IMPORTANT REFERENCE TABLES AND CHARTS

D1092186

Property

of

Dean J.

Hartman

STANDARD HANDBOOK FOR MECHANICAL ENGINEERS

OTHER McGRAW-HILL HANDBOOKS OF INTEREST

AMERICAN INSTITUTE OF PHYSICS · American Institute of Physics Handbook
AMERICAN SOCIETY OF MECHANICAL ENGINEERS · ASME Handbooks:
Engineering Tables
Metals Engineering—Design
Metals Engineering—Processes
Metals Properties
AMERICAN SOCIETY OF TOOL AND MANUFACTURING ENGINEERS:
Die Design Handbook
Handbook of Fixture Design
Manufacturing Planning and Estimating Handbook
Tool Engineers Handbook
BEEMAN · Industrial Power Systems Handbook
BRADY · Materials Handbook
BURINGTON · Handbook of Mathematical Tables and Formulas
BURINGTON AND MAY · Handbook of Probability and Statistics with Tables
CALLENDER · Time-Saver Standards
CARRIER AIR CONDITIONING COMPANY · Handbook of Air Conditioning System Design
CARROLL · Industrial Instrument Servicing Handbook
CONDON AND ODISHAW · Handbook of Physics
CONSIDINE · Process Instruments and Controls Handbook
CONSIDINE AND ROSS · Handbook of Applied Instrumentation
CROCKER · Piping Handbook
DAVIS · Handbook of Applied Hydraulics
DUDLEY · Gear Handbook
EMERICK · Heating Handbook
FACTORY MUTUAL ENGINEERING DIVISION · Handbook of Industrial Loss Prevention
FLUGGE · Handbook of Engineering Mechanics
HARRIS · Handbook of Noise Control
HARRIS AND CREDE · Shock and Vibration Handbook
HEYEL · The Foreman's Handbook
HUSKEY AND KORN · Computer Handbook
JURAN · Quality Control Handbook
KALLEN · Handbook of Instrumentation and Controls
KING AND BRATER · Handbook of Hydraulics
KLERER AND KORN · Digital Computer User's Handbook
KNOWLTON · Standard Handbook for Electrical Engineers
KOELLE · Handbook of Astronautical Engineering
KORN AND KORN · Mathematical Handbook for Scientists and Engineers
LASSER · Business Management Handbook
LEGRAND · The New American Machinists' Handbook
MACHOL · System Engineering Handbook
MAGILL, HOLDEN, AND ACKLEY · Air Pollution Handbook
MANAS · National Plumbing Code Handbook
MANTELL · Engineering Materials Handbook
MAYNARD · Industrial Engineering Handbook
MAYNARD · Top Management Handbook
MORROW · Maintenance Engineering Handbook
PERRY · Chemical Engineers' Handbook
PERRY · Engineering Manual
ROSSNAGEL · Handbook of Rigging
ROTHBART · Mechanical Design and Systems Handbook
SHAND · Glass Engineering Handbook
STANIAR · Plant Engineering Handbook
STREETER · Handbook of Fluid Dynamics
TOULOUKIAN · Retrieval Guide to Thermophysical Properties Research Literature
TRUXAL · Control Engineers' Handbook

STANDARD HANDBOOK FOR MECHANICAL ENGINEERS

Revised by a Staff of Specialists

THEODORE BAUMEISTER, Editor

Consulting Engineer; Stevens Professor Emeritus, Columbia University in the City of New York; Adjunct Professor of Mechanical Engineering, University of South Carolina

LIONEL S. MARKS, Editor, 1916 to 1951

Late Gordon McKay Professor of Mechanical Engineering, Harvard University

Seventh Edition

McGRAW-HILL BOOK COMPANY

New York San Francisco Toronto London Sydney

The Editor and the Publishers Will Be Grateful to Readers Who Notify Them of Any Inaccuracy or Important Omission in This Book

STANDARD HANDBOOK FOR MECHANICAL ENGINEERS

Copyright © 1958, 1967 by McGraw-Hill, Inc. All Rights Reserved.

Copyright renewed 1952 by Lionel S. Marks

Copyright 1916, 1924, 1930, 1941, 1951 by McGraw-Hill, Inc. All Rights Reserved. Printed in the United States of America. No part of this publication may be reproduced, stored in a retrieval system, or transmitted, in any form or by any means, electronic, mechanical, photocopying, recording, or otherwise, without the prior written permission of the publisher. *Library of Congress Catalog Card Number* 16-12915

04122

1234567890 LRMB 75432106987

First Edition
Eleven Printings

Second Edition
Seven Printings

Third Edition
Seven Printings

Fourth Edition
Thirteen Printings

Fifth Edition
Seven Printings

Sixth Edition
Eight Printings

LIST OF CONTRIBUTORS

Lewis H. Abraham, Senior Technical Staff, Product Development, Douglas Aircraft Company, Inc. *Aeronautics.*

Clarence B. Anderson, Associate Professor of Mechanical Engineering, The City University of New York. *Mechanics of Fluids.*

Eugene A. Avallone, Professor and Chairman, Department of Mechanical Engineering, The City University of New York. *Machine Elements.*

Eugene Ayres, Consulting Chemical Engineer, South Wellfleet, Mass. *Sources of Energy.*

Hilary E. Bacon, Consulting Chemical Engineer and Partner, Sheppard T. Powell and Associates, Baltimore, Md. *Corrosion.*

* **Robert A. Bareiss,** Senior Project Engineer, Lessells and Associates, Inc., Boston, Mass. *Machine Elements.*

Heard K. Baumeister, Senior Engineer, Systems Development Division, International Business Machines Corporation. *Mechanism. Optics.*

Martha C. Baumeister, Instructor, Department of Mathematics, University of Delaware. *Computers.*

Theodore Baumeister, III, Development Department, E. I. du Pont de Nemours & Co. *Computers.*

Philip E. Benner, Senior Application Engineer, Retired, General Electric Company; Engineering Consultant. *Direct-energy Conversion.*

C. H. Berry, late Gordon McKay Professor of Mechanical Engineering, Emeritus, Harvard University; and late Professor of Mechanical Engineering, Northeastern University. *Preferred Numbers.*

John A. Blume, Consulting Civil and Structural Engineer, San Francisco, Calif. *Structural Design of Buildings.*

* **William Bollay,** President, Aerophysics Development Corp. *Theory of Models. Wind Pressure on Structures.*

* **O. W. Boston,** Professor of Metal Processing, University of Michigan. *Metal Cutting Tools and Machines.*

F. G. Brickwedde, Evan Pugh Research Professor of Physics, The Pennsylvania State University. *Cryogenics.*

C. W. Briggs, Vice President-Technology, Steel Founders' Society of America. *Iron and Steel Castings.*

James A. Broadston, Director, Logistics, Rocketdyne, a Division of North American Aviation, Inc. *Surface Texture Designation, Production, and Control.*

Arthur L. Brown, Consultant in Fire Protection, Brookline, Mass. *Fire Protection.*

* **Arthur E. Bryson,** Associate Professor of Engineering Science, Harvard University. *High-speed Aerodynamics.*

* **Evers Burtner,** Associate Professor of Naval Architecture and Marine Engineering, Massachusetts Institute of Technology. *Marine Engineering.*

** Contributions by authors whose names are marked with an asterisk were made for the previous edition and have been revised or rewritten by others for this edition. The stated professional position in these cases is that held by the author at the time of his contribution.*

* **Frank W. Caldwell,** Former Director of Research, United Aircraft Corp. *Aircraft Propellers.*

Benson Carlin, Director of Research and Development, Air Shields, Inc., Hatboro, Pa. *Sound, Noise, and Ultrasonics.*

* **James H. Carpenter,** Director of Engineering Training, Carrier Corporation. *Air Conditioning.*

R. P. Carreker, Jr., Metallurgical Engineer, Research and Development Center, General Electric Company. *Non-Ferrous Metals.*

* **Miles N. Clair,** President, The Thompson and Lichtner Co., Brookline, Mass. *Cement, Mortar, and Concrete. Reinforced Concrete Construction.*

E. V. Crane, Consulting Engineer, Chief Engineer and Research Director (retired), E. W. Bliss Company. *Working Metals and Plastics.*

* **E. C. Crocker,** Senior Chemist, Arthur D. Little, Inc. *Non-Metallic Materials.*

* **E. M. Davis,** Technologist, U.S. Forest Products Laboratory, Madison, Wis. *Woodworking Machines.*

Chester L. Dawes, Associate Professor of Electrical Engineering, Emeritus, Harvard University; Vice President, New England Mica Company. *Electrical Engineering.*

B. B. Dayton, Chief Physicist, Consolidated Vacuum Corporation, Rochester, N.Y. *High-vacuum Pumps.*

* **J. P. Den Hartog,** Professor of Mechanical Engineering, Massachusetts Institute of Technology. *The Gyroscope.*

Carl H. de Zeeuw, Professor of Wood Products Engineering, State University College of Forestry at Syracuse. *Wood.*

* **W. S. Diehl,** Captain, U.S. Navy, Retired, Washington, D.C. *Aeronautics.*

Donald D. Dodge, Project Engineer, Ford Motor Company. *Nondestructive Testing.*

* **R. M. Donaldson,** Chief Hydraulic Engineer, Newport News Shipbuilding and Dry Dock Co. *Hydraulic Turbines.*

F. J. Edeskuty, Associate Group Leader, Cryogenics, Los Alamos Scientific Laboratory. *Cryogenics.*

* **F. R. Ellis,** Consulting Engineer, Hyde Park, Mass. *Heating and Ventilating.*

* **F. G. Ely,** Consultant, Research and Development Department, The Babcock & Wilcox Co. *Steam Boilers.*

* **Howard W. Emmons,** Professor of Engineering Science, Harvard University. *High-speed Aerodynamics.*

Vivian F. Estcourt, Consulting Engineer, Bechtel Corporation. *Geothermal Power.*

* **Harold Etherington,** Vice President, Nuclear Energy Products-Erco Division, ACF Industries, Incorporated. *Atomic Power.*

* **W. Theodore Everitt,** Staff Mechanical Engineer, Eastman Kodak Company. *Bearings with Rolling Contact.*

George H. Ewing, Vice President and Chief Engineer, Texas Eastern Transmission Corporation. *Pipeline Transmission.*

Elisha N. Fales, Aerodynamics Engineer, Atlantic Research Corporation, Alexandria, Va. *Windmills.*

Erich A. Farber, Professor and Research Professor of Mechanical Engineering, Director of the Solar Energy Laboratory, University of Florida. *Hot-air Engines.*

Edward A. Fenton, Technical Director, American Welding Society. *Welding.*

Edward W. Fisher, Chief Product Engineer, Garlock, Inc. *Packings.*

Leo P. Flood, Director of Engineering, City of New York Department of Air Pollution Control. *Atmospheric Pollution and Gas Cleaning.*

* *Contributions by authors whose names are marked with an asterisk were made for the previous edition and have been revised or rewritten by others for this edition. The stated professional position in these cases is that held by the author at the time of his contribution.*

Philip Franklin, Professor of Mathematics, Massachusetts Institute of Technology. *Mathematical Tables. Mathematics.*

Dudley D. Fuller, Professor of Mechanical Engineering, Columbia University. *Friction. Fluid Film Bearings.*

John E. Gray, President, Nuclear Utility Services, Inc. *Nuclear (Atomic) Power.*

* **Charles S. Grover,** Counsellor at Law, Boston, Mass. *Patents for Inventions.*

Albert Haertlein, late Gordon McKay Professor of Civil Engineering, Harvard University. *Surveying.*

E. F. Hammel, Jr., Group Leader, Cryogenics, Los Alamos Scientific Laboratory. *Cryogenics.*

* **R. M. Hardgrove,** Consultant, Research and Development Department, The Babcock & Wilcox Co. *Steam Boilers.*

George A. Hawkins, Dean of Engineering, Purdue University. *Thermal Properties of Substances and Thermodynamics.*

Harold V. Hawkins, Manager, Product Development and Engineering, Columbus McKinnon Corporation. *Pipeline Flexure Stresses. Materials Handling.*

Emil A. Hellebrand, Deputy Director, Propulsion and Vehicle Engineering Laboratory, NASA, George C. Marshall Space Flight Center. *Astronautics.*

* **K. C. D. Hickman,** Vice President and Director of Research, Aquastills, Inc.; Consultant in Water Conversion Engineering. *High-vacuum Pumps.*

William K. Hodson, President, H. B. Maynard and Company, Inc., Pittsburgh, Pa. *Control of Maintenance Costs.*

Hoyt C. Hottel, Professor of Fuel Engineering, Massachusetts Institute of Technology. *Radiant Heat Transfer.*

* **W. G. Hudson,** Consulting Engineer, Chicago, Ill. *Hoisting and Conveying.*

* **F. V. Hunt,** Rumford Professor of Physics and Gordon McKay Professor of Applied Physics, Harvard University. *Sound, Noise, and Ultrasonics.*

John R. Immer, President, Work Saving International, Management Consultants, Washington, D.C. *Industrial Plants.*

* **Arthur T. Ippen,** Professor of Hydraulics, Massachusetts Institute of Technology. *Mechanics of Liquids.*

Franklin Robert Jenkins, Patent Agent, Eatonton, Ga., *Patents for Inventions.*

Lewis V. Judson, Retired Physicist, Office of Weights and Measures, National Bureau of Standards. *Weights and Measures. General Properties of Materials.*

Serope Kalpakjian, Associate Professor, Department of Mechanical and Aerospace Engineering, Illinois Institute of Technology. *Metal-Removal Processes and Equipment.*

Igor J. Karassik, General Manager, Advance Products Division, Worthington Corporation. *Centrifugal and Axial Pumps.*

Hilmer Karlsson, Consultant, The Air Preheater Company, Inc. *Atmospheric Pollution and Gas Cleaning.*

Carl F. Kayan, Stevens Professor of Mechanical Engineering, Columbia University. *Refrigeration.*

Clyde E. Kesler, Professor of Theoretical and Applied Mechanics and of Civil Engineering, University of Illinois. *Cement, Mortar, & Concrete. Reinforced Concrete Design and Construction.*

G. W. Kessler, Vice President, Engineering, Boiler Division, The Babcock & Wilcox Company. *Steam Boilers.*

Stephen F. Kimball, Director, General Liability Service, Loss Prevention Department, Liberty Mutual Insurance Company. *Prevention of Accidents.*

* *Contributions by authors whose names are marked with an asterisk were made for the previous edition and have been revised or rewritten by others for this edition. The stated professional position in these cases is that held by the author at the time of his contribution.*

Reno C. King, Professor of Mechanical Engineering, New York University. *Pipe and Pipe Fittings.*

Walter J. Kleponis, Senior Negotiations Engineer, Steam Divisions, Westinghouse Electric Corporation. *Power-plant Heat Exchangers.*

* **Martin Kloomok,** Manager, Analysis and Computation Division, Product Development Laboratory, International Business Machines Corporation. *Automatic Computing Machines.*

P. H. Knowlton, Jr., Advance Systems Engineer, Large Steam Turbine-Generator Department, General Electric Company. *Steam Turbines.*

E. S. Krendel, Professor of Operations Research and Statistics, University of Pennsylvania. *Man- and Animal-generated Power.*

William C. Krutzsch, Manager-Engineering, Pump and Heat Transfer Division, Worthington Corporation. *Centrifugal and Axial Pumps.*

* **Arthur N. Kugler,** Chief Welding Engineer, Air Reduction Sales Company. *Welding.*

* **C. M. Larson,** Consulting Engineer, New Rochelle, N.Y. *Lubricants and Lubrication.*

* **Thomas P. Latimer,** Assistant General Manager, Turbo-Products Division, Clark Bros. Co. *Turbocompressors.*

W. A. Leech, Jr., Consulting Engineer, Swindell-Dresser Company. *Carbonization of Coal and Gas Making.*

Franklin J. Leerburger, Consulting Engineer, New York, N.Y. *Cost of Electric Power.*

Irving Lefkowitz, Professor of Engineering, Systems Research Center, Case Institute of Technology. *Instruments.*

E. Vernon Lewis, Associate Professor of Mathematics, Ursinus College. *Engineering Statistics and Quality Control.*

W. E. Lewis, Manager–Field Sales, Lectromelt Furnace Division, McGraw-Edison Company. *Electric Furnaces and Ovens.*

Lester C. Lichty, Robert Higgin Professor of Mechanical Engineering, Yale University. *Internal-combustion Engines.*

Benjamin S. Loeb, Division of Technical Information, U.S. Atomic Energy Commission. *Nuclear (Atomic) Power.*

Guy S. Longobardo, Advisory Engineer, Advanced Systems Development Division, International Business Machines Corporation. *Automatic Controls.*

Carl R. Loper, Jr., Associate Professor, Minerals and Metals Engineering, University of Wisconsin. *Foundry Practice and Equipment.*

William H. McAdams, Professor Emeritus of Chemical Engineering, Massachusetts Institute of Technology. *Transmission of Heat by Conduction and Convection.*

Neil MacCoull, Consulting Automotive Engineer, Lecturer in Mechanical Engineering, Columbia University. *Internal-combustion Engines: Automobiles.*

J. E. McDonald, President, Air-Boston Laboratory, Newton Lower Falls, Mass. *Centrifugal and Axial Fans.*

Charles W. MacGregor, Engineering Consultant and Manager of Advanced Technology, Systems Development Division, International Business Machines Corporation, Endicott, N.Y. *Mechanical Properties of Materials.*

C. Osborne Mackey, John Edson Sweet Professor of Engineering, Cornell University. *Mixtures of Gases and Vapors.*

Adolph Matz, Professor of Accounting, Wharton School of Finance and Commerce, University of Pennsylvania. *Cost Accounting.*

M. H. Mawhinney, Consulting Engineer, Salem, Ohio. *Combustion Furnaces.*

H. B. Maynard, President, Maynard Research Council, Pittsburgh, Pa. *Time and Motion Study.*

* *Contributions by authors whose names are marked with an asterisk were made for the previous edition and have been revised or rewritten by others for this edition. The stated professional position in these cases is that held by the author at the time of his contribution.*

R. R. Meigs, Vice President and Manager, Loss Prevention Department, Liberty Mutual Insurance Company. *Prevention of Accidents.*

* **H. W. Mergler,** Assistant Professor of Mechanical Engineering, Case Institute of Technology. *Automatic Control.*

George W. Michalec, Engineering Consultant, GPL Division, General Precision, Inc., Associate Professor of Mechanical Engineering, Stevens Institute of Technology. *Gearing.*

Finn C. Michelsen, Professor of Naval Architecture and Marine Engineering, University of Michigan. *Hydrofoil Craft and Air-Cushion Vehicles.*

John B. Middleton, Forester, Pennsylvania Electric Company. *Atmospheric Pollution and Gas Cleaning.*

Cort L. Miller, Engineer, Eastman Kodak Company. *Bearings with Rolling Contact.*

Roland E. Moore, Assistant Chief Engineer, Texas Eastern Transmission Corporation. *Pipeline Transmission.*

Reeves Morrisson, Assistant to the Chief Scientist, United Aircraft Corporation. *Gas Turbines.*

* **Howard E. Murphy,** Consulting Electrical Engineer, Cohasset, Mass. *Illumination.*

S. N. B. Murthy, Visiting Professor of Mechanical Engineering, Purdue University; Professor, Bangalore Institute of Technology, India. *Jet Propulsion and Aircraft Propellers.*

L. L. Newman, Chief Coal Technologist, Bureau of Mines. *Fuels.*

Edward Taylor Newton, Counsellor at Law; Senior Partner, Newton, Hopkins, Jones and Ormsby, Atlanta, Ga. *Patents for Inventions.*

Joseph P. Nicoletti, Vice President, John A. Blume and Associates, Engineers, San Francisco, Calif. *Structural Design of Buildings.*

B. W. Niebel, Professor and Head, Department of Industrial Engineering, The Pennsylvania State University. *Industrial Economics and Management.*

J. Hubert Noland, Professor of Electrical Engineering, University of South Carolina. *Electronics.*

Frederick H. Norton, Professor of Ceramics, Emeritus, Massachusetts Institute of Technology. *Refractories.*

John O'Keefe, Chief Mechanical and Electrical Engineer, Praeger-Kavanagh-Waterbury, Engineers-Architects, New York, N.Y. *Heating, Air-Conditioning and Ventilation.*

Nunzio J. Palladino, Professor and Head, Nuclear Engineering Department, The Pennsylvania State University. *Nuclear (Atomic) Power.*

Dan S. Park, Assistant to the President, Pennsylvania Electric Company. *Nuclear (Atomic) Power.*

Rienzi B. Parker, Jr., Chemical Engineering Consultant, Arthur D. Little, Inc. *Non-metallic Materials.*

John F. Partridge, District Industrial Engineer, New York Central System, Indianapolis, Ind. *Railway Engineering.*

Richard W. Perkins, Assistant Professor of Mechanical and Aerospace Engineering, Syracuse University. *Woodcutting Tools and Machines.*

* **H. W. Peterson,** Sales Engineer, Freyn Department, Koppers Company. *Gas Producers and Gas Cleaning.*

* **R. E. Peterson,** Manager, Mechanics Department, Westinghouse Research Laboratories, Westinghouse Electric Corp. *Gearing.*

Charles L. Pope, Engineering Supervisor, Eastman Kodak Company. *Bearings with Rolling Contact.*

** Contributions by authors whose names are marked with an asterisk were made for the previous edition and have been revised or rewritten by others for this edition. The stated professional position in these cases is that held by the author at the time of his contribution.*

* **Sheppard T. Powell**, Consulting Chemical Engineer, Baltimore, Md. *Corrosion.*

Bernard R. Queneau, Chief Metallurgical Engineer, Process Metallurgy-Steel Finishing, United States Steel Corporation. *Iron and Steel.*

William J. Rheingans, Consulting Engineer, Hydraulic Products Division, Allis-Chalmers Manufacturing Co. *Hydraulic Turbines.*

Raymond J. Rice, Consulting Engineer, New York, N.Y. *Illumination.*

L. M. Roberts, Special Consultant, Research-Cottrell, Inc. *Atmospheric Pollution and Gas Cleaning.*

* **Ernest L. Robinson**, Consulting Engineer, Schenectady, N.Y. *Stresses in Turbine Disk Wheels.*

Louis H. Roddis, Jr., President, Pennsylvania Electric Company. *Nuclear (Atomic) Power.*

* **Philip C. Rosenthal**, Chairman, Department of Mining and Metallurgy, University of Wisconsin. *Foundry Practice and Equipment.*

Adel F. Sarofim, Assistant Professor of Chemical Engineering, Massachusetts Institute of Technology. *Radiant Heat Transfer.*

* **W. E. Schaffnit, Jr.**, Engineer, Ingersoll-Rand Co. *Steam Condensation.*

Lyman F. Scheel, Supervisor of Fluid Mechanics, The Ralph M. Parsons Company, Los Angeles and New York. *Compressors.*

Zalman M. Shapiro, President, Nuclear Materials and Equipment Corporation. *Nuclear (Atomic) Power.*

* **C. Branson Smith**, Project Engineer, Pratt and Whitney Aircraft, United Aircraft Corp. *Aircraft Propellers.*

Kenneth A. Smith, Assistant Professor of Chemical Engineering, Massachusetts Institute of Technology. *Transmission of Heat by Conduction and Convection.*

Weston Smith, Managing Director, Weston Smith Associates, New York. *Analysis of Corporation Annual Reports.*

* **P. J. Snoy**, Die Engineer, E. W. Bliss Company. *Metal-Working Operations and Equipment.*

Gerhard E. Sonderman, Consulting Engineer, Singmaster and Breyer, New York. *Water.*

Robert F. Steidel, Jr., Professor of Mechanical Engineering, University of California, Berkeley. *Mechanics of Solids.*

Richard M. Stephani, Senior Design Engineer, Steam Divisions, Westinghouse Electric Corporation. *Power-Plant Heat Exchangers.*

V. H. Sussman, Director, Division of Air Pollution Control, Pennsylvania Department of Health. *Atmospheric Pollution and Gas Cleaning.*

George G. Sward, Consultant, Gardner Laboratory, Inc., Bethesda, Md. *Paints and Protective Coatings.*

* **Harold A. Thomas, Jr.**, Gordon McKay Professor of Civil and Sanitary Engineering, Harvard University. *Engineering Statistics and Statistical Quality Control.*

William T. Thomson, Professor of Engineering, University of California, Los Angeles, Calif. *Vibration.*

* **F. C. Thorn**, Research Director, Retired, The Garlock Packing Co. *Packings.*

A. J. Tigges, Consultant, General Public Utilities Corporation. *Atmospheric Pollution and Gas Cleaning.*

* **W. Turnwald**, Nordberg Manufacturing Co. *Steam Engines.*

Charles O. Velzy, Secretary-Treasurer, Charles R. Velzy Associates, Inc., White Plains, N.Y. *Incineration.*

* *Contributions by authors whose names are marked with an asterisk were made for the previous edition and have been revised or rewritten by others for this edition. The stated professional position in these cases is that held by the author at the time of his contribution.*

Charles R. Velzy, President, Charles R. Velzy Associates, Inc., White Plains, N.Y. *Incineration.*

W. A. Verrochi, Superintendent of Production, Pennsylvania Electric Company. *Atmospheric Pollution and Gas Cleaning.*

Joseph P. Vidosic, Regents' Professor and Acting Director, School of Mechanical Engineering, Georgia Institute of Technology. *Mechanics of Materials.*

Fred J. Villforth, Jr., Senior Project Mechanical Engineer, Texaco, Inc. *Lubricants and Lubrication.*

Philip C. Wagner, Principal Engineer, Jackson and Moreland Division, United Engineers and Constructors. *Power from the Tides.*

* **A. M. Wahl,** Advisory Engineer, Westinghouse Research Laboratories, Westinghouse Electric Corp. *Machine Elements.*

George L. West, Jr., Professor of Marine and Nuclear Engineering, University of Michigan. *Marine Engineering.*

* **J. H. Westbrook,** Research Associate, General Electric Research Laboratory, General Electric Company. *Nonferrous Metals.*

J. K. Whitteker, Specification Writer, Praeger-Kavanagh-Waterbury, Engineers-Architects, New York, N.Y. *Heating, Air-Conditioning and Ventilation.*

Glenn C. Williams, Professor of Chemical Engineering, Massachusetts Institute of Technology. *Transmission of Heat by Conduction and Convection.*

K. D. Williamson, Cryogenics Engineer, Los Alamos Scientific Laboratory. *Cryogenics.*

Frederick C. J. Willsea, Project Engineer, John A. Blume and Associates, Engineers, San Francisco, Calif. *Structural Design of Buildings.*

* **G. F. Wislicenus,** Professor of Aeronautical Engineering and Director of the Garfield Thomas Water Tunnel, The Pennsylvania State University. *Centrifugal Pumps.*

* **Edward Wrapp,** Associate Professor of Business Administration, Graduate School of Business Administration, Harvard University. *Industrial Economics and Management.*

E. F. Wright, Consulting Engineer, Advance Products Division, Worthington Corporation. *Pumps.*

John I. Yellott, Director, Yellott Solar Energy Laboratory, Phoenix, Ariz. *Solar Energy.*

M. J. Zucrow, Atkins Professor of Engineering, Purdue University. *Jet Propulsion and Aircraft Propellers.*

* *Contributions by authors whose names are marked with an asterisk were made for the previous edition and have been revised or rewritten by others for this edition. The stated professional position in these cases is that held by the author at the time of his contribution.*

PREFACE TO THE SEVENTH EDITION

This is the Golden Anniversary edition of the STANDARD HANDBOOK FOR MECHANICAL ENGINEERS. When the book was first published by Professor Marks in 1916 there were doubtless hopes that it would mature to a position of significance in the profession. The intervening fifty years have demonstrated its growth to classic proportions. Its progressive revision has culminated in this Seventh Edition—the work of more than one hundred contributors.

The editor has had the enthusiastic cooperation of his contributors, of his reviewers, and of his publishers to assure the publication of a book that will be useful to the professional engineer and to the student in the rapidly changing scope and practice of mechanical engineering.

For those who find history tantalizing, it is provocative to compare the table of contents of the first edition with that of this Seventh Edition. The additions include such new topics as computers and their adaptation to automatic controls, steam turbines of a million kilowatts capacity, boilers burning coal at the rate of half a dozen tons a minute, nuclear reactors and power plants, supersonic aircraft, astronautics, hovercraft, photoelasticity, air pollution, and water supply. But the many developments in such mundane areas as machine elements, metals, wood, plastics, machine tools, welding, adhesives, and piping, must not be forgotten. Even the treatment of such basic sciences as solid mechanics, thermodynamics and fluid dynamics, and of the increasingly important area of mathematics, has been overhauled to fit the modern demands imposed upon the mechanical engineer.

The profession has felt the impact of expansion of old practices and the introduction of new concepts. The editor has had to reconcile the need to keep the volume size within reasonable bounds with the need to offer the user the kind of comprehensive information that has made the book so useful over the years. In this effort he has had the enthusiastic cooperation of contributors, reviewers, and publishers, and of Theodore Baumeister III and Mrs. Martha W. C. Baumeister in the preparation of the all-important index. No handbook is any better than its index.

Meticulous care has been exercised to avoid errors—ultimately the responsibility of the editor. If any are included through inadvertence, the editor will be grateful for the help of readers in their elimination from subsequent printings of this edition.

THEODORE BAUMEISTER

WILLTOWN BLUFF, S.C.
December 31, 1966

PREFACE TO THE FIRST EDITION*

This Handbook is intended to supply both the practicing engineer and the student with a reference work which is authoritative in character and which covers the field of mechanical engineering in a comprehensive manner. It is no longer possible for a single individual or a small group of individuals to have so intimate an acquaintance with any major division of engineering as is necessary if critical judgment is to be exercised in the statement of current practice and the selection of engineering data. Only by the co-operation of a considerable number of specialists is it possible to obtain the desirable degree of reliability. This Handbook represents the work of fifty specialists.

Each contributor is to be regarded as responsible for the accuracy of his section. The number of contributors required to ensure sufficiently specialized knowledge for all the topics treated is necessarily large. It was found desirable to enlist the services of thirteen specialists for an adequate handling of the "Properties of Engineering Materials." Such topics as "Automobiles," "Aeronautics," "Illumination," "Patent Law," "Cost Accounting," "Industrial Buildings," "Corrosion," "Air Conditioning," "Fire Protection," "Prevention of Accidents," etc., though occupying relatively small spaces in the book, demanded each a separate writer.

A number of the contributions which deal with engineering practice, after examination by the Editor-in-Chief, were submitted by him to one or more specialists for criticism and suggestions. Their co-operation has proved of great value in securing greater accuracy and in ensuring that the subject matter does not embody solely the practice of one individual but is truly representative.

An accuracy of four significant figures has been assumed as the desirable limit; figures in excess of this number have been deleted, except in special cases. In the mathematical tables only four significant figures have been kept.

The Editor-in-Chief desires to express here his appreciation of the spirit of co-operation shown by the Contributors and of their patience in submitting to modifications of their sections. He wishes also to thank the Publishers for giving him complete freedom and hearty assistance in all matters relating to the book from the choice of contributors to the details of typography.

LIONEL S. MARKS

CAMBRIDGE, MASS.
April 23, 1916

* Excerpt.

CONTENTS

For the detailed contents of any section consult the title page of that section. The alphabetical index follows Section 18.

SYMBOLS AND ABBREVIATIONS

For symbols of chemical elements, see pp. 6–4 *ff*.; for abbreviations applying to metric weights and measures, see p. 1–72.

Pairs of parentheses, brackets, etc., are frequently used in this work to indicate corresponding values. For example, the statement that "the cost per kw of a 30,000-kw plant is $86; of a 15,000-kw plant, $98; and of an 8,000-kw plant, $112," is condensed as follows: The cost per kw of a 30,000 (15,000) [8,000]-kw plant is $86 (98) [112].

In the citation of references readers should always attempt to consult the latest edition of referenced publications.

A or Å	Angstrom unit = 10^{-10}m; 3.937×10^{-11} in.
A	mass number = N + Z
AA	arithmetical average
AAA	Am. Automobile Assoc.
AAR	Assoc. of Am. Railroads
AAS	Am. Astronautical Soc.
ABAI	Am. Boiler & Affiliated Industries
abs	absolute
a.c.	aerodynamic center
a-c	alternating current
ACI	Am. Concrete Inst.
ACM	Assoc. for Computing Machinery
ACRMA	Air Conditioning and Refrigerating Manufacturers Assoc.
ACS	Am. Chemical Soc.
ACSR	aluminum cable steel-reinforced
ACV	air cushion vehicle
A.D.	anno Domini (in the year of our Lord)
AEC	Atomic Energy Commission (U.S.)
a-f	audio frequency
AFBMA	Anti-friction Bearings Manufacturers' Assoc.
AFS	Am. Foundrymen's Soc.
AGA	Am. Gas Assoc.
AGMA	Am. Gear Manufacturers' Assoc.
ahp	air horsepower
AIChE	Am. Inst. of Chemical Engineers
AIEE	Am. Inst. of Electrical Engineers (see IEEE)
AIME	Am. Inst. of Mining Engineers
AIP	Am. Inst. of Physics
AISE	Am. Iron & Steel Engineers
AISI	Am. Iron and Steel Inst.
a.m.	ante meridiem (before noon)
a-m	amplitude modulation
Am. Mach.	Am. Machinist (New York)
AMA	Automobile Manufacturers' Assoc.; Acoustical Materials Assoc.
AMCA	Air Moving & Conditioning Assoc., Inc.
amp	amperes
amu	atomic mass unit
AN	ammonium nitrate (explosive); Army-Navy Specification
AN-FO	ammonium nitrate-fuel oil (explosive)
ANC	Army-Navy Civil Aeronautics Committee
ANS	Am. Nuclear Soc.
antilog	antilogarithm of
API	Am. Petroleum Inst.
approx	approximately
APWA	Am. Public Works Assoc.
AREA	Am. Railroad Eng. Assoc.
ARI	Air Conditioning and Refrigeration Inst.
ARS	Am. Rocket Soc.
ASA	Am. Standards Assoc. (see USASI)

ASCE	Am. Soc. of Civil Engineers
ASHAE	see ASHRAE
ASHRAE	Am. Soc. of Heating, Refrigerating, and Air Conditioning Engineers (formerly ASHAE and ASH&VE)
ASH&VE	see ASHRAE
ASLE	Am. Soc. of Lubricating Engineers
ASM	Am. Soc. for Metals
ASME	Am. Soc. of Mechanical Engineers
ASRE	Am. Soc. of Refrigerating Engineers (see ASHRAE)
ASST	Am. Soc. for Steel Treating
ASTM	Am. Soc. for Testing and Materials
ASTME	Am. Soc. of Tool & Manufacturing Engineers
atm	atmosphere
Auto. Ind.	Automotive Industries (New York)
avdp	avoirdupois
avg	average
AWG	Am. Wire Gage
AWPA	Am. Wood Preservation Assoc.
AWS	American Welding Soc.
AWWA	American Water Works Assoc.
b	barns
bar	barometer
B&S	Brown & Sharp (gage); Beams and Stringers
bbl	barrels
B.C.	before Christ
B.C.C.	body centered cubic
Bé	Baumé (degrees)
B.G.	Birmingham gage (hoop and sheet)
bgd	billions of gallons per day
BHN	Brinnell Hardness Number
bhp	brake horsepower
BLC	boundary layer control
B.M.	board measure; bench mark
bmep	brake mean effective pressure
B of M	Bureau of Mines
BOD	biochemical oxygen demand
bp	boiling point
bsfc	brake specific fuel consumption
BSI	British Standards Inst.
Btu	British thermal units
Btuh	Btu per hr
bu	bushels
Bull.	Bulletin
Buships	Bureau of Ships, USN
BWG	Birmingham wire gage
c	velocity of light
C	degrees Celsius (centigrade)
CAB	Civil Aeronautics Board
CAGI	Compressed Air & Gas Inst.
cal	calories
C-B-R	chemical, biological & radiological (filters)
CBS	Columbia Broadcasting System
cc	cubic centimeters
CCR	critical compression ratio
c to c	center to center
c.f.	centrifugal force
cf.	confer (compare)
cfh	cubic feet per hour
cfm	cubic feet per minute
C.F.R.	Cooperative Fuel Research
cfs	cubic feet per second
cg	center of gravity
cgs	centimeter-gram-second
Chem. Eng.	Chemical Eng'g (New York)
chu	centigrade heat unit
C.I.	cast iron
cir	circular
cir mil	circular mils
cm	centimeters
CME	Chartered Mech. Engr (IMechE)
C.N.	cetane number
coef	coefficient
COESA	U.S. Committee on Extension to the Standard Atmosphere
col	column
colog	cologarithm of
const	constant
cos	cosine of
$\cos^{-1}$	arc whose cosine is, inverse cosine of
cosh	hyperbolic cosine of
$\cosh^{-1}$	inverse hyperbolic cosine of
cot	cotangent of
$\cot^{-1}$	arc whose cotangent is (see $\cos^{-1}$)
coth	hyperbolic cotangent of
$\coth^{-1}$	inverse hyperbolic cotangent of
covers	coversed sine of
c.p.	circular pitch; center of pressure
cp	candle power
cp	coef of performance
CP	chemically pure
cpm	cycles per minute
cps	cycles per second

CSA	Canadian Standards Assoc.
csc	cosecant of
csc^{-1}	arc whose cosecant is (see cos^{-1})
csch	hyperbolic cosecant of
$csch^{-1}$	inverse hyperbolic cosecant of
cu	cubic
cyl	cylinder
db	decibel
d-c	direct current
def	definition
deg	degrees
diam	diameter
DO	dissolved oxygen
D_2O	deuterium (heavy water)
d.p.	diametral pitch; double pole
DPH	diamond pyramid hardness
DST	daylight saving time
d^2tons	breaking strength, d = chain wire diam, in.
DX	direct expansion
e	base of Napierian logarithmic system (=2.7182+)
EAP	equivalent air pressure
EDR	equivalent direct radiation
EEI	Edison Electric Inst.
eff	efficiency
e.g.	exempli gratia (for example)
ehp	effective horsepower
EHV	extra high voltage
El. Wld.	Electrical World (New York)
elec	electric
elong	elongation
emf	electromotive force
Engg.	Engineering (London)
Engr.	The Engineer (London)
ENT	emergency negative thrust
EP	extreme pressure (lubricant)
Eq.	equation
est	estimated
etc.	et cetera (and so forth)
et seq.	et sequens (and the following)
ev	electron volts
evap	evaporation
exp	exponential function of
exsec	exterior secant of
ext	external
F	degrees Fahrenheit
FAA	Federal Aviation Agency
F.C.	fixed carbon, %
FCC	Federal Communications Commission; Federal Construction Council
F.C.C.	face-centered-cubic (alloys)
ff.	following (pages)
fhp	friction horsepower
Fig.	figure
F.I.T.	Federal income tax
f-m	frequency modulation
F.O.B.	free on board (cars)
FP	fore perpendicular
FPC	Federal Power Commission
fpm	feet per minute
fps	feet per second; foot-pound-second system
F.S.	Federal Specifications
FSB	Federal Specifications Board
fsp	fiber saturation point
ft	feet
ft-c	foot candles
ft-L	foot lamberts
ft-lb	foot-pounds
g	acceleration due to gravity
g	grams
gal	gallons
gc	gigacycles per sec
GCA	ground-controlled approach
g-cal	gram-calories
gd	Gudermannian of
G.E.	General Electric Co.
GEM	ground effect machine
GFI	gullet feed index
G.M.	General Motors Co.
GNP	gross national product
gpcd	gallons per capita day
gpd	gallons per day; grams per denier
gpm	gallons per minute
gps	gallons per second
gpt	grams per tex
h	Planck's constant = 6.624×10^{-27}erg-sec
$\hbar$	Planck's constant, $\hbar = h/2\pi$
HEPA	high efficiency particulate matter
h-f	high frequency
hhv	high heat value
horiz	horizontal
hp	horsepower
h-p	high-pressure
HPAC	Heating, Piping, & Air Conditioning (Chicago)
hp-hr	horsepower-hour
hr	hours
HSS	high speed steel
H.T.	heat-treated
HTHW	high temperature hot water
Hz	hertz = 1 cps

IACS	International Annealed Copper Standard
IAeS	Institute of Aerospace Sciences
ibid.	ibidem (in the same place)
ICAO	International Civil Aviation Organization
ICC	Interstate Commerce Commission
ICE	Inst. of Civil Engineers
ICI	International Commission on Illumination
I.C.T.	International Critical Tables
I.D.	inside diameter
i.e.	id est (that is)
IEEE	Inst. of Electrical & Electronics Engineers (successor to AIEE, *q.v.*)
IES	Illuminating Engineering Soc.
i-f	intermediate frequency
IGT	Inst. of Gas Technology
ihp	indicated horsepower
IMechE	Inst. of Mechanical Engineers
imep	indicated mean effective pressure
Imp	Imperial
in.	inches
in.-lb	inch-pounds
INA	Inst. of Naval Architects
Ind. & Eng. Chem.	Industrial & Eng'g Chemistry (Easton, Pa)
int	internal
i-p	intermediate pressure
ipm	inches per minute
ipr	inches per revolution
IPS	iron pipe size
IRE	Inst. of Radio Engineers
IRS	Internal Revenue Service
ISO	International Organization for Standardization
isoth	isothermal
ISTM	International Soc. for Testing Materials
IUPAC	International Union of Pure & Applied Chemistry
J&P	joists & planks
Jour.	Journal
JP	jet propulsion fuel
K	isentropic exponent; conductivity
K	degrees Kelvin (Celsius abs)
K	Knudsen number
kB	kilo Btu (1000 Btu)
kc	kilocycles
kcps	kilocycles per sec
kg	kilograms
kg-cal	kilogram-calories
kg-m	kilogram-meters
kip	1000 lb or 1 kilo-pound
kips	thousands of pounds
km	kilometers
kmc	kilomegacycles per sec
kmcps	kilomegacycles per sec
kpsi	thousands of pounds per sq in.
ksi	one kip per sq in., 1000 psi
kts	knots
kva	kilovolt-amperes
kw	kilowatts
kwh	kilowatt-hours
l	liters
$\mathcal{L}$	Laplace operational symbol
lb	pounds
L.B.P.	length between perpendiculars
lim	limit
lin	linear
ln	Napierian logarithm of
loc. cit.	loco citato (place already cited)
log	common logarithm of
LOX	liquid oxygen explosive
l-p	low pressure
LPG	liquified petroleum gas
lpw	lumens per watt
L.W.L	load water line
m	meters
M	thousand; Mach number; moisture, %
ma	milliamperes
Machy.	Machinery (New York)
max	maximum
MBh	thousands of Btu per hr
mc	megacycles per sec
m.c.	moisture content
Mcf	thousand cubic feet
mcps	megacycles per sec
Mech. Eng.	Mechanical Eng'g (ASME)
mep	mean effective pressure
METO	maximum, except during take-off
mev	million electron volts
MF	maintenance factor
mhc	mean horizontal candles
mi	mile
MIL-STD	U.S. Military Standard
min	minutes; minimum
mip	mean indicated pressure
MKS	meter-kilogram-second system
MKSA	meter-kilogram-second-ampere system
ml	millilamberts

ml	milliliter = 1.000027 cc
mlhc	mean lower hemispherical candles
mm	millimeters
mm-free	mineral matter free
mmf	magnetomotive force
mp	melting point
MPC	maximum permissible concentration
mph	miles per hour
MRT	mean radiant temperature
ms	manuscript; milliseconds
msc	mean spherical candles
MSS	Manufacturers Standardization Soc. of the Valve & Fittings Industry
Mu	micron, micro
mw	megawatts
mw day	megawatt day
MWT	mean water temperature
n	polytropic exponent
N	number (in mathematical tables)
N	number of neutrons
N_s	specific speed
NA	not available
NAA	National Assoc. of Accountants
NACA	National Advisory Committee on Aeronautics (see NASA)
NACM	National Assoc. of Chain Manufacturers
NASA	National Aeronautics and Space Administration
nat.	natural
NBC	National Broadcasting Company
NBFU	National Board of Fire Underwriters
NBS	National Bureau of Standards
NCN	nitrocarbonitrate (explosive)
NDHA	National District Heating Assoc.
NEC	National Electrical Code
NEMA	National Electrical Manufacturers Assoc.
NFPA	National Fire Protection Assoc.
NLGI	National Lubricating Grease Institute
nm	nautical miles
No. (Nos.)	number(s)
NPSH	net positive suction head
NTP	normal temperature and pressure
O.D.	outside diameter (pipes)
O.H	open-hearth (steel)
O.N.	octane number
op. cit.	opere citato (work already cited)
OSW	Office of Saline Water
OTS	Office of Technical Services, U.S. Dept. of Commerce
oz	ounces
p. (pp.)	page (pages)
P.C.	propulsive coefficient
PE	polyethylene
PEG	polyethylene glycol
P.E.L.	proportional elastic limit
PETN	an explosive
pf	power factor
PFI	Pipe Fabrication Inst.
PIV	peak inverse voltage
p.m.	post meridiem (after noon)
PM	preventive maintenance
P.N.	performance number
ppb	parts per billion
PPI	plan position indicator
ppm	parts per million
press	pressure
Proc.	Proceedings
PSD	power spectral density, g^2/cps
psi	lb per sq in.
psia	lb per sq in. abs
psig	lb per sq in. gage
pt	point; pint
PVC	polyvinyl chloride
Q	10^{18} Btu
qt	quarts
q.v.	quod vide (which see)
r	roentgens
R	gas constant
R	deg Rankine (Fahrenheit abs); Reynolds number
rad	radius; radiation absorbed dose
RBE	see rem
R-C	resistor-capacitor
RCA	Radio Corporation of America
R&D	research & development
RDX	cyclonite, a military explosive
rem	Roentgen equivalent man (formerly RBE)
rev	revolutions
r-f	radio frequency
RMA	Rubber Manufacturers Assoc.
rms	square root of mean square
rpm	revolutions per minute
rps	revolutions per second

RSHF	room sensible heat factor
ry.	railway
s	entropy
S	sulphur, %
SAE	Soc. of Automotive Engineers
sat	saturated
SBI	Steel Boiler Inst.
scfm	standard cu ft per min
SCR	silicon controlled rectifier
sec	seconds; secant of
sec^{-1}	arc whose secant is (see cos^{-1})
Sec.	Section
sech	hyperbolic secant of
sech^{-1}	inverse hyperbolic secant of
segm	segment
SE No.	steam emulsion number
sfc	specific fuel comsumption, lb per hphr
sfm	surface feet per minute
sfpm	surface ft per minute
shp	shaft horsepower
SI	International System of Units (Le Système International d'Unites)
sin	sine of
sin^{-1}	arc whose sine is (see cos^{-1})
sinh	hyperbolic sine of
sinh^{-1}	inverse hyperbolic sine of
SNA&ME	Soc. of Naval Architects and Marine Engineers
SP	static pressure
sp	specific
specif	specification
sp gr	specific gravity
sp ht	specific heat
spp	species unspecified (botanical)
SPS	standard pipe size
sq	square
SSF	sec Saybolt Furol
SSU	seconds Saybolt Universal (same as SUS)
std	standard
SUS	Saybolt Universal seconds (same as SSU)
SWG	Standard (British) wire gage
TAC	Technical Advisory Committee on Weather Design Conditions (ASHRAE)
tan	tangent of
tan^{-1}	arc whose tangent is (see cos^{-1})
tanh	hyperbolic tangent of
tanh^{-1}	inverse hyperbolic tangent of
TDH	total dynamic head
TEL	tetraethyl lead
temp	temperature
THI	temperature-humidity (discomfort) index
thp	thrust horsepower
TNT	trinitrotoluol (explosive)
torr	= 1 mm Hg = 1.332 millibars (1/760) atm = (1.013250/760) dynes per sq cm
TP	total pressure
tph	tons per hour
tpi	turns per in.
TR	transmitter-receiver
Trans.	Transactions
T.S.	tensile strength
tsi	tons per sq in.
ttd	terminal temperature difference
UHF	ultra high frequency
UKAEA	United Kingdom Atomic Energy Authority
UL	Underwriters' Laboratory
ult	ultimate
UMS	universal maintenance standards
USAF	U.S. Air Force
USAS or USASI	USA Standard (USA Standards Inst., successor to ASA, *q.v.*)
USCG	U.S. Coast Guard
USCS	U.S. Commercial Standard
USDA	U.S. Dept. of Agriculture
USFPL	U.S. Forest Products Laboratory
USGS	U.S. Geologic Survey
USHEW	U.S. Dept. of Health, Education & Welfare
USN	U.S. Navy
USP	U.S Pharmacopoeia
USPHS	U.S. Public Health Service
USS	United States Standard
USSG	U.S. Standard Gage
VCF	visual confort factor
VCI	visual comfort index
VdI	Verein deutscher Ingenieure
vel	velocity
vers	versed sine of
vert	vertical
VHF	very high frequency
VI	viscosity index
viz.	videlicet (namely)
V.M.	volatile matter, %
vol	volume
VP	velocity pressure
vs.	versus

W&M	Washburn & Moen wire gage
w.g.	water gage
WHO	World Health Organization
W.I.	wrought iron
W.P.A.	Western Pine Assoc.
wt	weight
yd	yards
yr	year(s)
z	atomic number
z	figure of merit
Zeit	Zeitschrift
Δ	mass defect
μc	microcurie
σ, s	Boltzmann constant
μ	micro ($=10^{-6}$), as in μ sec, (see p. 1–72); micron $= 10^{-6}$ m (10^{-3} mm)

MATHEMATICAL SIGNS AND SYMBOLS

$+$	plus (sign of addition)
$+$	positive
$-$	minus (sign of subtraction)
$-$	negative
$\pm$ ($\mp$)	plus or minus (minus or plus)
$\times$	times, by (multiplication sign)
$\cdot$	multiplied by
$\div$	sign of division
$/$	divided by
$:$	ratio sign, divided by, is to
$::$	equals, as (proportion)
$<$	less than
$>$	greater than
$\ll$	much less than
$\gg$	much greater than
$=$	equals
$\equiv$	identical with
$\sim$	similar to
$\approx$	approximately equals
$\cong$	approximately equals, congruent
$\leq$	equal to or less than
$\geq$	equal to or greater than
$\mp$ $\neq$	not equal to
$\rightarrow$ $\doteq$	approaches
$\propto$	varies as
∞	infinity
$\sqrt{\ }$	square root of
$\sqrt[3]{\ }$	cube root of
$\therefore$	therefore
$\parallel$	parallel to
( ) [ ] { }	parentheses, brackets and braces; quantities enclosed by them to be taken together in multiplying, dividing, etc.
$\overline{AB}$	length of line from A to B
π	pi, $= 3.14159 +$
$^\circ$	degrees
$'$	minutes
$''$	seconds
$\angle$	angle
dx	differential of x
Δ	(delta) difference
Δx	increment of x
$\partial u/\partial x$	partial derivative of u with respect to x
$\int$	integral of
$\int_b^a$	integral of, between limits a and b
$\oint$	line integral around a closed path
Σ	(sigma) summation of
$f(x)$, $F(x)$	functions of x
$\exp x = e^x$	(e = naperian log base) (abbreviation for e^x)
∇	del or nabla, vector differential operator
∇^2	Laplacian operator
$\mathfrak{L}$	Laplace operational symbol
$4!$	factorial $4 = 1 \times 2 \times 3 \times 4$
$\lvert x \rvert$	absolute value of x
$\dot{x}$	first derivative of x with respect to time
$\ddot{x}$	second derivative of x with respect to time
$\mathbf{A} \times \mathbf{B}$	vector product; magnitude of **A** times magnitude of **B** times sine of the angle from **A** to **B**; $AB \sin \overline{AB}$
$\mathbf{A} \cdot \mathbf{B}$	scalar product; magnitude of **A** times magnitude of **B** times cosine of the angle from **A** to **B**; $AB \cos \overline{AB}$

In the writing out of formulas the practice described in the first paragraph of p. 2–24 is followed throughout this book.

SURFACE TEXTURE SYMBOLS (See also pp. 13-106 *et seq.*)

√ Surface Texture Symbol (ASA B46.2), Domestic
√ Surface Texture Symbol—machining allowance
× Surface Texture, Lay, angular in both directions
M Surface Texture, Lay, multidirectional
⊥ Surface Texture, Lay, perpendicular
‖ Surface Texture, Lay, parallel
C Surface Texture, Lay, circular
R Surface Texture, Lay, radial
~, √, ▽▽▽ Surface Texture Symbols, Foreign

SECTION 1

MATHEMATICAL TABLES AND WEIGHTS AND MEASURES

BY

PHILIP FRANKLIN, Professor of Mathematics, Massachusetts Institute of Technology.

LEWIS V. JUDSON, Retired Physicist, Office of Weights and Measures, National Bureau of Standards.

CONTENTS

MATHEMATICAL TABLES

By PHILIP FRANKLIN

WEIGHTS AND MEASURES

By LEWIS V. JUDSON

References for Mathematical Tables: Allen, "Six-place Tables," McGraw-Hill. Comrie, "Chambers Shorter Six-figure Mathematical Tables," Chemical Publishing. Dwight, "Mathematical Tables of Elementary and Some Higher Mathematical Functions," McGraw-Hill. Dwight, "Tables of Integrals and Other Mathematical Data," Macmillan. Jahnke and Emde, "Tables of Functions," B. G. Teubner, Leipzig, or Dover. Peirce-Foster, "A Short Table of Integrals," Ginn. "Mathematical Tables from Handbook of Chemistry and Physics," Chemical Rubber Co. "Handbook of Mathematical Functions," NBS.

Squares of Numbers

N	0	1	2	3	4	5	6	7	8	9	Avg diff
1.00	1.000	1.002	1.004	1.006	1.008	1.010	1.012	1.014	1.016	1.018	2
1	1.020	1.022	1.024	1.026	1.028	1.030	1.032	1.034	1.036	1.038	
2	1.040	1.042	1.044	1.047	1.049	1.051	1.053	1.055	1.057	1.059	
3	1.061	1.063	1.065	1.067	1.069	1.071	1.073	1.075	1.077	1.080	
4	1.082	1.084	1.086	1.088	1.090	1.092	1.094	1.096	1.098	1.100	
1.05	1.102	1.105	1.107	1.109	1.111	1.113	1.115	1.117	1.119	1.121	
6	1.124	1.126	1.128	1.130	1.132	1.134	1.136	1.138	1.141	1.143	
7	1.145	1.147	1.149	1.151	1.153	1.156	1.158	1.160	1.162	1.164	
8	1.166	1.169	1.171	1.173	1.175	1.177	1.179	1.182	1.184	1.186	
9	1.188	1.190	1.192	1.195	1.197	1.199	1.201	1.203	1.206	1.208	
1.10	1.210	1.212	1.214	1.217	1.219	1.221	1.223	1.225	1.228	1.230	
1	1.232	1.234	1.237	1.239	1.241	1.243	1.245	1.248	1.250	1.252	
2	1.254	1.257	1.259	1.261	1.263	1.266	1.268	1.270	1.272	1.275	
3	1.277	1.279	1.281	1.284	1.286	1.288	1.290	1.293	1.295	1.297	
4	1.300	1.302	1.304	1.306	1.309	1.311	1.313	1.316	1.318	1.320	
1.15	1.322	1.325	1.327	1.329	1.332	1.334	1.336	1.339	1.341	1.343	
6	1.346	1.348	1.350	1.353	1.355	1.357	1.360	1.362	1.364	1.367	
7	1.369	1.371	1.374	1.376	1.378	1.381	1.383	1.385	1.388	1.390	
8	1.392	1.395	1.397	1.399	1.402	1.404	1.407	1.409	1.411	1.414	
9	1.416	1.418	1.421	1.423	1.426	1.428	1.430	1.433	1.435	1.438	
1.20	1.440	1.442	1.445	1.447	1.450	1.452	1.454	1.457	1.459	1.462	
1	1.464	1.467	1.469	1.471	1.474	1.476	1.479	1.481	1.484	1.486	
2	1.488	1.491	1.493	1.496	1.498	1.501	1.503	1.506	1.508	1.510	
3	1.513	1.515	1.518	1.520	1.523	1.525	1.528	1.530	1.533	1.535	
4	1.538	1.540	1.543	1.545	1.548	1.550	1.553	1.555	1.558	1.560	
1.25	1.562	1.565	1.568	1.570	1.573	1.575	1.578	1.580	1.583	1.585	3
6	1.588	1.590	1.593	1.595	1.598	1.600	1.603	1.605	1.608	1.610	
7	1.613	1.615	1.618	1.621	1.623	1.626	1.628	1.631	1.633	1.636	
8	1.638	1.641	1.644	1.646	1.649	1.651	1.654	1.656	1.659	1.662	
9	1.664	1.667	1.669	1.672	1.674	1.677	1.680	1.682	1.685	1.687	
1.30	1.690	1.693	1.695	1.698	1.700	1.703	1.706	1.708	1.711	1.713	
1	1.716	1.719	1.721	1.724	1.727	1.729	1.732	1.734	1.737	1.740	
2	1.742	1.745	1.748	1.750	1.753	1.756	1.758	1.761	1.764	1.766	
3	1.769	1.772	1.774	1.777	1.780	1.782	1.785	1.788	1.790	1.793	
4	1.796	1.798	1.801	1.804	1.806	1.809	1.812	1.814	1.817	1.820	
1.35	1.822	1.825	1.828	1.831	1.833	1.836	1.839	1.841	1.844	1.847	
6	1.850	1.852	1.855	1.858	1.860	1.863	1.866	1.869	1.871	1.874	
7	1.877	1.880	1.882	1.885	1.888	1.891	1.893	1.896	1.899	1.902	
8	1.904	1.907	1.910	1.913	1.915	1.918	1.921	1.924	1.927	1.929	
9	1.932	1.935	1.938	1.940	1.943	1.946	1.949	1.952	1.954	1.957	
1.40	1.960	1.963	1.966	1.968	1.971	1.974	1.977	1.980	1.982	1.985	
1	1.988	1.991	1.994	1.997	1.999	2.002	2.005	2.008	2.011	2.014	
2	2.016	2.019	2.022	2.025	2.028	2.031	2.033	2.036	2.039	2.042	
3	2.045	2.048	2.051	2.053	2.056	2.059	2.062	2.065	2.068	2.071	
4	2.074	2.076	2.079	2.082	2.085	2.088	2.091	2.094	2.097	2.100	
1.45	2.102	2.105	2.108	2.111	2.114	2.117	2.120	2.123	2.126	2.129	
6	2.132	2.135	2.137	2.140	2.143	2.146	2.149	2.152	2.155	2.158	
7	2.161	2.164	2.167	2.170	2.173	2.176	2.179	2.182	2.184	2.187	
8	2.190	2.193	2.196	2.199	2.202	2.205	2.208	2.211	2.214	2.217	
9	2.220	2.223	2.226	2.229	2.232	2.235	2.238	2.241	2.244	2.247	

Moving the decimal point ONE place in *N* requires moving it TWO places in body of table (see p. 1–6).

Squares (*continued*)

N	0	1	2	3	4	5	6	7	8	9	Avg diff
1.50	2.250	2.253	2.256	2.259	2.262	2.265	2.268	2.271	2.274	2.277	**3**
1	2.280	2.283	2.286	2.289	2.292	2.295	2.298	2.301	2.304	2.307	
2	2.310	2.313	2.316	2.320	2.323	2.326	2.329	2.332	2.335	2.338	
3	2.341	2.344	2.347	2.350	2.353	2.356	2.359	2.362	2.365	2.369	
4	2.372	2.375	2.378	2.381	2.384	2.387	2.390	2.393	2.396	2.399	
1.55	2.402	2.406	2.409	2.412	2.415	2.418	2.421	2.424	2.427	2.430	
6	2.434	2.437	2.440	2.443	2.446	2.449	2.452	2.455	2.459	2.462	
7	2.465	2.468	2.471	2.474	2.477	2.481	2.484	2.487	2.490	2.493	
8	2.496	2.500	2.503	2.506	2.509	2.512	2.515	2.519	2.522	2.525	
9	2.528	2.531	2.534	2.538	2.541	2.544	2.547	2.550	2.554	2.557	
1.60	2.560	2.563	2.566	2.570	2.573	2.576	2.579	2.582	2.586	2.589	
1	2.592	2.595	2.599	2.602	2.605	2.608	2.611	2.615	2.618	2.621	
2	2.624	2.628	2.631	2.634	2.637	2.641	2.644	2.647	2.650	2.654	
3	2.657	2.660	2.663	2.667	2.670	2.673	2.676	2.680	2.683	2.686	
4	2.690	2.693	2.696	2.699	2.703	2.706	2.709	2.713	2.716	2.719	
1.65	2.722	2.726	2.729	2.732	2.736	2.739	2.742	2.746	2.749	2.752	
6	2.756	2.759	2.762	2.766	2.769	2.772	2.776	2.779	2.782	2.786	
7	2.789	2.792	2.796	2.799	2.802	2.806	2.809	2.812	2.816	2.819	
8	2.822	2.826	2.829	2.832	2.836	2.839	2.843	2.846	2.849	2.853	
9	2.856	2.859	2.863	2.866	2.870	2.873	2.876	2.880	2.883	2.887	
1.70	2.890	2.893	2.897	2.900	2.904	2.907	2.910	2.914	2.917	2.921	
1	2.924	2.928	2.931	2.934	2.938	2.941	2.945	2.948	2.952	2.955	
2	2.958	2.962	2.965	2.969	2.972	2.976	2.979	2.983	2.986	2.989	
3	2.993	2.996	3.000	3.003	3.007	3.010	3.014	3.017	3.021	3.024	
4	3.028	3.031	3.035	3.038	3.042	3.045	3.049	3.052	3.056	3.059	
1.75	3.062	3.066	3.070	3.073	3.077	3.080	3.084	3.087	3.091	3.094	**4**
6	3.098	3.101	3.105	3.108	3.112	3.115	3.119	3.122	3.126	3.129	
7	3.133	3.136	3.140	3.144	3.147	3.151	3.154	3.158	3.161	3.165	
8	3.168	3.172	3.176	3.179	3.183	3.186	3.190	3.193	3.197	3.201	
9	3.204	3.208	3.211	3.215	3.218	3.222	3.226	3.229	3.233	3.236	
1.80	3.240	3.244	3.247	3.251	3.254	3.258	3.262	3.265	3.269	3.272	
1	3.276	3.280	3.283	3.287	3.291	3.294	3.298	3.301	3.305	3.309	
2	3.312	3.316	3.320	3.323	3.327	3.331	3.334	3.338	3.342	3.345	
3	3.349	3.353	3.356	3.360	3.364	3.367	3.371	3.375	3.378	3.382	
4	3.386	3.389	3.393	3.397	3.400	3.404	3.408	3.411	3.415	3.419	
1.85	3.422	3.426	3.430	3.434	3.437	3.441	3.445	3.448	3.452	3.456	
6	3.460	3.463	3.467	3.471	3.474	3.478	3.482	3.486	3.489	3.493	
7	3.497	3.501	3.504	3.508	3.512	3.516	3.519	3.523	3.527	3.531	
8	3.534	3.538	3.542	3.546	3.549	3.553	3.557	3.561	3.565	3.568	
9	3.572	3.576	3.580	3.583	3.587	3.591	3.595	3.599	3.602	3.606	
1.90	3.610	3.614	3.618	3.621	3.625	3.629	3.633	3.637	3.640	3.644	
1	3.648	3.652	3.656	3.660	3.663	3.667	3.671	3.675	3.679	3.683	
2	3.686	3.690	3.694	3.698	3.702	3.706	3.709	3.713	3.717	3.721	
3	3.725	3.729	3.733	3.736	3.740	3.744	3.748	3.752	3.756	3.760	
4	3.764	3.767	3.771	3.775	3.779	3.783	3.787	3.791	3.795	3.799	
1.95	3.802	3.806	3.810	3.814	3.818	3.822	3.826	3.830	3.834	3.838	
6	3.842	3.846	3.849	3.853	3.857	3.861	3.865	3.869	3.873	3.877	
7	3.881	3.885	3.889	3.893	3.897	3.901	3.905	3.909	3.912	3.916	
8	3.920	3.924	3.928	3.932	3.936	3.940	3.944	3.948	3.952	3.956	
9	3.960	3.964	3.968	3.972	3.976	3.980	3.984	3.988	3.992	3.996	

$\pi^2 = 9.86960 \qquad 1/\pi^2 = 0.101321 \qquad e^2 = 7.38906$

Squares (*continued*)

N	0	1	2	3	4	5	6	7	8	9	Avg diff
2.00	4.000	4.004	4.008	4.012	4.016	4.020	4.024	4.028	4.032	4.036	4
1	4.040	4.044	4.048	4.052	4.056	4.060	4.064	4.068	4.072	4.076	
2	4.080	4.084	4.088	4.093	4.097	4.101	4.105	4.109	4.113	4.117	
3	4.121	4.125	4.129	4.133	4.137	4.141	4.145	4.149	4.153	4.158	
4	4.162	4.166	4.170	4.174	4.178	4.182	4.186	4.190	4.194	4.198	
2.05	4.202	4.207	4.211	4.215	4.219	4.223	4.227	4.231	4.235	4.239	
6	4.244	4.248	4.252	4.256	4.260	4.264	4.268	4.272	4.277	4.281	
7	4.285	4.289	4.293	4.297	4.301	4.306	4.310	4.314	4.318	4.322	
8	4.326	4.331	4.335	4.339	4.343	4.347	4.351	4.356	4.360	4.364	
9	4.368	4.372	4.376	4.381	4.385	4.389	4.393	4.397	4.402	4.406	
2.10	4.410	4.414	4.418	4.423	4.427	4.431	4.435	4.439	4.444	4.448	
1	4.452	4.456	4.461	4.465	4.469	4.473	4.477	4.482	4.486	4.490	
2	4.494	4.499	4.503	4.507	4.511	4.516	4.520	4.524	4.528	4.533	
3	4.537	4.541	4.545	4.550	4.554	4.558	4.562	4.567	4.571	4.575	
4	4.580	4.584	4.588	4.592	4.597	4.601	4.605	4.610	4.614	4.618	
2.15	4.622	4.627	4.631	4.635	4.640	4.644	4.648	4.653	4.657	4.661	
6	4.666	4.670	4.674	4.679	4.683	4.687	4.692	4.696	4.700	4.705	
7	4.709	4.713	4.718	4.722	4.726	4.731	4.735	4.739	4.744	4.748	
8	4.752	4.757	4.761	4.765	4.770	4.774	4.779	4.783	4.787	4.792	
9	4.796	4.800	4.805	4.809	4.814	4.818	4.822	4.827	4.831	4.836	
2.20	4.840	4.844	4.849	4.853	4.858	4.862	4.866	4.871	4.875	4.880	
1	4.884	4.889	4.893	4.897	4.902	4.906	4.911	4.915	4.920	4.924	
2	4.928	4.933	4.937	4.942	4.946	4.951	4.955	4.960	4.964	4.968	
3	4.973	4.977	4.982	4.986	4.991	4.995	5.000	5.004	5.009	5.013	
4	5.018	5.022	5.027	5.031	5.036	5.040	5.045	5.049	5.054	5.058	
2.25	5.062	5.067	5.072	5.076	5.081	5.085	5.090	5.094	5.099	5.103	5
6	5.108	5.112	5.117	5.121	5.126	5.130	5.135	5.139	5.144	5.148	
7	5.153	5.157	5.162	5.167	5.171	5.176	5.180	5.185	5.189	5.194	
8	5.198	5.203	5.208	5.212	5.217	5.221	5.226	5.230	5.235	5.240	
9	5.244	5.249	5.253	5.258	5.262	5.267	5.272	5.276	5.281	5.285	
2.30	5.290	5.295	5.299	5.304	5.308	5.313	5.318	5.322	5.327	5.331	
1	5.336	5.341	5.345	5.350	5.355	5.359	5.364	5.368	5.373	5.378	
2	5.382	5.387	5.392	5.396	5.401	5.406	5.410	5.415	5.420	5.424	
3	5.429	5.434	5.438	5.443	5.448	5.452	5.457	5.462	5.466	5.471	
4	5.476	5.480	5.485	5.490	5.494	5.499	5.504	5.508	5.513	5.518	
2.35	5.522	5.527	5.532	5.537	5.541	5.546	5.551	5.555	5.560	5.565	
6	5.570	5.574	5.579	5.584	5.588	5.593	5.598	5.603	5.607	5.612	
7	5.617	5.622	5.626	5.631	5.636	5.641	5.645	5.650	5.655	5.660	
8	5.664	5.669	5.674	5.679	5.683	5.688	5.693	5.698	5.703	5.707	
9	5.712	5.717	5.722	5.726	5.731	5.736	5.741	5.746	5.750	5.755	
2.40	5.760	5.765	5.770	5.774	5.779	5.784	5.789	5.794	5.798	5.803	
1	5.808	5.813	5.818	5.823	5.827	5.832	5.837	5.842	5.847	5.852	
2	5.856	5.861	5.866	5.871	5.876	5.881	5.885	5.890	5.895	5.900	
3	5.905	5.910	5.915	5.919	5.924	5.929	5.934	5.939	5.944	5.949	
4	5.954	5.958	5.963	5.968	5.973	5.978	5.983	5.988	5.993	5.998	
2.45	6.002	6.007	6.012	6.017	6.022	6.027	6.032	6.037	6.042	6.047	
6	6.052	6.057	6.061	6.066	6.071	6.076	6.081	6.086	6.091	6.096	
7	6.101	6.106	6.111	6.116	6.121	6.126	6.131	6.136	6.140	6.145	
8	6.150	6.155	6.160	6.165	6.170	6.175	6.180	6.185	6.190	6.195	
9	6.200	6.205	6.210	6.215	6.220	6.225	6.230	6.235	6.240	6.245	

Moving the decimal point ONE place in N requires moving it TWO places in body of table (see p. 1–6).

Squares (*continued*)

N	0	1	2	3	4	5	6	7	8	9	Avg diff
2.50	6.250	6.255	6.260	6.265	6.270	6.275	6.280	6.285	6.290	6.295	5
1	6.300	6.305	6.310	6.315	6.320	6.325	6.330	6.335	6.340	6.345	
2	6.350	6.355	6.360	6.366	6.371	6.376	6.381	6.386	6.391	6.396	
3	6.401	6.406	6.411	6.416	6.421	6.426	6.431	6.436	6.441	6.447	
4	6.452	6.457	6.462	6.467	6.472	6.477	6.482	6.487	6.492	6.497	
2.55	6.502	6.508	6.513	6.518	6.523	6.528	6.533	6.538	6.543	6.548	
6	6.554	6.559	6.564	6.569	6.574	6.579	6.584	6.589	6.595	6.600	
7	6.605	6.610	6.615	6.620	6.625	6.631	6.636	6.641	6.646	6.651	
8	6.656	6.662	6.667	6.672	6.677	6.682	6.687	6.693	6.698	6.703	
9	6.708	6.713	6.718	6.724	6.729	6.734	6.739	6.744	6.750	6.755	
2.60	6.760	6.765	6.770	6.776	6.781	6.786	6.791	6.796	6.802	6.807	
1	6.812	6.817	6.823	6.828	6.833	6.838	6.843	6.849	6.854	6.859	
2	6.864	6.870	6.875	6.880	6.885	6.891	6.896	6.901	6.906	6.912	
3	6.917	6.922	6.927	6.933	6.938	6.943	6.948	6.954	6.959	6.964	
4	6.970	6.975	6.980	6.985	6.991	6.996	7.001	7.007	7.012	7.017	
2.65	7.022	7.028	7.033	7.038	7.044	7.049	7.054	7.060	7.065	7.070	
6	7.076	7.081	7.086	7.092	7.097	7.102	7.108	7.113	7.118	7.124	
7	7.129	7.134	7.140	7.145	7.150	7.156	7.161	7.166	7.172	7.177	
8	7.182	7.188	7.193	7.198	7.204	7.209	7.215	7.220	7.225	7.231	
9	7.236	7.241	7.247	7.252	7.258	7.263	7.268	7.274	7.279	7.285	
2.70	7.290	7.295	7.301	7.306	7.312	7.317	7.322	7.328	7.333	7.339	
1	7.344	7.350	7.355	7.360	7.366	7.371	7.377	7.382	7.388	7.393	
2	7.398	7.404	7.409	7.415	7.420	7.426	7.431	7.437	7.442	7.447	
3	7.453	7.458	7.464	7.469	7.475	7.480	7.486	7.491	7.497	7.502	
4	7.508	7.513	7.519	7.524	7.530	7.535	7.541	7.546	7.552	7.557	
2.75	7.562	7.568	7.574	7.579	7.585	7.590	7.596	7.601	7.607	7.612	6
6	7.618	7.623	7.629	7.634	7.640	7.645	7.651	7.656	7.662	7.667	
7	7.673	7.678	7.684	7.690	7.695	7.701	7.706	7.712	7.717	7.723	
8	7.728	7.734	7.740	7.745	7.751	7.756	7.762	7.767	7.773	7.779	
9	7.784	7.790	7.795	7.801	7.806	7.812	7.818	7.823	7.829	7.834	
2.80	7.840	7.846	7.851	7.857	7.862	7.868	7.874	7.879	7.885	7.890	
1	7.896	7.902	7.907	7.913	7.919	7.924	7.930	7.935	7.941	7.947	
2	7.952	7.958	7.964	7.969	7.975	7.981	7.986	7.992	7.998	8.003	
3	8.009	8.015	8.020	8.026	8.032	8.037	8.043	8.049	8.054	8.060	
4	8.066	8.071	8.077	8.083	8.088	8.094	8.100	8.105	8.111	8.117	
2.85	8.122	8.128	8.134	8.140	8.145	8.151	8.157	8.162	8.168	8.174	
6	8.180	8.185	8.191	8.197	8.202	8.208	8.214	8.220	8.225	8.231	
7	8.237	8.243	8.248	8.254	8.260	8.266	8.271	8.277	8.283	8.289	
8	8.294	8.300	8.306	8.312	8.317	8.323	8.329	8.335	8.341	8.346	
9	8.352	8.358	8.364	8.369	8.375	8.381	8.387	8.393	8.398	8.404	
2.90	8.410	8.416	8.422	8.427	8.433	8.439	8.445	8.451	8.456	8.462	
1	8.468	8.474	8.480	8.486	8.491	8.497	8.503	8.509	8.515	8.521	
2	8.526	8.532	8.538	8.544	8.550	8.556	8.561	8.567	8.573	8.579	
3	8.585	8.591	8.597	8.602	8.608	8.614	8.620	8.626	8.632	8.638	
4	8.644	8.649	8.655	8.661	8.667	8.673	8.679	8.685	8.691	8.697	
2.95	8.702	8.708	8.714	8.720	8.726	8.732	8.738	8.744	8.750	8.756	
6	8.762	8.768	8.773	8.779	8.785	8.791	8.797	8.803	8.809	8.815	
7	8.821	8.827	8.833	8.839	8.845	8.851	8.857	8.863	8.868	8.874	
8	8.880	8.886	8.892	8.898	8.904	8.910	8.916	8.922	8.928	8.934	
9	8.940	8.946	8.952	8.958	8.964	8.970	8.976	8.982	8.988	8.994	

$\pi^2 = 9.86960 \qquad 1/\pi^2 = 0.101321 \qquad e^2 = 7.38906$

Squares (*continued*)

N	0	1	2	3	4	5	6	7	8	9	Avg diff
3.00	9.000	9.006	9.012	9.018	9.024	9.030	9.036	9.042	9.048	9.054	
1	9.060	9.066	9.072	9.078	9.084	9.090	9.096	9.102	9.108	9.114	6
2	9.120	9.126	9.132	9.139	9.145	9.151	9.157	9.163	9.169	9.175	
3	9.181	9.187	9.193	9.199	9.205	9.211	9.217	9.223	9.229	9.236	
4	9.242	9.248	9.254	9.260	9.266	9.272	9.278	9.284	9.290	9.296	
3.05	9.302	9.309	9.315	9.321	9.327	9.333	9.339	9.345	9.351	9.357	
6	9.364	9.370	9.376	9.382	9.388	9.394	9.400	9.406	9.413	9.419	
7	9.425	9.431	9.437	9.443	9.449	9.456	9.462	9.468	9.474	9.480	
8	9.486	9.493	9.499	9.505	9.511	9.517	9.523	9.530	9.536	9.542	
9	9.548	9.554	9.560	9.567	9.573	9.579	9.585	9.591	9.598	9.604	
3.10	9.610	9.616	9.622	9.629	9.635	9.641	9.647	9.653	9.660	9.666	
1	9.672	9.678	9.685	9.691	9.697	9.703	9.709	9.716	9.722	9.728	
2	9.734	9.741	9.747	9.753	9.759	9.766	9.772	9.778	9.784	9.791	
3	9.797	9.803	9.809	9.816	9.822	9.828	9.834	9.841	9.847	9.853	
4	9.860	9.866	9.872	9.878	9.885	9.891	9.897	9.904	9.910	9.916	
3.15	9.922	9.929	9.935	9.941	9.948	9.954	9.960	9.967	9.973	9.979	
6	9.986	9.992	9.998	10.005							
3.1							9.99	10.05	10.11	10.18	6
2	10.24	10.30	10.37	10.43	10.50	10.56	10.63	10.69	10.76	10.82	6
3	10.89	10.96	11.02	11.09	11.16	11.22	11.29	11.36	11.42	11.49	
4	11.56	11.63	11.70	11.76	11.83	11.90	11.97	12.04	12.11	12.18	7
3.5	12.25	12.32	12.39	12.46	12.53	12.60	12.67	12.74	12.82	12.89	
6	12.96	13.03	13.10	13.18	13.25	13.32	13.40	13.47	13.54	13.62	
7	13.69	13.76	13.84	13.91	13.99	14.06	14.14	14.21	14.29	14.36	
8	14.44	14.52	14.59	14.67	14.75	14.82	14.90	14.98	15.05	15.13	8
9	15.21	15.29	15.37	15.44	15.52	15.60	15.68	15.76	15.84	15.92	
4.0	16.00	16.08	16.16	16.24	16.32	16.40	16.48	16.56	16.65	16.73	
1	16.81	16.89	16.97	17.06	17.14	17.22	17.31	17.39	17.47	17.56	
2	17.64	17.72	17.81	17.89	17.98	18.06	18.15	18.23	18.32	18.40	
3	18.49	18.58	18.66	18.75	18.84	18.92	19.01	19.10	19.18	19.27	9
4	19.36	19.45	19.54	19.62	19.71	19.80	19.89	19.98	20.07	20.16	
4.5	20.25	20.34	20.43	20.52	20.61	20.70	20.79	20.88	20.98	21.07	
6	21.16	21.25	21.34	21.44	21.53	21.62	21.72	21.81	21.90	22.00	
7	22.09	22.18	22.28	22.37	22.47	22.56	22.66	22.75	22.85	22.94	10
8	23.04	23.14	23.23	23.33	23.43	23.52	23.62	23.72	23.81	23.91	
9	24.01	24.11	24.21	24.30	24.40	24.50	24.60	24.70	24.80	24.90	

$\pi^2 = 9.86960$ $(\pi/2)^2 = 2.46740$ $1/\pi^2 = 0.101321$

Explanation of Table of Squares (pp. 1–2 to 1–7).

This table gives the value of N^2 for values of N from 1 to 10, correct to four figures. (Interpolated values may be in error by 1 in the fourth figure.)

To find the square of a number *N* outside the range from 1 to 10, note that moving the decimal point ONE place in column N is equivalent to moving it TWO places in the body of the table. For example:

$(3.217)^2 = 10.35$ $(0.03217)^2 = 0.001035$ $(3217)^2 = 10350000$

This table can also be used inversely, to give square roots.

Squares (*continued*)

N	0	1	2	3	4	5	6	7	8	9	Avg diff
5.0	25.00	25.10	25.20	25.30	25.40	25.50	25.60	25.70	25.81	25.91	**10**
1	26.01	26.11	26.21	26.32	26.42	26.52	26.63	26.73	26.83	26.94	
2	27.04	27.14	27.25	27.35	27.46	27.56	27.67	27.77	27.88	27.98	
3	28.09	28.20	28.30	28.41	28.52	28.62	28.73	28.84	28.94	29.05	**11**
4	29.16	29.27	29.38	29.48	29.59	29.70	29.81	29.92	30.03	30.14	
5.5	30.25	30.36	30.47	30.58	30.69	30.80	30.91	31.02	31.14	31.25	
6	31.36	31.47	31.58	31.70	31.81	31.92	32.04	32.15	32.26	32.38	
7	32.49	32.60	32.72	32.83	32.95	33.06	33.18	33.29	33.41	33.52	
8	33.64	33.76	33.87	33.99	34.11	34.22	34.34	34.46	34.57	34.69	**12**
9	34.81	34.93	35.05	35.16	35.28	35.40	35.52	35.64	35.76	35.88	
6.0	36.00	36.12	36.24	36.36	36.48	36.60	36.72	36.84	36.97	37.09	
1	37.21	37.33	37.45	37.58	37.70	37.82	37.95	38.07	38.19	38.32	
2	38.44	38.56	38.69	38.81	38.94	39.06	39.19	39.31	39.44	39.56	
3	39.69	39.82	39.94	40.07	40.20	40.32	40.45	40.58	40.70	40.83	**13**
4	40.96	41.09	41.22	41.34	41.47	41.60	41.73	41.86	41.99	42.12	
6.5	42.25	42.38	42.51	42.64	42.77	42.90	43.03	43.16	43.30	43.43	
6	43.56	43.69	43.82	43.96	44.09	44.22	44.36	44.49	44.62	44.76	
7	44.89	45.02	45.16	45.29	45.43	45.56	45.70	45.83	45.97	46.10	
8	46.24	46.38	46.51	46.65	46.79	46.92	47.06	47.20	47.33	47.47	**14**
9	47.61	47.75	47.89	48.02	48.16	48.30	48.44	48.58	48.72	48.86	
7.0	49.00	49.14	49.28	49.42	49.56	49.70	49.84	49.98	50.13	50.27	
1	50.41	50.55	50.69	50.84	50.98	51.12	51.27	51.41	51.55	51.70	
2	51.84	51.98	52.13	52.27	52.42	52.56	52.71	52.85	53.00	53.14	
3	53.29	53.44	53.58	53.73	53.88	54.02	54.17	54.32	54.46	54.61	**15**
4	54.76	54.91	55.06	55.20	55.35	55.50	55.65	55.80	55.95	56.10	
7.5	56.25	56.40	56.55	56.70	56.85	57.00	57.15	57.30	57.46	57.61	
6	57.76	57.91	58.06	58.22	58.37	58.52	58.68	58.83	58.98	59.14	
7	59.29	59.44	59.60	59.75	59.91	60.06	60.22	60.37	60.53	60.68	
8	60.84	61.00	61.15	61.31	61.47	61.62	61.78	61.94	62.09	62.25	**16**
9	62.41	62.57	62.73	62.88	63.04	63.20	63.36	63.52	63.68	63.84	
8.0	64.00	64.16	64.32	64.48	64.64	64.80	64.96	65.12	65.29	65.45	
1	65.61	65.77	65.93	66.10	66.26	66.42	66.59	66.75	66.91	67.08	
2	67.24	67.40	67.57	67.73	67.90	68.06	68.23	68.39	68.56	68.72	
3	68.89	69.06	69.22	69.39	69.56	69.72	69.89	70.06	70.22	70.39	**17**
4	70.56	70.73	70.90	71.06	71.23	71.40	71.57	71.74	71.91	72.08	
8.5	72.25	72.42	72.59	72.76	72.93	73.10	73.27	73.44	73.62	73.79	
6	73.96	74.13	74.30	74.48	74.65	74.82	75.00	75.17	75.34	75.52	
7	75.69	75.86	76.04	76.21	76.39	76.56	76.74	76.91	77.09	77.26	
8	77.44	77.62	77.79	77.97	78.15	78.32	78.50	78.68	78.85	79.03	**18**
9	79.21	79.39	79.57	79.74	79.92	80.10	80.28	80.46	80.64	80.82	
9.0	81.00	81.18	81.36	81.54	81.72	81.90	82.08	82.26	82.45	82.63	
1	82.81	82.99	83.17	83.36	83.54	83.72	83.91	84.09	84.27	84.46	
2	84.64	84.82	85.01	85.19	85.38	85.56	85.75	85.93	86.12	86.30	
3	86.49	86.68	86.86	87.05	87.24	87.42	87.61	87.80	87.98	88.17	**19**
4	88.36	88.55	88.74	88.92	89.11	89.30	89.49	89.68	89.87	90.06	
9.5	90.25	90.44	90.63	90.82	91.01	91.20	91.39	91.58	91.78	91.97	
6	92.16	92.35	92.54	92.74	92.93	93.12	93.32	93.51	93.70	93.90	
7	94.09	94.28	94.48	94.67	94.87	95.06	95.26	95.45	95.65	95.84	
8	96.04	96.24	96.43	96.63	96.83	97.02	97.22	97.42	97.61	97.81	**20**
9	98.01	98.21	98.41	98.60	98.80	99.00	99.20	99.40	99.60	99.80	
10.0	100.0										

Moving the decimal point ONE place in *N* requires moving it TWO places in body of table (see p. 1–6).

Cubes of Numbers

N	0	1	2	3	4	5	6	7	8	9	Avg diff
1.00	1.000	1.003	1.006	1.009	1.012	1.015	1.018	1.021	1.024	1.027	**3**
1	1.030	1.033	1.036	1.040	1.043	1.046	1.049	1.052	1.055	1.058	
2	1.061	1.064	1.067	1.071	1.074	1.077	1.080	1.083	1.086	1.090	
3	1.093	1.096	1.099	1.102	1.106	1.109	1.112	1.115	1.118	1.122	
4	1.125	1.128	1.131	1.135	1.138	1.141	1.144	1.148	1.151	1.154	
1.05	1.158	1.161	1.164	1.168	1.171	1.174	1.178	1.181	1.184	1.188	
6	1.191	1.194	1.198	1.201	1.205	1.208	1.211	1.215	1.218	1.222	
7	1.225	1.228	1.232	1.235	1.239	1.242	1.246	1.249	1.253	1.256	
8	1.260	1.263	1.267	1.270	1.274	1.277	1.281	1.284	1.288	1.291	**4**
9	1.295	1.299	1.302	1.306	1.309	1.313	1.317	1.320	1.324	1.327	
1.10	1.331	1.335	1.338	1.342	1.346	1.349	1.353	1.357	1.360	1.364	
1	1.368	1.371	1.375	1.379	1.382	1.386	1.390	1.394	1.397	1.401	
2	1.405	1.409	1.412	1.416	1.420	1.424	1.428	1.431	1.435	1.439	
3	1.443	1.447	1.451	1.454	1.458	1.462	1.466	1.470	1.474	1.478	
4	1.482	1.485	1.489	1.493	1.497	1.501	1.505	1.509	1.513	1.517	
1.15	1.521	1.525	1.529	1.533	1.537	1.541	1.545	1.549	1.553	1.557	
6	1.561	1.565	1.569	1.573	1.577	1.581	1.585	1.589	1.593	1.598	
7	1.602	1.606	1.610	1.614	1.618	1.622	1.626	1.631	1.635	1.639	
8	1.643	1.647	1.651	1.656	1.660	1.664	1.668	1.672	1.677	1.681	
9	1.685	1.689	1.694	1.698	1.702	1.706	1.711	1.715	1.719	1.724	
1.20	1.728	1.732	1.737	1.741	1.745	1.750	1.754	1.758	1.763	1.767	
1	1.772	1.776	1.780	1.785	1.789	1.794	1.798	1.802	1.807	1.811	
2	1.816	1.820	1.825	1.829	1.834	1.838	1.843	1.847	1.852	1.856	
3	1.861	1.865	1.870	1.875	1.879	1.884	1.888	1.893	1.897	1.902	
4	1.907	1.911	1.916	1.920	1.925	1.930	1.934	1.939	1.944	1.948	**5**
1.25	1.953	1.958	1.963	1.967	1.972	1.977	1.981	1.986	1.991	1.996	
6	2.000	2.005	2.010	2.015	2.019	2.024	2.029	2.034	2.039	2.044	
7	2.048	2.053	2.058	2.063	2.068	2.073	2.078	2.082	2.087	2.092	
8	2.097	2.102	2.107	2.112	2.117	2.122	2.127	2.132	2.137	2.142	
9	2.147	2.152	2.157	2.162	2.167	2.172	2.177	2.182	2.187	2.192	
1.30	2.197	2.202	2.207	2.212	2.217	2.222	2.228	2.233	2.238	2.243	
1	2.248	2.253	2.258	2.264	2.269	2.274	2.279	2.284	2.290	2.295	
2	2.300	2.305	2.310	2.316	2.321	2.326	2.331	2.337	2.342	2.347	
3	2.353	2.358	2.363	2.369	2.374	2.379	2.385	2.390	2.395	2.401	
4	2.406	2.411	2.417	2.422	2.428	2.433	2.439	2.444	2.449	2.455	
1.35	2.460	2.466	2.471	2.477	2.482	2.488	2.493	2.499	2.504	2.510	**6**
6	2.515	2.521	2.527	2.532	2.538	2.543	2.549	2.554	2.560	2.566	
7	2.571	2.577	2.583	2.588	2.594	2.600	2.605	2.611	2.617	2.622	
8	2.628	2.634	2.640	2.645	2.651	2.657	2.663	2.668	2.674	2.680	
9	2.686	2.691	2.697	2.703	2.709	2.715	2.721	2.726	2.732	2.738	
1.40	2.744	2.750	2.756	2.762	2.768	2.774	2.779	2.785	2.791	2.797	
1	2.803	2.809	2.815	2.821	2.827	2.833	2.839	2.845	2.851	2.857	
2	2.863	2.869	2.875	2.881	2.888	2.894	2.900	2.906	2.912	2.918	
3	2.924	2.930	2.936	2.943	2.949	2.955	2.961	2.967	2.974	2.980	
4	2.986	2.992	2.998	3.005	3.011	3.017	3.023	3.030	3.036	3.042	
1.45	3.049	3.055	3.061	3.068	3.074	3.080	3.087	3.093	3.099	3.106	
6	3.112	3.119	3.125	3.131	3.138	3.144	3.151	3.157	3.164	3.170	
7	3.177	3.183	3.190	3.196	3.203	3.209	3.216	3.222	3.229	3.235	
8	3.242	3.248	3.255	3.262	3.268	3.275	3.281	3.288	3.295	3.301	**7**
9	3.308	3.315	3.321	3.328	3.335	3.341	3.348	3.355	3.362	3.368	

Moving the decimal point ONE place in N requires moving it THREE places in body of table (see p. 1–10).

Cubes (*continued*)

N	0	1	2	3	4	5	6	7	8	9	Avg diff
1.50	3.375	3.382	3.389	3.395	3.402	3.409	3.416	3.422	3.429	3.436	7
1	3.443	3.450	3.457	3.464	3.470	3.477	3.484	3.491	3.498	3.505	
2	3.512	3.519	3.526	3.533	3.540	3.547	3.554	3.561	3.568	3.575	
3	3.582	3.589	3.596	3.603	3.610	3.617	3.624	3.631	3.638	3.645	
4	3.652	3.659	3.667	3.674	3.681	3.688	3.695	3.702	3.709	3.717	
1.55	3.724	3.731	3.738	3.746	3.753	3.760	3.767	3.775	3.782	3.789	
6	3.796	3.804	3.811	3.818	3.826	3.833	3.840	3.848	3.855	3.863	
7	3.870	3.877	3.885	3.892	3.900	3.907	3.914	3.922	3.929	3.937	
8	3.944	3.952	3.959	3.967	3.974	3.982	3.989	3.997	4.005	4.012	8
9	4.020	4.027	4.035	4.042	4.050	4.058	4.065	4.073	4.081	4.088	
1.60	4.096	4.104	4.111	4.119	4.127	4.135	4.142	4.150	4.158	4.166	
1	4.173	4.181	4.189	4.197	4.204	4.212	4.220	4.228	4.236	4.244	
2	4.252	4.259	4.267	4.275	4.283	4.291	4.299	4.307	4.315	4.323	
3	4.331	4.339	4.347	4.355	4.363	4.371	4.379	4.387	4.395	4.403	
4	4.411	4.419	4.427	4.435	4.443	4.451	4.460	4.468	4.476	4.484	
1.65	4.492	4.500	4.508	4.517	4.525	4.533	4.541	4.550	4.558	4.566	
6	4.574	4.583	4.591	4.599	4.607	4.616	4.624	4.632	4.641	4.649	
7	4.657	4.666	4.674	4.683	4.691	4.699	4.708	4.716	4.725	4.733	
8	4.742	4.750	4.759	4.767	4.776	4.784	4.793	4.801	4.810	4.818	
9	4.827	4.835	4.844	4.853	4.861	4.870	4.878	4.887	4.896	4.904	9
1.70	4.913	4.922	4.930	4.939	4.948	4.956	4.965	4.974	4.983	4.991	
1	5.000	5.009	5.018	5.027	5.035	5.044	5.053	5.062	5.071	5.080	
2	5.088	5.097	5.106	5.115	5.124	5.133	5.142	5.151	5.160	5.169	
3	5.178	5.187	5.196	5.205	5.214	5.223	5.232	5.241	5.250	5.259	
4	5.268	5.277	5.286	5.295	5.304	5.314	5.323	5.332	5.341	5.350	
1.75	5.359	5.369	5.378	5.387	5.396	5.405	5.415	5.424	5.433	5.442	
6	5.452	5.461	5.470	5.480	5.489	5.498	5.508	5.517	5.526	5.536	
7	5.545	5.555	5.564	5.573	5.583	5.592	5.602	5.611	5.621	5.630	10
8	5.640	5.649	5.659	5.668	5.678	5.687	5.697	5.707	5.716	5.726	
9	5.735	5.745	5.755	5.764	5.774	5.784	5.793	5.803	5.813	5.822	
1.80	5.832	5.842	5.851	5.861	5.871	5.881	5.891	5.900	5.910	5.920	
1	5.930	5.940	5.949	5.959	5.969	5.979	5.989	5.999	6.009	6.019	
2	6.029	6.039	6.048	6.058	6.068	6.078	6.088	6.098	6.108	6.118	
3	6.128	6.139	6.149	6.159	6.169	6.179	6.189	6.199	6.209	6.219	
4	6.230	6.240	6.250	6.260	6.270	6.280	6.291	6.301	6.311	6.321	
1.85	6.332	6.342	6.352	6.362	6.373	6.383	6.393	6.404	6.414	6.424	
6	6.435	6.445	6.456	6.466	6.476	6.487	6.497	6.508	6.518	6.529	
7	6.539	6.550	6.560	6.571	6.581	6.592	6.602	6.613	6.623	6.634	11
8	6.645	6.655	6.666	6.677	6.687	6.698	6.708	6.719	6.730	6.741	
9	6.751	6.762	6.773	6.783	6.794	6.805	6.816	6.827	6.837	6.848	
1.90	6.859	6.870	6.881	6.892	6.902	6.913	6.924	6.935	6.946	6.957	
1	6.968	6.979	6.990	7.001	7.012	7.023	7.034	7.045	7.056	7.067	
2	7.078	7.089	7.100	7.111	7.122	7.133	7.144	7.156	7.167	7.178	
3	7.189	7.200	7.211	7.223	7.234	7.245	7.256	7.268	7.279	7.290	
4	7.301	7.313	7.324	7.335	7.347	7.358	7.369	7.381	7.392	7.403	
1.95	7.415	7.426	7.438	7.449	7.461	7.472	7.484	7.495	7.507	7.518	12
6	7.530	7.541	7.553	7.564	7.576	7.587	7.599	7.610	7.622	7.634	
7	7.645	7.657	7.669	7.680	7.692	7.704	7.715	7.727	7.739	7.751	
8	7.762	7.774	7.786	7.798	7.810	7.821	7.833	7.845	7.857	7.869	
9	7.881	7.892	7.904	7.916	7.928	7.940	7.952	7.964	7.976	7.988	

$\pi^3 = 31.0063$ $\quad 1/\pi^3 = 0.0322515+$

Cubes (*continued*)

N	0	1	2	3	4	5	6	7	8	9	Avg diff
2.00	8.000	8.012	8.024	8.036	8.048	8.060	8.072	8.084	8.096	8.108	12
1	8.121	8.133	8.145	8.157	8.169	8.181	8.194	8.206	8.218	8.230	
2	8.242	8.255	8.267	8.279	8.291	8.304	8.316	8.328	8.341	8.353	
3	8.365	8.378	8.390	8.403	8.415	8.427	8.440	8.452	8.465	8.477	
4	8.490	8.502	8.515	8.527	8.540	8.552	8.565	8.577	8.590	8.603	
2.05	8.615	8.628	8.640	8.653	8.666	8.678	8.691	8.704	8.716	8.729	13
6	8.742	8.755	8.767	8.780	8.793	8.806	8.818	8.831	8.844	8.857	
7	8.870	8.883	8.895	8.908	8.921	8.934	8.947	8.960	8.973	8.986	
8	8.999	9.012	9.025	9.038	9.051	9.064	9.077	9.090	9.103	9.116	
9	9.129	9.142	9.156	9.169	9.182	9.195	9.208	9.221	9.235	9.248	
2.10	9.261	9.274	9.287	9.301	9.314	9.327	9.341	9.354	9.367	9.381	
1	9.394	9.407	9.421	9.434	9.447	9.461	9.474	9.488	9.501	9.515	
2	9.528	9.542	9.555	9.569	9.582	9.596	9.609	9.623	9.636	9.650	
3	9.664	9.677	9.691	9.704	9.718	9.732	9.745	9.759	9.773	9.787	14
4	9.800	9.814	9.828	9.842	9.855	9.869	9.883	9.897	9.911	9.925	
2.15	9.938	9.952	9.966	9.980	9.994	10.008					14
2.1						9.94	10.08	10.22	10.36	10.50	14
2	10.65	10.79	10.94	11.09	11.24	11.39	11.54	11.70	11.85	12.01	15
3	12.17	12.33	12.49	12.65	12.81	12.98	13.14	13.31	13.48	13.65	16
4	13.82	14.00	14.17	14.35	14.53	14.71	14.89	15.07	15.25	15.44	18
2.5	15.62	15.81	16.00	16.19	16.39	16.58	16.78	16.97	17.17	17.37	20
6	17.58	17.78	17.98	18.19	18.40	18.61	18.82	19.03	19.25	19.47	21
7	19.68	19.90	20.12	20.35	20.57	20.80	21.02	21.25	21.48	21.72	23
8	21.95	22.19	22.43	22.67	22.91	23.15	23.39	23.64	23.89	24.14	24
9	24.39	24.64	24.90	25.15	25.41	25.67	25.93	26.20	26.46	26.73	26
3.0	27.00	27.27	27.54	27.82	28.09	28.37	28.65	28.93	29.22	29.50	28
1	29.79	30.08	30.37	30.66	30.96	31.26	31.55	31.86	32.16	32.46	30
2	32.77	33.08	33.39	33.70	34.01	34.33	34.65	34.97	35.29	35.61	32
3	35.94	36.26	36.59	36.93	37.26	37.60	37.93	38.27	38.61	38.96	34
4	39.30	39.65	40.00	40.35	40.71	41.06	41.42	41.78	42.14	42.51	36
3.5	42.88	43.24	43.61	43.99	44.36	44.74	45.12	45.50	45.88	46.27	39
6	46.66	47.05	47.44	47.83	48.23	48.63	49.03	49.43	49.84	50.24	40
7	50.65	51.06	51.48	51.90	52.31	52.73	53.16	53.58	54.01	54.44	42
8	54.87	55.31	55.74	56.18	56.62	57.07	57.51	57.96	58.41	58.86	44
9	59.32	59.78	60.24	60.70	61.16	61.63	62.10	62.57	63.04	63.52	47
4.0	64.00	64.48	64.96	65.45	65.94	66.43	66.92	67.42	67.92	68.42	49
1	68.92	69.43	69.93	70.44	70.96	71.47	71.99	72.51	73.03	73.56	52
2	74.09	74.62	75.15	75.69	76.23	76.77	77.31	77.85	78.40	78.95	54
3	79.51	80.06	80.62	81.18	81.75	82.31	82.88	83.45	84.03	84.60	58
4	85.18	85.77	86.35	86.94	87.53	88.12	88.72	89.31	89.92	90.52	59
4.5	91.12	91.73	92.35	92.96	93.58	94.20	94.82	95.44	96.07	96.70	62
6	97.34	97.97	98.61	99.25	99.90	100.54					64
6						100.5	101.2	101.8	102.5	103.2	7
7	103.8	104.5	105.2	105.8	106.5	107.2	107.9	108.5	109.2	109.9	7
8	110.6	111.3	112.0	112.7	113.4	114.1	114.8	115.5	116.2	116.9	7
9	117.6	118.4	119.1	119.8	120.6	121.3	122.0	122.8	123.5	124.3	7

Explanation of Table of Cubes (pp. 1–8 to 1–11).

This table gives the value of N^3 for values of N from 1 to 10, correct to four figures. (Interpolated values may be in error by 1 in the fourth figure.)

To find the cube of a number N outside the range from 1 to 10, note that moving the decimal point ONE place in column N is equivalent to moving it THREE places in the body of the table. **For example:**

$(4.852)^3 = 114.2 \qquad (0.4852)^3 = 0.1142 \qquad (485.2)^3 = 114200000$

This table may also be used inversely, to give cube roots.

Cubes (*continued*)

N	0	1	2	3	4	5	6	7	8	9	Avg diff
5.0	125.0	125.8	126.5	127.3	128.0	128.8	129.6	130.3	131.1	131.9	8
1	132.7	133.4	134.2	135.0	135.8	136.6	137.4	138.2	139.0	139.8	
2	140.6	141.4	142.2	143.1	143.9	144.7	145.5	146.4	147.2	148.0	
3	148.9	149.7	150.6	151.4	152.3	153.1	154.0	154.9	155.7	156.6	9
4	157.5	158.3	159.2	160.1	161.0	161.9	162.8	163.7	164.6	165.5	
5.5	166.4	167.3	168.2	169.1	170.0	171.0	171.9	172.8	173.7	174.7	
6	175.6	176.6	177.5	178.5	179.4	180.4	181.3	182.3	183.3	184.2	10
7	185.2	186.2	187.1	188.1	189.1	190.1	191.1	192.1	193.1	194.1	
8	195.1	196.1	197.1	198.2	199.2	200.2	201.2	202.3	203.3	204.3	
9	205.4	206.4	207.5	208.5	209.6	210.6	211.7	212.8	213.8	214.9	
6.0	216.0	217.1	218.2	219.3	220.3	221.4	222.5	223.6	224.8	225.9	11
1	227.0	228.1	229.2	230.3	231.5	232.6	233.7	234.9	236.0	237.2	
2	238.3	239.5	240.6	241.8	243.0	244.1	245.3	246.5	247.7	248.9	12
3	250.0	251.2	252.4	253.6	254.8	256.0	257.3	258.5	259.7	260.9	
4	262.1	263.4	264.6	265.8	267.1	268.3	269.6	270.8	272.1	273.4	
6.5	274.6	275.9	277.2	278.4	279.7	281.0	282.3	283.6	284.9	286.2	13
6	287.5	288.8	290.1	291.4	292.8	294.1	295.4	296.7	298.1	299.4	
7	300.8	302.1	303.5	304.8	306.2	307.5	308.9	310.3	311.7	313.0	14
8	314.4	315.8	317.2	318.6	320.0	321.4	322.8	324.2	325.7	327.1	
9	328.5	329.9	331.4	332.8	334.3	335.7	337.2	338.6	340.1	341.5	
7.0	343.0	344.5	345.9	347.4	348.9	350.4	351.9	353.4	354.9	356.4	15
1	357.9	359.4	360.9	362.5	364.0	365.5	367.1	368.6	370.1	371.7	
2	373.2	374.8	376.4	377.9	379.5	381.1	382.7	384.2	385.8	387.4	16
3	389.0	390.6	392.2	393.8	395.4	397.1	398.7	400.3	401.9	403.6	
4	405.2	406.9	408.5	410.2	411.8	413.5	415.2	416.8	418.5	420.2	17
7.5	421.9	423.6	425.3	427.0	428.7	430.4	432.1	433.8	435.5	437.2	
6	439.0	440.7	442.5	444.2	445.9	447.7	449.5	451.2	453.0	454.8	18
7	456.5	458.3	460.1	461.9	463.7	465.5	467.3	469.1	470.9	472.7	
8	474.6	476.4	478.2	480.0	481.9	483.7	485.6	487.4	489.3	491.2	
9	493.0	494.9	496.8	498.7	500.6	502.5	504.4	506.3	508.2	510.1	19
8.0	512.0	513.9	515.8	517.8	519.7	521.7	523.6	525.6	527.5	529.5	
1	531.4	533.4	535.4	537.4	539.4	541.3	543.3	545.3	547.3	549.4	20
2	551.4	553.4	555.4	557.4	559.5	561.5	563.6	565.6	567.7	569.7	
3	571.8	573.9	575.9	578.0	580.1	582.2	584.3	586.4	588.5	590.6	21
4	592.7	594.8	596.9	599.1	601.2	603.4	605.5	607.6	609.8	612.0	
8.5	614.1	616.3	618.5	620.7	622.8	625.0	627.2	629.4	631.6	633.8	22
6	636.1	638.3	640.5	642.7	645.0	647.2	649.5	651.7	654.0	656.2	
7	658.5	660.8	663.1	665.3	667.6	669.9	672.2	674.5	676.8	679.2	23
8	681.5	683.8	686.1	688.5	690.8	693.2	695.5	697.9	700.2	702.6	24
9	705.0	707.3	709.7	712.1	714.5	716.9	719.3	721.7	724.2	726.6	
9.0	729.0	731.4	733.9	736.3	738.8	741.2	743.7	746.1	748.6	751.1	25
1	753.6	756.1	758.6	761.0	763.6	766.1	768.6	771.1	773.6	776.2	
2	778.7	781.2	783.8	786.3	788.9	791.5	794.0	796.6	799.2	801.8	26
3	804.4	807.0	809.6	812.2	814.8	817.4	820.0	822.7	825.3	827.9	
4	830.6	833.2	835.9	838.6	841.2	843.9	846.6	849.3	852.0	854.7	27
9.5	857.4	860.1	862.8	865.5	868.3	871.0	873.7	876.5	879.2	882.0	
6	884.7	887.5	890.3	893.1	895.8	898.6	901.4	904.2	907.0	909.9	28
7	912.7	915.5	918.3	921.2	924.0	926.9	929.7	932.6	935.4	938.3	
8	941.2	944.1	947.0	949.9	952.8	955.7	958.6	961.5	964.4	967.4	29
9	970.3	973.2	976.2	979.1	982.1	985.1	988.0	991.0	994.0	997.0	
10.0	1000.0										

$\pi^3 = 31.0063$ $1/\pi^3 = 0.0322515+$

Moving the decimal point ONE place in N requires moving it THREE places in body of table (see p. 1–10).

Square Roots of Numbers

N	0	1	2	3	4	5	6	7	8	9	Avg diff
1.0	1.000	1.005	1.010	1.015	1.020	1.025	1.030	1.034	1.039	1.044	5
1	1.049	1.054	1.058	1.063	1.068	1.072	1.077	1.082	1.086	1.091	
2	1.095	1.100	1.105	1.109	1.114	1.118	1.122	1.127	1.131	1.136	
3	1.140	1.145	1.149	1.153	1.158	1.162	1.166	1.170	1.175	1.179	4
4	1.183	1.187	1.192	1.196	1.200	1.204	1.208	1.212	1.217	1.221	
1.5	1.225	1.229	1.233	1.237	1.241	1.245	1.249	1.253	1.257	1.261	
6	1.265	1.269	1.273	1.277	1.281	1.285	1.288	1.292	1.296	1.300	
7	1.304	1.308	1.311	1.315	1.319	1.323	1.327	1.330	1.334	1.338	
8	1.342	1.345	1.349	1.353	1.356	1.360	1.364	1.367	1.371	1.375	
9	1.378	1.382	1.386	1.389	1.393	1.396	1.400	1.404	1.407	1.411	
2.0	1.414	1.418	1.421	1.425	1.428	1.432	1.435	1.439	1.442	1.446	
1	1.449	1.453	1.456	1.459	1.463	1.466	1.470	1.473	1.476	1.480	3
2	1.483	1.487	1.490	1.493	1.497	1.500	1.503	1.507	1.510	1.513	
3	1.517	1.520	1.523	1.526	1.530	1.533	1.536	1.539	1.543	1.546	
4	1.549	1.552	1.556	1.559	1.562	1.565	1.568	1.572	1.575	1.578	
2.5	1.581	1.584	1.587	1.591	1.594	1.597	1.600	1.603	1.606	1.609	
6	1.612	1.616	1.619	1.622	1.625	1.628	1.631	1.634	1.637	1.640	
7	1.643	1.646	1.649	1.652	1.655	1.658	1.661	1.664	1.667	1.670	
8	1.673	1.676	1.679	1.682	1.685	1.688	1.691	1.694	1.697	1.700	
9	1.703	1.706	1.709	1.712	1.715	1.718	1.720	1.723	1.726	1.729	
3.0	1.732	1.735	1.738	1.741	1.744	1.746	1.749	1.752	1.755	1.758	
1	1.761	1.764	1.766	1.769	1.772	1.775	1.778	1.780	1.783	1.786	
2	1.789	1.792	1.794	1.797	1.800	1.803	1.806	1.808	1.811	1.814	
3	1.817	1.819	1.822	1.825	1.828	1.830	1.833	1.836	1.838	1.841	
4	1.844	1.847	1.849	1.852	1.855	1.857	1.860	1.863	1.865	1.868	
3.5	1.871	1.873	1.876	1.879	1.881	1.884	1.887	1.889	1.892	1.895	
6	1.897	1.900	1.903	1.905	1.908	1.910	1.913	1.916	1.918	1.921	
7	1.924	1.926	1.929	1.931	1.934	1.936	1.939	1.942	1.944	1.947	
8	1.949	1.952	1.954	1.957	1.960	1.962	1.965	1.967	1.970	1.972	
9	1.975	1.977	1.980	1.982	1.985	1.987	1.990	1.992	1.995	1.997	
4.0	2.000	2.002	2.005	2.007	2.010	2.012	2.015	2.017	2.020	2.022	
1	2.025	2.027	2.030	2.032	2.035	2.037	2.040	2.042	2.045	2.047	2
2	2.049	2.052	2.054	2.057	2.059	2.062	2.064	2.066	2.069	2.071	
3	2.074	2.076	2.078	2.081	2.083	2.086	2.088	2.090	2.093	2.095	
4	2.098	2.100	2.102	2.105	2.107	2.110	2.112	2.114	2.117	2.119	
4.5	2.121	2.124	2.126	2.128	2.131	2.133	2.135	2.138	2.140	2.142	
6	2.145	2.147	2.149	2.152	2.154	2.156	2.159	2.161	2.163	2.166	
7	2.168	2.170	2.173	2.175	2.177	2.179	2.182	2.184	2.186	2.189	
8	2.191	2.193	2.195	2.198	2.200	2.202	2.205	2.207	2.209	2.211	
9	2.214	2.216	2.218	2.220	2.223	2.225	2.227	2.229	2.232	2.234	

$\sqrt{\pi} = 1.77245+$ $1/\sqrt{\pi} = 0.56419$ $\sqrt{\pi/2} = 1.25331$ $\sqrt{e} = 1.64872$

Explanation of Table of Square Roots (pp. 1–12 to 1–15).

This table gives the values of $\sqrt{N}$ for values of N from 1 to 100, correct to four figures. (Interpolated values may be in error by 1 in the fourth figure.)

To find the square root of a number N outside the range from 1 to 100, divide the digits of the number into blocks of two (beginning with the decimal point), and note that moving the decimal point TWO places in N is equivalent to moving it ONE place in the square root of N. For example:

$\sqrt{2.718} = 1.648$ $\sqrt{271.8} = 16.48$ $\sqrt{0.0002718} = 0.01648$

$\sqrt{27.18} = 5.213$ $\sqrt{2718} = 52.13$ $\sqrt{0.002718} = 0.05213$

Square Roots (*continued*)

N	0	1	2	3	4	5	6	7	8	9	Avg diff
5.0	2.236	2.238	2.241	2.243	2.245	2.247	2.249	2.252	2.254	2.256	2
1	2.258	2.261	2.263	2.265	2.267	2.269	2.272	2.274	2.276	2.278	
2	2.280	2.283	2.285	2.287	2.289	2.291	2.293	2.296	2.298	2.300	
3	2.302	2.304	2.307	2.309	2.311	2.313	2.315	2.317	2.319	2.322	
4	2.324	2.326	2.328	2.330	2.332	2.335	2.337	2.339	2.341	2.343	
5.5	2.345	2.347	2.349	2.352	2.354	2.356	2.358	2.360	2.362	2.364	
6	2.366	2.369	2.371	2.373	2.375	2.377	2.379	2.381	2.383	2.385	
7	2.387	2.390	2.392	2.394	2.396	2.398	2.400	2.402	2.404	2.406	
8	2.408	2.410	2.412	2.415	2.417	2.419	2.421	2.423	2.425	2.427	
9	2.429	2.431	2.433	2.435	2.437	2.439	2.441	2.443	2.445	2.447	
6.0	2.449	2.452	2.454	2.456	2.458	2.460	2.462	2.464	2.466	2.468	
1	2.470	2.472	2.474	2.476	2.478	2.480	2.482	2.484	2.486	2.488	
2	2.490	2.492	2.494	2.496	2.498	2.500	2.502	2.504	2.506	2.508	
3	2.510	2.512	2.514	2.516	2.518	2.520	2.522	2.524	2.526	2.528	
4	2.530	2.532	2.534	2.536	2.538	2.540	2.542	2.544	2.546	2.548	
6.5	2.550	2.551	2.553	2.555	2.557	2.559	2.561	2.563	2.565	2.567	
6	2.569	2.571	2.573	2.575	2.577	2.579	2.581	2.583	2.585	2.587	
7	2.588	2.590	2.592	2.594	2.596	2.598	2.600	2.602	2.604	2.606	
8	2.608	2.610	2.612	2.613	2.615	2.617	2.619	2.621	2.623	2.625	
9	2.627	2.629	2.631	2.632	2.634	2.636	2.638	2.640	2.642	2.644	
7.0	2.646	2.648	2.650	2.651	2.653	2.655	2.657	2.659	2.661	2.663	
1	2.665	2.666	2.668	2.670	2.672	2.674	2.676	2.678	2.680	2.681	
2	2.683	2.685	2.687	2.689	2.691	2.693	2.694	2.696	2.698	2.700	
3	2.702	2.704	2.706	2.707	2.709	2.711	2.713	2.715	2.717	2.718	
4	2.720	2.722	2.724	2.726	2.728	2.729	2.731	2.733	2.735	2.737	
7.5	2.739	2.740	2.742	2.744	2.746	2.748	2.750	2.751	2.753	2.755	
6	2.757	2.759	2.760	2.762	2.764	2.766	2.768	2.769	2.771	2.773	
7	2.775	2.777	2.778	2.780	2.782	2.784	2.786	2.787	2.789	2.791	
8	2.793	2.795	2.796	2.798	2.800	2.802	2.804	2.805	2.807	2.809	
9	2.811	2.812	2.814	2.816	2.818	2.820	2.821	2.823	2.825	2.827	
8.0	2.828	2.830	2.832	2.834	2.835	2.837	2.839	2.841	2.843	2.844	
1	2.846	2.848	2.850	2.851	2.853	2.855	2.857	2.858	2.860	2.862	
2	2.864	2.865	2.867	2.869	2.871	2.872	2.874	2.876	2.877	2.879	
3	2.881	2.883	2.884	2.886	2.888	2.890	2.891	2.893	2.895	2.897	
4	2.898	2.900	2.902	2.903	2.905	2.907	2.909	2.910	2.912	2.914	
8.5	2.915	2.917	2.919	2.921	2.922	2.924	2.926	2.927	2.929	2.931	
6	2.933	2.934	2.936	2.938	2.939	2.941	2.943	2.944	2.946	2.948	
7	2.950	2.951	2.953	2.955	2.956	2.958	2.960	2.961	2.963	2.965	
8	2.966	2.968	2.970	2.972	2.973	2.975	2.977	2.978	2.980	2.982	
9	2.983	2.985	2.987	2.988	2.990	2.992	2.993	2.995	2.997	2.998	
9.0	3.000	3.002	3.003	3.005	3.007	3.008	3.010	3.012	3.013	3.015	
1	3.017	3.018	3.020	3.022	3.023	3.025	3.027	3.028	3.030	3.032	
2	3.033	3.035	3.036	3.038	3.040	3.041	3.043	3.045	3.046	3.048	
3	3.050	3.051	3.053	3.055	3.056	3.058	3.059	3.061	3.063	3.064	
4	3.066	3.068	3.069	3.071	3.072	3.074	3.076	3.077	3.079	3.081	
9.5	3.082	3.084	3.085	3.087	3.089	3.090	3.092	3.094	3.095	3.097	
6	3.098	3.100	3.102	3.103	3.105	3.106	3.108	3.110	3.111	3.113	
7	3.114	3.116	3.118	3.119	3.121	3.122	3.124	3.126	3.127	3.129	
8	3.130	3.132	3.134	3.135	3.137	3.138	3.140	3.142	3.143	3.145	
9	3.146	3.148	3.150	3.151	3.153	3.154	3.156	3.158	3.159	3.161	

Moving the decimal point TWO places in *N* requires moving it ONE place in body of table (see p. 1–12).

Square Roots (*continued*)

N	0	1	2	3	4	5	6	7	8	9	Avg diff
10.	3.162	3.178	3.194	3.209	3.225	3.240	3.256	3.271	3.286	3.302	16
1.	3.317	3.332	3.347	3.362	3.376	3.391	3.406	3.421	3.435	3.450	15
2.	3.464	3.479	3.493	3.507	3.521	3.536	3.550	3.564	3.578	3.592	14
3.	3.606	3.619	3.633	3.647	3.661	3.674	3.688	3.701	3.715	3.728	
4.	3.742	3.755	3.768	3.782	3.795	3.808	3.821	3.834	3.847	3.860	13
15.	3.873	3.886	3.899	3.912	3.924	3.937	3.950	3.962	3.975	3.987	
6.	4.000	4.012	4.025	4.037	4.050	4.062	4.074	4.087	4.099	4.111	12
7.	4.123	4.135	4.147	4.159	4.171	4.183	4.195	4.207	4.219	4.231	
8.	4.243	4.254	4.266	4.278	4.290	4.301	4.313	4.324	4.336	4.347	
9.	4.359	4.370	4.382	4.393	4.405	4.416	4.427	4.438	4.450	4.461	11
20.	4.472	4.483	4.494	4.506	4.517	4.528	4.539	4.550	4.561	4.572	
1.	4.583	4.593	4.604	4.615	4.626	4.637	4.648	4.658	4.669	4.680	
2.	4.690	4.701	4.712	4.722	4.733	4.743	4.754	4.764	4.775	4.785	
3.	4.796	4.806	4.817	4.827	4.837	4.848	4.858	4.868	4.879	4.889	10
4.	4.899	4.909	4.919	4.930	4.940	4.950	4.960	4.970	4.980	4.990	
25.	5.000	5.010	5.020	5.030	5.040	5.050	5.060	5.070	5.079	5.089	
6.	5.099	5.109	5.119	5.128	5.138	5.148	5.158	5.167	5.177	5.187	
7.	5.196	5.206	5.215	5.225	5.235	5.244	5.254	5.263	5.273	5.282	
8.	5.292	5.301	5.310	5.320	5.329	5.339	5.348	5.357	5.367	5.376	
9.	5.385	5.394	5.404	5.413	5.422	5.431	5.441	5.450	5.459	5.468	9
30.	5.477	5.486	5.495	5.505	5.514	5.523	5.532	5.541	5.550	5.559	
1.	5.568	5.577	5.586	5.595	5.604	5.612	5.621	5.630	5.639	5.648	
2.	5.657	5.666	5.675	5.683	5.692	5.701	5.710	5.718	5.727	5.736	
3.	5.745	5.753	5.762	5.771	5.779	5.788	5.797	5.805	5.814	5.822	
4.	5.831	5.840	5.848	5.857	5.865	5.874	5.882	5.891	5.899	5.908	8
35.	5.916	5.925	5.933	5.941	5.950	5.958	5.967	5.975	5.983	5.992	
6.	6.000	6.008	6.017	6.025	6.033	6.042	6.050	6.058	6.066	6.075	
7.	6.083	6.091	6.099	6.107	6.116	6.124	6.132	6.140	6.148	6.156	
8.	6.164	6.173	6.181	6.189	6.197	6.205	6.213	6.221	6.229	6.237	
9.	6.245	6.253	6.261	6.269	6.277	6.285	6.293	6.301	6.309	6.317	
40.	6.325	6.332	6.340	6.348	6.356	6.364	6.372	6.380	6.387	6.395	
1.	6.403	6.411	6.419	6.427	6.434	6.442	6.450	6.458	6.465	6.473	
2.	6.481	6.488	6.496	6.504	6.512	6.519	6.527	6.535	6.542	6.550	
3.	6.557	6.565	6.573	6.580	6.588	6.595	6.603	6.611	6.618	6.626	
4.	6.633	6.641	6.648	6.656	6.663	6.671	6.678	6.686	6.693	6.701	
45.	6.708	6.716	6.723	6.731	6.738	6.745	6.753	6.760	6.768	6.775	7
6.	6.782	6.790	6.797	6.804	6.812	6.819	6.826	6.834	6.841	6.848	
7.	6.856	6.863	6.870	6.877	6.885	6.892	6.899	6.907	6.914	6.921	
8.	6.928	6.935	6.943	6.950	6.957	6.964	6.971	6.979	6.986	6.993	
9.	7.000	7.007	7.014	7.021	7.029	7.036	7.043	7.050	7.057	7.064	

Square Roots of Certain Fractions

N	$\sqrt{N}$	N	$\sqrt{N}$	N	$\sqrt{N}$	N	$\sqrt{N}$	N	$\sqrt{N}$	N	$\sqrt{N}$
1/2	0.7071	3/5	0.7746	4/7	0.7559	1/9	0.3333	5/12	0.6455	9/16	0.7500
1/3	0.5774	4/5	0.8944	5/7	0.8452	2/9	0.4714	7/12	0.7638	11/16	0.8292
2/3	0.8165	1/6	0.4082	6/7	0.9258	4/9	0.6667	11/12	0.9574	13/16	0.9014
1/4	0.5000	5/6	0.9129	1/8	0.3536	5/9	0.7454	1/16	0.2500	15/16	0.9682
3/4	0.8660	1/7	0.3780	3/8	0.6124	7/9	0.8819	3/16	0.4330	1/32	0.1768
1/5	0.4472	2/7	0.5345	5/8	0.7906	8/9	0.9428	5/16	0.5590	1/64	0.1250
2/5	0.6325	3/7	0.6547	7/8	0.9354	1/12	0.2887	7/16	0.6614	1/50	0.1414

Square Roots (*continued*)

N	0	1	2	3	4	5	6	7	8	9	Avg diff
50.	7.071	7.078	7.085	7.092	7.099	7.106	7.113	7.120	7.127	7.134	**7**
1.	7.141	7.148	7.155	7.162	7.169	7.176	7.183	7.190	7.197	7.204	
2.	7.211	7.218	7.225	7.232	7.239	7.246	7.253	7.259	7.266	7.273	
3.	7.280	7.287	7.294	7.301	7.308	7.314	7.321	7.328	7.335	7.342	
4.	7.348	7.355	7.362	7.369	7.376	7.382	7.389	7.396	7.403	7.409	
55.	7.416	7.423	7.430	7.436	7.443	7.450	7.457	7.463	7.470	7.477	
6.	7.483	7.490	7.497	7.503	7.510	7.517	7.523	7.530	7.537	7.543	
7.	7.550	7.556	7.563	7.570	7.576	7.583	7.589	7.596	7.603	7.609	
8.	7.616	7.622	7.629	7.635	7.642	7.649	7.655	7.662	7.668	7.675	
9.	7.681	7.688	7.694	7.701	7.707	7.714	7.720	7.727	7.733	7.740	**6**
60.	7.746	7.752	7.759	7.765	7.772	7.778	7.785	7.791	7.797	7.804	
1.	7.810	7.817	7.823	7.829	7.836	7.842	7.849	7.855	7.861	7.868	
2.	7.874	7.880	7.887	7.893	7.899	7.906	7.912	7.918	7.925	7.931	
3.	7.937	7.944	7.950	7.956	7.962	7.969	7.975	7.981	7.987	7.994	
4.	8.000	8.006	8.012	8.019	8.025	8.031	8.037	8.044	8.050	8.056	
65.	8.062	8.068	8.075	8.081	8.087	8.093	8.099	8.106	8.112	8.118	
6.	8.124	8.130	8.136	8.142	8.149	8.155	8.161	8.167	8.173	8.179	
7.	8.185	8.191	8.198	8.204	8.210	8.216	8.222	8.228	8.234	8.240	
8.	8.246	8.252	8.258	8.264	8.270	8.276	8.283	8.289	8.295	8.301	
9.	8.307	8.313	8.319	8.325	8.331	8.337	8.343	8.349	8.355	8.361	
70.	8.367	8.373	8.379	8.385	8.390	8.396	8.402	8.408	8.414	8.420	
1.	8.426	8.432	8.438	8.444	8.450	8.456	8.462	8.468	8.473	8.479	
2.	8.485	8.491	8.497	8.503	8.509	8.515	8.521	8.526	8.532	8.538	
3.	8.544	8.550	8.556	8.562	8.567	8.573	8.579	8.585	8.591	8.597	
4.	8.602	8.608	8.614	8.620	8.626	8.631	8.637	8.643	8.649	8.654	
75.	8.660	8.666	8.672	8.678	8.683	8.689	8.695	8.701	8.706	8.712	
6.	8.718	8.724	8.729	8.735	8.741	8.746	8.752	8.758	8.764	8.769	
7.	8.775	8.781	8.786	8.792	8.798	8.803	8.809	8.815	8.820	8.826	
8.	8.832	8.837	8.843	8.849	8.854	8.860	8.866	8.871	8.877	8.883	
9.	8.888	8.894	8.899	8.905	8.911	8.916	8.922	8.927	8.933	8.939	
80.	8.944	8.950	8.955	8.961	8.967	8.972	8.978	8.983	8.989	8.994	
1.	9.000	9.006	9.011	9.017	9.022	9.028	9.033	9.039	9.044	9.050	
2.	9.055	9.061	9.066	9.072	9.077	9.083	9.088	9.094	9.099	9.105	**5**
3.	9.110	9.116	9.121	9.127	9.132	9.138	9.143	9.149	9.154	9.160	
4.	9.165	9.171	9.176	9.182	9.187	9.192	9.198	9.203	9.209	9.214	
85.	9.220	9.225	9.230	9.236	9.241	9.247	9.252	9.257	9.263	9.268	
6.	9.274	9.279	9.284	9.290	9.295	9.301	9.306	9.311	9.317	9.322	
7.	9.327	9.333	9.338	9.343	9.349	9.354	9.359	9.365	9.370	9.375	
8.	9.381	9.386	9.391	9.397	9.402	9.407	9.413	9.418	9.423	9.429	
9.	9.434	9.439	9.445	9.450	9.455	9.460	9.466	9.471	9.476	9.482	
90.	9.487	9.492	9.497	9.503	9.508	9.513	9.518	9.524	9.529	9.534	
1.	9.539	9.545	9.550	9.555	9.560	9.566	9.571	9.576	9.581	9.586	
2.	9.592	9.597	9.602	9.607	9.612	9.618	9.623	9.628	9.633	9.638	
3.	9.644	9.649	9.654	9.659	9.664	9.670	9.675	9.680	9.685	9.690	
4.	9.695	9.701	9.706	9.711	9.716	9.721	9.726	9.731	9.737	9.742	
95.	9.747	9.752	9.757	9.762	9.767	9.772	9.778	9.783	9.788	9.793	
6.	9.798	9.803	9.808	9.813	9.818	9.823	9.829	9.834	9.839	9.844	
7.	9.849	9.854	9.859	9.864	9.869	9.874	9.879	9.884	9.889	9.894	
8.	9.899	9.905	9.910	9.915	9.920	9.925	9.930	9.935	9.940	9.945	
9.	9.950	9.955	9.960	9.965	9.970	9.975	9.980	9.985	9.990	9.995	

$\sqrt{\pi} = 1.77245+$ $\quad 1/\sqrt{\pi} = 0.56419$ $\quad \sqrt{\pi/2} = 1.25331$ $\quad \sqrt{e} = 1.64872$

Moving the decimal point TWO places in *N* requires moving it ONE place in body of table (see p. 1–12).

Cube Roots of Numbers

N	0	1	2	3	4	5	6	7	8	9	Avg diff
1.0	1.000	1.003	1.007	1.010	1.013	1.016	1.020	1.023	1.026	1.029	
1	1.032	1.035	1.038	1.042	1.045	1.048	1.051	1.054	1.057	1.060	3
2	1.063	1.066	1.069	1.071	1.074	1.077	1.080	1.083	1.086	1.089	
3	1.091	1.094	1.097	1.100	1.102	1.105	1.108	1.111	1.113	1.116	
4	1.119	1.121	1.124	1.127	1.129	1.132	1.134	1.137	1.140	1.142	
1.5	1.145	1.147	1.150	1.152	1.155	1.157	1.160	1.162	1.165	1.167	
6	1.170	1.172	1.174	1.177	1.179	1.182	1.184	1.186	1.189	1.191	2
7	1.193	1.196	1.198	1.200	1.203	1.205	1.207	1.210	1.212	1.214	
8	1.216	1.219	1.221	1.223	1.225	1.228	1.230	1.232	1.234	1.236	
9	1.239	1.241	1.243	1.245	1.247	1.249	1.251	1.254	1.256	1.258	
2.0	1.260	1.262	1.264	1.266	1.268	1.270	1.272	1.274	1.277	1.279	
1	1.281	1.283	1.285	1.287	1.289	1.291	1.293	1.295	1.297	1.299	
2	1.301	1.303	1.305	1.306	1.308	1.310	1.312	1.314	1.316	1.318	
3	1.320	1.322	1.324	1.326	1.328	1.330	1.331	1.333	1.335	1.337	
4	1.339	1.341	1.343	1.344	1.346	1.348	1.350	1.352	1.354	1.355	
2.5	1.357	1.359	1.361	1.363	1.364	1.366	1.368	1.370	1.372	1.373	
6	1.375	1.377	1.379	1.380	1.382	1.384	1.386	1.387	1.389	1.391	
7	1.392	1.394	1.396	1.398	1.399	1.401	1.403	1.404	1.406	1.408	
8	1.409	1.411	1.413	1.414	1.416	1.418	1.419	1.421	1.423	1.424	
9	1.426	1.428	1.429	1.431	1.433	1.434	1.436	1.437	1.439	1.441	
3.0	1.442	1.444	1.445	1.447	1.449	1.450	1.452	1.453	1.455	1.457	
1	1.458	1.460	1.461	1.463	1.464	1.466	1.467	1.469	1.471	1.472	
2	1.474	1.475	1.477	1.478	1.480	1.481	1.483	1.484	1.486	1.487	
3	1.489	1.490	1.492	1.493	1.495	1.496	1.498	1.499	1.501	1.502	
4	1.504	1.505	1.507	1.508	1.510	1.511	1.512	1.514	1.515	1.517	
3.5	1.518	1.520	1.521	1.523	1.524	1.525	1.527	1.528	1.530	1.531	
6	1.533	1.534	1.535	1.537	1.538	1.540	1.541	1.542	1.544	1.545	
7	1.547	1.548	1.549	1.551	1.552	1.554	1.555	1.556	1.558	1.559	1
8	1.560	1.562	1.563	1.565	1.566	1.567	1.569	1.570	1.571	1.573	
9	1.574	1.575	1.577	1.578	1.579	1.581	1.582	1.583	1.585	1.586	
4.0	1.587	1.589	1.590	1.591	1.593	1.594	1.595	1.597	1.598	1.599	
1	1.601	1.602	1.603	1.604	1.606	1.607	1.608	1.610	1.611	1.612	
2	1.613	1.615	1.616	1.617	1.619	1.620	1.621	1.622	1.624	1.625	
3	1.626	1.627	1.629	1.630	1.631	1.632	1.634	1.635	1.636	1.637	
4	1.639	1.640	1.641	1.642	1.644	1.645	1.646	1.647	1.649	1.650	
4.5	1.651	1.652	1.653	1.655	1.656	1.657	1.658	1.659	1.661	1.662	
6	1.663	1.664	1.666	1.667	1.668	1.669	1.670	1.671	1.673	1.674	
7	1.675	1.676	1.677	1.679	1.680	1.681	1.682	1.683	1.685	1.686	
8	1.687	1.688	1.689	1.690	1.692	1.693	1.694	1.695	1.696	1.697	
9	1.698	1.700	1.701	1.702	1.703	1.704	1.705	1.707	1.708	1.709	

$\sqrt[3]{\pi} = 1.46459 \qquad 1/\sqrt[3]{\pi} = 0.682784$

Explanation of Table of Cube Roots (pp. 1–16 to 1–21).

This table gives the values of $\sqrt[3]{N}$ for all values of N from 1 to 1000, correct to four figures. (Interpolated values may be in error by 1 in the fourth figure.)

To find the cube root of a number N outside the range from 1 to 1000, divide the digits of the number into blocks of three (beginning with the decimal point), and note that moving the decimal point THREE places in column N is equivalent to moving it ONE place in the cube root of N. For example:

$$\sqrt[3]{2.718} = 1.396 \qquad \sqrt[3]{2718} = 13.96 \qquad \sqrt[3]{0.000002718} = 0.01396$$
$$\sqrt[3]{27.18} = 3.007 \qquad \sqrt[3]{27180} = 30.07 \qquad \sqrt[3]{0.00002718} = 0.03007$$
$$\sqrt[3]{271.8} = 6.477 \qquad \sqrt[3]{271800} = 64.77 \qquad \sqrt[3]{0.0002718} = 0.06477$$

Cube Roots *(continued)*

N	0	1	2	3	4	5	6	7	8	9	Avg diff
5.0	1.710	1.711	1.712	1.713	1.715	1.716	1.717	1.718	1.719	1.720	1
1	1.721	1.722	1.724	1.725	1.726	1.727	1.728	1.729	1.730	1.731	
2	1.732	1.734	1.735	1.736	1.737	1.738	1.739	1.740	1.741	1.742	
3	1.744	1.745	1.746	1.747	1.748	1.749	1.750	1.751	1.752	1.753	
4	1.754	1.755	1.757	1.758	1.759	1.760	1.761	1.762	1.763	1.764	
5.5	1.765	1.766	1.767	1.768	1.769	1.771	1.772	1.773	1.774	1.775	
6	1.776	1.777	1.778	1.779	1.780	1.781	1.782	1.783	1.784	1.785	
7	1.786	1.787	1.788	1.789	1.790	1.792	1.793	1.794	1.795	1.796	
8	1.797	1.798	1.799	1.800	1.801	1.802	1.803	1.804	1.805	1.806	
9	1.807	1.808	1.809	1.810	1.811	1.812	1.813	1.814	1.815	1.816	
6.0	1.817	1.818	1.819	1.820	1.821	1.822	1.823	1.824	1.825	1.826	
1	1.827	1.828	1.829	1.830	1.831	1.832	1.833	1.834	1.835	1.836	
2	1.837	1.838	1.839	1.840	1.841	1.842	1.843	1.844	1.845	1.846	
3	1.847	1.848	1.849	1.850	1.851	1.852	1.853	1.854	1.855	1.856	
4	1.857	1.858	1.859	1.860	1.860	1.861	1.862	1.863	1.864	1.865	
6.5	1.866	1.867	1.868	1.869	1.870	1.871	1.872	1.873	1.874	1.875	
6	1.876	1.877	1.878	1.879	1.880	1.881	1.881	1.882	1.883	1.884	
7	1.885	1.886	1.887	1.888	1.889	1.890	1.891	1.892	1.893	1.894	
8	1.895	1.895	1.896	1.897	1.898	1.899	1.900	1.901	1.902	1.903	
9	1.904	1.905	1.906	1.907	1.907	1.908	1.909	1.910	1.911	1.912	
7.0	1.913	1.914	1.915	1.916	1.917	1.917	1.918	1.919	1.920	1.921	
1	1.922	1.923	1.924	1.925	1.926	1.926	1.927	1.928	1.929	1.930	
2	1.931	1.932	1.933	1.934	1.935	1.935	1.936	1.937	1.938	1.939	
3	1.940	1.941	1.942	1.943	1.943	1.944	1.945	1.946	1.947	1.948	
4	1.949	1.950	1.950	1.951	1.952	1.953	1.954	1.955	1.956	1.957	
7.5	1.957	1.958	1.959	1.960	1.961	1.962	1.963	1.964	1.964	1.965	
6	1.966	1.967	1.968	1.969	1.970	1.970	1.971	1.972	1.973	1.974	
7	1.975	1.976	1.976	1.977	1.978	1.979	1.980	1.981	1.981	1.982	
8	1.983	1.984	1.985	1.986	1.987	1.987	1.988	1.989	1.990	1.991	
9	1.992	1.992	1.993	1.994	1.995	1.996	1.997	1.997	1.998	1.999	
8.0	2.000	2.001	2.002	2.002	2.003	2.004	2.005	2.006	2.007	2.007	
1	2.008	2.009	2.010	2.011	2.012	2.012	2.013	2.014	2.015	2.016	
2	2.017	2.017	2.018	2.019	2.020	2.021	2.021	2.022	2.023	2.024	
3	2.025	2.026	2.026	2.027	2.028	2.029	2.030	2.030	2.031	2.032	
4	2.033	2.034	2.034	2.035	2.036	2.037	2.038	2.038	2.039	2.040	
8.5	2.041	2.042	2.042	2.043	2.044	2.045	2.046	2.046	2.047	2.048	
6	2.049	2.050	2.050	2.051	2.052	2.053	2.054	2.054	2.055	2.056	
7	2.057	2.057	2.058	2.059	2.060	2.061	2.061	2.062	2.063	2.064	
8	2.065	2.065	2.066	2.067	2.068	2.068	2.069	2.070	2.071	2.072	
9	2.072	2.073	2.074	2.075	2.075	2.076	2.077	2.078	2.079	2.079	
9.0	2.080	2.081	2.082	2.082	2.083	2.084	2.085	2.085	2.086	2.087	
1	2.088	2.089	2.089	2.090	2.091	2.092	2.092	2.093	2.094	2.095	
2	2.095	2.096	2.097	2.098	2.098	2.099	2.100	2.101	2.101	2.102	
3	2.103	2.104	2.104	2.105	2.106	2.107	2.107	2.108	2.109	2.110	
4	2.110	2.111	2.112	2.113	2.113	2.114	2.115	2.116	2.116	2.117	
9.5	2.118	2.119	2.119	2.120	2.121	2.122	2.122	2.123	2.124	2.125	
6	2.125	2.126	2.127	2.128	2.128	2.129	2.130	2.130	2.131	2.132	
7	2.133	2.133	2.134	2.135	2.136	2.136	2.137	2.138	2.139	2.139	
8	2.140	2.141	2.141	2.142	2.143	2.144	2.144	2.145	2.146	2.147	
9	2.147	2.148	2.149	2.149	2.150	2.151	2.152	2.152	2.153	2.154	

Moving the decimal point THREE places in N requires moving it ONE place in body of table (see p. 1–16).

Cube Roots (*continued*)

N	0	1	2	3	4	5	6	7	8	9	Avg diff
10.	2.154	2.162	2.169	2.176	2.183	2.190	2.197	2.204	2.210	2.217	7
1.	2.224	2.231	2.237	2.244	2.251	2.257	2.264	2.270	2.277	2.283	6
2.	2.289	2.296	2.302	2.308	2.315	2.321	2.327	2.333	2.339	2.345	
3.	2.351	2.357	2.363	2.369	2.375	2.381	2.387	2.393	2.399	2.404	
4.	2.410	2.416	2.422	2.427	2.433	2.438	2.444	2.450	2.455	2.461	
15.	2.466	2.472	2.477	2.483	2.488	2.493	2.499	2.504	2.509	2.515	5
6.	2.520	2.525	2.530	2.535	2.541	2.546	2.551	2.556	2.561	2.566	
7.	2.571	2.576	2.581	2.586	2.591	2.596	2.601	2.606	2.611	2.616	
8.	2.621	2.626	2.630	2.635	2.640	2.645	2.650	2.654	2.659	2.664	
9.	2.668	2.673	2.678	2.682	2.687	2.692	2.696	2.701	2.705	2.710	
20.	2.714	2.719	2.723	2.728	2.732	2.737	2.741	2.746	2.750	2.755	4
1.	2.759	2.763	2.768	2.772	2.776	2.781	2.785	2.789	2.794	2.798	
2.	2.802	2.806	2.811	2.815	2.819	2.823	2.827	2.831	2.836	2.840	
3.	2.844	2.848	2.852	2.856	2.860	2.864	2.868	2.872	2.876	2.880	
4.	2.884	2.888	2.892	2.896	2.900	2.904	2.908	2.912	2.916	2.920	
25.	2.924	2.928	2.932	2.936	2.940	2.943	2.947	2.951	2.955	2.959	
6.	2.962	2.966	2.970	2.974	2.978	2.981	2.985	2.989	2.993	2.996	
7.	3.000	3.004	3.007	3.011	3.015	3.018	3.022	3.026	3.029	3.033	
8.	3.037	3.040	3.044	3.047	3.051	3.055	3.058	3.062	3.065	3.069	
9.	3.072	3.076	3.079	3.083	3.086	3.090	3.093	3.097	3.100	3.104	
30.	3.107	3.111	3.114	3.118	3.121	3.124	3.128	3.131	3.135	3.138	
1.	3.141	3.145	3.148	3.151	3.155	3.158	3.162	3.165	3.168	3.171	3
2.	3.175	3.178	3.181	3.185	3.188	3.191	3.195	3.198	3.201	3.204	
3.	3.208	3.211	3.214	3.217	3.220	3.224	3.227	3.230	3.233	3.236	
4.	3.240	3.243	3.246	3.249	3.252	3.255	3.259	3.262	3.265	3.268	
35.	3.271	3.274	3.277	3.280	3.283	3.287	3.290	3.293	3.296	3.299	
6.	3.302	3.305	3.308	3.311	3.314	3.317	3.320	3.323	3.326	3.329	
7.	3.332	3.335	3.338	3.341	3.344	3.347	3.350	3.353	3.356	3.359	
8.	3.362	3.365	3.368	3.371	3.374	3.377	3.380	3.382	3.385	3.388	
9.	3.391	3.394	3.397	3.400	3.403	3.406	3.409	3.411	3.414	3.417	
40.	3.420	3.423	3.426	3.428	3.431	3.434	3.437	3.440	3.443	3.445	
1.	3.448	3.451	3.454	3.457	3.459	3.462	3.465	3.468	3.471	3.473	
2.	3.476	3.479	3.482	3.484	3.487	3.490	3.493	3.495	3.498	3.501	
3.	3.503	3.506	3.509	3.512	3.514	3.517	3.520	3.522	3.525	3.528	
4.	3.530	3.533	3.536	3.538	3.541	3.544	3.546	3.549	3.552	3.554	
45.	3.557	3.560	3.562	3.565	3.567	3.570	3.573	3.575	3.578	3.580	
6.	3.583	3.586	3.588	3.591	3.593	3.596	3.599	3.601	3.604	3.606	
7.	3.609	3.611	3.614	3.616	3.619	3.622	3.624	3.627	3.629	3.632	
8.	3.634	3.637	3.639	3.642	3.644	3.647	3.649	3.652	3.654	3.657	2
9.	3.659	3.662	3.664	3.667	3.669	3.672	3.674	3.677	3.679	3.682	

Cube Roots of Certain Fractions

N	$\sqrt[3]{N}$	N	$\sqrt[3]{N}$	N	$\sqrt[3]{N}$	N	$\sqrt[3]{N}$	N	$\sqrt[3]{N}$	N	$\sqrt[3]{N}$
1/2	.7937	3/5	.8434	4/7	.8298	1/9	.4807	5/12	.7469	9/16	.8255
1/3	.6934	4/5	.9283	5/7	.8939	2/9	.6057	7/12	.8355	11/16	.8826
2/3	.8736	1/6	.5503	6/7	.9499	4/9	.7631	11/12	.9714	13/16	.9331
1/4	.6300	5/6	.9410	1/8	.5000	5/9	.8221	1/16	.3969	15/16	.9787
3/4	.9086	1/7	.5228	3/8	.7211	7/9	.9196	3/16	.5724	1/32	.3150
1/5	.5848	2/7	.6586	5/8	.8550	8/9	.9615	5/16	.6786	1/64	.2500
2/5	.7368	3/7	.7539	7/8	.9565	1/12	.4368	7/16	.7591	1/50	.2714

Cube Roots (*continued*)

N	0	1	2	3	4	5	6	7	8	9	Avg diff
50.	3.684	3.686	3.689	3.691	3.694	3.696	3.699	3.701	3.704	3.706	2
1.	3.708	3.711	3.713	3.716	3.718	3.721	3.723	3.725	3.728	3.730	
2.	3.733	3.735	3.737	3.740	3.742	3.744	3.747	3.749	3.752	3.754	
3.	3.756	3.759	3.761	3.763	3.766	3.768	3.770	3.773	3.775	3.777	
4.	3.780	3.782	3.784	3.787	3.789	3.791	3.794	3.796	3.798	3.801	
55.	3.803	3.805	3.808	3.810	3.812	3.814	3.817	3.819	3.821	3.824	
6.	3.826	3.828	3.830	3.833	3.835	3.837	3.839	3.842	3.844	3.846	
7.	3.849	3.851	3.853	3.855	3.857	3.860	3.862	3.864	3.866	3.869	
8.	3.871	3.873	3.875	3.878	3.880	3.882	3.884	3.886	3.889	3.891	
9.	3.893	3.895	3.897	3.900	3.902	3.904	3.906	3.908	3.911	3.913	
60.	3.915	3.917	3.919	3.921	3.924	3.926	3.928	3.930	3.932	3.934	
1.	3.936	3.939	3.941	3.943	3.945	3.947	3.949	3.951	3.954	3.956	
2.	3.958	3.960	3.962	3.964	3.966	3.968	3.971	3.973	3.975	3.977	
3.	3.979	3.981	3.983	3.985	3.987	3.990	3.992	3.994	3.996	3.998	
4.	4.000	4.002	4.004	4.006	4.008	4.010	4.012	4.015	4.017	4.019	
65.	4.021	4.023	4.025	4.027	4.029	4.031	4.033	4.035	4.037	4.039	
6.	4.041	4.043	4.045	4.047	4.049	4.051	4.053	4.055	4.058	4.060	
7.	4.062	4.064	4.066	4.068	4.070	4.072	4.074	4.076	4.078	4.080	
8.	4.082	4.084	4.086	4.088	4.090	4.092	4.094	4.096	4.098	4.100	
9.	4.102	4.104	4.106	4.108	4.109	4.111	4.113	4.115	4.117	4.119	
70.	4.121	4.123	4.125	4.127	4.129	4.131	4.133	4.135	4.137	4.139	
1.	4.141	4.143	4.145	4.147	4.149	4.151	4.152	4.154	4.156	4.158	
2.	4.160	4.162	4.164	4.166	4.168	4.170	4.172	4.174	4.176	4.177	
3.	4.179	4.181	4.183	4.185	4.187	4.189	4.191	4.193	4.195	4.196	
4.	4.198	4.200	4.202	4.204	4.206	4.208	4.210	4.212	4.213	4.215	
75.	4.217	4.219	4.221	4.223	4.225	4.227	4.228	4.230	4.232	4.234	
6.	4.236	4.238	4.240	4.241	4.243	4.245	4.247	4.249	4.251	4.252	
7.	4.254	4.256	4.258	4.260	4.262	4.264	4.265	4.267	4.269	4.271	
8.	4.273	4.274	4.276	4.278	4.280	4.282	4.284	4.285	4.287	4.289	
9.	4.291	4.293	4.294	4.296	4.298	4.300	4.302	4.303	4.305	4.307	
80.	4.309	4.311	4.312	4.314	4.316	4.318	4.320	4.321	4.323	4.325	
1.	4.327	4.329	4.330	4.332	4.334	4.336	4.337	4.339	4.341	4.343	
2.	4.344	4.346	4.348	4.350	4.352	4.353	4.355	4.357	4.359	4.360	
3.	4.362	4.364	4.366	4.367	4.369	4.371	4.373	4.374	4.376	4.378	
4.	4.380	4.381	4.383	4.385	4.386	4.388	4.390	4.392	4.393	4.395	
85.	4.397	4.399	4.400	4.402	4.404	4.405	4.407	4.409	4.411	4.412	
6.	4.414	4.416	4.417	4.419	4.421	4.423	4.424	4.426	4.428	4.429	
7.	4.431	4.433	4.434	4.436	4.438	4.440	4.441	4.443	4.445	4.446	
8.	4.448	4.450	4.451	4.453	4.455	4.456	4.458	4.460	4.461	4.463	
9.	4.465	4.466	4.468	4.470	4.471	4.473	4.475	4.476	4.478	4.480	
90.	4.481	4.483	4.485	4.486	4.488	4.490	4.491	4.493	4.495	4.496	
1.	4.498	4.500	4.501	4.503	4.505	4.506	4.508	4.509	4.511	4.513	
2.	4.514	4.516	4.518	4.519	4.521	4.523	4.524	4.526	4.527	4.529	
3.	4.531	4.532	4.534	4.536	4.537	4.539	4.540	4.542	4.544	4.545	
4.	4.547	4.548	4.550	4.552	4.553	4.555	4.556	4.558	4.560	4.561	
95.	4.563	4.565	4.566	4.568	4.569	4.571	4.572	4.574	4.576	4.577	
6.	4.579	4.580	4.582	4.584	4.585	4.587	4.588	4.590	4.592	4.593	
7.	4.595	4.596	4.598	4.599	4.601	4.603	4.604	4.606	4.607	4.609	
8.	4.610	4.612	4.614	4.615	4.617	4.618	4.620	4.621	4.623	4.625	
9.	4.626	4.628	4.629	4.631	4.632	4.634	4.635	4.637	4.638	4.640	

Moving the decimal point THREE places in *N* requires moving it ONE place in body of table (see p. 1–16).

Cube Roots (*continued*)

Cube roots of numbers from 100. to 499.

N	0.	1.	2.	3.	4.	5.	6.	7.	8.	9.	Avg diff
10	4.642	4.657	4.672	4.688	4.703	4.718	4.733	4.747	4.762	4.777	15
1	4.791	4.806	4.820	4.835	4.849	4.863	4.877	4.891	4.905	4.919	14
2	4.932	4.946	4.960	4.973	4.987	5.000	5.013	5.027	5.040	5.053	13
3	5.066	5.079	5.092	5.104	5.117	5.130	5.143	5.155	5.168	5.180	
4	5.192	5.205	5.217	5.229	5.241	5.254	5.266	5.278	5.290	5.301	12
15	5.313	5.325	5.337	5.348	5.360	5.372	5.383	5.395	5.406	5.418	
6	5.429	5.440	5.451	5.463	5.474	5.485	5.496	5.507	5.518	5.529	11
7	5.540	5.550	5.561	5.572	5.583	5.593	5.604	5.615	5.625	5.636	
8	5.646	5.657	5.667	5.677	5.688	5.698	5.708	5.718	5.729	5.739	10
9	5.749	5.759	5.769	5.779	5.789	5.799	5.809	5.819	5.828	5.838	
20	5.848	5.858	5.867	5.877	5.887	5.896	5.906	5.915	5.925	5.934	
1	5.944	5.953	5.963	5.972	5.981	5.991	6.000	6.009	6.018	6.028	
2	6.037	6.046	6.055	6.064	6.073	6.082	6.091	6.100	6.109	6.118	9
3	6.127	6.136	6.145	6.153	6.162	6.171	6.180	6.188	6.197	6.206	
4	6.214	6.223	6.232	6.240	6.249	6.257	6.266	6.274	6.283	6.291	
25	6.300	6.308	6.316	6.325	6.333	6.341	6.350	6.358	6.366	6.374	8
6	6.383	6.391	6.399	6.407	6.415	6.423	6.431	6.439	6.447	6.455	
7	6.463	6.471	6.479	6.487	6.495	6.503	6.511	6.519	6.527	6.534	
8	6.542	6.550	6.558	6.565	6.573	6.581	6.589	6.596	6.604	6.611	
9	6.619	6.627	6.634	6.642	6.649	6.657	6.664	6.672	6.679	6.687	
30	6.694	6.702	6.709	6.717	6.724	6.731	6.739	6.746	6.753	6.761	7
1	6.768	6.775	6.782	6.790	6.797	6.804	6.811	6.818	6.826	6.833	
2	6.840	6.847	6.854	6.861	6.868	6.875	6.882	6.889	6.896	6.903	
3	6.910	6.917	6.924	6.931	6.938	6.945	6.952	6.959	6.966	6.973	
4	6.980	6.986	6.993	7.000	7.007	7.014	7.020	7.027	7.034	7.041	
35	7.047	7.054	7.061	7.067	7.074	7.081	7.087	7.094	7.101	7.107	
6	7.114	7.120	7.127	7.133	7.140	7.147	7.153	7.160	7.166	7.173	6
7	7.179	7.186	7.192	7.198	7.205	7.211	7.218	7.224	7.230	7.237	
8	7.243	7.250	7.256	7.262	7.268	7.275	7.281	7.287	7.294	7.300	
9	7.306	7.312	7.319	7.325	7.331	7.337	7.343	7.350	7.356	7.362	
40	7.368	7.374	7.380	7.386	7.393	7.399	7.405	7.411	7.417	7.423	
1	7.429	7.435	7.441	7.447	7.453	7.459	7.465	7.471	7.477	7.483	
2	7.489	7.495	7.501	7.507	7.513	7.518	7.524	7.530	7.536	7.542	
3	7.548	7.554	7.560	7.565	7.571	7.577	7.583	7.589	7.594	7.600	
4	7.606	7.612	7.617	7.623	7.629	7.635	7.640	7.646	7.652	7.657	
45	7.663	7.669	7.674	7.680	7.686	7.691	7.697	7.703	7.708	7.714	5
6	7.719	7.725	7.731	7.736	7.742	7.747	7.753	7.758	7.764	7.769	
7	7.775	7.780	7.786	7.791	7.797	7.802	7.808	7.813	7.819	7.824	
8	7.830	7.835	7.841	7.846	7.851	7.857	7.862	7.868	7.873	7.878	
9	7.884	7.889	7.894	7.900	7.905	7.910	7.916	7.921	7.926	7.932	

Auxiliary Table of Two-thirds Powers and Three-halves Powers (see pp. 1–22 to 1–23)

(To assist in locating the decimal point)

N	$N^{2/3} (= \sqrt[3]{N^2})$	$N^{3/2} (= \sqrt{N^3})$
.0001	.002154	.000001
.001	.01	.00003162
.01	.0464	.001
.1	.2154	.03162278
.1	1.	1.
10.	4.64	31.62278
100.	21.54	1000.
1000.	100.	31622.78
10000.	464.16	1000000.

For complete table of three-halves powers, see pp. 1–22 to 1–23. That table, used inversely, provides a complete table of two-thirds powers.

Cube Roots (*continued*)

Cube roots of numbers from 500. to 1000.

N	0.	1.	2.	3.	4.	5.	6.	7.	8.	9.	Avg diff
50	7.937	7.942	7.948	7.953	7.958	7.963	7.969	7.974	7.979	7.984	**5**
1	7.990	7.995	8.000	8.005	8.010	8.016	8.021	8.026	8.031	8.036	
2	8.041	8.047	8.052	8.057	8.062	8.067	8.072	8.077	8.082	8.088	
3	8.093	8.098	8.103	8.108	8.113	8.118	8.123	8.128	8.133	8.138	
4	8.143	8.148	8.153	8.158	8.163	8.168	8.173	8.178	8.183	8.188	
55	8.193	8.198	8.203	8.208	8.213	8.218	8.223	8.228	8.233	8.238	
6	8.243	8.247	8.252	8.257	8.262	8.267	8.272	8.277	8.282	8.286	
7	8.291	8.296	8.301	8.306	8.311	8.316	8.320	8.325	8.330	8.335	
8	8.340	8.344	8.349	8.354	8.359	8.363	8.368	8.373	8.378	8.382	
9	8.387	8.392	8.397	8.401	8.406	8.411	8.416	8.420	8.425	8.430	
60	8.434	8.439	8.444	8.448	8.453	8.458	8.462	8.467	8.472	8.476	
1	8.481	8.486	8.490	8.495	8.499	8.504	8.509	8.513	8.518	8.522	
2	8.527	8.532	8.536	8.541	8.545	8.550	8.554	8.559	8.564	8.568	
3	8.573	8.577	8.582	8.586	8.591	8.595	8.600	8.604	8.609	8.613	**4**
4	8.618	8.622	8.627	8.631	8.636	8.640	8.645	8.649	8.653	8.658	
65	8.662	8.667	8.671	8.676	8.680	8.685	8.689	8.693	8.698	8.702	
6	8.707	8.711	8.715	8.720	8.724	8.729	8.733	8.737	8.742	8.746	
7	8.750	8.755	8.759	8.763	8.768	8.772	8.776	8.781	8.785	8.789	
8	8.794	8.798	8.802	8.807	8.811	8.815	8.819	8.824	8.828	8.832	
9	8.837	8.841	8.845	8.849	8.854	8.858	8.862	8.866	8.871	8.875	
70	8.879	8.883	8.887	8.892	8.896	8.900	8.904	8.909	8.913	8.917	
1	8.921	8.925	8.929	8.934	8.938	8.942	8.946	8.950	8.955	8.959	
2	8.963	8.967	8.971	8.975	8.979	8.984	8.988	8.992	8.996	9.000	
3	9.004	9.008	9.012	9.016	9.021	9.025	9.029	9.033	9.037	9.041	
4	9.045	9.049	9.053	9.057	9.061	9.065	9.069	9.073	9.078	9.082	
75	9.086	9.090	9.094	9.098	9.102	9.106	9.110	9.114	9.118	9.122	
6	9.126	9.130	9.134	9.138	9.142	9.146	9.150	9.154	9.158	9.162	
7	9.166	9.170	9.174	9.178	9.182	9.185	9.189	9.193	9.197	9.201	
8	9.205	9.209	9.213	9.217	9.221	9.225	9.229	9.233	9.237	9.240	
9	9.244	9.248	9.252	9.256	9.260	9.264	9.268	9.272	9.275	9.279	
80	9.283	9.287	9.291	9.295	9.299	9.302	9.306	9.310	9.314	9.318	
1	9.322	9.326	9.329	9.333	9.337	9.341	9.345	9.348	9.352	9.356	
2	9.360	9.364	9.368	9.371	9.375	9.379	9.383	9.386	9.390	9.394	
3	9.398	9.402	9.405	9.409	9.413	9.417	9.420	9.424	9.428	9.432	
4	9.435	9.439	9.443	9.447	9.450	9.454	9.458	9.462	9.465	9.469	
85	9.473	9.476	9.480	9.484	9.488	9.491	9.495	9.499	9.502	9.506	
6	9.510	9.513	9.517	9.521	9.524	9.528	9.532	9.535	9.539	9.543	
7	9.546	9.550	9.554	9.557	9.561	9.565	9.568	9.572	9.576	9.579	
8	9.583	9.586	9.590	9.594	9.597	9.601	9.605	9.608	9.612	9.615	
9	9.619	9.623	9.626	9.630	9.633	9.637	9.641	9.644	9.648	9.651	
90	9.655	9.658	9.662	9.666	9.669	9.673	9.676	9.680	9.683	9.687	
1	9.691	9.694	9.698	9.701	9.705	9.708	9.712	9.715	9.719	9.722	
2	9.726	9.729	9.733	9.736	9.740	9.743	9.747	9.750	9.754	9.758	
3	9.761	9.764	9.768	9.771	9.775	9.778	9.782	9.785	9.789	9.792	
4	9.796	9.799	9.803	9.806	9.810	9.813	9.817	9.820	9.824	9.827	
95	9.830	9.834	9.837	9.841	9.844	9.848	9.851	9.855	9.858	9.861	
6	9.865	9.868	9.872	9.875	9.879	9.882	9.885	9.889	9.892	9.896	
7	9.899	9.902	9.906	9.909	9.913	9.916	9.919	9.923	9.926	9.930	
8	9.933	9.936	9.940	9.943	9.946	9.950	9.953	9.956	9.960	9.963	
9	9.967	9.970	9.973	9.977	9.980	9.983	9.987	9.990	9.993	9.997	
100	10.00										

Moving the decimal point THREE places in *N* requires moving it ONE place in body of table (see p. 1–16).

Three-halves Powers of Numbers (see also p. 1–20)

N	0	1	2	3	4	5	6	7	8	9	Avg diff
1.	1.000	1.154	1.315	1.482	1.657	1.837	2.024	2.217	2.415	2.619	183
2.	2.828	3.043	3.263	3.488	3.718	3.953	4.192	4.437	4.685	4.939	237
3.	5.196	5.458	5.724	5.995	6.269	6.548	6.831	7.117	7.408	7.702	280
4.	8.000	8.302	8.607	8.917	9.230	9.546	9.866	10.190			313
4.								10.19	10.52	10.85	33
5.	11.18	11.52	11.86	12.20	12.55	12.90	13.25	13.61	13.97	14.33	35
6.	14.70	15.07	15.44	15.81	16.19	16.57	16.96	17.34	17.73	18.12	38
7.	18.52	18.92	19.32	19.72	20.13	20.54	20.95	21.37	21.78	22.20	41
8.	22.63	23.05	23.48	23.91	24.35	24.78	25.22	25.66	26.11	26.55	44
9.	27.00	27.45	27.90	28.36	28.82	29.28	29.74	30.21	30.68	31.15	46
10.	31.62	32.10	32.58	33.06	33.54	34.02	34.51	35.00	35.49	35.99	49
1.	36.48	36.98	37.48	37.99	38.49	39.00	39.51	40.02	40.53	41.05	51
2.	41.57	42.09	42.61	43.14	43.66	44.19	44.73	45.26	45.79	46.33	53
3.	46.87	47.41	47.96	48.50	49.05	49.60	50.15	50.71	51.26	51.82	55
4.	52.38	52.95	53.51	54.08	54.64	55.21	55.79	56.36	56.94	57.51	57
15.	58.09	58.68	59.26	59.85	60.43	61.02	61.62	62.21	62.80	63.40	59
6.	64.00	64.60	65.20	65.81	66.41	67.02	67.63	68.25	68.86	69.48	61
7.	70.09	70.71	71.33	71.96	72.58	73.21	73.84	74.47	75.10	75.73	63
8.	76.37	77.00	77.64	78.28	78.93	79.57	80.22	80.87	81.51	82.17	65
9.	82.82	83.47	84.13	84.79	85.45	86.11	86.77	87.44	88.10	88.77	66
20.	89.44	90.11	90.79	91.46	92.14	92.82	93.50	94.18	94.86	95.55	68
1.	96.23	96.92	97.61	98.30	99.00	99.69	100.38				69
1.							100.4	101.1	101.8	102.5	7
2.	103.2	103.9	104.6	105.3	106.0	106.7	107.4	108.2	108.9	109.6	7
3.	110.3	111.0	111.7	112.5	113.2	113.9	114.6	115.4	116.1	116.8	7
4.	117.6	118.3	119.0	119.8	120.5	121.3	122.0	122.8	123.5	124.3	7
25.	125.0	125.8	126.5	127.3	128.0	128.8	129.5	130.3	131.0	131.8	8
6.	132.6	133.3	134.1	134.9	135.6	136.4	137.2	138.0	138.7	139.5	8
7.	140.3	141.1	141.9	142.6	143.4	144.2	145.0	145.8	146.6	147.4	8
8.	148.2	149.0	149.8	150.5	151.3	152.1	153.0	153.8	154.6	155.4	8
9.	156.2	157.0	157.8	158.6	159.4	160.2	161.9	161.9	162.7	163.5	8
30.	164.3	165.1	166.0	166.8	167.6	168.4	169.3	170.1	170.9	171.8	8
1.	172.6	173.4	174.3	175.1	176.0	176.8	177.6	178.5	179.3	180.2	8
2.	181.0	181.9	182.7	183.6	184.4	185.3	186.1	187.0	187.9	188.7	9
3.	189.6	190.4	191.3	192.2	193.0	193.9	194.8	195.6	196.5	197.4	9
4.	198.3	199.1	200.0	200.9	201.8	202.6	203.5	204.4	205.3	206.2	9
35.	207.1	208.0	208.8	209.7	210.6	211.5	212.4	213.3	214.2	215.1	9
6.	216.0	216.9	217.8	218.7	219.6	220.5	221.4	222.3	223.2	224.2	9
7.	225.1	226.0	226.9	227.8	228.7	229.6	230.6	231.5	232.4	233.3	9
8.	234.2	235.2	236.1	237.0	238.0	238.9	239.8	240.8	241.7	242.6	9
9.	243.6	244.5	245.4	246.4	247.3	248.3	249.2	250.1	251.1	252.0	9
40.	253.0	253.9	254.9	255.8	256.8	257.7	258.7	259.7	260.6	261.6	10
1.	262.5	263.5	264.5	265.4	266.4	267.3	268.3	269.3	270.2	271.2	10
2.	272.2	273.2	274.1	275.1	276.1	277.1	278.0	279.0	280.0	281.0	10
3.	282.0	283.0	283.9	284.9	285.9	286.9	287.9	288.9	289.9	290.9	10
4.	291.9	292.9	293.9	294.9	295.9	296.9	297.9	298.9	299.9	300.9	10
45.	301.9	302.9	303.9	304.9	305.9	306.9	307.9	308.9	310.0	311.0	10
6.	312.0	313.0	314.0	315.0	316.1	317.1	318.1	319.1	320.2	321.2	10
7.	322.2	323.2	324.3	325.3	326.3	327.4	328.4	329.4	330.5	331.5	10
8.	332.6	333.6	334.6	335.7	336.7	337.8	338.8	339.9	340.9	342.0	10
9.	343.0	344.0	345.1	346.2	347.2	348.3	349.3	350.4	351.4	352.5	11

This table gives $N^{3/2}$ from $N = 1$ to $N = 100$. Moving the decimal point TWO places in N requires moving it THREE places in body of table. Thus:

$(7.23)^{3/2} = 19.44$ $(723.)^{3/2} = 19440$ $(0.0723)^{3/2} = 0.01944$

$(72.3)^{3/2} = 614.8$ $(7230.)^{3/2} = 614800$ $(0.723)^{3/2} = 0.6148$

Used inversely, table gives $M^{2/3}$ from $M = 1$ to $M = 1000$. Thus: $(0.6148)^{2/3} = 0.7230$.

Three-halves Powers (*continued*) (see also p. 1–20)

N	0	1	2	3	4	5	6	7	8	9	Avg diff
50.	353.6	354.6	355.7	356.7	357.8	358.9	359.9	361.0	362.1	363.1	11
1.	364.2	365.3	366.4	367.4	368.5	369.6	370.7	371.7	372.8	373.9	11
2.	375.0	376.1	377.1	378.2	379.3	380.4	381.5	382.6	383.7	384.8	11
3.	385.8	386.9	388.0	389.1	390.2	391.3	392.4	393.5	394.6	395.7	11
4.	396.8	397.9	399.0	400.1	401.2	402.3	403.4	404.6	405.7	406.8	11
55.	407.9	409.0	410.1	411.2	412.3	413.5	414.6	415.7	416.8	418.0	11
6.	419.1	420.2	421.3	422.4	423.6	424.7	425.8	426.9	428.1	429.2	11
7.	430.3	431.5	432.6	433.7	434.9	436.0	437.1	438.3	439.4	440.6	11
8.	441.7	442.9	444.0	445.1	446.3	447.4	448.6	449.7	450.9	452.0	11
9.	453.2	454.3	455.5	456.6	457.8	459.0	460.1	461.3	462.4	463.6	12
60.	464.8	465.9	467.1	468.2	469.4	470.6	471.7	472.9	474.1	475.3	12
1.	476.4	477.6	478.7	479.9	481.1	482.3	483.5	484.6	485.8	487.0	12
2.	488.2	489.4	490.6	491.7	492.9	494.1	495.3	496.5	497.7	498.9	12
3.	500.0	501.2	502.4	503.6	504.8	506.0	507.2	508.4	509.6	510.8	12
4.	512.0	513.2	514.4	515.6	516.8	518.0	519.2	520.4	521.6	522.8	12
65.	524.0	525.3	526.5	527.7	528.9	530.1	531.3	532.5	533.8	535.0	12
6.	536.2	537.4	538.6	539.8	541.1	542.3	543.5	544.7	546.0	547.2	12
7.	548.4	549.6	550.9	552.1	553.3	554.6	555.8	557.0	558.3	559.5	12
8.	560.7	562.0	563.2	564.5	565.7	566.9	568.2	569.4	570.7	571.9	12
9.	573.2	574.4	575.7	576.9	578.1	579.4	580.6	581.9	583.2	584.4	13
70.	585.7	586.9	588.2	589.4	590.7	591.9	593.2	594.5	595.7	597.0	13
1.	598.3	599.5	600.8	602.1	603.3	604.6	605.9	607.1	608.4	609.7	13
2.	610.9	612.2	613.5	614.8	616.0	617.3	618.6	619.9	621.2	622.4	13
3.	623.7	625.0	626.3	627.6	628.8	630.1	631.4	632.7	634.0	635.3	13
4.	636.6	637.9	639.2	640.4	641.7	643.0	644.3	645.6	646.9	648.2	13
75.	649.5	650.8	652.1	653.4	654.7	656.0	657.3	658.6	659.9	661.2	13
6.	662.6	663.9	665.2	666.5	667.8	669.1	670.4	671.7	673.0	674.4	13
7.	675.7	677.0	678.3	679.6	680.9	682.3	683.6	684.9	686.2	687.6	13
8.	688.9	690.2	691.5	692.9	694.2	695.5	696.8	698.2	699.5	700.8	13
9.	702.2	703.5	704.8	706.2	707.5	708.8	710.2	711.5	712.9	714.2	13
80.	715.5	716.9	718.2	719.6	720.9	722.3	723.6	725.0	726.3	727.7	13
1.	729.0	730.4	731.7	733.1	734.4	735.8	737.1	738.5	739.8	741.2	14
2.	742.5	743.9	745.3	746.6	748.0	749.3	750.7	752.1	753.4	754.8	14
3.	756.2	757.5	758.9	760.3	761.6	763.0	764.4	765.8	767.1	768.5	14
4.	769.9	771.2	772.6	774.0	775.4	776.8	778.1	779.5	780.9	782.3	14
85.	783.7	785.0	786.4	787.8	789.2	790.6	792.0	793.4	794.8	796.1	14
6.	797.5	798.9	800.3	801.7	803.1	804.5	805.9	807.3	808.7	810.1	14
7.	811.5	812.9	814.3	815.7	817.1	818.5	819.9	821.3	822.7	824.1	14
8.	825.5	826.9	828.3	829.7	831.1	832.6	834.0	835.4	836.8	838.2	14
9.	839.6	841.0	842.5	843.9	845.3	846.7	848.1	849.5	851.0	852.4	14
90.	853.8	855.2	856.7	858.1	859.5	860.9	862.4	863.8	865.2	866.7	14
1.	868.1	869.5	870.9	872.4	873.8	875.2	876.7	878.1	879.6	881.0	14
2.	882.4	883.9	885.3	886.8	888.2	889.6	891.1	892.5	894.0	895.4	14
3.	896.9	898.3	899.8	901.2	902.7	904.1	905.6	907.0	908.5	909.9	15
4.	911.4	912.8	914.3	915.7	917.2	918.6	920.1	921.6	923.0	924.5	15
95.	925.9	927.4	928.9	930.3	931.8	933.3	934.7	936.2	937.7	939.1	15
6.	940.6	942.1	943.5	945.0	946.5	948.0	949.4	950.9	952.4	953.9	15
7.	955.3	956.8	958.3	959.8	961.3	962.7	964.2	965.7	967.2	968.7	15
8.	970.2	971.6	973.1	974.6	976.1	977.6	979.1	980.6	982.1	983.5	15
9.	985.0	986.5	988.0	989.5	991.0	992.5	994.0	995.5	997.0	998.5	15
100.	1000.0										

Moving the decimal point TWO places in *N* requires moving it THREE places in body of table (see also auxiliary table on p. 1–20).

Reciprocals of Numbers

N	0	1	2	3	4	5	6	7	8	9	Avg diff
1.00		.9990	.9980	.9970	.9960	.9950	.9940	.9930	.9921	.9911	
1	.9901	.9891	.9881	.9872	.9862	.9852	.9843	.9833	.9823	.9814	−10
2	.9804	.9794	.9785	.9775	.9766	.9756	.9747	.9737	.9728	.9718	
3	.9709	.9699	.9690	.9681	.9671	.9662	.9653	.9643	.9634	.9625	
4	.9615	.9606	.9597	.9588	.9579	.9569	.9560	.9551	.9542	.9533	−9
1.05	.9524	.9515	.9506	.9497	.9488	.9479	.9470	.9461	.9452	.9443	
6	.9434	.9425	.9416	.9407	.9398	.9390	.9381	.9372	.9363	.9355	
7	.9346	.9337	.9328	.9320	.9311	.9302	.9294	.9285	.9276	.9268	
8	.9259	.9251	.9242	.9234	.9225	.9217	.9208	.9200	.9191	.9183	
9	.9174	.9166	.9158	.9149	.9141	.9132	.9124	.9116	.9107	.9099	−8
1.10	.9091	.9083	.9074	.9066	.9058	.9050	.9042	.9033	.9025	.9017	
1	.9009	.9001	.8993	.8985	.8977	.8969	.8961	.8953	.8945	.8937	
2	.8929	.8921	.8913	.8905	.8897	.8889	.8881	.8873	.8865	.8857	
3	.8850	.8842	.8834	.8826	.8818	.8811	.8803	.8795	.8787	.8780	
4	.8772	.8764	.8757	.8749	.8741	.8734	.8726	.8718	.8711	.8703	
1.15	.8696	.8688	.8681	.8673	.8666	.8658	.8651	.8643	.8636	.8628	
6	.8621	.8613	.8606	.8598	.8591	.8584	.8576	.8569	.8562	.8554	−7
7	.8547	.8540	.8532	.8525	.8518	.8511	.8503	.8496	.8489	.8482	
8	.8475	.8467	.8460	.8453	.8446	.8439	.8432	.8425	.8418	.8410	
9	.8403	.8396	.8389	.8382	.8375	.8368	.8361	.8354	.8347	.8340	
1.20	.8333	.8326	.8319	.8313	.8306	.8299	.8292	.8285	.8278	.8271	
1	.8264	.8258	.8251	.8244	.8237	.8230	.8224	.8217	.8210	.8203	
2	.8197	.8190	.8183	.8177	.8170	.8163	.8157	.8150	.8143	.8137	
3	.8130	.8123	.8117	.8110	.8104	.8097	.8091	.8084	.8078	.8071	−6
4	.8065	.8058	.8052	.8045	.8039	.8032	.8026	.8019	.8013	.8006	
1.25	.8000	.7994	.7987	.7981	.7974	.7968	.7962	.7955	.7949	.7943	
6	.7937	.7930	.7924	.7918	.7911	.7905	.7899	.7893	.7886	.7880	
7	.7874	.7868	.7862	.7855	.7849	.7843	.7837	.7831	.7825	.7819	
8	.7812	.7806	.7800	.7794	.7788	.7782	.7776	.7770	.7764	.7758	
9	.7752	.7746	.7740	.7734	.7728	.7722	.7716	.7710	.7704	.7698	
1.30	.7692	.7686	.7680	.7675	.7669	.7663	.7657	.7651	.7645	.7639	
1	.7634	.7628	.7622	.7616	.7610	.7605	.7599	.7593	.7587	.7582	
2	.7576	.7570	.7564	.7559	.7553	.7547	.7541	.7536	.7530	.7524	
3	.7519	.7513	.7508	.7502	.7496	.7491	.7485	.7479	.7474	.7468	
4	.7463	.7457	.7452	.7446	.7440	.7435	.7429	.7424	.7418	.7413	
1.35	.7407	.7402	.7396	.7391	.7386	.7380	.7375	.7369	.7364	.7358	−5
6	.7353	.7348	.7342	.7337	.7331	.7326	.7321	.7315	.7310	.7305	
7	.7299	.7294	.7289	.7283	.7278	.7273	.7267	.7262	.7257	.7252	
8	.7246	.7241	.7236	.7231	.7225	.7220	.7215	.7210	.7205	.7199	
9	.7194	.7189	.7184	.7179	.7174	.7168	.7163	.7158	.7153	.7148	
1.40	.7143	.7138	.7133	.7128	.7123	.7117	.7112	.7107	.7102	.7097	
1	.7092	.7087	.7082	.7077	.7072	.7067	.7062	.7057	.7052	.7047	
2	.7042	.7037	.7032	.7027	.7022	.7018	.7013	.7008	.7003	.6998	
3	.6993	.6988	.6983	.6978	.6974	.6969	.6964	.6959	.6954	.6949	
4	.6944	.6940	.6935	.6930	.6925	.6920	.6916	.6911	.6906	.6901	
1.45	.6897	.6892	.6887	.6882	.6878	.6873	.6868	.6863	.6859	.6854	
6	.6849	.6845	.6840	.6835	.6831	.6826	.6821	.6817	.6812	.6807	
7	.6803	.6798	.6793	.6789	.6784	.6780	.6775	.6770	.6766	.6761	
8	.6757	.6752	.6748	.6743	.6739	.6734	.6729	.6725	.6720	.6716	
9	.6711	.6707	.6702	.6698	.6693	.6689	.6684	.6680	.6676	.6671	

$1/\pi = 0.318310$ $1/e = 0.367879$

Moving the decimal point in either direction in *N* requires moving it in the OPPOSITE direction in body of table **(see p. 1–26).**

Reciprocals (*continued*)

N	0	1	2	3	4	5	6	7	8	9	Avg diff
1.50	.6667	.6662	.6658	.6653	.6649	.6645	.6640	.6636	.6631	.6627	−4
1	.6623	.6618	.6614	.6609	.6605	.6601	.6596	.6592	.6588	.6583	
2	.6579	.6575	.6570	.6566	.6562	.6557	.6553	.6549	.6545	.6540	
3	.6536	.6532	.6527	.6523	.6519	.6515	.6510	.6506	.6502	.6498	
4	.6494	.6489	.6485	.6481	.6477	.6472	.6468	.6464	.6460	.6456	
1.55	.6452	.6447	.6443	.6439	.6435	.6431	.6427	.6423	.6418	.6414	
6	.6410	.6406	.6402	.6398	.6394	.6390	.6386	.6382	.6378	.6373	
7	.6369	.6365	.6361	.6357	.6353	.6349	.6345	.6341	.6337	.6333	
8	.6329	.6325	.6321	.6317	.6313	.6309	.6305	.6301	.6297	.6293	
9	.6289	.6285	.6281	.6277	.6274	.6270	.6266	.6262	.6258	.6254	
1.60	.6250	.6246	.6242	.6238	.6234	.6231	.6227	.6223	.6219	.6215	
1	.6211	.6207	.6203	.6200	.6196	.6192	.6188	.6184	.6180	.6177	
2	.6173	.6169	.6165	.6161	.6158	.6154	.6150	.6146	.6143	.6139	
3	.6135	.6131	.6127	.6124	.6120	.6116	.6112	.6109	.6105	.6101	
4	.6098	.6094	.6090	.6086	.6083	.6079	.6075	.6072	.6068	.6064	
1.65	.6061	.6057	.6053	.6050	.6046	.6042	.6039	.6035	.6031	.6028	
6	.6024	.6020	.6017	.6013	.6010	.6006	.6002	.5999	.5995	.5992	
7	.5988	.5984	.5981	.5977	.5974	.5970	.5967	.5963	.5959	.5956	
8	.5952	.5949	.5945	.5942	.5938	.5935	.5931	.5928	.5924	.5921	
9	.5917	.5914	.5910	.5907	.5903	.5900	.5896	.5893	.5889	.5886	
1.70	.5882	.5879	.5875	.5872	.5869	.5865	.5862	.5858	.5855	.5851	−3
1	.5848	.5845	.5841	.5838	.5834	.5831	.5828	.5824	.5821	.5817	
2	.5814	.5811	.5807	.5804	.5800	.5797	.5794	.5790	.5787	.5784	
3	.5780	.5777	.5774	.5770	.5767	.5764	.5760	.5757	.5754	.5750	
4	.5747	.5744	.5741	.5737	.5734	.5731	.5727	.5724	.5721	.5718	
1.75	.5714	.5711	.5708	.5705	.5701	.5698	.5695	.5692	.5688	.5685	
6	.5682	.5679	.5675	.5672	.5669	.5666	.5663	.5659	.5656	.5653	
7	.5650	.5647	.5643	.5640	.5637	.5634	.5631	.5627	.5624	.5621	
8	.5618	.5615	.5612	.5609	.5605	.5602	.5599	.5596	.5593	.5590	
9	.5587	.5583	.5580	.5577	.5574	.5571	.5568	.5565	.5562	.5559	
1.80	.5556	.5552	.5549	.5546	.5543	.5540	.5537	.5534	.5531	.5528	
1	.5525	.5522	.5519	.5516	.5513	.5510	.5507	.5504	.5501	.5498	
2	.5495	.5491	.5488	.5485	.5482	.5479	.5476	.5473	.5470	.5467	
3	.5464	.5461	.5459	.5456	.5453	.5450	.5447	.5444	.5441	.5438	
4	.5435	.5432	.5429	.5426	.5423	.5420	.5417	.5414	.5411	.5408	
1.85	.5405	.5402	.5400	.5397	.5394	.5391	.5388	.5385	.5382	.5379	
6	.5376	.5373	.5371	.5368	.5365	.5362	.5359	.5356	.5353	.5350	
7	.5348	.5345	.5342	.5339	.5336	.5333	.5330	.5328	.5325	.5322	
8	.5319	.5316	.5313	.5311	.5308	.5305	.5302	.5299	.5297	.5294	
9	.5291	.5288	.5285	.5283	.5280	.5277	.5274	.5271	.5269	.5266	
1.90	.5263	.5260	.5258	.5255	.5252	.5249	.5247	.5244	.5241	.5238	
1	.5236	.5233	.5230	.5227	.5225	.5222	.5219	.5216	.5214	.5211	
2	.5208	.5206	.5203	.5200	.5198	.5195	.5192	.5189	.5187	.5184	
3	.5181	.5179	.5176	.5173	.5171	.5168	.5165	.5163	.5160	.5157	
4	.5155	.5152	.5149	.5147	.5144	.5141	.5139	.5136	.5133	.5131	
1.95	.5128	.5126	.5123	.5120	.5118	.5115	.5112	.5110	.5107	.5105	
6	.5102	.5099	.5097	.5094	.5092	.5089	.5086	.5084	.5081	.5079	
7	.5076	.5074	.5071	.5068	.5066	.5063	.5061	.5058	.5056	.5053	−2
8	.5051	.5048	.5045	.5043	.5040	.5038	.5035	.5033	.5030	.5028	
9	.5025	.5023	.5020	.5018	.5015	.5013	.5010	.5008	.5005	.5003	

Moving the decimal point in either direction in *N* requires moving it in the OPPOSITE direction in body of table (see p. 1–26).

Reciprocals (*continued*)

N	0	1	2	3	4	5	6	7	8	9	Avg diff
2.0	.5000	.4975	.4950	.4926	.4902	.4878	.4854	.4831	.4808	.4785	−24
1	.4762	.4739	.4717	.4695	.4673	.4651	.4630	.4608	.4587	.4566	−21
2	.4545	.4525	.4505	.4484	.4464	.4444	.4425	.4405	.4386	.4367	−20
3	.4348	.4329	.4310	.4292	.4274	.4255	.4237	.4219	.4202	.4184	−18
4	.4167	.4149	.4132	.4115	.4098	.4082	.4065	.4049	.4032	.4016	−17
2.5	.4000	.3984	.3968	.3953	.3937	.3922	.3906	.3891	.3876	.3861	−15
6	.3846	.3831	.3817	.3802	.3788	.3774	.3759	.3745	.3731	.3717	−14
7	.3704	.3690	.3676	.3663	.3650	.3636	.3623	.3610	.3597	.3584	−13
8	.3571	.3559	.3546	.3534	.3521	.3509	.3497	.3484	.3472	.3460	−12
9	.3448	.3436	.3425	.3413	.3401	.3390	.3378	.3367	.3356	.3344	−12
3.0	.3333	.3322	.3311	.3300	.3289	.3279	.3268	.3257	.3247	.3236	−11
1	.3226	.3215	.3205	.3195	.3185	.3175	.3165	.3155	.3145	.3135	−10
2	.3125	.3115	.3106	.3096	.3086	.3077	.3067	.3058	.3049	.3040	−10
3	.3030	.3021	.3012	.3003	.2994	.2985	.2976	.2967	.2959	.2950	−9
4	.2941	.2933	.2924	.2915	.2907	.2899	.2890	.2882	.2874	.2865	−8
3.5	.2857	.2849	.2841	.2833	.2825	.2817	.2809	.2801	.2793	.2786	−8
6	.2778	.2770	.2762	.2755	.2747	.2740	.2732	.2725	.2717	.2710	−8
7	.2703	.2695	.2688	.2681	.2674	.2667	.2660	.2653	.2646	.2639	−7
8	.2632	.2625	.2618	.2611	.2604	.2597	.2591	.2584	.2577	.2571	−7
9	.2564	.2558	.2551	.2545	.2538	.2532	.2525	.2519	.2513	.2506	−6
4.0	.2500	.2494	.2488	.2481	.2475	.2469	.2463	.2457	.2451	.2445	−6
1	.2439	.2433	.2427	.2421	.2415	.2410	.2404	.2398	.2392	.2387	−6
2	.2381	.2375	.2370	.2364	.2358	.2353	.2347	.2342	.2336	.2331	−6
3	.2326	.2320	.2315	.2309	.2304	.2299	.2294	.2288	.2283	.2278	−5
4	.2273	.2268	.2262	.2257	.2252	.2247	.2242	.2237	.2232	.2227	−5
4.5	.2222	.2217	.2212	.2208	.2203	.2198	.2193	.2188	.2183	.2179	−5
6	.2174	.2169	.2165	.2160	.2155	.2151	.2146	.2141	.2137	.2132	−5
7	.2128	.2123	.2119	.2114	.2110	.2105	.2101	.2096	.2092	.2088	−4
8	.2083	.2079	.2075	.2070	.2066	.2062	.2058	.2053	.2049	.2045	−4
9	.2041	.2037	.2033	.2028	.2024	.2020	.2016	.2012	.2008	.2004	−4

$1/\pi = 0.318310 \qquad 1/e = 0.367879$

Explanation of Table of Reciprocals (pp. 1–24 to 1–27).

This table gives the values of $1/N$ for values of N from 1 to 10, correct to four figures. (Interpolated values may be in error by 1 in the fourth figure.)

To find the reciprocal of a number N outside the range from 1 to 10, note that moving the decimal point any number of places in either direction in column N is equivalent to moving it the same number of places in the OPPOSITE direction in the body of the table. For example:

$$\frac{1}{3.217} = 0.3109 \qquad \frac{1}{3217.} = 0.000\ 3109 \qquad \frac{1}{0.003217} = 310.9$$

Reciprocals (*continued*)

N	0	1	2	3	4	5	6	7	8	9	Avg diff
5.0	.2000	.1996	.1992	.1988	.1984	.1980	.1976	.1972	.1969	.1965	−4
.1	.1961	.1957	.1953	.1949	.1946	.1942	.1938	.1934	.1931	.1927	
.2	.1923	.1919	.1916	.1912	.1908	.1905	.1901	.1898	.1894	.1890	
.3	.1887	.1883	.1880	.1876	.1873	.1869	.1866	.1862	.1859	.1855	
.4	.1852	.1848	.1845	.1842	.1838	.1835	.1832	.1828	.1825	.1821	−3
5.5	.1818	.1815	.1812	.1808	.1805	.1802	.1799	.1795	.1792	.1789	
.6	.1786	.1783	.1779	.1776	.1773	.1770	.1767	.1764	.1761	.1757	
.7	.1754	.1751	.1748	.1745	.1742	.1739	.1736	.1733	.1730	.1727	
.8	.1724	.1721	.1718	.1715	.1712	.1709	.1706	.1704	.1701	.1698	
.9	.1695	.1692	.1689	.1686	.1684	.1681	.1678	.1675	.1672	.1669	
6.0	.1667	.1664	.1661	.1658	.1656	.1653	.1650	.1647	.1645	.1642	
.1	.1639	.1637	.1634	.1631	.1629	.1626	.1623	.1621	.1618	.1616	
.2	.1613	.1610	.1608	.1605	.1603	.1600	.1597	.1595	.1592	.1590	
.3	.1587	.1585	.1582	.1580	.1577	.1575	.1572	.1570	.1567	.1565	−2
.4	.1563	.1560	.1558	.1555	.1553	.1550	.1548	.1546	.1543	.1541	
6.5	.1538	.1536	.1534	.1531	.1529	.1527	.1524	.1522	.1520	.1517	
.6	.1515	.1513	.1511	.1508	.1506	.1504	.1502	.1499	.1497	.1495	
.7	.1493	.1490	.1488	.1486	.1484	.1481	.1479	.1477	.1475	.1473	
.8	.1471	.1468	.1466	.1464	.1462	.1460	.1458	.1456	.1453	.1451	
.9	.1449	.1447	.1445	.1443	.1441	.1439	.1437	.1435	.1433	.1431	
7.0	.1429	.1427	.1425	.1422	.1420	.1418	.1416	.1414	.1412	.1410	
.1	.1408	.1406	.1404	.1403	.1401	.1399	.1397	.1395	.1393	.1391	
.2	.1389	.1387	.1385	.1383	.1381	.1379	.1377	.1376	.1374	.1372	
.3	.1370	.1368	.1366	.1364	.1362	.1361	.1359	.1357	.1355	.1353	
.4	.1351	.1350	.1348	.1346	.1344	.1342	.1340	.1339	.1337	.1335	
7.5	.1333	.1332	.1330	.1328	.1326	.1325	.1323	.1321	.1319	.1318	
.6	.1316	.1314	.1312	.1311	.1309	.1307	.1305	.1304	.1302	.1300	
.7	.1299	.1297	.1295	.1294	.1292	.1290	.1289	.1287	.1285	.1284	
.8	.1282	.1280	.1279	.1277	.1276	.1274	.1272	.1271	.1269	.1267	
.9	.1266	.1264	.1263	.1261	.1259	.1258	.1256	.1255	.1253	.1252	
8.0	.1250	.1248	.1247	.1245	.1244	.1242	.1241	.1239	.1238	.1236	
.1	.1235	.1233	.1232	.1230	.1229	.1227	.1225	.1224	.1222	.1221	
.2	.1220	.1218	.1217	.1215	.1214	.1212	.1211	.1209	.1208	.1206	
.3	.1205	.1203	.1202	.1200	.1199	.1198	.1196	.1195	.1193	.1192	
.4	.1190	.1189	.1188	.1186	.1185	.1183	.1182	.1181	.1179	.1178	−1
8.5	.1176	.1175	.1174	.1172	.1171	.1170	.1168	.1167	.1166	.1164	
.6	.1163	.1161	.1160	.1159	.1157	.1156	.1155	.1153	.1152	.1151	
.7	.1149	.1148	.1147	.1145	.1144	.1143	.1142	.1140	.1139	.1138	
.8	.1136	.1135	.1134	.1133	.1131	.1130	.1129	.1127	.1126	.1125	
.9	.1124	.1122	.1121	.1120	.1119	.1117	.1116	.1115	.1114	.1112	
9.0	.1111	.1110	.1109	.1107	.1106	.1105	.1104	.1103	.1101	.1100	
.1	.1099	.1098	.1096	.1095	.1094	.1093	.1092	.1091	.1089	.1088	
.2	.1087	.1086	.1085	.1083	.1082	.1081	.1080	.1079	.1078	.1076	
.3	.1075	.1074	.1073	.1072	.1071	.1070	.1068	.1067	.1066	.1065	
.4	.1064	.1063	.1062	.1060	.1059	.1058	.1057	.1056	.1055	.1054	
9.5	.1053	.1052	.1050	.1049	.1048	.1047	.1046	.1045	.1044	.1043	
.6	.1042	.1041	.1040	.1038	.1037	.1036	.1035	.1034	.1033	.1032	
.7	.1031	.1030	.1029	.1028	.1027	.1026	.1025	.1024	.1022	.1021	
.8	.1020	.1019	.1018	.1017	.1016	.1015	.1014	.1013	.1012	.1011	
.9	.1010	.1009	.1008	.1007	.1006	.1005	.1004	.1003	.1002	.1001	

Moving the decimal point in either direction in *N* requires moving it in the OPPOSITE direction in body of table **(see p. 1–26).**

Circumferences of Circles by Hundredths

(For circumferences by eighths, see p. 1–32)

D	0	1	2	3	4	5	6	7	8	9	Avg diff
1.0	3.142	3.173	3.204	3.236	3.267	3.299	3.330	3.362	3.393	3.424	31
.1	3.456	3.487	3.519	3.550	3.581	3.613	3.644	3.676	3.707	3.738	
.2	3.770	3.801	3.833	3.864	3.896	3.927	3.958	3.990	4.021	4.053	
.3	4.084	4.115	4.147	4.178	4.210	4.241	4.273	4.304	4.335	4.367	
.4	4.398	4.430	4.461	4.492	4.524	4.555	4.587	4.618	4.650	4.681	
1.5	4.712	4.744	4.775	4.807	4.838	4.869	4.901	4.932	4.964	4.995	
.6	5.027	5.058	5.089	5.121	5.152	5.184	5.215	5.246	5.278	5.309	
.7	5.341	5.372	5.404	5.435	5.466	5.498	5.529	5.561	5.592	5.623	
.8	5.655	5.686	5.718	5.749	5.781	5.812	5.843	5.875	5.906	5.938	
.9	5.969	6.000	6.032	6.063	6.095	6.126	6.158	6.189	6.220	6.252	
2.0	6.283	6.315	6.346	6.377	6.409	6.440	6.472	6.503	6.535	6.566	
.1	6.597	6.629	6.660	6.692	6.723	6.754	6.786	6.817	6.849	6.880	
.2	6.912	6.943	6.974	7.006	7.037	7.069	7.100	7.131	7.163	7.194	
.3	7.226	7.257	7.288	7.320	7.351	7.383	7.414	7.446	7.477	7.508	
.4	7.540	7.571	7.603	7.634	7.665	7.697	7.728	7.760	7.791	7.823	
2.5	7.854	7.885	7.917	7.948	7.980	8.011	8.042	8.074	8.105	8.137	
.6	8.168	8.200	8.231	8.262	8.294	8.325	8.357	8.388	8.419	8.451	
.7	8.482	8.514	8.545	8.577	8.608	8.639	8.671	8.702	8.734	8.765	
.8	8.796	8.828	8.859	8.891	8.922	8.954	8.985	9.016	9.048	9.079	
.9	9.111	9.142	9.173	9.205	9.236	9.268	9.299	9.331	9.362	9.393	
3.0	9.425	9.456	9.488	9.519	9.550	9.582	9.613	9.645	9.676	9.708	
.1	9.739	9.770	9.802	9.833	9.865	9.896	9.927	9.959	9.990	10.022	31
.1										10.02	3
.2	10.05	10.08	10.12	10.15	10.18	10.21	10.24	10.27	10.30	10.34	
.3	10.37	10.40	10.43	10.46	10.49	10.52	10.56	10.59	10.62	10.65	
.4	10.68	10.71	10.74	10.78	10.81	10.84	10.87	10.90	10.93	10.96	
3.5	11.00	11.03	11.06	11.09	11.12	11.15	11.18	11.22	11.25	11.28	
.6	11.31	11.34	11.37	11.40	11.44	11.47	11.50	11.53	11.56	11.59	
.7	11.62	11.66	11.69	11.72	11.75	11.78	11.81	11.84	11.88	11.91	
.8	11.94	11.97	12.00	12.03	12.06	12.10	12.13	12.16	12.19	12.22	
.9	12.25	12.28	12.32	12.35	12.38	12.41	12.44	12.47	12.50	12.53	
4.0	12.57	12.60	12.63	12.66	12.69	12.72	12.75	12.79	12.82	12.85	
.1	12.88	12.91	12.94	12.97	13.01	13.04	13.07	13.10	13.13	13.16	
.2	13.19	13.23	13.26	13.29	13.32	13.35	13.38	13.41	13.45	13.48	
.3	13.51	13.54	13.57	13.60	13.63	13.67	13.70	13.73	13.76	13.79	
.4	13.82	13.85	13.89	13.92	13.95	13.98	14.01	14.04	14.07	14.11	
4.5	14.14	14.17	14.20	14.23	14.26	14.29	14.33	14.36	14.39	14.42	
.6	14.45	14.48	14.51	14.55	14.58	14.61	14.64	14.67	14.70	14.73	
.7	14.77	14.80	14.83	14.86	14.89	14.92	14.95	14.99	15.02	15.05	
.8	15.08	15.11	15.14	15.17	15.21	15.24	15.27	15.30	15.33	15.36	
.9	15.39	15.43	15.46	15.49	15.52	15.55	15.58	15.61	15.65	15.68	

Explanation of Table of Circumferences (pp. 1–28 to 1–29).

This table gives the product of π times any number D from 1 to 10; that is, it is a table of multiples of π. (D = diameter.)

Moving the decimal point ONE place in column D is equivalent to moving it ONE place in the body of the table.

$$\text{Circumference} = \pi \times \text{diam} = 3.141593 \times \text{diam}$$

Conversely,

$$\text{Diameter} = \frac{1}{\pi} \times \text{circum} = 0.31831 \times \text{circum}$$

Circumferences by Hundredths (*continued*)

D	0	1	2	3	4	5	6	7	8	9	Avg diff
5.0	15.71	15.74	15.77	15.80	15.83	15.87	15.90	15.93	15.96	15.99	3
.1	16.02	16.05	16.08	16.12	16.15	16.18	16.21	16.24	16.27	16.30	
.2	16.34	16.37	16.40	16.43	16.46	16.49	16.52	16.56	16.59	16.62	
.3	16.65	16.68	16.71	16.74	16.78	16.81	16.84	16.87	16.90	16.93	
.4	16.96	17.00	17.03	17.06	17.09	17.12	17.15	17.18	17.22	17.25	
5.5	17.28	17.31	17.34	17.37	17.40	17.44	17.47	17.50	17.53	17.56	
.6	17.59	17.62	17.66	17.69	17.72	17.75	17.78	17.81	17.84	17.88	
.7	17.91	17.94	17.97	18.00	18.03	18.06	18.10	18.13	18.16	18.19	
.8	18.22	18.25	18.28	18.32	18.35	18.38	18.41	18.44	18.47	18.50	
.9	18.54	18.57	18.60	18.63	18.66	18.69	18.72	18.76	18.79	18.82	
6.0	18.85	18.88	18.91	18.94	18.98	19.01	19.04	19.07	19.10	19.13	
.1	19.16	19.20	19.23	19.26	19.29	19.32	19.35	19.38	19.42	19.45	
.2	19.48	19.51	19.54	19.57	19.60	19.63	19.67	19.70	19.73	19.76	
.3	19.79	19.82	19.85	19.89	19.92	19.95	19.98	20.01	20.04	20.07	
.4	20.11	20.14	20.17	20.20	20.23	20.26	20.29	20.33	20.36	20.39	
6.5	20.42	20.45	20.48	20.51	20.55	20.58	20.61	20.64	20.67	20.70	
.6	20.73	20.77	20.80	20.83	20.86	20.89	20.92	20.95	20.99	21.02	
.7	21.05	21.08	21.11	21.14	21.17	21.21	21.24	21.27	21.30	21.33	
.8	21.36	21.39	21.43	21.46	21.49	21.52	21.55	21.58	21.61	21.65	
.9	21.68	21.71	21.74	21.77	21.80	21.83	21.87	21.90	21.93	21.96	
7.0	21.99	22.02	22.05	22.09	22.12	22.15	22.18	22.21	22.24	22.27	
.1	22.31	22.34	22.37	22.40	22.43	22.46	22.49	22.53	22.56	22.59	
.2	22.62	22.65	22.68	22.71	22.75	22.78	22.81	22.84	22.87	22.90	
.3	22.93	22.97	23.00	23.03	23.06	23.09	23.12	23.15	23.18	23.22	
.4	23.25	23.28	23.31	23.34	23.37	23.40	23.44	23.47	23.50	23.53	
7.5	23.56	23.59	23.62	23.66	23.69	23.72	23.75	23.78	23.81	23.84	
.6	23.88	23.91	23.94	23.97	24.00	24.03	24.06	24.10	24.13	24.16	
.7	24.19	24.22	24.25	24.28	24.32	24.35	24.38	24.41	24.44	24.47	
.8	24.50	24.54	24.57	24.60	24.63	24.66	24.69	24.72	24.76	24.79	
.9	24.82	24.85	24.88	24.91	24.94	24.98	25.01	25.04	25.07	25.10	
8.0	25.13	25.16	25.20	25.23	25.26	25.29	25.32	25.35	25.38	25.42	
.1	25.45	25.48	25.51	25.54	25.57	25.60	25.64	25.67	25.70	25.73	
.2	25.76	25.79	25.82	25.86	25.89	25.92	25.95	25.98	26.01	26.04	
.3	26.08	26.11	26.14	26.17	26.20	26.23	26.26	26.30	26.33	26.36	
.4	26.39	26.42	26.45	26.48	26.52	26.55	26.58	26.61	26.64	26.67	
8.5	26.70	26.73	26.77	26.80	26.83	26.86	26.89	26.92	26.95	26.99	
.6	27.02	27.05	27.08	27.11	27.14	27.17	27.21	27.24	27.27	27.30	
.7	27.33	27.36	27.39	27.43	27.46	27.49	27.52	27.55	27.58	27.61	
.8	27.65	27.68	27.71	27.74	27.77	27.80	27.83	27.87	27.90	27.93	
.9	27.96	27.99	28.02	28.05	28.09	28.12	28.15	28.18	28.21	28.24	
9.0	28.27	28.31	28.34	28.37	28.40	28.43	28.46	28.49	28.53	28.56	
.1	28.59	28.62	28.65	28.68	28.71	28.75	28.78	28.81	28.84	28.87	
.2	28.90	28.93	28.97	29.00	29.03	29.06	29.09	29.12	29.15	29.19	
.3	29.22	29.25	29.28	29.31	29.34	29.37	29.41	29.44	29.47	29.50	
.4	29.53	29.56	29.59	29.63	29.66	29.69	29.72	29.75	29.78	29.81	
9.5	29.85	29.88	29.91	29.94	29.97	30.00	30.03	30.07	30.10	30.13	
.6	30.16	30.19	30.22	30.25	30.28	30.32	30.35	30.38	30.41	30.44	
.7	30.47	30.50	30.54	30.57	30.60	30.63	30.66	30.69	30.72	30.76	
.8	30.79	30.82	30.85	30.88	30.91	30.94	30.98	31.01	31.04	31.07	
.9	31.10	31.13	31.16	31.20	31.23	31.26	31.29	31.32	31.35	31.38	
10.0	31.42										

Moving the decimal point ONE place in *D* requires moving it ONE place in body of table (see p. 1–28.)

Areas of Circles by Hundredths

(For areas by eighths, see p. 1–32)

D	0	1	2	3	4	5	6	7	8	9	Avg diff
1.0	0.785	0.801	0.817	0.833	0.849	0.866	0.882	0.899	0.916	0.933	16
.1	0.950	0.968	0.985	1.003	1.021	1.039	1.057	1.075	1.094	1.112	18
.2	1.131	1.150	1.169	1.188	1.208	1.227	1.247	1.267	1.287	1.307	20
.3	1.327	1.348	1.368	1.389	1.410	1.431	1.453	1.474	1.496	1.517	21
.4	1.539	1.561	1.584	1.606	1.629	1.651	1.674	1.697	1.720	1.744	23
1.5	1.767	1.791	1.815	1.839	1.863	1.887	1.911	1.936	1.961	1.986	24
.6	2.011	2.036	2.061	2.087	2.112	2.138	2.164	2.190	2.217	2.243	26
.7	2.270	2.297	2.324	2.351	2.378	2.405	2.433	2.461	2.488	2.516	27
.8	2.545	2.573	2.602	2.630	2.659	2.688	2.717	2.746	2.776	2.806	29
.9	2.835	2.865	2.895	2.926	2.956	2.986	3.017	3.048	3.079	3.110	31
2.0	3.142	3.173	3.205	3.237	3.269	3.301	3.333	3.365	3.398	3.431	32
.1	3.464	3.497	3.530	3.563	3.597	3.631	3.664	3.698	3.733	3.767	34
.2	3.801	3.836	3.871	3.906	3.941	3.976	4.011	4.047	4.083	4.119	35
.3	4.155	4.191	4.227	4.264	4.301	4.337	4.374	4.412	4.449	4.486	37
.4	4.524	4.562	4.600	4.638	4.676	4.714	4.753	4.792	4.831	4.870	38
2.5	4.909	4.948	4.988	5.027	5.067	5.107	5.147	5.187	5.228	5.269	40
.6	5.309	5.350	5.391	5.433	5.474	5.515	5.557	5.599	5.641	5.683	42
.7	5.726	5.768	5.811	5.853	5.896	5.940	5.983	6.026	6.070	6.114	43
.8	6.158	6.202	6.246	6.290	6.335	6.379	6.424	6.469	6.514	6.560	45
.9	6.605	6.651	6.697	6.743	6.789	6.835	6.881	6.928	6.975	7.022	46
3.0	7.069	7.116	7.163	7.211	7.258	7.306	7.354	7.402	7.451	7.499	48
.1	7.548	7.596	7.645	7.694	7.744	7.793	7.843	7.892	7.942	7.992	49
.2	8.042	8.093	8.143	8.194	8.245	8.296	8.347	8.398	8.450	8.501	51
.3	8.553	8.605	8.657	8.709	8.762	8.814	8.867	8.920	8.973	9.026	53
.4	9.079	9.133	9.186	9.240	9.294	9.348	9.402	9.457	9.511	9.566	54
3.5	9.621	9.676	9.731	9.787	9.842	9.898	9.954	10.010			56
								10.01	10.07	10.12	6
.6	10.18	10.24	10.29	10.35	10.41	10.46	10.52	10.58	10.64	10.69	6
.7	10.75	10.81	10.87	10.93	10.99	11.04	11.10	11.16	11.22	11.28	
.8	11.34	11.40	11.46	11.52	11.58	11.64	11.70	11.76	11.82	11.88	
.9	11.95	12.01	12.07	12.13	12.19	12.25	12.32	12.38	12.44	12.50	
4.0	12.57	12.63	12.69	12.76	12.82	12.88	12.95	13.01	13.07	13.14	7
.1	13.20	13.27	13.33	13.40	13.46	13.53	13.59	13.66	13.72	13.79	
.2	13.85	13.92	13.99	14.05	14.12	14.19	14.25	14.32	14.39	14.45	
.3	14.52	14.59	14.66	14.73	14.79	14.86	14.93	15.00	15.07	15.14	
.4	15.21	15.27	15.34	15.41	15.48	15.55	15.62	15.69	15.76	15.83	
4.5	15.90	15.98	16.05	16.12	16.19	16.26	16.33	16.40	16.47	16.55	
.6	16.62	16.69	16.76	16.84	16.91	16.98	17.06	17.13	17.20	17.28	
.7	17.35	17.42	17.50	17.57	17.65	17.72	17.80	17.87	17.95	18.02	
.8	18.10	18.17	18.25	18.32	18.40	18.47	18.55	18.63	18.70	18.78	8
.9	18.86	18.93	19.01	19.09	19.17	19.24	19.32	19.40	19.48	19.56	

Explanation of Table of Areas of Circles (pp. 1–30 to 1–31).

Moving the decimal point ONE place in column *D* is equivalent to moving it TWO places in the body of the table. (*D* = diameter.)

$$\text{Area of circle} = \frac{\pi}{4} \times (\text{diam}^2) = 0.785398 \times (\text{diam}^2)$$

Conversely,

$$\text{Diam} = \sqrt{\frac{4}{\pi}} \times \sqrt{\text{area}} = 1.128379 \times \sqrt{\text{area}}$$

Areas of Circles by Hundredths (*continued*)

D	0	1	2	3	4	5	6	7	8	9	Avg diff
5.0	19.63	19.71	19.79	19.87	19.95	20.03	20.11	20.19	20.27	20.35	8
.1	20.43	20.51	20.59	20.67	20.75	20.83	20.91	20.99	21.07	21.16	
.2	21.24	21.32	21.40	21.48	21.57	21.65	21.73	21.81	21.90	21.98	
.3	22.06	22.15	22.23	22.31	22.40	22.48	22.56	22.65	22.73	22.82	
.4	22.90	22.99	23.07	23.16	23.24	23.33	23.41	23.50	23.59	23.67	9
5.5	23.76	23.84	23.93	24.02	24.11	24.19	24.28	24.37	24.45	24.54	
.6	24.63	24.72	24.81	24.89	24.98	25.07	25.16	25.25	25.34	25.43	
.7	25.52	25.61	25.70	25.79	25.88	25.97	26.06	26.15	26.24	26.33	
.8	26.42	26.51	26.60	26.69	26.79	26.88	26.97	27.06	27.15	27.25	
.9	27.34	27.43	27.53	27.62	27.71	27.81	27.90	27.99	28.09	28.18	
6.0	28.27	28.37	28.46	28.56	28.65	28.75	28.84	28.94	29.03	29.13	10
.1	29.22	29.32	29.42	29.51	29.61	29.71	29.80	29.90	30.00	30.09	
.2	30.19	30.29	30.39	30.48	30.58	30.68	30.78	30.88	30.97	31.07	
.3	31.17	31.27	31.37	31.47	31.57	31.67	31.77	31.87	31.97	32.07	
.4	32.17	32.27	32.37	32.47	32.57	32.67	32.78	32.88	32.98	33.08	
6.5	33.18	33.29	33.39	33.49	33.59	33.70	33.80	33.90	34.00	34.11	
.6	34.21	34.32	34.42	34.52	34.63	34.73	34.84	34.94	35.05	35.15	
.7	35.26	35.36	35.47	35.57	35.68	35.78	35.89	36.00	36.10	36.21	11
.8	36.32	36.42	36.53	36.64	36.75	36.85	36.96	37.07	37.18	37.28	
.9	37.39	37.50	37.61	37.72	37.83	37.94	38.05	38.16	38.26	38.37	
7.0	38.48	38.59	38.70	38.82	38.93	39.04	39.15	39.26	39.37	39.48	
.1	39.59	39.70	39.82	39.93	40.04	40.15	40.26	40.38	40.49	40.60	
.2	40.72	40.83	40.94	41.06	41.17	41.28	41.40	41.51	41.62	41.74	
.3	41.85	41.97	42.08	42.20	42.31	42.43	42.54	42.66	42.78	42.89	12
.4	43.01	43.12	43.24	43.36	43.47	43.59	43.71	43.83	43.94	44.06	
7.5	44.18	44.30	44.41	44.53	44.65	44.77	44.89	45.01	45.13	45.25	
.6	45.36	45.48	45.60	45.72	45.84	45.96	46.08	46.20	46.32	46.45	
.7	46.57	46.69	46.81	46.93	47.05	47.17	47.29	47.42	47.54	47.66	
.8	47.78	47.91	48.03	48.15	48.27	48.40	48.52	48.65	48.77	48.89	
.9	49.02	49.14	49.27	49.39	49.51	49.64	49.76	49.89	50.01	50.14	
8.0	50.27	50.39	50.52	50.64	50.77	50.90	51.02	51.15	51.28	51.40	13
.1	51.53	51.66	51.78	51.91	52.04	52.17	52.30	52.42	52.55	52.68	
.2	52.81	52.94	53.07	53.20	53.33	53.46	53.59	53.72	53.85	53.98	
.3	54.11	54.24	54.37	54.50	54.63	54.76	54.89	55.02	55.15	55.29	
.4	55.42	55.55	55.68	55.81	55.95	56.08	56.21	56.35	56.48	56.61	
8.5	56.75	56.88	57.01	57.15	57.28	57.41	57.55	57.68	57.82	57.95	
.6	58.09	58.22	58.36	58.49	58.63	58.77	58.90	59.04	59.17	59.31	14
.7	59.45	59.58	59.72	59.86	59.99	60.13	60.27	60.41	60.55	60.68	
.8	60.82	60.96	61.10	61.24	61.38	61.51	61.65	61.79	61.93	62.07	
.9	62.21	62.35	62.49	62.63	62.77	62.91	63.05	63.19	63.33	63.48	
9.0	63.62	63.76	63.90	64.04	64.18	64.33	64.47	64.61	64.75	64.90	
.1	65.04	65.18	65.33	65.47	65.61	65.76	65.90	66.04	66.19	66.33	15
.2	66.48	66.62	66.77	66.91	67.06	67.20	67.35	67.49	67.64	67.78	
.3	67.93	68.08	68.22	68.37	68.51	68.66	68.81	68.96	69.10	69.25	
.4	69.40	69.55	69.69	69.84	69.99	70.14	70.29	70.44	70.58	70.73	
9.5	70.88	71.03	71.18	71.33	71.48	71.63	71.78	71.93	72.08	72.23	
.6	72.38	72.53	72.68	72.84	72.99	73.14	73.29	73.44	73.59	73.75	
.7	73.90	74.05	74.20	74.36	74.51	74.66	74.82	74.97	75.12	75.28	
.8	75.43	75.58	75.74	75.89	76.05	76.20	76.36	76.51	76.67	76.82	
.9	76.98	77.13	77.29	77.44	77.60	77.76	77.91	78.07	78.23	78.38	16

Moving the decimal point ONE place in *D* requires moving it TWO places in body of table (see p. 1–30).

Circumferences and Areas of Circles by Eighths, etc.

(For tenths, see p. 1–28)

Diam	Circum	Area	Diam	Circum	Area	Diam	Circum	Area	Diam	Circum	Area
			7/8	2.749	.6013	4	12.57	12.57	9	28.27	63.62
1/64	.04909	.00019	57/64	2.798	.6230	1/16	12.76	12.96	1/8	28.67	65.40
1/32	.09817	.00077	29/32	2.847	.6450	1/8	12.96	13.36	1/4	29.06	67.20
3/64	.1473	.00173	59/64	2.896	.6675	3/16	13.16	13.77	3/8	29.45	69.03
1/16	.1963	.00307	15/16	2.945	.6903	1/4	13.35	14.19	1/2	29.85	70.88
5/64	.2454	.00479	61/64	2.994	.7135	5/16	13.55	14.61	5/8	30.24	72.76
3/32	.2945	.00690	31/32	3.043	.7371	3/8	13.74	15.03	3/4	30.63	74.66
7/64	.3436	.00940	63/64	3.093	.7610	7/16	13.94	15.47	7/8	31.02	76.59
1/8	.3927	.01227	1	3.142	.7854	1/2	14.14	15.90	10	31.42	78.54
9/64	.4418	.01553	1/16	3.338	.8866	9/16	14.33	16.35	1/8	31.81	80.52
5/32	.4909	.01917	1/8	3.534	.9940	5/8	14.53	16.80	1/4	32.20	82.52
11/64	.5400	.02320	3/16	3.731	1.108	11/16	14.73	17.26	3/8	32.59	84.54
3/16	.5890	.02761	1/4	3.927	1.227	3/4	14.92	17.72	1/2	32.99	86.59
13/64	.6381	.03241	5/16	4.123	1.353	13/16	15.12	18.19	5/8	33.38	88.66
7/32	.6872	.03758	3/8	4.320	1.485	7/8	15.32	18.67	3/4	33.77	90.76
15/64	.7363	.04314	7/16	4.516	1.623	15/16	15.51	19.15	7/8	34.16	92.89
1/4	.7854	.04909	1/2	4.712	1.767	5	15.71	19.63	11	34.56	95.03
17/64	.8345	.05542	9/16	4.909	1.917	1/16	15.90	20.13	1/8	34.95	97.21
9/32	.8836	.06213	5/8	5.105	2.074	1/8	16.10	20.63	1/4	35.34	99.40
19/64	.9327	.06922	11/16	5.301	2.237	3/16	16.30	21.14	3/8	35.74	101.6
5/16	.9817	.07670	3/4	5.498	2.405	1/4	16.49	21.65	1/2	36.13	103.9
21/64	1.031	.08456	13/16	5.694	2.580	5/16	16.69	22.17	5/8	36.52	106.1
11/32	1.080	.09281	7/8	5.890	2.761	3/8	16.89	22.69	3/4	36.91	108.4
23/64	1.129	.1014	15/16	6.087	2.948	7/16	17.08	23.22	7/8	37.31	110.8
3/8	1.178	.1104	2	6.283	3.142	1/2	17.28	23.76	12	37.70	113.1
25/64	1.227	.1198	1/16	6.480	3.341	9/16	17.48	24.30	1/8	38.09	115.5
13/32	1.276	.1296	1/8	6.676	3.547	5/8	17.67	24.85	1/4	38.48	117.9
27/64	1.325	.1398	3/16	6.872	3.758	11/16	17.87	25.41	3/8	38.88	120.3
7/16	1.374	.1503	1/4	7.069	3.976	3/4	18.06	25.97	1/2	39.27	122.7
29/64	1.424	.1613	5/16	7.265	4.200	13/16	18.26	26.53	5/8	39.66	125.2
15/32	1.473	.1726	3/8	7.461	4.430	7/8	18.46	27.11	3/4	40.06	127.7
31/64	1.522	.1843	7/16	7.658	4.666	15/16	18.65	27.69	7/8	40.45	130.2
1/2	1.571	.1963	1/2	7.854	4.909	6	18.85	28.27	13	40.84	132.7
33/64	1.620	.2088	9/16	8.050	5.157	1/8	19.24	29.46	1/8	41.23	135.3
17/32	1.669	.2217	5/8	8.247	5.412	1/4	19.63	30.68	1/4	41.63	137.9
35/64	1.718	.2349	11/16	8.443	5.673	3/8	20.03	31.92	3/8	42.02	140.5
9/16	1.767	.2485	3/4	8.639	5.940	1/2	20.42	33.18	1/2	42.41	143.1
37/64	1.816	.2625	13/16	8.836	6.213	5/8	20.81	34.47	5/8	42.80	145.8
19/32	1.865	.2769	7/8	9.032	6.492	3/4	21.21	35.78	3/4	43.20	148.5
39/64	1.914	.2916	15/16	9.228	6.777	7/8	21.60	37.12	7/8	43.59	151.2
5/8	1.963	.3068	3	9.425	7.069	7	21.99	38.48	14	43.98	153.9
41/64	2.013	.3223	1/16	9.621	7.366	1/8	22.38	39.87	1/8	44.37	156.7
21/32	2.062	.3382	1/8	9.817	7.670	1/4	22.78	41.28	1/4	44.77	159.5
43/64	2.111	.3545	3/16	10.01	7.980	3/8	23.17	42.72	3/8	45.16	162.3
11/16	2.160	.3712	1/4	10.21	8.296	1/2	23.56	44.18	1/2	45.55	165.1
45/64	2.209	.3883	5/16	10.41	8.618	5/8	23.95	45.66	5/8	45.95	168.0
23/32	2.258	.4057	3/8	10.60	8.946	3/4	24.35	47.17	3/4	46.34	170.9
47/64	2.307	.4236	7/16	10.80	9.281	7/8	24.74	48.71	7/8	46.73	173.8
3/4	2.356	.4418	1/2	11.00	9.621	8	25.13	50.27	15	47.12	176.7
49/64	2.405	.4604	9/16	11.19	9.968	1/8	25.53	51.85	1/8	47.52	179.7
25/32	2.454	.4794	5/8	11.39	10.32	1/4	25.92	53.46	1/4	47.91	182.7
51/64	2.503	.4987	11/16	11.58	10.68	3/8	26.31	55.09	3/8	48.30	185.7
13/16	2.553	.5185	3/4	11.78	11.04	1/2	26.70	56.75	1/2	48.69	188.7
53/64	2.602	.5386	13/16	11.98	11.42	5/8	27.10	58.43	5/8	49.09	191.7
27/32	2.651	.5591	7/8	12.17	11.79	3/4	27.49	60.13	3/4	49.48	194.8
55/64	2.700	.5800	15/16	12.37	12.18	7/8	27.88	61.86	7/8	49.87	197.9

Circumferences and Areas by Eighths (*continued*)

Diam	Circum	Area	Diam	Circum	Area	Diam	Circum	Area	Diam	Circum	Area
16	50.27	201.1	**19½**	61.26	298.6	**23**	72.26	415.5	**29**	91.11	660.5
⅛	50.66	204.2	⅝	61.65	302.5	⅛	72.65	420.0	¼	91.89	672.0
¼	51.05	207.4	¾	62.05	306.4	¼	73.04	424.6	½	92.68	683.5
⅜	51.44	210.6	⅞	62.44	310.2	⅜	73.43	429.1	¾	93.46	695.1
½	51.84	213.8	**20**	62.83	314.2	½	73.83	433.7	**30**	94.25	706.9
⅝	52.23	217.1	⅛	63.22	318.1	⅝	74.22	438.4	¼	95.03	718.7
¾	52.62	220.4	¼	63.62	322.1	¾	74.61	443.0	½	95.82	730.6
⅞	53.01	223.7	⅜	64.01	326.1	⅞	75.01	447.7	¾	96.60	742.6
17	53.41	227.0	½	64.40	330.1	**24**	75.40	452.4	**31**	97.39	754.8
⅛	53.80	230.3	⅝	64.80	334.1	¼	76.18	461.9	¼	98.17	767.0
¼	54.19	233.7	¾	65.19	338.2	½	76.97	471.4	½	98.96	779.3
⅜	54.59	237.1	⅞	65.58	342.2	¾	77.75	481.1	¾	99.75	791.7
½	54.98	240.5	**21**	65.97	346.4	**25**	78.54	490.9	**32**	100.5	804.2
⅝	55.37	244.0	⅛	66.37	350.5	¼	79.33	500.7	¼	101.3	816.9
¾	55.76	247.4	¼	66.76	354.7	½	80.11	510.7	½	102.1	829.6
⅞	56.16	250.9	⅜	67.15	358.8	¾	80.90	520.8	¾	102.9	842.4
18	56.55	254.5	½	67.54	363.1	**26**	81.68	530.9	**33**	103.7	855.3
⅛	56.94	258.0	⅝	67.94	367.3	¼	82.47	541.2	¼	104.5	868.3
¼	57.33	261.6	¾	68.33	371.5	½	83.25	551.5	½	105.2	881.4
⅜	57.73	265.2	⅞	68.72	375.8	¾	84.04	562.0	¾	106.0	894.6
½	58.12	268.8	**22**	69.12	380.1	**27**	84.82	572.6	**34**	106.8	907.9
⅝	58.51	272.4	⅛	69.51	384.5	¼	85.61	583.2	¼	107.6	921.3
¾	58.90	276.1	¼	69.90	388.8	½	86.39	594.0	½	108.4	934.8
⅞	59.30	279.8	⅜	70.29	393.2	¾	87.18	604.8	¾	109.2	948.4
19	59.69	283.5	½	70.69	397.6	**28**	87.96	615.8	**35**	110.0	962.1
⅛	60.08	287.3	⅝	71.08	402.0	¼	88.75	626.8	¼	110.7	975.9
¼	60.48	291.0	¾	71.47	406.5	½	89.54	637.9	½	111.5	989.8
⅜	60.87	294.8	⅞	71.86	411.0	¾	90.32	649.2	¾	112.3	1003.8

Areas of Circles. Diameters in Feet and Inches, Areas in Square Feet

Feet	Inches											
	0	1	2	3	4	5	6	7	8	9	10	11
0	.0000	.0055	.0218	.0491	.0873	.1364	.1963	.2673	.3491	.4418	.5454	.6600
1	.7854	.9218	1.069	1.227	1.396	1.576	1.767	1.969	2.182	2.405	2.640	2.885
2	3.142	3.409	3.687	3.976	4.276	4.587	4.909	5.241	5.585	5.940	6.305	6.681
3	7.069	7.467	7.876	8.296	8.727	9.168	9.621	10.08	10.56	11.04	11.54	12.05
4	12.57	13.10	13.64	14.19	14.75	15.32	15.90	16.50	17.10	17.72	18.35	18.99
5	19.63	20.29	20.97	21.65	22.34	23.04	23.76	24.48	25.22	25.97	26.73	27.49
6	28.27	29.07	29.87	30.68	31.50	32.34	33.18	34.04	34.91	35.78	36.67	37.57
7	38.48	39.41	40.34	41.28	42.24	43.20	44.18	45.17	46.16	47.17	48.19	49.22
8	50.27	51.32	52.38	53.46	54.54	55.64	56.75	57.86	58.99	60.13	61.28	62.44
9	63.62	64.80	66.00	67.20	68.42	69.64	70.88	72.13	73.39	74.66	75.94	77.24
10	78.54	79.85	81.18	82.52	83.86	85.22	86.59	87.97	89.36	90.76	92.18	93.60
11	95.03	96.48	97.93	99.40	100.9	102.4	103.9	105.4	106.9	108.4	110.0	111.5
12	113.1	114.7	116.3	117.9	119.5	121.1	122.7	124.4	126.0	127.7	129.4	131.0
13	132.7	134.4	136.2	137.9	139.6	141.4	143.1	144.9	146.7	148.5	150.3	152.1
14	153.9	155.8	157.6	159.5	161.4	163.2	165.1	167.0	168.9	170.9	172.8	174.8

If given diameter is not found in this table, reduce diameter to feet and decimals of a foot by aid of the following auxiliary table, and then find area from pp. 1–30 to 1–31.

From Inches and Fractions of an Inch to Decimals of a Foot

Inches	1	2	3	4	5	6	7	8	9	10	11
Feet	.0833	.1667	.2500	.3333	.4167	.5000	.5833	.6667	.7500	.8333	.9167

Inches	⅛	¼	⅜	½	⅝	¾	⅞
Feet	.0104	.0208	.0313	.0417	.0521	.0625	.0729

Example. 5 ft. 7⅜ in. = 5.0 + 0.5833 + 0.0313 = 5.6146 ft.

Segments of Circles, Given h/c

Given: h = height; c = chord. (For explanation of this table, see p. 1–38)

h/c	Diam/c	Diff	Arc/c	Diff	Area/$h \times c$	Diff	Central angle, v	Diff	h/Diam	Diff
.00			1.000	0	.6667	0	0.00°	458	.0000	4
1	25.010	12490	1.000	1	.6667	2	4.58	458	.0004	12
2	12.520	*4157	1.001	1	.6669	2	9.16	457	.0016	20
3	8.363	*2073	1.002	2	.6671	4	13.73	457	.0036	28
4	6.290	*1240	1.004	3	.6675	5	18.30	454	.0064	35
.05	5.050	*823	1.007	3	.6680	6	22.84°	453	.0099	43
6	4.227	*586	1.010	3	.6686	7	27.37	451	.0142	50
7	3.641	*436	1.013	4	.6693	8	31.88	448	.0192	58
8	3.205	*337	1.017	4	.6701	9	36.36	446	.0250	64
9	2.868	*268	1.021	5	.6710	10	40.82	442	.0314	71
.10	2.600	*217	1.026	6	.6720	11	45.24°	439	.0385	77
1	2.383	*180	1.032	6	.6731	12	49.63	435	.0462	83
2	2.203	*150	1.038	6	.6743	13	53.98	432	.0545	88
3	2.053	*127	1.044	7	.6756	14	58.30	427	.0633	94
4	1.926	*109	1.051	8	.6770	15	62.57	423	.0727	99
.15	1.817	*94	1.059	8	.6785	16	66.80°	418	.0826	103
6	1.723	*82	1.067	8	.6801	17	70.98	413	.0929	107
7	1.641	*72	1.075	9	.6818	18	75.11	409	.1036	111
8	1.569	*63	1.084	10	.6836	19	79.20	403	.1147	116
9	1.506	56	1.094	9	.6855	20	83.23	399	.1263	116
.20	1.450	50	1.103	11	.6875	21	87.21°	392	.1379	120
1	1.400	44	1.114	10	.6896	22	91.13	387	.1499	123
2	1.356	39	1.124	12	.6918	23	95.00	381	.1622	124
3	1.317	35	1.136	11	.6941	24	98.81	375	.1746	127
4	1.282	32	1.147	12	.6965	24	102.56	370	.1873	127
.25	1.250	28	1.159	12	.6989	25	106.26°	364	.2000	128
6	1.222	26	1.171	13	.7014	27	109.90	358	.2128	130
7	1.196	23	1.184	13	.7041	27	113.48	352	.2258	129
8	1.173	21	1.197	14	.7068	28	117.00	345	.2387	130
9	1.152	19	1.211	14	.7096	29	120.45	341	.2517	130
.30	1.133	17	1.225	14	.7125	29	123.86°	334	.2647	130
1	1.116	15	1.239	15	.7154	31	127.20	328	.2777	129
2	1.101	13	1.254	15	.7185	31	130.48	322	.2906	128
3	1.088	13	1.269	15	.7216	32	133.70	316	.3034	128
4	1.075	11	1.284	16	.7248	32	136.86	311	.3162	127
.35	1.064	10	1.300	16	.7280	34	139.97°	305	.3289	125
6	1.054	8	1.316	16	.7314	34	143.02	299	.3414	124
7	1.046	8	1.332	17	.7348	35	146.01	293	.3538	123
8	1.038	7	1.349	17	.7383	36	148.94	288	.3661	122
9	1.031	6	1.366	17	.7419	36	151.82	282	.3783	119
.40	1.025	5	1.383	18	.7455	37	154.64°	277	.3902	119
1	1.020	5	1.401	18	.7492	38	157.41	271	.4021	116
2	1.015	4	1.419	18	.7530	38	160.12	266	.4137	115
3	1.011	3	1.437	18	.7568	39	162.78	261	.4252	112
4	1.008	2	1.455	19	.7607	40	165.39	256	.4364	111
.45	1.006	3	1.474	19	.7647	40	167.95°	251	.4475	109
6	1.003	1	1.493	19	.7687	41	170.46	245	.4584	107
7	1.002	1	1.512	19	.7728	41	172.91	241	.4691	105
8	1.001	1	1.531	20	.7769	42	175.32	237	.4796	103
9	1.000	0	1.551	20	.7811	43	177.69	231	.4899	101
.50	1.000		1.571		.7854		180.00°		.5000	

* Interpolation may be inaccurate at these points.

Segments of Circles, Given h/D

Given: h = height; D = diameter of circle. (For explanation of this table, see p. 1–38)

h/D	Arc/D	Diff	Area/D^2	Diff	Central angle, v	Diff	Chord/D	Diff	Arc/Circum	Diff	Area/Circle	Diff
.00	0.000	2003	.0000	13	0.00°	2296	.0000	*1990	.0000	*638	.0000	17
1	.2003	*835	.0013	24	22.96	*956	.1990	*810	.0638	*265	.0017	31
2	.2838	*644	.0037	32	32.52	*738	.2800	*612	.0903	*205	.0048	39
3	.3482	*545	.0069	36	39.90	*625	.3412	*507	.1108	*174	.0087	47
4	.4027	*483	.0105	42	46.15	*553	.3919	*440	.1282	*154	.0134	53
.05	.4510	*439	.0147	45	51.68°	*504	.4359	*391	.1436	*139	.0187	58
6	.4949	*406	.0192	50	56.72	*465	.4750	*353	.1575	*130	.0245	63
7	.5355	*380	.0242	52	61.37	*435	.5103	*323	.1705	121	.0308	67
8	.5735	*359	.0294	56	65.72	*411	.5426	*298	.1826	114	.0375	71
9	.6094	*341	.0350	59	69.83	*391	.5724	*276	.1940	108	.0446	74
.10	.6435	*326	.0409	61	73.74°	*374	.6000	*258	.2048	104	.0520	78
1	.6761	*314	.0470	64	77.48	*359	.6258	*241	.2152	100	.0598	82
2	.7075	*302	.0534	66	81.07	*347	.6499	*227	.2252	96	.0680	84
3	.7377	*293	.0600	68	84.54	*335	.6726	*214	.2348	93	.0764	87
4	.7670	*284	.0668	71	87.89	*326	.6940	*201	.2441	91	.0851	90
.15	.7954	276	.0739	72	91.15°	316	.7141	*191	.2532	88	.0941	92
6	.8230	270	.0811	74	94.31	309	.7332	*181	.2620	86	.1033	94
7	.8500	263	.0885	76	97.40	302	.7513	*171	.2706	83	.1127	97
8	.8763	258	.0961	78	100.42	295	.7684	162	.2789	82	.1224	99
9	.9021	252	.1039	79	103.37	289	.7846	154	.2871	81	.1323	101
.20	0.9273	248	.1118	81	106.26°	284	.8000	146	.2952	79	.1424	103
1	0.9521	243	.1199	82	109.10	279	.8146	139	.3031	77	.1527	104
2	0.9764	240	.1281	84	111.89	274	.8285	132	.3108	76	.1631	107
3	1.0004	235	.1365	84	114.63	271	.8417	125	.3184	75	.1738	108
4	1.0239	233	.1449	86	117.34	266	.8542	118	.3259	74	.1846	109
.25	1.0472	229	.1535	88	120.00°	263	.8660	113	.3333	73	.1955	111
6	1.0701	227	.1623	88	122.63	260	.8773	106	.3406	72	.2066	112
7	1.0928	224	.1711	89	125.23	256	.8879	101	.3478	72	.2178	114
8	1.1152	222	.1800	90	127.79	254	.8980	95	.3550	70	.2292	115
9	1.1374	219	.1890	92	130.33	251	.9075	90	.3620	70	.2407	116
.30	1.1593	217	.1982	92	132.84°	249	.9165	85	.3690	69	.2523	117
1	1.1810	215	.2074	93	135.33	247	.9250	80	.3759	69	.2640	119
2	1.2025	214	.2167	93	137.80	245	.9330	74	.3828	68	.2759	119
3	1.2239	212	.2260	95	140.25	242	.9404	70	.3896	67	.2878	120
4	1.2451	210	.2355	95	142.67	241	.9474	65	.3963	67	.2998	121
.35	1.2661	209	.2450	96	145.08°	240	.9539	61	.4030	67	.3119	122
6	1.2870	208	.2546	96	147.48	238	.9600	56	.4097	66	.3241	123
7	1.3078	206	.2642	97	149.86	237	.9656	52	.4163	66	.3364	123
8	1.3284	206	.2739	97	152.23	235	.9708	47	.4229	65	.3487	124
9	1.3490	204	.2836	98	154.58	235	.9755	43	.4294	65	.3611	124
.40	1.3694	204	.2934	98	156.93°	233	.9798	39	.4359	65	.3735	125
1	1.3898	203	.3032	98	159.26	233	.9837	34	.4424	65	.3860	126
2	1.4101	202	.3130	99	161.59	231	.9871	31	.4489	64	.3986	126
3	1.4303	202	.3229	99	163.90	232	.9902	26	.4553	64	.4112	126
4	1.4505	201	.3328	100	166.22	230	.9928	22	.4617	64	.4238	126
.45	1.4706	201	.3428	99	168.52°	230	.9950	18	.4681	64	.4364	127
6	1.4907	201	.3527	100	170.82	230	.9968	14	.4745	64	.4491	127
7	1.5108	200	.3627	100	173.12	229	.9982	10	.4809	64	.4618	127
8	1.5308	200	.3727	100	175.41	230	.9992	6	.4873	63	.4745	128
9	1.5508	200	.3827	100	177.71	229	.9998	2	.4936	64	.4873	127
.50	1.5708		.3927		180.00°		1.0000		.5000		.5000	

* Interpolation may be inaccurate at these points.

Volumes of Spheres by Hundredths

D	0	1	2	3	4	5	6	7	8	9	Avg diff
1.0	.5236	.5395	.5556	.5722	.5890	.6061	.6236	.6414	.6596	.6781	173
.1	.6969	.7161	.7356	.7555	.7757	.7963	.8173	.8386	.8603	.8823	208
.2	.9048	.9276	.9508	.9743	.9983	1.0227					236
.2						1.023	1.047	1.073	1.098	1.124	25
.3	1.150	1.177	1.204	1.232	1.260	1.288	1.317	1.346	1.376	1.406	29
.4	1.437	1.468	1.499	1.531	1.563	1.596	1.630	1.663	1.697	1.732	33
1.5	1.767	1.803	1.839	1.875	1.912	1.950	1.988	2.026	2.065	2.105	38
.6	2.145	2.185	2.226	2.268	2.310	2.352	2.395	2.439	2.483	2.527	43
.7	2.572	2.618	2.664	2.711	2.758	2.806	2.855	2.903	2.953	3.003	48
.8	3.054	3.105	3.157	3.209	3.262	3.315	3.369	3.424	3.479	3.535	54
.9	3.591	3.648	3.706	3.764	3.823	3.882	3.942	4.003	4.064	4.126	60
2.0	4.189	4.252	4.316	4.380	4.445	4.511	4.577	4.644	4.712	4.780	66
.1	4.849	4.919	4.989	5.060	5.131	5.204	5.277	5.350	5.425	5.500	73
.2	5.575	5.652	5.729	5.806	5.885	5.964	6.044	6.125	6.206	6.288	80
.3	6.371	6.454	6.538	6.623	6.709	6.795	6.882	6.970	7.059	7.148	87
.4	7.238	7.329	7.421	7.513	7.606	7.700	7.795	7.890	7.986	8.083	94
2.5	8.181	8.280	8.379	8.478	8.580	8.682	8.785	8.888	8.992	9.097	102
.6	9.203	9.309	9.417	9.525	9.634	9.744	9.855	9.966	10.079		110
.6									10.08	10.19	11
.7	10.31	10.42	10.54	10.65	10.77	10.89	11.01	11.13	11.25	11.37	12
.8	11.49	11.62	11.74	11.87	11.99	12.12	12.25	12.38	12.51	12.64	13
.9	12.77	12.90	13.04	13.17	13.31	13.44	13.58	13.72	13.86	14.00	14
3.0	14.14	14.28	14.42	14.57	14.71	14.86	15.00	15.15	15.30	15.45	15
.1	15.60	15.75	15.90	16.06	16.21	16.37	16.52	16.68	16.84	17.00	16
.2	17.16	17.32	17.48	17.64	17.81	17.97	18.14	18.31	18.48	18.65	17
.3	18.82	18.99	19.16	19.33	19.51	19.68	19.86	20.04	20.22	20.40	18
.4	20.58	20.76	20.94	21.13	21.31	21.50	21.69	21.88	22.07	22.26	19
3.5	22.45	22.64	22.84	23.03	23.23	23.43	23.62	23.82	24.02	24.23	20
.6	24.43	24.63	24.84	25.04	25.25	25.46	25.67	25.88	26.09	26.31	21
.7	26.52	26.74	26.95	27.17	27.39	27.61	27.83	28.06	28.28	28.50	22
.8	28.73	28.96	29.19	29.42	29.65	29.88	30.11	30.35	30.58	30.82	23
.9	31.06	31.30	31.54	31.78	32.02	32.27	32.52	32.76	33.01	33.26	25
4.0	33.51	33.76	34.02	34.27	34.53	34.78	35.04	35.30	35.56	35.82	26
.1	36.09	36.35	36.62	36.88	37.15	37.42	37.69	37.97	38.24	38.52	27
.2	38.79	39.07	39.35	39.63	39.91	40.19	40.48	40.76	41.05	41.34	28
.3	41.63	41.92	42.21	42.51	42.80	43.10	43.40	43.70	44.00	44.30	30
.4	44.60	44.91	45.21	45.52	45.83	46.14	46.45	46.77	47.08	47.40	31
4.5	47.71	48.03	48.35	48.67	49.00	49.32	49.65	49.97	50.30	50.63	33
.6	50.97	51.30	51.63	51.97	52.31	52.65	52.99	53.33	53.67	54.02	34
.7	54.36	54.71	55.06	55.41	55.76	56.12	56.47	56.83	57.19	57.54	35
.8	57.91	58.27	58.63	59.00	59.37	59.73	60.10	60.48	60.85	61.22	37
.9	61.60	61.98	62.36	62.74	63.12	63.51	63.89	64.28	64.67	65.06	38

Explanation of Table of Volumes of Spheres (pp. 1–36 to 1–37).

Moving the decimal point ONE place in column D is equivalent to moving it THREE places in the body of the table. (D = diameter.)

$$\text{Volume of sphere} = \frac{\pi}{6} \times (\text{diam}^3) = 0.523599 \times (\text{diam}^3)$$

Conversely,

$$\text{Diam} = \sqrt[3]{\frac{6}{\pi}} \times \sqrt[3]{\text{volume}} = 1.240701 \times \sqrt[3]{\text{volume}}$$

Volumes of Spheres (*continued*)

D	0	1	2	3	4	5	6	7	8	9	Avg diff
5.0	65.45	65.84	66.24	66.64	67.03	67.43	67.83	68.24	68.64	69.05	40
.1	69.46	69.87	70.28	70.69	71.10	71.52	71.94	72.36	72.78	73.20	42
.2	73.62	74.05	74.47	74.90	75.33	75.77	76.20	76.64	77.07	77.51	43
.3	77.95	78.39	78.84	79.28	79.73	80.18	80.63	81.08	81.54	81.99	45
.4	82.45	82.91	83.37	83.83	84.29	84.76	85.23	85.70	86.17	86.64	47
5.5	87.11	87.59	88.07	88.55	89.03	89.51	90.00	90.48	90.97	91.49	48
.6	91.95	92.45	92.94	93.44	93.94	94.44	94.94	95.44	95.95	96.46	50
.7	96.97	97.48	97.99	98.51	99.02	99.54	100.06				52
.7							100.1	100.6	101.1	101.6	5
.8	102.2	102.7	103.2	103.8	104.3	104.8	105.4	105.9	106.4	107.0	5
.9	107.5	108.1	108.6	109.2	109.7	110.3	110.9	111.4	112.0	112.5	6
6.0	113.1	113.7	114.2	114.8	115.4	115.9	116.5	117.7	117.1	118.3	6
.1	118.8	119.4	120.0	120.6	121.2	121.8	122.4	123.6	123.0	124.2	
.2	124.8	125.4	126.0	126.6	127.2	127.8	128.4	129.1	129.7	130.3	
.3	130.9	131.5	132.2	132.8	133.4	134.1	134.7	135.3	136.0	136.6	
.4	137.3	137.9	138.5	139.2	139.8	140.5	141.2	141.8	142.5	143.1	7
6.5	143.8	144.5	145.1	145.8	146.5	147.1	147.8	148.5	149.2	149.8	
.6	150.5	151.2	151.9	152.6	153.3	154.0	154.7	155.4	156.1	156.8	
.7	157.5	158.2	158.9	159.6	160.3	161.0	161.7	162.5	163.2	163.9	
.8	164.6	165.4	166.1	166.8	167.6	168.3	169.0	169.8	170.5	171.3	
.9	172.0	172.8	173.5	174.3	175.0	175.8	176.5	177.3	178.1	178.8	8
7.0	179.6	180.4	181.1	181.9	182.7	183.5	184.3	185.0	185.8	186.6	
.1	187.4	188.2	189.0	189.8	190.6	191.4	192.2	193.0	193.8	194.6	
.2	195.4	196.2	197.1	197.9	198.7	199.5	200.4	201.2	202.0	202.9	
.3	203.7	204.5	205.4	206.2	207.1	207.9	208.8	209.6	210.5	211.3	
.4	212.2	213.0	213.9	214.8	215.6	216.5	217.4	218.3	219.1	220.0	9
7.5	220.9	221.8	222.7	223.6	224.4	225.3	226.2	227.1	228.0	228.9	
.6	229.8	230.8	231.7	232.6	233.5	234.4	235.3	236.3	237.2	238.1	
.7	239.0	240.0	240.9	241.8	242.8	243.7	244.7	245.6	246.6	247.5	
.8	248.5	249.4	250.4	251.4	252.3	253.3	254.3	255.2	256.2	257.2	10
.9	258.2	259.1	260.1	261.1	262.1	263.1	264.1	265.1	266.1	267.1	
8.0	268.1	269.1	270.1	271.1	272.1	273.1	274.2	275.2	276.2	277.2	
.1	278.3	279.3	280.3	281.4	282.4	283.4	284.5	285.5	286.6	287.6	11
.2	288.7	289.8	290.8	291.9	292.9	294.0	295.1	296.2	297.2	298.3	
.3	299.4	300.5	301.6	302.6	303.7	304.8	305.9	307.0	308.1	309.2	
.4	310.3	311.4	312.6	313.7	314.8	315.9	317.0	318.2	319.3	320.4	
8.5	321.6	322.7	323.8	325.0	326.1	327.3	328.4	329.6	330.7	331.9	
.6	333.0	334.2	335.4	336.5	337.7	338.9	340.1	341.2	342.4	343.6	12
.7	344.8	346.0	347.2	348.4	349.6	350.8	352.0	353.2	354.4	355.6	
.8	356.8	358.0	359.3	360.5	361.7	362.9	364.2	365.4	366.6	367.9	
.9	369.1	370.4	371.6	372.9	374.1	375.4	376.6	377.9	379.2	380.4	13
9.0	381.7	383.0	384.3	385.5	386.8	388.1	389.4	390.7	392.0	393.3	
.1	394.6	395.9	397.2	398.5	399.8	401.1	402.4	403.7	405.1	406.4	
.2	407.7	409.1	410.4	411.7	413.1	414.4	415.7	417.1	418.4	419.8	14
.3	421.2	422.5	423.9	425.2	426.6	428.0	429.4	430.7	432.1	433.5	
.4	434.9	436.3	437.7	439.1	440.5	441.9	443.3	444.7	446.1	447.5	
9.5	448.9	450.3	451.8	453.2	454.6	456.0	457.5	458.9	460.4	461.8	
.6	463.2	464.7	466.1	467.6	469.1	470.5	472.0	473.5	474.9	476.4	15
.7	477.9	479.4	480.8	482.3	483.8	485.3	486.8	488.3	489.8	491.3	
.8	492.8	494.3	495.8	497.3	498.9	500.4	501.9	503.4	505.0	506.5	16
.9	508.0	509.6	511.1	512.7	514.2	515.8	517.3	518.9	520.5	522.0	
10.0	523.6										

Moving the decimal point ONE place in *D* requires moving it THREE places in body of table (see p. 1–36).

Segments of Spheres

(h = height of segment; D = diam of sphere)

$\frac{h}{D}$	$\frac{\text{Vol segm}}{D^3}$	Diff	$\frac{\text{Vol segm}}{\text{Vol sphere}}$	Diff
0.00	0.0000		0.0000	
1	0.0002	2	0.0003	3
2	0.0006	4	0.0012	9
3	0.0014	8	0.0026	14
4	0.0024	10	0.0047	21
0.05	0.0038	14	0.0073	26
6	0.0054	16	0.0104	31
7	0.0073	19	0.0140	36
8	0.0095	22	0.0182	42
9	0.0120	25	0.0228	46
0.10	0.0147	27	0.0280	52
1	0.0176	29	0.0336	56
2	0.0208	32	0.0397	61
3	0.0242	34	0.0463	66
4	0.0279	37	0.0533	70
0.15	0.0318	39	0.0607	74
6	0.0359	41	0.0686	79
7	0.0403	44	0.0769	83
8	0.0448	45	0.0855	86
9	0.0495	47	0.0946	91
0.20	0.0545	50	0.1040	94
1	0.0596	51	0.1138	98
2	0.0649	53	0.1239	101
3	0.0704	55	0.1344	105
4	0.0760	56	0.1452	108
0.25	0.0818	58	0.1562	110
6	0.0878	60	0.1676	114
7	0.0939	61	0.1793	117
8	0.1002	63	0.1913	120
9	0.1066	64	0.2035	122
0.30	0.1131	65	0.2160	125
1	0.1198	67	0.2287	127
2	0.1265	67	0.2417	130
3	0.1334	69	0.2548	131
4	0.1404	70	0.2682	134
0.35	0.1475	71	0.2817	135
6	0.1547	72	0.2955	138
7	0.1620	73	0.3094	139
8	0.1694	74	0.3235	141
9	0.1768	74	0.3377	142
0.40	0.1843	75	0.3520	143
1	0.1919	76	0.3665	145
2	0.1995	76	0.3810	145
3	0.2072	77	0.3957	147
4	0.2149	77	0.4104	147
0.45	0.2227	78	0.4252	148
6	0.2305	78	0.4401	149
7	0.2383	78	0.4551	150
8	0.2461	78	0.4700	149
9	0.2539	78	0.4850	150
0.50	0.2618	79	0.5000	150

Explanation of Table on this page

Given, h = height of segment,
D = diameter of sphere.

To find the volume of the segment, form the ratio h/D and find from the table the value of (vol/D^3): then, by a simple multiplication,

$$\text{volume segment} = D^3 \times (\text{vol}/D^3)$$

The table gives also the ratio of the volume of the segment to the entire volume of the sphere.

NOTE. Area of zone $= \pi \times h \times D$.
(Use Table of Multiples of π, p. 1-28)

Explanation of Table on p. 1-34

Given, h = height of segment,
c = chord.

To find the diameter of the circle, the length of arc, or the area of the segment, form the ratio h/c, and find from the table the value of (diam/c), (arc/c), or (area/hc); then, by a simple multiplication,

$$\text{diam} = c \times (\text{diam}/c),$$
$$\text{arc} = c \times (\text{arc}/c),$$
$$\text{area} = h \times c \times (\text{area}/hc).$$

The table gives also the angle subtended at the center, and the ratio of h to D. See p. 2-17.

Explanation of Table on p. 1-35

Given, h = height of segment,
D = diameter of circle.

To find the chord, the length of arc, or the area of the segment, form the ratio h/D, and find from the table the value of (chord/D), (arc/D), or (area/D^2); then, by a simple multiplication,

$$\text{chord} = D \times (\text{chord}/D),$$
$$\text{arc} = D \times (\text{arc}/D),$$
$$\text{area} = D^2 \times (\text{area}/D^2).$$

The table gives also the angle subtended at the center, the ratio of the arc of the segment to the whole circumference, and the ratio of the area of the segment to the area of the whole circle. See p. 2-17.

NOTE. Vol segm $= \frac{1}{6} \pi h^2 (3D - 2h)$.

Regular Polygons

n = number of sides;
$v = 360°/n$ = angle subtended at the center by one side;

a = length of one side $= R\left(2 \sin \frac{v}{2}\right) = r\left(2 \tan \frac{v}{2}\right)$;

R = radius of circumscribed circle $= a\left(\frac{1}{2} \csc \frac{v}{2}\right) = r\left(\sec \frac{v}{2}\right)$;

r = radius of inscribed circle $= R\left(\cos \frac{v}{2}\right) = a\left(\frac{1}{2} \cot \frac{v}{2}\right)$;

$$\text{Area} = a^2\left(\tfrac{1}{4}\, n \cot \frac{v}{2}\right) = R^2(\tfrac{1}{2}\, n \sin v) = r^2\left(n \tan \frac{v}{2}\right).$$

n	v	$\frac{\text{Area}}{a^2}$	$\frac{\text{Area}}{R^2}$	$\frac{\text{Area}}{r^2}$	$\frac{R}{a}$	$\frac{R}{r}$	$\frac{a}{R}$	$\frac{a}{r}$	$\frac{r}{R}$	$\frac{r}{a}$
3	120°	0.4330	1.299	5.196	0.5774	2.000	1.732	3.464	0.5000	0.2887
4	90°	1.000	2.000	4.000	0.7071	1.414	1.414	2.000	0.7071	0.5000
5	72°	1.721	2.378	3.633	0.8507	1.236	1.176	1.453	0.8090	0.6882
6	60°	2.598	2.598	3.464	1.0000	1.155	1.000	1.155	0.8660	0.8660
7	51°.43	3.634	2.736	3.371	1.152	1.110	0.8678	0.9631	0.9010	1.038
8	45°	4.828	2.828	3.314	1.307	1.082	0.7654	0.8284	0.9239	1.207
9	40°	6.182	2.893	3.276	1.462	1.064	0.6840	0.7279	0.9397	1.374
10	36°	7.694	2.939	3.249	1.618	1.052	0.6180	0.6498	0.9511	1.539
12	30°	11.20	3.000	3.215	1.932	1.035	0.5176	0.5359	0.9659	1.866
15	24°	17.64	3.051	3.188	2.405	1.022	0.4158	0.4251	0.9781	2.352
16	22°.50	20.11	3.062	3.183	2.563	1.020	0.3902	0.3978	0.9808	2.514
20	18°	31.57	3.090	3.168	3.196	1.013	0.3129	0.3168	0.9877	3.157
24	15°	45.58	3.106	3.160	3.831	1.009	0.2611	0.2633	0.9914	3.798
32	11°.25	81.23	3.121	3.152	5.101	1.005	0.1960	0.1970	0.9952	5.077
48	7°.50	183.1	3.133	3.146	7.645	1.002	0.1308	0.1311	0.9979	7.629
64	5°.625	325.7	3.137	3.144	10.19	1.001	0.0981	0.0983	0.9968	10.18

Binomial Coefficients

(For table giving binomial coefficients for fractional values of n, see p. 2-28.)

$(n)_0 = 1$; $(n)_1 = n$; $(n)_2 = \frac{n(n-1)}{1 \times 2}$; $(n)_3 = \frac{n(n-1)(n-2)}{1 \times 2 \times 3}$; etc.; in general,

$(n)_r = \frac{n(n-1)(n-2)\ .\ .\ .\ (n-[r-1])}{1 \times 2 \times 3\ .\ .\ .\ \times r}$. Other notations: ${}_nC_r = \binom{n}{r} = (n)_r$.

n	$(n)_0$	$(n)_1$	$(n)_2$	$(n)_3$	$(n)_4$	$(n)_5$	$(n)_6$	$(n)_7$	$(n)_8$	$(n)_9$	$(n)_{10}$	$(n)_{11}$	$(n)_{12}$	$(n)_{13}$
1	1	1	...	...	...	...	...	...	...	...	...	...	...	...
2	1	2	1	...	...	...	...	...	...	...	...	...	...	...
3	1	3	3	1	...	...	...	...	...	...	...	...	...	...
4	1	4	6	4	1	...	...	...	...	...	...	...	...	...
5	1	5	10	10	5	1	...	...	...	...	...	...	...	...
6	1	6	15	20	15	6	1	...	...	...	...	...	...	...
7	1	7	21	35	35	21	7	1	...	...	...	...	...	...
8	1	8	28	56	70	56	28	8	1	...	...	...	...	...
9	1	9	36	84	126	126	84	36	9	1	...	...	...	...
10	1	10	45	120	210	252	210	120	45	10	1	...	...	...
11	1	11	55	165	330	462	462	330	165	55	11	1	...	...
12	1	12	66	220	495	792	924	792	495	220	66	12	1	...
13	1	13	78	286	715	1287	1716	1716	1287	715	286	78	13	1
14	1	14	91	364	1001	2002	3003	3432	3003	2002	1001	364	91	14
15	1	15	105	455	1365	3003	5005	6435	6435	5005	3003	1365	455	105

For $n = 14$, $(n)_{14} = 1$; for $n = 15$, $(n)_{14} = 15$, and $(n)_{15} = 1$.

Common Logarithms (1.00 to 2.00)

Number	0	1	2	3	4	5	6	7	8	9	Avg diff
1.00	0.0000	0004	0009	0013	0017	0022	0026	0030	0035	0039	**4**
1.01	0043	0048	0052	0056	0060	0065	0069	0073	0077	0082	
1.02	0086	0090	0095	0099	0103	0107	0111	0116	0120	0124	
1.03	0128	0133	0137	0141	0145	0149	0154	0158	0162	0166	
1.04	0170	0175	0179	0183	0187	0191	0195	0199	0204	0208	
1.05	0212	0216	0220	0224	0228	0233	0237	0241	0245	0249	
1.06	0253	0257	0261	0265	0269	0273	0278	0282	0286	0290	
1.07	0294	0298	0302	0306	0310	0314	0318	0322	0326	0330	
1.08	0334	0338	0342	0346	0350	0354	0358	0362	0366	0370	
1.09	0374	0378	0382	0386	0390	0394	0398	0402	0406	0410	
1.10	0.0414	0418	0422	0426	0430	0434	0438	0441	0445	0449	
1.11	0453	0457	0461	0465	0469	0473	0477	0481	0484	0488	
1.12	0492	0496	0500	0504	0508	0512	0515	0519	0523	0527	
1.13	0531	0535	0538	0542	0546	0550	0554	0558	0561	0565	
1.14	0569	0573	0577	0580	0584	0588	0592	0596	0599	0603	
1.15	0607	0611	0615	0618	0622	0626	0630	0633	0637	0641	
1.16	0645	0648	0652	0656	0660	0663	0667	0671	0674	0678	
1.17	0682	0686	0689	0693	0697	0700	0704	0708	0711	0715	
1.18	0719	0722	0726	0730	0734	0737	0741	0745	0748	0752	
1.19	0755	0759	0763	0766	0770	0774	0777	0781	0785	0788	
1.20	0.0792	0795	0799	0803	0806	0810	0813	0817	0821	0824	
1.21	0828	0831	0835	0839	0842	0846	0849	0853	0856	0860	
1.22	0864	0867	0871	0874	0878	0881	0885	0888	0892	0896	
1.23	0899	0903	0906	0910	0913	0917	0920	0924	0927	0931	
1.24	0934	0938	0941	0945	0948	0952	0955	0959	0962	0966	
1.25	0969	0973	0976	0980	0983	0986	0990	0993	0997	1000	**3**
1.26	1004	1007	1011	1014	1017	1021	1024	1028	1031	1035	
1.27	1038	1041	1045	1048	1052	1055	1059	1062	1065	1069	
1.28	1072	1075	1079	1082	1086	1089	1092	1096	1099	1103	
1.29	1106	1109	1113	1116	1119	1123	1126	1129	1133	1136	
1.30	0.1139	1143	1146	1149	1153	1156	1159	1163	1166	1169	
1.31	1173	1176	1179	1183	1186	1189	1193	1196	1199	1202	
1.32	1206	1209	1212	1216	1219	1222	1225	1229	1232	1235	
1.33	1239	1242	1245	1248	1252	1255	1258	1261	1265	1268	
1.34	1271	1274	1278	1281	1284	1287	1290	1294	1297	1300	
1.35	1303	1307	1310	1313	1316	1319	1323	1326	1329	1332	
1.36	1335	1339	1342	1345	1348	1351	1355	1358	1361	1364	
1.37	1367	1370	1374	1377	1380	1383	1386	1389	1392	1396	
1.38	1399	1402	1405	1408	1411	1414	1418	1421	1424	1427	
1.39	1430	1433	1436	1440	1443	1446	1449	1452	1455	1458	
1.40	0.1461	1464	1467	1471	1474	1477	1480	1483	1486	1489	
1.41	1492	1495	1498	1501	1504	1508	1511	1514	1517	1520	
1.42	1523	1526	1529	1532	1535	1538	1541	1544	1547	1550	
1.43	1553	1556	1559	1562	1565	1569	1572	1575	1578	1581	
1.44	1584	1587	1590	1593	1596	1599	1602	1605	1608	1611	
1.45	1614	1617	1620	1623	1626	1629	1632	1635	1638	1641	
1.46	1644	1647	1649	1652	1655	1658	1661	1664	1667	1670	
1.47	1673	1676	1679	1682	1685	1688	1691	1694	1697	1700	
1.48	1703	1706	1708	1711	1714	1717	1720	1723	1726	1729	
1.49	1732	1735	1738	1741	1744	1746	1749	1752	1755	1758	

Moving the decimal point n places to the right [or left] in the number requires adding $+n$ [or $-n$] in the body of the table (see p. 1–42).

Common Logarithms (1.00 to 2.00)

Number	0	1	2	3	4	5	6	7	8	9	Avg diff
1.50	0.1761	1764	1767	1770	1772	1775	1778	1781	1784	1787	3
1.51	1790	1793	1796	1798	1801	1804	1807	1810	1813	1816	
1.52	1818	1821	1824	1827	1830	1833	1836	1838	1841	1844	
1.53	1847	1850	1853	1855	1858	1861	1864	1867	1870	1872	
1.54	1875	1878	1881	1884	1886	1889	1892	1895	1898	1901	
1.55	1903	1906	1909	1912	1915	1917	1920	1923	1926	1928	
1.56	1931	1934	1937	1940	1942	1945	1948	1951	1953	1956	
1.57	1959	1962	1965	1967	1970	1973	1976	1978	1981	1984	
1.58	1987	1989	1992	1995	1998	2000	2003	2006	2009	2011	
1.59	2014	2017	2019	2022	2025	2028	2030	2033	2036	2038	
1.60	0.2041	2044	2047	2049	2052	2055	2057	2060	2063	2066	
1.61	2068	2071	2074	2076	2079	2082	2084	2087	2090	2092	
1.62	2095	2098	2101	2103	2106	2109	2111	2114	2117	2119	
1.63	2122	2125	2127	2130	2133	2135	2138	2140	2143	2146	
1.64	2148	2151	2154	2156	2159	2162	2164	2167	2170	2172	
1.65	2175	2177	2180	2183	2185	2188	2191	2193	2196	2198	
1.66	2201	2204	2206	2209	2212	2214	2217	2219	2222	2225	
1.67	2227	2230	2232	2235	2238	2240	2243	2245	2248	2251	
1.68	2253	2256	2258	2261	2263	2266	2269	2271	2274	2276	
1.69	2279	2281	2284	2287	2289	2292	2294	2297	2299	2302	
1.70	0.2304	2307	2310	2312	2315	2317	2320	2322	2325	2327	
1.71	2330	2333	2335	2338	2340	2343	2345	2348	2350	2353	
1.72	2355	2358	2360	2363	2365	2368	2370	2373	2375	2378	
1.73	2380	2383	2385	2388	2390	2393	2395	2398	2400	2403	
1.74	2405	2408	2410	2413	2415	2418	2420	2423	2425	2428	2
1.75	2430	2433	2435	2438	2440	2443	2445	2448	2450	2453	
1.76	2455	2458	2460	2463	2465	2467	2470	2472	2475	2477	
1.77	2480	2482	2485	2487	2490	2492	2494	2497	2499	2502	
1.78	2504	2507	2509	2512	2514	2516	2519	2521	2524	2526	
1.79	2529	2531	2533	2536	2538	2541	2543	2545	2548	2550	
1.80	0.2553	2555	2558	2560	2562	2565	2567	2570	2572	2574	
1.81	2577	2579	2582	2584	2586	2589	2591	2594	2596	2598	
1.82	2601	2603	2605	2608	2610	2613	2615	2617	2620	2622	
1.83	2625	2627	2629	2632	2634	2636	2639	2641	2643	2646	
1.84	2648	2651	2653	2655	2658	2660	2662	2665	2667	2669	
1.85	2672	2674	2676	2679	2681	2683	2686	2688	2690	2693	
1.86	2695	2697	2700	2702	2704	2707	2709	2711	2714	2716	
1.87	2718	2721	2723	2725	2728	2730	2732	2735	2737	2739	
1.88	2742	2744	2746	2749	2751	2753	2755	2758	2760	2762	
1.89	2765	2767	2769	2772	2774	2776	2778	2781	2783	2785	
1.90	0.2788	2790	2792	2794	2797	2799	2801	2804	2806	2808	
1.91	2810	2813	2815	2817	2819	2822	2824	2826	2828	2831	
1.92	2833	2835	2838	2840	2842	2844	2847	2849	2851	2853	
1.93	2856	2858	2860	2862	2865	2867	2869	2871	2874	2876	
1.94	2878	2880	2882	2885	2887	2889	2891	2894	2896	2898	
1.95	2900	2903	2905	2907	2909	2911	2914	2916	2918	2920	
1.96	2923	2925	2927	2929	2931	2934	2936	2938	2940	2942	
1.97	2945	2947	2949	2951	2953	2956	2958	2960	2962	2964	
1.98	2967	2969	2971	2973	2975	2978	2980	2982	2984	2986	
1.99	2989	2991	2993	2995	2997	2999	3002	3004	3006	3008	

Common Logarithms

Number	0	1	2	3	4	5	6	7	8	9	Avg diff
1.0	0.0000	0043	0086	0128	0170	0212	0253	0294	0334	0374	See pages 1–40 to 1–42
1.1	0414	0453	0492	0531	0569	0607	0645	0682	0719	0755	
1.2	0792	0828	0864	0899	0934	0969	1004	1038	1072	1106	
1.3	1139	1173	1206	1239	1271	1303	1335	1367	1399	1430	
1.4	1461	1492	1523	1553	1584	1614	1644	1673	1703	1732	
1.5	1761	1790	1818	1847	1875	1903	1931	1959	1987	2014	
1.6	2041	2068	2095	2122	2148	2175	2201	2227	2253	2279	
1.7	2304	2330	2355	2380	2405	2430	2455	2480	2504	2529	
1.8	2553	2577	2601	2625	2648	2672	2695	2718	2742	2765	
1.9	2788	2810	2833	2856	2878	2900	2923	2945	2967	2989	
2.0	0.3010	3032	3054	3075	3096	3118	3139	3160	3181	3201	21
2.1	3222	3243	3263	3284	3304	3324	3345	3365	3385	3404	20
2.2	3424	3444	3464	3483	3502	3522	3541	3560	3579	3598	19
2.3	3617	3636	3655	3674	3692	3711	3729	3747	3766	3784	18
2.4	3802	3820	3838	3856	3874	3892	3909	3927	3945	3962	17
2.5	3979	3997	4014	4031	4048	4065	4082	4099	4116	4133	17
2.6	4150	4166	4183	4200	4216	4232	4249	4265	4281	4298	16
2.7	4314	4330	4346	4362	4378	4393	4409	4425	4440	4456	16
2.8	4472	4487	4502	4518	4533	4548	4564	4579	4594	4609	15
2.9	4624	4639	4654	4669	4683	4698	4713	4728	4742	4757	15
3.0	0.4771	4786	4800	4814	4829	4843	4857	4871	4886	4900	14
3.1	4914	4928	4942	4955	4969	4983	4997	5011	5024	5038	14
3.2	5051	5065	5079	5092	5105	5119	5132	5145	5159	5172	13
3.3	5185	5198	5211	5224	5237	5250	5263	5276	5289	5302	13
3.4	5315	5328	5340	5353	5366	5378	5391	5403	5416	5428	13
3.5	5441	5453	5465	5478	5490	5502	5514	5527	5539	5551	12
3.6	5563	5575	5587	5599	5611	5623	5635	5647	5658	5670	12
3.7	5682	5694	5705	5717	5729	5740	5752	5763	5775	5786	12
3.8	5798	5809	5821	5832	5843	5855	5866	5877	5888	5899	11
3.9	5911	5922	5933	5944	5955	5966	5977	5988	5999	6010	11
4.0	0.6021	6031	6042	6053	6064	6075	6085	6096	6107	6117	11
4.1	6128	6138	6149	6160	6170	6180	6191	6201	6212	6222	10
4.2	6232	6243	6253	6263	6274	6284	6294	6304	6314	6325	10
4.3	6335	6345	6355	6365	6375	6385	6395	6405	6415	6425	10
4.4	6435	6444	6454	6464	6474	6484	6493	6503	6513	6522	10
4.5	6532	6542	6551	6561	6571	6580	6590	6599	6609	6618	10
4.6	6628	6637	6646	6656	6665	6675	6684	6693	6702	6712	10
4.7	6721	6730	6739	6749	6758	6767	6776	6785	6794	6803	9
4.8	6812	6821	6830	6839	6848	6857	6866	6875	6884	6893	9
4.9	6902	6911	6920	6928	6937	6946	6955	6964	6972	6981	9

$\log \pi = 0.4971$ $\quad \log \pi/2 = 0.1961$ $\quad \log \pi^2 = 0.9943$ $\quad \log \sqrt{\pi} = 0.2486$

$\log e = 0.4343$ $\quad \log (0.4343) = 0.6378 - 1$

These two pages give the common logarithms of numbers between 1 and 10, correct to four places. Moving the decimal point n places to the right [or left] in the number is equivalent to adding n [or $-n$] to the logarithm. Thus, $\log 0.017453 = 0.2419 - 2$, which may also be written $\bar{2}.2419$ or $8.2419 - 10$. See p. 2–5. Graphs, p. 2–84.

$$\log (ab) = \log a + \log b \qquad \log (a^N) = N \log a$$

$$\log \left(\frac{a}{b}\right) = \log a - \log b \qquad \log \left(\sqrt[N]{a}\right) = \frac{1}{N} \log a$$

Common Logarithms (*continued*)

Number	0	1	2	3	4	5	6	7	8	9	Avg diff
5.0	0.6990	6998	7007	7016	7024	7033	7042	7050	7059	7067	9
5.1	7076	7084	7093	7101	7110	7118	7126	7135	7143	7152	8
5.2	7160	7168	7177	7185	7193	7202	7210	7218	7226	7235	8
5.3	7243	7251	7259	7267	7275	7284	7292	7300	7308	7316	8
5.4	7324	7332	7340	7348	7356	7364	7372	7380	7388	7396	8
5.5	7404	7412	7419	7427	7435	7443	7451	7459	7466	7474	8
5.6	7482	7490	7497	7505	7513	7520	7528	7536	7543	7551	8
5.7	7559	7566	7574	7582	7589	7597	7604	7612	7619	7627	8
5.8	7634	7642	7649	7657	7664	7672	7679	7686	7694	7701	7
5.9	7709	7716	7723	7731	7738	7745	7752	7760	7767	7774	7
6.0	0.7782	7789	7796	7803	7810	7818	7825	7832	7839	7846	7
6.1	7853	7860	7868	7875	7882	7889	7896	7903	7910	7917	7
6.2	7924	7931	7938	7945	7952	7959	7966	7973	7980	7987	7
6.3	7993	8000	8007	8014	8021	8028	8035	8041	8048	8055	7
6.4	8062	8069	8075	8082	8089	8096	8102	8109	8116	8122	7
6.5	8129	8136	8142	8149	8156	8162	8169	8176	8182	8189	7
6.6	8195	8202	8209	8215	8222	8228	8235	8241	8248	8254	7
6.7	8261	8267	8274	8280	8287	8293	8299	8306	8312	8319	6
6.8	8325	8331	8338	8344	8351	8357	8363	8370	8376	8382	6
6.9	8388	8395	8401	8407	8414	8420	8426	8432	8439	8445	6
7.0	0.8451	8457	8463	8470	8476	8482	8488	8494	8500	8506	6
7.1	8513	8519	8525	8531	8537	8543	8549	8555	8561	8567	6
7.2	8573	8579	8585	8591	8597	8603	8609	8615	8621	8627	6
7.3	8633	8639	8645	8651	8657	8663	8669	8675	8681	8686	6
7.4	8692	8698	8704	8710	8716	8722	8727	8733	8739	8745	6
7.5	8751	8756	8762	8768	8774	8779	8785	8791	8797	8802	6
7.6	8808	8814	8820	8825	8831	8837	8842	8848	8854	8859	6
7.7	8865	8871	8876	8882	8887	8893	8899	8904	8910	8915	6
7.8	8921	8927	8932	8938	8943	8949	8954	8960	8965	8971	6
7.9	8976	8982	8987	8993	8998	9004	9009	9015	9020	9025	5
8.0	0.9031	9036	9042	9047	9053	9058	9063	9069	9074	9079	5
8.1	9085	9090	9096	9101	9106	9112	9117	9122	9128	9133	5
8.2	9138	9143	9149	9154	9159	9165	9170	9175	9180	9186	5
8.3	9191	9196	9201	9206	9212	9217	9222	9227	9232	9238	5
8.4	9243	9248	9253	9258	9263	9269	9274	9279	9284	9289	5
8.5	9294	9299	9304	9309	9315	9320	9325	9330	9335	9340	5
8.6	9345	9350	9355	9360	9365	9370	9375	9380	9385	9390	5
8.7	9395	9400	9405	9410	9415	9420	9425	9430	9435	9440	5
8.8	9445	9450	9455	9460	9465	9469	9474	9479	9484	9489	5
8.9	9494	9499	9504	9509	9513	9518	9523	9528	9533	9538	5
9.0	0.9542	9547	9552	9557	9562	9566	9571	9576	9581	9586	5
9.1	9590	9595	9600	9605	9609	9614	9619	9624	9628	9633	5
9.2	9638	9643	9647	9652	9657	9661	9666	9671	9675	9680	5
9.3	9685	9689	9694	9699	9703	9708	9713	9717	9722	9727	5
9.4	9731	9736	9741	9745	9750	9754	9759	9763	9768	9773	5
9.5	9777	9782	9786	9791	9795	9800	9805	9809	9814	9818	5
9.6	9823	9827	9832	9836	9841	9845	9850	9854	9859	9863	4
9.7	9868	9872	9877	9881	9886	9890	9894	9899	9903	9908	4
9.8	9912	9917	9921	9926	9930	9934	9939	9943	9948	9952	4
9.9	9956	9961	9965	9969	9974	9978	9983	9987	9991	9996	4

Degrees and Minutes Expressed in Radians (see also p. 1–69)

Degrees						Hundredths				Minutes	
1°	.0175	61°	1.0647	121°	2.1118	0°.01	.0002	0°.51	.0089	1′	.0003
2	.0349	2	1.0821	2	2.1293	2	.0003	2	.0091	2′	.0006
3	.0524	3	1.0996	3	2.1468	3	.0005	3	.0093	3′	.0009
4	.0698	4	1.1170	4	2.1642	4	.0007	4	.0094	4′	.0012
5°	.0873	65°	1.1345	125°	2.1817	.05	.0009	.55	.0096	5′	.0015
6	.1047	6	1.1519	6	2.1991	6	.0010	6	.0098	6′	.0017
7	.1222	7	1.1694	7	2.2166	7	.0012	7	.0099	7′	.0020
8	.1396	8	1.1868	8	2.2340	8	.0014	8	.0101	8′	.0023
9	.1571	9	1.2043	9	2.2515	9	.0016	9	.0103	9′	.0026
10°	.1745	70°	1.2217	130°	2.2689	0°.10	.0017	0°.60	.0105	10′	.0029
1	.1920	1	1.2392	1	2.2864	1	.0019	1	.0106	11′	.0032
2	.2094	2	1.2566	2	2.3038	2	.0021	2	.0108	12′	.0035
3	.2269	3	1.2741	3	2.3213	3	.0023	3	.0110	13′	.0038
4	.2443	4	1.2915	4	2.3387	4	.0024	4	.0112	14′	.0041
15°	.2618	75°	1.3090	135°	2.3562	.15	.0026	.65	.0113	15′	.0044
6	.2793	6	1.3265	6	2.3736	6	.0028	6	.0115	16′	.0047
7	.2967	7	1.3439	7	2.3911	7	.0030	7	.0117	17′	.0049
8	.3142	8	1.3614	8	2.4086	8	.0031	8	.0119	18′	.0052
9	.3316	9	1.3788	9	2.4260	9	.0033	9	.0120	19′	.0055
20°	.3491	80°	1.3963	140°	2.4435	0°.20	.0035	0°.70	.0122	20′	.0058
1	.3665	1	1.4137	1	2.4609	1	.0037	1	.0124	21′	.0061
2	.3840	2	1.4312	2	2.4784	2	.0038	2	.0126	22′	.0064
3	.4014	3	1.4486	3	2.4958	3	.0040	3	.0127	23′	.0067
4	.4189	4	1.4661	4	2.5133	4	.0042	4	.0129	24′	.0070
25°	.4363	85°	1.4835	145°	2.5307	.25	.0044	.75	.0131	25′	.0073
6	.4538	6	1.5010	6	2.5482	6	.0045	6	.0133	26′	.0076
7	.4712	7	1.5184	7	2.5656	7	.0047	7	.0134	27′	.0079
8	.4887	8	1.5359	8	2.5831	8	.0049	8	.0136	28′	.0081
9	.5061	9	1.5533	9	2.6005	9	.0051	9	.0138	29′	.0084
30°	.5236	90°	1.5708	150°	2.6180	0°.30	.0052	0°.80	.0140	30′	.0087
1	.5411	1	1.5882	1	2.6354	1	.0054	1	.0141	31′	.0090
2	.5585	2	1.6057	2	2.6529	2	.0056	2	.0143	32′	.0093
3	.5760	3	1.6232	3	2.6704	3	.0058	3	.0145	33′	.0096
4	.5934	4	1.6406	4	2.6878	4	.0059	4	.0147	34′	.0099
35°	.6109	95°	1.6581	155°	2.7053	.35	.0061	.85	.0148	35′	.0102
6	.6283	6	1.6755	6	2.7227	6	.0063	6	.0150	36′	.0105
7	.6458	7	1.6930	7	2.7402	7	.0065	7	.0152	37′	.0108
8	.6632	8	1.7104	8	2.7576	8	.0066	8	.0154	38′	.0111
9	.6807	9	1.7279	9	2.7751	9	.0068	9	.0155	39′	.0113
40°	.6981	100°	1.7453	160°	2.7925	0°.40	.0070	0°.90	.0157	40′	.0116
1	.7156	1	1.7628	1	2.8100	1	.0072	1	.0159	41′	.0119
2	.7330	2	1.7802	2	2.8274	2	.0073	2	.0161	42′	.0122
3	.7505	3	1.7977	3	2.8449	3	.0075	3	.0162	43′	.0125
4	.7679	4	1.8151	4	2.8623	4	.0077	4	.0164	44′	.0128
45°	.7854	105°	1.8326	165°	2.8798	.45	.0079	.95	.0166	45′	.0131
6	.8029	6	1.8500	6	2.8972	6	.0080	6	.0168	46′	.0134
7	.8203	7	1.8675	7	2.9147	7	.0082	7	.0169	47′	.0137
8	.8378	8	1.8850	8	2.9322	8	.0084	8	.0171	48′	.0140
9	.8552	9	1.9024	9	2.9496	9	.0086	9	.0173	49′	.0143
50°	.8727	110°	1.9199	170°	2.9671	0°.50	.0087	1°.00	.0175	50′	.0145
1	.8901	1	1.9373	1	2.9845					51′	.0148
2	.9076	2	1.9548	2	3.0020					52′	.0151
3	.9250	3	1.9722	3	3.0194					53′	.0154
4	.9425	4	1.9897	4	3.0369					54′	.0157
55°	.9599	115°	2.0071	175°	3.0543					55′	.0160
6	.9774	6	2.0246	6	3.0718					56′	.0163
7	.9948	7	2.0420	7	3.0892					57′	.0166
8	1.0123	8	2.0595	8	3.1067					58′	.0169
9	1.0297	9	2.0769	9	3.1241					59′	.0172
60°	1.0472	120°	2.0944	180°	3.1416					60′	.0175

Arc 1° = 0.0174533 Arc 1′ = 0.000290888 Arc 1″ = 0.00000484814
1 radian = 57°.295780 = 57° 17′.7468 = 57° 17′ 44″.806

Radians Expressed in Degrees

Rad.	Deg.	Rad.	Deg.	Rad.	Deg.	Rad.	Deg.	Rad.	Deg.	Interpolation	
0.01	0°.57	**.64**	36°.67	**1.27**	72°.77	**1.90**	108°.86	**2.53**	144°.96		
2	1°.15	**.65**	37°.24	8	73°.34	1	109°.43	4	145°.53	**.0002**	0°.01
3	1°.72	6	37°.82	9	73°.91	2	110°.01	**2.55**	146°.10	04	.02
4	2°.29	7	38°.39	**1.30**	74°.48	3	110°.58	6	146°.68	06	.03
.05	2°.86	8	38°.96	1	75°.06	4	111°.15	7	147°.25	08	.05
6	3°.44	9	39°.53	2	75°.63	**1.95**	111°.73	8	147°.82	**.0010**	0°.06
7	4°.01	**.70**	40°.11	3	76°.20	6	112°.30	9	148°.40	12	.07
8	4°.58	1	40°.68	4	76°.78	7	112°.87	**2.60**	148°.97	14	.08
9	5°.16	2	41°.25	**1.35**	77°.35	8	113°.45	1	149°.54	16	.09
.10	5°.73	3	41°.83	6	77°.92	9	114°.02	2	150°.11	18	.10
1	6°.30	4	42°.40	7	78°.50	**2.00**	114°.59	3	150°.69	**.0020**	0°.11
2	6°.88	**.75**	42°.97	8	79°.07	1	115°.16	4	151°.26	22	.13
3	7°.45	6	43°.54	9	79°.64	2	115°.74	**2.65**	151°.83	24	.14
4	8°.02	7	44°.12	**1.40**	80°.21	3	116°.31	6	152°.41	26	.15
.15	8°.59	8	44°.69	1	80°.79	4	116°.88	7	152°.98	28	.16
6	9°.17	9	45°.26	2	81°.36	**2.05**	117°.46	8	153°.55	**.0030**	0°.17
7	9°.74	**.80**	45°.84	3	81°.93	6	118°.03	9	154°.13	32	.18
8	10°.31	1	46°.41	4	82°.51	7	118°.60	**2.70**	154°.70	34	.19
9	10°.89	2	46°.98	**1.45**	83°.08	8	119°.18	1	155°.27	36	.21
.20	11°.46	3	47°.56	6	83°.65	9	119°.75	2	155°.84	38	.22
1	12°.03	4	48°.13	7	84°.22	**2.10**	120°.32	3	156°.42	**.0040**	0°.23
2	12°.61	**.85**	48°.70	8	84°.80	1	120°.89	4	156°.99	42	.24
3	13°.18	6	49°.27	9	85°.37	2	121°.47	**2.75**	157°.56	44	.25
4	13°.75	7	49°.85	**1.50**	85°.94	3	122°.04	6	158°.14	46	.26
.25	14°.32	8	50°.42	1	86°.52	4	122°.61	7	158°.71	48	.28
6	14°.90	9	50°.99	2	87°.09	**2.15**	123°.19	8	159°.28	**.0050**	0°.29
7	15°.47	**.90**	51°.57	3	87°.66	6	123°.76	9	159°.86	52	.30
8	16°.04	1	52°.14	4	88°.24	7	124°.33	**2.80**	160°.43	54	.31
9	16°.62	2	52°.71	**1.55**	88°.81	8	124°.90	1	161°.00	56	.32
.30	17°.19	3	53°.29	6	89°.38	9	125°.48	2	161°.57	58	.33
1	17°.76	4	53°.86	7	89°.95	**2.20**	126°.05	3	162°.15	**.0060**	0°.34
2	18°.33	**.95**	54°.43	8	90°.53	1	126°.62	4	162°.72	62	.36
3	18°.91	6	55°.00	9	91°.10	2	127°.20	**2.85**	163°.29	64	.37
4	19°.48	7	55°.58	**1.60**	91°.67	3	127°.77	6	163°.87	66	.38
.35	20°.05	8	56°.15	1	92°.25	4	128°.34	7	164°.44	68	.39
6	20°.63	9	56°.72	2	92°.82	**2.25**	128°.92	8	165°.01	**.0070**	0°.40
7	21°.20	**1.00**	57°.30	3	93°.39	6	129°.49	9	165°.58	72	.41
8	21°.77	1	57°.87	4	93°.97	7	130°.06	**2.90**	166°.16	74	.42
9	22°.35	2	58°.44	**1.65**	94°.54	8	130°.63	1	166°.73	76	.44
.40	22°.92	3	59°.01	6	95°.11	9	131°.21	2	167°.30	78	.45
1	23°.49	4	59°.59	7	95°.68	**2.30**	131°.78	3	167°.88	**.0080**	0°.46
2	24°.06	**1.05**	60°.16	8	96°.26	1	132°.35	4	168°.45	82	.47
3	24°.64	6	60°.73	9	96°.83	2	132°.93	**2.95**	169°.02	84	.48
4	25°.21	7	61°.31	**1.70**	97°.40	3	133°.50	6	169°.60	86	.49
.45	25°.78	8	61°.88	1	97°.98	4	134°.07	7	170°.17	88	.50
6	26°.36	9	62°.45	2	98°.55	**2.35**	134°.65	8	170°.74	**.0090**	0°.52
7	26°.93	**1.10**	63°.03	3	99°.12	6	135°.22	9	171°.31	92	.53
8	27°.50	1	63°.60	4	99°.69	7	135°.79	**3.00**	171°.89	94	.54
9	28°.07	2	64°.17	**1.75**	100°.27	8	136°.36	1	172°.46	96	.55
.50	28°.65	3	64°.74	6	100°.84	9	136°.94	2	173°.03	98	.56
1	29°.22	4	65°.32	7	101°.41	**2.40**	137°.51	3	173°.61		
2	29°.79	**1.15**	65°.89	8	101°.99	1	138°.08	4	174°.18		
3	30°.37	6	66°.46	9	102°.56	2	138°.66	**3.05**	174°.75		
4	30°.94	7	67°.04	**1.80**	103°.13	3	139°.23	6	175°.33		
.55	31°.51	8	67°.61	1	103°.71	4	139°.80	7	175°.90		
6	32°.09	9	68°.18	2	104°.28	**2.45**	140°.37	8	176°.47		
7	32°.66	**1.20**	68°.75	3	104°.85	6	140°.95	9	177°.04		
8	33°.23	1	69°.33	4	105°.42	7	141°.52	**3.10**	177°.62		
9	33°.80	2	69°.90	**1.85**	106°.00	8	142°.09	1	178°.19		
.60	34°.38	3	70°.47	6	106°.57	9	142°.67	2	178°.76		
1	34°.95	4	71°.05	7	107°.14	**2.50**	143°.24	3	179°.34		
2	35°.52	**1.25**	71°.62	8	107°.72	1	143°.81	4	179°.91		
3	36°.10	6	72°.19	9	108°.29	2	144°.39	**3.15**	180°.48		

Multiples of π

1	3.1416	180°
2	6.2832	360°
3	9.4248	540°
4	12.5664	720°
5	15.7080	900°
6	18.8496	1080°
7	21.9911	1260°
8	25.1327	1440°
9	28.2743	1620°
10	31.4159	1800°

Natural Sines and Cosines

Natural Sines at intervals of 0°.1, or 6′. (For 10′ intervals, see pp. 1–52 to 1–56)

Deg	°.0 =(0′)	°.1 (6′)	°.2 (12′)	°.3 (18′)	°.4 (24′)	°.5 (30′)	°.6 (36′)	°.7 (42′)	°.8 (48′)	°.9 (54′)			Avg diff
											0.0000	90°	
0°	0.0000	0017	0035	0052	0070	0087	0105	0122	0140	0157	0175	89	17
1	0175	0192	0209	0227	0244	0262	0279	0297	0314	0332	0349	88	17
2	0349	0366	0384	0401	0419	0436	0454	0471	0488	0506	0523	87	17
3	0523	0541	0558	0576	0593	0610	0628	0645	0663	0680	0698	86	17
4	0698	0715	0732	0750	0767	0785	0802	0819	0837	0854	0.0872	85	17
5	0.0872	0889	0906	0924	0941	0958	0976	0993	1011	1028	1045	84	17
6	1045	1063	1080	1097	1115	1132	1149	1167	1184	1201	1219	83	17
7	1219	1236	1253	1271	1288	1305	1323	1340	1357	1374	1392	82	17
8	1392	1409	1426	1444	1461	1478	1495	1513	1530	1547	1564	81	17
9	1564	1582	1599	1616	1633	1650	1668	1685	1702	1719	0.1736	80°	17
10°	0.1736	1754	1771	1788	1805	1822	1840	1857	1874	1891	1908	79	17
11	1908	1925	1942	1959	1977	1994	2011	2028	2045	2062	2079	78	17
12	2079	2096	2113	2130	2147	2164	2181	2198	2215	2233	2250	77	17
13	2250	2267	2284	2300	2317	2334	2351	2368	2385	2402	2419	76	17
14	2419	2436	2453	2470	2487	2504	2521	2538	2554	2571	0.2588	75	17
15	0.2588	2605	2622	2639	2656	2672	2689	2706	2723	2740	2756	74	17
16	2756	2773	2790	2807	2823	2840	2857	2874	2890	2907	2924	73	17
17	2924	2940	2957	2974	2990	3007	3024	3040	3057	3074	3090	72	17
18	3090	3107	3123	3140	3156	3173	3190	3206	3223	3239	3256	71	17
19	3256	3272	3289	3305	3322	3338	3355	3371	3387	3404	0.3420	70°	16
20°	0.3420	3437	3453	3469	3486	3502	3518	3535	3551	3567	3584	69	16
21	3584	3600	3616	3633	3649	3665	3681	3697	3714	3730	3746	68	16
22	3746	3762	3778	3795	3811	3827	3843	3859	3875	3891	3907	67	16
23	3907	3923	3939	3955	3971	3987	4003	4019	4035	4051	4067	66	16
24	4067	4083	4099	4115	4131	4147	4163	4179	4195	4210	0.4226	65	16
25	0.4226	4242	4258	4274	4289	4305	4321	4337	4352	4368	4384	64	16
26	4384	4399	4415	4431	4446	4462	4478	4493	4509	4524	4540	63	16
27	4540	4555	4571	4586	4602	4617	4633	4648	4664	4679	4695	62	16
28	4695	4710	4726	4741	4756	4772	4787	4802	4818	4833	4848	61	15
29	4848	4863	4879	4894	4909	4924	4939	4955	4970	4985	0.5000	60°	15
30°	0.5000	5015	5030	5045	5060	5075	5090	5105	5120	5135	5150	59	15
31	5150	5165	5180	5195	5210	5225	5240	5255	5270	5284	5299	58	15
32	5299	5314	5329	5344	5358	5373	5388	5402	5417	5432	5446	57	15
33	5446	5461	5476	5490	5505	5519	5534	5548	5563	5577	5592	56	15
34	5592	5606	5621	5635	5650	5664	5678	5693	5707	5721	0.5736	55	14
35	0.5736	5750	5764	5779	5793	5807	5821	5835	5850	5864	5878	54	14
36	5878	5892	5906	5920	5934	5948	5962	5976	5990	6004	6018	53	14
37	6018	6032	6046	6060	6074	6088	6101	6115	6129	6143	6157	52	14
38	6157	6170	6184	6198	6211	6225	6239	6252	6266	6280	6293	51	14
39	6293	6307	6320	6334	6347	6361	6374	6388	6401	6414	0.6428	50°	13
40°	0.6428	6441	6455	6468	6481	6494	6508	6521	6534	6547	6561	49	13
41	6561	6574	6587	6600	6613	6626	6639	6652	6665	6678	6691	48	13
42	6691	6704	6717	6730	6743	6756	6769	6782	6794	6807	6820	47	13
43	6820	6833	6845	6858	6871	6884	6896	6909	6921	6934	6947	46	13
44	6947	6959	6972	6984	6997	7009	7022	7034	7046	7059	0.7071	45°	12
45°	0.7071												
		°.9 =(54′)	°.8 (48′)	°.7 (42′)	°.6 (36′)	°.5 (30′)	°.4 (24′)	°.3 (18′)	°.2 (12′)	°.1 (6′)	°.0 (0′)	Deg	

(For graphs, see p. 2–84.)

Natural Cosines

Natural Sines and Cosines (*continued*)

Natural Sines at intervals of 0°.1, or 6′. (For 10′ intervals, see pp. 1–52 to 1–56)

Deg	°.0 =(0′)	°.1 (6′)	°.2 (12′)	°.3 (18′)	°.4 (24′)	°.5 (30′)	°.6 (36′)	°.7 (42′)	°.8 (48′)	°.9 (54′)			Avg diff
											0.7071	45°	
45°	0.7071	7083	7096	7108	7120	7133	7145	7157	7169	7181	7193	44	12
46	7193	7206	7218	7230	7242	7254	7266	7278	7290	7302	7314	43	12
47	7314	7325	7337	7349	7361	7373	7385	7396	7408	7420	7431	42	12
48	7431	7443	7455	7466	7478	7490	7501	7513	7524	7536	7547	41	12
49	7547	7559	7570	7581	7593	7604	7615	7627	7638	7649	0.7660	40°	11
50°	0.7660	7672	7683	7694	7705	7716	7727	7738	7749	7760	7771	39	11
51	7771	7782	7793	7804	7815	7826	7837	7848	7859	7869	7880	38	11
52	7880	7891	7902	7912	7923	7934	7944	7955	7965	7976	7986	37	11
53	7986	7997	8007	8018	8028	8039	8049	8059	8070	8080	8090	36	10
54	8090	8100	8111	8121	8131	8141	8151	8161	8171	8181	0.8192	35	10
55	0.8192	8202	8211	8221	8231	8241	8251	8261	8271	8281	8290	34	10
56	8290	8300	8310	8320	8329	8339	8348	8358	8368	8377	8387	33	10
57	8387	8396	8406	8415	8425	8434	8443	8453	8462	8471	8480	32	9
58	8480	8490	8499	8508	8517	8526	8536	8545	8554	8563	8572	31	9
59	8572	8581	8590	8599	8607	8616	8625	8634	8643	8652	0.8660	30°	9
60°	0.8660	8669	8678	8686	8695	8704	8712	8721	8729	8738	8746	29	9
61	8746	8755	8763	8771	8780	8788	8796	8805	8813	8821	8829	28	8
62	8829	8838	8846	8854	8862	8870	8878	8886	8894	8902	8910	27	8
63	8910	8918	8926	8934	8942	8949	8957	8965	8973	8980	8988	26	8
64	8988	8996	9003	9011	9018	9026	9033	9041	9048	9056	0.9063	25	7
65	0.9063	9070	9078	9085	9092	9100	9107	9114	9121	9128	9135	24	7
66	9135	9143	9150	9157	9164	9171	9178	9184	9191	9198	9205	23	7
67	9205	9212	9219	9225	9232	9239	9245	9252	9259	9265	9272	22	7
68	9272	9278	9285	9291	9298	9304	9311	9317	9323	9330	9336	21	6
69	9336	9342	9348	9354	9361	9367	9373	9379	9385	9391	0.9397	20°	6
70°	0.9397	9403	9409	9415	9421	9426	9432	9438	9444	9449	9455	19	6
71	9455	9461	9466	9472	9478	9483	9489	9494	9500	9505	9511	18	6
72	9511	9516	9521	9527	9532	9537	9542	9548	9553	9558	9563	17	5
73	9563	9568	9573	9578	9583	9588	9593	9598	9603	9608	9613	16	5
74	9613	9617	9622	9627	9632	9636	9641	9646	9650	9655	0.9659	15	5
75	0.9659	9664	9668	9673	9677	9681	9686	9690	9694	9699	9703	14	4
76	9703	9707	9711	9715	9720	9724	9728	9732	9736	9740	9744	13	4
77	9744	9748	9751	9755	9759	9763	9767	9770	9774	9778	9781	12	4
78	9781	9785	9789	9792	9796	9799	9803	9806	9810	9813	9816	11	3
79	9816	9820	9823	9826	9829	9833	9836	9839	9842	9845	0.9848	10°	3
80°	0.9848	9851	9854	9857	9860	9863	9866	9869	9871	9874	9877	9	3
81	9877	9880	9882	9885	9888	9890	9893	9895	9898	9900	9903	8	3
82	9903	9905	9907	9910	9912	9914	9917	9919	9921	9923	9925	7	2
83	9925	9928	9930	9932	9934	9936	9938	9940	9942	9943	9945	6	2
84	9945	9947	9949	9951	9952	9954	9956	9957	9959	9960	0.9962	5	2
85	0.9962	9963	9965	9966	9968	9969	9971	9972	9973	9974	9976	4	1
86	9976	9977	9978	9979	9980	9981	9982	9983	9984	9985	9986	3	1
87	9986	9987	9988	9989	9990	9990	9991	9992	9993	9993	9994	2	1
88	9994	9995	9995	9996	9996	9997	9997	9997	9998	9998	0.9998	1	0
89	0.9998	9999	9999	9999	9999	0000	0000	0000	0000	0000	1.0000	0°	0
90°	1.0000												
		°.9 =(54′)	°.8 (48′)	°.7 (42′)	°.6 (36′)	°.5 (30′)	°.4 (24′)	°.3 (18′)	°.2 (12′)	°.1 (6′)	°.0 (0′)	Deg	

Natural Cosines

Natural Tangents and Cotangents

Natural Tangents at intervals of 0°.1, or 6′. (For 10′ intervals, see pp. 1–52 to 1–56)

Deg	°.0 =(0′)	°.1 (6′)	°.2 (12′)	°.3 (18′)	°.4 (24′)	°.5 (30′)	°.6 (36′)	°.7 (42′)	°.8 (48′)	°.9 (54′)			Avg diff
											0.0000	90°	
0°	0.0000	0017	0035	0052	0070	0087	0105	0122	0140	0157	0175	89	17
1	0175	0192	0209	0227	0244	0262	0279	0297	0314	0332	0349	88	17
2	0349	0367	0384	0402	0419	0437	0454	0472	0489	0507	0524	87	17
3	0524	0542	0559	0577	0594	0612	0629	0647	0664	0682	0699	86	18
4	0699	0717	0734	0752	0769	0787	0805	0822	0840	0857	0.0875	85	18
5	0.0875	0892	0910	0928	0945	0963	0981	0998	1016	1033	1051	84	18
6	1051	1069	1086	1104	1122	1139	1157	1175	1192	1210	1228	83	18
7	1228	1246	1263	1281	1299	1317	1334	1352	1370	1388	1405	82	18
8	1405	1423	1441	1459	1477	1495	1512	1530	1548	1566	1584	81	18
9	1584	1602	1620	1638	1655	1673	1691	1709	1727	1745	0.1763	80°	18
10°	0.1763	1781	1799	1817	1835	1853	1871	1890	1908	1926	1944	79	18
11	1944	1962	1980	1998	2016	2035	2053	2071	2089	2107	2126	78	18
12	2126	2144	2162	2180	2199	2217	2235	2254	2272	2290	2309	77	18
13	2309	2327	2345	2364	2382	2401	2419	2438	2456	2475	2493	76	18
14	2493	2512	2530	2549	2568	2586	2605	2623	2642	2661	0.2679	75	19
15	0.2679	2698	2717	2736	2754	2773	2792	2811	2830	2849	2867	74	19
16	2867	2886	2905	2924	2943	2962	2981	3000	3019	3038	3057	73	19
17	3057	3076	3096	3115	3134	3153	3172	3191	3211	3230	3249	72	19
18	3249	3269	3288	3307	3327	3346	3365	3385	3404	3424	3443	71	19
19	3443	3463	3482	3502	3522	3541	3561	3581	3600	3620	0.3640	70°	20
20°	0.3640	3659	3679	3699	3719	3739	3759	3779	3799	3819	3839	69	20
21	3839	3859	3879	3899	3919	3939	3959	3979	4000	4020	4040	68	20
22	4040	4061	4081	4101	4122	4142	4163	4183	4204	4224	4245	67	21
23	4245	4265	4286	4307	4327	4348	4369	4390	4411	4431	4452	66	21
24	4452	4473	4494	4515	4536	4557	4578	4599	4621	4642	0.4663	65	21
25	0.4663	4684	4706	4727	4748	4770	4791	4813	4834	4856	4877	64	21
26	4877	4899	4921	4942	4964	4986	5008	5029	5051	5073	5095	63	22
27	5095	5117	5139	5161	5184	5206	5228	5250	5272	5295	5317	62	22
28	5317	5340	5362	5384	5407	5430	5452	5475	5498	5520	5543	61	23
29	5543	5566	5589	5612	5635	5658	5681	5704	5727	5750	0.5774	60°	23
30°	0.5774	5797	5820	5844	5867	5890	5914	5938	5961	5985	6009	59	24
31	6009	6032	6056	6080	6104	6128	6152	6176	6200	6224	6249	58	24
32	6249	6273	6297	6322	6346	6371	6395	6420	6445	6469	6494	57	25
33	6494	6519	6544	6569	6594	6619	6644	6669	6694	6720	6745	56	25
34	6745	6771	6796	6822	6847	6873	6899	6924	6950	6976	0.7002	55	26
35	0.7002	7028	7054	7080	7107	7133	7159	7186	7212	7239	7265	54	26
36	7265	7292	7319	7346	7373	7400	7427	7454	7481	7508	7536	53	27
37	7536	7563	7590	7618	7646	7673	7701	7729	7757	7785	7813	52	28
38	7813	7841	7869	7898	7926	7954	7983	8012	8040	8069	8098	51	28
39	8098	8127	8156	8185	8214	8243	8273	8302	8332	8361	0.8391	50°	29
40°	0.8391	8421	8451	8481	8511	8541	8571	8601	8632	8662	8693	49	30
41	8693	8724	8754	8785	8816	8847	8878	8910	8941	8972	9004	48	31
42	9004	9036	9067	9099	9131	9163	9195	9228	9260	9293	9325	47	32
43	9325	9358	9391	9424	9457	9490	9523	9556	9590	9623	0.9657	46	33
44	0.9657	9691	9725	9759	9793	9827	9861	9896	9930	9965	1.0000	45°	34
45°	1.0000												
		°.9 =(54′)	°.8 (48′)	°.7 (42′)	°.6 (36′)	°.5 (30′)	°.4 (24′)	°.3 (18′)	°.2 (12′)	°.1 (6′)	°.0 (0′)	Deg	

(For graphs, see p. 2–84.)

Natural Cotangents

Natural Tangents and Cotangents (*continued*)

Natural Tangents at intervals of 0°.1, or 6′. (For 10′ intervals, see pp. 1–52 to 1–56)

Deg	°.0 =(0′)	°.1 (6′)	°.2 (12′)	°.3 (18′)	°.4 (24′)	°.5 (30′)	°.6 (36′)	°.7 (42′)	°.8 (48′)	°.9 (54′)			Avg diff
											1.0000	45°	
45°	1.0000	0035	0070	0105	0141	0176	0212	0247	0283	0319	0355	44	35
46	0355	0392	0428	0464	0501	0538	0575	0612	0649	0686	0724	43	37
47	0724	0761	0799	0837	0875	0913	0951	0990	1028	1067	1106	42	38
48	1106	1145	1184	1224	1263	1303	1343	1383	1423	1463	1504	41	40
49	1504	1544	1585	1626	1667	1708	1750	1792	1833	1875	1.1918	40°	41
50°	1.1918	1960	2002	2045	2088	2131	2174	2218	2261	2305	2349	39	43
51	2349	2393	2437	2482	2527	2572	2617	2662	2708	2753	2799	38	45
52	2799	2846	2892	2938	2985	3032	3079	3127	3175	3222	3270	37	47
53	3270	3319	3367	3416	3465	3514	3564	3613	3663	3713	3764	36	49
54	3764	3814	3865	3916	3968	4019	4071	4124	4176	4229	1.4281	35	52
55	1.4281	4335	4388	4442	4496	4550	4605	4659	4715	4770	4826	34	55
56	4826	4882	4938	4994	5051	5108	5166	5224	5282	5340	5399	33	57
57	5399	5458	5517	5577	5637	5697	5757	5818	5880	5941	6003	32	60
58	6003	6066	6128	6191	6255	6319	6383	6447	6512	6577	6643	31	64
59	1.6643	6709	6775	6842	6909	6977	7045	7113	7182	7251	1.7321	30°	67
60°	1.732	1.739	1.746	1.753	1.760	1.767	1.775	1.782	1.789	1.797	1.804	29	7
61	1.804	1.811	1.819	1.827	1.834	1.842	1.849	1.857	1.865	1.873	1.881	28	8
62	1.881	1.889	1.897	1.905	1.913	1.921	1.929	1.937	1.946	1.954	1.963	27	8
63	1.963	1.971	1.980	1.988	1.997	2.006	2.014	2.023	2.032	2.041	2.050	26	9
64	2.050	2.059	2.069	2.078	2.087	2.097	2.106	2.116	2.125	2.135	2.145	25	9
65	2.145	2.154	2.164	2.174	2.184	2.194	2.204	2.215	2.225	2.236	2.246	24	10
66	2.246	2.257	2.267	2.278	2.289	2.300	2.311	2.322	2.333	2.344	2.356	23	11
67	2.356	2.367	2.379	2.391	2.402	2.414	2.426	2.438	2.450	2.463	2.475	22	12
68	2.475	2.488	2.500	2.513	2.526	2.539	2.552	2.565	2.578	2.592	2.605	21	13
69	2.605	2.619	2.633	2.646	2.660	2.675	2.689	2.703	2.718	2.733	2.747	20°	14
70°	2.747	2.762	2.778	2.793	2.808	2.824	2.840	2.856	2.872	2.888	2.904	19	16
71	2.904	2.921	2.937	2.954	2.971	2.989	3.006	3.024	3.042	3.060	3.078	18	17
72	3.078	3.096	3.115	3.133	3.152	3.172	3.191	3.211	3.230	3.251	3.271	17	19
73	3.271	3.291	3.312	3.333	3.354	3.376	3.398	3.420	3.442	3.465	3.487	16	22
74	3.487	3.511	3.534	3.558	3.582	3.606	3.630	3.655	3.681	3.706	3.732	15	24
75	3.732	3.758	3.785	3.812	3.839	3.867	3.895	3.923	3.952	3.981	4.011	14	28
76	4.011	4.041	4.071	4.102	4.134	4.165	4.198	4.230	4.264	4.297	4.331	13	32
77	4.331	4.366	4.402	4.437	4.474	4.511	4.548	4.586	4.625	4.665	4.705	12	37
78	4.705	4.745	4.787	4.829	4.872	4.915	4.959	5.005	5.050	5.097	5.145	11	44
79	5.145	5.193	5.242	5.292	5.343	5.396	5.449	5.503	5.558	5.614	5.671	10°	53
80°	5.671	5.730	5.789	5.850	5.912	5.976	6.041	6.107	6.174	6.243	6.314	9	
81	6.314	6.386	6.460	6.535	6.612	6.691	6.772	6.855	6.940	7.026	7.115	8	
82	7.115	7.207	7.300	7.396	7.495	7.596	7.700	7.806	7.916	8.028	8.144	7	
83	8.144	8.264	8.386	8.513	8.643	8.777	8.915	9.058	9.205	9.357	9.514	6	
84	9.514	9.677	9.845	10.02	10.20	10.39	10.58	10.78	10.99	11.20	11.43	5	
85	11.43	11.66	11.91	12.16	12.43	12.71	13.00	13.30	13.62	13.95	14.30	4	
86	14.30	14.67	15.06	15.46	15.90	16.35	16.83	17.34	17.89	18.46	19.08	3	
87	19.08	19.74	20.45	21.20	22.02	22.90	23.86	24.90	26.03	27.27	28.64	2	
88	28.64	30.14	31.82	33.69	35.80	38.19	40.92	44.07	47.74	52.08	57.29	1	
89	57.29	63.66	71.62	81.85	95.49	114.6	143.2	191.0	286.5	573.0	∞	0°	
90°	∞												
		°.9 =(54′)	°.8 (48′)	°.7 (42′)	°.6 (36′)	°.5 (30′)	°.4 (24′)	°.3 (18′)	°.2 (12′)	°.1 (6′)	°.0 (0′)	Deg	

Natural Cotangents

Natural Secants and Cosecants

Natural Secants at intervals of 0°.1, or 6′.

Deg	°.0 =(0′)	°.1 (6′)	°.2 (12′)	°.3 (18′)	°.4 (24′)	°.5 (30′)	°.6 (36′)	°.7 (42′)	°.8 (48′)	°.9 (54′)			Avg diff
											1.0000	90°	
0°	1.0000	0000	0000	0000	0000	0000	0001	0001	0001	0001	0002	89	0
1	0002	0002	0002	0003	0003	0003	0004	0004	0005	0006	0006	88	0
2	0006	0007	0007	0008	0009	0010	0010	0011	0012	0013	0014	87	1
3	0014	0015	0016	0017	0018	0019	0020	0021	0022	0023	0024	86	1
4	0024	0026	0027	0028	0030	0031	0032	0034	0035	0037	1.0038	85	1
5	1.0038	0040	0041	0043	0045	0046	0048	0050	0051	0053	0055	84	2
6	0055	0057	0059	0061	0063	0065	0067	0069	0071	0073	0075	83	2
7	0075	0077	0079	0082	0084	0086	0089	0091	0093	0096	0098	82	2
8	0098	0101	0103	0106	0108	0111	0114	0116	0119	0122	0125	81	3
9	0125	0127	0130	0133	0136	0139	0142	0145	0148	0151	1.0154	80°	3
10°	1.0154	0157	0161	0164	0167	0170	0174	0177	0180	0184	0187	79	3
11	0187	0191	0194	0198	0201	0205	0209	0212	0216	0220	0223	78	4
12	0223	0227	0231	0235	0239	0243	0247	0251	0255	0259	0263	77	4
13	0263	0267	0271	0276	0280	0284	0288	0293	0297	0302	0306	76	4
14	0306	0311	0315	0320	0324	0329	0334	0338	0343	0348	1.0353	75	5
15	1.0353	0358	0363	0367	0372	0377	0382	0388	0393	0398	0403	74	5
16	0403	0408	0413	0419	0424	0429	0435	0440	0446	0451	0457	73	5
17	0457	0463	0468	0474	0480	0485	0491	0497	0503	0509	0515	72	6
18	0515	0521	0527	0533	0539	0545	0551	0557	0564	0570	0576	71	6
19	0576	0583	0589	0595	0602	0608	0615	0622	0628	0635	1.0642	70°	7
20°	1.0642	0649	0655	0662	0669	0676	0683	0690	0697	0704	0711	69	7
21	0711	0719	0726	0733	0740	0748	0755	0763	0770	0778	0785	68	7
22	0785	0793	0801	0808	0816	0824	0832	0840	0848	0856	0864	67	8
23	0864	0872	0880	0888	0896	0904	0913	0921	0929	0938	0946	66	8
24	0946	0955	0963	0972	0981	0989	0998	1007	1016	1025	1.1034	65	9
25	1.1034	1043	1052	1061	1070	1079	1089	1098	1107	1117	1126	64	9
26	1126	1136	1145	1155	1164	1174	1184	1194	1203	1213	1223	63	10
27	1223	1233	1243	1253	1264	1274	1284	1294	1305	1315	1326	62	10
28	1326	1336	1347	1357	1368	1379	1390	1401	1412	1423	1434	61	11
29	1434	1445	1456	1467	1478	1490	1501	1512	1524	1535	1.1547	60°	11
30°	1.1547	1559	1570	1582	1594	1606	1618	1630	1642	1654	1666	59	12
31	1666	1679	1691	1703	1716	1728	1741	1753	1766	1779	1792	58	13
32	1792	1805	1818	1831	1844	1857	1870	1883	1897	1910	1924	57	13
33	1924	1937	1951	1964	1978	1992	2006	2020	2034	2048	2062	56	14
34	2062	2076	2091	2105	2120	2134	2149	2163	2178	2193	1.2208	55	15
35	1.2208	2223	2238	2253	2268	2283	2299	2314	2329	2345	2361	54	15
36	2361	2376	2392	2408	2424	2440	2456	2472	2489	2505	2521	53	16
37	2521	2538	2554	2571	2588	2605	2622	2639	2656	2673	2690	52	17
38	2690	2708	2725	2742	2760	2778	2796	2813	2831	2849	2868	51	18
39	2868	2886	2904	2923	2941	2960	2978	2997	3016	3035	1.3054	50°	19
40°	1.3054	3073	3093	3112	3131	3151	3171	3190	3210	3230	3250	49	20
41	3250	3270	3291	3311	3331	3352	3373	3393	3414	3435	3456	48	21
42	3456	3478	3499	3520	3542	3563	3585	3607	3629	3651	3673	47	22
43	3673	3696	3718	3741	3763	3786	3809	3832	3855	3878	3902	46	23
44	3902	3925	3949	3972	3996	4020	4044	4069	4093	4118	1.4142	45°	24
45°	1.4142												
		°.9 =(54′)	°.8 (48′)	°.7 (42′)	°.6 (36′)	°.5 (30′)	°.4 (24′)	°.3 (18′)	°.2 (12′)	°.1 (6′)	°.0 (0′)	Deg	

(For graphs, see p. 2–84.)

Natural Cosecants

Natural Secants and Cosecants (*continued*)

Natural Secants at intervals of 0°.1, or 6′.

Deg	°.0 =(0′)	°.1 (6′)	°.2 (12′)	°.3 (18′)	°.4 (24′)	°.5 (30′)	°.6 (36′)	°.7 (42′)	°.8 (48′)	°.9 (54′)			Avg diff
											1.4142	45°	
45°	1.4142	4167	4192	4217	4242	4267	4293	4318	4344	4370	4396	44	25
46	4396	4422	4448	4474	4501	4527	4554	4581	4608	4635	4663	43	27
47	4663	4690	4718	4746	4774	4802	4830	4859	4887	4916	4945	42	28
48	4945	4974	5003	5032	5062	5092	5121	5151	5182	5212	5243	41	30
49	5243	5273	5304	5335	5366	5398	5429	5461	5493	5525	1.5557	40°	31
50°	1.5557	5590	5622	5655	5688	5721	5755	5788	5822	5856	5890	39	33
51	5890	5925	5959	5994	6029	6064	6099	6135	6171	6207	6243	38	35
52	6243	6279	6316	6353	6390	6427	6464	6502	6540	6578	6616	37	37
53	6616	6655	6694	6733	6772	6812	6852	6892	6932	6972	7013	36	40
54	7013	7054	7095	7137	7179	7221	7263	7305	7348	7391	1.7434	35	42
55	1.7434	7478	7522	7566	7610	7655	7700	7745	7791	7837	7883	34	45
56	7883	7929	7976	8023	8070	8118	8166	8214	8263	8312	8361	33	48
57	8361	8410	8460	8510	8561	8612	8663	8714	8766	8818	8871	32	51
58	8871	8924	8977	9031	9084	9139	9194	9249	9304	9360	1.9416	31	54
59	1.9416	9473	9530	9587	9645	9703	9762	9821	9880	9940	2.0000	30°	58
60°	2.000	2.006	2.012	2.018	2.025	2.031	2.037	2.043	2.050	2.056	2.063	29	6
61	2.063	2.069	2.076	2.082	2.089	2.096	2.103	2.109	2.116	2.123	2.130	28	7
62	2.130	2.137	2.144	2.151	2.158	2.166	2.173	2.180	2.188	2.195	2.203	27	7
63	2.203	2.210	2.218	2.226	2.233	2.241	2.249	2.257	2.265	2.273	2.281	26	8
64	2.281	2.289	2.298	2.306	2.314	2.323	2.331	2.340	2.349	2.357	2.366	25	8
65	2.366	2.375	2.384	2.393	2.402	2.411	2.421	2.430	2.439	2.449	2.459	24	9
66	2.459	2.468	2.478	2.488	2.498	2.508	2.518	2.528	2.538	2.549	2.559	23	10
67	2.559	2.570	2.581	2.591	2.602	2.613	2.624	2.635	2.647	2.658	2.669	22	11
68	2.669	2.681	2.693	2.705	2.716	2.729	2.741	2.753	2.765	2.778	2.790	21	12
69	2.790	2.803	2.816	2.829	2.842	2.855	2.869	2.882	2.896	2.910	2.924	20°	13
70°	2.924	2.938	2.952	2.967	2.981	2.996	3.011	3.026	3.041	3.056	3.072	19	15
71	3.072	3.087	3.103	3.119	3.135	3.152	3.168	3.185	3.202	3.219	3.236	18	16
72	3.236	3.254	3.271	3.289	3.307	3.326	3.344	3.363	3.382	3.401	3.420	17	18
73	3.420	3.440	3.460	3.480	3.500	3.521	3.542	3.563	3.584	3.606	3.628	16	21
74	3.628	3.650	3.673	3.695	3.719	3.742	3.766	3.790	3.814	3.839	3.864	15	24
75	3.864	3.889	3.915	3.941	3.967	3.994	4.021	4.049	4.077	4.105	4.134	14	27
76	4.134	4.163	4.192	4.222	4.253	4.284	4.315	4.347	4.379	4.412	4.445	13	31
77	4.445	4.479	4.514	4.549	4.584	4.620	4.657	4.694	4.732	4.771	4.810	12	36
78	4.810	4.850	4.890	4.931	4.973	5.016	5.059	5.103	5.148	5.194	5.241	11	43
79	5.241	5.288	5.337	5.386	5.436	5.487	5.540	5.593	5.647	5.702	5.759	10°	52
80°	5.759	5.816	5.875	5.935	5.996	6.059	6.123	6.188	6.255	6.323	6.392	9	
81	6.392	6.464	6.537	6.611	6.687	6.765	6.845	6.927	7.011	7.097	7.185	8	
82	7.185	7.276	7.368	7.463	7.561	7.661	7.764	7.870	7.979	8.091	8.206	7	
83	8.206	8.324	8.446	8.571	8.700	8.834	8.971	9.113	9.259	9.411	9.567	6	
84	9.567	9.728	9.895	10.07	10.25	10.43	10.63	10.83	11.03	11.25	11.47	5	
85	11.47	11.71	11.95	12.20	12.47	12.75	13.03	13.34	13.65	13.99	14.34	4	
86	14.34	14.70	15.09	15.50	15.93	16.38	16.86	17.37	17.91	18.49	19.11	3	
87	19.11	19.77	20.47	21.23	22.04	22.93	23.88	24.92	26.05	27.29	28.65	2	
88	28.65	30.16	31.84	33.71	35.81	38.20	40.93	44.08	47.75	52.09	57.30	1	
89	57.30	63.66	71.62	81.85	95.49	114.6	143.2	191.0	286.5	573.0	∞	0°	
90°	∞												
		°.9 =(54′)	°.8 (48′)	°.7 (42′)	°.6 (36′)	°.5 (30′)	°.4 (24′)	°.3 (18′)	°.2 (12′)	°.1 (6′)	°.0 (0′)	Deg	

Natural Cosecants

Trigonometric Functions (at intervals of 10′)

Annex—10 in columns marked *. (For 0°.1 intervals, see pp. 1–46 to 1–51)

Degrees	Radians	Sines		Cosines		Tangents		Cotangents			
		Nat.	Log *	Nat.	Log *	Nat.	Log *	Nat.	Log		
0° 00′	0.0000	.0000	∞	1.0000	0.0000	.0000	∞	∞	∞	1.5708	90° 00′
10	0.0029	.0029	7.4637	1.0000	.0000	.0029	7.4637	343.77	2.5363	1.5679	50
20	0.0058	.0058	.7648	1.0000	.0000	.0058	.7648	171.89	.2352	1.5650	40
30	0.0087	.0087	.9408	1.0000	.0000	.0087	.9409	114.59	.0591	1.5621	30
40	0.0116	.0116	8.0658	.9999	.0000	.0116	8.0658	85.940	1.9342	1.5592	20
50	0.0145	.0145	.1627	.9999	.0000	.0145	.1627	68.750	.8373	1.5563	10
1° 00′	0.0175	.0175	8.2419	.9998	9.9999	.0175	8.2419	57.290	1.7581	1.5533	89° 00′
10	0.0204	.0204	.3088	.9998	.9999	.0204	.3089	49.104	.6911	1.5504	50
20	0.0233	.0233	.3668	.9997	.9999	.0233	.3669	42.964	.6331	1.5475	40
30	0.0262	.0262	.4179	.9997	.9999	.0262	.4181	38.188	.5819	1.5446	30
40	0.0291	.0291	.4637	.9996	.9998	.0291	.4638	34.368	.5362	1.5417	20
50	0.0320	.0320	.5050	.9995	.9998	.0320	.5053	31.242	.4947	1.5388	10
2° 00′	0.0349	.0349	8.5428	.9994	9.9997	.0349	8.5431	28.636	1.4569	1.5359	88° 00′
10	0.0378	.0378	.5776	.9993	.9997	.0378	.5779	26.432	.4221	1.5330	50
20	0.0407	.0407	.6097	.9992	.9996	.0407	.6101	24.542	.3899	1.5301	40
30	0.0436	.0436	.6397	.9990	.9996	.0437	.6401	22.904	.3599	1.5272	30
40	0.0465	.0465	.6677	.9989	.9995	.0466	.6682	21.470	.3318	1.5243	20
50	0.0495	.0494	.6940	.9988	.9995	.0495	.6945	20.206	.3055	1.5213	10
3° 00′	0.0524	.0523	8.7188	.9986	9.9994	.0524	8.7194	19.081	1.2806	1.5184	87° 00′
10	0.0553	.0552	.7423	.9985	.9993	.0553	.7429	18.075	.2571	1.5155	50
20	0.0582	.0581	.7645	.9983	.9993	.0582	.7652	17.169	.2348	1.5126	40
30	0.0611	.0610	.7857	.9981	.9992	.0612	.7865	16.350	.2135	1.5097	30
40	0.0640	.0640	.8059	.9980	.9991	.0641	.8067	15.605	.1933	1.5068	20
50	0.0669	.0669	.8251	.9978	.9990	.0670	.8261	14.924	.1739	1.5039	10
4° 00′	0.0698	.0698	8.8436	.9976	9.9989	.0699	8.8446	14.301	1.1554	1.5010	86° 00′
10	0.0727	.0727	.8613	.9974	.9989	.0729	.8624	13.727	.1376	1.4981	50
20	0.0756	.0756	.8783	.9971	.9988	.0758	.8795	13.197	.1205	1.4952	40
30	0.0785	.0785	.8946	.9969	.9987	.0787	.8960	12.706	.1040	1.4923	30
40	0.0814	.0814	.9104	.9967	.9986	.0816	.9118	12.251	.0882	1.4893	20
50	0.0844	.0843	.9256	.9964	.9985	.0846	.9272	11.826	.0728	1.4864	10
5° 00′	0.0873	.0872	8.9403	.9962	9.9983	.0875	8.9420	11.430	1.0580	1.4835	85° 00′
10	0.0902	.0901	.9545	.9959	.9982	.0904	.9563	11.059	.0437	1.4806	50
20	0.0931	.0929	.9682	.9957	.9981	.0934	.9701	10.712	.0299	1.4777	40
30	0.0960	.0958	.9816	.9954	.9980	.0963	.9836	10.385	.0164	1.4748	30
40	0.0989	.0987	.9945	.9951	.9979	.0992	.9966	10.078	.0034	1.4719	20
50	0.1018	.1016	9.0070	.9948	.9977	.1022	9.0093	9.7882	0.9907	1.4690	10
6° 00′	0.1047	.1045	9.0192	.9945	9.9976	.1051	9.0216	9.5144	0.9784	1.4661	84° 00′
10	0.1076	.1074	.0311	.9942	.9975	.1080	.0336	9.2553	.9664	1.4632	50
20	0.1105	.1103	.0426	.9939	.9973	.1110	.0453	9.0098	.9547	1.4603	40
30	0.1134	.1132	.0539	.9936	.9972	.1139	.0567	8.7769	.9433	1.4574	30
40	0.1164	.1161	.0648	.9932	.9971	.1169	.0678	8.5555	.9322	1.4544	20
50	0.1193	.1190	.0755	.9929	.9969	.1198	.0786	8.3450	.9214	1.4515	10
7° 00′	0.1222	.1219	9.0859	.9925	9.9968	.1228	9.0891	8.1443	0.9109	1.4486	83° 00′
10	0.1251	.1248	.0961	.9922	.9966	.1257	.0995	7.9530	.9005	1.4457	50
20	0.1280	.1276	.1060	.9918	.9964	.1287	.1096	7.7704	.8904	1.4428	40
30	0.1309	.1305	.1157	.9914	.9963	.1317	.1194	7.5958	.8806	1.4399	30
40	0.1338	.1334	.1252	.9911	.9961	.1346	.1291	7.4287	.8709	1.4370	20
50	0.1367	.1363	.1345	.9907	.9959	.1376	.1385	7.2687	.8615	1.4341	10
8° 00′	0.1396	.1392	9.1436	.9903	9.9958	.1405	9.1478	7.1154	0.8522	1.4312	82° 00′
10	0.1425	.1421	.1525	.9899	.9956	.1435	.1569	6.9682	.8431	1.4283	50
20	0.1454	.1449	.1612	.9894	.9954	.1465	.1658	6.8269	.8342	1.4254	40
30	0.1484	.1478	.1697	.9890	.9952	.1495	.1745	6.6912	.8255	1.4224	30
40	0.1513	.1507	.1781	.9886	.9950	.1524	.1831	6.5606	.8169	1.4195	20
50	0.1542	.1536	.1863	.9881	.9948	.1554	.1915	6.4348	.8085	1.4166	10
9° 00′	0.1571	.1564	9.1943	.9877	9.9946	.1584	9.1997	6.3138	0.8003	1.4137	81° 00′
		Nat.	Log *	Nat.	Log *	Nat.	Log *	Nat.	Log		
		Cosines		Sines		Cotangents		Tangents		Radians	Degrees

Trigonometric Functions (*continued*)

Annex—10 in columns marked *. (For 0°.1 intervals, see pp. 1-46 to 1-51)

Degrees	Radians	Sines Nat.	Sines Log *	Cosines Nat.	Cosines Log *	Tangents Nat.	Tangents Log *	Cotangents Nat.	Cotangents Log		
9° 00′	0.1571	.1564	9.1943	.9877	9.9946	.1584	9.1997	6.3138	0.8003	1.4137	81° 00′
10	0.1600	.1593	.2022	.9872	.9944	.1614	.2078	6.1970	.7922	1.4108	50
20	0.1629	.1622	.2100	.9868	.9942	.1644	.2158	6.0844	.7842	1.4079	40
30	0.1658	.1650	.2176	.9863	.9940	.1673	.2236	5.9758	.7764	1.4050	30
40	0.1687	.1679	.2251	.9858	.9938	.1703	.2313	5.8708	.7687	1.4021	20
50	0.1716	.1708	.2324	.9853	.9936	.1733	.2389	5.7694	.7611	1.3992	10
10° 00′	0.1745	.1736	9.2397	.9848	9.9934	.1763	9.2463	5.6713	0.7537	1.3963	80° 00′
10	0.1774	.1765	.2468	.9843	.9931	.1793	.2536	5.5764	.7464	1.3934	50
20	0.1804	.1794	.2538	.9838	.9929	.1823	.2609	5.4845	.7391	1.3904	40
30	0.1833	.1822	.2606	.9833	.9927	.1853	.2680	5.3955	.7320	1.3875	30
40	0.1862	.1851	.2674	.9827	.9924	.1883	.2750	5.3093	.7250	1.3846	20
50	0.1891	.1880	.2740	.9822	.9922	.1914	.2819	5.2257	.7181	1.3817	10
11° 00′	0.1920	.1908	9.2806	.9816	9.9919	.1944	9.2887	5.1446	0.7113	1.3788	79° 00′
10	0.1949	.1937	.2870	.9811	.9917	.1974	.2953	5.0658	.7047	1.3759	50
20	0.1978	.1965	.2934	.9805	.9914	.2004	.3020	4.9894	.6980	1.3730	40
30	0.2007	.1994	.2997	.9799	.9912	.2035	.3085	4.9152	.6915	1.3701	30
40	0.2036	.2022	.3058	.9793	.9909	.2065	.3149	4.8430	.6851	1.3672	20
50	0.2065	.2051	.3119	.9787	.9907	.2095	.3212	4.7729	.6788	1.3643	10
12° 00′	0.2094	.2079	9.3179	.9781	9.9904	.2126	9.3275	4.7046	0.6725	1.3614	78° 00′
10	0.2123	.2108	.3238	.9775	.9901	.2156	.3336	4.6382	.6664	1.3584	50
20	0.2153	.2136	.3296	.9769	.9899	.2186	.3397	4.5736	.6603	1.3555	40
30	0.2182	.2164	.3353	.9763	.9896	.2217	.3458	4.5107	.6542	1.3526	30
40	0.2211	.2193	.3410	.9757	.9893	.2247	.3517	4.4494	.6483	1.3497	20
50	0.2240	.2221	.3466	.9750	.9890	.2278	.3576	4.3897	.6424	1.3468	10
13° 00′	0.2269	.2250	9.3521	.9744	9.9887	.2309	9.3634	4.3315	0.6366	1.3439	77° 00′
10	0.2298	.2278	.3575	.9737	.9884	.2339	.3691	4.2747	.6309	1.3410	50
20	0.2327	.2306	.3629	.9730	.9881	.2370	.3748	4.2193	.6252	1.3381	40
30	0.2356	.2334	.3682	.9724	.9878	.2401	.3804	4.1653	.6196	1.3352	30
40	0.2385	.2363	.3734	.9717	.9875	.2432	.3859	4.1126	.6141	1.3323	20
50	0.2414	.2391	.3786	.9710	.9872	.2462	.3914	4.0611	.6086	1.3294	10
14° 00′	0.2443	.2419	9.3837	.9703	9.9869	.2493	9.3968	4.0108	0.6032	1.3265	76° 00′
10	0.2473	.2447	.3887	.9696	.9866	.2524	.4021	3.9617	.5979	1.3235	50
20	0.2502	.2476	.3937	.9689	.9863	.2555	.4074	3.9136	.5926	1.3206	40
30	0.2531	.2504	.3986	.9681	.9859	.2586	.4127	3.8667	.5873	1.3177	30
40	0.2560	.2532	.4035	.9674	.9856	.2617	.4178	3.8208	.5822	1.3148	20
50	0.2589	.2560	.4083	.9667	.9853	.2648	.4230	3.7760	.5770	1.3119	10
15° 00′	0.2618	.2588	9.4130	.9659	9.9849	.2679	9.4281	3.7321	0.5719	1.3090	75° 00′
10	0.2647	.2616	.4177	.9652	.9846	.2711	.4331	3.6891	.5669	1.3061	50
20	0.2676	.2644	.4223	.9644	.9843	.2742	.4381	3.6470	.5619	1.3032	40
30	0.2705	.2672	.4269	.9636	.9839	.2773	.4430	3.6059	.5570	1.3003	30
40	0.2734	.2700	.4314	.9628	.9836	.2805	.4479	3.5656	.5521	1.2974	20
50	0.2763	.2728	.4359	.9621	.9832	.2836	.4527	3.5261	.5473	1.2945	10
16° 00′	0.2793	.2756	9.4403	.9613	9.9828	.2867	9.4575	3.4874	0.5425	1.2915	74° 00′
10	0.2822	.2784	.4447	.9605	.9825	.2899	.4622	3.4495	.5378	1.2886	50
20	0.2851	.2812	.4491	.9596	.9821	.2931	.4669	3.4124	.5331	1.2857	40
30	0.2880	.2840	.4533	.9588	.9817	.2962	.4716	3.3759	.5284	1.2828	30
40	0.2909	.2868	.4576	.9580	.9814	.2994	.4762	3.3402	.5238	1.2799	20
50	0.2938	.2896	.4618	.9572	.9810	.3026	.4808	3.3052	.5192	1.2770	10
17° 00′	0.2967	.2924	9.4659	.9563	9.9806	.3057	9.4853	3.2709	0.5147	1.2741	73° 00′
10	0.2996	.2952	.4700	.9555	.9802	.3089	.4898	3.2371	.5102	1.2712	50
20	0.3025	.2979	.4741	.9546	.9798	.3121	.4943	3.2041	.5057	1.2683	40
30	0.3054	.3007	.4781	.9537	.9794	.3153	.4987	3.1716	.5013	1.2654	30
40	0.3083	.3035	.4821	.9528	.9790	.3185	.5031	3.1397	.4969	1.2625	20
50	0.3113	.3062	.4861	.9520	.9786	.3217	.5075	3.1084	.4925	1.2595	10
18° 00′	0.3142	.3090	9.4900	.9511	9.9782	.3249	9.5118	3.0777	0.4882	1.2566	72° 00′
		Cosines Nat.	Cosines Log *	Sines Nat.	Sines Log *	Cotangents Nat.	Cotangents Log *	Tangents Nat.	Tangents Log	Radians	Degrees

Trigonometric Functions (*continued*)

Annex—10 in columns marked *. (For 0°.1 intervals, see pp. 1-46 to 1-51)

Degrees	Radians	Sines Nat.	Sines Log *	Cosines Nat.	Cosines Log *	Tangents Nat.	Tangents Log *	Cotangents Nat.	Cotangents Log		
18° 00′	0.3142	.3090	9.4900	.9511	9.9782	.3249	9.5118	3.0777	0.4882	1.2566	72° 00′
10	0.3171	.3118	.4939	.9502	.9778	.3281	.5161	3.0475	.4839	1.2537	50
20	0.3200	.3145	.4977	.9492	.9774	.3314	.5203	3.0178	.4797	1.2508	40
30	0.3229	.3173	.5015	.9483	.9770	.3346	.5245	2.9887	.4755	1.2479	30
40	0.3258	.3201	.5052	.9474	.9765	.3378	.5287	2.9600	.4713	1.2450	20
50	0.3287	.3228	.5090	.9465	.9761	.3411	.5329	2.9319	.4671	1.2421	10
19° 00′	0.3316	.3256	9.5126	.9455	9.9757	.3443	9.5370	2.9042	0.4630	1.2392	71° 00′
10	0.3345	.3283	.5163	.9446	.9752	.3476	.5411	2.8770	.4589	1.2363	50
20	0.3374	.3311	.5199	.9436	.9748	.3508	.5451	2.8502	.4549	1.2334	40
30	0.3403	.3338	.5235	.9426	.9743	.3541	.5491	2.8239	.4509	1.2305	30
40	0.3432	.3365	.5270	.9417	.9739	.3574	.5531	2.7980	.4469	1.2275	20
50	0.3462	.3393	.5306	.9407	.9734	.3607	.5571	2.7725	.4429	1.2246	10
20° 00′	0.3491	.3420	9.5341	.9397	9.9730	.3640	9.5611	2.7475	0.4389	1.2217	70° 00′
10	0.3520	.3448	.5375	.9387	.9725	.3673	.5650	2.7228	.4350	1.2188	50
20	0.3549	.3475	.5409	.9377	.9721	.3706	.5689	2.6985	.4311	1.2159	40
30	0.3578	.3502	.5443	.9367	.9716	.3739	.5727	2.6746	.4273	1.2130	30
40	0.3607	.3529	.5477	.9356	.9711	.3772	.5766	2.6511	.4234	1.2101	20
50	0.3636	.3557	.5510	.9346	.9706	.3805	.5804	2.6279	.4196	1.2072	10
21° 00′	0.3665	.3584	9.5543	.9336	9.9702	.3839	9.5842	2.6051	0.4158	1.2043	69° 00′
10	0.3694	.3611	.5576	.9325	.9697	.3872	.5879	2.5826	.4121	1.2014	50
20	0.3723	.3638	.5609	.9315	.9692	.3906	.5917	2.5605	.4083	1.1985	40
30	0.3752	.3665	.5641	.9304	.9687	.3939	.5954	2.5386	.4046	1.1956	30
40	0.3782	.3692	.5673	.9293	.9682	.3973	.5991	2.5172	.4009	1.1926	20
50	0.3811	.3719	.5704	.9283	.9677	.4006	.6028	2.4960	.3972	1.1897	10
22° 00′	0.3840	.3746	9.5736	.9272	9.9672	.4040	9.6064	2.4751	0.3936	1.1868	68° 00′
10	0.3869	.3773	.5767	.9261	.9667	.4074	.6100	2.4545	.3900	1.1839	50
20	0.3898	.3800	.5798	.9250	.9661	.4108	.6136	2.4342	.3864	1.1810	40
30	0.3927	.3827	.5828	.9239	.9656	.4142	.6172	2.4142	.3828	1.1781	30
40	0.3956	.3854	.5859	.9228	.9651	.4176	.6208	2.3945	.3792	1.1752	20
50	0.3985	.3881	.5889	.9216	.9646	.4210	.6243	2.3750	.3757	1.1723	10
23° 00′	0.4014	.3907	9.5919	.9205	9.9640	.4245	9.6279	2.3559	0.3721	1.1694	67° 00′
10	0.4043	.3934	.5948	.9194	.9635	.4279	.6314	2.3369	.3686	1.1665	50
20	0.4072	.3961	.5978	.9182	.9629	.4314	.6348	2.3183	.3652	1.1636	40
30	0.4102	.3987	.6007	.9171	.9624	.4348	.6383	2.2998	.3617	1.1606	30
40	0.4131	.4014	.6036	.9159	.9618	.4383	.6417	2.2817	.3583	1.1577	20
50	0.4160	.4041	.6065	.9147	.9613	.4417	.6452	2.2637	.3548	1.1548	10
24° 00′	0.4189	.4067	9.6093	.9135	9.9607	.4452	9.6486	2.2460	0.3514	1.1519	66° 00′
10	0.4218	.4094	.6121	.9124	.9602	.4487	.6520	2.2286	.3480	1.1490	50
20	0.4247	.4120	.6149	.9112	.9596	.4522	.6553	2.2113	.3447	1.1461	40
30	0.4276	.4147	.6177	.9100	.9590	.4557	.6587	2.1943	.3413	1.1432	30
40	0.4305	.4173	.6205	.9088	.9584	.4592	.6620	2.1775	.3380	1.1403	20
50	0.4334	.4200	.6232	.9075	.9579	.4628	.6654	2.1609	.3346	1.1374	10
25° 00′	0.4363	.4226	9.6259	.9063	9.9573	.4663	9.6687	2.1445	0.3313	1.1345	65° 00′
10	0.4392	.4253	.6286	.9051	.9567	.4699	.6720	2.1283	.3280	1.1316	50
20	0.4422	.4279	.6313	.9038	.9561	.4734	.6752	2.1123	.3248	1.1286	40
30	0.4451	.4305	.6340	.9026	.9555	.4770	.6785	2.0965	.3215	1.1257	30
40	0.4480	.4331	.6366	.9013	.9549	.4806	.6817	2.0809	.3183	1.1228	20
50	0.4509	.4358	.6392	.9001	.9543	.4841	.6850	2.0655	.3150	1.1199	10
26° 00′	0.4538	.4384	9.6418	.8988	9.9537	.4877	9.6882	2.0503	0.3118	1.1170	64° 00′
10	0.4567	.4410	.6444	.8975	.9530	.4913	.6914	2.0353	.3086	1.1141	50
20	0.4596	.4436	.6470	.8962	.9524	.4950	.6946	2.0204	.3054	1.1112	40
30	0.4625	.4462	.6495	.8949	.9518	.4986	.6977	2.0057	.3023	1.1083	30
40	0.4654	.4488	.6521	.8936	.9512	.5022	.7009	1.9912	.2991	1.1054	20
50	0.4683	.4514	.6546	.8923	.9505	.5059	.7040	1.9768	.2960	1.1025	10
27° 00′	0.4712	.4540	9.6570	.8910	9.9499	.5095	9.7072	1.9626	0.2928	1.0996	63° 00′
		Cosines Nat.	Cosines Log *	Sines Nat.	Sines Log *	Cotangents Nat.	Cotangents Log *	Tangents Nat.	Tangents Log	Radians	Degrees

Trigonometric Functions (*continued*)

Annex—10 in columns marked *. (For 0°.1 intervals, see pp. 1–46 to 1–51)

Degrees	Radians	Sines		Cosines		Tangents		Cotangents			
		Nat.	Log *	Nat.	Log *	Nat.	Log *	Nat.	Log		
27° 00′	0.4712	.4540	9.6570	.8910	9.9499	.5095	9.7072	1.9626	0.2928	1.0996	63° 00′
10	0.4741	.4566	.6595	.8897	.9492	.5132	.7103	1.9486	.2897	1.0966	50
20	0.4771	.4592	.6620	.8884	.9486	.5169	.7134	1.9347	.2866	1.0937	40
30	0.4800	.4617	.6644	.8870	.9479	.5206	.7165	1.9210	.2835	1.0908	30
40	0.4829	.4643	.6668	.8857	.9473	.5243	.7196	1.9074	.2804	1.0879	20
50	0.4858	.4669	.6692	.8843	.9466	.5280	.7226	1.8940	.2774	1.0850	10
28° 00′	0.4887	.4695	9.6716	.8829	9.9459	.5317	9.7257	1.8807	0.2743	1.0821	62° 00′
10	0.4916	.4720	.6740	.8816	.9453	.5354	.7287	1.8676	.2713	1.0792	50
20	0.4945	.4746	.6763	.8802	.9446	.5392	.7317	1.8546	.2683	1.0763	40
30	0.4974	.4772	.6787	.8788	.9439	.5430	.7348	1.8418	.2652	1.0734	30
40	0.5003	.4797	.6810	.8774	.9432	.5467	.7378	1.8291	.2622	1.0705	20
50	0.5032	.4823	.6833	.8760	.9425	.5505	.7408	1.8165	.2592	1.0676	10
29° 00′	0.5061	.4848	9.6856	.8746	9.9418	.5543	9.7438	1.8040	0.2562	1.0647	61° 00′
10	0.5091	.4874	.6878	.8732	.9411	.5581	.7467	1.7917	.2533	1.0617	50
20	0.5120	.4899	.6901	.8718	.9404	.5619	.7497	1.7796	.2503	1.0588	40
30	0.5149	.4924	.6923	.8704	.9397	.5658	.7526	1.7675	.2474	1.0559	30
40	0.5178	.4950	.6946	.8689	.9390	.5696	.7556	1.7556	.2444	1.0530	20
50	0.5207	.4975	.6968	.8675	.9383	.5735	.7585	1.7437	.2415	1.0501	10
30° 00′	0.5236	.5000	9.6990	.8660	9.9375	.5774	9.7614	1.7321	0.2386	1.0472	60° 00′
10	0.5265	.5025	.7012	.8646	.9368	.5812	.7644	1.7205	.2356	1.0443	50
20	0.5294	.5050	.7033	.8631	.9361	.5851	.7673	1.7090	.2327	1.0414	40
30	0.5323	.5075	.7055	.8616	.9353	.5890	.7701	1.6977	.2299	1.0385	30
40	0.5352	.5100	.7076	.8601	.9346	.5930	.7730	1.6864	.2270	1.0356	20
50	0.5381	.5125	.7097	.8587	.9338	.5969	.7759	1.6753	.2241	1.0327	10
31° 00′	0.5411	.5150	9.7118	.8572	9.9331	.6009	9.7788	1.6643	0.2212	1.0297	59° 00′
10	0.5440	.5175	.7139	.8557	.9323	.6048	.7816	1.6534	.2184	1.0268	50
20	0.5469	.5200	.7160	.8542	.9315	.6088	.7845	1.6426	.2155	1.0239	40
30	0.5498	.5225	.7181	.8526	.9308	.6128	.7873	1.6319	.2127	1.0210	30
40	0.5527	.5250	.7201	.8511	.9300	.6168	.7902	1.6212	.2098	1.0181	20
50	0.5556	.5275	.7222	.8496	.9292	.6208	.7930	1.6107	.2070	1.0152	10
32° 00′	0.5585	.5299	9.7242	.8480	9.9284	.6249	9.7958	1.6003	0.2042	1.0123	58° 00′
10	0.5614	.5324	.7262	.8465	.9276	.6289	.7986	1.5900	.2014	1.0094	50
20	0.5643	.5348	.7282	.8450	.9268	.6330	.8014	1.5798	.1986	1.0065	40
30	0.5672	.5373	.7302	.8434	.9260	.6371	.8042	1.5697	.1958	1.0036	30
40	0.5701	.5398	.7322	.8418	.9252	.6412	.8070	1.5597	.1930	1.0007	20
50	0.5730	.5422	.7342	.8403	.9244	.6453	.8097	1.5497	.1903	0.9977	10
33° 00′	0.5760	.5446	9.7361	.8387	9.9236	.6494	9.8125	1.5399	0.1875	0.9948	57° 00′
10	0.5789	.5471	.7380	.8371	.9228	.6536	.8153	1.5301	.1847	0.9919	50
20	0.5818	.5495	.7400	.8355	.9219	.6577	.8180	1.5204	.1820	0.9890	40
30	0.5847	.5519	.7419	.8339	.9211	.6619	.8208	1.5108	.1792	0.9861	30
40	0.5876	.5544	.7438	.8323	.9203	.6661	.8235	1.5013	.1765	0.9832	20
50	0.5905	.5568	.7457	.8307	.9194	.6703	.8263	1.4919	.1737	0.9803	10
34° 00′	0.5934	.5592	9.7476	.8290	9.9186	.6745	9.8290	1.4826	0.1710	0.9774	56° 00′
10	0.5963	.5616	.7494	.8274	.9177	.6787	.8317	1.4733	.1683	0.9745	50
20	0.5992	.5640	.7513	.8258	.9169	.6830	.8344	1.4641	.1656	0.9716	40
30	0.6021	.5664	.7531	.8241	.9160	.6873	.8371	1.4550	.1629	0.9687	30
40	0.6050	.5688	.7550	.8225	.9151	.6916	.8398	1.4460	.1602	0.9657	20
50	0.6080	.5712	.7568	.8208	.9142	.6959	.8425	1.4370	.1575	0.9628	10
35° 00′	0.6109	.5736	9.7586	.8192	9.9134	.7002	9.8452	1.4281	0.1548	0.9599	55° 00′
10	0.6138	.5760	.7604	.8175	.9125	.7046	.8479	1.4193	.1521	0.9570	50
20	0.6167	.5783	.7622	.8158	.9116	.7089	.8506	1.4106	.1494	0.9541	40
30	0.6196	.5807	.7640	.8141	.9107	.7133	.8533	1.4019	.1467	0.9512	30
40	0.6225	.5831	.7657	.8124	.9098	.7177	.8559	1.3934	.1441	0.9483	20
50	0.6254	.5854	.7675	.8107	.9089	.7221	.8586	1.3848	.1414	0.9454	10
36° 00′	0.6283	.5878	9.7692	.8090	9.9080	.7265	9.8613	1.3764	0.1387	0.9425	54° 00′
		Nat.	Log *	Nat.	Log *	Nat.	Log *	Nat.	Log		
		Cosines		Sines		Cotangents		Tangents		Radians	Degrees

Trigonometric Functions (*continued*)

Annex—10 in columns marked *. (For 0°.1 intervals, see pp. 1–46 to 1–51)

Degrees	Radians	Sines Nat.	Sines Log *	Cosines Nat.	Cosines Log *	Tangents Nat.	Tangents Log *	Cotangents Nat.	Cotangents Log		
36° 00′	0.6283	.5878	9.7692	.8090	9.9080	.7265	9.8613	1.3764	0.1387	0.9425	54° 00′
10	0.6312	.5901	.7710	.8073	.9070	.7310	.8639	1.3680	.1361	0.9396	50
20	0.6341	.5925	.7727	.8056	.9061	.7355	.8666	1.3597	.1334	0.9367	40
30	0.6370	.5948	.7744	.8039	.9052	.7400	.8692	1.3514	.1308	0.9338	30
40	0.6400	.5972	.7761	.8021	.9042	.7445	.8718	1.3432	.1282	0.9308	20
50	0.6429	.5995	.7778	.8004	.9033	.7490	.8745	1.3351	.1255	0.9279	10
37° 00′	0.6458	.6018	9.7795	.7986	9.9023	.7536	9.8771	1.3270	0.1229	0.9250	53° 00′
10	0.6487	.6041	.7811	.7969	.9014	.7581	.8797	1.3190	.1203	0.9221	50
20	0.6516	.6065	.7828	.7951	.9004	.7627	.8824	1.3111	.1176	0.9192	40
30	0.6545	.6088	.7844	.7934	.8995	.7673	.8850	1.3032	.1150	0.9163	30
40	0.6574	.6111	.7861	.7916	.8985	.7720	.8876	1.2954	.1124	0.9134	20
50	0.6603	.6134	.7877	.7898	.8975	.7766	.8902	1.2876	.1098	0.9105	10
38° 00′	0.6632	.6157	9.7893	.7880	9.8965	.7813	9.8928	1.2799	0.1072	0.9076	52° 00′
10	0.6661	.6180	.7910	.7862	.8955	.7860	.8954	1.2723	.1046	0.9047	50
20	0.6690	.6202	.7926	.7844	.8945	.7907	.8980	1.2647	.1020	0.9018	40
30	0.6720	.6225	.7941	.7826	.8935	.7954	.9006	1.2572	.0994	0.8988	30
40	0.6749	.6248	.7957	.7808	.8925	.8002	.9032	1.2497	.0968	0.8959	20
50	0.6778	.6271	.7973	.7790	.8915	.8050	.9058	1.2423	.0942	0.8930	10
39° 00′	0.6807	.6293	9.7989	.7771	9.8905	.8098	9.9084	1.2349	0.0916	0.8901	51° 00′
10	0.6836	.6316	.8004	.7753	.8895	.8146	.9110	1.2276	.0890	0.8872	50
20	0.6865	.6338	.8020	.7735	.8884	.8195	.9135	1.2203	.0865	0.8843	40
30	0.6894	.6361	.8035	.7716	.8874	.8243	.9161	1.2131	.0839	0.8814	30
40	0.6923	.6383	.8050	.7698	.8864	.8292	.9187	1.2059	.0813	0.8785	20
50	0.6952	.6406	.8066	.7679	.8853	.8342	.9212	1.1988	.0788	0.8756	10
40° 00′	0.6981	.6428	9.8081	.7660	9.8843	.8391	9.9238	1.1918	0.0762	0.8727	50° 00′
10	0.7010	.6450	.8096	.7642	.8832	.8441	.9264	1.1847	.0736	0.8698	50
20	0.7039	.6472	.8111	.7623	.8821	.8491	.9289	1.1778	.0711	0.8668	40
30	0.7069	.6494	.8125	.7604	.8810	.8541	.9315	1.1708	.0685	0.8639	30
40	0.7098	.6517	.8140	.7585	.8800	.8591	.9341	1.1640	.0659	0.8610	20
50	0.7127	.6539	.8155	.7566	.8789	.8642	.9366	1.1571	.0634	0.8581	10
41° 00′	0.7156	.6561	9.8169	.7547	9.8778	.8693	9.9392	1.1504	0.0608	0.8552	49° 00′
10	0.7185	.6583	.8184	.7528	.8767	.8744	.9417	1.1436	.0583	0.8523	50
20	0.7214	.6604	.8198	.7509	.8756	.8796	.9443	1.1369	.0557	0.8494	40
30	0.7243	.6626	.8213	.7490	.8745	.8847	.9468	1.1303	.0532	0.8465	30
40	0.7272	.6648	.8227	.7470	.8733	.8899	.9494	1.1237	.0506	0.8436	20
50	0.7301	.6670	.8241	.7451	.8722	.8952	.9519	1.1171	.0481	0.8407	10
42° 00′	0.7330	.6691	9.8255	.7431	9.8711	.9004	9.9544	1.1106	0.0456	0.8378	48° 00′
10	0.7359	.6713	.8269	.7412	.8699	.9057	.9570	1.1041	.0430	0.8348	50
20	0.7389	.6734	.8283	.7392	.8688	.9110	.9595	1.0977	.0405	0.8319	40
30	0.7418	.6756	.8297	.7373	.8676	.9163	.9621	1.0913	.0379	0.8290	30
40	0.7447	.6777	.8311	.7353	.8665	.9217	.9646	1.0850	.0354	0.8261	20
50	0.7476	.6799	.8324	.7333	.8653	.9271	.9671	1.0786	.0329	0.8232	10
43° 00′	0.7505	.6820	9.8338	.7314	9.8641	.9325	9.9697	1.0724	0.0303	0.8203	47° 00′
10	0.7534	.6841	.8351	.7294	.8629	.9380	.9722	1.0661	.0278	0.8174	50
20	0.7563	.6862	.8365	.7274	.8618	.9435	.9747	1.0599	.0253	0.8145	40
30	0.7592	.6884	.8378	.7254	.8606	.9490	.9772	1.0538	.0228	0.8116	30
40	0.7621	.6905	.8391	.7234	.8594	.9545	.9798	1.0477	.0202	0.8087	20
50	0.7650	.6926	.8405	.7214	.8582	.9601	.9823	1.0416	.0177	0.8058	10
44° 00′	0.7679	.6947	9.8418	.7193	9.8569	.9657	9.9848	1.0355	0.0152	0.8029	46° 00′
10	0.7709	.6967	.8431	.7173	.8557	.9713	.9874	1.0295	.0126	0.7999	50
20	0.7738	.6988	.8444	.7153	.8545	.9770	.9899	1.0235	.0101	0.7970	40
30	0.7767	.7009	.8457	.7133	.8532	.9827	.9924	1.0176	.0076	0.7941	30
40	0.7796	.7030	.8469	.7112	.8520	.9884	.9949	1.0117	.0051	0.7912	20
50	0.7825	.7050	.8482	.7092	.8507	.9942	.9975	1.0058	.0025	0.7883	10
45° 00′	0.7854	.7071	9.8495	.7071	9.8495	1.0000	0.0000	1.0000	0.0000	0.7854	45° 00′
		Nat.	Log *	Nat.	Log *	Nat.	Log *	Nat.	Log		
		Cosines		Sines		Cotangents		Tangents		Radians	Degrees

Exponentials [e^n and e^{-n}]

n	e^n	Diff	n	e^n	Diff	n	e^n	n	e^{-n}	Diff	n	e^{-n}	n	e^{-n}
0.00	1.000	10	0.50	1.649	16	1.0	2.718*	0.00	1.000	−10	0.50	.607	1.0	.368*
.01	1.010	10	.51	1.665	17	.1	3.004	.01	0.990	−10	.51	.600	.1	.333
.02	1.020	10	.52	1.682	17	.2	3.320	.02	.980	−10	.52	.595	.2	.301
.03	1.030	11	.53	1.699	17	.3	3.669	.03	.970	−9	.53	.589	.3	.273
.04	1.041	10	.54	1.716	17	.4	4.055	.04	.961	−10	.54	.583	.4	.247
0.05	1.051	11	0.55	1.733	18	1.5	4.482	0.05	.951	−9	0.55	.577	1.5	.223
.06	1.062	11	.56	1.751	17	.6	4.953	.06	.942	−10	.56	.571	.6	.202
.07	1.073	10	.57	1.768	18	.7	5.474	.07	.932	−9	.57	.566	.7	.183
.08	1.083	11	.58	1.786	18	.8	6.050	.08	.923	−9	.58	.560	.8	.165
.09	1.094	11	.59	1.804	18	.9	6.686	.09	.914	−9	.59	.554	.9	.150
0.10	1.105	11	0.60	1.822	18	2.0	7.389	0.10	.905	−9	0.60	.549	2.0	.135
.11	1.116	11	.61	1.840	19	.1	8.166	.11	.896	−9	.61	.543	.1	.122
.12	1.127	12	.62	1.859	19	.2	9.025	.12	.887	−9	.62	.538	.2	.111
.13	1.139	11	.63	1.878	18	.3	9.974	.13	.878	−9	.63	.533	.3	.100
.14	1.150	12	.64	1.896	20	.4	11.02	.14	.869	−8	.64	.527	.4	.0907
0.15	1.162	12	0.65	1.916	19	2.5	12.18	0.15	.861	−9	0.65	.522	2.5	.0821
.16	1.174	11	.66	1.935	19	.6	13.46	.16	.852	−8	.66	.517	.6	.0743
.17	1.185	12	.67	1.954	20	.7	14.88	.17	.844	−9	.67	.512	.7	.0672
.18	1.197	12	.68	1.974	20	.8	16.44	.18	.835	−8	.68	.507	.8	.0608
.19	1.209	12	.69	1.994	20	.9	18.17	.19	.827	−8	.69	.502	.9	.0550
0.20	1.221	13	0.70	2.014	20	3.0	20.09	0.20	.819	−8	0.70	.497	3.0	.0498
.21	1.234	12	.71	2.034	20	.1	22.20	.21	.811	−8	.71	.492	.1	.0450
.22	1.246	13	.72	2.054	21	.2	24.53	.22	.803	−8	.72	.487	.2	.0408
.23	1.259	12	.73	2.075	21	.3	27.11	.23	.795	−8	.73	.482	.3	.0369
.24	1.271	13	.74	2.096	21	.4	29.96	.24	.787	−8	.74	.477	.4	.0334
0.25	1.284	13	0.75	2.117	21	3.5	33.12	0.25	.779	−8	0.75	.472	3.5	.0302
.26	1.297	13	.76	2.138	22	.6	36.60	.26	.771	−8	.76	.468	.6	.0273
.27	1.310	13	.77	2.160	21	.7	40.45	.27	.763	−7	.77	.463	.7	.0247
.28	1.323	13	.78	2.181	22	.8	44.70	.28	.756	−8	.78	.458	.8	.0224
.29	1.336	14	.79	2.203	23	.9	49.40	.29	.748	−7	.79	.454	.9	.0202
0.30	1.350	13	0.80	2.226	22	4.0	54.60	0.30	.741	−8	0.80	.449	4.0	.0183
.31	1.363	14	.81	2.248	22	.1	60.34	.31	.733	−7	.81	.445	.1	.0166
.32	1.377	14	.82	2.270	23	.2	66.69	.32	.726	−7	.82	.440	.2	.0150
.33	1.391	14	.83	2.293	23	.3	73.70	.33	.719	−7	.83	.436	.3	.0136
.34	1.405	14	.84	2.316	24	.4	81.45	.34	.712	−7	.84	.432	.4	.0123
0.35	1.419	14	0.85	2.340	23	4.5	90.02	0.35	.705	−7	0.85	.427	4.5	.0111
.36	1.433	15	.86	2.363	24			.36	.698	−7	.86	.423		
.37	1.448	14	.87	2.387	24	5.0	148.4	.37	.691	−7	.87	.419	5.0	.00674
.38	1.462	15	.88	2.411	24	6.0	403.4	.38	.684	−7	.88	.415	6.0	.00248
.39	1.477	15	.89	2.435	25	7.0	1097.	.39	.677	−7	.89	.411	7.0	.000912
0.40	1.492	15	0.90	2.460	24	8.0	2981.	0.40	.670	−6	0.90	.407	8.0	.000335
.41	1.507	15	.91	2.484	25	9.0	8103.	.41	.664	−7	.91	.403	9.0	.000123
.42	1.522	15	.92	2.509	26	10.0	22026.	.42	.657	−6	.92	.399	10.0	.000045
.43	1.537	16	.93	2.535	25			.43	.651	−7	.93	.395		
.44	1.553	15	.94	2.560	26	$\pi/2$	4.810	.44	.644	−6	.94	.391	$\pi/2$	.208
						$2\pi/2$	23.14						$2\pi/2$	.0432
0.45	1.568	16	0.95	2.586	26	$3\pi/2$	111.3	0.45	.638	−7	0.95	.387	$3\pi/2$	.00898
.46	1.584	16	.96	2.612	26	$4\pi/2$	535.5	.46	.631	−6	.96	.383	$4\pi/2$	.00187
.47	1.600	16	.97	2.638	26	$5\pi/2$	2576.	.47	.625	−6	.97	.379	$5\pi/2$	.000388
.48	1.616	16	.98	2.664	27	$6\pi/2$	12392.	.48	.619	−6	.98	.375	$6\pi/2$	.000081
.49	1.632	17	.99	2.691	27	$7\pi/2$	59610.	.49	.613	−6	.99	.372	$7\pi/2$	.000017
						$8\pi/2$	286751.						$8\pi/2$	.000003
0.50	1.649		1.00	2.718				0.50	0.607		1.00	.368		

* NOTE: Do not interpolate in this column.
$e = 2.71828$ $\quad 1/e = 0.367879$ $\quad \log_{10} e = 0.4343$ $\quad 1/(0.4343) = 2.3026$

$\log_{10}(0.4343) = \bar{1}.6378$ $\quad \log_{10}(e^n) = n(0.4343)$

For table of multiples of 0.4343, see p. 1–62. Graphs, p. 2–84.

Natural Logarithms

These two pages give the natural or Napierian logarithms (ln) of numbers between 1 and 10, correct to four places. Moving the decimal point n places to the right [or left] in the number is equivalent to adding n times 2.3026 [or n times $\bar{3}$.6974] to the logarithm. Base e = 2.71828+

n	n (2.3026)	n (0.6974–3)
1	2.3026	0.6974–3
2	4.6052	0.3948–5
3	6.9078	0.0922–7
4	9.2103	0.7897–10
5	11.5129	0.4871–12
6	13.8155	0.1845–14
7	16.1181	0.8819–17
8	18.4207	0.5793–19
9	20.7233	0.2767–21

Number	0	1	2	3	4	5	6	7	8	9	Avg diff
1.0	0.0000	0100	0198	0296	0392	0488	0583	0677	0770	0862	95
1.1	0953	1044	1133	1222	1310	1398	1484	1570	1655	1740	87
1.2	1823	1906	1989	2070	2151	2231	2311	2390	2469	2546	80
1.3	2624	2700	2776	2852	2927	3001	3075	3148	3221	3293	74
1.4	3365	3436	3507	3577	3646	3716	3784	3853	3920	3988	69
1.5	0.4055	4121	4187	4253	4318	4383	4447	4511	4574	4637	65
1.6	4700	4762	4824	4886	4947	5008	5068	5128	5188	5247	61
1.7	5306	5365	5423	5481	5539	5596	5653	5710	5766	5822	57
1.8	5878	5933	5988	6043	6098	6152	6206	6259	6313	6366	54
1.9	6419	6471	6523	6575	6627	6678	6729	6780	6831	6881	51
2.0	0.6931	6981	7031	7080	7129	7178	7227	7275	7324	7372	49
2.1	7419	7467	7514	7561	7608	7655	7701	7747	7793	7839	47
2.2	7885	7930	7975	8020	8065	8109	8154	8198	8242	8286	44
2.3	8329	8372	8416	8459	8502	8544	8587	8629	8671	8713	43
2.4	8755	8796	8838	8879	8920	8961	9002	9042	9083	9123	41
2.5	0.9163	9203	9243	9282	9322	9361	9400	9439	9478	9517	39
2.6	9555	9594	9632	9670	9708	9746	9783	9821	9858	9895	38
2.7	0.9933	9969	*0006	*0043	*0080	*0116	*0152	*0188	*0225	*0260	36
2.8	1.0296	0332	0367	0403	0438	0473	0508	0543	0578	0613	35
2.9	0647	0682	0716	0750	0784	0818	0852	0886	0919	0953	34
3.0	1.0986	1019	1053	1086	1119	1151	1184	1217	1249	1282	33
3.1	1314	1346	1378	1410	1442	1474	1506	1537	1569	1600	32
3.2	1632	1663	1694	1725	1756	1787	1817	1848	1878	1909	31
3.3	1939	1969	2000	2030	2060	2090	2119	2149	2179	2208	30
3.4	2238	2267	2296	2326	2355	2384	2413	2442	2470	2499	29
3.5	1.2528	2556	2585	2613	2641	2669	2698	2726	2754	2782	28
3.6	2809	2837	2865	2892	2920	2947	2975	3002	3029	3056	27
3.7	3083	3110	3137	3164	3191	3218	3244	3271	3297	3324	27
3.8	3350	3376	3403	3429	3455	3481	3507	3533	3558	3584	26
3.9	3610	3635	3661	3686	3712	3737	3762	3788	3813	3838	25
4.0	1.3863	3888	3913	3938	3962	3987	4012	4036	4061	4085	25
4.1	4110	4134	4159	4183	4207	4231	4255	4279	4303	4327	24
4.2	4351	4375	4398	4422	4446	4469	4493	4516	4540	4563	23
4.3	4586	4609	4633	4656	4679	4702	4725	4748	4770	4793	23
4.4	4816	4839	4861	4884	4907	4929	4951	4974	4996	5019	22
4.5	1.5041	5063	5085	5107	5129	5151	5173	5195	5217	5239	22
4.6	5261	5282	5304	5326	5347	5369	5390	5412	5433	5454	21
4.7	5476	5497	5518	5539	5560	5581	5602	5623	5644	5665	21
4.8	5686	5707	5728	5748	5769	5790	5810	5831	5851	5872	20
4.9	5892	5913	5933	5953	5974	5994	6014	6034	6054	6074	20

$\ln x = (2.3026) \log_{10} x$ $\log_{10} x = (0.4343) \ln x$

where 2.3026 = ln 10 and 0.4343 = $\log_{10} e$ (see p. 1–62) For graphs, see p. 2–84.

Natural Logarithms (*continued*)

Number	0	1	2	3	4	5	6	7	8	9	Avg diff
5.0	1.6094	6114	6134	6154	6174	6194	6214	6233	6253	6273	20
5.1	6292	6312	6332	6351	6371	6390	6409	6429	6448	6467	19
5.2	6487	6506	6525	6544	6563	6582	6601	6620	6639	6658	19
5.3	6677	6696	6715	6734	6752	6771	6790	6808	6827	6845	18
5.4	6864	6882	6901	6919	6938	6956	6974	6993	7011	7029	18
5.5	1.7047	7066	7084	7102	7120	7138	7156	7174	7192	7210	18
5.6	7228	7246	7263	7281	7299	7317	7334	7352	7370	7387	18
5.7	7405	7422	7440	7457	7475	7492	7509	7527	7544	7561	17
5.8	7579	7596	7613	7630	7647	7664	7681	7699	7716	7733	17
5.9	7750	7766	7783	7800	7817	7834	7851	7867	7884	7901	17
6.0	1.7918	7934	7951	7967	7984	8001	8017	8034	8050	8066	16
6.1	8083	8099	8116	8132	8148	8165	8181	8197	8213	8229	16
6.2	8245	8262	8278	8294	8310	8326	8342	8358	8374	8390	16
6.3	8405	8421	8437	8453	8469	8485	8500	8516	8532	8547	16
6.4	8563	8579	8594	8610	8625	8641	8656	8672	8687	8703	15
6.5	1.8718	8733	8749	8764	8779	8795	8810	8825	8840	8856	15
6.6	8871	8886	8901	8916	8931	8946	8961	8976	8991	9006	15
6.7	9021	9036	9051	9066	9081	9095	9110	9125	9140	9155	15
6.8	9169	9184	9199	9213	9228	9242	9257	9272	9286	9301	15
6.9	9315	9330	9344	9359	9373	9387	9402	9416	9430	9445	14
7.0	1.9459	9473	9488	9502	9516	9530	9544	9559	9573	9587	14
7.1	9601	9615	9629	9643	9657	9671	9685	9699	9713	9727	14
7.2	9741	9755	9769	9782	9796	9810	9824	9838	9851	9865	14
7.3	1.9879	9892	9906	9920	9933	9947	9961	9974	9988	*0001	13
7.4	2.0015	0028	0042	0055	0069	0082	0096	0109	0122	0136	13
7.5	2.0149	0162	0176	0189	0202	0215	0229	0242	0255	0268	13
7.6	0281	0295	0308	0321	0334	0347	0360	0373	0386	0399	13
7.7	0412	0425	0438	0451	0464	0477	0490	0503	0516	0528	13
7.8	0541	0554	0567	0580	0592	0605	0618	0631	0643	0656	13
7.9	0669	0681	0694	0707	0719	0732	0744	0757	0769	0782	12
8.0	2.0794	0807	0819	0832	0844	0857	0869	0882	0894	0906	12
8.1	0919	0931	0943	0956	0968	0980	0992	1005	1017	1029	12
8.2	1041	1054	1066	1078	1090	1102	1114	1126	1138	1150	12
8.3	1163	1175	1187	1199	1211	1223	1235	1247	1258	1270	12
8.4	1282	1294	1306	1318	1330	1342	1353	1365	1377	1389	12
8.5	2.1401	1412	1424	1436	1448	1459	1471	1483	1494	1506	12
8.6	1518	1529	1541	1552	1564	1576	1587	1599	1610	1622	12
8.7	1633	1645	1656	1668	1679	1691	1702	1713	1725	1736	11
8.8	1748	1759	1770	1782	1793	1804	1815	1827	1838	1849	11
8.9	1861	1872	1883	1894	1905	1917	1928	1939	1950	1961	11
9.0	2.1972	1983	1994	2006	2017	2028	2039	2050	2061	2072	11
9.1	2083	2094	2105	2116	2127	2138	2148	2159	2170	2181	11
9.2	2192	2203	2214	2225	2235	2246	2257	2268	2279	2289	11
9.3	2300	2311	2322	2332	2343	2354	2364	2375	2386	2396	11
9.4	2407	2418	2428	2439	2450	2460	2471	2481	2492	2502	11
9.5	2.2513	2523	2534	2544	2555	2565	2576	2586	2597	2607	10
9.6	2618	2628	2638	2649	2659	2670	2680	2690	2701	2711	10
9.7	2721	2732	2742	2752	2762	2773	2783	2793	2803	2814	10
9.8	2824	2834	2844	2854	2865	2875	2885	2895	2905	2915	10
9.9	2925	2935	2946	2956	2966	2976	2986	2996	3006	3016	10
10.0	2.3026										

Moving the decimal point n places to the right [or left] in the number requires adding n times 2.3026 [or n times (0.6974–3)] in the body of the table. See auxiliary table of multiples on top of the preceding page.

Hyperbolic Sines [$\sinh x = \frac{1}{2}(e^x - e^{-x})$]

x	0	1	2	3	4	5	6	7	8	9	Avg diff
0.0	.0000	.0100	.0200	.0300	.0400	.0500	.0600	.0701	.0801	.0901	100
1	.1002	.1102	.1203	.1304	.1405	.1506	.1607	.1708	.1810	.1911	101
2	.2013	.2115	.2218	.2320	.2423	.2526	.2629	.2733	.2837	.2941	103
3	.3045	.3150	.3255	.3360	.3466	.3572	.3678	.3785	.3892	.4000	106
4	.4108	.4216	.4325	.4434	.4543	.4653	.4764	.4875	.4986	.5098	110
0.5	.5211	.5324	.5438	.5552	.5666	.5782	.5897	.6014	.6131	.6248	116
6	.6367	.6485	.6605	.6725	.6846	.6967	.7090	.7213	.7336	.7461	122
7	.7586	.7712	.7838	.7966	.8094	.8223	.8353	.8484	.8615	.8748	130
8	.8881	.9015	.9150	.9286	.9423	.9561	.9700	.9840	.9981	1.012	138
9	1.027	1.041	1.055	1.070	1.085	1.099	1.114	1.129	1.145	1.160	15
1.0	1.175	1.191	1.206	1.222	1.238	1.254	1.270	1.286	1.303	1.319	16
1	1.336	1.352	1.369	1.386	1.403	1.421	1.438	1.456	1.474	1.491	17
2	1.509	1.528	1.546	1.564	1.583	1.602	1.621	1.640	1.659	1.679	19
3	1.698	1.718	1.738	1.758	1.779	1.799	1.820	1.841	1.862	1.883	21
4	1.904	1.926	1.948	1.970	1.992	2.014	2.037	2.060	2.083	2.106	22
1.5	2.129	2.153	2.177	2.201	2.225	2.250	2.274	2.299	2.324	2.350	25
6	2.376	2.401	2.428	2.454	2.481	2.507	2.535	2.562	2.590	2.617	27
7	2.646	2.674	2.703	2.732	2.761	2.790	2.820	2.850	2.881	2.911	30
8	2.942	2.973	3.005	3.037	3.069	3.101	3.134	3.167	3.200	3.234	33
9	3.268	3.303	3.337	3.372	3.408	3.443	3.479	3.516	3.552	3.589	36
2.0	3.627	3.665	3.703	3.741	3.780	3.820	3.859	3.899	3.940	3.981	39
1	4.022	4.064	4.106	4.148	4.191	4.234	4.278	4.322	4.367	4.412	44
2	4.457	4.503	4.549	4.596	4.643	4.691	4.739	4.788	4.837	4.887	48
3	4.937	4.988	5.039	5.090	5.142	5.195	5.248	5.302	5.356	5.411	53
4	5.466	5.522	5.578	5.635	5.693	5.751	5.810	5.869	5.929	5.989	58
2.5	6.050	6.112	6.174	6.237	6.300	6.365	6.429	6.495	6.561	6.627	64
6	6.695	6.763	6.831	6.901	6.971	7.042	7.113	7.185	7.258	7.332	71
7	7.406	7.481	7.557	7.634	7.711	7.789	7.868	7.948	8.028	8.110	79
8	8.192	8.275	8.359	8.443	8.529	8.615	8.702	8.790	8.879	8.969	87
9	9.060	9.151	9.244	9.337	9.431	9.527	9.623	9.720	9.819	9.918	96
3.0	10.02	10.12	10.22	10.32	10.43	10.53	10.64	10.75	10.86	10.97	11
1	11.08	11.19	11.30	11.42	11.53	11.65	11.76	11.88	12.00	12.12	12
2	12.25	12.37	12.49	12.62	12.75	12.88	13.01	13.14	13.27	13.40	13
3	13.54	13.67	13.81	13.95	14.09	14.23	14.38	14.52	14.67	14.82	14
4	14.97	15.12	15.27	15.42	15.58	15.73	15.89	16.05	16.21	16.38	16
3.5	16.54	16.71	16.88	17.05	17.22	17.39	17.57	17.74	17.92	18.10	17
6	18.29	18.47	18.66	18.84	19.03	19.22	19.42	19.61	19.81	20.01	19
7	20.21	20.41	20.62	20.83	21.04	21.25	21.46	21.68	21.90	22.12	21
8	22.34	22.56	22.79	23.02	23.25	23.49	23.72	23.96	24.20	24.45	24
9	24.69	24.94	25.19	25.44	25.70	25.96	26.22	26.48	26.75	27.02	26
4.0	27.29	27.56	27.84	28.12	28.40	28.69	28.98	29.27	29.56	29.86	29
1	30.16	30.47	30.77	31.08	31.39	31.71	32.03	32.35	32.68	33.00	32
2	33.34	33.67	34.01	34.35	34.70	35.05	35.40	35.75	36.11	36.48	35
3	36.84	37.21	37.59	37.97	38.35	38.73	39.12	39.52	39.91	40.31	39
4	40.72	41.13	41.54	41.96	42.38	42.81	43.24	43.67	44.11	44.56	43
4.5	45.00	45.46	45.91	46.37	46.84	47.31	47.79	48.27	48.75	49.24	47
6	49.74	50.24	50.74	51.25	51.77	52.29	52.81	53.34	53.88	54.42	52
7	54.97	55.52	56.08	56.64	57.21	57.79	58.37	58.96	59.55	60.15	58
8	60.75	61.36	61.98	62.60	63.23	63.87	64.51	65.16	65.81	67.47	64
9	67.14	67.82	68.50	69.19	69.88	70.58	71.29	72.01	72.73	73.46	71
5.0	74.20										

If $x > 5$, $\sinh x = \frac{1}{2}(e^x)$ and $\log_{10} \sinh x = (0.4343)x + 0.6990 - 1$, correct to four significant figures. For table of multiples of 0.4343, see p. 1–62. Graphs, p. 2–84.

Hyperbolic Cosines [$\cosh x = \frac{1}{2}(e^x + e^{-x})$]

x	0	1	2	3	4	5	6	7	8	9	Avg diff
0.0	1.000	1.000	1.000	1.000	1.001	1.001	1.002	1.002	1.003	1.004	1
1	1.005	1.006	1.007	1.008	1.010	1.011	1.013	1.014	1.016	1.018	2
2	1.020	1.022	1.024	1.027	1.029	1.031	1.034	1.037	1.039	1.042	3
3	1.045	1.048	1.052	1.055	1.058	1.062	1.066	1.069	1.073	1.077	4
4	1.081	1.085	1.090	1.094	1.098	1.103	1.108	1.112	1.117	1.122	5
0.5	1.128	1.133	1.138	1.144	1.149	1.155	1.161	1.167	1.173	1.179	6
6	1.185	1.192	1.198	1.205	1.212	1.219	1.226	1.233	1.240	1.248	7
7	1.255	1.263	1.271	1.278	1.287	1.295	1.303	1.311	1.320	1.329	8
8	1.337	1.346	1.355	1.365	1.374	1.384	1.393	1.403	1.413	1.423	10
9	1.433	1.443	1.454	1.465	1.475	1.486	1.497	1.509	1.520	1.531	11
1.0	1.543	1.555	1.567	1.579	1.591	1.604	1.616	1.629	1.642	1.655	13
1	1.669	1.682	1.696	1.709	1.723	1.737	1.752	1.766	1.781	1.796	14
2	1.811	1.826	1.841	1.857	1.872	1.888	1.905	1.921	1.937	1.954	16
3	1.971	1.988	2.005	2.023	2.040	2.058	2.076	2.095	2.113	2.132	18
4	2.151	2.170	2.189	2.209	2.229	2.249	2.269	2.290	2.310	2.331	20
1.5	2.352	2.374	2.395	2.417	2.439	2.462	2.484	2.507	2.530	2.554	23
6	2.577	2.601	2.625	2.650	2.675	2.700	2.725	2.750	2.776	2.802	25
7	2.828	2.855	2.882	2.909	2.936	2.964	2.992	3.021	3.049	3.078	28
8	3.107	3.137	3.167	3.197	3.228	3.259	3.290	3.321	3.353	3.385	31
9	3.418	3.451	3.484	3.517	3.551	3.585	3.620	3.655	3.690	3.726	34
2.0	3.762	3.799	3.835	3.873	3.910	3.948	3.987	4.026	4.065	4.104	38
1	4.144	4.185	4.226	4.267	4.309	4.351	4.393	4.436	4.480	4.524	42
2	4.568	4.613	4.658	4.704	4.750	4.797	4.844	4.891	4.939	4.988	47
3	5.037	5.087	5.137	5.188	5.239	5.290	5.343	5.395	5.449	5.503	52
4	5.557	5.612	5.667	5.723	5.780	5.837	5.895	5.954	6.013	6.072	58
2.5	6.132	6.193	6.255	6.317	6.379	6.443	6.507	6.571	6.636	6.702	64
6	6.769	6.836	6.904	6.973	7.042	7.112	7.183	7.255	7.327	7.400	70
7	7.473	7.548	7.623	7.699	7.776	7.853	7.932	8.011	8.091	8.171	78
8	8.253	8.335	8.418	8.502	8.587	8.673	8.759	8.847	8.935	9.024	86
9	9.115	9.206	9.298	9.391	9.484	9.579	9.675	9.772	9.869	9.968	95
3.0	10.07	10.17	10.27	10.37	10.48	10.58	10.69	10.79	10.90	11.01	11
1	11.12	11.23	11.35	11.46	11.57	11.69	11.81	11.92	12.04	12.16	12
2	12.29	12.41	12.53	12.66	12.79	12.91	13.04	13.17	13.31	13.44	13
3	13.57	13.71	13.85	13.99	14.13	14.27	14.41	14.56	14.70	14.85	14
4	15.00	15.15	15.30	15.45	15.61	15.77	15.92	16.08	16.25	16.41	16
3.5	16.57	16.74	16.91	17.08	17.25	17.42	17.60	17.77	17.95	18.13	17
6	18.31	18.50	18.68	18.87	19.06	19.25	19.44	19.64	19.84	20.03	19
7	20.24	20.44	20.64	20.85	21.06	21.27	21.49	21.70	21.92	22.14	21
8	22.36	22.59	22.81	23.04	23.27	23.51	23.74	23.98	24.22	24.47	23
9	24.71	24.96	25.21	25.46	25.72	25.98	26.24	26.50	26.77	27.04	26
4.0	27.31	27.58	27.86	28.14	28.42	28.71	29.00	29.29	29.58	29.88	29
1	30.18	30.48	30.79	31.10	31.41	31.72	32.04	32.37	32.69	33.02	32
2	33.35	33.69	34.02	34.37	34.71	35.06	35.41	35.77	36.13	36.49	35
3	36.86	37.23	37.60	37.98	38.36	38.75	39.13	39.53	39.93	40.33	39
4	40.73	41.14	41.55	41.97	42.39	42.82	43.25	43.68	44.12	44.57	43
4.5	45.01	45.47	45.92	46.38	46.85	47.32	47.80	48.28	48.76	49.25	47
6	49.75	50.25	50.75	51.26	51.78	52.30	52.82	57.35	57.89	54.43	52
7	54.98	55.53	56.09	56.65	57.22	57.80	58.38	58.96	59.56	60.15	58
8	60.76	61.37	61.99	62.61	63.24	63.87	64.52	65.16	65.82	66.48	64
9	67.15	67.82	68.50	69.19	69.89	70.59	71.30	72.02	72.74	73.47	71
5.0	74.21										

If $x > 5$, $\cosh x = \frac{1}{2}(e^x)$ and $\log_{10} \cosh x = (0.4343)x + 0.6990 - 1$, correct to four significant figures. For table of multiples of 0.4343, see p. 1-62. Graphs, p. 2-84.

Hyperbolic Tangents [$\tanh x = (e^x - e^{-x})/(e^x + e^{-x}) = \sinh x/\cosh x$]

x	0	1	2	3	4	5	6	7	8	9	Avg diff
0.0	.0000	.0100	.0200	.0300	.0400	.0500	.0599	.0699	.0798	.0898	100
1	.0997	.1096	.1194	.1293	.1391	.1489	.1587	.1684	.1781	.1878	98
2	.1974	.2070	.2165	.2260	.2355	.2449	.2543	.2636	.2729	.2821	94
3	.2913	.3004	.3095	.3185	.3275	.3364	.3452	.3540	.3627	.3714	89
4	.3800	.3885	.3969	.4053	.4137	.4219	.4301	.4382	.4462	.4542	82
0.5	.4621	.4700	.4777	.4854	.4930	.5005	.5080	.5154	.5227	.5299	75
6	.5370	.5441	.5511	.5581	.5649	.5717	.5784	.5850	.5915	.5980	67
7	.6044	.6107	.6169	.6231	.6291	.6352	.6411	.6469	.6527	.6584	60
8	.6640	.6696	.6751	.6805	.6858	.6911	.6963	.7014	.7064	.7114	52
9	.7163	.7211	.7259	.7306	.7352	.7398	.7443	.7487	.7531	.7574	45
1.0	.7616	.7658	.7699	.7739	.7779	.7818	.7857	.7895	.7932	.7969	39
1	.8005	.8041	.8076	.8110	.8144	.8178	.8210	.8243	.8275	.8306	33
2	.8337	.8367	.8397	.8426	.8455	.8483	.8511	.8538	.8565	.8591	28
3	.8617	.8643	.8668	.8693	.8717	.8741	.8764	.8787	.8810	.8832	24
4	.8854	.8875	.8896	.8917	.8937	.8957	.8977	.8996	.9015	.9033	20
1.5	.9052	.9069	.9087	.9104	.9121	.9138	.9154	.9170	.9186	.9202	17
6	.9217	.9232	.9246	.9261	.9275	.9289	.9302	.9316	.9329	.9342	14
7	.9354	.9367	.9379	.9391	.9402	.9414	.9425	.9436	.9447	.9458	11
8	.9468	.9478	.9488	.9498	.9508	.9518	.9527	.9536	.9545	.9554	9
9	.9562	.9571	.9579	.9587	.9595	.9603	.9611	.9619	.9626	.9633	8
2.0	.9640	.9647	.9654	.9661	.9668	.9674	.9680	.9687	.9693	.9699	6
1	.9705	.9710	.9716	.9722	.9727	.9732	.9738	.9743	.9748	.9753	5
2	.9757	.9762	.9767	.9771	.9776	.9780	.9785	.9789	.9793	.9797	4
3	.9801	.9805	.9809	.9812	.9816	.9820	.9823	.9827	.9830	.9834	4
4	.9837	.9840	.9843	.9846	.9849	.9852	.9855	.9858	.9861	.9863	3
2.5	.9866	.9869	.9871	.9874	.9876	.9879	.9881	.9884	.9886	.9888	2
6	.9890	.9892	.9895	.9897	.9899	.9901	.9903	.9905	.9906	.9908	2
7	.9910	.9912	.9914	.9915	.9917	.9919	.9920	.9922	.9923	.9925	2
8	.9926	.9928	.9929	.9931	.9932	.9933	.9935	.9936	.9937	.9938	1
2.9	.9940	.9941	.9942	.9943	.9944	.9945	.9946	.9947	.9949	.9950	1
3.	.9951	.9959	.9967	.9973	.9978	.9982	.9985	.9988	.9990	.9992	4
4.	.9993	.9995	.9996	.9996	.9997	.9998	.9998	.9998	.9999	.9999	1
5.	.9999	If $x > 5$, $\tanh x = 1.0000$ to four decimal places.									

Graphs, p. 2–84.

Multiples of 0.4343 ($0.43429448 = \log_{10} e$)

x	0	1	2	3	4	5	6	7	8	9
0.	0.0000	0.0434	0.0869	0.1303	0.1737	0.2171	0.2606	0.3040	0.3474	0.3909
1.	0.4343	0.4777	0.5212	0.5646	0.6080	0.6514	0.6949	0.7383	0.7817	0.8252
2.	0.8686	0.9120	0.9554	0.9989	1.0423	1.0857	1.1292	1.1726	1.2160	1.2595
3.	1.3029	1.3463	1.3897	1.4332	1.4766	1.5200	1.5635	1.6069	1.6503	1.6937
4.	1.7372	1.7806	1.8240	1.8675	1.9109	1.9543	1.9978	2.0412	2.0846	2.1280
5.	2.1715	2.2149	2.2583	2.3018	2.3452	2.3886	2.4320	2.4755	2.5189	2.5623
6.	2.6058	2.6492	2.6926	2.7361	2.7795	2.8229	2.8663	2.9098	2.9532	2.9966
7.	3.0401	3.0835	3.1269	3.1703	3.2138	3.2572	3.3006	3.3441	3.3875	3.4309
8.	3.4744	3.5178	3.5612	3.6046	3.6481	3.6915	3.7349	3.7784	3.8218	3.8652
9.	3.9087	3.9521	3.9955	4.0389	4.0824	4.1258	4.1692	4.2127	4.2561	4.2995

Multiples of 2.3026 ($2.3025851 = \ln 10 = 1/0.4343$)

x	0	1	2	3	4	5	6	7	8	9
0.	0.0000	0.2303	0.4605	0.6908	0.9210	1.1513	1.3816	1.6118	1.8421	2.0723
1.	2.3026	2.5328	2.7631	2.9934	3.2236	3.4539	3.6841	3.9144	4.1447	4.3749
2.	4.6052	4.8354	5.0657	5.2959	5.5262	5.7565	5.9867	6.2170	6.4472	6.6775
3.	6.9078	7.1380	7.3683	7.5985	7.8288	8.0590	8.2893	8.5196	8.7498	8.9801
4.	9.2103	9.4406	9.6709	9.9011	10.131	10.362	10.592	10.822	11.052	11.283
5.	11.513	11.743	11.973	12.204	12.434	12.664	12.894	13.125	13.355	13.585
6.	13.816	14.046	14.276	14.506	14.737	14.967	15.197	15.427	15.658	15.888
7.	16.118	16.348	16.579	16.809	17.039	17.269	17.500	17.730	17.960	18.190
8.	18.421	18.651	18.881	19.111	19.342	19.572	19.802	20.032	20.263	20.493
9.	20.723	20.954	21.184	21.414	21.644	21.875	22.105	22.335	22.565	22.796

Standard Distribution of Residuals (p. 2–33)

a = any positive quantity;
y = the number of residuals which are numerically $< a$;
r = the probable error of a single observation;
n = number of observations.

$\frac{a}{r}$	$\frac{y}{n}$	Diff
0.0	.000	54
1	.054	53
2	.107	53
3	.160	53
4	.213	51
0.5	.264	50
6	.314	49
7	.363	48
8	.411	45
9	.456	44
1.0	.500	42
1	.542	40
2	.582	37
3	.619	36
4	.655	33
1.5	.688	31
6	.719	29
7	.748	27
8	.775	25
9	.800	23
2.0	.823	20
1	.843	19
2	.862	17
3	.879	16
4	.895	13
2.5	.908	13
6	.921	10
7	.931	10
8	.941	9
9	.950	7
3.0	.957	6
1	.963	6
2	.969	5
3	.974	4
4	.978	4
3.5	.982	3
6	.985	2
7	.987	3
8	.990	1
9	.991	2
4.0	.993	6
5.0	.999	

Factors for Computing Probable Error (p. 2–33)

n	Bessel		Peters	
	$\frac{0.6745}{\sqrt{(n-1)}}$	$\frac{0.6745}{\sqrt{n(n-1)}}$	$\frac{0.8453}{\sqrt{n(n-1)}}$	$\frac{0.8453}{n\sqrt{n-1}}$
2	.6745	.4769	.5978	.4227
3	.4769	.2754	.3451	.1993
4	.3894	.1947	.2440	.1220
5	.3372	.1508	.1890	.0845
6	.3016	.1231	.1543	.0630
7	.2754	.1041	.1304	.0493
8	.2549	.0901	.1130	.0399
9	.2385	.0795	.0996	.0332
10	.2248	.0711	.0891	.0282
11	.2133	.0643	.0806	.0243
12	.2034	.0587	.0736	.0212
13	.1947	.0540	.0677	.0188
14	.1871	.0500	.0627	.0167
15	.1803	.0465	.0583	.0151
16	.1742	.0435	.0546	.0136
17	.1686	.0409	.0513	.0124
18	.1636	.0386	.0483	.0114
19	.1590	.0365	.0457	.0105
20	.1547	.0346	.0434	.0097
21	.1508	.0329	.0412	.0090
22	.1472	.0314	.0393	.0084
23	.1438	.0300	.0376	.0078
24	.1406	.0287	.0360	.0073
25	.1377	.0275	.0345	.0069
26	.1349	.0265	.0332	.0065
27	.1323	.0255	.0319	.0061
28	.1298	.0245	.0307	.0058
29	.1275	.0237	.0297	.0055
30	.1252	.0229	.0287	.0052
31	.1231	.0221	.0277	.0050
32	.1211	.0214	.0268	.0047
33	.1192	.0208	.0260	.0045
34	.1174	.0201	.0252	.0043
35	.1157	.0196	.0245	.0041
36	.1140	.0190	.0238	.0040
37	.1124	.0185	.0232	.0038
38	.1109	.0180	.0225	.0037
39	.1094	.0175	.0220	.0035
40	.1080	.0171	.0214	.0034
45	.1017	.0152	.0190	.0028
50	.0964	.0136	.0171	.0024
55	.0918	.0124	.0155	.0021
60	.0878	.0113	.0142	.0018
65	.0843	.0105	.0131	.0016
70	.0812	.0097	.0122	.0015
75	.0784	.0091	.0113	.0013
80	.0759	.0085	.0106	.0012
85	.0736	.0080	.0100	.0011
90	.0715	.0075	.0094	.0010
95	.0696	.0071	.0089	.0009
100	.0678	.0068	.0085	.0008

Compound Interest. Amount of a Given Principal

The amount A at the end of n years of a given principal P placed at compound interest to-day is $A = P \times x$ or $A = P \times y$ or $A = P \times z$, according as the interest (at the rate of r percent per annum) is compounded annually, semi-annually, or quarterly; the factor x or y or z being taken from the following tables.

Values of x. (Interest compounded annually; $A = P \times x$)

Years	$r = 2$	2½	3	3½	4	4½	5	6	7
1	1.0200	1.0250	1.0300	1.0350	1.0400	1.0450	1.0500	1.0600	1.0700
2	1.0404	1.0506	1.0609	1.0712	1.0816	1.0920	1.1025	1.1236	1.1449
3	1.0612	1.0769	1.0927	1.1087	1.1249	1.1412	1.1576	1.1910	1.2250
4	1.0824	1.1038	1.1255	1.1475	1.1699	1.1925	1.2155	1.2625	1.3108
5	1.1041	1.1314	1.1593	1.1877	1.2167	1.2462	1.2763	1.3382	1.4026
6	1.1262	1.1597	1.1941	1.2293	1.2653	1.3023	1.3401	1.4185	1.5007
7	1.1487	1.1887	1.2299	1.2723	1.3159	1.3609	1.4071	1.5036	1.6058
8	1.1717	1.2184	1.2668	1.3168	1.3686	1.4221	1.4775	1.5938	1.7182
9	1.1951	1.2489	1.3048	1.3629	1.4233	1.4861	1.5513	1.6895	1.8385
10	1.2190	1.2801	1.3439	1.4106	1.4802	1.5530	1.6289	1.7908	1.9672
11	1.2434	1.3121	1.3842	1.4600	1.5395	1.6229	1.7103	1.8983	2.1049
12	1.2682	1.3449	1.4258	1.5111	1.6010	1.6959	1.7959	2.0122	2.2522
13	1.2936	1.3785	1.4685	1.5640	1.6651	1.7722	1.8856	2.1329	2.4098
14	1.3195	1.4130	1.5126	1.6187	1.7317	1.8519	1.9799	2.2609	2.5785
15	1.3459	1.4483	1.5580	1.6753	1.8009	1.9353	2.0789	2.3966	2.7590
16	1.3728	1.4845	1.6047	1.7340	1.8730	2.0224	2.1829	2.5404	2.9522
17	1.4002	1.5216	1.6528	1.7947	1.9479	2.1134	2.2920	2.6928	3.1588
18	1.4282	1.5597	1.7024	1.8575	2.0258	2.2085	2.4066	2.8543	3.3799
19	1.4568	1.5987	1.7535	1.9225	2.1068	2.3079	2.5270	3.0256	3.6165
20	1.4859	1.6386	1.8061	1.9898	2.1911	2.4117	2.6533	3.2071	3.8697
25	1.6406	1.8539	2.0938	2.3632	2.6658	3.0054	3.3864	4.2919	5.4274
30	1.8114	2.0976	2.4273	2.8068	3.2434	3.7453	4.3219	5.7435	7.6123
40	2.2080	2.6851	3.2620	3.9593	4.8010	5.8164	7.0400	10.286	14.974
50	2.6916	3.4371	4.3839	5.5849	7.1067	9.0326	11.467	18.420	29.457
60	3.2810	4.3998	5.8916	7.8781	10.520	14.027	18.679	32.988	57.946

This table is computed from the formula $x = [1 + (r/100)]^n$

Values of y. (Interest compounded semi-annually; $A = P \times y$)

Years	$r = 2$	2½	3	3½	4	4½	5	6	7
1	1.0201	1.0252	1.0302	1.0353	1.0404	1.0455	1.0506	1.0609	1.0712
2	1.0406	1.0509	1.0614	1.0719	1.0824	1.0931	1.1038	1.1255	1.1475
3	1.0615	1.0774	1.0934	1.1097	1.1262	1.1428	1.1597	1.1941	1.2293
4	1.0829	1.1045	1.1265	1.1489	1.1717	1.1948	1.2184	1.2668	1.3168
5	1.1046	1.1323	1.1605	1.1894	1.2190	1.2492	1.2801	1.3439	1.4106
6	1.1268	1.1608	1.1956	1.2314	1.2682	1.3060	1.3449	1.4258	1.5111
7	1.1495	1.1900	1.2318	1.2749	1.3195	1.3655	1.4130	1.5126	1.6187
8	1.1726	1.2199	1.2690	1.3199	1.3728	1.4276	1.4845	1.6047	1.7340
9	1.1961	1.2506	1.3073	1.3665	1.4282	1.4926	1.5597	1.7024	1.8575
10	1.2202	1.2820	1.3469	1.4148	1.4859	1.5605	1.6386	1.8061	1.9898
11	1.2447	1.3143	1.3876	1.4647	1.5460	1.6315	1.7216	1.9161	2.1315
12	1.2697	1.3474	1.4295	1.5164	1.6084	1.7058	1.8087	2.0328	2.2833
13	1.2953	1.3812	1.4727	1.5700	1.6734	1.7834	1.9003	2.1566	2.4460
14	1.3213	1.4160	1.5172	1.6254	1.7410	1.8645	1.9965	2.2879	2.6202
15	1.3478	1.4516	1.5631	1.6828	1.8114	1.9494	2.0976	2.4273	2.8068
16	1.3749	1.4881	1.6103	1.7422	1.8845	2.0381	2.2038	2.5751	3.0067
17	1.4026	1.5256	1.6590	1.8037	1.9607	2.1308	2.3153	2.7319	3.2209
18	1.4308	1.5639	1.7091	1.8674	2.0399	2.2278	2.4325	2.8983	3.4503
19	1.4595	1.6033	1.7608	1.9333	2.1223	2.3292	2.5557	3.0748	3.6960
20	1.4889	1.6436	1.8140	2.0016	2.2080	2.4352	2.6851	3.2620	3.9593
25	1.6446	1.8610	2.1052	2.3808	2.6916	3.0420	3.4371	4.3839	5.5849
30	1.8167	2.1072	2.4432	2.8318	3.2810	3.8001	4.3998	5.8916	7.8781
40	2.2167	2.7015	3.2907	4.0064	4.8754	5.9301	7.2096	10.641	15.676
50	2.7048	3.4634	4.4320	5.6682	7.2446	9.2540	11.814	19.219	31.191
60	3.3004	4.4402	5.9693	8.0192	10.765	14.441	19.358	34.711	62.064

Formula: $y = [1 + (r/200)]^{2n}$

Values of z. (Interest compounded quarterly; $A = P \times z$; see opposite page)

Years	r = 2	2½	3	3½	4	4½	5	6	7
1	1.0202	1.0252	1.0303	1.0355	1.0406	1.0458	1.0509	1.0614	1.0719
2	1.0407	1.0511	1.0616	1.0722	1.0829	1.0936	1.1045	1.1265	1.1489
3	1.0617	1.0776	1.0938	1.1102	1.1268	1.1437	1.1608	1.1956	1.2314
4	1.0831	1.1048	1.1270	1.1496	1.1726	1.1960	1.2199	1.2690	1.3199
5	1.1049	1.1327	1.1612	1.1903	1.2202	1.2508	1.2820	1.3469	1.4148
6	1.1272	1.1613	1.1964	1.2326	1.2697	1.3080	1.3474	1.4295	1.5164
7	1.1499	1.1906	1.2327	1.2763	1.3213	1.3679	1.4160	1.5172	1.6254
8	1.1730	1.2206	1.2701	1.3215	1.3749	1.4305	1.4881	1.6103	1.7422
9	1.1967	1.2514	1.3086	1.3684	1.4308	1.4959	1.5639	1.7091	1.8674
10	1.2208	1.2830	1.3483	1.4169	1.4889	1.5644	1.6436	1.8140	2.0016
11	1.2454	1.3154	1.3893	1.4672	1.5493	1.6360	1.7274	1.9253	2.1454
12	1.2705	1.3486	1.4314	1.5192	1.6122	1.7108	1.8154	2.0435	2.2996
13	1.2961	1.3826	1.4748	1.5731	1.6777	1.7891	1.9078	2.1689	2.4648
14	1.3222	1.4175	1.5196	1.6288	1.7458	1.8710	2.0050	2.3020	2.6420
15	1.3489	1.4533	1.5657	1.6866	1.8167	1.9566	2.1072	2.4432	2.8318
16	1.3760	1.4900	1.6132	1.7464	1.8905	2.0462	2.2145	2.5931	3.0353
17	1.4038	1.5276	1.6621	1.8083	1.9672	2.1398	2.3274	2.7523	3.2534
18	1.4320	1.5661	1.7126	1.8725	2.0471	2.2378	2.4459	2.9212	3.4872
19	1.4609	1.6056	1.7645	1.9389	2.1302	2.3402	2.5705	3.1004	3.7378
20	1.4903	1.6462	1.8180	2.0076	2.2167	2.4473	2.7015	3.2907	4.0064
25	1.6467	1.8646	2.1111	2.3898	2.7048	3.0609	3.4634	4.4320	5.6682
30	1.8194	2.1121	2.4514	2.8446	3.3004	3.8285	4.4402	5.9693	8.0192
40	2.2211	2.7098	3.3053	4.0306	4.9138	5.9892	7.2980	10.828	16.051
50	2.7115	3.4768	4.4567	5.7110	7.3160	9.3693	11.995	19.643	32.128
60	3.3102	4.4608	6.0092	8.0919	10.893	14.657	19.715	35.633	64.307

Formula: $z = [1 + (r/400)]^{4n}$

Amount of an Annuity

The amount S accumulated at the end of n years by a given annual payment Y set aside at the end of each year is $S = Y \times v$, where the factor v is to be taken from the following table. (Interest at r percent per annum, compounded annually.)

Values of v

Years	r = 2	2½	3	3½	4	4½	5	6	7
1	1.0000	1.0000	1.0000	1.0000	1.0000	1.0000	1.0000	1.0000	1.0000
2	2.0200	2.0250	2.0300	2.0350	2.0400	2.0450	2.0500	2.0600	2.0700
3	3.0604	3.0756	3.0909	3.1062	3.1216	3.1370	3.1525	3.1836	3.2149
4	4.1216	4.1525	4.1836	4.2149	4.2465	4.2782	4.3101	4.3746	4.4399
5	5.2040	5.2563	5.3091	5.3625	5.4163	5.4707	5.5256	5.6371	5.7507
6	6.3081	6.3877	6.4684	6.5502	6.6330	6.7169	6.8019	6.9753	7.1533
7	7.4343	7.5474	7.6625	7.7794	7.8983	8.0192	8.1420	8.3938	8.6540
8	8.5830	8.7361	8.8923	9.0517	9.2142	9.3800	9.5491	9.8975	10.260
9	9.7546	9.9545	10.159	10.368	10.583	10.802	11.027	11.491	11.978
10	10.950	11.203	11.464	11.731	12.006	12.288	12.578	13.181	13.816
11	12.169	12.483	12.808	13.142	13.486	13.841	14.207	14.972	15.784
12	13.412	13.796	14.192	14.602	15.026	15.464	15.917	16.870	17.888
13	14.680	15.140	15.618	16.113	16.627	17.160	17.713	18.882	20.141
14	15.974	16.519	17.086	17.677	18.292	18.932	19.599	21.015	22.550
15	17.293	17.932	18.599	19.296	20.024	20.784	21.579	23.276	25.129
16	18.639	19.380	20.157	20.971	21.825	22.719	23.657	25.673	27.888
17	20.012	20.865	21.762	22.705	23.698	24.742	25.840	28.213	30.840
18	21.412	22.386	23.414	24.500	25.645	26.855	28.132	30.906	33.999
19	22.841	23.946	25.117	26.357	27.671	29.064	30.539	33.760	37.379
20	24.297	25.545	26.870	28.280	29.778	31.371	33.066	36.786	40.995
25	32.030	34.158	36.459	38.950	41.646	44.565	47.727	54.865	63.249
30	40.568	43.903	47.575	51.623	56.085	61.007	66.439	79.058	94.461
40	60.402	67.403	75.401	84.550	95.026	107.03	120.80	154.76	199.64
50	84.579	97.484	112.80	131.00	152.67	178.50	209.35	290.34	406.53
60	114.05	135.99	163.05	196.52	237.99	289.50	353.58	533.13	813.52

Formula: $v = \{[1 + (r/100)]^n - 1\} \div (r/100)$
$= (x - 1) \div (r/100)$

Principal Which Will Amount to a Given Sum

The principal P, which, if placed at compound interest to-day, will amount to a given sum A at the end of n years is $P = A \times x'$ or $P = A \times y'$ or $P = A \times z'$, according as the interest (at the rate of r percent per annum) is compounded annually, semi-annually, or quarterly; the factor x' or y' or z' being taken from the following tables.

Values of x'. (Interest compounded annually; $P = A \times x'$)

Years	r = 2	2½	3	3½	4	4½	5	6	7
1	.98039	.97561	.97087	.96618	.96154	.95694	.95238	.94340	.93458
2	.96117	.95181	.94260	.93351	.92456	.91573	.90703	.89000	.87344
3	.94232	.92860	.91514	.90194	.88900	.87630	.86384	.83962	.81630
4	.92385	.90595	.88849	.87144	.85480	.83856	.82270	.79209	.76290
5	.90573	.88385	.86261	.84197	.82193	.80245	.78353	.74726	.71299
6	.88797	.86230	.83748	.81350	.79031	.76790	.74622	.70496	.66634
7	.87056	.84127	.81309	.78599	.75992	.73483	.71068	.66506	.62275
8	.85349	.82075	.78941	.75941	.73069	.70319	.67684	.62741	.58201
9	.83676	.80073	.76642	.73373	.70259	.67290	.64461	.59190	.54393
10	.82035	.78120	.74409	.70892	.67556	.64393	.61391	.55839	.50835
11	.80426	.76214	.72242	.68495	.64958	.61620	.58468	.52679	.47509
12	.78849	.74356	.70138	.66178	.62460	.58966	.55684	.49697	.44401
13	.77303	.72542	.68095	.63940	.60057	.56427	.53032	.46884	.41496
14	.75788	.70773	.66112	.61778	.57748	.53997	.50507	.44230	.38783
15	.74301	.69047	.64186	.59689	.55526	.51672	.48102	.41727	.36245
16	.72845	.67362	.62317	.57671	.53391	.49447	.45811	.39365	.33873
17	.71416	.65720	.60502	.55720	.51337	.47318	.43630	.37136	.31657
18	.70016	.64117	.58739	.53836	.49363	.45280	.41552	.35034	.29586
19	.68643	.62553	.57029	.52016	.47464	.43330	.39573	.33051	.27651
20	.67297	.61027	.55368	.50257	.45639	.41464	.37689	.31180	.25842
25	.60953	.53939	.47761	.42315	.37512	.33273	.29530	.23300	.18425
30	.55207	.47674	.41199	.35628	.30832	.26700	.23138	.17411	.13137
40	.45289	.37243	.30656	.25257	.20829	.17193	.14205	.09722	.06678
50	.37153	.29094	.22811	.17905	.14071	.11071	.08720	.05429	.03395
60	.30478	.22728	.16973	.12693	.09506	.07129	.05354	.03031	.01726

Formula: $x' = [1 + (r/100)]^{-n} = 1/x$

Values of y'. (Interest compounded semi-annually; $P = A \times y'$)

Years	r = 2	2½	3	3½	4	4½	5	6	7
1	.98030	.97546	.97066	.96590	.96117	.95647	.95181	.94260	.93351
2	.96098	.95152	.94218	.93296	.92385	.91484	.90595	.88849	.87144
3	.94205	.92817	.91454	.90114	.88797	.87502	.86230	.83748	.81350
4	.92348	.90540	.88771	.87041	.85349	.83694	.82075	.78941	.75941
5	.90529	.88318	.86167	.84073	.82035	.80051	.78120	.74409	.70892
6	.88745	.86151	.83639	.81206	.78849	.76567	.74356	.70138	.66178
7	.86996	.84037	.81185	.78436	.75788	.73234	.70773	.66112	.61778
8	.85282	.81975	.78803	.75762	.72845	.70047	.67362	.62317	.57671
9	.83602	.79963	.76491	.73178	.70016	.66998	.64117	.58739	.53836
10	.81954	.78001	.74247	.70682	.67297	.64082	.61027	.55368	.50257
11	.80340	.76087	.72069	.68272	.64684	.61292	.58086	.52189	.46915
12	.78757	.74220	.69954	.65944	.62172	.58625	.55288	.49193	.43796
13	.77205	.72398	.67902	.63695	.59758	.56073	.52623	.46369	.40884
14	.75684	.70622	.65910	.61523	.57437	.53632	.50088	.43708	.38165
15	.74192	.68889	.63976	.59425	.55207	.51298	.47674	.41199	.35628
16	.72730	.67198	.62099	.57398	.53063	.49065	.45377	.38834	.33259
17	.71297	.65549	.60277	.55441	.51003	.46930	.43191	.36604	.31048
18	.69892	.63941	.58509	.53550	.49022	.44887	.41109	.34503	.28983
19	.68515	.62372	.56792	.51724	.47119	.42933	.39128	.32523	.27056
20	.67165	.60841	.55126	.49960	.45289	.41065	.37243	.30656	.25257
25	.60804	.53734	.47500	.42003	.37153	.32873	.29094	.22811	.17905
30	.55045	.47457	.40930	.35313	.30478	.26315	.22728	.16973	.12693
40	.45112	.37017	.30389	.24960	.20511	.16863	.13870	.09398	.06379
50	.36971	.28873	.22563	.17642	.13803	.10806	.08465	.05203	.03206
60	.30299	.22521	.16752	.12470	.09289	.06925	.05166	.02881	.01611

Formula: $y' = [1 + (r/200)]^{-2n} = 1/y$

Values of z'. (Interest compounded quarterly; $P = A \times z'$; see opposite page)

Years	$r = 2$	2½	3	3½	4	4½	5	6	7
1	.98025	.97539	.97055	.96575	.96098	.95624	.95152	.94218	.93296
2	.96089	.95138	.94198	.93268	.92348	.91439	.90540	.88771	.87041
3	.94191	.92796	.91424	.90074	.88745	.87437	.86151	.83639	.81206
4	.92330	.90512	.88732	.86989	.85282	.83611	.81975	.78803	.75762
5	.90506	.88284	.86119	.84010	.81954	.79952	.78001	.74247	.70682
6	.88719	.86111	.83583	.81132	.78757	.76453	.74220	.69954	.65944
7	.86966	.83991	.81122	.78354	.75684	.73107	.70622	.65910	.61523
8	.85248	.81924	.78733	.75670	.72730	.69908	.67198	.62099	.57390
9	.83564	.79908	.76415	.73079	.69892	.66849	.63941	.58509	.53550
10	.81914	.77941	.74165	.70576	.67165	.63923	.60841	.55126	.49960
11	.80296	.76022	.71981	.68159	.64545	.61126	.57892	.51939	.46611
12	.78710	.74151	.69861	.65825	.62026	.58451	.55086	.48936	.43486
13	.77155	.72326	.67804	.63570	.59606	.55893	.52415	.46107	.40570
14	.75631	.70546	.65808	.61393	.57280	.53447	.49874	.43441	.37851
15	.74137	.68809	.63870	.59291	.55045	.51108	.47457	.40930	.35313
16	.72673	.67115	.61989	.57260	.52897	.48871	.45156	.38563	.32946
17	.71237	.65464	.60164	.55299	.50833	.46733	.42967	.36334	.30737
18	.69830	.63852	.58392	.53405	.48850	.44687	.40884	.34233	.28676
19	.68451	.62281	.56673	.51576	.46944	.42732	.38903	.32254	.26754
20	.67099	.60748	.55004	.49810	.45112	.40862	.37017	.30389	.24960
25	.60729	.53630	.47369	.41845	.36971	.32670	.28873	.22563	.17642
30	.54963	.47347	.40794	.35154	.30299	.26120	.22521	.16752	.12470
40	.45023	.36903	.30255	.24810	.20351	.16697	.13702	.09235	.06230
50	.36880	.28762	.22438	.17510	.13669	.10673	.08337	.05091	.03113
60	.30210	.22417	.16641	.12358	.09181	.06823	.05072	.02806	.01555

Formula: $z' = [1 + (r/400)]^{-4n} = 1/z$

Annuity Which Will Amount to a Given Sum (Sinking Fund)

The annual payment, Y, which, if set aside at the end of each year, will amount with accumulated interest to a given sum S at the end of n years is $Y = S \times v'$, where the factor v' is given below. (Interest at r percent per annum, compounded annually.)

Values of v'

Years	$r = 2$	2½	3	3½	4	4½	5	6	7
2	.49505	.49383	.49261	.49140	.49020	.48900	.48780	.48544	.48309
3	.32675	.32514	.32353	.32193	.32035	.31877	.31721	.31411	.31105
4	.24262	.24082	.23903	.23725	.23549	.23374	.23201	.22859	.22523
5	.19216	.19025	.18835	.18648	.18463	.18279	.18097	.17740	.17389
6	.15853	.15655	.15460	.15267	.15076	.14888	.14702	.14336	.13980
7	.13451	.13250	.13051	.12854	.12661	.12470	.12282	.11914	.11555
8	.11651	.11447	.11246	.11048	.10853	.10661	.10472	.10104	.09747
9	.10252	.10046	.09843	.09645	.09449	.09257	.09069	.08702	.08349
10	.09133	.08926	.08723	.08524	.08329	.08138	.07950	.07587	.07238
11	.08218	.08011	.07808	.07609	.07415	.07225	.07039	.06679	.06336
12	.07456	.07249	.07046	.06848	.06655	.06467	.06283	.05928	.05590
13	.06812	.06605	.06403	.06206	.06014	.05828	.05646	.05296	.04965
14	.06260	.06054	.05853	.05657	.05467	.05282	.05102	.04758	.04434
15	.05783	.05577	.05377	.05183	.04994	.04811	.04634	.04296	.03979
16	.05365	.05160	.04961	.04768	.04582	.04402	.04227	.03895	.03586
17	.04997	.04793	.04595	.04404	.04220	.04042	.03870	.03544	.03243
18	.04670	.04467	.04271	.04082	.03899	.03724	.03555	.03236	.02941
19	.04378	.04176	.03981	.03794	.03614	.03441	.03275	.02962	.02675
20	.04116	.03915	.03722	.03536	.03358	.03188	.03024	.02718	.02439
25	.03122	.02928	.02743	.02567	.02401	.02244	.02095	.01823	.01581
30	.02465	.02278	.02102	.01937	.01783	.01639	.01505	.01265	.01059
40	.01656	.01484	.01326	.01183	.01052	.00934	.00828	.00646	.00467
50	.01182	.01026	.00887	.00763	.00655	.00560	.00478	.00344	.00238
60	.00877	.00735	.00613	.00509	.00420	.00345	.00283	.00188	.00121

Formula: $v' = (r/100) \div \{[1 + (r/100)]^n - 1\} = 1/v$

Present Worth of an Annuity

The capital C, which, if placed at interest today, will provide for a given annual payment Y for a term of n years before it is exhausted is $C = Y \times w$, where the factor w is given below. (Interest at r percent per annum, compounded annually.)

Values of w

Years	r = 2	2½	3	3½	4	4½	5	6	7
1	0.9804	0.9756	0.9709	0.9662	0.9615	0.9569	0.9524	0.9434	0.9346
2	1.9416	1.9274	1.9135	1.8997	1.8861	1.8727	1.8594	1.8334	1.8080
3	2.8839	2.8560	2.8286	2.8016	2.7751	2.7490	2.7232	2.6730	2.6243
4	3.8077	3.7620	3.7171	3.6731	3.6299	3.5875	3.5460	3.4651	3.3872
5	4.7135	4.6458	4.5797	4.5151	4.4518	4.3900	4.3295	4.2124	4.1002
6	5.6014	5.5081	5.4172	5.3286	5.2421	5.1579	5.0757	4.9173	4.7665
7	6.4720	6.3494	6.2303	6.1145	6.0021	5.8927	5.7864	5.5824	5.3893
8	7.3255	7.1701	7.0197	6.8740	6.7327	6.5959	6.4632	6.2098	5.9713
9	8.1622	7.9709	7.7861	7.6077	7.4353	7.2688	7.1078	6.8017	6.5152
10	8.9826	8.7521	8.5302	8.3166	8.1109	7.9127	7.7217	7.3601	7.0236
11	9.7868	9.5142	9.2526	9.0016	8.7605	8.5289	8.3064	7.8869	7.4987
12	10.575	10.258	9.9540	9.6633	9.3851	9.1186	8.8633	8.3838	7.9427
13	11.348	10.983	10.635	10.303	9.9856	9.6829	9.3936	8.8527	8.3577
14	12.106	11.691	11.296	10.921	10.563	10.223	9.8986	9.2950	8.7455
15	12.849	12.381	11.938	11.517	11.118	10.740	10.380	9.7122	9.1079
16	13.578	13.055	12.561	12.094	11.652	11.234	10.838	10.106	9.4466
17	14.292	13.712	13.166	12.651	12.166	11.707	11.274	10.477	9.7632
18	14.992	14.353	13.754	13.190	12.659	12.160	11.690	10.828	10.059
19	15.678	14.979	14.324	13.710	13.134	12.593	12.085	11.158	10.336
20	16.351	15.589	14.877	14.212	13.590	13.008	12.462	11.470	10.594
25	19.523	18.424	17.413	16.482	15.622	14.828	14.094	12.783	11.654
30	22.396	20.930	19.600	18.392	17.292	16.289	15.372	13.765	12.409
40	27.355	25.103	23.115	21.355	19.793	18.402	17.159	15.046	13.332
50	31.424	28.362	25.730	23.456	21.482	19.762	18.256	15.762	13.801
60	34.761	30.909	27.676	24.945	22.623	20.638	18.929	16.161	14.039

Formula: $w = [1 - [1 + (r/100)]^{-n}] \div [r/100] = v/x$

Annuity Provided for by a Given Capital

The annual payment Y provided for for a term of n years by a given capital C placed at interest today is $Y = C \times w'$. (Interest at r percent per annum, compounded annually; the fund supposed to be exhausted at the end of the term.)

Values of w'

Years	r = 2	2½	3	3½	4	4½	5	6	7
2	.51505	.51883	.52261	.52640	.53020	.53400	.53780	.54544	.55309
3	.34675	.35014	.35353	.35693	.36035	.36377	.36721	.37411	.38105
4	.26262	.26582	.26903	.27225	.27549	.27874	.28201	.28859	.29523
5	.21216	.21525	.21835	.22148	.22463	.22779	.23097	.23740	.24389
6	.17853	.18155	.18460	.18767	.19076	.19388	.19702	.20336	.20980
7	.15451	.15750	.16051	.16354	.16661	.16970	.17282	.17914	.18555
8	.13651	.13947	.14246	.14548	.14853	.15161	.15472	.16104	.16747
9	.12252	.12546	.12843	.13145	.13449	.13757	.14069	.14702	.15349
10	.11133	.11426	.11723	.12024	.12329	.12638	.12950	.13587	.14238
11	.10218	.10511	.10808	.11109	.11415	.11725	.12039	.12679	.13336
12	.09456	.09749	.10046	.10348	.10655	.10967	.11283	.11928	.12590
13	.08812	.09105	.09403	.09706	.10014	.10328	.10646	.11296	.11965
14	.08260	.08554	.08853	.09157	.09467	.09782	.10102	.10758	.11434
15	.07783	.08077	.08377	.08683	.08994	.09311	.09634	.10296	.10979
16	.07365	.07660	.07961	.08268	.08582	.08902	.09227	.09895	.10586
17	.06997	.07293	.07595	.07904	.08220	.08542	.08870	.09544	.10243
18	.06670	.06967	.07271	.07582	.07899	.08224	.08555	.09236	.09941
19	.06378	.06676	.06981	.07294	.07614	.07941	.08275	.08962	.09675
20	.06116	.06415	.06722	.07036	.07358	.07688	.08024	.08718	.09439
25	.05122	.05428	.05743	.06067	.06401	.06744	.07095	.07823	.08581
30	.04465	.04778	.05102	.05437	.05783	.06139	.06505	.07265	.08059
40	.03656	.03984	.04326	.04683	.05052	.05434	.05828	.06646	.07467
50	.03182	.03526	.03887	.04263	.04655	.05060	.05478	.06344	.07238
60	.02877	.03235	.03613	.04009	.04420	.04845	.05283	.06188	.07121

Formula: $w' = [r/100] \div [1 - [1 + (r/100)]^{-n}] = 1/w = v' + (r/100)$

Decimal Equivalents

From minutes and seconds into decimal parts of a degree

Min.	Degree	Sec.	Degree
0′	0°.0000	0″	0°.0000
1	.0167	1	.0003
2	.0333	2	.0006
3	.05	3	.0008
4	.0667	4	.0011
5′	.0833	5″	.0014
6	.10	6	.0017
7	.1167	7	.0019
8	.1333	8	.0022
9	.15	9	.0025
10′	0°.1667	10″	0°.0028
1	.1833	1	.0031
2	.20	2	.0033
3	.2167	3	.0036
4	.2333	4	.0039
15′	.25	15″	.0042
6	.2667	6	.0044
7	.2833	7	.0047
8	.30	8	.005
9	.3167	9	.0053
20′	0°.3333	20″	0°.0056
1	.35	1	.0058
2	.3667	2	.0061
3	.3833	3	.0064
4	.40	4	.0067
25′	.4167	25″	.0069
6	.4333	6	.0072
7	.45	7	.0075
8	.4667	8	.0078
9	.4833	9	.0081
30′	0°.50	30″	0°.0083
1	.5167	1	.0086
2	.5333	2	.0089
3	.55	3	.0092
4	.5667	4	.0094
35′	.5833	35″	.0097
6	.60	6	.01
7	.6167	7	.0103
8	.6333	8	.0106
9	.65	9	.0108
40′	0°.6667	40″	0°.0111
1	.6833	1	.0114
2	.70	2	.0117
3	.7167	3	.0119
4	.7333	4	.0122
45′	.75	45″	.0125
6	.7667	6	.0128
7	.7833	7	.0131
8	.80	8	.0133
9	.8167	9	.0136
50′	0°.8333	50″	0°.0139
1	.85	1	.0142
2	.8667	2	.0144
3	.8833	3	.0147
4	.90	4	.015
55′	.9167	55″	.0153
6	.9333	6	.0156
7	.95	7	.0158
8	.9667	8	.0161
9	.9833	9	.0164
60′	1.00	60″	0°.0167

From decimal parts of a degree into minutes and seconds (exact values)

Degree	Min. & sec.	Degree	Min. & sec.
0°.00	0′	0°.50	30′
1	0′ 36″	1	30′ 36″
2	1′ 12″	2	31′ 12″
3	1′ 48″	3	31′ 48″
4	2′ 24″	4	32′ 24″
0°.05	3′	0°.55	33′
6	3′ 36″	6	33′ 36″
7	4′ 12″	7	34′ 12″
8	4′ 48″	8	34′ 48″
9	5′ 24″	9	35′ 24″
0°.10	6′	0°.60	36′
1	6′ 36″	1	36′ 36″
2	7′ 12″	2	37′ 12″
3	7′ 48″	3	37′ 48″
4	8′ 24″	4	38′ 24″
0°.15	9′	0°.65	39′
6	9′ 36″	6	39′ 36″
7	10′ 12″	7	40′ 12″
8	10′ 48″	8	40′ 48″
9	11′ 24″	9	41′ 24″
0°.20	12′	0°.70	42′
1	12′ 36″	1	42′ 36″
2	13′ 12″	2	43′ 12″
3	13′ 48″	3	43′ 48″
4	14′ 24″	4	44′ 24″
0°.25	15′	0°.75	45′
6	15′ 36″	6	45′ 36″
7	16′ 12″	7	46′ 12″
8	16′ 48″	8	46′ 48″
9	17′ 24″	9	47′ 24″
0°.30	18′	0°.80	48′
1	18′ 36″	1	48′ 36″
2	19′ 12″	2	49′ 12″
3	19′ 48″	3	49′ 48″
4	20′ 24″	4	50′ 24″
0°.35	21′	0°.85	51′
6	21′ 36″	6	51′ 36″
7	22′ 12″	7	52′ 12″
8	22′ 48″	8	52′ 48″
9	23′ 24″	9	53′ 24″
0°.40	24′	0°.90	54′
1	24′ 36″	1	54′ 36″
2	25′ 12″	2	55′ 12″
3	25′ 48″	3	55′ 48″
4	26′ 24″	4	56′ 24″
0°.45	27′	0°.95	57′
6	27′ 36″	6	57′ 36″
7	28′ 12″	7	58′ 12″
8	28′ 48″	8	58′ 48″
9	29′ 24″	9	59′ 24″
0°.50	30′	1°.00	60′

Degree	Seconds
0°.000	0″.0
1	3″.6
2	7″.2
3	10″.8
4	14″.4
0°.005	18″
6	21″.6
7	25″.2
8	28″.8
9	32″.4
0°.010	36″

Common fractions

8 ths	16 ths	32 nds	64 ths	Exact decimal values
			1	.01 5625
		1	2	.03 125
			3	.04 6875
	1	2	4	.06 25
			5	.07 8125
		3	6	.09 375
			7	.10 9375
1	2	4	8	.12 5
			9	.14 0625
		5	10	.15 625
			11	.17 1875
	3	6	12	.18 75
			13	.20 3125
		7	14	.21 875
			15	.23 4375
2	4	8	16	.25
			17	.26 5625
		9	18	.28 125
			19	.29 6875
	5	10	20	.31 25
			21	.32 8125
		11	22	.34 375
			23	.35 9375
3	6	12	24	.37 5
			25	.39 0625
		13	26	.40 625
			27	.42 1875
	7	14	28	.43 75
			29	.45 3125
		15	30	.46 875
			31	.48 4375
4	8	16	32	.50
			33	.51 5625
		17	34	.53 125
			35	.54 6875
	9	18	36	.56 25
			37	.57 8125
		19	38	.59 375
			39	.60 9375
5	10	20	40	.62 5
			41	.64 0625
		21	42	.65 625
			43	.67 1875
	11	22	44	.68 75
			45	.70 3125
		23	46	.71 875
			47	.73 4375
6	12	24	48	.75
			49	.76 5625
		25	50	.78 125
			51	.79 6875
	13	26	52	.81 25
			53	.82 8125
		27	54	.84 375
			55	.85 9375
7	14	28	56	.87 5
			57	.89 0625
		29	58	.90 625
			59	.92 1875
	15	30	60	.93 75
			61	.95 3125
		31	62	.96 875
			63	.98 4375

WEIGHTS AND MEASURES

BY

Lewis V. Judson

REFERENCES: "International Critical Tables," McGraw-Hill. "Smithsonian Physical Tables," Smithsonian Institution. Landolt, "Landolt-Börnstein Zahlenwerte und Funktionen aus Physik, Chemie, Astronomie, Geophysik und Technik," Springer. "Handbook of Chemistry and Physics," Chemical Rubber Co. "Units of Weight and Measure; Definitions and Tables of Equivalents," Misc. Pub. 233, NBS. "Units and Systems of Weights and Measures; Their Origin, Development, and Present Status," Circ. 570, NBS. "Weights and Measures Standards of the United States, a Brief History," Misc. Pub. 247, NBS. "Standard Frequencies and Time Signals," Misc. Pub. 236, NBS. ICC, "Standard Time." Code of Federal Regulations, Title 49.

In the United States the measures of weight and length commonly employed are identical for practical purposes with the corresponding English units, but the capacity measures differ from those now in use in the British Empire, the U.S. gallon being defined as 231 cu in. and the bushel as 2,150.42 cu in., whereas the corresponding British Imperial units are, respectively, 277.42 cu in., and 2,219.36 cu in. (1 Imp gal = 1.2 U.S. gal, approx; 1 Imp bu = 1.03 U.S. bu, approx).

The metric system of weights and measures was legalized and its use made permissive in the United States by an Act of Congress, passed in 1866. In 1872, by the concurrent action of the principal governments of the world, it was agreed to establish an International Bureau of Weights and Measures near Paris. The convention was held, and the treaty signed in 1875. It was ratified by the United States in 1878.

Prior to 1893, the British Imperial yard and the British Imperial pound were regarded as the real standards of the United States. In 1893, the Office of Weights and Measures (now National Bureau of Standards) by executive order fixed the values of the United States yard and pound in terms of the meter and the kilogram, respec-

U.S. Customary Weights and Measures

Measures of Length

12 inches	= 1 foot
3 feet	= 1 yard
5½ yards = 16½ feet	= 1 rod, pole, or perch
40 poles = 220 yards	= 1 furlong
8 furlongs = 1,760 yards = 5,280 feet	= 1 mile
3 miles	= 1 league
4 inches	= 1 hand
9 inches	= 1 span

Nautical Units

6,076.11549 feet	= 1 international nautical mile
6 feet	= 1 fathom
120 fathoms	= 1 cable length
1 nautical mile per hr	= 1 knot

Surveyor's or Gunter's Measure

7.92 inches	= 1 link
100 links = 66 ft = 4 rods	= 1 chain
80 chains	= 1 mile
33⅓ inches	= 1 vara (Texas)

Measures of Area

144 square inches	= 1 square foot
9 square feet	= 1 square yard
30¼ square yards	= 1 square rod, pole, or perch
160 square rods = 10 square chains = 43,560 square feet = 5,645 sq varas (Texas)	= 1 acre
640 acres = 1 square mile	= 1 "section" of U.S. Govt. surveyed land
1 circular inch = area of circle 1 inch in diameter	= 0.7854 sq in.
1 square inch	= 1.2732 circular inches
1 circular mil	= area of circle 0.001 in. in diam
1,000,000 cir mils	= 1 circular inch

Measures of Volume

1,728 cubic inches	= 1 cubic foot
27 cubic feet	= 1 cubic yard
1 cord of wood	= 128 cubic feet
1 perch of masonry	= 16½ to 25 cu ft

U.S. Customary Weights and Measures—(*Continued*)

Measures of Volume

Liquid or Fluid Measure

4 gills	= 1 pint
2 pints	= 1 quart
4 quarts	= 1 gallon
7.4805 gallons	= 1 cubic foot

(There is no standard liquid barrel; by trade custom, 1 bbl of petroleum oil, unrefined = 42 gal)

Apothecaries' Liquid Measure

60 minims = 1 liquid dram or drachm
8 drams = 1 liquid ounce
16 ounces = 1 pint

Water Measure

The **miner's inch** is the quantity of water that will pass through an orifice 1 sq in. in cross section under a head of 4 to 6½ in., as fixed by statutes, and varies from 1/40 to 1/50 cu ft per sec. The units now most in use are 1 cu ft per sec and 1 gal per sec, the U.S. Reclamation Service employing the former. See p. 3-55 et seq.

Dry Measure

2 pints = 1 quart
8 quarts = 1 peck
4 pecks = 1 bushel

1 std bbl for fruits and vegetables = 7056 cu in. or 105 dry qt, struck measure

Shipping Measure

1 Register ton = 100 cu ft
1 U.S. shipping ton = 40 cu ft
= 32.14 U.S. bu or 31.14 Imp bu
1 British shipping ton = 42 cu ft
= 32.70 Imp bu or 33.75 U.S. bu

Board Measure

1 board foot = { 144 cu in. = volume of board; 1 ft sq and 1 in. thick }

The international log rule, based upon ¼ in. kerf, is expressed by the formula

$$X = 0.904762(0.22D^2 - 0.71D)$$

where X is the number of board feet in a 4 ft section of a log and D is the top diam in in. In computing the number of board feet in a log the taper is taken at ½ in. per 4 ft linear, and separate computation is made for each 4 ft section.

Weights
(The grain is the same in all systems)

Avoirdupois Weight

16 drams = 437.5 grains	= 1 ounce
16 ounces = 7,000 grains	= 1 pound
100 pounds	= 1 cental
2,000 pounds	= 1 short ton
2,240 pounds	= 1 long ton
1 std lime bbl, small	= 180 lb net
1 std lime bbl, large	= 280 lb net
Also (in Great Britain):	
14 pounds	= 1 stone
2 stone = 28 pounds	= 1 quarter
4 quarters = 112 pounds	= 1 hundredweight (cwt)
20 hundredweight	= 1 long ton

Troy Weight

24 grains	= 1 pennyweight (dwt)
20 pennyweights = 480 grains	= 1 ounce
12 ounces = 5,760 grains	= 1 pound

1 assay ton = 29,167 milligrams, or as many milligrams as there are troy ounces in a ton of 2,000 lb avoirdupois. Consequently, the number of milligrams of precious metal yielded by an assay ton of ore gives directly the number of troy ounces that would be obtained from a ton of 2,000 lb avoirdupois.

Apothecaries' Weight

20 grains	= 1 scruple ℈
3 scruples = 60 grains	= 1 dram ʒ
8 drams	= 1 ounce ℥
12 ounces = 5,760 grains	= 1 pound

Weight for Precious Stones

1 carat = 200 milligrams
(Used by almost all important nations)

Circular Measure

60 seconds	= 1 minute
60 minutes	= 1 degree
90 degrees	= 1 quadrant
360 degrees	= circumference
57.2957795 degrees (=57°17′44.806″)	= 1 radian (or angle having arc of length equal to radius)

tively, as 1 yd = 3,600/3,937 m and 1 lb = 453.5924277 g. By agreement in 1959 among the national standards laboratories of the English-speaking nations, the relations in use now are: 1 yd = 0.9144 m, whence 1 in. = 25.4 mm; and 1 lb = 0.45359237 kg, *i.e.*, 1 lb = 453.59237 g.

METRIC SYSTEM

The fundamental units of the metric system are the meter (the unit of length) and the kilogram (the unit of mass). The unit of volume, the cubic decimeter (which was also designated the liter), and the unit of mass, the kilogram, were originally derived from the meter. The kilogram and the meter are now defined independently, and the liter, although for many years defined as the volume of a kilogram of water at the temperature of its maximum density, 4 C, and under a pressure of 76 cm of mercury, is now equal to 1 cubic decimeter.

The Eleventh General Conference on Weights and Measures in 1960 adopted an expansion of the metric system in place of the original metric system by including other physical and engineering units. This expanded system is called, in French, **Le**

Système International d'Unités (abbreviated SI) and in English, **The International System of Units.** Engineers have not adopted it extensively. It should be pointed out that in this system, force is not expressed in kilograms of force but in Newtons (1 Newton = 1/9.80665 kg of force, *i.e.*, kiloponds, kgf) and that the system is a development of the MKSA system rather than the CGS system.

Metric Measures

Length

Unit	Symbol	Value in meters
Angstrom	A	0.000000001
Micron	μ	0.000001
Millimeter	mm	0.001
Centimeter	cm	0.01
Decimeter	dm	0.1
Meter (unit)	m	1.0
Dekameter	dam	10.0
Hectometer	hm	100.0
Kilometer	km	1,000.0
Megameter	....	1,000,000.0

Area

Unit	Symbol	Value in sq meters
....	....	....
....	....	....
Sq millimeter	mm^2	0.000001
Sq centimeter	cm^2	0.0001
Sq decimeter	dm^2	0.01
Sq meter (centiare)	m^2	1.0
Sq dekameter (are)	a	100.0
Hectare	ha	10,000.0
Sq kilometer	km^2	1,000,000.0
....	....	....

Volume

Unit	Symbol	Value in liters
Milliliter	ml	0.001
Liter (unit)	l	1.0
Kiloliter	kl	1,000.0
Also		
Centiliter	cl	0.01
Deciliter	dl	0.1
Dekaliter	dal	10.0
Hectoliter	hl	100.0
....	...	....

Cubic measure

Unit	Symbol	Value in cubic meters
Cubic kilometer	km^3	10^9
Cubic hectometer	hm^3	10^6
Cubic dekameter	dkm^3	10^3
Cubic meter	m^3	1
Cubic decimeter	dm^3	10^{-3}
Cubic centimeter	cm^3	10^{-6}
Cubic millimeter	mm^3	10^{-9}
Cubic micron	μ^3	10^{-18}

Mass

Unit	Symbol	Value in grams	Unit	Symbol	Value in grams
Microgram	γ	0.000001	Dekagram	dag	10.0
Milligram	mg	0.001	Hectogram	hg	100.0
Centigram	cg	0.01	Kilogram	kg	1,000.0
Decigram	dg	0.1	Quintal	q	100,000.0
Gram (unit)	g	1.0	Ton	t	1,000,000.0

The prefixes used to designate multiples and submultiples of metric units have also been used in recent years in connetion with other units. Examples are microinch and kilowatt.

The myriameter and the myriagram were formerly used but are no longer contained in international standards. The values of these units were 10,000 m and 10,000 g, respectively.

Other prefixes besides those originally used with metric units have come into use, but the prefix myria, formerly in use and signifying 10^4, is not now in the official list.

In the case of the prefixes for 10^{12} and 10^9 caution should be used, as these were erroneously interchanged in some instances from those given in the following list:

Tera	T	10^{12}	Centi	c	10^{-2}
Giga	G	10^9	Milli	m	10^{-3}
Mega	M	10^6	Micro	μ	10^{-6}
Kilo	k	10^3	Nano	n	10^{-9}
Hecto	h	10^2	Pico	p	10^{-12}
Deka	da	10^1	Femto	f	10^{-15}
Deci	d	10^{-1}	Atto	a	10^{-18}

It should be noted that the names of these units, the prefixes, and the symbols (except the A for angstrom) have an initial lowercase letter when used in text.

SYSTEMS OF UNITS

The principal units of interest to mechanical engineers can all be derived from the three units of **force, length,** and **time.** These three units may be chosen at pleasure; each such choice gives rise to a "system" of units. The following table gives the units of the four "systems" most often met with in the literature. [See second paragraph under Metric System (p. 1–71) for reference to a fifth system.]

In these systems the "standard pound body" and the "standard kilogram body" refer to two material standards of mass, carefully preserved at London and Paris, respectively (the U.S. pound is derived from the kilogram); the "standard locality" means sea level, 45 deg latitude, or, more strictly any locality in which the acceleration due to gravity has the value 980.665 cm per sec per sec = 32.1740 ft per sec per sec, which may be called the **standard acceleration.**

The **pound force** is the force required to support the standard pound body against gravity, *in vacuo*, in the standard locality; or, it is the force which, if applied to the standard pound body, supposed free to move, would give that body the "standard acceleration." The word "pound" is used for the unit of both force and mass and consequently is ambiguous. To avoid uncertainty it is desirable to call the units "pound force" and "pound mass," respectively.

The **kilogram force** is the force required to support the standard kilogram against gravity, *in vacuo*, in the standard locality; or, it is the force which, if applied to the standard kilogram body, supposed free to move, would give that body the "standard acceleration." The word "kilogram" is used for the unit of both force and mass and consequently is ambiguous. To avoid uncertainty it is desirable to call the units "kilogram force" and "kilogram mass," respectively.

The **poundal** is the force which, if applied to the standard pound body, would give that body an acceleration of 1 ft per sec per sec; *i.e.*, 1 poundal = 1/32.1740 lb force.

The **dyne** is the force which, if applied to the standard gram body, would give that body an acceleration of 1 cm per sec per sec; *i.e.*, 1 dyne = 1/980.665 of a gram force.

Systems of Units

Name of unit	Dimensions of units in terms of *F, L, T*	British "gravitational" system, or "foot-pound-second" system	Metric "gravitational" system, or "kilogram-meter-second" system	Metric "absolute" system, or "C. G. S." system	British "absolute" system (little used)
Force	F	1 lb	1 kg	1 dyne	1 poundal
Length	L	1 ft	1 m	1 cm	1 ft
Time	T	1 sec	1 sec	1 sec	1 sec
Velocity	L/T	1 ft per sec	1 m per sec	1 cm per sec	1 ft per sec
Acceleration	L/T^2	1 ft per sec^2	1 m per sec^2	1 cm per sec^2	1 ft per sec^2
Pressure	F/L^2	1 lb per ft^2	1 kg per m^2	1 dyne per cm^2	1 pdl per ft^2
Impulse or momentum	FT	1 lb-sec	1 kg-sec	1 dyne-sec	1 pdl-sec
Work or energy	FL	1 ft-lb	1 kg-m	1 dyne-cm = 1 "erg"	1 ft-pdl
Power	FL/T	1 ft-lb per sec	1 kg-m per sec	1 dyne-cm per sec	1 ft-pdl per sec
Mass	$F/(L/T^2)$	1 lb per (ft per sec^2) = 1 "slug."	1 kg per (m per sec^2) = 1 "metric slug."	1 dyne per (cm per sec^2) = 1 gram mass.	1 pdl per (ft per sec^2) = 1 pound

NOTE. The "slug" (also called the "geepound," or the "engineer's unit of mass"), the "metric slug," the "kilopond," and the "poundal" are rarely used in practice.

Other common units are as follows:

Work: 1 joule (absolute) = 10^7 ergs = 10,000,000 dyne-cm.
1 kilowatt-hour (absolute) = 3,600,000 joules (absolute) = 3,600 × 10^{10} dyne-cm.

Power: 1 horsepower = 550 ft-lb per sec.
1 poncelet = 100 kg-m per sec.
1 cheval-vapeur = 75 kg-m per sec = 1 metric horsepower = 1 pferde starke.
1 watt (absolute) = 1 joule (absolute) per sec = 1 × 10^7 dyne-cm per sec.
1 kilowatt = 1,000 watts = 10^{10} dyne-cm per sec.

A new horsepower of 550.220 ft-lb per sec, or 746 watts, has been proposed, but has not been accepted by mechanical engineers.

Prior to Jan. 1, 1948, the international system of electrical units was in general use instead of the absolute system.

$$1 \text{ international watt} = 1.000165 \text{ absolute watts}$$

The *weight* of a body (in a given locality) means a *force*, namely, the force required to support the body against gravity (in that locality). When no particular locality is specified, the standard locality may be assumed. Thus, the "standard weight" of the pound body is 1 lb force; the "standard weight" of the kilogram body is 1 kg force.

Force Equivalents

Dynes × 10^6	Kilograms	Pounds	Poundals
1	1.020 0.00848	2.248 0.3518	72.33 1.85933
0.9807 $\bar{1}$.99149	1	2.205 0.34334	70.93 1.85084
0.4448 $\bar{1}$.64819	0.4536 $\bar{1}$.65667	1	32.17 1.50750
0.01383 $\bar{2}$.14067	0.01410 $\bar{2}$.14916	0.03108 $\bar{2}$.49249	1

Heat Units. The units of heat commonly used are (1) the quantity of heat required to raise the temperature of 1 gram of water 1 C and (2) the quantity of heat required to raise the temperature of 1 pound of water 1 F. These units are (1) the **calorie** and (2) the **British thermal unit** or Btu. Work done in recent years on the International Steam Tables has led to the definition of the **IT calorie** and of the Btu in terms of other units. These definitions are

$$1 \text{ IT calorie} = \tfrac{1}{860} \text{ international watt-hour}$$
$$1 \text{ Btu} = 251.996 \text{ IT calories}$$

These units have been used on the following pages. The **kilocalorie,** sometimes called the kilogram calorie or large calorie, is equal to 1,000 calories and is used in engineering work in metric countries. The calorie is sometimes called the small calorie or gram calorie. (See also p. 4–10 *et seq.*)

The mean calorie (0 to 100 C) is about 1.001 IT calorie, and the corresponding mean Btu is approximately 779 ft-lb.

Mechanical Equivalent of Heat. The values now accepted as the work equivalents of the heat units are 778.2 ft-lb for the Btu and 4.1868 absolute joules for the IT calorie.

CONVERSION TABLES

Length Equivalents

Centimeters	Inches	Feet	Yards	Meters	Chains	Kilometers	Miles
1	0.3937 $\bar{1}.59517$	0.03281 $\bar{2}.51598$	0.01094 $\bar{2}.03886$	0.01 $\bar{2}.00000$	0.0_34971 $\bar{4}.69644$	10^{-5} $\bar{5}.00000$	0.0_56214 $\bar{6}.79335$
2.540 0.40483	**1**	0.08333 $\bar{2}.92082$	0.02778 $\bar{2}.44370$	0.0254 $\bar{2}.40483$	0.001263 $\bar{3}.10127$	0.0_4254 $\bar{5}.40483$	0.0_41578 $\bar{5}.19818$
30.48 1.48401	12 1.07918	**1**	0.3333 $\bar{1}.52288$	0.3048 $\bar{1}.48401$	0.01515 $\bar{2}.18046$	0.0_33048 $\bar{4}.48401$	0.0_31894 $\bar{4}.27736$
91.44 1.96114	36 1.55630	3 0.47712	**1**	0.9144 $\bar{1}.96114$	0.04545 $\bar{2}.65758$	0.0_39144 $\bar{4}.96114$	0.0_35682 $\bar{4}.75449$
100 2.00000	39.37 1.59517	3.281 0.51598	1.0936 0.03886	**1**	0.04971 $\bar{2}.69644$	0.001 $\bar{3}.00000$	0.0_36214 $\bar{4}.79335$
2012 3.30356	792 2.89873	66 1.81954	22 1.34242	20.12 1.30356	**1**	0.02012 $\bar{2}.30356$	0.0125 $\bar{2}.09691$
100000 5.00000	39370 4.59517	3281 3.51598	1093.6 3.03886	1000 3.00000	49.71 1.69644	**1**	0.6214 $\bar{1}.79335$
160934 5.20665	63360 4.80182	5280 3.72263	1760 3.24551	1609 3.20665	80 1.90309	1.609 0.20665	**1**

The equivalents are given in the heavier type. Logarithms of the equivalents are given immediately below. In some cases in this table and in those that follow, the equivalents have been rounded off, while the logarithm corresponds to the equivalent carried to a greater number of decimal places.

Subscripts after any figure, 0_3, 9_4, etc., mean that that figure is to be repeated the indicated number of times.

Length Equivalents

(As used by metrology laboratories for precise measurements, including measurements of surface texture.)*

Angstrom units	Surface texture, (U.S.), microin	Light bands,† monochromatic helium light count‡	Surface texture foreign, microns	Precision measurements,§ 0.0001 in.	Close-tolerance measurements, 0.001 in.	Metric measurements, mm	Inch measurements
1	0.003937 $\bar{3}.59517$	0.0003404 $\bar{4}.53199$	0.0001 $\bar{4}.0000$	0.0_43937 $\bar{5}.59517$	0.0_53937 $\bar{6}.59517$	0.0_61 $\bar{7}.00000$	0.0_83937 $\bar{9}.59517$
254 2.40483	**1**	0.086 $\bar{2}.93682$	0.0254 $\bar{2}.40483$	0.01 $\bar{2}.00000$	0.001 $\bar{3}.00000$	0.0_4254 $\bar{5}.40483$	0.0_51 $\bar{6}.00000$
2937.5 3.46797	11.566 1.06318	**1**	0.29375 $\bar{1}.46797$	0.11566 $\bar{1}.06318$	0.011566 $\bar{2}.06318$	0.0_329375 $\bar{4}.46797$	0.0_411566 $\bar{5}.06318$
10,000 4.00000	39.37 1.59517	3.404 0.53199	**1**	0.3937 $\bar{1}.59517$	0.03937 $\bar{2}.59517$	0.001 $\bar{3}.00000$	0.0_43937 $\bar{5}.59517$
25,400 4.40483	100 2.00000	8.646 0.93682	2.54 0.40483	**1**	0.1 $\bar{1}.00000$	0.00254 $\bar{3}.40483$	0.0001 $\bar{4}.00000$
254,000 5.40483	1000 3.00000	86.46 1.93682	25.4 1.40483	10 1.00000	**1**	0.0254 $\bar{2}.40483$	0.001 $\bar{3}.00000$
10,000,000 7.00000	39,370 4.59517	3404 3.53199	1000 3.00000	393.7 2.59517	39.37 1.59517	**1**	0.03937 $\bar{2}.59517$
4,000,000 8.40483	1,000,000 6.00000	86,460 4.93682	25,400 4.40483	10,000 4.00000	1000 3.00000	25.4 1.40483	**1**

* Computed by J. A. Broadston.

† One light band equals one-half corresponding wavelength. Visible-light wavelengths range from red at 6500A to violet at 4100A.

‡ One helium light band = 0.000011661 in. = 2937.5A; one krypton 86 light band = 0.0000119 in. = 3022.5A; one mercury 198 light band – 0.000021499 in. = 5460A.

§ The designations "precision measurements," etc., are not necessarily used in all metrology laboratories.

Conversion of Lengths*

	Inches to millimeters	Millimeters to inches	Feet to meters	Meters to feet	Yards to meters	Meters to yards	Miles to kilometers	Kilometers to miles
1	25.40	0.03937	0.3048	3.281	0.9144	1.094	1.609	0.6214
2	50.80	0.07874	0.6096	6.562	1.829	2.187	3.219	1.243
3	76.20	0.1181	0.9144	9.843	2.743	3.281	4.828	1.864
4	101.60	0.1575	1.219	13.12	3.658	4.374	6.437	2.485
5	127.00	0.1969	1.524	16.40	4.572	5.468	6.047	3.107
6	152.40	0.2362	1.829	19.69	5.486	6.562	9.656	3.728
7	177.80	0.2756	2.134	22.97	6.401	7.655	11.27	4.350
8	203.20	0.3150	2.438	26.25	7.315	8.749	12.87	4.971
9	228.60	0.3543	2.743	29.53	8.230	9.843	14.48	5.592

* EXAMPLE: 1 in. = 25.40 mm.

COMMON FRACTIONS OF AN INCH TO MILLIMETERS (FROM 1/64 TO 1 IN.)

64ths	Millimeters	64ths	Millimeters	64ths	Millimeters	64ths	Millimeters	64ths	Millimeters	64ths	Millimeters
1	0.397	13	5.159	25	9.922	37	14.684	49	19.447	57	22.622
2	0.794	14	5.556	26	10.319	38	15.081	50	19.844	58	23.019
3	1.191	15	5.953	27	10.716	39	15.478	51	20.241	59	23.416
4	1.588	16	6.350	28	11.112	40	15.875	52	20.638	60	23.812
5	1.984	17	6.747	29	11.509	41	16.272	53	21.034	61	24.209
6	2.381	18	7.144	30	11.906	42	16.669	54	21.431	62	24.606
7	2.778	19	7.541	31	12.303	43	17.066	55	21.828	63	25.003
8	3.175	20	7.938	32	12.700	44	17.462	56	22.225	64	25.400
9	3.572	21	8.334	33	13.097	45	17.859				
10	3.969	22	8.731	34	13.494	46	18.256				
11	4.366	23	9.128	35	13.891	47	18.653				
12	4.762	24	9.525	36	14.288	48	19.050				

DECIMALS OF AN INCH TO MILLIMETERS (FROM 0.01 IN. TO 0.99 IN.)

	0	1	2	3	4	5	6	7	8	9
.0		0.254	0.508	0.762	1.016	1.270	1.524	1.778	2.032	2.286
.1	2.540	2.794	3.048	3.302	3.556	3.810	4.064	4.318	4.572	4.826
.2	5.080	5.334	5.588	5.842	6.096	6.350	6.604	6.858	7.112	7.366
.3	7.620	7.874	8.128	8.382	8.636	8.890	9.144	9.398	9.652	9.906
.4	10.160	10.414	10.668	10.922	11.176	11.430	11.684	11.938	12.192	12.446
.5	12.700	12.954	13.208	13.462	13.716	13.970	14.224	14.478	14.732	14.986
.6	15.240	15.494	15.748	16.002	16.256	16.510	16.764	17.018	17.272	17.526
.7	17.780	18.034	18.288	18.542	18.796	19.050	19.304	19.558	19.812	20.066
.8	20.320	20.574	20.828	21.082	21.336	21.590	21.844	22.098	22.352	22.606
.9	22.860	23.114	23.368	23.622	23.876	24.130	24.384	24.638	24.892	25.146

MILLIMETERS TO DECIMALS OF AN INCH (FROM 1 TO 99 MM)

	0.	1.	2.	3.	4.	5.	6.	7.	8.	9.
0		0.0394	0.0787	0.1181	0.1575	0.1969	0.2362	0.2756	0.3150	0.3543
1	0.3937	0.4331	0.4724	0.5118	0.5512	0.5906	0.6299	0.6693	0.7087	0.7480
2	0.7874	0.8268	0.8661	0.9055	0.9449	0.9843	1.0236	1.0630	1.1024	1.1417
3	1.1811	1.2205	1.2598	1.2992	1.3386	1.3780	1.4173	1.4567	1.4961	1.5354
4	1.5748	1.6142	1.6535	1.6929	1.7323	1.7717	1.8110	1.8504	1.8898	1.9291
5	1.9685	2.0079	2.0472	2.0866	2.1260	2.1654	2.2047	2.2441	2.2835	2.3228
6	2.3622	2.4016	2.4409	2.4803	2.5197	2.5591	2.5984	2.6378	2.6772	2.7165
7	2.7559	2.7953	2.8346	2.8740	2.9134	2.9528	2.9921	3.0315	3.0709	3.1102
8	3.1496	3.1890	3.2283	3.2677	3.3071	3.3465	3.3858	3.4252	3.4646	3.5039
9	3.5433	3.5827	3.6220	3.6614	3.7008	3.7402	3.7795	3.8189	3.8583	3.8976

Area Equivalents

(1 hectare = 100 ares = 10,000 centiares or square meters)

Square meters	Square inches	Square feet	Square yards	Square rods	Square chains	Roods	Acres	Square miles or sections
1	1550	10.76	1.196	0.0395	0.002471	$0.0_{3}9884$	$0.0_{3}2471$	$0.0_{6}3861$
	3.19033	1.03197	0.07773	$\bar{2}.59700$	$\bar{3}.39288$	$\bar{3}.99495$	$\bar{4}.39288$	$\bar{7}.58670$
$0.0_{3}6452$	**1**	0.006944	$0.0_{3}7716$	$0.0_{4}2551$	$0.0_{5}1594$	$0.0_{6}6377$	$0.0_{6}1594$	$0.0_{9}2491$
$\bar{4}.80967$		$\bar{3}.84164$	$\bar{4}.88740$	$\bar{5}.40667$	$\bar{6}.20255$	$\bar{7}.80461$	$\bar{7}.20255$	$\overline{10}.39637$
0.09290	144	**1**	0.1111	0.003673	$0.0_{3}2296$	$0.0_{4}9183$	$0.0_{4}2296$	$0.0_{7}3587$
$\bar{2}.96803$	2.15836		$\bar{1}.04576$	$\bar{3}.56503$	$\bar{4}.36091$	$\bar{5}.96297$	$\bar{4}.36091$	$\bar{8}.55473$
0.8361	1296	9	**1**	0.03306	0.002066	$0.0_{3}8264$	0.0002066	$0.0_{6}3228$
$\bar{1}.92227$	3.11260	0.95424		$\bar{2}.51927$	$\bar{3}.31515$	$\bar{4}.91721$	$\bar{4}.31515$	$\bar{7}.50898$
25.29	39204	272.25	30.25	**1**	0.0625	0.02500	0.00625	$0.0_{5}9766$
1.40300	4.59333	2.43497	1.48072		$\bar{2}.79588$	$\bar{2}.39794$	$\bar{3}.79588$	$\bar{6}.98970$
404.7	627264	4356	484	16	**1**	0.4	0.1	0.0001562
2.60712	5.79745	3.63909	2.68484	1.20412		$\bar{1}.60206$	$\bar{1}.00000$	$\bar{4}.19382$
1012	1568160	10890	1210	40	2.5	**1**	0.25	$0.0_{3}3906$
3.00506	6.19539	4.03703	3.08278	1.60206	0.39794		$\bar{1}.39794$	$\bar{4}.59176$
4047	6272640	43560	4840	160	10	4	**1**	0.001562
3.60712	6.79745	4.63909	3.68484	2.20412	1.00000	0.60206		$\bar{3}.19382$
2589988		27878400	3097600	102400	6400	2560	640	**1**
6.41330		7.44527	6.49102	5.01030	3.80618	3.40824	2.80618	

Conversion of Areas*

	Sq in. to sq cm	Sq cm to sq in.	Sq ft to sq m	Sq m to sq ft	Sq yd to sq m	Sq m to sq yd	Acres to hectares	Hectares to acres	Sq mi to sq km	Sq km to sq mi
1	6.452	0.1550	0.0929	10.76	0.8361	1.196	0.4047	2.471	2.590	0.3861
2	12.90	0.3100	0.1858	21.53	1.672	2.392	0.8094	4.942	5.180	0.7722
3	19.35	0.4650	0.2787	32.29	2.508	3.588	1.214	7.413	7.770	1.158
4	25.81	0.6200	0.3716	43.06	3.345	4.784	1.619	9.884	10.360	1.544
5	32.26	0.7750	0.4645	53.82	4.181	5.980	2.023	12.355	12.950	1.931
6	38.71	0.9300	0.5574	64.58	5.017	7.176	2.428	14.826	15.540	2.317
7	45.16	1.085	0.6503	75.35	5.853	8.372	2.833	17.297	18.130	2.703
8	51.61	1.240	0.7432	86.11	6.689	9.568	3.237	19.768	20.720	3.089
9	58.06	1.395	0.8361	96.88	7.525	10.764	3.642	22.239	23.310	3.475

* EXAMPLE: 1 sq in. = 6.452 sq cm.

Volume and Capacity Equivalents

Cubic inches	Cubic feet	Cubic yards	U.S. Apothecary fluid ounces	U.S. quarts		U.S. gallons	U.S. bushels	Cubic decimeters or liters
				Liquid	Dry			
1	$0.0_{3}5787$ $\bar{4}.76246$	$0.0_{4}2143$ $\bar{5}.33109$	0.5541 $\bar{1}.74360$	0.01732 $\bar{2}.23845$	0.01488 $\bar{2}.17263$	$0.0_{2}4329$ $\bar{3}.63639$	$0.0_{3}4650$ $\bar{4}.66748$	0.01639 $\bar{2}.21450$
1728 3.23754	**1**	0.03704 $\bar{2}.56864$	957.5 2.98114	29.92 1.47599	25.71 1.41017	7.481 0.87393	0.8036 $\bar{1}.90502$	28.32 1.45205
46656 4.66891	27 1.43136	**1**	25853 4.41251	807.9 2.90736	694.3 2.84153	202.2 2.30530	21.70 1.33638	764.6 2.88341
1.805 0.25640	0.001044 $\bar{3}.01886$	$0.0_{4}3868$ $\bar{5}.58749$	**1**	0.03125 $\bar{2}.49485$	0.02686 $\bar{2}.42903$	0.007812 $\bar{3}.89279$	$0.0_{3}8392$ $\bar{4}.92388$	0.02957 $\bar{2}.47091$
57.75 1.76155	0.03342 $\bar{2}.52401$	0.001238 $\bar{3}.09264$	32 1.50515	**1**	0.8594 $\bar{1}.93418$	0.25 $\bar{1}.39794$	0.02686 $\bar{2}.42903$	0.9464 $\bar{1}.97606$
67.20 1.82737	0.03889 $\bar{2}.58983$	0.001440 $\bar{3}.15847$	37.24 1.57097	1.164 0.06582	**1**	0.2909 $\bar{1}.46376$	0.03125 $\bar{2}.49485$	1.101 0.04187
231 2.36361	0.1337 $\bar{1}.12607$	0.004951 $\bar{3}.69470$	128 2.10721	4 0.60206	3.437 0.53624	**1**	0.1074 $\bar{1}.03109$	3.785 0.57812
2150 3.33252	1.244 0.09498	0.04609 $\bar{2}.66362$	1192 3.07612	37.24 1.57097	32 1.50515	9.309 0.96891	**1**	35.24 1.54696
61.02 1.78550	0.03531 $\bar{2}.54795$	0.001308 $\bar{3}.11659$	33.81 1.52909	1.057 0.02394	0.9081 $\bar{1}.95812$	0.2642 $\bar{1}.42188$	0.02838 $\bar{2}.45297$	**1**

Conversion of Volumes or Cubic Measure *

	Cu in. to cu cm	Cu cm to cu in.	Cu ft to cu m	Cu m to cu ft	Cu yd to cu m	Cu m to cu yd	Gallons to cu ft	Cu ft to gallons
1	16.39	0.06102	0.02832	35.31	0.7646	1.308	0.1337	7.481
2	32.77	0.1220	0.05663	70.63	1.529	2.616	0.2674	14.96
3	49.16	0.1831	0.08495	105.9	2.294	3.924	0.4010	22.44
4	65.55	0.2441	0.1133	141.3	3.058	5.232	0.5347	29.92
5	81.94	0.3051	0.1416	176.6	3.823	6.540	0.6684	37.40
6	98.32	0.3661	0.1699	211.9	4.587	7.848	0.8021	44.88
7	114.7	0.4272	0.1982	247.2	5.352	9.156	0.9358	52.36
8	131.1	0.4882	0.2265	282.5	6.116	10.46	1.069	59.84
9	147.5	0.5492	0.2549	317.8	6.881	11.77	1.203	67.32

* EXAMPLE: 1 cu in. = 16.39 cu cm.

Conversion of Volumes or Capacities *

	Fluid ounces to cu cm	Cu cm to fluid ounces	Liquid pints to liters	Liters to liquid pints	Liquid quarts to liters	Liters to liquid quarts	Gallons to liters	Liters to gallons	Bushels to hecto-liters	Hecto-liters to bushels
1	29.57	0.03381	0.4732	2.113	0.9463	1.057	3.785	0.2642	0.3524	2.838
2	59.15	0.06763	0.9463	4.227	1.893	2.113	7.571	0.5284	0.7048	5.676
3	88.72	0.1014	1.420	6.340	2.839	3.170	11.36	0.7925	1.057	8.513
4	118.3	0.1353	1.893	8.454	3.785	4.227	15.14	1.057	1.410	11.35
5	147.9	0.1691	2.366	10.57	4.732	5.284	18.93	1.321	1.762	14.19
6	177.4	0.2092	2.839	12.68	5.678	6.340	22.71	1.585	2.114	17.03
7	207.0	0.2367	3.312	14.79	6.624	7.397	26.50	1.849	2.467	19.86
8	236.6	0.2705	3.785	16.91	7.571	8.454	30.28	2.113	2.819	22.70
9	266.2	2.3043	4.259	19.02	8.517	9.510	34.07	2.378	3.171	25.54

* EXAMPLE: 1 fluid oz = 29.57 cu cm.

Mass Equivalents

Kilograms	Grains	Ounces		Pounds		Tons		
		Troy and apoth	Avoirdupois	Troy and apoth	Avoirdupois	Short	Long	Metric
1	15432 4.18843	32.15 1.50719	35.27 1.54745	2.6792 0.42801	2.205 0.34333	$0.0_2 1102$ $\bar{3}.04230$	$0.0_3 9842$ $\bar{4}.99309$	0.001 $\bar{3}.00000$
$0.0_4 6480$ $\bar{5}.81157$	**1**	$0.0_2 2083$ $\bar{3}.31876$	$0.0_2 2286$ $\bar{3}.35902$	$0.0_3 1736$ $\bar{4}.23958$	$0.0_3 1429$ $\bar{4}.15490$	$0.0_7 7143$ $\bar{8}.85387$	$0.0_7 6378$ $\bar{8}.80465$	$0.0_7 6480$ $\bar{8}.81157$
0.03110 $\bar{2}.49281$	480 2.68124	**1**	1.09714 0.04026	0.08333 $\bar{2}.92082$	0.06857 $\bar{2}.83614$	$0.0_4 3429$ $\bar{5}.53511$	$0.0_4 3061$ $\bar{5}.48590$	$0.0_4 3110$ $\bar{5}.49281$
0.02835 $\bar{2}.45255$	437.5 2.64098	0.9115 $\bar{1}.95974$	**1**	0.07595 $\bar{2}.88056$	0.0625 $\bar{2}.79588$	$0.0_4 3125$ $\bar{5}.49485$	$0.0_4 2790$ $\bar{5}.44563$	$0.0_4 2835$ $\bar{5}.45255$
0.3732 $\bar{1}.57199$	5760 3.76042	12 1.07918	13.17 1.11944	**1**	0.8229 $\bar{1}.91532$	$0.0_3 4114$ $\bar{4}.61429$	$0.0_3 3673$ $\bar{4}.56508$	$0.0_3 3732$ $\bar{4}.57199$
0.4536 $\bar{1}.65667$	7000 3.84510	14.58 1.16386	16 1.20412	1.215 0.08468	**1**	0.0005 $\bar{4}.69897$	$0.0_3 4464$ $\bar{4}.64975$	$0.0_3 4536$ $\bar{4}.65667$
907.2 2.95770	140_6 7.14613	29167 4.46489	320_3 4.50515	2431 3.38571	2000 3.30103	**1**	0.8929 $\bar{1}.95078$	0.9072 $\bar{1}.95770$
1016 3.00691	15680_4 7.19535	32667 4.51411	35840 4.55437	2722 3.43492	2240 3.35025	1.12 0.04922	**1**	1.016 0.00691
1000 3.00000	15432356 7.18843	32151 4.50719	35274 4.54745	2679 3.42801	2205 3.34333	1.102 0.04230	0.9842 $\bar{1}.99309$	**1**

Conversion of Masses*

	Grains to grams	Grams to grains	Ounces (avdp) to grams	Grams to ounces (avdp)	Pounds (avdp) to kilograms	Kilograms to pounds (avdp)	Short tons (2000 lb) to metric tons	Metric tons (1000 kg) to short tons	Long tons (2240 lb) to metric tons	Metric tons to long tons
1	0.06480	15.43	28.35	0.03527	0.4536	2.205	0.907	1.102	1.016	0.984
2	0.1296	30.86	56.70	0.07055	0.9072	4.409	1.814	2.205	2.032	1.968
3	0.1944	46.30	85.05	0.1058	1.361	6.614	2.722	3.307	3.048	2.953
4	0.2592	61.73	113.40	0.1411	1.814	8.818	3.629	4.409	4.064	3.937
5	0.3240	77.16	141.75	0.1764	2.268	11.02	4.536	5.512	5.080	4.921
6	0.3888	92.59	170.10	0.2116	2.722	13.23	5.443	6.614	6.096	5.905
7	0.4536	108.03	198.45	0.2469	3.175	15.43	6.350	7.716	7.112	6.889
8	0.5184	123.46	226.80	0.2822	3.629	17.64	7.257	8.818	8.128	7.874
9	0.5832	138.89	255.15	0.3175	4.082	19.84	8.165	9.921	9.144	8.858

* EXAMPLE: 1 grain = 0.06480 grams.

Velocity Equivalents

Centimeters per sec	Meters per sec	Meters per min	Kilometers per hour	Feet per sec	Feet per min	Miles per hour	Knots
1	0.01	0.6 1.77815	0.036 $\bar{2}$.55630	0.03281 $\bar{2}$.51598	1.9685 0.29414	0.02237 $\bar{2}$.34965	0.01944 $\bar{2}$.28866
100 2.00000	1	60 1.77815	3.6 0.55630	3.281 0.51598	196.85 2.29414	2.237 0.34965	1.944 0.28866
1.667 0.22185	0.01667 $\bar{2}$.22185	1	0.06 $\bar{2}$.77815	0.05468 $\bar{2}$.73783	3.281 0.51598	0.03728 $\bar{2}$.57150	0.03240 $\bar{2}$.51050
27.78 1.44370	0.2778 $\bar{1}$.44370	16.67 1.22185	1	0.9113 $\bar{1}$.95968	54.68 1.73783	0.6214 $\bar{1}$.79335	0.53996 $\bar{1}$.73236
30.48 1.48401	0.3048 $\bar{1}$.48401	18.29 1.26217	1.097 0.04032	1	60 1.77815	0.6818 $\bar{1}$.83367	0.59248 $\bar{1}$.77268
0.5080 1.70586	0.005080 $\bar{3}$.70586	0.3048 $\bar{1}$.48401	0.01829 $\bar{2}$.26217	0.01667 $\bar{2}$.22185	1	0.01136 $\bar{2}$.05553	0.00987 $\bar{3}$.99453
44.70 1.65035	0.4470 $\bar{1}$.65035	26.82 1.42850	1.609 0.20670	1.467 0.16633	88 1.94448	1	0.86898 $\bar{1}$.93901
51.44 1.71133	0.5144 $\bar{1}$.71133	30.87 1.48949	1.852 0.26764	1.688 0.22732	101.3 2.00547	1.151 1.06100	1

Conversion of Linear and Angular Velocities *

	Cm per sec to feet per min	Feet per min to cm per sec	Cm per sec to miles per hour	Miles per hour to cm per sec	Feet per sec to miles per hour	Miles per hour to feet per sec	Radians per sec to rev per min	Rev per min to radians per sec
1	1.97	0.508	0.0224	44.70	0.682	1.47	9.55	0.1047
2	3.94	1.016	0.0447	89.41	1.364	2.93	19.10	0.2094
3	5.91	1.524	0.0671	134.1	2.045	4.40	28.65	0.3142
4	7.87	2.032	0.0895	178.8	2.727	5.87	38.20	0.4189
5	9.84	2.540	0.1118	223.5	3.409	7.33	47.75	0.5236
6	11.81	3.048	0.1342	268.2	4.091	8.80	57.30	0.6283
7	13.78	3.556	0.1566	312.9	4.773	10.27	66.84	0.7330
8	15.75	4.064	0.1790	357.6	5.455	11.73	76.39	0.8378
9	17.72	4.572	0.2013	402.3	6.136	13.20	85.94	0.9425

* **Example:** 1 cm per sec = 1.97 ft per min.

Acceleration Equivalents

Centimeters per sec per sec	Meters per sec per sec	Meters per hr per sec	Kilometers per hr per sec	Feet per hr per sec	Feet per sec per sec	Feet per min per min	Miles per hr per sec	Knots per sec
1	0.01 $\bar{1}$.00000	36.00 1.55630	0.036 $\bar{2}$.55630	118.1 2.07225	0.03281 $\bar{2}$.51599	118.1 2.07225	0.02237 $\bar{2}$.34965	0.01944 $\bar{2}$.29865
100 2.00000	1	3600 3.55630	3.6 0.55630	11811 4.07225	3.281 0.51599	11811 4.07225	2.237 0.34965	1.944 0.29865
0.02778 $\bar{2}$.44370	0.0002778 $\bar{4}$.44370	1	0.001 $\bar{3}$.00000	3.281 0.51599	0.0009113 $\bar{4}$.95968	3.281 0.51599	0.0006214 $\bar{4}$.79325	0.0005400 $\bar{4}$.73235
27.78 1.44370	0.2778 $\bar{1}$.44370	1000 3.00000	1	3281 3.51599	0.9113 $\bar{1}$.95968	3281 3.51599	0.6214 $\bar{1}$.79335	0.5400 $\bar{1}$.73235
0.008467 $\bar{3}$.92771	0.00008467 $\bar{5}$.92771	0.3048 $\bar{1}$.48401	0.0003048 $\bar{4}$.48401	1	0.0002778 $\bar{4}$.44370	1	0.0001894 $\bar{4}$.27737	0.0001646 $\bar{4}$.21640
30.48 1.48401	0.3048 $\bar{1}$.48401	1097 3.04030	1.097 0.04030	3600 3.55630	1	3600 3.55630	0.6818 $\bar{1}$.83366	0.4572 $\bar{1}$.66008
0.008467 $\bar{3}$.92771	0.00008467 $\bar{5}$.92771	0.3048 $\bar{1}$.48401	0.0003048 $\bar{4}$.48401	1	0.0002778 $\bar{4}$.44370	1	0.0001894 $\bar{4}$.27737	0.0001646 $\bar{4}$.21640
44.70 1.65035	0.4470 $\bar{1}$.65035	1609 3.20665	1.609 0.20665	5280 3.72263	1.467 0.13636	5280 3.72263	1	0.8690 $\bar{1}$.93901
51.44 1.71134	0.5144 $\bar{1}$.71134	1852 3.26764	1.852 0.26764	6076 3.78362	1.688 0.22732	6076 3.78362	1.151 0.06099	1

Conversion of Accelerations*

	Centimeters per sec per sec to ft per min per min	Kilometers per hr per sec to miles per hr per sec	Kilometers per hr per sec to knots per sec	Feet per sec per sec to miles per hr per sec	Feet per sec per sec to knots per sec	Feet per min per min to cm per sec per sec	Miles per hr per sec to kilometers per hr per sec	Miles per hr per sec to knots per sec	Knots per sec to miles per hr per sec	Knots per sec to kilometers per hr per sec
1	118.1	0.6214	0.5400	0.6818	0.4572	0.008467	1.609	0.8690	1.151	1.852
2	236.2	1.243	1.080	1.364	0.9144	0.01693	3.219	1.738	2.302	3.704
3	354.3	1.864	1.620	2.045	1.372	0.02540	4.828	2.607	3.452	5.556
4	472.4	2.485	2.160	2.727	1.829	0.03387	6.437	3.476	4.603	7.408
5	590.6	3.107	2.700	3.409	2.286	0.04233	8.046	4.345	5.754	9.260
6	708.7	3.728	3.240	4.091	2.743	0.05080	9.656	5.214	6.905	11.11
7	826.8	4.350	3.780	4.772	3.200	0.05927	11.27	6.083	8.056	12.96
8	944.9	4.971	4.320	5.454	3.658	0.06774	12.87	6.952	9.206	14.82
9	1063	5.592	4.860	6.136	4.115	0.07620	14.48	7.821	10.36	16.67

EXAMPLE: 1 cm per sec per sec = 118.1 ft per min per min.

Pressure Equivalents

Bars, megabaryes, or megadynes per sq cm	Kilograms per sq cm (metric atmospheres)	Pounds per sq in.	Short tons per sq ft	Atmospheres	Columns of mercury at temperature 0 C and g = 980.665 cm per sec²		Columns of water at temperature 15 C and g = 980.665 cm per sec²		
					Meters	Inches	Meters	Inches	Feet
1	1.0197 0.00848	14.50 1.16148	1.044 0.01882	0.9869 $\bar{1}$.99427	0.7501 $\bar{1}$.87510	29.53 1.47025	10.21 1.00886	401.8 2.60402	33.49 1.52485
0.9807 $\bar{1}$.99152	**1**	14.22 1.15300	1.024 0.01034	0.9678 $\bar{1}$.98579	0.7356 $\bar{1}$.86662	28.96 1.46177	10.01 1.00038	394.1 2.59556	32.84 1.51636
0.06895 $\bar{2}$.83852	0.07031 $\bar{2}$.84700	**1**	0.072 $\bar{2}$.85733	0.06805 $\bar{2}$.83280	0.05171 $\bar{2}$.71360	2.036 0.30876	0.7037 $\bar{1}$.84738	27.70 1.44254	2.309 0.36336
0.9576 $\bar{1}$.98119	0.9765 $\bar{1}$.98966	13.89 1.14267	**1**	0.9451 $\bar{1}$.97547	0.7183 $\bar{1}$.85628	28.28 1.45143	9.774 0.99006	384.8 2.58521	32.07 1.50604
1.0133 0.00573	1.0332 0.01420	14.70 1.16722	1.058 0.02453	**1**	0.76 $\bar{1}$.88081	29.92 1.47598	10.34 1.01459	407.1 2.60975	33.93 1.53058
1.3332 0.12490	1.3595 0.13338	19.34 1.28640	1.392 0.14373	1.316 0.11919	**1**	39.37 1.59517	13.61 1.13378	535.7 2.72894	44.64 1.64976
0.03386 $\bar{2}$.52975	0.03453 $\bar{2}$.53823	0.4912 $\bar{1}$.69124	0.03536 $\bar{2}$.54857	0.03342 $\bar{2}$.52402	0.02540 $\bar{2}$.40484	**1**	0.3456 $\bar{1}$.53861	13.61 1.13378	1.134 0.05460
0.09798 $\bar{2}$.99114	0.09991 $\bar{2}$.99962	1.421 0.15262	0.1023 $\bar{1}$.00996	0.09670 $\bar{2}$.98541	0.07349 $\bar{2}$.86622	2.893 0.46139	**1**	39.37 1.59517	3.281 0.51598
0.002489 $\bar{3}$.39598	0.002538 $\bar{3}$.40446	0.03609 $\bar{2}$.55745	0.002599 $\bar{3}$.41479	0.002456 $\bar{3}$.39024	0.001867 $\bar{3}$.27106	0.07349 $\bar{2}$.86622	0.02540 $\bar{2}$.40484	**1**	0.08333 $\bar{2}$.92082
0.02986 $\bar{2}$.47516	0.03045 $\bar{2}$.48364	0.4331 $\bar{1}$.63663	0.03119 $\bar{2}$.49397	0.02947 $\bar{2}$.46942	0.02240 $\bar{2}$.35024	0.8819 $\bar{1}$.94540	0.3048 $\bar{1}$.48401	12 1.07918	**1**

Conversion of Pressures *

	Pounds per sq in. to kilograms per sq cm	Kilograms per sq cm to pounds per sq in.	Atmospheres to pounds per sq in.	Pounds per sq in. to atmospheres	Atmospheres to kilograms per sq cm	Kilograms per sq cm to atmospheres
1	0.0703	14.22	14.70	0.0680	1.033	0.9678
2	0.1406	28.45	29.39	0.1361	2.066	1.936
3	0.2109	42.67	44.09	0.2041	3.100	2.904
4	0.2812	56.89	58.78	0.2722	4.133	3.871
5	0.3515	71.12	73.48	0.3402	5.166	4.839
6	0.4218	85.34	88.18	0.4083	6.199	5.807
7	0.4921	99.56	102.9	0.4763	7.233	6.775
8	0.5625	113.8	117.6	0.5444	8.266	7.743
9	0.6328	128.0	132.3	0.6124	9.299	8.711

* EXAMPLE: 1 lb per sq in. = 0.0703 kg per sq cm.

Energy or Work Equivalents

Joules	Kilogram-meters	Foot-pounds	Kilo-watt-hours	Metric horse-power-hours	Horse-power-hours	Liter-atmos-pheres	Kilo-calories	British thermal units
1	0.10197 $\bar{1}.00848$	0.7376 $\bar{1}.86780$	0.0_62778 $\bar{7}.44370$	0.0_63777 $\bar{7}.57711$	0.0_63725 $\bar{7}.57113$	0.009869 $\bar{3}.99427$	0.0_32388 $\bar{4}.37809$	0.0_39478 $\bar{4}.97670$
9.80665 0.9915207	**1**	7.233 0.85932	0.0_52724 $\bar{6}.43521$	0.0_537037 $\bar{6}.56863$	0.0_53653 $\bar{6}.56265$	0.09678 $\bar{2}.98579$	0.002342 $\bar{3}.36961$	0.009295 $\bar{3}.96825$
1.356 0.13220	0.1383 $\bar{1}.14068$	**1**	0.0_63766 $\bar{7}.57590$	0.0_651206 $\bar{7}.70932$	0.0_650505 $\bar{7}.70333$	0.01338 $\bar{2}.12647$	0.0_33238 $\bar{4}.51029$	0.001285 $\bar{3}.10890$
3.600×10^6 6.55630	3.671×10^5 5.56478	2.655×10^6 6.42410	**1**	1.3596 0.13342	1.341 0.12743	35528 4.55057	859.9 2.93443	3412 3.53303
2.648×10^6 6.42288	270000 5.43136	1.9529×10^6 6.29068	0.7355 $\bar{1}.86658$	**1**	0.9863 $\bar{1}.99401$	26131 4.41715	632.4 2.80098	2510 3.39961
2.6845×10^6 6.42887	2.7375×10^5 5.43735	1.98×10^6 6.29667	0.7457 $\bar{1}.87356$	1.0139 0.00598	**1**	26493 4.42314	641.2 2.80699	2544 3.40557
101.33 2.00573	10.333 1.01421	74.74 1.87353	0.0_42815 $\bar{5}.44952$	0.0_43827 $\bar{5}.58284$	0.0_43775 $\bar{5}.57686$	**1**	0.02420 $\bar{2}.38382$	0.09604 $\bar{2}.98246$
4187 3.62191	426.9 2.63036	3088 3.48971	0.001163 $\bar{3}.06558$	0.001581 $\bar{3}.19902$	0.001560 $\bar{3}.19304$	41.32 1.61618	**1**	3.968 0.59861
1055 3.02300	107.6 2.03178	778.2 2.89110	0.0_32931 $\bar{4}.46697$	0.0_33985 $\bar{4}.60042$	0.0_33930 $\bar{4}.59444$	10.41 1.01757	0.25200 $\bar{1}.40139$	**1**

Conversion of Energy, Work, Heat *

	Ft-lb to kilo-gram-meters	Kilo-gram-meters to ft-lb	Ft-lb to Btu	Btu to ft-lb	Kilo-gram-meters to kilo-calories	Kilo-calories to kilo-gram-meters	Joules to calories	Calories to joules
1	0.1383	7.233	0.001285	778.2	0.002342	426.9	0.2388	4.187
2	0.2765	14.47	0.002570	1,556.	0.004685	853.9	0.4777	8.374
3	0.4148	21.70	0.003855	2,334.	0.007027	1,281.	0.7165	12.56
4	0.5530	28.93	0.005140	3,113.	0.009369	1,708.	0.9554	16.75
5	0.6913	36.16	0.006425	3,891.	0.01172	2,135.	1.194	20.93
6	0.8295	43.40	0.007710	4,669.	0.01405	2,562.	1.433	25.12
7	0.9678	50.63	0.008995	5,447.	0.01640	2,989.	1.672	29.31
8	1.106	57.86	0.01028	6,225.	0.01874	3,415.	1.911	33.49
9	1.244	65.10	0.01156	7,003.	0.02108	3,842.	2.150	37.68

* EXAMPLE: 1 ft-lb = 0.1383 kg-m.

Power Equivalents

Horse-power	Kilo-watts	Metric horse-power	Ponce-lets	Kg-m per sec	Ft-lb per sec	Kilo-calories per sec	Btu per sec
1	0.7457 $\bar{1}.87256$	1.014 0.00599	0.7604 $\bar{1}.88105$	76.04 1.88105	550 2.74036	0.1781 $\bar{1}.25066$	0.7068 $\bar{1}.84936$
1.341 0.12743	**1**	1.360 0.13343	1.020 0.00848	102.0 2.00848	737.6 2.86780	0.2388 $\bar{1}.37813$	0.9478 $\bar{1}.97673$
0.9863 $\bar{1}.99402$	0.7355 $\bar{1}.86658$	**1**	0.75 $\bar{1}.87506$	75 1.87506	542.5 2.73438	0.1757 $\bar{1}.24467$	0.6971 $\bar{1}.84328$
1.315 0.11896	0.9807 $\bar{1}.99152$	1.333 0.12493	**1**	100 2.00000	723.3 2.85932	0.2342 $\bar{1}.36961$	0.9295 $\bar{1}.96825$
0.01315 $\bar{2}.11896$	0.009807 $\bar{3}.99152$	0.01333 $\bar{2}.12493$	0.01 $\bar{2}.00000$	**1**	7.233 0.85932	0.002342 $\bar{3}.36961$	0.009295 $\bar{3}.96825$
0.00182 $\bar{3}.25946$	0.001356 $\bar{3}.13220$	0.00184 $\bar{3}.26562$	0.00138 $\bar{3}.14067$	0.1383 $\bar{1}.14067$	**1**	$0.0_3 3238$ $\bar{4}.51029$	0.001285 $\bar{3}.10890$
5.615 0.74934	4.187 0.62187	5.692 0.75530	4.269 0.63036	426.9 2.63036	3088 3.48971	**1**	3.968 0.59861
1.415 0.15074	1.055 0.02320	1.434 0.15668	1.076 0.03178	107.6 2.03178	778.2 2.89110	0.2520 $\bar{1}.40138$	**1**

Conversion of Power *

	Horsepower to kilowatts	Kilowatts to horsepower	Metric horsepower to kilowatts	Kilowatts to metric horsepower	Horsepower to metric horsepower	Metric horsepower to horsepower
1	0.7457	1.341	0.7355	1.360	1.014	0.9863
2	1.491	2.682	1.471	2.719	2.028	1.973
3	2.237	4.023	2.206	4.079	3.042	2.959
4	2.983	5.364	2.942	5.438	4.055	3.945
5	3.729	6.705	3.677	6.798	5.069	4.932
6	4.474	8.046	4.412	8.158	6.083	5.918
7	5.220	9.387	5.147	9.520	7.097	6.904
8	5.966	10.73	5.883	10.88	8.111	7.891
9	6.711	12.07	6.618	12.24	9.125	8.877

* EXAMPLE: 1 horsepower = 0.7457 kilowatts.

Density Equivalents and Conversion Factors *

Equivalents					Conversion factors				
Grams per cu cm	Lb per cu in.	Lb per cu ft	Short tons (2,000 lb) per cu yd	Lb per U.S. gal		Grams per cu cm to lb per cu ft	Lb per cu ft to grams per cu cm	Grams per cu cm to short tons per cu yd	Short tons per cu yd to grams per cu cm
1	0.03613	62.43	0.8428	8.345	1	62.43	0.01602	0.8428	1.187
	$\bar{2}.55787$	1.79539	$\bar{1}.92572$	0.92143	2	124.86	0.03204	1.6856	2.373
27.68	**1**	1728	23.33	231	3	187.28	0.04805	2.5283	3.560
1.44217		3.23754	1.36792	2.36361	4	249.71	0.06407	3.3711	4.746
0.01602	0.0_35787	**1**	0.0135	0.1337	5	312.14	0.08009	4.2139	5.933
$\bar{2}.20466$	$\bar{4}.76245$		$\bar{2}.13033$	$\bar{1}.12613$	6	374.57	0.09611	5.0567	7.119
1.187	0.04287	74.07	**1**	9.902	7	437.00	0.11213	5.8995	8.306
0.07428	$\bar{2}.63212$	1.86964		0.99572	8	499.43	0.12814	6.7423	9.492
0.1198	0.004329	7.481	0.1010	**1**	9	561.85	0.14416	7.5850	10.679
$\bar{1}.07855$	$\bar{3}.63639$	0.87396	$\bar{1}.00432$		10	624.28	0.16018	8.4278	11.866

* Example: 1 gm per cu cm = 62.43 lb per cu ft.

Thermal Conductivity

Calories per sec per sq cm per cm per deg C	Watts per sq cm per cm per deg C	Calories per hr per sq cm per cm per deg C	Btu per hr per sq ft per ft per deg F	Btu per day per sq ft per in. per deg F
1	4.187	3,600	241.9	69,670
0.2388	1	860	57.79	16,641
0.0002778	0.001163	1	0.0672	19.35
0.004134	0.01731	14.88	1	288
0.00001435	0.00006009	0.05167	0.00347	1

Thermal Conductance

Calories per sec per sq cm per deg C	Watts per sq cm per deg C	Calories per hr per sq cm per deg C	Btu per hr per sq ft per deg F	Btu per day per sq ft per deg F
1	4.187	3,600	7,373	176,962
0.2388	1	860	1,761	42,267
0.0002778	0.001163	1	2.048	49.16
0.0001356	0.0005678	0.4882	1	24
0.000005651	0.00002366	0.02034	0.04167	1

Heat Flow

Calories per sec per sq cm	Watts per sq cm	Calories per hr per sq cm	Btu per hr per sq ft	Btu per day per sq ft
1	4.187	3,600	13,272	318,531
0.2388	1	860	3,170	76,081
0.0002778	0.001163	1	3.687	88.48
0.00007535	0.0003154	0.2712	1	24
0.000003139	0.00001314	0.01130	0.04167	1

Time

Kinds of Time. Three kinds of time are recognized by astronomers: sidereal, apparent solar, and mean solar time. The **sidereal day** is the interval between two consecutive transits of some fixed celestial object across any given meridian, or it is the interval required by the earth to make one complete revolution on its axis. This interval is constant, but it is inconvenient as a time unit because the noon of the sidereal day occurs at all hours of the day and night. The **apparent solar day** is the interval between two consecutive transits of the sun across any given meridian. On account of the variable distance between the sun and earth, the variable speed of the earth in its orbit, the effect of the moon, etc., this interval is not constant and consequently cannot be kept by any simple mechanism, such as clocks or watches. To overcome the objection noted above, the **mean solar day** was devised. The mean solar day is the length of the average apparent solar day. Like the sidereal day it is constant, and like the apparent solar day its noon always occurs at approximately the same time of day. By international agreement, beginning Jan. 1, 1925, the astronomical day, like the civil day, is from midnight to midnight. The hours of the astronomical day run from 0 to 24, and the hours of the civil day usually run from 0 to 12 A.M. and 0 to 12 P.M. In some countries the hours of the civil day also run from 0 to 24.

The Year. There are three different kinds of year used: the sidereal, the tropical, and the anomalistic. The **sidereal year** is the time taken by the earth to complete one revolution around the sun from a given star to the same star again. Its length is 365 days, 6 hours, 9 minutes, and 9 seconds. The **tropical year** is the time included between two successive passages of the vernal equinox by the sun, and since the equinox moves westward 50.2 seconds of arc a year, the tropical year is shorter by 20 minutes 23 seconds in time than the sidereal year. As the seasons depend upon the earth's position with respect to the equinox, the tropical year is the year of civil reckoning. The **anomalistic year** is the interval between two successive passages of the perihelion, *viz.*, the time of the earth's nearest approach to the sun. The anomalistic year is only used in special calculations in astronomy.

The Second. Although the second is ordinarily defined as 1/86,400 of the mean solar day, this is not sufficiently precise for many scientific purposes. Scientists have adopted more precise definitions for specific purposes: one in terms of the length of the tropical year 1900 and one in terms of a specific atomic frequency.

Frequency is the reciprocal of time; the unit of frequency is the **hertz** (Hz), defined as 1 cps. (See also Table 1, p. 15–5.)

The Calendar. The month depended originally upon the changes of the moon. The Mohammedan nations still use a lunar calendar with years of 12 lunar months, which contain 354 or 355 days in a specified cycle. According to their method of reckoning, the same month falls in different seasons and their calendars gain 1 year on ours about every 33 years. The **Julian calendar** (established 45 B.C. and now seldom used except in astronomy) discards all consideration of the moon and adopts 365¼ days as the true length of the year. The **Gregorian calendar,** now used in most of the civilized world, was adopted in Catholic countries of Europe in 1582 and in Great Britain and her colonies Jan. 1, 1752. For several years prior to the adoption of the Gregorian calendar the calendar year had begun on Mar. 25. When the change was made in Great Britain and her colonies, the year 1751 contained no January or February and no Mar. 1 to 24 inclusive. The calendar year 1751 was, therefore, short of a full year by 83 days. The calendar year 1752 was also 11 days short of a full year as the dates Sept. 3 to 13 inclusive, in that year, were dropped to correct the 11 day error that had accumulated during the use of the Julian calendar. The average length of the Gregorian calendar year is $365\frac{1}{4} - \frac{3}{400}$ days, or 365.2425 days. This is equivalent to 365 days, 5 hours, 49 minutes, 12 seconds. The length of the tropical year is 365.2422 days, or 365 days, 5 hours, 48 minutes, 46 seconds. Thus the Gregorian calendar year is longer than the tropical year by 0.0003 day, or 26 seconds. This difference amounts to 1 day in slightly more than 3,300 years and can properly be neglected.

Standard Time. Prior to 1883, each city of the United States had its own time, which was determined by the time of passage of the sun across the local meridian. A system of standard time had been used since its first adoption by the railroads in 1883 but was first legalized on Mar. 19, 1918, when Congress directed the Interstate Commerce Commission to establish limits of the standard time zones. The contiguous United States, which extends from 65 to 125 deg west longitude, is divided into four zones each of approximately 15 deg of longitude. The first or **Eastern zone** includes all territory between the Atlantic coast and an irregular line drawn from the United States–Canadian boundary just south of Drummond Island, through the Straits of Mackinac and the center of Lake Michigan, along the southern border of Michigan, through the central parts of the states of Indiana, Kentucky, and Tennessee, and along the western boundary of Georgia and the Apalachicola River to the Gulf of Mexico at Apalachicola Bay, Fla. The time of this zone is that of the 75 deg meridian, which is 5 hr slower than Greenwich time. The second or **Central zone** includes all territory between the line mentioned and an irregular line drawn from the United States–Canadian boundary at the boundary line between North Dakota and Montana, along the western and southern borders of North Dakota to the Missouri River, through Phillipsburg, Kans., along the western boundary of Oklahoma and Texas to the Rio Grande River, and to the Mexican border. The time is that of the 90 deg meridian. The third or **Mountain zone** includes all territory between the last-named line and an irregular line drawn from the United States–Canadian boundary at the northwest corner of Montana along the boundary between Montana and Idaho, the Salmon River, the western and southern borders of Idaho, through Utah and along the western border of Arizona to the United States–Mexican boundary on the Colorado River. The time is that of the 105 deg meridian. The fourth or **Pacific zone** includes all territory west of the last-named line to the Pacific coast except Alaska. The time is that of the 120 meridian. A fifth or **Alaska zone** includes Alaska only, the time being that of the 150 deg meridian. Standard time is uniform in each of these zones, and the time in one zone (except Alaska) differs by exactly 1 hr from the zone next to it. However, four different times are actually used in Alaska: Pacific, 120°; Yukon, 135°, Alaska, 150°; and Western Alaska, 165°. **Hawaii** is in the 150-deg zone, 10 hr slower than Greenwich time. Eastern time is observed in the Canal Zone; and Atlantic time, one hour faster than Eastern, is observed in Puerto Rico and the Virgin Islands.

In cities situated on the border line of two zones, the standard time of the easterly zone is commonly used; in such cities when the time is given, it should be specified as Eastern, Central, etc. The system of standard time had been adopted in almost all civilized countries and now is used by ships on the high seas. In many areas, clocks are advanced an hour during summer periods to give **Daylight Saving Time** (DST) instead of standard time.

Terrestrial Gravity

Standard acceleration of gravity is $g^0 = 980.665$ cm per sec per sec, or 32.1740 ft per sec per sec. This value g^0 is assumed to be the value of g at sea level and latitude 45 deg.

Acceleration of Gravity
(U.S. Coast and Geodetic Survey, 1912)

Latitude, deg	g		g/g^0	Latitude, deg	g		g/g^0
	Cm/sec²	Ft/sec²			Cm/sec²	Ft/sec²	
0	978.0	32.088	0.9973	50	981.1	32.187	1.0004
10	978.2	32.093	0.9975	60	981.9	32.215	1.0013
20	978.6	32.108	0.9979	70	982 6	32.238	1.0020
30	979.3	32.130	0.9986	80	983.1	32.253	1.0024
40	980.2	32.158	0.9995	90	983.2	32.258	1.0026

Correction for altitude above sea level: −0.3 cm per sec² for each 1,000 meters; −0.003 ft per sec² for each 1,000 ft.

Specific Gravity and Density

The **specific gravity of a solid or liquid** is the ratio of the mass of the body to the mass of an equal volume of water at some standard temperature. At the present time a temperature of 4 C (39 F) is commonly used by physicists, but the engineer uses 60 F. The specific gravity **of gases** is usually expressed in terms of hydrogen or air.

The **density** of a body is its mass per unit volume. If the gram is used as the unit of mass and the cubic centimeter or milliliter as the unit of volume, the figures representing the density are the same as the specific gravity of the body referred to water at 4 C as unity. The customary unit is pounds per cubic foot.

The specific gravity of liquids is usually measured by means of an hydrometer (see p. 3–54). Special arbitrary hydrometer scales are used in various trades and industries. The most common of these are the API and Baumé. The API (American Petroleum Institute) scale is approved by the American Petroleum Institute, the ASTM, the U.S. Bureau of Mines, and the National Bureau of Standards and is recommended for exclusive use in the United States petroleum industry, superseding the Baumé scale for liquids lighter than water. The relation between API degrees and specific gravity is expressed by the following equation:

$$\text{Degrees API} = \frac{141.5}{\text{sp gr } 60/60 \text{ F}} - 131.5$$

The specific gravities corresponding to the indications of the Baumé hydrometer are given in the following tables.

Specific Gravities at $\frac{60}{60}$ F Corresponding to Degrees API and Weights per U.S. Gallon at 60 F

$$\left(\text{Calculated from the formula, specific gravity} = \frac{141.5}{131.5 + \text{deg API}}\right)$$

Degrees API	Specific gravity	Lb per U.S. gallon	Degrees API	Specific gravity	Lb per U.S. gallon	Degrees API	Specific gravity	Lb per U.S. gallon	Degrees API	Specific gravity	Lb per U.S. gallon
10	1.0000	8.328	33	0.8602	7.163	56	0.7547	6.283	79	0.6722	5.595
11	0.9930	8.270	34	0.8550	7.119	57	0.7507	6.249	80	0.6690	5.568
12	0.9861	8.212	35	0.8498	7.076	58	0.7467	6.216	81	0.6659	5.542
13	0.9792	8.155	36	0.8448	7.034	59	0.7428	6.184	82	0.6628	5.516
14	0.9725	8.099	37	0.8398	6.993	60	0.7389	6.151	83	0.6597	5.491
15	0.9659	8.044	38	0.8348	6.951	61	0.7351	6.119	84	0.6566	5.465
16	0.9593	7.989	39	0.8299	6.910	62	0.7313	6.087	85	0.6536	5.440
17	0.9529	7.935	40	0.8251	6.870	63	0.7275	6.056	86	0.6506	5.415
18	0.9465	7.882	41	0.8203	6.830	64	0.7238	6.025	87	0.6476	5.390
19	0.9402	7.830	42	0.8155	6.790	65	0.7201	5.994	88	0.6446	5.365
20	0.9340	7.778	43	0.8109	6.752	66	0.7165	5.964	89	0.6417	5.341
21	0.9279	7.727	44	0.8063	6.713	67	0.7128	5.934	90	0.6388	5.316
22	0.9218	7.676	45	0.8017	6.675	68	0.7093	5.904	91	0.6360	5.293
23	0.9159	7.627	46	0.7972	6.637	69	0.7057	5.874	92	0.6331	5.269
24	0.9100	7.578	47	0.7927	6.600	70	0.7022	5.845	93	0.6303	5.246
25	0.9042	7.529	48	0.7883	6.563	71	0.6988	5.817	94	0.6275	5.222
26	0.8984	7.481	49	0.7839	6.526	72	0.6953	5.788	95	0.6247	5.199
27	0.8927	7.434	50	0.7796	6.490	73	0.6919	5.759	96	0.6220	5.176
28	0.8871	7.387	51	0.7753	6.455	74	0.6886	5.731	97	0.6193	5.154
29	0.8816	7.341	52	0.7711	6.420	75	0.6852	5.703	98	0.6166	5.131
30	0.8762	7.296	53	0.7669	6.385	76	0.6819	5.676	99	0.6139	5.109
31	0.8708	7.251	54	0.7628	6.350	77	0.6787	5.649	100	0.6112	5.086
32	0.8654	7.206	55	0.7587	6.316	78	0.6754	5.622			

The weights in this table are weights in air at 60 F with humidity 50 percent and pressure 760 mm.

Specific Gravities at $\frac{60}{60}$ F Corresponding to Degrees Baumé for Liquids Lighter than Water and Weights per U.S. Gallon at 60 F

(Calculated from the formula, specific gravity $\frac{60}{60}$ F $= \frac{140}{130 + \text{deg Baumé}}$)

Degrees Baumé	Specific gravity	Lb per gallon	Degrees Baumé	Specific gravity	Lb per gallon	Degrees Baumé	Specific gravity	Lb per gallon	Degrees Baumé	Specific gravity	Lb per gallon
10.0	1.0000	8.328	33.0	0.8589	7.152	55.0	0.7568	6.300	78.0	0.6731	5.602
11.0	0.9929	8.269	34.0	0.8537	7.108	56.0	0.7527	6.266	79.0	0.6699	5.576
12.0	0.9859	8.211	35.0	0.8485	7.065	57.0	0.7487	6.233	80.0	0.6667	5.549
13.0	0.9790	8.153	36.0	0.8434	7.022	58.0	0.7447	6.199	81.0	0.6635	5.522
14.0	0.9722	8.096	37.0	0.8383	6.980	59.0	0.7407	6.166	82.0	0.6604	5.497
15.0	0.9655	8.041	38.0	0.8333	6.939	60.0	0.7368	6.134	83.0	0.6573	5.471
16.0	0.9589	7.986	39.0	0.8284	6.898	61.0	0.7330	6.102	84.0	0.6542	5.445
17.0	0.9524	7.931	40.0	0.8235	6.857	62.0	0.7292	6.070	85.0	0.6512	5.420
18.0	0.9459	7.877	41.0	0.8187	6.817	63.0	0.7254	6.038	86.0	0.6482	5.395
19.0	0.9396	7.825	42.0	0.8140	6.777	64.0	0.7216	6.007	87.0	0.6452	5.370
20.0	0.9333	7.772	43.0	0.8092	6.738	65.0	0.7179	5.976	88.0	0.6422	5.345
21.0	0.9272	7.721	44.0	0.8046	6.699	66.0	0.7143	5.946	89.0	0.6393	5.320
22.0	0.9211	7.670	45.0	0.8000	6.661	67.0	0.7107	5.916	90.0	0.6364	5.296
23.0	0.9150	7.620	46.0	0.7955	6.623	68.0	0.7071	5.886	91.0	0.6335	5.272
24.0	0.9091	7.570	47.0	0.7910	6.586	69.0	0.7035	5.856	92.0	0.6306	5.248
25.0	0.9032	7.522	48.0	0.7865	6.548	70.0	0.7000	5.827	93.0	0.6278	5.225
26.0	0.8974	7.473	49.0	0.7821	6.511	71.0	0.6965	5.798	94.0	0.6250	5.201
27.0	0.8917	7.425	50.0	0.7778	6.476	72.0	0.6931	5.769	95.0	0.6222	5.178
28.0	0.8861	7.378	51.0	0.7735	6.440	73.0	0.6897	5.741	96.0	0.6195	5.155
29.0	0.8805	7.332	52.0	0.7692	6.404	74.0	0.6863	5.712	97.0	0.6167	5.132
30.0	0.8750	7.286	53.0	0.7650	6.369	75.0	0.6829	5.685	98.0	0.6140	5.110
31.0	0.8696	7.241	54.0	0.7609	6.334	76.0	0.6796	5.657	99.0	0.6114	5.088
32.0	0.8642	7.196				77.0	0.6763	5.629	100.0	0.6087	5.066

Specific Gravities at $\frac{60}{60}$ F Corresponding to Degrees Baumé for Liquids Heavier than Water

(Calculated from the formula, specific gravity $\frac{60}{60}$ F $= \frac{145}{145 - \text{deg Baumé}}$)

Degrees Baumé	Specific gravity	Degrees Baumé	Specific gravity	Degrees Baumé	Specific gravity	Degrees Baumé	Specific gravity	Degrees Baumé	Specific gravity	Degrees Baumé	Specific gravity
0	1.0000	12	1.0902	24	1.1983	36	1.3303	48	1.4948	60	1.7059
1	1.0069	13	1.0985	25	1.2083	37	1.3426	49	1.5104	61	1.7262
2	1.0140	14	1.1069	26	1.2185	38	1.3551	50	1.5263	62	1.7470
3	1.0211	15	1.1154	27	1.2288	39	1.3679	51	1.5426	63	1.7683
4	1.0284	16	1.1240	28	1.2393	40	1.3810	52	1.5591	64	1.7901
5	1.0357	17	1.1328	29	1.2500	41	1.3942	53	1.5761	65	1.8125
6	1.0432	18	1.1417	30	1.2609	42	1.4078	54	1.5934	66	1.8354
7	1.0507	19	1.1508	31	1.2719	43	1.4216	55	1.6111	67	1.8590
8	1.0584	20	1.1600	32	1.2832	44	1.4356	56	1.6292	68	1.8831
9	1.0662	21	1.1694	33	1.2946	45	1.4500	57	1.6477	69	1.9079
10	1.0741	22	1.1789	34	1.3063	46	1.4646	58	1.6667	70	1.9333
11	1.0821	23	1.1885	35	1.3182	47	1.4796	59	1.6860	......	....

Mohs Scale of Hardness

1. Talc.
2. Gypsum.
3. Calc-spar.
4. Fluorspar.
5. Apatite.
6. Feldspar.
7. Quartz.
8. Topaz.
9. Sapphire.
10. Diamond.

SECTION 2

MATHEMATICS

BY

PHILIP FRANKLIN, Professor of Mathematics, Massachusetts Institute of Technology.

THEODORE BAUMEISTER, III, Development Department, E. I. duPont de Nemours and Co., Inc.

MARTHA C. BAUMEISTER, Instructor, Department of Mathematics, University of Delaware.

CONTENTS

References (for Automatic Computing Machines, see page 2–99): Brenke, "Plane and Spherical Trigonometry," Dryden. Fine and Thompson, "Coordinate Geometry," Macmillan. Fine, "College Algebra," Ginn. Franklin, "Differential and Integral Calculus," McGraw-Hill. Franklin, "Methods of Advanced Calculus," McGraw-Hill. Hildebrand, "Introduction to Numerical Analysis," McGraw-Hill. Sokolnikoff and Sokolnikoff, "Higher Mathematics for Engineers and Physicists," McGraw-Hill. "Handbook of Mathematical Functions," NBS.

ARITHMETIC

BY

Philip Franklin

NUMERICAL COMPUTATION

Number of Significant Figures. In any engineering computation, the data are ordinarily the result of measurement and are correct only to a limited number of significant figures. Each of the numbers 3.840 and 0.003840 is said to be given "correct to four figures"; the true value lies in the first case between 3.8395 and 3.8405; in the second case, between 0.0038395 and 0.0038405. The **absolute error** is less than 0.001 in the first case, and less than 0.000001 in the second; but the **relative error** is the same in both cases, namely, an error of less than "one part in 3,840."

If a number is written as 384,000, the reader is left in doubt whether the number of correct significant figures is 3, 4, 5, or 6. This doubt can be removed by writing the number as 3.84×10^5, or 3.840×10^5, or 3.8400×10^5, or 3.84000×10^5.

In any numerical computation, the possible or desirable degree of accuracy should be decided on and the computation should then be so arranged that the required number of significant figures, and no more, is secured. Carrying out the work to a larger number of places than is justified by the data is to be avoided, (1) because the form of the results leads to an erroneous impression of their accuracy and (2) because time and labor are wasted in superfluous computation. The labor of working with six-place tables is nearly three times as great as that with four-place tables. In computations involving several steps, it is desirable to retain one extra figure until just before the final result is reached, in order to protect the last figure against the possible cumulative effect of small tabular errors. In **discarding superfluous figures,** if the first discarded figure is 5 or more, increase the preceding figure by 1. Thus, 3.14159, written correct to four figures, is 3.142; correct to three figures, 3.14. Again, 6.1297, correct to four figures, is 6.130.

Addition. In adding numbers, note that a doubtful final figure in any one number will render doubtful the whole column in which the figure lies; hence all figures to the right of that column are superfluous and contribute nothing to the accuracy of the result.

```
  0.2056x
  2.572xx
 14.25xxx
576.1xxxx
---------
593.1
```

Subtraction. The Austrian or "shop" method is recommended. The mental process is as follows, the figures here printed in boldface type being the only ones written down:

(3 plus how many is 12?) 3 plus **9** is 12; 1 to carry.
(7 plus how many is 15?) 7 plus **8** is 15; 1 to carry.
5 plus **2** is 7. 8 plus **6** is 14.

```
14752
 8463
~~~~~
 6289
```

This method is especially useful when it is desired to subtract from a given number the sum of several other numbers.

7 plus 1 is 8; plus 5 is 13; plus **9** is 22; 2 to carry.
5 plus 0 is 5; plus 2 is 7; plus **8** is 15; 1 to carry.
3 plus 1 is 4; plus 1 is 5; plus **2** is 7.
5 plus 3 is 8; plus **6** is 14.

```
14752
 3125 ┐
  101 │
 5237 ┘
~~~~~
 6289
```

The use of a wavy line to indicate subtraction is also recommended, as it will minimize the danger of adding when subtraction is intended.

Multiplication. In long examples in multiplication, the arrangement of work here illustrated is recommended, since it facilitates the abbreviation of the work by the omission, in practice, of all the figures on the right of the vertical line.

```
 4956
 8372
39648
 1486|8
  346|92
    9|912
41492|xxx
```

The **position of the decimal point** should be determined by reference to the first, or left-hand, figures of the numbers, rather than by "pointing off" so-and-so many places from the right-hand end. For the right-hand figures of a number are the least important ones, and in many cases are entirely unknown (especially when the slide rule or a desk calculator is used). The mental process for determining the decimal point is as follows:

1. If the multiplier is a number like 3.1416, with only one figure preceding the decimal point, think of this number as "a little over 3"; then the product must be "a little over three times the number which is being multiplied"; and this gives the position of the decimal point at once, by inspection.

2. If the multiplier is a number like 3,141.6 (or 0.000 003 141 6), think of this number as "about 3, with the point moved three places to the right" (or "about 3, with the point moved six places to the left"); then think what the answer would be if the multiplier were simply "about 3," and shift the decimal point accordingly.

Multiplication Tables. Crelle's large volume (Reimer, Berlin) gives the product of every three-figure number by every three-figure number; Peters (Reimer, Berlin), of every four-figure number by every two-figure number.

Division. In long division, where the numbers are given only approximately, the work can be much abbreviated without loss of accuracy by "cutting off" one figure of the divisor at each step, instead of "bringing down" a doubtful zero in the dividend. Thus, $3.1416 \div 2.3026 = 1.3644$.

```
23026)31416(1
      23026
 2303) 8390(3
       6909
  230) 1481(6
       1380
   23)  101(4
         92
    2)    9(4
```

To determine the **position of the decimal point** in a problem of fractional division, shift the point (mentally) in both numerator and denominator (the same number of places in each) until the denominator is a number in the "standard form," *i.e.*, a number with only one figure preceding the decimal point. (This will not change the value of the fraction.) Then estimate the approximate magnitude of the quotient by inspection. Thus:

$$\frac{0.2718}{3141.6} = \frac{0.000\ 2718}{3.1416} = \text{“about 0.000 09”} = 0.000\ 08652$$

$$\frac{31.416}{0.002718} = \frac{31{,}416}{2.718} = \text{“about 10,000”} = 11{,}558$$

Reciprocals. The reciprocal of N is $1/N$. Instead of dividing by a long number N, it is often better to multiply by the reciprocal of N. The table on pp. 1–24 to 1–27 gives the reciprocal of any number, correct to four figures. Barlow's table (Spon & Chamberlain, New York) gives the reciprocal of every four-figure number correct to seven figures (but without facilities for interpolation). The reciprocals of numbers having more than four figures are best found by the use of a large table of logarithms or a desk calculator with automatic division.

Reciprocals of $1 \pm x$ When x Is Small

$1/(1 + x) = 1 - x +$ (error $< x^2$, if x is between 0 and 1),
$\qquad\quad = 1 - x + x^2 -$ (error $< x^3$, if x is between 0 and 1).
$1/(1 - x) = 1 + x +$ (error $< x^2 + 2x^3$, if x is between 0 and $\frac{1}{2}$),
$\qquad\quad = 1 + x + x^2 +$ (error $< x^3 + 2x^4$, if x is between 0 and $\frac{1}{2}$).

NOTE. $1/(a \pm b) = (1/a)[1/(1 \pm x)]$, where $x = b/a$.

Notation by Powers of 10. All questions concerning the position of the decimal point are readily answered if each number is expressed in the "standard form," *i.e.*, as the product of two factors, one of which is a number with only one figure preceding the decimal point, while the other is a positive or negative power of 10. Thus, 3.1416×10^3 means 3.1416 with the point moved three places to the right, that is, 3141.6. Again,

3.1416×10^{-6} means 3.1416 with the point moved six places to the left, *i.e.*, 0.000 003 1416. This notation by powers of 10 should always be used in dealing with very large or very small numbers. Among electrical engineers its use is very general, even for numbers of moderate size.

Square Root. (1) If four figures of the root are sufficient, take the answer directly from the table of square roots, pp. 1–12 to 1–15. (2) To obtain a root of six or seven figures, use the formula: $\sqrt{N} = a + [(N - a^2)/2a]$ (approx), where a is the nearest value of $\sqrt{N}$ obtainable from the table, with three or four ciphers annexed. Here a^2 must be found exactly, by direct multiplication, so that at least three significant figures of the difference $N - a^2$ shall be known correctly; but this done, the division of $N - a^2$ by $2a$ should be carried to only three figures (logarithms or slide rule may be used).

NOTE. The simplest way to obtain any root of a seven-figure number correct to seven figures is to use a seven-place table of logarithms, if such a table is at hand.

Square Roots of 1 ± x When x Is Small

$$(1 + x)^{1/2} = 1 + \tfrac{1}{2}x - \text{(error less than } \tfrac{1}{8}x^2 \text{ if } 0 < x < 1),$$
$$= 1 + \tfrac{1}{2}x - \tfrac{1}{8}x^2 + \text{(error} < \tfrac{1}{16}x^3 \text{ if } 0 < x < 1).$$
$$(1 - x)^{1/2} = 1 - \tfrac{1}{2}x - \text{(error} < \tfrac{1}{8}x^2 + \tfrac{1}{10}x^3 \text{ if } 0 < x < \tfrac{1}{2}),$$
$$= 1 - \tfrac{1}{2}x - \tfrac{1}{8}x^2 - \text{(error} < \tfrac{1}{16}x^3 + \tfrac{1}{16}x^4 \text{ if } 0 < x < \tfrac{1}{2}).$$

NOTE. $\sqrt{a + b} = \sqrt{a}\,(1 + x)^{1/2}$, where $x = b/a$.

Cube Root. (1) If four figures of the root are sufficient, take the answer directly from the table of cube roots, pp. 1–16 to 1–21. (2) To obtain a root of six or seven figures, use the formula: $\sqrt[3]{N} = a + [(N - a^3)/3a^2]$ (approx), where a is the nearest value of $\sqrt[3]{N}$ obtainable from the table, with three or four ciphers annexed. Here a^3 must be found correct to seven or eight figures, by direct multiplication, so that at least three significant figures of the difference $N - a^3$ shall be known; but this done, the division of $N - a^3$ by $3a^2$ should be carried to only three or four figures (logarithms or the slide rule may be used).

NOTE. The simplest way to obtain any root of a seven-figure number correct to seven figures is to use a seven-place table of logarithms, if such a table is at hand.

Cube Roots of 1 ± x When x Is Small

$$(1 + x)^{1/3} = 1 + \tfrac{1}{3}x - \text{(error} < \tfrac{1}{9}x^2 \text{ if } 0 < x < 1),$$
$$= 1 + \tfrac{1}{3}x - \tfrac{1}{9}x^2 + \text{(error} < \tfrac{1}{16}x^3 \text{ if } 0 < x < 1).$$
$$(1 - x)^{1/3} = 1 - \tfrac{1}{3}x - \text{(error} < \tfrac{1}{9}x^2 + \tfrac{1}{10}x^3 \text{ if } 0 < x < \tfrac{1}{2}),$$
$$= 1 - \tfrac{1}{3}x - \tfrac{1}{9}x^2 - \text{(error} < \tfrac{1}{16}x^3 + \tfrac{1}{15}x^4 \text{ if } 0 < x < \tfrac{1}{2}).$$

NOTE. $\sqrt[3]{a + b} = \sqrt[3]{a}(1 + x)^{1/3}$, where $x = b/a$.

LOGARITHMS

Tables of Logarithms. The use of a table of logarithms greatly reduces the labor of multiplication, division, raising to powers, and extracting roots. The table on pp. 1–42 to 1–43 is carried out to four significant figures, and the following explanations should be sufficient to permit the use of the table readily, even by one without previous experience. For algebraic theory, see p. 2–25.

If more than four-figure accuracy is required, recourse must be had to a larger table. Five-place tables are available in great variety. If more than five figures are required, use a seven-place table: Schrön (Vieweg & Sohn, Braunschweig); Bruhns; Vega-Bremiker. If extreme accuracy is required, use the eight-place table by Bauschinger and Peters (Engelmann, Leipzig). For logarithmic paper, see p. 2–86.

To Find the Logarithm of Any Given (Positive) Number

1. WHEN THE GIVEN NUMBER IS BETWEEN 1 AND 10. An inspection of the table on pp. 1–42 to 1–43 shows that as the number increases from 1 to 9.99 . . . the logarithm of that number increases continuously from 0 to 0.999 . . . For example, log 2.97 = 0.4728; log 2.98 = 0.4742.

If the given number contains four significant figures, it is necessary to interpolate between the tabulated values, as follows:

To find log 2.973, notice that this number is $\frac{3}{10}$ of the way from 2.97 to 2.98; hence its logarithm will be (approx) $\frac{3}{10}$ of the way from 0.4728 to 0.4742. The difference here is 14 units, and $\frac{3}{10}$ of this difference is 4 (to the nearest unit); hence, by adding this 4 to 4728, log 2.973 = 0.4732. This process of interpolating should be performed mentally; the step of finding the tabular difference will be facilitated by a glance at the last column on the right, which gives, for each line of the table, the average of the differences along that line.

Again, to find log 4.098: From table, log 4.09 = 0.6117; adding $\frac{8}{10}$ of the difference (11), or about 9, gives: log 4.098 = 0.6126. Or better, since $\frac{8}{10}$ of the way forward is equal to $\frac{2}{10}$ of the way back, find in table log 4.10 = 0.6128, and *subtract* $\frac{2}{10}$ of 11, or 2, giving log 4.098 = 0.6126. It should be noted that any interpolated value may be in error by 1 in the last place.

If the given number contains more than four significant figures, it should be cut down to four figures (see p. 2–2), since the later figures will not affect the result in four-place computations.

2. When the given number is less than 1 or more than 10, it is simply necessary to notice that every such number can be regarded as obtainable from some number between 1 and 10 by merely shifting the decimal point (see p. 2–3); and that according to the rule at the foot of the table, moving the decimal point n places to the right (or left) in the number-column is equivalent to adding n (or $-n$) to the logarithm in the body of the table.

For example, to find log 2,973. Here 2,973 = 2.973×10^3 (*i.e.*, 2.973 with the decimal point moved 3 places to the right). From the table, log 2.973 = 0.4732. Hence, log 2,973 = 0.4732 + 3, which may be written as 3.4732.

Again, to find log 0.0002973. Here 0.0002973 = 2.973×10^{-4} (*i.e.*, 2.973 with the decimal point moved 4 places to the left). From the table, log 2.973 = 0.4732. Hence, log 0.0002973 = 0.4732 − 4. (This may be written as $\bar{4}.4732$, if desired, and is equal, of course, to −3.5268; this latter form, however, is not convenient in practice.)

It is thus evident that the logarithm of every positive number may be regarded as consisting of two parts: a decimal fraction, which is always positive (or zero); and a whole number, which may be positive, negative, or zero. The fractional part is called the **mantissa,** and is found from the table; the whole-number part is called the **characteristic,** and is determined by inspection.

To Find the Number Corresponding to a Given Logarithm

1. When the given logarithm is a positive decimal fraction (characteristic zero), simply reverse the process for finding the logarithm of a number between 1 and 10.

For example, given log N = 0.4732; to find N. In the body of the table it is seen that 0.4732 lies a little beyond 0.4728; hence N must lie a little beyond 2.97. By taking differences it is found that 0.4732 is in fact $\frac{4}{14}$ of the way from 0.4728 to the next higher logarithm; therefore, N must be $\frac{4}{14}$ of the way from 2.97 to the next higher number. But $\frac{4}{14}$ of 1 is 0.3 (to the nearest tenth), hence N = 2.973.

Again, given log N = 0.6126; to find N. Here, 0.6126 is $\frac{9}{11}$ of the way from 0.6117 to the next higher logarithm; therefore, N must be $\frac{9}{11}$ of the way from 4.09 to the next higher number. But $\frac{9}{11}$ of 1 is 0.8 (to the nearest tenth), hence N = 4.098.

2. When the given logarithm has any given value (characteristic not zero), proceed as follows: First, be sure the given logarithm is in the "standard form," *i.e.*, a positive decimal fraction (mantissa) plus a positive or negative whole number (characteristic). For example, if log N is originally given in the form log N = −3.5268, this must first be reduced to the (equivalent) form log N = 0.4732 − 4 (or $\bar{4}.4732$), before entering the table. Having the logarithm given in the standard form, suppose for the moment that the characteristic is zero, and find in the table the number corresponding to the given mantissa; then move the decimal point to the right or left according as the value of the characteristic is positive or negative.

For example, given log N = 0.4732 + 3; to find N. From the table, the number corresponding to 0.4732 is 2.973. The characteristic (+3) directs that the decimal point be moved 3 places to the right; hence N = 2.973×10^3 = 2,973.

Again, given log N = 0.4732 − 4; to find N. From the table, the number corresponding to 0.4732 is 2.973. The characteristic (−4) indicates that the decimal point is to be moved 4 places to the left; hence $N = 2.973 \times 10^{-4} = 0.0002973$.

The number corresponding to a given logarithm is called its **antilogarithm.** Thus, if log 2,973 = 0.4732 + 3, then 2973 = antilog (0.4732 + 3).

NOTE 1. In most tables of logarithms the decimal point is omitted, the tables being in fact not tables of logarithms, but tables of mantissas. This omission is of no consequence to the experienced computer but is often perplexing to one who makes only occasional use of such tables.

NOTE 2. Many computers prefer to write negative characteristics in the form of some positive number minus some multiple of 10; thus, 0.4732 − 4 = 6.4732 − 10; 0.4732 − 13 = 7.4732 − 20; etc.

Fundamental Properties of Logarithms. The usefulness of logarithms in computation depends on the following properties:

$$\log(ab) = \log a + \log b$$
$$\log(a/b) = \log a - \log b$$
$$\log(a^n) = n \log a$$
$$\log \sqrt[n]{a} = (1/n) \log a$$
$$\log 10^n = n$$

It is to be noted also that log 1 = 0, log 10 = 1, and log $(1/a) = -\log a$.

To Multiply by Logarithms. Find from the table the log of each factor, and add; the result will be the log of the product. Then find the product itself from the table.

EXAMPLE. Find $x = (4.098)(0.0002973)(72.1)$

Answer: $x = 8.784 \times 10^{-2} = 0.08784$

$$\begin{aligned} \log 4.098 &= 0.6126 \\ \log 0.0002973 &= 0.4732 - 4 \\ \log 72.1 &= \underline{0.8579 + 1} \\ \log x &= 1.9437 - 3 = 0.9437 - 2. \end{aligned}$$

To Divide by Logarithms. Method 1. Find from the table the log of the numerator and the log of the denominator, and subtract the second from the first; the result will be the logarithm of the quotient. Then find the quotient itself from the table.

EXAMPLE. Find $x = \dfrac{4.098}{0.0002973}$

Answer: $x = 1.378 \times 10^4 = 13780$

$$\begin{aligned} \log 4.098 &= 0.6126 \\ \log 0.0002973 &= \underline{0.4732 - 4} \\ \log x &= 0.1394 + 4 \end{aligned}$$

In order **to avoid negative mantissas** in cases where a larger mantissa would have to be subtracted from a smaller, modify the upper logarithm by adding and subtracting 1.

EXAMPLE. Find $x = \dfrac{0.0291}{63.4}$

Answer: $x = 4.590 \times 10^{-4} = 0.0004590$

$$\begin{aligned} \log 0.0291 &= 0.4639 - 2 = 1.4639 - 3 \\ \log 63.4 &= \underline{0.8021 + 1} = \underline{0.8021 + 1} \\ \log x &= 0.6618 - 4 \end{aligned}$$

But if the logarithms are written with the characteristics in front, and the "shop method" of subtraction is used (see p. 2-2), then no such special device is here required. Thus:

$$\begin{aligned} \log 0.0291 &= \bar{2}.4639 \\ \log 63.4 &= \underline{1.8021} \\ \log x &= \bar{4}.6618 \end{aligned}$$

To Divide by Logarithms. Method 2. Instead of subtracting the log of a number, it is often convenient to add the **cologarithm** of that number; the colog of N being defined by: colog $N = \log(1/N) = -\log N$.

To find the colog of a number, write the log of the number in the standard form, and subtract it from 1.0000 − 1, as in the following examples:

$$\begin{aligned} & 1.0000 - 1 \\ \log 69.5 &= \underline{0.8420 + 1} \\ \text{colog } 69.5 &= 0.1580 - 2 \end{aligned} \qquad \begin{aligned} & 1.0000 - 1 \\ \log 0.0002973 &= \underline{0.4732 - 4} \\ \text{colog } 0.0002973 &= 0.5268 + 3 \end{aligned}$$

This subtraction should be performed mentally. Thus, to subtract the mantissa, subtract each digit from 9 until the last non-zero digit is arrived at, and subtract this from 10; to subtract the characteristic, follow the regular rule of algebra ("reverse the sign and add"). Hence, if the logarithm itself is already written down, or can be read off from the table without interpolation, the cologarithm can be written down at once, by inspection. The use of cologarithms is not essential in logarithmic computation, but it often facilitates a compact arrangement of the work, especially in cases where the denominator of a fraction is itself the product of two or more factors.

To Find the nth Power of a Number by Logarithms. Find from the table the log of the number, and multiply it by n; the result will be the logarithm of the nth power of that number. Then find the power itself from the tables.

EXAMPLE 1. Find $x = (0.0291)^3$
Answer: $x = 2.464 \times 10^{-5} = 0.00002464$

$$\log 0.0291 = 0.4639 - 2$$
$$\times 3$$
$$\log x = 1.3917 - 6 = 0.3917 - 5$$

EXAMPLE 2. Find $x = (0.0291)^{1.41}$
Answer: $x = 6.825 \times 10^{-3} = 0.006825$

$$\log 0.0291 = 0.4639 - 2 = -1.5361$$
$$\times 1.41$$
$$15361$$
$$61444$$
$$15361$$
$$\log x = -2.1659 = 0.8341 - 3$$

To Find the nth Root of a Number by Logarithms. Find from the table the log of the number, and divide it by n; the result will be the log of the nth root of that number. Then find the root itself from the table.

EXAMPLE. Find $x = \sqrt[3]{4.098}$
Answer: $x = 1.600$

$$\log 4.098 = 0.6126$$
$$\log x = 0.2042$$

In order **to avoid fractional characteristics,** if the characteristic is not divisible by n, make it so divisible by adding and subtracting a suitable number before dividing.

EXAMPLE. Find $x = \sqrt[3]{0.0004590}$
Answer: $x = 7.714 \times 10^{-2} = 0.07714$

$$\log 0.0004590 = 0.6618 - \mathbf{4}$$
$$3)\mathbf{2}.6618 - \mathbf{6}$$
$$\log x = 0.8873 - 2$$

But if the characteristic is positive, it is simpler to write it in front of the mantissa, and then divide directly.

THE SLIDE RULE

The slide rule is an indispensable aid in all problems in multiplication, division, proportion, squares, square roots, etc., in which a limited degree of accuracy is sufficient. The ordinary 10 in. Mannheim rule (see below) gives three significant figures correctly; the 20 in. rule gives from three to four figures. For many problems the slide rule gives results more rapidly than a table of logarithms; it requires, however, more care in placing the decimal point in the answer. In all work with the slide rule, the position of the decimal point should be determined by inspection (see p. 2–3), only the sequence of digits being obtained from the instrument itself. Rapidity in the use of the instrument depends mainly on the skill with which the eye can estimate the values of the various divisions on the scale; expertness in this respect comes only with practice. The following explanations should be sufficient to permit the use of the ordinary slide rule successfully without previous experience and without knowledge of logarithms.

Multiplication and Division with a (Theoretical) Complete Logarithmic Scale. Consider a *complete* logarithmic scale (D, Fig. 1), assumed to extend indefinitely in both directions, only the main section, from 1 to 10, however, being usually available. Note that the divisions within the several sections are identical, except that the numeral attached to each division of any one section is ten times the numeral attached to the corresponding division in the preceding section. (The distances laid off from 1 are proportional to the logarithms of the corresponding numbers, the distance from 1 to 10 being taken as unity.) Consider also a duplicate scale C, numbered from 1 to 10, and arranged to slide along the fixed scale D as in the figures. By means of such a scale D and slide C any two numbers between 1 and 10 (and hence any two numbers whatever, with proper attention to the decimal point) can be multiplied or divided, as in the following examples.

TO MULTIPLY 4 BY 6. In Fig. 1, starting with point 1 of the fixed scale, run the eye along from 1 to 4; then set the 1 of the slide opposite this point 4, and *run the eye forward along the slide from* 1 *to* 6; the point thus reached on the fixed scale is 24, which is equal to 4 × 6. This process gives the distance from 1 to 4 *plus* the distance from 1 to 6, and is, in fact, a mechanical method of adding the logarithms of these numbers; hence the result is the product of the numbers.

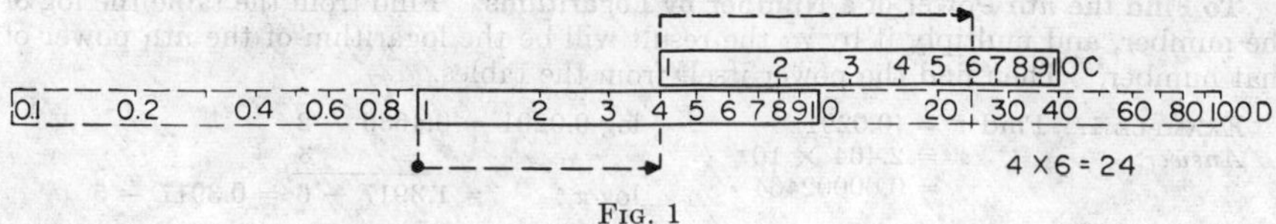

Fig. 1

To Divide 4 by 6. In Fig. 2, starting with the point 1 of the fixed scale, run the eye along from 1 to 4; then set the 6 of the slide opposite the point 4, and *run the eye backward along the slide from* 6 *to* 1; the point thus reached on the fixed scale is 0.667, which is equal to 4 ÷ 6. This process gives the distance from 1 to 4 *minus* the distance from 1 to 6 and is, in fact, a mechanical method of subtracting the logarithms of these numbers; hence the result is their quotient.

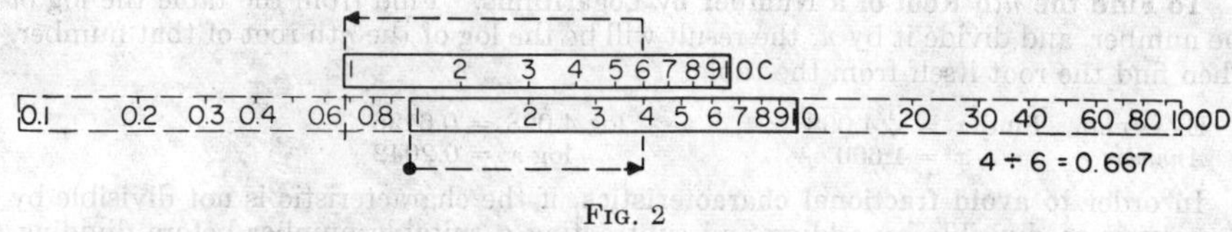

Fig. 2

Multiplication and Division, Using Only a Single Section of the Scale. If only the main section of scale *D* is available (as is usually the case in practice), the result of multiplication may fall beyond the scale, as it does in Fig. 1. In such cases *divide the first factor by* 10 *before beginning to multiply;* this will bring the result within the scale, without affecting the sequence of digits.

For example, to multiply 4 by 6. Having found that the setting shown in Fig. 1 is not successful, *reset the slide as in Fig.* 3, *with* 10 *instead of* 1 *opposite* 4; run the eye backward along the slide from 10 to 1, thus reaching the (unrecorded) point corresponding to 4 ÷ 10; then, continuing from this point, run the eye forward along the slide from 1 to 6, as before; the point finally reached on the main scale is 2.4, which has the same sequence of digits as the required value 24. After a little practice, this preliminary step of dividing by 10 will be performed almost intuitively. Whether or not this step is necessary in any given case can be determined by trial.

The **general rule of multiplication** may be stated as follows: To find the product of two factors, find one factor on the fixed scale; opposite this, set (tentatively) point 1 of the slide; on the slide find the second factor, and opposite this read the product on the main scale, if possible. If the product falls beyond the scale, begin over again, using point 10 of the slide instead of point 1.

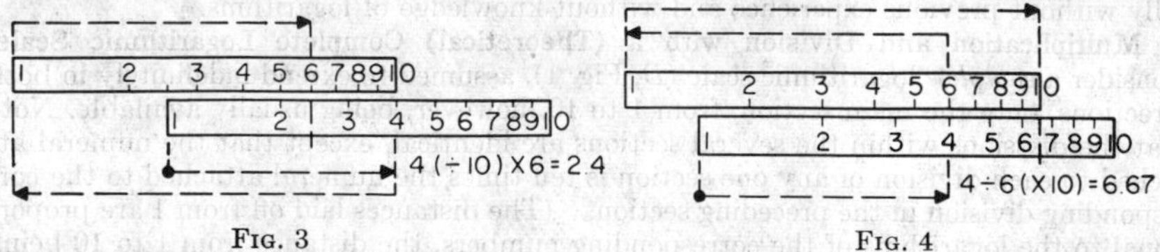

Fig. 3 Fig. 4

In division also, the result may fall beyond the main section of the scale, as it does in Fig. 2. In such cases, it suffices merely to *multiply the result by* 10 in order to bring it within the scale; this will not affect the sequence of digits.

For example, to divide 4 by 6, set the slide as in Fig. 4, and follow out mentally the steps indicated by the arrows. It will be noticed that the supplementary step of multiplying by

10 is performed by simply running the eye along the slide from 1 to 10 without resetting the slide; for this reason, division on the slide rule is slightly easier than multiplication.

The ordinary **Mannheim** slide rule has four scales, A, B, C, D, as shown in Fig. 5. Scales C and D are essentially the same as the C and D scales described above, and the principle just explained shows how they are used in multiplication and division. The fact that the D scale covers only the main section from 1 to 10 (all decimal points being omitted) is practically no restriction on the scope of the scale, as is seen in the preceding examples. A runner is provided, so that intermediate positions reached in the course of an extended computation may be indicated temporarily on the scale without the necessity of reading off their numerical values. The best runners are those which have no side frame to obscure the numerals.

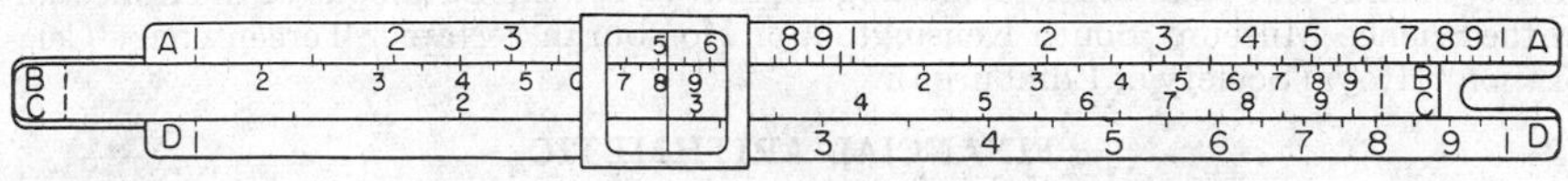

FIG. 5

In problems involving successive multiplications and divisions, arrange the work so that multiplication and division are performed alternately.

For example, to calculate $\frac{a \times b \times c}{d \times e}$, divide the product $a \times b$ by d; multiply this quotient by c; and divide this product by e. Each operation will require only one shifting either of the slide (for multiplication) or of the runner (for division).

To multiply a number of different quantities by a *constant multiplier* x, set the point 1 of slide opposite x, and read, by aid of the runner, the products of x by all the quantities which do not fall beyond the scale; then reset the slide, setting 10 instead of 1 opposite x, and read the products of x by all the remaining quantities.

To divide a number of different quantities by a *constant divisor* y, first find (by the slide rule) the quotient $1 \div y$, and then use this as a constant multiplier.

Scales A and B are exactly like scales C and D, except that they cover two sections of the complete logarithmic scale, the graduations being only half as fine. Either pair of scales may be used for multiplication and division; C and D give more accurate readings, but have the disadvantage that in the case of multiplication the slide must often be shifted to the other end in order to keep the result on the scale—an inconvenience which is not present when the less accurate scales A and B are employed.

By the use of both pairs of scales, problems in squares and square roots may be readily solved; for every number on A, except for the decimal point, is the square of the number directly below it on D (use the runner).

A scale of sines, tangents, and logarithms is often printed on the back of the slide. For further details concerning the use of the slide rule in various problems, see the instruction books furnished with each instrument: Cox, "Manual of the Mannheim Slide Rule"; Halsey, "Manual of the Slide Rule"; etc.

Other Types of Slide Rules. The **duplex slide rule** has two faces providing space for additional fixed as well as movable scales. The slide can be set and points read, on either side, by means of a runner encircling the whole rule with hairlines on each face. The additional scales frequently include inverted scales CI like C but numbered in the reverse order, and folded scales CF, DF, like C and D but starting with $\pi = 3.1416$, bringing the mark for 1 or 10 near the middle of the scale. These scales make possible the solution of more complicated problems with fewer settings of the slide. The **polyphase rule** is constructed like a Mannheim rule with the addition of a CI, or inverted C scale, on the slide and a fixed K scale. The K scale is like the D scale but covers three sections of the complete logarithmic scale, and so may be used with the D scale to find cube roots. The **log log slide rule** is of duplex type and carries on the fixed part a log ln scale in several parts. This may be used directly with the D scale (or B scale for some parts) to read the values of expotentials, e^x or natural logarithms, $\ln x$. And in conjunction with the C (or A scale for some parts) it may be used to find the value of a^b from a single setting, where b may have any (*e.g.*, fractional or negative) value. Scales for reading the hyperbolic sine, sinh x, and hyperbolic tangent, tanh x, are sometimes added. A number of **circular slide rules** are on the market, the best of which are operated by a milled thumbnut, like the stem wind of a watch. The advantage of the circular rule, aside from its compact size (some models are scarcely larger than a watch), lies in the fact that the scale is endless, so that the slide never has to be reset in order to bring the result within the scale. A disadvantage is found in the necessity of reading the figures in oblique positions, or else continually turning the instrument as a whole in the hand. There are also many **special slide rules,** adapted to various special types of computation, such as calculating discharge of water through pipes, horsepower of engines, dimensions of lumber, stadia measurements, and electric circuits. For a description of a large variety of slide rules and other calculating apparatus, see the Catalogue of the Collection in the Science Museum, South Kensington, or Horsburgh, "Napier Tercentenary Celebration" (Royal Society of Edinburgh).

FINANCIAL ARITHMETIC

For the facts that are commonly required in regard to compound interest, sinking funds, etc., see the headings of the tables on pp. 1–64 to 1–68. More extended tables may be found in Glover, "Tables of Applied Mathematics" (Ann Arbor, Mich., 1923).

GEOMETRY AND MENSURATION

BY

Philip Franklin

GEOMETRICAL THEOREMS

(For geometrical constructions, see p. 2–13)

Right Triangles. $a^2 + b^2 = c^2$. (See Fig. 1.) $\angle A + \angle B = 90°$ $p^2 = mn$. $a^2 = mc$. $b^2 = nc$. See also pp. 2–16, 2–43.

Oblique Triangles (see also pp. 2–16, 2–43). Sum of angles = 180°. An exterior angle = sum of the two opposite interior angles (Fig. 1).

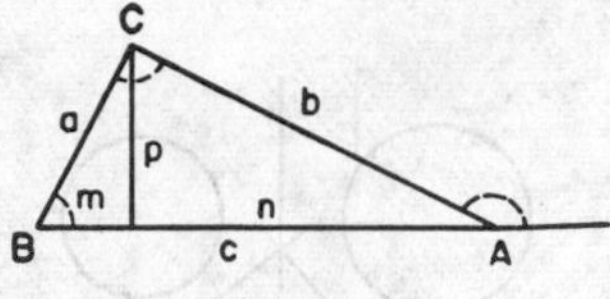

Fig. 1

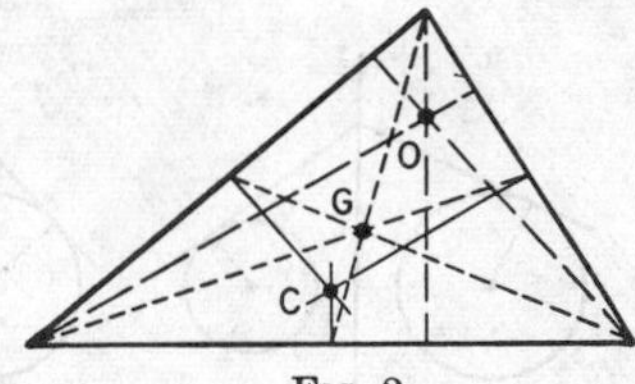

Fig. 2

The medians, joining each vertex with the middle point of the opposite side, meet in the center of gravity G (Fig. 2), which trisects each median.

The altitudes meet in a point called the **orthocenter,** O.

The perpendiculars erected at the mid-points of the sides meet in a point C, the center of the circumscribed circle. (In any triangle G, O, and C lie in line, and G is two-thirds of the way from O to C.)

The bisectors of the angles meet in the center of the inscribed circle (Fig. 3).

The largest side of a triangle is opposite the largest angle; it is less than the sum of the other two sides, and greater than their difference.

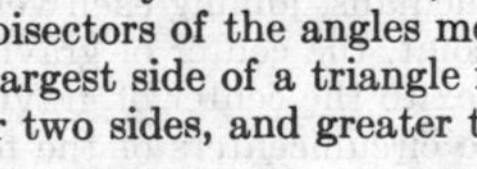

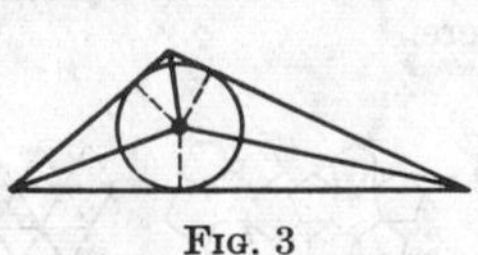

Fig. 3

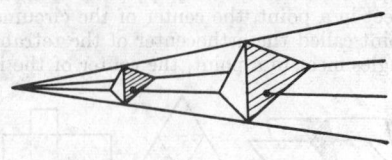

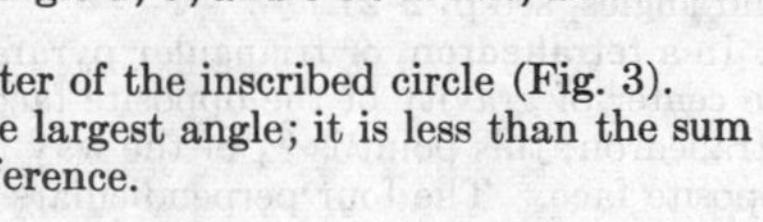

Fig. 4

Similar Figures. Any two similar figures, in a plane or in space, can be placed in "perspective," *i.e.*, so that straight lines joining corresponding points of the two figures will pass through a common point (Fig. 4). That is, of two similar figures, one is merely an enlargement of the other. Assume that each length in one figure is k times the corresponding length in the other; then each area in the first figure is k^2 times the corresponding area in the second, and each volume in the first figure is k^3 times the corresponding volume in the second. If two lines are cut by a set of parallel lines (or parallel planes), the corresponding segments are proportional.

The Circle (see also pp. 2–17, 2–48). An angle inscribed in a semicircle is a right angle (Fig. 5). An angle inscribed in a circle, or an angle between a chord and a tangent, is measured by half the intercepted arc (Fig. 6). An angle formed by any two lines which meet a circle is measured by half the sum or half the difference of the intercepted arcs, according as the point of intersection of the lines lies inside (Fig. 7) or outside the circle (Fig. 8).

A tangent is perpendicular to the radius drawn to the point of contact.

If a variable line through A (Figs. 9 and 10) cuts a circle in P and Q, then $\overline{AP} \times \overline{AQ}$ is constant; in particular, if A is an external point, $\overline{AP} \times \overline{AQ} = \overline{AT}^2$, where AT is the tangent from A.

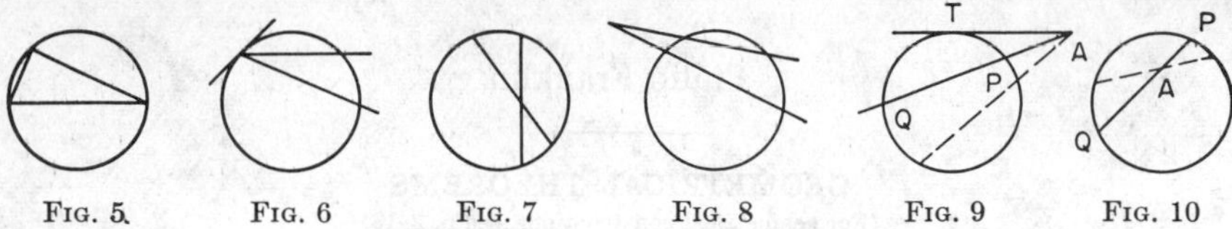

FIG. 5 FIG. 6 FIG. 7 FIG. 8 FIG. 9 FIG. 10

The radical axis (Fig. 11) of two circles is a straight line such that the tangents drawn from any point of this line to the two circles are of equal length. If the two circles intersect, the radical axis passes through their points of intersection. In any case, the radical axis bisects the common tangents of the two circles. The three radical axes of a set of three circles meet in a common point. (For equations, see p. 2–48.)

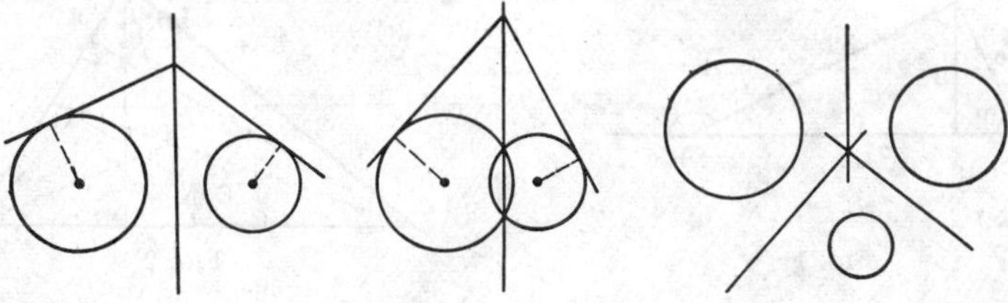

FIG. 11

Dihedral Angles. The dihedral angle between two planes is measured by a plane angle formed by two lines, one in each plane, perpendicular to the edge (Fig. 12). (For solid angles, see p. 2–21.)

In a **tetrahedron,** or triangular pyramid, the four medians, joining each vertex with the center of gravity of the opposite face, meet in a point, the center of gravity of the tetrahedron; this point is ¾ of the way from any vertex to the center of gravity of the opposite face. The four perpendiculars erected at the circumcenters of the four faces meet in a point, the center of the circumscribed sphere. The four altitudes meet in a point called the orthocenter of the tetrahedron. The planes bisecting the six dihedral angles meet in a point, the center of the inscribed sphere.

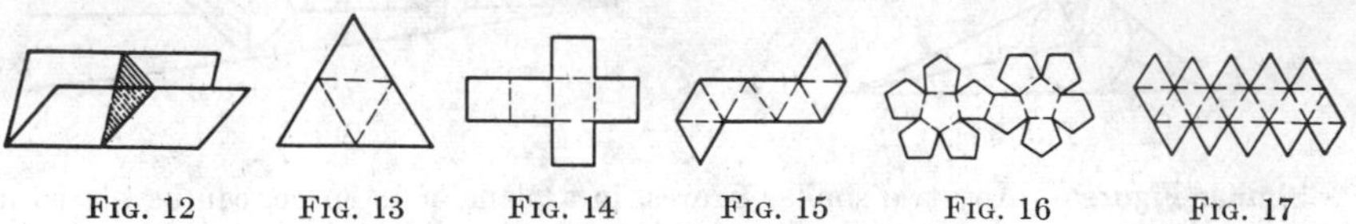

FIG. 12 FIG. 13 FIG. 14 FIG. 15 FIG. 16 FIG. 17

Regular Polyhedra (see also p. 2–21). Regular tetrahedron (Fig. 13), bounded by four equilateral triangles; cube (Fig. 14), bounded by six squares; octahedron (Fig. 15), bounded by eight equilateral triangles; dodecahedron (Fig. 16), bounded by twelve regular pentagons; icosahedron (Fig. 17), bounded by twenty equilateral triangles. Figures 13–17 show how these solids can be made by cutting the surface out of paper and folding it together.

The Sphere (see also p. 2–21). If AB is a diameter, any plane perpendicular to AB cuts the sphere in a circle, of which A and B are called the poles. A great circle on the sphere is formed by a plane passing through the center. A spherical triangle is bounded by arcs of great circles (see p. 2–45). In two polar triangles, each angle in one is the supplement of the corresponding side in the other. In two symmetrical triangles, the sides and angles of one are equal to the corresponding sides and angles of the other, but arranged in the reverse order (like right-handed and left-handed gloves).

GEOMETRICAL CONSTRUCTIONS

To Bisect a Line AB (Fig. 18). (1) From A and B as centers, and with equal radii, describe arcs intersecting in P and Q, and draw PQ, which will bisect AB in M. (2) Lay off $AC = BD$ = approximately half of AB, and then bisect CD.

To Draw a Parallel to a Given Line l **through a Given Point** A (Fig. 19). With point A as center draw an arc just touching the line l; with any point O of the line as

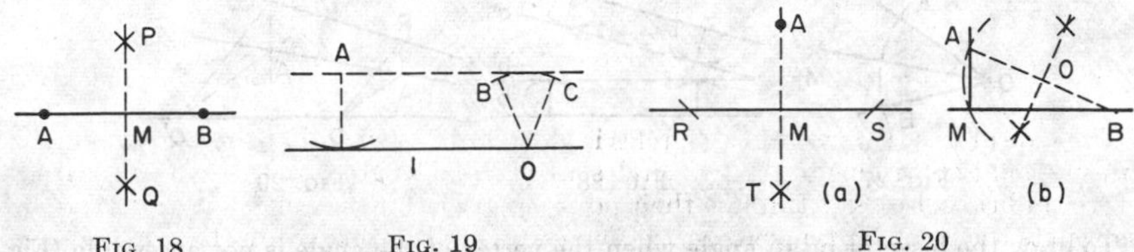

Fig. 18 Fig. 19 Fig. 20

center, draw an arc BC with the same radius. Then a line through A touching this arc will be the required parallel. Or, use a straight edge and triangle. Or, use a sheet of celluloid with a set of lines parallel to one edge and about ¼ in. apart ruled upon it.

To Draw a Perpendicular to a Given Line from a Given Point A **outside the Line** (Fig. 20). (1) With A as center, describe an arc cutting the line in R and S, and bisect RS in M. Then M is the foot of the perpendicular. (2) If A is nearly opposite one end of the line, take any point B of the line and bisect AB in O; then with O as center, and OA or OB as radius, draw an arc cutting the line in M. Or, (3) use a straightedge and triangle.

To Erect a Perpendicular to a Given Line at a Given Point P. (1) Lay off $PR = PS$ (Fig. 21), and with R and S as centers draw arcs intersecting at A. Then PA is the required perpendicular. (2) If P is near the end of the line, take any convenient point O (Fig. 22) above the line as center, and with radius OP draw an arc cutting the line in Q. Produce QO to meet the arc in A; then PA is the required perpendicular. (3) Lay off PB = 4 units of any scale (Fig. 23); from P and B as centers lay off $PA = 3$ and $BA = 5$; then APB is a right angle.

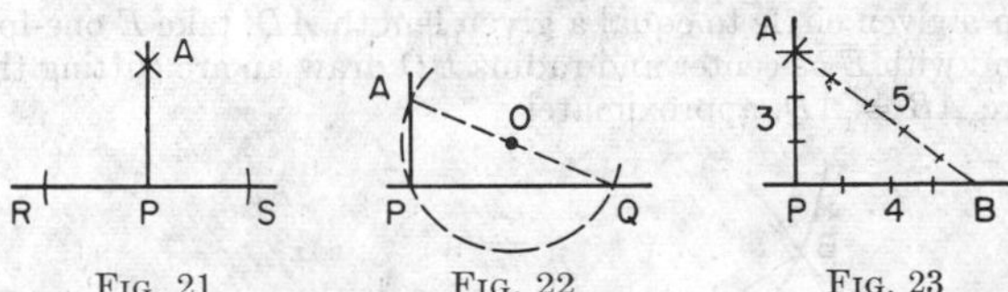

Fig. 21 Fig. 22 Fig. 23

To Divide a Line AB **into** n **Equal Parts** (Fig. 24). Through A draw a line AX at any angle, and lay off n equal steps along this line. Connect the last of these divisions with B, and draw parallels through the other divisions. These parallels will divide the given line into n equal parts. A similar method may be used to divide a line into parts which shall be proportional to any given numbers.

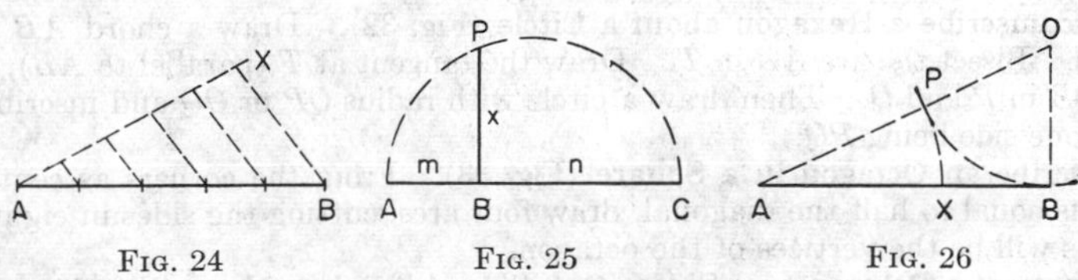

Fig. 24 Fig. 25 Fig. 26

To Construct a Mean Proportional (or Geometric Mean) between Two Lengths, m **and** n (Fig. 25). Lay off $AB = m$ and $BC = n$ and construct a semicircle on AC as diameter. Let the perpendicular erected at B meet the circumference at P. Then $BP = \sqrt{mn}$. (See p. 2–27.)

To Divide a Line AB in Extreme and Mean Ratio (the "golden section"). At one end, B, of the given line (Fig. 26), erect a perpendicular, BO, equal to half AB, and join OA. Along OA lay off $OP = OB$, and along AB lay off $AX = AP$. Then X is the required point of division; *i.e.*, $\overline{AX}^2 = AB \times BX$.

Numerically, $AX = \frac{1}{2}(\sqrt{5} - 1)(AB) = 0.618(AB)$.

To Bisect an Angle AOB (Fig. 27). Lay off $OA = OB$. From A and B as centers, with any convenient radius, draw arcs meeting in M; then OM is the required bisector.

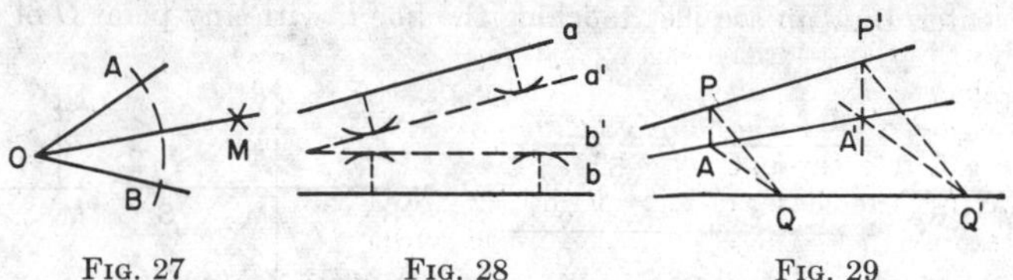

FIG. 27 FIG. 28 FIG. 29

To draw the bisector of an angle when the vertex of the angle is not accessible (Fig. 28). Parallel to the given lines a, b, and equidistant from them, draw two lines a', b' which intersect; then bisect the angle between a' and b'.

To Draw a Line through a Given Point A and in the Direction of the Point of Intersection of Two Given Lines, when this point of intersection is inaccessible (Fig. 29). Draw any two parallel lines PQ and $P'Q'$ as in the figure; through P' draw a line parallel to PA, and through Q' draw a line parallel to QA; let these lines intersect in A', and draw the line AA'. This line AA' will (if produced) pass through the intersection of the two given lines.

To Construct, Approximately, the Length of a Circular Arc (Rankine). In Fig. 30 draw a tangent at A. Prolong the chord BA to C, making $AC = \frac{1}{2}AB$. With C as center, and radius CB, draw an arc cutting the tangent in D. Then AD = arc AB, approximately (error about 4 min in an arc of 60 deg). Conversely, to find an arc AB on a given circle to equal a given length AD, take E one-fourth of the way from A to D, and with E as center and radius ED draw an arc cutting the circumference in B. Then arc $AB = AD$, approximately.

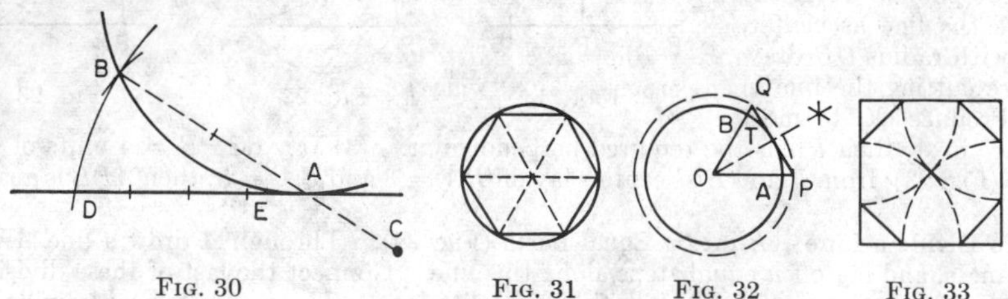

FIG. 30 FIG. 31 FIG. 32 FIG. 33

To Inscribe a Hexagon in a Circle (Fig. 31). Step around the circumference with a chord equal to the radius. Or, use a 60 deg triangle.

To Circumscribe a Hexagon about a Circle (Fig. 32). Draw a chord AB equal to the radius. Bisect the arc AB in T. Draw the tangent at T (parallel to AB), meeting OA and OB in P and Q. Then draw a circle with radius OP or OQ and inscribe in it a hexagon, one side being PQ.

To Inscribe an Octagon in a Square (Fig. 33). From the corners as centers, and with radius equal to half the diagonal, draw four arcs, cutting the sides in eight points. The points will be the vertices of the octagon.

To Construct a Polygon of n Sides, One Side AB Being Given (Fig. 34). With A as center and AB as radius, draw a semicircle, and divide it into n parts, of which $n - 2$ parts (counting from B) are to be used. Draw rays from A through these points of division, and complete the construction as in the figure (in which $n = 7$). Note that the center of the polygon must lie in the perpendicular bisector of each side.

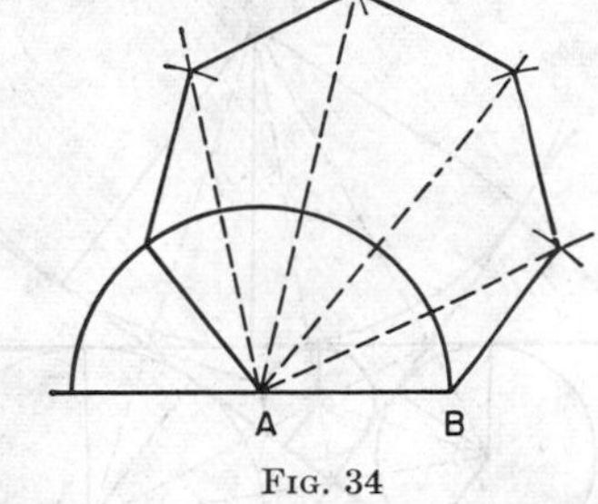

FIG. 34

To Draw a Tangent to a Circle from an external point A (Fig. 35). Bisect AC in M; with M as center and radius MC, draw arc cutting circle in P; then P is the required point of tangency.

To Draw a Common Tangent to Two Given Circles (Fig. 36). Let C and c be the centers and R and r the radii ($R > r$). From C as center, draw two concentric circles with radii $R + r$ and $R - r$; draw tangents to these circles from c; then draw parallels to these lines at distance r. These parallels will be the required common tangents.

To Draw a Circle through Three Given Points A, B, C, or to find the center of a given circular arc (Fig. 37). Draw the perpendicular bisectors of AB and BC; these will meet in the center, O.

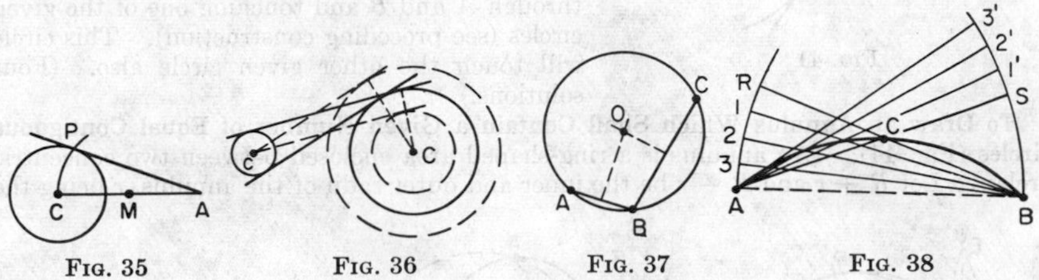

FIG. 35 FIG. 36 FIG. 37 FIG. 38

To Draw a Circular Arc through Three Given Points When the Center Is Not Available (Fig. 38). With A and B as centers, and chord AB as radius, draw arcs, cut by BC in R and by AC in S. Divide RA into n equal parts, 1, 2, 3, ... On BS produced take points 1′, 2′, 3′, . . . to give arcs $S1'$, $1'2'$, etc., all equal to $R1$. . . . Connect A with 1′, 2′, 3′, . . . and B with 1, 2, 3, ... Then the points of intersection of corresponding lines will be points of the required arc.

To Draw a Circle through Two Given Points, A, B, and Touching a Given Line, l (Fig. 39). Let AB meet line l in C. Draw any circle through A and B, and let CT be tangent to this circle from C. Along l, lay off CP and CQ equal to CT. Then either P or Q is the required point of tangency. (Two solutions.) Note that the center of the required circle lies in the perpendicular bisector of AB.

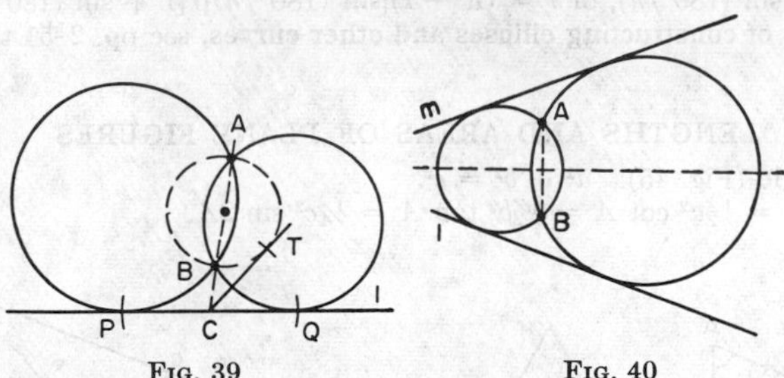

FIG. 39 FIG. 40

To Draw a Circle through One Given Point, A, and Touching Two Given Lines, l and m (Fig. 40). Draw the bisector of the angle between l and m, and let B be the reflection of A in this line. Then draw a circle through A and B and touching l (or m), as in preceding construction. (Two solutions.)

To Draw a Circle Touching Three Given Lines (Fig. 41). Draw the bisectors of the three angles; these will meet in the center O. (Four solutions.) The perpendiculars from O to the three lines give the points of tangency.

To Draw a Circle through Two Given Points A, B, and Touching a Given Circle (Fig. 42). Draw any circle through A and B, cutting the given circle in C and D. Let AB and CD meet in E, and let ET be tangent from E to the circle just drawn. With E as center, and radius ET, draw an arc cutting the given circle in P and Q. Either P or Q is the required point of contact. (Two solutions.)

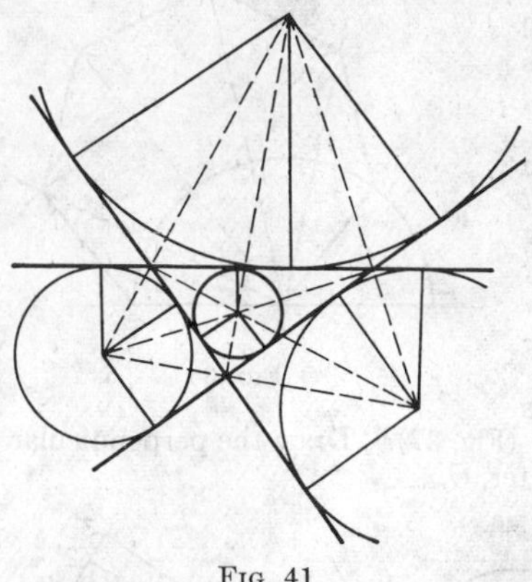

Fig. 41

To Draw a Circle through One Given Point, A, and Touching Two Given Circles (Fig. 43). Let S be a center of similitude for the two given circles, *i.e.*, the point of intersection of two external (or internal) common tangents. Through S draw any line cutting one circle in two points, the nearer of which shall be called P, and the other in two points, the more remote of which shall be called Q. Through A, P, Q draw a circle cutting SA in B. Then draw a circle through A and B and touching one of the given circles (see preceding construction). This circle will touch the other given circle also. (Four solutions.)

To Draw an Annulus Which Shall Contain a Given Number of Equal Contiguous Circles (Fig. 44). (An annulus is a ring-shaped area enclosed between two concentric circles.) Let $R + r$ and $R - r$ be the inner and outer radii of the annulus, r being the

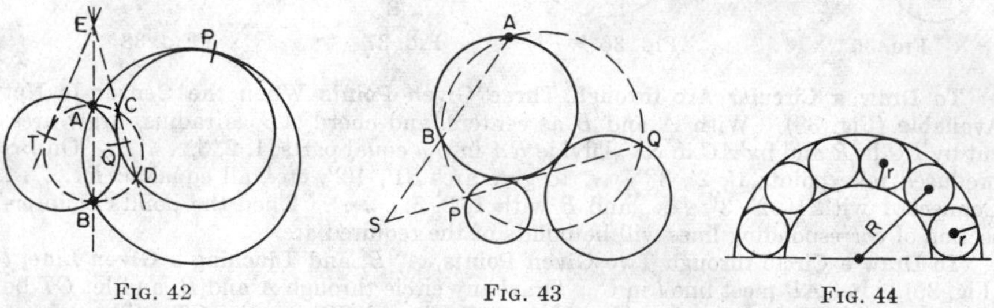

Fig. 42 Fig. 43 Fig. 44

radius of each of the n circles. Then the required relation between these quantities is given by $r = R \sin (180°/n)$, or $r = (R + r)[\sin (180°/n)]/[1 + \sin (180°/n)]$.

For methods of constructing ellipses and other curves, see pp. 2–51 to 2–63.

LENGTHS AND AREAS OF PLANE FIGURES

Right Triangle (Fig. 45). $a^2 + b^2 = c^2$.
Area $= \frac{1}{2}ab = \frac{1}{2}a^2 \cot A = \frac{1}{2}b^2 \tan A = \frac{1}{4}c^2 \sin 2A$.

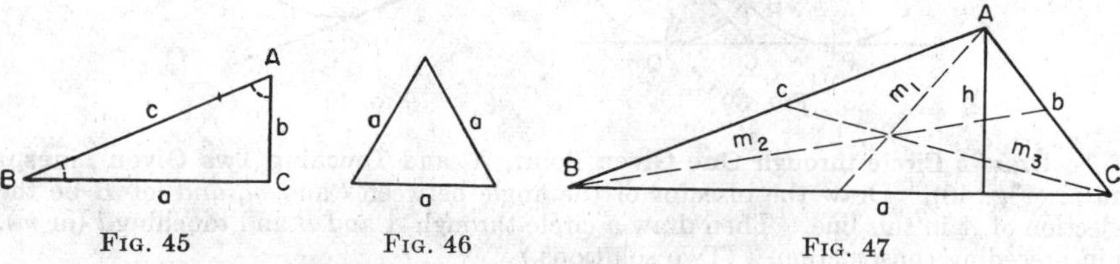

Fig. 45 Fig. 46 Fig. 47

Equilateral Triangle (Fig. 46). Area $= \frac{1}{4}a^2 \sqrt{3} = 0.43301a^2$.
Any Triangle (Fig. 47).

$s = \frac{1}{2}(a + b + c)$, $t = \frac{1}{2}(m_1 + m_2 + m_3)$.
$r = \sqrt{(s - a)(s - b)(s - c)/s}$ = radius inscribed circle.
$R = \frac{1}{2}a/\sin A = \frac{1}{2}b/\sin B = \frac{1}{2}c/\sin C$ = radius circumscribed circle.
Area $= \frac{1}{2}$ base $\times$ altitude $= \frac{1}{2}ah = \frac{1}{2}ab \sin C = rs = abc/4R$,
$= \sqrt{s(s - a)(s - b)(s - c)} = \frac{4}{3}\sqrt{t(t - m_1)(t - m_2)(t - m_3)}$,
$= r^2 \cot \frac{1}{2}A \cot \frac{1}{2}B \cot \frac{1}{2}C = 2R^2 \sin A \sin B \sin C$,
$= \pm\frac{1}{2}\{(x_1y_2 - x_2y_1) + (x_2y_3 - x_3y_2) + (x_3y_1 - x_1y_3)\}$, where (x_1,y_1), (x_2,y_2), (x_3,y_3) are coordinates of vertices. See also p. 2–45.

Rectangle (Fig. 48). Area $= ab = \frac{1}{2}D^2 \sin u$, where u = angle between diagonals D, D.

Rhombus (Fig. 49). Area $= a^2 \sin C = \frac{1}{2}D_1D_2$, where C = angle between two adjacent sides; D_1, D_2 = diagonals.

Parallelogram (Fig. 50). Area $= bh = ab \sin C = \frac{1}{2}D_1D_2 \sin u$, where u = angle between diagonals D_1 and D_2; $D_1^2 = 2(a^2 + b^2)$.

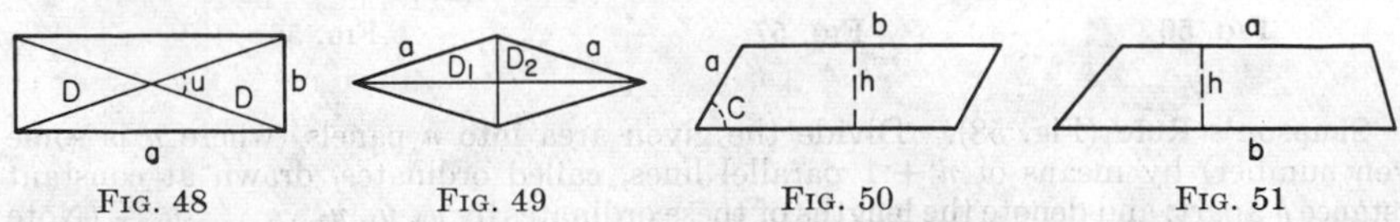

FIG. 48 FIG. 49 FIG. 50 FIG. 51

Trapezoid (Fig. 51). Area $= \frac{1}{2}(a + b)h = \frac{1}{2}D_1D_2 \sin u$, where bases a and b are parallel; u = angle between diagonals D_1 and D_2.

Quadrilateral Inscribed in a Circle (Fig. 52).

Area $= \frac{1}{2}D_1D_2 \sin u = \sqrt{(s - a)(s - b)(s - c)(s - d)} = \frac{1}{2}(ac + bd) \sin u$, where $s = \frac{1}{2}(a + b + c + d)$.

Any Quadrilateral (Fig. 53). Area $= \frac{1}{2}D_1D_2 \sin u$.

NOTE. $a^2 + b^2 + c^2 + d^2 = D_1^2 + D_2^2 + 4m^2$, where m = distance between midpoints of D_1 and D_2.

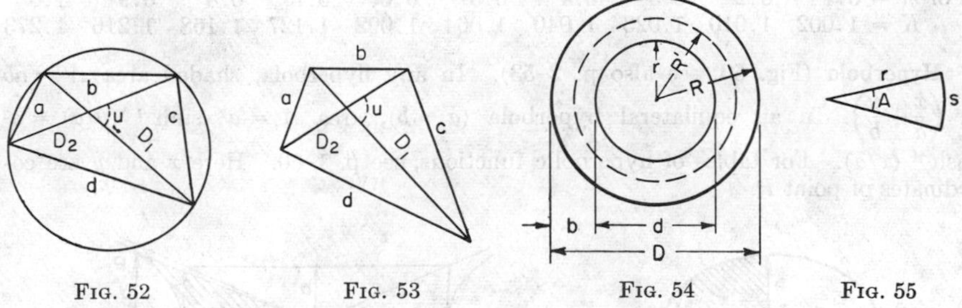

FIG. 52 FIG. 53 FIG. 54 FIG. 55

Polygons. See table, p. 1–39.

Circle. Area $= \pi r^2 = \frac{1}{2}Cr = \frac{1}{4}Cd = \frac{1}{4}\pi d^2 = 0.785398d^2$ (table, p. 1–30), where r = radius, d = diameter, C = circumference $= 2\pi r = \pi d$ (table, p. 1–28).

Annulus (Fig. 54). Area $= \pi(R^2 - r^2) = \pi(D^2 - d^2)/4 = 2\pi R'b$, where R' = mean radius $= \frac{1}{2}(R + r)$, and $b = R - r$.

Sector (Fig. 55). Area $= \frac{1}{2}rs = \pi r^2 A/360° = \frac{1}{2}r^2$ rad A, where rad A = radian measure of angle A, and s = length of arc $= r$ rad A (table, p. 1–44).

Segment (Fig. 56). Area $= \frac{1}{2}r^2(\text{rad } A - \sin A) = \frac{1}{2}[r(s - c) + ch]$, where rad A = radian measure of angle A (table, pp. 1–34 to 1–35, 1–44). For small arcs, $s = \frac{1}{3}(8c' - c)$, where c' = chord of half of the arc (Huygen's approximation).

NOTE. $c = 2\sqrt{h(d - h)}$; $c' = \sqrt{dh}$ or $d = c'^2/h$, where d = diameter of circle; $h = r(1 - \cos \frac{1}{2}A)$, $s = 2r$ rad $\frac{1}{2}A$.

Ribbon bounded by two parallel curves (Fig. 57). If a straight line AB moves so that it is always perpendicular to the path traced by its middle point G, then the area of the ribbon or strip thus generated is equal to the length of AB times the length of the path traced by G. (It is assumed that the radius of curvature of G's path is never less than $\frac{1}{2}AB$, so that successive positions of the generating line will not intersect.)

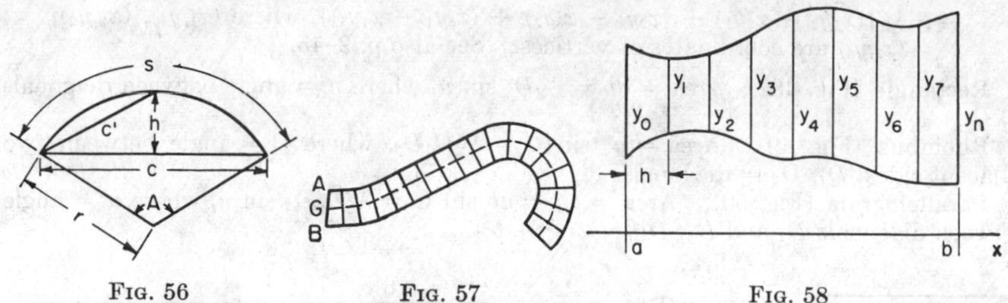

FIG. 56 FIG. 57 FIG. 58

Simpson's Rule (Fig. 58). Divide the given area into n panels (where n is some even number) by means of $n + 1$ parallel lines, called ordinates, drawn at constant distance h apart; and denote the lengths of these ordinates by $y_0, y_1, y_2, \ldots, y_n$. (Note that y_0 or y_n may be zero.) Area $= \frac{1}{3}h[y_0 + y_n) + 4(y_1 + y_3 + y_5 \ldots) + 2(y_2 + y_4 + y_6 \cdots)]$, approx. The greater the number of divisions, the more accurate the result.

NOTE. Taking $y = f(x)$, where x varies from $x = a$ to $x = b$, and $h = (b - a)/n$, then the error $= -\frac{1}{180}\frac{(b-a)^5}{n^4}f''''(X)$, where $f''''(X)$ is the value of the fourth derivative of $f(x)$ for some (unknown) value $x = X$, between a and b.

Ellipse (Fig. 59; see also p. 2–51). Area of ellipse $= \pi ab$. Area of shaded segment $= xy + ab \sin^{-1}(x/a)$. Length of perimeter of ellipse $= \pi(a + b)K$, where $K = (1 + \frac{1}{4}m^2 + \frac{1}{64}m^4 + \frac{1}{256}m^6 + \cdots)$, $m = (a - b)/(a + b)$.

For $m =$	0.1	0.2	0.3	0.4	0.5	0.6	0.7	0.8	0.9	1.0
$K =$	1.002	1.010	1.023	1.040	1.064	1.092	1.127	1.168	1.216	1.273

Hyperbola (Fig. 60; see also p. 2–53). In any hyperbola, shaded area $A = ab \ln\left(\frac{x}{a} + \frac{y}{b}\right)$. In an equilateral hyperbola ($a = b$), area $A = a^2 \sinh^{-1}(y/a) = a^2 \cosh^{-1}(x/a)$. For tables of hyperbolic functions, see p. 1–60. Here x and y are co-ordinates of point P.

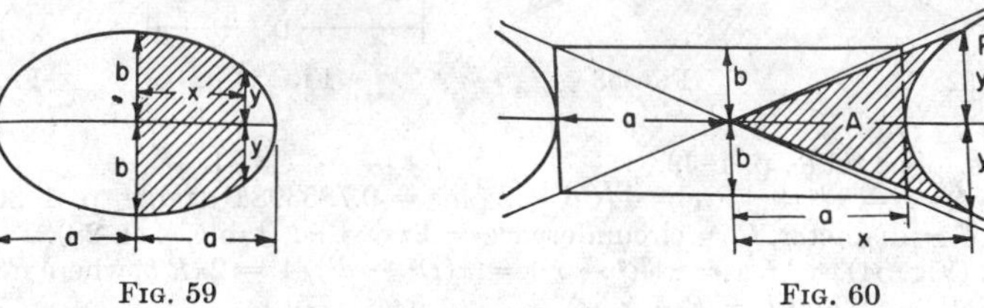

FIG. 59 FIG. 60

Parabola (Fig. 61; see also p. 2–49). Shaded area $A = \frac{2}{3}ch$. In Fig. 62, length of arc $OP = s = \frac{1}{2}PT + \frac{1}{2}p \ln \cot \frac{1}{2}u$. Here c = any chord; p = semilatus rectum; PT = tangent at P.

NOTE. $OT = OM = x$.

For lengths and areas of **other curves** see pp. 2–56 to 2–63.

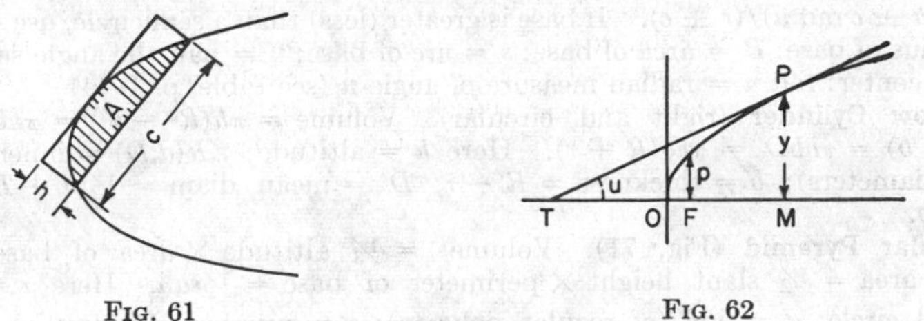

FIG. 61 FIG. 62

SURFACES AND VOLUMES OF SOLIDS

Regular Prism (Fig. 63). Volume $= \frac{1}{2}nrah = Bh$. Lateral area $= nah = Ph$. Here n = number of sides; B = area of base; P = perimeter of base.

Right Circular Cylinder (Fig. 64). Volume $= \pi r^2 h = Bh$. Lateral area $= 2\pi rh = Ph$. Here B = area of base; P = perimeter of base.

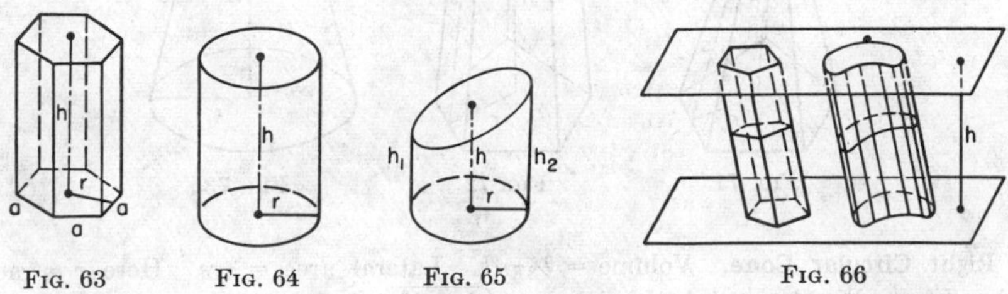

FIG. 63 FIG. 64 FIG. 65 FIG. 66

Truncated Right Circular Cylinder (Fig. 65). Volume $= \pi r^2 h = Bh$. Lateral area $= 2\pi rh = Ph$. Here h = mean height $= \frac{1}{2}(h_1 + h_2)$; B = area of base; P = perimeter of base.

Any Prism or Cylinder (Fig. 66). Volume $= Bh = Nl$. Lateral area $= Ql$. Here l = length of an element or lateral edge; B = area of base; N = area of normal section; Q = perimeter of normal section.

Any Truncated Prism or Cylinder (Fig. 67). Volume $= Nl$. Lateral area $= Qk$. Here l = distance between centers of gravity of areas of the two bases; k = distance

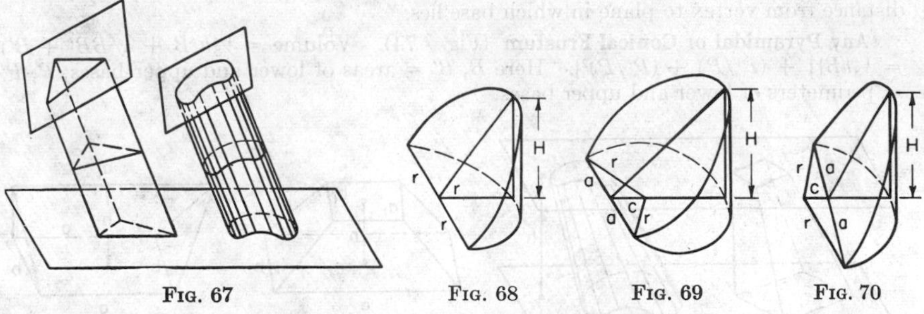

FIG. 67 FIG. 68 FIG. 69 FIG. 70

between centers of gravity of perimeters of the two bases; N = area of normal section; Q = perimeter of normal section. For a truncated triangular prism with lateral edges a,b,c, $l = k = \frac{1}{3}(a + b + c)$. Note that l and k will always be parallel to the elements.

Special Ungula of a Right Circular Cylinder (Fig. 68). Volume $= \frac{2}{3}r^2H$. Lateral area $= 2rH$. r = radius. (Upper surface is a semiellipse.)

Any Ungula of a right circular cylinder (Figs. 69 and 70). Volume $= H(\frac{2}{3}a^3 \pm cB)/(r \pm c) = H[a(r^2 - \frac{1}{3}a^2) \pm r^2c \text{ rad } u]/(r \pm c)$. Lateral area $= H(2ra \pm cs)/(r \pm c)$

$= 2rH(a \pm c \text{ rad } u)/(r \pm c)$. If base is greater (less) than a semicircle, use $+$ ($-$) sign. r = radius of base; B = area of base; s = arc of base; u = half the angle subtended by arc s at center; rad u = radian measure of angle u (see table, p. 1–44).

Hollow Cylinder (right and circular). Volume $= \pi h(R^2 - r^2) = \pi hb(D - b) = \pi hb(d + b) = \pi hbD' = \pi hb(R + r)$. Here h = altitude; $r,R(d,D)$ = inner and outer radii (diameters); b = thickness $= R - r$; D' = mean diam $= \frac{1}{2}(d + D) = D - b = d + b$.

Regular Pyramid (Fig. 71). Volume $= \frac{1}{3}$ altitude $\times$ area of base $= \frac{1}{6}hran$. Lateral area $= \frac{1}{2}$ slant height $\times$ perimeter of base $= \frac{1}{2}san$. Here r = radius of inscribed circle; a = side (of regular polygon); n = number of sides; $s = \sqrt{r^2 + h^2}$. Vertex of pyramid directly above center of base.

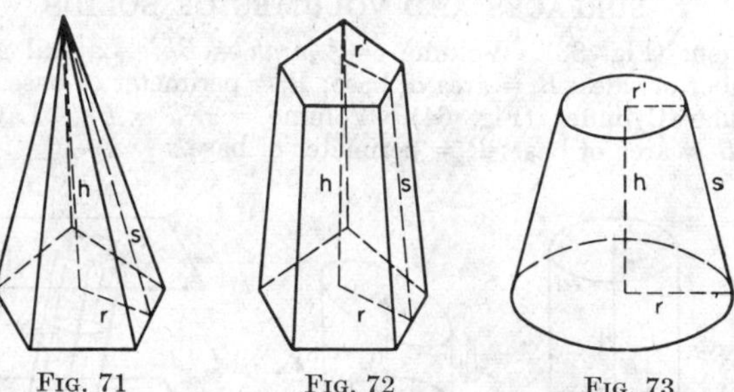

FIG. 71 FIG. 72 FIG. 73

Right Circular Cone. Volume $= \frac{1}{3}\pi r^2 h$. Lateral area $= \pi rs$. Here r = radius of base; h = altitude; s = slant height $= \sqrt{r^2 + h^2}$.

Frustum of Regular Pyramid (Fig. 72).

Volume $= \frac{1}{6}hran[1 + (a'/a) + (a'/a)^2]$.

Lateral area = slant height $\times$ half sum of perimeters of bases = slant height $\times$ perimeter of mid-section $= \frac{1}{2}sn(r + r')$. Here r,r' = radii of inscribed circles; $s = \sqrt{(r - r')^2 + h^2}$; a,a' = sides of lower and upper bases; n = number of sides.

Frustum of Right Circular Cone (Fig. 73). Volume $= \frac{1}{3}\pi r^2 h[1 + (r'/r) + (r'/r)^2] = \frac{1}{3}\pi h(r^2 + rr' + r'^2) = \frac{1}{4}\pi h[(r + r')^2 + \frac{1}{3}(r - r')^2]$. Lateral area $= \pi s(r + r')$; $s = \sqrt{(r - r')^2 + h^2}$.

Any Pyramid or Cone. Volume $= \frac{1}{3}Bh$. B = area of base; h = perpendicular distance from vertex to plane in which base lies.

Any Pyramidal or Conical Frustum (Fig. 74). Volume $= \frac{1}{3}h(B + \sqrt{BB'} + B') = \frac{1}{3}hB[1 + (P'/P) + (P'/P)^2]$. Here B, B' = areas of lower and upper bases; P, P' = perimeters of lower and upper bases.

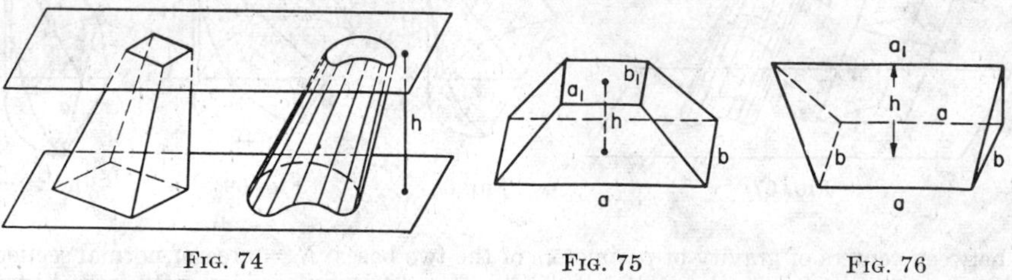

FIG. 74 FIG. 75 FIG. 76

Obelisk (frustum of a rectangular pyramid in Fig. 75).

Volume $= \frac{1}{6}h[(2a + a_1)b + (2a_1 + a)b_1] = \frac{1}{6}h[ab + (a + a_1)(b + b_1) + a_1b_1]$.

Wedge (rectangular base; a_1 parallel to a,a and at distance h above base in Fig. 76). Volume $= \frac{1}{6}hb(2a + a_1)$.

Sphere. Volume $= V = \frac{4}{3}\pi r^3 = 4.188790r^3 = \frac{1}{6}\pi d^3 = 0.523599d^3$ (table, p. 1–36) $= \frac{2}{3}$ volume of circumscribed cylinder. Area $= A = 4\pi r^2$ = four great circles (table, p. 1–30) $= \pi d^2 = 3.14159d^2$ = lateral area of circumscribed cylinder. Here r = radius; $d = 2r$ = diameter $= \sqrt[3]{6V/\pi} = 1.24070\sqrt[3]{V} = \sqrt{A/\pi} = 0.56419\sqrt{A}$.

Hollow Sphere, or spherical shell. Volume $= \frac{4}{3}\pi(R^3 - r^3) = \frac{1}{6}\pi(D^3 - d^3) = 4\pi R_1^2 t + \frac{1}{3}\pi t^3$. Here R,r = outer and inner radii; D,d = outer and inner diameters; t = thickness $= R - r$; R_1 = mean radius $= \frac{1}{2}(R + r)$.

Spherical Segment of One Base. Zone (spherical "cap" of Fig. 78). Volume $= \frac{1}{6}\pi h(3a^2 + h^2) = \frac{1}{3}\pi h^2(3r - h)$ (table, p. 1–38). Lateral area (of zone) $= 2\pi rh = \pi(a^2 + h^2)$.

NOTE. $a^2 = h(2r - h)$, where r = radius of sphere.

Any Spherical Segment. Zone (Fig. 77). Volume $= \frac{1}{6}\pi h(3a^2 + 3a_1^2 + h^2)$. Lateral area (zone) $= 2\pi rh$. Here r = radius of sphere. If the inscribed frustum of a cone be removed from the spherical segment, the volume remaining is $\frac{1}{6}\pi hc^2$, where c = slant height of frustum $= \sqrt{h^2 + (a - a_1)^2}$.

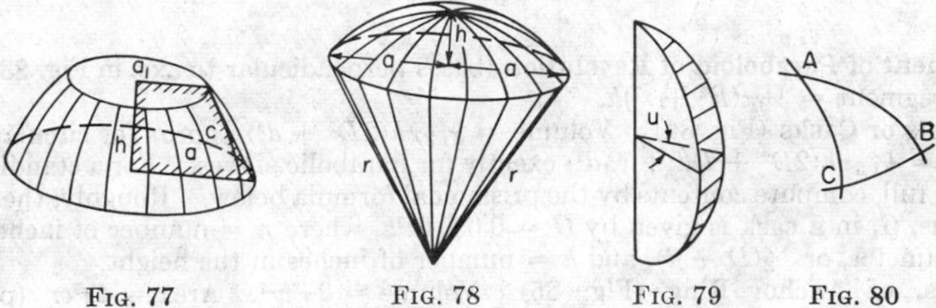

FIG. 77 FIG. 78 FIG. 79 FIG. 80

Spherical Sector (Fig. 78). Volume $= \frac{1}{3}r \times$ area of cap $= \frac{2}{3}\pi r^2 h$. Total area = area of cap + area of cone $= 2\pi rh + \pi ra$.

NOTE. $a^2 = h(2r - h)$.

Spherical wedge bounded by two plane semicircles and a **lune** (Fig. 79). Volume of wedge ÷ volume of sphere $= u/360°$. Area of lune ÷ area of sphere $= u/360°$. u = dihedral angle of the wedge.

Spherical triangle bounded by arcs of three great circles (Fig. 80). Area of triangle $= \pi r^2 E/180°$ = area of octant $\times E/90°$. E = spherical excess $= 180° - (A + B + C)$, where A, B, and C are angles of the triangle. See also p. 2–45.

Solid Angles. Any portion of a spherical surface subtends what is called a **solid angle** at the center of the sphere. If the area of the given portion of spherical surface is equal to the square of the radius, the subtended solid angle is called a **steradian,** and this is commonly taken as the unit. The entire solid angle about the center is called a **steregon,** so that 4π steradians = 1 steregon. A so-called "solid right angle" is the solid angle subtended by a quadrantal (or trirectangular) spherical triangle, and a "spherical degree" (now little used) is a solid angle equal to $\frac{1}{90}$ of a solid right angle. Hence 720 spherical degrees = 1 steregon, or π steradians = 180 spherical degrees. If u = the angle which an element of a cone makes with its axis, then the solid angle of the cone contains $2\pi(1 - \cos u)$ steradians.

Regular Polyhedra. A = area of surface; V = volume; a = edge.

Name of solid (see p. 2–12)	Bounded by	A/a^2	V/a^3
Tetrahedron	4 triangles	1.7321	0.1179
Cube	6 squares	6.0000	1.0000
Octahedron	8 triangles	3.4641	0.4714
Dodecahedron	12 pentagons	20.6457	7.6631
Icosahedron	20 triangles	8.6603	2.1817

Ellipsoid (Fig. 81). Volume $= \frac{4}{3}\pi abc$, where a, b, c = semiaxes.

Spheroid (or ellipsoid of revolution). The volume of any segment made by two planes perpendicular to the axis of revolution may be found accurately by the prismoidal formula below.

Paraboloid of Revolution (Fig. 82). Volume $= \frac{1}{2}\pi r^2 h = \frac{1}{2}$ volume of circumscribed cylinder.

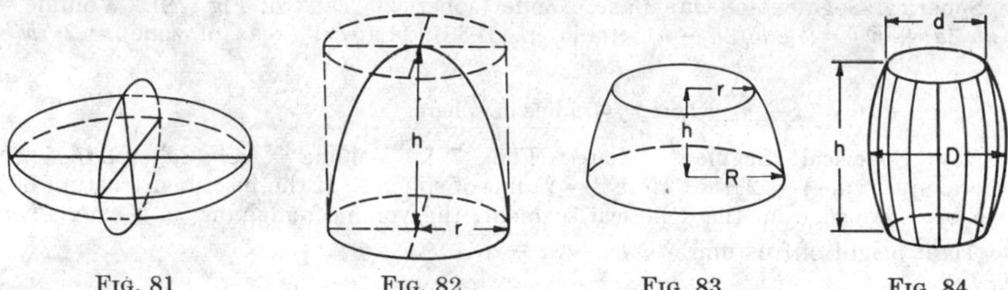

FIG. 81 FIG. 82 FIG. 83 FIG. 84

Segment of Paraboloid of Revolution (bases perpendicular to axis in Fig. 83). Volume of segment $= \frac{1}{2}\pi(R^2 + r^2)h$.

Barrels or Casks (Fig. 84). Volume $= \frac{1}{12}\pi h(2D^2 + d^2)$ approx for circular staves. Volume $= \frac{1}{15}\pi h(2D^2 + Dd + \frac{3}{4}d^2)$ exactly for parabolic staves. For a standing cask, partially full, compute contents by the prismoidal formula below. Roughly, the number of gallons, G, in a cask is given by $G = 0.0034n^2h$, where n = number of inches in the mean diameter, or $\frac{1}{2}(D + d)$, and h = number of inches in the height.

Torus, or Anchor Ring (Fig. 85). Volume $= 2\pi^2cr^2$. Area $= 4\pi^2cr$ (proof by theorems of Pappus).

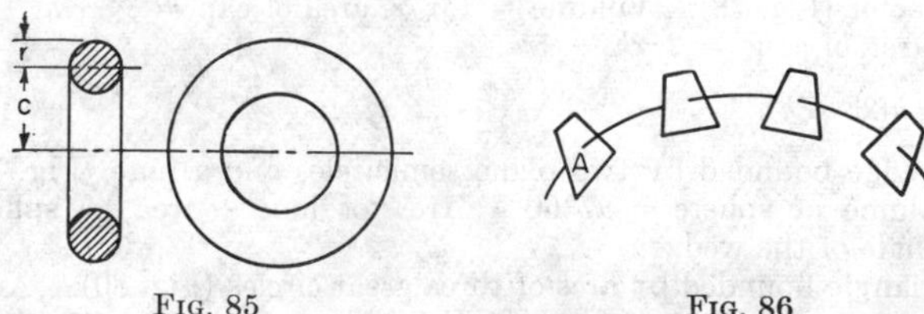

FIG. 85 FIG. 86

Theorems of Pappus. 1. Assume that a plane figure, area A, revolves about an axis in its plane but not cutting it; and let s = length of circular arc traced by its center of gravity. Then volume of the solid generated by A is $V = As$. For a complete revolution, $V = 2\pi rA$, where r = distance from axis to center of gravity of A.

2. Assume that a plane curve, length l, revolves about an axis in its plane but not cutting it; and let s = length of circular arc traced by its center of gravity. Then area of the surface generated by l is $S = ls$. For a complete revolution, $S = 2\pi rl$, where r = distance from axis to center of gravity of l.

NOTE. If V_1 or S_1 about any axis is known, then V_2 or S_2 about any parallel axis can be readily computed when the distance between the axes is known.

Generalized Theorems of Pappus. Consider any curved path of length s. If (1) a plane figure, area A [or (2) a plane curve, length l] moves so that its center of gravity slides along this curved path (Fig. 86), while the plane of A (or l) remains always perpendicular to the path, then (1) the volume generated by A is $V = As$ [and (2) the area generated by l is $S = ls$]. The path is assumed to curve so gradually that successive positions of A (or l) will not intersect.

Prismoidal Formula (Fig. 87). Volume $= \frac{1}{6}h(A + B + 4M)$, where h = altitude, A and B = areas of bases and M = area of a plane section midway between the bases.

This formula is exactly true for any solid lying between two parallel planes and such that the area of a section at distance x from one of these planes is expressible as a polynomial of not higher than the third degree in x. It is approximately true for many other solids.

Simpson's rule may be applied to finding volumes, if the ordinates y_1, y_2, be interpreted as the areas of plane sections, at constant distance h apart (p. 2–18).

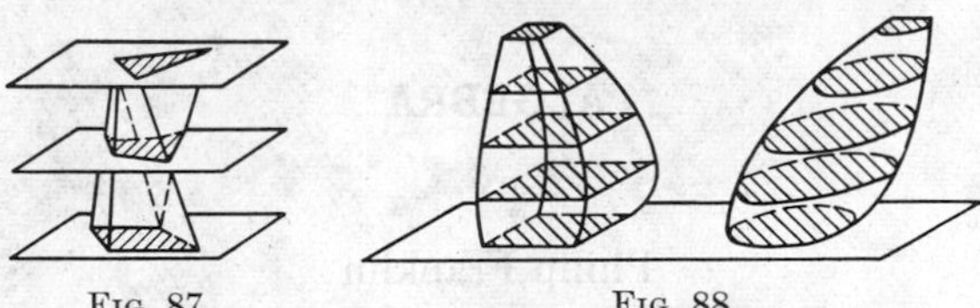

Fig. 87 Fig. 88

Cavalieri's Theorem. Assume two solids to have their bases in the same plane. If the plane section of one solid at every distance x above the base is equal in area to the plane section of the other solid at the same distance x above the base, then the volumes of the two solids will be equal. See Fig. 88.

ALGEBRA

BY

Philip Franklin

FORMAL ALGEBRA

Notation. The main points of separation in a simple algebraic expression are the $+$ and $-$ signs. Thus, $a + b \times c - d \div x + y$ is to be interpreted as $a + (b \times c) - (d \div x) + y$. In other words, the range of operation of the symbols $\times$ and $\div$ extends only so far as the next $+$ or $-$ sign. As between the signs $\times$ and $\div$ themselves, $a \div b \times c$ means, properly speaking, $a \div (b \times c)$; *i.e.*, the $\div$ sign is the stronger separative; but this rule is not always strictly followed, and in order to avoid ambiguity it is better to use the parentheses.

The range of influence of exponents and radical signs extends only over the next adjacent quantity. Thus, $2ax^3$ means $2a(x^3)$, and $\sqrt{2}\,ax$ means $(\sqrt{2})\,(ax)$. Instead of $\sqrt{2}\,ax$, it is safer, however, to write $\sqrt{2} \cdot ax$, or, better, $ax\sqrt{2}$.

Any expression within parentheses is to be treated as a single quantity. A horizontal bar serves the same purpose as parentheses.

The notation $a \cdot b$, or simply ab, means $a \times b$; and $a:b$, or a/b, means $a \div b$.

The symbol $|a|$ means the "absolute value of a," or numerical value regardless of sign; thus, $|-2| = |+2| = 2$.

The symbol $n!$ (where n is a whole number) is read: "n factorial," and means the product of the natural numbers from 1 to n, inclusive. Thus $1! = 1$; $2! = 1 \times 2$; $3! = 1 \times 2 \times 3$; $4! = 1 \times 2 \times 3 \times 4$; etc.

The symbol $\neq$ or $\nparallel$ means "not equal to"; $\pm$ means "plus or minus."

The symbol $\approx$ is sometimes used for "approximately equal to."

Addition and Subtraction. $a + b = b + a$.

$(a + b) + c = a + (b + c)$. $a - (-b) = a + b$. $a - a = 0$.

$a + (x - y + z) = a + x - y + z$. $a - (x - y + z) = a - x + y - z$.

A minus sign preceding a parenthesis operates to reverse the sign of every term within, when the parentheses are removed.

Multiplication and Simple Factoring. $ab = ba$. $(ab)c = a(bc)$. $a(b + c) = ab + ac$. $a(b - c) = ab - ac$. Also, $a \times (-b) = -ab$, and $(-a) \times (-b) = ab$; "unlike signs give minus; like signs give plus."

$(a + b)(a - b) = a^2 - b^2$.

$(a + b)^2 = a^2 + 2ab + b^2$, $(a - b)^2 = a^2 - 2ab + b^2$.

$(a + b)^3 = a^3 + 3a^2b + 3ab^2 + b^3$, $(a - b)^3 = a^3 - 3a^2b + 3ab^2 - b^3$, etc.

(See table of binomial coefficients, p. 1–39; also p. 2–26.)

$a^2 - b^2 = (a - b)(a + b)$, $\quad a^3 - b^3 = (a - b)(a^2 + ab + b^2)$.

$a^n - b^n = (a - b)(a^{n-1} + a^{n-2}b + a^{n-3}b^2 + \cdots + ab^{n-2} + b^{n-1})$.

$a^n + b^n$ is factorable by $a + b$ only when n is odd; thus,

$a^3 + b^3 = (a + b)(a^2 - ab + b^2)$.

$a^5 + b^5 = (a + b)(a^4 - a^3b + a^2b^2 - ab^3 + b^4)$, etc.

The following transformation is sometimes useful:

$$ax^2 + bx + c = a\left[\left(x + \frac{b}{2a}\right)^2 - \left(\frac{\sqrt{b^2 - 4ac}}{2a}\right)^2\right]$$

Fractions. If m is not zero, $\dfrac{ma + mb + mc}{mx + my} = \dfrac{a + b + c}{x + y}$; *i.e.*, both numerator and denominator of a fraction may be multiplied or divided by any quantity different from zero, without altering the value of the fraction.

To add two fractions, reduce each to a common denominator and add the numerators: $\dfrac{a}{b} + \dfrac{x}{y} = \dfrac{ay}{by} + \dfrac{bx}{by} = \dfrac{ay + bx}{by}$.

To multiply two fractions: $\dfrac{a}{b} \times \dfrac{x}{y} = \dfrac{ax}{by}$; $\dfrac{a}{b} \times x = \dfrac{a}{b} \times \dfrac{x}{1} = \dfrac{ax}{b}$.

To divide one fraction by another, invert the divisor and multiply:

$$\frac{a}{b} \div \frac{x}{y} = \frac{a}{b} \times \frac{y}{x} = \frac{ay}{bx} \qquad \frac{a}{b} \div x = \frac{a}{b} \times \frac{1}{x} = \frac{a}{bx}$$

Ratio and Proportion. The notation $a:b::c:d$, or the preferable form $a:b = c:d$, is read: "a is to b as c is to d," and means simply $(a/b) = (c/d)$, or $ad = bc$. a and d are called the "extremes," b and c the "means," and d the "fourth proportional" to a, b, and c. The "mean proportional" between two numbers is the square root of their product; also called the "geometric mean" of the numbers (p. 2–27). If $a/b = c/d$, then $(a + b)/b = (c + d)/d$, and $(a - b)/b = (c - d)/d$; whence also, $(a + b)/(a - b) = (c + d)/(c - d)$. If $a/x = b/y = c/z = \cdots = r$, then

$$(a + b + c + \cdots)/(x + y + z \cdots) = r$$

Variation. The notation $x \propto y$ is read: "x varies directly as y," or "x is directly proportional to y," and means $x = ky$, where k is some constant. To determine the constant k, it is sufficient to know any pair of values, as x_1 and y_1, which belong together; then $x_1 = ky_1$, and hence $x/x_1 = y/y_1$, or $x = (x_1/y_1)y$. The expression "x varies inversely as y," or "x is inversely proportional to y," means that x is proportional to $1/y$, or $x = k/y$.

Exponents. $a^{m+n} = a^m a^n$. $a^{m-n} = a^m/a^n$. $a^0 = 1$ (if $a \neq 0$). $a^{-m} = 1/a^m$. $(a^m)^n = a^{mn}$. $a^{1/n} = \sqrt[n]{a}$. Thus: $a^{1/2} = \sqrt{a}$, and $a^{1/3} = \sqrt[3]{a}$. $a^{m/n} = \sqrt[n]{a^m}$. Thus: $a^{2/3} = \sqrt[3]{a^2}$ and $a^{3/2} = \sqrt{a^3}$. $(\sqrt[n]{a})^n = a$. $(ab)^n = a^n b^n$. $(a/b)^n = a^n/b^n$. $(-a)^n = a^n$ if n is even. $(-a)^n = -a^n$ if n is odd. If n is positive and increases indefinitely, a^n becomes infinite if $a > 1$, and approaches 0 if $a < 1$ (a being always positive). Graphs, p. 2–84; series, p. 2–67.

Radicals. Except in the simple cases of square root and cube root, radical signs should always be replaced by fractional exponents: $\sqrt[n]{a} = a^{1/n}$. $(\sqrt[n]{a})^n = (a^{1/n})^n = a$. If n is odd, $\sqrt[n]{-a} = -\sqrt[n]{a}$; but if n is even, $\sqrt[n]{-a}$ is imaginary. Every positive number a has two square roots, one positive and the other negative; but the notation $\sqrt{a}$ always means the positive root; thus, $\sqrt{9} = 3$; $-\sqrt{9} = -3$. If the denominator of a fraction is of the form $\sqrt{a} \pm \sqrt{b}$, it is possible to "rationalize the denominator" by multiplying both numerator and denominator by $\sqrt{a} \mp \sqrt{b}$. Thus:

$$\frac{\sqrt{a} + \sqrt{b}}{\sqrt{a} - \sqrt{b}} = \frac{(\sqrt{a} + \sqrt{b})(\sqrt{a} + \sqrt{b})}{(\sqrt{a} - \sqrt{b})(\sqrt{a} + \sqrt{b})} = \frac{a + b + 2\sqrt{ab}}{a - b}$$

Logarithms. (For the use of logarithms in numerical computation, see p. 2–6.) The logarithm of a (positive) number N is the exponent of that power to which the base (10 or e) must be raised to produce N. Thus, $x = \log_{10} N$ means that $10^x = N$, and $x = \log_e N$ or $\ln N$ means that $e^x = N$. Logarithms to base 10 are called **common, denary,** or **Briggsian** logarithms. For table of four-place common logarithms see pp. 1–40 to 1–43.

Logarithms to base e are called **natural** or **Napierian** logarithms. Here $e = 1 + 1 + 1/2! + 1/3! + 1/4! + \cdots = 2.718281828459.\ .\ .$ For table of four-place natural logarithms see pp. 1–58, 1–59.

If the subscript 10 or e is omitted, the base must be inferred from the context, the

base 10 being used in numerical computation, and the base e in theoretical work. In either system,

$$\log(ab) = \log a + \log b \qquad \log(a^n) = n\log a \qquad \log 0 = -\infty$$
$$\log(a/b) = \log a - \log b \qquad \log(\sqrt[n]{a}) = (1/n)\log a \qquad \log 1 = 0$$
$$\log(1/n) = -\log n \qquad \log(\text{base}) = 1 \qquad \log\infty = \infty$$

The two systems are related as follows:

$$\log_{10} e = M = 0.4342944819\ldots \qquad \ln 10 = \log_e 10 = 1/M = 2.3025850930\ldots$$
$$\log_{10} x = 0.4343\log_e x \qquad \ln x = \log_e x = 2.3026\log_{10} x$$

For tables of multiples of M and $1/M$, see p. 1-62. For graphs of the logarithmic and exponential functions, see p. 2-84; series, p. 2-67.

Binomial Theorem. (For table of binomial coefficients, see pp. 1-39 and 2-28.)

Let $(n)_1 = n$, $(n)_2 = \dfrac{n(n-1)}{1\times 2}$, $\quad (n)_3 = \dfrac{n(n-1)(n-2)}{1\times 2\times 3}$

$$(n)_4 = \frac{n(n-1)(n-2)(n-3)}{1\times 2\times 3\times 4}, \ldots$$

Then, for any value of n, provided $|x| < 1$,

$$(1+x)^n = 1 + (n)_1x + (n)_2x^2 + (n)_3x^3 + (n)_4x^4 + \cdots$$

(If n is a positive integer, the series breaks off with the term in x^n, and is valid without restrictions on x, see p. 2-24.)

The most useful **special cases** are the following:

$$\sqrt{1+x} = (1+x)^{1/2} = 1 + \frac{1}{2}x - \frac{1}{8}x^2 + \frac{1}{16}x^3 - \frac{5}{128}x^4 + \cdots \qquad [|x| < 1]$$
$$\sqrt[3]{1+x} = (1+x)^{1/3} = 1 + \frac{1}{3}x - \frac{1}{9}x^2 + \frac{5}{81}x^3 - \frac{10}{243}x^4 + \cdots \qquad [|x| < 1]$$
$$\frac{1}{1+x} = (1+x)^{-1} = 1 - x + x^2 - x^3 + x^4 - \cdots \qquad [|x| < 1]$$
$$\frac{1}{\sqrt{1+x}} = (1+x)^{-1/2} = 1 - \frac{1}{2}x + \frac{3}{8}x^2 - \frac{5}{16}x^3 + \frac{35}{128}x^4 - \cdots \qquad [|x| < 1]$$
$$\frac{1}{\sqrt[3]{1+x}} = (1+x)^{-1/3} = 1 - \frac{1}{3}x + \frac{2}{9}x^2 - \frac{14}{81}x^3 + \frac{35}{243}x^4 - \cdots \qquad [|x| < 1]$$
$$\sqrt{(1+x)^3} = (1+x)^{3/2} = 1 + \frac{3}{2}x + \frac{3}{8}x^2 - \frac{1}{16}x^3 + \frac{3}{128}x^4 - \cdots \qquad [|x| < 1]$$
$$\frac{1}{\sqrt{(1+x)^3}} = (1+x)^{-3/2} = 1 - \frac{3}{2}x + \frac{15}{8}x^2 - \frac{35}{16}x^3 + \frac{315}{128}x^4 - \cdots \qquad [|x| < 1]$$

with corresponding formulas for $\sqrt{1-x}$, etc., obtained by reversing the signs of the odd powers of x. Also, provided $|b| < |a|$:

$$(a+b)^n = a^n\left(1+\frac{b}{a}\right)^n = a^n + (n)_1\,a^{n-1}b + (n)_2a^{n-2}b^2 + (n)_3a^{n-3}b^3 + \cdots$$

where $(n)_1$, $(n)_2$, etc., have the values given above.

Arithmetical Progression. In an arithmetical progression, a; $a+d$; $a+2d$; $a+3d$; . . . , each term is obtained from the preceding term by adding a constant, called the constant difference, d. If n is the number of terms, the last term is $l = a + (n-1)d$; the "average" term is $\frac{1}{2}(a+l)$; and the sum of the n terms is n times the average term, or $S = \frac{1}{2}n(a+l)$. The **arithmetical mean** between a and b is $(a+b)/2$.

Geometrical Progression. In a geometrical progression, a; ar; ar^2; ar^3; . . . , each term is obtained from the preceding term by multiplying by a constant, called the constant ratio, r. The nth term is ar^{n-1}. The sum of the first n terms is $S = a(r^n - 1)/(r - 1) = a(1 - r^n)/(1 - r)$. If r is a positive or negative fraction, that is, if $-1 < r < +1$, then r^n will approach zero as n increases, and the sum of n terms will approach $a/(1 - r)$ as a limit. The **geometric mean** between a and b is $\sqrt{ab}$; also called the **mean proportional** between a and b (p. 2–25; construction, p. 2–13).

The **harmonic mean** between a and b is $2ab/(a + b)$.

Summation of Certain Series by Second and Third Differences. Let a_1, a_2, a_3, . . . a_n be any series of n numbers, as in the first column of the adjoining scheme. By subtracting each number from the next following, form the column of "first differences," and by repeating this process, form the columns of second, third, etc., differences. If the kth differences are all equal, so that subsequent differences are all zero, the original series is called an arithmetical series of the kth order. In this special case the series can be summed as follows: Denote the numbers which stand at the head of the successive columns of differences by D', D'', D''', ... Then the nth term of the series is a_n, and the sum of the first n terms is S_n, where

Numbers	1st diff	2nd diff	3rd diff
−64	37	−18	6
−27	19	−12	6
− 8	7	− 6	6
− 1	1	0	6
0	1	6	·
1	7	·	
8	·		
·			

$$a_n = a_1 + (n-1)D' + \frac{(n-1)(n-2)}{1 \times 2} D'' + \frac{(n-1)(n-2)(n-3)}{1 \times 2 \times 3} D''' + \cdots$$

$$S_n = na_1 + \frac{n(n-1)}{1 \times 2} D' + \frac{n(n-1)(n-2)}{1 \times 2 \times 3} D'' + \frac{n(n-1)(n-2)(n-3)}{1 \times 2 \times 3 \times 4} D''' + \cdots$$

If the series is, for example, of the third order, each of these formulas will stop with the term involving D'''; and only a few terms of the series are required for the computation of the D's. (Differentials, p. 2–66.)

Sum of the Squares or Cubes of the First n Natural Numbers

$$1 + 2 + 3 + \cdots + (n-1) + n = \tfrac{1}{2}n(n+1)$$
$$1^2 + 2^2 + 3^2 + \cdots + (n-1)^2 + n^2 = \tfrac{1}{6}n(n+1)(2n+1)$$
$$1^3 + 2^3 + 3^3 + \cdots + (n-1)^3 + n^3 = [\tfrac{1}{2}n(n+1)]^2$$

Formula for Interpolation by Second Differences. In any ordinary table giving a quantity y as a function of a variable x, let it be required to find the value of y corresponding to a value of x which is not given directly in the table, but which lies between two tabulated values, as x_1 and x_2. If $x = x_1 + md$, where $d = x_2 - x_1$ = the constant interval between two successive x's, and m is some proper fraction, then the corresponding value of y will be given by the formula

$$y = y_1 + mD' + \frac{m(m-1)}{1 \times 2} D'' + \frac{m(m-1)(m-2)}{1 \times 2 \times 3} D''' + \cdots$$

where D', D'', D''', . . . are the first, second, third, . . . differences in the series of y's which begins with y_1 (see above), provided the function is of such a nature that the differences of higher orders become negligibly small.

The coefficients of D', D'', D''', . . . in the formula are the binomial coefficients for fractional values of m (see following table). The several terms of the formula (with careful attention to sign) are the successive corrections which must be added to y_1; the sum of these corrections should be rounded out to the nearest unit of the last significant place before adding. If $D' < 4$, the term involving D'', and later terms, can be neglected; the formula then reduces to $y = y_1 + mD'$, which is the familiar formula for ordinary, or "linear," interpolation. If $D''' < 8$ (or $D''''' < 12$, or $D'''''' < 16$), the term involving D''' (or D'''', or D''''') can be neglected.

Binomial Coefficients for Fractional Values of m

m	$(m)_2$	$(m)_3$	$(m)_4$	$(m)_5$
0.0	−0.0000	0.0000	−0.0000	0.0000
0.1	−0.0450	0.0285	−0.0207	0.0161
0.2	−0.0800	0.0480	−0.0336	0.0255
0.3	−0.1050	0.0595	−0.0402	0.0297
0.4	−0.1200	0.0640	−0.0416	0.0300
0.5	−0.1250	0.0625	−0.0391	0.0273
0.6	−0.1200	0.0560	−0.0336	0.0228
0.7	−0.1050	0.0455	−0.0262	0.0173
0.8	−0.0800	0.0320	−0.0176	0.0113
0.9	−0.0450	0.0165	−0.0087	0.0054

Here $(m)_2 = \frac{m(m-1)}{1 \times 2}$, $(m)_3 = \frac{m(m-1)(m-2)}{1 \times 2 \times 3}$, $(m)_4 = \frac{m(m-1)(m-2)(m-3)}{1 \times 2 \times 3 \times 4}$, etc. Compare p. 1–39.

Permutations. The number of possible permutations or arrangements of n different elements is $1 \times 2 \times 3 \times \cdots \times n = n!$ (read: "n factorial").

If among the n elements there are p equal ones of one sort, q equal ones of another sort, r equal ones of a third sort, etc., then the number of possible permutations is $(n!)/(p! \times q! \times r! \times \cdots)$, where $p + q + r + \cdots = n$.

Combinations. The number of possible combinations or groups of n elements taken r at a time (without repetition of any element within any one group) is $[n(n-1)(n-2)(n-3) \cdots (n-r+1)]/(r!) = (n)_r$. (See table of binomial coefficients, p. 1–39.) If repetitions are allowed, so that a group, for example, may contain as many as r equal elements, then the number of combinations of n elements taken r at a time is $(m)_r$, where $m_r = n + r - 1$.

NOTE: $(n)_1 + (n)_2 + \cdots + (n)_n = 2^n - 1$.

SOLUTION OF EQUATIONS IN ONE UNKNOWN QUANTITY

Roots of an Equation. An equation containing a single variable x will in general be true for some values of x and false for other values. Any value of x for which the equation is true is called a **root** of the equation. To "solve" an equation means to find all its roots. Any root of an equation, when substituted therein for x, will "satisfy" the equation. An equation which is true for all values of x, like $(x+1)^2 = x^2 + 2x + 1$, is called an **identity** (often written $(x+1)^2 \equiv x^2 + 2x + 1$).

Types of Equations

1. ALGEBRAIC EQUATIONS:

Of the first degree (linear), *e.g.*, $2x + 6 = 0$ (root: $x = -3$).
Of the second degree (quadratic), *e.g.*, $x^2 - 2x - 3 = 0$ (roots: $-1, 3$).
Of the third degree (cubic), *e.g.*, $x^3 - 6x^2 + 5x + 12 = 0$ (roots: $-1, 3, 4$).

2. TRANSCENDENTAL EQUATIONS:

Exponential equations, *e.g.*, $2^x = 32$ (root: $x = 5$); $2^x = -32$ (no real root).
Trigonometric equations, *e.g.*, $10 \sin x - \sin 3x = 4$ (roots: 30°, 150°).

Legitimate Operations on Equations. An equation which is true for a particular value of x will remain true for that value of x after any one of the following operations is performed:

Adding any quantity to both sides; subtracting any quantity from both sides; transposing any term from one side to the other, provided its sign be changed; multiplying or dividing both sides by any quantity which is not zero; changing the signs of all the terms; raising both sides to any positive integral power; extracting any odd root of both sides; extracting any even root of both sides, provided the $\pm$ sign is used; taking the logarithms of both sides (both sides being positive); taking the sin, cos, tan, etc., of both sides.

Notice, however, that the new equation obtained by some of these operations may possess "additional roots" which did not belong to the original equation. This occurs especially when both sides are squared; thus, $x = -2$ has only one root, namely, -2; but $x^2 = 4$, obtained by squaring, has not only the root -2 but also another root, $+2$.

Equations of the First Degree (Linear Equations). *Solution:* Collect all the terms involving x on one side of the equation, thus: $ax = b$, where a and b are known numbers. Then divide through by the coefficient of x, obtaining $x = b/a$ as the root.

Equations of the Second Degree (Quadratic Equations). *Solution:* Throw the equation into the standard form $ax^2 + bx + c = 0$. Then the two roots are

$$x_1 = \frac{-b + \sqrt{b^2 - 4ac}}{2a} \qquad x_2 = \frac{-b - \sqrt{b^2 - 4ac}}{2a}$$

The roots are real and distinct, coincident, or imaginary, according as $b^2 - 4ac$ is positive, zero, or negative. The sum of the roots is $x_1 + x_2 = -b/a$; the product of the roots is $x_1x_2 = c/a$.

Graphical Solution: Write the equation in the form $x^2 = px + q$, and plot the parabola $y_1 = x^2$, and the straight line $y_2 = px + q$. The abscissas of the points of intersection will be the roots of the equation. If the line does not cut the parabola, the roots are imaginary.

Equations of the Third Degree with Term in x^2 Absent. *Solution:* After dividing through by the coefficient of x^3, any equation of this type can be written $x^3 = Ax + B$. Let $p = A/3$ and $q = B/2$. The general solution is as follows:

CASE 1. $q^2 - p^3$ positive. One root is real, *viz.*,

$$x_1 = \sqrt[3]{q + \sqrt{q^2 - p^3}} + \sqrt[3]{q - \sqrt{q^2 - p^3}}$$

the other two roots are imaginary. If $\cosh u = q/p\sqrt{p}$, $x_1 = 2\sqrt{p} \cosh (u/3)$.

CASE 2. $q^2 - p^3$ = zero. Three roots real, but two of them equal.

$$x_1 = 2\sqrt[3]{q} \qquad x_2 = -\sqrt[3]{q} \qquad x_3 = -\sqrt[3]{q}$$

CASE 3. $q^2 - p^3$ negative. All three roots real and distinct. Determine an angle u between 0 and 180°, such that $\cos u = q/(p\sqrt{p})$. Then

$$x_1 = 2\sqrt{p} \cos (u/3)$$
$$x_2 = 2\sqrt{p} \cos (u/3 + 120°)$$
$$x_3 = 2\sqrt{p} \cos (u/3 + 240°)$$

Graphical Solution: Plot the curve $y_1 = x^3$, and the straight line $y_2 = Ax + B$. The abscissas of the points of intersection will be the roots of the equation.

Equations of the Third Degree (General Case). *Solution:* The general cubic equation, after dividing through by the coefficient of the highest power, may be written $x^3 + ax^2 + bx + c = 0$. To get rid of the term in x^2, let $x = x_1 - a/3$. The equation then becomes $x_1^3 = Ax_1 + B$, where $A = 3(a/3)^2 - b$, and $B = -2(a/3)^3 + b(a/3) - c$. Solve this equation for x_1, by the method above, and then find x itself from $x = x_1 - (a/3)$.

Graphical Solution: Without getting rid of the term in x^2, write the equation in the form $x^3 = -a[x + (b/2a)]^2 + [a(b/2a)^2 - c]$, and solve by the graphical method.

General Properties of Algebraic Equations. An algebraic equation of the nth degree in x is an equation of the type

$$a_0x^n + a_1x^{n-1} + a_2x^{n-2} + \cdots + a_{n-1}x + a_n = 0$$

where the a's are any given numbers (a_0 not zero), the expression on the left being called a **polynomial** of the nth degree in x. Such an equation will, in general, have n roots; but some of these n roots may be equal, and some may be imaginary. **Imaginary roots** always occur in pairs if the a's are all real numbers.

If the equation is written in the form: (a polynomial in x) = 0, then (1) if a is a root of the equation, $x - a$ is a factor of the polynomial; (2) if the polynomial can be factored in the form $(x - p)(x - q)(x - r) \cdots = 0$, each of the quantities p, q, r, . . . is a root of the equation; (3) if x is very large (either positive or negative), the higher powers of x are the most important; (4) if x is very small, the higher powers may be neglected.

Short Method of Substitution in a Polynomial. To find the value of $4x^4 - 14x^3 + 23x - 26$ when $x = 3$, for example, first arrange the terms in order of descending powers of x, and write the detached coefficients, with their signs, in a row, taking care to supply a zero coefficient for any missing term, including the constant term. Then, beginning at the left, bring down the first coefficient; multiply this by 3, and add to the second coefficient; multiply this result by 3 again, and add to the third coefficient; and so on. The final result, -11, is the value of the polynomial when $x = 3$.

4	−14	0	23	−26	(3
	12	−6	−18	15	
4	−2	−6	5	−11	

Short Method of Dividing a Polynomial by $x - a$. The device just explained gives not only the value of the polynomial when $x = 3$, but also the result of dividing the polynomial by $x - 3$. Thus, in the case illustrated, the quotient is $4x^3 - 2x^2 - 6x + 5$ and the remainder is -11. That is, $4x^4 - 14x^3 + 0x^2 + 23x - 26 = (x - 3)(4x^3 - 2x^2 - 6x + 5) - 11$.

Exponential Equations. To solve an equation of the form $a^x = b$, take the logarithms of both sides: $x \log a = \log b$, whence $x = (\log b)/(\log a)$. For example, if $3^x = 0.4$, $x = \log 0.4/\log 3 = (0.6021 - 1)/0.4771 = -0.3979/0.4771 = -0.8340$. Notice that the complete logarithm must be taken, not merely the mantissa.

Trigonometric Equations. (1) To solve $a \cos x + b \sin x = c$, where a and b are positive: Find the acute angle u for which $\tan u = b/a$, and the angle v (between 0 and 180°) for which $\cos v = c/\sqrt{a^2 + b^2}$. Then $x_1 = u + v$ and $x_2 = u - v$ are roots of the equation. (2) To solve $a \cos x - b \sin x = c$, where a and b are positive: Find u and v as above. Then $x_1 = -(u + v)$ and $x_2 = -(u - v)$ are roots of the equation.

General Method of Solution by Trial and Error. This method is applicable to a numerical equation of any form, and can be carried out to any desired degree of approximation. It is especially useful when a first approximation to a root is already known. Write the equation in the form $f(x) = 0$, where $f(x)$ means any function of x, and plot the curve $y = f(x)$ for a sufficient number of values of x to obtain a general idea of the shape of the curve. Then pick out the regions in which the curve appears to cross the axis of x, and plot the curve more accurately in each of these regions. Thus, by successive approximations, plotting the important parts of the curve on a larger and larger scale, determine as accurately as necessary the points where the curve crosses the axis, *i.e.*, the values of x which make $f(x)$ equal to zero.

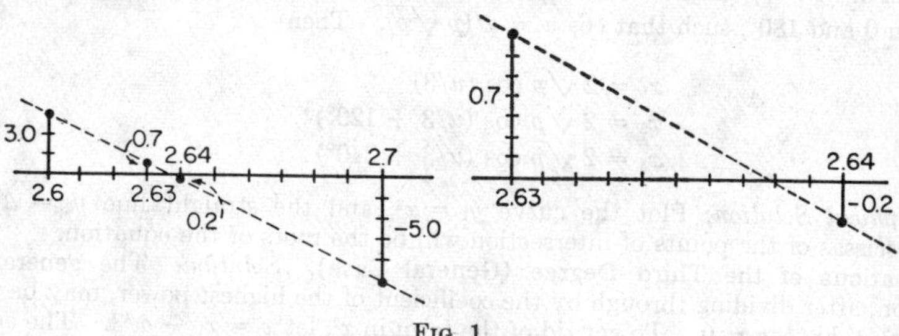

Fig. 1

Thus, suppose that $f(x) = 3.0$ when $x = 2.6$ and -5.0 when $x = 2.7$ (see Fig. 1). Then the curve must cross the axis somewhere between $x = 2.6$ and $x = 2.7$; and since it will not vary greatly from a straight line between those points, it is seen that it must cross near 2.64. Suppose the value of $f(x)$, when computed for $x = 2.64$, is -0.2, and when computed for $x = 2.63$ is $+0.7$; then the root lies between $x = 2.63$ and 2.64. Plotting this section on the larger scale, it is seen that the next guess should be about 2.638; and so on.

Instead of writing the original equation with all the terms on the left-hand side, it is often better to divide the expression into two parts, say $f_1(x)$ and $f_2(x)$, writing the equation in the form $f_1(x) = f_2(x)$. If then the two curves $y_1 = f_1(x)$ and $y_2 = f_2(x)$ be plotted separately, on the same diagram, the value of x corresponding to their point of intersection will be the desired root.

SOLUTION OF SIMULTANEOUS EQUATIONS

Meaning of a System of Simultaneous Equations. To solve a system of n simultaneous equations in n unknowns means to find all the sets of values of the unknowns (if any) which, when substituted in the given equations, will satisfy all the equations at the same time. If a system of equations has no solution, the equations are "inconsistent"; if it has an infinite number of solutions, the equations are "not all independent."

Simultaneous Equations of the First Degree in Two Unknowns

	Factors	
(1) $a_1x + b_1y = c_1$	b_2	$-a_2$
(2) $a_2x + b_2y = c_2$	$-b_1$	a_1

$$(a_1b_2 - a_2b_1)x = b_2c_1 - b_1c_2 \qquad \therefore x = (b_2c_1 - b_1c_2)/(a_1b_2 - a_2b_1)$$
$$(a_1b_2 - a_2b_1)y = a_1c_2 - a_2c_1 \qquad \therefore y = (a_1c_2 - a_2c_1)/(a_1b_2 - a_2b_1)$$

Here (1) is multiplied by b_2, (2) by $-b_1$, and the products added so as to eliminate y; again, (1) is multiplied by $-a_2$, (2) by a_1, and the products added so as to eliminate x. (The process is most conveniently performed as follows: Write the multipliers, as b_2 and $-b_1$, at the right of the equations; multiply the first term of each equation by its proper multiplier and add; then multiply the second term of each equation by its proper multiplier, and add; and so on. This is simpler than the common practice of multiplying out each equation separately before adding.) If $a_1b_2 - a_2b_1 = 0$, the equations have no solution when $c_1 \neq c_2$, and an infinite number of solutions when $c_1 = c_2$. The following **special solution** is possible when the sum and difference of the two unknowns are given:

Let	$x + y = m$ (1)	
and	$x - y = n$ (2)	
(1) + (2):	$2x = m + n$	$\therefore x = \frac{1}{2}(m + n)$
(1) − (2):	$2y = m - n$	$\therefore y = \frac{1}{2}(m - n)$

Simultaneous Equations of the Second Degree in Two Unknowns. CASE *a*. When the product of the unknowns, and their sum or difference, are given:

	$x + y = 5$	(1)
	$xy = 4$	(2)
Squaring (1),	$x^2 + 2xy + y^2 = 25$	
From (2),	$-4xy = -16$	
Adding,	$x^2 - 2xy + y^2 = 9$	
Hence,	$x - y = 3$ or -3	
But	$x + y = 5$ or 5	
Therefore,	$x = 4,\ y = 1$ or $x = 1,\ y = 4$	

$x - y = 3$	(1)
$xy = 4$	(2)
$x^2 - 2xy + y^2 = 9$	
$4xy = 16$	
$x^2 + 2xy + y^2 = 25$	
$x + y = 5$ or -5	
$x - y = 3$ or 3	
$x = 4,\ y = 1$ or $x = -1,\ y = -4$	

CASE *b*. When the product and the sum of the squares are given:

	$xy = 5$	(1)
	$x^2 + y^2 = 26$	(2)
From (1),	$2xy = 10$	(3)
(2) + (3):	$x^2 + 2xy + y^2 = 36$	(4)
(2) − (3):	$x^2 - 2xy + y^2 = 16$	(5)

$\sqrt{(4)}: x + y =$	6 or	6 or	−6 or	−6
$\sqrt{(5)}: x - y =$	4 or	−4 or	4 or	−4
$\therefore x =$	5 or	1 or	−1 or	−5
$\therefore y =$	1	5	−5	−1

CASE *c*. **When the sum or difference, and the sum of the squares, are given:**

$$\begin{array}{lrl} & x + y = 5 & (1)\\ & x^2 + y^2 = 17 & (2)\\ (1)^2: & x^2 + 2xy + y^2 = 25 & \\ (2): & x^2 + y^2 = 17 & \\ \hline (1)^2 - (2): & 2xy = 8 & \\ & xy = 4 & \end{array}$$

Then proceed as in Case *a*, above.

$$\begin{array}{lrl} & x - y = 3 & (1)\\ & x^2 + y^2 = 17 & (2)\\ (1)^2: & x^2 - 2xy + y^2 = 9 & \\ (2): & x^2 + y^2 = 17 & \\ \hline (1)^2 - (2): & -2xy = -8 & \\ & xy = 4 & \end{array}$$

Then proceed as in Case *a*, above.

CASE *d*. When one equation is of the first degree and the other of the second, as $ax + by = c$, and $Ax^2 + Bxy + Cy^2 + Dx + Ey + F = 0$: Solve the first equation for y in terms of x, and substitute in the second. This will give a quadratic equation in x. Solve this quadratic for the two values of x, and for each of these values of x find the corresponding value of y by substituting in the equation of the first degree.

Simultaneous Equations of the First Degree in *n* Unknowns. For example:

	Equation	Factors		
(*a*)	$2x - y + 3z + 5w = 29$	3	1	2
(*b*)	$5x + 2y - 2z + 3w = 15$	−5		
(*c*)	$3x - 4y + 7z - w = 12$		5	
(*d*)	$4x + 3y - 5z + 2w = 3$			−5
(*e*)	$-19x - 13y + 19z = 12$	−2	−31	
(*f*)	$17x - 21y + 38z = 89$	1		
(*g*)	$-16x - 17y + 31z = 43$		19	
(*h*)	$55x + 5y = 65$	16		
(*i*)	$285x + 80y = 445$	−1		
(*j*)	$595x = 595$;			

$$\begin{array}{ll} 595x = 595; & \therefore x = 1\\ 5y = 65 - 55x = 65 - 55 = 10; & \therefore y = 2\\ 19z = 12 + 19x + 13y = 12 + 19 + 26 = 57; & \therefore z = 3\\ 2w = 3 - 4x - 3y + 5z = 3 - 4 - 6 + 15 = 8; & \therefore w = 4 \end{array}$$

Here w is eliminated from (*a*) and (*b*), obtaining (*e*); from (*a*) and (*c*), obtaining (*f*); and from (*a*) and (*d*), obtaining (*g*). Then z is eliminated from (*e*) and (*f*), obtaining (*h*), and from (*e*) and (*g*), obtaining (*i*). Then y is eliminated from (*h*) and (*i*), obtaining (*j*), which contains only the single variable x. Hence $x = 1$. Now substituting this value of x in either (*h*) or (*i*), y is found; substituting these values of x and y in either (*e*), (*f*), or (*g*), z is found; and so on. (Solution by determinants, see p. 2–35.)

Approximate Solution of a Set of Simultaneous Equations of the First Degree When the Number of Equations is Greater Than the Number of Unknowns (Method of Least Squares).

CASE 1. SINGLE UNKNOWN QUANTITY. Given n equations in one unknown x; *e.g.*, n equally careful, independent measurements of some physical quantity:

$$x = x_1 \qquad x = x_2 \qquad \cdots x = x_n$$

As the "best" value of x, take the arithmetic mean, x_0, of the several determinations, namely, $x_0 = (x_1 + x_2 + \cdots + x_n)/n$. The quantities $v_1 = x_0 - x_1$, $v_2 = x_0 - x_2$, $\ldots v_n = x_0 - x_n$ are called the **residuals** of the observed values with respect to x_0, and their absolute values (*i.e.*, their numerical values without regard to sign) are denoted by $|v_1|, |v_2|, \ldots |v_n|$. (It can be shown that the sum of the squares of the residuals with respect to x_0 is smaller than the sum of the squares of the residuals with respect to any other value x_0'; hence the name of the method: "least squares.")

The quantities r and r_0, defined exactly by **Bessel's** formulas:

$$r = \frac{0.6745}{\sqrt{n-1}}\sqrt{v_1^2 + v_2^2 + \cdots + v_n^2}$$

$$r_0 = \frac{0.6745}{\sqrt{n(n-1)}}\sqrt{v_1^2 + v_2^2 + \cdots + v_n^2}$$

or given approximately by the simpler formulas of **Peters:**

$$r = \frac{0.8453}{\sqrt{n(n-1)}}(|v_1| + |v_2| + \cdots + |v_n|)$$

$$r_0 = \frac{0.8453}{n\sqrt{n-1}}(|v_1| + |v_2| + \cdots + |v_n|)$$

are called the **probable error of a single observation** (r), and the **probable error of the mean** (r_0), for the given series of observations. Note that $r_0 = r/\sqrt{n}$. For tables of the coefficients, see p. 1–63. This quantity r (or r_0) is best regarded as merely a conventional means of recording the relative precision of different sets of observations. If r is small, it may be inferred that most errors of the "accidental" class have been eliminated; but it should be especially noted that the smallness of r gives no information in regard to "constant" or "systematic" errors.

A statement like "x is equal to 2.36 with a probable error of 0.02," is written: $x = 2.36 \pm 0.02$, and is usually understood to mean that **the true value** of x, as far as can be told, **is just as likely to lie inside as outside the interval** from 2.34 to 2.38.

To test the **distribution of residuals,** arrange the residuals in order of magnitude, without regard to sign, and count the number, y, of residuals which are numerically less than some assigned value a; divide y by n, the total number of observations, and divide a by r, the probable error of a single observation. Do this for various values of a, and compare the results with the table on p. 1–63, which gives the standard distribution of residuals, as found from experience from a large number of different series of observations. In particular, the number of residuals numerically less than r should be about equal to the number numerically greater than r (if n is large). If any large discrepancy appears, the series of observations should be regarded as unsatisfactory.

NOTE. The "mean square error" sometimes met with is equal to the probable error divided by 0.6745.

CASE 2. SEVERAL UNKNOWN QUANTITIES. Assume that there have been obtained by measurement or observation n different equations of the first degree involving, say, three unknown quantities, x, y, z. There are then n simultaneous equations in three unknowns, and if $n > 3$ there will be, in general, no set of values of x, y, z which will satisfy all these n equations exactly. In such a case, the "best" set of values, x_0, y_0, z_0, may be found by the method of least squares as follows. (The process usually involves a large amount of labor; the use of a desk calculator is advisable.)

Given Equations

$$\begin{aligned} a_1x + b_1y + c_1z &= p_1 \\ a_2x + b_2y + c_2z &= p_2 \\ \cdot \quad \cdot \quad &\quad \cdot \\ a_nx + b_ny + c_nz &= p_n \end{aligned}$$

First, arrange the n given equations in the form indicated, being careful not to modify any of them by multiplication or division. (Any of the coefficients may of course be zero.)

Next, form the three "normal equations" as follows: (1) Multiply each of the given equations by the coefficient of x in that equation, and add; the result will be the first normal equation. (2) Multiply each of the given equations by the coefficient of y in that equation, and add; the result will be the second normal equation. (3) Similarly for the third. {Notation: $[aa] = a_1^2 + a_2^2 + \cdots + a_n^2$; $[ab] = a_1b_1 + a_2b_2 + \cdots + a_nb_n$; $[ap] = a_1p_1 + a_2p_2 + \cdots + a_np_n$; etc.}

Normal Equations

$$\begin{aligned} [aa]x_0 + [ab]y_0 + [ac]z_0 &= [ap] \\ [ba]x_0 + [bb]y_0 + [cc]z_0 &= [bp] \\ [ca]x_0 + [cb]y_0 + [cc]z_0 &= [cp] \end{aligned}$$

Finally, solve the three normal equations for the three unknowns in the usual way.

The quantities $v_1 = a_1x_0 + b_1y_0 + c_1z_0 - p_1$, etc., are called the **residuals** with respect to x_0, y_0, z_0. (It can be shown that the sum of the squares of the residuals with respect to x_0, y_0, z_0 is smaller than the corresponding quantity with respect to any other set of values, x_0', y_0', z_0'; this relation is taken as the criterion for the "best" set of values of x, y, z.)

One application of the above least-squares process is to find the constants defining a curve of assumed form best fitting a set of observed points. We illustrate for a straight line $y = mx + b$ best fitting a set of points x_i, y_i. We assume that the x_i are exact and only the y_i are subject to error. Here the normal equations are $m(xx) + b(x1) = (xy)$, $m(x1) + b(11) = (y1)$, where $(x1) = x_1 + x_2 + \cdots + x_n$, $(11) = 1 + 1 + \cdots + 1 = n$. Thus the second normal equation expresses the fact that the center of gravity of the points $(x_i/n, y_i/n)$ lies on the line of best fit.

The probable error of a single observation is

$$r = \frac{0.6745}{\sqrt{n-m}}\sqrt{v_1^2 + v_2^2 + \cdots + v_n^2}, \text{ or approx.}$$

$$r = \frac{0.8453}{\sqrt{n(n-m)}}(|v_1| + |v_2| + \cdots + |v_n|)$$

where m = the number of unknown quantities (here $m = 3$).

DETERMINANTS

Determinants are used chiefly in formulating theoretical results; they are seldom of use in numerical computation.

Evaluation of Determinants

Of the second order:

$$\begin{vmatrix} a & b_1 \\ a_2 & b_2 \end{vmatrix} = a_1b_2 - a_2b_1$$

Of the third order:

$$\begin{vmatrix} a_1 & b_1 & c_1 \\ a_2 & b_2 & c_2 \\ a_3 & b_3 & c_3 \end{vmatrix} = a_1\begin{vmatrix} b_2 & c_2 \\ b_3 & c_3 \end{vmatrix} - a_2\begin{vmatrix} b_1 & c_1 \\ b_3 & c_3 \end{vmatrix} + a_3\begin{vmatrix} b_1 & c_1 \\ b_2 & c_2 \end{vmatrix}$$
$$= a_1(b_2c_3 - b_3c_2) - a_2(b_1c_3 - b_3c_1) + a_3(b_1c_2 - b_2c_1)$$

Of the fourth order:

$$\begin{vmatrix} a_1 & b_1 & c_1 & d_1 \\ a_2 & b_2 & c_2 & d_2 \\ a_3 & b_3 & c_3 & d_3 \\ a_4 & b_4 & c_4 & d_4 \end{vmatrix} = a_1\begin{vmatrix} b_2 & c_2 & d_2 \\ b_3 & c_3 & d_3 \\ b_4 & c_4 & d_4 \end{vmatrix} - a_2\begin{vmatrix} b_1 & c_1 & d_1 \\ b_3 & c_3 & d_3 \\ b_4 & c_4 & d_4 \end{vmatrix} + a_3\begin{vmatrix} b_1 & c_1 & d_1 \\ b_2 & c_2 & d_2 \\ b_4 & c_4 & d_4 \end{vmatrix} - a_4\begin{vmatrix} b_1 & c_1 & d_1 \\ b_2 & c_2 & d_2 \\ b_3 & c_3 & d_3 \end{vmatrix}$$

etc. In general, to evaluate a determinant of the nth order, take the elements of the first column with signs alternately plus and minus, and form the sum of the products obtained by multiplying each of these elements by its corresponding **minor.** The minor corresponding to any element a_1 is the determinant (of next lower order) obtained by striking out from the given determinant the row and column containing a_1.

Properties of Determinants

1. The columns may be changed to rows and the rows to columns:

$$\begin{vmatrix} a_1 & b_1 & c_1 \\ a_2 & b_2 & c_2 \\ a_3 & b_3 & c_3 \end{vmatrix} = \begin{vmatrix} a_1 & a_2 & a_3 \\ b_1 & b_2 & b_3 \\ c_1 & c_2 & c_3 \end{vmatrix}$$

2. Interchanging two adjacent columns changes the sign of the result.

3. If two columns are equal, the determinant is zero.

4. If the elements of one column are m times the elements of another column, the determinant is zero.

5. To multiply a determinant by any number m, multiply all the elements of any one column by m.

6. $$\begin{vmatrix} a_1 + p_1 + q_1, & b_1 & c_1 \\ a_2 + p_2 + q_2, & b_2 & c_2 \\ a_3 + p_3 + q_3, & b_3 & c_3 \end{vmatrix} = \begin{vmatrix} a_1 & b_1 & c_1 \\ a_2 & b_2 & c_2 \\ a_3 & b_3 & c_3 \end{vmatrix} + \begin{vmatrix} p_1 & b_1 & c_1 \\ p_2 & b_2 & c_2 \\ p_3 & b_3 & c_3 \end{vmatrix} + \begin{vmatrix} q_1 & b_1 & c_1 \\ q_2 & b_2 & c_2 \\ q_3 & b_3 & c_3 \end{vmatrix}$$

7. $$\begin{vmatrix} a_1 & b_1 & c_1 \\ a_2 & b_2 & c_2 \\ a_3 & b_3 & c_3 \end{vmatrix} = \begin{vmatrix} a_1 + mb_1, & b_1 & c_1 \\ a_2 + mb_2, & b_2 & c_2 \\ a_3 + mb_3, & b_3 & c_3 \end{vmatrix}$$

Solution of Simultaneous Equations by Determinants

If
$$\begin{aligned} a_1x + b_1y + c_1z &= p_1 \\ a_2x + b_2y + c_2z &= p_2 \\ a_3x + b_3y + c_3z &= p_3 \end{aligned} \quad \text{where } D = \begin{vmatrix} a_1b_1c_1 \\ a_2b_2c_2 \\ a_3b_3c_3 \end{vmatrix} \neq 0,$$

then
$$\begin{aligned} x &= D_1/D, \\ y &= D_2/D, \text{ where } D_1 = \begin{vmatrix} p_1b_1c_1 \\ p_2b_2c_2 \\ p_3b_3c_3 \end{vmatrix}, D_2 = \begin{vmatrix} a_1p_1c_1 \\ a_2p_2c_2 \\ a_3p_3c_3 \end{vmatrix}, D_3 = \begin{vmatrix} a_1b_1p_1 \\ a_2b_2p_2 \\ a_3b_3p_3 \end{vmatrix} \\ z &= D_3/D, \end{aligned}$$

Similarly for a larger (or smaller) number of equations.

IMAGINARY OR COMPLEX QUANTITIES

In the algebra of imaginary or complex quantities, the objects on which the operations of the algebra are performed are not numbers in any ordinary sense of the word, but are best thought of as **points in a plane** (or as **vectors** drawn from a fixed origin to these points). The **"complex plane"** is determined by three fundamental points, O, U, i, arranged as in Fig. 2 and called the **zero point**, the **unit point**, and the **imaginary unit**

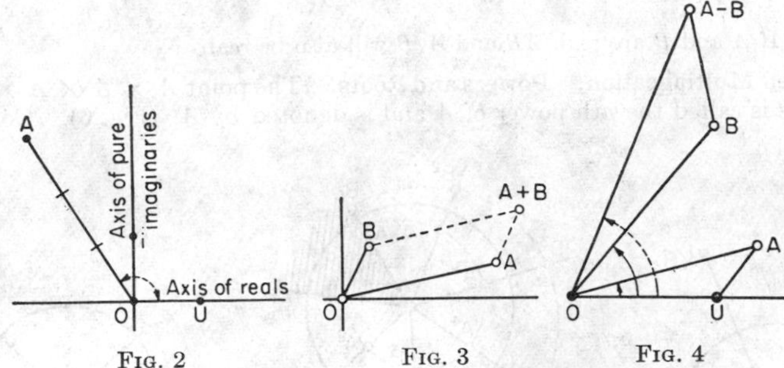

FIG. 2 FIG. 3 FIG. 4

point, respectively. All points on the line through O and U are called **real points**—positive if on the right of O, negative if on the left. All the remaining points in the plane are called **imaginary points**—those on the line through O and i being called the **pure imaginary points.**

The position of any point A in the plane may be determined by the *distance* from the origin O, measured in terms of OU as the unit length, and the *angle* φ which OA makes with the positive direction of the axis of reals. The distance r is sometimes called the modulus or absolute value of the point; the angle φ is sometimes called the amplitude or argument of the point. The notation $A = (3/120°)$ means the point whose *distance*, r, is 3 times OU, and whose *angle*, φ, is 120°. The development of the algebra depends wholly on the definitions of three fundamental operations denoted by $A + B$, $A \times B$, and e_A, as follows.

Addition and Subtraction. The **sum,** $A + B$, of two points A and B is defined as the point reached by starting from A and performing a journey equal in length and direction to the journey from O to B. That is, the vector from O to $A + B$ is the vector sum of the vectors OA and OB. In case A and B are not in line with O, the point $A + B$ is the fourth vertex of a parallelogram of which OA and OB are the sides (Fig. 3). Conversely, if any two points A and B are given, there is a definite point X such that $A = B + X$; this point X is called the **remainder,** A minus B, and is denoted by $A - B$. The point $O - B$ is denoted for brevity by $-B$. With these definitions of $A + B$ and $A - B$, all the ordinary laws of addition and subtraction that hold in the algebra of real numbers hold also in the algebra of complex quantities. In particular, the zero point O has all the formal properties of the number zero, and is denoted by 0.

NOTE. If A and B are "real" points, $A + B$ and $A - B$ will also be real.

Repeated Addition. Multiples and Submultiples. The point $A + A + A + \cdots + A$ to n terms is called the **nth multiple of** A and is denoted by nA. The points

$U, 2U, 3U, \ldots$ are denoted, for brevity, by $1, 2, 3, \ldots$. Conversely, if any point A and any positive integer n are given, there is a definite point X such that $nX = A$; this point X is called the n**th submultiple of A,** and is denoted by A/n. The points $U/2, U/3, \ldots$ are denoted, for brevity, by $\frac{1}{2}, \frac{1}{3}, \ldots$.

Multiplication and Division. The **product,** $A \times B$, or $A \cdot B$, or AB, of two points A and B is defined as the point whose angle is the sum of the angles of the given points, and whose distance is the product of the distances. (See Fig. 4.) Thus, if $A = (5/\underline{120°})$ and $B = (2/\underline{270°})$, then $AB = (10/\underline{30°})$. Conversely, if any two points A and B are given, provided B is not zero, there is a definite point X such that $A = BX$. This point X is called the **quotient,** A divided by B, and is denoted by A/B (where $B \neq 0$). Thus, the point A/B is a point whose angle is the angle of A minus the angle of B, and whose distance is the distance of A divided by the distance of B. The point U/B ($B \neq 0$) is called the **reciprocal** of the point B, and is denoted by $1/B$ (see Fig. 5). With these definitions of AB and A/B, the elementary laws of multiplication and division that hold in the algebra of real numbers hold also in the algebra of complex quantities. In particular, the point U has all the formal properties of the number unity, and is denoted by 1.

NOTE. If A and B are real, AB and A/B will also be real.

Repeated Multiplication. Powers and Roots. The point $A \times A \times A \times \cdots \times A$ to n factors is called the nth power of A and is denoted by A^n (Fig. 6). Conversely, if

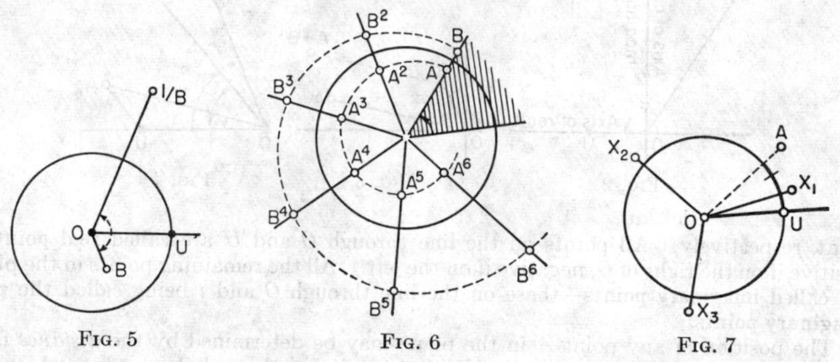

FIG. 5 FIG. 6 FIG. 7

any point A (not 0) and any positive integer n are given, there will be n distinct points X such that $X^n = A$; each of these points is called an n**th root of** A, some one of them, usually the one with the smallest positive angle, being denoted by $\sqrt[n]{A}$ or $A^{1/n}$. Thus, the point $\sqrt[n]{A}$ is a point whose distance is the nth root of the distance of A, and whose angle is $1/n$th of the angle of A. All the nth roots of A will lie on the circumference of a circle about O as center, and will divide that circumference into n equal parts (Fig. 7). Every point A (not 0) has two square roots, three cube roots, etc. Hence the theorem "If $A^n = B^n$ then $A = B$" does not hold in this algebra, and the ordinary rules for radical signs must be applied with caution. For example, if A and B are positive reals, $\sqrt{-A} \cdot \sqrt{-B} = -\sqrt{AB}$ and not $\sqrt{(-A)(-B)}$, which would give $+\sqrt{AB}$.

NOTE. If A is real and positive, $\sqrt[n]{A}$ will be real and positive; if A is real and negative, $\sqrt[n]{A}$ will be real if n is odd and imaginary if n is even.

Properties of i. The point i is the point whose distance is 1 and whose angle is 90 deg. It follows from the definition above that **multiplying any point** A **by** i **has the effect of rotating the point through an angle of +90°** without changing its distance from O. In particular, $i^2 = -1$, $i^3 = -i$, $i^4 = 1$, $i^5 = i$, etc.; $i = \sqrt{-1}$, $-i = -\sqrt{-1}$; where "1" denotes not the *number* one, but the *point* U.

Similarly, multiplying any point A by -1 has the effect of rotating the point through 180 deg.

First Standard Form for a Complex Quantity (Fig. 8). Any point A can be expressed in the form $x + iy$, where x and y are real points. For example, the three cube roots of 1 are 1, $-\frac{1}{2} + \frac{1}{2}i\sqrt{3}$, and $-\frac{1}{2} - \frac{1}{2}i\sqrt{3}$.
In general, $(x_1 + iy_1) + (x_2 + iy_2) = (x_1 + x_2) + i(y_1 + y_2)$

$$(x_1 + iy_1)(x_2 + iy_2) = (x_1x_2 - y_1y_2) + i(x_2y_1 + x_1y_2)$$

$$\frac{x_1 + iy_1}{x_2 + iy_2} = \frac{x_1x_2 + y_1y_2}{x_2^2 + y_2^2} + i\frac{x_2y_1 - x_1y_2}{x_2^2 + y_2^2}$$

If two complex quantities are equal, their real parts must be equal, and the coefficients of their pure imaginary parts must also be equal; *i.e.*, if $x_1 + iy_1 = x_2 + iy_2$, then $x_1 = x_2$ and $y_1 = y_2$. Thus a single equation between complex quantities is equivalent to two equations between real quantities.

Conjugate Imaginaries. Two points $A = x + iy$ and $B = x - iy$ are called conjugate imaginaries. Two such points are symmetrically situated with regard to the axis of reals. The sum and product of two conjugate imaginaries will be real.

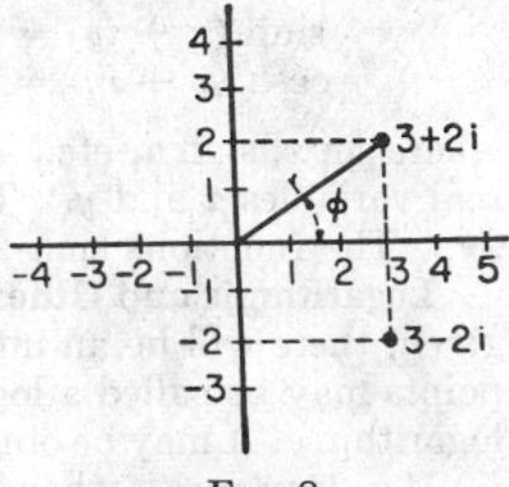

FIG. 8

Second Standard Form for a Complex Quantity. Since $x = r\cos\varphi$ and $y = r\sin\varphi$, any point $A = x + iy$ can be expressed as $A = r(\cos\varphi + i\sin\varphi)$, where r is real and positive (namely, the distance of A), and φ is real (namely the angle of A). For example, the three cube roots of 1 are 1, $\cos 120° + i\sin 120°$, and $\cos 240° + i\sin 240°$. In general,

$$[r_1(\cos\varphi_1 + i\sin\varphi_1)][r_2(\cos\varphi_2 + i\sin\varphi_2)] = r_1r_2[\cos(\varphi_1 + \varphi_2) + i\sin(\varphi_1 + \varphi_2)]$$

and

$$[r(\cos\varphi + i\sin\varphi)]^n = r^n[\cos(n\varphi) + i\sin(n\varphi)]$$ **(De Moivre's theorem)**

The **exponential function,** e^A, or exp A, of any point $A = x + iy$ is defined as the point whose distance is e^x and whose angle (measured in radians) is y; *i.e.*, $e^{x+iy} = e^x(\cos y + i\sin y)$. Here e^x means the ordinary exponential function of the real quantity x, where $e = 2.718$.

From this definition, the usual formal laws of exponents can be deduced: $e^Ae^B = e^{A+B}$, $(e^A)^n = e^{nA}$, $e^{-A} = 1/e^A$; $e^1 = e$, $e^0 = 1$.

The function e^A is a periodic function with a pure imaginary period $2\pi i$; **that is,** $e^{A\pm k2\pi i} = e^A$, where k is any positive integer.

If A is made to move along a line parallel to the axis of reals (or axis of pure imaginaries), the corresponding point e^A will move along a straight line through O (or along a circle about O as center).

Properties of $e^{i\varphi}$. The point $e^{i\varphi}$ is a point whose distance is 1 and whose angle is φ. If follows from the definitions above that **multiplying any point A by $e^{i\varphi}$ has the effect of rotating the point through an angle** φ, without changing its distance from O. In particular, $e^{i\pi} = -1$, $e^{-i\pi} = -1$; $e^{i\pi/2} = i$; $e^{-i\pi/2} = -i$; $e^{2\pi i} = 1$.

Third Standard Form for a Complex Quantity. Any point A can be expressed in the form $A = re^{i\varphi}$, where r is the distance and φ the angle of the point. For example, the three cube roots of 1 are 1, $e^{\frac{1}{3}2\pi i}$, $e^{\frac{2}{3}2\pi i}$. In general,

$$(r_1e^{i\varphi_1})(r_2e^{i\varphi_2}) = (r_1r_2)e^{i(\varphi_1+\varphi_2)}; \qquad (re^{i\varphi})^n = (r^n)e^{in\varphi}$$

If $x + iy = re^{i\varphi}$, then $r = \sqrt{x^2 + y^2}$, $\sin\varphi = y/r$, $\cos\varphi = x/r$, $\tan\varphi = y/x$.

If two complex quantities are equal, their distances will be equal, and their angles will differ at most by some multiple of 2π. Thus, if $r_1e^{i\varphi_1} = r_2e^{i\varphi_2}$ then $r_1 = r_2$ and $\varphi_1 = \varphi_2$ or $\varphi_2 \pm k2\pi$. Here again a single equation between complex quantities is equivalent to two equations between real quantities.

Definition of A^B. Let $A = re^{i\varphi}$; then $A^B = \exp[(\ln r + i\varphi)B]$.

For example, $i^i = e^{-\pi/2}$ where $i = \sqrt{-1}$.

If a is a positive real, $a^{x+iy} = a^x[\cos(y\ln a) + i\sin(y\ln a)]$.

Trigonometric and Hyperbolic Functions of a Complex Variable. If A is any point, then, by definition,

$$\sin A = \frac{e^{iA} - e^{-iA}}{2i} \qquad \cos A = \frac{e^{iA} + e^{-iA}}{2} \qquad \tan A = \frac{\sin A}{\cos A}$$

$$\sinh A = \frac{e^{A} - e^{-A}}{2} \qquad \cosh A = \frac{e^{A} + e^{-A}}{2} \qquad \tanh A = \frac{\sinh A}{\cosh A}$$

Hence the formulas that hold for these functions in the real case (pp. 2–42, 2–46, 2–67) hold also for the complex case. Further;

$$\begin{aligned}
\sin (x + iy) &= \sin x \cosh y + i \cos x \sinh y & \sin iy &= i \sinh y \\
\cos (x + iy) &= \cos x \cosh y - i \sin x \sinh y & \cos iy &= \cosh y \\
\sinh (x + iy) &= \sinh x \cos y + i \cosh x \sin y & \sinh iy &= i \sin y \\
\cosh (x + iy) &= \cosh x \cos y + i \sinh x \sin y & \cosh iy &= \cos y
\end{aligned}$$

where $\sin x$, $\sinh x$, etc., are the ordinary trigonometric and hyperbolic functions of the real variables x and y. The functions $\sin A$ and $\cos A$ are periodic with a real period 2π. The functions $\sinh A$ and $\cosh A$ are periodic with a pure imaginary period $2\pi i$.

Logarithmic and Other Inverse Functions of a Complex Variable. If any point A is given, there will be an infinite number of points X such that $e^x = A$; any one of these points may be called a logarithm of A, and be denoted by $\ln A$. All the values of the logarithm of A may be obtained from any one value by adding multiples of $2\pi i$.

If $x + iy = re^{i\varphi}$, then $\ln (x + iy) = \ln r + i\varphi \pm k \cdot 2\pi i$.

If any point A is given, there will be an infinite number of points X such that $\sin X = A$; any one of these may be denoted by $\sin^{-1} A$. The functions $\cos^{-1} A$, $\sinh^{-1} A$, etc., are defined in a similar way.

The elementary laws of operation which hold for these functions in the algebra of reals hold also, in a general way, in the algebra of complex quantities; but caution must be used, on account of the ambiguity in the symbols $\ln A$, $\sin^{-1}A$, etc., which denote many-valued functions. For a method of numerically computing possible correct determinations, see Franklin, "Fourier Methods," pp. 19–26, McGraw-Hill.

Differentiation of Functions of a Complex Variable. If $w = f(z)$, the derivative of w with respect to z is defined as

$$dw/dz = \lim \{[f(z + \Delta z) - f(z)]/\Delta z\}, \text{ when } \Delta z \text{ approaches } 0$$

It can be shown that $\lim [(\exp \Delta z - 1)/\Delta z] = 1$; hence $d(e^z) = e^z\, dz$, $d(\sin z) = \cos z\, dz$, etc., so that the formulas for differentiation here are the same as in the case of a real variable (p. 2–64).

Note. For the algebra of vector analysis, which differs in important respects from the algebra of complex quantities, see p. 2–96.

TRIGONOMETRY

BY

Philip Franklin

FORMAL TRIGONOMETRY

Angles or Rotations. An **angle** is generated by the rotation of a ray, as Ox, about a fixed point O in the plane. Every angle has an **initial line** (OA) from which the rotation started (Fig. 1), and a **terminal line** (OB) where it stopped; and the counterclockwise direction of rotation is taken as positive. Since the rotating ray may revolve as often as desired, angles of any magnitude, positive or negative, may be obtained. Two angles are **congruent** if they may be superposed so that their initial lines coincide and their terminal lines coincide; *i.e.*, two congruent angles are either equal or differ by some multiple of 360 deg. Two angles are **complementary** if their sum is 90 deg; **supplementary** if their sum is 180 deg. (The acute angles of a right-angled triangle are complementary.) If the initial line is placed so that it runs horizontally to the right, as in

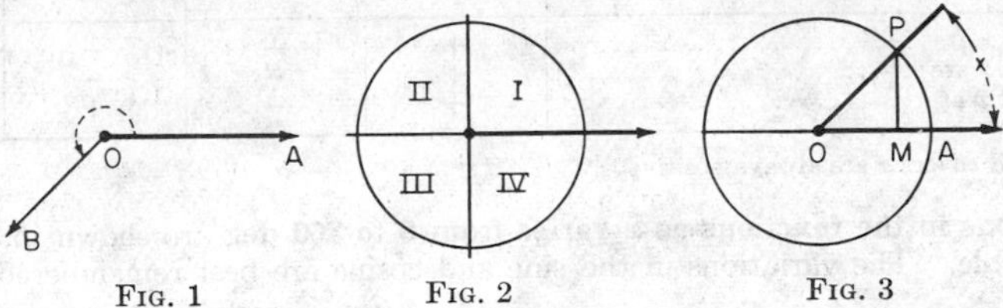

FIG. 1 FIG. 2 FIG. 3

Fig. 2, then the angle is said to be an angle in the 1st, 2nd, 3rd, or 4th **quadrant** according as the terminal line lies across the region marked I, II, III, or IV. The angles 0, 90, 180, 270 deg are called the quadrantal angles.

Units of Angular Measurement

1. SEXAGESIMAL MEASURE. (360 degrees = 1 revolution.) 1 degree = $1° = \frac{1}{90}$ of a right angle. The degree is usually divided into 60 equal parts called minutes (′), and each minute into 60 equal parts called seconds (″); while the second is subdivided decimally. But for many purposes it is more convenient to divide the degree itself into decimal parts, thus avoiding the use of minutes and seconds. (See tables, pp. 1–46 to 1–51.)

2. CENTESIMAL MEASURE, used chiefly in France. (400 grades = 1 revolution.) 1 grade = $\frac{1}{100}$ of a right angle. The grade is always divided decimally, the following terms being sometimes used: 1 "centesimal minute" = $\frac{1}{100}$ of a grade; 1 "centesimal second" = $\frac{1}{100}$ of a centesimal minute. In reading Continental books it is important to notice carefully which system is employed.

3. RADIAN, OR CIRCULAR, MEASURE. (π radians = 180 degrees.) 1 radian = the angle subtended by an arc whose length is equal to the length of the radius. The radian is constantly used in higher mathematics and in mechanics, and is always divided decimally. Table, pp. 1–44, 1–45.

1 radian = $57°.30 - = 57°.2957795131 = 57°\ 17'\ 44''.806247 = 180°/\pi$.

$1° = 0.01745\ \ldots$ radian = 0.01745 32925 radian.

$1' = 0.00029\ 08882$ radian.

$1'' = 0.00000\ 48481$ radian.

(For ten-place conversion tables, see the Smithsonian Tables of Hyperbolic Functions, Washington, D.C.)

Definitions of the Trigonometric Functions. Let x be any angle whose initial line is OA and terminal line OP (see Fig. 3). Drop a perpendicular from P on OA or OA produced. In the right triangle OMP, the three sides are MP = "side opposite" O (positive if running upward); OM = "side adjacent" to O (positive if running to the right); OP = "hypotenuse" or "radius" (may always be taken as positive); and the six ratios between these sides are the principal trigonometric functions of the angle x; thus:

$$\begin{aligned} \text{sine of } x &= \sin x = \text{opp/hyp} = MP/OP \\ \text{cosine of } x &= \cos x = \text{adj/hyp} = OM/OP \\ \text{tangent of } x &= \tan x = \text{opp/adj} = MP/OM \\ \text{cotangent of } x &= \cot x = \text{adj/opp} = OM/MP \\ \text{secant of } x &= \sec x = \text{hyp/adj} = OP/OM \\ \text{cosecant of } x &= \csc x = \text{hyp/opp} = OP/MP \end{aligned}$$

The last three are best remembered as the reciprocals of the first three:

$$\cot x = 1/\tan x \qquad \sec x = 1/\cos x \qquad \csc x = 1/\sin x$$

Other functions in use are the versed sine, the coversed sine, and the exterior secant:

$$\text{vers } x = 1 - \cos x \qquad \text{covers } x = 1 - \sin x \qquad \text{exsec } x = \sec x - 1$$

For graphs, see p. 2–84; series, p. 2–67.

Signs of the Trigonometric Functions

If x is in quadrant	I	II	III	IV
$\sin x$ and $\csc x$ are..........	+	+	−	−
$\cos x$ and $\sec x$ are..........	+	−	−	+
$\tan x$ and $\cot x$ are..........	+	−	+	−

Vers x and covers x are always positive.

Variations in the functions as x varies from 0 to 360 deg are shown in the accompanying table. The variations in the sine and cosine are best remembered by noting

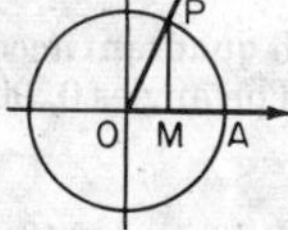

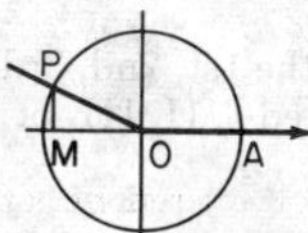

Fig. 4

the changes in the lines MP and OM (Fig. 4) in the "unit circle" (*i.e.*, a circle with radius = OP = 1), as P moves around the circumference.

x	0° to 90°	90° to 180°	180° to 270°	270° to 360°	Values at 30°	Values at 45°	Values at 60°
sin x	+0 to +1	+1 to +0	−0 to −1	−1 to −0	½	$\frac{1}{2}\sqrt{2}$	$\frac{1}{2}\sqrt{3}$
csc x	+∞ to +1	+1 to +∞	−∞ to −1	−1 to −∞	2	$\sqrt{2}$	$\frac{2}{3}\sqrt{3}$
cos x	+1 to +0	−0 to −1	−1 to −0	+0 to +1	$\frac{1}{2}\sqrt{3}$	$\frac{1}{2}\sqrt{2}$	½
sec x	+1 to +∞	−∞ to −1	−1 to −∞	+∞ to +1	$\frac{2}{3}\sqrt{3}$	$\sqrt{2}$	2
tan x	+0 to +∞	−∞ to −0	+0 to +∞	−∞ to −0	$\frac{1}{3}\sqrt{3}$	1	$\sqrt{3}$
cot x	+∞ to +0	−0 to −∞	+∞ to +0	−0 to −∞	$\sqrt{3}$	1	$\frac{1}{3}\sqrt{3}$
vers x	+0 to +1	+1 to +2	+2 to +1	+1 to +0			
covers x	+1 to +0	+0 to +1	+1 to +2	+2 to +1			

$\sqrt{2} = 1.4142$; $\frac{1}{2}\sqrt{2} = 0.7071$; $\sqrt{3} = 1.7321$; $\frac{1}{2}\sqrt{3} = 0.8660$; $\frac{1}{3}\sqrt{3} = 0.5774$; $\frac{2}{3}\sqrt{3} = 1.1547$.

Trigonometrical Tables. The tables on pp. 1–46 to 1–56 give the values of the principal trigonometric functions and of their logarithms, correct to four places of decimals, the angle advancing either by tenths of a degree (p. 1–46) or by 10 min (p. 1–52). These tables will be found adequate for most computations in which an accuracy of 1 part in 1,000 is sufficient. If much computing is to be done, it is advisable to use a separate volume of tables, containing more facilities for interpolation, and printed in larger type, such as the four-place tables of Huntington (Houghton Mifflin), with convenient marginal tabs; the five-place tables published by Macmillan or many others; the six-place tables of Bremiker; the standard seven-place tables of Schrön, Vega, or Bruhns (angles advancing by 10 sec); or the great eight-place of Bauschinger and Peters (angles advancing at intervals of 1 sec from 0 to 90 deg). The larger tables give only the logarithms of the functions, not the natural values.

To Find Any Function of a Given Angle. (Reduction to the first quadrant.) It is often required to find the functions of any angle x from a table that includes only angles between 0 and 90 deg. If x is not already between 0 and 360 deg, first "reduce to the first revolution" by simply adding or subtracting the proper multiple of 360 deg [for any function of (x) = the same function of $(x \pm n \times 360°)$]. Next **reduce to the first quadrant** as follows:

If x is between	90° and 180°	180° and 270°	270° and 360°
Subtract	90° from x	180° from x	270° from x
Then **sin x**	$= + \cos(x - 90°)$	$= - \sin(x - 180°)$	$= - \cos(x - 270°)$
csc x	$= + \sec(x - 90°)$	$= - \csc(x - 180°)$	$= - \sec(x - 270°)$
cos x	$= - \sin(x - 90°)$	$= - \cos(x - 180°)$	$= + \sin(x - 270°)$
sec x	$= - \csc(x - 90°)$	$= - \sec(x - 180°)$	$= + \csc(x - 270°)$
tan x	$= - \cot(x - 90°)$	$= + \tan(x - 180°)$	$= - \cot(x - 270°)$
cot x	$= - \tan(x - 90°)$	$= + \cot(x - 180°)$	$= - \tan(x - 270°)$
vers x	$= 1 + \sin(x - 90°)$	$= 1 + \cos(x - 180°)$	$= 1 - \sin(x - 270°)$
covers x	$= 1 - \cos(x - 90°)$	$= 1 + \sin(x - 180°)$	$= 1 + \cos(x - 270°)$

The "reduced angle" ($x - 90°$, or $x - 180°$, or $x - 270°$) will in each case be an angle between 0° and 90°, whose functions can then be found in the table.

Note. The formulas for sine and cosine are best remembered by aid of the unit circle.

To Find the Angle When One of Its Functions Is Given. In general, there will be two angles between 0 and 360 deg corresponding to any given function. The following tabulated rules show how to find these angles:

Given	First find from the tables an *acute* angle x_0 such that	Then the required angles x_1 and x_2 will be
$\sin x = +a$	$\sin x_0 = a$	x_0 and $180° - x_0$
$\cos x = +a$	$\cos x_0 = a$	x_0 and $[360° - x_0]$
$\tan x = +a$	$\tan x_0 = a$	x_0 and $[180° + x_0]$
$\cot x = +a$	$\cot x_0 = a$	x_0 and $[180° + x_0]$
$\sin x = -a$	$\sin x_0 = a$	$[180° + x_0]$ and $[360° - x_0]$
$\cos x = -a$	$\cos x_0 = a$	$180° - x_0$ and $[180° + x_0]$
$\tan x = -a$	$\tan x_0 = a$	$180° - x_0$ and $[360° - x_0]$
$\cot x = -a$	$\cot x_0 = a$	$180° - x_0$ and $[360° - x_0]$

The angles enclosed in brackets lie outside the range 0 to 180 deg and hence cannot occur as angles in a triangle.

For solution of trigonometric equations, see p. 2–30.

Relations between the Functions of a Single Angle (See Fig. 5).

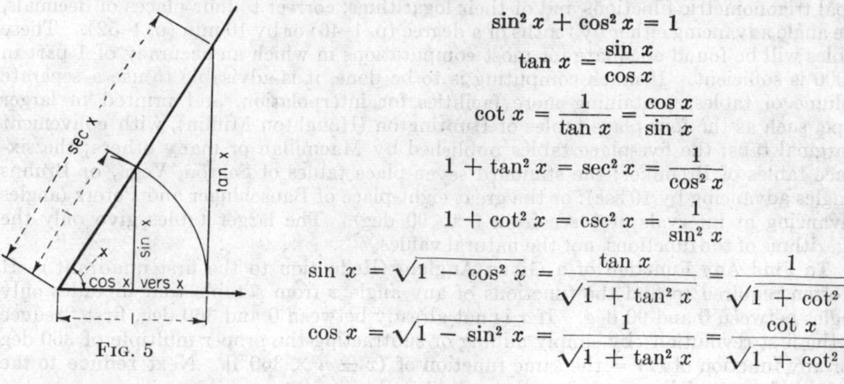

FIG. 5

$$\sin^2 x + \cos^2 x = 1$$

$$\tan x = \frac{\sin x}{\cos x}$$

$$\cot x = \frac{1}{\tan x} = \frac{\cos x}{\sin x}$$

$$1 + \tan^2 x = \sec^2 x = \frac{1}{\cos^2 x}$$

$$1 + \cot^2 x = \csc^2 x = \frac{1}{\sin^2 x}$$

$$\sin x = \sqrt{1 - \cos^2 x} = \frac{\tan x}{\sqrt{1 + \tan^2 x}} = \frac{1}{\sqrt{1 + \cot^2 x}}$$

$$\cos x = \sqrt{1 - \sin^2 x} = \frac{1}{\sqrt{1 + \tan^2 x}} = \frac{\cot x}{\sqrt{1 + \cot^2 x}}$$

Functions of Negative Angles. $\sin(-x) = -\sin x$; $\cos(-x) = \cos x$; $\tan(-x) = -\tan x$.

Functions of the Sum and Difference of Two Angles

$\sin(x + y) = \sin x \cos y + \cos x \sin y$.
$\cos(x + y) = \cos x \cos y - \sin x \sin y$.
$\tan(x + y) = (\tan x + \tan y)/(1 - \tan x \tan y)$.
$\cot(x + y) = (\cot x \cot y - 1)/(\cot x + \cot y)$.
$\sin(x - y) = \sin x \cos y - \cos x \sin y$.
$\cos(x - y) = \cos x \cos y + \sin x \sin y$.
$\tan(x - y) = (\tan x - \tan y)/(1 + \tan x \tan y)$.
$\cot(x - y) = (\cot x \cot y + 1)/(\cot y - \cot x)$.
$\sin x + \sin y = 2 \sin \tfrac{1}{2}(x + y) \cos \tfrac{1}{2}(x - y)$.
$\sin x - \sin y = 2 \cos \tfrac{1}{2}(x + y) \sin \tfrac{1}{2}(x - y)$.
$\cos x + \cos y = 2 \cos \tfrac{1}{2}(x + y) \cos \tfrac{1}{2}(x - y)$.
$\cos x - \cos y = -2 \sin \tfrac{1}{2}(x + y) \sin \tfrac{1}{2}(x - y)$.

$$\tan x + \tan y = \frac{\sin(x + y)}{\cos x \cos y};\ \cot x + \cot y = \frac{\sin(x + y)}{\sin x \sin y}$$

$$\tan x - \tan y = \frac{\sin(x - y)}{\cos x \cos y};\ \cot x - \cot y = \frac{\sin(y - x)}{\sin x \sin y}.$$

$\sin^2 x - \sin^2 y = \cos^2 y - \cos^2 x = \sin(x + y)\sin(x - y)$.
$\cos^2 x - \sin^2 y = \cos^2 y - \sin^2 x = \cos(x + y)\cos(x - y)$.
$\sin(45° + x) = \cos(45° - x)$; $\tan(45° + x) = \cot(45° - x)$.
$\sin(45° - x) = \cos(45° + x)$; $\tan(45° - x) = \cot(45° + x)$.

In the following transformations, a and b are supposed to be positive, $c = \sqrt{a^2 + b^2}$, A = the positive acute angle for which $\tan A = a/b$, and B = the positive acute angle for which $\tan B = b/a$:

$a \cos x + b \sin x = c \sin(A + x) = c \cos(B - x)$.
$a \cos x - b \sin x = c \sin(A - x) = c \cos(B + x)$.

Functions of Multiple Angles and Half Angles

$\sin 2x = 2 \sin x \cos x$; $\sin x = 2 \sin \tfrac{1}{2}x \cos \tfrac{1}{2}x$.
$\cos 2x = \cos^2 x - \sin^2 x = 1 - 2\sin^2 x = 2\cos^2 x - 1$.

$$\tan 2x = \frac{2 \tan x}{1 - \tan^2 x};\ \cot 2x = \frac{\cot^2 x - 1}{2 \cot x}.$$

$\sin 3x \quad = 3 \sin x - 4 \sin^3 x;\ \tan 3x = \dfrac{3 \tan x - \tan^3 x}{1 - 3 \tan^2 x}.$

$\cos 3x \quad = 4 \cos^3 x - 3 \cos x.$

$\sin (nx) \ = n \sin x \cos^{n-1} x - (n)_3 \sin^3 x \cos^{n-3} x + (n)_5 \sin^5 x \cos^{n-5} x - \cdots.$

$\cos (nx) = \cos^n x - (n)_2 \sin^2 x \cos^{n-2} x + (n)_4 \sin^4 x \cos^{n-4} x - \cdots,$

where $(n)_2$, $(n)_3$, . . . are the binomial coefficients (see p. 1–39).

$\sin \tfrac{1}{2}x = \pm\sqrt{\tfrac{1}{2}(1 - \cos x)}.\quad 1 - \cos x = 2 \sin^2 \tfrac{1}{2}x.$

$\cos \tfrac{1}{2}x = \pm\sqrt{\tfrac{1}{2}(1 + \cos x)}.\quad 1 + \cos x = 2 \cos^2 \tfrac{1}{2}x.$

$$\tan \tfrac{1}{2}x = \pm\sqrt{\frac{1 - \cos x}{1 + \cos x}} = \frac{\sin x}{1 + \cos x} = \frac{1 - \cos x}{\sin x}$$

$$\tan\left(\frac{x}{2} + 45°\right) = \pm\sqrt{\frac{1 + \sin x}{1 - \sin x}}.$$

Here the + or − sign is to be used according to the sign of the left-hand side of the equation.

Relations between Three Angles Whose Sum Is 180°

$\sin A + \sin B + \sin C = 4 \cos \tfrac{1}{2}A \cos \tfrac{1}{2}B \cos \tfrac{1}{2}C.$
$\cos A + \cos B + \cos C = 4 \sin \tfrac{1}{2}A \sin \tfrac{1}{2}B \sin \tfrac{1}{2}C + 1.$
$\sin A + \sin B - \sin C = 4 \sin \tfrac{1}{2}A \sin \tfrac{1}{2}B \cos \tfrac{1}{2}C.$
$\cos A + \cos B - \cos C = 4 \cos \tfrac{1}{2}A \cos \tfrac{1}{2}B \sin \tfrac{1}{2}C - 1.$
$\sin^2 A + \sin^2 B + \sin^2 C = 2 \cos A \cos B \cos C + 2.$
$\sin^2 A + \sin^2 B - \sin^2 C = 2 \sin A \sin B \cos C.$
$\tan A + \tan B + \tan C = \tan A \tan B \tan C.$
$\cot \tfrac{1}{2}A + \cot \tfrac{1}{2}B + \cot \tfrac{1}{2}C = \cot \tfrac{1}{2}A \cot \tfrac{1}{2}B \cot \tfrac{1}{2}C.$
$\cot A \cot B + \cot A \cot C + \cot B \cot C = 1.$
$\sin 2A + \sin 2B + \sin 2C = 4 \sin A \sin B \sin C.$
$\sin 2A + \sin 2B - \sin 2C = 4 \cos A \cos B \sin C.$

Inverse Trigonometric Functions. The notation $\sin^{-1} x$ (read: antisine of x, or inverse sine of x; sometimes written arc sin x) means the principal angle whose sine is x. Similarly for $\cos^{-1} x$, $\tan^{-1} x$, etc. (The principal angle means an angle between −90° and +90° in case of $\sin^{-1}$ and $\tan^{-1}$, and between 0° and 180° in the case of $\cos^{-1}$.) For graphs, see p. 2–84.

SOLUTION OF PLANE TRIANGLES

The "parts" of a plane triangle are its three sides, a, b, c, and its three angles A, B, C (A being opposite a, B opposite b, C opposite c, and $A + B + C = 180°$). A triangle is, in general, determined by any three parts (not all angles). To "solve" a triangle means to find the unknown parts from the known. The fundamental formulas are

$$\text{Law of sines: } \frac{a}{b} = \frac{\sin A}{\sin B}\qquad \text{Law of cosines: } c^2 = a^2 + b^2 - 2ab \cos C$$

Right Triangles. Use the definitions of the trigonometric functions, selecting for each unknown part a relation which connects that unknown with known quantities; then solve the resulting equations. Thus, in Fig. 6, if $C = 90°$, then $A + B = 90°$, $c^2 = a^2 + b^2$,

$$\sin A = a/c \qquad \cos A = b/c \qquad \tan A = a/b \qquad \cot A = b/a$$

If A is very small, use $\tan \tfrac{1}{2}A = \sqrt{(c - b)/(c + b)}$.

Oblique Triangles. There are four cases. It is highly desirable in all these cases to draw a sketch of the triangle approximately to scale before commencing the computation, so that any large numerical error may be readily detected.

Case 1. Given Two Angles (provided their sum is < 180 deg) and One Side (say a, Fig. 7). The third angle is known, since $A + B + C = 180°$. To find the remaining sides, use $b = \dfrac{a \sin B}{\sin A}$, $c = \dfrac{a \sin C}{\sin A}$. Or, drop a perpendicular from either B or C on the opposite side, and solve by right triangles.

Check: $c \cos B + b \cos C = a$.

Case 2. Given Two Sides (say a and b) and the Included Angle (C); and Suppose $a > b$ (Fig. 8).

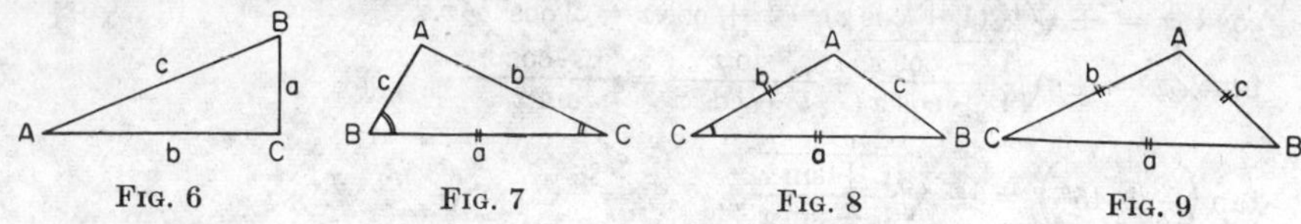

Fig. 6 Fig. 7 Fig. 8 Fig. 9

Method 1: Find c from $c^2 = a^2 + b^2 - 2ab \cos C$ [or $c^2 = (a - b)^2 + 2ab \text{ vers } C$]; then find the smaller angle, B, from $\sin B = (b/c) \sin C$; and finally, find A from $A = 180° - (B + C)$. *Check:* $a \cos B + b \cos A = c$.

Method 2: Find $\frac{1}{2}(A - B)$ from the law of tangents:

$$\tan \tfrac{1}{2}(A - B) = [(a - b)/(a + b)] \cot \tfrac{1}{2}C$$

and $\frac{1}{2}(A + B)$ from $\frac{1}{2}(A + B) = 90° - C/2$; hence $A = \frac{1}{2}(A + B) + \frac{1}{2}(A - B)$ and $B = \frac{1}{2}(A + B) - \frac{1}{2}(A - B)$. Then find c from $c = a \sin C/\sin A$ or $c = b \sin C/\sin B$. *Check:* $a \cos B + b \cos A = c$.

Method 3: Drop a perpendicular from A to the opposite side, and solve by right triangles.

Case 3. Given the Three Sides (provided the largest is less than the sum of the other two) (Fig. 9).

Method 1: Find the largest angle A (which may be acute or obtuse) from $\cos A = (b^2 + c^2 - a^2)/2bc$ {or $\text{vers } A = [a^2 - (b - c)^2]/2bc$} and then find B and C (which will always be acute) from $\sin B = b \sin A/a$ and $\sin C = c \sin A/a$. *Check:* $A + B + C = 180°$.

Method 2: Find A, B, and C from $\tan \frac{1}{2}A = r/(s - a)$, $\tan \frac{1}{2}B = r/(s - b)$, $\tan \frac{1}{2}C = r/(s - c)$, where $s = \frac{1}{2}(a + b + c)$, and $r = \sqrt{(s - a)(s - b)(s - c)/s}$. *Check:* $A + B + C = 180°$.

Method 3: If only one angle, say A, is required, use

$$\sin \tfrac{1}{2}A = \sqrt{(s - b)(s - c)/bc}$$

or

$$\cos \tfrac{1}{2}A = \sqrt{s(s - a)/bc}$$

according as $\frac{1}{2}A$ is nearer 0° or nearer 90°.

Case 4. Given Two Sides (say b and c) and the Angle opposite One of Them (B). This is the "ambiguous case" in which there may be two solutions, or one, or none (see Fig. 10).

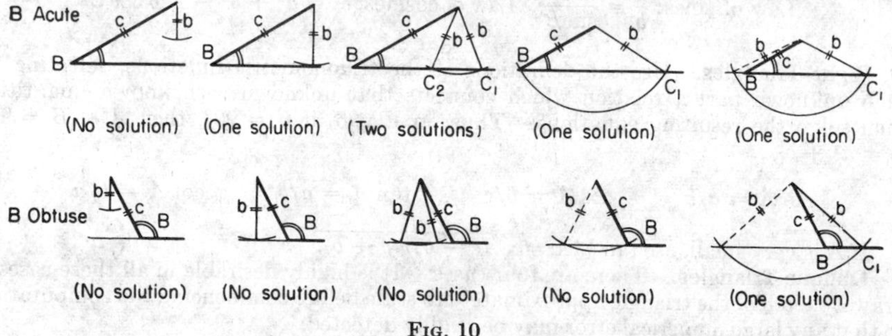

Fig. 10

First, try to find C from $\sin C = c \sin B/b$. If $\sin C > 1$, there is no solution. If $\sin C = 1$, $C = 90°$ and the triangle is a right triangle. If $\sin C < 1$, this determines two angles C, namely an acute angle C_1, and an obtuse angle $C_2 = 180° - C_1$. Then C_1 will yield a solution when and only when $C_1 + B < 180°$ (see Case 1); and similarly C_2 will yield a solution when and only when $C_2 + B < 180°$ (see Case 1).

Other Properties of Triangles (See also pp. 2–11, 2–16).

Area $= \frac{1}{2}ab \sin C = \sqrt{s(s-a)(s-b)(s-c)} = rs$, where $s = \frac{1}{2}(a + b + c)$, and r = radius of inscribed circle $= \sqrt{(s-a)(s-b)(s-c)/s}$.

Radius of circumscribed circle = R, where

$$2R = a/\sin A = b/\sin B = c/\sin C \qquad r = 4R \sin \frac{A}{2} \sin \frac{B}{2} \sin \frac{C}{2} = \frac{abc}{4Rs}$$

The length of the bisector of the angle C is

$$z = \frac{2\sqrt{abs(s-c)}}{a+b} = \frac{\sqrt{ab[(a+b)^2 - c^2]}}{a+b}$$

The median from C to the middle point of c is $m = \frac{1}{2}\sqrt{2(a^2 + b^2) - c^2}$.

SOLUTION OF SPHERICAL TRIANGLES

For the occasional solution of a spherical triangle the following formulas will be sufficient. For a detailed discussion, see any textbook on spherical trigonometry.

Let a, b, c be the sides of the spherical triangle, *i.e.*, portions of arcs of great circles of the sphere; and let A, B, C be the angles of the triangle; *i.e.*, the angles made by tangents drawn to the sides at their points of intersection on the sphere. The sum of the angles will always be greater than two right angles, and may be nearly six right angles. The angle $E = A + B + C - 180°$ is called the **spherical excess** of the triangle. (See also p. 2–21.)

$$\frac{\sin a}{\sin A} = \frac{\sin b}{\sin B} \qquad \frac{\sin b}{\sin B} = \frac{\sin c}{\sin C} \qquad \frac{\sin c}{\sin C} = \frac{\sin a}{\sin A}$$

$$\cos a = \cos b \cos c + \sin b \sin c \cos A$$

with similar formulas for $\cos b$ and $\cos c$.

$$\cos A = -\cos B \cos C + \sin B \sin C \cos a$$

with similar formulas for $\cos B$ and $\cos C$. Other sample formulas are

$$\sin a \cos B = \cos b \sin c - \sin b \cos c \cos A$$
$$\sin A \cos b = \cos B \sin C + \sin B \cos C \cos a$$

If $s = \frac{1}{2}(a + b + c)$ and $S = \frac{1}{2}(A + B + C)$

and if, $\tan r = \sqrt{\sin(s-a)\sin(s-b)\sin(s-c)/\sin s}$

and $\tan R = \sqrt{(-\cos S)/[\cos(S-A)\cos(S-B)\cos(S-C)]}$

then $\tan \frac{1}{2}A = (\tan r)/\sin(s-a)$, and $\tan \frac{1}{2}a = \tan R \cos(S-A)$

with similar formulas for $\tan \frac{1}{2}B$, $\tan \frac{1}{2}C$, and for $\tan \frac{1}{2}b$, $\tan \frac{1}{2}c$. (Here r and R are the radii, on the spherical surface, of the inscribed and circumscribed circles, respectively.) If $E = A + B + C - 180°$,

$$\tan \tfrac{1}{4}E = \sqrt{\tan \tfrac{1}{2}s \tan \tfrac{1}{2}(s-a) \tan \tfrac{1}{2}(s-b) \tan \tfrac{1}{2}(s-c)}$$

If E is small, then approximately, $\sin E = F/K^2$, where K = radius of sphere, and F = area of triangle, regarded as a plane triangle. In any case,

$$\frac{\text{Area of a spherical triangle}}{\text{Area of a great circle}} = \frac{\text{spherical excess}}{180°}$$

In the special case of a right spherical triangle, in which $C = 90°$,

$$\cos c = \cos a \cos b = \cot A \cot B \qquad \cos a = \cos A/\sin B \qquad \cos b = \cos B/\sin A$$
$$\sin A = \sin a/\sin c \qquad \cos A = \tan b/\tan c \qquad \tan A = \tan a/\sin b$$

HYPERBOLIC FUNCTIONS

The **hyperbolic sine, hyperbolic cosine,** etc., of any number x, are **functions of** x which are closely related to the exponential e^x, and which have formal properties very similar to those of the trigonometric functions, sine, cosine, etc. Their definitions and fundamental properties are as follows (see also p. 2–38; graphs, p. 2–84; table, p. 1–60; series, p. 2–68):

$\sinh x = \frac{1}{2}(e^x - e^{-x})$. $\quad \cosh x = \frac{1}{2}(e^x + e^{-x})$. $\quad \tanh x = \sinh x/\cosh x$.
$\operatorname{csch} x = 1/\sinh x$. $\quad \operatorname{sech} x = 1/\cosh x$. $\quad \coth x = 1/\tanh x$.
$\cosh^2 x - \sinh^2 x = 1$. $\quad 1 - \tanh^2 x = \operatorname{sech}^2 x$. $\quad 1 - \coth^2 x = -\operatorname{csch}^2 x$.
$\sinh(-x) = -\sinh x$. $\quad \cosh(-x) = \cosh x$. $\quad \tanh(-x) = -\tanh x$.
$\sinh(x \pm y) = \sinh x \cosh y \pm \cosh x \sinh y$.
$\cosh(x \pm y) = \cosh x \cosh y \pm \sinh x \sinh y$.
$\tanh(x \pm y) = (\tanh x \pm \tanh y)/(1 \pm \tanh x \tanh y)$.
$\sinh 2x = 2 \sinh x \cosh x$. $\quad \cosh 2x = \cosh^2 x + \sinh^2 x$.
$\tanh 2x = (2 \tanh x)/(1 + \tanh^2 x)$.
$\sinh \frac{1}{2}x = \sqrt{\frac{1}{2}(\cosh x - 1)}$. $\quad \cosh \frac{1}{2}x = \sqrt{\frac{1}{2}(\cosh x + 1)}$.
$\tanh \frac{1}{2}x = (\cosh x - 1)/(\sinh x) = (\sinh x)/(\cosh x + 1)$.

The hyperbolic functions are related to the rectangular hyperbola, $x^2 - y^2 = a^2$ (Fig. 12), in much the same way that the trigonometric functions are related to the

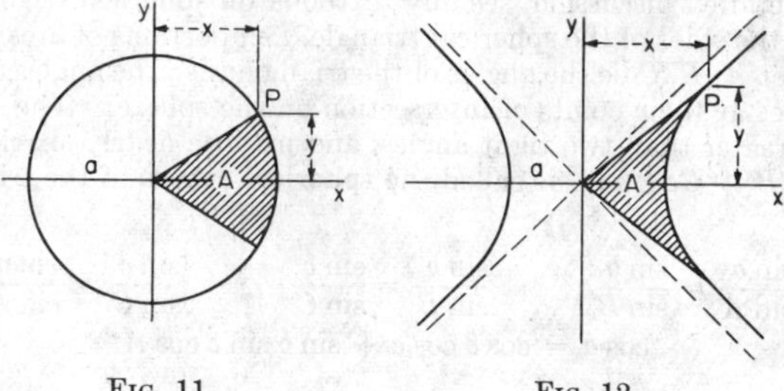

FIG. 11 FIG. 12

circle $x^2 + y^2 = a^2$ (Fig. 11); the analogy, however, concerns not angles but areas. Thus, in either figure, let A represent the shaded area, and let $u = A/a^2$ (a pure number). Then for the coordinates of the point P we have, in Fig. 11, $x = a \cos u$, $y = a \sin u$; and in Fig. 12, $x = a \cosh u$, $y = a \sinh u$.

The **inverse hyperbolic sine** of y, denoted by $\sinh^{-1}y$, is the number whose hyperbolic sine is y; that is, the notation $x = \sinh^{-1}y$ means $\sinh x = y$. Similarly for $\cosh^{-1}y$, $\tanh^{-1}y$, etc. These functions are closely related to the logarithmic function, and are especially valuable in the integral calculus. For graphs, see p. 2–85.

$$\sinh^{-1}(y/a) = \ln(y + \sqrt{y^2 + a^2}) - \ln a.$$
$$\cosh^{-1}(y/a) = \ln(y + \sqrt{y^2 - a^2}) - \ln a.$$
$$\tanh^{-1}\frac{y}{a} = \frac{1}{2}\ln\frac{a+y}{a-y}; \qquad \coth^{-1}\frac{y}{a} = \frac{1}{2}\ln\frac{y+a}{y-a}.$$

The **Gudermannian** of x (written gd x) is an angle u such that $x = \ln\tan(\frac{1}{4}\pi + \frac{1}{2}u)$. See Smithsonian Tables of the Hyperbolic Functions.

The **antigudermannian** of an angle u, denoted by $\operatorname{gd}^{-1} u$, is a number defined by $\operatorname{gd}^{-1} u = \ln\tan(\frac{1}{4}\pi + \frac{1}{2}u) = \int \sec u\, du = \sinh^{-1}(\tan u) = \cosh^{-1}(\sec u) = \tanh^{-1}(\sin u) = 2\tanh^{-1}(\tan \frac{1}{2}u)$. When u is small, $\operatorname{gd}^{-1}u = u + \frac{1}{6}u^3 + \frac{1}{24}u^5 + \frac{61}{5040}u^7 + \cdots$.

ANALYTICAL GEOMETRY

BY

Philip Franklin

THE POINT AND THE STRAIGHT LINE

Rectangular Coordinates (Fig. 1). Let $P_1 = (x_1, y_1)$, $P_2 = (x_2, y_2)$. Then, distance $P_1P_2 = \sqrt{(x_2 - x_1)^2 + (y_2 - y_1)^2}$; slope of $P_1P_2 = m = \tan u = (y_2 - y_1)/(x_2 - x_1)$; coordinates of mid-point are $x = \frac{1}{2}(x_1 + x_2)$, $y = \frac{1}{2}(y_1 + y_2)$; coordinates of point $1/n$th of the way from P_1 to P_2 are $x = x_1 + (1/n)(x_2 - x_1)$, $y = y_1 + (1/n)\ (y_2 - y_1)$.

Let m_1, m_2 be the slopes of two lines; then, if the lines are parallel, $m_1 = m_2$; if the lines are perpendicular to each other, $m_1 = -1/m_2$.

Equations of a Straight Line

1. Intercept Form (Fig. 2): $\dfrac{x}{a} + \dfrac{y}{b} = 1$. ($a$, b = intercepts of the line on the axes.)

2. Slope Form (Fig. 3): $y = mx + b$. ($m = \tan u$ = slope; b = intercept on the y-axis; see also Fig. 2, p. 2–84.)

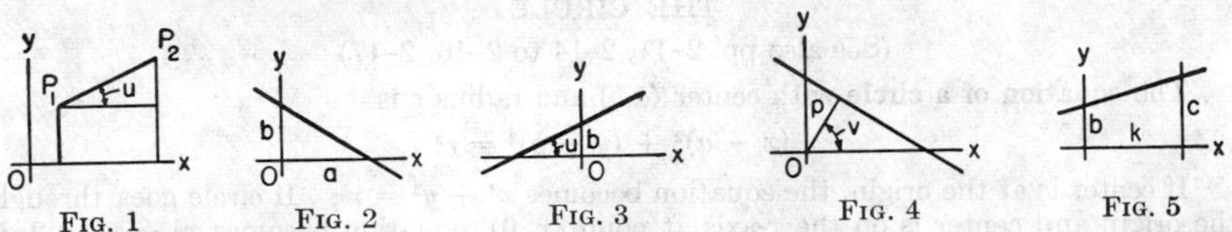

Fig. 1 Fig. 2 Fig. 3 Fig. 4 Fig. 5

3. Normal Form (Fig. 4): $x \cos v + y \sin v = p$. (p = perpendicular from origin to line; v = angle from the x-axis to p.)

4. Parallel-intercept Form (Fig. 5): $\dfrac{y - b}{c - b} = \dfrac{x}{k}$. ($b$, c = intercepts on two parallels at distance k apart.)

5. General Form: $Ax + By + C = 0$. [Here $a = -C/A$, $b = -C/B$, $m = -A/B$, $\cos v = A/R$, $\sin v = B/R$, $p = -C/R$, where $R = \pm\sqrt{A^2 + B^2}$ (sign to be so chosen that p is positive).]

6. Line through (x_1, y_1) with Slope m: $y - y_1 = m(x - x_1)$.

7. Line through (x_1, y_1) and (x_2, y_2): $y - y_1 = \dfrac{y_2 - y_1}{x_2 - x_1}(x - x_1)$.

8. Line Parallel to x-axis: $y = a$; to y-axis: $x = b$.

Angles and Distances

If u = angle from the line with slope m_1 to the line with slope m_2, then

$$\tan u = \frac{m_2 - m_1}{1 + m_2 m_1}. \qquad \text{If parallel, } m_1 = m_2. \quad \text{If perpendicular, } m_1 m_2 = -1.$$

If u = angle between the lines $Ax + By + C = 0$ and $A'x + B'y + C' = 0$, then

$$\cos u = \frac{AA' + BB'}{\pm\sqrt{(A^2 + B^2)(A'^2 + B'^2)}}. \qquad \text{If parallel, } A/A' = B/B'. \quad \text{If perpendicular, } AA' + BB' = 0.$$

The equations of the bisectors of the angles between the two lines just mentioned are

$$\frac{Ax + By + C}{\sqrt{A^2 + B^2}} \mp \frac{A'x + B'y + C'}{\sqrt{A'^2 + B'^2}} = 0$$

The equation of a line through (x_1, y_1) and meeting a given line $y = mx + b$ at an angle u, is

$$y - y_1 = \frac{m + \tan u}{1 - m \tan u}(x - x_1)$$

The distance from (x_0, y_0) to the line $Ax + By + C = 0$ is

$$D = \left|\frac{Ax_0 + By_0 + C}{\sqrt{A^2 + B^2}}\right|$$

where the vertical bars mean "the absolute value of."

The distance from (x_0, y_0) to a line which passes through (x_1, y_1) and makes an angle u with the x-axis is

$$D = (x_0 - x_1) \sin u - (y_0 - y_1) \cos u$$

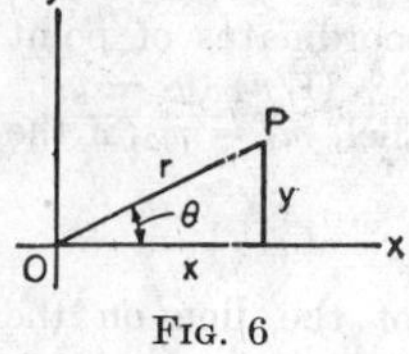

Fig. 6

Polar Coordinates (Fig. 6). Let (x, y) be the rectangular and (r, θ) the polar coordinates of a given point P. Then $x = r \cos \theta$; $y = r \sin \theta$; $x^2 + y^2 = r^2$.

Transformation of Coordinates. If origin is moved to point $(x_0\ y_0)$, the new axes being parallel to the old, $x = x_0 + x'$, $y = y_0 + y'$.

If axes are turned through the angle u, without change of origin,

$$x = x' \cos u - y' \sin u \qquad y = x' \sin u + y' \cos u$$

THE CIRCLE

(See also pp. 2–11, 2–14 to 2–16, 2–17)

The **equation of a circle** with center (a,b) and radius r is

$$(x - a)^2 + (y - b)^2 = r^2$$

If center is at the origin, the equation becomes $x^2 + y^2 = r^2$. If circle goes through the origin and center is on the x-axis at point $(r, 0)$, equation becomes $x^2 + y^2 = 2rx$. The **general equation** of a circle is

$$x^2 + y^2 + Dx + Ey + F = 0$$

It has center at $(-D/2, -E/2)$, and radius $= \sqrt{(D/2)^2 + (E/2)^2 - F}$ (which may be real, null, or imaginary).

The **equation of the radical axis** of two circles, $x^2 + y^2 + Dx + Ey + F = 0$ and $x^2 + y^2 + D'x + E'y + F' = 0$, is $(D - D')x + (E - E')y + (F - F') = 0$. The tangents drawn to two circles from any point of their radical axis are of equal length. If the circles intersect, the radical axis passes through their points of intersection (see p. 2–12).

The **equation of the tangent** to $x^2 + y^2 = r^2$ at (x_1, y_1) is $x_1x + y_1y = r^2$. The tangent to $x^2 + y^2 + Dx + Ey + F = 0$ at (x_1, y_1) is $x_1x + y_1y + \frac{1}{2}D(x + x_1) + \frac{1}{2}E(y + y_1) + F = 0$. The line $y = mx + b$ will be tangent to the circle $x^2 + y^2 = r^2$ if $b = r\sqrt{1 + m^2}$.

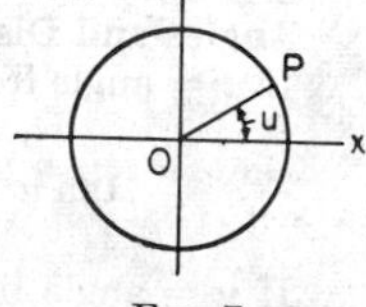

Fig. 7

Equations of Circle in Parametric Form. It is sometimes convenient to express the coordinates x and y of the moving point P (Fig. 7) in terms of an auxiliary variable, called a **parameter.** Thus, if the parameter be taken as the angle u from the x-axis to the radius vector OP, then the equations of the circle in parametric form will be $x = a \cos u$; $y = a \sin u$. For every value of the parameter u, there corresponds a point (x, y) on the circle. The ordinary equation $x^2 + y^2 = a^2$ can be obtained from the parametric equations by eliminating u.

THE PARABOLA

The **parabola** (see also p. 2–18) is the locus of a point which moves so that its distance from a fixed line (called the **directrix**) is always equal to its distance from a fixed point F (called the **focus**). See Fig. 8. The point halfway from focus to directrix is the **vertex,** O. The line through the focus, perpendicular to the directrix, is the **principal axis.** The breadth of the curve at the focus is called the **latus rectum, or parameter,** $=2p$, where p is the distance from focus to directrix. (Compare also Fig. 3, p. 2–84.)

NOTE. Any section of a right circular cone made by a plane parallel to a tangent plane of the cone will be a parabola.

Equation of Parabola, origin at vertex (Fig. 8): $y^2 = 2px$.

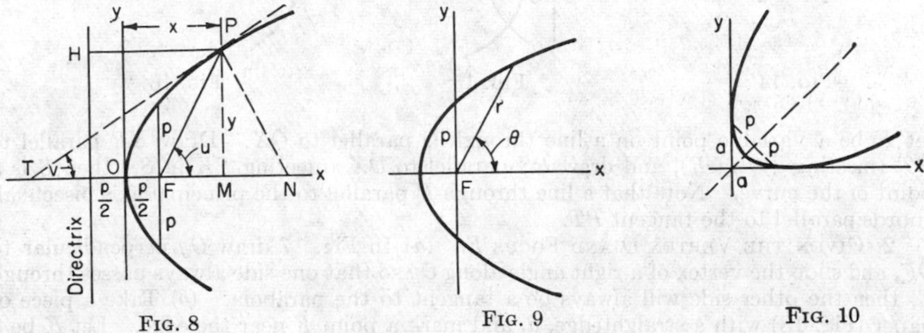

FIG. 8 FIG. 9 FIG. 10

Polar Equation of Parabola, referred to F as origin and Fx as axis (Fig. 9): $r = p/(1 - \cos\theta)$.

Equation Referred to the Tangents at the ends of the latus rectum as axes (Fig. 10): $x^{1/2} + y^{1/2} = a^{1/2}$, where $a = p\sqrt{2}$.

Equation of Tangent to $y^2 = 2px$ at (x_1,y_1): $y_1y = p(x + x_1)$. The line $y = mx + b$ will be tangent to $y^2 = 2px$ if $b = p/(2m)$.

The **tangent** PT at any point P bisects the angle between PF and PH (Fig. 8). A ray of light from F, reflected at P, will move off parallel to the principal axis. The

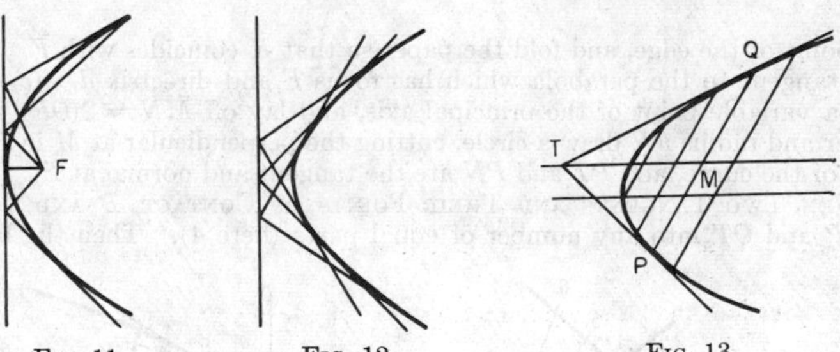

FIG. 11 FIG. 12 FIG. 13

subtangent, TM, is bisected at O. The **subnormal,** MN, is constant and equal to p. The locus of the foot of the perpendicular from the focus on a moving tangent is the tangent at the vertex (Fig. 11). The locus of the point of intersection of perpendicular tangents is the directrix (Fig. 12). The locus of the mid-points of a set of parallel chords whose slope is m is a straight line parallel to the principal axis at a distance p/m and is called a **diameter** (Fig. 13). If M is the mid-point of a chord PQ and if T is the point of intersection of the tangents at P and Q, then TM is parallel to the principal axis and is bisected by the curve (Fig. 13).

To Construct a Tangent to a Given Parabola. (1) At a given point of contact, P (Fig. 14): Find T so that $OT = OM$, or $FT = FP$. Then TP is the tangent at P.

Or, make $MN = p = 2(OF)$; then PN is the normal at P. (2) From a given external point, Q (Fig. 15): With Q as center and radius QF draw circle cutting the directrix in H; draw HP parallel to principal axis; then P is required point of contact. As check, note that QP is the perpendicular bisector of FH.

To Construct a Parabola. 1. Given Any Two Points, P and Q, the Tangent PT at One of Them, and the Direction of the Principal Axis OX. In Fig. 16,

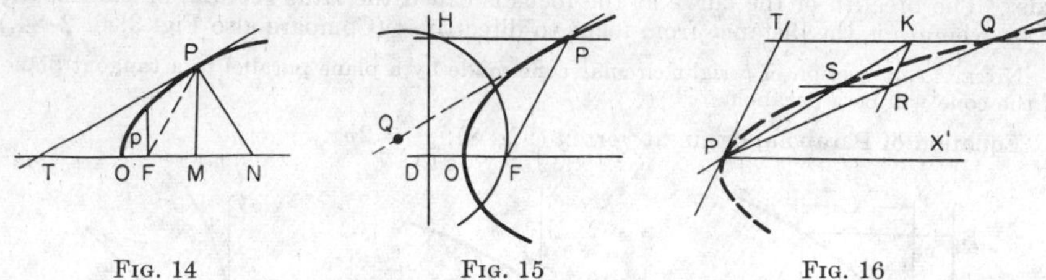

Fig. 14 Fig. 15 Fig. 16

let K be a variable point on a line through Q parallel to OX. Draw KR parallel to PT (meeting PQ in R), and draw RS parallel to OX (meeting PK in S); then S is a point of the curve. Note that a line through P parallel to the principal axis bisects all chords parallel to the tangent PT.

2. Given the Vertex O and Focus F. (*a*) In Fig. 17 draw Oy perpendicular to OF, and slide the vertex of a right angle along Oy so that one side always passes through F; then the other side will always be a tangent to the parabola. (*b*) Take a piece of paper (Fig. 18) with a straightedge, d, and mark a point F near the edge. Let K be a

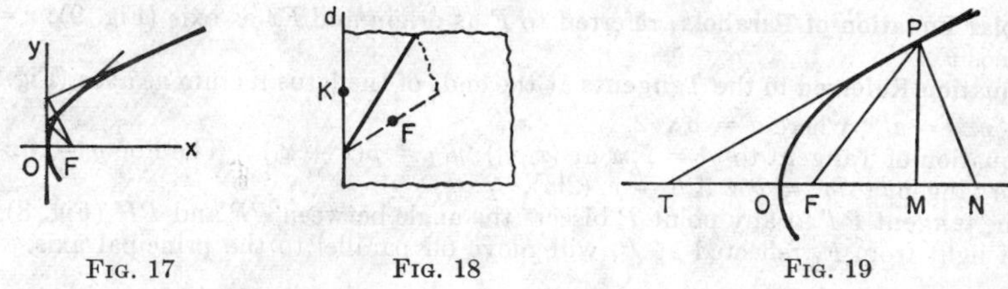

Fig. 17 Fig. 18 Fig. 19

variable point of the edge, and fold the paper so that K coincides with F. The crease will be a tangent to the parabola which has focus F and directrix d. (*c*) In Fig. 19, let M be a variable point of the principal axis, and lay off $MN = 2(OF) = p$. With F as center and radius FN draw a circle, cutting the perpendicular at M in P. Then P is a point of the curve, and PT and PN are the tangent and normal at P.

3. Given Two Tangents and Their Points of Contact, P and Q (Fig. 20). Divide TP and QT into any number of equal parts (here 4). Then the lines 11, 22,

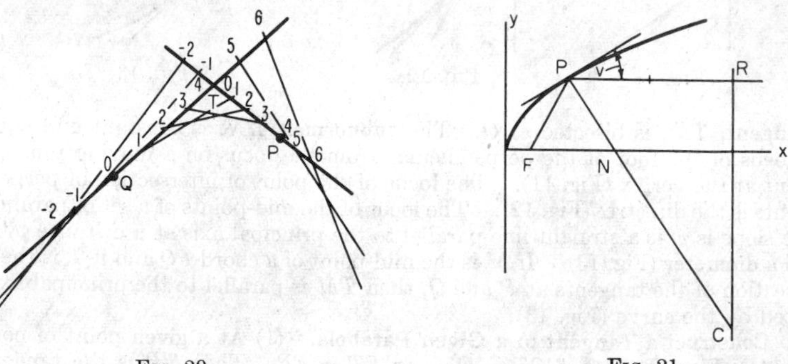

Fig. 20 Fig. 21

33, . . . will be tangents to the parabola. This method is especially advantageous in drawing rather flat arcs.

The **radius of curvature** of $y^2 = 2px$ at a point $P = (x,y)$ is $R = (p + 2x)^{3/2}/\sqrt{p}$, or $R = p/\sin^3 v$, where v = the angle which the tangent at P makes with PF (Fig. 21). At the vertex, $R = p$. To construct the radius of curvature at any point P, lay off $PR = 2(PF)$ parallel to the principal axis, and draw RC perpendicular to the axis, meeting the normal, PN, in C. Then C is the center of curvature for the point P, and a circle about C with radius CP will closely approximate the parabola in the neighborhood of P.

THE ELLIPSE

The **ellipse** (see also p. 2–18) has two **foci,** F and F' (Fig. 22), and two **directrices,** DH and $D'H'$. If P is any point of the curve, $PF + PF'$ is constant, $= 2a$; and PF/PH (or PF'/PH') is also constant, $= e$, where e is the **eccentricity** ($e < 1$). Either

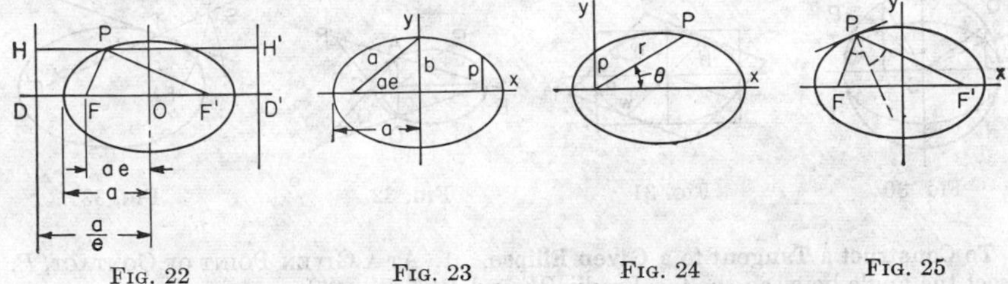

FIG. 22 FIG. 23 FIG. 24 FIG. 25

of these properties may be taken as the definition of the curve. The relations between e and the semiaxes a and b are as shown in Fig. 23. Thus, $b^2 = a^2(1 - e^2)$, $ae = \sqrt{a^2 - b^2}$, $e^2 = 1 - (b/a)^2$. The **semilatus rectum** $= p = a(1 - e^2) = b^2/a$. Note that b is always less than a, except in the special case of the circle, in which $b = a$ and $e = 0$.

Any section of a right circular cone made by a plane which cuts all the elements of one nappe of the cone will be an ellipse; if the plane is perpendicular to the axis of the cone, the ellipse becomes a circle.

Equation of Ellipse, center as origin:

$$\frac{x^2}{a^2} + \frac{y^2}{b^2} = 1 \qquad \text{or} \qquad y = \pm \frac{b}{a}\sqrt{a^2 - x^2}$$

If $P = (x,y)$ is any point of the curve, $PF = a + ex$, $PF' = a - ex$.

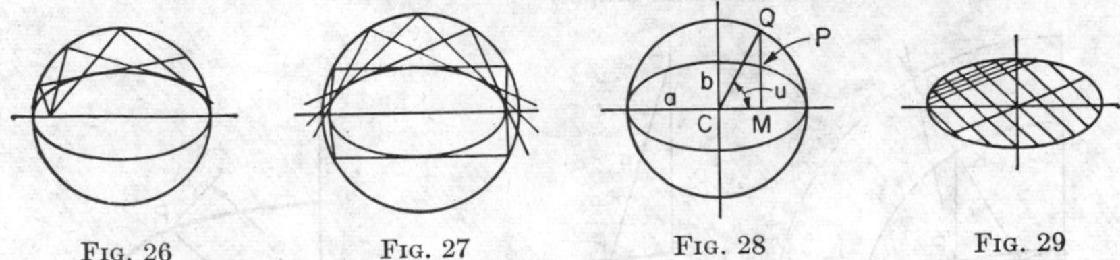

FIG. 26 FIG. 27 FIG. 28 FIG. 29

Equations of the Ellipse in Parametric Form $x = a \cos u$, $y = b \sin u$, where u is the eccentric angle of the point $P = (x,y)$. See Fig. 28.

Polar equation, focus as origin, axes as in Fig. 24: $r = p/(1 - e \cos \theta)$.

Equation of the Tangent at (x_1,y_1): $b^2x_1x + a^2y_1y = a^2b^2$.

The line $y = mx + k$ will be a tangent if $k = \pm\sqrt{a^2m^2 + b^2}$. The normal at any point P bisects the angle between PF and PF' (Fig. 25). The locus of the foot of the perpendicular from the focus on a moving tangent is the circle on the major axis as diameter (Fig. 26). The locus of the point of intersection of perpendicular tangents is a circle with radius $\sqrt{a^2 + b^2}$ (Fig. 27).

Ellipse as a Flattened Circle. Eccentric Angle. If the ordinates in a circle are diminished in a constant ratio, the resulting points will lie on an ellipse (Fig. 28). If

Q traces the circle with uniform velocity, the corresponding point P will trace the ellipse, with varying velocity. The angle u in the figure is called the eccentric angle of the point P.

Conjugate diameters are lines through the center, each of which bisects all the chords parallel to the other (Fig. 29). If m_1 and m_2 are the slopes, then $m_1m_2 = -b^2/a^2$. One pair of conjugate diameters are the diagonals of the rectangle circumscribing the ellipse. The eccentric angles of the ends of two conjugate diameters differ by 90 deg. Thus (Fig. 30), if CQ and CQ' are perpendicular radii in the circle, CP and CP' will be conjugate semidiameters in the ellipse. A parallelogram formed by tangents drawn parallel to a pair of conjugate diameters has a constant area, $= 4ab$ (Fig. 31). Also, if a', b' are conjugate semidiameters, and w the angle between them, then $a'^2 + b'^2 = a^2 + b^2$ and $a'b = ab/\sin w$.

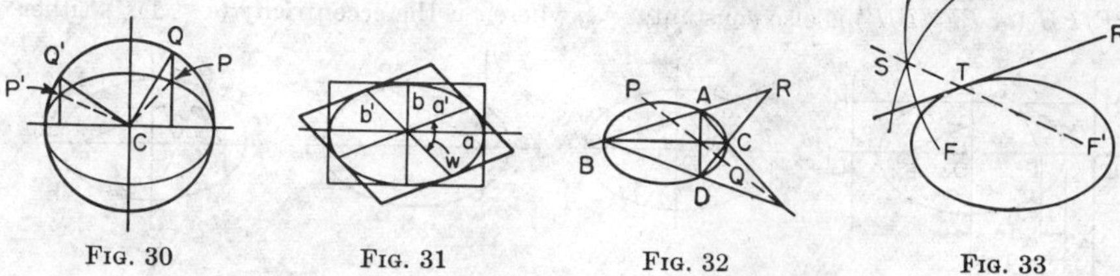

FIG. 30 FIG. 31 FIG. 32 FIG. 33

To Construct a Tangent to a Given Ellipse. 1. AT A GIVEN POINT OF CONTACT, P. Bisect the angle between the focal radii PF and PF' (Fig. 25).

2. FROM A GIVEN EXTERNAL POINT, R. (a) Through R draw any two lines cutting the ellipse, one in A and B, the other in C and D (Fig. 32). Through the point of intersection of AD and BC and the point of intersection of AC and BD, draw a line cutting the ellipse in P and Q. Then P and Q are the required points of contact. (b) With R as a center and radius RF, draw an arc; with F' as center and radius $2a$ draw an arc, intersecting the first in S; and let SF' meet the curve in T. Then T is the point of contact (Fig. 33).

To Construct an Ellipse, Given a and b. 1. In Fig. 34, with O as center, draw circles with radii a and b (and also a third circle with radius $a + b$). Let a variable ray through O cut these circles in J, K (and S); through J and K draw parallels to the axes, meeting in P. Then P is a point of the ellipse (and SP is the normal at P).

2. In Fig. 35, let P divide a line AB so that $PA = a$ and $PB = b$. Then if A and B slide on the axes, P will describe an ellipse.

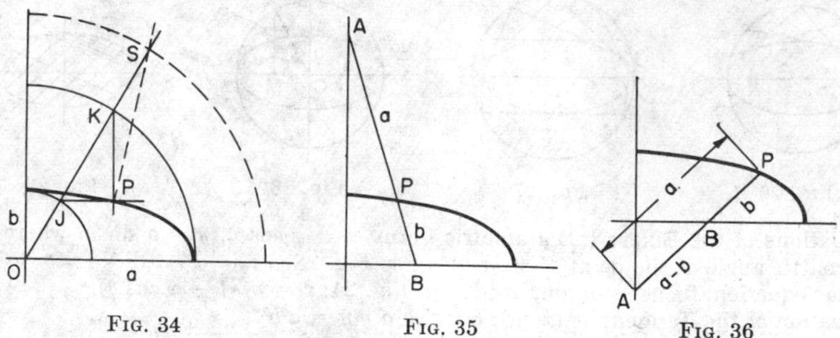

FIG. 34 FIG. 35 FIG. 36

3. In Fig. 36, let PBA be a straight line such that $PA = a$ and $PB = b$. Then if A and B slide on the axes, P will trace an ellipse. (Use a strip of paper, with the points P, B, and A marked on it.)

4. Find the foci, F and F', by striking an arc of radius a with center at B (Fig. 37). Drive pins at F, F', and B, and adjust a loop of thread around them. Then remove the pin at B, and replace it by a pencil point; by moving the pencil so as to keep the

string taut, the complete ellipse can be drawn at one sweep. Or, use a mechanical ellipsograph.

5. Apply the method of the following paragraph to the special case in which OP and OQ are perpendicular semiaxes.

To Construct an Ellipse, Given a Pair of Conjugate Semidiameters, OP and OQ. Complete the parallelogram, as in Fig. 38. Divide QD and QO into n equal parts, 1, 2, 3, . . . and 1′, 2′, 3′, ... Connect P with 1, 2, 3, . . . and P' with 1′, 2′, 3′ . . . . The points of intersection of corresponding lines will be points of the ellipse.

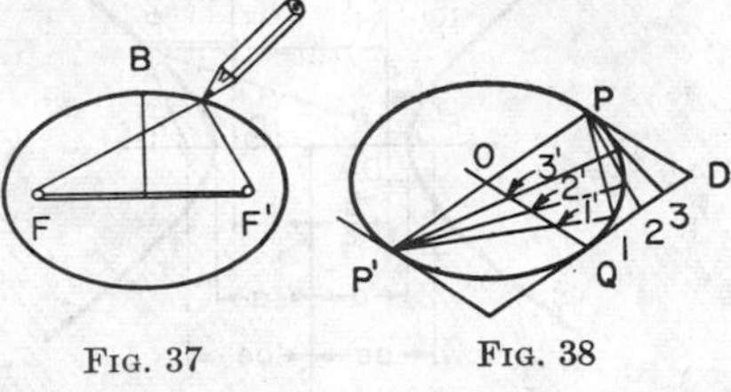

FIG. 37 FIG. 38

To Construct an Ellipse Approximately by Two Circular Arcs. In Fig. 39, lay off $OL = OA$ and $BS = BL = a - b$. Bisect SA in T, and draw THK perpendicular to BA. Then H is one center, with radius HA, and K is the other center, with radius KB. The junction point Q of the two arcs will fall a little outside the true ellipse.

The **radius of curvature of an ellipse at any point** $P = (x, y)$ is

$$R = a^2b^2(x^2/a^4 + y^2/b^4)^{3/2} = p/\sin^3 v$$

where v is the angle which the tangent at P makes with PF or PF'. At end of major axis, $R = b^2/a = MA$; at end of minor axis, $R = a^2/b = NB$ (see Fig. 40). To construct the radius of curvature at any other point P (Fig. 41), draw the normal at P (by bisecting the angle between PF and PF') and let it meet the major axis in N. At N draw a perpendicular to PN meeting PF in H. At H draw a perpendicular to PH meeting PN in C. Then C is the center of curvature for the point P, and a circle about C with radius CP will closely approximate the ellipse in the neighborhood of P. Note that, if the circle of curvature for P cuts the ellipse again at Q, then the tangent at P and the line PQ are equally inclined to the axis.

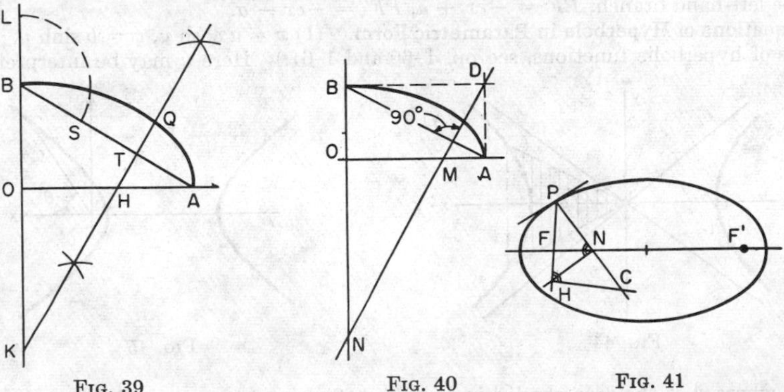

FIG. 39 FIG. 40 FIG. 41

THE HYPERBOLA

The **hyperbola** (see also p. 2–18) has two **foci,** F and F', at distances $\pm ae$ from the center, and two **directrices,** DH and $D'H'$, at distances $\pm a/e$ from the center (Fig. 42). If P is any point of the curve, $|PF - PF'|$ is constant, $= 2a$; and PF/PH (or PF'/PH') is also constant, $= e$ (called the **eccentricity**), where $e > 1$. Either of these properties may be taken as the definition of the curve. The curve has two branches which approach more and more nearly two straight lines called the **asymptotes.** Each asymptote makes with the principal axis an angle whose tangent is b/a. The relations between

e, a, and b are shown in Fig. 43: $b^2 = a^2(e^2 - 1)$, $ae = \sqrt{a^2 + b^2}$, $e^2 = 1 + (b/a)^2$. The semilatus rectum, or ordinate at the focus, is $p = a(e^2 - 1) = b^2/a$.

Any section of a right circular cone made by a plane which cuts both nappes of the cone will be a hyperbola. (Compare also Fig. 3, p. 2–84.)

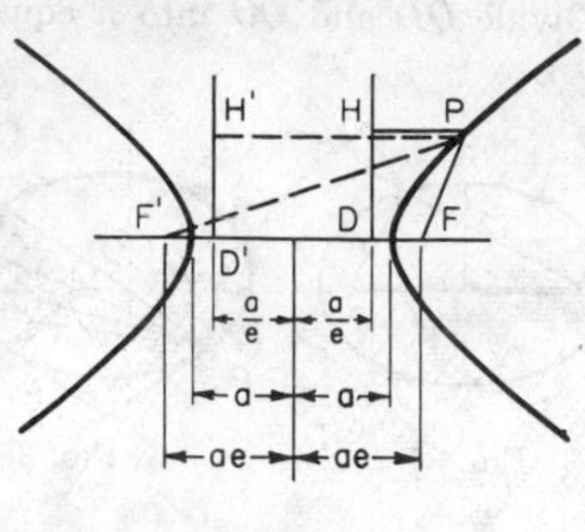

Fig. 42

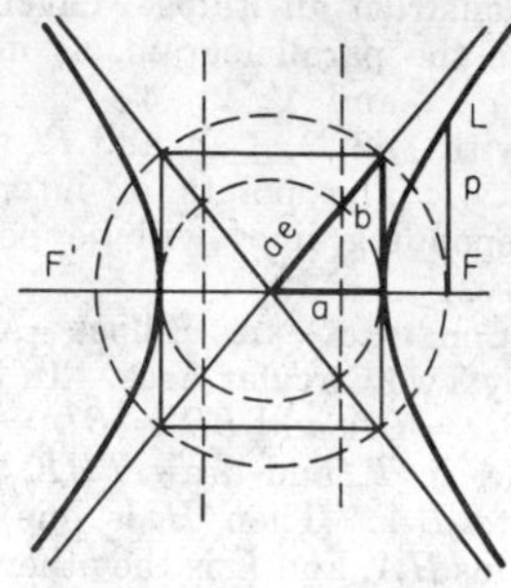

Fig. 43

Equation of the Hyperbola, center as origin:

$$\frac{x^2}{a^2} - \frac{y^2}{b^2} = 1 \qquad \text{or} \qquad y = \pm\frac{b}{a}\sqrt{x^2 - a^2}$$

If $P = (x,y)$ is on the right-hand branch, $PF = ex - a$, $PF' = ex + a$. If P is on the left-hand branch, $PF = -ex + a$, $PF' = -ex - a$.

Equations of Hyperbola in Parametric Form. (1) $x = a \cosh u$, $y = b \sinh u$. (For tables of hyperbolic functions, see pp. 1–60 and 1–61.) Here u may be interpreted as

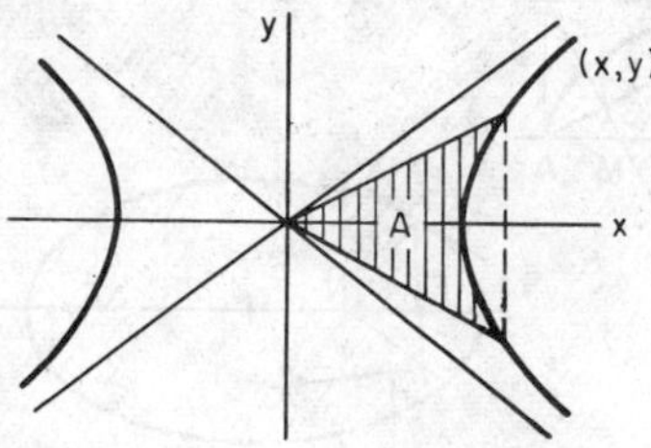

Fig. 44

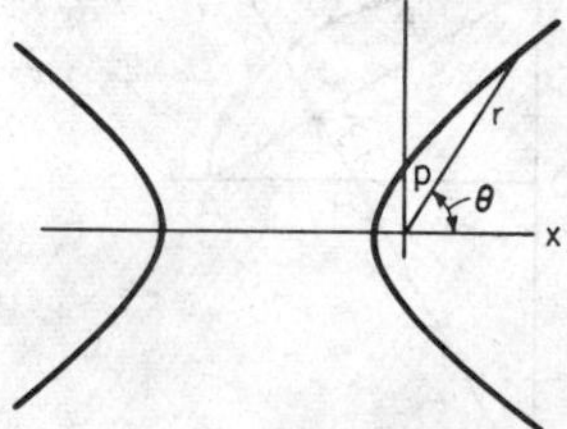

Fig. 45

A/ab, where A is the area shaded in Fig. 44. (2) $x = a \sec v$, $y = b \tan v$, where v is an auxiliary angle of no special geometric interest.

Polar equation, referred to focus as origin, axes as in Fig. 45:

$$r = p/(1 - e \cos \theta)$$

Equation of the Tangent at (x_1,y_1): $b^2x_1x - a^2y_1y = a^2b^2$. The line $y = mx + k$ will be a tangent if $k = \pm\sqrt{a^2m^2 - b^2}$. The tangent at any point P (Fig. 46) bisects the angle between PF and PF'. The locus of the foot of the perpendicular from the focus on a moving tangent is the circle on the principal axis as diameter (Fig. 47). The locus of the point of intersection of perpendicular tangents is a circle with radius $\sqrt{a^2 - b^2}$, which will be imaginary if $b > a$ (Fig. 48).

Properties of the Asymptotes (Fig. 49). If P is any point of the curve, the product of the perpendicular distances from P to the two asymptotes is constant, $= a^2b^2/(a^2 + b^2)$. Also, the product of the oblique distances (the distance to each asymptote being measured parallel to the other) is constant and equal to $\frac{1}{4}(a^2 + b^2)$. If a line cuts the hyperbola and its asymptotes, the parts of the line intercepted between the curve and the asymptotes are equal. The part of a tangent intercepted between the asymptotes is bisected by the point of contact. The triangle bounded by the asymptotes and a variable tangent is of constant area, $= ab$. If a line through Q perpendicular to the principal axis meets the asymptotes in R and S (see Fig. 49), then $\overline{QR} \times \overline{QS} = b^2$. If a line through Q parallel to the principal axis meets the asymptotes in U and V, then $\overline{QU} \times \overline{QV} = a^2$.

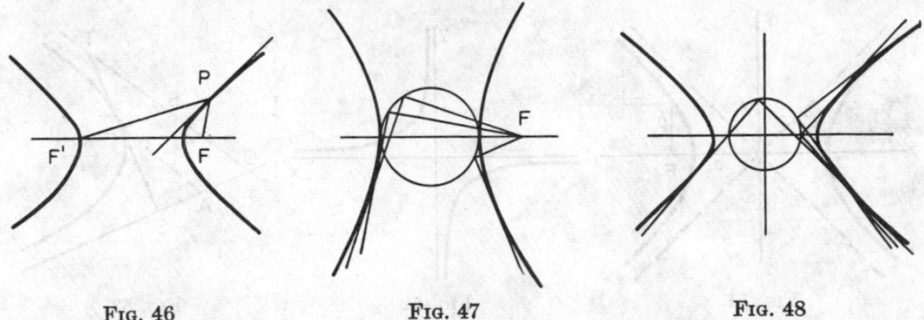

FIG. 46 FIG. 47 FIG. 48

Conjugate hyperbolas are two hyperbolas having the same asymptotes with semi-axes interchanged (Fig. 50). The equation of the hyperbola conjugate to $\dfrac{x^2}{a^2} - \dfrac{y^2}{b^2} = 1$ is $\dfrac{x^2}{a^2} - \dfrac{y^2}{b^2} = -1$.

Conjugate diameters are lines through the center, each of which bisects all the chords parallel to the other—a chord which does not meet the given hyperbola being under-

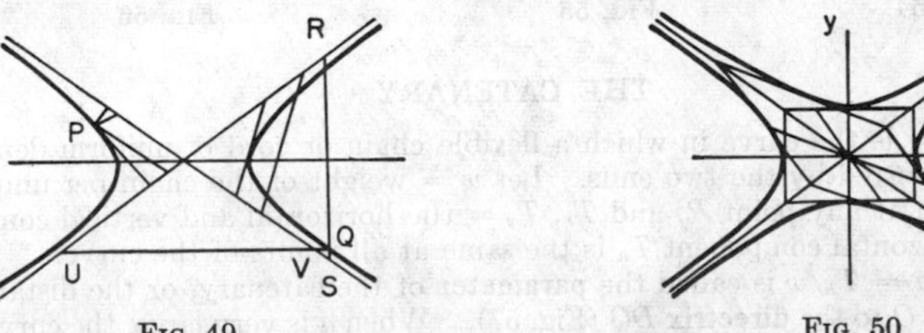

FIG. 49 FIG. 50

stood to be terminated by the conjugate hyperbola (Fig. 50). If m_1 and m_2 are the slopes, then $m_1m_2 = b^2/a^2$. Each asymptote, regarded as a diameter, is its own conjugate. If a parallelogram is formed by tangents drawn parallel to a pair of conjugate diameters, its vertices will lie on the asymptotes, and its area will be constant $= 4ab$. If a', b' are conjugate semidiameters, and w the angle between them, then $a'^2 - b'^2 = a^2 - b^2$, and $a'b' = ab/\sin w$.

Equilateral Hyperbola ($a = b$). Equation referred to principal axes (Fig. 51): $x^2 - y^2 = a^2$.

NOTE. $p = a$ (Fig. 51). Equation referred to asymptotes as axes (Fig. 52): $xy = a^2/2$. (See also Fig. 3, p. 2–84.)

Asymptotes are perpendicular. Eccentricity $= \sqrt{2}$. Any diameter is equal in length to its conjugate diameter.

To Construct a Tangent at any given point P of a hyperbola. In Fig. 53, draw PA and PB parallel to the asymptotes, and take $OS = 2(OA)$ and $OT = 2(OB)$. Then ST is the tangent at P.

To Construct a Hyperbola, given the asymptotes and any point P.

1. In Fig. 54 let TPT' be a variable line through P, and lay off $T'P' = TP$; then P' is a point of the curve.

2. In Fig. 55, draw PA and PB parallel to the asymptotes. Lay off $OA' = n(OA)$ and $OB' = (1/n)(OB)$, where n is any number; and through A' and B' draw parallels to the axes; these will meet in a point P' of the curve.

3. (Fig. 56). Take any point K in the ordinate PM, and draw OK meeting the line through P parallel to the x-axis in R. Draw a parallel to the x-axis through K and a parallel to the y-axis through R, meeting in Q. Then Q is a point of the curve.

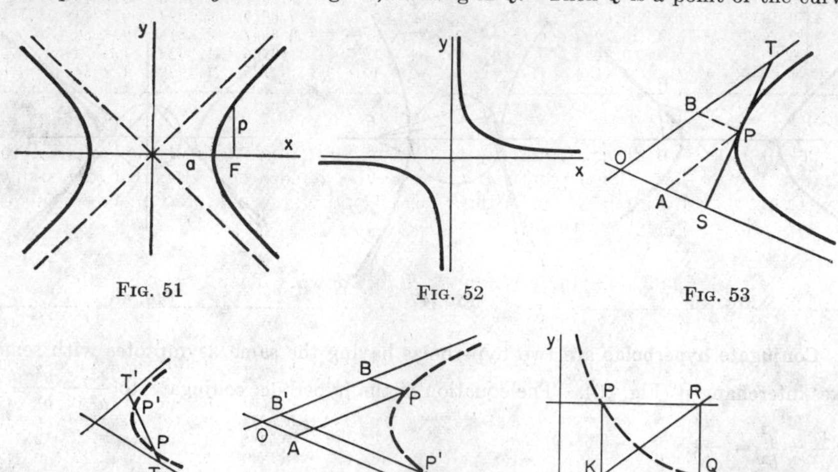

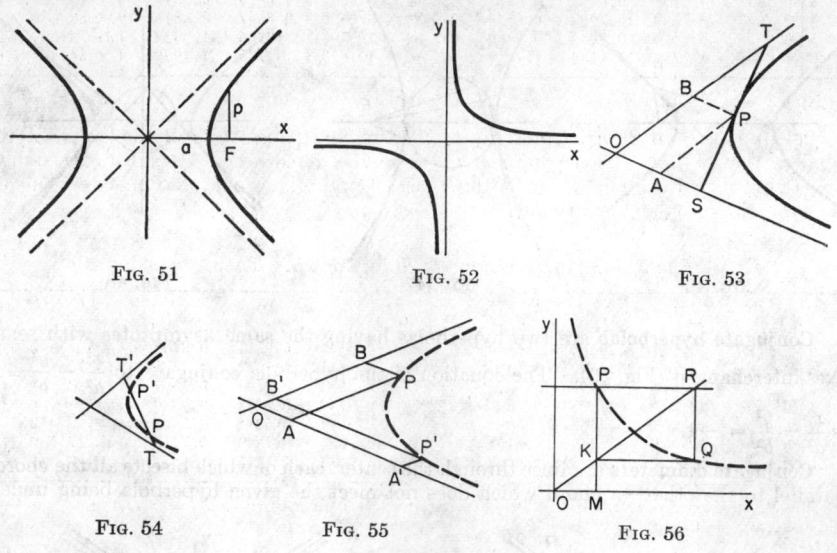

FIG. 51 FIG. 52 FIG. 53

FIG. 54 FIG. 55 FIG. 56

THE CATENARY

The **catenary** is the curve in which a flexible chain or cord of uniform density will hang when supported by the two ends. Let w = weight of the chain per unit length; T = the tension at any point P; and T_h, T_v = the horizontal and vertical components of T. The horizontal component T_h is the same at all points of the curve.

The length $a = T_h/w$ is called the **parameter** of the catenary, or the distance from the lowest point O to the **directrix** DQ (Fig. 57). When a is very large, the curve is very flat. For methods of finding a in any given case, see problems 1–6 below.

The rectangular **equation,** referred to the lowest point as origin, is $y = a\,[\cosh\,(x/a) - 1]$. (For table of hyperbolic functions, see p. 1–60.)

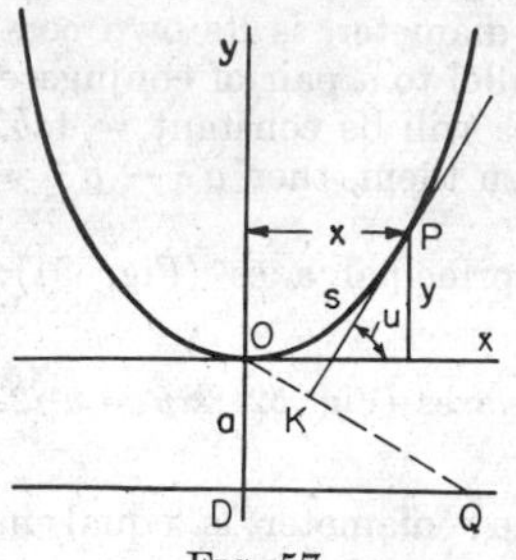

FIG. 57

In case of very flat arcs (a large), $y = \dfrac{x^2}{2a} + \cdots$; $s = x + \frac{1}{6}\dfrac{x^3}{a^2} + \cdots$, approx, so that in such a case the catenary closely resembles a parabola.

If the perpendicular from O to the tangent at P meets the directrix in Q, then DQ = arc $OP = s$ and $OQ = y + a$. The **radius of curvature** at P is $R = (y + a)^2/a$, which is equal in length to the portion of the normal intercepted between P and the directrix.

Problems on the Catenary (Fig. 57). When any two of the four quantities x, y, s, T/w are known, the remaining two, and also the parameter a, can be found, as follows:

1. GIVEN x AND y. Compute y/x, and find from Table 1 the value of the auxiliary variable z. Then compute $a = x/z$, $s = a \sinh z$, and $T = wa \cosh z$. Or, having z, find s/x and wx/T by using Tables 3 and 2 inversely, and hence (since x is known) compute s and T/w without the use of a.

Table 1. Giving z When y/x Is Known. Then $a = x/z$

y/x	0	1	2	3	4	5	6	7	8	9
0.0	0.0000	0.0200	0.0400	0.0600	0.0800	0.0999	0.1199	0.1398	0.1597	0.1795
0.1	0.1993	0.2191	0.2389	0.2586	0.2782	0.2978	0.3173	0.3368	0.3562	0.3756
0.2	0.3948	0.4140	0.4332	0.4522	0.4712	0.4901	0.5089	0.5276	0.5463	0.5648
0.3	0.5833	0.6016	0.6199	0.6381	0.6561	0.6741	0.6919	0.7097	0.7274	0.7449
0.4	0.7623	0.7797	0.7969	0.8140	0.8311	0.8480	0.8647	0.8814	0.8980	0.9145
0.5	0.9308	0.9471	0.9632	0.9792	0.9951	1.0109	1.0266	1.0422	1.0576	1.0730
0.6	1.0883	1.1034	1.1184	1.1334	1.1482	1.1629	1.1775	1.1920	1.2064	1.2207

NOTE. $y/x = (\cosh z - 1)/z$.

2. GIVEN x AND T/w. Compute wx/T, and find from Table 2 the value of the auxiliary variable z. Then compute $a = x/z$, $y = a(\cosh z - 1)$ and $s = a \sinh z$. Or, having z, find y/x and s/x by using Tables 1 and 3 inversely, and hence (since x is known) compute y and s without the use of a.

Table 2. Giving z When wx/T Is Known. Then $a = x/z$

wx/T	0	1	2	3	4	5	6	7	8	9
0.0	0.0000	0.0100	0.0200	0.0300	0.0400	0.0501	0.0601	0.0702	0.0803	0.0904
0.1	0.1005	0.1107	0.1209	0.1311	0.1414	0.1517	0.1621	0.1725	0.1830	0.1936
0.2	0.2042	0.2149	0.2256	0.2365	0.2474	0.2584	0.2695	0.2807	0.2920	0.3035
0.3	0.3150	0.3267	0.3385	0.3505	0.3626	0.3749	0.3874	0.4000	0.4129	0.4259
0.4	0.4392	0.4528	0.4666	0.4806	0.4950	0.5097	0.5248	0.5403	0.5562	0.5726
0.5	0.5894	0.6068	0.6249	0.6436	0.6632	0.6836	0.7051	0.7277	0.7517	0.7775
0.6	0.8053	0.8357	0.8695	0.9082	0.9541	1.0132	1.1110	......	......	......

NOTE. $wx/T = z/\cosh z$. If wx/T is less than 0.6627, there are two values of z, one less than 1.200 and one greater than 1.200; only the smaller of these values is tabulated. If wx/T is greater than 0.6627, the problem is impossible.

3. GIVEN x AND s. Compute s/x, and find from Table 3 the value of the auxiliary variable z. Then compute $a = x/z$, $y = a(\cosh z - 1)$, and $T = wa \cosh z$. Or, having z, find y/x and wx/T by using Table 1 and 2 inversely, and hence (since x is known) compute y and T/w without the use of a.

Table 3. Giving z When s/x Is Known. Then $a = x/z$

s/x	0	1	2	3	4	5	6	7	8	9
1.000	......	0.0245	0.0346	0.0424	0.0490	0.0548	0.0600	0.0648	0.0693	0.0735
1	0.0774	0.0812	0.0848	0.0883	0.0916	0.0948	0.0980	0.1010	0.1039	0.1067
2	0.1095	0.1122	0.1149	0.1174	0.1200	0.1224	0.1249	0.1272	0.1296	0.1319
3	0.1341	0.1363	0.1385	0.1407	0.1428	0.1448	0.1469	0.1489	0.1509	0.1529
4	0.1548	0.1567	0.1586	0.1605	0.1623	0.1642	0.1660	0.1678	0.1696	0.1713
1.005	0.1731	0.1748	0.1765	0.1782	0.1799	0.1815	0.1831	0.1848	0.1864	0.1880
6	0.1896	0.1911	0.1927	0.1942	0.1958	0.1973	0.1988	0.2003	0.2018	0.2033
7	0.2047	0.2062	0.2076	0.2091	0.2105	0.2119	0.2133	0.2147	0.2161	0.2175
8	0.2188	0.2202	0.2215	0.2229	0.2242	0.2255	0.2269	0.2282	0.2295	0.2308
9	0.2321	0.2334	0.2346	0.2359	0.2372	0.2384	0.2397	0.2409	0.2421	0.2434
1.01	0.2446	0.2565	0.2678	0.2787	0.2892	0.2993	0.3091	0.3186	0.3278	0.3367
2	0.3454	0.3539	0.3621	0.3702	0.3781	0.3859	0.3934	0.4009	0.4082	0.4153
3	0.4224	0.4293	0.4361	0.4428	0.4494	0.4559	0.4623	0.4686	0.4748	0.4809
4	0.4870	0.4930	0.4989	0.5047	0.5105	0.5162	0.5218	0.5274	0.5329	0.5383
1.05	0.5437	0.5490	0.5543	0.5595	0.5647	0.5698	0.5749	0.5799	0.5849	0.5898
6	0.5947	0.5996	0.6044	0.6091	0.6139	0.6186	0.6232	0.6278	0.6324	0.6369
7	0.6414	0.6459	0.6504	0.6548	0.6591	0.6635	0.6678	0.6721	0.6763	0.6806
8	0.6848	0.6889	0.6931	0.6972	0.7013	0.7053	0.7094	0.7134	0.7174	0.7213
9	0.7253	0.7292	0.7331	0.7369	0.7408	0.7446	0.7484	0.7522	0.7559	0.7597
1.10	0.7634	......	......	......	......	......	NOTE. $s/x = \sinh z/z$			

4. GIVEN y AND s. Then $\frac{T}{w} = \frac{s^2}{2y} + \frac{y}{2}$, $x = \left(\frac{s^2}{y} - y\right) \tanh^{-1}\left(\frac{y}{s}\right)$, $a = \frac{s^2}{2y} - \frac{y}{2}$. Or, if y/s is small, $x = s\left[1 - \frac{2}{3}\left(\frac{y}{s}\right)^2 - \frac{2}{15}\left(\frac{y}{s}\right)^4 - \cdots\right]$.

5. GIVEN y AND T/w. Then $a = \frac{T}{w} - y$, $x = \left(\frac{T}{w} - y\right) \cosh^{-1} \frac{T/w}{(T/w) - y}$. $s = \sqrt{2y(T/w) - y^2}$. Or, if $y(T/w)$ is small,

$$x = \sqrt{\frac{2yT}{w}}\left[1 - \frac{7}{12}\frac{wy}{T} - \cdots\right], \quad \frac{s - x}{s} = \frac{1}{3}\frac{wy}{T}, \text{ approx,}$$

$$s = \sqrt{\frac{2yT}{w}}\left[1 - \frac{1}{4}\frac{wy}{T} - \frac{1}{32}\left(\frac{wy}{T}\right)^2 - \frac{1}{128}\left(\frac{wy}{T}\right)^3 - \cdots\right].$$

6. GIVEN s AND T/w. Then $x = \frac{T}{w}\sqrt{1 - \left(\frac{ws}{T}\right)^2} \tanh^{-1}\left(\frac{ws}{T}\right)$,

$y = \frac{T}{w} - \frac{T}{w}\sqrt{1 - \left(\frac{ws}{T}\right)^2}$, $a = \frac{T}{w}\sqrt{1 - \left(\frac{ws}{T}\right)^2}$. Or, if ws/T is small,

$$x = s\left[1 - \frac{1}{6}\left(\frac{ws}{T}\right)^2 - \frac{11}{120}\left(\frac{ws}{T}\right)^4 - \cdots\right], \quad y = s\left[\frac{1}{2}\left(\frac{ws}{T}\right) + \frac{1}{8}\left(\frac{ws}{T}\right)^3 + \cdots\right],$$

$$a = \frac{T}{w}\left[1 - \frac{1}{2}\left(\frac{ws}{T}\right)^2 - \frac{1}{8}\left(\frac{ws}{T}\right)^4 - \cdots\right].$$

Given the Length $2L$ of a Chain Supported at Two Points A and B not in the Same Level, to Find a. (See Fig. 58; b and c are supposed known.) Let $(\sqrt{L^2 - b^2})/c = s/x$; enter Table 3 with this value of s/x, and find the corresponding value of the auxiliary variable z. Then $a = c/z$.

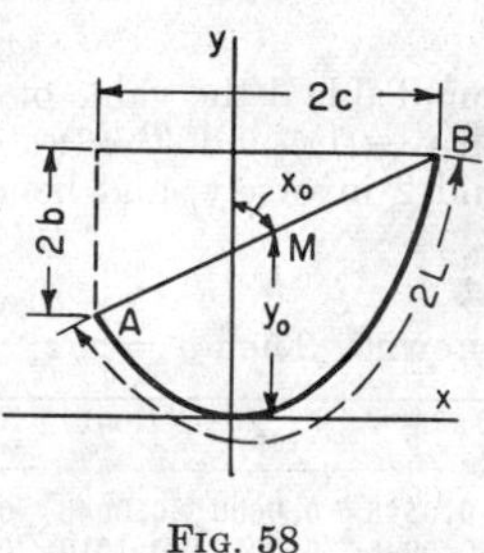

FIG. 58

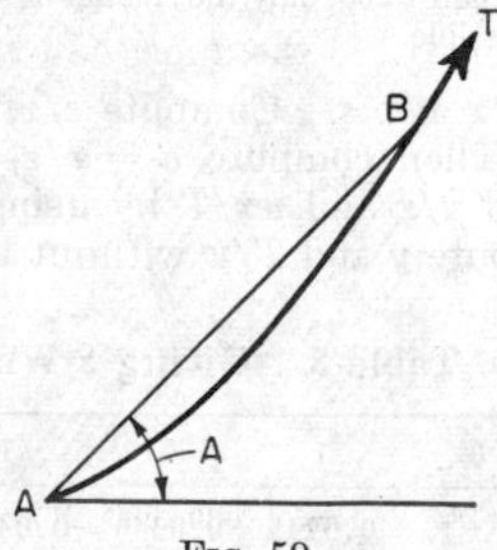

FIG. 59

NOTE. The coordinates of the mid-point M of AB (see Fig. 58) are $x_0 = a \tanh^{-1}(b/L)$, $y_0 = (L/\tanh z) - a$, so that the position of the lowest point is determined.

Correction for Sag in Chaining Uphill (Fig. 59). Let l = length of tape (corrected for stretch and temperature), w = weight per unit length of tape, A = angle between the chord AB and the horizontal.

If the tension P at the upper end is known, compute wl/P and find k from Table 4. If the tension Q at the lower end is known, compute wl/Q and find k from Table 5. In either case, chord $AB = l - kl$.

NOTE. $k = 1 - [(1 - \sqrt{1 - 2m \sin u + m^2})/(m \sin A)]$, where $m = wl/P$ and u is given by

$$(1 - \sqrt{1 - 2m \sin u + m^2}) \sec u = [\sinh^{-1}(\tan u) - \sinh^{-1}(\tan u - m \sec u)] \tan A.$$

Also, $Q = P - wl(1 - k) \sin A$, where k is the value in Table 4 corresponding to the given values of P and A.

Table 4. Giving k

$\frac{wl}{P}$	A = 0°	10°	20°	30°	40°	50°	60°	70°	80°
.01	.00000	000	000	000	000	000	000	000	000
.02	002	002	001	001	001	001	000	000	000
.03	004	004	003	003	002	002	001	000	000
.04	007	006	006	005	004	003	002	001	000
.05	011	010	009	008	006	004	003	001	000
.06	.00015	015	013	012	009	006	004	002	000
.07	020	020	018	016	012	009	005	003	001
.08	027	026	024	021	016	012	007	003	001
.09	034	033	031	026	021	015	009	004	001
.10	042	041	038	033	026	019	011	005	001
.11	.00051	050	046	040	032	023	014	007	002
.12	060	060	055	048	038	027	017	008	002
.13	070	070	065	057	045	032	020	009	002
.14	082	081	076	066	053	038	023	011	003
.15	094	094	087	076	061	044	027	013	003
.16	.00107	107	100	087	070	050	031	015	004
.17	121	121	113	099	079	057	035	017	004
.18	136	136	128	112	090	065	040	019	005
.19	151	152	143	125	101	073	045	021	006
.20	168	168	159	140	113	082	050	024	006

Table 5. Giving k

$\frac{wl}{Q}$	A = 0°	10°	20°	30°	40°	50°	60°	70°	80°
.01	.00000	000	000	000	000	000	000	000	000
.02	002	002	001	001	001	001	000	000	000
.03	004	004	003	003	002	001	001	000	000
.04	007	006	006	005	004	003	002	001	000
.05	011	010	009	008	006	004	002	001	000
.06	.00015	014	013	011	008	006	004	002	000
.07	020	020	018	015	011	008	005	002	001
.08	027	026	023	019	015	011	006	003	001
.09	034	032	029	024	019	013	008	004	001
.10	042	040	036	030	023	016	010	004	001
.11	.00051	048	043	036	028	019	011	005	001
.12	060	057	051	043	033	023	014	006	002
.13	070	067	060	050	038	026	016	007	002
.14	082	078	069	057	044	030	018	008	002
.15	094	089	079	066	050	035	021	010	002
.16	.00107	101	090	074	057	039	022	011	003
.17	121	114	101	084	064	044	026	012	003
.18	136	128	113	092	071	049	029	013	003
.19	151	142	125	103	079	054	032	015	004
.20	168	157	138	114	087	060	035	016	004

Correction for Stretch in Chaining Uphill. Let L = unstretched length of tape at working temperature, w = weight per unit length of tape, A = angle between chord AB and the horizontal, F = area of cross section, E = Young's modulus of elasticity (for steel, E = 29,000,000 psi), l = stretched length (along curve).

If the tension P at the upper end is known, compute wL/P and find m from Table 6. Then $l = L + (LP/FE)(1 - m)$.

If the tension Q at the lower end is known, compute wL/Q and find n from Table 7. Then $l = L + (LQ/FE)(1 + n)$.

Table 6. Giving m

$\frac{wL}{P}$	A = 0°	10°	20°	30°	40°	50°	60°	70°	80°	90°
.00	.000	.000	.000	.000	.000	.000	.000	.000	.000	.000
.10	.001	.010	.018	.026	.033	.039	.044	.047	.049	.050
.20	.003	.021	.038	.053	.067	.078	.088	.094	.099	.100

Table 7. Giving n

$\frac{wL}{Q}$	A = 10°	20°	30°	40°	50°	60°	70°	80°	90°
.00	.000	.000	.000	.000	.000	.000	.000	.000	.000
.10	.008	.016	.024	.032	.038	.043	.047	.049	.050
.20	.014	.031	.047	.062	.075	.086	.094	.099	.100

OTHER USEFUL CURVES

The **cycloid** is traced by a point on the circumference of a circle which rolls without slipping along a straight line. Equations of cycloid, in parametric form (axes as in Fig. 60): $x = a\ (\text{rad}\ u - \sin u)$, $y = a(1 - \cos u)$, where a is the radius of the rolling

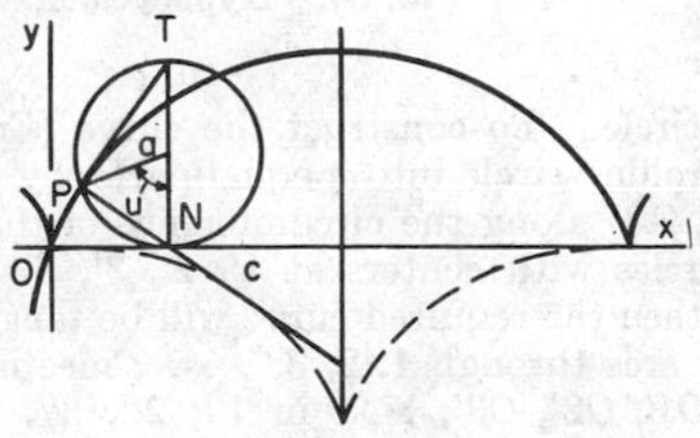

Fig. 60. Cycloid.

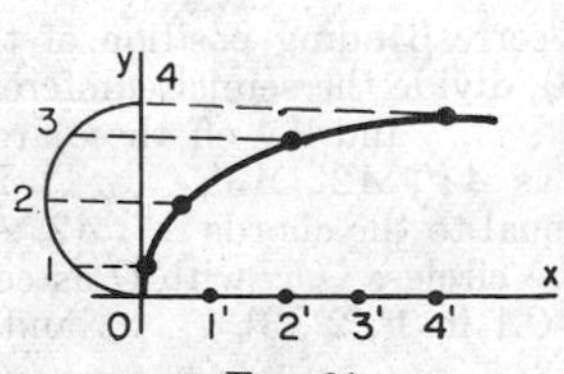

Fig. 61

circle, and rad u is the radian measure of the angle u through which it has rolled. The tangent and normal at any point pass through the highest and lowest points of the corresponding position of the generating circle. The **radius of curvature** at any point P is $PC = 4a \sin (u/2) = 2\sqrt{2ay}$ = twice the length of the normal, PN. The **evolute,** or locus of centers of curvature, is an equal cycloid. **To construct** a cycloid (Fig. 61), divide the semicircumference of the generating circle into n equal parts (here 4) and lay off these arcs along the base (from O to $4'$). Describe arcs with centers at $1'$, $2'$, . . . and radii equal to the chords $O1$, $O2$, . . . , and sketch the cycloid as a curve tangent to all of these arcs. Or, on horizontal lines through 1, 2, . . . lay off distances equal to $O1'$, $O2'$, etc. The points thus reached will lie on the cycloid.

The area of one arch $= 3\pi a^2$, length of arc of one arch $= 8a$. Area bounded by the ordinate of the point P corresponding to any value of u is $a^2(\tfrac{3}{2} \text{ rad } u - 2 \sin u + \tfrac{1}{4} \sin 2u) = \tfrac{3}{2}ax - \tfrac{1}{2} y\sqrt{(2a - y)y}$. Length of arc $OP = 4a(1 - \cos \tfrac{1}{2}u) = 4a - 2\sqrt{2a(2a - y)}$.

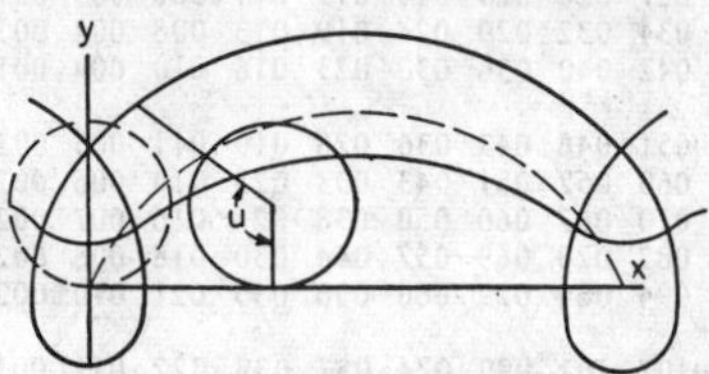

FIG. 62. Trochoid.

The **trochoid** is a more general curve, traced by any point on a radius of the rolling circle, at distance b from the center (Fig. 62). It is a prolate trochoid if $b < a$, and a curtate or looped trochoid if $b > a$. The equations in either case are $x = a \text{ rad } u - b \sin u$, $y = a - b \cos u$.

The **epicycloid** (or **hypocycloid**) is a curve generated by a point on the circumference of a circle of radius a which rolls without slipping on the outside (or inside) of a fixed circle of radius c. For the **equations,** put $b = a$ in the equations of the epi- or hypotrochoid, below. The normal at any point P passes through the point of contact N

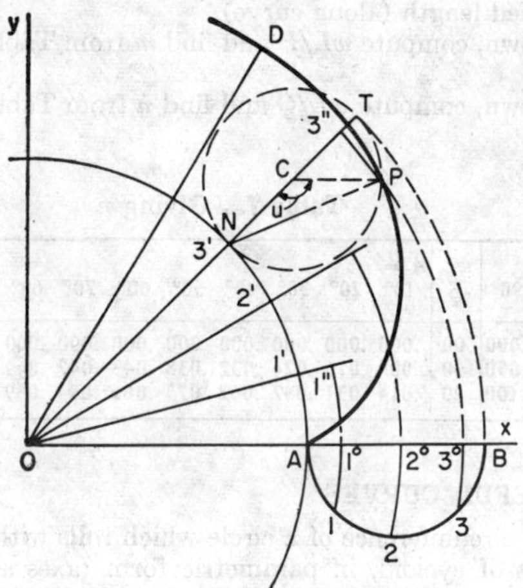

FIG. 63. Epicycloid.

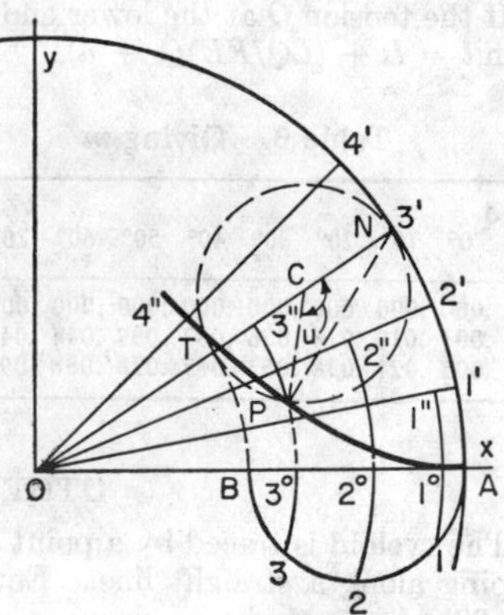

FIG. 64. Hypocycloid.

of the corresponding position of the rolling circle. To construct the curve (Figs. 63 and 64), divide the semicircumference of the rolling circle into n equal parts, by points 1, 2, 3 . . . , and lay off these arcs ($A1$, $A2$, $A3$) along the circumference of the base circle, as $A1'$, $A2'$, $A3'$, ... Describe circles with centers at $1'$, $2'$, $3'$, . . . and radii equal to the chords $A1$, $A2$, $A3$, . . . ; then the required curve will be tangent to all these circles. Or, with O as center, draw arcs through 1, 2, 3, . . . , meeting the radius OA in 1^0, 2^0, 3^0, . . . , and the radii $O1'$, $O2'$, $O3'$, . . . in $1''$, $2''$, $3''$, . . . ;

then from 1″, 2″, 3″, . . . lay off arcs equal to 1^01, 2^02, 3^03, . . . , respectively; the points thus reached will be points of the curve.

The area $OAP = \dfrac{a(c \pm a)(c \pm 2a)}{2c}$ (rad u − sin u), where the upper sign applies to the epicycloid, the lower to the hypocycloid, and rad u = the radian measure of the angle u shown in Figs. 63 and 64. Arc $AP = (4a/c)(c \pm a)(1 - \cos \tfrac{1}{2} u)$; arc $AD = (4a/c)(c \pm a)$. (In Fig. 64, D = 4″.)

Radius of curvature at any point P is $R = \dfrac{4a(c \pm a)}{c \pm 2a} \sin \tfrac{1}{2}u$; at A, $R = 0$; at D, $R = \dfrac{4a(c \pm a)}{c \pm 2a}$.

Special Cases. If $a = \tfrac{1}{2}c$, the hypocycloid becomes a straight line, diameter of the fixed circle (Fig. 65). In this case the hypotrochoid traced by any point rigidly connected with the rolling circle (not necessarily on the circumference) will be an ellipse. If $a = \tfrac{1}{4}c$, the curve generated will be the four-cusped hypocycloid, or **astroid** (Fig. 66), whose equation is $x^{2/3} + y^{2/3} = c^{2/3}$. If $a = c$, the epicycloid is the **cardioid,** whose equation in polar coordinates (axes as in Fig. 67) is $r = 2c(1 + \cos \theta)$. Length of cardioid = $16c$.

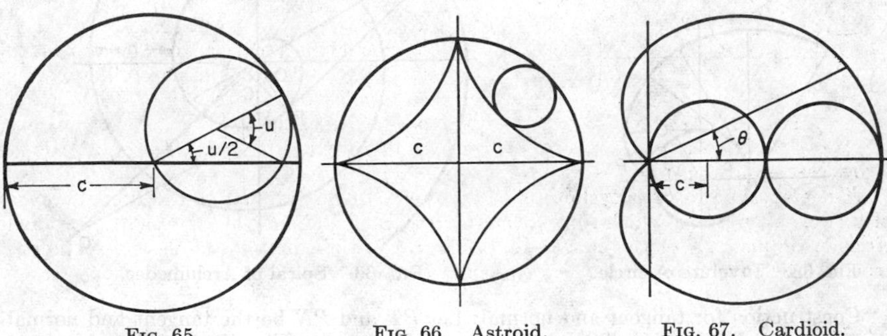

Fig. 65 Fig. 66. Astroid. Fig. 67. Cardioid.

The **epitrochoid** (or **hypotrochoid**) is a curve traced by any point rigidly attached to a circle of radius a, at distance b from the center, when this circle rolls without slipping on the outside (or inside) of a fixed circle of radius c. The equations are $x = (c \pm a) \cos \left(\dfrac{a}{c} u\right) \mp b \cos \left[\left(1 \pm \dfrac{a}{c}\right) u\right]$, $y = (c \pm a) \sin \left(\dfrac{a}{c} u\right) - b \sin \left[\left(1 \pm \dfrac{a}{c}\right) u\right]$, where u = the angle which the moving radius makes with the line of centers; take the upper sign for the epi- and the lower for the hypotrochoid. The curve is called prolate or curtate according as $b < a$ or $b > a$. When $b = a$, the special case of the epi- or hypocycloid arises.

The **involute of a circle** is the curve traced by the end of a taut string which is unwound from the circumference of a fixed circle, of radius c. If QP is the free portion of the string at any instant (Fig. 68), QP will be tangent to the circle at Q, and the length of QP = length of arc QA; hence the construction of the curve. The equations of the curve in parametric form (axes as in figure) are $x = c(\cos u + \text{rad } u \sin u)$, $y = c(\sin u - \text{rad } u \cos u)$, where rad u is the radian measure of the angle u which OQ makes with the x-axis. Length of arc $AP = \tfrac{1}{2}c(\text{rad } u)^2$; radius of curvature at P is QP. Polar equations, in terms of parameter v(= angle POQ), are $r = c \sec v$, rad $\theta = \tan v - \text{rad } v$. Here, $r = OP$, and rad θ = radian measure of angle AOP (Fig. 68).

The **spiral of Archimedes** (Fig. 69) is traced by a point P which, starting from O, moves with uniform velocity along a ray OP, while the ray itself revolves with uniform angular velocity about O. Polar equation: $r = k$ rad θ, or $r = a\ (\theta°/360°)$. Here $a = 2\pi k$ = the distance, measured along a radius, from each coil to the next.

In order to construct the curve, draw radii $O1$, $O2$, $O3$, . . . making angles $\frac{1}{n}\ (360°)$, $\frac{2}{n}\ (360°)$, $\frac{3}{n}\ (360°)$, . . . with Ox, and along these radii lay off distances equal to $\frac{1}{n}a, \frac{2}{n}a, \frac{3}{n}a$, . . . ; the points thus reached will lie on the spiral. The figure shows one-half of the curve, corresponding to positive values of θ.

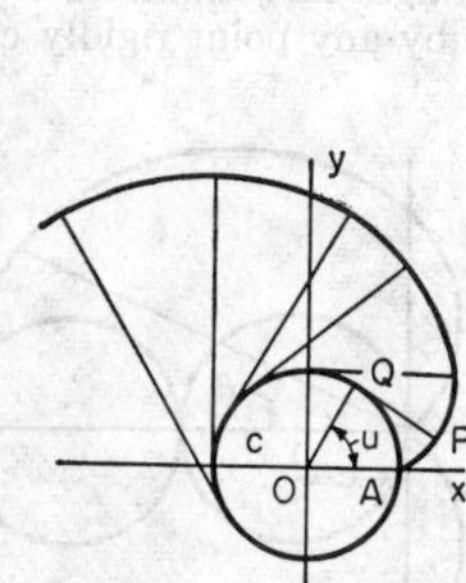

Fig. 68. Involute of circle.

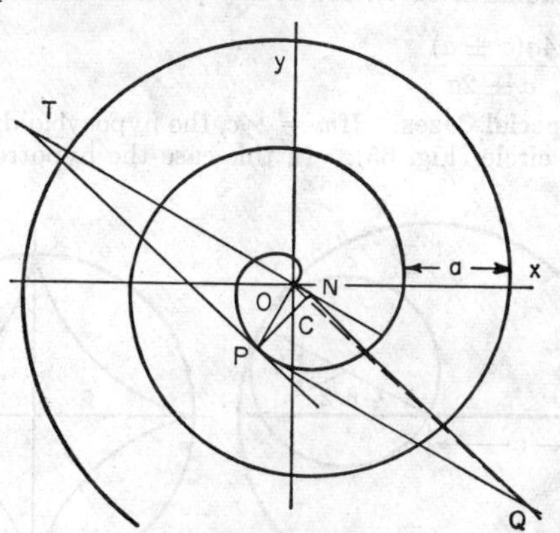

Fig. 69. Spiral of Archimedes.

Construction for tangent and normal: Let PT and PN be the tangent and normal at any point P, the line TON being perpendicular to OP. Then $OT = r^2/k$, and $ON = k$, where $k = a/(2\pi)$. Hence the construction.

The radius of curvature at P is $R = (k^2 + r^2)^{3/2}/(2k^2 + r^2)$. To construct the center of curvature, C, draw NQ perpendicular to PN and PQ perpendicular to OP; then OQ will meet PN in C. Length of arc $OP = \frac{1}{2}k$ [rad $\theta \sqrt{1 + (\text{rad } \theta)^2} + \sinh^{-1}$ (rad θ)]. After many windings, arc $OP = \frac{1}{2}r^2/k$, approx.

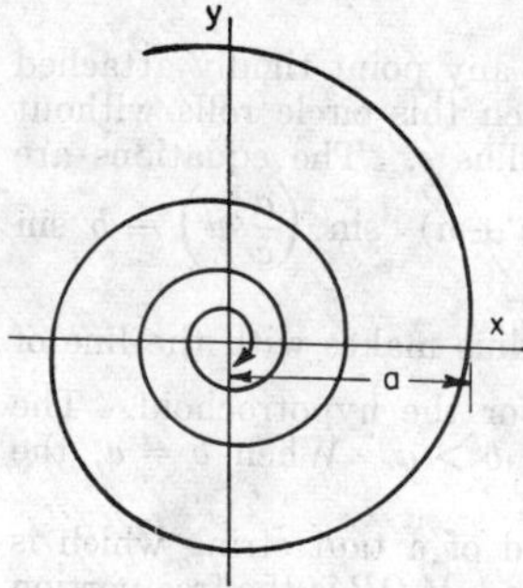

Fig. 70. Logarithmic spiral.

The **logarithmic spiral** (Fig. 70) is a curve which cuts the radii from O at a constant angle v, whose cotangent is m. Polar equation: $r = ae^{m \text{ rad } \theta}$. Here a is the value of r when $\theta = 0$. For large negative values of θ, the curve winds around O as an asymptotic point. If PT and PN are the tangent and normal at P, the line TON being perpendicular to OP (not shown in figure), then $ON = rm$, and $PN = r\sqrt{1 + m^2} = r/\sin v$. Radius of curvature at P is PN. The evolute of the spiral is an equal spiral whose axis makes an angle $\frac{1}{2}\pi - (\ln m)/m$ with the axis of the given spiral. Area swept out by the radius r from $r = 0$ (where $\theta = -\infty$) to $r = r$ is $A = r^2/4m$ = half the triangle OPT. Length of arc from O to $P = s = r/\cos v = PT$.

The **tractrix,** or Schiele's antifriction curve (Fig. 71), is a curve such that the portion PT of the tangent between the point of contact and the x-axis is constant $= a$. Its equation is $x = \pm a \left[\cosh^{-1}\frac{a}{y} - \sqrt{1 - \left(\frac{y}{a}\right)^2}\right]$, or, in parametric form, $x = \pm a(t - \tanh t)$, $y = a/\cosh t$. (For tables of hyperbolic functions, see p. 1–60.) The x-axis is an asymptote of the curve. Length of arc $BP = a \log_e (a/y)$. The evolute (locus of centers of curvature) is the catenary whose lowest point is at B, and whose directrix is Ox.

The **lemniscate** (Fig. 72) is the locus of a point P the product of whose distances from two fixed points F, F' is constant, equal to $\frac{1}{2}a^2$. The distance $FF' = a\sqrt{2}$. Polar equation is $r = a\sqrt{\cos 2\theta}$. Angle between OP and the normal at P is 2θ. The two branches of the curve cross at right angles at O. Maximum y occurs when $\theta = 30°$ and $r = a/\sqrt{2}$, and is equal to $\frac{1}{4}a\sqrt{2}$. Area of one loop $= a^2/2$.

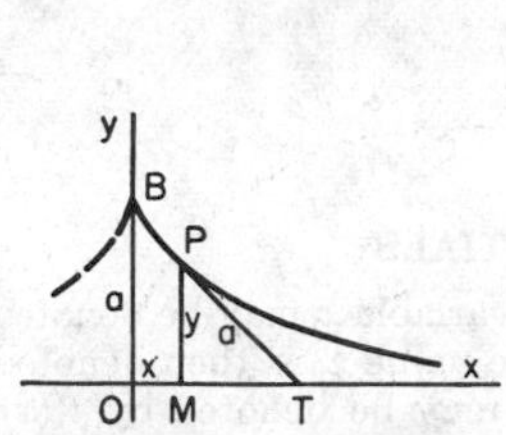

FIG. 71. Tractrix.

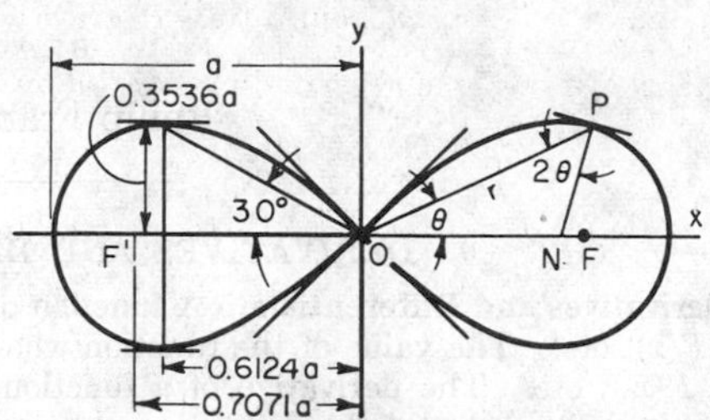

FIG. 72. Lemniscate.

The **helix** (Fig. 73) is the curve of a screw thread on a cylinder of radius r. The curve crosses the elements of the cylinder at a constant angle, v. The pitch, h, is the distance between two coils of the helix, measured along an element of the cylinder; hence $h = 2\pi r \tan v$. Length of one coil $= \sqrt{(2\pi r)^2 + h^2} = 2\pi r/\cos v$. To construct the projection of a helix on a plane containing the axis of the cylinder, draw a rectangle, breadth $2r$ and height h, to represent the plane, with a semicircle below it, as in the figure, to represent the base of the cylinder. Divide h into equal parts (here

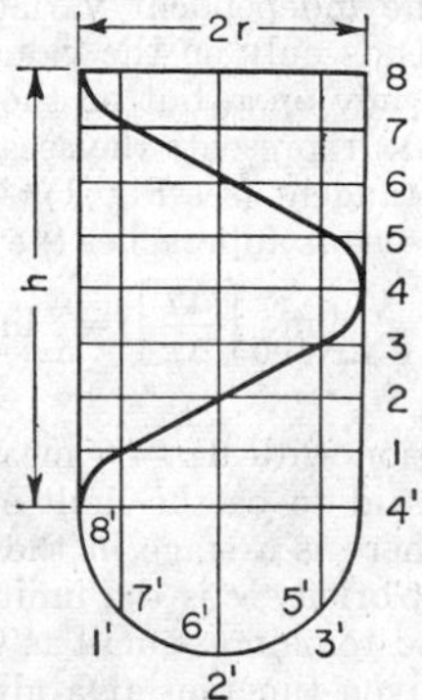

FIG. 73. Helix.

8), numbered from 1 to 8; think of the circumference as also divided into 8 equal parts, represented on the semicircle by numbers from 1′ to 4′ and back again from 4′ to 8′. Then the point of intersection of a horizontal line through 1, 2, . . . with a vertical line through 1′, 2′, . . . will be a point of the required projection. If the cylinder is rolled out on a plane, the development of the helix will be a straight line, with slope equal to $\tan v$.

DIFFERENTIAL AND INTEGRAL CALCULUS

BY

Philip Franklin

DERIVATIVES AND DIFFERENTIALS

Derivatives and Differentials. A **function** of a single variable x may be denoted by $f(x)$, $F(x)$, etc. The value of the function when x has the value x_0 is then denoted by $f(x_0)$, $F(x_0)$, etc. The **derivative** of a function $y = f(x)$ may be denoted by $f'(x)$, or by dy/dx. The value of the derivative at a given point $x = x_0$ is the **rate of change** of the function at that point; or, if the function is represented by a curve in the usual way (Fig. 1), the value of the derivative at any point shows the **slope of the curve** (*i.e.*, the slope of the tangent to the curve) at that point (positive if the tangent points upward, and negative if it points downward, moving to the right).

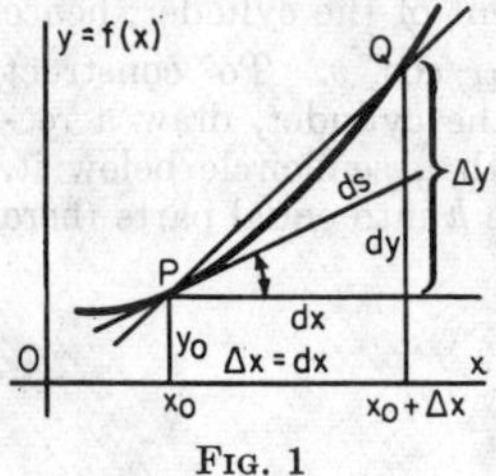

FIG. 1

The **increment** Δy (read: "delta y"), in y is the change produced in y by increasing x from x_0 to $x_0 + \Delta x$; *i.e.*, $\Delta y = f(x_0 + \Delta x) - f(x_0)$. The **differential**, dy, of y is the value which Δy would have if the curve coincided with its tangent. (The differential, dx, of x is the same as Δx when x is the independent variable.) Note that the derivative depends only on the value of x_0, while Δy and dy depend not only on x_0 but on the value of Δx as well. The ratio $\Delta y/\Delta x$ represents the secant slope, and dy/dx the slope of the tangent (see Fig. 1). If Δx is made to approach zero, the secant approaches the tangent as a limiting position, so that the derivative $= f'(x) = \dfrac{dy}{dx} = \lim\limits_{\Delta x \to 0} \left[\dfrac{\Delta y}{\Delta x}\right] = \lim\limits_{\Delta x \to 0} \left[\dfrac{f(x_0 + \Delta x) - f(x_0)}{\Delta x}\right]$. Also, $dy = f'(x)\,dx$.

The symbol "lim" in connection with $\Delta x \to 0$ means "the limit, as Δx approaches 0, of . . . ." (A constant c is said to be the **limit** of a variable u if, whenever any quantity m has been assigned, there is a stage in the variation-process beyond which $|c - u|$ is always less than m; or, briefly, c is the limit of u if the difference between c and u can be made to become and remain as small as we please.)

To find the derivative of a given function at a given point: (1) If the function is given only by a curve, measure graphically the slope of the tangent at the point in question; (2) if the function is given by a mathematical expression, use the following rules for differentiation. These rules give, directly, the differential, dy, in terms of dx; to find the derivative, dy/dx, divide through by dx.

Rules for Differentiation. (Here $u, v, w, \ldots$ represent any functions of a variable x, or may themselves be independent variables. a is a constant which does not change in value in the same discussion; $e = 2.71828$.)

1. $d(a + u) = du$. 2. $d(au) = a\,du$.
3. $d(u + v + w + \cdots) = du + dv + dw + \cdots$.
4. $d(uv) = u\,dv + v\,du$.
5. $d(uvw\ldots) = (uvw\ldots)\left(\dfrac{du}{u} + \dfrac{dv}{v} + \dfrac{dw}{w} + \cdots\right)$.
6. $d\dfrac{u}{v} = \dfrac{v\,du - u\,dv}{v^2}$. 7. $d(u^m) = mu^{m-1}\,du$.

Thus, $d(u^2) = 2u\,du$; $d(u^3) = 3u^2\,du$; etc.

8. $d\sqrt{u} = \dfrac{du}{2\sqrt{u}}$.

9. $d\left(\dfrac{1}{u}\right) = -\dfrac{du}{u^2}$.

10. $d(e^u) = e^u\,du$.

11. $d(a^u) = (\ln a)a^u\,du$.

12. $d\ln u = \dfrac{du}{u}$.

13. $d\log_{10} u = (\log_{10} e)\dfrac{du}{u} = (0.4343\ldots)\dfrac{du}{u}$.

14. $d\sin u = \cos u\,du$.

15. $d\csc u = -\cot u\csc u\,du$.

16. $d\cos u = -\sin u\,du$.

17. $d\sec u = \tan u\sec u\,du$.

18. $d\tan u = \sec^2 u\,du$.

19. $d\cot u = -\csc^2 u\,du$.

20. $d\sin^{-1} u = \dfrac{du}{\sqrt{1-u^2}}$.

21. $d\csc^{-1} u = -\dfrac{du}{u\sqrt{u^2-1}}$.

22. $d\cos^{-1} u = -\dfrac{du}{\sqrt{1-u^2}}$.

23. $d\sec^{-1} u = \dfrac{du}{u\sqrt{u^2-1}}$.

24. $d\tan^{-1} u = \dfrac{du}{1+u^2}$.

25. $d\cot^{-1} u = -\dfrac{du}{1+u^2}$.

26. $d\ln\sin u = \cot u\,du$.

27. $d\ln\tan u = \dfrac{2du}{\sin 2u}$.

28. $d\ln\cos u = -\tan u\,du$.

29. $d\ln\cot u = -\dfrac{2du}{\sin 2u}$.

30. $d\sinh u = \cosh u\,du$.

31. $d\,\mathrm{csch}\,u = -\mathrm{csch}\,u\coth u\,du$.

32. $d\cosh u = \sinh u\,du$.

33. $d\,\mathrm{sech}\,u = -\mathrm{sech}\,u\tanh u\,du$.

34. $d\tanh u = \mathrm{sech}^2 u\,du$.

35. $d\coth u = -\mathrm{csch}^2 u\,du$.

36. $d\sinh^{-1} u = \dfrac{du}{\sqrt{u^2+1}}$.

37. $d\,\mathrm{csch}^{-1} u = -\dfrac{du}{u\sqrt{u^2+1}}$.

38. $d\cosh^{-1} u = \dfrac{du}{\sqrt{u^2-1}}$.

39. $d\,\mathrm{sech}^{-1} u = -\dfrac{du}{u\sqrt{1-u^2}}$.

40. $d\tanh^{-1} u = \dfrac{du}{1-u^2}$.

41. $d\coth^{-1} u = \dfrac{du}{1-u^2}$.

42. $d(u^v) = (u^{v-1})(u\ln u\,dv + v\,du)$.

Derivatives of Higher Orders. The derivative of the derivative is called the second derivative; the derivative of this, the third derivative; and so on. If $y = f(x)$,

$$f'(x) = D_x y = \frac{dy}{dx} \qquad f''(x) = D_x^2 y = \frac{d^2y}{dx^2} \qquad f'''(x) = D_x^3 y = \frac{d^3y}{dx^3} \qquad \text{etc.}$$

NOTE. If the notation d^2y/dx^2 is used, this must not be treated as a fraction, like dy/dx, but as an inseparable symbol, made up of a symbol of operation d^2/dx^2, and an operand y.

The geometric meaning of the second derivative is this: if the original function $y = f(x)$ is represented by a curve in the usual way, then at any point where $f''(x)$ is *positive*, the curve is *concave upward*, and at any point where $f''(x)$ is *negative*, the curve is *concave downward* (Fig. 2). When $f''(x) = 0$, the curve usually has a **point of inflection.**

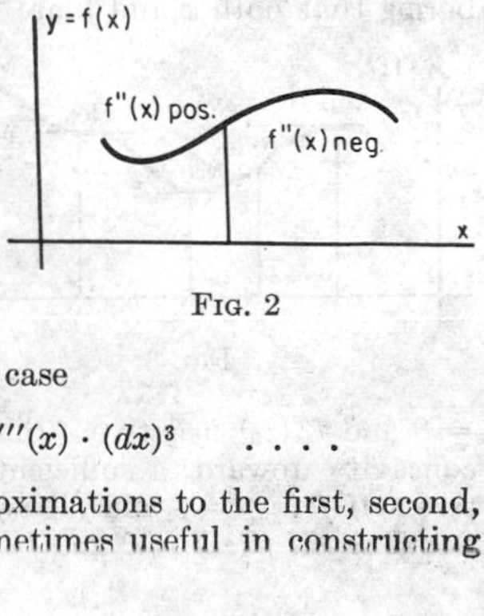

y = f(x)
f''(x) pos.
f''(x) neg.
x

FIG. 2

Differentials of Higher Orders. The differential of the differential is called the second differential; the differential of this, the third differential; etc. These quantities are of little importance except in the case where dx = a constant. In this case

$$dy = f'(x)\,dx \qquad d^2y = f''(x)\cdot(dx)^2 \qquad d^3y = f'''(x)\cdot(dx)^3 \qquad \ldots .$$

The first, second, third, etc., differentials are close approximations to the first, second, third, etc., differences (p. 2–27), and are, therefore, sometimes useful in constructing tables. Thus, denoting the first, second, third, etc., differences by D', D'', D''', etc., and, assuming always that dx = a constant,

$$D' = dy + \tfrac{1}{2}d^2y + \tfrac{1}{6}d^3y + \tfrac{1}{24}d^4y + \cdots$$

$$d^3y = D''' - \tfrac{3}{2}D'''' + \cdots$$

$$D'' = d^2y + d^3y + \tfrac{7}{12}d^4y + \cdots$$

$$d^2y = D'' - D''' + \tfrac{11}{12}D'''' + \cdots$$

$$D''' = d^3y + \tfrac{3}{2}d^4y + \cdots$$

$$dy = D' - \tfrac{1}{2}D'' + \tfrac{1}{3}D''' - \tfrac{1}{4}D'''' + \cdots$$

Functions of two or more variables may be denoted by $f(x, y, \ldots)$, $F(x, y, \ldots)$, etc. The derivative of such a function $u = f(x, y, \ldots)$ formed on the assumption that x is the only variable ($y, \ldots$ being regarded for the moment as constants) is called the **partial derivative of u with respect to x**, and is denoted by $f_x(x,y)$, or D_xu, or d_xu/dx, or $\partial u/\partial x$. Similarly, the partial derivative of u with respect to y is $f_y(x,y)$, or D_yu, or d_yu/dy, or $\partial u/\partial y$.

NOTE. In the third notation, d_xu denotes the differential of u formed on the assumption that x is the only variable. If the fourth notation, $\partial u/\partial x$, is used, this must not be treated as a fraction like du/dx; the $\partial/\partial x$ is a symbol of operation, operating on u, and the "∂x" must not be separated.

Partial derivatives of the second order are denoted by f_{xx}, f_{xy}, f_{yy}, or by Du, $D_x(D_yu)$, $D_y{}^2u$, or by $\partial^2u/\partial x^2$, $\partial^2u/\partial x\,\partial y$, $\partial^2u/\partial y^2$, the last symbols being "inseparable." Similarly for higher derivatives. Note that $f_{xy} = f_{yx}$.

If increments Δx, Δy (or dx, dy) are assigned to the independent variables x, y, the increment, Δu, produced in $u = f(x,y)$ is

$$\Delta u = f(x + \Delta x, y + \Delta y) - f(x,y)$$

while the **differential,** du, *i.e.*, the value which Δu would have if the partial derivatives of u with respect to x and y were constant, is given by

$$du = (f_x) \cdot dx + (f_y) \cdot dy$$

Here the coefficients of dx and dy are the values of the partial derivatives of u at the point in question.

If x and y are functions of a third variable t, then the equation

$$\frac{du}{dt} = (f_x)\frac{dx}{dt} + (f_y)\frac{dy}{dt}$$

expresses the rate of change of u with respect to t, in terms of the separate rate of change of x and y with respect to t.

For the graphical representation of $u = f(x,y)$, see p. 2–88.

Implicit Functions. If $f(x,y) = 0$, either of the variables x and y is said to be an implicit function of the other. To find dy/dx, either (1) solve for y in terms of x, and then find dy/dx directly; or (2) differentiate the equation through as it stands, remembering that both x and y are variables, and then divide by dx; or (3) use the formula $dy/dx = -(f_x/f_y)$, where f_x and f_y are the partial derivatives of $f(x,y)$ at the point in question.

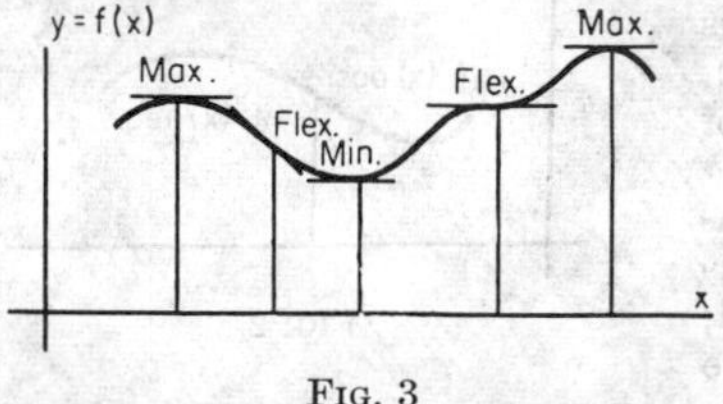

FIG. 3

MAXIMA AND MINIMA

A **function of one variable,** as $y = f(x)$, is said to have a **maximum** at a point $x = x_0$, if at that point the slope of the curve is zero and the concavity downward (see Fig. 3); a sufficient condition for a maximum is $f'(x_0) = 0$ and $f''(x_0)$ negative. Similarly, $f(x)$ has a **minimum** if the slope is zero and the concavity upward; a sufficient condition for a minimum is $f'(x_0) = 0$ and $f''(x_0)$ positive. If $f'(x_0) = 0$ and $f''(x_0) = 0$ and $f'''(x_0) \neq 0$, the point x_0 will be a **point of inflection.** If $f'(x_0) = 0$ and $f''(x_0) = 0$ and $f'''(x_0) = 0$, the point x_0 will be a maximum if $f''''(x_0) < 0$, and a minimum if $f''''(x_0) > 0$. It is usually sufficient, however, in any practical case, to find the values of x which make $f'(x) = 0$, and then decide, from a general knowledge of the curve or the sign of $f'(x)$ to the right and left of x_0, which of these values (if any) give maxima or minima, without investigating the higher derivatives.

A **function of two variables,** as $u = f(x,y)$, will have a **maximum** at a point (x_0,y_0) if at that point $f_x = 0$, $f_y = 0$, and $f_{xx} < 0$, $f_{yy} < 0$; and a **minimum** if at that point $f_x = 0$, $f_y = 0$, and $f_{xx} > 0$, $f_{yy} > 0$; provided, in each case, $(f_{xx})(f_{yy}) - (f_{xy})^2$ is positive. If $f_x = 0$ and $f_y = 0$, and f_{xx} and f_{yy} have opposite signs, the point (x_0,y_0) will be a "saddle point" of the surface representing the function.

EXPANSION IN SERIES

The range of values of x for which each of the series is convergent is stated at the right of the series.

Arithmetical and Geometrical Series, and the Binomial Theorem. See p. 2-26.

Exponential and Logarithmic Series

$$e^x = 1 + \frac{x}{1!} + \frac{x^2}{2!} + \frac{x^3}{3!} + \frac{x^4}{4!} + \cdots \qquad [-\infty < x < +\infty]$$

$$a^x = e^{mx} = 1 + \frac{m}{1!}x + \frac{m^2}{2!}x^2 + \frac{m^3}{3!}x^3 + \cdots \qquad [a > 0, -\infty < x < +\infty]$$

where $m = \ln a = (2.3026)(\log_{10} a)$.

$$\ln(1 + x) = x - \frac{x^2}{2} + \frac{x^3}{3} - \frac{x^4}{4} + \frac{x^5}{5} \cdots \qquad [-1 < x < +1]$$

$$\ln(1 - x) = -x - \frac{x^2}{2} - \frac{x^3}{3} - \frac{x^4}{4} - \frac{x^5}{5} - \cdots \qquad [-1 < x < +1]$$

$$\ln\left(\frac{1+x}{1-x}\right) = 2\left(x + \frac{x^3}{3} + \frac{x^5}{5} + \frac{x^7}{7} + \cdots\right) \qquad [-1 < x < +1]$$

$$\ln\left(\frac{x+1}{x-1}\right) = 2\left(\frac{1}{x} + \frac{1}{3x^3} + \frac{1}{5x^5} + \frac{1}{7x^7} + \cdots\right) \qquad [x < -1 \text{ or } +1 < x]$$

$$\ln x = 2\left[\frac{x-1}{x+1} + \frac{1}{3}\left(\frac{x-1}{x+1}\right)^3 + \frac{1}{5}\left(\frac{x-1}{x+1}\right)^5 + \cdots\right] \qquad [0 < x < \infty]$$

$$\ln(a + x) = \ln a + 2\left[\frac{x}{2a+x} + \frac{1}{3}\left(\frac{x}{2a+x}\right)^3 + \frac{1}{5}\left(\frac{x}{2a+x}\right)^5 + \cdots\right]$$
$$[0 < a < +\infty, -a < x < +\infty]$$

Series for the Trigonometric Functions. In the following formulas, *all angles must be expressed in radians.* If D = the number of degrees in the angle, and x = its radian measure, then $x = 0.017453D$.

$$\sin x = x - \frac{x^3}{3!} + \frac{x^5}{5!} - \frac{x^7}{7!} + \cdots \qquad [-\infty < x < +\infty]$$

$$\cos x = 1 - \frac{x^2}{2!} + \frac{x^4}{4!} - \frac{x^6}{6!} + \frac{x^8}{8!} - \cdots \qquad [-\infty < x < +\infty]$$

$$\tan x = x + \frac{x^3}{3} + \frac{2x^5}{15} + \frac{17x^7}{315} + \frac{62x^9}{2835} + \cdots \qquad [-\pi/2 < x < +\pi/2]$$

$$\cot x = \frac{1}{x} - \frac{x}{3} - \frac{x^3}{45} - \frac{2x^5}{945} - \frac{x^7}{4725} - \cdots \qquad [-\pi < x < +\pi]$$

$$\sin^{-1} y = y + \frac{y^3}{6} + \frac{3y^5}{40} + \frac{5y^7}{112} + \cdots \qquad [-1 \leqq y \leqq +1]$$

$$\tan^{-1} y = y - \frac{y^3}{3} + \frac{y^5}{5} - \frac{y^7}{7} + \cdots \qquad [-1 \leqq y \leqq +1]$$

$\cos^{-1} y = \frac{1}{2}\pi - \sin^{-1} y$; $\quad \cot^{-1} y = \frac{1}{2}\pi - \tan^{-1} y.$

Series for the Hyperbolic Functions (x a pure number)

$$\sinh x = x + \frac{x^3}{3!} + \frac{x^5}{5!} + \frac{x^7}{7!} + \cdots \qquad [-\infty < x < \infty]$$

$$\cosh x = 1 + \frac{x^2}{2!} + \frac{x^4}{4!} + \frac{x^6}{6!} + \cdots \qquad [-\infty < x < \infty]$$

$$\sinh^{-1} y = y - \frac{y^3}{6} + \frac{3y^5}{40} - \frac{5y^7}{112} + \cdots \qquad [-1 < y < +1]$$

$$\tanh^{-1} y = y + \frac{y^3}{3} + \frac{y^5}{5} + \frac{y^7}{7} + \cdots \qquad [-1 < y < +1]$$

General Formulas of Maclaurin and Taylor. If $f(x)$ and all its derivatives are continuous in the neighborhood of the point $x = 0$ (or $x = a$), then, for any value of x in this neighborhood, the function $f(x)$ may be expressed as a power series arranged according to ascending powers of x (or of $x - a$), as follows:

$$f(x) = f(0) + \frac{f'(0)}{1!}x + \frac{f''(0)}{2!}x^2 + \frac{f'''(0)}{3!}x^3 + \cdots + \frac{f^{(n-1)}(0)}{(n-1)!}x^{n-1} + (P_n)x^n \text{ (Maclaurin)}$$

$$f(x) = f(a) + \frac{f'(a)}{1!}(x-a) + \frac{f''(a)}{2!}(x-a)^2 + \frac{f'''(a)}{3!}(x-a)^3 + \cdots + \frac{f^{(n-1)}(a)}{(n-1)!}(x-a)^{n-1} + (Q_n)(x-a)^n \text{ (Taylor)}$$

Here $(P_n)x^n$, or $(Q_n)(x - a)^n$, is called the **remainder term;** the values of the coefficients P_n and Q_n may be expressed as follows:

$$P_n = [f^{(n)}(sx)]/n! = [(1-t)^{n-1}f^{(n)}(tx)]/(n-1)!$$
$$Q_n = \{f^{(n)}[a + s(x-a)]\}/n! = \{(1-t)^{n-1}f^{(n)}[a + t(x-a)]\}/(n-1)!$$

where s and t are certain unknown numbers between 0 and 1; the s-form is due to Lagrange, the t-form to Cauchy.

The error due to neglecting the remainder term is less than $(\overline{P}_n)x^n$, or $(\overline{Q}_n)(x - a)^n$, where $\overline{P}_n$, or $\overline{Q}_n$, is the largest value taken on by P_n, or Q_n, when s or t ranges from 0 to 1. If this error, which depends on both n and x, approaches 0 as n increases (for any given value of x), then the general expression with remainder becomes (for that value of x) a convergent infinite series.

The sum of the first few terms of Maclaurin's series gives a good approximation to $f(x)$ for values of x near $x = 0$; Taylor's series gives a similar approximation for values near $x = a$.

Reversing a Series. If $y = x + bx^2 + cx^3 + dx^4 + ex^5 + \cdots$, then $x = y - by^2 + (2b^2 - c)y^3 - (5b^3 - 5bc + d)y^4 + (14b^4 - 21b^2c + 6bd + 3c^2 - e)y^5 + \cdots$, provided the latter series is convergent.

Fourier's Series. Let $f(x)$ be a function which is finite in the interval from $x = -c$ to $x = +c$ and whose graph has finite arc length in that interval (see note below). Then, for any value of x between $-c$ and c,

$$f(x) = \tfrac{1}{2}a_0 + a_1 \cos\frac{\pi x}{c} + a_2 \cos\frac{2\pi x}{c} + a_3 \cos\frac{3\pi x}{c} + \cdots + b_1 \sin\frac{\pi x}{c} + b_2 \sin\frac{2\pi x}{c} + b_3 \sin\frac{3\pi x}{c} + \cdots$$

where the constant coefficients are determined as follows:

$$a_n = \frac{1}{c}\int_{-c}^{c} f(t)\cos\frac{n\pi t}{c}\,dt; \qquad b_n = \frac{1}{c}\int_{-c}^{c} f(t)\sin\frac{n\pi t}{c}\,dt.$$

In case the curve $y = f(x)$ is symmetrical with respect to the origin, the a's are all zero, and the series is a sine series. In case the curve is symmetrical with respect to the y-axis, the b's are all zero, and a cosine series results. (In this case, the series will be valid not only for values of x between $-c$ and c, but also for $x = -c$ and $x = c$.) A Fourier series can always be integrated term by term; but the result of differentiating term by term may not be a convergent series.

NOTE. If $x = x_0$ is a point of discontinuity, $f(x_0)$ is to be defined as $\frac{1}{2}[f_1(x_0) + f_2(x_0)]$, where $f_1(x_0)$ is the limit of $f(x)$ when x approaches x_0 from below, and $f_2(x_0)$ is the limit of $f(x)$ when x approaches x_0 from above.

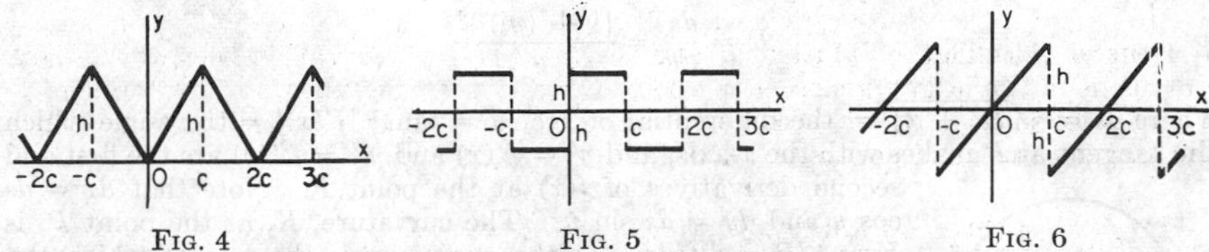

FIG. 4 FIG. 5 FIG. 6

Examples of Fourier's Series. If $y = f(x)$ is the curve in Figs. 4 to 6, then

In Fig. 4, $$y = \frac{h}{2} - \frac{4h}{\pi^2}\left(\cos\frac{\pi x}{c} + \frac{1}{9}\cos\frac{3\pi x}{c} + \frac{1}{25}\cos\frac{5\pi x}{c} + \cdots\right)$$

In Fig. 5, $$y = \frac{4h}{\pi}\left(\sin\frac{\pi x}{c} + \frac{1}{3}\sin\frac{3\pi x}{c} + \frac{1}{5}\sin\frac{5\pi x}{c} + \cdots\right)$$

In Fig. 6, $$y = \frac{2h}{\pi}\left(\sin\frac{\pi x}{c} - \frac{1}{2}\sin\frac{2\pi x}{c} + \frac{1}{3}\sin\frac{3\pi x}{c} - \cdots\right)$$

INDETERMINATE FORMS

In the following paragraphs, $f(x)$, $g(x)$ denote functions which approach 0; $F(x)$, $G(x)$ functions which increase indefinitely; and $U(x)$ a function which approaches 1, when x approaches a definite quantity a. The problem in each case is to find the limit approached by certain combinations of these functions when x approaches a. The symbol $\rightarrow$ is to be read "approaches" or "tends to."

CASE 1. "$\frac{0}{0}$." To find the limit of $f(x)/g(x)$ when $f(x) \rightarrow 0$ and $g(x) \rightarrow 0$, use the theorem that $\lim \frac{f(x)}{g(x)} = \lim \frac{f'(x)}{g'(x)}$, where $f'(x)$ and $g'(x)$ are the derivatives of $f(x)$ and $g(x)$. This second limit may be easier to find than the first. If $f'(x) \rightarrow 0$ and $g'(x) \rightarrow 0$, apply the same theorem a second time: $\lim \frac{f'(x)}{g'(x)} = \lim \frac{f''(x)}{g''(x)}$; and so on.

CASE 2. "$\frac{\infty}{\infty}$." If $F(x) \rightarrow \infty$ and $G(x) \rightarrow \infty$, then $\lim \frac{F(x)}{G(x)} = \lim \frac{F'(x)}{G'(x)}$, precisely as in Case 1.

CASE 3. "$0 \cdot \infty$." To find the limit of $f(x) \cdot F(x)$ when $f(x) \rightarrow 0$ and $F(x) \rightarrow \infty$, write $\lim [f(x) \cdot F(x)] = \lim \frac{f(x)}{1/F(x)}$, or $= \lim \frac{F(x)}{1/f(x)}$; then proceed as in Case 1 or Case 2.

CASE 4. The limit of combinations "0^0" or $[f(x)]^{g(x)}$; "1^∞" or $[U(x)]^{F(x)}$; "∞^0" or $[F(x)]^{b(x)}$ may be found since their logarithms are limits of the type evaluated in Case 3.

CASE 5. "$\infty - \infty$." If $F(x) \rightarrow \infty$ and $G(x) \rightarrow \infty$, write $\lim\ [F(x) - G(x)]$ $= \lim \dfrac{\dfrac{1}{G(x)} - \dfrac{1}{F(x)}}{\dfrac{1}{F(x) \cdot G(x)}}$; then proceed as in Case 1. Sometimes it is shorter to expand the functions in series. It should be carefully noticed that expressions like 0/0, ∞/∞, etc., do not represent mathematical quantities.

CURVATURE

The **radius of curvature** R of a plane curve at any point P (Fig. 7) is the distance, measured along the normal, on the concave side of the curve, to the **center of curvature,** C, this point being the limiting position of the point of intersection of the normals at P and a neighboring point Q, as Q is made to approach P along the curve. If the equation of the curve is $y = f(x)$,

$$R = \frac{ds}{du} = \frac{[1 + (y')^2]^{3/2}}{y''}$$

where $ds = \sqrt{dx^2 + dy^2}$ = the differential of arc, $u = \tan^{-1} [f'(x)]$ = the angle which the tangent at P makes with the x-axis, and $y' = f'(x)$ and $y'' = f''(x)$ are the first and second derivatives of $f(x)$ at the point P. Note that $dx = ds \cos u$ and $dy = ds \sin u$. The **curvature,** K, at the point P, is $K = 1/R = du/ds$; *i.e.*, the curvature is the rate at which the angle u is changing with respect to the length of arc s. If the slope of the curve is small, $K \approx f''(x)$.

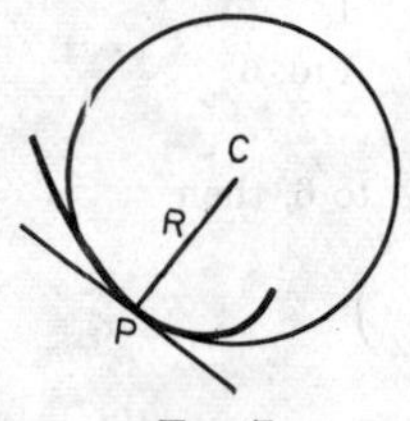

FIG. 7

If the equation of the curve in polar coordinates is $r = f(\theta)$, where r = radius vector and θ = polar angle, then

$$R = \frac{[r^2 + (r')^2]^{3/2}}{r^2 - rr'' + 2(r')^2}$$

where $r' = f'(\theta)$ and $r'' = f''(\theta)$.

The **evolute** of a curve is the locus of its centers of curvature. If one curve is the evolute of another, the second is called the **involute** of the first.

INDEFINITE INTEGRALS

An **integral** of $f(x)\,dx$ is any function whose differential is $f(x)\,dx$, and is denoted by $\int f(x)\,dx$. All the integrals of $f(x)\,dx$ are included in the expression $\int f(x)\,dx + C$, where $\int f(x)\,dx$ is any particular integral, and C is an arbitrary constant. The process of finding (when possible) an integral of a given function consists in recognizing by inspection a function which, when differentiated, will produce the given function; or in transforming the given function into a form in which such recognition is easy. The most common integrable forms are collected in the following brief table; for a more extended list, see Peirce, "Table of Integrals," Ginn, or Dwight, "Table of Integrals and other Mathematical Data," Macmillan.

GENERAL FORMULAS

1. $\int a\,du = a \int du = au + C.$ 2. $\int (u + v)\,dx = \int u\,dx + \int v\,dx.$

3. $\int u\,dv = uv - \int v\,du.$ 4. $\int f(x)\,dx = \int f[F(y)]F'(y)\,dy,\ x = F(y).$

5. $\int dy \int f(x,y)\,dx = \int dx \int f(x,y)\,dy.$

FUNDAMENTAL INTEGRALS

6. $\int x^n\,dx = \frac{x^{n+1}}{n+1} + C$, when $n \neq -1$.

7. $\int \frac{dx}{x} = \ln x + C = \ln cx.$ 8. $\int e^x\,dx = e^x + C.$

9. $\int \sin x\, dx = -\cos x + C.$ 10. $\int \cos x\, dx = \sin x + C.$

11. $\int \frac{dx}{\sin^2 x} = -\cot x + C.$ 12. $\int \frac{dx}{\cos^2 x} = \tan x + C.$

13. $\int \frac{dx}{\sqrt{1 - x^2}} = \sin^{-1} x + C = -\cos^{-1} x + c.$

14. $\int \frac{dx}{1 + x^2} = \tan^{-1} x + C = -\cot^{-1} x + c.$

Rational Functions

15. $\int (a + bx)^n\, dx = \frac{(a + bx)^{n+1}}{(n + 1)b} + C.$

16. $\int \frac{dx}{a + bx} = \frac{1}{b} \ln (a + bx) + C = \frac{1}{b} \ln c(a + bx).$

17. $\int \frac{1}{x^2} dx = -\frac{1}{x} + C.$ 18. $\int \frac{dx}{(a + bx)^2} = -\frac{1}{b(a + bx)} + C.$

19. $\int \frac{dx}{1 - x^2} = \tfrac{1}{2} \ln \frac{1 + x}{1 - x} + C = \tanh^{-1} x + C,$ when $x < 1$.

20. $\int \frac{dx}{x^2 - 1} = \tfrac{1}{2} \ln \frac{x - 1}{x + 1} + C = -\coth^{-1} x + C,$ when $x > 1$.

21. $\int \frac{dx}{a + bx^2} = \frac{1}{\sqrt{ab}} \tan^{-1} \left(\sqrt{\frac{b}{a}}x\right) + C$

22. $\int \frac{dx}{a - bx^2} = \frac{1}{2\sqrt{ab}} \ln \frac{\sqrt{ab} + bx}{\sqrt{ab} - bx} + C$

$= \frac{1}{\sqrt{ab}} \tanh^{-1} \left(\sqrt{\frac{b}{a}}x\right) + C$ $\Bigg\}$ $[a > 0, b > 0]$.

23. $\int \frac{dx}{a + 2bx + cx^2} = \frac{1}{\sqrt{ac - b^2}} \tan^{-1} \frac{b + cx}{\sqrt{ac - b^2}} + C \Big\} [ac - b^2 > 0].$

$= \frac{1}{2\sqrt{b^2 - ac}} \ln \frac{\sqrt{b^2 - ac} - b - cx}{\sqrt{b^2 - ac} + b + cx} + C$

$= -\frac{1}{\sqrt{b^2 - ac}} \tanh^{-1} \frac{b + cx}{\sqrt{b^2 - ac}} + C$ $\Bigg\}$ $[b^2 - ac > 0]$.

24. $\int \frac{dx}{a + 2bx + cx^2} = -\frac{1}{b + cx} + C,$ when $b^2 = ac$.

25. $\int \frac{(m + nx)\, dx}{a + 2bx + cx^2} = \frac{n}{2c} \ln (a + 2bx + cx^2) + \frac{mc - nb}{c} \int \frac{dx}{a + 2bx + cx^2}.$

26. In $\int \frac{f(x)\, dx}{a + 2bx + cx^2}$, if $f(x)$ is a polynominal of higher than the first degree, divide by the denominator before integrating.

27. $$\int \frac{dx}{(a + 2bx + cx^2)^p} = \frac{1}{2(ac - b^2)(p - 1)} \times \frac{b + cx}{(a + 2bx + cx^2)^{p-1}} + \frac{(2p - 3)c}{2(ac - b^2)(p - 1)} \int \frac{dx}{(a + 2bx + cx^2)^{p-}}.$$

28. $$\int \frac{(m + nx)\, dx}{(a + 2bx + cx^2)^p} = -\frac{n}{2c(p - 1)} \times \frac{1}{(a + 2bx + cx^2)^{p-1}} + \frac{mc - nb}{c} \int \frac{dx}{(a + 2bx + cx^2\ {}^p}.$$

29. $\int x^{m-1}(a+bx)^n\,dx = \frac{x^{m-1}(a+bx)^{n+1}}{(m+n)b} - \frac{(m-1)a}{(m+n)b}\int x^{m-2}(a+bx)^n\,dx,$

$= \frac{x^m(a+bx)^n}{m+n} + \frac{na}{m+n}\int x^{m-1}(a+bx)^{n-1}\,dx.$

Irrational Functions

30. $\int \sqrt{a+bx}\,dx = \frac{2}{3b}(\sqrt{a+bx})^3 + C.$

31. $\int \frac{dx}{\sqrt{a+bx}} = \frac{2}{b}\sqrt{a+bx} + C.$

32. $\int \frac{(m+nx)\,dx}{\sqrt{a+bx}} = \frac{2}{3b^2}(3mb - 2an + nbx)\sqrt{a+bx} + C.$

33. $\int \frac{dx}{(m+nx)\sqrt{a+bx}}$; substitute $y = \sqrt{a+bx}$, and use 21 and 22.

34. $\int \frac{f(x, \sqrt[n]{a+bx})}{F(x, \sqrt[n]{a+bx})}\,dx$; substitute $\sqrt[n]{a+bx} = y$.

35. $\int \frac{dx}{\sqrt{a^2-x^2}} = \sin^{-1}\frac{x}{a} + C = -\cos^{-1}\frac{x}{a} + c.$

36. $\int \frac{dx}{\sqrt{a^2+x^2}} = \ln(x + \sqrt{a^2+x^2}) + C = \sinh^{-1}\frac{x}{a} + c.$

37. $\int \frac{dx}{\sqrt{x^2-a^2}} = \ln(x + \sqrt{x^2-a^2}) + C = \cosh^{-1}\frac{x}{a} + c.$

38. $\int \frac{dx}{\sqrt{a+2bx+cx^2}} = \frac{1}{\sqrt{c}}\ln(b + cx + \sqrt{c}\sqrt{a+2bx+cx^2}) + C,$

when $c > 0$.

$= \frac{1}{\sqrt{c}}\sinh^{-1}\frac{b+cx}{\sqrt{ac-b^2}} + C,$ when $ac - b^2 > 0$.

$= \frac{1}{\sqrt{c}}\cosh^{-1}\frac{b+cx}{\sqrt{b^2-ac}} + C,$ when $b^2 - ac > 0$.

$= \frac{-1}{\sqrt{-c}}\sin^{-1}\frac{b+cx}{\sqrt{b^2-ac}} + C,$ when $c < 0$.

39. $\int \frac{(m+nx)\,dx}{\sqrt{a+2bx+cx^2}} = \frac{n}{c}\sqrt{a+2bx+cx^2} + \frac{mc-nb}{c}\int \frac{dx}{\sqrt{a+2bx+cx^2}}.$

40. $\int \frac{x^m\,dx}{\sqrt{a+2bx+cx^2}} = \frac{x^{m-1}X}{mc} - \frac{(m-1)a}{mc}\int \frac{x^{m-2}\,dx}{X}$

$- \frac{(2m-1)b}{mc}\int \frac{x^{m-1}\,dx}{X},$ when $X = \sqrt{a+2bx+cx^2}.$

41. $\int \sqrt{a^2+x^2}\,dx = \frac{x}{2}\sqrt{a^2+x^2} + \frac{a^2}{2}\ln(x + \sqrt{a^2+x^2}) + C,$

$= \frac{x}{2}\sqrt{a^2+x^2} + \frac{a^2}{2}\sinh^{-1}\frac{x}{a} + c.$

42. $\int \sqrt{a^2-x^2}\,dx = \frac{x}{2}\sqrt{a^2-x^2} + \frac{a^2}{2}\sin^{-1}\frac{x}{a} + C.$

43. $\int \sqrt{x^2-a^2}\,dx = \frac{x}{2}\sqrt{x^2-a^2} - \frac{a^2}{2}\ln(x + \sqrt{x^2-a^2}) + C,$

$= \frac{x}{2}\sqrt{x^2-a^2} - \frac{a^2}{2}\cosh^{-1}\frac{x}{a} + c.$

44. $\int \sqrt{a + 2bx + cx^2}\, dx = \frac{b + cx}{2c}\sqrt{a + 2bx + cx^2} + \frac{ac - b^2}{2c}\int \frac{dx}{\sqrt{a + 2bx + cx^2}} + C.$

Transcendental Functions

45. $\int a^x\, dx = \frac{a^x}{\ln a} + C.$

46. $\int x^n e^{ax}\, dx = \frac{x^n e^{ax}}{a}\left[1 - \frac{n}{ax} + \frac{n(n-1)}{a^2x^2} - \cdots \pm \frac{n!}{a^n x^n}\right] + C.$

47. $\int \ln x\, dx = x \ln x - x + C.$

48. $\int \frac{\ln x}{x^2}\, dx = -\frac{\ln x}{x} - \frac{1}{x} + C.$

49. $\int \frac{(\ln x)^n}{x}\, dx = \frac{1}{n+1}(\ln x)^{n+1} + C.$

50. $\int \sin^2 x\, dx = -\frac{1}{4}\sin 2x + \frac{1}{2}x + C = -\frac{1}{2}\sin x \cos x + \frac{1}{2}x + C.$

51. $\int \cos^2 x\, dx = \frac{1}{4}\sin 2x + \frac{1}{2}x + C = \frac{1}{2}\sin x \cos x + \frac{1}{2}x + C.$

52. $\int \sin mx\, dx = -\frac{\cos mx}{m} + C.$ 53. $\int \cos mx\, dx = \frac{\sin mx}{m} + C.$

54. $\int \sin mx \cos nx\, dx = -\frac{\cos (m+n)x}{2(m+n)} - \frac{\cos (m-n)x}{2(m-n)} + C.$

55. $\int \sin mx \sin nx\, dx = \frac{\sin (m-n)x}{2(m-n)} - \frac{\sin (m+n)x}{2(m+n)} + C.$

56. $\int \cos mx \cos nx\, dx = \frac{\sin (m-n)x}{2(m-n)} + \frac{\sin (m+n)x}{2(m+n)} + C.$

57. $\int \tan x\, dx = -\ln \cos x + C.$ 58. $\int \cot x\, dx = \ln \sin x + C.$

59. $\int \frac{dx}{\sin x} = \ln \tan \frac{x}{2} + C.$ 60. $\int \frac{dx}{\cos x} = \ln \tan\left(\frac{\pi}{4} + \frac{x}{2}\right) + C.$

61. $\int \frac{dx}{1 + \cos x} = \tan \frac{x}{2} + C.$ 62. $\int \frac{dx}{1 - \cos x} = -\cot \frac{x}{2} + C.$

63. $\int \sin x \cos x\, dx = \frac{1}{2}\sin^2 x + C.$ 64. $\int \frac{dx}{\sin x \cos x} = \ln \tan x + C.$

65.* $\int \sin^n x\, dx = -\frac{\cos x \sin^{n-1} x}{n} + \frac{n-1}{n}\int \sin^{n-2} x\, dx.$

66.* $\int \cos^n x\, dx = \frac{\sin x \cos^{n-1} x}{n} + \frac{n-1}{n}\int \cos^{n-2} x\, dx.$

67. $\int \tan^n x\, dx = \frac{\tan^{n-1} x}{n-1} - \int \tan^{n-2} x\, dx.$

68. $\int \cot^n x\, dx = -\frac{\cot^{n-1} x}{n-1} - \int \cot^{n-2} x\, dx.$

69. $\int \frac{dx}{\sin^n x} = -\frac{\cos x}{(n-1)\sin^{n-1} x} + \frac{n-2}{n-1}\int \frac{dx}{\sin^{n-2} x}$

70. $\int \frac{dx}{\cos^n x} = \frac{\sin x}{(n-1)\cos^{n-1} x} + \frac{n-2}{n-1}\int \frac{dx}{\cos^{n-2} x}.$

* If n is an odd number, substitute $\cos x = z$ or $\sin x = z$.

71.* $\int \sin^p x \cos^q x\,dx = \frac{\sin^{p+1} x \cos^{q-1} x}{p+q} + \frac{q-1}{p+q}\int \sin^p x \cos^{q-2} x\,dx,$

$= -\frac{\sin^{p-1} x \cos^{q+1} x}{p+q} + \frac{p-1}{p+q}\int \sin^{p-2} x \cos^q x\,dx.$

72.* $\int \sin^{-p} x \cos^q x\,dx = -\frac{\sin^{-p+1} x \cos^{q+1} x}{p-1} + \frac{p-q-2}{p-1}\int \sin^{-p+2} x \cos^q x\,dx.$

73.* $\int \sin^p x \cos^{-q} x\,dx = \frac{\sin^{p+1} x \cos^{-q+1} x}{q-1} + \frac{q-p-2}{q-1}\int \sin^p x \cos^{-q+2} x\,dx.$

74. $\int \frac{dx}{a+b\cos x} = \frac{2}{\sqrt{a^2-b^2}}\tan^{-1}\left(\sqrt{\frac{a-b}{a+b}}\tan \tfrac{1}{2}x\right) + C$, when $a^2 > b^2$,

$= \frac{1}{\sqrt{b^2-a^2}}\ln \frac{b + a\cos x + \sin x\sqrt{b^2-a^2}}{a+b\cos x} + C,$

$= \frac{2}{\sqrt{b^2-a^2}}\tanh^{-1}\left(\sqrt{\frac{b-a}{b+a}}\tan \tfrac{1}{2}x\right) + C,$ $[a^2 < b^2]$.

75. $\int \frac{\cos x\,dx}{a+b\cos x} = \frac{x}{b} - \frac{a}{b}\int \frac{dx}{a+b\cos x} + C.$

76. $\int \frac{\sin x\,dx}{a+b\cos x} = -\frac{1}{b}\ln(a+b\cos x) + C.$

77. $\int \frac{A + B\cos x + C\sin x}{a + b\cos x + c\sin x}\,dx = A\int \frac{dy}{a+p\cos y}$

$+ (B\cos u + C\sin u)\int \frac{\cos y\,dy}{a+p\cos y} - (B\sin u - C\cos u)\int \frac{\sin y\,dy}{a+p\cos y},$

where $b = p\cos u$, $c = p\sin u$ and $x - u = y$.

78. $\int e^{ax}\sin bx\,dx = \frac{a\sin bx - b\cos bx}{a^2+b^2}e^{ax} + C.$

79. $\int e^{ax}\cos bx\,dx = \frac{a\cos bx + b\sin bx}{a^2+b^2}e^{ax} + C.$

80. $\int \sin^{-1} x\,dx = x\sin^{-1} x + \sqrt{1-x^2} + C.$

81. $\int \cos^{-1} x\,dx = x\cos^{-1} x - \sqrt{1-x^2} + C.$

82. $\int \tan^{-1} x\,dx = x\tan^{-1} x - \tfrac{1}{2}\ln(1+x^2) + C.$

83. $\int \cot^{-1} x\,dx = x\cot^{-1} x + \tfrac{1}{2}\ln(1+x^2) + C.$

84. $\int \sinh x\,dx = \cosh x + C.$

85. $\int \tanh x\,dx = \ln\cosh x + C.$

86. $\int \cosh x\,dx = \sinh x + C.$

87. $\int \coth x\,dx = \ln\sinh x + C.$

88. $\int \operatorname{sech} x\,dx = 2\tan^{-1}(e^x) + C.$

89. $\int \operatorname{csch} x\,dx = \ln\tanh(x/2) + C.$

90. $\int \sinh^2 x\,dx = \tfrac{1}{2}\sinh x\cosh x - \tfrac{1}{2}x + C.$

91. $\int \cosh^2 x\,dx = \tfrac{1}{2}\sinh x\cosh x + \tfrac{1}{2}x + C.$

92. $\int \operatorname{sech}^2 x\,dx = \tanh x + C.$

93. $\int \operatorname{csch}^2 x\,dx = -\coth x + C.$

* If p or q is an odd number, substitute $\cos x = z$ or $\sin x = z$.

DEFINITE INTEGRALS

The definite integral of $f(x)\,dx$ from $x = a$ to $x = b$, denoted by $\int_a^b f(x)\,dx$, is the limit (as n increases indefinitely) of a sum of n terms:

$$\int_a^b f(x)\,dx = \lim_{n=\infty} [f(x_1)\,\Delta x + f(x_2)\,\Delta x + f(x_3)\,\Delta x + \cdots + f(x_n)\,\Delta x]$$

built up as follows: Divide the interval from a to b into n equal parts, and call each part Δx, $= (b - a)/n$; in each of these intervals take a value of x (say $x_1, x_2, \ldots x_n$), find the value of the function $f(x)$ at each of these points, and multiply it by Δx, the width of the interval; then take the limit of the sum of the terms thus formed, when the number of terms increases indefinitely, while each individual term approaches zero.

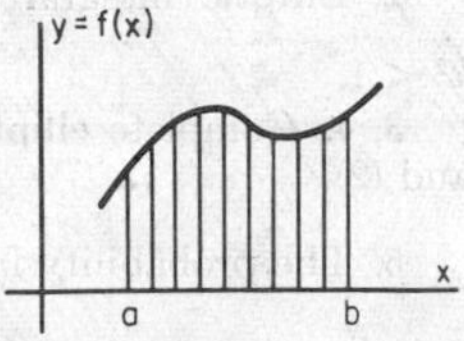

FIG. 8

Geometrically, $\int_a^b f(x)\,dx$ is the area bounded by the curve $y = f(x)$, the x-axis, and the ordinates $x = a$ and $x = b$ (Fig. 8); *i.e.*, briefly, the "area under the curve, from a to b." The **fundamental theorem** for the evaluation of a definite integral is the following:

$$\int_a^b f(x)\,dx = \left[\int f(x)\,dx\right]_{x=b} - \left[\int f(x)\,dx\right]_{x=a}$$

i.e., the definite integral is equal to the difference between two values of any one of the indefinite integrals of the function in question. In other words, the limit of a sum can be found whenever the function can be integrated.

Properties of Definite Integrals

$$\int_a^b = -\int_b^a; \quad \int_a^c + \int_c^b = \int_a^b$$

MEAN-VALUE THEOREM FOR INTEGRALS

$$\int_a^b F(x)f(x)\,dx = F(X)\int_a^b f(x)\,dx$$

provided $f(x)$ does not change sign from $x = a$ to $x = b$; here X is some (unknown) value of x intermediate between a and b.

MEAN VALUE. The **mean value** of $f(x)$ with respect to x, between a and b, is

$$\bar{f} = \frac{1}{b-a}\int_a^b f(x)\,dx$$

THEOREM ON CHANGE OF VARIABLE. In evaluating $\int_{x=a}^{x=b} f(x)\,dx$, $f(x)\,dx$ may be replaced by its value in terms of a new variable t and dt, and $x = a$ and $x = b$ by the corresponding values of t, provided that throughout the interval the relation between x and t is a one-to-one correspondence (*i.e.*, to each value of x there corresponds one and only one value of t, and to each value of t there corresponds one and only one value of x).

DIFFERENTIATION WITH RESPECT TO THE UPPER LIMIT. If b is variable, then $\int_a^b f(x)\,dx$ is a function of b, whose derivative is

$$\frac{d}{db}\int_a^b f(x)\,dx = f(b)$$

DIFFERENTIATION WITH RESPECT TO A PARAMETER

$$\frac{\partial}{\partial c}\int_a^b f(x,c)\,dx = \int_a^b \frac{\partial f(x,c)}{\partial c}\,dx$$

Functions Defined by Definite Integrals. The following definite integrals have received special names, and their values have been tabulated. (See, for example, Peirce, "Table of Integrals.")

1. Elliptic integral of the first kind $= F(u, k) = \int_0^u \frac{dx}{\sqrt{1 - k^2 \sin^2 x}}$ when $k^2 < 1$.

2. Elliptic integral of the second kind $= E(u, k) = \int_0^u \sqrt{1 - k^2 \sin^2 x}\,dx$, when $k^2 < 1$.

3, 4. Complete elliptic integrals of the first and second kinds; put $u = \pi/2$ in (1) and (2).

5. The probability integral $= \frac{2}{\sqrt{\pi}}\int_0^x e^{-x^2}\,dx$.

6. The gamma function $= \Gamma(n) = \int_0^\infty x^{n-1}e^{-x}\,dx$.

Approximate Methods of Integration. Mechanical Quadrature

1. Use Simpson's rule (p. 2–18) (see also Scarborough, "Numerical Mathematical Analyses," Johns Hopkins Press).
2. Expand the function in a converging power series, and integrate term by term.
3. Plot the area under the curve $y = f(x)$ from $x = a$ to $x = b$ on squared paper, and measure this area roughly by "counting squares," or more accurately, by the use of a planimeter, or by graphical means (see Franklin, "Methods of Advanced Calculus," McGraw-Hill).
4. Coradi's Mechanical Integraph provides a means of drawing on paper the curve $y = \int f(x)\,dx$, when the curve $y = f(x)$ is given, and can be used to facilitate the solution of certain differential equations.

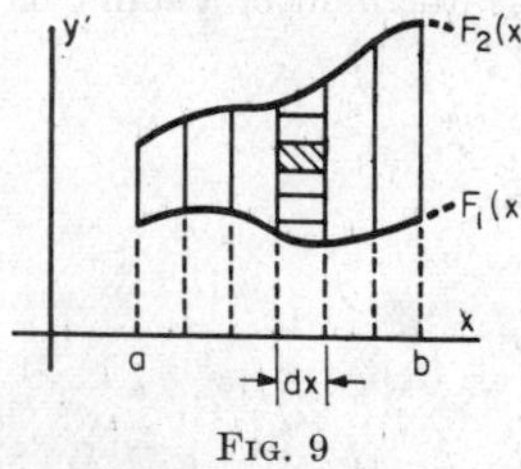

FIG. 9

Double Integrals. The notation $\iint f(x,y)\,dy\,dx$ means $\int[\int f(x,y)\,dy]\,dx$, the limits of integration in the inner, or first, integral being functions of x (or constants).

EXAMPLE. To find the weight of a plane area whose density, w, is variable, say $w = f(x,y)$. The weight of a typical element, $dx\,dy$, is $f(x,y)dx\,dy$. Keeping x and dx constant, and summing these elements from, say, $y = F_1(x)$ to $y = F_2(x)$, as determined by the shape of the boundary, the weight of a typical strip perpendicular to the x-axis is

$$dx\int_{y = F_1(x)}^{y = F_2(x)} f(x,y)\,dy$$

Finally, summing these strips from, say, $x = a$ to $x = b$, the weight of the whole area is

$$\int_{x=a}^{x=b}\left[dx\int_{y=F_1(x)}^{y=F_2(x)} f(x,y)\,dy\right], \text{ or, briefly, } \iint f(x,y)\,dy\,dx$$

DIFFERENTIAL EQUATIONS

An **ordinary differential equation** is one which contains a single independent variable, or argument, and a single dependent variable, or function, with its derivatives of various orders. **A partial differential equation** is one which contains a function of several independent variables, and its partial derivatives of various orders. The order of a differential equation is the order of the highest derivative which occurs in it. A solution of a differential equation is any relation between the variables, which, when substituted in the given equation, will satisfy it. The general solution of an ordinary differential equation of the nth order will contain n arbitrary constants. A differential equation is usually said to be solved when the problem is reduced to simple quadratures, *i.e.*, integrations of the form $y = \int f(x)\,dx$.

Methods of Solving Ordinary Differential Equations

Differential Equations of the First Order

1. If possible, separate the variables; *i.e.*, collect all the x's and dx on one side, and all the y's and dy on the other side; then integrate both sides, and add the constant of integration.

2. If the equation is homogeneous in x and y, the value of dy/dx in terms of x and y will be of the form $dy/dx = f(y/x)$. Substituting $y = xt$ will enable the variables to be separated. *Solution*: $\log_e x = \int \frac{dt}{f(t) - t} + C$.

3. The expression $f(x,y)\,dx + F(x,y)\,dy$ is an *exact differential* if $\frac{\partial f(x,y)}{\partial y} = \frac{\partial F(x,y)}{\partial x}$ ($=P$, say). In this case the solution of $f(x,y)\,dx + F(x,y)\,dy = 0$ is

$$\int f(x,y)\,dx + \int [F(x,y) - \int P\,dx]\,dy = C$$

or

$$\int F(x,y)\,dy + \int [f(x,y) - \int P\,dy]\,dx = C$$

4. Linear differential equation of the first order: $\frac{dy}{dx} + f(x)\cdot y = F(x)$. *Solution:* $y = e^{-P}[\int e^{P}F(x)\,dx + C]$, where $P = \int f(x)\,dx$.

5. Bernoulli's equation: $\frac{dy}{dx} + f(x)\cdot y = F(x)\cdot y^n$. Substituting $y^{1-n} = v$ gives $(dv/dx) + (1-n)f(x)\cdot v = (1-n)F(x)$, which is linear in v and x.

6. Clairaut's equation: $y = xp + f(p)$, where $p = dy/dx$. The solution consists of the family of lines given by $y = Cx + f(C)$, where C is any constant, together with the curve obtained by eliminating p between the equations $y = xp + f(p)$ and $x + f'(p) = 0$, where $f'(p)$ is the derivative of $f(p)$.

Differential Equations of the Second Order

7. $\frac{d^2y}{dx^2} = -n^2y$. *Solution:* $y = C_1 \sin(nx + C_2)$,

or $\quad y = C_3 \sin nx + C_4 \cos nx$.

8. $\frac{d^2y}{dx^2} = +n^2y$. *Solution:* $y = C_1 \sinh(nx + C_2)$,

or $\quad y = C_3e^{nx} + C_4e^{-nx}$

9. $\frac{d^2y}{dx^2} = f(y)$. *Solution:* $x = \int \frac{dy}{\sqrt{C_1 + 2P}} + C_2$, where $P = \int f(y)\,dy$.

10. $\frac{d^2y}{dx^2} = f(x)$. *Solution:* $y = \int P\,dx + C_1x + C_2$, where $P = \int f(x)\,dx$,

or $\quad y = xP - \int xf(x)\,dx + C_1x + C_2$.

11. $\frac{d^2y}{dx^2} = f\left(\frac{dy}{dx}\right)$. Putting $\frac{dy}{dx} = z$, $\frac{d^2y}{dx^2} = \frac{dz}{dx}$, $x = \int \frac{dz}{f(z)} + C_1$ and $y = \int \frac{z\,dz}{f(z)} + C_2$; then eliminate z from these two equations.

12. The equation for damped vibration: $\frac{d^2y}{dx^2} + 2b\frac{dy}{dx} + a^2y = 0$.

Case 1. If $a^2 - b^2 > 0$, let $m = \sqrt{a^2 - b^2}$. *Solution:*

$$y = C_1e^{-bx}\sin(mx + C_2) \quad \text{or} \quad y = e^{-bx}[C_3\sin(mx) + C_4\cos(mx)]$$

CASE 2. If $a^2 - b^2 = 0$, solution is $y = e^{-bx}(C_1 + C_2x)$.
CASE 3. If $a^2 - b^2 < 0$, let $n = \sqrt{b^2 - a^2}$. *Solution:*

$$y = C_1e^{-bx} \sinh (nx + C_2) \qquad \text{or} \qquad y = C_3e^{-(b+n)x} + C_4e^{-(b-n)x}$$

13. $\dfrac{d^2y}{dx^2} + 2b\dfrac{dy}{dx} + a^2y = c$. *Solution:* $y = \dfrac{c}{a^2} + y_1$, where y_1 = the solution of the corresponding equation with second member zero [see (12) above].

14. $\dfrac{d^2y}{dx^2} + 2b\dfrac{dy}{dx} + a^2y = c \sin (kx)$. *Solution:*

$$y = R \sin (kx - S) + y_1$$

where $R = c/\sqrt{(a^2 - k^2)^2 + 4b^2k^2}$, $\tan S = 2bk/(a^2 - k^2)$, and y_1 = the solution of the corresponding equation with second member zero [see (12) above].

15. $\dfrac{d^2y}{dx^2} + 2b\dfrac{dy}{dx} + a^2y = f(x)$. *Solution:* $y = y_0 + y_1$, where y_0 = any particular solution of the given equation, and y_1 = the general solution of the corresponding equation with second member zero [see (12) above].

If $b^2 < a^2$, $y_0 = \dfrac{1}{2\sqrt{b^2 - a^2}}\left[e^{m_1x}\int e^{-m_1x} f(x)\,dx - e^{m_2x}\int e^{-m_2x} f(x)\,dx\right]$.
where $m_1 = -b + \sqrt{b^2 - a^2}$ and $m^2 = -b - \sqrt{b^2 - a^2}$.

If $b^2 < a^2$, let $m = \sqrt{a^2 - b^2}$; then

$$y_0 = \frac{1}{m}e^{-bx}\left[\sin (mx)\int e^{bx} \cos (mx)\cdot f(x)\,dx - \cos (mx)\int e^{bx} \sin (mx)\cdot f(x)\,dx\right].$$

If $b^2 = a^2$, $y_0 = e^{-bx}\,[x\int e^{bx}f(x)\,dx - \int x\cdot e^{bx}f(x)\,dx]$.

Types 12–15 are examples of linear differential equations with constant coefficients. The solutions of such equations are often found most simply by the use of Laplace transforms. (See Franklin, "Fourier Methods," pp. 198–229, McGraw-Hill.)

LINEAR EQUATIONS

For the linear equation of the nth order

$$A_n(x)d^ny/dx^n + A_{n-1}(x)d^{n-1}y/dx^{n-1} + \cdots + A_1(x)\,dy/dx + A_0(x)y = E(x)$$

the general solution is $y = u + c_1u_1 + c_2u_2 + \cdots + c_nu_n$. Here u, the particular integral, is any solution of the given equation, and $u_1, u_2, \ldots, u_n$ form a fundamental system of solutions of the homogeneous equation obtained by replacing $E(x)$ by zero. A set of solutions is fundamental, or independent, if its Wronskian determinant $W(x)$ is not zero, where

$$W(x) = \begin{vmatrix} u_1 & u_2 & \cdots & u_n \\ u_1' & u_2' & \cdots & u_n' \\ \cdot & \cdot & \cdots & \cdot \\ \cdot & \cdot & \cdots & \cdot \\ \cdot & \cdot & \cdots & \cdot \\ u_1^{(n-1)} & u_2^{(n-1)} & \cdots & u_n^{(n-1)} \end{vmatrix}$$

For any n functions, $W(x) = 0$ if some one u_i is linearly dependent on the others, as $u_n = k_1u_1 + k_2u_2 + \cdots + k_{n-1}u_{n-1}$ with the coefficients k_i constant. And for n solutions of a linear differential equation of the nth order, if $W(x) \neq 0$, the solutions are linearly independent.

Constant Coefficients

To solve the homogeneous equation of the nth order $A_nd^ny/dx^n + A_{n-1}d^{n-1}y/dx^{n-1} + \cdots + A_1\,dy/dx + A_0y = 0$, $A_n \neq 0$, where $A_n, A_{n-1}, \ldots, A_0$ are constants, find the roots of the auxiliary equation

$$A_n p^n + A_{n-1}p^{n-1} + \cdots + A_1 p + A_0 = 0.$$

For each simple real root r, there is a term ce^{rx} in the solution. The terms of the solution are to be added together. When r occurs twice among the n roots of the auxiliary equation, the corresponding term is $e^{rx}(c_1 + c_2x)$. When r occurs three times, the corresponding term is $e^{rx}(c_1 + c_2x + c_3x^2)$, and so forth. When there is a pair of conjugate complex roots $a + bi$ and $a - bi$, the real form of the terms in the solution is $e^{ax}(c_1 \cos bx + d_1 \sin bx)$. When the same pair occurs twice, the corresponding term is $e^{ax}[(c_1 + c_2x) \cos bx + (d_1 + d_2x) \sin bx]$, and so forth.

Consider next the general non-homogeneous linear differential equation of order n, with constant coefficients, or

$$A_n d^n y/dx^n + A_{n-1}d^{n-1}y/dx^{n-1} + \cdots + A_1\, dy/dx + A_0 y = E(x).$$

We may solve this by adding any particular integral to the complementary function, or general solution, of the homogeneous equation obtained by replacing $E(x)$ by zero. The complementary function may be found from the rules just given. And the particular integral may be found by the methods of the following paragraphs.

Undetermined Coefficients

In the last equation, let the right member $E(x)$ be a sum of terms each of which is of the type k, $k \cos bx$, $k \sin bx$, ke^{ax}, kx, or more generally, kx^me^{ax}, $kx^me^{ax} \cos bx$, or $kx^me^{ax} \sin bx$. Here m is zero or a positive integer, and a and b are any real numbers. Then the form of the particular integral I may be predicted by the following rules.

Case 1. **$E(x)$ is a single term T.** Let D be written for d/dx, so that the given equation is $P(D)y = E(x)$, where $P(D) = A_nD^n + A_{n-1}D^{n-1} + \cdots + A_1D + A_0y$. With the term T associate the simplest polynomial $Q(D)$ such that $Q(D)T = 0$. For the particular types k, etc., $Q(D)$ will be D, $D^2 + b^2$, $D^2 + b^2$, $D - a$, D^2; and for the general types kx^me^{ax}, etc., $Q(D)$ will be $(D - a)^{m+1}$, $(D^2 - 2aD + a^2 + b^2)^{m+1}$, $(D^2 - 2aD + a^2 + b^2)^{m+1}$. Thus $Q(D)$ will always be some power of a first- or second-degree factor, $Q(D) = F^V$, $F = D - a$, or $F = D^2 - 2aD + a^2 + b^2$.

Use the method described under **Constant Coefficients** to find the terms in the solution of $P(D)y = 0$ and also the terms in the solution of $Q(D)P(D)y = 0$. Then assume that the particular integral I is a linear combination with unknown coefficients of those terms in the solution of $Q(D)P(D)y = 0$ which are not in the solution of $P(D)y = 0$. Thus if $Q(D) = F^q$ and F is *not* a factor of $P(D)$, assume $I = (Ax^{q-1} + Bx^{q-2} + \cdots + L)e^{ax}$ when $F = D - a$, and assume $I = (Ax^{q-1} + Bx^{q-2} + \cdots + L)e^{ax} \cos bx + (Mx^{q-1} + Nx^{q-2} + \cdots + R)e^{ax} \sin bx$ when $F = D^2 - 2aD + a^2 + b^2$. When F **is** a factor of $P(D)$ and the highest power of F which is a divisor of $P(D)$ is F^k, try the I above multiplied by x^k.

Case 2. **$E(x)$ is a sum of terms.** With each term in $E(x)$, associate a polynomial $Q(D) = F^q$ as before. Arrange in one group all the terms that have the same F. The particular integral of the given equation will be the sum of solutions of equations each of which has one group on the right. For any one such equation, the form of the particular integral is given as for Case 1, with q the highest power of F associated with any term of the group on the right.

After the form has been found in Case 1 or 2, the unknown coefficients follow when we substitute back in the given differential equation, equate coefficients of like terms, and solve the resulting system of simultaneous equations.

Variation of Parameters

Whenever a fundamental system of solutions $u_1, u_2, \ldots, u_n$ for the homogeneous equation is known, a particular integral of

$$A_n(x)d^n y/dx^n + A_{n-1}(x)d^{n-1}y/dx^{n-1} + \cdots + A_1(x)\, dy/dx + A_0(x)y = E(x)$$

may be found in the form $y = \Sigma v_k u_k$. In this and the next few summations, k runs from 1 to n. The v_k are functions of x, found by integrating their derivatives v_k', and these derivatives are the solutions of the n simultaneous equations $\Sigma v_k' u_k = 0$, $\Sigma v_k' u_k' = 0$, $\Sigma v_k' u_k'' = 0, \ldots, \Sigma v_k' u_k^{(n-2)} = 0$, $A_n(x)\Sigma v_k' u_k^{(n-1)} = E(x)$. To find the v_k from $v_k = \int v_k'\,dx + c_k$, any choice of constants will lead to a particular integral. The special choice $v_k = \int_0^x v_k'\,dx$ leads to the particular integral having $y, y', y'', \ldots, y^{(n-1)}$ each equal to zero when $x = 0$.

The Cauchy-Euler Equidimensional Equation. This has the form

$$k_n x^n d^n y/dx^n + k_{n-1}x^{n-1}d^{n-1}y/dx^{n-1} + \cdots + k_1 x\,dy/dx + k_0 y = F(x).$$

The substitution $x = e^t$, which makes

$$x\,dy/dx = dy/dt,$$
$$x^k\,dy^k/dx^k = (d/dt - k + 1)\cdots(d/dt - 2)(d/dt - 1)\,dy/dt$$

transforms this into a linear differential equation with constant coefficients. Its solution $y = g(t)$ leads to $y = g(\ln x)$ as the solution of the given Cauchy-Euler equation.

THE LAPLACE TRANSFORMATION

One form of operational calculus is the Laplace transformation and has as its basis the Laplace integral. When a differential equation expressed in terms of time, t, is operated upon by the Laplace integral, a new equation results which is expressed in terms of a complex variable of the form $\sigma + j\omega$. The transformed equation is in purely algebraic terms and may be manipulated algebraically to solve for the desired quantity as an explicit function of the complex variable. It is necessary to perform an inverse process to return to the time domain. There are essentially three reasons for the use of the Laplace transformation. They are (1) the solution of high-order differential equations may be performed by purely algebraic manipulation of the transformed equation; (2) boundary conditions are easily handled; (3) the Laplace-transform method is suited to the complex-variable theory associated with the Nyquist stability criterion.

In Laplace-transformation mathematics the following symbols and equations are used:

$f(t)$ = a function of time
s = a complex variable of the form $(\sigma + j\omega)$
$F(s)$ = an equation expressed in the transform variable s, resulting from operating on a function of time with the Laplace integral
$\mathcal{L}$ = an operational symbol indicating that the quantity which it prefixes is to be transformed into the frequency domain.

Therefore, $F(s) = \mathcal{L}[f(t)]$. The Laplace integral is defined as $\mathcal{L} = \int_0^\infty e^{-st}\,dt$. Therefore, $\mathcal{L}[f(t)] = \int_0^\infty e^{-st}f(t)\,dt$.

Direct Transforms. EXAMPLE:

$$f(t) = \sin\beta t$$
$$\mathcal{L}[f(t)] = \mathcal{L}(\sin\beta t) = \int_0^\infty \sin\beta t\,e^{-st}\,dt$$

but

$$\sin\beta t = \frac{e^{j\beta t} - e^{-j\beta t}}{2j}$$

$$\mathcal{L}(\sin\beta t) = \frac{1}{2j}\int_0^\infty (e^{j\beta t} - e^{-j\beta t})e^{-st}\,dt$$
$$= \frac{1}{2j}\left(\frac{-1}{s - j\beta}\right)e^{(-s+j\beta)t}\Big|_0^\infty - \frac{1}{2j}\left(\frac{-1}{s + j\beta}\right)e^{(-s-j\beta)t}\Big|_0^\infty$$
$$= \frac{\beta}{s^2 + \beta^2}.$$

Table 1 lists the transforms of common time-variable expressions normally encountered.

Transformation Calculus. By applying the preceding technique, the Laplace transform of derivative or integral functions can be derived.

Table 1. Laplace Transforms

(Thaler)

$f(t)$	$F(s) = \mathcal{L}[f(t)]$
1. A	A/s
2. $1 = u(t)$	$1/s$
3. $e^{-\alpha t}$	$\dfrac{1}{s+\alpha}$
4. $\dfrac{1}{\tau} e^{-t/\tau}$	$\dfrac{1}{\tau s + 1}$
5. $Ae^{-\alpha t}$	$\dfrac{A}{s+\alpha}$
6. $\sin \beta t$	$\dfrac{\beta}{s^2+\beta^2}$
7. $\cos \beta t$	$\dfrac{s}{s^2+\beta^2}$
8. $\dfrac{1}{\beta} e^{-\alpha t} \sin \beta t$	$\dfrac{1}{s^2 + 2\alpha s + \alpha^2 + \beta^2}$
9. $\dfrac{e^{-\alpha t}}{\beta - \alpha} - \dfrac{e^{-\beta t}}{\beta - \alpha}$	$\dfrac{1}{(s+\alpha)(s+\beta)}$
10. $\dfrac{Ae^{-\alpha t} - Be^{-\beta t}}{C}$ where $A = a - \alpha,\ B = a - \beta,\ C = \beta - \alpha$	$\dfrac{s+a}{(s+\alpha)(s+\beta)}$
11. $\dfrac{e^{-\alpha t}}{A} + \dfrac{e^{-\beta t}}{B} + \dfrac{e^{-\delta t}}{C}$ where $A = (\beta-\alpha)(\delta-\alpha)$, $B = (\alpha-\beta)(\delta-\beta)$, $C = (\alpha-\delta)(\beta-\delta)$	$\dfrac{1}{(s+\alpha)(s+\beta)(s+\delta)}$
12. t	$\dfrac{1}{s^2}$
13. t^2	$2/s^3$
14. t^n	$\dfrac{n!}{s^{n+1}}$
15. $d/dt[f(t)]$	$sF(s) - f(0^+)$
16. $d^2/dt^2\,[f(t)]$	$s^2F(s) - sf(0^+) - \dfrac{df}{dt}(0^+)$
17. $d^3/dt^3\,[f(t)]$	$s^3F(s) - s^2f(0^+) - s\dfrac{df(0^+)}{dt} - \dfrac{d^2f(0^+)}{dt^2}$
18. $\int f(t)dt$	$\dfrac{1}{s}\,[F(s) + \int f(t)dt\vert_{0^+}]$
19. $\dfrac{1}{\alpha} \sinh \alpha t$	$\dfrac{1}{s^2 - \alpha^2}$
20. $\cosh \alpha t$	$\dfrac{s}{s^2 - \alpha^2}$

The transform of a first derivative of a function of time is

$$\mathcal{L}\left[\frac{d}{dt}f(t)\right] = sF(s) - f(0^+)$$

where $F(s)$ = Laplace transform of $f(t)$
s = transform variable
$f(0^+)$ = initial value of $f(t)$, evaluated as t approaches zero from positive values.

For a step function of amplitude A at $t = 0, f(0^+) = A$ and $f(0^-) = 0$. The transform of a second derivative of a function of time

$$\frac{d}{dt}\left[\frac{d}{dt}f(t)\right] = f''(t)$$

is

$$\mathcal{L}[f''(t)] = s^2F(s) - sf(0^+) - f'(0^+).$$

The transform of $\int f(t)\, dt$ is

$$\mathcal{L}[\int f(t)\, dt] = \frac{f^{-1}(0^+)}{s} + \frac{F(s)}{s}.$$

where $f^{-1}(0^+) = \int f(t)\, dt$, evaluated as t approaches zero from positive values.

Inversion. When an equation has been transformed, an explicit solution for the unknown may be directly determined through algebraic manipulation. In automatic-control design, the equation is usually the differential equation describing the system, and the unknown is either the output quantity or the error. The solution gained from the transformed equation is expressed in terms of the complex variable s. For many design or analysis purposes, the solution in s is sufficient, but in some cases it is necessary to retransform the solution in terms of time. The process of passing from the complex-variable (frequency domain) expression to that of time (time domain) is called an **inverse transformation.** It is represented symbolically as

$$\mathcal{L}^{-1}F(s) = f(t).$$

For any $f(t)$ there is only one direct transform, $F(s)$. For any given $F(s)$ there is only one inverse transform $f(t)$. Therefore tables are generally used for determining inverse transforms. Very complete tables of inverse transforms may be found in Gardner and Barnes, "Transients in Linear Systems." As an example of the inversion procedure consider an equation of the form

$$K = \alpha x(t) + \int \frac{x(t)}{\beta}\, dt.$$

It is desired to obtain an expression for $x(t)$ resulting from an instantaneous change in the quantity K. Transforming the last equation yields

$$\frac{K}{s} = X(s)\alpha + \frac{X(s)}{s\beta} + \frac{f^{-1}(0^+)}{s}.$$

If

$$f^{-1}(0^+)/s = 0$$

then

$$X(s) = \frac{K/\alpha}{s + 1/\alpha\beta}$$

$$x(t) = \mathcal{L}^{-1}[X(s)] = \mathcal{L}^{-1}\frac{K/\alpha}{s + 1/\alpha\beta}.$$

From Table 1,

$$x(t) = \frac{K}{\alpha}e^{-t/\alpha\beta}.$$

GRAPHICAL REPRESENTATION OF FUNCTIONS

BY

Philip Franklin

For graphical methods in statistics, etc., see W. C. Brinton, "Graphical Methods for Presenting Facts," McGraw-Hill.

EQUATIONS INVOLVING TWO VARIABLES

Curve $y = f(x)$. To represent graphically any function, y, of a single variable, x, lay off the values of x as **abscissas** along a uniformly graduated horizontal axis, whose positive direction (as usually chosen) runs to the right, and at each point on this x-axis erect a perpendicular (called an **ordinate**) whose length represents the value of y at that point. The unit of measurement for the y-scale, whose positive direction (as usually chosen) runs upward, need not be the same as the unit for the x-scale. Draw a smooth curve through the extremities of the ordinates; this is the **graph** of the given function in rectangular coordinates, or the **curve** of the function.

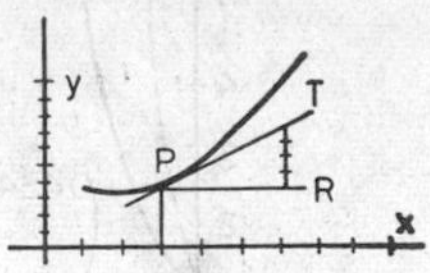

To measure graphically the rate of change of the function at any point P (Fig. 1), draw the tangent at P; then **rate of change** at $P = RT/PR$, where RT and PR are measured in units of the y-axis and x-axis, respectively. This ratio, which is positive if RT runs upward, negative if RT runs downward, is equal to the derivative of the function at the point P (see p. 2–64).

FIG. 1

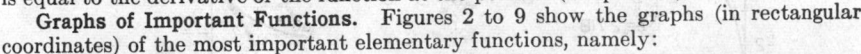

Graphs of Important Functions. Figures 2 to 9 show the graphs (in rectangular coordinates) of the most important elementary functions, namely:

The **linear function,** $y = mx + b$ (Fig. 2).

The **power functions,** $y = x^n$ [n positive (parabolic type); n negative (hyperbolic type)] (Fig. 3).

The **exponential function,** $y = 10^x$ or $y = e^x$, and the **logarithmic function,** $y = \log_{10} x$ or $y = \ln x$ (Fig. 4).

The **trigonometric functions** (Fig. 5), and the inverse trigonometric functions (Fig. 6).

The **hyperbolic functions** (Figs. 7 and 8) and the inverse hyperbolic functions (Fig. 9).

Various **special functions** (Figs. 10 to 12).

By a slight modification, each of these diagrams may be made to represent a somewhat more general function than that for which it is primarily intended. For, if x is replaced by $x - a$ in the equation, this merely requires renumbering the x-axis so that each number is moved a units to the left; and similarly, if y is replaced by $y - b$ in the equation, this merely requires renumbering the y-axis so that each number is moved b units downward. (Such a change is called a translation of the curve to the right, or upward.) Further, if x is replaced by x/c (or y by y/c) in the equation, it is merely necessary to multiply each of the numbers written along the x-axis (or y-axis) by c, in order to adapt the graph to the new equation. (Such a change is called a "stretching" of the curve along one of the axes.)

Empirical Curves. Any set of values of two variables x and y can be represented by plotting the points (x,y) on rectangular coordinate paper, and drawing a smooth curve through these points. The points which correspond to actual data should be clearly indicated by small circles or crosses, intermediate points being spoken of as interpolated points. While this process of graphically interpolating a continuous series of points *between* given values is usually fairly safe, the process of extrapolation—*i.e.*, extending the curve *beyond* the range of the given values—is dangerous.

To Find a Mathematical Equation to Fit a Given Empirical Curve. This problem is one which in general requires much patience and ingenuity. Only the simplest cases can be mentioned here.

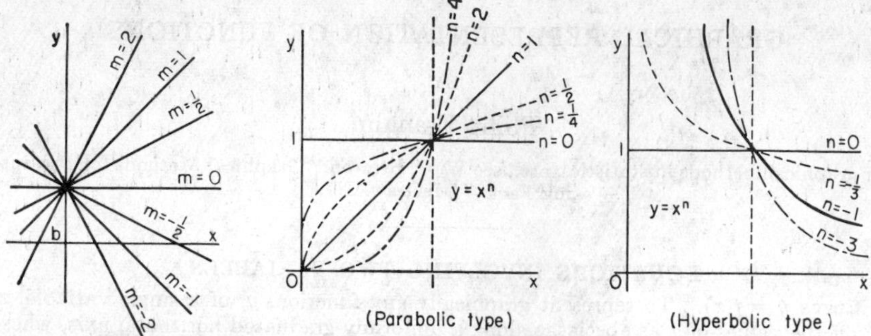

FIG. 2. Linear function, $y = mx + b$.

FIG. 3. Power function, $y = x^n$.

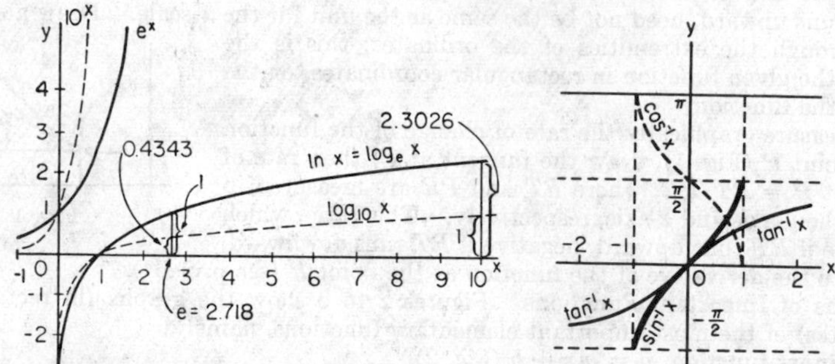

FIG. 4. Exponential function, 10^x or e^x. Logarithmic function, $\log_{10}x$ or $\ln_e x$.

FIG. 6. Inverse trigonometric functions.

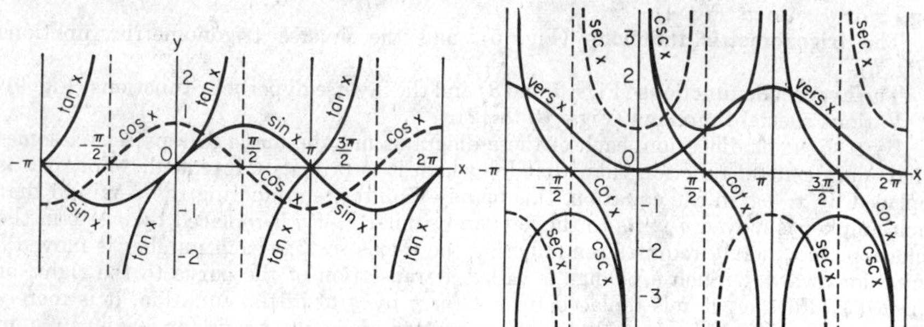

FIG. 5. Trigonometric functions.

CASE 1. If the given empirical curve is a straight line, then the law connecting the given values of x and y is $y = mx + b$, where $m =$ the slope of the line, and $b =$ the value of y at the point where the line crosses the y-axis. If the points lie only approximately on a straight line, the best position for this line can usually be found by stretching a black thread among the points; or, assume a law of the form $y = mx + b$, and, by substituting in this formula n pairs of values of x and y, obtain n equations connecting the coefficients m and b; various pairs of these equations may then be solved for m and b, and the average of the results taken. Or, if great accuracy is required, all n of the equations may be solved for m and b by the method of least squares (p. 2–32).

If any law of the form $f(x,y) = m \cdot F(x,y) + b$ is suspected, where $f(x,y)$ and $F(x,y)$ are any expressions involving either x or y or both x and y, such a law may be tested by plotting $F(x,y)$ instead of x, and $f(x,y)$ instead of y, on rectangular cross-section paper, and seeing whether or not the points lie on a straight line. If they do, the form of the law is verified, and the values of m and b can be read from the figure as before. For example, if $y^2 = mxy + b$, a straight line will be obtained by plotting y^2 against xy.

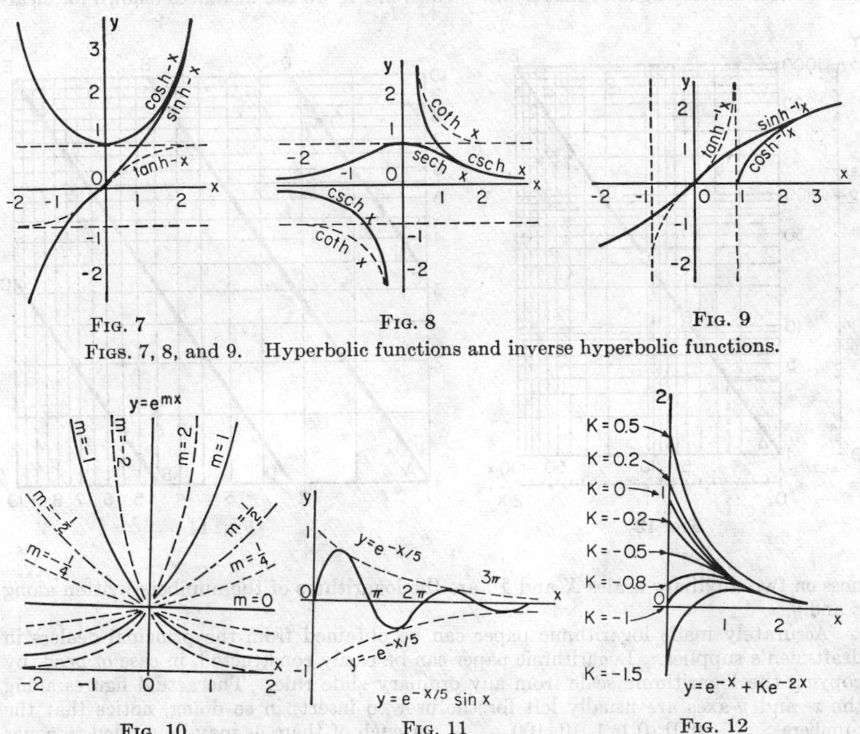

FIG. 7 FIG. 8 FIG. 9

FIGS. 7, 8, and 9. Hyperbolic functions and inverse hyperbolic functions.

FIG. 10 FIG. 11 FIG. 12

Again, if $xy = bx + my$, a straight line will be obtained by plotting y against y/x, since the equation may be written $y = b + m(y/x)$.

CASE 2. If a law of the form $y = cx^n$ is suspected, plot the points (x,y) on logarithmic paper (see below).

CASE 3. If a law of the form $y = c \cdot 10^{mx}$ (or $y = c \cdot e^{mx}$) is suspected, plot the points (x,y) on semilogarithmic paper (see below).

CASE 4. If the given curve resembles the logarithmic curve, $y = \log x$, interchange x and y and proceed as in Case 3.

CASE 5. If the given curve is a wavy line, resembling a sine or cosine curve, try an equation of the form $y = a \sin bx$ or $y = a \cos bx$. If the heights of the waves diminish as x increases, try an equation of the form $y = ae^{-nx} \sin bx$.

NOTE. Any periodic function (satisfying certain simple conditions) can be expressed by a Fourier series (p. 2–69).

CASE 6. A great variety of functions can be represented approximately by a polynomial of the form $y = a + bx + cx^2 + dx^3 + ex^4 + \cdots$, the first three or four terms being usually sufficient. To determine the coefficients a, b, c, . . . most accurately, substitute in the formula all the given pairs of values of x and y, and solve the resulting equations for a, b, c, . . . by the method of least squares (p. 2–32).

CASE 7. Many simple curves can be represented approximately by an equation of the hyperbolic form, $xy = c + bx + ay$, where a, b, and c are determined by substituting the coordinates of three conspicuous points of the curve. The lines $x = a$ and $y = b$ are the asymptotes of the hyperbola. The equation may also be written $(x - a)(y - b) = k$, where $k = ab + c$.

Logarithmic Cross-section Paper. In this form of cross-section paper (Fig. 13), the distance from the origin to any point on the x- or y-axis is equal to the logarithm of the number written against that point. Thus, in Fig. 13 the distances (shown for clearness on two auxiliary scales X and Y) are the logarithms of the numbers written along x and y.

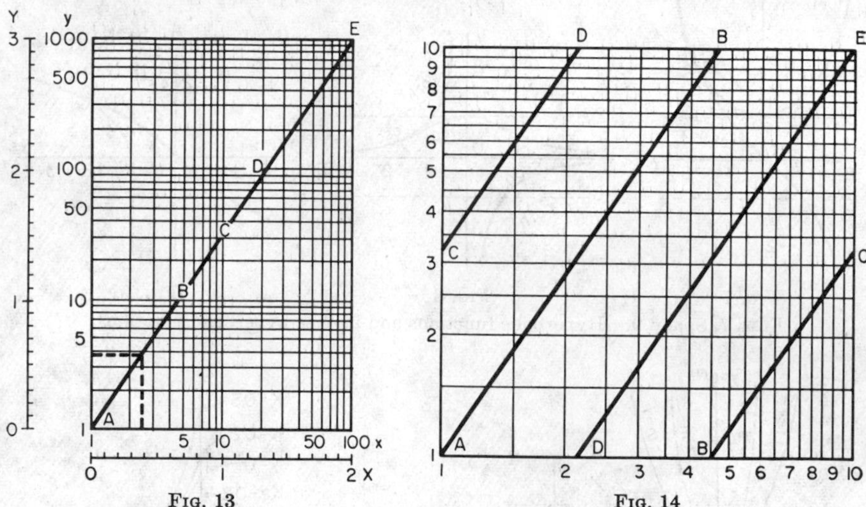

FIG. 13

FIG. 14

Accurately made logarithmic paper can be obtained from the principal dealers in draftsmen's supplies. Logarithmic paper can be easily constructed, in case of need, by copying the logarithmic scale from any ordinary slide rule. The actual figures along the x- and y-axes are usually left for the user to insert; in so doing, notice that the numbers . . . , 0.01, 0.1, 1, 10, 100, . . . , or such of them as may be needed to cover any given range of values, must be placed at the points of division which separate the main squares. It is often convenient, however, to omit the decimal point, numbering each square independently from 1 to 10. The length of the side of one square is called the *unit* or *base* of the logarithmic paper; the larger the unit, the finer the possible subdivisions of the scale.

To plot a point (x,y) on logarithmic paper, *e.g.*, the point (3,5), means to find the point of intersection of the vertical line marked $x = 3$ and the horizontal line marked $y = 5$. In interpolating between two lines, account should be taken of the fact that the divisions are not of uniform length.

Any equation of the form $y = cx^n$ when plotted on logarithmic paper will be represented by a straight line whose slope is n. For, if $y_1 = cx_1^n$ and $y_2 = cx_2^n$, then $y_1/y_2 = (x_1/x_2)^n$, or $(\log y_1 - \log y_2)/(\log x_1 - \log x_2) = n$. The slope must be measured by aid of an auxiliary *uniform* scale.

EXAMPLE. Let $y = x^{3/2}$. When $x = 1$, $y = 1$; plot this point A on the logarithmic paper, and draw the straight line AE with a slope equal to $3/2$ (Fig. 13). By the aid of this line, the value of y for any value of x between 1 and 100 can be read off directly; for example, if $x =$

2.50, $y = 3.95$, as shown by dotted lines, so that $(2.50)^{3/2} = 3.95$. To find the value of y for any value of x outside this range, note that moving the decimal point 2 places in x is equivalent to moving it 3 places in y. The line shown in Fig. 13 is thus equivalent to a complete table of three-halves powers.

It will be noticed that this line crosses four squares of the logarithmic paper. By superposing these four squares the whole diagram may be condensed into a single square (Fig. 14), in which, however, the scales for x and y now give only the sequence of digits in the answer, the position of the decimal point having to be determined by inspection.

To determine whether a given set of values, x and y, satisfies a law of the form $y = cx^n$, plot the values on logarithmic paper, and see whether they lie on a straight line; if they do, then the given values satisfy a law of this form; moreover, the slope of the line gives the value of n, and the value of y when $x = 1$ gives the value of c.

If the plotted points fail to lie exactly in line but form a curve slightly concave upward, try subtracting some constant b from all the y's, *i.e.*, move each point downward a distance equal to b units of the y-scale at that point. If it proves possible to choose b so that the resulting points lie in line, then the original values obey a law of the form $y - b = cx^n$, where n is again the slope of the line, and c is the value of $y - b$ when $x = 1$. (Conversely if the curve is concave *downward*, try *adding* b to all the y's; *i.e.*, move each point *upward;* if the new points lie in line, the original values obey a law of the form $y + b = cx^n$.) Another method of "straightening" the curve consists of adding some constant, $\pm a$, to all the values of x, which has the effect of shifting all the points to the right or left (by varying amounts), if this method succeeds, the original values obey a law of the form $y = c(x + a)^n$.

Semilogarithmic Cross-section Paper. This form of paper (Fig. 15) has a logarithmic scale along y and a uniform scale along x. The **scale value,** k, of the paper is the number which stands, on the x-axis, at a distance from the origin equal to the width of one of the main horizontal strips. Thus, in Fig. 15, each number shown along the auxiliary scale Y is the logarithm of the corresponding number along y, and each number shown along the auxiliary scale X is $1/k$th of the corresponding number along x (here $k = 5$). The number k, which may be chosen at pleasure, should be taken equal to some simple integer, as 1, 2, or 5, or some integral power of 10.

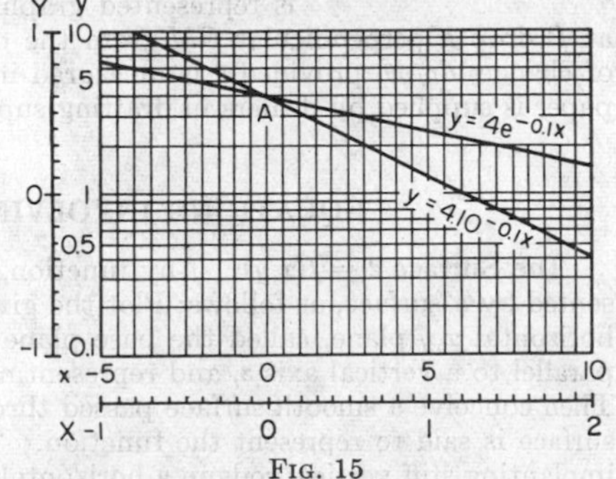

Fig. 15

In preparing the paper for use it is important to notice that the numbers $\cdots$, 0.01, 0.1, 1, 10, 100, . . . (or such of them as may be needed in any given case) must be placed along the y-axis at the points which mark the main lines of division between the horizontal strips; while the numbers $\cdots, -2k, -k, 0, +k, +2k, \cdots$ (or such of them as may be needed) must be placed along the x-axis at uniform intervals, each interval (from 0 to k, from k to $2k$, etc.) being equal to the width of one of the main horizontal strips. The width of one of these strips is called the *unit* or *base* of the semilogarithmic paper; the larger the unit, the finer the possible subdivisions of the scale.

To plot a point (x,y), as $x = 3$, $y = 5$, on semilogarithmic paper means to find the point of intersection of the vertical line marked $x = 3$ with the horizontal line marked $y = 5$.

Any equation of the form $y = c \cdot 10^{mx}$ (or $y = c \cdot e^{mx}$), when plotted on semilogarithmic paper with scale value k, will be represented by a straight line whose slope is km (or $0.4343\ km$). By a suitable choice of the scale value k, any given range of values of x can be brought within the size of the paper. Note that $e = 10^{0.4343}$.

Example. Given $y = 4 \cdot 10^{-0.1x}$ (or $y = 4 \cdot e^{-0.1x}$). In Fig. 15, when $x = 0$, $y = 4$. By plotting this point (A) on the semilogarithmic paper, with scale value 5, and drawing through it a straight line with slope equal to -0.5 (or -0.217) a graphical representation is obtained from which, for any value of x, the corresponding value of y can be read off. If it is desired to condense the figure, several horizontal strips may be superposed on a single strip; this of course renders the decimal point in the y-scale undetermined (unless a separate y-scale is provided for each section of the graph).

In order to determine whether a given set of values of x and y satisfies a law of the form $y = c \cdot 10^{mx}$ (or $y = c \cdot e^{mx}$), plot the values of x and y on semilogarithmic paper, with a suitable scale value k, and see whether they lie on a straight line; if they do so, the law is satisfied, and the values of m and c may be found as follows: m = the slope of the line divided by k (or the slope of the line divided by $0.4343k$), and c = the value of y when $x = 0$.

If the plotted points fail to lie exactly in line, but form a curve slightly concave upward, try subtracting some constant b from all the y's, and plot the values thus modified; if b can be so chosen that the revised points lie in line, then the original values obey a law of the form $y - b = c \cdot 10^{mx}$ (or $y - b = c \cdot e^{mx}$), where m and c are to found as before. If the curve is concave downward, add b, instead of subtracting; and replace $y - b$ by $y + b$ in the law.

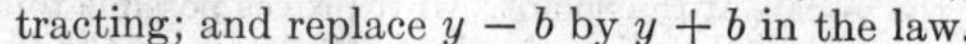

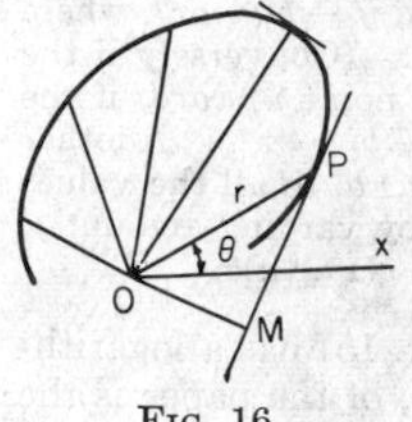

FIG. 16

Curves in Polar Coordinates. Any function, r, of a single variable, θ, can be represented by a curve in polar coordinates (p. 2–48). Lay off the given values of θ as angles, the initial line Ox running toward the right, and the counterclockwise direction about the origin being taken as positive. Along the terminal side of each angle θ, lay off the corresponding value of r, forward if r is positive, backward if r is negative; and pass a smooth curve through the points thus determined.

The rate of change of r with respect to θ at a given point P is represented graphically as follows (Fig. 16): On the tangent at P drop a perpendicular OM from the origin: then $r(MP/OM)$ represents the rate of change, $dr/d\theta$, provided θ is measured in radians. Specially ruled polar coordinate paper is supplied by dealers in drafting supplies.

EQUATIONS INVOLVING THREE VARIABLES

The Surface $z = f(x,y)$. Any function, z, of two variables, x and y, may be represented by a surface, as follows: Plot the given pairs of values of x and y as points in a horizontal x,y plane, called the base plane; at each of these points erect an ordinate, parallel to a vertical axis z, and representing by its length the value of z at that point. Then conceive a smooth surface passed through the extremities of these ordinates: this surface is said to represent the function. In practice, the ordinates may be made by implanting stiff vertical rods in a horizontal board of soft wood which serves as the base plane; the surface may then be constructed by filling in the spaces with plaster of paris. Or, more simply, pieces of cardboard may be cut out to represent parallel plane sections of the surface, and then stood on edge in slots cut in the board to receive them. The units employed along x, y, and z need not be equal to each other.

Contour-line Charts. All the points of a surface $z = f(x,y)$ which are at any given height above the base plane form a curve on the surface, called a contour line of the surface. If each of these contour lines be projected on the base plane, and each labeled with the value of z to which it corresponds, a complete representation of the function $z = f(x,y)$ is obtained, all in one plane. A topographical map, with contour lines showing elevations above the sea, and a weather map, with contour lines showing barometric pressure, are familiar examples. If there are several values of z corresponding to any given point (x,y), there will be several contour lines whose projections pass through that point.

Contour-line Charts for Simultaneous Equations [of the form $z = f(x,y)$, $w = F(x,y)$]. In Fig. 17, plot the function $z = f(x,y)$ by contour lines on an x-y plane, and plot the function $w = F(x,y)$ by contour lines on the same x-y plane. Then every point on the diagram (either directly or by interpolation) is the intersection of four curves—an x-curve, a y-curve, a z-curve, and a w-curve. Here, by "curve" is meant any line, straight or curved. By the aid of such a diagram, when the values of any two of these four variables are given, the values of the other two can be found. The method of use consists simply in entering the diagram along the two given curves (or lines), tracing them to their point of intersection, and then coming out again along the two curves (or lines) whose values are required. The best manner of numbering the curves is indicated in the figure.

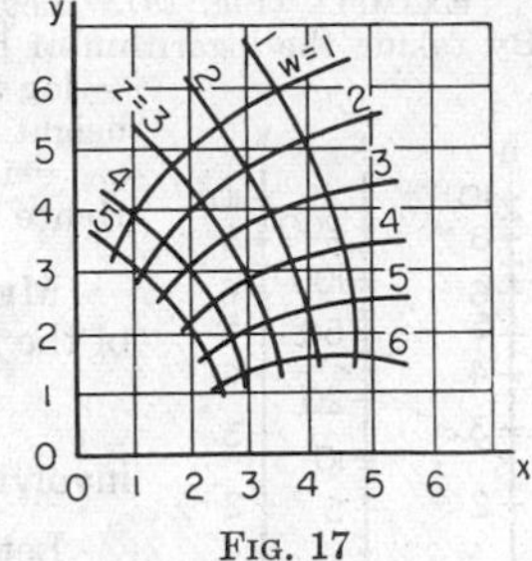

FIG. 17

ALIGNMENT CHARTS

Alignment Charts for Three Variables, t, u, v. Any relation between three variables, t, u, v, which can be thrown into one of the forms listed in later paragraphs, can be represented graphically by a very convenient form of diagram called an alignment chart. In the simplest form of an alignment chart for three variables there are three scales (straight or curved), along which the values of the three variables, t, u, v, are marked in such a way that any three values of t, u, v which satisfy the given equation are represented by three points which lie in line. Hence, if the values of any two of the variables are given, the corresponding value of the third can be found by simply drawing a straight line through the two given points and reading the value of the point where it crosses the third scale.

The most important methods of constructing alignment charts for three variables are described below. Where several methods are applicable in a given case, the best one must be determined largely by trial. For further information, see d'Ocagne, "Traité de Nomographie," Gauthier-Villars, Paris; Runge, "Graphical Methods," Columbia University Press; Peddle, "Construction of Graphical Charts," McGraw-Hill; Lipka, "Graphical and Mechanical Computation," Wiley; Kraitchik, "Alignment Charts," Van Nostrand; Douglass and Adams, "Elements of Nomography," McGraw-Hill.

METHOD 1. Given, an equation which can be thrown into the form

$$f_1(u) + f_2(v) = f_3(t)$$

where $f_1(u)$ is a function of u alone, $f_2(v)$ a function of v alone, etc. An alignment chart may be constructed as follows:

Choice of Moduli to Fit Size of Paper. Let $f_1(u')$ be the smallest and $f_1(u'')$ the largest value of $f_1(u)$ likely to be needed, and let h be the height of the available space on the paper. Then find a simple number, m_1, such that m_1 times $f_1(u'') - f_1(u')$ shall not exceed h. Similarly, find a simple number m_2 such that m_2 times $f_1(v'') - f_1(v')$ shall not exceed h.

Also, compute a third modulus, m_3 by the formula

$$m_3 = (m_1 m_2)/(m_1 + m_2)$$

Construction of the First Two Scales. Draw two parallel vertical axes, at any distance, k, apart. On the first axis, marked u, starting with any convenient origin, lay off the distances $x = m_1 f_1(u)$ for successive values of u, labeling each point thus plotted with the corresponding value of u. Similarly, on the second axis, marked v, starting with any convenient origin, lay off $y = m_2 f_2(v)$ for successive values of v, labeling each point with the corresponding value of v. The u-scale and the v-scale are thus completed.

Construction of the Third Scale. Draw a third line, t, parallel to the first two lines, dividing the distance k in the ratio m_1/m_2; that is, the distance from u to t is $m_1 k/(m_1 + m_2)$. Compute the value t_0 corresponding to any convenient values u_0 and v_0, and label with this value, t_0, the point where the t-axis is cut by a straight line joining the points u_0 and v_0. Using this point t_0 as an anchorage, lay off along the t-line the scale determined by $z = m_3 f_3(t)$ where $m_3 = (m_1 m_2)/(m_1 + m_2)$. The third scale is thus completed, and the chart is ready for use.

Note that the units of measurement for x, y, and z (which do not appear on the completed chart) must of course be the same. Note also that to ensure accuracy on the third scale, especially if the modulus m_3 is small, it is well to compute more than one anchorage point, t_0.

The construction is greatly facilitated by the use of previously constructed uniform and logarithmic scales with various moduli.

EXAMPLE (Fig. 18). Let $uv^{1.41} = t$, for a range of values of u and v between 1 and 10. By taking the logarithm of both sides, reduce the equation to the form $\log u + 1.41 \log v = \log t$. Here $f_1(u) = \log u$, $f_2(v) = 1.41 \log v$, $f_3(t) = \log t$. For a height of paper $h = 10$, and a width $k = 5$, we may take $m_1 = 10$ and $m_2 = 10/1.41 = 7.00$; whence $m_3 = 4.15$ and $m_1k/(m_1 + m_2) = 2.92$. Hence the chart is readily constructed, as shown.

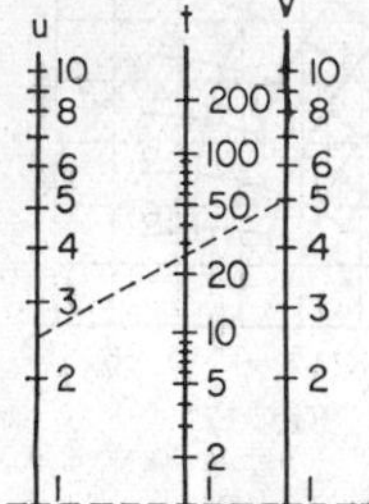

FIG. 18

METHOD 1a. Method 1 may be readily extended to equations of the form

$$f_1(u) + f_2(v) + f_3(w) = f_4(t)$$

involving four variables, t, u, v, w.

Let $f_1(u) + f_2(v) = q$ and chart this equation by Method 1. Then chart the equation $q + f_3(w) = f_4(t)$ by the same method, using as one of the scales the q-scale already drawn. (The q-scale need not be graduated; the position of the q-axis is all that is important.) In reading the completed chart, we use two index lines, one joining points u and v, and cutting the q-axis in an (unlabeled) point q; the other joining points w and t, and cutting the q-axis in the same (unlabeled) point q. Thus when any three of the four variables are given, the fourth can be found.

A further extension to equations of the same form involving five or more variables is obvious.

EXAMPLE (Fig. 19). Let $t = w\sqrt{uv}$ whence $\frac{1}{2}\log u + \frac{1}{2}\log v + \log w = \log t$. Here $f_1(u) = \frac{1}{2}\log u$, $f_2(v) = \frac{1}{2}\log v$, $f_3(w) = \log w$, and $f_4(t) = \log t$.

FIG. 19

METHOD 2. Given, an equation which can be thrown into the form

$$f_1(u) = f_2(v) \cdot f_3(t)$$

where $f_1(u)$ is a function of u alone, $f_2(v)$ a function of v alone, etc. First, choose two "moduli" m_1 and m_2 (to fit size of paper) exactly as in Method 1.

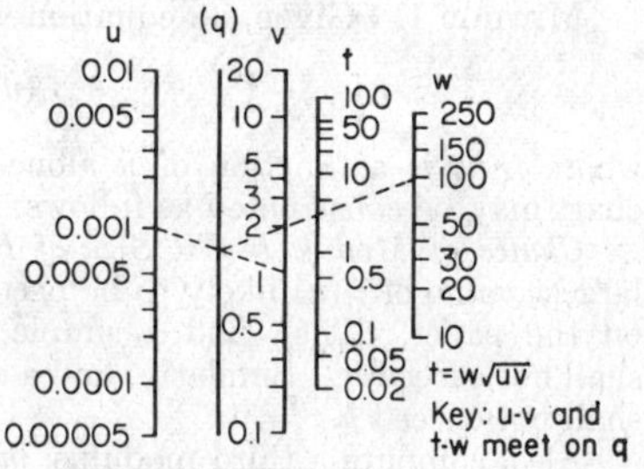

Second, draw two parallel vertical axes, AX and BY, oppositely directed, the diagonal line AB being of any convenient length k. With A and B as origins, lay off along these axes the distances

$$x = m_1f_1(u) \quad \text{and} \quad y = m_2f_2(v)$$

for successive values of u and v, respectively, and label each point thus plotted with the corresponding value of u (or v). The u- and v-scales are thus completed.

Third, on BY select a point F at any convenient distance, l, from B; compute an auxiliary modulus, n, by the formula $n = lm_1/m_2$; and lay off along AX an auxiliary scale, $x' = nf_3(t)$ for successive values of t, marking each point (temporarily) with the corresponding value of t. Then transfer this auxiliary scale to the axis AB by means of projecting lines drawn through the point F, marking each point (permanently) with the corresponding value of t. The t-scale, along the axis AB, is thus completed, and the chart is ready for use.

As a check, note that along the t-axis, the distance z from A to any point labeled t should be given by

$$v = km_1f_3(t)/[m_1f_3(t) + m_2]$$

Indeed the points of the t-scale may be laid down independently by the use of this formula, if desired, instead of by the graphical method above described.

This type of chart is known as a Z-chart.

EXAMPLE (Fig. 20). Let $u = 0.196\, t^3 v$, where u is to range from 0 to 150,000 and v from 0 to 15,000. The equation may be written $u = (10v)\,(0.0196t^3)$.

Here $f_1(u) = u$, $f_2(v) = 10v$, $f_3(t) = 0.0196t^3$.

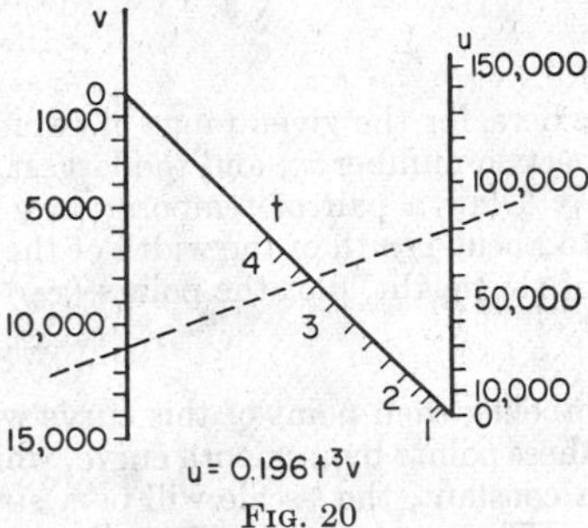

FIG. 20

The theory underlying Methods 1 and 2 depends only on simple properties of similar triangles. The following methods are based on certain standard equations of the straight line in analytical geometry, and the notation in what follows has been suggested by the form of these equations.

Notation. In each of the equations which follow, U stands for any function of u alone, V for any function of v alone, and $F_1(t)$, $F_2(t)$ for any functions of t alone. Any of these functions may reduce to a constant. The axes of x, y, and y' which are mentioned are of merely temporary use in constructing the diagram, and the letters x, y, y' should not be written on the chart. It is not necessary that the axes be at right angles, provided the x of a point is always measured parallel to the x-axis, and its y parallel to the y-axis.

METHOD 3. Given, an equation which can be thrown into the form

$$U \cdot F_1(t) + V \cdot F_2(t) = 1$$

where, for the given range of values of u and v, the largest variations in U and V are less than a certain number m.

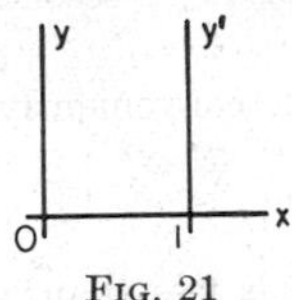

FIG. 21

Draw a pair of (temporary) x,y axes (Fig. 21), and through the point $x = 1$ draw a third axis, which may be called the axis of y', parallel to the axis of y. In ordinary cases, the unit of measurement along x should be nearly equal to the full width of the paper. Now choose a unit for y and y' such that m times this unit will about equal the height of the paper, and plot, in the usual way, the points (x,y) given by

$$x = \frac{F_2(t)}{F_1(t) + F_2(t)} \qquad y = \frac{1}{F_1(t) + F_2(t)}$$

labeling each point with the value of t to which it corresponds. Connect these points by a smooth curve, which gives the t-scale of the diagram. [If $F_1(t)/F_2(t)$ = a constant, the t-scale will prove to be a straight line parallel to the y-axis.]

Then, using the same units as above, plot along y the points given by $y = U$, labeling each point with the corresponding value of u; and plot along y' the points given by $y' = V$, labeling each of these points with the corresponding value of v. This gives the u- and v-scales of the diagram. The three scales being thus constructed, the x-axis may now be erased, and the diagram is ready for use. Any three points t, u, v which lie in line correspond to three values of t, u, v, which satisfy the given equation. The numbering on each scale should be shown at sufficiently frequent intervals to permit of easy interpolation.

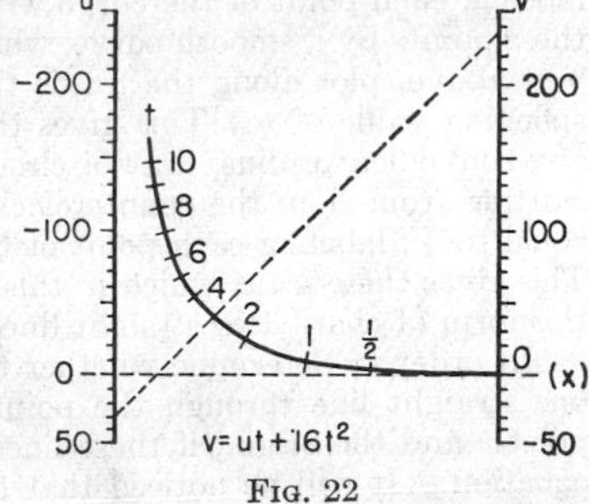

FIG. 22

EXAMPLE (Fig. 22). Let $v = ut + 16t^2$, which reduces to the form $(-u/16)\,(1/t) + (v/16)\,(1/t^2) = 1$. Here $U = -u/16$, $V = v/16$, $F_1(t) = 1/t$, $F_2(t) = 1/t^2$ and $x = 1/(1 + t)$, $y = t^2/(1 + t)$.

NOTE. If $m = \infty$, values of u and v which give large values of U and V cannot be shown within the limits of the paper. In such cases, the chart may be supplemented by a second chart, made according to Method 4, below.

METHOD 4. Given, an equation which can be thrown into the form

$$\frac{F_1(t)}{U} + \frac{F_2(t)}{V} = 1$$

where, for the given range of values of u and v, the largest variation in U is less than a certain number m, and the largest variation in V is less than a certain number n.

Draw a pair of temporary x,y axes, and having chosen a unit for the x-axis equal to about $1/m$th of the width of the paper, and a unit for the y-axis equal to about $1/n$th of the height, plot the points (x,y) given by

$$x = F_1(t) \qquad y = F_2(t)$$

labeling each point of this curve with the value of t to which it corresponds. Connect these points by a smooth curve, which gives the t-scale of the diagram. [If $F_1(t)/F_2(t) =$ a constant, the t-scale will be a straight line through the origin.]

Then, using the same units as above, plot along x the values of U, labeling each point with the corresponding value of u; and plot along y the values of V, labeling each point with the corresponding value of v. This gives the u- and v-scales of the diagram. On the chart as thus completed, any three points t, u, v which lie in line correspond to three values of t, u, v which satisfy the given equation.

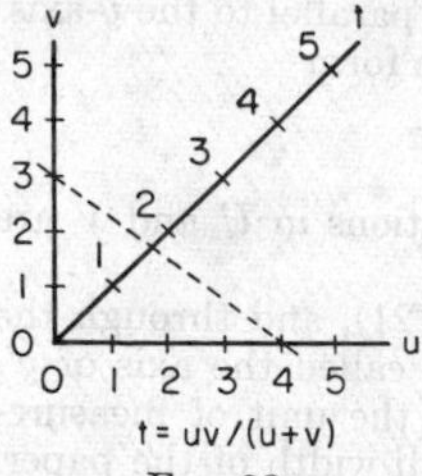

FIG. 23

EXAMPLE (Fig. 23). Let $t = (uv)/(u + v)$, which may be written in the form $t/v + t/u = 1$. Here $U = u$, $V = v$, $F_1(t) = t$, $F_2(t) = t$.

NOTE. If $m = \infty$ and $n = \infty$, values of u and v which give large values of U and V cannot be shown within the limits of the paper. In such cases the chart may be supplemented by a second chart, made according to Method 3, above.

METHOD 5. Given, an equation which can conveniently be thrown into the form

$$F_2(t) = V \cdot F_1(t) + U$$

where, for the given range of values of t, the largest variation in $F_1(t)$ is less than a certain number m, and the largest variation in $F_2(t)$ is less than a certain number n.

Draw a pair of temporary x,y axes, and, having chosen a unit for x equal to about $1/m$th of the width of the paper and a unit for y equal to about $1/n$th of the height, plot the points (x,y) given by

$$x = F_1(t) \qquad y = F_2(t)$$

labeling each point of the curve with the value of t to which it corresponds. Connect these points by a smooth curve, which forms the t-scale. Next using the same unit for y as above, plot along the y-axis the values of U labeling each point with the corresponding value of u. This gives the u-scale. Finally, with the origin as center, and any convenient radius, draw a circle cutting the x-axis in A. Along this circular arc, starting from A in the counterclockwise direction, lay off the angles whose slopes are equal to V, labeling each point of the arc with the value of v to which it corresponds. This gives the v-scale, which in this case, however, plays a peculiar role, since, in using this form of chart, two straight lines are required instead of one. Thus:

In order to determine whether three values, t, u, v, satisfy the given equation, lay one straight line through the points t and u, and another straight line through the point v and the origin; if these lines are parallel, the three values of t, u, v satisfy the equation. It will be noticed that the function of the v-scale here is to measure, in a certain sense, the slope of the line joining t and u. A chart of this type may be called "an alignment chart with a sliding scale for one of the variables."

EXAMPLE. Let $\sin u = \sin 60° \sin t - \cos 60° \cos t \cos v$ (Fig. 24), which may be put in the form $(\sin 60° \sin t) = \cos v\,(\cos 60° \cos t) + \sin u$. Here $F_1(t) = \cos 60° \cos t$, $F_2(t) = \sin 60° \sin t$, $U = \sin u$, $V = \cos v$.

Alignment Charts for Four Variables. The extension of Methods 3, 4, and 5 to the case of four variables, say r, s, u, v consists essentially in replacing the t-scale of the earlier diagram by a network of two scales, one for r and one for s. The point where a curve $r = r_1$ and a curve $s = s_1$ intersect may be spoken of as the point (r_1,s_1). In the following equations, U denotes as before any function of u alone V any function of v alone; while $F_1(r,s)$ and $F_2(r,s)$ represent any functions of r and s.

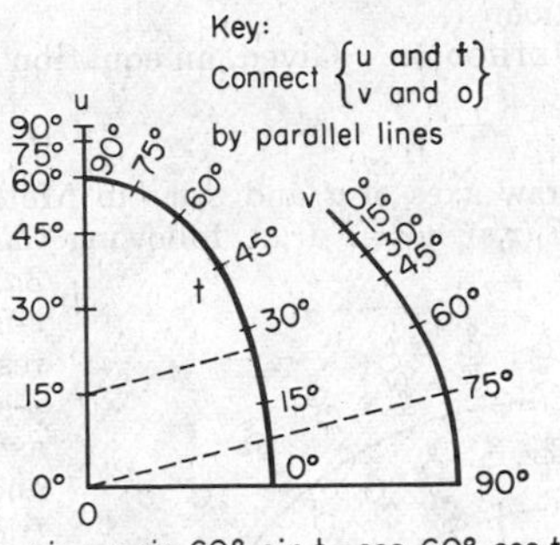

Fig. 24

Method 3*a*. Given, an equation of the form

$$U \cdot F_1(r,s) + V \cdot F_2(r,s) = 1$$

Draw axes x, y, and y' as in Method 3, and plot the network of curves given by the equations

$$x = \frac{F_2(r,s)}{F_1(r,s) + F_2(r,s)} \qquad y = \frac{1}{F_1(r,s) + F_2(r,s)}$$

To do this (Fig. 25), find the point (x,y) that corresponds to each given pair of values of r and s, by direct substitution in the equations for x and y. Connect all the points for which $r = 1$ by a curve, and label it $r = 1$; connect all the points for which $r = 2$ by another curve, and label it $r = 2$; etc. This gives the family of r-curves. Similarly, through all the points for which $s = 1$ draw a curve labeled $s = 1$; through all the points for which $s = 2$ draw a curve labeled $s = 2$; etc. This gives the family of s-curves, intersecting the family of r-curves. Note, however, that if it is possible to eliminate s (or r) from the equations that give x and y, the resulting equation in x, y, and r (or x, y, and s) can often be plotted directly for each given value of r (or of s).

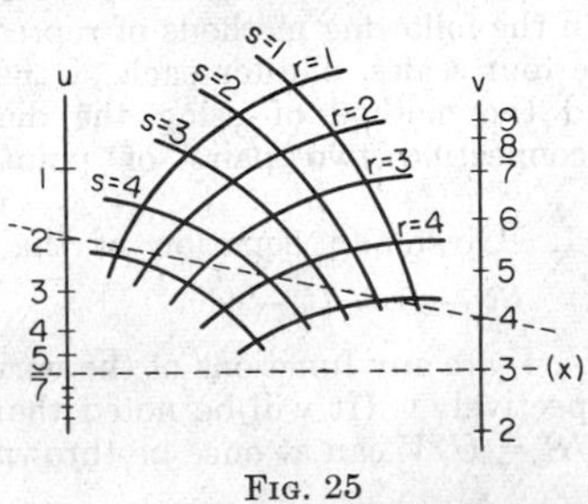

Fig. 25

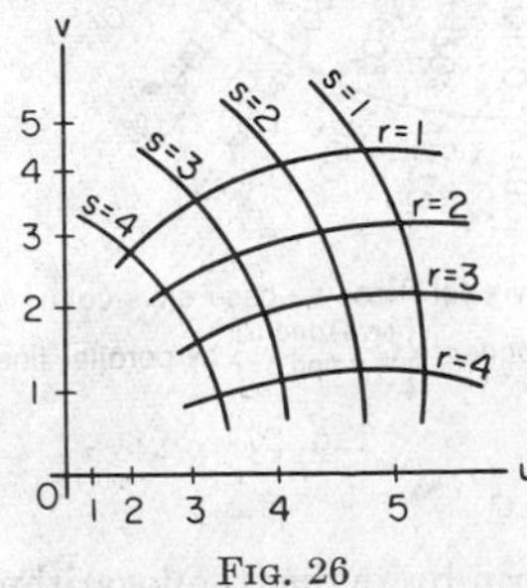

Fig. 26

Next, construct the u- and v-scales along the axes of y and y' as in Method 3. (The letters x, y, and y', and the units used in plotting along these axes, should be omitted from the finished diagram, as should also the axis of x.)

In the chart, as thus completed, any three points, (r,s),u, and v which lie in a straight line, correspond to values of r, s, u, v which satisfy the given equation. Hence, when any three of these four values are given, the fourth can be found from the chart.

Method 4*a*. Given, an equation of the form

$$\frac{F_1(r,s)}{U} + \frac{F_2(r,s)}{V} = 1$$

Draw axes of x and y as in Method 4, and plot the network of curves given by

$$x = F_1(r,s) \qquad y = F_2(r,s)$$

To do this, follow the plan outlined for a similar case under Method 3*a*, labeling each curve of the r-family (Fig. 26) with the corresponding value of r, and each curve of the s-family with the corresponding value of s. Next, construct the u- and V-scales along the x- and y-axes, precisely as in Method 4. Then any three points, (r,s), u, and v, which lie in a straight line correspond to values of r, s, u, v which satisfy the given equation.

METHOD 5a. Given, an equation of the form

$$F_2(r,s) = V \cdot F_1(r,s) + U$$

Draw axes of x and y, as in Method 5, and plot the network of curves given by $x = F_1(r,s)$, $y = F_2(r,s)$, following the plan outlined for a similar case under Method 3a, and labeling each curve of the r-family (or s-family) with the value of r (or s) to which it corresponds. Next, construct the u-scale along the y-axis, and the v-scale along a circular arc, precisely as in Method 5. Then any three points, (r,s), u, and v, which are so related that the line through (r,s) and u is parallel to the line joining v with the origin, will correspond to values of r, s, u, v which satisfy the given equation.

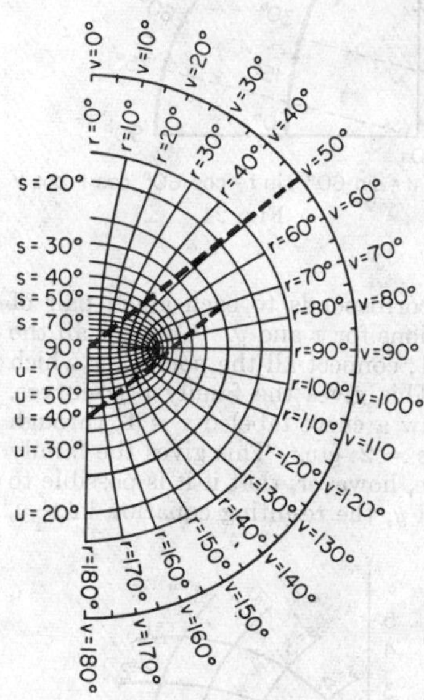

FIG. 27

EXAMPLE Method 5a (Fig. 27). Let $\cot v = \cot r \cos s + \csc r \sin s \cot u$, which may be written $(\cos r \cot s) = \cot v\ (\sin r \csc s) - \cot u$. Here $U = -\cot u$, $V = \cot v$, $F_1(r,s) = \sin r \csc s$, $F_2(r,s) = \cos r \cot s$, whence

$$\frac{x^2}{\csc^2 s} + \frac{y^2}{\cot^2 s} = 1 \qquad \frac{x^2}{\sin^2 r} - \frac{y^2}{\cos^2 r} = 1$$

so that the s-curves are ellipses and the r-curves hyperbolas.

Parallel Charts, or Proportional Charts, for Four Variables. In the following methods of representation there are four scales, one for each of the four variables, and the method of using the diagram consists in connecting two pairs of points by parallel lines.

METHOD 1. Given, an equation of the form

$$R - S = U - V$$

where R, S, U, V are any functions of the variables r, s, u, v, respectively. (It will be noted that any proportion $R/S = U/V$ can at once be thrown into this form by taking the logarithm of both sides.)

In Fig. 28, draw four vertical axes, y_1, y_2, y_1', y_2', such that the distance between y_1 and y_1' (which may be zero) is equal to the distance between y_2 and y_2', and so that the four zero points lie in line. Along these axes, using the same unit for all, plot the points given by $y_1 = R$, $y_1' = S$, $y_2 = U$, $y_2' = V$, and label each point with the value of r, s, u, or v to which it corresponds. (The letters y_1, y_2, y_1', y_2' are temporary, and should not appear on the diagram.) Then if the line joining two points r and u is parallel to the line joining two points s and v, the four values of r, s, u, v will satisfy the given equation. In this and the following methods, a parallel ruler, or a pair of draftsman's triangles, will be useful in reading the chart. A "key" stating which points are to be joined with which should be clearly given on the diagram.

EXAMPLE (Fig. 28). Let $32.2vr = us^2$, or $\log r - 2 \log s = \log u - \log (32.2v)$. Here $R = \log r$, $S = 2 \log s$, $U = \log u$, $V = \log (32.2v)$.

METHOD 2. Given, an equation of the form

$$\frac{R}{S} = \frac{U}{V}$$

In Fig. 29, draw a pair of axes, x,y, and parallel to them (or coinciding with them) a second pair of axes, x_1,y_1. Using any convenient horizontal unit, plot along x and x_1 the points given by $x = R$, $x_1 = U$, and using any convenient vertical unit, plot along y and y_1 the points given by $y = S$, $y_1 = V$. Label each point with the value of r, s, u, v, to which it corresponds. (The letters x, y, x_1, y_1 should not appear on the diagram.) Then if the line joining two points r and s is parallel to the line joining two points u and v, the four values r, s, u, v will satisfy the given equation.

METHOD 3. Given, an equation of the form

$$R - S = \frac{V}{U}$$

In Fig. 30, take a pair of axes, x,y, and through the point $x = 1$ draw a third axis, y', parallel to y. Also, take a second pair of axes, x_2,y_2, parallel to (or coinciding with)

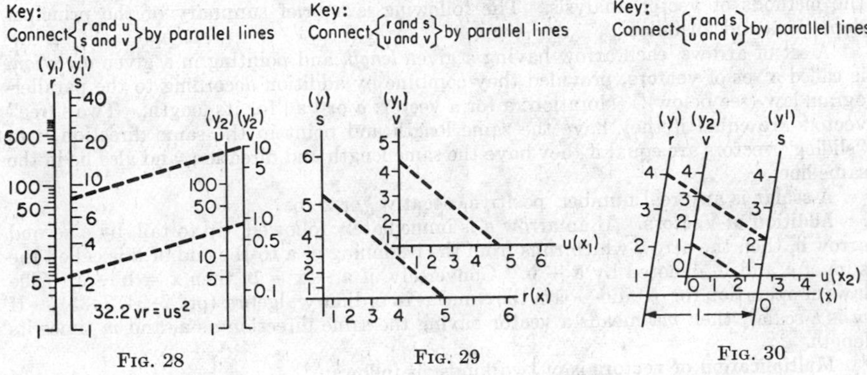

FIG. 28 FIG. 29 FIG. 30

the axes of x and y. Having chosen a suitable unit for x and x_2, and a suitable unit for y, y', and y_2, lay off the values of R and S along y and y', respectively, labeling each point with the value of r or s to which it corresponds; and lay off the values of U and V along x_2 and y_2, labeling each point with the value of u or v to which it corresponds. Then if the line joining two points r and s is parallel to the line joining two points u and v, the four values r, s, u, v will satisfy the given equation.

For further examples, see Strachan, Nomographic Solutions for Formulas of Various Types, *Trans. ASCE*, **78**, 1915.

VECTOR ANALYSIS

BY

Philip Franklin

Many problems involving directed magnitudes can be advantageously treated by the methods of vector analysis. The following is a brief summary of the principal definitions and formulas.

A set of arrows, each arrow having a given *length* and pointing in a given *direction,* is called a set of **vectors,** provided they combine by addition according to the parallelogram law (see below). Notation: **a** for a vector; *a* or | **a** | for its length. Two "free" vectors are equal if they have the same length and point in the same direction; two "sliding" vectors are equal if they have the same length and direction, and also lie in the same line.

A **scalar** is any real number, positive, negative, or zero.

Addition of Vectors. If an arrow **a** is immediately followed, tip to tail, by a second arrow **b**, then the arrow which runs from the beginning of **a** to the end of **b** is called the **sum** of **a** and **b**, denoted by $\mathbf{a} + \mathbf{b}$. Conversely, if $\mathbf{a} + \mathbf{x} = \mathbf{b}$, then $\mathbf{x} = \mathbf{b} - \mathbf{a}$. The laws of operation for $+$ and $-$ are the same as in ordinary algebra (pp. 2–24, 2–35). If m is a scalar, then $m\mathbf{a}$ means a vector having the same direction as **a**, and m times its length.

Multiplication of vectors is of two kinds, as follows:

The **scalar product,** or dot product, of two vectors **a** and **b,** denoted by $\mathbf{a}\cdot\mathbf{b}$—or by $(\mathbf{ab})$ in round parentheses—is defined as the scalar quantity $ab \cos \theta$, where θ is the angle between **a** and **b.**

EXAMPLE. If **F** is a force whose point of application moves along a vector distance **x**, then $\mathbf{F}\cdot\mathbf{x}$ = *work* done by **F** this during displacement.

PECULIARITIES OF SCALAR PRODUCTS. (1) Since $\mathbf{a}\cdot\mathbf{b}$ is not a vector, expressions like $(\mathbf{a}\cdot\mathbf{b})\cdot\mathbf{c}$ will not occur; (2) from $\mathbf{a}\cdot\mathbf{x} = \mathbf{a}\cdot\mathbf{y}$ we cannot infer that $\mathbf{x} = \mathbf{y}$, hence, quotients will not occur; (3) from $\mathbf{a}\cdot\mathbf{b} = 0$, it follows that **a** is **perpendicular** to **b** (unless **a** or **b** is zero).

On the other hand, scalar products are like ordinary products in the following respects: $\mathbf{a}\cdot\mathbf{b} = \mathbf{b}\cdot\mathbf{a}$, and $(\mathbf{a} + \mathbf{b})\cdot(\mathbf{c} + \mathbf{d}) = \mathbf{a}\cdot\mathbf{c} + \mathbf{a}\cdot\mathbf{d} + \mathbf{b}\cdot\mathbf{c} + \mathbf{b}\cdot\mathbf{d}$; also, $m(\mathbf{a}\cdot\mathbf{b}) = (m\mathbf{a}\cdot\mathbf{b}) = \mathbf{a}\cdot(m\mathbf{b})$, where m is any scalar.

The **vector product,** or cross product, of two vectors **a** and **b,** denoted by $\mathbf{a} \times \mathbf{b}$ or by $[\mathbf{ab}]$ in square brackets—is defined as the *vector* whose length is $ab \sin \theta$, where θ is the angle between **a** and **b,** and whose direction is perpendicular to the plane of **a** and **b** (in such a sense that a right-handed screw advancing along $\mathbf{a} \times \mathbf{b}$ would turn **a** toward **b**). The angle θ must be between 0 and 180°.

EXAMPLE. If **F** is a force acting on a particle whose radius vector is **r**, then $\mathbf{r} \times \mathbf{F}$ = the *torque* of **F** about the origin.

PECULIARITIES OF VECTOR PRODUCTS. (1) $\mathbf{a} \times \mathbf{b} = -\mathbf{b} \times \mathbf{a}$, so that the order of the factors is always important; (2) $\mathbf{a} \times \mathbf{a} = 0$; (3) it is *not* true that $\mathbf{a} \times (\mathbf{b} \times \mathbf{c}) = (\mathbf{a} \times \mathbf{b}) \times \mathbf{c}$; (4) from $\mathbf{a} \times \mathbf{x} = \mathbf{a} \times \mathbf{y}$ it does *not* follow that $\mathbf{x} = \mathbf{y}$; hence, quotients will not occur; (5) from $\mathbf{a} \times \mathbf{b} = 0$, it follows that **a** and **b** are **parallel** (unless **a** or **b** is zero).

On the other hand, as in ordinary algebra,

$$(\mathbf{a} + \mathbf{b}) \times (\mathbf{c} + \mathbf{d}) = \mathbf{a} \times \mathbf{c} + \mathbf{a} \times \mathbf{d} + \mathbf{b} \times \mathbf{c} + \mathbf{b} \times \mathbf{d}$$

provided the order of factors in each product is preserved; also, $m(\mathbf{a} \times \mathbf{b}) = (m\mathbf{a}) \times \mathbf{b} = \mathbf{a} \times (m\mathbf{b})$, where m is any scalar. Further laws are

$$\mathbf{a}\cdot(\mathbf{b} \times \mathbf{c}) = \mathbf{b}\cdot(\mathbf{c} \times \mathbf{a}) = \mathbf{c}\cdot(\mathbf{a} \times \mathbf{b}) \quad \text{and} \quad \mathbf{a} \times (\mathbf{b} \times \mathbf{c}) = (\mathbf{a}\cdot\mathbf{c})\mathbf{b} - (\mathbf{a}\cdot\mathbf{b})\mathbf{c}.$$

Vector Differentiation. If $\mathbf{r} = \mathbf{f}(t)$ gives a vector $\mathbf{r}$ as a function of a scalar t, then $d\mathbf{r}/dt = \lim \{[\mathbf{f}(t + \Delta t) - \mathbf{f}(t)]/\Delta t\}$ as Δt approaches zero.

$$d(\mathbf{a} + \mathbf{b}) = d\mathbf{a} + d\mathbf{b} \qquad d(m\mathbf{a}) = m(d\mathbf{a}) + (dm)\mathbf{a}$$
$$d(\mathbf{a}\cdot\mathbf{b}) = (d\mathbf{a})\cdot\mathbf{b} + \mathbf{a}\cdot(d\mathbf{b}) \qquad d(\mathbf{a} \times \mathbf{b}) = (d\mathbf{a}) \times \mathbf{b} + \mathbf{a} \times (d\mathbf{b})$$

EXAMPLE. If $\mathbf{r} = \mathbf{f}(t)$ gives the position vector of a moving particle as a function of the time t, then $d\mathbf{r}/dt =$ its vector velocity, $\mathbf{v}$, and $d\mathbf{v}/dt =$ its vector acceleration, $\mathbf{a}$. If $\mathbf{m}$ and $\mathbf{n}$ are unit vectors in the direction of the tangent and normal to the path at the time t, then $\mathbf{v} = v\mathbf{m}$, where $v = ds/dt =$ the (scalar) path velocity, and $d\mathbf{m} = [(ds/R)]\mathbf{n}$, where $R =$ the (scalar) radius of curvature of the path. Then

$$\mathbf{a} = \frac{d(v\mathbf{m})}{dt} = \frac{dv}{dt}\mathbf{m} + v\frac{d\mathbf{m}}{dt} = \frac{dv}{dt}\mathbf{m} + \frac{v^2}{R}\mathbf{n}\cdot$$

Here dv/dt and v^2/R are the familiar expressions for the components of acceleration along the tangent and normal.

Newtonian Mechanics

In many linkages and machine elements it is often convenient to choose several sets of cartesian coordinate systems for the determination of the acceleration, stress, and other pertinent properties of the several parts. (See also p. 8–3 *et seq.*) Formulas have been derived that facilitate the simultaneous use of these several systems which are most often rendered in vector notation.

The first set of axes, X_o, Y_o, Z_o, has its origin at O. This set is considered fixed in space. The second set of axes, X', Y', Z', has its origin at Q. The position of Q, measured in the first system, is r_q. The second set is always parallel to the first, *i.e.*, $X' \| X_o$, $Y' \| Y_o$, $Z' \| Z_o$; and is in general translating in the first system with a velocity $\boldsymbol{V}_q$, *i.e.*, the velocity of the origin Q measured in the first system. The third set of axes, X, Y, Z, also has its origin at Q and therefore is not translating in the second system but is in general rotating in the second system with an angular velocity of $\boldsymbol{\omega}$. Neither $\boldsymbol{V}_q$ nor $\boldsymbol{\omega}$ is constant, but they change at a rate of $\boldsymbol{a}_q$ and $\dot{\boldsymbol{\omega}}$, respectively.

The point in the mechanism whose dynamic properties are to be considered usually possesses a position, $\boldsymbol{r}$; a velocity, $\boldsymbol{V}$; and an acceleration, $\boldsymbol{a}$; all measured in the X, Y, Z system. The purpose is to find the position, velocity, and acceleration of this point in fixed space, *i.e.*, in the first system, the X_o, Y_o, Z_o set, which are $\boldsymbol{r}_o$, $\boldsymbol{V}_o$, and $\boldsymbol{a}_o$, respectively:

$$\boldsymbol{r}_o = \boldsymbol{r}_q + \boldsymbol{r} \qquad \boldsymbol{V}_o = \boldsymbol{V}_q + \boldsymbol{\omega} \times \boldsymbol{r} + \boldsymbol{V}$$
$$\boldsymbol{a}_o = \boldsymbol{a}_q + \dot{\boldsymbol{\omega}} \times \boldsymbol{r} + \boldsymbol{\omega} \times (\boldsymbol{\omega} \times \boldsymbol{r}) + 2(\boldsymbol{\omega} \times \boldsymbol{V}) + \boldsymbol{a}.$$

Analytic Representation

Let $\mathbf{i}$, $\mathbf{j}$, $\mathbf{k}$ represent three vectors of unit magnitude along the three mutually perpendicular lines OX, OY, OZ, respectively, forming a right-hand system. Then the vector $\mathbf{r}$ may be represented by $\mathbf{r} = a\mathbf{i} + b\mathbf{j} + c\mathbf{k}$. Also, for any scalar m, $m\mathbf{r} = ma\,\mathbf{i} + mb\,\mathbf{j} + mc\,\mathbf{k}$.

Let $\mathbf{r}_1 = a_1\mathbf{i} + b_1\mathbf{j} + c_1\mathbf{k}$ and $\mathbf{r}_2 = a_2\mathbf{i} + b_2\mathbf{j} + c_2\mathbf{k}$. Then the sum $\mathbf{r}_1 + \mathbf{r}_2 = (a_1 + a_2)\mathbf{i} + (b_1 + b_2)\mathbf{j} + (c_1 + c_2)\mathbf{k}$. The scalar product $\mathbf{r}_1\cdot\mathbf{r}_2 = a_1a_2 + b_1b_2 + c_1c_2$. The vector product

$$\mathbf{r}_1 \times \mathbf{r}_2 = (b_1c_2 - b_2c_1)\mathbf{i} + (c_1a_2 - c_2a_1)\mathbf{j} + (a_1b_2 - a_2b_1)\mathbf{k}.$$

$$\mathbf{r}_1 \times \mathbf{r}_2 = \begin{vmatrix} \mathbf{i} & \mathbf{j} & \mathbf{k} \\ a_1 & b_1 & c_1 \\ a_2 & b_2 & c_2 \end{vmatrix} \quad \text{and} \quad \mathbf{r}_1\cdot(\mathbf{r}_2 \times \mathbf{r}_3) = \begin{vmatrix} a_1 & b_1 & c_1 \\ a_2 & b_2 & c_2 \\ a_3 & b_3 & c_3 \end{vmatrix}.$$

Differential Operators

By definition, $\nabla = \text{del} = \mathbf{i}\frac{\partial}{\partial x} + \mathbf{j}\frac{\partial}{\partial y} + \mathbf{k}\frac{\partial}{\partial z}$ and $\nabla^2 = \text{Laplacian} = \nabla \cdot \nabla = \frac{\partial^2}{\partial x^2} + \frac{\partial^2}{\partial y^2} + \frac{\partial^2}{\partial z^2}$ $\nabla S = \text{grad } S = \frac{\partial S}{\partial x}\mathbf{i} + \frac{\partial S}{\partial y}\mathbf{j} + \frac{\partial S}{\partial z}\mathbf{k}$, the gradient of a scalar function $S(x,y,z)$. For a vector function $\mathbf{V}(x,y,z) = P\mathbf{i} + Q\mathbf{j} + R\mathbf{k}$, the divergence of $\mathbf{V}$ is $\nabla\cdot\mathbf{V} = \frac{\partial P}{\partial x} + \frac{\partial Q}{\partial y} + \frac{\partial R}{\partial z}$. And the curl of $\mathbf{V}$ is

$$\nabla \times \mathbf{V} = \text{curl } \mathbf{V} = \text{rot } \mathbf{V} = \begin{vmatrix} \mathbf{i} & \mathbf{j} & \mathbf{k} \\ \frac{\partial}{\partial x} & \frac{\partial}{\partial y} & \frac{\partial}{\partial z} \\ P & Q & R \end{vmatrix}.$$

The **divergence theorem** states that if $\mathbf{F}$ is a vector function and V is a volume bounded by a surface S, then

$$\iiint_V \text{div } \mathbf{F}\, dv = \iiint_V \nabla\cdot\mathbf{F}\, dv = \iint_S \mathbf{F}\cdot d\mathbf{S}.$$

The integrations are to be carried out over the volume V and the surface S. And if $\mathbf{n}$ is the unit outward normal and $dS = |d\mathbf{S}|$ is the scalar element of surface, $d\mathbf{S} = \mathbf{n}\, dS$, $\mathbf{F}\cdot d\mathbf{S} = \mathbf{F}\cdot\mathbf{n}\, dS$.

Stokes's theorem states that if $\mathbf{F}$ is a vector function and S is a surface bounded by a simple closed curve C, then

$$\int_C \mathbf{F}\cdot d\mathbf{r} = \iint_S \text{curl } \mathbf{F}\cdot d\mathbf{S} = \iint_S (\nabla \times \mathbf{F})\cdot d\mathbf{S}.$$

Here, $d\mathbf{r} = dx\ \mathbf{i} + dy\ \mathbf{j} + dz\ \mathbf{k}$. The theorem implies that the surface integral of $(\nabla \times \mathbf{F})$ over any surface S which is bounded by C is equal to the line integral of $\mathbf{F}$ over the contour C, taken in the direction related to that of $\mathbf{n}$ (in $d\mathbf{S} = \mathbf{n}\, dS$) by the right-hand rule.

COMPUTERS

BY

Theodore Baumeister III and Martha C. Baumeister

REFERENCES: Manuals of the computer manufacturers. Ralston and Wilf, "Mathematical Methods for Digital Computers," Wiley. *Datamation Magazine*. *Communications* and *Jour. ACM*. McCracken, "A Guide to FORTRAN Programming," Wiley.

COMPUTER TYPES

There are four general types of computers: analog, digital, hybrid, and special-purpose. Analog and digital computers are so named because of the way they handle problems. In an **analog computer,** the physical components which comprise the hardware of the computer are connected together to form an analogous model of the problem. Thus, for each part of the problem, there must exist a piece of hardware, such as a summer, an integrator, or a pot, and all parts of the problem are solved simultaneously. In a **digital computer,** the hardware is not apportioned in this way but is used over and over to perform the different logical and arithmetical calculations which represent the different portions of the problem. The results of these calculations are temporarily stored in the computer memory for later use. The problem is solved sequentially, with the hardware being used to calculate first one part of the problem and then another. The **hybrid computer** usually consists of analog and digital computers linked together by the necessary translating equipment. **Special-purpose computers** take on many forms, ranging from the thermostat in a home heating system to the large computers used for directing chemical processes or for controlling operations in power systems or refineries.

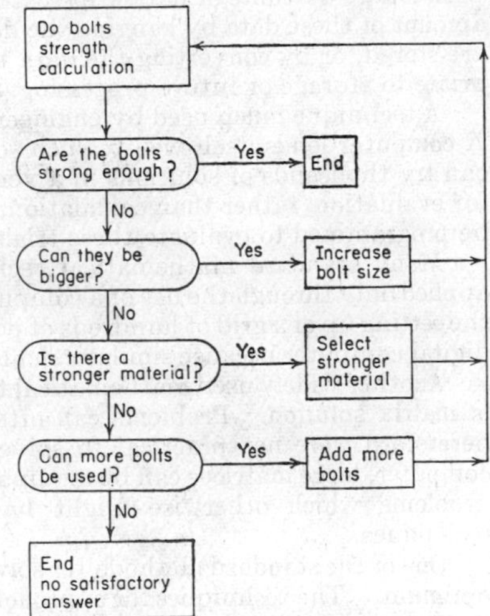

FIG. 1. Typical digital-computer flow chart.

USING COMPUTERS

Preparatory to writing the computer program in any appropriate language is a step known as flow charting. A **flow chart** (Fig. 1) is essentially a diagram, generally using a standard notation, representing a step-by-step statement of the sequence of operations which will construct a solution to the problem. In many cases, much more time and effort are expended in creating the flow chart than in creating the computer program from that point on. These cases are usually where people do not understand the problem or its method of solution as well as was first thought. In many instances, the greatest reward from the computer program is the increased understanding of the problem associated with the creation of the flow chart.

Some kinds of problems are not well enough understood to permit a complete computer solution. In these cases, the computer is used to assist the man solving the problem. Input is prepared, a computer solution is made, the output is examined, and a decision is then made about what course to pursue for future investigations. This decision making is known as **closing the outer loop.** On other kinds of jobs, great pains may be taken to provide the programming so that the computer itself may close the outer loop without human intervention. This is, of course, most desirable from a production viewpoint but may be, in many cases, not practical or even not possible.

DIGITAL COMPUTERS

Solution Techniques

A **simulation** (another word for model) of a system is used whenever it is desirable to watch the succession of many interrelated events or when there is interplay between the system itself and outside forces. Examples are problems in man-machine interaction and in the modeling of business systems. Typical man-machine problems are the servicing of automatic equipment by a crew of operators and the repair by a maintenance crew of equipment subject to unpredictable breakdown. A business-system model consists of the interactions between businesses and the rest of the economy, *e.g.*, competitive buyers in a raw-materials market or competitive manufacturers marketing their products. Business models often involve transportation and warehousing of commodities.

Physical or chemical systems may also be modeled; *e.g.*, for the application of automatic control valves in pipelines, a model is made with portions which represent the attributes of the control system, the valve, the piping system, and the fluid. Such a model, when tested, can indicate whether fluid hammer will occur or whether valve action is fast enough, or it can be used to demonstrate pressure and temperature conditions in the fluid when subject to control by the valve.

One of the major uses of the digital computer is **data reduction.** In installations where large amounts of data are recorded and kept, it is often advisable to reduce the amount of these data by ganging the data together, by averaging the data before they are stored, or by converting the data to a more useful form, e.g., a form more appropriate to storage or future processing.

A technique much used by engineers is the solving of equations by **trial and error.** A computer lends itself well to such solutions because of its speed and accuracy. It can try thousands of solutions in a very short time, thus freeing technical manpower for evaluation, rather than calculation, of these trials. The computer itself can often be programmed to evaluate these trials.

Many standard mathematical techniques such as **relaxation** can be practicably applied only through the use of a computer. A typical relaxation problem may require the setting up of a grid of hundreds of points. Such a problem lends itself ideally to the digital computer because similar calculations are done at many points within the grid.

Another widely used mathematical technique becoming more available to engineers is **matrix solution.** Problems can often be stated in terms of large matrices, which heretofore were not practical to solve. With the advent of the high-speed digital computer, large matrices can be manipulated at reasonable cost. This permits solving problems which otherwise might have required the development of specialized techniques.

One of the standard methods for solving many problems in real life is to **approach an optimum.** The techniques for approaching an optimum point depend on the nature of the surface, or terrain, on which the optimizing is done. This work is called **hill climbing,** and many of the techniques represent in great detail mechanisms a man might use in climbing a hill in a fog. The effort is, of course, to attain expeditiously the highest point on the hill without being confused by lower, local peaks. Sometimes, as in the case of cost functions, it is not the maximum point, but a minimum, that is sought. In such cases, the techniques are the same, but the signs are reversed.

There is a class of problems which is characterized by values or cost functions which plot as families of parallel straight lines. These are functions of many variables, perhaps hundreds. The fact that the value function is linear enables a particular method of solution known as **linear programming** to be considered. The area of solution to a linear-programming problem is circumscribed by limits on the magnitudes of the variables. These limits are imposed by the real world and must also plot as straight lines, usually in many dimensions. The statements of these limits describe a space bounded by them which is called the **solution space.** All linear-programming algorithms search about in the corners of this solution space to find the point at which the cost function is minimized or the value function maximized. All modern computer-service centers have available large, efficient, high-speed, standard programs for solving linear-programming problems.

Many **standard engineering calculations** have been applied to computers. Some typical examples are (1) pipe-flange rating under ASME pressure-vessel codes; (2) calculation of critical speeds for rotating shafts with various load and support configurations; (3) volume-versus-depth calibration for tanks equipped with various standard heads (in some cases, the tanks need not be level); (4) calculation of flow rates and pressure drops of fluids in piping systems (this kind of calculation is not as standardized as many others, and in general, these programs are very special-purpose for the particular application).

Also available with most digital computers are programs for the solution of **statistical problems.** The most widely used and the cheapest and simplest both to formulate and to solve are programs of **linear statistics,** which involve a technique known as **regression,** or **least squares.** In some areas, however, linear statistics will not suffice. For these problems, there exist more specialized programs which involve **nonlinear** statistical techniques. This type of problem is more difficult and expensive both to state and to solve, and in certain cases no solution can be obtained. An engineer with some training can easily learn to do linear statistics for particular problems. However, the difficulties that may be encountered with nonlinear solutions should not be underestimated.

A class of problems susceptible to **Monte Carlo** solution became practical with the advent of digital computers. The Monte Carlo technique is used when the list of possible conditions in which the activity under investigation can find itself is too large or too complex to be easily stated. As its name implies, the Monte Carlo technique uses random numbers (which are easily made available to the computer) to determine statistically what conditions exist or what changes will take place. A large number of solutions is then run, and statistical inferences are drawn. Typical problems solved by this technique are **machine-scheduling** and **queuing-theory** problems. Many simulators also utilize this technique.

There are available a number of programs, such as **APT,** which are used in the development of control tapes for automatic control of machine tools. Essential features of such programs are (1) that they produce output information as close as possible to that required by the machine-tool controller, and (2) that they permit a simple and yet versatile statement of the configuration of the machine, its working surfaces, and the part to be produced.

Computers have been widely used by engineering organizations (with individuals of widely varying skills) in such diverse areas as process control, economic evaluation, industrial-engineering decisions, cost estimating, and curve and graph plotting.

Obtaining Programs

There are many ways to obtain digital-computer programs. Each type of computer has a user group, *e.g.*, the **SHARE** Organization, which has as members those installations using the largest IBM computers commercially available. This group has thousands of programs, which do everything from taking square roots, through statistical analyses, to standard linear-programming codes. Programs are available from such user groups or through computer manufacturers' representatives and are generally free.

Another source of programs, generally more tailored to engineering problems, is the professional society, *e.g.*, the AIChE. In general, the program, with a sample problem and a complete description of how the program works and of the calculations performed, is available at a nominal price.

Another method of obtaining a particular program is to **purchase** the program and the operating information. Organizations with programs or programming groups frequently trade with other such organizations. Many service centers which rent computer service also rent the use of certain programs, e.g., piping-stress flexibility programs and linear-programming codes. Since the writing of a program may cost many thousands of dollars, it is generally cheaper to rent it from someone who already has it.

Another way of obtaining programs, **contract programming,** is to have them written to specification by individuals or organizations specializing in this service.

A last source, generally limited to programs peculiar to a particular machine, is the computer manufacturer. In some cases, however, the computer manufacturer, if he foresees wide application of the program, may arrange to supply machine-capable personnel to share the burden of preparation.

Using Digital Computers

Using a computer is different from almost every other job. A computer has no common sense; it will do exactly what it has been instructed to do—no more, no less. A computer does not know the meaning of the word *reasonable.* Unless it has been programmed to examine an answer, it will only produce a solution, not judge it. An algebraic expression may be perfectly good mathematically for all values of its independent variable—positive, negative, or zero—but the real-life situation may not tolerate negative values. The computer can be instructed to select the useful solutions, but the statement of the logic and calculations required must be exact. It must be perfect. It must be unambiguous. Each possible answer to each logical question that is asked must be provided. If a problem proposed for computer solution does not have these properties, it cannot be solved on the computer. In general, it is possible for any technical person to learn to use a computer. It may well be, however, that problems which appear quite simple are difficult to state for computer solution. Professional programmers should therefore always be consulted before a problem is programmed for a computer. It is often advisable to leave the computer programming entirely to persons trained in this and to have other technical people act as their advisors and directors. Such a function is provided by the in-house programming staff or sometimes by programmers available from outside. Professional programmers are familiar with the idiosyncrasies of computers. They are aware, for example, of a famous source of error in the use of digital computers—the problem of **round-off, or truncation.** As an illustration, in most digital computers $\frac{1}{3} \times 3$ is not equal to 1. If the *division* is done first, the answer may be .333 . . . 3 (as many 3s as there are digits in the computer). This answer, when multiplied by 3, results in .999 . . . 9. Thus, the computer is forced to tell you that 1 divided by 3 and then multiplied by 3 is not equal to 1. This is not as trivial as it may at first seem. Since there are literally thousands of such operations performed, the accumulated errors can be most meaningful. There are techniques for correcting this trouble; the professional programmer knows them.

Computer work has another unique feature, called **debugging.** In a not unusually large computer program, there may be tens of thousands of computer instructions. Each one of these must be **exactly right.** This is not to be confused with "approximately right." It is not a question of practicality; it is a question of logic. In general, it is not possible to write a computer program that is error-free the first time it is used. The program must be tried and fixed several times. In complicated programs, as many as 50 or 100 trials are not uncommon. It is also not uncommon to find an error that has existed for several years and that no one has ever noticed before. This often happens long after the original program writers have transferred to other work. A well-documented program, preferably written in a language such as FORTRAN, will greatly shorten the time it takes for new people to become familiar with it.

One of the problems which confront computer users is that of **compatibility among** computers. It is generally desirable to have programs made so that they will be applicable, with very slight modifications, to several computers. If this has been done, the replacement of one computer by another in the course of time will not result in a serious loss of available programs or in excessive reprogramming costs. (Companies replace their computers much as individuals trade in their automobiles.) One prevailing way to attain this end is to use special-purpose or general-purpose languages which are not computer-oriented, i.e., which do not contain operations peculiar to any one computer but instead describe the problem solution in a general way. Examples of these languages include the algebraic languages, particularly **FORTRAN,** named for FORmula TRANslator, which is available for nearly every technical computer and is the most widely used technical programming language in this country. Another technical computing language of the algebraic type is **ALGOL. COBOL** (for COmmon Business Oriented Language) is an English-language system which describes in stylized English words and phrases the calculations and logic to be performed. COBOL has at present two drawbacks: (1) it is wordy, and (2) it has so far been developed primarily for dealing with business or data-processing problems. All three of these languages have the attribute that with relatively little training one can learn to read and write programs in them. This means that, if there is any doubt about what calculations are being performed, one can read the code and determinate it exactly. In addition, there are special languages more particularly suited to certain special classes of problems.

Nearly all computer users have available to them a variety of machines of different sizes, speeds, and costs. Speed ratios, and consequently cost ratios, can be determined for each computer under consideration (see Table 1). In general, it is preferable to use a computer that is too large and too fast; if the problem turns out to be larger than anticipated (and this happens more often than not), reprogramming for another computer in the middle of the work is thus avoided.

Table 1. Typical Internal Speeds and Maximum Main-memory Size of Representative Large-scale Digital Computers

	IBM 7040	IBM 7090	Sperry Rand 1107	CDC 3600	Sperry Rand 1108
Time (microseconds):					
Clear and add	16	4.4	4	2	0.75
Add to accumulator	16	4.4	4	2	0.75
Store	16	4.4	4	2	0.75
Floating add*	24	22	14	4	2.6
Maximum main memory (words)	32,768	32,768	65,536	262,144	131,072

* In most computers, this time depends on the actual numbers being added.

Special-purpose Languages

The following digital-computer languages are representative of current practice, but in the rapidly developing computer business, they can be expected to become outmoded or altered. **APT** and **AUTOPROMPT** are languages developed to assist in the creation of automatic-control tapes for metal-cutting machinery. **FORTRAN, ALGOL,** and **MAD** are essentially general-purpose algebraic languages for solving problems the solutions to which can be stated in logic and arithmetic. Each provides special editing features to permit the preparation of readable output.

COMIT, LISP, and **SLIP** are list-processing languages. There are classes of problems (many in the simulation and industrial-engineering fields) which lend themselves to statements of a list-processing nature.

Simscript is, as the name implies, a simulator language. It is useful for writing general-purpose simulators, particularly for problems of man-machine interaction or man or machine versus environment.

Currently, a host of other problems are being worked on, and specific languages are being tailored to such tasks as searching lawbooks for applicable decisions and patent searching. There are programs being built which permit description of the bonds in chemical elements. All these programs have, as a major feature, large files of information which must be readily scanned in response to relatively vague questions.

Digital-programming Terms

Programming is the writing of instructions to direct the machine to do a particular calculation or task. The set of instructions so coded is referred to as a **program.**

The program may be fairly simple, such as, "Find the positive square root of a given number," or fairly complicated, such as, "Construct a heat balance." The instructions to the computer are generally in the imperative mode and are written as a series of **commands,** *e.g.*, to read a card, to punch a card, to read a number, to add one number to another, to ask if one number is larger than another. When these commands are expressed in the particular **bit** configuration of the machine, they are referred to as **code,** or **machine code.** A command is also referred to as an **instruction** or **operation.** In general, it is not convenient to write programs in the language of the machine. Instead, various languages more convenient to the person preparing the program are used. The simplest of these is called an **assembler** language. In an assembly system, machine commands, written in a mnemonic pseudocode, are interpreted and prepared in the machine code. For example, TRA is a mnemonic command meaning "transfer." In machine language, this is 0020. A more sophisticated form of translator is a **compiler,** in which the program is stated in a form different from the machine instructions and the compiler generates machine instructions corresponding to the problem statement in the compiler language. One of the tasks that an interpreter or a compiler does is translate; that is, it reads information in one language and converts it to equivalent information in another language. The basic piece of information for most engineering programming is the **word.** Words often are numbers, which, of course, have digits. Some of the numbers are fairly small, and the location of the decimal point is easily described. Such numbers are generally kept in a form known as **fixed point,** where a decimal point is assumed to be at a certain place in the number. On the other hand, there are numbers intermediate in the calculation which may be very large or very small. These are best handled in a system called **floating point.** In this system, a number is kept as two parts: (1) a **mantissa** containing the actual digits of the number, and (2) the **exponent.** The exponent is the power of 10 (in binary machines, the power of 2) to which the 10 (2) must be raised. The number that results from raising the 10 (2) to the power of the exponent is multiplied by the mantissa to obtain the value desired (see Table 2). Machines which can handle floating-point addition, subtraction, multiplication, and division are called **floating-point machines.** All the larger modern computers have such equipment.

Table 2. Representation of Numbers in Floating Point in Decimal and Binary Computers

Number	Alternate form	Decimal representation		Typical octal representation in a binary computer	
		Mantissa	Exponent (of 10)	Mantissa (octal)[a]	Exponent (of 2) (octal)
200	$0.2 * 10^3$	.2	3	∧62	10
−100	$-0.1 * 10^3$	−.1	3	−∧62	7
2	$0.2 * 10^1$	.2	1	∧4	2
−0.2	$-0.2 * 10^0$	−.2	0	−∧63143...[b]	−2
−0.02	$-0.2 * 10^{-1}$	−.2	−1	−∧50753...[b]	−5
1	$0.1 * 10^1$	.1	1	∧4	1
0	$0 * 10^0$	0	0	∧0	0

[a] The symbol ∧ represents the binary point.
[b] Many multiples of 0.1, 0.01, etc., are not exactly expressible as binary fractions.

Information in most digital computers is stored in a binary form, i.e., by a zero or a 1. These binary **bits** are merely normal numbers, base 2, and are strung together into words which are usually from 20 to 48 bits in length. In a **binary machine,** these bits are one continuous binary number working from right to left. In a **decimal machine,** these bits are broken up into groups, and the machine hardware is built to deal with each group as a decimal digit. In an **alphabetical and decimal,** or **alphadecimal,** machine, the machine hardware is arranged to deal with these groups of bits as numbers and letters. In a binary machine, the information is translated to binary form when it is read into the machine, the calculations are done in binary (which is convenient to the machine), and the information is retranslated from binary for output. These translations are done in the computer (see Table 3). Sometimes it is necessary to refer to portions of a binary number. This is generally done by grouping the bits together, three at a time, whereupon they become the equivalent of base-8 numbers, or **octal.** For example, the binary number 100110001010, when grouped in triples, may be expressed as 4612, which is its octal representation. No machine is made as an octal machine. Octal is merely a convenience for the user in referring to information in a binary machine.

Table 3. Binary-Octal-Decimal Conversion[a]

Decimal	Octal[b]	Binary[b]
0	0	000000
1	1	000001
2	2	000010
3	3	000011
4	4	000100
5	5	000101
6	6	000110
7	7	000111
8	10	001000
9	11	001001
10	12	001010
11	13	001011
0.50000	∧40	∧100000
0.25000	∧20	∧010000
0.12500	∧10	∧001000
0.06250	∧04	∧000100
0.03125	∧02	∧000010
0.015625	∧01	∧000001

[a] Moving a number one place to the left multiplies by 10 in decimal, by 8 in octal, and by 2 in binary.

[b] The symbol ∧ represents the binary point.

Alphabetic information can also be stored in a binary machine. In this case, the bits in the machine words are considered as being in six-bit groups, each group representing a letter. The word is then said to contain **BCD,** or binary-coded decimal information. For example, if 010001 represents A, 010010 represents B, 010011 represents C, and 110000 represents a blank, then in a 36-bit word ABC is 010001010010010011110000110000110000 (in octal, 212223606060).

Converting computer output into a form which will be easily understood by the user is called an **edit.** Programming an edit is called **editing** and includes inserting decimal points, arranging columns with decimal points lined up, and adding headings, titles, and other descriptive information. Editing is basic to the field of business programming—in printing paychecks, for example—and also most technical people want their answers in some edited form. The techniques of editing are also used to make plots, histograms, contours, and other pictorial representations. The use of line plotters which can accept digital-computer output and of computer routines which can do coordinate-axis transformations results in excellent drawings in plan, elevation, perspective, and stereo for three-dimensional viewing.

To solve any problem at all, one must be able to read the **input** data which define the specific problem at hand and to write the **output** answers. If the reading or writing is done on magnetic tape, it is necessary to have the ability to **rewind** the tape when finished. Words in the computer are generally made available by their computer **address,** a name for the location in memory where the word is stored. The address then constitutes "the name of the information" in the same way that a location in a city is given by its address and not by its description. Just as a house has an address even when no numbers are displayed on it, so it is with the computer. The addresses are not listed anywhere.

It is often found convenient in programming to break the program down into a number of smaller parts called **subprograms,** or **subroutines.** Two words often used in connection with subroutines are **open,** meaning that a few lines of coding are all that is required and that these few lines are repeated as needed whenever the operation is used, and **closed,** which means that the routine is supplied once and that each time the particular operation is used, the same code is used but with different **arguments** to provide the different answers. In most digital computers, a relatively few logical operations, called **tests,** may be performed upon numbers in the machine. A typical test determines whether a number is equal to zero, greater than zero, or less than zero. A string of instructions to be performed a definite number of times for the calculation desired is generally arranged in what is termed a **loop,** meaning that at the end of the last instruction a transfer of control is made back to the first instruction, so that the series is performed again and again until certain criteria are met.

As high-speed computers are very expensive per hour of computation, it is desirable to have the computer operate as fast as possible with minimum human intervention to slow it down. To assist the operator in the many chores associated with the handling of programs and data, there are **systems routines** (also called **executive routines** or **monitors**), in which specially coded cards are used to direct the computer, *e.g.*, to translate from the user language to the machine language, to load the machine-language program, and to read the data and compute the answers as required. These routines usually have the ability to make additions from a **library** of standard subroutines which have been previously stored on tape. Monitors, input-output routines, compilers, and, indeed, all routines which are to be used by everyone are generally classed as **software.** Computer manufacturers have discovered that customers are often more concerned about the effectiveness of the software than they are about the speed of the hardware.

A **flow chart,** or flow diagram, is a logical pictorial statement of the steps to be undertaken and their order of execution to obtain a solution for the problem at hand. A flow chart also shows the logical tests that must be made to determine which calculation should be performed in cases where alternate paths may be available.

Digital Hardware Terms

The physical body of the computer, the **hardware,** consists of the memory, tapes, readers, printers, punches, arithmetic registers, control units—in fact, all the physical components of the computer itself. For a computer to do its work, there must be a statement of the input information upon which it is to work. This information may be prepared on standard 80-column punched cards, which are read into the computer through a **card reader.** If they are read directly to the computer, the operation is said to be **on-line;** if they are read in a card reader and converted or written onto a tape before being read by the computer, the operation is said to be **off-line.** A **tape** consists of a reel of Mylar®, or equivalent, with a special coating which can retain magnetic information. It is similar in many respects to the tape in a home tape recorder and can be read by a computer. When the information is read from cards or tape, it is stored in the **memory** of the computer. In general, the main memory of the computer is **random access;** that is, any piece of information can be obtained upon demand without having to wait for other pieces to go past. Such memory is generally in the form of **magnetic cores** consisting of small rings with electronically interesting hysteresis curves which permit the storage of information. In addition to the core memory or core storage, which is usually high speed, there are two slower-speed forms of memory: (1) the **magnetic disk,** similar to a large phonograph record, and (2) the **magnetic drum,** where the recording face is not on the sides of plates but on the outer surface of the drum. The disk and drum are cheaper than core memory. The operation of the computer is controlled through its **console,** which displays indicators of the status of the computer operation. The calculations are performed inside the computer by taking information from the memory and storing it in **registers,** which do the computer work. There the information (1) may be shifted to the right or left; (2) may be dealt with arithmetically; (3) may be asked certain logical questions, e.g., whether the sign of the number is plus or minus; and (4) may be returned to the memory. The memory is usually compartmented into sections, each of which is addressable (definable in terms of its **address**). The minimum-sized piece of information available in a digital computer generally consists of one **bit.** This is the logical equivalent of a zero or a 1 and can suffice to answer a question "yes" or "no." A group of bits taken together (sometimes called a **byte**) may represent (1) a number or (2) an alphabetic character or punctuation. A group of bits taken together (in most computers, 36 bits) is called a **word** and is all available at one time under one address. Many computers have a particular register, known as an **accumulator,** where the answers for most arithmetic operations appear. When the calculation is finished, the answers may be (1) punched onto a card, (2) printed on an **on-line** printer (one attached to the computer), or (3) written on tape for **off-line** printing (printing on equipment not attached to the computer). In many cases, the equipment which does off-line conversion both to and from tape will have a **plugboard,** permitting fast rearrangement of the information from the input document (IBM card) to the tape or from the tape to the printed form. For speed, some computers do not write one card's worth of information on a tape at a time but gather the information into larger groups, called **records** or **blocks,** which must then be broken up by the tape-to-print equipment. Information on tape is usually called a block or a record. On some equipment, there is, at the end of the last record on a tape, a set of magnetic pulses, called a **tape mark** or **end-file mark,** to signal the end of a set of information. In addition, for speed, some computers do not write directly from high-speed memory onto their magnetic tapes but transfer the information from the high-speed memory to an auxiliary memory, the **output buffer.** The computer then continues computations, and simultaneously the output system of the computer takes over the job of transferring the information from the buffer onto the tape. Some computer systems also have **input buffers** to do an equivalent job. Milliseconds (10^{-3} sec), microseconds (10^{-6} sec), and nanoseconds (10^{-9} sec) are variously used to measure the speed of operations in the computer.

Many special-purpose computers and some general-purpose computers with special-purpose connections to the outside world have translating equipment to convert electrical voltages from outside sources to numbers as they are stored in the digital computer. This equipment is also used when the computer is connected to some outside device to be run in **real time,** i.e., when the calculation is to be performed coincidentally with an actual occurrence outside. One of the features then required is the ability to interrupt the computer. If there are to be many such real-time input devices, **a multiplexer,** or coordinator, is often required.

ANALOG COMPUTERS

Components

The present-day analog computer is electrical; generally, all problem variables are represented by a d-c voltage between ±100 volts. Basic analog-computer components are shown in Fig. 2.

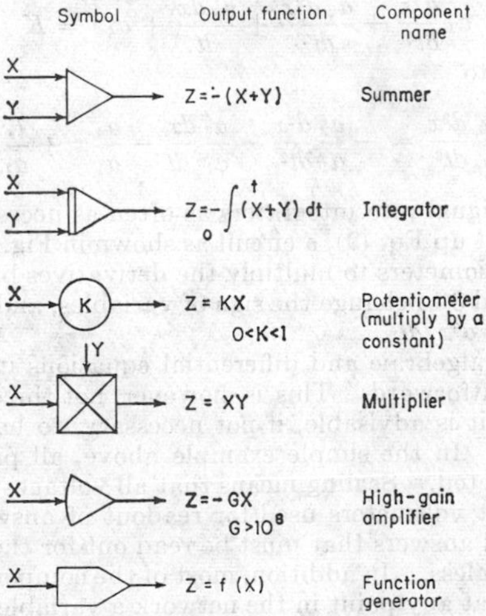

Symbol	Output function	Component name
(X, Y inputs)	$Z = -(X+Y)$	Summer
(X, Y inputs)	$Z = -\int_0^t (X+Y)\,dt$	Integrator
(X input, K)	$Z = KX$, $0<K<1$	Potentiometer (multiply by a constant)
(X, Y inputs)	$Z = XY$	Multiplier
(X input)	$Z = -GX$, $G>10^8$	High-gain amplifier
(X input)	$Z = f(X)$	Function generator

FIG. 2. Analog-computer components.

A **summer** is used to perform addition; the sign of the answer is opposite to that of the input components. To perform subtraction, the sign of the subtrahand must be changed (*e.g.*, run through another summer with nothing added to it). An **integrator,** which generally integrates with respect to time, is the component which gives the analog computer its ability to solve problems stated in terms of differential equations. Also, the integrator requires a mechanism to reset it to its initial conditions. A **potentiometer** (also called a **pot**) is used to multiply an incoming variable (a voltage) by a constant factor which is less than 1. A **multiplier** multiplies two variables together.

A **function generator** is a specially prepared device to provide an arbitrary function $f(X)$ for a given input signal X. For Monte Carlo solutions, a signal generator providing random output is used.

A **high-gain amplifier** produces an output which is over 10^8 times the sum of the input voltages (with the sign reversed). A high-gain amplifier is a part of both the summer and the integrator, which differ only in the way the high-gain amplifier is connected and in some additional components. Often the hardware representing an amplifier can be used either as a summer or as an integrator. It is cheaper to buy high-gain amplifiers that do not have this multiple use, so there are summers and integrators that are not interchangeable merely by using different connections. The use of the high-gain amplifier for division is illustrated by Fig. 3. Voltage X goes in.

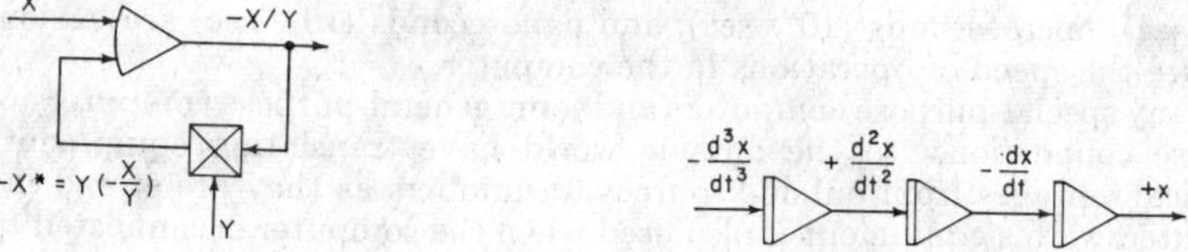

FIG. 3. High-gain amplifier used for division.

FIG. 4. Integration in an analog computer.

Assume that $(-X/Y)$ comes out. The $(-X/Y)$ goes to the multiplier; $(-X/Y) \cdot (Y) = -X^*$ comes out of the multiplier and goes into the amplifier to be added to X. $(-X/Y)$ is the only output value for which X^* will balance X, and no current will flow. Any unbalance between X and $-X^*$ will be raised by 10^8 by the amplifier and fed back into the multiplier, where it goes back in with reversed sign.

Using Analog Computers

Consider the equation

$$a_1 \frac{d^3x}{dt^3} + \frac{a_2\, d^2x}{dt^2} + \frac{a_3\, dx}{dt} + a_4 x = K \tag{1}$$

This can be converted to

$$\frac{d^3x}{dt^3} = -\frac{a_2}{a_1}\frac{d^2x}{dt^2} - \frac{a_3}{a_1}\frac{dx}{dt} - \frac{a_4}{a_1}x + \frac{K}{a_1} \tag{2}$$

To integrate, run the signal into integrators as often as necessary and get a setup as shown in Fig. 4. To set up Eq. (**2**), a circuit as shown in Fig. 5 is required. Figure 5 shows the use of potentiometers to multiply the derivatives by their respective coefficients, of summers 2 and 3 to change the sign of variables, and of summer 1 to sum up the component parts of d^3x/dt^3.

The translations of algebraic and differential equations into an analog-computer diagram appear straightforward. This is, however, not the case. In all reasonably complicated problems, it is advisable, if not necessary, to have a competent analog programmer available. In the simple example above, all problems associated with scaling have been neglected. **Scaling** means that all voltages must be between +100 and −100 volts. Most voltmeters used for readout of answers are only precise to 0.1 volt. Therefore, all answers that must be read out for the user must be scaled to avoid becoming meaningless. In addition, most of the components are precise to only 1 part in 10^4, so that if at any point in the network a variable becomes less than that part of the total voltage, it can either be completely lost or be considered at twice its correct value. This error can then be propagated to the point that the so-called *answers* represent errors or noise and not the problem under investigation. The solution to this problem, particularly, requires skillful analog programming.

Another problem that usually confronts the analog user is that each symbol on his flow chart represents some electronic hardware in the racks of the computer. In many problems, there are not nearly enough pieces. Much of the cost of obtaining answers may well be spent in overcoming this limitation.

A typical way to save components is to remove excess summers and do the summing at the integrators. For example, in Fig. 5, removing summer 1 and summing at integrator 4 changes the signs of all quantities involved, permitting removal of summers 2 and 3 but putting one in as No. 7 (see Fig. 6), with a net gain of two summers.

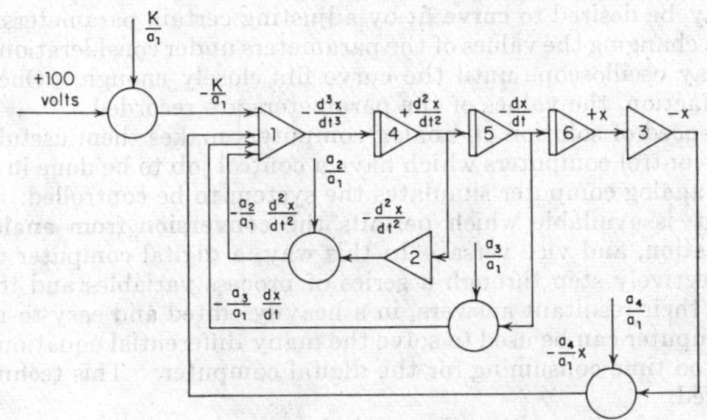

FIG. 5. Diagram representing Eq. (2).

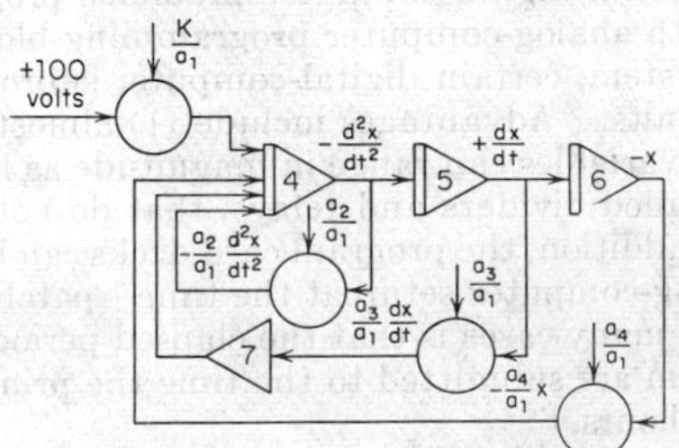

FIG. 6

The results of an analog simulation may be recorded in several ways. The most common method is with an **X-Y plotter,** which allows the plotting of one variable versus another as a graph. Another common form of graphic display is on a **cathode-ray tube,** which requires the use of the repetitive-operation feature called **rep-op.** Here, the computer is switched from reset to operate and back at a frequency of up to 50 cps, so that the voltages created can be plotted repetitively on a cathode-ray tube and appear to stand still. Also, by this method, the effect of changing one of the problem variables can be easily and quickly determined. This is often done in curve fitting.

Solution Techniques

An analog computer is adapted especially to the solution of problems containing differential equations. As it is equipped with integrators, it is also well suited to the handling of non-steady-state problems. And, as the name **analog** implies, the type of problem for which it is ideally adapted is simulation. It is often more easily used in simulation of fluid-flow problems than is the digital computer.

Another use of an analog computer is the testing of instruments by simulating various process conditions to which the instruments respond. In this kind of work, the analog computer is programmed to act as the rest of the system, the instrument under consideration is installed as part of the setup, and then tests are run.

Trial-and-error solutions of the Monte Carlo type are fairly easy to accomplish through the use of a random-signal generator. If an optimal set of conditions is required, the random-function generator supplies test variables, and part of the computer records those values which produce the better result. In the course of a few minutes, many combinations can be tried. Practically speaking, operation is stopped at this point, with reasonable certainty of an optimal solution. The advantage over a digital computer in this kind of work is the great number of trials that can be made in a short time.

If an equation has been programmed and certain values of process variables are known, it may be desired to **curve fit** by adjusting certain parameters. This can be done easily by changing the values of the parameters under consideration and observing the cathode-ray oscilloscope until the curve fits closely enough. Once the curve is fitted to satisfaction, the values of the parameters are recorded.

The high speed of solution on analog computers makes them useful for preparing test input for control computers which have a control job to be done in real time. In this case, the analog computer simulates the system to be controlled.

Equipment is available which permits the **conversion from analog voltages to digital information,** and vice versa. In this way, a digital computer can be used to read in or selectively step through a series of process variables and to record them, together with their resultant answers, in a heavily edited and easy-to-read form, and the analog computer can be used to solve the many differential equations which would otherwise be too time-consuming for the digital computer. This technique is not, as yet, widely used.

Programs are being written for digital computers which simulate an analog computer of considerable size. **MIDAS,** for example, is a digital-computer program which permits running on a digital computer problems programmed in analog-computer language, i.e., with analog-computer programming blocks such as summers and integrators. In this system, certain digital-computer subroutines act as the analog-computer operational units. Advantages include (1) almost negligible amplitude- or time-scaling problems (variables can range in magnitude as high as 10^{30}), and (2) new programming blocks, called **dividers** and **relays,** that do not have to be programmed from components. In addition, the program card decks can be easily saved and represent the complete analog-computer setup at the time—patch board, pot settings, and all. A disadvantage in many cases is that the elapsed period from the time the cards representing the program are submitted to the time the printed answers are returned may be in the order of hours.

SECTION 3

MECHANICS OF SOLIDS AND FLUIDS

BY

ROBERT F. STEIDEL, Jr., Professor of Mechanical Engineering, University of California, Berkeley.

DUDLEY D. FULLER, Professor of Mechanical Engineering, Columbia University.

CLARENCE B. ANDERSON, Associate Professor of Mechanical Engineering, The City University of New York.

CONTENTS

MECHANICS OF SOLIDS
By ROBERT F. STEIDEL, JR.

FRICTION
By DUDLEY D. FULLER

MECHANICS OF FLUIDS
By CLARENCE B. ANDERSON

MECHANICS OF SOLIDS

BY

Robert F. Steidel, Jr.

REFERENCES: Beer and Johnston, "Mechanics for Engineers," McGraw-Hill. Halfman, "Dynamics," Addison-Wesley. Ham and Crane, "Mechanics of Machinery," McGraw-Hill. Higdon and Stiles, "Engineering Mechanics," Prentice-Hall. Holowenko, "Dynamics of Machinery," Wiley. Housner and Hudson, "Applied Mechanics," Van Nostrand. Meriam, "Mechanics," Wiley. Synge and Griffith, "Principles of Mechanics," McGraw-Hill. Timoshenko and Young, "Advanced Dynamics," McGraw-Hill. Timoshenko and Young, "Engineering Mechanics," McGraw-Hill.

PHYSICAL MECHANICS

Definitions

Force is the action of one body on another which will cause acceleration of the second body unless acted on by an equal and opposite action counteracting the effect of the first body. It is a **vector** quantity.

Time is a measure of the sequence of events. In Newtonian mechanics it is an absolute quantity. In relativistic mechanics it is relative to the *frames of reference* in which the sequence of events is observed.

Inertia is that property of matter which causes a resistance to any change in the motion of a body.

Mass is a quantitative measure of *inertia*.

Acceleration of gravity. Every object which falls in a vacuum at a given position on the earth's surface will have the same acceleration g. Accurate values of the acceleration of gravity as measured *relative* to the earth's surface include the effect of the earth's rotation and flattening at the poles. The international gravity formula for the acceleration of gravity at the earth's surface is $g = 32.0881(1 + 0.005305 \sin^2 \phi - 0.0000059 \sin^2 2\phi)$ ft/sec², where ϕ is latitude in degrees. For extreme accuracy, the local acceleration of gravity must also be corrected for the presence of large water or land masses and for height above sea level. The absolute acceleration of gravity for a non-rotating earth discounts the effect of the earth's rotation and is rarely used, except outside the earth's atmosphere. If g_0 represents the absolute acceleration at sea level, the absolute value at an altitude h is $g = g_0R^2/(R + h)^2$, where R is the radius of the earth, approximately 3,960 mi.

Weight is the resultant force of attraction on the mass of a body due to a gravitational field. On the earth, units of weight are based upon an acceleration of gravity of 32.1740 ft/sec².

Linear momentum is the product of mass and the linear velocity of a particle and is a vector. The moment of the linear-momentum vector about a fixed axis is the **angular momentum** of the particle about that fixed axis. For a rigid body rotating about a fixed axis, angular momentum is defined as the product of moment of inertia and angular velocity, each measured about the fixed axis.

An increment of **work** is defined as the product of an incremental displacement and the component of the force vector in the direction of the displacement or the component of the displacement vector in the direction of the force. The increment of work done by a couple acting on a body during a rotation of $d\theta$ in the plane of the couple is $dU = M\,d\theta$.

Energy is defined as the capacity of a body to do work by reason of its motion or configuration (see **Work and Energy**).

A vector is a directed line segment that has both magnitude and direction. In script or text, a vector is distinguished from a scalar V by a boldface type **V**. The magnitude of the scalar is the magnitude of the vector, $V = |\mathbf{V}|$.

A frame of reference is a specified set of geometric conditions to which other locations, motion, and time are referred. In Newtonian mechanics, the fixed stars are referred to as the **primary (inertial) frame of reference.** Relativistic mechanics denies the existence of a primary reference frame and holds that all reference frames must be described relative to each other.

SYSTEMS AND UNITS OF MEASUREMENTS

In *absolute systems,* the units of **length, mass,** and **time** are considered fundamental quantities, and all other units including that of **force** are derived.

In *gravitational systems,* the units of **length, force,** and **time** are considered fundamental qualities, and all other units including that of **mass** are derived. The standard unit of force in the United States is the avoirdupois pound or the weight of 1/2.204622 kg at any location where the acceleration of gravity is 32.1740 ft/sec^2.

General Laws

Newton's Laws

I. If a balanced force system acts on a particle at rest, it will remain at rest. If a balanced force system acts on a particle in motion, it will remain in motion in a straight line without acceleration.

II. If an unbalanced force system acts on a particle, it will accelerate in proportion to the magnitude and in the direction of the resultant force.

III. When two particles exert forces on each other, these forces are equal in magnitude, opposite in direction, and collinear.

Fundamental Experiment. The basic relation between mass, acceleration, and force is contained in Newton's second law of motion. If a particle is isolated in a primary (inertial) frame of reference, the acceleration $\mathbf{a}_1$, $\mathbf{a}_2$, $\mathbf{a}_3$, . . . of the particle produced by forces $\mathbf{F}_1$, $\mathbf{F}_2$, $\mathbf{F}_3$, . . . will be directly proportional so that $\mathbf{F}_1/\mathbf{a}_1 = \mathbf{F}_2/\mathbf{a}_2 = \mathbf{F}_3/\mathbf{a}_3 = \cdot\cdot\cdot = \mathbf{F}/\mathbf{a} = \text{constant} = m$. The constant ratio m is known as the **mass** of the body. It is a quantitative measure of inertia or the resistance to change in velocity. When described in terms of the fundamental experiment, mass is a derived unit. It is on this basis that engineering uses the gravitational system of units.

Fundamental Equation. Force = mass × acceleration. An alternative form states that the resultant force is equal to the time rate of change of momentum, $\mathbf{F} = d(m\mathbf{v})/dt$.

Law of the Conservation of Mass. The mass of a body remains unchanged by any ordinary physical or chemical change to which it may be subjected.

Law of the Conservation of Energy. The principle of conservation of energy requires that the total mechanical energy of a system remain unchanged if it is subjected only to forces which depend on position or configuration.

Law of the Conservation of Momentum. The linear momentum of a system of bodies is unchanged if there is no resultant external force on the system. The angular momentum of a system of bodies about a fixed axis is unchanged if there is no resultant external moment about this axis.

Law of Mutual Attraction (Gravitation). Two particles attract each other with a force F proportional to their masses m_1 and m_2 and inversely proportional to the square of the distance r between them, or $F = km_1m_2/r^2$ in which k is the gravitational constant. The value of the gravitational constant is $k = 6.673 \times 10^{-8}\ \text{cm}^3\ \text{g}^{-1}\ \text{sec}^{-2}$ in cgs or **absolute units,** or $k = 3.44 \times 10^{-8}\ \text{ft}^4\ \text{lb}^{-1}\ \text{sec}^{-4}$ in **engineering** or **gravitational units.** It should be pointed out that the unit of force F in the cgs system is the **dyne** and is derived, while the unit of force in the gravitational system is the **pound-force** and is a fundamental quantity.

Example. Each of two solid steel spheres 6 in. in diam will weigh 32.0 lb on the earth's surface. This is the force of attraction between the earth and the steel sphere. The force of mutual attraction between the spheres if they are just touching is 0.000000136 lb.

STATICS OF RIGID BODIES

General Considerations

If the forces acting on a rigid body do not produce any acceleration, they must neutralize each other, *i.e.*, form a **system of forces in equilibrium.** Equilibrium is said to be **stable** when the body with the forces acting upon it returns to its original position after being displaced a very small amount from that position; **unstable** when the body tends to move still further from its original position than the very small displacement; and **neutral** when the forces retain their equilibrium when the body is in its new position.

External and Internal Forces. The forces by which the individual particles of a body act on each other are known as internal forces. All other forces are called external forces. If a body is supported by other bodies while subject to the action of forces, deformations and forces will be produced at the points of support or contact and these internal forces will be distributed throughout the body until equilibrium exists and the body is said to be in a state of tension, compression or shear. The forces exerted by the body on the supports are known as **reactions.** They are equal in magnitude and opposite in direction to the forces with which the supports act on the body, known as **supporting forces.** The supporting forces are external forces applied to the body.

In considering a body at a definite section, it will be found that all the internal forces act in pairs, the two forces being equal and opposite. The external forces act singly.

General Law. When a body is at rest, the forces acting externally to it must form an equilibrium system. This law will hold for any part of the body, in which case the forces acting at any section of the body become external forces when the part on either side of the section is considered alone. In the case of a **rigid body,** any two forces of the same magnitude, but acting in opposite directions in any straight line, may be added or removed without change in the action of the forces acting on the body, provided the strength of the body is not affected.

Composition, Resolution, and Equilibrium of Forces

The **resultant** of several forces acting at a point is a force which will produce the same effect as all the individual forces acting together.

Forces Acting on a Body at the Same Point. The resultant R of two forces F_1 and F_2 applied to a rigid body at the same point is represented in magnitude and direction by the diagonal of the parallelogram formed by F_1 and F_2 (see Figs. 1 and 2).

$$R = \sqrt{F_1^2 + F_2^2 + 2F_1F_2 \cos a}$$

$$\sin a_1 = (F_2 \sin a)/R \qquad \sin a_2 = (F_1 \sin a)/R$$

When $a = 90$ deg, $R = \sqrt{F_1^2 + F_2^2}$, $\sin a_1 = F_2/R$, and $\sin a_2 = F_1/R$.

When $a = 0$ deg, $R = F_1 + F_2$ }
When $a = 180$ deg, $R = F_1 - F_2$ } Forces act in same straight line.

A force R **may be resolved into two component forces** intersecting anywhere on R and acting in the same plane as R, by the reverse of the operation shown by Figs. 1 and 2; and by repeating the operation with the components, R may be resolved into any number of component forces intersecting R at the same point and in the same plane.

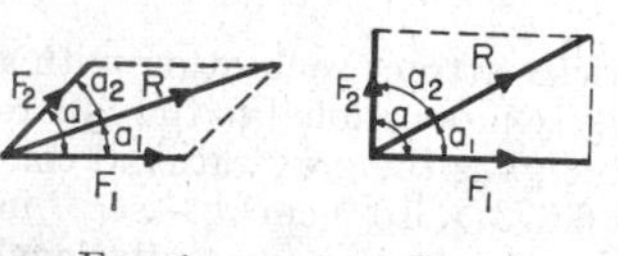

FIG. 1 FIG. 2

Resultant of Any Number of Forces Applied to a Rigid Body at the Same Point. Resolve each of the given forces F into components along three rectangular coordinate axes. If A, B, and C are the angles made with XX, YY, and ZZ, respectively, by any force F, the components will be $F \cos A$ along XX, $F \cos B$ along YY, $F \cos C$ along ZZ; add the components of all the forces along each axis algebraically and obtain $\Sigma F \cos A = \Sigma X$ along XX, $\Sigma F \cos B = \Sigma Y$ along YY, and $\Sigma F \cos C = \Sigma Z$ along ZZ.

The resultant $R = \sqrt{(\Sigma X)^2 + (\Sigma Y)^2 + (\Sigma Z)^2}$. The angles made by the resultant with the three axes are A_r with XX, B_r with YY, C_r with ZZ, where

$$\cos A_r = \Sigma X/R \qquad \cos B_r = \Sigma Y/R \qquad \cos C_r = \Sigma Z/R$$

The **direction of the resultant** can be determined by plotting the algebraic sums of the components.

If the forces are all in the same plane, the components of each of the forces along one of the three axes (say, ZZ) will be 0; *i.e.*, angle $C_r = 90°$ and $R = \sqrt{(\Sigma X)^2 + (\Sigma Y)^2}$, $\cos A_r = \Sigma X/R$, and $\cos B_r = \Sigma Y/R$.

For equilibrium, it is necessary that $R = 0$; *i.e.*, ΣX, ΣY, and ΣZ must each be equal to zero.

General Law. In order that a number of forces acting at the same point shall be in equilibrium, the algebraic sum of their components along any *three* coordinate axes must each be equal to zero. When the forces all act in the same plane, the algebraic sum of their components along any *two* coordinate axes must each equal zero.

When the Forces Form a System in Equilibrium. Three unknown forces can be determined if the lines of action of the forces are *all* known and are in different planes. If the forces are all in the same plane, the lines of action being known, only *two* unknown forces can be determined. If the lines of action of the unknown forces are *not* known, only *one* unknown force can be determined in either case.

Couples and Moments

Couple. Two parallel forces of equal magnitude, Fig. 3, which act in opposite directions and are not collinear, form a couple. **A couple cannot be reduced to a single force.**

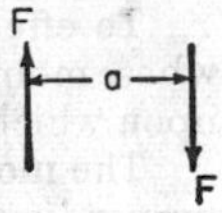

Displacement and Change of a Couple. The forces forming a couple may be moved about and their magnitude and direction changed, provided they always remain parallel to each other, remain either in the original plane or one parallel to it, and provided the product of one of the forces and the perpendicular distance between the two is constant and the direction of rotation remains the same.

F a F

Fig. 3

Moment of a Couple. The moment of a couple is the product of the magnitude of one of the forces and the perpendicular distance between the lines of action of the forces. Fa = moment of couple; a = arm of couple. If the forces are measured in pounds and the distance a in feet, the **unit of rotation moment** is the foot-pound. If the force is measured in kilograms and the distance in meters, the unit is the meter-kilogram. In the cgs system the unit of rotation moment is 1 cm-dyne.

Rotation moments of couples acting in the same plane are conventionally considered to be positive for counterclockwise moments and negative for clockwise moments, although it is only necessary to be consistent within a given problem. The magnitude, direction, and sense of rotation of a couple are completely determined by its moment axis, or moment vector, which is a line drawn perpendicular to the plane in which the couple acts, with an arrow indicating the direction from which the couple will appear to have right-handed rotation; the length of the line represents the magnitude of the moment of the couple. See Fig. 4, in which AB represents the magnitude of the moment of the couple. Looking along the line in the direction of the arrow, the couple will have right-handed rotation in any plane perpendicular to the line.

A B

Fig. 4

Composition of Couples. Couples may be combined by adding their moment vectors geometrically, in accordance with the parallelogram rule, in the same manner in which forces are combined.

Couples lying in the same or parallel planes are added algebraically. Let +40, −60, and +100 ft-lb be the moments of three couples in the same or parallel planes; their resultant is a single couple lying in the same or in a parallel plane, whose moment is $\Sigma M = +40 - 60 + 100 = +80$ ft-lb.

If the polygon formed by the moment vectors of several couples closes itself, the couples form an equilibrium system. Two couples will balance each other when they lie in the same or parallel planes, and have the same moment in magnitude, but opposite in sign.

Combination of a Couple and a Single Force in the Same Plane (Fig. 5). Given a force $F = 20$ lb acting as shown at distance x from YY, and a couple whose moment is -60 ft-lb in the same or a parallel plane, to find the resultant. A couple may be changed to any other couple in the same or a parallel plane having the same moment and same sign. Let the couple consist of two forces of 20 lb each and let the arm be 3 ft. Place the couple in such a manner that one of its forces is opposed to the given force at p. This force of the couple and the given force being of the same magnitude and opposite in direction will neutralize each other, leaving the other force of the couple acting at a distance of 3 ft from p and parallel and equal to the given force $F = 20$.

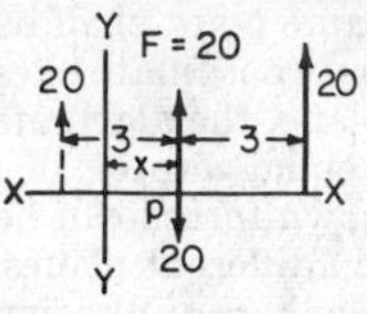

Fig. 5

General Rule. The resultant of a couple and a single force lying in the same or parallel planes is a single force, equal in magnitude, in the same direction and parallel to the single force, and acting at a distance from the line of action of the single force equal to the moment of the couple divided by the single force. The moment of the resultant force about any point on the line of action of the given single force must be of the same sense as that of the couple, positive if the moment of the couple is positive, and negative if moment of couple is negative. If the moment of the couple in Fig. 5 had been $+60$ instead of -60, the resultant would have been a force of 20 lb acting in the same direction and parallel to F, but at a distance of 3 ft to the left of it (shown dotted), making the moment of the resultant about any point on F positive.

To effect a parallel displacement of a single force F over a distance a, a couple whose moment is Fa must be added to the system. The sense of the couple will depend upon which way it is desired to displace force F.

The moment of a force with respect to a point is the product of the force F and the perpendicular distance from the point to the line of action of the force.

The Moment of a Force with Respect to a Straight Line. If the force is resolved into components parallel and perpendicular to the given line, the moment of the force with respect to the line is the product of the magnitude of the perpendicular component and the distance from its line of action to the given line.

Forces with Different Points of Application

Composition of Forces. If each force **F** is resolved into components parallel to three rectangular coordinate axes XX, YY, and ZZ, the magnitude of the resultant is $R = \sqrt{(\Sigma X)^2 + (\Sigma Y)^2 + (\Sigma Z)^2}$, and its line of action makes angles A_r, B_r, and C_r with axes XX, YY, and ZZ, where $\cos A_r = \Sigma X/R$, $\cos B_r = \Sigma Y/R$, and $\cos C_r = \Sigma Z/R$; and there are three couples which may be combined by their moment vectors into a single resultant couple having the moment $M_r = \sqrt{(M_x)^2 + (M_y)^2 + (M_z)^2}$, whose moment vector makes angles of A_m, B_m, and C_m with axes XX, YY, and ZZ, such that $\cos A_m = M_x/M_r$, $\cos B_m = M_y/M_r$, and $\cos C_m = M_z/M_r$. If this single resulting couple is in the same plane as the single resulting force at the origin or a plane parallel to it, the system may be reduced to a single force **R** acting at a distance from **R** equal to M_r/R. If the couple and force are not in the same or parallel planes, it is impossible to reduce the system to a single force. If $\mathbf{R} = 0$, *i.e.*, if ΣX, ΣY, and ΣZ all equal zero, the system will reduce to a single couple whose moment is $\mathbf{M}_r$. If $\mathbf{M}_r = 0$, *i.e.*, if M_x, M_y, and M_z all equal zero, the resultant will be a single force **R**.

When the forces are all in the same plane, cosine of one of the angles A_r, B_r, or $C_r = 0$, say, $C_r = 90$ deg. Then $R = \sqrt{(\Sigma X)^2 + (\Sigma Y)^2}$, $M_r = \sqrt{M_x^2 + M_y^2}$, and the final resultant is a force equal and parallel to R, acting at a distance from R equal to M_r/R.

A system of forces in the same plane can always be replaced by either a couple or a single force. If $\mathbf{R} = 0$ and $\mathbf{M}_r > 0$, the resultant is a couple. If $\mathbf{M}_r = 0$ and $\mathbf{R} > 0$, the resultant is a single force.

A rigid body is in equilibrium when acted upon by a system of forces whenever $\mathbf{R} = 0$ and $\mathbf{M}_r = 0$, *i.e.*, when the following six conditions hold true: $\Sigma X = 0$, $\Sigma Y = 0$, $\Sigma Z = 0$, $M_x = 0$, $M_y = 0$, and $M_z = 0$. When the system of forces is in the same plane, equilibrium prevails when the following three conditions hold true: $\Sigma X = 0$, $\Sigma Y = 0$, $\Sigma M = 0$.

Forces Applied to Support Rigid Bodies

The external forces in equilibrium acting upon a body may be statically determinate or indeterminate according to the number of unknown forces existing. When the forces are all in the same plane and act at a common point, two unknown forces may be determined if their lines of action are known, one if unknown.

When the forces are all in the same plane and are parallel, two unknown forces may be determined if the lines of action are known, one if unknown.

When the forces are anywhere in the same plane, three unknown forces may be determined if their lines of action are known, if they are not parallel or do not pass through a common point; if the lines of action are unknown, only one unknown force can be determined.

If the forces all act at a common point but are in different planes, three unknown forces can be determined if the lines of action are known, one if unknown.

If the forces act in different planes but are parallel, three unknown forces can be determined if their lines of action are known, one if unknown.

The first step in the solution of problems in statics is the determination of the supporting forces. The following data are required for the complete knowledge of supporting forces: magnitude, direction, and point of application. According to the nature of the problem, none, one, or two of these quantities are known.

One Fixed Support. The point of application, direction, and magnitude of the load are known. See Fig. 6. As the body on which the forces act is in equilibrium, the supporting force P must be equal in magnitude and opposite in direction to the resultant of the loads L.

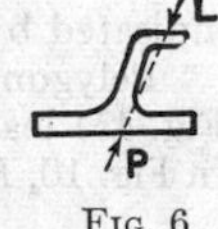

FIG. 6

In the case of a **rolling surface,** the point of application of the support is obtained from the center of the connecting bolt A (Fig. 7), both the direction and magnitude being unknown. The point of application and line of action of the support at B are known, being determined by the rollers.

When three forces acting in the same plane on the same rigid body are in equilibrium, their lines of action must pass through the same point O. The load L is known in magnitude and direction. The line of action of the support at B is known on account of the rollers. The point of application of the support at A is known. The three forces are in equilibrium and are in the same plane; therefore, the lines of action must meet at the point O.

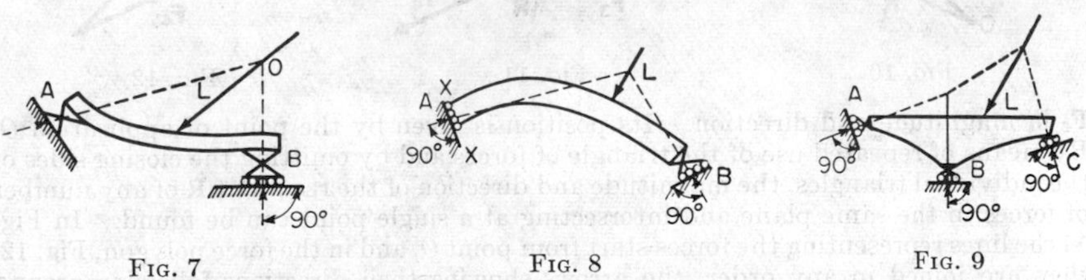

FIG. 7 FIG. 8 FIG. 9

In the case of the rolling surfaces shown in Fig. 8, the direction of the support at A is known, the magnitude and point of application unknown. The line of action and point of application of the supporting force at B are known, its magnitude unknown. The lines of action of the three forces must meet in a point, and the supporting force at A must be perpendicular to the plane XX. In the case shown in Fig. 9, the directions and points of application of the supporting forces are known, and the magnitudes unknown. The lines of action of resultant of supports A and B, the support at C and load L must meet at a point. Resolve the resultant of supports at A and B into components at A and B, their direction deing determined by the rollers.

If a member of a truss or frame in equilibrium is pinned at two points and loaded at these two points only, the line of action of the forces exerted on the member or by the member at these two points must be along a line connecting the pins.

If the external forces acting upon a rigid body in equilibrium are all in the same plane, the equations $\Sigma X = 0$, $\Sigma Y = 0$, and $\Sigma M = 0$ must be satisfied. When trusses, frames, and other structures are under discussion, these equations are usually used as $\Sigma V = 0$, $\Sigma H = 0$, $\Sigma M = 0$, where V and H represent vertical and horizontal components, respectively.

The **supports** are said to be **determinate statically** when the laws of equilibrium are sufficient for their determination. When the conditions are not sufficient for the determination of the supports or other forces, the structure is said to be **statically indeterminate**; the unknown forces can then be determined from considerations involving the deformation of the material.

When several bodies are so connected to one another as to make up a rigid structure, the forces at the points of connection must be considered as internal forces and are not taken into consideration in the determination of the supporting forces for the structure as a whole.

The distortion of any practically rigid structure under its working loads is so small as to be negligible when determining supporting forces. When the forces acting at the different joints in a built-up structure cannot be determined by dividing the structure up into parts, the structure is said to be **statically indeterminate internally.** A structure may be statically indeterminate internally and still be statically determinate externally.

Fundamental Problems in Graphical Statics

A force may be represented by a straight line in a determined position, and its magnitude by the length of the straight line. The direction in which it acts may be indicated by an arrow.

Polygon of Forces. The parallelogram of two forces intersecting each other (see Fig. 45) leads directly to the graphic composition by means of the triangle of forces. In Fig. 10, R is called the **closing side,** and represents the resultant of the forces $\mathbf{F}_1$ and

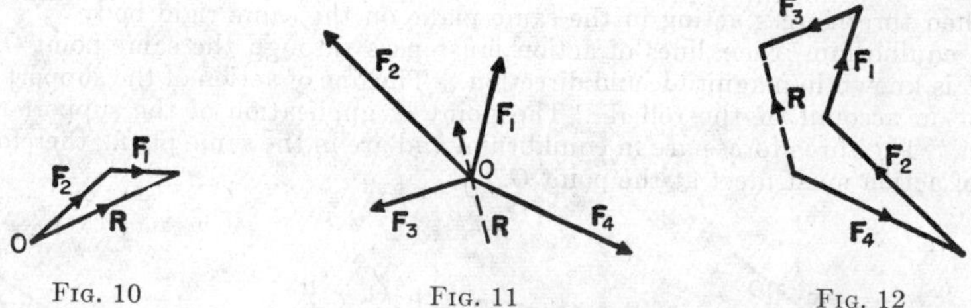

FIG. 10 FIG. 11 FIG. 12

$\mathbf{F}_2$ in magnitude and direction. Its position is given by the point of application O. By means of repeated use of the triangle of forces and by omitting the closing sides of the individual triangles, the magnitude and direction of the resultant $\mathbf{R}$ of any number of forces in the same plane and intersecting at a single point can be found. In Fig. 11 the lines representing the forces start from point O, and in the force polygon, Fig. 12, they are joined in any order, the arrows showing their directions following around the polygon in the same direction. The magnitude of the resultant at the point of application of the forces is represented by the closing side $\mathbf{R}$ of the force polygon; its direction, as shown by the arrow, is counter to that in the other sides of the polygon.

If the forces are in equilibrium, R must equal zero, *i.e.,* **the force polygon must close.**

If in a closed polygon one of the forces is reversed in direction, this force becomes the resultant of all the others.

If the **forces** do **not** all lie **in the same plane,** the diagram becomes a polygon in space. The resultant $\mathbf{R}$ of this system may be obtained by adding the forces in space.

The resultant is the vector which closes the space polygon. The space polygon may be projected onto three coordinate planes, giving three related plane polygons. Any two of these projections will involve all static equilibrium conditions and will be sufficient for a full description of the force system (see Fig. 13).

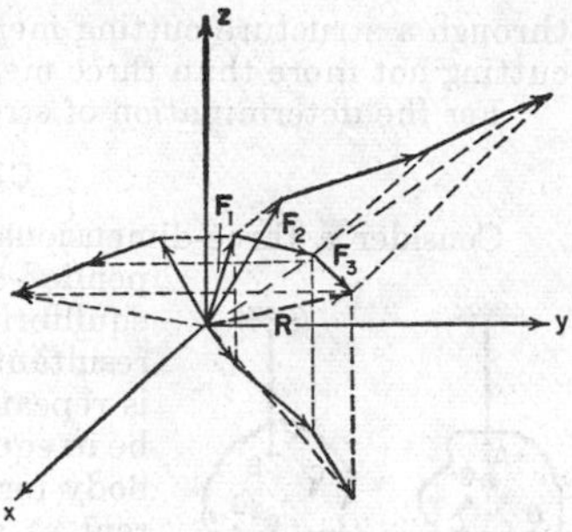

FIG. 13

Determination of Stresses in Members of a Statically Determinate Plane Structure with Loads at Rest

It will be assumed that the loads are applied at the joints of the structure, *i.e.*, at the points where the different members are connected, and that the connections are pins with no friction. The stresses in the members must then be along lines connecting the pins, unless any member is loaded at more than two points by pin connections. If the members are straight, the forces exerted on them or by them must coincide with the axes of the members. In other words, there shall be no bending stresses in any of the members of the structure.

Equilibrium. In order that the whole structure should be in equilibrium, it is necessary that the external forces (loads and supports) shall form a balanced system. Graphical and analytical methods are both of service.

Supporting Forces. When the supporting forces are to be determined, it is not necessary to pay any attention to the make-up of the structure under consideration so long as it is practically rigid; the loads may be taken as they occur, or the resultant of the loads may be used instead. When the stresses in the members of the structure are being determined, the loads *must* be distributed at the joints where they belong.

Method of Joints. When all the external forces have been determined, any joint at which there are not more than two unknown forces may be taken and these unknown forces determined by the methods of the stress polygon, resolution or moments. In Fig. 14, let O be the joint of a structure and **F** be the only known force; but let $O1$ and $O2$ be two members of the structure joined at O. Then the lines of action of the unknown forces are known and their magnitude may be determined (1) by a **stress polygon** which, for equilibrium, must close; (2) by resolution into H and V components, using the condition of equilibrium $\Sigma H = 0, \Sigma V = 0$; or (3) by moments, using any convenient point on the line of action of $O1$ and $O2$ and the condition of equilibrium $\Sigma M = 0$. No more than *two* unknown forces can be determined. In this manner, proceeding from joint to joint, the stresses in all the members of the truss can usually be determined if the structure is statically determinate internally.

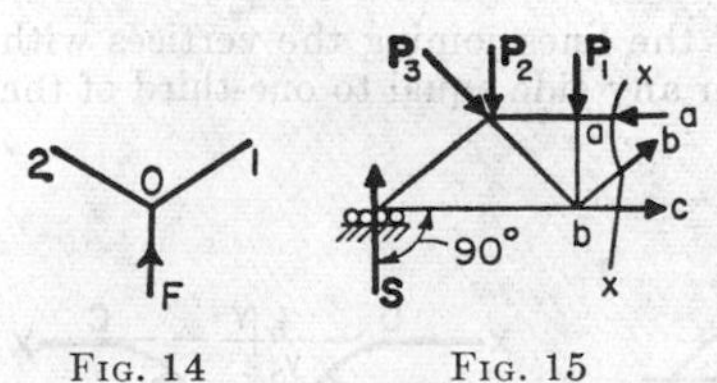

FIG. 14 FIG. 15

Method of Sections. The structure may be divided into parts by passing a section through it cutting some of its members; one part may then be treated as a rigid body and the external forces acting upon it determined. Some of these forces will be the stresses in the members themselves. For example, let xx (Fig. 15) be a section taken through a truss loaded at P_1, P_2, and P_3, and supported on rollers at S. As the whole truss is in equilibrium, any part of it must be also, and consequently the part shown to the left of xx must be in equilibrium under the action of the forces acting externally to it. Three of these forces are the stresses in the members aa, bb, and bc, and are the unknown forces to be determined. They can be determined by applying the condition of equilibrium of forces acting in the same plane but not at the same point. $\Sigma H = 0$, $\Sigma V = 0$, $\Sigma M = 0$. The three unknown forces can be determined only if they are not parallel or do not pass through the same point; if, however, the forces are parallel or meet in a point, two unknown forces only can be determined. Sections may be passed through a structure cutting members in any convenient manner, as a rule, however, cutting not more than three members, unless members are unloaded.

For the determination of stresses in framed structures, see Sec. 12.

CENTER OF GRAVITY

Consider a three-dimensional body of any size, shape, and weight. If it is suspended as in Fig. 16 by a cord from any point A, it will be in equilibrium under the action of the tension in the cord and the resultant of the gravity or body forces W. If the experiment is repeated by suspending the body from point B, it will again be in equilibrium. If the lines of action of the resultant of the body forces were marked in each case, they would be concurrent at a point G known as the **center of gravity** or **center of mass.** Whenever the density of the body is uniform, it will be a constant factor and like geometric shapes of different densities will have the same center of gravity. The term **centroid** is used in this case since the location of the center of gravity is of geometric concern only. If densities are nonuniform, like geometric shapes will have the same centroid but different centers of gravity.

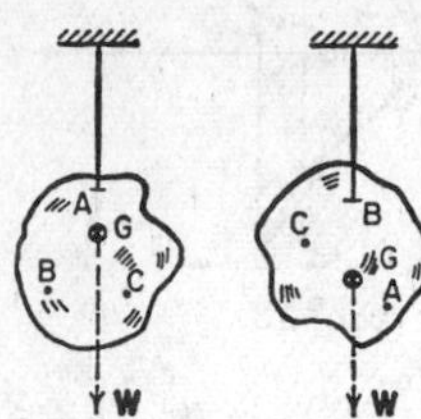

Fig. 16

Centroids of Technically Important Lines, Areas, and Solids

Centroids of Lines

Straight Line. The centroid is at its middle point.

Circular Arc, AB, Fig. 17(a): $x_0 = r \sin c/\text{rad } c$; $y_0 = 2r \sin^2 \frac{1}{2}c/\text{rad } c$. (rad c = angle c measured in radians; see p. 1–44.)

Circular Arc, AC, Fig. 17(b): $x_0 = r \sin c/\text{rad } c$; $y_0 = 0$.

Quadrant, AB, Fig. 18: $x_0 = y_0 = 2r/\pi = 0.6366r$.

Semicircumference, AC, Fig. 18: $y_0 = 2r/\pi = 0.6366r$; $x_0 = 0$.

Combination of Arcs and Straight Line, Fig. 19: AD and BC are two quadrants of radius r. $y_0 = \{(AB)r + 2[0.5\pi r(r - 0.6366r)]\} \div [AB + 2(0.5\pi r)]$.

Centroids of Plane Areas

Triangle. Centroid lies at the intersection of the lines joining the vertices with the mid-points of the sides, and at a distance from any side equal to one-third of the corresponding altitude.

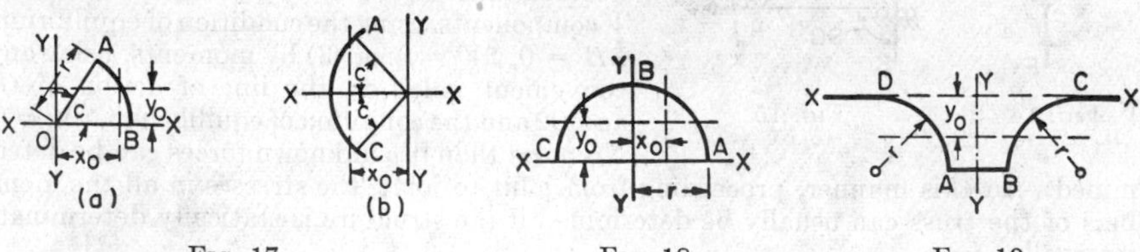

Fig. 17 Fig. 18 Fig. 19

Parallelogram. Centroid lies at the point of intersection of the diagonals.

Trapezoid (Fig. 20). Centroid lies on the line joining the middle points m and n of the parallel sides. The distances h_a and h_b are

$$h_a = h(a + 2b)/3(a + b) \qquad h_b = h(2a + b)/3(a + b)$$

Draw $BE = a$ and $CF = b$; EF will then intersect mn at centroid.

Any Quadrilateral. The centroid of any quadrilateral may be determined by the general rule for areas, or graphically by dividing it into two sets of triangles by means of the diagonals. Find the centroid of each of the four triangles and connect the centroids of the triangles belonging to the same set. The intersection of these lines will be centroid of area. Thus, in Fig. 21, O, O_1, O_2, and O_3 are, respectively, the centroids of the triangles ABD, ABC, BDC, and ACD. The intersection of O_1O_3 with OO_2 gives the centroids.

Segment of a Circle (Fig. 22): $x_0 = \frac{2}{3}r \sin^3 c/(\text{rad } c - \cos c \sin c)$. A segment may be considered to be a sector from which a triangle is subtracted, and the general rule applied.

Sector of a Circle (Fig. 23): $x_0 = \frac{2}{3}r \sin c/\text{rad } c$; $y_0 = \frac{4}{3}r \sin^2 \frac{1}{2}c/\text{rad } c$.

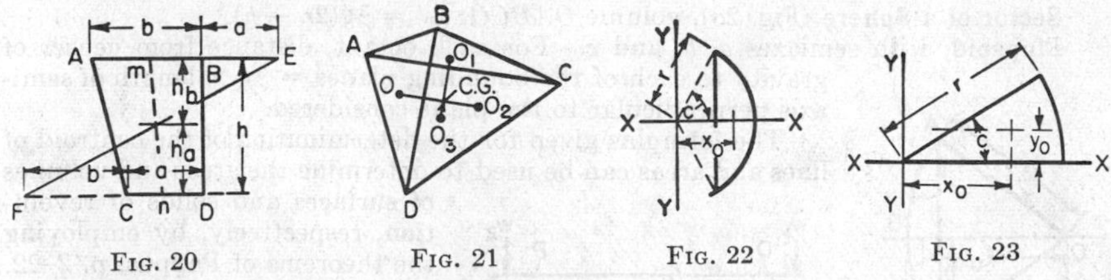

FIG. 20 FIG. 21 FIG. 22 FIG. 23

Semicircle: $x_0 = \frac{4}{3}r/\pi = 0.4244r$; $y_0 = 0$.

Quadrant (90 deg sector): $x_0 = y_0 = \frac{4}{3}r/\pi = 0.4244r$.

Parabolic Half Segment (Fig. 24): Area ABO: $x_0 = \frac{3}{5}x_1$; $y_0 = \frac{3}{8}y_1$.

Parabolic Spandrel (Fig. 24): Area AOC: $x_0' = \frac{3}{10}x_1$; $y_0' = \frac{3}{4}y_1$.

Quadrant of an Ellipse (Fig. 25): Area OAB: $x_0 = \frac{4}{3}(a/\pi)$; $y_0 = \frac{4}{3}(b/\pi)$.

The centroid of a figure such as that shown in Fig. 26 may be determined as follows: Divide the area $OABC$ into a number of parts by lines drawn perpendicular to the

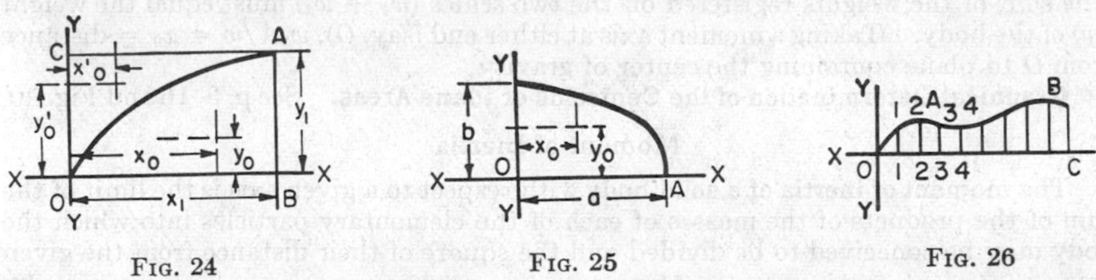

FIG. 24 FIG. 25 FIG. 26

axis XX, *e.g.*, 11, 22, 33, etc. These parts will be approximately either triangles, rectangles, or trapezoids. The area of each division may be obtained by taking the product of its mean height and its base. The centroid of each area may be obtained as previously shown. The sum of the moments of all the areas about XX and YY, respectively, divided by the sum of the areas will give approximately the distances from the center of gravity of the whole area to the axes XX and YY. The greater the number of areas taken the more nearly exact the result.

CENTROIDS OF SOLIDS

Prism or Cylinder with Parallel Bases. The centroid lies in the center of the line connecting the centers of gravity of the bases.

Oblique Frustum of a Right Circular Cylinder (Fig. 27). Let 1 2 3 4 be the plane of symmetry. The distance from the base to the centroid is $\frac{1}{2}h + (r^2 \tan^2 c)/8h$, where c is the angle of inclination of the oblique section to the base. The distance of the centroid from the axis of the cylinder is $r^2 \tan c/4h$.

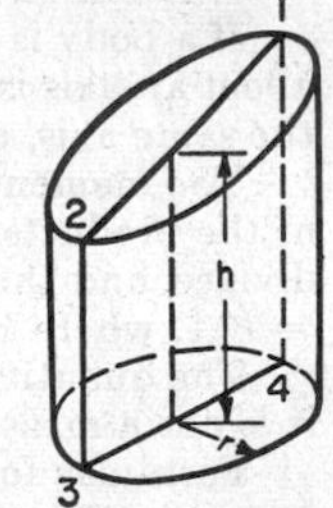

FIG. 27

Pyramid or Cone. The centroid lies in the line connecting the centroid of the base with the vertex and at a distance of one-fourth of the altitude above the base.

Truncated Pyramid. If h is the height of the truncated pyramid and A and B the areas of its bases, the distance of its centroid from the surface of A is

$$h(A + 2\sqrt{AB} + 3B)/4(A + \sqrt{AB} + B)$$

Truncated Circular Cone. If h is the height of the frustum and R and r the radii of the bases, the distance from the surface of the base whose radius is R to the centroid is $h(R^2 + 2Rr + 3r^2)/4(R^2 + Rr + r^2)$.

Segment of a Sphere (Fig. 28), volume ABC: $x_0 = 3(2r - h)^2/4(3r - h)$.

Hemisphere. $x_0 = 3r/8$.

Hollow Hemisphere. $x_0 = 3(R^4 - r^4)/8(R^3 - r^3)$, where R and r are, respectively, the outer and inner radii.

Sector of a Sphere (Fig. 28), volume $OABCO$: $x_0' = \frac{3}{8}(2r - h)$.

Ellipsoid, with semiaxes a, b, and c. For each octant, distance from center of gravity to each of the bounding planes = $\frac{3}{8}$ × length of semiaxis perpendicular to the plane considered.

The formulas given for the determination of the centroid of lines and areas can be used to determine the areas and volumes of surfaces and solids of revolution, respectively, by employing the theorems of Pappus, p. 2–22.

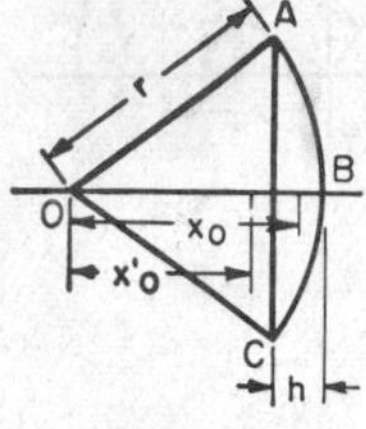

Fig. 28

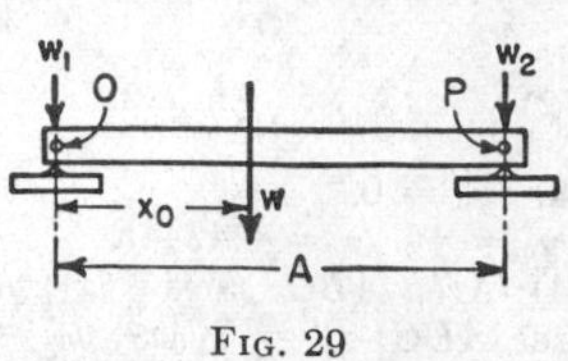

Fig. 29

Determination of Center of Gravity of a Body by Experiment. The center of gravity may be determined by hanging the body up from different points and plumbing down; the point of intersection of the plumb lines will give the center of gravity. It may also be determined as shown in Fig. 29. The body is placed on knife-edges which rest on platform scales. The sum of the weights registered on the two scales $(w_1 + w_2)$ must equal the weight (w) of the body. Taking a moment axis at either end (say, O), $w_2A/w = x_0$ = distance from O to plane containing the center of gravity.

Graphical Determination of the Centroids of Plane Areas. See p. 3–16 and Fig. 40.

Moment of Inertia

The **moment of inertia of a solid body** with respect to a given axis is the limit of the sum of the products of the masses of each of the elementary particles into which the body may be conceived to be divided and the square of their distance from the given axis.

If $dm = dw/g$ represents the mass of an elementary particle and y its distance from an axis, the moment of inertia I of the body about this axis will be $I = \int y^2\,dm = \int y^2\,dw/g$.

The moment of inertia may be expressed in weight units ($I_w = \int y^2\,dw$), in which case the moment of inertia in weight units, I_w, is equal to the moment of inertia in mass units, I, multiplied by g.

If $I = k^2m$, the quantity k is called the **radius of gyration** or the **radius of inertia.**

If a body is considered to be composed of a number of parts, its moment of inertia about an axis is equal to the sum of the moments of inertia of the several parts about the same axis, or $I = I_1 + I_2 + I_3 + \cdots + I_n$.

The **moment of inertia of an area** with respect to a given axis is the limit of the sum of the products of the elementary areas into which the area may be conceived to be divided and the square of their distance (y) from the axis in question. $I = \int y^2\,dA = k^2A$, where k = **radius of gyration.**

The quantity $Sy^2\,dA$ is more properly referred to as the *second moment of area* since it is not a measure of *inertia* in a true sense.

Formulas for moments of inertia and radii of gyration of various areas are given on pp. 5–37 to 5–40.

Relation between the Moments of Inertia of an Area and a Solid. The moment of inertia of a solid of elementary thickness about an axis is equal to the moment of inertia of the area of one face of the solid about the same axis multiplied by the mass per unit volume of the solid times the elementary thickness of the solid.

Moments of Inertia about Parallel Axes. The moment of inertia of an area or solid about any given axis is equal to the moment of inertia about a parallel axis through the center of gravity plus the square of the distance between the two axes times the area or mass.

In Fig. 30(*a*), the moment of inertia of the area *ABCD* about axis *YY* is equal to I_0 (or the moment of inertia about Y_0Y_0 through the center of gravity of the area and parallel to *YY*) plus x_0^2A, where A = area of *ABCD*. In Fig. 30(*b*), the moment of inertia of the mass *m* about $YY = I_0 + x_0^2m$. Y_0Y_0 passes through the centroid of the mass and is parallel to *YY*.

Polar Moment of Inertia. The polar moment of inertia, Fig. 31, is taken about an axis perpendicular to the plane of the area. Referring to Fig. 31, if I_y and I_x be the moments of inertia of the area *A* about *YY* and *XX*, respectively, then the polar moment of inertia $I_p = I_x + I_y$, or the polar moment of inertia is equal to the sum of the moments of inertia about any two axes at right angles to each other in the plane of the area and intersecting at the pole.

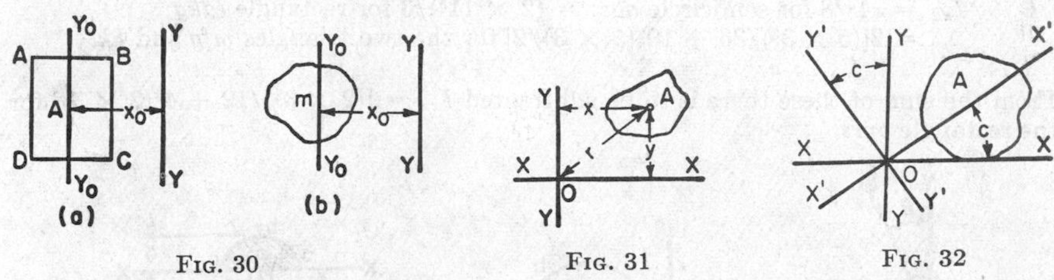

FIG. 30 FIG. 31 FIG. 32

Product of Inertia. This quantity will be represented by I_{xy} and is $\int\int xy\, dy\, dx'$ where x and y are the coordinates of any elementary part into which the area may be conceived to be divided. I_{xy} may be positive or negative, depending upon the position of the area with respect to the coordinate axes *XX* and *XY*.

Relation between Moments of Inertia about Axes Inclined to Each Other. Referring to Fig. 32, let I_y and I_x be the moments of inertia of the area *A* about *YY* and *XX*, respectively, I_y' and I_x' the moments about *Y'Y'* and *X'X'*, and I_{xy} and I_{xy}' the products of inertia for *XX* and *YY*, and *X'X'* and *Y'Y'*, respectively. Also, let *c* be the angle between the respective pairs of axes, as shown. Then,

$$I_y' = I_y \cos^2 c + I_x \sin^2 c + I_{xy} \sin 2c$$
$$I_x' = I_x \cos^2 c + I_y \sin^2 c - I_{xy} \sin 2c$$
$$I_{xy}' = \frac{(I_x - I_y)}{2} \sin 2c + I_{xy} \cos 2c$$

Principal Moments of Inertia. In every plane area, a given point being taken as the origin, there is at least one pair of rectangular axes in the plane of the area about one of which the moment of inertia is a maximum, and a minimum about the other. These moments of inertia are called the **principal moments of inertia,** and the axes about which they are taken are the **principal axes of inertia.** One of the conditions for principal moments of inertia is that the product of inertia I_{xy} shall equal zero. **Axes of symmetry** of an area are always principal axes of inertia.

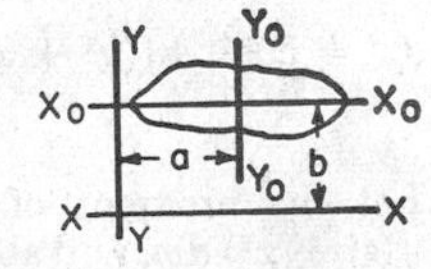

FIG. 33

Relation between Products of Inertia and Parallel Axes. In Fig. 33, X_0X_0 and Y_0Y_0 pass through the center of gravity of the area parallel to the given axes *XX* and *YY*. If I_{xy} be the product of inertia for *XX* and *YY*, and $I_{x_0y_0}$ that for X_0X_0 and Y_0Y_0, then $I_{xy} = I_{x_0y_0} + abA$.

Mohr's Circle. The **principal moments of inertia** and the location of the **principal axes of inertia** for any point of a plane area may be established graphically as follows.

Given at any point *A* of a plane area (Fig. 34), the moments of inertia I_x and I_y about axes *X* and *Y*, and the product of inertia I_{xy} relative to *X* and *Y*. The graph shown in Fig. 34(*b*) is plotted on rectangular coordinates with moments of inertia as abscissas and products of inertia as ordinates. Lay out $Oa = I_x$ and $ab = I_{xy}$ (upward for positive products of inertia, downward for negative). Lay out $Oc = I_y$ and $cd =$ *negative of* I_{xy}. Draw circle with *bd* as diameter. This is **Mohr's circle.** The *maximum* moment of inertia is $I_x' = Of$; the *minimum* moment of inertia is $I_y' = Og$. The principal axes of inertia are located as follows. From axis AX (Fig. 34(*a*)) lay out angular distance $\theta = \frac{1}{2} < bef$. This locates axis AX', one principal axis ($I_x' = Of$). The other principal axis of inertia is AY', perpendicular to AX' ($I_x' = Og$).

The **moment of inertia of any area** may be considered to be made up of the sum or difference of the known moments of inertia of simple figures. For example, the dimensioned figure shown in Fig. 35 represents the section of a rolled shape with hole *oprs* and may be divided into the semicircle *abc*, rectangle *edkg*, and triangles *mfg* and *hkl*, from which the rectangle *oprs* is to be subtracted. Referring to axis XX,

$$I_{xx} = \pi 4^4/8 \text{ for semicircle } abc; = (2 \times 11^3)/3 \text{ for rectangle } edkg;$$
$$= 2[(5 \times 3^3)/36 + 10^2(5 \times 3)/2] \text{ for the two triangles } mfg \text{ and } hkl$$

From the sum of these there is to be subtracted $I_{xx} = [(2 \times 3^2)/12 + 4^2(2 \times 3)]$ for the rectangle *oprs*.

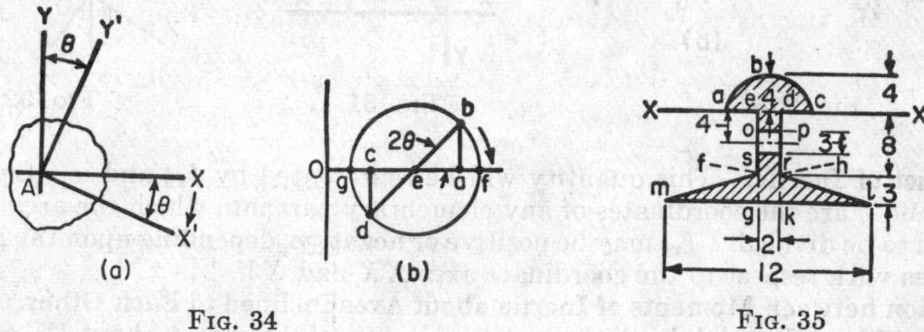

FIG. 34 FIG. 35

If the moment of inertia of the whole area is required about an axis parallel to XX, but passing through the center of gravity of the whole area, $I_0 = I_{xx} - x_0^2A$, where x_0 = distance from XX to center of gravity. The **moments of inertia of built-up sections** used in structural work may be found in the same manner, the moments of inertia of the different **rolled sections** being given in Sec. 12.

Moments of Inertia of Solids. For moments of inertia of solids about parallel axes, $I_x = I_0 + x_0^2m$; see p. 3–15.

Moment of Inertia with Reference to Any Axis. Let a mass particle *dm* of a body have *x*, *y*, and *z* as coordinates, XX, YY, and ZZ being the coordinate axes and O the origin. Let $X'X'$ be any axis passing through the origin and making angles of A, B, and C with XX, YY, and ZZ, respectively. The moment of inertia with respect to this axis then becomes equal to

$$I_x' = \cos^2 A \int(y^2 + z^2)\,dm + \cos^2 B \int(z^2 + x^2)\,dm + \cos^2 C \int(x^2 + y^2)\,dm - 2\cos B \cos C \int yz\,dm - 2\cos C \cos A \int zx\,dm - 2\cos A \cos B \int xy\,dm$$

Let the moment of inertia about $XX = I_x = \int(y^2 + z^2)\,dm$, about $YY = Iy = \int(z^2 + x^2)\,dm$, and about $ZZ = I_z = \int(x^2 + y^2)\,dm$. Let the products of inertia about the three coordinates axes be

$$I_{yz} = \int yz\,dm \qquad I_{zx} = \int zx\,dm \qquad I_{xy} = \int xy\,dm$$

Then the moment of inertia I_x' becomes equal to

$$I_x \cos^2 A + I_y \cos^2 B + I_z \cos^2 C - 2I_{yz} \cos B \cos C - 2I_{zx} \cos C \cos A - 2I_{xy} \cos A \cos B$$

The moment of inertia of any solid may be considered to be made up of the sum or difference of the moments of inertia of simple solids of which the moments of inertia are known.

Moments of Inertia of Important Solids (Homogeneous)

$m = w/g$ = mass per unit of volume of the body
$M = W/g$ = total mass of body
r = radius. I = moment of inertia (mass units)
$I_w = I \times g$ = moment of inertia (weight units)

Solid circular cylinder about its axis: $I = \pi r^4 ma/2 = Mr^2/2$. ($a$ = length of axis of cylinder.)

Solid circular cylinder about an axis through the center of gravity and perpendicular to axis of cylinder: $I = M[r^2 + (a^2/3)]/4$.

Hollow circular cylinder about its axis: $I = \pi ma(r_1^4 - r_2^4)/2$. ($r_1$ and r_2 = outer and inner radii; a = length.)

Thin hollow circular cylinder about its axis: $I = Mr^2$.

Solid sphere about a diameter: $I = 8m\pi r^5/15 = 2Mr^2/5$.

Thin hollow sphere about a diameter: $I = 2Mr^2/3$.

Thick hollow sphere about a diameter: $I = 8m\pi(r_1^5 - r_2^5)/15$. ($r_1$ and r_2 are outer and inner radii.)

Rectangular prism about an axis through center of gravity and perpendicular to a face whose dimensions are a and b: $I = M(a^2 + b^2)/12$.

Solid right circular cone about an axis through its apex and perpendicular to its axis: $I = 3M[(r^2/4) + h^2]/5$. (h = altitude of cone, r = radius of base.)

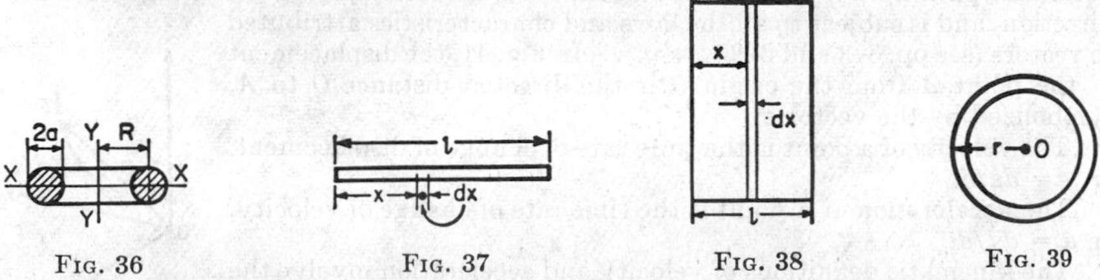

FIG. 36 FIG. 37 FIG. 38 FIG. 39

Solid right circular cone about its axis of revolution: $I = 3Mr^2/10$.

Ellipsoid with semiaxes a, b, and c: I about diameter $2c$ (z-axis) $= 4m\pi abc\,(a^2 + b^2)/15$. [Equation of ellipsoid: $(x^2/a^2) + (y^2/b^2) + (z^2/c^2) = 1$.]

Ring with Circular Section (Fig. 36): $I_{yy} = \frac{1}{2}m\pi^2Ra^2(4R^2 + 3a^2)$; $I_{xx} = m\pi^2Ra^2[R^2 + (5a^2/4)]$.

Approximate Moments of Inertia of Solids. In order to determine the moment of inertia of a solid, it is necessary to know all its dimensions. In the case of a rod of mass M, Fig. 37, and length l, with shape and size of the cross section unknown, making the approximation that the weight is all concentrated along the axis of the rod, the moment of inertia about YY will be $I_{yy} = \int_0^l (M/l)x^2\,dx = Ml^2/3$.

A thin plate may be treated in the same way (Fig. 38): $I_{yy} = \int^l (M/l)x^2\,dx$. Here the mass of the plate is assumed as concentrated at its middle layer.

Thin Ring, or Cylinder (Fig. 39). Assume the mass, M, of the ring or cylinder to be concentrated at a distance r from O. The moment of inertia about an axis through O perpendicular to plane of ring or along axis of cylinder will be $I = Mr^2$; this will be greater than the exact moment of inertia, and r is sometimes taken as the distance from O to the center of gravity of the cross section of the rim.

Flywheel Effect. The moment of inertia of a solid is often called flywheel effect in the solution of problems dealing with rotating bodies, and is usually expressed in pounds per square foot (I_w).

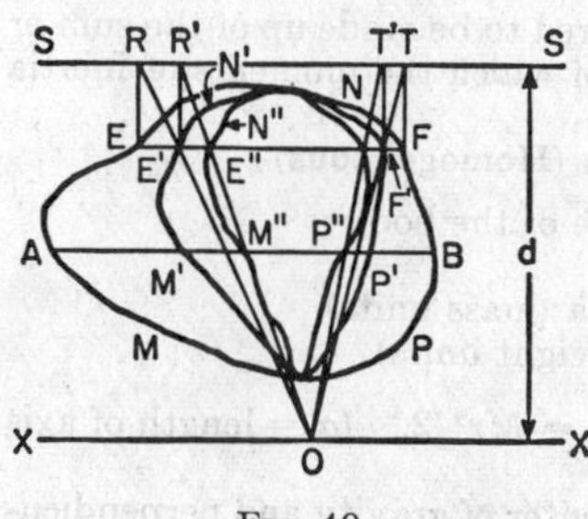

Fig. 40

Graphical Determination of the Centroids and Moments of Inertia of Plane Areas. Required, to find the center of gravity of the area MNP, Fig. 40, and its moment of inertia about any axis XX.

Draw any line SS parallel to XX and at a distance d from it. Draw a number of lines such as AB and EF across the figure parallel to XX. From E and F draw ER and FT perpendicular to SS. Select as a pole any point O on XX, preferably the point nearest the area, and draw OR and OT, cutting EF at E' and F'. If the same construction is repeated, using other lines parallel to XX, a number of points will be obtained, which, if connected by a smooth curve, will give the area $M'N'P'$. Project E' and F' on to SS by lines $E'R'$ and $F'T'$. Join F' and T' with O, obtaining E'' and F''; connect the points obtained using other lines parallel to XX and obtain an area $M''N''P''$. The area $M'N'P' \times d =$ moment of area MNP about the line XX, and the distance from XX to the centroid $MNP =$ area $M'N'P' \times d/$area MNP. Also, area $M''N''P'' \times d^2 =$ moment of inertia of MNP about XX. The areas $M'N'P'$ and $M''N''P''$ can best be obtained by use of a planimeter.

KINEMATICS

Kinematics is the study of the motion of bodies without reference to the forces causing that motion or the mass of the bodies.

The **displacement** of a point is the directed distance that a point has moved on a geometric path from a convenient origin. It is a **vector,** having both magnitude and direction, and is subject to all the laws and characteristics attributed to vectors (see pp. 3–3 and 2–96 *et seq.*). In Fig. 41, the displacement of the point A from the origin O is the directed distance O to A, symbolized by the vector **s**.

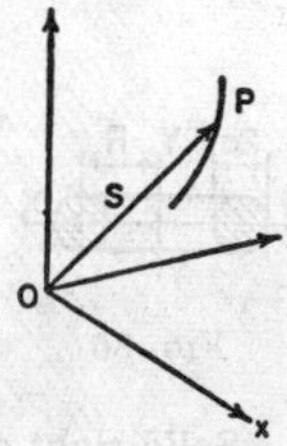

The **velocity** of a point is the time rate of change of displacement, or $\mathbf{v} = d\mathbf{s}/dt$.

The **acceleration** of a point is the time rate of change of velocity, or $\mathbf{a} = d\mathbf{v}/dt$.

Fig. 41

The kinematic definitions of velocity and acceleration involve the four variables, *displacement, velocity, acceleration,* and *time.* If we eliminate the variable of time, a third equation of motion is obtained, $ds/v = dt = dv/a$. This differential equation, together with the definitions of velocity and acceleration, make up the *three kinematic equations* of motion, $v = ds/dt$, $a = dv/dt$, and $a\,ds = v\,dv$. These differential equations are usually limited to the scalar form when expressed together since the last can only be properly expressed in terms of the scalar dt. The first two, since they are definitions for velocity and acceleration, are **vector equations.**

A **space-time curve** offers a convenient means for the study of the motion of a point. The **slope of the curve** at any point will represent the **velocity** at that time. In Fig. 42 (a) the slope is constant, as the graph is a straight line; the velocity is therefore uniform. In Fig. 42 (b) the slope of the curve varies from point to point, and the velocity must also vary. At p and q the slope is zero; therefore, the velocity of the point at the corresponding times must also be zero.

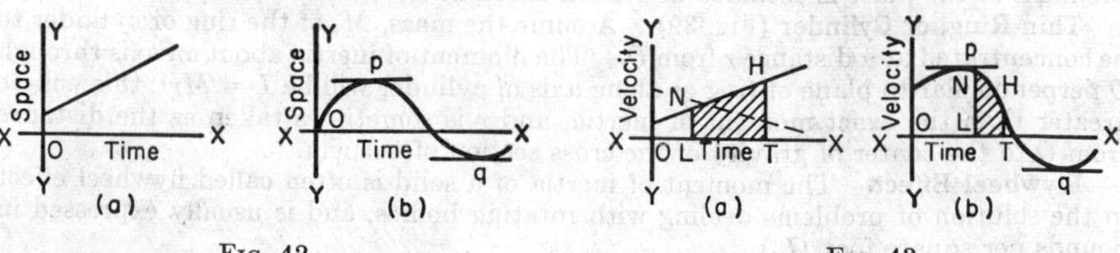

Fig. 42

Fig. 43

A **velocity-time curve** offers a convenient means for the study of acceleration. The **slope of the curve at** any point will represent the **acceleration** at that time. In Fig. 43(*a*) the slope is constant, so the acceleration must be constant. In the case represented by the full line, the acceleration is positive, so the velocity is increasing. The dotted line shows a negative acceleration and therefore a decreasing velocity. In Fig. 43(*b*) the slope of the curve varies from point to point, so the acceleration must also vary. At p and q the slope is zero; therefore, the acceleration of the point at the corresponding times must also be zero. The area under the velocity-time curve between any two ordinates such as NL and HT will represent the distance moved in time interval LT. In the case of the uniformly accelerated motion shown by the full line in Fig. 43(*a*), the area $LNHT$ is $\frac{1}{2}(NL + HT) \times (OT - OL)$ = mean velocity multiplied by the time interval = space passed over during this time interval. In Fig. 43(*b*) the mean velocity can be obtained from the equation of the curve by means of the calculus, or graphically by approximation of the area.

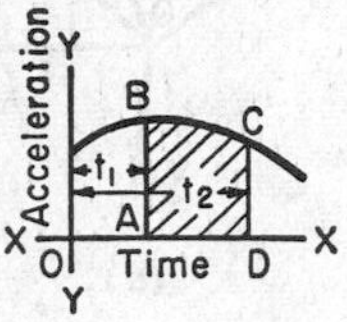

FIG. 44

An **acceleration-time curve** (Fig. 44) may be constructed by plotting accelerations as ordinates, and times as abscissas. The area under this curve between any two ordinates will represent the total increase in velocity during the time interval. The area $ABCD$ represents the total increase in velocity between time t_1 and time t_2.

General Expressions Showing the Relations between Space, Time, Velocity, and Acceleration for Rectilinear Motion

Special Motions

Uniform Motion. If the **velocity** is **constant,** the **acceleration** must be **zero,** and the point has uniform motion. The space-time curve becomes a straight line inclined toward the time axis [Fig. 42(*a*)]. The velocity-time curve becomes a straight line parallel to the time axis. For this motion $a = 0$, v = constant, and $s = s_0 + vt$.

Uniformly Accelerated or Retarded Motion. If the **velocity is not uniform** but the **acceleration is constant,** the point has uniformly accelerated motion; the acceleration may be either positive or negative. The space-time curve becomes a parabola and the velocity-time curve becomes a straight line inclined toward the time axis, Fig. 43(*a*). The acceleration-time curve becomes a straight line parallel to the time axis. For this motion a = constant, $v = v_0 + at$, $s = s_0 + v_0t + \frac{1}{2}at^2$.

If the point starts from rest, $v_0 = 0$. Care should be taken concerning the sign + or − for acceleration.

Table 1

Variables	$s = f(t)$	$v = f(t)$	$a = f(t)$	$a = f(s,v)$
Displacement....	....	$s = s_0 + \int_{t_0}^{t} vdt$	$s = s_0 + \int_{t_0}^{t}\int_{t_0}^{t} a\,dt\,dt$	$s = s_0 + \int_{v_0}^{v} (v/d)\,dv$
Velocity........	$v = ds/dt$	....	$v = v_0 + \int_{t_0}^{t} adt$	$\int_{v_0}^{v} v\,dv = \int_{s}^{s_0} a\,ds$
Acceleration.....	$a = d^2s/dt^2$	$a = dv/dt$	....	$a = v\,dv/ds$

Composition and Resolution of Velocities and Acceleration

Resultant Velocity. A velocity is said to be the resultant of two other velocities when it is represented by a vector that is the geometric sum of the vectors representing the other two velocities. This is the **parallelogram of motion.** In Fig. 45, **v** is the resultant of $\mathbf{v}_1$ and $\mathbf{v}_2$ and is represented by the diagonal of a parallelogram of which $\mathbf{v}_1$ and $\mathbf{v}_2$ are the sides; or it is the third side of a triangle of which $\mathbf{v}_1$ and $\mathbf{v}_2$ are the other two sides.

FIG. 45

Polygon of Motion. The parallelogram of motion may be extended to the polygon of motion. Let $\mathbf{v}_1$, $\mathbf{v}_2$, $\mathbf{v}_3$, $\mathbf{v}_4$ [Fig. 46(*a*)] show the directions of four velocities imparted in the same plane to point O. If the lines $\mathbf{v}_1$, $\mathbf{v}_2$, $\mathbf{v}_3$, $\mathbf{v}_4$ [Fig. 46(*b*)] are drawn parallel to and proportional to the velocities imparted to point O, $\mathbf{v}$ will represent the resultant velocity imparted to O. It will make no difference in what order the velocities are taken in constructing the motion polygon. As long as the arrows showing the direction of the motion follow each other in order about the polygon, the resultant velocity of the point will be represented in magnitude by the closing side of the polygon, but opposite in direction.

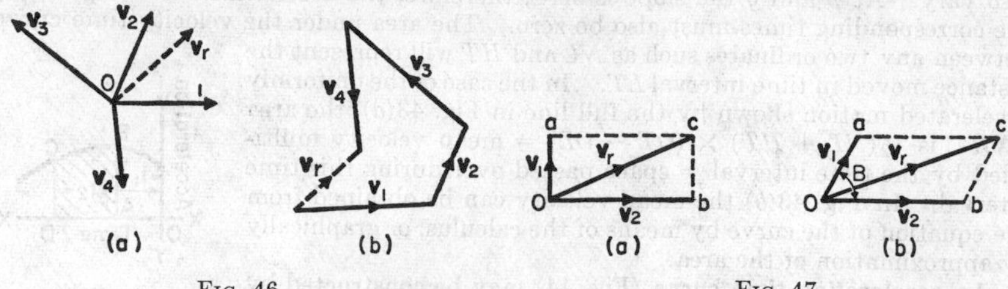

FIG. 46 FIG. 47

Resolution of Velocities. Velocities may be resolved into **component velocities** in the same plane, as shown by Fig. 47. Let the velocity of point O be v_r. In Fig. 47(*a*) this velocity is resolved into two components in the same plane as v_r and at right angles to each other.

$$v_r = \sqrt{(v_1)^2 + (v_2)^2}$$

In Fig. 10(*b*) the components are in same plane as v_r, but are not at right angles to each other. In this case,

$$v_r = \sqrt{(v_1)^2 + (v_2)^2 + 2v_1v_2 \cos B}$$

If the components v_1 and v_2 and angle B are known, the direction of v_r can be determined. $\sin bOc = (v_1/v_r) \sin B$. $\sin cOa = (v_2/v_r) \sin B$. Where v_1 and v_2 are at right angles to each other, $\sin B = 1$.

Resultant Acceleration. Accelerations may be combined and resolved in the same manner as velocities, but in this case the lines or vectors represent accelerations instead of velocities. If the acceleration had components of magnitude a_1 and a_2, the magnitude of the resultant acceleration would be $\sqrt{a = (a_1)^2 + (a_2)^2 + 2a_1a_2 \cos B}$, where B is the angle between the vectors a_1 and a_2.

Curvilinear Motion in a Plane

The linear velocity, $v = ds/dt$ of a point in curvilinear motion, is the same as for rectilinear motion. Its direction is tangent to the path of the point. In Fig. 48(*a*), let $p_1p_2p_3$ be the path of a moving point, and v_1, v_2, v_3 represent its velocity at points p_1, p_2, p_3, respectively. If O be taken as a pole Fig. 48(*b*) and vectors v_1, v_2, v_3 representing the velocities of the point at p_1, p_2, and p_3 be drawn, the curve connecting the terminal points of these vectors is known as the **hodograph** of the motion. This velocity diagram is applicable only to motions all in the same plane.

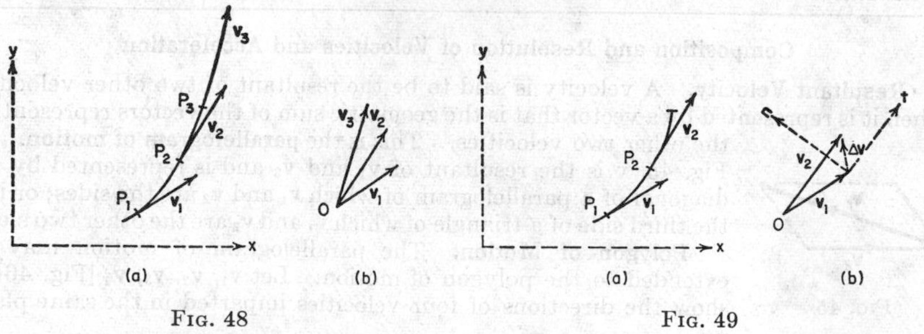

FIG. 48 FIG. 49

Acceleration. Tangents to the curve, Fig. 48(b), indicate the directions of the **instantaneous velocities.** The direction of the tangents does not, as a rule, coincide with the direction of the accelerations as represented by tangents to the path. If the acceleration a at some point in the path is resolved by means of a parallelogram into components tangent and normal to the path, the normal acceleration $a_n = v^2/\rho$, where ρ = radius of curvature of the path at the point in question, and the tangential acceleration $a_t = dv/dt$, where v = velocity tangent to the path at the same point. $a = \sqrt{a_n^2 + a_t^2}$. The normal acceleration is constantly directed toward the center of the path.

EXAMPLE. Figure 49 shows a point moving in a curvilinear path. At p_1 the velocity is $\mathbf{v}_1$; at p_2 the velocity is $\mathbf{v}_2$. If these velocities are drawn from pole O [Fig. 49(b)], $\Delta\mathbf{v}$ will be the difference between $\mathbf{v}_2$ and $\mathbf{v}_1$. The acceleration during travel p_1p_2 will be $\Delta\mathbf{v}/\Delta t$, where t Δt is the time interval. The approximation becomes closer to instantaneous acceleration as shorter intervals Δt are employed. The acceleration $\Delta\mathbf{v}/\Delta t$ can be resolved into normal and tangential components leading to $\mathbf{a}_n = \Delta\mathbf{v}_n/\Delta t$, normal to the path, and $\mathbf{a}_r = \Delta\mathbf{v}_\rho/\Delta t$, tangential to the path.

Velocity and *acceleration* may be expressed in **polar coordinates** such that $v = \sqrt{v_r^2 + v_\theta^2}$ and $a = \sqrt{a_r^2 + a_\theta^2}$. Figure 50 may be used to explain the r and θ coordinates.

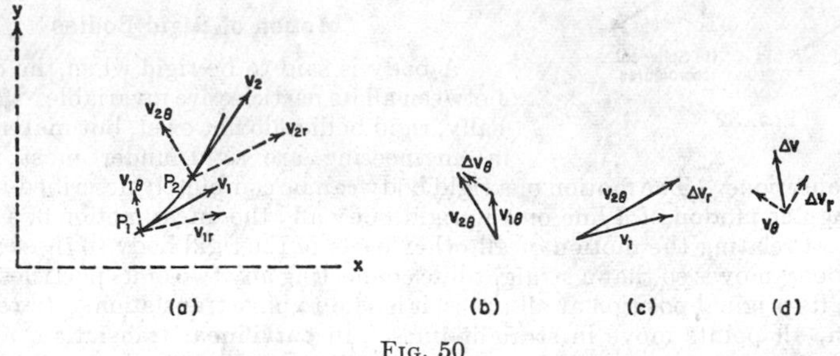

FIG. 50

EXAMPLE. At p_1 the velocity is $\mathbf{v}_1$, with components $\mathbf{v}_{1r}$ in the r-direction and $\mathbf{v}_{1\theta}$ in the θ-direction. At p_2 the velocity is $\mathbf{v}_2$, with components $\mathbf{v}_{2r}$ in the r-direction and $\mathbf{v}_{2\theta}$ in the θ-direction. It is evident that the difference in velocities $\mathbf{v}_2 - \mathbf{v}_1 = \Delta\mathbf{v}$ will have components $\Delta\mathbf{v}_r$ and $\Delta\mathbf{v}_\theta$, giving rise to accelerations $\mathbf{a}_r$ and $\mathbf{a}_\theta$ in a time interval Δt.

In polar coordinates, $v_r = dr/dt$, $a_r = d^2r/dt^2 - r(d\theta/dt)^2$, $v_\theta = r(d\theta/dt)$, and $a_\theta = r(d^2\theta/dt^2) + 2(dr/dt)(d\theta/dt)$.

If a point P moves on a circular path of radius r with an angular velocity of ω and an angular acceleration of α, the linear velocity of the point P is $v = \omega r$ and the two components of the linear acceleration are $a_n = v^2/r = \omega^2 r = v\omega$ and $a_t = \alpha r$.

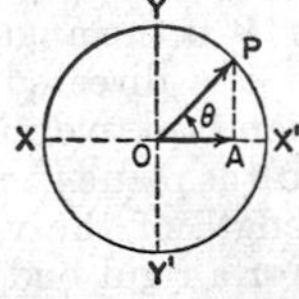

FIG. 51

If the angular velocity is constant, the point P travels equal circular paths in equal intervals of time. The projected displacement, velocity, and acceleration of the point P on the x- and y-axes are sinusoidal functions of time, and the motion is said to be **harmonic motion.** Angular velocity is usually expressed in radians per second, and when the number (N) of revolutions traversed per minute (rpm) by the point P is known, the angular velocity of the radius r is $\omega = 2\pi N/60 = 0.10472N$. In Fig. 51, let the angular velocity of the line OP be a constant ω. Let the point P start at X' and move to P in time t. Then the angle $\theta = \omega t$. If $OP = r$, $X'A = r - OA = r - r\cos\omega t = s$. The velocity V of the point A on the x-axis will equal $ds/dt = \omega r \sin \omega t$, and the acceleration $a = dv/dt = -\omega^2 r \cos\omega t$. The period τ is the time necessary for the point P to complete one cycle of motion $\tau = 2\pi/\omega$, and it is also equal to the time necessary for A to complete a full cycle on the x-axis from X' to X and return.

Curvilinear Motion in Space

If **three dimensions** are used, velocities and accelerations may be resolved into components not in the same plane by what is known as the **parallelepiped of motion.** Three coordinate systems are widely used, cartesian, cylindrical, and spherical. In **cartesian coordinates,** $v = \sqrt{v_x^2 + v_y^2 + v_z^2}$ and $a = \sqrt{a_x^2 + a_y^2 + a_z^2}$. In **cylindrical coordinates,** the radius vector **R** of displacement lies in the *r-z* plane, which is at an angle with the *x-z* plane. Referring to (*a*) of Fig. 52, the θ coordinate is perpendicular to the *r-z* plane. In this system, $v = \sqrt{v_r^2 + v_\theta^2 + v_z^2}$ and $a = \sqrt{a_r^2 + a_\theta^2 + a_z^2}$, where $v_r = dr/dt$, $a_r = d^2r/dt^2 - r(d\theta/dt)^2$, $v_\theta = r(d\theta/dt)$, and $a_\theta = r(d^2\theta/dt^2) + 2(dr/dt)(d\theta/dt)$. In **spherical coordinates,** the three coordinates are the *R* coordinate, the θ coordinate, and the ϕ coordinate as in (*b*) of Fig. 52. The velocity and acceleration are $v = \sqrt{v_R^2 + v_\theta^2 + v_\phi^2}$ and $a = \sqrt{a_r^2 + a_\theta^2 + a_\phi^2}$, where $v_R = dR/dt$, $v_\phi = R(d\phi/dt)$, $v_\theta = R\cos\phi(d\theta/dt)$, $a_R = d^2R/dt^2 - R(d\phi/dt)^2 - R\cos^2\phi\,(d\theta/dt)^2$, $a_\phi = R(d^2\phi/dt^2) + R\cos\phi\sin\phi\,(d\theta/dt)^2 + 2(dR/dt)(d\phi/dt)$, and $a_\theta = R\cos\phi\,(d^2\theta/dt^2) + 2[(dR/dt)\cos\phi - R\sin\phi\,(d\phi/dt)]\,d\theta/dt$.

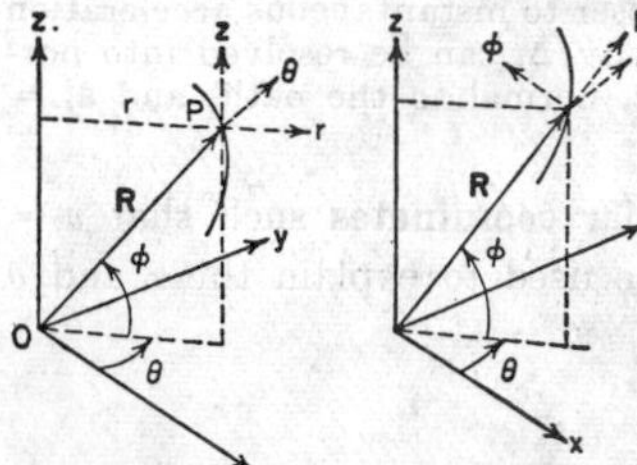

(a) Cylindrical coordinates (b) Spherical coordinates

FIG. 52

Motion of Rigid Bodies

A body is said to be **rigid** when the distances between all its particles are invariable. Theoretically, rigid bodies do not exist, but materials used in engineering are rigid under most practical working conditions. The motion of a rigid body can be completely described by knowing the **angular motion** of a line on the rigid body and the **linear motion** of a point on this line and relating the motion of all other parts of the rigid body to these motions. If a rigid body moves so that a straight line connecting any two of its particles remains parallel to its original position at all times, it is said to have **translation.** In **rectilinear translation,** all points move in straight lines. In **curvilinear translation,** all points move on congruent curves but without rotation. **Rotation** is defined as angular motion about an axis, which may or may not be fixed. Rigid body motion in which the paths of all particles lie on parallel planes is called **plane motion.**

Angular Motion

Angular displacement is the change in angular position of a given line as measured from a convenient reference line. In Fig. 53, consider the motion of the line *AB* as it moves from its original position *A′B′*. The angle between lines *AB* and *A′B′* is the angular displacement of line AB, symbolized as $\boldsymbol{\theta}$. It is a directed quantity and is a vector. The usual notation used to designate angular displacement is a vector normal to the plane in which the angular displacement occurs. The length of the vector is proportional to the magnitude of the angular displacement. For a rigid body moving in three dimensions, the line *AB* may have angular motion about any three orthogonal axes. For example, the angular displacement can be described in cartesian coordinates as $\boldsymbol{\theta} = \boldsymbol{\theta}_x + \boldsymbol{\theta}_y + \boldsymbol{\theta}_z$, where $\theta = \sqrt{\theta_x^2 + \theta_y^2 + \theta_z^2}$.

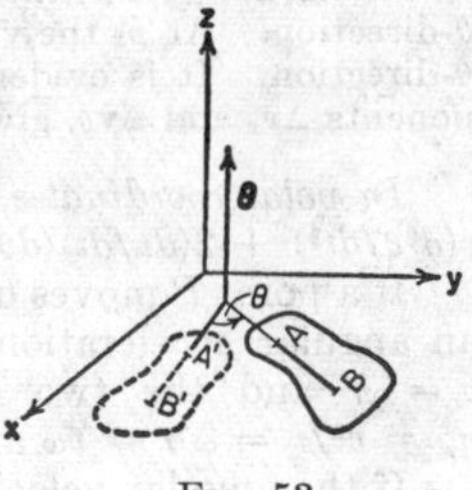

FIG. 53

Angular velocity is defined as the time rate of change of angular displacement, $\boldsymbol{\omega} = d\boldsymbol{\theta}/dt$. Angular velocity may also have components about any three orthogonal axes.

Angular acceleration is defined as the time rate of change of angular acceleration, $\boldsymbol{\alpha} = d\boldsymbol{\omega}/dt = d^2\boldsymbol{\theta}/dt^2$. Angular acceleration may also have components about any three orthogonal axes.

The *kinematic equations* of angular motion of a line are analogous to those for the motion of a point. In referring to Table 1, $\omega = d\theta/dt$, $\alpha = d\omega/dt$, and $\alpha\, d\theta = \omega\, d\omega$. Substitute θ for *s*, ω for *v*, and α for *a*.

Motion of a Rigid Body in a Plane

Plane motion is the motion of a rigid body such that the paths of all particles of that rigid body lie on parallel planes.

Instantaneous Axis. When the axis about which any body may be considered to rotate changes its position, any one position is known as an instantaneous axis, and the line through all positions of the instantaneous axis as the **centrode.**

When the velocity of two points in the same plane of a rigid body having plane motion is known, the instantaneous axis for the body will be at the intersection of the lines drawn from each point and perpendicular to its velocity. See Fig. 54, in which A and B are two points on the rod AB, $\mathbf{v}_1$ and $\mathbf{v}_2$ representing theirdvelocities. O is the instantaneous axis for AB; $\therefore$ point C will h ave velocity shown in a line perpendicular to OC.

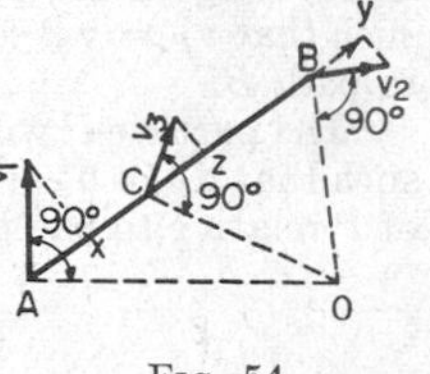

Fig. 54

Linear velocities of points in a body rotating about an instantaneous axis are proportional to their distances from this axis. In Fig. 54, $\mathbf{v}_1:\mathbf{v}_2:\mathbf{v}_3 = AO:OB:OC$. If the velocities of A and B were parallel, the lines OA and OB would also be parallel and there would be no instantaneous axis. The motion of the rod would be translation, and all points would be moving with the same velocity in parallel straight lines.

If a body has plane motion, the components of the velocities of any two points in the body along the straight line joining them must be equal. Ax must be equal to By and Cz in Fig. 54.

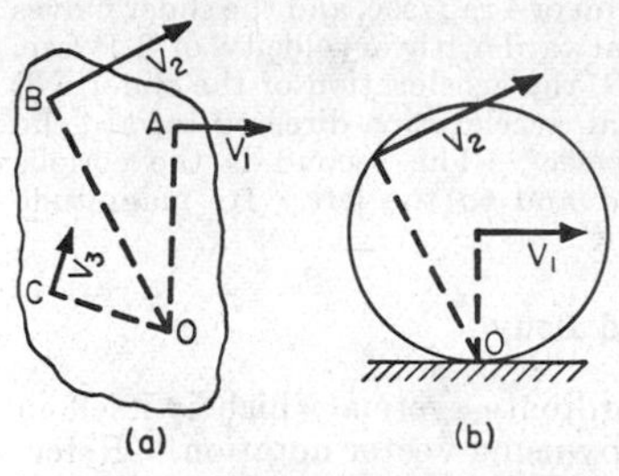

Fig. 55

Example. In Fig. 55(a), the velocities of points A and B are known—they are $\mathbf{v}_1$ and $\mathbf{v}_2$ respectively. To find the instantaneous axis of the body, perpendiculars AO and BO are drawn. O, at the intersection of the perpendiculars, is the **instantaneous axis** of the body. To find the velocity of any other point, like C, line OC is drawn and $\mathbf{v}_3$ erected perpendicular to OC with magnitude equal to $v_1(CO/AO)$. The **angular velocity** of the body will be $\omega = v_1/AO$ or v_2/BO or v_3/CO. The instantaneous axis of a wheel rolling on at rack without slipping [Fig. 55(b)] lies at the point of contact, O, which has zero linear velocity. All points of the wheel will have velocities perpendicular to radii to O and proportional in magnitudes to their respective distances from O.

Another way to describe the plane motion of a rigid body is with the use of **relative motion.** In Fig. 56 the velocity of point A is $\mathbf{v}_1$. The angular velocity of the line AB is v_1/r_{AB}. The velocity of B relative to A is $\omega_{AB} \times r_{AB}$. Point B is considered to be

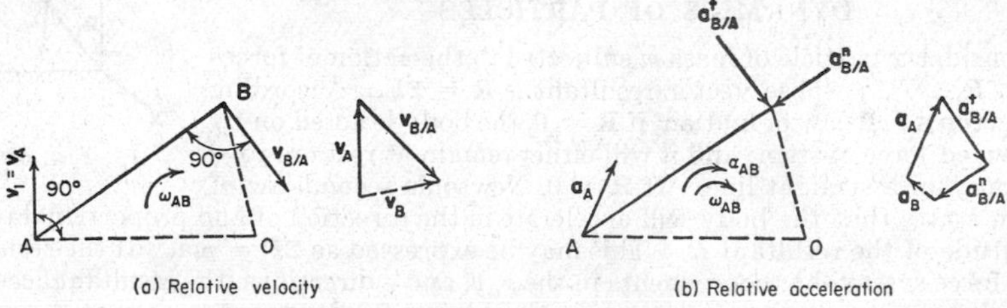

Fig. 56

moving on a circular path around A as a center. The direction of the relative velocity of B to A would be tangent to the circular path in the direction that ω_{AB} would make B move. The velocity of B is the vector sum of the velocity of A added to the velocity of B relative to A, $\mathbf{v}_B = \mathbf{v}_A + \mathbf{v}_{B/A}$.

The **acceleration** of B is the vector sum of the acceleration of A added to the acceleration of B relative to A, $\mathbf{a}_B = \mathbf{a}_A + \mathbf{a}_{B/A}$. Care must be taken to include the complete relative acceleration of B to A. If B is considered to move on a circular path about A, with a velocity relative to A, it will have an acceleration relative to A that has both normal and tangential components: $\mathbf{a}_{B/A} = \mathbf{a}_{B^n/A} + \mathbf{a}_{B^t/A}$.

If B is a point on a path which lies on the same rigid body as the line AB, a **particle P traveling on the path** will have a velocity $\mathbf{v}_P$ at the instant P passes over point B such that $\mathbf{v}_P = \mathbf{v}_A + \mathbf{v}_{B/A} + \mathbf{v}_{P/B}$, where the velocity $\mathbf{v}_{P/B}$ is the velocity of P relative to path B.

The particle P will have an acceleration $\mathbf{a}_P$ at the instant P passes over the point B such that $\mathbf{a}_P = \mathbf{a}_A + \mathbf{a}_{B/A} + \mathbf{a}_{P/B} + 2\omega_{AB} \times \mathbf{v}_{P/B}$. The term $\mathbf{a}_{P/B}$ is the acceleration of P relative to the path at point B. The last term, $2\mathbf{v}_{P/B}\omega_{AB}$, is frequently referred to as the **coriolis acceleration.** The direction is always normal to the path in a sense which would rotate the head of the vector $\mathbf{v}_{P/B}$ about its tail in the direction of the angular velocity of the rigid body ω_{AB}.

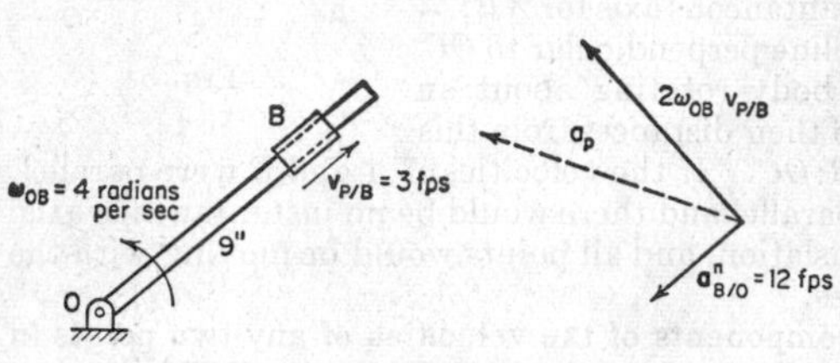

FIG. 57

EXAMPLE. In Fig. 57, arm OB is rotating counterclockwise about O with a constant angular velocity of 38 rpm or 4 rad/sec, and the slider moves outward with a velocity of 3 ft/sec. At an instant when the slider is 9 in. from the center O, the acceleration of the slider will have two components. One component is the normal acceleration directed toward the center O. Its magnitude is $\omega^2 r = (4)^2(9/12) = 12$ ft/sec². The second is the coriolis acceleration directed normal to the arm OB, upward and to the left. Its magnitude is $2\omega v = 2(4)(3) = 24$ ft/sec².

General Motion of a Rigid Body

The general motion of a point moving in a coordinate system which is itself in motion is complicated and can best be summarized by using vector notation. Referring to Fig. 58, let the point P be displaced a vector distance $\mathbf{R}$ from the origin O of a moving reference frame x, y, z which has a velocity $\mathbf{v}_o$ and an acceleration $\mathbf{a}_o$. If point P has a velocity and an acceleration relative to the moving reference plane, let these be $\mathbf{v}_r$ and $\mathbf{a}_r$. The angular velocity of the moving reference frame is ω, and the origin of the moving reference frame is displaced a vector distance $\mathbf{R}_1$ from the origin of a primary (fixed) reference frame X, Y, Z. The velocity and acceleration of P are $\mathbf{v}_P = \mathbf{v}_o + \omega \times \mathbf{R} + \mathbf{v}_r$ and $\mathbf{a}_P = \mathbf{a}_o + (d\omega/dt) \times \mathbf{R} + \omega \times (\omega \times \mathbf{R}) + 2\omega \times \mathbf{v}_r + \mathbf{a}_r$.

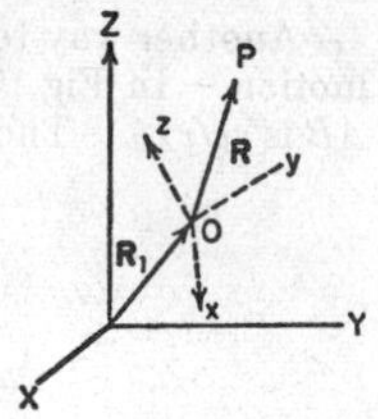

FIG. 58

DYNAMICS OF PARTICLES

Consider a particle of mass m subjected to the action of forces $\mathbf{F}_1, \mathbf{F}_2, \mathbf{F}_3 \ldots$, whose vector resultant is $\mathbf{R} = \Sigma\mathbf{F}$. According to Newton's first law of motion, if $\mathbf{R} = 0$, the body is acted on by a balanced force system, and it will either remain at rest or move uniformly in a straight line. If $\mathbf{R} = 0$, Newton's second law of motion states that the body will accelerate in the direction of and proportional to the magnitude of the resultant R. This may be expressed as $\Sigma\mathbf{F} = m\mathbf{a}$. If the resultant of the force system has components in the x, y, and z directions, the resultant acceleration will have proportional components in the x, y, and z direction so that $F_x = ma_x$, $F_y = ma_y$, and $F_z = ma_z$. If the resultant of the force system varies with time, the acceleration will also vary with time.

In **rectilinear motion,** the acceleration and the direction of the unbalanced force must be in the direction of motion. **Forces must be in balance and the acceleration equal to zero in any direction other than the direction of motion.**

EXAMPLE 1. The body in Fig. 59 weighs 100 lb and is subjected to an external horizontal force of 40 lb applied in the direction shown. The coefficient of friction between the body and the inclined plane is 0.1. Required, the velocity of the body at the end of 5 sec, if it starts from rest.

First determine all the forces acting externally on the body. These are the applied force F = 40 lb, the weight W = 100 lb, and the force with which the plane reacts on the body. This latter force can be resolved into component forces, one normal and one parallel to the surface of the plane. Motion will be downward along the plane since a static analysis will show that the body will slide downward unless the static coefficient of friction is greater than 0.269. In the direction normal to the surface of the plane, the forces must be balanced. The normal force is $(3/5)(40) + (4/5)(100) = 104$ lb. The frictional force is $104 \times 0.1 = 10.4$ lb. The unbalanced force acting on the body along the plane is $(3/5)(100) - (4/5)(40) - 10.5 = 17.6$ lb downward. $F = ma = (100/g)a$; therefore, $a = 0.176\,g$. The body is acted upon by constant forces and starts from rest; therefore, $v = \int_0^5 a\,dt$, and at the end of 5 sec, the velocity would be 28.35 ft/sec.

EXAMPLE 2. Find the constant force necessary to start from rest a train weighing 100 tons and give it a speed of 30 mph in 1 min; track to be level and straight, train resistance to be constant and equal to 12 lb per ton. The external forces acting upon the train

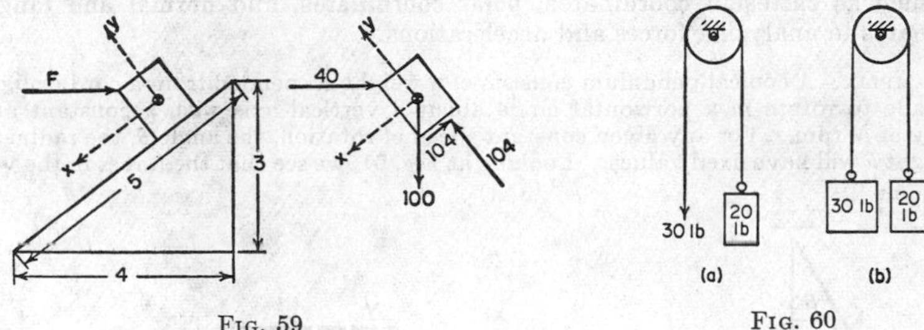

FIG. 59

FIG. 60

are the resistance of $100 \times 12 = 1{,}200$ lb, the constant force F pulling the train along the level track, the force of gravity equal to weight of train, and the reaction of the track. The forces normal to the track form a balanced system, but, as the train is to be started from rest and given a velocity, the forces acting along the track must form an unbalanced system. A velocity of 30 mph = 44 fps; to acquire this velocity in 60 sec requires an acceleration of 44/60, as $a = v/t$. The unbalanced force to give the train this acceleration is $F = ma = (100 \times 2{,}000/g)(44/60) = 4{,}560$ lb. The total tractive force required is, therefore, $4{,}560 + 1{,}200 = 5{,}760$ lb. If the train is on a grade, the problem is the same, with the addition of another force acting along the track, *i.e.*, the component of the weight along the track.

EXAMPLE 3. The force with which a rope acts on a body is equal and opposite to the force with which the body acts on the rope, and each is equal to the tension in the rope. In Fig. 60(a), neglecting the weight of the pulley and the rope, the tension in the cord must be the force of 30 lb. For the 20 lb weight, the unbalanced force is $30 - 20 = 10$ lb in the upward direction, *i.e.*, $30 - 20 = (20/g)a$, and $a = 16.1$ ft/sec² upward. In Fig. 60(b) the 30 lb force is replaced by a 30 lb weight. The unbalanced force is still $30 - 20 = 10$ lb, but it now acts on two weights so that $30 - 20 = (50/g)a$ and $a = 6.44$ ft/sec². The 20 lb weight is accelerated upward, and the 30 lb weight is accelerated downward. The tension in the rope is equal to 20 lb plus the unbalanced force necessary to give it an upward acceleration of $g/5$ or $T = 20 + (20/g)(g/5) = 24$ lb. The tension is also equal to 30 lb less the unbalanced force necessary to give it a downward acceleration of $g/5$ or $T = 30 - (30/g)(g/5) = 24$ lb.

General Formulas for the Motion of a Body under the Action of a Constant Unbalanced Force

Let s = space in ft, a = acceleration in ft per sec per sec; v = velocity in ft per sec, v_0 = initial velocity in ft per sec, h = height in ft, F = force; m = mass, w = weight, g = acceleration due to gravity.

Initial velocity = 0	Initial velocity = v
$F = ma = (w/g)a$	$F = ma = (w/g)a$
$v = at$	$v = v_0 + at$
$s = \frac{1}{2}at^2 = \frac{1}{2}vt$	$s = v_0t + \frac{1}{2}at^2 = \frac{1}{2}v_0t + \frac{1}{2}vt$
$v = \sqrt{2as}$	
$= \sqrt{2gh}$ (falling freely from rest)	

If a body is to be moved in a straight line by a force, the line of action of this force must pass through its center of gravity.

General Rule for the Solution of Problems When the Forces Are Constant in Magnitude and Direction. Resolve all the forces acting on the body into two components, one in the direction of the body's motion and one at right angles to it. Add the components in the direction of the body's motion algebraically and find the **unbalanced force,** if any exists.

In **curvilinear motion,** a particle moves along a curved path, and the resultant of the unbalanced force system may have components in directions other than the direction of motion. **The acceleration in any given direction is proportional to the component of the resultant in that direction.** It is common to utilize orthogonal coordinate systems such as **cartesian coordinates, polar coordinates,** and **normal and tangential coordinates** in analyzing forces and accelerations.

Example. A conical pendulum consists of a weight suspended from a cord or light rod and made to rotate in a horizontal circle about a vertical axis with a constant angular velocity of N rpm. For any given constant speed of rotation, the angle θ, the radius r, and the height h will have fixed values. Looking at Fig. 61, we see that the forces in the vertical

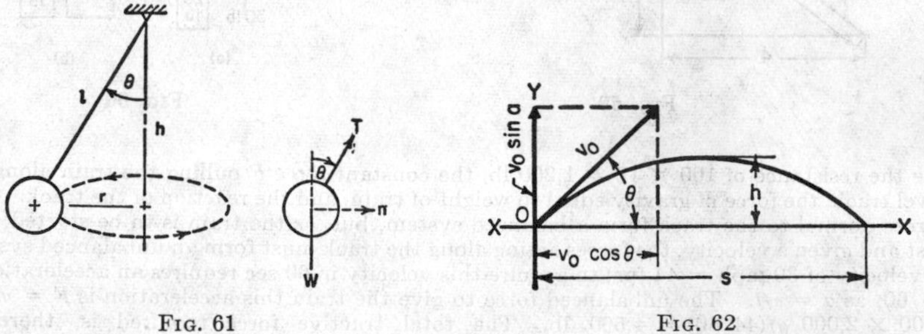

Fig. 61 Fig. 62

direction must be balanced, $T \cos \theta = w$. The forces in the direction normal to the circular path of rotation are unbalanced such that $T \sin \theta = (w/g)a_n = (w/g)\omega^2 r$. Substituting $r = l \sin \theta$ in this last equation gives the value of the tension in the cord $T = (w/g)l\omega^2$. Dividing the second equation by the first and substituting $\tan \theta = r/h$ yields the additional relation that $h = g/\omega^2$.

An unresisted projectile has a motion compounded of the vertical motion of a falling body, and of the horizontal motion due to the horizontal component of the velocity of projection. In Fig. 62 the only force acting after the projectile starts is gravity, which causes an acceleration downward. The horizontal component of the original velocity v_0 is not changed by gravity. The projectile will rise until the velocity given to it by gravity is equal to the vertical component of the starting velocity v_0, and the equation $v_0 \sin \theta = gt$ gives the time t required to reach the highest point in the curve. The same time will be taken in falling if the surface XX is level, and the projectile will therefore be in flight $2t$ sec. The distance $s = v_0 \cos \theta \times 2t$, and the maximum height of ascent $h = (v_0 \sin \theta)^2/2g$. The expressions for the coordinates of any point on the path of the projectile are: $x = (v_0 \cos \theta)t$, and $y = (v_0 \sin \theta)t - \frac{1}{2}gt^2$, giving $y = x \tan \theta - (gx^2/2v_0^2 \cos^2 \theta)$ as the equation for the curve of the path. The radius of curvature of the highest point may be found by using the general expression $v^2 = gr$ and solving for r, v being taken equal to $v_0 \cos \theta$.

Simple Pendulum. The period of oscillation $= \tau = 2\pi \sqrt{l/g}$, where l is the length of the pendulum and the length of the swing is not great compared to l.

Centrifugal and Centripetal Forces. When a body revolves about an axis, some connection must exist capable of applying force enough to the body to constantly deviate it toward the axis. This deviating force is known as **centripetal force.** The equal and opposite resistance offered by the body to the connection is called a **centrifugal force** (c.f.). The acceleration toward the axis necessary to keep a particle moving in a circle about that axis is v^2/r; therefore, the force necessary is $ma = mv^2/r = wv^2/gr = w\pi^2N^2r/900g$, where N = rpm. This force is constantly directed toward the axis.

The centrifugal force of a solid body revolving about an axis is the same as if the whole mass of the body were concentrated at its center of gravity. Centrifugal force $= wv^2/gr = mv^2/r = w\omega^2r/g$, where w and m are the weight and mass of the whole body, r is the distance from the axis about which the body is rotating to the center of gravity of the body, ω the angular velocity of the body about the axis in radians, and v the linear velocity of the center of gravity of the body.

Balancing

A rotating body is said to be in **standing balance** when its center of gravity coincides with the axis upon which it revolves. Standing balance may be obtained by resting the axis carrying the body upon two horizontal plane surfaces, as in Fig. 63. If the center of gravity of the wheel A coincides with the center of the shaft B, there

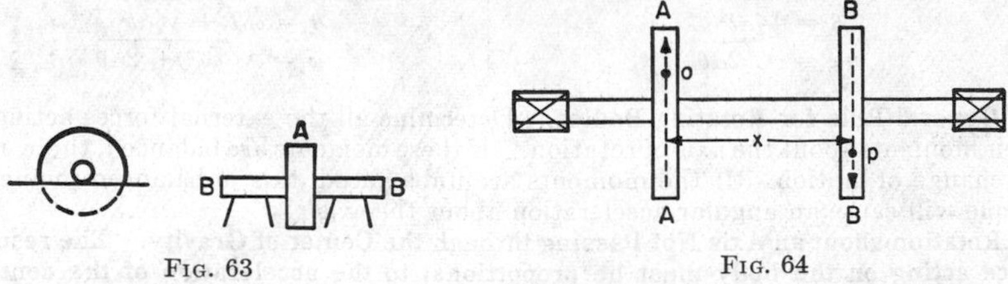

FIG. 63 FIG. 64

will be no movement, but if the center of gravity does not coincide with the center of the shaft, the shaft will roll until the center of gravity of the wheel comes directly under the center of the shaft. The center of gravity may be brought to the center of the shaft by adding or taking away weight at proper points on the diameter passing through the center of gravity and the center of the shaft. Weights may be added to or subtracted from any part of the wheel so long as its center of gravity is brought to the center of the shaft.

A rotating body may be in standing balance and not in **dynamic balance.** In Fig. 64, AA and BB are two disks whose centers of gravity are at o and p, respectively. The shaft and the disks are in standing balance if the disks are of the same weight and the distances of o and p from the center of the shaft are equal, and o and p lie in the same axial plane but on opposite sides of the shaft. Let the weight of each disk be w and the distances of o and p from the center of the shaft each be equal to r. The force exerted on the shaft by AA is equal to $w\omega^2r/g$, where ω is the angular velocity of shaft. Also, the force exerted on shaft by $BB = w\omega^2r/g$. These two equal and opposite parallel forces act at a distance x apart and constitute a couple with a moment tending to rotate the shaft, as shown by the arrows, of $(w\omega^2r/g)x$. A couple cannot be balanced by a single force, so two forces at least must be added to or subtracted from the system to get dynamic balance.

Systems of Particles. The principles of motion for a single particle can be extended to cover a **system of particles.** In this case, **the vector resultant of all external forces acting on the system of particles must equal the total mass of the system times the acceleration of the mass center, and the direction of the resultant must be the direction of the acceleration of the mass center.** This is the **principle of motion of the mass center.**

Rotation of Solid Bodies in a Plane about Fixed Axes

For a rigid body revolving in a plane about a fixed axis, **the resultant moment about that axis must be equal to the product of the moment of inertia (about that axis) and the angular acceleration,** $\Sigma M_0 = I_0\alpha$. This is a general statement which includes the particular case of rotation about an axis that passes through the center of gravity.

Rotation about an Axis Passing through the Center of Gravity. The rotation of a body about its center of gravity can only be caused or changed by a **couple.** See Fig. 65. If a single force F is applied to the wheel, the axis immediately acts on the wheel with an equal force to prevent translation, and the result is a couple (moment Fr) acting on the body and causing rotation about its center of gravity.

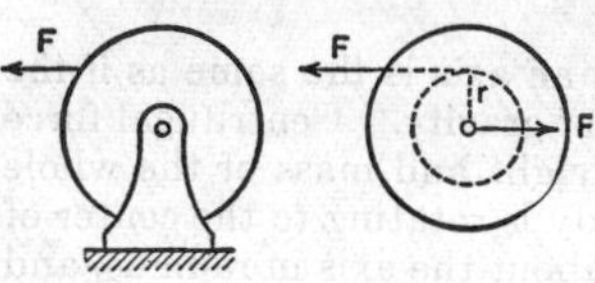

Fig. 65

General formulas for rotation of a body about a fixed axis through the center of gravity, if a constant unbalanced moment is applied (Fig. 65).

Let θ = angular displacement, radians, ω = angular velocity, radians per sec, α = angular acceleration, radians per sec per sec, M = unbalanced moment, ft-lb, I = moment of inertia (mass), g = acceleration due to gravity, t = time of application of M.

Initial angular velocity = 0	Initial angular velocity = ω_0
$M = I\alpha$	$M = I\alpha$
$\theta = \frac{1}{2}\alpha t^2$	$\theta = \omega_0 t + \frac{1}{2}\alpha t^2$
$\omega = \sqrt{2\alpha\theta}$	$\omega = \sqrt{\omega_0^2 + 2\alpha\theta}$

General Rule for Rotating Bodies. Determine all the external forces acting and their moments about the axis of rotation. If these moments are balanced, there will be no change of motion. If the moments are unbalanced, this unbalanced moment or **torque** will cause an angular acceleration about the axis.

Rotation about an Axis Not Passing through the Center of Gravity. The resultant force acting on the body must be proportional to the acceleration of the center of gravity and directed along its line of action. If the axis of rotation does not pass through the center of gravity, the center of gravity will have a resultant acceleration with a component $a_n = \omega^2 r$ directed toward the axis of rotation and a component $a_t = \alpha r$ tangential to its circular path. The resultant force acting on the body must also have two components, one directed normal and one directed tangential to the path of the center of gravity. The line of action of this resultant does not pass through the center of gravity because of the unbalanced moment $M_0 = I_0\alpha$ but at a point Q, as in Fig. 66. The point of application of this resultant is known as the **center of percussion** and may be **defined** as the point of application of the resultant of all the forces tending to cause a body to rotate about a certain axis. It is the point at which a suspended body may be struck without causing any pressure on the axis passing through the point of suspension.

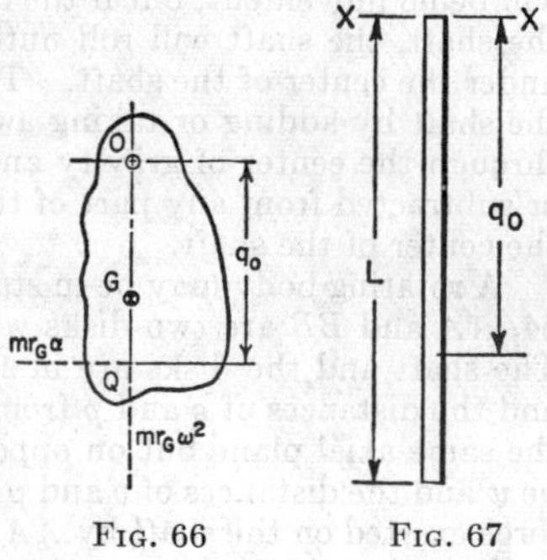

Fig. 66 Fig. 67

Center of Percussion. The distance from the axis of suspension to the center of percussion is $q_0 = I/mx_0$, where I = moment of inertia of the body about its axis of suspension to the center of gravity of the body.

Examples. 1. Find the center of percussion of the homogeneous rod (Fig. 67) of length L and mass m, suspended at XX.

$$q_0 = \frac{I}{mx_0}; \qquad I \text{ (approx)} = \frac{m}{L}\int_0^L x^2\,dx; \qquad r_0 = \frac{L}{2}; \qquad \therefore q_0 = \frac{2}{L^2}\int_0^L x^2\,dx = 2L/3$$

2. Find the center of percussion of a solid cylinder, of mass m, resting on a horizontal plane. In Fig. 68, the instantaneous center of the cylinder is at A. The center of percussion will, therefore, be a height above the plane equal to $q_0 = I/mx_0$. Since $I = (mr^2/2) + mr^2$ and $x_0 = r$, $q_0 = 3r/2$.

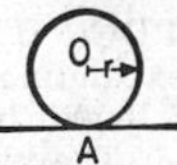

FIG. 68

Wheel or Cylinder Rolling down a Plane. In this case the component of the weight along the plane tends to make it roll down and is treated as a force causing rotation. The forces acting on the body should be resolved into components along the line of motion and perpendicular to it. If the forces are all known, their resultant is at the center of percussion. If one force is to be determined (the exact conditions as regards slipping or not slipping must be known), the center of percussion can be determined and the unknown force found.

Relation between the Center of Percussion and Radius of Gyration. $q_0 = I/mx_0 = k^2/x_0 \therefore k^2 = x_0q_0$ where k = radius of gyration. Therefore, the radius of gyration is a mean proportional between the distance from the axis of oscillation to the center of percussion and the distance from the same axis to the center of gravity.

Interchangeability of Center of Percussion and Axis of Oscillation. If a body is suspended from an axis, the center of percussion for that axis can be found. If the body be suspended from this center of percussion as an axis, the original axis of suspension will then become the center of percussion. The center of percussion is sometimes known as the **center of oscillation.**

Period of Oscillation of a Compound Pendulum. The length of an equivalent simple pendulum is the distance from the axis of suspension to the center of percussion of the body in question. To find the **period of oscillation** of a body about a given axis, find the distance $q_0 = I/mx_0$ from that axis to the center of percussion of the swinging body. The length of the simple pendulum that will oscillate in the same time is this distance q_0. The period of oscillation for the equivalent single pendulum is $\tau = 2\pi \sqrt{q_0/g}$.

Determination of Moment of Inertia by Experiment. To find the moment of inertia of a body, suspend it from some axis not passing through the center of gravity and, by swinging it, determine the period of a single oscillation in seconds. The known values will then be τ = time of single oscillation, x_0 = distance from axis to center of gravity, and m = mass of rod. The length of the equivalent simple pendulum is $q_0 = I/mx_0$. Substituting this value of q_0 in $\tau = 2\pi \sqrt{q_0/g}$ gives $\tau = 2\pi \sqrt{I/mx_0g}$, from which $\tau^2 = 4\pi^2 I/mx_0g$, or $I = mx_0g\tau^2/4\pi^2$.

Plane Motion of a Rigid Body

Plane motion may be considered to be a combination of translation and rotation (see **Kinematics**). For translation, Newton's second law of motion must always be satisfied, and the resultant of the external force system must be equal to the product of the mass times the acceleration of the center of gravity in any system of coordinates. In rotation, the body moving in plane motion will not have a fixed axis. When the methods of relative motion are being used, any point on the body may be used as a reference axis to which the motion of all other points is referred.

The sum of the moments of all external forces about the reference axis must be equal to the vector sum of the centroidal moment of inertia times the angular acceleration and the moment of the resultant force about the reference axis.

EXAMPLE. Determine the forces acting on the piston pin A and the crank pin B of the connecting rod of a reciprocating engine shown in Fig. 69 for a position of 30 deg from

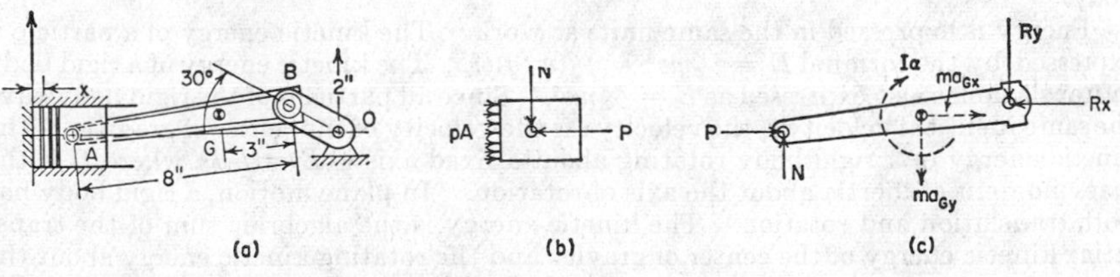

FIG. 69

TDC. The crankshaft speed is constant at 2,000 rpm. Assume that the pressure of expanding gases on the 4 lb piston at this point is 100 lb/in.². The connecting rod weighs 5 lb and has a centroidal radius of gyration of 3 in.

The kinematics of the problem are such that the angular velocity of the crank is $\omega_{OB} = 209.4$ rad/sec clockwise, the angular velocity of the connecting rod is $\omega_{AB} = 45.7$ rad/sec counterclockwise, and the angular acceleration is $\alpha_{AB} = 5{,}790$ rad/sec² clockwise. The linear acceleration of the piston is 7,230 ft/sec² in the direction of the crank. From the free-body diagram of the piston, the horizontal component of the piston pin force is $100 \times (\pi/4)(5^2) - P = (4/32.2)(7{,}230)$, $P = 1{,}037.624$ lb. The acceleration of the center of gravity G is the vector sum of the component accelerations $\mathbf{a}_G = \mathbf{a}_A + \mathbf{a}_A{}^n + \mathbf{a}_{G_A}{}^t$ where $a_G{}^n/R = r_{AG}{}^2 = 5/12(45.7)^2 = 870$ ft/sec² and $a_G{}^t/A = r_{AG}\omega^2 = 5/12(5{,}790) = 2{,}412$ ft/sec². The resultant acceleration of the center of gravity is 6,893 ft/sec² in the x-direction and 1,154 ft/sec² in the negative y-direction. The resultant of the external force system will have corresponding components such that $ma_{Gx} = (4/32.2)(6{,}893) = 972.3$ lb and $ma_{Gy} = (4/32.2)(1{,}154) = 143.5$ lb. The three remaining unknown forces can be found from the three equations of motion for the connecting rod.

Taking the sum of the moments of the external forces about the reference axis B, $(N) \times (8) \cos(7.18°) - (1{,}037.6) \times (2) \sin 30° = (5/32.2)(3/12)^2(5{,}790)(12) - (972.3) \times (3) \sin(7.18°) - (143.5) \times (3) \cos(7.18°)$. From this equation, $N = 116$ lb. Taking the sum of the external forces in the x- and y-directions, $1.037.6 - R_x = 972.3$; $R_x = 65.3$ lb; $R_y - 116 = 143.5$; and $R_z = 259.5$ lb.

WORK AND ENERGY

Work. When a body is displaced against resistance or accelerated, work must be done upon it. An increment of work is defined as the product of an incremental displacement and the component of the force vector in the direction of the displacement or the product of the component of the incremental displacement and the force in the direction of the force. $dU = F \cdot ds \cos \alpha$, where α is the angle between the vector displacement and the vector force. The increment of work done by a couple M acting in a body during an increment of angular rotation $d\theta$ in the plane of the couple is $dU = M\, d\theta$. In a force-displacement or moment-angle diagram, called a **work diagram** (Fig. 70), force is plotted as a function of displacement. The area under the curve represents the work done, which is equal to $\int_{s_1}^{s_2} F\, ds \cos \alpha$ or $\int_{\theta_1}^{\theta_2} M\, d\theta$.

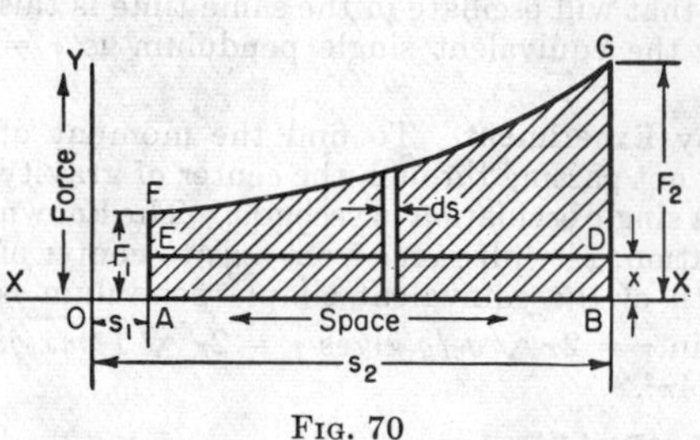

FIG. 70

Units of Work. When the force of 1 lb acts through the distance of 1 ft, **1 ft-lb** of work is done. The **foot-ton** unit is sometimes used. In countries using the metric system the unit employed is the **meter-kilogram.**

Energy. A body is said to possess energy when it can do work. A body may possess this capacity through its **position** or **condition.** When a body is so held that it can do work, if released, it is said to possess energy of position or **potential energy.** When a body is moving with some velocity, it is said to possess energy of motion or **kinetic energy.** An example of potential energy is a body held suspended by a rope; the position of the body is such that if the rope be removed work can be done by the body.

Energy is expressed in the same units as work. The kinetic energy of a particle is expressed by the formual $E = \frac{1}{2}mv^2 = \frac{1}{2}(w/g)v^2$. The kinetic energy of a rigid body in translation is also expressed as $E = \frac{1}{2}mv^2$. Since all particles of the rigid body have the same identical velocity v, the velocity v is the velocity of the center of gravity. The kinetic energy of a rigid body rotating about a fixed axis is $E = I_0\omega^2$, where I_0 is the mass moment of inertia about the axis of rotation. In plane motion, a rigid body has both translation and rotation. The kinetic energy is the algebraic sum of the translating kinetic energy of the center of gravity and the rotating kinetic energy about the center of gravity, $E = \frac{1}{2}mv^2 + \frac{1}{2}I\omega^2$. Here the velocity v is the velocity of the center of gravity, and the moment inertia I is the centroidal moment of inertia.

If a force which varies acts through a space on a body of mass m, the work done is $\int_{s_1}^{s} F\,ds$, and if the work is all used in giving kinetic energy to the body it is equal to $\frac{1}{2}m(v_2^2 - v_1^2)$ = **change in kinetic energy,** where v_2 and v_1 are the velocities at distances s_2 and s_1, respectively. This is a specific statement of the law of conservation of energy. **The principle of conservation of energy requires that the mechanical energy of a system remain unchanged if it is subjected only to forces which depend on position or configuration.**

Certain problems in which the velocity of a body at any point in its straightline path when acted upon by varying forces is required can be easily solved by the use of a **work diagram.**

In Fig. 70, let a body start from rest at A and be acted upon by a force that varies in accordance with the diagram $AFGBA$. Let the resistance to motion be a constant force $= x$. Find the velocity of the body at point B. The area $AFGBA$ represents the work done upon the body and the area $AEDBA$ (= force $x \times$ distance AB) represents the work that must be done to overcome resistance. The difference of these areas, or *EFGDE,* will represent work done in excess of that required to overcome resistance, and consequently is equal to the increase in kinetic energy. Equating the work represented by the area $EFGDE$ to $\frac{1}{2}wv^2/g$ and solving for v will give the required velocity at B. If the body did not start from rest, this area would represent the change in kinetic energy, and the velocity could be obtained by the formula: Work $= \frac{1}{2}(w/g)(v_1^2 - v_0^2)$, v_1 being the required velocity.

General Rule for Rectilinear Motion. Resolve each force acting on the body into components, one of which acts along the line of motion of the body and the other at right angles to the line of motion. Take the sum of all the components acting in the direction of the motion and multiply this sum by the distance moved through for constant forces. (Take the average force times distance for forces that vary.) This product will be the total work done upon the body. If there is no unbalanced component, there will be no change in kinetic energy and consequently no change in velocity. If there is an unbalanced component, the change in kinetic energy will be this unbalanced component multiplied by the distance moved through.

The **work done by a system of forces acting on a body** is equal to the algebraic sum of the work done by each force taken separately.

Power is the rate at which work is performed, or the number of units of work performed in unit time. The units of power employed by engineers are the **horsepower,** or 33,000 ft-lb per min = 550 ft-lb per sec, and the **kilowatt** = 1.341 hp = 737.55 ft-lb per sec.

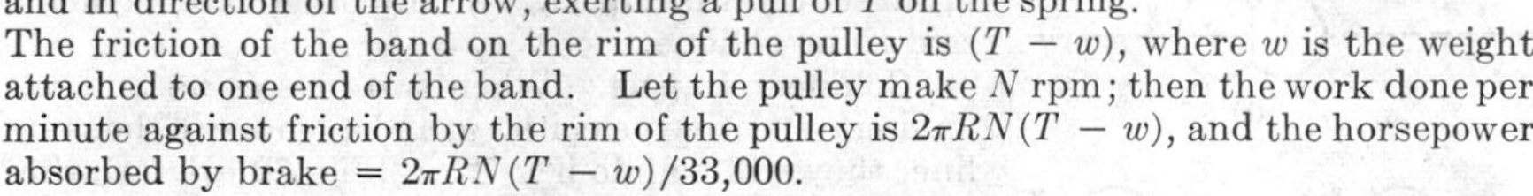

FIG. 71

Friction Brake. In Fig. 71 a pulley revolves under the band and in direction of the arrow, exerting a pull of T on the spring. The friction of the band on the rim of the pulley is $(T - w)$, where w is the weight attached to one end of the band. Let the pulley make N rpm; then the work done per minute against friction by the rim of the pulley is $2\pi RN(T - w)$, and the horsepower absorbed by brake $= 2\pi RN(T - w)/33{,}000$.

IMPULSE AND MOMENTUM

The product of force and time is defined as linear impulse. The impulse of a constant force over a time interval $t_2 - t_1$ is $F(t_2 - t_1)$. If the force is not constant in magnitude but is constant in direction, the impulse is $\int_{t_1}^{t_2} F\,dt$. The dimensions of linear impulse are (force) $\times$ (time) in pound-seconds.

Impulse is a **vector** quantity which has the direction of the resultant force. Impulses may be added vectorially by means of a vector polygon, or they may be resolved into components by means of a parallelogram. The **moment of a linear**

impulse may be found in the same manner as the moment of a force. The linear impulse is represented by a directed line segment, and the moment of the impulse is the product of the magnitude of the impulse and the perpendicular distance from the line segment to the point about which the moment is taken. **Angular impulse** over a time interval $t_2 - t_1$ is a product of the sum of applied moments on a rigid body about a reference axis and time. The dimension for angular impulse are (force) $\times$ (time) $\times$ (displacement) in foot-pound-seconds. **Angular impulse and linear impulse cannot be added.**

Momentum is also a vector quantity and can be added and resolved in the same manner as force and impulse. The dimensions of linear momentum are (force) $\times$ (time) in pound-seconds and are identical to linear impulse. An alternate statement of Newton's second law of motion is that the resultant of an unbalanced force system must be equal to the time rate of change of linear momentum, $\Sigma\mathbf{F} = d(m\mathbf{v})/dt$.

If a variable force acts for a certain time on a body of mass m, the quantity $\int_{t_1}^{t_2} F\,dt = m(v_1 - v_2)$ = the change of momentum of the body.

The **moment of momentum** can be determined by the same methods as those used for the moment of a force or moment of an impulse. The dimensions of the moment of momentum are (force) $\times$ (time) $\times$ (displacement) in foot-pound-seconds.

In **plane motion** the angular momentum of a rigid body about a reference axis perpendicular to the plane of motion is the sum of the moments of linear momenta of all particles in the body about the reference axes. Specifically, **the angular momentum of a rigid body in plane motion is the vector sum of the angular momentum about the reference axis and the moment of the linear momentum of the center of gravity about the reference axis,** $\mathbf{H}_0 = I_0\omega + \mathbf{d} \times m\mathbf{v}$.

In three-dimensional rotation about a fixed axis, the angular momentum of a rigid body has components along three coordinate axes, which involve both the moments of inertia about the x, y, and z axes, $I_{0_{xx}}$, $I_{0_{yy}}$, and $I_{0_{zz}}$, and the products of inertia, $I_{0_{xy}}$, $I_{0_{xz}}$, and $I_{0_{yz}}$; $H_{0_x} = I_{0_{xx}} \cdot \omega_x - I_{0_{xy}} \cdot \omega_y - I_{0_{xz}} \cdot \omega_z$, $H_{0_y} = -I_{0_{xy}} \cdot \omega_x + I_{0_{yy}} \cdot \omega_y - I_{0_{yz}} \cdot \omega_z$, and $H_{0_z} = -I_{0_{xz}}\omega_x - I_{0_{zy}} \cdot \omega_y + I_{0_{zz}} \cdot \omega_z$, where $\mathbf{H}_0 = \mathbf{H}_{0_x} + \mathbf{H}_{0_y} + \mathbf{H}_{0_z}$.

These same equations may express the angular momentum of a rigid body in general three-dimensional motion. In this case the reference axis O must be the center of gravity.

Impact

The collision between two bodies, where relatively large forces result over a comparatively short interval of time, is called **impact.** A straight line perpendicular to the plane of contact of two colliding bodies is called the **line of impact.** If the centers of gravity of the two bodies lie on the line of contact, the impact is called **central impact,** in any other case, **eccentric impact.** If the linear momenta of the centers of gravity are also directed along the line of impact, the impact is **collinear or direct central impact.** In any other case impact is said to be **oblique.**

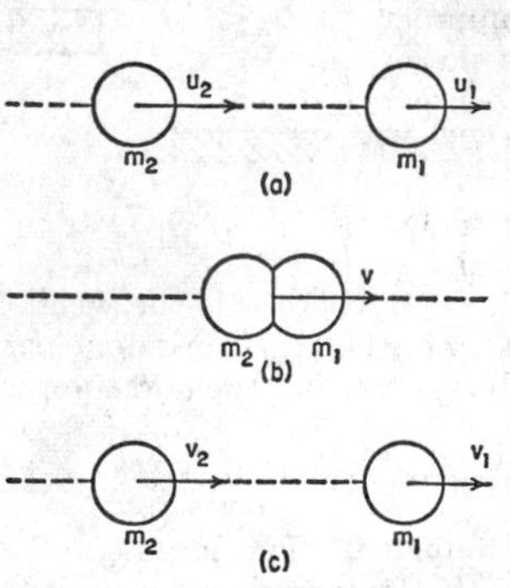

Fig. 72

Collinear Impact. When two masses m_1 and m_2, having respective velocities u_1 and u_2, move in the same line, they will collide if $u_2 > u_1$ [Fig. 72(*a*)]. During collision [Fig. 72(*b*)], kinetic energy is absorbed in the deformation of the bodies. There follows a period of restoration which may or may not be complete. If complete restoration of the energy of deformation occurs, the impact is **elastic.** If the restoration of energy is incomplete, the impact is referred to as **inelastic.** After collision [Fig. 72(*c*)], the bodies continue to move with changed velocities of v_1 and v_2. Since the contact forces on one body are equal to and opposite the contact forces on the other, the sum of the linear momenta of the two bodies is conserved; $m_1u_1 + m_2u_2 = m_1v_1 + m_2v_2$.

The law of conservation of momentum states that the linear momentum of a system of bodies is unchanged if there is no resultant external force on the system.

Coefficient of Restitution. The ratio of the velocity of separation $v_1 - v_2$ to the velocity of approach $u_2 - u_1$ is called the **coefficient of restitution** e. $e = (v_1 - v_2)/(u_2 - u_1)$.

The value of e will depend on the shape and material properties of the colliding bodies. In elastic impact, the coefficient of restitution is unity and there is no energy loss. A coefficient of restitution of zero indicates perfectly inelastic or plastic impact, where there is no separation of the bodies after collision and the energy loss is a maximum. In **oblique impact,** the coefficient of restitution applies only to those components of velocity along the line of impact or normal to the plane of impact. The coefficient of restitution between two materials can be measured by making one body many times larger than the other so that m_2 is infinitely large in comparison to m_1. The velocity of m_2 is unchanged for all practical purposes during impact and $e = -v_1/u_1$. For a small ball dropped from a height H upon an extensive horizontal surface and rebounding to a height h, $e = \sqrt{h/H}$.

Impact of Jet Water on Flat Plate. When a jet of water strikes a flat plate perpendicularly to its surface, the force exerted by the water on the plate is wv/g, where w is the weight of water striking the plate in a unit of time and v is the velocity. When the jet is inclined to the surface by an angle, A, the pressure is $(wv/g) \cos A$.

Variable Mass

If the mass of a body is variable such that mass is either being added or ejected, an alternate form of Newton's second law of motion must be used which accounts for changes in mass:

$$\mathbf{F} = m\frac{d\mathbf{v}}{dt} + \frac{dm}{dt}\mathbf{u}$$

The mass m is the instantaneous mass of the body, and dv/dt is the time rate of change of the absolute velocity of mass m. The velocity u is the velocity of the mass m relative to the added or ejected mass, and dm/dt is the time rate of change of mass. In this case, care must be exercised in the choice of coordinates and expressions of sign. If mass is being added, dm/dt is plus, and if mass is ejected, dm/dt is minus.

Fields of Force—Attraction

The space within which the action of a physical force comes into play on bodies lying within its boundaries is called the **field of the force.**

The **strength** or **intensity of the field** at any given point is the relation between a force F acting on a mass m at that point and the mass. Intensity of field $= i = F/m$; $F = mi$.

The **unit of field intensity** is the same as the unit of acceleration, *i.e.*, 1 ft per sec per sec, or 1 m per sec per sec. The intensity of a field of force may be represented by a line (or **vector**).

A field of force is said to be **homogeneous** when the intensity of all points is uniform and in the same direction.

A field of force is called a **central field of force** with a center O, if the direction of the force acting on the mass particle m in every point of the field passes through O and its magnitude is a function only of the distance r from O to m. A line so drawn through the field of force that its direction coincides at every point with that of the force prevailing at that point is called a **line of force.**

Rotation of Solid Bodies about Any Axis

The general moment equations for three-dimensional motion are usually expressed in terms of the angular momentum. For a reference axis O, which is either a fixed axis or the center of gravity, $M_{0_x} = (dH_{0_x}/dt) - H_{0_y} \cdot \omega_z + H_{0_z} \cdot \omega_y$, $M_{0_y} = (dH_{0_y}/dt) - H_{0_z} \cdot \omega_x + H_{0_x} \cdot \omega_z$, and $M_{0_z} = (dH_{0_z}/dt) - H_{0_x}\omega_y + H_{0_y}\omega_x$. If the coordinate axes are oriented to coincide with the principal axes of inertia, $I_{0_{xx}}$, $I_{0_{yy}}$, and $I_{0_{zz}}$, a similar set of three differential equations results, involving moments, angular velocity, and angular acceleration; $M_{0_x} = I_{0_{xx}}(d\omega_x/dt) + (I_{0_{zz}} - I_{0_{yy}})\omega_y \cdot \omega_z$, $M_{0_y} = I_{0_{yy}}(d\omega_y/dt) + (I_{0_{xx}} - I_{0_{zz}})\omega_z \cdot \omega_x$, and $M_{0_z} = I_{0_{zz}}(d\omega_z/dt) + (I_{0_{yy}} - I_{0_{xx}})\omega_x\omega_y$. These equations are known as **Euler's equations of motion** and may apply to any rigid body.

Gyroscopic motion can be explained in terms of Euler's equations. Let I_1, I_2, and I_3 represent the principal moments of inertia of a gyroscope spinning with a constant angular velocity ω, about axis 1, the subscripts 1, 2, and 3 representing a right-hand set of reference axes. If the gyroscope is precessed about the third axis, a vector moment results along the second axis such that $M_2 = (I_1 - I_3)\omega_3\omega_1$. In the practical case where I_1 is much larger than I_3, the gyroscopic moment can be approximated by $M = I\omega\Omega$, where Ω is the rate of precession, ω the rate of spin, and I the moment of inertia about the spin axis.

THE GYROSCOPE (by J. P. Den Hartog)

REFERENCES: Meriam, "Dynamics," Wiley. Halfman, "Dynamics," Addison-Wesley. Timoshenko and Young, "Advanced Dynamics," McGraw-Hill. Ferry, "Applied Gyrodynamics," Wiley. Rawlings, "The Theory of the Gyroscopic Compass," Macmillan.

The elementary facts about gyroscopic forces may be briefly illustrated by the following example. Given, a wheel or disk, of weight w and radius R, spinning rapidly about its axis OA (Fig. 73), and mounted in gimbal rings in such a way that its center is stationary, while its axis is free to point in any direction in space (see Fig. 74). Let k = the radius of gyration of the wheel about its axis. (If all the weight is in the rim, $k^2 = R^2$; if the wheel is a homogeneous disk, $k^2 = R^2/2$.) Now suppose that the axle end A is constrained to move between two smooth fixed guides, forming a slot as in Fig. 73, and suppose that a force Q is applied to pull the point A along the slot. Then, (1) as far as the motion of A along the slot is concerned, it makes no difference whether the disk is rotating or not; in fact, $Qb = (w/g)(k^2/2)(dv/b\ dt)$, where Qb is the moment of Q about the center O, and dv/dt is the (linear) acceleration of the point A along the slot; (2) if the wheel is rotating, then the mere motion of A along the slot will call into play a strong lateral pressure P (called a gyroscopic reaction) against one of the guides.

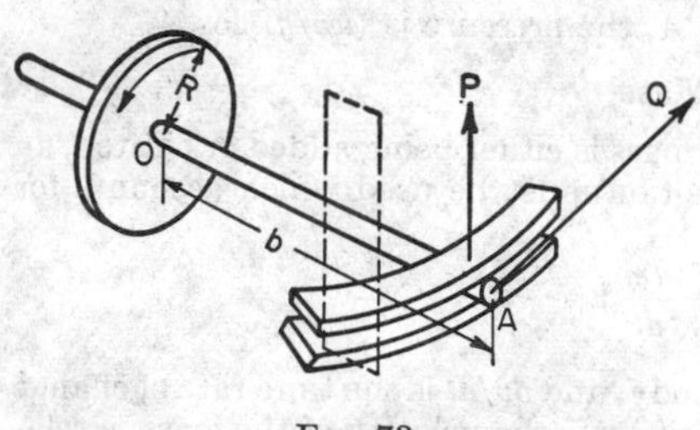

FIG. 73

Which one of the two guides the force P will act against depends on the direction of spin, and is best determined by the following rule (Huntington, *Eng. News*, July 21, 1910): If the applied force Q is thought of as due to the pressure of a flat board against the side of the revolving axle (the board being perpendicular to Q as shown in dotted line in Fig. 73), then the axle will strive to move in the direction in which it would naturally roll if the board were rough. Thus, in Fig. 73, the axle end A will push against the *upper* guide and would actually move in the direction of the P arrow if the guide were not present.

The magnitude of the gyroscopic force P at any instant is proportional to the spinning velocity, and also to the velocity of A along the slot, being given by

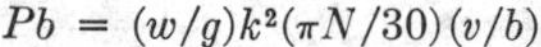

$$Pb = (w/g)k^2(\pi N/30)(v/b)$$

where Pb = the moment of P about the center, v = the linear velocity of the point A along the slot at the instant in question, N = rpm in the spinning velocity of the wheel, and g = 32.17 ft per sec per sec.

FIG. 74

It should be noted that the gyroscopic reaction P against the fixed guide does not depend on the magnitude of the accelerating force Q, except in so far as Q is necessary to create the velocity v, in case A starts from rest; when once the velocity v has been established, Q can be made zero, and both v and P will (neglecting friction) continue constant. On the other hand, if the guide is movable and exerts a pressure $P' = P$

against the axle at A, this force will itself maintain the velocity v (called the precessional velocity) of the point A along the guide. In brief, *the end of the axle of a rotating gyroscope always tends to move at right angles to any force impressed upon it.*

For example, suppose an airplane is driven by a right-handed propeller (turning like a right-handed screw when moving forward); if a gust of wind or other force turns the machine to the *left,* the gyroscopic action of the propeller will make the forward end of the shaft strive to *rise;* if the wing surface is large, this motion will be practically prevented by the resistance of the air, and the gyroscopic forces become effective merely as internal stresses, whose maximum value can be computed by the formula above. Similarly, if the airplane is dipped *downward,* the gyroscopic action will make the forward end of the shaft strive to turn to the *left.*

In the Brennan monorail car, the slot is parallel to the rail, so that a force Q, applied automatically at the axle end when the car starts to tip, will be converted gyroscopically into a strong righting moment Pb, which forces the car back into a position of lateral equilibrium. Numerical case: If $w = 3{,}200$ lb, $k = 1.4$ ft, $b = 2$ ft, and spinning velocity $= 3{,}000$ rpm, then a force Q of 50 lb acting for ½ sec will produce at the end of that time a precessional velocity of 1 fps along the slot, with a resulting lateral force against the guide of nearly 16,000 lb. The displacement of the point A along the slot will be about 6 deg. An essential feature of the apparatus is a device for bringing the axle back into the ready position after each period of activity.

Modern **applications** of the gyroscope are based on one of the following properties: (1) a gyroscope mounted in three gimbal rings so as to be entirely free angularly in all directions will retain its direction *in space* in the absence of outside couples; (2) if the axis of rotation of a gyroscope turns or precesses in space, a couple or torque acts on the gyroscope (and conversely on its frame).

Devices operating on the first principle are satisfactory only for short durations, say less than half an hour, because no gyroscope is entirely without outside couple. The friction couples at the various gimbal bearings, although small, will precess the axis of rotation so that after a while the axis of rotation will have changed its direction in space. The chief device based on the first principle is the **airplane compass,** which is a freely mounted gyro, keeping its direction in space during fast maneuvers of a fighting airplane. No magnetic compass will indicate correctly during such maneuvers. After the plane is back on an even keel in steady flight, the magnetic compass once more reads the true magnetic north, and the gyro compass has to be reset to point north again.

An example of a device operating on the second principle is the **automatic pilot** for keeping a vehicle on a given course. This device has been installed on torpedoes, ships, and airplanes. When the ship or plane turns from the chosen course, a couple is exerted on the gyro axis, which makes it precess and this operates electric contacts or hydraulic or pneumatic valves. These again operate on the rudders, through relays, and bring the ship back to its course.

Another application is the ship **antirolling** gyroscope. This very large gyroscope spins about a vertical axis and is mounted in a ship so that the axis can be tipped fore and aft by means of an electric motor, the precession motor. The gyro can exert a large torque on the ship about the fore-and-aft axis, which is along the "rolling" axis. The sign of the torque is determined by the direction of rotation of the precession motor, which in turn is controlled by electric contacts operated by a small pilot gyroscope on the ship, which feels which way the ship rolls and gives the signals to apply a countertorque.

The **turn-indicator** for airplanes is a gyro, the frame of which is held by springs. When the airplane turns, it makes the gyro axis turn with it, and the resultant couple is delivered by the springs. Thus the elongation of the springs is a measure of the rate of turn, which is suitably indicated by a pointer.

The most complicated and ingenious application of the gyroscope is the **marine compass.** This is a pendulously suspended gyroscope which is affected by gravity and also by the earth's rotation so that the gyro axis is in equilibrium only when it points north, *i.e.,* when it lies in the plane formed by the local vertical and by the earth's north-south axis. If the compass is disturbed so that it points away from north, the action of the earth's rotation will restore it to the correct north position in a few hours.

FRICTION

BY

Dudley D. Fuller

References: Bowden and Tabor, "The Friction and Lubrication of Solids," Oxford. Fuller, "Theory and Practice of Lubrication for Engineers," Wiley. Ham and Crane, "Mechanics of Machinery," McGraw-Hill. Bevan, "Theory of Machines," Longmans. Shigley, "Mechanical Design," McGraw-Hill. Rabinowicz, "Friction and Wear of Materials," Wiley.

Friction is the resistance that is encountered when two solid surfaces slide or tend to slide over each other. The surfaces may be either dry or lubricated. In the first case, when the surfaces are free from contaminating fluids, or films, the resistance is called **dry friction.** The friction of brake shoes on the rim of a wheel is an example of dry friction.

When the rubbing surfaces are separated from each other by a very thin film of lubricant, the friction is that of **boundary** (or **greasy**) **lubrication.** The lubrication depends in this case on the strong adhesion of the lubricant to the material of the rubbing surfaces; the layers of lubricant slip over each other instead of the dry surfaces. A journal when starting, reversing, or turning at very low speed under a heavy load is an example of the condition that will cause boundary lubrication. Other examples are gear teeth (especially hypoid gears), cutting tools, wire-drawing dies, power screws, bridge trunions, and the running-in process of most lubricated surfaces.

When the lubrication is arranged so that the rubbing surfaces are separated by a fluid film, and the load on the surfaces is carried entirely by the hydrostatic or hydrodynamic pressure in the film, the friction is that of **complete** (or **viscous**) **lubrication.** In this case, the frictional losses are due solely to the internal fluid friction in the film. Oil ring bearings, bearings with forced feed of oil, pivoted shoe-type thrust and journal bearings, bearings operating in an oil bath, hydrostatic oil pads, oil lifts, and step bearings are instances of complete lubrication.

Incomplete lubrication or mixed lubrication takes place when the load on the rubbing surfaces is carried partly by a fluid viscous film and partly by areas of boundary lubrication. The friction is intermediate between that of fluid and boundary lubrication. Incomplete lubrication exists in bearings with drop-feed, waste-packed, or wick-fed lubrication, or on parallel surface bearings.

STATIC AND SLIDING COEFFICIENTS OF FRICTION

In the absence of friction, the resultant of the forces between the surfaces of two bodies pressing upon each other is normal to the surface of contact. With friction, the resultant deviates from the normal.

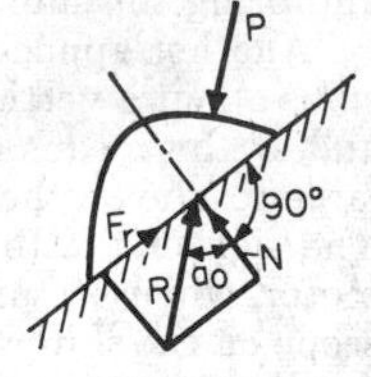

Fig. 1

If one body is pressed against another by a force P, as in Fig. 1, the first body will not move, provided the angle a_0 included between the line of action of the force and a normal to the surfaces in contact does not exceed a certain value which depends upon the nature of the surfaces. The resultant force R has the same magnitude and line of action as the force P. In Fig. 1, R is resolved into two components: a force N normal to the surfaces in contact and a force F_r parallel to the surfaces in contact. From the above statement it follows that

$$F_r \leqq N \tan a_0 \leqq N f_0$$

Table 1. Coefficients of Static and Sliding Friction
(Reference letters indicate the lubricant used; numbers in parentheses give the sources. See footnote)

Materials	Static		Sliding	
	Dry	Greasy	Dry	Greasy
Hard steel on hard steel	0.78 (1)	0.11 (1, *a*)	0.42 (2)	0.029 (5, *h*)
		0.23 (1, *b*)		0.081 (5, *c*)
		0.15 (1, *c*)		0.080 (5, *i*)
		0.11 (1, *d*)		0.058 (5, *j*)
		0.0075 (18, *p*)		0.084 (5, *d*)
		0.0052 (18, *h*)		0.105 (5, *k*)
				0.096 (5, *l*)
				0.108 (5, *m*)
				0.12 (5, *a*)
Mild steel on mild steel	0.74 (19)		0.57 (3)	0.09 (3, *a*)
				0.19 (3, *u*)
Hard steel on graphite	0.21 (1)	0.09 (1, *a*)		
Hard steel on babbitt (ASTM No. 1)	0.70 (11)	0.23 (1, *b*)	0.33 (6)	0.16 (1, *b*)
		0.15 (1, *c*)		0.06 (1, *c*)
		0.08 (1, *d*)		0.11 (1, *d*)
		0.085 (1, *e*)		
Hard steel on babbitt (ASTM No. 8)	0.42 (11)	0.17 (1, *b*)	0.35 (11)	0.14 (1, *b*)
		0.11 (1, *c*)		0.065 (1, *c*)
		0.09 (1, *d*)		0.07 (1, *d*)
		0.08 (1, *e*)		0.08 (11, *h*)
Hard steel on babbitt (ASTM No. 10)		0.25 (1, *b*)		0.13 (1, *b*)
		0.12 (1, *c*)		0.06 (1, *c*)
		0.10 (1, *d*)		0.055 (1, *d*)
		0.11 (1, *e*)		
Mild steel on cadmium silver				0.097 (2, *f*)
Mild steel on phosphor bronze			0.34 (3)	0.173 (2, *f*)
Mild steel on copper lead				0.145 (2, *f*)
Mild steel on cast iron		0.183 (15, *c*)	0.23 (6)	0.133 (2, *f*)
Mild steel on lead	0.95 (11)	0.5 (1, *f*)	0.95 (11)	0.3 (11, *f*)
Nickel on mild steel			0.64 (3)	0.178 (3, *x*)
Aluminum on mild steel	0.61 (8)		0.47 (3)	
Magnesium on mild steel			0.42 (3)	
Magnesium on magnesium	0.6 (22)	0.08 (22, *y*)		
Teflon on Teflon	0.04 (22)			0.04 (22, *f*)
Teflon on steel	0.04 (22)			0.04 (22, *f*)
Tungsten carbide on tungsten carbide	0.2 (22)	0.12 (22, *a*)		
Tungsten carbide on steel	0.5 (22)	0.08 (22, *a*)		
Tungsten carbide on copper	0.35 (23)			
Tungsten carbide on iron	0.8 (23)			
Bonded carbide on copper	0.35 (23)			
Bonded carbide on iron	0.8 (23)			
Cadmium on mild steel			0.46 (3)	
Copper on mild steel	0.53 (8)		0.36 (3)	0.18 (17, *a*)
Nickel on nickel	1.10 (16)		0.53 (3)	0.12 (3, *w*)
Brass on mild steel	0.51 (8)		0.44 (6)	
Brass on cast iron			0.30 (6)	
Zinc on cast iron	0.85 (16)		0.21 (7)	
Magnesium on cast iron			0.25 (7)	
Copper on cast iron	1.05 (16)		0.29 (7)	
Tin on cast iron			0.32 (7)	
Lead on cast iron			0.43 (7)	
Aluminum on aluminum	1.05 (16)		1.4 (3)	
Glass on glass	0.94 (8)	0.01 (10, *p*)	0.40 (3)	0.09 (3, *a*)
		0.005 (10, *q*)		0.116 (3, *v*)
Carbon on glass			0.18 (3)	
Garnet on mild steel			0.39 (3)	
Glass on nickel	0.78 (8)		0.56 (3)	
Copper on glass	0.68 (8)		0.53 (3)	
Cast iron on cast iron	1.10 (16)		0.15 (9)	0.070 (9, *d*)
				0.064 (9, *n*)
Bronze on cast iron			0.22 (9)	0.077 (9, *n*)
Oak on oak (parallel to grain)	0.62 (9)		0.48 (9)	0.164 (9, *r*)
				0.067 (9, *s*)
Oak on oak (perpendicular)	0.54 (9)		0.32 (9)	0.072 (9, *s*)
Leather on oak (parallel)	0.61 (9)		0.52 (9)	
Cast iron on oak			0.49 (9)	0.075 (9, *n*)
Leather on cast iron			0.56 (9)	0.36 (9, *t*)
				0.13 (9, *n*)
Laminated plastic on steel			0.35 (12)	0.05 (12, *t*)
Fluted rubber bearing on steel				0.05 (13, *t*)

(1) Campbell, *Trans. ASME*, 1939; (2) Clarke, Lincoln, and Sterrett, *Proc. API*, 1935; (3) Beare and Bowden, *Phil. Trans. Roy. Soc.*, 1935; (4) Dokos, *Trans. ASME*, 1946; (5) Boyd and Robertson, *Trans. ASME*, 1945; (6) Sachs, *Zeit. f. angew. Math. und Mech.*, 1924; (7) Honda and Yama la, *Jour. I of M*, 1925; (8) Tomlinson, *Phil. Mag.*, 1929; (9) Morin, *Acad. Roy. des Sciences*, 1838; (10) Claypoole, *Trans. ASME*, 1943; (11) Tabor, *Jour. Applied Phys.*, 1945; (12) Eyssen, General Discussion on Lubrication, *ASME*, 1937; (13) Brazier and Holland-Bowyer, General Discussion on Lubrication, *ASME*, 1937; (14) Bur-

where $f_0 = \tan \alpha_0$ is called the **coefficient of friction of rest** (or of **static friction**) and α_0 is the **angle of friction of rest** (or angle of **repose**).

If the normal force N between the surfaces is kept constant, and the tangential force F_r is gradually increased, there will be no motion while $F_r < Nf_0$. A state of *impending motion* is reached when F_r nears the value of Nf_0. If one surface slides over the other, being pressed together by a normal force N, a frictional force F resisting the motion must be overcome. This force is usually smaller than F_r. The force F is commonly expressed as $F = fN$, where f is the **coefficient of sliding friction,** or **kinetic friction.** In the range of practical velocities of sliding, the coefficients of sliding friction are smaller than the coefficients of static friction. With small velocities of sliding and very clean surfaces, the two coefficients do not differ appreciably.

Under moderate pressures, the frictional force is proportional to the normal load on the rubbing surfaces. It is independent of the pressure per unit area of the surfaces. The coefficient of friction is approximately independent of the rubbing speed, when the speed is sufficiently low so as not to affect the temperature of the surface; at higher velocities, the coefficient of friction decreases as the velocity increases.

The coefficients of friction for dry surfaces (dry friction) depend on the materials sliding over each other and on the finished condition of the surfaces. With greasy (boundary) lubrication, the coefficients depend both on the materials and conditions of the surfaces and on the lubricants employed.

Coefficients of friction are sensitive to atmospheric dust and humidity, oxide films, surface finish, velocity of sliding, temperature, vibration, and the extent of contamination. In many instances the degree of contamination is perhaps the most important single variable. For example, in the table below, values for the static coefficient of friction of steel on steel are listed, and, depending upon the degree of contamination of the specimens, the coefficient of friction varies effectively from ∞ (infinity) to 0.013.

Coefficients of Static Friction for Steel on Steel

Test condition	f_0	Ref.*
Degassed at elevated temp in high vacuum	∞ (weld on contact)	20
Grease-free in vacuum	0.78	1
Grease-free in air	0.39	8
Clean and coated with oleic acid	0.11	1
Clean and coated with solution of stearic acid	0.013	21

* See footnote to Table 1.

The most effective lubricants for non-fluid lubrication are generally those which react chemically with the solid surface and form an adhering film that is attached to the surface with a chemical bond. This action depends upon the nature of the lubricant and upon the reactivity of the solid surface. The table below indicates that a fatty acid, such as found in animal, vegetable, and marine oils, reduces the coefficient of friction markedly only if it can react effectively with the solid surface. Paraffin oil is almost completely non-reactive.

Values in Table 1 of sliding and static coefficients have been selected largely from recent investigations where these variables have been very carefully controlled. They

FOOTNOTE, TABLE 1 (cont.)

well, *Jour. SAE*, 1942; (15) Stanton, "Friction," Longmans; (16) Ernst and Merchant, Conference on Friction and Surface Finish, M.I.T., 1940; (17) Gongwer, Conference on Friction and Surface Finish, M.I.T., 1940; (18) Hardy and Bircumshaw, *Proc. Roy. Soc.*, 1925; (19) Hardy and Hardy, *Phil. Mag.*, 1919; (20) Bowden and Young, *Proc. Roy. Soc.*, 1951; (21) Hardy and Doubleday, *Proc. Roy. Soc.*, 1923; (22) Bowden and Tabor, "The Friction and Lubrication of Solids," Oxford; (23) Shooter, *Research*, 4, 1951.

(*a*) Oleic acid; (*b*) Atlantic spindle oil (light mineral); (*c*) castor oil; (*d*) lard oil; (*e*) Atlantic spindle oil plus 2 percent oleic acid; (*f*) medium mineral oil; (*g*) medium mineral oil plus ½ percent oleic acid; (*h*) stearic acid; (*i*) grease (zinc oxide base); (*j*) graphite; (*k*) turbine oil plus 1 percent graphite; (*l*) turbine oil plus 1 percent stearic acid; (*m*) turbine oil (medium mineral); (*n*) olive oil; (*p*) palmitic acid; (*q*) ricinoleic acid; (*r*) dry soap; (*s*) lard; (*t*) water; (*u*) rape oil; (*v*) 3-in-1 oil; (*w*) octyl alcohol; (*x*) triolein; (*y*) 1 percent lauric acid in paraffin oil.

are representative values for smooth surfaces. It has been generally observed that sliding friction between hard materials is smaller than that between softer surfaces.

Coefficients of Static Friction at Room Temperature*

Surfaces	Clean	Paraffin oil	Paraffin oil + 1% lauric acid	Degree of reactivity of solid
Nickel	0.7	0.3	0.28	Low
Chromium	0.4	0.3	0.3	Low
Platinum	1.2	0.28	0.25	Low
Silver	1.4	0.8	0.7	Low
Glass	0.9		0.4	Low
Copper	1.4	0.3	0.08	High
Cadmium	0.5	0.45	0.05	High
Zinc	0.6	0.2	0.04	High
Magnesium	0.6	0.5	0.08	High
Iron	1.0	0.3	0.2	Mild
Aluminum	1.4	0.7	0.3	Mild

* From reference 22 of footnote to Table 1.

Effect of Surface Films. Campbell[1]* observed a lowering of the coefficient of friction when oxide or sulphide films were present on metal surfaces. The reductions listed in the following table were obtained with oxide films formed by heating in air at temperatures from 100 to 500 C, and sulphide films produced by immersion in a 0.02 percent sodium sulphide solution.

Static Coefficients of Friction f_o

	Clean and dry	Oxide film	Sulphide film
Steel-steel	0.78	0.27	0.39
Brass-brass	0.88		0.57
Copper-copper	1.21	0.76	0.74

Effect of Sliding Velocity. It has generally been observed that coefficients of friction reduce on dry surfaces as sliding velocity increases. (See results of railway brake-shoe tests below.) Dokos[4] measured this reduction in friction for mild steel on medium steel. Values are for the average of four tests with high contact pressures.

Sliding velocity, in. per sec	0.0001	0.001	0.01	0.1	1	10	100
f	0.53	0.48	0.39	0.31	0.23	0.19	0.18

Effect of Surface Finish. The degree of surface roughness has been found to influence the coefficient of friction. Burwell[14] evaluated this effect for conditions of boundary or greasy friction. The values listed below are for sliding coefficients of friction, hard steel on hard steel.

	Surface					
	Superfinished	Ground	Ground	Ground	Ground	Grit-blasted
Roughness, microinches	2	7	20	50	65	55
Mineral oil	0.128	0.189	0.360	0.372	0.378	0.212
Mineral oil + 2% oleic acid	0.116	0.170	0.249	0.261	0.230	0.164
Oleic acid	0.099	0.163	0.195	0.222	0.238	0.195
Mineral oil + 2% sulphonated sperm oil	0.095	0.137	0.175	0.251	0.197	0.165

* Superior numbers refer to sources in footnote to Table 1.

Solid Lubricants. In certain applications solid lubricants are used successfully. Boyd and Robertson[5] with pressures ranging from 50,000 to 400,000 psi found sliding coefficients of friction, f, for hard steel on hard steel as follows: powdered mica, 0.305; powdered soapstone, 0.306; lead iodide, 0.071; silver sulphate, 0.054; graphite, 0.058; molybdenum disulphide, 0.033; tungsten disulphide, 0.037; stearic acid, 0.029.

Coefficients of Static Friction for Special Cases

Masonry and Earth. Dry masonry on brickwork, 0.6–0.7; timber on polished stone, 0.40; iron on stone, 0.3–0.7; masonry on dry clay, 0.51; masonry on moist clay, 0.33.

Earth on Earth. Dry sand, clay, mixed earth, 0.4–0.7; damp clay, 1.0; wet clay, 0.31; shingle and gravel, 0.8–1.1.

Natural Cork. On cork, 0.59; on pine with grain, 0.49; on glass, 0.52; on dry steel, 0.45; on wet steel, 0.69; on hot steel, 0.64; on oiled steel, 0.45; water-soaked cork on steel, 0.56; oil-soaked cork on steel, 0.42.

Coefficients of Sliding Friction for Special Cases

Soapy Wood. Lesley gives for wood on wood, copiously lubricated with tallow, stearine, and soft soap (as used in launching practice), a starting coefficient of friction equal to 0.036, diminishing to an average value of 0.019 for the first 50 ft of motion of the ship. Rennie gives 0.0385 for wood on wood, lubricated with soft soap, under a load of 56 psi.

Asbestos-fabric Brake Material. The coefficient of sliding friction f of asbestos fabric against a cast-iron brake drum, according to Taylor and Holt (*NBS*, 1940) is 0.35 to 0.40 when at normal temperature. It drops somewhat with rise in brake temperature up to 300 F. With a further increase in brake temperature 300 to 500 F the value of f may show an increase caused by disruption of the brake surface.

Steel Tires on Steel Rails (Galton).

Speed mph	Start	6.8	13.5	27.3	40.9	54.4	60
Values of f	0.242	0.088	0.072	0.07	0.057	0.038	0.027

Railway Brake Shoes on Steel Tires. Galton and Westinghouse give, for cast-iron brakes, the following values for f, which decrease rapidly with the speed of the rim; the coefficient f decreases also with time, as the temperature of the shoe increases.

Speed, mph	10	20	30	40	50	60
f, when brakes were applied	0.32	0.21	0.18	0.13	0.10	0.06
f, after 5 sec	0.21	0.17	0.11	0.10	0.07	0.05
f, after 12 sec	....	0.13	0.10	0.08	0.06	0.05

Schmidt and Schrader confirm the marked decrease in the coefficient of friction with the increase of rim speed. They also show an irregular slight decrease in the value of f with higher shoe pressure on the wheel, but they did not find the drop in friction after a prolonged application of the brakes. Their observations are as follows:

Speed, mph	20	30	40	50	60
Coefficient of friction	0.25	0.23	0.19	0.17	0.16

Wood Brake Blocks. According to Klein, f is practically constant for velocities from 200 to 4,000 fpm and for pressures from 7 to 142 psi. The following values of f are for wood on lengthwise fiber brake blocks carefully machined:

	Beech	Oak	Poplar	Elm	Willow
Cast iron	0.29–0.37	0.30–0.34	0.35–0.40	0.36–0.37	0.46–0.47
Wrought iron	0.54	0.51–0.40	0.65–0.60	0.60–0.49	0.63–0.60

The higher values apply for cast iron when the brake wheel is cleaned with gasoline, the lower when it is only wiped clean; the reverse holds for wrought iron.

Hydraulic Hoists. According to Lang, for bronze or lignum vitae sliding surfaces on bronze, f is constant for slow reversing motion and for pressures of 30 to 1,500 psi. For surfaces continuously lubricated, $f = 0.06$; for surfaces wet with water through numerous slots, 0.10; for surfaces running dry and creaking, up to 0.30.

Stuffing Boxes Packed with Hemp, Cotton, or Leather. f is constant for hydraulic pressures between 15 and 750 psi. For **hemp or cotton packing,** loose or woven, soaked in hot tallow, smooth rod, box not set up too tightly so that the packing is still elastic, usual dimensions—even after months of use, $f = 0.06$ to 0.11 (see also *Am. Mach.*, Feb. 3, 1898). When the packing is rendered difficult by unfavorable conditions, $f =$ up to 0.25. For well-made **leather packing rings** of soft leather $f = 0.03$ to 0.07; if of hard, stiff tanned leather, 0.10 to 0.13; under unfavorable conditions such as rough piston and dirty water, up to 0.20. The coefficient of friction is found to change inversely to the diameter of the cylinder. The depth of the leather does not influence the friction.

Grindstones. The coefficient of friction between coarse-grained sandstone and cast iron is $f = 0.21$ to 0.24; for steel, 0.29; for wrought iron, 0.41 to 0.46, according as the stone is freshly trued or dull; for fine-grained sandstone (wet grinding) $f = 0.72$ for cast iron, 0.94 for steel, and 1.0 for wrought iron.

Honda and Yamada give $f = 0.28$ to 0.50 for carbon steel on emery, depending on the roughness of the wheel.

Rubber Tires on Pavement. Arnoux gives $f = 0.67$ for dry macadam, 0.71 for dry asphalt, 0.81 for wet asphalt, and 0.17 to 0.06 for soft, slippery roads. For a cord tire on a sand-filled brick surface in fair condition, Agg (*Bull.* 88, *Iowa State College Engineering Experiment Station,* 1928) gives the following values of f depending on the inflation of the tire:

Inflation pressure, psi	Dry pavement		Wet pavement	
	Static f_0	Sliding f	Static f_0	Sliding f
40	0.90	0.85	0.74	0.69
50	0.88	0.84	0.64	0.58
60	0.80	0.76	0.63	0.56

Tests of the Goodrich Company on wet brick pavement with balloon tires of different treads gave the following values of f:

	Coefficients of friction			
	Static (before slipping)		Sliding (after slipping)	
Speed, mph	5	30	5	30
Smooth tire	0.49	0.28	0.43	0.26
Circumferential grooves	0.58	0.42	0.52	0.36
Angular grooves at 60 deg	0.75	0.55	0.70	0.39
Angular grooves at 45 deg	0.77	0.55	0.68	0.44

Sleds. For **unshod wooden runners** on smooth wood or stone surfaces, $f = 0.07$ (0.15) when tallow (dry soap) is used as a lubricant (= 0.38 when not lubricated); on snow and ice, $f = 0.035$. For **runners with metal shoes** on snow and ice, $f = 0.02$. Rennie found for steel on ice, $f = 0.014$. However, as the temperature falls, the coefficient of friction will get larger. Bowden cites the following data for brass on ice:

Temp. C	f
0	0.025
−20	0.085
−40	0.115
−60	0.14

Compound Sliding. A body sliding across another may be deflected crosswise from its original direction by a small force. This explains the ease with which an automobile may skid on the road or with which a plug gage can be inserted into a hole if it is rotated while being pushed in.

ROLLING FRICTION

Rolling is substituted frequently for sliding friction, as in the case of wheels under vehicles, balls or rollers in bearings, rollers under skids when moving loads; frictional resistance to the rolling motion is substantially smaller than to sliding motion. The coefficient of rolling friction $f_r = P/L$ where L is the load and P is the frictional resistance.

The frictional resistance P to the rolling of a cylinder under a load L applied at the center of the roller (Fig. 2) is inversely proportional to the radius r of the roller; $P = \frac{k}{r} L$.

Table 2. Coefficients of Rolling Friction, f_r, for Wheels with Steel and Pneumatic Tires

Wheel	Inflation press, psi	Load, lb	Concrete	Blue-grass sod	Tilled loam	Loose sand	Loose snow 10–14″ deep
2.5 × 36 steel	..	1,000	0.010	0.087	0.384	0.431	0.106
4 × 24 steel	..	500	0.034	0.082	0.468	0.504	0.282
4.00–18 4-ply	20	500	0.034	0.058	0.366	0.392	0.210
4 × 36 steel	..	1,000	0.019	0.074	0.367	0.413	
4.00–30 4-ply	36	1,000	0.018	0.057	0.322	0.319	
4.00–36 4-ply	36	1,000	0.017	0.050	0.294	0.277	
5.00–16 4-ply	32	1,000	0.031	0.062	0.388	0.460	
6 × 28 steel	..	1,000	0.023	0.094	0.368	0.477	0.156
6.00–16 4-ply	20	1,000	0.027	0.060	0.319	0.338	0.146
6.00–16 4-ply*	30	1,000	0.031	0.070	0.401	0.387	
7.50–10 4-ply†	20	1,000	0.029	0.061	0.379	0.429	
7.50–16 4-ply	20	1,500	0.023	0.055	0.280	0.322	
7.50–28 4-ply	16	1,500	0.026	0.052	0.197	0.205	
8 × 48 steel	..	1,500	0.013	0.065	0.236	0.264	0.118
7.50–36 4-ply	16	1,500	0.018	0.046	0.185	0.177	0.0753
9.00–10 4-ply†	20	1,000	0.031	0.060	0.331	0.388	
9.00–16 6-ply	16	1,500	0.042	0.054	0.249	0.272	0.099

* Skid-ring tractor tire.
† Ribbed tread tractor tire.
All other pneumatic tires with implement-type tread.

If r is in inches, values of k are as follows: hardwood on hardwood, 0.02; iron on iron, steel on steel, 0.002; hard polished steel on hard polished steel, 0.0002 to 0.0004.

Data on rolling friction are scarce. Noonan and Strange give, for steel rollers on steel plates and for loads varying from light to those causing a permanent set of the material, the following values of k: surfaces well finished and clean, 0.0005 to 0.001; surfaces well oiled, 0.001 to 0.002; surfaces covered with silt, 0.003 to 0.005; surfaces rusty, 0.005 to 0.01.

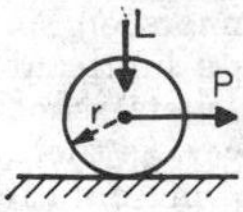

If a load L is moved on rollers (Fig. 3) and if k and k' are the respective coefficients of friction for the lower and upper surfaces, the frictional force $P = (k + k')L/d$.

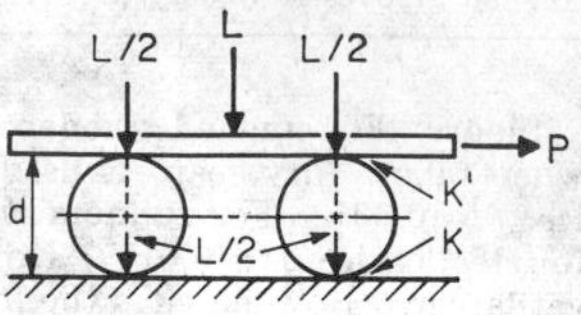

Fig. 2 Fig. 3

McKibben and Davidson (*Agri. Eng.*, 1939) give the data in Table 2 on the rolling resistance of various types of wheels for typical road and field conditions.

Moyer found the following average values of f_r for pneumatic rubber tires properly inflated and loaded: hard road, 0.008; dry, firm, and well-packed gravel, 0.012; wet loose gravel, 0.06.

FRICTION OF MACHINE ELEMENTS

Work of Friction—Efficiency. In a simple machine or assemblage of two elements, the work done by an applied force P acting through the distance s is measured by the product Ps. The useful work done is less and is measured by the product Ll of the resistance L by the distance l through which it acts. The **efficiency** e of the machine is the ratio of the useful work performed to the total work received, or $e = Ll/Ps$. The **work expended in friction** W_f is the difference between the total work received and the useful work, or $W_f = Ps - Ll$. The **lost-work** ratio $= V = W_f/Ll$, and $e = 1/(1 + V)$.

If a machine consists of a train of mechanisms having the respective efficiencies, $e_1, e_2, e_3 \ldots e_n$, the combined efficiency of the machine is equal to the product of these efficiencies.

Efficiencies of Machines and Machine Elements. The following values for machine elements are from "Elements of Machine Design," by Kimball and Barr. Those for machines are from Goodman's "Mechanics Applied to Engineering." The quantities given are percentage efficiencies.

Common bearing (singly)	96–98	Belting	96–98
Common bearing, long lines of shafting	95	Pin-connected chains (bicycle)	95–97
Roller bearings	98	High-grade transmission chains	97–99
Ball bearings	99	Weston pulley block (½ ton)	30–47
Spur gear, including bearings		Epicycloidal pulley block	40–45
Cast teeth	93	1 ton steam hoist or windlass	50–70
Cut teeth	96	Hydraulic windlass	60–80
Bevel gear, including bearings		Hydraulic jack	80–90
Cast teeth	92	Cranes (steam)	60–70
Cut teeth	95	Overhead traveling cranes	30–50
Worm gear		Locomotives (drawbar hp/ihp)	65–75
Thread angle, 30°	85–95	Hydraulic couplings, max	98
Thread angle, 15°	75–90		

Wedges

Sliding in V Guides. If a wedge-shaped slide having an angle $2b$ is pressed into a V guide by a force P (Fig. 4) the force normal to the wedge faces will be $N = P/\sin b$, and the frictional force opposing motion along the axis of the wedge is $F = fN = fP/\sin b = f'P$, where $f' = f/\sin b$ is improperly called the coefficient of friction. In these formulas, the fact that the elasticity of the materials permits an advance of the wedge into the guide under the load P has been neglected. The common efficiency for V guides is $e = 0.88$ to 0.90.

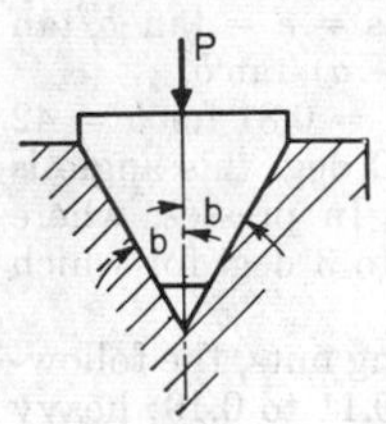

FIG. 4

Taper Keys. In Fig. 5 if the key be moved in the direction of the force P, the force H must be overcome. The supporting reactions K_1, K_2, and K_3 together with the required force P may be obtained by drawing the force polygon (Fig. 6). The friction angles of these faces are a_1, a_2, and a_3, respectively. In Fig. 6, draw AB parallel to H in Fig. 5, and lay it off to scale to represent H. From the point A, draw AC parallel to K_1, *i.e.*, making the angle $b + a_1$ with AB; from the other extremity of AB, draw BC parallel to K_2 in Fig. 5. AC and CB then give the magnitudes of K_1 and K_2, respectively. Now through C draw CD parallel to K_3 to its intersection with AD which has been drawn through A parallel to P. The magnitudes of K_3 and P are then given by the lengths of CD and DA.

By calculation,

$$K_1/H = \cos a_2/\cos (b + a_1 + a_2)$$
$$P/K_1 = \sin (b + a_1 + a_3)/\cos a_3$$
$$P/H = \cos a_2 \sin (b + a_1 + a_3)/\cos a_3 \cos (b + a_1 + a_2)$$

If $a_1 = a_2 = a_3 = a$, then $P = H \tan (b + 2a)$, and efficiency $e = \tan b/\tan (b + 2a)$. Force required to loosen the key $= P_1 = H \tan (2a - b)$. In order for the key not to slide out when force P is removed, it is necessary that $b < (a_1 + a_3)$, or $b < 2a$.

The forces acting upon the taper key of Fig. 7 may be found in a similar way (see Fig. 8).

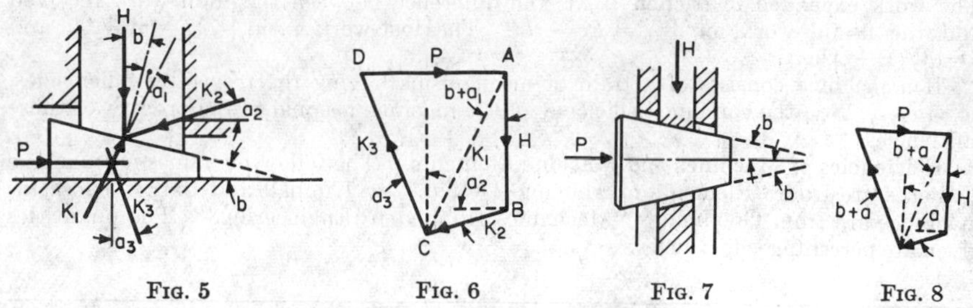

FIG. 5 FIG. 6 FIG. 7 FIG. 8

$$\begin{aligned} P &= 2H \cos a \sin (b + a)/\cos (b + 2a) \\ &= 2H \tan (b + a)/[1 - \tan a \tan (b + a)] \\ &= 2H \tan (b + a) \text{ approx} \end{aligned}$$

The force to loosen the key is $P_1 = 2H \tan (a - b)$ approx, and the efficiency $e = \tan b/\tan (b + a)$. The key will be self-locking when $b < a$, or, more generally, when $2b < (a_1 + a_3)$.

Screws

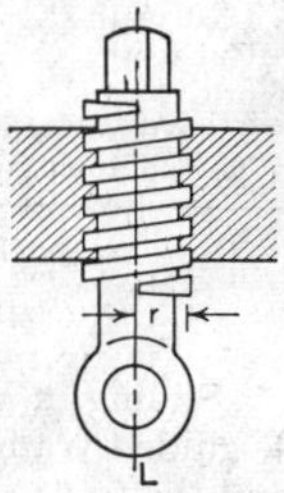

Screws with Square Threads (Fig. 9). Let r = mean radius of the thread = ½ (radius at root + outside radius), and l = pitch (or lead of a single-threaded screw), both in inches; b = angle of inclination of thread to a plane at right angles to the axis of screw ($\tan b = l/2\pi r$); and f = coefficient of sliding friction = $\tan a$. Then, for a screw in uniform motion (friction of the root and outside surfaces being neglected) there is required a force P acting at right angles to the axis at the distance r. $P = L \tan (b \pm a) = L(l \pm 2\pi rf)/(2\pi r \mp fl)$, where the upper signs are for motion in a direction opposed to that of L and the lower for motion in the same direction as that of L. When $b \leqq a$, the screw will not "overhaul" (or move under the action of the load L).

FIG. 9

The **efficiency** for motion opposed to direction in which L acts $= e = \tan b/\tan (b + a)$; for motion in the same direction in which L acts, $e = \tan (b - a)/\tan b$.

The value of e is a maximum when $b = 45 \text{ deg} - \frac{1}{2}a$; *e.g.*, $e_{max} = 0.81$ for $b = 42$ deg and $f = 0.1$. Since e increases rapidly for values of b up to 20 deg, this angle is generally not exceeded; for $b = 20$ deg, and $f_1 = 0.10$, $e = 0.74$. In presses, where the mechanical advantage is required to be great, b is taken down to 3 deg, for which value $e = 0.34$ with $f = 0.10$.

Kingsbury found for square-threaded screws running in loose-fitting nuts, the following coefficients of friction: lard oil, 0.09 to 0.25; heavy mineral oil, 0.11 to 0.19; heavy oil with graphite, 0.03 to 0.15.

Ham and Ryan give for screws the following values of coefficients of friction, with medium mineral oil: high-grade materials and workmanship, 0.10; average quality materials and workmanship, 0.12; poor workmanship, 0.15.

The use of castor oil as a lubricant lowered f from 0.10 to 0.066.

The coefficients of friction of a **plain collar thrust bearing** used with a **power screw** with medium mineral oil were: soft steel on cast iron, 0.12; hardened steel on cast iron, 0.09; soft steel on bronze, 0.08; hardened steel on bronze, 0.06.

The coefficients of static friction (at starting) were 30 percent higher.

Screws with V Threads. Let c = half the angle between the faces of a thread. Then, using the same notation as for square-threaded screws, for a screw in motion (neglecting friction of root and outside surfaces),

$$P = L(l \pm 2\pi rf \sec d)/(2\pi r \mp lf \sec d)$$

d is the angle between a plane normal to the axis of the screw through the point of the resultant thread friction, and a plane which is tangent to the surface of the thread at the same point (see Groat, *Proc. Engs. Soc. West. Penn*, **34**). Sec d = sec c $\sqrt{1 - (\sin b \sin c)^2}$. For small values of b this reduces practically to sec d = sec c, and, for all cases the approximation, $P = L(l \pm 2\pi rf \sec c)/(2\pi r \mp lf \sec c)$ is within the limits of probable error in estimating values to be used for f.

The **efficiencies** are: $e = \tan b(1 - f \tan b \sec d)/(\tan b + f \sec d)$ for motion opposed to L, and $e = (\tan b - f \sec d)/\tan b(1 + f \tan b \sec d)$ for motion with L. If we let $\tan d' = f \sec d$, these equations reduce, respectively, to $e = \tan b/\tan (b + d')$ and $e = \tan (b - d')/\tan b$. Negative values in the latter case merely mean that the thread will not overhaul. Subtract the values from unity for actual efficiency, considering the external moment and not the load L as being the driver. The efficiency of a V thread is lower than that of a square thread of the same helix angle, since $d' > a$.

For a **V-threaded screw and nut,** let r_1 = outside radius of thread, r_2 = radius at root of thread, $r = (r_1 + r_2)/2$, $\tan d' = f \sec d$, r_0 = mean radius of nut seat = $1.5r$ (approx) and f' = coefficient of friction between nut and seat.

To tighten up the nut the turning moment required is $M = Pr + Lr_0f = Lr\,[\tan (d' + b) + 1.5f']$. **To loosen** $M = Lr[\tan (d' - b) + 1.5f']$.

The **total tension in a bolt** due to tightening up with a moment M is $T = 2\pi M/(l + fl \sec b \sec d \operatorname{cosec} b + f'3\pi r)$. $T \div$ area at root gives unit pure tensile stress induced, S_t. There is also a unit torsional stress: $S_s = 2(M - 1.5rf'T)/\pi r_2^3$. The equivalent combined stress is $S = 0.35S_t + 0.65\sqrt{S_t^2 + 4S_s^2}$.

Kingsbury, from tests on U.S. standard bolts, finds efficiencies for tightening up nuts from 0.06 to 0.12, depending upon the roughness of the contact surfaces and the character of the lubrication.

Toothed and Worm Gearing

The efficiency of **spur and bevel gearing** depends on the material and the workmanship of the gears and on the lubricant employed. For high-speed gears of good quality the efficiency of the gear transmission is 99 percent; with slow-speed gears of average workmanship the efficiency of 96 percent is common. On the average, efficiencies of 97 to 98 percent can be considered normal.

In **helical gears,** where considerable transverse sliding of the meshing teeth on each other takes place, the friction is much greater. If b and c are, respectively, the spiral angles of the teeth of the driving and driven helical gears (*i.e.*, the complements of their angles of inclination), $b + c$ is the shaft angle of the two gears, and $f = \tan a$ is the coefficient of sliding friction of the teeth, the efficiency of the gear transmission is $e = [\cos b \cos (c + a)]/[\cos c \cos (b - a)]$.

In the case of **worm gearing** when the shafts are normal to each other ($b + c = 90$), the efficiency is $e = \tan c/\tan (c + a) = (1 - pf/2\pi r)/(1 + 2\pi rf/p)$, where c is the spiral angle of the worm wheel, or the lead angle of the worm; p the lead, or pitch of the worm thread; and r the mean radius of the worm. Typical values of f are as follows:

Rubbing speed of worm, fpm	100	200	300	500	800	1200
Phosphor-bronze wheel, polished-steel worm	0.054	0.045	0.039	0.030	0.024	0.020
Single-threaded cast-iron worm and gear	0.060	0.051	0.047	0.034	0.025	

Journals and Bearings

Friction of Journal Bearings. If P = total load on journal in lb, l = journal length in in., and $2r$ = journal diam in in., then $p = P/2rl$ = mean normal pressure, psi of the projected area of the journal. Also, if f_1 be the **coefficient of journal friction,** the **moment of journal friction** for a cylindrical journal is $M = f_1Pr$ in in.-lb. The **work expended in friction** at a speed of n rpm is $W_f = 2\pi Mn = 6.283f_1Prn$ in.-lb per min. For the **conical bearing** (Fig. 10) the mean radius $r_m = (r + R)/2$ is to be used.

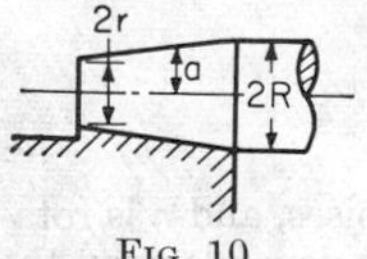

Fig. 10

Values of Coefficient of Friction. For very low velocities of rotation (*e.g.*, below 10 rpm), high loads, and with good lubrication, the coefficient of friction approaches the value of greasy friction, 0.07 to 0.15 (see Table 1 above). This is also the "pull-out" coefficient of friction *on starting* the journal. With higher velocities, a fluid film is established between the journal and bearing, and the values of the coefficient of friction depend on the speed of rotation, the pressure on the bearing, and the viscosity of the oil. For journals running in complete bearing bushings, with a small clearance, *i.e.*, with the diameter of the bushing slightly larger than the diameter of the journal, the experimental data of McKee give approximate values of the coefficient of friction as in Fig. 11.

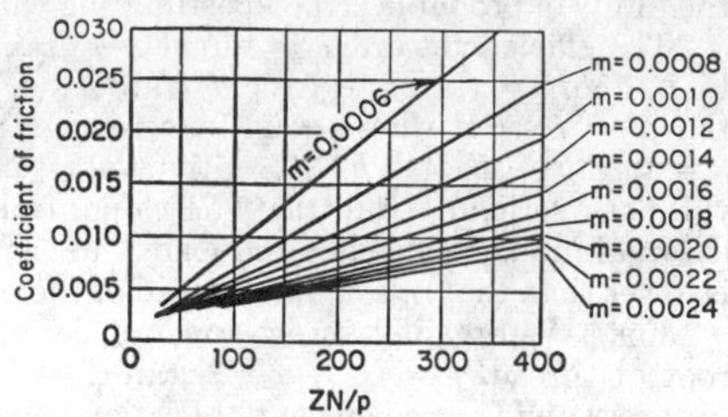

Fig. 11. Coefficient of friction of journal.

If d_1 is the diameter of the bushing in inches, d the diameter of the journal in inches, then $(d_1 - d)$ is the diametral clearance and $m = (d_1 - d)/d$ is the clearance ratio. The diagram of McKee (Fig. 11) gives the coefficient of friction as a function of the characteristic number ZN/p, where N is the rpm, $p = P/dl$ the average pressure, psi, on the projected area of the bearing, where P is the load, lb; l the length of bushing, in.; Z the absolute viscosity of the oil in centipoises (see p. 3–53). Approximate values of Z at 100 (130) deg F are as follows: light machine oil, 30 (16); medium machine oil, 60 (25); medium-heavy machine oil, 120 (40); heavy machine oil, 160 (60).

For purposes of design of ordinary machinery with bearing pressures from 50 to 300 psi and speeds of 100 to 3,000 rpm, values for the coefficient of journal friction can be taken from 0.008 to 0.020.

Thrust Bearings

Frictional Resistance. Step bearings or pivots may be used to resist the end thrust of shafts. Let L = total load, lb in the direction of the shaft axis; dA = an elementary area of the thrust-bearing surface, sq in.; y = distance of the area dA from its axis of revolution, in.; p = pressure on dA due to load L, psi; and f = coefficient of sliding friction. Then, **moment of thrust friction** $= M = fp \int y\, dA$ in in.-lb; and the **work expended in friction** per min at n rpm $= W_f = 2\pi M n$ in in.-lb.

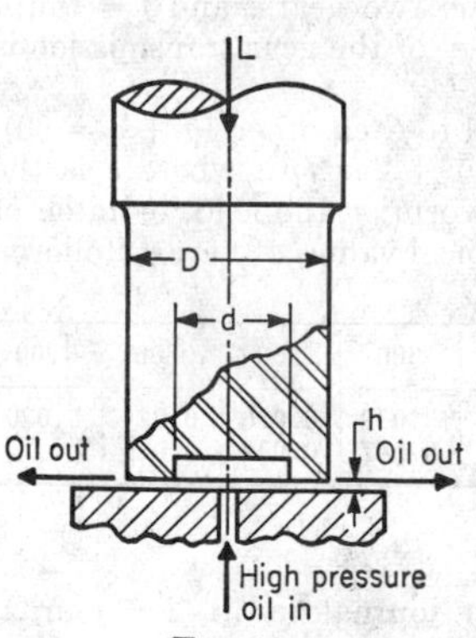

Fig. 12

For a **ring-shaped flat step bearing** such as that shown in Fig. 12 (or a **collar bearing**), $M = \frac{1}{3} fL(D^3 - d^3)/(D^2 - d^2)$, where D and d are in in. For a **flat circular step bearing,** $d = 0$, and $M = \frac{1}{3} fLD$.

The value of the coefficient of sliding friction is 0.08 to 0.15 when the speed of rotation is very slow. At higher velocities when a collar or step bearing is used, f = 0.04 to 0.06. If the design provides for the formation of a load carrying oil film, as in the case of the Kingsbury thrust bearing, the coefficient of friction has values f = 0.001 to 0.0025.

Where oil is supplied from an external pump with such pressure as to separate the surfaces and provide an oil film of thickness h (Fig. 12), the frictional moment is

$$M = \frac{Z \times n(D^4 - d^4)}{67 \times 10^7 \times h}$$

where h is the film thickness, in., Z is viscosity of lubricant in centipoises, and n is rotation speed, rpm. With this kind of lubrication the frictional moment depends upon the

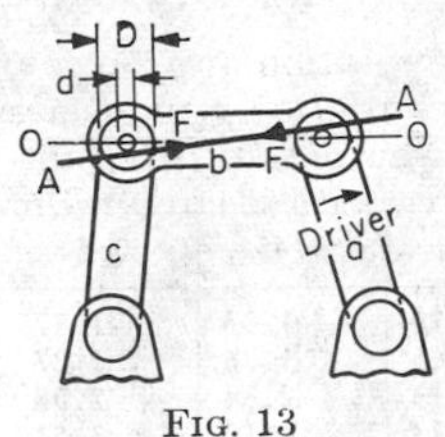

FIG. 13

speed of rotation of the shaft and actually approaches zero for zero shaft speeds. The thrust load will be carried on a film of oil regardless of shaft rotation for as long as the pump continues to supply the required volume and pressure (see also Sec. 8).

EXAMPLE. A hydrostatic thrust bearing carries 101,000 lb, D is 16 in., d is 10 in., oil film thickness, h, is 0.006 in., oil viscosity, Z, 30 centipoises at operating temperature, and n is 750 rpm. Substituting these values, the frictional torque, M, is 310 in.-lb. The oil supply pressure was 82.5 psi; the oil flow, 12.2 gpm.

Frictional Forces in Pin Joints of Mechanisms

In the absence of friction, or when the effect of friction is negligible, the force transmitted by the link b from the driver a to the driven link c (Figs. 13 and 14) acts through the center line OO of the pins connecting the link b with links a and c. With friction, this line of action shifts to the line AA, tangent to small circles of diameter d. The diameter d of the circle, called the **friction circle,** for each individual joint, is equal to fD, where D is the diameter of the pin and f is the coefficient of friction between the pin and the link. The choice of the proper disposition of the tangent AA with respect to the two friction circles is dictated by the consideration that friction always opposes the action of the linkage. The force F opposes the motion of a; therefore, with friction it acts on a longer lever than without friction (Figs. 13 and 14). On the other hand, the force F drives the link c; friction hinders its action, and the equivalent lever is shorter with friction than without friction; the friction throws the line of action toward the center of rotation of link c.

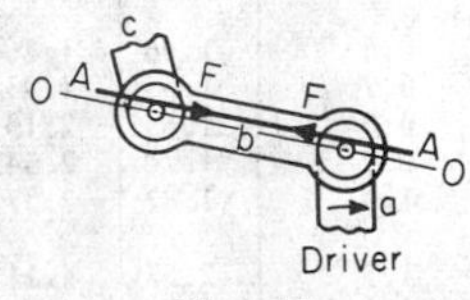

FIG. 14

EXAMPLE. An engine eccentric (Fig. 15) is a joint where the friction loss may be large. For the dimensions shown and with a torque of 250 in.-lb applied to the rotating shaft, the resultant horizontal force, with no friction, will act through the center of the eccentric and be 250/(2.5 sin 60) or 115.5 lb. With friction coefficient 0.1, the resultant force (which for a long rod remains approximately horizontal) will be tangent to the friction circle of radius 0.1×5, or 0.5 in., and have a magnitude of $250/(2.5 \sin 60 + 0.5)$, or 93.8 lb.

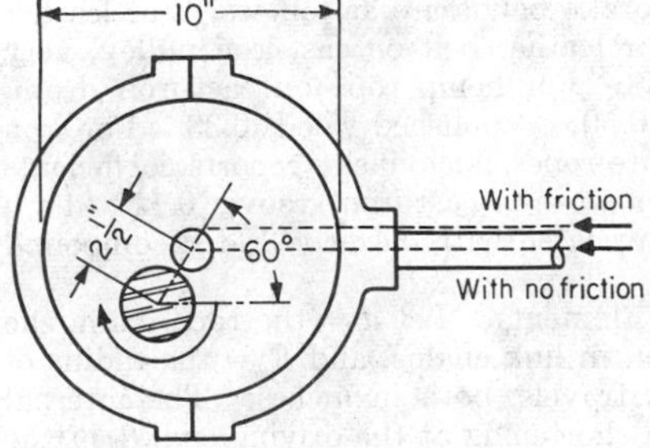

FIG. 15

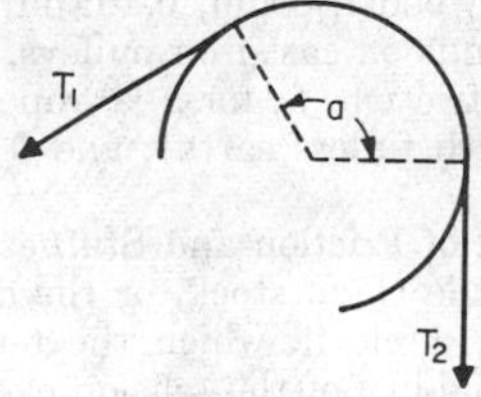

FIG. 16

Tension Elements

Frictional Resistance. In Fig. 16, let T_1 and T_2 be the tensions with which a rope, belt, chain, or brake band is strained over a drum, pulley, or sheave, and let the rope or belt be on the point of slipping from T_2 toward T_1 by reason of the difference of tension $T_1 - T_2$. Then $T_1 - T_2$ = circumferential force P transferred by friction must be equal to the frictional resistance W of the belt, rope, or band on the drum or pulley. Also, let a = angle subtending the arc of contact between the drum and tension element, measured in radians. Then, disregarding centrifugal forces,

$$T_1 = T_2 e^{fa} \quad \text{and} \quad P = (e^{fa} - 1)T_1/e^{fa} = (e^{fa} - 1)T_2 = W$$

where e = base of the Napierian system of logarithms = 2.718 +.

Table 3. Values of e^{fa}

$\frac{a°}{360°}$	*f*								
	0.1	0.15	0.2	0.25	0.3	0.35	0.4	0.45	0.5
0.1	1.06	1.1	1.13	1.17	1.21	1.25	1.29	1.33	1.37
0.2	1.13	1.21	1.29	1.37	1.46	1.55	1.65	1.76	1.87
0.3	1.21	1.32	1.45	1.60	1.76	1.93	2.13	2.34	2.57
0.4	1.29	1.46	1.65	1.87	2.12	2.41	2.73	3.10	3.51
0.425	1.31	1.49	1.70	1.95	2.23	2.55	2.91	3.33	3.80
0.45	1.33	1.53	1.76	2.03	2.34	2.69	3.10	3.57	4.11
0.475	1.35	1.56	1.82	2.11	2.45	2.84	3.30	3.83	4.45
0.5	1.37	1.60	1.87	2.19	2.57	3.00	3.51	4.11	4.81
0.525	1.39	1.64	1.93	2.28	2.69	3.17	3.74	4.41	5.20
0.55	1.41	1.68	2.00	2.37	2.82	3.35	3.98	4.74	5.63
0.6	1.46	1.76	2.13	2.57	3.10	3.74	4.52	5.45	6.59
0.7	1.55	1.93	2.41	3.00	3.74	4.66	5.81	7.24	9.02
0.8	1.65	2.13	2.73	3.51	4.52	5.81	7.47	9.60	12.35
0.9	1.76	2.34	3.10	4.11	5.45	7.24	9.60	12.74	16.90
1.0	1.87	2.57	3.51	4.81	6.59	9.02	12.35	16.90	23.14
1.5	2.57	4.11	6.59	10.55	16.90	27.08	43.38	69.49	111.32
2.0	3.51	6.59	12.35	23.14	43.38	81.31	152.40	285.68	535.49
2.5	4.81	10.55	23.14	50.75	111.32	244.15	535.49	1,174.5	2,575.9
3.0	6.59	16.90	43.38	111.32	285.68	733.14	1,881.5	4,828.5	12,391
3.5	9.02	27.08	81.31	244.15	733.14	2,199.90	6,610.7	19,851	59,608
4.0	12.35	43.38	152.40	535.49	1,881.5	6,610.7	23,227	81,610	286,744

$e^{\pi} = 23.1407$. $\log e^{\pi} = 1.3643764$.

f is the coefficient of friction of repose (f_0) when there is no slip of the belt or band on the drum and the coefficient of sliding friction (f) when slip takes place. In addition to the values given below, see p. 3–40.

Average values of f_0 for belts, ropes, and brake bands are as follows: For leather belt on slightly greasy wood pulley, 0.47. For leather belt on cast-iron pulley, very greasy, 0.12; slightly greasy, 0.28; moist, 0.38. For hemp rope on cast-iron drum, 0.25; on wooden drum, 0.40; on rough wood, 0.50; on polished wood, 0.33. For iron brake bands on cast-iron pulleys, 0.18. For wire ropes, Tichvinsky reports coefficients of static friction, f_0, for a ⅝ rope (8 × 19) on a worn-in cast-iron groove: 0.113 (dry); 0.124 (with fullers earth); and 0.104 (when lubricated with Texaco Crater compound No. 1).

Effect of Friction and Stiffness in Tension Elements. Let d = the rope diam, the diam of the chain stock, or the diam of the pin in link chains, and R = the radius of the pitch circle in which the tension element travels, both in inches. The internal friction rigidity of the tension element causes a shortening at the driving end T_1 of the lever arm R an amount h_1 in inches, and at the following end a lengthening of the lever arm R an amount $= h_2$ in. Then, for simultaneous winding on and off, $T_1(R - h_1) = T_2(R + h_2)$. Approximately, $h_1 = h_2 = h$, whence $h_1 + h_2 = 2h$ (approx) and $T_1 = [1 + (2h/R)]T_2$.

This results in a frictional loss, and the efficiency of transmission is $e = 1 - (2h/R)$. If the tension element is only wound on the drum, $h_1 = 0$ and $T_1 = [1 + (h/R)]T_2$, with the corresponding efficiency $e = 1 - h/R$.

For **chains** the coefficient of friction between the link faces or pivots is $f = 0.2$ to 0.3; when d = the diam of the link pin, $h = fd/2$.

For **hemp ropes,** $h = 0.03d^2$ to $0.09d^2$ according to the construction, material, and condition of the rope.

The **elastic rigidity** of the material is not a factor in simultaneous winding on and off, since the lever arm R is increased equally at the points of winding on and off; the work expended in bending the tension element as it is wound on is recovered as it straightens out in unwinding. But if there is only winding on, the effect of the bending is to be taken into account.

Efficiency of rope and chain sheaves at low speeds, including journal friction (180 deg contact):

For fixed sheaves, chain, and wire rope, $e = 0.94$ to 0.96.

For floating sheaves, chain, and wire rope, $e = 0.97$.

Hemp rope sheaves:

Rope diam., in......	5/8	1	1½	1¾	2
Fixed sheaves: e =	0.95–0.96	0.91–0.96	0.89–0.93	0.84–0.92	0.85–0.91
Floating sheaves: e =	0.97	0.96	0.95	0.94	0.93

MECHANICS OF FLUIDS

BY

Clarence B. Anderson

REFERENCES: Shames, "Mechanics of Fluids," McGraw-Hill. Streeter, "Fluid Mechanics," McGraw-Hill. Rouse, "Elementary Mechanics of Fluids," Wiley. Shapiro, "The Dynamics and Thermodynamics of Compressible Fluid Flow," Parts I and II from vol. I, Ronald Press. Binder, "Fluid Mechanics," Prentice-Hall. Report of Fluid Meters Committee, ASME. Langhaar, "Dimensional Analysis and Theory of Models," Wiley.

Notation

A = area
b = width
c = speed of sound
c_P = specific heat at constant pressure
c_V = specific heat at constant volume
C_D = discharge coefficient
d = diameter
D = diameter
E = bulk modulus
E = modulus of elasticity
f = friction factor
F = force
g = acceleration of gravity
h = vertical distance or depth
h_f = loss of head
I = moment of inertia
J = mechanical equivalent of heat
k = ratio of specific heats, c_P/c_V
K = loss factor
l = length
L = length
m = hydraulic radius
M = mass
n = coefficient of roughness
p = perimeter
P = pressure
q = heat added to fluid
Q = fluid flow rate or discharge
r = radius
R = perfect gas constant
R = reaction force
Re = Reynolds number
s = slant distance
s.g. = specific gravity
S = speed of pressure wave
S = hydraulic slope
t = time
T = temperature
T = thickness
U = internal energy
U = velocity
v = volume
v = local velocity
V = average velocity
w = specific weight
W = weight
$\mathcal{W}$ = work done on the fluid
x = direction
y = direction or vertical distance
z = direction or vertical direction
α = angle
ϵ = roughness
θ = angle
θ = function of
μ = dynamic viscosity
ν = kinematic viscosity
ρ = mass density
σ = surface tension
τ = shearing stress
ϕ = function of

PROPERTIES OF FLUIDS

A fluid is defined as a substance which deforms continuously when subjected to a shear stress, however small that shear stress may be. Fluid properties are defined from the macroscopic viewpoint, which is concerned with the average properties of many molecules.

The **velocity** V of a fluid is defined with respect to some axis system that in engineering practice is usually stationary with respect to the earth's surface. The units of velocity are ft sec^{-1}.

The **density** ρ is the mass per unit volume of the fluid and is not to be confused with **specific weight** w, the weight per unit volume. The interrelation of density and specific weight is $w = g\rho$, where g is the acceleration of gravity. The units of density are slug ft^{-3} or lb sec^2 ft^{-4}.

The **specific gravity,** s.g. or sp gr, is the ratio of the density of a substance to that of water at 39.2 F.

The **pressure** P is the force exerted by a fluid per unit area and has the units of lb ft^{-2}. Because thermodynamic laws and relations are used in fluid mechanics, P is defined as absolute pressure unless specifically stated otherwise (see also Sec. 4). For convenience, pressures are often expressed in pounds per square inch, inches of water, inches of mercury, or millibars, so caution must be observed when substituting in formulas. When pressure is given with respect to atmospheric pressure, it is called gage pressure. Thus, a pressure of 5.3 lb in.$^{-2}$ gage, or 5.3 psig, when the atmospheric pressure is 15 lb in.$^{-2}$, is equivalent to 20.3 lb in.$^{-2}$, or 2,923 lb ft^{-2}. Standard atmospheric pressure is defined as 2,116 lb ft^{-2}, or 14.7 lb in.$^{-2}$. To avoid confusion, units of pressure are often written as psia, lb in.$^{-2}$ abs, psfa, lb ft^{-2} abs; psig, where abs and a stand for absolute and g stands for gage. The **temperature** T has units of R, degrees Rankine.

When a fluid flows such that its velocities are free of macroscopic fluctuations, the flow is said to be *laminar*. The flow is *turbulent* when the velocities are subject to macroscopic fluctuations. Smoke rising from a cigarette in still air at first illustrates laminar flow and then turbulent flow when the swirls and eddies appear and continue.

When the flow is laminar, Newton's viscosity law states that the applied shear stress τ is proportional to the rate of deformation or to the velocity gradient normal to the velocity, dV/dy. The constant of proportionality μ is the **absolute** or **dynamic viscosity,** $\tau = \mu\, dV/dy$. A Newtonian fluid has a linear relation between the applied shear stress and the rate of deformation, while for a non-Newtonian fluid the relation is non-linear.

In the cgs system the unit of dynamic viscosity is the *poise*, having dimensions of gr sec^{-1} cm^{-1} or dyne sec cm^{-2}. The customary unit is the *centipoise*, having dimensions of poise $\times$ 10^{-2}. The dynamic viscosity of water at 68.4 F and atmospheric pressure is 1.0 centipoise. In the English system the units of dynamic viscosity are slug ft^{-1} sec^{-1} or lb sec ft^{-2}. To convert the dynamic viscosity in centipoise to units of lb sec ft^{-2}, multiply by 2.083×10^{-5}.

The **kinematic viscosity** ν is the dynamic viscosity divided by the density $\nu = \mu/\rho$. In the cgs system the unit of kinematic viscosity is the *stoke*, having dimensions of cm^2 sec^{-1}. It is customary to use the *centistoke* which is stoke $\times$ 10^{-2}. In the English system the dimensions of kinematic viscosity are ft^2 sec^{-1}. To convert kinematic viscosity in centistoke to units of ft^2 sec^{-1}, multiply by 1.076×10^{-5}.

Viscosity can be determined experimentally. A few such experiments are the laminar flow of a fluid in a duct, the damping of a torsional or spherical pendulum, the rate of rise or fall of a spherical body in a fluid, or the torque exerted on a stationary cylinder when a fluid fills the annular space between it and a rotating cylinder. Industrially, viscosity is measured by observing the time necessary for a fluid to flow from a filled container of specified dimensions through an opening in the bottom of the container. Empirical relations exist to convert the efflux time to kinematic viscosity. In the United States the **Saybolt Universal** viscometer is commonly used for petroleum products and lubricating oils. For heavy oils the **Saybolt Furol** viscometer is used. Dimensions of these viscometers are prescribed by the ASTM. In England the **Redwood** viscometer and in Germany the **Engler** viscometer are used.

The value of the kinematic viscosity in stokes can be obtained from the following approximation equations where t is the efflux time in seconds:

Saybolt Universal, when $32 < t < 100$ . . . . $\nu = 0.00226t - 1.95/t$
  When $t > 100$ . . . . $\nu = 0.00220t - 1.35/t$
Saybolt Furol, when $25 < t < 40$ . . . . $\nu = 0.0224t - 1.84/t$
  When $t > 40$ . . . . $\nu = 0.0216t - 0.60/t$
Redwood No. 1 (English), when $34 < t < 100$ . . $\nu = 0.00260t - 1.79/t$
  When $t > 100$ . . . . $\nu = 0.00247t - 0.50/t$
Redwood Admiralty (English) . . . . $\nu = 0.027t - 20/t$
Engler (German) . . . . $\nu = 0.00147t - 3.74/t$

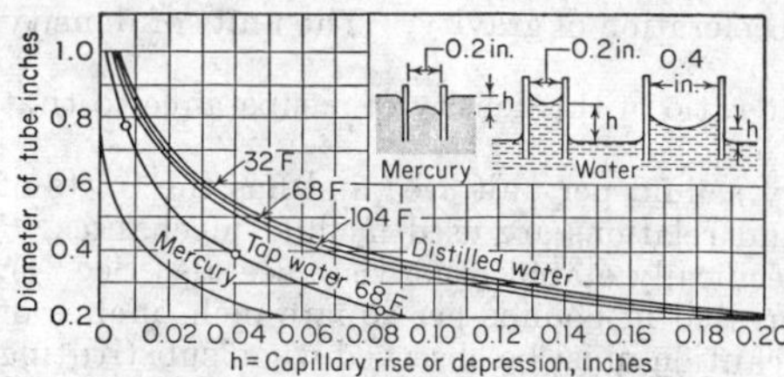

FIG. 1. Capillarity in circular glass tubes. (*From "Hydraulics" by Daugherty, McGraw-Hill Book Co.,* 1937. *Used by permission.*)

The **bulk modulus** E of a substance is given by $E = \rho\, dP/d\rho$. The bulk modulus for water is about 3×10^5 lb in.$^{-2}$, and for mercury about 4.7×10^6 lb in.$^{-2}$. For gases, E depends on the thermodynamic process. For an isothermal change of state, $E = P$, and for an isentropic change of state, $E = kP$, where k is the ratio of specific heats. A change of pressure of 10 lb in.$^{-2}$ produces a change in the density of water of approximately 6.7×10^{-5} slug ft^{-3}, while for air under standard conditions and an isentropic change of state, the change in density is approximately 1×10^{-3} slug ft^{-3}. As a consequence, water and other liquids are generally treated as *incompressible*, while gases are treated as *compressible* fluids (see also Sec. 4).

The **speed of sound** c in a fluid or any medium is given by $c^2 = E/\rho = dP/d\rho$. The speed of sound in water is about 4,700 ft sec^{-1}, while in air under standard conditions and an isentropic change of state, the speed of sound is about 1,100 ft sec^{-1}. Within experimental error, measured values of the speed of sound in a gas are equal to the speed of sound for an isentropic process. Thus, the speed of sound in an ideal gas is taken to be $c^2 = kP/\rho = kgRT$ without the superfluous statement that the process is isentropic. In an ideal gas the speed of sound is a function of the temperature only (see also Sec. 12).

The **surface tension** σ of a liquid is the WORK done in extending the surface of the liquid one unit area. The units of surface tension are ft lb ft^{-2} or lb ft^{-1}. The value of surface tension depends on which liquid and fluid are in contact at the free surface of the liquid, for example, water-air, water–carbon dioxide, or water-oil. When one of the fluids is a gas, changes in its pressure and temperature usually cause little change in the surface tension of the liquid. In problems of atomization an estimate of the energy per pound of liquid required to produce droplets of a given size can be obtained by multiplying the value of the surface tension by the change in the surface area of the pound of liquid.

Capillary action is due to the surface tension, **cohesion** of the liquid molecules, and the **adhesion** of the liquid molecules and the molecules on the surface of a solid. A liquid wets the solid surface when adhesion is greater than cohesion. When a tube is partially immersed

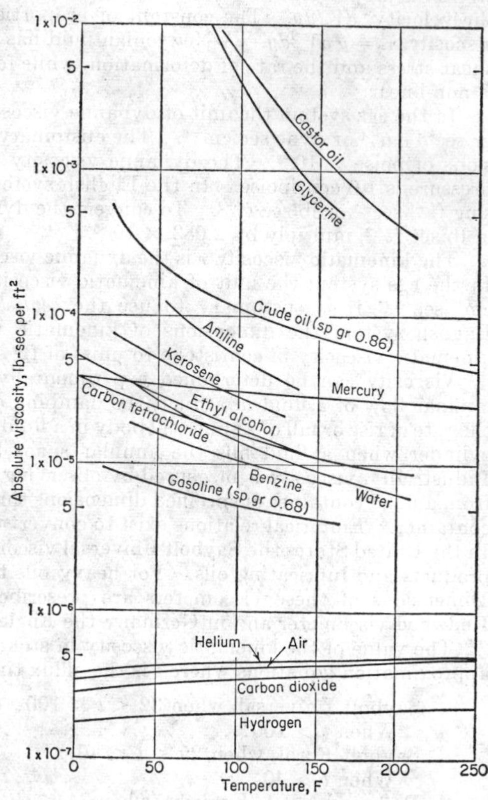

FIG. 2. Absolute viscosities μ of certain gases and liquids. (*From "Fluid Mechanics" by Streeter, McGraw-Hill Book Co.,* 1958. *Used by permission.*)

in a liquid, the liquid will rise in the tube if it wets the surface of the tube and will be depressed if it does not wet the tube. The amount of vertical rise or depression due to capillary action *alone* is shown in Fig. 1 for water and mercury in circular, clean glass tubes, when the gas is air. The effect of capillarity in manometers may be usually avoided by using glass tubes having an internal diameter of ⅜ in. or larger. Whatever the tube diameter, all readings should be taken at the middle of the meniscus, the curved surface of the liquid in the tube, whether the tube is vertical or slanted.

For a fluid in motion it is convenient to define reference and real values assumed by the pressure, temperature, density, etc. The first of these values, called **static** conditions, occurs when the fluid properties are measured at zero relative velocity between the fluid and the measuring instrument. The second of these values, called **stagnation** conditions, occurs when fluid properties are measured when

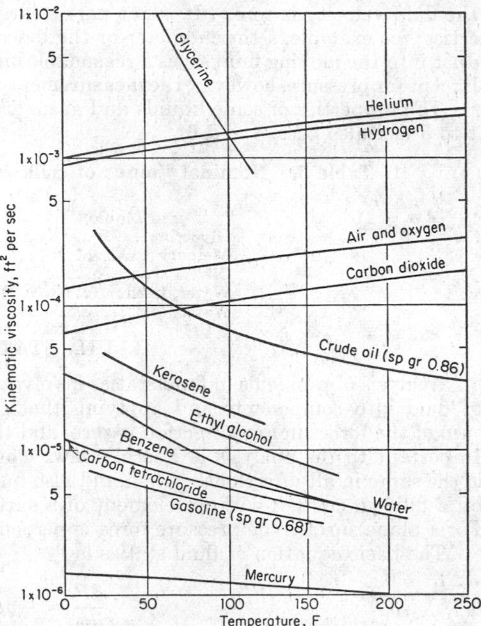

FIG. 3. Kinematic viscosities ν of certain gases at 14.7 lb in.$^{-2}$ and liquids. (*From "Fluid Mechanics" by Streeter, McGraw-Hill Book Co.*, 1958. *Used by permission.*)

Table 1. Densities of Liquids at 14.7 lb in.$^{-2}$ and 60 F

Liquid	Density ρ, slug ft^{-3}	Specific weight w, lb ft^{-3}
Alcohol, ethyl	1.53	49.3
Benzene	1.71	54.9
Carbon tetrachloride	3.09	99.5
Gasoline, sp gr 0.68	1.32	42.5
Glycerine	2.45	78.8
Kerosene	1.56	50.2
Mercury	26.3	848
Oil, crude sp gr 0.86	1.65	53.1
Water, fresh	1.94	62.4
Water, salt	1.99	64.0

Table 2. Surface Tension of Liquids in Contact with Air at 68 F
(From Streeter, "Fluid Mechanics," McGraw-Hill)

Liquid	Surface tension σ, lb/ft
Alcohol, ethyl	0.00153
Benzene	0.00198
Carbon tetrachloride	0.00183
Kerosene	0.0016–0.0022
Water	0.00498
Mercury	
In air	0.0352
In water	0.0269
In vacuum	0.0333
Oil	
Lubricating	0.0024–0.0026
Crude	0.0016–0.0026

the fluid velocity is zero. It is not particularly difficult to measure stagnation properties; for example, a thermometer or thermocouple protruding through the walls of a duct into the moving fluid gives a reasonable indication of the stagnation temperature. Except for pressure, however, the measurement of static conditions presents difficulties.

The properties of some liquids and gases are given in Figs. 2 and 3 and in Tables 1 to 3 (see also Secs. 4 and 6).

Table 3. Nominal Values of Bulk Modulus for Certain Liquids

Liquid	Bulk modulus, lb in^{-2}
Glycerine	630,000
Mercury	3,800,000
Oil	225,000
Water, fresh	300,000
Water, salt	330,000

FLUID STATICS

Analysis of problems in fluid statics involves resolving the forces exerted by a body of fluid into components and applying the static equilibrium laws: The algebraic sum of the forces in any direction is zero, and the summation of the moments is zero. Important to the analysis is **Pascal's law:** The pressure at a point in a static fluid is the same in all directions. It should also be noted that the pressure force exerted by a fluid in contact with an element of a surface is perpendicular to that element. For a plane surface the pressure force is perpendicular to the surface.

The basic equation of fluid statics is

$$\frac{dP}{dy} = -g\rho$$

where y is the vertical direction, parallel to the gravitational force, measured positively upward from a datum plane. The equation indicates the pressure in the fluid decreases as the vertical distance increases. Furthermore, dP is zero when dy is zero, and so the pressure is constant over a horizontal plane within the fluid.

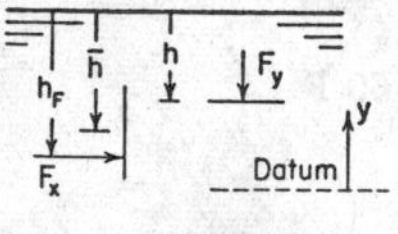

Fig. 4. Forces on submerged surfaces.

Liquids. For most cases the density of a liquid can be considered constant and the basic equation integrated to give $P = gh = wh$, where h is measured downward from the free surface of the liquid (Fig. 4). When atmospheric pressure acts on the liquid surface, the gage pressure at depth h is $P = wh$. When pressure P_a acts on the liquid surface, the pressure at depth h is $P = P_a + wh$.

The vertical force F_y exerted by a liquid on a horizontal surface of area A is obtained by integration:

$$F_y = \int P\, dA = whA$$

The **magnitude** of F_y equals the weight of the liquid above the surface, and its **location** can be determined because it acts through the center of mass, or centroid, of the liquid above the surface. The **direction** of F_y depends on which side of the horizontal surface is of interest.

The horizontal force F_x exerted by a liquid on a vertical surface is

$$F_x = \int P\, dA = w\int h\, dA = w\bar{h}A$$

where $\bar{h}$ is the depth to the centroid of the surface and is defined by $\bar{h}A = \int h\, dA$. The *magnitude* of F_x then equals the pressure at the centroid, $P = w\bar{h}$, times the area of the surface. The location of F_x is found by taking moments about an axis lying in the free surface,

$$h_F F_x = \int hP\, dA = w\int h^2\, dA$$

Then

$$h_F = \frac{\int h^2\, dA}{\bar{h}A} = \frac{I}{\bar{h}A}$$

where I is the moment of inertia of the vertical surface about an axis lying in the free surface. Using the parallel-axis theorem of moments of inertia,

$$h_F = \bar{h} + \frac{\bar{I}}{\bar{h}A}$$

where $\bar{I}$ is the moment of inertia of the surface about an axis lying in the surface, passing through its centroid, and parallel to the free surface. The *direction* of F_x depends on which side of the surface is of interest.

EXAMPLE. Determine the force and its location acting on a rectangular vertical gate 3 ft wide and 5 ft high at the bottom of tank with water 12 ft deep. $F_x = w\bar{h}A = 62.4 \times (7 + 5/2) \times (3 \times 5) = 8{,}892$ lb. $h_F = \bar{h} + \bar{I}/\bar{h}A = (7 + 5/2) + [1/12 \times 3 \times (5)^3]/[(7 + 5/2) \times (3 \times 5)] = 9.5 + 0.219 = 9.72$ ft below the free surface.

Plane areas (Fig. 5) inclined at angle θ to the free surface are a special case of vertical surfaces. The slant distance S is measured along the area from an origin in the free surface. The magnitude of the force acting on one side of the surface is

$$F = w\int h\,dA = w \sin\theta \int s\,dA = w\bar{s}A \sin\theta$$

The force is located at

$$S_F = \frac{I}{\bar{s}A} = \bar{s} + \frac{\bar{I}}{\bar{s}A}$$

where $\bar{s}$ is the slant distance to the centroid of the area.

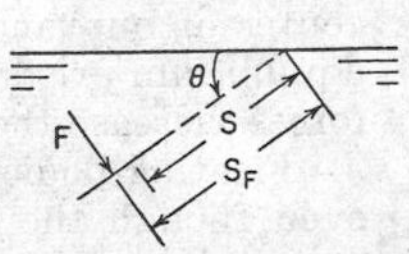

FIG. 5. Inclined surface.

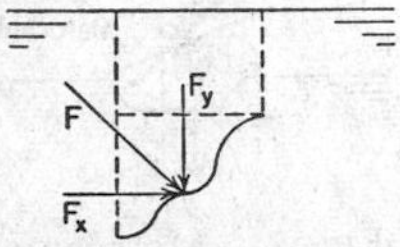

FIG. 6. Force on irregular surface.

For irregular surfaces (Fig. 6), the force and its location are found from the vertical and horizontal forces. The vertical component of the force equals the weight of liquid above the surface and acts through the centroid of the volume of liquid above the surface. The horizontal component of the force equals the force on a vertical projection of the irregular surface and acts at $\bar{h}$ of the projection as for any vertical surface. The total force $F = \sqrt{F_x^2 + F_y^2}$. The force and its location acting on the underside of a surface can be determined by considering first that the liquid extends above the surface and then reversing the direction of the force acting on the upper side.

Gases. In general the density of a gas cannot be considered constant. Integrating the basic equation depends on establishing another relationship. For an **ideal isothermal gas** the variation of pressure with elevation y is

$$P_2 = P_1 e^{-g\rho_1/P_1(y_2-y_1)} = P_1 e^{-(y_2-y_1)/RT_1}$$

For an **ideal isentropic gas** the variation of pressure with elevation is

$$P_2 = P_1 \left[1 - \frac{k-1}{k}\frac{1}{RT_1}(y_2 - y_1)\right]^{k/k-1}$$

where k is the ratio of specific heats.

At sea level the properties of the standard atmosphere are defined as $P = 2{,}116$ lb ft^{-2} = 29.92 in. Hg = 14.7 psia, T = 59 F = 519 R, $\rho = 2.378 \times 10^{-3}$ slug ft^{-3}, and $w = 0.07651$ lb ft^{-3}. The temperature is assumed to decrease linearly with altitude at the rate of -0.00357 R ft^{-1} to an altitude of 35,300 ft. Since $T = 519 - 0.00357y$, the pressure at altitude y is

$$P = 2{,}116(1 - 6.88 \times 10^{-6}y)^{5.26}$$

The force exerted by a gas in contact with a surface can be determined by integration. For calculation purposes, the pressure can often be considered constant since it does not vary greatly with height and the force is taken to act at the centroid of the surface.

Buoyancy. Archimedes' principle states that a solid body submerged in a fluid at rest is buoyed up by a force equal in magnitude to the weight of the displaced fluid. The buoyant force F_f acts at the center of gravity of the displaced volume of fluid, called the center of buoyancy. The resultant force F on any submerged body equals the difference in the buoyant force and the weight of the body,

$$F = F_f - W = gv(\rho_f - \rho_b) = v(w_f - w_b)$$

where v is the volume of displaced fluid, and subscripts f and b indicate the fluid and body, respectively. The sign of F will indicate whether the body has a tendency to rise or sink in the fluid. F will be negative for a raindrop and positive for a bubble in soda. The equation can be utilized to determine experimentally the specific weight of a fluid or the volume of the displaced fluid. For any body that is floating on a liquid the buoyant force equals the weight of the body, $W = vw_f$.

The stability of a submerged body can be determined from the positions of the center of buoyancy and the center of gravity of the body. If the center of buoyancy is above the center of gravity, the body is in stable equilibrium and if displaced will return to its original position. If the center of buoyancy and center of gravity are coincident, the body is in neutral equilibrium and if displaced will remain in the new position. If the center of buoyancy is below the center of gravity, unstable equilibrium exists and if the body is displaced the unbalanced forces increase the displacement.

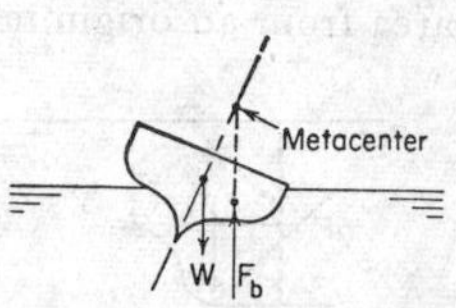

Fig. 7. Metacenter.

Floating bodies, such as rafts, boats, and barges, are stable even though the center of buoyancy is below the center of gravity because for small displacements the center of buoyancy shifts and a righting couple is produced. The point where a vertical through the new center of buoyancy cuts the original vertical (now inclined), through the center of gravity, is called the metacenter. The distance along the original vertical between the metacenter and center of gravity is called the metacentric height. A large value for the metacentric height indicates a large righting couple and a rapid recovery from a displacement (see Fig. 7). If a floating body is displaced until the righting couple is negative, the body will capsize (see also Sec. 11).

A **hydrometer** is a specially prepared float used to measure specific weight or specific gravity of a liquid by utilizing the equation $w_f = W/v$. The most common hydrometer is made of glass and has a graduate stem above a hollow bulb which contains weight such as mercury or bird shot to make the instrument float upright. The weight W of the hydrometer being known, graduations on the stem serve to measure the depth to which the hydrometer sinks (the submerged volume) but are marked in units of specific weight or gravity. By altering the weight and submerged volume, any desired degree of sensitivity can be obtained.

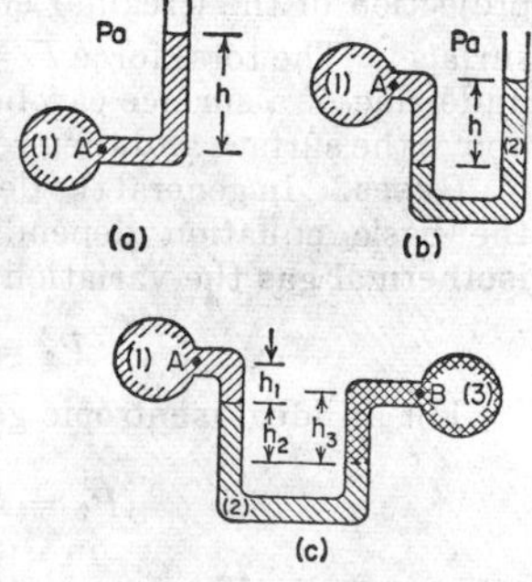

Fig. 8. Manometers.

Manometers are instruments which measure difference in pressure by means of a static column of liquid(s). Manometers have a wide variety of forms and can be analyzed by the equation $P = wh$ and the fact that the pressure is constant over a horizontal plane in a liquid. In Fig. 8, which shows three examples of manometers, P_a denotes ambient or atmospheric pressure.

Example. For Fig. 8(*a*), $P_a + w_1h_1 = P_A$. If liquid (1) is water, $h_1 = 10$ in. and $P_a = 14.7$ psia,

$$P_A = 14.7 \times 144 + 62.4 \times {}^{10}\!/\!_{12} = 2{,}116 + 52 = 2{,}168 \text{ psfa} = 15.1 \text{ psia}$$

Example. For Fig. 8(*c*), with three liquids, (1), (2), and (3),

$$P_A + w_1h_1 + w_2h_2 - w_3h_3 = P_B \quad \text{or} \quad P_A - P_B = w_3h_3 - w_1h_1 - w_2h_2$$

If a manometer tube has a small internal diameter, it is necessary to correct for the capillary rise or depression of the meniscus.

FLUIDS IN MOTION

Streamlines are lines drawn in the moving fluid so that they are always tangent to the velocity vectors of the fluid particles at any given time. There is no velocity component perpendicular to the streamlines nor can any two streamlines cross each other. The streamlines that pass through each point of a closed curve of infinitesimal area form a **streamtube.** Because the streamtube is composed of streamlines no fluid crosses the walls of a streamtube. The flow is **steady** if the fluid properties, such as pressure, density, and velocity, do not change with time at a given section of a streamtube, and, conversely, the flow is **unsteady** if these characteristics do change with time.

For steady flow the mass per unit time passing through any section of a streamtube is constant. To obtain the mass per unit time for the entire flow, the mass per unit time for each streamtube is summed over the flow cross section, such as the cross-sectional area of a pipe, river, channel, or free jet. If the velocity is constant over the cross section but varies only in the direction of flow, the flow is one-dimensional. If the velocity varies over the cross section and in the direction of flow, the flow is two- or three-dimensional. **One-dimensional flows** are rare in nature, but the analytical solutions are simple in form. **Two- and three-dimensional flows** are approximated as one-dimensional flows by utilizing the average velocity and the one-dimensional analytical results adjusted to reflect two- and three- dimensional flows by means of experimentally determined correction factors or coefficients.

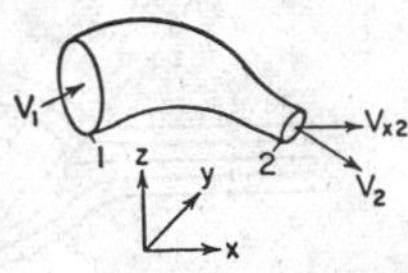

FIG. 9. Momentum notation.

Using the average velocity, the descriptive equations for steady flow of a liquid are (Fig. 9):

1. **Continuity** (Conservation of mass)

$$Q = AV = A_1V_1 = A_2V_2$$

2. **Momentum** (Conservation of momentum)

$$\Sigma F_x = \rho Q(V_{x2} - V_{x1})$$
$$\Sigma F_y = \rho Q(V_{y2} - V_{y1})$$
$$\Sigma F_z = \rho Q(V_{z2} - V_{z1})$$

3. **Energy** (Conservation of energy)

$$Jq_{12} + \mathcal{W}_{12} = J(U_2 - U_1) + \frac{P_2 - P_1}{w} + \frac{V_2^2 - V_1^2}{2g} + z_2 - z_1$$

For the special case of an adiabatic flow, $q_{12} = 0$, no work done, $\mathcal{W}_{12} = 0$, and no change in internal energy, $U_2 = U_1$, the energy equation for a liquid is

$$\frac{P_2}{w} + \frac{V_2^2}{2g} + z_2 = \frac{P_1}{w} + \frac{V_1^2}{2g} + z_1$$

This is known as **Bernoulli's equation.** The term P/w, having units of feet, is called the **static pressure head** and because of the specific weight w is in feet of the liquid that is **flowing.** If a manometer containing mercury is used to measure the static pressure of flowing water, the feet of mercury must be converted to feet of water. The term $V^2/2g$ is the **velocity head,** and the term z is the **potential head.** Since the pressure terms appear on both sides of Bernoulli's equation, the pressure can be expressed in terms of absolute or gage pressure, the correction for converting from absolute to gage pressure canceling out. It is generally more convenient to use gage pressure, which will be done hereafter unless specifically noted.

If a solid body is immersed in a flowing liquid, the liquid is diverted around the body. There is a point on the upstream portion of the body called the stagnation point where the fluid velocity is zero and the pressure is the stagnation pressure P_0 (see Fig. 10). Applying Bernoulli's equation along a small streamtube which contains the stagnation point gives

$$\frac{P_0}{w} = \frac{P_1}{w} + \frac{V_1^2}{2g}$$

or

$$P_0 = P_1 + \frac{\rho V_1^2}{2}$$

The term $\rho V/2$ is commonly called the **dynamic or impact pressure** of the liquid.

In the momentum equation, for example, the term ΣF_x is the sum of the *external* forces in the x direction acting *on* the whole free body of liquid between sections 1 and 2. The term V_{x2} is the x component of the velocity at section 2 and is constant over section 2 (Fig. 9).

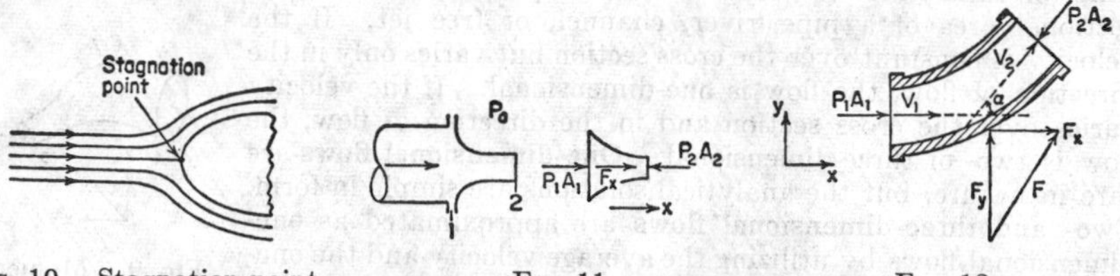

FIG. 10. Stagnation point. FIG. 11 FIG. 12

Dynamic Forces

Whenever the momentum of a liquid is changed in direction or magnitude, or both, there is an external force acting **on** the liquid, and, by Newton's laws, the liquid exerts a reaction force. It is suggested that each problem involving change of momentum be solved as a separate problem, setting up a coordinate system and drawing the free body of liquid with the forces acting on it.

EXAMPLE. Water flows through a frictionless nozzle (Fig. 11) under the following conditions: $P_1 = 50$ psig, $P_a = 0$ psig, $d_1 = 12$ in., and $d_2 = 6$ in. Determine the force exerted by the water on the nozzle. The free body of the liquid in the nozzle is shown where the force on the liquid is F_x, assumed positive to the right. Bernoulli's equation gives $V_1^2/2g + (50 \times 144)/62.4 = V_2^2/2g$, since $z_1 = z_2$. From the continuity equation $V_2 = V_1(d_1/d_2)^2 = 4V_1$. Then $V_1^2 = (64.4 \times 50 \times 144)/[(16 - 1) \times 62.4] = 495$, $V_1 = 22.25$ ft sec^{-1}, $V_2 = 89.0$ ft sec^{-1}, and $Q = [\pi/4(1)^2]22.25 = 17.47$ ft^3 sec^{-1}. The momentum equation is

$$P_1A_1 - P_2A_2 + F_x = \rho Q(V_{2x} - V_{1x})$$
$$50 \times 144 \times \pi/4(1)^2 - 0 + F_x = 1.935 \times 17.47 \times (89.0 - 22.25)$$

or $F_x = -3{,}395$ lb. The force on the water is negative, to the left. The water exerts a force of 3,395 lb on the nozzle to the right.

If a liquid flows through a **pipe bend** (Fig. 12), the sectioning is conveniently done at sections where the flow is straight and the pressure constant across the flow. The forces acting on the liquid are

$$F_x = P_2A_2 \cos\alpha - P_1A_1 + \rho Q(V_2 \cos\alpha - V_1)$$
$$F_y = P_2A_2 \sin\alpha + \rho Q V_2 \sin\alpha$$
$$F = \sqrt{F_x^2 + F_y^2}$$

where F_x and F_y are assumed to act in the direction of the positive axis. If, on solving, the sign of F_x is negative, it acts opposite to the assumed direction, and similarly for F_y. The resultant force F acts at the angle $\theta = \tan^{-1}(F_y/F_x)$. If the cross section changes from 1 to 2, the pressure at 2 can be determined from Bernoulli's equation.

It is often necessary in practice to **anchor** pipe bends as the forces may be large enough to cause excessive pipe deflection. This is particularly true when the quantity flow and velocity are high. **Expansion** joints, often used in pipelines to avoid stressing the pipe, permit some motion of the pipe, and the forces exerted by the liquid at the bends must be provided for (see also Secs. 5 and 8).

When a **free jet** (Fig. 13) is **deflected by a curved surface** or vane which is tangent to the jet at the point of contact, the forces on the liquid are $F_x = \rho Q(V_2 \cos x - V_1)$ and $F_y = \rho Q V_2 \sin \alpha$. The resultant force on the liquid is $F = \sqrt{F_x^2 + F_y^2}$ and it acts at the angle $\theta = \tan^{-1}(F_y/F_x)$. If the initial and final velocities are the same the equations can be written $F_x = \rho QV(\cos \alpha - 1)$ and $F_y = \rho QV \sin \alpha$.

If the deflecting surface has a velocity U (Fig. 14), the mass deflected per unit time is $\rho A(V - U)$. The forces exerted on the liquid are

$$F_x = \rho A(V - U)[(V - U) \cos \alpha - (V - U)] = \rho A(V - U)^2(\cos \alpha - 1)$$
$$F_y = \rho A(V - U)[(V - U) \sin \alpha - 0] = \rho A(V - U)^2 \sin \alpha$$

The x-direction force exerted on the vane is

$$R_x = -F_x = \rho A(V - U)^2(1 - \cos \alpha)$$

The power produced is $R_x U = \rho AU(V - U)^2(1 - \cos \alpha)$.

Power-producing machines (see Sec. 9) utilizing the change in the direction of the momentum are called impulse turbines. The deflecting vanes are arranged

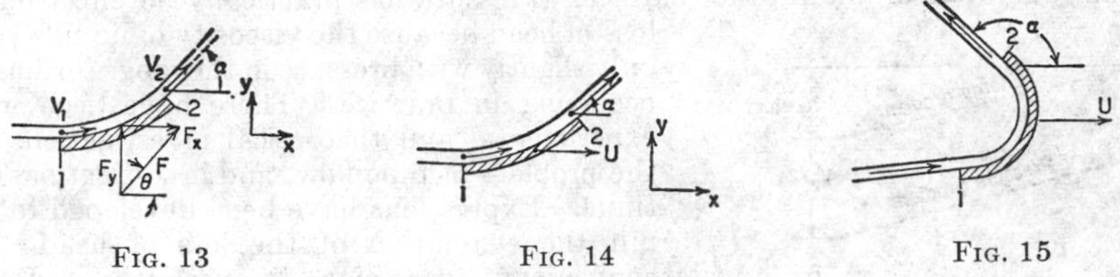

FIG. 13 FIG. 14 FIG. 15

so that the entire mass of the liquid jet is deflected and the power produced is $\rho AVU(V - U)(1 - \cos \alpha)$. Maximum power is produced when $\alpha = 180$ deg and $U = V/2$. It is not practical to have $\alpha = 180$ deg since the liquid leaving a vane would strike the succeeding vane and, owing to a change of momentum, would result in a loss of power (see Fig. 15).

It should be noted that what path the liquid takes in going from section 1 to section 2 or what happens to it between these sections is of no consequence in determining the force acting on the liquid if the conditions at (1) and (2) are known.

If a **body is immersed in a moving fluid** or is in motion relative to the fluid, determining the forces acting on the body would involve knowing the velocity and pressure distributions before and after the body and integrating for the momentum change over all the streamtubes affected by the presence of the body. Except for a few special cases, these forces are measured experimentally. The force in the direction of motion is the **drag,** and the force transverse to the motion is the **lift.** (For a detailed discussion of drag and lift see Secs. 11 and 12, *e.g.*, buildings, bridges, chimneys, wires, airplanes, and automobiles.)

Flow of Liquids in Ducts

When a liquid flows in a duct, it may or may not completely fill the duct. The case of the liquid not filling the duct, of having a free surface, is called **open-channel flow.** When the liquid completely fills the duct, the case is known simply as **duct flow.**

The liquid has no velocity at the wall of the duct, while within the duct it has velocity. The liquid is then subjected to a shearing stress at the wall. This shearing stress is known as **friction.** The distance the effect of the shearing stress at the wall extends into the fluid is known as the thickness of the boundary layer or as the **boundary layer.** If a liquid is allowed to flow smoothly into a duct, the boundary layer starts at the entrance and grows continuously until it fills the duct. The flow while the boundary layer is growing is called **generating flow.** When the boundary layer completely fills the duct, that is, when the effect of the wall shearing stress extends completely across the duct, the flow is called **established flow.**

Established Duct Flow. Because there is work done by the liquid against friction, Bernoulli's equation cannot be used. The energy equation is written as

$$h_f = \frac{P_1 - P_2}{w} + \frac{V_1^2 - V_2^2}{2g} + z_1 - z_2$$

where h_f represents the lost energy or head between sections 1 and 2 (Fig. 16). If the area at section 1 equals the area at section 2, then $V_1 = V_2$ from the continuity equation and the loss of head is

$$h_f = \frac{P_1 - P_2}{w} + z_1 - z_2$$

If, in addition, the pipe is horizontal, the loss of head is

$$h_f = \frac{P_1 - P_2}{w}$$

The loss of head depends on (1) the kind of liquid flowing, its density and viscosity; (2) the velocity of the liquid; (3) the size of the duct; (4) the length of the duct; and (5) the roughness of the interior surface. Pressure has practically no effect on the loss of head because the viscosity of liquids varies only slightly with pressure in the ranges ordinarily occurring in practice. There have been many experimental and theoretical investigations into the problem of pipe flow, and investigations continue. Expressions have been developed to permit the evaluation of the loss of head. One convenient expression to use is the **Darcy-Weisbach** equation,

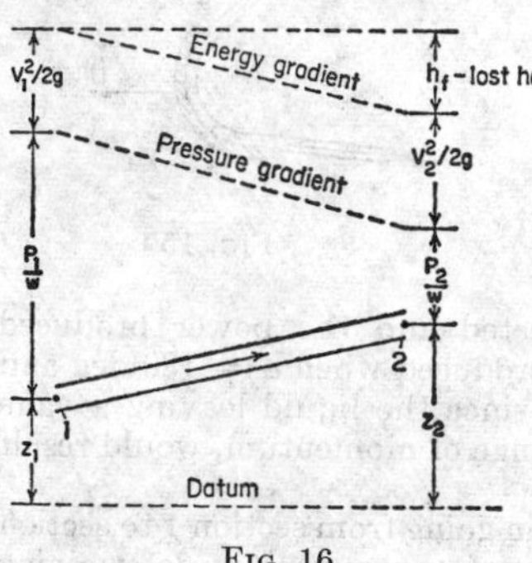

Fig. 16

$$h_f = f\frac{L}{4m}\frac{V^2}{2g}$$

in which f is known as the **friction factor** and is dimensionless; L is the length of the duct; m is the hydraulic radius, defined as the ratio of the cross-sectional area of flow A divided by wetted perimeter p (the perimeter of A in contact with the solid surface), or $m = A/p$; V is the velocity; and g is the acceleration of gravity. This equation is applicable for either metric or English units, as long as the quantities are consistently expressed.

The Darcy-Weisbach equation is valid for a duct of any shape of cross section. For **circular ducts** and pipes, the value of $m = \pi d^2/4\pi d$ so that $4m = d$. The head-loss equation thus assumes its more familiar form,

$$h_f = f\frac{L}{d}\frac{V^2}{2g}$$

This equation applies for either laminar or turbulent flow. Whether the flow is laminar or turbulent determines the value of the friction factor f, which can, in general, be expressed as a function of the ratio of inertial to viscous forces Re known as the **Reynolds number** and of the so-called **relative roughness,** ϵ/d. The roughness ϵ is a length characterizing the hydraulically effective roughness of any pipe surface and is derived from experiment. Thus $f = \phi(Re, \epsilon/d)$. The application of the head-loss equation therefore requires knowledge concerning this function.

For **laminar flow** the shear is due entirely to molecular forces. The velocity is zero at the wall and reaches its maximum in the center of the pipe. The velocity distribution is parabolic and occurs in such a way that maximum velocity is twice the average velocity. The local disturbances in the liquid due to rough surfaces are insignificant compared with the energy required to overcome the viscous shearing stresses. The shearing stress τ is proportional to the dynamic viscosity μ and to the rate of deformation dV/dy (transverse velocity gradient), or $\tau = \mu(dV/dy)$.

The friction factor f has a value of $64/Re$ as long as laminar flow prevails over the entire section. This condition is satisfied if the **Reynolds number,** $Re = \rho Vd/\mu = Vd/\nu$, is smaller than approximately 2,000. There is no sharp division between laminar and turbulent flows as characterized by the value of Reynolds number. Turbulent flow may occur with a value of Re as low as 1,200. Under extraordinarily quiet conditions laminar flow may exist at Reynolds numbers much higher than 2,000. Generally, it may be taken that the critical Reynolds number is 2,000, below which the flow is laminar and the critical zone, where the flow may be either laminar or turbulent, is about 2,000 to 4,000. Above a Reynolds number of 4,000 the flow is generally turbulent.

The **roughness of the interior pipe surfaces** has no influence on laminar flow except as it affects the cross-sectional area. For laminar flow the friction factor $f = 64/Re$ and the head-loss equation becomes $h_f = (64/Re)(L/d)(V^2/2g) = 32VL\mu/g\rho d^2$. The equivalent of this equation was independently and experimentally determined by Hagen in 1839 and Poiseuille in 1840.

For **turbulent flow** the shear is due to molecular forces and, principally, to the transfer of momentum due to the violent mixing or eddying within the liquid. Individual fluid particles no longer follow paths that can be predicted except by statistical methods. Owing to the mixing process superimposed on the rectilinear motion, velocity distributions are much more uniform than for laminar flow, and head losses increase greatly through the shearing stresses created by the eddying. Only near the wall does the flow remain laminar, and there in a relatively thin layer. If the roughness protuberances of the wall surfaces remain submerged in this laminar flow and do not affect the friction factor f, the flow is known as **smooth pipe flow.** The friction factor is still dependent on Reynolds number only but by a different functional relationship given first by von Kármán, $1/\sqrt{f} = 1.74 - 2 \log (18.6/R_e \sqrt{f})$.

When the thickness of the laminar layer is decreased by penetration of turbulent eddying toward the wall (practically expressed by higher Reynolds numbers), the roughness protuberances become exposed to the turbulent motion and in turn affect it. With still higher Reynolds numbers the thickness of the laminar layer becomes small compared to the height of the roughness protuberances and the degree of turbulence is entirely determined by the hydraulically effective roughness of these normally minute wall proturberances. The equation for such **completely turbulent flow,** established by Prandtl and von Kármán, is $1/\sqrt{f} = 1.74 + 2 \log (2\epsilon/d)$.

Between the smooth pipe and completely turbulent flows is the transition range of turbulent flows where both the Reynolds number and the relative roughness ϵ/d have effect. Colebrook combined both equations empirically into a single function

$$\frac{1}{\sqrt{f}} = -2 \log \left(\frac{2.51}{Re \sqrt{f}} + \frac{\epsilon}{3.7d}\right)$$

These equations are presented graphically in Fig. 17 (Moody, *Trans. ASME*, Nov., 1944). The determination of f for use in the Darcy-Weisbach equation requires therefore knowledge of Re and ϵ/d. Values of ϵ in feet for most commercial pipe surfaces are listed in Table 4.

Table 4. Absolute Roughness Classification of Pipe Surfaces for Selection of Friction Factor f in Fig. 17

Commercial pipe surfaces (new)	Absolute roughness ϵ, ft
Glass, drawn brass, copper, lead	Smooth
Wrought iron, steel	0.00015
Asphalted cast iron	0.0004
Galvanized iron	0.0005
Cast iron	0.00085
Wood stave	0.0006–0.003
Concrete	0.001–0.01
Riveted steel	0.003–0.03

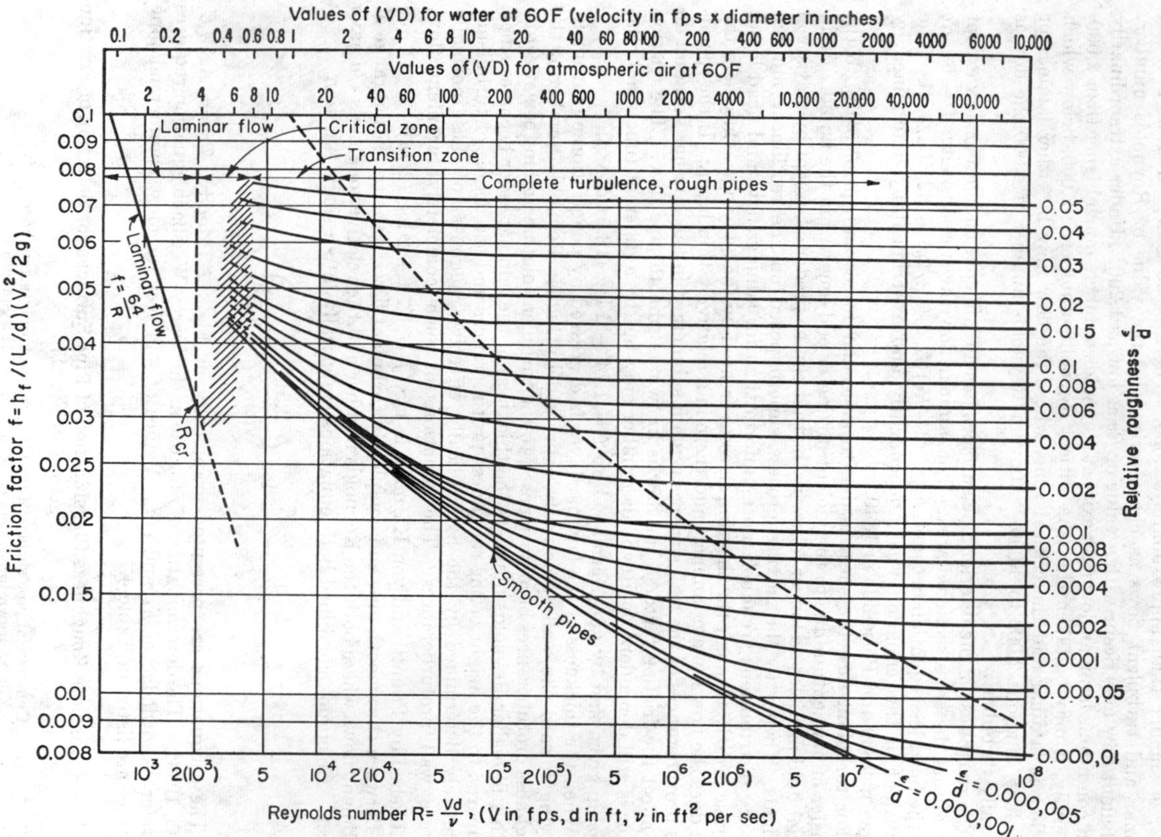

FIG. 17. Friction factors for flow in pipe.

Simple Duct Problems. The approach to simple duct problems is the same for non-circular and circular ducts. For circular ducts or pipes the diameter d is used in the calculations.

$$h_f = f\frac{L}{d}\frac{V^2}{2g} \qquad f = \theta\left(\frac{\rho V d}{\mu}, \frac{\epsilon}{d}\right) \qquad Q = AV$$

For non-circular ducts substitute $4m$ for d in the equations, where m is the hydraulic radius.

$$h_f = f\frac{L}{4m}\frac{V^2}{2g} \qquad f = \theta\left(\frac{4\rho V m}{\mu}, \frac{\epsilon}{4m}\right) \qquad Q = AV$$

There are three pipe flow cases introductory to more complicated problems:

a. Given: $Q, L, \rho, \mu, \epsilon, d$. Find: h_f
b. Given: $h_f, L, \rho, \mu, \epsilon, d$. Find: Q
c. Given: $h_f, L, \rho, \mu, \epsilon, Q$. Find: d

For *case (a)* the values of the Reynolds number and the relative roughness are calculated. The value of f is obtained from Fig. 17, and h_f is calculated by substituting the head-loss equation.

EXAMPLE. Determine the head loss for the flow of 2,000 gpm of water at 50 F through 500 ft of cast-iron pipe having an internal diameter of 10 in.

$$V = \frac{Q}{A} = \frac{(2{,}000 \times 0.1337 \times 1/60)}{\frac{\pi}{4}\left(\frac{10}{12}\right)^2} = 8.17 \text{ ft sec}^{-1}$$

(See Sec. 1 for conversion tables.)

$$Re = \frac{Vd}{\nu} = \frac{8.17\ (10/12)}{1.40 \times 10^{-5}} = 4.86 \times 10^5$$

$$\frac{\epsilon}{d} = \frac{0.00085}{10/12} = 0.00102$$

From Fig. 17, by interpolation, $f = 0.02$.

Then

$$h_f = 0.02 \times \frac{500}{10/12} \times \frac{(8.17)^2}{64.4} = 12.4 \text{ ft}$$

EXAMPLE. For the example above determine the pressure at section (2) if $P_1 = 10$ psi, $z_1 = 150$ ft, and $z_2 = 100$ ft.

$$P_2 = P_1 + w(-h_f + z_1 - z_2) = 10 \times 144 + 62.4(-12.4 + 50)$$
$$= 1{,}440 + 2{,}346 = 3{,}786 \text{ lb ft}^{-2} = 26.3 \text{ psi}$$

For *case (b)*, V cannot be determined directly, but can be determined by trial and error. The first trial value of f can be assumed at the known value of ϵ/d (Fig. 17). The head-loss equation can be solved for the first trial value of V from which a trial value of Reynolds number is obtained. Using this trial value of Reynolds number and the known ϵ/d, a second trial value of f is obtained. The process is continued until the values of V calculated are repeated. Having determined V, the value of Q is calculated.

EXAMPLE. Gasoline (sp gr 0.68) at 60 F flows through a 6 in. Schedule 40 welded-steel pipe with a head loss of 10 ft in 500 ft. Determine the flow.

$$d = 6.625 - 2(0.280) = 6.065 \text{ in.} = 0.505 \text{ ft}$$

(See Sec. 8 for dimensions of steel pipe.)

$$\frac{\epsilon}{d} = \frac{0.00015}{0.505} = 0.0003$$

The trial f is assumed as 0.015. Substituting the head-loss equation,

$$V^2 = \frac{2gh_f d}{fL} = \frac{64.4 \times 10 \times 0.505}{0.015 \times 500} = 4.33$$
$$V = 2.08 \text{ ft sec}^{-1}$$

The trial Reynolds number is $Re = (2.08 \times 0.505)/(5 \times 10^{-6}) = 2.1 \times 10^5$. The second trial f is 0.017. The second trial velocity is 1.95 ft sec^{-1}, and the Reynolds number is 1.97×10^5. At this Reynolds number the friction factor is again 0.017, and the velocity will repeat in value. The quantity flow is $Q = \pi/4(0.505)^2 \times 1.95 = 0.39$ ft^3 sec^{-1}.

For *case* (*c*), V and d are unknown so that neither Re nor ϵ/d can be calculated. The procedure is to assume a value of f and to calculate d using the head-loss equation and the equation of continuity. Use this value of d to calculate Reynolds number and ϵ/d. Determine the new value of f from Fig. 17, and repeat the procedure until the value of f is repeated and all the equations are satisfied.

EXAMPLE. Water at 50 F is to flow at the rate of 500 ft^3 sec^{-1} through a concrete pipe 5,000 ft long with head loss of no more than 50 ft. Determine the diameter of the pipe. Using the continuity equation, the head-loss equation can be solved for the diameter

$$d^5 = \frac{8fLQ^2}{g\pi^2 h_f} = \frac{8 \times 5{,}000 \times (500)^2}{32.2\pi^2 \times 50} f = 6.34 \times 10^5 f$$

Using the continuity equation, the Reynolds number can be written as:

$$Re = \frac{4Q}{\pi \nu d} = \frac{4 \times 500}{\pi \times 1.40 \times 10^{-5} \times d} = \frac{4.55 \times 10^7}{d}$$

The relative roughness, using a value for ϵ of 0.005 ft, is $\epsilon/d = 0.005/d$. Assume that $f = 0.02$; then $d = 6.61$ ft, $Re = 6.88 \times 10^6$, $\epsilon/d = 0.00076$, and from Fig. 17, $f = 0.018$. Repeating the process for $f = 0.018$ gives $d = 6.47$ ft, $Re = 7.03 \times 10^6$, $\epsilon/d = 0.00077$, and from Fig. 17, $f = 0.018$. Therefore, $d = 6.47$ ft. Since the head loss is to be no more than 50 ft, a concrete pipe having an internal diameter of 6.47 ft or larger is selected. If commercial concrete pipe is used, the size chosen will depend on availability.

The flow of water generally gives high Reynolds numbers in **practice;** for most commercial pipes, an average value of f between 0.02 and 0.03 will quickly lead to a final result in trial-and-error procedures for diameter. For problems involving low Reynolds numbers and for liquids with high viscosities, the trial steps of the calculation will generally have to be repeated more than once. The accuracy may never be expected to be greater than 3 to 5 percent. Extreme refinement in computing head losses and capacity is unwarranted.

Differences in performance may be expected after water has been flowing and standing in pipes for long periods. Some specific data show an increase in friction of 20 percent with a 4 in. wrought-iron pipe after a few months; of 70 percent with a 48 in. cast-iron pipe after 17 years; and of 20 percent in a large aqueduct after 1 year's growth of slime. Russell quotes a study on cast-iron pipes for municipal water works in which 10 to 60 in. pipes showed a doubling in the f value after 20 years, while in 4 to 8 in. pipes f increases 100 percent in 8 years and 500 percent in 20 years. An ample margin in f values should be provided for long-term service (see also Pigott, *Mech. Eng.*, Aug., 1933, and Kemler, *Trans. ASME*, 55, 1933).

The principles that resulted in the Colebrook function relating f to the Reynolds number and the relative roughness ϵ/d led to an equation for the velocity distribution in circular pipes. This equation gives the velocity v at any point y (measured from the wall of pipe along a radius) in terms of f, of the average velocity, and of the pipe radius $r_0 = d/2$. This relation is generally applicable regardless of whether f is determined for smooth or rough pipe flow or for the transition region (see Rouse, *op. cit.*). $v/V = \sqrt{f}\,(2.15 \log y/r_0 + 1.43) + 1$. The maximum velocity is given by $V_{max}/V = 1.43\sqrt{f} + 1$. The quantity V/V_{max} is generally known as the **pipe factor.** The average velocity is found at a constant distance from the center of $0.78r_0$.

For laminar flow in a pipe the velocity distribution is parabolic. The maximum velocity occurs at the center of the pipe and is twice the average velocity, $V_{max} = V/2$.

The head losses in pipelines due to **valves and fittings** are called **minor losses.** Such losses are misnamed because in many installations they are greater than the friction loss in the straight section of the pipe. With one exception, that of the sudden expansion, the minor loss is experimentally determined. The minor head loss is expressed either in terms of the velocity head of the flowing liquid or as equal to the loss in additional lengths of pipe; $h_f = (f\,L/d)V^2/2g = K\,V^2/2g$, or $h_f = f(L/d)V^2/2g$.

The head loss for a sudden contraction, $d_2/d_1 = 0.5$, is $0.33V_1^2/2g$ (Table 5). The loss factor K for sudden enlargements and contractions and for exits is given in terms of the velocity head before the fitting. The head loss for a fully open 3 in. globe valve is equivalent to the head loss in $340 \times 3/12 = 85$ ft of 3 in. pipe (Table 6).

Table 5. Representative Values of Loss Factor (K)

(Crane Co., Tech. Paper 410, Flow of Fluids)

		K
Sudden enlargement		$\left[1 - \frac{d_1^2}{d_2^2}\right]^2$
Sudden contraction	$d_2/d_1 = 0.1$	0.47
	$d_2/d_1 = 0.3$	0.42
	$d_2/d_1 = 0.5$	0.33
	$d_2/d_1 = 0.7$	0.22
	$d_2/d_1 = 0.9$	0.03
Entrance*		
Projecting inward		0.78
Sharp-edged		0.50
Slightly rounded		0.23
Well-rounded		0.04
Exit		
Projecting, sharp-edged, rounded		1.0

* From O'Brien and Hickox, "Applied Fluid Mechanics," McGraw-Hill.

Table 6. Representative Equivalent Length in Pipe Diameters (L/d) of Various Valves and Fittings

(Crane Co., Tech. Paper 410, Flow of Fluids)

	L/D
Globe valves, fully open	340
Angle valves, fully open	145
Gate valves, fully open	13
¾ open	35
½ open	160
¼ open	190
Swing check valves, fully open	135
In line, ball check valves, fully open	150
Butterfly valves, 6 in. and larger, fully open	20
90 deg standard elbow	20–30
45 deg standard elbow	16
90 deg long radius elbow	20
90 deg street elbow	50
45 deg street elbow	26
Standard tee	
Flow through run	20
Flow through branch	60

EXAMPLE. A pipeline of 6 in. standard steel pipe 150 ft long connects two open tanks containing water at 60 F with a difference in the elevations of the free surfaces of 20 ft. The pipeline contains a submerged square-edged entry and exit, six 90 deg standard elbows, and two fully open globe valves. Determine the quantity flow. The head loss, 20 ft, is used up in supplying the loss at entry, the friction loss in the pipe, the losses in the elbows and valves, and the exit loss. Since $d = 6.065$ in. $= 0.505$ ft,

$$20 = \left(0.5 + f\frac{150}{0.505} + 6 \times f \times 30 + 2 \times f \times 340 + 1\right)\frac{V^2}{2g}$$

$$= (1.5 + 1{,}157 \times f)\frac{V^2}{2g}$$

Assume $f = 0.02$; then $V = 7.22$ ft sec^{-1}, $\epsilon/d = 0.00003$, $VD = 7.22 \times 6.065 = 43.8$, and, from Fig. 17, $f = 0.016$. Solving again for velocity $V = 8.02$ ft sec^{-1}, it is found that $VD = 48.5$ and that f does not change. The quantity flow is

$$Q = \frac{\pi}{4} \times (0.505)^2 \times 8.02 = 1.60 \text{ ft}^3 \text{ sec}^{-1}$$

Solutions to pipeline problems proceed in the same manner as do the simple pipe problems.

When two or more pipes of different diameters and roughnesses are connected in **series** and the pipeline contains valves and fittings, the head-loss equation is written for the pipeline and the continuity equation is utilized to simplify it. Suppose a series pipeline consists of two pipes denoted by the subscripts 1 and 2, that pipe 2 is downstream of pipe 1, that the entrance loss factor to pipe 1 is K_e, that there is a sudden expansion between the pipes, that there is a valve with loss factor K_v in pipe 2, and that the exit loss factor of pipe 2 is 1.0. The head-loss equation is

$$h_f = K_e \frac{V_1^2}{2g} + f_1 \frac{L_1}{d_1} \frac{V_1^2}{2g} + \left(1 - \frac{d_1^2}{d_2^2}\right)^2 \frac{V_1^2}{2g} + K_v \frac{V_2^2}{2g} + f_2 \frac{L_2}{d_2} \frac{V_2^2}{2g} + 1.0 \frac{V_2^2}{2g}$$

Using the continuity equation $V_1 d_1^2 = V_2 d_2^2$, V_2 can be eliminated from the head-loss equation, thus giving

$$h_f = \frac{V_1^2}{2g} \left[K_e + \left(1 - \frac{d_1^2}{d_2^2}\right)^2 + K_v \left(\frac{d_1}{d_2}\right)^4 + 1.0 \left(\frac{d_1}{d_2}\right)^4 + f_1 \frac{L_1}{d_1} + f_2 \frac{L_2}{d_2} \left(\frac{d_1}{d_2}\right)^4 \right]$$

If Q and the characteristics of the pipes are given, the values of f_1 and f_2 can be determined and the value of h_f found. If h_f and the characteristics of the pipe are given, the solution for Q is by trial and error. For the first trial assume f_1 equals f_2 and solve for V_1 and V_2. These values are used to determine new values for the f's which are used to obtain the second trial values for the velocities. The procedure is continued until the values for the f's are repeated. Then Q is calculated. The same technique is used for more than two pipes in series.

When two or more pipes are connected in **parallel,** the head loss for each of the pipes is the same and at either of the junction points the quantity flow into the junction equals the quantity flow out of the junction. Suppose a parallel system consists of two pipes, denoted by the subscripts 1 and 2. Then $h_{f1} = h_{f2} = h_f$ and $Q = Q_1 + Q_2$, where Q is the quantity into or out of the system. If h_f is given along with the pipe and liquid properties, the solution is that of a simple pipe problem. If only Q is known, the solution is trial and error. For the first trial assume a value for Q_1, solve for h_f, and use this value of h_f to solve for Q_2. With h_f as the ordinate and $(Q - Q_1 - Q_2)$ as the abscissa, plot the result of the first trial. If $(Q - Q_1 - Q_2)$ for the first trial is negative, assume a smaller value for Q_1 on the second trial or a larger value if $(Q - Q_1 - Q_2)$ is positive, and complete the calculations for the second trial. Plot the result of the second trial, and connect the results of the two trials by a straight line. The intersection of the straight line and the ordinate gives an estimation of h_f, which can be used to calculate Q_1 and Q_2 as a check.

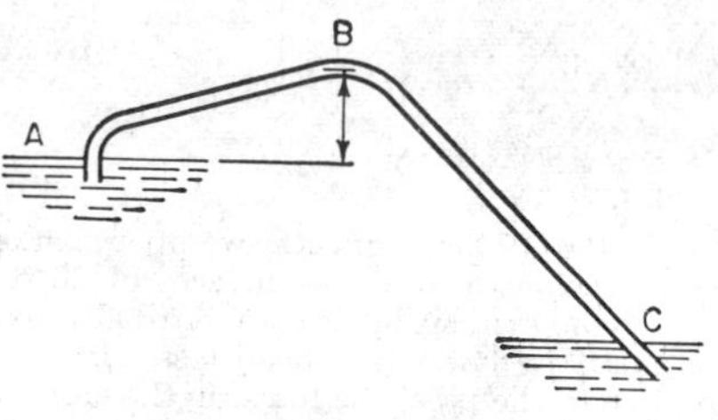

FIG. 18. Siphon.

Branching pipelines are handled in a manner similar to that of the parallel pipe system. Assume a value for h_f in one of the pipes, and calculate the quantities in the separate branches. With h_f as the ordinate and $(Q_{in} - Q_{out})$ at the branch point as the abscissa, plot the result of the first trial. Assuming a different value of h_f in one of the pipes and depending on whether $(Q_{in} - Q_{out})$ is positive or negative, a second trial is made. Connecting the results of the two trials by a straight line, a value for h_f when $(Q_{in} - Q_{out})$ equals zero is obtained, which can be used to recalculate $(Q_{in} - Q_{out})$ as a check.

Siphons are arrangements of pipe or hose which cause liquids to flow from one level, A in Fig. 18, to a lower level C over an intermediate summit B. Before the flow will start, the pipe must be filled with liquid. The minimum absolute pressure in the pipe can be determined from the energy equation after calculating the head loss, including the minor losses. Should the minimum absolute pressure be equal to or less than the vapor pressure of the liquid at its temperature, it is an indication that vapor might form and that the siphon might no longer function. If the pressure at B is near the vapor pressure of the liquid, dissolved gases such as air may be liberated in sufficient quantities, collect, and stop the flow unless there is a provision for removing them.

Generally, when a problem involves the flow of a warm or hot liquid, the minimum pressure in the pipe should be determined to check whether it is below the vapor pressure of the liquid. If it is, a correction may be necessary.

When the fluid flowing in a pipe or pipeline is a **gas,** such as air, caution should be observed. When a gas flows through a pipe, its velocity does not remain constant as does that of a liquid but increases with the length of the pipe owing to a decrease in its density. Solving a pipe or pipeline problem for the flow of a gas as though the gas were a liquid can lead to large errors. See Secs. 4 and 12 for flow of gases in pipes.

Open-channel flow occurs when the liquid does not fill the duct and when it has a free surface exposed to the atmosphere or to a gas. The fact that the surface pressure remains constant in the direction of flow distinguishes this free-surface flow from that in closed conduits. Free-surface flow is encountered in canals, flumes, and rivers, also in sewers, tunnels, and some circulating systems kept under gas or air pressure. The great variety of shapes of cross sections complicates the treatment of this condition.

With steady motion in a long open channel of relatively uniform cross section, the stream surface adjusts itself parallel to the bottom and to the energy gradient. If the parallelism is assumed and used in the Darcy-Weisbach equation for pipe friction, then $\Delta z = h_f = f \dfrac{L}{4m} \dfrac{V^2}{2g}$, in which Δz is the difference in surface elevation over a distance L of the channel, f is the Darcy-Weisbach friction coefficient, m is the hydraulic radius, and V is the mean velocity. Since the hydraulic slope, or the energy dissipation per unit length, is $S = \Delta z/L = h_f/L$ for the condition of steady uniform flow, the equation may be written in the form $V = \sqrt{8g/f}\,\sqrt{mS}$ (in which it was first stated by Chézy) with a factor C instead of $\sqrt{8g/f}$. As f is dependent on the Reynolds number Re and on the relative roughness $\epsilon/4m$ for pipes, C is subject to the same influences. A number of factors make values of C less certain for open channels than values of f for circular pipes. For open channels the shape factor is seldom represented adequately in the hydraulic radius m. Also, since water flow predominates in problems of open channel flow, Reynolds numbers are generally high, so that the relative roughness is usually the determining factor. For this reason the Manning equation, $V = 1.486m^{2/3}S^{1/2}/n$, has been widely used. This substitutes $1.486m^{1/6}/n$ for the Chézy C. The coefficient of roughness n is practically equal to the Kutter n (see Table 7). The variation of C with $m^{1/6}$ indicates the importance of relative roughness, since $C = 1.486m^{1/6}/n = \sqrt{8g/f}$ or $1/\sqrt{f} = 0.0926m^{1/6}/n$ (ft-sec units). The Manning equation may be applied to closed conduits when Reynolds numbers and absolute roughness are high. See Table 8 for values of m.

Table 7. Values of Coefficient of Roughness n for Open Channels

Type of channel	n
ARTIFICIAL CHANNELS OF UNIFORM CROSS SECTION	
Sides and bottom lined with well-planed timber evenly laid	0.009
Neat cement plaster, smoothest pipes	0.010
Cement plaster (3 cement to 1 sand), smooth iron pipes	0.011
Unplaned timber evenly laid, ordinary iron pipes	0.012
Ashlar masonry, best brickwork, well-laid new sewer pipe	0.013
(This last value should be used for the previous categories, if in doubt as to the excellence of construction and the maintenance free from slime, rust, or other growths and deposits.)	
Average brickwork, foul planks, foul iron pipes, ordinary sewer pipes after average uneven settlement and average fouling	0.015
Good rubble masonry, concrete laid in rough forms, poor brickwork, heavily incrusted iron pipes	0.017
CHANNELS SUBJECT TO NON-UNIFORMITY OF CROSS SECTION	
Excellent clean canals in firm gravel, of fairly uniform section; rough rubble, "dry paving"	0.020
Ordinary earth canals and rivers in good order, free from large stones and heavy weeds	0.025
Canals and rivers with many stones and weeds	0.03–0.04

Open concrete, masonry, metal, or timber flumes can be cleaned periodically, and the removal of slime, weeds, silt deposits, etc., increases their capacity considerably. For earth channels this is not readily done and for pipes it is more difficult and expensive and may be impracticable. Open flumes are subject to rapid ice formation in winter in northern latitudes, to upstream retarding wind action, and to very rapid vegetable growth in many localities. These cause a rapid drop in discharging capacity and should be allowed for by increased cross section or slope, or both. Channels in earth are also subject to loss of water by seepage, sometimes so considerable as to require special investigation. The state of uniformity of cross section is as important as mere local roughness. A channel with frequent minute changes of cross section must be regarded as a rough channel even if the sides and bottom are smooth in appearance. A circular section flowing only one-third or less full usually has a larger value of n than the same section flowing more than half full.

Table 8. Values of the Hydraulic Radius m for Various Cross Sections

(m = cross-sectional area ÷ wetted perimeter)

Form of cross section	Value of m
Circle, flowing full, also half full	$d/4$
Square, no top (depth = width = d)	$d/3$
Half square (width = $2d$, depth = d)	$d/2$
Trapezoidal channels (bottom width = b; depth = d):	
Half regular hexagon, side slopes 60 deg	$d/2$
Channel with 45 deg side slopes	$(bd + d^2)/(b + 2.83d)$
Channel with side slopes 1½ hor to 1 vert	$(bd + 1.5d^2)/(b + 3.61d)$
Channel with side slopes 2 hor to 1 vert	$(bd + 2d^2)/(b + 4.47d)$
Wide, shallow stream	d (approx)

All canals should be designed to have velocities high enough to prevent silt deposits and to retard vegetable growths. Earth channels must not have such high velocities as to scour loose the material of the sides and bottom. Approximate values of eroding velocities, in fps, are for fine sand, 1.5, non-colloidal silt, 2, fine gravel, 3, colloidal silts, 3.75, coarse gravel, 4 (see Rouse, "Engineering Hydraulics").

Open-channel Problem. It is necessary to carry 150 cu ft of water per sec in a rectangular unplaned timber flume whose width is to be twice the depth of water ($m = d/2$). What are the required dimensions for various slopes of the flume? *Solution:* For unplaned timber a value of $n = 0.013$ is safe. For assumed values of d = 3, 4, 5, and 6 ft, the cross-sectional areas of stream are 18, 32, 50, and 72 sq ft and the mean velocities for 150 cfs are 8.3, 4.7, 3.0, and 2.1 fps, respectively. By the Manning formula, $S = \frac{n^2V^2}{2.208m^{4/3}}$, and, for the corresponding values of m (1.5, 2, 2.5, and 3 ft), the slopes are found to be 3.1, 0.67, 0.20, and 0.077 ft per 1,000 ft, respectively, for the above assumed sizes. If it is required to find the dimensions of a canal with some desired depth or width for a given discharge and fixed slope, the procedure is to assume trial dimensions, calculate the mean velocity (= Q/area) and see if the value of m calculated by the Manning formula agrees closely with the m for the assumed dimensions. If not, new trials are made until there is close agreement. If the *shape* is fixed, *e.g.*, a semicircle or a 90 deg V flume, so that V = given Q ÷ (const × d^2), and m = const × d, the value of d may be calculated directly by the Manning formula.

Generating Flow. While the boundary layer is growing and before it fills the pipe, it is not strictly proper to apply the friction factor based on established flow to determine the head loss. However, the generating flow section is generally short when compared to the pipe length in which established flow is present, for most engineering applications. Consequently, no significant error is introduced in considering that established flow exists for the entire length of the pipe. (For discussions of generating flow see Rohsenow and Choi, "Heat, Mass, and Momentum Transfer," Prentice-Hall, and Knudsen and Katz, "Fluid Dynamics and Heat Transfer," McGraw-Hill.)

Flow Measurement

(See also Sec. 16.)

A wide variety of instruments and techniques is used to measure the quantity flow of a fluid. The need for accuracy in the measurement of fluid flow depends on the application of the information. In some cases extreme accuracy is needed, while in others only a rough estimate is required. Industrially, a small error in the measurement of large quantities of a fluid can mean a loss of income.

The most accurate method of determining the flow rate is to **weigh** the fluid that passes a given section for a measured period of time. Of course, this method is not always practicable. **Volumetric** measurements of a liquid can be made by using a calibrated tank.

There are available **positive displacement meters. Disk meters** have a disk that wobbles or nutates within a chamber so that each time the disk nutates a known volume of fluid passes through the meter. By counting the nutations in a time interval, the flow rate can be determined. **Rotary-vane** meters have spring-loaded vanes mounted on an eccentric drum in a circular cavity. Each time the drum rotates, a fixed volume of fluid passes through the meter. **Gear** and **lobe meters** have meshed gears and lobes that permit a fixed volume of fluid to pass through the meter for each revolution of the rotors. Accuracies of 1 percent or better are common with positive displacement meters in good condition.

The determination of flow often involves the measurement of **static pressure.** Static pressure is the pressure exerted by the fluid normal to the streamlines, and it will be constant across the flow if the streamlines are parallel. If the streamlines are curved, the static pressure varies across the flow. A small hole, called a **static pressure tap** or **piezometer opening,** in the walls of a duct is used in the determination of the fluid static pressure at the wall (Fig. 19), $P_A = w_2h - w_1(h + z)$. The diameter of

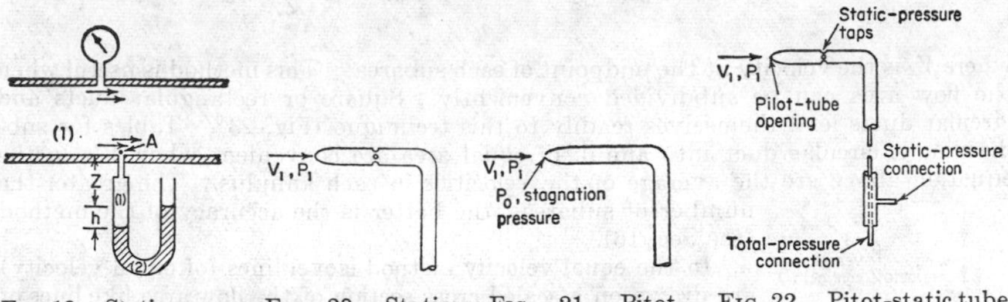

FIG. 19. Static pressure taps.

FIG. 20. Static pressure probe.

FIG. 21. Pitot tube.

FIG. 22. Pitot-static tube.

the hole should be small, usually about ⅛ in. diam, the edges of the hole should be free of burrs, and the wall of the duct should be smooth in the vicinity of the hole. The static pressure can be measured by some suitable means, such as a manometer or pressure gage. (If air is trapped in a liquid manometer system and one is not aware of it, the calculation of pressure can be in error. Provision should be made to bleed off any trapped air. Also, pressure gages indicate the pressure at their bases, and if there is a difference in the elevation of the gage and the pressure tap, this should be accounted for.)

A smooth tube with a rounded nose that has radial holes in the portion behind the nose is used to measure the static pressure P_1 within the flow. This tube (Fig. 20) is a **static-pressure tube** or **probe.**

A **Pitot tube** has an opening at the nose and is a useful and accurate instrument in determining the velocity of fluid. When the fluid in the tube is static, the pressure at the nose is stagnation pressure P_0. Writing Bernoulli's equation between the free stream and the stagnation point gives (Fig. 21) $V_1^2 = [2(P_0 - P_1)]/\rho$.

The Pitot tube and static-pressure probe are combined into one instrument called the **Pitot-static tube** (Fig. 22) with the Pitot tube inside the static-pressure probe. The dynamic pressure, $\rho V_1^2/2 = P_0 - P_1$, can be measured directly by placing a differential manometer across the total and static-pressure connections.

The static-pressure, Pitot, and Pitot-static tubes should be aligned closely along the streamlines to ensure accuracy and should not have a cross section large enough to affect the velocity in the duct. For most engineering applications these tubes can be used without calibration. Other instruments variously used to measure the velocity of a fluid include cup anemometers, vane anemometers, and hot-wire anemometers (see Sec. 16).

The density and viscosity of a liquid are dependent on the static temperature. The measurement of the **static temperature** of a flowing liquid does not entail the difficulties encountered in the measurement of the static temperature of a flowing gas but can be made directly by placing a temperature-sensing element in the flowing liquid.

If the velocity has been determined at points in a liquid stream, the flow rate can be obtained by summation methods. In the **equal-area** method the flow area A is

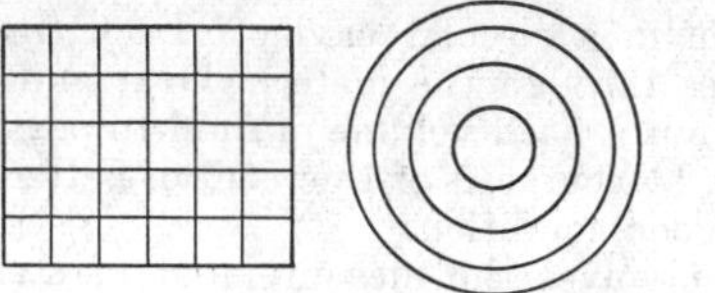

Fig. 23. Equal subareas.

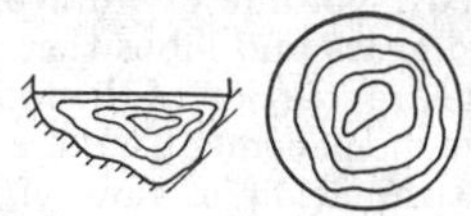

Fig. 24. Isovels.

subdivided into n small and equal areas A'. The total flow is approximated by

$$Q = A'(V_1 + V_2 + \cdots + V_n) = A' \sum_{i=1}^{n} V_i$$

where V_i is the velocity at the midpoint of each subarea. This method is useful when the flow area can be subdivided conveniently. Square or rectangular ducts and circular ducts lend themselves readily to this technique (Fig. 23). Tables for subdividing a circular duct into annuli of equal area are convenient when V's in the equation above are the average of the velocities in each annulus. The greater the number of subareas, the better is the accuracy of the method (see Sec. 16).

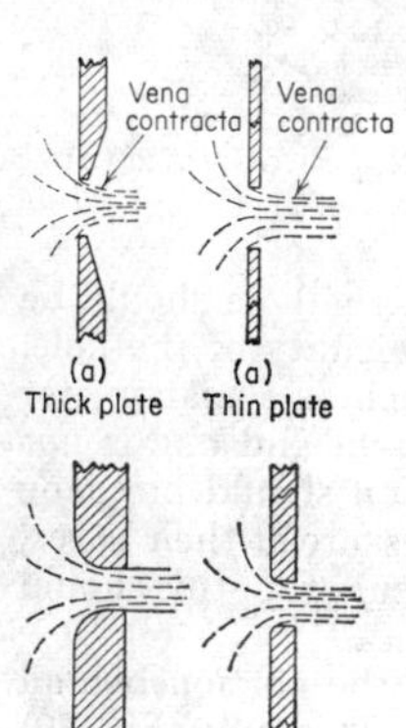

Fig. 25. Types of orifices, thick plate and thin plate.

In the **equal velocity** method **isovel** lines (of equal velocity) are drawn on a scaled cross section of the flow area like lines of constant elevation on a map (Fig. 24). The area between any two isovels times the average value of the two isovels approximates the flow rate between the isovels. Summation over the entire area gives the total flow rate. The greater the number of velocities, the more accurately the isovels can be drawn and the better is the accuracy of the method.

If it is known that the flow in a pipe is laminar, the flow rate can be determined because the average velocity is one-half the velocity at the center. When the flow is turbulent, the average velocity is found at a distance from the center of $0.78r_0$. In either of these cases the section of pipe where the velocity measurements are made should be a considerable distance downstream from any valve, fitting, or obstacle which disturbs the velocity profile.

Devices coming under the general heading of **rate meters** or **obstruction meters** are placed in the liquid stream to determine the flow rate; included are orifices, flow nozzles, venturis, weirs, rotameters, and electromagnetic meters (see Sec. 16).

An **orifice** is a hole, usually circular, in a plate placed in the wall of a tank or mounted between flanges in a pipe. A **standard orifice** is circular and has a sharp square upstream corner so that the issuing jet is in contact with the orifice only at that edge (Fig. 25*a*). The downstream edge is beveled if the orifice plate is thick. As the liquid flows through the orifice, its momentum causes the jet to contract. The section of minimum cross section, the vena contracta, occurs at a distance from the orifice about one-half its diameter. When the orifice is mounted in the side of a tank and the jet is free, it is assumed that the static pressure in the jet at the vena contracta is atmospheric. If the area of the tank is large compared to the area of the vena contracta, the ideal velocity of the jet is $V_i = \sqrt{2gh}$, which is obtained by writing Bernoulli's equation between the free surface and the vena contracta (Fig. 26). The actual average velocity at the vena contracta is about 0.98 to 0.99 of the ideal velocity. The area of the vena contracta is about 0.62 of the area of the orifice. Hence, letting A be the area of the orifice, the discharge of a standard tank orifice is

$$Q = 0.61A\sqrt{2gh}$$

Q being in cu ft per sec when A is in ft^2, h in ft and g in ft sec^{-2}. The value 0.61 is called the **discharge coefficient** C_D, which is defined as the ratio of the actual quantity of flow to the ideal quantity of flow or $C_D = Q_{\text{actual}}/Q_{\text{ideal}} = Q/Q_{\text{ideal}}$. (This is the *general definition* for the discharge coefficient of any device when the fluid is a liquid.)

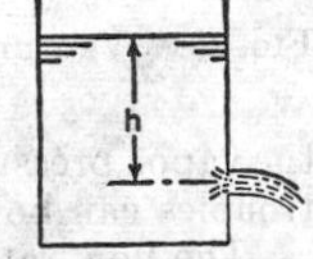

Fig. 26. Tank orifice.

For a **rounded-approach orifice** [Fig. 25(*b*)], when the entrance curve is not too abrupt and is followed by a short length (¼ to ½ diam) of constant diameter, there is no contraction. When mounted in a tank, the coefficient of discharge for a good smooth orifice is about 0.97; for the very best orifice it is about 0.99; for an orifice with abrupt curvature, causing some contraction and cross currents, it may be as low as 0.90. Rounding the upstream edge of a tank orifice [Fig. 25(*c*)] so that the radius of curvature is not larger than 10 percent of the orifice diameter will give a discharge coefficient of about 0.80.

The discharge for a well-made sharp-edged or rounded-approach orifice will be within 3 percent of the calculated value, provided (1) the orifice is located at least 3 diam from any side wall, (2) the head is at least twice the orifice diameter, and (3) the diameter of the orifice is accurately measured, for an error in the diameter causes twice that error in the calculated discharge.

For best results the orifice must be calibrated in the exact position of use and under the same conditions of use. The orifice must be carefully maintained to prevent rounding of the sharp edge, corrosion, or the accumulation of rust and dirt if accuracy within 1 percent is desired.

Pipe orifices are those placed in a pipe, usually between flanges (Fig. 27). The ideal discharge is obtained by writing Bernoulli's equation between 1 and 2 and utilizing the continuity equation,

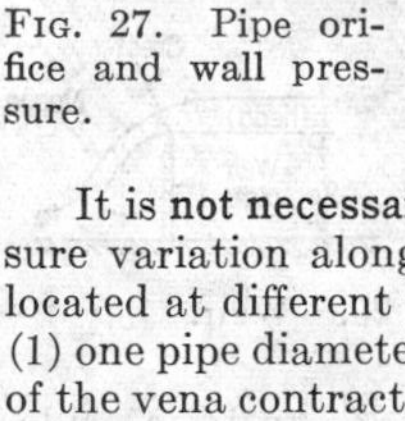

$$Q_{\text{ideal}} = A_2\sqrt{\frac{2(P_1 - P_2)}{\rho[1 - (d_2/d_1)^4]}}$$

where $1 - (d_2/d_1)^4$ is the correction for the velocity of approach. The actual discharge is given by:

$$Q = C_D A_2\sqrt{\frac{2(P_1 - P_2)}{\rho[1 - (d_2/d_1)^4]}}$$

where C_D is the experimentally determined discharge coefficient.

Wall pressure
(1) (2)
Fig. 27. Pipe orifice and wall pressure.

It is **not necessary** to measure the pressure P_2 at the orifice. Because of the pressure variation along the wall of the pipe (Fig. 27) the static pressure taps can be located at different points on either side of the orifice. Usually the taps are located (1) one pipe diameter upstream and one-half pipe diameter downstream in the vicinity of the vena contracta, (2) at the corners on either side of the orifice plate (corner taps), or (3) in the flanges on either side of the orifice plate (flange taps). P_1 and P_2 are the pressures measured at the upstream and downstream static-pressure taps, respectively, and the value of C_D depends on the location of the taps. When using experimentally determined values of the discharge coefficient to obtain the flow rate, the static-pressure taps must be located in the same positions as those used in the experiment to determine C_D (see Sec. 16).

The **Venturi meter** (Fig. 28) consists of a well-rounded convergent section at the entrance, a throat of constant diameter, and a divergent section with an included angle of not more than 15 ± deg. The overall pressure loss of a Venturi is less than the pipe orifice or nozzle, making it a useful metering device when the pressure loss in a system is critical. The pressure connections are usually made to ring piezometers, consisting of circumferential passageways communicating to the interior of the meter by four or more small holes equally spaced around the meter. The object is to assure obtaining the average static pressure by avoiding dependence on a single tap, which is subject to possible local disturbances. The ring piezometers are often cast as part of the meter tube. The nominal size of a Venturi meter is that of the pipeline in which it is to be placed. The throat diameter is usually between 0.25 and 0.75 of the upstream diameter, depending on the flow rate to be expected and on the pressure in the pipeline. The throat velocity should be great enough to cause a measurable indication on the gage used but not so great that the throat pressure is below the vapor pressure of the liquid. If the throat pressure is below atmospheric pressure, troubles can be encountered with air leaking into the gage connections.

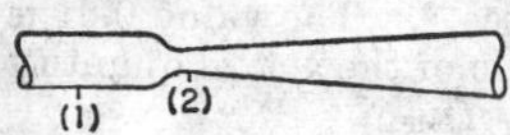

FIG. 28. Venturi meter.

The flow rate through the Venturi meter is

$$Q = C_D A_2 \sqrt{\frac{2(P_1 - P_2)}{\rho[1 - (d_1/d_2)^4]}}$$

The coefficient of discharge depends on the nature of the flow and the design of the Venturi, with a normal range of 0.98 to 0.99 for a well-designed meter.

Flow nozzles have rounded entrance sections and throat sections. The coefficient of discharge for a well-designed flow nozzle approaches that of a Venturi.

When a pipe orifice, flow nozzle, or Venturi is mounted in a **position** that is **other than horizontal,** the flow rate is given by

$$Q = C_D A_2 \sqrt{\frac{2g[(P_1 - P_2)/w + z_1 - z_2]}{1 - (d_2/d_1)^4}}$$

where z_1 and z_2 are the elevations of the upstream and downstream pressure taps, respectively.

It is not always possible to install a pipe orifice, flow nozzle, or Venturi under the same conditions used in obtaining the published values of the coefficient of discharge. For reasonable accuracy the meter should be preceded by at least 10 diam of straight pipe. If the pipeline preceding the meter contains fittings and valves which disrupt the velocity profile, the approach to the meter should be lengthened to 30 or more diam of straight pipe. The approach section becomes more important as the diameter ratio d_1/d_2 increases. When the meter is calibrated in place, the coefficient of discharge may differ from the published values (in the rare case it may be greater than unity) because of the effect of the pipeline ahead of the meter (see Sec. 16 for further details on flow meters).

A **weir** is an open-channel structure over which water flows. The top surface of a weir is termed the crest. The simplest form of a weir is a plate (Fig. 29). The upstream face of the weir plate should be vertical and smooth. The crest should have a sharp square upstream corner and a top flat portion from 1/16 to 1/8 in. wide, beveled on the downstream side, so that the water does not touch the crest again after leaving the upstream corner. The approach channel should extend far enough upstream or be baffled so that the velocity distribution in the channel is normal and the surface free of waves. The rate of flow of the weir is a function of the head h, measured above the crest. The head should be measured a distance upstream from

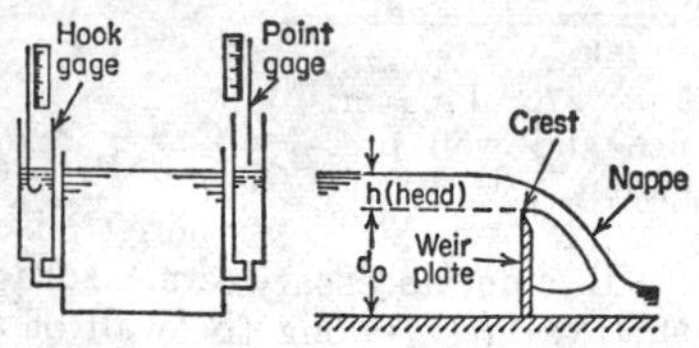

FIG. 29. Weir.

the weir equal to at least four times the maximum head to be encountered. Unless these conditions are satisfied, the experimentally determined coefficients do not apply.

For a **rectangular suppressed weir** the weir plate occupies the full width of a rectangular channel. The crest is level, and the smooth vertical walls of the channel extend downstream beyond the crest to prevent lateral spreading of the water jet or nappe. The underside of the nappe must be vented to the atmosphere; otherwise the water will entrain the air, create a partial vacuum, and possibly cling to the downstream face of the weir plate. The theoretical discharge over a weir of width l is $Q = \frac{2}{3}Clh\sqrt{2gh}$. The actual discharge is $Q = 3.33lh^{3/2}$ as determined by Francis, who found an experimental discharge coefficient $C = 0.62$. The units of Q are cu ft per sec, and l and h are in ft. The Francis formula is widely used by engineers and is reliable within 1 to 3 percent for heads above 0.3 ft when the approach velocity is small. The Rehbock formula is probably the best formula for rectangular suppressed weirs; $Q = [3.234 + 5.347/(320h - 3) + 0.428\,h/d_0]lh^{3/2}$, where d_0 is the height of weir or the depth of water at zero head (see "Precise Weir Measurements and Discussions," *Trans. ASCE*, 93, 1929). The formula includes a correction for the velocity of approach for normal, or fairly uniform, velocity distribution in the upstream channel. Although the equation is not dimensionally correct, it gives values agreeing within less than 1 percent with experiments on weirs from 0.2 to 4 ft in height with heads from 0.1 to 2 ft, subject to the ratio h/d_0 not exceeding 4.

A rectangular notch weir (Fig. 30) has a contraction at each side as well as at the crest. The discharge is reduced as though the length of the weir were decreased by $0.1h$ for each end contraction. The Francis formula is $Q = 3.33(l - 0.2h)h^{3/2}$. This formula must not be used unless l is at least $2h$. The weir need not be located in a rectangular channel. If it is not, the minimum distance from any point on the edges of the weir to the sides and bottom of the channel should be at least $2h$ to $3h$.

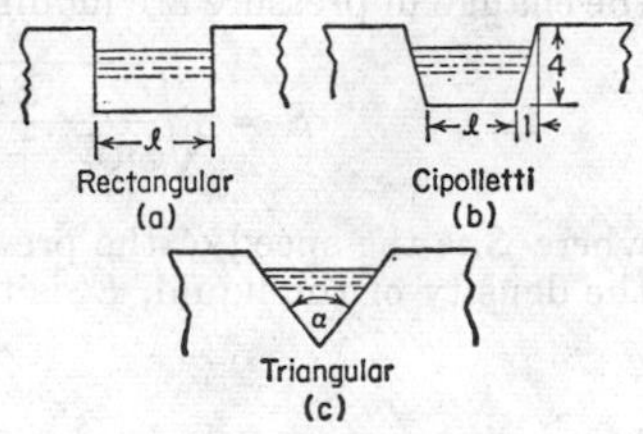

FIG. 30. Notch weirs.

Cipolletti found that a trapezoidal notch with the end slopes of one horizontal to four vertical just compensated for the end contractions of a rectangular notch weir. Accordingly, the simple Francis formula, $Q = 3.33lh^{3/2}$, may be used for the *Cipolletti trapezoidal weir* (Fig. 30). The crest length l must be at least $2h$, and the minimum distance from the edges of the weir to the sides or bottom of the channel should be at least $2h$ to $3h$ to avoid a velocity-of-approach correction.

Triangular notch weirs (Fig. 30) are convenient to use for measuring flows that vary from a moderate maximum to a very small minimum and for achieving the same degree of accuracy, when desired, for high and low discharges. The theoretical equation for the discharge is $Q = C\frac{8}{15}h^2\sqrt{2gh}\tan\alpha/2$, where C is the discharge coefficient, α is the notch angle, and h is the head above the vertex. An approximate formula for a 90 deg weir is $Q = 2.5h^{2.5}$. The discharge coefficient C has a value from 0.58 to 0.59, based on experiments at Cornell University, with heads up to 3 ft and vertex angles of 28, 60, 90, and 120 deg. The average coefficient 0.58 was found for the 60 and 90 deg weirs and 0.59 for the 28 and 120 deg weirs.

The two most commonly used **head gages** are illustrated in Fig. 29. The **hook gage** is raised until the point just pierces the surface, and the **point gage** is lowered until the point just touches the surface. In each case the reading when the water surface is level with the crest must be taken into account in order to determine the head. While the head measurements can be made in the open channel, it is better if a stilling box or well is used. The stilling well can be a small pipe connected to the side of the channel through a piezometer opening, which assists in damping the surges or waves in the channel.

The formulas given for the various weirs apply for sharp upstream edges. A rounding of the edges increases the discharge especially at low heads. For accurate determination of the flow rate it is best to calibrate the weirs in place.

Unsteady Flow

The term "unsteady flow" applies to those flows in which the average characteristics, such as velocity and pressure, are varying with time. Water hammer and the rate of flow from a tank when the free surface is rising or falling are two examples of unsteady flow.

Water hammer sounds as though someone is hitting the pipe with a hammer and is due to a sudden change in the velocity of any flowing liquid, not only water. When the velocity is changed instantaneously by an amount ΔV, the resultant change in momentum causes a change in pressure of $\Delta P = -\rho c \, \Delta V$.

EXAMPLE. If the velocity of water is suddenly **reduced** by 10 ft sec^{-1}, the **rise** in pressure is

$$\Delta P = 1.94 \times 4{,}720 \times 10 = 91{,}500 \text{ psf} = 635 \text{ psi}$$

and the pressure wave travels at the speed of sound in water, 4,720 ft sec^{-1}

The pressure wave that is the result of a rise in pressure (a decrease in the velocity) is termed a compression wave and one that is the result of a fall in pressure is termed an expansion wave.

When the liquid is flowing in an elastic pipe, both the speed of a pressure wave and the change in pressure are modified by the expansion of the pipe so that

$$S = \sqrt{\frac{EE'}{[\rho(E' + Ed/T)]}} \qquad \text{and} \qquad \Delta P = -\rho S \, \Delta V$$

where S is the speed of the pressure wave, E is the bulk modulus of the liquid, ρ is the density of the liquid, E' is the modulus of elasticity of the pipe material, d is the

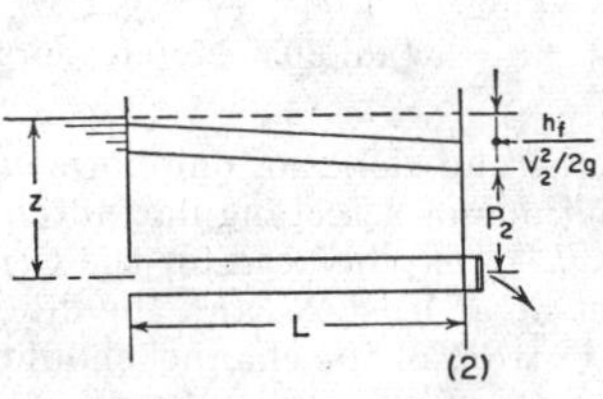

FIG. 31. Pressure ahead of open valve in pipeline.

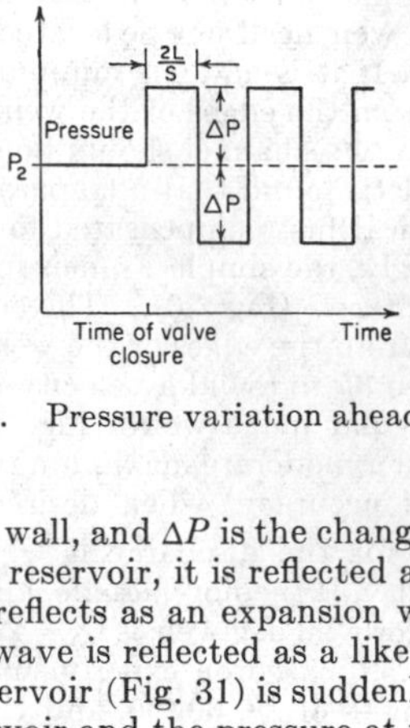

FIG. 32. Pressure variation ahead of closed valve.

diameter of the pipe, T is the thickness of the pipe wall, and ΔP is the change in pressure. When a pressure wave in a pipe comes to a reservoir, it is reflected as a wave of the opposite type. Thus a compression wave reflects as an expansion wave at a reservoir, and vice versa. At a solid boundary a wave is reflected as a like wave.

If a valve at the end of a pipe connected to a reservoir (Fig. 31) is suddenly closed, a compression wave travels up the pipe to the reservoir and the pressure at the valve is ΔP **plus** the static pressure that existed at the valve before it was closed. The speed at which the compression wave travels is S. When the compression wave reaches the reservoir, it is reflected as an expansion wave which travels down the pipe to the closed valve where it is reflected as an expansion wave. After the expansion wave is reflected, the pressure at the valve is ΔP **below** the static pressure that existed at the valve before it was closed. Were it not for friction, compression and expansion waves would travel up and down the pipe alternately and indefinitely. The time taken for the pressure waves to make the round trip from the valve to the reservoir and back to the valve is $t = 2L/S$. The pressure ahead of the valve is shown in Fig. 32 as a function of time. Friction will alter this pressure history by reducing the amplitude of the pressure waves until equilibrium is attained.

To prevent the full rise in pressure, the valve should close in a time greater than $2L/S$. When the closure time is greater than $2L/S$, the pressure history at the valve can be approximated from a step-by-step analysis or estimated by $\Delta P \approx 2\rho VL/\Delta t_c$, where Δt_c is the closure time.

Adequately proportioned **air chambers** or **surge tanks** are installed to absorb almost entirely the excess pressure when it is not feasible to close the valve slowly. Water hammer may occur in a pipeline due to loose valve seats or washers, as happens in a house. The phenomenon of reflected compression and expansion waves is utilized in the **hydraulic ram** to pump water and to supercharge internal combustion engines.

The **time required to drain a tank** (Fig. 33) can be approximated, which often suffices for engineering purposes, by neglecting the acceleration of the liquid. At a given time the change in the liquid volume in the tank equals the difference in the volumes in and out of the tank:

$$A_z\,dz = (Q_{\text{in}} - Q_{\text{out}})\,dt$$

or

$$t = \int_{z_1}^{z_2} \frac{(A_z\,dz)}{(Q_{\text{in}} - Q_{\text{out}})} = \int_{z_1}^{z_2} \frac{(A_z\,dz)}{(Q_{\text{in}} - A_{\text{out}}V_{\text{out}})}$$

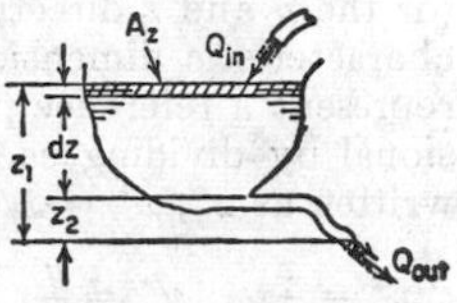

FIG. 33

The velocity at the exit V_{out} is expressed in terms of z by summing the losses due to friction and minor losses in the exiting pipeline and equating them to the head loss z. While the value of the friction factor will vary with time, owing to the changing exit velocity, it can be assumed constant because the solution is an approximate one.

The integration can be completed if A_z is expressible in terms of z, and Q_{in} is constant, expressed in terms of z, or zero. If A_z cannot be easily expressed in terms of z, a graphical or step-by-step integration may be used.

THEORY OF MODELS AND DIMENSIONAL ANALYSIS

Engineering problems that are too complicated for mathematical, graphical, or computer solution are generally studied by experimentation. Problems to which solutions are available are also often studied experimentally, if for no other reason than to check any assumptions made in the analysis. The experiments are conducted full scale (**prototype**) or other than full scale (**model**). The procedure of employing a model is used extensively in the design of ships, airplanes, pumps, and turbines, as well as in problems dealing with heat transfer and complex elastic structures. In each case, a model is constructed which is geometrically similar to the prototype. When an experiment is made on a model, it is necessary to determine the conditions under which the data are applicable to the prototype and can be used to predict its performance. Whether an experiment is conducted on the prototype or model, there can be quite a few variables involved in a given problem. One difficulty that arises is how to report the data when, for example, the number of variables is six. Another difficulty is the large number of experimental runs required if each variable takes on different values while all the other variables are held constant. The theory of models and dimensional analysis deals with these conditions and difficulties.

The **theory of models** applies to those engineering problems that can be completely or partially defined in terms of fundamental equations, which describe the system, and boundary-initial conditions. While only problems involving liquids are considered here, the same technique applies to fluids in general and to such problems as heat transfer and stress analysis.

The fundamental equations for the conservation of mass, momentum, and energy of a liquid are available (see p. 3–55 and references). The momentum equations are often identified by the name Navier-Stokes. Whether or not the boundary and initial conditions can be written depends on the complexity of the problem. It may be impossible to write boundary conditions which are faithful to the problem, as in the case of the equation for the inside surface of a rough pipe. Even when the fundamental equations and boundary conditions are written, the analytical solution often cannot be obtained. Mathematically simplifying the problem to the extent that a solution is obtained is helpful in understanding the more complex situation. But it is not necessary to have the analytical solution to apply the techniques of the theory of models.

To illustrate the application of the theory of models, consider a problem involving the three-dimensional steady flow of a viscous liquid. The momentum equation for the x direction is

$$-\frac{\partial P}{\partial x} + \mu\left(\frac{\partial^2 u}{\partial x^2} + \frac{\partial^2 u}{\partial y^2} + \frac{\partial^2 u}{\partial z^2}\right) = \rho\left(u\frac{\partial u}{\partial x} + v\frac{\partial u}{\partial y} + w\frac{\partial u}{\partial z}\right)$$

where the left-hand side of the equation is the sum of the external pressure and viscous forces acting on a differential element of the liquid; the right-hand side is the change of momentum of the liquid or the so-called inertia force; and u, v, w are the components of the velocity along the x-, y-, and z-axes, respectively. The momentum equations for the y and z directions are of the same type. Let l represent some reference or characteristic dimension of the problem, V_r represent a reference velocity, and P_r represent a reference pressure. The variables of the equation are made non-dimensional by dividing each by its reference value. Thus, x/l is a non-dimensional x, written as x^*, $x^* = x/l$. The variables of the momentum equation then become

$$x^* = \frac{x}{l} \qquad y^* = \frac{y}{l} \qquad z^* = \frac{z}{l} \qquad u^* = \frac{u}{V_r} \qquad v^* = \frac{v}{V_r} \qquad w^* = \frac{w}{V_r} \qquad P^* = \frac{P}{P_r}$$

and their substitution in the momentum equation gives

$$-\frac{P_r}{\rho V_r^2}\frac{\partial P^*}{\partial x^*} + \frac{1}{\rho V_r l/\mu}\left(\frac{\partial^2 u^*}{\partial x^{*2}} + \frac{\partial^2 u^*}{\partial y^{*2}} + \frac{\partial^2 u^*}{\partial z^{*2}}\right) = u^*\frac{\partial u^*}{\partial x^*} + v^*\frac{\partial u^*}{\partial y^*} + w^*\frac{\partial u^*}{\partial z^*}$$

Since the equation is now non-dimensional, the coefficients $P_r/\rho V_r^2$ and $\rho V_r l/\mu$ are non-dimensional. Coefficients such as these are called dimensionless or π groups and bear the name of men prominent in the study of fluid mechanics, heat transfer, etc.

The coefficient $\rho V_r l/\mu$ is the **Reynolds number** and is the ratio of the inertia force to the viscous force. When the Reynolds number is small, the viscous is large compared to the inertia force and the flow is laminar. When the Reynolds number is large, the inertia force is large compared to the viscous force and the flow is turbulent. For the case of flow in a pipe the reference values are chosen as the average velocity V and the diameter d; $Re = \rho V d/\mu = V d/\nu$.

The coefficient $P_r/\rho V_r^2$ is the **Euler number** and is the ratio of the pressure force to the inertia force. In experimentation and calculations the **pressure coefficient,** $P/\rho V^2/2$, equal to twice the Euler number, is used. For the case of flow in a horizontal pipe the reference values are chosen as the average velocity V and the difference of the entrance and exit pressures ΔP, $\Delta P/\rho V^2$.

When the non-dimensional equations for the model and prototype are identical, the data of the model are transferable by equating the dimensionless groups. For example, the pressure drop measured on pipe 1 gives the pressure drop of a geometrically similar pipe 2, provided

$$\left(\frac{\Delta P}{\rho V^2}\right)_1 = \left(\frac{\Delta P}{\rho V^2}\right)_2 \qquad \left(\frac{\rho V d}{\mu}\right)_1 = \left(\frac{\rho V d}{\mu}\right)_2$$

Combining the Euler and Reynolds numbers gives

$$\Delta P_2 = \Delta P_1 \frac{\rho_1}{\rho_2}\left(\frac{\mu_2}{\mu_1}\right)^2\left(\frac{d_1}{d_2}\right)^2$$

It should be noted that the liquids flowing in pipes 1 and 2 need not be the same. To predict the flow of oil in a pipe, experiments can be made on a model using water.

There are other dimensionless groups. Consider a ship which when moving through the water creates waves. The shape of the free surface will be affected by the force of gravity. The momentum equation, in the z direction only, is

$$-\frac{\partial P}{\partial z} - \frac{g}{\rho} + \mu\left(\frac{\partial^2 w}{\partial x^2} + \frac{\partial^2 w}{\partial y^2} + \frac{\partial^2 w}{\partial z^2}\right) = \rho\left(u\frac{\partial w}{\partial x} + v\frac{\partial w}{\partial y} + w\frac{\partial w}{\partial z}\right)$$

Non-dimensionalizing this equation gives

$$-\frac{P_r}{\rho V_r^2} - \frac{1}{V_r^2/gl} + \frac{1}{\rho V_r l/\mu}\left(\frac{\partial^2 w^*}{\partial x^{*2}} + \frac{\partial^2 w^*}{\partial y^{*2}} + \frac{\partial^2 w^*}{\partial z^{*2}}\right) = u^*\frac{\partial w^*}{\partial x^*} + v\frac{\partial w^*}{\partial y^*} + w^*\frac{\partial w^*}{\partial z^*}$$

where V_r^2/gl is the **Froude number,** or the ratio of the inertia force to the force of gravity. Taking as reference values the ship's length L and velocity V, it is necessary that the Euler number, $P/\rho V^2$, the Reynolds number, $\rho VL/\mu$, and the Froude number, V^2/gL, be the same for model and prototype if similarity is to exist.

There are times when the condition of similarity presents the experimenter with additional difficulties: A ship is to operate in fresh water at 20 knots and the 1/9 scale model is to be towed in a fresh-water tank. The equality of Reynolds numbers requires that the model speed be $V_m = V_p L_p/L_m = 180$ knots. The equality of the Froude numbers requires that the model speed be $V_m = V_p \sqrt{L_m/L_p} = 6\frac{2}{3}$ knots. This dilemma is resolved by towing the model at 6⅔ knots because the gravity force predominates the viscous force. Theoretical corrections are made to account for the viscous force.

When surface tension is important in a problem, the inclusion of the surface tension force in the momentum equation results in the **Weber** number, $\rho V_r^2 l/\sigma$.

Dimensional analysis is a procedural technique whereby the variables that are assumed to be significant in a given problem can be formed into dimensionless groups, the number of groups being less than the number of variables. This is a great advantage because fewer experimental runs are then required to establish a relationship between the groups than between the variables. Dimensional analysis does not presume that the user has any knowledge of the fundamental equations. However, the more knowledgeable the user, the more applicable are the results.

The theorems on which dimensional analysis is based are: (1) Any equation which is dimensionally homogeneous can be put into such a form that the variables enter the equations only through certain dimensionless groups. (2) It can be proved that any dimensionless combination must be expressible as a product of powers of the variables.

The variables that enter into a problem can be expressed in terms of basic dimensions. The basic dimensions may be taken as mass M, length L, and time t. Utilizing these basic dimensions, the dimensions of velocity are Lt^{-1}, which follows from the definition of velocity, and the dimensions of force are MLt^{-1}, which follows from Newton's second law. The basic dimensions of common variables are given in Table 9.

Table 9. Common Variables and Their Dimensions in Terms of Mass, Length, and Time

Variable	Dimension	Variable	Dimension
Mass	M	Work, energy, or heat	ML^2t^{-2}
Length	L	Power	ML^2t^{-3}
Time	t	Pressure or stress	$ML^{-1}t^{-2}$
Area	L^2	Dynamic viscosity	$ML^{-1}t^{-1}$
Volume	L^3	Kinematic viscosity	L^2t^{-1}
Linear velocity	Lt^{-1}	Surface tension	Mt^{-2}
Linear acceleration	Lt^{-2}	Temperature	ML^2t^{-2}
Density	ML^{-3}	Momentum	MLt^{-1}
Angle	None	Angular momentum	ML^2t^{-1}
Force	MLt^{-2}	Moment of momentum	ML^2t^{-1}
Moment or torque	ML^2t^{-2}	Moment of inertia	ML^2

The choice of basic dimensions is largely a matter of convenience. They may be taken as force, length, and time or as mass, length, time, and temperature.

To illustrate the steps of dimensional analysis, consider the problem of pressure drop of a liquid flowing through a horizontal pipe. Assume that the variables which affect the pressure drop ΔP are the average velocity V, density ρ, and viscosity μ of the liquid and the length L, diameter d, and the roughness ϵ of the pipe. The functional relationship between these variables can be expressed by the dimensionally homogeneous equation,

$$\Delta P = \phi(V,\rho,\mu,L,d,\epsilon)$$

Any π product of these variables has the form

$$\pi = P^a V^b \rho^c \mu^e L^f d^g \epsilon^h$$

where π is a dimensional combination or product, not 3.1416. Substituting the basic dimensions for each of the variables gives

$$M^0L^0t^0 = (ML^{-1}t^{-2})^a(Lt^{-1})^b(ML^{-3})^c(ML^{-1}t^{-1})^e(L)^f(L)^g(L)^h$$

To satisfy dimensional homogeneity the exponents for each basic dimension must be equal on both sides of the equation, giving the set of linear algebraic equations:

$$\begin{aligned} 0 &= a + c + e \\ 0 &= -a + b - 3c - e + f + g + h \\ 0 &= -2a - b - e \end{aligned}$$

The coefficient matrix of this set is called the dimensional matrix:

$$\begin{pmatrix} 1 & 0 & 1 & 1 & 0 & 0 & 0 \\ -1 & 1 & -3 & -1 & 1 & 1 & 1 \\ -2 & -1 & 0 & -1 & 0 & 0 & 0 \end{pmatrix}$$

As a *rule of thumb*, m variables described by n basic dimensions can be formed into $(m - n)$ dimensionless groups. In this case $(m - n) = (7 - 3) = 4$. There is a *theorem* that the number of dimensionless groups equals $(m - r)$, where r is the rank of the dimensional matrix. In this case $(m - r) = (7 - 3) = 4$. The rule of thumb does not always yield the correct number.

In the set of linear algebraic equations there are seven unknowns with only three equations. However, since the set is consistent, four of the unknowns can be specified arbitrarily. Let a, e, f, and h be the arbitrary unknowns and, in particular, let $a = 1$ because a function for ΔP is sought. Solving for c, b, and g gives

$$\begin{aligned} c &= -1 - e \\ b &= -2 - e \\ g &= -e - f - h \end{aligned}$$

Then

$$\begin{aligned} \pi &= (\Delta P)(V)^{-2-e}(\rho)^{-1-e}(\mu)^e(L)^f(d)^{-e-f-h}(\epsilon)^h \\ &= \frac{\Delta P}{\rho V^2}\left(\frac{\mu}{\rho V d}\right)^e\left(\frac{L}{d}\right)^f\left(\frac{\epsilon}{d}\right)^h \end{aligned}$$

which can be written as:

$$\frac{\Delta P}{\rho V^2} = \theta\left(\frac{\rho V d}{\mu}, \frac{L}{d}, \frac{\epsilon}{d}\right)$$

The number of variables in the problem has been reduced from seven to four. Furthermore, this is a satisfactory grouping of the variables into dimensionless groups. It is known from the theory of models that for a problem involving pressure and viscous forces, two of the dimensionless groups must be the Reynolds number and the Euler number. Any other grouping of the variables by dimensional analysis that did not include the Reynolds and Euler numbers would have been unacceptable.

Before using dimensional analysis one should make a very serious attempt to find the fundamental equations for a problem and, if possible, write the boundary conditions. Utilizing the theory of models, the significant dimensionless groups are found. Dimensional analysis will yield the remaining dimensionless groups, provided the steps are arranged to yield also the significant groups.

The success of dimensional analysis depends on the knowledge and ability of the user. Failure to include an important variable gives incomplete results. Often the user will attempt to include all the variables he can think of that might have a connection with the problem in order to cover all of the possibilities. This attempt leads to one dimensionless group for each additional variable, and the principal advantage of dimensional analysis is lost. Having found the dimensionless groups, the functional relationship is established by experimentation, which is conducted by varying the value of the dimensionless group.

SECTION 4

HEAT

BY

G. A. HAWKINS, Dean of Engineering, Purdue University.
C. O. MACKEY, John Edson Sweet Professor of Engineering, Cornell University.
WILLIAM H. McADAMS, Professor Emeritus of Chemical Engineering, Massachusetts Institute of Technology.
G. C. WILLIAMS, Professor of Chemical Engineering, Massachusetts Institute of Technology.
K. A. SMITH, Assistant Professor of Chemical Engineering, Massachusetts Institute of Technology.
HOYT C. HOTTEL, Professor of Fuel Engineering, Massachusetts Institute of Technology.
ADEL F. SAROFIM, Assistant Professor of Chemical Engineering, Massachusetts Institute of Technology.

CONTENTS

THERMAL PROPERTIES OF SUBSTANCES AND THERMODYNAMICS

BY

G. A. Hawkins

REFERENCES: DeGroot, "Thermodynamics of Irreversible Processes," Interscience. Dodge, "Chemical Engineering Thermodynamics," McGraw-Hill. Epstein, "Textbook of Thermodynamics," Wiley. Fares, "Thermodynamics," Macmillan. Glasstone, "Thermodynamics for Chemists," Van Nostrand. Guggenheim, "Thermodynamics," Interscience. Jones and Hawkins, "Engineering Thermodynamics," Wiley. Keenan, "Thermodynamics," Wiley. Keenan and Keyes, "Thermodynamic Properties of Steam," Wiley. Lee and Sears, "Thermodynamics," Addison-Wesley. Lewis and Randall, "Thermodynamics," McGraw-Hill. Mooney, "Mechanical Engineering Thermodynamics," Prentice-Hall. Obert, "Elements of Thermodynamics and Heat Transfer," McGraw-Hill. Rocard, "Thermodynamique," Masson et Cie., Editeurs, Paris. Rossini, "Chemical Thermodynamics," Wiley. Rossini, "Thermodynamics and Physics of Matter," Princeton. Ruhemann, "Separation of Gases," Clarendon Press. Tables of Thermal Properties of Gases, *NBS Circ.* 564. Tribus, "Thermostatics and Thermodynamics," Van Nostrand. Van Wylen, "Thermodynamics," Wiley. Weber, "Thermodynamics for Chemical Engineers," Wiley. Wenner, "Thermochemical Calculations," McGraw-Hill. Urangham, "The Theory and Practice of Heat Engines," Cambridge. Zemansky, "Heat and Thermodynamics," McGraw-Hill.

THERMAL PROPERTIES OF SUBSTANCES

Measurement of Temperature

Thermometers. The basis for establishing a temperature scale to serve as a primary standard is the fact that at constant temperature, the pressure-volume product for a pure gas approaches a constant finite value as the pressure approaches zero. The scale of the **hydrogen thermometer** is based on this fact. Because of the complexity and difficulty of using such a thermometer precisely the Seventh General Conference of Weights and Measures, representing 31 nations, adopted in 1927 the more readily usable **International Temperature Scale** based on basic fixed points. These are: temperature of equilibrium between liquid and gaseous oxygen at the pressure of 1 standard atmosphere (oxygen point) −182.97 C; between ice and air-saturated water at normal atmospheric pressure (ice point) 0.000 C (changed to 0.01 C in 1960); between liquid water and its vapor at the pressure of 1 standard atmosphere (steam point) 100.000 C; between liquid sulphur and its vapor at the pressure of 1 standard atmosphere (sulphur point) 444.00 C; between solid silver and liquid silver at normal atmospheric pressure (silver point) 960.5 C; between solid gold and liquid gold at normal atmospheric pressure (gold point) 1063 C. For ordinary use, the mercury thermometer agrees closely with the International Temperature scale, but above 500 F the divergence between the two scales may be appreciable.

The usual **mercury thermometer** can be used to about 600 F; this limit may be extended to 1000 F if the capillary tube above the mercury is filled with nitrogen or carbon dioxide under high pressure. The lower temperature limit for the mercury thermometer is −39 F. For lower temperatures, alcohol, pentane, or petroleum ether may be used as the thermometric substance. For stem exposure corrections, see Temperature Measurements, p. 16–14. Temperatures are also measured by means of thermocouples, resistance thermometers, and various forms of **pyrometers** (see pp. 16–13 to 16–18).

At the 1948 meeting of the General Conference of Weights and Measures, the word **Celsius** was adopted to replace the adjective **centigrade.** The use of the term

Celsius avoids confusion in the French language. All other temperature scales are designated by the first letter of the inventor's name: F for Fahrenheit, R for Reaumur, K for Kelvin, and R for Rankine. It was logical to designate the international scale by C, in recognition of its inventor (in 1742), Anders Celsius, a Swedish astronomer. In 1960, the General Conference changed the defining fixed point from the ice point to the triple point of water, 0.01 C, which is more easily reproduced than is the ice point. The triple point is the condition under which three phases of matter can coexist in equilibrium. By this action, the interval between the triple point and steam became 99.99 deg instead of 100 and the international scale ceased to be a "centigrade scale." The word "Celsius" is accordingly used in the material that follows. (See Celsius versus Centigrade, the Nomenclature of the Temperature Scale of Science, *Science*, **136**, Apr. 20, 1962, pp. 254–255.)

Thermometer Scales. Let F and C denote the readings on the Fahrenheit and Celsius (or centigrade) scales, respectively, for the same temperature. Then

$$C = \tfrac{5}{9}(F - 32) \qquad F = \tfrac{9}{5}C + 32$$

Table 1 gives corresponding readings on the two scales.

Table 1. Conversion of Thermometer Readings

DEGREES CELSIUS TO DEGREES FAHRENHEIT

C	F	C	F	C	F	C	F	C	F	C	F
−40	−40.0	+5	+41.0	+40	+104.0	+175	+347	+350	+662	+750	+1382
−38	−36.4	6	42.8	41	105.8	180	356	355	671	800	1472
−36	−32.8	7	44.6	42	107.6	185	365	360	680	850	1562
−34	−29.2	8	46.4	43	109.4	190	374	365	689	900	1652
−32	−25.6	9	48.2	44	111.2	195	383	370	698	950	1742
−30	−22.0	10	50.0	45	113.0	200	392	375	707	1000	1832
−28	−18.4	11	51.8	46	114.8	205	401	380	716	1050	1922
−26	−14.8	12	53.6	47	116.6	210	410	385	725	1100	2012
−24	−11.2	13	55.4	48	118.4	215	419	390	734	1150	2102
−22	− 7.6	14	57.2	49	120.2	220	428	395	743	1200	2192
−20	− 4.0	15	59.0	50	122.0	225	437	400	752	1250	2282
−19	− 2.2	16	60.8	55	131.0	230	446	405	761	1300	2372
−18	− 0.4	17	62.6	60	140.0	235	455	410	770	1350	2462
−17	+ 1.4	18	64.4	65	149.0	240	464	415	779	1400	2552
−16	3.2	19	66.2	70	158.0	245	473	420	788	1450	2642
−15	5.0	20	68.0	75	167.0	250	482	425	797	1500	2732
−14	6.8	21	69.8	80	176.0	255	491	430	806	1550	2822
−13	8.6	22	71.6	85	185.0	260	500	435	815	1600	2912
−12	10.4	23	73.4	90	194.0	265	509	440	824	1650	3002
−11	12.2	24	75.2	95	203.0	270	518	445	833	1700	3092
−10	14.0	25	77.0	100	212.0	275	527	450	842	1750	3182
− 9	15.8	26	78.8	105	221.0	280	536	455	851	1800	3272
− 8	17.6	27	80.6	110	230.0	285	545	460	860	1850	3362
− 7	19.4	28	82.4	115	239.0	290	554	465	869	1900	3452
− 6	21.2	29	84.2	120	248.0	295	563	470	878	1950	3542
− 5	23.0	30	86.0	125	257.0	300	572	475	887	2000	3632
− 4	24.8	31	87.8	130	266.0	305	581	480	896	2050	3722
− 3	26.6	32	89.6	135	275.0	310	590	485	905	2100	3812
− 2	28.4	33	91.4	140	284.0	315	599	490	914	2150	3902
− 1	30.2	34	93.2	145	293.0	320	608	495	923	2200	3992
0	32.0	35	95.0	150	302.0	325	617	500	932	2250	4082
+ 1	33.8	36	96.8	155	311.0	330	626	550	1022	2300	4172
2	35.6	37	98.6	160	320.0	335	635	600	1112	2350	4262
3	37.4	38	100.4	165	329.0	340	644	650	1202	2400	4352
4	39.2	39	102.2	170	338.0	345	653	700	1292	2450	4442

TABLES OF VALUES FOR INTERPOLATION IN THE ABOVE TABLE

Degrees Celsius................	1	2	3	4	5	6	7	8	9
Degrees Fahrenheit............	1.8	3.6	5 4	7.2	9.0	10.8	12.6	14.4	16.2

Table 1. Conversion of Thermometer Readings—(*Continued*)

DEGREES FAHRENHEIT TO DEGREES CELSIUS*

F	*C*	*F*	*C*	*F*	*C*	*F*	*C*	*F*	*C*	*F*	*C*
−40	−40.00	+30	−1.11	+80	+26.67	+250	+121.11	+500	+260.00	+900	+482.22
−38	−38.89	31	−0.56	81	27.22	255	123.89	505	262.78	910	487.78
−36	−37.78	32	0.00	82	27.78	260	126.67	510	265.56	920	493.33
−34	−36.67	33	+0.56	83	28.33	265	129.44	515	268.33	930	498.89
−32	−35.56	34	1.11	84	28.89	270	132.22	520	271.11	940	504.44
−30	−34.44	35	1.67	85	29.44	275	135.00	525	273.89	950	510.00
−28	−33.33	36	2.22	86	30.00	280	137.78	530	276.67	960	515.56
−26	−32.22	37	2.78	87	30.56	285	140.55	535	279.44	970	521.11
−24	−31.11	38	3.33	88	31.11	290	143.33	540	282.22	980	526.67
−22	−30.00	39	3.89	89	31.67	295	146.11	545	285.00	990	532.22
−20	−28.89	40	4.44	90	32.22	300	148.89	550	287.78	1000	537.78
−18	−27.78	41	5.00	91	32.78	305	151.67	555	290.55	1050	565.56
−16	−26.67	42	5.56	92	33.33	310	154.44	560	293.33	1100	593.33
−14	−25.56	43	6.11	93	33.89	315	157.22	565	296.11	1150	621.11
−12	−24.44	44	6.67	94	34.44	320	160.00	570	298.89	1200	648.89
−10	−23.33	45	7.22	95	35.00	325	162.78	575	301.67	1250	676.67
− 8	−22.22	46	7.78	96	35.56	330	165.56	580	304.44	1300	704.44
− 6	−21.11	47	8.33	97	36.11	335	168.33	585	307.22	1350	732.22
− 4	−20.00	48	8.89	98	36.67	340	171.11	590	310.00	1400	760.00
− 2	−18.89	49	9.44	99	37.22	345	173.89	595	312.78	1450	787.78
0	−17.78	50	10.00	100	37.78	350	176.67	600	315.56	1500	815.56
+ 1	−17.22	51	10.56	105	40.55	355	179.44	610	321.11	1550	843.33
2	−16.67	52	11.11	110	43.33	360	182.22	620	326.67	1600	871.11
3	−16.11	53	11.67	115	46.11	365	185.00	630	332.22	1650	898.89
4	−15.56	54	12.22	120	48.89	370	187.78	640	337.78	1700	926.67
5	−15.00	55	12.78	125	51.67	375	190.55	650	343.33	1750	954.44
6	−14.44	56	13.33	130	54.44	380	193.33	660	348.89	1800	982.22
7	−13.89	57	13.89	135	57.22	385	196.11	670	354.44	1850	1010.00
8	−13.33	58	14.44	140	60.00	390	198.89	680	360.00	1900	1037.78
9	−12.78	59	15.00	145	62.78	395	201.67	690	365.56	1950	1065.56
10	−12.22	60	15.56	150	65.56	400	204.44	700	371.11	2000	1093.33
11	−11.67	61	16.11	155	68.33	405	207.22	710	376.67	2050	1121.11
12	−11.11	62	16.67	160	71.11	410	210.00	720	382.22	2100	1148.89
13	−10.56	63	17.22	165	73.89	415	212.78	730	387.78	2150	1176.67
14	−10.00	64	17.78	170	76.67	420	215.56	740	393.33	2200	1204.44
15	− 9.44	65	18.33	175	79.44	425	218.33	750	398.89	2250	1232.22
16	− 8.89	66	18.89	180	82.22	430	221.11	760	404.44	2300	1260.00
17	− 8.33	67	19.44	185	85.00	435	223.89	770	410.00	2350	1287.78
18	− 7.78	68	20.00	190	87.78	440	226.67	780	415.56	2400	1315.56
19	− 7.22	69	20.56	195	90.55	445	229.44	790	421.11	2450	1343.33
20	− 6.67	70	21.11	200	93.33	450	232.22	800	426.67	2500	1371.11
21	− 6.11	71	21.67	205	96.11	455	235.00	810	432.22	2550	1398.89
22	− 5.56	72	22.22	210	98.89	460	237.78	820	437.78	2600	1426.67
23	− 5.00	73	22.78	215	101.67	465	240.55	830	443.33	2650	1454.44
24	− 4.44	74	23.33	220	104.44	470	243.33	840	448.89	2700	1482.22
25	− 3.89	75	23.89	225	107.22	475	246.11	850	454.44	2750	1510.00
26	− 3.33	76	24.44	230	110.00	480	248.89	860	460.00	2800	1537.78
27	− 2.78	77	25.00	235	112.78	485	251.67	870	465.56	2850	1565.59
28	− 2.22	78	25.56	240	115.56	490	254.44	880	471.11	2900	1593.33
29	− 1.67	79	26.11	245	118.33	495	257.22	890	476.67	2950	1621.11

TABLE OF VALUES FOR INTERPOLATION IN THE ABOVE TABLE

Degrees Fahrenheit	1	2	3	4	5	6	7	8	9
Degrees Celsius*	0.56	1.11	1.67	2.22	2.78	3.33	3.89	4.44	5.00

* All decimals in the table are repeating decimals; 37.78 is really 37.777 . . . .

If the pressure readings of a constant-volume hydrogen thermometer are extrapolated to zero pressure, it is found that the corresponding temperatures is −273.16 C, or −459.69 F. It is convenient to have a so-called **absolute temperature scale** on which zero corresponds with zero pressure on the hydrogen thermometer. Such a scale has fundamental thermodynamic significance and agrees very closely with the thermodynamic temperature scale. The absolute scales in use are:

Degrees Kelvin (K) = degrees Celsius + 273.16

Degrees Rankin (R) = degrees Fahrenheit + 459.69

Fixed Temperatures. Standard samples for calibration of temperature-measuring instruments at certain fixed points are available from the National Bureau of Standards with certificates giving the exact freezing point of each lot of metal. These are: tin 449.4 F (231.9 C); lead, 621.2 (327.3); zinc, 787.1 (419.5); aluminum, 1220.2 (660.1); copper, 1981.4 (1083.0).

Convenient standards for use in less precise calibrations are listed in Table 2. Additional information which may be found useful in estimating temperatures is presented in Tables 3 to 9.

Table 2. Standards for Less Precise Calibrations

Substance	Deg F	Deg C	Substance	Deg F	Deg C
Liquid naphthalene boils at	424.33	217.9	Liquid copper-silver eutectic solidifies at	1434	779.0
Liquid tin solidifies at	449.4	231.9	Solid silver melts at	1760.9	960.5
Liquid benzophenone boils at	582.6	305.9	Solid gold melts at	1945.4	1063
Liquid lead solidifies at	621.2	327.3	Liquid copper solidifies at	1981.4	1083
Liquid zinc solidifies at	787.1	419.5	Solid nickel melts at	2646	1452
Liquid sulphur boils at	832.28	444.60	Solid palladium melts at	2831	1555
Liquid antimony solidifies at	1166.9	630.5	Solid platinum melts at	3223	1773
Liquid aluminum (97.7 percent pure) solidifies at	1218	659	Solid alumina melts at	3722	2050
			Solid tungsten melts at	6134	3390

Table 3. Melting Points of Non-metallic Elements, Deg F

Helium	−456*	Argon	−309	Phosphorus	111
Hydrogen	−434	Krypton	−272	Iodine	236.3
Neon	−416	Xenon	−220	Sulphur	235
Fluorine	−367	Chlorine	−150.9	Silicon	2588
Oxygen	−360	Bromine	+ 19	Carbon	>6500
Nitrogen	−346				

* At 25 atm.

Table 4. Melting Points of Various Solids, Deg F

(For pure metals, see p. 6–67; for refractories see p. 6–209 and 6–215)

Alloys:		Fusible alloys:		Enamel colors	1760
Bismuth solder	200–262	33 Bi + 33 Pb + 33 Sn	250	India rubber	257
Brass and bronze (about)	1650	18 Bi + 36 Pb + 46 Sn	305	Paraffin	129
80 Cu + 20 Zn	1845	10 Bi + 40 Pb + 50 Sn	324	Phosphorus	111
50 Cu + 50 Zn	1615			Porcelain	2820
20 Cu + 80 Zn	1300	Tin solder	275–350	Potassium	143.6
Delta metal	1742	Blast-furnace slag	2370–2600	Sodium	207.5
20 Sn + 80 Pb	530	Borax	1040	Spermaceti	120
50 Sn + 50 Pb	400	Cast iron, gray	2460–2550	Stearine	122
80 Sn + 20 Pb	388	Cast iron, white	1920–2010	Steel	2370–2550
		Chlorides:		Wrought iron	2460–2640
		Calcium	1422		
		Potassium	1474		
		Sodium	1479		
		Zinc	689		

Table 5. Melting Points of Reactor Materials, Deg F

(Power's Data Sheet No. 317, *Power*, Jan., 1959)

Material	Deg F	Material	Deg F
Niobium carbide, NbC	6800	Beryllium carbide, Be_2C	3812
Graphite, C	6700	Aluminum oxide, Al_2O_3	3722
Zirconium carbide, ZrC	6400	Beryllium silicide, $2BeO{\cdot}SiO_2$	3630
Zirconium nitride, ZrN	5400	Beryllium oxide-aluminum, $BeO{\cdot}Al_2O_3$	3470
Zirconium oxide, ZrO_2	4900	Zirconium beryllide, $ZrBe_9$	3180
Beryllium oxide, BeO	4568	Zirconium disilicide, $ZrSi_2$	3090
Zirconium silicides, Zr_3Si_2, Zr_4Si_3, Zr_6Si_5	4010–4080	Titanium, Ti	3074
Aluminum nitride, AlN	4060	Zirconium aluminide, $ZrAl_2$	3000
Beryllium nitride, Be_3N_4	4000		

Table 6. Freezing Points of Liquids at Atmospheric Pressure, Deg F

Liquid	Deg F	Liquid	Deg F	Liquid	Deg F
Ammonia	−107.8	Calcium chloride (sat sol)	− 40	Methyl alcohol	−144.2
Aniline	20.8	Ether	−180	Rapeseed oil	25.7
Benzol	41.9	Ethyl alcohol	−174.6	Turpentine	<−75
Carbon bisulphide	−168.1	Glycerin	64	Sulphuric acid	−105
Carbon dioxide	−110.2	Naphthalene	176	Salt (NaCl) sol, sat	− 0.4
Chloroform	− 82.3	Linseed oil	− 4	Sea water	27.5
		Mercury	− 38.8	Toluene	−149

Mixtures of glycerin and water (Bolley)			Mixtures of ethyl alcohol and water (F. Beilstein)			
Percent by weight of glycerin	Specific gravity	Freezing point, deg F	Percent by weight of alcohol	Freezing point, deg F	Percent by weight of alcohol	Freezing point, deg F
10	1.0245	30.2	2.58	30.2	21.7	10.4
20	1.0498	27.5	5.22	28.4	23.8	6.8
30	1.0771	20.8	7.36	26.6	26.0	3.2
40	1.1045	1.0	9.58	24.8	28.0	− 0.4
45	1.1183	−15.2	11.50	23.0	30.0	− 4.0
50	1.1320	−25.6	13.27	21.2	33.5	−11.2
60	1.1582	Below −31.0	16.53	17.6	37.3	−18.4
			19.09	14.0	41.2	−25.6

Table 7. Boiling Points at Atmospheric Pressure, Deg F

Substance	Deg F	Substance	Deg F	Substance	Deg F
Zinc	1665	Glycerin	554	Turpentine	320.0
Sulphur	832	Phosphorus	536	Toluene	231.0
Mercury	675	Naphthalene	424	Sodium chloride (sat sol)	226.4
Linseed oil	549	Aniline	364	Helium	−452.0
Paraffin	572	Calcium chloride (sat sol)	356		

Expansion of Bodies by Heat

Coefficients of Expansion. The coefficient of linear expansion of a solid is defined as the increment of length in a unit of length for a rise in temperature of 1 deg. Likewise, the **coefficient of cubical expansion** of a solid, liquid, or gas is the increment of volume of a unit volume for a rise of temperature of 1 deg. Denoting these coefficients by a' and a''', respectively,

$$a' = \frac{1}{l}\frac{dl}{dt} \qquad a''' = \frac{1}{V}\frac{dV}{dt}$$

in which l denotes length, V volume, and t temperature. For homogeneous solids $a''' = 3a'$ and the **coefficient of superficial expansion** $a'' = 2a'$.

The coefficients of expansion are, in general, dependent upon the temperature, but for ordinary ranges of temperature, constant mean values may be taken. If lengths, areas, and volumes at 32 F (0 C) be taken as standard, then these magnitudes at other

Table 8. Boiling Points of Hydrocarbons, Deg F

(Reference: Arthur and Elizabeth Rose, "The Condensed Chemical Dictionary," 6th ed., Reinhold, 1961)

Name	Chemical formula	Deg F
PARAFFINS OR ALKANES: C_nH_{2n+2}		
Methane	CH_4	−258.9
Ethane	C_2H_6	−127.5
Propane	C_3H_8	− 44.5
Butane	C_4H_{10}	31.1
Pentane	C_5H_{12}	96.9
Hexane	C_6H_{14}	155.6
Heptane	C_7H_{16}	209.1
Octane	C_8H_{18}	258.2
Nonane	C_9H_{20}	303.2
Decane	$C_{10}H_{22}$	345.2
OLEFINS OR ALKENES: C_nH_{2n}		
Ethylene	C_2H_4	−152.5
Propylene	C_3H_6	− 53.8
1-Butene	C_4H_8	20.8
1-Pentene	C_5H_{10}	86.0
DIOLEFINS OR DIENES: C_nH_{2n-2}		
1,3-Butadiene	C_4H_6	24.1
Isoprene	C_5H_8	93.3
ACETYLENES OR ALKINES: C_nH_n		
Acetylene	C_2H_2	−119.2
AROMATIC SERIES		
Benzene	C_6H_6	176.1
Toluene	C_7H_8	231.2
Ethylbenzene	C_8H_{10}	277.1
Naphthalene	$C_{10}H_8$	424.2

Table 9. Relation of Color to Temperature of Iron or Steel

Color	Deg F	Color	Deg F
Dark blood red, black red	990	Orange, free scaling heat	1650
Dark red, blood red, low red	1050	Light orange	1725
Dark cherry red	1175	Yellow	1825
Medium cherry red	1250	Light yellow	1975
Cherry, full red	1375	White	2200
Light cherry, light red	1550		

temperatures t_1 and t_2 are related as follows:

$$\frac{l_1}{l_2} = \frac{1 + a't_1}{1 + a't_2} \qquad \frac{A_1}{A_2} = \frac{1 + a''t_1}{1 + a''t_2} \qquad \frac{V_1}{V_2} = \frac{1 + a'''t_1}{1 + a'''t_2}$$

Since for solids and liquids the expansion is small, the preceding formulas for these bodies become approximately

$$l_2 - l_1 = a'l_1(t_2 - t_1) \qquad A_2 - A_1 = a''A_1(t_2 - t_1)$$
$$V_2 - V_1 = a'''V_1(t_2 - t_1)$$

For certain metals, the variation of the coefficient of expansion with temperature is given by an equation in which, denoting by l_0 the length at 32 F, and by l the length at temperature t, the following relation is obtained:

$$l = l_0 \left[1 + a\left(\frac{t - 32}{1000}\right) + b\left(\frac{t - 32}{1000}\right)^2 \right]$$

Information relative to the constants in this equation is presented in Table 10.

Table 10. Constants for the Equation

Metal	1000 a	1000 b	Temperature range, deg F
Aluminum	12.58	3.0	32–1130
Cast iron	5.441	1.747	32–1160
Ingot iron	6.375	1.636	32–1380
Malleable iron	6.503	1.622	32– 930
Ingot steel	6.212	1.623	32–1380
Copper	9.278	1.244	32–1160
Nickel	7.652	1.023	32–1830

Gruneisen finds that a' varies directly as the specific heat.

Additional information regarding the compressibility of water, coefficients of expansion, and linear shrinkage of castings is presented in Tables 11 to 13.

Table 11. Compressibility of Water $(v_f - v) \times 10^5$
(Abstracted from Keenan and Keyes, "Thermodynamic Properties of Steam")

Pressure, psia	Temperature, deg F								
	32	100	200	300	400	500	600	700	705.4
Saturated liquid p, psia	0.08854	0.9492	11.526	67.013	247.31	680.8	1542.9	3093.7	3206.2
Saturated liquid 100 v_f, cu ft per lb	1.6022	1.6132	1.6634	1.7449	1.8369	2.0432	2.3629	3.692	5.030
1,000	5.7	5.1	5.4	6.9	8.7	6.4			
1,500	8.4	7.5	8.1	10.4	14.1	17.3			
2,000	11.0	9.9	10.8	13.8	19.5	27.8	32.6		
2,500	13.7	12.3	13.4	17.2	24.8	37.7	61.9		
3,000	16.3	14.7	16.0	20.7	30.0	47.1	87.9		
3,206.2	17.5	15.7	17.1	22.2	32.1	51.0	98.0	354	0
4,000	21.5	19.2	21.0	27.5	40.0	64.5	132.2	821	2079
5,000	26.7	23.6	26.0	34.0	49.6	80.5	169.3	1017	2309
6,000	31.7	27.8	30.8	40.5	58.7	96.1	202.9		

The coefficients of cubical expansion for different gases at ordinary temperatures are about the same. From 0 to 212 F and at atmospheric pressure, the values multiplied by 1,000 are as follows: for NH_3, 2.11; CO, 2.04; CO_2, 2,07; H_2, 2.03; NO, 2.07.

Units of Force and Mass

Force, mass, length, and time are related by Newton's second law of motion, which may be expressed as

$$F \sim ma$$

In order to write this as an equality, a constant must be introduced which has magnitude and dimensions. For convenience, the constant may be designated as $1/g_c$. Thus,

$$F = \frac{ma}{g_c}$$

Since this equation must be homogeneous insofar as the dimensions are concerned, the units for g_c are mL/t^2F. Consider a 1-lb mass, lb_m, in the earth's gravitational field, where the acceleration is 32.1740 ft/sec². The force exerted on the pound mass will

Table 12. Coefficients of Expansion

(For pure metals, see p. 6–10 and 6–67)

COEFFICIENTS OF LINEAR EXPANSION
(Mean values of 10,000a' between 32 and 212 F)

Metals	
Aluminum bronze	0.094
Brass, cast	0.104
Brass, wire	0.107
Bronze	0.100
Constantan (60 Cu, 40 Ni)	0.095
German silver	0.102
Iron:	
Cast	0.059
Soft forged	0.063
Wire	0.080
Magnalium (85 Al, 15 Mg)	0.133
Phosphor bronze	0.094
Solder	0.134
Speculum metal	0.107
Steel:	
Bessemer, rolled hard	0.056
Bessemer, rolled soft	0.063
Nickel (10% Ni)	0.073
Type metal	0.108
Other Materials	
Bakelite, bleached	0.122
Brick	0.053
Caoutchouc	0.372
Carbon—coke	0.030
Cement, neat	0.060
Concrete	0.080
Ebonite	0.468
Glass:	
Thermometer	0.045
Hard	0.033
Plate and crown	0.050
Flint	0.044
Pyrex	0.018
Granite	0.04–0.05
Graphite	0.044
Gutta percha	0.875
Ice	0.283
Limestone	0.023–0.05
Marble	0.02–0.09
Masonry	0.025–0.050
Paraffin:	
32 F–61 F	0.592
61 F–100 F	0.724
100 F–120 F	2.612
Porcelain	0.02
Quartz:	
Parallel to axis	0.044
Perpend. to axis	0.074
Quartz, fused	0.0028
Rubber	0.428
Vulcanite	0.400
Wood (‖ to fiber):	
Ash	0.053
Chestnut and maple	0.036
Oak	0.027
Pine	0.030
Across the fiber:	
Chestnut and pine	0.019
Maple	0.027
Oak	0.030

COEFFICIENTS OF CUBICAL EXPANSION
(Mean values of 1,000a''' at ordinary room temperatures)

Liquids	
Acetic acid	0.60
Alcohol (ethyl)	0.61
Alcohol (methyl)	0.80
Benzene	0.77
Benzol	0.70
Calcium chloride ($CaCl_2$), 5 to 50% solution	0.28
Chloroform	0.77
Ether	0.92
Glycerin	0.28
Hydrochloric acid	0.27
Hydrochloric acid, 50% solution	0.52
Mercury	0.10
Olive oil	0.41
Petroleum, Pennsylvania	0.50
Petroleum, California	0.43
Petroleum, Texas	0.42
Phenol (C_6H_6O)	0.50
Rapeseed oil	0.50
Salt, 1.6% solution	0.60
Salt, 26% solution	0.24
Sulphuric acid	0.31
Sulphuric acid, 50% solution	0.45
Turpentine	0.54
Water	0.115
Solids	
Fluorspar	0.035
Ice (4 to 30 F)	0.62
Paraffin wax	0.61
Rock salt	0.67
Sulphur	0.40
Wood (beech)	0.016
Wood (pine)	0.028

Table 13. Linear Shrinkage of Castings

Bar iron, rolled	1:55
Bell metal	1:65
Bismuth	1:265
Brass	1:65
Bronze	1:63
Cast iron	1:96
Gun metal	1:134
Iron, fine grained	1:72
Lead	1:92
Steel castings	1:50
Steel, puddled	1:72
Steel, wrought	1:64
Tin	1:128
Zinc, cast	1:624
8 Cu + 1 Sn (by wt)	1:13

be defined as the pound force, lb_f. This system of units gives for g_c the following magnitude and dimensions:

$$1\ lb_f = \frac{(1\ lb_m)(32.174\ ft/sec^2)}{g_c}$$

hence

$$g_c = 32.174\ lb_m ft/lb_f sec^2$$

g_c may be used with other units, in which case the numerical value changes. The numerical value of g_c for four systems of units is

$$g_c = 32.174\frac{lb_m ft}{lb_f sec^2} = 1\frac{slug\ ft}{lb_f sec^2} = 1\frac{lb_m ft}{pdl\ sec^2} = 1\frac{g\ cm}{dyne\ sec^2}$$

Consider now the relationship which involves weight, a gravitational force, and mass by applying the basic equation for a body of fixed mass acted upon by a gravitational force g and no other force. The acceleration of the mass caused by the gravitational force is the acceleration due to gravity g.

Substituting gives the relationship between weight and mass

$$w = \frac{mg}{g_c}$$

If the gravitational acceleration is constant, the weight and mass are in a fixed proportion to each other; hence for accounting purposes in mass balances they can be used interchangeably. This is not possible if g is a variable.

We may now write the relation between mass m and weight w as

$$w = m\frac{g}{g_c}$$

The constant g_c is used throughout the following paragraphs.

Measurement of Heat

Units of Heat. Many units of heat have been dependent on the experimentally determined properties of some substance. To eliminate experimental variations, the unit of heat may be defined in terms of fundamental units. The International Steam Table Conference (London, 1929) defines the Steam Table (IT) calorie as $\frac{1}{860}$ of a watthour. One British thermal unit (Btu) is defined as 251.996 IT cal, or 778.26 ft-lb.

Previously, the Btu was defined as the heat necessary to raise one pound of water one degree Fahrenheit at some arbitrarily chosen temperature level. Similarly, the calorie was defined as the heat required to heat one gram of water one degree Celsius at 15 C (or at 17.5 C). These units are roughly the same in value as those mentioned above.

Heat Capacity and Specific Heat. The heat capacity of a material is the amount of heat transferred to raise unit mass of a material 1 deg in temperature. The ratio of the amount of heat transferred to raise unit mass of a material 1 deg to that required to raise unit mass of water 1 deg at some specified temperature is the **specific heat** of the material. For most engineering purposes, heat capacities may be assumed numerically equal to specific heats. Two heat capacities are generally used, that at constant pressure c_p and that at constant volume c_v. For unit mass, the instantaneous heat capacities are defined as

$$\left(\frac{\partial h}{\partial t}\right)_p = c_p \qquad \left(\frac{\partial u}{\partial t}\right)_v = c_v$$

Over a range in temperature, the mean heat capacities are given by

$$c_{pm} = \frac{1}{t_2 - t_1}\int_{t_1}^{t_2} c_p\,dt \qquad c_{vm} = \frac{1}{t_2 - t_1}\int_{t_1}^{t_2} c_v\,dt$$

Denoting by c the heat capacity, the heat required to raise the temperature of w lb of a substance from t_1 to t_2 is $Q = mc(t_2 - t_1)$, provided c is a constant.

In general, c varies with the temperature, though for moderate temperature ranges a constant mean value may be taken. If, however, c is taken as variable, then $Q = m\int_{t_1}^{t_2} c\,dt$. The *mean* heat capacity from 0 to t deg is given by $c_m = \frac{1}{t}\int_0^t c\,dt$. If $c = a_1 + a_2t + a_3t^2 + \cdots$

$$c_m = a_1 + \tfrac{1}{2}a_2t + \tfrac{1}{3}a_3t^2 + \cdots$$

Data relative to the specific heat of water, mean specific heats for solids and liquids, the specific heat of gases at 1 atm, and the mean specific heat of iron are presented in Tables 14 to 19.

Specific Heat of Solids. For elements near room temperature, the specific heat may be approximated by the rule of Dulong and Petit, that the specific heat at constant

Table 14. Specific Heat of Water at Constant Pressure

(Interpolated from Keenan and Keyes tables)

Temp, deg F	Pressure, psia			
	1,000	2,000	4,000	6,000
200	1.0	1.0	0.99	0.98
400	1.07	1.06	1.05	1.04
600	....	1.45	1.29	1.21
680	....	....	1.77	1.45

Table 15. Specific Heat of Water at 1 Atm (I.C.T.)

Temp, deg F	32	50	100	150	212
c_p	1.001	1.002	1.004	1.009	1.021

Table 16. Mean Specific Heats of Various Solids and Liquids between 32 and 212 F, Btu/lb F

(For gases, see p. 4–12 and Fig. 1; for pure metals, pp. 6–10 and 6–67; for refractories, pp. 6–209) and 6–215

Substance	Specific heat
Solids	
Alloys:	
Bismuth-tin	0.040–0.045
Bell metal	0.086
Brass, yellow	0.0883
Brass, red	0.090
Bronze	0.104
Constantan	0.098
D'Arcet's metal	0.050
German silver	0.095
Lipowitz's metal	0.040
Nickel steel	0.109
Rose's metal	0.050
Solders (Pb and Sn)	0.040–0.045
Type metal	0.0388
Wood's metal	0.040
40 Pb + 60 Bi	0.0317
25 Pb + 75 Bi	0.030
Asbestos	0.20
Ashes	0.20
Bakelite	0.3–0.4
Basalt (lava)	0.20
Borax	0.229
Brick	0.22
Carbon-coke	0.203
Chalk	0.215
Charcoal	0.20
Cinders	0.18
Coal	0.3
Concrete	0.156
Cork	0.485
Corundum	0.198
Dolomite	0.222
Ebonite	0.33
Glass:	
Normal	0.199
Crown	0.16
Flint	0.12
Gneiss	0.18
Granite	0.195
Graphite	0.201
Gypsum	0.259
Hornblende	0.195
Humus (soil)	0.44
Ice:	
−4 F	0.465
32 F	0.487
India rubber (Para)	0.27–0.48
Kaolin	0.224
Limestone	0.217
Marble	0.210
Oxides:	
Alumina (Al_2O_3)	0.183
Cu_2O	0.111
Lead oxide (PbO)	0.055
Lodestone	0.156
Magnesia	0.222
Magnetite (Fe_3O_4)	0.168
Silica	0.191
Soda	0.231
Zinc oxide (ZnO)	0.125
Paraffin wax	0.69
Porcelain	0.22
Quartz	0.17–0.28
Quicklime	0.217
Salt, rock	0.21
Sand	0.195
Sandstone	0.22
Serpentine	0.25
Sulphur	0.180
Talc	0.209
Tufa	0.33
Vulcanite	0.331
Wood:	
Fir	0.65
Oak	0.57
Pine	0.67
Liquids	
Acetic acid	0.51
Acetone	0.544
Alcohol (absolute)	0.58
Aniline	0.49
Benzol	0.40
Chloroform	0.23
Ether	0.54
Ethyl acetate	0.478
Ethylene glycol	0.602
Fusel oil	0.56
Gasoline	0.50
Glycerin	0.58
Hydrochloric acid	0.60
Kerosene	0.50
Naphthalene	0.31
Machine oil	0.40
Mercury	0.033
Olive oil	0.40
Paraffin oil	0.52
Petroleum	0.50
Sulphuric acid	0.336
Sea water	0.94
Toluene	0.40
Turpentine	0.42
Molten metals:	
Bismuth (535–725 F)	0.036
Lead (590–680 F)	0.041
Sulphur (246–297 F)	0.235
Tin (460–660 F)	0.058

Table 17. Constants for Kopp's Law

Elements	Specific heats of the atoms	Elements	Specific heats of the atoms
Heavy elements	6.4	Oxygen	4.0
Boron	2.7	Phosphorus	5.4
Carbon	1.8	Silicon	3.5
Fluorine	5.0	Sulphur	5.4
Hydrogen	2.3		

Table 18. Specific Heats of Gases at 1 Atm

Gas	Symbol	Equation for C_p in Btu per mol	Temp range, deg R	Source
Oxygen	O_2	$11.515 - \left(\frac{172}{\sqrt{T}}\right) + \left(\frac{1530}{T}\right)$	540–5000	a
		$11.515 - \left(\frac{172}{\sqrt{T}}\right) + \left(\frac{1530}{T}\right) + \left(\frac{0.05(T - 4000)}{1000}\right)$	5000–9000	a
Nitrogen	N_2	$9.47 - \left(\frac{3.47 \times 10^3}{T}\right) + \left(\frac{1.16 \times 10^6}{T^2}\right)$	540–5000	a
Carbon monoxide	CO	$9.46 - \left(\frac{3.29 \times 10^3}{T}\right) + \left(\frac{1.07 \times 10^6}{T^2}\right)$	540–5000	a
Hydrogen	H_2	$5.76 + \left(\frac{0.578T}{1000}\right) + \left(\frac{20}{\sqrt{T}}\right)$	540–4000	a
		$5.76 + \left(\frac{0.578T}{1000}\right) + \left(\frac{20}{\sqrt{T}}\right) - \left(\frac{0.33(T - 4000)}{1000}\right)$	4000–9000	a
Water	H_2O	$19.86 - \left(\frac{597}{\sqrt{T}}\right) + \left(\frac{7500}{T}\right)$	540–5000	a*
Carbon dioxide	CO_2	$16.2 - \left(\frac{6.53 \times 10^3}{T}\right) + \left(\frac{1.41 \times 10^6}{T^2}\right)$	540–6300	a
Methane	CH_4	$4.22 + 8.211 \times 10^{-3}T$	492–1800	b
		$27.0 - \frac{14,400}{T}$	1800–5940	b
Ethylene	C_2H_4	$6.0 + 8.33 \times 10^{-3}T$	720–1400	c
Ethane	C_2H_6	$6.6 + 13.33 \times 10^{-3}T$	720–1440	c
Ethyl alcohol	C_2H_6O	$4.5 + 21.1 \times 10^{-3}T$	680–1120	c
Methyl alcohol	CH_4O	$2.0 + 16.67 \times 10^{-3}T$	680–1100	c
Benzene	C_6H_6	$6.5 + 28.9 \times 10^{-3}T$	520–1120	c
Octane	C_8H_{18}	$14.4 + 53.3 \times 10^{-3}T$	720–1440	c
Dodecane	$C_{12}H_{26}$	$19.6 + 80.0 \times 10^{-3}T$	720–1440	c

[a] Sweigert and Beardsley, Empirical Specific Heat Equations Based upon Spectroscopic Data, *Ga. School Tech., State Eng. Expt. Sta. Bull.* 2, 1938.

[b] Schwarz, Die Spezifischen Wärmen der Gase als Hilfswerte zur Berechnung von Gleichgewichten, *Arch. Eisenhüttenw.*, **9,** 1936, p. 389.

[c] Parks and Huffman, *ACS, Mon.* 60, 1932.

* Approximate. An equation based on the most recent data is given by Keyes in *J. Chem. Phys.*, **15,** Aug. 1947, p. 602.

Table 19. Mean Specific Heat of Iron (c_m) between 32 and t F (Oberhoffer)

t	600	800	1000	1200	1400	1600	1800	2000	2250	2500
c_m	0.127	0.133	0.139	0.148	0.167	0.170	0.169	0.168	0.167	0.167

volume for one atomic weight of any solid element is 6.4. For solid compounds at about room temperature, Kopp's approximation is often useful. This states that the specific heat of a solid compound at room temperature is equal to the sum of the specific heats of the atoms forming the compound. The values given in the following Table 17 are to be used in connection with Kopp's law.

EXAMPLE. Specific heat of the atoms of Na_2SO_4 = 2(6.4) + 5.4 + 4(4) = 34.2. Molecular weight Na_2SO_4 = 142. Specific heat = 34.2/142 = 0.24: (I.C.T. value = 0.20). Errors of 20 percent are not uncommon using Kopp's law.

Specific Heats of Gases. For monatomic gases, the specific heats do not vary with temperature, and k, the value of c_p/c_v, is 1.66. For diatomic gases (oxygen, nitrogen, etc.), the specific heats vary with temperature but for many purposes may be assumed constant over considerable ranges of temperature. For diatomic gases, k is approximately 1.40. For more complex gases, generalizations are not possible. Specific heat increases with molecular complexity, and the value of k decreases (see also Table 24).

Properties of gases are, usually, most readily correlated on the mol basis. **A pound mol** is the mass in pounds equal to the molecular weight. Thus 1 pound mol of oxygen is 32 lb. At the same pressure and temperature, the volume of one mol is the same for all perfect gases, *i.e.*, following the gas laws. For perfect gases, $Mc_p - Mc_v = AMR = 1.987$.

$$c_v = AR/(k - 1) \qquad c_p = ARk/(k - 1)$$

On a molal basis, the average values of specific heat for some of the more common gases are given by Fig. 1. These values have been corrected to zero pressure but they

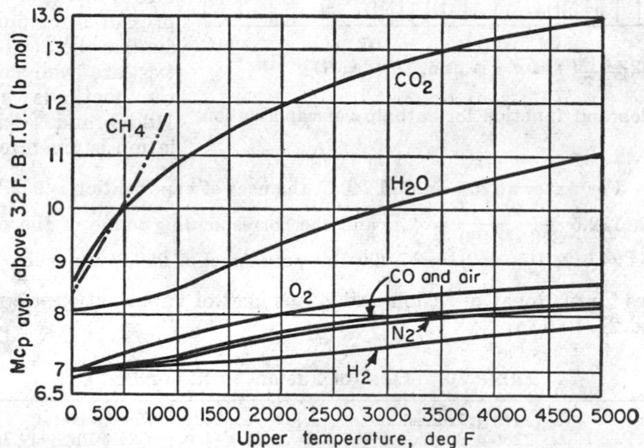

Fig. 1. Values of the mean molal specific heat at constant pressure, above 32 F.

are practically the same at 1 atm. Table 18 gives equations for specific heats for several gases at a constant pressure of 1 atm.

Specific Heat of Mixtures. If w_1 lb of a substance at temperature t_1 and with specific heat c_1 is mixed with w_2 lb of a second substance at temperature t_2 and with specific heat c_2, provided chemical reaction, heat evolution, or heat absorption do not occur, the specific heat of the mixture is

$$c_m = (w_1c_1 + w_2c_2)/(w_1 + w_2)$$

and the temperature of the mixture is

$$t_m = (w_1c_1t_1 + w_2c_2t_2)/(w_1c_1 + w_2c_2)$$

In general, $t_m = \Sigma wct/\Sigma wc$.

To raise the temperature of w_1 lb of a substance having a specific heat c_1 from t_1 to t_m, the weight w_2 of a second substance required is

$$w_2 = w_1c_1(t_m - t_1)/c_2(t_2 - t_m)$$

For mixing two bodies of the same (perfect) gas at constant pressure,

$$t_m = [(V_1 + V_2)/(V_1/T_1 + V_2/T_2)] - 459.69$$

Specific Heat of Solutions. For aqueous solutions of salts, the specific heat may be estimated by assuming the specific heat of the solution equal to that of the water alone. Thus, for a 20 percent by weight solution of sodium chloride in water, the specific heat would be approximately 0.8.

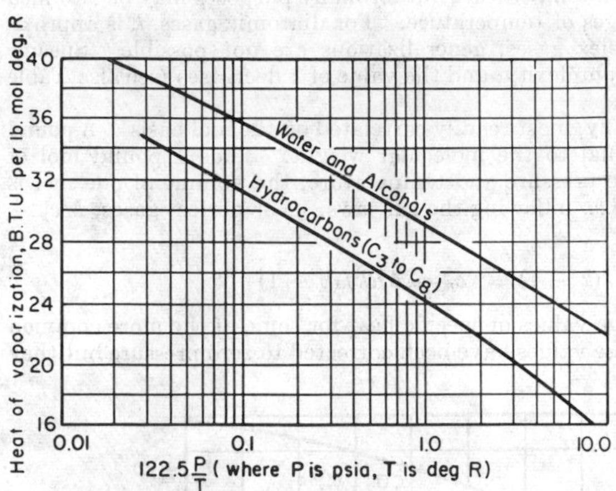

FIG. 2. Hildebrand function for enthalpy of vaporization.

Latent Heats. For pure substances, the heat effects accompanying changes in state at constant pressure are known as latent effects, because no temperature change is evident. Heat of fusion, vaporization, sublimation, and change in crystal form are examples. Heats of vaporization at low pressures for pure liquids of similar chemical characteristics are well correlated by the methods proposed by Hildebrand. Such a correlation is given in Fig. 2.

EXAMPLE. For water at 25 psia and 240 F, the heat of vaporization is 952 Btu. Referring to Fig. 2, $122.5 \frac{25}{240 + 460} = 4.4$, and the corresponding value of the molal heat of vaporization is $24.6(240 + 460) = 17{,}200$ But per lb mol or 956 Btu per lb.

The values for the heat of fusion and latent heat of vaporization are presented in Tables 20 and 21.

Table 20. Heat of Fusion,* Btu per Lb

Aluminum	171.0	Potassium	26.2	Wood's metal,	
Bismuth	22.0	Silver	44.0	25.8 Pb + 14.7 Sn	
Cadmium	23.4	Sodium	49.5	+ 52.4 Bi + 7.1 Cd	15.1
Chromium	136.0	Sulphur	16.7	Acetic acid, $C_2H_4O_2$	88.4
Cobalt	115.2	Tin	25.4	Benzene, C_6H_6	54.5
Copper	88.2	Zinc	47.0	Diphenyl, $C_{12}H_{10}$	47.0
Gold	28.7	Alloys:		Ethyl alcohol, C_2H_6O	45.0
Iron	117.0	30.5 Pb + 69.5 Sn	30.6	Glycerol, $C_3H_8O_3$	85.0
Lead	10.0	36.9 Pb + 63.1 Sn	28.0	Methyl alcohol, CH_4O	29.5
Mercury	5.0	64.7 Pb + 36.3 Sn	21.0	Napnthalene, $C_{10}H_8$	64.0
Nickel	130.0	77.8 Pb + 22.2 Sn	17.0	Phenol, C_6H_6O	52.2
Palladium	65.0	Rose's metal,		Ice	144.0
Phosphorus	9.0	24.0 Pb + 27.3 Sn			
Platinum	49.0	+ 48.7 Bi	12.3		

* Data compiled from "Handbook of Chemistry and Physics," 43d ed., Chemical Rubber Publishing Co.; "Chemical Engineers' Handbook," 3d ed., McGraw-Hill; Kelley, *U.S. Bureau of Mines Bull.* 476, 1949; "Smithsonian Physical Tables," 8th ed. (rev.), 1st reprint, 1934.

Table 21. Latent Heat of Vaporization at Atmospheric Pressure, Btu per Lb

Ethyl alcohol	367	Hexane	156	Hydrogen	194
Methyl alcohol	482	Heptane	133	Nitrogen	86
Aniline	198	Octane	128	Oxygen	92
Benzene	172	Decane	110	Chlorine	121
Toluene	151	Gasoline	133–145	Sulphur	120
Chloroform	110	Kerosene	105–110	Acetone	239
Ether	162	Turpentine	126	Carbon bisulphide	152
Diphenyl	134			Carbon tetrachloride	83.5

Vapor Pressures. At a specified temperature, a pure liquid can exist in equilibrium contact with its vapor at but one pressure, its vapor pressure. A plot of these pressures against the corresponding temperatures is known as a vapor-pressure curve.

Various values for the evaporation temperatures of certain liquids at a pressure of 1 atm are presented in Table 22.

Table 22. Evaporation Temperatures of Certain Liquids at Pressures up to 1 Atm
(See also special tables, pp. 4-38 to 4-56, for other liquids and for vapor pressures at higher pressures)

Substance	Pressures, mm of mercury					
	10	100	200	400	600	760
	Temperature, deg F					
Acetone	− 25.6	45.1	71.2	101.7	121.1	133.1
Benzene	− 9.5	71.2	109.4	141.9	163.7	176.2
Carbon tetrachloride	− 4.0	72.2	102.3	134.6	156.1	170.2
Chloroform	− 22.0	49.1	77.3	108	128.8	142.0
Diphenyl	246.0	357.5	400.5	441.1	471.8	493.0
Ethyl alcohol	26.6	94.8	118.8	145.5	162.4	173.0
Ethyl ether	− 56.2	17.6	35.4	63.5	83.1	94.2
Ethylene glycol	190.5	280.5	313.0	348.8	372.0	384.7
Methyl alcohol	3.74	69.6	93.7	121.0	138.2	148.4
Mercury	363	501	555	613.5	650.5	672.5
Water	52.3	123.8	141.2	176.5	200.4	212.0

GENERAL PRINCIPLES OF THERMODYNAMICS

Thermodynamics is the study which deals with energy, the various concepts and laws describing the conversion of one form of energy to another and the various systems employed to effect the conversions. Thermodynamics deals in general with systems in equilibrium. By means of its fundamental concepts and basic laws the behavior of an engineering system may be described when the various variables are altered. Thermodynamics covers a very broad field and includes many systems, for example, those dealing with chemical, thermal, mechanical, and electrical force fields and potentials. The quantity of matter under consideration is called the **system,** and everything else is spoken of as the **surroundings.** With a **closed system** there is no interchange of matter between system and surroundings; with an **open system** there is such an interchange. Any change that the system may undergo is known as a **process.** Any process or series of processes in which the system returns to its original condition or state is called a **cycle.**

Heat is energy **in transit** from one mass to another because of a temperature difference between the two. Whenever a force of any kind acts through a distance, **work** is done. Like heat, work is also energy in transit. Work is to be differentiated from the capacity of a quantity of energy to do work.

Notation

A = $1/J = 1/778$ Btu per ft-lb
B = availability (by definition, $B = H - T_oS$)
c_p = specific heat at constant pressure
c_v = specific heat at constant volume
E, e = total energy associated with a system
g = local acceleration of gravity, ft per sec^2
g_c = a dimensional constant
H, h = enthalpy, Btu (by definition $h = u + Apv$)
J = mechanical equivalent of heat = 778.26 ft-lb per Btu = 4.1861 joules per cal
k = c_p/c_v
m = mass of substance under consideration, lb_m
M = molecular weight
p = absolute pressure, lb per sq ft
Q, q = quantity of heat absorbed by the system from the surroundings, Btu
R = ideal gas constant

R_u = universal gas constant
S, s = entropy
t = temperature, deg F
$T = t + 459.69$ = absolute temperature = deg R
T_o = sink or discard temperature
U, u = internal energy
V = linear velocity, fps (or total volume)
v = volume
w = weight of substance under consideration, lb_f
W = external work performed on surroundings during change of state, ft-lb
$Y = \left(\frac{p_1}{p_2}\right)^{(k-1)/k} - 1$
z = distance above or below chosen datum
Z = free energy (by definition, $Z = H - TS$)
ψ = Helmholtz free energy (by definition, $\psi = U - TS$)

In this notation, small letters usually denote magnitudes referred to unit mass of the substance, capital letters corresponding magnitudes referred to m units of mass. Thus, v denotes the volume of 1 lb, $V = mv$, the volume of m lb. Similarly, $U = mu$, $S = ms$, etc. Subscripts are used to indicate different states; thus, p_1, v_1, T_1, u_1, s_1 refer to state 1, p_2, v_2, T_2, u_2, s_2 refer to state 2. Q_{12} is used to denote the heat absorbed by a body during the change from state 1 to state 2, and W_{12} denotes the external work done during the same change.

The two fundamental and general laws of thermodynamics are: (1) Energy may be neither created nor destroyed. (2) It is impossible to bring about any change or series of changes the sole net result of which is transfer of energy as heat from a low to a high temperature; in other words, heat will not of itself flow from low to high temperatures.

The **first law of thermodynamics,** one of the very important laws of nature, is the law of conservation of energy. Although the law has been stated in a variety of ways, all have essentially the same meaning. The following are examples ot typical statements: whenever energy is transformed from one form to another, energy is always conserved; energy can neither be created nor destroyed; the sum total of all energy remains constant. The energy conservation hypothesis was stated by a number of investigators; however, experimental evidence was not available until the famous work of J. P. Joule.

It has long been the custom to designate the law of conservation of energy, the first law of thermodynamics, when it is used in the analysis of engineering systems involving heat transfer and work. Statements of the first law may be written as follows: heat and work are mutually convertible; or, since energy can neither be created nor destroyed, the total energy associated with an energy conversion remains constant.

Before the first law may be applied to the analysis of engineering systems it is necessary to express it in some form of expression. Thus it may be stated for an **open system** as

$$\begin{bmatrix}\text{Net amount of}\\ \text{energy added to}\\ \text{system as heat}\\ \text{and all forms}\\ \text{of work}\end{bmatrix} + \begin{bmatrix}\text{Stored}\\ \text{energy}\\ \text{of mass}\\ \text{entering}\\ \text{system}\end{bmatrix} - \begin{bmatrix}\text{Stored}\\ \text{energy}\\ \text{of mass}\\ \text{leaving}\\ \text{system}\end{bmatrix} = \begin{bmatrix}\text{Net increase}\\ \text{in stored}\\ \text{energy of}\\ \text{system}\end{bmatrix}$$

For an open system with fluid entering only at section 1 and leaving only at section 2 and with no electrical, magnetic, or surface-tension effects, this equation may be written as

$$JQ - W + \int \left(Jh_1 + \frac{V_1^2}{2g_c} + \frac{gz_1}{g_c}\right) \delta m_1 - \int \left(Jh_2 + \frac{V_2^2}{2g_c} + \frac{gz_2}{g_c}\right) \delta m_2$$
$$= JU_f - JU_i + \frac{m_f V_f^2 - m_i V_i^2}{2g_c} + \frac{g}{g_c}(m_f z_f - m_i z_i)$$

The subscripts i and f refer to entire systems before and after the process occurs. δm refers to a differential quantity of matter.

It must be remembered that all terms in the first-law equation must be expressed in the same units.

For a **closed stationary system,** the first-law expression reduces to

$$JQ - W = J(U_2 - U_1)$$

For an **open system** fixed in position but undergoing **steady flow,** *e.g.*, a turbine or reciprocating steam engine, for a mass flow rate of m is

$$JQ - W = m\left[J(h_2 - h_1) + \frac{V_2^2 - V_1^2}{2g_c} + \frac{g}{g_c}(z_2 - z_1)\right]$$

In a **steady-flow** process, the mass rate of flow into the apparatus is equal to the mass rate of flow out and, in addition, at any point in the apparatus, the conditions are unchanging with time.

Since for many processes the last two terms are often negligible they will be omitted for simplicity except when such omission would introduce appreciable error.

Work done in overcoming a fluid pressure is measured by $W = \int p\,dv$, where p is the pressure *effectively* applied to the surroundings for doing work and dv represents the change in volume of the system.

Reversible and Irreversible Processes. A reversible process is one in which **both** the system and the surroundings may be returned to their original states. After an irreversible process, this is not possible. No process involving friction or an unbalanced potential can be reversible. No loss in ability to do work is suffered because of a reversible process but there is always a loss in ability to do work because of an irreversible process. All actual processes are irreversible. Any series of reversible processes that starts and finishes with the system in the same state is called a **reversible cycle.**

Steady-flow Processes. With **steady flow,** the conditions at any point in an apparatus through which a fluid is flowing do not change progressively with time. Steady-flow processes involving only mechanical effects are equivalent to similar nonflow processes occurring between two weightless frictionless diaphragms or pistons moving at constant pressure with the system as a whole in motion. Under these circumstances, the total work done by or on a unit amount of fluid is made up of that done on the two diaphragms $p_2v_2 - p_1v_1$ and that done on the rest of the surroundings $\int p\,dv - p_2v_2 + p_1v_1$. Differentiating, $p\,dv - d(pv) = -v\,dp$. The net, useful flow work done on the surroundings is $-\int v\,dp$. This is often called the shaft work. The net, useful or shaft work differs from the total work by $p_2v_2 - p_1v_1$. The first-law equaton may be written to indicate this result for a unit mass flow rate as

$$Jq - W_{\text{net}} = J(u_2 - u_1) + p_2v_2 - p_1v_1 + \frac{1}{2g_c}(V_2^2 - V_1^2) + \frac{g}{g_c}(z_2 - z_1)$$

or since by definition

$$Ju + pv = Jh$$

$$Jq - W_{\text{net}} = J(h_2 - h_1) + \frac{1}{2g_c}(V_2^2 - V_1^2) + \frac{g}{g_c}(z_2 - z_1)$$

If all net work effects are mechanical,

$$Jq + \int v\,dp = J(h_2 - h_1) + \frac{1}{2g_c}(V_2^2 - V_1^2) + \frac{g}{g_c}(z_2 - z_1)$$

Since in evaluating $\int v\,dp$ the pressure is that *effectively* applied to the surroundings, the integration cannot usually be performed except for reversible processes.

If a fluid is passed adiabatically through a conduit (*i.e.*, without heat exchange with the conduit), without doing any net or useful work, and if velocity and potential effects are negligible, $h_2 = h_1$. A process of the kind indicated is the Joule-Thomson flow (see p. 4-68) and the ratio $(\partial T/\partial p)$ for such a flow is the Joule-Thomson coefficient.

If a fluid is passed through a non-adiabatic conduit without doing any net or useful work and if velocity and potential effects are negligible, $q = h_2 - h_1$. This equation is important in the calculation of heat balances on flow apparatus, *e.g.*, condensers, heat exchangers, and coolers.

In many engineering processes the movement of materials is not independent of time; hence the steady-flow equations do not apply. For example, the process of oxygen discharging from a storage bottle represents a transient condition. The pressure within the bottle changes as the amount of oxygen in the tank decreases. The analysis of some transient processes is very complex; however, in order to show the general approach, a simple case will be considered.

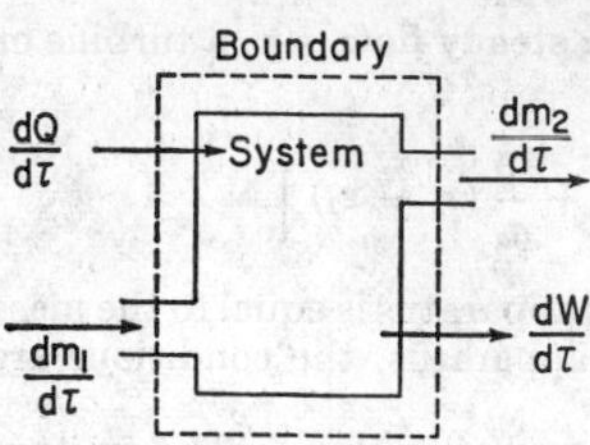

Fig. 3. Variable-flow system.

The quantity of material flowing into and out of the engineering system shown in Fig. 3 varies with time. The amount of work and the heat transfer crossing the system boundary are likewise dependent upon time. According to the law of conservation of mass, the rate of change of mass within the system is equal to the net rate of mass flow into and out of the system. Hence, in terms of mass flow rates,

$$\frac{dm_s}{d\tau} = \frac{dm_1}{d\tau} - \frac{dm_2}{d\tau}$$

For a finite period of time, this relation may be expressed as

$$\Delta m_s = \Delta m_1 - \Delta m_2$$

The first law may be written as follows:

$$J\frac{dU_s}{d\tau} = J\frac{dQ}{d\tau} + \frac{dW}{d\tau} + \left(Jh_1 + \frac{V_1^2}{2g_c} + \frac{g}{g_c}z_1\right)\frac{dm_1}{d\tau} - \left(Jh_2 + \frac{V_2^2}{2g_c} + \frac{g}{g_c}z_2\right)\frac{dm_2}{d\tau}$$

Under non-steady-flow conditions the variables h, V, z may change with time as well as flow rate, in which case the solution is very involved.

If steady-flow conditions prevail, then ΔU_s is equal to 0 and the integrands are independent of time, in which case the above equation reduces to the familiar steady-flow relation.

The **second law of thermodynamics** is a statement that conversion of heat to work is limited by the temperature at which conversion occurs. It may be shown that:

1. No cycle can be more efficient than a reversible cycle operating between given temperature limits.
2. The efficiency of all reversible cycles absorbing heat only at a single constant higher temperature T_1 and rejecting heat only at a single constant lower temperature T_2 must be the same.
3. For all such cycles, the efficiency is

$$e = \frac{W}{Q_1} = \frac{T_1 - T_2}{T_1}$$

This is usually called the **Carnot cycle efficiency.** By the first law $W = Q_1 + Q_2$,

$$(Q_1 + Q_2)/Q_1 = (T_1 - T_2)/T_1$$

By algebraic rearrangement,

$$(Q_1/T_1) + (Q_2/T_2) = 0$$

Clapeyron Equation

$$\frac{dp}{dT} = \frac{Q}{ATV_{12}}$$

This important relation is useful in calculations relating to constant-pressure evaporation of pure substances. In that case the equation may be written

$$v_{fg} = \frac{h_{fg}}{AT} \frac{1}{(dp/dT)}$$

where the symbols are as on pp. 4–15 and 4–16.

Entropy. For reversible cyclical processes in which the temperature varies during heat absorption and rejection, *i.e.*, for any *reversible cycle*, $\int \frac{dQ}{T} = 0$. Consequently, for any *reversible process*, $\int \frac{dQ}{T}$ is not a function of the particular *reversible path* followed. This integral is called the entropy change, or $\int_1^2 \frac{dQ_{\text{rev}}}{T} = S_2 - S_1 = S_{12}$. The entropy of a substance is dependent only on its state or condition. Mathematically, dS is a complete or perfect differential and S is a point function in contrast with Q and W which are path functions. For any reversible process, the change in entropy of the system and surroundings is zero, whereas for any irreversible process, the net entropy change is positive.

All actual processes are irreversible and therefore occur with a decrease in the amount of energy available for doing work, *i.e.*, with an increase in unavailable energy. The increase in unavailable energy is the product of two factors, T_0 the lowest available temperature for heat discard (practically always the temperature of the atmosphere) and the net change in entropy. The increase in unavailable energy is $T_0 \, \Delta S_{\text{net}}$. Any process that occurs of itself (any spontaneous process) will proceed in such a direction as to result in a net increase in entropy. This is an important concept in the application of thermodynamics to chemical processes.

Availability of a system or quantity of energy is defined as $B = h - T_0 s$. In this equation, all quantities except T_0 refer to the system irrespective of the state of the surroundings. T_0 is the lowest temperature available for heat discard. The preceding definition assumes the absence of velocity, potential, and similar effects. When these are not negligible, proper allowance must be made, *e.g.*, $B = h - T_0 s + \frac{V^2}{2g_c} + \frac{g}{g_c} z$. By substitution of $Q = T_0(S_2 - S_1)$ in the appropriate first-law expressions, it may be shown that for any steady-flow process, or for any constant-pressure non-flow process, decrease in availability is equal to the maximum possible (reversible) net work effect with sink for heat discard at T_0.

The availability function B is of particular value in the thermodynamic analysis of changes occurring in the stages of a turbine and is of general utility in determining thermodynamic efficiencies, *i.e.*, the ratio of actual work performed during a process to that which theoretically should have been performed.

Free energy, the Gibbs function, is defined as

$$Z = H - TS$$

This function is of particular importance in processes where chemical changes occur. For reversible isothermal steady-flow processes, or for reversible constant-pressure isothermal non-flow processes, change in free energy is equal to net work.

Helmholtz free energy, $\psi = U - TS$, is equal to the work during a constant-volume isothermal reversible non-flow process.

All three of these functions B, Z, and ψ are point functions, and like E, H, and S their differentials are complete or perfect.

Perfect Differentials. Maxwell Relations. If z is some function of x and y, in general

$$dz = \left(\frac{\partial z}{\partial x}\right)_y dx + \left(\frac{\partial z}{\partial y}\right)_x dy$$

Substituting M for $\left(\frac{\partial z}{\partial x}\right)_y$ and N for $\left(\frac{\partial z}{\partial y}\right)_x$

$$dz = M\,dx + N\,dy$$

But $\frac{\partial}{\partial y}\left(\frac{\partial z}{\partial x}\right) = \frac{\partial}{\partial x}\left(\frac{\partial z}{\partial y}\right)$ or $\frac{\partial M}{\partial y} = \frac{\partial N}{\partial x}$. This is Euler's criterion for integrability. A perfect differential has the characteristics of dz stated above. Many important thermodynamic relations may be derived from the appropriate point function by the use of this relation. Some of these relations follow:

Table 23. Maxwell Relations
(A is a conversion factor, 1/778 Btu per ft-lb)

Function	Differential	Maxwell relation
$\Delta u = q - W$	$du = T\,ds - Ap\,dv$	$\left(\frac{\partial T}{\partial v}\right)_s = -A\left(\frac{\partial p}{\partial s}\right)_v$
$h = u + Apv$	$dh = T\,ds + Av\,dp$	$\left(\frac{\partial T}{\partial p}\right)_s = A\left(\frac{\partial v}{\partial s}\right)_p$
$\psi = u - Ts$	$d\psi = -s\,dT - Ap\,dv$	$\left(\frac{\partial s}{\partial v}\right)_T = A\left(\frac{\partial p}{\partial T}\right)_v$
$z = h - Ts$	$dz = -s\,dT + Av\,dp$	$\left(\frac{\partial s}{\partial p}\right)_T = -A\left(\frac{\partial v}{\partial T}\right)_p$

By holding certain variables constant, a second set of relations is obtained:

Differential	Independent variable held constant	Relation
$du = T\,ds - Ap\,dv$	s	$\left(\frac{\partial u}{\partial v}\right)_s = -Ap$
	v	$\left(\frac{\partial u}{\partial s}\right)_v = T$
$dh = T\,ds + Av\,dp$	s	$\left(\frac{\partial h}{\partial p}\right)_s = Av$
	p	$\left(\frac{\partial h}{\partial s}\right)_p = T$
$d\psi = -s\,dT - Ap\,dv$	T	$\left(\frac{\partial \psi}{\partial v}\right)_T = -Ap$
	v	$\left(\frac{\partial \psi}{\partial T}\right)_v = -s$
$dz = -s\,dT + Av\,dp$	T	$\left(\frac{\partial z}{\partial p}\right)_T = Av$
	p	$\left(\frac{\partial z}{\partial T}\right)_p = -s$

By equating these various terms in the third column which are equal, one may obtain

$$\left(\frac{\partial u}{\partial s}\right)_v = \left(\frac{\partial h}{\partial s}\right)_p \qquad \left(\frac{\partial u}{\partial v}\right)_s = \left(\frac{\partial \psi}{\partial v}\right)_T$$

$$\left(\frac{\partial h}{\partial p}\right)_s = \left(\frac{\partial z}{\partial p}\right)_T \qquad \left(\frac{\partial z}{\partial T}\right)_p = \left(\frac{\partial \psi}{\partial T}\right)_v$$

By mathematical manipulation of equations previously given, the following important relations may be formulated:

$$c_v = \left(\frac{\partial q}{\partial T}\right)_v = T\left(\frac{\partial s}{\partial T}\right)_v = \left(\frac{\partial u}{\partial T}\right)_v$$

$$c_p = \left(\frac{\partial q}{\partial T}\right)_p = T\left(\frac{\partial s}{\partial T}\right)_p = \left(\frac{\partial h}{\partial T}\right)_p$$

$$c_p - c_v = AT\left(\frac{\partial v}{\partial T}\right)_p\left(\frac{\partial p}{\partial T}\right)_v$$

$$\left(\frac{\partial c_v}{\partial v}\right)_T = AT\left(\frac{\partial^2 p}{\partial T^2}\right)_v \qquad \left(\frac{\partial c_p}{\partial p}\right)_T = -AT\left(\frac{\partial^2 v}{\partial T^2}\right)_p$$

Relations involving q, u, h, and s:

$$dq = c_v\,dT + AT\left(\frac{\partial p}{\partial T}\right)_v dv = c_p\,dT - AT\left(\frac{\partial v}{\partial T}\right)_p dp$$

$$du = c_v\,dt + A\left[T\left(\frac{\partial p}{\partial T}\right)_v - p\right]dv$$

$$dh = c_p\,dT - A\left[T\left(\frac{\partial v}{\partial T}\right)_p - v\right]dp$$

$$ds = c_v\frac{dT}{T} + A\left(\frac{\partial p}{\partial T}\right)_v dv = c_p\frac{dT}{T} - A\left(\frac{\partial v}{\partial T}\right)_p dp$$

Since $q - AW = u_{12}$ and $h = u + Apv$, for reversible processes,

$$du = T\,ds - Ap\,dv \qquad \text{and} \qquad dh = du + Ap\,dv + Av\,dp$$

it follows that

$$Av = -T\left(\frac{\partial s}{\partial p}\right)_T + \left(\frac{\partial h}{\partial p}\right)_T$$

But from Table 23, $$A\left(\frac{\partial v}{\partial T}\right)_p = -\left(\frac{\partial s}{\partial p}\right)_T$$

Therefore, $$\left(\frac{\partial h}{\partial p}\right)_T = A\left[v - T\left(\frac{\partial v}{\partial T}\right)_p\right]$$

Similarly, $$\left(\frac{\partial u}{\partial v}\right)_T = -A\left[p - T\left(\frac{\partial p}{\partial T}\right)_v\right]$$

These last two equations give in terms of p, v, and T the necessary relations that must hold for any system, however complex. An equation in p, v, and T for the properties of a substance is called an equation of state. These two equations applicable to any substance or system are known as **thermodynamic equations of state.**

Presentation of Thermal Properties. Before the laws of thermodynamics can be applied and quantitative results obtained in the analysis of an engineering system, it is necessary to have available the properties of the system, some of which are temperature, pressure, internal energy, entropy, and enthalpy. In general, the property of a pure substance under equilibrium conditions may be expressed as a function of two other properties. This is based on the assumption that certain effects, such as gravitational and magnetic, are not important for the condition under investigation. The various properties of a pure substance under equilibrium conditions may be expressed by an equation of state, which in general form follows:

$$p = f(T,v)$$

In this relation the pressure is shown to be a function of both the temperature and the specific volume. Many special forms of equations of state are used in the analysis of engineering systems. Plots of the properties of various pure substances are very useful in studies dealing with thermodynamics. Two-dimensional plots, such as $p - v$, $p - h$, $p - T$, $T - s$, etc., show phase relations and are important in the analysis of cycles.

The constants in the equations of state are usually based on experimental data. The properties may be presented in many different ways, some of which are:

1. As equations of state, *e.g.*, the perfect gas laws and the van der Waals equation.
2. As charts or graphs.
3. As tables.
4. As approximations which may be useful when more reliable data are not available.

Ideal Gas Laws. At low pressures and high enough temperatures, in the absence of chemical reaction, all gases approach a condition such that their P-V-T properties may be expressed by the simple relation

$$pv = RT$$

If v is expressed as volume per unit weight, the value of the constant R will be different for different gases. If v is expressed as the volume of one molecular weight of gas, then R_u is the same for all gases in any chosen system of units. Hence $R = R_u/M$.

Table 24. Properties of Various Gases
(Approximate values[a] at 68 F and 14.7 psia)

Gas	Symbol	Mol wt	Sp gr, air = 1.00	Sp vol, cu ft per lb	Gas constant R, ft-lb per lb, deg F	Sp heat, c_p, Btu per lb, deg F	$c_p/c_v = k$	Boiling point at atm press, deg F	Critical temp, deg F	Critical press psia
Acetylene(ethyne)	C_2H_2	26.0	0.907	14.75	59.4	0.350	1.30	−118	96	910
Air	..	29.0	1.000	13.26	53.3	0.241	1.40	−317	−221	546
Ammonia	NH_3	17.0	0.596	22.51	91.0	0.523	1.32	− 28	270	1,638
Argon	A	39.9	1.379	9.51	38.7	0.124	1.67	−302	−187	705
N-Butane	C_4H_{10}	58.1	2.067	6.61	26.5	0.395	1.11	31	307	528
Butene-1(Butylene α)	C_4H_8	56.1	1.935	6.85	27.5	0.360	1.11	21	291	621
Carbon dioxide	CO_2	44.0	1.529	8.72	35.1	0.205	1.30	−109	88	1,072
Carbon monoxide	CO	28.0	0.967	13.70	55.2	0.243	1.40	−313	−218	514
Chlorine	Cl_2	70.9	2.486	5.41	21.8	0.115	1.33	− 30	291	118
Ethane	C_2H_6	30.0	1.049	12.77	51.5	0.386	1.22	−127	90	717
Ethyl chloride	C_2H_5Cl	64.5	2.365	5.96	24.0	0.275	1.13	54	370	764
Ethylene	C_2H_4	28.0	0.975	13.69	55.1	0.400	1.22	−155	50	747
Freon(F-12)	CCl_2F_2	120.9	4.520	3.18	12.6	.....	1.13	− 21	233	580
Helium	He	4.0	0.1381	95.9	386.3	1.250	1.66	−452	−450	33
Hydrogen	H_2	2.0	0.0695	191.5	766.8	3.420	1.41	−423	−400	188
Hydrogen chloride	HCl	36.5	1.268	10.53	42.4	0.191	1.41	−121	124	1,198
Hydrogen sulphide	H_2S	34.1	1.190	11.26	45.2	0.243	1.30	− 75	212	1,306
Isobutane(2-Methyl propane)	C_4H_{10}	58.1	2.018	6.61	26.5	0.392	1.11	14	273	543
Methane	CH_4	16.0	0.554	24.0	96.4	0.593	1.32	−258	−116	672
Methyl chloride	CH_3Cl	50.5	1.785	7.60	30.6	0.240	1.20	− 11	289	966
Natural gas[b]	..	19.5	0.667	19.75	79.1	0.560	1.27	−240	− 80	670
Neon	Ne	20.2	0.696	19.06	76.4	0.248	1.64	−410	−380	389
Nitric oxide	NO	30.0	1.037	12.80	51.5	0.231	1.40	−240	−137	954
Nitrogen	N_2	28.0	0.967	13.66	55.2	0.247	1.41	−320	−232	492
Nitrous oxide	N_2O	44.0	1.530	8.72	35.1	0.221	1.31	−129	98	1,053
Oxygen	O_2	32.0	1.105	12.00	48.3	0.217	1.40	−297	−182	730
Pentane	C_5H_{12}	72.1	2.471	5.33	21.3	0.40	1.06	97	387	485
Propane	C_3H_8	44.1	1.562	8.72	35.0	0.393	1.15	− 48	204	632
Propene(propylene)	C_3H_6	42.1	1.451	9.14	36.8	0.358	1.14	− 52	198	661
Sulphur dioxide	SO_2	64.1	2.264	5.99	24.0	0.154	1.26	14	315	1,141

[a] Approximate values listed are adapted from the following sources: "CAGI Handbook." Rose and Rose, "Condensed Chemical Dictionary," Reinhold. "Handbook of Chemistry and Physics," Chemical Rubber Publishing Co. Selected Values of Physical and Thermodynamic Properties of Hydrocarbons and Related Compounds, *API Research Project* 44, 1953. Selected Values of Chemical Thermodynamic Properties, *NBS Circ.* 500, 1952.

[b] Representative value; exact characteristics require knowledge of exact constituents.

In general, for any amount of gas, the ideal gas equation becomes

$$pV = NMRT$$

where V is now the total gas volume, N is the number of moles of gas in the volume V, M is the molecular weight, and $R_u = MR$ the universal gas constant.

For all ideal gases, $R_u = MR$ in lb-ft is 1,546. One pound mol of any perfect gas occupies a volume of 359 cu ft at 32 F and 1 atm.

For many engineering purposes. use of the gas laws is permissible up to pressures of 100 to 200 psi if the absolute temperatures are at least twice the critical temperatures. Below the critical temperature, errors introduced by use of the gas laws may usually be neglected up to 15 psi pressure although errors of 5 percent are often met when dealing with saturated vapors.

The **van der Waals equation of state,** $p = [BT/(v - b)] - a/v^2$, is a modification of the ideal gas law which is sometimes useful at high pressures. The quantities B, a, and b are constants.

Approximate *P-V-T* Relations. For most gases, suitable P-V-T data are not available. An approximation useful under such circumstances is based on the observation of van der Waals that in terms of reduced properties most gases approximate a common **reduced equation of state.** The reduced quantities are the actual ones divided by the corresponding critical quantities, *e.g.*, the reduced temperature $T_R = T_{\text{actual}}/T_{\text{critical}}$, the reduced volume $v_R = v_{\text{actual}}/v_{\text{critical}}$, the reduced pressure $p_R = p_{\text{actual}}/p_{\text{critical}}$. The gas laws may be made to apply to any non-perfect gas by the introduction of a correction factor μ

$$pV = \mu N R_u T$$

When the gas laws apply, $\mu = 1$ and on a molal basis $\mu = pV/R_uT$. If on a plot of μ versus p_R lines of constant T_R are drawn, for different substances these are found to fall in narrow bands. Single T_R lines may be drawn to represent approximately the various bands. This has been done in Fig. 4. To use the chart, only the critical pressure and temperature of the gas need be known.

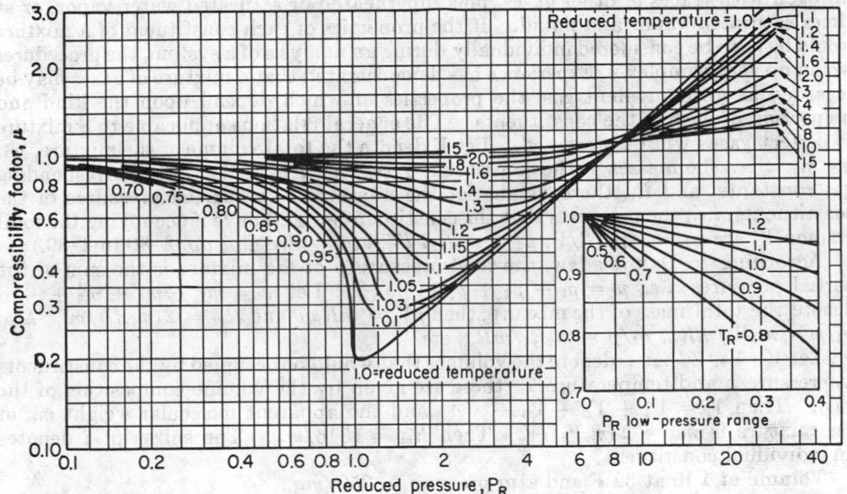

FIG. 4. Compressibility factors of gases and vapors. (*From Hougen and Watson, "Chemical Process Principles," Wiley.*)

EXAMPLE. Find the volume of 1 lb of steam at 5,500 psia and 1200 F (by steam tables, $v = 0.1516$ cu ft per lb).

For water, critical temperature = 705.4 F; critical pressure = 3,206.4 psia; reduced temp = 1660/1165 = 1 43; reduced pressure = 5,500/3206.4 = 1.72; μ (see Fig. 4) = 0.83.
$v = 0.83 \dfrac{(1546)(1660)}{(18)(5500)(144)} = 0.149$ cu ft. Error = 100(0.152 − 0.149)/0.152 = 1.7 percent. If the gas laws had been used, the error would have been 17 percent.

For gases not conforming to these charts, satisfactory approximations may be obtained by using so-called pseudo constants, empirically chosen.

Table 25. Pseudocritical Constants

Gas	T_c', deg K	p_c' atm
Helium	8.3	10.3
Hydrogen	41.3	20.8
Neon	52.3	33.9

No entirely satisfactory method for calculation for gaseous mixtures has been developed, but the use of average critical constants as proposed by Kay (*Ind. Eng., Chem.*, **28**, 1936, p. 1014) is easy and gives satisfactory results under conditions considerably removed from the critical. He assumes the gaseous mixture can be treated as if it were a single pure gas with a pseudocritical pressure and temperature estimated by a method of molar averaging.

$$(T_c)_{\text{mixture}} = (T_c)_a y_a + (T_c)_b y_b + (T_c)_c y_c + \cdots$$
$$(p_c)_{\text{mixture}} = (p_c)_a y_a + (p_c)_b y_b + (p_c)_c y_c + \cdots$$

where $(T_c)_a$ is the critical temperature of pure a, etc.; $(p_c)_a$ is the critical pressure of pure a, etc.; and y_a is the mol fraction of a, etc. For a gaseous mixture made up of gases a, b, c, etc., the pseudocritical constants having been determined, the gaseous mixture is handled on the μ charts as if it were a single pure gas.

Ideal Gas Mixtures. Many of the fluids involved in engineering systems are physical mixtures of the permanent gases or one or more of these with superheated or saturated vapors. For example, normal atmospheric air is a mixture of oxygen and nitrogen with traces of other gases, plus superheated or saturated water vapor, or at times saturated vapor and liquid. If the properties of each constituent of a mixture would have to be considered individually during an analysis of a system, the procedures would be very complex. Experience has demonstrated that a mixture of gases may be regarded as an equivalent gas, the properties of which depend upon the kind and proportion of each of the constituents. The general relations applicable to a mixture of perfect gases will be presented. Let V denote the total volume of the mixture, m_1, m_2, m_3, . . . the masses of the constituent gases, R_1, R_2, R_3, . . . the corresponding gas constants, and R_m the constant for the mixture. The **partial pressures** of the constituents, *i.e.*, the pressures that the constituents would have if occupying the total volume V, are $p_1 = m_1R_1T/V$, $p_2 = m_2R_2T/V$, etc. (See also pp. 4–80 to 4–89.)

According to Dalton's law, the **total pressure** p **of the mixture** is the sum of the partial pressures; *i.e.*, $p = p_1 + p_2 + p_3 + \cdots$. Let $m = m_1 + m_2 + m_3 + \cdots$ denote the total mass of the mixture; then $pV = mR_mT$ and $R_m = \Sigma(m_iR_i)/m$. Also $p_1/p = m_1R_1/mR_m$, $p_2/p = m_2R_2/mR_m$, etc.

Let V_1, V_2, V_3 . . . denote the volumes that would be occupied by the constituents at pressure p and temperature T (these are given by the volume composition of the gas). Then $V = V_1 + V_2 + V_3 + \cdots$ and the apparent molecular weight m_m of the mixture is $m_m = \Sigma(m_iV_i)/V$. Then $R_m = 1546/m_m$. The subscript i denotes an individual constituent.

Volume of 1 lb at 32 F and atm pressure $= 359/m_m$.

Mass of 1 cu ft at 32 F and atm pressure $= 0.002788m_m$.

The specific heats of the mixture are, respectively,

$$c_p = \Sigma(m_ic_{pi})/m \qquad c_v = \Sigma(m_ic_{vi})/m$$

Internal Energy, Enthalpy, and Entropy of an Ideal Gas. If an ideal gas with constant specific heats changes from an initial state p_1, V_1, T_1 to a final state p_2, V_2, T_2, the following equations hold:

$$u_2 - u_1 = mc_v(T_2 - T_1) = A(p_2v_2 - p_1v_1)/(k - 1)$$
$$h_2 - h_1 = mc_p(T_2 - T_1) = Ak(p_2v_2 - p_1v_1)/(k - 1)$$

$$s_2 - s_1 = m\left(c_v \ln \frac{T_2}{T_1} + AR \ln \frac{v_2}{v_1}\right) = m\left(c_p \ln \frac{T_2}{T_1} - AR \ln \frac{p_2}{p_1}\right)$$
$$= m\left(c_p \ln \frac{v_2}{v_1} + c_v \ln \frac{p_2}{p_1}\right)$$

In general, the energy per unit mass is $u = c_vT + u_0$, the enthalpy is $h = c_pT + h_0$, and the entropy is $s = c_v \ln T + AR \ln v + s_0 = c_p \ln T - AR \ln p + s_0' = c_p \ln v + c_p \ln p = s_0''$.

The two fundamental equations for ideal gases are

$$dq = c_v\, dT + Ap\, dv \qquad dq = c_p\, dT - Av\, dp$$

Special Changes of State for Ideal Gases

(Specific heats assumed constant)

In the following formulas, the subscripts 1 and 2 refer to the initial and final states, respectively.

1. Constant Volume: $p_2/p_1 = T_2/T_1$.

$$Q_{12} = U_2 - U_1 = mc_v(t_2 - t_1) = AV(p_2 - p_1)/(k - 1)$$
$$W_{12} = 0 \qquad s_2 - s_1 = mc_v \ln (T_2/T_1)$$

2. Constant Pressure: $V_2/V_1 = T_2/T_1$.

$$W_{12} = p(V_2 - V_1) = mR(t_2 - t_1)$$
$$Q_{12} = mc_p(t_2 - t_1) = AkW_{12}/(k - 1)$$
$$s_2 - s_1 = mc_p \ln (T_2/T_1)$$

3. Isothermal (Constant Temperature): $p_2/p_1 = V_1/V_2$.

$$U_2 - U_1 = 0 \qquad W_{12} = mRT \ln (V_2/V_1) = p_1V_1 \ln (V_2/V_1)$$
$$Q_{12} = AW_{12} \qquad s_2 - s_1 = Q_{12}/T = mAR \ln (V_2/V_1)$$

4. Reversible Adiabatic. Isentropic: $p_1V_1^k = p_2V_2^k$.

$$T_2/T_1 = (V_1/V_2)^{k-1} = (p_2/p_1)^{(k-1)/k}$$
$$AW_{12} = U_1 - U_2 = mc_v(t_1 - t_2) \qquad Q_{12} = 0 \qquad s_2 - s_1 = 0$$
$$W_{12} = (p_1V_1 - p_2V_2)/(k - 1) = p_1V_1[1 - (p_2/p_1)^{(k-1)/k}]/(k - 1)$$

5. Polytropic. This name is given to the change of state which is represented by the equation $pV^n = \text{const}$. A polytropic curve usually represents actual expansion and compression curves in motors and air compressors for pressures up to a few hundred pounds. By giving n different values and assuming specific heats constant, the preceding changes may be made special cases of the polytropic change, thus,

For $n = 1$,	$pv = \text{const}$	isothermal
$n = k$,	$pv^k = \text{const}$	isentropic
$n = 0$,	$p = \text{const}$	constant pressure
$n = \infty$,	$v = \text{const}$	constant volume

For a polytropic change of an ideal gas (for which c_v is constant), the specific heat is given by the relation $c_n = c_v(n - k)/(n - 1)$; hence for $1 < n < k$, c_n is negative. This is approximately the case in **air compression** up to a few hundred pounds pressure. The following are the principal formulas:

$$p_1V_1^n = p_2V_2^n \qquad T_2/T_1 = (V_1/V_2)^{n-1} = (p_2/p_1)^{(n-1)/n}$$
$$W_{12} = (p_1V_1 - p_2V_2)/(n - 1) = p_1V_1[1 - (p_2/p_1)^{(n-1)/n}]/(n - 1)$$
$$Q_{12} = mc_n(t_2 - t_1)$$
$$AW_{12}:U_2 - U_1:Q_{12} = k - 1:1 - n:k - n$$

The quantity $(p_1/p_2)^{(k-1)/k} - 1$ occurs frequently in calculations for perfect gases.

Determination of Exponent n. Lay off successive values of p and V, measured at chosen points on the curve under investigation, on logarithmic cross-section paper; or, lay off values of log p and log V on ordinary cross-section paper. If n is a constant, the points will lie in a straight line, and the slope of the line gives the value of n.

If two representative points (p_1, V_1 and p_2, V_2) be chosen, then

$$n = (\log p_1 - \log p_2)/(\log V_2 - \log V_1)$$

Several pairs of points should be used to test the constancy of n.

Changes of State with Variable Specific Heat. In case of a considerable range of temperature, the assumption of constant specific heat is not permissible, and the equations referring to changes of state must be suitably modified. Experiments on the specific heat of various gases show that the specific heat may sometimes be taken as a linear function of the temperature: thus, $c_v = a + bT$; $c_p = a' + b'T$. In that case, the following expressions apply for the change of internal energy and entropy, respectively:

$$U_2 - U_1 = m[a(T_2 - T_1) + 0.5b(T_2^2 - T_1^2)]$$
$$S_2 - S_1 = m[a \ln (T_2/T_1) + b(T_2 - T_1) + AR \ln (V_2/V_1)]$$

and for an isentropic change,

$$W_{12} = J(U_1 - U_2)$$
$$AR \ln (V_1/V_2) = a \ln (T_2/T_1) + b(T_2 - T_1)$$

For more complex specific-heat relations (see Table 18), integration of the equations between specified limits must be undertaken.

Graphical Representation. The change of state of a substance may be shown graphically by taking any two of the six variables p, V, T, S, U, H as independent coordinates and drawing a curve to represent the successive values of these two variables as the change proceeds. While any pair may be chosen, there are three systems of graphical representation that are specially useful.

1. p and V. The curve (Fig. 5) represents the simultaneous values of p and V during the change (reversible) from state 1 to state 2. The area between the curve and the axis OV is given by the integral $\int_{V_1}^{V_2} p\,dV$ and therefore represents the external work W_{12} done by the gas during the change. The area included by a closed cycle represents the work of the cycle (as in the indicator diagram of the steam engine).

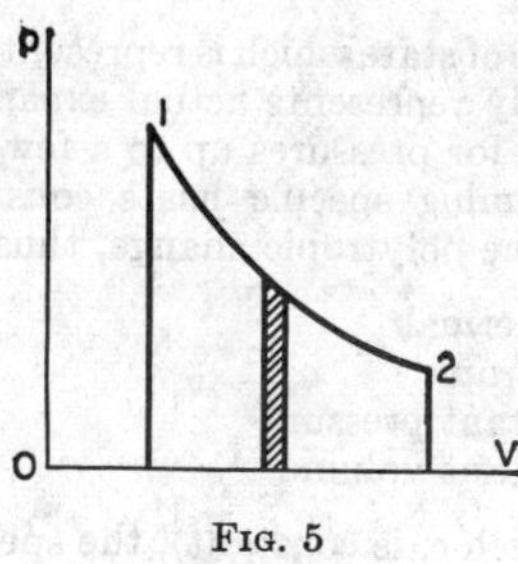

Fig. 5

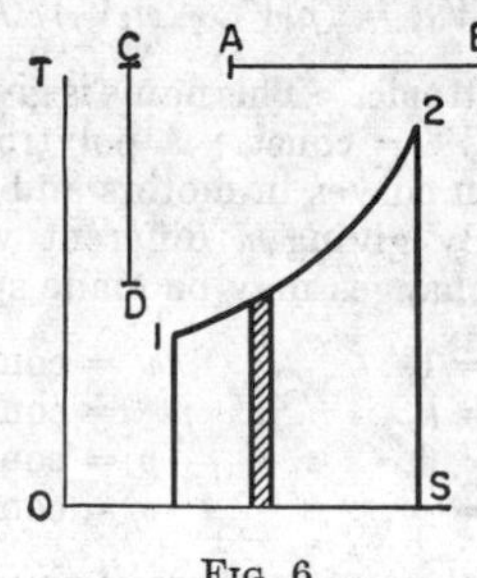

Fig. 6

2. T and S (Fig. 6). The absolute temperature T is taken as the ordinate, the entropy S as the abscissa. The area between the curve of change of state and the S-axis is given by the integral $\int_{S_1}^{S_2} T\,dS$, and it therefore represents the heat Q_{12} absorbed by the substance from external sources provided there are no irreversible effects. On the T-S diagram, an isothermal is a straight line, as AB, parallel to the S-axis; a *reversible* adiabatic is a straight line, as CD, parallel to the T-axis.

In the case of internal generation of heat through friction, as in steam turbines, the increase of entropy is given by $\int_{T_1}^{T_2} \frac{dQ'}{T}$ (see p. 4–19) and the area under the curve represents the heat Q' thus generated. In this case, an adiabatic is *not* a straight line parallel to the T-axis.

3. H and S. In the system of representation devised by Dr. Mollier, the enthalpy H is taken as the ordinate and the entropy S as the abscissa. If on this diagram (Fig. 7) a line of constant pressure, as 12, be drawn, the heat absorbed during the change at constant pressure is given by $Q_{12} = H_2 - H_1$, and this is represented by the line segment 23. The **Mollier diagram** is specially useful in problems that involve the flow of fluids, throttling, and the action of steam in turbines. A Mollier diagram for steam is presented in Fig. 22.

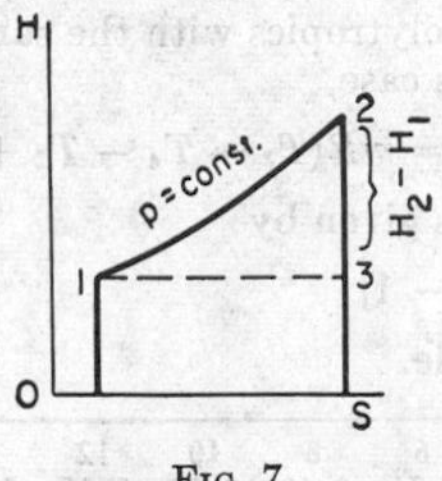

Fig. 7

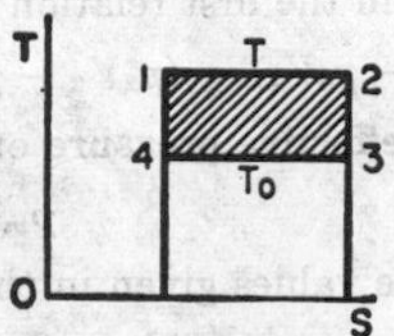

Fig. 8. Carnot cycle.

Ideal Cycles with Perfect Gases

Gases are used as heat mediums in several important types of motors. In air compressors, air engines, and air refrigerating machines, atmospheric air is the medium. In the internal-combustion engine, the medium is a mixture of products of combustion. Motors using gases are operated in certain well-defined cycles, which are described below. In the analyses given, ideal conditions that cannot be attained by actual motors are assumed. However, conclusions derived from such analyses are usually approximately valid for the modified actual cycle.

In the following, the subscripts 1, 2, 3, etc., refer to corresponding points shown in the figures. The work of the cycle is denoted by (W) and the net heat absorbed by (Q).

Carnot Cycle. The Carnot cycle (Fig. 8) is of historic interest. It consists of two isothermals and two isentropics. The heat absorbed along the upper isothermal 12 is $Q_{12} = mART \ln (V_2/V_1)$, and the heat transformed into work, represented by the cycle area, is $A(W) = Q_{12}[1 - (T_0/T)]$.

Hence,

$$(W) = mR(T - T_0) \ln (V_2/V_1)$$

If the cycle is traversed in the reverse sense, $Q_{43} = mART_0 \ln (V_3/V_4)$ is the heat absorbed from the cold body (brine), and the ratio $Q_{43}:A(W) = T_0:(T - T_0)$ is the **coefficient of performance** of the refrigerating machine.

Otto and Diesel Cycles. The ideal cycles usually employed for internal-combustion engines may be classified in two groups: (1) explosive—Otto, (2) non-explosive—Diesel, Joule.

Otto Cycle (Fig. 9 for pressure-volume plane, Fig. 10 for temperature-entropy plane). Isentropic compression 12 is followed by ignition and rapid heating at constant

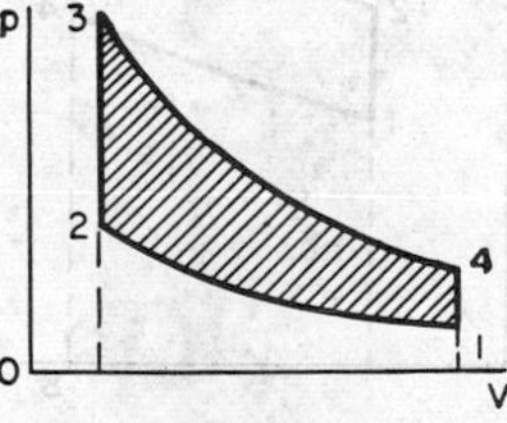

Fig. 9. Otto cycle.

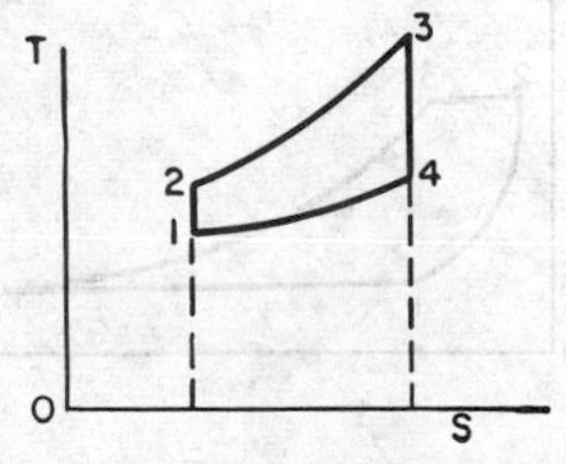

Fig. 10. Otto cycle.

volume, 23. This is followed by isentropic expansion, 34. Assuming constant specific heats the following relations hold:

$$\frac{T_2}{T_1} = \frac{T_3}{T_4} = \left(\frac{p_2}{p_1}\right)^{\frac{k-1}{k}} = \left(\frac{p_3}{p_4}\right)^{\frac{k-1}{k}} = \left(\frac{V_1}{V_2}\right)^{k-1}$$

$$Q_{23} = mc_v(T_3 - T_2)$$

$$(W) = JQ_{23}[1 - (T_1/T_2)] = Jmc_v(T_3 - T_4 - T_2 + T_1)$$

$$\text{Efficiency} = 1 - \frac{T_1}{T_2} = 1 - \left(\frac{V_2}{V_1}\right)^{k-1} = 1 - \left(\frac{p_1}{p_2}\right)^{\frac{k-1}{k}}$$

If the compression and expansion curves are polytropics with the same value of n, replace k by n in the first relation above. In this case,

$$(W) = [(p_3V_3 - p_4V_4) - (p_2V_2 - p_1V_1)]/(n - 1) = mR(T_3 - T_4 - T_2 + T_1)/(n - 1)$$

The **mean effective pressure** of the diagram is given by

$$p_m = ap_1[(p_3/p_2) - 1]$$

where a has the values given in the following table.

	$p_2/p_1 =$ 3	4	5	6	8	10	12	14	16
(n = 1.4)	a = 1.70	1.94	2.13	2.31	2.62	2.88	3.10	3.31	3.50
(n = 1.3)	a = 1.69	1.92	2.11	2.28	2.57	2.81	3.03	3.22	3.39
(n = 1.2)	a = 1.68	1.90	2.08	2.25	2.51	2.74	2.94	3.12	3.27

Diesel Cycle. In the Diesel oil engine, air is compressed to a high pressure. Fuel is then injected into the air, which is at a temperature above the ignition point, and it burns at nearly constant pressure (23, in Fig. 11). Isentropic expansion of the products of combustion is followed by exhaust and suction of fresh air, as in the Otto cycle.

Fig. 11. Diesel cycle.

The work obtained is

$$(W) = Jm[c_p(T_3 - T_2) - c_v(T_4 - T_1)]$$

and the efficiency of the ideal cycle is

$$1 - [(T_4 - T_1)/k(T_3 - T_2)]$$

The **Joule cycle,** also called the **Brayton cycle** (Fig. 12), consists of two isentropics and two constant-pressure lines. The following relations hold:

$$V_3/V_2 = V_4/V_1 = T_3/T_2 = T_4/T_1$$

$$\frac{T_2}{T_1} = \frac{T_3}{T_4} = \left(\frac{V_1}{V_2}\right)^{k-1} = \left(\frac{V_4}{V_3}\right)^{k-1} = \left(\frac{p_2}{p_1}\right)^{\frac{k-1}{k}}$$

$$(W) = Jmc_p(T_3 - T_2 - T_4 + T_1)$$

$$\text{Efficiency} = (W)/JQ_{23} = 1 - (T_1/T_2)$$

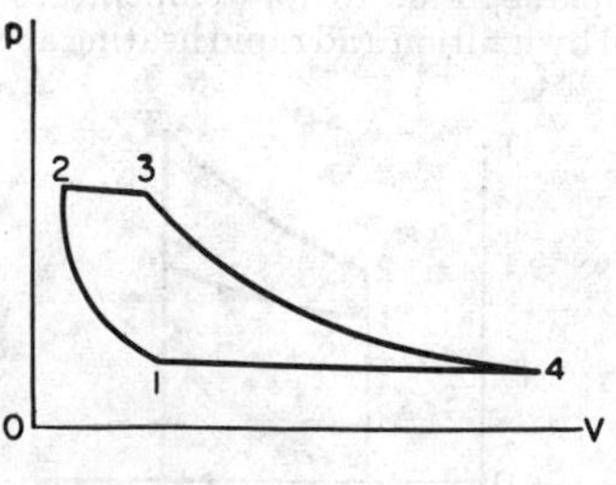

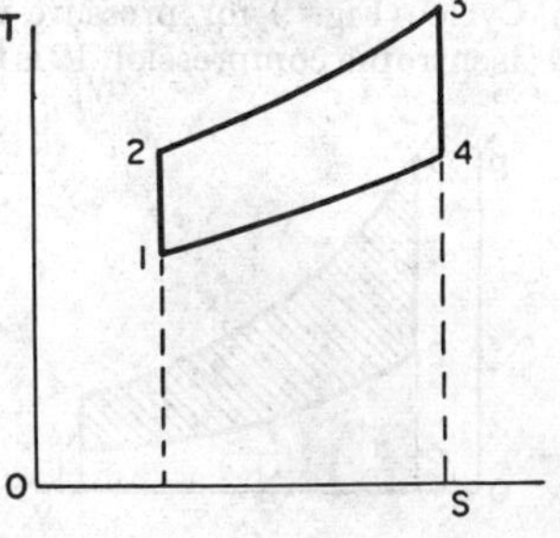

Fig. 12. Joule, or Brayton cycle.

The Joule cycle has assumed renewed importance as a basis for analysis of gas turbine operation.

Stirling Cycle. The Stirling engine may be visualized as a cylinder with a piston at each end. Between the pistons is a regenerator. The cylinder is assumed to be insulated except for a contact with a hot reservoir at one end and a contact with a cold reservoir at the other end.

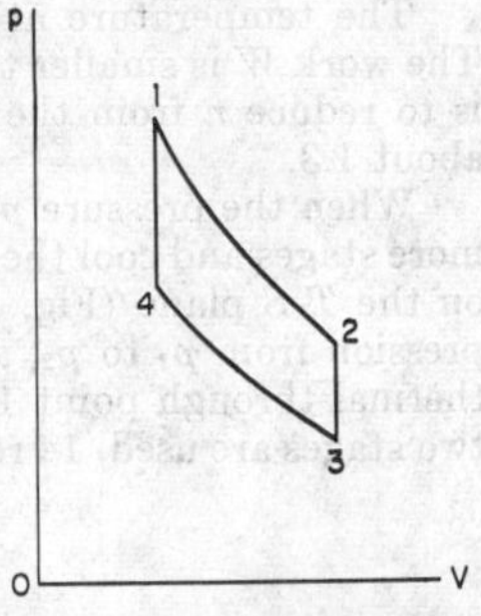

Starting with state 1, Fig. 13, heat from the hot reservoir is added to the gas at T_H (or $T_H - dT$). During the reversible isothermal process, the left piston moves outward, doing work as the system volume increases and the pressure falls. Both pistons are then moved to the right at the same rate to keep the system volume constant (process 2–3). No heat transfer occurs with either reservoir. As the gas passes through the regenerator, heat is transferred from the gas to the regenerator, causing the gas temperature to fall to T_L by the time the gas leaves the right end of the regenerator. For this heat-transfer process to be reversible, the temperature of the regenerator at each point must equal the gas temperature at that point. Hence there is a temperature gradient through the regenerator from T_H at the left end to T_L at the right end. No work is accomplished during this process. During the path 3–4, heat is removed from the gas at T_L (or $T_L + dT$) to the reservoir at T_L. To hold the gas temperature constant, the right piston is moved inward—doing work on the gas, with a resulting increase in pressure. During process 4–1, both pistons are moved to the left at the same rate to keep the system volume constant. The pistons are closer together during this process than they were during process 2–3, since $V_4 = V_1 < V_2 = V_3$. No heat is transferred to either reservoir. As the gas passes back through the regenerator, the energy stored in the regenerator during 2–3 is returned to the gas. The gas emerges from the left end of

FIG. 13. Stirling cycle.

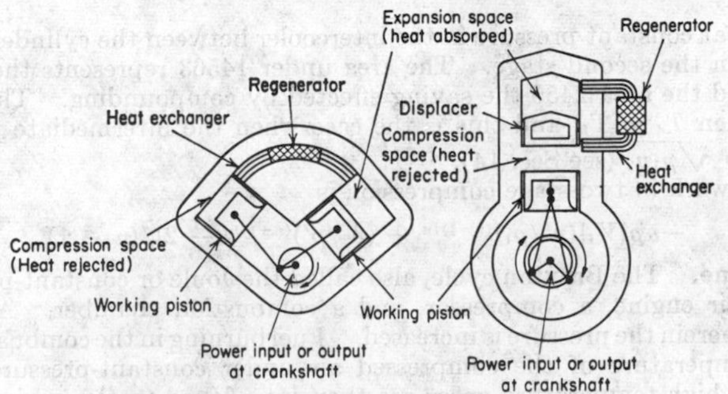

FIG. 14. Two main types of Stirling engine; (1) left, double-cylinder, two-piston; (2) right, single-cylinder, piston-plus-displacer. Each has two variable-volume working spaces filled with the working fluid—one for expansion and one for compression of the gas. Spaces are at different temperatures—the extreme temperatures of the working cycle—and are connected by a duct, which holds the regenerator and heat exchangers. (*International Science & Technology, May,* 1962.)

the regenerator at the temperature T_H. No work is performed during this process since the volume remains constant. Thus the cycle is completed and is externally reversible. The system exchanges a net amount of heat with only the two energy reservoirs T_H and T_L. Two types of Stirling engines are shown in Fig. 14. Extensive research-and-development effort has been devoted to the Stirling engines for future use as prime movers in space power systems operating on solar energy. (See also Sec. 9.)

Air Compression. It is assumed that the compressor works under ideal reversible conditions without clearance and without friction losses and that the changes are over ranges where the gas laws are applicable. Where the gas laws cannot be used, analysis in terms of μ charts (p. 4–23) is convenient. If the compression from p_1 to p_2 (Fig. 15) follows the law pV^n = const, the work represented by the indicator diagram is

$$-W = n(p_2V_2 - p_1V_1)/(n-1) = np_1V_1[(p_2/p_1)^{(n-1)/n} - 1]/(n-1)$$

The temperature at the end of compression is given by $T_2/T_1 = (p_2/p_1)^{(n-1)/n}$. The work W is smaller the smaller the value of n, and the purpose of the water jacket is to reduce n from the isentropic value 1.4. Under usual working conditions, n is about 1.3.

When the pressure p_2 is high, it is advantageous to divide the process into two or more stages and cool the air between the cylinders. The saving effected is best shown on the T-S plane (Fig. 16). With single-stage compression, 12 represents the compression from p_1 to p_2, and if the constant-pressure line 23 is drawn cutting the isothermal through point 1 in point 3, the area 1′1233′ represents the work W. When two stages are used, 14 represents the compression from p_1 to an intermediate pressure

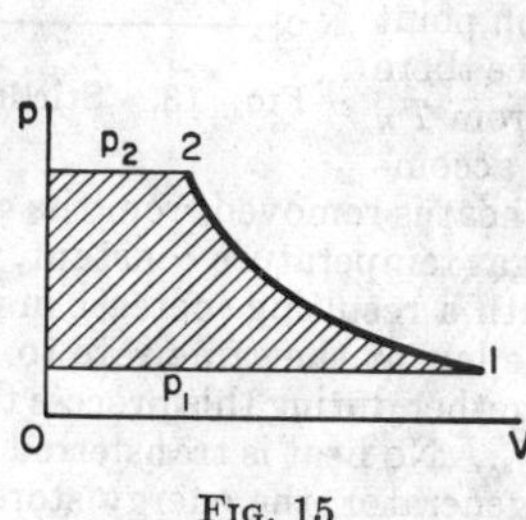

FIG. 15

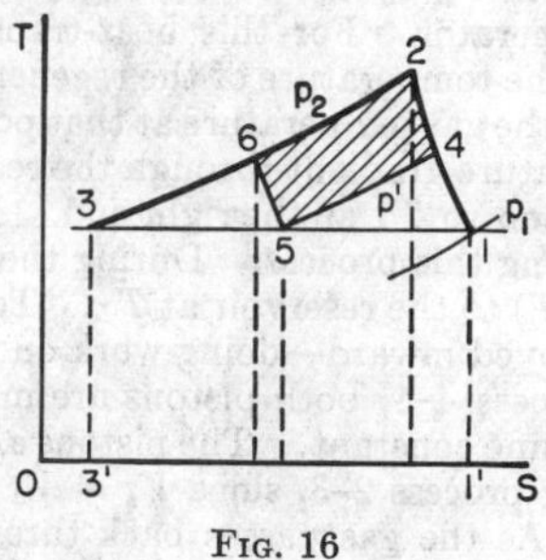

FIG. 16

FIGS. 15 and 16. Air-compressor cycle.

p', 45 cooling at constant pressure in the intercooler between the cylinders, and 56 the compression in the second stage. The area under 14563 represents the work of the two stages and the area 2456 the saving effected by compounding. This saving is a maximum when $T_4 = T_6$, and this is the case when the intermediate pressure p' is given by $p' = \sqrt{p_1p_2}$ (see Sec. 14).

The total work in two-stage compression is

$$-np_1V_1[(p'/p_1)^{(n-1)/n} + (p_2/p')^{(n-1)/n} - 2]/(n-1)$$

Gas Turbine. The Brayton cycle, also called the Joule or constant-pressure cycle, employs an air engine, a compressor, and a combustion chamber. Air enters the compressor wherein the pressure is increased. Fuel burning in the combustion chamber raises the temperature of the compressed air under constant-pressure conditions. The resulting high-temperature gases are then introduced to the engine where they expand and perform work. The excess work of the engine over that required to compress the air is available for operating other devices, such as a generator.

Basically, the simple gas-turbine cycle is the same as the Brayton cycle, except that the air compressor and engine are replaced by an axial flow compressor and gas turbine. Air is compressed in the compressor, after which it enters a combustion chamber where the temperature is increased while the pressure remains constant. The resulting high-temperature air then enters the turbine, thereby performing work. For more detailed information regarding the actual gas-turbine cycles the reader is referred to Sec. 9.

Vapors

General Characteristics of Vapors. Let a gas be compressed at constant temperature; then, provided this temperature does not exceed a certain critical value, the gas begins to liquefy at a definite pressure, which depends upon the temperature. At the beginning of liquefaction, a unit mass of gas will also have a definite volume v_g, depending on the temperature. In Fig. 17, AB represents the compression and the point B gives the **saturation** pressure and volume. If the compression is continued, the pressure remains constant with the temperature, as indicated by BC, until at C the substance is in the liquid state with the volume v_f.

The curves v_f and v_g giving the volumes for various temperatures at the end and beginning of liquefaction, respectively, may be called the **limit curves.** A point B on curve v_g represents the state of **saturated vapor;** a point C on the curve v_f represents the liquid state; and a point M between B and C represents a mixture of vapor and liquid of which the part $x = MC/BC$ is vapor and the part $1 - x = BM/BC$ is liquid. The ratio x is called the **quality of the mixture.** The region between the curves v_f and v_g is thus the region of liquid and vapor mixtures. The region to the right of curve v_g is the region of **superheated vapor.** The curve v_g dividing these regions represents the so-called **saturated vapor.**

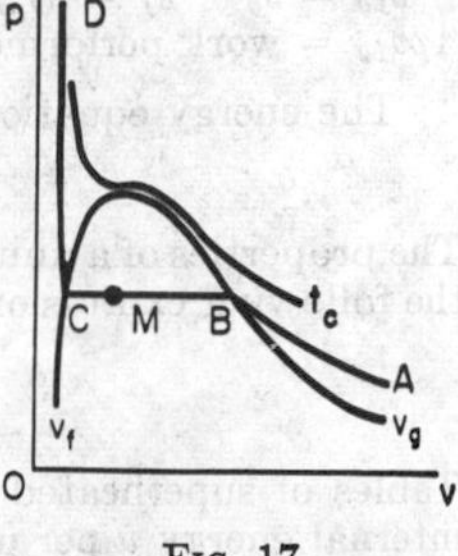

FIG. 17

For saturated vapor or a mixture of vapor and liquid, the pressure is a function of the temperature only, and the volume of the mixture depends upon the temperature and quality x. That is, $p = f(t)$, $v = F(t, x)$.

For the vapor in the superheated state, the volume depends on pressure and temperature $[v = F_1(p, t)]$, and these may be varied independently.

Critical State. If the temperature of the gas lies above a definite temperature t_c called the **critical temperature,** the gas cannot be liquefied by compression alone. The saturation pressure corresponding to t_c is the **critical pressure** and is denoted by p_c. At the critical state, the limit curves v_f and v_g merge; hence for temperatures above t_c, it is impossible to have a mixture of vapor and liquid. Table 26 gives the critical data for various gases; also the boiling temperature t_b corresponding to atmospheric pressure.

Table 26. Critical Data for Various Gases
(Condensed from "International Critical Tables")

Substance	t_b deg F	t_c deg F	p_c atm	v_c cu ft per lb	Substance	t_b deg F	t_c deg F	p_c atm	v_c cu ft per lb
Air	−317.6	−220.3	37.2	0.0457	C_2H_6	−127.5	90.0	48.2	0.079
Helium	−452.0	−450.2	2.26	0.231	C_3H_8	− 48.1	206.26	42.01	0.071
Hydrogen	−422.9	−399.8	12.8	0.516	C_4H_{10}	31.5	307.4	37.48	0.071
Argon	−302.3	−187.7	48.0	0.03	C_5H_{12}	97.0	387.0	33	0.069
Nitrogen	−320.4	−232.8	33.5	0.053	C_6H_{14}	156.1	454.6	29.5	0.0685
Oxygen	−297.2	−181.8	49.7	0.037	C_7H_{16}	209.2	517.1	27.65	0.0685
Bromine	137.8	575.6	......	......	C_8H_{18}	259.2	565.7	24.8	0.0685
Chlorine	− 30.3	291.3	76.1	0.028	C_2H_2	−118.5	96.3	62	0.0693
HCl	−121	124.5	81.6	0.038	C_2H_4	−155.0	49.3	50.9	0.073
H_2S	− 74.9	212.7	88.9	......	C_6H_6	176	551.4	47.7	0.0526
NO	−239.8	−136.7	65.0	0.031	C_7H_8	231.3	609.1	41.6	0.055
N_2O	−129.1	97.7	71.7	0.036	CH_4O	147.3	464.0	78.7	0.059
MH_3	− 28	270.3	111.5	0.068	C_2H_6O	173.0	469.6	63.1	0.058
H_2O	212	705.45	218.53	0.0503	C_3H_6O	133	455	47	0.060
SO_2	14	315.0	77.7	0.031	$C_4H_{10}O$	101.8	380.8	35.5	0.061
CO	−313.6	−220.33	34.53	0.053	$CHCl_3$	142.2	505.4	......	0.031
CO_2	−109.3	88.0	73.0	0.035	CH_3Cl	− 10.25	289.6	65.8	0.043
CS_2	115.3	523.4	76.0	......	C_2H_5Cl	54.9	369.0	52	0.0485
CH_4	−258.5	−116.5	45.8	0.099					

Thermal Properties of Saturated Vapors and of Vapor and Liquid Mixtures

Notation

v_f, v_g = volume of 1 lb of saturated liquid and vapor, respectively, cu ft
c_f, c_g = specific heat of saturated liquid and vapor, respectively
h_f, h_g = specific enthalpy of saturated liquid and vapor, respectively
u_f, u_g = specific internal energy of saturated liquid and vapor, respectively

s_f, s_g = specific entropy of saturated liquid and vapor, respectively
$v_{fg} = v_g - v_f$ = increase of volume during vaporization
$h_{fg} = h_g - h_f$ = heat of vaporization, or heat required to vaporize 1 lb of liquid at constant pressure and temperature

r may be used for h_{fg} when several heats of vaporization (as r_1, r_2, r_3, etc.) are under consideration.

$u_{fg} = u_g - u_f$ = increase of internal energy during vaporization
$s_{fg} = s_g - s_f = h_{fg}/T$ = increase of entropy during vaporization
Apv_{fg} = work performed during vaporization

The energy equation applied to the vaporization process is

$$h_{fg} = u_{fg} + Apv_{fg}$$

The properties of a unit mass of a mixture of liquid and vapor of quality x are given by the following expressions:

$$v = v_f + xv_{fg} \qquad u = u_f + xu_{fg}$$
$$h = h_f + xh_{fg} \qquad s = s_f + xs_{fg}$$

Tables of superheated vapor usually give values of v, h, and s per unit mass. The internal energy u per unit mass can be found from the equation

$$u = h - Apv$$

or with p in psi,

$$u = h - 0.1852pv$$

Charts for Saturated and Superheated Vapors

Certain properties of vapor mixtures and superheated vapors may be shown graphically by means of charts. Such charts show the behavior of vapors and have a practical application in the solution of certain problems.

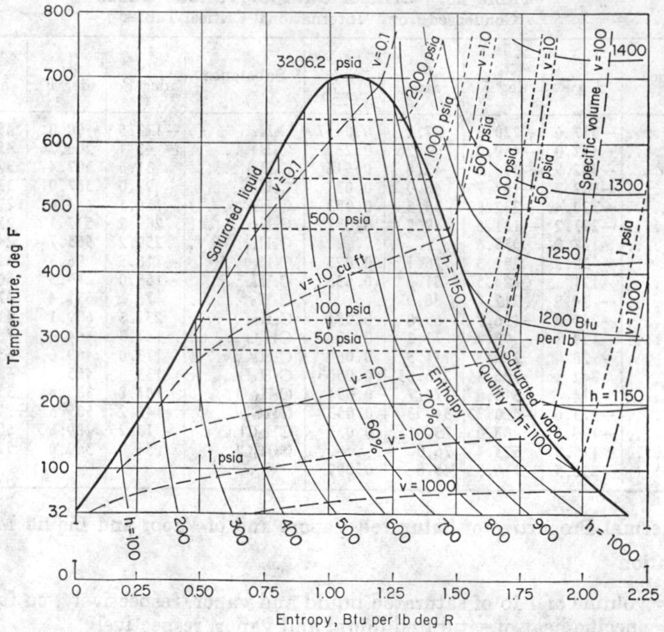

FIG. 18. Temperature-entropy diagram for steam. (*Data from Keenan and Keyes, "Thermodynamic Properties of Steam," Wiley.*)

Temperature-Entropy Chart. Figure 18 shows the temperature-entropy chart for water vapor. The liquid curve is obtained by plotting corresponding values of T and s_f, and the saturation curve by plotting values of T and s_g. The values are taken from Tables 28 and 29. The two curves merge into each other at the critical temperature $T = 1165.1$ R. Between these two curves, constant pressure lines are also lines of constant temperature; but at the saturation curve the constant pressure lines show a

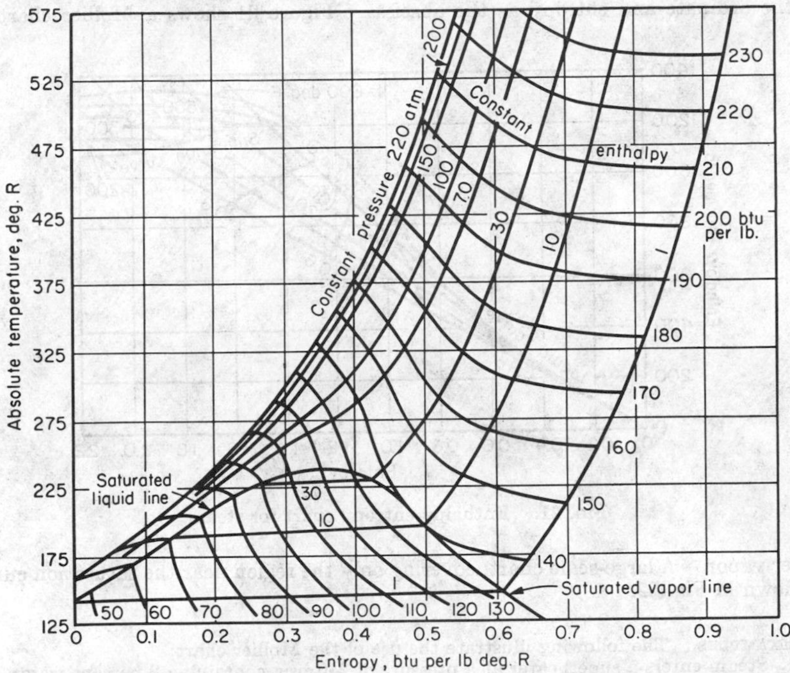

FIG. 19. Temperature-entropy diagram for air. (*From Williams, Thermodynamic Properties of Air at Low Temperature, Trans. AICE*, **39**, *Feb.*, 1943.)

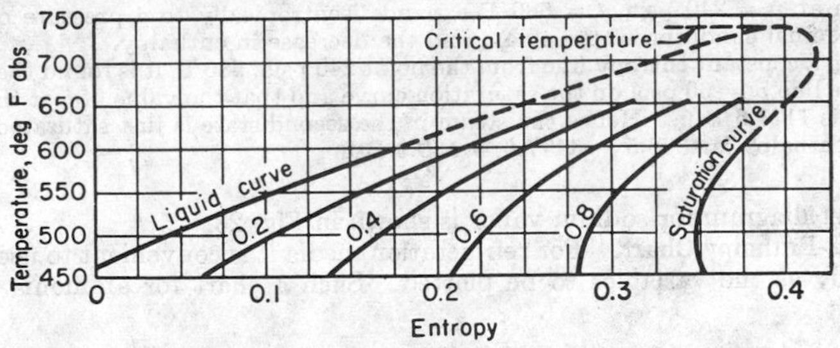

FIG. 20. Temperature-entropy chart for isobutane.

sharp break with rising temperature. The constant quality lines $x = 0.2$, 0.4, etc., are equally spaced between the liquid and saturation curves.

Figure 19 is a temperature-entropy chart for air.

Figure 20 shows a temperature-entropy chart for isobutane. The form of the saturation curve is worthy of note. In the case of water vapor, this curve has a negative slope throughout; but in the case of isobutane, the curve has a positve slope except near the critical temperature. In the case of water vapor, therefore, isentropic expansion of dry vapor (s = const) will be accompanied by condensation, isentropic compression by superheating. For isobutane, in the region where the saturation curve has the positive slope, the conditions are reversed; isentropic expansion is accompanied by superheating, isentropic compression by condensation.

Enthalpy-Entropy Chart (Mollier Chart). In this chart, the enthalpy h is taken as the ordinate and entropy as the abscissa. Figure 21 shows a Mollier chart for

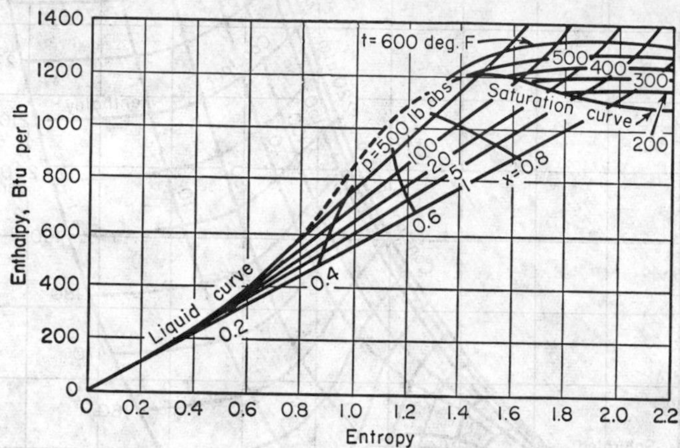

FIG. 21. Enthalpy-entropy chart for steam.

water vapor. A large-scale chart, covering only the region near the saturation curve, is shown in Fig. 22.

EXAMPLES. The following illustrate the use of the Mollier chart:

1. Steam enters a superheater at a pressure of 240 psia containing 2 percent water. It leaves the superheater at a temperature of 580 F. Required the heat per pound of steam to effect this change.

The initial and final points are located on the Mollier chart. From the enthalpy scale, $h_1 = 1184.2$ and $h_2 = 1308.5$; therefore $q_{12} = 1308.5 - 1184.2 = 124.3$ Btu.

2. Steam at $p = 240$ psia, $t = 580$ F expands isentropically to a pressure of 60 psia. Required the final condition of the steam and the decrease in enthalpy.

Following a constant entropy line from the point 240 psia, 580 F, it is found that this line intersects the line $p = 60$ psia on the saturation curve and that the value of h at the point of intersection is 1177.6 Btu. Hence the steam in the second state is just saturated, and the decrease in enthalpy is $1308.5 - 1177.6 = 130.9$ Btu.

A Mollier diagram for sodium vapor is shown in Fig. 23.

Pressure-Enthalpy Chart. For refrigeration media it is convenient to use pressure and enthalpy as the variables to be plotted. Such a chart for ammonia is shown in Fig. 24.

Changes of State. Superheated Vapors and Mixtures of Liquid and Vapor

Isothermal. In the only important cases, the fluid is a mixture of liquid and vapor in both initial and final states.

$$t = \text{const} \qquad p = \text{const} \qquad x_1, x_2 = \text{initial and final qualities}$$
$$Q_{12} = mh_{fg}(x_2 - x_1) \qquad U_2 - U_1 = mu_{fg}(x_2 - x_1)$$
$$W_{12} = mpv_{fg}(x_2 - x_1) \qquad S_2 - S_1 = Q_{12}/T$$

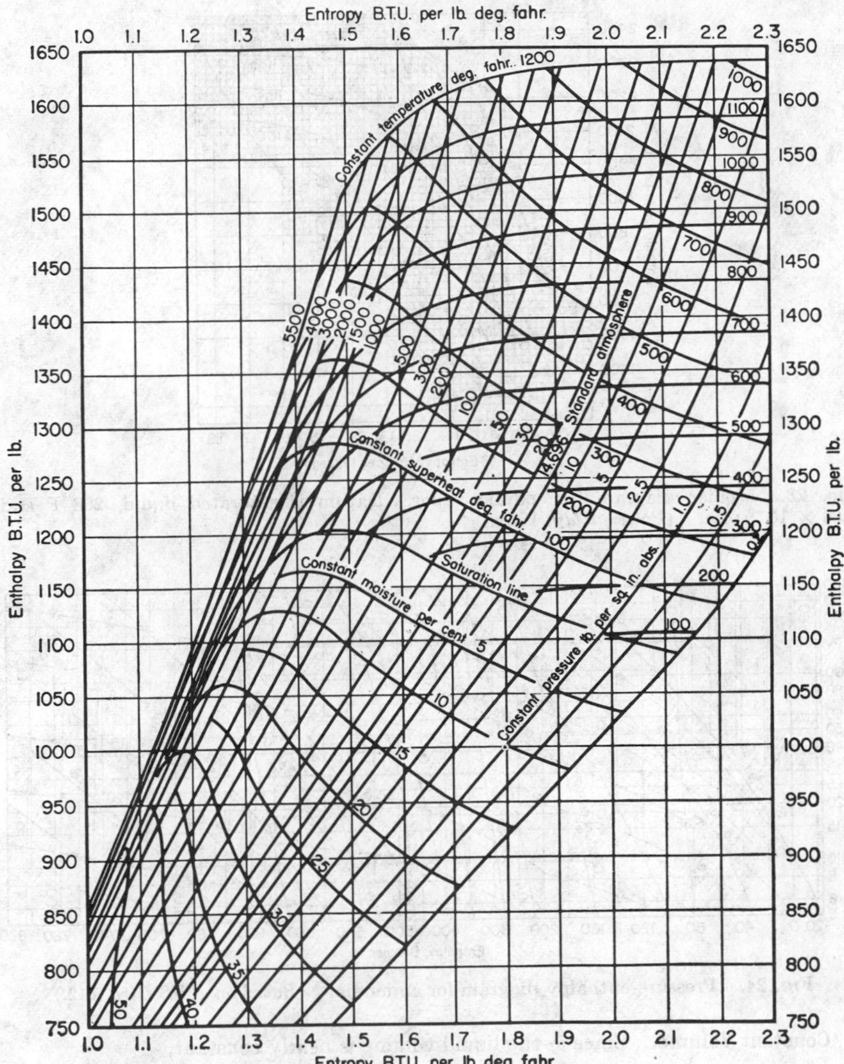

FIG. 22. Enthalpy-entropy (Mollier) chart for steam. *(From "Steam, Its Generation and Use," The Babcock & Wilcox Co.,* 1963.)

Constant Pressure. If the fluid is a mixture at the beginning and end of the change, the constant pressure change is also isothermal. If the initial state is in the mixture region and the final state is that of a superheated vapor, the following are the equations for Q_{12}, etc. Let h_2, u_2, v_2, and s_2 be the properties of 1 lb of superheated vapor in the final state 2: then

$$Q_{12} = m(h_2 - h_1) \qquad h_1 = h_{f1} + x_1 h_{fg1}$$
$$U_2 - U_1 = m(u_2 - u_1) \qquad u_1 = u_{f1} + x_1 u_{fg1}$$
$$S_2 - S_1 = m(s_2 - s_1) \qquad s_1 = s_{f1} + x_1 s_{fg1}$$
$$W_{12} = mp(v_2 - v_1) \qquad v_1 = v_{f1} + x_1 v_{fg1}$$

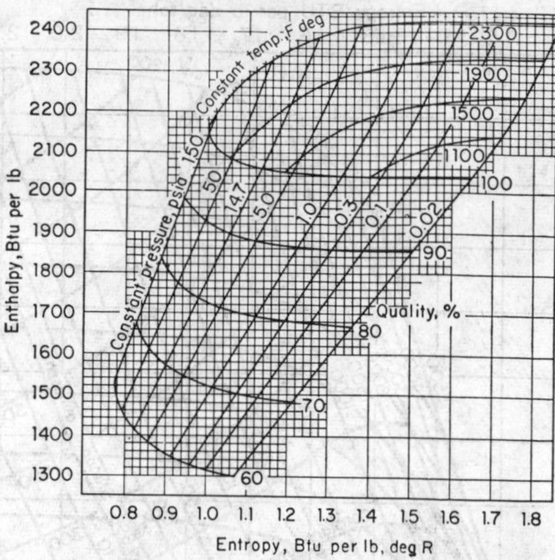

FIG. 23. Mollier diagram for sodium vapor. Datum is saturated liquid, 208 F and 1.68×10^{-9} psia. (*Power, July,* 1961.)

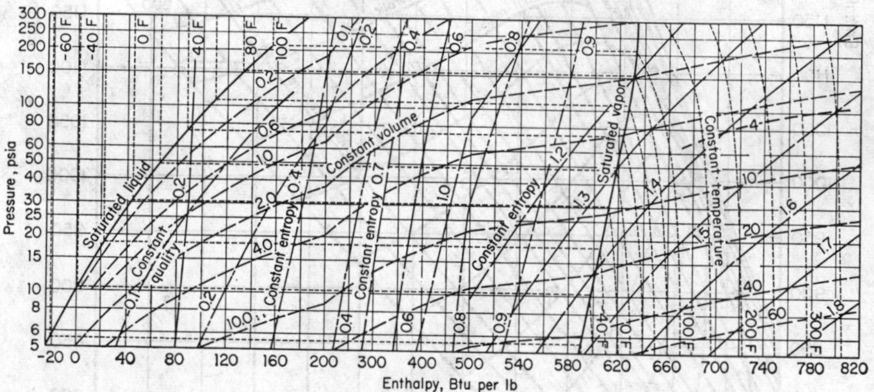

FIG. 24. Pressure-enthalpy diagram for ammonia. (*Based on NBS Circ.* 142.)

Constant Volume. Since v_f the liquid volume is nearly constant,

$$x_1 v_{fg1} = x_2 v_{fg2}$$

$$x_2 = x_1 v_{fg1}/v_{fg2} \quad \text{or} \quad x_2 = x_1 v_{g1}/v_{g2} \text{ approx}$$

$$Q_{12} = U_2 - U_1 = m(u_2 - u_1) \qquad W_{12} = 0$$

Isentropic. $s =$ const.
If the fluid is a mixture in the initial and final states,

$$s_{f1} + x_1 s_{fg1} = s_{f2} + x_2 s_{fg2}$$

If the initial state is that of superheated vapor,

$$s_1 = s_{f2} + x_2 s_{fg2}$$

in which s_1 is read from the table of superheated vapor. The final value x_2 is determined from one of these equations, and the final internal energy u_2 is then

$$u_{f2} + x_2 u_{fg2} \qquad Q_{12} = 0 \qquad W_{12} = J(U_1 - U_2) = Jm(u_1 - u_2)$$

For water vapor, the relation between p and v during an isentropic change may be represented approximately by the equation pv^n = constant. The exponent n is not constant, but varies with the initial quality and initial pressure, as shown in Table 27.

Table 27. Values of n (Water Vapor)

Initial quality	Initial pressure, psia											
	20	40	60	80	100	120	140	160	180	200	220	240
1.00	1.131	1.132	1.133	1.134	1.136	1.137	1.138	1.139	1.141	1.142	1.143	1.145
0.95	1.127	1.128	1.129	1.130	1.131	1.131	1.132	1.133	1.134	1.135	1.136	1.137
0.90	1.123	1.123	1.124	1.124	1.125	1.125	1.126	1.126	1.127	1.127	1.128	1.129
0.85	1.119	1.119	1.119	1.119	1.120	1.120	1.120	1.120	1.120	1.120	1.120	1.121
0.80	1.115	1.115	1.114	1.114	1.114	1.114	1.113	1.113	1.113	1.113	1.112	1.112
0.75	1.111	1.110	1.110	1.109	1.109	1.108	1.107	1.106	1.106	1.105	1.104	1.104

The isentropic expansion of superheated steam is fairly represented by pv^n = const, with $n = 1.315$.

The volume at the end of expansion (or compression) is $V_2 = V_1(p_1/p_2)^{1/n}$, and the external work is

$$W_{12} = (p_1V_1 - p_2V_2)/(n - 1) = p_1V_1[1 - (p_2/p_1)^{(n-1)/n}]/(n - 1)$$

If the initial state is in the region of superheat and the final state in the mixture region, two values of n must be used: $n = 1.315$ for the expansion to the state of saturation, and the appropriate value from the first row of Table 27 for the expansion of the mixture.

Tables of Thermal Properties of Vapors

Steam. Tables 28 to 30, abstracted from Keenan and Keyes, "Thermodynamic Properties of Steam," give internationally accepted values which are believed to be correct within very narrow tolerance. They are a representation of the results obtained from an organized body of research and agreed to in a series of international conferences.

Table 28. Properties of Saturated Steam

(From Keenan and Keyes, "Thermodynamic Properties of Steam")

(h_f and s_f are measured from 32F)

Abs press, psi	Temp, deg F	Specific volume		Enthalpy			Entropy			Internal energy
		Liquid	Vapor	Liquid	Evap	Vapor	Liquid	Evap	Vapor	Evap
1.0	101.74	0.01614	333.6	69.70	1036.3	1106.0	0.1326	1.8456	1.9782	974.6
1.2	107.92	0.01616	280.9	75.87	1032.7	1108.6	0.1435	1.8193	1.9628	970.3
1.4	113.26	0.01618	243.0	81.20	1029.6	1110.8	0.1528	1.7971	1.9498	966.7
1.6	117.99	0.01620	214.3	85.91	1026.9	1112.8	0.1610	1.7776	1.9386	963.5
1.8	122.23	0.01621	191.8	90.14	1024.5	1114.6	0.1683	1.7605	1.9288	960.6
2.0	126.08	0.01623	173.73	93.99	1022.2	1116.2	0.1749	1.7451	1.9200	957.9
2.2	129.62	0.01624	158.85	97.52	1020.2	1117.7	0.1809	1.7311	1.9120	955.5
2.4	132.89	0.01626	146.38	100.79	1018.3	1119.1	0.1864	1.7183	1.9047	953.3
2.6	135.94	0.01627	135.78	103.83	1016.5	1120.3	0.1916	1.7065	1.8981	951.2
2.8	138.79	0.01629	126.65	106.68	1014.8	1121.5	0.1963	1.6957	1.8920	949.2
3.0	141.48	0.01630	118.71	109.37	1013.2	1122.6	0.2008	1.6855	1.8863	947.3
4.0	152.97	0.01636	90.63	120.86	1006.4	1127.3	0.2198	1.6427	1.8625	939.3
5.0	162.24	0.01640	73.52	130.13	1001.0	1131.1	0.2347	1.6094	1.8441	933.0
6.0	170.06	0.01645	61.98	137.96	996.2	1134.2	0.2472	1.5820	1.8292	927.5
7.0	176.85	0.01649	53.64	144.76	992.1	1136.9	0.2581	1.5586	1.8167	922.7
8.0	182.86	0.01653	47.34	150.79	988.5	1139.3	0.2674	1.5383	1.8057	918.4
9.0	188.28	0.01656	42.40	156.22	985.2	1141.4	0.2759	1.5203	1.7962	914.6
10	193.21	0.01659	38.42	161.17	982.1	1143.3	0.2835	1.5041	1.7876	911.1
11	197.75	0.01662	35.14	165.73	979.3	1145.0	0.2903	1.4897	1.7800	907.8
12	201.96	0.01665	32.40	169.96	976.6	1146.6	0.2967	1.4763	1.7730	904.8
13	205.88	0.01667	30.06	173.91	974.2	1148.1	0.3027	1.4638	1.7665	901.9
14	209.56	0.01670	28.04	177.61	971.9	1149.5	0.3083	1.4522	1.7605	899.3
14.696	212.00	0.01672	26.80	180.07	970.3	1150.4	0.3120	1.4446	1.7566	897.5
15	213.03	0.01672	26.29	181.11	969.7	1150.8	0.3135	1.4415	1.7549	896.7
16	216.32	0.01674	24.75	184.42	967.6	1152.0	0.3184	1.4313	1.7497	894.3
17	219.44	0.01677	23.39	187.56	965.5	1153.1	0.3231	1.4218	1.7449	892.0
18	222.41	0.01679	22.17	190.56	963.6	1154.2	0.3275	1.4128	1.7403	889.9
19	225.24	0.01681	21.08	193.42	961.9	1155.3	0.3317	1.4043	1.7360	887.8
20	227.96	0.01683	20.089	196.16	960.1	1156.3	0.3356	1.3962	1.7319	885.8
21	230.57	0.01685	19.192	198.79	958.4	1157.2	0.3395	1.3885	1.7280	883.9
22	233.07	0.01687	18.375	201.33	956.8	1158.1	0.3431	1.3811	1.7242	882.0
23	235.49	0.01689	17.627	203.78	955.2	1159.0	0.3466	1.3740	1.7206	880.2
24	237.82	0.01691	16.938	206.14	953.7	1159.8	0.3500	1.3672	1.7172	878.5
25	240.07	0.01692	16.303	208.42	952.1	1160.6	0.3533	1.3606	1.7139	876.8
26	242.25	0.01694	15.715	210.62	950.7	1161.3	0.3564	1.3544	1.7108	875.2
27	244.36	0.01696	15.170	212.75	949.3	1162.0	0.3594	1.3484	1.7078	873.6
28	246.41	0.01698	14.663	214.83	947.9	1162.7	0.3623	1.3425	1.7048	872.1
29	248.40	0.01699	14.189	216.86	946.5	1163.4	0.3652	1.3368	1.7020	870.5
30	250.33	0.01701	13.746	218.82	945.3	1164.1	0.3680	1.3313	1.6993	869.1
31	252.22	0.01702	13.330	220.73	944.0	1164.7	0.3707	1.3260	1.6967	867.7
32	254.05	0.01704	12.940	222.59	942.8	1165.4	0.3733	1.3209	1.6941	866.3
33	255.84	0.01705	12.572	224.41	941.6	1166.0	0.3758	1.3159	1.6917	864.9
34	257.08	0.01707	12.226	226.18	940.3	1166.5	0.3783	1.3110	1.6893	863.5
35	259.28	0.01708	11.898	227.91	939.2	1167.1	0.3807	1.3063	1.6870	862.3
36	260.95	0.01709	11.588	229.60	938.0	1167.6	0.3831	1.3017	1.6848	861.0
37	262.57	0.01711	11.294	231.26	936.9	1168.2	0.3854	1.2972	1.6826	859.8
38	264.16	0.01712	11.015	232.89	935.8	1168.7	0.3876	1.2929	1.6805	858.5
39	265.72	0.01714	10.750	234.48	934.7	1169.2	0.3898	1.2886	1.6784	857.2

Table 28. Properties of Saturated Steam—*(Continued)*

Abs press, psi	Temp, deg F	Specific volume		Enthalpy			Entropy			Internal energy
		Liquid	Vapor	Liquid	Evap	Vapor	Liquid	Evap	Vapor	Evap
40	267.25	0.01715	10.498	236.03	933.7	1169.7	0.3919	1.2844	1.6763	856.1
41	268.74	0.01716	10.258	237.55	932.6	1170.2	0.3940	1.2803	1.6743	855.0
42	270.21	0.01717	10.029	239.04	931.6	1170.7	0.3960	1.2764	1.6724	853.8
43	271.64	0.01719	9.810	240.51	930.6	1171.1	0.3980	1.2726	1.6706	852.7
44	273.05	0.01720	9.601	241.95	929.6	1171.6	0.4000	1.2687	1.6687	851.6
45	274.44	0.01721	9.401	243.36	928.6	1172.0	0.4019	1.2650	1.6669	850.5
46	275.80	0.01722	9.209	244.75	927.7	1172.4	0.4038	1.2613	1.6652	849.5
47	277.13	0.01723	9.025	246.12	926.7	1172.9	0.4057	1.2577	1.6634	848.4
48	278.45	0.01725	8.848	247.47	925.8	1173.3	0.4075	1.2542	1.6617	847.4
49	279.74	0.01726	8.678	248.79	924.9	1173.7	0.4093	1.2508	1.6601	846.4
50	281.01	0.01727	8.515	250.09	924.0	1174.1	0.4110	1.2474	1.6585	845.4
51	282.26	0.01728	8.359	251.37	923.0	1174.4	0.4127	1.2432	1.6569	844.3
52	283.49	0.01729	8.208	252.63	922.2	1174.8	0.4144	1.2409	1.6553	843.3
53	284.70	0.01730	8.062	253.87	921.3	1175.2	0.4161	1.2377	1.6538	842.4
54	285.90	0.01731	7.922	255.09	920.5	1175.6	0.4177	1.2346	1.6523	841.5
55	287.07	0.01732	7.787	256.30	919.6	1175.9	0.4193	1.2316	1.6509	840.6
56	288.23	0.01733	7.656	257.50	918.8	1176.3	0.4209	1.2285	1.6494	839.7
57	289.37	0.01734	7.529	258.67	917.9	1176.6	0.4225	1.2255	1.6480	838.7
58	290.50	0.01736	7.407	259.82	917.1	1176.9	0.4240	1.2226	1.6466	837.8
59	291.61	0.01737	7.289	260.96	916.3	1177.3	0.4255	1.2197	1.6452	836.9
60	292.71	0.01738	7.175	262.09	915.5	1177.6	0.4270	1.2168	1.6438	836.0
61	293.79	0.01739	7.064	263.20	914.7	1177.9	0.4285	1.2140	1.6425	835.2
62	294.85	0.01740	6.957	264.30	913.9	1178.2	0.4300	1.2112	1.6412	834.3
63	295.90	0.01741	6.853	265.38	913.1	1178.5	0.4314	1.2085	1.6399	833.4
64	296.94	0.01742	6.752	266.45	912.3	1178.8	0.4328	1.2059	1.6387	832.6
65	297.97	0.01743	6.655	267.50	911.6	1179.1	0.4342	1.2032	1.6374	831.8
66	298.99	0.01744	6.560	268.55	910.8	1179.4	0.4356	1.2006	1.6362	831.0
67	299.99	0.01745	6.468	269.58	910.1	1179.7	0.4369	1.1981	1.6350	830.2
68	300.98	0.01746	6.378	270.60	909.4	1180.0	0.4383	1.1955	1.6338	829.4
69	301.96	0.01747	6.291	271.61	908.7	1180.3	0.4396	1.1930	1.6326	828.6
70	302.92	0.01748	6.206	272.61	907.9	1180.6	0.4409	1.1906	1.6315	827.8
71	303.88	0.01749	6.124	273.60	907.2	1180.8	0.4422	1.1881	1.6303	827.0
72	304.83	0.01750	6.044	274.57	906.5	1181.1	0.4435	1.1857	1.6292	826.3
73	305.76	0.01751	5.966	275.54	905.8	1181.3	0.4447	1.1834	1.6281	825.5
74	306.68	0.01752	5.890	276.49	905.1	1181.6	0.4460	1.1810	1.6270	824.7
75	307.60	0.01753	5.816	277.43	904.5	1181.9	0.4472	1.1787	1.6259	824.0
76	308.50	0.01754	5.743	278.37	903.7	1182.1	0.4484	1.1764	1.6248	823.3
77	309.40	0.01754	5.673	279.30	903.1	1182.4	0.4496	1.1742	1.6238	822.5
78	310.29	0.01755	5.604	280.21	902.4	1182.6	0.4508	1.1720	1.6228	821.7
79	311.16	0.01756	5.537	281.12	901.7	1182.8	0.4520	1.1698	1.6217	821.0
80	312.03	0.01757	5.472	282.02	901.1	1183.1	0.4531	1.1676	1.6207	820.3
81	312.89	0.01758	5.408	282.91	900.4	1183.3	0.4543	1.1654	1.6197	819.6
82	313.74	0.01759	5.346	283.79	899.7	1183.5	0.4554	1.1633	1.6187	818.9
83	314.59	0.01760	5.285	284.66	899.1	1183.8	0.4565	1.1612	1.6177	818.2
84	315.42	0.01761	5.226	285.53	898.5	1184.0	0.4576	1.1592	1.6168	817.5
85	316.25	0.01761	5.168	286.39	897.8	1184.2	0.4587	1.1571	1.6158	816.8
86	317.07	0.01762	5.111	287.24	897.2	1184.4	0.4598	1.1551	1.6149	816.1
87	317.88	0.01763	5.055	288.08	896.5	1184.6	0.4609	1.1530	1.6139	815.4
88	318.68	0.01764	5.001	288.91	895.9	1184.8	0.4620	1.1510	1.6130	814.8
89	319.48	0.01765	4.948	289.74	895.3	1185.1	0.4630	1.1491	1.6121	814.1

Table 28. Properties of Saturated Steam—(*Continued*)

Abs press, psi	Temp, deg F	Specific volume		Enthalpy			Entropy			Internal energy
		Liquid	Vapor	Liquid	Evap	Vapor	Liquid	Evap	Vapor	Evap
90	320.27	0.01766	4.896	290.56	894.7	1185.3	0.4641	1.1471	1.6112	813.4
91	321.06	0.01767	4.845	291.38	894.1	1185.5	0.4651	1.1452	1.6103	812.8
92	321.83	0.01768	4.796	292.18	893.5	1185.7	0.4661	1.1433	1.6094	812.2
93	322.60	0.01768	4.747	292.98	892.9	1185.9	0.4672	1.1413	1.6085	811.5
94	323.36	0.01769	4.699	293.78	892.3	1186.1	0.4682	1.1394	1.6076	810.9
95	324.12	0.01770	4.652	294.56	891.7	1186.2	0.4692	1.1376	1.6068	810.2
96	324.87	0.01771	4.606	295.34	891.1	1186.4	0.4702	1.1358	1.6060	809.6
97	325.61	0.01772	4.561	296.12	890.5	1186.6	0.4711	1.1340	1.6051	808.9
98	326.35	0.01772	4.517	296.89	889.9	1186.8	0.4721	1.1322	1.6043	808.3
99	327.08	0.01773	4.474	297.65	889.4	1187.0	0.4731	1.1304	1.6035	807.7
100	327.81	0.01774	4.432	298.40	888.8	1187.2	0.4740	1.1286	1.6026	807.1
102	329.25	0.01775	4.350	299.90	887.6	1187.5	0.4759	1.1251	1.6010	805.9
104	330.66	0.01777	4.271	301.37	886.5	1187.9	0.4778	1.1216	1.5994	804.7
106	332.05	0.01778	4.194	302.82	885.4	1188.2	0.4796	1.1182	1.5978	803.5
108	333.42	0.01780	4.120	304.26	884.3	1188.6	0.4814	1.1149	1.5963	802.4
110	334.77	0.01782	4.049	305.66	883.2	1188.9	0.4832	1.1117	1.5948	801.2
112	336.11	0.01783	3.981	307.06	882.1	1189.2	0.4849	1.1085	1.5934	800.0
114	337.42	0.01784	3.914	308.43	881.1	1189.5	0.4866	1.1053	1.5919	798.9
116	338.72	0.01786	3.850	309.79	880.0	1189.8	0.4883	1.1022	1.5905	797.8
118	339.99	0.01787	3.788	311.12	879.0	1190.1	0.4900	1.0992	1.5891	796.7
120	341.25	0.01789	3.728	312.44	877.9	1190.4	0.4916	1.0962	1.5878	795.6
122	342.50	0.01791	3.670	313.75	876.9	1190.7	0.4932	1.0933	1.5865	794.5
124	343.72	0.01792	3.614	315.04	875.9	1190.9	0.4948	1.0903	1.5851	793.4
126	344.94	0.01793	3.560	316.31	874.9	1191.2	0.4964	1.0874	1.5838	792.3
128	346.13	0.01794	3.507	317.57	873.9	1191.5	0.4980	1.0845	1.5825	791.3
130	347.32	0.01796	3.455	318.81	872.9	1191.7	0.4995	1.0817	1.5812	790.2
132	348.48	0.01797	3.405	320.04	872.0	1192.0	0.5010	1.0790	1.5800	789.2
134	349.64	0.01799	3.357	321.25	871.0	1192.2	0.5025	1.0762	1.5787	788.2
136	350.78	0.01800	3.310	322.45	870.1	1192.5	0.5040	1.0735	1.5775	787.2
138	351.91	0.01801	3.264	323.64	869.1	1192.7	0.5054	1.0709	1.5763	786.2
140	353.02	0.01802	3.220	324.82	868.2	1193.0	0.5069	1.0682	1.5751	785.2
142	354.12	0.01804	3.177	325.98	867.2	1193.2	0.5083	1.0657	1.5740	784.3
144	355.21	0.01805	3.134	327.13	866.3	1193.4	0.5097	1.0631	1.5728	783.3
146	356.29	0.01806	3.094	328.27	865.3	1193.6	0.5111	1.0605	1.5716	782.3
148	357.36	0.01808	3.054	329.39	864.5	1193.9	0.5124	1.0580	1.5705	781.4
150	358.42	0.01809	3.015	330.51	863.6	1194.1	0.5138	1.0556	1.5694	780.5
152	359.46	0.01810	2.977	331.61	862.7	1194.3	0.5151	1.0532	1.5683	779.5
154	360.49	0.01812	2.940	332.70	861.8	1194.5	0.5165	1.0507	1.5672	778.5
156	361.52	0.01813	2.904	333.79	860.9	1194.7	0.5178	1.0483	1.5661	777.6
158	362.03	0.01814	2.869	334.86	860.0	1194.9	0.5191	1.0459	1.5650	776.8
160	363.53	0.01815	2.834	335.93	859.2	1195.1	0.5204	1.0436	1.5640	775.8
162	364.53	0.01817	2.801	336.98	858.3	1195.3	0.5216	1.0414	1.5630	775.0
164	365.51	0.01818	2.768	338.02	857.5	1195.5	0.5229	1.0391	1.5620	774.1
166	366.48	0.01819	2.736	339.05	856.6	1195.7	0.5241	1.0369	1.5610	773.2
168	367.45	0.01820	2.705	340.07	855.7	1195.8	0.5254	1.0346	1.5600	772.3
170	368.41	0.01822	2.675	341.09	854.9	1196.0	0.5266	1.0324	1.5590	771.4
172	369.35	0.01823	2.645	342.10	854.1	1196.2	0.5278	1.0302	1.5580	770.5
174	370.29	0.01824	2.616	343.10	853.3	1196.4	0.5290	1.0280	1.5570	769.7
176	371.22	0.01825	2.587	344.09	852.4	1196.5	0.5302	1.0259	1.5561	768.8
178	372.14	0.01826	2.559	345.06	851.6	1196.7	0.5313	1.0238	1.5551	767.9

Table 28. Properties of Saturated Steam—(*Continued*)

Abs press, psi	Temp, deg F	Specific volume		Enthalpy			Entropy			Internal energy
		Liquid	Vapor	Liquid	Evap	Vapor	Liquid	Evap	Vapor	Evap
180	373.06	0.01827	2.532	346.03	850.8	1196.9	0.5325	1.0217	1.5542	767.1
182	373.96	0.01829	2.505	347.00	850.0	1197.0	0.5336	1.0196	1.5532	766.2
184	374.86	0.01830	2.479	347.96	849.2	1197.2	0.5348	1.0175	1.5523	765.4
186	375.75	0.01831	2.454	348.92	848.4	1197.3	0.5359	1.0155	1.5514	764.6
188	376.64	0.01832	2.429	349.86	847.6	1197.5	0.5370	1.0136	1.5506	763.8
190	377.51	0.01833	2.404	350.79	846.8	1197.6	0.5381	1.0116	1.5497	763.0
192	378.38	0.01834	2.380	351.72	846.1	1197.8	0.5392	1.0096	1.5488	762.1
194	379.24	0.01835	2.356	352.64	845.3	1197.9	0.5403	1.0076	1.5479	761.3
196	380.10	0.01836	2.333	353.55	844.5	1198.1	0.5414	1.0056	1.5470	760.6
198	380.95	0101838	2.310	354.46	843.7	1198.2	0.5425	1.0037	1.5462	759.8
200	381.79	0.01839	2.288	355.36	843.0	1198.4	0.5435	1.0018	1.5453	759.0
205	383.86	0.01842	2.234	357.58	841.1	1198.7	0.5461	0.9971	1.5432	757.1
210	385.90	0.01844	2.183	359.77	839.2	1199.0	0.5487	0.9925	1.5412	755.2
215	387.89	0.01847	2.134	361.91	837.4	1199.3	0.5512	0.9880	1.5392	753.2
220	389.86	0.01850	2.087	364.02	835.6	1199.6	0.5537	0.9835	1.5372	751.3
225	391.79	0.01852	2.0422	366.09	833.8	1199.9	0.5561	0.9792	1.5353	749.5
230	393.68	0.01854	1.9992	368.13	832.0	1200.1	0.5585	0.9750	1.5334	747.7
235	395.54	0.01857	1.9579	370.14	830.3	1200.4	0.5608	0.9708	1.5316	745.9
240	397.37	0.01860	1.9183	372.12	828.5	1200.6	0.5631	0.9667	1.5298	744.1
245	399.18	0.01863	1.8803	374.08	826.8	1200.9	0.5653	0.9627	1.5280	742.4
250	400.95	0.01865	1.8438	376.00	825.1	1201.1	0.5675	0.9588	1.5263	740.7
260	404.42	0.01870	1.7748	379.76	821.8	1201.5	0.5719	0.9510	1.5229	737.3
270	407.78	0.01875	1.7107	383.42	818.5	1201.9	0.5760	0.9436	1.5196	733.9
280	411.05	0.01880	1.6511	386.98	815.3	1202.3	0.5801	0.9363	1.5164	730.7
290	414.23	0.01885	1.5954	390.46	812.1	1202.6	0.5841	0.9292	1.5133	727.5
300	417.33	0.01890	1.5433	393.84	809.0	1202.8	0.5879	0.9225	1.5104	724.3
320	423.29	0.01899	1.4485	400.39	803.0	1203.4	0.5952	0.9094	1.5046	718.3
340	428.97	0.01908	1.3645	406.66	797.1	1203.7	0.6022	0.8970	1.4992	712.4
360	434.40	0.01917	1.2895	412.67	791.4	1204.1	0.6090	0.8851	1.4941	706.8
380	439.60	0.01925	1.2222	418.45	785.8	1204.3	0.6153	0.8738	1.4891	701.3
400	444.59	0.0193	1.1613	424.0	780.5	1204.5	0.6214	0.8630	1.4844	695.9
420	449.39	0.0194	1.1061	429.4	775.2	1204.6	0.6272	0.8527	1.4799	690.8
440	454.02	0.0195	1.0556	434.6	770.0	1204.6	0.6329	0.8426	1.4755	685.7
460	458.50	0.0196	1.0094	439.7	764.9	1204.6	0.6383	0.8330	1.4713	680.7
480	462.82	0.0197	0.9670	444.6	759.9	1204.6	0.6436	0.8237	1.4673	675.7

Table 28. Properties of Saturated Steam—(*Continued*)

Abs press, psi	Temp, deg F	Specific volume		Enthalpy			Entropy			Internal energy
		Liquid	Vapor	Liquid	Evap	Vapor	Liquid	Evap	Vapor	Vapor
500	467.01	0.0197	0.9278	449.4	755.0	1204.4	0.6487	0.8147	1.4634	1118.6
520	471.07	0.0198	0.8915	454.1	750.1	1204.2	0.6536	0.8060	1.4596	1118.4
540	475.01	0.0199	0.8578	458.6	745.4	1204.0	0.6584	0.7976	1.4560	1118.3
560	478.85	0.0200	0.8265	463.0	740.8	1203.8	0.6631	0.7893	1.4524	1118.2
580	482.58	0.0201	0.7973	467.4	736.1	1203.5	0.6676	0.7813	1.4489	1118.0
600	486.21	0.0201	0.7698	471.6	731.6	1203.2	0.6720	0.7734	1.4454	1117.7
620	489.75	0.0202	0.7440	475.7	727.2	1202.9	0.6763	0.7658	1.4421	1117.5
640	493.21	0.0203	0.7198	479.8	722.7	1202.5	0.6805	0.7584	1.4389	1117.3
660	496.58	0.0204	0.6971	483.8	718.3	1202.1	0.6846	0.7512	1.4358	1117.0
680	499.88	0.0204	0.6757	487.7	714.0	1201.7	0.6886	0.7441	1.4327	1116.7
700	503.10	0.0205	0.6554	491.5	709.7	1201.2	0.6925	0.7371	1.4296	1116.3
720	506.25	0.0206	0.6362	495.3	705.4	1200.7	0.6963	0.7303	1.4266	1116.0
740	509.34	0.0207	0.6180	499.0	701.2	1200.2	0.7001	0.7237	1.4237	1115.6
760	512.36	0.0207	0.6007	502.6	697.1	1199.7	0.7037	0.7172	1.4209	1115.2
780	515.33	0.0208	0.5843	506.2	692.9	1199.1	0.7073	0.7108	1.4181	1114.8
800	518.23	0.0209	0.5687	509.7	688.9	1198.6	0.7108	0.7045	1.4153	1114.4
820	521.08	0.0109	0.5538	513.2	684.8	1198.0	0.7143	0.6983	1.4126	1114.0
840	523.88	0.0210	0.5396	516.6	680.8	1197.4	0.7177	0.6922	1.4099	1113.6
860	526.63	0.0211	0.5260	520.0	676.8	1196.8	0.7210	0.6862	1.4072	1113.1
880	529.33	0.0212	0.5130	523.3	672.8	1196.1	0.7243	0.6803	1.4046	1112.6
900	531.98	0.0212	0.5006	526.6	668.8	1195.4	0.7275	0.6744	1.4020	1112.1
920	534.59	0.0213	0.4886	529.8	664.9	1194.7	0.7307	0.6687	1.3995	1111.5
940	537.16	0.0214	0.4772	533.0	661.0	1194.0	0.7339	0.6631	1.3970	1111.0
960	539.68	0.0214	0.4663	536.2	657.1	1193.3	0.7370	0.6576	1.3945	1110.5
980	542.17	0.0215	0.4557	539.3	653.3	1192.6	0.7400	0.6521	1.3921	1110.0
1,000	544.61	0.0216	0.4456	542.4	649.4	1191.8	0.7430	0.6467	1.3897	1109.4
1,050	550.57	0.0218	0.4218	550.0	639.9	1189.9	0.7504	0.6334	1.3838	1108.0
1,100	556.31	0.0220	0.4001	557.4	630.4	1187.8	0.7575	0.6205	1.3780	1106.4
1,150	561.86	0.0221	0.3802	564.6	621.0	1185.6	0.7644	0.6079	1.3723	1104.7
1,200	567.22	0.0223	0.3619	571.7	611.7	1183.4	0.7711	0.5956	1.3667	1103.0
1,250	572.42	0.0225	0.3450	578.6	602.4	1181.0	0.7776	0.5836	1.3612	1101.2
1,300	577.46	0.0227	0.3293	585.4	593.2	1178.6	0.7840	0.5719	1.3559	1099.4
1,350	582.35	0.0229	0.3148	592.1	584.0	1176.1	0.7902	0.5604	1.3506	1097.5
1,400	587.10	0.0231	0.3012	598.7	574.7	1173.4	0.7963	0.5491	1.3454	1095.4
1,450	591.73	0.0233	0.2884	605.2	565.5	1170.7	0.8023	0.5379	1.3402	1093.3
1,500	596.23	0.0235	0.2760	611.6	556.3	1167.9	0.8082	0.5269	1.3351	1091.0
1,600	604.90	0.0239	0.2548	624.1	538.0	1162.1	0.8196	0.5053	1.3249	1086.7
1,700	613.15	0.0243	0.2304	636.3	519.6	1155.9	0.8306	0.4843	1.3149	1081.8
1,800	621.03	0.0247	0.2179	648.3	501.1	1149.4	0.8412	0.4637	1.3049	1076.8
1,900	628.58	0.0252	0.2021	660.1	482.4	1142.4	0.8516	0.4433	1.2949	1071.4
2,000	635.82	0.0257	0.1878	671.7	463.4	1135.1	0.8619	0.4230	1.2849	1065.0
2,200	649.46	0.0268	0.1625	694.8	424.4	1119.2	0.8820	0.3826	1.2646	1053.1
2,400	662.12	0.0280	0.1407	718.4	382.7	1101.1	0.9023	0.3411	1.2434	1038.6
2,600	673.94	0.0295	0.1213	743.0	337.2	1080.2	0.9232	0.2973	1.2205	1021.9
2,800	684.99	0.0310	0.1035	770.1	284.7	1054.8	0.9459	0.2487	1.1946	1001.2
3,000	695.36	0.0346	0.0858	802.5	217.8	1020.3	0.9731	0.1885	1.1615	972.7
3,200	705.11	0.0444	0.0580	872.4	62.0	934.4	1.0320	0.0532	1.0852	898.4
3,206.2	705.40	0.0503	0.0503	902.7	0	902.7	1.0580	0	1.0580	872.9

Table 29. Superheated Steam Tables

(Abstracted from Keenan and Keyes, "Thermodynamic Properties of Steam")
(v = specific volume, cu ft per lb; h = enthalpy, Btu per lb; s = entropy)

Pressure, psia (Saturation temp, deg F)		Temperature of steam, deg F								
		340	380	420	460	500	550	600	650	700
20	v	23.60	24.82	26.04	27.25	28.46	29.97	31.47	32.97	34.47
(227.96)	h	1210.8	1229.7	1248.7	1267.6	1286.6	1310.5	1334.4	1358.6	1382.9
	s	1.8053	1.8285	1.8505	1.8716	1.8918	1.9160	1.9392	1.9671	1.9829
40	v	11.684	12.315	12.938	13.555	14.168	14.930	15.688	16.444	17.198
(267.25)	h	1207.0	1226.7	1246.2	1265.5	1284.8	1309.0	1333.1	1357.4	1381.9
	s	1.7252	1.7493	1.7719	1.7934	1.8140	1.8385	1.8619	1.8843	1.9058
60	v	7.708	8.143	8.569	8.988	9.403	9.917	10.427	10.935	11.441
(292.71)	h	1203.0	1223.6	1243.6	1263.4	1283.0	1307.4	1331.8	1356.3	1380.9
	s	1.6766	1.7135	1.7250	1.7470	1.7678	1.7927	1.8162	1.8388	1.8605
80	v	5.718	6.055	6.383	6.704	7.020	7.410	7.797	8.180	8.562
(312.03)	h	1198.8	1220.3	1240.9	1261.1	1281.1	1305.8	1330.5	1355.1	1379.9
	s	1.6407	1.6669	1.6909	1.7134	1.7346	1.7598	1.7836	1.8063	1.8281
100	v	4.521	4.801	5.071	5.333	5.589	5.906	6.218	6.527	6.835
(327.81)	h	1194.3	1216.8	1238.1	1258.8	1279.1	1304.2	1329.1	1354.0	1378.9
	s	1.6117	1.6391	1.6639	1.6869	1.7085	1.7340	1.7581	1.7810	1.8029
120	v	......	3.964	4.195	4.418	4.636	4.902	5.165	5.426	5.683
(341.25)	h	......	1213.2	1235.3	1256.5	1277.2	1302.6	1327.7	1352.8	1377.8
	s	......	1.6156	1.6413	1.6649	1.6869	1.7127	1.7370	1.7601	1.7822
140	v	......	3.365	3.569	3.764	3.954	4.186	4.413	4.638	4.861
(353.02)	h	......	1209.4	1232.3	1254.1	1275.2	1300.9	1326.4	1351.6	1376.8
	s	......	1.5950	1.6217	1.6458	1.6683	1.6945	1.7190	1.7423	1.7645
160	v	......	2.914	3.098	3.273	3.443	3.648	3.849	4.048	4.244
(363.53)	h	......	1205.5	1229.3	1251.6	1273.1	1299.3	1325.0	1350.4	1375.7
	s	......	1.5766	1.6042	1.6291	1.6519	1.6785	1.7033	1.7268	1.7491
180	v	......	2.563	2.732	2.891	3.044	3.230	3.411	3.588	3.764
(373.06)	h	......	1201.4	1226.1	1249.1	1271.0	1297.6	1323.5	1349.2	1374.7
	s	......	1.5596	1.5884	1.6139	1.6373	1.6642	1.6894	1.7130	1.7355
200	v	......	......	2.438	2.585	2.726	2.895	3.060	3.221	3.380
(381.79)	h	......	......	1222.9	1246.5	1268.9	1295.8	1322.1	1348.0	1373.6
	s	......	......	1.5738	1.6001	1.6240	1.6513	1.6767	1.7006	1.7232
220	v	......	......	2.198	2.335	2.465	2.621	2.772	2.920	3.066
(389.86)	h	......	......	1219.5	1243.8	1266.7	1294.1	1320.7	1346.8	1372.6
	s	......	......	1.5603	1.5874	1.6117	1.6395	1.6652	1.6892	1.7120
260	v	......	......	1.8257	1.9483	2.063	2.199	2.330	2.457	2.582
(404.42)	h	......	......	1212.4	1238.3	1262.3	1290.5	1317.7	1344.3	1370.4
	s	......	......	1.5354	1.5642	1.5897	1.6184	1.6447	1.6692	1.6922
300	v	......	......	1.5513	1.6638	1.7675	1.8891	2.005	2.118	2.227
(417.33)	h	......	......	1204.8	1232.5	1257.6	1286.8	1314.7	1341.8	1368.3
	s	......	......	1.5126	1.5434	1.5701	1.5998	1.6268	1.6517	1.6751
350	v	......	......	......	1.3984	1.4923	1.6010	1.7036	1.8021	1.8980
(431.72)	h	......	......	......	1224.8	1251.5	1282.1	1310.9	1338.5	1365.5
	s	......	......	......	1.5197	1.5481	1.5792	1.6070	1.6325	1.6563
400	v	......	......	......	1.1978	1.2851	1.3843	1.4770	1.5654	1.6508
(444.59)	h	......	......	......	1216.5	1245.1	1277.2	1306.9	1335.2	1362.7
	s	......	......	......	1.4977	1.5281	1.5607	1.5894	1.6155	1.6398

Table 29. Superheated Steam Tables—(*Continued*)

Pressure, psia (Saturation temp, deg F)		Temperature of steam, deg F								
		500	550	600	650	700	750	800	900	1000
450	*v*	1.1231	1.2154	1.3005	1.3810	1.4584	1.5337	1.6074	1.7516	1.8928
(456.28)	*h*	1238.4	1272.0	1302.8	1331.9	1359.9	1387.3	1414.3	1467.7	1521.0
	s	1.5095	1.5437	1.5735	1.6003	1.6250	1.6481	1.6699	1.7108	1.7486
500	*v*	0.9927	1.0798	1.1591	1.2333	1.3044	1.3732	1.4405	1.5715	1.6996
(467.01)	*h*	1231.3	1266.7	1298.6	1328.4	1357.0	1384.8	1412.1	1466.0	1519.6
	s	1.4919	1.5279	1.5588	1.5863	1.6115	1.6350	1.6571	1.6982	1.7363
550	*v*	0.8852	0.9686	1.0431	1.1124	1.1783	1.2419	1.3038	1.4241	1.5414
(476.94)	*h*	1223.7	1261.2	1294.3	1324.9	1354.0	1382.3	1409.9	1464.3	1518.2
	s	1.4751	1.5131	1.5451	1.5734	1.5991	1.6228	1.6452	1.6868	1.7250
600	*v*	0.7947	0.8753	0.9463	1.0115	1.0732	1.1324	1.1899	1.3013	1.4096
(486.21)	*h*	1215.7	1255.5	1289.9	1321.3	1351.1	1379.7	1407.7	1462.5	1516.7
	s	1.4586	1.4990	1.5323	1.5613	1.5875	1.6117	1.6343	1.6762	1.7147
700	*v*	......	0.7277	0.7934	0.8525	0.9077	0.9601	1.0108	1.1082	1.2024
(503.10)	*h*	......	1243.2	1280.6	1313.9	1345.0	1374.5	1403.2	1459.0	1513.9
	s	......	1.4722	1.5084	1.5391	1.5665	1.5914	1.6147	1.6573	1.6963
800	*v*	......	0.6154	0.6779	0.7328	0.7833	0.8308	0.8763	0.9633	1.0470
(518.23)	*h*	......	1229.8	1270.7	1306.2	1338.6	1369.2	1398.6	1455.4	1511.0
	s	......	1.4467	1.4863	1.5190	1.5476	1.5734	1.5972	1.6407	1.6801
900	*v*	......	0.5264	0.5873	0.6393	0.6863	0.7300	0.7716	0.8506	0.9262
(531.98)	*h*	......	1215.0	1260.1	1298.0	1332.1	1363.7	1393.9	1451.8	1508.1
	s	......	1.4216	1.4653	1.5002	1.5303	1.5570	1.5814	1.6257	1.6656
1,000	*v*	......	0.4533	0.5140	0.5640	0.6084	0.6492	0.6878	0.7604	0.8294
(544.61)	*h*	......	1198.3	1248.8	1289.5	1325.3	1358.1	1389.2	1448.2	1505.1
	s	......	1.3961	1.4450	1.4825	1.5141	1.5418	1.5670	1.6121	1.6525
1,100	*v*	......	......	0.4632	0.5020	0.5445	0.5830	0.6191	0.6866	0.7503
(556.30)	*h*	......	......	1236.7	1280.5	1318.3	1352.4	1384.3	1444.5	1502.2
	s	......	......	1.4251	1.4656	1.4989	1.5276	1.5535	1.5995	1.6405
1,200	*v*	......	......	0.4016	0.4498	0.4909	0.5277	0.5617	0.6250	0.6843
(567.22)	*h*	......	......	1223.5	1271.0	1311.0	1346.4	1379.3	1440.7	1499.2
	s	......	......	1.4052	1.4491	1.4843	1.5142	1.5409	1.5879	1.6293
1,400	*v*	......	......	0.3174	0.3668	0.4062	0.4403	0.4714	0.5281	0.5805
(587.10)	*h*	......	......	1193.0	1250.6	1295.5	1334.0	1369.1	1433.1	1493.2
	s	......	......	1.3639	1.4171	1.4567	1.4893	1.5177	1.5666	1.6093
1,600	*v*	......	......	......	0.3027	0.3417	0.3743	0.4034	0.4553	0.5027
(604.90)	*h*	......	......	......	1227.3	1278.7	1320.9	1358.4	1425.3	1487.0
	s	......	......	......	1.3800	1.4303	1.4660	1.4964	1.5476	1.5914
1,800	*v*	......	......	......	0.2506	0.2907	0.3225	0.3502	0.3986	0.4421
(621.03)	*h*	......	......	......	1200.3	1260.3	1307.0	1347.2	1417.4	1480.8
	s	......	......	......	1.3515	1.4044	1.4438	1.4765	1.5301	1.5752
2,000	*v*	......	......	......	0.2058	0.2489	0.2806	0.3074	0.3532	0.3935
(635.82)	*h*	......	......	......	1167.0	1240.0	1292.0	1335.5	1409.2	1474.5
	s	......	......	......	1.3139	1.3783	1.4223	1.4576	0.5139	1.5380
2,200	*v*	......	......	......	0.1633	0.2135	0.2457	0.2721	0.3159	0.3538
(649.46)	*h*	......	......	......	1121.0	1217.4	1276.0	1323.3	1400.8	1468.2
	s	......	......	......	1.2665	1.3515	1.4010	1.4393	1.4986	1.5465

Table 30. Steam Table for Use in Condenser Calculations

(Abstracted from Keenan and Keyes, "Thermodynamic Properties of Steam")

Temp, deg F, t	Abs pressure		Specific volume	Enthalpy			Entropy	
	Psi	In. Hg	Sat vapor, v_g	Sat liquid, h_f	Evap, h_{fg}	Sat vapor, h_g	Sat liquid, s_f	Sat vapor, s_g
	p							
50	0.17811	0.3626	1703.2	18.07	1065.6	1083.7	0.0361	2.1264
52	0.19182	0.3906	1587.6	20.07	1064.4	1084.5	0.0400	2.1199
54	0.20642	0.4203	1481.0	22.07	1063.3	1085.4	0.0439	2.1136
56	0.2220	0.4520	1382.4	24.06	1062.2	1086.3	0.0478	2.1072
58	0.2386	0.4858	1291.1	26.06	1061.0	1087.1	0.0517	2.1010
60	0.2563	0.5218	1206.7	28.06	1059.9	1088.0	0.0555	2.0948
62	0.2751	0.5601	1128.4	30.05	1058.8	1088.9	0.0593	2.0886
64	0.2951	0.6009	1055.7	32.05	1057.6	1089.7	0.0632	2.0826
66	0.3164	0.6442	988.4	34.05	1056.5	1090.6	0.0670	2.0766
68	0.3390	0.6903	925.9	36.04	1055.5	1091.5	0.0708	2.0706
70	0.3631	0.7392	867.9	38.04	1054.3	1092.3	0.0745	2.0647
72	0.3886	0.7912	813.9	40.04	1053.2	1093.2	0.0783	2.0588
74	0.4156	0.8462	763.8	42.03	1052.1	1094.1	0.0820	2.0530
76	0.4443	0.9046	717.1	44.03	1050.9	1094.9	0.0858	2.0473
78	0.4747	0.9666	673.6	46.02	1049.8	1095.8	0.0895	2.0416
80	0.5069	1.0321	633.1	48.02	1048.6	1096.6	0.0932	2.0360
82	0.5410	1.1016	595.3	50.01	1047.5	1097.5	0.0969	2.0304
84	0.5771	1.1750	560.2	52.01	1046.4	1098.4	0.1005	2.0249
86	0.6152	1.2527	527.3	54.00	1045.2	1099.2	9.1042	2.0195
88	0.6556	1.3347	496.7	56.00	1044.1	1100.1	0.1079	2.0141
90	0.6982	1.4215	468.0	57.99	1042.9	1100.9	0.1115	2.0087
92	0.7432	1.5131	441.3	59.99	1041.8	1101.8	0.1151	2.0034
94	0.7906	1.6097	416.2	61.98	1040.7	1102.6	0.1187	1.9981
96	0.8407	1.7117	392.8	63.98	1039.5	1103.5	0.1223	1.9929
98	0.8935	1.8192	370.9	65.97	1038.4	1104.4	0.1259	1.9877
100	0.9492	1.9325	350.4	67.97	1037.2	1105.2	0.1295	1.9826
102	1.0078	2.0519	331.1	69.96	1036.1	1106.1	0.1330	1.9775
104	1.0695	2.1775	313.1	71.96	1034.9	1106.9	0.1366	1.9725
106	1.1345	2.3099	296.2	73.95	1033.8	1107.8	0.1401	1.9675
108	1.2029	2.4491	280.3	75.95	1032.7	1108.6	0.1436	1.9626
110	1.2748	2.5955	265.4	77.94	1031.6	1109.5	0.1471	1.9577
112	1.3504	2.7494	251.4	79.94	1030.4	1110.3	0.1506	1.9529
114	1.4298	2.9111	238.2	81.93	1029.2	1111.1	0.1541	1.9481
116	1.5130	3.0806	225.8	83.93	1028.1	1112.0	0.1576	1.9433
118	1.6006	3.2589	214.2	85.92	1026.9	1112.8	0.1610	1.9386
120	1.6924	3.4458	203.27	87.92	1025.8	1113.7	0.1645	1.9339
122	1.7888	3.6420	192.95	89.92	1024.6	1114.5	0.1679	1.9293
124	1.8897	3.8475	183.25	91.91	1023.4	1115.3	0.1714	1.9247
126	1.9955	4.0629	174.10	93.91	1022.3	1116.2	0.1748	1.9202
128	2.1064	4.2887	165.47	95.91	1021.1	1117.0	0.1782	1.9156
130	2.2225	4.5251	157.34	97.90	1020.0	1117.9	0.1816	1.9112
132	2.3440	4.7725	149.66	99.90	1018.8	1118.7	0.1849	1.9067
134	2.4712	5.0314	142.42	101.90	1017.6	1119.5	0.1883	1.9023
136	2.6042	5.3022	135.58	103.90	1016.4	1120.3	0.1917	1.8980
138	2.7432	5.5852	129.12	105.89	1015.3	1121.2	0.1950	1.8937
140	2.8886	5.8812	123.01	107.89	1014.1	1122.0	0.1984	1.8894
142	3.0440	6.1903	117.23	109.89	1012.9	1122.8	0.2016	1.8851
144	3.1990	6.5132	111.77	111.89	1011.7	1123.6	0.2049	1.8809
146	3.365	6.850	106.60	113.89	1010.6	1124.5	0.2083	1.8768
148	3.537	7.202	101.71	115.89	1009.4	1125.3	0.2116	1.8726
150	3.718	7.569	97.07	117.89	1008.2	1126.1	0.2149	1.8685

Mercury Vapor. Properties of mercury vapor are presented in Table 31.

Table 31. Properties of Mercury Vapor

(h_f and s_f are measured from 32 F)

By L. A. Sheldon, General Electric Co.

Pressure, psia, p	Temp, deg F, t	Specific vol, cu ft, per lb, v_g	Enthalpy, Btu: Sat liquid, h_f	Enthalpy, Btu: Vaporization, h_{fg}	Enthalpy, Btu: Sat vapor, h_g	Entropy: Sat liquid, s_f	Entropy: Vaporization, s_{fg}	Entropy: Sat vapor, s_g
0.4	402.3	114.5	13.81	128.1	141.9	0.02094	0.1486	0.1696
0.6	426.1	78.23	14.70	127.6	142.3	0.02195	0.1441	0.1660
0.8	443.8	59.71	15.36	127.2	142.6	0.02269	0.1408	0.1635
1.0	458.1	48.45	15.89	126.9	142.8	0.02328	0.1382	0.1615
1.5	485.1	33.14	16.90	126.3	143.2	0.02436	0.1337	0.1580
2	505.2	25.31	17.65	125.8	143.5	0.02514	0.1304	0.1556
3	535.4	17.34	18.78	125.2	144.0	0.02629	0.1258	0.1521
4	558.0	13.26	19.62	124.7	144.3	0.02714	0.1225	0.1497
5	576.2	10.77	20.30	124.3	144.6	0.02780	0.1200	0.1478
6	591.4	9.096	20.87	123.9	144.8	0.02834	0.1179	0.1462
7	605.0	7.882	21.37	123.6	145.0	0.02882	0.1161	0.1450
8	616.8	6.963	21.81	123.4	145.2	0.02923	1.1146	0.1439
9	627.5	6.244	22.21	123.2	145.4	0.02960	0.1133	0.1429
10	637.3	5.661	22.58	122.9	145.5	0.02993	0.1121	0.1420
15	676.5	3.892	24.04	122.1	146.1	0.03124	0.1074	0.1387
20	706.2	2.983	25.15	121.4	146.6	0.03220	0.1041	0.1363
25	730.4	2.429	26.05	120.9	146.9	0.03297	0.1016	0.1345
30	750.9	2.053	26.81	120.4	147.2	0.03360	0.09953	0.1331
35	769.0	1.781	27.49	120.0	147.5	0.03416	0.09774	0.1319
40	784.8	1.576	28.08	119.7	147.8	0.03464	0.09621	0.1308
45	799.3	1.414	28.62	119.4	148.0	0.03507	0.09486	0.1299
50	812.5	1.284	29.11	119.1	148.2	0.03546	0.09364	0.1291
60	836.1	1.086	29.99	118.6	148.6	0.03614	0.09154	0.1276
70	856.6	0.9436	30.75	118.1	148.9	0.03672	0.08976	0.1264
80	874.8	0.8349	31.43	117.7	149.1	0.03725	0.08824	0.1254
90	891.6	0.7497	32.06	117.3	149.4	0.03771	0.08687	0.1245
100	906.9	0.6811	32.63	117.0	149.6	0.03813	0.08565	0.1237
120	934.4	0.5767	33.60	116.4	150.1	0.03887	0.08353	0.1224
140	958.3	0.5012	34.55	115.9	150.4	0.03951	0.08175	0.1212
160	979.9	0.4438	35.35	115.4	150.8	0.04007	0.08019	0.1202
180	999.6	0.3990	36.09	115.0	151.1	0.04058	0.07881	0.1193

Diphenyl $(C_6H_5)_2$ has the following properties (Chipman and Peltier, *Ind. Eng. Chem.*, Nov., 1929, p. 1106): boiling point, 491.5 F; density of the liquid, 53 lb per cu ft; density of saturated vapor, 0.242 lb per cu ft; heat of vaporization, 134 Btu per lb: all measured at the boiling point. The specific heat at constant pressure is given by the relation $c_p = 0.279 + 0.000667t$. The vapor pressures (p, psia) at various temperatures (t, deg F) are as follows:

t	200	250	300	350	400	450	500
p	0.060	0.227	0.701	1.832	4.117	8.638	16.29
t	550	600	650	700	750	800	
p	28.54	47.01	73.55	110.1	158.6	221.0	

Dowtherm A is the eutectic mixture of diphenyl oxide and diphenyl containing 73.5 percent of diphenyl oxide and 26.5 percent of diphenyl and melting at 53.6 F. It is used as a liquid heating medium at elevated temperatures. Its low vapor pressure permits high temperature without attendant high pressures. Table 32 (Badger, *Ind. Eng. Chem.*, Sept., 1937) gives properties of this eutectic.

Table 32. Properties of Saturated Dowtherm A*

Temp, deg F	Pressure, psia	Enthalpy, Btu per lb, above 53.6 F			Specific heat, liquid	Density, lb per cu ft	
		Sat liquid, h_f	Vaporization, h_{fg}	Sat vapor, h_g		Liquid	Vapor
500.0	14.7	222.0	123	345	0.63	54.1	0.28
510.0	18.1	228.0	121	349	0.63	53.7	0.32
520.0	20.4	234.0	120	354	0.64	53.2	0.36
530.0	22.7	240.0	119	359	0.64	53.0	0.40
540.0	25.1	247.0	118	365	0.65	52.7	0.44
550.0	27.0	253.0	117	370	0.65	52.3	0.48
560.0	30.8	260.0	115	375	0.65	51.9	0.54
570.0	34.6	267.0	114	381	0.66	51.6	0.60
580.0	36.6	274.0	112	386	0.66	51.2	0.67
590.0	41.4	281.0	111	392	0.66	50.8	0.75
600.0	44.3	288.0	110	398	0.66	50.4	0.88
610.0	46.2	295.0	109	404	0.67	50.1	1.00
620.0	53.0	302.0	107	409	0.67	49.8	1.10
630.0	57.6	309.0	106	415	0.67	49.3	1.17
640.0	63.6	316.0	105	421	0.67	49.1	1.24
650.0	68.4	323.0	104	427	0.67	48.6	1.29
660.0	74.2	330.0	102	432	0.68	48.4	1.34
670.0	80.8	337.0	101	438	0.68	47.9	1.40
680.0	87.7	344.0	99	443	0.68	47.5	1.5
690.0	95.4	351.0	98	449	0.68	47.2	1.6
700.0	104.0	358.0	97	455	0.68	46.9	1.7
710.0	113.0	365.0	95	460	0.68	46.3	1.8
720.0	119.0	372.0	93	465	0.68	45.9	1.9
730.0	131.0	379.0	92	471	0.68	45.5	2.1
740.0	142.0	386.0	90	476	0.68	44.9	2.3
750.0	150.0	393.0	89	482	0.68	44.4	2.5

* Dowtherm E boils at 350 F and freezes at 0 F. Additional information on this fluid is available from the "Dowtherm Handbook," published by the Dow Chemical Company, Midland, Michigan.

Pure Hydrocarbons. The vapor pressures of various commercially important pure hydrocarbons are shown graphically in Fig. 25.

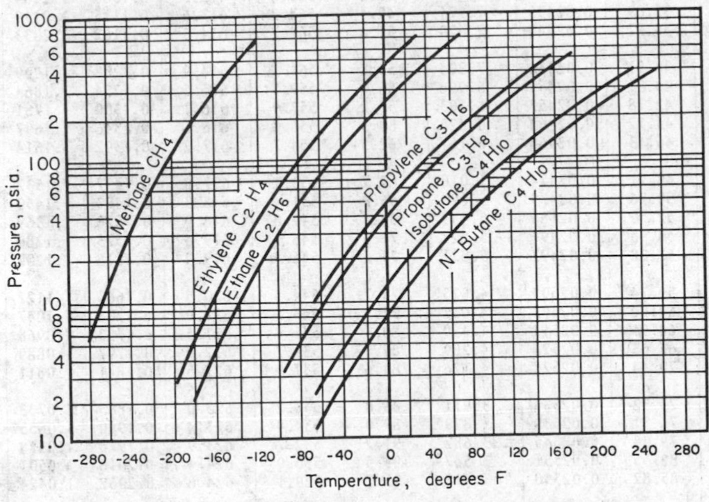

Fig. 25. Vapor pressures of pure hydrocarbons.

Ammonia Vapor. The properties of saturated and superheated ammonia vapor have been determined accurately by the NBS (*Circ.* 142, 1923). The principal properties are given in Tables 33 and 34 and Fig. 24. Properties of **aqua-ammonia** are given in Fig. 26.

In these tables, the entropy s_f and the heat of the liquid h_f are taken as zero at −40 F instead of at 32 F, as is customary in most tables.

Table 33. Properties of Saturated Ammonia

(h_f and s_f are measured from −40 F)

Temp, deg F,	Pressure, psia,	Specific volume, cu ft per lb		Enthalpy, Btu			Entropy		
t	p	Sat liquid, v_f	Sat vapor, v_g	Sat liquid, h_f	Vaporization, h_{fg}	Sat vapor, h_g	Sat liquid, s_f	Vaporization, s_{fg}	Sat vapor, s_g
−40	10.41	0.02322	24.86	0.0	597.6	597.6	0.000	1.4242	1.4242
−38	11.04	0.02326	23.53	2.1	596.2	598.3	0.0051	1.4142	1.4193
−36	11.71	0.02331	22.27	4.3	594.8	599.1	0.0101	1.4043	1.4144
−34	12.41	0.02335	21.10	6.4	593.5	599.9	0.0151	1.3945	1.4096
−32	13.14	0.02340	20.00	8.5	592.1	600.6	0.0201	1.3847	1.4048
−30	13.90	0.02345	18.97	10.7	590.7	601.4	0.0250	1.3751	1.4001
−28	14.71	0.02349	18.00	12.8	589.3	602.1	0.0300	1.3655	1.3955
−26	15.55	0.02354	17.09	14.9	587.9	602.8	0.0350	1.3559	1.3909
−24	16.42	0.02359	16.24	17.1	586.5	603.6	0.0399	1.3464	1.3863
−22	17.34	0.02364	15.43	19.2	585.1	604.3	0.0448	1.3370	1.3818
−20	18.30	0.02369	14.68	21.4	583.6	605.0	0.0497	1.3277	1.3774
−18	19.30	0.02374	13.97	23.5	582.2	605.7	0.0545	1.3184	1.3729
−16	20.34	0.02378	13.29	25.6	580.8	606.4	0.0594	1.3092	1.3686
−14	21.43	0.02383	12.66	27.8	579.3	607.1	0.0642	1.3001	1.3643
−12	22.56	0.02384	12.06	30.0	577.8	607.8	0.0690	1.2910	1.3600
−10	23.74	0.02393	11.50	32.1	576.4	608.5	0.0738	1.2820	1.3558
− 8	24.97	0.02399	10.97	34.3	574.9	609.2	0.0786	1.2730	1.3516
− 6	26.26	0.02404	10.47	36.4	573.4	609.8	0.0833	1.2641	1.3474
− 4	27.59	0.02409	9.991	38.6	571.9	610.5	0.0880	1.2553	1.3433
− 2	28.98	0.02414	9.541	40.7	570.4	611.1	0.0928	1.2465	1.3393
0	30.42	0.02419	9.116	42.9	568.9	611.8	0.0975	1.2377	1.3352
2	31.92	0.02424	8.714	45.1	567.3	612.4	0.1022	1.2290	1.3312
4	33.47	0.02430	8.333	47.2	565.8	613.0	0.1069	1.2204	1.3273
6	35.09	0.02435	7.971	49.4	564.2	613.6	0.1115	1.2119	1.3234
8	36.77	0.02440	7.629	51.6	562.7	614.3	0.1162	1.2033	1.3195
10	38.51	0.02446	7.304	53.8	561.1	614.9	0.1208	1.1949	1.3157
12	40.31	0.02451	6.996	56.0	559.5	615.5	0.1254	1.1864	1.3118
14	42.18	0.02457	6.703	58.2	557.9	616.1	0.1300	1.1781	1.3081
16	44.12	0.02462	6.425	60.3	556.3	616.6	0.1346	1.1697	1.3043
18	46.13	0.02468	6.161	62.5	554.7	617.2	0.1392	1.1614	1.3006
20	48.21	0.02474	5.910	64.7	553.1	617.8	0.1437	1.1532	1.2969
22	50.36	0.02479	5.671	66.9	551.4	618.3	0.1483	1.1450	1.2933
24	52.59	0.02485	5.443	69.1	549.8	618.9	0.1528	1.1369	1.2897
26	54.90	0.02491	5.227	71.3	548.1	619.4	0.1573	1.1288	1.2861
28	57.28	0.02497	5.021	73.5	546.4	619.9	0.1618	1.1207	1.2825
30	59.74	0.02503	4.825	75.7	544.8	620.5	0.1663	1.1127	1.2790
32	62.29	0.02508	4.637	77.9	543.1	621.0	0.1708	1.1047	1.2755
34	64.91	0.02514	4.459	80.1	541.4	621.5	0.1753	1.0968	1.2721
36	67.63	0.02521	4.289	82.3	539.7	622.0	0.1797	1.0889	1.2686
38	70.43	0.02527	4.126	84.6	537.9	622.5	0.1841	1.0811	1.2652
40	73.32	0.02533	3.971	86.8	536.2	623.0	0.1885	1.0733	1.2618
42	76.31	0.02539	3.823	89.0	534.4	623.4	0.1930	1.0655	1.2585
44	79.38	0.02545	3.682	91.2	532.7	623.9	0.1974	1.0578	1.2552
46	82.55	0.02551	3.547	93.5	530.9	624.4	0.2018	1.0501	1.2519
48	85.82	0.02558	3.418	95.7	529.1	624.8	0.2062	1.0424	1.2486
50	89.19	0.02564	3.294	97.9	527.3	625.2	0.2105	1.0348	1.2453
52	92.66	0.02571	3.176	100.2	525.5	6.257	0.2149	1.0272	1.2421

Table 33. Properties of Saturated Ammonia—(*Continued*)

Temp, deg F,	Pressure, psia,	Specific volume, cu ft per lb		Enthalpy, Btu			Entropy		
		Sat liquid,	Sat vapor,	Sat liquid,	Vaporization,	Sat vapor,	Sat liquid,	Vaporization,	Sat vapor,
t	p	v_f	v_g	h_f	h_{fg}	h_g	s_f	s_{fg}	s_g
54	96.23	0.02577	3.063	102.4	523.7	626.1	0.2192	1.0197	1.2389
56	99.91	0.02584	2.954	104.7	521.8	626.5	0.2236	1.0121	1.2357
58	103.7	0.02590	2.851	106.9	520.0	626.9	0.2279	1.0046	1.2325
60	107.6	0.02597	2.751	109.2	518.1	627.3	0.2322	0.9972	1.2294
62	111.6	0.02604	2.656	111.5	516.2	627.7	0.2365	0.9897	1.2262
64	115.7	0.02611	2.565	113.7	514.3	628.0	0.2408	0.9823	1.2231
66	120.0	0.02618	2.477	116.0	512.4	628.4	0.2451	0.9750	1.2201
68	124.3	0.02625	2.393	118.3	510.5	628.8	0.2494	0.9676	1.2170
70	128.8	0.02632	2.312	120.5	508.6	629.1	0.2537	0.9603	1.2140
72	133.4	0.02639	2.235	122.8	506.6	629.4	0.2579	0.9531	1.2110
74	138.1	0.02646	2.161	125.1	504.7	629.8	0.2622	0.9458	1.2080
76	143.0	0.02653	2.089	127.4	502.7	630.1	0.2664	0.9386	1.2050
78	147.9	0.02661	2.021	129.7	500.7	630.4	0.2706	0.9314	1.2020
80	153.0	0.02668	1.955	132.0	498.7	630.7	0.2749	0.9242	1.1991
82	158.3	0.02675	1.892	134.3	496.7	631.0	0.2791	0.9171	1.1962
84	163.7	0.02684	1.831	136.6	494.7	631.3	0.2833	0.9100	1.1933
86	169.2	0.02691	1.772	138.9	492.6	631.5	0.2875	0.9029	1.1904
88	174.8	0.02699	1.716	141.2	490.6	631.8	0.2917	0.8958	1.1875
90	180.6	0.02707	1.661	143.5	488.5	632.0	0.2958	0.8888	1.1846
92	186.6	0.02715	1.609	145.8	486.4	632.2	0.3000	0.8818	1.1818
94	192.7	0.02723	1.559	148.2	484.3	632.5	0.3041	0.8748	1.1789
96	198.9	0.02731	1.510	150.5	482.1	632.6	0.3083	0.8678	1.1761
98	205.3	0.02739	1.464	152.9	480.0	632.9	0.3125	0.8608	1.1733
100	211.9	0.02747	1.419	155.2	477.8	633.0	0.3166	0.8539	1.1705
105	228.9	0.02769	1.313	161.1	472.3	633.4	0.3269	0.8366	1.1635
110	247.0	0.02790	1.217	167.0	466.7	633.7	0.3372	0.8194	1.1566
115	266.2	0.02813	1.128	173.0	460.9	633.9	0.3474	0.8023	1.1497
120	286.4	0.02836	1.047	179.0	455.0	634.0	0.3576	0.7851	1.1427

Table 34. Properties of Superheated Ammonia

(Condensed from *NBS Circ.* 142, 1923)

(v = specific volume in cu ft per lb; h = enthalpy in Btu per lb; s = entropy. h_f and s_f are measured from −40 F)

Pressure, psia	Temp of saturated vapor, deg F		Temperature of superheated vapor, deg F								
			−30	−20	−10	0	10	20	30	40	50
		v	26.58	27.26	27.92	28.58	29.24	29.90	30.55	31.20	31.85
10	−41.34	h	603.2	608.5	613.7	618.9	624.0	629.1	634.2	639.3	644.4
		s	1.4420	1.4542	1.4659	1.4773	1.4884	1.4992	1.5097	1.5200	1.5301
		v	....	....	13.74	14.09	14.44	14.78	15.11	15.45	15.78
20	−16.64	h	....	....	610.0	615.5	621.0	626.4	631.7	637.0	642.3
		s	....	....	1.3784	1.3907	1.4025	1.4138	1.4248	1.4356	1.4460
		v	....	....	....	9.250	9.492	9.731	9.966	10.20	10.43
30	−0.57	h	....	....	....	611.9	617.8	623.5	629.1	634.6	640.1
		s	....	....	....	1.3371	1.3497	1.3618	1.3733	1.3845	1.3953
		v	....	....	....	....	....	7.203	7.387	7.568	7.746
40	11.66	h	....	....	....	....	....	620.4	626.3	632.1	637.8
		s	....	....	....	....	....	1.3231	1.3353	1.3470	1.3583
		v	....	....	....	....	....	....	5.838	5.988	6.135
50	21.67	h	....	....	....	....	....	....	623.4	629.5	635.4
		s	....	....	....	....	....	....	1.3046	1.3169	1.3286
			100	120	140	160	180	200	240	280	320
		v	4.190	4.371	4.548	4.722	4.893	5.063	5.398	5.730	
80	44.40	h	658.7	670.4	681.8	693.2	704.4	715.6	738.1	760.7	
		s	1.3199	1.3404	1.3598	1.3784	1.3963	1.4136	1.4467	1.4781	
		v	3.304	3.454	3.600	3.743	3.883	4.021	4.294	4.562	
100	56.05	h	655.2	667.3	679.2	690.8	702.3	713.7	736.5	759.4	
		s	1.2891	1.3104	1.3305	1.3495	1.3678	1.3854	1.4190	1.4507	
		v	2.712	2.842	2.967	3.089	3.190	3.326	3.557	3.783	
120	66.02	h	651.6	664.2	676.5	688.5	700.2	711.8	734.9	758.0	
		s	1.2628	1.2850	1.3058	1.3254	1.3441	1.3620	1.3960	1.4281	
		v	2.288	2.404	2.515	2.622	2.727	2.830	3.030	3.227	3.420
140	74.79	h	647.8	661.1	673.7	686.0	698.0	709.9	733.3	756.7	780.0
		s	1.2396	1.2628	1.2843	1.3045	1.3236	1.3418	1.3763	1.4088	1.4395
		v	1.969	2.075	2.175	2.272	2.365	2.457	2.635	2.809	2.980
160	82.64	h	643.9	657.8	670.9	683.5	695.8	707.9	731.7	755.3	778.9
		s	1.2186	1.2429	1.2652	1.2859	1.3054	1.3240	1.3591	1.3919	1.4229
		v	1.720	1.818	1.910	1.999	2.084	2.167	2.328	2.484	2.637
180	89.78	h	639.9	654.4	668.0	681.0	693.6	705.9	730.1	753.9	777.7
		s	1.1992	1.2247	1.2477	1.2691	1.2891	1.3081	1.3436	1.3768	1.4081
		v	1.520	1.612	1.698	1.780	1.859	1.935	2.082	2.225	2.364
200	96.34	h	635.6	650.9	665.0	678.4	691.3	703.9	728.4	752.5	776.5
		s	1.1809	1.2077	1.2317	1.2537	1.2742	1.2935	1.3296	1.3631	1.3947
		v	....	1.443	1.525	1.601	1.675	1.745	1.881	2.012	2.140
220	102.42	h	....	647.3	662.0	675.8	689.1	701.9	726.8	751.1	775.3
		s	....	1.1917	1.2167	1.2394	1.2604	1.2801	1.3168	1.3507	1.3825
		v	....	1.302	1.380	1.452	1.521	1.587	1.714	1.835	1.954
240	108.09	h	....	643.5	658.8	673.1	686.7	699.8	725.1	749.8	774.1
		s	....	1.1764	1.2025	1.2259	1.2475	1.2677	1.3049	1.3392	1.3712
		v	....	1.182	1.257	1.326	1.391	1.453	1.572	1.686	1.796
260	113.42	h	....	639.5	655.6	670.4	684.4	697.7	723.4	748.4	772.9
		s	....	1.1617	1.1889	1.2132	1.2354	1.2560	1.2938	1.3258	1.3608

Properties of Other Refrigerants. Complete and consistent data are not available on most of the working fluids used for refrigeration. The data presented in this section on refrigerating fluids other than ammonia are, in many cases, not of as high order of accuracy as the values given for steam (see also Sec. 18).

Table 35. Properties of Saturated Sulphur Dioxide

(h_f and s_f are measured from −40 F)

Temp, deg F, t	Pressure, psia, p	Specific volume, cu ft per lb		Enthalpy, Btu			Entropy		
		Sat liquid, v_f	Sat vapor, v_g	Sat liquid, h_f	Vaporization, h_{fg}	Sat vapor, h_g	Sat liquid, s_f	Vaporization, s_{fg}	Sat vapor, s_g
−40	3.136	0.01044	22.42	0.00	178.6	178.6	0.0000	0.4256	0.4256
−30	4.331	0.01053	16.56	2.93	177.0	179.9	0.00674	0.4119	0.4186
−20	5.883	0.01062	12.42	5.98	175.1	181.1	0.01366	0.3983	0.4119
−10	7.863	0.01072	9.44	9.16	173.0	182.1	0.02075	0.3847	0.4054
0	10.35	0.01082	7.28	12.44	170.6	183.1	0.02795	0.3712	0.3992
10	13.42	0.01092	5.682	15.80	168.1	183.9	0.03519	0.3579	0.3931
20	17.18	0.01103	4.487	19.20	165.3	184.5	0.04241	0.3447	0.3871
30	21.70	0.01114	3.581	22.64	162.4	185.0	0.04956	0.3316	0.3812
40	27.10	0.01126	2.887	26.12	159.3	185.4	0.05668	0.3187	0.3754
50	33.45	0.01138	2.348	29.61	156.0	185.6	0.06370	0.3060	0.3697
60	40.90	0.01150	1.926	33.10	152.5	185.6	0.07060	0.2935	0.3641
70	49.62	0.01163	1.590	36.58	148.9	185.5	0.07736	0.2811	0.3585
80	59.68	0.01176	1.321	40.05	145.1	185.2	0.08399	0.2690	0.3529
90	71.25	0.01190	1.104	43.50	141.2	184.7	0.09038	0.2569	0.3473
100	84.52	0.01204	0.9262	46.90	137.2	184.1	0.09657	0.2452	0.3417
110	99.76	0.01219	0.7804	50.26	133.1	183.3	0.1025	0.2336	0.3361
120	120.9	0.01236	0.6598	53.58	128.8	182.4	0.1083	0.2222	0.3305
130	136.5	0.01253	0.5595	56.85	124.4	181.2	0.1138	0.2110	0.3247
140	158.6	0.01272	0.4758	60.04	119.9	179.9	0.1189	0.1999	0.3189

Table 36. Properties of Superheated Sulphur Dioxide

(v = specific volume in cu ft per lb; h = enthalpy in Btu per lb; s = entropy. h_f and s_f are measured from −40 F)

Pressure, psia	Temp of saturated vapor, deg F		Temperature of superheated vapor, deg F								
			0	20	40	60	80	100	120	140	160
6	−19.37	v	12.75	13.34	13.93	14.52	15.11	15.69	16.26	16.82	17.35
		h	184.3	187.5	190.7	193.9	197.2	200.5	203.8	207.1	210.4
		s	0.4185	0.4254	0.4320	0.4383	0.4444	0.4504	0.4561	0.4618	0.4672
10	− 1.34	v	7.545	7.939	8.316	8.681	9.038	9.389	9.736	10.08	10.42
		h	183.2	186.7	190.1	193.5	196.9	200.3	203.7	207.1	210.5
		s	0.4005	0.4080	0.4151	0.4216	0.4280	0.4341	0.4400	0.4457	0.4512
15	14.43	v	....	5.192	5.470	5.734	5.988	6.233	6.471	6.705	6.937
		h	....	185.4	189.2	192.8	196.4	199.9	203.3	206.7	210.1
		s	....	0.3927	0.4005	0.4078	0.4144	0.4208	0.4268	0.4326	0.4383
20	26.44	v	....	....	4.035	4.251	4.454	4.648	4.834	5.015	5.193
		h	....	....	187.8	191.8	195.6	199.3	202.9	206.5	209.9
		s	....	....	0.3896	0.3972	0.4043	0.4109	0.4173	0.4232	0.4290
25	36.33	v	....	....	3.181	3.363	3.536	3.696	3.848	3.998	4.145
		h	....	....	186.1	190.6	194.7	198.6	202.4	206.0	209.6
		s	....	....	0.3793	0.3880	0.3958	0.4029	0.4095	0.4157	0.4216
			60	80	100	120	140	160	180	200	220
30	44.76	v	2.747	2.907	3.052	3.189	3.318	3.443	3.565	3.685	3.803
		h	189.3	193.8	197.9	201.8	205.6	209.3	212.9	216.5	220.1
		s	0.3797	0.3885	0.3960	0.4029	0.4094	0.4154	0.4211	0.4266	0.4318
40	58.83	v	1.980	2.121	2.246	2.360	2.465	2.565	2.662	2.755	2.845
		h	185.9	191.3	196.1	200.4	204.6	208.5	212.3	216.0	219.7
		s	0.3654	0.3754	0.3842	0.3918	0.3988	0.4053	0.4113	0.4169	0.4223
60	80.29	v	....	....	1.288	1.403	1.514	1.608	1.689	1.751	1.819
		h	....	....	191.4	197.0	201.9	206.5	210.7	214.8	218.7
		s	....	....	0.3640	0.3738	0.3822	0.3896	0.3964	0.4026	0.4084
80	96.88	v	....	....	0.993	1.084	1.163	1.232	1.292	1.347	1.400
		h	....	....	185.6	192.5	198.6	203.9	208.7	213.3	217.5
		s	....	....	0.3457	0.3580	0.3682	0.3769	0.3846	0.3915	0.3978

Table 37. Properties of Carbon Dioxide

(h_f and s_f are measured from 32 F)

Temp, deg F, t	Pressure, psia, p	Density, lb per cu ft: Sat liquid	Density, lb per cu ft: Sat vapor	Enthalpy, Btu: Sat liquid, h_f	Enthalpy, Btu: Vaporization, h_{fg}	Enthalpy, Btu: Sat vapor, h_g	Entropy: Sat liquid, s_f	Entropy: Sat vapor, s_g
−40	145.87	69.8	1.64	−38.5	136.5	98.0	−0.0850	0.2400
−35	161.33	69.1	1.83	−35.8	134.3	98.5	−0.0793	0.2367
−30	177.97	68.3	2.02	−33.1	132.1	99.0	−0.0735	0.2336
−25	195.85	67.6	2.23	−30.4	129.8	99.4	−0.0676	0.2306
−20	215.02	66.9	2.44	−27.7	127.5	99.8	−0.0619	0.2277
−15	235.53	66.1	2.66	−24.9	125.0	100.1	−0.0560	0.2250
−10	257.46	65.3	2.91	−22.1	122.4	100.3	−0.0500	0.2220
− 5	280.85	64.5	3.17	−19.4	120.0	100.6	−0.0440	0.2198
0	305.76	63.6	3.46	−16.7	117.5	100.8	−0.0381	0.2173
5	332.2	62.8	3.77	−14.0	115.0	101.0	−0.0322	0.2151
10	360.4	61.9	4.12	−11.2	112.2	101.0	−0.0264	0.2124
15	390.2	61.0	4.49	− 8.4	109.4	101.0	−0.0204	0.2100
20	421.8	60.0	4.89	− 5.5	106.3	100.8	−0.0144	0.2071
25	455.3	59.0	5.33	− 2.5	103.1	100.6	−0.0083	0.2043
30	490.6	58.0	5.81	+ 0.4	99.7	100.1	−0.0021	0.2012
35	528.0	57.0	6.35	3.5	95.8	99.3	+0.0039	0.1975
40	567.3	55.9	6.91	6.6	91.8	98.4	0.0099	0.1934
45	608.9	54.7	7.60	9.8	87.5	97.3	0.0160	0.1892
50	652.7	53.4	8.37	2.9	83.2	96.1	0.0220	0.1852
55	698.8	52.1	9.27	16.1	78.7	94.8	0.0282	0.1809
60	747.4	50.7	10.2	19.4	74.0	93.4	0.0345	0.1767
65	798.6	49.1	11.3	22.9	68.9	91.8	0.0412	0.1724
70	852.4	47.3	12.6	26.6	62.7	89.3	0.0482	0.1665
75	909.3	45.1	14.2	30.9	54.8	85.7	0.0562	0.1587
80	969.3	42.4	16.2	35.6	44.0	79.6	0.0649	0.1464
85	1032.7	38.2	19.1	41.7	27.5	69.2	0.0761	0.1265
88	1072.1	32.9	25.4	Critical point at 88.43 F				

Table 38. Properties of Ethyl Chloride and of Methyl Chloride

Temp, deg F, t	Ethyl chloride					Methyl chloride				
	Pressure, psia, p	Specific vol of vapor, cu ft per lb, v_g	Enthalpy, Btu from 32 F			Pressure, psia, p	Specific vol of vapor, cu ft per lb, v_g	Enthalpy, Btu from 32 F		
			Sat liquid, h_f	Vaporization, h_{fg}	Sat vapor, h_g			Sat liquid, h_f	Vaporization, h_{fg}	Sat vapor, h_g
−20	2.16	29.54	−19.0	177.6	158.6	11.75	8.09	−19.0	186.4	167.4
−15	2.53	26.07	−17.2	176.8	159.6	13.43	7.22	−17.19	185.3	168.1
−10	2.94	22.95	−15.4	175.9	160.5	15.00	6.46	−15.38	184.2	168.8
− 5	3.41	20.28	−13.5	175.1	161.6	16.79	5.80	−13.58	183.1	169.5
0	3.93	18.04	−11.7	174.2	162.5	18.80	5.18	−11.75	182.0	170.2
+ 5	4.50	16.10	− 9.8	173.4	163.6	21.00	4.65	− 9.93	180.8	170.9
10	5.13	14.36	− 8.1	172.6	164.5	23.30	4.18	− 8.06	179.6	171.6
15	5.86	12.86	− 6.3	171.8	165.5	25.92	3.78	− 6.24	178.5	172.2
20	6.65	11.56	− 4.4	170.9	166.5	28.8	3.41	− 4.32	177.3	172.9
25	7.48	10.35	− 2.5	170.1	167.6	31.9	3.09	− 2.48	176.1	173.6
30	8.40	9.22	− 0.6	169.2	168.6	35.2	2.81	− 0.62	174.9	174.3
35	9.42	8.27	+ 1.3	168.4	169.6	38.7	2.54	+ 1.25	173.7	174.9
40	10.53	7.43	3.2	167.5	170.7	42.6	2.31	3.15	172.4	175.6
45	11.77	6.70	5.1	166.6	171.7	47.0	2.10	5.04	171.2	176.2
50	13.20	6.04	6.9	165.6	172.5	51.5	1.93	6.88	169.9	176.8
55	14.67	5.42	8.9	164.6	173.5	56.4	1.76	8.80	168.6	177.4
60	16.45	4.84	10.8	163.6	174.4	61.6	1.61	10.70	167.3	178.0
65	18.17	4.38	12.8	162.6	175.4	67.3	1.48	12.63	166.0	178.6
70	20.03	4.00	14.7	161.6	176.3	73.3	1.34	14.52	164.6	179.2
75	22.11	3.65	16.6	160.6	177.2	79.2	1.24	16.46	163.3	179.7
80	24.33	3.39	18.6	159.5	178.1	85.3	1.14	18.36	161.9	180.2
85	26.67	3.17	20.6	158.5	179.1	94.1	1.05	20.26	160.5	180.7
90	29.24	2.99	22.6	157.3	179.9	102.1	0.98	22.13	159.1	181.2
95	32.03	2.83	24.6	156.1	180.6	110.3	0.906	24.07	157.7	181.8
100	34.93	2.70	26.6	154.9	181.5	118.8	0.85	26.06	156.3	182.3
105	37.97	2.61	28.6	153.8	182.4	128.1	0.804	28.02	154.9	182.9
110	41.10	2.51	30.5	152.6	183.1	137.6	0.765	30.03	153.4	183.5

Table 39. Properties of Propane and Butane

Temp, deg F	Propane (C_3H_8) (Heat measurements are from 0 F)						Butane (C_4H_{10}) (Heat measurements are from 0 F)					
	Pressure, psia	Specific volume of vapor, cu ft per lb	Enthalpy, Btu per lb		Entropy		Pressure, psia	Specific volume of vapor, cu ft per lb	Enthalpy, Btu per lb		Entropy	
			Liquid h_f	Vapor h_g	Liquid S_f	Vapor S_g			Liquid h_f	Vapor h_g	Liquid S_f	Vapor S_g
−70	7.37	12.9	−37.0	152.5	−0.086	0.400						
−60	9.72	9.93	−32.0	155.0	−0.074	0.393						
−50	12.6	7.74	−26.5	158.0	−0.061	0.389						
−40	16.2	6.13	−21.5	160.0	−0.049	0.384						
−30	20.3	4.93	−16.0	163.0	−0.036	0.380						
−20	25.4	4.00	−11.0	165.0	−0.024	0.377						
−10	31.4	3.26	−5.5	168.0	−0.012	0.374						
0	38.2	2.71	0	170.5	0.000	0.371	7.3	11.10	0	170.5	0.000	0.371
+10	46.0	2.27	5.5	173.5	0.012	0.370	9.2	8.95	5.5	174.0	0.011	0.370
20	55.5	1.90	11.0	176.0	0.024	0.368	11.6	7.23	10.5	177.5	0.022	0.370
30	66.3	1.60	17.0	179.0	0.035	0.366	14.4	5.90	16.0	181.5	0.033	0.371
40	78.0	1.37	23.0	182.0	0.047	0.366	17.7	4.88	21.5	185.0	0.044	0.371
50	91.8	1.18	29.0	185.0	0.059	0.365	21.6	4.07	27.0	188.5	0.056	0.373
60	107.1	1.01	35.0	188.0	0.070	0.364	26.3	3.40	33.0	192.5	0.067	0.374
70	124.0	0.883	41.0	190.5	0.082	0.364	31.6	2.88	38.5	196.0	0.078	0.375
80	142.8	0.770	47.5	193.5	0.093	0.364	37.6	2.46	44.5	199.5	0.089	0.376
90	164.0	0.673	54.0	196.5	0.105	0.364	44.5	2.10	51.0	203.0	0.100	0.377
100	187.0	0.591	60.5	199.0	0.116	0.363	52.2	1.81	57.0	206.5	0.111	0.378
110	212.0	0.521	67.0	201.0	0.128	0.363	60.8	1.58	63.5	210.5	0.122	0.380
120	240.0	0.459	73.5	202.5	0.140	0.363	70.8	1.38	70.0	213.5	0.134	0.382
130	......	......	......	......	......	.....	81.4	1.21	76.5	217.0	0.145	0.384
140	......	......	......	......	......	.....	92.6	1.07	83.5	221.0	0.157	0.386

Table 40. Properties of Freon 11 and Freon 12

Temp, deg F	Freon 11 (CCl_3F) (Heat measurements are from −40 F)						Freon 12 (CCl_2F_2) (Heat measurements are from −40 F)					
	Pressure, psia	Specific volume of vapor, cu ft per lb	Enthalpy, Btu per lb: Liquid h_f	Enthalpy, Btu per lb: Vapor h_g	Entropy: Liquid S_f	Entropy: Vapor S_g	Pressure, psia	Specific volume of vapor, cu ft per lb	Enthalpy, Btu per lb: Liquid h_f	Enthalpy, Btu per lb: Vapor h_g	Entropy: Liquid S_f	Entropy: Vapor S_g
−40	0.739	44.2	0.00	87.48	0.0000	0.2085	9.3	3.91	0.00	73.50	0.0000	0.1752
−30	1.03	32.3	1.97	88.67	0.0046	0.2064	12.0	3.09	2.03	74.70	0.00471	0.1739
−20	1.42	24.1	3.94	89.87	0.0091	0.2046	15.3	2.47	4.07	75.87	0.00940	0.1727
−10	1.92	18.2	5.91	91.07	0.0136	0.2030	19.2	2.00	6.14	77.05	0.01403	0.1717
0	2.55	13.9	7.89	92.27	0.0179	0.2015	23.9	1.64	8.25	78.21	0.01869	0.1709
10	3.35	10.8	9.88	93.48	0.0222	0.2003	29.3	1.35	10.39	79.36	0.02328	0.1701
15	3.82	9.59	10.88	94.09	0.0244	0.1997	32.4	1.23	11.48	79.94	0.02556	0.1698
20	4.34	8.52	11.87	94.69	0.0264	0.1991	35.7	1.12	12.55	80.49	0.02783	0.1695
25	4.92	7.58	12.88	95.30	0.0285	0.1986	39.3	1.02	13.66	81.06	0.03008	0.1692
30	5.56	6.75	13.88	95.91	0.0306	0.1981	43.2	0.939	14.76	81.61	0.03233	0.1689
35	6.26	6.07	14.88	96.51	0.0326	0.1976	47.3	0.862	15.87	82.16	0.03458	0.1686
40	7.03	5.45	15.89	97.11	0.0346	0.1972	51.7	0.792	17.00	82.71	0.03680	0.1683
45	7.88	4.90	16.91	97.72	0.0366	0.1968	56.4	0.730	18.14	83.26	0.03903	0.1681
50	8.80	4.42	17.92	98.32	0.0386	0.1964	61.4	0.673	19.27	83.78	0.04126	0.1678
55	9.81	4.00	18.95	98.93	0.0406	0.1960	66.7	0.622	20.41	84.31	0.04348	0.1676
60	10.9	3.63	19.96	99.53	0.0426	0.1958	72.4	0.575	21.57	84.82	0.04568	0.1674
70	13.4	2.99	22.02	100.73	0.0465	0.1951	84.8	0.493	23.90	85.82	0.05009	0.1670
80	16.3	2.49	24.09	101.93	0.0504	0.1947	98.8	0.425	26.28	86.80	0.05446	0.1666
90	19.7	2.09	26.18	103.12	0.0542	0.1942	114.3	0.368	28.70	87.74	0.05882	0.1662
100	23.6	1.76	28.27	104.30	0.0580	0.1938	131.6	0.319	31.16	88.62	0.06316	0.1658
110	28.1	1.50	30.40	105.47	0.0617	0.1935	150.7	0.277	33.65	89.43	0.06749	0.1654
120	33.2	1.28	32.53	106.63	0.0654	0.1933	171.8	0.240	36.16	90.15	0.07180	0.1649
130	39.0	1.10	34.67	107.78	0.0691	0.1931	194.9	0.208	38.69	90.76	0.07607	0.1644

Table 41. Properties of Freon 21 and Freon 22

Temp, deg F	Freon 22 ($CHClF_2$) (Heat measurements are from −40 F)						Freon 21 ($CHCl_2F$) (Heat measurements are from −40 F)					
	Pressure, psia	Specific volume of vapor, cu ft per lb	Enthalpy, Btu per lb		Entropy		Pressure, psia	Specific volume of vapor, cu ft per lb	Enthalpy, Btu per lb		Entropy	
			Liquid h_f	Vapor h_g	Liquid S_f	Vapor S_g			Liquid h_f	Vapor h_g	Liquid S_f	Vapor S_g
−40	15.31	3.279	0.00	100.46	0.0000	0.2394	1.36	32.1	0.00	114.6	0.0000	0.2730
−30	19.72	2.590	2.62	101.63	0.0062	0.2367	1.89	23.6	2.36	115.8	0.0055	0.2695
−20	25.01	2.074	5.28	102.79	0.0123	0.2341	2.58	17.7	4.71	117.0	0.0109	0.2663
−10	31.29	1.681	7.96	103.92	0.0182	0.2316	3.46	13.4	7.07	118.2	0.0162	0.2633
0	38.79	1.373	10.63	105.02	0.0240	0.2293	4.58	10.3	9.44	119.4	0.0214	0.2606
10	47.63	1.130	13.29	106.08	0.0296	0.2272	5.98	8.08	11.81	120.6	0.0265	0.2581
15	52.63	1.028	14.63	106.61	0.0313	0.2262	6.80	7.18	13.01	121.2	0.0291	0.2569
20	57.98	0.9369	15.98	107.13	0.0352	0.2253	7.70	6.39	14.21	121.8	0.0316	0.2559
25	63.75	0.8552	17.34	107.63	0.0377	0.2244	8.70	5.71	15.40	122.4	0.0341	0.2548
30	69.93	0.7816	18.74	108.13	0.0409	0.2235	9.79	5.11	16.61	123.0	0.0365	0.2538
35	76.59	0.7157	20.20	108.62	0.0439	0.2226	11.0	4.59	17.83	123.6	0.0390	0.2528
40	83.72	0.6559	21.70	109.09	0.0469	0.2218	12.3	4.13	19.04	124.2	0.0414	0.2519
45	91.31	0.6024	23.20	109.54	0.0499	0.2209	13.8	3.73	20.27	124.8	0.0439	0.2510
50	99.4	0.5537	24.73	109.98	0.0528	0.2201	15.3	3.37	21.49	125.4	0.0463	0.2502
55	108.0	0.5099	26.27	110.39	0.0558	0.2193	17.0	3.10	22.73	126.0	0.0487	0.2493
60	117.2	0.4695	27.83	110.78	0.0588	0.2185	18.9	2.77	23.98	126.6	0.0511	0.2486
70	137.2	0.4000	30.99	111.49	0.0648	0.2168	23.1	2.30	26.49	127.8	0.0559	0.2471
80	159.7	0.3417	34.27	112.13	0.0708	0.2151	28.0	1.92	29.03	129.0	0.0606	0.2458
90	184.8	0.2928	37.61	112.67	0.0768	0.2133	33.6	1.62	31.59	130.1	0.0652	0.2446
100	212.6	0.2517	40.98	113.06	0.0827	0.2115	40.0	1.37	34.18	131.3	0.0699	0.2434
110	243.4	0.2167	44.35	113.29	0.0886	0.2096	47.4	1.17	36.79	132.4	0.0745	0.2424
120	277.3	0.1871	47.85	113.52	0.0945	0.2078	55.7	1.00	39.46	133.5	0.0791	0.2414
130	313.5	0.1629	51.5	113.71			65.1	0.862	42.13	134.6	0.0837	0.2405

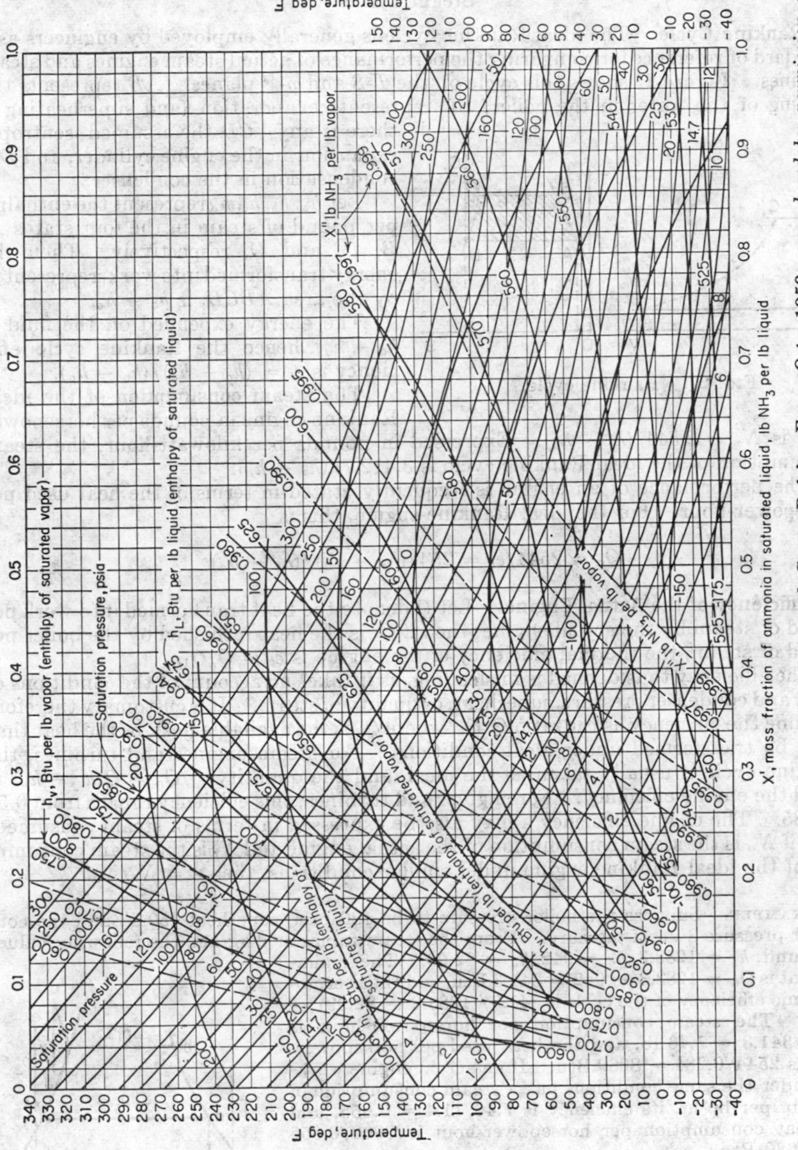

FIG. 26. Properties of aqua-ammonia. (*Kohloss and Scott, Refrig. Eng., Oct., 1950, reproduced by permission of ASHRAE.*)

Steam Cycles

Rankine Cycle. The ideal Rankine cycle is generally employed by engineers as a standard of reference for comparing the performance of actual steam engines and steam turbines. Figure 27 shows this cycle on the T-S and p-V planes. AB represents the heating of the water in the boiler, BC represents evaporation (and superheating if there is any), CD the assumed isentropic expansion in the engine cylinder, and DA condensation in the condenser.

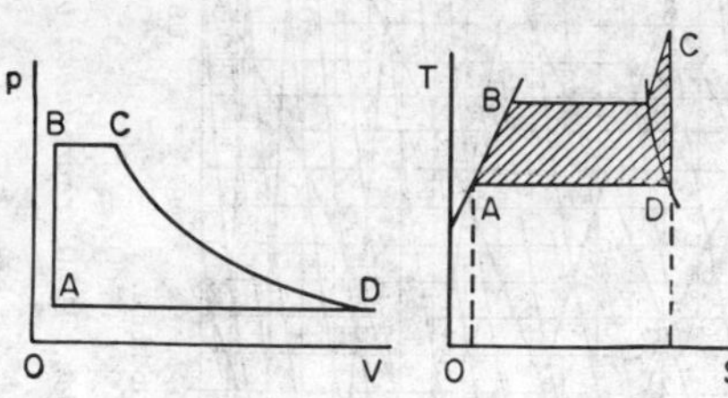

Fig. 27. Rankine cycle.

Let h_a, h_b, h_c, h_d represent the enthalpy per pound of steam in the four states A, B, C, and D, respectively. Then the energy transformed into work, represented by the area $ABCD$, is $h_c - h_d$.

The energy expended on the fluid is $h_c - h_a$; hence the **Rankine cycle efficiency** is $e_t = (h_c - h_d)/(h_c - h_a)$.

The **steam consumption** of the ideal Rankine engine in pounds per horsepower hour is $N_r = 2{,}544/(h_c - h_d)$. Expressed in pounds per kilowatt-hour, the steam consumption of the ideal Rankine cycle is $3{,}412.7/(h_c - h_d)$.

The performance of an engine is frequently stated in terms of the heat used per horsepower-hour. For the ideal Rankine engine, this is

$$Q_r = 2544/e_t = 2544(h_c - h_a)/(h_c - h_d)$$

Efficiency of the Actual Engine. Let Q denote the heat transformed into work per pound of steam by the actual engine; then if Q_1 is the heat furnished by the boiler per pound of steam, the **thermal efficiency of the engine** is $e_t = Q/Q_1$.

The efficiency thus defined is misleading, as it takes no account of the conditions of boiler and condenser pressure, superheat, or quality of steam. It is customary therefore to define the efficiency as the ratio Q/Q_a, where Q_a is the **available heat,** or the heat that could be transformed under ideal conditions. For steam engines and turbines, the Rankine cycle is usually taken as the ideal, and the quantity $Q/Q_a = Q(h_c - h_d)$ is called the **engine efficiency.** For engines and turbines, this efficiency ranges from 0.50 to 0.85. The engine efficiency e may also be expressed in terms of steam consumed; thus, if N_a is the steam consumption of the actual engine and N_r is the steam consumption of the ideal Rankine engine under similar conditions, then $e = N_r/N_a$.

Example. Suppose the boiler pressure to be 180 psia, superheat 150 F, and the condenser pressure 3 in. of mercury. From the steam tables or diagram, the following values are found: $h_c = 1283.3$, $h_d = 942$, $h_a = 82.99$. The available heat is $Q_a = 1283.3 - 942 = 341.3$ Btu, and the thermodynamic efficiency of the cycle is $341.3/(1283.3 - 82.99) = 0.284$. The steam consumption per horsepower-hour is $2{,}544/341.3 = 7.46$ lb, and the heat used per horsepower-hour is $2544/0.284 = 8960$ Btu. If an actual engine working under the same conditions has a steam consumption of 11.4 lb. per hp-hr, its efficiency is $7.46/11.4 = 0.655$, and its heat consumption per horsepower-hour is $8960/0.655 = 13{,}680$ Btu.

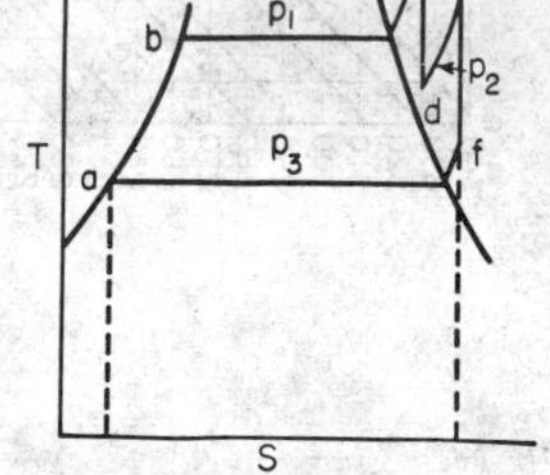

Fig. 28. Reheating cycle.

Reheating Cycle. Let the steam after expansion from p_1 to an intermediate pressure p_2 (cd, Fig. 28) be reheated at constant pressure p_2, as indicated by de. Then follows the isentropic expansion to pressure p_3, represented by ef.

The energy absorbed by 1 lb of steam is $h_c - h_a$ from the boiler, and $h_e - h_d$ from the reheating. The work done, neglecting the energy required to operate the boiler feed pump, etc., is $h_c - h_d + h_e - h_f$. Hence the efficiency of the cycle is

$$e_t = \frac{h_c - h_d + h_e - h_f}{h_c - h_a + h_e - h_d}$$

Bleeding Cycle. In the **regenerative** or bleeding cycle, steam is drawn from the turbine at one or more stages and used to heat the feed water. Figure 29 shows a diagrammatic arrangement for bleeding at one stage. Entering the turbine is $1 + w$ lb, of steam at p_1, t_1, and enthalpy h_1. At the bleeding point w lb at p_2, t_2, h_2 enters the feed-water heater. The remaining 1 lb passes through the turbine and condenser and enters the feed-water heater as water at temperature t_3. Let t' denote the temperature of the water leaving the heater, and h' the corresponding enthalpy of the liquid. Then the equation for the interchange of heat in the heater is

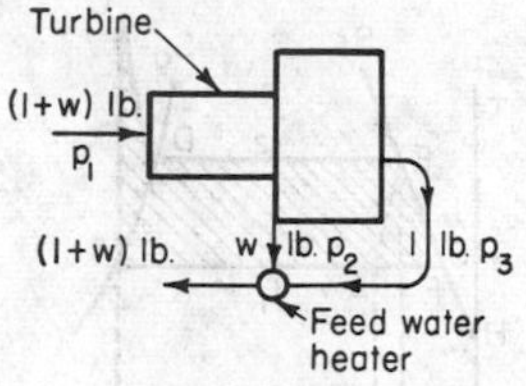

$$w(h_2 - h') = h' - h_{f3}$$

Fig. 29. Regenerative feed-water heating.

The work done by the bled steam is $w(h_1 - h_2)$ and that by the 1 lb of steam going completely through the turbine is $h_1 - h_3$. Total work $= w(h_1 - h_2) + (h_1 - h_3)$ if work to the pumps is neglected. The heat supplied between feed-water heater and turbine is $(1 + w)(h_1 - h')$. Hence the ideal efficiency of the cycle is

$$e_t = \frac{w(h_1 - h_2) + h_1 - h_3}{(1 + w)(h \;\; - h')}$$

For a full discussion of reheating and regenerative cycles, see *Trans. ASME*, **45,** articles by Wohlenberg, and by Hirschfield and Ellenwood. See also Stodola, "Steam and Gas Turbines," Loewenstein's translation, 1927, p. 1310; Bartlett, "Steam Turbine Performance and Economics," McGraw-Hill; Salisbury, "Steam Turbines and Their Cycles," Wiley; Lee, "Theory and Design of Steam and Gas Turbines," McGraw-Hill; Potter, "Power Plant Theory and Design," Ronald.

The heat from **nuclear reactors** is used for heating services or, through thermodynamic cycles, for power purposes. The reactor coolant transfers the heat generated by fission so as to be used directly, or through an intermediate heat-exchange system, avoiding radioactive contamination. Steam is the preferred thermodynamic fluid in practice so that the Rankine-cycle performance standards with regenerative and reheat variations, prevail. Adaptation of gas-turbine cycles, using various gases, can be expected as allowable reactor temperatures are raised.

Many engineers and scientists are actively engaged in research dealing with the location, production, utilization, transmission, storage, and distribution of new forms of energy. Examples are the study of the energy released in the fusion of hydrogen nuclei and research in solar energy. Considerable effort is being expended in studying the feasibility of combining the gas turbine with a steam-generating plant. The possibility of efficiency improvement over the steam cycle is due to the higher inlet temperatures associated with the gas turbine. Significant advances are predicted in the near future in expanding our energy sources and reserves. (See Sec. 9.)

REFRIGERATION

(See also Sec. 18)

Vapor-compression Machines. The essential parts of a vapor-compression system are the same as in the system using air, except that the expansion cylinder is replaced by an expansion valve through which the liquified medium flows from the high-pressure condensing coils to the low-pressure brine coils. The cycle of operation is best shown on the *T-S* plane (Fig. 30). The point *B* represents the state of the refrigerating medium leaving the brine coils and entering the compressor. Usually in this state the fluid is nearly dry saturated vapor; *i.e.*, point *B* is near the saturation curve S_g. *BC* represents the assumed reversible adiabatic compression, during which the fluid is usually superheated. In the state C, the superheated vapor passes into the cooling coils and is cooled at constant pressure, as indicated by CD, and then condensed at temperature T_2, as shown by DE. The liquid now flows through the expansion valve into the brine coils. This is a throttling process, and the final-state point A is located on the T_1-line in such a position as to make the enthalpy for state A (= area $OHGAA_1$) equal to the enthalpy at E (= area $OHEE_1$). The mixture of liquid and vapor now absorbs heat from the brine and vaporizes, as indicated by AB.

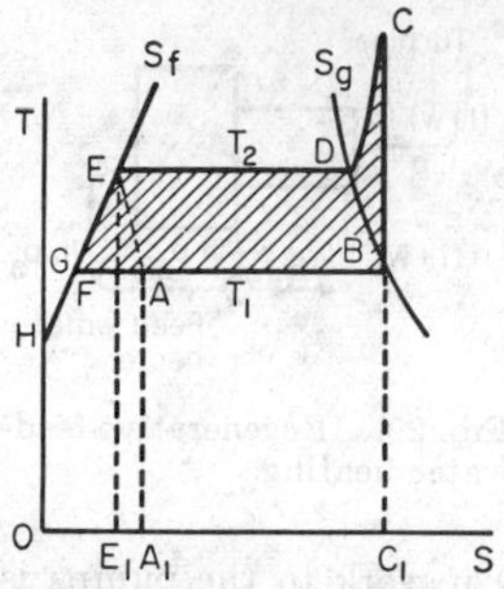

FIG. 30. Vapor-compression refrigeration cycle.

The **heat absorbed from the brine,** represented by area A_1ABC_1, is

$$Q_1 = h_b - h_a = h_b - h_e$$

The **heat rejected to the cooling water,** represented by area C_1CDEE_1, is

$$Q_2 = h_c - h_e = c_p(T_c - T_d) + r_2 \qquad \text{approx}$$

where r_2 denotes the enthalpy of vaporization at the upper temperature T_2, and c_p the specific heat of the superheated vapor. The **work** that must be **supplied per pound of fluid circulated** is $W = J(Q_2 - Q_1) = J(h_c - h_b)$. The ratio $JQ_1/W = (h_b - h_e)/(h_c - h_b)$ is sometimes called the **coefficient of performance.**

If Q denotes the heat to be absorbed from the brine per hour, then the **quantity of fluid circulated per hour** is $m = Q/(h_b - h_a)$; or, if B is taken on the saturation curve, $m = Q/(h_{g1} - h_{f2})$.

The work per hour is $W = Jm(h_c - h_{g1}) = JQ(h_c - h_{g1})/(h_{g1} - h_{f2})$ ft-lb, and the **horsepower required** is $H = Q(h_c - h_{g1})/2544(h_{g1} - h_{f2})$.

If v_{g1} is the volume of the saturated vapor at the temperature T_1 in the brine coils, and n the number of working strokes per minute, the **displacement volume of the compressor cylinder** is $V = mv_{g1}/60n$.

The values of h_{g1}, h_{f2} in the preceding formulas are found in the tables of saturated vapors. The enthalpy h_c of the superheated vapor may be determined in the case of ammonia from Table 34 for superheated ammonia. (See also Fig. 24.)

The work necessary for operating a refrigerator, although usually supplied through the compressor, may be supplied in other ways. Thus in **absorption refrigerators** (see Secs. 12, 18) an absorbent, usually water, absorbs the refrigerant, usually ammonia. The water, by its affinity for the ammonia, has, in a thermodynamic sense, ability to do work. Having absorbed the ammonia and thereby lost its ability to do work, the water may have its work capacity restored by passing the ammonia-water solution through a rectifying column from which water and ammonia emerge. With operation under a suitable pressure, the ammonia is condensed to a liquid. This, in turn, may be evaporated, yielding refrigeration, the ammonia vapors being once again absorbed in the water. Thermodynamically the analysis for these absorption cycles is similar to to that for compression cycles. See Fig. 26 for properties of aqua-ammonia.

THERMODYNAMICS OF FLOW OF COMPRESSIBLE FLUIDS

REFERENCES: Stodola, "Steam and Gas Turbines," Loewenstein's translation, McGraw-Hill. Ruhemann, "Separation of Gases," Clarendon Press. Berry, *Mech. Eng.*, Nov., 1929. Walker, Lewis, McAdams, and Gilliland, "Principles of Chemical Engineering," McGraw-Hill. Kennan, "Thermodynamics," Wiley. Shapiro, "The Dynamics and Thermodynamics of Compressible Fluid Flow," Ronald. Hall, "Thermodynamics of Fluid Flow," Prentice-Hall. Murphy, "Similitude in Engineering," Ronald. Binder, "Advanced Fluid Dynamics and Fluid Machinery," Prentice-Hall. Goldstein, "Modern Developments in Fluid Dynamics," Vols. I, II, Oxford. Streeter, "Fluid Mechanics," McGraw-Hill. Rotty, "Introduction to Gas Dynamics," Wiley. Schlichting, "Boundary Layer Theory," translated by J. Keston, McGraw-Hill.

Important examples of the flow of compressible fluids are the following: (1) the flow of air and steam through orifices and short tubes or nozzles, as in the steam turbine, (2) the flow of compressed air, steam, and illuminating gas in long mains, (3) the flow of low-pressure gases, as furnace gases in ducts and chimneys or air in ventilating ducts, (4) the flow of gases in moving channels, as in the centrifugal fan.

Notation

Let A = area of section, sq ft
C = empirically determined coefficient of discharge
D = inside diameter of pipe, ft
$d = 12D$ = inside diameter of pipe, in.
F_{12} = energy expended in overcoming internal and external friction between sections A_1 and A_2
F' = energy used in overcoming friction, ft-lb per lb of fluid flowing
f = friction factor = $4f'$
g = 32.2 = local acceleration of gravity, ft per sec²
g_c = a dimensional constant
h = enthalpy, Btu per lb
J = 778.3
$k = c_p/c_v$
L = equivalent length of pipe, ft
m = mass of fluid flowing past a given section per sec, lb
μ = viscosity, centipoises
P = pressure, psia
ΔP = differential pressure across nozzle, psi
p = pressure of fluid at given section, lb per sq ft abs
p_m = critical flow pressure
Q_{12} = heat entering the flowing fluid between sections A_1 and A_2
q = volume of fluid flowing past section, cfm
R = ideal gas constant
ρ = density, lb per cu ft
T = temperature R
V = mean velocity at the given section, fps
v = specific volume
w = weight of fluid flowing past a given section per sec, lb
z = height from center of gravity of flow to a fixed base level, ft

The cross sections of the tube or channel are denoted by A_1, A_2, etc. (Fig. 31), and the various magnitudes pertaining to these sections are denoted by corresponding subscripts. Thus, at section A_1, the velocity, specific volume, and pressure are, respectively, V_1, v_1, p_1; at section A_2, they are V_2, v_2, p_2.

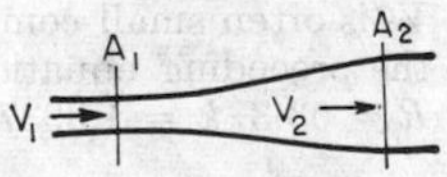

FIG. 31

Fundamental Equations. In the interpretation of fluid-flow phenomena, three fundamental equations are of importance.

1. The continuity equation, or material balance,

$$\frac{A_1V_1}{v_1} = \frac{A_2V_2}{v_2} \quad \text{or} \quad \frac{dv}{v} = \frac{dA}{A} + \frac{dV}{V}$$

2. The first law or energy balance for steady flow,

$$Jq = J(h_2 - h_1) + \frac{V_2^2 - V_1^2}{2g_c} + \frac{g}{g_c}(z_2 - z_1)$$

3. The available energy balance for a steady-flow process, based on unit weight, is

$$v\,dp + \frac{V\,dV}{g} + dF + dz = 0$$

In the processes here discussed, no net external or shaft work is performed.

For most actual processes, the third equation cannot be integrated because the actual path is not known. Usually, adiabatic flow is assumed, but occasionally the assumption of isothermal conditions may be more nearly correct.

Flow through Orifices and Nozzles. As a compressible fluid passes through a nozzle, drop in pressure and simultaneous increase in velocity result. By assuming the type of flow, *e.g.*, adiabatic, it is possible to calculate from the properties of the fluid the required area for the cross section of the nozzle at any point in order that the flowing fluid may just fill the provided space. From this calculation, it is found that for all compressible fluids the nozzle form must first be converging but eventually, if the pressure drops sufficiently, a place is reached where to accommodate the increased volume due to the expansion the nozzle must become diverging in form. The smallest cross section of the nozzle is called the throat, and the pressure at the throat is the **critical flow pressure** (not to be confused with the previously mentioned critical pressure, p. 4–31). If the nozzle is cut off at the throat with no diverging section and the pressure at the discharge end is progressively decreased, with fixed inlet pressure, the amount of fluid passing increases until the discharge pressure equals the critical, but further decrease in discharge pressure does not result in increased flow. This is not true for thin plate orifices. For any particular gas, the ratio of critical to inlet pressure is approximately constant. For gases, $p_m/p_1 = 0.53$ approx; for saturated steam the ratio is about 0.575; and for moderately superheated steam it is about 0.55.

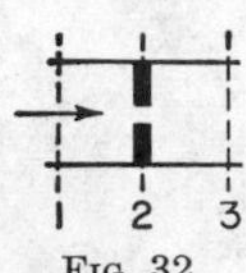

FIG. 32

Formulas for Orifice Computations. The general fundamental relation is given by the energy balance $(V_2^2 - V_1^2)/2g_c = -Jh_{12}$. Referring to Fig. 32, let section 2 be taken at the orifice, section 3 is somewhat beyond the orifice on the downstream side, and section 1 is before the orifice on the upstream side. Then

$$V_2 = C\sqrt{2g_cJ(h_1 - h_2)} \bigg/ \sqrt{1 - \left(\frac{A_2}{A_1}\right)^2 \left(\frac{v_1}{v_2}\right)^2}$$

The coefficient of discharge factor C is discussed on p. 16–19.

The volume of gas passing is V_2A_2 cu ft per sec, and the quantity is $V_2A_2\rho$. For ideal gases, assuming reversible adiabatic expansion through the orifice,

$$V_2 = C\sqrt{2g_cp_1v_1\frac{k}{k-1}\left[1 - \left(\frac{p_2}{p_1}\right)^{\frac{k-1}{k}}\right]} \bigg/ \sqrt{1 - \left(\frac{A_2}{A_1}\right)^2 \left(\frac{p_2}{p_1}\right)^{\frac{2}{k}}}$$

$$m = CA_2p_2\sqrt{\frac{2g_c}{RT_1}\frac{k}{k-1}\left(\frac{p_1}{p_2}\right)^{\frac{k-1}{k}}\left[\left(\frac{p_1}{p_2}\right)^{\frac{k-1}{k}} - 1\right]} \bigg/ \sqrt{1 - \left(\frac{A_2}{A_1}\right)^2 \left(\frac{p_2}{p_1}\right)^{\frac{2}{k}}}$$

V_1 is often small compared with V_2, and under these conditions the denominators in the preceding equations become approximately equal to unity. For air, assuming $R = 53.3$, $k = 1.3937$, and V_1 negligible,

$$m = 2.05CA_2p_2\sqrt{(1/T_1)(p_1/p_2)^{0.283}[(p_1/p_2)^{0.283} - 1]}$$

Although the preceding formulas are generally applicable under the assumed conditions, it must be remembered that irrespective of the value of p_3, p_2 cannot become less than p_m. When p_3 is less than p_m, the flow rate becomes independent of the downstream pressure; for ideal gases,

$$m = CA_2p_1\sqrt{\frac{g_c}{RT_1}k\left(\frac{2}{k+1}\right)^{(k+1)/(k-1)}}$$

or for air

$$m = 0.53Cp_1\frac{A_2}{\sqrt{T_1}}$$

The following formula (see ASME Power Test Code No. 10 for 1949) is useful for calculating the flow rate, in cubic feet per minute, of any gas (provided no condensation occurs) through a nozzle for pressure drops less than the critical range:

$$q_1 = \frac{31.5Cd_2^2Y'}{\rho_1}\sqrt{\rho_2\,\Delta P}$$

In this equation,

$$Y' = \left(\frac{k}{k-1}\right)^{1/2}\left(\frac{P_2}{P_1}\right)^{\frac{1}{k}}\sqrt{\left[1-\left(\frac{P_2}{P_1}\right)^{\frac{k-1}{k}}\right]\Big/\left(1-\frac{P_2}{P_1}\right)\left[1-\left(\frac{d_n}{d_1}\right)^4\left(\frac{P_2}{P_1}\right)^{\frac{2}{k}}\right]}$$

where P_1 = static pressure on upstream side of nozzle, P_2 = static pressure on downstream side of nozzle, d_1 = diameter of pipe upstream of nozzle, d_n = nozzle throat diameter. Values of Y' are given in Table 42.

Table 42. Values for Y'

P_2/P_1	$k = 1.40$, d_2/d_1					$k = 1.35$, d_2/d_1					$k = 1.30$, d_2/d_1				
	0	0.2	0.3	0.4	0.5	0	0.2	0.3	0.4	0.5	0	0.2	0.3	0.4	0.5
1.00	1.000	1.001	1.004	1.013	1.033	1.000	1.001	1.004	1.013	1.033	1.000	1.001	1.004	1.013	1.033
0.99	0.995	0.995	0.999	1.007	1.027	0.994	0.995	0.999	1.007	1.027	0.994	0.995	0.998	1.007	1.026
0.98	0.989	0.990	0.993	1.002	1.021	0.989	0.990	0.993	1.001	1.020	0.988	0.989	0.992	1.001	1.020
0.97	0.984	0.985	0.988	0.996	1.015	0.983	0.984	0.987	0.995	1.014	0.983	0.983	0.986	0.995	1.013
0.96	0.978	0.979	0.982	0.990	1.009	0.978	0.978	0.981	0.990	1.008	0.977	0.977	0.980	0.989	1.007
0.95	0.973	0.974	0.977	0.985	1.002	0.972	0.973	0.976	0.984	1.001	0.971	0.972	0.974	0.982	1.000
0.94	0.967	0.968	0.971	0.979	0.996	0.966	0.967	0.970	0.978	0.995	0.965	0.966	0.968	0.976	0.993
0.93	0.962	0.963	0.965	0.973	0.990	0.961	0.961	0.964	0.972	0.989	0.959	0.960	0.962	0.970	0.987
0.92	0.956	0.957	0.960	0.967	0.984	0.955	0.955	0.958	0.966	0.982	0.953	0.954	0.956	0.964	0.980
0.91	0.951	0.951	0.954	0.961	0.978	0.949	0.950	0.952	0.960	0.976	0.947	0.948	0.950	0.957	0.973
0.90	0.945	0.946	0.948	0.956	0.971	0.943	0.944	0.946	0.953	0.969	0.941	0.942	0.944	0.951	0.966
0.89	0.939	0.940	0.943	0.950	0.965	0.937	0.938	0.940	0.947	0.963	0.935	0.935	0.938	0.945	0.959
0.88	0.934	0.934	0.937	0.944	0.959	0.931	0.932	0.934	0.941	0.956	0.929	0.929	0.932	0.938	0.953
0.87	0.928	0.928	0.931	0.938	0.953	0.925	0.926	0.926	0.935	0.950	0.922	0.923	0.926	0.932	0.946
0.86	0.922	0.923	0.925	0.932	0.946	0.919	0.920	0.922	0.929	0.943	0.916	0.917	0.919	0.926	0.939
0.85	0.916	0.917	0.919	0.926	0.940	0.913	0.914	0.916	0.923	0.936	0.910	0.911	0.913	0.923	0.932
0.84	0.910	0.911	0.913	0.920	0.933	0.907	0.908	0.910	0.916	0.930	0.904	0.904	0.907	0.919	0.925
0.83	0.904	0.905	0.907	0.913	0.927	0.901	0.902	0.904	0.910	0.923	0.897	0.898	0.900	0.916	0.918
0.82	0.898	0.899	0.901	0.907	0.920	0.895	0.895	0.898	0.904	0.917	0.891	0.891	0.894	0.900	0.911
0.81	0.892	0.893	0.895	0.901	0.914	0.889	0.889	0.891	0.897	0.910	0.885	0.885	0.887	0.893	0.904
0.80	0.886	0.887	0.889	0.895	0.907	0.883	0.883	0.885	0.891	0.903	0.878	0.879	0.880	0.886	0.897
0.79	0.880	0.881	0.883	0.889	0.901	0.876	0.877	0.879	0.834	0.896	0.872	0.872	0.874	0.880	0.890
0.78	0.874	0.875	0.877	0.882	0.894	0.870	0.870	0.872	0.878	0.889	0.865	0.865	0.868	0.873	0.883
0.77	0.868	0.869	0.871	0.876	0.887	0.864	0.864	0.866	0.871	0.882	0.859	0.859	0.861	0.866	0.876
0.76	0.862	0.862	0.864	0.869	0.881	0.857	0.858	0.859	0.865	0.876	0.852	0.852	0.854	0.859	0.869
0.75	0.856	0.856	0.858	0.863	0.874	0.851	0.851	0.853	0.858	0.869	0.845	0.846	0.848	0.852	0.862
0.74	0.849	0.850	0.852	0.857	0.867	0.844	0.845	0.846	0.851	0.862	0.839	0.839	0.841	0.845	0.855
0.73	0.843	0.844	0.845	0.850	0.860	0.838	0.838	0.840	0.845	0.855	0.832	0.832	0.834	0.838	0.848
0.72	0.837	0.837	0.839	0.844	0.854	0.831	0.831	0.833	0.838	0.848	0.825	0.825	0.827	0.831	0.841
0.71	0.830	0.831	0.832	0.837	0.847	0.825	0.825	0.827	0.831	0.840	0.818	0.819	0.820	0.824	0.834
0.70	0.824	0.824	0.826	0.830	0.840	0.818	0.818	0.820	0.824	0.833	0.811	0.812	0.813	0.817	0.826

If the velocity of approach is zero (as with a nozzle taking in air from the outside) d_1 is infinite and d_2/d_1 is zero.

Where the pressure drop through the orifice is small, the hydraulic formulas (pp. 3–55 and 3–68) applicable to incompressible fluids may be employed for gases and other compressible fluids.

In general, the formulas of the preceding section are applicable to nozzles. When so used however, the proper value of the discharge coefficient must be employed. For steam nozzles, this may be as high as 0.94 to 0.96, although for many orifice installations it is as low as 0.50 to 0.60. Steam nozzles constitute a most important type, and calculations for these are best carried out with the aid of a Mollier or similar chart.

Formulas for Discharge of Steam. When the back pressure p_3 is less than the critical pressure p_m, the discharge depends upon the area of orifice A_2 and reservoir pressure p_1. There are three formulas widely used to express, approximately, the discharge m of **saturated** steam in terms of A_2 and p_1 as follows:

1. Napier's equation, $m = A_2 p_1/70$.
2. Grashof's formula, $m = 0.0165 A_2 p_1^{0.97}$.
3. Rateau's formula, $m = A_2 p_1(16.367 - 0.96 \log p_1)/1{,}000$.

In these formulas, A_2 is to be taken in square inches, p_1 in pounds per square inch. Napier's formula is merely convenient as a rough check. Formulas 2 and 3 are applicable to well-rounded convergent orifices, in which case the coefficient of discharge may be taken as 1; *i.e.*, no correction is required. For flow of **superheated** steam, see also p. 9–61.

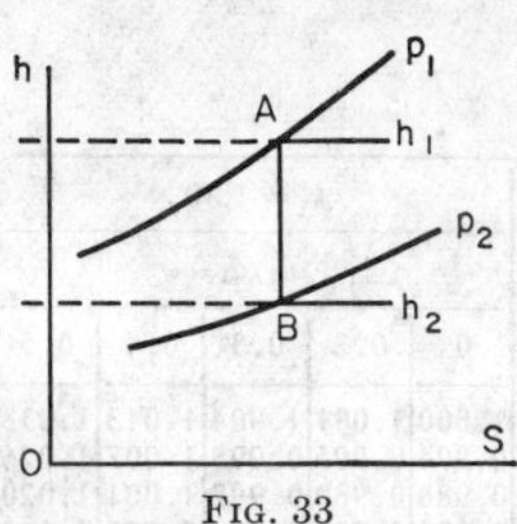

FIG. 33

When the back pressure p_2 is greater than the critical flow pressure p_m, the velocity and discharge are found most conveniently from the general formulas of flow. From the steam tables (p. 4–38) or from the **Mollier chart** (p. 4–35), find the initial enthalpy h_1 and the enthalpy h_2 after isentropic expansion; also the specific volume v_2 (see Fig. 33). Then

$$V_2 = 223.7\sqrt{h_1 - h_2} \qquad \text{and} \qquad m = A_2V_2/v_2$$

The same method is used in the case of steam initially superheated.

EXAMPLE. Required the discharge through an orifice ½ in. diam of steam at 140 psia superheated 110 F, back pressure, 90 psia.

From the Mollier chart and the steam tables, $h_1 = 1255.7$, $h_2 = 1214$, $v_2 = 5.30$ cu ft.

$$V_2 = 233.7\sqrt{1{,}255.7 - 1{,}214} = 1{,}455$$
$$A_2 = 0.1964 \text{ sq in.} = (0.1964/144) \text{ sq ft}$$
$$m = A_2V_2/v_2 = (0.1964/144) \times (1{,}455/5.30) = 0.372 \text{ lb per sec}$$

This calculation assumes ideal conditions, and the results must be multiplied by the correct coefficient of discharge to get actual results.

Flow through Converging-Diverging Nozzles. At the throat, or smallest cross section of the nozzle (Fig. 34), the pressure of saturated steam takes the value $p_m = 0.57p_1$. The quantity discharged is fixed by the area A_2 of the throat and the initial pressure p_1. For saturated steam, Grashof's or Rateau's formula (see above) may be used. The diverging part of the nozzle permits further expansion to the back pressure p_3, the velocity of the jet meanwhile increasing from $V_m(= V_2)$, the critical velocity at the throat, to V_3 given by the fundamental equation $V_3 = 223.7\sqrt{h_1 - h_3}$.

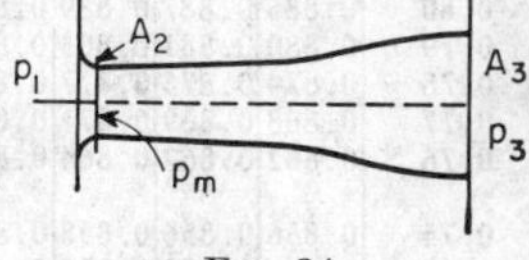

FIG. 34

The frictional resistances in the nozzle have the effect of decreasing the jet energy $V_3^2/2g_c$ and correspondingly increasing the enthalpy of the flowing fluid. Thus, if h_3 is the enthalpy in the final state with frictionless expansion, $h_3'(>h_3)$ is the enthalpy when friction is taken into account; hence $(V_3')^2/2g_c = J(h_1 - h_3')$ is less than $V_3^2/2g_c = J(h_1 - h_3)$. The loss of kinetic energy, in Btu, is $h_3' - h_3$, and the ratio of this loss to the available kinetic energy, *i.e.* $(h_3' - h_3)/(h_1 - h_3)$, is denoted by y.

The **design of a nozzle for a given discharge** m with pressures p_1 and p_3 is most conveniently effected with the aid of the Mollier chart. Determine p_m, the critical pressure, and h_1, h_m, h_3, assuming frictionless flow. Then

$$V_m = 223.7\sqrt{h_1 - h_m} \qquad \text{and} \qquad V_3' = 223.7\sqrt{(1 - y)(h_1 - h_3)}$$

Next find v_m and v_3'. Then, from the equation of continuity,

$$A_m = mv_m/V_m \qquad \text{and} \qquad A_3' = mv_3'/V_3'$$

The following example illustrates the method.

EXAMPLE. Required the throat and end sections of a nozzle to deliver 0.7 lb of steam per sec. The initial pressure is 160 psia, the back pressure 15 psia, and the steam is initially superheated 100 F; $y = 0.15$.

The critical pressure is $160 \times 0.55 = 88$ lb. On the Mollier chart (Fig. 35), the point A representing the initial state is located, and line of constant entropy (frictionless adiabatic) is drawn from A. This cuts the curves $p = 88$ and $p = 15$ in the points B and C, respectively. The three values of h are found to be $h_1 = 1253$, $h_m = 1199$, $h_3 = 1067$. Of the available drop in enthalpy, $h_1 - h_3 = 185.5$ Btu, 15 percent or 27.9 Btu is lost through friction. Hence, $CD = 27.9$ is laid off and D is projected horizontally to point C' on the curve $p = 15$. Then C' represents the final state of the steam, and the quality is found to be $x = 0.943$. The specific volume in the state C' is $26.29 \times 0.943 = 24.8$ cu ft. Likewise, the specific volume for the state B is found to be 5.29 cu ft/lb.

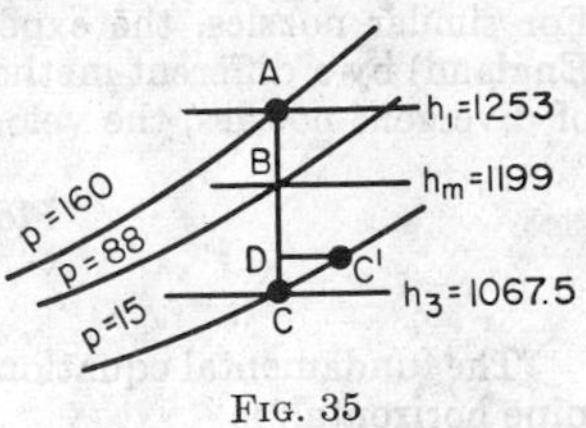

FIG. 35

For the velocities at throat and end sections,

$$V_m = 223.7\sqrt{1{,}253 - 1{,}199} = 1{,}643 \text{ fps}$$
$$V_3 = 223.7\sqrt{185.5 - 27.9} = 2{,}813 \text{ fps}$$
$$A_m = (0.7 \times 5.29)/1{,}643 = 0.00225 \text{ sq ft} = 0.324 \text{ sq in.}$$
$$A_3 = (0.7 \times 24.8)/2{,}813 = 0.00617 \text{ sq ft} = 0.89 \text{ sq in.}$$

The diameters are $d_m = 0.643$ in. and $d_3 = 1.064$ in.

Divergence of Nozzles. Figure 36 gives, for various ratios of expansion, the required "divergence" of the nozzle, *i.e.*, the ratio of the area of any section to the throat area. Thus in the case of saturated steam, if the final pressure is 1/15 of the initial pressure the ratio of the areas is 3.25. The curves apply to frictionless flow; the effect of friction is to increase the divergence.

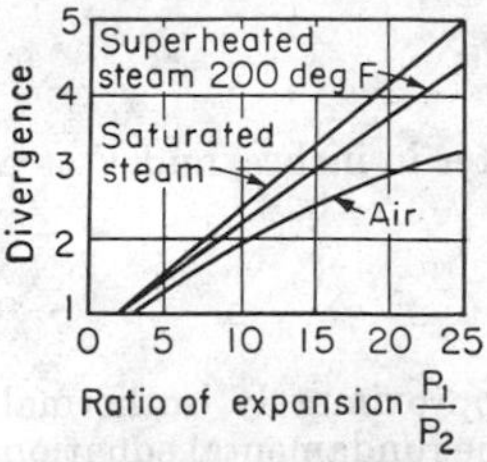

FIG. 36

Theory of Supersaturation. Certain discrepancies between the discharge of saturated steam through an orifice as calculated from the preceding theory and the discharge actually observed are explained by a hypothesis first advanced by Martin, *viz.*, that steam when expanded rapidly, as in turbine nozzles, becomes supersaturated; in other words, the condensation required by the ordinary theory of adiabatic expansion does not occur on account of the rapidity of the expansion (see Goodenough, *Power*, Sept. 27, Oct. 4, 1927).

The effect of supersaturation in turbines is a loss of energy, the amount of which may be 1.5 to 3 percent of the available energy of the steam.

Flow of Wet Steam. When the steam entering a nozzle is wet, the speed of the water particles at exit is not the same as the speed of the steam. Denoting by V the speed of the steam, the speed of the water drops is fV, and f may vary perhaps 0.20 to 0.05 or less, depending on the pressure. The actual velocity V of the steam is greater than the velocity V_0 calculated on the usual assumption that steam and water have the same velocity. If x is the quality of the steam, the ratio of these velocities is

$$V/V_0 = 1/\sqrt{x + f^2(1 - x)}$$

Thus with $x = 0.92$, $f = 0.15$, $V/V_0 = 1.036$. Since the discharge is practically proportional to the steam velocity, the actual discharge in this case is 3.6 percent greater than the discharge computed on the usual assumptions.

Velocity Coefficients. Loss of Energy y. On account of friction losses, the actual velocity V attained by the jet is less than the velocity V_0 calculated under ideal conditions. That is, $V = xV_0$, where x (< 1) is a velocity coefficient. The coefficient x is connected with the coefficient y, giving the loss of energy, by the relation, $y = 1 - x^2$.

The elaborate and accurate experiments of the General Electric Co. on turbine nozzles (Warren and Keenan, *Trans. ASME,* **48**, p. 33) give for convergent nozzles values of x in excess of 0.98, with a corresponding loss of energy $y = 0.025$ to 0.04. For similar nozzles, the experiments of the Steam Nozzles Research Committee (of England) by a different method give values of x around 0.96, or $y = 0.08$. In the case of divergent nozzles, the velocity coefficient may be somewhat lower.

Flow of Fluids in Circular Pipes

(See pp. 3–55 et seq.)

The fundamental equation as previously given on a unit weight basis, assuming the pipe horizontal, is

$$(V\,dV/g) + v\,dp + dF = 0$$

The friction term dF includes not only losses due to frictional flow along the pipe but also those due to fittings, valves, etc., as well as losses occasioned by any enlargement or contraction of the pipe as, for instance, the loss occurring when a fluid passes from a pipe into a tank. For long straight pipes of uniform diameter, dF is approximately equal to $2f'(V^2\,dL/gD)$. It is usual to express friction due to fittings, etc., in terms of additional length of pipe, adding this to the actual pipe length to get the equivalent pipe length.

$$f' = f/4 \text{ for data on pp. 3–58 et seq.}$$

Integration of the fundamental equation leads to two sets of formulas.

1. For pressure drops, small relative to the initial pressure, the specific volume v and the velocity V may be assumed constant. Then approximately

$$p_1 - p_2 = 2f'V^2L/vgD$$

Expressing pressure in pounds per square inch, p', the diameter in inches, and V as a function of wv/d^2, this equation becomes

$$p_1' - p_2' = 174.2f'w^2vL/d^5$$

2. For considerable pressure drops, when dealing with approximately isothermal flow of gases and vapors to which the gas laws are applicable, the fundamental equation on a weight basis may be integrated to give

$$p_1^2 - p_2^2 = \frac{2w^2RT}{gA^2}\ln\frac{v_2}{v_1} + \frac{4f'RTw^2L}{gA^2D}$$

Coefficients of Friction. The coefficient of friction f is not a constant but is a function of the dimensionless expression $\mu/\rho Vd$ or $\mu v/Vd$, which is the reciprocal of the Reynolds number. McAdams and Sherwood (*Mech. Eng.*, Oct., 1926) formulate the expression

$$f' = 0.0054 + 0.375(\mu v/Vd)$$

This formula is applicable to water and other fluids. For high-pressure steam, the second term in the expression is small and f' is approximately equal to 0.0054. Babcock has suggested the approximation $f' = 0.0027(1 + 3.6/d)$ for steam.

Values of $f = 4f'$ as a function of pipe surface are given by Fig. 17, p. 3–60.

For predicting the capacity of a given pipe operating on a chosen fluid with fixed pressure drop, the use of Fig. 37 eliminates the trial-and-error methods usually involved. Figure 38 gives the viscosity of various gases. For conversion factors, see Hawkins, Solberg, and Sibbitt, Units and Conversion Factors for Absolute Viscosity, *Power Plant Eng.*, Nov., 1941; and pp. 3–49 *et seq.*

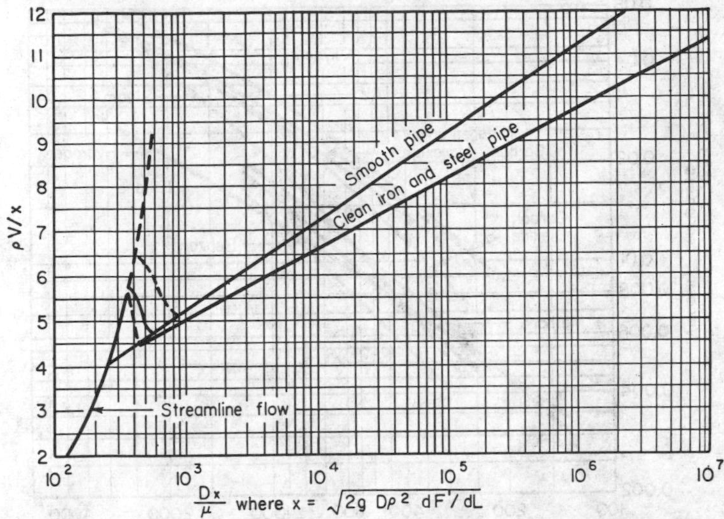

FIG. 37. Chart for estimating rate of flow from the pressure gradient.

EXAMPLE. Air at 68 F is flowing isothermally through a straight standard 1 in. pipe (I.D. = 1.049 in.). The pipe is 200 ft long, the pressure at the pipe inlet is 60 psig, and the pressure drop through the pipe is 5 psi. The average density of the air in the pipe is

$$\rho_{avg} = 0.0753[(60 + 14.7) + (55 + 14.7)]/(2 \times 14.7) = 0.370 \text{ lb per cu ft}$$

$$F' = \frac{(5.0)(144)}{0.370} = 1945 \text{ ft-lb}_f \text{ per lb}_f \qquad D = \frac{1.049}{12} = 0.0875 \text{ ft}$$

$$x = \sqrt{\frac{2(32.2)(0.0875)(0.370)^2(1{,}945)}{200}} = 2.74$$

$$\mu = 0.018 \text{ centipoise (Fig. 38), or } (0.018)(0.000672) = 0.0000121 \text{ in lb-ft-sec units}$$

$$\frac{Dx}{\mu} = \frac{(0.0875)(2.74)}{0.0000121} = 19{,}800 \text{ and from Fig. 37 the corresponding value of } \frac{\rho V}{x} \text{ is } 7.05$$

$$V = \frac{7.05(2.74)}{0.370} = 52.2 \text{ ft per sec}$$

$$m = AV\rho = \frac{(3.1416)(0.0875)^2}{4}(52.2)(0.370) = 0.116 \text{ lb per sec}$$

Resistances due to fittings, expressed in terms of L/D, are as follows: 90 deg elbows, 1–2½ (3–6) [7–10] in., 30 (40) [50]; 90 deg curves, radius of center line of curve 2–8 pipe diameters, 10; globe valves, 1–2½ (3–6) [7–10] in., 45 (60) [75]; tees, 1–4 in., 60. The resistance in energy units, due to sudden enlargement in a pipe, is approximately $(V_1 - V_2)^2/2g$. For sudden contraction it is $1.5(1 - r)V_2^2/2g(3 - r)$, where $r = A_2/A_1$.

Throttling

Throttling or Wiredrawing. When a fluid flows from a region of higher pressure into a region of lower pressure through a valve or constricted passage, it is said to be throttled or wiredrawn. Examples are seen in the passage of steam through pressure-reducing valves, in the flow through ports and passages in the steam engine, and in the expansion valve of the refrigerating machine.

The general equation applicable to throttling processes is

$$(V_2^2 - V_1^2)/2g_c = (h_1 - h_2)J$$

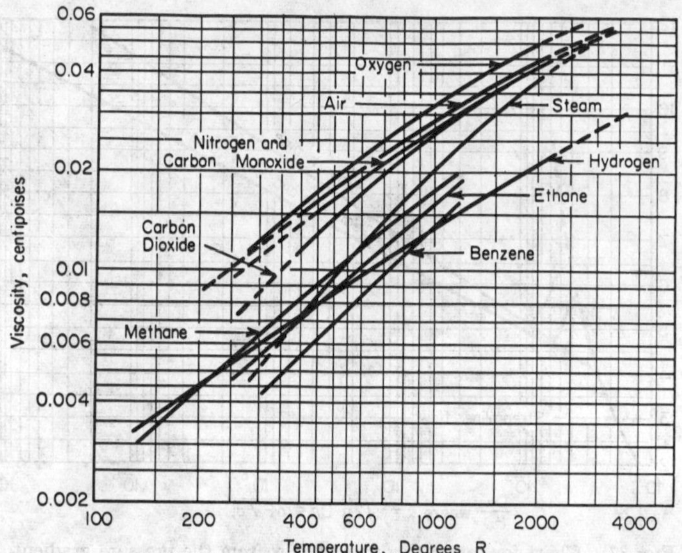

FIG. 38. Viscosity of gases.

The velocities V_2 and V_1 are practically equal, and it follows that $h_1 = h_2$; *i.e.*, in a throttling process there is no change in enthalpy.

For a mixture of liquid and vapor, $h = h_f + xh_{fg}$; hence the equation of throttling is $h_{f1} + x_1h_{fg1} = h_{f2} + x_2h_{fg2}$. In the case of a perfect gas, $h = c_pT + h_0$; hence the equation of throttling is $c_pT_1 + h_0 = c_pT_2 + h_0$, or $T_1 = T_2$.

Joule-Thomson Effect. The investigations of Joule and Lord Kelvin showed that a gas drops in temperature when throttled. This is not universally true. For some gases, notably hydrogen, the temperature rises for throttling processes over ordinary ranges of temperature and pressure. Whether there is a rise or fall in temperature depends on the particular range of pressure and temperature over which the change occurs. For every gas, there is one temperature at which no temperature change occurs during a Joule-Thomson expansion; this is called the **inversion temperature.** Below this temperature, a gas cools on throttling; above this temperature, its temperature rises. The ratio of the observed drop in temperature to the drop in pressure, *i.e.*, dT/dp, is the **Joule-Thomson coefficient.**

The variations of the Joule-Thomson coefficient, for **air,** with both temperature and pressure, can be determined from the constant enthalpy curves of Fig. 19. Values of the coefficient for **steam** vary from 0.465 at 300 deg to 0.165 at 530 F, the unit being degrees per pound per square inch.

The **cooling effect produced by throttling** has been applied to the liquefaction of gases (see p. 18–26).

Loss Due to Throttling. A throttling process in a cycle of operations always introduces a loss of efficiency. If T_0 is the temperature corresponding to the back pressure, the loss of available energy is the product of T_0 and the increase of entropy during the throttling process. The following example illustrates the calculation in the case of ammonia passing through the expansion valve of a refrigerating machine.

EXAMPLE. The liquid ammonia at a temperature of 70 F passes through the valve into the brine coil in which the temperature is 20 deg and the pressure is 48.21 psia. The initial enthalpy of the liquid ammonia (see Table 33) is $h_{f1} = 120.5$, and therefore the final enthalpy is $h_{f2} + x_2h_{fg2} = 64.7 + 553.1x_2 = 120.5$, whence $x_2 = 0.101$. From the table, the initial entropy is $s_{f1} = 0.254$. The final entropy is $s_{f2} + (x_2h_{fg2}/T_2) = 0.144 + 0.101 \times 1.153 = 0.260$. $T_0 = 20 + 460 = 480$; hence the loss of refrigerating effect is $480 \times (0.260 - 0.254) = 2.9$ Btu.

COMBUSTION

Fuels. For special properties of various fuels, see Sec. 7. In general, fuels may be classed under three heads: (1) gaseous fuels, (2) liquid fuels, (3) solid fuels.

The combustible elements that characterize fuels are carbon, hydrogen, and, in some cases, sulphur. The complete combustion of carbon gives, as a product, carbon dioxide, CO_2; the combustion of hydrogen gives water, H_2O.

Combustion of Gaseous and Liquid Fuels

Combustion Equations. The approximate molecular weights of the important elements and compounds entering into combustion calculations are:

Gas	H_2	O_2	N_2	CO	CO_2	H_2O	CH_4	C_2H_4	C_2H_6O
Molecular weight	2	32	28	28	44	18	16	28	46

For the elements C and H, the equations of complete combustion are

$$\begin{cases} C + O_2 = CO_2 \\ 12\text{ lb} + 32\text{ lb} = 44\text{ lb} \end{cases} \qquad \begin{matrix} H_2 + \tfrac{1}{2}O_2 = H_2O \\ 2\text{ lb} + 16\text{ lb} = 18\text{ lb} \end{matrix}$$

For a combustible compound, as CH_4, the equation may be written

$$CH_4 + x \cdot O_2 = y \cdot CO_2 + z \cdot H_2O$$

Taking, as a basis, 1 molecule of CH_4 and making a balance of the atoms on the two sides of the equation, it is seen that

$$y = 1 \qquad z = 2 \qquad 2x = 2y + z \qquad \text{or} \qquad x = 2$$

Hence,

$$\begin{cases} CH_4 + 2O_2 = CO_2 + 2H_2O \\ 16\text{ lb} + 64\text{ lb} = 44\text{ lb} + 36\text{ lb} \end{cases}$$

The coefficients in the combustion equation give the combining volumes of the gaseous components. Thus, in the last equation 1 cu ft of CH_4 requires for combustion 2 cu ft of oxygen and the resulting gaseous products of combustion are 1 cu ft of CO_2 and 2 cu ft of H_2O. The coefficients multiplied by the corresponding molecular weights give the combining weights. These are conveniently referred to 1 lb of the fuel. In the combustion of CH_4, for example, 1 lb of CH_4 requires $64/16 = 4$ lb of oxygen for complete combustion and the products are $44/16 = 2.75$ lb of CO_2 and $36/16 = 2.25$ lb of H_2O.

Air Required for Combustion. The composition of air is approximately 0.232 O_2 and 0.768 N_2 on a pound basis, or 0.21 O_2 and 0.79 N_2 by volume. For exact analyses, it may be necessary sometimes to take account of the water vapor mixed with the air, but ordinarily this may be neglected.

The minimum amount of air required for the combustion of 1 lb of a fuel is the quantity of oxygen required, as found from the combustion equation, divided by 0.232. Likewise, the minimum volume of air required for the combustion of 1 cu ft of a fuel gas is the volume of oxygen divided by 0.21. For example, in the combustion of CH_4 the air required per pound of CH_4 is $4/0.232 = 17.24$ lb and the volume of air per cubic foot of CH_4 is $2/0.21 = 9.52$ cu ft. Ordinarily, more air is provided than is required for complete combustion. Let a denote the minimum amount required and xa the quantity of air admitted; then $x - 1$ is the **excess coefficient.**

Products of Combustion. The products arising from the complete combustion of a fuel are CO_2, H_2O, and, if sulphur is present, SO_2. Accompanying these are the nitrogen brought in with the air and the oxygen in the excess of air. Hence the products of complete combustion are principally CO_2, H_2O, N_2, and O_2. The **presence of CO indicates incomplete combustion.** The composition of the products of combustion is readily calculated from the combustion equations, as shown by the following illustrative example:

EXAMPLE. A producer gas having the volume composition given is burned with 20 percent excess of air; required the volume composition of the exhaust gases.

		Coefficients in reaction equations			Coefficients multiplied by V		
	V	O_2	CO_2	H_2O	O_2	CO_2	H_2O
H_2	0.08	0.5	0	1	0.04	0	0.08
CO	0.22	0.5	1	0	0.11	0.22	0
CH_4	0.024	2	1	2	0.048	0.024	0.048
CO_2	0.066	0	1	0	0	0.066	0
N_2	0.61	0	0	0	0	0	0
	1.0				0.198	0.31	0.128

For 1 cu ft of the producer gas, 0.198 cu ft of O_2 is required for complete combustion. The minimum volume of air required is 0.198/0.21 = 0.943 cu ft and with 20 percent excess the air supplied is 0.943 × 1.2 = 1.132 cu ft. Of this, 0.238 cu ft is oxygen and 0.894 cu ft is N_2. Consequently, for 1 cu ft of the fuel gas, the exhaust gas contains

CO_2	0.31 cu ft	or	CO_2	15.7 percent
H_2O	0.128 cu ft		H_2O	6.5 percent
N_2	0.61 + 0.894 = 1.504 cu ft		N_2	75.8 percent
O_2 (excess)	0.238 − 0.198 = 0.040 cu ft		O_2	2.0 percent
	1.982 cu ft			100.0 percent

Volume Contraction. As a result of chemical action, there is often a change of volume; for example, in the reaction $2H_2 + O_2 = 2H_2O$, three volumes (two of H_2 and one of O_2) contract to two volumes of water vapor. In the example just given, the volume of producer gas and air supplied is 1 cu ft gas + 1.132 cu ft air = 2.132 cu ft, and the corresponding volume of the exhaust gas is 1.982 cu ft, showing a contraction of about 7 percent. For a hydrocarbon having the composition C_mH_n, the relative volume contraction is $[1 - (n/4)]$; thus for CH_4 and C_2H_4 there is no change of volume, for C_2H_2 the contraction is half the volume, and for C_2H_6 there is an increase of one-half in volume.

The change of volume accompanying a chemical reaction, such as a combustion, causes a corresponding change in the gas constant R. Let R' denote the constant for the mixture of gas and air (1 lb of gas and xa lb of air) before combustion, and R'' the constant of the mixture of resulting products of combustion. Then, if y is the resulting contraction of volume, $R''/R' = (1 + xa - y)/(1 + xa)$.

Heat of Combustion. Usually, a chemical change is accompanied by the generation or absorption of heat. The union of a combustible with oxygen produces heat, and the heat thus generated when 1 lb of combustible is completely burned is called the **heat of combustion** or the **heat value** of the combustible. Heat values are determined experimentally by calorimeters in which the products of combustion are cooled to the initial temperature and the heat absorbed by the cooling medium is measured. This is called the **high heat value.**

The heat transferred (heat of combustion) during a combustion reaction is computed on either a constant-pressure or a constant-volume basis. The first law is used in the analysis of either process.

1. The **heat value at constant volume** (H_v). Consider a constant-volume combustion process where several reactants combine under proper conditions to form one or more products. The heat of combustion under constant-volume conditions (H_v) according to the first law may be expressed as follows:

$$H_v = \Sigma(Nu)_P - \Sigma(Nu)_R$$

The term N refers to the amount of material and the symbol u signifies the internal energy per unit quantity of material. The subscripts P and R refer to the products and reactants respectively. Hence, it may be concluded that H_v is equal to the change in internal energy. The heat of combustion under constant-volume conditions may also be described as the quantity of heat transferred from a calorimeter to the external surroundings when the temperature and volume of the combustion products are brought to the temperature and volume, respectively, of the gaseous mixture before burning.

2. The **heat value at constant pressure** (H_p). For a constant-pressure process the

first law may be expressed as

$$H_p = \Sigma(Nu)_P - \Sigma(Nu)_R + pV_P - pV_R$$

Here the symbols p and V refer to the pressure and total volume respectively. Usually in combustion reactions that part of the change in internal energy resulting from a volume change is small in comparison to the total change; hence it may usually be neglected. Assuming therefore that the internal energy change for a constant-volume reaction is approximately equal to that for a constant-pressure change, the following equation results:

$$H_p = H_v + p(V_P - V_R)$$

Since H_v is equal to the change in internal energy, this relation may be changed to enthalpy values, from which it may be concluded that H_p is equal to the change in enthalpy. The heat of combustion under constant-pressure conditions may also be described as the heat transferred from a calorimeter when the pressure and temperature of the products are brought back to the pressure and temperature, respectively, of the gaseous mixture before burning.

If the reactants and products are assumed to be ideal gases, then the relation for (H_p) may be expressed as follows, where ΔN represents the change in number of moles and R the universal gas constant:

$$H_p = H_v + \Delta NRT$$

From this relation the heat transferred (heat of combustion) at constant pressure may be found from the heat of reaction at constant volume, or vice versa, if the temperature and molar-volume change are known.

If there is no change of volume due to the combustion, the heat values H_p and H_v are the same. When there is a contraction of volume, H_p exceeds H_v by the heat equivalent of the work done on the gas during the contraction. For example, in the burning of CO according to the equation $CO + \frac{1}{2}O_2 = CO_2$, there is a contraction of ½ volume. Taking 62 F as the temperature, the volume of 1 lb CO at atmospheric pressure is 13.6 cu ft; hence the equivalent of the work done at atmospheric pressure is $\frac{1}{2} \times 13.6 \times 2116/778 = 18.5$ Btu, which is about 0.4 percent of the heat value of CO. Since the difference between H_p and H_v is small in most fuels, it is usually neglected.

It is also to be noted that heat values vary with the initial temperature (which is also the final temperature), but the variation is usually negligible.

Heat Value per Unit Volume. Since the consumption of a fuel gas is more easily measured by volume than by mass, it is convenient to express heat values in terms of volumes. For this purpose, a standard temperature and pressure must be assumed. It is customary to take atmospheric pressure (14.70 psi) as standard, but there is diversity of practice in the matter of a **standard temperature.** The temperature of 68 F (20 C) is generally accepted in metric countries and has been recommended by the American delegates to the meeting of the International Committee of Weights and Measures and also by the ASME Power Test Codes Committee. The American Gas Assoc. uses 60 F as the standard temperature of reference. Conversion of density and heat values from 68 to 60 F of dry (saturated) gas is obtained by multiplying by the factor 1.0154 (1.0212). Conversion of specific volumes of dry (saturated) gas is obtained by multiplying by the factor 0.9848 (0.9792).

If the gas is at some other pressure and temperature, say p_1 psia and T_1 deg R, the heat value per cubic foot is found by multiplying the heat value per cubic foot under standard conditions by $35.9p_1/T_1$.

The heat values of a few of the more common fuels per pound and per cubic foot are given in Table 43 (see also Sec. 7).

Heat Value per Unit Volume of Mixture. Let a denote the volume of air required for the combustion of 1 cu ft of fuel gas and xa the value of air actually admitted, $(x - 1)a$ being therefore the excess. Then the volume of the mixture of fuel gas and air is $1 + xa$, and the quotient $H/(1 + xa)$ may be called the heat value per cubic foot of mixture. This magnitude is useful in comparing the relative volumes of mixture

Table 43. Heats of Combustion

Fuel	Chemical symbol	High heat value, Btu		Low heat value, Btu	
		Per lb	Per cu ft[a]	Per lb	Per cu ft[a]
Carbon to CO_2	C	14,096			
Carbon to CO	C	3,960			
CO to CO_2	CO	4,346	316.0		
Sulphur to SO_2	S	3,984			
Hydrogen	H_2	61,031	319.4	51,593	270.0
Methane	CH_4	23,890	994.7	21,518	896.0
Ethane	C_2H_6	22,329	1742.6	20,431	1594.5
Propane	C_3H_8	21,670	2480.1	19,944	2282.6
Butane	C_4H_{10}	21,316	3215.6	19,679	2968.7
Pentane	C_5H_{12}	21,095	3950.2	19,513	3654.0
Hexane (liquid)	C_6H_{14}	20,675	......	19,130	
Octane (liquid)	C_8H_{18}	20,529	......	19,029	
n-Decane (liquid)	$C_{10}H_{22}$	20,371	......	19,175	
Ethylene	C_2H_4	21,646	1576.1	20,276	1477.4
Propene (propylene)	C_3H_6	21,053	2299.4	19,683	2151.3
Acetylene (ethyne)	C_2H_2	21,477	1451.4	20,734	1402.0
Benzene	C_6H_6	18,188	3687.5	17,446	3539.3
Toluene (methyl benzene)	C_7H_8	18,441	4410.1	17,601	4212.6
Methanol (methyl alcohol, liquid)	CH_4O	9,758	......	7,658	
Ethanol (ethyl alcohol, liquid)	C_2H_6O	12,770	......	9,620	
Naphthalene (solid)	$C_{10}H_8$	17,310	......	13,110	

[a] Measured as a gas at 68 F and 14.70 psia. Multiply by 1.0154 for 60 F and 14.70 psia.

required with different fuel gases. Thus a lean gas, as blast-furnace gas or producer gas, has a low heat value H, but the value of a is correspondingly low. On the other hand, a rich gas, like natural gas, has a high heat value but requires a large volume of air for combustion.

Low and High Heat Values. Any fuel containing hydrogen yields water as one product of combustion. At atmospheric pressure, the partial pressure of the water vapor in the resulting combustion gas mixture will usually be sufficiently high to cause water to condense out if the temperature is allowed to fall below 120 to 140 F. This causes liberation of the heat of vaporization of any water condensed. The low heat value is evaluated assuming no water vapor condensed, whereas the high heat value is calculated assuming all water vapor condensed.

To facilitate calculations of the temperature attained by combustion, it is desirable to make use of the **low heat value.** The necessity of taking into account the heat of vaporization of the water vapor and the difference between the specific heats of liquid water and of water vapor is thus avoided. The high heat of combustion exceeds the low heat of combustion by the difference between the heat actually given up on cooling the products to the initial temperature and that which would have been given up if the products had remained in the gaseous state. A bomb calorimeter (constant volume) gives practically correct values of the high heat value; a gas calorimeter (constant pressure) gives values which, for the usual fuels, may be incorrect by a fraction of 1 percent. The quantity to be subtracted from the high heat value to obtain the low heat value will vary with the composition of the fuel; an approximate value is 1050 m, where m is the number of pounds of H_2O formed per pound of fuel burned.

In Germany, the low heat value of the fuel is used in calculating efficiencies of internal-combustion engines. In the United States, the high value is specified by the ASME Power Test Codes.

Heat of Formation. The change in enthalpy resulting when a compound is formed from its elements isothermally and at constant pressure is numerically equal to, but of opposite sign to, the heat of formation, $\Delta H_f = -Q_f$. It is equal to the difference between the heats of combustion of the constituents forming the compound and the heat of combustion of the compound itself. The following values for heats of formation are in Btu per pound of the compound. The elements before the change and the compounds formed are assumed in their ordinary stable states at 65 F and 1 atm. A plus sign indicates heat evolved on forming the compound, a minus sign heat absorbed from the surroundings.

Table 44. Products of Combustion

(From Marks, "The Airplane Engine")

Fuel	Chemical formula	Molecular weight $O_2 = 32$	Specific weight, lb per cu ft at 68 F and 14.70 lb per sq in.	Volume of air necessary for combustion of unit volume of fuel at same temperature and pressure	Products of combustion of 1 cu ft of fuel in theoretical amount of air, cu ft			Weight of air necessary for combustion of unit weight of fuel	Products of combustion of 1 lb of fuel in theoretical amount of air, lb		
					CO_2	H_2O	N_2		CO_2	H_2O	N_2
Oxygen	O_2	32	0.0831								
Nitrogen	N_2	28.08	0.0727								
Air			0.0753								
Hydrogen	H_2	2.016	0.0052	2.39	0	1	1.89	34.2	0.0	8.94	26.28
Steam	H_2O	18.016									
Carbon monoxide	CO	28.00	0.0727	2.39							
Carbon dioxide	CO_2	44.00	0.1142								
Methane	CH_4	16.03	0.0416	9.55	1	2	7.55	17.21	2.75	2.248	13.22
Ethane	C_2H_6	30.05	0.0779	16.71	2	3	13.21	16.07	2.93	1.799	12.34
Propane	C_3H_8	44.06	0.1142	23.87	3	4	18.87	15.65	3.00	1.635	12.02
Butane	C_4H_{10}	58.1	0.1506	30.94	4	5	24.53	15.44	3.03	1.551	11.86
Pentane	C_5H_{12}	72.1	0.1869	38.08	5	6	30.2	15.31	3.05	1.499	11.76
Hexane	C_6H_{14}	86.1	0.2232	45.3	6	7	35.8	15.22	3.07	1.465	11.69
Heptane	C_7H_{16}	100.1	0.2596	52.5	7	8	41.5	15.15	3.08	1.439	11.64
Octane	C_8H_{18}	114.1	0.2959	59.7	8	9	47.2	15.11	3.08	1.421	11.60
Nonane	C_9H_{20}	128.2	0.3323	66.8	9	10	52.8	15.07	3.09	1.406	11.57
Benzene	C_6H_6	78.0	0.2025	35.8	6	3	28.3	13.26	3.38	0.693	10.18
Toluene	C_7H_8	92.1	0.2388	42.9	7	4	34.0	13.50	3.35	0.783	10.36
Xylene	C_8H_{10}	106.2	0.2752	50.1	8	5	39.6	13.57	3.31	0.845	10.42
Cyclohexane	C_6H_{12}	84.0	0.2180	43.0	6	6	34.0	14.76	3.14	1.285	11.34
Ethylene	C_2H_4	28.03	0.0728	14.32	2	2	11.32	14.76	3.14	1.285	11.34
Propylene	C_3H_6	42.0	0.1090	21.48	3	3	16.98	14.76	3.14	1.285	11.34
Butylene	C_4H_8	64.1	0.1454	28.64	4	4	22.64	14.76	3.14	1.285	11.34
Acetylene	C_2H_2	26.02	0.0675	11.93	2	1	9.43	13.26	3.38	0.693	10.18
Allylene	C_3H_4	40.0	0.1038	19.09	3	2	15.09	13.78	3.30	0.900	10.59
Napthalene	$C_{10}H_8$	128.1	0.3322	57.3	10	4	45.28	12.93	3.44	0.563	9.93
Methyl alcohol	CH_4O	32.0	0.0830	7.16	1	2	5.66	6.46	1.37	1.125	4.96
Ethyl alcohol	C_2H_6O	46.0	0.1194	14.32	2	3	11.32	8.99	1.91	1.174	6.90

Fuels. Methane, CH_4 (gas), 2001.4; ethane, C_2H_6 (gas), 1206.1; propane, C_3H_8 (vapor), 1008.5; acetylene, C_2H_2 (gas), −3747; ethylene, C_2H_4 (gas), −805.3; benzene, C_6H_6 (vapor), −459; toluene, C_7H_8 (vapor), −234.9; methyl alcohol, CH_3OH (liquid), 3227.3; ethyl alcohol, C_2H_5OH (liquid), 2623.3.

Inorganic Compounds. Al_2O_3, 6710; CaO, 4869; $CaCO_3$, 5206; FeO, 1611; Fe_2O_3, 2238; Fe_3O_4, 2075; FeS_2, 532.7; HCL(gas), 1089, HNO_3 (liquid), 1190; H_2O (liquid), 6827; H_2S (gas), 279.9; H_2SO_4 (liquid), 3555.8; K_2O, 164.7; MgO, 6522; MnO, 2449; NO, −1296; N_2O, −803.5; Na_2O, 2888; NH_3, 1163; NH_4CL, 1480; NiO, 1407; P_2O_5, 5394; PbO (red), 423.0; PbO_2, 489.1; SO_2, 1933; SO_3, 2112; SnO, 904.7; ZnO, 1847.

Table 45. Internal Energy of Gases

(Btu per lb mol above 520 R)
(From L. C. Lichty, "Internal Combustion Engines," 1939, p. 582, derived from data given by Hershey, Eberhardt, and Hottel, *Trans. SAE*, **31,** 1936, p. 409)

Temp, R	O_2	N_2	Air	CO_2	H_2O	H_2	CO	*Apv*
520	0	0	0	0	0	0	0	1,033
540	100	97	97	139	122	96	97	1,072
560	200	196	196	280	244	193	196	1,112
580	301	295	295	424	357	291	295	1,152
600	402	395	395	570	490	390	396	1,192
700	920	896	897	1,320	1,110	887	896	1,390
800	1,449	1,399	1,403	2,120	1,734	1,386	1,402	1,589
900	1,989	1,905	1,915	2,965	2,366	1,886	1,913	1,787
1000	2,539	2,416	2,431	3,852	3,009	2,387	2,430	1,986
1100	3,101	2,934	2,957	4,778	3,666	2,889	2,954	2,185
1200	3,675	3,461	3,492	5,736	4,399	3,393	3,485	2,383
1300	4,262	3,996	4,036	6,721	5,030	3,899	4,026	2,582
1400	4,861	4,539	4,587	7,731	5,740	4,406	4,580	2,780
1500	5,472	5,091	5,149	8,764	6,468	4,916	5,145	2,979
1600	6,092	5,652	5,720	9,819	7,212	5,429	5,720	3,178
1700	6,718	6,224	6,301	10,896	7,970	5,945	6,305	3,376
1800	7,349	6,805	6,889	11,993	8,741	6,464	6,899	3,575
1900	7,985	7,393	7,485	13,105	9,526	6,988	7,501	3,773
2000	8,629	7,989	8,087	14,230	10,327	7,517	8,109	3,972
2100	9,279	8,592	8,698	15,368	11,146	8,053	8,722	4,171
2200	9,934	9,203	9,314	16,518	11,983	8,597	9,339	4,369
2300	10,592	9,817	9,934	17,680	12,835	9,147	9,961	4,568
2400	11,252	10,435	10,558	18,852	13,700	9,703	10,588	4,766
2500	11,916	11,056	11,185	20,033	14,578	10,263	11,220	4,965
2600	12,584	11,682	11,817	21,222	15,469	10,827	11,857	5,164
2700	13,257	12,313	12,453	22,419	16,372	11,396	12,499	5,362
2800	13,937	12,949	13,095	23,624	17,288	11,970	13,144	5,561
2900	14,622	13,590	13,742	24,836	18,217	12,549	13,792	5,759
3000	15,309	14,236	14,394	26,055	19,160	13,133	14,443	5,958
3100	16,001	14,888	15,051	27,281	20,117	13,723	15,097	6,157
3200	16,693	15,543	15,710	28,513	21,086	14,319	15,754	6,355
3300	17,386	16,199	16,369	29,750	22,066	14,921	16,414	6,554
3400	18,080	16,855	17,030	30,991	23,057	15,529	17,078	6,752
3500	18,776	17,512	17,692	32,237	24,057	16,143	17,744	6,951
3600	19,475	18,171	18,356	33,487	25,067	16,762	18,412	7,150
3700	20,179	18,833	19,022	34,741	26,085	17,385	19,082	7,348
3800	20,887	19,496	19,691	35,998	27,110	18,011	19,755	7,547
3900	21,598	20,162	20,363	37,258	28,141	18,641	20,430	7,745
4000	22,314	20,830	21,037	38,522	29,178	19,274	21,107	7,944
4100	23,034	21,500	21,714	39,791	30,221	19,911	21,784	8,143
4200	23,757	22,172	22,393	41,064	31,270	20,552	22,462	8,341
4300	24,482	22,845	23,073	42,341	32,326	21,197	23,140	8,540
4400	25,209	23,519	23,755	43,622	33,389	21,845	23,819	8,738
4500	25,938	24,194	24,437	44,906	34,459	22,497	24,499	8,937
4600	26,668	24,869	25,120	46,193	35,535	23,154	25,179	9,136
4700	27,401	25,546	25,805	47,483	36,616	23,816	25,860	9,334
4800	28,136	26,224	26,491	48,775	37,701	24,480	26,542	9,533
4900	28,874	26,905	27,180	50,069	38,791	25,418	27,226	9,731
5000	29,616	27,589	27,872	51,365	39,885	25,819	27,912	9,930
5100	30,361	28,275	28,566	52,663	40,983	26,492	28,600	10,129
5200	31,108	28,961	29,262	53,963	42,084	27,166	29,289	10,327
5300	31,857	29,648	29,958	55,265	43,187	27,842	29,980	10,526
5400	32,607	30,337	30,655	56,569	44,293	28,519	30,674	10,724

Internal Energy and Enthalpy of Gases. Table 45 gives the internal energy of various common gases in Btu per lb mol measured above 520 R (60 F). The corresponding values of the enthalpy are obtained by adding the value of APv from the last column.

Temperature Attained by Combustion. Excluding the effect of dissociation, the temperature attained at the end of combustion may be calculated by a simple energy balance. The heat of combustion less the heat lost by conduction and radiation during the process is equal to the increase in internal energy of the products mixture if the combustion is at constant volume; or, if the combustion is at constant pressure, the difference is equal to the increase in enthalpy of the products mixture.

EXAMPLE. To calculate the temperature of combustion of a fuel gas having the composition H_2 = 0.50, CO = 0.46, CO_2 = 0.04. The gas is burned with 15 percent excess air at constant volume, and the initial temperature is 62 F; *i.e.*, T = 522 R.

The volume compositions of the initial mixture of fuel gas and air and of the mixture of products are, respectively:

Initial: H_2, 0.50; CO, 0.46; CO_2, 0.04; O_2, 0.552; N_2, 2.098
Products: H_2O, 0.50; CO_2, 0.50; O_2, 0.072; N_2, 2.098

Since a volume composition is also a mol composition, the products mixture may be regarded as made up of 0.5 mol each of H_2O and CO_2, 0.072 mol of O_2, and 2.098 mols of N_2. If values are taken from Table 45, the heat generated by combustion of the fuel mixture is $0.50 \times 2 \times 51{,}593 + 0.46 \times 28 \times 4346 = 107{,}569$ Btu. The internal energy u of the products mixture at T = 522 is now calculated. For 0 5 mol H_2O + 0.5 mol CO_2 + 0.072 mol O_2 + 2.098 mols N_2 this is 6.1 + 6.95 + 0.72 + 20.34 = 34.11 Btu.

The energy u of the mixture is next calculated for various assumed temperatures, the proper values being taken from Table 45

T_2 assumed	4700	4800	4900	5000	5100
Energy 0.5 mol H_2O	18,308	18,851	19,396	19,943	20,492
Energy 0.5 mol CO_2	23,742	24,388	25,035	25,683	26,331
Energy 0.072 mol O_2	1,973	2,026	2,079	2,132	2,185
Energy 2.098 mols N_2	54,596	55,018	56,447	57,882	59,321
u_2 =	97,619	100,283	102,957	105,640	108,329
u_1 =	34	34	34	34	34
	97,585	100,249	102,923	105,606	108,295

If the heat of combustion, 107,569 Btu, is entirely used in the increase of energy, the temperature attained lies somewhere between 5000 and 5100; by interpolation, the value 5073 deg is obtained.

Loss of heat during combustion may readily be taken into account; thus if 10 percent of the heat of combustion is lost, the amount available for increasing the energy of the products is $107{,}569 \times 0.90 = 96{,}812$ Btu, and this increase gives T_2 = 4671 deg. If the fuel is burned at constant pressure, H_p is used instead of H_v and values of h are determined from Table 45 instead of values of u.

Effect of Dissociation. The maximum temperature that can be obtained by the combustion of any fuel is limited by the dissociation of the products formed. The dissociation and equilibriums involved in high-temperature combustion are exceedingly complex, involving such chemical species as CO_2, CO, H_2O, H_2, H, OH, N_2, NO, N, O_2, and O. Equilibrium constants for the reactions involved are given in Lewis and von Elbe, "Combustion, Flames, and Explosions of Gases," pp. 382–383, Macmillan, 1938. Calculations of this type are facilitated by the use of charts. See Hottel, Williams, and Satterfield, "Thermodynamic Charts for Combustion Processes," Wiley.

Calculated flame temperatures, allowing for dissociation, for gaseous fuels with stated amounts of air present are given in Table 46. The combustion is assumed to be adiabatic and at 14.7 psia.

In the case of **explosion** in the **internal-combustion engine,** the figures in Table 46 will be somewhat changed. The effect of compression is to increase both the initial temperature and the initial pressure. The resulting increase in the explosion temperature will tend to increase the dissociation, the increase of pressure will tend to reduce it. The net effect will be a small reduction.

Combustion of Liquid Fuels. For properties of fuel oils, heat values, etc., see pp. 7–20 to 7–30. Calculations for the burning of liquid fuels are fundamentally the same as for gaseous fuels. Liquid fuels are almost always gasified before or during actual combustion.

Tizard and Pye (*Automobile Engr.*, Feb., 1921) give the following result on a theoretically correct mixture of benzene vapor and air at 212 F and atmospheric pressure. This was compressed to ⅕ of its volume and exploded. It was assumed that no heat was lost during explosion. With no dissociation, the maximum temperature reached is 5473 F and the maximum pressure 658 psi. With dissociation, the maximum temperature is 4811 F and the maximum pressure 600.7 psi. Similar results are found for other liquid fuels, as alcohol, kerosene, etc.

Table 46. Flame Temperatures, Deg R, at 14.7 Psia, Allowing for Dissociation
(Satterfield, "Generalized Thermodynamics of High-temperature Combustion," Sc.D. thesis, M.I.T., 1946)

Fuel	Percent of theoretical air				
	80	90	100	120	140
Hydrogen	4,210	4,330	4,390	4,000	3,670
Carbon monoxide	4,280	4,370	4,320	4,140	3,850
Methane	4,050	....	4,010	3,660	3,330
Carbureted water gas	3,940	....	4,150	3,820	3,510
Coal gas	3,920	....	4,050	3,780	3,440
Natural gas	4,010	....	4,180	3,840	3,520
Producer gas	3,040	....	3,330	3,130	2,970
Blast-furnace gas	2,810	....	3,060	2,920	2,750

The volumetric compositions of the fuels of Table 46 are given below:

Fuels	CO	H_2	CH_4	C_2H_6	Illuminants (assumed C_2H_4)	CO_2	O_2	N_2
H_2	.....	100.0						
CO	100.0							
CH_4	.....	.....	100.0					
Carbureted water gas	24.1	32.5	9.0	2.2	10.3	4.6	0.6	16.7
Coal gas	5.9	53.2	29.6	....	2.7	1.4	0.7	6.5
Natural gas	.....	.....	78.8	14.0	....	0.4	...	6.8
Producer gas	26.0	3.0	0.5	....	....	2.50	...	56.0
Blast-furnace gas	26.5	3.5	0.2	....	....	12.8	0.1	56.9

As the temperature falls after reaching the maximum, the uncombined CO and H_2 burn with the oxygen present, and when the temperature has reached about 3000 F the combustion is practically complete. Thus in the internal-combustion engine dissociation has the effect of reducing the explosion temperature and pressure and afterward of raising the expansion curve. The effect on the efficiency is not large. For an engine using benzene according to the conditions just noted, the ideal efficiency with no heat loss and without dissociation was found by Tizard and Pye to be 35.9 percent; with dissociation and subsequent recombination, it was found to be 33.8 percent.

Combustion of Solid Fuels

For properties of solid fuels, heat values, etc., see pp. 7–2 to 7–20.

Air Required for Combustion. Let c, h, and o, denote, respectively, the parts of carbon, hydrogen, and oxygen in 1 lb of the fuel. Then the **minimum amount of oxygen** required for complete combustion is $2.67c + 8h - o$ lb, and the **minimum quantity of air** required is $a = (2.67c + 8h - o)/0.23 = 11.6[c + 3(h - o/8)]$ lb.

With air at 62 F and at atmospheric pressure, the minimum volume of air required is $v_m = 147[c + 3(h - o/8)]$ cu ft. In practice, an excess of air over that required for combustion is admitted to the furnace. The actual quantity admitted per pound of fuel may be denoted by xa. Then x = amount admitted ÷ minimum amount.

Combustion Products. If v_m is the minimum volume of air required for complete combustion and xv_m the actual volume supplied, then the products will contain per pound of fuel, $O_2 = 0.21v_m(x - 1)$ cu ft, $N_2 = 0.79\ xv_m$ cu ft.

From the reaction equation $C + O_2 = CO_2$, the volume of CO_2 formed is equal to the volume of oxygen required for the carbon constituent alone; hence volume of $CO_2 = 0.21v_mc/[c + 3(h - 0.125o)]$.

Of the *dry* gaseous products (*i.e.*, without water), the CO_2 content by volume is therefore given by the expression

$$CO_2 = 0.21c/[xc + (x - 0.21)3(h - 0{,}125o)]$$

The combined CO_2 and O_2 content is

$$CO_2 + O_2 = 0.21 \left\{1 - 0.79 \Big/ \left[\frac{x + cx}{3(h - 0.125o) - 0.21}\right]\right\}$$

If the fuel is all carbon, the combined CO_2 and O_2 is by volume 21 percent of the gaseous products. The more hydrogen contained in the fuel, the smaller is the $CO_2 + O_2$ content. The CO_2 content depends in the first instance on the excess of air. Thus, for pure carbon, it is $CO_2 = 0.21/x$.

The excess of air may be calculated from the composition of the gases and that of the fuel. Thus

$$x = 0.21 \left[\frac{c}{[CO_2]} + 3(h - 0.125o)\right] \Big/ [c + 3(h - 0.125o)]$$

in which $[CO_2]$ denotes the percent by volume of the CO_2 in the dry gas.

The temperature of combustion is calculated by the same method as for gaseous fuels.

Loss Due to Incomplete Combustion. The loss due to incomplete combustion of the carbon in the fuel, in Btu per lb of fuel, is

$$L = 10{,}136C \times CO/(CO + CO_2)$$

where 10,136 = difference in heat evolved in burning 1 lb of carbon to CO_2 and to CO; CO and CO_2 = percentages by volume of carbon monoxide and carbon dioxide as found by analysis; and C = fraction of quantity of carbon in the fuel which is actually burned and passes up the stack, either as CO or CO_2. The presence of 1 percent of CO in the flue gases will represent a decrease in the boiler efficiency of 4.5 percent. An additional loss is caused by passage through the grate to the ashpit of any unburned or partly burned fuel.

It is generally assumed that high CO_2 readings are indicative of good combustion and, hence, of high efficiencies. Such readings are not satisfactory when considered apart from the CO determination. The best percentage of CO_2 to maintain varies with different fuels and is lower for those with a high hydrogen content than for fuel mainly composed of carbon.

Hydrogen in a fuel increases the nitrogen content of the flue gases. This is due to the fact that the water vapor formed by the combustion of hydrogen will condense at the temperature at which the analysis is made, while the nitrogen which accompanied the oxygen maintains its gaseous form and passes in that form into the sampling apparatus. For this reason, where highly volatile coals containing considerable hydrogen are burned, the flue gas contains an apparently increased amount of nitrogen. The effect is even more pronounced when burning gaseous or liquid hydrocarbon fuels.

The amount of flue gases per pound of fuel, including moisture formed by the hydrogen component, is approximately $= 3.02[N/(CO_2 + CO)]C + (1 - A)$, where A = percent of ash as found in test. The quantity of dry flue gases per pound of fuel may be approximated from the formula: $W_2 = C[11CO_2 + 8O + 7(CO + N)]/3(CO_2 + CO)$. In these formulas, the amount of gas is per pound of dry or moist fuel as the percentage of C is referred to a dry or moist basis.

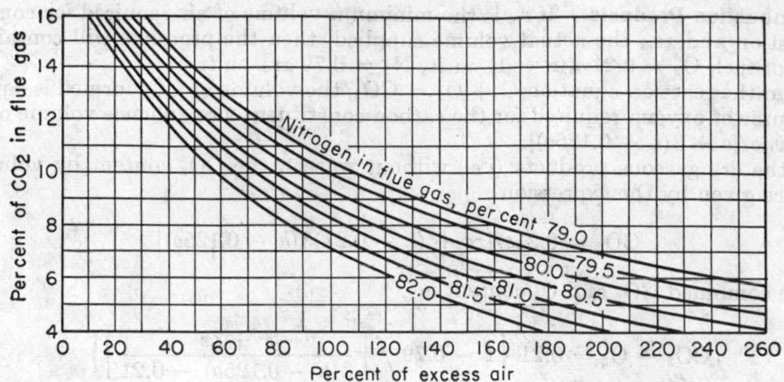

FIG. 39. Ratio of air supplied per pound of combustible to that theoretically required.

The ratio of air supplied per pound of fuel to the air theoretically required is

$$\frac{W_1}{W} = \frac{3.02C\left(\dfrac{N}{CO_2 + CO}\right)}{34.56\left(\dfrac{C}{3} + H - \dfrac{O}{8}\right)}.$$

The ratio of air supplied per pound of combustible to that theoretically required is $N/[N - 3.782(O - \frac{1}{2}CO)]$, on the assumption that all the nitrogen in the flue gas comes from the air supplied. Figure 39 gives the value of this ratio for varying flue-gas analyses where there is no CO present.

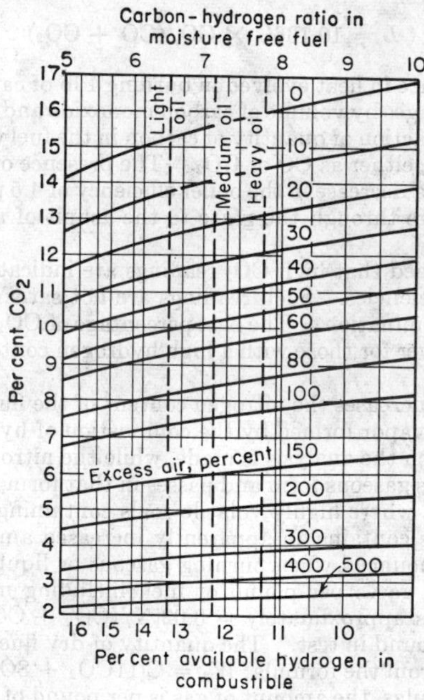

FIG. 40. Relation of CO_2 to excess air for oil fuels.

For petroleum fuels with hydrogen content from 9 to 16 percent, the excess air can be determined from the CO_2 content of the flue gases (with no CO present) by the use of Fig. 40. The curves are based on the assumption of 0.4 percent sulphur in the oil.

Surface Combustion. If, after forcing combustible gas through a porous mass of refractory material, igniting, and allowing it to burn in the air with the usual flame, air is forced in with the gas so that the resulting explosive mixture flows with too great velocity for backfiring to occur, the flame becomes non-luminous and, as the surface of the refractory mass is heated up, gradually disappears from the surface of the material, which glows under the action of the surface combustion. The combustion, which is supported by the oxygen admitted with the gas and is not influenced by the oxygen in front of the refractory mass, may be perfect with a minimum of excess air. In the case of a porous slab or diaphragm, the combustion takes place within a distance of from ⅛ to ¼ in. from the surface. This method of heating has been applied to muffles and crucibles, where the porous refractory material, in the form of small lumps, is closely packed in the interspaces. Muffles can be kept steadily at a temperature of 2700 F (3600 F attainable) with the use of only one-half the amount of gas required in the older method of firing. The advantages of this method of combustion, according to Prof. W. A. Bone (*Engineering*, Apr. 14, 1911), are that combustion is accelerated by the incandescent surface, the heat developed can be concentrated just where it is required, very high temperatures are attainable without the use of regenerators, and the energy is converted into radiant form which is transmitted very rapidly to the object exposed to it.

Surface combustion has been applied to boilers, the tubes being packed throughout their length with pieces of firebrick, the air-gas mixture entering each tube through a ¾ in. hole in a fireclay plug or nozzle (which serves to protect the joints in the tube sheet) at the front end. For gas firing, 3 to 6 in. tubes have been used, and 9 to 12 in. for oil firing, the oil being first vaporized in a chamber at the firing end of the tube. The combustion is confined to about 4-in. next to the admission nozzles. In one boiler, it was found that 70 (22) [8] percent of the total evaporation took place over the first (2d) [3d] third of the length of the tubes (*Engineering*, May 10, 1912). The length of the boiler is not increased for greater capacities, the increased capacity being obtained by an increase in the diameter of the boiler and the use of a greater number of tubes.

In another type of surface-combustion furnace, the air-fuel mixture impinges directly on a bed of refractory material and a zone of combustion forms at that surface in the bed at which the velocity of the mixture equals the rate of flame propagation in the mixture. With this type, the delivery tube is accessible for cleaning.

The term surface combustion is also applied to a furnace in which the combustible mixture discharges into a refractory-lined tube or tunnel of small dimensions opening out into a furnace. As the tube or tunnel surface heats to incandescence, the combustion is accelerated and is completed before the mixture leaves it (see Blake, *Proc. Engrs'. Soc. West. Penna.*, 1920).

MIXTURES OF AIR AND WATER VAPOR

BY

C. O. Mackey

REFERENCES: Berry, Humidity Computations, *Combustion*, Aug., Sept., Oct., 1934. "ASHRAE Guide and Data Book." Keenan and Keyes, "Thermodynamic Properties of Steam," Wiley. Threlkeld, "Thermal Environmental Engineering," Prentice-Hall. Ellenwood and Mackey, "Thermodynamic Charts," Wiley.

For general relationships see p. 4–24. For air conditioning see pp. 12–120 to 12–153.

Atmospheric Humidity. The atmosphere is a mixture of air and water vapor. Dalton's law of partial pressures (for the mixture) and the ideal gas law (for each constituent) may safely be assumed to apply. The **total pressure** B (barometric pressure) is the sum of the **vapor pressure** p_v and the **air pressure** p_a.

The temperature of the atmosphere, as indicated by an ordinary thermometer, is the **dry-bulb temperature** t_d. If the atmosphere is cooled under constant total pressure, the partial pressures remain constant until a temperature is reached at which condensation of vapor begins. This temperature is the **dew point** t_c (condensation temperature) and is the saturation temperature, or boiling point, corresponding to the actual vapor pressure p_v. If a thermometer bulb is covered with absorbent material, *e.g.*, linen, wet with distilled water and exposed to the atmosphere, evaporation will cool the water and the thermometer bulb to the **wet-bulb temperature** t_w. This is the temperature given by a psychrometer (see p. 4–81). The wet-bulb temperature lies between the dry-bulb temperature and the dew point. These three temperatures are distinct except for a saturated atmosphere, for which they are identical. For each of these temperatures, there is a corresponding vapor pressure. The actual vapor pressure p_v corresponds with the dew point t_c. The vapor pressures p_d and p_w, corresponding with t_d and t_w, do not represent pressures actually appearing in the atmosphere but are used in computations.

Relative humidity r is the ratio of the actual vapor pressure to the pressure of saturated vapor at the prevailing dry-bulb temperature $r = p_v/p_d$. Within the limits of usual accuracy, this equals the ratio of actual vapor density to the density of saturated vapor at dry-bulb temperature, $r = \rho_v/\rho_d$. It is to be noted that relative humidity is a property of the vapor alone; it has nothing to do with the fact that the vapor is mixed with air. It is a method of expressing the departure of the vapor from saturation.

Molal humidity f is the mass of water vapor in mols per one mol of air. The laws of Dalton and Avogadro state that the molal composition of a mixture is proportional to the distribution of partial pressures, or $f = p_v/p_a = p_v/(B - p_v)$.

Specific humidity (humidity ratio) W is the mass of water vapor (pounds or grains) per pound of air. Mass in pounds equals mass in mols multiplied by the molecular weight. The molecular weight of water is 18, and the equivalent molecular weight of air is 28.97. The ratio $28.97/18 = 1.608$, or 1.61 with ample accuracy. Thus $W = f/1.61$.

Air density ρ_a is the pounds of air in one cubic foot. **Vapor density** ρ_v is the pounds of vapor in one cubic foot. **Mixture density** ρ_m is the sum of these, *i.e.*, the pounds of air plus vapor in one cubic foot.

Notation. The subscripts a, v, m, and f apply to air, vapor, mixture, and liquid water, respectively. The subscripts d and w apply to conditions pertaining to the dry- and wet-bulb temperature, respectively.

Humidity Measurements. Many methods are in use: (1) The **dew-point** method measures the temperature at which condensation begins; water-vapor pressure can then be found from steam tables. Dew-point apparatus can either cool a surface or compress and expand moist air. (2) **Hygrometers** measure relative humidity, often by using the change in dimensions of a hygroscopic material such as human hair, wood, or paper; these instruments are simple and inexpensive but require frequent calibration. The electrical resistance of an electrolytic film can also be used as an indication of relative humidity. (3) The wet- and dry-bulb **psychrometer** is widely used. Humidity measurements of air flowing in ducts can be made with psychrometers that use mercury-in-glass thermometers, thermocouples, or resistance thermometers. Humidity measurements of still air can be made with sling psychrometers or aspiration psychrometers. Psychrometric wet-bulb temperatures must be corrected to obtain thermodynamic wet-bulb temperatures, or there must be adequate air motion past the wet-bulb thermometer, 800 to 900 fpm (with duct walls at air temperature), to ensure a proper balance between radiation and convection. (Carrier and Mackey, *Trans. ASME*, 1937, p. 33.) (4) **Chemical analysis** by the use of dessicants such as sulphuric acid, phosphorus pentoxide, lithium chloride, or silica gel can be used as primary standards of humidity measurement.

Table 1 gives the pressure-temperature relations for saturated water vapor over water or ice.

Table 1. Vapor Pressure of Water in In. Hg at 32 F
(Ice below 32 F)
(From Keenan and Keyes, "Thermodynamic Properties of Steam")

t	0	1	2	3	4	5	6	7	8	9
−40	0.0039									
−30	0.0071	0.0067	0.0062	0.0058	0.0055	0.0051	0.0048	0.0045	0.0043	0.0041
−20	0.0126	0.0119	0.0112	0.0106	0.0100	0.0094	0.0089	0.0084	0.0079	0.0075
−10	0.0220	0.0208	0.0197	0.0187	0.0176	0.0167	0.0158	0.0149	0.0141	0.0133
− 0	......	0.0358	0.0339	0.0322	0.0305	0.0289	0.0274	0.0259	0.0246	0.0233
+ 0	0.0377	0.0397	0.0419	0.0441	0.0465	0.0489	0.0514	0.0541	0.0569	0.0598
10	0.0629	0.0661	0.0695	0.0730	0.0767	0.0806	0.0847	0.0889	0.0933	0.0980
20	0.103	0.108	0.113	0.119	0.124	0.130	0.137	0.143	0.150	0.157
30	0.165	0.172	0.180	0.188	0.196	0.204	0.212	0.220	0.229	0.238
40	0.248	0.258	0.268	0.278	0.289	0.300	0.312	0.324	0.336	0.349
50	0.363	0.376	0.391	0.405	0.420	0.436	0.452	0.469	0.486	0.504
60	0.522	0.541	0.560	0.580	0.601	0.622	0.644	0.667	0.690	0.714
70	0.739	0.765	0.791	0.818	0.846	0.875	0.905	0.935	0.967	0.999
80	1.032	1.066	1.102	1.138	1.175	1.213	1.253	1.293	1.335	1.378
90	1.422	1.467	1.513	1.561	1.610	1.660	1.712	1.765	1.819	1.875
100	1.933	1.992	2.052	2.114	2.178	2.243	2.310	2.379	2.449	2.521

The following equations give various properties in terms of pressure in inches Hg and temperature in degrees F.

Relative humidity: $r = p_v/p_d$ (1)

Specific humidity: $W = p_v/1.61(B - p_v)$ lb/lb dry air (2)

Volume of mixture per pound of dry air:

$$v_a = \frac{1}{\rho_a} = 0.754(t_d + 460)/(B - rp_d) \quad \text{cu ft} \tag{3}$$

Volume of mixture per pound of mixture:

$$v_m = \frac{1}{\rho_m} = v_a/(1 + W) \quad \text{cu ft} \tag{4}$$

The **enthalpy** of a mixture of dry air and steam, when each constituent is assumed to be an ideal gas, in Btu per pound of dry air, is the sum of the enthalpy of 1 lb of dry air and the enthalpy of the W lb of steam mixed with that air. The specific enthalpy of dry air (above 0 F) is $h_a = 0.240t_d$ (up to 130 F, the specific heat of dry air is 0.240; at higher temperatures, it is larger). The specific enthalpy of low-pressure steam (saturated or superheated) is nearly independent of the vapor pressure and depends only on t_d. An empirical equation for the specific enthalpy of low-pressure steam for the range of temperatures from −40 F to 250 F is

$$h_v = 1{,}062 + 0.44t_d \qquad \text{Btu/lb} \tag{5}$$

The enthalpy of a mixture of air and steam is

$$h_m = 0.240t_d + W(1{,}062 + 0.44t_d) \tag{6}$$

The specific heat of a mixture of dry air and steam per pound of dry air may be called **humid specific heat** and is $0.240 + 0.44W$ Btu/lb dry air. For a steady-flow process without change of specific humidity, heat transfers per pound of dry air may be computed as the product of humid specific heat and change in dry-bulb temperature.

Thermodynamic Wet-bulb Temperature (Temperature of Adiabatic Saturation). The thermodynamic wet-bulb temperature t^* is an important property of state of mixtures of dry air and superheated steam; it is the temperature at which water (or ice), by evaporating into a mixture of air and steam, will bring the mixture to saturation at the same temperature in a steady-flow process in the absence of external heat transfer. For a mixture of dry air and saturated steam only, $t^* = t_d$; when $r < 1$, $t^* < t_d$. By writing energy and mass balances for the process of adiabatic saturation with water supplied at t^*, the following equation may be derived:

$$W = W^* - \frac{(0.240 + 0.44W^*)(t_d - t^*)}{1{,}094 + 0.44t_d - t^*} \tag{7}$$

where W^* = specific humidity for saturation at t^* and total pressure of B.

The enthalpy of a mixture of dry air and **saturated** steam at the total pressure B and thermodynamic wet-bulb temperature t^* exceeds the enthalpy of a mixture of dry air and **superheated** steam at the same B and t^*, for

$$h_m^* = h_m + (W^* - W)h_f^*$$

A property of the mixture that remains constant for constant B and t^* has been called the **Σ function,** for

$$\Sigma^* = h_m^* - W^*h_f^* = \Sigma = h_m - Wh_f^*$$

Examples. 1. A mixture of dry air and **saturated** steam; $B = 24$ in. Hg; $t_d = 76$ F.
Partial pressure of water vapor: from Table 1,

$$p_v = p_d = 0.905 \text{ in. Hg}$$

Partial pressure of dry air: $p_a = B - p_v = 23.095$ in. Hg.
Specific humidity: from Eq. (**2**),

$$W = 0.905/1.61(23.095) = 0.0243 \text{ lb/lb dry air}$$

Volume of mixture per pound of dry air: from Eq. (**3**),

$$v_a = 0.754(536)/23.095 = 17.5 \text{ cu ft}$$

Volume of mixture per pound of mixture: from Eq. (**4**),

$$v_m = 17.5/1.0243 = 17.1 \text{ cu ft}$$

Enthalpy of mixture: from Eq. (**6**),

$$h_m = 0.240(76) + 0.0243(1{,}095) = 44.85 \text{ Btu/lb dry air}$$

2. A mixture of dry air and **superheated** steam: $B = 24$ in. Hg; $t_d = 76$ F; $t_w = t^* = 62$ F.
Pressure of saturated steam at $t^* = 0.560$ in. Hg (from Table 1) and from Eq. (**2**)

$$W^* = 0.560/1.61(23.44) = 0.01484 \text{ lb/lb dry air}$$

Specific humidity: from Eq. (**7**),

$$W = 0.01484 - \frac{0.2465(14)}{1{,}065.4} = 0.0116 \text{ lb/lb dry air}$$

Partial pressure of water vapor: from Eq. (**2**),

$$0.0116 = p_v/1.61(24 - p_v)$$

and

$$p_v = 0.44 \text{ in. Hg}$$

Relative humidity: from Eq. (**1**), $r = 0.44/0.905 = 0.486$.
Volume of mixture per pound of dry air: from Eq. (**3**),

$$v_a = 0.754(536)/23.56 = 17.2 \text{ cu ft}$$

Volume of mixture per pound of mixture: from Eq. (**4**),

$$v_m = 17.2/1.0116 = 17.0 \text{ cu ft}$$

Enthalpy of mixture: from Eq. (**6**),

$$h_m = 0.240(76) + 0.0116(1{,}095) = 30.95 \text{ Btu/lb dry air}$$

Psychrometric Charts. For occasional use, algebraic equations are less confusing and more reliable; for frequent use, a **psychrometric chart** may be preferable. A disadvantage of charts is that each applies for only one value of barometric pressure, usually 760 mm or 30 in. Hg. Correction to other barometric readings is not simple. The equations have the advantage that the actual barometric pressure is taken into account. The equations are often more convenient for equal accuracy or more accurate for equal convenience.

Psychrometric charts are usually plotted, as indicated by Fig. 1, with dry-bulb temperature as abscissa and specific humidity as ordinate. Since the specific humidity is determined by the vapor pressure and the barometric pressure (which is constant for a given chart), and is nearly proportional to the vapor pressure, a second ordinate scale, departing slightly from uniform graduations, will give the vapor pressure. The saturation curve ($r = 1.0$) gives the specific humidity and vapor pressure for a mixture of air and saturated vapor. Similar curves below it give results for various values of relative humidity. Inclined lines of one set carry fixed values of the wet-bulb temperature, and those of another set carry fixed values of v_a, cubic feet per pound of air. Many charts carry additional scales of enthalpy or Σ function.

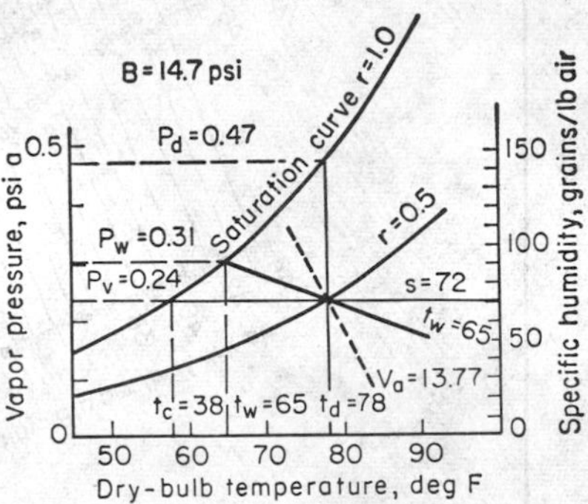

FIG. 1. Skeleton humidity chart.

Any two values will locate the point representing the state of the atmosphere, and the desired values can be read directly.

Figures 2 and 3 are psychrometric charts from the General Electric Company and Ellenwood and Mackey, "Thermodynamic Charts," covering a dry-bulb temperature range from 32 to 300 F. They are accurate only for a barometric pressure of 29.92 in. Hg.

Air-conditioning processes alter the temperature and specific humidity of the atmosphere. The weight of dry air remains constant and consequently computations are best based upon 1 lb of dry air.

Liquid water may enter or leave the apparatus. Its weight m_f lb per lb of air is often merely the difference between the specific humidities of the entering and leaving atmospheres. Its specific enthalpy at the observed or assumed temperature of supply

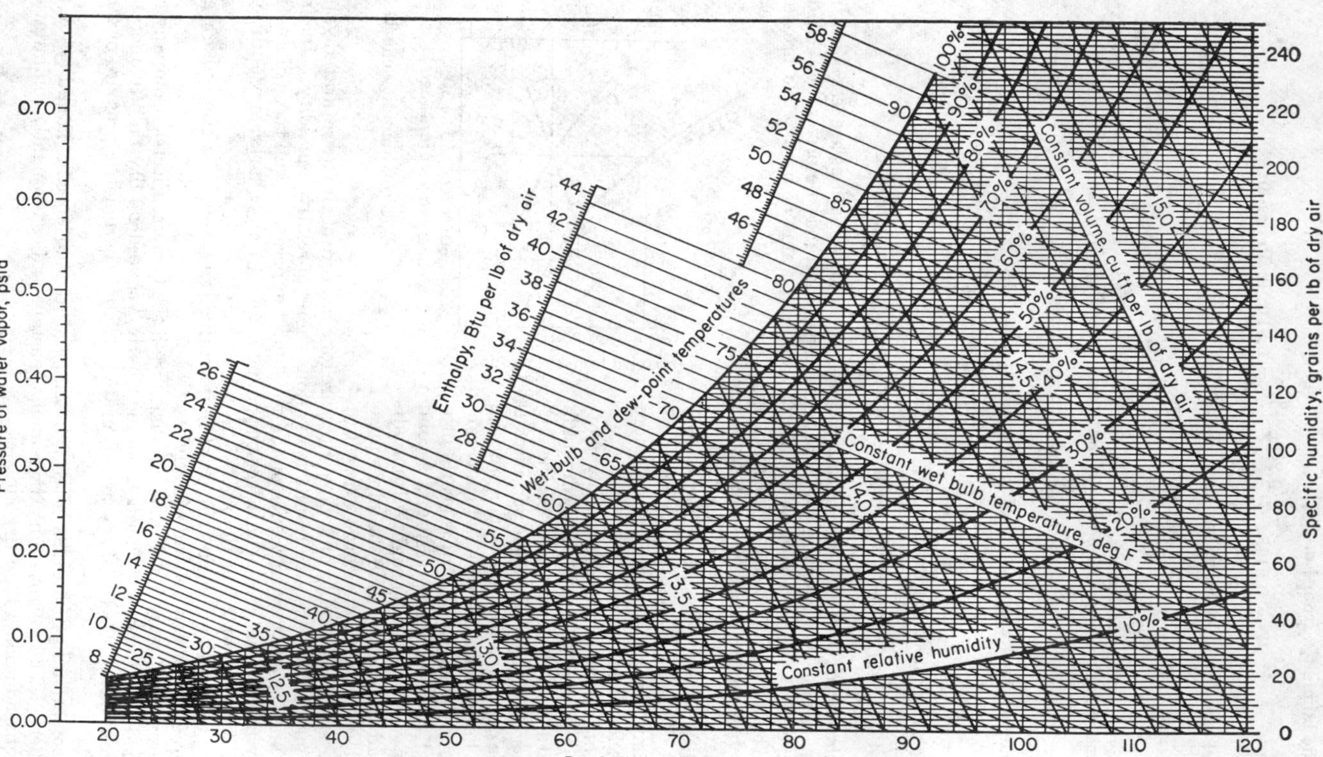

FIG. 2. Humidity chart for low temperatures. Barometric pressure = 14.696 psia. *(Copyright by General Electric Co. Adapted by permission.)*

or removal t_f is

$$h_f = t_f - 32 \text{ Btu per lb of liquid} \tag{8}$$

Because most air conditioning involves steady-flow processes, thermal results are computed by the steady flow equation, written for 1 lb of air. Using subscript 1 for entering atmosphere and liquid water, and for heat supplied; and 2 for departing

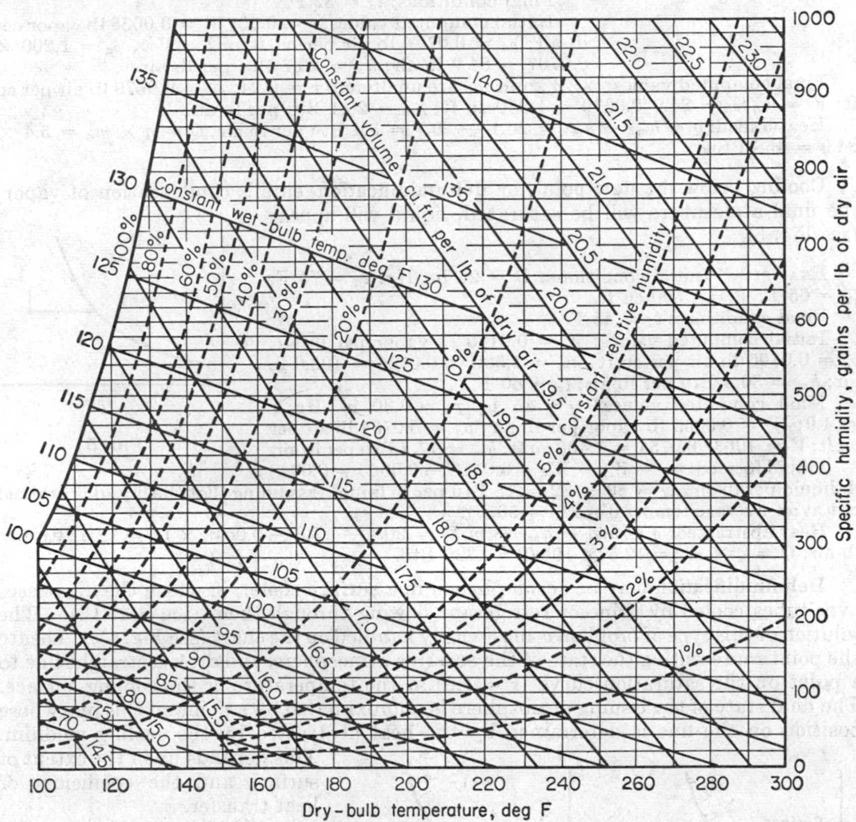

FIG. 3. Humidity chart for medium temperatures. (*From Ellenwood and Mackey, "Vapor Charts," Wiley.*)

atmosphere and water, and for heat abstracted; the equation becomes (in the absence of work)

$$h_{m1} + m_{f1}h_{f1} + q_1 = h_{m2} + m_{f2}h_{f2} + q_2 \text{ Btu per lb air} \tag{9}$$

Either or both values of m_f or q may be zero.

In terms of the sigma function, the steady-flow equation becomes

$$\Sigma_1 + W_1(t_{w1} - 32) + m_{f1}h_{f1} + q_1 = \Sigma_2 + W_2(t_{w2} - 32) + m_{f2}h_{f2} + q_2 \text{ Btu per lb air} \tag{10}$$

Unit processes involved in air conditioning include heating and cooling an atmosphere above its dew point, cooling below the dew point, adiabatic saturation, and mixing of two atmospheres. These, in various sequences, make it possible to start with any given atmosphere and produce an atmosphere of any required characteristics.

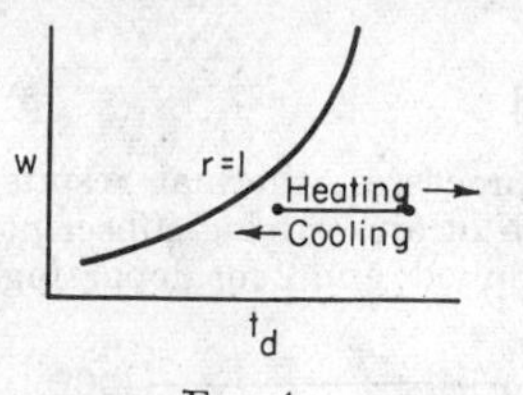

FIG. 4

Heating and cooling above the dew point entail no condensation of vapor. Barometric pressure and composition being unaltered, partial pressures remain constant. The process is represented in Fig. 4.

EXAMPLE. Initial conditions: $B = 28$ in. Hg; $t_d = 60$ F; $t_w = 50$ F; $p_v = 0.26$ in. Hg; $V = 1{,}200$ cu ft.

Final conditions: $t_d = 82$ F.

Initial computed values: $r = 0.50$; $W = 0.0058$ lb vapor per lb air; $\rho_a = 0.0707$ lb air per cu ft; $m_a = V \times \rho_a = 1{,}200 \times 0.0707 = 84.9$ lb air; $h_m = 20.7$ Btu per lb air.

Final computed values: p_v, W, and m_a are unaltered; $r = 0.24$; $\rho_a = 0.0679$ lb air per cu ft; $V = m_a/\rho_a = 84.9/0.0679 = 1{,}250$ cu ft; $h_m = 26.1$ Btu per lb air.

Heat added: $q = h_{m2} - h_{m1} = 26.1 - 20.7 = 5.4$ Btu per lb air; $Q = q \times m_a = 5.4 \times 84.9 = 458$ Btu.

Cooling below the dew point, or **dehumidification,** entails condensation of vapor; the final atmosphere will be saturated, liquid will appear (see Fig. 5).

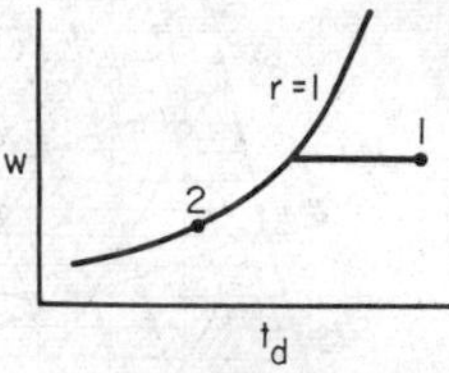

FIG. 5

EXAMPLE. Initial conditions: $B = 29$ in. Hg; $t_d = 75$ F; $t_w = 65$ F; $V = 1{,}500$ cu ft.

Final conditions: $t_d = 45$ F.

Initial computed values: $W = 0.0113$ lb vapor per lb air; $\rho_a = 0.0706$ lb air per cu ft; $m_a = 1{,}500 \times 0.0706 = 106.0$ lb air; $h_m = 30.4$ Btu per lb air; $t_c = 60$ F.

Final computed values: $t_d = 45$ F; $p_v = 0.30$ in. Hg; $r = 1.0$; $W = 0.0065$ lb vapor per lb air; $\rho_a = 0.0754$ lb air per cu ft; $V = 106.0/0.0754 = 1{,}406$ cu ft; $h_m = 17.8$ Btu per lb air.

Liquid formed: $m_f = W_1 - W_2 = 0.0113 - 0.0065 = 0.0048$ lb liquid per lb air; $h_f = 50 - 32 = 18$ Btu per lb liquid (assuming that the liquid is drained out at an average temperature $t_f = 50$ F).

Heat abstracted: $q = h_{m1} - h_{m2} - m_f h_f = 30.4 - 17.8 - 0.0048 \times 18 = 12.5$ Btu per lb air; $Q = q \times m_a = 12.5 \times 106.0 = 1325$ Btu.

Dehumidification may be accomplished in a **surface cooler,** in which the air passes over tubes cooled by brine or refrigerant flowing through them (see Sec. 12). The solution of this type of problem is most easily handled on the chart (see Fig. 6). Locate the point representing the state of the entering atmosphere, and draw a straight line to a point on the saturation curve ($r = 1.0$) at the temperature of the cooling surface. The final state of the issuing atmosphere is approximated by a point on this line whose position on the line is determined by the heat abstracted by the cooling medium. This depends upon the extent of surface and the coefficient of heat transfer.

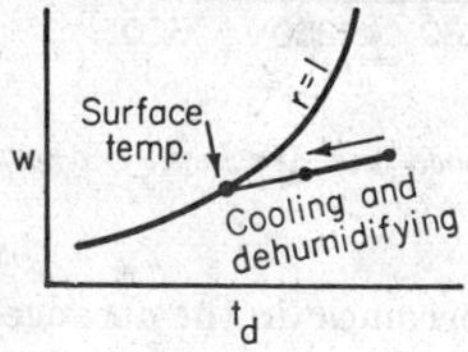

FIG. 6

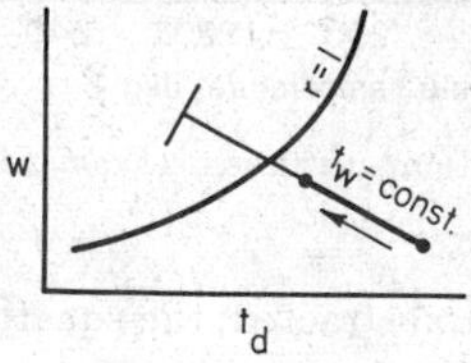

FIG. 7

Adiabatic saturation (humidification) may be conducted in a spray chamber through which atmosphere flows. A large excess of water is recirculated through spray nozzles, and evaporation is made up by a suitable water supply. After the process has been operating for some time, the water in the spray chamber will have been cooled to the temperature of adiabatic saturation, which differs from the wet-bulb temperature only because of radiation and velocity errors that affect the wet-bulb thermometer. No heat is added or abstracted; the process is adiabatic. The heat of vaporization for the water that is evaporated is supplied by the cooling of the air passing through the chamber. The wet-bulb temperature of the atmosphere is constant throughout the chamber (Fig. 7). If the chamber is sufficiently large, the issuing atmosphere will be saturated at the wet-bulb temperature of the entering atmosphere; *i.e.*, as the atmosphere passes through the chamber, t_w remains constant, t_d is reduced from its initial value to t_w, and t_c is increased from its initial value to t_w. In a chamber of commercial size, the action may terminate somewhat short of this, the precise end point being determined by the duration and effectiveness of contact between air and spray water. In any case, the weight of water evaporated equals the increase in the specific humidity of the atmosphere.

EXAMPLE. Initial conditions $B = 30$ in. Hg; $t_d = 78$ F; $t_w = 55$ F; $r = 0.20$; $W = 28$ grains vapor per lb air.

Final condition: $t_d = t_w = 55$ F; $r = 1.0$; $W = 64$ grains vapor per lb air.

Water evaporated: $W_2 - W_1 = 64 - 28 = 36$ grains water per lb air.

The design of the spray chamber to produce this result is necessarily based upon experience with like apparatus previously built.

In practice, the spray chamber is preceded and followed by heating coils, the first to warm the entering atmosphere to the desired value of t_w, determined by the prescribed final specific humidity, the second to warm the issuing atmosphere to the desired temperature, and simultaneously to reduce its relative humidity to the desired value.

The **spray chamber** that is used for adiabatic saturation (humidification) in winter may be used for dehumidification in summer by supplying the spray nozzles with refrigerated water instead of recirculated water. In this case, the issuing atmosphere will be saturated at the temperature of the spray water, which will be held at the desired dew point. Subsequent heating of the atmosphere to an acceptable temperature will simultaneously reduce the relative humidity to the desired value.

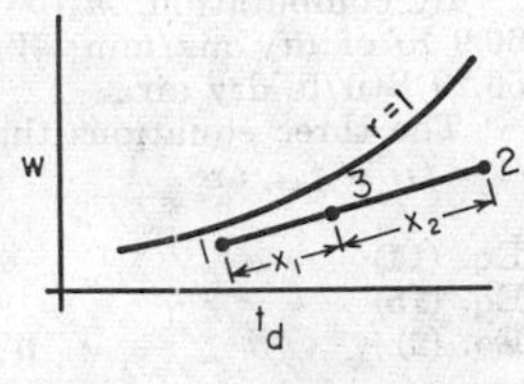

FIG. 8

Mixing Two Atmospheres. In recirculating ventilation systems, two atmospheres (1 and 2) are mixed to form a third (3). The state of the final atmosphere is readily found graphically on the psychrometric chart (see Fig. 8). Locate the points 1 and 2 representing the states of the initial atmospheres. Connect these points by a straight line. Locate a point that divides this line into segments inversely proportional to the weights of air in the respective atmospheres. The division point represents the state of the final mixture, so long as it falls below the saturation curve ($r = 1$). If the final point falls above the saturation curve, as in Fig. 9, condensation will ensue, and the true final point 4 is found by drawing a line from the apparent point 3, parallel to the lines of constant wet-bulb temperature, to its intersection with the saturation curve. From all the points involved, readings of specific humidity may be taken, including point 3 when it falls above the saturation curve, and in this case the difference between W_3 and W_4 will be the weight of condensate, pounds per pound air.

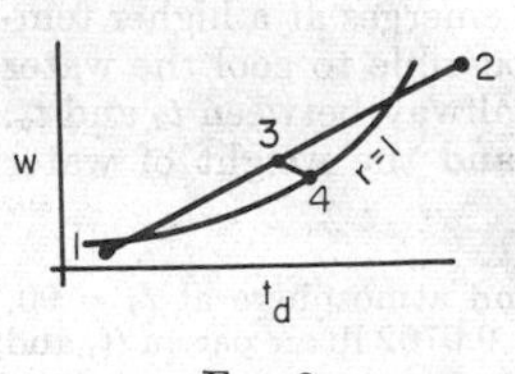

FIG. 9

If the chart is sectional and the two points do not fall in the same section, or in any case in which it is preferred, the same method may be carried out arithmetically.

For adiabatic mixing in a steady-flow process of two masses of "moist" air, each at the total pressure of B,

$$m_{a3} = m_{a1} + m_{a2} \tag{11}$$

In the absence of condensation,

$$m_{a3}W_3 = m_{a1}W_1 + m_{a2}W_2 \tag{12}$$

and

$$m_{a3}h_{m3} = m_{a1}h_{m1} + m_{a2}h_{m2} \tag{13}$$

When condensation occurs, assume that the condensate is removed at the final temperature t_4 and that the final mixture consists of dry air and saturated water vapor at this same temperature. The weight of condensate is

$$m_c = m_{a1}W_1 + m_{a2}W_2 - m_{a3}W_4 \tag{14}$$

where W_4 is the specific humidity for saturation at temperature t_4 and total pressure B. Also

$$m_{a1}h_{m1} + m_{a2}h_{m2} = m_{a2}h_{m4} + m_c h_{f4} \qquad \textbf{(15)}$$

In the case of condensation, a trial solution is necessary to find the temperature t_4 that will satisfy these relations.

EXAMPLES. 1. Two thousand cu ft of air per min at $t_{d1} = 80$ F and $t_{w1} = 65$ F are mixed in an adiabatic, steady-flow process with one thousand cu ft of air per min at $t_{d2} = 95$ F and $t_{w2} = 75$ F; the total pressure of each mixture is 29 in. Hg.

By computation, $m_{a1} = 140$ lb dry air/min; $W_1 = 0.010$ lb/lb dry air; $m_{a2} = 67.6$ lb dry air/min; $W_2 = 0.0146$ lb/lb dry air.

From Eq. (**11**), $m_{a3} = 207.6$ lb dry air/min.

From Eq. (**12**), $W_3 = 0.0116$ lb/lb dry air.

From Eq. (**6**), $h_{m1} = 30.3$ Btu/lb dry air and $h_{m2} = 38.9$ Btu/lb dry air.

From Eq. (**13**), $h_{m3} = 33.1$ Btu/lb dry air.

From Eq. (**6**), $t_{d3} = 84.9$ F.

2. Fifteen hundred cu ft of air per min at $t_{d1} = 0$ F and $r_1 = 0.8$ are mixed in an adiabatic, steady-flow process with one thousand cu ft of air per min at $t_{d2} = 100$ F and $r_2 = 0.9$; the total pressure of each mixture is 30 in. Hg.

By computation, $m_{a1} = 129.6$ lb of dry air/min; $W_1 = 0.000626$ lb/lb dry air; $m_{a2} = 66.9$ lb of dry air/min; $W_2 = 0.03824$ lb/lb dry air; $h_{m1} = 0.90$ Btu/lb dry air; $h_{m2} = 66.29$ Btu/lb dry air.

The three equations that must be satisfied by a choice of the terminal temperature, $t_4 = t_{d4} = t_{w4}$, are

Eq. (**14**) $\qquad m_c = 2.64 - 196.5W_4$

Eq. (**15**) $\qquad 4551 = 196.5h_{m4} + m_c h_{f4}$

Eq. (**2**) $\qquad W_4 = p_{v4}/1.61(30 - p_{v4}) \quad$ for $r_4 = 1$

The value of t_4 that satisfies these equations is 55 F; condensation amounts to 0.84 lb per min.

The **cooling tower** is a chamber in which outdoor atmosphere flows through a spray of entering hot water, which is to be cooled. The temperature of the water is reduced in part by the warming of the air, and in greater part by the evaporation of a portion of the water. The atmosphere enters at given conditions and emerges at a higher temperature and usually saturated ($r = 1$). It is commonly possible to cool the water below the temperature of the entering air, often to about halfway between t_d and t_w. The volume of atmosphere per pound of entering water and the weight of water evaporated are to be computed.

EXAMPLE. A cooling tower is to receive water at 120 F and atmosphere at $t_d = 90$, $t_w = 80$, whence $p_v = 0.92$, $W = 0.0196$ lb vapor per lb air, $\rho_a = 0.0702$ lb air per cu ft, and $h_m = 43.2$. The water is to be cooled to 85 F. What volume of atmosphere must be passed through the tower, and what weight of water will be lost by evaporation?

The issuing atmosphere will be assumed to be saturated at 115 F. Then $t_d = 115$ F, $p_v = 3.0$ in. Hg, $W = 0.0690$ lb vapor per lb air, $\rho_a = 0.0623$ lb air per cu ft, and $h_m = 104.4$ Btu per lb air.

The two unknowns are the weight of air to be passed through the tower and the weight of water to be evaporated. The two equations are the water-weight balance and the enthalpy balance (the steady-flow equation for zero heat transfer to or from outside). Assume that 1 lb water enters, of which x lb are evaporated. The water-weight balance $1 + m_aW_1 = 1 - x + m_aW_2$ becomes $x = m_a(W_2 - W_1) = m_a(0.0690 - 0.0196) = 0.0494m_a$. The enthalpy balance $1 \times (120 - 32) + m_ah_{m1} = (1 - x)(85 - 32) + m_ah_{m2}$ becomes $88 + 43.2m_a = 53(1 - x) + 104.4m_a$; whence, $53x = 53 - 88 + m_a(104.4 - 43.2) = -35 + 61.2m_a$.

Solving these simultaneous equations, $x = 0.0295$ lb water evaporated per pound of water entering and $m_a = 0.597$ lb air per pound water entering.

In an **evaporative condenser** vapor is condensed within tubes that are cooled by the evaporation of water flowing over the outside of the tubes; the water evaporates into the atmosphere. The computation of results is similar to that for the cooling tower.

Combustion Computations. The total weight of water vapor in the flue-gas mixture is the sum of that arriving with the air and fuel and that resulting from the combustion of hydrogen and hydrocarbons. The weight of dry flue gases is computed from the chemical equations. The vapor pressure in the flue gas can be computed, and from this the dew point of the flue gas can be estimated on the assumption that the dry gases do not influence the vapor pressure. If the fuel contains an appreciable amount of sulphur, the flue gas will carry enough sulphur oxides to change the result markedly. The vapor pressure of sulphurous acid (SO_2 dissolved in water) is less than the vapor pressure of pure water; that of sulphuric acid (SO_3 dissolved in water) is much more so. Accordingly, the dew point will be higher. The dew point of flue gas, neglecting sulphur oxides, often falls not far from 120 F. Actual dew points above 250 F have been observed in flue gas arising from high-sulphur coal. (See Yeaw and Shnidman, Flue Products of Industrial Fuels, *Ind. Eng. Chem.*, **28**, p. 999, 1936.)

TRANSMISSION OF HEAT BY CONDUCTION AND CONVECTION

BY

W. H. McAdams, G. C. Williams, and K. A. Smith

REFERENCES: McAdams, "Heat Transmission," McGraw-Hill. Eckert and Drake, "Heat and Mass Transfer," McGraw-Hill. Carslaw and Jaeger, "Conduction of Heat in Solids," Oxford. Jakob, "Heat Transfer," vols. I and II, Wiley. Grober, Erk, and Grigull, "Fundamentals of Heat Transfer," translated by J. Moszynski, McGraw-Hill. Wilkes, "Heat Insulation," Wiley. Kays and London, "Compact Heat Exchangers," McGraw-Hill. "Thermophysical Properties Data Book," Purdue University.

Notation and Units

The units are based on feet, pounds, hours, degrees Fahrenheit, and Btu. Any other consistent set may be used in the dimensionless relations given, but for the dimensional equations the units of this table must be used.

A = area of heat-transfer surface, sq ft
A_i = inside area
A_o = outside area
A_m = average value of A, sq ft
a = an empirical constant
C_p = specific heat at constant pressure, Btu per lb per deg F
D = diameter, ft
D_o = outside diam, ft
D_i = inside diam, ft
D' = diameter, in.
D_o' = outside diam, in.
D_i' = inside diam, in.
e = base of natural logarithms, 2.718
G = mass velocity, equals w/S, lb per hr per sq ft of cross section occupied by fluid
G_{max} = mass velocity through minimum free area in a row of pipes normal to fluid stream, lb per hr per sq ft
g_c = conversion factor, equal to 4.18×10^8 (mass lb)(ft)/(force lb)(hr)^2
g_L = local acceleration due to gravity, 4.18×10^8 ft per hr per hr at sea level
h = local individual coefficient of heat transfer, equals $dq/dA\ \Delta t$, Btu per hr sq ft deg F diff
$h_c + h_r$ = combined coefficient by conduction, convection, and radiation between surface and surroundings
h_m = mean value of h for entire surface, based on $(\Delta t)_m$
$h_{a.m.}$ = average h, arbitrarily based on arithmetic-mean temperature difference
h_s = heat-transfer coefficient through scale deposits
J = mechanical equivalent of heat, 778 ft-lb per Btu
k = thermal conductivity, Btu per hr per sq ft per unit temperature gradient deg F per ft

$$k_m = -\frac{1}{t_1 - t_2}\int_1^2 k\,dt$$

k_f = k at the "film" temperature, $t_f = (t + t_w)/2$
l = thickness of material normal to heat flow, ft
L = length of heat-transfer surface, heated length, ft
N = number of rows of tubes
N_{Gr} = Grashof number, $L_c^3 \rho_f^2 g_L \beta_f (\Delta t)_s / \mu_f^2$
Q = quantity of heat, Btu
q = total rate of heat flow, Btu per hr
$\dot{\mathbf{q}}$ = heat-flux vector, Btu per hr per sq ft
$\dot{\mathbf{q}}_x$ = x-component of heat-flux vector
R = thermal resistances, $1/UA$, $1/hA$, $1/(h_c + h_r)A_0$
R_g = gas constant, 1,546/mol. wt, 53.35 for air
$\mathcal{R}$ = recovery factor
r = radius, ft
S = cross section, filled by fluid, in plane normal to direction of fluid flow, sq ft
T = temperature, deg R = $t + 460$
T_1, T_2 = inlet and outlet bulk temperatures, respectively, of warmer fluid, deg F
t = bulk temperature (based on heat balance), deg F
t_w = wall temperature, deg F
t_1, t_2 = inlet and outlet bulk temperatures of colder fluid, deg F
t_i, t_o = temperatures of fluid inside and outside, deg F
t_f = $(t + t_w)/2$
t_{sat} = saturation temperature, deg F
U = over-all coefficient of heat transfer, Btu per hr per sq ft per deg F; U_i, U_o based on inside and outside surface, respectively
V = mean velocity, fph
V_s = average velocity, volumetric rate divided by cross section filled by fluid, fps
V_{sm} = maximum velocity, through minimum cross section, fps
x = one of the axes of a Cartesian reference frame, ft
X = $(t_2 - t_1)/(T_1 - t_1)$
w = mass rate of flow per tube, lb per hr per tube
Z = $(T_1 - T_2)/(t_2 - t_1)$
α = a dimensional constant
β = volumetric coefficient of thermal expansion, having units of reciprocal of Fahrenheit temperature
Γ = mass rate of flow, lb/(hr) (ft of wetted periphery measured on a plane normal to direction of fluid flow); = $w/\pi D$ for a vertical and $w/2L$ for a horizontal tube
γ = ratio of specific heats, c_p/c_v; 1.4 for air
∇ = gradient operator
Δt = temperature difference, deg F
$(\Delta t)_{ave}$, $(\Delta t)_{l.m.}$ = arithmetic and logarithmic means of terminal temperature differences, respectively, deg F
$(\Delta t)_m$ = true mean value of the terminal temperature differences, deg F
$(\Delta t)_o$ = over-all temperature difference, deg F
$(\Delta t)_s$ = temperature difference between surface and surroundings, deg F
λ = latent heat (enthalpy) of vaporization, Btu per lb
μ = viscosity at bulk temperature, lb per hr per ft; equals 2.42 times centipoises; equals 116,000 times viscosity in (lb force) (sec)/sq ft
μ_f = viscosity, lb per hr per ft, at arithmetic mean of wall and fluid temperatures
μ_w = viscosity at wall temperature, lb per hr per ft
ρ = density, lb per cu ft
ρ_∞ = density of stream of great depth, lb per cu ft
σ = surface tension, (lb force) per ft

Subscripts:

l = liquid
v = vapor

Preliminary Statements. The transfer of heat is usually considered to occur by three processes:

1. **Conduction** is the transfer of heat from one part of a body to another part or to another body by short-range interaction of molecules and/or electrons.

2. **Convection** is the transfer of heat by the combined mechanisms of fluid mixing and conduction.

3. **Radiation** is the emission of energy in the form of electromagnetic waves. All bodies above absolute zero temperature radiate. Radiation incident on a body may be absorbed, reflected, and transmitted. (See p. 4–108 *et seq.*)

Table 1. Thermal Conductivities of Metals*

(k = Btu per hr per sq ft per deg F per ft)

$k_t = k_{t_0} - a(t - t_0)$

Substance	Temp range, deg F	k_{t_0}	a
Metals:			
Aluminum	70–700	130	0.03
Antimony	70–212	10.6	0.006
Beryllium	70–700	80	0.027
Cadmium	60–212	53.7	0.01
Cobalt	70	28	....
Copper	70–700	232	0.032
Germanium	70	34	....
Gold	60–212	196	....
Iron, pure	70–700	41.5	0.025
Iron, wrought	60–212	34.9	0.002
Steel (1% C)	60–212	26.2	0.002
Lead	32–500	20.3	0.006
Magnesium	32–370	99	0.015
Mercury	32	4.8	....
Molybdenum	32–800	79	0.016
Nickel	70–560	36	0.0175
Palladium	70	39	....
Platinum	70–800	41	0.0014
Plutonium	70	5	....
Rhodium	70	88	....
Silver	70–600	242	0.058
Tantalum	212	32	....
Thallium	32	29	....
Thorium	70–570	17	−0.0045
Tin	60–212	36	0.0135
Titanium	70–570	9	0.001
Tungsten	70–570	92	0.02
Uranium	70–770	14	−0.007
Vanadium	70	20	—
Zinc	60–212	65	0.007
Zirconium	32	11	—
Alloys:			
Admiralty metal	68–460	58.1	−0.054
Brass	−265–360	61.0	−0.066
(70% Cu, 30% Zn)	360–810	84.6	0
Bronze, 7.5% Sn	130–460	34.4	−0.042
7.7% Al	68–392	39.1	−0.038
Constantan	−350–212	12.7	−0.0076
(60% Cu, 40% Ni)	212–950	10.1	−0.019
Dural 24S (93.6% Al, 4.4% Cu, 1.5% Mg,	−321–550	63.8	−0.083
0.5% Mn)	550–800	130.	+0.038
Inconel X (73% Ni 15% Cr, 7% Fe, 2.5% Ti)	27–1070	7.62	−0.0068
Manganin (84% Cu,	1070–1650	3.35	−0.0111
12% Mn, 4% Ni)	−256–212	11.5	−0.015
Monel (67.1% Ni, 29.2% Cu, 1.7% Fe, 1.0% Mn)	−415–1470	12.0	−0.008
Nickel silver (64% Cu, 17% Zn, 18% Ni)	68–390	18.1	−0.0156

* For refractories, see p. 6–209 and 6–215 for pipe coverings, p. 8–251 for building materials, pp. 4–95 to 97. Conversion factors for various units are given on p. 1–85. Tables 3–7 were revised by G. B. Wilkes.

Thermal Conductivity of Nickel-Chromium Alloys with Iron

$k_t = k_{t_0} - a(t - t_0)$

AISI Number	Temp, range, deg F	k_{t_0}	a
301, 302, 303, 304 (303 Se, 304 L)	95–1650	8.08	−0.0052
310 (3105)	32–1650	6.85	−0.0072
314	80–572	10.01	−0.00124
	572–1650	8.20	−0.0045
316 (316 L)	− 60–1750	7.50	−0.0042
321, 347 (348)	−100–1650	8.22	−0.0050
403, 410 (416, 416 Se, 420)	−100–1850	15.0	0
430 [430 F, 430 F (Se)]	122–1650	12.60	−0.0012
440 C	212–932	12.77	−0.0043
446	32–1850	12.96	−0.0050
501, 502	80–1520	21.4	+0.0037

Properties of Molten Metals*

Metal and melting point	Temperature, deg F	k, Btu/(hr)(ft)(deg F)	ρ, lb/cu ft	c_p, Btu/(lb)(deg F)	μ, lb/(ft)(hr)
Bismuth (520F)	600	9.5	625	0.0345	3.92
	1000	9.0	608	0.0369	2.66
	1400	9.0	591	0.0393	1.91
Lead (621F)	700	10.5	658	0.038	5.80
	900	11.4	650	0.037	4.65
	1300	.....	633	.....	3.31
Mercury (−38F)	50	4.7	847	0.033	3.85
	300	6.7	826	0.033	2.66
	600	8.1	802	0.032	2.09
Potassium (147F)	300	26.0	50.4	0.19	0.90
	800	22.8	46.3	0.18	0.43
	1300	19.1	42.1	0.18	0.31
Sodium (208F)	200	49.8	58.0	0.33	1.69
	700	41.8	53.7	0.31	0.68
	1300	34.5	48.6	0.30	0.43
Na, 56 wt %, K, 44 wt % (66.2F)	200	14.8	55.4	0.270	1.40
	700	15.9	51.3	0.252	0.570
	1300	16.7	46.2	0.249	0.389
Na, 22 wt %, K, 78 wt % (12F)	200	14.1	53.0	0.226	1.19
	750	15.4	48.4	0.210	0.500
	1400		43.1	0.211	0.353
Pb, 44.5 wt %, Bi, 55.5 wt % (257F)	300	5.23	657	0.035	
	700	6.85	639	0.035	3.71
	1200	.....	614	.....	2.78

* Based largely on the "Liquid-Metals Handbook," 2d ed., United States Government Printing Office, Washington, D.C., 1952.

Table 2. Thermal Conductivities of Liquids and Gases

Substance	Temp, deg F	k	Substance	Temp, deg F	k
LIQUIDS			GASES		
Acetone	68	0.103	Air (see below)	32	0.0140
Ammonia	45	0.29	Ammonia, vapor	32	0.0126
Aniline	32	0.104	Ammonia	212	0.0192
Benzol	86	0.089	Argon	32	0.00915
Carbon bisulphide	68	0.0931	Carbon dioxide	32	0.0084
Ethyl alcohol	68	0.105		212	0.0128
Ether	68	0.0798	Carbon monoxide	32	0.0135
Glycerin, USP, 95%	68	0.165	Chlorine	32	0.0043
Kerosene	68	0.086	Ethane	32	0.0106
Methyl alcohol	68	0.124	Ethylene	32	0.0101
n-Pentane	68	0.0787	Helium	32	0.0818
Petroleum ether	68	0.0758	*n*-Hexane	32	0.0072
Toluene	86	0.086	Hydrogen	32	0.0966
Water	32	0.343		212	0.124
	140	0.377	Methane	32	0.0175
Oil, castor	39	0.104	Neon	32	0.0267
Oil, olive	39	0.101	Nitrogen	32	0.0140
Oil, turpentine	54	0.0734	Nitrous oxide	32	0.0088
Vaseline	59	0.106		212	0.0090
			Nitric oxide	32	0.0138
			Oxygen	32	0.0142
			n-Pentane	32	0.0074
			Sulphur dioxide	32	0.005

Thermal Conductivities of Air and Steam*

Temperature, deg F	32	200	400	600	800	1000
Air, 1 atm	0.0140	0.0181	0.0225	0.0266	0.0303	0.0337
Steam, 1 psia	......	0.0132	0.0184	0.0238	0.0292	0.0345

* Values from F. G. Keyes, *Tech. Rept.* 37, Project Squid (Apr. 1, 1952).

CONDUCTION

The **basic Fourier conduction law** for an isotropic material is

$$\dot{\mathbf{q}} = -k\nabla t \tag{1}$$

In Cartesian coordinates, the x-component of this equation is $\dot{q}_x = -k(\partial t/\partial x)$, and if the heat flow is unidimensional, $q = \dot{q}A(x) = -kA(x)(dt/dx)$. This states that the steady-state rate of heat conduction q is proportional to the cross-sectional $A(x)$ normal to the direction of flow and to the temperature gradient $\partial t/\partial x$ along the conduction path. The proportionality constant k is called the **"true" thermal conductivity** of the material.

The thermal conductivity of a given material varies with temperature, and the mean thermal conductivity is defined by

$$k_m = \frac{1}{t_0' - t_i'}\int_{t_i'}^{t_0'} k\,dt$$

Over moderate range, k varies linearly with t, and hence k_m is the value of k at the arithmetic mean of t_i' and t_0'.

For unidimensional heat flow through a material of thickness l

$$q\int_0^l \frac{dx}{A(x)} = \int_{t_i'}^{t_0'} k\,dt = k_m(t_i' - t_0') \tag{2}$$

with an obvious definition for the mean area:

$$\frac{q}{A_m} = k_m(t_i' - t_0')$$

For flat plates, $A_m = A_i = A_0$; for hollow cylinders, $A_m = (A_0 - A_i)/\ln(A_0/A_i)$; for hollow spheres, $A_m = \sqrt{A'A_0}$. For more complex shapes, Eq. (**1**) must be employed. Mean areas may then be evaluated by a graphical procedure (Awbery and Schofield, *Proc. 5th Intern. Congr. Refrig.*, **3**, 1929, pp. 591–610) or by the relaxation procedure (Emmons, *Trans. ASME*, **65**, 1943, pp. 607–612).

Table 3. Thermal Conductivities of Miscellaneous Solid Substances*

(Values of k are to be regarded as rough average values for the temperature range indicated)

Material	Bulk density, lb per cu ft	Temp, deg F	k
Asbestos board, compressed asbestos and cement	123.	86.	0.225
Asbestos millboard	60.5	86.	0.070
Asbestos wool	25.	212.	0.058
Ashes, soft wood	12.5	68.	0.018
Ashes, volcanic	51.	300.	0.123
Carbon black	12.	133.	0.012
Cardboard, corrugated	...	...	0.037
Celluloid	87.3	86.	0.12
Cellulose sponge, du Pont	3.4	82.	0.033
Concrete, sand. and gravel	142.	75.	1.05
Concrete, cinder	97.	75.	0.41
Charcoal, powder	11.5	63.	0.029
Cork, granulated	5.4	23.	0.028
Cotton wool	5.0	100.	0.035
Diamond	151.	70.	320.
Earth plus 42 % water	108.	0.	0.62
Fiber, red	80.5	68.	0.27
"Flotofoam" (U.S. Rubber Co.)	1.6	92.	0.017
Glass, pyrex	139	200.	0.59
Glass, soda lime	...	200.	0.59
Graphite, solid	93.5	122.	87.
Gravel	116.	68.	0.22
Gypsum board	51.	99.	0.062
Ice	57.5	...	1.26
Kaolin wool	10.6	800.	0.059
Leather, sole	62.4	...	0.092
Mica	122.	...	0.25
Pearlite, Arizona, spherical shell of siliceous material	9.1	112.	0.035
Polystyrene, expanded "Styrofoam"	1.7	...	0.021
Pumice, powdered	49.	300.	0.11
Quartz, crystal, perpendicular to C-axis	...	−300.	12.5
		0.	4.3
		300.	2.3

Material	Bulk density, lb per cu ft	Temp, deg F	k
Quartz, crystal, parallel to C-axis	...	−300.	25.0
		0.	8.3
		300.	4.2
Rubber, hard	74.3	100.	0.092
Rubber, soft, vulcanized	68.6	86.	0.08
Sand, dry	94.8	68.	0.188
Sawdust, dry	13.4	68.	0.042
Silica, fused	...	200.	0.83
Silica gel, powder	32.5	131.	0.049
Soil, dry	...	68.	0.075
Soil, dry, including stones	127.	68.	0.30
Snow	7–31	32.	0.34–1.3
Titanium oxide, finely ground	52.	1000.	0.041
Wool, pure	5.6	86.	0.021
Zirconia grain	113.	600.	0.11
Woods, oven dry, across grain†:			
Aspen	26.	85.	0.069
Bald cypress	24.	85.	0.063
Balsa	10.	85.	0.034
Basswood	24.	85.	0.058
Douglas Fir	29.	85.	0.063
Elm, rock	48.	85.	0.097
Fir, white	26.	85.	0.069
Hemlock	29.	85.	0.066
Larch, western	36.	85.	0.078
Maple, sugar	43.	85.	0.094
Oak, red	42.	85.	0.099
Pine, southern yellow	35.	85.	0.078
Pine, white	25.	85.	0.060
Red cedar, western	21.	85.	0.053
Redwood	25.	85.	0.062
Spruce	21.	85.	0.052

* The thermal conductivity of different materials varies greatly. For metals and alloys k is high, while for certain insulating materials, such as glass wool, cork, and kapok, it is very low. In general, k varies with the temperature, but in the case of metals, the variation is relatively small. With most other substances, k increases with rising temperatures, but in the case of many crystalline materials, the reverse is true.

† With heat flow parallel to the grain, k may be 2 to 3 times that with heat flow perpendicular to the grain; the values for wood are taken chiefly from J. D. MacLean, *Trans. ASHRAE*, **47**, 1941, p. 323.

Table 4. Thermal Conductivities for Building Insulation

Material	Bulk density, lb per cu ft	Temp, deg F	k
Balsam wool, blanket	3.6	70.	0.021
Cabot's Quilt, eel-grass	15.6	86.	0.027
Glass wool, blanket	3.25	100.	0.022
Hairfelt, blanket	11.0	86.	0.022
Insulating boards, Insulite, Celotex, etc.	12–19	100.	0.027–0.031
Kapok, "DryZero," blanket	1.6	75.	0.019
Redwood bark, loose, shredded, "Palco Bark"	4.0	100.	0.025
Rock wool, loose	7.	117.	0.024
Sil-O-Cel powder	10.6	86.	0.026
Vermiculite, loose, "Zonolite"	8.2	60.	0.038

Table 5. Thermal Conductivities of Material for Refrigeration and Extreme Low Temperatures

Material	Bulk density, lb per cu ft	Temp, deg F	k	Material	Bulk density, lb per cu ft	Temp, deg F	k
Corkboard	6.9	100	0.022	Rubber board, expanded, "Rubatex"	4.9	100	0.018
		−100	0.018			−100	0.015
		−300	0.010			−300	0.004
Fiberglas with asphalt coating (board)	11.0	100	0.023	Silica aerogel, powder, "Santocel"	5.3	100	0.013
		−100	0.014			0	0.012
		−300	0.007			−100	0.010
Glass blocks, expanded, "Foamglas"	10.6	100	0.036	Vegetable fiberboard, asphalt coating	14.4	100	0.028
		−100	0.033			−100	0.021
		−300	0.018			−300	0.013
Mineral wool board, "Rockcork"	14.3	100	0.024	Foams: Polystyrene[a]	2.9	−100	0.015
		−100	0.017	Polyurethane[b]	5.0	−100	0.019
		−300	0.008				

[a] Test space pressure, 1.0 atm; $k = 0.0047$ at 10^{-5} mm Hg.
[b] Test space pressure, 1.0 atm; $k = 0.007$ at 10^{-3} mm Hg.

Table 6. Thermal Conductivities of Insulating Materials for High Temperatures

Material	Bulk density, lb per cu ft	Max temp, deg F	100 F	300 F	500 F	1000 F	1500 F	2000 F
Asbestos paper, laminated.......	22.	400	0.038	0.042				
Asbestos paper, corrugated......	16.	300	0.031	0.042				
Diatomaceous earth, silica, powder......................	18.7	1500	0.037	0.045	0.053	0.074		
Diatomaceous earth, asbestos and bonding material.........	18.	1600	0.045	0.049	0.053	0.065		
Fiberglas block, PF612.........	2.5	500	0.023	0.039				
Fiberglas block, PF614.........	4.25	500	0.021	0.033				
Fiberglas block, PF617.........	9.	500	0.020	0.033				
Fiberglas, metal mesh blanket, #900......................	......	1000	0.020	0.030	0.040			
Glass blocks, average values....	14–24	1600	.....	0.046	0.053	0.074		
Hydrous calcium silicate, "Kaylo"......................	11.	1200	0.032	0.038	0.045			
85% magnesia...................	12.	600	0.029	0.035				
Micro-quartz fiber, blanket.....	3.	3000	0.021	0.028	0.042	0.075	0.108	0.142
Potassium titanate, fibers.......	71.5	....	.....	0.022	0.024	0.030		
Rock wool, loose................	8–12	....	0.027	0.038	0.049	0.078		
Zirconia grain..................	113.	3000	.....	.....	0.108	0.129	0.163	0.217

Table 7. Thermal Conductance across Air Spaces

[Btu per (hr) (sq ft) (deg F)—Reflective Insulation]

Air space, in.	Direction of heat flow	Temp diff, deg F	Mean temp, deg F	Aluminum surfaces, $\epsilon = 0.05$	Ordinary surfaces, non-metallic, $\epsilon = 0.90$
Horizontal, ¾–4 across.......	Upward	20.	80.	0.60	1.35
Vertical, ¾–4 across.........	Across	20.	80.	0.49	1.19
Horizontal, ¾ across.........	Downward	20.	75.	0.30	1.08
Horizontal, 4 across..........	Downward	20.	80.	0.19	0.93

CONDUCTION AND CONVECTION

Phenomena of Heat Transmission. In many practical cases of heat transmission —e.g., boilers, condensers, the cooling of engine cylinders—heat is transmitted from one fluid to another through a wall separating the two. The processes occurring in the fluids may be extremely complex. However, to facilitate discussion, it is convenient to imagine that most of the fluid offers no resistance to heat transmission but that a thin film of fluid adjacent to the wall offers considerable resistance. This situation is depicted in Fig. 1. Then, by definition,

$$q = h_i A_i (t_i - t_i') = \frac{k}{l} A_m (t_i' - t_0) = h_0 A_0 (t_0' - t_0)$$

The terms h_i and h_0 are the **film coefficients,** or **unit conductances,** of the films f_1 and f_2, respectively, and k is the thermal conductivity of the wall. Since q, A, $t_i - t_i'$, and $t_0' - t_0$ are susceptible to direct measurement, h_i and h_0 are simply defined quantities and the propriety of the above equation does not rest upon the heuristic film concept. Indeed, for laminar flow, the film concept is a gross misrepresentation, and yet the definition of a film coefficient (or heat-transfer coefficient) remains convenient and valid.

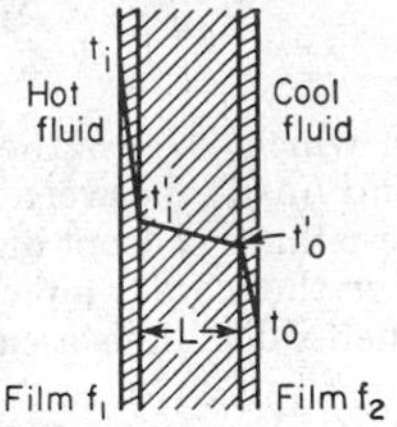

Fig. 1. Temperature gradients in heat flow through a wall.

If t_i' and t_0' are eliminated from the above equation, a relation is obtained for steady flow through several resistances in series:

$$q = \frac{t_i - t_0}{(1/h_i A_i) + (l/k A_m) + (1/h_0 A_0)} \tag{3}$$

Each of the terms in the denominator represents a resistance to heat transfer. There may also be a resistance $1/h_sA_s$, due to the presence of a scale deposit on the surface. Thus, if the over-all heat transfer is given by $q = UA(t_i - t_0)$, then the total thermal resistance is given by

$$1/UA = (1/h_iA_i) + (l/kA_m) + (1/h_oA_o) + (1/h_sA_s) \tag{4}$$

Coefficients for scale deposits are given in Table 8.

Table 8. Heat Transfer Coefficients (h_s) for Scale Deposits from Water[a]

[For use in Eq. (4)]

Temp of heating medium	Up to 240 F		240 to 400 F	
Temp of water	125 F or less		Above 125 F	
Water velocity, fps	3 and less	Over 3	3 and less	Over 3
Distilled	2,000	2,000	2,000	2,000
Sea water	2,000	2,000	1,000	1,000
Treated boiler feed water	1,000	2,000	500	1,000
Treated make-up for cooling tower	1,000	1,000	500	500
City, well, Great Lakes	1,000	1,000	500	500
Brackish, clean river water	500	1,000	330	500
River water, muddy, silty[b]	330	500	250	330
Hard (over 15 grains per gal)	330	330	200	200
Chicago Sanitary Canal	130	170	100	130

Miscellaneous cases: Refrigerating liquids, brine, clean petroleum distillates, organic vapors, 1,000; refrigerant vapor, 500; vegetable oils, 330; fuel oil (topped crude), 200.

[a] From standards of Tubular Exchanger Manufacturers Assoc., 1952.

[b] Delaware, East River (N.Y.), Mississippi, Schuylkill, and New York Bay.

Mean Temperature Difference. The basic equation for any steadily operated heat exchanger is $dq = U(\Delta t)_o\, dA$, in which U is the over-all coefficient (Eq. (4)), $(\Delta t)_o$ is the over-all temperature difference between hot and cold fluids, and dq/dA is the local rate of flow per unit surface. In order to apply this relation to a finite exchanger, it is necessary to integrate it. The assumptions usually made are constant U, constant mass rates of flow, no changes in phase, constant specific heats, and negligible heat losses. The resulting equation for parallel or countercurrent flow of fluids is

$$q = UA(\Delta t)_m = UA[(\Delta t)_{01} - (\Delta t)_{02}]/\ln[(\Delta t)_{01}/(\Delta t)_{02}] \tag{5a}$$

in which $(\Delta t)_m$ is the logarithmic mean of the terminal temperature differences, $(\Delta t)_{01}$ and $(\Delta t)_{02}$, between hot and cold fluid. The value of UA is evaluated from the resistance concept of Eq. (4) and the values of h are obtained from the following pages. For the more complex cases of multipass and cross flow, $(\Delta t)_m$ is given by Fig. 2. The shell-side fluid is assumed to be well mixed by suitable baffles.

Example: Assume an exchanger in which the hot fluid enters at 400 F and leaves at 327 F; the cold fluid enters at 100 F and leaves at 283 F. Assuming U independent of temperature, what will be the true mean temperature difference from hot to cold fluid, (1) for counterflow and (2) for a reversed current apparatus with one well-baffled pass in the shell and two equal passes in the tubes?

1. With counterflow, the terminal differences are 400 − 283 = 117 F and 327 − 100 = 227 F; the logarithmic mean difference is 110/0.662 = 166 F.

2. Z = (400 − 327)/(283 − 100) = 0.4; X = (283 − 100)/(400 − 100) = 0.61; from section A of Fig. 2, Y = 0.9 = $(\Delta t)_m/166$; $(\Delta t)_m$ = 149 F.

If one of the temperatures remains constant, as in a condenser or in an evaporative cooler, Eq. (5a) applies for parallel flow, counterflow, reversed current, and cross flow.

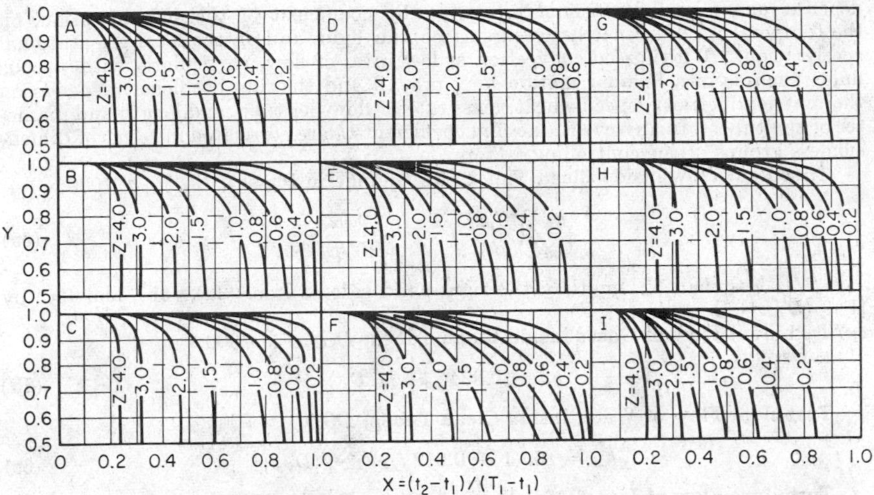

FIG. 2. (*A*) One shell pass and two tube passes; (*B*) two shell passes and four tube passes; (*C*) three shell passes and six tube passes; (*D*) four shell passes and eight tube passes; (*E*) cross flow, one shell pass and one tube pass; (*F*) single-pass cross-flow exchanger, both fluids unmixed; (*G*) single-pass cross-flow exchanger, one fluid mixed, other unmixed; (*H*) two-pass cross-flow exchanger, shell fluid mixed, tube fluid unmixed, shell fluid flowing across second and first passes in series; (*I*) same as *H*, but shell fluid crosses first and second passes in series.

$$Y = \text{ordinate} = \frac{\text{true mean temp difference}}{\text{logarithmic mean temp difference for counter flow}}$$

For the other symbols see p. 4–90. (*From Trans. ASME*, **62**, 1940, pp. 283–294.)

If U varies considerably with temperature, the apparatus should be considered to be divided into stages, in each of which variation of U with temperature or temperature difference is linear. Then for parallel or counterflow operation, the following relation may be applied to each stage:

$$q = A[U_2(\Delta t)_{01} - U_1(\Delta t)_{02}]/\ln\,[U_2(\Delta t)_{01}/U_1(\Delta t)_{02}] \qquad \textbf{(5b)}$$

The above discussion focuses on the concepts of an over-all coefficient and a mean-temperature difference. An alternative approach focuses on the concepts of effectiveness and the number of transfer units. The alternatives are basically equivalent, but one or the other may enjoy a computational advantage. The latter method is presented in detail by Kays and London and by Mickley and Korchak (*Chem. Eng.*, **69**, 1962, pp. 181–188 and 239–242).

FILM COEFFICIENTS

The important physical properties which affect film coefficients (see p. 4–97) are thermal conductivity, viscosity, density, and specific heat. Factors within the control of the designer include fluid velocity and shape and arrangement of the heating surface. With forced flow of gases or water, under the conditions usually met in practice, the flow is turbulent (see p. 3–49), and under these conditions the film coefficient can be greatly increased by increasing the velocity of the fluid at the expense of a greater power requirement. For a given velocity and fluid, the film coefficient depends upon the direction of flow of fluid relative to the heating surface. With free or natural convection, for a given arrangement of surface, the film coefficient depends on an additional fluid property, the coefficient of thermal expansion, on the temperature difference between surface and fluid, and on the local gravitational acceleration. With forced convection at low rates of flow, particularly with viscous fluids such as oils, laminar motion may prevail and the film coefficient depends on thermal conductivity, specific heat, mass rate of flow per tube, and length and diameter of the tube. In any event, the film coefficients h are correlated in terms of dimensionless groups of the controlling factors.

Turbulent Flow inside Clean Tubes (No Change in Phase), $DG/\mu_f > 7000$:

$$\frac{h_m}{C_pG}\left(\frac{C_p\mu_f}{k_f}\right)^{2/3} = \frac{0.023}{(DG/\mu_f)^{0.2}} \tag{6a}$$

For L/D less than 60, multiply the right-hand side of Eqs. (**6a**), (**6b**), and (**6c**) by $[1 + (D/L)^{0.7}]$.

Turbulent Flow of Gases inside Clean Tubes, $DG/\mu_f > 7000$:

$$h_m = 0.024C_pG^{0.8}/(D_i')^{0.2} \tag{6b}$$

Turbulent Flow of Water inside Clean Tubes, $DG/\mu_f > 7000$:

$$h_m = 160(1 + 0.012\,t_f)V_s^{0.8}/(D_i')^{0.2} \tag{6c}$$

Turbulent Flow of Liquid Metals inside Clean Tubes, ($C_p\mu/k < 0.05$): The equation of Sleicher and Tribus ("Recent Advances in Heat Transfer," p. 281, McGraw-Hill, 1961) is recommended for isothermal tube walls—

$$\frac{h_mD}{k} = 6.3 + 0.016\left(\frac{DGC_p}{k}\right)^{0.91}\left(\frac{C_p\mu}{k}\right)^{0.3} \tag{6d}$$

Turbulent Flow of Gases or Water in Annuli. Use Eq. (**6b**) or (**6c**), with D' taken as the clearance, inches.

Water in Coiled Pipes. Multiply h_m for the straight pipe by the term $[1 + (3.5\,D_i/D_c)]$, where D_i is the inside diameter of the pipe and D_c is that of the coil.

Turbulent Boundary Layer on a Flat Plate, $V_\infty\rho_f x/\mu_f > 4 \times 10^5$, no pressure gradient:

$$\frac{h}{\rho_fC_pV_\infty}\left(\frac{C_p\mu}{k}\right)_f^{2/3} = \frac{0.0148}{(\rho_fV_\infty x/\mu_f)^{0.2}} \tag{6e}$$

$$\frac{h_m}{\rho_fC_pV_\infty}\left(\frac{C_p\mu}{k}\right)_f^{2/3} = \frac{0.0185}{(\rho_fV_\infty L/\mu_f)^{0.2}} \tag{6f}$$

Fluid Flow Normal to a Single Tube, D_oG/μ_f from 1000 to 50,000:

$$\frac{h_mD_o}{k_f} = 0.26\left(\frac{D_oG}{\mu_f}\right)^{0.6}\left(\frac{C_p\mu}{k}\right)_f^{0.3} \tag{7}$$

Gas Flow Normal to a Single Tube, D_oG/μ_f from 1000 to 50,000:

$$h_m = 0.30C_pG^{0.6}/(D_o')^{0.4} \tag{7a}$$

Fluid Flow Normal to a Bank of Staggered Tubes, D_oG_{max}/μ_f from 2000 to 40,000:

$$\frac{h_mD_o}{k_f} = K\left(\frac{C_p\mu}{k}\right)_f^{1/3}\left(\frac{D_oG_{max}}{\mu_f}\right)^{0.6} \tag{8}$$

Values of K for N Rows Deep

N	1	2	3	4	5	6	7	10
K	0.24	0.25	0.27	0.29	0.30	0.31	0.32	0.33

Water Flow Normal to a Bank of Staggered Tubes, D_oG_{max}/μ_f from 2000 to 40,000:

$$h_m = 370(1 + 0.0067t_f)V_{sm}^{0.6}/(D_o')^{0.4} \tag{8a}$$

For baffled exchangers, to allow for leakage of fluids around the baffles, use 60 per-cent of the values of h_m from Eq. (**8**); for tubes in line, deduct 25 per cent from the values of h_m given by Eq. (**8**).

Water Flow in Layer Form over Horizontal Tubes, $4\Gamma/\mu < 2100$

$$h_{\text{a.m.}} = 150(\Gamma/D_o')^{1/3} \quad \textbf{(9)}$$

for Γ ranging from 100 to 1,000 lb of water per hr per ft (each side).

Water Flow in Layer down Vertical Tubes, $w/\pi D > 500$

$$h_m = 120\Gamma^{1/3} \quad \textbf{(9a)}$$

Table 9. Typical Values of h_m for Heating and Cooling, Forced Convection
($D_o' = 1.31$ in., $D_i' = 1.05$ in.)

Fluid and arrangement	t_f, deg F	Velocity: Fps[a]	Velocity: Lb per hr per sq ft	Btu per hr per sq ft per deg F	Eq. No.
Air inside tubes	...	$V_s = 31.8$,	$G = 8600$	8.0	6b
Air normal to staggered tubes	170	$V_s = 8.92$,	$G_m = 2000$	7.5	8
Water inside tubes	100	$V_s = 5.0$,	$G = 1.12 \times 10^6$	1260	6c
Water normal to staggered tubes	100	$V_s = 2.0$,	$G_m = 0.448 \times 10^6$	800	8a
Trickle cooler, water	...		$\Gamma = 100$ lb per hr per ft	640	9
Falling water film, vertical tube	...		$\Gamma = 1{,}000$ lb per hr per ft	1200	9a

[a] Velocity in fps at 70 F and 1 atm = $G/3600\rho$.

Heat Transfer to Gases Flowing at Very High Velocities. If a non-reactive gas stream is brought to rest adiabatically, as at the true stagnation point of a blunt body, the temperature rise will be

$$t_s - t_\infty = V^2/2g_cJC_p \quad \textbf{(9b)}$$

where t_s is the stagnation temperature and t_∞ is the temperature of the free stream moving at velocity V. At every other point on the body, the gas is brought to rest partly by pressure changes and partly by viscous effects in the boundary layer. In general, this process is not adiabatic, even though the body transfers no heat. The thermal conductivity of the gas will transfer heat from one layer of gas to another. At an insulated surface, the gas temperature will therefore be neither the free-stream temperature nor the stagnation temperature. In general, the rise in gas temperature will be given by the equation

$$t_{aw} - t_\infty = \mathcal{R}(t_s - t_\infty) = \mathcal{R}V^2/2g_cJC_p \quad \textbf{(9c)}$$

where t_{aw} is the gas temperature at the adiabatic wall and $\mathcal{R}$ is the recovery factor.

If a given point on the surface of a body is not at the temperature t_{aw} given by Eq. (**9c**) with the proper local value of $\mathcal{R}$ inserted, there will be a transfer of heat to or from the body. This suggests defining the coefficient of heat transfer in the usual way, except that the difference $t_w - t_{aw}$ should be used:

$$q/A = h(t_\infty - t_{aw}) = h[t_w - (t + \mathcal{R}V^2/2g_cJC_p)] \quad \textbf{(9d)}$$

where t_w is the surface temperature of the heated wall. With this modification, it is found that the correlations for h are nearly independent of Mach number; *e.g.*, Eq. (**6a**) may be used for turbulent, compressible flow in a pipe. Obviously, $\mathcal{R} = 1.0$ at a forward stagnation point. For flows parallel to surfaces which have little or no curvature in the direction of flow, the following are recommended:

Laminar flow $\qquad \mathcal{R} = \left(\dfrac{C_p\mu}{k}\right)^{1/2}$

Turbulent flow $\qquad \mathcal{R} = \left(\dfrac{C_p\mu}{k}\right)^{1/3}$

Very little is presently known about point values of the recovery factor for flow over more complex shapes. Thus, special thermocouples should be used to measure the temperature of high-velocity gas streams (Hottel and Kalitinsky, *Jour. Applied Mechanics*, 1945, pp. A25–A32; and Franz, *Jahrb* 1938 *deut. Luftfahrt-Forsch* II, pp. 215–218). Eckert (*Trans. ASME*, **78**, 1956, pp. 1273–1283) recommends that all property values be evaluated at a film temperature defined by

$$t_f = (t_\infty + t_w)/2 + 0.22(t_{aw} - t_\infty) \tag{9e}$$

Nielsen (*NACA Wartime Rept.* L-179) gives graphs for predicting the heat transfer and pressure drop for air flow at Mach numbers up to 1.0, in tubes having a uniform wall temperature.

Heat transfer from a reacting gas to a surface is treated by Lees ("Recent Advances in Heat and Mass Transfer," p. 161, McGraw-Hill).

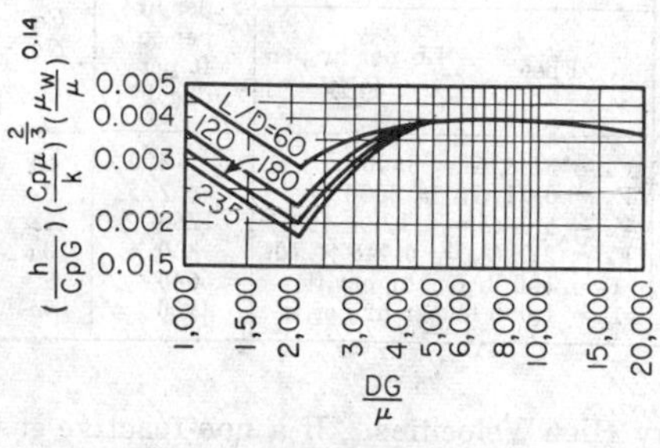

FIG. 3. Heating and cooling of viscous oils flowing inside tubes. [The curves for DG/μ below 2,100 are based on Eq. (**10**).]

Laminar Flow.

PIPE FLOW, $DG/\mu < 2100$. Use the Sieder-Tate modification of the Graetz equation for isothermal tube walls and $wC_p/kL > 10$:

$$h_{a.m.}D/k = 2.0(wC_p/kL)^{1/3}(\mu/\mu_w)^{0.14} \tag{10}$$

or

$$(h_{a,m.}/C_pG)(C_p\mu/k)^{2/3}(\mu_w/\mu)^{0.14} = 1.85(D/L)^{1/3}(DG/\mu)^{-2/3} \tag{10a}$$

As shown in Fig. 3, as DG/μ increases from 2,100 to 7,000, the effect of L/D diminishes and finally becomes negligible for $L/D > 60$.

LAMINAR BOUNDARY LAYER ON A FLAT PLATE, $\rho V_\infty x/\mu < 4 \times 10^5$. Isothermal plate, no pressure gradient:

$$\frac{h}{\rho_f C_p V_\infty}\left(\frac{C_p\mu}{k}\right)_f^{2/3} = \frac{0.332}{(\rho_f V_\infty x/\mu_f)^{1/2}} \tag{10b}$$

$$\frac{h_m}{\rho_f C_p V_\infty}\left(\frac{C_p\mu}{k}\right)_f^{2/3} = \frac{0.664}{(\rho_f V_\infty L/\mu_f)^{1/2}}$$

Extended Surfaces. Fin efficiency is defined as the ratio of the mean temperature difference from surface to fluid divided by the temperature difference from fin to fluid at the base or root of the fin. Graphs of fin efficiency for extended surfaces of various types are given by Gardner (*Trans. ASME*, **67**, pp. 621–628, 1945). Heat transfer coefficients for various extended surfaces are given by Kays and London.

Natural Convection. Heat transfer by natural convection is governed by relations of the form

$$\frac{h_m L_c}{k_f} = f[L_c^3\rho_f^2 g_L \beta_f (\Delta t)_s/\mu_f^2,\ (C_p\mu/k)_f] \tag{11}$$

where β_f is defined by the equation $\rho_f = \rho_\infty[1 - \beta_f(\Delta t)_s]$. For perfect gases, $\beta_f = 1/T_\infty$. The dimensionless group $L_c^3\rho_f^2 g_L\beta_f(\Delta t)_s/\mu_f^2 \equiv N_{Gr}$ represents the ratio of the product (inertial force times buoyant force) to (viscous force squared).

If the flow is of the laminar-boundary-layer type and if $(C_p\mu/k)_f > 1$, an effective correlation is

$$\frac{h_m L_c}{k_f} = B_1[N_{Gr}(C_p\mu/k)_f]^{0.25} \tag{11a}$$

where B_1 is a weak function of $(C_p\mu/k)_f$. Similarly, for $(C_p\mu/k)_f < 1$,

$$\frac{h_m L_c}{k_f} = B_2[N_{Gr}(C_p\mu/k)_f{}^2]^{0.25} \tag{11b}$$

Vertical Flat Plates. For this case, $L = L_c$ and the flow in the laminar-boundary-layer type will be laminar if

$$(C_p\mu/k)_f > 1;\ 10^9 > N_{Gr}(C_p\mu/k)_f > 10^4$$
$$(C_p\mu/k)_f < 1;\ ? > N_{Gr}(C_p\mu/k)_f{}^2 > 10^4$$

Lefevre (*Rept. Heat* 113, National Engineering Laboratory, Great Britian, Aug. 1956) gives an interpolation formula which contains the proper limiting forms and is in complete agreement with existing numerical results:

$$\frac{h_m L_c}{k_f} = \left[\frac{N_{Gr}(C_p\mu/k)^2}{2.435 + 4.884(C_p\mu/k)_f{}^{1/2} + 4.953(C_p\mu/k)_f}\right]^{0.25} \tag{11c}$$

If $(C_p\mu/k)_f$ is in the vicinity of unity and if $N_{Gr}(C_p\mu/k)_f > 10^9$, the boundary layer will be turbulent and

$$\frac{hL}{k_f} = 0.13[N_{Gr}(C_p\mu/k)_f]^{1/3} \tag{11d}$$

Horizontal Cylinders. Replace L in the vertical-flat-plate formulas by $\pi D_o/2$.

Heated Horizontal Plates Facing Upward or Cooled Horizontal Plates Facing Downward.

$$2 \times 10^7 > N_{Gr}(C_p\mu/k)_f > 10^5 \qquad \frac{h_m L}{k_f} = 0.54[N_{Gr}(C_p\mu/k)_f]^{0.25} \tag{11e}$$

$$N_{Gr}(C_p\mu/k)_f > 2 \times 10^7 \qquad \frac{h_m L}{k_f} = 0.14[N_{Gr}(C_p\mu/k)_f]^{1/3} \tag{11f}$$

Heated Horizontal Plates Facing Downward or Cooled Horizontal Plates Facing Upward.

$$3 \times 10^{10} > N_{Gr}(C_p\mu/k)_f > 3 \times 10^5 \qquad \frac{hL}{k_f} = 0.27[N_{Gr}(C_p\mu/k)_f]^{0.25} \tag{11g}$$

Equations (**11c**) to (**11g**) should not be considered reliable if $(C_p\mu/k)_f$ differs greatly from unity.

For more complex systems, it is best to consult plots of experimental data (McAdams).

For any particular fluid, the above equations may be greatly simplified. For air which is at room temperature and atmospheric pressure and is subjected to the gravitational attraction at sea level:

Vertical Plates.

$$10^3 > L^3(\Delta t)_s > 10^{-2} \qquad h_m = 0.28[(\Delta t)_s/L]^{0.25} \tag{12a}$$
$$L^3(\Delta t)_s > 10^3 \qquad h_m = 0.19(\Delta t)_s{}^{1/3} \tag{12b}$$

Horizontal Cylinders.

$$10^2 > D^3(\Delta t)_s > 10^{-3} \qquad h_m = 0.25[(\Delta t)_s/D]^{0.25} \tag{12c}$$
$$D^3(\Delta t)_s > 10^2 \qquad h_m = 0.19(\Delta t)_s{}^{1/3} \tag{12d}$$

Heated Horizontal Plates Facing Upward or Cooled Horizontal Plates Facing Downward.

$$10 > L^3(\Delta t)_s > 0.1 \qquad h_m = 0.27[(\Delta t)_s/L]^{0.25} \tag{12e}$$
$$10^4 > L^3(\Delta t)_s > 10 \qquad h_m = 0.22(\Delta t)_s{}^{1/3} \tag{12f}$$

HEATED HORIZONTAL PLATES FACING DOWNWARD OR COOLED HORIZONTAL PLATES FACING UPWARD.

$$10^4 > L^3(\Delta t)_s > 0.1 \qquad h_m = 0.12[(\Delta t)_s/L]^{0.25} \tag{12g}$$

Condensing Vapors. If the condensate of a single pure vapor, saturated or supersaturated, wets the surface, film-type condensation is obtained. The rate of heat transfer equals $h_m(\Delta t)_m$, where $(\Delta t)_m$ is the mean difference between the saturation temperature and the temperature of the surface. As long as the condensate flow is laminar ($4\Gamma/\mu_f < 2{,}100$), the following dimensionless equations may be used:

For **horizontal tubes,**

$$h_mD/k = 0.73[D^3\rho^2\lambda g_L/k\mu_fN(\Delta t)_m]^{0.25} = 0.76(D^3\rho^2 g_L/\mu_f\Gamma)^{1/3} \tag{13}$$

For **vertical tubes,**

$$h_mL/k = 0.94[L^3\rho^2\lambda g_L/k\mu_f(\Delta t)_m]^{0.25} = 0.93(L^3\rho^2 g_L/\mu_f\Gamma)^{1/3} \tag{13a}$$

The equations show that a tube of given dimensions, for the usual case where L/ND is greater than 2.76, is more effective in a horizontal than in a vertical position. Thus for $L/ND = 100$, a horizontal tube gives an average h which is 2.5 times that for a vertical tube. Since there is but little variation in the thermal conductivity or viscosity of the condensate at the condensing temperature at 1 atm, there is little variation in h_m. Thus with horizontal tubes, h_m may be taken as 200 to 400 for the following vapors condensing at atmospheric pressure: benzene, carbon tetrachloride, dichlormethane, dichlordifluoromethane, diphenyl ethyl alcohol, heptane, hexane, methyl alcohol, octane, toluene, and xylene. Ammonia gives h_m of 1,000, and mixtures of steam and organic vapors, forming immiscible condensates, give h_m ranging from 250 to 750, increasing with increasing proportion of steam. With film-type condensation of clean steam on horizontal tubes, h_m ranges from 1,000 to 3,000 see Eq. (**13**). With vertical tubes 10 to 20 ft long, ripples form in the film; values of h_m from Eq. (**13a**) should be increased 20 percent.

For long vertical tubes, $4\Gamma/\mu_f$ may exceed 2100; in that case:

$$h_m(\mu_f^2/k_f^3\rho_f^2 g_L)^{1/3} = 0.0077(4\Gamma/\mu_f)^{0.4} \tag{13b}$$

The presence of **non-condensible gas,** such as air, seriously reduces h, and consequently all vapor-heated apparatus should be well-vented.

With steam, small traces of certain promoters (Nagle, U.S. Patent 1,995,361) such as oleic acid and benzyl mercaptan become adsorbed in a very thin layer on the surface of the tubes, preventing the condensate from wetting the metal and inducing dropwise condensation, which gives much higher values of h_m (7,000 to 70,000) than film-type condensation. However, with dirty or corroded surfaces, it is difficult to maintain dropwise condensation. Figure 4 shows over-all coefficients U_o for condensing steam at 1 atm on a vertical 10 ft length of copper tube, 5/8 in. O.D., 0.049 in. wall, at various water velocities.

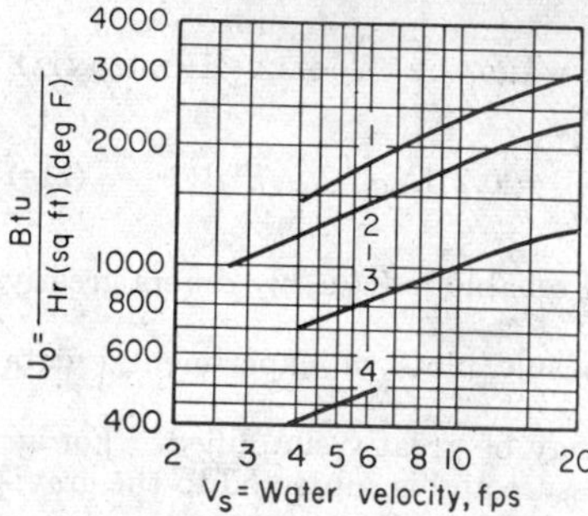

FIG. 4. **Over-all coefficients between condensing steam and water.** Curve 1, chrome-plated copper, oleic acid; curve 2, copper, benzyl mercaptan; curve 3, copper, oleic acid; curve 4, admiralty metal, no promoter.

Boiling Liquids. The nature of the heat transfer from a submerged heater to a pool of boiling water is shown in Fig. 5. Other liquids exhibit the same qualitative features. In the range AB, heat transfer to the liquid occurs solely by natural convection, and evaporation occurs at the free surface of the pool. In the range BC, **nucleate boiling** occurs. Bubbles form at active nuclei on the heating surface, detach, and rise to the pool surface. At point C, the heat flux passes through a maximum at a temperature difference called the **critical** Δt. In the range CD, transitional boiling occurs. At point D, the transition is complete and the heating surface is completely blanketed by a vapor film. This is the point of minimum heat flux, or the **Leidenfrost point.** In the range DE, the heating surface continues to be blanketed by a vapor film.

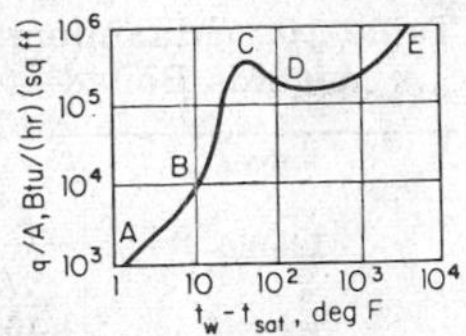

FIG. 5. Boiling of water at 212 F on a platinum surface.

The range AB is adequately correlated by the usual natural-convection equations. No truly adequate correlation is available for the range BC because the complex processes of nucleation and interfacial interaction are only partially understood. However, the relation due to Rohsenow (*Trans. ASME*, **74**, 1952, pp. 969–976) is one of the best and can be reliably used for modest extrapolations of existing data.

$$\frac{C_{p,l}(t_w - t_{sat})}{\lambda} = C_{fs}\left[\frac{q/A}{\mu_l \lambda}\sqrt{\frac{g_c\sigma}{g_L(\rho_l - \rho_v)}}\right]^{1/3}\left(\frac{C_{p,l}\mu_l}{k_l}\right)^{1.7} \tag{14a}$$

The value of the constant C_{fs} is intimately dependent on the nature of the particular fluid-solid pair and must be determined by experiment. It usually assumes values in the range $0.003 < C_{fs} < 0.05$ and is not affected by moderate subcooling or the shape of the heating surface.

Zuber (*USAEC Rept.* AECU-4439, June, 1959) has presented a theoretical equation for the maximum heat flux from a flat, horizontal surface. The analysis is based on considerations of hydrodynamic stability. For saturated liquids,

$$(q/A)_{max} = K_1\rho_v\lambda\left[\frac{\sigma g_L g_c(\rho_l - \rho_v)}{\rho_v^2}\right]^{1/4}\left(\frac{\rho_l}{\rho_l + \rho_v}\right)^{1/2} \tag{14b}$$

$$0.12 < K_1 < 0.157 \qquad \text{(theoretical)}$$

Berenson (Sc.D. thesis, Mechanical Engineering Department, MIT, 1960) used a similar analysis and obtained a relation which is identical for $\rho_l \gg \rho_v$, but he found that $K_1 = 0.18$ gives better agreement with the data. The theoretical basis of this equation has been subject to attack, but the correlation appears to be the best available. Zuber also performed an analysis for subcooled liquids and proposed a modification which is also in excellent agreement with experiment:

$$(q/A)_{max} = K_1\rho_v[\lambda + C_{p,l}(t_{sat} - t_l)]\left[\frac{\sigma g_L g_c(\rho_l - \rho_v)}{\rho_v^2}\right]^{0.25}\left(\frac{\rho_l}{\rho_l + \rho_v}\right)^{1/2}$$
$$\left\{1 + \frac{5.33(\rho_l C_{p,l}k_l)^{1/2}(t_{sat} - t_l)}{\rho_v[\lambda + C_{p,l}(t_{sat} - t_l)]}\left[\frac{g_L(\rho_l - \rho_v)\rho_v^2}{\sigma^3 g_c^3}\right]^{1/8}\right\} \tag{14c}$$

Zuber's hydrodynamic analysis of the Leidenfrost point yields

$$(q/A)_{min} = K_2\lambda\rho_v\left[\frac{\sigma g_L g_c(\rho_l - \rho_v)}{\rho_l^2}\right]^{1/4} \qquad 0.144 < K_2 < 0.177 \tag{14d}$$

Berenson finds better agreement with the data if $K_2 = 0.09$. For very small wires, the heat flux will exceed that predicted by this flat-plate formula. A reliable prediction of the critical temperature is not available.

For nucleate boiling accompanied by forced convection, the heat flux may be approximated by the sum of the heat flux for pool boiling alone and the heat flux for forced convection alone. This procedure will not be satisfactory at high qualities, and no satisfactory correlation exists for the maximum heat flux.

For a given liquid and boiling pressure, the nature of the surface may substantially influence the flux at a given (Δt), Table 10. These data may be used as rough approximations for a bank of submerged tubes. Film coefficients for scale deposits are given in Tablo 8.

Table 10. Maximum Flux and Corresponding Over-all Temperature Difference for Liquids Boiled at 1 Atm with a Submerged Horizontal Steam-heated Tube

Liquid	Aluminum		Copper		Chromium-plated copper		Steel	
	$\frac{q/A}{1000}$	$(\Delta t)_o$	$\frac{q/A}{1000}$	$(\Delta t)_o$	$\frac{q/A}{1000}$	$(\Delta t)_o$	$\frac{q/A}{1000}$	$(\Delta t)_o$
Ethyl acetate........	41	70	61	55	77	55		
Benzene............	51	80	58	70	73	100	82	100
Ethyl alcohol........	55	80	85	65	124	65		
Methyl alcohol......	..	..	100	95	110	110	155	110
Distilled water......	..	..	230	85	350	75	410	150

For forced-circulation evaporators, vapor binding is also encountered. Thus with liquid benzene entering a 4-pass steam-jacketed pipe at 0.9 fps, up to the point where 60 percent by weight was vaporized, the maximum flux of 60,000 Btu per hr per sq ft was obtained at an over-all temperature difference of 60 F; beyond this point, the coefficient and flux decreased rapidly, approaching the values obtained in superheating vapor, see Eq. (**6b**). For comparison, in a natural convection evaporator, a maximum flux of 73,000 Btu per hr per sq ft was obtained at $(\Delta t)_o$ of 100 F.

Combined Convection and Radiation Coefficients. In some cases of heat loss, such as that from bare and insulated pipes, where loss is by convection to the air and radiation to the walls of the enclosing space it is convenient to use a combined convection and radiation coefficient $(h_c + h_r)$. The rate of heat loss thus becomes

$$q = (h_c + h_r)A(\Delta t)_s \tag{15}$$

where $(\Delta t)_s$ is the temperature difference, deg F, between the surface of the hot body and the walls of the space. In evaluating $(h_c + h_r)$, h_c should be calculated by the appropriate convection formula [see Eqs. (**11c**) to (**11g**)] and h_r from the equation

$$h_r = 0.00685\epsilon(T_{av}/100)^3$$

where ϵ is the black body coefficient of the radiating surface, p. 4–111, T_{av} is the average temperature of the surface and the enclosing walls, deg R. For oxidized bare steel pipe, the sum $h_c + h_r$ may be taken directly from Table 11.

Table 11. Values of $(h_c + h_r)$

(For horizontal bare or insulated standard steel pipe of various sizes and for flat plates in a room at 80 F)

Nominal pipe diam, in.	$(\Delta t)_s$, temperature difference, deg F, from surface to room														
	50	100	150	200	250	300	400	500	600	700	800	900	1000	1100	1200
½	2.12	2.48	2.76	3.10	3.41	3.75	4.47	5.30	6.21	7.25	8.40	9.73	11.20	12.81	14.65
1	2.03	2.38	2.65	2.98	3.29	3.62	4.33	5.16	6.07	7.11	8.25	9.57	11.04	12.65	14.48
2	1.93	2.27	2.52	2.85	3.14	3.47	4.18	4.99	5.89	6.92	8.07	9.38	10.85	12.46	14.28
4	1.84	2.16	2.41	2.72	3.01	3.33	4.02	4.83	5.72	6.75	7.89	9.21	10.66	12.27	14.09
8	1.76	2.06	2.29	2.60	2.89	3.20	3.88	4.68	5.57	6.60	7.73	9.05	10.50	12.10	13.93
12	1.71	2.01	2.24	2.54	2.82	3.13	3.83	4.61	5.50	6.52	7.65	8.96	10.42	12.03	13.84
24	1.64	1.93	2.15	2.45	2.72	3.03	3.70	4.48	5.37	6.39	7.52	8.83	10.28	11.90	13.70
FLAT PLATES															
Vertical..............	1.82	2.13	2.40	2.70	2.99	3.30	4.00	4.79	5.70	6.72	7.86	9.18	10.64	12.25	14.06
HFU.................	2.00	2.35	2.65	2.97	3.26	3.59	4.31	5.12	6.04	7.07	8.21	9.54	11.01	12.63	14.45
HFD.................	1.58	1.85	2.09	2.36	2.63	2.93	3.61	4.38	5.27	6.27	7.40	8.71	10.16	11.76	13.57

HFU, horizontal, facing upward; HFD, horizontal, facing downward.

Heat Transmission through Pipe Insulation. (McMillan, *Trans. ASME*, 1915.) For any number of layers of insulation on any size of pipe, Eqs. (**2**), (**4**), and (**15**) combine to give

$$\frac{q_o}{A_o} = \frac{(\Delta t)_o}{\frac{r_o}{k_1}\ln\frac{r_2}{r_1} + \frac{r_o}{k_2}\ln\frac{r_3}{r_2} + \cdots + \frac{1}{h_c + h_r}} \tag{16}$$

where q_o/A_o is the Btu per hr per sq ft of outer surface of the last layer; $(\Delta t)_o$ is the over-all temperature difference (deg F) between pipe and air; r_o is the radius, feet, of the

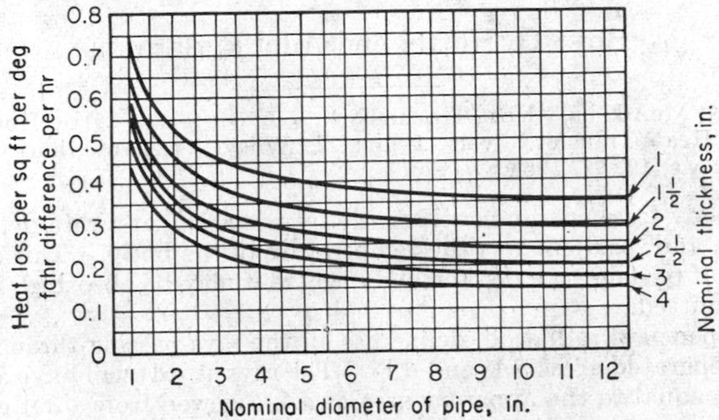

Fig. 6. Variation with pipe size of over-all coefficient U_o for a given thickness of insulation, for $k = 0.042$.

outer surface; r_1 is the outside radius, feet, of the pipe, $r_2 = r_1 +$ thickness of first layer of insulation, foot; $r_3 = r_2$ plus the thickness of second layer, etc.; and k_1, k_2, k_3, etc., are the conductivities of the respective layers. For average indoor conditions, $h_c + h_r$ is often taken as 2 as an approximation, since a substantial error in $h_c + h_r$ will have but little effect on the over-all loss of heat. Figure 6 shows the variation in U_o with pipe size and thickness of insulation (for $k = 0.042$) for pipe and air temperatures of 375 and 75 F, respectively.

RADIANT-HEAT TRANSFER

BY

Hoyt C. Hottel and Adel F. Sarofim

REFERENCES: McAdams, "Heat Transmission," 3d ed. (chap. IV by Hottel), McGraw-Hill. Jakob, "Heat Transfer," vols. I and II, Wiley. Viskanta and Grosh, Applied Mechanics Reviews, **17, 91,** 1964.

A heated body loses energy continuously by radiation, at a rate dependent on the shape, the size, and, particularly, the temperature of the body. This emitted radiation is capable of passage to a distant body, where it may be absorbed, reflected, scattered, or transmitted.

Consider a pencil of radiation, defined as all the rays passing through each of two small, widely separated areas dA_1 and dA_2. The rays at dA_1 will have a solid angle of divergence $d\Omega_1$, equal to the apparent area of dA_2 (viewed from dA_1) divided by the square of the separating distance. Let the normal to dA_1 make the angle θ_1 with the pencil. The flux density q [energy/(time)(area normal to beam)] per unit solid angle of divergence is called the **intensity** I, and the flux $d\dot{Q}$ (energy/time) through area dA_1 (of apparent area $dA_1 \cos \theta_1$ normal to the beam) is therefore given by

$$d\dot{Q} = dA_1 \cos \theta_1 \, dq_1 = I \, dA_1 \cos \theta_1 \, d\Omega_1 \qquad \textbf{(1)}$$

The intensity I along a pencil, in the absence of absorption or scatter, is constant (unless the beam passes into a medium of different refractive index n; $I_1/n_1^2 = I_2/n_2^2$).

The **emissive power** of a surface is the flux density [energy/(time)(surface area)] due to emission from it throughout a hemisphere. If the intensity I of emission from a surface is independent of the angle of emission, Eq. (**1**) may be used to show that the surface emissive power is πI, though the emission is throughout 2π steradians.

Black-body Radiation

Engineering calculations of thermal radiation from surfaces is best keyed to the radiation characteristics of the **black body, or ideal radiator.** The characteristic properties of a black body are that it absorbs all the radiation incident on its surface and that the quality and intensity of the radiation it emits are completely determined by its temperature. The total radiative flux throughout a hemisphere from a black surface of area A and absolute temperature T is given by the **Stefan-Boltzmann law:** $\dot{Q} = A\sigma T^4$ or $q = \sigma T^4$. The Stefan-Boltzmann constant has the value 0.1713×10^{-8} Btu/(sq ft)(hr)(deg R)^4, 5.67×10^{-4} ergs/(sq cm)(sec)(deg K)^4; 5.67×10^{-8} watts/(sq m)(deg K)^4, or 1.00×10^{-8} chu/(sq ft)(hr)(deg K)^4. From the above definition of emissive power, σT^4 is the total emissive power of a black body, called E; and the intensity I_B of emission from a black body is E/π, or $\sigma T^4/\pi$.

The spectral distribution of energy flux from a black body is expressed by Planck's law

$$E_\lambda \, d\lambda = \frac{c_1 \lambda^{-5}}{e^{c_2/\lambda T} - 1} \, d\lambda \qquad \textbf{(2)}$$

wherein $E_\lambda \, d\lambda$ is the hemispherical flux density lying in the wavelength range λ to $\lambda + d\lambda$. With E_λ (called the monochromatic emissive power) in ergs/(sq cm)(cm)(sec), λ in cm, and T in deg K, the values of c_1 and c_2 are 3.74×10^{-5} erg cm^2/sec and 1.4387 cm deg K. It may be shown from Planck's law that, of the total energy flux from a black body at any temperature, the fraction f in wavelengths below λ is dependent only on λT. Values of f versus λT appear in Table 1.

Table 1. Fraction f of Black-body Radiation below λ
(λT = microns × deg K)

λT	1200	1600	1800	2000	2200	2400	2600	2800	3000	3200
f	0.002	0.020	0.039	0.067	0.101	0.140	0.183	0.228	0.273	0.318
λT	3400	3600	3800	4000	4200	4500	4800	5100	5500	6000
f	0.362	0.404	0.443	0.480	0.516	0.564	0.608	0.646	0.691	0.738
λT	6500	7000	7600	8400	10000	12000	14000	20000	50000	
f	0.776	0.808	0.839	0.871	0.914	0.945	0.963	0.986	0.999	

Table 1 indicates that half of black-body radiation lies on either side of a wavelength given by λT = 4107 microns deg K and that the twofold range of λT of 2600 to 5426 spans half the energy. The use of Table 1 will be illustrated later.

Radiative Exchange between Surfaces of Solids

The ratio of the total radiating power of a real surface to that of a black surface at the same temperature is called the **emittance** of the surface (for a perfectly plane surface, the **emissivity**), designated by ϵ. Subscripts λ, θ, and n may be assigned to differentiate monochromatic, directional, and surface-normal values, respectively, from the total hemispherical value. If radiation is incident on a surface, the fraction absorbed is called the **absorptance (absorptivity)**, a term in which two subscripts may be appended, the first to identify the temperature of the surface and the second to identify the quality of the incident radiation. **Kirchoff's law** states that the emittance ϵ_1 of a surface at temperature T_1 equals the absorptance α_{11} which the surface exhibits for radiation from a source at its own temperature; *i.e.*, a surface of relatively low radiating power is also a poor absorber (or good reflector) of radiation from a source at its own temperature. Under practically all conditions, monochromatic emissivity ϵ_λ and absorptivity α_λ are the same. If they do not change with wavelength, the surface is called **gray,** and $\epsilon_\lambda = \alpha_\lambda = \epsilon = \alpha$. Since ϵ_λ and α_λ do not change rapidly with temperature, the total emittance or absorptance of a gray surface changes but little with its temperature.

Consider radiative exchange between a body of area A_1 and temperature T_1 and its black surroundings at T_2. The net interchange

$$\dot{Q}_{1\rightleftharpoons 2} = A_1(\epsilon_1\sigma T_1^4 - \alpha_{12}\sigma T_2^4) \tag{3}$$

From what has preceded, it is clear that

$$\epsilon_1 = \int_0^1 \epsilon_\lambda \, df_{\lambda T_1} \qquad \text{and} \qquad \alpha_{12} = \int_0^1 \epsilon_\lambda \, df_{\lambda T_2} \tag{4}$$

i.e., that ϵ_1 (or α_{12}) is the area under a curve of ϵ_λ versus f, read as a function of λT at T_1 (or T_2) from Table 1. A selective surface is one whose ϵ_λ changes from a high (low) to a low (high) value as λ increases. According to Eqs. (**3**) and (**4**), ϵ_1 and α_{12} for such surfaces are markedly different when $T_2/T_1 \gg 1$; *e.g.*, when T_1 = 530 R (ambient temperature) and T_2 = 10800 R (effective solar temperature), $\epsilon_1 = 0.9$ and $\alpha_{12} = 0.1 - 0.2$ for a white paint, but ϵ_1 can be as low as 0.12 and α_{12} above 0.9 for a thin layer of copper oxide on bright aluminum.

Although values of emittances and absorptances depend in very complex ways on the real and imaginary components of the refractive index and on the geometrical structure of the surface layer, some generalizations are possible.

Polished Metals. (1) ϵ_λ is quite low in the infrared and, for $\lambda > 8\mu$, can be adequately approximated by $0.00365\sqrt{r/\lambda}$, where r is the resistivity in ohm-cm and λ is in microns; at shorter wavelengths, ϵ_λ increases and, for many metals, has values of 0.4 to 0.8 in the visible (0.4–0.7μ). ϵ_λ is approximately proportional to the square root of the absolute temperature ($\epsilon_\lambda \propto \sqrt{r}$ and $r \propto T$) in the far infrared ($\lambda > 8\mu$), is temperature insensitive in the near infrared (0.7–1.5μ), and decreases slightly with temperature in the visible. (2) Total emittance is substantially proportional to absolute temperature; at moderate temperature, $\epsilon_n = 0.58T\sqrt{r_0/T_0}$, where T is in degrees K. (3) Total absorptance of a metal at T_1 for radiation from a black or gray source at T_2 is equal to the emissivity evaluated at the geometric mean of T_1 and T_2. (4) The ratio of hemispherical to normal emittance (absorptance) varies from 1.33 at very low ϵ's (α's) to about 1.03 at an $\epsilon(\alpha)$ of 0.4.

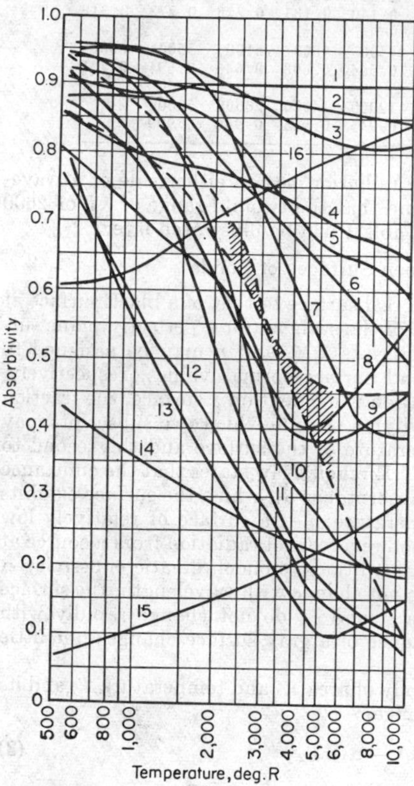

Fig. 1. Variation of absorptivity with temperature of radiation source. (1) Slate composition roofing; (2) linoleum, red brown; (3) asbestos slate; (4) soft rubber, gray; (5) concrete; (6) porcelain; (7) vitreous enamel, white; (8) red brick; (9) cork; (10) white Dutch tile; (11) white chamotte; (12) MgO, evaporated; (13) anodized aluminum; (14) aluminum paint; (15) polished aluminum; (16) graphite. The two dotted lines bound the limits of data on gray paving brick, asbestos paper, wood, various cloths, plaster of paris, lithopone, and paper.

Unless extraordinary pains are taken to prevent oxidation, however, a metallic surface may exhibit several times the emittance or absorptance of a polished specimen. The emittance of iron and steel, for example, varies widely with degree of oxidation and roughness—clean metallic surfaces have an emittance of from 0.05–0.45 at ambient temperatures to 0.4–0.7 at high temperatures; oxidized and/or rough surfaces range from 0.6–0.95 at low temperatures to 0.9–0.95 at high temperatures.

Refractory Materials. Grain size and concentration of trace impurities are important. (1) Most refractory materials have an ϵ_λ of 0.8 to 1.0 at wavelengths beyond 2 to 4 microns; ϵ_λ decreases rapidly toward shorter wavelengths for materials that are white in the visible but retains its high value for black materials such as FeO and Cr_2O_3. Small concentrations of FeO and Cr_2O_3 or other colored oxides can cause marked increases in the emittance of materials that are normally white. ϵ_λ for refractory materials varies little with temperature. (2) Refractory materials generally have a total emittance which is high (0.7 to 1.0) at ambient temperatures and decreases with increase in temperature; a change from 1850 to 2850 F may cause a decrease in ϵ of one-fourth to one-third. (3) The emittance and absorptance increase with increase in grain size over a grain-size range of 1–200 μ. (4) The ratio ϵ/ϵ_n of hemispherical to normal emissivity of polished surfaces varies with refractive index from 1 at $n = 0$ to 0.93 at $n = 1.5$ (common glass) and back to 0.96 at $n = 3$. (5) The ratio ϵ/ϵ_n for a surface composed of particulate matter which scatters isotropically varies with ϵ from 1 when $\epsilon = 1$ to 0.8 when $\epsilon = 0.07$. (6) The total absorptance shows a decrease with increase in temperature of the radiation source similar to the decrease in emittance with increase in the specimen temperature. Figure 1 shows the effect of the temperature of the radiation source on the absorptance of surfaces of various materials at room temperature. It will be noted that polished aluminum (line 15) and anodized aluminum (line 13), representative of metals and non-metals, respectively, respond oppositely to a change in the temperature of the radiation source. The absorptance of surfaces for sunlight may be read from the right of Fig. 1, assuming sunlight to consist of black-body radiation from a source at 10800 R.

From Fig. 1 it is seen that, when T_2 is not too different from T_1, α_{12} may be expressed

Table 2. Emissivity of Surfaces

Surface	Temp,* deg F	Emissivity*
Metals and Their Oxides		
Aluminum:		
Highly polished	440–1070	0.039–0.057
Polished	73	0.040
Rough plate	78	0.055–0.07
Oxidized at 1110 F	390–1110	0.11–0.19
Oxide	530–1520	0.63–0.26
Alloy 75ST	75	0.10
75ST, repeated heating	450–900	0.22–0.16
Brass:		
Highly polished	497–710	0.03–0.04
Rolled plate, natural	72	0.06
Rolled, coarse-emeried	72	0.20
Oxidized at 1110 F	390–1110	0.61–0.59
Chromium	100–1000	0.08–0.26
Copper:		
Electrolytic, polished	176	0.02
Comm'l plate, polished	66	0.030
Heated at 1110 F	390–1110	0.57–0.57
Thick oxide coating	77	0.78
Cuprous oxide	1470–2010	0.66–0.54
Molten copper	1970–2330	0.16–0.13
Dow metal, cleaned, heated	450–750	0.24–0.20
Gold, highly polished	440–1160	0.02–0.40
Iron and steel:		
Pure Fe, polished	350–1800	0.05–0.37
Wrought iron, polished	100–480	0.28
Smooth sheet iron	1650–1900	0.55–0.60
Rusted plate	67	0.69
Smooth oxidized iron	260–980	0.78–0.82
Strongly oxidized	100–480	0.95
Molten iron and steel	2730–3220	0.40–0.45
Lead:		
99.96%, unoxidized	260–440	0.06–0.08
Gray oxidized	75	0.28
Oxidized at 390 F	390	0.63
Mercury, pure clean	32–212	0.09–0.12
Molybdenum filament	1340–4700	0.10–0.29
Monel metal, K5700		
Washed, abrasive soap	75	0.17
Repeated heating	450–1610	0.46–0.65
Nickel and alloys:		
Electrolytic, polished	74	0.05
Electroplated, not polished	68	0.11
Wire	368–1844	0.10–0.19
Plate, oxid. at 1110 F	390–1110	0.37–0.48
Nickel oxide	1200–2290	0.59–0.86
Copper-nickel, polished	212	0.06
Nickel-silver, polished	212	0.14
Nickelin, gray oxide	70	0.26
Nichrome wire, bright	120–1830	0.65–0.79
Nichrome wire, oxid	120–930	0.95–0.98
ACI-HW (60Ni, 12Cr); firm black ox. coat	520–1045	0.89–0.82
Platinum, polished plate	440–2960	0.05–0.17
Silver, pure polished	440–1160	0.02–0.03
Stainless steels:		
Type 316, cleaned	75	0.28
316, repeated heating	450–1600	0.57–0.66
304, 42 hr at 980 F	420–980	0.62–0.73
310, furnace service	420–980	0.90–0.97
Allegheny #4, polished	212	0.13
Tantalum filament	2420–5430	0.194–0.33
Thorium oxide	530–1520	0.58–0.21
Tin, bright	76	0.04–0.06
Tungsten, aged filament	80–6000	0.03–0.35
Zinc, 99.1%, comm'l, polished	440–620	0.05
Galv., iron, bright	82	0.23
Galv., gray oxid	75	0.28
Refractories, Building Materials, Paints, Misc.		
Alumina, 50μ grain size	1850–2850	0.39–0.28
Alumina-silica, cont'g	1850–2850	
0.4% Fe_2O_3	....	0.61–0.43
1.7% Fe_2O_3	....	0.73–0.62
2.9% Fe_2O_3	....	0.78–0.68
Al paints (vary with am't lacquer body, age)	212	0.27–0.67
Asbestos	100–700	0.93–0.95
Candle soot; lampblack-water glass	70–700	0.95 ± 0.01
Carbon plate, heated	260–1160	0.81–0.79
Oil layers:		
Lube oil, 0.01″ on pol. Ni	68	0.82
Linseed, 1–2 coats on Al	68	0.56–0.57
Rubber, soft gray reclaimed	76	0.86
Misc. I: shiny black lacquer, planed oak, white enamel, serpentine, gypsum, white enamel paint, roofing paper, lime plaster, black matte shellac	70	0.87–0.91
Misc. II: glazed porcelain, white paper, fused quartz, polished marble, rough red brick, smooth glass, hard glossy rubber, flat black lacquer, water, electrographite	70	0.92–0.96

* When two temperatures and two emissivities are given they correspond, first to first and second to second, and linear interpolation is permissible.

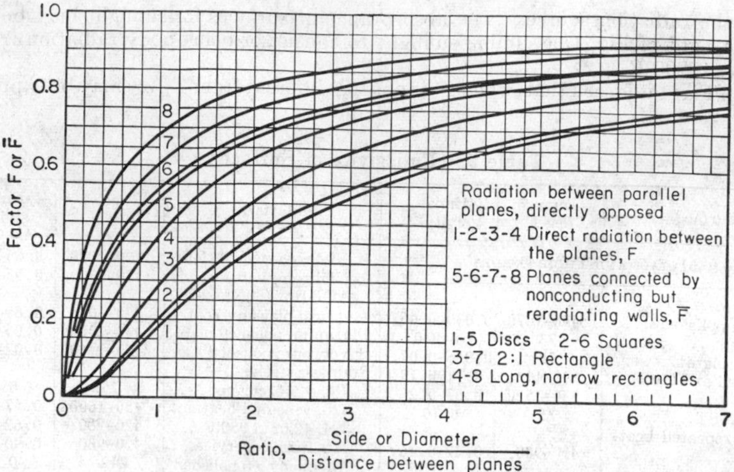

FIG. 2. Values of the factor F or $\bar{F}$ for parallel planes directly opposed.

as $\epsilon_1(T_2/T_1)^n$. For this case, Eq. (**3**) becomes

$$\dot{Q}_{1,\text{net}} = \sigma A_1 \epsilon_{AV}(1 + n/4)(T_1^4 - T_2^4) \tag{5}$$

where ϵ_{AV} is evaluated at the arithmetic mean of T_1 and T_2.

Table 2 gives the emittance of various surfaces and emphasizes the variation possible in a single material. The values in the table apply, with a few exceptions, to normal radiation from the surface.

For opaque materials, the **reflectance** ρ is the complement of the absorptance. The directional distribution of the reflected radiation depends on the material, its degree of roughness or grain size, and if a metal, its state of oxidation. Polished surfaces of homogeneous materials reflect specularly. In contrast, the intensity of the radiation reflected from a **perfectly diffuse,** or **Lambert,** surface is independent of direction. The directional distribution of reflectance of many oxidized metals, refractory materials, and natural products approximates that of a perfectly diffuse reflector. A better model, adequate for many calculational purposes, is achieved by assuming that the total reflectance ρ is the sum of diffuse and specular components ρ_D and ρ_S.

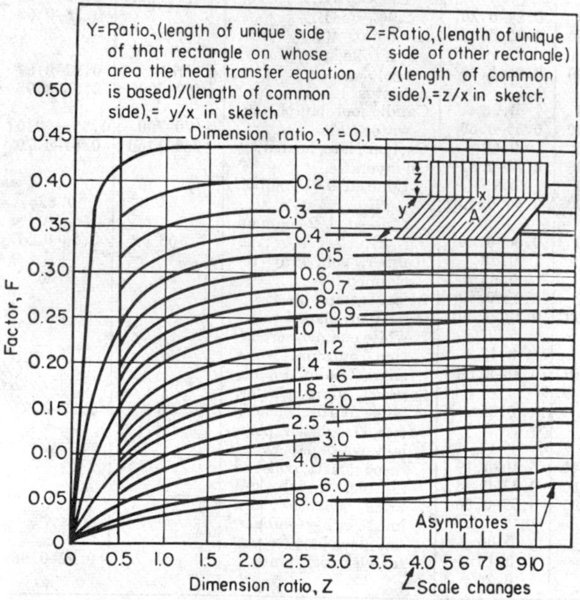

FIG. 3. Values of the factor F for perpendicular adjacent rectangles.

Black-surface Enclosures. When several surfaces are present, the need arises for evaluating a geometrical factor F, called the **view factor.** Restriction is temporarily to black surfaces, the intensity from which is independent of angle of emission. Define F_{12} as the fraction of the radiation leaving surface A_1 in all directions which is intercepted by surface A_2. Since the net interchange between A_1 and A_2 must be zero when their temperatures are alike, it follows that $A_1F_{12} = A_2F_{21}$. This product, having the dimensions of area, will be called the **direct-interchange area** and be designated for brevity by $\overline{12}$ ($\equiv \overline{21}$). It is sometimes designated $\overline{s_1s_2}$. Clearly, $\overline{11} + \overline{12} + \overline{13} + \cdots = A_1$; and when A_1 cannot "see" itself, $\overline{11} = 0$. Values of F have been calculated for various surface arrangements and appear for opposed parallel rectangles and disks of equal size as lines 1 to 4 of Fig. 2, for perpendicular adjacent rectangles in Fig. 3, and for an infinite plane parallel to a system of rows of parallel tubes as lines 1 and 3 of Fig. 4. Multiple graphical integration to determine F is unnecessary for surfaces in two-dimensional systems (third dimension infinite). In the cross-sectional view, the sum of lengths of crossed strings from the ends of A_1 to the ends of A_2 less the sum of uncrossed strings from and to the same points, all divided by 2, equals A_1F_{12} ($\equiv \overline{12}$) per unit length normal to the drawing. For other cases, see *NACA-TN* 2836, Dec. 1952.

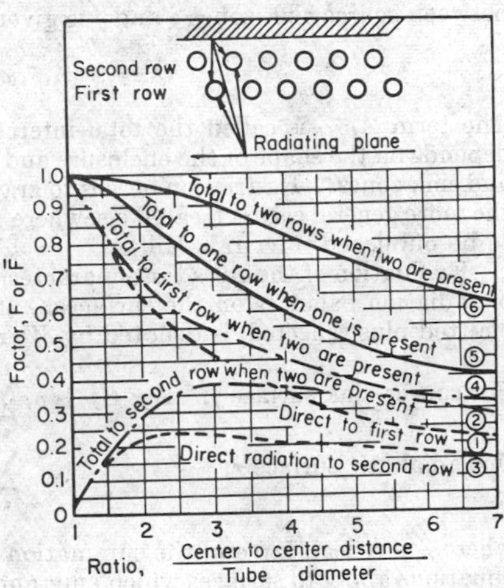

FIG. 4. Values of F or $\bar{F}$ for a plane parallel to rows of tubes.

The view factor F may often be evaluated from that for simpler configurations by the application of three principles: that of reciprocity, $A_iF_{ij} = A_jF_{ji}$; that of conservation, $\Sigma F_{ij} = 1$; and that due to Yamauti, showing that the exchange areas AF between two pairs of surfaces are equal when there is a one-to-one correspondence for all sets of symmetrically placed pairs of elements in the two surface combinations.

EXAMPLE. The exchange area between the two squares 1 and 4 of Fig. 5 is to be evaluated. The following exchange areas may be obtained from the values, in Fig. 3, of F for common-side rectangles $\overline{13} = 0.24$, $\overline{24} = 2 \times 0.29 = 0.58$, $\overline{(1+2)(3+4)} = 3 \times 0.32 = 0.96$. Expression of $\overline{(1+2)(3+4)}$ in terms of its components yields $\overline{(1+2)(3+4)} = \overline{13} + \overline{14} + \overline{23} + \overline{24}$. And by the Yamauti principle $\overline{14} = \overline{23}$, since for every pair of elements in 1 and 4, there is a corresponding pair in 2 and 3. Therefore,

$$\overline{14} = [\overline{(1+2)(3+4)} - \overline{13} - \overline{24}]/2 = 0.07$$

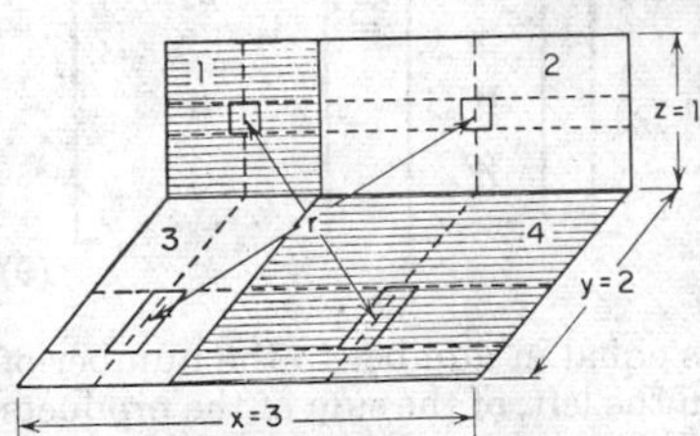

FIG. 5. Illustration of the Yamauti principle.

Figure 2 may be used in the same way. Another example is the evaluation of AF for exchange between the outside of the smaller of two coaxial cylinders and the inside of the larger when they are *not* coextensive, given the view factor for coextensive cylinders (Leuenberger and Person, *ASME Paper* 56-A-144).

Enclosures Containing Gray Sources and Sinks, Refractory Surfaces, and No Absorbing Gas. The calculation of interchange between a source and a sink under conditions involving successive multiple reflections from other source-sink surfaces in the enclosure, as well as reradiation from refractory surfaces, can become complicated. Let a **zone** of a furnace enclosure be an area small enough to make all elements of itself have substantially equivalent "views" of the rest of the enclosure. (In a furnace containing a symmetry plane, parts of a single zone would lie on either side of the plane.) Zones are of two classes, source-sink surfaces, designated by numerical subscripts and having areas $A_1, A_2, \ldots$ and emissivities $\epsilon_1, \epsilon_2, \ldots$; and surfaces at which the net radiant-heat flux is zero (fulfilled by the average refractory wall where difference between internal convection and external loss is minute compared with incident radiation), designated by letter subscripts starting with r, and having areas $A_r, A_s, \ldots$. It may be shown (McAdams, chap. IV by Hottel) that the net radiation interchange between source-sink zones i and j is given by

$$\dot{Q}_{i\rightleftharpoons j} = A_i\mathfrak{F}_{ij}\sigma T_i^4 - A_j\mathfrak{F}_{ji}\sigma T_j^4 \tag{6}$$

The term $A_i\mathfrak{F}_{ij}$ is called the **total-interchange area** shared by areas A_i and A_j and depends on the shape of the enclosure and the emissivity and absorptivity of the source and sink zones. Restriction here is to gray source-sink zones, for which $A_i\mathfrak{F}_{ij} = A_j\mathfrak{F}_{ji}$; the more general case is treated elsewhere (Hottel and Sarofim, "Radiative Transport," to be published, McGraw-Hill).

Evaluation of the $A\mathfrak{F}$'s that characterize an enclosure involves solution of a system of radiation balances on the surfaces. If at a surface the total leaving-flux density, emitted plus reflected, is denoted by W, radiation balances take the form

For source-sink surface j: $$A_j\epsilon_jE_j + \rho_j\sum_i \overline{(ij)}W_i = A_jW_j \tag{7}$$

For adiabatic surface r: $$\sum_i \overline{(ir)}W_i = A_rW_r \tag{8}$$

where ρ is reflectance and the summation is over all surfaces in the enclosure. These equations apply to surfaces which emit and reflect diffusely (*i.e.*, their leaving intensity W_i/π is independent of direction—of j). Most non-metallic, tarnished, or rough metal surfaces correspond reasonably well to this restriction (but see p. 4-17). In matrix notation, Eqs. (7) and (8) become

$$\begin{bmatrix} \overline{11} - \frac{A_1}{\rho_1} & \overline{12} & \cdots & \overline{1r} & \overline{1s} & \cdots \\ \overline{12} & \overline{22} - \frac{A_2}{\rho_2} & \cdots & \overline{2r} & \overline{2s} & \cdots \\ \cdots & \cdots & \cdots & \cdots & \cdots & \cdots \\ \overline{1r} & \overline{2r} & \cdots & \overline{rr} - A_r & \overline{rs} & \cdots \\ \overline{1s} & \overline{2s} & \cdots & \overline{rs} & \overline{ss} - A_s & \cdots \\ \cdots & \cdots & \cdots & \cdots & \cdots & \cdots \end{bmatrix} \begin{bmatrix} W_1 \\ W_2 \\ \cdots \\ W_r \\ W_s \\ \cdots \end{bmatrix} = \begin{bmatrix} -\frac{A_1\epsilon_1}{\rho_1}E_1 \\ -\frac{A_2\epsilon_2}{\rho_2}E_2 \\ \cdots \\ 0 \\ 0 \\ \cdots \end{bmatrix} \tag{9}$$

This represents a system of simultaneous equations equal in number to the number of rows of the first matrix. Each equation consists, on the left, of the sum of the products of the members of a row of the first matrix and the corresponding members of the W-column matrix, and, on the right, of the member of that row in the third matrix. With the above set of equations solved for W_i, the net flux at any surface A_i is given by

$$\dot{Q}_{i,\text{net}} = \frac{A_i\epsilon_i}{\rho_i}(E_i - W_i) \tag{10}$$

Refractory temperature is obtained from $W_r = E_r = \sigma T_r^4$.

The more general use of Eq. (9) is to obtain the set of total-interchange areas $A\mathfrak{F}$ which constitute a complete description of the effect of shape, size, and emissivity on radiative flux, independent of the presence or absence of other transfer mechanisms.

It may be shown that

$$A_i\mathfrak{F}_{ij} \equiv A_j\mathfrak{F}_{ji} \equiv \overline{S_iS_j} = \frac{A_i\epsilon_i}{\rho_i}\frac{A_j\epsilon_j}{\rho_j}\left(-\frac{D_{ij}'}{D}\right) \tag{11}$$

where D is the determinant of the coefficient matrix in Eq. (**9**) and D_{ij}' is the cofactor of its ith row and jth column, or -1^{i+j} times the minor of D formed by crossing out the ith row and jth column.

As an example, consider radiant interchange between concentric gray spheres of inner and outer radii r_1 and r_2.

$$A_1\mathfrak{F}_{12} = \frac{A_1\epsilon_1}{\rho_1}\frac{A_2\epsilon_2}{\rho_2}\frac{\overline{12}}{\begin{vmatrix}\overline{11}-\dfrac{A_1}{\rho_1} & \overline{12}\\ \overline{12} & \overline{22}-\dfrac{A_2}{\rho_2}\end{vmatrix}}$$

$\overline{12} = A_1$; $\overline{11} = 0$; $\overline{22} = A_2 - \overline{21} = A_2 - \overline{12} = A_2 - A_1$. Substitution gives

$$A_1\mathfrak{F}_{12} = \frac{A_1\epsilon_1}{\rho_1}\frac{A_2\epsilon_2}{\rho_2}\frac{A_1}{\begin{vmatrix}-A_1/\rho_1 & A_1\\ A_1 & A_2 - A_1 - A_2/\rho_2\end{vmatrix}} = \frac{1}{\dfrac{1}{A_1\epsilon_1} + \dfrac{1}{A_2}\left(\dfrac{1}{\epsilon_2} - 1\right)} \tag{12}$$

This case includes that of infinite parallel planes ($\mathfrak{F} = 1/[1/\epsilon_1 + 1/\epsilon_2 - 1]$), and that of a small body A_1 enclosed in a large one ($A_1\mathfrak{F}_{12} = A_1\epsilon_1$).

Many furnace problems are adequately handled by dividing the enclosure into but two source-sink zones A_1 and A_2, and any number of no-flux zones, A_r, A_s, ... For this case Eq. (**11**) yields

$$\frac{1}{A_1\mathfrak{F}_{12}}\left(\equiv\frac{1}{A_2\mathfrak{F}_{21}}\right) = \frac{1}{A_1}\left(\frac{1}{\epsilon_1} - 1\right) + \frac{1}{A_2}\left(\frac{1}{\epsilon_2} - 1\right) + \frac{1}{A_1\bar{F}_{12}} \tag{13}$$

Here the expression $A_1\bar{F}_{12}$ ($\equiv A_2\bar{F}_{21}$) represents the total interchange area for the limiting case of a black source and black sink (the refractory emissivity is of no moment). The factor $\bar{F}$ is known exactly for a few geometrically simple cases and may be approximated for others. If A_1 and A_2 are equal parallel disks, squares, or rectangles, connected by non-conducting but reradiating refractory walls, then $\bar{F}$ is given by Fig. 2, lines 5 to 8. If A_1 represents an infinite plane and A_2 is one or two rows of infinite parallel tubes in a parallel plane, and if the only other surface is a refractory surface behind the tubes, $\bar{F}_{12}$ is given by line 5 or 6 of Fig. 4. If an enclosure may be divided into several radiant-heat sources or sinks A_1, A_2, etc., and the rest of the enclosure (reradiating refractory surface) may be lumped together as A_r at a uniform temperature T_r, then the total-interchange area for zone pairs in the black system is given by

$$A_1\bar{F}_{12}\ (\equiv A_2\bar{F}_{21}) = \overline{12} + \frac{(\overline{1r})(\overline{r2})}{A_r - \overline{rr}} \tag{14}$$

For the two-source-sink-zone system to which Eq. (**13**) applies, Eq. (**14**) simplifies to $A_1\bar{F}_{12} = \overline{12} + 1/(1/\overline{1r} + 1/\overline{2r})$; and if A_1 and A_2 each can see none of itself, there is further simplification to

$$A_1\bar{F}_{12} = \overline{12} + \frac{1}{1/(A_1 - \overline{12}) + 1/(A_2 - \overline{12})} = \frac{A_1A_2 - (\overline{12})^2}{A_1 + A_2 - 2(\overline{12})} \tag{15}$$

which necessitates the evaluation of but one geometrical factor F.

Equation (**13**) covers a major fraction of problems of radiant-heat interchange between source and sink in a furnace enclosure. The error due to single zoning of source and sink is small even if the "views" of the enclosure from different parts of each zone are quite different, provided the emissivity is fairly high; the error in $\bar{F}$ is zero if it is obtainable from Fig. 2 or 4, small if Eq. (**14**) is used and the variation in temperature over the refractory is small. Approach to any desired accuracy can be made by use of Eq. (**11**) with division of the surfaces into more zones.

From the definitions of F, $\bar{F}$, and $\mathfrak{F}$ it is to be noted that

$$F_{11} + F_{12} + F_{13} + \cdots + F_{1r} + F_{1s} + \cdots = 1$$
$$\bar{F}_{11} + \bar{F}_{12} + \bar{F}_{13} + \cdots = 1$$
$$\mathfrak{F}_{11} + \mathfrak{F}_{12} + \mathfrak{F}_{13} + \cdots = \epsilon_1$$

EXAMPLE. A furnace chamber of rectangular parallelepipedal form is heated by the combustion of gas inside vertical radiant tubes lining the side walls. The tubes are 5 in. O.D., on 12 in. centers. The stock forms a continuous plane on the hearth. Roof and end walls are refractory. Dimensions are shown in Fig. 6. The radiant tubes and stock are gray bodies having emissivities 0.8 and 0.9, respectively. What is the net rate of heat transmission to the stock by radiation when the mean temperature of the tube surface is 1500 F and that of the stock is 1200 F?

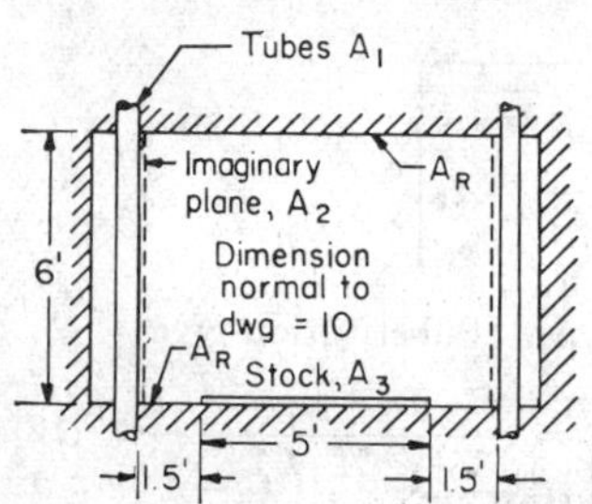

FIG. 6. Dimensions of a furnace chamber.

This problem must be broken up into two parts, first considering the walls with their refractory-backed tubes. To imaginary planes A_2 of area 6 × 10 ft and located parallel to and inside the rows of radiant tubes, the tubes emit radiation $\sigma T_1^4 A_1 \mathfrak{F}_{12}$, which equals $\sigma T_1^4 A_2 \mathfrak{F}_{21}$. To find $\mathfrak{F}_{21}$ use Fig. 4, line 5, from which $\bar{F}_{21} = 0.81$. Then from Eq. (**13**),

$$\mathfrak{F}_{21} = 1/[(1/0.81) + (1/1 - 1) + (12/5\pi)(1/0.8 - 1)] = 0.702$$

This amounts to saying that the system of refractory-backed tubes is equal in radiating power to a continuous plane A_2 replacing the tubes and refractory back of them, having a temperature equal to that of the tubes and an equivalent or effective emissivity of 0.702.

The new simplified furnace now consists of an enclosure formed by two 6 × 10 ft radiating side walls (area A_2, of emissivity 0.702), a 5 × 10 ft receiving plane on the floor (A_3), and refractory surfaces (A_R) to complete the enclosure (ends, roof, and floor side strips); the desired heat transfer is

$$q_{2\rightleftharpoons 3} = \sigma(T_1^4 - T_3^4)A_2\mathfrak{F}_{23}$$

To evaluate $\mathfrak{F}_{23}$, start with the direct interchange factor F_{23}. $F_{23} = F$ from (A_2) to (A_3 + a strip of A_R alongside A_3 which has a common edge with A_2) minus F from (A_2) to (the strip only). These two F's may be evaluated from Fig. 3. For the first F, $Y = 6/10$, $Z = 6.5/10$, $F = 0.239$; for the second F, $Y = 6/10$, $Z = 1.5/10$, $F = 0.100$. Then $F_{23} = 0.239 - 0.10 = 0.139$. Now $\bar{F}$ may be evaluated. From Eq. (**14**) *et seq.*,

$$A_2\bar{F}_{23} = \overline{23} + \frac{1}{(1/\overline{2R} + 1/\overline{3R})}; \quad \bar{F}_{23} = F_{23} + \frac{1}{(1/F_{2R}) + (A_2/A_3)(1/F_{3R})}$$

Since A_2 "sees" A_R, A_3, and some of itself (the plane opposite), $F_{2R} = 1 - F_{22} - F_{23}$. F_{22}, the direct interchange factor between parallel 6 × 10 ft rectangles separated by 8 ft, may be taken as the geometric mean of the factors for 6 ft squares separated by 8 ft, and 10 ft squares separated by 8 ft. These come from Fig. 2, line 2, according to which $F_{22} = \sqrt{0.13 \times 0.255} = 0.182$. Then $F_{2R} = 1 - 0.182 - 0.139 = 0.679$. The other required direct factor is $F_{3R} = 1 - F_{32} = 1 - F_{23}A_2/A_3 = 1 - 0.139 \times 120/50 = 0.666$. Then $\bar{F}_{23} = 0.139 + \dfrac{1}{(1/0.679) + (120/50)(1/0.666)} = 0.336$. Having $\bar{F}_{23}$, we may now evaluate the factor $\mathfrak{F}_{23}$.

$$\mathfrak{F}_{23} = \frac{1}{(1/0.336) + [(1/0.702) - 1] + (120/50)[(1/0.9) - 1]} = 0.273$$

$$q_{\text{net}} = \sigma(T_1^4 - T_3^4)A_2\mathfrak{F}_{23} = 0.171(19.6^4 - 16.6^4)(120)(0.273)$$
$$= 402{,}000 \text{ Btu per hr}$$

A result of interest is obtained by dividing the term $A_2\mathfrak{F}_{23}(120 \times 0.273$, or 32.7) by the actual area A_1 of the radiating tubes $\left(\frac{5\pi}{12} \times 60 \times 2 = 157 \text{ sq ft}\right)$. This is $32.7/157 = 0.208$, which means that the net radiation from a tube to the stock is 20.8 percent as much as if the tube were black and completely surrounded by black stock.

Enclosures of Surfaces That Are Not Diffuse Reflectors. The total-interchange-area concept has been generalized to include surfaces the reflectance ρ of which can be divided into a diffuse, or Lambert-reflecting, component ρ_D and a specular component ρ_S independent of angle of incidence, with $\epsilon + \rho_S + \rho_D = 1$. In application to concentric spheres or infinite cylinders, with A_1 the inner surface, the method yields (Sarofim and Hottel, *JHT, ASME,* 1966)

$$A_1\mathfrak{F}_{12} \equiv \overline{S_1S_2} = \frac{1}{\dfrac{1}{A_1\epsilon_1} + \dfrac{1}{A_2}\left(\dfrac{1}{\epsilon_2} - 1\right) + \dfrac{\rho_{S2}}{1 - \rho_{S2}}\left(\dfrac{1}{A_1} - \dfrac{1}{A_2}\right)}$$

When there is no specular reflectance, the third term in the denominator drops out, in agreement with Eq. (**12**). When the reflectance is exclusively specular, the denominator becomes $1/A_1\epsilon_1 + \rho_{S2}/A_1(1 - \rho_{S2})$, easily derivable from first principles.

Flames, Combustion Products, and Particle Clouds

The radiation from a flame is due to radiation from burning soot particles of microscopic and submicroscopic dimensions, from suspended larger particles of coal, coke, or ash, and from the water vapor and carbon dioxide in the hot gaseous combustion products. The contribution of radiation emitted by the combustion process itself, so-called *chemiluminescence,* is relatively negligible. Common to these problems is the effect of the shape of the emitting volume on the radiative flux; this will be considered first.

Mean Beam Lengths. Evaluation of radiation from a non-isothermal volume is beyond the scope of this section (see Hottel and Cohen, *AICE Jour.,* 1958). If a volume emitter is isothermal and at a temperature T, the ratio of the emission from an element dA of its envelope, in the direction θ and throughout the solid angle $d\Omega$, to that from a black surface within the same angle and at T is called the **gas emissivity.** Clearly, ϵ depends on the path length L through the volume to dA. A hemispherical volume radiating to a spot on the center of its base represents the only case in which L is independent of direction. Flux at that spot relative to hemispherical black-body flux is thus an alternative way to visualize emissivity. The flux density to an area of interest on the envelope of an emitter volume of any shape can be matched by that at the base of a hemispherical volume of some radius L, which will be called the **mean beam length.** It is found that, although the ratio of L to a characteristic dimension D of the shape varies with opacity, the variation is small enough for most engineering purposes to permit use of a constant ratio, L_M/D, where L_M is the **average mean beam length.** L_M can be defined to apply to a spot on the envelope or to any portion of its area. An important limiting case is that of opacity approaching zero ($PD \to 0$, where P = partial pressure of the emitter constituent). For this case, L (called L_0) equals 4 × (ratio of gas volume to bounding area) when interest is in radiation to the entire envelope. For the range of PD encountered in practice, L (now L_M) is always less. For various shapes, 0.8 to 0.95 times L_0 has been found optimum (see Table 3); for shapes not reported in Table 3, a factor of 0.88 (or $L_M = 0.88L_0 = 3.5V/A$) is recommended.

Soot luminosity is important where combustion occurs under such conditions that the hydrocarbons in the flame are subject to heat in the absence of sufficient air well mixed on a molecular scale. Because soot particles are small relative to the wavelength of radiation of interest (diameters 200 to 1,400A), the monochromatic emissivity ϵ_λ depends on the total particle volume per unit volume of space f_v, regardless of particle size. It is given by

$$\epsilon_\lambda = 1 - e^{-Kf_vL/\lambda}$$

where L is the path length. Integration of the above over the energy spectrum gives the total emissivity ϵ as

$$\epsilon \approx 1 - 1/(1 + KTf_v L/C_2)^4$$

where C_2 is the second Planck constant. K/C_2 can be obtained from the complex refractive index of soot, in turn dependent on its hydrogen-carbon ratio H/C. Based

Table 3. Mean Beam Lengths for Volume Radiation

Shape	Characteristic dimension, D	L_0/D	L_M/D
Sphere	Diameter	0.67	0.63
Infinite cylinder	Diameter	1	0.94
Semi-infinite cylinder, radiating to:			
Center of base	Diameter	1	0.90
Entire base	Diameter	0.81	0.65
Right-circle cylinder, ht = diam, radiating to:			
Center of base	Diameter	0.76	0.71
Whole surface	Diameter	0.67	0.60
Right-circle cylinder, ht = 0.5 diam, radiating to:			
End	Diameter	0.47	0.43
Side	Diameter	0.52	0.46
Total surface	Diameter	0.50	0.45
Right-circle cylinder, ht = 2 × diam, radiating to:			
End	Diameter	0.73	0.60
Side	Diameter	0.82	0.76
Total surface	Diameter	0.80	0.73
Infinite cylinder, half-circle cross section, radiating to spot on middle of flat side	Radius		1.26
Rectangular parallelepipeds:			
1:1:1 (cube)	Edge	0.67	0.60
1:1:4, radiating to:			
1 × 4 face	Shortest edge	0.90	0.82
1 × 1 face	Shortest edge	0.86	0.71
Whole surface	Shortest edge	0.89	0.81
1:2:6, radiating to:			
2 × 6 face	Shortest edge	1.18	
1 × 6 face	Shortest edge	1.24	
1 × 2 face	Shortest edge	1.18	
Whole surface	Shortest edge	1.2	
Infinite parallel planes	Clearance	2.00	1.76
Space outside infinite bank of tubes, centers on equilateral triangles; tube diam = clearance	Clearance	3.4	2.8
Same, except tube diam = 0.5 clearance	Clearance	4.45	3.8
Same, except tube centers on squares, diam = clearance	Clearance	4.1	3.5

on a study of coals, K/C_2 varies from 4.8 cm^{-1} deg K^{-1} at $H/C = 0$ to 2.4 at $H/C = 0.4$; some experimental work at Ijmuiden on two oil-flame types leads to 4.4 and 9.8. A tentative value of 5 cm^{-1} deg K^{-1} (85 ft^{-1} deg R^{-1}) is recommended.

There is at present no method of predicting soot concentration of a luminous flame analytically; reliance must be placed on experimental measurement on flames similar to that of interest. Visual observation is misleading; a flame so bright as to hide the wall behind it may be far from a "black" radiator. The International Flame Foundation at Ijmuiden has recorded data on many luminous flames from gas, oil, and coal (see *Jour. Inst. Fuel*, 1956–present). Addition of 0.1 to non-luminous-gas emissivity to allow for soot luminosity is often sufficient if calculations of total flame emission are to be based on a mean flame temperature; this is because emission from the flame comes more from its cool envelope than from its hot core, especially as its emissivity goes up.

Clouds of Large Black Particles. The emissivity of a cloud of particles with perimeter large compared with wavelength is $1 - e^{-(a/v)L}$, where a/v is the projected area of the particles in unit volume of space. If the particles have no dimples (a particle can "see" none of itself), a/v is $(a'/v)/4$, where a' is the actual surface area; and if the particles are uniform, $a/v = cA = cA'/4$, where A and A' are the projected and total areas of each particle and c is the particle concentration. As an example, consider heavy fuel oil atomized to a surface-mean particle diameter of d microns, burned with 20 percent excess air to produce coke residue particles having the original drop diameter, and suspended in combustion products at 2200 F. The flame emissivity due to the particles along a path of L ft will be

$$\epsilon = 1 - e^{-4.9L/d}$$

With 200μ particles and an L of 10 ft, the particle contribution to emissivity will be 0.22. Soot luminosity will increase this; particle burnout will decrease it. The combined emissivity due to several kinds of emitters can be calculated from the separately calculated emissivities provided only one of these (gaseous combustion products) is a selective emitter. If $\epsilon_G,\epsilon_p,\epsilon_S$ are the separate emissivities due to gas, massive particles, and soot, all calculated as though no other emitter were present, the combined emissivity is $1 - (1 - \epsilon_G)(1 - \epsilon_p)(1 - \epsilon_S)$. The emissivity of a cloud of gray particles of surface emissivity ϵ_m lies between values predicted from the use of exponents of $(a/v)L$ and $\epsilon_m(a/v)L$ in the cloud-emissivity relationship, because of multiple scatter by reflection. Particles with perimeter lying between 0.5 and 5 times the λ of interest are difficult to handle (see Van der Hulst, "Light Scattering by Small Particles," Wiley, 1957).

Gaseous Combustion Products. Radiation from water vapor and carbon dioxide occurs in spectral bands in the infrared. In magnitude it overshadows convection at furnace temperatures. The emissivity ϵ_G of a CO_2-containing gas volume depends on gas temperature T_G, on the CO_2 partial-pressure–beam-length product P_CL, and to a much lesser extent, on the total pressure. Figure 7 gives ϵ_G for carbon dioxide at a total pressure of 1 atm. The gas absorptivity α_G equals the emissivity when the absorbing gas and the emitter are at the same temperature. When the emitter surface temperature is T_S, α_G is $(T_G/T_S)^{0.65}$ times the ϵ_G read from Fig. 7 at T_S instead of T_G and at P_CLT_S/T_G instead of P_CL. If, at constant P_CL, the total pressure P_T is increased above 1 atm, ϵ_G and α_G increase a small fraction due to line broadening. Over the range of $P_C + P_T$ of 1 to 10 atm, a multiplying factor $(P_C + P_T)^m$ may be used to estimate the effect. m is 0.06, 0.09, or 0.11 (0.008, 0.01, or 0.03) at T_G = 500 R (2000 R), when $(P_C + P_T)L$ is 10, 4, or 0.5 ft atm; it is at maximum in the PL range 0.1–1.0; it decreases as temperature rises.

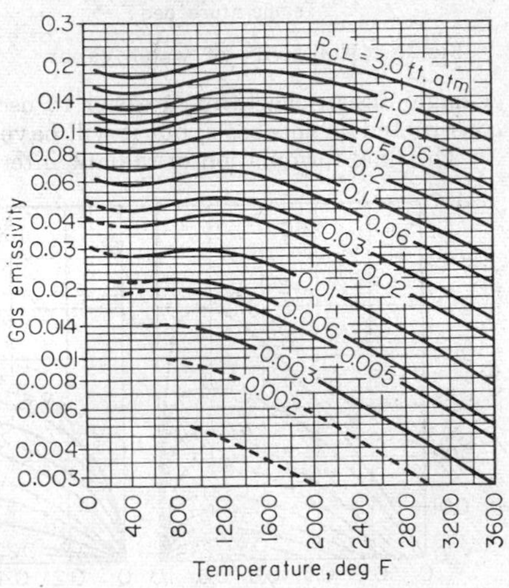

FIG. 7. Emissivity of carbon dioxide.

For water vapor, the gas emissivity depends on T_G and P_wL and on total pressure P_T and on the partial pressure of water vapor P_w. Emissivity due to water vapor is given in Fig. 8 as a function of T_G and P_wL, for the special case of $P_w = 0$ and $P_T = 1$. Allowance for departure from these special conditions is made by multiplying ϵ_G from Fig. 8 by a factor C_w read from Fig. 9 as a function of $(P_w + P_T)$ and P_wL. The absorptivity α_G of water vapor for black-body radiation is ϵ_G from Fig. 8, read at T_S and at $P_wL(T_S/T_G)$ instead of P_wL, then multiplied by $(T_G/T_S)^{0.45}$. The correction factor C_w still applies.

When carbon dioxide and water vapor are present together, the total radiation due to both is somewhat less than the sum of the separately calculated effects because each gas is somewhat opaque to radiation from the other. The amount $\Delta\epsilon$ by which to reduce the sum of ϵ_G for CO_2 and ϵ_G for H_2O (each evaluated as if the other were absent) to obtain the ϵ_G due to the two together is read from Fig. 10. The same type of correction applies in calculating α_G.

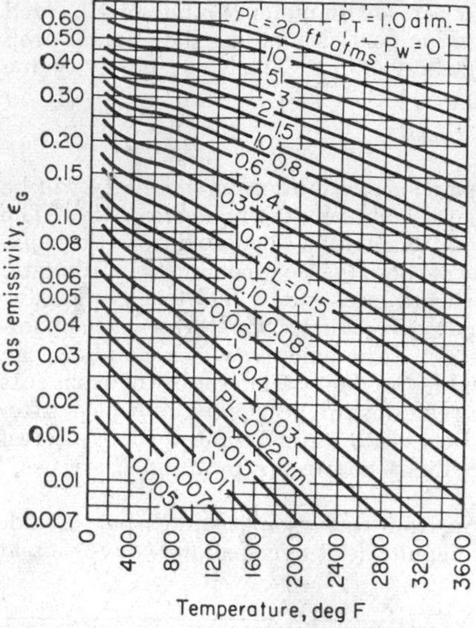

FIG. 8. Emissivity of water vapor.

Effective use can sometimes be made of the fact that, at furnace temperatures and for gases containing H_2O and CO_2 in a fixed ratio, ϵ_G decreases with rising temperature in such a way that the product $(\epsilon_G)(T_G)$ depends almost exclusively on $(P_c + P_w)L$.

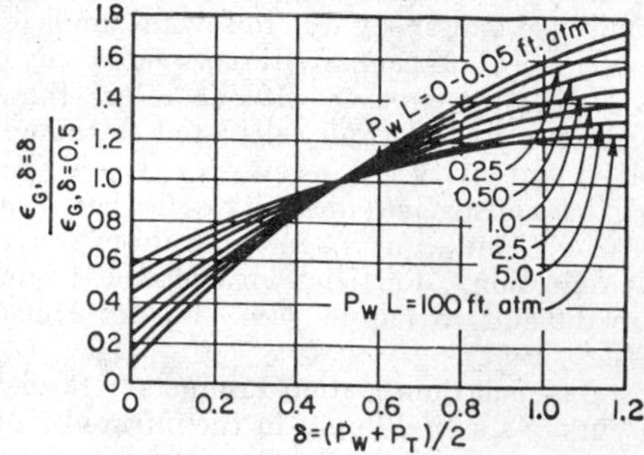

FIG. 9. Correction for effects of total pressure and partial pressure on water-vapor radiation.

A single design chart, much easier to use than Figs. 7 to 10 in combination, may be constructed on this basis; but it will have validity over a restricted range of variables.

The final formulation of radiant interchange between a gas and its bounding sur-

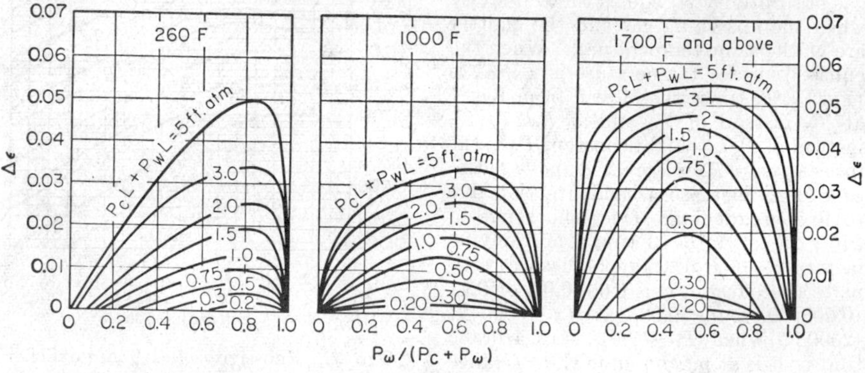

FIG. 10. Correction for superimposed radiation from mixtures of carbon dioxide and water vapor.

face, when the gas contains CO_2 and H_2O, is then

$$q = \sigma\epsilon_S'[\epsilon_G T_G^4 - \alpha_G T_S^4] \equiv 0.171\epsilon_S'[\epsilon_G(T_G/100)^4 - \alpha_G(T_S/100)^4] \qquad \textbf{(16)}$$

If the surface is gray, multiplication by ϵ_S makes proper allowance for reduction in the primary beam from gas to surface and surface to gas, respectively; but some of the gas radiation initially reflected from the surface has further opportunity for absorption at the surface because the gas is but incompletely opaque to the reflected beam. Consequently, the factor to allow for surface emissivity lies between ϵ_S and unity, nearer the latter the more transparent the gas (low PL) and the more convoluted the surface. In the emissivity range of most industrial surface, 0.7 to 1.0, an adequate approximation consists in use of an effective emissivity ϵ_S' halfway between the actual value of ϵ_S and unity.

EXAMPLE. Flue gas containing 9.5 percent CO_2 and 7.1 percent H_2O, wet basis, flows through a bank of tubes of 1.5 in. O.D. on equilateral triangular centers 4.5 in. apart. In a section in which the gas and tube surface temperatures are 1700 and 1000 F, what is the heat-transfer rate per square foot of tube area, due to gas radiation only? Tube surface emissivity = 0.8.

$$L_M = 3.8 \times 4.5/12 = 1.43 \text{ ft} \qquad P_cL = 0.135 \text{ ft atm} \qquad P_wL = 0.102 \text{ ft atm}$$

From Fig. 7, for CO_2: $\epsilon_G = 0.080$, $\alpha_G = 0.084$.
From Fig. 8, for H_2O: $\epsilon_G = 0.050$, $\alpha_G = 0.076$.
From Fig. 9, $c_u = 1.1$.
From Fig. 10, $\Delta\epsilon = 0.003$, $\Delta\alpha = 0.009$.

$$\epsilon_{G,\text{Total}} = 0.08 + 0.05 \times 1.1 - 0.003 = 0.132$$
$$\alpha_{G,\text{Total}} = 0.084 + 0.076 \times 1.1 - 0.002 = 0.166$$

The effective surface-emissivity factor $\epsilon_s = (0.8 + 1)/2 = 0.9$. From Eq. (**16**),

$$q = 0.9 \times 0.171(0.132 \times 21.6^4 - 0.166 \times 14.6^4) = 3260 \text{ Btu/ft}^2\text{hr}$$

equivalent to a convection coefficient of $^{3260}/_{700}$, or 4.6. The emissivity of an "equivalent gray" flame is $(0.132 \times 21.6^4 - 0.166 \times 14.6^4)/(21.6^4 - 14.6^4) = 0.123$.

Enclosures—Combustion Chambers

The so-called *radiant section* of a furnace presents a heat-transfer problem in which there enters the combined action of direct radiation from the flame to the stock or heat sink and radiation from the flame to refractory surfaces and thence back through the flame (with partial absorption) to the sink, convection, and external losses. Solutions of the problem based on varying degrees of simplification are available, including allowance for temperature variation in both gas and refractory walls (Hottel and Cohen, *AIChE Jour.*, 1958). A less rigorous treatment suffices, however, for handling many problems. There are two limiting cases: the long chamber with gas temperature varying only in the direction of gas flow and the compact chamber containing a gas or flame at a uniform temperature. The latter will be considered first.

The following simple mathematical model of a furnace chamber is found to make substantially correct predictions of the relation among the dominant variables for a wide range of furnace types: The gas mass and flame transfer heat as though at a mean temperature T_G; the gas is gray; the bounding walls of total area A_T are divisible into a heat-sink surface A_1, gray and at a single temperature T_1, and an adiabatic refractory area A_r, convection to which and external loss from which are negligible. The net radiative flux from gas to sink must be proportional to the difference in their black emissive powers; the proportionality constant, of dimension area, will by analogy to the treatment of surface interchange be called $A_1\mathfrak{F}_{1G}$ (or, in more recent nomenclature, the total-interchange area $\overline{GS_1}$), a term allowing for both direct gas-to-sink interchange and indirect exchange via multiple reflection and refractory action. It may be shown from Eq. (**11**) [with exchange areas redefined to include gas transmittance (McAdams, chap. IV by Hottel)] that

$$\frac{1}{\mathfrak{F}_{1G}} = \frac{1}{\epsilon_1} - 1 + \frac{1}{\epsilon_G\left[1 + \dfrac{A_r/A_1}{\epsilon_G/(1-\epsilon_G)F_{r1}}\right]} \tag{17}$$

For the commonly encountered case of the sink consisting of a row of tubes mounted on a refractory wall, A_1 is the area of the whole plane in which the tubes lie, T_1 is tube surface temperature, and ϵ_1 is the effective emissivity of the tube-row–refractory-wall combination, as in the earlier numerical example associated with Fig. 6, where $\epsilon_1 = 0.702$. One further simplification is to replace A_1/A_T by C, the "cold" fraction of the wall, and to approximate F_{r1} by C (the speckled-furnace model). The net radiative flux from the gas is then

$$A_1\mathfrak{F}_{1G}\sigma(T_G^4 - T_1^4) \qquad \text{or} \qquad \frac{A_T}{(1/\epsilon_G) + (1/C\epsilon_1) - 1}\sigma(T_G^4 - T_1^4)$$

If the convective flux from gas to sink is $A_1h_1(T_G - T_1)$ (and this is small compared with radiation), convection may be linearized in T^4 to give $A_1h_1(T_G - T_1) = A_1(h_1/4\sigma T_{G1}^3)\sigma(T_G^4 - T_1^4)$. T_{G1} in the dimensionless term in the first parentheses may be approximated as the arithmetic mean of T_G and T_1 (guessed the first time around, in calculating). The total flux may now be written

$$\dot{Q}_{G,\text{net}} = \left[\frac{A_T}{(1/\epsilon_G) + (1/C\epsilon_1) - 1} + \frac{A_1h}{4\sigma T_{G1}^3}\right]\sigma(T_G^4 - T_1^4) \equiv (\overline{GS}_1)_{r,c}\sigma(T_G^4 - T_1^4) \tag{18}$$

The equation defines the pseudo-interchange-area term $(\overline{GS}_1)_{r,c}$, which allows for both radiative and convective flux. With this equation of flux, there must be combined an energy balance. If T_0 is the base temperature, H_{in} the entering hourly enthalpy of air and fuel above that base, B the amount by which the leaving-gas temperature is less than the radiating temperature T_G, $\dot{m}c_p$ the hourly heat capacity of the combustion products over the temperature interval $T_G - B$ to T_0, the energy balance is

$$H_{in} - \dot{Q}_G = (T_G - B - T_0)\dot{m}c_p$$

If the same mean specific heat is used to define a kind of adiabatic flame temperature T_{AF} as $T_0 + H_{in}/\dot{m}c_p$, these relations may be combined with (**18**) to eliminate the unknown T_G and give the dimensionless relation

$$\mu'D' + \tau^4 = (1 + B' - \mu')^4 \tag{19}$$

where μ' = reduced furnace efficiency, the actual efficiency $\dot{Q}_G/H_{in}$ times the temperature ratio $(T_{AF} - T_0)/T_{AF}$

D' = reduced firing density

$$\frac{H_{in}}{\sigma A_T T_{AF}^3(T_{AF} - T_0)}\frac{A_T}{(\overline{GS}_1)_{r,c}} \text{ or } D\frac{A_T}{(\overline{GS}_1)_{r,c}}$$

τ = reduced sink temperature, T_1/T_{AF}

B' = B/T_{AF}, the ratio of the gas-temperature drop, from mean radiating point to chamber outlet, to the adiabatic flame temperature

Equation (**19**) says that the efficiency of the chamber is a function of the firing density, the heat-sink temperature, and the gas-temperature drop B (at this point the one arbitrary quantity); and the firing-density term makes due allowance for any operating variables such as fuel type, excess air, or air preheat which affect flame temperature or gas emissivity, for fractional occupancy of the walls by sink surfaces, and for sink emissivity. If the furnace gas is well stirred, B' approaches zero. The resulting idealized furnace may be called the "well-stirred speckled-walled gray-gas combustion chamber"; its characteristics are shown in, Fig. 11, where Eq. (**19**) with $B' = 0$ is plotted, together with shaded areas indicating the operating regimes of various types of furnaces. Note the significant properties of the function presented: (1) As firing rate D' goes down, the efficiency rises and approaches $1 - \tau$ in the limit. (2) Changes in sink temperature have little effect if $\tau < 0.3$. (3) As the furnace walls approach complete coverage by a black sink ($C\epsilon_1 \rightarrow 1$) and as convection becomes unimportant, the effect of flame emissivity on D' becomes one of inverse proportionality; thus at very high firing rates where μ' approaches inverse proportionality to D', efficiency of heat transfer varies directly as ϵ_G (gas-turbine chambers), but at low firing rates ϵ_G has relatively

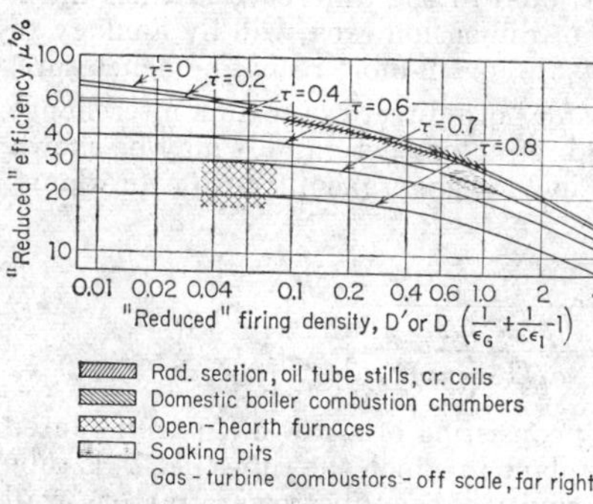

FIG. 11. The thermal performance of "well-stirred" furnace chambers.

little effect. (4) When $C\epsilon_1 \ll 1$ because of a non-black sink or much refractory surface, the effect of changing flame emissivity is to produce a much less than proportional effect on heat flux.

The factor B—the allowance for imperfect stirring—must be estimated. Values in the range 200 to 300 F have been found to produce data correlation for a series of tests on marine boilers. B increases with increase in μ' or decrease in D'; in the absence of data on the type of furnace of interest, a tentative recommendation is that $B' = \mu'/4$.

Equation (**19**) and Fig. 11 serve as a framework for correlating the performance of furnaces with flow patterns—plug flow, parabolic profile, and recirculatory flow—differing from the well-stirred model (Hottel and Sarofim, *Int. Jl. Mass and Ht. Trans.*, 1965). As expected, plug-flow furnaces show somewhat higher efficiency, mild-recirculation types somewhat lower efficiency, and strong-recirculation furnaces performances closely similar to that of the well-stirred model. Equation (**19**) has also been used to correlate data on the radiant section of a tube still in which τ varied from 0.34 to 0.47. The assumption of a mean τ of 0.4 and a value of B' of $\mu'/4$ leads, from Eq. (**19**), to

$$\mu' D A_T / (\overline{GS}_1)_{r,c} = (1 - \tfrac{3}{4}\mu')^4 - (0.4)^4$$

Though $(\overline{GS}_1)_{r,c}$ varied with gas temperature and excess air, its mean value was used. The average deviation of 10 measured performance points from the above relation was only 3.8 percent, even though no constants of the equation were determined empirically from furnace data (Hottel, *Jour. Inst. Fuel*, 1961).

Equation (**19**) is capable of covering a wide range of furnace types; its structure makes it safer to use than the many empirical relations in the literature.

The Long Chamber. When the gas-temperature transverse to the flow direction is reasonably uniform and the chamber is long compared with its mean hydraulic radius, the opposed upstream and downstream fluxes through the flow cross section will substantially cancel (*e.g.*, tunnel kilns, billet-reheating furnaces, the numerical example of p. 4–116). Under these conditions, the radiative contribution to local flux may be formulated in terms of local temperatures and of view factors or exchange areas evaluated as for a two-dimensional system. The local flux density at the sink A_1 is then

$$q(T_G,T_1) = \mathfrak{F}_{1G}\sigma(T_G^4 - T_1^4) + h_1(T_G - T_1) \quad \textbf{(20)}$$

where q is written to indicate that it is a function of T_G and T_1 and $\mathfrak{F}_{1G}$ is evaluated as in Eq. (**17**). If $\dot{m}c_p$ is the hourly heat capacity of the gas stream, the temperature of which changes by dT_G over the sink area increment dA_1, then

$$[q(T_G,T_1)]\, dA_1 = -\dot{m}c_p\, dT_G$$

From this it is clear that the reciprocal of the mean height of a curve of $1/q$ versus $\dot{m}c_pT_G$ over the gas-temperature interval of interest is q_{avg}. Three points generally suffice.

SECTION 5

STRENGTH OF MATERIALS

BY

CHARLES W. MacGREGOR, Engineering Consultant and Manager of Advanced Technology, Systems Development Division, International Business Machines Corporation, Endicott, N.Y.

J. P. VIDOSIC, Regents' Professor and Acting Director, School of Mechanical Engineering, Georgia Institute of Technology.

HAROLD V. HAWKINS, Manager, Product Development and Engineering, Columbus McKinnon Corporation.

WILLIAM T. THOMSON, Professor of Engineering, University of California, Los Angeles.

DONALD D. DODGE, Project Engineer, Ford Motor Company.

CONTENTS

MECHANICAL PROPERTIES OF MATERIALS

BY

Charles W. MacGregor

REFERENCES: Smith, "Testing of Materials," Van Nostrand. Timoshenko, "Strength of Materials," Part II, Van Nostrand. Moore and Kommers, "Fatigue of Metals," McGraw-Hill. Hatt and Scofield, "Laboratory Manual of Testing Materials," McGraw-Hill. Nádai, "Theory of Flow and Fracture of Solids," McGraw-Hill. "ASTM Standards," ASTM. "Creep Data," ASME. Gibbons, "Materials Testing Machines," Instruments Publishing Co. Marin, "Engineering Materials," Prentice-Hall. Lubahn and Felgar, "Plasticity and Creep of Metals," Wiley. Finnie and Heller, "Creep of Engineering Materials," McGraw-Hill. "Proceedings of the International Conference on Fatigue of Metals," IMechE, 1956.

In a **tension test** the **stress-strain diagram** is constructed by plotting the stress S_o (determined by dividing the axial load P by the original area of cross section A_o) as ordinate *vs.* the strain ϵ_o (obtained by dividing the increment in gage length ΔL_o by the original gage length L_o) as abscissa. The strain ϵ_o is obtained from axial strain measurements. Since both A_o and L_o are constants, the diagram has the same shape as one for which the axial load P is plotted against the deformation ΔL_o. Typical curves for metals are shown in Figs. 1 to 3. The elastic portion of such a diagram is a straight line (**Hooke's** law) and the slope of this line, or the ratio of stress to strain within the elastic range, is the **modulus of elasticity** E **(Young's modulus).** As the stress is increased, a point is reached where a further increase will show a departure of the curve from the straight line. The greatest stress intensity for which stress is still **proportional to strain is called the proportional elastic limit** (indicated by PEL in Fig. 3). This is not strictly the same as the **elastic limit.** The elastic limit is the greatest stress which can be applied without leaving a permanent deformation upon complete release of the load. To determine the elastic limit, it is necessary to load and unload the specimen with increasing values of the load until a permanent set is found after complete unloading. Since this procedure is time-consuming and since the elastic limit so determined differs little from the proportional limit, the true elastic limit is seldom obtained in actual practice.

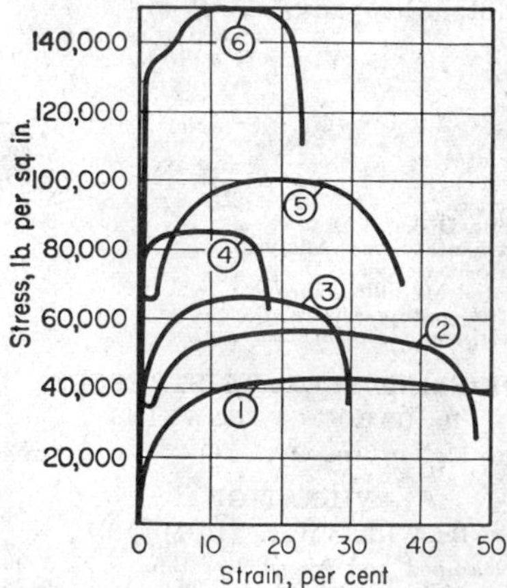

Fig. 1. Comparative stress-strain diagrams: (1) soft brass; (2) low-carbon steel; (3) hard bronze; (4) cold-rolled steel; (5) medium-carbon steel, annealed; (6) medium-carbon steel, heat-treated.

If the stress is increased further, the stress-strain curve departs more and more from the straight line. Unloading the specimen at point X (Fig. 3), the portion XX' is linear and is essentially parallel to the original line OX''. The horizontal distance OX' is called the **permanent set** corresponding to the stress at X. This is the basis for the construction of the arbitrary **yield strength.** To determine the yield strength, a straight line XX' is drawn parallel to the initial elastic line OX'' but displaced from it by an arbitrary value of permanent strain. The permanent strain commonly used is 0.20

percent of the original gage length. The intersection of this line with the curve determines the stress value called the yield strength. In reporting the yield strength, the amount of permanent set should be specified. The arbitrary yield strength is used especially for those materials not exhibiting a natural yield point such as for non-ferrous metals, but it is not limited to these.

If a specimen is completely unloaded from point X in Fig. 3 and is then reloaded, the curve will follow a continuation of the curve OX as though no unloading had taken place.

A natural **yield point** is present in annealed carbon steels, especially those of low carbon content. The yield point has been defined as the stress for which a marked increase in strain occurs without a corresponding increase in stress. In such steels, both an upper and a lower yield point are usually present. Following initial yielding, the stress drops and the curve remains approximately horizontal for a period of deformation before it begins to rise again. The **upper yield point** is the stress from which the initial drop occurs. The **lower yield point** is sometimes taken as the lowest value of stress after the initial dropoff and before the load begins to rise continuously, or more properly as the average stress during this interval as indicated in Fig. 2. The term yield point should not be used in connection with materials where the stress-strain diagram does not become horizontal or does not show an actual drop of stress with increase of strain in the region of yield.

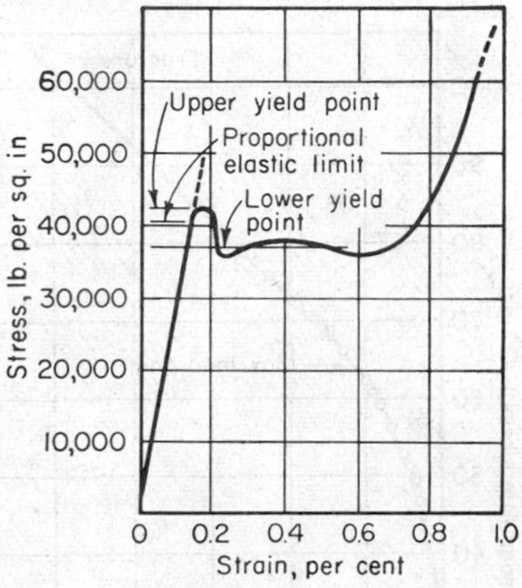

FIG. 2. Yielding of annealed steel.

Upon further deformation the load reaches a maximum value and then drops somewhat before fracture. The **tensile strength** is obtained by dividing the maximum load during the test by the original cross-sectional area. A measure of the **ductility** of the material after fracture is given by the **percent elongation** and also by the **reduction of area.** The percent elongation after fracture is determined by dividing the change in the original gage length by the original gage length, this ratio multiplied by 100 percent. The original gage length should always be stated in reporting percent elongation values. The percent reduction of area after fracture is the ratio of the change in the original area determined at the smallest cross section to the original area of cross section, this ratio multiplied by 100 percent (see also Tables 1-3).

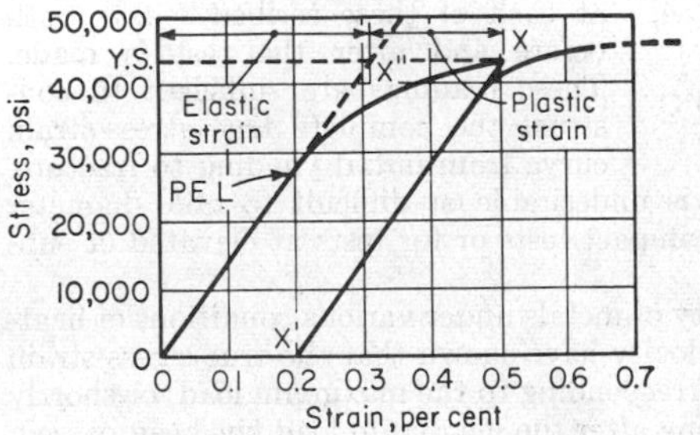

FIG. 3. General stress-strain diagram.

In a **compression test,** most ductile metals have stress-strain relations very similar to the tensile values in the early part of the curve. As the area of cross section increases, the curve usually rises instead of falling as in the ordinary form of tension test. For this reason the curve does not reach an analytic maximum as in the case of tension, and unless shearing, splitting, or crumbling occurs there may not be any fracture and consequently no definite **compressive strength** may be quoted. Where fracture does occur, the compressive strength is the maximum which a material is capable of developing.

The **true stress-strain diagram** (see MacGregor, The Tension Test, *Proc. ASTM*, **40,** 1940, pp. 508-534; also The True Stress-strain Tension Test—Its Role in Modern Materials Testing, *Jour. Franklin Inst.*, **238,** Nos. 2 and 3, Aug. and Sept., 1944, pp. 111-135, 159-176) for the tension test is constructed by plotting the true stress S, determined by dividing the axial load P by the instantaneous area of cross section A, as ordinate *vs.* the true strain $\epsilon = \ln (A_o/A)$ as abscissa where A_o is the original area and A the instantaneous area of cross section as shown in Fig. 4. Simultaneous readings of the axial load and the dimension or dimensions required to compute the minimum instantaneous area of cross section are taken throughout the test to fracture. This is called the **multiload method.** For round bars, the true strain ϵ, which is equal to the true reduction of area q', is $2 \ln (d_o/d)$, where d_o and d are the original and instantaneous diameters, respectively. The true axial strain is thus determined from diameter measurements. The same diameter measurements serve to compute the true stress. If the test specimen is of rectangular cross section, where the ratio of width to thickness is less than 6, the instantaneous area of cross section is $A = \frac{1}{3}h(b + 2c)$ where h, c, and b are, respectively, the width at the center of the cross section parallel to the long side, the thickness at the center parallel to the short side, and the thickness at the ends of the cross section. The method is applicable to bars of any cross section.

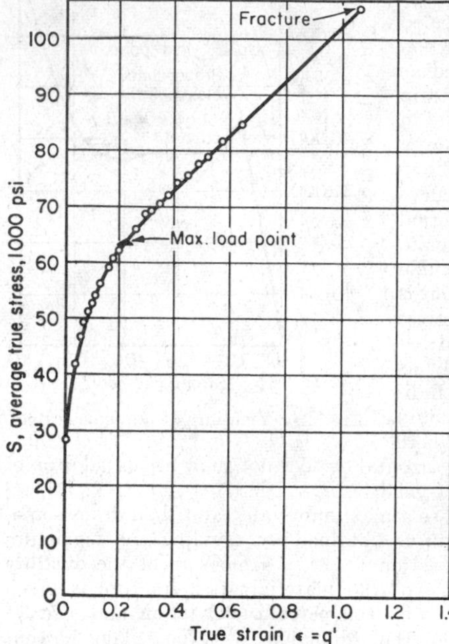

Fig. 4. True stress-strain curve for 20°C annealed mild steel.

Another procedure for constructing the true stress-strain curve is the **two-load method** (see reference above, on true stress-strain diagram) where no strain readings are taken throughout the test, and only the maximum and fracture loads noted. A tapered test bar, scribed with fine lateral marks at intervals along its length, is used. The dimension or dimensions governing the areas of cross section are measured at each of these scribed marks both before and after the test is made. These readings are sufficient to construct the complete true stress-strain curve from initial yielding to fracture. The method is especially useful where it is undesirable or difficult to take diameter readings during the test, as for high-speed impact tests or for tests at elevated or subatmospheric temperatures.

Experiments conducted on a wide variety of metals under various conditions of heat-treatment, cold work, temperature, and velocity have shown that the true stress-strain curve is essentially linear from the point corresponding to the maximum load, or shortly thereafter, to fracture. During local necking after the maximum load has been passed, a three-dimensional state of stress is present in the locally constricted region. The axial stresses, which are much greater than the lateral stresses, are not distributed exactly uniformly over the cross section. The stress value $S = P/A$ represents the average of the true axial stresses. Tests have indicated that this average true stress is usually not greatly different from the stress which would be present if a necked region had not been allowed to form and the material subjected to a purely uniform uniaxial state of stress.

The mechanical properties determined from the true stress-strain curve in addition to the yield point or yield strength are listed in Table 4.

P_u, P_b, A_u, A_b, A_o are, respectively, the max load, the fracture load, the area of cross section at max load, the area of cross section at fracture, and the original area of cross section.

With the exception of the elastic constants and the proportional limit, the remaining mechanical properties determined from the ordinary stress-strain curve are empirical. The true stress-strain method is a more rational approach and is more sensitive to

Table 1. Typical Mechanical Properties at Room Temperature

(Based on ordinary stress-strain values)

Metal	Tensile strength, kpsi	Yield strength, kpsi	Ultimate elongation, percent	Reduction of area, percent	Brinell No.
Cast iron	18–60	8–40	0	0	100–300
Wrought iron	45–55	25–35	35–25	55–30	100
Commercially pure iron, annealed	42	19	48	85	70
Hot rolled	48	30	30	75	90
Cold rolled	100	95	.....	.....	200
Structural steel, ordinary	50–65	30–40	40–30	.....	120
Low alloy, high strength	65–90	40–80	30–15	70–40	150
Steel, SAE 1300, annealed	70	40	26	70	150
Quenched, drawn 1300 F	100	80	24	65	200
Drawn 1000 F	130	110	20	60	260
Drawn 700 F	200	180	14	45	400
Drawn 400 F	240	210	10	30	480
Steel, SAE 4340, annealed	80	45	25	70	170
Quenched, drawn 1300 F	130	110	20	60	270
Drawn 1000 F	190	170	14	50	395
Drawn 700 F	240	215	12	48	480
Drawn 400 F	290	260	10	44	580
Cold-rolled steel, SAE 1112	84	76	18	45	160
Stainless steel, 18–8	85–95	30–35	60–55	75–65	145–160
Steel castings, heat-treated	60–125	30–90	33–14	65–20	120–250
Aluminum, pure, rolled	13–24	5–21	35–5	.....	23–44
Aluminum-copper alloys, cast	19–23	12–16	4–0	.....	50–80
Wrought, heat-treated	30–60	10–50	33–15	.....	50–120
Aluminum die castings	30	.....	2		
Aluminum alloy 17ST	56	34	26	39	100
Aluminum alloy 51ST	48	40	20	35	105
Copper, annealed	32	5	58	73	45
Copper, hard drawn	68	60	4	55	100
Brasses, various	40–120	8–80	60–3	.....	50–170
Phosphor bronze	40–130	.....	55–5	.....	50–200
Tobin bronze, rolled	63	41	40	52	120
Magnesium alloys, various	21–45	11–30	17–0.5	.....	47–78
Monel metal, 70Ni, 30Cu	100	50	35	.....	170
Molybdenum, arc-cast	97	91	28 [1″g. l.]	40	260
Zirconium, crystal bar	24–43	8–26	24–54	25–75	70–130
Titanium (99.0 Ti), annealed bar	95	80	47	27	
Ductile iron, Grade 90–65–02, as cast	95–105	70–75	2.5–5.5	.....	225–265

Compressive strength of cast iron, 80,000 to 150,000 psi.
Compressive yield strength of all metals, except those cold-worked, = tensile yield strength.

changes in both metallurgical and mechanical conditions of the material. It gives a more accurate picture of the ductility through the use of the true uniform and local necking strains of Table 4. It can be correlated with stress-strain values in other tests such as torsion, notched-beam impact, combined-stress tests, and in metal-forming problems, for which the ordinary stress-strain approach is inadequate.

Table 5 lists typical true stress-strain properties for a few materials tested in tension. The true stress-strain approach can be used for compression tests as well; for ductile metals the two curves are often quite close for moderate strain values.

Methods are also available for determining the stress-strain curves of a material from **bending** and **torsion** tests. (See Nádai, "Theory of Flow and Fracture of Solids," McGraw-Hill, 1950, pp. 349, 359.)

To represent the stress-strain relations for **combined stress tests** in ductile metals, where stresses are present on each of the faces of a cubical element of the material, effective stress, S, and effective strain, ϵ, values can be used. For combined stress tests

$$S = \frac{\sqrt{2}}{2}\sqrt{(S_1 - S_2)^2 + (S_2 - S_3)^2 + (S_3 - S_1)^2}$$

$$\epsilon = \frac{\sqrt{2}}{3}\sqrt{(\epsilon_1 - \epsilon_2)^2 + (\epsilon_2 - \epsilon_3)^2 + (\epsilon_3 - \epsilon_1)^2}$$

Table 2. Elastic Constants of Metals

(Mostly from tests of R. W. Vose)

Metal	*E* Modulus of elasticity (Young's modulus), 1,000,000 psi	*G* Modulus of rigidity (shearing modulus), 1,000,000 psi	*K* Bulk modulus, 1,000,000 psi	μ Poisson's ratio
Cast steel	28.5	11.3	20.2	0.265
Cold-rolled steel	29.5	11.5	23.1	0.287
Stainless steel 18–8	27.6	10.6	23.6	0.305
All other steels, including high-carbon, heat-treated	28.6–30.0	11.0–11.9	22.6–24.0	0.283–0.292
Cast iron	13.5–21.0	5.2–8.2	8.4–15.5	0.211–0.299
Malleable iron	23.6	9.3	17.2	0.271
Copper	15.6	5.8	17.9	0.355
Brass, 70–30	15.9	6.0	15.7	0.331
Cast brass	14.5	5.3	16.8	0.357
Tobin bronze	13.8	5.1	16.3	0.359
Phosphor bronze	15.9	5.9	17.8	0.350
Aluminum alloys, various	9.9–10.3	3.7–3.9	9.9–10.2	0.330–0.334
Monel metal	25.0	9.5	22.5	0.315
Inconel	31	11		
Z-nickel	30	11		
Beryllium copper	17	7		
Elektron (magnesium alloy)	6.3	2.5	4.8	0.281
Titanium (99.0 Ti), annealed bar	15–16			
Zirconium, crystal bar	11–14			
Molybdenum, arc-cast	48–52			

For the bulk modulus and Poisson's ratio, see pp. 5–21, 5–24.

Table 3. Mechanical Properties of Stone and Brick*

	Specific gravity	Compressive strength, psi	Modulus of elasticity, psi	Absorption of water, parts by weight	Coefficient of expansion per deg F	Modulus of rupture, psi
Granite	2.67	19,400	7,300,000	1/150	0.0000040	1,850
Limestone	2.53	9,500	8,460,000	1/38	0.0000045	1,400
Limestone, oolithic	2.48	6,700	7,000,000	1/23	0.0000045	
Marble	2.72	12,700	8,000,000	1/300	0.0000045	1,400
Sandstone	2.22	9,300	3,000,000	1/24	0.0000055	1,400
Trap	2.96	20,000	12,000,000			
Slate	2.77	14,000	14,000,000	1/430	0.0000058	7,700
Brick						
Common	2.00	4,000	2,000,000	1/8		
Hard-burned	2.10	8,000	4,000,000	1/6		
Paving	2.42	10,000	7,000,000	1/100		
Sand-lime	1.85	3,500	1,000,000	1/10		
Brick masonry						
In lime mortar		0.14 × compressive strength of brick				
In cement mortar		0.23 × compressive strength of brick				

* Other strength functions: shearing strength of brick and stone is from 10 to 20 percent of the compressive strength; tensile strength is 4 percent of compressive strength; modulus of rupture is 15 percent of compressive strength. Poisson's ratio is 1/4.

where S_1, S_2, and S_3 are the true principal stresses and ϵ_1, ϵ_2, and ϵ_3 are the true principal strains. The true principal stresses and strains are defined as in the case of pure tension discussed above. A curve is then constructed by plotting S as a function of ϵ, and this will generally agree well with the true stress-strain curve obtained from a tension test on the material for true strain values as large as 0.20.

Table 4. Mechanical Properties from True Stress-Strain Curve in the Tension Test

Mechanical Property	Definition
True stress at max load	$S_u = P_u/A_u$
True fracture stress	$S_b = P_b/A_b$
Min modulus of strain hardening	$\delta S/\delta \epsilon$ after P_{max}
True uniform strain	$\epsilon_u = \ln (A_o/A_u)$
True fracture strain	$\epsilon_b = \ln (A_o/A_b)$
True local necking strain	$\epsilon_n = \ln (A_u/A_b)$
Strain energy per unit volume	$T_s = \int^{\epsilon_b} S\, d\epsilon$

Table 5. Typical True Stress-Strain Properties

Material	True stress at max load, psi	True fracture stress, psi	Min modulus of strain hardening, psi	True uniform strain	True local necking strain	True fracture strain
SAE—1112 steel (annealed)	83,800	117,800	56,800	0.243	0.628	0.871
SAE—1045 steel (annealed)	109,700	142,700	89,700	0.197	0.374	0.571
Chrome iron	114,900	192,800	74,500	0.094	1.056	1.150
Turbine bolt steel	147,200	263,000	104,600	0.0649	0.939	1.0049
Brass	78,000	101,900	70,150	0.388	0.350	0.738
Monel metal	131,400	189,000	74,400	0.384	0.847	1.231

Testing Rates. In routine testing, a constant rate of crosshead motion is often maintained. This does not provide a constant true strain rate in the specimen even if the slack in the grips and the deformation of the specimen heads are negligible. The relation between the true strain rate $\dot{\epsilon}$ and the ordinary strain rate $\dot{\epsilon}_o$ in the test specimen is $\dot{\epsilon} = \dot{\epsilon}_o/1 + \epsilon_o$ where ϵ_o is the ordinary strain $\Delta L_o/L_o$. The true strain rate decreases as the strain increases even through $\dot{\epsilon}_o$ or the rate of change of gage length is kept constant. To maintain a constant true strain rate $\dot{\epsilon}$ for a round specimen it is necessary to adjust the speed of the machine so that the diameter d changes with time t by the relation

$$d = d_o e^{-\dot{\epsilon}t/2}$$

Such adjustments can easily be made. (Cf. MacGregor and Fisher, Tension Tests at Constant True Strain Rates, *Jour. Applied Mechanics*, Dec., 1945.) For most materials and testing temperatures, an increased strain rate will result in an increase in the stress necessary to produce a given strain. If strain aging takes place, this may be reversed. The magnitude of the effect is larger at elevated temperatures. At room temperature, variations in strain rate as much as 10 to 1 produce quite small changes in stress for ductile metals such as copper, aluminum, or steel. Tin, lead, and other low-melting metals are much more sensitive to small variations in strain rates even at room temperature. Very large effects may be produced in all metals at room temperature by high-speed impact.

The **type of fracture in tension** gives some indication of the quality of the material, but this is considerably affected by the testing temperature, speed of testing, the shape and size of the test piece, and other conditions. Contraction is greatest in tough and ductile materials and least in brittle materials. In general, fractures are either of the **shear** or of the **separation** (loss of cohesion) types. Flat tensile specimens of ductile metals often show shear failures if the ratio of width to thickness is greater than 6:1. Separation failures occur in brittle materials, such as certain cast irons. Combinations of both shear and separation failures are common on round specimens of ductile metal. Failure often starts at the axis in a necked region and produces a relatively flat area which grows until the material shears along a cone-shaped surface at the outside of the specimen, resulting in what is known as the cup-and-cone fracture. Double cup-and-cone and rosette fractures sometimes occur. Several types of tensile fractures are shown in Fig. 5.

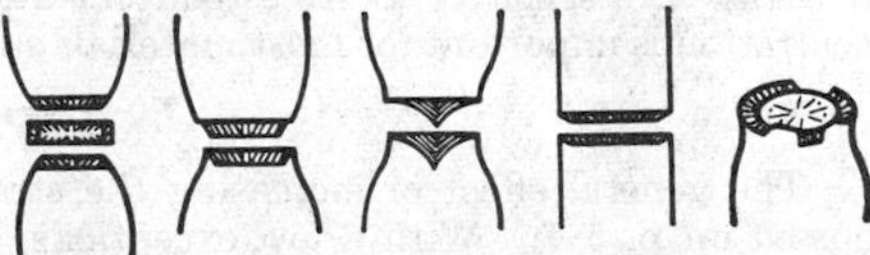

Fig. 5. Typical metal fractures in tension.

Fracture under compression does not appear in ductile metals since the material merely flows laterally as the height is decreased. The fracture (Fig. 6) of brittle materials depends upon the ratio of height to lateral dimension, the friction between the compression platens and the specimen, and the shape of the specimen. Fracture is usually of the shear type with sliding along inclined planes starting at the surface on which the pressure is applied.

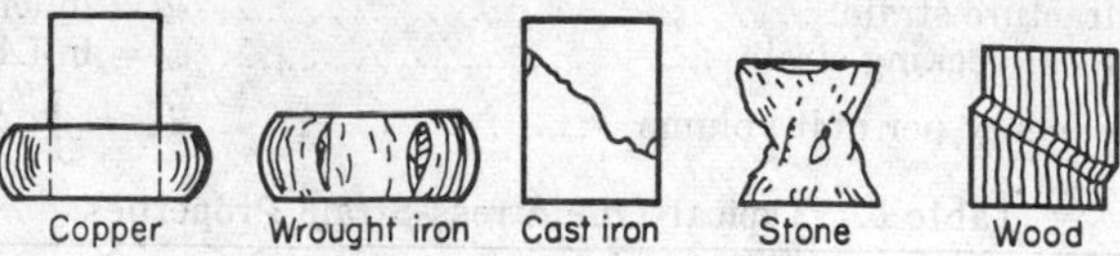

Fig. 6. Typical compression fractures.

Plasticity is the property of a material which permits it to undergo a permanent change in shape without fracture. An ideally plastic material undergoes no strain hardening (measured by the increase in stress necessary to produce further plastic deformation). Almost all metallic materials show some strain hardening. Plastic yielding is governed by a difference of the principal stresses. The two most widely accepted conditions which the principal stresses must satisfy for initial yielding of a ductile metal are the **maximum shearing stress criterion** and the **distortion energy criterion.** If the principal stresses are $S_1 > S_2 > S_3$, plastic flow will occur by the former if

$$S_1 - S_3 = \pm S_0$$

and according to the latter if

$$(S_1 - S_2)^2 + (S_2 - S_3)^2 + (S_3 - S_1)^2 = 2S_0^2$$

where S_o is the yield stress in simple tension.

Stress Concentration

In a structure or machine part having a notch or any abrupt change in cross section, the maximum stress will occur at this position and will be greater than the stress calculated by elementary formulas based upon simplified assumptions as to the stress distribution. The ratio of this maximum stress to the nominal stress (calculated by the elementary formulas) is the stress concentration factor K. This is a constant for the particular shape and is independent of the material, provided it is isotropic. The stress concentration factor may be determined theoretically in many cases from the mathematical theory of elasticity. It may also be determined experimentally by the use of **photoelasticity,** in which transparent models are examined under polarized light; by fracture tests on models of brittle material; or by measuring the local strains on the actual metal part with strain gages of small gage lengths. The factors shown in Figs. 7 to 14 were determined from both photoelastic tests and the theory of elasticity. Stress concentration is not important for ductile metals under static loading since any plastic flow will eliminate it, in whole or in part, through a redistribution of stress. Brittle materials are sensitive to stress concentration even under static loading. Stress concentration is important for most materials subjected to fluctuating or oscillating stresses.

IMPACT

The general effect of increasing the strain rate on mechanical properties was discussed on p. 5–7. With a few exceptions, most of the investigations on impact have been carried out on notched-bar specimens in bending. No stress-strain information which is directly useful in design is provided by such tests, but the energy needed to fracture a standard specimen is a sensitive indicator of the metallurgical condition of the material. The **Charpy** and the **Izod** (Fig. 28) tests are widely used for this purpose. In each, the specimen is struck by a swinging pendulum and the energy absorbed in the fracture is measured. A striking velocity of 17.5 fps is employed in the Charpy test and 11.5 fps for the Izod test.

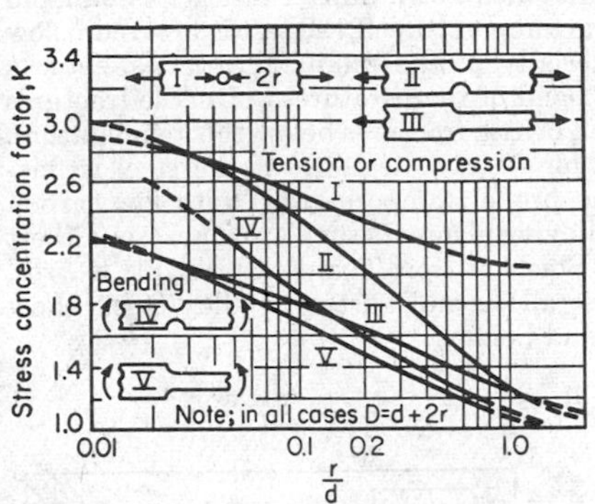

FIG. 7. Flat plate with semicircular fillets and grooves or with holes, in tension or compression.

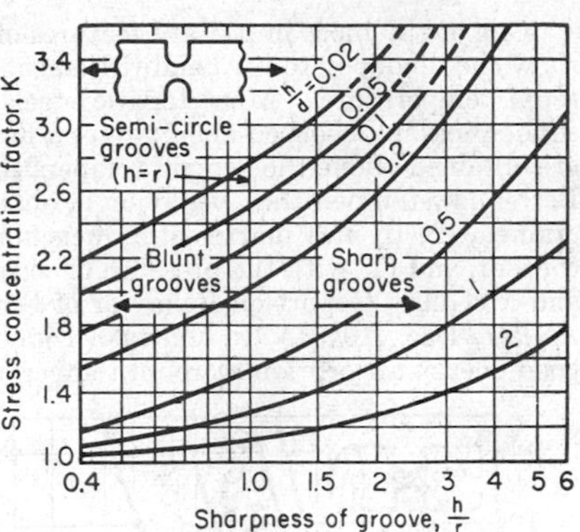

FIG. 8. Flat plate with grooves, in tension.

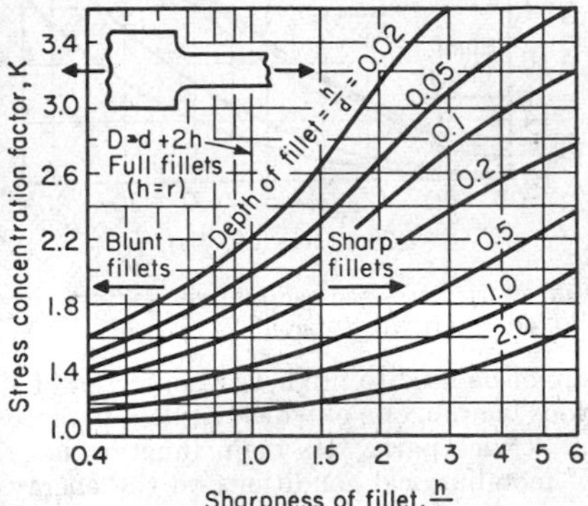

FIG. 9. Flat plate with fillets, in tension.

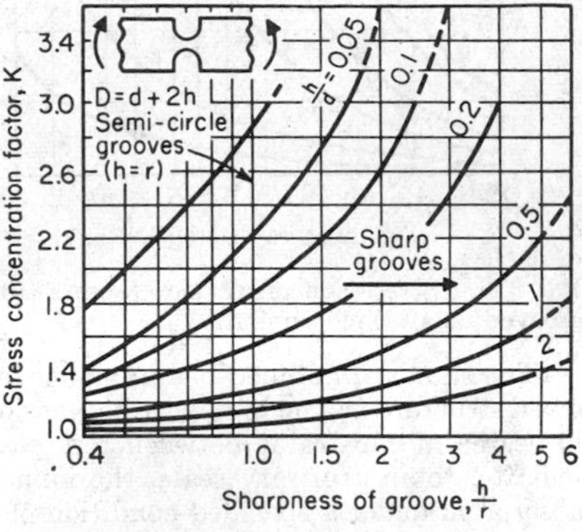

FIG. 10. Flat plate with grooves, in bending.

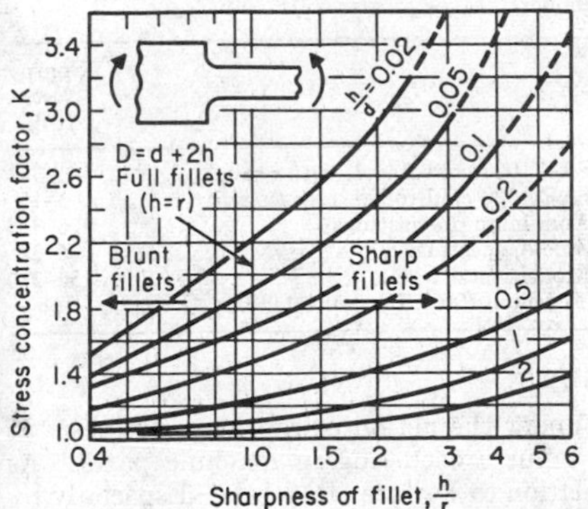

FIG. 11. Flat plate with fillets, in bending.

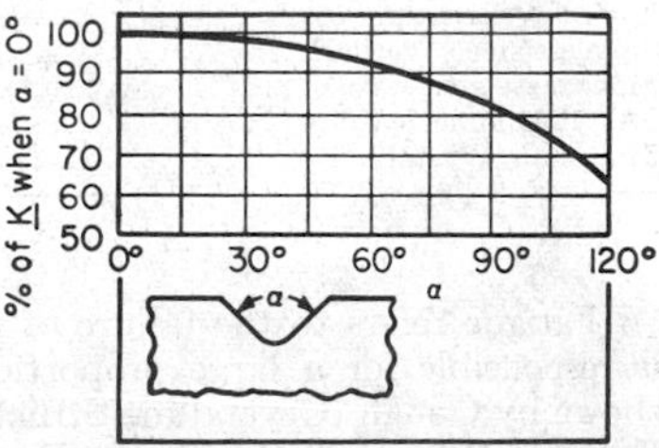

FIG. 12. Flat plate with angular notch, in tension or bending.

FIGS. 7 to 12. Stress-concentration factors for flat plates of width D reduced to width d by grooves or fillets of depth h or holes of radius r.

One of the most important features of the notched-beam impact test is its ability to show the tendency toward embrittlement as the temperature of the test is lowered below room temperature. Most ferritic steels, especially of the unkilled varieties, show a sudden loss in absorbed energy over a narrow band of temperatures. Ductile fractures are obtained above the dropoff temperature and brittle fractures below this temperature. Better low-temperature behavior is obtained for ferritic steels (1) if the steel is fine-grained, (2) by full martensitic quenching and proper tempering, (3) with low carbon content, and (4) with the presence of certain alloying elements such as nickel (see Gillett and McGuire, Report on Behavior of Ferritic Steels at Low Temperatures, Pt. I, *Proc. ASTM*, Dec., 1945). In contrast, copper-base alloys and austenitic alloy steels show good energy absorption at room temperature and below.

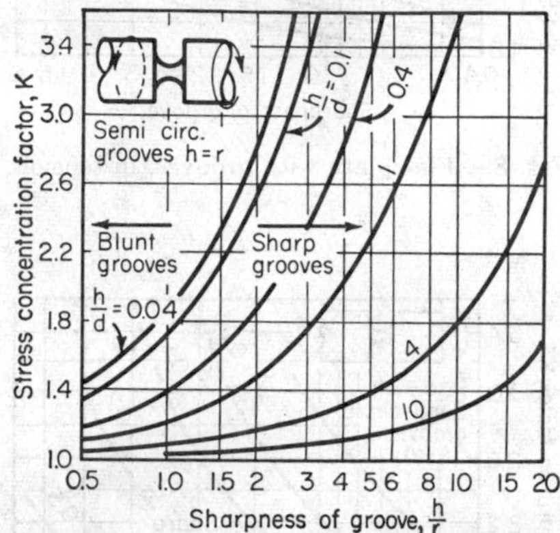

Fig. 13. Stress-concentration factors for grooved shafts in torsion.

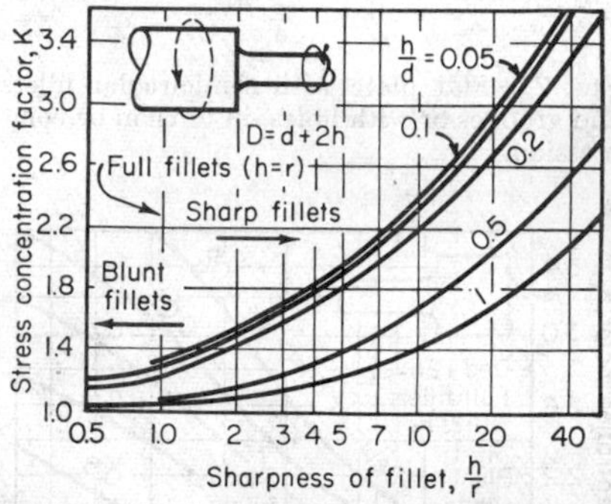

Fig. 14. Stress-concentration factors for filleted shaft in torsion.

The standard notched-beam impact tests cannot be used to predict the behavior of a given structure or machine part because of various factors, one of which is the difference in degree of constraint between test piece and service part. Its main function is to indicate, to an arbitrary scale, the influence of metallurgical conditions on the energy absorption under a specified condition of constraint.

Table 6. Impact Strengths

(Random values)

	Charpy test, ft-lb		Charpy test, ft-lb
Commercially pure iron	20	SAE 1020 cold-rolled, with grain	3–35
Low-alloy structural steel	25–50	SAE 1020 cold-rolled, cross grain	3–15
Stainless steels, various	35–65	Aluminum die castings	0.6–3.5
Manganese steel	10–35	Zinc die castings	6–20
SAE 1020 annealed	3–20	Monel metal	150–230
Zirconium, crystal bar	3–75	Titanium (99.0 Ti), annealed bar	18

FATIGUE

Fatigue refers to the failure of materials under the action of repeated stresses. It is responsible for a large proportion of the failures occurring in machine parts. As shown by Gough (Crystalline Structure in Relation to Failure of Metals—Especially by Fatigue, *Proc. ASTM*, **33,** Pt. II, 1933), fatigue failure is the result of slip occurring along certain crystallographic directions accompanied by local crystal fragmentation rupturing the atomic bonds, and thus leading to the formation of submicroscopic cracks which soon become visible cracks.

In **fatigue testing,** a specimen is subjected to periodically varying stresses by means of mechanical or magnetic devices. The applied stresses may alternate between equal positive and negative values, from zero to maximum positive or negative values, or between unequal positive and negative values. The most common loading is alternate tension and compression of equal numerical values obtained by rotating a smooth cylindrical specimen while under a bending load. A series of fatigue tests are made on a number of specimens of the material at different stress levels. The stress endured is then plotted against the number of cycles sustained. By choosing lower and lower stresses, a value may be found which will not produce failure, regardless of the number of applied cycles. This stress value is called the **fatigue limit.** The diagram is called the stress-cycle diagram or ***S-N* diagram.** Instead of recording the data on cartesian coordinates, stress is plotted either *vs.* the logarithm of the number of cycles (Fig. 15) or both stress and cycles are plotted to logarithmic scales. Both diagrams show a relatively sharp bend in the curve near the fatigue limit for ferrous metals. The fatigue limit may be established for most steels between 2 and 10 million cycles. Non-ferrous metals usually show no clearly defined fatigue limit. The *S-N* curves in these cases indicate a continuous decrease in stress values to several hundred million cycles, and both the stress value and the number of cycles sustained should be reported.

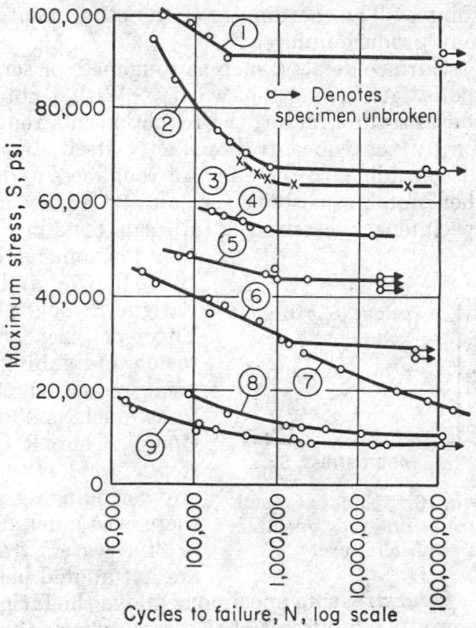

FIG. 15. *S-N* diagrams from fatigue tests: (1) 1.20 C steel, quenched, drawn 860 F; (2) SAE 3420, quenched, drawn 1200 F; (3) alloy structural steel; (4) SAE 1050, quenched, drawn 1200 F; (5) SAE 4130, normalized, annealed; (6) ordinary structural steel; (7) Duralumin; (8) copper, annealed; (9) cast iron. (Reversed bending.)

The mean stress (the average of the maximum and minimum stress values for a cycle) has a pronounced influence on the stress range (the algebraic difference between the maximum and minimum stress values). Several empirical formulas and graphical methods such as the "Modified Goodman Diagram" have been developed to show the influence of the mean stress on the stress range for failure (see Moore and Kommers, "The Fatigue of Metals," McGraw-Hill; "Prevention of the Failure of Metals under Repeated Stress," Wiley). Much further work is needed on this phase of the fatigue problem. A simple but conservative procedure (see Soderberg, Working

Table 7. Typical Approximate Fatigue Limits for Reversed Bending

Metal	Tensile strength, kpsi	Fatigue limit, kpsi	Metal	Tensile strength, kpsi	Fatigue limit, kpsi
Cast iron	20–50	6–18	Copper	32–50	12–17
Malleable iron	50	24	Monel	70–120	20–50
Cast steel	60–80	24–32	Phosphor bronze	55	12
Armco iron	44	24	Tobin bronze, hard	65	21
Plain carbon steels	60–150	25–75	Cast aluminum alloys	18–40	6–11
SAE 6150 heat-treated	200	80	Wrought aluminum alloys	25–70	8–18
Nitraloy	125	80	Magnesium alloys	20–45	7–17
Brasses, various	25–75	7–20	Molybdenum, are cast	98	80
Zirconium crystal bar	52	16–18	Titanium (Ti-75A)	91	45

Stresses, *Jour. Applied Mechanics*, **2**, Sept., 1935) is to plot the variable stress S_v (one-half the stress range) as ordinate *vs.* the mean stress S_m as abscissa (Fig. 16). At zero mean stress, the ordinate is the fatigue limit under completely reversed stress. Yielding will occur if the mean stress exceeds the yield stress S_0, and this establishes the extreme right-hand point of the diagram. A straight line is drawn between these two points. The coordinates of any other point along this line are values of S_m and S_v which may produce failure.

Surface defects, such as roughness or scratches, and notches or shoulders, all reduce the fatigue strength of a part. With a notch of prescribed geometric form and known concentration factor, the reduction in strength is appreciably less than would be called for by the concentration factor itself, but the various metals differ widely in their susceptibility to the effect of roughness and concentrations, or **notch sensitivity**. Further, notch sensitivity seems to be higher, and ordinary fatigue strength lower in large specimens, necessitating full-scale tests in many cases (see Peterson, Stress Concentration Phenomena in Fatigue of Metals, *Trans. ASME*, **55**, 1933, p. 157, and Buckwalter and Horger, Investigation of Fatigue Strength of Axles, Press Fits, Surface Rolling and Effect of Size, *Trans. ASM*, **25**, Mar. 1937, p. 229). **Corrosion** and **galling** (due to rubbing of mating surfaces) cause great reduction of fatigue strengths, sometimes amounting to as much as 90 percent of the original endurance limit (see Gough, Contact Corrosion under Pressure, *Nat. Phys. Lab. Rept., Dept. Ind. Sci. Research,* 1935, p. 150). Although any corroding agent is productive of severe corrosion fatigue, there is so much difference between the effects of "sea water" or "tap water" from different localities that numerical values are not quoted here.

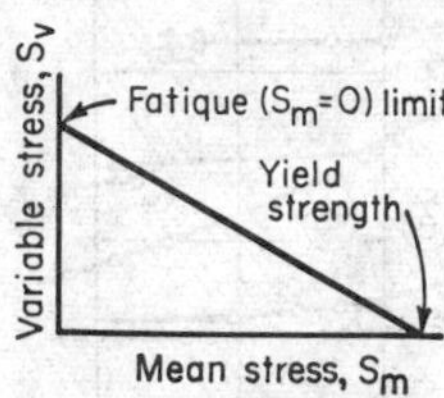

Fig. 16. Effect of mean stress on the variable stress for failure.

Overstressing specimens above the fatigue limit for periods shorter than necessary to produce failure at that stress reduces the fatigue limit in a subsequent test. Similarly, **understressing** below the fatigue limit may increase it. Shot peening, nitriding, and cold work usually improve fatigue properties.

No very good over-all correlation exists between fatigue properties and any other mechanical property of a material. The best correlation is between the fatigue limit under completely reversed bending stress and the ordinary tensile strength. For many ferrous metals, the fatigue limit is approximately 0.40 to 0.60 times the tensile strength if the latter is below 200,000 psi. Low-alloy high-yield-strength steels often show higher values than this. The fatigue limit for non-ferrous metals is approximately 0.20 to 0.50 times the tensile strength. The fatigue limit in reversed shear is approximately 0.57 times that in reversed bending.

Fatigue failure is particularly dangerous since the incipient cracks are often invisible and the final failure may occur with disastrous suddenness in high-speed machinery or vehicles. The progress of the crack in its early stages is extremely slow (deForest, The Rate of Growth of Fatigue Cracks, *Trans. ASME*, **58**, 1936, p. A23), and losses attendant on service failure may be largely avoided with periodic inspection by special means, and rejection or repair of parts in which cracks have started. One of the best means for this inspection is the **magnaflux method,** in which the part (necessarily ferrous magnetic) is magnetized and covered with a fine magnetic powder. In the vicinity of a crack there is a disturbance of the magnetic flux, and the magnetic powder gathers there, effectively marking the crack. With non-magnetic materials other procedures are used, such as the **Zyglo method** in which the part is immersed in a special activated penetrating oil and viewed under black light. Periodic inspection of all vital parts by these methods is becoming standard practice in the transportation and high-speed-machinery fields.

Surface fatigue occurs under highly concentrated compressive loading between two rolling members, such as in ball bearings, cams, and gear teeth, and results in a flaking or spalling of the material on one or both surfaces. This is usually caused by high shearing stresses below the surface (see Buckingham, "Dynamic Loads on Gear Teeth," ASME; Almen, Lubricants and False Brinelling of Ball and Roller Bearings,

Mech. Eng., June, 1937; Stribeck, Kugellager für beliebige Balastrung, translated by Hess, *Trans. ASME*, **29,** 1907, p. 367).

CREEP

Experience has shown that, for the design of equipment subjected to sustained loading at elevated temperatures, little reliance can be placed on the usual short-time tensile properties of metals at those temperatures. Under the application of a constant load it has been found that materials, both metallic and non-metallic, show a gradual flow or **creep** even for stresses below the proportional limit at elevated temperatures (see Kanter and Spring, Long-time or Flow Tests on Carbon Steels at Various Temperatures with Particular Reference to Stresses below the Proportional Limit, *Proc. ASTM*, **28,** Pt. II, 1928, p. 80). Similar effects are present in low-melting metals such as lead at room temperature. The deformation which can be permitted in the satisfactory operation of most high-temperature equipment is limited.

In metals, creep is a plastic deformation caused by slip occurring along crystallographic directions in the individual crystals, together with some flow of the grain boundary material. After complete release of load, a small fraction of this plastic deformation is recovered with time. Most of the flow is non-recoverable for metals.

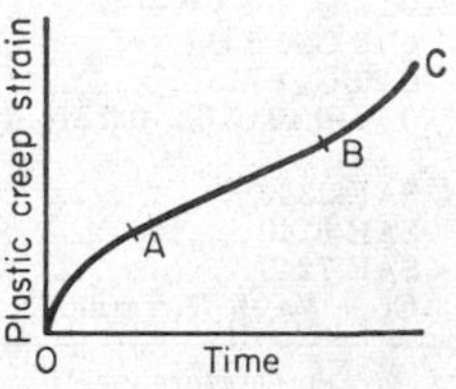

FIG. 17. Typical creep curve.

Since the early creep experiments (see Andrade, On the Viscous Flow in Metals and Allied Phenomena, *Proc. Roy. Soc.*, 1910) many different types of tests have come into use. The most common are the **long-time creep test** under constant tensile load and the **stress-rupture** test. Other special forms are the **stress-relaxation test** and the **constant-strain-rate test.**

The **long-time creep test** is conducted by applying a dead weight to one end of a lever system, the other end being attached to the specimen surrounded by a furnace and held at constant temperature. The axial deformation is read periodically throughout the test and a curve is plotted of the strain ϵ_0 as a function of time t (Fig. 17). This is repeated for various loads at the same testing temperature. The portion of the curve OA in Fig. 17 is the region of **primary creep,** AB the region of **secondary creep,** and BC that of **tertiary creep.** The strain rates, or the slopes of the curve, are decreasing, constant, and increasing, respectively, in these three regions. Since the period of the creep test is usually much shorter than the duration of the part in service, various extrapolation procedures are followed (see McVetty, Working Stresses for High Temperature Service, *Mech. Eng.*, **56,** No. 3, Mar., 1939, p. 149, and Creep of Metals at Elevated Temperatures; the Hyperbolic-sine Relation between Stress and Creep Rate, *Trans. ASME*, **65,** 1943, pp. 761–767).

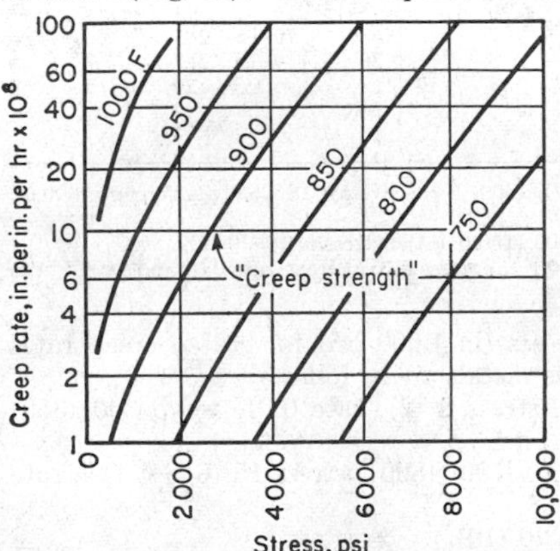

FIG. 18. Creep rates for 0.35 carbon steel.

In practical applications the region of constant-strain rate (secondary creep) is often used to estimate the probable deformation throughout the life of the part. It is thus assumed that this rate will remain constant during periods beyond the range of the test data. The working stress is chosen so that this total deformation will not be excessive. An arbitrary **creep strength,** which is defined as the stress which at a given temperature will result in 1 percent deformation in 100,000 hr, has received a certain amount of recognition, but it is advisable to determine the proper stress for each individual case from diagrams of stress versus creep rate (Fig. 18) (see "Creep Data," ASTM and ASME, 1938).

Table 8. Stresses for Given Creep Rates and Temperatures

(Compiled from ASME and ASTM "Creep Data")
Based on 1,000 hr tests. Stresses in 1,000 psi

Material	Creep rate 0.1 percent per 1,000 hr					Creep rate 0.01 percent per 1,000 hr				
Temperature, deg F	800	900	1000	1100	1200	800	900	1000	1100	1200
Wrought steels:										
SAE 1015	17–27	11–18	3–12	2–7	1	10–18	6–14	3–8	1	
0.20C, 0.50 Mo	26–33	18–25	9–16	2–6	1–2	16–24	11–22	4–12	2	1
0.10–.25 C, 4–6 Cr + Mo	22	15–18	9–11	3–6	2–3	14–17	11–15	4–7	2–3	1–2
SAE 4140	27–33	20–25	7–15	4–7	1–2	19–28	12–19	3–8	2–4	1
SAE 1030–1045	8–25	5–15	5	2	1	5–15	3–7	2–4	1	
Commercially pure iron	7	.....	4	...	3	5	.....	2		
0.15 C, 1–2.5 Cr, 0.50 Mo	25–35	18–28	8–20	6–8	3–4	20–30	12–18	3–12	2–5	1–2
SAE 4340	20–40	15–30	2–12	1–3	...	8–20	.....	1–6		
SAE X3140	7–10	.....	5–4	...	...	3–8	.....	1–2		
0.20 C, 4–6 Cr	30	10–20	7–10	1	...	.....	.....	3–5		
0.25 C, 4–6 Cr + W	30	10–15	4–10	2–8	...	.....	6–11	2–7		
0.16 C, 1.2 Cu	.....	18	10–15	3	1	.....	10–18	7–12		
0.20 C, 1 Mo	35	27	12	...	...	25	12	6		
0.10–0.40 C, 0.2–0.5 Mo, 1–2 Mn	30–40	12–20	4–14	...	...	25–28	8–15	2–8	...	0.5
SAE 2340	7–12	5	2							
SAE 6140	30	12	4	...	...	7	6	1		
SAE 7240	30	21	6–15	2	...	30	11	3–9	1	
Cr + Va + W, various	20–70	14–30	5–15	...	...	18–50	8–18	2–13		
Temperature, deg F	1100	1200	1300	1400	1500	1000	1100	1200	1300	1400
Wrought chrome-nickel steels:										
"18–8"[a]	10–18	5–11	3–10	2–5	2.5	11–16	5–12	2–10	...	1–2
10–25 Cr, 10–30 Ni[b]	10–20	5–15	3–10	2–5	...	.....	6–15	3–10	2–8	1–3
Temperature, deg F	800	900	1000	1100	1200	800	900	1000	1100	1200
Cast steels:										
0.20–0.40 C	10–20	5–10	3	...	...	8–15	.....	1		
0.10–0.30 C, 0.5–1 Mo	28	20–30	6–12	2	...	20	10–15	2–5		
0.15–0.30 C, 4–6 Cr + Mo	25–30	15–25	8–15	8	...	20–25	9–15	2–7	2	
"18–8"[c]	.....	.....	20–25	15	10	.....	.....	20	15	8
Cast iron	20	8	4	...	...	10	.....	2		
Cr Ni cast iron	.....	.....	9	...	...	.....	.....	3		

[a] Additional data. At creep rate 0.1 percent and 1000 (1600) F the stress is 18–25 (1); at creep rate 0.01 percent at 1500 F, the stress is 0.5.

[b] Additional data. At creep rate 0.1 percent and 1000 (1600) F the stress is 10–30 (1).

[c] Additional data. At creep rate 0.1 percent and 1600 F the stress is 3; at creep rate 0.01 and 1500 F, the stress is 2–3.

Additional temperatures (deg F) and stresses (in 1,000 psi) for stated creep rates (percent per 1,000 hr) for **wrought non-ferrous** metals are as follows:

60–40 Brass. Rate 0.1, temp. 350 (400), stress 8 (2); rate 0.01, temp 300 (350) [400], stress 10 (3) [1].

Phosphor Bronze. Rate 0.1, temp 400 (550) [700] {800}, stress 15 (6) [4] {1}; rate 0.01, temp 400 (550) [700], stress 8 (4) [2].

Nickel. Rate 0.1, temp 800 (1000), stress 20 (10).

70 *Cu*, 30 *Ni*. Rate 0.1, temp 600 (750), stress 28 (13–18); rate 0.01, temp 600 (750), stress 14 (8–9).

Aluminum Alloy 17*S* (*Duralumin*). Rate 0.1, temp 300 (500) [600], stress 22 (5) [1.5].

Lead, pure (*commercial*) [0.03 percent Ca], at 110 F, for rate 0.1 percent the stress range, psi, is 150–180 (60–140) [200–220]; for rate of 0.01 percent, 50–90 (10–50) [110–150].

Structural changes may occur during a creep test thus altering the metallurgical condition of the metal. In some cases, premature rupture appears at a low fracture strain in a normally ductile metal indicating that the material has become embrittled.

This is a very insidious condition and difficult to predict. The **stress-rupture test** (see Thielemann and Parker, Fracture of Steels at Elevated Temperatures after Prolonged Loading, *Metals Technol.*, Apr., 1939) is well adapted to study this effect. It is conducted by applying a constant load to the specimen in the same manner as for the long-time creep test. The nominal stress is then plotted *vs.* the time for fracture at constant temperature on a log-log scale (Fig. 19).

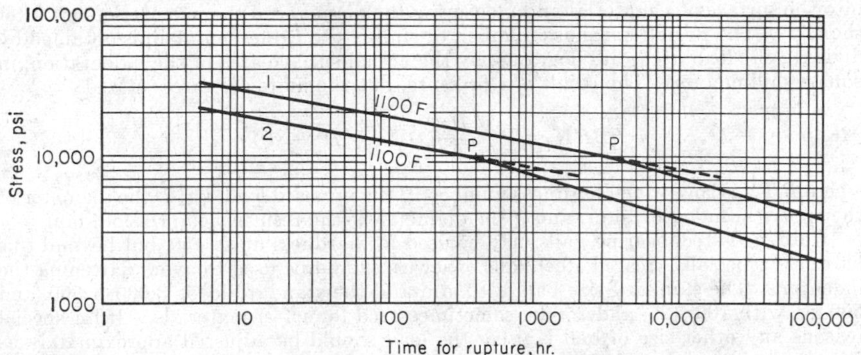

FIG. 19. Relation between time for failure and stress for a 3 percent chromium steel. (*Thielemann.*)

The stress reaction is measured in the **constant-strain-rate test** while the specimen is deformed at a constant strain rate. In the **relaxation test,** the decrease of stress with time is measured while the total strain (elastic + plastic) is maintained constant. The latter test has direct application to the loosening of turbine bolts and to similar problems. Although some correlation has been indicated between the results of these various types of tests, no general correlation is yet available and it has been found necessary to make tests under each of these special conditions to obtain satisfactory results.

The interrelationship between strain rate and temperature in the form of a velocity-modified temperature (see MacGregor and Fisher, A Velocity-modified Temperature for the Plastic Flow of Metals, *Jour. Applied Mechanics*, Mar., 1945) simplifies the creep problem in reducing the number of variables.

HARDNESS

Hardness has been variously defined as resistance to local penetration, to scratching, to machining, to wear or abrasion, and to yielding. The multiplicity of definitions, and corresponding multiplicity of hardness measuring instruments, together with the lack of a fundamental definition, indicates that hardness may not be a fundamental property of a material but rather a composite one including yield strength, work hardening, true tensile strength, modulus of elasticity, and others.

Scratch hardness is measured by **Mohs scale** of minerals (see p. 1–86) which is so arranged that each mineral will scratch the mineral of the next lower number. In recent mineralogical work and in certain microscopic metallurgical work, jeweled scratching points either with a set load or else loaded to give a set width of scratch have been used (see Talmadge, Quantitative Standards for Hardness of the Ore Minerals, *Econ. Geol.*, **20,** 1925, p. 531; and Bierbaum, The Microcharacter, *Trans. ASST*, **18,** 1930, p. 1009). Hardness in its relation to machinability and to wear and abrasion is generally dealt with in direct machining or wear tests, and little attempt is made to separate hardness itself, as a numerically expressed quantity, from the results of such tests.

The resistance to localized penetration, or **indentation hardness,** is widely used industrially as a measure of hardness, and indirectly as an indicator of other desired properties in a manufactured product. The indentation tests described below are essentially non-destructive, and in most applications may be considered non-marring, so that they may be applied to each piece produced, and through the empirical relationships of hardness to such properties as tensile strength, fatigue strength, and impact strength, pieces likely to be deficient in these latter properties may be detected and rejected.

Brinell hardness is determined by forcing a hardened sphere under a known load into the surface of a material and measuring the diameter of the indentation left after the test. The **Brinell hardness number,** or simply the **Brinell number,** is obtained by dividing the load used, in kilograms, by the actual surface area of the indentation, in square millimeters. The result is a pressure, but the units are rarely stated.

$$BHN = P \Bigg/ \frac{\pi D}{2} (D - \sqrt{D^2 - d^2})$$

where BHN is the Brinell hardness number; P the imposed load, kg; D the diameter of the spherical indentor, mm; and d the diameter of the resulting impression, mm.

Hardened-steel bearing balls may be used for hardness up to 450, but beyond this hardness especially treated steel balls or jewels should be used to avoid flattening the indentor. The standard size ball is 10 mm and the standard loads 3,000, 1,500, and 500 kg, with 100, 125, and 250 kg sometimes used for softer materials. If for special reasons any other size of ball is used, the load should be adjusted approximately as follows: for iron and steel, $P = 30D^2$; for brass, bronze, and other soft metals, $P = 5D^2$; for extremely soft metals, $P = D^2$ (see "Methods of Brinell Hardness Testing," ASTM E10–61T). Readings obtained with other than the standard ball and loadings should have the load and ball size appended, as such readings are only approximately equal to those obtained under standard conditions.

The size of the specimen should be sufficient to ensure that no part of the plastic flow around the impression reaches a free surface, and in no case should the thickness be less than 10 times the depth of the impression. The load should be applied steadily and should remain on for at least 15 sec in the case of ferrous materials and 30 sec in the case of most non-ferrous materials. Longer periods may be necessary on certain soft materials that exhibit creep at room temperature. In testing thin materials, it is not permissible to pile up several thicknesses of material under the indentor, as the readings so obtained will invariably be lower than the true readings. With such materials, smaller indentors and loads, or different methods of hardness testing, are necessary.

In the standard Brinell test, the diameter of the impression is measured with a low-power hand microscope, but for production work there are available several testing machines which automatically measure the depth of the impression and from this give readings of hardness. Such machines should be frequently calibrated on test blocks of known hardness.

In the **Rockwell method** of hardness testing, the depth of penetration of an indentor under certain arbitrary conditions of test is determined. The indentor may be either a steel ball of some specified diameter or a spherical-tipped conical diamond of 120 deg angle and 0.2 mm tip radius, called a "Brale." A *minor load* of 10 kg is first applied which causes an initial penetration and holds the indentor in place. Under this condition, the dial is set to zero and the major load applied. The values of the latter are 60, 100, or 150 kg. Upon removal of the major load, the reading is taken while the minor load is still on. The hardness number may then be read directly from the scale which measures penetration, and this scale is so arranged that soft materials with deep penetrations give low hardness numbers.

A variety of combinations of indentor and major load are possible; the most commonly used are R_B using as indentor a $\frac{1}{16}$-in. ball and a major load of 100 kg and R_C using a Brale as indentor and a major load of 150 kg (see "Rockwell Hardness and Rockwell Superficial Hardness of Metallic Materials," ASTM E18–61).

As compared with the Brinell test, the Rockwell method makes a smaller indentation, may be used on thinner material, and is much more rapid since hardness numbers are read directly and need not be calculated. However, the Brinell test may be made without special apparatus and is somewhat more widely recognized for laboratory use. There is also a **Rockwell superficial hardness test** similar to the regular Rockwell, except that the indentation is much shallower.

The **Vickers** method of hardness testing is similar in principle to the Brinell in that it expresses the result in terms of the pressure under the indentor and uses the same units, kilograms per square millimeter. The indentor is a diamond in the form of a square pyramid with an apical angle of 136 deg, the loads are much lighter, varying between 1 and 120 kg, and the impression is measured by means of a medium-power compound microscope.

$$V = P/0.5393d^2$$

where V is the Vickers hardness number, sometimes called the **diamond-pyramid hardness** (*DPH*); P the imposed load, kg; and d the diagonal of indentation, mm. The Vickers method is more flexible and is considered to be more accurate than either the Brinell or the Rockwell, but the equipment is more expensive than either of the others and the Rockwell is somewhat faster in production work (ASTM E92–57).

Among the other hardness methods may be mentioned the **Scleroscope,** in which a diamond-tipped "hammer" is dropped on the surface and the rebound taken as an index of hardness. This type of apparatus is seriously affected by the resilience as well as the hardness of the material and has largely been superseded by other methods. In the **Monotron** method, a penetrator is forced into the material to a predetermined depth and the load required is taken as the indirect measure of the hardness. This is the reverse of the Rockwell method in principle, but the loads and indentations are smaller than those of the latter. In the **Herbert pendulum,** a 1 mm steel or jewel ball resting on the surface to be tested acts as the fulcrum for a 4 kg compound pendulum of 10 sec period. The swinging of the pendulum causes a rolling indentation in the material, and from the behavior of the pendulum several factors in hardness, such as **work hardenability,** may be determined which are not revealed by other methods. Although the Herbert results are of considerable significance, the instrument is suitable for laboratory use only (see Herbert, The Pendulum Hardness Tester, and Some Recent Developments in Hardness Testing, *Engineer*, **135,** 1923, pp. 390 and 686). In the **Herbert cloudburst** test, a shower of steel balls, dropped from a predetermined height, dulls the surface of a hardened part in proportion to its softness and thus reveals defective areas. A variety of **mutual indentation methods** (Cowdrey, Hardness by Mutual Indentation, *Proc. ASTM*, **30,** Pt. II, 1930, p. 559), in which crossed cylinders or prisms of the material to be tested are forced together, give results comparable with the Brinell test. These are particularly useful on wires and on materials at high temperatures.

The relation among the scales of the various hardness methods is not exact, since no two measure exactly the same sort of hardness, and a relationship determined on steels of different hardnesses will be found only approximately true with other materials. The **Vickers-Brinell relation** is nearly linear up to at least 400, with the Vickers approximately 5 percent higher than the Brinell (actual values run from +2 to +11 percent) and nearly independent of the material. Beyond 500, the values become more widely divergent owing to the flattening of the Brinell ball. The **Brinell-Rockwell relation** is fairly satisfactory and is shown in Fig. 20. Approximate relations for the **Shore Scleroscope** are also given on the same plot.

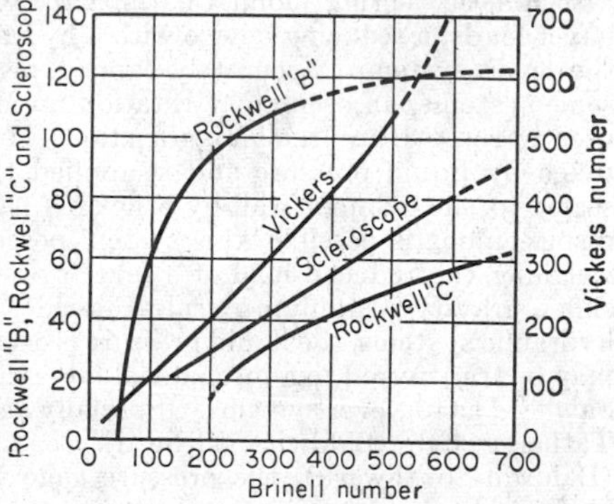

FIG. 20. Hardness scales.

The **hardness of wood** is defined by the ASTM as the load in pounds required to force a ball 0.444 in. diam into the wood to a depth of 0.222 in., the speed of penetration being ¼ in. per min. For a summary of the work in hardness see Williams, "Hardness and Hardness Measurements," ASM, 1942.

TESTING OF MATERIALS

Testing Machines. Machines for the mechanical testing of materials usually contain elements (1) for gripping the specimen, (2) for deforming it, and (3) for measuring the load required in performing the deformation. Some machines (ductility testers) omit the measurement of load and substitute a measurement of deformation, whereas other machines include the measurement of both load and deformation through apparatus either integral with the testing machine (stress-strain recorders) or auxiliary to it (strain gages). In most general-purpose testing machines, the deformation is controlled as the independent variable and the resulting load measured, and in many special-purpose machines, particularly those for light loads, the load is controlled and the resulting deformation is measured. Special features may include those for constant rate of loading (pacing disks), for constant rate of straining, for constant load maintenance, and for cyclical load variation (fatigue).

A nut-and-screw combination, driven through clutches and change gears, was formerly common for **producing deformation,** but this arrangement has been largely superseded by a pump and hydraulic cylinder. The hydraulic arrangement is quieter, more flexible in control, and more durable, but cannot maintain constant deformation

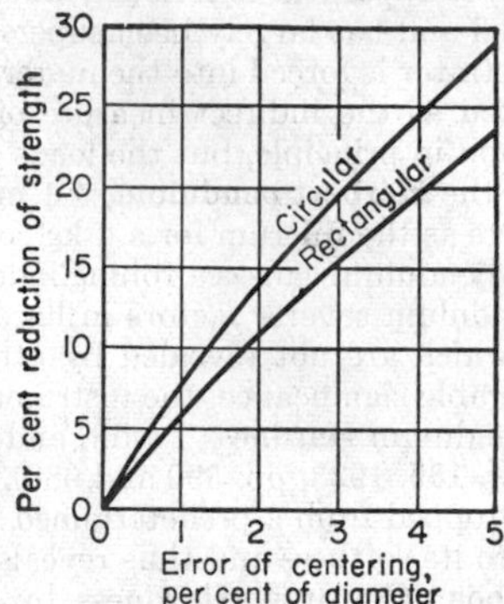

Fig. 21. Effect of centering errors on brittle test specimens.

for any length of time on account of leakage. **In weighing light loads,** direct weights are accurate, but unless lead shot or water is used small variations in load are inconvenient. Ordinary springs used for this purpose are not sufficiently accurate, but the "Iso-Elastic" spring (John Chatillon & Sons, New York) has negligible errors. For larger loads, a reducing device with a **hydraulic weighing system** has largely displaced the lever system. Accurately lapped pistons may be made nearly frictionless; in some systems, an oscillatory rotation imposed on either the piston or the cylinder is used to remove any remaining friction. In the Emery hydraulic support, the load is taken by liquid pressure and is applied through a piston of considerable clearance sealed to the cylinder wall by a flexible flat metal diaphragm; although only minute displacement is possible, this system possesses great accuracy and sensitivity. For weighing the reduced load of a lever system, there may be used dead weights (lead shot), gravity pendulums, scale-and-rider combinations, or Iso-Elastic springs. In hydraulic systems, the liquid pressure is occasionally balanced by hydrostatic head, but may be transferred to a mechanical force through small pistons or Emery supports and balanced as for lever systems. Specially accurate pressure gages may be used (Emery-Tatnall system, Baldwin-Southwark Corp., Philadelphia); in the Tate-Emery system (Baldwin-Southwark), the pressure gage element is used as a null indicator, being balanced by Iso-Elastic springs, and gives particularly accurate and sensitive readings. Many systems have included means of **recording automatically** the load and deformation of the test piece, but few have been satisfactory until recent years (Emery-Tatnall and Tate-Emery). (For further information, see Gibbons, "Materials Testing Machines," Instruments Publishing Co., also in *Instruments*, **7**, **8**, 1934–1935, and *Bull. ASTM*, Oct., 1939.)

Grips should not only hold the test specimen against slippage but should also apply the load in the desired manner. Centering of the load is of great importance in compression testing, and should not be neglected in tension testing if the material is brittle. Figure 21 shows the theoretical errors due to off-center loading; the results are directly applicable to compression tests using swivel loading blocks. Swivel (ball-and-socket) holders or compression blocks should be used with all except the most ductile materials, and, in compression testing of brittle materials (concrete, stone, brick), any rough faces should be smoothly capped with plaster of paris or, for greater strength, a mixture of two-thirds plaster of paris and one-third portland cement. Serrated grips may be used to hold ductile materials or the shanks of other holders in tension; a taper of 1 in 6 on the wedge faces gives a self-tightening action without excessive jamming. Ropes are ordinarily held by wet eye splices, but braided ropes or small cords may be given several turns over a fixed pin and then clamped. Wire ropes should be zincked into forged sockets (solder and lead have insufficient strength).

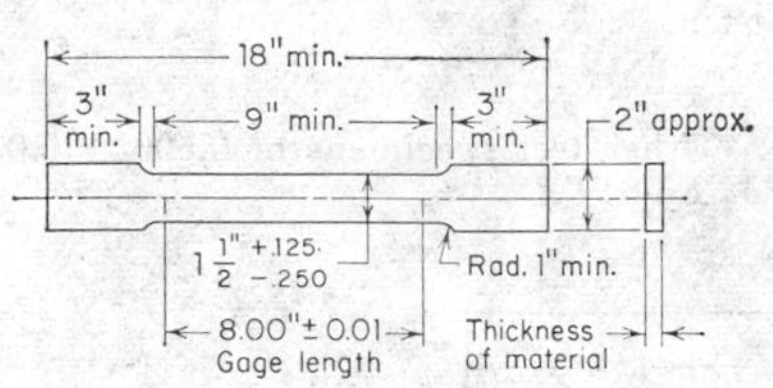

Fig. 22. Tension specimen for plate stock. (*ASTM E*8-61*T*.)

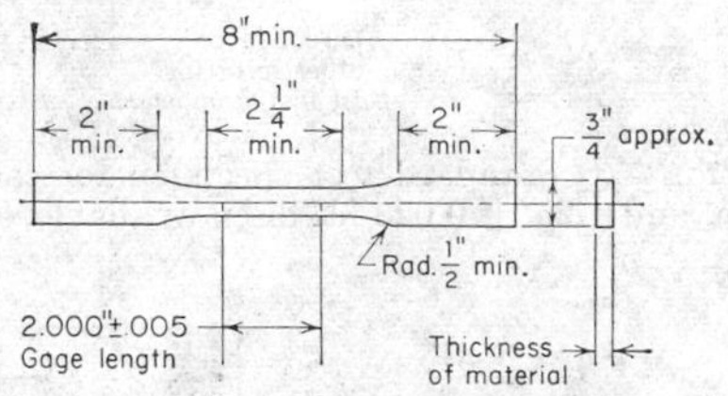

Fig. 23. Tension specimen for sheet metal. (*ASTM E*8-61*T*.)

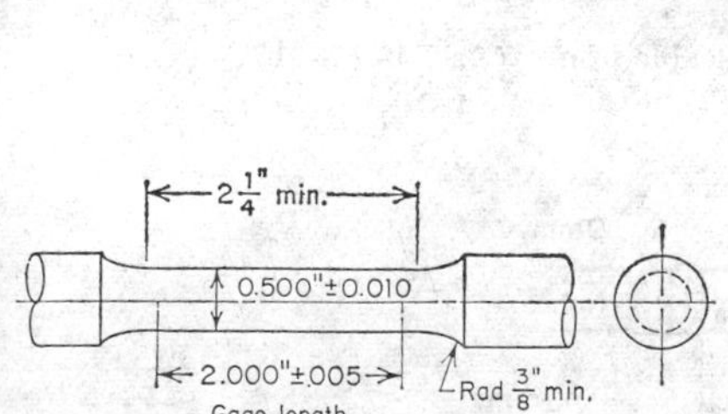

Fig. 24. Test specimens, 2-in. gage length, ½-in. diam. Others available for 0.350- and 0.250-in. diam. (*ASTM E*8-61*T*.)

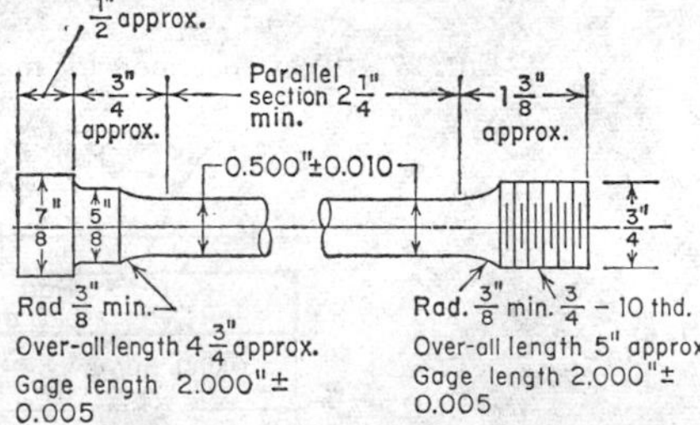

Fig. 25. Ends for standard round-tension-test specimen. Others also available. (*ASTM E*8-61*T*.)

Accuracy and Calibration. ASTM E4-61T requires that commercial machines shall have errors of less than 1 percent within the "loading range" when checked against acceptable standards of comparison at at least five suitably spaced loads. The "loading range" may be any range through which the preceding requirements for accuracy are satisfied, except that it shall not extend below 100 times the least load to which the machine will respond or which can be read on the indicator. The use of calibration plots or tables to correct the results of an otherwise inaccurate machine is not permitted under any circumstances. Machines with errors less than 0.1 percent are commercially available (Tate-Emery, and others), and somewhat greater accuracy is possible in the most refined research apparatus.

Dead loads may be used to check machines of low capacity; accurately calibrated proving levers may be used to extend the range of available weights. Various elastic devices (such as the Morehouse proving ring) made of specially treated steel, with sensitive distortion-measuring devices, and calibrated by dead weights at the Bureau of Standards are among the most satisfactory means of checking the higher loads.

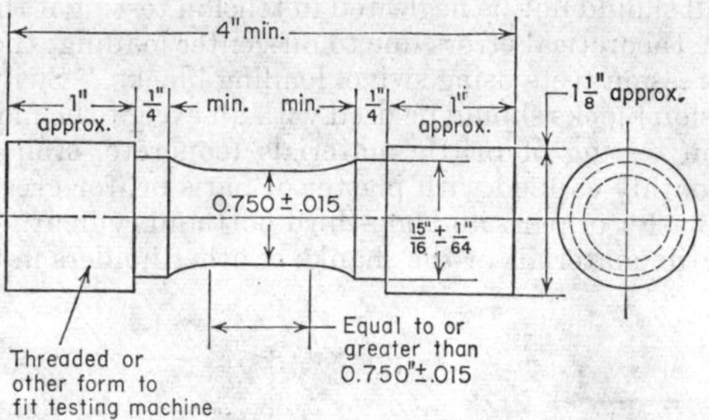

FIG. 26. Standard test specimen for cast iron. Other test specimens of 0.500 ± 0.010 in. and 1.25 ± 0.025 in. diam available. (*ASTM E*8-61*T*.)

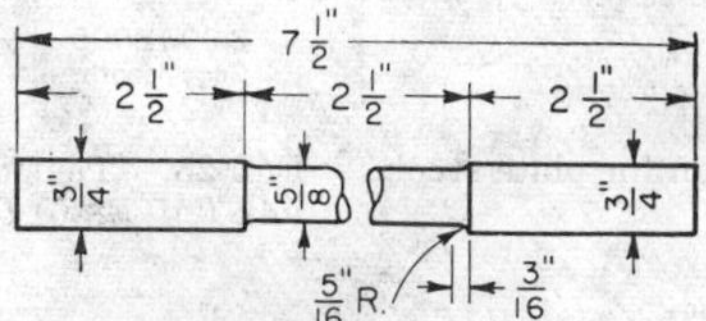

FIG. 27. Test specimen for malleable iron. (*ASTM E*8-61*T*.)

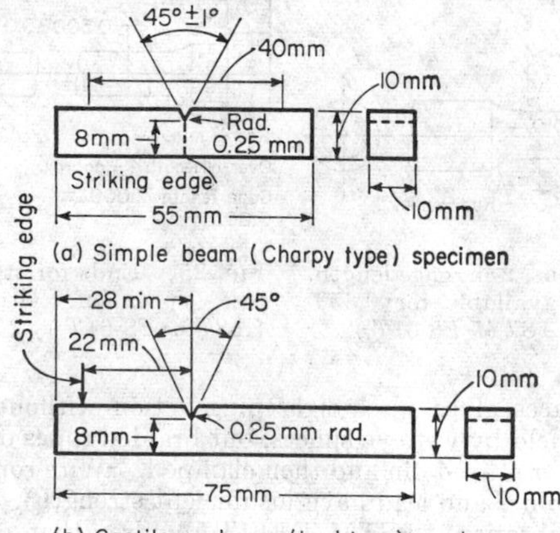

FIG. 28. Impact-test specimens. Others available. (*ASTM E*23-62.)

Standard **forms of test specimens** (ASTM) are shown in Figs. 22 to 28. In wrought materials, and particularly in those which have been cold-worked, different properties may be expected in different directions with respect to the direction of the applied work, and the test specimen should be cut from the parent material in such a way as to give the strength in the desired direction. With the exception of fatigue specimens and specimens of extremely brittle materials, surface finish is of little practical importance, although extreme roughness tends to decrease the ultimate elongation.

MECHANICS OF MATERIALS

BY

J. P. Vidosic

References: Timoshenko and MacCullough, "Elements of Strength of Materials," Van Nostrand. Seely, "Advanced Mechanics of Materials," Wiley. Timoshenko and Goodier, "Theory of Elasticity," McGraw-Hill. Phillips, "Introduction to Plasticity," Ronald. Van Den Broek, "Theory of Limit Design," Wiley. Hetényi, "Handbook of Experimental Stress Analysis," Wiley. Dean and Douglas, "Semi-Conductor and Conventional Strain Gages," Academic Press.

Main Symbols

Unit Stress	
Stress, apparent	S
Pure shearing	S_v or S_s
True (ideal) stress	T
Proportional elastic limit	S_p
Yield point	S_y
Ultimate strength, tension	S_M
Ultimate compression	S_c
Vertical shear in beams	S_v
Modulus of rupture	S_R
Moment	
Bending	M
Torsion	M_t
External Action	
Force	P
Weight of body	G
Weight of load	W
External shear	V
Modulus of Elasticity	
Longitudinal	E
Shearing	G

Bulk	K
Modulus of resilience	U_p
Ultimate resilience	U_R
Geometrical	
Length	l
Area	A
Volume	V
Velocity	v
Radius of gyration	r
Rectangular moment of inertia	I
Polar moment of inertia	I_P or J
Deformation	
Gross, longitudinal	e
Unit, longitudinal	s
Angular	d or α
Lateral	s'
Poisson's ratio	μ
Reciprocal of Poisson's ratio	n
Radius	r
Deflection	f

SIMPLE STRESSES AND STRAINS

Deformations are changes in form produced by external forces or loads that act on non-rigid bodies. Deformations are **longitudinal,** e, a lengthening (+) or shortening (−) of the body; and **angular,** d, a change of angle between the faces.

Unit deformation (dimensionless number) is the deformation in unit distance. Unit longitudinal deformation $s = e/l$ (Fig. 1). Unit angular deformation $\tan \alpha$ equals α approx (Fig. 2).

Accompanying a longitudinal deformation e is a **lateral** deformation e' (Fig. 1). The ratio of s'/s is **Poisson's ratio** μ. Values of μ are: glass, 0.244; brass, 0.333; copper, 0.333; cast iron, 0.270; wrought iron, 0.278; steel, 0.303; lead, 0.430; concrete, 0.10 to 0.20 at working stresses and 0.25 at higher stresses.

Stress is an internal distributed force; it is the internal mechanical reaction of the material accompanying deformation. Stresses always occur in pairs. Stresses are **normal** [tensile stress (+) and compressive stress (−)]; and **tangential,** or **shearing.**

Intensity of stress, or **unit stress,** S, psi, is the amount of force per unit of area of surface (Fig. 3). P is the load acting through the center of gravity of the area. The uniformly distributed normal stress is

$$S = P/A$$

When the stress is not uniformly distributed, $S = dP/dA$.

A **long rod** will stretch under its own weight G and a terminal load P (see Fig. 4). The total elongation e is that due to the terminal load plus that due to one-half the weight of the rod considered as acting at the end.

$$e = [Pl + (Gl/2)]/AE$$

The maximum stress is at the upper end.

When a **load is carried by several paths** to a support, the different paths take portions of the load in proportion to their stiffness, which is controlled by material (E) and by design.

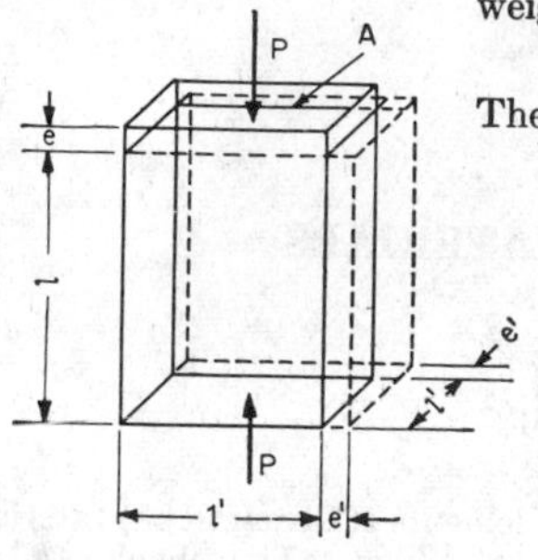

Fig. 1

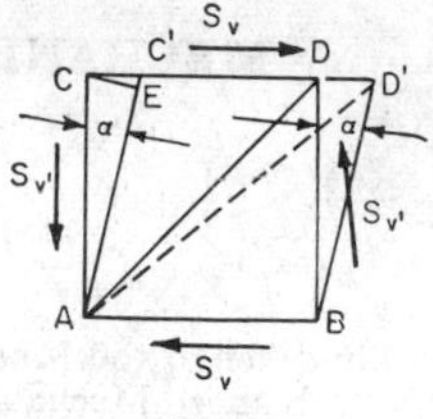

Fig. 2

Example. Two pairs of bars rigidly connected (with the same elongation) carry a load P_0 (Fig. 5). A_1, A_2 and E_1, E_2 and P_1, P_2 and S_1, S_2 are cross sections, moduli of elasticity, loads, and stresses of the bars, respectively; e = elongation.

$$e = P_1l/(E_1A_1) = P_2l/(E_2A_2) \quad P_0 = 2P_1 + 2P_2$$
$$S_2 = P_2/A_2 = \tfrac{1}{2}[P_0E_2/(E_1A_1 + E_2A_2)] \quad S_1 = \tfrac{1}{2}[P_0E_1/(E_1A_1 + E_2A_2)]$$

Temperature Stresses. When the deformation arising from change of temperature is prevented, temperature stresses arise that are proportional to the amount of deformation that is prevented. Let a = coefficient of expansion per degree of temperature, l_1 = length of bar at temperature t_1, and l_2 = length at temperature t_2. Then

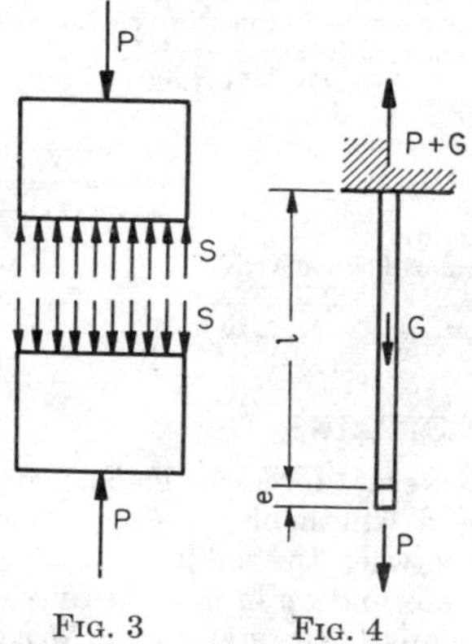

Fig. 3 Fig. 4

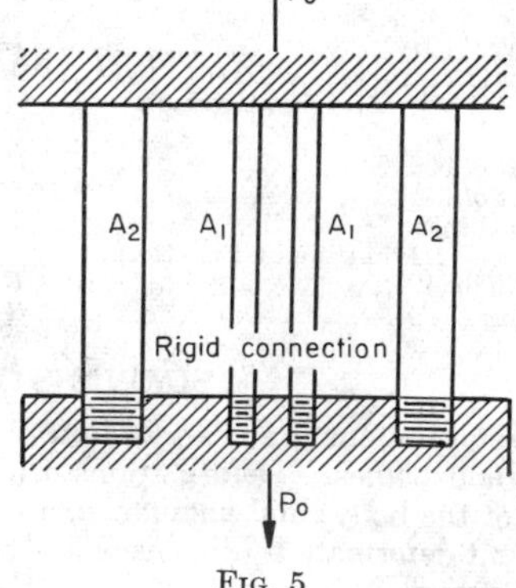

Fig. 5

$$l_2 = l_1[1 + a(t_2 - t_1)]$$

If, subsequently, the bar is cooled to a temperature t_1, the proportionate deformation is $s = a(t_2 - t_1)$ and the corresponding unit stress $S = Ea \times (t_2 - t_1)$. For **coefficients of expansion,** see p. 4–6. In the case of steel, a change of temperature of 12 F will cause in general a unit stress of 2,340 psi.

Shearing stresses (Fig. 2) act tangentially to the surface of contact and do not change length of sides of elementary volume; they **change the angle between faces** and the **length of diagonal.** Two pairs of shearing stresses must act together. **Shearing stress intensities are of equal magnitude on all four faces of an element.** $S_v = S_v'$ (Fig. 6).

In the presence of **pure shear** on external faces (Fig. 6), the **resultant stress** S on one diagonal plane at 45 deg is pure tension and on the other diagonal plane pure com-

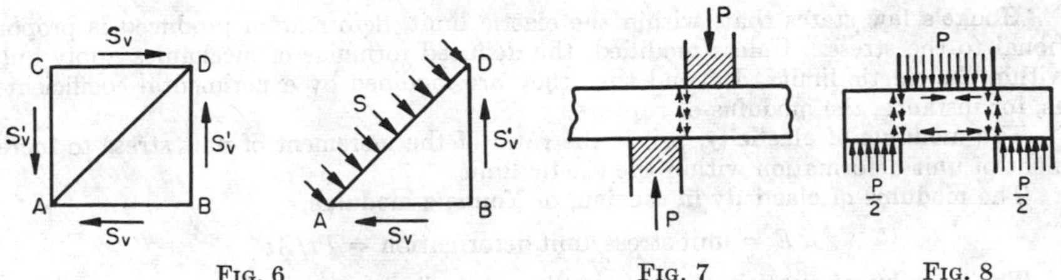

Fig. 6 Fig. 7 Fig. 8

pression; $S = S_v = S_v'$. S on diagonal plane is called "diagonal tension" by writers on reinforced concrete. Failure under pure shear is difficult to produce experimentally, except under torsion and certain special cases. Figure 7 shows an ideal case and Fig. 8 a common form of test piece that introduces bending stresses.

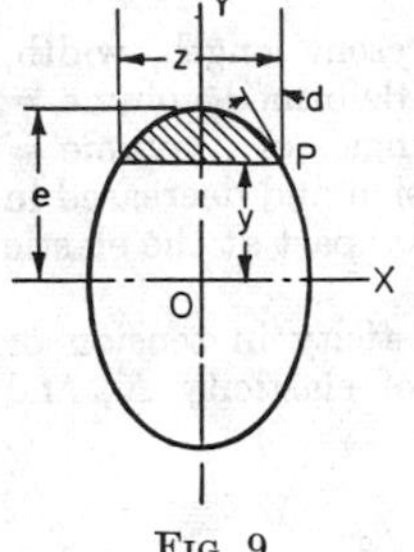

Fig. 9

Let Fig. 9 represent the section of area A on which a shearing force V acts. Then, if pure shear should exist, $S_v = V/A$. This would be uniformly distributed over the area A. When **shear is accompanied by bending (transverse shear in beams)**, the unit shear S_v increases from the extreme fiber to the neutral axis OX. The unit shear parallel to axis OX at any point y distant from the neutral axis as at P (Fig. 9) is

$$S_v = \left(V \int_y^e yz\,dy \right) \Big/ Iz$$

where I is the moment of inertia of the cross section about OX.

For a **rectangular cross section** (Fig. 10*a*),

$$S_v = \frac{3}{2}\frac{V}{bh}\left[1 - \left(\frac{2y}{h}\right)^2\right] \qquad S_v\,(\text{max}) = \frac{3}{2}\frac{V}{bh} = \frac{3}{2}\frac{V}{A}, \text{ for } y = 0$$

For a **circular cross section** (Fig. 10*b*),

$$S_v = \frac{4}{3}\frac{V}{\pi r^2}\left[1 - \left(\frac{y}{r}\right)^2\right] \qquad S_v\,(\text{max}) = \frac{4}{3}\frac{V}{\pi r^2} = \frac{4}{3}\frac{V}{A}, \text{ for } y = 0$$

For a **circular ring** (thickness small in comparison with the major diameter), S_v (max) $= 2V/A$, for $y = 0$.

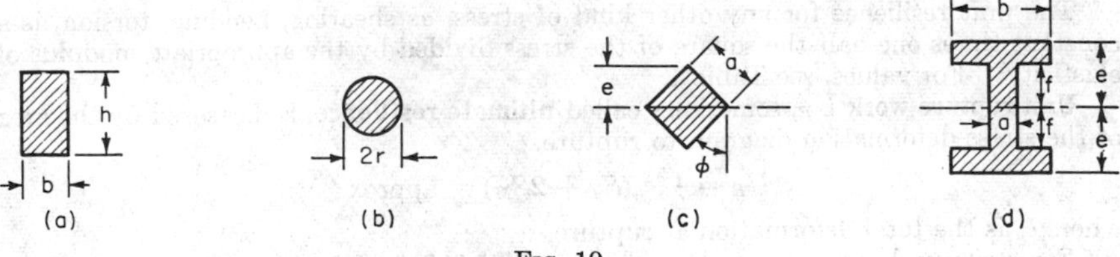

Fig. 10

For a **square cross section** (diagonal vertical, Fig. 10*c*),

$$S_v = \frac{V\sqrt{2}}{a^2}\left[1 + \frac{y\sqrt{2}}{a} - 4\left(\frac{y}{a}\right)^2\right] \qquad S_v\,(\text{max}) = 1.591\frac{V}{A}, \text{ for } y = \frac{e}{4}$$

For an **I-shaped cross section** (Fig. 10*d*),

$$S_v\,(\text{max}) = \frac{3}{4}\frac{V}{a}\left[\frac{be^2 - (b-a)f^2}{be^3 - (b-a)f^3}\right] \text{ for } y = 0$$

Elasticity is the ability of a material to return to its original dimensions after the removal of stresses. The **elastic limit** S_p is the limit of stress within which the deformation completely disappears after the removal of stress; *i.e.*, no set remains.

Hooke's law states that, within the elastic limit, deformation produced is proportional to the stress. Unless modified, the deduced formulas of mechanics apply only within the elastic limit. Beyond this, they are modified by experimental coefficients, as, for instance, the modulus of rupture.

The modulus of elasticity, psi, is the ratio of the increment of unit stress to increment of unit deformation within the elastic limit.

The **modulus of elasticity in tension,** or **Young's modulus,**

$$E = \text{unit stress/unit deformation} = Pl/Ae$$

The modulus of elasticity in compression is similarly measured.

The **modulus of elasticity in shear** or **coefficient of rigidity,** $G = S_v/\alpha$ where α is expressed in radians (see Fig. 2).

The **bulk modulus of elasticity** K is the ratio of normal stress, applied to all six faces of a cube, to the change of volume.

Change of volume under normal stress. Let l, d, and b represent length, width, and thickness; μ = Poisson's ratio; s = unit deformation. Then deformed volume = $(1 + s)l(1 - \mu s)b(1 - \mu s)d \approx (1 + s - 2\mu s)lbd$. Fractional change of volume $\approx$ $(1 - 2\mu)s$. When μ is less than ½, the volume is increased in tension and decreased in compression. For steel ($\mu \approx$ ⅓), change of volume is about 1/3,000 part at the elastic limit.

The following relationships exist between the modulus of elasticity in tension or compression E, modulus of elasticity in shear G, bulk modulus of elasticity K, and Poisson's ratio μ:

$$E = 2G(1 + \mu)$$
$$G = E/2(1 + \mu)$$
$$\mu = (E - 2G)/2G$$
$$K = E/3(1 - 2\mu)$$
$$\mu = (3K - E)/6K$$

Resilience U (in.-lb) is the potential energy stored up in a deformed body. The amount of resilience is equal to the work required to deform the body from zero stress to stress S, when S does not exceed the elastic limit. For normal stress, resilience = work of deformation = average force times deformation = $\frac{1}{2}Pe = \frac{1}{2}AS \times Sl/E = \frac{1}{2}S^2V/E$.

Modulus of resilience U_p (in.-lb per cu in.), or **unit resilience,** is the elastic energy stored up in a cubic inch of material at the elastic limit. For normal stress,

$$U_p = \tfrac{1}{2}S_p{}^2/E$$

The unit resilience for any other kind of stress, as shearing, bending, torsion, is a constant times one-half the square of the stress divided by the appropriate modulus of elasticity. For values, see Table 1.

Unit rupture work U_R, sometimes called **ultimate resilience,** is measured by the area of the stress-deformation diagram to rupture.

$$U_R = \tfrac{1}{3}e_u(S_y + 2S_M) \quad \text{approx}$$

where e_u is the total deformation at rupture.

For structural steel, $U_R = \frac{1}{3} \times \frac{27}{100} \times [35{,}000 + (2 \times 60{,}000)] = 13{,}950$ in.-lb per cu in.

Example 1. A load P = 40,000 lb compresses a wooden block of cross-sectional area A = 10 sq in. and length = 10 in., an amount $e = \frac{4}{100}$ in. Stress $S = \frac{1}{10} \times 40{,}000 =$ 4,000 psi. Unit elongation $s = \frac{4}{100} \div 10 = \frac{1}{250}$. Modulus of elasticity $E = 4{,}000 \div \frac{1}{250}$ = 1,000,000 psi. Unit resilience $U_p = \frac{1}{2} \times 4{,}000 \times 4{,}000/1{,}000{,}000 = 8$ in.-lb per cu in.

Example 2. A weight G = 5,000 lb falls through a height h = 2 ft; V = number of cubic inches required to absorb the shock without exceeding a stress of 4,000 psi. Neglect compression of block. Work done by falling weight = Gh = 5,000 × 2 × 12 in.-lb. Resilience of block = V × 8 in.-lb = 5,000 × 2 × 12. Therefore, V = 15,000 cu in.

Thermal Stresses. A bar will change its length when its temperature is raised (or lowered) by the amount $\Delta l_o = \alpha l_o(t_2 - 32)$. The linear coefficient of thermal expansion,

Table 1. Resilience per Unit of Volume, U_p

(S = longitudinal stress; S_v = shearing stress; E = tension modulus of elasticity; G = shearing modulus of elasticity)

		Torsion	
Tension or compression	$\frac{1}{2}S^2/E$	Solid, circular	$\frac{1}{4}S_v^2/G$
Shear	$\frac{1}{2}S_v^2/G$	Hollow, radii R_1 and R_2	$\frac{(R_1^2+R_2^2)}{R_1^2}\frac{1}{4}\frac{S_v^2}{G}$
Beams (free ends)		Springs	
Rectangular section, bent in arc of circle; no shear	$\frac{1}{6}S^2/E$	Carriage	$\frac{1}{6}S^2/E$
Ditto, circular section	$\frac{1}{8}S^2/E$	Flat spiral, rect. section	$\frac{1}{24}S^2/E$
		Helical: axial load, circular wire	$\frac{1}{4}S_v^2/G$
Concentrated center load; rectangular cross section	$\frac{1}{18}S^2/E$	Helical: axial twist	$\frac{1}{8}S^2/E$
Ditto, circular cross section	$\frac{1}{24}S^2/E$	Helical: axial twist, rect. section	$\frac{1}{6}S^2/E$
Uniform load, rectangular cross section	$\frac{5}{36}S^2/E$		
I-beam section, concentrated center load	$\frac{3}{32}S^2/E$		

α, is assumed constant at normal temperatures and l_o is the length at 32 F. If this expansion (or contraction) is prevented, a **thermal-time stress** is developed, equal to $S = E\alpha(t_2 - t_1)$, as the temperature goes from t_1 to t_2. In thin flat plates the stress becomes $S = E\alpha(t_2 - t_1)/(1 - \mu)$; μ is Poisson's ratio. Such stresses can occur in castings containing large and small sections. Similar stresses also occur when heat flows through members because of the difference in temperature between one point and another. The heat flowing across a length b as a result of a linear drop in temperature Δt equals $Q = k\,A\Delta t/b$ Btu per hr. The thermal conductivity, k, is in Btu per hr per sq ft per deg F per in. of thickness. The **thermal-flow stress** is then $S = E\alpha Qb/kA$. Note, when Q is substituted, the stress becomes $S = E\alpha\Delta t$ as above, only t is now a function of distance rather than time.

Example. A cast-iron plate 3 ft square and 2 in. thick is used as a fire wall. The temperature is 330 F on the hot side and 160 F on the other. What is the thermal-flow stress developed across the plate?

$$S = E\alpha\Delta t = 13 \times 10^6 \times 6.5 \times 10^{-6} \times 170 = 14{,}360 \text{ psi}$$

or

$$Q = 2.3 \times 9 \times 170/2 = 1760 \text{ Btu per hr}$$

and

$$S = 13 \times 10^6 \times 6.5 \times 10^{-6} \times 1760 \times 2/2.3 \times 9 = 14{,}360 \text{ psi}$$

COMBINED STRESSES

Simple stresses, defined as such by the flexure and torsion theories, lie in planes normal or parallel to the line of action of the forces. Normal, as well as shearing, stresses may, however, exist in other directions. A particle out of a loaded member will contain normal and shearing stresses as shown in Fig. 11. Note that the four shearing stresses must be of the same magnitude, if equilibrium is to be satisfied.

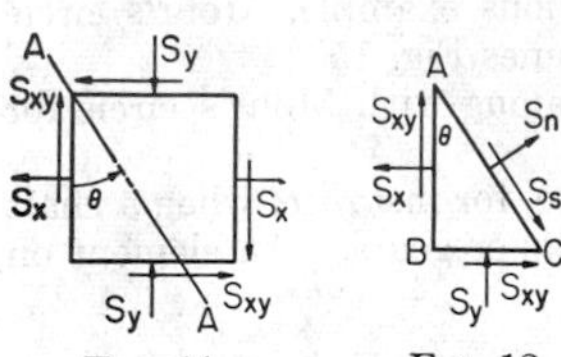

Fig. 11　Fig. 12

If the particle is "cut" along the plane $\overline{AA}$, equilibrium will reveal that, in general, normal as well as shearing stresses act upon the plane $\overline{AC}$ (Fig. 12). The normal stress on plane $\overline{AC}$ is labeled S_n and shearing, S_s. The application of equilibrium yields

$$S_n = \frac{S_x + S_y}{2} + \frac{S_x - S_y}{2}\cos 2\theta + S_{xy}\sin 2\theta$$

and

$$S_s = \frac{S_x - S_y}{2}\sin 2\theta - S_{xy}\cos 2\theta$$

A *sign convention* must be used. A tensile stress is positive while compression is negative. A shearing stress is positive when directed as on plane $\overline{AB}$ of Fig. 12; *i.e.*, when the shearing stresses on the vertical planes form a clockwise couple, the stress is positive.

The planes defined by $\tan 2\theta = 2\,S_{xy}/S_x - S_y$, the *principal planes*, contain the **principal stresses**—maximum and minimum normal stresses. These stresses are

$$S_M,\, S_m = \frac{S_x + S_y}{2} \pm \sqrt{\left(\frac{S_x - S_y}{2}\right)^2 + S_{xy}{}^2}$$

The radical in the equation yields the **maximum and minimum shearing stresses.** These act upon the planes, $\tan 2\theta = -\dfrac{S_x - S_y}{2S_{xy}}$.

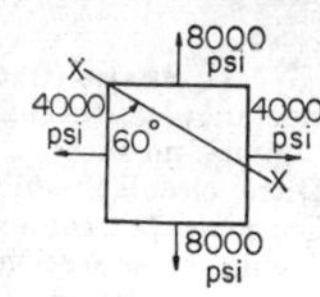

FIG. 13

EXAMPLE. The steam in a boiler subjects a particular particle on the boiler shell to a circumferential stress of 8,000 psi and a longitudinal stress of 4,000 psi as shown in Fig. 13. Find the stresses acting on the plane $\overline{XX}$, making an angle of 60 deg with the direction of the 8,000 psi stress. Find the principal stresses and locate the principal planes. Also find the maximum-minimum shearing stresses.

$$60 \text{ deg } S_n = \frac{4{,}000 + 8{,}000}{2} + \frac{4{,}000 - 8{,}000}{2}(-\,0.5000) + 0 = 7{,}000 \text{ psi}$$

$$60 \text{ deg } S_s = \frac{4{,}000 - 8{,}000}{2}(0.8660) - 0 = -\,1{,}732 \text{ psi}$$

$$S_{M,m} = \frac{4{,}000 + 8{,}000}{2} \pm \sqrt{\left(\frac{4{,}000 - 8{,}000}{2}\right)^2 + 0} = 6{,}000 \pm 2{,}000 = 8{,}000 \text{ and } 4{,}000 \text{ psi}$$

$$\text{at } \tan 2\theta = \frac{2 \times 0}{4{,}000 - 8{,}000} = 0 \quad \text{or} \quad \theta = 90 \text{ deg and } 0 \text{ deg}$$

$$S_{s\,M,m} = \pm\sqrt{\left(\frac{4{,}000 - 8{,}000}{2}\right)^2 + 0} = \pm\,2{,}000 \text{ psi}$$

Mohr's Stress Circle. The biaxial stress field with its combined stresses can be represented graphically by the Mohr stress circle. For instance, for the particle given in Fig. 11, Mohr's circle is as shown in Fig. 14. The stress *sign convention* previously defined must be adhered to. Furthermore, in order to locate the point (on Mohr's circle) that yields the stresses on a plane θ degrees from the vertical side of the particle (such as plane $\overline{AA}$ in Fig. 11), 2θ degrees must be laid off in the same direction from the radius to (S_x, S_{xy}). For the previous example, Mohr's circle becomes Fig. 15.

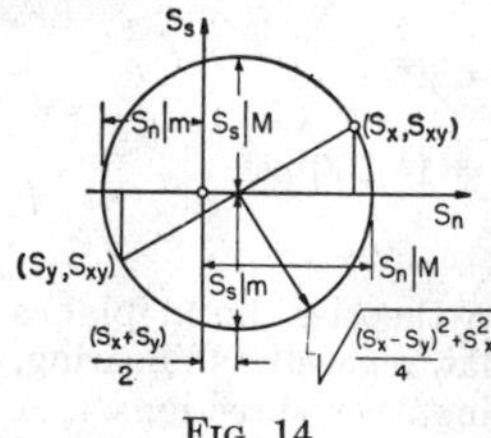

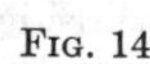

FIG. 14

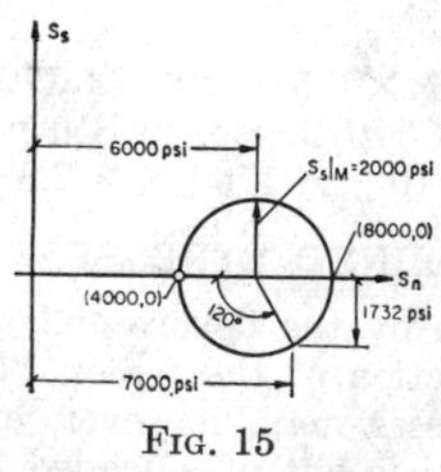

FIG. 15

Eight special stress fields are shown in Figs. 16 to 23, along with Mohr's circle for each.

Combined Loading. Combined flexure and torsion arise, for instance, when a shaft twisted by a torque, M_t, is bent by forces produced by belts or gears. An element on

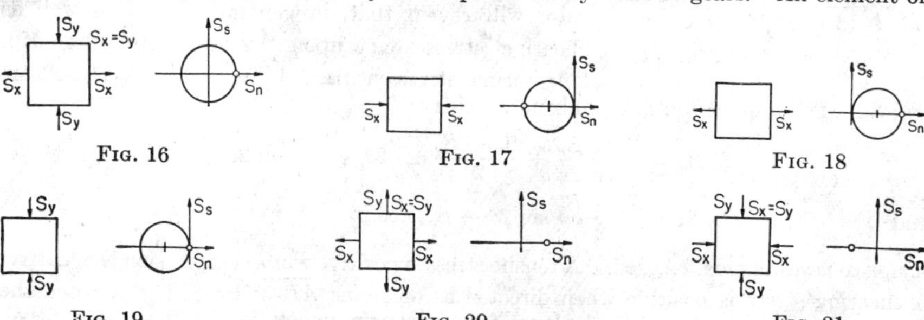

FIG. 16 FIG. 17 FIG. 18

FIG. 19 FIG. 20 FIG. 21

FIG. 22 FIG. 23

the surface, such as $ABCD$ on the shaft of Fig. 24, is subjected to a flexure stress $S_x = Mc/I = 8\ Fl/\pi d^3$ and a torsional shearing stress $S_{xy} = M_t c/J = 16\ M_t/\pi d^3$. These stresses will induce combined stresses. The maximum combined stresses will be

$$S_n = \tfrac{1}{2}(S_x \pm \sqrt{S_x{}^2 + 4S_{xy}{}^2})$$

and

$$S_s = \pm\ \tfrac{1}{2}\sqrt{S_y{}^2 + 4S_{xy}{}^2}$$

The above situation applies to any case of normal stress with shear, as when a bolt is under both tension and shear. A beam particle subjected to both flexure and transverse shear is another case.

Combined torsion and longitudinal loads exist on a propeller shaft. A particle on this shaft will contain a tensile stress computed using $S = F/A$ and a torsion shearing stress equal to $S_s = M_t c/J$. The free body of a particle on the surface will be the same as that of Fig. 24. A particle on the surface of a vertical turbine shaft is subjected to direct compression and torsion.

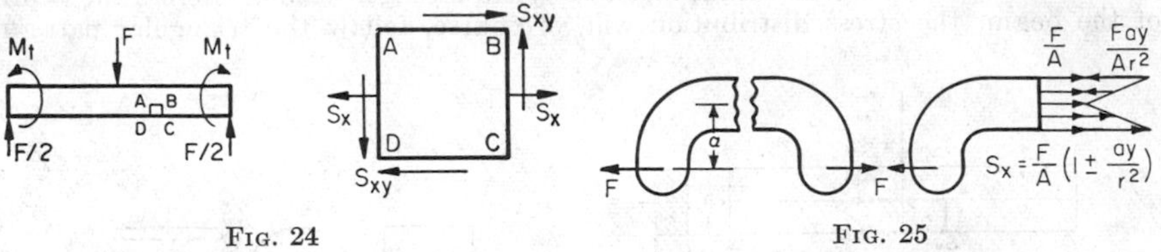

FIG. 24 FIG. 25

When combined loading results in stresses of the same type and direction the addition is algebraic. Such a situation exists on an offset link like that of Fig. 25.

Mohr's Strain Circle. Strain equations can also be derived for plane-strain fields. Strains e_x and e_y are the extensional strains (tension or compression) occurring at a point in two right-angle directions, and the change of the angle between them is γ_{xy}. The strain e at the point in any direction a at an angle θ with the x-direction derives as

$$e_a = \frac{e_x + e_y}{2} + \frac{e_x - e_y}{2}\cos 2\theta + \frac{\gamma_{xy}}{2}\sin 2\theta$$

Similarly, the shearing strain γ_{ab} (change in the original right angle between directions a and b) is defined by

$$\gamma_{ab} = (e_x - e_y)\sin 2\theta + \gamma_{xy}\cos 2\theta$$

Inspection easily reveals that the above equations for e_a and γ_{ab} are mathematically identical to those for S_n and S_s. Thus, once a sign convention is established, a Mohr circle for strain can be constructed and used as the stress circle is used. The strain e is positive when an extension and negative when a contraction. If the direction associated with the first subscript a rotates counterclockwise during straining with respect to the direction indicated by the second subscript b, the shearing strain is positive; if clockwise, it is negative. In constructing the circle, positive extensional strains will be plotted to the right as abscissas and positive **half-shearing** strains will be plotted upwards as ordinates.

For the strains shown in Fig. 26a, Mohr's strain circle becomes that shown in Fig. 26b. The extensional strain in the direction a, making an angle of θ_a with the

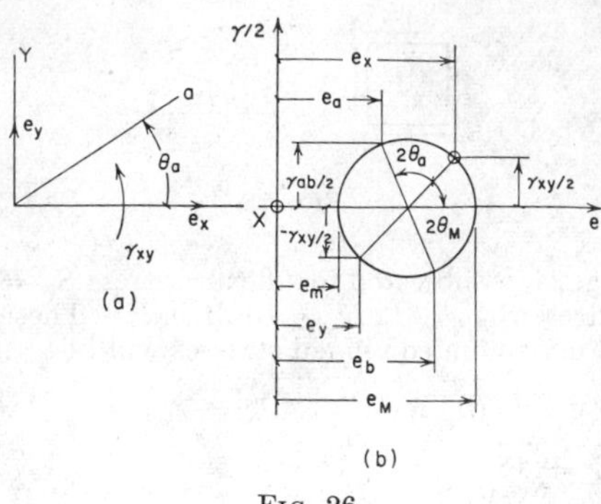

FIG. 26

x-direction, is e_a, and the shearing strain is γ_{ab} counterclockwise. The strain 90° away is e_b. The maximum principal strain is e_M at an angle θ_M clockwise from the x-direction. The other principal or minimum strain is e_m 90° away.

PLASTIC DESIGN

Early efforts in stress analysis were based on limit loads, that is, loads which stress a member "wholly" to the yield strength. Euler's famous column paper ("Sur la Force des Colonnes," Academie des Sciences de Berlin, 1757) deals with the column problem this way. More recently, the concept of limit loads, referred to as **limit,** or **plastic, design,** has found strong application in the design of certain structures. The theory presupposes a ductile material, absence of stress raisers, and fabrication free of embrittlement. Local load overstress is allowed, provided the structure does not deform appreciably.

To visualize the limit-load approach, consider a simple beam of uniform section subjected to a concentrated load at midspan, as depicted in Fig. 27a. According to elastic theory, the outermost fiber on each side and at midspan—the section of maximum bending moment—will first reach the yield-strength value. Across the depth of the beam, the stress distribution will, of course, follow the triangular pattern,

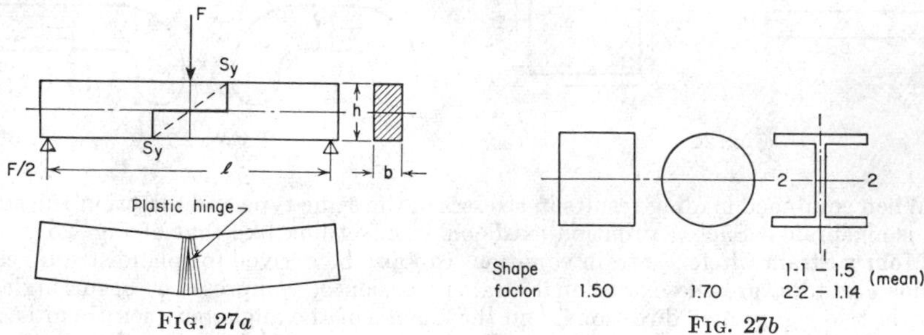

FIG. 27a FIG. 27b

becoming zero at the neutral axis. If the material is ductile, the stress in the outermost fibers will remain at the yield value until every other fiber reaches the same value as the load increases. Thus the stress distribution assumes the rectangular pattern before the *plastic hinge* forms and failure ensues.

The problem is that of finding the final limit load. Elastic-flexure theory gives the maximum load—triangular distribution—as

$$F_y = \frac{2S_y bh^2}{3l}$$

For the rectangular stress distribution, the limit load becomes

$$F_L = \frac{S_y bh^2}{l}$$

The ratio $F_L/F_y = 1.50$—an increase of 50 percent in load capability. The ratio F_L/F_y has been named **shape factor** (Jenssen, Plastic Design in Welded Structures Promises New Economy and Safety, *Welding Jour.*, March, 1959). See Fig. 27b for shape factors for some other sections. The shape factor may also be determined by dividing the first moment of area about the neutral axis by the section modulus.

A constant-section beam with both ends fixed, supporting a uniformly distributed load, illustrates another application of the plastic-load approach. The bending-moment diagram based on the elastic theory drawn in Fig. 28 (broken line) shows a moment at the center equal to one-half the moment at either end. A preferable situation, it might be argued, is one in which the moments are the same at the three stations—solid line. Thus, applying equilibrium to, say, the left half of the beam yields a bending moment at each of the three plastic hinges of

$$M_L = \frac{wl^2}{16}$$

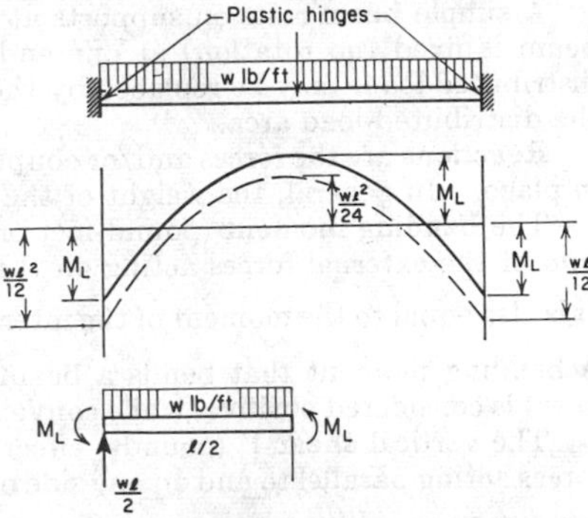

Fig. 28

DESIGN STRESSES

If a machine part is safely to transmit loads acting upon it, a permissible maximum stress must be established and used in the design. This is the allowable stress, the working stress, or, preferably, the **design stress.** The design stress should not waste material, yet should be large enough to prevent failure in case loads exceed expected values, or other uncertainties react unfavorably.

The design stress is determined by dividing the applicable material property—yield strength, ultimate strength, fatigue strength—by a **factor of safety.** The factor should be selected only after all **uncertainties** have been thoroughly considered. Among these are the uncertainty with respect to the magnitude and kind of operating load, the reliability of the material from which the component is made, the assumptions involved in the theories used, the environment in which the equipment might operate, the extent to which localized and fabrication stresses might develop, the uncertainty concerning causes of possible failure, and the endangering of human life in case of failure. Factors of safety vary from industry to industry, being the result of accumulated experience with a class of machines or a kind of environment. Many codes, such as the ASME code for power shafting, recommend design stresses found safe in practice.

In general, the **ductility** of the material determines the property upon which the factor should be based. Materials having an elongation of over 5 percent are considered ductile. In such cases, the factor of safety is based upon the yield strength or the endurance limit. For materials with an elongation under 5 percent, the ultimate strength must be used because these materials are **brittle** and so fracture without yielding.

Factors of safety based on yield are often taken **between 1.5 and 4.0.** For more reliable materials or better-known design and operating conditions, the lower factors are appropriate. In the case of untried materials or otherwise uncertain conditions, the higher factors are safer. The same values can be used when loads vary, but in such cases they are applied to the fatigue or endurance strength. When the ultimate strength determines the design stress (in the case of brittle materials), the factors of safety can be doubled.

Thus, under static loading, the design stress for, say, SAE-1020, which has a yield strength of 45,000 psi, may be taken at 45,000/2, or 22,500 psi, if a reasonably certain design condition exists. A Class 30 cast-iron part might be designed at 30,000/5 or 6,000 psi. A 2017S-O aluminum-alloy component (13,000 psi endurance strength) could be computed at a design stress of 13,000/2.5 or 5,200 psi in the usual fatigue-load application.

BEAMS

(For properties of structural steel and wooden beams, see Sec. 12.)

Notation

R = reaction
M = bending moment
W = total distributed load
S_s or S_v = transverse shearing unit stress
Z = horizontal shearing unit stress
I = rectangular moment of inertia

w = distributed load per longitudinal unit
P = concentrated load
V or Q = total vertical shear
S = unit normal apparent stress
I_P = polar moment of inertia
r = radius of curvature
i = slope
f = deflection
l = distance between supports

A **simple beam** rests on supports at its ends which permit rotation. A **cantilever beam** is fixed (no rotation) at one end. When computing reactions and moments, distributed loads may be replaced by their resultants acting at the center of gravity of the distributed-load area.

Reactions are the forces and/or couples acting at the supports and holding the beam in place. In general, the weight of the beam should be accounted for.

The **bending moment** (pound-feet or pound-inches) at any section is the algebraic sum of the external forces acting on the beam on one side of the section, $M = \Sigma Fx$. It is also equal to the moment of the internal-stress forces at the section, $M = \int s(dA)y$. A bending moment that bends a beam convex downward (tensile stress on bottom fiber) is considered **positive,** while convex upward (compression on bottom) is **negative.**

The **vertical shear** V (pounds) effective on a section is the algebraic sum of all the forces acting parallel to and on one side of the section, $V = \Sigma F$. It is also equal to the sum of the transverse shear stresses acting on the section, $V = \int S_s\, dA$.

Moment and shear diagrams may be constructed by plotting to scale the particular entity as the ordinate for each section of the beam. Such diagrams show in continuous form the variation along the length of the beam.

Moment-Shear Relation. The shear V is the first derivative of moment with respect to distance along the beam, $V = dM/dx$. This relationship does not, however, account for any sudden changes in moment.

Examples. Figure 29 illustrates a simple beam subjected to a uniform load. $M = R_1x - wx \times \frac{x}{2} = \frac{wlx}{2} - \frac{wx^2}{2}$ and $V = R_1 - wx = \frac{wl}{2} - wx$. Note also that $V = \frac{d}{dx}\left(\frac{wlx}{2} - \frac{wx^2}{2}\right) = \frac{wl}{2} - wx$.

Figure 30 below is a simple beam carrying a uniformly varying load; $M = R_1x - h\frac{x}{l} \times \frac{x}{2} \times \frac{x}{3} = \frac{hlx}{6} - \frac{hx^3}{6l}$, if h is in pounds per foot and weight of beam is neglected. The vertical shear $V = R_1 - \frac{hx}{l} \times \frac{x}{2} = \frac{hl}{6} - \frac{hx^2}{2l}$. Note again that $V = \frac{d}{dx}\left(\frac{hlx}{6} - \frac{hx^3}{6l}\right) = \frac{hl}{6} - \frac{hx^2}{2l}$.

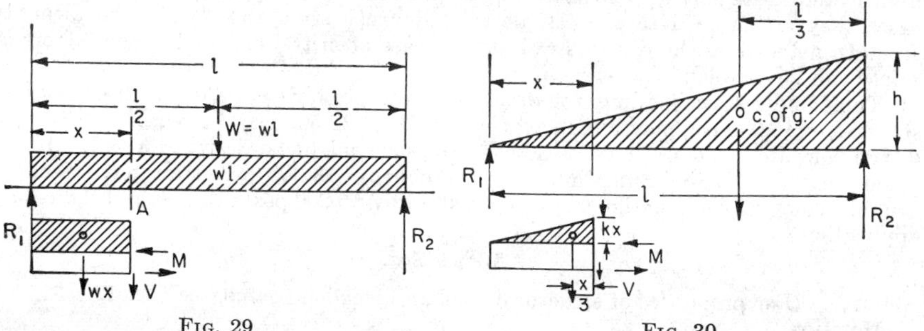

Fig. 29 Fig. 30

Table 2 gives the reactions, bending-moment equations, vertical shear equations, and the deflection of some of the more common types of beams.

Table 2. Beams of Uniform Cross Section, Loaded Transversely

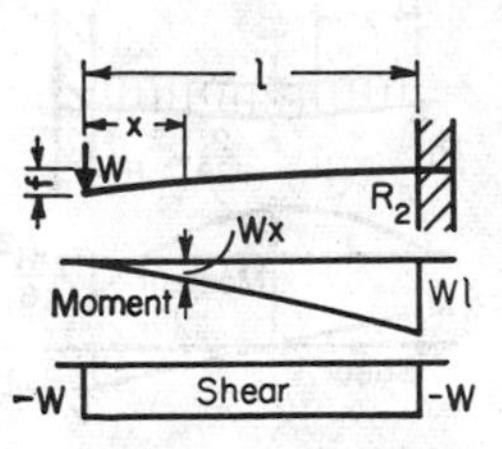

$$R_2 = W$$
$$M_x = -Wx$$
$$M_{\max} = -Wl,\ (x = l)$$
$$Q_x = -W$$
$$f = \frac{Wl^3}{3EI}\ (\max)$$

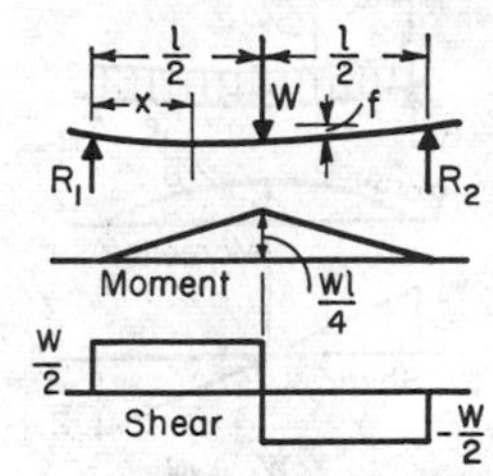

$$R_1 = \frac{W}{2},\ R_2 = \frac{W}{2}$$
$$M_x = \frac{Wx}{2}$$
$$M_{\max} = \frac{Wl}{4},\ \left(x = \frac{l}{2}\right)$$
$$Q_x = \pm\frac{W}{2}$$
$$f = \frac{W}{EI}\frac{l^3}{48}\ (\max)$$

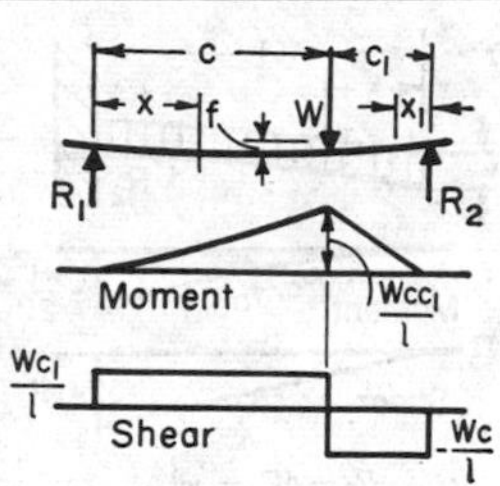

$$R_1 = \frac{Wc_1}{l},\ R_2 = \frac{Wc}{l}$$
$$M_x = \frac{Wc_1x}{l},\ M_{x'} = \frac{Wcx_1}{l}$$
$$M_{\max} = \frac{Wcc_1}{l},\ (x_1 = c_1 \text{ or } x = c)$$
$$Q_x = \frac{Wc_1}{l},\ Q_{x1} = \frac{Wc}{l}$$
$$f = \frac{Wc_1}{3EIl}\left[\frac{c(l + c_1)}{3}\right]^{3/2}\ (\max)$$

Max f occurs at $x = \sqrt{c(l + c_1)/3}$

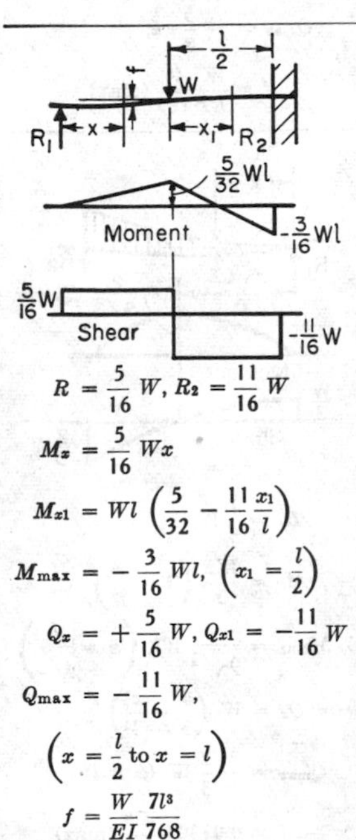

$$R = \frac{5}{16}W,\ R_2 = \frac{11}{16}W$$
$$M_x = \frac{5}{16}Wx$$
$$M_{x1} = Wl\left(\frac{5}{32} - \frac{11}{16}\frac{x_1}{l}\right)$$
$$M_{\max} = -\frac{3}{16}Wl,\ \left(x_1 = \frac{l}{2}\right)$$
$$Q_x = +\frac{5}{16}W,\ Q_{x1} = -\frac{11}{16}W$$
$$Q_{\max} = -\frac{11}{16}W,$$
$$\left(x = \frac{l}{2} \text{ to } x = l\right)$$
$$f = \frac{W}{EI}\frac{7l^3}{768}$$

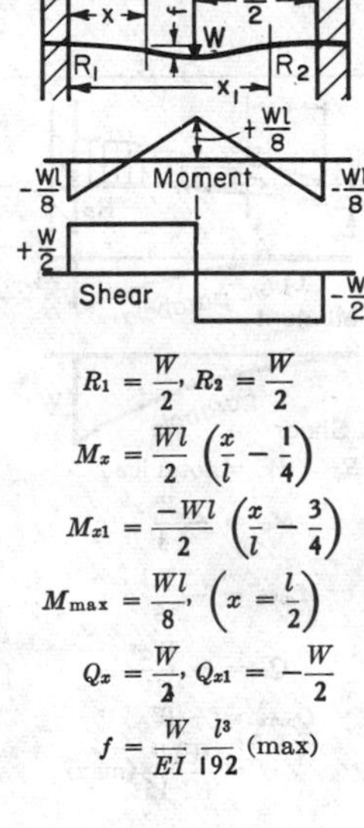

$$R_1 = \frac{W}{2},\ R_2 = \frac{W}{2}$$
$$M_x = \frac{Wl}{2}\left(\frac{x}{l} - \frac{1}{4}\right)$$
$$M_{x1} = \frac{-Wl}{2}\left(\frac{x}{l} - \frac{3}{4}\right)$$
$$M_{\max} = \frac{Wl}{8},\ \left(x = \frac{l}{2}\right)$$
$$Q_x = \frac{W}{2},\ Q_{x1} = -\frac{W}{2}$$
$$f = \frac{W}{EI}\frac{l^3}{192}\ (\max)$$

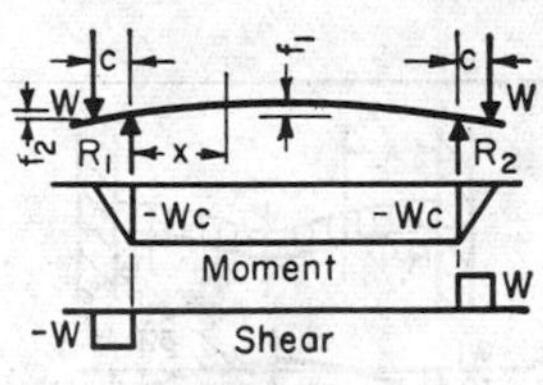

$$R_1 = W$$
$$R_2 = W$$
$$M_x = -Wc = \text{const}$$
$$Q_{W \text{ to } R_1} = -W$$
$$Q_{R_1 \text{ to } R_2} = 0$$
$$Q_{R_2 \text{ to } W} = +W$$
$$f_1 = \frac{Wcl^2}{EI8}\ (\max)$$
$$f_2 = \frac{W}{EI}\frac{c^2}{3}\left(c + \frac{3l}{2}\right)\ (\max)$$

Table 2. Beams of Uniform Cross Section, Loaded Transversely—(*Continued*)

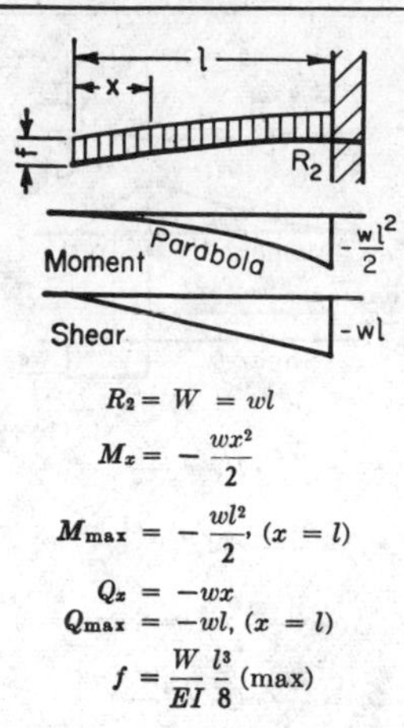

$$R_2 = W = wl$$
$$M_x = -\frac{wx^2}{2}$$
$$M_{max} = -\frac{wl^2}{2},\ (x = l)$$
$$Q_x = -wx$$
$$Q_{max} = -wl,\ (x = l)$$
$$f = \frac{W}{EI}\frac{l^3}{8}\ \text{(max)}$$

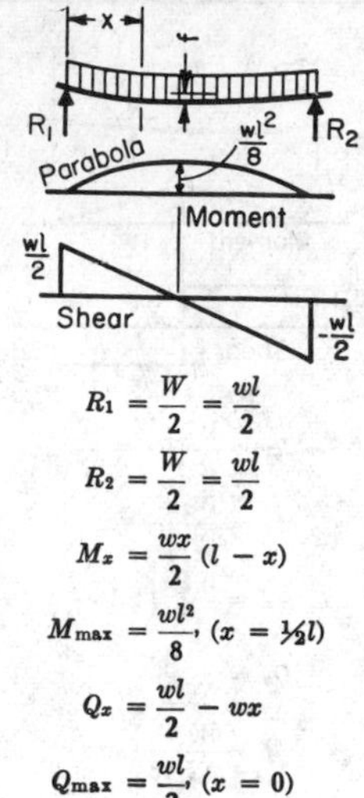

$$R_1 = \frac{W}{2} = \frac{wl}{2}$$
$$R_2 = \frac{W}{2} = \frac{wl}{2}$$
$$M_x = \frac{wx}{2}(l - x)$$
$$M_{max} = \frac{wl^2}{8},\ (x = \tfrac{1}{2}l)$$
$$Q_x = \frac{wl}{2} - wx$$
$$Q_{max} = \frac{wl}{2},\ (x = 0)$$
$$f = \frac{W}{EI}\frac{5l^3}{384}\ \text{(max)}$$

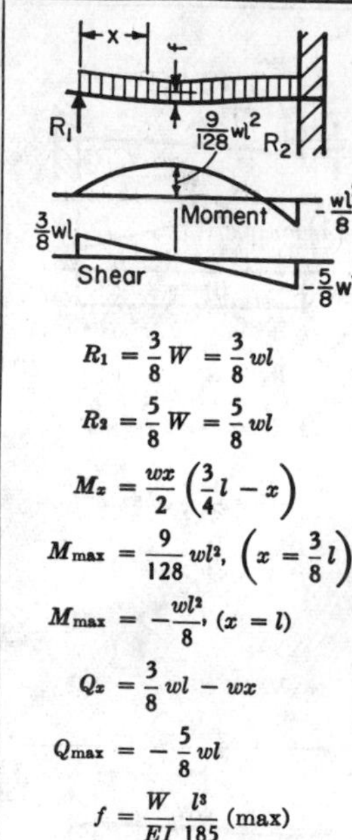

$$R_1 = \frac{3}{8}W = \frac{3}{8}wl$$
$$R_2 = \frac{5}{8}W = \frac{5}{8}wl$$
$$M_x = \frac{wx}{2}\left(\frac{3}{4}l - x\right)$$
$$M_{max} = \frac{9}{128}wl^2,\ \left(x = \frac{3}{8}l\right)$$
$$M_{max} = -\frac{wl^2}{8},\ (x = l)$$
$$Q_x = \frac{3}{8}wl - wx$$
$$Q_{max} = -\frac{5}{8}wl$$
$$f = \frac{W}{EI}\frac{l^3}{185}\ \text{(max)}$$

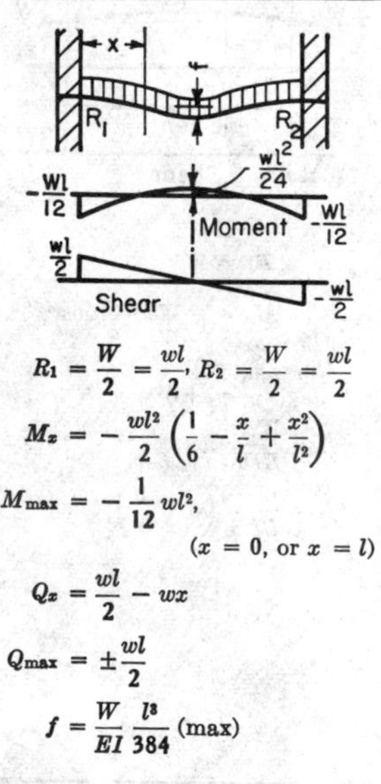

$$R_1 = \frac{W}{2} = \frac{wl}{2},\ R_2 = \frac{W}{2} = \frac{wl}{2}$$
$$M_x = -\frac{wl^2}{2}\left(\frac{1}{6} - \frac{x}{l} + \frac{x^2}{l^2}\right)$$
$$M_{max} = -\frac{1}{12}wl^2,\quad (x = 0, \text{ or } x = l)$$
$$Q_x = \frac{wl}{2} - wx$$
$$Q_{max} = \pm\frac{wl}{2}$$
$$f = \frac{W}{EI}\frac{l^3}{384}\ \text{(max)}$$

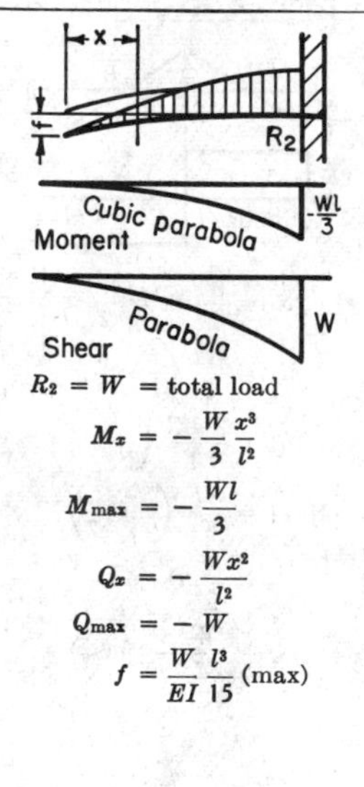

$$R_2 = W = \text{total load}$$
$$M_x = -\frac{W}{3}\frac{x^3}{l^2}$$
$$M_{max} = -\frac{Wl}{3}$$
$$Q_x = -\frac{Wx^2}{l^2}$$
$$Q_{max} = -W$$
$$f = \frac{W}{EI}\frac{l^3}{15}\ \text{(max)}$$

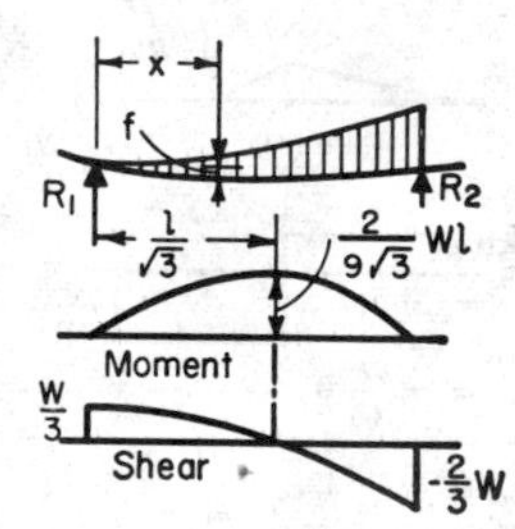

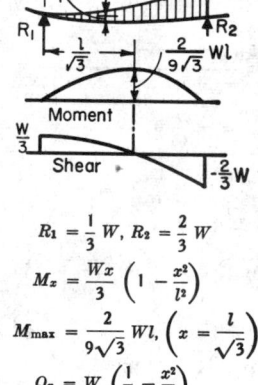

$$R_1 = \frac{1}{3}W,\ R_2 = \frac{2}{3}W$$
$$M_x = \frac{Wx}{3}\left(1 - \frac{x^2}{l^2}\right)$$
$$M_{max} = \frac{2}{9\sqrt{3}}Wl,\ \left(x = \frac{l}{\sqrt{3}}\right)$$
$$Q_x = W\left(\frac{1}{3} - \frac{x^2}{l^2}\right)$$
$$Q_{max} = -\frac{2}{3}W,\ (x = l)$$
$$f = 0.01304\frac{Wl^3}{EI}\ \text{(max)}$$

Table 2. Beams of Uniform Cross Section, Loaded Transversely—(*Continued*)

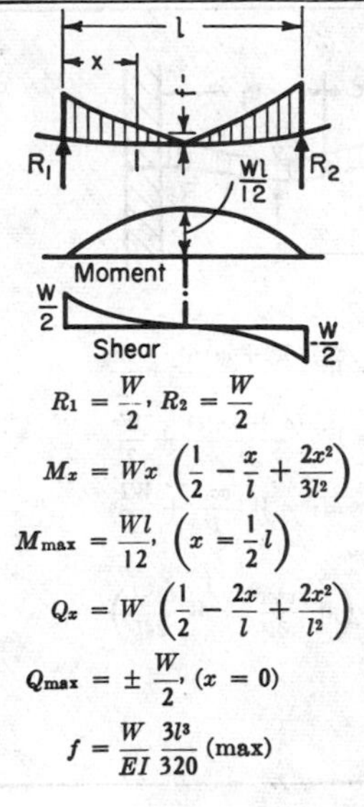

$$R_1 = \frac{W}{2},\ R_2 = \frac{W}{2}$$

$$M_x = Wx\left(\frac{1}{2} - \frac{x}{l} + \frac{2x^2}{3l^2}\right)$$

$$M_{max} = \frac{Wl}{12},\ \left(x = \frac{1}{2}l\right)$$

$$Q_x = W\left(\frac{1}{2} - \frac{2x}{l} + \frac{2x^2}{l^2}\right)$$

$$Q_{max} = \pm\frac{W}{2},\ (x = 0)$$

$$f = \frac{W}{EI}\frac{3l^3}{320}\ (\max)$$

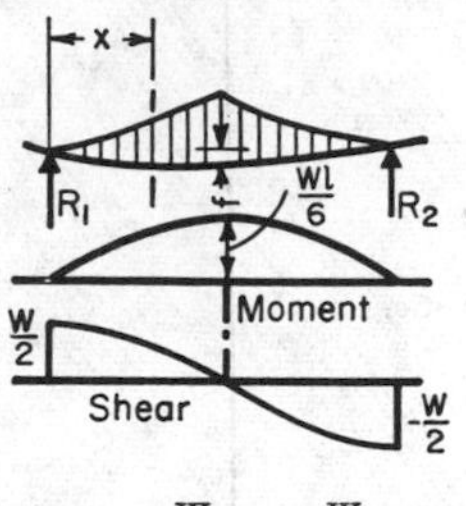

$$R_1 = \frac{W}{2},\ R_2 = \frac{W}{2}$$

$$M_x = Wx\left(\frac{1}{2} - \frac{2}{3}\frac{x^2}{l^2}\right)$$

$$M_{max} = \frac{Wl}{6},\ \left(x = \frac{1}{2}l\right)$$

$$Q_x = W\left(\frac{1}{2} - \frac{2x^2}{l^2}\right)$$

$$Q_{max} = \pm\frac{W}{2},\ (x = 0)$$

$$f = \frac{W}{EI}\frac{l^3}{60}\ (\max)$$

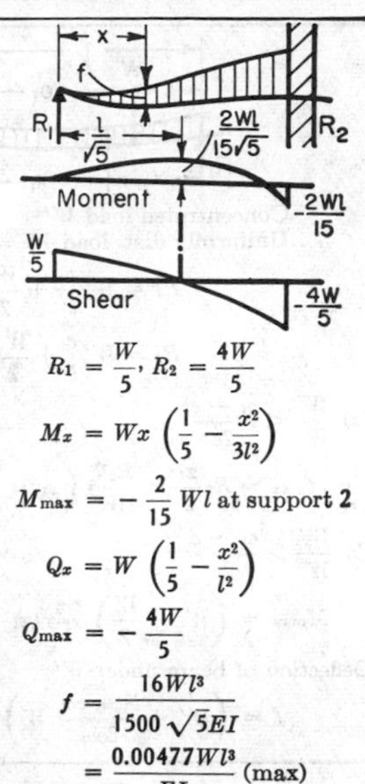

$$R_1 = \frac{W}{5},\ R_2 = \frac{4W}{5}$$

$$M_x = Wx\left(\frac{1}{5} - \frac{x^2}{3l^2}\right)$$

$$M_{max} = -\frac{2}{15}Wl \text{ at support 2}$$

$$Q_x = W\left(\frac{1}{5} - \frac{x^2}{l^2}\right)$$

$$Q_{max} = -\frac{4W}{5}$$

$$f = \frac{16Wl^3}{1500\sqrt{5}EI} = \frac{0.00477Wl^3}{EI}\ (\max)$$

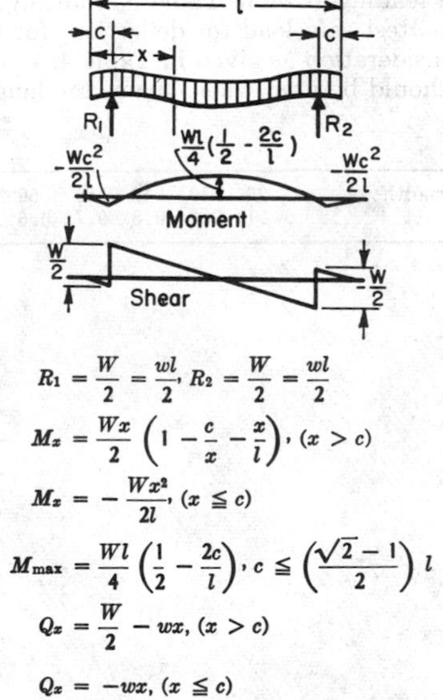

$$R_1 = \frac{W}{2} = \frac{wl}{2},\ R_2 = \frac{W}{2} = \frac{wl}{2}$$

$$M_x = \frac{Wx}{2}\left(1 - \frac{c}{x} - \frac{x}{l}\right),\ (x > c)$$

$$M_x = -\frac{Wx^2}{2l},\ (x \leqq c)$$

$$M_{max} = \frac{Wl}{4}\left(\frac{1}{2} - \frac{2c}{l}\right),\ c \leqq \left(\frac{\sqrt{2}-1}{2}\right)l$$

$$Q_x = \frac{W}{2} - wx,\ (x > c)$$

$$Q_x = -wx,\ (x \leqq c)$$

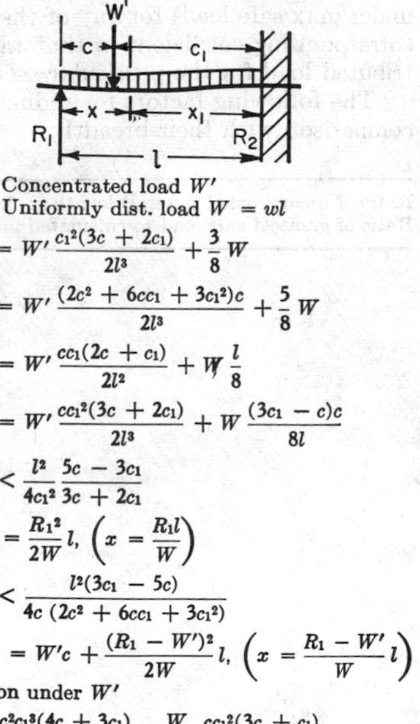

Concentrated load W'
Uniformly dist. load $W = wl$

$$R_1 = W'\frac{c_1^2(3c + 2c_1)}{2l^3} + \frac{3}{8}W$$

$$R_2 = W'\frac{(2c^2 + 6cc_1 + 3c_1^2)c}{2l^3} + \frac{5}{8}W$$

$$M_2 = W'\frac{cc_1(2c + c_1)}{2l^2} + W\frac{l}{8}$$

$$M_{W'} = W'\frac{cc_1^2(3c + 2c_1)}{2l^3} + W\frac{(3c_1 - c)c}{8l}$$

(*a*) $\dfrac{W'}{W} < \dfrac{l^2}{4c_1^2}\dfrac{5c - 3c_1}{3c + 2c_1}$

$$M_{c\,max} = \frac{R_1^2}{2W}l,\ \left(x = \frac{R_1 l}{W}\right)$$

(*b*) $\dfrac{W'}{W} < \dfrac{l^2(3c_1 - 5c)}{4c\,(2c^2 + 6cc_1 + 3c_1^2)}$

$$M_{c1\,max} = W'c + \frac{(R_1 - W')^2}{2W}l,\ \left(x = \frac{R_1 - W'}{W}l\right)$$

Deflection under W'

$$f = \frac{W'}{EI}\frac{c^2c_1^3(4c + 3c_1)}{12l^3} + \frac{W}{EI}\frac{cc_1^2(3c + c_1)}{48l}$$

Table 2. Beams of Uniform Cross Section, Loaded Transversely—(*Continued*)

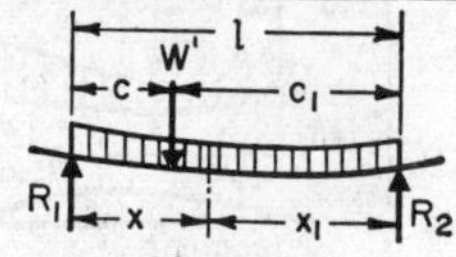

Concentrated load W'
Uniformly dist. load $W = wl$; $c < c_1$

$$R_1 = W'\frac{c_1}{l} + \frac{W}{2}$$

$$R_2 = W'\frac{c}{l} + \frac{W}{2}$$

(a) $\frac{W'}{W} < \frac{c_1 - c}{2c}$

$$M_{\max} = R_2\frac{x_1}{2} = \frac{R_2^2 l}{2W}, \left(x_1 = \frac{R_2 l}{W}\right)$$

(b) $\frac{W'}{W} > \frac{c_1 - c}{2c}$

$$M_{\max} = \left(W' + \frac{W}{2}\right)\frac{cc_1}{l}, (x_1 = c_1)$$

Deflection of beam under W':

$$f = \left(W' + \frac{l^2 + cc_1}{8cc_1}W\right)\frac{c^2c_1^2}{3EIl}$$

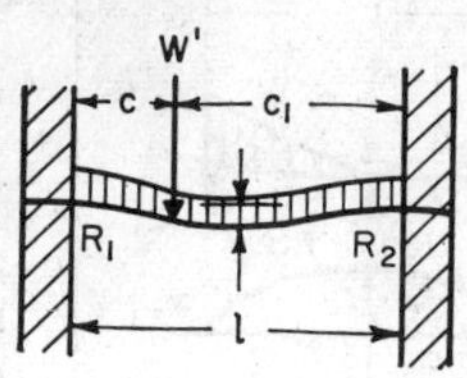

$c < c_1$

$$R_1 = W'\frac{(3c + c_1)c_1^2}{l^3} + \frac{W}{2}$$

$$R_2 = W'\frac{(c + 3c_1)c^2}{l^3} + \frac{W}{2}$$

$$M_{\max} = M_1 = W'\frac{cc_1^2}{l^2} + \frac{Wl}{12}$$

Deflection under W'

$$f = \frac{1}{EI}\left(W'\frac{c^3c_1^3}{3l^3} + W\frac{c^2c_1^2}{24l}\right)$$

Maximum Safe Load on Steel Beams. To obtain max safe load (or max deflection under max safe load) for any of the conditions of loading given in Table 5, multiply the corresponding coefficient in that table by the greatest safe load (or deflection) for distributed load for the particular section under consideration as given in Table 4.

The following factors for reducing the load should be used when beams are long in comparison with their breadth:

Ratio of unsupported (lateral) length to flange width or breadth	20	30	40	50	60	70
Ratio of greatest safe load to calculated load	1	0.9	0.8	0.7	0.6	0.5

Table 3. Uniformly Distributed Loads on Rectangular Beams 1 In. Wide*

(Calculated for unit fiber stress of 1,000 psi: nominal size)
TOTAL LOAD IN POUNDS, INCLUDING WEIGHT OF BEAM

Span, ft	Depth of beam in inches										
	6	7	8	9	10	11	12	13	14	15	16
5	800	1090	1420	1800	2220	2690	3200	3750	4350	5000	5690
6	670	910	1180	1500	1850	2240	2670	3130	3630	4170	4740
7	570	780	1010	1290	1590	1920	2280	2680	3110	3570	4060
8	500	680	890	1120	1390	1680	2000	2350	2720	3130	3560
9	440	600	790	1000	1230	1490	1780	2090	2420	2780	3160
10	400	540	710	900	1110	1340	1600	1880	2180	2500	2840
11	360	490	650	820	1010	1220	1450	1710	1980	2270	2590
12	330	450	590	750	930	1120	1330	1560	1810	2080	2370
13	310	420	550	690	850	1030	1230	1440	1680	1920	2190
14	290	390	510	640	790	960	1140	1340	1560	1790	2030
15	270	360	470	600	740	900	1070	1250	1450	1670	1900
16	250	340	440	560	690	840	1000	1170	1360	1560	1780
17	230	320	420	530	650	790	940	1100	1280	1470	1670
18	220	300	400	500	620	750	890	1040	1210	1390	1580
19	210	290	380	470	590	710	840	990	1150	1320	1500
20	200	270	360	450	560	670	800	940	1090	1250	1420
22	180	250	320	410	500	610	730	850	990	1140	1290
24	160	230	290	370	460	560	670	780	910	1040	1180
26	150	210	270	340	420	520	610	720	840	960	1090
28	140	190	250	320	390	480	570	670	780	890	1010
30	130	180	240	300	370	450	530	630	730	830	950

* This table is convenient for wooden beams. For any other fiber stress S', multiply the values in table by $S'/1{,}000$. See Sec. 12 for properties of wooden beams of commercial sizes.

Table 4. Approximate Safe Loads in Pounds on Steel Beams

(Pencoyd Iron Works)

Allowable fiber stress for steel, 16,000 psi (basis of table); for iron, reduce values given in table by one-eighth. Beams supported at both ends.

L = distance between supports, ft
A = sectional area of beam, sq in.
D = depth of beam, in.
a = interior area, sq in.
d = interior depth, in.
w = total working load, net tons

Shape of section	Greatest safe load, lb		Deflection, in.	
	Load in middle	Load distributed	Load in middle	Load distributed
Solid rectangle	$\frac{890AD}{L}$	$\frac{1780AD}{L}$	$\frac{wL^3}{32AD^2}$	$\frac{wL^3}{52AD^2}$
Hollow rectangle	$\frac{890(AD - ad)}{L}$	$\frac{1780(AD - ad)}{L}$	$\frac{wL^3}{32(AD^2 - ad^2)}$	$\frac{wL^3}{52(AD^2 - ad^2)}$
Solid cylinder	$\frac{667AD}{L}$	$\frac{1333AD}{L}$	$\frac{wL^3}{24AD^2}$	$\frac{wL^3}{38AD^2}$
Hollow cylinder	$\frac{667(AD - ad)}{L}$	$\frac{1333(AD - ad)}{L}$	$\frac{wL^3}{24(AD^2 - ad^2)}$	$\frac{wL^3}{38(AD^2 - ad^2)}$
Even-legged angle or tee	$\frac{885AD}{L}$	$\frac{1770AD}{L}$	$\frac{wL^3}{32AD^2}$	$\frac{wL^3}{52AD^2}$
Channel or Z bar	$\frac{1525AD}{L}$	$\frac{3050AD}{L}$	$\frac{wL^3}{53AD^2}$	$\frac{wL^3}{85AD^2}$
Deck beam	$\frac{1380AD}{L}$	$\frac{2760AD}{L}$	$\frac{wL^3}{50AD^2}$	$\frac{wL^3}{80AD^2}$
I beam	$\frac{1795AD}{L}$	$\frac{3390AD}{L}$	$\frac{wL^3}{58AD^2}$	$\frac{wL^3}{93AD^2}$

Table 5. Coefficients for Correcting Values in Table 4 for Various Methods of Support and of Loading

Conditions of loading	Maximum relative safe load	Maximum relative deflection under max relative safe load
Beam Supported at Ends		
Load uniformly distributed over span	1.0	1.0
Load concentrated at center of span	½	0.80
Two equal loads symmetrically concentrated	$l/4c$	
Load increasing uniformly to one end	0.974	0.976
Load increasing uniformly to center	¾	0.96
Load decreasing uniformly to center	3/2	1.08
Beam Fixed at One End, Cantilever		
Load uniformly distributed over span	¼	2.40
Load concentrated at end	⅛	3.20
Load increasing uniformly to fixed end	⅜	1.92
Beam Continuous over Two Supports Equi-distant from Ends		
Load uniformly distributed over span:		
1. If distance $a > 0.2071l$	$l^2/4a^2$	
2. If distance $a < 0.2071l$	$\dfrac{l}{l - 4a}$	
3. If distance $a = 0.2071l$	5.83	
Two equal loads concentrated at ends	$l/4a$	

l = length of beam; c = distance from support to nearest concentrated load; a = distance from support to end of beam.

Theory of Flexure

A bent beam is shown in **Fig. 31.** The concave side is in compression and the convex side in tension. These are divided by the **neutral plane** of zero stress $A'B'BA$. The intersection of the neutral plane with the face of the beam is the **neutral line or elastic curve** AB. The intersection of the neutral plane with the cross section is the **neutral axis** NN'.

It is assumed that a beam is prismatic, of a length at least 10 times its depth, and that the external forces are all at right angles to the axis of the beam and in a plane of symmetry, and that flexure is slight. Other assumptions are: (1) That the material is homogeneous, and obeys Hooke's law. (2) That **stresses are within the elastic limit.** (3) That every layer of material is free to expand and contract longitudinally and laterally under stress as if separate from other layers. (4) That the tensile and compressive moduli of elasticity are equal. (5) That the cross section remains a plane surface. (The assumption of plane cross sections is only strictly true when the shear is constant or zero over the cross section, and when the shear is constant throughout the length of the beam.)

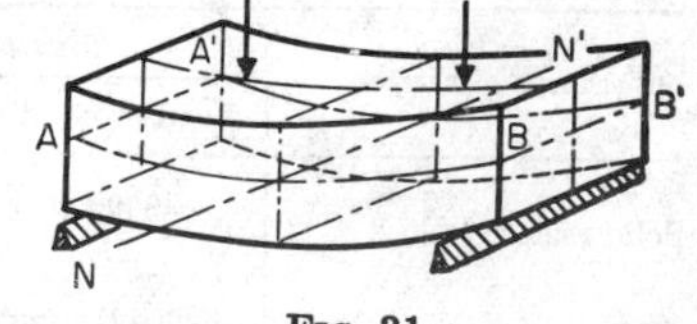

Fig. 31

It follows then that: (1) The internal forces are in horizontal balance. (2) The **neutral axis contains the center of gravity** of the cross section, when there is no resultant axial stress. (3) The stress intensity varies directly with the distance from the neutral axis.

The moment of the elastic forces about the neutral axis, *i.e.*, the **stress moment** or **moment of resistance,** is $M = SI/c$, where S is an elastic unit stress at outer fiber whose distance from the neutral axis is c; and I is the rectangular moment of inertia about the neutral axis.

Table 6. Properties of Various Cross Sections

(I = moment of inertia; I/c = section modulus; $r = \sqrt{I/A}$ = radius of gyration)

Section	Moment of inertia	Section modulus	Radius of gyration
$I = \frac{bh^3}{12}$ $\frac{I}{c} = \frac{bh^2}{6}$ $r = \frac{h}{\sqrt{12}} = 0.289h$	$\frac{bh^3}{3}$ $\frac{bh^2}{3}$ $\frac{h}{\sqrt{3}} = 0.577h$	$\frac{b^3h^3}{6(b^2+h^2)}$ $\frac{b^2h^2}{6\sqrt{b^2+h^2}}$ $\frac{bh}{\sqrt{6(b^2+h^2)}}$	$\frac{bh}{12}(h^2\cos^2 a + b^2\sin^2 a)$ $\frac{bh}{6}\left(\frac{h^2\cos^2 a + b^2\sin^2 a}{h\cos a + b\sin a}\right)$ $\sqrt{\frac{h^2\cos^2 a + b^2\sin^2 a}{12}}$
$I = \frac{b}{12}(H^3 - h^3)$ $\frac{I}{c} = \frac{b}{6}\frac{H^3 - h^3}{H}$ $r = \sqrt{\frac{H^3 - h^3}{12(H-h)}}$	$\frac{H^4 - h^4}{12}$ $\frac{1}{6}\frac{H^4 - h^4}{H}$ $\sqrt{\frac{H^2 + h^2}{12}}$	$\frac{H^4 - h^4}{12}$ $\frac{\sqrt{2}}{12}\frac{H^4 - h^4}{H}$ $\sqrt{\frac{H^2 + h^2}{12}}$	$\frac{bh^3}{36};\ c = \frac{2}{3}h$ $\frac{bh^2}{24}$ $\frac{h}{\sqrt{18}}$
$I = \frac{bh^3}{12}$ $\frac{I}{c} = \frac{bh^2}{12}$ $r = \frac{h}{\sqrt{6}}$	$\frac{5\sqrt{3}}{16}R^4$ $\frac{5}{8}R^3$ $\sqrt{\frac{5}{24}}R$	$\frac{5\sqrt{3}}{16}R^3$	$\frac{1 + 2\sqrt{2}}{6}R^4$ $0.6906R^3$ $0.475R$

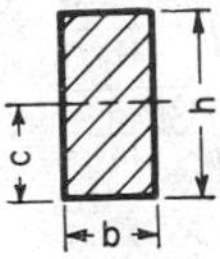

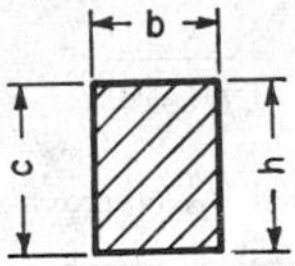

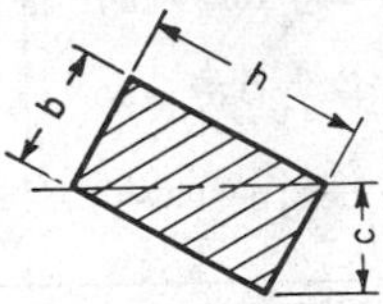

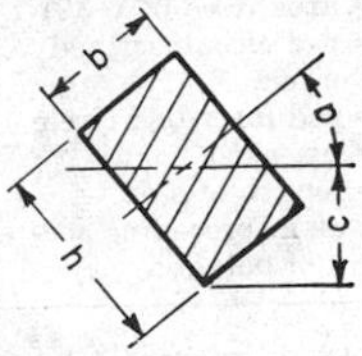

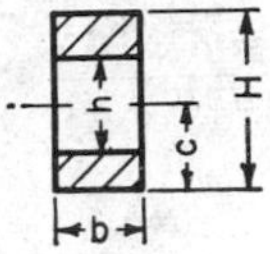

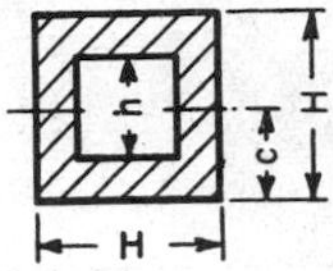

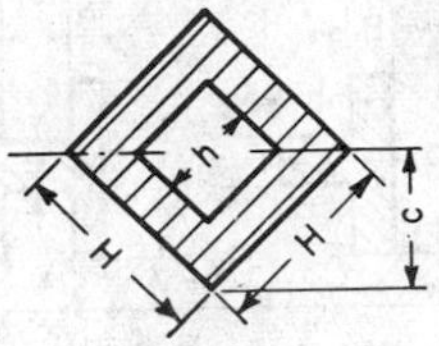

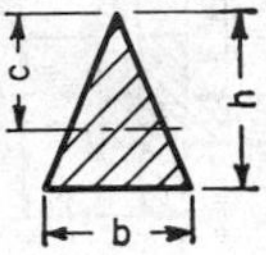

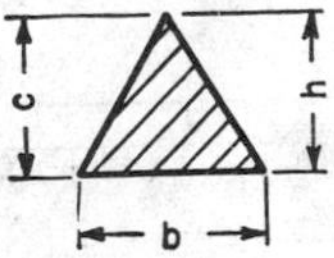

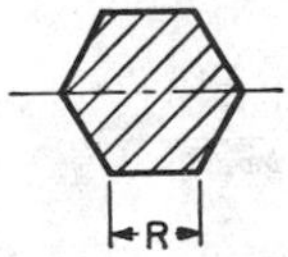

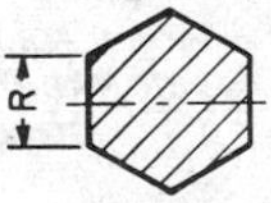

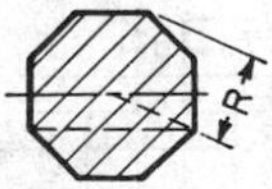

Square, axis same as first rectangle, side $= h$; $I = h^4/12$; $I/c = h^3/6$; $r = 0.289h$.
Square, diagonal taken as axis: $I = h^4/12$; $I/c = 0.1179h^3$; $r = 0.289h$.

Table 6. Properties of Various Cross Sections—*(Continued)*

Section	Moment of inertia	Section modulus	Radius of gyration
Equilateral Polygon A = area, (see p. 1–39) R = rad circumscribed circle r = rad inscribed circle n = no. sides a = length of side Axis as in preceding section of octagon	$I = \frac{A}{24}(6R^2 - a^2)$ $= \frac{A}{48}(12r^2 + a^2)$ $= \frac{AR^2}{4}$ (approx)	$\frac{I}{c} = \frac{I}{r}$ $= \frac{I}{R\cos\frac{180°}{n}}$ $= \frac{AR}{4}$ (approx)	$\sqrt{\frac{6R^2 - a^2}{24}} \approx \frac{R}{2}$ $\sqrt{\frac{12r^2 + a^2}{48}}$
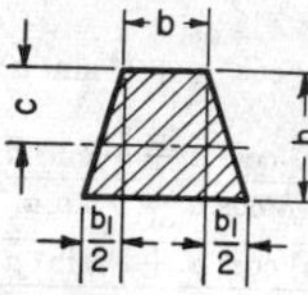 b, c, h, $\frac{b_1}{2}$, $\frac{b_1}{2}$	$I = \frac{6b^2 + 6bb_1 + b_1^2}{36(2b + b_1)} h^3$ $c = \frac{1}{3}\frac{3b + 2b_1}{2b + b_1} h$	$\frac{I}{c} = \frac{6b^2 + 6bb_1 + b_1^2}{12(3b + 2b_1)} h^2$	$\frac{h\sqrt{12b^2 + 12bb_1 + 2b_1^2}}{6(2b + b_1)}$
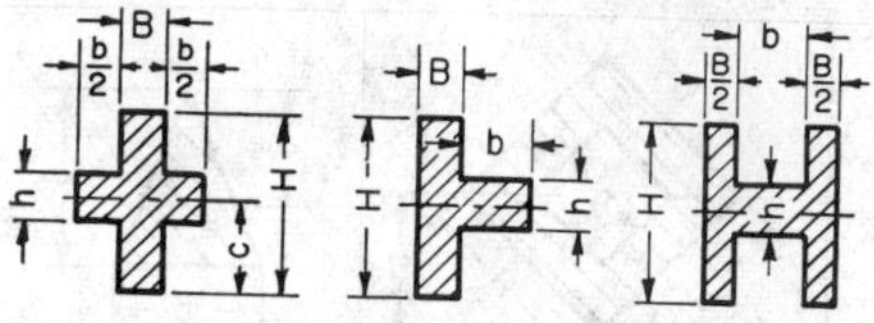 B, $\frac{b}{2}$, $\frac{b}{2}$, h, H, c; B, b, h, H; b, $\frac{B}{2}$, $\frac{B}{2}$, H, h		$I = \frac{BH^3 + bh^3}{12}$ $\frac{I}{c} = \frac{BH^3 + bh^3}{6H}$	$\sqrt{\frac{BH^3 + bh^3}{12(BH + bh)}}$
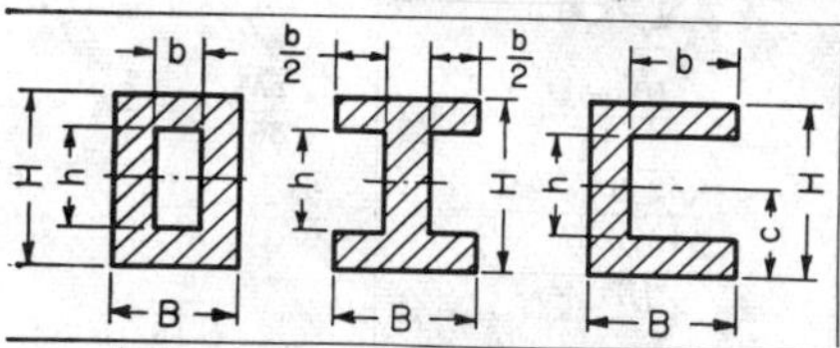 b, $\frac{b}{2}$, H, h, B; $\frac{b}{2}$, h, H, B; b, h, H, c, B		$I = \frac{BH^3 - bh^3}{12}$ $\frac{I}{c} = \frac{BH^3 - bh^3}{6H}$	$\sqrt{\frac{BH^3 - bh^3}{12(BH - bh)}}$
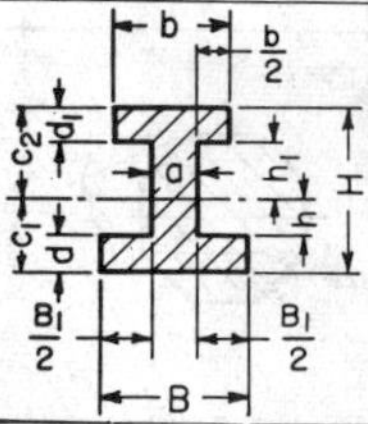 b, $\frac{b}{2}$, c_2, d_1, a, h_1, h, H, c_1, d, $\frac{B_1}{2}$, $\frac{B_1}{2}$, B	$I = \frac{1}{3}(Bc_1^3 - B_1h^3 + bc_2^3 - b_1h_1^3)$ $c_1 = \frac{1}{2}\frac{aH^2 + B_1d^2 + b_1d_1(2H - d_1)}{aH + B_1d + b_1d_1}$		$\sqrt{\frac{I}{(Bd + bd_1) + a(h + h_1)}}$
a, c_2, c_1, h, d, $\frac{b}{2}$, $\frac{b}{2}$, B; a, H, h, d, b, B; $\frac{a}{2}$, $\frac{a}{2}$, H, d, c_2, c_1, b, B			$I = \frac{1}{3}(Bc_1^3 - bh^3 + ac_2^3)$ $c_1 = \frac{1}{2}\frac{aH^2 + bd^2}{aH + bd}$ $c_2 = H - c_1$ $r = \sqrt{\frac{I}{[Bd + a(H - d)]}}$
r, d	$I = \frac{\pi d^4}{64} = \frac{\pi r^4}{4} = \frac{A}{4} r^2$ $= 0.05d^4$ (approx)	$\frac{I}{c} = \frac{\pi d^3}{32} = \frac{\pi r^3}{4} = \frac{A}{4} r$ $= 0.1d^3$ (approx)	$\frac{r}{2} = \frac{d}{4}$

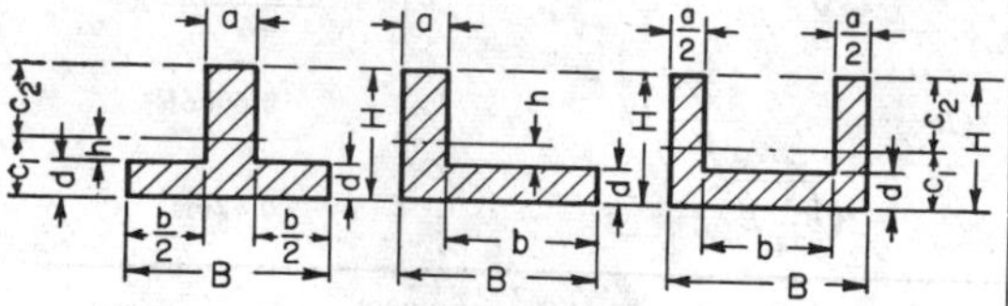

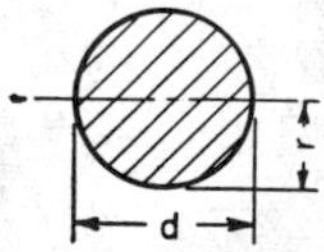

Table 6. Properties of Various Cross Sections—(*Continued*)

Section	Moment of inertia	Section modulus	Radius of gyration
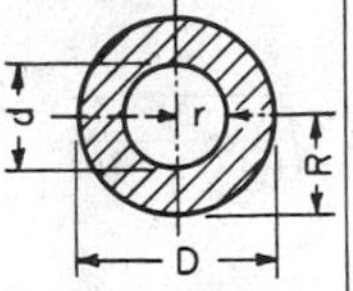 d, r, R, D $d_m = \frac{1}{2}(D + d)$ $s = \frac{1}{2}(D - d)$	$I = \frac{\pi}{64}(D^4 - d^4)$ $= \frac{\pi}{4}(R^4 - r^4)$ $= \frac{1}{4}A(R^2 + r^2)$ $= 0.05(D^4 - d^4)$ (approx)	$\frac{I}{c} = \frac{\pi}{32}\frac{D^4 - d^4}{D}$ $= \frac{\pi}{4}\frac{R^4 - r^4}{R}$ $= 0.8d_m^2 s$ (approx) when $\frac{s}{d_m}$ is very small	$\frac{\sqrt{R^2 + r^2}}{2} = \frac{\sqrt{D^2 + d^2}}{4}$
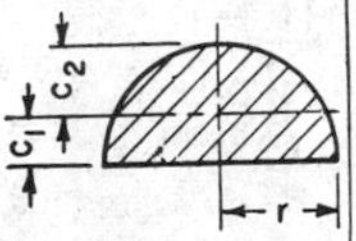 c_2, c_1, r	$I = r^4\left(\frac{\pi}{8} - \frac{8}{9\pi}\right)$ $= 0.1098r^4$	$\frac{I}{c_2} = 0.1908r^3$ $\frac{I}{c_1} = 0.2587r^3$ $c_1 = 0.4244r$	$\frac{\sqrt{9\pi^2 - 64}}{6\pi}r = 0.264r$
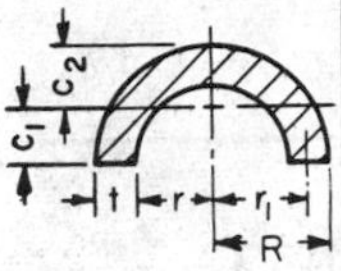 c_2, c_1, t, r, r_1, R	$I = 0.1098(R^4 - r^4)$ $- \frac{0.283R^2r^2(R - r)}{R + r}$ $= 0.3tr_1^3$ (approx) when $\frac{t}{r_1}$ is very small	$c_1 = \frac{4}{3\pi}\frac{R^2 + Rr + r^2}{R + r}$ $c_2 = R - c_1$	$\sqrt{\frac{2I}{\pi(R^2 - r^2)}}$ $= 0.31r_1$ (approx)
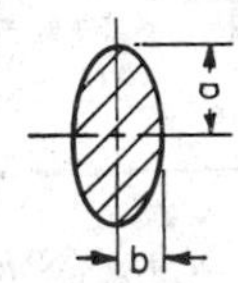 a, b	$I = \frac{\pi a^3 b}{4} = 0.7854a^3b$	$\frac{I}{c} = \frac{\pi a^2 b}{4} = 0.7854a^2b$	$\frac{a}{2}$
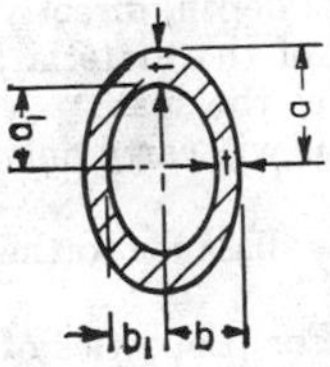 a_1, a, t, b_1, b	$I = \frac{\pi}{4}(a^3b - a_1^3b_1)$ $= \frac{\pi}{4}a^2(a + 3b)t$ (approx)	$\frac{I}{c} = \frac{\pi}{4}a(a + 3b)t$ (approx)	$\sqrt{\frac{I}{(\pi ab - a_1b_1)}} =$ $\frac{a}{2}\sqrt{\frac{a + 3b}{a + b}}$ (approx)
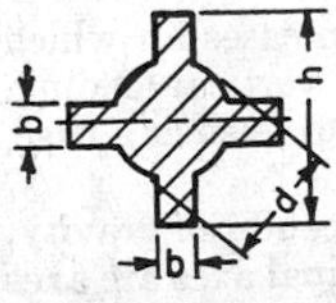 b, h, d, b	$I = \frac{1}{12}\left[\frac{3\pi}{16}d^4 + b(h^3 - d^3) + b^3(h - d)\right]$	$\frac{I}{c} = \frac{1}{6h}\left[\frac{3\pi}{16}d^4 + b(h^3 + d^3) + b^3(h - d)\right]$	$\sqrt{\frac{I}{\pi\frac{d^2}{4} + 2b(h - d)}}$ (approx)
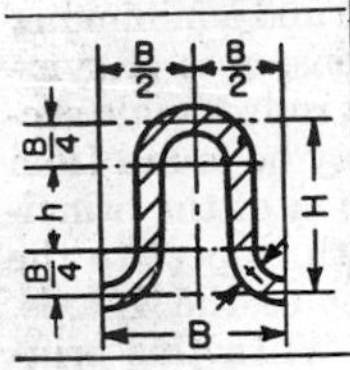 $\frac{B}{2}$, $\frac{B}{2}$, $\frac{B}{4}$, h, $\frac{B}{4}$, H, t, B	$I = \frac{t}{4}\left(\frac{\pi B^3}{16} + B^2h + \frac{\pi Bh^2}{2} + \frac{2}{3}h^3\right)$ $h = H - \frac{1}{2}B$	$\frac{I}{c} = \frac{2I}{H + t}$	$\sqrt{\frac{I}{2\left(\frac{\pi B}{4} + h\right)t}}$

Table 6. **Properties of Various Cross Sections**—(*Continued*)

Section	Moment of inertia and section modulus	Radius of gyration
Corrugated sheet iron, parabolically curved	$I = \frac{64}{105}(b_1h_1^3 - b_2h_2^3)$, where $h_1 = \frac{1}{2}(H + t)$ | $b_1 = \frac{1}{4}(B + 2.6t)$ $h_2 = \frac{1}{2}(H - t)$ | $b_2 = \frac{1}{4}(B - 2.6t)$ $\frac{I}{c} = \frac{2I}{H + t}$	$r = \sqrt{\frac{3I}{t(2B + 5.2H)}}$

Approximate values of *least* radius of gyration r

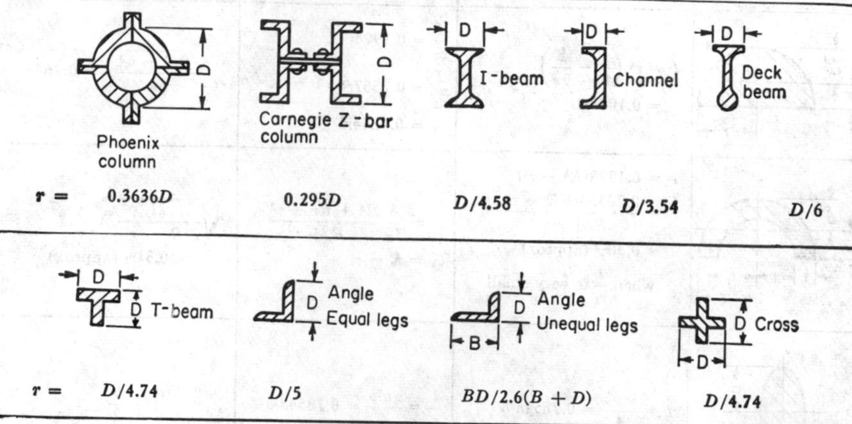

Section	Phoenix column	Carnegie Z-bar column	I-beam	Channel	Deck beam
$r =$	$0.3636D$	$0.295D$	$D/4.58$	$D/3.54$	$D/6$

Section	T-beam	Angle, equal legs	Angle, unequal legs	Cross
$r =$	$D/4.74$	$D/5$	$BD/2.6(B + D)$	$D/4.74$

This formula is for the **strength of beams.** For rectangular beams, $M = \frac{1}{6}Sbh^2$, where b = breadth, and h = depth; *i.e.*, the elastic **strength of beam sections** varies as follows: (1) for equal width, as the square of the depth; (2) for equal depth, directly as the width; (3) for equal depth and width, directly as the strength of the material; (4) if span varies, then for equal depth, width and material, inversely as the span.

If a beam is cut in halves horizontally, the two halves laid side by side will carry only one-half as much as the original beam.

The term **section modulus** is given to the value of I/c, where c is the distance to the fiber carrying greatest stress. Moment of inertia of cross section = I.

Tables 6 to 8 give the properties of various beam cross sections. For properties of structural-steel shapes, see Sec. 12.

Oblique Loading. It should be noted that Table 6 includes certain cases for which the horizontal axis is not a neutral axis, assuming the common case of vertical loading. The rectangular section with the diagonal as a horizontal axis (Table 6) is such a case. These cases must be handled by the principles of oblique loading.

Every section of a beam has two principal axes passing through the center of gravity, and these two axes are always at right angles to each other. The **principal axes** are axes with respect to which the moment of inertia is, respectively, a maximum and a minimum, and for which the product of inertia is zero. For symmetrical sections, axes of symmetry are always principal axes. **For unsymmetrical sections,** like a rolled angle section (Fig. 32), the inclination of the principal axis with the X-axis may be found from the formula $\tan 2\theta = 2I_{xy}/(I_y - I_x)$, in which θ = angle of inclination of the principal axis to the X-axis, I_{xy} = the product of inertia of the section with respect to the X- and Y-axes, I_y = moment of inertia of the section with respect to the Y-axis, I_x = moment of inertia of the section with respect to the X-axis. When this principal axis has been found, the other principal axis is at right angles to it.

Calling the moments of inertia with respect to the principal axes, I_x' and I_y', the unit stress existing anywhere in the section at a point whose coordinates are x and y (Fig. 33) is $S = (My \cos \alpha/I_x') + (Mx \sin \alpha/I_y')$, in which M = bending moment with respect to the section in question, α = the angle which the plane of bending moment or the plane of the loads makes with the y-axis, $M \cos \alpha$ = the component of bending moment causing bending about the principal axis which has been designated as the X-axis, $M \sin \alpha$ = the component of bending moment causing bending about the principal axis which has been designated as the Y-axis. The sign of the two terms for unit stress may be determined by inspection in the usual way, and the result will be tension or compression as determined by the algebraic sum of the two terms.

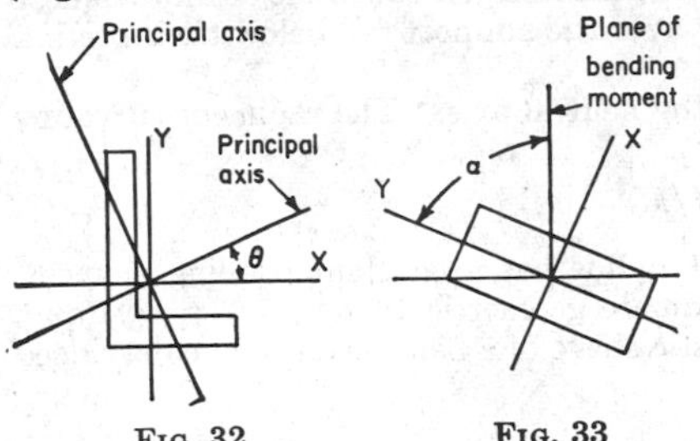

FIG. 32 FIG. 33

In general, it may be stated that when the plane of the bending moment coincides with one of the principal axes, then the other principal axis is the neutral axis. This is the ordinary case, in which the ordinary formula for unit stress may be applied. When the plane of the bending moment does not coincide with one of the principal axes, then the above formula for oblique loading may be applied.

Internal Moment beyond the Elastic Limit

Ordinarily, the expression $M = SI/c$ is used for stresses above the elastic limit, in which case S becomes an experimental coefficient S_R, the **modulus of rupture,** and the formula is empirical. The true relation is obtained by applying to the cross section a stress-strain diagram from a tension and compression test, as in Fig. 34. Figure 34 shows the side of a beam of depth d under flexure beyond its elastic limit; line 1–1 shows the distorted cross section; line 3–3, the usual rectilinear relation of stress to strain; and line 2–2, an actual stress-strain diagram, applied to the cross section of the beam, compression above and tension below. The neutral axis is then below the gravity axis. The **outer material** may be expected to develop **greater ultimate strength** than in simple stress, on account of the reinforcing action of material nearer the neutral axis that is not yet overstrained. This leads to an **equalization of stress** over the cross section. S_R exceeds the ultimate strength S_M in tension as follows: for cast iron, $S_R = 2S_M$; for sandstone, $S_R = 3S_M$; for concrete, $S_R = 2.2S_M$; for wood (green), $S_R = 2.3S_M$.

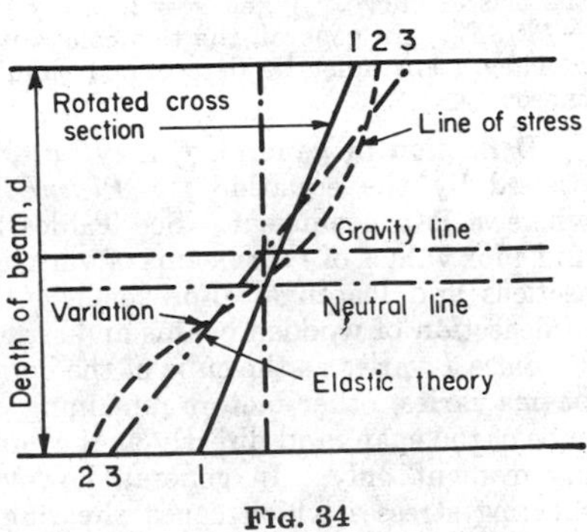

FIG. 34

In the case of steel I beams, failure begins practically when the elastic limit in the compression flange is reached.

Because of the support of adjoining material, the **elastic limit in flexure** S_p is also greater than in tension, depending upon the relation of breadth to depth of section. For the same breadth, the difference decreases with increase of height. No difference will occur in the case of an I beam, or with hard materials. Bauschinger quotes for soft steel plates, 1.27; Considère, 1.37; Hatt, 1.5 (*Railroad Gaz.*, 1899).

Wide plates will not expand and contract freely, and the value of E will be increased on account of side constraint. As a consequence of lateral contraction of the fibers of the tension side of a beam and lateral swelling of fibers at the compression side, the cross section becomes distorted to a trapezoidal shape, and the neutral axis is at the cg of the trapezoid. Strictly, this shape is one with a curved perimeter, the radius being r/μ, where r is the radius of the neutral line of the beam, and μ is Poisson's ratio.

Deflection of Beams

When a beam is subjected to bending, the fibers on one side elongate, while the fibers on the other side shorten (Fig. 35). These changes in length cause the beam to deflect. All points on the beam except those directly over the support fall below their original position, as shown in Figs. 31 and 35.

The **elastic curve** is the curve taken by the neutral axis. The radius of **curvature** at any point is

$$r = EI/M$$

A beam bent to a **circular curve** of constant radius has a constant bending moment.

Replacing r in the equation by its approximate geometrical value, $1/r = d^2y/(dx)^2$, the fundamental equation from which the elastic curve of a bent beam can be developed and the deflection of any beam obtained is,

$$M = EI\, d^2y/(dx)^2 \qquad \text{(approx)}$$

Substituting the value of M, in terms of x, and integrating once, gives the slope of the tangent to the elastic curve of the beam at point x; $\tan i = dy/dx = \int_0^x M\, dx/EI$. Since i is usually small, $\tan i = i$, expressed in radians. A second integration gives the vertical deflection of any point of the elastic curve from its original position.

Example. In the cantilever beam shown in Fig. 35, the bending moment at any section $= -P(l - x) = EI\, d^2y/(dx)^2$. Integrate and determine constant by the condition that when $x = 0$, $dy/dx = 0$. Then $EI\, dy/dx = -Plx + \frac{1}{2}Px^2$. Integrate again, and determine constant by the condition that when $x = 0$, $y = 0$. Then $EIy = -\frac{1}{2}Plx^2 + Px^3/6$. This is the equation of the elastic curve. When $x = l$, $y = f = -Pl^3/3EI$. In general, the two constants of integration must be determined simultaneously.

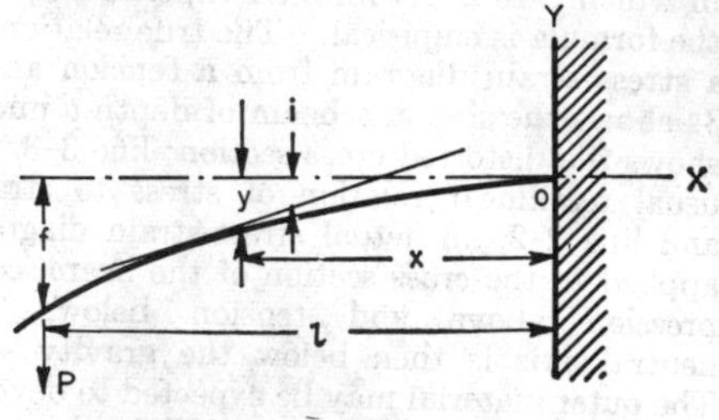

Fig. 35

Deflection in general, f, may be expressed by the equation $f = Pl^3/mEI$, where m is a coefficient. See Tables 2 and 4 for values of f for beams of various sections and loadings. For coefficients of deflection of wooden beams and structural steel shapes, see Sec. 12.

Since I varies as the cube of the depth, the **stiffness,** or inverse deflection, **of various beams** varies, other factors remaining constant, inversely as the load, inversely as the cube of the span, and directly as the cube of the depth. This deflection is due to bending moment only. In general, however, the bending of beams involves transverse shearing stresses which cause **shearing strains** and thus **add to the total deflection.** These strains may affect substantially the strength as well as the deflection of beams. When deflection due to transverse shear is to be accounted for, the differential equation of the elastic curve takes the form,

$$EI\frac{d^2y}{dx^2} = EI\left(\frac{d^2y_b}{dx^2} + \frac{d^2y_s}{dx^2}\right) = M - \frac{kEI}{AG} \times \frac{d^2M}{dx^2}$$

where k is a factor dependent upon the beam cross section. Sergius Sergev, in "The Effect of Shearing Forces on the Deflection and Strength of Beams" (*Univ. of Wash. Exp. Sta. Bull.* 114) gives $k = 1.2$ for rectangular sections, 10/9 for circular sections, and 2.4 for I beams. He also points out that in the case of a deep, rectangular-section cantilever, carrying a concentrated load at the free end, the deflection due to shear may be up to 3.1 percent of that due to bending moment; if this beam supports a uniformly distributed load, it may be up to 4.1 percent. A deep, simple beam deflection may increase up to 15.6 percent when carrying a uniformly distributed load and up to 12.5 percent when the load is concentrated at mid-span. These added deflections can be even larger for I beams.

Design of beams may be based on **strength** (stress) or on **stiffness** if deflection must be limited. When more than one beam shares a load, each beam will assume a portion of the load that is proportional to its stiffness. **Superposition** may be used in connection with both stresses and deflections.

EXAMPLE (Fig. 36). Two wooden stringers—one (A) 8 × 16 in. in cross section and 20 ft in span, the other (B) 8 in. × 8 in. × 16 ft—carry the center load P_0 = 22,000 lb. Required, the load carried by each stringer. The deflections, f, of the two stringers must be equal. Load on $A = P_1$, and on $B = P_2$. $f = P_1l_1^3/48EI_1 = P_2l_2^3/48EI_2$. Then $P_1/P_2 = l_2^3I_1/l_1^3I_2 = 4$. $P_0 = P_1 + P_2 = 4P_2 + P_2$, whence $P_2 = 22{,}000/5 =$ 4,400 lb and $P_1 = 4 \times 4{,}400 =$ 17,600 lb.

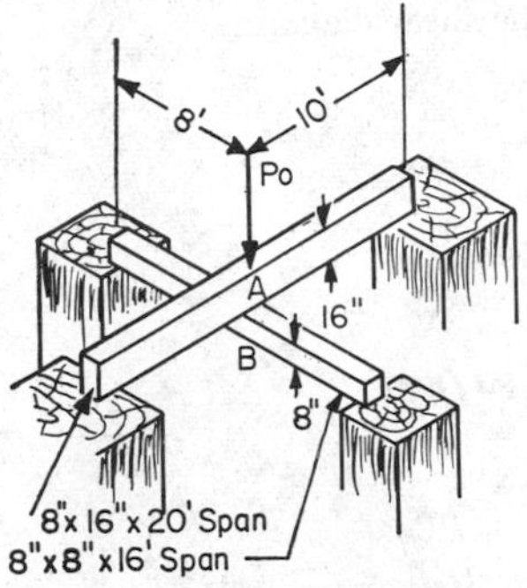

FIG. 36

Relation between Deflection and Stress

Combine the formula $M = SI/c = Pl/n$, where n is a constant, P = load, and l = span, with formula $f = Pl^3/mEI$, where m is a constant. Then

$$f = C''Sl^2/Ec$$

where C'' is a new constant $= n/m$. Other factors remaining the same, the **deflection varies directly as the stress and inversely as E.** If the span is constant, a shallow beam will submit to greater deformations than a deeper beam without exceeding a safe stress. If depth is constant, a beam of double span will attain a given deflection with only one-quarter the stress. Values of n, m, and C'' are given in Table 7 (for other values, see Table 2):

Table 7

Beam	Load	n	m	C''
Cantilever	Concentrated at end	1	3	1/3
Cantilever	Uniform	2	8	1/4
Simple	Concentrated at center	4	48	1/12
Simple	Uniform	8	384/5	5/48
Fixed ends	Concentrated at center	8	192	1/24
Fixed ends	Uniform	12	384	1/32
One end fixed One end supported	Concentrated at center	16/3	768/7	7/144
One end fixed One end supported	Uniform	128/9	185	1/13
Simple	Uniformly varying, maximum at center	6	60	1/10

Graphical Relations

Referring to Fig. 37, the shear V acting at any section is equal to the total load on the right of the section, or

$$V = \int w\,dx$$

Since $w\,dx$ is the product of w, a loading intensity (which is expressed as a vertical height in the load diagram), by dx, an elementary length along the horizontal, evidently $w\,dx$ is the area of a small vertical strip of the **load diagram**. Then $\int w\,dx$ is the summation of all such vertical strips between two indefinite points. Thus, to obtain the shear in any section mn, find the area of the load diagram up to that section, and draw a second diagram called the **shear diagram,** any ordinate of which is proportional to the shear, or to the area in the load diagram to the right of mn. Since $V = dM/dx$,

$$\int V\,dx = M$$

By similar reasoning, a **moment diagram** may be drawn, such that the ordinate at any point is proportional to the area of the shear diagram to the right of that point. Since $M = EI\, d^2f/(dx)^2$,

$$\int M\, dx = EI[(df/dx) + C] = EI(i + C)$$

if I is constant. Here C is a constant of integration. Thus i, the slope or grade of the elastic curve at any point, is proportional to the area of the moment diagram $\int M\, dx$ up to that point; and a **slope diagram** may be derived from the moment diagram in the same manner as the moment diagram was derived from the shear diagram.

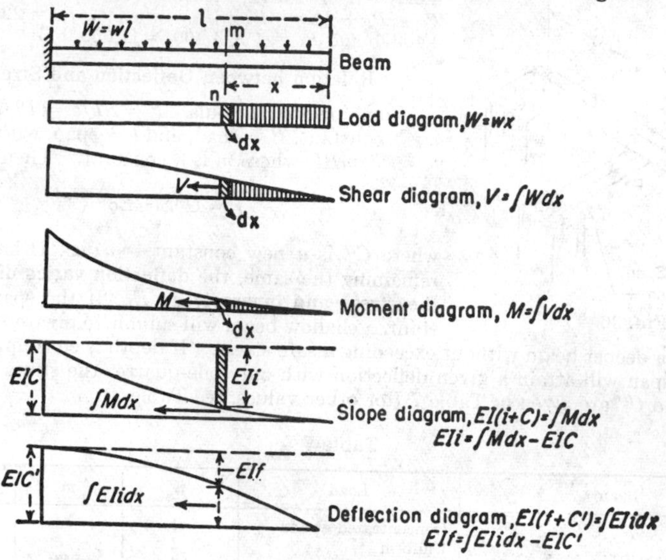

Fig. 37

If I is not constant, draw a new curve whose ordinates are M/I and use these M/I ordinates just as the M ordinates were used in the case where I was constant; that is, $\int(M/I)\, dx = E(i + C)$. The ordinate at any point of the slope curve is thus proportional to the area of the M/I curve to the right of that point. Again, since $iE = E\, df/dx$,

$$\int iE\, dx = \int E\, df = E(f + C')$$

and thus the ordinate f to the elastic curve at any point is proportional to the area of the slope diagram $\int i\, dx$ up to that point. The equilibrium polygon may be used in drawing the **deflection curve** directly from the M/I diagram.

Thus, the five curves of load, shear, moment, slope, and deflection are so related that each curve is derived from the previous one by a process of graphical integration, and with proper regard to scales the deflection is thereby obtained.

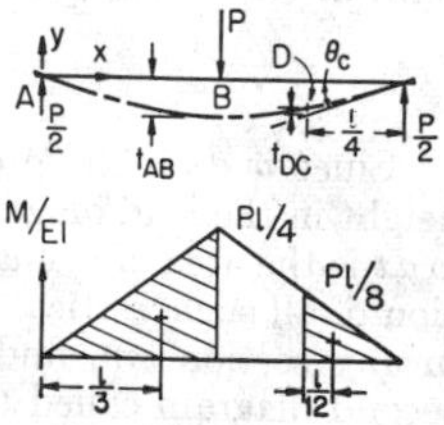

The vertical distance from any point A (Fig. 38) on the elastic curve of a beam to the tangent at any other point B equals the moment of the area of the M/EI diagram from A to B about A. This distance, the **tangential deviation, t_{AB},** may be used with the slope-area relation and the geometry of the elastic curve to obtain deflections. These theorems, together with the equilibrium equations, can be used to compute reactions in the case of statically **indeterminate beams.**

Fig. 38

EXAMPLE. The deflections of points B and D are

$$y_B = -t_{AB} = \text{moment area } \frac{M}{EI}\bigg|_A^B = -\frac{1}{EI} \times \frac{Pl}{4} \times \frac{l}{4} \times \frac{l}{3} = -\frac{Pl^3}{48EI}$$

$$\theta_C = \Delta\theta\bigg|_B^C = \text{area } \frac{M}{EI}\bigg|_B^C = \frac{1}{EI} \times \frac{Pl}{4} \times \frac{l}{4} = \frac{Pl^2}{16EI}$$

$$y_D = -\left(\theta_C \times \frac{l}{4} - t_{DC}\right) = -\frac{Pl^2}{16EI} \times \frac{l}{4} \times \frac{1}{EI} \times \frac{Pl}{8} \times \frac{l}{8} \times \frac{l}{12} = -\frac{11Pl^3}{768EI}$$

Resilience of Beams

The external work of a load gradually applied to a beam, and which increases from zero to P, is $\frac{1}{2}Pf$ and equals the **resilience** U. But, from the formulas $P = nSI/cl$ and $f = nSl^2/mcE$, where n and m are constants that depend upon loading and supports, S = fiber stress, c = distance from neutral axis to outer fiber, and l = length of span. Substitute for P and f, and

$$U = \frac{n^2}{m}\left(\frac{k}{c}\right)^2 \cdot \frac{S^2V}{2E}$$

where k is the radius of gyration, and V the volume of the beam. For values of U, see Table 1.

The resilience of beams of similar cross section at a given stress is proportional to their volumes. The **internal resilience,** or the elastic deformation energy in the material of a beam in a length x is dU, and

$$U = \tfrac{1}{2}\int M^2\, dx/EI = \tfrac{1}{2}\int M\, di$$

where M is the moment at any point x, and di is the angle between the tangents to the elastic curve at the ends of dx. The values of resilience and deflection in special cases are easily developed from this equation.

Rolling Loads

Rolling or **moving loads** are those loads which may change their position on a beam. Figure 39 represents a beam with two equal concentrated moving loads, such as two wheels on a crane girder, or the wheels of a truck on a bridge. Since the maximum

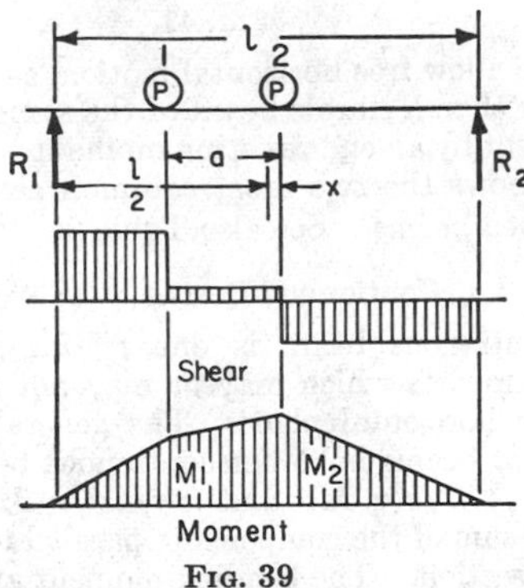

FIG. 39

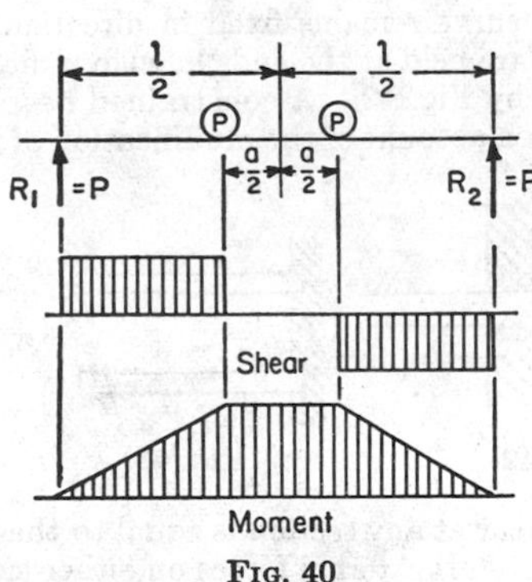

FIG. 40

moment occurs where the shear is zero, it is evident from the shear diagram that the maximum moment will occur under a wheel. $x < a/2$:

$$R_1 = P\left(1 - \frac{2x}{l} + \frac{a}{l}\right)$$

$$M_2 = \frac{Pl}{2}\left(1 - \frac{a}{l} + \frac{2x}{l}\frac{a}{l} - \frac{4x^2}{l^2}\right)$$

$$R_2 = P\left(1 + \frac{2x}{l} - \frac{a}{l}\right)$$

$$M_1 = \frac{Pl}{2}\left(1 - \frac{a}{l} - \frac{2a^2}{l^2} + \frac{2x}{l}\frac{3a}{l} - \frac{4x^2}{l^2}\right)$$

$$M_2 \text{ max when } x = \tfrac{1}{4}a$$

$$M_1 \text{ max when } x = \tfrac{3}{4}a$$

$$M_{max} = \frac{Pl}{2}\left(1 - \frac{a}{2l}\right)^2 = \frac{P}{2l}\left(l - \frac{a}{2}\right)^2$$

EXAMPLE. Two wheel loads of 3,000 lb each, spaced on 5 ft centers, move on a span of $l = 15$ ft, $x = 1.25$ ft, and $R_2 = 2{,}500$ lb. $\therefore\ M_{max} = M_2 = 2{,}500 \times 6.25 = 15{,}600$ lb-ft.

Figure 40 shows the condition when two equal loads are equally distant on opposite sides of the center. The moment is equal under the two loads.

If the **two moving loads** are **of unequal weight,** the condition for **maximum moment** is that the maximum moment will occur under the heavy wheel when the center of the beam bisects the distance between the resultant of the loads and the heavy wheel. Figure 41 shows this position and the shear and moment diagrams.

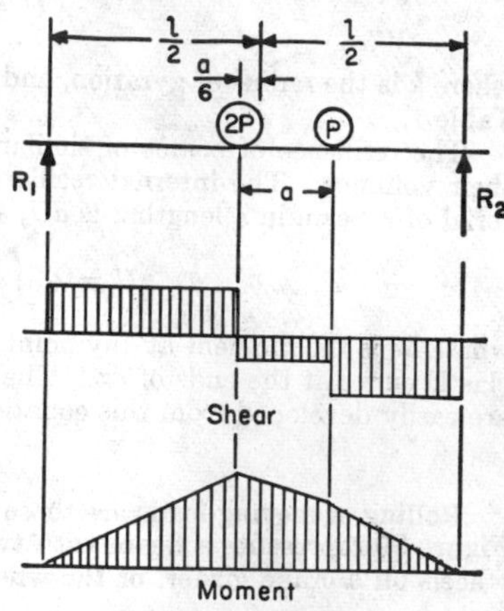

FIG. 41

When **several wheel loads** constituting a system occur, the several suspected wheels must be examined in turn to determine which will cause the greatest moment. The **position for the greatest moment** that can occur under a given wheel is, as stated, when the center of the span bisects the distance between the wheel in question and the resultant of all the loads then on the span. The **position for maximum shear** at the support will be when one wheel is passing off the span.

Constrained Beams

Constrained beams are those so held or "built in" at one or both ends that the tangent to the elastic curve remains fixed in direction. These beams are held at the ends in such a manner as to allow free horizontal motion, as illustrated by Fig. 42. A constrained beam is stiffer than a simple beam of the same material, on account of the modification of the moment by an end resisting moment. Figure 43 shows the two most common cases of constrained beams. See also Table 2.

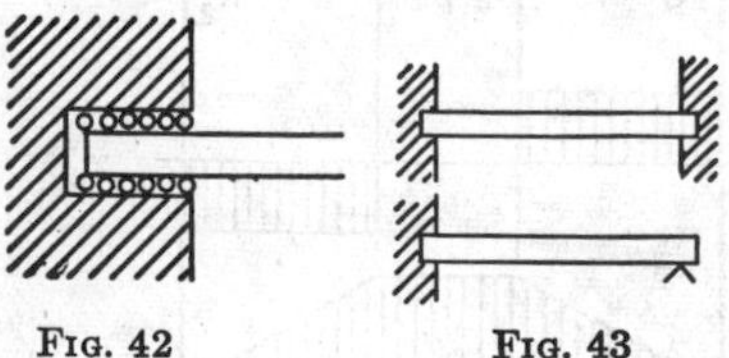
FIG. 42 FIG. 43

Continuous Beams

A continuous beam is one resting upon several supports which may or may not be in the same horizontal plane. The general discussion for beams holds for continuous beams. $S_vA = V$, $SI/c = M$, and $d^2f/dx^2 = M/EI$. The **shear** at any section is equal to the algebraic sum of the components parallel to the section of all external forces on either side of the section. The bending moment at any section is equal to the moment of all external forces on either side of the section. The relations stated above between shear and moment diagrams hold true for continuous beams. The bending moment at any section is equal to the bending moment at any other section, plus the shear at that section times its arm, plus the product of all the intervening external forces times their respective arms. To illustrate (Fig. 44):

$$V_x = R_1 + R_2 + R_3 - P_1 - P_2 - P_3$$

$$M_x = R_1(l_1 + l_2 + x) + R_2(l_2 + x) + R_3x - P_1(l_2 + c + x) - P_2(b + x) - P_3a$$

$$M_x = M_3 + V_3x - P_3a$$

Table 8 gives the value of the moment at the various supports of a uniformly loaded continuous beam over equal spans, and it also gives the values of the shears on each side of the supports. Note that the shear is of opposite sign on either side of the supports and that the sum of the two shears is equal to the reaction.

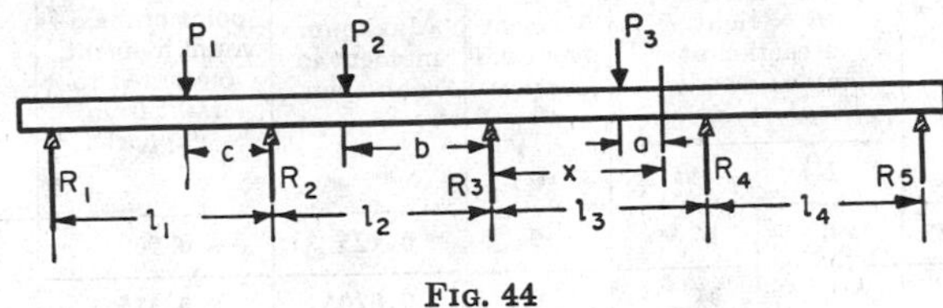

Fig. 44

Figure 45 shows the relation between the moment and shear diagrams for a uniformly loaded continuous beam of four equal spans (see Table 8). Table 8 also gives the **maximum bending moment** which will occur **between supports,** and in addition the position of this moment and the points of inflection (see Fig. 46).

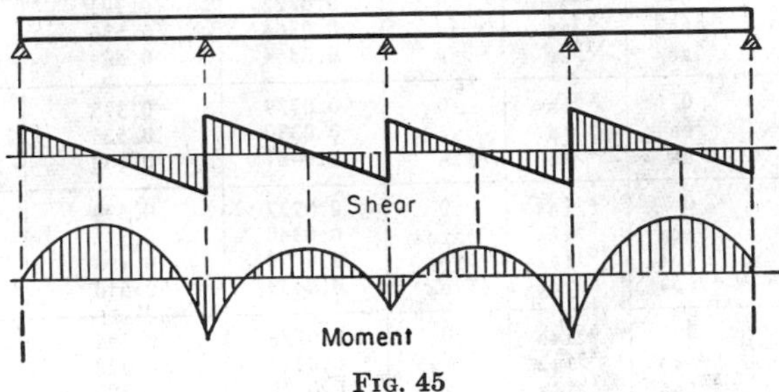

Fig. 45

Figure 46 shows the values of the functions for a uniformly loaded continuous beam resting on three equal spans with four supports.

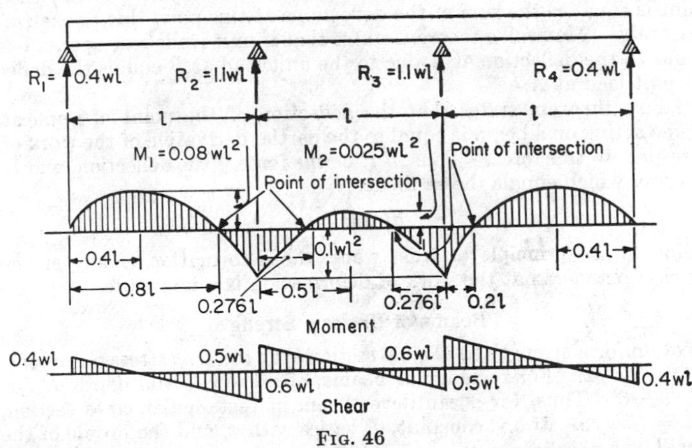

Fig. 46

Continuous beams are **stronger and much stiffer than simple beams.** However, a small, unequal subsidence of piers will cause serious changes in sign and magnitude of the bending stresses, reactions, and shears.

Table 8. Uniformly Loaded Continuous Beams over Equal Spans

(Uniform load per unit length = w; length of each span = l)

Number of supports	Notation of support of span	Shear on each side of support. L = left, R = right. Reaction at any support is $L + R$		Moment over each support	Maximum moment in each span	Distance to point of maximum moment, measured to right from support	Distance to point of inflection, measured to right from support
		L	R				
2	1 or 2	0	1/2	0	0.125	0.500	None
3	1	0	3/8	0	0.0703	0.375	0.750
	2	5/8	5/8	1/8	0.0703	0.625	0.250
4	1	0	4/10	0	0.080	0.400	0.800
	2	6/10	5/10	1/10	0.025	0.500	0.276, 0.724
5	1	0	11/28	0	0.0772	0.393	0.786
	2	17/28	15/28	3/28	0.0364	0.536	0.266, 0.806
	3	13/28	13/28	2/28	0.0364	0.464	0.194, 0.734
6	1	0	15/38	0	0.0779	0.395	0.789
	2	23/38	20/38	4/38	0.0332	0.526	0.268, 0.783
	3	18/38	19/38	3/38	0.0461	0.500	0.196, 0.804
7	1	0	41/104	0	0.0777	0.394	0.788
	2	63/104	55/104	11/104	0.0340	0.533	0.268, 0.790
	3	49/104	51/104	8/104	0.0433	0.490	0.196, 0.785
	4	53/104	53/104	9/104	0.0433	0.510	0.215, 0.804
8	1	0	56/142	0	0.0778	0.394	0.789
	2	86/142	75/142	15/142	0.0338	0.528	0.268, 0.788
	3	67/142	70/142	11/142	0.0440	0.493	0.196, 0.790
	4	72/142	71/142	12/142	0.0405	0.500	0.215, 0.785
Values apply to		wl	wl	wl^2	wl^2	l	l

The numerical values given are coefficients of the expressions at the foot of each column.

Maxwell's Theorem. When a number of loads rest upon a beam, the deflection at any point is equal to the sum of the deflections at this point due to each of the loads taken separately. Maxwell's theorem states that if unit loads rest upon a beam at two points A and B, the deflection at A due to the unit load at B equals the deflection at B due to the unit load at A.

Castigliano's theorem states that the deflection of the point of application of an external force acting on a beam is equal to the partial derivative of the work of deformation with respect to this force. Thus, if P be the force, f the deflection, and U the work of deformation, which equals the resilience,

$$dU/dP = f$$

According to the **principle of least work,** the deformation of any structure takes place in such a manner that the work of deformation is a minimum.

Beams of Uniform Strength

Beams of uniform strength so vary in section that the unit stress S remains constant, and I/c varies as M. For **rectangular beams,** of breadth b and depth d, $I/c = bd^2/6$; and $M = Sbd^2/6$. Thus, for a cantilever beam of rectangular cross section, under a load P, $Px = Sbd^2/6$. If b is constant, d^2 varies with x, and the profile of the shape of the beam will be a parabola, as Fig. 47. **If d is constant, b will vary as x and the beam will be triangular in plan, as shown in Fig. 48.**

Table 9. Beams of Uniform Strength (in Bending)

1. Fixed at One End, Load P Concentrated at Other End

Beam	Cross section	Elevation and plan	Formulas
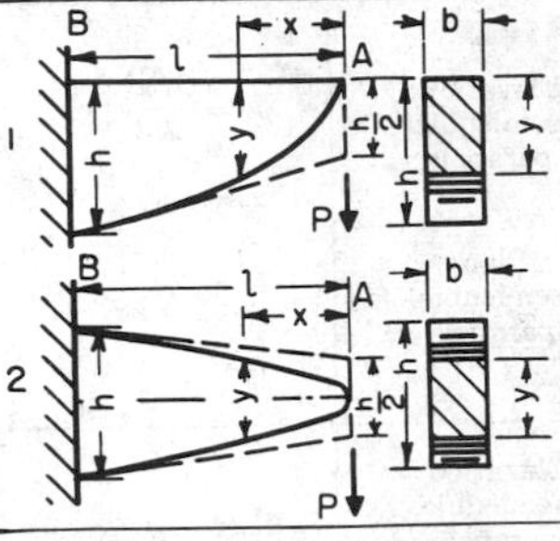 1, 2	Rectangle: width (b) constant, depth (y) variable	Elevation: 1, top, straight line; bottom, parabola. 2, complete parabola Plan: rectangle	$y^2 = \frac{6P}{bS_s}x$ $h = \sqrt{\frac{6Pl}{bS_s}}$ Deflection at A: $f = \frac{8P}{bE}\left(\frac{l}{h}\right)^3$
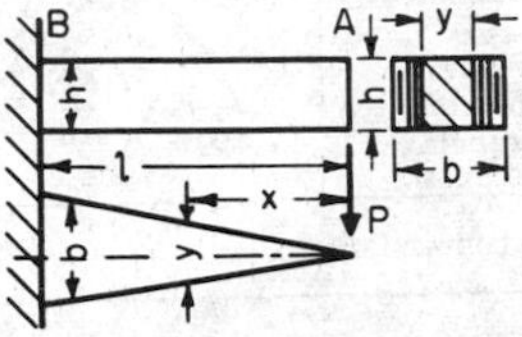	Rectangle: width (y) variable, depth (h) constant	Elevation: rectangle Plan: triangle	$y = \frac{6P}{h^2S_s}x$ $b = \frac{6Pl}{h^2S_s}$ Deflection at A: $f = \frac{6P}{bE}\left(\frac{l}{h}\right)^3$
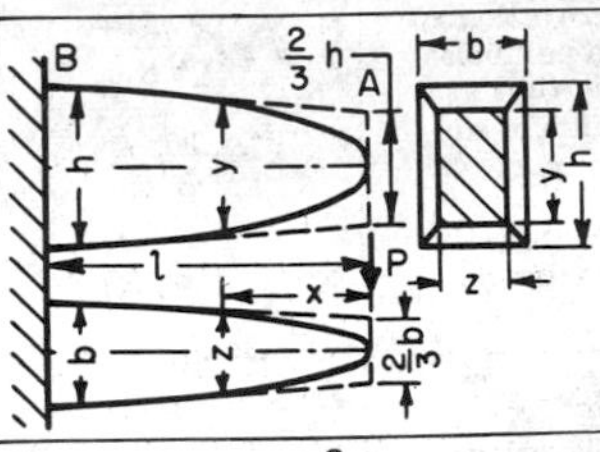	Rectangle: width (z) variable, depth (y) variable $\frac{z}{y} = k$ (const)	Elevation: cubic parabola Plan: cubic parabola	$y^3 = \frac{6P}{kS_s}x$ $z = ky$ $h = \sqrt[3]{\frac{6Pl}{kS_s}}$ $b = kh$
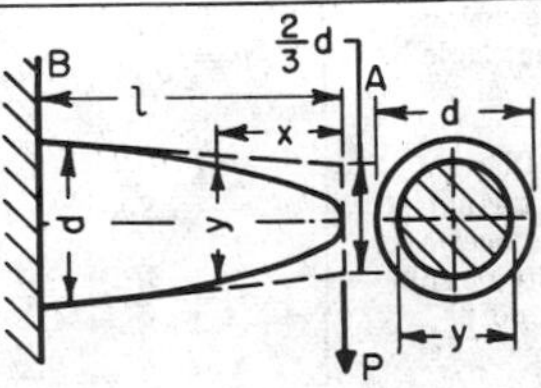	Circle: diam (y) variable	Elevation: cubic parabola Plan: cubic parabola	$y^3 = \frac{32P}{\pi S_s}x$ $d = \sqrt[3]{\frac{32Pl}{\pi S_s}}$

2. Fixed at One End, Load P Uniformly Distributed over l

Beam	Cross section	Elevation and plan	Formulas
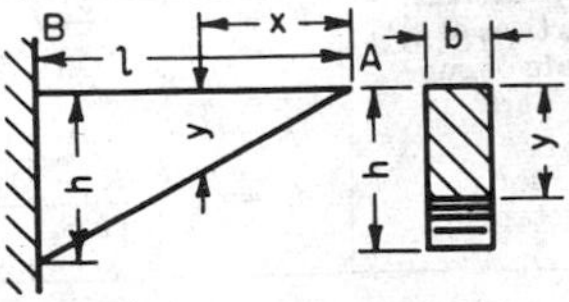	Rectangle: width (b) constant, depth (y) variable	Elevation: triangle Plan: rectangle	$y = x\sqrt{\frac{3P}{blS}}$ $h = \sqrt{\frac{3Pl}{bS_s}}$ $f = 6\frac{P}{bE}\left(\frac{l}{h}\right)^3$
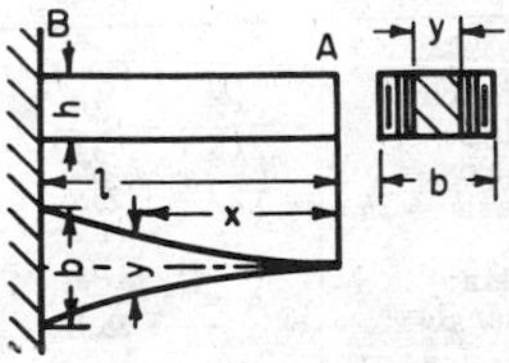	Rectangle: width (y) variable, depth (h) constant	Elevation: rectangle Plan: two parabolic curves with vertices at free end	$y = \frac{3Px^2}{lS_sh^2}$ $b = \frac{3Pl}{S_sh^2}$ Deflection at A: $f = \frac{3P}{bE}\left(\frac{l}{h}\right)^3$

Table 9. Beams of Uniform Strength (in Bending)—*(Continued)*

2. Fixed at One End, Load P Uniformly Distributed over l

Beam	Cross section	Elevation and plan	Formulas
	Rectangle: width (z) variable, depth (y) variable, $\frac{z}{y} = k$	Elevation: semicubic parabola Plan: semicubic parabola	$y^3 = \frac{3Px^2}{kS_s l}$ $z = ky$ $h = \sqrt[3]{\frac{3Pl}{kS_s}}$ $b = kh$
	Circle: diam (y) variable	Elevation: semicubic parabola Plan: semicubic parabola	$y^3 = \frac{16P}{\pi l S_s} x^2$ $d = \sqrt[3]{\frac{16Pl}{\pi S_s}}$

3. Supported at Both Ends, Load P Concentrated at Point C

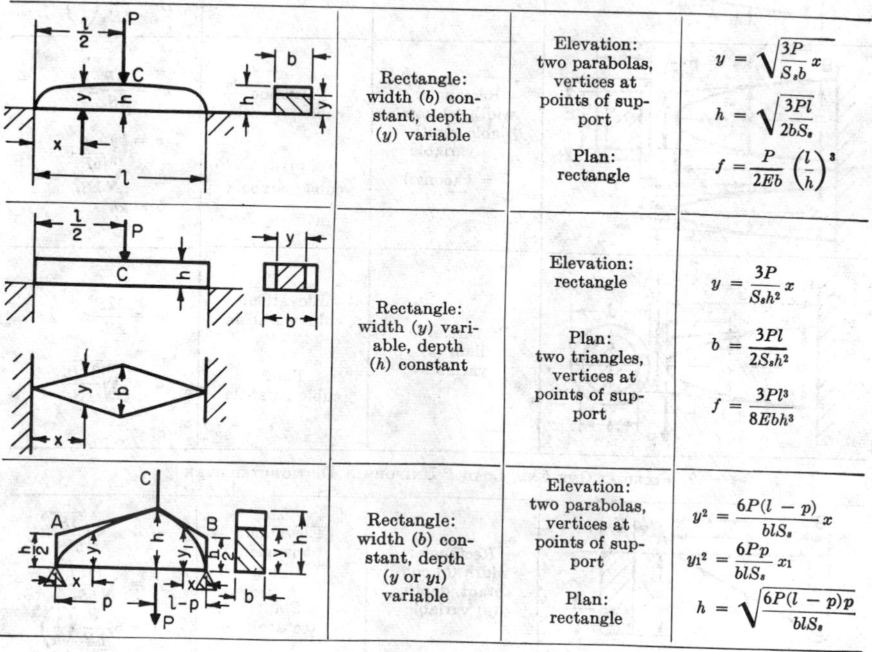

Beam	Cross section	Elevation and plan	Formulas
	Rectangle: width (b) constant, depth (y) variable	Elevation: two parabolas, vertices at points of support Plan: rectangle	$y = \sqrt{\frac{3P}{S_s b} x}$ $h = \sqrt{\frac{3Pl}{2bS_s}}$ $f = \frac{P}{2Eb}\left(\frac{l}{h}\right)^3$
	Rectangle: width (y) variable, depth (h) constant	Elevation: rectangle Plan: two triangles, vertices at points of support	$y = \frac{3P}{S_s h^2} x$ $b = \frac{3Pl}{2S_s h^2}$ $f = \frac{3Pl^3}{8Ebh^3}$
	Rectangle: width (b) constant, depth (y or y_1) variable	Elevation: two parabolas, vertices at points of support Plan: rectangle	$y^2 = \frac{6P(l - p)}{blS_s} x$ $y_1^2 = \frac{6Pp}{blS_s} x_1$ $h = \sqrt{\frac{6P(l - p)p}{blS_s}}$

Load P Moving across Span

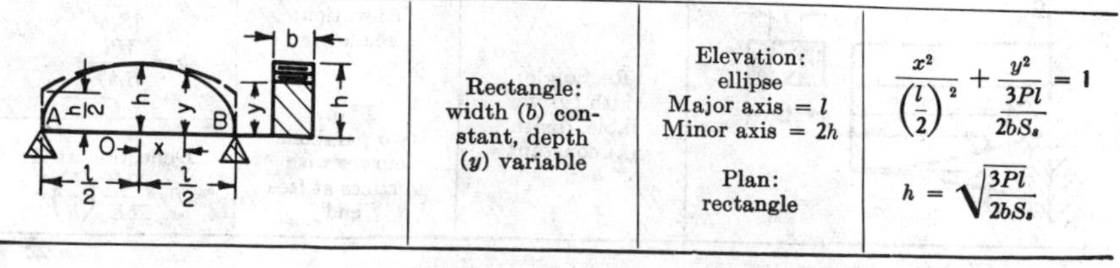

Beam	Cross section	Elevation and plan	Formulas
	Rectangle: width (b) constant, depth (y) variable	Elevation: ellipse, Major axis $= l$, Minor axis $= 2h$ Plan: rectangle	$\frac{x^2}{\left(\frac{l}{2}\right)^2} + \frac{y^2}{\frac{3Pl}{2bS_s}} = 1$ $h = \sqrt{\frac{3Pl}{2bS_s}}$

Table 9. Beams of Uniform Strength (in Bending)—(*Continued*)

4. Supported at Both Ends, Load P Uniformly Distributed over l

Beam	Cross section	Elevation and plan	Formulas
	Rectangle: width (b) constant, depth (y) variable	Elevation: ellipse Plan: rectangle	$\frac{x^2}{\left(\frac{l}{2}\right)^2} + \frac{y^2}{\frac{3Pl}{4bS_s}} = 1$ $h = \sqrt{\frac{3Pl}{4bS_s}}$ Deflection at O: $f = \frac{1}{64}\frac{Pl^3}{EI} = \frac{3}{16}\frac{P}{bE}\left(\frac{l}{h}\right)^3$
	Rectangle: width (y) variable, depth (h) constant	Elevation: rectangle Plan: two parabolas with vertices at center of span	$y = \frac{3P}{S_s h^2}\left(x - \frac{x^2}{l}\right)$ $b = \frac{3Pl}{4S_s h^2}$

Shear at the end of a beam necessitates a modification of the forms determined above. The area required to resist shear will be P/S_v in a cantilever and R/S_v in a simple beam. The dotted extensions in Figs. 47 and 48 show the changes necessary to enable these

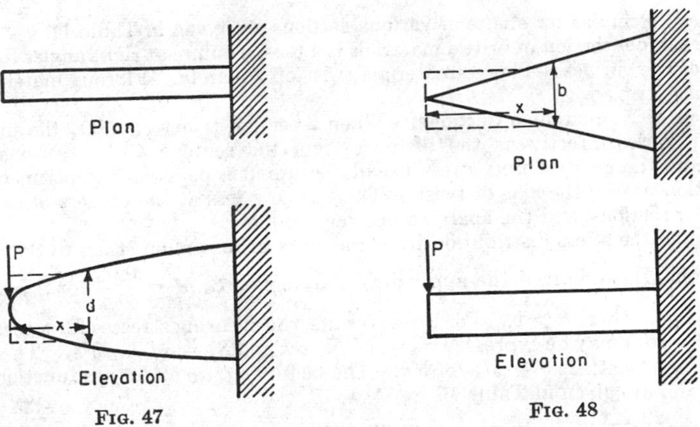

Fig. 47

Fig. 48

cantilevers to resist shear. The waste in material and extra cost in fabricating, however, make many of the forms impractical, except for cast iron.

Table 9 shows some of the simple **sections of uniform strength.** In none of these, however, is shear taken into account.

TORSION

Under torsion, a bar (Fig. 49) is twisted by a couple of the value Pp. Elements of the surface become helices of angle d, and a radius rotates through an angle a in a length l, both d and a being expressed in radians. S_v = shearing unit stress at distance r from center; I_P = polar moment of inertia; G = shearing modulus of elasticity. It is assumed that the cross sections remain plane surfaces. The strain on the cross section is wholly tangential, and is zero at the center of the section. $ld = ra$.

In the case of a **circular cross section,** the stress S_v increases directly as the distance of the strained element from the center.

The polar moment of inertia I_P for any section may be obtained from $I_P = I_1 + I_2$, where I_1 and I_2 are the rectangular moments of inertia of the section about any two lines at right angles to each other, through the center of gravity.

The **external twisting moment** M_t is balanced by the internal resisting moment.

For strength, $M_t = S_v I_P / r$.

For stiffness, $M_t = aGI_P/l$.

FIG. 49

The torsional resilience $U = \frac{1}{2}Ppa = S_v^2 I_P l / 2r^2 G = a^2 G I_P / 2l$.

The state of stress on an element taken from the surface of the shaft, as in **Fig. 50,** is pure shear. Pure tension exists at right angles to one 45 deg helix and pure compression at right angles to the opposite helix.

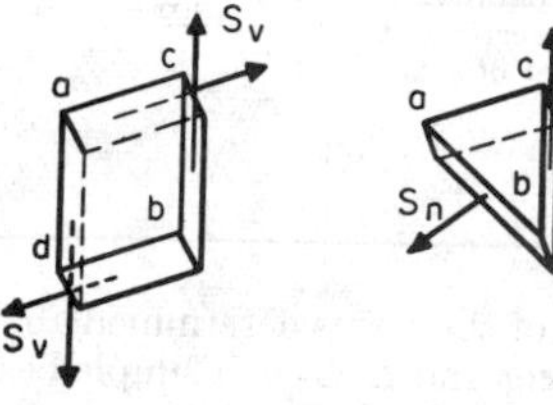

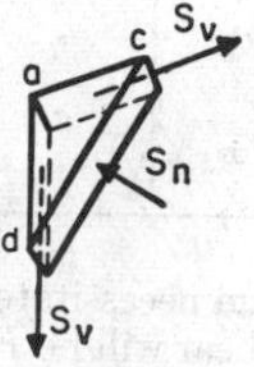

FIG. 50

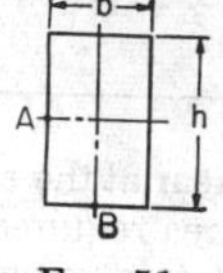

FIG. 51

Reduced **formulas for shafts of various sections** are given in Table 11.

Failure under torsion in brittle materials is a tensile failure at right angles to a helical element of the surface. Plastic materials twist off squarely. Fibrous materials separate in long strips.

Torsion of Non-circular Sections. When a section is not circular, the unit stress no longer varies directly as the distance from the center. Cross sections become warped, and the greatest unit stress usually occurs at a point on the perimeter of the cross section *nearest* the axis of twist. There is no stress at the corners of square and rectangular sections, and the analyses become complex.

Assuming the stress distribution from the point of maximum stress to the corner to be parabolic, Bach derived the approximate expression $S_s M = \dfrac{9M_t}{2b^2h}$ for a rectangular section, b by h, where $h > b$. For closer results, the shearing stresses for a **rectangular section (Fig. 51) may be expressed** $S_A = M_t/\alpha_A b^2 h$ **and** $S_B = M_t/\alpha_B b^2 h$. The angle of twist for these shafts is $\theta = M_t l/\beta G b^3 h$. The factors α_A, α_B and β are functions of the ratio h/b and are given in Table 10.

Table 10. Factors for Torsion of Rectangular Shafts

h/b	1.00	1.50	1.75	2.00	2.50	3.00	4.00	5.00	6.00	8.00	10.0	∞
α_A	0.208	0.231	0.239	0.246	0.258	0.267	0.282	0.291	0.299	0.307	0.312	0.333
α_B	0.208	0.269	0.291	0.309	0.336	0.355	0.378	0.392	0.402	0.414	0.421	
β	0.141	0.196	0.214	0.229	0.249	0.263	0.281	0.291	0.299	0.307	0.312	0.333

In the case of **composite sections,** such as a tee or angle, the torque that can be resisted is $M_t = G\,\theta\Sigma\beta h b^3$; the summation applies to each of the rectangles into which the section can be divided. The maximum stress occurs on the component rectangle having the largest b value. It is computed from

$$S_A = M_t \beta_A b_A / \alpha_A \Sigma \beta h b^3$$

Torque, deflection, and work relations for some additional sections are given in Table 11.

Table 11. Torsion of Shafts of Various Cross Sections

(For strength and stiffness of shafts, see Sec. 8)

Cross section	Torsional resisting moment M_t	Angular twist, θ_1 (length = 1 in., radius = 1 in.)		Work of torsion (V = volume)
		In terms of torsional moment	In terms of max shear	
d	$\frac{\pi}{16} d^3 S_v$	$\frac{M_t}{GI_P} = \frac{32}{\pi d^4}\frac{M_t}{G}$	$2\frac{S_{v_{max}}}{G}\frac{1}{d}$	$\frac{1}{4}\frac{S_{v\,max}^2}{G}V$ (Note 1)
d, D	$\frac{\pi}{16}\frac{D^4 - d^4}{D} S_v$	$\frac{32}{\pi(D^4 - d^4)}\frac{M_t}{G}$	$2\frac{S_{v_{max}}}{G}\frac{1}{D}$	$\frac{1}{4}\frac{S_{v\,max}^2}{G}\frac{D^2 + d^2}{D^2}V$ (Note 2)
B, A, h, b	$\frac{\pi}{16} b^2 h S_v$ $(h > b)$	$\frac{16}{\pi}\frac{b^2 + h^2}{b^3 h^3}\frac{M_t}{G}$	$\frac{S_{v_{max}}}{G}\frac{b^2 + h^2}{bh^2}$	$\frac{1}{8}\frac{S_{v\,max}^2}{G}\frac{b^2 + h^2}{h^2}V$ (Note 3)
h, b	$\frac{2}{9} b^2 h S_v$ $(h > b)$	$3.6\frac{b^2 + h^2}{b^3 h^3}\frac{M_t}{G}$*	$0.8\frac{S_{v_{max}}}{G}\frac{b^2 + h^2}{bh^2}$*	$\frac{4}{45}\frac{S_{v\,max}^2}{G}\frac{b^2 + h^2}{h^2}V$ (Note 4)
h, h	$\frac{2}{9} h^3 S_v$	$7.2\frac{1}{h^4}\frac{M_t}{G}$	$1.6\frac{S_{v_{max}}}{G}\frac{1}{h}$	$\frac{8}{45}\frac{S_{v\,max}^2}{G}V$ (Note 5)
b, b, b	$\frac{b^3}{20} S_v$	$46.2\frac{1}{b^4}\frac{M_t}{G}$	$2.31\frac{S_{v_{max}}}{G}\frac{1}{b}$	
b, b	$\frac{b^3}{1.09} S_v$	$0.967\frac{1}{b^4}\frac{M_t}{G}$	$0.9\frac{S_{v_{max}}}{G}\frac{1}{b}$	

* When	h/b = 1	2	4	8
Coefficient 3.6 becomes	= 3.56	3.50	3.35	3.21
Coefficient 0.8 becomes	= 0.79	0.78	0.74	0.71

NOTES. (1) $S_{v_{max}}$ at circumference. (2) $S_{v_{max}}$ at outer circumference. (3) $S_{v_{max}}$ at A; $S_{vB} = 16M_t/\pi bh^2$. (4) $S_{v_{max}}$ at middle of side h; in middle of b, $S_v = 9M_t/2bh^2$. (5) $S_{v\max}$ at middle of side.

COLUMNS AND INSTABILITY

Members subjected to direct compression can be grouped into three classes. **Compression blocks** are so short (slenderness ratios below 30) that bending of member is not pending. At the other limit, columns so slender that bending is primary, are the **long columns** defined by Euler's theory. The intermediate columns, quite common in practice, are called **short columns.**

Long columns and the more slender short columns usually fail by **buckling** when the **critical load** is reached. This is a matter of **instability**; that is, the column may continue to yield and deflect even though the load is not being increased above critical. The **slenderness ratio** is the unsupported length divided by the least radius of gyration, parallel to which it can bend.

Long columns are handled by **Euler's column formula,**

$$P_{cr} = n\pi^2 EI/l^2 = n\pi^2 EA/(l/r)^2$$

The **coefficient** n accounts for **end conditions.** When the column is pivoted at both ends, $n = 1$; when one end is fixed and other rounded, $n = 2$; when both are fixed, $n = 4$; and when one end is fixed with the other free, $n = \frac{1}{4}$. The slenderness ratio that separates long columns from short ones depends upon the modulus of elasticity and the yield strength of the column material. When Euler's formula results in $(P_{cr}/A) > S_y$, strength rather than buckling causes failure, and the column ceases to be long. In round numbers, this **critical slenderness ratio** falls between 120 and 150. Table 12 gives additional facts concerning long columns.

Table 12. Strength of Round-ended Columns According to Euler's Formula

Material	Cast iron	Wrought iron	Low-carbon steel	Medium-carbon steel
Ultimate compressive strength, psi	107,000	53,400	62,600	89,000
Allowable compressive stress, psi (maximum)	7,100	15,400	17,000	20,000
Modulus of elasticity	14,200,000	28,400,000	30,600,000	31,300,000
Factor of safety	8	5	5	5
Smallest I allowable at worst section, in.^{4}	$\frac{Pl^2}{17,500,000}$	$\frac{Pl^2}{56,000,000}$	$\frac{Pl^2}{60,300,000}$	$\frac{Pl^2}{61,700,000}$
Limit of ratio, $l/r >$	50.0	60.6	59.4	55.6
Rectangle ($r = b\sqrt{1/12}$), $l/b >$	14.4	17.5	17.2	16.0
Circle ($r = \frac{1}{4}d$), $l/d >$	12.5	15.2	14.9	13.9
Circular ring of small thickness ($r = d\sqrt{1/8}$), $l/d >$	17.6	21.4	21.1	19.7

(P = allowable load, lb; l = length of column, in.; b = smallest dimension of a rectangular section, in.; d = diameter of a circular section, in.; r = least radius of gyration of section.)

Short Columns. The stress in a short column may be considered partly due to compression and partly due to bending. A theoretical equation has not been derived. Empirical, though rational, expressions are, in general, based on the assumption that the permissible stress must be reduced below that which could be permitted were it due to compression only. The manner in which this reduction is made determines the type of equation as well as the slenderness ratio beyond which the equation does not apply. Figure 52 illustrates the situation. Some typical formulas are given in Table 13.

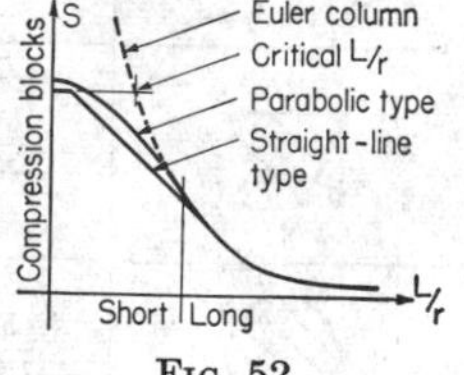

FIG. 52

EXAMPLE. A machine member unsupported for a length of 15 in. has a square cross section 0.5 in. on a side. It is to be subjected to compression. What maximum safe load can be applied centrally, according to the AISC formula? At the computed load, what size section (also square) would be needed, if it were to be designed according to the AREA formula?

$$l/r = 15/.5/\sqrt{12} = 104, \therefore \text{short column}$$

$$P/A = 17{,}000 - 0.485\ (104)^2 = 11{,}730$$

or

$$P = .25 \times 11{,}730 = 2{,}940 \text{ lb}$$

and

$$\frac{2{,}940}{a^2} \leq 15{,}000 - 50\ (15/a/\sqrt{12}) = 15{,}000 - \frac{2600}{a}$$

thus

$$a^2 - 0.173a - 0.196 = 0 \qquad \text{or} \qquad a = 0.536 \text{ in.}$$

Table 13. Typical Short-column Formulas

Formula	Material	Code	Slenderness ratio
$S_w = 17{,}000\text{–}0.485\left(\frac{l}{r}\right)^2$	Carbon steels	AISC	$l/r < 120$
$S_w = 16{,}000\text{–}70\ (l/r)$	Carbon steels	Chicago	$l/r < 120$
$S_w = 15{,}000\text{–}50\left(\frac{l}{r}\right)$	Carbon steels	AREA	$l/r < 150$
$S_w = 19{,}000\text{–}100\ (l/r)$	Carbon steels	Am. Br. Co.	$60 < \frac{l}{r} < 120$
$* S_{cr} = 135{,}000 - \frac{15.9}{c}\left(\frac{l}{r}\right)^2$	Alloy-steel tubing	ANC	$\frac{l}{\sqrt{c}\,r} < 65$
$S_w = 9{,}000\text{–}40\left(\frac{l}{r}\right)$	Cast iron	NYC	$\frac{l}{r} < 70$
$* S_{cr} = 34{,}500 - \frac{245}{\sqrt{c}}\left(\frac{l}{r}\right)$	2017ST Aluminum	ANC	$\frac{l}{\sqrt{c}\,r} < 94$
$* S_{cr} = 5{,}000 - \frac{0.5}{c}\left(\frac{l}{r}\right)^2$	Spruce	ANC	$\frac{l}{\sqrt{c}\,r} < 72$
$* S_{cr} = S_y\left[1 - \frac{S_y}{4n\pi^2 E}\left(\frac{l}{r}\right)^2\right]$	Steels	Johnson	$\frac{l}{r} < \sqrt{\frac{2n\pi^2 E}{S_y}}$
$\dagger\ S_{cr} = \dfrac{S_y}{1 + \frac{ec}{r^2}\sec\left(\frac{l}{r}\sqrt{\frac{P}{4AE}}\right)}$	Steels	Secant	$\frac{l}{r} <$ critical

* S_{cr} = theoretical maximum, c = end fixity coefficient,
$c = 2$, both ends pivoted, $c = 2.86$, one pivoted, other fixed,
$c = 4$, both ends fixed, $c = l$, one fixed, one free.
† e is initial eccentricity at which load is applied to center of column cross section.

Combined Flexure and Longitudinal Force. Figure 53 shows a bar under flexure due to transverse and longitudinal loads. The maximum fiber stress S is made up of S_0, due to the direct action of load P, and S_b, due to the entire bending moment M. M is the algebraic sum of two bending moments, M_1 due to longitudinal load (+ for compression and − for tension), and M_2 due to transverse load. $M = M_2 \pm M_1$. Here $M_1 = Pf$ and $f = CS_bl^2/Ec$. *For the Case of Longitudinal Compression.* $S_bI/c = M_2 + CPS_bl^2/Ec$, or $S_b = M_2c/(I - CPl^2/E)$. The maximum stress is $S = S_b + S_0$ compression. The constant C for the case of Fig. 53 is derived from the equations $P'l/4 = S_bI/c$ and $f = P'l^3/48EI$. Solving for f; $f = \frac{1}{12}S_bl^2/Ec$, or $C = \frac{1}{12}$. For a beam supported at the ends and uniformly loaded, $C = \frac{5}{48}$. Other cases can be similarly calculated.

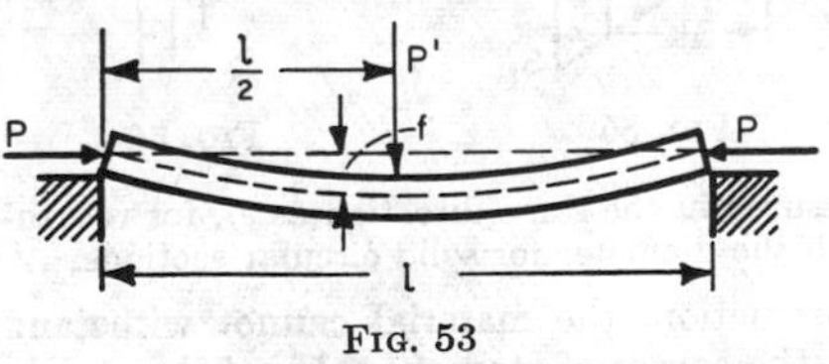

FIG. 53

For the Case of Longitudinal Tension. $M = M_2 - Pf$, and $S_b = M_2c/(I + CPl^2/E)$. The maximum stress is $S = S_b + S_0$, tension.

ECCENTRIC LOADS

When **short blocks** are **loaded eccentrically** in compression or in tension, *i.e.*, not through the center of gravity (cg), a combination of axial and bending stress results.

The maximum unit stress S_M is the algebraic sum of these two unit stresses.

In **Fig. 54** a load P acts in a line of symmetry at the distance e from cg; r = radius

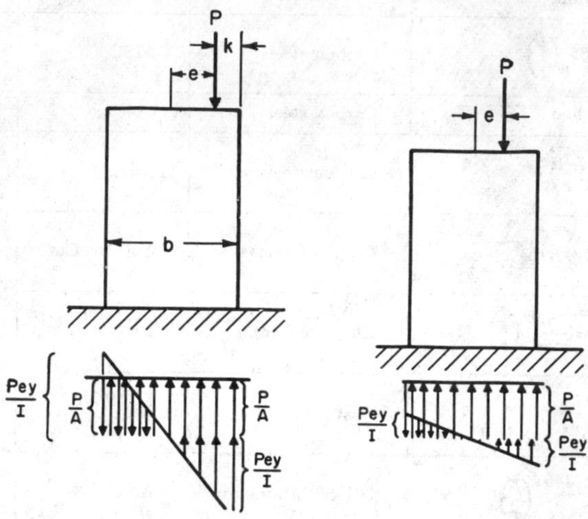

Fig. 54

of gyration. The unit stresses are (1) S_c, due to P, as if it acted through cg, and (2) S_b, due to the bending moment of P acting with a leverage of e about cg. Thus unit stress S at any point y is

$$S = S_c \pm S_b$$
$$= (P/A) \pm Pey/I$$
$$= S_c(1 \pm ey/r^2)$$

y is positive for points on the same side of cg as P, and negative on the opposite side. For a **rectangular cross section** of width b, the maximum stress $S_M = S_c(1 + 6e/b)$. When P is outside the middle third of width b and is a compressive load, tensile stresses occur.

For a **circular cross section** of diameter d, $S_M = S_c(1 + 8e/d)$. The stress due to the weight of the solid will modify these relations.

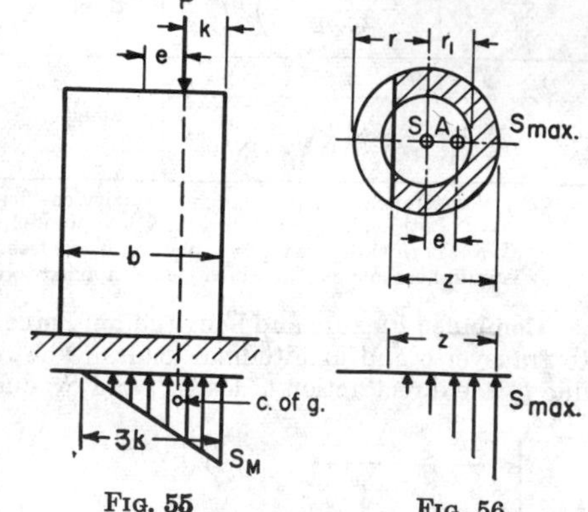

Fig. 55 Fig. 56

Note. In these formulas e is measured from the gravity axis, and gives tension when e is greater than one-sixth the width (measured in the same direction as e), for rectangular sections; and when greater than one-eighth the diameter for solid circular sections.

If, as in certain classes of masonry construction, the **material cannot withstand tensile stress and** thus no tension can occur, the center of moments (Fig. 55) is taken at the center of stress. For a **rectangular section,** P acts at distance k from the nearest edge. Length under compression = $3k$, and $S_M = \frac{2}{3}P/hk$. For a **circular section,** $S_M = [0.372 + 0.056(k/r)]P/k\sqrt{rk}$, where r = radius and k = distance of P from circumference. For a **circular ring,** S = average compressive stress on cross-section produced by P; e = eccentricity of P; z = length of diameter under compression (Fig. 56). Values of z/r and of the ratio of S_{max} to average S are given in Tables 14 and 15.

Chimney Problem. Weight of chimney = 563,000 lb; e = 1.56 ft; O.D. of chimney = 10 ft 8 in.; I.D. = 6 ft 6½ in. Overturning moment = Pe = 878,000 ft-lb, $r_1/r = 0.6$. $e/r = 0.29$. This gives $(z/r) > 2$. Therefore, the entire area of the base is under compression.

Table 14. Values of the Ratio z/r (Fig. 56)

$\frac{e}{r}$	$\frac{r_1}{r}$ = 0.0	0.5	0.6	0.7	0.8	0.9	1.0	$\frac{e}{r}$
0.25	2.00	...	...	...	...	...	...	0.25
0.30	1.82	...	...	...	...	...	...	0.30
0.35	1.66	1.89	1.98	...	...	...	...	0.35
0.40	1.51	1.75	1.84	1.93	...	...	...	0.40
0.45	1.37	1.61	1.71	1.81	1.90	...	...	0.45
0.50	1.23	1.46	1.56	1.66	1.78	1.89	2.00	0.50
0.55	1.10	1.29	1.39	1.50	1.62	1.74	1.87	0.55
0.60	0.97	1.12	1.21	1.32	1.45	1.58	1.71	0.60
0.65	0.84	0.94	1.02	1.13	1.25	1.40	1.54	0.65
0.70	0.72	0.75	0.82	0.93	1.05	1.20	1.35	0.70
0.75	0.59	0.60	0.64	0.72	0.85	0.99	1.15	0.75
0.80	0.47	0.47	0.48	0.52	0.61	0.77	0.94	0.80
0.85	0.35	0.35	0.35	0.36	0.42	0.55	0.72	0.85
0.90	0.24	0.24	0.24	0.24	0.24	0.32	0.49	0.90
0.95	0.12	0.12	0.12	0.12	0.12	0.12	0.25	0.95

Table 15. Values of the Ratio S_{max}/S_{avg}

(In determining S average, use load P divided by total area of cross section)

$\frac{e}{r}$	$\frac{r_1}{r}$ = 0.0	0.5	0.6	0.7	0.8	0.9	1.0	$\frac{e}{r}$
0.00	1.00	1.00	1.00	1.00	1.00	1.00	1.00	0.00
0.05	1.20	1.16	1.15	1.13	1.12	1.11	1.10	0.05
0.10	1.40	1.32	1.29	1.27	1.24	1.22	1.20	0.10
0.15	1.60	1.48	1.44	1.40	1.37	1.33	1.30	0.15
0.20	1.80	1.64	1.59	1.54	1.49	1.44	1.40	0.20
0.25	2.00	1.80	1.73	1.67	1.61	1.55	1.50	0.25
0.30	2.23	1.96	1.88	1.81	1.73	1.66	1.60	0.30
0.35	2.48	2.12	2.04	1.94	1.85	1.77	1.70	0.35
0.40	2.76	2.29	2.20	2.07	1.98	1.88	1.80	0.40
0.45	3.11	2.51	2.39	2.23	2.10	1.99	1.90	0.45
0.50	3.55	2.80	2.61	2.42	2.26	2.10	2.00	0.50
0.55	4.15	3.14	2.89	2.67	2.42	2.26	2.17	0.55
0.60	4.96	3.58	3.24	2.92	2.64	2.42	2.26	0.60
0.65	6.00	4.34	3.80	3.30	2.92	2.64	2.42	0.65
0.70	7.48	5.40	4.65	3.86	3.33	2.95	2.64	0.70
0.75	9.93	7.26	5.97	4.81	3.93	3.33	2.89	0.75
0.80	13.87	10.05	8.80	6.53	4.93	3.96	3.27	0.80
0.85	21.08	15.55	13.32	10.43	7.16	4.50	3.77	0.85
0.90	38.25	30.80	25.80	19.85	14.60	7.13	4.71	0.90
0.95	96.10	72.20	62.20	50.20	34.60	19.80	6.72	0.95
1.00	∞	∞	∞	∞	∞	∞	∞	1.00

Area under compression = 55.8 sq ft; I = 546; $S = (563{,}000/55.8) \pm (878{,}000 \times 5.33)/546 = 18{,}700$ (max) and 1,500 (min) lb compression per sq ft. From Table 15, by interpolation, $S_{max}/S_{avg} = 1.85$. $\therefore S_{max} = (563{,}000/55.8) \times 1.85 = 18{,}685$ lb per sq ft.

The **kern** is the area around the center of gravity of a cross section within which any load applied will produce stress of only one sign throughout the entire cross section. Outside the kern, a load produces stresses of different sign. Figure 57 shows kerns (shaded) for various sections.

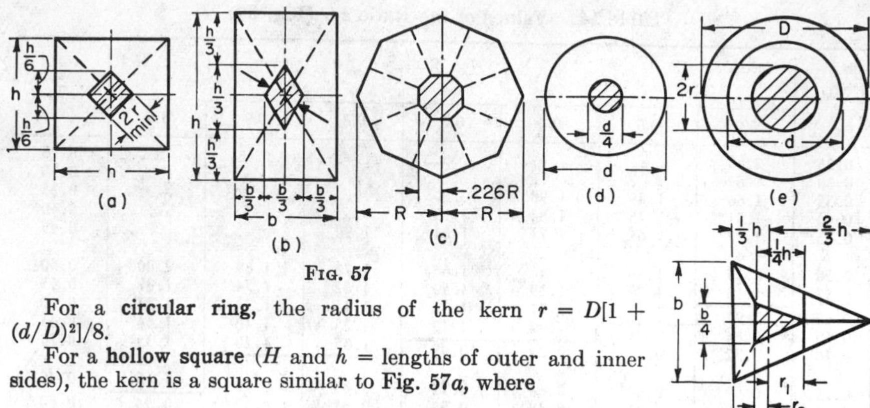

FIG. 57

For a **circular ring,** the radius of the kern $r = D[1 + (d/D)^2]/8$.

For a **hollow square** (H and h = lengths of outer and inner sides), the kern is a square similar to Fig. 57*a*, where

$$r_{\min} = \frac{H}{6}\frac{1}{\sqrt{2}}\left[1 + \left(\frac{h}{H}\right)^2\right] = 0.1179H\left[1 = \left(\frac{h}{H}\right)^2\right]$$

For a **hollow octagon** R_a and R_i = radii of circles circumscribing the outer and inner sides; thickness of wall $= 0.9239(R_a - R_i)$], the kern is an octagon similar to Fig. 57*c*, where $0.2256R$ becomes $0.2256R_a[1 + (R_i/R_a)^2]$.

CURVED BEAMS

The application of the flexure formula for a straight beam to the case of a curved beam results in error. When all "fibers" of a member have the same center of curvature, the **concentric-** or common-type of curved beam exists (see Fig. 58). Such a beam is defined by the Winkler-Bach theory. The stress at a point y units from the centroidal axis is

$$S = \frac{M}{AR}\left[1 + \frac{y}{Z\,(R + y)}\right]$$

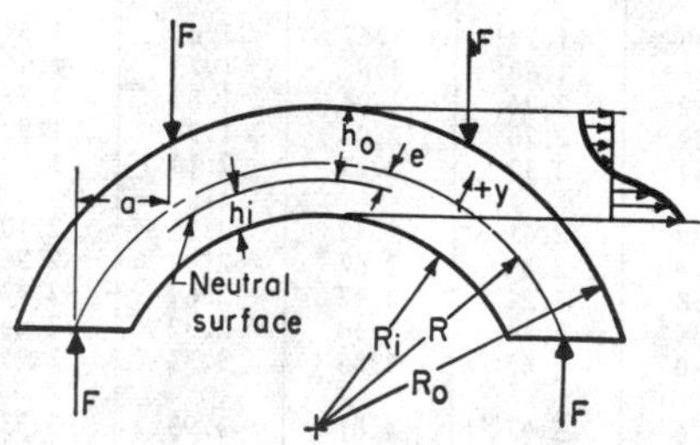

FIG. 58

M is the bending moment, positive when it increases curvature; Y is positive when measured toward the convex side; A is the cross-sectional area; R is the radius of the centroidal axis; Z **is a cross-section property** defined by

$$Z = -\frac{1}{A}\int \frac{y}{R + y}\,dA$$

Analytical expressions for Z of certain sections are given in Table 16. Z can also be found by **graphical** integration methods (see any advanced strength book). The **neutral surface** shifts toward the center of curvature, or inside fiber, an amount equal to $e = ZR/(Z + 1)$. The Winkler-Bach theory, though practically satisfactory, disregards radial stresses as well as lateral deformations and assumes pure bending. The

Table 16. Analytical Expressions for Z

Section	Expression
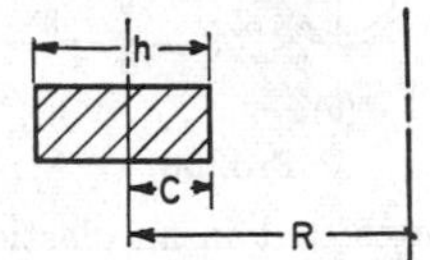 Rectangle (h, C, R)	$Z = -1 + \frac{R}{h}\left(\ln \frac{R+C}{R-C}\right)$
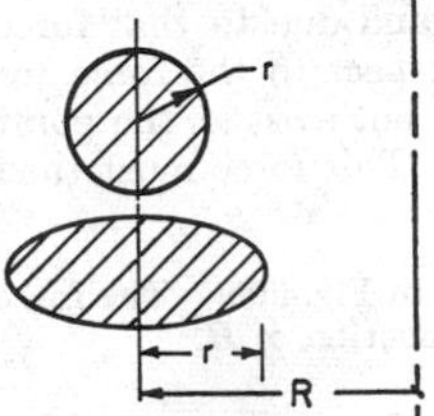 Circle / ellipse (r, R)	$Z = -1 + 2\left(\frac{R}{r}\right)\left[\frac{R}{r} - \sqrt{\left(\frac{R}{r}\right)^2 - 1}\right]$
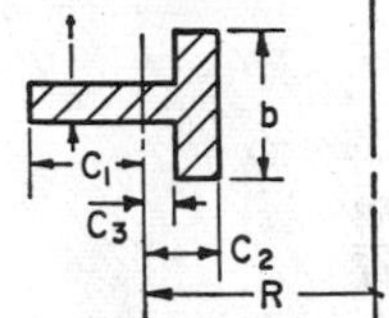 T-section (t, b, C_1, C_2, C_3, R)	$Z = -1 + \frac{R}{A}\left[t \ln(R + C_1) + (b - t) \ln(R - C_3) - b \ln(R - C_2)\right]$ and $A = tC_1 - (b - t)C_3 + bC_2$
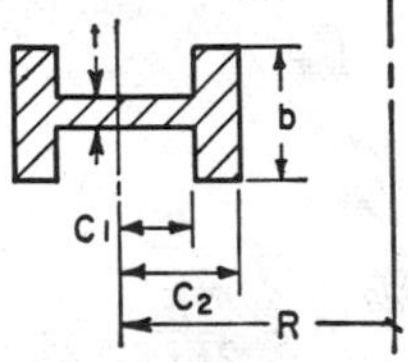 I-section (t, b, C_1, C_2, R)	$Z = -1 + \frac{R}{A}\left[b \ln\left(\frac{R + C_2}{R - C_2}\right) + (t - b) \ln\left(\frac{R + C_1}{R - C_1}\right)\right]$ $A = 2\left[(t - b)C_1 + bC_2\right]$

maximum stress occurring on the inside fiber is $S = Mh_i/AeR_i$, while that on the outside fiber is $S = Mh_o/AeR_o$.

Example. A split steel ring of rectangular cross section is subjected to a diametral force of 1,000 lb as shown in Fig. 59*a*. Compute the stress at the point 0.5 in. from the outside fiber on plane *mm*. Also compute the maximum stress.

$$Z = -1 + \frac{R}{h}\left(\ln \frac{R+C}{R-C}\right) = -1 + \frac{10}{4}\left(\ln \frac{10+2}{10-2}\right) = 0.0133$$

$$S_{1.5} = \frac{M}{AR}\left[1 + \frac{y}{Z\,(R+y)}\right] + \frac{F}{A} = \frac{-1{,}000 \times 10}{8 \times 10}\left[1 + \frac{1.5}{0.0133\,(10 + 1.5)}\right] + \frac{1{,}000}{8}$$

$$= -1{,}250 + 125 = -1{,}125 \text{ psi (compr.)}$$

$$S_M = \frac{-1{,}000}{8}\left[1 + \frac{-2}{0.0133\,(10-2)}\right] + \frac{1{,}000}{8} = 2{,}230 + 125 = 2{,}355 \text{ psi}$$

or $$e = \frac{ZR}{Z+1} = \frac{0.0133 \times 10}{0.0133 + 1} = 0.131$$

and $$S_M = \frac{Mh_i}{AeR_i} + \frac{P}{A} = \frac{1{,}000 \times 1.87}{8 \times 0.131 \times 8} + \frac{1{,}000}{8} = 2{,}355 \text{ psi}$$

The **deflection** in curved beams can be computed by means of the moment-area theory. If the origin of axes is taken at the point whose deflection is wanted, it can be shown that the component displacements in the x and y directions are

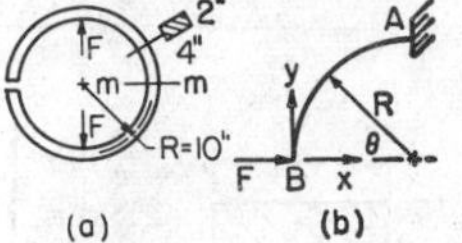

FIG. 59

$$\Delta_x = \int_0^s \frac{Myds}{EI} \quad \text{and} \quad \Delta_y = \int_0^s \frac{Mxds}{EI}$$

The resultant deflection is then equal to $\Delta_0 = \sqrt{\Delta_x^2 + \Delta_y^2}$ in the direction defined by $\tan \theta = \Delta_y/\Delta_x$. Deflections can also be found conveniently by use of **Castigliano's theorem.** It states that in an elastic system the displacement in the direction of a force (or couple) and due to that force (or couple) is the partial derivative of the strain energy with respect to the force (or couple). Stated mathematically, $\Delta_z = \partial U/\partial F_z$. If a force does not exist at the point and/or in the direction desired, a dummy force may be applied. This force must then be eliminated by equating it to zero at the end.

EXAMPLE. **A quadrant of radius R is fixed at one end as shown in Fig. 59b. The force F is applied in the radial direction at the free end B. Find the deflection of B.**

By moment area:

$$y = R \sin \theta \qquad x = R(1 - \cos \theta)$$
$$ds = Rd\theta \qquad M = FR \sin \theta$$
$$_B\Delta_x = \frac{FR^3}{EI} \int_0^{\pi/2} \sin^2 d\theta = \frac{\pi FR^3}{4EI}$$
$$_B\Delta_y = \frac{FR^3}{EI} \int_0^{\pi/2} \sin \theta \, (1 - \cos \theta) d\theta = -\frac{FR^3}{2EI}$$

and
$$\Delta_B = \frac{FR^3}{2EI}\sqrt{1 + \pi^2/4}$$

at
$$\theta_x = \tan^{-1}\left(-\frac{FR^3}{2EI} \times \frac{4EI}{\pi FR^3}\right) = \tan^{-1}\frac{2}{\pi} = 32.5 \text{ deg}$$

By Castigliano:

$$_B\Delta_x = \frac{\partial U}{\partial F} = \frac{\partial}{\partial F}\int_0^{\pi/2} \frac{F^2R^3}{2EI} \sin^2\theta \, d\,\theta = \frac{\pi FR^3}{4EI}$$
$$_B\Delta_y = \frac{\partial U}{\partial F_y} = \frac{\partial}{\partial F_y}\int_0^{\pi/2} \frac{[FR \sin \theta - F_yR\,(1 - \cos \theta)]^2\, Rd\theta}{2EI} = -\frac{FR^3}{2EI}$$

The F_y, assumed downwards, is equated to zero, after the integration and differentiation are performed to find $_B\Delta_y$. The remainder of the computation is exactly as in the moment-area method.

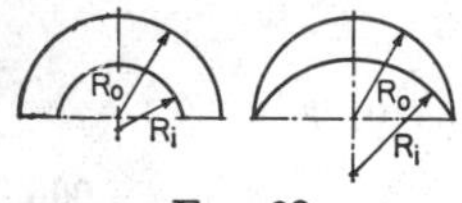

FIG. 60

Eccentrically Curved Beams. These beams, **Fig. 60**, are bounded by arcs having different centers of curvature. In addition, it is possible for either radius to be the larger one. The one in which the section depth shortens as the central section is approached may be called the **arch beam.** When the central section is the largest, the beam is of the crescent type. **Crescent I** denotes the beam of larger outside radius and **crescent II** of larger inside radius. The stress at the **central section** of such beams may be found from $S = KMC/I$. In the case of rectangular cross section, the equation becomes $S = 6KM/bh^2$ where M is the bending moment, b is the width of the beam section, and h its height. The **stress factors** K for the **inner boundary**, established from photoelastic data, are given on Table 17. The outside radius is denoted by R_o and the inside by R_i. The geometry of crescent beams is such that the stress can be larger in **off-center sections.** The stress at the central section determined above must then be multiplied by the **position factor** k, given in Table 18. As in the concentric beam, the **neutral surface** shifts slightly toward the inner boundary (see Vidosic, Curved Beams with Eccentric Boundaries, *Trans. ASME*, **79**, pp. 1317–1321).

Table 17. Stress Factors for Inner Boundary at Central Section

1. For the arch-type beams

(a) $K = 0.834 + 1.504 \dfrac{h}{R_o + R_i}$ if $\dfrac{R_o + R_i}{h} < 5.$

(b) $K = 0.899 + 1.181 \dfrac{h}{R_o + R_i}$ if $5 < \dfrac{R_o + R_i}{h} < 10.$

(c) In the case of larger section ratios use the equivalent beam solution.

2. For the crescent I-type beams

(a) $K = 0.570 + 1.536 \dfrac{h}{R_o + R_i}$ if $\dfrac{R_o + R_i}{h} < 2.$

(b) $K = 0.959 + 0.769 \dfrac{h}{R_o + R_i}$ if $2 < \dfrac{R_o + R_i}{h} < 20.$

(c) $K = 1.092 \left(\dfrac{h}{R_o + R_i}\right)^{0.0298}$ if $\dfrac{R_o + R_i}{h} > 20.$

3. For the crescent II-type beams

(a) $K = 0.897 + 1.098 \dfrac{h}{R_o + R_i}$ if $\dfrac{R_o + R_i}{h} < 8.$

(b) $K = 1.119 \left(\dfrac{h}{R_o + R_i}\right)^{0.0378}$ if $8 < \dfrac{R_o + R_i}{h} < 20.$

(c) $K = 1.081 \left(\dfrac{h}{R_o + R_i}\right)^{0.0270}$ if $\dfrac{R_o + R_i}{h} > 20.$

Table 18. Crescent-beam Position Stress Factors

Angle θ, deg	k	
	Inner	Outer
10	$1 + 0.055\,H/h$	$1 + 0.03\,H/h$
20	$1 + 0.164\,H/h$	$1 + 0.10\,H/h$
30	$1 + 0.365\,H/h$	$1 + 0.25\,H/h$
40	$1 + 0.567\,H/h$	$1 + 0.467\,H/h$
50	$1.521 - \dfrac{(0.5171 - 1.382\,H/h)^{1/2}}{1.382}$	$1 + 0.733\,H/h$
60	$1.756 - \dfrac{(0.2416 - 0.6506\,H/h)^{1/2}}{0.6506}$	$1 + 1.123\,H/h$
70	$2.070 - \dfrac{(0.4817 - 1.298\,H/h)^{1/2}}{0.6492}$	$1 + 1.70\,H/h$
80	$2.531 - \dfrac{(0.2939 - 0.7084\,H/h)^{1/2}}{0.3542}$	$1 + 2.383\,H/h$
90		$1 + 3.933\,H/h$

Note: All formulas are valid for $0 < H/h \leq 0.325$. Formulas for the inner boundary, except for 40 deg, may be used to $H/h \leq 0.36$. H = distance between centers.

IMPACT

A force or stress is considered **suddenly applied** when the duration of load application is less than one-half the **fundamental natural period** of vibration of the member upon which the force acts. Under impact, a compression wave propagates through the member at a velocity $c = \sqrt{E/\rho}$, where ρ is the mass density. As this compression wave travels back and forth by reflection from one end of the bar to the other, a maximum stress is produced which is many times larger than what it would be statically. An exact determination of this stress is most difficult. However, if conservation of kinetic and strain energies is applied, the **impact stress** is found to be

$$S' = S \sqrt{\frac{W}{W_b}\left(\frac{3W}{3W + W_b}\right)}$$

The weight of the striking mass is here denoted by W, that of the struck bar by W_b, while S is the static stress, W/A (A is the cross-sectional area of the bar). Above is the case of **sudden impact.** When the ratio W/W_b is small, the stress computed by above equation may be erroneous. A better solution of this problem may result from

$$S' = S + S\sqrt{\frac{W}{W_b} + \frac{2}{3}}$$

If a weight W falls a distance h before striking a bar of mass W_b, energy conservation will yield the relation

$$S' = S\left[1 + \sqrt{1 + \frac{2h}{e} \times \left(\frac{3W}{3W + W_b}\right)}\right]$$

The elongation $e = \varepsilon l = Sl/E$. When the striking mass W is assumed rigid, the elasticity factor is taken equal to 1. Thus the equation becomes

$$S' = S\,(1 + \sqrt{1 + 2h/e})$$

If, in addition, h is taken equal to zero (**sudden impact**), the radical equals 1, and so the stress becomes $S' = 2S$. Since Hooke's law is applicable, the relations

$$e' = e\,(1 + \sqrt{1 + 2h/e}) \qquad \text{and} \qquad e' = 2e$$

are also true for the same conditions.

The expression may be converted, by using $v^2 = 2gh$, to

$$S' = S\,(1 + \sqrt{1 + v^2/eg})$$

This might be called the **energy impact** form. If the **natural frequency,** f_n, of the bar is **used,** the stress equation is

$$S' = S\,(1 + \sqrt{1 + 0.204\,hf_n^2})$$

In general, the **maximum impact stress** in a **beam** and a **shaft** can be approximated from the simplified falling-weight equation. It is necessary, though, to substitute the maximum **deflection,** y, for e, in the case of beams, and for the **angle of twist,** θ, in the case of shafts. Of course $S = MC/I$ and M_tC/J respectively. Thus

$$S' = S\left(1 + \sqrt{1 + \frac{2h}{y\ (\text{or}\ \theta)}}\right)$$

For a more exact solution, elastic yield in each member must be considered. The theory then yields

$$S' = S\left[1 + \sqrt{1 + 2h/y\left(\frac{35W}{35W + 17W_b}\right)}\right]$$

for a **simply supported beam** struck in the middle by a weight W.

THEORY OF ELASTICITY

Loaded members in which the stress distribution cannot be estimated fail of solution by elementary strength-of-material methods. To such cases, the more advanced, mathematical principles of the **theory of elasticity** must be applied. When this is not possible, experimental stress analysis has to be used. Because of the complexity of solution, only some of the more practical problems have been solved by the theory of elasticity. The more general concepts and methods are presented.

Two kinds of forces may act on a body. **Surface forces** are distributed over the surface as the result of, for instance, the pressure of one body on another. Forces due to gravity, inertia, magnetism, etc., which act over the entire volume of a body, are called **body forces.** Both surface and body forces can be best handled if resolved into three orthogonal components. Surface forces are thus designated $\bar{X}$, $\bar{Y}$, and $\bar{Z}$, while body forces are labeled X, Y, and Z.

In general, there exists a normal stress σ and a shearing stress τ at each point of a loaded member. It is convenient to deal with components of each of these stresses on each of six orthogonal planes that bound the point element. Thus there are at each point **six stress components,** σ_x, σ_y, σ_z, $\tau_{xy} = \tau_{yx}$, $\tau_{xz} = \tau_{zx}$, and $\tau_{yz} = \tau_{zy}$. Similarly, if the normal unit strain is designated by the letter $\mathcal{E}$ and shearing unit strain by γ, the **six components of strain** are defined by

$$\mathcal{E}_x = \partial u/\partial x \qquad \mathcal{E}_y = \partial v/\partial y \qquad \mathcal{E}_z = \partial w/\partial z$$
$$\gamma_{xy} = \partial u/\partial y + \partial v/\partial x \qquad \gamma_{yz} = \partial v/\partial z + \partial w/\partial y$$

and

$$\gamma_x = \partial u/\partial z + \partial w/\partial x$$

The elastic **displacements** of particles on the body in the x, y, and z directions are identified as the u, v, and w **components,** respectively.

Since metals have the usually assumed elastic as well as isotropic properties, Hooke's law holds. Therefore the interrelationships between stress and strain can easily be obtained.

$$\mathcal{E}_x = \frac{1}{E}[\sigma_x - \mu(\sigma_y + \sigma_z)]$$
$$\mathcal{E}_y = \frac{1}{E}[\sigma_y - \mu(\sigma_x + \sigma_z)]$$
$$\mathcal{E}_z = \frac{1}{E}[\sigma_z - \mu(\sigma_x + \sigma_y)]$$
$$\gamma_{xy} = \tau_{xy}/G \qquad \gamma_{xz} = \tau_{xz}/G$$

and

$$\gamma_{yz} = \tau_{yz}/G$$

The general case of strain can be obtained by superposing the elongation strains upon the shearing strains.

Problems depending upon theories of elasticity are considerably simplified if the stresses are all parallel to one plane or if all deformations occur in planes perpendicular to the length of the member. The first case is one of **plane stress,** as when a thin plate of uniform thickness is subjected to central, boundary forces parallel to the plane of the plate. The second is a case of **plane strain,** such as a gate subjected to hydrostatic pressure, the intensity of which does not vary along the gate's length. All particles therefore displace at right angles to the length and so cross sections remain plane. In plane-stress problems, three of the six stress components vanish, thus leaving only σ_x, σ_y, and τ_{xy}. Similarly, in plane strain, only $\mathcal{E}_x$, $\mathcal{E}_y$, and γ_{xy} will not equal zero, thus the same three stresses σ_x, σ_y, and τ_{xy} remain to be considered.

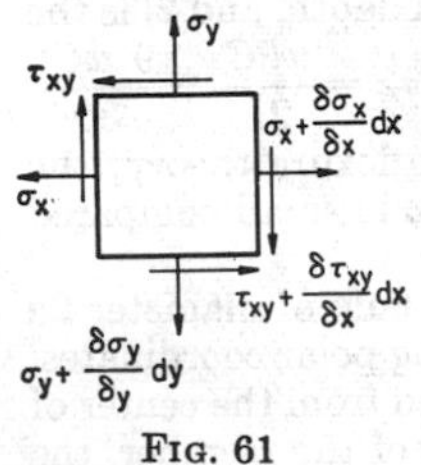

FIG. 61

Plane problems can thus be represented by the element shown in Fig. 61. Equilibrium considerations applied to this particle result in the **differential equations of equilibrium** which reduce to

$$\frac{\partial \sigma_x}{\partial x} + \frac{\partial \tau_{xy}}{\partial y} + X = 0$$

and

$$\frac{\partial \sigma_y}{\partial y} + \frac{\partial \tau_{xy}}{\partial x} + Y = 0.$$

Since the two differential equations of equilibrium are insufficient to find the three stresses, a third equation must be used. This is the **compatibility equation** relating the three strain components. It is

$$\frac{\partial^2 \mathcal{E}_x}{\partial y^2} + \frac{\partial^2 \mathcal{E}_y}{\partial x^2} = \frac{\partial^2 \gamma_{xy}}{\partial x \partial y}$$

If strains are expressed in terms of the stresses, the compatibility equation becomes

$$\left(\frac{\partial^2}{\partial x^2} + \frac{\partial^2}{\partial y^2}\right)(\sigma_x + \sigma_y) = 0$$

Now, in any **two-dimensional** problem, the compatibility equation along with the differential equilibrium equations must be simultaneously solved for the three unknown stresses. This is accomplished using **stress functions,** which permit the integration and satisfy boundary conditions in each particular situation.

In **three-dimensional** problems, the third dimension must be considered. This results in three differential equations of equilibrium, as well as three compatibility equations. The six stress components can thus be found. The complexity involved in the solution of these equations is such, however, that only a few special cases have been solved.

In certain problems, such as rotating circular disks, **polar coordinates** become more convenient. In such cases, the stress components in a two-dimensional field are the **radial stress,** σ_r, the **tangential stress,** σ_θ, and the **shearing stress,** $\tau_{r\theta}$. In terms of these stresses the **polar differential equations** become

$$\frac{\partial \sigma_r}{\partial r} + \frac{1}{r}\frac{\partial \tau_{r\theta}}{\partial \theta} + \frac{\sigma_r - \sigma_\theta}{r} + R = 0$$

and

$$\frac{1}{r}\frac{\partial \sigma_\theta}{\partial \theta} + \frac{\partial \tau_{r\theta}}{\partial r} + \frac{2\tau_{r\theta}}{r} = 0$$

The body force per unit volume is represented by R. The **compatibility equation in** polar coordinates is

$$\left(\frac{\partial^2}{\partial r^2} + \frac{1}{r}\frac{\partial}{\partial r} + \frac{1}{r^2}\frac{\partial^2}{\partial \theta^2}\right)\left(\frac{\partial^2 \phi}{\partial r^2} + \frac{1}{r}\frac{\partial \phi}{\partial r} + \frac{1}{r^2}\frac{\partial^2 \phi}{\partial \theta^2}\right) = 0$$

ϕ is again a stress function of r and θ that will provide a solution of the differential equations and satisfy boundary conditions. As an example, the exact solution of a **simply supported beam** carrying a uniformly distributed load, w, yields

$$\sigma_x = \frac{w}{2I}(l^2 - x^2)\,y + \frac{w}{2I}\left(\frac{2y^3}{3} - \frac{2c^2y}{5}\right)$$

The origin of coordinates is at the center of the beam, $2c$, is the beam depth, and $2l$ is the span length. Thus the maximum stress at $x = 0$ and $y = C$ is $\sigma_x = \dfrac{wl^2C}{2I} + \dfrac{9\ wC^3}{30}$. The first term represents the stress as obtained by the elementary flexure theory; the second is a correction. The second term becomes negligible when c is small compared to l.

The important case of a **flat plate** of unit width with a **circular hole** of diameter $2a$ at its center, subjected to a uniform tensile load, has been solved using polar coordinates. If S is the uniform stress at some distance from the hole, r is measured from the center of the hole, and θ is the angle of r with respect to the longitudinal axis of the member, the stresses are

$$\sigma_r = \frac{S}{2}\left(1 - \frac{a^2}{r^2}\right) + \frac{S}{2}\left(1 + \frac{3a^4}{r^4} - \frac{4a^2}{r^2}\right)\cos 2\theta$$

$$\sigma_\theta = \frac{S}{2}\left(1 + \frac{a^2}{r^2}\right) - \frac{S}{2}\left(1 + \frac{3a^4}{r^4}\right)\cos 2\theta$$

$$\tau_{r\theta} = -\frac{S}{2}\left(1 - \frac{3a^4}{r^4} + \frac{2a^2}{r^2}\right)\sin 2\theta$$

CYLINDERS AND SPHERES

A **thin-wall cylinder** has a wall thickness such that the assumption of constant stress across the wall results in negligible error. Cylinders having internal-diameter–to–thickness (D/t) ratios greater than 10 are usually considered thin-walled. Boilers, drums, tanks, and pipes are often treated as such. Equilibrium equations reveal the circumferential, or hoop, stress to be $S = pr/t$ under an internal pressure p (see Fig. 62). If the cylinder is closed at the ends, a longitudinal stress of $pr/2t$ is developed. The tensile stress developed in a thin hollow sphere subjected to internal pressure is also $pr/2t$.

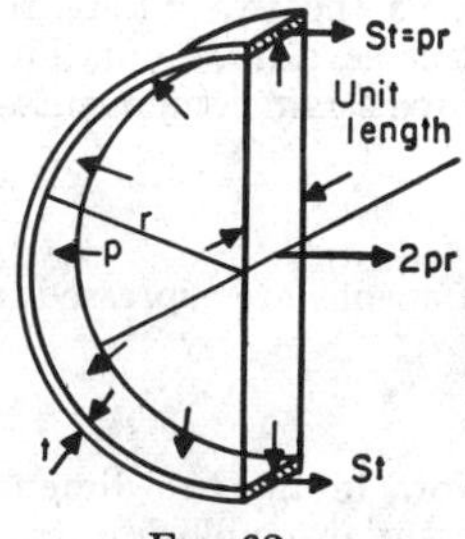

Fig. 62

When thin-walled cylinders, such as vacuum tanks and submarines, are subjected to **external pressure, collapse** becomes the mode of failure. The shell is assumed perfectly round and of uniform thickness, the material obeys Hooke's law, the radial stress is negligible, and the normal stress distribution is linear. Other, lesser assumptions are also made. Using the theory of elasticity, R. G. Sturm (*Univ. of Ill. Exp. Sta. Bull.*, No. 12, Nov. 11, 1941) derived the **collapsing pressure** as

$$W_c = KE\left(\frac{t}{D}\right)^3 \text{ psi}$$

The factor K, a numerical coefficient, depends upon the L/D and D/t ratios (D is outside-shell diameter), the kind of end support, and whether pressure is applied radially only, or at the ends as well. **Figures 63 to 66, reproduced from the bulletin, supply the K values. N on these charts indicates the number of lobes into which the shell col-**

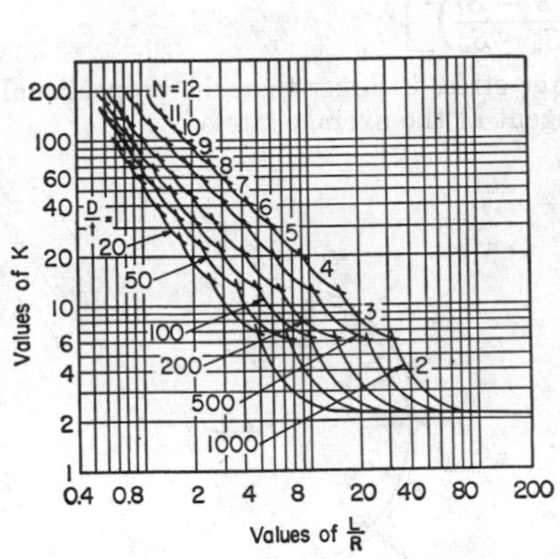

Fig. 63. Radial external pressure with simply supported edges.

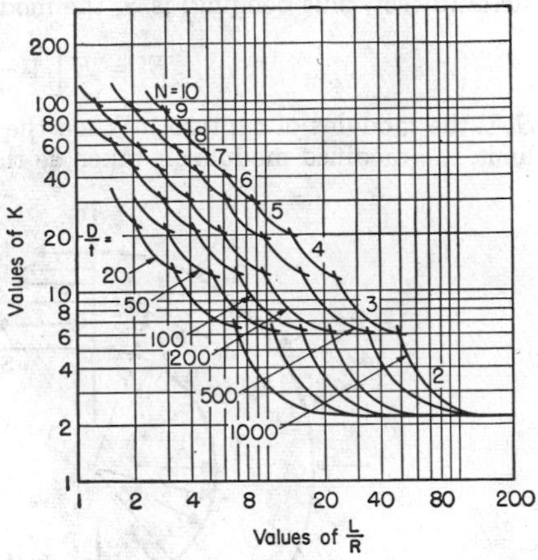

Fig. 64. Radial external pressure with fixed edges.

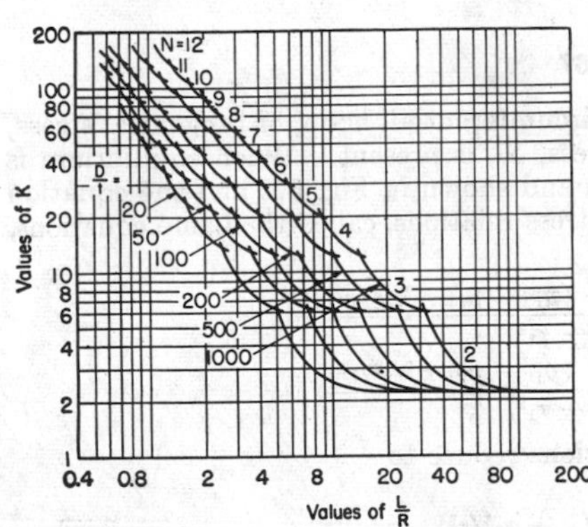

Fig. 65. Radial and end external pressure with simply supported edges.

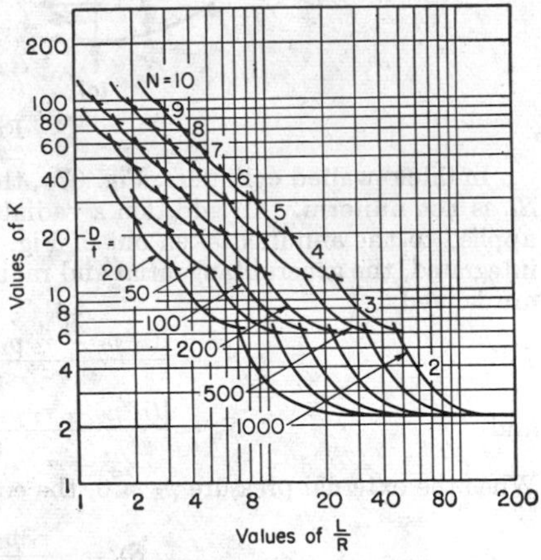

Fig. 66. Radial and end external pressure with fixed edges.

Figs. 63–66. Collapse factor K for round cylinders. $\mu = 0.30$; $W_c = KE\left(\frac{t}{D}\right)^3$; W_c = collapsing pressure; K = coefficient depending on L/R and D/t given by curves; E = modulus of elasticity of the material; t = thickness of shell; D = outside diameter of cylinder. (*From Univ. of Ill. Bull.*)

lapses. These values are for materials having Poisson's ratio of 0.3. It may also be pointed out that in the case of long cylinders (infinitely long, theoretically) the value of K approaches $2/(1 - \mu^2)$.

When the **cylinder is stiffened with rings,** the shell may be assumed to be divided into a series of shorter shells, equal in length to the ring spacing. The previous equation can then be applied to a ring-to-ring length of cylinder. However, the flexural rigidity of the combined stiffener and shell, EI_c, necessary to withstand the pressure is $EI_c = W_s D^3 L_s/24$. W_s is the pressure, L_s the length between rings, and I_c the combined moment of inertia of the ring and that portion of the shell assumed acting with the ring.

In some instances, cylinders collapse only after a stress in excess of the elastic limit has been reached; that is, **plastic range** stresses are present. In such cases the same equation applies, but the modulus of elasticity must be modified.

When the average stress, S_a, is less than the proportional limit, S_p, and the maximum stress (direct, plus bending) is S, the modified modulus

$$E' = E\left[1 - \frac{1}{4}\left(\frac{S - S_l}{S_u - S_a}\right)^2\right]$$

S_u is the modulus of rupture. When the average stress is larger than the proportional limit, the modified modulus is taken as the tangent at the average stress.

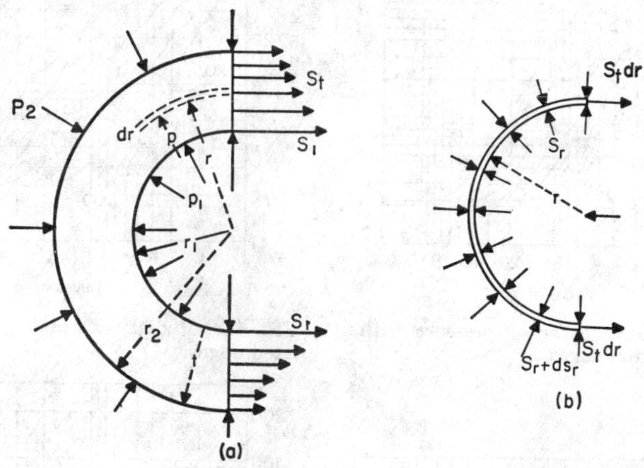

FIG. 67

In **thick-walled cylinders,** Fig. 67*a*, the circumferential, hoop, or tangential stress, S_t, is not uniform. In addition a radial stress, S_r, is present. When equilibrium is applied to the annulus taken out of Fig. 67*a* and shown in Fig. 67*b* and the equation integrated, the general tangential and radial stress relations, called the **Lamé** equations, are derived.

$$S_t = \frac{[(r_1^2p_1 - r_2^2p_2) + (p_1 - p_2)\, r_1^2r_2^2/r^2]}{(r_2^2 - r_1^2)}$$

and

$$S_r = \frac{[(r_1^2p_1 - r_2^2p_2) - (p_1 - p_2)\, r_1^2r_2^2/r^2]}{(r_2^2 - r_1^2)}$$

When the external pressure $p_2 = 0$, the equations reduce to

$$S_t = \frac{r_1^2p_1}{r_2^2 - r_1^2}\,(1 + r_2^2/r^2)$$

and

$$S_r = \frac{r_1^2p_1}{r_2^2 - r_1^2}\,(1 - r_2^2/r^2)$$

At the inner boundary the tangential elongation, ε_t, is equal to

$$\varepsilon_t = (S_t - \mu S_r)/E.$$

The increase in the bore radius, Δr_1, resulting therefrom is

$$\Delta r_1 = \frac{r_1 p_1}{E_h}\left(\frac{1 + r_1^2/r_2^2}{1 - r_1^2/r_2^2} + \mu\right)$$

Similarly a solid shaft of r radius under external pressure p_2 will have its radius decreased by the amount

$$\Delta r = -\frac{rp_2}{E_s}(1 - \mu)$$

In the case of a **press or shrink fit,** $p_1 = p_2 = p$. The sum of Δr_1 and Δr_1 absolute is the radial interference; twice this sum is the **diametral interference,** Δ, or

$$\Delta = 2r_1 p\left[\frac{1}{E_h}\left(\frac{1 + r_1^2/r_2^2}{1 - r_1^2/r_2^2} + \mu\right) + \frac{1 - \mu}{E_s}\right]$$

If the hub and shaft materials are the same, $E_h = E_s = E$, and

$$\Delta = \frac{4r_1r_2^2p}{E\,(r_2^2 - r_1^2)}$$

If the equation is solved for p and this value substituted in Lamé's equation, the maximum tangential stress on the inner surface of the hub is found to be

$$S_t = \frac{E\Delta}{4r_1r_1^2}(r_2^2 + r_1^2)$$

Example. The barrel of a field gun has an outside diameter of 9 in. and a bore of 4.7 in. An internal pressure of 16,000 psi is developed during firing. What maximum stress occurs in the barrel? An investigation of Lamé's equations for internal pressure reveals the maximum stress to be the tangential one on the inner surface. Thus,

$$S_t = p_1\frac{(r_1^2 + r_2^2)}{r_2^2 - r_1^2} = \frac{16{,}000\,(2.39^2 + 4.5^2)}{4.5^2 - 2.39^2} = 31{,}900 \text{ psi}$$

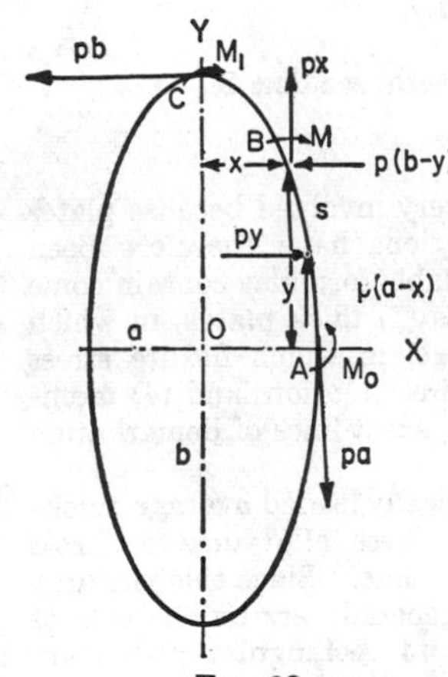

Fig. 68

Oval Hollow Cylinders. In Fig. 68, let a and b be the semiminor and semimajor axes. The bending moments at A and C will then be

$$M_0 = (pa^2/2) - (pI_x/2S) - (pI_y/2S)$$
$$M_1 = M_0 - p(a^2 - b^2)/2$$

where I_x and I_y are the moments of inertia of the arc AC about the x and y axes, respectively. The **bending moment at any point** will be

$$M = M_0 - (pa^2/2) + (px^2/2) + (py^2/2)$$

Thick Hollow Spheres. With an **internal pressure** p, where $p < T/0.65$,

$$r_2 = r_1[T + 0.4p)/(T - 0.65p)]^{1/3}$$

The maximum tensile stress is on the inner surface, in the direction of the circumference. With an **external pressure** p, where $p < T/1.05$,

$$r_2 = r_1[T/(T - 1.05p)]^{1/3}$$

In both cases T is the true stress.

PRESSURE BETWEEN BODIES WITH CURVED SURFACES

(See Hertz, "Gesammelte Werke," Vol. 1, pp. 159 *et seq.*, Barth.)

Two Spheres. The radius A of the compressed area is obtained from the formula $A^3 = 0.68P(c_1 + c_2)/[(1/r_1) + (1/r_2)]$, in which P is the compressing force, c_1 and c_2 ($= 1/E_1$ and $1/E_2$) are reciprocals of the respective moduli of elasticity, and r_1 and r_2

are the radii. (Reciprocal of Poisson's ratio assumed to be $n = 10/3$.) The **greatest contact pressure** in the middle of the compressed surface will be $S_{max} = 1.5(P/\pi A^2)$, and

$$S_{max}^3 = 0.235P[(1/r_1) + (1/r_2)]^2/(c_1 + c_2)^2$$

The **total deformation** of the two spheres will be Y, which is obtained from

$$Y^3 = 0.46P^2(c_1 + c_2)^2[(1/r_1) + (1/r_2)]$$

For $c_1 = c_2 = 1/E$, *i.e.*, **two spheres with the same modulus of elasticity,** it follows that $A^3 = 1.36\ P/E[(1/r_1) + (1/r_2)]$, $S_{max}^3 = 0.059PE^2[(1/r_1) + (1/r_2)]^2$, and $Y^3 = 1.84P^2[(1/r_1) + (1/r_2)]/E^2$. If the radii of these spheres are also equal, $A^3 = 0.68Pr/E = 0.34Pd/E$; $S_{max}^3 = 0.235PE^2/r^2 = 0.94PE^2/d^2$; and $Y^3 = 3.68P^2/E^2r = 7.36P^2/E^2d$.

Sphere and Flat Plate. In this case, $r_1 = r$ and $r_2 = \infty$, and the above formulas become $A^3 = 0.68Pr(c_1 + c_2) = 1.36Pr/E$, and

$$S_{max}^3 = 0.235P/r^2(c_1 + c_2)^2 = 0.059PE^2/r^2$$
$$Y^3 = 0.46P^2(c_1 + c_2)^2/r = 1.84P^2/E^2r$$

Two Cylinders. The width b of the rectangular pressure surface is obtained from $(b/4)^2 = 0.29P(c_1 + c_2)/l[(1/r_1) + (1/r_2)]$, where r_1 and r_2 are the radii, and l the length

$$S_{max}^2 = (4P/\pi bl)^2 = 0.35P[(1/r_1) + (1/r_2)]/l(c_1 + c_2)$$

For cylinders with the same moduli of elasticity, $c_1 = c_2 = 1/E$, and $(b/4)^2 = 0.58P/El[(1/r_1) + (1/r_2)]$; and $S_{max}^2 = 0.175PE[(1/r_1) + (1/r_2)]/l$. When $r_1 = r_2 = r$, $(b/4)^2 = 0.29Pr/El$, and $S_{max}^2 = 0.35PE/lr$.

Cylinder and Flat Plate. Here $r_1 = r$, $r_2 = \infty$, and the above formulas reduce to $(b/4)^2 = 0.29Pr(c_1 + c_2)/l = 0.58Pr/El$, and

$$S_{max}^2 = 0.35P/lr(c_1 + c_2) = 0.175PE/lr$$

For application to ball and roller bearings and to gear teeth, see Sec. 8.

FLAT PLATES

The analysis of flat plates subjected to **lateral loads** is very involved because plates bend in all vertical planes. Strict mathematical derivations have therefore been accomplished only in some special cases. Most of the available formulas contain some amount of rational empiricism. Plates may be classified as (1) **thick plates,** in which transverse shear is important; (2) **average-thickness plates,** in which flexure stress predominates; (3) **thin plates,** which depend in part upon direct tension; and (4) **membranes,** which are subject to direct tension only. However, exact lines of demarkation do not exist.

The flat-plate formulas given apply primarily to symmetrically loaded **average-thickness plates** of constant thickness. In the mathematical analyses, allowance for stress redistribution, because of slight local yielding, is usually not made. Since this yielding, especially in ductile materials, is beneficial, the formulas generally err on the side of safety. Certain cases of symmetrically loaded **circular and rectangular plates** are presented in Figs. 69 and 70. The maximum stresses are calculated from

$$S_M = k\frac{wr^2}{t^2} \qquad S_M = k\frac{P}{t^2} \qquad \text{or} \qquad S_M = k\frac{C}{t^2}$$

The first equation is for a uniformly distributed load, w, psi; the second supports a concentrated load, P, pounds; and the third, a couple, C, per unit length. Combinations of these loadings may be treated by superposition. The factors k are given on Tables 19 and 20, R is the radius of circular plates or one side of rectangular plates, and t is the plate thickness.

The **maximum deflection** for the same cases is given by

$$y_M = k_1 \frac{wr^4}{Et^3}, \qquad y_M = k_1 \frac{Pr^2}{Et^3} \qquad \text{and} \qquad y_M = k_1 \frac{Cr^2}{Et^3}$$

The factors k_1 are also given in the tables. For additional information, including shells, refer to ASME Handbook, "Metals Engineering: Design," McGraw-Hill.

[$r = R$ for circular plates;
r = smaller side for rectangular plates]

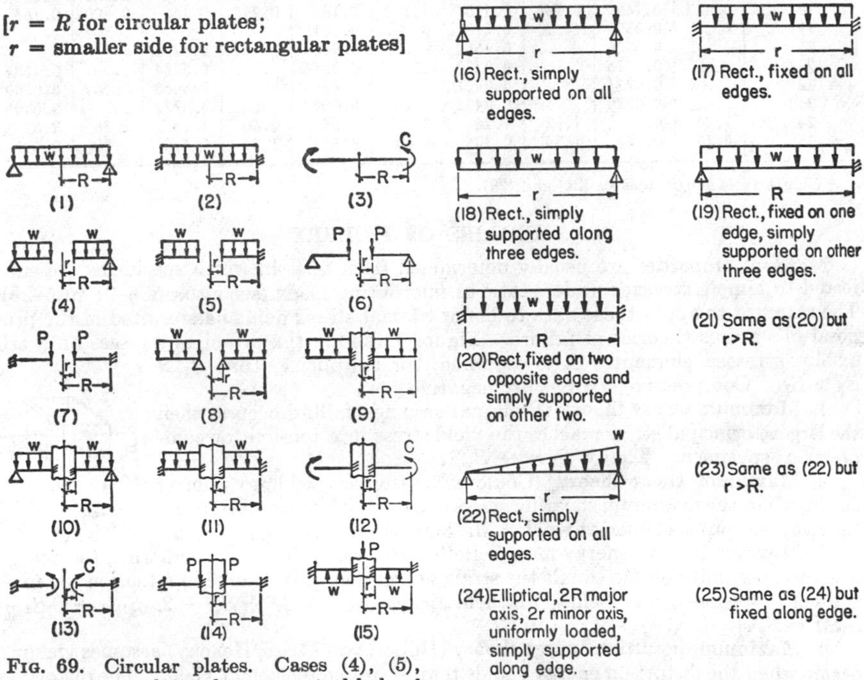

Fig. 69. Circular plates. Cases (4), (5), (6), (7), (8), and (13) have a central hole of radius r; cases (9), (10), (11), (12), (14), and (15) have a central piston of radius r to which the plate is fixed.

Fig. 70. Rectangular and elliptical plates. [R is the longer dimension except in cases (21) and (23).]

Table 19. Coefficients k and k_1 for Circular Plates

($\mu = 0.3$)

R/r	1.25		1.5		2		3		4		5	
Case	k	k_1	k	k_1	k	k_1	k	k_1	k	k_1	k	k_1
1	1.24	0.696										→
2	0.75	0.171										→
3	6.0	4.2										→
4	0.592	0.184	0.976	0.414	1.440	0.664	1.880	0.824	2.08	0.830	2.19	0.813
5	0.105	0.0025	0.259	0.0129	0.481	0.057	0.654	0.130	0.708	0.163	0.730	0.176
6	1.10	0.341	1.26	0.519	1.48	0.672	1.88	0.734	2.17	0.724	2.34	0.704
7	0.195	0.0036	0.320	0.024	0.455	0.081	0.670	0.171	1.00	0.218	1.30	0.238
8	0.660	0.202	1.19	0.491	2.04	0.902	3.34	1.220	4.30	1.300	5.10	1.310
9	0.135	0.0023	0.410	0.0183	1.04	0.0938	2.15	0.293	2.99	0.448	3.69	0.564
10	0.122	0.00343	0.336	0.0313	0.740	0.1250	1.21	0.291	1.45	0.417	1.59	0.492
11	0.072	0.00068	0.1825	0.005	0.361	0.023	0.546	0.064	0.627	0.092	0.668	0.112
12	6.865	0.2323	7.448	0.6613	8.136	1.493	8.71	2.555	8.930	3.105	9.036	3.418
13	6.0	0.196	6.0	0.485	6.0	0.847	6.0	0.940	6.0	0.801	6.0	0.658
14	0.115	0.00129	0.220	0.0064	0.405	0.0237	0.703	0.062	0.933	0.092	1.13	0.114
15	0.090	0.00077	0.273	0.0062	0.710	0.0329	1.54	0.110	2.23	0.179	2.80	0.234

Table 20. Coefficients k and k_1 for Rectangular and Elliptical Plates

($\mu = 0.3$)

R/r	1.0		1.5		2.0		3.0		4.0	
Case	k	k_1	k	k_1	k	k_1	k	k_1	k	k_1
16	0.25	0.0443	0.346	0.0843	0.40	0.1106	0.45	0.1336	0.471	0.1400
17	0.308	0.0138	0.454	0.0240	0.497	0.0277	0.500	0.028	0.500	0.028
18	0.672	0.140	0.768	0.160	0.792	0.165	0.798	0.166	0.800	0.166
19	.....	0.030	.....	0.070	.....	0.101				
20	.....	0.0209	.....	0.0582	.....	0.0987	.....	0.1276		
21*	.....	0.0216	.....	0.0270	.....	0.0284	.....	0.0284	.....	0.0284
22	.....	0.0221	.....	0.0421	.....	0.0553	.....	0.0668	.....	0.0700
23*	.....	0.0220	.....	0.0436	.....	0.0592	.....	0.0772	.....	0.0908
24	1.24	0.70	1.92	1.26	2.26	1.58	2.60	1.88	2.78	2.02
25	0.75	0.171	1.34	0.304	1.63	0.379	1.84	0.419	1.90	0.431

* Length ratio is r/R in cases (21) and (23).

THEORIES OF FAILURE

Material properties are usually determined from tests in which specimens are subjected to **simple stresses** under static or fluctuating loads (see also pp. 5–21 to 5–29). The attempt to apply these data to **bi- or triaxial stress fields** has resulted in the proposal of various theories of failure. Figure 71 shows the principal stresses on a triaxially stressed element. It is assumed, for simplicity, that $S_1 > S_2 > S_3$. Compressive stresses are negative.

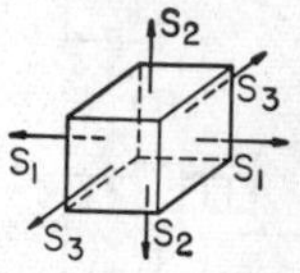

Fig. 71

1. **Maximum stress theory** (Rankine) assumes failure occurs when the largest principal stress reaches the yield stress in a tension (or compression) specimen. That is $S_1 = \pm S_y$.

2. **Maximum shear theory** (Coulomb) assumes yielding (failure) occurs when the maximum shearing stress equals that in a simple tension (or compression) specimen at yield. Mathematically, $S_1 - S_3 = \pm S_y$.

3. **Maximum strain energy theory** (Beltrami) assumes failure occurs when the energy absorbed per unit volume equals the strain energy per unit volume in a tension (or compression) specimen at yield. Mathematically, $S_1^2 + S_2^2 + S_3^2 - 2\mu(S_1S_2 + S_2S_3 + S_3S_1) = S_y^2$.

4. **Maximum distortion energy theory** (Huber, von Mises, Hencky) assumes yielding occurs when the distortion energy equals that in simple tension at yield. The distortion energy, that portion of the total energy which causes distortion rather than volume change, is

$$U_d = \frac{1+\mu}{3E}(S_1^2 + S_2^2 + S_3^2 - S_1S_2 - S_2S_3 - S_3S_1)$$

Thus failure is defined by

$$S_1^2 + S_2^2 + S_3^2 - (S_1S_2 + S_2S_3 + S_3S_1) = S_y^2$$

5. **Maximum strain theory** (Saint-Venant) claims failure occurs when the maximum strain equals the strain in simple tension at yield or $S_1 - \mu(S_2 + S_3) = S_y$.

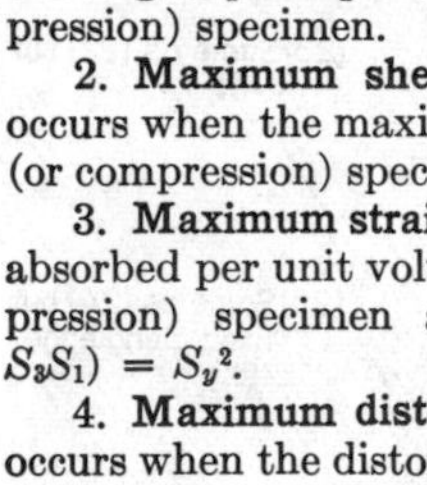

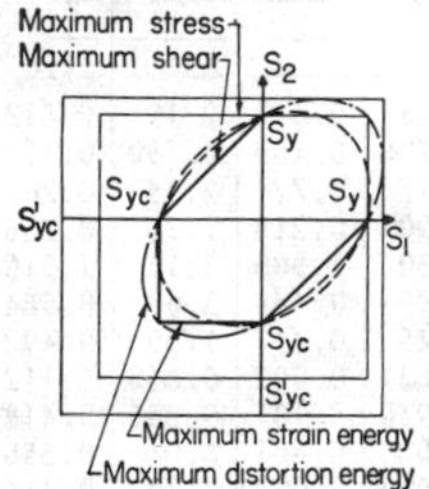

Fig. 72

6. **Internal friction theory** (Mohr). When the ultimate strengths in tension and compression are the same, this theory reduces to that of maximum shear. For principal stresses of opposite sign, failure is defined by $S_1 - \left(\frac{S_{uc}}{S_u}\right) S_2 = -S_{uc}$; if the signs are the same $S_1 = S_u$ or $-S_{uc}$, where S_{uc} is the ultimate strength in compression. If the principal stresses are both either tension or compression, then the larger one, say S_1, must equal S_u when S_1 is tension or S_{uc} when S_1 is compression.

A graphical representation of the first four theories applied to a biaxial stress field is presented in Fig. 72. Stresses outside the bounding lines in the case of each theory mean failure (yield or fracture). A comparison with experimental data proves the **distortion energy theory** (4) best for ductile materials of equal tension-compression properties. When these properties are unequal, the internal energy theory (6) appears best. In practice, judging by some accepted codes, the maximum shear theory (2) is generally used for ductile materials, and the maximum stress theory (1) for brittle materials.

Fatigue failures cannot be related, theoretically, to elastic strength and thus to the theories described. However, experimental results justify this, at least to a limited extent. Therefore, the theory evaluation given above holds for **fluctuating stresses,** provided that principal stresses at the maximum load are used and the **endurance strength** in simple bending is substituted for the yield strength.

EXAMPLE. A steel shaft, 4 in. in diameter, is subjected to a bending moment of 120,000 in.-lb, as well as a torque. If the yield strength in tension is 40,000 psi, what maximum torque can be applied under the (*a*) maximum shear theory and (*b*) the distortion energy theory?

$$S_x = \frac{Mc}{I} = \frac{120{,}000 \times 2}{12.55} = 19{,}100 \text{ psi} \qquad S_{xy} = \frac{TC}{J} = \frac{T \times 2}{25.1} = 0.0798T$$

and

$$S_{M,m} = \frac{S_x}{2} \pm \sqrt{\left(\frac{S_x}{2}\right)^2 + S_{xy}^2}$$

(*a*) $S_M - S_m = S_y$ or $2\sqrt{\left(\frac{19{,}100}{2}\right)^2 + (0.0798T)^2} = (40{,}000)^2$

or $T = 221{,}000$ in.-lb.

(*b*)

$$S_M^2 + S_m^2 - S_M S_m = S_y^2$$

substituting and simplifying,

$$(9{,}550)^2 + 3\sqrt{\left(\frac{19{,}100}{2}\right)^2 + (0.0798T)^2} = (40{,}000)^2$$

or $T = 255{,}000$ in.-lb.

PLASTICITY

The reaction of materials to stress and strain in the plastic range is not yet fully defined. However, some concepts and theories have been proposed.

Ideally, a **purely elastic material** is one complying explicitly with Hooke's law. In a **viscous material,** the shearing stress is proportional to the shearing strain. The **purely plastic material** yields indefinitely, but only after reaching a certain stress. Combinations of these are the **elastico-viscous** and the **elastico-plastic** materials.

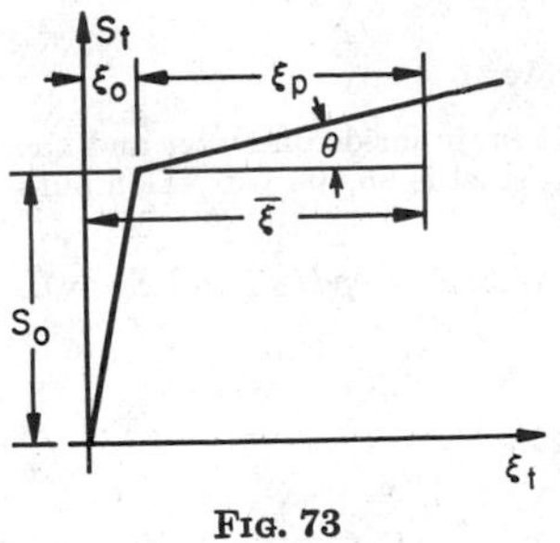

FIG. 73

Engineering materials are not ideal, but usually contain some of the elastico-plastic characteristics. The **total strain** ε_t is the sum of the **elastic strain** ε_o plus the **plastic strain** ε_p, as shown in Fig. 73, where the stress-strain curve is approximated by two straight lines. The **natural strain,** which is at the same time the total strain, is $\bar{\varepsilon} = \int_{l_o}^{l} dl/l = \ln\ (l/l_o)$. In this equation, l is the instantaneous length, while l_o is the original length. In terms of the normal strain, the natural strain becomes $\bar{\varepsilon} = \ln(1 + \varepsilon_o)$. Since it is assumed that the volume remains constant, $l/l_o = A_o/A$, and so the natural stress becomes $\bar{S} = P/A = \frac{P}{A_o}(1 + \varepsilon_o)$. A_o is the original cross-sectional area. If the natural stress is plotted against the natural strain on log-log paper, the graph is very nearly a straight line. The plastic-range relation is thus approximated by $\bar{S} = K\bar{\varepsilon}^n$, where the proportionality factor K and the **strain-hardening coefficient** n are determined from best fits to experimental data. Values of K and n determined by Low and Garofalo (*Proc. Soc. Exp. Stress Anal.*, Vol. IV, No. 2, 1947) are given in Table 21.

The geometry of Fig. 73 can be used to arrive at a second approximate relation

$$\bar{S} = S_o + (\varepsilon_p - \varepsilon_o)\tan\theta = S_o\left(1 - \frac{H}{E}\right) + \varepsilon_p H$$

where $H = \tan\theta$ is a kind of **plastic modulus.**

The **deformation theory of plastic flow** for the general case of combined stress is developed using the above concepts. Certain additional assumptions involved include: principal plastic-strain directions are the same as principal stress directions; the elastic strain is negligible compared to plastic strain; and the ratios of the three principal shearing strains—$(\bar{\varepsilon}_1 - \bar{\varepsilon}_2)$, $(\bar{\varepsilon}_2 - \bar{\varepsilon}_3)$, $(\bar{\varepsilon}_3 - \bar{\varepsilon}_1)$—to the principal shearing stresses—$(\bar{S}_1 - \bar{S}_2)/2$, $(\bar{S}_2 - \bar{S}_3)/2$, $(\bar{S}_3 - \bar{S}_1)/2$—are equal. The relations between the principal strains and stresses in terms of the simple tension quantities become

$$\begin{aligned}\bar{\varepsilon}_1 &= \bar{\varepsilon}/\bar{S}\,[\bar{S}_1 - (\bar{S}_2 + \bar{S}_3)/2]\\ \bar{\varepsilon}_2 &= \bar{\varepsilon}/\bar{S}\,[\bar{S}_2 - (\bar{S}_3 + \bar{S}_1)/2]\\ \bar{\varepsilon}_3 &= \bar{\varepsilon}/\bar{S}\,[\bar{S}_3 - (\bar{S}_1 + \bar{S}_2)/2]\end{aligned}$$

If these equations are added, the plastic flow theory is expressed:

$$\frac{\bar{S}}{\bar{\varepsilon}} = \sqrt{\frac{[(\bar{S}_1 - \bar{S}_2)^2 + (\bar{S}_2 - \bar{S}_3)^2 + (\bar{S}_3 - \bar{S}_1)^2]/2}{2\,(\bar{\varepsilon}_1^2 + \bar{\varepsilon}_2^2 + \bar{\varepsilon}_3^2)/3}}$$

Table 21. Constants *K* and *n* for Sheet Materials

Material	Treatment	*K*, psi	*n*
0.05%C rimmed steel	Annealed	77,100	0.261
0.05%C killed steel	Annealed & tempered	73,100	0.234
Decarburized 0.05 C steel	Annealed in wet H_2	75,500	0.284
0.05/0.07% Phos. low C	Annealed	93,330	0.156
SAE-4130	Annealed	169,400	0.118
SAE-4130	Normalized & tempered	154,500	0.156
Type 430 stainless	Annealed	143,000	0.229
Alcoa 24-S	Annealed	55,900	0.211
Reynolds R-301	Annealed	48,450	0.211

In the above equation

$$\sqrt{\tfrac{1}{2}[(\bar{S}_1 - \bar{S}_2)^2 + (\bar{S}_2 - \bar{S}_3)^2 + (\bar{S}_3 - \bar{S}_1)^2]} = \bar{S}_e$$

and

$$\sqrt{\tfrac{2}{3}[\bar{\varepsilon}_1^2 + \bar{\varepsilon}_2^2 + \bar{\varepsilon}_3^2]} = \varepsilon_e$$

are the effective, or significant, stress and strain respectively.

Example. An annealed, stainless-steel type 430 tank is 41 in. in inside diameter and has a wall 0.375 in. thick. The ultimate strength of the stainless steel is 85,000 psi. Compute the maximum strain as well as the pressure at fracture.

The tank constitutes a biaxial stress field where $S_1 = pd/2t$, $S_2 = pd/4t$, and $S_3 = 0$. Taking the power stress-strain relation

$$\bar{S}_e = K\bar{\varepsilon}_e^n \quad \text{or} \quad \bar{\varepsilon}/\bar{S} = \bar{S}_e^{\left(\frac{1-n}{n}\right)}\Big/K^{1/n}$$

thus

$$\bar{\varepsilon}_1 = \frac{\bar{S}_e^{\left(\frac{1-n}{n}\right)}}{K^{1/n}}\left[\frac{3}{4}\bar{S}_1\right] \quad \bar{\varepsilon}_2 = 0,$$

and

$$\bar{\varepsilon}_3 = \frac{\bar{S}_e^{\left(\frac{1-n}{n}\right)}}{K^{1/n}}\left[-\frac{3}{4}\bar{S}_1\right] = -\bar{\varepsilon}_1$$

The maximum-shear theory, which is applicable to a ductile material under combined stress, is acceptable here. Thus rupture will occur at $\bar{S}_1 - \bar{S}_3 = \bar{S}_1 = \bar{S}_u$, and

$$\bar{S}_e = \sqrt{\frac{1}{2}\left[\left(\frac{\bar{S}_1}{2}\right)^2 + \left(\frac{\bar{S}_1}{2}\right)^2 + \bar{S}_1^2\right]} = \sqrt{\frac{3}{4}\bar{S}_1^2} = \left(\frac{3}{4}\right)^{1/2}\bar{S}_u$$

So
$$\bar{\varepsilon}_1 = \frac{[(3/4)^{1/2}\bar{S}_u]^{\frac{1-n}{n}}}{K^{1/n}}\left(\frac{3}{4}\bar{S}_u\right) = \left[\frac{3}{4}\right]^{\frac{1+0.229}{0.458}}\left(\frac{85{,}000}{143{,}000}\right)^{\frac{1}{0.229}}$$
$$= 0.0475 \text{ in./in.}$$

And, since $\bar{S}_u = S_1 = \dfrac{pd}{2t}$, then $p = \dfrac{2t\bar{S}_u}{d}$ or $p = \dfrac{2 \times 0.375 \times 85{,}000}{41} = 1{,}550$ psi

ROTATING DISKS

Rotating circular disks may be of various profiles, of constant thickness or variable thickness, with or without centrally and non-centrally located holes, and with radial, tangential, and shearing stresses.

Solution starts with the differential equations of equilibrium and compatibility (see p. 5–62 *et seq.*) and the subsequent application of appropriate boundary conditions for the derivation of working stress equations.

If the disk thickness is small compared with the diameter, the variation of stress with thickness can be assumed to be negligible, symmetry eliminating the shearing stress. In the rotating case, the disk weight is neglected, but its inertia force becomes the body-force term in the equilibrium equations.

Thus solved, the stress components in a solid disk become

$$\sigma_r = \frac{3+\mu}{8}\rho\omega^2(R^2 - r^2)$$

$$\sigma_\theta = \frac{3+\mu}{8}\rho\omega^2R^2 - \frac{1+3\mu}{8}\rho\omega^2r^2$$

where μ = Poisson's ratio
ρ = mass density in lb-sec²/in.⁴
ω = angular speed in radians/sec
R = outside disk radius
r = radius to point in question

The largest stresses occur at the center of the solid disk and are

$$\sigma_r = \sigma_\theta = \frac{3+\mu}{8}\rho\omega^2R^2$$

A disk with a central hole of radius r_h (no external forces) is subjected to the following stresses:

$$\sigma_r = \frac{3+\mu}{8}\rho\omega^2\left(R^2 + r_h^2 - \frac{R^2r_h^2}{r^2} - r^2\right)$$

$$\sigma_\theta = \frac{3+\mu}{8}\rho\omega^2\left(R^2 + r_h^2 + \frac{R^2r_h^2}{r^2} - \frac{1+3\mu}{3+\mu}r^2\right)$$

The maximum radial stress, $\sigma_r|_M$, occurs at $r = \sqrt{Rr_h}$, and

$$\sigma_r|_M = \frac{3+\mu}{8}\rho\omega^2(R - r_h)^2$$

The largest tangential stress, $\sigma_\theta|_M$, exists at the inner boundary, and

$$\sigma_\theta|_M = \frac{3+\mu}{4}\rho\omega^2\left(R^2 + \frac{1-\mu}{3+\mu}r_h^2\right)$$

As the hole radius r_h approaches zero, the tangential stress assumes a value twice that at the center of a rotating solid disk, given above.

Stresses in Turbine Disks. Explicit solutions for cases other than those cited are not available, so approximate solutions, such as those proposed by Stodola, Thompson, Hetényi, and Robinson, are necessary. Manson (The Determination of Elastic Stresses in Gas-turbine Disks, *NACA Rept.* 871, 1947) uses the calculus of finite differences.

The customary, simplifying assumptions of axial symmetry—no variation of stress in the thickness direction and a completely elastic stress situation—are made. The differential equations of equilibrium and compatibility are rewritten in finite-difference form.

Solution of the finite-difference equations, appreciation of their linear nature, and successive application of them yield the stresses at any station in terms of those at a boundary station such as r_0. The equations thus derived are

$$\begin{aligned}\sigma_{r,n} &= A_{r,n}\sigma_{t,r_0} + B_{r,n}\\ \sigma_{t,n} &= A_{t,n}\sigma_{t,r_0} + B_{t,n}\end{aligned} \tag{1}$$

The finite-difference expressions yield Eqs. (**2**), which permit the coefficients at station n to be computed from those at station $n - 1$.

$$\begin{aligned}A_{r,n} &= K_nA_{r,n-1} + L_nA_{t,n-1}\\ A_{t,n} &= K_n'A_{r,n-1} + L_n'A_{t,n-1}\\ B_{r,n} &= K_nB_{r,n-1} + L_nB_{t,n-1} + M_n\\ B_{t,n} &= K_n'B_{r,n-1} + L_n'B_{t,n-1} + M_n'\end{aligned} \tag{2}$$

The coefficients at the first station can be established by inspection. For a solid disk, for instance, where both stresses are equal to the tangential stress at the center, the coefficients in Eqs. (**1**) are $A_{r,n} = A_{t,n} = 1$ and $B_{r,n} = B_{t,n} = 0$. In the case of the disk with a central hole, where $\sigma_{r,r_h} = 0$, $A_{r,r_h} = B_{r,r_h} = B_{t,r_h} = 0$ and $A_{t,r_1} = 1$. Knowing these, all others can be found from Eqs. (**2**).

At the outer boundry, $\sigma_{r,R} = A_{r,R}\sigma_{t,r_0} + B_{r,R}$ and $\sigma_{t,r_0} = (\sigma_{r,R} - B_{r,R})/A_{r,R}$. The radial and tangential stresses at each station are successively obtained, knowing σ_{t,r_0} and all the coefficients, using Eqs. (**1**).

The remaining coefficients in Eqs. (**2**), extracted from the finite-difference equations, are defined below, where E is Young's modulus at the temperature of the point in question, h is the profile thickness, α is the thermal coefficient of expansion, ΔT is the temperature increment above that at which the thermal stress is zero, μ is Poisson's ratio, ω is the angular velocity of disk, and ρ is the mass density of disk material.

$$\begin{aligned}C_n &= r_nh_n\\ C_n' &= \mu_n/E_n + [(1 + \mu_n)(r_n - r_{n-1})/(2E_nr_n)]\\ D_n &= \tfrac{1}{2}(r_n - r_{n-1})h_n\\ D_n' &= 1/E_n + [(1 + \mu_n)(r_n - r_{n-1})/(2E_nr_n)]\\ F_n &= r_{n-1}h_{n-1}\\ F_n' &= (\mu_{n-1}/E_{n-1}) - [(1 + \mu_{n-1})(r_n - r_{n-1})/(2E_{n-1}r_{n-1})]\\ G_n &= \tfrac{1}{2}(r_n - r_{n-1})h_{n-1}\\ G_n' &= (1/E_{n-1}) - [(1 + \mu_{n-1})(r_n - r_{n-1})/(2E_{n-1}r_{n-1})]\\ H_n &= \tfrac{1}{2}\omega^2(r_n - r_{n-1})(\rho_nh_nr_n^2 + \rho_{n-1}h_{n-1}r^2_{n-1})\\ H_n' &= \alpha_n\,\Delta T_n - \alpha_{n-1}\,\Delta T_{n-1}\\ K_n &= (F_n'D_n - F_nD_n')/(C_n'D_n - C_nD_n')\\ K_n' &= (C_nF_n' - C_n'F_n)/(C_n'D_n - C_nD_n')\\ L_n &= (G_n'D_n + G_nD_n')/(C_n'D_n - C_nD_n')\\ L_n' &= -(C_n'G_n + C_nG_n')/(C_n'D_n - C_nD_n')\\ M_n &= (H_n'D_n + H_nD_n')/(C_n'D_n - C_nD_n')\\ M_n' &= (C_n'H_n + C_nH_n')/(C_n'D_n - C_nD_n')\end{aligned}$$

Stations need not be equally spaced between the two boundaries. It is best to space them more closely where the profile, temperature, or other property is changing rapidly. In cases of sudden or abrupt section changes, it is best to fair in across the change; the material density should, however, be adjusted to give a total mass equal to the actual. Six to ten stations are often sufficient.

The modulus of elasticity has a significant effect, and its exact value at the temperature of each station should be used. The coefficients of thermal expansion are usually averaged for the temperature between the station and that at which no thermal stress occurs.

The first two Eqs. (**2**) and the last two must be worked simultaneously.

At the outer boundary, loads external to the disk may be imposed, e.g., the radial stress $\sigma_{r,R}$ from the centrifuged pull of a bucket. At the center, the disk may be shrunk on a shaft with the fit pressures causing a radial external push at this boundary.

Numerical solutions are most expeditiously accomplished by use of a table with column-to-column procedures.

Disks with Non-central Holes. This case has not been solved explicitly, but approximations are useful (*e.g.*, Armstrong, Stresses in Rotating Tapered Disks with Noncentral Holes, Ph.D. dissertation, Iowa State University, 1960). The area between the holes is considered removed and replaced by uniform spokes, each one with a cross-sectional area equal to the original minimum spoke area and with a length equal to the diameter of the non-central holes. The higher stress in such a spoke results in an additional extension, which is then applied to the outer annulus according to thin-ring theory and based on the average radius of the ring. The additional stress is considered constant and is added to the tangential stress which would be present in a disk of the same dimensions but filled (that is, no non-central holes).

The stress in the substitute spoke is computed by adjusting the stress at the hole-center radius in the solid or filled disk in proportion to the areas, or $S_{sp} = \sigma_{r,h}(A_g/A_{sp})$, where $\sigma_{r,h}$ is the radial stress in the filled disk at the radius of the hole circle, A_g is the gross circumferential area at the same radius of the filled disk, and A_{sp} is the area of the substitute spoke. The increase in total strain is $\delta = \sigma_{r,h}/E[(A_g/A_{sp}) - 1]l_{sp}$, where l_{sp} is the length of the substitute spoke.

The spoke-effect correction to be applied to the tangential stress is therefore $\sigma_{\theta c} = \delta E/r'$, where r' is the average outer-rim or annulus radius. This is added to the tangential stress found at the corresponding radius in the filled disk. The final step is to adjust the tangential and radial stresses as determined for stress concentrations caused by the holes in the actual disk. The factors for this adjustment are those in an infinite plate of uniform thickness having the same size hole. The method is claimed to yield stresses within 5 percent of those measured photoelastically at points of highest stress.

EXPERIMENTAL STRESS ANALYSIS

Analytical methods of stress analysis can reach limits of applicability. Many experimental techniques have been suggested and tried; several have been developed to a state of great usefulness, e.g., photoelasticity, strain-gage measurement, brittle coating, and birefringent coating.

Photoelasticity

Most transparent materials exhibit temporary double refraction, or **birefringence,** when stressed. Light is resolved into components along the two principal plane directions. The effect is temporary as long as the elastic stress is not exceeded and is in direct proportion to the applied load. The stress magnitude can be established by the amount of component wave retardation, as given in the white and black band field (fringe pattern) obtained when a monochromatic light source is used. The polariscope, consisting of the light source, the polarizer, the model in a loading frame, an analyzer (same as polarizer), and a screen or camera, is used to produce and evaluate the fringe effect. Quarter-wave plates may be placed on either side of the model, making the light components through the model independent of the absolute orientation of polarizer and analyzer. The polarizer is a plane polariscope and yields the directions of principal stresses (the isoclinics); the analyzer is a circular polariscope yielding the fringes (isochromatics) as well.

Figure 74 shows the fringe pattern and the 20° isoclinics of a disk loaded radially at four places.

The isochromatics in the fringe pattern depict the **difference** between principal stresses. At free boundaries where the normal stress is zero, the difference automatically becomes the tangential stress. Starting at such a boundary and proceding into the interior, the stresses can be separated by numerical calculation.

The Stress-Optic Law. In a transparent, isotropic plate subjected to a biaxial stress field within the elastic limit, the relative retardation, R_t, between the two components produced by temporary double refraction is $R_t = Ct(p - q) = n\lambda$, where C is the stress-optic coefficient, t is the plate thickness, p and q are the principal stresses, n is the fringe order (the number of fringes which have passed the point during application of load), and λ is the wavelength of monochromatic light used. Thus, $(p - q)/2 = \tau\Big|_M = (n\lambda)/2Ct = nf/t$.

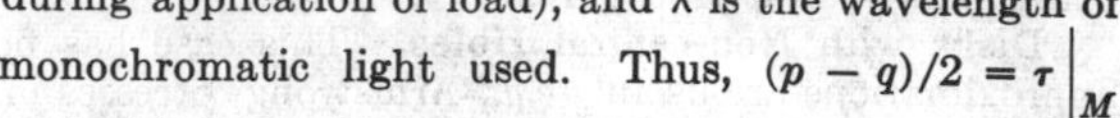

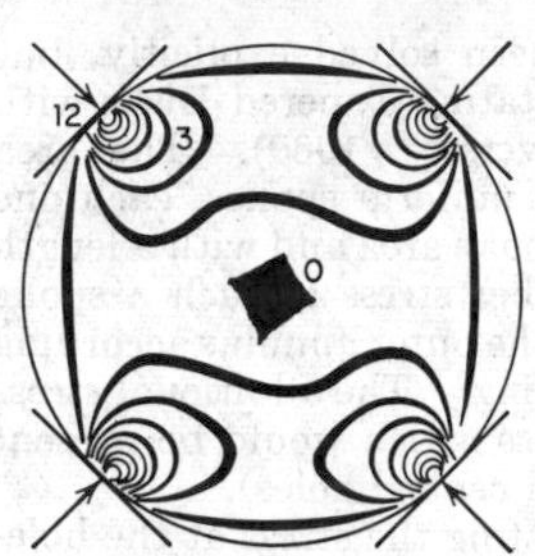

(a) Fringe pattern

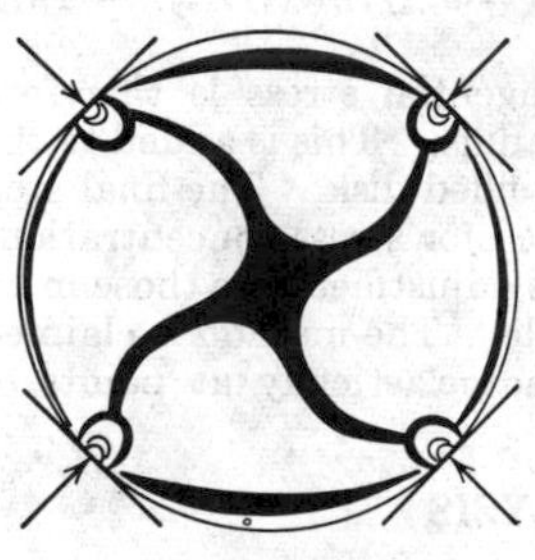
(b) 20° isoclinics

Fig. 74

If the **material-fringe value** f is determined with the same light source (generally a mercury-vapor lamp emitting light having a wavelength of 5461 A units) as used in the model study, the maximum shearing stress, or one-half the difference between the principal stresses, is directly determined. The calibration is a matter of obtaining the material-fringe value in psi per fringe per inch.

Isoclinics, or the direction of the principal planes, can be obtained with a plane polariscope. A new isoclinic parameter is observed each time the polarizer and analyzer are rotated simultaneously into a new position. A white-light source reveals a more distinct isoclinic, as the black curve is more distinguishable against a colored background.

Isostatics, or stress trajectories, are curves the tangents to which represent the progressive change in principal-plane directions. They are constructed graphically using the isoclinics. Since there are two principal planes at each point, two families of orthogonal curves are drawn. Care must be exercised in the drawing of trajectories for practical accuracy.

Stress Separation. If knowledge of each principal stress is required, the photoelastic data must be treated to separate the stresses from the difference given by the data. If the sum of the two stresses is also obtained somehow, a simultaneous solution of the sum and difference values will yield each principal stress. One can also start at a boundary where the normal stress value is zero. There, the photoelastic reading gives the principal stress parallel to the boundary. Starting with the single value, methods have been developed which can be used to proceed with the separation. Typical of the former are lateral-extensometer, iteration, and membrane-analogy techniques; typical of the latter are the slope-equilibrium, shear-difference, graphical-integration, and alternating-summation methods, and oblique incidence (see p. 5–77). Often, however, the surface stresses are the maximum valued ones. (See Frocht, "Photoelasticity," McGraw-Hill.)

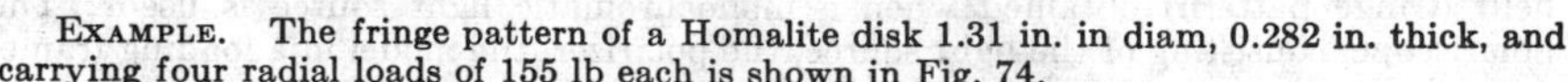

Example. The fringe pattern of a Homalite disk 1.31 in. in diam, 0.282 in. thick, and carrying four radial loads of 155 lb each is shown in Fig. 74.

A closed solution is not known. However, by counting the fringe order at any point, the stress can be determined photoelastically. For instance, the dark spot at the center marks a fringe of zero order, as do the disk edges except in the immediate vicinity of the concentrated loads. The point at the center, which remained dark throughout the loading, is an isotropic point (zero stress difference and normal stresses are equal in all directions). Counting out from the center toward the load, the first "circular" fringe is of order

3. Therefore, anywhere along it $(p - q)/2 = \tau\Big|_M = nf/t = 3 \times 65/0.282 = 692$ psi. Carefully inspected, fringe 12 can be counted at the point of load application. Therefore, $\tau\Big|_M = 12 \times 65/0.282 = 2{,}770$ psi.

Three-dimensional Photoelasticity

Stress "freezing" and slicing, wherein a plastic model is brought up to its critical temperature, loaded as desired, and while loaded, slowly brought back to room temperature, are techniques which freeze the fringe pattern into the model. The model can be cut into slices without disturbing the "frozen" strains. Two-dimensional models are usually machined from plate stock, and three-dimensional models are cast. The frozen stress model is sliced so that the desired information can be obtained by normal incidence using the previous formulations.

When normal incidence is not possible, **oblique incidence** becomes necessary. Oblique-incidence patterns are usable in two-dimensional as well as three-dimensional stress separation. The measurement of fractional fringes is often required when using oblique incidence. With a crossed, circular, monochromatic polariscope, oriented to the principal stresses at a point, the analyzer is rotated through some angle ϕ until

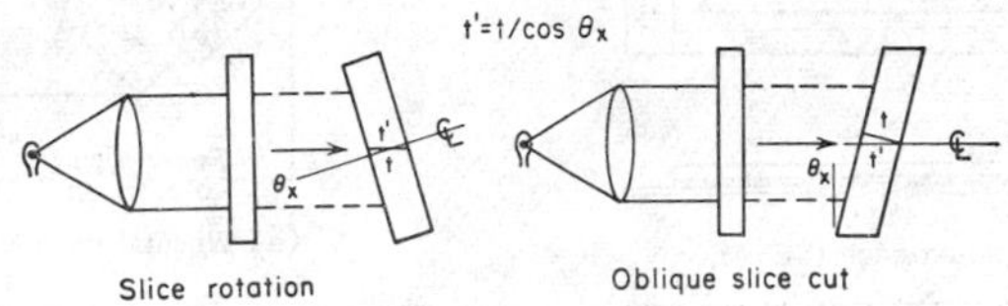

Fig. 75

extinction occurs. The fringe value n is $n = n_n \pm \phi/180$, where n_n is the order of the last visible fringe. Whether the fractional term is added or subtracted depends upon the direction in which the analyzer is rotated (established by inspection).

Oblique-incidence calculations are based on the stress-optic law: $n_n = R_t = t(p - q)/f = tp/f - tq/f = n_p - n_q$. Also, when polarized light is directed through the slice at an angle θ_x to a principal plane, either by rotating the slice away from normal to the light ray or by cutting it at the angle θ_x (see Fig. 75), the fringe order becomes

$$n_{\theta_x} = \frac{t'}{f}(p' - q') = \frac{t}{f \cos \theta_x}(p - q \cos^2 \theta_x)$$
$$= (n_p - n_q \cos^2 \theta_x)/\cos \theta_x$$

Solving algebraically,

$$n_p = (n_{\theta_x} \cos \theta_x - n_n \cos^2 \theta_x)/\sin^2 \theta_x$$

and

$$n_q = (n_{\theta_x} \cos \theta_x - n_n)/\sin^2 \theta_x$$

If orders n_n and n_{θ_x} are thus measured at a point, n_p and n_q can be computed. The principal stresses are then determined from $p = fn_p/t$ and $q = fn_q/t$.

The material-fringe value f in these equations is at the "freezing" temperature (critical temperature). The angle of incidence, as well as the fringe orders, must be accurately measured if errors are to be minimized.

Bonded Metallic Gages

Strain measurements down to one-millionth of an inch per inch are possible with electrical-resistance wire gages. Such gages can be used to measure surface strains (stress by Hooke's law) on any shape or size of object. Figure 76 illustrates schematically the gage construction with a grid of fine alloy wire or thin foil, bonded to paper and covered for protection with a felt pad. In use, the gage is cemented rigidly to the surface of the member to be analyzed. The strain relation is $\epsilon = (\Delta R/R)(1/G_f)$ in./in. Thus, if the resistance R and gage factor G_f (given by the gage manufacturer) are known and the change in resistance ΔR is measured, the strain which caused the resistance change can be determined and Hooke's law can be applied to determine the stress.

Gages must be properly selected in accordance with manufacturer's recommendations. The surface to which the gage is applied must be clean, the proper cement must be used, and the gage assembly must be coated for protection against environmental conditions (e.g., moisture).

A gaging unit, usually a Wheatstone bridge or a ballast circuit (see Fig. 77 and p. 15–42), is needed to detect the signal resulting from the change in resistance of the strain gage. The strain and, therefore, the signal are often too small for direct handling, so that amplification is needed, with a metering discriminator for magnitude evaluation.

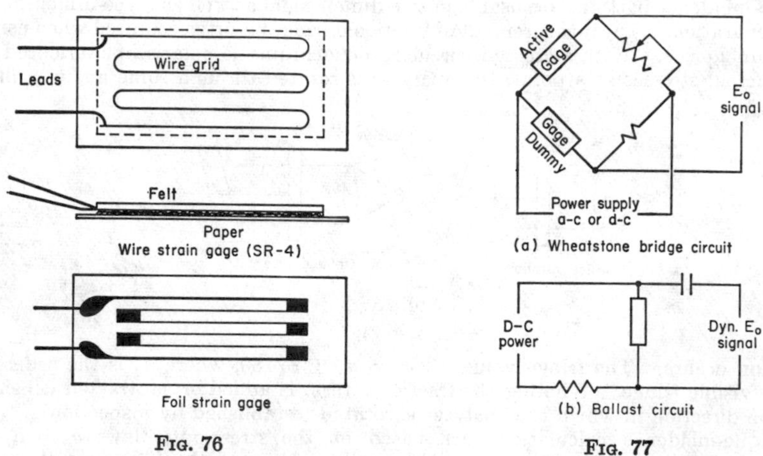

Fig. 76

Fig. 77

The signal is read or recorded by a galvanometer, oscilloscope, or other device. Equipment specifically constructed for strain measurement is available to indicate or record the signal directly in strain units.

Static strains are best gaged on a **Wheatstone bridge**, with strain gages wired to it as indicated in Fig. 77(*a*). With the bridge set so that the only unbalance is the change of resistance in the active-strain gage, the potential difference between the output terminals becomes a measurement of strain. Since the gage is sensitive to temperature as well as strain, it will measure the combined effect. However, if a "dummy" gage, cemented to an unstressed piece of the same metal subjected to the same climatic conditions, is wired into the bridge leg adjacent to the one containing the "active" gage, the electric-resistance temperature effect is cancelled out. Thus the active gage reports only that which is taking place in the stressed plate. The power supply can be either a-c or d-c.

It is sometimes useful to make both gages active—e.g., mounted on opposite sides of a beam, with one gage subjected to tension and the other to compression. Temperature effects are still compensated, but the bridge output is doubled. In other instances, it may be desirable to make all four bridge arms active gages. The experimenter must determine the most practical arrangement for the problem at hand and must bear in mind that the bridge unbalances in proportion to the difference in the strains of gages located in adjacent legs and to the sum of strain in gages located in opposite legs.

Dynamic strains can be detected using circuits such as the **ballast** type shown in Fig. 77*b*. The capacitor coupling passes only rapidly varying or dynamic strains.

The capacitor's infinite impedance to a steady voltage filters out any static effects or strains. The circuit is d-c powered.

Transverse Sensitivity. Grid-type gages possess some strain sensitivity in the direction perpendicular to the gage axis. In a uniaxial stress field, this transverse sensitivity is of no concern because the gage factor was obtained in such a field. However, in a biaxial stress field, neglect of transverse sensitivity will give slightly erroneous strains. When accounted for, the true strains in the axial direction of gage, ϵ_1, and at right angles to it, ϵ_2, are $\epsilon_1 = (1 - \mu k)(\epsilon_{a1} - k\epsilon_{a2})/(1 - k^2)$ and $\epsilon_2 = (1 - \mu k)(\epsilon_{a2} - k\epsilon_{a1})/(1 - k^2)$. Where the apparent strains are $\epsilon_{a1} = \Delta R_1/RG_f$ and $\epsilon_{a2} = \Delta R_2/RG_f$, measured by cementing a gage in each direction 1 and 2. The factor μ is Poisson's ratio of the material to which gages are cemented, and k (usually provided by the gage manufacturer) is the coefficient of transverse sensitivity of the gage. The gage is cemented to the test piece, a uniaxial stress is applied in its axial direction, and the resistance change and strain are measured. The gage factor $G_1 = \Delta R_1/R\epsilon_1$ is computed. A uniaxial stress is next applied transversely to the gage. Again the resistance change and strain are measured and G_2 computed. Then $k = (G_2 + \mu G_1)/(G_1 + \mu G_2)$.

Strain Rosettes. In a general biaxial stress field, the principal plane directions, as well as the stresses, are unknown. Thus, three gages mounted in three differing

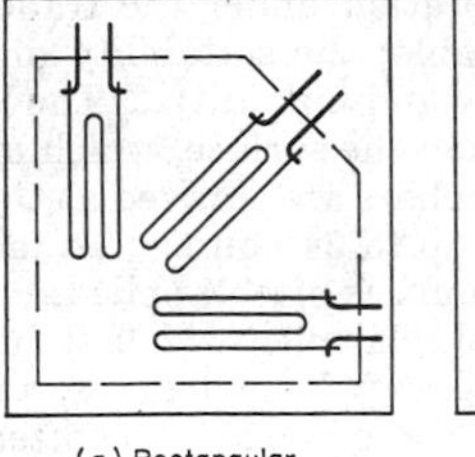

(a) Rectangular

(b) Equiangular

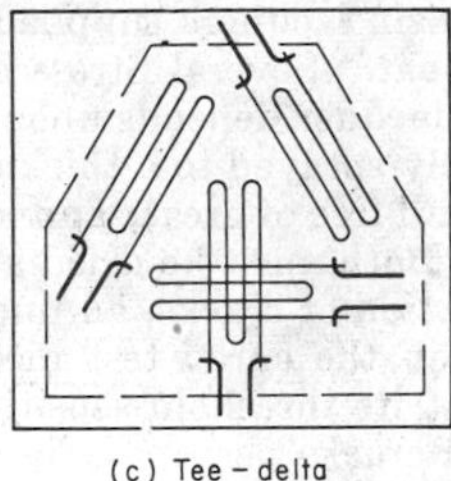

(c) Tee – delta

FIG. 78

directions are needed if the three unknowns are to be determined. Three standard gage combinations, called strain rosettes, are commercially available and are best for the purpose. These are the *rectangular strain rosette* (Fig. 78*a*), which covers a minimum of area and is, therefore, best where the strain gradient is high; the *equiangular strain rosette* (Fig. 78*b*), where the gages do not overlap and which can be used where the strain gradient is low; the *T-delta strain rosette* (Fig. 78*c*), which occupies no more area than the equiangular rosette and which provides an extra check, or "insurance" gage. The wiring and instrumentation of gages in rosettes do not differ from those of individual gages.

The true strains along the gage-length directions are found according to the following equations, in which $R_n = \Delta R_n/RF_1(1 - k^2)$ and $b = 1/k$.

RECTANGULAR ROSETTE. (See Fig. 78*a*.)

$$\epsilon_1 = R_1 - R_3/b$$
$$\epsilon_2 = R_2(1 + 1/b) - (1/b)(R_1 + R_3)$$
$$\epsilon_3 = R_3 - R_1/b$$

EQUIANGULAR ROSETTE. (See Fig. 78*b*.)

$$\epsilon_1 = R_1 - (1/b)(R_2 + R_3)$$
$$\epsilon_2 = R_2 - (1/b)(R_1 + R_3)$$
$$\epsilon_3 = R_3 - (1/b)(R_1 + R_3)$$

T-DELTA ROSETTE. (See Fig. 78c.)

$$\epsilon_1 = R_1(1 + 1/b) - (1/b)(R_3 + R_4)$$
$$\epsilon_2 = R_2(1 + 1/b) - (1/b)(R_3 + R_4)$$
$$\epsilon_3 = R_3 - (1/b)R_4$$
$$\epsilon_4 = R_4 - (1/b)R_3$$

Foil Gages. Foil gages are produced from thin foil by photoetching techniques and are applied, instrumented, read, and evaluated just like the wire-grid type. Foil gages, being much thinner, may be applied easily to curved surfaces, have lower transverse sensitivity, exhibit negligible hysteresis under cycling loads, creep little under sustained loads, and can be stacked on top of each other.

Brittle-coating Analysis

Brittle coatings which adhere to the surface well can reveal the strain in the underlying material. Probably the first such coating used was mill scale, a thin iron oxide which forms on hot-rolled steel stock. Many coatings such as whitewash, Portland cement, and shellac have been tried.

The most popular of presently available strain-indicating brittle coatings are the wood-rosin lacquers supplied by the Magnaflux Corporation under the trade name **Stresscoat.** Several Stresscoat compositions are available; the suitability of a particular lacquer depends upon the prevailing temperature and humidity. The lacquer is usually sprayed to a thickness of 0.004 to 0.008 in. upon the surface, which must be clean and free of grease and loose particles. Calibration bars are sprayed at the same time. Both must be dried at an even temperature for up to 24 hours. To facilitate observation of cracks, an undercoating of bright aluminum is often applied.

When the cured test piece is subjected to loads, the lacquer will first begin to crack at its threshold sensitivity in the area of the largest principal stress, with the parallel cracks perpendicular to the principal stress. This information is often sufficient, as it reveals the critical area and the direction of normal stress.

The threshold sensitivity of Stresscoat lacquers is 600 to 800 microinches per inch in a uniaxial stress field. Exact control of lacquer selection, thickness, curing, and testing temperatures may reduce the threshold to 400 microinches per inch. If desired, the approximate strain (probably within 10 percent) may be established using the calibration strip sprayed with the test part. The strip is placed in a loading device and bent as a cantilever beam by means of a cam at the free end, causing the coating to crack on the tension surface. Crack spacing varies with the strain, being close at the fixed end and diminishing toward the free end down to threshold sensitivity values. The strip is placed in a holder containing strain graduations. A visual comparison of cracks on the test-part surface with those on the strip reveals the strain magnitude which caused the cracks.

Birefringent Coatings

A birefringent coating is one which becomes double refractive when strained. The principle is quite old, but plastics, which adhere to all kinds of materials, which have stable optical-strain constants, and which are sufficiently sensitive to be practical, are of recent development. The trade name applied to this technique is **Photostress.** Photostress plastics can be obtained either as thin sheets (0.040, 0.080, and 0.120 in.) or in liquid form. The sheet material can be bonded to a surface with a special adhesive. The liquid can be brushed or sprayed on, or the part can be dipped in the liquid. The layer should be at least 0.004 in. thick. It is often necessary to apply several successive coatings, with heat curing of each layer in turn. Two sheet types and two liquids are available; these differ in stretching ability and in magnitude of the strain-optical constant. Each of the sheet materials is available metalized on one face, to reflect polarized light even when cemented to a dull surface.

The principles involved are the same as those for conventional photoelasticity. One frequent advantage is the fact that the plastic (sheet or liquid) can be applied directly to the part, which can then be subjected to actual operating loads. A special reflecting polariscope must be used. It contains only one polarizer and quarter-wave disk because the light passes back through the same pair after reflection by the stressed surface-plastic interface. The only limitation rests in the geometry of the structural component to be examined; not only must it be possible to apply the plastic to the surface, but the surface must be accessible to light.

The strain-optic law, since the light passes the plastic thickness twice, becomes

$$p - q = \frac{n}{2t} \frac{E}{K(1 + \mu)}$$

where n is fringe order, E is modulus, μ is Poisson's ratio of workpiece material, and K (supplied by the manufacturer) is the strain-optic coefficient of the plastic. As in conventional photoelasticity, isoclinics are present as well.

PIPELINE FLEXURE STRESSES CAUSED BY EXPANSION OR MOVEMENT OF SUPPORTS

BY

Harold V. Hawkins

REFERENCES: Shipman, Design of Steam Piping to Care for Expansion, *Trans. ASME*, 1929. Wahl, Stresses and Reactions in Expansion Pipe Bends, *Trans. ASME*, 1927. Hovgaard, The Elastic Deformation of Pipe Bends, *Jour. Math. Phys.*, Nov., 1926, and Oct., 1928. M. W. Kellog Co., "The Design of Piping Systems," Wiley.

For details of Pipe and Pipe Fittings see Sec. 8.

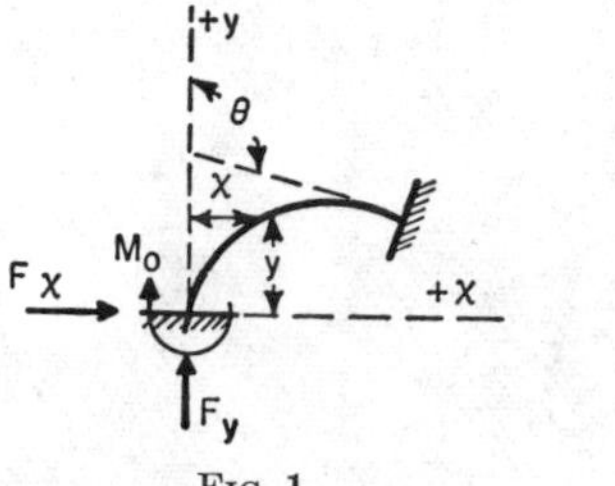

FIG. 1

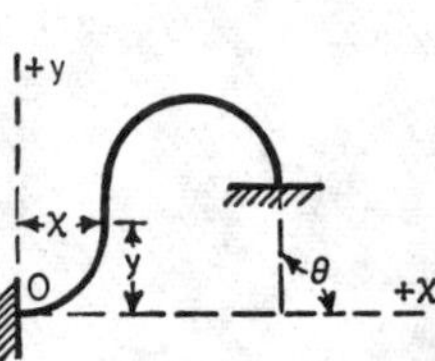

FIG. 2

Nomenclature (see **Figs. 1 and 2**).

M_0 = end moment at origin, in.-lb
M = max moment, in.-lb
F_x = end reaction at origin in x-direction, lb
F_y = end reaction at origin in y-direction, lb
$S_l = (Mr/I)\alpha$ = max unit longitudinal flexure stress, psi
$S_t = (Mr/I)\beta$ = max unit transverse flexure stress, psi
$S_s = (Mr/I)\gamma$ = max unit shearing stress, psi
Δx = relative deflection of ends of pipe parallel to x-direction caused by either temperature change or support movement, or both, in.
Δy = same as Δx but parallel to y-direction, in. Note that Δx and Δy are positive if under the change in temperature the end opposite the origin tends to move in a positive x- or y-direction, respectively.
t = wall thickness of pipe, in.
r = mean radius of pipe cross section, in.
λ = constant = tR/r^2
I = moment of inertia of pipe cross section about pipe center line, in.^{4}
E = modulus of elasticity of pipe at *actual working* temperature, psi
K = flexibility index of pipe. $K = 1$ for all straight pipe sections, $K = (10 + 12\lambda^2)/(1 + 12\lambda^2)$ for all curved pipe sections where $\lambda > 0.335$ (see Fig. 3)
α, β, γ = ratios of actual max longitudinal flexure, transverse flexure, and shearing stresses to Mr/I for curved sections of pipe (see Fig. 3)
A, B, C, F, G, H = constants given by Table 2
θ = angle of intersection between tangents to direction of pipe at reactions
$\Delta\theta$ = change in θ caused by movements of supports, or by temperature change, or both, radians
ds = an infinitesimal element of length of pipe
s = length of a particular curved section of pipe, in.
R = radius of curvature of pipe center line

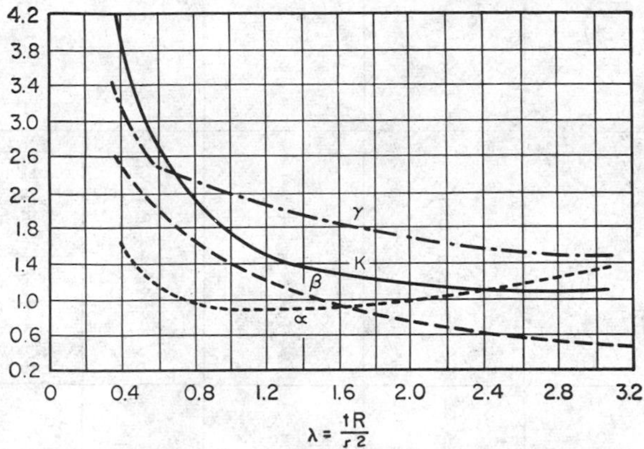

FIG. 3. Flexure constants of initially curved pipes.

Table 1. General Equations for Pipelines in One Plane

Type of supports	Unsymmetrical	Symmetrical about y-axis
Both ends fully fixed	$M_0 = \frac{EI\Delta x(CF - AB) + EI\Delta y(BF - AG)}{2ABF + CGH - B^2H - A^2G - CF^2}$ $F_x = \frac{EI\Delta x(CH - A^2) + EI\Delta y(BH - AF)}{2ABF + CGH - B^2H - A^2G - CF^2}$ $F_y = \frac{EI\Delta x(BH - AF) + EI\Delta y(GH - F^2)}{2ABF + CGH - B^2H - A^2G - CF^2}$ $\Delta\theta = 0$	$M_0 = \frac{EI\Delta xF}{GH - F^2}$ $F_x = \frac{EI\Delta xH}{GH - F^2}$ $F_y = 0$ $\Delta\theta = 0$
Both ends hinged	$M_0 = 0$ $F_x = \frac{EI\Delta xC + EI\Delta yB}{CG - B^2}$ $F_y = \frac{EI\Delta xB + EI\Delta yG}{CG - B^2}$ $\Delta\theta = \frac{\Delta x(AB - CF) + \Delta y(AG - BF)}{CG - B^2}$	$M_0 = 0$ $F_x = \frac{EI\Delta x}{G}$ $F_y = 0$ $\Delta\theta = \frac{-\Delta xF}{G}$
Origin end only hinged, other end fully fixed	$M_0 = 0$ $F_x = \frac{EI\Delta xC + EI\Delta yB}{CG - B^2}$ $F_y = \frac{EI\Delta xB + EI\Delta yG}{CG + B^2}$ $\Delta\theta = \frac{\Delta x(AB - CF) + \Delta y(AG - BF)}{CG + -B^2}$	
In general for any specific rotation $\Delta\theta$ and movement Δx and Δy	$M_0 = \frac{EI\Delta x(CF - AB) + EI\Delta y(BF - AG) + EI\Delta\theta(CG - B^2)}{2ABF + CGH - A^2G - CF^2 - B^2H}$ $F_x = \frac{EI\Delta x(CH - A^2) + EI\Delta y(BH - AF) + EI\Delta\theta(CF - AB)}{2ABF + CGH - A^2G - CF^2 - B^2H}$ $F_y = \frac{EI\Delta x(BH - AF) + EI\Delta y(GH - E^2) + EI\Delta\theta(BF - AG)}{2ABF + CGH - A^2G - CF^2 - B^2H}$	

Table 2. Values of A, B, C, F, G, and H for Various Piping Elements

	$A = K\int x\,ds$	$B = K\int xy\,ds$	$C = K\int x^2\,ds$	$F = K\int y\,ds$	$G = K\int y^2\,ds$	$H = K\int ds$
s, (x_1, y), (x_2, y)	$\frac{s}{2}(x_1 + x_2)$	Ay	$s\left(\frac{s^2}{3} + x_1x_2\right)$	sy	Fy	s
S, (x, y_2), (x, y_1)	sx	$\frac{A}{2}(y_1 + y_2)$	Ax	$\frac{s}{2}(y_1 + y_2)$	$s\left(\frac{s^2}{3} + y_1y_2\right)$	s
S, (x_2, y_2), (x_1, y_1)	$\frac{s}{2}(x_1 + x_2)$	$\frac{A}{3}(y_1 + y_2) + \frac{s}{6}(x_1y_1 + x_2y_2)$	$\frac{s}{3}(x_1^2 + x_1x_2 + x_2^2)$	$\frac{s}{2}(y_1 + y_2)$	$\frac{s}{3}(y_1^2 + y_1y_2 + y_2^2)$	s
(x, y) (upper semicircle)	πKRx	$A\left(y + \frac{2R}{\pi}\right)$	$A\left(x + \frac{R^2}{2x}\right)$	$(\pi y + 2R)KR$	$Fy + \left(2y + \frac{\pi}{2}R\right)KR^2$	πKR
(x, y) (lower semicircle)		$A\left(y - \frac{2R}{\pi}\right)$		$(\pi y - 2R)KR$	$Fy - \left(2y - \frac{\pi}{2}R\right)KR^2$	
(x, y) (quarter circle)	$\left(\frac{\pi x}{2} - R\right)KR$	$Ay + \left(x - \frac{R}{2}\right)KR^2$	$Ax + \left(\frac{\pi R}{4} - x\right)KR^2$	$\left(\frac{\pi y}{2} + R\right)KR$	$Fy + \left(\frac{\pi R}{4} + y\right)KR^2$	$\frac{\pi KR}{2}$

(x, y)	$\left(\frac{\pi x}{2}+R\right)KR$	$Ay+\left(x+\frac{R}{2}\right)KR^2$	$Ax+\left(\frac{\pi R}{4}+x\right)KR^2$	$\left(\frac{\pi y}{2}+R\right)KR$	$Fy+\left(\frac{\pi R}{4}+y\right)KR^2$	$\frac{\pi KR}{2}$
(x, y)		$Ay-\left(x+\frac{R}{2}\right)KR^2$		$\left(\frac{\pi y}{2}-R\right)KR$	$Fy+\left(\frac{\pi R}{4}-y\right)KR^2$	
(x, y)	$\left(\frac{\pi x}{2}-R\right)KR$	$Ay-\left(x-\frac{R}{2}\right)KR^2$	$Ax+\left(\frac{\pi R}{4}-x\right)KR^2$	$\left(\frac{\pi y}{2}-R\right)KR$	$Fy+\left(\frac{\pi R}{4}-y\right)KR^2$	
(x, y) 45°	$\left(\frac{\pi x}{4}-\frac{R}{\sqrt{2}}\right)KR$	$Ay+\left[\left(1-\frac{\sqrt{2}}{2}\right)x-\frac{R}{4}\right]KR^2$	$Ax+\left[\left(\frac{\pi}{8}+\frac{1}{4}\right)R-\frac{x\sqrt{2}}{2}\right]KR^2$	$\left[\frac{\pi y}{4}+\left(1-\frac{\sqrt{2}}{2}\right)R\right]KR$	$Fy+\left[\left(1-\frac{\sqrt{2}}{2}\right)y+\left(\frac{\pi}{8}-\frac{1}{4}\right)R\right]KR^2$	$\frac{\pi KR}{4}$
(x, y) 45°		$Ay-\left[\left(1-\frac{\sqrt{2}}{2}\right)x-\frac{R}{4}\right]KR^2$		$\left[\frac{\pi y}{4}-\left(1-\frac{\sqrt{2}}{2}\right)R\right]KR$	$Fy-\left[\left(1-\frac{\sqrt{2}}{2}\right)y-\left(\frac{\pi}{8}-\frac{1}{4}\right)R\right]KR^2$	
45° (x, y)	$\left(\frac{\pi x}{4}+\frac{R}{\sqrt{2}}\right)KR$	$Ay+\left[\left(1-\frac{\sqrt{2}}{2}\right)x+\frac{R}{4}\right]KR^2$	$Ax+\left[\left(\frac{\pi}{8}+\frac{1}{4}\right)R+\frac{x\sqrt{2}}{2}\right]KR^2$	$\left[\frac{\pi y}{4}+\left(1-\frac{\sqrt{2}}{2}\right)R\right]KR$	$Fy+\left[\left(1-\frac{\sqrt{2}}{2}\right)y+\left(\frac{\pi}{8}-\frac{1}{4}\right)R\right]KR^2$	
(x, y) 45°		$Ay-\left[\left(1-\frac{\sqrt{2}}{2}\right)x+\frac{R}{4}\right]KR^2$		$\left[\frac{\pi y}{4}-\left(1-\frac{\sqrt{2}}{2}\right)R\right]KR$	$Fy-\left[\left(1-\frac{\sqrt{2}}{2}\right)y-\left(\frac{\pi}{8}-\frac{1}{4}\right)R\right]KR^2$	
θ_1 θ_2 (x, y)	$[x(\theta_2-\theta_1)-R(\sin\theta_2-\sin\theta_1)]KR$	$Ay-\left[x(\cos\theta_2-\cos\theta_1)+\frac{R}{2}(\sin^2\theta_2-\sin^2\theta_1)\right]KR^2$	$Ax-\left[x(\sin\theta_2-\sin\theta_1)-\frac{R}{4}(\sin 2\theta_2-\sin 2\theta_1)-\frac{R}{2}(\theta_2-\theta_1)\right]KR^2$	$[y(\theta_2-\theta_1)-R(\cos\theta_2-\cos\theta_1)]KR$	$Fy-\left[y(\cos\theta_2-\cos\theta_1)+\frac{R}{4}(\sin 2\theta_2-\sin 2\theta_1)-\frac{R}{2}(\theta_2-\theta_1)\right]KR^2$	$(\theta_2-\theta_1)KR$

General Discussion

Under the effect of changes in temperature of the pipeline, or of movement of support reactions (either translation or rotation), or both, the determination of stress distribution in a pipe becomes a statically indeterminate problem. In general the problem may be solved by a slight modification of the standard arch theory: $\Delta x = -K\int My\, ds/EI$, $\Delta y = K\int Mx\, ds/EI$, and $\Delta\theta = K\int M\, ds/EI$ where the constant K is introduced to correct for the increased flexibility of a curved pipe, and where the integration is over the entire length of pipe between supports. In Table 1 are given equations derived by this method for moment and thrust at one reaction point for pipes in one plane that are fully fixed, hinged at both ends, hinged at one end and fixed at the other, or partly fixed. If the reactions at one end of the pipe are known, the moment distribution in the entire pipe then can be obtained by simple statics.

Since an initially curved pipe is more flexible than indicated by its moment of inertia, the constant K is introduced. Its value may be taken from Fig. 3, or computed from the equation given below. $K = 1$ for all straight pipe sections since they act according to the simple flexure theory.

In Fig. 3 are given the flexure constants K, α, β, and γ for initially curved pipes as functions of the quantity $\lambda = tR/r^2$. The flexure constants are derived from the equations

$$K = (10 + 12\lambda^2)/(1 + 12\lambda^2),\ \text{when } \lambda > 0.335$$

$$\alpha = \tfrac{2}{3}K\sqrt{(5 + 6\lambda^2)/18}$$

$$\beta = 18\lambda/(1 + 12\lambda^2)$$

$$\gamma = [8\lambda - 36\lambda^3 + (32\lambda^2 + \tfrac{20}{3})\sqrt{\tfrac{4}{3}\lambda^2 - \tfrac{5}{18}}]/(1 + 12\lambda^2),\ \text{when } \lambda < 0.58$$

$$= (12\lambda^2 + 18\lambda - 2)/(1 + 12\lambda^2),\ \text{when } \lambda > 0.58$$

The increased flexibility of the curved pipe is brought about by the tendency of its cross section to flatten. This flattening causes a transverse flexure stress whose maximum is S_t. Because the maximum longitudinal and maximum transverse stresses do not occur at the same point in the pipe's cross section, the resulting maximum shear is not one-half the difference of S_l and S_t; it is S_s. In the straight sections of the pipe, $\alpha = 1$, the transverse stress disappears, and $\gamma = \tfrac{1}{2}$. This discussion of S_s does not include the uniform transverse or longitudinal tension stresses induced by the internal pressure in the pipe; their effects should be added if appreciable.

Table 2 gives values of the constants A, B, C, F, G, and H for use in equations listed in Table 1. The values may be used (1) for the solution of any pipeline, or (2) for the derivation of equations for standard shapes composed of straight sections and arcs of circles as in Fig. 5. Equations for shapes not given may be obtained by algebraic addition of those given. All measurements are from the left-hand end of the pipeline. Reactions and stresses are very greatly influenced by end conditions. Formulas are given to cover the extreme conditions. The following suggestions and comments should be considered when laying out a pipeline:

Avoid expansion bends, and design the entire pipeline to take care of its own expansion.

The movement of the equipment to which the ends of the pipe line are attached must be included in the Δx and Δy of the equations.

Maximum flexibility is obtained by placing **supports** and **anchors** so that they will not interfere with the natural movement of the pipe.

That shape is most efficient in which the **maximum length of pipe** is **working** at the maximum safe stress.

Excessive **bending moment at joints** is more likely to cause trouble than excessive stresses in pipe walls. Hence, keep pipe joints away from points of high moment.

Reactions and stresses are greatly influenced by **flattening of the cross section** of the curved portions of the pipeline.

It is recommended that **cold springing** allowances be discounted in stress calculations.

Application to Two- and Three-plane Pipelines. Pipelines in more than one plane may be solved by the successive application of the preceding data, dividing the pipeline into two or more one-plane lines.

EXAMPLE. The unsymmetrical pipeline of Fig. 4 has fully fixed ends. From Table 2 use $K = 1$ for all sections, since only straight segments are involved.

Table 3. Example Showing Determination of Integrals

Part of pipe	Values of integrals					
	A	B	C	F	G	H
0–1	$\frac{a^2}{2}$	0	$\frac{a^3}{3}$	0	0	a
1–2	ab	$\frac{ab^2}{2}$	a^2b	$\frac{b^2}{2}$	$\frac{b^3}{3}$	b
2–3	$\frac{c}{2}(2a + c)$	$\frac{bc}{2}(2a + c)$	$\frac{c^3}{3} + ac(a + c)$	bc	b^2c	c
Total 0–3	$\frac{a^2}{2} + ab + \frac{c}{2}(2a + c)$	$\frac{ab^2}{2} + \frac{bc}{2}(2a + c)$	$\frac{a^3}{3} + a^2b + \frac{c^3}{3} + ac(a + c)$	$\frac{b^2}{2} + bc$	$\frac{b^3}{3} + b^2c$	$a + b + c$

Upon introduction of $a = 120$ in., $b = 60$ in., and $c = 180$ in., into the preceding relations (Table 3) for A, B, C, F, G, H, the equations for the reactions at 0 from Table 1 become

$$M_0 = EI\Delta x(-7.1608 \times 10^{-5}) + EI\Delta y(-8.3681 \times 10^{-5})$$
$$F_x = EI\Delta x(+1.0993 \times 10^{-5}) + EI\Delta y(+3.1488 \times 10^{-6})$$
$$F_y = EI\Delta x(+3.1488 \times 10^{-6}) + EI\Delta y(+1.33717 \times 10^{-6})$$

Also it follows that

$$M_1 = M_0 + F_ya = EI\ \Delta x(+3.0625 \times 10^{-4}) + EI\ \Delta y(+7.6779 \times 10^{-5})$$
$$M_2 = M_1 - F_xb = EI\ \Delta x(+2.4029 \times 10^{-4}) + EI\ \Delta y(-1.1215 \times 10^{-4})$$
$$M_3 = M_2 + F_yc = EI\ \Delta x(+8.0707 \times 10^{-4}) + EI\ \Delta y(+1.2854 \times 10^{-4})$$

Thus the maximum moment M occurs at 3.

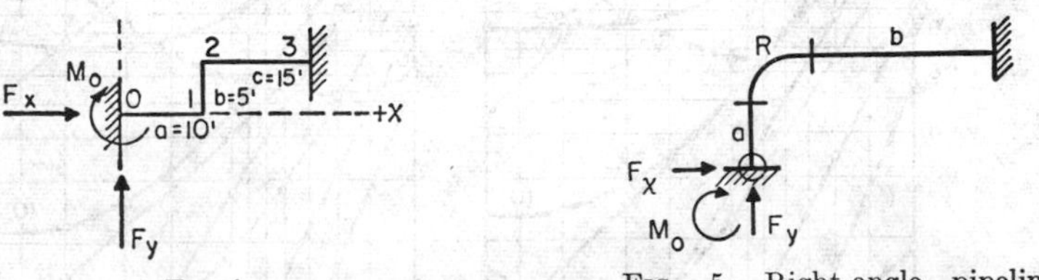

FIG. 4

FIG. 5. Right-angle pipeline.

The total maximum longitudinal fiber stress ($\alpha = 1$ for straight pipe)

$$= \frac{F_x}{2\pi rt} \pm \frac{M_3r}{I}$$

There is no transverse flexure stress since all sections are straight. The maximum shearing stress is either (1) one-half of the maximum longitudinal fiber stress as given above, (2) one-half of the hoop-tension stress caused by any internal radial pressure that might exist in the pipe, or (3) one-half the difference of the maximum longitudinal fiber stress and hoop-tension stress, whichever of these three possibilities is numerically greatest.

The equations of Table 1 may be employed to develop the solution of generalized types of pipe configurations for which Fig. 5 is a typical example. If only temperature changes are considered, the reactions for the right-angle pipeline (Fig. 5) may be determined from the following equations:

$$M_0 = C_1EI\ \Delta x/R^2$$
$$F_x = C_2EI\ \Delta x/R^3$$
$$F_y = C_3EI\ \Delta x/R^3$$

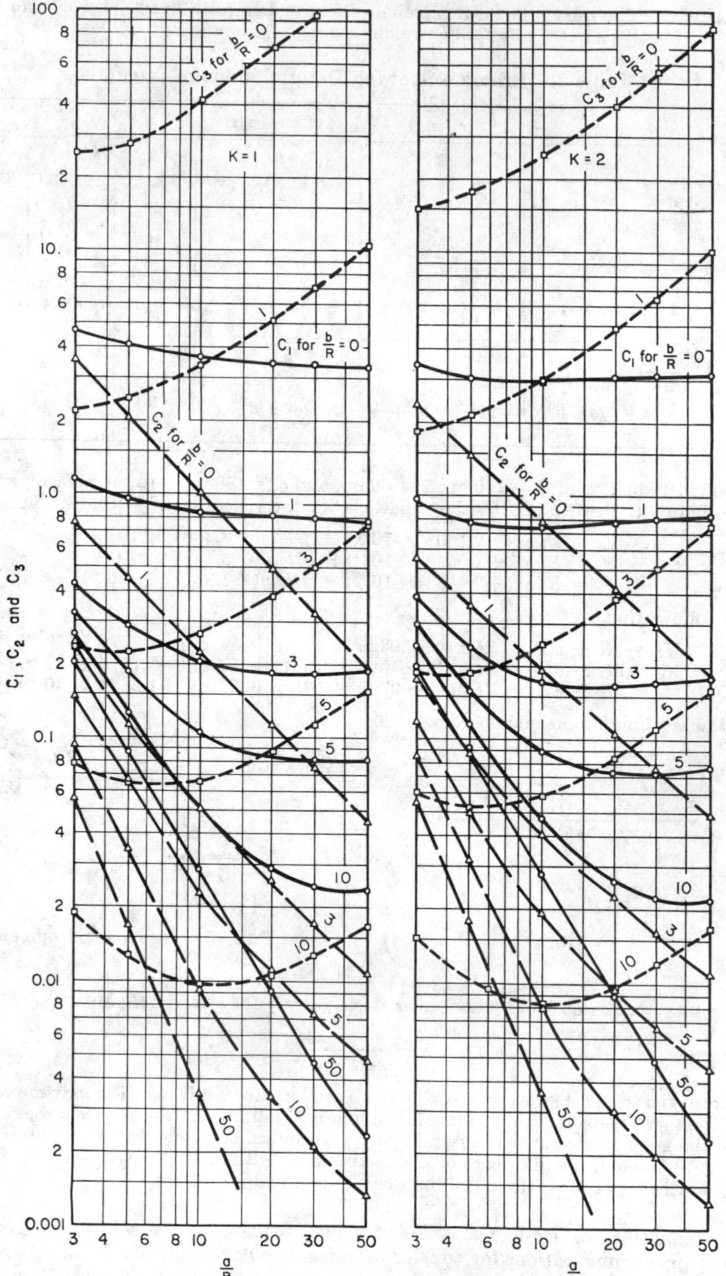

FIG. 6. Reactions for right-angle pipelines.

In these equations, Δx is the x-component of the deflection between reaction points caused by temperature change only. The values of C_1, C_2, and C_3 are given in Fig. 6 for $K = 1$ and $K = 2$. For other values of K, interpolation may be employed.

EXAMPLE. With $a/R = 20$ and $b/R = 3$, the value of C_1 is 0.185 for $K = 1$ and 0.165 for $K = 2$. If $K = 1.75$, the interpolated value of C_1 is 0.175.

Elimination of Flexure Stresses. Pipeline flexure stresses that normally would result from movement of supports or from the tendency of the pipes to expand under temperature change often may be avoided entirely through the use of expansion joints (see p. 8–245). Their use may simplify both the design of the pipeline and the support structure. When using expansion joints the following suggestions should be considered: (1) select expansion joint carefully for maximum temperature range (and deflection) expected so as to prevent damage to expansion fitting; (2) provide guides to limit movement at expansion joint to direction permitted by joint; (3) provide adequate anchors at one end of each straight section or along their mid-length, forcing movement to occur at expansion joint yet providing adequate support for pipeline; (4) mount expansion joints adjacent to an anchor point to prevent sagging of the pipeline under its own weight and don't depend upon the expansion joint for stiffness—it is intended to be flexible; (5) give consideration to effects of corrosion, since corrugated character of expansion joints makes cleaning difficult.

VIBRATION

BY

William T. Thomson

REFERENCES: Den Hartog, "Mechanical Vibration," McGraw-Hill. Freberg and Kemler, "Elements of Mechanical Vibration," Wiley. Hansen and Chenea, "Mechanics of Vibration," Wiley. Myklestad, "Fundamentals of Vibration Analysis," McGraw-Hill. Thomson, "Mechanical Vibrations," Prentice-Hall. Timoshenko," Vibration Problems in Engineering," Van Nostrand.

The simplest vibrating system is one of a single degree of freedom, the motion of which can be described by a single coordinate x, as shown in Fig. 1. The mass attached to the spring has freedom to vibrate in the vertical direction, and the mass of the spring will be considered to be small in comparison to it.

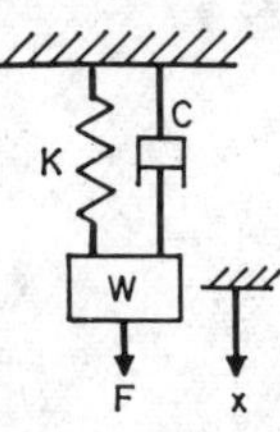

FIG. 1

Free Vibrations. When the system previously described is put into motion by an initial displacement or velocity, the oscillations will gradually diminish in amplitude, because of resisting forces which are always present. These damping forces may arise from various sources, such as air or fluid resistance, internal friction of the material of the vibrating body, or friction between sliding surfaces. When a body is vibrating in air or in a liquid and velocities are small, the resisting force is very nearly proportional to the velocity and equal to $c\dot{x}$. The differential equation of motion then becomes

$$\frac{W}{g}\ddot{x} + c\dot{x} + kx = 0 \tag{1}$$

where $\dot{x}$ and $\ddot{x}$ are the first and second derivatives of x with respect to time.

The general solution of this equation in terms of the initial displacement x_0 and initial velocity $\dot{x}_0$ is

$$x = e^{-\zeta\omega_n t}\left[x_0 \cos\omega_d t + \left(\frac{\dot{x}_0 + \zeta\omega_n x_0}{\omega_d}\right)\sin\omega_d t\right] \tag{2}$$

where the symbols used are related to the original quantities as follows:

$$\omega_n = \sqrt{\frac{kg}{W}} = \frac{2\pi}{\tau} = \text{undamped natural frequency, radians per sec}$$

$$\tau = \text{period of free vibration with no damping, } \zeta = 0$$

$$\omega_d = \omega_n\sqrt{1-\zeta^2} = \frac{2\pi}{\tau_d}$$

$$\tau_d = \text{period of free vibration with damping } \zeta$$

$$\zeta = c/c_c = \text{damping factor}$$

$$c_c = 2\sqrt{\frac{kW}{g}} = \text{critical damping}$$

By substituting $x_0 = A \sin\alpha$ and $\dfrac{\dot{x}_0 + \zeta\omega_n x_0}{\omega_d} = A\cos\alpha$, Eq. (**2**) can also be written as

$$x = A\,e^{-\zeta\omega_n t}\sin(\omega_d t + \alpha) \tag{3}$$

In general, damping, ζ, is small, and the difference between ω_d and ω_n is a small quantity of the second order. It can be assumed, therefore, that small damping forces do not affect the period of free vibration, which is

$$\tau = 2\pi\sqrt{\frac{W}{kg}} = 2\pi\sqrt{\frac{\delta_{st}}{g}} \tag{4}$$

where δ_{st} is the statical deflection of the spring under the action of the weight W.

Logarithmic Decrement. A convenient way to determine the amount of damping present in an oscillatory system is to measure the rate of decay of free oscillations shown in Fig. 2. This is best expressed by the logarithmic decrement, which is defined as the natural logarithm of the ratio of any two successive amplitudes, which results in the equation

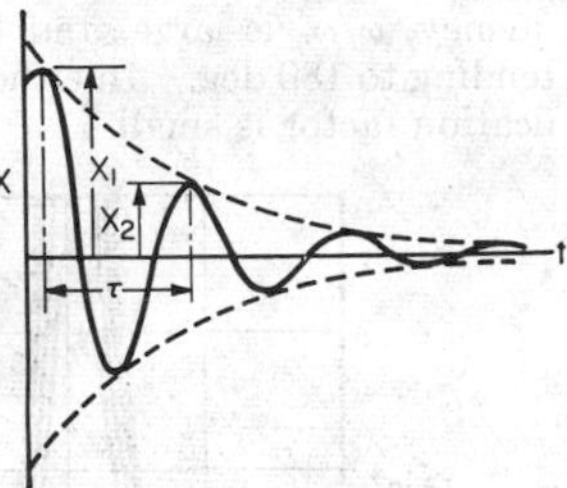

FIG. 2

$$\delta = \ln\frac{x_i}{x_{i+1}} = \frac{2\pi\zeta}{\sqrt{1-\zeta^2}} \cong 2\pi\zeta \tag{5}$$

The logarithmic decrement can also be obtained from the resonance curve of forced vibration as

$$\delta = \left(\frac{f_2 - f_1}{f_n}\right)\pi \tag{6}$$

where f_n is the resonant frequency and f_1 and f_2 are frequencies on each side of resonance, for which the amplitude is 0.707 times the amplitude at resonance. Since $f_n/(f_2 - f_1)$ is a measure of the sharpness of the resonance curve, it is often referred to as the Q of the system.

$$Q = \frac{f_n}{f_2 - f_1} = \frac{1}{2\zeta} \tag{7}$$

Forced Vibration. When a harmonic disturbing force $P \sin \omega t$ acts on the spring-mass system, the differential equation becomes

$$\frac{W}{g}\ddot{x} + c\dot{x} + kx = P \sin \omega t \tag{8}$$

The resulting vibration will consist of two parts, free damped vibration such as that represented by Eq. (**2**) and forced vibration. The free vibration will be damped out in a short time, after which only the forced vibration will exist.

The expression for the forced vibration has the form

$$x = X \sin(\omega t - \phi) \tag{9}$$

where the amplitude and phase are given by the following equations

$$X = \frac{P}{k}\,\frac{1}{\sqrt{\left[1 - \left(\frac{\omega}{\omega_n}\right)^2\right]^2 + 4\zeta^2\left(\frac{\omega}{\omega_n}\right)^2}} \tag{10}$$

$$\phi = \tan^{-1}\frac{2\zeta\frac{\omega}{\omega_n}}{1 - \left(\frac{\omega}{\omega_n}\right)^2} \tag{11}$$

The first factor on the right side of Eq. (**10**) is the **zero frequency deflection,** *i.e.*, the statical deflection which would result if a steady force of magnitude P was applied to the spring of stiffness k. The second factor is due to dynamical conditions and is called the magnification factor. The phase angle given by Eq. (**11**) determines the amount the displacement lags behind the disturbing force, in radians. In Fig. 3, the magnification factor and phase angle are plotted against ω/ω_n for various values of the damping factor ζ.

When the disturbing force has a very low frequency as compared with the natural frequency of the system, the ratio ω/ω_n is small and the magnification factor approaches unity with phase approaching zero. When the disturbing force has a very high frequency, ω/ω_n is large, and the magnification factor approaches zero with phase angle tending to 180 deg. In either of these extreme cases the effect of damping on the magnification factor is small.

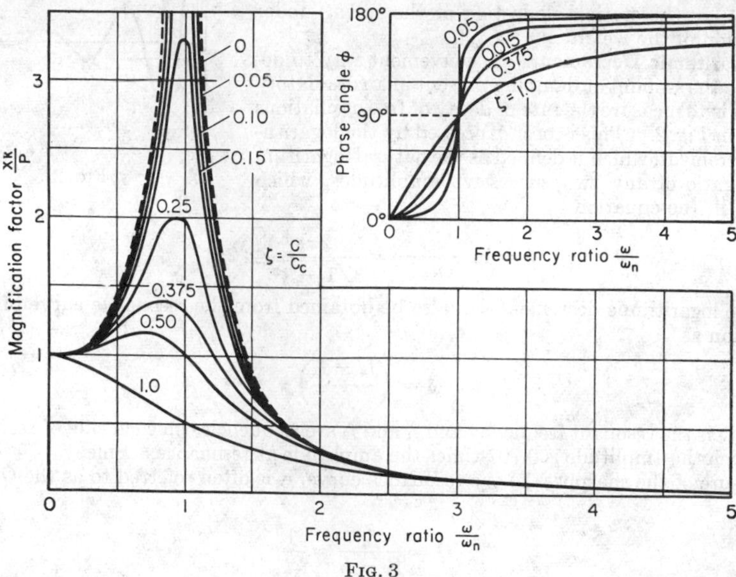

Fig. 3

When ω approaches ω_n a condition of resonance is encountered, and the amplitude of vibration is limited only by the amount of damping present. The phase angle in this neighborhood also undergoes a large variation and has the value of 90 deg at $\omega/\omega_n = 1.0$.

Structural Damping. In structural analysis, it is found that damping is encountered proportional to displacement but out of phase with the velocity of harmonic oscillation. For such cases the following differential equation applies

$$\frac{W}{g}\ddot{x} + (1 + i\gamma)\,kx = P \sin \omega t \tag{12}$$

where γ is the structural damping coefficient (usually between 0 and 0.05). The magnification factor then becomes

$$\frac{1}{\sqrt{\left[1 - \left(\frac{\omega}{\omega_n}\right)^2\right]^2 + \gamma^2}} \tag{13}$$

and its resonant value becomes $\frac{1}{\gamma}$, in contrast to $\frac{1}{2\zeta}$ of the viscous damping. Thus, in the neighborhood of resonance, structural damping behaves like viscous damping of value 2ζ.

Energy Method. Examination of the frequency equation $\omega_d = \omega_n\sqrt{1 - \zeta^2}$ indicates that damping can usually be neglected when determining the resonant frequencies of the system. For an undamped system, the total energy is a constant, and there is a continual interchange between the potential and kinetic energy. Thus the maximum kinetic energy of the system as it moves through the equilibrium position is equal to the maximum potential energy at the extreme displacement, where the velocity is zero.

The energy principle can be used for the determination of the fundamental frequency of multidegree and continuous systems as well as that of single-degree systems. For such systems, it is necessary to assume some form of deflection distribution $y(x)$, from which the kinetic and potential energies to be equated are calculated. This procedure, known as Rayleigh's method, gives surprisingly accurate values of the fundamental frequency.

As an example, the effect of the mass of the spring of the system of Fig. 1 (which was previously neglected) on the natural frequency, can be determined by Rayleigh's method as follows. Let w be the total weight of the spring, which will be considered to be small in comparison to the end weight W. Assuming the displacement amplitude of any point a distance y from the fixed end to be $x_0\frac{y}{l}$, where x_0 is the amplitude of W, the kinetic energy of the system becomes

$$T_{\max} = \frac{1}{2}\frac{W}{g}\dot{x}_0^2 + \frac{1}{2}\frac{w}{g}\int_0^l \left(\frac{\dot{x}_0 y}{l}\right)^2 dy$$
$$= \frac{1}{2g}\left(W + \frac{w}{3}\right)\omega^2 x_0^2 \tag{14}$$

Equating this to the maximum potential energy

$$U_{\max} = \tfrac{1}{2} k x_0^2 \tag{15}$$

the natural frequency of the system including the mass of the spring becomes

$$\omega_n = \sqrt{\frac{kg}{W + \frac{1}{3}w}} \tag{16}$$

Equation (16) indicates that one-third of the weight of the spring should be added to the end weight for a more accurate estimate of the natural frequency of the system of Fig. 1.

As a second example, the Rayleigh procedure is applied to a single-span beam of uniform mass and stiffness. In this case, the end fixity F is defined as the moment developed at the ends, divided by the end moment for a perfectly rigid support. For instance, $F = 0$ for pinned supports, while $F = 1$ for rigidly clamped supports. Using statical deflection for any value of F, the stiffness and mass of an equivalent spring-mass system can be determined, from which the fundamental frequency can be expressed in the form

$$f_1 = \frac{\alpha}{2\pi}\sqrt{\frac{EIg}{Wl^3}} \tag{17}$$

where E = modulus of elasticity
I = moment of inertia of cross-sectional area about neutral axis
W = total weight of beam
l = length of beam
g = 386 in. per sec²
α = coefficient depending on F

The coefficient α and the equivalent stiffness and mass are plotted in Fig. 4 as functions of F.

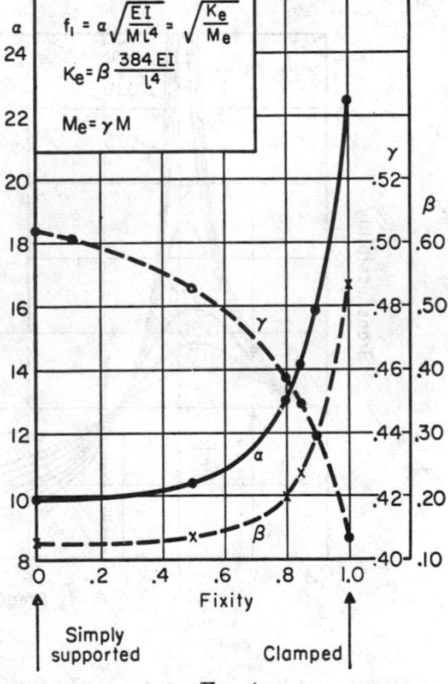

Fig. 4

Non-linear Vibrations. There are many systems where the parameters m, k, and c do not remain constant but will vary with the displacement. For example, the restoring force of the simple pendulum for large angles is not proportional to the angle, nor is the inductance of a coil with iron core constant with current. Such systems are classified as non-linear in that the superposition theorem does not hold.

We will point out here certain characteristics of a system with non-linear restoring force when excited harmonically. Fig. 5 (*a*) indicates the usual resonance curve for a

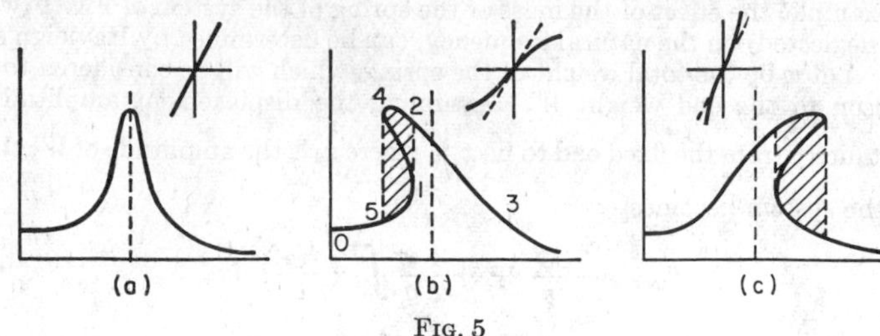

FIG. 5

linear system with constant stiffness. For a softening spring, the resonance curve will bend toward the lower frequencies, as shown in (*b*), while for a hardening spring the curve will bend toward the higher frequencies, as shown in (*c*). These characteristics of the non-linear system lead to instability in the amplitude for the region shown shaded in Fig. 5. For instance, with the softening spring, the amplitude takes the course 0,1,2,3, with increasing frequency, and course 3,2,4,5,0 with decreasing frequency, and amplitudes in the shaded region are not possible.

Vibration Isolation. Vibrations originating from machines or other sources are in general transmitted to the neighboring structure, to the detriment of the environment. To reduce the transmitted vibrations, isolators in the form of springs, rubber mounts, or cork padding are frequently used. As an example, automobile engines are supported on rubber mounts to reduce the transmission of engine vibrations to the remainder of the car.

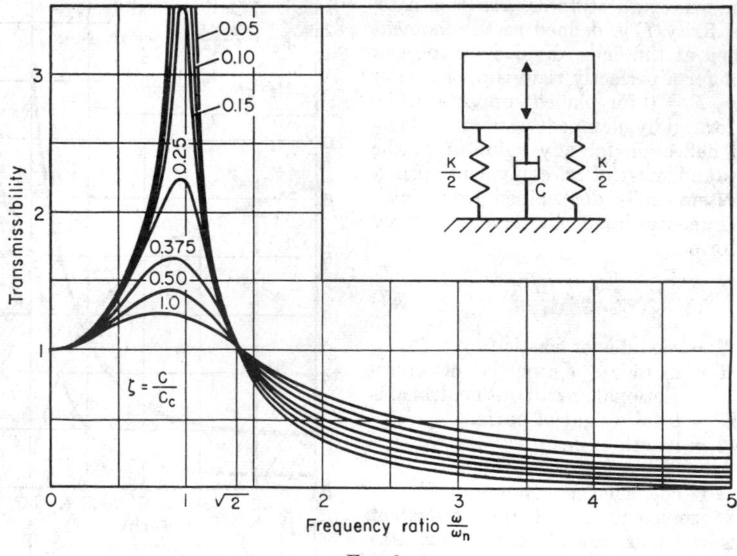

FIG. 6

Of interest here is the ratio of the force transmitted to the disturbing force, this ratio being designated as the **transmissibility.** Assuming that the isolator can be represented by a spring and a dashpot, as shown in Fig. 6, the force transmitted is the vector sum of the spring and dashpot force which is

$$F_{TR} = \sqrt{(kx)^2 + (c\omega x)^2} = kx\sqrt{1 + \left(2\zeta\frac{\omega}{\omega_n}\right)^2} \tag{18}$$

The amplitude is equal to that of forced vibration given by Eq. (10), and hence the transmissibility becomes

$$\frac{F_{TR}}{F_0} = \frac{\sqrt{1 + 4\zeta^2\left(\frac{\omega}{\omega_n}\right)^2}}{\sqrt{\left[1 - \left(\frac{\omega}{\omega_n}\right)^2\right]^2 + 4\zeta^2\left(\frac{\omega}{\omega_n}\right)^2}} \tag{19}$$

which is plotted in Fig. 6. The above ratio is less than 1 if ω/ω_n is greater than $\sqrt{2}$ and decreases with increasing values of ω/ω_n. Thus for an isolator to perform its function the natural frequency ω_n of the supported structure must be small in comparison to the frequency ω of the disturbing force.

The actual design of an isolator frequently offers difficulties when very low natural frequencies are required. Since $\omega_n \cong \sqrt{\frac{g}{\delta_{st}}}$, the statical deflection δ_{st} necessary for small ω_n is often beyond the practical range.

The relationship between the disturbing frequency f in cycles per minute, the statical deflection δ in inches, and the percent reduction in vibration, defined as $R = (1-\text{transmissibility})$, is

$$f = 188\sqrt{\frac{1}{\delta}\left(\frac{2-R}{1-R}\right)} \tag{20}$$

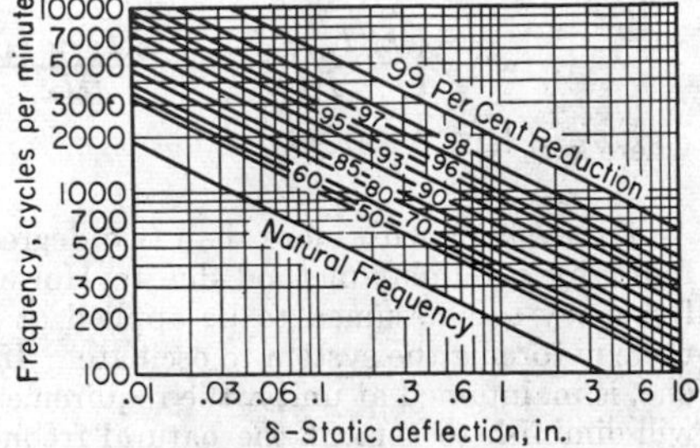

FIG. 7. Vibration isolation, frequency–static deflection chart. (*Reprinted with permission from Freberg and Kemler, "Elements of Mechanical Vibration," Wiley*).

a plot of which is shown as Fig. 7.

In Fig. 8 are shown two applications of isolators. In (*a*) the isolation is accomplished by springs, while in (*b*) the bearings are supported in rubber rings. Commercial isolators of all shapes and sizes are available as standard equipment.

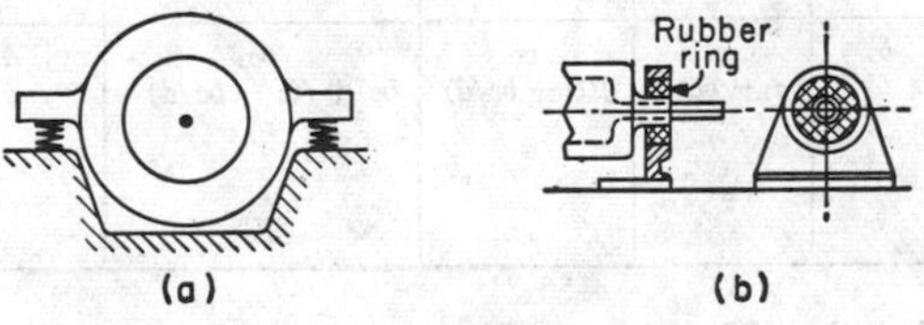

FIG. 8

Torsional Vibrations of Shafts. The simplest case of a torsional system is shown in Fig. 9, in which a circular disk is attached to a uniform shaft. By twisting the shaft, torsional vibrations of the system can be produced.

The differential equation of torsional vibration is

$$I\ddot{\theta} + c\dot{\theta} + k\theta = 0 \tag{21}$$

where I is the mass moment of inertia of the disk; c the coefficient of viscous damping; $k = GI_p/l$, the torsional stiffness of the shaft; G = shear modulus; I_p = polar moment of inertia of shaft cross section; and l = length of shaft. Since this equation is identical in form to that of the linear spring-mass system, the same form of solution exists, and the natural frequency will be

$$f_n = \frac{1}{2\pi}\sqrt{\frac{k}{I}} = \frac{1}{2\pi}\sqrt{\frac{GI_p}{lI}} \tag{22}$$

For a system consisting of two disks and a shaft, as shown in **Fig. 10**, the frequency equation is

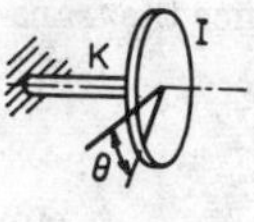

Fig. 9 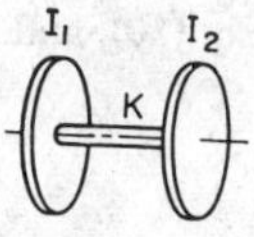 Fig. 10 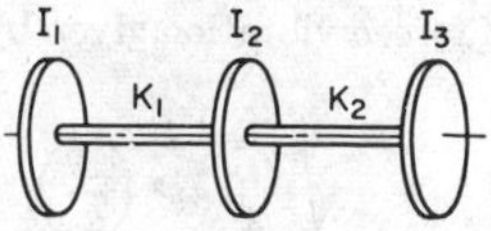 Fig. 11 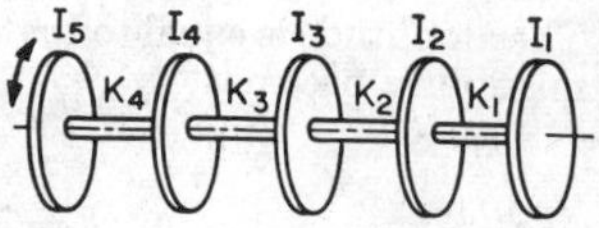 Fig. 12

$$f = \frac{1}{2\pi}\sqrt{\frac{(I_1 + I_2)\,GI_p}{lI_1I_2}} \tag{23}$$

If three disks are connected by shafts of stiffness k_1 and k_2, as in Fig. 11, the two natural frequencies can be obtained from the equation

$$\omega^4 - \left[\frac{k_1(I_1 + I_2)}{I_1I_2} + \frac{k_2(I_2 + I_3)}{I_2I_3}\right]\omega^2 + \frac{k_1k_2(I_1 + I_2 + I_3)}{I_1I_2I_3} = 0 \tag{24}$$

where $k = \dfrac{GI_p}{l}$.

For systems with more than two degrees of freedom, the natural frequencies can be found by a tabular method due to Holzer. In this method, an oscillatory torque of frequency ω is assumed to be applied at some point, such as the left end of Fig. 12, thereby forcing the system to oscillate. If the amplitude at any point, such as the right end, is maintained at unity, the requirement of the applied torque will depend on ω and will diminish to zero at the natural frequencies of the system. Thus, by assuming a frequency ω and summing the inertia torques, a plot of the required applied torque *vs.* frequency will establish all the natural frequencies of the system. The same procedure can be applied to linear spring-mass systems with several springs and masses. The following table illustrates the tabular computational procedure of Holzer's method.

Mass no.	I	$I\omega^2$	Angular displacement θ, radians	$I\omega^2\theta$	$\Sigma I\omega^2\theta$	Torsional stiffness k	Twist of section $\frac{1}{k}\Sigma I\omega^2\theta$
1	a	b	c	bc	bc	d	bc/d
2	e	f	$c - bc/d$	$f(c - bc/d)$	$bc + f(c - bc/d)$	g	
3							
.							
.							
n					T_n		

Balancing of Rotating Machines. An important requirement of all rotating machines is that the rotation axis coincide with one of the principal axes of inertia of the body. This requirement is difficult to satisfy exactly in the process of manufacturing, and hence balancing becomes necessary, especially for high-speed machines. This is evident from the fact that the magnitude of any unbalance is equal to the centrifugal force $m\omega^2r$.

The condition of unbalance of a rotating body may be classified as static or dynamic unbalance. In the case of static unbalance, the unbalance appears in a single axial plane and on the same side of the axis of rotation, as shown in Fig. 13 (*a*). Consequently this type of unbalance can be detected by a static test, where the rotor is placed on a pair of parallel rails. In practice, however, the effect of the unbalance is magnified by rotation. The unbalance of a thin disk is essentially static unbalance.

In the case of dynamic unbalance, the unbalance can be in a single axial plane and on opposite sides of the rotation axis, as in Fig. 13 (*b*), or in two different axial planes, as shown in Fig. 13 (*c*). In (*b*) it is possible for the center of gravity to lie on the rotation axis, and hence the rotor may be in static balance. However, under rotation, the two unbalance forces form a couple, which has a tendency to rock the axis of rotation. The unbalance indicated in (c) is the most general case, where the rotor is in static and dynamic unbalance.

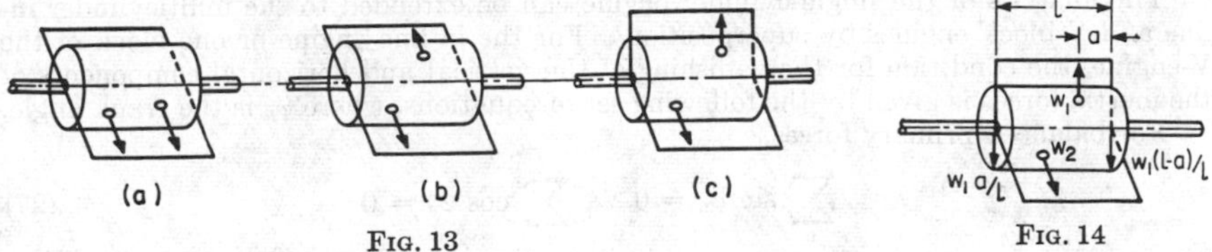

FIG. 13

FIG. 14

In all cases, a complete balance can be obtained by adding or removing correcting weights in two arbitrary and separated transverse planes. In general the end planes of the rotor are convenient correction planes; *e.g.* for the rotor of Fig. 14, with unbalance w_1 and w_2, the correction weights at the ends are $w_1 \frac{a}{l}$ and $w_1 \frac{(l-a)}{l}$ in the axial plane of w_1, and w_2 may be resolved similarly. Combining the necessary corrections for each unbalance, a single weight at each end placed at a proper radial distance will completely balance the rotor.

The determination of the magnitude and angular position of the unbalance is the task of the balancing machine. All balancing machines are provided with elastically supported bearings in which the rotor may spin (Fig. 15). Because of unbalance, the bearings will oscillate laterally, and the amplitude and phase of the rotor are indicated with respect to an arbitrary rotor position by electrical pickups and strobo-flash light.

In the case in which the rotor is very long and flexible, the position of the unbalance will depend on the elastic configuration of the rotor, which is dependent on the speed of rotation, its temperature, etc. In such cases, it is necessary to balance the rotor in its normal operating environment and speed by means of a portable balancing instrument.

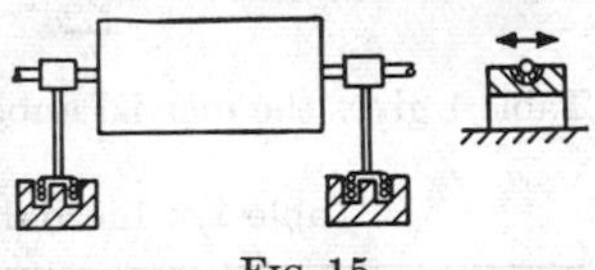

FIG. 15

Inertial Unbalance of Reciprocating Engines. The moving parts of a reciprocating engine produce dynamic forces which may result in undesirable vibrations. Rotating parts such as the crankshaft can be balanced; however, translating parts, such as the piston, and parts, like the connecting rod, with a more complex motion of combined rotation and translation cannot be so easily balanced.

In the calculation for the unbalanced forces in a single-cylinder engine, the moving parts are divided into a reciprocating weight and a rotating weight. This is accomplished by assigning portions of the connecting-rod weight to the piston end and the crank end. In general this division of the connecting rod into two lumped masses will lead to errors in the moment of inertia and consequently in the torque equation; however, the force analysis can be considered to be exact.

Assuming the rotating weight to be counterbalanced, only the reciprocating weight is of concern, and the force equation for the single-cylinder engine becomes

$$\begin{aligned} F &= m_{rec}\, r\omega^2 \left(\cos \omega t + \frac{r}{l} \cos 2\omega t \right) \\ &= \quad X_1 \quad + \quad X_2 \end{aligned} \tag{25}$$

The component X_1, which alternates once per revolution, is referred to as the primary force, while the component X_2, which alternates twice per revolution, is called the secondary force.

In addition to the inertia force, there will be an unbalanced torque about the crankshaft axis due to the reciprocating weight which is given by the equation

$$T = \frac{1}{2} m_{rec}\, r^2\omega^2 \left(\frac{r}{2l} \sin \omega t - \sin 2\omega t - \frac{3r}{2l} \sin 3\omega t \cdot \cdot \cdot \right) \tag{26}$$

This torque, however, is in general considered together with the torque due to the power stroke, and the torsional oscillations resulting from these excitations are minimized by means of the pendulum-type absorber or the torsional damper, consisting of a floating disk within a closed hub filled with viscous fluid.

The analysis of the single-cylinder engine can be extended to the multicylinder in-line and V-block engines by superposition. For the in-line engine or one block of the V-engine, the condition for the vanishing of the vertical and horizontal components of the inertia forces is given by the following set of equations, where φ_n is the crank angle.

For balanced primary forces,

$$\sum_n \sin \varphi_n = 0 \qquad \sum_n \cos \varphi_n = 0 \tag{27}$$

For balanced secondary forces,

$$\sum_n \sin 2\varphi_n = 0 \qquad \sum_n \cos 2\varphi_n = 0 \tag{28}$$

In addition to these requirements, it is evident that pitching and yawing moments may exist in the multicylinder engine. For such moments to be zero, the following sets of equations must also be satisfied, where l_n is the distance from the rotation axis to the nth cylinder.

For balanced primary moments,

$$\sum_n l_n \sin \varphi_n = 0 \qquad \sum_n l_n \cos \varphi_n = 0 \tag{29}$$

For balanced secondary moments,

$$\sum_n l_n \sin 2\varphi_n = 0 \qquad \sum_n l_n \cos 2\varphi_n = 0 \tag{30}$$

Table 1 gives the inertial unbalance of typical engines.

Table 1. Inertial Unbalance of Four Stroke per Cycle Engines

No. cylinders	Crank arrangement, φ_n	Unbalanced forces				Unbalanced moments about 1st cylinder			
		$\Sigma \sin \varphi_n$	$\Sigma \cos \varphi_n$	$\Sigma \sin 2\varphi_n$	$\Sigma \cos 2\varphi_n$	$\Sigma l_n \sin \varphi_n$	$\Sigma l_n \cos \varphi_n$	$\Sigma l_n \sin 2\varphi_n$	$\Sigma l_n \cos 2\varphi_n$
1		0	X_1	0	X_2				
2	0–180	0	0	0	$2X_2$	0	lX_1	0	$2lX_2$
4	0–180–180–0	0	0	0	$4X_2$	0	0	0	$6lX_2$
4	0–90–270–180	0	0	0	0	lX_1	$3lX_1$	0	0
6	0–120–240–240–120–0	0	0	0	0	0	0	0	0
8	0–180–90–270–270–90–180–0	0	0	0	0	0	0	0	0
90 deg–V8	0–90–270–180	0	0	0	0	Rotating primary couple of constant magnitude $\sqrt{10}\ lX_1$ which may be completely counterbalanced			

Vibration Absorbers. In certain cases a secondary spring-mass system, called the absorber, can be effectively designed to reduce the vibrations of the system. If a system is forced to vibrate at a frequency ω_1, an absorber k_2, W_2, tuned to the same frequency $\omega_1 = \sqrt{\dfrac{k_2 g}{W_2}}$, will introduce an opposing force equal to that of the disturbing force to suppress completely the vibratory motion of the original system. Since the counterforce of the absorber is equal to the inertial force $\dfrac{W_2}{g}\omega^2 X_2$ of the secondary mass, the size of the absorber system is established by the magnitude of the disturbing force and the allowable amplitude of the secondary mass.

An absorber of this type has limitations in that it is effective only at a single frequency and also in that two other resonant frequencies in the neighborhood of the suppressed frequency will be introduced. Thus, for a variable-frequency disturbance, such as the automobile engine, the simple spring-mass absorber is useless. For the variable-speed rotational system, the pendulum-type absorber shown in Fig. 16 is ideally suited in that its natural frequency is proportional to the rotational speed and hence such an absorber will always remain in tune with the disturbing torque. With r very much smaller than R, the gravitational field g is replaced by the centrifugal field $\omega^2 R$, so that the natural frequency of the pendulum becomes

$$\omega_n = \omega \sqrt{\frac{R}{r}} \tag{31}$$

In the actual absorber, a U-shaped counterweight, fitted loosely by two pins, as shown in Fig. 17, is used, and the effective pendulum length is here equal to $r = r_1 - r_2$.

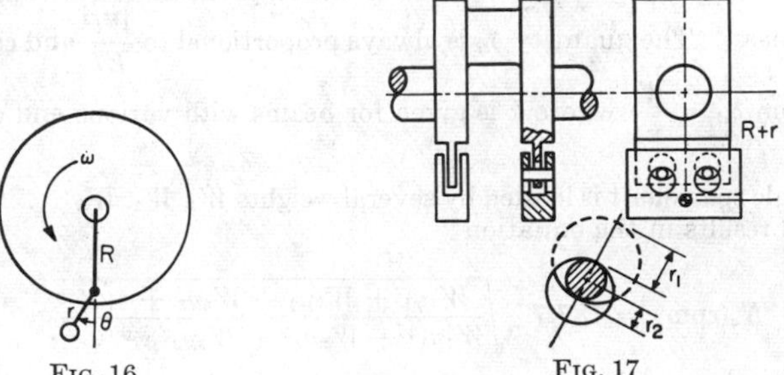

Fig. 16 Fig. 17

As an example, in the six-cylinder four-cycle engine, there will be three power strokes per revolution, and to absorb the torsional vibrations at this frequency, R/r must be equal to 9. The countertorque imparted by the centrifugal absorber of weight W is $\frac{W}{g}\omega^2 R^2 \theta$.

Critical Speed. At certain speeds, known as critical speeds, rotating shafts become dynamically unstable with large lateral amplitudes. This phenomenon is due to the resonance frequency when the rotation speed in revolutions per second corresponds to the natural frequencies of lateral vibration of the shaft.

Consider first a vertical shaft with a centrally mounted thin disk of weight W, as shown in Fig. 18. We will assume that the center of gravity of the disk is a distance e from the geometric center corresponding to the center of the shaft. When rotating at speed ω the angle between x and e will depend on whether ω is less or greater than ω_n, the natural frequency of lateral vibration. With zero damping this angle will be zero for $\omega < \omega_n$ and 180 deg for $\omega > \omega_n$, and in either case the centrifugal force acting on the shaft is

$$\frac{W}{g}\omega^2(x + e) \tag{32}$$

where x may be positive or negative. The elastic restoring force of the shaft is kx, k being the lateral stiffness of the shaft at the disk, or $48\ EI/l^3$, if the ends of the shaft are considered pinned; and by equating these two forces and replacing kg/W by ω_n^2, we arrive at the result

$$x = \frac{e\left(\frac{\omega}{\omega_n}\right)^2}{1 - \left(\frac{\omega}{\omega_n}\right)^2} \tag{33}$$

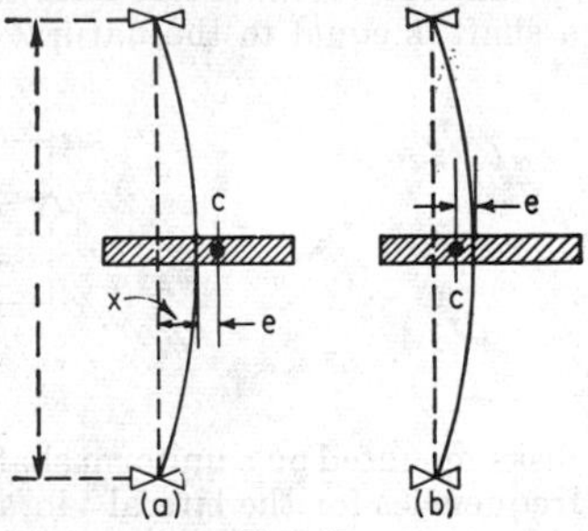

Fig. 18

As stated previously, x and e have the same sign for $\omega < \omega_n$ and opposite signs for $\omega > \omega_n$, the two conditions being illustrated by Figs. 18 (*a*) and (*b*).

When $\omega = \omega_n$ a condition of resonance is encountered and the amplitude x becomes excessively large, which often leads to failure. Thus the critical speed of the system coincides with the natural frequency of lateral vibration of the system, which for the single-disk case is

$$\omega_n = \sqrt{\frac{kg}{W}} \tag{34}$$

In simple cases, where the mass can be considered to be concentrated at a single point, the critical speed can be found from the equation

$$N_c(\text{rpm}) = \frac{60}{2\pi}\,\omega_n = \frac{60}{2\pi}\sqrt{\frac{g}{\delta_{st}}} = 187.7/\sqrt{\delta_{st}} \tag{35}$$

where δ_{st} is the statical deflection, measured in inches, of the shaft at the position of the concentrated mass. The quantity δ_{st} is always proportional to $\frac{Wl^3}{EI}$ and can be readily determined from $\delta_{st} = \frac{W}{k}$, where k is given for beams with various end conditions in Table 2.

When a single span shaft is loaded by several weights $W_1, W_2, W_3 \ldots$, Rayleigh's energy method results in the equation

$$N_c(\text{rpm}) = 187.7\sqrt{\frac{W_1y_1 + W_2y_2 + W_3y_3 + \cdots}{W_1y_1^2 + W_2y_2^2 + W_3y_3^2 + \cdots}} \tag{36}$$

for the first critical speed.

The deflections y_1, y_2, y_3, etc., may be determined from static loads W_1, W_2, W_3, etc., for the first approximation, after which a recalculation of the deflection due to dynamic loads W_1y_1, W_2y_2, W_3y_3, etc., will improve the accuracy. N_c calculated from the first approximation of static loads is generally within 1 percent of the correct value.

One other procedure for the calculation of the natural frequency of lateral vibration of shafts carrying several weights is given by Dunkerley. This formula is given as

$$\frac{1}{\omega_c^2} = \frac{1}{\omega_0^2} + \frac{1}{\omega_1^2} + \frac{1}{\omega_2^2} + \frac{1}{\omega_3^2} + \cdots \tag{37}$$

where ω_c = critical speed of entire shaft assembly, radians per sec
ω_0 = critical speed of shaft only
ω_1 = critical speed of shaft carrying only W_1
ω_2 = critical speed of shaft carrying only W_2, etc.

Lateral Vibrations of Shafts on Three Supports. The critical speed of rotation of a shaft is equal to the natural frequency of the shaft in lateral vibration. For two

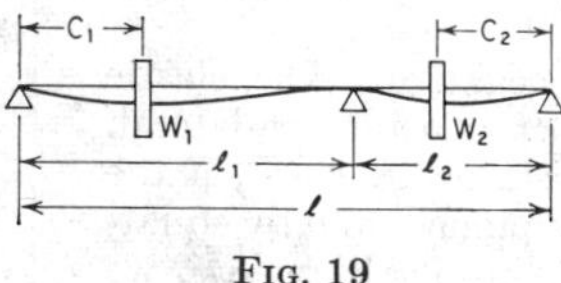

FIG. 19

disks mounted on a uniform shaft and simply supported at three points, the two natural frequencies for the lateral vibration can be computed from the equation (Fig. 19)

$$N_{cpm} = 187.7\sqrt{\frac{1}{2(ac-b^2)}\left[\frac{c}{W_1} + \frac{a}{W_2} \pm \sqrt{\left(\frac{c}{W_1} + \frac{a}{W_2}\right)^2 - \frac{4(ac-b^2)}{W_1W_2}}\,\right]}$$

where the three influence coefficients are given as

$$a = \frac{1}{12ll_1^2EI}\left[4l_1^2(l - c_1)^2c_1^2 - c_1(-c_1^3 + l^2c_1 - l_2^2c_1)(l^2 - l_2^2 - c_1^2)\right]$$

$$b = \frac{1}{12ll_1l_2EI}\left[2l_1l_2c_1c_2(l^2 - c_1^2 - c_2^2) - c_1c_2(l^2 - l_2^2 - c_1^2)(l^2 - l_1^2 - c_2^2)\right]$$

$$c = \frac{1}{12ll_2^2EI}\left[4l_2^2(l - c_2)^2c_2^2 - c_2(-c_2^3 + l^2c_2 - l_1^2c_2)(l^2 - l_1^2 - c_2^2)\right]$$

Lateral Vibrations of Uniform Beams. For uniform beams vibrating in flexure, the natural frequencies are expressible in the form

$$f_n \text{ (cycles per sec)} = c_n \sqrt{\frac{g\,EI}{wl^4}} \tag{38}$$

where EI = flexural stiffness, lb-in.²
w = weight per unit length, lb per in.
l = length of beam, in.
g = 386 in. per sec²
c_n = number depending on boundary conditions and mode number.

The following table gives values of c_n for the first five natural frequencies of beams with six different boundary conditions.

Beam configuration	c_1	c_2	c_3	c_4	c_5
Simply supported ends	1.56	6.28	14.1	25.1	39.3
Clamped-free	0.560	3.57	9.82	19.2	31.8
Free-free or clamped-clamped	3.58	9.82	19.2	31.8	47.5
Clamped-hinged or hinged-free	2.45	7.96	16.6	28.4	43.3

Longitudinal and Torsional Vibration of Uniform Rods. The equations for the natural frequencies of slender uniform rods in longitudinal or torsional vibration are identical except for the stiffness factor and can be written as

$$f(\text{cps}) = c_n \sqrt{\frac{g\,AE}{wl^2}} \quad \text{(longitudinal)} \tag{39}$$

$$= c_n \sqrt{\frac{g\,AG}{wl^2}} \quad \text{(torsional)} \tag{40}$$

where E = modulus of elasticity, psi
A = cross-sectional area, sq in.
w = weight per unit length, lb per in.
l = length, in.
g = 386 in. per sec²
G = shear modulus, psi
c_n = number depending on boundary conditions and mode number n, as shown in accompanying table. The same number c_n applies for the two equations above.

End conditions	c_n, $n = 1, 2, 3, \ldots$
Free-free or clamped-clamped	$\frac{1}{2}n$
Clamped-free	$\frac{1}{4}(2n - 1)$

Vibration of Membranes. Assume that the membrane in a perfectly flexible and infinitely thin sheet of uniform material and thickness is uniformly stretched in all directions in its plane by a tension so large that the fluctuation in this tension due to the small deflections during vibrations can be neglected.

Let S = uniform tension per unit length of boundary
A = area of membrane
w = weight of membrane per unit area

The frequency of the fundamental mode of vibration of the membrane is

$$f = \frac{\alpha}{2\pi}\sqrt{\frac{gS}{wA}} \tag{41}$$

where α for various shapes of the boundary is as follows:

Shape	α
Circle	4.261
Square	4.443
Quadrant of a circle	4.551
60° sector of a circle	4.616
Equilateral triangle	4.774
Semicircle	4.803
Rectangle 3 × 2	4.624
Rectangle 2 × 1	4.967
Rectangle 3 × 1	5.736

The frequencies of higher modes of vibrations of a circular membrane are given by the equation

$$f_{n,m} = \frac{\alpha_{nm}}{2\pi a}\sqrt{\frac{gS}{w}} \tag{42}$$

where a = radius of circular membrane
α_{nm} = constant given in table below and depending on number n of nodal diameters and number m of nodal circles (the boundary circle is included in m).

m \ n	0	1	2	3	4	5
1	2.40	3.83	5.13	6.38	7.59	8.78
2	5.52	7.02	8.42	9.76	11.06	12.3
3	8.65	10.17	11.6	13.02	14.4	15.7
4	11.8	13.3	14.8	16.2	17.6	19.0
5	14.9	16.5	18.0	19.4	20.8	22.2
6	18.1	19.6	21.1	22.6	24.0	25.4
7	21.2	22.8	24.3	25.7	27.2	28.6
8	24.4	25.9	27.4	28.9	30.4	31.8

Vibration of Plates. It is assumed that the plate consists of a perfectly elastic, homogeneous, isotropic material, and that it has a uniform thickness, considered small in comparison with its other dimensions. The deflections are assumed to be small in comparison with the thickness of the plates.

Let h = thickness of plate
$D = Eh^3/12(1 - \nu^2)$ = flexural rigidity of plate (ν is Poisson's ratio)
d = weight per unit volume of material of plate.

The frequencies of the consecutive modes of vibration of a rectangular plate with the sides a and b and simply supported along the edges are

$$f_{mn} = \frac{\pi}{2}\sqrt{\frac{gD}{hd}}\left(\frac{m^2}{a^2} + \frac{n^2}{b^2}\right) \tag{43}$$

where m = 1, 2, 3 . . .
n = 1, 2, 3 . . .

For the fundamental type of vibration of a square plate,

$$f = (\pi/a^2)\sqrt{gD/dh} \tag{44}$$

Consecutive frequencies of a square plate with free edges are given by the equation

$$f_i = (\alpha_i/2\pi a^2)\sqrt{gD/dh} \tag{45}$$

in which α_i is a constant depending on the mode of vibration. For the three lowest modes, the values of this constant are

$$\alpha_1 = 14.10 \qquad \alpha_2 = 20.56 \qquad \alpha_3 = 23.91$$

Circular Plate Clamped at the Boundary. Equation (**45**) can be used for calculating frequencies, α denoting in this case the radius of the boundary. Denoting with m the number of nodal circles and with n the number of nodal diameters, the magnitude of the factor α_i in Eq. (**45**) will be given by the following table. The table also gives values of α_i in Eq. (**45**) for a circular plate with free boundary.

m	Plate clamped at boundary			Plate with free boundary			
	$n = 0$	$n = 1$	$n = 2$	$n = 0$	$n = 1$	$n = 2$	$n = 3$
0	10.21	21.22	34.84	.....	.....	5.251	12.23
1	39.78	.....	.....	9.076	20.52	35.24	52.91
2	88.90	.....	.....	38.52	59.86		

Circular Plate Fixed at the Center. The constant α_i for consecutive modes of vibration having s nodal circles is as follows:

$m =$	0	1	2	3
$\alpha_i =$	3.75	20.91	60.68	119.7

VIBRATION-MEASURING INSTRUMENTS

(See also p. 5–77; Secs. 15 and 16)

Vibrations to be measured can be classified as either (1) periodic, (2) shock or transient, or (3) random or statistical.

Of these, periodic motion is best understood, and instruments for measuring frequency, amplitude, velocity, acceleration, or wave slope are well developed. In the measurement of shocks the same quantities mentioned above may be of interest; however, in general, peak accelerations are of prime importance. In the case of random motions a frequency spectrum of mean-square values is desirable, and the instrumentation for such measurements is quite complex and somewhat recent in development.

The seismic spring-mass system of Fig. 20 represents the basic transducer element of many vibration measuring instruments. Depending on the frequency range utilized, displacement, velocity, or acceleration is indicated by the relative motion of the suspended mass with respect to the case. Since vibrations are often too small for mechanical indication, the relative motion is generally converted to electrical voltage by motion of a coil in a magnetic field.

The relationship between the amplitude X of the harmonic motion to be measured and the relative displacement Z of the seismic mass is given by the equations

$$Z = \frac{\left(\frac{\omega}{\omega_n}\right)^2 X}{\sqrt{\left[1 - \left(\frac{\omega}{\omega_n}\right)^2\right]^2 + \left[2\zeta\left(\frac{\omega}{\omega_n}\right)\right]^2}} \tag{46}$$

$$\varphi = \tan^{-1}\frac{2\zeta\left(\frac{\omega}{\omega_n}\right)}{1 - \left(\frac{\omega}{\omega_n}\right)^2} \tag{47}$$

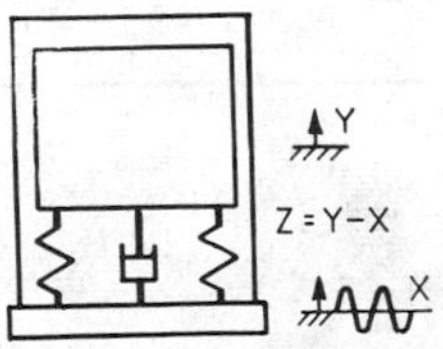

Fig. 20

Table 2. Stiffness of Elements

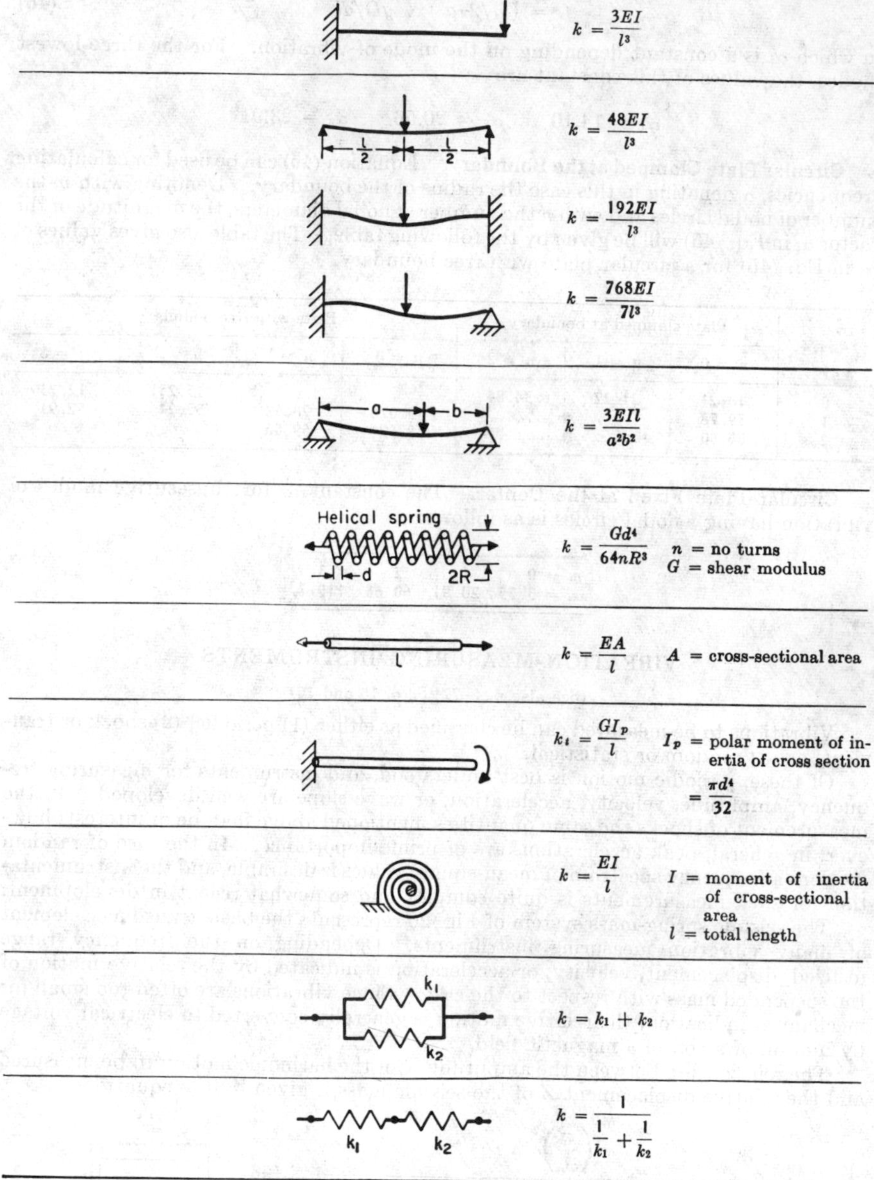

$k = \frac{3EI}{l^3}$	
$k = \frac{48EI}{l^3}$	
$k = \frac{192EI}{l^3}$	
$k = \frac{768EI}{7l^3}$	
$k = \frac{3EIl}{a^2b^2}$	
$k = \frac{Gd^4}{64nR^3}$	n = no turns G = shear modulus
$k = \frac{EA}{l}$	A = cross-sectional area
$k_t = \frac{GI_p}{l}$	I_p = polar moment of inertia of cross section $= \frac{\pi d^4}{32}$
$k = \frac{EI}{l}$	I = moment of inertia of cross-sectional area l = total length
$k = k_1 + k_2$	
$k = \frac{1}{\frac{1}{k_1} + \frac{1}{k_2}}$	

and plotted in Fig. 21. These equations indicate that the parameters involved are the frequency ratio ω/ω_n and the damping factor ζ. For minimum amplitude and phase distortion, ζ is chosen in the neighborhood of 0.7.

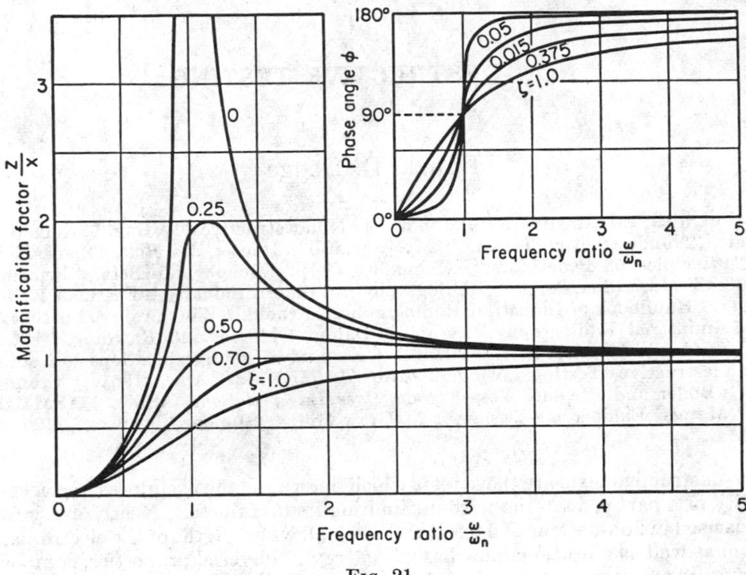

Fig. 21

Accelerometers are high-natural frequency instruments, and their useful frequency range is below resonance. For small values of ω/ω_n, Eq. (**46**) becomes approximately

$$Z \cong \frac{1}{\omega_n^2} (\omega^2 X)$$

and the relative motion becomes proportional to the acceleration.

Displacement and velocity instruments are low natural frequency devices and their useful range is in a region $\omega/\omega_n \gg 1$, or, from Eq. (**46**),

$$Z \cong X$$

However, both velocity and displacement for harmonic motion can be obtained from accelerometers by means of electronic integrators.

Aside from the seismic-mass type of transducer, there are a variety of other vibration-measuring devices, which are listed as follows.

Electrical-resistance strain gage consists of a grid of fine wire cemented to the vibrating object to measure fluctuating strains. These wires are also used as suspensions for seismic weights in some accelerometers.

Piezoelectric transducer utilizes quartz or barium titanate crystals, has high natural frequencies, and must in general be used together with a low-pass filter to cut out frequency components in the neighborhood of resonance.

Variable reluctance differential transformer consists of a primary with carrier-frequency excitation and of opposing secondary coils which indicate a voltage due to displacement of an iron core attached to the vibrating structure.

NON-DESTRUCTIVE TESTING

BY

Donald D. Dodge

REFERENCES: McMaster, "Handbook of Nondestructive Testing," Ronald. McGonnagle, "Nondestructive Testing," McGraw-Hill. Heuter and Bolt, "Sonics," Wiley. Betz, "Principles of Penetrants," Magnaflux Corp. Doane and Betz, "Principles of Magnaflux," Magnaflux Corp. "Radiography in Modern Industry," Eastman Kodak Co. Crowther, "Handbook of Industrial Radiography," Arnold. Wiltshire, "A Further Handbook of Industrial Radiography," Arnold. Banks, Oldfield, and Rawding, "Ultrasonic Flaw Detection in Metals," Prentice-Hall. Commonly Used Specifications and Standards for Nondestructive Testing, *Nondestructive Testing,* Mar.–Apr., 1961. "Standards," ASTM. Boiler and Pressure Vessel Code, *Case Interpretations,* ASME. ASME Handbook, "Metals Engineering-Design," McGraw-Hill. "Standards," Secs. J420, J425–J428, SAE.

Non-destructive tests are those tests which determine the usefulness, serviceability, or quality of a part or material without limiting its usefulness. Nearly every form of energy is used in non-destructive tests, including all wavelengths of the electromagnetic spectrum as well as vibrational mechanical energy. Physical properties, composition, and structure are determined; defects are detected; and thickness is measured. These tests are here divided into the following basic methods: **magnetic-particle, penetrant, radiographic, ultrasonic, eddy-current, microwave,** and **infrared.** Numerous techniques are utilized in the application of each test method. Table 1 gives a summary of principal non-destructive testing methods.

Magnetic-particle Methods

Magnetic-particle testing (see also p. 13–12) is a non-destructive method for detecting discontinuities at or near the surface in **ferro-magnetic materials.** The test object is intensely magnetized, and then finely divided magnetic particles are applied to its surface. When properly oriented to the induced magnetic field, a discontinuity creates a leakage field which attracts and holds the particles, forming a visible indication. Magnetic-field direction and character are dependent upon how the magnetizing force is applied and upon the type of current used. For best sensitivity, the **magnetizing current** must flow in a direction parallel to the principal direction of the expected defect. Circular fields, produced by passing current through the object, are almost completely contained within the test object. Longitudinal fields, produced by coils or yokes, create external poles and a general-leakage field. Alternating, direct, or half-wave direct current may be used for the location of surface defects. Half-wave direct current is most effective for locating subsurface defects. Magnetic particles may be applied dry or as a wet suspension in a liquid similar to kerosene. Colored **dry powders** are advantageous when testing for subsurface defects and when testing objects which have rough surfaces, such as castings, forgings, and weldments. **Wet particles** are preferred for detection of very fine cracks, such as fatigue or grinding cracks. Fluorescent wet particles are used to inspect complex objects with the aid of ultraviolet light. Application of particles while magnetizing current is on (continuous method) produces stronger indications than obtained if the particles are applied after the current is shut off (residual method). Interpretation of subsurface-defect indications requires experience. Demagnetization of the test object after inspection is advisable.

Table 1. Summary of Principal Non-destructive Test Methods

Method	Principle	Material	Detects	Advantages	Limitations
Magnetic particle	*General:* Concentration of particles at a defect aids visual inspection	All materials	Surface discontinuities	Low cost Fluorescing test materials improve indications	Parts must be clean No standards
	Magnetic particles are attracted by leakage flux at surface flaws of magnetized object	Magnetic materials	Surface flaws such as cracks, laps, seams, and pits Some near-surface flaws	Simple to perform Easy to interpret Fast Can be attenuated	Requires high-current source Materials must be magnetic Parts should be demagnetized Residual magnetism effects
	Electrified particles blown onto object are attracted by local field at flaw	Nonconductors Porcelain enamel parts Glass-to-metal seals Plastics	Surface cracks	Simple equipment Easy to perform Very sensitive	Not applicable to thin enamel coatings Only surface flaws detected
Penetrant	*Liquid penetrant* is drawn into surface flaws by capillary action, then revealed by developer material	Nonporous materials Metals Plastics Glazed ceramics	Surface flaws such as cracks, porosity, pits, seams, and laps	Simple to perform Inexpensive Applicable to complex shapes On-site inspection	Only surface flaws detected Surfaces must be clean Penetrant washes out of wide defects
	Filtered particles are deposited at surface; fluid is absorbed by additional area of crack	Porous materials such as unfired clay, carbon, sintered parts, and concrete	Surface cracks	Easy to perform Simple equipment Sensitive	Only surface cracks detected Particle size 100 mesh or less Not applicable to thin enamel coatings
Ultrasonic	*General:* Mechanical vibrational waves (frequency range 1–25 mc) are propagated into test object. This energy is reflected and scattered by inhomogeneities, or becomes resonant. Information interpreted from cathode-ray tube *Pulse:* Selected frequency used for flaw detection *Resonance:* Varying frequency used for thickness or bond	Metals Plastics Ceramics Glass Rubber Graphite Concrete	Cracks Inclusions Porosity Laminations Bursts Grain size Lack of bond Lack of penetration or fusion in welds Thickness variations	High sensitivity Fast Penetrates up to 30 ft steel Accurately locates flaw Can be automated Access to only one side needed Various energy modes available	Difficulty with complex shapes Surface roughness may affect test Defect orientation affects test Comparative standards only Requires couplant Operator skill required Usually no permanent record

Table 1. Summary of Principal Non-destructive Test Methods—(*Continued*)

Method	Principle	Material	Detects	Advantages	Limitations
Radiation	*General:* Penetrating radiation is differentially absorbed by materials, depending upon thickness and type of material	All materials	Internal defects such as inclusions, porosity, shrink, hot tears, cracks, cold shuts, and coarse structure in cast metals; lack of fusion, lack of penetration in welds Thickness	Standards established Internal defects detected Accepted by codes and industry Permanent film record Automatic thickness gaging	Health precautions necessary Defect must be at least 2% of total section thickness Film processing requires time, facilities, and care Difficulty with complex shapes
	X-ray source produces radiation electrically, by deceleration of electrons			Versatile—energy adjustable Fluoroscopy available Accelerator minimizes scatter Thickness up to 30 in. steel can be tested	Electric power and water required Equipment heavy and costly Shielded area usually required
	Gamma source produces radiation in decay of radioactive material			Portable Low cost Thickness up to 10 in. steel can be tested	Government license required Energy cannot be adjusted or turned off Source must be replaced
Eddy current	A-c coil induces eddy currents in test object. Flaws and material properties affect flow of currents	Metals	Material composition Structure Cracks Voids Inclusions Size Coating thickness	Versatile Special coils easily made Can be automated Sensitive to surface and near-surface inhomogeneities Many frequencies available	Sensitive to many variables Sensitivity varies with depth Reference standards needed Response often comparative

Electrified-particle testing indicates minute cracks in non-conducting materials. Particles of calcium carbonate are positively charged as they are blown through a spray gun at the test object. If the object is metal backed, such as porcelain enamel, no preparation other than cleaning is necessary. When not metal backed, the object must be dipped in an aqueous penetrant solution and dried. The penetrant remaining in cracks provides a mobile electron supply for the test. A readily visible powder indication forms at a crack due to the attraction of the positively charged particles.

Penetrant Methods

Liquid-penetrant testing is used to locate defects open to the surface of **non-porous materials.** The test object must be thoroughly cleaned before testing. Penetrating liquid is applied to the surface of a test object by a brush, spray, or dip method. A time allowance (1 to 30 min) is required for liquid penetration of surface defects. Excess penetrant is then carefully removed from the surface, and an absorptive coating, known as **developer,** is applied to the object to draw penetrant out of defects, thus showing their location, shape, and approximate size. The developer is typically a fine powder, such as talc, in suspension in alcohol. Penetrating-liquid types are (1) for test in visible light, and (2) for test under near ultraviolet light (3,650 A). Sensitivity of penetrant testing is greatest when a fluorescent penetrant is observed in a semidarkened location. After testing, the penetrant and developer are removed by washing with water, sometimes aided by an emulsifier, or with a solvent.

In **filtered-particle** testing, cracks in **porous objects** (100 mesh or smaller) are indicated by the difference in absorption between a cracked and a flawfree surface. A fluid containing suspended particles is sprayed on a test object. If a crack exists, particles are filtered out and concentrate at the surface as liquid flows into the additional absorbent area created by the crack. Fluorescent or colored particles are used to locate defects in unfired dried clay, certain fired ceramics, concrete, some powdered metals, carbon, and partially sintered tungsten and titanium carbides.

Radiographic Methods

Radiographic test methods employ X-rays, gamma rays, or similar penetrating radiation to reveal flaws, defects, composition, thickness, or structure of objects. Electromagnetic-energy wavelengths in the region of 0.01 to 10 A (1 A = 10^{-8} cm) are used to examine the interior of opaque materials. Penetrating radiation proceeds from its source in straight lines to the test object. Rays are differentially absorbed by the object, depending upon the energy of the radiation and the nature and thickness of the material.

X-rays of a variety of wavelengths result when high-speed electrons in a vacuum tube are suddenly stopped. An X-ray tube contains a heated filament (cathode) and a target (anode); **radiation intensity** is almost directly proportional to filament current (ma); tube voltage (kv) determines the penetration capability of the rays. As tube voltage increases, shorter wavelengths and more intense X-rays are produced. When the energy of penetrating radiation increases, the difference in attenuation between materials decreases. Consequently, more film-image contrast is obtained at lower voltage, and a greater range of thickness can be radiographed at one time at higher voltage.

Gamma rays of a specific wavelength are emitted from the disintegrating nuclei of natural radioactive elements, such as radium, and from a variety of artificial radioactive isotopes produced in nuclear reactors. Cobalt 60, iridium 192, thulium 170, and cesium 137 are commonly used for industrial radiography. **Half-life** of an isotope is the time required for half of the radioactive material to decay. This time ranges from a few hours to many years (see also p. 9–162).

A **radiograph** is a photographic record produced by passage of penetrating radiation onto a film. A void or reduced mass appears as a darker image on the film because of the lesser absorption of energy and the resulting additional exposure of the film. The quantity of X-rays absorbed by a material generally increases as the atomic number increases.

Radiographic films vary in speed, contrast, and grain size. Slow films generally have smaller grain size and produce more contrast. Slow films are used where optimum sharpness and maximum contrast are desired. Fast films are used where objects with large differences in thickness are to be radiographed or where sharpness and contrast can be sacrificed to shorten exposure time. Exposure of a radiographic film comes from direct radiation and scattered radiation. **Direct radiation** is desirable, image-forming radiation; **scattered radiation,** which occurs in the object being X-rayed or in neighboring objects, produces undesirable images on the film and loss of contrast. **Intensifying screens** made of 0.005- or 0.010-in.-thick lead are often used for radiography at voltages above 100 kv. The lead filters out much of the low-energy scatter radiation. Under action of X-rays or gamma rays above 88 kv, a lead screen also emits electrons which, when in intimate contact with the film, produce additional coherent darkening of the film. Exposure time can be materially reduced by use of intensifying screens above and below the film.

A radiograph is a shadow picture since X-rays and gamma rays follow the laws of light in shadow formation. Four factors determine the best **geometric sharpness** of a picture: (1) The effective focal-spot size of the radiation source should be as small as possible. (2) The source-to-object distance should be adequate for proper definition of the area of the object farthest from the film. (3) The film should be as close as possible to the object. (4) The area of interest should be in the center of and perpendicular to the X-ray beams and parallel to the X-ray film.

Penetrameters are used to indicate the **contrast** and **definition** which exist in a radiograph. The type generally used in the United States is a small rectangular plate of the same material as the object being X-rayed. It is uniform in thickness (usually 2 percent of the object thickness) and has holes drilled through it. ASTM specifies hole diameters one, two, and four times the thickness of the penetrameter. Step, wire, and bead penetrameters are also used. (See ASTM Materials Specification E-94.)

Because of the variety of factors which relate to the production and measurement of an X-ray image, **operating factors** are generally selected from reference tables or graphs which have been established through empirical methods.

All materials may be inspected by radiographic means, but there are limitations to the configurations of materials. With optimum techniques, wires 0.0001 in. in diameter can be resolved in small electrical components. At the other extreme, welded-steel pressure vessels with 20-in. wall thickness can be routinely inspected by use of high-energy accelerators as a source of radiation. **Neutron radiation** penetrates extremely dense materials such as lead more readily than X-rays or gamma rays.

Radiographic specifications are published by ASTM, ASME, AWS, and API, primarily for detecting lack of penetration or lack of fusion in welded objects. Cast-metal objects are radiographed to detect conditions such as shrink, porosity, hot tears, cold shuts, inclusions, coarse structure, and cracks.

The usual method of utilizing penetrating radiation is film. However, Geiger counters, semiconductors, phosphors (fluoroscopy), photoconductors (xeroradiography), scintillation crystals, and vidicon tubes (image intensifiers) are also used.

The **dangers** connected with exposure of the human body to X-rays and gamma rays should be fully understood by any person responsible for the use of radiation equipment. NBS is a prime source of information concerning radiation safety. USAEC specifies maximum permissible exposure to be 1.25 r per quarter year. (See p. 9–181.)

Ultrasonic Methods

Ultrasonic non-destructive test methods (see also p. 12–185 *et seq.*) employ high-frequency mechanical vibrational energy to detect and locate structural discontinuities or differences and to measure thickness of a variety of materials. An electric pulse is generated in a test instrument and transmitted to a transducer, which converts the electric pulse into mechanical vibrations. These low-energy-level vibrations are transmitted through a coupling liquid into the test object, where the ultrasonic energy is attenuated, scattered, reflected, or resonated to indicate conditions of the material comprising the object. Reflected, transmitted, or resonant-sound energy is reconverted to electrical energy by a transducer and returned to the test instrument, where it is amplified. The received energy is then usually displayed on a cathode-ray tube. The presence, position, and amplitude of echoes indicate conditions of the test-object material.

Materials capable of being tested by ultrasonic energy are those which transmit vibrational energy. Metals are tested in dimensions of up to 30 ft. Non-cellular plastics, ceramics, glass, new concrete, organic materials, and rubber can be tested. Each material has a characteristic sound velocity, which is a function of its density and modulus (elastic or shear) (see Table 1, p. 12–177).

Material characteristics determinable through ultrasonics include structural discontinuities, such as flaws and unbonds, physical constants and metallurgical differences, and thickness (measured from one side). A common application of ultrasonics is the inspection of welds for inclusions, porosity, lack of penetration, and lack of fusion. Other applications include location of unbond in nuclear-fuel elements, machinery maintenance, liquid-contaminant particle counting, and medical applications. Automatic testing is frequently possible in manufacturing applications.

Two different test principles are used in ultrasonic testing. **Resonance** principles are used for precise measurement of test-object thickness from one side. **Pulse** principles are used for flaw detection and other applications. Ultrasonic pulse systems are further classified as either **pulse echo,** in which a single transducer is used, or **through transmission,** in which separate sending and receiving transducers are used. Pulse-echo systems are more common. In either system, ultrasonic energy must be transmitted into, and received from, the test object through a **coupling medium,** since air will not transmit ultrasound of these frequencies. Water, oil, grease, and glycerine are commonly used couplants. Two types of testing are used: contact and immersion. In **contact** testing, the transducer is placed directly on the test object. In **immersion** testing, the transducer and test object are separated from one another in a tank filled with water or by a column of water or by a liquid-filled wheel. Immersion testing eliminates transducer wear and facilitates scanning of the test object. Scanning systems usually have paper-printing equipment for readout of test information.

Ultrasonic transducers are piezoelectric units which convert electric energy into acoustic energy and convert acoustic energy into electric energy of the same frequency. Quartz, barium titanate, lithium sulphate, lead metaniobate, and lead zirconate titanate are commonly used transducer crystals, which are generally mounted with a damping backing in a housing. Transducers range in size from $\frac{1}{16}$ to 5 in. and are of circular or rectangular shape. Ultrasonic beams can be focused to improve resolution and definition. Transducer characteristics and beam patterns are dependent upon frequency, size, crystal material, and construction.

Test frequencies used range from 40 kc to 20,000 mc. Flaw-detection and thickness-measurement applications use frequencies between 500 kc and 25 mc, with 2.25 mc being most commonly employed for flaw detection. Low frequencies (40 kc to 1.0 mc) are used on materials of low elastic modulus or large grain. High frequencies (2.25 mc to 25 mc) provide better resolution of smaller defects and are used on fine-grain materials and thin sections. Frequencies above 25 mc are employed for investigation and measurement of physical properties related to acoustic attenuation.

Wave vibrational modes other than longitudinal are effective in detecting off-oriented flaws or other characteristics not detectable by the longitudinal mode. Wedges of plastic, water, or other material are inserted between the transducer face and the test object to convert, by refraction, to shear, transverse, surface, or Lamb vibrational modes. As in optics, Snell's law expresses the relationship between incident and refracted beam angles; i.e., the ratio of the sines of the angle from the normal, of the incident and refracted beams in two mediums, is equal to the ratio of the mode acoustic velocities in the two mediums.

Limiting conditions for ultrasonic testing may be the test-object shape, surface roughness, grain size, material structure, defect orientation, selectivity of discontinuities, and the skill of the operator.

Standards for acceptance are established in many government, national-society, and company specifications (see references, p. 5–106). Evaluation is made by comparing (visually or by automated electronic means) received signals with signals obtained from reference blocks containing flat-bottom holes between 1/64 and 8/64 in. diam or from parts containing known defects.

Eddy-current Methods

Eddy-current non-destructive tests are based upon correlation between electromagnetic properties and physical or structural properties of a test object. Eddy currents are induced in **metals** whenever they are brought into an a-c magnetic field (see also p. 15–23). These eddy currents create a secondary magnetic field, which opposes the inducing magnetic field. The presence of discontinuities or material variations alters eddy currents, thus changing the apparent impedance of the inducing coil or of a detection coil. Coil impedance indicates the magnitude and phase relationship of the eddy currents to their inducing magnetic-field current. This relationship is dependent upon the mass, conductivity, permeability, and structure of the metal and upon the frequency, intensity, and distribution of the alternating magnetic field. Conditions such as heat treatment, composition, hardness, phase transformation, case depth, cold working, strength, size, thickness, cracks, seams, and inhomogeneities are indicated by eddy-current tests. Correlation data must usually be obtained to determine whether test conditions for desired characteristics of a particular test object can be established. Because of the many factors which cause variation in electromagnetic properties of metals, care must be taken that the instrument response to the condition of interest in not nullified or duplicated by variations due to other conditions.

Alternating-current **frequencies** between 1 and 5,000,000 cps are used for eddy-current testing. Test frequency determines the depth of current penetration into the test object, due to the a-c phenomenon of "skin effect." Depth of current penetration is the depth at which the eddy currents are equal to 37 percent of their value at the surface. In a plane conductor, depth of penetration varies inversely as the square root of the product of conductivity, permeability, and frequency. High-frequency eddy currents are more sensitive to surface defects or conditions, while low-frequency eddy currents are sensitive also to deeper internal defects or conditions.

Test coils are of three general types: the **circular** coil, which surrounds an object; the **bobbin** coil, which is inserted within an object; and the **probe** coil, which is placed on the surface of an object. Coils are further classified as **absolute,** when testing is conducted without direct comparison with a reference object in another coil, or **differential,** when comparison is made through use of two coils connected in series opposition. Many variations of these basic coil types are utilized. Axial length of a circular test coil should not be more than 4 in., and its shape should correspond closely to the shape of the test object for best results. Coil diameter should be no more than twice the test-object diameter for consistent and useful results. Coils may be of the air-core or magnetic-core type.

Instrumentation for the analysis and presentation of electrical signals resulting from eddy-current testing includes a variety of means, ranging from meters to vectorscopes. Instrument, meter, or alarm circuits are adjusted to be sensitive only to signals of a certain electrical phase, so that selected conditions are indicated while others are ignored (see also p. 15–34 *et seq.*). Automatic testing is frequently possible.

Thickness measurement of metallic and non-metallic coatings on metals is performed using eddy-current principles. Coating thicknesses measured typically range from 0.0001 to 0.100 in. For measurement to be possible, metallic-coating conductivity must differ from that of the base metal.

Microwave Methods

Microwave test methods utilize electromagnetic energy to determine characteristics of **non-metallic substances,** either solid or liquid. Frequencies used range from 1 to 3,000 kmc/sec. Microwaves generated in a test instrument are transmitted by a wave guide through air to the test object. Analysis of reflected or transmitted energy indicates certain material characteristics, such as moisture content, composition, structure, density, degree of cure, aging, and presence of flaws. Other applications include thickness and displacement measurement in the range of 0.001 in. to more than 12 in. Materials that can be tested include most solid and liquid non-metals, such as chemicals, minerals, plastics, wood, ceramics, glass, and rubber.

Infrared Methods

Infrared non-destructive tests involve the detection of infrared electromagnetic energy emitted by a test object. Infrared radiation is produced naturally by all matter at all temperatures above absolute zero. Materials emit radiation at varying intensities, depending upon their temperature and surface characteristics. A **passive** infrared system detects the natural radiation of an unheated test object, while an **active** system employs a source to heat the test object, which then radiates infrared energy to a detector. Sensitive indication of temperature or temperature distribution through infrared detection is useful in locating irregularities in materials, in processing, or in the functioning of parts. Emission in the infrared range of 0.8 to 15 microns is collected optically, filtered, detected, and amplified by a test instrument which is designed around the characteristics of the detector material. Temperature variations on the order of 0.01 F can be indicated by meter or graphic means. Infrared theory and instrumentation are based upon radiation from a black body; therefore, **emissivity correction** must be made electrically in the test instrument or arithmetically from instrument readings (see also p. 4–108 *et seq.*).

SECTION 6

MATERIALS OF ENGINEERING

BY

LEWIS V. JUDSON, Retired Physicist, Office of Weights and Measures, National Bureau of Standards.

BERNARD R. QUENEAU, Chief Metallurgical Engineer, Process Metallurgy-Steel Finishing, United States Steel Corporation.

C. W. BRIGGS, Vice President—Technology, Steel Founders' Society of America.

R. P. CARREKER, Jr., Metallurgical Engineer, Research and Development Center, General Electric Co.

HILARY E. BACON, Consulting Chemical Engineer and Partner, Sheppard T. Powell and Associates.

GEORGE G. SWARD, Consultant, Gardner Laboratory, Inc., Bethesda, Md.

CARL H. de ZEEUW, Professor of Wood Products Engineering, State University College of Forestry at Syracuse.

RIENZI B. PARKER, Jr., Chemical Engineering Consultant, Arthur D. Little, Inc.

FREDERICK H. NORTON, Professor of Ceramics, Emeritus, Massachusetts Institute of Technology; Consultant, Arthur D. Little, Inc.

CLYDE E. KESLER, Professor of Theoretical and Applied Mechanics and of Civil Engineering, University of Illinois.

GERHARD E. SONDERMAN, Consulting Engineer, Singmaster and Breyer, New York.

FRED J. VILLFORTH, Jr., Senior Project Mechanical Engineer, Texaco, Inc.

CONTENTS

CORROSION

By HILARY E. BACON

PAINTS AND PROTECTIVE COATINGS

By GEORGE G. SWARD

WOOD

By CARL H. de ZEEUW

NON-METALLIC MATERIALS

By RIENZI B. PARKER, Jr., and Associates

REFRACTORIES

By FREDERICK H. NORTON

CEMENT, MORTAR, AND CONCRETE

By CLYDE E. KESLER

WATER

By GERHARD E. SONDERMAN

LUBRICANTS AND LUBRICATION

By FRED J. VILLFORTH, Jr.

GENERAL PROPERTIES OF MATERIALS

BY

Lewis V. Judson

REFERENCES: "International Critical Tables," McGraw-Hill. "Smithsonian Physical Tables," Smithsonian Institution. Landolt, "Landolt-Börnstein Zahlenwerte und Funktionen aus Physik, Chemie, Astronomie, Geophysik und Technik," Springer. "Handbook of Chemistry and Physics," Chemical Rubber Co. "Book of ASTM Standards," ASTM. "ASRE Refrigerating Data Book," ASRE. Brady, "Materials Handbook," McGraw-Hill. Mantell, "Engineering Materials Handbook," McGraw-Hill. International Union of Pure and Applied Chemistry, Butterworth Scientific Publications.

Chemistry

Every **elementary substance** is made up of exceedingly small particles called **atoms** which are all alike and which cannot be further subdivided or broken up by **chemical processes.** It will be noted that this statement is virtually a definition of the term elementary substance and a limitation of the term chemical process. There are as many different classes or families of atoms as there are **chemical elements.**

Two or more atoms, either of the same kind or of different kinds, are, in the case of most elements, capable of uniting with one another to form a higher order of distinct particles called **molecules.** If the molecules or atoms of which any given material is composed are all exactly alike, the material is a **pure substance.** If they are not all alike, the material is a **mixture.**

If the atoms which compose the molecules of any pure substance are all of the same kind, the substance is, as already stated, an **elementary substance.** If the atoms which compose the molecules of a pure chemical substance are not all of the same kind, the substance is a **compound substance.**

The atoms are to be considered as the smallest particles which occur separately in the structure of molecules of either compound or elementary substances, so far as can be determined by ordinary chemical analysis. The molecule of an element consists of a definite (usually small) number of its atoms. The molecule of a compound consists of one or more atoms of each of its several elements, the numbers of the various kinds of atoms and their arrangement being definite and fixed and determining the character of the compound. This notion of molecules and their constituent atoms is useful for interpreting the observed fact that chemical reactions—*e.g.* the analysis of a compound into its elements, the synthesis of a compound from the elements, or the changing of one or more compounds into one or more different compounds—take place so that the masses of the various substances concerned in a given reaction stand in definite and fixed ratios.

It appears from recent researches that some substances which cannot by any available means be decomposed into simpler substances and which must, therefore, be defined as elements, are continually undergoing spontaneous changes or **radioactive transformation** into other substances which can be recognized as physically and chemically different from the original substance. Radium is an element by the definition given and may be considered as made up of atoms. But it is assumed that these atoms, so called because they resist all efforts to break them up and are, therefore, apparently indivisible, nevertheless split up spontaneously, at a rate which scientists have not been able to influence in any way, into other atoms, thus forming other elementary substances of totally different properties.

The view generally accepted at present is that the atoms of all the chemical elements, including those not yet known to be radioactive, consist of several kinds of still smaller particles, three of which are known as **protons, neutrons,** and **electrons.** The

Chemical Elements[a]

Element	Symbol	Atomic No.	Atomic weight[b]	Valence
Actinium	Ac	89		
Aluminum	Al	13	26.9815	3
Americium	Am	95		
Antimony	Sb	51	121.75	3, 5
Argon[c]	Ar	18	39.948	0
Arsenic[d]	As	33	74.9216	3, 5
Astatine	At	85		
Barium	Ba	56	137.34	2
Berkelium	Bk	97		
Beryllium	Be	4	9.0122	2
Bismuth	Bi	83	208.980	3, 5
Boron[d]	B	5	10.811[l]	3
Bromine[e]	Br	35	79.904[m]	1, 3, 5
Cadmium	Cd	48	112.40	2
Calcium	Ca	20	40.08	2
Californium	Cf	98		
Carbon[d]	C	6	12.01115[l]	2, 4
Cerium	Ce	58	140.12	3, 4
Cesium[k]	Cs	55	132.905	1
Chlorine[f]	Cl	17	35.453[m]	1, 3, 5, 7
Chromium	Cr	24	51.996[m]	2, 3, 6
Cobalt	Co	27	58.9332	2, 3
Columbium (see Niobium)				
Copper	Cu	29	63.546[m]	1, 2
Curium	Cm	96		
Dysprosium	Dy	66	162.50	3
Einsteinium	Es	99		
Erbium	Er	68	167.26	3
Europium	Eu	63	151.96	2, 3
Fermium	Fm	100		
Fluorine[g]	F	9	18.9984	1
Francium	Fr	87		
Gadolinium	Gd	64	157.25	3
Gallium[k]	Ga	31	69.72	2, 3
Germanium	Ge	32	72.59	2, 4
Gold	Au	79	196.967	1, 3
Hafnium	Hf	72	178.49	4
Helium[c]	He	2	4.0026	0
Holmium	Ho	67	164.930	3
Hydrogen[h]	H	1	1.00797[l]	1
Indium	In	49	114.82	1, 2, 3
Iodine[d]	I	53	126.9044	1, 3, 5, 7
Iridium	Ir	77	192.2	2, 3, 4, 6
Iron	Fe	26	55.847[m]	2, 3
Krypton[c]	Kr	36	83.80	0
Lanthanum	La	57	138.91	3
Lead	Pb	82	207.19	2, 4
Lithium[i]	Li	3	6.939	1
Lutetium	Lu	71	174.97	3
Magnesium	Mg	12	24.312	2
Manganese	Mn	25	54.9380	2, 3, 4, 6, 7
Mendelevium	Md	101		
Mercury[e]	Hg	80	200.59	1, 2
Molybdenum	Mo	42	95.94	3, 4, 5, 6
Neodymium	Nd	60	144.24	3
Neon[c]	Ne	10	20.183	0
Neptunium	Np	93		
Nickel	Ni	28	58.71	2, 3, 4
Niobium	Nb	41	92.906	2, 3, 4, 5
Nitrogen[f]	N	7	14.0067	3, 5
Nobelium	No	102		
Osmium	Os	76	190.2	2, 3, 4, 6, 8
Oxygen[f]	O	8	15.9994[l]	2
Palladium	Pd	46	106.4	2, 4
Phosphorus[d]	P	15	30.9738	3, 5
Platinum	Pt	78	195.09	2, 4
Plutonium	Pu	94		
Polonium	Po	84		2, 4
Potassium	K	19	39.102	1

Chemical Elements[a]—(*Contiuned*)

Element	Symbol	Atomic No.	Atomic weight[b]	Valence
Praseodymium	Pr	59	140.907	3
Promethium	Pm	61		5
Protactinium	Pa	91		
Radium	Ra	88		2
Radon[f]	Rn	86		0
Rhenium	Re	75	186.2	1, 4, 7
Rhodium	Rh	45	102.905	3, 4
Rubidium	Rb	37	85.47	1
Ruthenium	Ru	44	101.07	3, 4, 6, 8
Samarium	Sm	62	150.35	3
Scandium	Sc	21	44.956	3
Selenium[d]	Se	34	78.96	2, 4, 6
Silicon[d]	Si	14	28.086[l]	4
Silver	Ag	47	107.868[m]	1
Sodium	Na	11	22.9898	1
Strontium	Sr	38	87.62	2
Sulphur[d]	S	16	32.064[l]	2, 4, 6
Tantalum	Ta	73	180.948	4, 5
Technetium	Tc	43		
Tellurium[d]	Te	52	127.60	2, 4, 6
Terbium	Tb	65	158.924	3
Thallium	Tl	81	204.37	1, 3
Thorium	Th	90	232.038	3
Thulium	Tm	69	168.934	3
Tin	Sn	50	118.69	2, 4
Titanium	Ti	22	47.90	3, 4
Tungsten	W	74	183.85	3, 4, 5, 6
Uranium	U	92	238.03	4, 6
Vanadium	V	23	50.942	1, 2, 3, 4, 5
Xenon[c]	Xe	54	131.30	0
Ytterbium	Yb	70	173.04	2, 3
Yttrium	Y	39	88.905	3
Zinc	Zn	30	65.37	2
Zirconium	Zr	40	91.22	4

Note: Table courtesy IUPAC and Butterworth Scientific Publications.

[a] All the elements for which atomic weights are listed are metals, except as otherwise indicated. No atomic weights are listed for most radioactive elements, as these elements have no fixed value.

[b] The atomic weights are based upon nuclidic mass of $C^{12} = 12$.

[c] Inert gas. [d] Metalloid. [e] Liquid. [f] Gas.

[g] Most active gas. [h] Lightest gas. [i] Lightest metal. [j] Not placed. [k] Liquid at 25 C.

[l] The atomic weight varies because of natural variations in the isotopic composition of the element. The observed ranges are boron, ±0.003; carbon, ±0.00005; hydrogen, ±0.00001; oxygen, ±0.0001; silicon, ±0.001; sulphur, ±0.003.

[m] The atomic weight is believed to have an experimental uncertainty of the following magnitude: bromine, ±0.001; chlorine, ±0.001; chromium, ±0.001; copper, ±0.001; iron, ±0.003; silver, ±0.001. For other elements, the last digit given is believed to be reliable to ±0.5.

protons are bound together in the atomic nucleus with other particles, including neutrons, and are positively charged. The neutrons are particles having approximately the mass of a proton but are uncharged. The electrons are negatively charged particles, all alike, external to the nucleus, and sufficient in number to neutralize the nuclear charge in an atom. The differences between the atoms of different chemical elements are due to the different numbers of these smaller particles composing them. According to the original Bohr theory, an ordinary atom is conceived as a stable system of such electrons revolving in closed orbits about the nucleus like the planets of the solar system around the sun. In a hydrogen atom, there is 1 proton and 1 electron; in a radium atom, there are 88 electrons surrounding a nucleus 226 times as massive as the hydrogen nucleus. Only a few, in general the outermost or valence electrons of such an atom, are subject to rearrangement within, or ejection from, the atom, thereby enabling it, because of its increased energy, to combine with other atoms to form molecules of either elementary substances or compounds. The **atomic number** of an element is the number of excess positive charges on the nucleus of the atom. The essential feature that distinguishes one element from another is this charge of the nucleus. It also determines the position of the element in the periodic table. Modern researches have shown the existence of **isotopes,** that is, two or more species of atoms having the same atomic number and thus occupying the same place in the periodic system, but differing somewhat in atomic weight. These isotopes are chemically identical and are merely different species of the same chemical element. Most of the ordinary inactive

Solubility of Inorganic Substances in Water

(Number of grams of the anhydrous substance soluble in 1,000 g of water. The common name of the substance is given in parenthesis.)

	Composition	Temperature, deg F		
		32	122	212
Aluminum sulphate	$Al_2(SO_4)_3$	313	521	891
Aluminum potassium sulphate (potassium alum)	$Al_2K_2(SO_4)_4 \cdot 24H_2O$	30	170	1540
Ammonium bicarbonate	NH_4HCO_3	119		
Ammonium chloride (sal ammoniac)	NH_4Cl	297	504	760
Ammonium nitrate	NH_4NO_3	1183	3440	8710
Ammonium sulphate	$(NH_4)_2SO_4$	706	847	1033
Barium chloride	$BaCl_2 \cdot 2H_2O$	317	436	587
Barium nitrate	$Ba(NO_3)_2$	50	172	345
Calcium carbonate (calcite)	$CaCO_3$	0.018 (1)	....	0.88
Calcium chloride	$CaCl_2$	594	....	1576
Calcium hydroxide (hydrated lime)	$Ca(OH)_2$	1.77	....	0.67
Calcium nitrate	$Ca(NO_3)_2 \cdot 4H_2O$	931	3561	3626
Calcium sulphate (gypsum)	$CaSO_4 \cdot 2H_2O$	1.76	2.06	1.69
Copper sulphate (blue vitriol)	$CuSO_4 \cdot 5H_2O$	140	334	753
Ferrous chloride	$FeCl_2 \cdot 4H_2O$	644 (4)	820	1060
Ferrous hydroxide	$Fe(OH)_2$	0.0067 (3)		
Ferrous sulphate (green vitriol or copperas)	$FeSO_4 \cdot 7H_2O$	156	482	
Ferric chloride	$FeCl_3$	730	3160	5369
Lead chloride	$PbCl_2$	6.73	16.7	33.3
Lead nitrate	$Pb(NO_3)_2$	403	....	1255
Lead sulphate	$PbSO_4$	0.042 (2)		
Magnesium carbonate	$MgCO_3$	0.13 (3)		
Magnesium chloride	$MgCl_2 \cdot 6H_2O$	524	....	723
Magnesium hydroxide (milk of magnesia)	$Mg(OH)_2$	0.009 (3)		
Magnesium nitrate	$Mg(NO_3)_2 \cdot 6H_2O$	665	903	
Magnesium sulphate (Epsom salts)	$MgSO_4 \cdot 7H_2O$	269	500	710
Potassium carbonate (potash)	K_2CO_3	893	1216	1562
Potassium chloride	KCl	284	435	566
Potassium hydroxide (caustic potash)	KOH	971	1414	1773
Potassium nitrate (saltpeter or niter)	KNO_3	131	851	2477
Potassium sulphate	K_2SO_4	74	165	241
Sodium bicarbonate (baking soda)	$NaHCO_3$	69	145	
Sodium carbonate (sal soda or soda ash)	$NaCO_3 \cdot 10H_2O$	204	475	452
Sodium chloride (common salt)	$NaCl$	357	366	392
Sodium hydroxide (caustic soda)	$NaOH$	420	1448	3388
Sodium nitrate (Chile saltpeter)	$NaNO_3$	733	1148	1755
Sodium sulphate (Glauber salts)	$Na_2SO_4 \cdot 10H_2O$	49	466	422
Zinc chloride	$ZnCl_2$	2044	4702	6147
Zinc nitrate	$Zn(NO_3)_2 \cdot 6H_2O$	947		
Zinc sulphate	$ZnSO_4 \cdot 7H_2O$	419	768	807

(1) 59 F. (2) 68 F. (3) In cold water. (4) 50 F.

Solubility of Gases in Water

(By volume, at atmospheric pressure)

t (deg F) =	32	68	212	t (deg F) =	32	68	212
Air	0.032	0.020	0.012	Hydrogen	0.023	0.020	0.018
Acetylene	1.89	1.12		Hydrogen sulphide	5.0	[illegible].8	0.87
Ammonia	1250	700	......	Hydrochloric acid	560	480	
Carbon dioxide	1.87	0.96	0.26	Nitrogen	0.026	0.017	0.0105
Carbon monoxide	0.039	0.025	......	Oxygen	0.053	0.034	0.0185
Chlorine	5.0	2.5	0.00	Sulphuric acid	87	43	

Approximate Specific Gravities and Densities

(Water at 39 F and normal atmospheric pressure taken as unity)

For more detailed data on any material, see the section dealing with the properties of that material. Data given are for usual room temperatures.

Substance	Specific gravity	Avg density, lb per cu ft
Metals, Alloys, Ores		
Aluminum, cast-hammered	2.55–2.80	165
Aluminum, bronze	7.7	481
Brass, cast-rolled	8.4–8.7	534
Bronze, 7.9 to 14% Sn	7.4–8.9	509
Bronze, phosphor	8.88	554
Copper, cast-rolled	8.8–8.95	556
Copper ore, pyrites	4.1–4.3	262
German silver	8.58	536
Gold, cast-hammered	19.25–19.35	1205
Gold coin (U.S.)	17.18–17.2	1073
Iridium	21.78–22.42	1383
Iron, gray cast	7.03–7.13	442
Iron, cast, pig	7.2	450
Iron, wrought	7.6–7.9	485
Iron, spiegel-eisen	7.5	468
Iron, ferrosilicon	6.7–7.3	437
Iron ore, hematite	5.2	325
Iron ore, limonite	3.6–4.0	237
Iron ore, magnetite	4.9–5.2	315
Iron slag	2.5–3.0	172
Lead	11.34	710
Lead ore, galena	7.3–7.6	465
Manganese	7.42	475
Manganese ore, pyrolusite	3.7–4.6	259
Mercury	13.546	847
Monel metal, rolled	8.97	555
Nickel	8.9	537
Platinum, cast-hammered	21.5	1330
Silver, cast-hammered	10.4–10.6	656
Steel, cold-drawn	7.83	489
Steel, machine	7.80	487
Steel, tool	7.70–7.73	481
Tin, cast-hammered	7.2–7.5	459
Tin ore, cassiterite	6.4–7.0	418
Tungsten	19.22	1200
Uranium	18.7	1170
Zinc, cast-rolled	6.9–7.2	440
Zinc, ore, blende	3.9–4.2	253
Various Solids		
Cereals, oats, bulk	0.41	26
Cereals, barley, bulk	0.62	39
Cereals, corn, rye, bulk	0.73	45
Cereals, wheat, bulk	0.77	48
Cork	0.22–0.26	15
Cotton, flax, hemp	1.47–1.50	93
Fats	0.90–0.97	58
Flour, loose	0.40–0.50	28
Flour, pressed	0.70–0.80	47
Glass, common	2.40–2.80	162
Glass, plate or crown	2.45–2.72	161
Glass, crystal	2.90–3.00	184
Glass, flint	3.2–4.7	247
Hay and straw, bales	0.32	20
Leather	0.86–1.02	59
Paper	0.70–1.15	58

Substance	Specific gravity	Avg density, lb per cu ft
Potatoes, piled	0.67	44
Rubber, caoutchouc	0.92–0.96	59
Rubber goods	1.0–2.0	94
Salt, granulated, piled	0.77	48
Saltpeter	2.11	132
Starch	1.53	96
Sulphur	1.93–2.07	125
Wool	1.32	82
Timber, air-dry		
Apple	0.66–0.74	44
Ash, black	0.55	34
Ash, white	0.64–0.71	42
Birch, sweet, yellow	0.71–0.72	44
Cedar, white, red	0.35	22
Cherry, wild red	0.43	27
Chestnut	0.48	30
Cypress	0.45–0.48	29
Fir, Douglas	0.48–0.55	32
Fir, balsam	0.40	25
Elm, white	0.56	35
Hemlock	0.45–0.50	29
Hickory	0.74–0.80	48
Locust	0.67–0.77	45
Mahogany	0.56–0.85	44
Maple, sugar	0.68	43
Maple, white	0.53	33
Oak, chestnut	0.74	46
Oak, live	0.87	54
Oak, red, black	0.64–0.71	42
Oak, white	0.77	48
Pine, Oregon	0.51	32
Pine, red	0.48	30
Pine, white	0.43	27
Pine, Southern	0.61–0.67	38–42
Pine, Norway	0.55	34
Poplar	0.43	27
Redwood, California	0.42	26
Spruce, white, red	0.45	28
Teak, African	0.99	62
Teak, Indian	0.66–0.88	48
Walnut, black	0.59	37
Willow	0.42–0.50	28
Various Liquids		
Alcohol, ethyl (100%)	0.789	49
Alcohol, methyl (100%)	0.796	50
Acid, muriatic, 40%	1.20	75
Acid, nitric, 91%	1.50	94
Acid, sulphuric, 87%	1.80	112
Chloroform	1.500	95
Ether	0.736	46
Lye, soda, 66%	1.70	106
Oils, vegetable	0.91–0.94	58
Oils, mineral, lubricants	0.88–0.94	57
Turpentine	0.861–0.867	54

Approximate Specific Gravities and Densities—(*Continued*)

Substance	Specific gravity	Avg density, lb per cu ft
Various Liquids		
Water, 4 C, max. density	1.0	62.428
Water, 100 C	0.9584	59.830
Water, ice	0.88–0.92	56
Water, snow, fresh fallen	0.125	8
Water, sea water	1.02–1.03	64
Gases, see pp. 4–20 and 4–72		
Ashlar Masonry		
Granite, syenite, gneiss	2.4–2.7	159
Limestone	2.1–2.8	153
Marble	2.4–2.8	162
Sandstone	2.0–2.6	143
Bluestone	2.3–2.6	153
Rubble Masonry		
Granite, syenite, gneiss	2.3–2.6	153
Limestone	2.0–2.7	147
Sandstone	1.9–2.5	137
Bluestone	2.2–2.5	147
Marble	2.3–2.7	156
Dry Rubble Masonry		
Granite, syenite, gneiss	1.9–2.3	130
Limestone, marble	1.9–2.1	125
Sandstone, bluestone	1.8–1.9	110
Brick Masonry		
Hard brick	1.8–2.3	128
Medium brick	1.6–2.0	112
Soft brick	1.4–1.9	103
Sand-lime brick	1.4–2.2	112
Concrete Masonry		
Cement, stone, sand	2.2–2.4	144
Cement, slag, etc	1.9–2.3	130
Cement, cinder, etc	1.5–1.7	100
Various Building Mat'ls		
Ashes, cinders	0.64–0.72	40–45
Cement, portland, loose	1.5	94
Portland cement	3.1–3.2	196
Lime, gypsum, loose	0.85–1.00	53–64
Mortar, lime, set	1.4–1.9	103
		94
Mortar, portland cement	2.08–2.25	135
Slags, bank slag	1.1–1.2	67–72
Slags, bank screenings	1.5–1.9	98–117
Slags, machine slag	1.5	96
Slags, slag sand	0.8–0.9	49–55
Earth, etc., Excavated		
Clay, dry	1.0	63
Clay, damp, plastic	1.76	110
Clay and gravel, dry	1.6	100
Earth, dry, loose	1.2	76
Earth, dry, packed	1.5	95
Earth, moist, loose	1.3	78
Earth, moist, packed	1.6	96
Earth, mud, flowing	1.7	108
Earth, mud, packed	1.8	115
Riprap, limestone	1.3–1.4	80–85
Riprap, sandstone	1.4	90
Riprap, shale	1.7	105
Sand, gravel, dry, loose	1.4–1.7	90–105
Sand, gravel, dry, packed	1.6–1.9	100–120
Sand, gravel, wet	1.89–2.16	126
Excavations in Water		
Sand or gravel	0.96	60
Sand or gravel and clay	1.00	65
Clay	1.28	80
River mud	1.44	90
Soil	1.12	70
Stone riprap	1.00	65
Minerals		
Asbestos	2.1–2.8	153
Barytes	4.50	281
Basalt	2.7–3.2	184
Bauxite	2.55	159
Bluestone	2.5–2.6	159
Borax	1.7–1.8	109
Chalk	1.8–2.8	143
Clay, marl	1.8–2.6	137
Dolomite	2.9	181
Feldspar, orthoclase	2.5–2.7	162
Gneiss	2.7–2.9	175
Granite	2.6–2.7	165
Greenstone, trap	2.8–3.2	187
Gypsum, alabaster	2.3–2.8	159
Hornblende	3.0	187
Limestone	2.1–2.86	155
Marble	2.6–2.86	170
Magnesite	3.0	187
Phosphate rock, apatite	3.2	200
Porphyry	2.6–2.9	172
Pumice, natural	0.37–0.90	40
Quartz, flint	2.5–2.8	165
Sandstone	2.0–2.6	143
Serpentine	2.7–2.8	171
Shale, slate	2.6–2.9	172
Soapstone, talc	2.6–2.8	169
Syenite	2.6–2.7	165
Stone, Quarried, Piled		
Basalt, granite, gneiss	1.5	96
Limestone, marble, quartz	1.5	95
Sandstone	1.3	82
Shale	1.5	92
Greenstone, hornblend	1.7	107
Bituminous Substances		
Asphaltum	1.1–1.5	81
Coal, anthracite	1.4–1.8	97
Coal, bituminous	1.2–1.5	84
Coal, lignite	1.1–1.4	78
Coal, peat, turf, dry	0.65–0.85	47
Coal, charcoal, pine	0.28–0.44	23
Coal, charcoal, oak	0.47–0.57	33
Coal, coke	1.0–1.4	75
Graphite	1.64–2.7	135
Paraffin	0.87–0.91	56
Petroleum	0.87	54
Petroleum, refined (kerosene)	0.78–0.82	50
Petroleum, benzine	0.73–0.75	46
Petroleum, gasoline	0.70–0.75	45
Pitch	1.07–1.15	69
Tar, bituminous	1.20	75
Coal and Coke, Piled		
Coal, anthracite	0.75–0.93	47–58
Coal, bituminous, lignite	0.64–0.87	40–54
Coal, peat, turf	0.32–0.42	20–26
Coal, charcoal	0.16–0.23	10–14
Coal, coke	0.37–0.51	23–32

elements have been shown to consist of a mixture of isotopes. This convenient atomic model should be regarded as only a working hypothesis for coordinating a number of phenomena about which much yet remains to be known. (See also p. 9-158.)

Calculation of the Percentage Composition of Substances. Add together the atomic weights of the elements in the compound to obtain its molecular weight. Multiply the atomic weight of the element to be calculated by the number of atoms present (indicated in the formula by a subscript number) and by 100, and divide by the molecular weight of the compound. For example, hematite iron ore (Fe_2O_3) contains 69.94 percent of iron by weight, determined as follows: Molecular weight of Fe_2O_3 = $(55.84 \times 2) + (16 \times 3) = 159.68$. Percentage of iron in compound = $(55.84 \times 2) \times 100/159.68 = 69.94$.

Specific Gravity and Density of Water at Atmospheric Pressure

(Weights are *in vacuo*)

Temp, deg C	Specific gravity	Density, lb per cu ft	Temp, deg C	Specific gravity	Density, lb per cu ft	Temp, deg C	Specific gravity	Density, lb per cu ft	Temp, deg C	Specific gravity	Density, lb per cu ft
0	0.99987	62.4183	20	0.99823	62.3164	40	0.99224	61.9428	60	0.98324	61.380
2	0.99997	62.4246	22	0.99780	62.2894	42	0.99147	61.894	62	0.98220	61.315
4	1.00000	62.4266	24	0.99732	62.2598	44	0.99066	61.844	64	0.98113	61.249
6	0.99997	62.4246	26	0.99681	62.2278	46	0.98982	61.791	66	0.98005	61.181
8	0.99988	62.4189	28	0.99626	62.1934	48	0.98896	61.737	68	0.97894	61.112
10	0.99973	62.4096	30	0.99567	62.1568	50	0.98807	61.682	70	0.97781	61.041
12	0.99952	62.3969	32	0.99505	62.1179	52	0.98715	61.624	72	0.97666	60.970
14	0.99927	62.3811	34	0.99440	62.0770	54	0.98621	61.566	74	0.97548	60.896
16	0.99897	62.3623	36	0.99371	62.0341	56	0.98524	61.505	76	0.97428	60.821
18	0.99862	62.3407	38	0.99299	61.9893	58	0.98425	61.443	78	0.97307	60.745

Compressibility of Liquids

If v_1 and v_2 are the volumes of the liquids at pressures of p_1 and p_2 atm, respectively, at any temperature, the coefficient of compressibility b is given by the equation

$$b = \frac{1}{v_1} \times \frac{v_1 - v_2}{p_2 - p_1}$$

The value of $b \times 10^6$ for oils at low pressures at about 70 F varies from about 55 to 80; for mercury at 32 F, it is 3.9; for chloroform at 32 F, it is 100 and increases with the temperature to 200 at 140 F; for ethyl alcohol, it increases from about 100 at 32 F and low pressures to 125 at 104 F; for glycerin, it is about 24 at room temperature and low pressure.

Volume of Water as a Function of Pressure and Temperature

(From "International Critical Tables")

Temperature, deg F (C)	Pressure in atmospheres								
	0	500	1,000	2,000	3,000	4,000	5,000	6,500	8,000
32(0)	1.0000	0.9769	0.9566	0.9223	0.8954	0.8739	0.8565	0.8361	
68(20)	1.0016	0.9804	0.9619	0.9312	0.9065	0.8855	0.8675	0.8444	0.8244
122(50)	1.0128	0.9915	0.9732	0.9428	0.9183	0.8974	0.8792	0.8562	0.8369
176(80)	1.0287	1.0071	0.9884	0.9568	0.9315	0.9097	0.8913	0.8679	0.8481

Composition of Air

The percent volumetric composition of dry air at sea level is N_2, 78.03; O_2, 20.99; A, 0.94; CO_2, 0.03; H_2, 0.01; Ne, 0.00123; He, 0.0004; Kr, 0.00005; Xe, 0.000006. For ordinary purposes, this is taken as N_2, 79; O_2, 21. On this basis, the ratio of N_2 to O_2 is 3.76. On the basis of mass or weight, the percent composition is N_2, 75.5; O_2, 23.2, A, 1.33; CO_2, 0.045 or approximately N_2, 76.8; O_2, 23.2 and the nitrogen-oxygen weight ratio is 3.32 (data from "International Critical Tables," vol. 1, p. 393, McGraw-Hill).

Basic Properties of Several Metals

(Staff contribution)*

Material	Density, g per cm³	Coefficient of thermal expansion, in. per in. per deg F × 10⁻⁶	Thermal conductivity, Btu per hr per ft per deg F	Specific heat, Btu per lb per deg F	Approximate melting temp, deg F	Modulus of elasticity, psi × 10⁶	Poisson's ratio	Yield stress, psi × 10³	Ultimate stress, psi × 10³	Elongation, percent
Aluminum, 2024-T3	2.77	12.6	110	0.23	940	10.6	0.33	50	70	18
Aluminum, 6061-T6	2.70	13.5	90	0.23	1080	10.6	0.33	40	45	17
Aluminum, 7079-T6	2.74	13.7	70	0.23	900	10.4	0.33	68	78	14
Beryllium, QMV	1.85	6.4–10.2	85	0.45	2340	40–44	0.024–0.030	27–38	33–51	1–3.5
Copper, pure	8.90	9.2	227	0.092	1980	17.0	....	See "Metals Handbook"		
Gold, pure	19.32	....	172	0.031	1950	10.8	0.42	.....	18	30
Lead, pure	11.34	29.3	21.4	0.031	620	2.0	0.40–0.45	1.3	2.6	20–50
Magnesium AZ31B-H24 (sheet)	1.77	14.5	55	0.25	1100	6.5	0.35	22	37	15
Magnesium, HK31A-H24	1.79	14.0	66	0.13	1100	6.4	0.35	29	37	8
Molybdenum, wrought	10.3	3.0	83	0.07	4730	40.0	0.32	80	120–200	Small
Nickel, pure	8.9	7.2	53	0.11	2650	32.0	....	See "Metals Handbook"		
Platinum	21.45	5.0	40	0.031	3217	21.3	0.39	.....	20–24	35–40
Plutonium, alpha phase	19.0–19.7	30.0	4.8	0.034	1184	14.0	0.15–0.21	40	60	Small
Silver, pure	10.5	11.0	241	0.056	1760	10–11	0.37	8	18	48
Steel, AISI C1020 (hot-worked)	7.85	8.4	27	0.10	2750	29–30	0.29	48	65	36
Steel, AISI 304 (sheet)	8.03	9.9	9.4	0.12	2600	28	0.29	39	87	65
Tantalum	16.6	3.6	31	0.03	5425	27.0	0.35	.....	50–145	1–40
Thorium, induction melt	11.6	6.95	21.7	0.03	3200	7–10	0.27	21	32	34
Titanium, B 120VCA (aged)	4.85	5.2	4.3	0.13	3100	14.8	0.3	190	200	9
Tungsten	19.3	2.5	95	0.033	6200	50	0.28	.....	18–600	1–3
Uranium D-38	18.97	4.0–8.0	17	0.028	2100	24	0.21	28	56	4

Notes: Room-temperature properties are given.
For further information, consult the "Metals Handbook" or a manufacturer's publication.

* Compiled by Anders Lundberg, University of California, and reproduced by permission.

IRON AND STEEL

BY

B. R. Queneau

REFERENCES: "Metals Handbook," ASM. ASTM Standards, Part 1. SAE Handbook. "Steel Products Manual," AISI.

CLASSIFICATION OF IRON AND STEEL

Iron (Fe) is not a high-purity metal commercially but contains other chemical elements which have a large effect on its physical and mechanical properties. The amount and distribution of these elements are dependent upon the method of manufacture. The most important commercial forms of iron are listed below.

Pig iron is the product of the blast furnace and is made by the reduction of iron ore.

Cast iron is an alloy of iron containing so much carbon that, as cast, it is not appreciably malleable at any temperature.

Gray cast iron is an iron which, as cast, has combined or cementitic carbon not in excess of a eutectoid percentage—the balance of the carbon occurring as graphite flakes. The term "gray iron" is derived from the characteristic gray fracture of this metal.

White cast iron contains carbon in the combined form. The presence of cementite or iron carbide (Fe_3C) makes this metal hard and brittle, and the absence of graphite gives the fracture a white color.

Malleable cast iron is an alloy in which all the combined carbon in a special white cast iron has been changed to free or temper carbon by suitable heat-treatment.

Nodular (ductile) cast iron is produced by adding alloys of magnesium or cerium to molten iron. These additions cause the graphite to form into small nodules, resulting in a higher-strength, ductile iron.

Ingot iron is an open-hearth iron very low in carbon, manganese, and other impurities.

Wrought iron is a ferrous material aggregated from a solidifying mass of pasty particles of highly refined metallic iron with which is incorporated, without subsequent fusion, a minutely and uniformly distributed quantity of slag.

Steel is a malleable alloy of iron and carbon, usually containing substantial quantities of manganese.

Carbon steel is steel that owes its distinctive properties chiefly to the carbon it contains.

Alloy steel is steel that owes its distinctive properties chiefly to some element or elements other than carbon, or jointly to such other elements and carbon. Some alloy steels necessarily contain an important percentage of carbon, even as much as 1.25 percent. There is no agreement about where to draw the line between the alloy steels and the carbon steels.

Bessemer steel, open-hearth steel, basic oxygen steel, and **electric-furnace steel** are steels made by the Bessemer, open-hearth, basic-oxygen-furnace, and electric-furnace processes, irrespective of carbon content.

PIG IRON

Iron ore is reduced in a blast furnace to form **pig iron,** which is the raw material for practically all iron and steel products. Formerly, nearly 90 percent of the iron ore used in the United States came from the Lake Superior district; the ore had the advantages of high quality and the cheapness with which it could be mined and transported by way of the Great Lakes. The higher-grade ores in these deposits have incurred such heavy depletion that the steel industry must depend in the future on concentrates produced from low-grade ores such as the taconites and on foreign ores.

The **blast furnace** consists of a vertical shaft over 20 ft in diameter and 100 ft high containing a descending column of iron ore, coke, and limestone and a large volume of ascending hot gas. The gas is produced by the burning of the coke in the hearth of the furnace and contains about 34 percent carbon monoxide. This gas reduces the iron ore to metallic iron, which melts and picks up considerable quantities of carbon, manganese, phosphorus, sulphur, and silicon. The **gangue** (mostly silica) of the iron ore and the ash in the coke combine with the limestone to form the blast-furnace slag. The pig iron and slag are drawn off at intervals from the hearth through the iron notch and cinder notch, respectively. The modern blast furnace produces 2,000 to 3,500 tons of pig iron per day. The blast furnace produces iron for three general applications: (1) conversion pig irons, which are used to make many varieties of steel; (2) pig iron for use in foundries for making castings; and (3) ferroalloys, which contain a considerable percentage of another metallic element and are used as addition agents in steelmaking. Compositions of commercial irons are listed in Table 1.

Table 1. Types of Pig Iron for Steelmaking and Foundry Use
(Compiled from "Steel Products Manual," AISI, 1949.)

Pig Iron and Blast-furnace Ferroalloys				
Designation	Chemical composition, percent*			Principal use
	Si	P	Mn	
Bessemer	1.00–3.00	0.076–1.00	1.00–1.25	Acid Bessemer steel
Basic	1.00–1.50	0.400 max	1.01–2.00	Open-hearth and basic-oxygen steel
Foundry, northern	1.00–1.50	0.300–0.500	0.40–0.75	A wide variety of castings
Foundry, southern	1.75–3.50	0.501–0.700	0.50–1.25	Cast-iron pipe
Ferromanganese	0.50–1.00	0.2–0.35	78–82	Addition of manganese to steel or cast iron
Ferrosilicon (silvery pig)	5.00–17.00	0.300 max	1.00–2.00	Addition of silicon to steel or cast iron

* Carbon content not specified. Sulphur specified 0.05 percent max.

COMMERCIALLY PURE IRON

Commercial quantities of **electrolytic iron** have been produced since 1904, but for economic reasons, most of the processes have been short-lived. Electrolytic iron is brittle as deposited so that it can be readily pulverized to produce a high-purity iron power. Typical compositions of different irons are given in Table 2.

Table 2. Typical Compositions of Wrought Iron, Ingot Iron, Electrolytic Iron, and Steel (Percent)

Material	C	Mn	P	S	Si	Slag by weight
Wrought iron (hand-puddled)	0.06	0.05	0.068	0.009	0.10	2.0
Wrought iron (Byers)	0.08	0.02	0.062	0.010	0.16	1.20
Ingot iron (Armco)	0.015	0.020	0.005	0.025	Trace	
Electrolytic iron	0.006	.....	0.005	0.005	0.005	
Low-carbon steel	0.06	0.40	0.012	0.030	0.009	

WROUGHT IRON

Wrought iron is the oldest form of iron made by man. It is still produced in small quantities, primarily by the Byers process. The normal wrought iron contains a considerable amount of slag, giving it the characteristic fibrous structure. It can readily be worked and welded at temperatures close to its melting point. It can be obtained in the form of plates, sheets, structural shapes, bars, pipe, and tubing. The principal use for wrought iron is in the form of pipe for mildy corrosive conditions. Table 3 gives the ASTM mechanical-test requirements for Grade A, double-refined bars, and Grade B, single-refined bars.

Table 3. Mechanical Properties of Wrought Iron (Round, Square, and Hexagonal Bars)
(ASTM A189–63)

	Under 1⅝ in. in diam or thickness	1⅝ in. and up to but not incl 2½ in. in diam or thickness	2½ in. and over in diam or thickness and flat bars
GRADE A—DOUBLE-REFINED			
Tensile strength, psi	48,000–54,000	47,000–54,000	46,000–54,000
Yield point, min psi	0.60 T.S.	0.55 T.S.	0.50 T.S.
Elongation in 8 in., min %	28	25	22
Reduction of area, min %	45	40	35
GRADE B—SINGLE-REFINED			
Tensile strength, min psi	48,000	47,000	46,000
Yield point, min psi	0.60 T.S.	0.55 T.S.	0.50 T.S.
Elongation in 8 in., min %	25	22	20
Reduction of area, min %	40	35	30

INGOT IRON

Ingot iron (Armco iron) is a relatively pure iron which is made in a basic open-hearth furnace in a manner similar to that used for steel. The refining operation is carried on considerably further by the addition of a very pure grade of iron ore, which oxidizes out the impurities to a low point. A high furnace temperature is required for this operation owing to the high melting point of pure iron. A typical analysis of ingot iron is given in Table 2.

Physical constants: sp gr, 7.866; melting point, 2802 F; specific heat at 77 F, 0.108; heat of fusion, 117 Btu per lb; thermal conductivity at 212 F, 465 Btu per hr per sq ft per in. per deg F; thermal coefficient of expansion at 212 F, 7 millionths per deg F; electrical resistivity at 32 F, 9.50 microhm-cm; temperature coefficient of electrical resistance between 32 and 212 F, 0.0031 per deg F. Many of these constants are affected considerably by small changes in composition, grain size, or mechanical treatment.

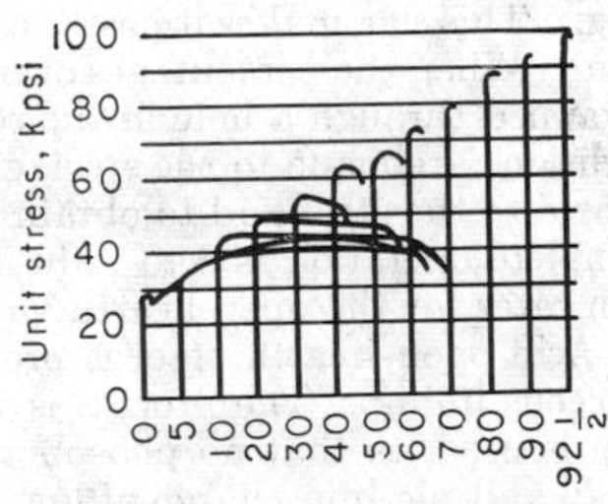

FIG. 1. Effect of cold rolling on the stress-strain relations of Armco ingot iron. (*Kenyon and Burns.*)

Mechanical Properties. The average mechanical properties of ingot iron after various treatments are given in Table 4.

Young's modulus for ingot iron is 29,300,000 psi both in tension and compression, and the shear modulus is 11,800,000 psi. Poisson's ratio is 0.28. The **effect of cold rolling** on the tensile strength, yield strength, elongation, and shape of the stress-strain curve is shown in Fig. 1. Ingot iron welds evenly and easily; it holds paint well and has superior enameling properties; it has a high magnetic permeability at high inductions and low retentivity.

Uses. In galvanized-sheet form for culverts, flumes, roofing and siding; in plate form in oil tanks, water tanks, boilers, gas holders, and large pipe; in enameled form for ranges, refrigerators, tables and kitchen furniture, lighting fixtures, and similar articles. The purity of ingot iron makes it valuable as melting stock in making high-grade tool steel.

Table 4. Mechanical Properties of Ingot Iron
(R. L. Kenyon, "Metals Handbook," ASM, 1948.)

	Hot-rolled rods or plates	Dead soft	Cold-worked (approx max)	Forgings			
				Fin-ished cold	Fin-ished hot	Finished hot, annealed	Finished hot, quenched 1725 F in water
Tensile yield strength, kpsi	26–32	19	.....	27	19	18	30
Tensile strength, kpsi	42–48	38	100	44	42	41	47
Elongation, %	22–28	43–48	.....	42	45	47	36
Gage length, in	8	2	.....	2	2	2	2
Reduction of area, %	65–78	70–77	65–70	76	77	71	70
Hardness, BHN	82–100	67	220	101	90	82	110

STEEL

Steel Manufacturing

Steel is produced from pig iron by the removal of impurities in an open-hearth furnace, a basic oxygen furnace, a Bessemer converter, or an electric furnace. In the United States, over 80 percent of steel is produced in the **basic open-hearth** furnace. This is a reverberatory furnace having a capacity up to 550 tons. The hearth has a basic lining of magnesia and dolomite, and the roof is made of high-grade silica or basic brick. A practice in wide use for making structural steels is to charge limestone, iron ore, and scrap and then melt the scrap with an oxidizing flame. When melting is well advanced, molten pig iron is added, and a reaction takes place between the iron oxide and the impurities in the pig iron. The rate of this reaction and the initial melting of scrap can be increased by the addition of oxygen to the furnace by roof lances. The acid slag formed by the oxidation of silicon and manganese is run off, and with further heating, the lime comes up through the bath, causing a violent boil and forming a basic slag. This slag makes it possible to remove a large percentage of the phosphorus in the iron. When the percentages of impurities are lowered to the desired extent, the metal is tapped through a hole in the rear of the furnace and poured into a ladle. Various additions are made to the steel, either in the furnace before tapping or in the ladle, to deoxidize the steel and to obtain the desired composition. The time required for the complete operation is 6 to 12 hr, depending on the rate of oxygen injection. Production rates for the open hearth vary from 25 to 60 tons per furnace hr.

Acid open-hearth steel is produced in an open-hearth furnace having an acid or siliceous lining. The process is very similar to the basic process except that an acid slag is used, so that no phosphorus can be removed from the steel. This requires a scrap and pig-iron charge of low phosphorus content.

Bessemer steel is made in a pear-shaped converter which is mounted on trunnions so as to be tilted easily for charging and pouring. Molten pig iron is poured into the converter, and air is blown through the liquid metal. Heat is liberated by the oxidation of the impurities—silicon, manganese, and carbon. When the carbon has been nearly eliminated, the metal is recarburized by the addition of alloys containing carbon, manganese, and silicon. From 8 to 30 tons of steel are made in one blow requiring only 10 or 20 min.

Acid Bessemer steel is made in a converter having a siliceous lining and is the only Bessemer steel made in the United States, for our ores are not suitable for the production of pig iron for **basic Bessemer steel**. The latter is made in a converter having a magnesite lining, and limestone is added during the process to form a basic slag which removes a large proportion of the phosphorus in the pig. The process requires a pig iron very high in phosphorus, whereas the basic open-hearth process can use pig iron containing phosphorus in all but the highest amounts.

Basic Oxygen Steel. A recent development in steelmaking is the process in which pure oxygen (99+ percent) is blown vertically under high pressure (175 psi) onto the surface of molten iron. The vessels are similar in shape to the Bessemer converters but range in size from 30 to 300 tons. Because of the excess heat available with oxygen blowing, considerable scrap can be added during the blow. Production rates of well over 300 tons per furnace hr can be attained. The comparatively low investment cost and low cost of operation have already made this the second-largest producer of steel in the world, and with time it will probably replace the basic open hearth as the major steelmaking process.

Electric Steel. The electric furnace commonly used in the production of electric steel is the three-phase arc furnace in which the electric arc heats the bath. The furnace has a basic lining and is usually charged with cold steel scrap. When the bath is molten, the impurities are removed by oxidation by the use of iron oxide or by the introduction of gaseous oxygen. The resultant slag is then removed, and a new slag is formed from lime, sand, and spar. This slag may be made carbidic by the addition of coke dust, and the oxygen content of the steel is reduced to a low level. Alloying elements are then added to meet the specified composition, and the heat is tapped into a ladle. The **induction furnace** is simply a melting furnace to which the various metals are added to make the desired alloy. When steel scrap is used as a charge, it will be a high-grade scrap the composition of which is well known (see also Sec. 7).

Vacuum Casting. Hydrogen in amounts as low as 5 ppm may cause internal flakes in large steel sections. By pouring the liquid steel in a vacuum chamber, it is possible to reduce the hydrogen to about 1 ppm. Vacuum casting is used extensively for large forgings such as electrical rotors. Carbon deoxidation is also carried out in a vacuum but is carried out for the purpose of reducing the oxygen content in the steel to less than 0.001 percent by removal of oxygen as carbon monoxide. This treatment substantially decreases the number of non-metallic inclusions in the steel and is used for bearings and other high-quality steels.

Steel Ingots. After being refined by one of the preceding methods, the steel is tapped into a ladle and poured into iron ingot molds. Many defects in rolled-steel products may be introduced by incorrect ingot practice, and the production of high-grade steel requires great care at this stage.

Steels in which no gas evolution occurs on solidification are called **killed steels.** When the steel cools in the mold, shrinkage of the steel on solidifying causes **piping**—the cavity, or "pipe," being found usually in the upper portion of the ingot. To minimize this condition, a large-end-up mold is used together with a refractory "hot top" which supplies molten steel to the main body of the ingot while solidification proceeds. This minimizes the amount of metal that has to be discarded on account of pipe, but the top discard still amounts to 10 or 15 percent of the total weight of the ingot.

To reduce the cost of hot tops and the large percentage of metal discard when making mild steel for structural purposes, the steel is not fully deoxidized. This results in blowholes in the steel on solidification; the presence of these blowholes minimizes piping by distributing small voids throughout the ingot instead of having one large one in the upper center of the ingot. If not exposed at the surface of the ingot, these blowholes weld together during rolling. Steel deoxidized in this manner is called **semikilled steel.** If the steel is deoxidized still less in the ladle, a reaction takes place during solidification in which the oxygen and the carbon in the steel form carbon monoxide, which is freely evolved from the ingot. The intensity of this reaction affects the ingot structure greatly. If the reaction is allowed to go to completion, the product is called **rimmed steel,** but if the reaction is stopped after a short while by preventing, in a mechanical manner, further evolution of gas from the top of the ingot, the steel is called **capped steel.** The gas evolution results in an outer skin on the ingot which is clean and very low in carbon. In capped steel, the skin is thinner and there is less segregation or concentration of impurities than in rimmed steel. The presence of this nearly pure iron skin enables the production of an excellent surface finish on the rolled product, and therefore sheet and strip are made nearly exclusively from rimmed or capped steel.

Some defects besides the occurrence of pipe in rolled-steel products are segregation, ingot cracks, seams, scabs, laps, and inclusions. **Segregation,** or the concentration of impurities, occurs in all steels upon solidification, but it can be minimized by proper mold design and low pouring temperatures. Rough mold surfaces or molds containing cracks or cavities interfere with the normal contraction of the ingot, and transverse cracks in the ingot skin may result. Cracks thus produced soon have their surfaces oxidized, and when the ingot is rolled out, these defects will be elongated in the direction of rolling and are called **seams.** Any oxidized crack or blowhole at the surface will roll out into a seam. Improper pouring conditions such as splashing of steel in the molds will form **scabs.** When rolling with grooved rolls which are not properly designed or set up, fins are liable to result from the flow of metal between the flat bodies of the rolls. If the fin is thin and wide, it will be folded over when the steel passes through the next set of rolls and will form a **lap. Non-metallic inclusions** consisting of sulphides, silicates, etc., are found to some extent in all steels and are introduced in the refining and deoxidation of the steel. Steels containing many inclusions are said to be "dirty," but the presence of these inclusions, unless they are large in size, is not necessarily detrimental to the physical properties.

Pipe, segregation, and inclusions are defects in the steel which cannot be remedied to any large extent. Surface defects such as seams, laps, and scabs can be removed by **chipping** the surface with air hammers, **scarfing** or **deseaming** with oxyacetylene torches, grinding, or by machining. To inspect the surface of steel products, the scale can be removed by **pickling** in acid, by the use of a torch in **flame scaling,** or by mechanical means.

Mechanical Treatment of Steel

At present, all but 2 or 3 percent of the total steel produced is cast in the form of ingots and then subjected to some form of mechanical treatment. The solid ingot is heated to between 2000 and 2600 F, depending on the composition of the steel, and then hot-worked by rolling, pressing, or hammering. **Hot work** consists of any mechanical treatment at temperatures above the thermal critical range of the steel. Considerable improvement in mechanical properties is obtained by hot work. It will increase to some extent the yield and tensile strength, but it is especially beneficial to the ductility of the steel since it breaks up the dendritic structure in the ingot and minimizes the effects of segregation and inclusions. The temperature at which hot work is completed is important and should be above the thermal critical range, but as near to it as practicable, the exact temperature depending upon the carbon and alloy content.

The effect of **rolling** is to elongate the inclusions in the direction of rolling, giving the steel excellent properties on samples taken parallel to this direction, although tests on samples taken in a transverse direction will not have as high mechanical properties. **Hammer forging** is more effective than rolling in that working can be done in more than one direction thus eliminating directional properties to the steel. The slow application of pressure in a **forging press** works the interior of a large forging more effectively than hammering; the press is used to a large extent for large high-quality forgings. Rolling, hammering, or pressing effectively breaks up the coarse crystallization of a cast ingot when a reduction in area of 3 or 4 to 1 has been obtained.

Shaping of steel by rolling is adopted whenever possible because of the rapidity of the operation and its relatively low cost. Rolling operations are carried out in mills which derive their name from the name of the product that they produce. Thus an ingot may be rolled into blooms in a blooming mill and slabs in a slabbing mill. In the blooming mill, the ingot is reduced by several passes to a **bloom,** having dimensions about 6 in. square or larger. The bloom may then be further reduced to a **billet** which is somewhere between 1¼ and 6 in. square. The names blooms and billets still apply if the products are rectangular in form when the widths are less than twice the thickness. However, if the width far exceeds the thickness of the rectangular section, it is called a **slab.** Blooms are rolled on finishing mills into *structural shapes, rails, wheels, sheet bar* for further rolling into sheet, and **skelp** to be used in the manufacture of pipe. Blooms may also be used for forging purposes. Slabs are rolled into plates and coils of hot-rolled sheets. Billets are rolled into rods, bars, bands, hoops, small shapes, and seamless tubes.

Cold work is work done on the metal below the thermal critical range and usually is done at atmospheric temperature. It greatly increases the yield strength and tensile strength, especially the former, and reduces the ductility. It includes operations such as cold rolling, cold pressing, twisting, and wire drawing. Large tonnages of sheets are cold-rolled which greatly improves their surface finish as well as increases their strength (see p. 6–30 for cold-rolled sheet).

The **extrusion** process shapes metal into the desired form by forcing it through a die under pressure. The advantages of extrusion are that it reduces scrap loss and labor and machining costs and is economically more suitable for both small-unit or large-scale production of odd-shaped pieces. **Cold** extrusion of steel markedly increases the mechanical properties and is therefore used extensively in production of ordnance. A low-carbon, aluminum-killed steel is normally used, and a phosphate coating serves as an excellent lubricant. For higher-alloy and stainless steels **hot** extrusion is necessary. Hot extrusion achieved practicality with the invention of the **Ugine-Sejournet** process, which solved the basic problem of lubrication by using glass. The glass melts at the high temperatures involved and forms a lubricating film over the section to be extruded. The problem of scale-free heating is solved in several ways, including heating in a barium chloride bath, induction heating, heating in molten salt baths, and using controlled heating atmospheres. The process is being improved continuously by changes in dies, presses, and operating speeds, and it is probably the best method for forming alloys with poor hot-working characteristics.

Constitution and Structure of Steel

As a result of the methods of production, the following elements are always present in steel: carbon, manganese, phosphorus, sulphur, silicon, and traces of oxygen, nitrogen, and aluminum. Various alloying elements are frequently added, such as nickel, chromium, copper, molybdenum, and vanadium. The most important of the above elements in steel is carbon, and it is necessary to understand the effect of carbon on the internal structure of the steel to understand the heat-treatment of carbon and low-alloy steels.

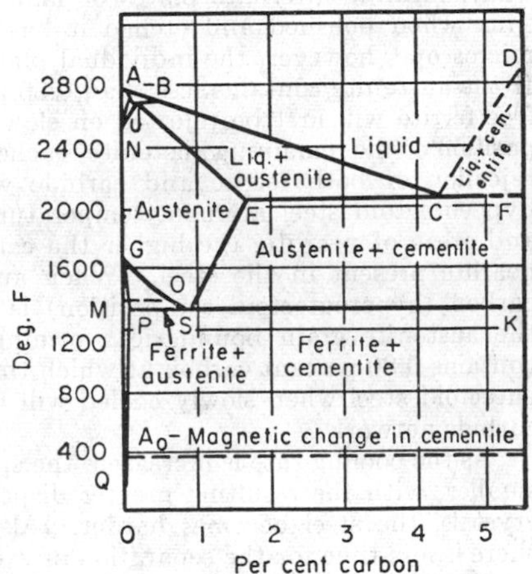

FIG. 2. Iron–iron carbide equilibrium diagram.

In Fig. 2 is the iron–iron carbide equilibrium diagram which shows the phases that are present in steels of various carbon contents over a range of temperatures under equilibrium conditions. Pure iron when heated to 1670 F changes its internal crystalline structure from a body-centered cubic arrangement of atoms, **alpha iron,** to a face-centered cubic structure, **gamma iron.** At 2535 F, it changes back to the body-centered cubic structure, **delta iron,** and at 2802 F the iron melts. When carbon is added to iron, it is found that it has only slight solid solubility in alpha iron (less than 0.001 percent at room temperature). On the other hand, gamma iron will hold up to 2.0 percent carbon in solution at 2066 F. The alpha iron containing carbon or any other element in solid solution is called **ferrite,** and the gamma iron containing elements in solid solution is called **austenite.** Usually when not in solution in the iron, the carbon forms a compound Fe_3C (iron carbide) which is extremely hard and brittle and is known as **cementite.**

The temperatures at which the phase changes occur are called **critical points** (or temperatures) and, in the diagram, represent equilibrium conditions. In practice there is a lag in the attainment of equilibrium, and the critical points are found at lower temperatures on cooling and at higher temperatures on heating than those given, the difference increasing with the rate of cooling or heating.

The various critical points have been designated by the letter A; when obtained on cooling, they are referred to as Ar, on the heating as Ac. The various critical points are distinguished from each other by numbers after the letters, being numbered in the order in which they occur as the temperature increases. Ac_0 represents the magnetic change in cementite on heating; Ac_1, the beginning of transformation of ferrite to austenite on heating (line PSK); Ac_2, the magnetic change in ferrite on heating (line MO); Ac_3, the end of transformation of ferrite to austenite on heating (line $GOSK$); and Ac_4, the change from austenite to delta iron on heating (line NJ). On cooling, the critical points would be referred to as Ar_4, Ar_3, Ar_2, Ar_1, and Ar_0, respectively. It must be remembered that the diagram represents the pure iron–iron carbide system. The varying amounts of impurities in commercial steels affect to a considerable extent the position of the curves and especially the lateral position of point S.

Carbon steel in equilibrium at room temperature will have present both ferrite and cementite. The physical properties of the ferrite are approximately those of pure iron and are characteristic of the metal. The presence of cementite does not in itself cause steel to be hard, but rather it is the shape and distribution of the carbides in the iron that determines the hardness of the steel. The fact that the carbides can be dissolved in austenite is the basis of the heat-treatment of steel since the steel can be heated above the critical temperature (above line $GOSE$ in the diagram) to dissolve all the carbides, and then suitable cooling through the cooling range will produce the desired size and distribution of carbides in the ferrite.

If austenite containing 0.80 percent carbon (**eutectoid** composition) is slowly cooled through the critical temperature, ferrite and cementite are rejected simultaneously, forming alternate plates or lamellae. This microstructure is called **pearlite** since when polished and etched it has a pearly luster. When examined under a microscope, however, the individual plates of cementite can easily be distinguished. If the austenite contains less than 0.80 percent carbon (**hypoeutectoid** composition), free ferrite will first be rejected on slow cooling through the critical until the composition of the remaining austenite reaches 0.80 percent carbon when the simultaneous rejection of both ferrite and carbide will again occur, producing pearlite. So a hypoeutectoid steel at room temperature will be composed of areas of free ferrite and areas of pearlite, the higher the carbon percentage, the greater the amount of pearlite present in the steel. When austenite containing more than 0.80 percent carbon (**hypereutectoid** composition) is slowly cooled, cementite is thrown out at the austenite grain boundaries, forming a cementite network until the austenite contains 0.80 percent carbon at which time pearlite is again formed. Thus, a hypereutectoid steel when slowly cooled will have areas of pearlite surrounded by a thin carbide network.

As the cooling rate is increased, the spacing between the pearlite lamellae becomes smaller; with the resulting greater dispersion of carbide preventing slip in the iron crystals, the steel becomes harder. Also, with an increase in the rate of cooling, there is less time for the separation of excess ferrite or cementite and the equilibrium amount of these constituents will not be precipitated before the austenite transforms to pearlite. Thus with a fast rate of cooling, pearlite may contain more or less carbon than given by the eutectoid composition. When the cooling rate becomes very rapid (as obtained by quenching), the carbon does not have sufficient time to separate out in the form of carbide, and the austenite transforms to a highly stressed structure supersaturated with carbon called **martensite.** This structure is exceedingly hard but brittle and requires **tempering** to increase the ductility. Tempering consists of heating martensite to some temperature below the critical causing the carbide to precipitate in the form of small spheroids. The higher the tempering temperature, the larger the carbide particle size, the greater the ductility of the steel, and the lower the hardness.

In a carbon steel, it is possible to have a structure consisting either of parallel plates of carbide in a ferrite matrix, the distance between the plates depending upon the rate of cooling, or of carbide spheroids in a ferrite matrix, the size of the spheroids depending upon the temperature to which the hardened steel was heated. (Some spheroidization occurs when pearlite is heated, but only at high temperatures close to the critical temperature range.)

Heat-treating Operations

The following definitions of terms have been adopted by the ASTM, SAE, and ASM in substantially identical form.

Heat-treatment. An operation, or combination of operations, involving the heating and cooling of a metal or an alloy in the solid state, for the purpose of obtaining certain desirable conditions or properties.

Quenching. Rapid cooling by immersion in liquids or gases or by contact with metal.

Hardening. Heating and quenching certain iron-base alloys from a temperature either within or above the critical range for the purpose of producing a hardness superior to that obtained when the alloy is not quenched. Usually restricted to the formation of martensite.

Annealing is a heating and cooling operation implying usually a relatively slow cooling. The purpose of such a heat-treatment may be (1) to remove stresses; (2) to induce softness; (3) to alter ductility, toughness, electrical, magnetic, or other physical properties; (4) to refine the crystalline structure; (5) to remove gases; or (6) to produce a definite microstructure. The temperature of the operation and the rate of cooling depend upon the material being heat-treated and the purpose of the treatment. Certain specific heat-treatments coming under the comprehensive term annealing are as follows:

Full Annealing. Heating iron-base alloys above the critical temperature range, holding above that range for a proper period of time, followed by slow cooling to below that range. The annealing temperature is generally about 100 F above the upper limit of the critical temperature range, and the time of holding is usually not less than 1 hr for each inch of section of the heaviest objects being treated. The objects being treated are ordinarily allowed to cool slowly in the furnace. They may, however, be removed from the furnace and cooled in some medium that will prolong the time of cooling as compared with unrestricted cooling in the air.

Process Annealing. Heating iron-base alloys to a temperature below or close to the lower limit of the critical temperature range followed by cooling as desired. This heat-treatment is commonly applied in the sheet and wire industries, and the temperatures generally used are from 1000 to 1300 F.

Normalizing. Heating iron-base alloys to approximately 100 F above the critical temperature range followed by cooling to below that range in still air at ordinary temperature.

Patenting. Heating iron-base alloys above the critical temperature range followed by cooling below that range in air, in molten lead, or a molten mixture of nitrates or nitrites maintained at a temperature usually between 800 to 1050 F, depending on the carbon content of the steel and the properties required of the finished product. This treatment is applied in the wire industry to medium- or high-carbon steel as a treatment to precede further wire drawing.

Spheroidizing. Any process of heating and cooling steel that produces a rounded or globular form of carbide. The following spheroidizing methods are used: (1) Prolonged heating at a temperature just below the lower critical temperature, usually followed by relatively slow cooling. (2) In the case of small objects of high-carbon steels, the spheroidizing result is achieved more rapidly by prolonged heating to temperatures alternately within and slightly below the critical temperature range. (3) Tool steel is generally spheroidized by heating to a temperature of 1380 to 1480 F for carbon steels and higher for many alloy tool steels, holding at heat from 1 to 4 hr and cooling slowly in the furnace.

Tempering (also termed **Drawing**). Reheating hardened steel to some temperature below the lower critical temperature, followed by any desired rate of cooling.

Although the terms "tempering" and "drawing" are practically synonymous as used in commercial practice, the term "tempering" is preferred.

Figure 3 summarizes the rates of decomposition of a eutectoid carbon steel over a range of temperatures. Various cooling rates are shown diagrammatically, and it will be seen that the faster the rate of cooling, the lower the temperature of transformation, and the harder the product formed. At around 1000 F, the austenite transforms rapidly to fine pearlite; to form martensite it is necessary to cool very rapidly through this temperature range to avoid the formation of pearlite before the specimen reaches the temperature for the formation of martensite. The minimum rate of cooling that is required to form a fully martensite structure is called the **critical cooling rate.** No matter at what rate the steel is cooled, the only products of transformation of this steel will be pearlite or martensite. However, if the steel is given an interrupted quench in a molten bath at some temperature between 400 and 1000 F, an acicular structure, called **Bainite,** of considerable toughness, combining high strength with high ductility, is obtained, and this heat-treatment is known as austempering. A somewhat similar heat-treatment called martempering can be utilized to produce a fully martensitic structure of high hardness, but free of the cracking, distortion, and residual stresses often associated with such a structure. Instead of quenching to room temperature, the steel is quenched to just above the martensitic transformation temperature and held for a short time to permit equalization of the temperature gradient throughout the piece. Then the steel may be cooled relatively slowly through the martensitic transformation range without superimposing thermal stresses on those introduced during transformation. The limitation of austempering and martempering for carbon steels is that these two heat-treatments can be applied only to articles of small cross section, since the rate of cooling in salt baths is not sufficient to prevent the formation of pearlite in samples or more than ½-in. diameter.

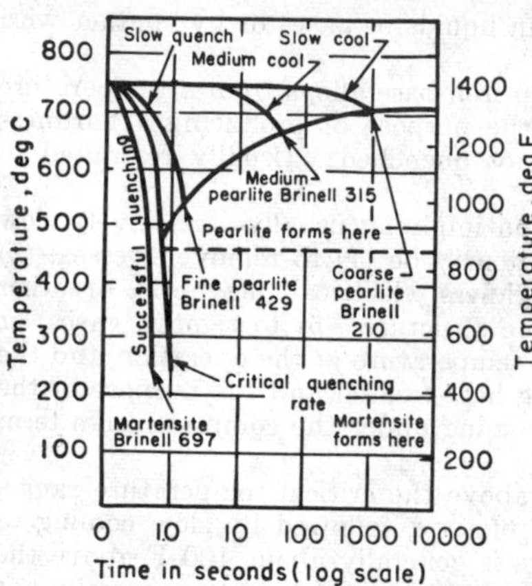

FIG. 3. Influence of cooling rate on the product of transformation in a eutectoid carbon steel.

The maximum hardness obtainable in a high-carbon steel with a fine pearlite structure is approximately 400 Brinell, although a martensitic structure would have a hardness of approximately 700 Brinell. Besides being able to obtain structures of greater hardness by forming martensite, a spheroidal structure will have considerably higher proof stress (*i.e.*, stress to cause a permanent deformation of 0.01 percent) and ductility than a lamellar structure of the same tensile strength and hardness. It is essential, therefore, to form martensite when optimum properties are desired in the steel. This can be done with a piece of steel having a small cross section by heating the steel above the critical and quenching in water; but when the cross section is large, the cooling rate at the center of the section will not be sufficiently rapid to prevent the formation of pearlite. The characteristic of steel that determines its capacity to harden throughout the section when quenched is called **hardenability.** This term should not be confused with the ability of a steel to attain a certain hardness. The intensity of hardening, *i.e.*, the maximum hardness of the martensite formed, is largely dependent upon the carbon content of the steel

Determination of Hardenability. The standard method of determining the capacity of a steel to harden is the **Jominy hardenability test.** This test consists of heating a steel bar 3 in. long and 1 in. diam to the desired austenitizing temperature and quenching one end in water, allowing the other end to air-cool. A continuous change in cooling rate is obtained along the bar varying from 600 deg per sec at 1⁄16 in. from the quenched end to 4 deg per sec on the other. Rockwell C hardness measurements are then made at 1/16 in. intervals along the bar, and a plot is made of hardness versus the distance from the quenched end. Since the cooling rate is known for any given position along the Jominy bar, the relation is obtained between the cooling rate and the hardness developed in the steel. In addition, the cooling rates for many simple geometric shapes such as bars and plates in different quenching mediums have been determined, so that it is possible to predict the hardness that will be developed in a given steel part if the Jominy hardenability curve is known; or if a minimum hardness is required in a given steel article, it is possible to specify the minimum Jominy hardenability needed to develop the required hardness in a given quenching medium. For the detailed procedure of the Jominy test and its application, see the 1955 SAE Handbook.

Three main factors affect the hardenability of steel: (1) austenite composition; (2) austenite grain size; and (3) amount, nature, and distribution of undissolved or insoluble particles in the austenite. The austenite composition will determine the rate of decomposition, in the range of 1000 F. The slower the rate of decomposition, the larger the section that can be hardened throughout, and therefore the greater the hardenability of the steel. Everything else being equal, the higher the carbon content, the greater the hardenability. The question of **austenitic grain size** is of considerable importance in any steel that is to be heat-treated since it affects the properties of the steel to a considerable extent. When a steel is heated to just above the critical temperature, small polyhedral grains of austenite are formed. With increase in temperature, there is an increase in the size of grains, until at temperatures close to the melting point the grains are very large. The relation between the grain size developed and the heating temperature will vary considerably among steels on account of variations in the deoxidation practice. By suitable deoxidation, steels can be made to be coarse grained at comparatively low temperatures, and others are fine-grained over a considerable range of temperatures. Since the transformation of austenite usually starts at grain boundaries, a fine-grained steel will transform more rapidly than a coarse-grained steel because the latter has much less surface area bounding the grains than a steel with a fine grain size. Everything else being equal, coarse-grained austenite will have a higher hardenability than fine-grained. Small particles in the austenite will act as nuclei for the beginning of transformation in a manner similar to grain boundaries, and therefore the presence of a large number of small particles (sometimes submicroscopic in size) will result in low hardenability.

Determination of Austenitic Grain Size. The subject of austenite grain size is of considerable interest because of the fact that the grain size developed during heat-treatment has a large effect on the physical properties of the steel. In steels of similar chemical analysis, the steel developing the finer austenitic grain size will have a lower hardenability, but will, in general, have greater toughness, show less tendency to crack or warp on quenching, be less susceptible to grinding cracks, have lower internal stresses, and retain less austenite than coarse grained steel. It is for these reasons that most alloy steels are fine-grain steels. There are several methods of determining the grain-size characteristics of a steel, the one most commonly used in steel specifications being the **McQuaid-Ehn test.** In this test, a representative sample is carburized for 8 hr at 1700 F and cooled slowly. The high-carbon case on slow cooling will reject cementite at the austenite grain boundaries, and, by polishing and etching, the grains will be clearly seen under a microscope. There are several ways to report the grain size observed under the microscope, the one used most extensively being the ASTM index numbers. The numbers are based on the formula: number of grains per square inch at $100x = 2^{N-1}$, in which N is the grain-size index. The usual range in steels will be from 1 to 128 grains per sq in. at $100x$, and the corresponding ASTM numbers will be 1 to 8. Steels having an ASTM grain size of 1 to 4 are usually considered coarse-grained, and those from 5 to 8 are fine-grained steels. It should be noted that the McQuaid-Ehn test will give only the grain size developed in the steels when heated to one temperature for a given length of time. To determine fully the grain-size characteristics of a steel, tests should be made over a range of temperatures, but the McQuaid-Ehn test has proved of great help to both producers and consumers of steel since the test is inexpensive and reproducible. For further information on grain size, reference should be made to the ASM Metals Handbook.

EFFECT OF ALLOYING ELEMENTS ON THE PROPERTIES OF STEEL

When relatively large amounts of alloying elements are added to steel, the characteristic behavior of carbon steels is obliterated. Most **alloy steel** is medium- or high-carbon steel to which various elements have been added to modify its properties to an appreciable extent, but it still owes its distinctive characteristics to the carbon that it contains. The percentage of alloy element required for a given purpose ranges from a few hundredths of 1 percent to possibly as high as 5 percent.

When ready for service, these steels will usually contain only two constituents, ferrite and carbide. The only way that an alloying element can affect the properties of the steel is to change the dispersion of carbide in the ferrite, change the properties

Table 5. Trends of Influence of the Alloying Elements

Element	As dissolved in ferrite, strength	As dissolved in austenite, hardenability	As undissolved carbide in austenite, fine grain, toughness	As dispersed carbide in tempering, high temp strength and toughness	As fine non-metallic dispersion, fine grain, toughness
Al	Moderate	Mild	None	None	Very strong
Cr	Mild	Strong	Strong	Moderate	Slight
Co	Strong	Negative	None	None	None
Cb	Little	Strong	Strong	Strong	None
Cu	Strong	Moderate	None	None	None
Mn	Strong	Moderate	Mild	Mild	Slight
Mo	Moderate	Strong	Strong	Strong	None
Ni	Mild	Mild	None	None	None
P	Strong	Mild	None	None	None
Si	Moderate	Moderate	None	None	Moderate
Ta	Moderate ?	Strong ?	Strong	Strong	None
Ti	Strong	Strong	Very strong	Little ?	Moderate
W	Moderate	Strong	Strong	Strong	None
V	Mild	Very strong	Very strong	Very strong	Moderate ?

of the ferrite, or change the properties of the carbide. The effect on the distribution of carbide is the most important factor, since in sections amenable to close control of structure, carbon steel is only moderately inferior to alloy steel. However, in large sections where carbon steels will fail to harden throughout the section even on a water quench, the hardenability of the steel can be increased by the addition of any alloying element (except possibly cobalt). The increase in hardenability permits the hardening of a larger section of alloy steel than of plain carbon steel. The quenching operation does not have to be so drastic. Consequently, there is a smaller difference in temperature between the surface and center during quenching, and cracking and warping resulting from sharp temperature gradients in a steel during hardening can be avoided. The elements most effective in increasing the hardenability of steel are manganese, silicon, and chromium.

Elements such as molybdenum, tungsten, and vanadium are effective in increasing the hardenability when dissolved in the austenite, but are usually present in the austenite in the form of carbides. The main advantage of these carbide-forming elements is that they prevent the agglomeration of carbides in tempered martensite. Tempering relieves the internal stresses in the hardened steel and causes spheroidization of the carbide particles with resultant loss in hardness and strength. The presence of these stable carbide-forming elements enables higher tempering temperatures to be used without sacrificing strength. This permits these alloy steels to have a greater ductility for a given strength, or, conversely, greater strength for a given ductility, than plain carbon steels.

The third factor which contributes to the strength of alloy steel is the presence of the alloying element in the ferrite. Any element in solid solution in a metal will increase the strength of the metal, so that these elements will materially contribute to the strength of hardened and tempered steels. The elements most effective in strengthening the ferrite are phosphorus, silicon, manganese, nickel, molybdenum, tungsten, and chromium.

A final important effect of alloying elements is their influence on the austenitic grain size. Martensite formed from a fine-grained austenite has considerably greater resistance to shock than when formed from a coarse-grained austenite. The oxides formed by the deoxidation of the steel by different elements apparently prevent grain growth above the critical temperature over a considerable temperature range. Aluminum is the most effective element to form grain-growth inhibitors; most killed steels have some aluminum added during deoxidation. The presence of finely scattered carbides in the austenite appears to have a similar effect on the austenite grain size, so the elements forming stable carbides will also contribute to the formation of a fine-grained austenite.

In Table 5, a summary of the effects of various alloying elements is given. It must be remembered that this table indicates only the trends of the various elements, and the fact that one element has an important influence on one factor does not prevent it from having an equally strong influence on another one.

PRINCIPLES OF HEAT-TREATMENT OF IRON AND STEEL

When heat-treating a steel for a given part, certain precautions have to be taken to develop optimum mechanical properties in the steel. Some of the major factors that have to be taken into consideration are outlined below.

Heating. The first step in the heat-treatment of steel is the heating of the material to above the critical to make it fully austenitic. The **heating rate** should be sufficiently slow to avoid injury to the material through excessive thermal and transformational stresses. In general, hardened steel should be heated more slowly and uniformly than is necessary for soft stress-free materials. Large sections should not be placed in a hot furnace, the allowable size depending upon the carbon and alloy content. For high-carbon steels, care should be taken in heating sections as small as 2 in. diam, and in medium-carbon steels precautions are required for size over 6 in. diam. The **maximum temperature** selected will be determined by the chemical composition of the steel and its grain-size characteristics. In hypoeutecitod steel (below 0.80 percent carbon), a temperature just above the upper critical range is used, and in hypereutectoid steels (above 0.80 percent carbon), a temperature between the lower and the upper critical is generally used so as to avoid heating to high temperatures with consequent grain growth. See Table 6 for heat-treating temperatures

Table 6. Temperatures for Heat-treatments for Carbon Steels
(ASM Metals Handbook, 1948)

AISI steel No.	Normalize, deg F	Anneal, deg F	Quench, deg F	AISI steel No.	Normalize, deg F	Anneal, deg F	Quench, deg F
C1010	1650–1750	1000–1350	1650–1700	C1050	1550–1650	1525–1600	1475–1550
C1020	1650–1750	1000–1350	1600–1675	C1060	1525–1625	1500–1575	1450–1550
C1030	1600–1675	1250–1375*	1575–1650	C1070	1525–1625	1500–1575	1450–1550
C1035	1575–1650	1575–1650*	1525–1600	C1080	1525–1625	1500–1575*	1450–1550
C1040	1575–1650	1550–1625*	1500–1575	C1095	1525–1625	1500–1575*	1450–1550
C1045	1550–1650	1525–1600	1475–1550				

* For spheroidizing, anneal at 1250 to 1375 F.

for plain carbon steels. The **time** at maximum temperature should be such that a uniform temperature is obtained throughout the cross section of the steel. Care should be taken to avoid undue length of time at temperature since this will result in undesirable grain growth, scaling, or decarburization of the surface. A practical figure often given for the total time in the hot furnace is ½ hr per in. of cross-sectional thickness. When the steel has attained a uniform temperature, the **cooling rate** must be such as to develop the desired structure: slow cooling rates (furnace or air cooling) to develop the softer pearlitic structures and high cooling rates (quenching) to form the hard martensitic structures. In selecting a **quenching medium** (see ASM Metals Handbook), it is important to select the quenching medium for a particular job on the basis of size, shape, and allowable distortion before choosing the steel composition. It is convenient to classify steels in two groups on the basis of depth of hardening: shallow hardening and deep hardening. **Shallow-hardening steels** may be defined as those which, in the form of 1 in. diam rounds, have, after brine quenching, a completely martensitic shell not deeper than ¼ in. The shallow-hardening steels are those of low or no alloy content, whereas the deep-hardening steels have a substantial content of those alloying elements that increase penetration of hardening, notably chromium, manganese, and nickel. The high cooling rates required to harden shallow-hardening steel produce severe distortion in all but simple, symmetrical shapes having a low ratio of length to diameter or thickness. Plain carbon steels cannot be used for complicated shapes where distortion must be avoided. In this case, water quenching must be abandoned and a less active quench used which materially reduces the temperature gradient during quenching. Certain oils are satisfactory but are incapable of hardening shallow-hardening steels of substantial size. A change in steel composition is required with a change from water to an oil quench. Quenching in oil does not entirely prevent distortion. When the degree of distortion produced by oil quenching is objectionable, recourse is taken to air hardening. The cooling rate in air is very much slower than in oil or water, so an exceptionally high alloy content is required. This means that a high price is paid for the advantage gained, both in terms of metal cost and loss in machinability, though it may be well justified when applied to expensive tools. In this case, danger of cracking is negligible.

Liquids for Quenching Shallow-hardening Steels. Shallow-hardening steels require extremely rapid surface cooling in the quench particularly in the temperature range around 1020 F. A submerged water spray will give the fastest and most reproducible quench practicable. Such a quench is limited in application to simple short objects which are not likely to warp. Because of difficulty in obtaining symmetrical flow of the water relative to the work, the spray quench is conducive to warping. The ideal practical quench is one that will give the required surface cooling without agitation of the bath. The addition of ordinary salt, sodium chloride, greatly improves the performance of water in this respect, the best concentration being around 10 percent. Most inorganic salts are effective in suppressing the formation of vapor at the surface of the steel and thus aid in cooling steel uniformly and eliminating the formation of soft spots. To minimize the formation of vapor, water-base quenching liquids must be kept cold, preferably under 70 F. The addition of some other soluble materials to water such as soap is extremely detrimental because of increased formation of vapor.

Liquids for Quenching Deep-hardening Steels. When oil quenching is required, use a steel of sufficient alloy content to produce a completely martensitic structure at the surface over the heaviest section of the work. To minimize the possibility of cracking, especially when hardening tool steels, keep the quenching oil warm, preferably between 100 and 150 F. If this expedient is insufficient to prevent cracking, the work may be removed just before the start of the hardening transformation and cooled in air. Whether or not transformation has started can be determined with a permanent magnet, the work being completely non-magnetic before transformation if completely hardened by the quench.

The cooling characteristics of quenching oils are difficult to evaluate and have not been satisfactorily correlated with the physical properties of the oils as determined by the usual tests. The standard tests are important with regard to secondary requirements of quenching oils. Low viscosity assures free draining of oil from the work and therefore low oil loss. A high flash and fire point assures a high boiling point and reduces the fire hazard which is increased by keeping the oil warm. A low carbon residue indicates stability of properties with continued use and little sludging. The steam-emulsion number should be low to assure low water content, water being objectionable because of its vapor film forming tendency and high cooling power. A low saponification number assures that the oil is of mineral base and not subject to organic deterioration of fatty oils which give rise to offensive odors. Viscosity index is a valuable property for maintenance of composition.

Effect of the Condition of Surface. The factors that affect the depth of hardening are the hardenability of the steel, the size of specimen, the quenching medium, and finally the condition of the surface of the steel before quenching. Steel that carries a heavy coating of scale will not cool so rapidly as a steel that is comparatively scale free, and soft spots may be produced; or, in extreme cases, complete lack of hardening may result. It is therefore essential to minimize scaling as much as possible. Decarburization can also produce undesirable results such as non-uniform hardening and thus lower the resistance of the material to alternating stresses.

Tempering of fully hardened steel is carried out for relief of quenching stresses and for the recovery of a limited degree of toughness and ductility. The operation will give almost any desired combination of properties by proper selection of the time-temperature conditions. Table 7 gives the Brinell hardness obtained in several

Table 7. Brinell Hardness of Carbon and Alloy Steels

Composition of steel	Brinell hardness when hardened and tempered at						
	As quenched	200 F	400 F	600 F	800 F	1000 F	1200 F
0.35 carbon	550	534	495	415	352	269	217
0.80 carbon	697	712	653	555	461	363	269
1.2 carbon	728	755	682	601	477	375	285
AISI 2340	668	614	534	461	375	307	237
AISI 1340	627	614	539	469	401	311	241
AISI 5140	601	589	545	477	408	331	262
AISI 4140	614	614	545	485	429	363	302
AISI 6145	601	601	555	485	415	363	302
0.70 C; 18 W; 4 Cr; 1 V	720	720	682	663	668	710	653

carbon and alloy steels when tempered for 1 hr at various temperatures. It should be emphasized that steel should be tempered immediately after hardening to prevent cracking caused by internal stresses. When pyrometers are not available, the tempering temperatures may be controlled by the examination of the roughly polished surface of the metal. A thin film of oxide forms upon the steel, the color of this film varying with the tempering temperature. Although variations will occur with different steels, the following temperatures are given with their corresponding **colors:** 400 F, faint straw; 440 F, straw; 475, deep straw; 520, bronze; 540, purple; 590, full blue; 640, light blue.

The Relation of Design to Heat-treatment

Care must be taken in the design of a machine part to prevent cracking or distortion during heat-treatment. With proper design the entire piece may be heated and cooled at approximately the same rate during the heat-treating operation. A light section should never be joined to a heavy section. Sharp reentrant angles should be avoided. Sharp corners and inadequate fillets produce serious stress concentration, causing the actual service stresses to build up to a point where they amount to two to five times the normal working stress calculated by the engineer in the original layout. The use of generous fillets is especially desirable with all high-strength alloy steels.

It is well for the designer to remember that the modulus of elasticity of all commercial steels, either carbon or alloy, is the same so far as practical designing is concerned. The deflection under load of a given part is, therefore, entirely a function of the section of the part and is not affected by the composition or heat-treatment of the steel. Consequently if a part deflects excessively, a change in design is necessary; either a heavier section must be used or the points of support must be increased.

CASEHARDENING

The production of articles having a soft ductile interior and a very hard surface can be accomplished by carburizing a low-carbon steel at an elevated temperature and then quenching. The process of carburizing followed by hardening is known as casehardening.

Carburizing methods can be divided into three groups: pack carburizing where a solid carburizing agent is used, gas carburizing, and liquid carburizing. In **pack carburizing,** the usual compound contains 20 percent metallic carbonates (mostly barium carbonate) bound to a hardwood charcoal by the use of oil, tar, or molasses. Sometimes up to 20 percent coke is added in order to increase the rate of heat transfer. Before using again, used compound should have some new compound added to make up for loss of carbonates, powdering of the compound, and burning of the charcoal and coke. One part new compound is often added to 3 parts used compound, but with care in handling this can be cut down to 1 part new to 5 parts old.

Carburizing boxes are usually made from a high-nickel-chromium heat-resisting alloy. Cast-steel or welded-steel plate boxes may be substituted when the boxes are used infrequently or when the work being carburized is large and nonsymmetrical. Work should be packed with its longest dimension vertical, and the minimum amount of compound should be used so as to decrease the heating time. Normal **carburizing temperatures** are around 1700 F, but for nickel steels a temperature of 1650 F is used and for shallow-case depth, temperatures as low as 1550 F. It is difficult to prevent variations of 0.010 in. in case depth, and therefore, it is standard practice to specify case depths of at least 0.025 in. when pack carburizing. By using a minimum of carburizing compound, the over-all carburizing time for a case of 0.040 to 0.050 in. will be about 9 hr. The pack method of carburizing is adaptable to both batch and continuous furnace operation; warping is held to a minimum. The main disadvantages are the time consumed in heating the charge and the high labor cost of packing and unpacking.

Gas carburizing is being developed and may eventually replace other methods. Low labor costs and automatic quenching reduce the operating costs to a low figure, but the high initial investment is justified only by large units operating at high output. The carburizing gases used are carbon monoxide, methane, ethane, and propane. The hydrocarbons will break down, if undiluted, liberating an excessive amount of carbon in the form of soot on all exposed surfaces. By diluting with gases such as nitrogen and hydrogen, the amount of free carbon deposit will be decreased. Cases of 0.040 to 0.050 in. can be obtained in 4 hr at 1700 F. By suitable adjustment of time, temperature, and gas composition, the surface carbon content and the carbon gradient can be varied to meet almost any requirement.

Liquid carburizing is done in activated baths of calcium cyanamid, sodium or potassium cyanide, and controlling chemicals which govern the decomposition of the cyanides. The baths are operated at between 1500 and 1650 F, and cases of 0.020 in. are obtained in 90 min. For case depths of more than about 0.030 in. it is more economical to use either pack or gas carburizing. The process is extremely flexible, easily controlled, and particularly well adapted to small units. With continuous operation and automatic quenching, labor costs are low.

The type of **steel for carburizing** will depend upon section and distortion limits of the finished part and the stresses to which it will be subjected. Plain carbon steels of between 0.15 and 0.25 percent carbon are used extensively and after heat-treatment will develop core strengths as high as 100,000 psi. To develop higher core strengths, it is necessary to have alloying elements such as nickel, chromium, manganese, or molybdenum to give sufficient hardenability. In regard to the correct **heat-treatment,** it must be remembered that a carburized steel is a duplex material having a high-carbon case and a low-carbon core with a more or less gradual transition from one to the other. Two critical temperatures are thus involved in the hardening of a carburized part.

Annealing and Hardening of Carburized Parts. To minimize distortion, a part should be annealed at a temperature 50 F above the carburizing temperature and the rate of cooling from the annealing temperature should be regulated to provide the required structure for best machinability. For **hardening,** there are three treatments in general use. First, a direct quench from the carburizing temperature into a suitable quenching medium. This method was not used until recently except with parts of regular shape because of the danger of cracking and distortion. With the advent of steels that maintain a fine grain size at carburizing temperatures, distortion is found to be less by direct quenching than by any other method. A second treatment is to cool slowly from the carburizing temperature, reheat to above the critical of the case, and quench. This facilitates handling of large quantities of carburized parts delivered discontinuously from a batch-type furnace and minimizes the retention of austenite in the high-carbon case. The old "double-quench" method in which the part was slowly cooled from the carburizing temperature, reheated and quenched from above the core critical temperature, then reheated and quenched from above the critical of the case is no longer favored.

Cyaniding. Where it is necessary to have only a superficial hard wear-resisting surface, a rapid method of casehardening is to use a molten cyanide bath. The bath usually consists of sodium cyanide with sodium chloride and sodium carbonate to retard the decomposition of the cyanide. The cyaniding should be carried out at a temperature just above the critical of the core, and the steel should be quenched directly from the cyanide bath. A uniform case depth of around 0.010 in. is obtained in 1 hr in both carbon and low-alloy steels, and besides carbon the case will contain very hard iron nitrides which increase the wear resistance of the surface of the steel part. Cyanide baths are frequently used simply as a heating medium in connection with the hardening of steels to prevent surface decarburization and produce work with a clean surface.

Nitriding. The introduction of nitrogen into the outer surface of steel parts in order to give an extremely hard, wear-resisting case is called nitriding. The treatment consists in heating steel to a temperature of 950 to 1000 F inside a chamber through which a controlled stream of ammonia gas is passed. The treatment usually lasts 50 to 90 hr depending upon the composition of the steel and the depth to which it is desired to effect nitrification. The nitriding temperature is below the thermal critical range and even below the usual tempering temperature so that the mechanical properties of the previously heat-treated core metal are not affected by nitriding. The big advantage of nitriding is that hardening is accomplished without a quenching operation, so that complicated shapes and articles of uneven cross section can be treated with safety. The steel used is usually heat-treated before machining, rough-machined, given a heat-treatment at the nitriding temperature without ammonia in order to produce whatever slight distortion is likely to occur, then the part is finish machined and nitrided. Besides wear resistance, nitriding aids in the retention of hardness at elevated temperatures and to some extent increases the resistance to corrosion. The disadvantages of nitriding include high cost, time of operation, and need for expert attention.

Stock for Nitriding. A series of steel alloys containing aluminum, known as **Nitralloy,** give the best results in the nitriding process. The compositions of the most commonly used nitriding steels are given in Table 8 (ASM Metals Handbook, 1948).

Table 8. Compositions of Nitriding Steels (Nitralloy), Percent

Alloying metal	C	Mn	Si	Al	Cr	Mo
Nitralloy 125 (Type H)	0.20–0.30	0.40–0.70	0.20–0.40	0.85–1.20	0.90–1.40	0.15–0.25
Nitralloy 135 (Type G)	0.30–0.40	0.40–0.70	0.20–0.40	0.85–1.20	0.90–1.40	0.15–0.25
Nitralloy 135 Modified (aircraft specification)	0.38–0.45	0.40–0.70	0.20–0.40	0.85–1.20	1.40–1.80	0.30–0.45
Nitralloy N*	0.20–0.27	0.40–0.70	0.20–0.40	0.85–1.20	1.00–1.30	0.20–0.30
Nitralloy 230 (Alamo)	0.25–0.35	0.40–0.70	0.20–0.40	0.85–1.20	....	0.60–1.00
Nitralloy EZ (Type G† with Se)	0.30–0.40	0.50–1.10	0.20–0.40	0.85–1.20	1.00–1.50	0.15–0.25

* Ni, 3.5. † Se, 0.15–025.

Flame hardening is the local heating of steel above the critical temperature so that on subsequent quenching a hardened layer will be produced. The depth of the flame-hardened layer will vary from 1/16 to about 1/4 in. depending upon the service requirements. For local hardening or for hardening the surface of large steel parts, this method has been very useful, especially since distortion of the part is kept to a minimum. The chemical analysis of the steel has to be such as to respond readily to heat-treatment. For plain carbon steels, the carbon content should be between 0.35 to 0.70 percent, although steels with higher carbon content may be flame hardened if care is taken to prevent surface cracking. To obtain satisfactory results by flame hardening, the character of the flame, its distance from the surface of the work, its speed of travel, and the timing of the quench must all be under perfect control. After quenching, tempering is essential to relieve the stresses, a temperature of 400 F usually being sufficient. Flame hardening may be adapted to castings, forgings, or rolled sections irrespective of size. Typical applications are for the hardening of gear teeth, cams, wheel treads, rail ends, and many machine parts.

Local hardening can also be accomplished by local heating with electricity. Resistance heating is useful in hardening local sections of some forgings and castings, but in general its principal application is for heating parts having a uniform cross section. Induction heating is well adapted for the surface hardening of cylindrical parts. Crankshaft bearings are hardened by the patented **Tocco** process by applying a high-frequency current to the bearing section for a few seconds. When the steel is heated to the desired depth, water is sprayed on the heated surface through holes in the inductor blocks surrounding the bearing. The extent of the heated zone can be so closely controlled that the fillets will remain soft while the bearing surface is hardened, thereby reducing the possibility of fatigue failure without sacrificing wear resistance at the bearing surface.

A hard working surface also can be obtained **on a ductile backing steel** by use of composite steels or surfacing by welding. **Composite steels** consist of two or more steels of different composition and are used for hacksaw blades, shear blades, knives of all types, lathe tools, drills, dies, vault steels, jail bars, and stoker bars. The usual method of making composite steel is to cast molten steel around a steel insert in a mold. For best results the insert is pickled to remove all oxide and may even be plated with a protective coating of iron. **Surfacing by welding** (see Sec. 13) permits the use of hard facing alloys on steel parts subject to abrasion. In addition to increasing the life of equipment and decreasing costs, hard facing can be used for salvaging or reclaiming worn parts. No single type of hard-facing material is satisfactory for all applications. Various facing alloys of widely different composition are used for different requirements of hardness and shock resistance. These alloys may be divided into four groups: (1) alloy steels containing less than 20 percent of alloying elements such as chromium, tungsten, and manganese which are comparatively economical and possess greatest shock resistance; (2) ferrous alloys containing more than 20 percent alloying elements and are therefore harder and give longer service; (3) non-ferrous alloys of cobalt, chromium, and tungsten which are resistant to wear and corrosion and maintain a high hardness at elevated temperatures; and (4) tungsten, boron, or tantalum carbides supported in a matrix of cobalt or nickel. These carbides are the hardest facing alloys and give the maximum resistance to abrasion.

Clad Steels. A clad steel plate is a composite plate made of mild steel with a cladding of corrosion- or heat-resistant metal on one or both sides.

The cladding may consist of various grades of stainless steels, nickel, Monel, Inconel, cupronickel, or silver. There are many ways of producing clad steel, but the usual method is to make a "sandwich" of two mild steel plates and two cladding plates separated by an inert material in the center. The sandwich is welded around the edges to prevent oxidation on heating and is rolled at about 2200 F. During rolling, welding occurs and the plates are reduced to the desired thickness. The edges are sheared and the sandwich separates into two plates, each clad on one face. The thickness of the clad material may vary from 5 to 50 percent of the thickness of the clad plate but normally is held to 10 or 20 percent. The clad steels are available in the form of plate, sheet, and strip and may be obtained as wire.

The clad steels are used in place of solid corrosion- or heat-resistant materials and thus are found in a wide variety of industries. They are also used where corrosion is a minor problem but where freedom from contamination of the materials handled is essential. In addition to savings in material costs, the clad steels are frequently easier to fabricate than solid plates of the cladding material. Their high heat conductivity is another factor in their selection for many applications. For instance for cooking vessels, in the canning, varnish, and soap industries, the inside of such vessels must be stainless, but the higher heat conductivity of the mild-steel backing prevents hot spots and burning that occur with solid stainless vessels. Clad steels are used for processing equipment in the chemical, food, beverage, drug, paper, textile, oil, and associated industries.

Chromizing. Chromizing of low-carbon steel is effective in improving corrosion resistance by developing a surface containing up to 40 percent chromium. Some forming operations can be carried out on chromized material. Most chromizing is accomplished by packing the steel to be treated in a powdered mixture of chromium and alumina and then heating to above 2300 F for 3 or 4 hr in a reducing atmosphere. Another method is to expose the parts to be treated to gaseous chromium compounds at temperatures above 1550 F. Flat rolled sheets for corrosive applications such as auto mufflers can thus be chromized in open-coil annealing facilities.

COMMERCIAL STEELS

The variety of applications of steel for engineering purposes is due to the wide range of physical properties obtainable by changes in carbon content and heat-treatment. For the ASTM specifications, see Table 21. Applications of carbon steels are given in Table 9. Carbon steels can be subdivided roughly into three groups: (1) low-carbon steel, 0.05 to 0.25 percent carbon, for use where only moderate strength is required together with considerable plasticity; (2) machinery steels, 0.30 to 0.55 percent carbon, which can be heat-treated to develop high strength; and (3) tool steels, containing from 0.60 to 1.30 percent carbon (this range also includes rail and spring steels).

Table 9. Applications of Carbon Steels

Percent C	Uses
0.05–0.10	Sheet, strip, tubing, wire nails
0.10–0.20	Rivets, screws, parts to be case-hardened
0.20–0.35	Structural steel, plate, forgings such as camshafts
0.35–0.45	Machinery steel—shafts, axles, connecting rods, etc.
0.45–0.55	Large forgings—crankshafts, heavy-duty gears, etc.
0.60–0.70	Bolt-heading and drop-forging dies, rails, setscrews
0.70–0.80	Shear blades, cold chisels, hammers, pickaxes, band saws
0.80–0.90	Cutting and blanking punches and dies, rock drills, hand chisels
0.90–1.00	Springs, reamers, broaches, small punches, dies
1.00–1.10	Small springs and lathe, planer, shaper, and slotter tools
1.10–1.20	Twist drills, small taps, threading dies, cutlery, small lathe tools
1.20–1.30	Files, ball races, mandrels, drawing dies, razors

Low-carbon Steels. Of the many low-carbon-steel products, sheet and strip steels are becoming increasingly important. The consumption of steel in the sheet and tinplate industry has accounted for approximately 50 percent of the total steel production in the United States. This large production has been made possible by the development of the continuous sheet and strip rolling mills. Applications in which large quantities of sheet are employed are tinplate for food containers; black, galvanized, and terne-coated sheets for building purposes; and high-quality sheets for automobiles, furniture, refrigerators, and countless other stamped, formed, and welded products. The difference between **sheet** and **strip** is based on width and is arbitrary. The difference between hot- and cold-rolled products is that in hot rolling the steel is heated before the final rolling and in cold rolling it is not. Cold working produces a better surface finish, improves the mechanical properties, and permits the rolling of thinner-gage material than hot rolling. Approximate mechanical properties of cold-rolled strip steel are given in Table 10.

Sheets for deep-drawing applications must be dead soft so as to have a maximum amount of plasticity. They must also have a relatively fine grain size, since a large grain size will cause a rough finish, an "orange-peel" effect, on the deep-drawn article. The sharp yield point characteristic of low-carbon steel must be eliminated to prevent sudden local elongations in the sheet during forming, which result in strain markings called **stretcher strains or Lüders, lines.** This can be done by cold working (Fig. 1), a reduction of only 1 percent in thickness usually being sufficient. This cold reduction is usually done by cold rolling, known as **temper rolling,** followed by alternate bending and reverse bending in a roller leveler. Temper rolling must always precede roller leveling because soft-annealed sheets will "break" (yield locally) in the roller leveler. An important phenomenon in these temper-rolled low-carbon sheets is the return of the sharp yield point after a period of time. This is known as **aging** in steel. The return of the yield point is accompanied by an increase in hardness and a loss in ductility. Greater reductions by temper rolling decrease the rate of the aging process, and an increase in temperature greatly increases its rate. It is therefore necessary to fabricate the sheets soon after temper rolling in order to avoid stretcher strains. Non-aging sheets can be supplied from aluminum killed steels, but the higher cost of killed steel usually restricts its use to severe drawing applications.

Table 10. Approximate Mechanical Properties for Various Tempers of Cold-rolled Strip Steel

(ASTM A109–62T)

Temper	Tensile strength, psi	Elongation in 2 in. for 0.050 in. thickness of strip, percent	Remarks
No. 1 (hard)	90,000 ± 10,000	3 ± 2	Intended for flat blanking only.
No. 2 (half hard)	65,000 ± 10,000	10 ± 6	Intended for bending up to 90 deg across the rolling direction. (No bending along the rolling direction.)
No. 3 (quarter hard)	55,000 ± 10,000	20 ± 7	For shallow drawing and stamping. Bends 180 deg across the rolling direction. Bends up to 90 deg along the rolling direction.
No. 4 (skin-rolled)	48,000 ± 6,000	32 ± 8	For fairly deep drawing where no surface strain or fluting is permissible. Bends 180 deg in any direction.
No. 5 (dead soft)	44,000 ± 6,000	39 ± 6	For deep drawing where stretcher strains or fluting are permissible. Also for drifting, erroneously called "extrusion." Bends 180 deg in any direction.

High-strength hot-rolled, cold-rolled, and galvanized sheets are now available with specified yield strengths. By the use of small alloy additions of columbium or vanadium, it is possible to meet the requirements of ASTM A375–62T for hot-rolled sheets—50,000 psi yield point, 70,000 psi tensile strength, and 22 percent elongation in 2 in. By further alloy additions, sheets are produced to a minimum of 65,000 psi yield point, 80,000 psi tensile strength, and 16 percent elongation in 2 in. The sheets are available in coil form and are used extensively for metallic buildings and for welding into tubes for construction of furniture, etc.

Structural Steels. Bridges and buildings have been constructed for years with structural carbon steel meeting the requirements of ASTM A7 and A373 (Table 11). In 1962, ASTM approved a new structural steel with a minimum yield point of 36,000 psi (ASTM A36), which was developed to fill the need for a higher-strength carbon steel. The controlled chemistry provides good weldablity, and the steel furnishes a significant improvement in the economics of steel construction. The structural carbon steels are available in plates, shapes, and bars in the hot-rolled condition. A uniform strength over a range of section thicknesses is provided by varying the amount of carbon, manganese, and silicon.

A special group of high-strength, low-alloy steels has been used for both the construction and the transportation industries. These steels, having yield points at the 50,000-psi level, are covered by ASTM A242 for both welded and riveted construction. This specification was adopted in 1941 to cover a large number of proprietary high-strength, low-alloy steels with better atmospheric corrosion resistance than structural carbon steel. While the minimum mechanical requirements of the steel were defined, the chemical specification only limits the carbon, manganese, and sulphur contents and does not specify alloying elements. In order to clarify the weldability of the steel, two new specifications have been added—ASTM A440, covering steels intended for use with riveted and bolted fabrication, and ASTM A441, covering a manganese-vanadium steel intended for use with welded fabrication. It should be noted in Table 11 that although the high-strength steels have the same chemical composition regardless of gage, the mechanical properties vary with section thickness.

The family of constructional steels is rounded out by heat-treated alloy steels having yield strengths at the 100,000-psi level. These steels are not as yet covered by ASTM but are covered by military specifications and, for pressure-vessel applications, by ASME Code Case 1204. They are available in plates, shapes, and bars and are readily welded. Since they are heat-treated to tempered martensitic structure, they retain excellent toughness at temperatures as low as −50 F. Major cost savings have been effected by using these steels in the construction of pressure vessels, in mining and earth-moving equipment, and for major members of large steel structures.

Table 11. Mechanical Properties of Constructional Steels

ASTM designation	Thickness range, in.	Yield point, min psi	Tensile strength, psi	Elongation in 8 in., min percent	Suitability for welding
Structural carbon steel:					
ASTM A7–61T	All thicknesses	33,000	60,000–75,000	21	No
ASTM A373–58T	To 4, incl	32,000	58,000–75,000	21	Yes
ASTM A36–62T	To 4, incl	36,000	58,000–80,000	20	Yes
High-strength, low-alloy steel:					
ASTM A242–63T }	To ¾, incl	50,000	70,000 min	18	Yes
ASTM A440–63T }	Over ¾ to 1½, incl	46,000	67,000 min	19	No
ASTM A441–63T }	Over 1½ to 4, incl	42,000	63,000 min	16	Yes
Heat-treated constructional alloy steel:					
None	To 2½, incl	100,000	115,000–135,000	18*	Yes
	Over 2½ to 6, incl	90,000	105,000–135,000	17*	Yes

* Elongation in 2 in., min.

For the economical construction of cryogenic vessels operating from room temperature down to the temperature of liquid nitrogen (−320 F), a 9 percent nickel-alloy steel has been developed. The mechanical properties as specified by ASTM A353 are 60,000 psi min yield strength and 90,000 psi min tensile strength for Grade A, and 65,000 psi and 95,000 psi, respectively, for Grade B. The minimum Charpy keyhole impact requirement is 15 ft-lb at −320 F. For lower temperatures, it is necessary to use austenitic stainless steel (see p. 6–39).

Machinery Steels. A large variety of carbon and alloy steels has been used in the automotive and allied industries. Complete specifications are published by AISI on all types of steel, and these specifications should be referred to for detailed information.

A numerical index is used to identify the compositions of AISI steels. A capital-letter prefix is used to indicate the steelmaking process. The letter B indicates an acid Bessemer carbon steel; C, a basic open-hearth carbon steel; and E, an electric-furnace alloy steel. A series of four numerals designates the composition; the first two indicate the alloy type, and the last two indicate, as far as feasible, the average carbon content in "points," or hundredths of 1 percent. Thus C-1020 is a carbon steel with a carbon range of 0.18 to 0.23 made in the basic open hearth, and E-2512 is a 5 percent nickel steel with 0.09 to 0.14 carbon made in the electric furnace. The compositions for the standard steels are listed in Tables 12*a* and *b*. A group of steels developed during World War II, known as **NE steels,** has been discontinued, although the better

Table 12*a*. Chemical Composition of AISI Carbon Steels

AISI grade designation	Chemical composition ranges and limits, percent			
	C	Mn	P	S
C-1005	0.06 max	0.35 max	0.04 max	0.05 max
C-1006	0.08 max	0.25–0.40	0.04 max	0.05 max
C-1008	0.10 max	0.25–0.50	0.04 max	0.05 max
C-1010	0.08–0.13	0.30–0.60	0.04 max	0.05 max
C-1011	0.08–0.13	0.60–0.90	0.04 max	0.05 max
C-1012	0.10–0.15	0.30–0.60	0.04 max	0.05 max
C-1013	0.11–0.16	0.50–0.80	0.04 max	0.05 max
C-1015	0.13–0.18	0.30–0.60	0.04 max	0.05 max
C-1016	0.13–0.18	0.60–0.90	0.04 max	0.05 max
C-1017	0.15–0.20	0.30–0.60	0.04 max	0.05 max
C-1018	0.15–0.20	0.60–0.90	0.04 max	0.05 max
C-1019	0.15–0.20	0.70–1.00	0.04 max	0.05 max
C-1020	0.18–0.23	0.30–0.60	0.04 max	0.05 max
C-1021	0.18–0.23	0.60–0.90	0.04 max	0.05 max
C-1022	0.18–0.23	0.70–1.00	0.04 max	0.05 max
C-1023	0.20–0.25	0.30–0.60	0.04 max	0.05 max
C-1024	0.19–0.25	1.35–1.65	0.04 max	0.05 max
C-1025	0.22–0.28	0.30–0.60	0.04 max	0.05 max
C-1026	0.22–0.28	0.60–0.90	0.04 max	0.05 max
C-1027	0.22–0.29	1.20–1.50	0.04 max	0.05 max
C-1029	0.25–0.31	0.60–0.90	0.04 max	0.05 max
C-1030	0.28–0.34	0.60–0.90	0.04 max	0.05 max
C-1031	0.28–0.34	0.30–0.60	0.04 max	0.05 max
C-1033	0.30–0.36	0.70–1.00	0.04 max	0.05 max
C-1034	0.32–0.38	0.50–0.80	0.04 max	0.05 max
C-1035	0.32–0.38	0.60–0.90	0.04 max	0.05 max
C-1036	0.30–0.37	1.20–1.50	0.04 max	0.05 max
C-1037	0.32–0.38	0.70–1.00	0.04 max	0.05 max
C-1038	0.35–0.42	0.60–0.90	0.04 max	0.05 max
C-1039	0.37–0.44	0.70–1.00	0.04 max	0.05 max
C-1040	0.37–0.44	0.60–0.90	0.04 max	0.05 max
C-1041	0.36–0.44	1.35–1.65	0.04 max	0.05 max
C-1042	0.40–0.47	0.60–0.90	0.04 max	0.05 max
C-1043	0.40–0.47	0.70–1.00	0.04 max	0.05 max
C-1044	0.43–0.50	0.30–0.60	0.04 max	0.05 max
C-1045	0.43–0.50	0.60–0.90	0.04 max	0.05 max
C-1046	0.43–0.50	0.70–1.00	0.04 max	0.05 max
C-1048	0.44–0.52	1.10–1.40	0.04 max	0.05 max
C-1049	0.46–0.53	0.60–0.90	0.04 max	0.05 max
C-1050	0.48–0.55	0.60–0.90	0.04 max	0.05 max
C-1051	0.45–0.56	0.85–1.15	0.04 max	0.05 max
C-1052	0.47–0.55	1.20–1.50	0.04 max	0.05 max
C-1053	0.48–0.55	0.70–1.00	0.04 max	0.05 max
C-1054	0.50–0.60	0.50–0.80	0.04 max	0.05 max
C-1055	0.50–0.60	0.60–0.90	0.04 max	0.05 max
C-1059	0.55–0.65	0.50–0.80	0.04 max	0.05 max
C-1060	0.55–0.65	0.60–0.90	0.04 max	0.05 max
C-1061	0.54–0.65	0.75–1.05	0.04 max	0.05 max
C-1064	0.60–0.70	0.50–0.80	0.04 max	0.05 max
C-1065	0.60–0.70	0.60–0.90	0.04 max	0.05 max
C-1066	0.60–0.71	0.85–1.15	0.04 max	0.05 max
C-1069	0.65–0.75	0.40–0.70	0.04 max	0.05 max
C-1070	0.65–0.75	0.60–0.90	0.04 max	0.05 max
C-1071	0.65–0.76	0.75–1.05	0.04 max	0.05 max
C-1074	0.70–0.80	0.50–0.80	0.04 max	0.05 max
C-1075	0.70–0.80	0.40–0.70	0.04 max	0.05 max
C-1078	0.72–0.85	0.30–0.60	0.04 max	0.05 max
C-1080	0.75–0.88	0.60–0.90	0.04 max	0.05 max
C-1084	0.80–0.93	0.60–0.90	0.04 max	0.05 max
C-1085	0.80–0.93	0.70–1.00	0.04 max	0.05 max
C-1086	0.80–0.93	0.30–0.50	0.04 max	0.05 max
C-1090	0.85–0.98	0.60–0.90	0.04 max	0.05 max
C-1095	0.90–1.03	0.30–0.50	0.04 max	0.05 max
B-1006	0.08 max	0.45 max	0.07–0.12	0.06 max
B-1010	0.13 max	0.30–0.60	0.07–0.12	0.06 max

Table 12a. Chemical Composition of AISI Carbon Steels—(*Continued*)

AISI grade designation	Chemical composition ranges and limits, percent			
	C	Mn	P	S
	FREE-CUTTING STEELS			
C-1108	0.08–0.13	0.50–0.80	0.04 max	0.08–0.13
C-1109	0.08–0.13	0.60–0.90	0.04 max	0.08–0.13
C-1115	0.13–0.18	0.60–0.90	0.04 max	0.08–0.13
C-1117	0.14–0.20	1.00–1.30	0.04 max	0.08–0.13
C-1118	0.14–0.20	1.30–1.60	0.04 max	0.08–0.13
C-1119	0.14–0.20	1.00–1.30	0.04 max	0.24–0.33
C-1120	0.18–0.23	0.70–1.00	0.04 max	0.08–0.13
C-1126	0.23–0.29	0.70–1.00	0.04 max	0.08–0.13
C-1132	0.27–0.34	1.35–1.65	0.04 max	0.08–0.13
C-1137	0.32–0.39	1.35–1.65	0.04 max	0.08–0.13
C-1138	0.34–0.40	0.70–1.00	0.04 max	0.08–0.13
C-1139	0.35–0.43	1.35–1.65	0.04 max	0.12–0.20
C-1140	0.37–0.44	0.70–1.00	0.04 max	0.08–0.13
C-1141	0.37–0.45	1.35–1.65	0.04 max	0.08–0.13
C-1144	0.40–0.48	1.35–1.65	0.04 max	0.24–0.33
C-1145	0.42–0.49	0.70–1.00	0.04 max	0.04–0.07
C-1146	0.42–0.49	0.70–1.00	0.04 max	0.08–0.13
C-1151	0.48–0.55	0.70–1.00	0.04 max	0.08–0.13
C-1211	0.13 max	0.60–0.90	0.07–0.12	0.08–0.15
C-1212	0.13 max	0.70–1.00	0.07–0.12	0.16–0.23
B-1111	0.13 max	0.60–0.90	0.07–0.12	0.08–0.15
B-1112	0.13 max	0.70–1.00	0.07–0.12	0.16–0.23

alloys have been included in the AISI steels. The NE steels that were retained are those with the first two digits 86, 87, or 98. A group of steels known as **H steels,** which are similar to the standard AISI steels, is being produced with a specified Jominy hardenability; these steels are identified by a suffix H added to the conventional series number. In general, these steels have a somewhat greater allowable variation in chemical composition but a smaller variation in hardenability than would be normal for a given grade of steel. This smaller variation in hardenability results in greater reproducibility of the mechanical properties of the steels on heat-treatment; therefore, H steels are becoming increasingly important in machinery steels.

Boron steels are designated by the letter B inserted between the second and third digits, *e.g.*, 50B40. The effectiveness of boron in increasing hardenability was a discovery of the late thirties, when it was noticed that heats treated with complex deoxidizers (containing boron) showed exceptionally good hardenability, high strength, and ductility after heat-treatment. It was found that as little as 0.0005 percent of boron increased the hardenability of steels with 0.15 to 0.60 carbon; whereas, boron contents of over 0.005 percent had an adverse effect on hot workability. Boron steels achieve special importance in times of alloy shortages, for they can replace such critical alloying elements as nickel, molybdenum, chromium, and manganese and, when properly heat-treated, possess physical properties comparable to the alloy grades they replace. Additional advantages for the use of boron in steels are a decrease in susceptibility to flaking, formation of less adherent scale, greater softness in the unhardened condition, and better machinability.

Specific applications of these steels cannot be given since the selection of a steel for a given part must depend upon an intimate knowledge of factors such as the availability and cost of the material, the detailed design of the part, and the severity of the service to be imposed. However the mechanical properties desired in the part to be heat-treated will determine to a large extent the carbon and alloy content of the steel. Table 13 gives a résumé of mechanical properties that can be expected on heat-treating AISI steels and Table 14 gives an indication of the effect of mass on the mechanical properties of heat-treated steels.

The low-carbon AISI steels are used for carburized parts, cold-headed bolts and

Table 12*b*. Chemical Compositions of AISI Alloy Steels

AISI No.	Chemical composition ranges and limits, percent							
	C	Mn	P, max	S, max	Si	Ni	Cr	Other
				MANGANESE STEELS				
1330	0.28–0.33	1.60–1.90	0.040	0.040	0.20–0.35			
1335	0.33–0.38	1.60–1.90	0.040	0.040	0.20–0.35			
1340	0.38–0.43	1.60–1.90	0.040	0.040	0.20–0.35			
1345	0.43–0.48	1.60–1.90	0.040	0.040	0.20–0.35			
				NICKEL-CHROMIUM STEELS				
3140	0.38–0.43	0.70–0.90	0.040	0.040	0.20–0.35	1.10–1.40	0.55–0.75	
E-3310	0.08–0.13	0.45–0.60	0.025	0.025	0.20–0.35	3.25–3.75	1.40–1.75	
				MOLYBDENUM STEELS				
								Mo
4012	0.09–0.14	0.75–1.00	0.040	0.040	0.20–0.35	....	....	0.15–0.25
4023	0.20–0.25	0.70–0.90	0.040	0.040	0.20–0.35	....	....	0.20–0.30
4024	0.20–0.25	0.70–0.90	0.040	0.035–0.050	0.20–0.35	....	....	0.20–0.30
4027	0.25–0.30	0.70–0.90	0.040	0.040	0.20–0.35	....	....	0.20–0.30
4028	0.25–0.30	0.70–0.90	0.040	0.035–0.050	0.20–0.35	....	....	0.20–0.30
4037	0.35–0.40	0.70–0.90	0.040	0.040	0.20–0.35	....	....	0.20–0.30
4042	0.40–0.45	0.70–0.90	0.040	0.040	0.20–0.35	....	....	0.20–0.30
4047	0.45–0.50	0.70–0.90	0.040	0.040	0.20–0.35	....	....	0.20–0.30
4063	0.60–0.67	0.75–1.00	0.040	0.040	0.20–0.35	....	....	0.20–0.30
				CHROMIUM-MOLYBDENUM STEELS				
4118	0.18–0.23	0.70–0.90	0.040	0.040	0.20–0.35	....	0.40–0.60	0.08–0.15
4130	0.28–0.33	0.40–0.60	0.040	0.040	0.20–0.35	....	0.80–1.10	0.15–0.25
4135	0.33–0.38	0.70–0.90	0.040	0.040	0.20–0.35	....	0.80–1.10	0.15–0.25
4137	0.35–0.40	0.70–0.90	0.040	0.040	0.20–0.35	....	0.80–1.10	0.15–0.25
4140	0.38–0.43	0.75–1.00	0.040	0.040	0.20–0.35	....	0.80–1.10	0.15–0.25
4142	0.40–0.45	0.75–1.00	0.040	0.040	0.20–0.35	....	0.80–1.10	0.15–0.25
4145	0.43–0.48	0.75–1.00	0.040	0.040	0.20–0.35	....	0.80–1.10	0.15–0.25
4147	0.45–0.50	0.75–1.00	0.040	0.040	0.20–0.35	....	0.80–1.10	0.15–0.25
4150	0.48–0.53	0.75–1.00	0.040	0.040	0.20–0.35	....	0.80–1.10	0.15–0.25
				NICKEL-CHROMIUM-MOLYBDENUM STEELS				
4320	0.17–0.22	0.45–0.65	0.040	0.040	0.20–0.35	1.65–2.00	0.40–0.60	0.20–0.30
4337	0.35–0.40	0.60–0.80	0.040	0.040	0.20–0.35	1.65–2.00	0.70–0.90	0.20–0.30
E-4337	0.35–0.40	0.65–0.85	0.025	0.025	0.20–0.35	1.65–2.00	0.70–0.90	0.20–0.30
4340	0.38–0.43	0.60–0.80	0.040	0.040	0.20–0.35	1.65–2.00	0.70–0.90	0.20–0.30
E-4340	0.38–0.43	0.65–0.85	0.025	0.025	0.20–0.35	1.65–2.00	0.70–0.90	0.20–0.30
				MOLYBDENUM STEELS				
4422	0.20–0.25	0.70–0.90	0.040	0.040	0.20–0.35	....	....	0.35–0.45
4427	0.24–0.29	0.70–0.90	0.040	0.040	0.20–0.35	....	....	0.35–0.45
4520	0.18–0.23	0.45–0.65	0.040	0.040	0.20–0.35	....	....	0.45–0.60
				NICKEL-MOLYBDENUM STEELS				
								Mo
4615	0.13–0.18	0.45–0.65	0.040	0.040	0.20–0.35	1.65–2.00	....	0.20–0.30
4617	0.15–0.20	0.45–0.65	0.040	0.040	0.20–0.35	1.65–2.00	....	0.20–0.30
4620	0.17–0.22	0.45–0.65	0.040	0.040	0.20–0.35	1.65–2.00	....	0.20–0.30
4621	0.18–0.23	0.70–0.90	0.040	0.040	0.20–0.35	1.65–2.00	....	0.20–0.30
				NICKEL-CHROMIUM-MOLYBDENUM STEELS				
4718	0.16–0.21	0.70–0.90	0.040	0.040	0.20–0.35	0.90–1.20	0.35–0.55	0.30–0.40
4720	0.17–0.22	0.50–0.70	0.040	0.040	0.20–0.35	0.90–1.20	0.35–0.55	0.15–0.25

Table 12b. Chemical Compositions of AISI Alloy Steels—(*Continued*)

AISI No.	Chemical composition ranges and limits, percent							
	C	Mn	P, max	S, max	Si	Ni	Cr	Other
	NICKEL-MOLYBDENUM STEELS							
4815	0.13–0.18	0.40–0.60	0.040	0.040	0.20–0.35	3.25–3.75	....	0.20–0.30
4817	0.15–0.20	0.40–0.60	0.040	0.040	0.20–0.35	3.25–3.75	....	0.20–0.30
4820	0.18–0.23	0.50–0.70	0.040	0.040	0.20–0.35	3.25–3.75	....	0.20–0.30
	CHROMIUM STEELS							
5015	0.12–0.17	0.30–0.50	0.040	0.040	0.20–0.35	....	0.30–0.50	
5046	0.43–0.50	0.75–1.00	0.040	0.040	0.20–0.35	....	0.20–0.35	
5115	0.13–0.18	0.70–0.90	0.040	0.040	0.20–0.35	....	0.70–0.90	
5120	0.17–0.22	0.70–0.90	0.040	0.040	0.20–0.35	....	0.70–0.90	
5130	0.28–0.33	0.70–0.90	0.040	0.040	0.20–0.35	....	0.80–1.10	
5132	0.30–0.35	0.60–0.80	0.040	0.040	0.20–0.35	....	0.75–1.00	
5135	0.33–0.38	0.60–0.80	0.040	0.040	0.20–0.35	....	0.80–1.05	
5140	0.38–0.43	0.70–0.90	0.040	0.040	0.20–0.35	....	0.70–0.90	
5145	0.43–0.48	0.70–0.90	0.040	0.040	0.20–0.35	....	0.70–0.90	
5147	0.45–0.52	0.70–0.95	0.040	0.040	0.20–0.35	....	0.85–1.15	
5150	0.48–0.53	0.70–0.90	0.040	0.040	0.20–0.35	....	0.70–0.90	
5155	0.50–0.60	0.70–0.90	0.040	0.040	0.20–0.35	....	0.70–0.90	
5160	0.55–0.65	0.75–1.00	0.040	0.040	0.20–0.35	....	0.70–0.90	
E-50100	0.95–1.10	0.25–0.45	0.025	0.025	0.20–0.35	....	0.40–0.60	
E-51100	0.95–1.10	0.25–0.45	0.025	0.025	0.20–0.35	....	0.90–1.15	
E-52100	0.95–1.10	0.25–0.45	0.025	0.025	0.20–0.35	....	1.30–1.60	
	CHROMIUM-VANADIUM STEELS							
								V
6118	0.16–0.21	0.50–0.70	0.040	0.040	0.20–0.35	....	0.50–0.70	0.10–0.15
6120	0.17–0.22	0.70–0.90	0.040	0.040	0.20–0.35	....	0.70–0.90	0.10 min
6150	0.48–0.53	0.70–0.90	0.040	0.040	0.20–0.35	....	0.80–1.10	0.15 min
	NICKEL-CHROMIUM-MOLYBDENUM STEELS							
								Mo
8115	0.13–0.18	0.70–0.90	0.040	0.040	0.20–0.35	0.20–0.40	0.30–0.50	0.08–0.15
8615	0.13–0.18	0.70–0.90	0.040	0.040	0.20–0.35	0.40–0.70	0.40–0.60	0.15–0.25
8617	0.15–0.20	0.70–0.90	0.040	0.040	0.20–0.35	0.40–0.70	0.40–0.60	0.15–0.25
8620	0.18–0.23	0.70–0.90	0.040	0.040	0.20–0.35	0.40–0.70	0.40–0.60	0.15–0.25
8622	0.20–0.25	0.70–0.90	0.040	0.040	0.20–0.35	0.40–0.70	0.40–0.60	0.15–0.25
8625	0.23–0.28	0.70–0.90	0.040	0.040	0.20–0.35	0.40–0.70	0.40–0.60	0.15–0.25
8627	0.25–0.30	0.70–0.90	0.040	0.040	0.20–0.35	0.40–0.70	0.40–0.60	0.15–0.25
8630	0.28–0.33	0.70–0.90	0.040	0.040	0.20–0.35	0.40–0.70	0.40–0.60	0.15–0.25
8637	0.35–0.40	0.75–1.00	0.040	0.040	0.20–0.35	0.40–0.70	0.40–0.60	0.15–0.25
8640	0.38–0.43	0.75–1.00	0.040	0.040	0.20–0.35	0.40–0.70	0.40–0.60	0.15–0.25
8642	0.40–0.45	0.75–1.00	0.040	0.040	0.20–0.35	0.40–0.70	0.40–0.60	0.15–0.25
8645	0.43–0.48	0.75–1.00	0.040	0.040	0.20–0.35	0.40–0.70	0.40–0.60	0.15–0.25
8650	0.48–0.53	0.75–1.00	0.040	0.040	0.20–0.35	0.40–0.70	0.40–0.60	0.15–0.25
8655	0.50–0.60	0.75–1.00	0.040	0.040	0.20–0.35	0.40–0.70	0.40–0.60	0.15–0.25
8660	0.55–0.65	0.75–1.00	0.040	0.040	0.20–0.35	0.40–0.70	0.40–0.60	0.15–0.25
8720	0.18–0.23	0.70–0.90	0.040	0.040	0.20–0.35	0.40–0.70	0.40–0.60	0.20–0.30
8735	0.33–0.38	0.75–1.00	0.040	0.040	0.20–0.35	0.40–0.70	0.40–0.60	0.20–0.30
8740	0.38–0.43	0.75–1.00	0.040	0.040	0.20–0.35	0.40–0.70	0.40–0.60	0.20–0.30
8742	0.40–0.45	0.75–1.00	0.040	0.040	0.20–0.35	0.40–0.70	0.40–0.60	0.20–0.30
8822	0.20–0.25	0.75–1.00	0.040	0.040	0.20–0.35	0.40–0.70	0.40–0.60	0.30–0.40
	SILICON-MANGANESE STEELS							
9255	0.50–0.60	0.70–0.95	0.040	0.040	1.80–2.20	....		
9260	0.55–0.65	0.70–1.00	0.040	0.040	1.80–2.20	....		
9262	0.55–0.65	0.75–1.00	0.040	0.040	1.80–2.20	....	0.25–0.40	

Table 12*b*. Chemical Compositions of AISI Alloy Steels—(*Continued*)

AISI No.	Chemical composition ranges and limits, percent							
	C	Mn	P, max	S, max	Si	Ni	Cr	Other
	NICKEL-CHROMIUM-MOLYBDENUM STEELS							
								Mo
E-9310	0.08–0.13	0.45–0.65	0.025	0.025	0.20–0.35	3.00–3.50	1.00–1.40	0.08–0.15
9840	0.38–0.43	0.70–0.90	0.040	0.040	0.20–0.35	0.85–1.15	0.70–0.90	0.20–0.30
9850	0.48–0.53	0.70–0.90	0.040	0.040	0.20–0.35	0.85–1.15	0.70–0.90	0.20–0.30

Table 13. Mechanical Properties of Certain AISI Steels with Various Heat-treatments

(Sections up to 1½ in. diam or thickness)

Draw temp, deg F	Tensile, strength, kpsi	Yield point, kpsi	Reduction of area, percent	Elong in 2 in., percent	Brinell hardness	Tensile strength, kpsi	Yield point, kpsi	Reduction of area, percent	Elong in 2 in., percent	Brinell hardness
	AISI C 1040 quenched in water at 1500 F					AISI 1340 normalized at 1585 F, quenched in oil at 1550 F				
600	125	104	46	11	260	227	206	43	11	448
800	119	91	53	13	250	181	166	51	13	372
1000	110	78	58	15	220	140	121	58	17.5	297
1100	108	71	60	17	216	125	103	62	20	270
1200	104	66	62	20	210	115	88	65	23	250
1300	98	60	64	22	205	110	78	68	25.5	234
	AISI 2340 normalized at 1600 F, quenched in oil at 1425 F					AISI 3140 normalized at 1600 F, quenched in oil at 1500 F				
600	222	205	43	11	437	228	209	42	11	448
800	180	165	50	14	372	187	168	51	13	372
1000	139	122	58	19	297	140	128	59	18	352
1100	121	108	62	22	270	125	112	63	21.5	332
1200	110	95	65	25	250	112	100	66	24	297
1300	99	85	67	27	240	105	90	68	27.5	283
	AISI 4042 normalized at 1600 F, quenched in oil at 1500 F					AISI 4140 normalized at 1600 F, quenched in oil at 1500 F				
600	231	210	41	12	448	225	208	42.5	10	426
800	175	158	50	14	372	180	163	49	13	372
1000	140	125	58	19	297	135	120	57	18	283
1100	125	110	62	23	260	120	105	61	20	250
1200	113	99	65	26	234	108	195	62	22.5	228
1300	105	92	68	30	210	100	88	63	25	216
	AISI 4340 normalized at 1600 F, quenched in oil at 1525 F					AISI 4640 normalized at 1600 F, quenched in oil at 1500 F				
600	250	230	40	9	484	225	208	43	11	448
800	211	200	44	10	426	182	168	50	13	372
1000	173	160	52	12.5	352	141	125	58	19	283
1100	158	140	56	15	313	125	109	62	22.5	260
1200	140	123	60	18	283	110	93	64	26	234
1300	123	108	63	22.5	250	100	81	66	27.5	222
	AISI 5140 normalized at 1575 F, quenched in oil at 1500 F					AISI 8640 normalized at 1600 F, quenched in oil at 1525 F				
600	232	211	43	11	448	240	220	42	10	472
800	190	162	49	12.5	372	202	188	45	12.5	415
1000	140	124	58	17.5	283	165	148	53	16	332
1100	123	108	62	21	250	145	130	57	18	297
1200	110	95	65	24	228	130	113	61	21	283
1300	100	88	68	29	210	116	100	63	22.5	250

rivets, and for similar applications where high quality is required. The AISI 1100 series are low-carbon **free-cutting** steels for high-speed screw-machine stock and other machining purposes. These steels have high sulphur present in the steel in the form of manganese sulphide inclusions causing the chips to break short on machining. Manganese and phosphorus harden and embrittle the steel which also contributes toward free machining. For a further improvement in machinability, **lead** is added to steel. The usual range is from 0.20 to 0.35 percent lead.

Table 14. Effect of Mass of Specimen on the Mechanical Properties of Some AISI Steels

Diam of section, in.	Tensile strength, kpsi	Yield point, kpsi	Reduction of area, percent	Elong in 2 in., percent	Brinell hardness	Tensile strength, kpsi	Yield point, kpsi	Reduction of area, percent	Elong in 2 in., percent	Brinell hardness
AISI C 1040 water quenched, tempered at 1000 F						AISI 3140 oil quenched, tempered at 1000 F				
1	110	78	58	15	230	140	121	54	15	297
2	98	65	49	20	194	130	108	50	17	260
3	93	59	48	23	185	123	99	48	19	250
4	90	57	47	24.5	180	118	94	46	20	240
5	89	54	46	25	180	115	91	43	19	230
AISI 4140, oil quenched, tempered at 1000 F						AISI 8640, oil quenched, tempered at 1000 F				
1	145	128	56	18	297	168	145	44	16	332
2	143	125	58	19	297	153	132	45	20	313
3	137	118	59	20	283	138	117	46	22	283
4	126	110	60	18	270	129	108	46	23	270
5	122	105	59	17	260	126	105	45	23	260

Cold-finished carbon-steel bars are used for bolts, nuts, typewriter and cash-register parts, motor and transmission power shafting, piston pins, bushings, oil-pump shafts and gears, etc. Average mechanical properties of cold-drawn steel are given in Table 15. Besides improved mechanical properties, cold-finished steel has better machining properties than hot-rolled products. The surface finish and dimensional accuracy are also greatly improved by cold finishing.

Table 15. Average Physical Properties of Cold-drawn Steel

(ASM Metals Handbook, 1948)

(Sizes ⅝ to 2 in. diam, test specimens 2 × 0.505 in.)

AISI steels	Tensile strength, kpsi	Yield strength, kpsi	Elongation in 2 in., percent	Reduction of area, percent	Brinell hardness	AISI steels	Tensile strength, kpsi	Yield strength, kpsi	Elongation in 2 in., percent	Reduction of area, percent	Brinell hardness
C-1010	67	55.0	25.0	57	137	C-1045	102	86.7	15.0	35	207
C-1015	71	60.3	22.0	55	149	B-1112	87	73.9	17.0	45	183
C-1020	75	63.7	20.0	52	156	C-1120	78	66.3	19.5	49	159
C-1025	80	68.0	18.5	50	163	C-1117	80	68.0	19.0	51	163
C-1030	87	73.9	17.5	48	179	C-1118	82.5	70.1	18.5	50	167
C-1035	92	78.2	17.0	45	187	C-1137	105	89.2	16.0	35	217
C-1040	97	82.4	16.0	40	197	C-1141	112	95.2	14.0	30	223

Forging steels, between 0.30 and 0.40 percent carbon, are used for axles, bolts, pins, connecting rods, and similar applications. These steels are readily forged and, after heat-treatment, develop considerably higher mechanical properties than low-carbon steels. For heavy sections where high strength is required, such as in crankshafts and heavy-duty gears, the carbon may be increased to 0.40 to 0.50 percent and sufficient alloy content used to obtain the necessary hardenability.

TOOL STEELS

The application of tool steels can generally be fitted into one of the following categories or types of operations: cutting, shearing, forming, drawing, extruding, rolling, and battering. Each of these operations requires in the tool steel a particular physical property or a combination of such metallurgical characteristics as hardness, strength, toughness, wear resistance, and resistance to heat softening, before optimum performance can be realized. These considerations are of prime importance in tool selection; but hardenability, permissible distortion, surface decarburization during heat treatment, and machinability of the tool steel are a few of the additional factors to be weighed in reaching a final decision. In actual practice, the final selection of a tool steel represents a compromise of the most desirable physical properties with the best over-all economic performance. Tool steels have been identified and classified by the SAE and the AISI into six major groups, based upon quenching methods, applications, special characteristics, and use in specific industries. These six classes are water-hardening, shock-resisting, cold-work, hot-work, high-speed, and special-purpose tool steels. A simplified classification of these six basic types and their subdivisions is given in Table 16.

Table 16. Simplified Tool-steel Classification

Major grouping	Symbol	Types
Water-hardening tool steels	W	
Shock-resisting tool steels	S	
Cold-work tool steels	O	Oil hardening
	A	Medium-alloy air hardening
	D	High-carbon, high-chromium
Hot-work tool steels	H	H1-H19* chromium base
		H20-H39 tungsten base
		H40-H59 molybdenum base
High-speed tool steels	T	Tungsten base
	M	Molybdenum base
Special-purpose tool steels	F	Carbon-tungsten
	L	Low-alloy
	P	Mold steels
		P1-P19 low carbon
		P20-P39 other types

* Each subdivision is further identified as to type by a suffix number which follows the letter symbol.

Water-hardening tool steels, containing 0.70 to 1.30 percent carbon, are widely used because of their low cost, good toughness, and excellent machinability. They are shallow-hardening steels, unsuitable for non-deforming applications because of high warpage, and possess poor resistance to softening at elevated temperatures. Water-hardening tool steels have the widest applications of all major groups and are used for files, twist drills, shear knives, chisels, hammers, and forging dies.

Shock-resisting tool steels, with chromium-tungsten, silicon-molybdenum, or silicon-manganese as the dominant alloys, combine good hardenability with outstanding toughness. A tendency to distort easily is their greatest disadvantage. However, oil quenching can minimize this characteristic.

Cold-work tool steels are divided into three groups: oil-hardening, medium-alloy air-hardening, and high-carbon, high-chromium. In general, this class possesses high wear resistance and hardenability, develops little distortion, but at best is only average in toughness and in resistance to heat softening. Machinability ranges from good in the oil-hardening grade to poor in the high-carbon, high-chromium steels.

Hot-work tool steels are either chromium- or tungsten-based alloys possessing fine non-deforming, hardenability, toughness, and resistance to heat softening characteristics, with fair machinability and wear resistance. Either air or oil hardening can be employed. Applications are blanking, forming extrusion and casting dies where temperatures may rise to 1000 F.

High-speed tool steels, the best-known tool steels, possess the best combination of all properties excepting toughness, which is not critical for high-speed cutting operations, and are either tungsten- or molybdenum-base types. Cobalt is added in some cases to improve the cutting qualities in roughing operations. They retain considerable hardness at a red heat. Very high heating temperatures are required for the heat-treatment of high-speed steel and, in general, the tungsten-cobalt high-speed steels require higher quenching temperatures than the molybdenum steels. High-speed steel should be tempered at about 1100 F to increase the toughness; owing to a secondary hardening effect, the hardness of the tempered steels may be higher than as quenched.

Special-purpose tool steels are comprised of the low-carbon, low-alloy, carbon-tungsten, mold, and other miscellaneous types.

SPRING STEEL

For small springs, steel is often supplied to spring manufacturers in a form that requires no heat-treatment except perhaps a low-temperature anneal to relieve forming strains. Types of previously treated steel wire for small helical springs are **music wire** which has been given a special heat-treatment called patenting and then cold-drawn to develop a high yield strength, **hard-drawn wire** which is of lower quality than music wire since it is usually made of lower grade material and is seldom patented, and **oil-tempered wire** which has been quenched and tempered. The wire usually has a Brinell hardness between 352 and 415, although this will depend on the application of the spring and the severity of the forming operation. Steel for small flat springs has either been cold-rolled or quenched and tempered to a similar hardness.

Steel for both helical and flat springs which is hardened and tempered after forming is usually supplied in an annealed condition. Plain carbon steel is satisfactory for small springs; for large springs it is necessary to use alloy steels such as chrome-vanadium or silicon-manganese steel in order to obtain a uniform structure throughout the cross section. Table 17 gives the chemical composition and heat-treatment of several spring steels. It is especially important for springs that the surface of the steel be free from all defects.

Table 17. Type of Steel and Heat-treatment for Large Hot-formed Flat, Leaf, and Helical Springs

AISI steel	Normalizing temp,* deg F	Quenching temp,† deg F	Tempering temp, deg F
C1074	1525–1575	1450–1525	700– 850
C1095	1575–1625	1475–1525	850–1050
4068	1550–1600	1500–1525	850–1050
6150	1600–1650	1600–1650	850–1050
9260	1600–1650	1600–1650	850–1050
5150	1600–1650	1475–1525	850–1050
8650	1600–1650	1600–1650	850–1050

* These normalizing temperatures should be used as the forming temperature whenever feasible.
† Quench in oil at 110 to 140 F.

STAINLESS STEELS

Corrosion- and Heat-resisting Steels. Certain alloys of iron and chromium are highly resistant to corrosion and oxidation at high temperatures and maintain considerable strength at these temperatures. These alloys sometimes contain nickel and small percentages of silicon, molybdenum, tungsten, copper, and other elements. This large and complex group of alloys is known as **stainless steels,** and they are normally classified in one of three groups: (A) **austenitic steels,** containing both nickel and chromium; (B) **martensitic steels,** which are hardenable alloys containing up to 18 percent chromium and which are martensitic when quenched; and (C) **ferritic steels,** which are low-carbon, non-hardenable alloys containing up to 27 percent chromium. (See Table 18*a*.)

Group A (Austenitic). The addition of substantial quantities of Ni to high-chromium alloys stabilizes the austenite to such an extent that the alloys are austenitic at room temperature. The most common composition is 18 Cr and 8 Ni (known as **18-8**), and many modifications have been developed for special applications (Table 18).

They cannot be hardened except by cold work, although excellent properties in the lower nickel grades are obtained in this manner (see Table 19). These alloys are highly resistant to many acids, including hot or cold nitric acid. They have excellent toughness at temperatures as low as liquid helium (−452 F) and are useful for parts subjected to severe stresses at elevated temperatures. The 25 Cr alloys can be used up to 2000 F without excessive scaling. The group of alloys for use at these elevated temperatures—known as **superalloys**—in which iron is a comparatively unimportant element is covered on pp. 6-42 to 6-45.

The austenitic stainless steels are not highly resistant to hot sulphurous gases and are sometimes subject to intergranular corrosion if chromium carbides are present in the grain boundaries. These carbides form during prolonged exposure in the 800 to 1600 F temperature range. Normal corrosion resistance can be restored by heating the steel above 1700 F and cooling rapidly. When titanium or columbium is added to a low-carbon 18-8 (types 321 and 347, respectively), the steel is relatively immune to this intergranular attack. Two newer grades, 304L and 316L, with a carbon content below 0.03 percent have been developed to minimize the amount of carbide precipitation. They find excellent application where welding is involved and postannealing is impractical.

Group B (Martensitic). The hardenable alloys can be heat-treated to a high hardness and because of their oxidation resistance are used extensively for cutlery, razor blades, surgical and dental instruments, springs for high-temperature operation, ball valves and seats, and similar applications. Compositions and obtainable properties are given in Table 18 and 19, respectively. The hardening-temperature range depends on composition, but in general, the higher the quenching temperature, the harder the article. Oil quenching is preferable, but with thin and intricate shapes, hardening should be obtained by cooling in air. Tempering at 800 F does not lower the hardness of the part, and in this condition these steels show remarkable resistance to fruit and vegetable acids, lye, ammonia, and other corrosive agents to which cutlery may be subjected.

Group C (Ferritic). This group is frequently called **stainless iron** because of its low carbon content. The alloys possess considerable ductility, ability to be worked hot or cold, and excellent corrosion resistance and are relatively inexpensive. Although these low-carbon chromium alloys cannot be hardened by heat-treatment, they can be hardened to a considerable extent by cold working. Alloys containing 16 to 18 percent Cr are probably the most useful of the straight chromium steels because of their forming and medium-deep-drawing properties. They are used extensively for kitchen equipment, dairy machinery, interior decorative work, automobile trimmings, and chemical equipment (to resist nitric acid corrosion).

For resisting oxidizing conditions at high temperatures, the Cr content is increased to between 25 and 30 percent. These alloys are useful for all types of furnace parts not subjected to high stress. Since the oxidation resistance is independent of carbon content, soft, forgeable alloys low in carbon can be rolled into plates, shapes, and sheets, and hard and wear-resistant castings can be made from higher-carbon, nonforgeable alloys.

The compositions and mechanical properties of the ferritic alloys are given in Tables 18 and 19, respectively.

There are many non-standard grades of stainless steels developed for specific applications. An important group is the **precipitation-hardening alloys,** which consist essentially of the 18-8 composition to which age-hardening elements such as titanium, columbium, aluminum, copper, and molybdenum have been added. Typical compositions are **stainless W,** with 17 Cr, 7 Ni, 0.70 Ti, and 0.20 Al; **17-7 PH,** with 17 Cr, 7 Ni, and 1.00 Al; and **AM 350,** with 17 Cr, 4 Ni, 3 Mo, and 0.10 N. Typical properties obtained in the 17-7 PH by solution annealing at 1400 F and cooling and aging at 1050 F are 185,000 psi yield strength, 200,000 psi tensile strength, and 9 percent elongation. These precipitation-hardening stainless steels are available in coils, sheets, strip, plate, forging billets, bars, rods, and wire. Because strength does not vary with bar size and can be developed in any thickness, many new applications are feasible. Final-machining operations can be performed before heat-treatment if allowance is made for

Table 18a. Compositions of Standard Grades of Wrought Stainless and Heat-resisting Steels
(AISI, 1959)

AISI type	Nominal composition, percent					
	C	Mn, max	Si, max	Cr	Ni	Other[a]
			Austenitic Steels			
201	0.15 max	7.50[b]	1.00	16.00–18.00	3.50–5.50	0.25 max N
202	0.15 max	10.00[c]	1.00	17.00–19.00	4.00–6.00	0.25 max N
301	0.15 max	2.00	1.00	16.00–18.00	6.00–8.00	
302	0.15 max	2.00	1.00	17.00–19.00	8.00–10.00	
302B	0.15 max	2.00	3.00[d]	17.00–19.00	8.00–10.00	
303	0.15 max	2.00	1.00	17.00–19.00	8.00–10.00	0.15 min S
303(Se)	0.15 max	2.00	1.00	17.00–19.00	8.00–10.00	0.15 min Se
304	0.08 max	2.00	1.00	18.00–20.00	8.00–12.00	
304L	0.03 max	2.00	1.00	18.00–20.00	8.00–12.00	
305	0.12 max	2.00	1.00	17.00–19.00	10.00–13.00	
308	0.08 max	2.00	1.00	19.00–21.00	10.00–12.00	
309	0.20 max	2.00	1.00	22.00–24.00	12.00–15.00	
309S	0.08 max	2.00	1.00	22.00–24.00	12.00–15.00	
310	0.25 max	2.00	1.50	24.00–26.00	19.00–22.00	
310S	0.08 max	2.00	1.50	24.00–26.00	19.00–22.00	
314	0.25 max	2.00	3.00[e]	23.00–26.00	19.00–22.00	
316	0.08 max	2.00	1.00	16.00–18.00	10.00–14.00	2.00–3.00 Mo
316L	0.03 max	2.00	1.00	16.00–18.00	10.00–14.00	2.00–3.00 Mo
317	0.08 max	2.00	1.00	18.00–20.00	11.00–15.00	3.00–4.00 Mo
321	0.08 max	2.00	1.00	17.00–19.00	9.00–12.00	5 × C min Ti
347	0.08 max	2.00	1.00	17.00–19.00	9.00–13.00	10 × C min Cb-Ta
348	0.08 max	2.00	1.00	17.00–19.00	9.00–13.00	10 × C min Cb-Ta 0.10 max Ta
			Martensitic Steels			
403	0.15 max	1.00	0.50	11.50–13.00		
410	0.15 max	1.00	1.00	11.50–13.50		
414	0.15 max	1.00	1.00	11.50–13.50	1.25–2.50	
416	0.15 max	1.25	1.00	12.00–14.00	....	0.15 min S
416(Se)	0.15 max	1.25	1.00	12.00–14.00	....	0.15 min Se
420	0.15 min	1.00	1.00	12.00–14.00		
431	0.20 max	1.00	1.00	15.00–17.00	1.25–2.50	
440A	0.60–0.75	1.00	1.00	16.00–18.00	....	0.75 max Mo
440B	0.75–0.95	1.00	1.00	16.00–18.00	....	0.75 max Mo
440C	0.95–1.20	1.00	1.00	16.00–18.00	....	0.75 max Mo
501	0.10 min	1.00	1.00	4.00–6.00	....	0.40–0.65 Mo
502	0.10 max	1.00	1.00	4.00–6.00	....	0.40–0.65 Mo
			Ferritic Steels			
405	0.08 max	1.00	1.00	11.50–14.50	....	0.10–0.30 Al
430	0.12 max	1.00	1.00	14.00–18.00		
430F	0.12 max	1.25	1.00	14.00–18.00	....	0.15 min S
430F(Se)	0.12 max	1.25	1.00	14.00–18.00	....	0.15 min Se
446	0.20 max	1.50	1.00	23.00–27.00	....	0.25 max N

[a] Other elements in addition to those shown below are as follows: Phosphorus is 0.06 percent max in types 201, 202, 416, 416(Se), 430F, 430F(Se); 0.045 percent max in types 301, 302, 302B, 304, 304L, 305, 308, 309, 309S, 310, 310S, 314, 316, 316L, 317, 321, 347, 348; 0.20 percent max in types 303 and 303(Se). Sulphur is 0.030 percent max in types 201, 202, 301, 302, 302B, 304, 304L, 305, 308, 309, 309S, 310, 310S, 314, 316, 316L, 317, 321, 347, 348, 403, 405, 410, 414, 420, 430, 431, 440A, 440B, 440C, 446, 501 and 502; 0.15 percent min in types 303, 416, and 430F.

[b] Mn range, 5.50 to 7.50.

[c] Mn range, 7.50 to 10.00.

[d] Si range, 2.00 to 3.00.

[e] Si range, 1.50 to 3.00.

Table 18b. Nominal Compositions of Non-standard Grades of Wrought Stainless Steel

Tentative designation	Nominal composition, percent						
	C	Mn	Si	Cr	Ni	Mo	Other
308L	0.025	1.75	0.40	21.00	10.00		
316F	0.06	1.50	0.50	18.00	13.00	2.25	0.13 P, 0.15 S
317L	0.025	1.75	0.50	18.50	13.50	3.25	
329	0.07	0.60	0.50	27.50	4.50	2.25	
347F(Se)	0.05	1.25	0.50	17.50	9.50	....	0.13 P, 0.30 Se, 0.60 Cb
418	0.17	0.40	0.30	12.75	2.00	....	3.00 W
420F	0.38	0.45	0.35	13.50	.....	....	0.21 Se or 0.18 S
422	0.20	0.65	0.50	12.00	0.75	1.00	1.00 W, 0.30 V
440F	1.00	0.40	0.40	17.00	.....	....	0.18 Se or 0.08 S
442	0.06	0.50	0.50	21.00			
443	0.06	0.50	0.50	21.00	.....	....	1.00 Cu
Stainless W	0.07	0.50	0.50	16.75	6.75	....	0.80 Ti, 0.20 Al
17-4 PH	0.04	0.40	0.50	16.50	4.25	....	0.25 Cb, 3.60 Cu
17-7 PH	0.07	0.70	0.40	17.00	7.00	....	1.15 Al
PH 15-7 Mo	0.07	0.70	0.40	15.00	7.00	2.25	1.15 Al
AM-350	0.10	0.75	0.35	16.50	4.25	2.75	0.10 N
AM-355	0.13	0.85	0.35	15.50	4.25	2.75	0.12 N
16-18	0.05	0.50	0.40	16.00	19.00		
20-29 Cu-Mo	0.05	0.75	1.00	20.00	29.00	2.20	3.20 Cu
17-10 P	0.12	0.75	0.50	17.00	10.50	....	0.28 P
HMN	0.30	3.50	0.50	18.50	9.50	....	0.25 P
Tenelon	0.08	14.50	0.50	17.00	.....	....	0.40 N

the slight growth that occurs. Wide application of these steels is made by the aircraft industry because of their high strength-to-weight ratio and strength at elevated temperatures.

Ultrahigh-strength Steels

The low-alloy hardenable steels have been used for years in many applications requiring tensile strengths in the order of 200,000 psi; however, the strength level of commercial steel has been raised progressively to well over 300,000 psi, partially because of the demands of the missile industry. Improvements in both strength and ductility were initially obtained by modifying the standard engineering steels AISI 4140 (chromium-molybdenum) and AISI 4340 (nickel-chromium-molybdenum) by increasing the silicon content from 0.25 to about 1.50 percent and by adding 0.05 percent vanadium. These steels contain over 0.40 percent carbon, and when oil-quenched and tempered between 500 and 600 F, develop yield strengths of 240,000 psi, tensile strengths of 280,000 psi, and elongation in 2 in. of about 10 percent. Similar properties can be obtained in hot-work die steels, known as 5 Cr-Mo-V and containing 0.40 carbon, 1.0 silicon, 5.0 chromium, 1.3 molybdenum, and 0.5 vanadium. The extremely high hardenability of these steels permits air cooling from the austenitizing temperature and thus minimizes residual stresses. In addition, tempering is performed at 1000 F, thus reducing residual stresses in weldments and giving the best combination of strength and toughness in quenched and tempered steels.

A major increase in properties of alloy steels has been obtained experimentally by **Ausforming.** In this process, the steel is first austenitized by heating above the critical and is then cooled to a temperature below that required for pearlite formation and strained by an operation such as rolling. It is then quenched to martensite and tempered to produce the desired combination of strength and ductility. Ausforming a 5 Cr-Mo-V steel can raise the yield strength to 370,000 psi by a 50 percent reduction in area at 900 F followed by quenching and double tempering at 950 F. A similar process, known as **zerolling,** can develop yield strengths close to 300,000 psi in austenitic stainless steels. By rolling the stainless at temperatures below 0 F, a high-strength martensite is formed which has excellent toughness even at low temperatures.

Table 19. Nominal Mechanical Properties of Standard Stainless Steels

Grade	Condition	Tensile strength, psi	0.2 percent yield strength, psi	Elongation in 2 in., percent	Reduction of area, percent	Hardness	
						Rockwell	BHN
Austenitic Steels							
201	Annealed	115,000	55,000	55	...	B90	...
	¼-hard	125,000[a]	75,000[a]	20[a]	...	C25	...
	½-hard	150,000[a]	110,000[a]	10[a]	...	C32	...
	¾-hard	175,000[a]	135,000[a]	5[a]	...	C37	...
	Full-hard	185,000[a]	140,000[a]	4[a]	...	C41	...
202	Annealed	105,000	55,000	55	...	B90	...
	¼-hard	125,000[a]	75,000[a]	12[a]	...	C27	...
301	Annealed	110,000	40,000	60	...	B85	165
	¼-hard	125,000[a]	75,000[a]	25[a]	...	C25	...
	½-hard	150,000[a]	110,000[a]	15[a]	...	C32	...
	¾-hard	175,000[a]	135,000[a]	12[a]	...	C37	...
	Full-hard	185,000[a]	140,000[a]	8[a]	...	C41	...
302	Annealed	90,000	37,000	55	65	B82	155
	¼-hard (sheet, strip)	125,000[a]	75,000[a]	12[a]	...	C25	...
	Cold drawn (bar, wire)[b]	To 350,000	....	...	...	...	...
302B	Annealed	95,000	40,000	50	65	B85	165
303, 303(Se)	Annealed	90,000	35,000	50	55	B84	160
304	Annealed	85,000	35,000	55	65	B80	150
304L	Annealed	80,000	30,000	55	65	B76	140
305	Annealed	85,000	37,000	55	70	B82	156
308	Annealed	85,000	35,000	55	65	B80	150
309, 309S	Annealed	90,000	40,000	45	65	B85	165
310, 310S	Annealed	95,000	40,000	45	65	B87	170
314	Annealed	100,000	50,000	45	60	B87	170
316	Annealed	85,000	35,000	55	70	B80	150
	Cold drawn (bar, wire)[b]	To 300,000	....	...	...	...	...
316L	Annealed	78,000	30,000	55	65	B76	145
317	Annealed	90,000	40,000	50	55	B85	160
321	Annealed	87,000	35,000	55	65	B80	150
347, 348	Annealed	92,000	35,000	50	65	B84	160
Martensitic Steels							
403, 410, 416, 416(Se)	Annealed	75,000	40,000	30	65	B82	155
	Hardened[c]	....	....	...	...	C43	410
	Tempered at						
	400 F	190,000	145,000	15	55	C41	390
	600 F	180,000	140,000	15	55	C39	375
	800 F	195,000	150,000	17	55	C41	390
	1000 F	145,000	115,000	20	65	C31	300
	1200 F	110,000	85,000	23	65	B97	225
	1400 F	90,000	60,000	30	70	B89	180
414	Annealed	120,000	95,000	17	55	C22	235
	Hardened[c]	....	....	...	...	C44	426
	Tempered at						
	400 F	200,000	150,000	15	55	C43	415
	600 F	190,000	145,000	15	55	C41	400
	800 F	200,000	150,000	16	58	C43	415
	1000 F	145,000	120,000	20	60	C34	325
	1200 F	120,000	105,000	20	65	C24	260
420, 420F	Annealed	95,000	50,000	25	55	B92	195
	Hardened[d]	....	....	...	...	C54	540
	Tempered at						
	600 F	230,000	195,000	8	25	C50	500

Table 19. Nominal Mechanical Properties of Standard Stainless Steels—(*Continued*)

Grade	Condition	Tensile strength, psi	0.2 percent yield strength, psi	Elongation in 2 in., percent	Reduction of area, percent	Hardness	
						Rockwell	BHN
431	Annealed	125,000	95,000	20	60	C24	260
	Hardened[d]	....	....	...	...	C45	440
	Tempered at						
	400 F	205,000	155,000	15	55	C43	415
	600 F	195,000	150,000	15	55	C41	400
	800 F	205,000	155,000	15	60	C43	415
	1000 F	150,000	130,000	18	60	C34	325
	1200 F	125,000	95,000	20	60	C24	260
440A	Annealed	105,000	60,000	20	45	B95	215
	Hardened[d]	....	....	...	...	C56	570
	Tempered						
	600 F	260,000	240,000	5	20	C51	510
440B	Annealed	107,000	62,000	18	35	B96	220
	Hardened[d]	....	....	...	...	C58	590
	Tempered						
	600 F	280,000	270,000	3	15	C55	555
440C, 440F	Annealed	110,000	65,000	13	25	B97	230
	Hardened[d]	....	....	...	...	C60	610
	Tempered						
	600 F	285,000	275,000	2	10	C57	580
501	Annealed	70,000	30,000	28	65	...	160
502	Annealed	70,000	30,000	30	75	B80	150
			Ferritic Steels				
405	Annealed	70,000	40,000	30	60	B80	150
430	Annealed	75,000	45,000	30	60	B82	155
430F, 430F(Se)	Annealed	80,000	55,000	25	60	B86	170
446	Annealed	80,000	50,000	23	50	B86	170

[a] Minimum.
[b] Depending on size and amount of cold reduction.
[c] Hardening temperature 1800 F, 1-in.-diam bars.
[d] Hardening temperature 1900 F, 1-in.-diam bars.

A series of high-nickel-alloy steels, known as **maraging steels** and containing little carbon, have been developed with an exceptional combination of high strength and fracture toughness. As annealed, these maraging steels develop a soft, ductile, iron-nickel martensitic structure than can readily be machined and shaped and later strengthened by a simple aging treatment. The nominal composition is 18 percent nickel, 7 to 9 cobalt, 3 to 5 molybdenum, and 0.1 to 0.8 titanium. Each of these elements has a strengthening effect, and they are adjusted to develop the required combination of strength and toughness. The heat-treatment consists of heating to 1500 F for 1 hr, air-cooling to room temperature, and aging 3 hr at 900 F. Typical properties as annealed are 110,000 psi strength, 150,000 psi tensile strength, 18 percent elongation, and 72 percent reduction in area. As aged, the corresponding tensile properties are 300,000 psi, 12 percent, and 60 percent. These steels retain excellent notch toughness to temperatures of −320 F and also have high-temperature strength retention remaining above 220,000 psi tensile strength at 800 F. The consistency of test results should encourage wide engineering applications of these new high-strength steels.

Special-property Alloys

Iron-nickel alloys are used extensively in the electrical industry owing to their exceptional magnetic properties. Alloys containing 20 to 30 Ni are non-magnetic and are used to some extent for non-magnetic parts in electrical machinery. Alloys having a high permeability and low hysteresis loss have a composition between 45 and 80 Ni., two of the better known being **Permalloy** with 78.5 Ni and **Hipernik** with 50 Ni. **Perminvar** (45 Ni, 25 Co) has a constant permeability over a range of flux densities. The magnetic properties of various alloys are given in Table 20.

Another important group of iron-nickel base alloys are those with low coefficients of expansion. **Invar,** containing 36 Ni, has an exceedingly low coefficient of linear expansion. Within limits of atmospheric temperature change, its expansion is proportional to the temperature and it is, therefore, used for secondary standards of length. **Elinvar** (32 Ni with small percentages of Cr, W, Mn, Si, and C) not only has a low coefficient of expansion but also has a constant modulus of elasticity over the temperature range of 0 to 100 F and is thus useful in hairsprings for watches and springs for other precision instruments. **Platinite,** a 46 Ni alloy, has the same thermal coefficient of expansion as platinum; and **Dumet wire,** a 42 Ni alloy covered with copper to prevent gassing at the seal, is used to replace platinum as the "seal-in" wire in incandescent lamps and vacuum tubes.

Table 20. Magnetic Properties of Various Alloys

(ASM Metals Handbook, 1948)

Material[a]	Initial permeability	Maximum permeability	Hysteresis loss, ergs per cc per cycle[b]	Residual induction, gausses	Coercive force, oersteds	Saturation value, gausses[c]	Resistivity, microhm-cm
Ingot iron	250	7,000	5,000	13,000	1.0	21,600	11
4% silicon-iron	600	6,000	3,500	12,000	0.5	20,000	50
78.5 Permalloy, quenched	10,000	105,000	200	6,000	0.05	10,700	16
45 Permalloy	2,700	23,000	1,200	8,000	0.3	16,000	45
3.8–78.5 Cr-Permalloy	12,000	62,000	200	4,500	0.05	8,000	65
3.8–78.5 Mo-Permalloy	20,000	75,000	200	5,000	0.05	8,500	55
45–25 Perminvar, baked	400	2,000	2,500	3,000	1.2	15,500	19
7–45–25 Mo-Perminvar, baked	550	3,700	2,600	4,300	0.65	10,300	80
70–7.5 Perminvar, annealed	750	3,500	.....	.....	0.8	12,000	16
5–79 Mo-Supermalloy	100,000	800,000	20	6,000	0.004	8,000	60

[a] Single numbers preceding the word Permalloy signify the nickel content, and double numbers signify first the content of chromium or molybdenum, and second the nickel content, the balance being iron in each case. The two large numbers before Perminvar indicate the nickel and cobalt contents, respectively, and the small initial number indicates the molybdenum content.

[b] For saturation value of the flux density.

[c] Saturation value of the intrinsic induction.

Electrical sheet steels are alloys of iron and silicon with C, Mn, P, and S kept as low as possible. The silicon increases the electrical resistivity of iron and greatly decreases the hysteresis loss; silicon-alloy sheets are used in almost all magnetic circuits where alternating current is used. For transformers, the silicon content is around 5 percent, but in structures subjected to vibration, such as motor armatures, the silicon is usually kept below 4 percent because of the brittleness of high silicon sheets.

Austenitic manganese steel (Hadfield's manganese steel) is a non-magnetic alloy containing around 12 Mn and 1 C. It is relatively soft but work-hardens on the surface when subjected to severe abrasion, so that it is extremely useful in crushing machinery, for railroad crossings and frogs, tractor shoes, etc. As cast, this alloy is partly martensitic and, therefore, hard and brittle. By quenching from a high temperature (1900 F), a homogeneous austenite is retained and the alloy has the high toughness, strength, and ductility characteristic of austenitic steels.

ASTM Specifications

The ASTM Standards, 1964, contain over 200 specifications for ferrous materials and products. For detailed specifications and for chemical analyses reference should be made to these Standards. The specifications contain also details of the preparation of test specimens, the location from which they should be taken, and permissible variations in the dimensions of material ordered.

The tensile properties specified for structural and boiler steels are given in Table 21.

Table 21. ASTM Specifications

ASTM No.	Grade	Tensile strength, kpsi	Min yield point, kpsi	Min elong, percent	
				In 8 in.	In 2 in.
	STRUCTURAL AND RIVET STEEL				
A7-61T	Steel for bridges and buildings	60–75	33	21	24
A36-62T	Structural steel	58–80	36	20	23
A94-62T	Structural silicon steel	70–75	45	17	20
A283-58	Structural-quality carbon-steel plates (2 in. thick and under)				
	Grade A	45–55	24	27	30
	Grade B	50–60	27	25	28
	Grade C	55–65	30	23	27
	Grade D	60–72	33	21	24
A284-55T	Carbon-silicon plates				
	Grade A	50	25	25	28
	Grade B	55	27.5	23	27
A113-58	Structural steel for locomotives				
	Grade A	60–72	33	21	24
	Grade B	50–62	27	24	28
A131-61	Structural steel for ships	58–71	32	21	24
A242-63T	Low-alloy structural steel	70	50	18	
A141-58	Structural rivet steel	52–62	28	24	
	BOILER STEEL PLATES AND RIVETS				
A30-56	Boiler and firebox steel for locomotives:				
	flange	55–65	30	24	28
	firebox, Grade A	55–65	30	25	29
	Grade B	48–58	26	27	30
A285-57T	Carbon steel plates, flange, and firebox quality:				
	Grade A	45–55	24	28	31
	Grade B	50–60	27	26	29
	Grade C	55–65	30	24	28
A212-61T	Carbon-silicon steel plates				
	Grade A	65–77	35	20	23
	Grade B	70–85	38	18	21
A202-56	Chromium-manganese-silicon steel plates				
	Grade A	75–90	45	18	21
	Grade B	85–100	47	17	20
A31-55	Boiler-rivet steel				
	Grade A	45–55	23	27	
	Grade B	58–68	29	22	

WIRE, SHEETS, AND BARS

Wire and Sheet-metal Gages. Wire and black and galvanized sheet metal of the smaller thicknesses are made to various gages. Steel wire is usually made to the Washburn and Moen (W & M) or Roebling gage. The U.S. standard for sheet metal is based upon weight per square foot; the tabulated values are the corresponding thicknesses for wrought iron weighing 480, and for steel and open-hearth iron weighing 489.6 lb per cu ft. Stubs steel-wire gage is also used for numbered twist drill sizes (see Sec. 13). The Birmingham wire gage is used in the U.S. for brass wire. The Brown and Sharpe gage is a uniform geometrical progression, each gage being equal to 0.89053 times the preceding gage. See Sec. 15 for more data on the Brown and Sharpe gage.

Weights of Rolled Sheet Steel

Gage No.	Weight per sq ft, lb		Gage No.	Weight per sq ft, lb		Gage No.	Weight per sq ft, lb		Gage No.	Weight per sq ft, lb	
	BWG	USSG		BWG	USSG		BWG	USSG		BWG	USSG
7-0's	....	20.00	6	8.2824	8.125	18	1.9992	2	29	0.5304	0.5625
6-0's	....	18.75	7	7.344	7.5	19	1.7126	1.75	30	0.4896	0.5
5-0's	....	17.50	8	6.732	6.875	20	1.428	1.50	31	0.408	0.4375
0000	18.5232	16.25	9	6.0384	6.25	21	1.3056	1.375	32	0.3672	0.4063
000	17.34	15	10	5.4672	5.625	22	1.1424	1.25	33	0.3264	0.375
00	15.504	13.75	11	4.896	5	23	1.02	1.125	34	0.2856	0.3438
0	13.872	12.50	12	4.4972	4.375	24	0.8976	1	35	0.2040	0.3125
1	12.24	11.25	13	3.876	3.75	25	0.816	.875	36	0.1632	0.2813
2	11.5872	10.625	14	3.3864	3.125	26	0.7344	.75	37	....	0.2656
3	10.5672	10	15	2.9376	2.813	27	0.6528	.6875	38	....	0.25
4	9.7104	9.375	16	2.651	2.5	28	0.5712	.625			
5	8.976	8.75	17	2.3664	2.25						

Properties of Steel Wire

(Breaking stress = 100,000 psi)

No., Roebling gage	Breaking load, lb	Weight, lb per 1,000 ft	No., Roebling gage	Breaking load, lb	Weight, lb per 1,000 ft	No., Roebling gage	Breaking load, lb	Weight, lb per 1,000 ft	No., Roebling gage	Breaking load, lb	Weight, lb per 1,000 ft
6-0's	16,619	558.4	6	2,895	97.3	17	229	7.70	27	23.0	0.763
5-0's	14,522	487.9	7	2,461	82.7	18	174	5.83	28	20.0	0.676
0000	12,130	407.6	8	2,061	69.3	19	132	4.44	29	18.0	0.594
000	10,292	345.8	9	1,720	57.8	20	96	3.23	30	15.0	0.517
00	8,605	289.1	10	1,431	48.1	21	80	2.70	31	14.0	0.481
0	7,402	248.7	11	1,131	38.0	22	62	2.07	32	13.0	0.446
1	6,290	211.4	12	866	29.1	23	49	1.65	33	9.5	0.319
2	5,433	182.5	13	665	22.3	24	42	1.40	34	7.9	0.264
3	4,676	157.1	14	503	16.9	25	31	1.06	35	7.1	0.238
4	3,976	133.6	15	407	13.7	26	25	0.855	36	6.4	0.214
5	3,365	113.1	16	312	10.5						

Galvanized-sheet Gage

Galvanized-sheet gage no.	Gage weights			Mean thickness, in.	Galvanized-sheet gage no.	Gage weights			Mean thickness, in.
	Oz per sq ft	Psf	Psi			Oz per sq ft	Psf	Psi	
8	112.5	7.0312	0.048828	0.1681	20	26.5	1.6562	0.011502	0.0396
9	102.5	6.4062	0.044488	0.1532	21	24.5	1.5312	0.010634	0.0366
					22	22.5	1.4062	0.0097656	0.0336
10	92.5	5.7812	0.040148	0.1382	23	20.5	1.2812	0.0088976	0.0306
11	82.5	5.1562	0.035807	0.1233	24	18.5	1.1562	0.0080295	0.0276
12	72.5	4.5312	0.031467	0.1084					
13	62.5	3.9062	0.027127	0.0934	25	16.5	1.0312	0.0071615	0.0247
14	52.5	3.2812	0.022786	0.0785	26	14.5	0.90625	0.0062934	0.0217
					27	13.5	0.84375	0.0058594	0.0202
15	47.5	2.9688	0.020616	0.0710	28	12.5	0.78125	0.0054253	0.0187
16	42.5	2.6562	0.018446	0.0635	29	11.5	0.71875	0.0049913	0.0172
17	38.5	2.4062	0.016710	0.0575					
18	34.5	2.1562	0.014974	0.0516	30	10.5	0.65625	0.0045573	0.0157
19	30.5	1.9062	0.013238	0.0456	31	9.5	0.59375	0.0041233	0.0142
					32	9.0	0.56250	0.0039062	0.0134

Comparison of Standard Gages*

(Thickness in decimals of an inch)

Gage No.	BWG; Stubs Iron Wire	AWG; B&S	U.S. Steel Wire; Am. Steel & Wire; Washburn & Moen; Steel Wire	U.S. Standard (old)	SWG	Manufacturers' standard
0000000	.....	....	0.4900	0.5000	0.500	
000000	.....	0.580000	0.4615	0.4687	0.464	
00000	.....	0.516500	0.4305	0.4375	0.432	
0000	0.454	0.460000	0.3938	0.4062	0.400	
000	0.425	0.409642	0.3625	0.3750	0.372	
00	0.380	0.364796	0.3310	0.3437	0.348	
0	0.340	0.324861	0.3065	0.3125	0.324	
1	0.300	0.289297	0.2830	0.2812	0.300	
2	0.284	0.257627	0.2625	0.2656	0.276	
3	0.259	0.229423	0.2437	0.2500	0.252	0.2391
4	0.238	0.204307	0.2253	0.2344	0.232	0.2242
5	0.220	0.181940	0.2070	0.2187	0.212	0.2092
6	0.203	0.162023	0.1920	0.2031	0.192	0.1943
7	0.180	0.144285	0.1770	0.1875	0.176	0.1793
8	0.165	0.128490	0.1620	0.1719	0.160	0.1644
9	0.148	0.114423	0.1483	0.1562	0.144	0.1495
10	0.134	0.101897	0.1350	0.1406	0.128	0.1345
11	0.120	0.090742	0.1205	0.1250	0.116	0.1196
12	0.109	0.080808	0.1055	0.1094	0.104	0.1046
13	0.095	0.071962	0.0915	0.0937	0.092	0.0897
14	0.083	0.064084	0.0800	0.0781	0.080	0.0747
15	0.072	0.057068	0.0720	0.0703	0.072	0.0673
16	0.065	0.050821	0.0625	0.0625	0.064	0.0598
17	0.058	0.045257	0.0540	0.0562	0.056	0.0538
18	0.049	0.040303	0.0475	0.0500	0.048	0.0478
19	0.042	0.035890	0.0410	0.0437	0.040	0.0418
20	0.035	0.031961	0.0348	0.0375	0.036	0.0359
21	0.032	0.028462	0.03175	0.0344	0.032	0.0329
22	0.028	0.025346	0.0286	0.0312	0.028	0.0299
23	0.025	0.022572	0.0258	0.0281	0.024	0.0269
24	0.022	0.020101	0.0230	0.0250	0.022	0.0239
25	0.020	0.017900	0.0204	0.0219	0.020	0.0209
26	0.018	0.015941	0.0181	0.0187	0.018	0.0179
27	0.016	0.014195	0.0173	0.0172	0.0164	0.0164
28	0.014	0.012641	0.0162	0.0156	0.0148	0.0149
29	0.013	0.011257	0.0150	0.0141	0.0136	0.0135
30	0.012	0.010025	0.0140	0.0125	0.0124	0.0120
31	0.010	0.008928	0.0132	0.0109	0.0116	0.0105
32	0.009	0.007950	0.0128	0.0102	0.0108	0.0097
33	0.008	0.007080	0.0118	0.0094	0.0100	0.0090
34	0.007	0.006305	0.0104	0.0086	0.0092	0.0082
35	0.005	0.005615	0.0095	0.0078	0.0084	0.0075
36	0.004	0.005000	0.0090	0.0070	0.0076	0.0067
37	.....	0.004453	0.0085	0.0066	0.0068	0.0064
38	.....	0.003965	0.0080	0.0062	0.0060	0.0060
39	.....	0.003531	0.0075	......	0.0052	
40	.....	0.003144	0.0070	......	0.0048	

* Principal uses—BWG: strips, bands, hoops, and wire; AWG or B&S: non-ferrous sheets, rod, and wire; U.S. Steel Wire: steel wire except music wire; U.S. Standard (old): stainless steel sheets; SWG: English legal standard wire gage; manufacturers' standards: uncoated steel sheets.

Weights of Square and Round Steel Bars

(For iron, subtract 2 percent)

Size, in.	Weight, lb per lin ft		Size, in.	Weight, lb per lin ft		Size, in.	Weight, lb per lin ft		Size, in.	Weight, lb per lin ft	
	Square	Round		Square	Round		Square	Round		Square	Round
0	....	....	3	30.60	24.03	6	122.4	96.1	9	275.4	216.3
1/16	0.013	0.010	1/16	31.89	25.05	1/16	125.0	98.2	1/16	279.2	219.3
1/8	0.053	0.042	1/8	33.20	26.08	1/8	127.6	100.2	1/8	283.1	222.4
3/16	0.120	0.094	3/16	34.54	27.13	3/16	130.2	102.2	3/16	287.0	225.4
1/4	0.213	0.167	1/4	35.91	28.21	1/4	132.8	104.3	1/4	290.9	228.5
5/16	0.332	0.261	5/16	37.31	29.30	5/16	135.5	106.4	5/16	294.9	231.6
3/8	0.478	0.376	3/8	38.73	30.42	3/8	138.2	108.5	3/8	298.8	234.7
7/16	0.651	0.511	7/16	40.18	31.55	7/16	140.9	110.7	7/16	302.8	237.8
1/2	0.850	0.668	1/2	41.65	32.71	1/2	143.7	112.8	1/2	306.9	241.0
9/16	1.076	0.845	9/16	43.15	33.89	9/16	146.4	115.0	9/16	310.9	244.2
5/8	1.328	1.043	5/8	44.68	35.09	5/8	149.2	117.2	5/8	315.0	247.4
11/16	1.607	1.262	11/16	46.23	36.31	11/16	152.1	119.4	11/16	319.1	250.6
3/4	1.913	1.502	3/4	47.81	37.55	3/4	154.9	121.7	3/4	323.2	253.9
13/16	2.245	1.763	13/16	49.42	38.81	13/16	157.8	123.9	13/16	327.4	257.1
7/8	2.603	2.044	7/8	51.05	40.10	7/8	160.7	126.2	7/8	331.6	260.4
15/16	2.988	2.347	15/16	52.71	41.40	15/16	163.6	128.5	15/16	335.8	263.7
1	3.400	2.670	4	54.40	42.73	7	166.6	130.9	10	340.0	267.0
1/16	3.838	3.015	1/16	56.11	44.07	1/16	169.6	133.2	1/16	344.3	270.4
1/8	4.303	3.380	1/8	57.85	45.44	1/8	172.6	135.6	1/8	348.6	273.8
3/16	4.795	3.766	3/16	59.62	46.83	3/16	175.6	137.9	3/16	352.9	277.1
1/4	5.313	4.172	1/4	61.41	48.23	1/4	178.7	140.4	1/4	357.2	280.6
5/16	5.857	4.600	5/16	63.23	49.66	5/16	181.8	142.8	5/16	361.6	284.0
3/8	6.428	5.049	3/8	65.08	51.11	3/8	184.9	145.2	3/8	366.0	287.4
7/16	7.026	5.518	7/16	66.95	52.58	7/16	188.1	147.7	7/16	370.4	290.9
1/2	7.650	6.008	1/2	68.85	54.07	1/2	191.3	150.2	1/2	374.9	294.4
9/16	8.301	6.519	9/16	70.78	55.59	9/16	194.5	152.7	9/16	379.3	297.9
5/8	8.978	7.051	5/8	72.73	57.12	5/8	197.7	155.3	5/8	383.8	301.5
11/16	9.682	7.604	11/16	74.71	58.67	11/16	200.9	157.8	11/16	388.4	305.0
3/4	10.413	8.178	3/4	76.71	60.25	3/4	204.2	160.4	3/4	392.9	308.6
13/16	11.170	8.773	13/16	78.74	61.85	13/16	207.5	163.0	13/16	397.5	312.2
7/8	11.953	9.388	7/8	80.80	63.46	7/8	210.9	165.6	7/8	402.1	315.8
15/16	12.763	10.024	15/16	82.89	65.10	15/16	214.2	168.2	15/16	406.7	319.5
2	13.600	10.681	5	85.00	66.76	8	217.6	170.9	11	411.4	323.1
1/16	14.463	11.359	1/16	87.14	68.44	1/16	221.0	173.6	1/16	416.1	326.8
1/8	15.353	12.058	1/8	89.30	70.14	1/8	224.5	176.3	1/8	420.8	330.5
3/16	16.270	12.778	3/16	91.49	71.86	3/16	227.9	179.0	3/16	425.5	334.2
1/4	17.213	13.519	1/4	93.71	73.60	1/4	231.4	181.8	1/4	430.3	338.0
5/16	18.182	14.280	5/16	95.96	75.36	5/16	234.9	184.5	5/16	435.1	341.7
3/8	19.178	15.062	3/8	98.23	77.15	3/8	238.5	187.3	3/8	439.9	345.5
7/16	20.201	15.866	7/16	100.53	78.95	7/16	242.1	190.1	7/16	444.8	349.3
1/2	21.250	16.690	1/2	102.85	80.78	1/2	245.7	192.9	1/2	449.7	353.2
9/16	22.326	17.534	9/16	105.20	82.62	9/16	249.3	195.8	9/16	454.6	357.0
5/8	23.428	18.400	5/8	107.58	84.49	5/8	252.9	198.7	5/8	459.5	360.9
11/16	24.557	19.287	11/16	109.98	86.38	11/16	256.6	201.5	11/16	464.4	364.8
3/4	25.713	20.195	3/4	112.41	88.29	3/4	260.3	204.5	3/4	469.4	368.7
13/16	26.895	21.123	13/16	114.87	90.22	13/16	264.0	207.4	13/16	474.4	372.6
7/8	28.103	22.072	7/8	117.35	92.17	7/8	267.8	210.3	7/8	479.5	376.6
15/16	29.338	23.042	15/16	119.86	94.14	15/16	271.6	213.3	15/16	484.5	380.5

Weights of Flat Rolled Steel, Pounds per Linear Foot*

(The last line of the table gives weights per square feet)

(For iron, subtract 2 percent)

Width, in.	Thickness, in.															
	1/16	1/8	3/16	1/4	5/16	3/8	7/16	1/2	9/16	5/8	11/16	3/4	13/16	7/8	15/16	1
1/4	0.053	0.106	0.159	0.213	0.27	0.32	0.37	0.43	0.48	0.53	0.58	0.64	0.69	0.74	0.80	0.85
1/2	0.106	0.213	0.319	0.425	0.53	0.64	0.74	0.85	0.96	1.06	1.17	1.28	1.38	1.49	1.59	1.70
3/4	0.159	0.319	0.478	0.638	0.80	0.96	1.12	1.28	1.43	1.59	1.75	1.91	2.07	2.23	2.39	2.55
1	0.213	0.425	0.638	0.850	1.06	1.23	1.49	1.70	1.91	2.13	2.34	2.55	2.76	2.98	3.19	3.40
2	0.425	0.850	1.275	1.700	2.13	2.55	2.98	3.40	3.83	4.25	4.68	5.10	5.53	5.95	6.38	6.80
3	0.638	1.275	1.913	2.550	3.19	3.83	4.46	5.10	5.74	6.38	7.01	7.65	8.29	8.93	9.56	10.20
4	0.850	1.700	2.550	3.400	4.25	5.10	5.95	6.80	7.65	8.50	9.35	10.20	11.05	11.90	12.75	13.60
5	1.063	2.125	3.188	4.250	5.31	6.38	7.44	8.50	9.56	10.63	11.69	12.75	13.81	14.88	15.94	17.00
6	1.275	2.550	3.825	5.100	6.38	7.65	8.93	10.20	11.48	12.75	14.03	15.30	16.58	17.85	19.13	20.40
7	1.488	2.975	4.463	5.950	7.44	8.93	10.41	11.90	13.39	14.88	16.36	17.85	19.34	20.83	22.31	23.80
8	1.700	3.400	5.100	6.800	8.50	10.20	11.90	13.60	15.30	17.00	18.70	20.40	22.10	23.80	25.50	27.20
9	1.913	3.825	5.738	7.650	9.56	11.48	13.39	15.30	17.21	19.13	21.04	22.95	24.86	26.78	28.69	30.60
10	2.125	4.250	6.375	8.500	10.63	12.75	14.88	17.00	19.13	21.25	23.38	25.50	27.63	29.75	31.88	34.00
20	4.25	8.50	12.75	17.00	21.25	25.50	29.75	34.00	38.25	42.50	46.80	51.0	55.30	59.50	63.8	68.00
30	6.38	12.75	19.13	25.50	31.88	38.25	44.63	51.00	57.38	63.75	70.10	76.5	82.90	89.30	95.6	102.00
40	8.50	17.00	25.50	34.00	42.50	51.00	59.50	68.00	76.50	85.00	93.50	102.0	110.50	119.00	127.5	136.00
12	2.55	5.10	7.65	10.20	12.75	15.30	17.85	20.40	22.95	25.50	28.05	30.60	33.15	35.70	38.25	40.80

* For other widths the weights are obtainable by addition; for example, 54 × 3/4 in. = [(10 × 5) + 4] × 3/4 in., and weight = (10 × 12.75) + 10.20 = 137.7 lb. Similarly, for greater thicknesses, the weights are obtainable by addition.

IRON AND STEEL CASTINGS

BY

Charles W. Briggs

References: "Metals Handbook," ASM. "Cast Metals Handbook," AFS. "Gray Iron Castings Handbook," Gray Iron Founders' Society. "Malleable Iron Castings," Malleable Founders' Society. "Steel Castings Handbook," Steel Founders' Society. Briggs, "The Metallurgy of Steel Castings," McGraw-Hill.

CLASSIFICATION OF CASTINGS

Cast-iron Castings. The term **cast iron** covers a wide range of iron-carbon-silicon alloys containing from 2.0 to 4.0 percent carbon and 0.25 to 3.00 percent silicon in combination with varying percentages of manganese, sulphur, and phosphorus, and sometimes one or more alloying elements, such as nickel, chromium, molybdenum, copper, vanadium, and titanium. Cast irons may be grouped broadly into two classes.

Gray Cast Iron. A cast iron that contains a relatively large percentage of its carbon in the form of graphite. It has a gray fracture. It may be a plain or an alloy cast iron varying from 20,000 to 60,000 psi, minimum tensile strength. The soft irons are readily machined and are used for the ordinary run of machine construction work. Strong iron castings are adapted for medium and heavy sections where strength properties are desirable.

Chilled-iron Castings. Cast iron with some section purposely cooled by chills so fast that the carbon is retained in the combined form (white iron) while other sections are allowed to cool more slowly, retaining the carbon in the form found in gray iron. Such castings as crusher jaws, chilled rolls, or car wheels, requiring hard surfaces for wear resistance and soft bodies, are made from low-silicon irons.

Special Processed Irons. Cast iron produced by licensed or patented controlled processes that permit the achievement of specific cast irons for specific purposes. **Meehanite** is the name of numerous cast irons each having a different combination of mechanical and engineering properties. Four general classification types are produced: (1) general engineering, (2) heat resisting, (3) wear resisting, and (4) corrosion resisting. Tensile strengths vary from 25,000 to 55,000 psi, and, when oil-quenched and tempered a strength of 75,000 psi can be obtained. **Nodular iron,** or ductile iron, is cast iron with the graphite substantially spherulitic or in nodular shape and substantially free of flake graphite. There are primarily two grades: an as-cast grade and a graphitizing annealed grade. Tensile strengths vary from 60,000 to 120,000 psi.

Malleable-iron Castings. Malleable iron is a mixture of iron and carbon including small amounts of silicon, manganese, phosphorus and sulphur, which, after being cast, is converted, by heat-treatment, into a matrix of ferrite containing nodules of temper carbon. The ordinary malleable-iron grade has a tensile strength from 50,000 to 55,000 psi. The pearlite malleable grade is 60,000 psi, and the heat-treated pearlite malleable irons develop tensile strengths of upwards of 85,000 psi. Most malleable-iron castings weigh from a few ounces to 100 lb. Machinery and automotive castings are outstanding applications.

Steel Castings. There are two main classes of steel castings: carbon and alloy. There are five classes of commercial steel castings: (1) **low-carbon steels** (carbon content below 0.20 percent), (2) **medium-carbon steels** (carbon between 0.20 and 0.50 percent), (3) **high-carbon steels** (carbon content above 0.50 percent), (4) **low-alloy steels** (alloy content totaling less than 8 percent), (5) **high-alloy steels** (alloying content totaling greater than 8 percent). The tensile strength of cast steel varies from

60,000 to 250,000 psi depending on composition and heat-treatment. Steel castings are produced weighing from a few ounces to over 200 tons. They are used in the transportation, machinery, and allied fields. Steel castings should be selected where strength, toughness, and reliability are essential.

CAST IRON

Composition. The properties of cast iron are regulated by the control of the amount, type, size, and distribution of the various carbon formations. The important factors are (1) casting design, (2) chemical composition, (3) type of melting scrap, (4) melting process, (5) rate of cooling in the mold, and (6) subsequent heat-treatment.

It is not advisable to specify cast irons by chemical composition. Different foundries use different ranges of composition to secure the desired properties, owing to differences in raw materials, melting practices, etc. In general, the engineer who must be familiar with many metals need not know the intimate details of the production of each. Therefore, the method of producing the irons and their composition should be left to the discretion of the foundryman and his metallurgist, who are familiar with the many composition variables to obtain the properties which the engineer desires. Since cast irons are now specified on the basis of tensile strength, long tables of compositions for various classes of cast iron are not given, because they are of little value.

The carbon in cast iron is of two types: (1) **combined carbon** as iron carbide and (2) **graphite,** present as a mechanical admixture. The graphite is in the form of dispersed flakes occupying from 6 to 10 percent of the volume of the typical gray irons. These flakes impair the continuity of the matrix to such an extent that they exert a very pronounced effect upon the mechanical properties of the metal. An increase in the amount of graphite present in cast iron, such as an increase in the flake size or an unfavorable distribution of the graphite, affects adversely the strength of the metal.

Silicon has a powerful softening effect. Its presence in cast iron reduces the ability of the iron to retain carbon in chemical combination. With very little silicon, the iron retains all its carbon in combination and produces white iron. With about 3 percent silicon, almost no carbon can be held in chemical combination. Manganese, chromium, molybdenum, titanium, and vanadium promote the retention of carbon in the combined form (carbide stabilizers) and counteract silicon. Nickel and copper improve the matrix and increase the strength of the iron, but they do not lessen the amount of graphite present and keep the iron readily machinable.

Mechanical Properties

The **tensile strength** of cast iron, including the special irons, varies from 20,000 to 80,000 psi. Eight classes of increasing strength are recognized by ASTM A48-60T for gray iron castings. Some of the property values that may be obtained are listed in Tables 1 to 3 and Fig. 1. The tensile test is the standard strength test for cast iron. The dimensions of the test bar employed depend on the thickness of the walls of the controlling section of the casting, as indicated in Table 1. Test bars are cast to shape and machined to size. The length of the test bar varies, depending on the bar diameter. Tensile strengths range from 20,000 to 60,000 psi for the eight grades.

Table 1. Cast-iron-test-bar Thicknesses

Casting-wall thickness, in.	Machined test-bar diam, in.	As-cast test-bar diam, in.
0.25-0.50	0.50	0.88
0.51-1.00	0.75	1.20
1.01-2.00	1.25	2.00
Over 2 in.	To be agreed upon	

The **elastic limit** of cast iron is close to its ultimate breaking strength. Gray iron can sustain indefinitely a static load just short of the tensile strength without distortion or breakage. Gray iron has low ductility and breaks without perceptible distortion. Since gray iron does not distort prior to breaking it is essential that service stresses be known or that a conservative safety factor be employed.

With static loading the ultimate strength of cast iron in tension is less than that shown in compression; the impact strength of most cast irons is low.

The tensile strength of gray iron is reduced by temperatures over 700 F, and gray iron is limited to a maximum temperature of 450 F when used under the ASME code for unfired pressure vessels. Within this range there is no perceptible change in the tensile strength of gray irons. The **damping capacity,** or the ability to absorb vibration, is high. High-strength pearlite irons, such as **meehanite,** or nodular iron, have the highest damping capacities of all engineering metals; this accounts for the common selection of cast iron for machinery bases and housings. The endurance limit of gray cast iron is from 12,000 to 24,000 psi. Meehanite metal of the GA type is reported at 28,000 psi in the quenched and tempered condition.

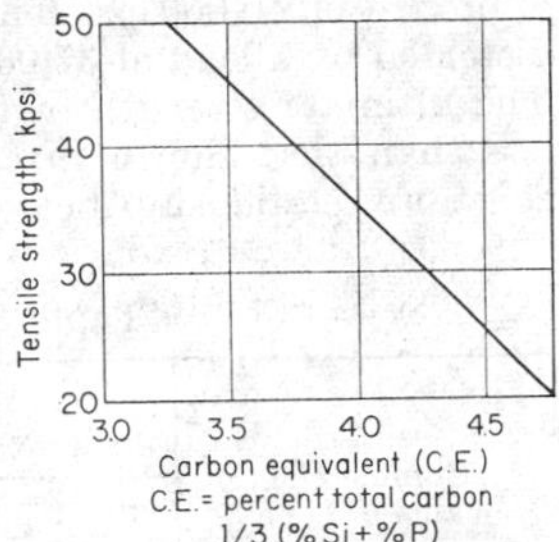

FIG. 1. General relation of tensile strength to carbon equivalent for gray cast iron in 1.2-in.-diameter cast test bars. (*Reprinted by permission from "Gray Iron Castings Handbook," Gray Iron Founders' Society, Inc., Copyright*, 1957.)

The ease of **machining** gray irons usually is inversely proportional to the strength of the casting. Chilling, heat-treatment, and alloy additions reduce the machineability. The white irons, or chilled-iron castings, are widely used for machinery parts to resist wear. High-alloy cast irons of the chromium, nickel, and silicon types are especially resistant to sulphur and acid corrosion.

Corrosion Resistance. Ordinary grades of cast iron offer considerable resistance to underground corrosion; water pipes have given constant service for over 100 years. Chromium (15 to 30 percent) imparts a protective coating to cast iron which is especially resistant to sulphur and acid corrosion. High-nickel (18 to 22 percent Ni) cast irons (Ni-Resist) are austenitic in structure and extremely corrosion resistant to many acids and alkalies. High-silicon (11 to 17 percent Si) cast irons (**Duriron, Tantiron,** etc.) are remarkably good for withstanding all acids except hydrofluoric and hot concentrated hydrochloric acid.

Table 2. Gray Cast Iron

Carbon equivalent	Tensile strength, psi	Modulus of elasticity in tension at ½ load, psi × 10^6	Modulus of rupture, psi	Deflection in 18 in. span, in.	Shear strength, psi	Endurance limit, psi	Compressive strength, psi	Brinell hardness, 3000 kg load	Izod impact, unnotched, ft-lb
4.8	20,400	8.0	48,300	0.370	29,600	10,000	72,800	146	3.6
4.6	22,400	8.7	49,200	0.251	33,000	11,400	91,000	163	3.6
4.5	25,000	9.7	58,700	0.341	35,500	11,800	95,000	163	4.9
4.3	29,300	10.5	63,300	0.141	37,000	12,300	90,900	179	2.2
4.1	32,500	13.6	73,200	0.301	44,600	16,500	120,800	192	4.2
4.0	35,100	13.3	77,000	0.326	47,600	17,400	120,800	196	4.4
3.7	40,900	14.8	84,200	0.308	47,300	19,600	119,100	215	3.9
3.3	47,700	20.0	92,000	0.230	60,800	25,200	159,000	266	4.4

General Information on Properties. Cast iron is widely used in engineering and allied industries because of the ease with which it may be cast, its moderate cost, and its wide range of useful properties. The engineer should realize that the term "cast iron" is a general term used to designate a class of materials including soft, weak irons; hard, brittle irons; and strong cast irons. Modern engineering practice classifies gray irons according to minimum-tensile-strength properties. The bulk of commercial gray irons is found in the classes from 25,000 to 50,000 psi. However, irons upward to 80,000 psi are obtainable by special processes, compositions, and treatments.

Gray iron breaks without perceptible distortion because of its low ductility. However, a gray iron of 40,000 psi tensile strength could indefinitely sustain a static load equivalent to a stress of about 37,000 psi without distortion or breakage, whereas a bronze of 40,000 psi tensile strength and 18,000 psi yield point would be grossly distorted by a load of 37,000 psi; in fact, it would continue to distort and soon break. The ultimate strength of gray iron in tension under conditions of static loading is less than that shown in compression, transverse loading, and shear. There is no constant relationship between the Brinell hardness and the tensile strength of cast

Table 3. Alloy and Special Alloy Cast Irons

Commercial name or type	Average composition, percent						Mechanical properties		Resistant to
	Total carbon	Ni	Cr	Si	Mo	Other elements	BHN	Tensile strength, psi	
Ni	2.61	1.08	.....	2.38	....	....	269	51,500	Wear
Ni-Cr	2.79	0.50	0.20	2.44	....	....	250	56,700	Wear
Ni-Cr-No	2.72	0.85	0.15	2.35	1.05	....	306	70,000	Wear
Ni-Hard	3.50	4.50	1.50	0.60	....	....	675	35,000	Wear
Nitrided cast iron	3.00	.....	1.25	1.25	0.15	Al 1.00	...	......	Wear
Cr	3.70	.....	0.75	1.10	....	Mn 0.50	250	35,000	Wear
High Cr	2.60	.....	26.70	0.33	....	....	477	......	Wear
Oil quenched	3.00	1.20	0.40	1.50	....	....	480	......	Wear
Ni-Resist	3.00	13.50	3.20	1.60	....	Cu 6.48	140	24,000	Heat and corrosion
Ni-Mo	3.25	1.00	.....	2.00	0.40	....	156	26,000	Heat
Cr	3.00	.....	1.00	2.00	....	....	...	40,000	Heat
17% Cr	2.00	.....	17.00	1.75	....	....	420	70,000	Oxidation

iron; while strong irons are somewhat harder, tensile strength cannot be consistently predicted from hardness tests. The modulus of elasticity of cast iron is proportioned to the tensile strength. The effective modulus of elasticity at 25 percent of the ultimate strength ranges from 12 million psi for the weaker irons to 18 million for the strong gray irons. Cast iron has little or no impact or shock resistance properties.

Iron Foundry Practice

Cast iron is produced from pig iron, cast-iron scrap, and steel scrap. There are eight classes of pig iron based on increasing phosphorus content. Each class has a number of grades; ASTM A43-60 recognizes 243 grades. The steel used is medium to light in character, such as clippings and punchings from structural steel plate. Melting is done mostly in cupolas, although air furnaces and electric furnaces are used. The cupola is a low-cost melting unit and can melt any type of cast iron desired. Uniformity of composition and mechanical properties can be held within fairly close limits. The other melting units have an advantage that adjustments to the composition can be made to the bath. The molten iron is poured into sand molds. Castings from a few ounces to upwards of 100 tons are produced. (See also Sec. 13.)

Obsolete Terms. Engineers should guard against the use of such terms as **semisteel** and **high-test cast iron**; both terms are obsolete. "Semisteel" was used in connection with cast iron made with steel in the melting charge, but the metal produced has none of the characteristics of steel. It is strictly a cast iron, and today most operators use some steel in their charge. The term "high-test cast iron" was used to designate a gray iron having a tensile strength greater than that of ordinary cast iron.

Purchase Specification for Cast-iron Castings

Engineers should purchase cast-iron castings to the ASTM specifications. They are known and understood by cast-iron founders. The most generally used specification is ASTM A48-60T Gray Iron Castings, summarized as follows:

Gray-iron castings are classified according to **tensile strength.** The following minimum values are specified:

Class No.	20	25	30	35	40	50	60
Tensile strength, min, kpsi	20	25	30	35	40	50	60

Transverse tests are optional. The following minimum breaking loads are specified:

Thickness of critical casting section, in.	Test bar	Diam of test bar, in.	Span length, in.	Class No. 20	25	30	35	40	50	60
				Min breaking load at center, lb						
0.50 and under	A	0.875	12	900	1,025	1,150	1,275	1,400	1,675	1,925
0.51–1.00	B	1.20	18	1,800	2,000	2,200	2,400	2,600	3,000	3,400
1.01 and up	C	2.00	24	6,000	6,800	7,600	8,300	9,100	10,300	12,500

The **test bars** are cast separately from the casting but made under the same sand conditions as the casting and receive the same thermal treatment.

Other ASTM specifications for cast iron are as follows: A126-61T Gray Iron Castings for Valves, Flanges and Pipe Fittings; A159-58 Gray Iron Castings, Automotive; A278-61T Gray Iron Castings for Pressure-containing Parts for Temperatures up to 650 deg F; A319-53 Gray Iron Castings for Elevated Temperatures for Non-pressure-containing Parts; A74-42 Cast Iron Soil Pipe and Fittings; A142-61 Cast Iron Culvert Pipe; A377-57 Cast Iron Pressure Pipe; A436-61T Gray Iron Castings, Austenitic. The methods of testing cast-iron castings are as follows: A256-46 Compression Testing of Cast Iron; A327-54 Impact Testing of Cast Iron; A438-60T Transverse Testing of Gray Cast Iron.

Tolerances for Gray-iron Castings

Pattern shrinkage tolerances compensate for the shrinkage of gray iron on cooling from solidification to room temperature. The value of 1 percent, or approximately ⅛ in. per ft, is the one commonly used. The amount of shrinkage varies somewhat with the size of the casting and the resistance offered by the mold as follows:

Pattern dimension, in.	Type of construction	Shrinkage allowance, in. per ft
Up to 24	Open	⅛
25–48	Open	1/10
Over 48	Open	1/12
Up to 24	Cored	⅛
25–36	Cored	1/10
Over 36	Cored	1/12
High-alloy irons up to 48	.....	5/32

Casting finish tolerances (unmachined) are related to the pattern tolerances. The purchaser should allow, for miscellaneous castings, a dimensional tolerance approximately one-half of the maximum shrinkage tolerance or ±1/16 in. (0.06 in.) for castings approaching a foot in length. Certain small castings, such as cams, camshafts, etc., are being held to ±1/32 in. (0.03 in.). Medium-size castings (3 ft in length) are produced to a value of ±3/20 in. Tolerances for heavy-cored areas are ±1/10 in. per ft. Tolerances for highly repetitive jobs, such as automotive cylinder blocks, can be held to ±1/64 in. (0.015 in.) for length up to an 8 in. span. Over 8 in., a tolerance of ±1/32 in. is considered normal.

Machine finish tolerances are normally 3/32 to 1/8 in. In the machine-tool industry, where casting of 100 to 2,000 lb is common, machining allowances of 3/16 in. to 1/4 in. usually are specified. The following table shows some common machining tolerances or allowances:

Pattern size, in.	Bore, in.	Finish, in.*
Up to 12	1/8	3/32
13–24	3/16	1/8
25–42	1/4	3/16
43–60	5/16	1/4
61–80	3/8	5/16
81–120	7/16	3/8
Over 120	Special instructions required	

* Surfaces to be machined should be located in the lower, or "drag," sections of the mold for minimum machine tolerances. Additional finish allowances of 1/32 to 1/16 in. greater than shown may be desirable if certain upper, or "cope," surfaces are to be machined.

Nodular (Ductile) Cast Iron

Nodular iron is a cast iron produced by adding to it graphite spherulitic alloys, such as magnesium and cerium. The addition causes the graphite to form as small nodules or spheroids instead of as the normal angular flakes. Quality-control processes are required to produce cast iron of high strengths with reasonable amounts of ductility.

As-cast grades of ductile iron have a tensile strength between 60,000 and 105,000 psi with an elongation of 10.0 to 1.0 percent, depending on composition. Annealing increases the elongation to 10 to 25 percent with a tensile strength of 60,000 to 75,000 psi. Normalized and tempered specimens have a tensile strength of 90,000 to 120,000 psi with an elongation of 2.0 to 5.0 percent. The varying composition of the base metal, the methods of nodularizing, and the control measures account for the wide range of tensile values in these test bars.

The notched impact value as measured by the standard Charpy specimen is very low, being less than 5 ft-lb approx at room temperatures. The endurance limit varies from 35,000 to 40,000 for tensile strengths of 70,000 to 95,000 psi. The material appears to have the advantages of cast iron (fluidity, low melting point, good machinability) with the tensile strength of carbon cast steel.

Nodular iron can be produced by any of the furnaces used for the melting of cast iron, although the electric-arc furnaces produce more closely controlled nodular iron. **Specifications for nodular iron** have been prepared by ASTM: A339–55 Nodular-iron Castings; A395–61 Cast Nodular Iron for Pressure Containing Parts for Use at Elevated Temperatures; A396–58 High Strength Nodular Iron Castings; A436–61 Austenitic Gray Iron Castings.

The property requirements for the low- and high-strength grades are as follows:

	A339		A396	
	60–45–10	80–60–03	100–70–03	120–90–02
Tensile strength, min psi	60,000	80,000	100,000	120,000
Yield strength, min psi	45,000	60,000	70,000	90,000
Elongation in 2 in., min %	10	3*	3	2

* Where strength is the prime requirement, the elongation requirement may be waived by agreement.

Tensile test bars (0.505 in. diam) are machined from coupons of three different section thicknesses: ½, 1, and 3 in. The coupons are to be cast at the same time the castings are cast and are to be of a comparable section thickness.

The **application** of nodular iron in brief summary is as follows:

Type	BHN	Characteristics	Application
60–45–10	140–190	Annealed ferritic matrix, good machinability and ductility	Valves, pumps, and pressure parts
80–60–03	200–270	Pearlitic matrix, as-cast high strength	Heavy-duty machinery gears, rolls, statically loaded castings
100–70–03 120–90–02	240–300 270–350	Normalized and tempered or quenched and tempered	Wear-resistant parts, pinions, gears, cams, guides, rollers

The engineer should employ factors of safety similar to those used for cast iron. Materials with less than 5 percent ductility are not usually considered as ductile materials. Notched-impact properties are low, and shock-loading applications need confirming service testing.

MALLEABLE-IRON CASTINGS

Composition. Malleable-iron castings may be broadly divided as follows: (1) standard malleable irons, (2) pearlitic malleable irons, (3) special malleable irons, and (4) cupola malleable irons. The chemical composition of the white iron from which the standard malleable iron is produced falls generally within the following limits: carbon 2.00 to 2.70, silicon 1.20 to 0.80, manganese less than 0.55, phosphorus less than 0.20, and sulphur less than 0.18 percent. Pearlitic malleable irons are made from a chemical composition similar to that of standard malleable iron together with additional alloys or so heat-treated that some of the carbon in the resultant material is in the combined form. Special malleable irons consist principally of those with a high silicon content, those alloyed with copper, and those alloyed with copper and molybdenum. High-silicon malleable permits short annealing times. Copper is used as an alloy to increase strength and endurance limit. The copper-molybdenum malleable iron is used for extra-high strengths. Cupola malleable-iron composition is carbon 2.80 to 3.30, silicon 1.10 to 0.60, and manganese 0.40 to 0.65 percent. Most of the commercial malleable is produced in the standard grade.

Mechanical Properties. The tensile strength of malleable irons vary from 50 to 110 kpsi approx. The tensile strength of the standard grade is from 50 to 60 kpsi approx. Specification minimum values for malleable irons are given in Table 4.

Table 4. Specification Minimum Properties of Malleable Irons

Type	ASTM specification	Tensile strength, min psi	Yield point, min psi	Elongation, min percent	BHN, typical range
Cupola.......	A197–47	40,000	30,000	5	
Standard.....	A47–61(32510)	50,000	32,500	10	110–130
Standard.....	A47–61(35018)	53,000	35,000	18	120–145
Pearlitic......	A220–61T(45010)	65,000	45,000	10	163–207
Pearlitic......	A220–61T(45007)	68,000	45,000	7	163–217
Pearlitic......	A220–61T(48004)	70,000	48,000	4	163–229
Pearlitic......	A220–61T(50007)	75,000	50,000	7	179–229
Pearlitic......	A220–61T(53004)	80,000	53,000	4	197–241
Pearlitic......	A220–61T(60003)	80,000	60,000	3	197–255
Pearlitic......	A220–61T(80003)	100,000	80,000	2	241–269

Standard malleable iron has an average endurance limit of 54,630 psi and an endurance ratio of 0.575. The notch-fatigue ratio is 0.33. The ultimate strength of malleable iron in shear is roughly 90 percent of the ultimate tensile strength. The modulus of rigidity is about 11 million psi. The impact resistance of standard-grade malleable iron, measured by the Charpy test, keyhole notch, is 6.5 to 8.0 ft-lb.

Malleable iron has excellent machinability. With SAE 1112 steel rated at the base value of 100, the following ratings have been given:

Malleable irons	Machinability value	BHN
Standard	120	110–145
Pearlitic	90	180–200
Pearlitic	80	200–240

Malleable iron has a high resistance to atmospheric corrosion and finds wide use as pole-line hardware, bridge railings, panels, street signs, etc. Malleable-iron castings are used extensively for automobile, agricultural-implement, conveyor, and handling equipment, and in electrical, power, and railroad industries.

Specifications and Use. ASTM specification A47–61 Malleable Iron Castings leads the field in production volume and is the standard grade of malleable, consisting largely of ferrite interspersed by nodules of free carbon; A220–61T Pearlitic Malleable Iron Castings, which contains some carbon in the combined form through special heat-treatment and by alloying to make it pearlitic, has rapidly increased in use during the past decade; A197–47 Cupola Malleable Iron has been almost completely supplanted by the other classes. Specification values are given in Table 4. Another standard specification, A338–61, covers Malleable Iron Flanges, Pipe Fillings, and Valve Parts for Railroad, Marine and Other Heavy Duty Service at Temperatures up to 650 F.

Processing Methods. The production of malleable-iron castings consists of two steps: the manufacture of the white-iron casting and its subsequent conversion into the tough malleable product. This conversion is accomplished by heating the white iron to 1500 to 1600 F. If this temperature is maintained, the combined carbon (Fe_3C) will be dissolved and will tend to precipitate out as a "temper" carbon. The resultant matrix consists of iron interspersed with nodules of tempered graphite.

Castings having sections over 2 in. do not lend themselves to production in malleable iron. There are very few malleable castings that weigh over 500 lb. Most castings weigh from a few ounces to less than 100 lb. Fusion welding is not recommended.

Tolerances for Malleable-iron Castings

Pattern shrinkage tolerances for malleable-iron castings are approximately ⅛ in. per ft. Draft allowances are 1/64 in. per in. for production patterns; ¼ in. per in. for loose patterns.

Casting-finish tolerances (unmachined) for green-sand molding on the basis of outside dimensions are: up to 4 in., ±1/32; 4 to 8 in., ±3/64; 8 to 12 in., ±1/16; 12 to 24 in., ±⅛ in. Shell-molding tolerances are about two-thirds of these values.

Machine finish allowances recommended for malleable-iron castings are: (1) milling—1/16 to 3/32 for small castings, ⅛ to 3/16 for medium castings, and somewhat greater for large castings weighing 100 lb or more; (2) reaming—3/32 in. on the diameter for cored holes under 1 in., ⅛ to 3/16 in. on the diameter for medium holes, and more for large holes; (3) turning or boring—diameters larger than 5 in., ¼ to ⅜ in. on the diameter.

STEEL CASTINGS

Composition. There are five classes of commercial steel castings:

1. Low-carbon steels (carbon below 0.20 percent)
2. Medium-carbon steels (carbon between 0.20 and 0.50 percent)
3. High-carbon steels (carbon above 0.50 percent)
4. Low-alloy steels (total alloy less than 8 percent)
5. High-alloy steels (total alloy more than 8 percent)

Carbon-steel Castings. Carbon-steel castings contain less than 1.70 percent C, along with other elements normally present. These elements may be present in percentages ranging as follows: Mn 0.50 to 1.00, Si 0.20 to 0.70, max P 0.05, and max

S 0.06. In addition, carbon-steel castings contain small percentages of other elements, which were not added but were residual in the scrap steel used as part of the melting charge.

The medium-carbon class, constituting the bulk of the steel casting output, is the regular grade product. Low- and high-carbon grades have been developed for specialized products and uses.

Alloy-steel Castings. A steel casting is considered to be an alloy-steel casting if the alloying elements, either residual or added, are present in percentages greater than the following: Mn, 1.00; Si, 0.70; Cu, 0.50; Cr, 0.25; Mo, 0.10; V, 0.05; W, 0.05; Al, 0.05; Ti, 0.05. Limitations on phosphorus and sulphur contents apply to cast alloy steels as well as to cast carbon steels unless they are specified for the purpose of producing an alloying effect. The low-alloy casting class represents a considerable portion of the total steel-casting production in this country. High-alloy steel castings of the heat- and corrosion-resistant type are similar to the wrought stainless steels (see p. 6-39).

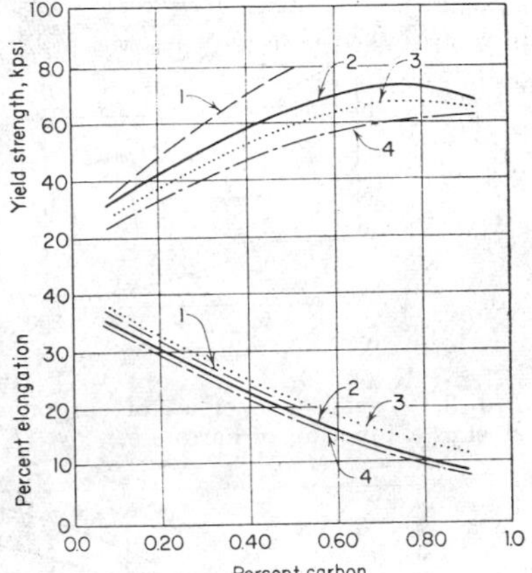

FIG. 2. Yield strength and elongation vs. carbon content for carbon cast steels. (1) Water quenched and tempered—1200 F. (2) Normalized. (3) Normalized and tempered—1200 F. (4) Annealed.

Weight Range. Steel castings range from a few ounces to many tons. The largest on record had a finished weight of 230 tons. Steel castings may be made of any thickness down to about ¼ in.

Mechanical Properties. The outstanding mechanical properties of cast steel are strength, ductility, and resistance to impact. Steel castings possess high rigidity and are capable of withstanding both high and low temperatures, are weldable and have excellent endurance properties.

The mechanical properties of carbon steel are shown in Figs. 2 and 3. The properties of low-alloy cast steels are given in Figs. 4 and 5. In the heat- and corrosion-resistant class of alloy castings there are 46 class designations. Table 7 lists the ASTM requirements for heat and corrosion alloy castings; the strength values normally expected are from 10 to 25 percent above the specification minimum values.

Tensile and Yield Strength. Ferritic steels of a given hardness or hardenability have the same tensile strength whether cast, rolled, wrought, or welded, regardless of the alloy content. For design purposes involving tensile and yield properties, rolled, wrought, cast, and welded steels can be interchanged with the fullest confidence.

Ductility. If the ductility properties of steels are compared with their hardness values, cast, wrought, rolled steels and welds are almost identical. The longitudinal properties of the forged and rolled steels are slightly higher than those of cast steel or weld metal. The transverse properties are lower, by an amount that depends on the degree of working. Since most service conditions involve several directions of loading, the securing of uniform directional properties of cast steel is sometimes particularly advantageous.

Impact. The notched-bar impact test is often used as a measurement of the toughness of materials. Cast steels have excellent impact resistance at normal and low temperatures. Generally, wrought steels are tested in the direction of rolling, and show higher impact values than cast steels of similar composition. Transverse impact values will be 50 to 70 percent of these values. Cast steels do not show directional properties. If the directional properties are averaged for wrought steels, the values obtained are comparable to the values obtained for cast steels of similar composition. The **hardenability** of cast steels is influenced by composition and other

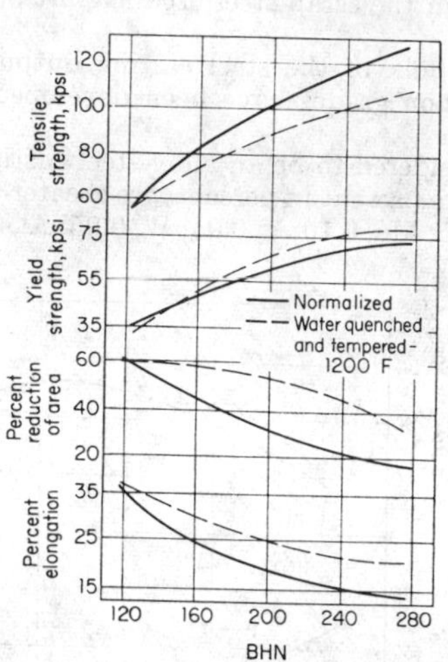

FIG. 3. Tensile properties of carbon cast steel as a function of hardness.

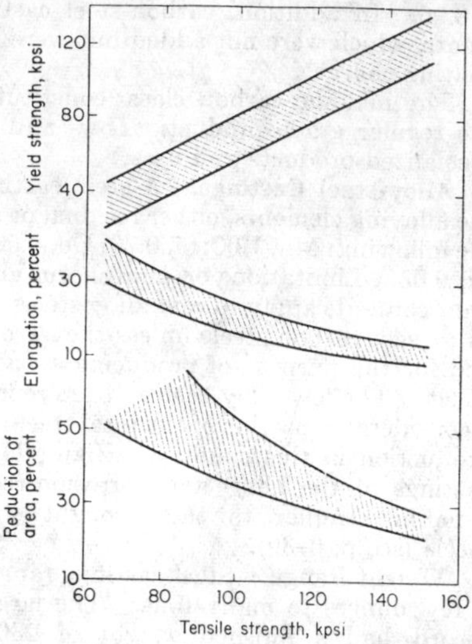

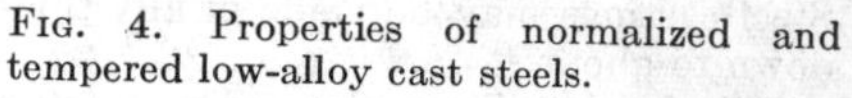

FIG. 4. Properties of normalized and tempered low-alloy cast steels.

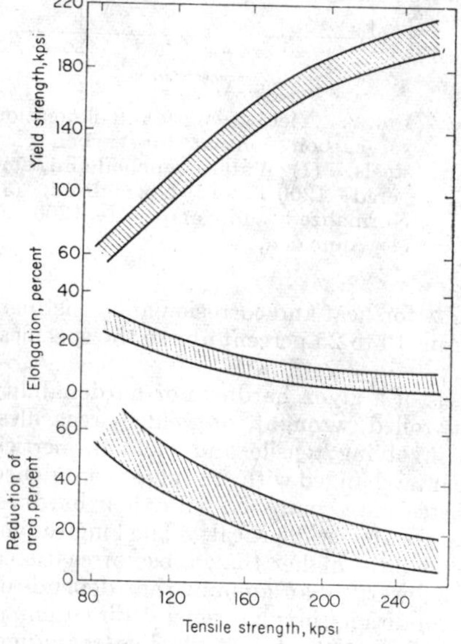

FIG. 5. Properties of quenched and tempered low-alloy cast steels.

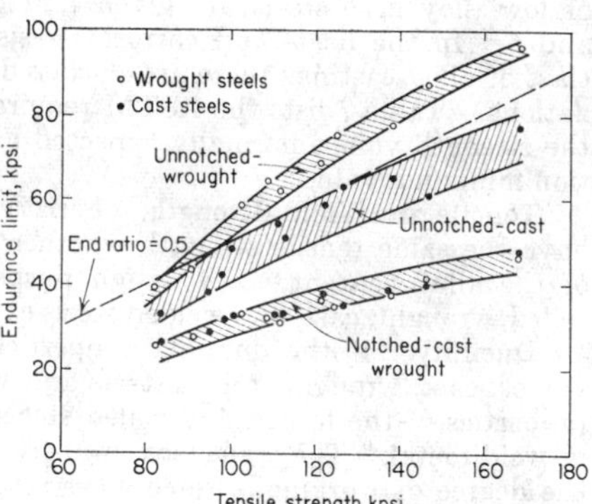

FIG. 6. Variation of endurance limit with tensile strength for comparable carbon and low-alloy and wrought steels.

variables in the same manner as the hardenability of wrought steels. The ratio of the **endurance limit** to the tensile strength for cast steel varies from 0.42 to 0.50, depending somewhat upon the composition and heat-treatment of the steel. The notch-fatigue ratio varies from 0.28 to 0.32 for cast steels and is the same for wrought steels (Fig. 6).

In wear resistance testing, cast steels react similarly to rolled steels and give corresponding values, depending on composition, structure, and hardness. Carbon cast steels of approximately 0.50 percent C and low-alloy cast steels of the chromium, chromium-molybdenum, nickel-chromium, chromium-vanadium, and medium-manganese types, all of which contain more than 0.40 percent C, have given excellent resistance to wear in service.

Corrosion Resistance. Cast steel and wrought steel of similar composition and heat-treatment appear to be equally resistant to corrosion in the same environments. Small amounts of copper in cast steel increase the resistance of steel to atmospheric corrosion. High-alloy cast steels of chromium and chromium-nickel types are normally used for corrosion resistance.

Table 5. Machinability Index for Cast Steels

Steel	BHN	Conventional		Metcut*	
		Carbide	HSS	HSS	Carbide
B1112 Free machining steel (wrought)	179	..	100		
1020 Annealed	122	10	90	160	400
1020 Normalized	134	6	75	135	230
1040 Double normalized	185	11	70	130	400
1040 Normalized and annealed	175	10	75	135	380
1040 Normalized	190	6	65	120	325
1040 Normalized and oil quenched	225	6	45	80	310
1330 Normalized	187	2	40	75	140
1330 Normalized and tempered	160	3	65	120	230
4130 Annealed	175	4	55	95	260
4130 Normalized and spheroidized	175	3	50	90	200
4340 Normalized and annealed	200	3	35	60	210
4340 Normalized and spheroidized	210	6	55	95	290
4340 Quenched and tempered	300	2	25	45	200
4340 Quenched and tempered	400	½	20	35	180
8430 Normalized and tempered @ 1200 F	200	3	50	90	200
8430 Normalized and tempered @ 1275 F	180	4	60	110	240
8630 Normalized	240	2	40	75	180
8630 Annealed	175	5	65	120	290

* The metcut speed index number is the actual cutting speed (surface ft per min) which will give 1 hr tool life in turning.

Heat Resistance. Although not comparable to the high-alloy steels of the nickel-chromium type especially designed for heat resistance, the 4.0 to 6.5 percent Cr cast steels, particularly with additions of 0.75 to 1.25 W, or 0.40 to 0.70 Mo and 0.75 to 1.00 Ti, show good strength and considerable resistance to scaling at 1000 F and below.

The **machinability** of carbon and alloy cast steels is comparable to that of wrought steels having equivalent strength, ductility, and hardness, and similar microstructure. Factors influencing the machinability of cast steel are as follows: (1) Microstructure has a definite effect on the machinability of cast steels. In some cases it is possible to improve machining characteristics as much as 100 to 200 percent through heat-treatments, which alter the microstructure. (2) Generally speaking, hardness alone cannot be taken as the criterion for predicting tool life in the cutting of cast steels. (3) In general, for a given structure, the plain carbon steels possess better machining properties than the alloy steels. (4) The tool life of carbon (1040) cast steel, when machined with carbides, varies as the ratio of ferrite to pearlite in its microstructure, the $^{60}/_{40}$ ratio machining best. (5) To obtain equivalent tool life, the skin of a cast steel should be machined at approximately one-half of the cutting speed recommended for the base metal. The machinability of various carbon and low-alloy cast steels is given in Table 5.

The **welding** of steel castings presents the same problems as the welding of wrought steels.

Purchase Specifications for Steel Castings. Most steel castings are purchased according to mechanical property specifications rather than according to the SAE or AISI numbering system for ranges of chemical composition. These composition ranges are used as the basis of purchase requirements when the purchaser is considering certain definite engineering properties, such as wear resistance, weldability, high temperature service, and corrosion resistance. Engineers should purchase steel castings to the ASTM specifications. They are jointly prepared by purchasers and manufacturers of steel castings and are well known and understood by steel foundrymen. The most generally used specifications are ASTM A27–60 Mild- to Medium-strength Carbon-steel Castings for General Application and A148–60, High-strength Steel Castings for Structural Purposes. A summary of these specifications is given in Table 6. The values specified in the table are minimum values used as rejection limits. The normal expected values of cast steel meeting these requirements are from 10 to 40 percent above the specification minimums.

Table 6. ASTM Requirements for Steel Castings, Mechanical Properties

Grade	Tensile strength, min kpsi	Yield point, min, kpsi	Elongation in 2 in., min, percent	Reduction of area, min, percent
		ASTM A27–60		
60–30	60	30	24	35
65–35	65	35	24	35
70–36	70	36	22	30
		ASTM A148–60		
80–40	80	40	18	30
80–50	80	50	22	35
90–60	90	60	20	40
105–85	105	85	17	35
120–95	120	95	14	30
150–125	150	125	9	22
175–145	175	145	6	12

Other ASTM specifications for steel castings are as follows: A128–60, Austenitic-Manganese-Steel Castings; A95–44, Carbon-steel Castings for Valves, Flanges, and Fittings for High-temperature Service; A216–60T, Carbon-steel Castings Suitable for Fusion Welding for High-temperature Service; A217–60T, Alloy-steel Castings Suitable for Fusion Welding for High-temperature Service; A296–60T, Corrosion-resistant Iron-Chromium and Iron-Chromium-Nickel-Alloy Castings for General Applications; A297–60T, Heat-resistant Iron-Chromium and Iron-Chromium-Nickel-Alloy Castings for General Application; A351–61T, Ferritic and Austenitic Steel Castings for High-temperature Service; A352–60T, Ferritic Steel Castings for Pressure-containing Parts Suitable for Low-temperature Service; A356–60T, Heavy-walled Carbon and Low-alloy Steel Castings for Steam Turbines; A362–52T, Iron-Chromium and Iron-Chromium-Nickel-Alloy Tubular Centrifugal Castings for General Applications; A389–60T, Alloy-steel Castings Normalized and Drawn for High-pressure and Elevated-temperature Service; A447–50, Chromium-Nickel-Iron-Alloy Castings (25–12 Class) for High-temperature Service; A448–50, Nickel-Chromium-Iron-Alloy Castings (35–15 Class) for High-temperature Service.

A summary of the requirements for the heat and corrosion specifications A296 and A297 is given in Table 7 to indicate the types of stainless steels cast in steel foundries.

Steel Melting Practice. Steel for steel castings is produced commercially by almost all the currently used processes of making steel: open-hearth (acid and basic), electric-arc (acid and basic), converter (side-blown, acid), and electric-induction.

The melting methods employed are similar to those for ingot production, except the acid electric-arc and high-frequency furnace practices which apply directly to steel-casting production. The primary differences between the production of steel for castings and for ingots are that the steel for castings must always be a dead-killed steel having a high degree of fluidity. Approximately 75 grades of carbon and alloy cast steels and 40 grades of heat- and corrosion-resistant alloy-steel castings are being made by the industry.

Table 7. ASTM Requirements for Corrosion and Heat-resistant Alloy-steel Castings

Specification and heat treatment		Mechanical properties—min			Chemical composition percent—max					
Specification	Class	Tensile strength, psi	Yield point, psi	Elong in 2 in., percent	C	Mn	Si	Ni	Cr	Mo
ASTM A296–60T	CA-15	90,000	65,000	18	0.15	1.00	1.50	1.00	11.5–14	0.50
	CB-30	65,000	30,000	...	0.30	1.00	1.50	2.00	18–21	
	CC-50	55,000	......	...	0.50	1.00	1.50	4.00	26–30	
	CE-30	80,000	40,000	10	0.30	1.50	2.00	8–11	26–30	
	CF-8	65,000	28,000	35	0.08	1.50	2.00	8–11	18–21	
	CF-8C	70,000	30,000	30	0.08	1.50	2.00	9–12	18–21	
	CF-8M	70,000	30,000	30	0.08	1.50	2.00	9–12	18–21	2.00–3.00
	CF-16F	70,000	30,000	25	0.16	1.50	2.00	9–12	18–21	
	CF-20	70,000	30,000	30	0.20	1.50	2.00	8–11	18–21	
	CG-12	70,000	28,000	35	0.12	1.50	2.00	10–13	20–23	
	CH-20	70,000	30,000	30	0.20	1.50	2.00	12–15	22–26	
	CK-20	65,000	28,000	30	0.20	2.00	2.00	19–22	23–27	
	CA-40	90,000	65,000	18	0.20–.40	1.00	1.50	1	11.5–14	0.5
	CF-3	65,000	28,000	35	0.03	1.50	2.00	8–12	17–21	
	CF-3M	70,000	30,000	30	0.03	1.50	1.50	9–13	17–21	2–3
	CG-8M	75,000	35,000	25	0.08	1.50	1.50	9–13	18–21	3–4
ASTM A297–60T	HC	55,000	......	...	0.50	1.00	2.00	4.00	26–30	0.50
	HE	85,000	40,000	9	0.20–.50	2.00	2.00	8–11	26–30	0.50
	HF	70,000	35,000	25	0.20–.40	2.00	2.00	8–12	18–23	0.50
	HH	75,000	35,000	10	0.20–.50	2.00	2.00	11–14	24–28	0.50
	HI	70,000	35,000	10	0.20–.50	2.00	2.00	14–18	26–30	0.50
	HK	65,000	35,000	10	0.20–.60	2.00	2.00	18–22	24–28	0.50
	HT	65,000	......	4	0.35–.75	2.00	2.50	33–37	13–17	0.50
	HU	65,000	......	4	0.35–.75	2.00	2.50	37–41	17–21	0.50
	HW	60,000	......	...	0.35–.75	2.00	2.50	58–62	10–14	0.50
	HX	60,000	......	...	0.35–.75	2.00	2.50	64–68	15–19	0.50
	HD	75,000	35,000	8	0.50	1.50	2.00	4–7	26–30	0.50
	HL	65,000	35,000	10	0.20–.60	2.00	2.00	18–22	28–32	0.50
	HN	63,000	......	8	0.20–.50	2.00	2.00	23–27	19–23	0.50

Tolerances for Steel Castings

Pattern shrinkage tolerances for steel castings vary from $\frac{9}{32}$ to $\frac{1}{16}$ in. per ft. The figure often used is $\frac{3}{16}$ in. per ft, but its universal adoption would lead to trouble and errors in steel casting dimensions and tolerances. The best policy is to discuss pattern shrinkage tolerances with the foundry that is to make the castings.

Minimum Section Thickness. The fluidity of steel in comparison with other metals is known to be low. In order that sections be completely run, it is necessary that a minimum value of section thickness be adopted as a function of the largest dimension of the casting. Values suggested for design use are as follows:

Minimum section thickness, in.	Maximum length of section, in.
¼	12
½	50

Casting finish tolerances (unmachined) are based on the longest dimension of the casting, and the values vary, depending on the type of pattern equipment employed. The average tolerances are given in Table 8.

Machine finish tolerances to be added to the casting section for machining purposes will depend entirely on the casting design, and definite values cannot be established for all casting designs but guides can be suggested to designers. Table 9 presents a guide to machine allowances on gears, wheels, and circular-shaped and flat castings.

Table 8. Dimensional Tolerances for Steel Castings*

(Deviation from the design dimension)

Pattern type	Blueprint dimension, in.			
	0–3.0	3.1–7.0	7.1–20.0	20.1–100.0
Metal match plate	+1/32, −1/16	+3/32, −1/16	+1/8, −1/16	+1/8, −1/8
Metal pattern mounted on cope and drag boards	+1/16, −1/16	+3/32, −3/32	+1/8, −3/32	+7/32, −1/8
Hardwood pattern mounted on cope and drag boards	+3/32, −1/16	+1/8, −3/32	+1/8, −3/32	+1/4, −5/32

* Surfaces that are not to be machined.

Table 9. A Guide to Machine-finish Allowances*

Circular shapes		Bores		Flat shapes	
Casting diam, in.	Allowance on outside radius, in.	Bore diam, in.	Allowance on bore radius, in.	Greatest casting dimension, in.	Allowance, in.
Up to 18	1/4	Up to 1	Cast solid	Up to 12	3/16
18–36	5/16	2–7	1/4	12–24	1/4
36–48	3/8	7–12	3/8	24–48	5/16
48–72	1/2	12–20	1/2	48–96	3/8
72–108	5/8			96 and up	1/2
108 and up†	3/4				

* These allowances apply to short orders and may be reduced somewhat on production runs which permit adequate pilot work to be done. They also indicate that a flat surface is more easily produced than a true circle.

† Machine allowances for castings greater than 15 ft should be determined through consultation with the producing foundry.

Precision-casting Processes

Investment Process. This is the "lost wax" method used by ancient craftsmen, readapted after the First World War for jewelry and denture manufacture, and used extensively in the Second World War for aircraft engine parts. Patterns are formed by pressure injection of wax or plastic into a precision metallic die. Patterns, either singly or in groups, are fitted with wax gates and risers for casting metals and precoated with a fine silica mixture by spraying or dipping. This is followed by a coarser "stucco" coat. The assembly is then placed in a flask and covered (invested) with a slurry of refractory material which is chemically bonded. Entrapped air is removed by vibrating the filled flask or by application of vacuum. After the mold has set, the pattern is melted out, and the mold is heated slowly to 1900 F. Metal is poured into the hot mold at proper casting temperatures. Silica, zircon, zirconia, or sillimanite in powder form are used as investments for casting steels and irons.

A modification of the above is the use of frozen mercury as the pattern. The frozen pattern is dipped several times in a refractory mixture to build upon investment around the frozen mercury pattern. The mercury is melted out and the mold fired to a hard ceramic shell.

Carbon steels, low-alloy steels, stainless steels, high-alloy base alloys are produced normally in weights from a few ounces to 4 and 6 lb. A limited number of patterns for castings in the 20 to 100 lb weight class have been produced.

Shell Molding. A thermosetting sand and resin mixture is applied mechanically to a hot pattern plate for a controlled time to form a plastic layer adjacent to the pattern. Excess sand mixture is dumped off the pattern. The shell is cured on the pattern and then stripped from the pattern. Matching shells, with shell cores inserted for complex parts, are pasted or clamped together for pouring. Shells may be backed with sand or shot or may receive metal unsupported. The resin burns out of the sand, allowing the mold to crumble away from the solidified casting.

All the ferrous metals are cast in the shell-molding process—carbon- and low-alloy steel castings, gray-iron, nodular-iron, and malleable-iron castings, as well as stainless steels. Current commercial production is largely castings ranging from ½ to 20 lb in weight. Castings up to 36 in. in length have been made and shell-making equipment for patterns 72 × 48 in. is projected.

CO_2 Process. CO_2 is applied under pressure to a core or mold composed of silica sand mixed with a sodium silicate binder. The CO_2 reacts with the sodium silicate to form a silica gel which sets a hard rigid mold or core. Cast-iron and steel castings are produced in molds of this type.

True Centrifugal Castings. Cast-iron or steel molds are used in a horizontal-spindle machine for the casting of tubular castings such as liners, tubes, etc. Weighed molten metal is poured into the metal mold while spinning. Centrifugal force permits uniformly thick wall sections to form. A wide range of sizes is produced commercially.

Graphite Mold Process. This is a process for the manufacture of permanent molds for casting steel car wheels. The mold cavity is machined in a graphite block. Matching mold halves are clamped together and the metal poured under pressure. Quick chilling of graphite molds improves strength of castings. Surface finishes are superior to those produced by sand casting. Production sizes range up to 200 lb.

Ceramicast Process. The mold is formed of a mixture of fine ceramic material and ethyl silicate, which is elastic for a time during the setting period, thus facilitating stripping the mold from the pattern. The process is used for alloy and stainless-steel castings. Sizes range from a few ounces to 20 lb, and upwards of 20 in. in diameter.

Ceramic Molds. Various ceramic bodies and metal pattern dies are processed with presses to form molds. The molds are then fired to high temperature and poured with carbon, low-alloy, and stainless steels. Castings of any size can be produced. There is limited commercial application at the present.

Use of Steel Castings

All major construction industries employ steel castings. They constitute the major truck construction for railroad cars and are employed in large numbers in road-building equipment, trucks, trailers, agricultural equipment, tractors, hoists, and power shovels. Steel castings are also employed as valves, fittings, and other parts for refinery and chemical industries. Large castings find service in rolling mills, ships, and marine, mining, logging, and machine-tool industries. The military requires ordnance, naval, and aircraft castings. If service requirements include dynamic loading and impact and fatigue-stress conditions, then steel castings are employed.

Casting Design

Maximum service and properties can be obtained from castings only when they are properly designed. Design rules for castings have been prepared in detail to aid design engineers in preparing efficient designs. Engineers are referred to the following publications, which are procured: "Steel Castings Handbook," Steel Founders' Soc., 21010 Center Ridge Rd., Rocky River, Ohio, 44116; "Casting Design Handbook," Am. Soc. for Metals, Metals Park, Ohio; "Design of Ferrous Castings," Am. Foundrymen's Soc., Des Plaines, Ill.; "Gray Iron Castings Handbook," Gray Iron Founders' Soc., 930 National City E. 6 Bldg., Cleveland, Ohio; "Malleable Iron Castings," Malleable Founders' Soc., 781 Union Commerce Bldg., Cleveland, Ohio.

NON-FERROUS METALS

BY

R. P. Carreker, Jr.

ACKNOWLEDGEMENT: Consultation and information provided by the following individuals facilitated the revision of this section: A. N. Holden, J. H. Westbrook, G. Oxx, and H. T. McHenry, General Electric Co.; R. S. Burr, Anaconda American Brass Co.; E. L. Hill, The Dow Chemical Co.; E. W. Horvick, American Zinc Inst.; J. B. Long, Tin Research Inst.; H. J. Rowe, Aluminum Co. of America; M. P. Buck, The International Nickel Co.; E. F. Erbin, Titanium Metals Corp.

REFERENCES: "Metals Handbook," 8th ed., ASM. Hoyt, "Metals and Alloys Data Book," Reinhold. Smithells, "Metals Reference Book," Interscience. Hampel, "Rare Metals Handbook," Reinhold. Everhart *et al.*, "Mechanical Properties of Metals and Alloys," GPO. Kohl, "Materials Technology for Electron Tubes," Reinhold. Savitsky (Sherby, ed.), "The Influence of Temperature on the Mechanical Properties of Metals and Alloys," Stanford Univ. Press. Wulff, Taylor, and Shaler, "Metallurgy for Engineers," Wiley. Guy, "Elements of Physical Metallurgy," Addison-Wesley. ASM Review of Metal Literature. ASTM Standards. Brady, "Materials Handbook," McGraw-Hill. Weiss, "Aerospace Structural Metals Handbook," Syracuse Univ. Press. For a comprehensive list of trade terms, compositions, properties, and manufacturers of commercially available alloys, see Woldman and Metzler, "Engineering Alloys," ASM. See also publications of various metals-producing companies.

Seven **non-ferrous metals** are of primary commercial importance: copper, zinc, lead, tin, aluminum, nickel, and magnesium. Some 40 other elements are frequently alloyed with these to make the commercially important alloys. There are also about 15 minor metals that have important specific uses. The properties of these elements are given in Table 1. (See also Sec. 4, Thermal Properties of Bodies; Sec. 5, Mechanical Properties of Materials; p. 6–3 *et seq.*, General Properties of Materials.)

Metallic Properties. Metals are substances that characteristically are opaque crystalline solids of high reflectivity having good electrical and thermal conductivities, a positive chemical valence, and, usually, the important combination of considerable strength and the ability to flow before fracture. These characteristics are exhibited by the metallic elements (*e.g.*, iron, copper, aluminum), or **pure metals,** and by combinations of elements (*e.g.*, steel, brass, dural), or **alloys.** Metals are composed of many small **crystals,** which have grown individually until they have filled the intervening spaces by abutting neighboring crystals. Although the external shape of these crystals and their orientation with respect to each other are usually random, within each such **grain,** or crystal, the atoms are arranged on a regular three-dimensional lattice. Most metals are arranged according to one of the three common types of **lattice,** or **crystal structure:** face-centered cubic, body-centered cubic, or hexagonal close-packed. (See Table 1.)

The several properties of metals are influenced to varying degrees by the testing or service **environment** (temperature, surrounding medium) and the **internal structure** of the metal, which is a result of its chemical composition and previous history such as casting, hot rolling, cold extrusion, annealing, and heat-treatment. These relationships, and the discussions below, are best understood in the framework of the several phenomena that may occur in metals processing and service and their general effect on metallic structure and properties.

Ores, Extraction, and Refining. All metals begin with the mining of ores and are successively brought through suitable physical and chemical processes to arrive at commercially useful degrees of purity. At the higher-purity end of this process

Table 1. Physical Constants of the Principal Alloy-forming Elements*

	Atomic No.	Atomic weight	Density, lb per cu in.	Melting point, deg F	Boiling point, deg F	Specific heat†	Latent heat of fusion, Btu per lb	Linear coef of thermal exp. per deg F × 10^{-6}	Btu per sq ft per hr per in. per deg F	Electrical resistivity, microhm-cm	Modulus of elasticity (tension), psi × 10^6	Crystal structure‡	Transition temp, deg F	Symbol
Aluminum	13	26.97	0.09751	1220.4	3740	0.215	170	13.3	1740	2.655	10	FCC		Al
Antimony	51	121.76	0.239	1166.9	2620	0.049	68.9	4.7–6.0	131	39.0	11.3	Rhom		Sb
Arsenic	33	74.91	0.207	1497	1130	0.082	159	2.6	....	35	11	Rhom		As
Barium	56	137.36	0.13	1300	2980	0.068	.....	(10)	....	50	1.8	BCC		Ba
Beryllium	4	9.02	0.0658	2340	5020	0.52	470	6.9	1100	5.9	37	HCP		Be
Bismuth	83	209.00	0.354	520.3	2590	0.029	22.5	7.4	58	106.8	4.6	Rhom		Bi
Boron	5	10.82	0.083	3812	4620	0.309	.....	4.6	....	1.8 × 10^{12}	....	?		B
Cadmium	48	112.41	0.313	609.6	1409	0.055	23.8	16.6	639	6.83	8	HCP		Cd
Calcium	20	40.08	0.056	1560	2625	0.149	100	12	871	3.43	3	FCC/BCC	867	Ca
Carbon	6	12.010	0.0802	6700	8730	0.165	.....	0.3–2.4	165	1375	0.7	Hex/D		C
Cerium	58	140.13	0.25	1460	4380	0.042	27.2	.....	....	78	....	HCP/FCC/?	572/1328	Ce
Chromium	24	52.01	0.260	3350	4500	0.11	146	3.4	464	13	36	BCC/FCC	3344	Cr
Cobalt	27	58.94	0.32	2723	6420	0.099	112	6.8	479	6.24	30	HCP/FCC/HCP	783/2048	Co
Columbium	41	92.91	0.310	4380	5970	0.065	.....	4.0	....	13.1	15	BCC		Cb
Copper	29	63.54	0.324	1981.4	4700	0.092	91.1	9.2	2730	1.673	16	FCC		Cu
Gadolinium	64	156.9	0.287	......	....	......	.....	.....	....	....	....	HCP		Gd
Gallium	31	69.72	0.216	85.5	3600	0.0977	34.5	10.1	232	56.8	1	O		Ga
Germanium	32	72.60	0.192	1756	4890	0.086	205.7	(3.3)	....	60 × 10^6	11.4	D		Ge
Gold	79	197.2	0.698	1945.4	5380	0.031	29.0	7.9	206	2.19	12	FCC		Au
Hafnium	72	178.6	0.473	3865	9700	0.0351	.....	(3.3)	....	32.4	20	HCP/BCC	3540	Hf
Hydrogen	1	1.0080	3.026 × 10^{-6}	−434.6	−422.9	3.45	27.0	.....	1.18	....	....	Hex		H
Indium	49	114.76	0.264	313.5	3630	0.057	12.2	18	175	8.37	1.57	FCT		In
Iridium	77	193.1	0.813	4449	9600	0.031	47	3.8	406	5.3	75	FCC		Ir
Iron	26	55.85	0.284	2802	4960	0.108	117	6.50	523	9.71	28.5	BCC/FCC/BCC	1663/2554	Fe
Lanthanum	57	138.92	0.223	1535	8000	0.0448	.....	.....	....	59	5	HCP/FCC/?	662/1427	La
Lead	82	207.21	0.4097	621.3	3160	0.031	11.3	16.3	241	20.65	2.6	FCC		Pb
Lithium	3	6.940	0.019	367	2500	0.79	286	31	494	11.7	1.7	BCC		Li
Magnesium	12	24.32	0.0628	1202	2030	0.25	160	14	1100	4.46	6.5	HCP		Mg
Manganese	25	54.93	0.268	2273	3900	0.115	115	12	....	185	23	CCX/CCX/ FCT/?	1340/2010/ 2080	Mn
Mercury	80	200.61	0.4896	−37.97	675	0.033	4.9	33.8	58	94.1	....	Rhom		Hg
Molybdenum	42	95.95	0.369	4750	8670	0.061	126	3.0	1020	5.17	50	BCC		Mo

Table 1. Physical Constants of the Principal Alloy-forming Elements* (*Continued*)

	Atomic No.	Atomic weight	Density, lb per cu in.	Melting point, deg F	Boiling point, deg F	Specific heat†	Latent heat of fusion, Btu per lb	Linear coef of thermal exp. per deg F × 10^{-6}	Btu per sq ft per hr per in. per deg F	Electrical resistivity, microhm-cm	Modulus of elasticity (tension), psi × 10^6	Crystal structure‡	Transition temp, deg F	Symbol
Nickel	28	58.69	0.322	2651	4950	0.105	133	7.4	639	6.84	30	FCC		Ni
Nitrogen	7	14.008	0.042×10^{-3}	−346	−320.4	0.247	11.2	....	0.147	....	....	Hex		N
Osmium	76	190.2	0.813	4900	9900	0.031	....	2.6	....	9.5	80	HCP		Os
Oxygen	8	16.000	0.048×10^{-3}	−361.8	−297.4	0.218	5.9	....	0.171	....	....	C		O
Palladium	46	106.7	0.434	2829	7200	0.058	69.5	6.6	494	10.8	17	FCC		Pd
Phosphorus	15	30.98	0.0658	111.4	536	0.177	9.0	70	....	10^{17}	....	C		P
Platinum	78	195.23	0.7750	3224.3	7970	0.032	49	4.9	494	9.83	21	FCC		Pt
Plutonium	94	239	0.686	1229	....	.....	....	50–65	....	150	....	?	6 Forms	Pu
Potassium	19	39.096	0.031	145	1420	0.177	26.1	46	697	6.15	0.5	BCC		K
Radium	88	226.05	0.18	1300	.....	.....	....	.....	....	....	....	?		Ra
Rhenium	75	186.31	0.765	5733	10,700	0.0326	76	.....	....	21	75	HCP		Re
Rhodium	45	102.91	0.4495	3571	8100	0.059	.....	4.6	610	4.5	54	FCC		Rh
Selenium	34	78.96	0.174	428	1260	0.084	29.6	21	3	12	8.4	MC/Hex	248	Se
Silicon	14	28.06	0.084	2605	4200	0.162	607	1.6–4.1	581	10^5	16	D		Si
Silver	47	107.88	0.379	1760.9	4010	0.056	45.0	10.9	2900	1.59	11	FCC		Ag
Sodium	11	22.997	0.035	207.9	1638	0.295	49.5	39	929	4.2	1.3	BCC		Na
Sulphur	16	32.066	0.0748	246.2	832.3	0.175	16.7	36	1.83	2×10^{23}	....	Rhom/FCC	204	S
Tantalum	73	180.88	0.600	5420	9570	0.036	.....	3.6	377	12.4	27	BCC		Ta
Tellurium	52	127.61	0.225	840	2530	0.047	13.1	9.3	41	2×10^5	6	Hex		Te
Thallium	81	204.39	0.428	577	2655	0.031	9.1	16.6	2700	18	1.2	HCP/BCC	446	Tl
Thorium	90	232.12	0.422	3348	8100	0.0355	35.6	6.2	....	18.6	11.4	FCC		Th
Tin	50	118.70	0.264	449.4	4120	0.054	26.1	13	464	11.5	6	D/BCT	55	Sn
Titanium	22	47.90	0.164	3074	6395	0.139	187	4.7	1190	47.8	16.8	HCP/BCC	1650	Ti
Tungsten	74	183.92	0.697	6150	10,700	0.032	79	2.4	900	5.5	50	BCC		W
Uranium	92	238.07	0.687	2065	7100	0.028	19.8	11.4	186	29	29.7	O/Tet/BCC	1229/1427	U
Vanadium	23	50.95	0.217	3452	5430	0.120	.....	4.3	215	26	18.4	BCC/?	2822	V
Zinc	30	65.38	0.258	787	1663	0.092	43.3	9.4–22	784	5.92	12	HCP		Zn
Zirconium	40	91.22	0.23	3326	9030	0.066	.....	3.1	116	41.0	11	HCP/BCC	1585	Zr

* From ASM Metals Handbook revised and supplemented where necessary from Hampel's "Rare Metals Handbook" and elsewhere.

† Cal per g per deg C at room temperature equals Btu per lb per deg F at room temperature.

‡ FCC = face-centered cubic; BCC = body-centered cubic; C = cubic; HCP = hexagonal closest packing; Rhom = rhombohedral; Hex = hexagonal; FCT = face-centered tetragonal; O = orthorhombic; FCO = face-centered orthorhombic; CCX = cubic complex; D = diamond cubic; BCT = body-centered tetragonal; MC = monoclinic.

sequence, scrap metal is frequently combined with that derived from ore. Availability of suitable ores and the extracting and refining processes used are specific for each metal and largely determine the price of the metal and the impurities that are usually present in commercial metals.

Melting. Once a metal arrives at a useful degree of purity, it is brought to the desired combination of shape and properties by a series of physical processes, each of which influences the internal structure of the metal. The first of these is usually melting, during which several elements can be combined to produce an alloy of the desired composition. Depending upon the metal, its container, the surrounding atmosphere, the addition of alloy-forming materials, or exposure to vacuum, various chemical reactions may be utilized in the melting stage to achieve optimum results.

Casting. The molten metal of desired composition is poured into some type of mold in which the heat of fusion is dissipated and the melt becomes a solid of suitable shape for the next stage of manufacture. Such castings are used directly (*e.g.*, sand casting, die casting, permanent-mold casting) or transferred to subsequent operations (*e.g.*, ingots to rolling, billets to forging or extrusion). The obvious advantage of using castings without subsequent major processing is cheapness. The typical cast-

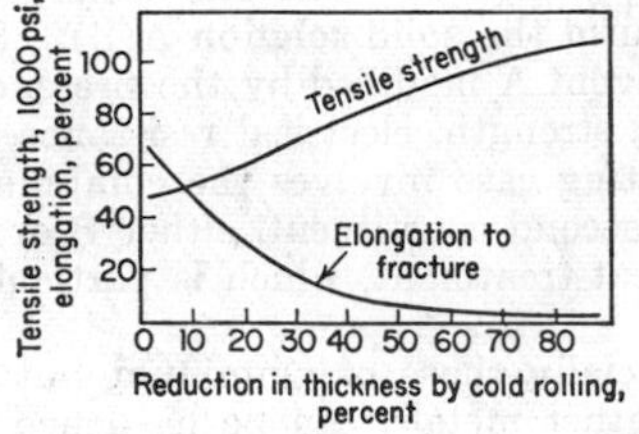

FIG. 1. Effect of cold rolling on annealed brass (Cu 72, Zn 28).

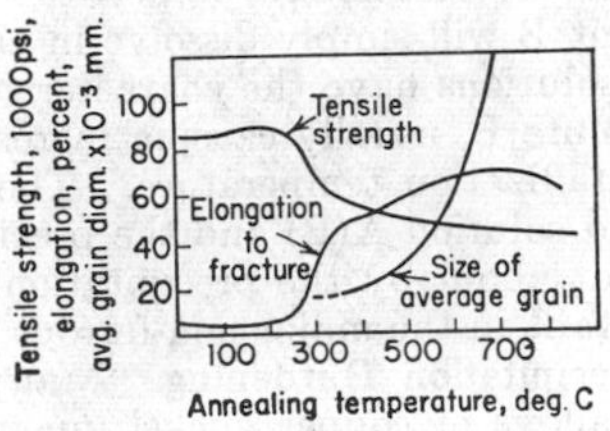

FIG. 2. Effect of annealing on cold-rolled brass (Cu 72, Zn 28).

ing has, to a greater or lesser degree, a large crystal size (**grain size**), extraneous **inclusions** from slag or mold, and **porosity** caused by gas evolution and/or shrinking during solidification. The foundryman's art lies in minimizing the possible defects in castings while maximizing the economies of the process.

Metalworking. (See also p. 13–14 *et seq.*) The major portion of all metals is subjected to additional shape and size changes in the solid state. These metalworking operations substantially alter the internal structure and eliminate many of the defects typical of castings. The usual sequence involves first **hotworking** and then, quite often, **coldworking.** Some metals are only hot-worked, some only cold-worked; most are both hot- and cold-worked. These terms have a special meaning in metallurgical usage.

A cast metal consists of an aggregate of variously oriented grains, each one a single crystal. Upon deformation, the grains flow by a process involving the slip of blocks of atoms over each other, along definite crystallographic planes. The metal is hardened, strengthened, and rendered less ductile, and further deformation becomes more difficult. This is an important method of increasing the strength of non-ferrous metals. The effect of progressive **cold rolling** on brass (Fig. 1) is typical. Terms such as "soft," "quarter hard," "half hard," and "full hard" are frequently used to indicate the degree of hardening produced by such working. For most metals, the hardness resulting from cold working is stable at room temperature, but with lead, zinc, or tin, it will decrease with time.

Upon **annealing, or heating the cold-worked metal,** the first effect is to relieve macrostresses in the object without loss of strength; indeed, the strength is often increased slightly. Above a certain temperature, softening commences and proceeds rapidly with increase in temperature (Fig. 2). The cold-worked distorted metal undergoes a change called **recrystallization.** New grains form and grow until they have consumed the old, distorted ones. The temperature at which this occurs in a given time, called the **recrystallization temperature,** is lower and the resulting grain size finer, the more severe the working of the original piece. If the original working is carried out above this temperature, it does not harden the piece, and the operation is termed **hot working.** If the annealing temperature is increased beyond the recrystallization temperature or if the piece is held at temperature for a long time, the average grain size increases. This generally softens and decreases the strength of the piece still further.

Hot working occurs when deformation and annealing proceed simultaneously, so that the resulting piece of new size and shape emerges in a soft condition roughly similar to the annealed condition.

Alloys. The above remarks concerning structure and property control through casting, hot working, cold working, and annealing generally apply both to pure metals and to alloys. The addition of alloying elements makes possible other means for controlling properties. In some cases, the addition to a metal A of a second element B simply results in the appearance of some new crystals of B as a **mixture** with crystals of A; the resulting properties tend to be an average of A and B. In other cases, an entirely new substance will form—the **intermetallic compound** AB, having its own set of distinctive properties (usually hard and brittle). In still other cases, element B will simply dissolve in element A to form the **solid solution** A(B). Such solid solutions have the characteristics of the **solvent** A modified by the presence of the **solute** B, usually causing increased hardness, strength, electrical resistance, and recrystallization temperature. The most interesting case involves the combination of solid solution A(B) and the precipitation of a second constituent, either B or AB, brought about by the precipitation-hardening heat-treatment, which is particularly important in the major non-ferrous alloys.

Precipitation Hardening. Many alloys, especially those of aluminum but also some alloys of copper, nickel, magnesium, and other metals, can be hardened and strengthened by heat-treatment. The heat-treatment is usually a two-step process which involves (1) a solution heat-treatment followed by rapid quenching and (2) a precipitation or aging treatment to cause separation of a second phase from solid solution and thereby cause hardening. These alloys after a solution treatment are comparatively soft and consist of homogeneous grains of solid solution generally indistinguishable microscopically from a pure metal. If very slowly cooled from the solution-treatment temperature, the alloy will deposit crystals of a second constituent, the amount of which increases as the temperature decreases. Rapid cooling after a solution treatment will retain the supersaturated solution at room temperature, but if the alloy is subsequently reheated to a suitable temperature, fine particles of a new phase will form and in time will grow to a microscopically resolvable size. At some stage in this precipitation process the hardness, the tensile strength, and particularly the yield strength of the alloy will be considerably increased. If the reheating treatment is carried out for too long a time, the alloy will overage and soften. The temperature and time for both solution and precipitation heat-treatments must be closely controlled to obtain the best results. To some extent, precipitation hardening may be superimposed upon hardening resulting from cold working. Precipitation-hardened alloys have an unusually high ratio of proportional limit to tensile strength, but the endurance limit in fatigue is not increased to nearly the same extent.

Effect of Environment. The properties of metals under the "normal" conditions of 70 F and 50 percent relative humidity in clean air can be markedly changed under other conditions, with the various metals differing greatly in their degree of response to such changing conditions. The subject of **corrosion** is both important and highly specific (see p. 6-124 *et seq.*). **Oxidation** is a chemical reaction specific to each metal and, wherever important, is so treated. The **effect of temperature,** however, can be profitably considered in general terms. The primary consequence of increase in temperature is increased atom movement, or **diffusion.** In the discussion above, the effects of recrystallization, hot working, solution treatment, and precipitation were all made possible by increased diffusion at elevated temperatures. The temperature at which such atom movements become appreciable is roughly proportional to the melting point of the metal. If their melting points are expressed on an absolute-temperature scale, then various metals can be expected to exhibit comparable effects at about the same fraction of their melting points. Thus, the recrystallization temperatures of lead, zinc, aluminum, copper, nickel, molybdenum, and tungsten are successively higher. The consequent rule of thumb is that alloys do not have useful structural strength at temperatures above about 0.5 of their melting temperatures.

COPPER AND ITS ALLOYS

REFERENCE: Butts, "Copper," Reinhold.

Commercial Coppers. Most copper is refined electrolytically from anodes of crude **blister copper. Lake copper** originates in the Great Lakes district; it is not electrolytically refined but is of high purity and conductivity. **Secondary copper,** if electrolytically refined, is equal to primary copper, but if fire-refined, it may be less pure and is commonly used as casting copper, produced for brass-foundry use in making alloys.

The electrolytic refining operation produces **cathodes** that may measure about 3 ft square and weigh 180 to 300 lb. Cathodes may be used directly as melting stock for making alloys, but if copper is to be rolled to fabricated forms, it is melted and cast into wire bars, cakes, or billets. The remelting, or so-called "refining operation," involves melting in a large fuel-fired reverberatory furnace, oxidizing to eliminate sulphur and gas absorbed from the fuel, and "poling" to reduce the oxygen to about 0.04 percent. When correctly refined, castings solidify with an approximately level surface, the gas evolved during solidification balancing the shrinkage that would otherwise occur. This is known as **tough-pitch copper.** It has a density of 8.4 to 8.7 g per cc when cast, 8.89 to 8.92 when worked and annealed.

The presence of **oxygen** is desirable in making the copper slightly harder and, before electrolytic refining was adopted, was useful in neutralizing the effect of certain impurities. Oxygen is harmful if the copper is to be welded or otherwise heated in a reducing gas, as it causes an embrittlement of the copper and renders it useless. **Deoxidized copper** is usually made by adding phosphorus, but this decreases the conductivity. Most copper tubing is made of phosphorus-deoxidized copper. **Oxygen-free copper** of high conductivity and density is now available, made by casting without contact with air. Like deoxidized copper, this is more ductile than tough-pitch copper and is immune to embrittlement by hot reducing gases encountered in some service conditions and frequently in brazing or heat-treating operations.

Table 2. ASTM Specification Properties of Copper Wire

Diam, in.	Hard-drawn wire		Medium-drawn wire			Soft-annealed wire	
	Tensile strength, kpsi, min.	Elongation, percent in 60 in., min	Tensile strength, kpsi		Elongation, percent in 60 in., min	Tensile strength, kpsi, max	Elongation, percent in 10 in., min
			Min	Max			
0.460	49	3.75*	42	49	3.75*	36	35
0.325	54.5	2.40*	45	52	3.0*	36	35
0.229	59	1.79*	48	55	2.25*	37	30
0.162	62.1	1.14	49	56	1.15	37	30
0.114	64.3	1.02	50	57	1.06	37	30
0.081	65.7	0.95	51	58	1.00	38.5	25
0.057	66.4	0.89	52	59	0.94	38.5	25
0.040	67	0.85	53	60	0.88	38.5	25
Electrical resistivity, ohms (mile pound)	910.15		905.44†			875.2	
Microhms per cm cube	1.7930		1.7837‡			1.7241	

* Elongation in 10 in. gage length.
† On wire below 0.324 in. diam, 896.15 for larger wires.
‡ On wire below 0.324 in. diam, 1.7654 for larger wires.

Table 3. Composition and Properties of Wrought-copper-base Alloys

Material	Cabra alloy No.	Form tested	Nominal composition, percent					Machinability index	Tensile strength, kpsi		Elongation, percent in 2 in.		Yield strength (0.5% extension under load), kpsi		Rockwell B hardness		Melting point, deg F	Density, lb per cu ft	Coef-no. of expansion (avg 77–572 deg F) per deg F × 10⁻⁶	Elec conductivity (annealed) percent IACS	Thermal conductivity, Btu per hr per sq ft per ft per deg F
			Cu	Zn	Pb	Sn	Others		Hard	Soft	Hard	Soft	Hard	Soft	Hard	Soft					
Coppers																					
Electrolytic tough-pitch copper	110	Sheet	99.92	...	...	...	0.04 O	20	50	32	12	50	45	10	50	F40	1981	556	9.8	101	226
		Wire	...	...	...	...	...	...	55	35	1.5	35									
		Rod	...	...	...	...	...	...	44	32	16	55	44	10	47	F40					
Oxygenfree copper	102	...	99.95	...	...	...	...	20	50	32	16	55	45	10	47	F40	1981	558	9.8	101	226
Phosphorus deoxidized copper	122	...	99.9+	...	...	...	0.02 P	20	48	32	15	50	40	10	50	F45	1981	558	9.8	85	199
Tellurium copper	145	...	99.5	...	...	...	0.50 Te	80	44	33	15	...	41	8	43	...	1980	558	9.8	90	215
Sulphur copper	147	...	99.7	...	...	...	0.30 S	90	50	34	12	42	48	10	45	...	1980	558	9.8	95	216
Zirconium copper	150	...	99.8+	...	...	...	0.12 Zr	20	80	56	5	25	75	48	75	69	1976	558	9.8	85	...
Beryllium copper	172	...	97.4	...	...	...	2.15 Be, 0.35 Ni	20	118	70	4	45	85	30	102	70	1750	515	9.3	17	46
Beryllium copper, H.T.	172	...	97.4	...	...	...	2.15 Be, 0.35 Ni	...	190	175	2	5	97	95	114	112	...	...	...	25	64
Chromium copper	182	...	99.1	...	...	...	0.85 Cr, 0.05 Si	20	72	63	25	25	61	45	77	65	1975	555	9.8	90	187
Plain Brasses																					
Gilding, 95%	210	Sheet	95.0	5.0	...	...	...	20	56	34	5	45	50	10	64	F46	1950	553	10.0	56	135
Commercial bronze, 90%	220	Sheet	90.0	10.0	...	...	...	20	61	37	5	45	54	10	70	F53	1910	549	10.2	44	109
Red brass, 85%	230	Sheet	85.0	15.0	...	...	...	30	70	40	5	47	57	12	77	F59	1880	546	10.4	37	92
		Tube	85.0	15.0	...	...	...	30	70	40	8	55	58	12	77	F60					
Low brass, 80%	240	Sheet	80.0	20.0	...	...	...	30	74	44	7	50	59	14	82	F61	1830	541	10.6	32	81
		Wire	80.0	20.0	...	...	...	30	107	44	5	55									
Cartridge brass, 70%	260	Sheet	70.0	30.0	...	...	...	30	76	47	8	62	63	15	82	F64	1750	532	11.1	28	70
Yellow brass	270	Sheet	65.0	35.0	...	...	...	30	74	47	8	62	60	15	80	F64	1710	529	11.3	27	67
		Wire	65.0	35.0	...	...	...	30	110	50	8	60									
		Rod	65.0	35.0	...	...	...	30	...	48	...	65	...	16	...	F65					
Muntz metal	280	Sheet	60.0	40.0	...	...	...	40	70	54	10	45	50	21	75	F80	1660	524	11.6	28	71

Leaded Brasses																					
Leaded commercial bronze	314	Rod	89.0	9.25	1.75	....	.....	80	52	37	18	45	45	12	58	F55	1900	551	10.2	42	104
Low-leaded brass (tube)	335	Tube	67.0	32.5	0.5	....	.....	60	75	47	7	60	60	15	80	F64	1720	530	11.2	26	67
Low-leaded brass	335	Sheet	64.5	35.0	0.5	....	.....	60	74	47	8	62	60	15	80	F64	1700	529	11.3	26	67
Medium-leaded brass	340	Sheet	64.5	34.5	1.0	....	.....	70	74	47	7	60	60	15	80	F64	1700	529	11.3	26	67
High-leaded brass (tube)	342	Tube	67.0	31.4	1.6	....	.....	90	75	52	7	50	60	20	80	F75	1710	531	11.3	26	67
High-leaded brass	342	Sheet	62.5	35.75	1.75	....	.....	90	74	49	7	52	60	17	80	F68	1670	529	11.3	26	67
Extra-high-leaded brass	356	Sheet	62.5	35.0	2.5	....	.....	100	74	49	7	50	60	17	80	F68	1660	530	11.4	26	67
Free-cutting brass	360	Rod	61.5	35.5	3.0	....	.....	100	58	49	25	53	45	18	78	F68	1650	530	11.4	26	67
Leaded Muntz metal	365	Sheet	60.0	39.5	0.5	....	.....	60	...	54	....	45	...	20	...	F80	1650	525	11.6	28	71
Free-cutting Muntz metal	370	Tube	60.5	38.4	1.1	....	.....	70	80	54	6	40	60	20	85	F80	1650	525	11.6	27	69
Forging brass	377	Rod	60.0	38.0	2.0	....	.....	80	...	52	....	45	...	20	...	F78	1640	527	11.5	27	69
Architectural bronze	385	Rod	57.0	40.0	3.0	....	.....	90	60	60	....	30	...	20	...	65	1630	529	11.6	28	71
Tin and Aluminum Brasses																					
Admiralty	442	Tube	71.0	28.0	....	1.0	.....	30	...	53	....	65	...	22	...	F75	1720	531	11.2	25	64
		Sheet	71.0	28.0	....	1.0	.....	30	...	48	....	25	...	18	...	F70					
Naval brass	464	Rod	60.0	39.25	....	0.75	.....	30	75	57	20	47	53	25	82	55	1650	525	11.8	26	67
		Sheet	60.0	39.25	....	0.75	.....	30	70	62	17	40	58	30	75	60					
Leaded naval brass	485	Rod	60.0	37.5	1.75	0.75	.....	70	75	57	15	40	53	25	82	55	1650	526	11.8	26	67
Manganese bronze (A)	675	Rod	58.5	39.2	....	1.0	1.0 Fe; 0.3 Mn	30	84	65	19	33	60	30	90	65	1630	522	11.8	24	61
Aluminum brass	687	Tube	76.0	22.0	....	....	2.0 Al	30	...	60	....	55	...	27	...	F77	1780	520	10.3	23	58
Phosphor Bronzes (Tin Bronzes)																					
Phosphor bronze, 5% (A)	510	Sheet	95.0	....	....	5.0	.....	20	81	47	10	64	75	19	87	26	1920	554	9.9	18	47
Phosphor bronze, 8% (C)	521	Sheet	92.0	....	....	8.0	.....	20	93	55	10	70	72	...	93	F75	1880	549	10.1	13	36
Phosphor bronze, 10% (D)	524	Sheet	90.0	....	....	10.0	.....	20	100	66	13	68	...	28	97	55	1830	548	10.2	11	29
Phosphor bronze, 1.25% (E)	502	Sheet	98.75	....	....	1.25	Trace P	20	65	40	8	48	50	14	75	F60	1970	554	9.9	48	120
Aluminum Bronzes																					
Aluminum bronze, 5%	...	Sheet	95.0	....	....	....	5.0 Al	20	92	55	7	65	65	22	92	35	1940	510	....	17.7	48
Aluminum bronze, 8%	...	Sheet	92.0	....	....	....	8.0 Al	20	105	65	7	60	65	25	96	50	1905	486	9.95	14.8	42
		Rod	92.0	....	....	....	8.0 Al	20	80	65	30	65	50	25							
Aluminum bronze	...	Rod	90.0	....	....	....	9.5 Al; 0.5 Fe	20	95	80	16	22	55	40	...	...	1910	473	9.40	12.6	35
Cupronickel and Nickel Silver																					
Cupronickel, 30%	715	Tube	70.0	.....	....	....	30.0 Ni	20	...	60	....	45	...	25	...	45	2260	585	9.0	4.6	17
Cupronickel, 10%	706	Tube	88.4	.....	....	....	10 Ni; 1.25 Fe	20	60	44	15	46	57	22	68	25	2093	559	9.3	9.2	26
Nickel-silver, 18% (A)	752	Sheet	65.0	17.0	....	....	18.0 Ni	20	85	58	3	40	74	25	87	40	2030	546	9.0	6.0	19
Nickel-silver, 18% (B)	770	Sheet	55.0	27.0	....	....	18.0 Ni	30	100	60	3	40	85	27	91	55	1930	542	9.3	5.5	17
Silicon Bronzes																					
High-silicon bronze (A)	655	Sheet	94.8	.....	....	....	Max: 1.60 Fe; 1.50 Zn	30	94	60	8	60	58	25	93	62	1880	532	10.0	7.0	21
		Rod	Min	.....	....	....	3.50 Si; 1.50 Mn; 0.75 Sn	...	92	58	22	60	55	22	90	60					
Low-silicon bronze (B)	651	Wire	96.0	.....	....	....	Max: 0.80 Fe; 1.50 Zn	30	90	50	12	40	67	35	...	...	1940	546	9.9	12	33
		Rod	Min	.....	....	....	2.00 Si; 0.75 Mn; 1.60 Sn	...	70	40	15	50	55	15	80	F55					

This table is largely prepared from "Alloy Data" of the Copper and Brass Research Association, New York. Values shown are typical and should not be used for specification purposes since they vary with the size and shape tested and with manufacturing variables. Tests on sheet 0.040 in. thick; rod 1 in. diam, wire 0.080 in. diam, tube 1 in. O.D. by 0.065 in. wall thickness. "Hard" corresponds to commercial hard-drawn temper. Higher values of yield and tensile strength and hardness are obtained by a greater amount of cold working, but this is limited to relatively narrow sheets and to rod, wire, and tube of small diameter.

* Elongation on 10 in. gage length.

H.T. = precipitation heat-treatment on form shown; F = Rockwell F hardness.

Copper may be rolled extensively at any temperature up to about 1900 F but is preferably hot-worked at 1600 F. **Sheet copper** for roofing is sometimes used as it leaves the rolls, but for other purposes it is commonly employed after it has been cold-rolled to increase its hardness and strength. **Copper wire** about 0.04 in. diam is commonly made by drawing from a hot-rolled rod without annealing, but smaller sizes may involve intermediate anneals. Copper shapes for switch parts are made by **extrusion,** brushes and commutator sections by rolling and **drawing.** Copper for **electrical purposes** must be very pure; the presence of even traces of certain impurities (particularly phosphorus, arsenic, iron, titanium, and silicon) decreases the conductivity very considerably. Such copper should have a minimum copper content of 99.90 percent (silver being counted as copper) and a resistance, measured on a drawn and annealed wire, not exceeding 0.15436 ohm per m,g at 20 C (ASTM specification B5–43). Selected values of the strength of copper wire from ASTM specifications B5–46, B2–52, and B3–56 are shown in Table 2.

Copper containing small amounts of **silver** retains the effect of cold working to a higher temperature than pure copper (about 610 F compared with about 400 F). This is useful where comparatively high temperatures are to be withstood, as in soldering operations or for stressed conductors designed to operate at moderately elevated temperatures. **Tellurium** and **sulphur** are added to enhance the machinability of copper with minimum sacrifice in conductivity. Similarly, **chromium** and **zirconium** are added to increase elevated-temperature strength with little decrease in conductivity. **Beryllium copper** is a precipitation-hardening alloy that combines moderate conductivity with very high strength. (Typical heat-treatment, 1450 F for 1 hr; water quench, 600 F for 3 hr.) See Table 3.

Copper alloys are useful because of their good thermal or electrical conductivity, good cold- or hot-working properties, machinability, or corrosion resistance. For high thermal or electrical conductivity, commercially pure copper should be used; if greater strength combined with high conductivity is required, alloys containing zirconium or other elements are used. The cheapest copper alloy is **brass** of high zinc content and is used unless high corrosion resistance under stress or the special mechanical properties of other alloys are required. When good cold-working properties are desired, as in deep-drawing or forming operations, a brass with 30 to 35 percent zinc is used. **Leaded brass** is used when much machining must be done, particularly for automatic-screw-machine work. For high elastic strength, the **tin bronzes** are used. The **alloys** of copper with **aluminum** or **silicon** or **nickel** are good for corrosion resistance. Several hundred different copper alloys are available, but requirements can generally be met satisfactorily by one or more of the alloys listed in Table 3.

BRASSES

The useful copper-zinc alloys contain up to 40 percent zinc. Those with 30 to 35 percent find the greatest application as they are cheap, very ductile, and readily worked. With decreasing zinc content, the alloys approach copper more and more in their properties and improve in corrosion resistance. **Season cracking** may occur with high-zinc brasses but rarely with 15 percent zinc or below; this is spontaneous cracking, occurring on exposure to atmospheric corrosion, in brass objects with high residual tensile stresses at the surface. It may be prevented by avoiding the production of internal macrostresses or by removing such stresses by relief annealing at 475 to 530 F without softening the work. It should be noted that alloys susceptible to spontaneous season cracking, even if they are free from internal strains, will crack when exposed to corrosive conditions under high service stresses.

The 5 to 20 percent zinc alloys find application because of freedom from season cracking, because of their red color, and because their high melting point is desirable in brazing operations. The properties of these alloys are included in Table 3. Figures 1 and 2 show the effect of progressive cold rolling and progressive annealing on a brass containing 30 percent zinc. Cold working increases the hardness and tensile strength and decreases the ductility as measured by elongation or reduction in area. Annealing below a certain temperature has practically no effect, but in the recrystallization range a rapid decrease in strength and increase in ductility occurs. At this point, the effect of cold working is almost entirely removed. Heating beyond this point results in the growth of the grains with comparatively little further increase in ductility. Figures 3 and 4 show the variation of properties of brass with composition after annealing at the temperatures indicated.

Table 4 summarizes the ASTM specification requirements for 65/35 brass of various rolled and annealed tempers. Practically all wrought-copper alloys are used in the cold-worked condition to gain additional strength. Articles are often made from annealed stock and depend on the work of the forming operation to shape and harden them. When the work involved is too small to do this, brass rolled with a degree of temper depending on requirements should be used.

Brass for springs should be rolled as hard as consistent with the subsequent forming operations. For articles requiring sharp bends, or for deep-drawing operations, annealed brass must be used. In general, the smaller grain sizes are to be preferred.

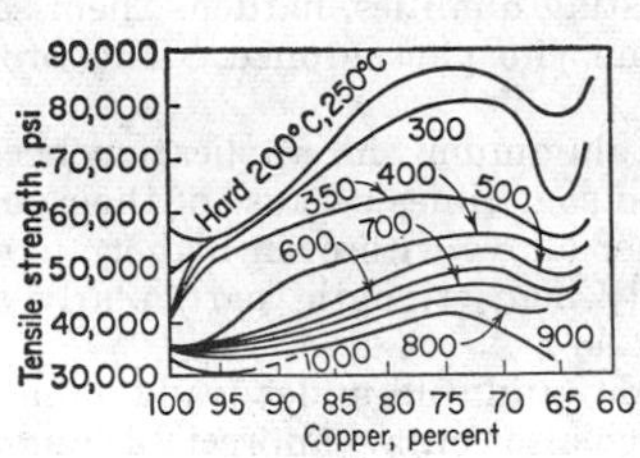

FIG. 3. Tensile strengths of copper-zinc alloys.

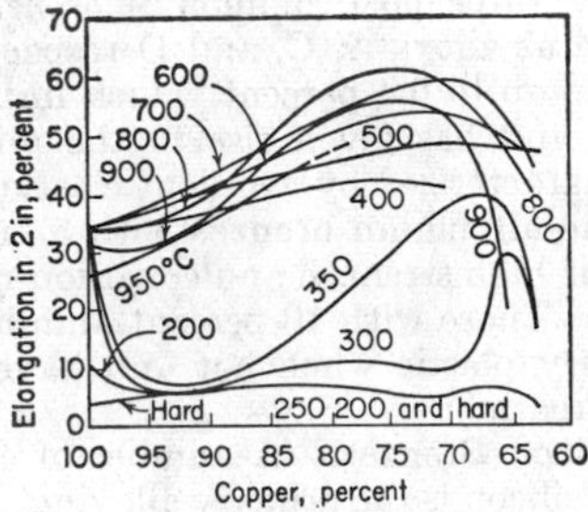

FIG. 4. Per cent elongation in 2 in. of copper-zinc alloys.

Table 4. Properties of Rolled Yellow Brass
(ASTM specification B36–61)

Temper	Nominal grain size, mm	Annealing temp, F, (approx)[b]	Tensile strength, psi Min	Tensile strength, psi Max	Rockwell hardness
Annealed A	0.120	1300	....	....	F50–62
B	0.070	1180	....	....	52–67
C	0.050	1070	....	....	61–73
D	0.035	930	....	....	65–76
E	0.025	800	....	....	67–79
	0.015	700	....	....	72–85
	Nominal reduction, B. & S. gage No.[a]	Percentage reduction of thickness			
Quarter hard	1	10.9	49,000	59,000	B40–65
Half hard	2	20.7	55,000	65,000	57–74
Three-quarter hard	3	29.4	62,000	72,000	70–80
Hard	4	37.1	68,000	78,000	76–84
Extra hard	6	50.0	79,000	89,000	83–89
Spring	8	60.5	86,000	95,000	87–92
Extra spring	10	68.7	90,000	99,000	88–93

[a] Since the B & S scale is a uniform geometric progression (see p. 6–46) the actual reduction in thickness of one number will decrease as the piece is progressively cold-rolled, but since the actual thickness also decreases, the effect of cold work remains approximately the same.

[b] The grain size obtained after a given annealing treatment is dependent on the prior grain size and on the amount of final rolling.

The addition of **lead** to brass renders it free cutting and remarkably machinable. Additions of 0.75 to 1.25 percent of **tin** improve the corrosion resistance. **Aluminum** is added to brass to improve the corrosion resistance particularly in condenser-tube applications. **Manganese bronze** is a complex brass with hot-working properties, high strength, and abrasion resistance. **Naval brass** is used as boat shafting.

All the brasses may be hot-worked if they are free from lead, particularly those alloys containing 60 percent or less of copper, for these contain a constituent, beta, which is extremely plastic at high temperatures even in the presence of lead. Alloys for extrusion and hot pressing are all in this range.

Extruded sections of many copper alloys are made in a wide variety of shapes. In addition to those used architecturally for moldings, etc., extrusion is important to the engineer since many objects such as pinions, hinges, brackets, and lock barrels can be made directly from extruded bars. Special extruded shapes used as stock for automatic screw-machine operations frequently reduce scrap considerably.

BRONZES

The three most common *tin bronzes* contain about 4.5, 8, and 10 percent tin and are known as alloys A, C, and D respectively. They usually contain phosphorus, from a trace up to 0.4 percent, which improves the casting qualities, hardens them somewhat, and has given rise to the misleading name **phosphor bronze.** The bronzes are characterized by excellent elastic properties.

The **aluminum bronzes** with 5 and 8 percent aluminum find application because of their high strength and corrosion resistance, and sometimes because of their golden color. Those with 10 percent aluminum and other alloys with even higher amounts are very plastic when hot and have exceptionally high strength, particularly after heat-treatment.

Silicon Bronzes. A number of alloys are made (and sold under trade names) in which silicon is the primary alloying agent but which also contain appreciable amounts of zinc, iron, tin, or manganese. These alloys are as corrosion-resistant as copper (slightly more so in some solutions) and possess excellent hot workability with high strength. Their outstanding characteristic is that of ready weldability by all methods. The alloys are extensively fabricated by arc or acetylene welding into tanks and vessels for hot-water storage and chemical processing.

The **cupronickels** and so-called **nickel silvers** are white in color and find application on this account, and because of their comparative freedom from tarnishing under atmospheric conditions. Nickel silver is the base for most silver-plated ware. The cupronickels are extremely malleable and may be worked extensively without annealing. Because of their excellent corrosion resistance, they are used for condenser tubes for most severe service. Alloys containing nickel have the best high-temperature properties of any copper alloy.

PROCESSING OF COPPER ALLOYS

Fabrication. Practically any of the copper alloys listed in Table 3 can be obtained in sheet, rod, and wire form and many in the form of tubes. Most of them, in the annealed condition, will withstand extensive amounts of cold work and may be shaped to the desired form by deep drawing, flanging, forming, bending, and similar operations. If extensive cold work is planned, the material should be purchased in the annealed condition. Very extensive operations need intermediate annealing either to avoid failure of the metal or to minimize the power consumption. This is done at 900 to 1300 F, depending on the alloy, and is usually followed by air cooling. Because of the ready workability of brass, it is often cheaper to use than steel. Brass may be drawn at higher speeds than ferrous metals and with less wear on the tools. In cupping operations, a take-in of 45 percent is usual and on some jobs, may be larger. Brass hardened by cold working is softened by annealing at about 1100 F.

Welding. Deoxidized copper will weld satisfactorily by the oxyacetylene method. Sufficient heat input to overcome its high heat conductivity must be maintained by the use of torches considerably more powerful than those customary for steel, and preferably by preheating the work in addition. The filler rod must be deoxidized.

Tough-pitch copper will not give high-strength welds because of embrittlement due to the oxygen content. Copper may be arc-welded, using either metallic, inert-gas tungsten-arc, or carbon-arc welding with experienced operators. Filler rods of phosphor bronze or silicon bronze will give strong welds more consistently and are used where the presence of a weld of different composition and corrosion-resistance characteristics is not harmful. Brass may be welded by the oxyacetylene process but not with the arc. A filler rod of about the same composition is used, although silicon is frequently added to prevent zinc fumes. (See also p. 13–39 *et. seq.*)

The copper-silicon alloys are characterized by remarkable ease of welding by all methods. The conductivity is not too high, and the alloy is to a large extent self-fluxing.

All copper alloys, except those containing large amounts of aluminum, can be readily soft-**soldered** or silver-soldered. **Brazing** is possible only with those alloys whose melting points are sufficiently greater than that of the solder used.

Machining. Free-cutting brass rod has been for years the standard material for automatic screw-machine work where the very highest machinability is necessary. The use of this material will often result in considerable savings over steel at a lower base price. Most copper alloys are readily machined by usual methods using standard tools designed for steel but at higher speeds. Consideration of the wide range of characteristics presented by various types of copper alloys and the adaptation of the machining practice to the particular material concerned will give greatly improved results. For purposes of machining, copper alloys can be divided into three groups depending on their structure and related characteristics:

Group A is composed of alloys of homogeneous structure; copper, the wrought bronzes up to 10 percent tin, brasses and nickel silvers up to 37 percent zinc, aluminum bronzes up to 8 percent aluminum, the silicon bronzes, and cupronickel. These alloys are all tough and ductile and form a long continuous chip. When they are severely cold-worked, they approach the second classification in their characteristics.

Group B includes lead-free alloys of duplex structure. Some cast bronzes and most of the high-strength copper alloys in the wrought condition belong in this group. They form a continuous but brittle chip by a process of intermittent shearing against the tool edge which causes chatter unless work and tool are rigid.

Group C. Many of the basic brases and bronzes are rendered particularly fit for machining operations by the addition of 0.5 to 3.0 percent of lead. This exists in the structure as minute uniformly distributed droplets which apparently serve the function of breaking up the chip and lubricating the tool. Chips are fine, almost needlelike, and readily removed. Very little heat is evolved, but the tendency to chatter is greater than in Type A alloy. Lead additions may be made to most copper alloys, but its low melting point makes hot working impossible. Tellurium and sulphur additions are used in place of lead when the combination of hot workability and good machinability is desired.

For lathe turning, the tough alloys of Group A need a sharp top rake angle (20 to 30 deg for copper and cupronickel; 12 to 16 deg for the brasses, bronzes, and silicon bronzes with high-speed tools; 8 to 12 deg with carbide tools except for copper for which 16 is recommended). Type C (leaded) materials should have a much smaller rake to minimize chatter, a maximum of 8 deg with high-speed steels and 3 to 6 deg with carbide. Type B materials are intermediate, working best with 6 to 12 deg with high-speed tools, 3 to 8 deg with carbide, the higher angle being used with the tougher materials. Side clearance angle should be 5 to 7 deg except for tough "sticky" materials like copper and cupronickel, where a side rake of 10 to 15 deg will give better service.

Many copper alloys will drill satisfactorily with the standard helix angle of 30 deg. Straight fluted tools (helix angle 0 deg) are preferable for the leaded Group C alloys. An angle of 10 deg is to be preferred for Group B and 40 deg for copper and cupronickel. Feeds may generally be 2 to 3 times those used for steel. With Type B alloy, a fairly coarse feed helps breaking up the chip, and with Type A a fine feed and high speed gives best results provided that sufficient feed be used to prevent rubbing and work hardening.

Corrosion Resistance. All copper alloys are highly resistant to atmospheric attack, but for outdoor exposure those containing over 80 percent of copper (or copper itself) are preferred because of their resistance to **season cracking.**

Water pipes are commonly made of deoxidized copper, red brass, and yellow brass, the last being least resistant to acid waters. Alloys with over 80 percent copper, such as red brass, the silicon-copper alloys, cupronickel, or aluminum bronze, are generally more resistant to corrosion than the alloys with low copper content. Deoxidized copper, arsenical copper, or Admiralty brass have proved satisfactory for condenser tubes operating with fresh water. In sea water, copper is less suitable because of its inability to form protective films. Admiralty brass was for years the standard alloy for sea-water installations; as now made it contains minute additions of arsenic, antimony, or phosphorus to retard dezincification, which is in effect selective corrosion of the alloy with redeposition of copper. Aluminum brass and the cupronickels are preferred for the most severe sea-water service.

Copper and its alloys are not suitable for use in oxidizing acidic solutions or in the presence of moist free ammonia, or mercury. They are also subject to velocity effects in solutions.

Effect of Temperature. Copper and all its alloys increase in strength slightly and uniformly as temperature decreases from room temperature. No low-temperature brittleness is encountered. Copper is useless for prolonged stressed service much above 400 F, but some of its alloys may be used up to 550 F. For service above this, the cupronickel and copper-aluminum alloys alone have satisfactory properties. Aluminum bronzes, particularly those containing 10 percent aluminum, find application for valve seats in internal-combustion engines. For specific data, see Burghoff, Blank, and Maddigan, *Proc. ASTM*, **42,** 1942, p. 668; "Compilation of Available High-temperature Creep Data of Metals and Alloys," ASTM and ASME, 1938; "Symposium on the Effect of Temperature on the Properties of Metals," ASTM and ASME, 1931; White and Siebert, "Literature Survey of Low-temperature Properties of Metals," Edwards; Mechanical Properties of Metals at Low Temperatures, *NBS Circ.* 520, 1952.

COPPER-BASE ALLOYS FOR CASTING

(See "Cast Metals Handbook," AFS.)

Table 5 shows the composition of the important copper-base casting alloys together with typical properties to be expected from sand castings. Test results obtained on standard test pieces (either attached to the casting or separately poured) indicate the quality of the metal used but not the specific properties of the casting itself because of variations of thickness, soundness, and other factors. The ideal casting is one with a fairly uniform metal section with ample fillets and a gradual transition from thin to thick parts.

By far the greatest tonnage of copper castings is made by the **sand-casting** process, and alloys 3A and 4A are the most popular for general-purpose work. **Brass die castings** are made when greater accuracy of dimensions or a better surface finish is desired. While inferior in properties to hot-pressed parts, die castings are adaptable to a wider range of design, for they may be made with intricate coring and with considerable variation in section thickness.

NICKEL AND NICKEL ALLOYS

(Based largely on information supplied by International Nickel Co.)

The majority of the world's production of nickel comes from the sulphide deposits in Ontario. After intermediate processing, the pure metal is achieved by electrolysis or by decomposition of nickel carbonyl. In either case, the metal is then melted and cast into ingots for further working. **Monel,** an important alloy of nickel, is made by reducing an intermediate smelting product, copper-nickel matte, without separating the metals from each other. Other alloys are made in the usual way by incorporation of the elements in the molten state.

The nominal composition and typical properties of nickel and various nickel-rich alloys are summarized in Tables 6 to 8.

Table 5. Composition and Properties of Copper-base Alloys for Sand Castings

Common name	ASTM No.	Nominal composition, percent				Tensile strength, kpsi	Yield strength, kpsi	Elongation in 2 in., percent	Castability, 1 = best	Conductivity, percent IACS	Machinability index*	Weldability
		Cu	Sn	Pb	Zn							
Tin bronze	1A	88	10	...	2	40	18	20	3	11	50	Fair
Tin bronze	1B	88	8	...	4	40	18	20	3	12	50	Fair
High-leaded tin bronze	3A	80	10	10	...	25	12	8	1	10	80	Poor
Leaded red brass	4A	85	5	5	5	30	14	20	2	15	90	Poor
Commercial red brass	4B	83	4	6	7	29	12	15	2	...	90	Poor
Leaded yellow brass	6A	71	1	3	25	35	12	25	4	20	80	Poor
Special copper-alloy castings heat-treated to combine high strength and conductivity		99.85				28	18	40	8	80	20	...
		99 (0.8 Cr, 0.1 Si)				50	32	16	8	80	20	...
		97 (2.6 Co, 0.4 Be)				90	70	10	9	45	10	...

* 100 = free-cutting brass.

Table 6. Composition of Nickel Alloys

Alloy designation*		Nominal composition, percent							
New	Old	Ni	C	Mn	Fe	Si	Cu	Cr	Others
Nickel 200	A nickel	99.5	0.06	0.25	0.15	0.05	0.05		
Nickel 201	L nickel	99.5	0.01	0.20	0.15	0.05	0.05		
Nickel 211	D nickel	95.0	0.10	4.75	0.05	0.05	0.03		
Nickel 233	330 nickel	99.5	0.09	0.18	0.05	0.03	0.03		0.07 Mg
†Duranickel 301	Z nickel	94.0	0.15	0.25	0.15	0.55	0.05		4.5 Al, 0.5 Ti
†Monel 400	Monel	66.0	0.12	0.90	1.35	0.15	31.5		
†Monel R405	R Monel	66.0	0.18	0.90	1.35	0.15	31.5	....	0.050 S
†Monel K-500	K Monel	65.0	0.15	0.60	1.00	0.15	29.5	....	2.8 Al, 0.50 Ti
†Inconel 600	Inconel	76.0	0.04	0.20	7.20	0.20	0.10	15.8	
†Inconel 718	Inconel 718	52.5	0.04	0.20	18.0	0.20	0.10	19.0	0.6 Al, 0.80 Ti, 5.2 Cb, 3.0 Mo
†Inconel X-750	Inconel X	73.0	0.04	0.70	6.75	0.30	0.05	15.0	0.8 Mo, 2.5 Ti, 0.85 Cb
†Incoloy 800	Incoloy	32.0	0.04	0.75	46.0	0.35	0.30	20.5	
†Ni-0-Nel 825	Ni-0-Nel	41.8	0.03	0.65	30.0	0.35	1.80	21.5	0.15 Al, 0.9 Ti, 0.5 Mo
‡Hastelloy A		57	0.1	2	20	1.0	.....	....	20 Mo
‡Hastelloy B		65	0.1	0.5	5	0.5	.....	....	28 Mo
‡Hastelloy C		58	0.1	1.0	5.0	1.0	.....	14	17 Mo, 5 W
‡Hastelloy D		85	....	1.0	.....	10.0	3.0	....	1.0 Al
62-15 Ni-Cr		62	0.2	0.5	Bal	1.0	.....	15	
80-20 Ni-Cr		77	0.1	1.0	0.5	1.3	.....	20	

* Alloy designations follow the usage of International Nickel Co.† or Haynes Stellite Co.‡

Table 7. Physical Properties of Nickel Alloys

Alloy no.	Density, lb per cu in.	Modulus of elasticity, 10^6 psi	Specific heat (70 F), Btu/lb deg F	Thermal expansion (70–200 F), in./in./deg F $\times 10^6$	Thermal conductivity (70 F), Btu/ft² hr/in./deg F	Electrical resistivity, ohms/cir. mil/ft	Curie temp, deg F (annealed)
200	0.321	30	0.109	7.4	436	66	680
201	0.321	30					
211	0.315	30	.....	7.4	306	102	
233	0.321	30					
301	0.298	30	.....	7.2	420	260	
400	0.319	26	0.102	7.7	400	307	600
R405	0.319	26	0.102	7.7	151	307	35
K-500	0.306	26	0.100	7.6	121	370	−40
600	0.304	31	0.106	7.4	103	620	−192
718	0.296	29	.....	7.2	78	751	−175
800	0.290	28	0.12	7.9	80	559	−175
825	0.294	28	.....	7.8	77	645	−320
‡Hastelloy A	0.318	27	.....	6.1	116		
‡Hastelloy B	0.334	30	.....	5.6	78		
‡Hastelloy C	0.323	28	.....	6.3	87		
Hastelloy D	0.282	29	.....	6.1	145		
65-15 Ni-Cr	0.296	...	.....	7.6	...	675	
80-20 Ni-Cr	0.303	31	.....	...	...	650	

‡ As in Table 6.

Commercially pure nickel, known as **nickel 200**, is available as sheet, rod, wire, tubing, and other fabricated forms. It is used where the thermal or electrical properties of nickel are required and where corrosion resistance is needed in parts that have to be worked extensively.

Commercial nickel may be forged or rolled at 1600 to 2300 F. It becomes increasingly harder below 1600 F but has no brittle range. The recrystallization temperature of cold-worked pure nickel is about 660 F, but commercial nickel recrystallizes at about 1100 F and is usually annealed at temperatures between 1100 and 1750 F.

The addition of certain elements to nickel renders it susceptible to a precipitation or aging treatment to increase its strength and hardness. In the unhardened or

Table 8. Mechanical Properties of Nickel and Its Alloys

Alloy	Form and temper tested	Yield strength (0.2% offset), kpsi	Tensile strength, kpsi	Elongation, percent in 2 in.	Brinell hardness
Nickel 200*	Rod, hot-rolled	15–45	60–85	55–40	90–120
	Rod, cold-drawn	60–90	80–115	35–15	125–230
	Rod, annealed	15–30	55–80	55–40	90–120
	Wire, spring temper	130–155	135–165	10–2	
Duranickel 301	Rod, cold-drawn	50–130	90–150	35–15	175–300
	Rod, drawn, heat-treated	120–150	160–190	20–7	300–380
	Wire, spring, heat-treated	....	190–250	10–5	
	Rod, hot-rolled	35–85	90–120	50–25	150–225
Monel 401†	Rod, hot-rolled	40–65	80–95	45–30	140–185
	Rod, drawn, annealed	25–40	70–85	50–35	110–140
	Strip, annealed	25–45	70–85	50–30	61–73‡
	Strip, full hard	90–130	110–140	15–2	>98‡
	Wire, spring temper	130–160	140–170	10–2	
Monel K 500	Rod, hot-rolled	40–90	90–120	45–25	140–240
	Rod, cold-drawn	70–100	100–135	35–13	175–260
	Rod, drawn, heat-treated	100–130	140–170	30–15	265–320
	Wire, spring, heat-treated	150–175	160–200	8–3	
Inconel 600	Rod, hot-rolled	39–90	85–120	45–30	140–210
	Rod, cold-drawn	70–125	95–150	30–15	180–290
	Wire, spring temper	150–175	165–185	10–2	
Cast nickel 200	As cast	20–30	45–60	30–15	80–125
Cast Monel 400	As cast	32–40	65–90	45–25	125–150
Cast Inconel 600	As cast	30–45	70–95	30–10	160–190
Hastelloy A	As cast	42–45	69–77	12–8	155–200
	Rolled and annealed	47–52	110–120	48–40	200–215
Hastelloy B	As cast	55–57	75–82	9–6	190–230
	Rolled and annealed	60–65	130–140	45–40	210–235
Hastelloy C	As cast	45–48	72–80	15–10	175–215
	Rolled and annealed	55–65	115–128	50–25	160–210
Hastelloy D	As cast	36–40	36–40	0	50–55§
62-15 Ni-Cr	Wire	40–160	95–175	35–2	83‡
80-20 Ni-Cr	Wire	63	110	25	85–90‡

* Properties of nickel 201 are approximately 20% softer than those of nickel 200.
† Properties of Monel R405 and nickel 211 are approx the same as Monel.
‡ Rockwell B scale.
§ Rockwell C scale.

quenched state, Duranickel 301 fabricates almost as easily as pure nickel and when finished may be hardened by heating for about 8 hr at 1000 to 1100 F. Intermediate anneals during fabrication are at 1650 to 1750 F. The increase in strength due to aging may be superimposed on that due to cold work.

Nickel castings are made in dry sand molds, but need special technique because of the high temperatures involved. The addition of 1½ percent silicon and lesser amounts of carbon and manganese is necessary to obtain good casting properties.

Alloys of nickel with 2 to 5 percent manganese are used generally for spark-plug electrodes, an application that requires resistance to hot corrosive gases. They are slightly stronger than nickel but have, in general, the same properties.

Copper-nickel Alloys. Alloys containing less than 50 percent nickel are discussed under Copper Alloys, pp. 6–76 to 6–79. An important nickel-rich alloy is known by the trade name **Monel 400** (see Tables 6 to 8). It combines high strength, high ductility, and excellent resistance to corrosion. It is a homogenous solid solution alloy; hence its strength can be increased by cold working alone. In the annealed state, its tensile strength is about 70,000 psi, and this may be increased to 170,000 in the hardest drawn wires. It is available in practically all fabricated forms. Monel 400 is hot-worked in the range 1600 to 2150 F after rapid heating in a reducing but sulphur-free atmosphere. It must be cold-worked in the same manner as mild steel, but requires more power. Very heavily cold-worked Monel 400 may commence to recrystallize at 800 F, but in normal practice no softening will occur below 1200 F. Annealing is done in boxes for 2 to 6 hr at about 1400 F or open for 2 to 5 min at about 1725 F. Non-scaling atmospheres are desirable and sulphur-free atmospheres essential.

Because of its toughness, Monel 400 must be machined with slower cutting speed and lighter cuts than mild steel. High-speed tools are necessary. The special grade of Monel containing sulphur (Monel R405) should be used where high cutting speeds must be maintained. This alloy is essentially the same as the sulphur-free alloy in mechanical properties and corrosion resistance, and it can be hot-forged.

The short-time tensile strengths of Monel at elevated temperatures are summarized in Table 9.

The fatigue endurance limit of Monel 400 is about 35,000 (47,000) psi when annealed (hard-drawn). The action of corrosion during fatigue is much less drastic on Monel 400 than on steels of equal or higher endurance limit. McAdam found a limit of 30,000 psi in brackish water.

Monel 400 may be welded by the usual electric and gas methods but needs special fluxes. The gas flame should be slightly reducing and the work done rapidly without rewelding. Flux-coated electrodes should be used for arc welding. Spot and seam welding can be used on thin sheet. Soft soldering, brazing, and silver soldering are readily applied.

Monel 400 is highly resistant to atmospheric action, sea water, steam, foodstuffs, and many industrial chemicals. It deteriorates rapidly in the presence of moist chlorine and ferric, stannic, or mercuric salts in acid solutions. It must not be exposed when hot to molten metals, sulphur, or gaseous products of combustion containing sulphur.

If about 2.75 percent aluminum is added to the base 70/30 nickel-copper alloy, it becomes susceptible to precipitation hardening. This alloy (trade name Monel K500) is available in rod, strip, tubing, sheet, and wire form. It is sufficiently ductile in the annealed state to permit drawing, forming, bending, or other cold-working operations but work-hardens rapidly and requires more power than mild steel. It is hot-worked at 1700 to 2150 F and should be cooled and quenched from about 1600 F if the metal is to be further worked or to be hardened. Heat-treatment consists of quenching from 1600 F, cold working if desired, and reheating for 10 to 16 hr at 1000 to 1100 F. If no cold working is intended, the quench may be omitted on sections less than 2 in. thick, and the alloy hardened at 1100 F. The properties of the heat-treated alloy remain quite stable, at least up to 1000 F for several months. It is non-magnetic down to −150 F.

Inconel 600 is a high-strength non-magnetic (−40 F) nickel-chromium-iron alloy which is used widely for corrosion- and heat-resisting purposes at temperatures up to 2200 F in non-sulphidizing atmospheres. In sulphidizing atmospheres, the maximum recommended temperature is 1500 F. Inconel X 750 is an age-hardenable modification suitable for stressed applications in the range 1200 to 1500 F.

High-temperature Properties of Nickel Alloys. The combination of useful strength and oxidation resistance makes nickel alloys frequent choices for high-temperature service. Table 9 indicates the changes in mechanical properties with temperature, and Table 10 expresses the limiting service temperatures for major nickel alloys in various environments.

Low-temperature Properties of Nickel Alloys. Several nickel-base alloys have very good properties at low temperatures in contrast to ferrous alloys where impact strength (the index of brittleness) falls off very rapidly with decreasing temperature. The impact strength remains nearly constant with most nickel-rich alloys, while the tensile and yield strengths increase as they do in the other alloys. Specific data on low-temperature properties may be found in Mudge, *Inco Mag.*, **19,** No 1; White and Siebert, "Literature Survey of Low-temperature Properties of Metals," Edwards; and "Mechanical Properties of Metals at Low Temperatures," *NBS Circ.* 520, 1952.

A series of nickel-rich alloys with molybdenum and some other elements are sold under the trade name of **Hastelloy** (see Table 6). Hastelloy D is a nickel-silicon alloy. These materials are exceptionally resistant to corrosion by hot concentrated acids such as hydrochloric, sulphuric, and nitric. Hastelloy B has good strength at elevated temperatures; its properties are given in the section on high-temperature metals. The properties of the nickel-rich nickel-chromium electrical-resistor alloys are also given there.

Magnetic Properties of Nickel Alloys. Nickel is slightly ferromagnetic but loses its magnetism at a temperature of 695 F when pure. In commercial nickel, this temperature is about 650 F. Monel is feebly magnetic and loses all ferromagnetism above 200 F. Monel K500 is non-magnetic down to at least −110 F. The degree

Table 9. Short-time High-temperature Properties of Hot-rolled Nickel and Its Alloys*

	Temperature, deg F							
	70	600	800	1000	1200	1500	1800	2000
Nickel 200†								
Tensile strength, kpsi	73	83	76	46	34	25	8	
Yield strength, 0.2% offset, kpsi	24	22	21	17	15			
Elongation, percent in 2 in.	49	50	52	55	57	65	91	
Monel 400								
Tensile strength, kpsi	81	78	71	51	30	16	8	
Yield strength, 0.2% offset, kpsi	32	28	29	23	18	9		
Elongation, percent in 2 in.	46	51	52	29	34	58	45	
Inconel 600								
Tensile strength, kpsi	85	79	83	79	71	32	15	11
Yield strength, 0.2% offset, kpsi	36	27	28	22	22			
Elongation, percent in 2 in.	50	51	50	21	5	23	51	67

* See also data on metals and alloys for use at elevated temperatures p. 6–110.

† Nickel 200 is not recommended for use above 600 F; low-carbon nickel 201 is the preferred substitute.

Table 10. Limiting Temperatures or Usual Service Temperatures, Deg F*

Service or environment	Nickel 200	Monel alloy 400	Inconel alloy 600	Incoloy alloy 800	Other alloys
Ammonia synthesis	.....	.....	750–1200		
Ammonia dissociation	.....	.....	1700–1800		
Carburizing	.....	.....	1550–1750	1550–1750	
Carbonitriding	.....	.....	1550–1750		
Fused salts:					
Neutral heat-treating	.....	.....	1550–1750		
Sodium hydroxide	.....	.....	1500†		
Sodium nitrate	.....	.....	....	....	Alloy 201–1000†
Gases:					
Air	1900†	1000†	2150†	2000†	Alloy 702–2400†
Chlorine	1000†	800†	1000†	650†	
Fluorine	1000†	900†	750†		
Hydrogen chloride	950†	450†	900†	800†	
Hydrogen fluoride	1400†	1200†	1200†		
Hydrogen	2300†	2000†	2300†	2300†	
Glass	.....	.....	2300†	....	Alloys 301, 400, K-500‡
Liquid metals:					
Sodium, potassium, sodium-potassium					
Static	1650†	1100†	1650†	1600†	
Dynamic	.....	.....	1300†		
Mercury, static	600†	.....	900†		
Nitriding	.....	.....	900–1050		
Steam	800†	800†	1800†	1800†	

* "Handbook of Huntington Alloys," International Nickel Co.

† Limiting temperatures.

‡ Water-cooled molds for fluoride glass.

of ferromagnetism and the temperature sensitivity are very susceptible to variations in composition and mechanical and thermal treatment.

An important group of magnetic alloys are the nickel-irons, and their modifications, of exceptionally high permeability. Other nickel-iron alloys are used for their special thermal expansion and thermoelastic properties.

Nickel Electroplates. Electroplating accounts for about 10 percent of the total annual consumption of nickel. Normal nickel electroplate has properties approximating those of wrought nickel, but special baths and techniques can give very much harder plates. Bonds between nickel and base metal are usually strong. The largest use of nickel plate is for corrosion protection of iron and steel parts and zinc base die castings for automotive use. A 1.5 to 3 mil nickel plate is covered with a chromium plate only about 1/100 as thick to give a bright, tarnish-resistant, hard surface. Nickel electro-deposits are also used to facilitate brazing of chromium containing alloys, to reclaim worn parts, and for electroformed parts, such as dies for phonograph records.

ALUMINUM AND ITS ALLOYS

(Based largely on information supplied by Aluminum Co. of America.)

References: Edwards, Frary, and Jeffries, "The Aluminum Industry," McGraw-Hill. Fink *et al.*, "Physical Metallurgy of Aluminum Alloys," ASM. von Zeerleder, "Technology of Light Metals," Elsevier.

Aluminum owes most of its applications to its low density and to the relatively high strength of its alloys, although other uses depend upon its comparatively good corrosion resistance, good working properties, or electrical or thermal conductivity and reflectivity. Commercial aluminum is a soft and ductile metal and is used for many applications where high strength is not necessary. It is available in extruded or rolled forms and can be **hardened** by cold working but not by heat-treatment. The alloys of aluminum possess better casting and machining characteristics and better mechanical properties and, therefore, are used more extensively than the pure metal.

Aluminum Alloys for Sand Castings. The compositions and typical properties of aluminum alloys used for foundry work are listed in Table 11. Most of these are based on either aluminum-copper or aluminum-silicon systems with additions to improve the casting or service characteristics. Among **aluminum-copper** alloys, the one containing 8 percent copper has been used longest as a general-purpose alloy, although the additions of silicon and iron to this improve the casting characteristics, particularly in rendering the alloy less hot-short. Additions of zinc to this alloy, CS22, are made to improve the machinability. The 4 percent alloys do not have as good casting properties as those containing 8 percent copper.

Alloys containing 12 percent copper are slightly stronger than the 8 percent alloy but considerably less tough. They owe their employment to the fact that it is easy to produce castings free from leaks in this alloy, although they have now been largely replaced by aluminum-silicon alloys.

Alloy CG1 which has a small magnesium content retains a larger percentage of its strength and hardness up to comparatively high temperatures. It was developed primarily for pistons but is used in other high-temperature applications. It age-hardens spontaneously after casting, and further hardening may be produced by a precipitation heat-treatment at a moderate temperature, particularly if this follows a solution heat-treatment.

Aluminum-silicon alloys have come into considerable use because of their excellent casting qualities and resistance to corrosion. The alloys are not hot-short and are easy to cast sound in thin or thick sections. They are rather difficult to machine. The most commonly used aluminum-silicon alloy is that containing 5 percent silicon (S2). Alloy S2 solidifies normally with a coarse hypereutectic structure, but this is "modified" before casting by the addition of a small amount of sodium to give a fine eutectic structure of greater strength and toughness. With all alloys containing substantial amounts of silicon, the iron content must be low to avoid brittleness.

Aluminum-magnesium alloys are superior to practically all other aluminum casting alloys with respect to resistance to corrosion and machinability. In addition, these alloys exhibit good to exceptional combinations of mechanical strength and ductility. Two important alloys of this group are ASTM G1 and G3. In general, however, the alloys are difficult to cast into intricate or pressure-tight castings, and carefully controlled foundry practices are required to minimize a marked tendency for oxidation of the molten alloys.

Permanent Mold-casting Alloys. Alloys for casting in permanent molds must be free from hot-shortness. The silicon alloys mentioned above are extensively used, also those containing copper, and alloys with both silicon and copper.

Table 11. Compositions and Typical Mechanical Properties of Aluminum Casting Alloys*

Alloy designation				Chemical composition, percent‡ (remainder Al)										
ASTM	Aluminum Co.	Reynolds	Am. Smelting and Refining Co.	Cu	Si	Mg	Fe	Other	Treatment	Yield strength, kpsi†	Tensile strength, kpsi†	Elongation, percent in 2 in.†	Endurance limit, kpsi	Electrical conductivity, percent IACS
SAND-CASTING ALLOYS														
S2	43	43	050	...	5.0	...	...	....	SC	9	19	6.0	6.5	37
	45	45	....	...	10.0	...	...	....	SC	10	21	4.5	6.0	31
S9	47	...	....	...	12.5	...	...	....	SC	11	26	8.0	6.0	40
CS4	108	108	430	4.0	3.0	...	...	....	SC	14	21	2.0	8.5	31
	112	112	....	7.0	...	...	1.2	1.7 Zn	SC	14	23	1.5	9.0	30
CG1	122	122	1000.3	10.0	...	0.2	1.2	....	SC	21	26	0.5	9.5	34
CN21	142	142	401.5 Ni	4.0	...	1.5	...	2.0 Ni	SC	24	28	1.0	8.0	36
CN21	142	142	....	...	...	...	...	....	T2	18	27	1.0	6.5	44
CN21	142	142	....	...	...	...	...	....	T61	32	37	0.5	8.0	37
CN21	142	142	....	...	...	...	...	....	T571	28	32	0.5	8.0	
C1	195	195	....	4.0	...	...	...	....	T4	16	31	8.5	6.0	35
C1	195	195	....	...	...	...	...	....	T6	22	36	5.0	6.5	
C1	195	195	....	...	...	...	...	....	T62	31	40	2.0	7.0	37
	212	212	....	8.0	1.2	...	1.0	....	SC	14	22	2.0	8.0	30
G1	214	214	....	...	...	3.8	...	....	SC	12	25	9.0	5.5	35
GS1	B214	B214	024	...	1.8	3.8	...	....	SC	13	20	2.0	...	38
G3	220	220	....	...	...	10.0	...	....	T4	25	45	14.0	7	21
SC5	A334	A334	....	3.0	4.0	0.3	...	....	SC	16	25	2.0	8.5	31
SC21	355	355	....	1.3	5.0	0.5	...	....	T6	25	35	3.5	8.5	36
SC21	355	355	....	...	...	...	...	....	T51	23	28	1.5	7.0	43
SG1	356	356	....	...	7.0	0.3	...	....	T4	16	28	6.0	...	39
SG1	356	356	....	...	...	...	...	....	T6	22	32	4.0	8.0	39
SG1...	356	356	....	...	...	...	...	....	T51	20	25	2.0	7.5	43
	645	645	....	2.5	...	...	1.2	11.0 Zn	....	20	29	4.0	7.5	33
PERMANENT MOLD-CASTING ALLOYS														
S2	43	43	050	...	5.0	...	...	....	CC	9	24	6.0	...	41
SC1	A108	A108	....	4.5	5.5	...	...	....	CC	16	28	2.0	...	37
	B113	B113	....	7.0	1.7	...	1.2	....	CC	19	28	2.0	...	29
CS22	C113	C113	....	7.0	3.5	...	1.2	2.0 Zn	CC	24	30	1.0	...	27
CG1	122	122	....	10.0	...	0.2	1.2	....	CC	26	31	1.0	...	34
SN41	A312	A312	....	0.8	12.0	1.0	...	2.5 Ni	T551	28	36	0.5	...	29
CN21	142	142	401.5 Ni	4.0	...	1.5	...	2.0 Ni	CC	24	34	1.0	...	34
CN21	142	142	....	...	...	...	...	....	T61	42	47	0.5	9.5	
CN21	142	142	....	...	...	...	...	....	T571	34	40	0.0	10.5	34
CS4	B195	B195	....	4.5	2.5	...	...	....	T4	22	40	10.0	9.5	35
CS4	B195	B195	....	...	...	...	...	....	T6	33	45	5.0	10.0	50
GZ1	A214	A214	004 Zn	...	...	3.8	...	1.8 Zn	CC	16	27	5.0		
SC21	355	355	....	1.3	5.0	0.5	...	....	T6	26	43	4.0	9.0	39
SC21	355	355	....	...	...	...	...	....	T51	24	30	2		
SG1	356	356	....	...	7.0	0.3	...	....	T4	18	32	9	...	39
SG1	356	356	....	...	...	...	...	....	T6	24	40	5	...	41

Table 11. Compositions and Typical Mechanical Properties of Aluminum Casting Alloys*—(*Continued*)

Alloy designation				Chemical composition, percent‡ (remainder Al)					Treatment	Yield strength, kpsi†	Tensile strength, kpsi†	Elongation, percent in 2 in.†	Endurance limit, kpsi	Electrical conductivity, percent IACS
ASTM	Aluminum Co.	Reynolds	Am. Smelting and Refining Co.	Cu	Si	Mg	Fe	Other						
						Die-casting Alloys								
S9	13	13	0120	...	12.0	...	...	....	DC	18	33	1.8	15.0	36
S2	43	43	....	...	5.0	...	...	....	DC	13	29	3.5	...	41
	81	...	....	7.0	3.0	...	...	....	DC	24	32	1.3	16.0	28
	83	...	....	2.0	3.0	...	...	....	DC	14	30	3.5	14.5	30
SC1	85	85	450	4.0	5.0	...	...	....	DC	19	35	2.7	17.0	28
	218	218	....	...	...	8.0	...	....	DC	23	38	5.0	18.0	25

* These values are largely taken from data published by the Aluminum Co. of America. They are typical values and should not be used for specification purposes. Aluminum-base alloys for casting are covered by ASTM specification B179–55. Sand castings are covered by B26–55T. Treatments SC, CC, and DC refer to alloy in the sand-cast, chill-cast, or die-cast conditions, respectively. T2 is an annealing treatment for removing casting stresses. T4 is a solution heat-treatment followed by rapid cooling and aging at room temperature. T6, T61, and T62 are solution heat treatments followed by precipitation. Treatments T51, T551, and T571 are precipitation treatments only.

† Tensile properties are on ½ in. diam sand-cast, or ½ in. diam chill or die-cast specimens, tested without machining surface. Yield strength corresponds to 0.2 percent offset. Endurance limit is based on 500,000,000 cycles on R. R. Moore type of machine and machined specimens.

‡ All these alloys may contain, as impurities, iron in amounts not to exceed 0.4 up to 1.0 percent, silicon 0.2 to 1.2 percent, and manganese up to about 0.3 percent, according to the alloy. An intentional addition of titanium up to 0.2 percent is often made.

Common uses for some of the casting alloys (Aluminum Co. designations) are as follows: 43, A214, cooking utensils and pipe fittings; 122, 142, pistons and cylinder heads; 108 intricate pressure-tight castings; 212 intricate castings; 13, large intricate parts; A334, pressure-tight castings; 218, marine fittings; 214, dairy and food equipment.

In the United States, the greater use of permanent mold castings is for internal-combustion-engine pistons for which light weight, low thermal expansion, and good properties at high temperatures are desirable. Most of these are cast in alloy CG1. Most of these alloys can be heat-treated to improve their properties or to render them less liable to dimensional change during use.

Die-casting Alloys. Aluminum alloys for pressure die-casting must possess considerable fluidity and be free from hot-shortness. The physical properties are usually of less importance than the casting qualities. Absorption of iron is difficult to avoid under operating conditions but should be kept low.

Aluminum-alloy Designations. Wrought alloys are designated by a four-digit number following the system adopted by the Aluminum Association in 1954. The first digit indicates the alloy type, according to the major alloying element. The second digit indicates specific alloy modifications. The last two digits identify the specific aluminum alloy or indicate the aluminum purity. In most cases, the last two digits correspond to the alloy number in the former alloy-designation system (as 2024 was formerly 24S). The first digit is assigned according to the principal alloying element: 1 = 99+ percent aluminum, 2 = copper, 3 = manganese, 4 = silicon, 5 = magnesium, 6 = magnesium and silicon, 7 = zinc.

The **temper designation** indicates the treatment the alloy has received in arriving at its present condition and associated properties. The temper of an alloy is indicated by the letters O, F, H, or T followed by one or more numbers. In wrought alloys, O indicates annealed; F, as-fabricated; T, heat-treated; H, cold-worked. Specific heat-treatments and degrees of cold working are indicated by numbers, *e.g.*, T7 or H14. When an alloy is customarily used only in the as-cast condition, the temper designation in omitted. If the alloy is used in both the as-cast and the

Table 12. Composition and Typical Room-temperature Properties of Wrought-aluminum Alloys*

Aluminum Assoc. alloy designation†	Nominal composition, percent (balance aluminum)					Temper‡	Density, lb per cu in.	Electrical conductivity, % IACS	Brinell hardness, 500 kg load, 10 mm ball	Tensile mechanical properties			Endurance limit, kpsi
	Cu	Si	Mn	Mg	Other elements					0.2% offset TYS, kpsi	UTS, kpsi	Elong, % in 2 in.	
						Work-hardened Alloys							
1100	....	...	...	....	....	0	0.098	59	23	5	13	35	5
						H14	.....	...	32	16	17.5	9	7
						H18	.....	57	44	22	24	5	8.5
3003	....	...	1.2	...	....	0	0.099	50	28	6	16	30	7
						H14	.....	41	40	19	21.5	8	9
						H18	.....	40	55	26	29	4	10
5052	....	...	...	2.5	0.25 Cr	0	0.096	40	45	12	27	25	17
						H14	.....	...	67	31	37	10	18
						H18	.....	40	85	36	41	7	19
5056	....	...	0.1	5.2	0.1 Cr	0	0.095	29	...	22	42	35	20
						H18	.....	27	...	59	63	10	22
						Heat-treated Alloys							
2011	5.5	...	...	....	0.5 Pb 0.5 Bi	T3	0.102	40	95	48	55	15	18
						T6	.....	...	97	39	57	17	18
2014	4.4	0.8	0.8	0.4	....	0	0.101	40	45	14	27	18	13
						T4	.....	...	105	40	62	20	20
						T6	.....	...	135	60	70	13	18
Alclad 2014	....	...	...	....	....	0	0.101	40	...	10	25	21	18
						T4	.....	...	...	37	61	22	37
						T6	.....	...	...	60	68	11	41
2017	4.0	...	0.5	0.5	....	0	0.101	45	45	10	26	20	13
						T4	.....	30	105	40	62	20	18
2020	4.5	...	0.5	....	0.2 Cd, 1.3 Li	T6	0.098	...	...	77	84	7	
2024	4.4	...	0.5	1.5	....	0	0.100	50	47	11	27	19	13
						T3	.....	...	120	50	70	18	20
						T4	.....	30	120	48	68	20	20

Table 12. Composition and Typical Room-temperature Properties of Wrought-aluminum Alloys—(*Continued*)

Aluminum Assoc. alloy designation†	Nominal composition, percent (balance aluminum)					Temper‡	Density, lb per cu in.	Electrical conductivity, % IACS	Brinell hardness, 500 kg load, 10-mm ball	Tensile mechanical properties			Endurance limit, kpsi
	Cu	Si	Mn	Mg	Other elements					0.2% offset TYS, kpsi	UTS, kpsi	Elong, % in 2 in.	
Alclad 2024	....	...	...	....	....	0	0.100	...	...	11	26	18	40
						T3	.....	...	...	44	64	19	40
						T4	.....	...	...	42	64	11	41
2025	4.5	0.8	0.8	....	....	T6	0.101	40	110	37	58	19	18
2219	6.1	...	0.3	....	0.15 Zr	0	.....	...	...	10	25	20	
					0.10 V	T42	.....	...	...	27	53	20	
					0.06 Ti	T87	.....	...	130	57	69	10	
6151	....	1.0	...	0.6	0.25 Cr	T6	0.098	45	100	43	48	17	11
6053	....	0.7	...	1.3	0.25 Cr	0	0.097	45	26	8	16	25	8
						T4	.....	40	62	20	30	22	13
						T6	.....	40	80	32	37	14	13
6061	0.25	0.6	...	1.0	0.25 Cr	0	0.098	45	30	8	18	22	9
						T6	.....	...	95	40	45	12	13.5
6063	....	0.4	...	0.7	....	T42	0.098	50	42	13	22	20	9.5
						T6	.....	55	73	31	35	12	9.5
7075	1.6	...	...	2.5	5.6 Zn	0	0.101	...	60	15	33	17	
					0.3 Cr	T6	.....	30	150	72	82	11	24
Alclad 7075	....	...	...	....	....	0	0.101	...	...	14	32	17	
						T6	.....	...	...	67	76	11	
7178	2.0	...	...	2.7	0.3 Cr, 6.8 Zn	T6	.....	...	...	78	88	10	

Notes:
* Typical values for 0.064-in.-thick sheet.
† Aluminum Association Standardized System of Alloy Designation adopted October, 1954.
‡ Standard temper designations: 0 = fully annealed. H14 and H18 correspond to half-hard and hard strain-hardened tempers. T3 = solution treated and then cold-worked; T4 = solution heat-treated; T6 = solution treated and then artificially aged; T42 = as fabricated.

heat-treated conditions, the letter F is used to indicate the as-cast condition. T2 indicates an annealed casting.

Wrought-aluminum alloys (Table 12) are divided into two classes: those hardened and strengthened by cold working alone and those which owe their improved properties to heat-treatment. Some of the latter alloys age-harden spontaneously at room temperature, although other wrought alloys of both types need to be heated moderately.

The most important work-hardening alloys are commercially pure aluminum (1100) or the 1.25 percent manganese alloy (3003). Both of these are available in a wide range of sheet, rod, tube, and wire sizes and extruded shapes. The 3003 alloy is used extensively for the manufacture of cooking utensils, conduit pipe, and other products where strength and hardness somewhat greater than those of pure aluminum are desired. These alloys can be hardened by cold work but are not heat-treated except when annealed to remove hardness resulting from cold work.

Where high strength is necessary, it is usual to use an alloy of the **duralumin** type. The most common is 2024. This alloy is readily hot-worked. It hardens spontaneously at room temperature after solution heat-treatment. Extensive cold working must be done within a few hours after quenching. Cold working following age-hardening is less easy but gives the highest strength obtainable with the alloys. For aircraft construction, 2017 has been largely superseded by 2024 because this alloy has a higher strength. 6061 and 6063 have better fabricating qualities in the quenched condition. Alloy 6053 is used because of its combination of good physical properties and corrosion resistance. It is available in various rolled structural shapes; most architectural extruded sections are made from it. Alloy 2219 is by far the most weldable of the high-strength heat-treatable alloys. Alloy 7178 is the highest-strength heat-treatable alloy commercially available today and is considerably more easily welded than 6065.

Most of the heat-treatable alloys are less resistant to corrosion than is pure aluminum or aluminum-manganese alloy; alloy 6053 is an exception. The corrosion resistance of the duralumin-type alloys is greatest in the quenched condition. Oil quenching and artificial aging decrease the resistance still further. Many of the heat-treatable alloys are available in sheet form with an integral coating of high-purity aluminum or corrosion-resistant alloy on each side; the thickness of each layer is approximately 2½ to 10 percent of the total, depending upon the alloy and gage. These products, known as **alclad alloys,** possess an excellent resistance to corrosion. Because of electrolytic action, exposed cut edges of the base metal are protected, and ordinary bare rivets can be used. The strength is slightly less than that of bare sheet of similar gage.

A new type of wrought-aluminum commodity, designated **APM,** has elevated-temperature strength, stability, and resistance to creep superior to any known aluminum alloy. The process consists of making a compact of fine, high-purity aluminum powder containing large but controlled amounts of aluminum oxide, followed by extruding, rolling, or forging into a final product. Alloy XAP001 contains 6 percent oxide and has 47 percent IACS conductivity, 37,000 psi tensile strength, 27,000 psi yield strength, and 13 percent elongation at normal temperature. As high as 800 F, the tensile strength is 11,000 psi, with 10,000 psi yield strength and 4 percent elongation. (See Table 13.)

Heat-treatment. Intermediate annealing to relieve cold work is done at a temperature of about 650 F for pure aluminum and 5052 or about 750 F for 3003. The rate of cooling is unimportant. The heat-treatable alloys are best cold-worked when in the quenched condition after heat-treatment. They may be fully annealed only by heating to 750 to 800 F and cooling slowly to 500 F. A partial softening of heat-treated material can be obtained by an ordinary anneal at 650 F.

The heat-treatable alloys must have a double heat-treatment: one at a high temperature to dissolve the alloy constituents later responsible for hardening and the other at a low temperature to permit them to cause precipitation hardening of the alloy. The second action may take place spontaneously at room temperatures on some alloys and is then known as *natural aging,* but on other alloys it has to be carried

Table 13. Typical Tensile Properties of Aluminum Alloys at Elevated Temperatures

Alloy and temper	Property*	Temperature, deg F 75	300	400	500	700
Wrought						
1100-H18	T.S.	24,000	17,500	6,000	3,500	1,500
	Y.S.	21,000	14,000	3,000	2,000	1,000
	El.	15	16	70	85	95
3003-H18	T.S.	29,000	23,000	17,000	10,500	3,000
	Y.S.	25,000	16,000	8,000	5,000	2,000
	El.	10	12	15	25	60
3004-H18	T.S.	40,000	32,000	23,000	11,500	4,000
	Y.S.	34,000	22,000	9,500	5,000	2,500
	El.	6	14	27	70	100
2017-T4	T.S.	60,000	40,000	25,000	13,000	4,500
	Y.S.	37,000	33,500	20,000	9,500	3,000
	El.	22	16	25	35	100
2024-T4	T.S.	68,000	46,000	27,000	14,000	5,000
	Y.S.	44,000	38,000	21,000	9,500	3,500
	El.	22	22	25	45	100
5052-H16	T.S.	39,000	32,000	25,000	12,000	5,000
	Y.S.	34,000	27,000	11,000	8,000	2,500
	El.	10	16	35	80	120
6053-T6	T.S.	39,000	25,000	13,000	6,000	2,500
	Y.S.	33,000	22,000	10,000	3,500	2,000
	El.	20	17	30	—7	0 9
6061-T6	T.S.	45,000	31,000	19,000	7,500	3,000
	Y.S.	40,000	29,000	15,000	5,000	2,000
	El.	17	18	25	55	105
7075-T6	T.S.	82,000	28,000	14,000	11,000	6,000
	Y.S.	72,000	22,000	11,000	8,000	4,000
	El.	11	32	55	60	75
XAP001	T.S.	37,000	......	21,000	19,000	14,500
	Y.S.	24,000	......	18,000	16,000	14,000
	El.	17	......	16	17	

Alloy and temper	Temperature, deg F 75	300	400	500	600
Sand Castings					
122-T2	25,000	25,000	22,000	17,000	8,000
	20,000	17,000	14,000	11,000	4,500
	1.0	1.2	1.5	3.0	14.0
122-T61	36,000	35,000	22,000	10,000	8,000
	30,000	30,000	16,000	5,000	4,500
	1.0	1.2	2.0	6.0	14.0
142	28,000	28,000	22,000	12,000	7,500
	24,000	24,000	18,000	5,000	3,500
	1.0	1.0	1.0	9.0	10.0
195-T4	31,000	24,000	15,000	9,500	4,000
	16,000	13,000	9,000	6,000	3,000
	8.5	9.0	20.0	25.0	80.0
355-T4	30,000	30,000	13,000	8,000	6,000
	20,000	25,000	9,000	5,000	3,500
	5.0	3.0	12.0	22.0	30.0
356-T4	28,000	21,000	13,000	8,000	4,500
	16,000	15,000	9,000	5,500	3,000
	6.0	7.0	8.0	20.0	45.0
Permanent Mold Castings					
122-T551	37,000	33,000	26,000	18,000	10,000
	35,000	29,000	20,000	12,500	6,000
	0	0	1	3	10
A132-T551	36,000	31,000	23,000	17,500	11,000
	28,000	22,000	13,000	9,500	5,000
	0.5	1	2	2	8
142-T571	40,000	37,000	28,000	15,000	9,000
	34,000	33,000	22,000	9,000	5,000
	0	1	2	10	30
B195-T4	36,000	30,000	15,000	7,500	4,000
	22,000	20,000	9,000	5,000	2,500
	7.5	8	12	25	65
355-T4	38,000	31,000	12,000	8,000	4,500
	23,000	25,000	9,000	6,000	3,000
	6		20	25	50

* T.S., tensile strength, psi; Y.S., yield strength, 0.2 percent offset, psi; El., elongation in 2 in., percent.

Tensile tests made on ASTM standard test pieces, 0.5-in. diam, maintained at elevated temperatures for 10,000 hrs except for M257 and M276 where data are for 1,000 hr heating.

Speed of straining 0.1 in. per min per in. of gage length.

out at a somewhat elevated temperature referred to as *artificial aging* or precipitation treatment. The correct treatment for the various alloys is given in Table 14. The solution treatment is usually done in a nitrate bath or in a furnace with forced air circulation. The temperature must be controlled closely. The solution heat-treatment of duralumin should be followed by a rapid quench, preferably in cold water since slower quenches in hot water or oil, although they minimize distortion, render the alloy susceptible to intergranular corrosion. In the alloys that age spontaneously at room temperature, hardening starts immediately after quenching and is practically complete in four days. Severe cold-forming operations must be done within less than an hour after quenching. If it is desired to hold the alloy for later cold-working, aging may be retarded by storing the quenched material at low temperatures, *e.g.*, in ice, which will permit working up to 24 hr, or in "dry ice" (solid CO_2) which will retard aging almost indefinitely.

Table 14. Conditions for Heat-treatment of Aluminum Alloys

Alloy	Solution heat-treatment*		Precipitation heat-treatment		
	Temperature, deg F	Temper designation	Temperature, deg F	Time of aging	Temper designation
2014	925–950	T4	315–325	18 hr	T6
2017	930–950	T4	Room	4 days	
2017A	875–950	T4	Room	4 days	
2024	910–930	T4	Room	4 days	
6053	960–980	T4	315–325	18 hr	T6
6061	960–980	T4	315–325	18 hr	T6
7075	860–930	W	205–215 } †	4–6 hr	T6
			310–320	8–10 hr	

* In a molten nitrate bath, the time varies from 10 to 60 min depending upon the size of the load and the thickness of the material. In an air furnace, proper allowance must be made for a slower rate of bringing the load up to temperature. For heavy material, a longer time at temperature may be necessary. All quenching is performed in cold water.

† This is a two-stage treatment with air cooling to room temperature between the low-temperature and the high-temperature stage. Covered by U.S. Patent 1,858,092.

Machining (see pp. 13–69 to 13–102). Many aluminum alloys are easily machined without special technique. Pure aluminum and the aluminum-manganese alloys are hard to machine unless special tools are used with greater rake than is customary for steel. In general, such tools are similar to those used for working wood but should be harder. Cemented hard carbide tools are almost essential for aluminum-silicon alloys. The casting alloys containing copper and all the wrought heat-treated alloys possess good machinability. For products in which physical properties are subordinate to high machinability, as in automatic screw machine work, alloy 2011 is used. The additions of lead and bismuth render this free-cutting.

Riveting is the most commonly used method of joining aluminum alloys, especially in structures of the heat-treatable alloys that cannot be welded without loss of strength. In general, rivets of similar composition to the base metal are used. When heat-treatable rivets are driven cold, it is important that they be used in the freshly quenched condition prior to aging, but they may be kept for long times in cold storage. Large rivets can sometimes be driven hot from their solution treatment temperature, depending on contact with tools and surrounding metal to produce an effective quench.

Welding (see Sec. 13). The wrought-aluminum alloys are readily welded by experienced operators by either the fusion or resistance method. Fusion welding of the strong alloys is not recommended unless subsequent heat-treatment is possible, but spot and seam welding can be done if automatically controlled. Most casting alloys may be welded, but experience is necessary to overcome the danger of strains and cracks resulting from thermal contraction. Welding should be done prior to heat-treatment. The rod used should generally be of the same composition as the alloy. Aluminum alloys can be **soldered,** but the resultant joints are rarely satisfactory and are not recommended for highly stressed parts or for joints that cannot be given adequate protection against corrosion action.

Corrosion Resistance. Although aluminum is chemically active, the presence of a firmly adherent self-healing oxide coat on the surface prevents action except under conditions that tend to remove this surface film. Concentrated nitric and acetic acids are handled in aluminum not only because of its resistance to attack but also because any resulting corrosion products are colorless. For the same reason, aluminum is employed in the preparation of foods and beverages. Hydrochloric acid and most alkalies dissolve the protective film at the surface and permit fairly rapid attack. Moderately alkaline soaps and the like can be used with aluminum if a small amount of sodium silicate is added. Aluminum is very resistant to sulphur and most of its gaseous compounds.

Ordinary atmospheric corrosion is resisted by aluminum and most of its alloys, and they may be used without any protective coating. The pure metal is most resistant to attack, and additions of alloying elements usually decrease resistance, particularly after heat-treatment. Under severe conditions of exposure such as may prevail on shipboard or where the metal is continually in contact with wood or other absorbent material in the presence of moisture, a protective coat of paint is desirable as an added precaution.

Table 15. Aluminum Electrical Conductors

Form, alloy,* treatment†	Tensile strength, kpsi	Minimum electrical conductivity, percent IACS
Redraw rod (0.375 in. diam):		
EC-O	9–14	62.8
EC-H12	12–17	62.5
EC-H14	14–20	62.4
EC-H16	16–24	62.3
5005-O	14–20	54.3
5005-H12	17–23	54.0
5005-H14	20–76	53.9
5005-H16	24–30	53.8
Wire (0.0801 in. diam):		
EC-H19	26 min	62.0
5005-H19	37	53.5
Bus conductor:		
EC-H111 (extruded)	9 min	62.0
EC-H17 (cold-finished)	17	62.0
No. 2EC-T6:	29	55.0
6061-T6 (extruded)	38	40.0
6063-T6 (extruded)	30	53.0

* Nominal compositions—Ec: 99.6 min Al; 2EC: 0.4 Si, 0.6 Mg; 5005. . . : 0.8 Mg; 6061: 0.6 Si, 1.3 Mg, 0.25 Cu, 0.25 Cr; 6063: 0.4 Si, 0.7 Mg.

† Treatments: O = annealed; H-12, 14, 16, 19 = cold-worked; T-6 = solution-treated, aged.

The resistance to corrosion of aluminum alloys may be augmented by coating the material with a surface layer of high-purity aluminum, or in some cases an alloy, which is rolled as an integral part of the sheet. The corrosion resistance of any of the alloys may be improved by giving an **anodizing treatment,** which comprises making the parts to be treated the anode in an electrolytic bath (chromic, sulphuric, or oxalic acid). This produces a tough adherent coating of aluminum oxide. The film will be colorless on pure aluminum and tends to be gray or colored on alloys containing silicon, copper, or other constituents. This film is very adherent and cannot be readily detached by bending or ordinary fabricating processes. If a colored finish is desired, the electrolytically oxidized article may be treated with a dye solution. Chemical methods are available for producing a similar but thinner film without electrolytic action by mere dipping in hot alkaline oxidizing solution or applying a paste.

When painting or lacquering aluminum it is important that the surface be properly prepared, prior to the application of the paint. A thin anodic film makes an excellent paint base, or the metal may be chemically treated with a dilute phosphoric acid solution. Where corrosive conditions are to be met, zinc chromate may be used as the pigment in the primer coat and aluminum paint for the top.

Aluminum Conductors. On a weight basis, aluminum has twice the electrical conductance of copper; on a volume basis, the conductivity of aluminum is about 62 percent that of copper. For electrical applications, aluminum is used as a special, high-purity grade (EC) or as relatively dilute alloys designed to improve strength with minimum sacrifice in conductivity. Table 15 lists common conductor alloys and gives their strengths and conductivities in various forms and treatments. In power-transmission lines, the necessary strength for long spans is obtained by stranding aluminum wires about a core wire of steel (**ACSR**).

MAGNESIUM AND MAGNESIUM ALLOYS

(Based largely on data supplied by the Dow Chemical Co.)

REFERENCES: Publications of The Dow Chemical Co. "Metals Handbook," ASM. Beck, "Technology of Magnesium and Its Alloys," Hughes.

Magnesium is the lightest metal of structural importance (108 lb per cu ft). Its principal applications are in aircraft, in portable and manually operated tools, and in moving and reciprocating parts of machinery (particularly textile and printing machinery and lawn mowers). Because of its chemical activity, it is used in pyrotechnical materials and for sacrificial galvanic protection of other metals exposed to corrosive mediums.

Commercially pure magnesium contains a minimum of 99.8 percent magnesium. Aluminum, iron, silicon, and manganese are the chief impurities. The major part of the magnesium produced is used in the form of magnesium-rich alloys. Aluminum is the chief addition, with smaller amounts of zinc and manganese being used in nearly all cases. These alloys can be heat-treated and aged to increase their strength. Designs employing magnesium should take into account the low value of the modulus of elasticity (6.5×10^6 psi) and the high thermal coefficient of expansion (14×10^{-6} per deg F at 32 F, and 16×10^{-6} for the range 68 to 752 F). See Tables 16 and 17 for compositions and properties.

Alloys of the Mg-Al-Zn system are most used for sand and permanent-mold **castings.** Alloy AZ63A is the most difficult to use. Pressure tightness is most easily obtained in castings of alloy EZ33A. Most permanent-mold castings are made with AM100A and AZ92A alloys. The casting alloy K1A was developed for applications requiring high damping capacity; its damping capacity exceeds that of cast iron. The normal unhindered shrinkage factor can be reduced to as low as ⅛ in. per ft on large castings or where shrinkage is restricted by cores.

Magnesium-alloy **forgings** are used for applications requiring higher properties than are obtainable in castings. They are generally press-forged. Alloy AZ61 is a general-purpose alloy, while alloy AZ80 is used for the highest-strength press forgings of simple design. This alloy may be aged to increase its strength when required.

A wide range of **extruded shapes** is available in a number of alloy compositions. Alloys AZ31, AZ61, and AZ80 increase in cost and strength in the order named. Impact extrusion is now used for small symmetrical tubular parts.

Sheet is available in several alloys (see Table 17), in both the soft-annealed and the hard-rolled form. Magnesium-alloy sheet is usually hot-formed at temperatures between 400 and 650 F, although simple bends of large radius can be made cold.

The development of jet engines and high-velocity aircraft, missiles, and spacecraft has accelerated the development of new magnesium-base alloys with improved elevated-temperature properties. These alloys have been obtained by the addition of some combination of **rare earths,** manganese, zirconium, and thorium. Such alloys have extended the temperatures at which magnesium can be used in structural applications to as high as 700 to 800 F.

Joining. Magnesium alloys may be joined by riveting or welding. Riveting is most widely employed. Aluminum-alloy rivets are used; 5052 is preferred since contact corrosion is minimized, although other alloys can be used (with some danger from contact corrosion). All rivets should be anodized to prevent such attack.

Table 16. Typical Mechanical Properties of Magnesium Casting Alloys, Tensile Yield Strength, Separately Cast Test Bars

Alloy	Condition or temper*	Nominal composition, percent					Tensile strength, kpsi	Tensile yield strength, kpsi	Elongation, percent in 2 in.	Shear, kpsi	Bearing strength, kpsi		BHN	Electrical conductivity, percent IACS‡
		Al	Zn	Mn, min	Zr	Other					Ultimate	Yield		
Sand-casting alloys:														
AM100A	-T6	10.0	...	0.10	...	....	40	22	1	22	...	...	70	14
AZ63A	-F	6.0	3.0	....	...	....	29	14	6	18	60	40	50	14
	-T4						40	13	12	17	60	44	55	12
	-T5						30	14	4	17	60	40	55	
	-T6						40	19	5	20	75	52	73	15
AZ81A	-T4	7.5	0.7	0.13	...	....	40	12	15	17	60	44	55	12
AZ91C	-F	8.7	0.7	0.13	...	....	24	14	2	18	60	40	52	13
	-T4						40	12	14	17	60	44	53	11
	-T5						26	17	3	...	...	...	...	
	-T6						40	19	5	20	75	52	66	13
AZ92A	-F	9.0	2.0	0.10	...	....	24	14	2	18	50	46	65	12
	-T4						40	14	9	20	68	46	63	10
	-T5						26	16	2	19	50	46	70	
	-T6						40	21	2	22	80	65	84	14
EK41A	-T6	....	...	....	0.7	4.0 RE†	25	18	3	20	59	41	50	24
EZ33A	-T5	....	2.5	....	0.8	3.5 RE	23	15	3	22	57	40	50	25
HK31A	-T6	....	...	....	0.8	3.5 Th	32	15	8	22	61	40	55	22
HZ32A	-T5	....	2.0	....	0.8	3.5 Th	30	14	7	22	60	37	57	27
K1A	-F	....	...	....	0.7	....	25	7	19	8	...	...	..	31
QE22A	-T6	....	...	....	0.7	2.0 RE, 2.5 Ag	40	30	4	23	...	...	...	25
ZE41A	-T5	....	4.0	....	0.7	1.3 RE	30	20	3.5	22	70	51	62	31
ZH62A	-T5	....	5.5	....	0.8	1.8 Th	40	25	6	23	72	49	70	27
ZK51A	-T5	....	4.5	....	0.8	....	40	24	8	22	72	47	65	27
ZK61A	-T6	....	6.0	....	0.8	....	45	28	10	26	...	...	70	27
Permanent-mold-casting alloys:														
AM100A	-F	10.0	...	0.10	...	....	22	12	2	18	...	...	53	12
	-T4						40	13	10	20	...	...	52	10
	-T6						40	16	4	21	...	...	60	14
	-T61						40	22	1	22	...	...	70	15
AZ63A	-F	6.0	3.0	....	...	....	...	...	....	...	...	...	50	14
	-T4						...	...	....	...	...	...	55	12
	-T5						...	...	....	...	...	...	55	
	-T6						...	...	....	...	...	...	73	15
AZ81A	-T4	7.5	0.7	0.13	...	....	...	...	....	...	...	...	55	12

Table 16. Typical Mechanical Properties of Magnesium Casting Alloys, Tensile Yield Strength, Separately Cast Test Bars—*(Continued)*

Alloy	Condition or temper*	Nominal composition, percent					Tensile strength, kpsi	Tensile yield strength, kpsi	Elongation, percent in 2 in.	Shear, kpsi	Bearing strength, kpsi		BHN	Electrical conductivity, percent IACS‡
		Al	Zn	Mn, min	Zr	Other					Ultimate	Yield		
AZ91C	-F	8.7	0.7	0.13	...	...	24	14	2	18	...	...	52	13
	-T4						40	12	14	17	...	...	53	11
	-T5						26	17	3	...	...	...	...	...
	-T6						40	19	5	20	...	...	66	13
AZ92A	-F	9.0	2.0	0.10	...	...	24	14	2	18	...	...	65	12
	-T4						40	14	10	20	...	...	63	10
	-T5						25	16	1	19	...	...	69	...
	-T6						40	21	2	22	...	...	80	14
EK41A	-T6	...	...	...	0.7	4.0 RE	26	19	3	...	...	...	50	24
EZ33A	-T5	...	2.5	...	0.8	3.5 RE	23	15	3	...	...	...	50	25
Die-casting alloys:														
AZ91A	-F	...	...	...	...	...	33	22	3	22	...	...	63	
AZ91B	-F	...	...	...	...	...	33	22	3	22	...	...	63	

* -F = as cast; -T4 = artificially aged; -T4 = solution heat-treated; -T6 = solution heat-treated plus artificially aged.

† Re = rare earths.

‡ Percent electrical conductivity/100 approximately equals thermal conductivity in cgs units.

Table 17. Properties of Wrought-magnesium Alloys

Alloy and temper*	Nominal composition, percent					Physical properties			Room-temperature mechanical properties (typical)							
	Al	Mn	Th	Zn	Zr	Density, lb per cu in	Thermal conductivity, cgs units, 68 F	Electrical resistivity, microhm-cm, 68 F	Tensile strength, kpsi	Tensile yield strength, kpsi	Elongation in 2 in., percent	Compressive yield strength, kpsi	Shear strength, kpsi	Bearing strength, kpsi Ult	Bearing strength, kpsi Yield	BHN
Extruded Bars, Rods, Shapes																
AZ31B-F	3.0	...	...	1.0	...	0.0639	0.18	9.2	38	29	15	14	19	56	33	49
AZ61A-F	6.5	...	...	1.0	...	0.0647	0.14	12.5	45	33	16	19	22	68	40	60
AZ80A-T5	8.5	...	...	0.5	...	0.0649	0.12	14.5	55	40	7	35	24	60	58	82
HM31A-T5	...	1.2 min	3.0	...	...	0.0651	0.25	6.6	44	38	8	27	22	62	49	63
									43	34	13	23	21	62	44	63
ZK21A-F	...	...	...	2.3	0.6	0.0645	0.30	5.4	42	33	10	25	21	60	46	
ZK60A-F	...	...	...	5.7	0.5	0.0659	0.28	6.0	49	38	14	33	24	76	56	75
-T5	...	...	...	5.7	0.5	0.0659	0.29	5.7	53	44	11	36	26	79	59	82
(P)ZK60B-T5	...	...	...	5.8	0.5	0.0661	0.30	5.5	49	38	17	40	25	76	65	
Extruded Tube																
AZ31B-F	3.0	...	...	1.0	...	0.0639	0.18	9.2	36	24	16	12	...	...	...	46
AZ61A-F	6.5	...	...	1.0	...	0.0647	0.14	12.5	41	24	14	16	...	...	...	50
ZK21A-F	...	...	...	2.3	0.6	0.0645	0.30	5.4	41	35	6	17				
ZK60A-F	...	...	...	5.7	0.5	0.0659	0.28	6.0	47	35	13	25	...	...	...	75
-T5	...	...	...	5.7	0.5	0.0659	0.29	5.7	50	40	11	30	...	...	...	82
Sheet and Plate																
AZ31B-H24	3.0	...	...	1.0	...	0.0639	0.18	9.2	42	32	15	26	29	77	47	73
									40	29	17	23	28	72	45	
									39	27	19	19	27	70	40	
AZ31B-O	3.0	...	...	1.0	...	0.0639	0.18	9.2	37	22	21	16	26	66	37	56
HK31A-H24	...	...	3.0	...	0.7	0.0647	0.27	6.1	38	30	9	23	26	67	41	57
									37	28	10	23	26	65	41	57
									39	31	14	25	27	68	44	
HK31A-O	...	...	3.0	...	0.7	0.0647	0.25	6.6	33	20	23	14	24	58	28	
HM21A-T8	...	0.6	2.0	...	...	0.0640	0.33	5.0	35	23	11	19	19	63	37	56
									37	27	12	23	...	67	41	
Tooling Plate																
AZ31-B	3.0	...	...	1.0	...	0.0639	0.18	9.2	35	19	12	10				
Tread Plate																
AZ31B	3.0	...	...	1.0	...	0.0639	0.18	9.2	35	19	14	11				52

* Temper: -F = as fabricated; -H24 = strain-hardened, then partially annealed; -O = fully annealed; -T5 = artificially aged; -T8 = solution heat-treated, cold-worked, then artificially aged

Note: For all above alloys: coefficient of thermal expansion = 0.0000145; modulus of elasticity = 6,500,000 psi; modulus of rigidity = 2,400,000 psi; Poisson's ratio = 0.35.

Adhesive bonding is now an accepted method for joining magnesium. It offers advantages in weight saving, fatigue strength, and corrosion resistance.

Arc welding with inert-gas (helium or argon) shielding of the molten metal produces satisfactory joints. Butt joints are preferred, but any type of joint permissible for mild steel can be used. After welding, a stress-relief anneal is necessary to relieve the welding stresses. Typical times are 15 min at 500 F for soft-annealed alloys and 1 hr at 400 F for hard-rolled alloys. (See also Sec. 13.)

Machining. Magnesium in all its forms is a free-machining metal. Standard tools such as those used for brass and steel can be used with slight modification. Relief angles should be from 7 to 12 deg, and the rake angles from 0 to 15 deg. High-speed steel is satisfactory and is used for most drills, taps, and reamers. The hard grades of cemented carbides are better for production work and should be used where the tool design permits it. Finely divided magnesium constitutes a fire hazard, and good housekeeping in the machine shop is essential. (See also Sec. 13.)

Corrosion Resistance and Surface Protection. Magnesium alloys display good resistance to ordinary inland atmospheric exposure, to most alkalies, and to many organic chemicals. Marine atmospheric exposure and most acids and salts attack them rapidly. Galvanic couples formed by contact with most other metals, or by impregnation of the surface with other metals during fabrication, can cause rapid attack of the magnesium under conditions of wet corrosion. Protective treatments are available. Prior to shipment, most magnesium parts are pickled in a solution of sodium dichromate and nitric acid (chrome pickle); This forms a protective film on the surface and makes an excellent base for painting. Other protective and decorative finishes are also available.

ZINC AND ZINC ALLOYS

(Based largely on data supplied by The New Jersey Zinc Co. and the American Zinc Inst.)

Zinc, one of the least expensive non-ferrous metals, is produced from sulphide, silicate, or carbonate ores by a process involving concentration and roasting followed either by reduction of the zinc ore by carbon and simultaneous distillation of the zinc in batch or continuous retorts or by leaching out the oxide with sulphuric acid and electrolyzing the solution after purification. Distilled zinc contains impurities (principally Pb, Cd, and Fe) that may be eliminated by fractional redistillation to produce zinc of 99.99 + percent purity. Metal of equal purity can be produced by the electrolytic process. Zinc reaches the market in the form of slabs, 1 to 1½ in. thick, 8½ to 10 in. wide, 18 to 20 in. long. In this form, it is frequently called **spelter.**

The important grades of zinc available in the United States are covered by ASTM specification B6–62T, Table 18.

Table 18. ASTM Specification B6–62T for Slab Zinc

Grade	Max percent			Zinc, min percent
	Lead	Iron	Cadmium	
Special high grade	0.003	0.003	0.003	99.99
High grade	0.07	0.02	0.07	99.9
Intermediate	0.20	0.03	0.50	99.5
Brass special	0.60	0.03	0.50	99.0
Prime western	1.60	0.05	0.50	98.0

The special high-grade zinc is used in the manufacture of die castings, where impurities have a marked harmful effect on corrosion resistance and dimensional stability. **Galvanizing** (which consumes by far the largest proportion of zinc) utilizes principally Prime western zinc, but large tonnages of high-grade zinc are used in continuous galvanizing mills. All grades are used for rolled-zinc products as the presence of impurities is often desirable for their strengthening effect. For brass manufacture and other alloys, there is an increasing tendency toward the use of high grades of zinc.

Wrought Zinc. Zinc rolled in the form of sheet, strip, or plate of various thicknesses is used extensively. It is usually made from commercial slab zinc. It is produced by hot rolling unless some stiffness and temper are required, in which case one or more of the finishing passes are done cold. The softer, purer grades of zinc are used for deep drawing or forming operations, and the less pure metal is used for weather strip, roofing, and other applications where some stiffness is necessary, or where specific chemical properties are desired, as in photoengravers' plates.

Nearly all rolled zinc is custom-rolled to meet the customer's requirements (see ASTM B69–39). Duplication of characteristics is obtained by careful control of composition and rolling treatment and by application of control tests such as dynamic ductility, temper, hardness, and dynamic bend. Fundamental data for structural design may be obtained from creep tests at room temperature. Zinc should not be used in applications where continuous high stresses are involved.

Alloys of zinc containing 0.65 to 1.25 percent copper are significantly stronger than unalloyed zinc and possess good ductility and working properties. They can be worked-hardened and may be employed for parts that must withstand loads somewhat higher than would be permissible in unalloyed zinc. The addition of about 0.01 percent magnesium (*Trans. AIME*, 1930, p. 481) to this alloy increases the creep resistance considerably, and the alloy finds some application for roofing and the like with design stresses up to 10,000 psi. Magnesium additions, however, decrease the ductility and general fabricating characteristics.

The usual tensile test is practically meaningless with zinc because the creep that occurs even at quite small loads causes the breaking load to vary with testing speed; the results are unrelated to service conditions. The speed in tensile testing is usually controlled at 0.25 in. per min under which conditions the soft grades of rolled zinc will have a tensile strength of 16,000 to 19,000, hard-rolled impure zinc 19,000 to 26,000, and the zinc-copper-magnesium alloy in the cold-worked condition as much as 50,000 psi. The elongation will vary between 5 and 65 percent but bears no direct relation to formability because of the different speed of testing. The properties of zinc vary with the direction of testing, and the across-grain tensile values will be approximately 20 percent higher than those obtained with the direction of the grain, although the elongations are correspondingly lower. A comparatively new series of zinc alloys containing titanium has been developed for applications requiring increased strength and creep resistance and/or low thermal expansion. A typical analysis is copper 0.5 to 0.8, titanium 0.08 to 0.16, and as maximum values 0.20 lead, 0.015 iron, 0.01 cadmium, 0.01 manganese, 0.02 chromium.

Zinc strip or sheet can be fabricated by the usual methods, **cupping, forming, etc.,** provided it is not at too low a temperature. A take-in of 40 percent on the first cupping operation is usual. Warm soapy water is widely used as a lubricant. The soft grades are self-annealing at room temperature, and only the harder alloys need intermediate annealing between operations as most other metals do. When necessary, the hard zincs are annealed at 212 F and the zinc-copper alloys at about 440 F. Welding is possible, and soldering is exceptionally easy. Simple extrusion of rods, molding, and tubing is possible but expensive because of the slow speeds necessary. The impact extrusion process, however, is being more and more widely used for producing battery cups and similar articles.

Zinc is resistant to atmospheric **corrosion** but is attacked by acids and alkalies. Soap tends to inhibit the action of water. Surface finishes for corrosion resistance or improving the appearance are readily applied. These include electroplating with copper, nickel, and chromium, lacquering, enameling, or chemically coating.

Zinc Die Castings. Zinc alloys are particularly suited for making die castings since the melting point is reasonably low, resulting in long die life even with ordinary steels, and a high accuracy and good surface finish are possible.

The alloys at present used for die castings in the United States are practically limited to those covered by the ASTM specification B86–63. Nominal compositions and typical properties of die-cast test pieces are given in Table 19. The low limits of impurities are necessary to avoid disintegration of the castings by intergranular corrosion under moist atmospheric conditions. The presence of magnesium prevents this effect if the impurities are not higher than the specification values. The mechanical properties in Table 19 are average figures for die-cast tensile-test pieces of 0.25 in. diam or impact specimens 0.25 in. square. Specification values for these properties, if used, would naturally be lower than the typical ones quoted and, in the case of the actual castings, considerable variations must be expected.

The zinc die-casting alloys are somewhat similar in general properties. Alloy XXIII is distinguished by excellent retention of impact strength and dimension.

Table 19. Properties of Zinc-base Die-casting Alloys

	Alloy AG40A (XXIII)	Alloy AG41A (XXV)
Capacitor, %:		
Copper	0.25, max	0.75–1.25
Aluminum	3.5 –4.3	3.5 –4.3
Magnesium	0.020–0.05	0.03–0.08
Iron, max	0.100	0.100
Lead, max	0.005	0.007
Cadmium, max	0.004	0.005
Tin, max	0.003	0.005
Zinc	Remainder	Remainder
Typical properties		
Tensile strength, psi	35,000	40,000
Elongation, percent in 2 in.	10	5
Brinell Hardness, 500 kg/10 mm ball	65	80
Charpy impact, ft-lb	35	35
Electrical resistivity, 77 F, microhm-cm^3	64	67
Electrical conductivity, 77 F $\times 10^3$ mho cm^3	155	151
Thermal conductivity, Btu per ft per sq ft per hr per deg F	66	62
Thermal expansion $\times 10^{-6}$ per deg F	15.2	15.2
Density, lb per cu ft	410	415
Melting point, deg F	728	727

Alloy XXV has somewhat greater impact strength and some growth in dimension when used at temperatures near 212 F. For normal-temperature service, there is little choice between XXIII and XXV.

A measurement of the expansion of the die casting after exposure to water vapor at 203 F for 10 days is a suitable index of stability and freedom from susceptibility to intergranular corrosion but analysis for impurity content is more widely used.

Aging of Die Castings. Because of changes occurring in the structure of zinc die castings, they commence to shrink immediately after removal from the mold, the change being about two-thirds complete in 5 weeks. The maximum extent of this is about 0.001 in. per in. Alloy XXIII (copper-free) is unaffected, and alloy XXV, with 1 percent copper, is not greatly affected at room temperature. Alloy XXIII may be partly stabilized with respect to shrinkage by heating for 3 to 6 hr at 212 F. The castings should be at temperature for this period of time and may be cooled normally in air to room temperature.

Effect of Temperature on Zinc and Zinc Alloys. The properties of zinc and zinc alloys are very sensitive to temperature. Creep resistance decreases rapidly with increasing temperature, and this must be considered in designing articles to withstand continous loads.

Ductility and general fabricating characteristics increase with temperature. Forming and drawing operations on strip or sheet zinc should not be attempted below 70 F, and the more severe operations can be performed more readily at somewhat higher temperatures (up to 125 F).

Zinc and zinc alloys become somewhat brittle below the range 0 to 32 F, depending on the particular composition, but recover their normal properties on reaching room temperature again. Even at low temperature, the die-casting alloys have residual impact strength superior to ordinary cast iron.

TITANIUM AND ZIRCONIUM ALLOYS

REFERENCES: "Handbook on Titanium Metal," Titanium Metals Corp. of America, New York. Abkowitz, Burke, and Hiltz, "Titanium in Industry," Van Nostrand. McQuillan and McQuillan, "Titanium," Butterworth.

Although **titanium** and titanium alloys have been commercially available for less than 15 years, they have already become important structural metals because of their unusual combination of properties. These alloys have strengths comparable with alloy steels while the weight is only 60 percent that of steel. In addition, the corrosion resistance of titanium alloys is far superior to aluminum and even exceeds that of stainless steel under most conditions, particularly those involving salt-water spray. Titanium's low magnetic permeability is also notable.

Titanium is prepared by calcium or magnesium reduction of the chlorinated oxide to yield "sponge," which is then melted in consumable-electrode arc furnaces to ingots.

Table 20. Typical Compositions of Titanium Alloys

	Alloy designation	C	Nominal composition, weight percent							
			N	O	Al	Fe	Mn	Mo	V	Other
1	Iodide titanium	0.01	0.002	0.005	0.02	0.01	0.01	0.001		
2	A-40	0.20								
3	Ti-65A	0.10	0.05	0.015	....	0.12				
4	Ti-75A	0.10	0.08	.....	....	0.20				
5	Ti-100A	0.07	.....	.....	....	0.30				
6	A110 At (α, W)	0.20	.....	.....	5	....	....	.....	...	2.5 Sn
7	Ti-6Al-4V* ($\alpha\beta$, W)	0.10	0.05	.....	6	0.25	0.10	.....	4	
8	Ti-3Mn-1A1 ($\alpha\beta$, W)	0.20	.....	.....	1.5	....	3.0			
9	Ti-8Al-1Mo-IV ($\alpha\beta$, W)	....	.....	.....	8	....	....	1	1	
10	Ti-4Al-3Mo-1V* ($\alpha\beta$)	....	.....	.....	4	....	....	3	1	
11	Ti-6Al-6V-2Sn* ($\alpha\beta$)	....	.....	.....	6	....	....	.....	6	2.0 Sn
12	Ti-8Mn ($\alpha\beta$)	0.20	.....	.....	....	....	8			
13	C 130 AM ($\alpha\beta$)	0.20	.....	.....	4	....	4			
14	RS-140 ($\alpha\beta$)	0.20	.....	.....	5	1.25	....	.....	...	2.75 Cr
15	Ti-155A ($\alpha\beta$)	0.10	0.08	.....	5	1.5	....	1.2	...	1.4 Cr
16	Ti-13V-11Cr-3Al* (β, W)	....	.....	.....	3	....	....	.....	13	11.0 Cr

Note: α = all alpha; β = all beta; $\alpha\beta$ = both α and β; W = weldable.
* Also available in higher-strength (20,000 to 40,000 psi) heat-treated condition.

Electrolytic methods of recovery have been studied experimentally. Material of special purity may be prepared by powder-metallurgy techniques or by thermal decomposition of the iodide. Titanium is one of the most abundant metals in the earth's crust, and as costs are reduced by improvements in production methods, consumption should rise rapidly.

The allotropic transformation in titanium from HCP to BCC at about 1560 F affords opportunity for property variation by heat-treatment comparable with that for steels. The various titanium alloys are usually classified in terms of the crystal structure: commercially pure, all-alpha (HCP) weldable, alpha-beta (two-phase) weldable, alpha-beta non-weldable, and all-beta (BCC). No all-beta alloy is yet available commercially. The mechanical properties of titanium and its alloys, particularly commercially pure titanium, depend markedly on the content of fractional percentages of C, O, N, H, and Fe. (See Tables 20 and 21.)

Zirconium metal's most important application was formerly as a getter (i.e., absorber) for gases in electronic tubes. The chief consumption of zirconium at present is in nuclear energy where its combination of high corrosion resistance and low neutron-absorption cross section offers special advantages (see p. 6–117). For getter applications parts of the tube are built of zirconium, and the construction is such that they will be heated during operation of the tube and thus be able to absorb gas continuously. In chemical inertness the metal resembles tantalum and, if its cost can be reduced, it should be valuable for chemical-processing equipment. Aqua regia, concentrated hydrochloric acid, and 50 percent sodium hydroxide do not attack

Table 21. Mechanical Properties of Titanium Alloys (Annealed Condition)

Alloy No. (see Table 20)	Room temperature					400 F			800 F			Max recom. temp, deg F, for 1,000 hr service
	Yield strength, kpsi	Tensile strength, kpsi	Elong., percent in 2 in.	Hardness†	V-notch Charpy impact, ft-lb	Yield strength, kpsi	Tensile strength, kpsi	Elong., percent in 2 in.	Yield strength, kpsi	Tensile strength, kpsi	Elong., percent in 2 in.	
1	15	35	55	VPN 60	150							
2	45	50	22	....	90	21	37	40	12	25	22	1000
3	55	65	20	R_c 30	...	...	...	...	...	...	...	1000
4	70	80	15	R_b 98	25	36	53	29	19	31	21	1000
5	90	100	15	R_c 30								
6	100	115	10	....	20	82	100	17	63	82	16	1200
7*	120	130	10	R_c 34	18	102	110	15	79	96	15	850
8	110	120	10	....	...	85	97	18	58	75	22	
9	125	135	10	....	...	94	101	20	75	81	18	
10*	155	180	5	R_c 40	...	136	157	6	111	140	8	
11*	170	180	8	....	...	144	153	15				
12	110	120	10	....	...	85	110	18	55	85	20	
13	130	140	10	....	15	110	120	17	88	105	22	800
14	140	150	10	....	15	120	140	17	93	117	19	700
15	140	150	12	R_c 38	15	110	130	17	91	109	21	650
16*	160	170	4	....	...	142	163	8	128	137	10	

* Also available in higher-strength (20,000 to 40,000 psi) heat-treated condition.

† VPN = Vickers pyramid hardness scale; R_c = Rockwell C hardness scale.

it at 212 F. The metallurgical characteristics of zirconium are, in many respects, quite similar to those of titanium.

LOW-MELTING METALS AND ALLOYS

Metals with low melting temperatures offer a diversity of industrial applications. In this field, much use is made of the **eutectic**-type alloy, in which two or more elements are combined in proper proportion so as to have a minimum melting temperature. Such alloys melt at a specific temperature, as does a pure metal, rather than over a range of temperature, as with most alloys.

Liquid Metals. A few metals are used in their liquid state. **Mercury** (mp, 37.97 F) is the only metal that is liquid below room temperature. In addition to its use in thermometers, scientific instruments, and electrical contacts, it is a constituent of some very low-melting alloys. Its application in dental amalgams is unique and familiar to all. It has been used as a heat-exchange fluid, as have **sodium** and the sodium-potassium alloy **NaK** (see p. 6–117).

Table 22. Composition Specifications for Lead, Percent

	Corroding lead	Chemical lead*	Common desilverized lead A	Common desilverized lead B	Copper lead
Silver, max	0.0015	0.020	0.002	0.002	0.020
Silver, min	......	0.002			
Copper, max	0.0015	0.080	0.0025	0.0025	0.080
Copper, min	......	0.040	......	......	0.040
Silver, plus copper, max	0.0025				
Arsenic, max	0.0015				
Antimony plus tin, max	0.0095				
Arsenic, antimony, and tin together, max	......	0.002	0.015	0.015	0.015
Zinc, max	0.0015	0.001	0.002	0.002	0.002
Iron, max	0.002	0.002	0.002	0.002	0.002
Bismuth, max	0.05	0.005	0.15	0.25	0.010
Lead (by difference) min	99.94	99.90	99.85	99.73	99.85

*Chemical lead designates undesilverized lead from southeast Missouri ores.

Tin. Moving up the temperature scale, there is tin (mp, 449.4 F), the largest single use of which is for coating steel to make **tinplate; solders** and **bronze** are the next largest uses. Tin may be applied to steel, copper, or cast iron either by hot dipping in a molten bath or by electrodeposition. Normally thinner tin coatings are achieved by hot tinning. Electrodeposited tin is a matte coating, but it can be brightened to the brilliance of hot-dipped coatings by reflowing in hot oils or, in the case of tinplate, by induction, convection, or radiation heating. Alloys of 12 to 25 percent tin, balance lead, are applied to steel by hot dipping and are known as **terneplate.**

Modern **pewter** is a tarnish-resistant alloy composed of 91 to 93 percent tin, 6 to 7 percent antimony, and 1 to 2 percent copper. Old pewter, first used about 200 years ago, contained sufficient lead to cause the surface to darken with age.

REFERENCES: Publications of the Tin Research Institute, Inc. Hedges, "Tin and Its Alloys," St. Martin's Press. Mantell, "Tin," Reinhold.

Lead. Several varieties of pig lead are recognized by ASTM specifications, *e.g.*, those listed in Table 22. **Corroding lead** is the highest-purity commercial lead and is used for making white lead. **Chemical lead** is extensively employed in chemical plants for withstanding corrosion, particularly of sulphuric acid. Its copper content confers added stiffness. **Common lead** is the usual grade for alloying.

Antimonal lead is used in places where greater strength is needed. For storage-battery plates, lead containing 6 to 7 percent antimony is used. In the cast condition, this has a tensile strength of about 7,000 psi with an elongation of about 22 percent, density 677 lb per cu ft. Lead for sheathing telephone and electric-power cables is usually made of an alloy containing about 1 percent antimony. This alloy, when extruded as cable sheath and aged 1 month at room temperature, has a tensile strength of 2,750 to 3,050 psi at a testing speed of 0.25 in. per min per in. of free length, elongation 30 to 40 percent, and endurance limit 800 psi (50 million cycles at 700 per min).

Cast lead-antimony alloys containing 6 to 14 percent antimony have a tensile strength of 7,000 to 8,000 psi with elongation decreasing from 24 to 10 percent. The lead-antimony alloys, particularly in the range 2 to 8 percent antimony, are susceptible to heat-treatment, which considerably increases their strength. This treatment is rarely employed in practice. An alloy also used for cable sheathing is ordinary chemical lead with about 0.06 percent copper. Alloys with 0.1 percent or less tellurium or 0.01 to 0.10 percent calcium have been proposed for special purposes where higher creep and fatigue resistance are needed. Alloys with larger amounts of calcium (0.8 percent) and smaller quantities of alkali metals are used to a limited extent as bearing metals. Lead for coating steel (terneplate) and copper contains 5 to 25 percent tin to aid adhesion to the base metal (see Tin, above). Lead is an important constituent of alloys with tin and copper and of type metals.

Type Metals. The principal type metals are listed in Table 23; composition variations are encountered in practice. Electrotype metal serves only as a backing

Table 23. Composition and Properties of Type Metals*

Service	Composition, percent			Melting point, deg F	Brinell hardness
	Sn	Sb	Pb		
Electrotype	3	3	94	570	14
Linotype	4	12	84	475	22
Stereotype	6	14	80	500	24
Monotype	8	16	76	515	26
Foundry	14	24	62	605	32

* Gonser and Epstein, *Metals & Alloys*, **8,** 1937, p. 59.

to the shell and does not need to be hard. In the linotype machine, the metal must be fluid and capable of rapid solidification; hence metal of very nearly eutectic composition is used. It is rarely used as the actual printing surface and, therefore, need not be so hard as stereotype and monotype metals. Foundry type is used for hand setting and needs greater hardness to withstand handling and repeated use.

Fusible Alloys. (See Table 24.) These alloys are used typically as fusible links in sprinkler heads, as electric cutouts, as fire-door links, for making castings, for patterns in making match plates, for making electroforming molds, for setting punches in multiple dies, and for dyeing cloth. Some fusible alloys can be cast or sprayed on wood, paper, and other materials without damaging the base materials, and many of these alloys can be used for making hermetic seals. Since some of these alloys melt below the boiling point of water, they can be used in bending tubing. The properly prepared tubing is filled with the molten alloy and allowed to solidify, and after bending, the alloy is melted out by immersion of the tube in boiling water. The volume changes during the solidification of a fusible alloy are, to a large extent, governed by the bismuth content of the alloy. As a general rule, alloys containing more than about 55 percent bismuth expand and those containing less than about 48 percent bismuth contract during solidification; those containing 48 to 55 percent bismuth exhibit little change in volume. The change in volume due to cooling of the solid metal is a simple linear shrinkage, but some of the fusible alloys owe much of their industrial importance to other volume changes, caused by change in structure of the solid alloy, which permit the production of castings having dimensions equal to, or greater than, those of the mold in which the metal was cast.

For fire-sprinkler heads with a rating of 160 F, **Wood's metal** is used for the fusible-solder-alloy link. Wood's metal gives the most suitable degree of sensitivity at this temperature, but in tropical countries and in situations where industrial processes create a hot atmosphere (*e.g.*, baking ovens, foundries), solders having a higher melting point must be used. Alloys of eutectic compositions are used since they melt sharply at a specific temperature.

Fusible alloys are also used as molds for thermoplastics, for the production of artificial jewelry in pastes and plastic materials.

Table 24. Fusible Alloys

Alloy composition, percent					Melting range, deg F		
Sn	Bi	Pb	Cd	Others	Solidus	Eutectic	Liquidus
12.0	....	.....	....	82.0 Ga, 6.0 Zn	...	63†	
8.0	....	.....	....	92.0 Ga	...	68†	
8.3	44.7	22.6	5.3	19.1 In	...	117†	
12.0	49.0	18.0	....	21.0 In	...	136†	
12.77	48.0	25.63	9.6	4.0 In	142	....	149
13.2	49.3	26.3	9.8	1.4 Ga	149	....	151
13.1	49.5	27.3	10.1	....	...	158†	
12.5	50.0	25.0	12.5	(Wood's)	158	....	162
13.3	50.0	26.7	10.0	(Lipowitz's)	158	....	163
13.0	42.0	35.0	10.0	....	158	....	176
13.0	40.0	37.0	10.0	....	158	....	185
24.5	45.3	17.9	12.3	....	158	....	190
11.3	42.5	37.7	8.5	....	158	....	194
15.4	38.4	30.8	15.4	....	158	....	207
....	51.7	40.2	8.1	....	...	198†	
15.5	52.5	32.0	....	....	...	205†	
20.0	50.0	30.0	....	(Onion's or Lichtenberg's)	205	....	212
18.8	50.0	31.2	....	(Newton's)........	205	....	207
25.0	50.0	25.0	....	(D'Arcet's)	205	....	208
22.0	50.0	28.0	....	(Rose's)	205	....	230
34.2	46.1	19.7	....	(Malotte's)	205	....	253
33.0	34.0	33.0	....	....	205	....	289
25.9	53.9	.....	20.2	....	...	217†	
25.0	50.0	.....	25.0	....	217	....	235
34.5	44.5	.....	21.0	....	217	....	248
14.5	48.0	28.5	....	9.0 Sb	217	....	440
1.0	55.0	44.0	....	....	243	....	248
50.0	....	.....	....	50.0 In	243	....	260
48.0	....	.....	....	52.0 In	...	243†	
.....	55.5	44.5	....	....	...	255†	
46.0	....	.....	17.0	37.0 Tl	...	262†	
40.0	56.0	.....	....	4.0 Zn	...	266†	
41.6	57.4	1.0	....	....	273	....	275
43.0	57.0	.....	....	....	...	281†	
48.8	10.2	41.0	....	....	288	....	331
.....	60.0	.....	40.0	....	...	291†	
51.2	....	30.6	18.2	....	...	293†	
40.0	....	42.0	18.0	....	293	....	320
56.5	....	.....	....	43.5 Tl	...	338†	
67.0	....	.....	33.0	....	...	349†	
63.0	....	37.0	....	....	...	361†	
.....	47.5	.....	....	52.5 Tl	...	370†	
92.0	....	.....	....	8.0 Zn	....	390†	
.....	....	.....	17.0	83.0 Tl	...	397†	
96.5	....	.....	....	3.5 Ag	...	430†	
99.25	....	.....	....	0.75 Cu	...	441†	

* From "Fusible Alloys Containing Tin," Booklet 175, Tin Research Inst., Inc., May, 1963.
† Indicates eutectic alloy.

Solders are non-ferrous filler metals used in a joining process wherein coalescence between metal parts is produced by heating to suitable temperatures below those of the base metals and generally below 800 F. (See Table 25.) ASTM specification B32–60aT permits a variation of −1 percent in tin content for alloys containing a nominal composition of 10 percent or more tin. The eutectic composition (63 percent tin) has the lowest melting point (361 F) of the binary tin-lead solders. For joints in copper pipe and cables, a wide melting range is needed; a 50 percent tin, 50 percent lead solder alloy is used most advantageously. An alloy of 95 percent tin, 5 percent

Table 25. Composition, Uses, and Melting Ranges for Selected Solder Alloys
(ASTM specification B32–60aT)

Nominal composition, percent				Melting range, deg F		Uses
Sn	Pb	Sb	Ag	Solidus	Liquidus	
70	30	...	...	361	378	Coating metals
63	37	...	...	361	361	Eutectic solder alloy, electronics
60	40	...	...	361	374	General-purpose, electronics
50	50	...	...	361	421	General-purpose, plumbing
45	55	...	...	361	441	Radiator cores, roofing seams
40	60	...	...	361	460	Wiping solder, general-purpose
35	65	...	...	361	477	Machine and torch soldering
30	70	...	...	361	491	Machine and torch soldering
25	75	...	...	361	511	Machine and torch soldering
20	80	...	...	361	531	Auto-body repair
15	85	...	...	440	550	Radiator solder
10	90	...	...	514	570	Coating metals
5	95	...	...	572	596	Wiping solder
2	98	...	...	601	611	Soldering-can sideseams
40	58	2	...	365	448	General-purpose, not recommended for use on zinc-containing materials
35	63.2	1.8	...	365	470	
30	68.4	1.6	...	364	482	Torch or machine soldering, except on zinc-containing materials
25	73.7	1.3	...	364	504	
20	79	1	...	363	517	Machine soldering and coating of metals, except zinc-containing materials
95	....	5	...	450	464	Joints on copper: electrical, plumbing, heating; not recommended for zinc-containing materials
...	97.5	...	2.5	580	580	For use on copper, brass with torch heating; not recommended in humid environments due to its known susceptibility to corrosion
1	97.5	...	1.5	588	588	For use on copper, brass with torch heating

antimony also is used for joining copper water pipe, and this alloy has higher strength at hot-water temperatures than the tin-lead solders. Antimonial solders should not be used to join basis metals containing zinc (*e.g.*, galvanized iron, brass). Tin-antimony, tin-silver, and cadmium-silver solder alloys are used for higher-temperature applications than are permissible with tin-lead alloys.

Brazing filler metals are defined by the AWS as metals to be added when making a braze. A filler metal has a melting temperature above 800 F, but below that of the base metals being joined. The AWS-ASTM have classified brazing filler metals according to their nominal composition (see Table 26); composition and melting points are given in Table 27.

REFERENCE: AWS, "Brazing Manual," Reinhold.

Table 26. Brazing Filler Metals
(AWS specification A5.8, ASTM specification B260–56T)

AWS-ASTM filler-metal classification	Base metals joined
BAlSi (aluminum-silicon)	Aluminum and aluminum alloys
BCuP (copper-phosphorus)	Copper and copper alloys; limited use on tungsten and molybdenum; should not be used on ferrous or nickel-base metals
BAg (silver)	Ferrous and non-ferrous metals except aluminum and magnesium; iron, nickel, cobalt-base alloys; thin-base metals
BCu (copper)	Ferrous and non-ferrous metals except aluminum and magnesium
RBCuZn (copper-zinc)	Ferrous and non-ferrous metals except aluminum and magnesium; corrosion resistance generally inadequate for joining copper, silicon, bronze, copper, nickel, or stainless steel
BMg (magnesium)	Magnesium-base metals
BNi (nickel)	AISI 300 and 400 stainless steels; nickel- and cobalt-base alloys; also carbon steel, low-alloy steels, and copper where specific properties are desired

Table 27. Brazing Alloys*

Designation	Composition, percent				Melting range, deg F	
	Ag	Cu	Zn	Cd	First melting point	Point of complete liquefaction
A.S.T.M. 1	10	52	38	<0.5	1510	1600
A.S.T.M. 2	20	45	35	<0.5	1430	1500
A.S.T.M. 3	20	45	30	5	1430	1500
A.S.T.M. 4	45	30	25	....	1250	1370
A.S.T.M. 5	50	34	16	....	1280	1425
A.S.T.M. 6	65	20	15	....	1280	1325
A.S.T.M. 7	70	20	10	....	1335	1390
A.S.T.M. 8	80	16	4	....	1360	1460
A.S.T.M. 50–50	...	50	50	....	1595	1620
A.S.T.M. 52–48	...	52	48	....	1600	1620
Black Button	1Pb	27.3	64.7	7.5 Sn	1385	1440
Easy-Flo†	50	15.50	16.5	18 Cd	1160	1175
Sil-fos†	15	80	...	5 P	1300	1300
Phos Copper†	..	93	...	7 P	1317	1470

* See ASTM specification B260–52T (Brazing Solders).
† Proprietary alloy.

BEARING METALS

Babbitt metal is a general term used for soft tin and lead-base alloys which are cast as bearing surfaces on steel, bronze, or cast-iron shells. Babbitts have excellent **embedability** (ability to embed foreign particles in itself) and **conformability** (ability to deform plastically to compensate for irregularities in bearing assembly) characteristics. These alloys may be run satisfactorily against a soft-steel shaft. The limitations of Babbitt alloys are liability to spreading under high, steady loads and to cracking under high, fluctuating loads. These limitations apply more particularly at higher temperatures, for increase in temperature between 68 and 212 F about halves the metal's strength. By suitable design of the bearing assembly, a properly

Table 28. Composition and Physical Properties[a] of Babbitt Alloys
(ASTM specification B23–61)

Alloy grade No.[b]	Nominal composition, percent				Yield point,[c] psi		Ultimate tensile strength in compression,[d] psi		BHN	
	Sn	Sb	Pb	Cu	68 F	212 F	68 F	212 F	68 F	212 F
1	91	4.5	....	4.5	4,400	2,650	12,850	6,950	17.0	8.0
2	89	7.5	....	3.5	6,100	3,000	14,900	8,700	24.5	12.0
3	84	8.0	....	8.0	6,600	3,150	17,600	9,900	27.0	14.5
7	10.0	15.0	75.0	...	3,550	1,600	15,650	6,150	22.5	10.5
8	5.0	15.0	80.0	...	3,400	1,750	15,600	6,150	20.0	9.5
13	6.0	10.0	Rem.							
15[e]	1.0	16.0	Rem.	...	.....	.....	......	.....	21.0	13.0

[a] The compression-test specimens were cylinders 1.5 in. long and 0.5 in. diam, machined from chill castings 2 in. long and 0.75 in. diam. Brinell tests were made on the bottom face of parallel machined specimens cast in a 2-in. diam by 0.625 in. deep steel mold at room temperature.

[b] Alloy grade No. 9 was discontinued in 1946, and Nos. 4 to 6, 10 to 12, 16, and 19 were discontinued in 1959.

[c] The values for yield point were taken from stress-strain curves at a deformation of 0.125 percent reduction of gage length.

[d] The ultimate-strength values were taken as the unit load necessary to produce a deformation of 25 percent of the length of the specimen.

[e] Also nominal arsenic 0.10 percent.

chosen Babbitt alloy can be made to give satisfactory service in all but the most stringent conditions.

The important tin- and lead-base (Babbitt) bearing alloys are listed in Table 28. Alloy No. 1 is used in internal-combustion engines. Numbers 2 and 3, containing more antimony, are harder and less likely to pound out. Alloy Nos. 7, 8, 13, and 15 are lead-base Babbitts which will function satisfactorily under moderate conditions of load and speed. Alloy No. 15 is an arsenical alloy and, with its better high-temperature hardness, finds the largest-volume use of the three lead-base alloys because of its ability to withstand higher loads and to provide longer fatigue life.

Cadmium-base bearing alloys are cadmium-nickel (containing about 1.5 percent nickel and 0.4 to 0.75 percent copper) and cadmium-silver (containing about 0.5 to 2 percent silver). These alloys are harder than Babbitts and have less conformability than white-metal alloys. Although they possess a higher fatigue strength (particularly at elevated temperatures) than Babbitts, they are more liable to corrosion by acidic lubricants.

Silver bearings have an excellent record in heavy-duty applications in aircraft engines and Diesels. For reciprocating engines, silver bearings normally consist of electrodeposited silver on a steel backing with an overlay of 0.001 to 0.005 in. of lead. An indium flash on top of the lead overlay is used to increase corrosion resistance of the material.

Aluminum alloys are used in high load-carrying applications but have not replaced Babbitts for equipment operating under a steady, undirectional load. Three major alloys are in use: (1) 6.25 percent tin, 1 percent nickel, and 1 percent copper; (2) 1 to 3 percent cadmium with varying amounts of silicon, copper, and nickel; and (3) 20 to 30 percent tin alloy containing up to 3 percent copper. The first two alloy types may be used as either solid-cast or steel-backed bearings, but the third type is backed by steel for support.

Mention should be made of **cast iron** as a bearing material. The flake graphite in cast iron develops a glazed surface which is useful at surface speeds up to 130 fpm and at loads up to 150 psi approx. Because of the poor conformability of cast iron, good alignment and freedom from dirt are essential.

Copper-base bearing alloys have a wide range of bearing properties that fit them for many applications. Used alone or in combination with steel, Babbitt (white metal), and graphite, the bronzes and copper-leads meet the conditions of load and speed given in Table 29. **Copper-lead alloys** are cast onto steel backing strips in very thin layers (0.02 in.) to provide bearing surfaces.

Aluminum bronzes and **silicon bronzes** are used for high-strength and oxidation-resistant bearings. These materials must have the best possible lubrication, or heating, with subsequent failure, will result.

Porous bearing materials are used in light- and medium-duty applications as small-size bearings and bushings. Since they can operate for long periods without an additional supply of lubricant, such bearings are useful in inaccessible or inconvenient places where lubrication would be difficult. Porous bearings are made by pressing mixtures of copper and tin (bronze), and often graphite or Teflon or iron and graphite, and sintering these in a reducing atmosphere without melting. By controlling the conditions under which the bearings are made, porosity may be adjusted so that interconnecting voids of up to 35 percent of the total volume may be available for impregnation by lubricants. ASTM specifications for these bearings are given in Table 30.

Miscellaneous. A great variety of materials, *e.g.*, rubber, wood, phenolic, carbon-graphite, cermets, ceramics, and plastics, are in use for special applications. Carbon-graphite is used where contamination by oil or grease lubricants is undesirable (*e.g.*, textile machinery, pharmaceutical equipment, milk and food processing) and for elevated-temperature applications. Notable among plastic materials are Teflon and nylon, the polycarbonate Lexan, and the acetal Delrin. Since Lexan and Delrin can be injection-molded easily, bearings can be formed quite economically from these materials.

Table 29. Copper-base Bearing Metals

Specification designations		Nominal composition, percent						Minimum tensile strength, kpsi	Uses
ASTM	Other	Cu	Sn	Pb	Zn	P	Other		
B144–52:									
Alloy 3A	SAE 64	80	10	10	...	....	....	25	Heavy loads and high speeds; backing for Babbitt-lined bearings, wrist-pin bushings, valve rocker-arm bushings, crankshaft bearings; electric-motor bushings; lathe, railroad-car, rolling-mill, and trunnion bearings
Alloy 3B	SAE 660	83	7	7	3	....	....	30	Medium loads and speeds; general utility; automotive generators, distributors, guide bushings, starters, main bearings for presses, spindle bushings for trucks, sleeve bushings
Alloy 3C	....	85	5	9	1	....	....	25	Medium loads and speeds; similar to alloy 3B
Alloy 3D	SAE 67	78	7	15	...	....	....	25	Medium loads and high speeds; pump bushings, gas-engine bearings, and drum bushings for cranes, hydraulic glands, etc.
Alloy 3E	AMS 4840	70	5	25	...	....	....	21	Light-to-moderate loads and high speeds; unsuitable for extremely heavy compressive and shock loads; pump bushings, compressor bearings, underwater service
B148–52:									
Alloy 9C	....	85	...	....	...	....	4 Fe, 11Al	75	Bushings for power shovels, roll-neck bearings, turntable bushings, machine-tool bearings, guidepost bushings, boring-bar bushings
B22–61:									
Alloy A	....	80	19	0.25 max	...	1.0 max	....	24*	Bridge turntable plates for contact with hardened-steel disks at low speeds under pressures not over 3,000 psi
Alloy B	....	83	16	0.25 max	...	1.0 max	....	18*	As with alloy A above, low speeds with pressure not over 2,500 psi; with hard steel, 1,500 psi; with trunnions of movable bridges, 2,500 psi; bearing and expansion plates
Alloy C	....	82 max	10	10	...	0.10	0.10 Ni		Machinery bearings, bearing and expansion plates under pressures not to exceed 1,000 psi
Alloy D	....	89 max	10	0.30 max	2.0	0.05 max	....	40	Gears, worm gears, and similar parts which are subject to other than compressive stresses
Alloy E	....	65	...	0.20 max	23	....	3 Fe, 5 Al, 4 Mn	110	Bushings for bridge pins and similar applications where angular movement is slight and compressive stresses may attain 8,000 psi

Table 29. Copper-base Bearing Metals—(*Continued*)

Specification designations		Nominal composition, percent						Minimum tensile strength, kpsi	Uses
ASTM	Other	Cu	Sn	Pb	Zn	P	Other		
	SAE 40	85	5	5	5	....	....	35	Light loads and low-to-medium speeds; bearing shells, automotive-transmission thrust washers, manifold bearings, pump sleeves, spring bushings
	SAE 62	88	10	....	2	....	....	45	Heavy loads and low speeds; piston-pin bushings, valve guides, worm bearings, linkage bushings for machine tools
	SAE 620	88	8	....	4	....	....	40	Heavy loads and low speeds; bushings for aircraft landing gear, bridge bearings, trunnions, machine-tool bearings
	SAE 63	88	10	....	2	....	....	40	Heavy loads, low speeds, and severe working conditions; earth-moving machinery, locomotive bearings, gear bushings, automotive spindle bushings, packaging machinery
	....	75	...	25	..	...	....	18	Moderate loads and speeds; main and connecting-rod bearings, large motor bearings

* Deformation limit (min psi)—compressive stress producing permanent set of 0.001 in. on machined sand-cast specimens 1 in. square area by 1 in. high.

Table 30. Metal-powder-sintered Bearings (Oil-impregnated)
(ASTM specification B202–60T)

	Grade I Copper base		Grade II—Iron base			
			Class A			Class B
	Class A	Class B	A_1	A_2	A_3	
Copper, %	87.5–90.5	82.6–88.5	....	....	....	7.0–11.0 18.0–22.0
Iron, %	1.0 max	1.0 max	96.25 min	95.9 min	95.5 min	Rem.*
Tin, %	9.5–10.5	9.5–10.5				
Lead, %	....	2.0–4.0				
Zinc, max %	....	0.75				
Nickel, max %	....	0.35				
Antimony, max %	....	0.25				
Carbon, max %	1.75†	1.75†				
Silicon, max %	....	....	0.3	0.3	0.3	
Aluminum, max %	....	....	0.2	0.2	0.2	
Other elements, %	0.5	0.5	3.0	3.0	3.0	3.0
Combined carbon,‡ %	....	....	0.25–0.60	0.60–1.0		
Density (g per cm³)	6.4–6.8	6.5–6.9	5.7 –6.1	5.7 –6.1	5.7–6.1	5.8–6.2

* Total of iron plus copper shall be 97 percent, min.

† Commonly graphite. A maximum of 1.5 percent of another type of solid lubricant may be substituted.

‡ The combined carbon may be a metallographic estimate of the carbon in the iron.

METALS AND ALLOYS FOR USE AT ELEVATED TEMPERATURES

REFERENCES: "High Temperature High Strength Alloys," AISI. Simmons and Krivobok, Compilation of Chemical Compositions and Rupture Strength of Super-strength Alloys, *ASTM Tech. Pub.* 170-A. "Metals Handbook," ASM. Smith, "Properties of Metals at Elevated Temperatures," McGraw-Hill. Clark, "High-temperature Alloys," Pittman. Cross, Materials for Gas Turbine Engines, *Metal Progress,* March, 1965. Hampel, "Rare Metals Handbook," Reinhold.

Metals are used for an increasing variety of applications at elevated temperatures, "elevated" being a relative term that depends upon the specific metal and the specific service environment. Elevated-temperature properties of the common metals and alloys are cited in the several preceding subsections. This subsection deals with metals and alloys whose prime use is in high-temperature applications. (Typical maximum temperatures are compressors, 750 F; steam turbines, 1100 F; gas turbines,

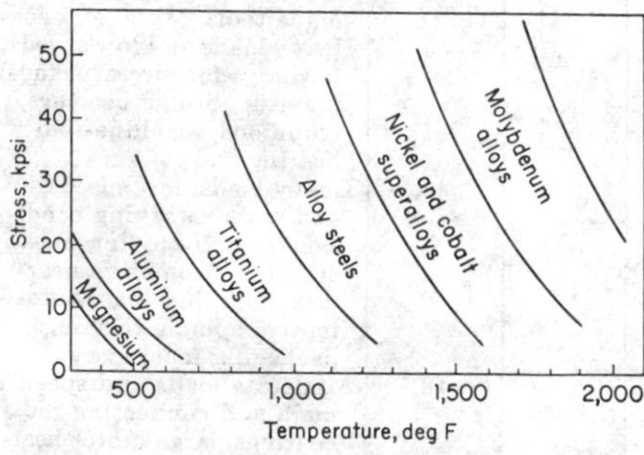

FIG. 5. Stress-temperature application ranges for various alloy types. (Stress to produce rupture in 1,000 hr.)

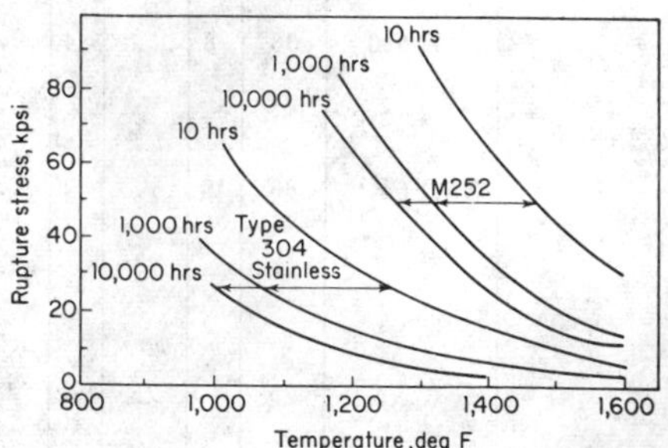

FIG. 6. Effect of time on the rupture strength of type 304 stainless steel and alloy M252.

2000 F; resistance-heating elements, 2400 F; electronic vacuum tubes, 3500 F; and lamps, 4500 F.) In general, alloys for high-temperature service must have melting points above the operating temperature, low vapor pressures at that temperature, resistance to attack (oxidation, sulphidation, corrosion) by the environment, and sufficient strength to withstand the applied load for the service life without deforming beyond permissible limits. At high temperatures, atomic diffusion becomes appreciable, so that time is an important factor with respect to surface chemical reactions, to **creep,** or slow deformation, under constant load, and to internal changes within the alloy during service. The effects of time and temperature are conveniently combined by the empirical **Larson-Miller parameter** $P = T(C + \log t) \times 10^{-3}$, where T = test temp in deg R (deg F + 460) and t = test time in hr. The constant C depends upon the material but is frequently taken to be 20.

A great many alloys have been developed specifically for such applications. The selection of an alloy for a specific high-temperature application is strongly influenced by service conditions (stress, stress fluctuations, temperature, heat shock, atmosphere, service life), and there are hundreds of alloys from which to choose. The following illustrations should be regarded as examples. Vendor literature and more extensive reference volumes should be consulted.

Figure 5 indicates the general stress-temperature range in which various alloy types find application in elevated-temperature service. Figure 6 indicates the important effect of time on the strength of alloys at high temperatures, comparing a familiar stainless steel (type 304) with a widely used **superalloy** (M252).

Common Heat-resisting Alloys. A number of alloys containing large amounts of **chromium and nickel** are available. These have excellent oxidation resistance at elevated temperatures. Several of them have been developed as electrical-resistance heating elements; others are modifications of stainless steels, developed for general corrosion resistance. Selected data on these alloys are summarized in Table 31. The maximum temperature value given is for resistance to oxidation with a reasonable life. At higher temperatures, failure will be rapid because of scaling. At lower temperatures, much longer life will be obtained. At the maximum useful temperature, the metal may be very weak and frequently must be supported to prevent sagging. Under load, these alloys are generally useful only at considerably lower temperatures, say up to 1200 F max, depending upon permissible creep rate and the load.

Superalloys were developed largely to meet the needs of aircraft gas turbines, but they have also been used in other applications demanding high strength at high temperatures. These alloys are based on nickel and/or cobalt, to which are added (typically) chromium for oxidation resistance and a complex of other elements which

Table 31. Properties of Common Heat-resisting Alloys

Name or SAE type	Max temp for oxidation resistance, deg F	Chemical composition, percent					Specific gravity	Coef of linear expansion per deg F × 10^{-6} (0–1200 F)	Stress to rupture in 1,000 hr, kpsi			0.2 percent offset yield strength, kpsi		
		C	Cr	Ni	Fe	Other			1200 F	1500 F	1800 F	Room	1000 F	1200 F
62 Ni, 15 Cr....	1700	....	15	62	Bal	....	8.19	9.35						
80 Ni, 20 Cr....	2100	....	20	80	...	....	8.4	9.8	....	....	...	63		
Kanthal.......	2450	....	25	....	Bal	3 Co, 5 Al	7.15							
Alloy 10.......	2450	....	37	....	Bal	7.5 Al	6.9							
Inconel.......	2000	....	13	79	Bal	....	8.4	.....	14.5	3.7	...	36	22	22
1015..........	1000	0.15	....	....	Bal	....	7.8	8.36	2.7	....	...	42	20	10
502..........	1150	0.12	5	....	Bal	0.5 Mo	7.8	7.31	6	1.5	...	27	18	12
446..........	2000	0.12	26	0.3	Bal	....	7.6	6.67	4	1.2	...			
304..........	1650	0.06	18	9	Bal	....	7.9	10.4	11	3.5	...	32	14	11
347..........	1650	0.08	18.5	11.5	Bal	0.8 Cb	8.0	10.7	20	....	...	41	31	26
316..........	1650	0.07	18	13	Bal	2.5 Mo	8.0	10.3	25	7	...	41	22	21
310..........	2000	0.12	25	20	Bal	....	7.9	9.8	13.2	3.0	2.7	34	28	25
321..........	1650	0.06	18	10	Bal	0.5 Ti	8.0	10.7	17.5	3.7	...	39	27	25
NA 22 H......	2200	0.5	28	48	Bal	5W	...	8.6	30	18	3.6			

contribute to hot strength, both by solid solution hardening and by forming relatively stable dispersions of fine particles. Hardening by cold work, hardening by precipitation-hardening heat-treatments, and hardening by deliberately arranging for slow precipitation during service are all methods used to enhance the properties of these alloys. **Fabrication** of these alloys is difficult since they are designed to resist distortion even at elevated temperatures. Forging temperatures of about 2300 F are used with small reductions and slow rates of working. Many of these alloys are fabricated by precision casting. Cast alloys that are given a strengthening heat-treatment often have better properties than wrought alloys, but the shapes that can be made are limited.

Vacuum melting is an important factor in the production of superalloys. The advantages which result from its application include the ability to melt higher percentages of reactive metals, improved mechanical properties (particularly fatigue strength), decreased scatter in mechanical properties, and improved billet-to-bar stock-conversion ratios in wrought alloys.

Tables 32 to 35 list compositions and properties of some superalloys, and Fig. 7 indicates the temperature dependence of the rupture strength of a number of such alloys.

Cast tool alloys are another important group of materials having high-temperature strength and wear resistance. They are principally alloys of cobalt, chromium, and tungsten. They are hard and brittle, and they must be cast and ground to shape. Their most important application is for hard-facing, but they compete with high-speed steels and cemented carbides for many applications, in certain instances being superior to both. (See also p. 6–122 *et. seq.*) Typical compositions are given in Table 36; typical properties are elastic modulus = 35×10^6 psi; density = 8.8; hardness, BHN = room temp 660, 1500 F 435, and 2000 F 340.

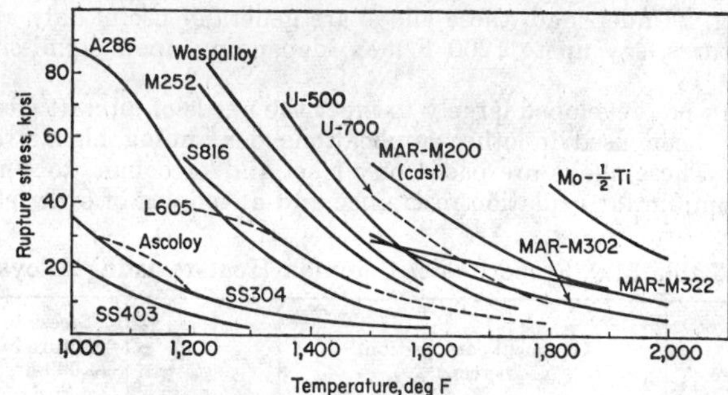

FIG. 7. Temperature dependence of the rupture strength of some high-temperature alloys. (Stress to produce rupture in 1,000 hr.).

For still higher temperature applications, the possible choices are limited to a few metals with high melting points, all characterized by limited availability and by difficulty of extraction and fabrication. Alloys of metals such as chromium, columbium, molybdenum, tantalum, and tungsten are still in relatively early stages of development. Table 37 cites properties of some of these new alloys.

Table 32. Wrought Superalloys, Composition‡

Common designation	Chemical composition, percent												
	C	Mn	Si	Cr	Ni	Co	Mo	W	Cb	Ti	Al	Fe	Other
19-9D L	0.2	0.5	0.6	19	9	...	1.2	1.25	0.3	0.3	...	Bal	
Timken	0.1	0.5	0.5	16	25	...	6	...	..	...	...	Bal	0.15N
L.C. N-155	0.1	0.5	0.5	20	20	20	3	2	1	...	...	Bal	0.15N
S-590	0.4	0.5	0.5	20	20	20	4	4	4	...	...	Bal	
S-816	0.4	0.5	0.5	20	20	Bal	4	4	4	...	...	4	
Inconel-X	0.05	0.5	0.4	15	73	...	..	...	1	2.5	0.9	7	
Nimonic-80	0.05	0.7	0.5	20	76	...	..	...	..	2.3	1.0	0.5	
K-42-B	0.05	0.7	0.7	18	42	22	..	...	..	2.0	0.2	14	
Hastelloy B	0.1	0.5	0.5	..	65	...	28	...	..	...	...	6	0.4V
M 252†	0.10	1.0	0.7	19	53.5	10	10	...	..	2.5	0.75	2	
Inco 700	0.12	2.0*	1.0*	15	48	28	3	...	..	2.2	2.8	5	
J 1570	0.20	0.1*	0.2*	20	29	37.5	..	7	..	4.1	...	2	
HS-R235	0.10	...	...	16	Bal	1.5	6	...	..	3.0	1.8	8	
Hastelloy X	0.10	...	...	21	48	2.0	9	1.0	..	...	...	18	
HS 25 (L605)	0.05	1.5	1.0*	20	10	53	..	15	..	...	...	1.0	
A-286	0.05	...	...	15	26	...	1.3	...	..	2.0	0.35	55	0.3V

* Max.

† Waspaloy has a similar composition (except for lower Mo content), and similar properties.

‡ For a complete list of superalloys, both wrought and cast, experimental and under development, see *ASTM Spec. Pub.* 170, "Compilation of Chemical Compositions and Rupture Strengths of Superstrength Alloys."

Chromium with room-temperature ductility has been prepared experimentally as a pure metal and as strong high-temperature alloys. It is not generally available on a commercial basis, but active development is under way (1965).

Columbium (also known as **niobium**) is available as a pure metal and in several alloys. Alloys of columbium are used in nuclear applications at temperatures above 1600 F approx because of their low thermal neutron cross section, high strength, and good corrosion resistance in liquid or gaseous alkali-metal atmospheres. Their oxida-

Table 33. Wrought Superalloys, Properties

Common designation	Max temp under load, deg F	Coef of expansion, in. per in. per deg F × 10^{-6} (70–1200 F)	Specific gravity	Stress to rupture, kpsi: At 1200 F, 1,000 hr	Stress to rupture, kpsi: At 1500 F, 100 hr	Stress to rupture, kpsi: At 1500 F, 1,000 hr	Short-time tensile strengths, kpsi: Yield, 0.2% offset, Room	Yield, 1200 F	Yield, 1500 F	Yield, 1800 F	Ultimate, Room	Ultimate, 1200 F	Ultimate, 1500 F	Ultimate, 1800 F
19-9 DL	1200	9.7	7.75	38	17	10	115	39	30	..	140	75	33	13
Timken	1350	9.25	8.06	36	13.5	9	96*	70*	16*	..	134	90	40	18
L.C. N-155	1400	9.4	8.2	48	20.0	15	53	40	33	12	115	53	35	19
S-590	1450	8.0	8.34	40	19.0	15	78*	70	47	20	140	82	60	22
S-816	1500	8.3	8.66	53	29.0	18	63*	45	41	..	140	112	73	25
Inconel X	1500	8.4	8.33	68	30.0	17	100	79	50	6	160	120	60	9
Nimonic-80A	1450	7.56	....	56	24	15	80*	73	47	..	150	101	69	
K-42-B	1400	8.5	8.23	38	22	15	105	84	52	..	158	117	54	
Hastelloy B	1450	6.9	9.24	36	17	10	58	42	..	..	135	94	66	24
M 252	1500	7.55	8.25	70	26	18	90	75	65	..	160	140	80	20
Inco 700	1600	8.32	8.16	85	42	27	105	93	82	..	170	140	95	
J 1570	1600	8.42	8.66	84	34	24	81	70	71	17	152	135	82	20
HS-R235	1600	8.34	7.88	70	35	23	100	90	80	22	170	145	83	25
Hastelloy X	1350	....	....	30	14	10	56	41	37	..	113	83	52	15
HS 25 (L605)	1500	....	....	54	22	18	70	35	..	..	...	75	50	23
A-286	1350	....	....	45	13.8	7.7								

* 0.02 percent offset.

Table 34. Cast Superalloys, Composition

Common designation	Chemical composition, percent: C	Mn	Si	Cr	Ni	Co	Mo	W	Cb	Fe	Other
Vitallium (Haynes 21)	0.25	0.6	0.6	27	2	Bal	6	..	..	1	
61 (Haynes 23)	0.4	0.6	0.6	26	1.5	Bal	..	5	..	1	
422-19 (Haynes 30)	0.4	0.6	0.6	26	16	Bal	6	..	..	1	
X-40 (Haynes 31)	0.4	0.6	0.6	25	10	Bal	..	7	..	1	
S-816	0.4	0.6	0.6	20	20	Bal	4	4	4	5	
HE 1049	0.45	0.7	0.7	25	10	45	..	15	..	1.5	0.4B
Hastelloy C	0.10	0.8	0.7	16	56	1	17	4	..	5.0	0.3V

Table 35. Cast Superalloys, Properties

Common designation	Max temp under load, deg F	Coef of expansion, in. per in. per deg F × 10^{-6} (70–1200 F)	Specific gravity	Stress to rupture in 1,000 hr, kpsi: 1200 F	1500 F	1800 F	Short-time tensile values, kpsi: Yield strength, 0.2% offset, Room	Yield, 1200 F	Yield, 1500 F	Yield, 1800 F	Ultimate, Room	Ultimate, 1200 F	Ultimate, 1500 F	Ultimate, 1800 F
Vitallium (Haynes 21)	1500	8.35	8.3	44	14	7	82	71	49	..	101	89	59	33
61 (Haynes 23)	1500	8.5	8.53	47	22	5.5	58	74	40	33	105	97	58	45
422-19 (Haynes 30)	1500	8.07	8.31	....	21	7	55	37*	48	..	98	59*	64	37
X-40 (Haynes 31)	1500	8.18	8.60	46	23	9.8	74	37*	44	..	101	77*	59	29
S-816	1500	8.27	8.66	46	21	9.8	..	..	..	..	112			
HE 1049	1650	....	8.9	75	35	7	80	72	62	36	90	82	81	52
Hastelloy C	....	7.73	8.91	12.5	14.5	1.4	54	50	..	..	130	87	51	19

* Specimen not aged.

tion resistance at temperatures above 1800 F approx is so poor that columbium-base alloys are not useful in such an environment.

Alloys of columbium are also regarded as the best **superconducting materials** available. This is a rapidly changing field. Currently, the most important high-field superconductors are the alloys of columbium and zirconium and the compound Cb_3Sn. At a magnetic field of 50,000 gauss, the Cb-25 Zr alloy has a critical field of about 90,000 gauss. Wire of this alloy is ductile and can easily be wound into a coil. The columbium-tin compound has a critical field of over 200,000 gauss and a critical current at 100,000 gauss in the range of 10^4 to 10^5 amp per cm^2. This compound is brittle and must either be used as a very thin coating on a ductile substrate

Table 36. Typical Compositions of Cast Tool Alloys

Name	C	Cr	W	Co	Fe	V	Ta	B	Other
Rexalloy	3	32	20	45					
Stellite 98 M2	3	28	18	35	9	4	0.1	0.1	3 Ni
Tantung G-2	3	15	21	40	...	...	19	0.2	
Borcoloy No. 6	0.7	5	18	20	Bal	1.3	...	0.7	6 Mo
Colmonoy WCR 100	...	10	15	..	Bal	...	...	3	

Table 37. Properties of Selected Refractory Alloys

Alloy	Melting temp, deg F	Density, lb per in.³ at 75 F	Elastic modulus at 75 F, kpsi	Ductile-to-brittle transition temp, deg F	Tensile strength, kpsi (recrystallized condition)				
					75 F	1800 F	2200 F	3000 F	3500 F
Chromium	3450	0.760	42	625	...	12	8		
Columbium	4474	0.310	16	−185	45	12	10		
F48 (15 W, 5 Mo, 1 Zr, 0.05 C)			25		121	75	50		
Cb74 or Cb752 (10 W, 2 Zr)		0.326			84	60	36		
Molybdenum	4730	0.369	47	85	75	34	22	6	3
Mo (½ Ti)					110	70	48	8	4
TZM (0.5 Ti, 0.08 Zr)					130	85	70	14	5
Tantalum	5425	0.600	27	<−320	30	22	15	8	4
Ta (10 W)					...	65	35	12	8
Rhenium	5460	0.759	68	<75	170	85	60	25	11
Tungsten	6170	0.697	58	645	85	36	32	19	10
W (10 Mo)					...	...	...	28	10
W (2 ThO_2)					...	...	40	30	25

or be prepared as a coil in such a way that the compound is formed by high-temperature reaction of columbium and tin after winding the coil.

Molybdenum is similar to tungsten in most of its properties. It can be prepared in the massive form by powder metallurgy or by inert-atmosphere or vacuum-arc melting. Its most serious limitation is its ready formation of a volatile oxide at temperatures of 1400 F approx. Intensive development efforts are now directed toward finding suitable means of surface protection. In the worked form, it is inferior to tungsten in melting point, tensile strength, vapor pressure, and hardness, but in the recrystallized condition, the ultimate strength and elongation are higher. Tensile strengths up to 350,000 psi have been reported for hard-drawn wire, and to 170,000 psi for soft wire. In the hard-drawn condition, molybdenum has an elongation of 2 to 5 percent, but after recrystallizing, this increases to 10 to 25 percent. Young's modulus is 50 million psi. It costs about the same as tungsten, per pound, but its density is much less. It has considerably better forming properties than tungsten and is extensively used for anodes, grids, and supports in vacuum tubes, lamps, and X-ray tubes. Molybdenum is generally used for winding electric furnaces for temperatures up to 3000 F. As it must be protected against oxidation, such furnaces are usually operated in hydrogen. It is the common material for contacts in mercury switches. Its principal use is still as an alloying addition to steels, especially tool steels and high-temperature steels.

Molybdenum alloys are finding increased use in aerospace and commercial structural applications. They are generally stronger than columbium alloys but are not ductile in the welded condition. Molybdenum alloys are resistant to alkali-metal corrosion.

Tantalum has a melting point that is surpassed only by tungsten. Its early use was as an electric-lamp filament material. It is more ductile than molybdenum or tungsten; the elongation for annealed material may be as high as 40 percent. The tensile strength of annealed sheet is about 50,000 psi. It is used for grids and plates in electronic power tubes. Its most important uses are in chemical-processing equipment, where its high rate of heat transfer (compared with glass or ceramics) is particularly important, although it is equivalent to glass in corrosion resistance. Its corrosion resistance also makes it attractive for surgical implants. Like tungsten and molybdenum, it is prepared by powder metallurgy, so the size of the piece that can be fabricated is limited by the size of the original pressed compact. Tantalum carbide is used in cemented-carbide tools, where it decreases the tendency to seizure and cratering. The stability of the anodic oxide film on tantalum leads to rectifier and capacitor applications. Tantalum and its **alloys** become competitive with columbium at temperatures above 2700 F. As in the case of columbium, these materials are resistant to liquid or vapor metal corrosion and have excellent ductility even in the welded condition.

Tungsten has the highest melting point of all metals. The massive metal is usually prepared by powder metallurgy from hydrogen-reduced powder. As a metal, its chief use is as filaments in incandescent lamps and electronic tubes, since its vapor pressure is low at high temperatures. Tensile strengths over 600,000 psi have been reported for fine tungsten wires; in larger sizes (1.0 mm), tensile strength is only 200,000 psi. The hard-drawn wire has an elongation of 2 to 4 percent, but the recrystallized wire is brittle. Young's modulus is 60 million psi. It can be sealed directly to hard glass and so is used for lead-in wires. A considerable proportion of tungsten rod and sheet is used for electrical contacts in the form of disks cut from rod or sheet and brazed to supporting elements. The major part of the tungsten used is made into ferroalloys for addition to steels or into tungsten carbide for cutting tools. Other applications include elements of electronic tubes, X-ray tube anodes, and arc-welding electrodes. **Alloys** of tungsten that are commercially available are W-3 Re, W-25 Re, and thoriated tungsten. The rhenium-bearing alloys are more ductile than unalloyed tungsten at room temperature. Thoriated tungsten is stronger than unalloyed tungsten at temperatures up to the recrystallization temperature.

METALS AND ALLOYS FOR ATOMIC-ENERGY APPLICATIONS

(See also Sec. 9.)

REFERENCES: Glasstone, "Principles of Nuclear Reactor Engineering," Van Nostrand. Hausner and Roboff, "Materials for Nuclear Power Reactors," Reinhold.

The advent of atomic energy has not only created a demand for new metals and alloys but has also focused attention on certain properties and combinations of properties which theretofore had been of little consequence. Reactor technology requires special materials for fuels, fuel cladding, moderators, reflectors, controls, heat-transfer mediums, operating mechanisms, and auxiliary structures. Some of the properties pertinent to such applications are given in a general way in Table 38. In general, outside the reflector, only normal engineering requirements need be considered.

Nuclear Properties. A most important consideration in the design of a nuclear reactor is the control of the number and speed of the neutrons resulting from fission of the fuel. It is thus apparent that the designer must have knowledge of the effectiveness of various materials in slowing down neutrons or in capturing them. The slowing-down power depends not only on the relative energy loss per atomic collision but also on the number of collisions per second per unit volume. The former will be larger, the lower the atomic weight, and the latter larger, the greater the atomic

Table 38. Requirements of Materials for Nuclear Reactor Components

Component	Neutron-absorption cross section	Effect in slowing neutrons	Strength	Resistance to radiation damage	Thermal conductivity	Corrosion resistance	Cost	Other	Typical material
Moderator and reflector	Low	High	Adequate	....	....	High	Low	Low atomic wt	H_2O, graphite, Be
Fuel*......	Low		Adequate	High	High	High	Low	....	U, Th, Pu
Control rod	High	....	Adequate	Adequate	High	....	....	....	Cd, B_4C
Shield.....	High	High	High	......	....	....	....	High γ radiation absorption	Concrete
Cladding...	Low	....	Adequate	....	High	High	Low	....	Al, Zr, stainless steel
Structural..	Low	....	High	Adequate	....	High	....	....	Zr, stainless steel
Coolant....	Low	....	....	....	High	....	....	Low corrosion rate, high heat capacity	H_2O, Na, NaK, CO_2, He

* U, Th, and Pu are used as fuels in the forms of metals, oxides, and carbides.

density and the higher the probability of a scattering collision. The effectiveness of a moderator is frequently expressed in terms of the moderating ratio, the ratio of the slowing-down power to the capture cross section. The capturing and scattering tendencies are measured in terms of nuclear cross section in barns (10^{-24} sq cm). Data for some of the materials of interest are given in Tables 39 to 41. The absorption data apply to slow, or thermal, neutrons; entirely different cross sections obtain for fast neutrons, for which few materials have significantly high capture affinity. Fast neutrons have energies of about 10^6 ev, while slow, or thermal, neutrons have energies of about 2.5×10^{-2} ev. Special consideration must frequently be given to the presence of small amounts of high cross-section elements such as Co or W which are either normal

Table 39. Moderating Properties of Materials*

Moderator	Slowing-down power, cm^{-1}	Moderating ratio
H_2O....................	1.53	70
D_2O....................	0.177	21,000
He........................	1.6×10^{-5}	83
Be........................	0.16	150
BeO.......................	0.11	180
C (graphite)..............	0.063	170

* Adapted from Glasstone, "Principles of Nuclear Reactor Engineering," Van Nostrand.

Table 40. Slow-neutron Absorption by Structural Materials*

Material	Relative neutron absorption per cu cm $\times 10^3$	Relative neutron absorption for pipes of equal strength, 68 F	Melting point, deg F
Magnesium..........	3.5	10	1200
Aluminum...........	13	102	1230
Stainless steel....	226	234	2730
Zirconium..........	12.6	16	3330

* Leeser, *Materials & Methods*, **41**, 1955, p. 98.

Table 41. Slow-neutron Absorption Cross Sections*

Low		Intermediate		High	
Element	Cross section, barns	Element	Cross section, barns	Element	Cross section, barns
Oxygen	0.0016	Zinc	1.0	Manganese	12
Carbon	0.0045	Columbium	1.2	Tungsten	18
Beryllium	0.009	Barium	1.2	Tantalum	21
Fluorine	0.01	Strontium	1.3	Chlorine	32
Bismuth	0.015	Nitrogen	1.7	Cobalt	35
Magnesium	0.07	Potassium	2.0	Silver	60
Silicon	0.1	Germanium	2.3	Lithium	67
Phosphorus	0.15	Iron	2.4	Gold	95
Zirconium	0.18	Molybdenum	2.4	Hafnium	100
Lead	0.18	Gallium	2.8	Mercury	340
Aluminum	0.22	Chromium	2.9	Iridium	470
Hydrogen	0.32	Thallium	3.3	Boron	715
Calcium	0.42	Copper	3.6	Cadmium	3,000
Sodium	0.48	Nickel	4.5	Samarium	8,000
Sulphur	0.49	Tellurium	4.5	Gadolinium	36,000
Tin	0.6	Vanadium	4.8		
		Antimony	5.3		
		Titanium	5.8		

* Leeser, *Materials & Methods*, **41**, 1955, p. 98.

incidental impurities in nickel alloys and steels or important components of high-temperature alloys.

Effects of Radiation. Irradiation affects the properties of solids in a number of ways: dimensional changes; decrease in density; increase in hardness, yield, and tensile strengths; decrease in ductility; decrease in electrical conductivity or change in magnetic susceptibility. Another consideration is the activation of certain alloying elements by irradiation. $Tantalum^{181}$ and Co^{60} have moderate radioactivity but long half-lives; isotopes having short lives but high-activity levels include Cr^{51}, Mn^{56}, and Fe^{59}.

Metallic Coolants. The need for the efficient transfer of large quantities of heat in a reactor has led to widespread use of several metallic coolants. These have raised new problems of pumping, valving, and corrosion. In addition to their thermal and flow properties, consideration must also be given the nuclear properties of prospective coolants. Extensive thermal, flow, and corrosion data on metallic coolants are given in the Liquid Metals Handbook, published by USAEC. The resistance of common materials to liquid sodium and NaK are given qualitatively in Table 42.

Table 42. Resistance of Materials to Liquid Sodium and NaK*

	Good	Limited	Poor
<1000 F	Carbon steels, low-alloy steels, alloy steels, stainless steels, nickel alloys, cobalt alloys, refractory metals, beryllium, aluminum oxide, magnesium oxide, aluminum bronze	Gray cast iron, copper, aluminum alloys, magnesium alloys, glasses	Sb, Bi, Cd, Ca, Au, Pb, Se, Ag, S, Sn, Teflon
1000–1600 F	Armco iron, stainless steels, nickel alloys,† cobalt alloys, refractory metals‡	Carbon steels, alloy steels, Monel, titanium, zirconium, beryllium, aluminum oxide, magnesium oxide	Gray cast iron, copper alloys, Teflon, Sb, Bi, Cd, Ca, Au, Pb, Se, Ag, S, Sn, Pt, Si, magnesium alloys

* For more complete details, see Liquid Metals Handbook.
† Except Monel.
‡ Except titanium and zirconium.

Water, however, remains the most-used coolant; it is used under pressure as a single-phase liquid, as a boiling two-phase coolant, or as steam in a superheat reactor.

Fuels. There are, at present, only three fissionable materials, U^{233}, U^{235}, and Pu^{239}. Of these, only U^{235} occurs naturally as an isotopic "impurity" with natural uranium U^{238}. $Uranium^{233}$ may be prepared from natural thorium, and Pu^{239} from U^{238} by neutron bombardment. Both uranium and thorium are prepared by conversion of the oxide to the tetrafluoride and subsequent reduction to the metal.

The properties of **uranium** are considerably affected by the three allotropic changes which it undergoes, the low-temperature forms being highly anisotropic. The strength of the metal is low (see Table 43) and decreases rapidly with increasing

Table 43. Mechanical Properties of Metals for Nuclear Reactors

Material	Room temperature						Elevated temp*		
	Longitudinal			Transverse					
	Yield strength, kpsi	Ult strength, kpsi	Elong,† per-cent	Ult str, kpsi	Elong,† per-cent	Charpy impact ft-lb	deg F	Ult str, kpsi	Elong, per-cent
Beryllium									
cast, extruded and annealed..	....	40.	1.82	16.6	0.18	....	392	62.	23.5
flake, extruded and annealed	....	63.7	5.0	25.5	0.30	....	752	43.	29.
powder, hot-extruded......	39.5	81.8	15.8	45.2	2.3	4.1	1112	23	8.5
powder, vacuum hot pressed	32.1	45.2	2.3	45.2	2.3	0.8	1472	5.2	10.5
Zirconium									
Kroll-50% CW..........	....	82.6	....	....	....	14.8	250	32.	
Kroll-annealed..........	....	49.0	....	....	....	....	500	23.	
iodide..................	15.9	35.9	31.	....	....	2.5–6.0	700	17.	
							900	12.	
							1500	3.	
Uranium..................	25.	53.	<10	....	....	15.	302	27.	
							1112	12.	
Thorium..................	27.	37.5	40.	....	....	....	570	22.	
							930	17.5	

* All elevated-temperature data on beryllium for hot-extruded powder; on zirconium for iodide material.

† Beryllium is extremely notch-sensitive. The tabulated data have been obtained under very carefully controlled conditions, but ductility values in practice will be found in general to be much lower and essentially zero in the transverse direction.

temperature. The corrosion resistance is also poor. Aluminum-base alloys containing uranium-aluminum intermetallic compounds have been used to achieve improved properties. **Thorium** is even softer than uranium but is very ductile. Like uranium it corrodes readily, particularly at elevated temperatures. Owing to its crystal structure, its properties are isotropic. **Plutonium** is unusual in possessing six allotropic forms, many of which have anomalous physical properties. The electrical resistivity of the alpha phase is greater than that for any other metallic element. Because of the poor corrosion resistance of nuclear-fuel metals, most fuels in power reactors today are in the form of oxide UO_2, ThO_2, or PuO_2, or mixtures of these. The carbides UC and UC_2 are also of interest in reactors using liquid-metal coolants.

Control-rod Materials. Considerations of neutron absorption cross sections and melting points limit the possible control-rod materials to a very small group of elements, of which only four—boron, cadmium, hafnium, and gadolinium—have thus far been prominent. **Boron** is a very light metal of high hardness ($\sim$3000 Knoop) prepared by thermal or hydrogen reduction of BCl_3. Because of its high melting point, solid shapes of boron are prepared by powder-metallurgy techniques. Boron has a very high electrical resistivity at room temperature but becomes conductive at high temperatures. The metal in bulk form is oxidation-resistant below 1000 C but reacts readily with most halogens at only moderate temperatures. Rather than the elemental form, boron is generally used as boron steel or as the carbide, oxide, or nitride. **Cadmium** is a highly ductile metal of moderate hardness which is recovered as a by-product in zinc smelting. Its properties greatly resemble those of zinc. The relatively low melting point renders it least attractive as a control rod of the four metals cited. **Hafnium** metal is reduced from hafnium tetrachloride by sodium and subsequently purified by the iodide hot-wire process. It is harder and less readily worked than zirconium, to which it is otherwise very similar in both chemical and physical properties. Hafnium reacts easily with oxygen, and its properties are sensitive to traces of most gases. The very high absorption cross section of **gadolinium** renders it advantageous for fast-acting control rods. This metal is one of the rare earths and as yet is of very limited availability. It is most frequently employed as the oxide. Certain of the other rare-earth metals may eventually find similar application.

Beryllium. Great interest attaches to beryllium because it is unique among the metals with respect to its very low neutron-absorption cross section and high neutron-slowing power. It may also serve as a source of neutrons when subjected to alpha-particle bombardment. Beryllium is currently prepared almost entirely by magnesium reduction of the fluoride, although fused-salt electrolysis is also practicable and has been used. The high affinity of the metal for oxygen and nitrogen renders its processing and fabrication especially difficult. Prior to the intensive effort applied to the problem during World War II, beryllium was regarded as almost hopelessly brittle. Now special techniques, such as vacuum hot pressing, or vacuum casting followed by hot extrusion of clad slugs, have led to material having marginally acceptable, though highly directional, mechanical properties. The extreme toxicity of beryllium powder necessitates special precautions in all operations.

Zirconium. Zirconium's importance in nuclear technology derives from its low neutron-absorption cross section, excellent corrosion resistance, and high strength at moderate temperatures. The metal is produced by magnesium reduction of the tetrachloride (Kroll process). A subsequent refining by the iodide hot-wire process was formerly customary but is now no longer required. The Kroll product is usually converted to ingot form by consumable-electrode-arc melting. An important step in the processing for many applications is the difficult chemical separation of the 1½ to 3 percent hafnium with which zirconium is contaminated. Unless removed, this small hafnium content results in a prohibitive increase in absorption cross section from 0.18 to 3.5 barns. The mechanical properties of zirconium are particularly sensitive to the impurity content and the fabrication technique. In spite of the high melting point, the mechanical properties are poor at high temperatures, principally because of the allotropic transformation at 1585 F. A satisfactory annealing temperature is 1100 F. The low-temperature corrosion behavior is excellent but can be seriously affected by impurities. The oxidation resistance at high temperatures is poor. Special alloys (Zircoloys) have been developed having greatly improved oxidation resistance in the intermediate-temperature range. These alloys have a nominal content of 1.5 percent Sn and minor additions of iron-group elements.

Stainless Steel. Although stainless steel has a higher thermal neutron-absorption cross section than do the zirconium alloys, its good corrosion resistance, high strength, low cost, and ease of fabrication make it a strong competitor with zirconium alloys as a fuel-cladding material for water-cooled power-reactor applications. Types 348 and 304 stainless have been used in major reactors.

JEWELRY METALS

Gold is used primarily as a monetary standard; the small amount put to metallurgical use is for jewelry or decorative purposes, in dental work, for fountain-pen nibs, and as an electrodeposited protective coating. An alloy with palladium has been used as a platinum substitute for laboratory vessels, but its present price is so high that it does not compete with platinum.

Silver has the highest electrical conductivity of any metal, and it found some use in bus bars during World War II, when copper was in short supply. Since its density is higher than that of copper and since Government silver frequently has deleterious impurities, it offers no advantage over copper as an electrical conductor. Heavy-duty electrical contacts are usually made of silver. It is used in aircraft bearings and solders. Its largest commercial use is in tableware as sterling silver, which contains 92.5 percent silver (the remainder is usually copper). United States coinage contained 90 percent silver, 10 percent copper

Platinum has many uses because of its high melting point, chemical inertness, and catalytic activity. It is the standard catalyst for the oxidation of sulphur dioxide in the manufacture of sulphuric acid. Because it is inert toward most chemicals, even at elevated temperatures, large amounts are used for laboratory apparatus. It is the only metal that can be used for an electric heating element above 2300 F without a protective atmosphere. Thermocouples of platinum with platinum-rhodium alloy are standard for high temperatures. Platinum and platinum alloys are used in large amounts in feeding mechanisms of glass-working equipment to ensure constancy of the orifice dimensions that fix the size of glass products. They are also used for electrical contacts, in dental work, in aircraft spark-plug electrodes, and as jewelry.

Palladium follows platinum in importance and abundance among the platinum metals and resembles platinum in most of its properties. Its density and melting point are the lowest of the platinum metals, and it forms an oxide coating at a dull-red heat so that it cannot be heated in air above 800 F approx. In the finely divided form, it is an excellent hydrogenation catalyst. It is as ductile as gold and is beaten into leaf as thin as gold leaf. Its hardened alloys find some use in dentistry, jewelry, and electrical contacts.

Iridium is one of the platinum metals. Its chief uses are as a hardener for platinum jewelry alloys and as platinum contacts. Its alloys with osmium are used for tipping fountain-pen nibs. It is the most corrosion-resistant element known.

Rhodium is used mainly as an alloying addition to platinum. It is a component of many of the pen-tipping alloys. Because of its high reflectivity and freedom from oxidation films, it is frequently used as an electroplate for jewelry and for reflectors for motion-picture projectors, aircraft searchlights, and the like.

POWDER METALLURGY

References: Schwartzkopf, "Powder Metallurgy," Macmillan. Goetzal, "Treatise on Powder Metallurgy," Interscience.

Powder metallurgy involves (1) the production of metal powders of suitable characteristics and (2) consolidation of the powder to the desired density and cohesion by pressing and a subsequent or simultaneous heating operation known as sintering. Sintering may involve the formation of a liquid phase or may be carried out below the melting point of all constituents. Reasons for the use of powder metallurgy include (1) the ability to fabricate refractory or reactive metals, (2) the ability homogeneously to combine dissimilar materials, (3) the ability to produce metal of controlled porosity or permeability, (4) the ability to produce large numbers of certain small parts more cheaply than by competitive conventional techniques. The maximum weight of a piece that it is feasible to make by powder metallurgy is ordinarily about 1 lb, although much larger pieces can and have been made.

The strength, and more particularly the ductility, of powder metallurgy products are almost always inferior to those obtained by casting or forging, although by special means, such as additional working and annealing, better properties can be obtained. Typical properties of sintered metals are given in Tables 44 and 45 and are there compared with those for typical cast and wrought metals. An exception to the general trend shown in the tables is the comparatively recent development of sintered aluminum powder (see p. 6–89). This material, which incorporates a controlled amount of oxide, has elevated-temperature properties superior to those of any conventional cast- or wrought-aluminum alloy.

A considerable body of empirical knowledge is now at hand with respect to powder characteristics, die design, pressing techniques, sintering atmospheres, etc. (see particularly Goetzal). In general, these problems become more acute the larger and more complex the piece and the more reactive the metal.

Table 44. Mechanical Properties of Sintered Copper and Iron
(Goetzal in Wulf, "Powder Metallurgy," ASM, 1942)

Material and treatment	Density	Brinell hardness	Tensile strength, kpsi	Elongation, percent in 2 in.	Yield strength, kpsi
COPPER					
Compacted at 50 tons per sq in.	7.87	73	1	0	
Sintered 8 hr at 800 C	7.90	34	16	9.5	
Repressed at 50 tons per sq in.	8.39	70	22	4.0	
Repressed and resintered at 800 C	8.37	39	25	17	
After 25% cold reduction, annealed	8.35	39	17	16.5	
After 50% cold reduction, annealed	8.59	41	25	22	
After 75% cold reduction, annealed	8.82	44	33	27.5	
Cast and wrought copper, annealed	8.96	....	32	50	
IRON					
Compacted at 50 tons per sq in.	6.23	70	0.5	0	0
Sintered 8 hr above 1000 C	6.68	47	27	10	0
Repressed at 50 tons per sq in.	7.27	67	43	5	0
Repressed and resintered above 1000 C	7.23	63	35	21	19
25% cold reduction, annealed	7.40	63.5	30	15	
50% cold reduction, annealed	7.69	68.5	32.8	21.5	
75% cold reduction, annealed	7.75	68.5	33.8	26.0	
Electrolytic iron, cast and annealed	7.87	67	37	50	15
HOT-PRESSED BRASS					
90 Cu, 10 Zn, pressed at 900 C	....	....	30	22	17
90 Cu, 10 Zn, cast and wrought	....	....	37	45	10
80 Cu, 20 Zn, pressed at 900 C	....	....	37	34	18
80 Cu, 20 Zn, cast and wrought	....	....	44	50	14
70 Cu, 30 Zn, pressed at 800 C	....	....	38	16	12
70 Cu, 30 Zn, cast and wrought	....	....	47	62	15
50 Cu, 50 Zn, pressed at 700 C	....	....	21	0	21

Table 45. Comparison of Mechanical Properties of SAE and Sintered Steels
(Stern, *Trans. AIME*, **166**, 1946, p. 556)

Treatment	SAE 1020		SAE 1040		SAE 1060		SAE 1080	
	SAE	Sin.	SAE	Sin.	SAE	Sin.	SAE	Sin.
FURNACE-COOLED								
Yield point, kpsi	43	37	52	40	59	42	62	57
Tensile strength, kpsi	66	55	88	61	95	69	102	79
Elongation, percent	35	25	29	21	24	13.5	20	7.5
Reduction in area, percent	55	27	60	22	51	12.5	48	5.5
OIL-QUENCHED AND DRAWN AT 1300 F								
Yield point, kpsi	38	35	55	39	72	44	80	50
Tensile strength, kpsi	60	52	82	55	98	63	100	69
Elongation, percent	35	35	30	30	26	18.5	23	10.5
Reduction in area, percent	65	40	60	35	61	22	56	10.5
OIL-QUENCHED AND DRAWN AT 800 F								
Yield point, kpsi	57	50	76	55	105	65	125	80
Tensile strength, kpsi	77	65	110	76	144	91	175	106
Elongation, percent	30	25	19	18	17	13.5	12	8
Reduction in area, percent	58	25	48	19	48	12	40	6.5

The sintered specimens were prepared from electrolytic iron powder and graphite. All specimens were pressed at 50 tons per sq in., presintered 15 min at 2000 F, repressed at 50 tons per sq in., and sintered 1 hr at 2000 F. The sintered alloys do not contain the manganese and silicon of the SAE steels.

CEMENTED CARBIDES

REFERENCE: Schwartzkopf and Kieffer, "Refractory Hard Metals," Macmillan. Also see powder-metallurgy references p. 6–120.

Cemented hard carbides constitute a highly important class of materials in modern technology. They are most generally produced by powder-metallurgy techniques. However, some special parts are produced by casting, and flame spraying and arc deposition have recently become prominent, particularly in hard-facing applications. The bulk of the cemented carbides are still based on tungsten monocarbide, WC, although new types have been introduced in recent years based on TiC and on Cr_3C_2. The most important application of the cemented carbides is as cutting tools, but a considerable volume is also used for dies and wear-resistant applications.

Table 46. Composition and Properties of Cemented Carbides

Composition, percent	Specific gravity	Hardness, Rockwell A	Transverse rupture strength, kpsi	Young's modulus, psi × 10^6
WC + 3 Co	15.25	92.7	170	97.5
WC + 4.5 Co	15.05	92.3	200	90.5
WC + 6 Co	14.85	90–92	225	88
WC + 9 Co	14.6	90	275	
WC + 13 Co	14.15	89	300	80
WC + 10 TaC + 6 Co	14.7	91	220	
WC + 12 TiC + 6 Co	11.2	92	160	
WC + 10 TaC + 15 TiC + 8 Co	11.7	92	165	72
WC + 15 TaC + 15 TiC + 15 Co	11.4	90	190	67
WC + 2 TaC + 1 CbC + 20 Co*	13.4	86	380	
WC + 6 TaC + 11 TiC + 2 CbC + 9 Co*	11.1	92	250	
TiC + 10–40 Ni	5.5–6.5	83–90	160	55
Cr_3C_2 + 2 WC + 15 Ni	7.0	88	100	

* Approximate values for a typical grade; compositions and properties for others in this grouping may vary considerably.

Carbides are produced by adding carbon to the powdered metal or oxide (or to mixtures of two or more metals or oxides) and then heating in a reducing atmosphere to a temperature in the neighborhood of 2600 F. The time and temperature must be controlled to give the proper carbon content of the carbides and appropriate particle size. Special properties are claimed for WC-TiC compositions made by reaction in molten nickel alloy, the so-called "menstruum process." The finely granular carbide powder, however made, is intimately mixed with the powdered metal binder (cobalt for the WC grades) by prolonged ball milling, and then pressed and sintered or hot pressed. In some instances, parts are presintered at low temperatures (~1500 F) to give them sufficient strength to be ground or cut to more complex shapes than can be formed by pressing. Shrinkage of the sintered material must be allowed for. Final sintering is then carried out at a much higher temperature, specific for each composition. While the final sintering is usually done below the melting point of the binder metal, a liquid ternary phase is usually formed which is largely responsible for the densification and bond strength. Tungsten carbide grades are usually sintered in hydrogen, but the newer TiC grades are vacuum sintered. (See Table 46.)

The strength and hardness of the cemented carbides are controlled by varying the amount of the binder metal; the lower the binder content, the harder and more brittle the composite. The strength and toughness may also be improved by reduction in the particle size of the carbides. Admixtures of other carbides to a given base are usually made to control oxidation resistance, thermal conductivity, or elastic modulus.

The modulus of elasticity of tungsten carbide is about 102 × 10^6 psi—higher than any other known material. The compressive strength of cemented tungsten carbide varies between 900 and 500 kpsi, depending on cobalt content. Thermal expansion is about 3.3×10^{-6} per deg F. Thermal conductivity is about 500 Btu per hr per sq ft per in. per deg F for cemented tungsten carbide, decreasing to 185 for the double tungsten-titanium carbides. A low thermal conductivity seems to favor resistance to cratering in machining steels, but in machining cast iron and other materials with discontinuous chip the high thermal conductivity and superior hardness of tungsten carbide are desirable. The lower moduli of the carbide compositions containing tantalum or titanium permit greater deflection before fracture than the harder tungsten carbides. The chromium carbide and particularly the titanium carbide bases have superior oxidation resistance at high temperatures. Their critical materials content is very low. The titanium carbide grades have the further advantages of low density and excellent high-temperature strength. The chromium carbides have a unique feature for gaging applications in that they have about the same expansion coefficient as steels so that results are not affected by ambient temperature variations when working with steel.

Shaped tips for lathe and other cutting tools are copper-welded, brazed, or silver-soldered to a steel shank both for cheapness and for support of the brittle tip. In designing tips, it is important to avoid large changes of thickness and to design the backer so that stresses due to thermal contraction after brazing cannot crack the tip. In designing tools, it is important to use the lowest rake angle possible so that the tool may have the maximum support. Other applications of hard carbides include lathe centers, gage tips, guides of various kinds, Brinell balls, and the like. The piece should be shaped as closely as possible to final size before sintering, but a limited amount of forming can be done by grinding with special silicon carbide or diamond-impregnated wheels (see p. 6–171). Numerous other uses are also found for the cemented carbides, *e.g.*, wear-resistant tips for plug and snap gages, scribers, files, wiredrawing dies, thread guides in the manufacture of synthetic fibers, die linings, and wear plates of many kinds. The standardization and application of carbide grades has been ably described by Miller (*Metal Progress*, **63**, 1953. p. 75). (See also Sec. 13.)

CORROSION

BY

Hilary E. Bacon

References: Cushman and Gardner, "Corrosion and Preservation of Iron and Steel," McGraw-Hill. Rawdon, Protective Metal Coatings, *ACS Monograph* 40, Reinhold. Uhlig, "The Corrosion Handbook," Wiley. Evans, "The Corrosion of Metals," Edward Arnold. Friend, "The Corrosion of Iron and Steel," Longmans. Speller, "Corrosion—Cause and Prevention," McGraw-Hill. Kallen, Corrosion, *Power*, Dec., 1956, pp. 74–106. DePaul, "Corrosion and Wear Handbook," McGraw-Hill. Polar, "A Guide to Corrosion Resistance," Climax Molybdenum Co. Zapffe, "Stainless Steels," ASM. La Que and Copson, Corrosion Resistance of Metals and Alloys, *ACS Monograph* 158, Reinhold. Bregman, "Corrosion Inhibitors," Macmillan.

GENERAL CONSIDERATIONS

Corrosion is a destructive attack on metals which may be chemical or electrochemical in nature. Direct chemical corrosion is limited to unusual conditions involving highly corrosive environments or high temperature or both. Examples are metals in contact with strong acids or alkalies and the formation of iron oxide by dissociation of water in contact with overheated boiler tubes. However, most of the phenomena involving corrosion of metals containing or submerged in water, or atmospheric corrosion by films of moisture, are electrochemical in nature.

The **mechanism** of electrochemical corrosion is most obvious in the case of electrically coupled dissimilar metals such as zinc and copper submerged in water, so that zinc forms the anode and copper the cathode of a galvanic cell. The reaction proceeds in two parts: (1) the **anodic reaction,** in which the metal dissolves in the electrolyte in the form of positively charged ions, and (2) the **cathodic reaction,** in which positively charged hydrogen ions plate out as atomic hydrogen on the cathodic surface. The electrons released by the anodic reaction flow through the metallic circuit to the cathode, where they neutralize an exactly equivalent number of hydrogen ions.

Anodic reaction: $M \rightarrow M^+ + e$

Cathodic reaction: $H^+ + e \rightarrow H$ (atomic)

The hydrogen film will eventually cover and **polarize** the cathodic surface, stopping the flow of electrons. The positive metal ions released near the surface of the anode combine with negative hydroxide ions from the water to form a neutral metal hydroxide, which frequently coats the anodic surface.

Over-all reaction: $M^+ + OH^- \rightarrow MOH$

Thus under favorable conditions the electrochemical reaction will stifle itself at the cathode or anode or both.

The commoner case is a single metal in which the surface is heterogeneous in polarity, composed of small discrete anodic and cathodic areas so close together as to be indistinguishable. Small potential differences arise from minor variations in composition, surface finish, stress, deposits or inclusions, or concentration differences of electrolytic or gaseous solutes in the adjacent liquid phase. Penetration proceeds at the anodic areas resulting in a wide variety of pitting, roughening, or wastage. The cathodic hydrogen film and anodic insoluble precipitates are equally important stifling factors and can be utilized to retard corrosion.

An index of the driving force of the electrochemical reaction is the potential or emf of the galvanic cell, which is the sum of the potentials of the half-cells formed by the anode and cathode and the water surrounding them. These potentials are characteristic of the metal (or other electrode material) and vary with ionic content of the electrolyte, temperature, and other factors. Specific **electrode potentials** are qualified by fixing the equilibrium concentration of metal ions, conventionally, at 1 molal (one gram-molecular weight per liter); they can only be determined by currentless measurement, in the absence of electrode reaction. Otherwise, they are altered by polarization by an increment known as the **overvoltage,** related to the energy changes at the electrodes. The **hydrogen overvoltage** is associated with the release of hydrogen at the cathode.

These basic facts concerning mechanism are fundamental to explanation of electrochemical corrosion phenomena and methods of prevention.

FACTORS IN ELECTROCHEMICAL CORROSION

Metal. The tendency of a metal to dissolve in water, which is known as **solution pressure,** can be measured by the (currentless) electrical potential which must be applied in order to prevent any action when the metal is immersed in a solution of one of its salts at standard (1 molal) concentration. From such information, the metals may be arranged in a series in the order of their solution pressures:

Electromotive Force Series of Metals

Magnesium	Iron	Copper
Beryllium	Cadmium	Mercury
Aluminum	Nickel	Silver
Manganese	Tin	Palladium
Zinc	Lead	Platinum
Chromium	Hydrogen (zero)	Gold

Although the standard concentration of metal salts and complete absence of polarization currents are never encountered in practice, this series nevertheless lists the metals in order of decreasing corrodibility. When two metals in contact are immersed in water, that which is above the other in this series becomes anodic, suffers corrosion, and protects the other metal by rendering it cathodic.

The **electrolyte** is the controllable dominant factor. Normally the water in contact with metals contains impurities such as salts, gases, and vapors. Its **electrolytic activity** is a function of ions which increase its conductivity; thus high salinity promotes electrochemical corrosion. More important, water is rarely **neutral** (pH = 7.0) but is either **acidic** (pH below 7.0) or **basic** (pH above 7.0). (For definition and explanation of pH, see p. 9–47.) The excess of hydrogen ions accompanying a decreasing pH increases the driving force and the reaction rate of electrochemical corrosion; hence acids and acidic salts produce a corrosive environment. Conversely, an overbalance of hydroxyl ions (high pH) depresses electrochemical corrosion and may provide excellent protection even without film formation—as when caustic, ammonia, or amines are added to condensate or demineralized or completely softened water.

Oxygen. Gaseous oxygen dissolved in water reacts with the protective atomic hydrogen on cathodic areas of metallic surfaces, destroys the film by **depolarization,** and permits corrosion to continue. The rate of corrosion is roughly limited by the rate of diffusion of dissolved oxygen to the metal surface, and thus extensive oxygen attack occurs at or near the water line. Dissolved oxygen is dominant in the vast majority of corrosion problems, many of which can be completely solved by thorough mechanical, thermal, or chemical deaeration of water. Figures 1 and 2 give the solubility of oxygen in parts per million in water in contact with saturated air at various pressures from 10 psi gage to a vacuum of 28 in. Hg and at temperatures up to 230 F. An entirely secondary action of dissolved oxygen is to oxidize the ferrous hydroxide, formed by the union of the metal and hydroxide ions, to the insoluble ferric state.

Factors Stimulating Corrosion. In practice, conditions which promote corrosion may be inferred from what has been said about metals, electrolytes, and dissolved oxygen. Any condition of non-uniformity within the metal, such as may arise from improper annealing or cold working, may increase the heterogeneity and intensity of polarity differences, and obviously the use of **dissimilar metals** may cause one of them to corrode, as in the case of aluminum heat-exchanger tubes adjacent to iron tie rods in the tube bundle. Non-uniformity of concentrations in the electrolyte produces **concentration cells** and is thus favorable to corrosive attack. It is well known that non-uniformity in distribution of dissolved oxygen renders the areas exposed to low oxygen concentration anodic with respect to those in contact with higher oxygen concentration. Thus, **turbulence** and entrained air cause corrosion at the inlet ends of condenser tubes and on the tube sheet. The depolarization of the hydrogen film by dissolved oxygen (and hence corrosion) occurs more rapidly on some metals than on others, zinc and aluminum being less active than iron, and is catalyzed by the presence of **mill scale.** **Atmospheric corrosion** is stimulated by a damp atmosphere since this maintains a film of water on the metal, providing the essential electrolyte. Other factors are **acid gases** in the atmosphere or sulphur

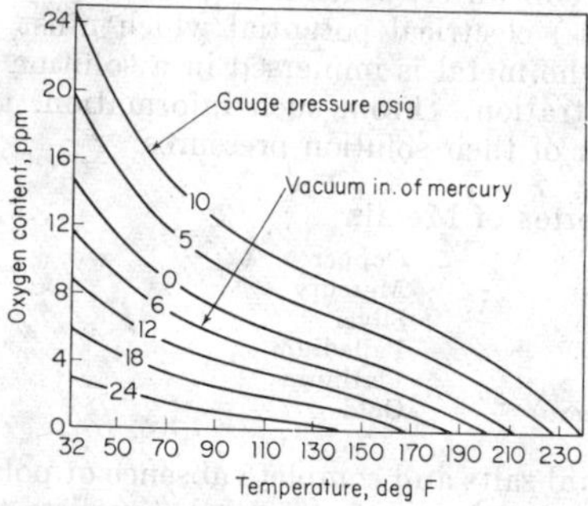

Fig. 1. Solubility of oxygen in water under saturated air at pressures up to 10 psi. (To convert ppm to cc per liter multiply by 0.698.)

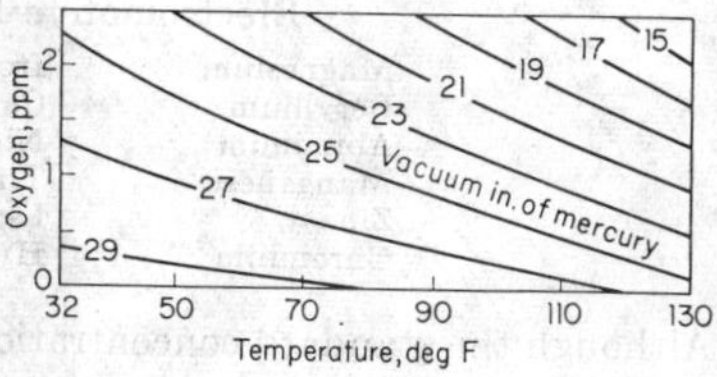

Fig. 2. Solubility of oxygen in water under saturated air at pressures down to 29 in. vacuum.

compounds from cinders, coke, coal dust, etc.; salts that dissociate to produce an acid reaction; oxygen dissolved in the water film. All these factors, although sometimes in other form, apply to **immersed corrosion** and to **underground corrosion.**

Factors inhibiting corrosion are likewise deduced from the foregoing relations of metals, electrolytes, and dissolved oxygen to electrochemical corrosion. Protective measures include the use of **sacrificial anodes** such as zinc or magnesium, the impression of a counter emf by various **cathodic protection** devices, and **passivation** of metals (so treating them as to reduce their solubility in acids and the rate of precipitation from other metal ions from solutions). Contact with the electrolyte is prevented by various **protective coatings,** either applied or precipitated from solution, as in the case of calcium carbonate, hydrated chromium and iron oxides.

Electrolysis, which is not to be confused with the fact that corrosion is fundamentally an electrochemical phenomenon, is generally caused by the leakage of current from electric circuits and may take place at a point far removed from where the leakage occurs. Electric-railway track feeder and return systems and improperly grounded welding equipment have caused many cases of corrosion due to electrolysis. Undue emphasis is often given to this phase of the corrosion problem. Stray currents of extremely feeble intensity and voltage may serve to accelerate corrosion, even when they have not initiated it. Corrosion due to electrolysis can be minimized by providing thorough insulation, grounding all metallic conduits, avoiding combinations of dissimilar metals in a circuit, and maintaining apparatus in an electronegative state with reference to possible sources of current, either by a "drainage" system or by "tying up" with some sources of current of a higher potential (Thalmann).

CORROSION RESISTANCE OF VARIOUS METALS

Iron and Steel. Under similar conditions, iron and steel corrode at practically the same rate, but the distribution of the corrosion may be different for the two. The slag interspersed through wrought iron may result in a generally distributed attack under atmospheric corrosion rather than a severely localized (pitting) attack. In underground corrosion and in continuous immersion in water, tests have not shown much difference between the two materials.

Polished surfaces resist corrosion much better than rougher surfaces. Variations in surface finish may have a greater influence than ordinary variations in chemical composition other than pronounced segregation. The presence of mill scale on the surface favors localized or irregularly distributed corrosion. Frequently a polished surface will withstand exposure for a considerable length of time before showing signs of corrosion.

External conditions overbalance composition of the metal in determining rates of corrosion. Oxygen determines the commencement of corrosion of iron and steel under ordinary conditions; it not only acts as a depolarizer but also unites with ferrous iron at the corrosion anodes. In the general absence of oxygen, corrosion drops to a negligible rate. In local absence of oxygen, a differential oxygen cell may be set up which serves to accelerate corrosion in the oxygen-poor portion. In salt solutions, corrosion depends both upon the amount of oxygen present and upon the salt in solution.

Rust may accelerate corrosion and cause pitting. The probable explanation (Evans) is that surface accumulations of rust shield the underlying metal from free access to oxygen, thus rendering such portions anodic (corrodible) with respect to unshielded areas to which oxygen has freer access (cathodic areas). Under certain conditions of exposure, especially atmospheric, rust may form so continuous and adherent a coating that it protects the underlying metal from further corrosive attack. This is especially true of copper-bearing steel and iron under atmospheric exposure. Rust adheres much better to cast iron than to rolled iron or steel; the superior corrosion resistance of cast iron is attributable in large measure to this fact.

Cold working of metals results in an increased rate of attack by **acids;** it also increases heterogeneity in metals, which may lead to increased rate of corrosion. Local cold working, as in the rolling of boiler tubes, builds up internal stresses and greatly increases corrosion rates of such parts; thorough annealing after cold working is the remedy.

Stress Corrosion. The effect of corrosion on a metal which is under stress is often much more severe than under ordinary conditions. This is particularly true of metal members subjected simultaneously to fatigue stress and to corrosion. Under such conditions, the number of stress applications required for failure of the metal is very much less than under non-corrosive conditions. A condition of internal stress, such as may result from cold working, severe heat-treatment, or local overheating as in welding may also serve to accentuate the destructive effect of what otherwise would be a mild corrosive attack. For example, hard-drawn brass tubing may crack under the action of relatively slight surface corrosion, or the heads of rivets may snap off. Tightly drawn-up bolts of certain non-ferrous metals may behave similarly.

Alloys of commercially pure iron with either **cobalt, nickel,** or **copper** in small amounts (0.25 to 0.30 percent) are more resistant to atmospheric corrosion than the original iron from which they were made; all such alloys tend to form protective rust coatings. Copper or nickel alloyed in small concentrations have no certain effect one way or another on corrosion of steel in fresh or salt waters. **Manganese** and copper retard corrosion when alloyed with iron or steel. The results of extensive exposure tests of black steel sheets of different copper contents (*Trans. ASTM*, 1918–1946) have shown that for black sheets exposed to the atmosphere the presence of a small amount of copper, *e.g.*, 0.20 percent, is very advantageous. Although such materials rust readily when exposed to the atmosphere, the rusting is not progressive. Unlike the rust coating that forms on ordinary steel, the coating on copper-bearing steel is smoother, more adherent, and relatively impervious, and serves to protect the underlying metal. As with ordinary steel, the "life" of copper-bearing steel likewise varies with the conditions to which it is subjected. In ASTM tests of 16 gage sheet steel and iron, in a marine atmosphere at Annapolis, Md., the first failure occurred after 26 years of continuous exposure, whereas, in the atmosphere of Pittsburgh, Pa., all the specimens failed within 5 years.

According to other ASTM tests, the presence of copper in the same amounts as in the materials used in atmospheric exposure tests does not materially improve the life of steel immersed continuously in water, either in treated city water (Washington), brackish river water (Annapolis), or acid mine water (Pittsburgh). Data leading to similar conclusions concerning the life of underground structures were obtained in the soil-corrosion tests carried out by the NBS.

Certain low-alloy low-carbon steels with an alloy content below 5 percent (see Table 12*b*, p. 6–34) have an improved corrosion resistance. These steels have a relatively high yield strength and tensile strength, and permit thin sections which would not be admissible without the improved corrosion resistance.

Stainless steels depend primarily on the presence of chromium for their resistance to corrosion and heat; they fall into three groups (see p. 6–39). W. E. McFee (*Ind. & Eng. Chem.*, **48,** 10, pp. 1964–70) published a diagram showing commercially available alloys and recommended careful selection for specific applications. The **martensitic** and **ferritic** types are magnetic, hardenable, and useful for cutlery, machine parts, and resistance to atmospheric corrosion; **austenitic** types, of which type 304 (18 Cr, 8 Ni) is the most familiar form, are not hardenable but are more widely useful for resistance to corrosive liquids. **Passivity** is due to a surface condition which, in the austenitic alloys, is a self-repairing oxide film preserved in an oxidizing environment, *e.g.*, nitric acid. Passivity may be lost if oxygen is withdrawn, as in crevices or under a bit of foreign matter in stagnant water. Corrosion resistance can be seriously impaired by welding or improper heat-treatment, whereby the metal becomes susceptible to intercrystalline corrosion. This can be overcome by proper alloy additions stabilizing the material. Paul and Moran (*ACS Monograph* 158, p. 375 *et seq.*) note the effectiveness of **halide ions** in penetrating the passivating films, causing severe pitting or stress-corrosion cracking. Thus, when moisture condenses within idle steam turbines, it can form droplets of chloride solution from an imperceptible film of boiler-water salts and cause pinhole penetrations. **Stress-corrosion cracking** has become more important because of the use of austenitic stainless-steel pipe and tubing in high-pressure power stations of both the conventional and the nuclear type. Alloys containing molybdenum (such as types 216 and 329) are more resistant to halides than type 304.

Cast Iron. Corrosion occurs in buried cast iron in certain types of soil. The product of this **graphitic corrosion** plugs the hole so that a pipe, if undisturbed, is still serviceable in low-pressure systems. Cast iron can be greatly improved in corrosion resistance by alloying elements, such as chromium and nickel. **Silicon cast iron** (13 to 14 percent Si) is resistant to most acids and many other chemicals, though not to alkalies; as the iron is weak and brittle, its use is limited to shapes cast to size. Trade names for this type of alloy are Duriron, Corrosiron, and Tantiron (see p. 6–53). **Nickel cast iron** (13 to 15 percent Ni) has high corrosion resistance toward many chemicals and to dilute acids and has the advantage of superior strength and toughness (see Table 7, p. 6–63).

Metals in Brine. According to the work of N. B. Smith (*Ice and Refrig.*, **12**) with neutral calcium chloride brine (sp gr 1.2), copper alloys are most corrosion-resistant, wrought iron, steel, and cast iron constitute an intermediate group, and lead, solder, and zinc constitute a group having lower corrosion resistance. The durability of any metal in brine, however, varies with the condition of the brine. For general purposes, a pH of 8.5 (pH 7.0 being the neutral point) is recommended. Brine with a high pH is corrosive to aluminum and zinc. The corrosiveness of a brine is increased two or three times by saturating it with air. Damage from corrosion fatigue in salt water which is deaerated is less than in fresh water containing air. Chromium is the most effective alloying element for increasing corrosion-fatigue strength in the absence of hydrogen sulphide, and nickel is best in the presence of hydrogen sulphide.

CORROSION PROBLEMS IN STEAM-GENERATING PLANTS

(See also Sec. 9)

Corrosion of Boilers

Central steam-electric power-station equipment containing or submerged in water at moderate temperatures and pressures suffers corrosion due to the same electrochemical mechanism as that described on p. 6–125 and is affected by similar accelerating and retarding factors and corrective measures. At saturation temperatures above moderately low pressures, a second mechanism predominates, in which iron removes oxygen from water or steam, forming iron oxide and releasing hydrogen:

$$3Fe + 4H_2O \rightarrow Fe_3O_4 + 8H$$

It is noteworthy that this mechanism does not require the intervention of dissolved gaseous oxygen in the water, which is often the rate-limiting factor in the electrochemical corrosion discussed earlier in this subsection.

The stable oxide at boiler temperatures in a non-oxidizing environment is **magnetite,** Fe_3O_4 (ferrous ferrite). A normal protective skin of magnetite is formed from the underlying steel. One theory (Potter) holds that loosely adherent magnetite is formed at the water-oxide interface by ferrous ions diffusing through the oxide film and that dense, hard magnetite is formed at the oxide-steel interface by OH^- ions diffusing inward through the film. Both reactions release hydrogen. The magnetite formed at the oxide-steel interface is dense and adherent, that at the water-oxide interface less so. This surface also receives increments of oxide precipitated from iron brought in from the preboiler cycle, forming ferrous hydroxide and ultimately magnetite:

$$3Fe(OH)_2 \rightarrow Fe_3O_4 + 2H_2O + H_2$$

Under favorable conditions all boiler and superheater surfaces are covered with a thin film of black magnetic oxide formed by the above mechanism, but it is constantly being broken down, and repaired with the release of hydrogen. Consequently, the concentration of **hydrogen in steam** (usually of the order of 1 to 2 parts per billion) is an index to the rate of corrosion and in critical cases may be followed by recording instruments as a guide to operation. (Hydrogen release by the second reaction above is of a smaller order of magnitude.)

Although the control of internal corrosion in boilers operated at low pressures and high pressures is similar, the problem becomes more complex as the temperature and pressure are elevated. The modern trend toward very large boilers, with operating pressures of 2,000 psi becoming commonplace, has introduced new forms of corrosion which were not encountered in low-pressure boilers.

The special corrosion problems affecting modern boilers are described by Hecht, Partridge, Schroeder, and Whirl. A comprehensive discussion of various types of corrosion in marine boilers has been published by Slater and Parr. Although this relates primarily to marine practice, their identification of the types of attack is applicable to corrosion occurring in stationary boilers.

Factors in Corrosion of Boilers

Scale. In earlier times, the conditioning of feed water was less exacting than now required, and it was common practice to permit accumulations of scale or sludge on the tube surfaces. Such deposits there formed a physical dam between the water and the metal, and corrosion was prevented. In recent years, scale and sludge formations have been minimized or eliminated by modern feed-water conditioning, so that control of corrosion has become essential for the protection of equipment.

Non-condensible gases released from water in boilers are probably the greatest single cause of corrosion in boiler tubes, drums, economizers, and superheaters. **Oxygen** corrosion produces rapid pitting, and it is recognized that the rate of corrosion is directly proportional to the dissolved oxygen concentration of the feed water. Other dissolved gases, such as carbon dioxide, hydrogen sulphide, and compounds which release gaseous products also accelerate the rate of attack at high pressures and temperatures.

The removal of gases from feed water is effected in modern steam stations by mechanical (vacuum) and thermal deaeration, by the addition of chemicals, or by a combination of those processes. The basic method is to heat the water by direct contact with steam in either open heaters or in the more efficient type known as **deaerating heaters.** In general the water is sprayed, atomized, or trickled over a stack of metal trays, to present the largest possible surface, while steam is admitted and directed so as to sweep out the non-condensible gases as they flash out of solution. By the use of steam at not less than 5 psi (227 F), efficient distribution, and liberal venting through a vent condenser, residual oxygen can be reduced to 0.005 ml per liter. Refined testing methods have recorded values as low as 0.001 or below. The removal of other dissolved gases is likewise effected by contact heaters or by deaerators, but some gases which form compounds with water (ammonia, carbon dioxide) may not be reduced to as low a level as dissolved oxygen. (See also p. 9–46.)

Removal of residual oxygen by chemicals generally follows thermal deaeration as insurance against impaired efficiency. Several chemicals can be added to water which will remove oxygen; these include, in chronological order of use, **tannins, ferrous hydroxide, sodium sulphite,** and **hydrazine.** This type of treatment is known as scavenging. Gallo-tannins behave like alkaline pyrogallol (as used in gas analysis) in scrubbing oxygen from water at elevated temperatures, but are limited to low-pressure boilers. Ferrous hydroxide was used in an earlier high-pressure station, but the iron oxide produced in the system would not be tolerated today. Sodium sulphite is currently the chemical most widely used for removing traces of oxygen remaining in water after thermal deaeration.

The rate of reaction of trace concentrations of sulphite and oxygen as found in feed water is slow, but can be greatly speeded up by the addition of **catalysts.** Cobalt nitrate is most widely used for this purpose, although copper sulphate has also been employed. A few years ago excess sulphite in concentrated boiler waters was maintained between 20 and 40 ppm, or higher. Such dosages are now known to be unnecessary and may actually cause trouble in high-pressure boilers. An excess of 10 to 20 ppm is generally satisfactory up to 900 psi, 3 to 7 ppm up to 1,500 psi, while above this level, sulphite may cause difficulty by decomposing.

Hydrazine hydrate ($N_2H_4.H_2O$) is a powerful reducing agent and will effectively prevent oxygen corrosion if properly applied and controlled. There is evidence that it functions on the surface of metal and suspended matter, and can coexist with dissolved oxygen. The residual quantities maintained in boiler water vary from 0.02 to 0.10 ppm. Rate of feed required depends on oxygen input, number of concentrations, and other factors. At high temperature, hydrazine partially breaks down to form ammonia, and the rate of input should be held to a level permitting a detectable residual, but just below the point of ammonia increase. The use of this material should be adequately controlled by informed persons. Recent experience has demonstrated that it is very effective in preventing corrosion and for limiting the quantity of black iron oxide (Fe_2O_4) in boilers.

The effect of pH on corrosion at feed-water and boiler-water temperatures is similar to its effect on electrochemical corrosion at ordinary temperatures, *i.e.*, the solution pressure of iron is sharply depressed as the pH is elevated. In the absence of oxygen, iron pickup becomes negligible in most feed-water circuits as the pH is elevated to 9.0, and in boilers, at a level of 10.2 to 11.0. Industrial boilers operating at moderate pressures (below 1,000 psi) are treated with caustic soda, if it is not already present as a result of make-up treatment, to maintain an alkalinity which will buffer the water within the desired range. Exceptions are central power-station boilers operated at higher pressures and low make-up, in which caustic may attack the protective iron oxide film with the production of a sodium-iron compound:

$$FeO + 2NaOH \rightarrow Fe(ONa)_2 + H_2O$$

The necessary concentrations do not occur in the main body of the boiler water but can develop in the concentrating film next to the tube wall or under porous deposits of metal oxides. In the first case, the result is a **broad, smooth groove** which reduces the wall thickness to the point of failure. In the second case, jagged pits are filled with magnetic iron oxide produced by reaction of the exposed steel. The failure occurs as a pinhole leak. To prevent these types of corrosion, some high pressure boilers are operated with "zero caustic" treatment, either by maintaining all alkalinity in the form of trisodium phosphate ("captive alkalinity") or by eliminating sodium salts altogether and using only ammonia and hydrazine to maintain a pH of about 8.5 to 9.0. This latter treatment is also necessary to produce steam of satisfactory quality from once-through boilers and in certain other special cases.

The commonest cause of low pH of boiler water is **carbon dioxide** released by decomposition of bicarbonates and carbonates in the make-up water, and in a great majority of cases this requires continuous treatment to maintain proper alkalinity. Occasionally, process condensate contains contaminants which, on pyrolysis at boiler temperatures, yield excessive amounts of CO_2 or other acid constituents. Examples are sucrose in sugar-evaporator condensate, furfural, and various organic products that are processed by steam. An unusual cause of acid attack is ferric chloride left in deep pits after acid cleaning. At boiler temperatures this salt yields hydrochloric acid which rapidly attacks the metal to point of failure.

Copper, nickel, and **zinc** are often found in boiler sludge and deposits, their sources being in non-ferrous-alloy tubes of condensers, evaporators, and heat exchangers. Much of the copper is metallic, in the form of either a spongy mass or very thin sheets. If thin films develop on the boiler tubes, they may provide a mechanism for concentration of solids beneath them, leading to the type of damage described above where caustic is present in the boiler water. Masses of spongy copper bonded to the metal in boiler drums are often found covering corroded areas. Whether the formation of metallic copper occurs by reduction of the oxide or salts by hydrogen or occurs by galvanic action is uncertain.

Histories of tube failures in high-pressure boilers almost always report the presence of excessive amounts of metal oxides, dominated by **black iron oxide,** frequently in the form of a loose, fluffy sludge that accumulates in crevices and at the ends of boiler drums. This may be harmless even when present in considerable quantities. However, on the surface of the boiler tubes the layer of magnetic iron oxide may far exceed the desired thin protective film, the excess being derived from the underlying metal or the preboiler circuits, or both. Mention has been made (p. 6–129) of the diffusion of ferrous ions from the underlying metal and of hydroxyl ions from the interface with water—forming, respectively, dense or loose magnetic iron oxide. When the thickness exceeds several mils (depending on pressure and temperature), **acid cleaning** may be necessary to prevent damage to the metal.

Hydrogen damage is caused by the diffusion of hydrogen through steel, reacting with carbon to form methane, which builds up high local stresses at the interfaces between grains, forming voids which may ultimately produce failure. Decarburization is visible to varying degrees in the microstructure (Partridge *et al.*). Hydrogen damage is found only in the steel underlying an area where visible corrosion has occurred and is a common problem in the operation of high-pressure boilers.

There are several mechanisms by which the film on the surface of the boiler metal may be destroyed at an abnormally rapid rate, followed by the re-formation *in situ* of magnetic iron oxide in such a manner that failure develops. These mechanisms occur in areas subjected to rates of heat input above the average for the boiler furnace, which may be as high as 200,000 Btu per sq ft per hr. Under these conditions it is difficult to maintain a thin, impervious protective film on the tube surfaces, and water of the highest quality, with very adequate rates of circulation, must be furnished to these sections of the boiler. Deposit-producing impurities such as silica or iron cannot be tolerated because precipitation is accelerated by high temperatures, and, in turn, the temperature is raised by even a very slight addition to the normal film, or by very thin scale. The deterioration thus feeds on itself and progresses to point of failure unless the boiler is effectively acid-cleaned. At excessively high temperatures the dissociation reaction which is catalyzed by the oxide surface becomes so rapid that the underlying metal cannot be protected. The cause of abnormal heat input and temperature conditions may be flame impingement or the impact of radiant heat; film boiling; or steam blanketing, caused by deficient circulation of water, which is usually avoided by boiler design.

The several corrosion phenomena described above and other types of destructive attack on boiler steel can often be identified by cutting a section of metal from the damaged area, mounting it in plastic, polishing and etching the surface, and taking photomicrographs which will show fine details of grain structure. Boetcher described identifying characteristics of several types of failure which can be classified by this technique. In **corrosion fatigue,** caused by alternating stresses set up by vibration or other periodic mechanical or thermal changes, the attack develops along a concentration of stress and the cracks are predominantly transcrystalline. In severe cases, cracking is produced by periodic stress alone without the interaction of a corrosive medium, but where both mechanisms occur, corrosion penetrates into the metal with the crack. By contrast, high-temperature **creep cracks** resulting from slow plastic flow under sufficient stress and temperature are predominantly intercrystalline and not related to corrosion. Study of properly prepared photomicrographs by a competent metallurgist may reveal the thermal history of the specimen in terms of maximum temperature and duration.

Caustic embrittlement, although not strictly classifiable as corrosion, is caused by a selective attack at the grain boundaries, believed to be due to the protective action of silica on the crystal faces. Necessary conditions are high stress and slow leakage accompanied by evaporation which will permit the caustic to build up to many times the concentration maintained in the boiler water. A third condition is the "embrittling character" of the boiler water.

Embrittlement of boiler steel was a dominant factor in boiler water conditioning for many years. Statistical studies revealed an association of embrittlement failures with high caustic concentrations in the boiler water while relative immunity appeared to be conferred by the presence of sodium sulfate in certain ratios to the caustic. The ASME "Suggested Rules for Care of Power Boilers" recommended specific sulphate-alkalinity ratios in the 1926 and subsequent editions, but research and field experience have failed to confirm the merits of sulphates and have developed more effective inhibitors. These include tannins and related organic substances (suitable only for low-pressure boilers) and sodium nitrate. The "captive alkalinity," or "zero caustic," conditioning described above is also a successful corrective measure. With the advent of forged and welded drums and the disappearance of riveted joints, opportunities for embrittlement are limited to the rolled joints between boiler tubes and the tube sheets or headers, where embrittlement has occurred in a few cases. Zapffe contends that penetration of hydrogen into the crystalline structure, its reactions and formation of gaseous products, explains cracking ascribed by others to caustic embrittlement.

The **boiler economizer** is particularly susceptible to pitting attack since it is the first high-temperature surface to be exposed to oxygen dissolved in the feed water. The water passing through it has a relatively low pH value and contains no inhibiting chemicals. Effective treatment consists of deaeration of feed water and treatment with alkaline and reducing chemicals. In some cases, a portion of the boiler water is recirculated through the economizer.

Superheater corrosion is due largely to the reaction between metal and steam at high temperatures. A secondary cause is carry-over of boiler-water salts. In this case, high concentrations of sodium hydroxide may form on the tube walls with direct chemical attack or may bake on the walls and cause blistering.

Corrosion in Preboiler Equipment

The feed-water circuits of a modern steam plant usually begin with the surface condensers of turbogenerators or steam-condensing process equipment and include direct-contact or tubular feed-water heaters, surge tanks, pumps, and piping. The metals in this equipment present a large surface area to the circulating feed water, and appreciable iron, copper, and alloying components go into solution and enter the boilers to become constituents of boiler sludge. This metal pickup is kept within tolerable limits by deaerating in condenser hot wells or feed-water heaters at the earliest point in the cycle where the pressure is adequate, and by maintaining the pH at as high a level as possible. Where the make-up is softened by hot-process treatment and is an appreciable percentage of the feed water, the pH is usually 9.5 or higher and presents no control problem. Where ion-exchange or evaporation processes are used to produce make-up, or large amounts of condensate are recovered, the normal alkalinity and pH of the feed water may be too low to give the desired protection. The usual control measure is continuous feed of caustic soda, ammonia, or a neutralizing amine. To minimize input of chemicals, boiler blowdown may be reçirculated to the surge tank of the deaerating heater or some other low-pressure point. Measures for specific control of feed-water pH should aim at a level not below 8.5, and marked reduction in metal pickup is accomplished by raising the pH to 9.0 or a little higher. Ammonia may be present in the water supply in sufficient amounts for pH control or may be added in the form of ammonium sulphate, hydroxide, or other compounds, but its concentration in contact with brass condenser tubes or other parts must be limited, as it forms highly soluble cupric-ammonium compounds which wash away readily. This is accelerated by dissolved oxygen. Ammonia initiates stress corrosion of yellow-brass alloys in some cases.

In studies of **ammonia, cyclohexylamine,** and **morpholine,** Bigger and others found that these alkalizing materials differed greatly in their distribution between the vapor phase and the liquid phase. For a given concentration in the steam leaving the boiler, morpholine provides the highest fraction in the first-formed film of condensate in turbines, low-pressure heaters, etc., and thus is the most effective of the three for this treatment. Cyclohexylamine has been used to protect condensate return lines of building heating systems but because of its volatility is lost at the deaerating heater and at vents in the system. Roughly twice as much morpholine or cyclohexylamine must be used, in parts per million, as the free CO_2 which must be neutralized. Where **hydrazine** is used to prevent oxygen corrosion, partial breakdown contributes ammonia which must be considered in balancing the pH control treatment.

Corrosion of Other Steam-plant Equipment

Condenser tubes are attacked by circulating cooling water, which may be relatively non-aggressive river or lake water, highly polluted, brackish or sea water, or water recirculated through spray ponds or cooling towers. Tube materials must be carefully selected for resistance to the specific water supply. The metals include Admiralty, Muntz, aluminum brass and aluminum bronze, cupronickel, redbrass, and copper. Resistance depends upon building up, by initial corrosion, a uniform protective film. Admiralty brass (Cu 70 percent, Zn 29 percent, Sn 1 percent), the most widely used condenser tube material, is normally satisfactory for sea-water or polluted fresh-water service over a wide range and is usually inhibited with a fraction of 1 percent of arsenic, antimony, or phosphorus. For very severe conditions it may be replaced by aluminum brass (Cu 76 percent, Al 2 percent, Zn 22 percent) and 70–30 or 80–20 cupronickel, which are both resistant to impingement pitting and dezincification. Where the latter is persistent, either cupronickel or aluminum bronze (Cu 93.5 percent, Al balance) is used to eliminate zinc. Red brass and copper are not suitable for salt or brackish water, but deoxidized copper has special uses in process and refrigeration equipment (see pp. 6–83 *et seq.*).

Even when the material is resistant to corrosive constituents dissolved in the water, attack may occur through several mechanisms: (1) **deposit attack** on areas shielded by adhering foreign matter, producing a local oxygen deficiency and making the underlying metal anodic; (2) **dezincification,** in which both components of the metal are dissolved and the copper is redeposited as a porous plug or layer; (3) **impingement** of air bubbles, usually only near the inlet end, preventing protective film formation or causing undercutting; and (4) **corrosion fatigue** due to unusual stresses or vibration. **Season cracking** due to the latter can be eliminated by proper annealing.

Pumps may be corroded by the solvent action of the liquid passing through them (see Sec. 14). When dissimilar metals in contact are used, *e.g.*, a cast-iron body with brass glands, seats etc., autoelectrolysis is almost certain to result when brines or other electrolytes are pumped. If it is not possible to confine the construction to one metal, the less resistant metal should be used only for easily renewable parts.

Corrosion may result from the leakage of current from the driving motor. This can be prevented by using an insulating coupling between the pump and motor shafts.

Air in the pump, either free or in solution in the liquid pumped, accelerates corrosion. Pumps should be vented so that they may be completely filled with the liquid they are handling.

Manufacturers' design and selection of materials for **boiler feed pumps** are based on a questionnaire covering the mineral analysis, pH, and chemical treatment of the feed water, as well as temperature and pressure conditions. Corrosion-erosion attack is aggravated by water of high purity, which is frequently required, because of absence of alkaline salts to buffer the pH at a high enough level. For such service, alloys of high chromium content may be necessary, while ordinary ferrous metals of proper physical characteristics are acceptable for feed water containing appreciable alkalinity with the pH controlled at 8.5 or above. Bronze parts may be attacked by highly alkaline water from hot-process softening systems.

CORROSION OF EQUIPMENT IN CHEMICAL PLANTS

Chemical plants as a rule are subject to severe damages caused by corrosion. Not only must consideration be given to providing for continuity of operation in order to meet production schedules, but the products of corrosion may detract from the quality of manufactured goods. Maintenance expense is often an important item in manufacturing costs, and an economic balance between the selection of more expensive special materials and equipment upkeep is usually an important operating problem, requiring study and judgment for its satisfactory solution.

Removal of hydrogen from cathodic surfaces by oxygen is often the controlling reaction. When non-oxidizing acids are present, depolarizatlon by hydrogen evolution may overshadow hydrogen oxidation. When an oxidizing acid such as nitric is present, oxidation of the hydrogen film occurs, and is independent of the presence of dissolved oxygen. Strong **nitric acid** passivates iron or steel and reduces the corrosion rate.

Caustic alkalinity attacks silica and corrodes high-silicon alloys. Lead, zinc, aluminum, and tin are attacked by caustic solutions. Hydroxide alkalinity is more effective than carbonate or bicarbonate alkalinity in covering iron or steel surfaces with a protective film. The hydroxide film is more dense and impermeable.

Temperature plays an important role in corrosion by chemicals; as in other types of corrosion, the rate is sharply increased by higher temperatures.

When strong **sulphuric acid** is stored in steel tanks, and the level fluctuates through comparatively wide limits, air is drawn in or expelled. Moisture in the air is absorbed by the strong acid with which unsubmerged surfaces are wetted, thus reducing its strength. This occurs mostly along the side walls, and the diluted acid corrodes the steel. Damage to tanks can be eliminated by installing a desiccator unit on the breather, thus drying all air entering the acid storage tank and consequently preventing corrosion due to formation of weak acid.

In chemical plants where **corrosive vapors or gases** are discharged to the atmosphere, serious corrosion of steel throughout the plant may take place. In many instances it is impracticable to prevent the escape of these gases or to provide special metals which would resist corrosion from this source. Often the most economical solution to the problem is to design steel structures with extra thickness of metal so that even after considerable corrosion, sufficient metal remains to provide the structural strength required. Under such atmospheric conditions, some plants, in designing reinforced concrete, place reinforcing steel further from the surface than would be done if only structural strength were considered. In this case, economy in design is sacrificed to gain better protection for the reinforcing steel.

Tanks or basins used for **storage of acids or alkalies** can be protected by special brick and cement linings. Such linings are usually bonded to the steel by means of an impervious membrane which is designed to withstand the special conditions existing.

Solvents liberated when enamel is baked on wire may be burned by means of catalytic combustion which, because of the catalyst, ignite at relatively low temperatures. This method of disposal prevents damage to painted surfaces when the solvent vapors are discharged through stacks to the atmosphere.

In the **contact process for manufacturing sulphuric acid,** it is customary to use cast iron for constructing coolers serving the final absorption towers. When oleum is produced, it has been found necessary to substitute steel pipe with cast-steel bands in preference to cast iron. Sulphur trioxide reacts with silicon in the cast iron, causing rupture of the metal. Coolers of this type are designed for very low velocities of the acid passing through the pipes. This prevents removal of the iron sulphate film which forms and protects the cast iron or steel used in this equipment. Heat transfer is sacrificed in order to obtain long life of the equipment.

Chemical Equipment. The development of corrosion-resistant steels (p. 6–39), of high-nickel alloys (p. 6–80), and of ferrosilicon alloys (p. 6–63) has extended greatly the uses of the ferrous materials in the chemical field. **Stainless-clad** steel sheet is available for applications that require good thermal conductivity in addition to the corrosion resistance of stainless steel. **Enameled steel** or iron ware is used widely, but most enamels are generally attacked by alkalies. **Rubber-lined tanks** and other chemical equipment, together with hard-rubber piping and connectors, now serve a very useful purpose. The number of non-ferrous metals and alloys useful for chemical equipment is exceedingly large. **Lead** is widely used, and the development of lead-lined steel pipe and tanks has greatly extended its sphere of usefulness. **Nickel,** nickel-clad steel, and alloys high in nickel are widely used. Special **aluminum bronzes** that have been modified by the addition of some other element such as iron are now coming into use for handling acids. For certain uses, especially when natural flavors and odors must be retained, **silver** is used.

CORROSION OF PIPES AND STRUCTURES

Underground Pipes. Steel, wrought iron, cast iron, and lead often corrode severely in certain natural soils. Soils containing organic or carbonaceous matter, such as coke, coal, or cinders, or impregnated with acid wastes from manufacturing plants are highly corrosive in their action. The autoelectrolysis of iron buried in soils is recurrent, since oxygen is always present in sufficient amount to act as a depolarizer.

The NBS investigation of soil corrosion, summarized in *NBS Circ.* C450, 1945, has established the following facts:

1. **Ferrous Metals.** Serious corrosion underground occurs in the absence of stray currents, although electrical currents, which did not originate in power plants, have been detected on pipelines. Soil conditions play a major role. Wrought iron and steel corroded at approximately the same rate, and the presence of copper in the steel did not improve its corrosion resistance. In certain soils, the corrosion rate of cast iron was greater than that of steel. The removal of mill and foundry scale from the surface did not greatly affect the rate of corrosion. Depth of pitting was directly proportional to duration of exposure in certain soils, but in others the pit depth increased very slowly after the soil conditions had become stabilized. Distribution of corrosion tended to become more uniform as the exposure period increased.

2. **Non-ferrous Metals.** No metal was found outstandingly superior under all conditions. The corrosion rate (loss of weight and depth of penetration) was, with but few exceptions, greater for ferrous than non-ferrous metals. The presence of chlorides, bicarbonates, and sulphates in the soil retarded the rate of corrosion of **lead,** although in certain soils, as in tidal marshes, the rate of attack did not decrease with

time. **Copper** and high-copper alloys corroded very slowly in most soils, the presence of sulphides being the principal accelerator of corrosion, with the rate of attack being particularly high in cinders. High-zinc brass became weak and brittle by dezincification in some soils. **Zinc** corroded rapidly in a few soils, the rate being proportional to the duration of exposure. This limits the effective life of galvanized coatings on ferrous metals. The useful service is proportional to the thickness of the zinc coating; a coating of 2.8 oz per sq ft prevented the formation of pits for 10 years, except in one very corrosive soil. Over a 10-year period, the loss of weight of galvanized steel was one-half, or less, that of the companion bare steel. Three **aluminum** alloys corroded rapidly under most of the soil conditions to which they were exposed.

3. Pipes buried in **mixtures of two dissimilar soils** or in two unlike soils in contact (not mixed) generally corrode more rapidly than in either of the two soils separately. Lead in a mixture or simple contact of dissimilar soils will often corrode markedly. Pipes buried in trenches fulfill these conditions of soils in contact or mixed. Metals corrode at the junction line of dissimilar soils. Cast iron in soils takes on a coating of rust and soil, pits being filled with carbon and black iron oxide. Lead shows both the gray and brown oxides when corroded in soils. Potentials up to 1 volt may be generated readily by placing unlike metals in a given soil or by using one metal in two dissimilar soils.

4. **Bituminous coatings** are widely used, especially natural asphalt and blown asphalt made from oil residuum and coal tar pitch. Coatings of this last substance were somewhat inferior to others in the NBS investigation in that they were more susceptible to soil stresses, temperature changes, softening, and brittleness, although they were more resistant to water absorption. The method of application of all such coatings is important. Dipping, brushing, and spraying methods are all used. For severe soil conditions, the coating should be reinforced by wrapping the coated pipe spirally with a strong fabric of some kind which has been impregnated with a waterproof bituminous mixture. For exceptionally severe corrosive soil conditions, pipes may be encased in concrete.

Asbestos-cement pipes were not deteriorated by 4 years' exposure in a variety of soils.

Pipes are often destroyed by the action of **dissimilar metals** to which they are connected, such as brass valves. Short connections, readily replaced, should be used on either side of the brass fittings.

Application of a negative potential booster to diminish potential differences in electrical rails has proved to be an effective means of reducing electrolysis of underground iron and steel, such as gas and water mains.

Bridges, Roofs, Stacks, etc. Iron and steel structures are corroded by the presence in the atmosphere of moisture and waste products from manufacturing and metallurgical plants such as carbon dioxide, sulphur dioxide, chlorine, ammonia, zinc and acid fumes, and soot. As a rule, they are not corroded in a dry atmosphere. To minimize the corrosive effects of gases, protective coatings (see p. 6–143) are used. Metal work exposed to the action of sulphur fumes should be covered with brick or with a paint highly resistant to sulphur dioxide. Bridges are now protected by means of so-called **drip floors** placed over the floor proper. The failure of **metal smokestacks** by corrosion occurs only during idle periods and particularly in the summer. Deposits of soot and fly ash assist very materially in this by absorbing the corrosive gases in the products of combustion. These combine with atmospheric water vapor, and the corrosive attack is essentially that of a weak acid. The ordinary materials used for the construction of smokestacks do not differ very much among themselves in their resistance to the corrosive attack, although there is some indication that some of the newly developed low-alloy steels are superior.

Concrete Structures. The alkaline nature of cement assures great permanence to structural steel embedded in concrete. This has been repeatedly confirmed by the examination of the steel in reinforced-concrete buildings which have been demolished. The following information on deterioration by corrosion resulting from electrical current is from *NBS Tech. Paper* 18.

When current passes from an iron anode into concrete, oxides of iron form on the anode, occupying about 2.2 times the volume of the equivalent iron, and giving rise to mechanical pressure (sometimes as high as 4,700 psi) which may result in cracking the concrete. At temperatures below 113 F, and with a potential gradient less than 60 volts per ft, this action is very slight, even in wet concrete.

Concrete near the cathode, or metal through which the current leaves the concrete, becomes softened and remains brittle and friable after drying, destroying the bond between the iron and concrete. This effect is noted at all voltages, high or low, and is due to the concentration of sodium or potassium near the cathode. The content of these elements in the cement should therefore be kept low.

Salt (NaCl), or calcium chloride, should never be added to concrete used in structures that will be subject to electrolytic action. Concrete in contact with salt water is very susceptible to electrolysis. In structures exposed to the action of salts, pickling solutions, etc., the potential gradient must be kept low. In the absence of metallic electrodes, the action of the current is similar to slow seepage, the water-soluble elements in the concrete migrating toward the cathode. Grounding of electric conductors in such a structure is equivalent to installing electrodes.

Waterproofing compounds when mixed with concrete have but little effect in preventing electrolysis. Waterproofing membranes, properly applied, are fairly efficacious in preventing the entry of earth currents. Painting or otherwise coating the reinforcing metal may minimize the danger from electrolysis, but it prevents proper bonding between the metal and the concrete.

All d-c circuits within a building should be kept free from grounds. All pipe lines entering a building should be installed with insulating joints outside the building; if passing through, they should have insulating joints on both sides of the building. If the potential drop around the isolated section is 8 volts or more, the isolated section should be shunted by a copper cable. Lead-covered cable should be kept out of contact with the building.

All metallic structures within a building should be interconnected, provided that all lines entering the building are installed with insulating joints, but they should not be grounded to any ground plate lying outside the insulating joints. Maintaining the reinforcing metal negative is worse than no protection at all.

Cinder concrete is frequently used in certain types of building construction. When the concrete is properly made and poured so as to eliminate voids adjacent to the reinforcing steel, very satisfactory service can be relied upon. If it is porous, pipes buried in it sometimes suffer severe corrosive attack by the acid-forming constituents that may be present. Proper precautions should be taken to neutralize any acidity in the cinder especially that which is in immediate contact with the pipes.

An important use of cement in preventing corrosion is the use of **cement linings for pipes** carrying water. They have proved very useful for corrosive waters such as mine drainage as well as for less severe service, as in water mains. The process is now being applied regularly to cast-iron pipe and also to steel pipe even as small as that used in ordinary water service. A special type coupling for cement-lined pipe is required. Lead-lined couplings are very useful.

Lead embedded in concrete is sometimes severely corroded as a result of free lime present. Lead shower-bath pans are a common example. Protection of the surface of the lead by a bituminous coating is always recommended, and the use of alumina cement, as an added precaution, can also be recommended. Aluminum and aluminum alloys in intimate contact with plaster or cement may suffer corrosion for the same reasons. Similar precautionary measures are advisable.

METHODS FOR MINIMIZING CORROSION

Corrosion may be minimized by (1) the use of a coating of protective metal such as zinc, tin, lead, nickel, or copper; (2) the production of oxide, phosphate, or similar coatings on iron and steel surfaces; (3) the application of protective paints (p. 6–143); and (4) rendering the surface of the metal passive.

Coating Metals with Zinc. Galvanizing. Zinc is applied to metal surfaces by the Sherardizing process, by dipping into a bath of molten zinc, by electrodeposition, or by metal spraying.

In the **Sherardizing process,** the articles, after being thoroughly cleaned by pickling and sandblasting, are placed in a metal drum together with zinc dust and heated to a temperature of from 500 to 600 F, depending on their size and shape, the drum being rotated so as to promote "rumbling" of the contents. The coating that results is not pure zinc, but an alloy of about 90 percent zinc and 10 percent iron (melting point, 1260 F approx), and is highly resistant to corrosion. The process is especially suited for screws, bolts and nuts, chains, pipe fittings, nails, small castings, and such other articles as may conveniently be placed within the drum. The cost varies with the character of the articles coated. The term **electro-Sherardizing,** which is often used, merely connotes that the Sherardizing furnace is heated electrically. By a suitable annealing or heat-treatment, the zinc coating produced on sheet and wire by hot dipping can be converted into a very similar alloy coating. A cheap method used for nails, etc., consists in rumbling them in zinc dust. The coating is inferior in quality.

In the **hot process,** the articles after being thoroughly cleaned are dipped into a bath of molten zinc. The bath must be maintained at a temperature somewhat higher than the melting point of zinc, which necessitates a large fuel consumption and also results in a considerable loss of zinc (approx 10 percent). A greater source of loss is the iron-zinc alloy (dross) which forms as a heavy sediment in the zinc bath. That portion of the zinc surface through which the material to be coated enters the zinc bath must be kept covered with a flux; ammonium chloride and zinc chloride are widely used for this. The process is used almost exclusively for sheet and pipe, and, until recently, for wire also. Exposed structural steel work, such as towers, is generally zinc coated by this means. Sheet and wire are coated by mechanical means, pipe and structural shapes by hand. Many irregular shapes (pots, vats, tubs, etc.) and small shapes (bolts, nuts, nails, screws) are coated by hand. For the latter, some means for removing excess zinc, such as centrifuges or shaking devices, is generally used. A very small percentage of aluminum renders the zinc bath very fluid and is favored by many in coating irregular shapes. One or two percent tin is often added in the coating of sheets in order to obtain a very uniform coating and to improve the surface appearance. A coating applied by hot dipping never consists of a simple layer of zinc. It is always of a composite nature, the layer adjacent to the base metal consisting of zinc-iron alloys. This layer is relatively brittle and, thereby, imposes some limitations on hot-dipped galvanized sheet and wire for certain uses. By a recent process, formation of the alloy can be practically eliminated. A coating of 1 oz per sq ft of exposed surface is considered very suitable for most conditions of service.

The **electrolytic or cold process** consists in setting up the articles to be coated as cathodes in an electrolytic bath of soluble zinc salts, the anode being metallic zinc. Small articles are placed in metallic baskets in contact with the basket and with each other, the basket being attached to the cathode of the system. Both the acid sulphate and the cyanide bath are used, the latter particularly for small articles and, with suitable addition agents, for the recently developed "bright" coatings. The use of zinc plating on a large commercial scale has been advanced by its application to the coating or steel wire. The high ductility of the pure zinc coating obtained is the outstanding feature of such a coating. The ease of control of the uniformity and thickness is also advantageous. The coating of sheet steel by plating appears to be imminent.

In the **metal spraying or metallizing process,** metal wire or powder is fed at a controlled rate into the flame of an oxygas or oxyacetylene torch. The impingement of this atomized metal on a prepared surface produces a layer of flattened and interlocked particles which are mechanically bonded to the surface being coated. To ensure good adhesion, the surface of the base material must be clean and roughened, for example, by sandblasting. The process is especially useful for applying thick coatings to limited areas, for rebuilding or reclamation of worn or undersized parts (such as cylinders, shafts, or pistons), and is also used to supply protective and decorative coatings. The deposited metal is less dense than cast metal; porosity in the coating may be overcome by cold work, heat-treatment, increasing the thickness of the coating, or by using two or more metals in the same coating. Sprayed coatings of zinc, aluminum, and cadmium need not be entirely free from pores as these metals are anodic to iron and steel. On the other hand, coatings of metals which are cathodic to iron and steel—for example, nickel, stainless steel, copper, tin, or lead—should be as free from pores as possible since the base metal would be attacked through the pores of the coating. Sprayed coatings of zinc or aluminum range from 0.001 to perhaps 0.015 in. in thickness, depending upon the severity of exposure. The porous characteristics of the sprayed coats furnish an excellent base for the application of paints, varnishes, and other corrosion-inhibiting or protecting mediums. The process is readily adapted to production coating of small articles of metal or of non-metallic materials such as wood, leather, or plastics, and is particularly useful for coating large assembled structures such as bridges, towers, storage tanks, and canal gates. Sprayed coatings of aluminum and of chromium-nickel alloys are used for protection against a combination of high temperature and corrosive action, for example, in the oil industry and in furnace equipment.

Cadmium behaves similarly to zinc as a coating metal for iron in affording electrochemical protection from corrosion. Cadmium coatings are applied commercially by electroplating and are preferred by many, the claim being made that a thin coating of cadmium gives the same degree of protection as a thicker one of zinc. This is true to some extent under marine conditions, but in an industrial atmosphere, where sulphur compounds are present, the useful life of cadmium coatings is shorter than that of comparable zinc coatings.

Coating with Tin, Lead, Nickel, Copper, or Chromium. Coatings of **tin** or of a **tin-lead alloy** are used principally on thin sheets of iron, being applied as a rule in a manner similar to that of the hot process of galvanizing. When so-called **terneplate** is made, a mixture of tin (25 percent) and lead (75 percent) is generally used. Such coatings, if free from pinholes, are highly resistant to corrosion. The excellent "paintholding" properties of terneplate fit it for many uses in building construction. Its "lubricating properties," in drawing and stamping processes, assist greatly in the manufacture of containers and fuel tanks.

Lead coatings on steel are most efficient in a polluted atmosphere as in industrial centers. In rural atmosphere, pinhole corrosion is soon evident. A "bonding" agent, either as an alloy in the lead or as an undercoat, is necessary for the process commonly used in applying lead coating, *i.e.*, the hot-dip process.

In coating or electroplating with **nickel or copper,** the object to be coated is made the cathode, the anode consisting of a block of the metal to be deposited, and the electrolyte, a solution of the metal to be deposited. In nickel plating, a copper coating is generally applied before the nickel to render the latter more adherent and more corrosion-resistant by making the entire coating more impervious. **Chromium** coatings which are now widely used are also produced by electroplating from chromic acid solutions. They are nearly always applied as a very thin finish on a nickel coating and are almost perfect in their tarnish resistance. Coatings of these three metals protect the underlying, or base metal from corrosion only in so far as they exclude air and moisture. Hence, the imperviousness of such coatings as determined by the conditions of deposition is of very great importance. Chromium plating on account of its great hardness is also used to some extent as a protection against wear and abrasion.

Copper is sometimes applied in coats integral with the base metal. Copper is cast around a steel billet which is afterward worked down to the required size. Most of the steel coated in this way is used for wire and gives a combination of high electrical conductivity and high tensile properties. It is also used for purposes requiring the combination of high corrosion resistance and strength as in concrete revetment mats used in river control. Steel clad with nickel or stainless steel is also available commercially.

Aluminum coatings cannot be made by electrodeposition in the ordinary way, although aluminum has been deposited from complex organic liquids in the form of coatings on steel. Aluminum coatings are usually produced by mechanical means. Such a coating has proved very useful on duralumin (p. 6–89), but on iron or steel its usefulness is limited by the brittleness of the intermediate alloy layer which generally forms.

Steel coated by immersion in molten aluminum (see below) resists atmospheric corrosion admirably. Its rough unattractive appearance restricts its use.

Calorizing is a process by which a coating of aluminum and aluminum-iron alloys is produced on iron and steel (brass, copper, or nickel may also be calorized) which protects the metal against high temperatures because of the formation of aluminum oxide on the surface. It does not protect against ordinary corrosion in the atmosphere or in liquids. Sulphurous acid and carbon monoxide have no appreciable effect on calorized metal. Bending or working of calorized metal should be done at a bright-red heat; threading must be done before calorizing, followed by chasing of the threads to make them fit smoothly without breaking the coating; dimensions and weights are increased by calorizing. Thermal and electrical conductivities are not appreciably changed. The base metal is soft-annealed by the process. A few uses are soot-blowing apparatus, carbonizing boxes, furnace parts, and condenser and economizer tubes. Good results are regularly obtainable up to a temperature of 1700 F and in some cases to 1830 F. Calorizing is carried out either by a powder or a dip process. In the powder process, the parts to be treated are placed in a tight receptacle partly filled with a mixture of finely divided metallic aluminum and aluminum oxide. The air is replaced by hydrogen, and the receptacle is subjected to a high temperature for a time that depends on the depth of penetration of aluminum desired. In the dip process, the parts are fluxed, then immersed in molten aluminum, and then heated to promote alloying. This method gives a thinner coating of aluminum alloy but is much more expeditious. A calorized surface resists continued temperatures up to 1800 F but begins to burn at approximately 2000 F, whereas ordinary steel begins at about 930 F. It is not affected by ordinary oxidizing furnace conditions.

Calite, which may be considered as representative of a large class of heat-resistant alloys, is an alloy of iron, nickel, and aluminum and resists oxidization up to 2200 F for an indefinite time and, for short periods, up to 2370 F. The protective oxide formed does not snap off on quenching from extremely high temperatures. It is practically non-corrodible under ordinary conditions of exposure. Many other combinations, containing chromium and nickel as essential alloying constituents, are commercially available.

A process termed **chromizing,** similar in its operation to calorizing, uses powdered chromium or ferrochromium, the articles to be coated being heated while embedded in the powdered metal within a hydrogen or other non-oxidizing atmosphere. It has only a very limited commercial application.

Magnetic Oxide on Iron Surfaces. In the **Bower-Barff process,** the iron or steel articles to be coated are heated in a closed retort to a temperature of 1600 F, after which superheated steam is admitted. This results in the formation of red oxide (Fe_2O_3) and magnetic oxide (Fe_3O_4). Carbon monoxide is then admitted to the retort to reduce the red oxide to magnetic oxide, which is highly resistant to corrosion. Each operation takes about 20 min. The glossy black coating of magnetic oxide on **Russia iron** is produced by laying up sheets of iron with powdered charcoal between, the whole mass being then heated and hammered.

Iron and steel may also be **oxide-coated** by electrolytic means, the object to be coated being made the anode (anodic oxidation) in an alkaline solution. Such coatings are primarily for appearance such as for cast-iron stove parts. Though experimentally successful, the commercial application of the process is limited. The **Chemag process,** a German development, is of this kind.

Phosphate Coatings for Rust-proofing Iron and Steel. (Eckelmann, *Chem. & Met. Eng.*, Dec. 24, 1919.) In the **Coslett process,** iron or steel articles immersed for 3 or 4 hr in a boiling solution, made by mixing iron fillings with concentrated H_3PO_4 (sufficient to form a paste) and then adding to weak phosphoric acid, become coated with a rust-resisting deposit of basic ferrous phosphate. This process was improved by the addition of an oxidizing agent, the **Parkerizing** process, and later by the addition of other accelerators (**Bonderizing**). The phosphate coating, in itself, affords only a very slight degree of protection against corrosion. Oiling the coating improves the corrosion resistance greatly and imparts an attractive lustrous black appearance. Coatings of this kind are not suitable for severe out-of-doors service. Phosphating a steel surface is an excellent method of priming prior to subsequent painting or lacquering. The phosphate is applied by spraying. It finds extensive application for automobile bodies and is known commercially as **Bonder-**

izing and **Granodizing.** Some of the phosphate treatments are electrolytically applied. The phosphate treatment is also applicable to zinc surfaces. The advantages of this latter process over the Bower-Barff and similar process are in greater cheapness and simplicity and the use of low temperatures.

Treatments somewhat analogous to the Parkerizing treatment are widely used for the treatment of magnesium alloys prior to the application of other types of coatings, such as aluminum-pigmented spar varnish and pyroxalin coatings of the Duco type.

Protection of Aluminum Alloys. Wrought-aluminum alloys are largely used for aircraft purposes. Alloys containing copper as an essential alloy constituent, in sheet form, are susceptible to intercrystalline corrosive attack which results in the material becoming very brittle with little or no surface evidence of the change. Aluminum alloys containing magnesium or magnesium and silicon, and the newer alloys containing zinc and chromium as the essential alloying constituents, are very stable under prolonged weathering conditions. The protective coatings used on aluminum alloys depend on the severity of the service. A preliminary anodizing treatment to produce a film of oxide on the surface (formed by making the article the anode of a cell with chromic, sulphuric, or oxalic acid as the electrolyte) is now common practice. Such a surface oxide coating forms an excellent basis for the application of other coatings. Aluminum-pigmented spar varnish is excellent for this. For very severe marine conditions, the only coatings that give permanent protection are those of aluminum.

Alclad products are made by casting a shell of corrosion-resisting aluminum (2S or 72S) around a billet of aluminum alloy. Fabrication of the coated or clad billet produces sheet, rod, wire, and various rolled and extruded shapes which possess the physical properties of the alloy and the corrosion resistance of the aluminum cladding. Tubing clad only on the inside is also available. Aluminum coating applied by the metal-spraying process is useful, especially for heavy pieces and assembled structures.

The **passivating of iron surfaces** may be accomplished in several ways, the most common consisting of immersion of the metal in nitric acid (sp gr 1.4) after it has been highly polished. Other methods consist in immersing the metal in fuming sulphuric acid, potassium ferrocyanide, or potassium chromate solution or in chromic acid; coating with a manganese dioxide paint; cathodic pickling in a weak acid solution, the metal being made the cathode in a circuit of low voltage; treatment with arsenic-sodium nitrite, etc. This condition of passivity is temporary and, thus far, passivating has been of doubtful value, except for stainless steel for which it is a regular practice. A chromate treatment now used commercially on zinc surfaces is somewhat analogous to some of the above treatments.

Treatment of **cooling water** to form protective films is widely applied in recirculating cooling-tower systems as well as once-through systems serving refrigeration or process condensers, heat exchanges, etc. Deposition of **calcium carbonate scale** may be controlled to avoid interference with heat transfer while still protecting the metal, by adjusting the methyl-orange alkalinity, calcium hardness, and pH of the water so that the Langelier **Calcium Carbonate Saturation Index** is slightly positive (0.1 to 0.3) for the existing temperature and total solids. Powell has published a graph which may be used for calculating the Index from the above variables. The control may require reduction of calcium hardness by lime or zeolite softening; reduction of alkalinity by lime softening or feeding sulphuric acid, which is widely practiced; adjustment of pH downward or upward with alkalies or acids. Total solids, reflecting ionic strength as a factor in scale formation, must be controlled by blowdown, preferably under 1,500 to 2,000 ppm. Chlorination is usually needed to destroy organic slimes which inhibit crystalline scale formation.

Addition of enough **sodium dichromate** and caustic to maintain 200 to 500 ppm Na_2CrO_4 oxidizes ferrous iron to form a tough, self-healing film of mixed oxides of the two metals, covering anodic areas. Optimum pH is about 8.5. The chromate residual requirements rise with temperature and salinity; if enough is not maintained, pitting will result, and the rapid formation of ferrous ions will consume more chromate than would be needed to give more complete protection. To avoid prohibitive chemical cost and waste-disposal problems, the system must be operated at maximum concentration and minimum blowdown. Because of toxicity hazard, exposure of personnel to tower-drift spray or water discharging into funnels or sumps must be avoided. Chromate treatment is excellent for entirely closed bearing-cooling systems, circulating through copper-alloy heat exchangers cooled by a secondary flow of corrosive characteristics, *e.g.*, sea water.

Various **polyphosphates** are added to cooling water to form protective films and also to sequester scale-forming components by **"threshold" treatment.** Effectiveness approaching complete protection may require 10 to 30 ppm in terms of orthophosphate (PO_4), and the pH is controlled at 6.5 or lower to avoid precipitation of orthophosphates and control scale. In the **dianodic** treatment, both phosphate and chromate are maintained at a total concentration of the order of 60 ppm in either a 1:2 or 2:1 ratio.

Another modification is the use of chromated organic compounds, such as glucosates, to extend the covering power of the film with lower chromium concentrations.

Slushing oils are usually non-drying oils or greases which remain soft for prolonged periods, are strongly adhesive on metals, but can readily be removed when desired. The best protection to metals is afforded by acid-free semisolid oils applied in a melted condition. Types of commercial slushing oils are petroleum residues, mixtures of lithopone and iron oxide with heavy petroleum residues, petrolatumlike compounds emulsified with chromate solutions, blown vegetable oils, soft asphalts thinned, rosin-base materials. A specification proposed several years ago is as follows: Coating shall adhere firmly at all temperatures to which it will be exposed; coating shall be readily removable with cotton waste wet with kerosene; polished iron, steel, copper, or brass shall show no staining when exposed to weather at any temperature below 212 F for not less than 5 days; in the salt-spray test, no rust shall be formed in 24 hr, practically none in 5 days, and no appreciable rust in 60 days. Typical formulas are: (1) 20 g rosin of "H" grade + 100 g petrolatum (USP) + 10 cc kerosene. The rosin is melted and mixed with the hot petrolatum after which the kerosene is stirred in. Rosin greatly increases the adhesiveness of the petrolatum. Wax may be added to raise the melting point of the petrolatum if necessary. (2) 3 parts candelilla wax, 6 parts "H" rosin, 50 parts petrolatum (USP). (3) 2 parts carnauba wax, 5 parts "H" rosin, 50 parts petrolatum (USP). In each case, melt the ingredients together at 255 F, stir and cool. Flow an excess over the metal surface (*NBS Tech. Paper* 176 and *Circ.* 200 and 214). Lanolin is the best grease to use as a basis of slushing oils. A small amount of sodium chromate is desirable in slushing greases unless all traces of water have been eliminated.

PAINTS AND PROTECTIVE COATINGS

BY

George G. Sward

REFERENCES: Bigos (ed.), "Painting Manual," Steel Structures Painting Council. Deniston, "The Science of Wood Finishing," The Research Press. Fisher, "What You Should Know about Paint," Schnell Publishing Co. Payne, "Organic Coating Technology," Wiley. Roberts, "Organic Coatings—Their Properties, Selection and Use," GPO.

Paint is a mixture of filmogen (film-forming material, binder) and pigment. The pigment imparts color, and the filmogen, continuity; together, they create opacity. Most paints require volatile thinner to reduce their consistencies to a level suitable for application.

In conventional oil-base paint, the filmogen is a vegetable oil. Driers are added to shorten drying time. The thinner is usually petroleum spirits.

In water-thinned paints, the filmogen may be a material dispersible in water, such as solubilized linseed oil or casein, an emulsified polymer, such as butadiene-styrene, a cementitious material, such as portland cement, or a soluble silicate.

Varnish is a blend of resin and drying oil, or other combination of filmogens, in volatile thinner. A solution of resin alone is a **spirit varnish,** *e.g.*, shellac varnish. A blend of resin and drying oil is an **oleoresinous varnish,** *e.g.*, spar varnish. A blend of non-resinous, non-oleaginous filmogens requiring a catalyst to promote the chemical reaction necessary to produce a solid film is a **catalytic coating.**

Enamel is paint that dries relatively harder, smoother, and glossier than the ordinary type. These changes come from the use of varnish instead of oil as the liquid portion. The varnish may be oleoresinous, spirit, or catalytic.

Lacquer is a term that has been used to designate several types of painting materials; it now generally means a spirit varnish or enamel, based usually on cellulose nitrate or cellulose acetate-butyrate.

PAINT INGREDIENTS

The ingredients of paints are drying and semidrying vegetable oils, resins, plasticizers, thinners (solvents), driers or other catalysts, portland cement, etc., and pigments.

Drying oils dry (become solid) when exposed in thin films to air. The drying starts with a chemical reaction of the oil with oxygen. Subsequent or simultaneous polymerization completes the change. The most important drying oil is linseed oil. **Raw linseed oil** requires 3 or 4 days to dry. Addition of small percentages of driers shortens the time to 5 to 10 hr.

Heat-treating, or cooking, bodies (thickens) oil. If driers are added during the cooking, the product is **boiled oil.** Boiled oil is made with a minimum of cooking to avoid discoloration, and also by adding concentrated driers to raw oil. **Blown oil** is made by bubbling air (oxygen) through the oil.

Soybean oil, with poorer drying properties than linseed oil, is classed as a **semidrying oil. Tung oil** dries much faster than linseed oil, but the film wrinkles so much that it is reminiscent of frost; heat-treatment eliminates this tendency. Tung oil gels after a few minutes cooking at high temperatures. It is more resistant to alkali than linseed oil. Its chief use is in oleoresinous varnishes. **Oiticica oil** resembles tung oil in many of its properties. **Castor oil** is non-drying, but heating chemically "dehydrates" it and converts it to a drying oil. The dehydrated oil resembles tung oil but is slower drying and less alkali-resistant. **Fish oil,** extracted from the menhaden and the sardine, has considerable use in paints and varnishes. **Non-drying oils,** like coconut oil, are used in some baking enamels. An oxidizing **hydrocarbon oil,** made from petroleum, contains no esters or fatty acids.

The drying properties of oils are linked to the amount and nature of unsaturated compounds. By molecular distillation or solvent extraction the better drying portions of an oil can be separated. Drying is also improved by changing the structure of the unsaturated compounds (isomerization) and by modifying the oils with small amounts of such compounds as phthalic acid and maleic acid. The latter process borders on varnish making.

Driers are oil-soluble compounds of certain metals, mainly lead, manganese, and cobalt. They accelerate the drying of coatings made with oil. The metals are introduced into the coatings by cooking their oxides or salts in the varnish or oil, or by addition of separately prepared compounds. Certain types of synthetic non-oil coatings (catalytic coatings) dry by baking or by the action of a **catalyst** other than conventional drier. Drier action begins only after the coating has been applied. Catalyst action usually begins immediately upon its addition to the coating; hence, addition is delayed until the coating is about to be used.

Resins. Both natural and synthetic resins are used. **Natural resins** include fossil types from trees now extinct, recent types (rosin, Manila, and dammar), lac (secretion of an insect), and asphalts (gilsonite). **Synthetic resins** include ester gum, phenolic, alkyd, urea, melamine, amide, epoxy, urethane, vinyl, styrene, rubber, petroleum, terpene, cellulose nitrate, cellulose acetate, and ethyl cellulose. In general, the natural resins are compatible with drying oils, or may be made so, and are used in both oleoresinous and spirit varnishes; many are suitable for spirit varnishes only.

Non-resinous Filmogens. Some filmogens are neither oil nor resin. Among these are casein, soybean protein, glue, starch, portland cement, and water-soluble silicates, all of which are used in water-thinned paint. The latexes might also be included.

Plasticizers. In an oleoresinous varnish the oil acts as a softening agent or plasticizer for the resin. There are other natural compounds and substances, and many synthetic ones, for plasticizing film formers such as the cellulosics. Plasticizers include blown vegetable oils, camphor, dibutyl phthalate, tricresyl phosphate, dibutyl sebacate, dibutyl tartrate, tributyl citrate, methyl abietate, and chlorinated biphenyl.

Thinners. As the consistency of the film-forming portion of most paints and varnishes is too high for easy application, thinners (**solvents**) are needed to reduce it. If the non-volatile portion is already liquid, the term thinner is used; if solid, the term solvent is used. **Petroleum spirits** has largely replaced turpentine for thinning paints in the factory. **Turpentine** is sometimes preferred for on-the-job thinning of architectural paints. The coal-tar products—toluene, xylene, and solvent naphtha—are used where solvency better than that given by petroleum spirits is needed. Esters, alcohols, and ketones are standard for cellulosic lacquers. Chlorinated solvents are required for some of the synthetic resins. Finally, water is used to thin emulsion and paint sold over the counter, to be thinned at point of use.

Pigments may be natural or synthetic, organic or inorganic, opaque or non-opaque, white or colored, chemically active or inert. Factors entering into the selection of a pigment are color, opacity, particle size, compatibility with other ingredients, resistance to light, heat, alkali, and acid, and cost. The most important pigments are: **white**—basic carbonate white lead, basic sulphate white lead, zinc oxide, leaded zinc oxide, titanium dioxide, lithopone; **red**—iron oxides, red lead (for rust prevention rather than color), chrome orange, molybdate orange, toluidine red, para red, phthalocyanine; **yellow**—iron oxide, chrome yellow, zinc yellow (for rust prevention rather than color), Hansa; **green**—chrome green, chrome oxide; **blue**—iron, ultramarine, phthalocyanine; **extenders** (non-opaque), *i.e.*, magnesium silicate, calcium silicate, calcium carbonate, barium sulphate, aluminum silicate.

Miscellany. Paint contains many other ingredients, minor in amount but important in function, such as emulsifiers, antifoamers, and thickeners.

PAINTS

Paste paint contains only a part of the oil and thinner needed for the complete paint; the balance is added by the user. Multiple-pigment pastes contain from 65 to 80 percent of pigment; white lead soft paste, 87 percent; white lead heavy paste, 91 percent; red lead paste, 92 percent.

Aluminum paint is a mixture of aluminum pigment and varnish; from 1 to 2 lb of pigment per gal of varnish. The aluminum is in the form of thin flakes. In the paint film, the flakes "leaf"; *i.e.*, they overlap like leaves fallen from trees. Leafing gives aluminum paint its metallic appearance and its impermeability to moisture. Aluminum paint ranks high as a reflector of the sun's radiation and as a retainer of heat in hot-air or hot-water pipes or tanks.

Bituminous Paint. Hard asphalts, like gilsonite, cooked with drying oils, and soft asphalts and coal tar, cut back with thinner, may be used to protect metal and masonry wherever their black color is not objectionable.

Calcimine, a mixture of glue and pigment, is sold as dry powder to be mixed with water. **Casein paint** is a mixture of casein, solubilizing agent, and pigment; it is sold both as dry powder and as paste. **Emulsion paints** are emulsions in water of oil or varnish base mixed with pigment. The **latex paints** (acrylic, butadiene-styrene, polyvinylacetate, etc.) belong to this class. Calcimine and casein paints are used mainly on interior plaster and masonry surfaces, and may be used on wood that has been primed. Emulsion paints are designed for both exterior and interior masonry and are more washable than casein paints. Calcimine is not washable.

Electrical Paint. Most paints, especially those not water-thinned, are electrically insulating to a high degree. Electrically conductive paint contains large percentages of metal powder or carbon pigment.

Strippable coatings are intended to give temporary protection to articles during storage or shipment.

Luminous paints are of two kinds: **phosphorescent,** which continue to glow after removal of the activating energy; and **fluorescent,** which glow only during activation. Activation may be by sunlight, artifical light, ultraviolet radiation, or by radioactive compound added to the paint. The last method makes paint self-luminous by eliminating the need for activation by light. The luminous properties are due to zinc sulphide, calcium sulphide and strontium sulphide pigments.

Ship-bottom Paint. Ocean-going steel ships require antifouling paint over the anticorrosive primer. Red lead or zinc yellow is used in the primer. **Antifouling** paints contain ingredients, such as cuprous oxide and mercuric oxide, that are toxic to barnacles and other marine organisms. For rapid drying, so that the time in dry dock is kept short, the vehicle is usually a spirit varnish, such as vinyl, and rosin-coal tar solutions. During World War II, the U.S. Navy developed **hot plastic** ship-bottom paint. It is applied by spray gun in a relatively thick film and dries or sets as it cools. **Copper powder paint** is suitable for small wooden craft.

Fire-retardant Paint. Most paint films contain less combustible matter than does wood. To this extent, they are fire-retardant. In addition they cover splinters and fill in cracks. However, flames and intense heat will eventually ignite the wood, painted or not. The most that ordinary paint can do is to delay ignition. Special compositions fuse and give off flame-smothering fumes, or convert to spongy heat-insulating masses, when heated. The relatively thick film and low resistance to abrasion and cleaning make these coatings unsuited for general use as paint, unless conventional decorative paints are applied over them. However, steady improvement in paint properties is being made.

Traffic paint is quick-drying, so that traffic is inconvenienced as little as possible. Rough texture and absence of gloss increase visibility. Tiny glass beads may be added for greater night visibility. Bituminous paints are sometimes used on light-colored pavements.

Heat-reflecting Paint. Light colors reflect more of thesun's radiation than do dark colors. White is somewhat better than aluminum, but, for some uses, aluminum may retain its reflecting power longer. On heating radiators, flat paint (any color) radiates more heat than aluminum- or copper-bronze paint.

Heat-resistant Paint. **Silicone** paint is the most heat-resistant paint yet developed. Its first use was as an insulation varnish for electric motors, but types for other uses, such as on stoves and heaters, have been developed. Since it must be cured by baking, it is primarily a product finish.

Fungicides should be added to paint that is to be used in bakeries, breweries, sugar refineries, dairies, and other places where fungi flourish. Among suitable fungicides are mercuric chloride, organo-mercuric compounds, and chlorinated phenols. Fungi infected surfaces should be sterilized before they are painted. Scrub them with mild alkali; if infection is severe, add a disinfectant.

Wood preservatives of the paintable type are used extensively to treat wood windows, doors, and cabinets. They reduce rotting that may be promoted by water that enters at joints. They comprise solutions of compounds, such as chlorinated phenols, and copper and zinc naphthenates, in petroleum thinner. Water repellents, such as paraffin wax, are sometimes added but may interfere with satisfactory painting.

Clear **water repellents** are treatments for masonry to prevent wetting by water. Older types are solutions of waxes, drying oils, or metallic soaps. Silicone solutions, recently developed, are superior, both in repelling water and in effect on appearance.

Painting

Exterior Architectural Painting. Surfaces must be clean and dry, except that wood to be painted with emulsion paint will tolerate a small amount of moisture and masonry to be painted with portland cement–base paint should be damp. Scrape or melt the resin from the knots in wood, or scrub it off with paint thinner or alcohol. As an extra precaution, seal the knots with shellac varnish, aluminum paint, or proprietary knot sealer. When painting wood for the first time, fill nail holes and cracks with putty, after the priming coat has dried. If the wood had been painted before, remove loose paint with a scraper, wire brush, or sandpaper. Prime all bare wood. In bad cases of cracking and scaling, remove all of the paint by dry scraping or with paint and varnish remover or with a torch.

Until 1943, the usual paint exterior contained about 65 percent pigment, 30 percent raw linseed oil, and 5 percent thinner and drier. To stretch the supply of linseed oil during the recent war, manufacturers reduced the percentage of oil to about 23 and increased the thinner correspondingly. They bodied (thickened) about half of the oil to get suitable consistency. This "oil conservation" paint gave such good results that practically all oil-base house paints now contain substantial percentages of bodied oil.

Paint on new wood should be from 4 to 5 mils thick. This usually requires three coats. A system consisting of non-penetrating primer and special finish coat may permit the minimum to be reached with two coats. Repainting should be frequent enough to preserve a satisfactory thickness of the finish coat. Non-penetrating primers stick on some types of wood better than regular house paint does.

Interior Architectural Painting. Interior paints are used primarily for decoration, illumination, and sanitation. Enamels are used for kitchen and bathroom walls, where water resistance and easy cleaning are needed; semiglossy and flat types are used on walls and ceilings where it is desired to avoid glare. Wet plaster will eventually destroy oil-base paints. Fresh plaster must be allowed to dry out. Water from leaks and condensation must be kept away from aged plaster. Several coats of paint with low permeability to water vapor make an effective vapor barrier.

Painting Concrete and Masonry. Moisture in concrete and masonry brings alkali to the surface where it can destroy oil paint. Allow 2 to 6 months for these materials to dry out before painting; a year or more, if they are massive. Emulsion paints may be used on damp concrete or masonry if there is reason to expect the drying to continue. Portland cement paint, sometimes preferred for masonry, is especially suitable for first painting of porous surfaces such as cinder block. Before applying this paint, wet the surface so that capillarity will not extract the water from the paint. Scrubbing the paint into the surface with a stiff brush of vegetable fiber gives the best job, but good jobs are also obtained with usual brushes or by spraying. Keep the paint damp for 2 or 3 days so that it will set properly. Chlorinated rubber, chlorinated paraffin, synthetic rubber, and vinyl paints are much used on concrete, especially for swimming pools, because of their high resistance to alkali.

Painting Steel. Preparation of steel for painting, type of paint, and condition of exposure are closely related. Methods of preparation, arranged in order of increasing thoroughness, include (1) removal of oil with solvent; (2) removal of dirt, loose rust, and loose mill scale with scraper or wire brush; (3) flame cleaning; (4) sand blasting; (5) pickling; (6) phosphating. Exposure environments, arranged in order of increasing severity, include (*a*) dry interiors, or arid regions; (*b*) rural or light industrial areas, normally dry; (*c*) frequently wet; (*d*) continuously wet; (*e*) corrosive chemical. Paint systems for condition (*a*) often consist of a single coat of low-cost paint. For other conditions, the systems comprise one or two coats of rust-inhibitive primer, and one or more finish coats, selected according to severity of conditions.

The primer contains one or more rust-inhibitive pigments, selected mainly from red lead, zinc yellow, and zinc dust. It may also contain zinc oxide, iron oxide, and extender pigments. Of equal importance is the binder, especially for the top coats. For above-water surfaces, linseed oil and alkyd varnish give good service; for underwater surfaces, other binders, like phenolic and vinyl resin, are better. Chemical-resistant binders include epoxy, synthetic rubber, chlorinated rubber, vinyl, and neoprene.

Paint for structural steel is normally air-drying. Large percentages for factory-finished steel are catalytic-cured, or are baked.

Galvanized Iron. Allow new galvanized iron to weather for 6 months before painting. If there is not enough time, treat it with a proprietary etching solution. For the priming coat, without pretreatment, a paint containing a substantial amount of zinc dust should be used. If the galvanizing has weathered, the usual primers for steel are also good.

Tinplate is an excellent base for paint. The grease should be washed off with paint thinner and the same primer used as for steel. Much tin roofing is painted with iron oxide paints.

Painting Copper. The only preparation needed is washing off any grease and roughening the surface, if it is a polished one. Special primers are not needed. Paint or varnish all copper to prevent corrosion products from staining the adjoining paint.

Painting Aluminum. The surface must be clean and free from grease. Highly polished sheet should be etched with phosphoric acid or chromic acid. Zinc-yellow primers give the best protection against corrosion. The only preparation needed for interior aluminum is to have the surface clean; anticorrosive primers are not needed.

Magnesium and its alloys corrode readily, especially in marine atmospheres. Red-lead primers must not be used. For factory finishing, it is customary to chromatize the metal and then apply a zinc-yellow primer.

Water-tank Interiors. Among the best paints for these are asphaltic compositions. For drinking-water tanks, select one that imparts no taste. Zinc-dust paints made with phenolic varnish are also good.

Wood Products. Finishes may be lacquer or varnish, or their corresponding enamels. High-quality clear finishes may require 10 to 15 operations, such as sanding, staining, filling, sealing, and finishing. Furniture finishing is done mostly by spray. Small articles are often finished by tumbling; shapes like broom handles, by squeegeeing.

Plastics. Carefully balanced formulations are necessary for satisfactory adhesion, to avoid crazing and to prevent migration of plasticizer.

Paint-destroying Agencies. Heavy dew, hot sun, and marine atmospheres shorten the life of paint. Industrial zones where the atmosphere is contaminated with hygroscopic and acidic substances make special attention to painting programs necessary. Dampness within masonry and plaster walls brings alkali to the surface where it can destroy oil-base paints. Interior paints on dry surfaces endure indefinitely; they need renewal to give new color schemes or when it becomes impractical to wash them. Dry temperate climates are favorable to long life of exterior paints.

Application. Most industrial finishing is done with spray guns. In electrostatic spraying, the spray is charged and attracted to the grounded target. Overspray is largely eliminated. Other methods of application include dipping, flowing, tumbling, doctor blading, rolling, fluid bed, and screen stenciling.

An increasing proportion of maintenance painting is being done with spray and hand roller. The spray requires up to 25 percent more paint than the brush, but the advantage of speed is offsetting. The roller requires about the same amount of paint as the brush.

Dry finishing is done by flame-spraying powdered pigment-filmogen compositions or by immersing heated articles in a **fluid bed** of the powdered composition.

Spreading Rates. When applied by brush, approximate spreading rates for paints on various surfaces are as follows:

Surface	Type	First coat, sq ft per gal	Second and third coats, sq ft per gal
Wood	Oil	400–500	500–600
Wood, primed	Emulsion	500–600	500–600
Structural steel	Oil	450–600	650–900
Sheet metal	Oil	500–600	550–650
Brick and concrete	Oil	200–300	400–500
Brick and concrete	Cement	100–125	125–175
Brick and concrete	Emulsion	200–300	400–500
Smooth plaster	Oil	550–650	550–650
Smooth plaster	Casein	500–600	500–600
Smooth plaster	Emulsion	400–500	500–600
Concrete floors	Enamel	400–500	550–650
Wood floors	Varnish	550–650	550–650

VARNISH

Oleoresinous varnishes are classed according to oil length, *i.e.*, the number of gallons of oil per 100 lb of resin. Short oil varnishes contain up to 10 gal of oil per 100 lb of resin; medium, from 15 to 25 gal; long, over 30 gal.

Floor varnish is of medium length and is often made with modified phenolic resins, tung, and linseed oils. It should dry overnight to a tough hard film. Some floor varnishes are rather thin and penetrating so that they leave no surface film. They show scratches less than the orthodox type.

Spar varnish is of long oil length, made usually with phenolic or modified-phenolic resins, tung or dehydrated castor oil, and linseed oil. Other spar varnishes are of the alkyd and urethane types. Spar varnishes dry to a medium-hard glossy film that is resistant to water, actinic rays of the sun, and moderate concentrations of chemicals.

Chemical-resistant varnishes are designed to withstand acid, alkali, and other chemicals. They are usually made of synthetic resins, such as chlorinated rubber, cyclized rubber, phenolic resin, melamine, urea-aldehyde, vinyl and epoxy resin. Some of these must be dried by baking. **Catalytic varnish** is made with a non-oxidizing film-former, and is cured with a catalyst, such as hydrochloric acid or certain amines. **Flat varnish** is made by adding materials, such as finely divided silica or metallic soap, to glossy varnish. Synthetic latex or other emulsion, or aqueous dispersion, such as glue, is sometimes called **water varnish.**

Lacquer. The word lacquer has been used for (1) spirit varnishes used especially for coating brass and other metals, (2) Japanese or Chinese lacquer, (3) coatings in which cellulose nitrate (**pyroxylin**), cellulose acetate, or cellulose acetate–butyrate is the dominant ingredient, (4) oleoresinous baking varnishes for interior of food cans.

Present-day lacquer primarily refers to cellulosic coatings, clear or pigmented. These lacquers dry by evaporation. By proper choice of solvents, they are made to dry rapidly. Besides cellulosic compounds, they contain resins, plasticizers, and solvent. Cellulose acetate, cellulose acetate–butyrate, and cellulose acetate–propionate lacquers are non-flammable, and the clear forms have better exterior durability than the cellulose nitrate type. Cellulose acetate and cellulose acetate–butyrate are superior to cellulose nitrate for **airplane dopes** because they are non-flammable; the cellulose acetate–butyrate is superior to the acetate because it remains taut in humid weather.

Although cellulosic derivatives dominate the lacquer field, compositions containing vinyls, chlorinated hydrocarbons, or other synthetic thermoplastic polymers are included.

Lac is a resinous material secreted by an insect that lives on the sap of certain trees. Most of it comes from India. After removal of dirt, it is marketed in the form of grains, called seed-lac; cakes, called button lac; or flakes, called shellac. Lac contains up to 7 percent of wax, which is removed to make the refined grade. A bleached, or white, grade is also available.

Shellac varnish is made by "cutting" the resin in alcohol; the cut is designated by the pounds of lac per gallon of alcohol, generally 4 lb. Shellac varnish should always be used within 6 to 12 months of manufacture as some of the lac combines with the alcohol to form a soft, sticky material.

WOOD

BY

Carl H. de Zeeuw

REFERENCES: Brown, Panshin, and de Zeeuw, "Textbook of Wood Technology," McGraw-Hill. "Design of Wood Aircraft Structures," ANC-18, Munitions Board Aircraft Committee, 1951. Freas and Selbo, Fabrication and Design of Glued Laminated Wood Structural Members, *U.S. Dept. Agr. Tech. Bull.* No. 1069, 1954. Hunt and Garratt, "Wood Preservation," McGraw-Hill. "National Design Specification for Stress-grade Lumber and Its Fastenings," National Lumber Manufacturers Assoc., 1962. Stamm and Harris, "Chemical Processing of Wood," Chemical Publishing. "Technical Data on Plywood," Douglas Fir Plywood Assoc. "Wood Handbook," *U.S. Dept. Agr. Handbook* No. 72, 1955. Scofield and O'Brien, "Modern Timber Engineering," Southern Pine Assoc.

COMPOSITION, STRUCTURE, AND NOMENCLATURE

Wood is a naturally formed organic material consisting essentially of elongated tubular elements called **cells** arranged in a parallel manner for the most part. These cells vary in dimensions and wall thickness with position in the tree, age, conditions of growth, and kind of tree. The walls of the cells are formed principally of chain molecules of cellulose, polymerized from glucose residues and oriented as a partly crystalline material. These chains are aggregated in the cell wall at a variable angle, roughly parallel to the axis of the cell. The cells are cemented by an amorphous material called **lignin**. The complex structure of the gross wood approximates a rhombic system. The direction parallel to the grain and the axis of the stem is longitudinal (**L**), the two axes across the grain are radial (**R**) and tangential (**T**) with respect to the cylinder of the tree stem. This anisotropy and the molecular orientation accounts for the major differences in physical properties with respect to direction which are present in wood.

Natural variability of any given physical measurement in wood approximates the normal probability curve. It is traceable to the differences in the growth of individual samples and at present cannot be controlled. For engineering purposes, statistical evaluation is employed for determination of safe working limits.

Timber is classified broadly as **hardwood,** which is produced by the broad-leaved trees (*angiosperms*), such as oak, maple, ash; and **softwood,** the product of coniferous trees (*gymnosperms*), such as pines, larch, spruce, hemlock. The terms "hard" and "soft" have no relation to actual hardness of the wood, as can be seen by reference to Table 2. **Sapwood** is the living wood of pale color on the outside of the stem. **Heartwood** is the inner core of physiologically inactive wood in a tree and is usually darker in color, somewhat heavier, due to infiltrated material, and more decay-resistant than the sapwood. Other terms relating to wood, veneer, and plywood are defined in ASTM D9–30, D1038–52, and the Wood Handbook.

Standard nomenclature of timber is based on commercial practice which groups woods of similar technical qualities but separate botanical identities under a single name. For listings of domestic hardwoods and softwoods see ASTM D1165–52 and the Wood Handbook.

The **chemical composition** of woody cell walls is generally about 40 to 50 percent cellulose, 15 to 35 percent lignin, less than 1 percent mineral, 20 to 35 percent hemicellulose, and the remainder extractable matter of a variety of sorts. Softwoods and hardwoods have about the same cellulose content.

PHYSICAL PROPERTIES OF WOOD

Moisture Relations

Wood is a hygroscopic material which contains water in varying amounts, depending upon the relative humidity and temperature of the surrounding atmosphere. **Equilibrium conditions** are established as shown in Fig. 1. The standard reference condition for wood is **ovendry weight,** which is determined by drying at 100 to 105 C to constant weight.

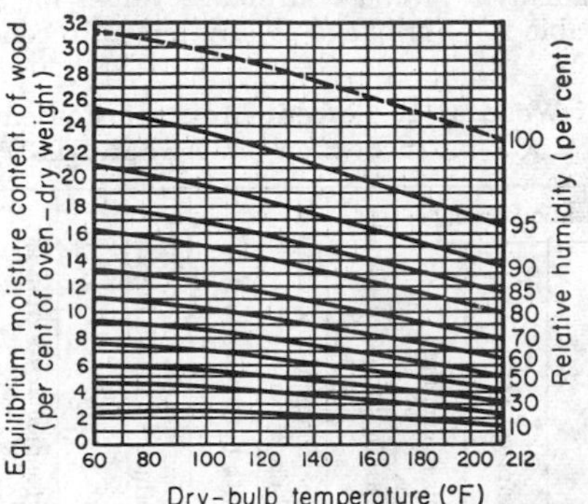

FIG. 1. Relation of dry bulb temperature, relative humidity, and equilibrium moisture content of wood. (From *USDA Tech. Bull.* 1069).

Moisture content of wood is the weight of water expressed as a percentage of the ovendry weight. The water is absorbed solely in the intermolecular regions of the cell wall up to 31 percent depending on the kind of wood and the temperature. The maximum value for this type of absorption is called the **fiber saturation point** (fsp) and is usually taken as 28 percent for room temperature. Additional water is taken into the cell cavities as "free water" and may be in excess of 700 percent. **Air-dry wood** has 12 to 15 percent moisture content. **Green wood** contains from 40 to 100 percent water for ordinary ranges of specific gravities.

Strength properties remain constant as long as the wood is above the fiber saturation point. Changes in moisture content in the cell wall cause the strength to vary inversely in a manner similar to compound interest. Computations for adjustment of strength data with moisture changes below the fiber saturation point can be made using the values from Table 1 as x in the annual compound interest tables (Sec. 1) and the change in moisture content percentage in place of the number of years.

Table 1. Strength Changes in Wood as Related to Specific Gravity and Moisture Content

(From the Wood Handbook)

Strength property	Specific gravity*		Change in percent for 1 percent change in moisture content†
	Green wood	Air-dry wood, 12 percent m.c.	
Static bending:			
Fiber stress at prop. limit, psi	$10{,}200\ G^{1.25}$	$16{,}700\ G^{1.25}$	5
Modulus of rupture, psi	$17{,}600\ G^{1.25}$	$25{,}700\ G^{1.25}$	4
Modulus of elasticity, kpsi	$2{,}360\ G$	$2{,}800\ G$	2
Impact bending:			
Height of drop to failure, in	$114\ G^{1.75}$	$94.6\ G^{1.75}$	0.5
Compression parallel to grain:			
Fiber stress at prop. limit, psi	$5{,}250\ G$	$8{,}750\ G$	5
Maximum crushing strength, psi	$6{,}730\ G$	$12{,}200\ G$	6
Modulus of elasticity, kpsi	$2{,}910\ G$	$3{,}380\ G$	
Compression perpendicular to grain:			
Fiber stress at prop. limit, psi	$3{,}000\ G^{2.25}$	$4{,}630\ G^{2.25}$	5.5
Hardness:			
End, lb	$3{,}740\ G^{2.25}$	$4{,}800\ G^{2.25}$	4
Side, lb	$3{,}420\ G^{2.25}$	$3{,}770\ G^{2.25}$	2.5

* The properties and values should be read as equations; for example, modulus of rupture for green wood = $17{,}600\ G^{1.25}$, where G represents the specific gravity of ovendry wood based on volume at the moisture condition indicated.

† The percentages are to be applied successively, as in compound interest calculations.

Dimensional Changes

Shrinking or swelling of wood is the result of change in water content within the cell wall; because of the anisotropic nature of the wall the changes will be unequal for the several axes. Shrinkage is expressed as percentage of dimensional change based on the green or fully swollen size. **Longitudinal shrinkage** from green to ovendry ranges from 0.1 to 0.3 percent and is usually neglected. Across the grain, total shrinkage averages about 50 percent greater tangentially than radially. Average shrinkage values for a number of commercial woods are shown in Table 2. Shrinkage to any moisture con-

Table 2. Strength and Related Properties of Wood at 12 Percent Moisture Content (Average Values from Tests on Clear Pieces 2 × 2 in. in Section per ASTM D143)*

Kind of wood	Specific gravity, ovendry volume	Density at 12% m.c. lb per cu ft	Shrinkage in percent from green to ovendry condition based on dimension when green		Static Bending			Maximum crushing strength parallel to grain, psi	Compression perpendicular to grain at proportional limit, psi	Tensile strength perpendicular to grain, psi†	Impact bending, height of drop in inches for failure with 50 lb hammer	Shear strength parallel to grain, psi	Hardness perpendicular to grain av. of R and T
			Rad.	Tan.	Fiber stress at proportional limit, psi	Modulus of rupture, psi	Modulus of elasticity, kpsi						
Hardwoods													
Ash, white	0.64	42	4.9	7.9	8,900	15,400	1,770	7,410	1,410	940	43	1,950	1,320
Basswood	0.40	26	6.6	9.3	5,900	8,700	1,460	4,730	450	350	16	990	410
Beech	0.67	45	5.1	11.0	8,700	14,900	1,720	7,300	1,250	1,010	41	2,010	1,300
Birch, yellow	0.66	43	7.2	9.2	10,100	16,600	2,010	8,170	1,190	920	55	1,880	1,260
Cherry, black	0.53	35	3.7	7.1	9,000	12,300	1,490	7,110	850	560	29	1,700	950
Chestnut	0.45	30	3.4	6.7	6,100	8,600	1,230	5,320	760	460	19	1,080	540
Cottonwood, eastern	0.43	28	3.9	9.2	5,700	8,500	1,370	4,910	470	580	20	930	430
Elm, American	0.55	35	4.2	9.5	7,600	11,800	1,340	5,520	850	660	39	1,510	830
Elm, rock	0.66	44	4.8	8.1	8,000	14,800	1,540	7,050	1,520	.....	56	1,920	1,320
Sweetgum	0.55	36	5.4	10.2	6,600	12,500	1,640	6,320	660	760	32	1,600	850
Hickory, shagbark	0.77	50	7.0	10.5	10,700	20,200	2,160	9,210	2,170	.....	67	2,430	
Mahogany ‡ (Swietenia spp)	0.51	34	3.5	4.8	7,960	11,460	1,500	6,800	1,100	750	..	1,230	800
Maple, sugar	0.68	44	4.9	9.5	9,500	15,800	1,830	7,830	1,810	.....	39	2,330	1,450
Oak, red, northern	0.66	44	4.0	8.2	8,500	14,300	1,820	6,760	1,250	800	43	1,780	1,290
Oak, white	0.71	48	5.3	9.0	8,200	15,200	1,780	7,440	1,320	800	37	2,000	1,360
Poplar, yellow	0.45	29	4.2	7.6	6,200	10,100	1,580	5,540	560	540	24	1,190	540
Tupelo, black	0.55	35	4.4	7.7	7,300	9,600	1,200	5,520	1,150	500	22	1,340	810
Walnut, black	0.56	38	5.2	7.1	10,500	14,600	1,680	7,580	1,250	690	34	1,370	1,010
Softwoods													
Cedar, western red	0.34	23	2.4	5.0	5,300	7,700	1,120	5,020	610	220	17	860	350
Cypress	0.48	32	3.8	6.2	7,200	10,600	1,440	6,360	900	270	24	1,000	510
Douglas fir, coast	0.51	34	4.8	7.6	7,800	12,200	1,950	7,430	870	340	31	1,160	710
Hemlock, eastern	0.43	28	3.0	6.8	6,100	8,900	1,200	5,410	800	.....	21	1,060	500
Hemlock, western	0.44	29	4.3	7.9	6,800	10,100	1,490	6,210	680	310	26	1,170	580
Larch, western	0.59	38	4.5	9.1	8,300	13,900	1,960	8,110	980	430	35	1,410	830
Pine, red	0.47	31	3.8	7.2	7,000	11,000	1,630	6,070	650	460	26	1,210	560
Pine, ponderosa	0.42	28	3.9	6.3	6,300	9,200	1,260	5,270	740	400	17	1,160	450
Pine, eastern white	0.37	24	2.1	6.1	5,700	8,600	1,240	4,800	510	310	18	900	380
Pine, western white	0.42	27	2.6	5.3	6,200	9,500	1,510	5,620	540	.....	23	850	370
Pine, shortleaf	0.54	36	4.4	7.7	7,700	12,800	1,760	7,070	1,000	470	33	1,310	690
Redwood	0.42	28	2.6	4.4	6,900	10,000	1,340	6,150	860	240	19	940	480
Spruce, sitka	0.42	28	4.3	7.5	6,700	10,200	1,570	5,610	710	370	25	1,150	510
Spruce, white	0.45	28	4.7	8.2	6,500	9,800	1,340	5,470	570	360	20	1,080	480

* Tabulated from Wood Handbook, *Tropical Woods* No. 95, and unpublished data from the U.S. Forest Products Laboratory.

† Tensile strength parallel to grain to be taken as equal to modulus of rupture in bending.

‡ Central American *Swietenia* spp.

dition can be estimated by assuming that the change is linear from green to ovendry and that about half occurs in drying to 12 percent.

Swelling in polar liquids other than water is inversely related to the size of the molecule of the liquid. It has been shown that the tendency to hydrogen bonding on the dielectric constant are close, direct indicators of the swelling power of water-free organic liquids. In general, the strength values for wood swollen in any polar liquid are similar when there is equal swelling of the wood.

Swelling in aqueous solutions of sulphuric and phosphoric acids, zinc chloride, and sodium hydroxide above pH 8 may be as much as 25 percent greater in the transverse direction than in water. The transverse swelling may be accompanied by longitudinal shrinkage up to 5 percent. The swelling reflects a chemical change in the cell walls, and the accompanying strength changes are related to the degradation of the cellulose.

Dimensional stabilization of wood cannot be completely attained. Two or three coats of varnish, enamel, or synthetic lacquer may be 50 to 85 percent efficient in preventing short-term dimensional changes. Metal foil embedded in multiple coats of varnish may be 90 to 95 percent efficient in short-term cycling. The best long-term stabilization results from internal bulking of the cell wall by the use of materials such as phenolic resins polymerized *in situ* or water solutions of polyethylene glycol (PEG) on green wood. The presence of the bulking agents alters the physical properties of the treated wood. Phenol increases electrical resistance, hardness, compression strength, weight, and decay resistance but lowers the impact strength. Polyethylene glycol maintains strength values at the green-wood level, reduces electrical resistance, and can only be finished with polyurethane resins. (See Stamm for further discussion.)

Specific Gravity and Density

Specific gravity, G_m, of wood at a given moisture condition m is the ratio of the weight of the ovendry wood W_o to the weight of water displaced by the sample at the given moisture condition w_m.

$$G_m = W_o/w_m$$

This definition is required because volume and weight are constant only under special conditions. The **weight density of wood** D (unit weight) at any given moisture content, is the weight of ovendry wood and the contained water divided by the volume of the piece at that same moisture content. Average values for specific gravity ovendry and weight density at 12 percent moisture content are given in Table 2. Specific gravity of solid, dry wood substance based on helium displacement is 1.46, or about 91 lb per cu ft.

Conversion of weight density from one moisture condition to another can be accomplished by the following equation (Skaar):

$$D_2 = D_1 \frac{100 + M_2}{100 + M_1 + 0.0135\, D_1(M_2 - M_1)}$$

D_1 is the weight density, lb per cu ft, which is known for some moisture condition M_1. D_2 is desired weight density at a moisture content M_2. Moisture contents M_1 and M_2 are expressed in percent.

Specific gravity and strength properties vary directly in an exponential relationship $S = KG^n$. Table 1 gives values of K and the exponent n for various strength properties. The equation is based on more than 160 kinds of wood and yields estimated average values for wood in general. This relationship is the best general index to wood quality.

Thermal Properties

The **coefficients of thermal expansion** in wood vary with the structural axes. According to Weatherwax and Stamm (*Trans. ASME*, **69,** 1947, p. 421), the longitudinal coefficient for the temperature range + 50 C to − 50 C averages 3.39×10^{-6} per deg C and is independent of specific gravity. Across the grain, for an average specific gravity ovendry of 0.46, the radial coefficient α_r is 25.7×10^{-6} per deg C and the tangential α_t is 34.8×10^{-6} per deg C. Both α_r and α_t vary with specific gravity approximately to the first power. Thermal expansions are usually overshadowed by the larger dimensional changes due to moisture.

Thermal conductivity of wood varies principally with the direction of heat flow with respect to the grain. **Transverse conductivity** can be calculated by MacLean's equation (*Heating, Piping, Air Conditioning*, **13,** 1941):

$$K = G\,(1.39 + CM) + 0.165$$

where G is specific gravity, based on ovendry weight and volume at given moisture content M, percent. The constant C has two values: for moisture contents under 40 percent, $C = 0.028$; for moisture contents of 40 percent or more, $C = 0.038$. **Longitudinal conductivity** is 2.25 to 2.75 times greater than transverse.

Fuel value of wood depends primarily upon the weight of dry cell-wall material plus tannin and resins. Moisture in wood decreases fuel value because of heat loss in vaporizing the water. An approximate relation is

$$\text{Btu per lb} = H\left(100 - \frac{m.c.}{7} \Big/ 100 + m.c.\right)$$

where H is heat of combustion, averaging 8500 Btu for hardwoods and 9000 Btu for conifers, and *m.c.* is moisture content of the wood in percent. (See p. 7–18 for fuel values and p. 4–69 *et seq.* for combustion.)

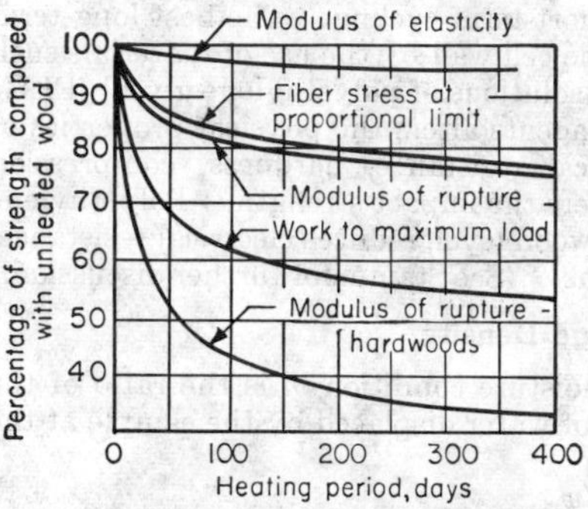

Fig. 2. Effect of heating in water at 200 F on bending strength. Wood tested after cooling to room temperature and drying to 12 percent moisture content. All curves for softwoods except as noted. (*From Wood Handbook*)

Ignition of wood depends on the exothermic-reaction temperature, which is 273 C approx, the presence of inflammable extractives, and the shape and size of the cross section. Thin, outstanding edges ignite readily, while chamfered, heavy timbers are slow to catch fire. Long-continued heating below the exothermic-reaction temperature can cause ignition.

The **immediate effect of temperature on strength properties** is given by an inverse, linear relationship; changes in specific gravity cause direct displacement of the curves, while moisture content changes result in direct variation of the slopes of the curves. These effects are reversible if the heating time is short. A predicting equation for strength-temperature changes based on Kollmann's experiments is:

$$S_2 = S_1 - (37.35)\,G_o(T_2 - T_1)\left[1 + 0.0756\,\frac{m.c.}{100}\right]$$

where S_2 is a strength value desired, S_1 is a known strength, G_o is specific gravity on an ovendry basis for the wood, T_2 and T_1 are temperatures, deg F, corresponding to the strength values, and *m.c.* is moisture content, percent.

Permanent effects of heat on strength of wood show a direct dependence on time, temperature, and moisture content. Figure 2 illustrates the effect of time of heating on the bending strengths when the other factors are constant. A rough estimate of the effect of moisture is that any given value shown will be less than half as great for ovendry wood. The effect of steam or temperatures above 280 F on wet wood is to cause accelerated hydrolysis and increased rate of strength loss.

Fire-retardant treatment will provide wood which will flame only as long as an external source of heat exists. No treatment can make wood "fireproof" or prevent charring. The best chemicals for fire-retardant treatment are the mono- and diammonium salts. Zinc chloride is also widely used but can cause serious strength losses. Neither of these salts cause corrosive action on metal in contact with the treated lumber. Commercial formulations employ the above salts in combination with borax, boric acid, phosphoric acid, and magnesium chloride. The range of retentions of dry salt in pounds per cubic foot for these fire-retardant materials is from 5 to 6 for thicknesses up to 2 in., from 2 to 3 for lumber up to 4 in. Minimum penetration is specified as ½ in.

Electrical Properties

The **direct-current electrical resistance** of wood is dependent principally on the moisture content and secondarily on density, grain direction, temperature, minerals, and extractives. According to Clark and Williams (*Jour. Phys. Chem.* **37,** 1933, p. 119), the specific resistance for ovendry wood ranges from 3×10^{17} to 3×10^{18} ohm-cm and at 16 percent moisture content decreases to 10^8 ohm-cm. In general, the logarithm of the conductivity (reciprocal of the resistance) will increase linearly with moisture content of the wood up to the fiber saturation point. At this level the specific resistance approximates that of water (10^5 to 10^6 ohm-cm) and increases only slightly up to maximum water content.

Electrical-resistance moisture meters measure the resistance between two pins driven into the wood and, when calibrated for species and temperature range, are accurate to within 2 percent for moisture contents between 7 and 25 percent in the surface layers of the wood. Resistance meters are unreliable when used with salt-treated wood.

The **alternating-current characteristics of wood** have been summarized by Skaar (*N.Y. State Coll. Forestry Tech. Publ.* 69, 1948) as follows: The **dielectric constant of wood** without regard to kind is directly proportional to the density at a given moisture content, increases with the latter factor, decreases slightly with increases in frequency of the alternating current, and is 30 to 50 percent greater in the longitudinal- than in the perpendicular-to-grain directions.

Wood in Relation to Sound

The **transmission of sound in wood** for a given direction with respect to the grain is described by the expression $v = \sqrt{E/\rho}$, in which v is the velocity of sound in wood, in. per sec, E is the dynamic Young's modulus, psi, and ρ is the density of the wood, slugs per cu in. Kitazawa (*Jour. Forest Products Research Soc.*, **2,** No. 5, 1952, p. 228) has shown that the directional variation of dynamic modulus with respect to the axes of the wood can be described by Hankinson's formula below. The dynamic modulus is about 10 percent higher than the static value and varies inversely with moisture changes by approximately 1.3 percent for each percent change in moisture content.

Non-destructive testing of wood for the determination of elastic moduli is carried out by resonance techniques analogous to those used with steel and concrete. For details, see Kitazawa, *loc. cit.* These methods are particularly useful for a variable material such as wood, since a series of tests can be carried out on a single sample.

Durability of Wood

Decay resistance of timber varies widely between different kinds of trees and between individuals of the same kind. Heartwood is more resistant than sapwood due to lower permeability and presence of toxic extractives. Experience of the U.S. Forest Products Laboratory shows **high natural decay resistance** of the heartwood for the following important commercial timbers: northern white cedar, southern cypress, western red cedar, redwood, chestnut, black locust, and black walnut. **Moderate decay resistance** is associated with the heartwood of Douglas fir, eastern white pine, southern yellow pine, western larch, white oak, and red gum. Other kinds of native timbers have little or no resistance in an untreated condition.

Wood-destroying fungi are primitive forms of plant life which utilize either the lignin portion (white rots) or the cellulose (brown rots) for food. Control of moisture, air, or temperature, limits or halts the metabolic process. Optimum conditions for growth are 20 to 25 percent moisture content, 20 percent of wood volume as air, and temperatures from 75 to 95 F. Wood which is saturated with water because of complote submersion has too little air for fungus growth and will remain unattacked. Freezing of wood will not kill the fungus but will cause dormancy. However, elevated temperature from 120 to 145 F will kill even the most resistant fungi. Normal conditions for kiln drying and steaming for preservation treatment fall within the temperature range for sterilization. Service conditions usually preclude control of the growth factors, and fungus growth is inhibited by chemical impregnation of the wood.

Resistance of wood to insect activity is poor in sapwood, while heartwood, particularly if resinous, is less subject to attack. **Termites** of the subterranean type are the most serious wood-destroying insect group in the United States. These insects remove the wood internally leaving few signs of their activity. The cellulose of the wood is acted on by protozoa in the insect intestine and converted to sugars for food. Control of termites is best effected by construction features which prevent the insects from gaining entry to a structure (see *U.S. Dept. Agr. Farmers' Bull.*, 1949, p. 1911). In addition, the soil may be poisoned or the wood pressure-treated with toxic chemicals.

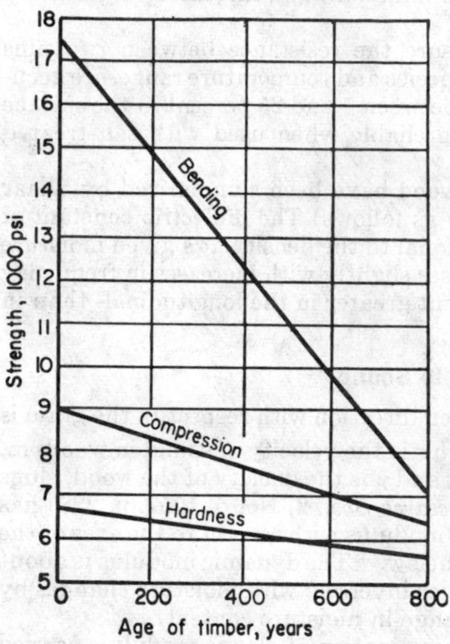

Fig. 3. Strength loss with age in a hardwood (*Zelkowa serrata*). (From *Sci. Rpts. Saikyo Univ.* No. 7, 1955).

Wood-boring beetles can also cause extensive damage. Their activity can be noted by the presence of small surface holes and evicted sawdust. Heat sterilization and thorough surface coatings of paint or varnish are the best control measures.

Marine organisms will attack and destroy any known kind of wood under the proper conditions in tropical waters. The heartwood of imported timbers such as green heart (*Ocotea rodiaei* Mez.); certain *Eucalyptus* spp., such as turpentine and jarrah; azobe (*Lophira procera* Chev.); and manbarklak (*Eschweilera* spp.) will be durable in coastal waters of the United States. None of the native timbers can be classed as durable under these same conditions unless pressure-treated with creosote to refusal.

Resistance of wood to chemical action is best in the less permeable heartwood of the conifers. Aqueous solutions of sodium hydroxide, sulphuric, hydrochloric, and nitric acids cause most damage since swelling and degradation are simultaneous. Temperature changes for a given solution act roughly with the logarithm of time.

Submersion of timber in water will prevent fungus action as noted but will eventually cause deterioration of the wood due to hydrolysis of the cellulose. This change correlates with strength tests in bending and compression. Excavated piles of about 260 years of age have shown shear failures in the early wood zones.

Long exposure of wood to the atmosphere also causes changes in the cellulose. A study by Kohara and Okamoto of sound old timbers of a softwood and hardwood of known ages from temple roof beams shows that the percentage of cellulose decreases steadily over a period up to 1,400 years while the lignin remains almost constant. These changes are reflected in strength losses (Fig. 3). Impact properties approximate a loss that is nearly linear with the logarithm of time.

STRENGTH AND ELASTIC PROPERTIES OF WOOD

Primary Strength Data

Primary data on the strength of small pieces of air-dry wood, free from defects, are shown in Table 2. Additional data and tests on green material can be found in the Wood Handbook and *U.S. Dept. Agr. Bull.* 479. Test methods are given in ASTM D143 and are similar to those used in other English-speaking countries. Data on foreign timbers imported into the United States can be found in Armstrong, The Strength Properties of Timber, *Dept. Sci. Ind. Research* (*Brit.*) *Forest Products Research Bull.* 28, London, 1953.

Rheological Properties of Wood

Wood exhibits pronounced visco-elastic characteristics. Under suddenly applied loads there is an immediate deformation approximating the classical pattern, followed by a logarithmic increase with time. Because of this time-dependent relation, the rate of loading is an important factor to consider in the testing and use of wood. Impact and dynamic measures of elasticity for small samples are about 10 percent higher than for static. The strength values are even more influenced by rate (see p. 6–158). Impact strengths are also affected by this relationship but present methods of calculating have little meaning, except for height of drop as shown in Table 2, and this for comparative purposes only.

Damping capacity of wood is superior to most structural materials. Expressed in terms of the logarithmic decrement δ, which is one-half the damping capacity, Greenhill (*Jour. Council Sci. Ind. Research*, **9,** 4, 1936, p. 265) determined a value $\delta = 0.035$ in flexure for sitka spruce. Kimball (*Jour. Applied Mechanics*, **8,** 1941) quoted $\delta = 0.0049$ for mild steel and 0.0034 for aluminum as comparative values.

The **fatigue properties of woods** have not been intensively investigated because they are less sensitive to repeated loads than is the case for more highly crystalline materials. Below the fatigue limit, wood will dissipate an unlimited amount of energy as heat without damage. The U.S. Forest Products Laboratory has found that small cantilever bending specimens subjected to fully reversed stresses at 12 percent moisture content and 75 F have an apparent endurance load of about 30 percent of the modulus of rupture of standard static tests after 30 billion cycles.

Load Direction and Relation to Grain of Wood

All strength properties vary with the orthotropic axes of the wood in a manner which is approximated by an expression first given in *Air Serv. Info. Circ.*, **III,** No. 259, 1921, and is commonly known as **Hankinson's formula:**

$$N = \frac{PQ}{P \sin^2\theta + Q \cos^2\theta}$$

Where N = allowable stress induced by a load acting at an angle to the grain direction, psi; P = allowable stress parallel to the grain, psi; Q = allowable stress perpendicular to the grain, psi; and θ = angle between direction of load and direction of grain.

The deviation of the grain from the long axis of the member to which the load is applied is known as **slope of grain** and is determined by measuring the length of run in inches along the axis for a 1 in. deviation of the grain from the axis. Koehler (*U.S. Forest Products Laboratory Rept.* 1585, 1943) gives complete methods and discussions on slope of grain determination. The effect of grain slope on the important strength properties is shown by Table 3.

Stress-graded construction lumber is produced under lumber-association grading rules constructed on the basis of engineering studies made by the USFPL (see Wood Handbook and ASTM 245). Natural variability within a species, time-dependant stress behavior, and overload factors are taken into account. The actual size and location of knots, checks, splits, wane, and slope of grain are used as criteria for assignment of grade. Table 4 shows the grades established for a number of kinds of wood and their allowable unit stresses. Stresses for other kinds of wood are available in the National Design Specification.

With the exception of southern pine, methods of grading vary for the different sizes and contemplated uses. For example, bending members (J & P, B & S) are graded essentially as simple beams on the extent and placement of defects in the middle third. Any change in the size of a piece requires regrading of the member. Furthermore, it is assumed the lumber is green at time of use unless the grade is specially marked. A single use classification exists for southern pine; no regrading is required when a piece is cut in length, and the original assigned stress still applies. In addition, the strength advantage to be gained by kiln drying (KD) is utilized in certain grades so marked, and, for the first time, grades are set up for 1-in. boards and other members smaller than 2 × 4-in. nominal section.

Machine-stress rating evaluates the modulus of elasticity in bending by passing the piece through a series of rolls. The stress grade is assigned by a computer programmed on a correlation between the modulus of elasticity and the breaking strength. Use of these machines is expanding rapidly. It is anticipated that machine-stress-graded lumber will be more consistent than visually graded lumber and will also be more widely available.

Adjustments for Working Stresses

Modifications of the unit stresses in Table 4 should be made, if applicable, before employing these values in design as working stresses. The principal adjustment is for **duration of load.** Unit allowable stresses have been assigned on the basis of a 10-year loading period, and since the strength of wood varies with the log of time (see Rheology), other load periods can safely use modified stresses. Unit values from Table 4, excluding E for column computations, can be increased as follows: 15 percent for 2 months duration; as for snow; 25 percent for 7 days duration; 33⅓ percent for wind or earthquake; 100 percent for impact. When a member is fully stressed to maximum design load for more than ten years either continuously or cumulatively, use working stresses 90 percent of those in Table 4.

Table 3. Strength of Wood Members with Various Grain Slopes as Percentages of Straight-grained Members

(From Wood Handbook)

Maximum slope of grain in member	Static bending		Impact bending; drop height to failure (50 lb hammer), percent	Maximum crushing strength parallel to grain, percent
	Modulus of rupture, percent	Modulus of elasticity, percent		
Straight-grained	100	100	100	100
1 in 25	96	97	95	100
1 in 20	93	96	90	100
1 in 15	89	94	81	100
1 in 10	81	89	62	99
1 in 5	55	67	36	93

Moisture conditions which will cause the lumber in use to remain either dry or permanently above the fiber saturation point will employ the same values of stress as shown in Table 4, except that where lumber is fully submerged, compression parallel to the grain is reduced 10 percent, compression perpendicular to the grain is reduced one-third, and Young's modulus is decreased by one-eleventh.

GLUED-LAMINATED WOOD

The term **glued-laminated** wood, or **glulam,** refers to construction in which a wooden member, either straight or curved, is formed by assembling a set of boards or plank with glue so that the grain of all laminations is essentially parallel to the length of the member. Such construction offers wide latitude for formation of high-strength complex shapes, supplies large members far in excess of sawn solid sections, as, for example, dredge spuds 30 by 30 in. and 85 ft long; also, it allows the production of large, fully seasoned members without the long drying period required in the past. The cost of the glue and a normal one-third loss in material from rough to finished form make glued-laminated shapes more expensive than comparable sawn-solid sizes and at present restricts this construction to the special classes noted above.

Table 4. Allowable Unit Stresses for Stress-grade Lumber

(Condensed from National Design Specification 1962 ed.)
(The allowable unit stresses below are for normal loading conditions. For service conditions see text.)

Species and commercial grade[a]		Allowable unit stresses, psi				Modulus of elasticity E, psi
		Extreme fiber in bending f and tension parallel to grain t[c]	Horizontal shear H	Compression perpendicular to grain $c\ \perp$	Compression parallel to grain c	
Douglas Fir, All Regions						
Dense select structural[b]	LF	2,050	120	455	1,500	1,760,000
Select structural	LF	1,900	120	415	1,400	1,760,000
1750 f industrial	LF	1,750	120	415	1,400	1,760,000
1500 f industrial	LF	1,500	120	390	1,200	1,760,000
1200 f industrial	LF	1,200	95	390	1,000	1,760,000
Dense select structural[b]	J&P	2,050	120	455	1,650	1,760,000
Select structural	J&P	1,900	120	415	1,500	1,760,000
Dense construction[b]	J&P	1,750	120	455	1,400	1,760,000
Construction	J&P	1,500	120	390	1,200	1,760,000
Standard	J&P	1,200	95	390	1,000	1,760,000
Dense select structural[b]	B&S	2,050	120	455	1,500	1,760,000
Select structural	B&S	1,900	120	415	1,400	1,760,000
Dense construction[b]	B&S	1,750	120	455	1,200	1,760,000
Construction	B&S	1,500	120	390	1,000	1,760,000
Dense select structural[b]	P&T	1,900	120	455	1,650	1,760,000
Select structural	P&T	1,750	120	415	1,500	1,760,000
Dense construction[b]	P&T	1,500	120	455	1,400	1,760,000
Construction	P&T	1,200	120	390	1,200	1,760,000
Selected decking	Decking	1,500	...	390	.....	1,760,000
Commercial decking	Decking	1,200	...	390	.....	1,760,000
Douglas Fir, Inland Region (W.P.A.) (2-in. thick only; 15% moisture)						
Dense select structural MC 15	LF	2,300	125	455	1,700	1,760,000
Select structural MC 15	LF	2,100	125	415	1,550	1,760,000
1500 f industrial MC 15	LF	1,750	125	390	1,400	1,760,000
1200 f industrial MC 15	LF	1,500	110	390	1,200	1,760,000
Dense select structural MC 15	J&P	2,300	125	455	1,850	1,760,000
Select structural MC 15	J&P	2,100	125	415	1,650	1,760,000
Dense construction MC 15	J&P	2,050	125	455	1,600	1,760,000
Construction MC 15	J&P	1,750	125	390	1,400	1,760,000
Standard MC 15	J&P	1,500	110	390	1,200	1,760,000
Hemlock, Western (Coast and Inland)						
Select structural	LF	1,600	100	365	1,100	1,540,000
1500 f industrial	LF	1,500	100	365	1,000	1,540,000
1200 f industrial	LF	1,200	80	365	900	1,540,000
Select structural	J&P	1,600	100	365	1,200	1,540,000
Construction	J&P	1,500	100	365	1,100	1,540,000
Standard	J&P	1,200	80	365	1,000	1,540,000
Construction	B&S	1,500	100	365	1,000	1,540,000
Construction	P&T	1,200	100	365	1,100	1,540,000
Selected decking[g]	Decking	1,300	...	365	.....	1,540,000
Commercial decking[g]	Decking	1,000	...	365	.....	1,540,000

Table 4. Allowable Unit Stresses for Stress-grade Lumber—(*Continued*)

Species and commercial grade[a]		Allowable unit stresses, psi: Extreme fiber in bending f and tension parallel to grain t[c]	Horizontal shear H	Compression perpendicular to grain $c \perp$	Compression parallel to grain c	Modulus of elasticity E, psi
Hemlock, Inland Region (W.P.A.) (2 in. thick only; 15% moisture)						
Select structural MC15	LF	1,800	105	365	1,200	1,540,000
1500 f industrial MC 15	LF	1,650	105	365	1,150	1,540,000
1200 f industrial MC 15	LF	1,450	90	365	1,050	1,540,000
Select structural MC 15	J&P	1,800	105	365	1,300	1,540,000
Construction MC 15	J&P	1,650	105	365	1,250	1,540,000
Standard MC 15	J&P	1,450	90	365	1,150	1,540,000
Pine, Southern[d]						
Dense structural 86 KD[b,e,f]	2″ thick only	3,000	165	455	2,250	1,760,000
Dense structural 72 KD[b,e,f]	2″ thick only	2,500	150	455	1,950	1,760,000
Dense structural 65 KD[b,e,f]	2″ thick only	2,250	135	455	1,800	1,760,000
Dense structural 58 KD[b,e,f]	2″ thick only	2,050	120	455	1,650	1,760,000
No. 1 dense KD[b,e,f]	2″ thick only	2,050	135	455	1,750	1,760,000
No. 1 KD[e]	2″ thick only	1,750	135	390	1,500	1,760,000
No. 2 dense KD[b,e,f]	2″ thick only	1,750	120	455	1,300	1,760,000
No. 2KD[e]	2″ thick only	1,500	120	390	1,100	1,760,000
Dense structural 86[b,f]	2″ thick only	2,900	150	455	2,200	1,760,000
Dense structural 72[b,f]	2″ thick only	2,350	135	455	1,800	1,760,000
Dense structural 65[b,f]	2″ thick only	2,050	120	455	1,600	1,760,000
Dense structural 58[b,f]	2″ thick only	1,750	105	455	1,450	1,760,000
No. 1 dense[b,f]	2″ thick only	1,750	120	455	1,550	1,760,000
No. 1	2″ thick only	1,500	120	390	1,350	1,760,000
No. 2 dense[b,f]	2″ thick only	1,400	105	455	1,050	1,760,000
No. 2	2″ thick only	1,200	105	390	900	1,760,000
Dense structural 86[b,f]	3″ & 4″ thick	2,900	150	455	2,200	1,760,000
Dense structural 72[b,f]	3″ & 4″ thick	2,350	135	455	1,800	1,760,000
Dense structural 65[b,f]	3″ & 4″ thick	2,050	120	455	1,600	1,760,000
Dense structural 58[b,f]	3″ & 4″ thick	1,750	105	455	1,450	1,760,000
No. 1 dense SR[b,f]	3″ & 4″ thick	1,750	120	455	1,750	1,760,000
No. 1 SR	3″ & 4″ thick	1,500	120	390	1,500	1,760,000
No. 2 dense SR[b,f]	3″ & 4″ thick	1,400	105	455	1,050	1,760,000
No. 2 SR	3″ & 4″ thick	1,200	105	390	900	1,760,000
Dense structural 86[b,f]	5″ thick & up	2,400	150	455	1,800	1,760,000
Dense structural 72[b,f]	5″ thick & up	2,000	135	455	1,550	1,760,000
Dense structural 65[b,f]	5″ thick & up	1,800	120	455	1,400	1,760,000
Dense structural 58[b,f]	5″ thick & up	1,600	105	455	1,300	1,760,000
No. 1 dense SR[b,f]	5″ thick & up	1,600	120	455	1,500	1,760,000
No. 1 SR	5″ thick & up	1,400	120	390	1,300	1,760,000
No. 2 dense SR[b,f]	5″ thick & up	1,400	105	455	1,050	1,760,000
No. 2 SR	5″ thick & up	1,200	105	390	900	1,760,000
Industrial 86 KD[e]	1″, 1¼″ and 1½″ thick	2,600	165	390	1,950	1,760,000
Industrial 72 KD[e]	1″, 1¼″ and 1½″ thick	2,200	150	390	1,650	1,760,000
Industrial 65 KD[e]	1″, 1¼″ and 1½″ thick	2,000	135	390	1,550	1,760,000
Industrial 58 KD[e]	1″, 1¼″ and 1½″ thick	1,750	120	390	1,400	1,760,000

Table 4. Allowable Unit Stresses for Stress-grade Lumber—(*Continued*)

Species and commercial grade[a]		Allowable unit stresses, psi				
		Extreme fiber in bending f and tension parallel to grain t[c]	Horizontal shear H	Compression perpendicular to grain c ⊥	Compression parallel to grain c	Modulus of elasticity E, psi
Pine, Southern[d]						
Industrial 50 KD[e]	1″, 1¼″ and 1½″ thick	1,500	120	390	1,100	1,760,000
Industrial 86	1″, 1¼″ and 1½″ thick	2,500	150	390	1,900	1,760,000
Industrial 72	1″, 1¼″ and 1½″ thick	2,000	135	390	1,550	1,760,000
Industrial 65	1″, 1¼″ and 1½″ thick	1,750	120	390	1,350	1,760,000
Industrial 58	1″, 1¼″ and 1½″ thick	1,500	105	390	1,250	1,760,000
Industrial 50	1″, 1¼″ and 1½″ thick	1,200	105	390	900	1,760,000
Select	Decking	1,750	120	390	1,350	1,760,000
Select No. 1	Decking	1,200	105	390	900	1,760,000
No. 2	Decking	1,200	105	390	900	1,760,000

[a] Abbreviations: J&P = joists and planks; B&S = beams and stringers; P&T = posts and timbers; LF = light framing; KD: see note [e]; SR = stress rated.

[b] These grades meet the requirements for density.

[c] In tension members the slope of grain limitations applicable to the middle portion of the length of the joist and plank and beam and stringer grades used shall apply throughout the length of the piece.

[d] All stress-grades under the 1956 Grading Rules are all-purpose grades and apply to all sizes. Pieces so graded may be cut to shorter lengths without impairment of the stress rating of the shorter pieces.

Grade restrictions provided by the 1956 Grading Rules apply to the entire length of the piece, and each piece is suitable for use in continuous spans, over double spans or under concentrated loads without regrading for special shear or other special stress requirements.

The following variations apply to lumber in service under wet conditions or where the moisture content is at or above fiber saturation point, as when continuously submerged, (*a*) the allowable unit stresses in bending, tension parallel to grain and horizontal shear shall be limited in all thicknesses to the stresses indicated for thicknesses of 5″ and up; (*b*) the allowable unit stresses for compression parallel to grain shall be limited to the stresses indicated for thicknesses of 5″ and up reduced by 10 percent.

[e] KD = kiln dried in accordance with the provisions of paragraphs 219 and 220 of the 1956 Grading Rules.

[f] Longleaf may be specified by substituting "Longleaf" for "Dense" in the grade name, and when so specified the same allowable stresses shall apply.

[g] The grades apply for tongued-and-grooved material 2 and 4 in. in nominal thickness and 6-in. or more in nominal width. Stresses recommended are limited to conditions where the lumber is used as planks.

Glues and Gluing Practice

Glues for structural laminating are classified for interior or exterior use on the basis of resistance to the moisture conditions to be encountered in service. **Casein** is the most widely used adhesive and is employed where the moisture content of the timbers is lower than 20 percent, as for most indoor uses. This glue is inexpensive and will set at temperatures under 70 F. **Synthetic resins** are required for glued members which will be above 20 percent moisture content in use. All resins used in laminating are of the thermosetting types since joints made with the thermoplastic glues will creep under sustained loads. The hot-setting resins, such as straight phenol-formaldehyde, are generally avoided because the large size of the timbers makes it difficult to attain the proper setting temperatures at the glue line. For information on glues, see page 6–172 and Freas and Selbo, *U.S. Dept. Agr. Bull.* 1069.

Preparation of wood for gluing requires conditioning to moisture contents of 5 to 6 percent for interior uses and 10 to 12 percent for material to be used outdoors. Just prior to glue application the lumber should be machined, preferably on a double surfacer, using cuts no greater than ¹⁄₁₆ in., and at a feed speed to produce 20 to 30 knife marks to the inch. Uniformity of thickness is important, and variation should not exceed 0.010 to 0.016 in. for good results.

Gluing practice should conform closely to the manufacturer's recommendations for use of a given glue. The process of forming a glue joint is essentially a complex reaction in physical chemistry. Quality of the bond formed depends on the mixing and the pot life of the adhesive, assembly time, pressure, curing temperature, and surface preparation.

Preservative Treatment of Glued-laminated Members

In those cases in which decay hazard requires protection of the finished structure, this can be supplied either by treatment of the member after gluing and framing or the lumber can be treated prior to the laminating. When treatment is applied to a complete member, the glue line must be waterproof and capable of resisting the high temperature and chemical action of the preservative without delamination. For this application the thermosetting phenol derivatives have given best service. When treatment prior to lamination is necessary, creosote has proven to be compatible for both Douglas fir and southern pine with the exterior-use resin adhesives. Good joints are possible using impregnated lumber, if retention is moderate and a final light surfacing is carried out after treatment and before gluing.

Allowable Unit Stresses for Structural Glued-laminated Lumber

The determination of stresses is made on the basis of statistical study of the occurrence of knots in the various lumber grades (see *U.S. Dept. Agr. Tech. Bull.* 1069), the effect of slope of grain and slope of scarf, and the assumption that the beams will be laminated horizontally. Table 5 shows the allowable unit stresses for Douglas fir and southern pine structural glued-laminated lumber as developed by the West Coast Lumbermen's Association and the Southern Pine Inspection Bureau, respectively.

Modifications of allowable stresses required for grain slope in laminae, end joints, and vertical laminations can be found in Scofield and O'Brien, "Modern Timber Engineering." For the curved parts of bent members the allowable unit stress in bending is multiplied by a **curvature factor:** $1 - 2{,}000\ (t/R)^2$, in which t is the lamination thickness, in., R is the radius of curvature of a lamina, in., and the ratio t/R is not to exceed $1/125$ for softwoods and $1/100$ for hardwoods. The **radial stresses** induced in curved members by bending moments may be taken into account by methods given in paragraph 903-C-2, National Design Specification. Stresses shown in Table 5 should also be modified for load duration (see p. 6–158).

PLYWOOD

Plywood is the name given to a wood panel glued under pressure from an odd number of layers or plies of veneer or veneer and lumber, in which alternate plies are laid with the grain at right angles. The alternation of grain direction in adjacent plies equalizes the sheet in the two face directions in strength, stiffness, and dimensional changes.

Balanced construction in plywood results in minimum warpage in the sheet. Balance is determined by considering veneer thickness, shrinkage, elasticity, moisture content, and grain angle as factors in the moments of pairs of plies about the neutral axis of the sheet. Balance is especially critical in thin sheets.

The two outside veneer sheets in a plywood panel are known as the **faces** or **face and back.** The interior ply or plies whose grain direction parallels the face is a **core,** if single, or **centers,** if more than one is used. The interior plies whose grain is perpendicular to that in the faces are the **cross bands.** Plywood stock sheets range from three to seven plies and 1/8 to 1 3/16 in. thick and are usually 4 by 8 ft in surface. Special smaller sizes are produced to order, particularly in hardwoods. Lengths up to 30 ft can be made at the mills by splicing. Commercial thicknesses and ply construction of Douglas fir plywood are shown in Table 7.

Plywood can be made of veneers cut from any kind of wood; however, technical difficulties of glue compatibility and veneer cutting restrict production plywood to a few kinds of wood. Depending on the botanical identity of the wood in the sheets, plywood is classed as hardwood or softwood. For both classes the sheets are made in two types that reflect the moisture resistance of the glue joints. Douglas fir plywood, which is the principal constructional plywood in the U.S., is made as (1) **interior,** a type that will maintain its shape and most of its strength when occasionally subjected to a thorough wetting and subsequent normal drying; and (2) **exterior,** a type of plywood which must retain its shape and strength when repeatedly wet and dried under adverse conditions and be suitable for permanent outdoor exposure. The latter is also called **marine plywood.** Interior plywood is usually bonded with soybean glue or an extended resin adhesive, while exterior panels are made with hot-pressed phenol resins. The **grade of plywood** is based on the quality of the veneers on the faces of the sheet. Veneer grades for Douglas fir and most other western softwoods are A, B, C, and D, in decreasing order of quality. Hardwood veneers are graded as 1, 2, 3, 4, with number 1 as highest quality. The **grade designation** of plywood will include the type and the veneer grades, as, for example, Ext-DFPA·Plyshield·(A-C), in which the face is grade A and the back C. The inner plies of commercial Douglas fir panels are made up with grade C for exterior type and grade D for the interior-type plywood. The various grades of Douglas fir plywood are shown in Table 6.

Strength of Plywood

The allowable stress values for solid wood cannot be transposed directly to plywood because of the alternation of ply directions and the fact that knots and other major defects are confined to single plies. Precise equations for strength, based on the composite section and involving all plies, are given in Design of Wood Aircraft Structures, *ANC Bull.* 18. These calculations are involved and yield too refined answers for most applications.

Recommended Working Stresses for Douglas Fir Plywood

Approximate methods for the calculation of plywood strength have been developed and tested by the USFPL (R-1630, Apr., 1956). These methods are suitable for estimating the strength and stiffness of plywood and are sufficiently accurate for general design use, provided that the plywood is not stressed to buckling. Working stresses based on this system for various grades of Douglas fir are shown in Table 6. These stresses should be used only with the restrictions in the following paragraphs.

Tension and compression approximations take into account only those plies with grain parallel to load direction. Consequently, the choice of stress in the table must be made on basis of face-grain direction with respect to load direction. The values for parallel (‖) to face grain, perpendicular (⊥) to face grain, and 3 ply as against 5 or more plies differ because the inner plies are poorer grade veneer which carry lower stresses. Stress direction at 45 deg to face grain requires the full cross-sectional area to be used in computations because none of the plies in the sheet are parallel to the load direction. Calculations will be simplified for standard plywood constructions by the use of the section properties given in Table 7.

Bending load for plywood, based on *Bull.* 1630, is calculated by a modified flexure formula $M = KSI/c$, in which M is the bending moment; S is the unit stress for extreme fiber in bending of those plies in the parallel-to-span direction; I is the moment of inertia computed on basis of plies parallel to span only; c is the distance from neutral axis to outermost fiber of the outermost ply having its grain in the direction of the span; $K = 1.50$ for 3 ply plywood having the grain of the outer plies perpendicular to the span; $K = 0.85$ for all other plywood.

Deflection in bending is approximated by the usual equations, except that the moment of inertia I is a composite term made up of the sum of the moments of inertia for the plies parallel to span, plus one-twentieth that of the plies perpendicular to span. For thin sheets of plywood (¼ in. and under), the perpendicular plies contribute less than 10 percent to the total and may be neglected in calculations. However, as sheet thickness increases, the I perpendicular approaches the value of I parallel, and must be included.

Shear in plywood is of two types. The stress listed in Table 6 as shear in plane perpendicular (⊥) to plies is that developed in the plywood web of a built-up "I," or

Table 5. Allowable Unit Stresses for Structural Glued-laminated Lumber

(The allowable unit stresses below are for normal loading conditions. For service adjustments see text.)
(From National Design Specification)

Species and grade combinations			Allowable unit stresses in pounds per square inch							
Outer laminations		Inner laminations	Extreme fiber in bending, f*		Tension parallel to grain, t		Compression parallel to grain, c		Horizontal shear, H	Compression perpendicular to grain, $c \perp$
Grade	Number, each side	Grade	From 4 to 14 laminations	15 or more laminations	From 4 to 14 laminations	15 or more laminations	From 4 to 14 laminations	15 or more laminations		
Dry conditions of use (The modulus of elasticity E is 1,800,000 psi)										
Douglas Fir, Coast Region										
Select structural	All	Select structural	2,600	2,600	2,600	2,600	2,200	2,200	165	415
Select structural	Two	Construction	2,600	2,600	2,600	2,600	2,000	2,000	165	415
Clear (close grain)†	One	Construction	2,600	2,600	2,200	2,400	1,900	2,000	165	385
Dense construction	All	Dense construction	2,400	2,600	2,600	2,600	2,200	2,300	165	450
Dense construction	1/14 of total	Construction	2,400	2,600	2,200	2,400	1,900	2,000	165	450
Select structural	One	Construction	2,400	2,600	2,200	2,400	1,900	2,000	165	415
Select structural	Two	Standard	2,600	2,600	2,400	2,400	2,000	2,000	165	415
Select structural	One	Standard	2,200	2,200	2,000	2,400	1,800	1,900	165	415
Construction	All	Construction	2,000	2,200	2,200	2,400	1,900	2,000	165	385
Construction	One	Standard	2,000	2,200	2,000	2,400	1,800	1,900	165	385
Standard	All	Standard	1,600	2,000	2,000	2,400	1,800	1,900	165	385
Pine, Southern										
No. 1 dense	All	No. 1 dense	3,000	3,000	3,000	3,000	2,400	2,500	200	450
B & B dense	One	No. 1	3,000	3,000	2,600	2,600	2,100	2,100	200	450
No. 1 dense	1/14 of total	No. 1	3,000	3,000	2,600	2,600	2,100	2,100	200	450
B & B dense	One	No. 2 dense	2,800	2,800	3,000	3,000	2,400	2,400	200	450
No. 1 dense	1/5 of total	No. 2 dense	2,800	3,000	2,800	3,000	2,300	2,400	200	450
No. 1	All	No. 1	2,600	2,600	2,600	2,600	2,100	2,100	200	385
B & B dense	1/14 of total	No. 2	2,400	2,800	2,600	2,600	2,000	2,000	200	450
B & B	One	No. 2	2,400	2,400	2,600	2,600	2,000	2,000	200	385
No. 1	1/5 of total	No. 2	2,400	2,600	2,400	2,600	2,000	2,000	200	385
No. 2 dense	All	No. 2 dense	2,000	2,600	2,600	3,000	2,200	2,300	200	450
No. 2 dense	1/14 of total	No. 2	2,000	2,600	2,200	2,600	1,900	2,000	200	450

No. 2	All	No. 2	1,800	2,200	2,200	2,600	1,900	2,000	200	385
No. 1	1/5 of total	No. 3	1,800	2,400	2,400	2,500	1,900	2,000	200	385
No. 2	1/5 of total	No. 3	1,800	2,200	2,200	2,300	1,900	1,900	200	385
Wet conditions of use (The modulus of elasticity E is 1,600,000 psi)										
Douglas Fir, Coast Region										
Select structural	All	Select structural	2,000	2,000	2,000	2,000	1,600	1,600	145	275
Select structural	Two	Construction	2,000	2,000	1,800	1,800	1,500	1,500	145	275
Clear (close grain)†	One	Construction	2,000	2,000	1,800	1,800	1,400	1,400	145	260
Dense construction	All	Dense construction	2,000	2,200	2,000	2,000	1,600	1,700	145	305
Dense construction	1/14 of total	Construction	2,000	2,200	1,800	1,800	1,400	1,400	145	305
Select structural	One	Construction	2,000	2,000	1,800	1,800	1,400	1,400	145	275
Select structural	Two	Standard	2,000	2,000	1,800	1,800	1,400	1,400	145	275
Select structural	One	Standard	1,800	1,800	1,600	1,800	1,300	1,400	145	275
Construction	All	Construction	1,600	1,800	1,800	1,800	1,400	1,400	145	260
Construction	One	Standard	1,600	1,800	1,600	1,800	1,300	1,400	145	260
Standard	All	Standard	1,200	1,600	1,600	1,800	1,300	1,400	145	260
Pine, Southern										
No. 1 dense	All	No. 1 dense	2,400	2,400	2,400	2,400	1,800	1,800	175	300
B & B dense	One	No. 1	2,400	2,400	2,000	2,000	1,500	1,500	175	300
No. 1 dense	1/14 of total	No. 1	2,400	2,400	2,000	2,000	1,500	1,500	175	300
B & B dense	One	No. 2 dense	2,200	2,200	2,400	2,400	1,700	1,700	175	300
No. 1 dense	1/5 of total	No. 2 dense	2,200	2,400	2,200	2,400	1,700	1,700	175	300
No. 1	All	No. 1	2,000	2,000	2,000	2,000	1,500	1,500	175	260
B & B dense	1/14 of total	No. 2	1,800	2,200	2,000	2,000	1,500	1,500	175	300
B & B	One	No. 2	1,800	2,000	2,000	2,000	1,500	1,500	175	260
No. 1	1/5 of total	No. 2	2,000	2,000	2,000	2,000	1,400	1,500	175	260
No. 2 dense	All	No. 2 dense	1,600	2,000	2,000	2,400	1,600	1,700	175	300
No. 2 dense	1/14 of total	No. 2	1,600	2,000	1,800	2,000	1,400	1,400	175	300
No. 2	All	No. 2	1,400	1,800	1,800	2,000	1,400	1,400	175	260
No. 1	1/5 of total	No. 3	1,400	1,900	1,900	2,000	1,400	1,400	175	260
No. 2	1/5 of total	No. 3	1,400	1,700	1,800	1,900	1,400	1,400	175	260

* The allowable unit stresses in bending in Table 5 apply only when the wide faces of the laminations are placed normal to the direction of the load. For allowable stresses in bending when the loading is applied parallel to the planes of the laminations, see the applicable specification indicated in text.

† The rate of growth and density requirements of inner laminations shall apply to clear outer laminations.

Note. Members with intermediate working stresses will satisfy most design requirements. Members with the highest working stresses are available when special strength requirements are needed. Where larger sizes are desired, those combinations with lower stresses should be used.

box beam. The second kind of shear is set up in the plane of the plies as normal horizontal shear in a beam. Because the cells of the wood in a direction normal to their length are deformed at low stress levels, the shear is limited in this case by the plies perpendicular to stress direction. Such shear action is called **rolling shear** in plywood. Stress concentrations as exist between flanges and webs of "I" and box beams and framing members at edges of panels should be computed using 50 percent of tabulated rolling-shear stress.

Table 6. Allowable Unit Stresses for Plywood (Douglas Fir and Western Larch)

(For grades and thicknesses listed in USCS45–60)

(Values given are for permanent loads; for normal 10-year loading, increase by 10 percent.)

DRY LOCATION

Type of stress	Ext A-A	Ext A-B Ext A-C	Ext concrete form B-B Ext B-C Ext C-C Int concrete form B-B Int sheathing C-D Int sheathing C-D (ext glue)	All other grades conforming to USCS45–60, with Coast Douglas fir faces and backs and with inner plies of Douglas fir or any Western softwood species listed in Groups 1, 2, or 3 of USCS122–60 (apply the following percentages to stresses for corresponding Ext grade)
Extreme fiber in bending				
Face grain ∥ to span	2,188	2,000	1,875	100%
Face grain ⊥ to span	1,875	1,875	1,875	65
Tension				
∥ to face grain (3 ply only*)	2,188	2,000	1,875	100%‡
⊥ to face grain	1,875	1,875	1,875	65%
± 45° to face grain	337	320	310	75%
Compression				
∥ to face grain (3 ply only*)	1,605	1,460	1,375	100%‡
⊥ to face grain	1,375	1,375	1,375	60%
± 45° to face grain	496	472	460	70%
Bearing (on face)	405	405	405	100%
Shear, rolling, in plane of plies†				
∥ or ⊥ to face grain	79	72	68	75%
± 45°	105	96	90	75%
Shear in plane ⊥ to plies				
∥ or ⊥ to face grain	260	240	225	80%
± 45°	520	480	450	80%
Modulus of elasticity in bending				
Face grain ∥ to span	1,600,000	1,600,000	1,600,000	100%
Face grain ⊥ to span	1,600,000	1,600,000	1,600,000	60%

* For tension or compression, ∥ to grain, in 5 ply or thicker, use values for 3 ply, but in next lower grade.

† For the flange-web joints of beams having plywood webs and for joints between the skin and framing members located at the edges of stressed-skin plywood panels, these values shall be reduced by 50 percent.

‡ For 5 or more plies, use 80 percent.

Example: The working stress in compression ∥ for A-D 5-ply (1,100 psi) is found by multiplying the value for Exterior A-C 5-ply, 1375 psi, by 80%, the reduction factor shown in the last column and footnotes * and ‡.

WET OR DAMP LOCATION

Where moisture content will exceed 16%, decrease by 20% values shown for dry location for following properties:

Extreme fiber in bending, tension and compression both ∥ and ⊥ to the grain and at 45°, and bearing. (No change in values for rolling shear or modulus of elasticity.)

Shrinkage in Plywood

The range of possibilities in kinds of wood, combinations within a sheet, thickness, and numbers of plies makes the tabulation of shrinkage data impossibly cumbersome. Calculations can be made using the methods given by C. B. Norris in "Techniques of Plywood." Studies have been made by the U.S. Forest Products Laboratory for 3 ply panels of one kind of wood, and of equal ply thicknesses, dried from soaked to oven-dry condition, and ranging in thickness from 1/10 to 1/2 in. Shrinkage in such panels averages 0.45 percent parallel to the face grain and 0.67 percent perpendicular to the face grain, and varies from 0.2 to 1 percent and 0.3 to 1.2 percent, respectively.

Shrinkage of plywood in the direction of the sheet thickness approximates that of a sawn-solid piece of the same kind and dimension.

Table 7. Moments of Inertia, Section Moduli, and Veneer Areas for Selected Plywood Constructions

(12 in. widths)

(From "Technical Data on Plywood," Douglas Fir Plywood Assoc.)

Net plywood thickness	No. of plies	Veneer thickness (nominal), in.			Parallel‡ plies only			Perpendicular‡ plies only		
		Faces§	Centers	Crossband	Area, sq. in.	Moment of inertia I, in.⁴	Section modulus S, in.³	Area, sq. in.	Moment of inertia I, in.⁴	Section modulus S, in.³
1/8″—S†	3	1/16	1/16	.....	0.75	0.0017	0.027	0.75	0.0002	0.0077
3/16″—S	3	1/12	1/12	.....	1.25	0.0060	0.064	1.00	0.0006	0.0139
1/4″—R*	3	1/12	1/12	.....	2.00	0.0150	0.120	1.00	0.0006	0.0139
1/4″—S	3	1/9	1/9	.....	1.67	0.0143	0.114	1.33	0.0014	0.0247
5/16″—R	3	1/10+	1/10+	.....	2.50	0.0294	0.188	1.25	0.0011	0.0215
5/16″—S	3	1/8	1/8	.....	2.25	0.0286	0.183	1.50	0.0020	0.0312
3/8″—R	3	1/8	1/8	.....	3.00	0.0509	0.271	1.50	0.0020	0.0312
3/8″—S	3	1/8	3/16	.....	2.25	0.0461	0.246	2.25	0.0066	0.0704
3/8″—S	5	1/10	1/12	2@1/12	2.50	0.0377	0.201	2.00	0.0150	0.120
7/16″—S	5	1/10	1/10	2@1/10	2.85	0.0575	0.263	2.40	0.0260	0.1735
1/2″—R	5	1/10	1/10	2@1/10	3.60	0.0990	0.396	2.40	0.0260	0.1735
1/2″—S	5	1/8	1/8	2@1/10	3.60	0.0926	0.370	2.40	0.0324	0.1995
9/16″—S	5	1/8	1/8	2@1/8	3.75	0.1273	0.452	3.00	0.0507	0.271
5/8″—R	5	1/8	1/8	2@1/8	4.50	0.1934	0.619	3.00	0.0507	0.271
5/8″—S	5	1/8	3/16	2@1/8	4.50	0.1670	0.534	3.00	0.0771	0.352
11/16″—S	5	1/8	1/8	2@3/16	3.75	0.202	0.588	4.50	0.123	0.492
3/4″—R	5	1/8	1/8	2@3/16	4.50	0.299	0.798	4.50	0.123	0.492
3/4″—S	5	1/8	3/16	2@3/16	4.50	0.251	0.670	4.50	0.171	0.608
3/4″—S	7	1/8	2@1/12	3@1/8	4.50	0.286	0.763	4.50	0.136	0.503
13/16″—S	7	1/8	2@1/8	3@1/8	5.25	0.343	0.845	4.50	0.193	0.617
7/8″—S	7	1/8	2@5/32	3@1/8	6.00	0.427	0.976	4.50	0.243	0.707
15/16″—S	7	1/8	2@3/16	3@1/8	6.75	0.525	1.120	4.50	0.299	0.797
1″—S	7	1/8	2@1/8	3@3/16	5.25	0.540	1.080	6.75	0.460	1.131
1 1/16″—S	7	1/8	2@1/6	3@3/16	6.00	0.615	1.157	6.75	0.585	1.305
1 1/8″—R¶	7	1/10	2@3/16	3@3/16	6.90	0.798	1.419	6.66	0.627	1.115
1 1/8″—S	7	1/8	2@3/16	3@3/16	6.75	0.771	1.371	6.75	0.653	1.395
1 3/16″—S	7	1/8	2@7/32	3@3/16	7.50	0.912	1.538	6.75	0.763	1.526

* Rough. † Sanded. ‡ Refers to direction of face grain. § For sanded panels, thickness is before sanding. ¶ Interior floor panel 2·4·1 grade.

PRESERVATIVE TREATMENT OF WOOD

Since few woods are resistant to deterioration under adverse conditions, and the sterilization provided by steam treating and kiln drying is not permanent, the principal method for protection of wood in service is the introduction of toxic chemicals into the wood.

Materials for Protection Against Biological Action

Oils and oil-borne preservatives are the chief materials in use today. **Coal tar creosote,** which is the most widely used, is a by-product distilled from the coal tar produced by high-temperature carbonization of bituminous coal. It consists of a heterogeneous mixture of liquid and solid hydrocarbons having a continuous boiling range from about 200 C to 325 C. Analysis methods, as given by the American Wood Preservers Assoc., are important since the chemical composition and related toxicity of coal tar creosote is variable. The fraction distilling in the 200 to 275 C range appears to be the most toxic. As a means of reducing cost or increasing penetration, **creosote-coal tar solutions** and **creosote-petroleum solutions** have been used extensively. Such solutions are used in proportions as high as 50 percent. Toxicity of the petroleum solutions is reduced in a ratio greater than indicated by the percentage of diluent added. **Pentachlorophenol** in volatile petroleum carriers is nearly as important a preservative as creosote and is favored where cleanliness and paintability are necessary. Usual concentrations of pentachlorophenol for wood treatment are not less than 5 percent by weight. This produces a solution in the same range of cost as coal tar creosote and can be used in roughly the same range of retentions as the latter.

Water-borne solutions of inorganic salts have advantages over the oils in greater ease of penetration and freedom from fire hazards and odor; however, they do cause swelling and some react with metal. The principal preservative of this class is chromated zinc chloride. Some other salts used are: acid cupric chromate (Celcure), ammoniacal copper arsenate (Chemonite), chromated copper arsenate (Green salt or Erdalith), chromated zinc arsenate (Boliden salt), copperized chromated zinc chloride. Retention for salts used in wood preserving is stated in pounds of dry salt per cubic foot of material.

Preparation of Material

Wood which is to be pressure treated must be peeled to hasten drying and permit maximum preservative absorption. Barking can be done by hand shaving or in a peeling machine which smoothes and straightens the poles. Machine peeling results in lower pole strengths and lesser penetration for many kinds of wood.

Seasoning ordinarily is done by air drying to about 15 percent moisture content. When green material must be used for treating, two seasoning methods are common. **Steam conditioning** is usually used with southern pine. The wood in the treating cylinder is steamed for several hours at about 30 psi following which a vacuum is drawn on the charge for several hours. MacLean (*U.S. Dept. Agr. Misc. Publ.* 224, rev. 1953) has worked out charts showing cycles required and temperatures attained for various sizes of material. **Boiling under vacuum** (Boulton process) is extensively used for Douglas fir and red oak. The charge in a cylinder is submerged in hot oil, and a vacuum drawn so that the water boils out of the wood.

Adzing, boring, framing, and all other cutting should be completed prior to treatment since this will ensure all surfaces are adequately penetrated.

Incising is a process by which chisel-pointed teeth are forced into the side grain of the wood to about half-inch depths. Primary purpose is to expose more end grain and give greater penetration in woods such as western red cedar and Douglas fir.

Methods for Preservative Treatment

Wood can be treated with preservatives under pressure in closed vessels, by dipping, hot and cold soak, and diffusion. On the basis of volume of material treated for use in engineered structures, the pressure treatments are most important.

Three pressure systems are standard today: **full-cell** (Bethell), **Lowry**, and **Rueping.** All employ a combination of pressure and vacuum in sequence on material contained in a pressure vessel. The essential difference is the use of an initial vacuum or pressure. The full-cell process draws a vacuum on the charge, then introduces the preservative without breaking the vacuum, so that a maximum of preservative can be forced into the wood. The Lowry system uses atmospheric pressure at the start, and the Rueping process employs a positive initial pressure. The latter two systems are also called **empty-cell processes** because the air under pressure in the wood will expand at the end of the cycle to force out excess preservative from cell cavities, leaving a minimum retention for maximum penetration. The Rueping process is the most efficient in this respect and is now the principal creosoting process in use in this country. Typical pressure–time cycles for the three processes are shown in Fig. 4. The temperature during the treatment depends mostly on the preservative. Creosote oils are usually used in the range of 180 to 200 F. Salt solutions are used at temperatures from atmospheric to 200 F. Higher temperatures with salts may cause difficulties in reactions with the wood and embrittlement (see p. 6–154).

Fire-retardant treatments of wood use the same pressure methods and equipment as that used for preservation. Salts similar to those used to protect against fungus attack are employed (see above), but in much greater quantities, up to refusal. This high proportion of inorganic material can have a dulling effect on machine tools. The three principal materials used are chromated zinc chloride (FR), Minalith, and Pyresote. (See also p. 12–195.)

Allowable working stresses for preservative-treated lumber should be reduced to account for damage due to the treating process. Tests made by the U.S. Forest Products Laboratory of preservative-treated lumber when undergoing bending and compression perpendicular to grain show reductions in stress in extreme fiber from a few percent up to 25 percent, depending on the treating conditions. Compression parallel to grain is affected less and modulus of elasticity very little. The effect on

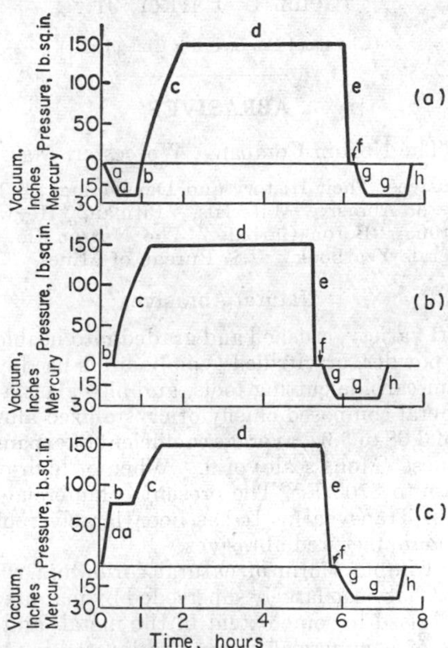

FIG. 4. Typical pressure diagrams for pressure preservative treatment of wood. (*From Hunt and Garratt, "Wood Preservation," McGraw-Hill.*) (*a*)—Full-cell process: *a*, preliminary vacuum period; *b*, filling cylinder with preservative; *c*, pressure rising to maximum; *d*, maximum pressure maintained; *e*, pressure released; *f*, preservative withdrawn; *g*, final vacuum period; *h*, vacuum released. (*b*)—Lowry process: *b*, filling cylinder with preservative at atmospheric pressure; *c* to *h*, pressure period and final vacuum, as in (*a*). (*c*)—Rueping process: *aa*, preliminary air pressure applied; *b*, filling cylinder, while pressure is maintained; *c* to *h*, pressure period and final vacuum, as in (*a*).

horizontal shear can be estimated by inspection for increase in shakes and checks after treatment. Keeping temperatures, heating periods, and pressures to a minimum for required penetration and retention will hold the loss in working stress to a reasonable figure.

COMMERCIAL LUMBER STANDARDS

Standard abbreviations for lumber description and **size standards** for yard lumber are given in the Wood Handbook.

Cross-sectional **dimensions** and **section properties** for beams, stringers, joists, planks, and posts are given in Sec. 12.

Standard patterns for finish lumber are shown in publications of the grading and dressing rules for the various lumber associations.

Information and **specifications for commercial plywood** are given in Commercial Standards: CS45–55 for Douglas-fir Plywood and CS35–49 for Hardwood Plywood.

NON-METALLIC MATERIALS

BY

Rienzi B. Parker, Jr.

(Chemical Engineering Consultant)

ABRASIVES

(The Norton Company, Worcester, Mass.)

REFERENCES: "Abrasives: Their History and Development," The Norton Co. Searle, "Manufacture and Use of Abrasive Materials," Pitman. Heywood, "Grinding Wheels and Their Uses," Penton. "Boron Carbide," The Norton Co. "Abrasive Materials," annual review in "Minerals Yearbook," U.S. Bureau of Mines.

Natural Abrasives

Diamond of the **bort** variety, crushed and graded into usable sizes and bonded with synthetic resin, metal powder, or vitrified-type bond, is used extensively for grinding tungsten- and tantalum-carbide cutting tools, and also glass, stone and ceramics.

Corundum is a mineral composed chiefly of crystallized alumina (93 to 97 percent Al_2O_3) with a density of 3.68 to 3.94, average coefficient of expansion of about 0.0000045 per deg F, and a hardness (Mohs scale) of 9. When of high purity, it is insoluble in acids and melts at close to 3700 F. The present commercial source of corundum is South Africa (Northern Transvaal). It has been largely replaced by harder, more uniform and efficient, manufactured abrasives.

Emery, a cheap and impure form of natural corundum which has been used for centuries as an abrasive, has been largely superseded by manufactured aluminum oxide for grinding. It is still used to some extent in the metal- and glass-polishing trades. The principal deposits of commercial emery are located in Asia Minor and on the island of Naxos.

Garnet. Certain deposits of garnet having a hardness between quartz and corundum are used in the manufacture of abrasive paper. **Quartz** is also used for this purpose. Garnet costs about twice as much as quartz and generally lasts proportionately longer.

Buhrstones and millstones are generally made from cellular quartz. Chasers (or stones running on edge) are also made from the same mineral.

Oilstones. Most oilstones used today in metalworking and wood-working shops are made of manufactured aluminum oxide, in three grits, fine, medium, and coarse. The great majority of oilstones are quarried in Arkansas and are known as "Arkansas" and "Washita" stones. The **Arkansas stone** is a true novaculite, homogeneous, gritty, and of a fine, siliceous composition. The hard variety is used for sharpening tools requiring a very fine edge, such as those of surgeons, engravers, and dentists. The soft variety is more porous and coarser and is used for less exacting work. **Washita stone** is less dense, more porous, and of the same general composition. The chief use is for whetstones and for coarser tools.

Pumice, of volcanic origin, is extensively used in leather, felt, and woolen industries and in the manufacture of polish for wood, metal, and stone. An artificial pumice is made from sand and clay in five grades of hardness, grain, and fineness.

Infusorial earth or **tripoli** resembles chalk or clay in physical properties. It can be distinguished by absence of effervescence with acid, is generally white or gray in color, but may be brown or even black. Owing to its porosity, it is very absorptive.

It is used extensively in polishing powders, scouring soaps, etc., and, on account of its porous structure, in the manufacture of dynamite as a holder of nitroglycerin, also as a non-conductor for steam pipes and as a filtering medium. It is also known as **diatomaceous silica.**

Manufactured Abrasives

Manufactured abrasives have largely superseded the natural abrasives for commercial use, owing to a much closer control of chemical composition and crystal structure, thus enabling the maintenance of uniform hardness and cutting qualities.

Crystalline alumina consists essentially of the same mineral as corundum, but the physical properties such as crystal structure, size, and shape of grain are so controlled as to produce the most desirable abrasives for specific types of grinding. The method of cooling the pig of ore and the percentages of impurities present (TiO_2, Fe_2O_3, and SiO_2), although usually less than 5 percent total, greatly influence the properties of the product. Crystalline alumina has a conchoidal fracture, and the grains, when crushed or broken, possess sharp cutting points and edges. Manufactured aluminum oxide, particularly the fines, is also an excellent refractory material for electric-furnace parts, laboratory ware, and many special industrial installations. As an abrasive it is best adapted to the grinding of high-tensile-strength materials such as steel and annealed malleable iron. Manufactured corundum is available under several trade names such as **Borolon,**® **Aloxite,**® **Lionite,**® and **Alundum.**® A product made by fusing chemically purified alumina (Al_2O_3) is not so tough as the material of 95 percent purity but is better adapted to certain operations such as precision grinding of sensitive steels.

Silicon carbide (SiC) (see p. 6–122) corresponding to the mineral moissanite has been found in meteors. The hardness is between that of corundum and diamond; the specific gravity is 3.2. It is insoluble in acid and infusible. It decomposes above 4060 F. It is manufactured by fusing together coke and sand in an electric furnace of the resistance type. Sawdust is used also in the batch and burns away leaving passages for the carbon monoxide to escape. The grains are characterized by great brittleness. Abrasives of silicon carbide are best adapted to the grinding of low-tensile-strength materials such as cast iron, brass, bronze, marble, concrete, stone, and glass. It is available under several trade names such as **Carborundum,**® **Carbolon,**® and **Crystolon.**®

Boron carbide (B_4C), a recent addition to commercial manufactured abrasives, has a scratch hardness greater than that of silicon carbide. It is available under the trade name of **Norbide,**® and is being used in loose grain form for the lapping of cemented-carbide tools. In the form of molded shapes, it is used for pressure blast nozzles, wire-drawing dies, bearing surfaces for gages, etc.

Grinding Wheels

Vitrified Process. In wheels, segments, and other abrasive shapes of this type, the abrasive grains are bonded with a glass or porcelain obtained by mixing the grains with such materials as clays and feldspars in various proportions, molding the wheel, drying, and firing at a temperature of 2500 F approx. It is possible to manufacture wheels as large as 60 in. diam by this process, and even larger wheels may be obtained by building up with segments. Most of the grinding wheels and shapes (segments, cylinders, bricks, etc.) now manufactured are of the vitrified type and are very satisfactory for general grinding operations.

Silicate Process. Wheels and shapes of the silicate type are manufactured by mixing the abrasive grain with sodium silicate (water glass) and fillers that are more or less inert, molding the wheel by tamping, and baking at a moderate temperature. Silicate bonded wheels are considered relatively "mild acting" and, in the form of large wheels, are still used to some extent for grinding-edge tools in place of the old-fashioned sandstone wheels.

Organic Bonded Wheels. Organic bonds are used for high-speed wheels, and are equally well adapted to the manufacture of very thin wheels because of their flexibility compared with vitrified wheels. There are three distinct types in the group. The **shellac process** consists of mixing abrasive grains with shellac, heating the mass until the shellac is viscous, stirring, cooling, crushing, forming in molds, and reheating sufficiently to permit the shellac to set firmly upon cooling. Wheels made by this process are used for saw gumming, roll grinding, ball-race and cam grinding, and in the cutlery trade. In the **rubber process** the bond is either natural or synthetic rubber. The initial mixture of grain, rubber, and sulphur (and such special ingredients as accelerators, fillers, and softeners) may be obtained by rolling or other methods. Having formed the wheel, the desired hardness is then developed by vulcanization. Wheels can be made in a wide variety of grain combinations and grades and have a high factor of safety as regards resistance to breakage in service. Wheels made by the rubber process are used for cutoff service on wet-style machines, ball-race punchings, feed wheels and centerless grinders, and for grinding stainless-steel billets and welds, which usually require a high-quality finish. With the **resinoid process,** the practice is to form the wheel by the cold-press process using a synthetic resin. After heating, the resultant bond is an insoluble, infusible product of notable strength and resiliency. Resinoid bond is used for the majority of high-speed wheels in foundries, welding shops, and billet shops, and also for cutoff wheels. The rate of stock removal is generally in direct proportion to the peripheral speed. Resinoid bonded wheels are capable of being operated at speeds as high as 9,500 sfpm, as contrasted with 6,500 sfpm for most vitrified bonds.

The **grain** size or grit of a wheel is determined by the size or combination of sizes of abrasive grain used. The Grinding Wheel Institute has standardized sizes 8, 10, 12, 14, 16, 20, 24, 30, 36, 46, 54, 60, 70, 80, 90, 100, 120, 150, 180, 200, 220, and 240. The finer sizes, known as flours, are designated as 280, 320, 400, 500, 600, 800, 900, or as F, FF, FFF, and XF.

The **grade** is the hardness or relative strength of bonding of a grinding wheel. The wheel from which grain particles are easily broken away, causing it to wear rapidly, is called soft, and one that is able to retain its particles longer is called hard. The complete range of grade letters used for the order of increasing hardness is

Soft → Hard

A, B, C, D, E, F, G, H, I, J, K, L, M, N, O, P, Q, R, S, T, U, V, W, X, Y, Z

Flint, garnet, emery, corundum, and the manufactured abrasives can be held on paper or cloth by glue or a resin cement. Abrasive papers are used chiefly for wood and the cloths for metal work.

Crushed steel is made by heating high-grade crucible steel to white heat and quenching in a bath of cold water. The fragments are then crushed to sizes ranging from fine powder to 1⁄16 in. diam. They are classified as diamond crushed steel, diamond steel, emery, and steelite, used chiefly in the stone, brick, glass, and metal trades.

Rouge and **crocus** are finely powdered oxide of iron used for buffing and polishing. Rouge is the red oxide; crocus is purple.

ADHESIVES

By Thomas D. Perry

(Consultant to Rohm & Haas Co.)

References: Braude, "Adhesives," Chemical Publishing Co. Sutermeister and Browne, "Casein and Its Industrial Applications," Reinhold. Perry, "Modern Wood Adhesives," Pitman. Del Monte, "Technology of Adhesives," Reinhold. Knight, "Adhesives for Wood," Chemical Publishing Co.

Glue is the term usually applied to materials of natural origin, as animal, vegetable (starch), casein, and soybean; **adhesive** is the more recent term generally used for synthetic bonding agents. **Cements** often refer to specific adhesives for rubber, glass, stone, leather, etc., and **pastes** to those for paper goods.

Animal glue is derived from by-products of the packing industry, hides and bones particularly. It is available in flake or granulated form and, for use, is dissolved in water at temperatures from 120 to 160 F. Bone and hide glues are usually blended to establish standard grades. Glue is the standard by which other adhesives are judged for strength. Animal glue joints, when tested dry, are stronger than the wood but deteriorate rapidly when wet, or exposed to mold, fungi, or insect pests. Glue is used mainly for assembly work, since cost largely eliminates it from the plywood field.

The method of grading glue is that of the National Association of Glue Manufacturers, adopted in 1930, and complete data can be obtained from them.

Casein glue is a product of the dried curds of milk, lime, and other chemical ingredients, mixed cold. It is used for both plywood and assembly work but is comparatively costly. Casein glue bonds are water-resistant but are subject to deterioration from mold and fungi. Casein latex is a combination used for metal-to-wood bonds, as in plywood with metal faces (sometimes called **Plymetal**).

Soybean glue is derived from soybean meal after the oil has been extracted. It is a dry powder and is combined with lime, caustic soda, silicate of soda, etc. It is widely used in Douglas fir plywood, is low in cost, and is moderately water-resistant. As with other alkaline materials, it must be used on woods with discrimination, to avoid staining.

Vegetable glue is usually made from cassava (tapioca) flour, dissolved with caustic soda. Other starches, corn or potato, are sometimes used. Being low in cost, it is extensively used for the plywood of low- and medium-priced furniture. It makes a thick viscous mixture and must be mechanically spread. Vegetable-glue bonds show excellent strength when dry, but weaken under moisture exposure and are attacked by mold and fungi.

Silicate of soda glues find use as quick-sticking adhesives for corrugated boxes and in the low-cost plywood field, particularly for box shooks, where the lack of durability is not a serious handicap.

Albumin glue is soluble dried blood, with minor additives. It gives strong durable bonds when coagulated in plywood joints at temperatures of 160 to 180 F. It was the first of the wood adhesives to be set under heat, a step that encouraged the development of the **resin** adhesives. While highly moisture resistant, it deteriorates with age and under attack by mold and fungi.

Synthetic Adhesives

Synthetic or resin-type adhesives have become important recently. Most of them exhibit better water resistance than the glues mentioned above and are more durable under weather exposure. In general they can be cured (hardened or polymerized) under heat in minutes, in contrast with the hours of clamping time required for most glues and adhesives at normal room temperatures. Some of them can be hardened by the use of chemical catalysts (hardeners) but must be kept under pressure for several hours. Resin adhesives, as a rule, are immune to molds, fungi, and insect attacks.

Urea-formaldehydes cure under heat (200 to 225 F) and can be cured at room temperatures, with proper catalysts, at 70 F and up, but not below 70 F. They are available in liquid or powder form, the liquids having a separate catalyst added at the time of use. The powders usually have an incorporated catalyst and are mixed with water at the time of use. Ureas are generally combined with substantial amounts of extenders (such as wheat flours), often up to 2 parts adhesive powder to 1 part extender. This brings them within a favorable cost range for use in high-grade furniture, pianos, cabinets, interior plywood, doors, and the like, which may be used in homes and offices in humid climates. They have largely displaced animal and vegetable glues for such applications. They are distinctly water-resistant with low extender ratios, but higher extender ratios appreciably reduce this water resistance. In general they are not considered suitable for weather or marine exposures.

Phenol-formaldehydes are available in powder, liquid, and film form, the latter (**Tego**) being especially useful with thin veneers (under $\frac{1}{30}$ in.), where spreading is difficult. Resulting plywood is waterproof, weather- and marineproof, and is widely used in air and water craft. Powders are reduced to liquid form, usually with water as a solvent, and fillers (such as walnut-shell flour), up to about 20 percent of the weight of the adhesive powder, improve the spreading qualities. No catalysts are required, and normal cure is under heat at 250 to 325 F. Some suppliers provide acid catalysts for room temperature work, at 70 F and up, but the resulting bonds are not considered the equivalent of hot pressing. Phenolics are extensively used for **exterior-type** plywood, under rigid specifications (CS-45–55 for softwood plywood and CS-35–49 for hardwood). Properly made phenolic-resin adhesive joints in heat-bonded plywood exhibit extreme durability, even outlasting the wood under severe exposures. Phenolics are used chiefly for such plywood and seldom for assembly joints.

Resorcinol-formaldehyde is particularly adaptable to laminating timbers and boat parts, since it will cure at 75 F and up, but no lower. Its durability is increased by curing assemblies in tightly sealed chambers up to about 200 F, when it is equal to that of the phenolics. It is often combined with phenolics to lower temperature requirements and costs; and with ureas to increase their water resistance, under which conditions they are called **fortified ureas.** It is only available in liquid form with a separate catalyst and is in the higher cost ranges.

Melamine-formaldehyde is a type of urea with improved water resistance closely approaching that of the phenolics. It can be cured only with heat. It is often combined with ureas. When uncombined it has the advantage of being practically colorless.

Polyvinyl resin emulsions are available, premixed, and on a "ready-to-use" basis. They have the advantage of a very quick "tack" and require a minimum of half an hour under pressure at room temperatures. They can be used only at normal room temperatures, weakening under substantial heat, and are not water-resistant. However, they find wide use in assembly joints and special plywood constructions, because of their short time pressure requirements.

There are several other chemically derived adhesives, related to the plastics, which are suitable for special uses. These include resins of the polyamide, polyester, and epoxy types. The latter exhibit excellent adhesion to metallic and other surfaces, high strength, low water sensitivity, and high thermal stability. Suppliers should be consulted for details.

Packaged Glues. Casein and urea resin adhesives are available in package form for retail sales, requiring only mixing with water and curing at room temperature. Various proprietary liquid glues are similarly available. Most of these latter are based on animal or fish glues with various chemical additions. They may be useful for small shops where volume does not justify the mechanical preparation and application required in regular factory operation.

Cements

Plastic bonding agents constitute a class of heat-applied cements, valuable for bonding metal to metal, metal to rubber, or metal to wood. **Reanite,**® is a modified rubber, and **Cycleweld,**® is a combination of rubber and other plastics. **Kotol,**® a thermoplastic cement, is used for cementing metal to rubber. These allow very strong joints to be made conveniently and, in some instances, replace welding.

Pyroxylin cement is made by dissolving scrap celluloid or other pyroxylin material in a lacquer solvent. It is a very convenient water-resistant cement for repair-shop use.

Rubber cements are available in two types: the latex or compounded-latex type and the solvent rubber-cement type. The **latex type** finds use as a fabric and fiber cement, especially for combining layers of cloth in shoe construction. It has good durability. **Solvent rubber cements** are produced by dissolving freshly milled rubber, preferably natural crepe, in naphtha, benzol, or other solvent. This produces a viscous tacky adhesive for the permanent cementing of rubber or the temporary sticking of paper, cloth, etc.

Magnesia cement consists of calcined magnesia mixed with a 30 percent solution of magnesium chloride. It hardens to a stonelike mass with considerable capacity for binding organic matter.

Putties

Litharge and glycerine combine to make an oil-resistant filler of considerable strength.

Plastic wood is a combination of wood flour, resins, and a nitrocellulose cement, of great utility for filling nailholes, cracks, etc.

Putty, made by mixing whiting with linseed oil, was once used almost exclusively for setting glass windows. **Glazing compounds** of greater flexibility and durability are gradually replacing putty.

BELTING MATERIALS

By V. J. Mlejneck

(Formerly with Graton & Knight Company)

(See also p. 8–70)

Leather Belts. High-quality leather belting is made of leather cut from the part of the hide that is back of the shoulders and close to the backbone. Such leather is uniform and has min stretch and max elasticity. Strips cut from this section, properly matched and joined together, will produce a straight, smooth-running belt. Single belting can regularly be obtained up to about 3⁄16 in. thick, double (two-ply) belting up to about ⅜ in. thick. Belting of over two plies is made to suit individual conditions. Very wide belting is generally made by joining two or more strips laterally.

Federal specification KK-B-201b for flat leather belting specifies that the average stretch shall not exceed 15 percent at a tensile stress of 2,500 psi. The leather shall have a minimum tensile strength of not less than 3,300 psi and an average of not less than 4,000 psi for single-ply and not less than 3,750 psi for double-ply.

Care of Leather Belting. Belting should not be allowed to dry out and become harsh and brittle. If found to be drying out, it should be treated with liquid dressing. Surface dirt should be removed before the dressing is applied, and only as much as is readily absorbed should be applied at one time. Both sides of the belt should be treated for best results. Liquid dressings formulated by a belting manufacturer are available.

Commercial sizes of leather belting range from ½ to 72 in. in width, the width increasing by ⅛ in. up to 1 in., by ¼ in. up to 3 in., by ½ in. up to 5 in., by 1 in. up to 10 in. and above that by 2 in. increments.

Rubber belts are made by impregnating layers of fabric and/or cord with natural or synthetic rubber compounds to form "plies" which are bonded into an integral belt by vulcanization in heated presses. Their advantages are high strength, low stretch growth, resistance to moisture, good flexibility, long wear resistance, and low original cost. Rubber belts are available in many types for different service conditions and horsepower loads. All belting manufacturers provide free design services upon request. Rubber belts should never be treated with leather-belt dressings or other dressings which contain oils that soften and weaken rubber compounds. Rubber-belt strengths are specified in pounds per inch width per ply. Standard duct breaking strengths in a belt have been set by the Rubber Manufacturers Assoc. at the following minimums:

28 oz—280 lb per in. per ply
32 oz—300 lb per in. per ply
35 oz—320 lb per in. per ply

where belt duct weights are based on the raw fabric weight of a 36 × 42 in. size sample. Commercial sizes run from 1 to 60 in. Special belts of rayon, nylon, or steel-cable construction are available in strengths far exceeding the above.

Cotton belts, when woven, have a tensile strength of 5,000 psi approx; when sewed, from 6,500 to 7,500 psi.

BRICKING MATERIALS, BLOCKS, AND TILE

References: Plummer and Reardon, "Principles of Brick Engineering, Handbook of Design," Structural Clay Products Institute. Stang, Parsons, and McBurney, Compressive Strength of Clay Brick Walls, *B of S Research Paper* 108. ASTM specifications covering paving brick, building brick, sewer brick, and fire brick. Hunting, "Building Construction," Wiley.

The Committee on Nomenclature and Definitions (E-8) of the ASTM has published the following definition of brick:

Brick—In the case of structural and road building material, a small unit, solid or practically so, commonly in the form of a rectangular prism, formed from inorganic, non-metallic substances and hardened in its finished shape by heat or chemical action. NOTE—The term is also used collectively for a number of such units, as "a carload of brick." In the present state of the art, the term brick, when used without a qualifying adjective, should be understood to mean such a unit, or a collection of such units, made from clay or shale hardened by heat. When other substances are used, the term brick should be suitably qualified unless specifically indicated by the context.

It is, therefore, officially recognized that unless suitably qualified, a brick is a unit of burned clay or shale.

Brick (Common). Any brick made primarily for building purposes and not especially treated for texture or color, but including clinker and over-burnt brick.

Brick (Facing). A brick made especially for facing purposes, usually treated to produce surface texture or made of selected clays or otherwise treated to produce the desired color.

Brick are manufactured by the dry-press, the stiff-mud, or the soft-mud process. The **dry-press brick** are made in molds under high pressure and from relatively dry clay mixes. Usually all six surfaces are smooth and even, with geometrical uniformity. The **stiff-mud brick** are made from mixes of clay or shale with more moisture than in the dry-press process, but less moisture than used in the soft-mud process. The clay is extruded from an auger machine in a ribbon and cut by wires into the required lengths. These brick may be side-cut or end-cut, depending on the cross section of the ribbon and the length of the section cut off. The two faces cut by wires are rough in texture, the other faces may be smooth or artifically textured. The **soft-mud process** uses a wet mix of clay which is placed in molds under slight pressure.

The various **methods of burning** commonly used are described as scove kilns, tunnel kilns, round or downdraft kilns, continuous kilns, and permanent kilns. Properties vary greatly, depending on the burning conditions. In tunnel kilns, all brick are burned approximately the same. Placed on cars, the brick move slowly through the tunnel and into gradually increasing temperatures, until the maximum of approximately 2000 F is reached. From there on, they are gradually cooled.

Brick are highly resistant to freezing and thawing, to attacks of acids and alkalies, and to fire. They furnish good thermal insulation and good insulation against sound transference.

Building Brick Made from Clay or Shale

(Standard specifications, ASTM, C62-49)

Designation*	Min compressive strength (brick flatwise), psi gross area		Max water absorption by 5 hr boil, percent		Max saturation coefficient†	
	Avg of 5	Indiv.	Avg of 5	Indiv.	Avg of 5	Indiv.
Grade SW	3,000	2,500	17.0	20.0	0.78	0.80
Grade MW	2,500	2,200	22.0	25.0	0.88	0.90
Grade NW	1,500	1,250	No limit		No limit	

* Grade SW includes brick intended for use where a high degree of resistance to frost action is desired and the exposure is such that the brick may be frozen when permeated with water.

Grade MW includes brick intended for use where exposed to temperatures below freezing but unlikely to be permeated with water or where a moderate and somewhat non-uniform degree of resistance to frost action is permissible.

Grade NW includes brick intended for use as back-up or interior masonry, or if exposed, for use where no frost action occurs; or if frost action occurs, where the average annual precipitation is less than 20 in.

† The saturation coefficient is the ratio of absorption by 24 hr submersion in cold water to that after 5 hr submersion in boiling water.

Paving brick are made of clay or shale usually by the stiff-mud or dry-press process. Brick for use as paving brick are burned to vitrification. The common requirements are as follows: size, $8\frac{1}{2} \times 2\frac{1}{2} \times 4$, $8\frac{1}{2} \times 3 \times 3\frac{1}{2}$, $8\frac{1}{2} \times 3 \times 4$, with permissible variations of $\frac{1}{8}$ in. in either transverse dimension, and $\frac{1}{4}$ in. in length.

Although brick have always been used in construction, their use has been limited, until recently, to resisting compressive-type loadings. By adding steel in the mortar joints to take care of tensile stresses, **reinforced brick masonry** extends the use of brick masonry to additional types of building construction such as floor slabs.

Sand-lime brick are made from a mixture of sand and lime, molded under pressure and cured under steam at 200 F. They are usually a light gray in color and are used primarily for backing brick and for interior facing.

Cement brick are made from a mixture of cement and sand, manufactured in the same manner as sand-lime brick. In addition to their use as backing brick, they are used where there is no danger of attack from acid or alkaline conditions.

Firebrick (see p. 6–206).

Specialty Brick. A number of types of specialty brick is available for important uses, particularly where refractory characteristics are needed. These include **alumina** brick, **silicon carbide** brick, and **boron carbide** brick (see pp. 6–171, 6–214).

Other Structural Blocks. Important structural units which fall outside the classic definition of brick are as follows: **Concrete blocks** are made with portland cement as the basic binder. The choice of aggregate ranges from relatively dense aggregate such as sand to light aggregate such as coal cinders. **Gypsum blocks** are generally used for fire protection in non-load-bearing situations. **Glass blocks** are available where transparency is desired. **Structural clay tile** is widely used in both load-bearing and non-load-bearing situations; variety of complex shapes is available for hollow-wall construction. For classification of all these products with respect to dimensions and specifications for usage, the references should be consulted.

CERAMICS

By Robert S. Feigelson

(Stanford University)

References: Kingery, "Introduction to Ceramics," Wiley. Norton, "Elements of Ceramics," Addison-Wesley. "Carbon Encyclopedia of Chemical Technology," Interscience. Humenik, "High-temperature Inorganic Coatings," Reinhold. Kingery, "Ceramic Fabrication Processes," MIT.

Ceramic materials are a diverse group of non-metallic, inorganic solids with a wide range of compositions and properties. Their structure may be either crystalline or glassy. The desired properties are often achieved by high-temperature treatment (firing or burning).

Traditional ceramics are products based on the silicate industries, where the chief raw materials are naturally occurring minerals such as the clays, silica, feldspar and talc. While silicate ceramics dominate the industry, newer ceramics, sometimes referred to as **electronic** or **technical** ceramics, are playing a major role in many applications.

Manufacture. Typically, the manufacture of traditional-ceramic products involves blending of the finely divided starting materials with water to form a plastic mass which can be formed into the desired shape. The plasticity of clay constituents in water leads to excellent forming properties. Formation processes include extrusion, pressing, and ramming. Unsymmetrical articles can be formed by "slip-casting" techniques, where much of the water is taken up by a porous mold. After the water content of formed articles has been reduced by drying, the ware is **fired** at high temperature for fusion and/or reaction of the components and for attainment of the desired properties. Firing temperatures can usually be considerably below the fusion point of the pure components through the use of a **flux,** often the mineral feldspar. Following burning, a vitreous ceramic coating, or **glaze,** may be applied to render the surface smooth and impermeable.

Quite different is the **fusion casting** of some refractories and refractory blocks (see p. 6–206) and most glasses (see p. 6–187), where formation of the shaped article is carried out after fusion of the starting materials.

Properties. The physical properties of ceramic materials are strongly dependent on composition, microstructure (phases present and their distribution), and the history of manufacture. Volume pore concentration can vary widely (0 to 30 percent) and can influence shock resistance, strength, and permeability. Most traditional ceramics have a glassy phase, a crystalline phase, and some porosity. The last can be eliminated at the surface by glazing. Most ceramic materials are resistant to large compressive stresses but fail readily in tension. Resistance to abrasion, heat, and stains, chemical stability, rigidity, good weatherability, and brittleness characterize many common ceramic materials.

Products. Many traditional-ceramic products are referred to as **whiteware** and include pottery, semivitreous wares, electrical porcelains, sanitary ware, and dental porcelains. Building products include brick and structural tile and conduit (see p. 6–175). Refractory blocks (pp. 6–206 and 8–225) and many abrasives (p. 6–171) are ceramic products. Porcelain **enamels** for metals are opacified, complex glasses which are designed to match the thermal-expansion properties of the substrate. Important **technical ceramics** include magnetic ceramics, with magnetic properties but relatively high electrical resistance; nuclear ceramics, including uranium dioxide fuel elements; barium titanate as a material with very high dielectric constant. Several of the pure oxide ceramics with superior physical properties are being used in electrical and missile applications where high melting and deformation temperatures and stability in oxygen are important.

CLEANSING MATERIALS

By Douglas Melzard

(Arthur D. Little, Inc.)

References: McCutcheon, "Detergents and Emulsifiers," McCutcheon, Inc. Schwartz, Perry, and Berch, "Surface Active Agents and Detergents," Interscience. *ASTM Special Tech. Pub.* 197. Niven, "Industrial Detergency," Reinhold.

Cleansing is the removal of dirt, soil, and impurities from surfaces of all kinds. Means of soil attachment to the surface include simple entrapment in interstices, electrostatically held dirt, wetting of the surface with liquid soils, and soil-surface chemical reaction. A variety of cleansing systems has been developed which are difficult to classify since several soil-removal mechanisms are often involved. A liquid suspending medium, an active cleansing agent, and mechanical action are usually combined. The last may involve mechanical scrubbing, bath agitation, spray impingement, or ultrasonic energy. Cleansing involves detachment from the surface, suspension of solids or emulsification of liquids, or dissolution, either physical or by chemical reaction.

Organic Solvents

Both **petroleum solvents** (mineral spirits or naphtha) and **chlorinated hydrocarbons** (trichloroethylene and perchloroethylene) are used to remove solvent-soluble oils, fats, waxes, and greases as well as to flush away insoluble particulates. Petroleum solvents are used in both soak-tank and spray equipment. Chlorinated hydrocarbons are widely used in vapor degreasing (where the metal stock or part is bathed in the condensing vapor), their high vapor density and non-flammability being advantageous. Solvent recovery by distillation can be used if the operation is of sufficient size. Both solvent types are used in garment **dry cleaning** with solvent-soluble detergents.

Emulsifiable solvent cleansers contain a penetrating solvent and dissolved emulsifying agent. Following soaking, the surface is flushed with hot water, the resulting emulsion carrying away both soil and solvent. These cleaners are usually extended with kerosinelike solvents.

Alkali Cleansers

Alkali cleansers are water-soluble inorganic compounds, often strong cleansers. Carbonates, phosphates, pyrophosphates, and caustic soda are common, with numerous applications in plant maintenance, material processing, and process-water treatment. Cleansing mechanisms vary from beneficial water softening and suspension of solids to chemical reaction in the solubilization of fats and oils. Certain of these compounds are combined with **detergents** to improve efficiency; these are referred to as **builders.** Boiler and process-equipment scales can sometimes be controlled or removed with selected alkali cleansers. (See also p. 6-201 *et seq.* and p. 9-44 *et seq.*)

Synthetic Detergents

Detergents concentrate strongly at a solid-liquid or liquid-liquid interface and are thus characterized as **surface active.** In contrast to soaps, they can be tailored to perform over a wide range of conditions of temperature, acidity, and presence of dissolved impurities with little or no foaming. Detergents promote **wetting** of the surface by the suspending medium (usually water), **emulsification** of oils and greases, and **suspension** of solids without redeposition, the last function being the prime criterion of a good detergent. Detergents are classified as **anionic** (negatively charged in solution), **cationic** (positively charged), and **nonionic.** Germicidal properties may influence detergent choice.

For specific applications, the supplier should be consulted since there is a large variety of available formulations and since many detergent systems contain auxiliary compounds which may be diluents, foam promotors, or alkali chemicals. Additives are designed for pH control, water softening, and enhanced suspending power. Formulations have been developed for cleaning food and dairy-process equipment, metals processing, metal cleaning prior to electroplating, textile fiber and fabric processing, and industrial building maintenance. Strong, improperly selected detergent systems can cause deterioration of masonry or marble floors, aluminum window frames, water-based paints, and floor tiles, whereas detergents matched to the job at hand can result in increased plant efficiency.

Soaps, the oldest surface-active cleansers, lack the versatility of synthetic detergents but are widely used in the home and in the laundry industry. Properties depend on the fat or oil and alkali used in their preparation and include solvent-soluble soaps for dry cleaning.

Chemical cleaners which attack specific soils include dilute acid for metal oxide removal, for the cleaning of soldered or brazed joints, and for the removal of carbonate scale in process equipment. Oxalic acid (usually with a detergent) is effective on rust.

Chelating agents are organic compounds which complex with several metal ions and can aid in removal of common boiler scales and metal oxides from metal surfaces.

Aerosol-dispensed cleaners produce a mist of water and detergent.

Steam cleaning in conjunction with a detergent is effective on grease-laden machinery.

For cleaning **automobiles,** a weak solution of nonionic detergent followed by hose rinsing is effective. There are numerous cleansers for the **hands,** including Boraxo,® soap jelly and sawdust, lard for loosening oil grime, and linseed oil for paints; repeated use of solvents can be hazardous. **Windows** are cleaned with plain water or water plus detergent. Considerable effort has been devoted to complex cleaning techniques for electrical equipment, aircraft exteriors, internal-combustion engines, and other valuable equipment.

CORDAGE

The term **cordage** denotes any flexible string or line. Usage includes wrapping, baling, hauling, and power transmission in portable equipment. **Twine** and **cord** generally imply lines of ⅜ in. diam or less, with larger sizes being referred to as **rope.**

Cordage fibers for twine, cable, or rope vary in choice, depending on end-use requirements. For fiber properties, see p. 6-182. Of the **natural fibers** which have been used (abaca, sisal, hemp, cotton, and jute), abaca or manila is predominate in heavy cordage. Hemp is used for small, tarred lines, and henequen for agricultural binder twine.

Rope is made by twisting yarns into strands, with the strands (usually three) **twisted** (laid) into a line. The line twist may be S or Z (see p. 10–10), generally opposite to the twist of the strands, which, in turn, is opposite to the twist of the yarns. The term **lay** designates the number of turns of the strands per unit length of rope but may also characterize the rope properties, a function of the degree of twist of each component. Grades range from **soft lay** (high ultimate strength) to **hard lay** (high abrasion resistance). Cable-laid rope results from twisting together conventional, three-strand rope.

Synthetic fibers are gaining usage in cordage because of resistance to rot, high strength, and other special properties. These fibers include nylon for strength, polyester (Dacron) for strength and dimensional stability, vinyls for chemical-plant use, fiber glass for electrical and chemical properties, and polypropylene for strength and flotation (see p. 8–126).

Braided cordage has been used largely for small-diameter lines such as sash cord and clothesline. However, braided lines are now available in larger diameters, with lines up to 3-in. diam under development. The strength of braided rope is slightly superior, and the line has less tendency to elongate in tension and cannot rotate or unlay under load. These properties are balanced against a somewhat higher cost than that of twisted rope.

A No. 1 common-lay rope will conform to the strength and weight table of the Federal Specification TR601A listed below.

Weight and Strength of Different Sizes of Manila Rope, Specification Values

(From U.S. government specification TR601A, dated Nov. 26, 1935, and formulated jointly by cordage manufacturers and government representatives)

Approx diam, in.	Circumference, in.	Max net weight, lb per ft	Min breaking strength, lb	Approx diam, in.	Circumference, in.	Max net weight, lb per ft	Min breaking strength, lb	Approx diam, in.	Circumference, in.	Max net weight, lb per ft	Min breaking strength, lb
3/16	5/8	0.015	450	13/16	2½	0.195	6,500	1 13/16	5½	0.895	26,500
¼	¾	0.020	600	15/16	2¾	0.225	7,700	2	6	1.08	31,000
5/16	1	0.029	1,000	1	3	0.270	9,000	2¼	7	1.46	41,000
3/8	1 1/8	0.041	1,350	1 1/16	3¼	0.313	10,500	2 5/8	8	1.91	52,000
7/16	1¼	0.053	1,750	1 3/16	3½	0.360	12,000	3	9	2·42	64,000
½	1½	0.075	2,650	1¼	3¾	0.418	13,500	3¼	10	2.99	77,000
9/16	1¾	0.104	3,450	1 5/16	4	0.480	15,000	3 5/8	11	3.67	91,000
11/16	2	0.133	4,400	1½	4½	0.600	18,500	4	12	4.36	105,000
¾	2¼	0.167	5,400	1 5/8	5	0.744	22,500				

The approximate length of coil is 1,200 ft for diam 7/16 in. and larger. For smaller sizes it is longer; up to 3,000 ft for 3/16 in. diam.

For comparison, a **nylon rope** of a given diameter will have about 3 times the breaking strength given above and a **polyester rope** about 2½ times the strength of manila. Both have substantially greater flex and abrasion resistance.

ELECTRICAL INSULATING MATERIALS

By John T. Blake

(Simplex Wire and Cable Co.)

(See also Sec. 15.)

REFERENCES: Plastics Compositions for Dielectrics, *Ind. & Eng. Chem.*, **38**, 1946, p. 1090. High Dielectric Ceramics, *Ind. & Eng. Chem.*, **38**, 1946, p. 1097. Polystyrene Plastics as High Frequency Dielectrics, *Ind. & Eng. Chem.*, **38**, 1946, p. 1121. Paper Capacitors Containing Chlorinated Impregnants, *Ind. & Eng. Chem.*, **38**, 1946, p. 1110. "Contributions of the Chemist to Dielectrics," National Research Council, 1947. National Research Council, Conference on Electrical Insulation, (1) Annual Report, (2) Annual

Digest of Literature on Dielectrics. Von Hippel, "Dielectric Materials and Applications," Wiley.

The insulating properties of any material are dependent upon **dielectric strength,** or the ability to withstand high voltages without breakdown; **ohmic resistance,** or the ability to prevent leakage of small currents; and **power loss,** or the absorption of electrical energy that is transformed into heat. Power loss depends upon a number of influences, particularly the molecular symmetry of the insulation and frequency of the voltage, and is the basis of power factor, an important consideration whenever efficient handling of alternating currents is concerned, and a dominating consideration when high frequencies are used, as in radio circuits. Materials may have one of these qualities to a far greater extent than the other; *e.g.,* air has a very high specific resistance but very little dielectric strength and no power loss at any frequency; glass has great dielectric strength yet much lower resistance than air. The **ideal insulator** is one having the maximum dielectric strength and resistance, minimum power loss, and also mechanical strength and chemical stability. Moisture is by far the greatest enemy of insulation, consequently the absence of hygroscopic quality is desirable.

The common insulating materials are described below. For their electrical properties, see p. 15–26.

Rubber. See Rubber and Rubberlike Materials, p. 6–197.

Mica and Mica Compounds. Mica is a natural mineral varying widely in color and composition, and occurs in sheets that can be subdivided down to a thickness of 0.00025 in. White mica is best for electrical purposes. The green shades are the softest varieties, and the white amber from Canada is the most flexible. Mica has high insulating qualities, the best grades having a dielectric strength of 12,000 volts per tenth of a millimeter. Its lack of flexibility, its non-uniformity, and its surface leakage are disadvantages. To offset these, several mica products have been developed, in which small pieces of mica are built up into finished shapes by means of binders such as shellac, gum, and phenolic resins.

Micanite® consists of thin sheets of mica built into finished forms with insulating cement. It can be bent when hot and machined when cold, and is obtainable in thicknesses of 0.01 to 0.12 in. Flexible micanite plates, cloth, and paper are also obtainable in various thicknesses. **Megohmit®** is similar to micanite except that it is claimed not to contain adhesive matter. It can be obtained in plates, paper, linen, and finished shapes. **Megotalc,®** built up from mica and shellac, is similar to the above-named products and is obtainable in similar forms.

Insulating Varnishes. Two general types of insulating varnish are used: (1) asphalt, bitumen, or wax, in petroleum solvent, and (2) drying-oil varnishes based on natural oils compounded with resins from natural or synthetic sources. Varnishes have changed greatly in the last few years, since new oils have become available, and particularly since phenolic and alkyd resins have been employed in their manufacture.

Silicone varnishes (see p. 6–205) harden by baking and have electrical properties similar to those of the phenol-aldehyde resins. They are stable at temperatures up to 300 F. They can be used as wire coatings, and such wire is used in the manufacture of motors that can operate at high temperatures.

Impregnating Compounds. Bitumens and waxes are used to impregnate motor and transformer coils, the melted mix being forced into the coil in a vacuum tank, forming a solid insulation when cooled. Brittle compounds, which gradually pulverize due to vibration in service, and soft compounds, which melt and run out under service temperatures, should be avoided as far as possible.

Oil. Refined grades of petroleum oils are extensively used for the insulation of transformers, switches, and lightning arresters. The following specification covers the essential points:

Specific gravity, 0.860; flash test, not less than 335 F; cold test, not more than 14 F; viscosity (Saybolt) at 100 F, not more than 120 sec; loss on evaporation (8 hr at 200 F), not more than 0.5 percent; dielectric strength, not less than 35,000 volts; freedom from water, acids, alkalies, saponifiable matter, mineral matter, or free sulphur. Moisture is particularly dangerous in oil.

Petroleum oils are used for the impregnation of kraft or manila paper, after wrapping on copper conductors, to form high-voltage power cables for service up to 300,000 volts. Oil-impregnated paper insulation is sensitive to moisture, and such cables must be lead-sheathed. The transmission of power at high voltages in underground systems is universally accomplished by such cables.

Chlorinated Hydrocarbons. Chlorinated hydrocarbons have the advantage of being non-flammable and are used as filling compounds for transformers and condensers where this property is important. Chlorinated naphthalene and chlorinated diphenyl are typical of this class of material. They vary from viscous oils to solids, with a wide range of melting points.

Impregnated Fabrics. Fabrics serve as a framework to hold a film of insulating material and must, therefore, be of proper thickness, texture, and mechanical strength, and free from nap and acidity. A wide variety of drying varnishes is used for the impregnation, and the dipping is followed by baking in high-temperature towers. Varnished cambric is used for the wrapping of coils and for the insulation of conductors. These cables have high power factor and must be kept free of moisture, but they are desirable for resisting electrical surges.

Thermosetting substances of the phenol-aldehyde type (see p. 6–194) and of the urea-formaldehyde type first soften and then undergo a chemical reaction which converts them quickly to a strong infusible product. Good properties are available in the phenolics, while numerous special types have been developed for high heat resistance, low-power-factor arc resistance, and other specialized properties. A wide variety of resins is available. The urea plastics are lacking in heat resistance but are suitable for general-purpose molding and have fair arc resistance.

Thermoplastic resins (see Plastics, p. 6–192) are used for molding and extruding electrical insulations. They differ from the thermosetting resins in that they do not become infusible. **Polyethylene** softens between 210 and 240 F. Its dielectric strength and resistivity are high, its power factor is only 0.0003, and its dielectric constant is 2.28. It is used extensively in high-frequency and radar applications and as insulation on some power and communication cables. **Teflon**® is a fluorocarbon resin which has electrical properties similar to those of polyethylene. Its softening point is 750 F approx, and it extrudes and molds with difficulty; however, more tractable grades of Teflon are now available. It is resistant to nearly all chemicals and solvents.

Nylon is a synthetic plastic with interesting mechanical and electrical properties. It has only fair water resistance. Its melting point is 390 to 480 F, and it is used for the molding of coil forms. It can be extruded onto wire in thin layers. Such wires are used in place of the conventional varnish-coated magnet wires in coils and motors. Operation may be at temperatures up to 260 F. (See also p. 6–183.)

Paper. Except in lead-sheathed telephone cables, the present tendency is to use paper only as a backing or framework for an insulating film or compound, owing to its hygroscopic qualities. **Manila** and **kraft** papers possess the best dielectric and mechanical strength and, when coated with good insulating varnish, are excellent insulators. Various types of paraffined paper are used in condensers. (See also p. 6–190.)

Silicone rubber (see p. 6–205) is a rubberlike material of good physical properties (tensile strength, 400 to 700 psi; elongation, 200 percent). It can be operated for long periods of time at temperatures up to 300 F or intermittently up to 480 F.

Ceramics and **glasses** find wide usage as insulating materials where brittleness and lack of flexibility are unimportant. (See pp. 6–177 and 6–187.)

Polymeric (plastic) films, particularly the polyester and flourocarbon types, are being used increasingly where fabrication of the electrical component permits either wrapping or insertion of film chips.

FIBERS AND FABRICS

By Milton M. Platt and Robert E. Sebring

(Fabric Research Laboratories, Inc.)

(See also Cordage, p. 6–179.)

References: Matthews-Mauersberger, "The Textile Fibers," Wiley. Von Bergen and Krauss, "Textile Fiber Atlas," Textile Book Publishers, Inc. Hess, "Textile Fibers and Their Use," Lippincott. Sherman and Sherman, "The New Fibers," Van Nostrand. Kaswell, "Textile Fibers, Yarns and Fabrics," Reinhold. "Harris' Handbook of Textile Fibers," Waverly House. Kaswell, "Wellington Sears Handbook of Industrial Textiles," Wellington Sears Co. Fiber Charts, *Textile World*, McGraw-Hill. ASTM Standards.

Fibers are threadlike structural materials, adaptable for spinning, weaving, felting, and similar applications. They may be of natural or synthetic origin and of inorganic or organic composition. **Fabrics** are defined by the ASTM as "planar structures produced by interlacing yarns, fibers, or filaments." A **bonded fabric** (or non-woven fabric) consists of a web of fibers held together with a cementing medium which does not form a continuous sheet of adhesive material. A **braided fabric** is produced by interlacing several ends of yarns such that the paths of the yarns are not parallel to the fabric axis. A **knitted fabric** is produced by interlooping one or more ends of yarn. A **woven fabric** is produced by interlacing two or more sets of yarns, fibers, or filaments such that the elements pass each other essentially at right angles and one set of elements is parallel to the fabric axis. A woven narrow fabric is 12 in. or less in width and has a selvage on either side.

Inorganic Fibers

Asbestos is the only mineral fiber of natural origin. Synthetic mineral fibers are **spun glass, rock wool,** and **slag wool.** These fibers can endure high temperatures without substantial loss of strength. Glass fibers possess a higher strength-to-weight ratio at the elastic limit than do other common engineering materials (see also pp. 6–188 and 6–203).

Metal filaments (wires) are used as textile fibers where their particular material properties are important.

Natural Organic Fibers

The **animal fibers** include **wool** from sheep, **mohair** from goats, **camel's hair,** and **silk.** Wool is the most important of these, and it may be processed to reduce its susceptibility to moth damage and shrinkage. Silk is no longer of particular economic importance, having been supplanted by one or another of the synthetic fibers for most applications.

The **vegetable fibers** of greatest utility consist mainly of cellulose and may be classified as follows: seed hairs, such as cotton; bast fibers, such as flax, hemp, jute, and ramie; and vascular fibers. Those containing the most cellulose are the most flexible and elastic and may be bleached white most easily. Those which are more lignified tend to be stiff, brittle, and hard to bleach. Vegetable fibers are much less hygroscopic than wool or silk.

Mercerized cotton is cotton fiber that has been treated with strong caustic soda while under tension. The fiber becomes more lustrous, stronger, and more readily dyeable.

Synthetic Organic Fibers

In recent years, a large and increasing portion of commercial fiber production has been of synthetic or semisynthetic origin. These fibers provide generally superior mechanical properties and greater resistance to degradation than do natural organic fibers and are available in a variety of forms and compositions for particular end-use applications. Generic categories of man-made fibers have been established by the Textile Fiber Products Identification Act, 15 USC 70, 72 Stat. 1717.

Among the important fibers are **rayons,** made from regenerated cellulose, plain or acetylated, which has been put into a viscous solution and extruded through the holes of a spinneret into a setting bath. The types most common at present are **viscose** and **acetate.** Cuprammonium rayon, saponified acetate rayon, and high-wet-modulus rayon are also manufactured and have properties which make them suitable for particular applications. Rayon is generally less expensive than other synthetic fibers.

In contrast to these regenerated fibers are a variety of polymer fibers which are chemically synthesized. The most important is **nylon,** including nylon 6,6, a condensation polymer of hexamethylene diamine-adipic acid, and nylon 6, a polymer of caprolactam. Nylon possesses outstanding mechanical properties and is widely used in industrial fabrics. Other polymer fibers possess mechanical or chemical properties which make them a specific material of choice for specialized applications. These include **polyester** fibers, made from polyethylene terephthalate; **acrylic** and **modacrylic** fibers, made from copolymers of acrylonitrile and other chemicals; **Saran,**® a polymer composed essentially of vinylidene chloride; and the **olefins,** including polyethylenes and polypropylene. Additional man-made organic fibers are currently of less importance—their production has been discontinued, or they are still in a development state or in limited commercial use.

As part of their manufacture, substantially all synthetic fibers are **drawn** (hot- or cold-stretched) after extrusion to achieve desirable changes in properties. Generally, increases in draw increase breaking strength and modulus and decrease ultimate elongation.

Proximate Identification of Fibers. Fibers are most accurately distinguished under the microscope, with the aid of chemical reagents and stains. A useful rough test is burning, in which the odor of burned meat distinguishes animal fibers from vegetable and synthetic fibers. Animal fibers, cellulose acetate, and nylon melt before burning and fuse to hard rounded beads. Cellulose fibers burn off sharply. Cellulose acetate dissolves in either acetone or chloroform containing some alcohol.

Heat Endurance. Fibers of organic origin lose strength when heated over long periods of time above certain temperatures: cellulose, 300 F; cellulose acetate, 200 F; nylon, 435 F; casein, 212 F; and glass, 600 F.

Creep. Textile fibers exhibit the phenomenon of creep at relatively low loads. When a textile fiber is subjected to load, it suffers three kinds of distortion: (1) an elastic deformation, closely proportioned to load and fully and instantly recoverable upon load removal; (2) a primary creep, which increases at a decreasing rate with time and which is fully, but not instantaneously, recoverable upon load removal; and (3) a secondary creep, which varies obscurely with time and load and is completely nonrecoverable upon load removal. The relative amounts of these three components, acting to produce the total deformation, vary with the different fibers. The two inelastic components give rise to mechanical hysteresis on loading and unloading.

Felts and Fabrics

A **felt** is a compacted formation of randomly entangled fibers. Wool felt is cohesive because the scaly structure of the wool fibers promotes mechanical interlocking of the tangled fibers. Felts can be made with blends of natural or synthetic fibers, and they may be impregnated with resins, waxes, or lubricants for specific mechanical uses. Felts are available in sheets or cut into washers or shaped gaskets in a wide range of thicknesses and densities for packing, for vibration absorption, for heat insulation, or as holders of lubricant for bearings.

Fabrics are woven or knitted from **yarns.** Continuous-filament synthetic fibers can be made into monofilament or multifilament yarns with little or no twist. Natural fibers, of relatively short length, and synthetic **staple** fibers, which are purposely cut into short lengths, must be twisted together to form yarns. The amount of twist in yarns and the tension and arrangement of the weaving determine the appearance and mechanical properties of fabrics. Staple-fiber fabrics retain less than 50 percent of the intrinsic fiber strength, but values approaching 100 percent are retained with continuous-filament yarns. Industrial fabrics can be modified by mechanical and chemical treatments, as well as by coatings and impregnations, to meet special demands for strength and other mechanical, chemical, and electrical properties or to resist insect, fungus, and bacterial action and flammability.

Nomenclature. There are literally dozens of different numbering systems for expressing the relationship between yarn weight and length, all differing and each used in connection with particular fiber types or in different countries. The most common currently used unit is the **denier,** which is the weight in grams of 9,000 m of yarn. A universal system, based on the **tex** (the weight in grams of 1,000 m of yarn), has been approved by the International Standards Organization and by the ASTM, and this is expected eventually to supersede the present multisystem usage. Relative strengths of fibers and yarns are expressed as the **tenacity,** which reflects the

Table 1. Fiber Properties*

Kind	Source	Length of fiber, in.	Width or diam of cells, microns	Specific gravity	Moisture regain,‡ percent	Chemical description	Principal uses
Cotton	Plant seed hair	5/8-2	8-27	1.52	8.5	Cellulose	Industrial, household, apparel
Jute†	Plant bast	50-80	15-20	1.48	13.7	Lignocellulose	Bagging, twine, carpet backing
Wool	Animal	2-16	10-50	1.32	17	Protein	Apparel, household, industrial
Viscose	Manufactured	Any	8-43	1.52	11	Regenerated cellulose	Apparel, industrial, household
Cellulose acetate	Manufactured	Any	12-46	1.33	6	Cellulose ester	Apparel, industrial, household
Nylon	Manufactured	Any	8	1.14	4.2	Polyamide	Apparel, industrial, household
Casein	Manufactured	Any	11-28	1.3	4.1	Protein	Apparel
Flax†	Plant bast	12-36	15-17	1.5	12	Cellulose	Household, apparel, industrial
Hemp†	Plant bast	.....	18-23	1.48	12	Cellulose	Twine, halyards, rigging
Sisal†	Plant leaf	30-48	10-30	....	....	Lignocellulose	Twine, cordage
Manila†	Plant leaf	60-140	10-30	....	....	Lignocellulose	Rope, twine, cordage
Ramie†	Plant bast	3-10	24-70	1.52	....	Cellulose	Household, apparel, seines
Silk	Silkworm	Any	5-23	1.35	11	Protein	Apparel, household, industrial
Glass	Manufactured	Any	3	2.5	0	Fused metal oxides	Industrial, household
Dacron	Manufactured	Any	8	1.38	0.4	Polyester	Apparel, industrial, household

* Adapted from Smith, Textile Fibers, *Proc. ASTM*, 1944; Appel, A Survey of the Synthetic Fibers, *Am. Dyestuff Reporter*, **34**, 1945, pp. 21–26; and other sources.

† These fibers are commercially used as bundles of cells. They vary greatly in width. Width figures given are for the individual cells.

‡ In air at 70 F and 65 percent relative humidity.

Table 2. Tensile Properties of Single Fibers*

Fiber	Breaking tenacity, gpd	Extension at break, percent	Elastic recovery at corresponding strain, percent	Elastic modulus,† gpd
Glass	6.0-7.3	3.0-4.0	100 at 2.9	200-300
Fortisan (rayon)	6.0-7.0	6	100 at 1.2 60 at 2.4	150-200
Flax	2.6-7.7	2.7-3.3	65 at 2	
Nylon 6, 6	4.6-9.2	16-32	100 at 8	25-50
Nylon 6	4.5-8.6	16-40	100 at 8	25-50
Silk	2.4-5.1	10-25	92 at 2	75-125
Saran	1.1-2.3	15-25	95 at 10	
Cotton	3.0-4.9	3-7	74 at 2	50-100
Steel (90,000 psi T.S.)	0.9	28	....	300
Steel (music wire)	3.5	8	....	300
Viscose rayon	1.5-5.0	15-30	82 at 2	50-150
Wool	1.0-1.7	25-35	99 at 2	25-40
Acetate rayon	1.3-1.5	23-34	100 at 1	25-40
Polyester	4.4-7.8	10-25	100 at 2	50-80
Polypropylene	4.0-7.0	15-25	95 at 7	15-50
Polytetrafluoroethylene	1.7	13	....	

* From Kaswell, "Wellington Sears Handbook of Industrial Textiles," Wellington Sears Co., Inc.

† From Kaswell, "Textile Fibers, Yarns, and Fabrics," Reinhold.

specific gravity and the average cross section of the yarn. Units are grams per denier (gpd) or grams per tex (gpt).

Many textiles can sustain high-energy impact loads because of their considerable elongation before rupture. The total work done per unit length on a fiber or yarn which is extended to the point of rupture can be approximated by multiplying the specific strength by one-half the final extension of that length.

Yarn twist direction is expressed as S or Z twist, with the near-side helical paths of a twisted yarn held in a vertical position comparable in direction of slope to the center portion of one of these letters. Amount of twist is expressed in turns per inch (tpi).

Fabrics are characterized by the composition of the fiber material, the type of weave or construction, the count (the number of yarns per inch in the warp and the filling directions), and the weight of the fabric, usually expressed in ounces per running yard. **Cover factor** is the ratio of fabric surface covered by yarn to the total fabric surface. **Packing factor** is the ratio of fiber volume to total fabric volume.

Tables 1 to 3 give physical data and other information about commercial fibers and yarns. The tabulated quantities involving the denier should be regarded as approximate; they are not absolute values such as are used in engineering calculations.

Table 3. Temperature and Chemical Effects on Textiles*

Fiber	Temperature limit, deg F	Resistance to chemicals	Resistance to mildew
Cotton	Yellows 250; decomposes 300	Poor resistance to acids	Attacked
Flax	275	Poor resistance to acids	Attacked
Silk	Decomposes 300	Attacked	Attacked
Glass	Softens 1350	Resists	Resists
Nylon 6	Sticky 400; melts 420–430	Generally good	Resists
Nylon 6, 6	Sticky 455; melts 482	Generally good	Resists
Viscose rayon	Decomposes 350–400	Poor resistance to acids	Attacked
Acetate	Sticky 350–400; melts 500	Poor resistance to acids	Resists
Wool	Decomposes 275	Poor resistance to alkalies	Attacked
Asbestos	1490	Resists	Resists
Polyester	Sticky 455; melts 480	Generally good	Resists
Polypropylene	Softens 300–310; melts 325–335	Generally good	Resists
Polyethylene	Softens 225–235; melts 230–250	Generally good	Resists
Jute	275	Poor resistance to acids	Attacked

* From Fiber Chart, *Textile World*, McGraw-Hill, 1962.

FREEZING PREVENTIVES

Common salt is sometimes used to prevent the freezing of water; it does not, however, lower the freezing point sufficiently to be of use in very cold weather, and in concentrated solution tends to "creep" and to crystallize all over the receptacle. It also tends to corrode metals. For freezing temperatures, see p. 18–16.

Calcium chloride ($CaCl_2$) is a white solid substance widely used for preventing freezing of solutions and (owing to its great hygroscopic power) for keeping sizing materials and other similar substances moist. It does not "creep" as in the case of salt. It does not rust metal but attacks solder.

Calcium chloride solutions are much less corrosive on metal if made alkaline by the use of lime, and also if a trace of sodium chromate is present. They are not suitable for use in automobile radiators, because of corrosive action while hot, and because of tendency of any spray therefrom to ruin the insulation of spark plugs and high tension cables. For freezing temperatures, see p. 18–16.

Glycerol is a colorless, viscid liquid without odor and miscible with water in all proportions. It should have a specific gravity of approximately 1.25. It has no effect on metals but disintegrates rubber and loosens up iron rust.

Denatured alcohol is free from the disadvantages of calcium chloride, salt, and glycerin solutions, but is volatile from water mixtures which run hot. A solution containing 50 percent alcohol becomes inflammable, but it is rarely necessary to use more than 30 percent. See p. 6–201.

Methyl alcohol (**Zerone®**), variously trade named, is sold widely for automobile antifreeze. It is a desirable and effective antifreeze, but care must be taken not to breathe its fumes, which are poisonous.

Ethylene glycol (**Prestone®, Zerex®**) is used as a freezing preventive and also permits the use of high jacket temperatures in aircraft and other engines. Sp gr 1.125 (1.098) at 32 (77) F; boiling point, 387 F; specific heat, 0.575 (0.675) at 68 (212) F. Miscible with water in all proportions.

Non-freezing Percentages by Volume in Solution

Temperature, deg F	20	10	0	−10
Methyl alcohol	13	20	25	30
Prestone	17	25	32	38
Alcohol	17	26	34	42
Glycerine	22	33	40	47

GLASS

References: *Journal of American Ceramic Society,* Columbus, Ohio. *Journal of the Society of Glass Technology,* Sheffield, England. Morey, "Properties of Glass," Reinhold. Scholes, "Handbook of the Glass Industry," Ogden-Watney. "Non-silica Glasses," *Chem. & Met. Eng.,* Mar., 1946. Phillips, "Glass the Miracle-maker," Pitman. Long, "Propriétés physiques et fusion du verre," Dunod. Eitel-Pirani-Scheel, "Glastechnische Tabellen," Springer. Jebsen-Marwedel, "Glastechnische Fabrikationsfehler," Springer.

Glass is an inorganic product of fusion which has cooled to a rigid condition without crystallizing. It is obtained by melting together silica, alkali, and stabilizing ingredients, such as lime, alumina, lead, and barium. Bottle, plate, and window glass usually contain SiO_2, Al_2O_3, CaO, and Na_2O. Small amounts of the oxides of manganese and selenium are added to obtain colorless glass.

Special glasses, such as fiber glass, laboratory ware, thermometer glass, and optical glass, require different manufacturing methods and different compositions. The following oxides are either substituted for or added to the above base glass: B_2O_3, ZnO, K_2O, As_2O_3, PbO, etc., to secure the requisite properties. Colored glasses are obtained by adding the oxides of iron, manganese, copper, selenium, cobalt, chromium, etc., or colloidal gold.

Molten glass possesses the ability to be fabricated in a variety of ways and to be cooled down to room temperature rapidly enough to prevent crystallization of the constituents. It is a rigid material at ordinary temperatures but may be remelted and molded any number of times by the application of heat. Ordinary glass is melted at about 2600 F and will soften enough to lose its shape at about 1100 F.

Properties of Glass. The following data are for ordinary glass; specific gravity 2.3 to 2.6; tensile strength, 10,000 psi; compressive strength, 50,000 psi; modulus of elasticity, 10,000,000 psi; coefficient of expansion, 40 to 60 $\times 10^{-7}$ per deg F; thermal conductivity, 0.4 to 0.6 Btu per sq ft per ft per deg F per hr; specific heat, 0.16 to 0.20.

Glass always breaks under a tensile stress even though it strongly resists an applied compressive force. The value obtained for crushing strength depends on the material of the plates used and upon the precision of the testing apparatus. Glass resists atmospheric corrosion and is one of the best materials for resisting the attack of water, bases, and acids, with the exception of hydrofluoric acid.

Most glass is opaque to ultraviolet light. Quartz transmits well into the ultraviolet. Glass transmits infrared light and heat; special color filters and heat absorbers may be used to transmit or absorb particular wave-length ranges.

Window glass is a soda-lime-silica glass, fabricated in continuous sheets up to a width of 6 ft. The sheets are made in two thicknesses, SS and DS, which are, respectively, 1/16 and 1/8 in. Both thicknesses are made in A, B, C, and D grades.

Plate glass is similar in composition to window glass. It is fabricated in continuous sheets up to a width of 15 ft and is polished on both sides. It may be obtained in various thicknesses and grades.

Safety glass consists of two layers of plate glass firmly held together by an intermediate layer of organic material, such as polyvinyl butyral. Safety glass is ordinarily ¼ in. thick but can be obtained in various thicknesses. This plate is shatterproof and is used for windshields, bank cashier's windows, etc.

Toughened glass is made from sheet glass in thicknesses up to 1 in. It possesses great mechanical strength, which is obtained by rapidly chilling the surfaces while the glass is still hot. This process sets up a high compression on the glass surfaces, which have the capacity of withstanding very high tensile forces.

Wire glass is a glass having an iron wire screen thoroughly embedded in it. It offers about 1½ times the resistance to bending that plain glass does; even thin sheets may be walked on. If properly made, it does not fall apart when cracked by shocks or heat, and is consequently fireproof. It is used for flooring, skylights, fireproof doors, fire walls, etc. It must be ordered exactly to measure, as it cannot be readily cut. Less light passes through it than through plain glass.

Pressed glass is made by forming heat-softened glass in molds under pressure. Such articles as cheap tableware, insulators, and glass blocks are made by this process.

Glass insulators are pressed and are made in a variety of shapes and sizes for both low and high voltages. Glass is a good conductor in the molten condition but is a good insulator at ordinary temperatures. The dielectric constant and specific resistance of glass can be varied within wide limits, making it an ideal material for many electrical purposes.

Glass blocks find wide application for building purposes, and are made 3⅞ in. thick in the following sizes: 6 × 6, 8 × 8, 12 × 12 in. The thermal conductivity of a glass block panel, for a thickness of 3⅞ in., is 0.49 Btu per sq ft per hr per deg F. The solar heat transmission can be varied within wide limits by using different colored glasses and by changing the reflection by means of surface configurations. The light transmission can be varied from 25 to 80 percent by changing the surface configurations of the blocks.

Fiber glass is a term used to designate articles that consist of a multitude of tiny glass filaments ranging in size from 0.0001 to 0.01 in. in diam. The larger fibers are used in air filters; those 0.0005 in. in diam, for thermal insulation; and the 0.0001 to 0.0002 in. diam fibers, for glass fabrics, which are stronger than ordinary textiles of the same size. Insulating tapes made from glass fabric have found wide application in electrical equipment, such as motors and generators and for mechanical uses.

Glass is used for many structural purposes, such as store fronts and table tops, and is available in thicknesses of $\frac{5}{16}$ and $\frac{7}{16}$ in., and 72 × 130 in.

Cellular glass is a puffed variety with about 5 million cells per cubic foot. It is a good heat insulator and makes a durable marine float.

Pyrex is the registered trade-mark of the Corning Glass Works. Many compositions of glass appear under that brand, the most notable perhaps being the low-expansion borosilicate glasses containing no metals of the magnesia-lime-zinc group and no heavy metals. Physical properties: modulus of elasticity, 8,800,000 psi; sp gr, 2.25; refractive index, 1.4754; dispersion, 0.00738; linear thermal expansion coefficient (65 to 660 F), 0.0000020; specific heat, 0.20; thermal conductivity, 0.21 Btu per sq ft per in. per deg F per hr; can be used without softening up to 1200 to 1300 F. Principal uses are for chemical ware, baking ware, high-tension insulators, sight glasses for chemical apparatus, boiler gage glasses, glass pipe lines for chemical plants, railroad lantern globes, and battery jars. Chemical ware withstands the test of plunging from molten paraffin at 390 F into ice water. Other manufacturers produce similar glasses.

Fused quartz is made by melting rock crystal or purest quartz sand in the electric furnace. It is unaffected by changes of temperature, is fireproof and acid-resistant, does not conduct electricity, and has practically no expansion under heat. It is used considerably for high-temperature laboratory apparatus. See Plastics, p. 6–192, for glass substitutes.

NATURAL STONES

By David Rostoker

(Corning Glass Works)

REFERENCES: Kessler, Insley, and Sligh, *Jour. Res. NBS*, **25**, pp. 161–206. Birch, Schairer, and Spicer, Handbook of Physical Constants, *Geol. Soc. Am. Special Paper* 36. Currier, Geological Appraisal of Dimension Stone Deposits, *USGS Bull.* 1109.

A **stone** or a **rock** is a naturally occurring composite of minerals. Stone has been used for thousands of years as a major construction material because it possesses qualities of strength, durability, architectural adaptibility, and aesthetic satisfaction. There are two principal branches of the natural-stone industry—**dimension** stone and **crushed** or broken stone. The uses of the latter vary from aggregate to riprap, in which stones in a broad range of sizes are used as structural support in a matrix or to provide weathering resistance. Dimension stones are blocks or slabs of stone processed to specifications of size, shape, and surface finish. The largest volume today lies in the use of slabs varying from 1 to 4 in. in thickness that are mounted on a structure as a protective and aesthetic veneer.

There are two major types of natural stone: **igneous** and **metamorphic** stones, composed of tightly interlocking crystals of one or more minerals, and **sedimentary** rocks, composed of cemented mineral grains in which the cement may or may not be of the same composition as the grains. The major groups of natural stone used commercially are:

Granite, a visibly crystalline rock made of silicate minerals, primarily feldspar and quartz. Commercially, "granite" refers to all stones geologically defined as plutonic, igneous, and gneissic.

Marble, generally a visibly crystalline carbonate rock; however, microcrystalline rocks, such as onyx, travertine, and serpentine, are usually included by the trade as long as they can take a polish.

Limestone, a sedimentary rock composed of calcium or magnesium carbonate grains in a carbonate matrix.

Sandstone, a sedimentary rock composed chiefly of cemented, sand-sized quartz grains. In the trade, quartzites are usually grouped with sandstones although these rocks tend to fracture through, rather than around, the grains. **Conglomerate** is a term used for a sandstone containing aggregate in sizes from the gravel range up.

The above stones can be used almost interchangeably as dimension stone for architectural or structural purposes.

Slate, a fine-grained rock characterized by marked cleavages by which the rock can be split easily into relatively thin slabs. Because of this characteristic, slate was at one time widely used for roofing tiles. It is used today for electrical boards and blackboards, and it has recently become popular for steps, risers, spandrels, flagstones, and other building uses.

Miscellaneous stones, such as traprock (fine-grained black volcanic rock), greenstone, or argillite, are commonly used as crushed or broken stone but rarely as dimension stone.

The table of physical properties contains the range of values that can be obtained from stones in various orientations relative to their textural and structural anisotropy. For a particular application, where one property must be exactly determined, the value must be obtained along a specified axis.

Selected Terms Applying to the Use of Dimension Stone

Anchor, a metal tie or rod used to fasten stone to backup units.

Arris, the meeting of two surfaces producing an angle, corner, or edge.

Ashlar, a facing of square or rectangular stones having sawed, dressed, or squared beds.

Bond stones, stones projecting a minimum of 4 in. laterally into the backup wall; used to tie the wall together.

Cut stone, finished dimension stone—ready to set in place. The finish may be polished, honed, grooved (for foot traffic), or broken face.

Bearing wall, a wall supporting a vertical load in addition to its own weight.

Cavity wall, a wall in which the inner and outer parts are separated by an air space but are tied together with cross members.

Composite wall, a wall in which the facing and backing are of different materials and are united with bond stones to exert a common reaction under load. It is considered preferable, however, not to require the facing to support a load; thus the bond stones merely tie the facing to the supporting wall, as in the case of a veneer.

Veneer or faced wall, a wall in which a thin facing and the backing are of different materials but are not so bonded as to exert a common reaction under load.

Physical and Thermal Properties of Common Stones

Type of stone	Density, lb per cu ft	Compressive strength $\times 10^{-3}$, psi	Rupture modulus $\times 10^{-3}$, psi (ASTM C99–52)	Shearing strength $\times 10^{-3}$, psi	Young's modulus $\times 10^{-6}$, psi	Modulus of rigidity $\times 10^{-6}$, psi	Poisson's ratio	Abrasion-hardness index (ASTM C241–51)	Porosity, volume percent	48-hr water absorption (ASTM C97–47)	Thermal conductivity, Btu per ft per hr per deg F	Coefficient of thermal expansion $\times 10^{-6}$, per deg F
Granite	160–190	13–55	1.4–5.5	3.5–6.5	4–16	2–6	0.05–0.2	37–88	0.6–3.8	0.02–0.58	20–35	3.6–4.6
Marble	165–179	8–27	0.6–4.0	1.3–6.5	5–11.5	2–4.5	0.1–0.2	8–42	0.4–2.1	0.02–0.45	8–36	3.0–8.5
Slate	168–180	9–10	6–15	2.0–3.6	6–16	2.5–6	0.1–0.3	6–12	0.1–1.7	0.01–0.6	12–26	3.3–5.6
Sandstone	119–168	5–20	0.7–2.3	0.3–3.0	0.7–10	0.3–4	0.1–0.3	2–26	1.9–27.3	2.0–12.0	4–40	3.9–6.7
Limestone	117–175	2.5–28	0.5–2.0	0.8–3.6	3–9	1–4	0.1–0.3	1–24	1.1–31.0	1.0–10.0	20–32	2.8–4.5

PAPER

By R. Claire Canty and F. G. Perry, Jr.

(Arthur D. Little, Inc.)

REFERENCES: Calkin, "Modern Pulp and Papermaking," Reinhold. Griffin and Little, "Manufacture of Pulp and Paper," McGraw-Hill. Guthrie, "The Economics of Pulp and Paper," State College of Washington Press. "Dictionary of Paper," American Pulp and Paper Assoc. Sutermeister, "Chemistry of Pulp and Papermaking," Wiley. Casey, "Pulp and Paper—Chemistry and Technology," Interscience. TAPPI Technical Information Sheets. TAPPI Monograph Series. "Index of Federal Specifications, Standards and Handbooks," GSA. Lockwoods Directory of the Paper and Allied Trades.

Paper Grades

Specific paper qualities are achieved in a number of ways: (1) By selecting the composition of the furnish for the paper machine. Usually more than one pulp (prepared by different pulping conditions or processes) is required. The ratio of long-fibered pulp (softwood) to short-fibered pulp (hardwood or mechanical type), the reused-fiber content, and the use of non-fibrous fillers and chemical additives are important factors. (2) By varying the paper-machine operation. Fourdrinier wire machines are most common, although multicylinder machines and high-speed tissue machines with Yankee driers are also used. (3) By using various finishing operations (*e.g.*, calendering, supercalendering, coating, and laminating).

There is a tremendous number of paper grades, which are, in turn, used in a wide variety of converted products. The following broad classifications are included as a useful guide:

Sanitary papers are tissue products characterized by bulk, opacity, softness, and water absorbency.

Glassine, greaseproof, and waxing papers—in glassine, high transparency and density, low grease penetration, and uniformity of formation are important requirements.

Food-board products require a good brightness and should be odorless and have good tear, tensile, and fold-endurance properties, opacity, and printability.

Boxboard and a variety of other board products are made on multicylinder machines, where layers of fiber are built up to the desired thickness. Interior plys are often made from wastepaper furnishes, while surface plys are from bleached, virgin fiber. Boards are often coated for high brightness and good printing qualities.

Printing papers include publication papers (magazines), book papers, bond and ledger papers, newsprint, and catalog papers. In all cases, printability, opacity, and dimensional stability are important.

Linerboard and **bag paper** are principally unbleached, long-fiber, kraft products of various weights. Their principal property requirements are high tensile and bursting strengths.

Corrugating medium, in combined fiberboard, serves to hold the two linerboards apart in rigid, parallel separation. Stiffness is the most important property, together with good water absorbency for ease of corrugation.

Pulps

The most important source of fiber for paper pulps is wood, although numerous other vegetable substances are used. Reused fiber (wastepaper) constitutes about 30 percent of the total furnish used in paper, principally in boxboard and other packaging or printing papers.

There are three basic processes used to convert wood to papermaking fibers: mechanical, chemical, and "chemimechanical."

Mechanical Pulping (Groundwood). Here, the entire log is reduced to fibers by grinding against a stone cylinder, the simplest route to papermaking fiber. Wood fibers are mingled with extraneous materials which can cause weakening and discoloration in the finished paper. Nonetheless, the resulting pulp imparts good bulk and opacity to a printing sheet. Some long-fibered chemical pulp is usually added. Groundwood is used extensively in low-cost, short-service, and throwaway papers, *e.g.*, newsprint and catalog paper.

Chemical Pulping. Fiber separation can also be accomplished by chemical treatment of wood chips to dissolve the lignin that cements the fibers together. From 40 to 50 percent of the log is extracted, resulting in relatively pure cellulosic fiber. There are two major chemical-pulping processes, which differ both in chemical treatment and in the nature of the pulp produced. In **sulphate pulping,** also referred to as the **kraft** or **alkaline** process, the pulping chemicals must be recovered and reused for economic reasons. Sulphate pulps result in papers of high physical strength, bulk, and opacity; low unbleached brightness; slow beating rates; and relatively poor sheet-formation properties. Both bleached and unbleached sulphate pulps are used in packaging papers, container board, and a variety of printing and bond papers. In **sulphite pulping,** the delignifying agents are sulphurous acid and an alkali, with several variations of the exact chemical conditions in commercial use. In general, sulphite pulps have lower physical strength properties and lower bulk and opacity than kraft pulps, with higher unbleached brightness and better sheet-formation properties. The pulps are blended with groundwood for newsprint and are used in printing and bond papers, tissues, and glassine.

"Chemimechanical" processes combine both chemical and mechanical methods of defibration, the most important commercial process being the NSSC (Neutral Sulphite Semi Chemical). A wide range of yields and properties can be obtained.

Bleaching

Chemical pulps may be bleached to varying degrees of brightness, depending on the end use. During some bleaching operations, the remaining lignin is removed and residual coloring matter destroyed. Alternatively, a non-delignifying bleach lightens the color of high-lignin pulps.

Refining

The final character of the pulp is developed in the **refining** (beating) operation. Pulp fibers are fibrillated, hydrated, and cut. The fibers are roughened and frayed, and a gelatinous substance is produced. This results in greater fiber coherence in the finished paper.

Sizing, Loading, and Coating

Sizing is used, principally in book papers, to make the paper water-repellent and to enhance interfiber bonding and surface characteristics. Sizing materials may be premixed with the pulp or applied after sheet formation.

Loading materials, or **fillers,** are used by the papermaker to smooth the surface, to provide ink affinity, to brighten color, and to increase opacity. The most widely used filler is clay.

Coatings consisting of pigment and binder are often applied to the base stock to create better printing surfaces. A variety of particulate, inorganic materials are combined with binders such as starch or casein in paper coatings. Coating is generally followed by calendering.

Converting and Packaging

A host of products is made from paper; the converting industry represents a substantial portion of the total paper industry. Principal products are in the fine-paper and book-paper fields. Slush pulps are used to make molded pulp products such as egg cartons and paper plates.

Combinations of paper laminated with other materials such as plastic film and metal foil have found wide use in the packaging market.

PLASTICS

By Harris J. Bixler

(Amicon Corporation)

REFERENCES: "Modern Plastics Encyclopedia," McGraw-Hill. Reinhold Plastics Applications Series, Reinhold. Roff, "Fibres, Plastics and Rubbers," Butterworth. Lee and Neville, "Epoxy Resins," McGraw-Hill. Billmeyer, "Textbook of Polymer Science," Interscience. Schmidt and Marlies, "Principles of High Polymer Theory and Practice," McGraw-Hill.

Plastics are materials which are wholly or in part composed of long, chainlike molecules called **high polymers.** While carbon is the element common to all commercial high polymers, hydrogen, oxygen, nitrogen, sulphur, halogens, and silicon can be present in varying proportions. High polymers may be divided into two classes: **thermoplastic** and **thermosetting.** The former reversibly melt to become highly viscous liquids and, upon cooling, solidify to give, depending on their structure, elastic, ductile, tough, or brittle solids. Melting temperatures range from 100 to 300 C. The thermosetting polymers are infusible without thermal or mechanical degradation. Many thermosetting polymers are prepared by curing thermoplastic **prepolymers** or **"B-stage"** resins. **Curing** (a chain-linking chemical reaction) is usually initiated with heat. The more highly cured the polymer, the higher its heat-distortion temperature and the harder and more brittle it becomes.

Thermoplastics

Thermoplastic polymers are often used with only minor additions (colorants, stabilizers, lubricants). Important characteristics are low density, low cost, toughness, optical clarity, ease of forming complex shapes, low thermal conductivity, chemical resistance, flexibility, and useful electrical properties. Fabrication into plastic objects is achieved by compression, injection, blow, and slush molding; vacuum forming; melt extrusion; solvent casting; stamping; calendering; and powder-metallurgy processes

Table 1. Thermoplastics—Properties and Uses

Item	High-density polyethylene	Low-density polyethylene	Polypropylene
Key properties	Chemical resistance, strength, low cost	Electrical properties, flexibility, low cost	Toughness, gloss, light weight, heat resistance
Major uses	Film, bleach, bottles, pipe	Film, containers, wire coating	Housewares, appliance parts, tank liners
Density, g per cc	0.94–0.96	0.91–0.93	0.90–0.92
Tensile strength, psi	3,100–5,500	1,000–2,300	3,500–6,000
Tensile modulus, psi × 10^{-5}	0.4–1.5	0.17–0.35	1–2
Maximum continuous-use temp, deg F	250	180–212	200–320
Molding temp, deg F	300–800	275–700	350–600
Dielectric strength, volts per mil	440–600	420–700	450–650
Dielectric constant, 1,000 cps	2.30–2.35	2.25–2.35	2.3
Dissipation factor, 1,000 cps	Less than 0.0002	Less than 0.0005	0.0002–0.0008
Water absorption, 24 hr, percent	Less than 0.01	Less than 0.015	Less than 0.02

Item	Cellulose acetate	Rigid vinyl	Plasticized vinyl
Key properties	Low cost, toughness, clarity, colorability	Compounding flexibility, low cost, chemical resistance	Compounding flexibility, low cost, pliability
Major uses	Door knobs, blister packs, appliance housings	Conduit, pipe, building panels	Tubing, gaskets, upholstery, footwear
Density, g per cc	1.26–1.34	1.35–1.45	1.16–1.35
Tensile strength, psi	1,900–8,300	5,000–9,000	1,500–3,500
Tensile modulus, psi × 10^{-5}	1.0–4.0	4–6	
Maximum continuous-use temp, deg F	140–220	120–160	150–175
Molding temp, deg F	260–490	285–400	285–385
Dielectric strength, volts per mil	200–300	375–750	275–900
Dielectric constant, 1,000 cps	3.5–7.0	3.0–3.3	4.0–8.0
Dissipation factor, 1,000 cps	0.01–0.06	0.01–0.02	0.07–0.16
Water absorption, 24 hr, percent	1.9–6.5	0.07–0.4	0.15–0.75

Item	Cellulose acetate butyrate	Nylon 6, 6	Polymethyl methacrylate (Lucite or Plexiglas)	Polytetrafluoroethylene (Teflon)
Key properties	Impact resistance, clarity, weatherability	Toughness, low coefficient of friction, machinability	Crystal clarity, strength, weatherability, colorability	Thermal stability, low coefficient of friction, chemical resistance
Major uses	Outdoor signs, lenses	Gears, bearings, hinges, fibers	Automotive lenses, shaped glazing, signs	Gaskets, non-stick surfaces, insulation, electrical applications
Density, g per cc	1.15–1.22	1.09–1.14	1.17–1.20	2.13–2.22
Tensile strength, psi	2,600–6,900	7,000–12,000	7,000–11,000	2,000–4,500
Tensile modulus, psi × 10^{-5}	0.5–2.0	2.6–4.0	4.5	0.58
Maximum continuous-use temp, deg F	140–220	270–300	140–190	550
Molding temp, deg F	265–480	470–720	300–500	
Dielectric strength, volts per mil	250–350	340–410	350–400	430

Table 1. Thermoplastics—Properties and Uses—(*Continued*)

Item	Cellulose acetate butyrate	Nylon 6, 6	Polymethyl methacrylate (Lucite or Plexiglas)	Polytetrafluoroethylene (Teflon)
Dielectric constant, 1,000 cps	3.3–6.3	4.0–4.5	3.0–3.5	2.0
Dissipation factor, 1,000 cps	0.01–0.04	0.02–0.04	0.03–0.05	Less than 0.0002
Water absorption, 24 hr, percent	0.9–2.2	0.4–1.5	0.3–0.4	0.00

Item	Polystyrene (general-purpose)	High-impact polystyrene	ABS acrylonitrile butadiene-styrene
Key properties	Low cost, crystal clarity	Low cost, impact strength, craze resistance	Toughness, strength, processability
Major uses	Food containers, lighting panels, film	Appliance housing, luggage, pipe and fittings	Automotive accessories, refrigerator liners, telephone sets
Density, g per cc	1.05–1.07	0.98–1.10	1.01–1.15
Tensile strength, psi	5,000–9,000	2,000–6,800	2,400–9,000
Tensile modulus, psi $\times 10^{-5}$	4–5	2–4.5	1–4
Maximum continuous-use temp, deg F	150–170	140–175	140–250
Molding temp, deg F	265–600	250–600	300–600
Dielectric strength, volts per mil	400–600	300–600	310–400
Dielectric constant, 1,000 cps	2.4–2.65	2.4–4.5	2.4–4.75
Dissipation factor, 1,000 cps	Less than 0.0003	0.0004–0.002	0.002–0.012
Water absorption, 24 hr, percent	0.03–0.05	0.1–0.3	0.1–0.3

(see also Sec. 13). The starting material in these processes is bulk polymer in the form of small particles called **molding powders,** extruded sheet, or **plastisol.** Plastisols are liquid or semisolid dispersions of finely powdered polymer in a non-volatile, non-migrating liquid, which result in a homogeneous, tough mass upon heating. Expanded, or **foamed,** thermoplastics are finding widespread use as thermal insulation and cushioning material. Hollow beads (or, in some cases, a plastisol) containing a heat-triggerable blowing agent are charged into a heated mold where the polymer softens, is expanded by the blowing agent, and upon cooling, solidifies to a low-density (as low as 2 lb per cu ft) open- or closed-cell plastic foam with low thermal conductivity.

Filled thermoplastics (primarily vinyls) containing up to 50 percent by weight of fillers such as asbestos, wood flour, clay, titania, or carbon black are used in flooring tile, electrical-wire insulation, and pipe or conduit.

Table 1 summarizes the **physical properties** and **major end uses** of a number of thermoplastics of industrial importance.

Thermosetting Plastics

Most **thermosetting plastics** are composite structures, being either multicomponent laminates or blends of polymer and particulate or fibrous fillers. The selection and blending or laminating together (called **compounding**) of suitable polymers and fillers are the heart of thermosetting-plastics technology. These plastics are noted for thermal and dimensional stability, chemical resistance, strength, durability, and good electrical properties. The costs of thermosetting plastics vary considerably—from very cheap phenolics for container caps, through dinnerware-quality melamine-formaldehydes, to highly engineered epoxy and phenolic composites for space vehicles.

Compounding is done in Banbury and dough mixers, ribbon blenders, rubber mills, extruders, or for fibrous fillers like cellulose and asbestos, a papermaker's beater (beater addition products).

Fillers include wood flour, silica, mica, clay, glass fiber, cellulose, asbestos, and natural and synthetic textile fibers. To promote adhesion between the filler and the polymeric binder, the former is frequently precoated with sizing agents.

Fabrication (shaping and/or curing) is done by injection, compression, and transfer molding; press laminating; casting; tunnel-oven curing (sheet stock and extrudates); lay-up; and bag molding. For lay-up, bag molding, and laminating, prepolymer impregnation of woven and non-woven felts may be the sole compounding step. Although heat is usually employed to accelerate curing, many room-temperature–curing plastics are now in use. (See also Sec. 13.)

Polyurethane foams are a unique class of thermosetting plastics. By mixing two relatively low-viscosity liquids (prepolymer and blowing, plus curing agents), an expanded foam can be formed and cured in minutes at room temperature. These have found widespread use as poured-in-place insulation.

Tables 2 to 4 summarize the **physical properties** and **major end uses** of a number of industrially important thermosets.

Table 2. Properties and Uses of Phenol-formaldehyde Plastics

	No filler	Mica-filled
Key properties	Low cost, chemical and heat resistance	Good strength, electrical properties, temperature stability
Major uses	Impregnating resins, buttons, electrical connectors	Electrical components, abrasive products, brake shoes
Density, g per cc	1.25–1.3	1.65–1.92
Tensile strength, psi	7,000–8,000	6,500–7,000
Tensile modulus, psi × 10^{-5}	7.5–10	30–50
Maximum continuous-use temp, deg F	250	250–300
Molding temp, deg F	270–320	280–350
Dielectric strength, volts per mil	250–400	250–400
Dielectric constant, 1,000 cps	4.5–6.0	4.4–5.5
Dissipation factor, 1,000 cps	0.03–0.08	0.03–0.04
Water absorption, 24 hr, percent	0.1–0.2	0.01–0.05

Table 3. Properties and Uses of Melamine-formaldehyde and Polyester Plastics

	Melamine-formaldehyde		Polyester woven cloth—reinforced
	No filler	Alpha cellulose-filled	
Key properties	Heat resistance, moisture resistance, toughness, scratch resistance	Same as for no filler plus added strength and toughness	Low cost, high strength-to-weight ratio, versatility, abrasion resistance
Major uses	Buttons, decorative laminates, adhesives, textile finishes	Dinnerware, utensil handles, housewares, electrical moldings	Boats, auto bodies, large lay-ups, wall siding, pipe, filament-wound pressure tanks
Density, g per cc	1.48	1.47–1.52	1.5–2.1
Tensile strength, psi	....	7,000–13,000	30,000–50,000
Tensile modulus, psi × 10^{-5}	....	12–14	15–45
Maximum continuous-use temp, deg F	210	210	300–350
Molding temp, deg F	300–350	280–370	70–250
Dielectric strength, volts per mil		250–400	350–500
Dielectric constant, 1,000 cps	....	7.8–9.2	4.2–6.0
Dissipation factor, 1,000 cps	....	0.015–0.036	0.01–0.06
Water absorption, 24 hr, percent	0.3–0.5	0.1–0.6	0.05–0.5

Table 4. Properties and Uses of Epoxy and Silicone Thermosetting Plastics

	Epoxy, mineral-filled	Flexibilized epoxy, no filler	Silicone, mineral-filled
Key properties	Inertness, low shrinkage upon curing, high strength	Adhesion, low shrinkage upon curing, chemical resistance, flexibility	Thermal and oxidative stability, low-temperature flex, excellent electrical properties
Major uses	Potting of electrical components, adhesives	Adhesives, caulking compounds, surface coatings	Potting compounds, electronic components, sealants, gaskets
Density, g per cc	1.6–2.0	1.15–1.25	1.81–2.82
Tensile strength, psi	7,000–13,000	2,000–10,000	3,000–3,500
Tensile modulus, psi $\times 10^{-5}$	3.5	0.01–3.5	
Maximum continuous-use temp, deg F	250–550	250–300	Greater than 600
Molding temp, deg F	....	....	310–370
Dielectric strength, volts per mil	400–550	235–400	200–400
Dielectric constant, 1,000 cps	3.2–4.0	3–5	3.8–6.3
Dissipation factor, 1,000 cps	0.008–0.03	0.012–0.05	0.002–0.005
Water absorption, 24 hr, percent	0.04–0.1	0.27–0.25	0.13

ROOFING MATERIALS

(Bird & Son, East Walpole, Mass.)

REFERENCES: Abraham, "Asphalts and Allied Substances," Van Nostrand. ASTM Tentative Standards. Grondal, "Certigrade Handbook of Red Cedar Shingles," Red Cedar Shingle Bureau, Seattle, Wash.

Asphalt. Asphalts are bitumens, and the one most commonly seen in roofing and paving is obtained from petroleum residuals. These are obtained by the refining of petroleum. The qualities of asphalt are affected by the nature of the crude and the process of refining. When the flux asphalts obtained from the oil refineries are treated by blowing air through them while the asphalt is maintained at a high temperature, a material is produced which is very stable and has good weathering properties.

Coal Tar. Coal tar is more susceptible to temperature change than asphalt; therefore, for roofing purposes its use is usually confined to flat decks.

Asphalt prepared roofing is manufactured by impregnating a dry roofing felt with a hot asphaltic saturant. A coating consisting of a harder asphalt compounded with a fine mineral **filler** is applied to the weather side of the saturated felt. Into this coating is embedded mineral **surfacing** such as mineral granules, powdered talc, mica, or soapstone. The reverse side of the roofing has a very thin coating of the same asphalt which is usually covered with powdered talc or mica to prevent the roofing from sticking in the package. The surfacing used on **smooth-surfaced roll roofing** is usually powdered talc or mica. The surfacing used on **mineral- or slate-surfaced roll roofing** is roofing granules either in natural colors prepared from slate or artifical colors usually made by applying a coating to a rock granule base. **Asphalt shingles** usually have a granular surfacing. They are made in strips and as individual shingles. The different shapes and sizes of these shingles provide single, double, and triple coverage of the roof deck.

Materials Used in Asphalt Prepared Roofing. The **felt** is usually composed of a continuous sheet of felted fibers of selected rag, specially prepared wood, and high-quality waste papers. The constituents may be varied to give a felt with the desired qualities of strength, absorbency, and flexibility. (See p. 6-184.)

The most satisfactory roofing **asphalts** are obtained by air-blowing a steam- or vacuum-refined petroleum residual. Saturating asphalts must possess a low viscosity in order for the felt to become thoroughly impregnated. Coating asphalts must have good weather-resisting qualities and possess a high fusion temperature in order that there will be no flowing of the asphalt after the application to the roof.

Asphalt built-up roof coverings usually consist of several layers of asphalt-saturated felt with a continuous layer of hot-mopped asphalt between the layers of felt. The top layer of such a roof covering may consist of a hot mopping of asphalt only, a top pouring of hot asphalt with slag or gravel embedded therein, or a mineral-surfaced cap sheet embedded in a hot mopping of asphalt.

Wood shingles are usually manufactured in three different lengths: 16, 18, and 24 in. There are three grades in each length; the No. 1 is the best, and the No. 3 is intended for purposes where the presence of defects is not objectionable. Red-cedar shingles of good quality are obtainable from the Pacific Coast; in the South, red cypress from the Gulf states is preferable. Redwood shingles come 5½ butts to 2 in.; lesser thicknesses are more liable to crack and have shorter life. Shingles 8 in. wide or over should be split before laying. Dimension shingles of uniform width are obtainable. Various stains are available for improved weathering resistance and altered appearance.

Asbestos shingles are composed of portland cement reinforced with asbestos fiber and are formed under pressure. They resist the destructive effects of time, weather, and fire. Asbestos shingles (American method) weigh about 500 lb per square (roofing to cover 100 sq ft) and carry Underwriter's Class A label. Asbestos shingles are made in a variety of colors and shapes. Asbestos roofing shingles have either a smooth surface or a textured surface which represents wood graining.

Slate should be hard and tough and have a well-defined vein that is not too coarse. Approximate weight varies from 650 to 850 lb per square. Slate roofing is available in a variety of sizes and colors and has good fire resistance, but it is regarded as expensive. (See p. 6–189.)

Metallic roofings are usually laid in large panels, often strengthened by corrugating, but they are sometimes cut into small sizes bent into interlocking shapes and laid to interlock with adjacent sheets or shingles. Metallic-roofing panels of both aluminum and steel are available with a variety of prefinished surface treatments to enhance weatherability. Metal tile and metal shingles are usually made of copper, copper-bearing galvanized steel, tinplate, zinc, or aluminum. The lightest metal shingle is the one made from aluminum, which weighs approximately 40 lb per square. The metal radiates solar heat, resulting in lower temperatures beneath than with most other types of uninsulated roofs.

Roofing cements and **coatings** are usually made from asphalt, asbestos fiber, and solvents to make the cement workable. The cements are used for flashings and repairs and contain slow-drying oils so that they will remain plastic on long exposure. Roof coatings are used to renew old asphalt roofings. Asphalt-base aluminum roof coatings are used to renew old asphalt roofs.

Tile. Hard-burned clay tiles with overlapping or interlocking edges cost about the same as slate. They should have a durable glaze and be well made. Unvitrified tiles with slip glaze are satisfactory in warm climates, but only vitrified tiles should be used in the colder regions. Tile roofs weigh from 750 to 1,200 lb per square. Properly made, tile does not deteriorate, is a poor conductor of heat and cold, and is not so brittle as slate.

RUBBER AND RUBBERLIKE MATERIALS

By C. C. Davis

(Boston Woven Hose and Rubber Co.)

References: Dawson and Porritt, "Rubber: Physical and Chemical Properties," Research Association of British Rubber Manufacturers. Davis and Blake, "The Chemistry and Technology of Rubber," Reinhold. ASTM Standards on Rubber Products. "Rubber Red Book. Directory of the Rubber Industry," *The Rubber Age*. Flint, "The Chemistry and Technology of Rubber Latex," Van Nostrand. "The Vanderbilt Handbook," R. T. Vanderbilt Co. Whitby, Davis, and Dunbrook, "Synthetic Rubber," Wiley. "Rubber Bibliography," Rubber Division, American Chemical Society. Noble, "Latex in Industry," *The Rubber Age*. "Annual Report on the Progress of Rubber Technology," Institution of the Rubber Industry.

To avoid confusion by the use of the word **rubber** for a variety of natural and synthetic products, the term **elastomer** has come into use, particularly in scientific and technical literature, as a name for both natural and synthetic materials which are elastic or resilient and in general resemble natural rubber in feeling and appearance.

The utility of rubber and synthetic elastomers is increased by compounding. In the raw state, elastomers are soft and sticky when hot, and hard or brittle when cold. **Vulcanization** extends the temperature range within which they are flexible and elastic. In addition to vulcanizing agents, ingredients are added to make elastomers stronger, tougher, and harder, to make them age better, to color them, and in general to modify them to meet the needs of service conditions. Few rubber products today are made from rubber or other elastomers alone.

The elastomers of greatest commercial and technical importance today are natural rubber, GR-S, Neoprene, nitrile rubbers and Butyl.

Natural rubber of the best quality is prepared by coagulating the latex of the *Hevea brasiliensis* tree, cultivated chiefly in the Far East. This represents nearly all of the natural rubber on the market today.

Unloaded vulcanized rubber will stretch to approximately ten times its length and at this point will bear a **load** of 10 tons per sq in. It can be compressed to one-third its thickness thousands of times without injury. When most types of vulcanized rubber are stretched, their resistance increases in greater proportion than the extension. Even when stretched almost to the point of rupture, they recover very nearly their original dimensions on being released, and then gradually recover a part of the residual distortion.

Freshly cut or torn raw rubber possesses the power of **self-adhesion** which is practically absent in vulcanized rubber. Cold water preserves rubber, but if exposed to the air, particularly to the sun, rubber goods tend to become hard and brittle. Dry heat up to 120 F has little deteriorating effect; at temperatures of 360 to 400 F rubber begins to melt and becomes sticky; at higher temperatures, it becomes entirely carbonized. Unvulcanized rubber is **soluble** in gasoline, naphtha, carbon bisulphide, benzene, petroleum ether, turpentine, and other liquids.

Most rubber is **vulcanized,** *i.e.*, made to combine with sulphur or sulphur-bearing organic compounds or with other chemical cross-linking agents. Vulcanization, if properly carried out, improves mechanical properties, eliminates tackiness, renders the rubber less susceptible to temperature changes, and makes it insoluble in all known solvents. It is impossible to dissolve vulcanized rubber unless it is first decomposed. Other ingredients are added for general effects as follows:

To increase tensile strength and resistance to abrasion: carbon black, precipitated pigments, as well as organic vulcanization accelerators.

To cheapen and stiffen: whiting, barytes, talc, silica, silicates, clays, fibrous materials.

To soften (for purposes of processing or for final properties): bituminous substances, coal tar and its products, vegetable and mineral oils, paraffin, petrolatum, petroleum oils, asphalt.

Vulcanization accessories, dispersion and wetting mediums, etc.: magnesium oxide, zinc oxide, litharge, lime, stearic and other organic acids, degras, pine tar.

Protective agents (natural aging, sunlight, heat, flexing): condensation amines, waxes.

Coloring pigments: iron oxides, especially the red grades, lithopone, titanium oxide, chromium oxide, ultramarine blue, carbon and lampblacks, and organic pigments of various shades.

Specifications should state suitable physical tests. Tensile strength and extensibility tests are of importance and differ widely with different compounds.

GR-S is an outgrowth and improvement of German Buna S. The quantity now produced far exceeds all other synthetic elastomers. It is made from butadiene and styrene, which are produced from petroleum. These two materials are copolymerized directly to GR-S, which is known as a butadiene-styrene copolymer. GR-S has recently been improved, and now gives excellent results in tires.

Neoprene is made from acetylene, which is converted to vinylacetylene, which in turn combines with hydrogen chloride to form chloroprene. The latter is then polymerized to Neoprene.

Nitrile rubbers, an outgrowth of German Buna N or Perbunan, are made by a process similar to that for GR-S, except that acrylonitrile is used instead of styrene. This type of elastomer is a butadiene-acrylonitrile copolymer.

Butyl, one of the most important of the synthetic elastomers, is made from petroleum raw materials, the final process being the copolymerization of isobutylene with a very small proportion of butadiene or isoprene.

Polysulphide rubbers having unique resistance to oxidation and to softening by solvents are commercially available and are sold under the trade-mark "Thiokol.®"

Many new elastomeric materials are assuming industrial importance. **Ethylene-propylene** rubbers are notable in their potential low cost and oxidation resistance. **Polyurethane** elastomers can have a tensile strength up to twice that of conventional rubber, and solid articles as well as foamed shapes can be cast into the desired form using prepolymer shapes as starting materials. **Silicone** rubbers have the advantages, of a wide range of service temperatures and room-temperature curing. **Flourocarbon** elastomers are available for high-temperature service.

No one of these elastomers is satisfactory for all kinds of service conditions, but rubber products can be made to meet a large variety of service conditions.

The following examples show some of the important properties required of rubber products and some typical services where these properties are of major importance:

Resistance to abrasive wear: auto-tire treads, conveyor-belt covers, soles and heels, cables, hose covers.

Resistance to tearing: auto inner tubes, tire treads, footwear, hot-water bags, hose covers, belt covers.

Resistance to flexing: auto tires, transmission belts, V belts, mountings, footwear.

Resistance to high temperatures: auto tires, auto inner tubes, belts conveying hot materials, steam hose, steam packing.

Resistance to cold: airplane parts, automotive parts, auto tires, refrigeration hose.

Minimum heat build-up: auto tires, transmission belts, V belts, mountings.

High resilience: auto inner tubes, sponge rubber, mountings, elastic bands, thread, sandblast hose, jar rings.

High rigidity: packing, soles and heels, valve cups, suction hose, battery boxes.

Long life: fire hose, transmission belts, tubing.

Electrical resistivity: electricians' tape, switchboard mats, electricians' gloves.

Electrical conductivity: hospital flooring, nonstatic hose, matting.

Impermeability to gases: balloons, life rafts, gasoline hose, special diaphragms.

Resistance to ozone: ignition distributor gaskets, ignition cables, windshield wipers.

Resistance to sunlight: wearing apparel, hose covers, bathing caps.

Resistance to chemicals: tank linings, hose for chemicals.

Resistance to oils: gasoline hose, oil-suction hose, paint hose, creamery hose, packinghouse hose, special belts, tank linings, special footwear.

Stickiness: cements, electricians' tapes, adhesive tapes, pressure-sensitive tapes.

Low specific gravity: airplane parts, forestry hose, balloons.

No odor or taste: milk tubing, brewery and wine hose, nipples, jar rings.

Special colors: ponchos, life rafts, welding hose.

The following table gives a comparison of some important characteristics of the most important elastomers when vulcanized. The lower part of the table indicates, for a few representative rubber products, preferences in the use of different elastomers for different service conditions without consideration of cost.

Specifications for rubber goods may cover the chemical, physical, and mechanical properties, such as elongation, tensile strength, permanent set, and oven tests, minimum rubber content, exclusion of reclaimed rubber, maximum free and combined sulphur contents, maximum acetone and chloroform extracts, ash content, and many construction requirements. It is preferable, however, to specify properties such as resilience, hystereses, static or dynamic shear and compression modulus, flex fatigue and cracking, creep, electrical properties, stiffening, heat generation, compression set,

Comparative Properties of Elastomers

	Natural rubber	GR-S	Neoprene	Nitrile rubbers	Butyl	Thiokol®
Tensile properties	Excellent	Good	Very good	Good	Good	Fair
Resistance to abrasive wear	Excellent	Good	Very good	Good	Good	Poor
Resistance to tearing	Very good	Poor	Good	Fair	Very good	Poor
Resilience	Excellent	Good	Good	Fair	Poor	Poor
Resistance to heat	Good	Fair	Good	Excellent	Good	Poor
Resistance to cold	Excellent	Good	Good	Good	Excellent	Poor
Resistance to flexing	Excellent	Good	Very good	Good	Excellent	Poor
Aging properties	Excellent	Excellent	Good	Good	Excellent	Good
Cold flow (creep)	Very low	Low	Low	Very low	Fairly low	High
Resistance to sunlight	Fair	Fair	Excellent	Good	Excellent	Excellent
Resistance to oils and solvents	Poor	Poor	Good	Excellent	Fair	Excellent
Permeability to gases	Fairly low	Fairly low	Low	Fairly low	Very low	Very low
Electrical insulation	Fair	Excellent	Fair	Poor	Excellent	Good
Flame resistance	Poor	Poor	Good	Poor	Poor	Poor
Auto-tire tread	Preferred	Alternate				
Inner tube	Alternate	....	....	....	Preferred	
Conveyor-belt cover	Preferred	....	Alternate			
Tire sidewall	Alternate	Preferred				
Transmission belting	Preferred	....	Alternate			
Druggist sundries	Preferred					
Gasoline and oil hose	....	....	....	Preferred		
Lacquer and paint hose	....	....	....	....	....	Preferred
Oil-resistant footwear	....	....	Preferred			
Balloons	Alternate	....	Preferred			
Jar rings	Alternate	Preferred				
Wire and cable insulation	Alternate	Preferred				

resistance to oils and chemicals, permeability, brittle point, etc., in the temperature range prevailing in service, and to leave the selection of the elastomer to a competent manufacturer.

Latex, imported in stable form from the Far East, is used for various rubber products. In the manufacture of such products, the latex must be compounded for vulcanizing and otherwise modifying the properties of the rubber itself. Important products made directly from compounded latex include surgeons' and household gloves, thread, bathing caps, rubberized textiles, balloons, and sponge. A recent important use of latex is for "foam sponge," which may be several inches thick and used for cushions, mattresses, etc.

Gutta-percha and **balata,** also natural products, are akin to rubber chemically but more leathery and thermoplastic, and are used for some special purposes, principally for submarine cables, golf balls, and various minor products.

Rubber Derivatives

Rubber derivatives are chemical compounds and modifications of rubber, some of which have become of commercial importance.

Chlorinated rubber, produced by the action of chlorine on rubber in solution, is non-rubbery, incombustible, and extremely resistant to many chemicals. As commercial **Parlon,** it finds use in corrosion-resistant paints and varnishes, in inks, and in adhesives.

Rubber hydrochloride, produced by the action of hydrogen chloride on rubber in solution, is a strong, extensible, tear-resistant, moisture-resistant, oil-resistant material, marketed as **Pliofilm** in the form of tough transparent films for wrappers, packaging material, etc.

Cyclized rubber is formed by the action of certain agents, *e.g.*, sulphonic acids and chlorostannic acid, on rubber, and is a thermoplastic, non-rubbery, tough or hard product. One form, **Thermoprene,** is used in the **Vulcalock process** for adhering rubber to metal, wood, and concrete, and in chemical-resistant paints. **Pliolite,** which has high resistance to many chemicals and has low permeability, is used in special paints, paper, and fabric coatings. **Marbon-B** has exceptional electrical properties and is valuable for insulation. **Hypalon** (chlorosulphonated polyethylene) is highly resistant to many important chemicals, notably ozone and concentrated sulphuric acid, for which other rubbers are unsuitable.

SOLVENTS

By C. G. Harford

(Arthur D. Little, Inc.)

REFERENCES: Sax, "Dangerous Properties of Industrial Materials," Reinhold. Perry, "Chemical Engineer's Handbook," McGraw-Hill.

The use of solvents has become widespread throughout industry. The health of personnel and the fire hazards involved should always be considered. Generally, solvents are **organic liquids** which vary greatly in solvent power, flammability, volatility, and toxicity.

Solvents for Polymeric Materials

A wide choice of solvents and solvent combinations is available for use with organic polymers in the manufacture of polymer-coated products and unsupported films. For a given polymer, the choice of solvent system is often critical in terms of solvent power, cost, safety, and evaporation rate. In such instances, the supplier of the base polymer should be consulted.

Alcohols

Methyl alcohol (methanol), is now made synthetically. It is completely miscible with water and most organic liquids. It evaporates rapidly and is a good solvent for dyes, gums, shellac, nitrocellulose, and some vegetable waxes. It is widely used as an antifreeze for automobiles, in shellac solutions, spirit varnishes, stain and paint removers. It is toxic; imbibition or prolonged breathing of the vapors can cause blindness. It should be used only in well-ventilated spaces. Flash point 52 F.

Ethyl alcohol (ethanol) is produced by fermentation and synthetically. For industrial use it is generally denatured and sold under various trade names. There are numerous formulations of specially denatured alcohols which can legally be used for specified purposes.

This compound is miscible with water and most organic solvents. It evaporates rapidly and, because of its solvent power, low cost, and agreeable odor, finds a wide range of uses. The common uses are antifreeze (see Freezing Preventives, p. 6–186), shellac solvent, in mixed solvents, spirit varnishes, and solvent for dyes, oils, and animal greases.

Denatured alcohols are toxic when taken orally. The effect of ethyl-alcohol vapors when breathed in high concentration can produce the physiological effects of alcoholic liquors. It should be used in well-ventilated areas. Flash point 60 to 62 F.

Isopropyl alcohol (isopropanol) is derived mainly from petroleum gases. It is not as good a solvent as denatured alcohol although it can be used as a substitute for ethyl alcohol in some instances. It is used as a rubbing alcohol and in lacquer thinners. Flash point is 52 F.

Butyl alcohol (normal butanol) is used extensively in lacquer and synthetic resin compositions and also in penetrating oils, metal cleaners, insect sprays, and paints for application over asphalt. It is an excellent blending agent for otherwise incompatible materials. Flash point is 84 F.

Esters

Ethyl acetate dissolves a large variety of materials, such as nitrocellulose, oils, fats, gums, and resins. It is used extensively in nitrocellulose lacquers, candy coatings, food flavorings, and in chemical synthesis. On account of its high rate of evaporation, it finds a use in paper, leather, and cloth coatings and cements. Flash point 24 F.

Butyl acetate is the acetic-acid ester of normal butanol. This ester is used extensively for dissolving various cellulose esters, mineral and vegetable oils, and many synthetic resins, such as the vinylites, polystyrene, methyl methacrylate, and chlorinated rubber. It is also a good solvent for natural resins. It is the most important solvent used in lacquer manufacture. It is useful in the preparation of perfumes and synthetic flavors. Flash point 72 F.

Amyl acetate, sometimes known as banana oil, is used mainly in lacquers. Its properties are somewhat like those of butyl acetate. Flash point 70 F.

Hydrocarbons

The **aromatic hydrocarbons** are derived from coal-tar distillates, the most common of which are benzene, toluene, xylene (also known as benzol, toluol, and xylol), and highflash solvent naphtha.

Benzene is an excellent solvent for fats, vegetable and mineral oils, rubber, chlorinated rubber; it is also used as a solvent in paints, lacquers, inks, paint removers, asphalt, coal tar. This substance should be used with caution. Flash point 12 F.

Toluene. General uses are about the same as benzol, in paints, lacquers, rubber solutions, and solvent extractions. Flash point 40 F.

Xylene is used in the manufacture of dyestuffs and other synthetic chemicals and as a solvent for paints, rubber, lacquer, and varnishes. Flash point 63 F.

Hi-flash naphtha or **coal-tar naphtha** is used mainly as a diluent in lacquers, synthetic enamels, paints, and asphaltic coatings. Flash point 100 F.

Petroleum

These hydrocarbons, derived from petroleum, are, next to water, the cheapest and most universally used solvents.

V. M. & P. naphtha, sometimes called **benzine,** is used by paint and varnish makers as a solvent or diluent. It finds wide use as a solvent for fats, oils, greases and is used as a diluent in paints and lacquers. It is also used as an extractive agent as well as in some specialized fields of cleansing (fat removal). It is used to compound rubber cement, inks, varnish removers. It is relatively non-toxic. Flash point 20 to 45 F.

Mineral spirits, also called **Stoddard solvent,** is extensively used in dry cleaning because of its high flash point and clean evaporation. It is also widely used in turpentine substitutes for oil paints. Flash point 100 to 110 F.

Kerosine, a No. 1 fuel oil, is a good solvent for petroleum greases, oils, and fats. Flash point 100 to 165 F.

Chlorinated Solvents

Carbon tetrachloride is a colorless non-flammable liquid with a chloroformlike odor. It is an excellent solvent for fats, oils, greases, waxes, and resins and is used in dry cleaning and in degreasing of wool, cotton waste, and glue. It is also used in rubber cements and adhesives, as an extracting agent, and in fire extinguishers. It should be used only in well-ventilated spaces; prolonged inhalation is extremely dangerous.

Trichlorethylene is somewhat similar to carbon tetrachloride but is slower in evaporation rate. It is the solvent most commonly used for vapor degreasing of metal parts. It is also used in the manufacture of dyestuffs and other chemicals. It is an excellent solvent and is used in some types of paints, varnishes, and leather coatings.

Tetrachlorethylene, also called **perchlorethylene,** is non-flammable and has uses similar to those of carbon tetrachloride and trichlorethylene. Its chief use is in dry cleaning; it is also used somewhat in metal degreasing.

Ketones

Acetone is an exceptionally active solvent for a wide variety of organic materials, gases, liquids, and solids. It is completely miscible with water and also with most of the organic liquids. It can also be used as a blending agent for otherwise immiscible liquids. It is used in the manufacture of pharmaceuticals, dyestuffs, lubricating compounds, and pyroxylin compositions. It is a good solvent for cellulose acetate, ethyl cellulose, vinyl and methacrylate resins, chlorinated rubber, asphalt, camphor, and various esters of cellulose, including smokeless powder, cordite, etc. Some of its more common uses are in paint and varnish removers, the storing of acetylene, and the dewaxing of lubricating oils. It is the basic material for the manufacture of iodoform and chloroform. It is also used as a denature for ethyl alcohol. Flash point 0 F.

Methylethylketone (MEK) can be used in many cases where acetone is used as a general solvent, *e.g.*, in the formulation of pyroxylin cements and in compositions containing the various esters of cellulose. Flash point 30 F.

THERMAL INSULATIONS

By Peter E. Glaser
(Arthur D. Little, Inc.)

REFERENCES: "Guide and Data Book," ASHRAE. Glaser, "Aerodynamically Heated Structures," Prentice-Hall. Timmerhaus, "Advances in Cryogenic Engineering," Plenum. Wilkes, "Heat Insulation," Wiley.

Thermal insulations consisting of a single material, a mixture of materials, or a composite structure are chosen to reduce heat flow. **Insulating effectiveness** is judged on the basis of thermal conductivity and depends on the physical and chemical structure of the material. The heat transferred through an insulation results from **solid conduction, gas conduction,** and **radiation.** Solid conduction is reduced by small-size particles or fibers in loose-fill insulation and by thin cell walls in foams. Gas conduction is reduced by providing large numbers of small pores (either interconnected or closed off from each other) of the order of the mean free paths of the gas molecules, by substituting gases of low thermal conductivity, or by evacuating the pores to a low pressure. Radiation is reduced by adding materials which absorb, reflect, or scatter radiant energy. (See also pp. 4-95, 96, 97, 106.)

The **performance** of insulations depends on the temperature of the bounding surfaces and their emittance, the insulation density, the type and pressure of gas within the pores, the moisture content, the thermal shock resistance, and the action of mechanical loads and vibrations. In **transient** applications, the heat capacity of the insulation (affecting the rate of heating or cooling) has to be considered.

The **form** of the **insulations** can be loose fill (bubbles, fibers, flakes, granules, powders), flexible (batting, blanket, felt, multilayer sheets and tubular), rigid (block, board, brick, custom-molded, sheet and pipe covering), cemented, foamed-in-place, or sprayed.

The **choice of insulations** is dictated by the service-temperature range as well as by design criteria and economic considerations.

Cryogenic Temperatures (below −150 F)

(See also Sec. 18.)

At the low temperatures experienced with cryogenic liquids, **evacuated multilayer insulations,** consisting of a series of radiation shields of high reflectivity separated by low-conductivity spacers, are effective materials. Radiation-shield materials are aluminum foils or aluminized polyester films used in combination with spacers of thin polyester fiber or glass-fiber papers; radiation shields of crinkled, aluminized polyester film without spacers are also used. To be effective, multilayer insulations require a vacuum of at least 10^{-4} mm Hg. **Evacuated powder** and **fiber insulations** can be effective at gas pressures up to 0.1 mm Hg over a wide temperature range. **Powders** include colloidal silica (8×10^{-7} in. particle diam), silica aerogel (1×10^{-6} in.), synthetic calcium silicate (0.001 in.), and perlite (an expanded form of glassy volcanic lava particles, 0.05 in. diam). Powder insulations can be **opacified** with copper, aluminum, or carbon particles to reduce radiant-energy transmission. **Fiber insulations** consist of mats of fibers arranged in ordered parallel layers either without binders or with a minimum of binders. Glass fibers (10^{-5} in. diam) are used most frequently. For large process installations and cold boxes, unevacuated perlite powder or mineral fibers are useful.

Foamed organic plastics, using either fluorinated hydrocarbons or other gases as expanding agents, are partially evacuated when gases within the closed cells condense when exposed to low temperatures. Polystyrene and polyurethane foams are used frequently. **Gastight barriers** are required to prevent a rise in thermal conductivity with aging due to diffusion of air and moisture into the foam insulation. Gas barriers are made of aluminum foil, polyester film, and polyester film laminated with aluminum foil.

Refrigeration, Heating, and Air Conditioning (up to 250 F)

At temperatures associated with commercial refrigeration practice and building insulation, **vapor barriers** resistant to the diffusion of water vapor should be installed on the warm side of most types of insulations if the temperature within the insulation is expected to fall below the dew point (this condition would lead to condensation of water vapor within the insulation and result in a substantial decrease in insulating effectiveness). Vapor barriers include oil- or tar-impregnated paper, paper laminated with aluminum foil, and polyester films. Insulations which have an impervious outer skin or structure require a **vaportight sealant** at exposed joints to prevent collection of moisture or ice underneath the insulation. (See also Secs. 12 and 18.)

Loose-fill insulations include powders and granules such as perlite, vermiculite (an expanded form of mica), silica aerogel, calcium silicate, expanded organic plastic beads, granulated cork (bark of the cork tree), granulated charcoal, redwood wool (fiberized bark of the redwood tree), and synthetic fibers. The most widely used fibers are those made of glass, rock, or slag produced by centrifugal attenuation or attenuation by hot gases.

Flexible or **blanket insulations** include those made from organically bonded glass fibers; rock wool, slag wool, macerated paper, or hair felt placed between or bonded to paper laminate (including vapor-barrier material) or burlap; foamed organic plastics in sheet and pad form (polyurethane, polyethylene); and elastomeric closed-cell foam in sheet, pad, or tube form.

Rigid or **board insulations** (obtainable in a wide range of densities and structural properties) include foamed organic plastics such as polystyrene (extruded or molded beads); polyurethane, polyvinyl chloride, phenolics, and ureas; balsa wood, foamed glass, and corkboard (compressed mass of baked-cork particles).

Moderate Temperatures (up to 1200 F)

The widest use of a large variety of insulations is in the temperature range associated with power plants and industrial equipment. Inorganic insulations are available for this temperature range, with several capable of operating over a wider temperature range.

Loose-fill insulations include diatomaceous silica (fossilized skeletons of microscopic organisms), perlite, vermiculite, and fibers of glass, rock, or slag. Board and blanket insulations of various shapes and degrees of flexibility and density include glass and mineral fibers, asbestos paper, and millboard [asbestos is a heat-resistant fibrous mineral obtained from Canadian (chrysotile) or South African (amosite) deposits]; asbestos fibers bonded with sodium silicate, 85 percent basic magnesium carbonate, expanded perlite bonded with calcium silicate, calcium silicate reinforced with asbestos fibers, expanded perlite bonded with cellulose fiber and asphalt, organic bonded mineral fibers, and cellulose fiberboard.

Sprayed insulation (macerated paper or fibers and adhesive or frothed plastic foam), **insulating concrete** (concrete mixed with expanded perlite or vermiculite), and **foamed-in-place plastic insulation** (prepared by mixing polyurethane components, pouring the liquid mix into the void, and relying on action of generated gas or vaporization of a low-boiling fluorocarbon to foam the liquid and fill the space to be insulated) are useful in special applications.

Reflective insulations form air spaces bounded by surfaces of high reflectivity to reduce the flow of radiant energy. Surfaces need not be mirror-bright to reflect long-wavelength radiation emitted by objects below 500 F. Materials for reflective insulation include aluminum foil cemented to one or both sides of kraft paper and aluminum particles applied to the paper with adhesive. Where several reflective surfaces are used, they have to be separated during the installation to form air spaces.

High Temperatures (above 1500 F)

At the high temperatures associated with furnaces and process applications, physical and chemical stability of the insulation in an oxidizing, reducing, or neutral atmosphere or vacuum may be required. **Loose-fill insulations** include glass fibers (1000 F useful temperature limit), asbestos fibers (1200 F), fibrous potassium titanate (1900 F), alumina-silica fibers (2300 F), microquartz fibers (2500 F), opacified colloidal alumina (2400 F in vacuum), zirconia fibers (3000 F), alumina bubbles (3300 F), zirconia bubbles (4300 F), and carbon and graphite fibers (4500 F in vacuum or an inert atmosphere).

Rigid insulations include reinforced and bonded colloidal silica (2000 F), bonded diatomaceous earth brick (2500 F), insulating firebrick (see Refractories, p. 6–206), and anisotropic, pyrolitic graphite (100-to-1 ratio of thermal conductivity parallel to surface and across thickness).

Reflective insulations, forming either an air space or an evacuated chamber between spaced surfaces, include stainless steel, molybdenum, tantalum, or tungsten foils and sheets.

Insulating cements are based on asbestos, mineral, or refractory fibers bonded with mixtures of clay or sodium silicate. Lightweight, castable insulating materials consisting of mineral or refractory fibers in a calcium aluminate cement are useful up to 2500 F.

Ablators are composite materials capable of withstanding high temperatures and high gas velocities for limited periods with minimum erosion by subliming and charring at controlled rates. Materials include asbestos, carbon, graphite, silica, nylon or glass fibers in a high-temperature resin matrix (epoxy or phenolic resin), and cork compositions.

SILICONES

Silicones are organosilicon oxide polymers characterized by remarkable temperature stability, chemical inertness, waterproofness, and excellent dielectric properties. The investigations of Prof. Kipping in England for over forty years established a basis for the recent developments of the numerous industrially-important products now being made by the Dow-Corning Corp. of Midland, Mich., and by the General Electric Co. Among these products are the following:

Water repellents in the form of extremely thin films which can be formed on paper, cloth, ceramics, glass, plastics, leather, powders, or other surfaces. These have great value for the protection of delicate electrical equipment in moist atmospheres.

Oils with high flash points (above 600 F), low pour points (−120 F), and with a constancy of viscosity notably superior to petroleum products in the range from 500 to −100 F (see Fig. 1, p. 6–244). They are practically incombustible. They are in use for hydraulic servomotor fluids, damping fluids, dielectric liquids for transformers, heat-transfer mediums, etc., and are of special value in aircraft because of the rapid and extreme temperature variations to which aircraft are exposed. At present they are not available as lubricants except under light loads.

Greases and compounds for plug cocks, spark plugs, and ball bearings which must operate at extreme temperatures and speeds.

Varnishes and resins for use in electrical insulation where temperatures are high. Layers of glass cloth impregnated with or bounded by silicone resins withstand prolonged exposure to temperatures up to 500 F. They form paint finishes of great resistance to chemical agents and to moisture. They have many other industrial uses.

Silicone rubbers which retain their resiliency for −50 to 520 F but with much lower strength than some of the synthetic rubbers. They are used for shaft seals, oven gaskets, refrigerator gaskets, and vacuum gaskets.

REFRACTORIES

BY

F. H. Norton

References: Buell, "The Open-hearth Furnace," 3 vols., Penton. *Bull.* R-2-E, The Babcock & Wilcox Co. "Refractories," General Refractories Co. Chesters, "Steel Plant Refractories," United Steel Companies, Ltd. "Modern Refractory Practice," Harbison Walker Refractories Co. Green and Stewart, "Ceramics: A Symposium," British Ceramic Soc. Norton, "Refractories," 3d ed., McGraw-Hill. ASTM Standards on Refractory Materials (Committee C-8). Trinks, "Industrial Furnaces," Vol. I, Wiley. Campbell, "High Temperature Technology," Wiley.

TYPES OF REFRACTORIES

Fire-clay Refractories. Fire-clay brick are made from fire clays, which comprise all refractory clays that are not white burning. Fire clays can be divided into plastic clays and hard flint clays; they may also be classified as to alumina content.

Firebricks are usually made of a blended mixture of flint clays and plastic clays which is then formed, after mixing with water, to the required shape. Some or all of the flint clay may be replaced by highly burned or calcined clay, called **grog.** A large proportion of the modern bricks is molded by the dry-press or power-press process where the forming is carried out under high pressure and with a low water content. Some extruded and hand-molded brick are still made.

The dried bricks are burned either in periodic or tunnel kilns at temperatures varying between 2200 and 2700 F. Tunnel kilns give continuous production and a uniform temperature of burning.

Fire-clay bricks are used for boiler settings, kilns, malleable-iron furnaces, incinerators, and many portions of steel and non-ferrous metal furnaces. They are resistant to spalling and stand up well under many slag conditions, but are not generally suitable for use with high-lime slags, fluid-coal-ash slags, or under severe load conditions.

High-alumina brick are manufactured from raw materials rich in alumina, such as diaspore and bauxite. They are graded into groups with 50, 60, 70, 80, and 90 percent alumina content. When well fired, these brick contain a large amount of mullite and less of the glassy phase than is present in the firebricks. Corundum is also present in many of these bricks. High-alumina brick are generally used for unusually severe temperature or load conditions. They are employed extensively in limekilns and rotary cement kilns, the ports and regenerators of glass tanks, and for slag resistance in some metallurgical furnaces; their price is higher than that for firebrick.

Silica brick are manufactured from crushed ganister rock containing about 97 to 98 percent silica. A bond consisting of 2 percent lime is used, and the bricks are fired in periodic kilns at temperatures of 2700 to 2800 F for several days until a stable volume is obtained. They are especially valuable where a good strength is required at high temperatures. Recently, superduty silica brick are finding some use in the steel industry. They have a lowered alumina content, and often a lowered porosity.

Silica brick are used extensively in coke ovens, the roofs and walls of open-hearth furnaces, in the roofs and side walls of glass tanks, and as linings of acid electric steel furnaces. Although silica brick is readily **spalled** (cracked by a temperature change) below red heat, it is very stable if the temperature is kept above this range, and for this reason stands up well in regenerative furnaces. Any structure of silica brick should be heated up slowly to the working temperature; a large structure often requires 2 weeks or more to bring up.

Magnesite brick are made from crushed magnesium oxide which is produced by calcining raw magnesite rock to high temperatures. A rock containing several percent of iron oxide is preferable as this permits the rock to be fired at a lower temperature than if pure materials were used. Magnesite brick are generally fired at a comparatively high temperature in periodic or tunnel kilns, though large tonnages of unburned brick are now produced. The latter are made with special grain sizing and a bond such as an oxychloride. A large proportion of magnesite brick made in this country uses raw material extracted from sea water.

Magnesite brick are basic and are used whenever it is necessary to resist high-lime slags such as in the basic open-hearth furnace. They also find use in furnaces for the lead- and copper-refining industry. The highly-pressed unburned brick find extensive-use as linings for cement kilns. Magnesite brick are not so resistant to spalling as fire-clay brick.

Dolomite. This rock contains a mixture of $Mg(OH)_2$ and $Ca(OH)_2$, is calcined, and is used in granulated form for furnace bottoms.

Chrome brick are manufactured in much the same way as magnesite brick but are made from natural chromite ore. Commerical ores always contain magnesia and alumina. Unburned hydraulically pressed chrome brick are also made.

Chrome bricks are very resistant to all types of slag. They are used as separators between acid and basic refractories, also in soaking pits and floors of forging furnaces. The unburned hydraulically pressed brick now find extensive use in the walls of the open-hearth furnace and are often enclosed in a metal case. Chrome bricks are used in sulphite-recovery furnaces and to some extent in the refining of nonferrous metals. Basic bricks combining various proportions of magnesite and chromite are now made in large quantities and have advantages over either material alone for some purposes.

The **insulating firebrick** is a class of brick which consists of a highly porous fire clay or kaolin. They are light in weight (about ½ to ⅙ that of fireclay), low in thermal conductivity, and yet sufficiently resistant to temperature to be used successfully on the hot side of the furnace wall, thus permitting thin walls of low thermal conductivity and low heat content. The low heat content is particularly valuable in saving fuel and time on heating up, allows rapid changes in temperature to be made, and permits rapid cooling. These bricks are made in a variety of ways, such as mixing organic matter with the clay and later burning it out to form pores; or a bubble structure can be incorporated in the clay-water mixture which is later preserved in the fired brick. The insulating firebricks are classified into several groups according to the maximum use limit; the ranges are up to 1600, 2000, 2300, 2600, and above 2800 F.

Insulating refractories are used mainly in the heat-treating industry for furnaces of the periodic type; the low heat content permits noteworthy fuel savings as compared with firebrick. They are also used extensively in stress-relieving furnaces, chemical-process furnaces, oil stills or heaters, and in the combustion chambers of domestic-oil-burner furnaces. They usually have a life equal to the heavy brick that they replace. They are particularly suitable for constructing experimental or laboratory furnaces because they can be cut or machined readily to any shape. However, they are not resistant to fluid slag.

There are a number of types of **special brick,** obtainable from individual manufactories. High-burned kaolin refractories are particularly valuable under conditions of severe temperature and heavy load, or severe spalling conditions, as in the case of high-temperature oil-fired boiler settings, or piers under enameling furnaces. Another brick for the same uses is a high-fired brick of Missouri aluminous clay.

There are a number of bricks on the market made from electrically fused materials, such as fused mullite, fused alumina, and fused zircon. These bricks although high in cost are particularly suitable for certain severe conditions, such as bottoms and walls of glass-melting furnaces.

Bricks of **silicon carbide** (see p. 6–171), either nitride or clay-bonded, have a high thermal conductivity and find use in muffle walls and as a slag-resisting material.

Other types of refractory that find certain limited use are **forsterite, and zirconia.** Acid-resisting brick consisting of a dense body like stoneware are used for lining tanks and conduits in the chemical industry. Carbon blocks are used as linings for the crucibles of blast furnaces.

The **chemical composition** of some of the refractories is given in Table 1. The **physical properties** are given in Table 2. Reference should be made to ASTM standards for details of standard tests.

Standard and Special Shapes

There are a large number of **standard refractory shapes** carried in stock by most manufacturers. Their catalogues should be consulted in selecting these shapes, but the common ones are shown in Table 3. These shapes have been standardized by the American Refractories Institute and by the Bureau of Simplification of the U.S. Department of Commerce.

Table 1. Chemical Composition of Typical Refractories[a]

No.	Refractory type	SiO_2	Al_2O_3	Fe_2O_3	TiO_2	CaO	MgO	Cr_2O_3	SiC	Alkalies	Resistance to: Siliceous steel-slag	High-lime steel-slag	Fused mill-scale	Coal-ash slag
1	Alumina (fused)	8–10	85–90	1–1.5	1.5–2.2	...	...	..	.....	0.8–1.3[c]	E	G	F	G
2	Chrome	6	23	15[b]	......	...	17	38	.....	....	G	E	E	G
3	Chrome (unburned)	5	18	12[b]	......	...	32	30	.....	....	G	E	E	G
4	Fire clay (high-heat duty)	50–57	36–42	1.5–2.5	1.5–2.5	...	...	..	.....	1–3.5[c]	F	P	P	F
5	Fire clay (super-duty)	52	43	1	2	...	...	..	.....	2[c]	F	P	F	F
6	Forsterite	34.6	0.9	7.0	......	1.3	55.4							
7	High-alumina	22–26	68–72	1–1.5	3.5	...	...	..	.....	1–1.5[c]	G	F	F	F
8	Kaolin	52	45.4	0.6	1.7	0.1	0.2	..	.....	....	F	P	G[d]	F
9	Magnesite	3	2	6	......	3	86	..	.....	....	P	E	E	E
10	Magnesite (unburned)	5	7.5	8.5	......	2	64	10	.....	....	P	E	E	E
11	Magnesite (fused)	.....	.....	.....	......	...	...	..	.....	....	F	E	E	E
12	Refractory porcelain	25–70	25–60	.....	......	...	...	..	.....	1–5	G	F	F	F
13	Silica	96	1	1	......	2	...	..	.....	....	E	P	F	P
14	Silicon carbide (clay bonded)	7–9	2–4	0.3–1	1	...	...	..	85–90	....	E	G	F	E
15	Sillimanite (mullite)	35	62	0.5	1.5	...	...	..	.....	0.5[c]	G	F	F	F
16	Insulating fire-brick (2600 F)	57.7	36.8	2.4	1.5	0.6	0.5	..	.....	....	P	P	G[e]	P

[a] Much of this data has been taken from a table prepared by Trostel, *Chem. and Met. Eng.*, Nov., 1938.
[b] As FeO.
[c] Includes lime and magnesia.
[d] Excellent if left above 1200 F.
[e] Oxidizing atmosphere.
E = Excellent. G = Good. F = Fair. P = Poor.

Regenerator tile sizes, $a \times b \times c$ are: 18×6 or 9×3; 18×9 or 12×4; $22\frac{1}{2} \times 6$ or 9×3; $22\frac{1}{2} \times 9$ or 12×4; $27 \times 9 \times 3$; 27×9 or 12×4; $31\frac{1}{2} \times 12 \times 4$; $36 \times 12 \times 4$.

The following **arch, wedge, and key bricks** have maximum dimensions, $a \times b \times c$ of $9 \times 4\frac{1}{2} \times 2\frac{1}{2}$ in. The minimum dimensions a', b', c', are as noted: No. 1 arch, $c' = 2\frac{1}{8}$; No. 2 arch, $c' = 1\frac{3}{4}$; No. 3 arch, $c' = 1$; No. 1 wedge, $c' = 1\frac{7}{8}$; No. 2 wedge, $c' = 1\frac{1}{2}$; No. 3 wedge, $c' = 2$; No. 1 key, $b' = 4$; No. 2 key, $b' = 3\frac{1}{2}$; No. 3 key, $b' = 3$; No. 4 key, $b' = 2\frac{1}{4}$; edge skew, $b' = 1\frac{1}{2}$; feather edge, $c' = \frac{1}{8}$; No. 1 neck, $a' = 3\frac{1}{2}$, $c' = \frac{5}{8}$; No. 2 neck, $a' = 2\frac{1}{2}$, $c = \frac{5}{8}$; No. 3 neck, $a' = 0$, $c' = \frac{5}{8}$; end skew, $a' = 6\frac{3}{4}$; side skew, $b' = 2\frac{1}{4}$; jamb brick, $9 \times 2\frac{1}{2}$; bung arch, $c' = 2\frac{3}{8}$.

Special shapes are more expensive than the standard refractories, and, as they are usually hand-molded, will not be so dense or uniform in structure as the regular brick. When special shapes are necessary, they should be laid out as simply as possible and the maximum size should be kept down below 30 in. if possible. It is also desirable to make all special shapes with the vertical dimension as an even multiple of 2½ in. plus one joint so that they will bond in with the rest of the brickwork.

Table 2. Physical Properties of Typical Refractories[a]

(Refractory numbers refer to Table 1)

Refractory No.	Fusion point, Deg F	Fusion point, Pyrometric cone	Deformation under load, percent at deg F and lb per sq in.	Spalling resistance	Reheat shrinkage after 5 hr, percent at (deg F)	Wt. of straight 9 in. brick, lb
1	3390+	39+	1 at 2730 and 50	Good	+0.5 (2910)	9–10.6
2	3580+	41+	Shears 2740 and 28	Poor	−0.5 to 1.0 (3000)	11.0
3	3580+	41+	Shears 2955 and 28	Fair	−0.5 to 1.0 (3000)	11.3
4	3060–3170	31–33	2.5–10 at 2460 and 25	Good	±0 to 1.5 (2550)	7.5
5	3170–3200	33–34	2–4 at 2640 and 25	Excellent	±0 to 1.5 (2910)	8.5
6	3430	40	10 at 2950	Fair	....	9.0
7	3290	36	1–4 at 2640 and 25	Excellent	−2 to 4 (2910)	7.5
8	3200	34	0.5 at 2640 and 25	Excellent	−0.7 to 1.0 (2910)	7.7
9	3580+	41+	Shears 2765 and 28	Poor	−1 to 2 (3000)	10.0
10	3580+	41+	Shears 2940 and 28	Fair	−0.5 to 1.5 (3000)	10.7
11	3580+	41+		Fair	....	10.5
12	2640–3000	16–30		Good		
13	3060–3090	31–32	Shears 2900 and 25	Poor[b]	+0.5 to 0.8 (2640)	6.5
14	3390	39	0–1 at 2730 and 50	Excellent	+2[c] (2910)	8–9.3
15	3310–3340	37–38	0–0.5 at 2640 and 25	Excellent	−0 to 0.8 (2910)	8.5
16	2980–3000	29–30	0.3 at 2200 and 10	Good	−0.2 (2600)	2.25

Refractory No.	Porosity	Specific heat 60–1200 F	Mean coefficient of thermal expansion from 60 F shrinkage point × 10⁵	Mean thermal conductivity, Btu per sq ft per hr per deg F per in. thickness — Mean temperatures between the hot and cold face, deg F: 200	400	800	1200	1600	2000	2400
1	20–26	0.20	0.43	..	20	22	24	27	30	32
2	20–26	0.20	0.56	..	8	9	10	11	12	12
3	10–12	0.21								
4	15–25	0.23	0.25–0.30	5	6	7	8	10	11	12
5	12–15	0.23	0.25–0.30	6	7	8	9	10	12	13
6	23–26	0.25								
7	28–36	0.23	0.24	6	7	8	9	10	12	13
8	18	0.22	0.23	..	....	11	12	13	13	14
9	20–26	0.27	0.56–0.83	..	40	35	30	27	26	25
10	10–12	0.26								
11	20–30	0.27	0.56–0.80							
12	.....	0.23	0.30	..	14	15	17	18	19	20
13	20–30	0.23	0.46[d]	..	8	10	12	13	14	15
14	13–28	0.20	0.24	..	....	100	80	65	55	50
15	20–25	0.23	0.30	..	10	11	12	13	14	15
16	75	0.22	0.25	..	1.6	2.0	2.6	3.2	3.8	

[a] Much of this data has been taken from a table prepared by Trostel, *Chem. and Met. Eng.*, Nov., 1938.
[b] Excellent if left above 1200 F.
[c] Oxidizing atmosphere.
[d] Up to 0.56 at red heat.

Refractory Mortars, Coatings, Plastics, Castables, and Ramming Mixtures

Practically all brickwork is laid up with some type of jointing material to give a more stable structure and to seal the joints. This material may be ground fire clay or a specially prepared mortar containing grog to reduce the shrinkage. The bonding mortars may be divided into three general classes. The first are **air-setting mortars** which often contain chemical or organic binder to give a strong bond when dried or fired at comparatively low temperatures. Many of the air-setting mortars should not be used at extremely high temperatures because the fluxing action of the air-setting ingredient reduces the fusion point. The second class is called **heat-setting mortar** and requires temperatures of over 2000 F to produce a good bond. These mortars vary in vitrifying point, some producing a strong bond in the lower temperature ranges, and the others requiring very high temperatures to give good strength. The third classification comprises **special-base mortars** such as silica, magnesite, silicon carbide, or chrome, which are specially blended for use with their respective bricks. The chrome-base mortar may be satisfactorily used with fire-clay bricks in many cases.

The refractory bonding mortars should preferably be selected on the advice of the manufacturer of the refractory to obtain good service, although there are a considerable number of independent manufacturers of mortars who supply an excellent prod-

Table 3. Sizes and Shapes of Firebrick

(All dimensions in in.)

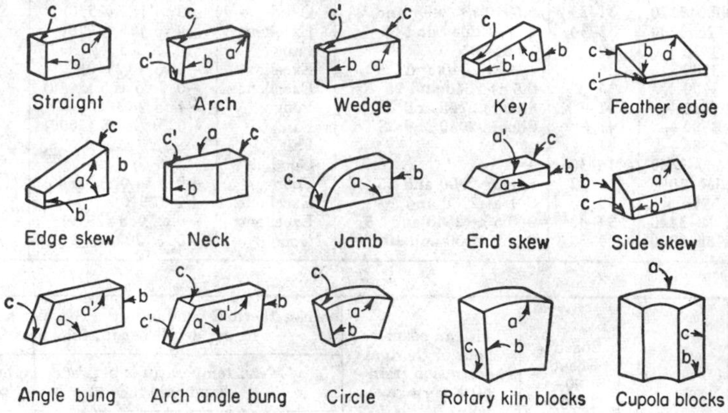

Straight Arch Wedge Key Feather edge

Edge skew Neck Jamb End skew Side skew

Angle bung Arch angle bung Circle Rotary kiln blocks Cupola blocks

Name of bricks	Straight bricks			Name of bricks	Straight bricks		
	Length *a*	Width *b*	Thickness *c*		Length *a*	Width *b*	Thickness *c*
9 in. straight	9	4½	2½	9 × 4½ × 3 in. straight	9	4½	3
Small 9 in.	9	3½	2½	9 × 6 × 3 in. straight	9	6	3
Soap	9	2¼	2½	13½ in. straight	13½	6	2½
Checker	9	2¾	2¾	Bridge block	13½	6	3
Split brick	9	4½	1¼	Stock-hole tile	18	9	4½
2 in. brick	9	4½	2	Square-edge tile	12	12	3
Large 9 in.	9	6¾	2½	No. 101 square bung	13	4½	3
Flat back straight	9	6	2½	Open-hearth checker	10½	4½	4½

uct. From 300 to 400 lb of dry mortar per thousand brick is required for thin joints, which are desirable in most furnace construction. For thicker trowel joints, up to 500 lb per thousand brick is required. In the case of chrome-base mortars, 600 lb per thousand brick shoud be allowed, and for magnesite cement 800 lb.

The working properties of the bonding mortar are important. Mortars for insulating refractories should be carefully selected as many of the commercial products do not retain water sufficiently long to enable a good joint to be made. There are special mortars for this purpose which are entirely satisfactory.

Coatings are used to protect the hot surface of the refractories, especially when they are exposed to dust-laden gases or slags. These coatings usually consist of ground grog and fire clay of a somewhat coarser texture than the mortar. There are also chrome-base coatings which are quite resistant to slags, and in a few cases natural clays containing silica and feldspar are satisfactory.

The coatings can be applied to the surface of the brickwork with a brush in thin layers about 1/16 in. thick, or they may be sprayed on with a cement gun, the latter method generally giving the best results. Some types of coating can be put on in much thicker layers, but care should be taken to assure that the coating selected will fit the particular brick used, otherwise it is apt to peel off in service. The coating seals the pores and openings in the brickwork and presents a more continuous and impervious service to the action of the furnace gases and slag. It is not a cure-all for refractory troubles.

Table 4. Additional Arch, Wedge, and Key Bricks

Name of shape	a	b	b'	c	c'	Name of shape	a	b	c'
Large 9 in. No. 1 wedge.	9	6¾	....	2½	1⅞	13½ in. No. 1 wedge..	13½	6	2¾‡
Large 9 in. No. 2 wedge.	9	6¾	....	2½	1½	13½ in. No. 2 wedge..	13½	6	2½‡
No. 1 flat-back arch....	9	6	....	3½	2½	13½ in. No. 3 wedge..	13½	6	2‡
No. 2 flat-back arch....	9	6	....	3½	2	No. 102 angle bung...	12¾*	4½	‡
9 × 6 in. No. 1 key....	9	6	5⅜	2½†	.....	No. 103 arch bung....	13	4½	2⅝‡
9 × 6 in. No. 1 key....	9	6	4 13/16	2½†	.....	No. 104 arch angle bung............	12¾*	4½	2⅝‡
13½ in. No. 1 key.....	13½	6	5	2½†	.....	No. 105 arch bung....	13	4½	2⅞†
13½ in. No. 2 key.....	13½	6	4⅜	2½†	.....				

* a' = 11⅜. † = 2½ or 3. ‡ = 3.

Table 5. Circle Bricks and Blocks

(The dimensions $a \times b \times c$ of circle bricks are 9 × 4½ × 2½; of rotary kiln blocks 9 × 9 × 4; of 6 in. cupola block 9 × 6 × 4; or 9 in. cupola block 9 × 4½ × 9 in.)

Name of brick	Diameter of circle: Outside	Diameter of circle: Inside	No. of bricks to a circle	Name of brick	Diameter of circle: Outside	Diameter of circle: Inside	No. of bricks to a circle	Name of brick	Diameter of circle: Outside	Diameter of circle: Inside	No. of bricks to a circle
24 in. Circle brick	33	24	12	9–90 Rotary kiln block	108	90	38	No. 90 6 in. Cupola block	102	90	36
36 in. Circle brick	45	36	16	9–96 Rotary kiln block	114	96	40	No. 96 6 in. Cupola block	108	96	38
48 in. Circle brick	57	48	20	9–102 6 in. kiln block	120	102	42	No. 102 6 in. Cupola block	114	102	40
60 in. Circle brick	69	60	24	No. 30 6 in. Cupola block	42	30	15	No. 108 6 in. Cupola block	120	108	42
72 in. Circle brick	81	72	28	No. 36 6 in. Cupola block	48	36	17	No. A 9 in. Cupola block	25	16	9
84 in. Circle brick	93	84	32	No. 42 6 in. Cupola block	54	42	19	No. B 9 in. Cupola block	30	21	11
9–48 Rotary kiln block	66	48	23	No. 48 6 in. Cupola block	60	48	21	No. C 9 in. Cupola block	36	27	13
9–54 Rotary kiln block	72	54	25	No. 54 6 in. Cupola block	66	54	23	No. D 9 in. Cupola block	39	30	14
9–60 Rotary kiln block	78	60	27	No. 60 6 in. Cupola block	72	60	25	No. E 9 in. Cupola block	49	40	17
9–66 Rotary kiln block	84	66	29	No. 66 6 in. Cupola block	78	66	27	No. F 9 in. Cupola block	60	51	21
9–72 Rotary kiln block	90	72	31	No. 72 6 in. Cupola block	84	72	29	No. G 9 in. Cupola block	69	60	24
9–78 Rotary kiln block	96	78	33	No. 78 6 in. Cupola block	90	78	31	No. H 9 in. Cupola block	82	73	29
9–84 Rotary kiln block	102	84	36	No. 84 6 in. Cupola block	96	84	33				

Plastics and ramming mixtures are generally a mixture of fire clay and coarse grog of somewhat the same composition as the original fire-clay brick. They are used in repairing furnace walls which have been damaged by spalling or slag erosion, and also for making complete furnace walls in certain installations such as small boiler furnaces. They are also used to form special or irregular shapes, in temporary wooden forms, in the actual furnace construction.

Some of the plastics and ramming mixtures contain silicate of soda and are air-setting, so that a strong structure is produced as soon as the material is dry. Others have as a base chrome ore or silicon carbide, which make a mixture having a high thermal conductivity and a good resistance to slag erosion. These mixtures are often used in the water walls of large boiler furnaces; they are rammed around the tubes and held in place by small studs welded to the tube walls. The chrome plastic has been used with good success for heating-furnace floors and subhearths of open-hearth furnaces.

Castable mixes are a refractory concrete usually containing high-alumina cement to give the setting properites. These find considerable use in forming intricate furnace parts in wooden molds; large structures have been satisfactorily cast by this method. This type of mixture is much used for baffles in boilers where it can be cast in place around the tubes. Lightweight castables with good insulating properties are used to line furnace doors.

Furnace Walls

The modern tendency in furnace construction is to make a comparatively thin wall, anchored and supported at frequent intervals by castings or heat-resisting alloys which, in turn, are held by a structural framework so that the weight of the refractory is carried by the framework and does not rest on the base. The wall may be made of heavy refractories backed up with insulating material, or of insulating refractory. Table 6 gives heat losses and heat contents of a number of wall combinations and may enable the designer to pick out a wall section to suit his purpose. Solid walls built with standard 9 in. brick are made up in various ways, but the hot face has usually four header courses and one stretcher course alternating.

Many modern furnaces are constructed with air-cooled walls, with refractory blocks held in place against a casing by alloy steel holders. Sectional walls made up with steel panels having lightweight insulating refractories attached to the inner surface are also used and are especially valuable for use in the upper parts of large boiler furnaces, oil stills, and similar types of construction. The sections can be made up at the plant and shipped as a unit. They have the advantage of low cost because of the light ironwork required to support them.

Many failures in furnace construction result from improper expansion joints. Expansion joints should usually be installed at least every 10 ft, although in some low-temperature structures the spacing may be greater. For high-temperature construction, the expansion joint allowance per foot in inches should be as follows: fire clay, $\frac{1}{16}$ to $\frac{3}{32}$; high alumina, $\frac{3}{32}$ to $\frac{1}{8}$; silica, $\frac{1}{8}$ to $\frac{3}{16}$; magnesite, $\frac{1}{4}$; chrome, $\frac{5}{32}$; forsterite, $\frac{1}{4}$. Figure 1 shows some typical examples of expansion joints. Corrugated cardboard is often used in the joints.

The **roof** of the furnace is usually either a sprung arch or a suspended arch. A **sprung arch** is generally made of standard shapes using an inside radius equal to the total span. In most cases, it is necessary to build a form on which the arch is sprung. The arch dimensions can be calculated when the span and rise are known by the use of the table on p. 1–34. The number of bricks per course is then easily determinable.

In the case of arches with a considerable rise, it has been found that an inverted catenary shape is better than a circular shape for stability, and it is possible to run the side walls of the furnace right down to the floor in one continuous arch with almost complete elimination of the ironwork. The catenary can be readily laid out by hanging a flexible chain from two points of a vertical wall.

The **suspended arch** is used when it is desirable to have a flat roof (curved suspended arches are also made); it presents certain advantages in construction and repair but is more difficult to insulate than the sprung arch. Special suspended arch shapes are

Table 6. Transmitted Heat Losses and Heat-storage Capacities of Wall Structures under Equilibrium Conditions

(Based on still air at 80 F)

(Condensed from "B & W Insulating Firebrick" Bulletin of The Babcock & Wilcox Co.)

Thickness, in.		Hot face temperature, deg F									
Wall	Of insulating refractory and firebrick	1200		1600		2000		2400		2800	
		HL	HS	HL	HS	HL	HS	HL	HS	HL	HS
4½	4½ 20	355	1,600	537	2,300	755	2,900				
	4½ 28	441	2,200	658	3,100	932	4,000	1,241	4,900	1,589	5,900
	4½ FB	1,180	8,400	1,870	11,700	2,660	14,800	3,600	18,100	4,640	21,600
7	4½ 28 + 2½ 20	265	3,500	408	4,900	567	6,500	751	8,100	970	9,800
	4½ FB	423	12,500	660	17,700	917	23,000	1,248	28,200		
9	4½ 28 + 4½ 20	203	4,100	311	5,900	432	7,900	573	9,900	738	12,200
	4½ FB + 4½ 20	285	13,700	437	19,200	615	24,800				
	9 20	181	3,100	280	4,300	395	5,500				
	9 28	233	4,100	349	5,800	480	7,500	642	9,300	818	11,100
	9 FB	658	15,800	1,015	21,600	1,430	27,600	1,900	34,000	2,480	40,300
11½	9 28 + 2½ 20	169	5,700	260	8,000	364	10,500	484	13,100	623	15,800
	9 FB + 2½ 20	335	22,300	514	31,400	718	40,600	962	50,400	1,233	60,300
	9 28 + 4½ 20	143	6,500	217	9,300	305	12,300	404	15,300	514	18,700
	9 FB + 4½ 20	241	24,100	367	34,500	516	44,800	690	55,100		
13½	9 20 + 4½ FB	165	5,300	255	7,300	348	9,900				
	9 28 + 4½ FB	200	6,900	302	9,700	415	12,600	556	15,700	710	19,100
	13½ FB	452	22,300	700	31,000	980	39,900	1,310	49,100	1,683	58,300
16	13½ FB + 2½ 20	275	31,200	423	43,300	588	56,300	780	70,000	994	84,200
18	9 20 + 9 FB	147	8,500	225	11,900	319	15,700				
	9 28 + 9 FB	175	10,700	266	15,100	375	19,700	493	24,600	635	29,800
	13½ FB + 4½ 20	210	34,100	318	48,400	440	62,600	587	77,500	753	92,600
	18 FB	355	28,800	532	40,300	745	52,200	1,000	64,200	1,283	76,500
20½	18 FB + 2½ 20	234	39,000	356	55,400	500	72,000	665	89,200	847	107,000
22½	18 FB + 4½ 20	182	43,200	281	61,000	392	79,200	519	97,700	667	117,600
	22½ FB	287	36,000	435	49,500	612	64,100	814	78,800	1,040	93,400

HL = heat loss in Btu per sq ft per hr. HS = heat storage capacity in Btu per sq ft. 20 = 2000 F insulating refractory. 28 = 2800 F insulating refractory. FB = fire-clay brick.

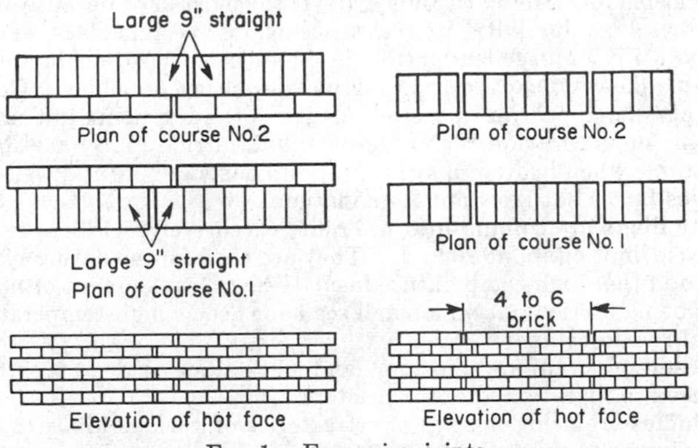

Fig. 1. Expansion joints.

commercially available. The insulating refractory is suited to this type of construction because the steel supports are light and the heat loss is low.

SELECTION OF REFRACTORIES

The selection of the most suitable refractory for a given purpose demands experience in furnace construction. A brick that costs twice as much as another brand and gives twice the life is preferable since the total cost includes the laying cost. Furthermore, a brick that gives longer service reduces the shutdown period of the furnace. Where slag or abrasion is severe, brick with a dense structure is desirable. If spalling conditions are important, a brick with a more flexible structure is better, although there are cases where a very dense structure gives better spalling resistance than a more open one.

High-lime slag can be taken care of with magnesite, chrome, or high-alumina brick, but if severe temperature fluctuations are encountered also, no brick will give long life. For coal-ash slag, dense fire-clay bricks give fairly good service if the temperature is not high. At the higher temperatures, a chrome-plastic or silicon-carbide refractory often proves successful. When the conditions are unusually severe, air- or water-cooled walls must be resorted to; the water-cooled stud-tube wall has been very successful in boiler furnaces.

With a general freedom from slag, it is often most economical to use an insulating refractory. Although this brick may cost more per unit, it allows thinner walls, so that the total construction cost may be no greater than the regular brick. The substitution of insulating refractory for heavy brick in periodic furnaces has sometimes halved the fuel consumption.

The stability of a refractory installation depends largely on the bricklaying. The total cost, in addition to the bricks, of laying brick varies with the type of construction, locality, and refractory.

RECENT DEVELOPMENTS IN REFRACTORIES

Pure-oxide refractories have been developed to permit fabrication of parts such as tubes, crucibles, and special shapes. Alumina (Al_2O_3) is the most readily formed into non-porous pieces and, up to its softening point of 3690 F, is most useful. Mullite ($2SiO_2 \cdot 3Al_2O_3$), softening at 3290 F, is used for thermocouple-protection tubes, crucibles, and other small pieces. Magnesium oxide (MgO), fusing at 5070 F, is resistant to metals and slags. Zirconia (ZrO_2), softening at 4600 F, is very sensitive to temperature changes but can be stabilized with a few percent of lime. Beryllium oxide (BeO), softening at 4660 F, has a very high thermal conductivity but must be fabricated with great care because of health hazards. Thoria (ThO_2) softens at 5520 F and has been used in crucibles for melting active metals and as a potential nuclear fuel.

Refractory carbides, sulphides, borides, silicides, and nitrides have been developed for special uses. Many have high softening points, but all have limited stability in an oxidizing atmosphere. Sililon carbide (SiC) is the most used because of its high thermal and electrical conductivity, its resistance against certain slags, and its relatively good stability in air. Molybdenum silicide ($MoSi_2$) also has considerable resistance to oxidation and, like SiC, can be used for metal-melting crucibles. Cerium sulphide (CeS_2) is a metallic-appearing material of high softening point but no resistance to oxidation. Zirconium nitride (ZrN) and titanium nitride (TiN) are also metalliclike but are not stable when heated in air. Graphite has valuable and well-known refractory properties but is not resistant to oxidation.

Refractory fibers are coming into use quite extensively. Fibers of silica-alumina glass have a use limit of about 2000 F. They are used for insulating blankets, expansion joints, and other high-temperature insulation. Development of higher-temperature fibers is being carried out on a small scale for use as high-temperature insulation or mechanical reenforcement.

Nuclear fuels of uranium, thorium, and plutonium oxides or carbides are now extensively used in high-temperature reactors.

Space vehicles are using nozzles of refractories of various kinds to withstand the high temperatures and erosion. Nose cones of sintered alumina are now used extensively because of their excellent refractory and electrical properties. Heat shields to protect space vehicles upon reentry are an important use of special refractories.

PHYSICAL PROPERTIES OF HIGH-PURITY REFRACTORIES

In Table 7 are shown the properties of some of the more important pure refractory materials. It should be realized that, as purer materials become available and testing methods become more refined, some of these values will be changed.

Table 7. Physical Properties of Some Dense,* Pure Refractories

Material	Density, per cc	Modulus of rupture, 10^3 psi at 70 F	Modulus of rupture, 10^3 psi at 1800 F	Modulus of elasticity, 10^6 psi at 70 F	Fusion point, deg F	Linear coef of expansion, 10^{-6} in. per in. per deg F between 65 and 1800 F	Thermal conductivity, Btu per in. per sq ft per deg F at 212 F	Thermal conductivity, Btu per in. per sq ft per deg F at 1800 F	Specific heat	Thermal stress resistance	Electrical resistivity, ohm cm at 70 F	Electrical resistivity, ohm cm at 1800 F
Al_2O_3	3.97	100	60	53	3690	5.0	210	55	0.26	Good	$>10^{14}$	10^7
BeO	3.03	20	10	45	4660	4.9	1450	130	0.50	Very good	$>10^{14}$	10^8
MgO	3.58	14	12	31	5070	7.5	240	47	0.25	Poor	$>10^{14}$	10^7
ThO_2	10.00	12	7	21	5520	5.0	62	20	0.06	Fair	$>10^{14}$	10^5
ZrO_2	5.60	20	15	22	4600	5.5	15	15	0.14	Fair	10^8	500
UO_2	10.96	12	...	25	5070	5.6	58	20	0.06	Fair		
SiC	3.22	24	24	68	5000+	2.2	390	145	0.20	Excel.	10	4
BC	2.52	50	40	42	4440	2.5	200	145	0.36	Good	0.5	
BN	2.25	7	1	12	5000	2.6	150	130	0.39	Good	10^{10}	104
$MoSi_2$	6.20	100	40	50	3890	5.1	220	100	0.11	Good	10^{-6}	
C	2.22	3	4	2	7000	2.2	870	290	0.34	Good	10^{-3}	10^{-2}

* Porosity, 0 to 5 percent. † Stabilized.

REFERENCES: Norton, "Refractories," 3d ed.; Green and Stewart, "Ceramics: A Symposium;" Ryschkewitsch, "Oxydekramik der Einstuffsystemme," Springer; Campbell, "High Temperature Technology;" Kingery, "Property Measurements at High Temperatures," Wiley.

CEMENT, MORTAR, AND CONCRETE

BY

Clyde E. Kesler

References: Taylor, Thompson, and Smulski, "Concrete, Plain and Reinforced," Wiley. MacMillan, "Basic Principles of Concrete Making," McGraw-Hill. Blanks and Kennedy, "The Technology of Cement and Concrete," Wiley. Troxell and Davis, "Composition and Properties of Concrete," McGraw-Hill. Baker, "Treatise on Masonry Construction," Wiley. Committee 613, "Recommended Practice for Selecting Proportions for Concrete," and Committee 614, "Recommended Practice for Measuring, Mixing and Placing Concrete," American Concrete Inst.

CEMENT

Normal portland cement is used for concrete, for reinforced concrete, and either with or without lime, for mortar and stucco. It is made from a mixture of about 80 percent carbonate of lime (limestone, chalk, or marl) and about 20 percent clay (in the form of clay, shale, or slag). After being intimately mixed, the materials are finely ground by a wet or dry process and then calcined in kilns to a clinker. When cool, this clinker is ground to a fine powder. During the grinding, a small amount of gypsum is usually added to regulate the setting of the cement. The chemical analysis of 32 American type I cements gives the following average percentage composition: silica (SiO_2), 21.92; alumina (Al_2O_3), 6.91; iron oxide (Fe_2O_3), 2.91; calcium oxide(CaO), 62.92; magnesium oxide (MgO), 2.54; sulphuric oxide (SO_3), 1.72; alkalies (R_2O_3), 0.82; loss on ignition, 1.50; insoluble residue 0.20.

Types and Kinds of Cements. Five types of portland cements are covered by ASTM specification C150.

Normal portland cement, type I, is used for purposes for which another type having special properties is not required. Most structures, pavements, and reservoirs are built with type I cement.

Modified portland cement, type II, generates less heat from its hydration and is more resistant to sulphate attacks than type I. This cement is used in structures having large cross sections, such as large abutments and heavy retaining walls. It may also be used in drainage where a moderate sulphate concentration exists.

High-early-strength portland cement, type III, is used when high strengths are required in a few days. Use of high-early-strength will allow earlier removal of forms and shorter periods of curing.

Low-heat portland cement, type IV, generates less heat during hydration than type II and is used for mass concrete constructions such as large dams where high temperature rises would create special problems. Type IV cement gains strength more slowly than type I. The tricalcium aluminate content is limited to 7 percent.

Sulphate-resisting portland cement, type V, is a special cement, not readily available, to be used when concrete is exposed to severe sulphate attack. Type V cements gain strength more slowly than type I cement. The tricalcium aluminate content is limited to a maximum of 5 percent.

Air-entraining portland cements purposely cause air, in minute, closely spaced bubbles, to occur in concrete. Entrained air makes the concrete more resistant to the effects of repeated freezing and thawing and of the deicing agents used on pavements. To obtain such cements, air-entraining agents are interground with the cement clinker during manufacture. Types I to III can be obtained as air-entraining cements and are then designated as types IA, IIA, and IIIA.

Portland blast-furnace slag cements are made by grinding granulated high-quality slag with portland-cement clinker. Portland blast-furnace slag cement type IS and air-entraining portland blast-furnace slag cement type IS-A are covered by ASTM specification C205. Provisions are also made for moderate-heat-of-hydration cements (MH) and moderate-sulphate-resistance cements (MS), or both (MH-MS). Type IS cements initially gain strength more slowly but have about the same 28-day strength as type I cements.

White portland cement is used for architectural and ornamental work because of its white color. It is high in alumina and contains less than 0.5 percent iron. The best brands are true portlands in composition.

Portland-pozzolan cement is a blended cement made by intergrinding portland cement and pozzolanic materials. Two types, type IP (portland-pozzolan cement) and type IP-A (air-entraining portland-pozzolan cement), are covered in ASTM specification C340.

Masonry cement, ASTM specification C91, is a blended cement used in place of job cement-lime mixtures to reduce the number of materials handled and to improve the uniformity of the mortar. These cements are made by combining either natural or portland cements with fattening materials such as hydrated lime and, sometimes, with air-entraining admixtures.

Waterproofed cement is sometimes used where a waterproof or water-repellent concrete or mortar is particularly desirable. It is cement ground with certain soaps and oils. The effectiveness is limited to 3 or 4 ft of water pressure.

Pozzolana cement has been used under certain conditions for concrete not exposed to the air. It is made by mixing and grinding together slaked lime and granulated blast-furnace slag or other material similar to natural lava, without burning. The ancient cements were mixtures of lime and volcanic material.

Natural cement is sometimes used, either with or without lime, for common mortar for brick or stonework. It is manufactured from limestone containing clay. The chemical constituents are similar to those of portland cement. Formerly, it was made from the rock just as it came from the quarry, so that its chemical composition varied with the composition of the rock, but now greater care is used in maintaining uni-

Chemical limits	Percentages				
	Normal	Moderate heat	High early strength	Low heat	Resistant
Silicon dioxide (SiO_2), min	....	21.0			
Aluminum oxide (Al_2O_2), max	....	6.0			[a]
Ferric oxide (Fe_2O_3), max	....	6.0	.....	6.5	[a]
Magnesium oxide (MgO), max	5.0	5.0	5.0	5.0	4.0
Sulphur trioxide (SO_3)					
When $3CaO \cdot Al_2O_3$ is 8 % or less, max	2.5	2.5	3.0	2.3	2.3
When $3CaO \cdot Al_2O_3$ is more than 8 %, max	3.0	.....	4.0		
Loss on ignition, max	3.0	3.0	3.0	3.0	3.0
Insoluble residue, max	0.75	0.75	0.75	0.75	0.75
Tricalcium silicate ($3CaO \cdot SiO_2$),[b] max	....	.....	.....	35	
Dicalcium silicate ($2CaO \cdot SiO_2$),[b] min	....	.....	.....	40	
Tricalcium aluminate ($3CaO \cdot Al_2O_3$),[b] max	....	8	15[c]	7	5
Sum of tricalcium silicate and tricalcium aluminate, max	....	58[d]			

[a] The tricalcium aluminate shall not exceed 5 percent, and the tetracalcium aluminoferrite ($4CaO \cdot Al_2O_2 \cdot Fe_2O_2$) plus twice the amount of tricalcium aluminate shall not exceed 20 percent.

[b] Expressing chemical limitations by means of calculated assumed compounds does not necessarily mean that the oxides are actually or entirely present as such compounds; ASTM Specifications for Portland Cement (C150) indicates how the percentages of tricalcium silicate, dicalcium silicate, tricalcium aluminate, and tetracalcium aluminoferrite shall be calculated from the chemical analyses.

[c] When moderate sulphate resistance is required for type III cement, tricalcium aluminate may be limited to 8 percent. When high sulphate resistance is required, the tricalcium aluminate may be limited to 5 percent.

[d] This limit applies when moderate heat of hydration is required and tests for heat of hydration are not requested.

formity. The unground rock is fed directly to the kilns, calcined at a temperature much lower than that required for portland cement, and then crushed and ground.

Portland-cement Tests. Cement should be tested for all but unimportant work. Tests should be made in accordance with the standard specifications of the ASTM or with the Federal specifications where they apply. Samples should be taken at the mill, and tests completed before shipments are made. When this is not possible, samples should be taken at random from sound packages, one from every 10 bbl or 40 bags, and mixed. The total sample should weigh about 6 lb. ASTM requirements for standard portland cements are as shown in the table on page 6–217.

The **autoclave soundness test** consists of determining the expansion of a 1-in.-sq neat cement bar 10 in. long which, after 24-hr storage in 90 percent or greater humidity, is placed in an autoclave, where the pressure is raised to 295 psi in about 1 hr, maintained for 3 hr, and then brought back to normal in 1½ hr. Cements that show over 1 percent expansion may show unsoundness after some years of service; the ASTM allows a maximum of 0.80 percent.

Time of Setting. Initial set should not be less than 45 min when Vicat needle is used or 60 min when Gilmore needle is used. Final set should be within 10 hr. Cement paste must remain plastic long enough to be properly placed and yet submit to finishing operation in a reasonable time.

Compressive Strength. Minimum requirements for average compressive strength of not less than three 2-in. cubes composed of 1 part (by weight) cement and 2.75 parts standard graded mortar sand, tested in accordance with ASTM method C109, are as follows:

Age of test, days	Storage of test pieces	Compressive strength, psi				
		Normal	Moderate heat	High early strength	Low heat	Sulphate resistant
1	1 day moist air	.....	.....	1,700		
3	1 day moist air, 2 days water	1,200	1,000	3,000		
7	1 day moist air, 6 days water	2,100	1,800	.....	800	1,500
28	1 day moist air, 27 days water	3,500	3,500	.....	2,000	3,000

LIME

Common lime, or **quicklime,** when slaked or hydrated, is used for interior plastering and for lime mortar. Mixed with cement, it is used for lime and cement mortar and for stucco. Mortars made with lime alone are not satisfactory for thick walls because of slow-setting qualities. They must never be used under water. Lime is made by burning pure limestone in kilns about 40 ft high by 10 ft diam at temperatures ranging from 1400 to 2000 F. A typical percentage chemical composition is calcium oxide (CaO), 97; iron oxide (Fe_2O_3), 1.3; silica (SiO_2), 1.0; magnesium oxide (MgO), 0.7. Quicklime slakes rapidly with water with much heat evolution, forming calcium hydrate (CaH_2O_2). With proper addition of water, it becomes plastic, and the volume of putty obtained is 2 or 3 times the loose volume of the lime before slaking, and its weight is about 2½ times the weight of the lime. Plastic lime sets by drying, by crystallization of calcic hydrate, and by absorbing carbonic acid from the air. The process of hardening is very slow. Popping is likely to occur in plastic unless the lime is sound, as indicated by an autoclave test at 120-psi pressure for 2 hr.

Magnesium lime, used for the same purposes as common or high-calcium lime, contains more than 20 percent magnesium oxide. It slakes more slowly, evolves less heat, expands less, sets more rapidly, and produces higher-strength mortars than does high-calcium quicklime.

Pulverized and granulated limes slake completely much more quickly than ordinary lump lime. They are sometimes waterproofed by the addition of stearates and other compounds similar to those used in cement for the same purpose. The waterproofing treatment retards the slaking.

Hydrated lime is a finely divided white powder manufactured by slaking quicklime with the requisite amount of water. It has the advantage over lime slaked on the job of giving a more uniform product, free from unslaked lime. It does not have plasticity or water retention equal to freshly slaked quicklime.

Hydraulic hydrated lime is used for blending with portland cement and as a masonry cement. It is the hydrated product of calcined impure limestone which contains enough silica and alumina to permit the formation of calcium silicates.

AGGREGATES

Sand

Sand to be used for mortar, plaster, and concrete should consist of clean, hard, uncoated grains free from organic matter, vegetable loam, alkali, or other deleterious substances. Vegetable or organic impurities are particularly harmful. A quantity of vegetable matter so small that it cannot be detected by the eye may render a sand absolutely unfit for use with cement. Stone screenings, slab, or other hard inert material may be substituted for or mixed with sand. Sand for concrete should range in size from fine to coarse, with not less than 95 percent (preferably not more than 30 percent) passing a No. 4 sieve, not less than 10 percent retained on a No. 50 sieve, and not more than 5 percent (or 8 percent, if screenings) passing a No. 100 sieve. A straight-line gradation on a graph, with percentages passing plotted as ordinates to normal scale and sieve openings as abscissas to logarithmic scale, gives excellent results.

The grading of sand for mortar depends upon the width of joint, but normally not less than 95 percent should pass a No. 8 sieve, and it should grade uniformly from coarse to fine without more than 8 percent passing a No. 100 sieve.

Sand for plaster should have at least 90 percent passing a No. 8 sieve and not more than 5 percent passing the No. 100 sieve.

Silt or clayey material passing a No. 200 sieve in excess of 2 percent is objectionable.

Test of Sand. Sand for use in important concrete structures should always be tested. The strength of concrete and mortar depends to a large degree upon the quality of the sand and the coarseness and relative coarseness of the grains. Sand or other fine aggregate when made into a mortar of 1 part portland cement to 3 parts fine aggregate by weight should show a tensile strength at least equal to the strength of 1:3 mortar of the same consistency made with the same cement and standard sand. Sand for use in mortar in the 1:3 mortar test should show a strength of at least 90 percent of the standard sand. If the aggregate is of poor quality, then the proportion of cement in the mortar or concrete should be increased to secure the desired strength. If the strength is less than 90 percent that of Ottawa sand mortar, the aggregate should be rejected unless compression tests of concrete made with the selected aggregates pass the requirements. The standard Ottawa sand will pass a No. 20 sieve and be retained on a No. 30 sieve. This sand is supplied by the Ottawa Silica Co., Ottawa, Ill. The compressive strength of 2-in. cubes made from a cement and sand mixture with a 0.9 water-cement ratio and a flow of 100 percent should equal 90 percent of the strength of similar cubes made with graded Ottawa sand.

The ASTM standard test (C40) for the presence of injurious organic compounds in natural sands for cement mortar or concrete is as follows: A 12-oz graduated glass prescription bottle is filled to the 4½-oz mark with the sand to be tested. A 3 percent solution of sodium hydroxide (NaOH) in water is then added until the volume of sand and liquid, after shaking, gives a total volume of 7 liquid oz. The bottle is stoppered, shaken thoroughly, and then allowed to stand for 24 hr. A standard-reference-color solution of potassium dichromate in sulphuric acid is prepared as directed in ASTM D154. The color of the clear liquid above the sand is then compared with the standard-color solution; if the liquid is darker than the standard color, further tests of the sand should be made before it is used in mortar or concrete. The standard color is similar to light amber.

Coarse Aggregate

Broken Stone and Gravel. Coarse aggregate for concrete may consist of broken stone, gravel, slab, or other hard inert material with similar characteristics. The particles should be clean, hard, durable, and free from vegetable or organic matter, alkali, or other deleterious matter and should range in size from material retained on the No. 4 sieve to the coarsest size permissible for the structure. For reinforced concrete and small masses of unreinforced concrete, the maximum size should be that which will readily pass around the reinforcement and fill all parts of the forms. Either 1- or 1½-in. diam is apt to be the maximum. For heavy mass work, the maximum size may run up to 3 in. or larger.

Lightweight aggregates are usually pumice, lava, slag, burned clay, or shale and cinders from coal or coke. They should be well graded, with ample fines, and should have a mortar strength ratio, in comparison with graded Ottawa sand, of at least 70 percent. Their application is largely for concrete units and floor slabs where saving in weight is important and where special thermal insulation or acoustical properties are desired.

Heavyweight aggregates are generally iron or other metal punchings, ferrophosphate, hematite, magnetite, barite, limenite, and similar heavy stones and rocks. They are used in concrete for counterweights, dry docks, and shielding against rays from nuclear reactions.

Fineness Modulus. The fineness modulus, which is used in the Abrams method as an index of the characteristics of the aggregates, is the sum of the cumulative percentages (divided by 100) which would be retained by all the sieves in a special sieve analysis. The sieves used in this method are Nos. 100, 50, 30, 16, 8, and 4 for fine aggregates and these plus the ⅜-, ¾-, 1½-, and 3-in. sizes for coarse aggregates. A high fineness modulus indicates a relatively low surface area because the particles are relatively large, which means less water required and, therefore, a higher concrete strength. Aggregates of widely different gradation may have the same fineness modulus.

ASTM standard sieves for analysis of aggregates for concrete are of the following sizes of opening and wire:

Sieve No.	100	50	30	16	8	4
Sieve opening, in.	0.0059	0.0117	0.0234	0.0469	0.0937	0.187
Wire diam, in.	0.0043	0.0085	0.0154	0.0256	0.0394	0.0606
Sieve size, in.	⅜	¾	1	1½	2	3
Sieve opening, in.	0.375	0.750	1.00	1.50	2.00	3.00
Wire diam, in.	0.0894	0.1299	0.1496	0.1807	0.1988	0.2283

WATER

Water for concrete or mortar should be clean and free from oil, acid, alkali, organic matter, or other deleterious substance. Cubes or briquettes made with it should show strength equal to those made with distilled water. Water fit for drinking is normally satisfactory for use with cement. However, many waters not suitable for drinking may be suitable for concrete. Water with less than 2,000 ppm of total dissolved solids can usually be used safely for making concrete. (See also p. 6–234 *et seq.*)

Seawater can be used as mixing water for plain concrete, although 28-day strength may be lower than for normal concrete. If seawater is used in reinforced concrete, care must be taken to provide adequate cover with a dense air-entrained concrete to minimize risks of corrosion. Seawater should not be used with prestressed concrete.

ADMIXTURES

Admixtures are substances, other than the normal ingredients, added to mortars or concrete for altering the normal properties so as to improve them for a particular purpose. Admixtures are frequently used to entrain air, increase workability, accelerate or retard setting, provide a pozzolanic reaction with lime, reduce shrinkage, and reduce bleeding. However, before using an admixture, consideration must be given to its effect on properties other than the one which is being improved. Most important is consideration of possible changes in the basic mix which might make the admixture unnecessary.

Air-entraining agents constitute one of the most important groups of admixtures. They entrain air in small, closely spaced, separated bubbles in the concrete, greatly improving resistance to freezing and thawing and to deicing agents.

Accelerators are used to decrease the setting time and increase early strength. They permit shorter curing periods, earlier form removal, and placing at lower temperatures. Calcium chloride is the most frequently used accelerator and can be used in amounts up to 2 percent of the weight of the cement.

Retarders increase the setting time. They are particularly useful in hot weather and in grouting operations.

Other admixtures may be classed as gas-forming agents, pozzolanic materials, curing aids, water-repelling agents, and coloring agents.

MORTARS

Properties desirable in a mortar include (1) good plasticity or workability, (2) low volume change or volume change of the same character as the units bonded, (3) low absorption, (4) low solubility and thus freedom from efflorescence, (5) good strength in bond and ample strength to withstand applied loads, (6) high resistance to weathering.

Lime mortar consists of lime paste and sand and is made by slaking lime and mixing it with sand or by making up lime putty in advance to be mixed with sand when needed.

The quality of the lime putty is greatly affected by the procedure used in slaking the quicklime. The method given by the ASTM (C5) is as follows:

Directions for Slaking. For **quick-slaking lime,** always add the lime to the water, not the water to the lime. Have enough water at first to cover all the lime completely. Have a plentiful supply of water available for immediate use—a hose throwing a good stream, if possible. Watch the lime constantly. At the slightest appearance of escaping steam, hoe thoroughly and quickly and add enough water to stop the steaming. Do not be afraid of using too much water with this kind of lime.

For **medium-slaking lime,** add the water to the lime. Add enough water so that the lime is about half submerged. Hoe occasionally if steam starts to escape. Add a little water now and then if necessary to prevent the putty from becoming dry and crumbly. Be careful not to add any more water than required, and not too much at a time.

For **slow-slaking lime,** add enough water to the lime to moisten it thoroughly. Let it stand until the reaction has started. Cautiously add more water, a little at a time, taking care that the mass is not cooled by the fresh water. Do not hoe until the slaking is practically complete. If the weather is very cold, it is preferable to use hot water, but if this is not available, the mortar box may be covered in some way to retain the heat.

Lime mortar, because of its slow hardening, is not widely used at the present time; it is suitable for interior non-load-bearing walls. Proportions customarily stated are 2.5 to 3 volumes dry and loose sand to 1 volume lime putty. In practice, unless carefully supervised, the proportion of sand is apt to be greater than this, as the mortar man determines the proportion by the way the mortar falls from his hoe in mixing. Actually, the proportions of mortar should be determined by the characteristics of the masonry, particularly as to absorption. Quicklime is now sold in 80-lb bags, although previously in 200-lb casks. The weight of quicklime and sand required to produce 1 cu yd of lime mortar (as given in Table 1) is based on work by Clair and on the use of well-graded mortar sand with a specific gravity of 2.65.

Lime-and-cement mortar is made of mortar cement, lime putty or hydrated lime, and sand in proportions, by volume, normally of 1 cement, 1 or 2 lime, and 5 or 6 sand. This type of mortar is particularly suited for masonry of all kinds. Mortar with unslaked lime should be made up several days before cement is added. When wanted for use, the cement is mixed into the mass and is immediately used. Only small quantities of cement should be mixed with the lime and sand at a time so that there will be no danger of the cement attaining a set before the mortar is used. The time between mixing in of cement and the use of mortar should be limited to 2 hr. Prepared hydrated lime and mortar cements are increasingly being used in place of lime putty for the type of work where lime-and-cement mortars apply. Table 2 gives the quantities required to produce 1 cu yd of lime-and-cement mortar and is based on work done by Clair.

Cement mortar is composed of cement and sand or screenings mixed with water. Proportions in practice are ordinarily, by dry and loose volumes, 1 part cement to 2 parts sand (1:2) or 1 part cement to 3 parts sand (1:3). Cement mortars are used for masonry where high strength is required or where the work is to be subjected to the action of water. Table 3 gives the quantities of sand and cement required for 1 cu yd of cement mortar. If the specific gravity of the sand and cement being used is known and also the actual water requirements, the quantities for 1 cu yd of mortar

Table 1. Quantities Required per Cubic Yard of Lime-sand Mortar for 50 Percent Flow

Volume mixtures desired		Weights of constituents, lb		Water addition, gal
Lime putty	Dry sand	Quicklime	Mortar sand, damp	
1	3	195	2,640	69
1	4	154	2,780	63
1	5	127	2,870	60
1	6	107	2,900	60
1	7	93	2,940	59
1	9	74	3,020	54

Table 2. Quantities Required per Cubic Yard of Lime-cement-sand Mortar for 50 Percent Flow

Volume mixtures desired			Weight of constituents, lb			Water addition, gal
Cement	Lime putty	Dry sand	Cement	Quick-lime	Mortar sand, damp	
1	0.1	3	805	20	2,680	41
1	1	4	555	140	2,470	57
1	1	5	475	120	2,630	54
1	1	6	405	100	2,690	52
1	2	5	420	210	2,320	67
1	2	7	325	160	2,530	61
1	2	9	270	135	2,700	56

can be determined accurately by the sum of the absolute volumes of the solids. The strength of portland-cement mortar (1) increases with the proportion of cement, (2) in general, increases with the coarseness of the sand, (3) increases with the density of the mortar, and (4) decreases with increase in water-cement ratio. With the same aggregate, the strongest and most impermeable mortar is that containing the largest percentage of cement in a given volume of mortar. With the same percentage of cement, the strongest mortar is that which has the greatest density. A small addition of hydrated lime or lime putty, not exceeding 10 percent by weight of the cement, is sometimes used to increase the workability or watertightness of the mortar, but the same results can usually be obtained by increasing the proportion of cement. Unslaked or imperfectly slaked lime must never be used, as it will expand and disintegrate the mortar. Table 4 shows the effect of different gradings of sand upon the strength of mortar.

Mortar for stonework is generally in practice 1 cement, 1 lime putty, and 6 sand. Lime mortar should not be used for thick walls, as it hardens very slowly, nor should it be used for masonry under water or in wet soil or for structures requiring great

Table 3. Volume of Compacted Plastic Portland Cement Mortar and Quantities of Materials per Cubic Yard*

(Taylor, Thompson, and Smulski)

Relative proportions by volume: Cement†	Sand‡	Volume: Cubic feet from 1 bag of cement weighing 94 lb	Cubic feet from 1 bbl (4 bags) cement containing 4 cu ft	Materials for 1 cu yd, based on barrel of 4 bags or 4 cu ft: Packed cement, bbl	Loose sand, cu yd	Relative proportions by volume: Cement†	Sand‡	Volume: Cubic feet from 1 bag of cement weighing 94 lb	Cubic feet from 1 bbl (4 bags) cement containing 4 cu ft	Materials for 1 cu yd, based on barrel of 4 bags or 4 cu ft: Packed cement, bbl	Loose sand, cu yd
1	0	0.80	3.2	8.31	0.0	1	4½	3.91	15.6	1.72	1.15
1	½	1.02	4.1	6.61	0.49	1	5	4.28	17.1	1.58	1.17
1	1	1.38	5.5	4.88	0.72	1	5½	4.64	18.5	1.46	1.19
1	1½	1.74	7.0	3.87	0.86	1	6	5.00	20.0	1.35	1.20
1	2	2.11	8.4	3.21	0.95	1	6½	5.36	21.4	1.26	1.21
1	2½	2.47	9.9	2.74	1.01	1	7	5.72	22.9	1.18	1.22
1	3	2.83	11.3	2.39	1.06	1	7½	6.08	24.3	1.11	1.23
1	3½	3.19	12.8	2.12	1.10	1	8	6.44	25.8	1.05	1.24
1	4	3.55	14.2	1.90	1.13						

* Variations in the fineness of the sand and cement and in the consistency of the mortar may affect the values by 10 percent in either direction.

† Cement as packed by manufacturer (4 bags = 1 bbl). ‡ Coarse bank and measured loose.

Table 4. Tests by New York Board of Water Supply of 1:3 Mortar Made with Sands of Different Mechanical Analyses

(Taylor, Thompson, and Smulski)

Percentages passing sieves				Tensile test, psi		Compression test, psi	
No. 4	No. 8	No. 50	No. 100	7 days	90 days	7 days	90 days
100	70	12	5	213	613	2690	5640
100	86	21	6	263	412	1915	4660
100	99	26	2	177	325	905	2170
100	97	28	6	178	282	1070	1500
100	94	44	12	139	228	905	1130
100	100	52	14	122	170	275	810
100	100	94	48	80	149	330	490

Table 5. Amount of Mortar Required for a Cubic Yard of Stone Masonry

(Baker)

Description of masonry	Mortar, cu yd: Min	Max
Ashlar, 18 in. courses and ¼ in. joints	0.03	0.04
Ashlar, 12 in. courses and ¼ in. joints	0.06	0.08
Rubble, small, rough stones	0.33	0.40
Rubble, large stones, rough hammer-dressed	0.20	0.30
Squared stone masonry, 18 in. courses and ¾ in. joints	0.12	0.15
Squared stone masonry, 12 in. courses and ¾ in. joints	0.20	0.25

strength or which are subject to shock. Lime-and-cement mortar may be used for masonry above water. The amount of mortar required for 1 cu yd of masonry is given in Table 5.

Brick mortar may be made with portland cement and sand, natural cement and sand, lime and sand, or mortar cement and sand. An easy-working mixture suitable for laying brick exposed to severe weathering, for chimneys, and in load-bearing walls is obtained by mixing hydrated lime with water to a creamy consistency, putting in the sand (5 or 6 parts to 1 of hydrated lime), and letting the mixture stand from 1 to 3 days. One part of cement, based on the volume of hydrated lime, is added when the mortar is wanted for use. A good mixture for non-load-bearing walls and mild exposure is 1 cement, 2 lime putty, 7 to 9 sand. On important work where freedom from efflorescence, cracking, and leakage of walls is desired, the mortar is subjected to tests for soluble salts, volume change, absorption, and water retention. The absorption rate of the masonry units to be bonded is determined, and the mortar is adjusted accordingly. High absorption rates during the first 10 min require highly water-retentive mortars and thus higher lime contents, such as 1 cement, 1½ lime, 5 sand. Bond and actual water-penetration tests may be made on wall assemblies. The amount of mortar required in laying brickwork is given in Table 6.

Table 6. Amount of Mortar Required for Brickwork

(From investigations of Taylor and Thompson)

Mortar for common brick (20 brick per cu ft,* size 8 × 3¾ × 2¼ in., with ⅜ in. joints)			Mortar for selected face brick† (8.8 brick per sq ft, size 7¾ × 3½ × 2¼ in., with 5/16 in. joints)			Mortar for pressed face brick‡ (7½ brick per sq ft, size 8¼ × 4 × 2¼ in., with ¼ in. joints)		
Thickness of joints, in.	Cu ft per cu ft of masonry	Cu ft per 1,000 brick	Thickness of joints, in.	Cu ft per sq ft of surface	Cu ft per 1,000 brick	Thickness of joints, in.	Cu ft per sq ft of surface	Cu ft per 1,000 brick
½	0.37	19.4	⅜	0.07	8.4	¼	0.05	6.8
⅜	0.28	14.0	5/16	0.06	6.8	3/16	0.035	4.7
¼	0.19	9.0	¼	0.05	5.6	⅛	0.02	2.6

* Actual brick laid in wall. For figuring quantities use 22½ brick per cu ft.
† Laid with headers every sixth course. ‡ Laid running bond (all stretchers).

Mortars for Plastering. Common or lime mortar for interior plastering consists of lime, clean coarse sand, and hair or fiber. ASTM (C5) recommendations for white and base coats are as follows:

After slaking, the putty shall be prepared for use as follows:

1. **White Coat.** After the action has ceased, run off the putty through a No. 10 sieve and store for a minimum of 2 weeks unless the manufacturer provides different direction.
2. **Base Coats.** After the action has ceased, run off the putty through a No. 8 sieve. Add sand up to equal parts by weight, all of the hair required, and store for a minimum of 2 weeks.

The mortar should be protected from freezing. One hundred lb, or 1.25 cu ft, of quicklime will make about 3½ cu ft of lime putty or paste. The volume of a lime barrel is about 3 cu ft. **Back plaster** is a scratch coat applied to the back of laths fastened to the boarding between the studs. **Scratch coat** consists of mortar of lime, sand, and considerable hair—about 2 to 2½ bu to 200 lb of quicklime. It is put directly on the laths. **Brown coat** consists of mortar with less hair, about 1 to 1½ bu per 200 lb of quicklime. When three-coat work is used, this is troweled directly on to the scratch coat. **Skim coat** is a finish coat composed of lime putty and fine white sand. It is placed in two layers and troweled to a hard finish. **Gaged skim coat** is skimming mixed with a certain amount of plaster of paris, which makes it practically a hard finish. **Hard finish** consists of 1 part lime putty to 1 or 2 parts plaster of paris.

Keene's cement, which is an anhydrous calcined gypsum with an accelerator, is much used as a hard-finish plaster.

Gypsum plaster (ASTM C28) lacks the plasticity and sand-carrying capacity of lime plaster but is widely used because of its more rapid hardening and drying and because of the uniformity obtainable as the result of its being put up in bags ready-mixed for use.

Gypsum ready-mixed plaster should contain not more than 3 cu ft of mineral aggregate per 100 lb of calcined gypsum plaster, to which may be added fiber and material to control setting time and workability. Gypsum neat plaster used in place of sanded plaster for second coat should contain at least 66 percent $CaSO_4 \cdot \frac{1}{2}H_2O$; the remainder may be fiber and retarders. Calcined gypsum for finishing coat may be white or gray. If it contains no retarder, it should set between 20 and 40 min; if retarded, it should set between 40 min and 6 hr.

Cement plaster is used where a very hard or strong plaster is required, *e.g.*, for thin metal-lath partitions or as a fire protection. It should contain not more than 2 parts sand, by dry and loose volume, to 1 part portland cement. Lime putty or hydrated lime is added up to 15 percent by volume of the cement.

Two-coat work is used for the cheaper class of houses for plastering on wood laths. For the first coat, the mortar is usually spread on in one layer on the walls and two layers on the ceiling, is smoothed with a **darby** (a board with two handles), and when nearly dry, is floated with a wooden hand float. The finish coat may be of skim or hard finish. The total thickness will be ½ to ⅝ in.

Three-coat work has a first or scratch coat of mortar spread on and scratched when nearly dry. The second coat or brown coat consists of mortar, which is smoothed off, darbied, and floated with a wooden hand float. This is then covered, for the third coat, with skim or hard finish. The first coat on metal or wire lathing for three-coat work requires a fatter mortar than for laths; ¾-in. grounds or rails are generally used. The total thickness for three-coat work is, therefore, from ¾ to ⅞ in.

Under moisture conditions where the plaster will not dry rapidly, **curing** at temperatures above 60 and below 90 F is absolutely necessary if cracking is to be avoided.

Stucco is used for exterior plastering and is applied to brick or stone or is plastered onto wood or metal lath. For covering wooden buildings, the stucco is plastered either on wood lath or on metal lath in three coats, using mortar similar to that for brick or stone. Concrete in northern climates exposed to frost should never be plastered but should be finished by rubbing down with carborundum brick or similar tool when the surface is comparatively green. It may also be tooled in various ways. Whenever stucco is used, extreme care must be taken to get a good bond to the supporting surface.

For three-coat work on masonry or wood lath, the first or scratch coat should average ¼ in. thick outside the lath or surface of the brick. The thickness of the second coat should be ⅜ to ½ in., while the finish coat should be thin, *i.e.*, ⅛ in. or not more than ¼ in. The second coat should generally be applied 24 hr after the first or scratch coat. The finish coat should not be applied in less than 1 week after the second coat. Proportions of mix for all coats may be ⅕ part hydrated lime, 1 part portland cement, 3 parts fairly coarse sand, measured by volume. Stucco work should not be put on in freezing weather and must be kept moist for at least 7 days after application of the mortar.

Coloring of Stucco. Mineral colors, if used, should be of such composition that they will not be affected by cement, lime, or the weather. The best method is to use colored sands when possible. The most satisfactory results with colored mortar are obtained by using white portland cement. Prepared patented stuccos which are combinations of cement, sand, plasticizers, waterproofing agents, and pigment are widely used.

CONCRETE

Concrete is made by mixing cement and an aggregate composed of hard inert particles of varying size, such as a combination of sand or broken-stone screenings, with gravel, broken stone, lightweight aggregate, or other material. Portland cement should always be used for reinforced concrete, for mass concrete subjected to stress, and for all concrete laid under water.

Proportioning Concrete. Compressive strength is generally accepted as the principal measure of the quality of concrete, and although this is not entirely true, there is an approximate relation of compressive strength to the other mechanical properties. Methods of proportioning generally aim to give concrete of a predetermined compressive strength.

The concrete mixture is proportioned or designed for a particular condition in various ways: (1) arbitrary selection based on experience and common practice, such as 1 part cement, 2 parts sand, 4 parts stone (written **1:2:4**); (2) proportioning on the basis of the water-cement ratio, either assumed from experience or determined by trial mixtures with the given materials and conditions; (3) combining materials on the basis of either the voids in the aggregates or mechanical-analysis curves so as to obtain the least voids and thus concrete of the maximum density for a given cement content.

The method of arbitrary selection, formerly in most common use, has been largely displaced by the water-cement-ratio method. The arbitrary-proportioning method by volume or weight is simple to use but is not economical, nor does it give the best possible results with a given aggregate. In a modification of this method, the minimum cement content is specified along with a maximum water content per bag of cement. The water-cement-ratio method depends on the principle that the strength of the concrete with given aggregates and cement bears a direct relation to the ratio of the water to the cement present. The smaller the water-cement ratio, as long as the mix is workable, the higher the strength of the resulting concrete. Methods devised by Abrams and based on the use of the fineness modulus of the aggregates make it possible to compute the proportions of cement with the fine and coarse aggregates so as to give the most economical mixtures. As the water-cement-ratio–strength relation changes for different materials, it is necessary to make preliminary tests of the materials to determine their exact water-cement-ratio–strength relation.

Steps in proportioning by the water-cement-ratio method:

1. Select the proper water-cement ratio for the job; see Tables 7 and 11.
2. Select the proper slump, see Table 9.
3. Estimate the quantity of water needed to provide the required slump. Table 8 gives the approximate quantities needed for a 3-in. slump. To raise or decrease the slump 1 in., raise or lower the amount of water 3 percent.
4. Select the maximum size of aggregate that will be suitable for the job. The maximum size is determined by the aggregate available, spacing of reinforcement, and thickness of section.
5. Determine the percentage of the total aggregate that is fine aggregate from Table 8.
6. Compute the starting-mix proportions. Adjustment can be made on the job, but it is better to make trial mixes in the laboratory since only by actually mixing and testing the concrete can its properties be known. The specific gravity of the cement, specific gravity of the aggregates, and moisture content of the aggregates are needed to compute the mix quantities. The quantities for 1 cu yd can be computed as follows:

a. Determine the cement content from Table 8 or by dividing the water content, step 3, by the water-cement ratio, step 1.

b. Add the absolute volume of water to the absolute volume of the cement and subtract this volume from 1 cu yd. If the concrete is air-entrained, the volume of air must also be subtracted at this point. The volume remaining is the amount of aggregates needed.

c. Compute the quantities of fine and coarse aggregates needed from the percentage of the total that is fine aggregate, given in Table 8. The computed quantities of aggregates may be different from those shown in Table 8 because of different water content and different specific gravities of aggregates.

The trial batches or first job batches may indicate adjustments needed for workability, slump, or strength.

If the above computations are not made, the suggested proportions in Table 8 may be used for trial batches.

Table 7 is given by ACI as a guide for selection of the maximum water-cement ratio from the standpoint of the exposure of the concrete.

In Table 11, the maximum water content includes the free moisture contained in the aggregates. The water absorbed into the pores of the aggregate is not available for hydration of the cement and is therefore not included in the water content. The water of absorption is usually less than 1 percent by weight. The coarser the aggregate (high fineness modulus), the less free water it will contain. Average allowances for free moisture are as follows in percentage of the dry weight of the material:

	Dry	Damp	Wet
Gravel	0.2	1.0	2.0
Sand	2.0	4.0	7.0

The **dry rodded weight** is determined by filling a container, of a diameter approximately equal to the depth, with the aggregate in three equal layers, each layer being rodded 25 times using a bullet-pointed rod ⅝ in. diam and 24 in. long.

Measurement of materials is usually done by weight. The bulking effect of moisture, particularly on the fine aggregate, makes it difficult to keep proportions uniform when volume measurement is used. Water is batched by volume or weight.

Table 7. Maximum Permissible Water-Cement Ratios (Gal per Bag) for Different Types of Structures and Degrees of Exposure

(From Recommended Practice for Selecting Proportions for Concrete, *ACI Std.* 613.)

Type of structure	Exposure conditions[a]					
	Severe wide range in temperature or frequent alternations of freezing and thawing (air-entrained concrete only)			Mild temperature, rarely below freezing, or rainy or arid		
	In air	At the waterline or within the range of fluctuating water level or spray		In air	At the waterline or within the range of fluctuating water level or spray	
		In fresh water	In seawater or in contact with sulphates[b]		In fresh water	In seawater or in contact with sulphates[b]
Thin sections, such as railings, curbs, sills, ledges, ornamental or architectural concrete, reinforced piles, and pipe and all sections with less than 1 in. concrete cover over reinforcing	5.5	5.0	4.5[c]	6	5.5	4.5[c]
Moderate sections, such as retaining walls, abutments, piers, girders, beams	6.0	5.5	5.0[c]	*d*	6.0	5.0[c]
Exterior portions of heavy (mass) sections	6.5	5.5	5.0[c]	*d*	6.0	5.0[c]
Concrete deposited by tremie under water	...	5.0	5.0	...	5.0	5.0
Concrete slabs laid on the ground	6.0	...	...	*d*		
Concrete protected from the weather, interiors of buildings, concrete below ground	*d*	...	...	*d*		
Concrete which will later be protected by enclosure or backfill but which may be exposed to freezing and thawing for several years before such protection is offered	6.0	...	...	*d*		

[a] Air-entrained concrete should be used under all conditions involving severe exposure and may be used under mild-exposure conditions to improve workability of the mixture.

[b] Soil or ground water containing sulphate concentrations of more than 0.2 percent.

[c] When sulphate-resisting cement is used, maximum water-cement ratio may be increased by 0.5 gal per bag.

[d] Water-cement ratio should be selected on basis of strength and workability requirements.

Mixing. In order to get good concrete, the cement and aggregates must be throughly mixed so as to obtain a homogeneous mass and coat all particles with the cement paste. Mixing may be done either by hand or by machine, although hand mixing is rare today. **Hand mixing** must be done thoroughly on a watertight mixing platform. A good method of hand mixing is as follows: The sand is measured and spread on the platform, then a proper amount of cement is placed on the top and the two materials mixed until the color is uniform. In the meantime, screened gravel or stone is placed in the measuring box on the platform. After removing the box, the gravel is hollowed out slightly in the center and the sand and cement are shoveled on top, covering the gravel with a layer of even thickness. The water is poured on top of these layers and the whole mass is mixed by shovels, each shovelful of material being turned and spread on the platform about 2 ft from its original position. The operation is repeated several times. As a rule, four turnings are sufficient.

Machine-mixed concrete is employed almost universally. The mixing time for the usual batch mixer of 1 cu yd or less capacity should not be less than 1 min from the time all materials are in the mixer until the time of discharge. Larger mixers require 25 percent increase in mixing time per ½-cu-yd increase in capacity. Increased mixing

Table 8. Quantities of Material for 1 Cubic Yard of Concrete

(For coarse sand, fineness modulus of about 2.90, and 3 to 4 in. of slump.)
(Adapted from "Design of Concrete Mixtures," ST100, Portland Cement Assoc.)

Water-cement ratio, gal per sack	Entrained air,* percent	Water, gal	Cement, sack per yd	Fine aggregate, lb	Coarse aggregate, lb	Fine aggregate, percent of total aggregate
NON-AIR-ENTRAINED						
For ¾-in.-max-size aggregate:						
5	2	41	8.2	1,180	1,650	42
6	2	41	6.9	1,280	1,650	44
7	2	41	5.9	1,360	1,650	45
8	2	41	5.2	1,410	1,650	46
For 1-in.-max-size aggregate:						
5	1.5	39	7.8	1,100	1,820	38
6	1.5	39	6.5	1,210	1,820	40
7	1.5	39	5.6	1,280	1,820	41
8	1.5	39	4.9	1,330	1,820	42
For 1½-in.-max-size aggregate:						
5	1	36	7.2	1,030	2,030	34
6	1	36	6.0	1,120	2,030	36
7	1	36	5.2	1,190	2,030	37
8	1	36	4.5	1,240	2,030	38
AIR-ENTRAINED						
For ¾-in.-max-size aggregate:						
5	6	36	7.2	1,190	1,650	42
6	6	36	6.0	1,280	1,650	44
7	6	36	5.2	1,350	1,650	45
8	6	36	4.5	1,400	1,650	46
For 1-in.-max-size aggregate:						
5	6	34	6.8	1,090	1,820	37
6	6	34	5.7	1,180	1,820	39
7	6	34	4.9	1,240	1,820	41
8	6	34	4.3	1,290	1,820	42
For 1½-in.-max-size aggregate:						
5	5	32	6.4	1,000	2,030	33
6	5	32	5.4	1,080	2,030	35
7	5	32	4.6	1,140	2,030	36
8	5	32	4.0	1,190	2,030	37

* For non-air-entrained concrete, this is the expected amount of entrapped air.

times up to 5 min increase the workability and the strength of the concrete. Mixing should always continue until the mass is homogeneous.

Concrete mixers of the batch type give more uniform results; few continuous mixers are used. Batch mixers are either (1) rotating mixers, consisting of a revolving drum or a square box revolving about its diagonal axis and usually provided with deflectors and blades to improve the mixing; or (2) paddle mixers, consisting of a stationary box with movable paddles which perform the mixing. Paddle mixers work better with relatively dry, high-sand, small-size aggregate mixtures and mortars and are less widely used than rotating mixers.

Ready-mixed concrete is (1) proportioned and mixed at a central plant (central-mixed concrete) and transported to the job in plain trucks or agitator trucks, or (2) proportioned at a central plant and mixed in a mixer truck (truck-mixed concrete) equipped with water tanks, during transportation. Ready-mixed concrete is largely displacing job-mixed concrete in metropolitan areas. The truck agitators and mixers are essentially rotary mixers mounted on trucks. There is no deleterious effect on the concrete if it is used within 1 hr after the cement has been added to the aggregates.

Materials for concrete are also **centrally batched,** particularly for road construction, and transported to the site in batcher trucks with compartments to keep aggregates separated from the cement. The truck discharges into the charging hopper of the job mixer. Road mixers sometimes are arranged in series—the first mixer partly mixes the materials and discharges into a second mixer, which completes the mixing.

Consistency of Concrete. The consistency to be used depends upon the character of the structure. The proportion of water in the mix is of vital importance. A very wet mixture of the same cement content is much weaker than a dry or mushy mixture. Dry concrete can be employed in dry locations for mass foundations provided that it is carefully spread in layers not over 6 in. thick and is thoroughly rammed. Medium, or quaking, concrete is adapted for ordinary mass-concrete uses, such as foundations, heavy walls, large arches, piers, and abutments. Mushy concrete is suitable as rubble concrete and reinforced concrete, for such applications as thin building walls, columns, floors, conduits, and tanks. A medium, or quaking, mixture has a tenacious, jellylike consistency which shakes on ramming; a mushy mixture will settle to a level surface when dumped in a pile and will flow very sluggishly into the forms or around the reinforcing bars; a dry mixture has the consistency of damp earth.

Table 9. Suggested Slump

Class of concrete	Limiting values of slump, in.	
	Min	Max
Caissons, heavy foundations, massive walls	1	4
Road slabs, floor slabs on ground, pavements	1	4
Ordinary reinforced building walls	4	6
Slabs, beams, girders	4	7
Thin walls, columns	4	7

The two methods in common use for measuring the consistency or workability of concrete are the slump test and the flow test. In the **slump test,** which is the more widely used of the two, a form shaped as a frustum of a cone is filled with the concrete and immediately removed. The slump is the subsidence of the mass below its height when in the cone. The form has a base of 8 in. diam, a top of 4 in. diam, and a height of 12 in. It is filled in three 4-in. layers of concrete, each layer being rodded by 25 strokes of a ⅝-in. rod, 24 in. long and bullet-pointed at the lower end.

A test using the penetration of a half sphere, called the **Kelly Ball test,** is sometimes used for field control purposes. A 1-in. penetration by the Kelly Ball corresponds to about 2 in. of slump.

Usual limitations on the consistency of concrete as measured by the slump test are given in Table 9.

The **consistency** of concrete has some relation to its **workability,** but a lean mix may be unworkable with a given slump and a rich mix may be very workable. Certain admixtures tend to lubricate the mix and, therefore, increase the workability at certain slumps. The slump at all times should be as small as possible consistent with the requirements of handling and placing. A slump over 7 in. is usually accompanied by segregation and low strength of concrete.

Forms for concrete should maintain the lines required and prevent leakage of mortar. The pressure on forms is equivalent to that of a liquid with the same density as the concrete, and of the depth placed within 2 hr. Dressed lumber or plywood is used for exposed surfaces, and rough lumber for unexposed areas. Wood or steel forms should be oiled before placing concrete.

Placement of concrete for most structures is by chutes or buggies. Chutes should have a slope not less than one vertical to two horizontal; the use of flatter slopes encourages the use of excess water, leading to segregation and low strengths. Buggies are preferable to chutes because they handle drier concrete and allow better placement control. Drop-bottom buckets are desirable for large projects and dry concrete. Concrete pumped through pipelines by mechanically applied pressure is sometimes economical for construction spread over large areas. Concrete for tunnels is placed by pneumatic pumps. Underwater concrete is deposited by drop-bottom bucket or by a tremie or pipe. Such concrete should have a cement-content increase of 15 percent to allow for loss of cement in placement.

Compaction of concrete (working it into place) is accomplished by manual spading, by walking in, or "booting," the concrete, and by tampers or vibrators. Vibrators are applied to the outside of the forms and to the surface or interior of the concrete; they should be used with care to avoid producing segregation. The frequency of vibrators is usually between 2,000 and 4,000 pulsations per min.

Curing of concrete is necessary to ensure proper hydration. Concrete should be kept moist for a period of at least 7 days, and the temperature should not be allowed to fall below 50 F for at least 3 days. Sprayed-on membrane curing compounds may be used to retain moisture. Special precautions must be taken in cold weather and in hot weather.

Quality Control of Concrete. Control methods include measuring materials by weight, allowing for the water content of the aggregates; careful limitation of the total water quantity to that designed; frequent tests of the aggregates and changing the proportions as found necessary to maintain yield and workability; constant checks on the consistency by the slump test; careful attention to the placing of steel and the filling of forms; layout of the concrete distribution system so as to eliminate segregation; check on the quality of the concrete as placed by means of specimens made from it as it is placed in the forms; and careful attention to proper curing of the concrete. The field specimens of concrete are usually 6 in. diam by 12 in. high for aggregates up to 1½ in. max size and 8 by 16 in. for 3-in. aggregate. They are made by rodding the concrete in three layers, each layer being rodded 25 times using a ⅝-in.-diam bullet-pointed rod 24 in. long.

Weight of Concrete. The following are average weights, lb per cu ft, of portland-cement concrete:

Sand-cinder concrete	112	Limestone concrete	148
Burned-clay or shale concrete	105	Sandstone concrete	143
Gravel concrete	148	Traprock concrete	155

Watertightness. Concrete can be made practically impervious to water by proper proportioning, mixing, and placing. Leakage through concrete walls is usually due to poor workmanship or occurs at the joints between 2 days' work or through cracks formed by contraction. New concrete can be bonded to old by wetting the old surface, plastering it with neat cement, and then placing the concrete before the neat cement has set. It is almost impossible to prevent contraction cracks entirely, although a sufficient amount of reinforcement may reduce their width so as to permit only seepage of water. For best results, a low-volume-change cement should be used with a concrete of a quaking consistency; the concrete should be placed carefully so as to leave no visible stone pockets, and the entire structure should be made without joints and preferably in one continuous operation. The best waterproofing agent is an additional proportion of cement in the mix. The concrete should contain not less than 6 bags of cement per cu yd.

For maximum watertightness, mortar and concrete may require more fine material than would be used for maximum strength. Gravel produces a more-watertight concrete than broken stone under similar conditions. Patented compounds are on the market for producting watertight concrete, but under most conditions, equally good results can be obtained for less cost by increasing the percentage of cement in the mix. Membrane waterproofing, consisting of asphalt or tar with layers of felt or tarred paper, is advisable where it is expected that cracks will occur. Mortar troweled on very hard may produce watertight work.

Concrete to be placed through water should contain at least 7 bags of cement per cu yd and should be of a quaking consistency.

According to Fuller and Thompson (*Trans. ASCE*, **59,** p. 67), watertightness increases (1) as the percentage of cement is increased and in a very much larger ratio; (2) as the maximum size of stone is increased, provided the mixture is homogeneous; (3) materially with age; and (4) with thickness of the concrete, but in a much larger ratio. It decreases uniformly with increase in pressure and rapidly with increase in the water-cement ratio.

Air-entrained Concrete. The entrainment of from 3 to 6 percent by volume of air in concrete by means of vinsol resin or other air-bubble-forming compounds has, under certain conditions, improved the resistance of concrete in roads to frost and salt attack. The air entrainment increases the workability and reduces the compressive strength and the weight of the concrete. As the amount of air entrainment produced by a given percentage of vinsol resin varies with the cement, mixture, aggregates, slump, and mixing time, good results are dependent on very careful control.

Concrete for Masonry Units. Mixtures for concrete masonry units, which are widely used for walls and partitions, employ aggregates of a maximum size of ½ in. and are proportioned either for casting or for machine manufacture. Cast units are made in steel or wooded forms and employ concrete slumps of from 2 to 4 in. The proportions used are 1 part cement and 3 to 6 parts aggregate by dry and loose volumes. The forms are stripped after 24 hr, and the blocks piled for curing. Most **blocks** are made by machine, using very dry mixtures with only enough water present to enable the concrete to hold together when formed into a ball. The proportions used are 1 part cement and 4 to 8 parts aggregate by dry and loose volumes. The utilization of such a lean and dry mixture is possible because the blocks are automatically tamped and vibrated in steel molds. The blocks are stripped from the molds at once, placed on racks on trucks, and cured either in air or in steam. High-pressure-steam (50 to 125 psi) curing develops the needed strength of the blocks in less than 24 hr. Most concrete blocks are made with lightweight aggregates such as cinders and burned clay or shale in order to reduce the weight and improve their acoustical and thermal insulating properties. These aggregates not only must satisfy the usual requirements for gradation and soundness but must be limited in the amount of coal, iron, sulphur, and phosphorus present because of their effect on durability, discoloration and staining, fire resistance, and the formation of "pops." Pops form on the surface of concrete blocks using cinders or burned clay and shale as a result of the increase in volume of particles of iron, sulphur, and phosphorus when acted on by water, oxygen, and the alkalies of the cement.

Strength of Concrete

The strength of concrete increases (1) with the quantity of cement in a unit volume, (2) with the decrease in the quantity of mixing water relative to the cement content, and (3) with the density of the concrete. Strength is decreased by an excess of sand over that required to fill the voids in the stone and give sufficient workability. The volume of fine aggregate should not exceed 60 percent of that of coarse aggregate 1½-in. max size or larger.

Compressive Strength. Table 11 give the results obtainable with first-class materials and under first-class conditions. Growth in strength with age depends in a large measure upon the consistency characteristics of the cement and upon the curing conditions. Table 10 gives the change in relative strength with age for several water-cement ratios and a wide range of consistencies for a cement with a good age-strength gain relation. Many normal portland cements today show very little gain in strength after 28 days.

Tensile Strength. The tensile strength of concrete is of less importance than the crushing strength, as it is seldom relied upon. The true tensile strength is about 8 percent of the compression strength and must not be confused with the tensile fiber stress in a concrete beam, which is greater.

Recently, a method of obtaining the tensile of concrete by loading a cylinder in compression along two diametrically opposite generators has come into use. Nearly all the concrete in the plane of the two load strips is in tension. The tensile strength may be computed as $T = 2P/\pi ld$, where T = splitting tensile strength, psi; P = maximum load, lb; l = length of cylinder, in.; d = diameter of cylinder, in. Average values of tensile splitting strength are given in Table 11.

Transverse Strength. There is an approximate relationship between the tensile fiber stress of plain concrete beams and their compressive strength. The modulus of rupture is greatly affected by the size of the coarse aggregate and its bond and transverse strength. Quartzite generally gives low-modulus-of-rupture concrete. Table 11 indicates that the relation of the modulus of rupture of plain concrete beams at 28 days to the water-cement ratio is similar to that of the compressive strength of concrete to the water-cement ratio.

The transverse or beam test is generally used for checking the quality of concrete used for roads. The standard beam is 6 by 6 by 20 in., tested on an 18-in. span and loaded at the one-third points.

The strength of concrete in direct **shear** is about 20 percent of the compressive strength.

Table 10. Variation of Compressive Strength with Age
(Strength at 28 days taken as 100)

Water-cement ratio by volume, gal per bag of cement	3 days	7 days	28 days	3 months	1 year
5	40	75	100	125	145
7	30	65	100	135	155
9	25	50	100	145	165

Table 11. Strength of Plain Concrete at 28 Days

Max water content, gal per bag of cement	5	5.5	6	6.5	7.0
Compressive strength, psi	4,000	3,700	3,350	3,000	2,650
Modulus of rupture, psi	650	625	600	550	500
Tensile strength (split cyl. method), psi	350	325	300	275	250

Deleterious Actions and Materials

Freezing retards the setting and hardening of portland-cement concrete and is likely to lower its strength permanently. On exposed surfaces such as walls and side walks placed in freezing weather, a thin scale may crack from the surface. Natural cement is completely ruined by freezing.

Concrete laid in freezing weather or when the temperature is likely to drop to freezing should have the materials heated and should be protected from the frost, after laying, by suitable covering or artificial heat. The use of calcium chloride, salt, or other ingredients in sufficient quantities to significantly lower the temperature of freezing is not permitted since the concrete would be adversely affected.

Mica and Clay in Sand. Mica in sand, if over 2 percent, reduces the density of mortar and consequently its strength, sometimes to a very large extent. In crushed-stone screenings, the effect of the same percentage of mica in the natural state is less marked. Black mica, which has a different crystalline form, is not injurious to mortar. Clay in sand may be injurious because it may introduce too much fine material or form balls in the concrete. When not excessive in quantity, it may increase the strength and watertightness of a mortar of proportions 1:3 or leaner.

Mineral oils which have not been disintegrated by use do not injure concrete when applied externally. Animal fats and vegetable oils tend to disintegrate concrete unless it has thoroughly hardened. Concrete after it has thoroughly hardened resists the attack of diluted organic acids but is disintegrated even by dilute inorganic acids; protective treatments are magnesium fluosilicate, sodium silicate, or linseed oil. Green concrete is injured by manure but is not affected after it has thoroughly hardened.

Electrolysis injures concrete under certain conditions, and electric current should be prevented from passing through it. (See also p. 6–136 *et seq.*)

Seawater attacks cement and may disintegrate concrete. Deleterious action is greatly accelerated by frost. To prevent serious damage, the concrete must be made with a sulphate-resisting cement, a rich mix (not leaner than 1:2:4), and exceptionally good aggregates, including a coarse sand, and must be allowed to harden thoroughly, at least 7 days, before it is touched by the seawater. Although tests indicate that there is no essential difference in the strengths of mortars gaged with fresh water and with seawater, the latter tends to retard the setting and may increase the tendency of the reinforcement to rust.

WATER

BY

G. E. Sonderman

REFERENCES: Spiegler, "Salt Water Purification," Wiley. Ellis, "Fresh Water from the Ocean," Ronald. Saline Water Conversion Report, *OSW Annual Reports*, Dept. of the Interior. "Water Quality and Treatment," AWWA. Water, *Chem. Eng.*, June 10, 1963. "Drinking Water Standards," U.S. Public Health Service, 1962. Arnold, Thermal Pollution of Surface Supplies, *Jour. AWWA*, Nov., 1962.

Water Resources

Oceans cover 70 percent of the earth's surface and are the basic source of all water. Ocean waters contain about 3½ percent by weight of dissolved materials, generally varying from 32,000 to 36,000 ppm and as high as 42,000 ppm in the Persian Gulf.

About 50 percent of the sun's energy falling on the ocean causes evaporation. The vapors form clouds which precipitate pure water as rain. While most rain falls on the sea, land rainfall returns to the sea in rivers or percolates into the ground and back to the sea or is reevaporated. This is known as the **hydrological cycle.** It is a closed distillation cycle, without additions or losses from outer space or from the interior of the earth.

Water supply to the United States depends on an annual rainfall averaging 30 in. and equal to 1,564,800 billion gal per year, or 4,560 billion gal per day. About 72 percent returns to the atmosphere by direct evaporation and transpiration from trees and plants. The remaining 28 percent, or 1,277 billion gal daily, is the maximum supply available. This is commonly called **runoff** and properly includes both surface and underground flows. Between 33 and 40 percent of runoff appears as ground water.

Two-thirds of the runoff passes into the ocean as flood flow in one-third of the year. By increased capture, it would be possible to retain about one-half of the 1,277 billion gal, or 638 billion gal, per day as **maximum usable water.**

Withdrawal use is the quantity of water removed from the ground or diverted from a body of surface water. **Consumptive use** is the portion of such water that is discharged to the atmosphere or incorporated in growing vegetation or in industrial or food products.

The estimated withdrawal use of water in the United States in 1960 was 322 billion gal per day, including some saline waters (see Table 1).

Table 1. Water Use in the United States, 1960*
(All quantities in billion gallons per day)

	Total withdrawal	Fresh water	Saline water	Consumptive use
Irrigation	135	135	...	107
Public water utilities	22	22	...	4
Rural domestic	6	6	...	5
Industrial and misc	61	53	8	9
Steam-electric plants	98	76	22	0.3
Total	322	292	30	125.3

* Compiled from data by Picton, MacKichan, and others.

Fresh-water withdrawal is about 23 percent of runoff, and consumptive use is about 10 percent of runoff. The consumptive use of water for irrigation is about 64 percent, but another 15 percent is allowed for transmission and distribution losses.

Dividing total water withdrawal by the population of the United States shows a 1960 water use, the **Water Index,** of 1,750 gal per capita day (gpcd). It reflects the great industrial and agricultural uses of water because man can survive on a theoretical minimum of 1 qt of water per day. The average **household use** of water in American urban areas is 30 to 60 gpcd. But since municipal waterworks also supply industrial customers, the average **production of water utilities** is 140 gpcd, ranging from 40 to 400 gpcd. These figures include 15 percent distribution losses.

Additions to water resources for the future can be made by (1) increase in storage reservoirs, (2) injection of used water or flood water into underground strata called **aquifers,** (3) covering reservoirs with films to reduce evaporation, (4) rainmaking, (5) saline-water conversion.

It is equally important to improve the efficient use of water supplies by (1) multiple use of cooling water, (2) use of air cooling instead of water cooling, (3) use of cooling towers, (4) reclamation of waste waters, both industrial and sewage, (5) abatement of pollution by treatment rather than by dilution, which requires additional fresh water.

Measurements and Definitions

Water **quantities** in this country are measured by U.S. gallons, the larger unit being 1,000 U.S. gal. For agriculture and irrigation, water use is measured in acre-feet, *i.e.*, the amount of water covering 1 acre of surface to a depth of 1 ft. In the British-standard area, the imperial gallon is used. In metric-system areas, water is measured in kilograms and the larger unit is the metric ton, which equals a cubic meter of water, expressed as m^3.

Conversion Table

1 acre-ft	=	325,850 U.S. gal or 326 M approx
1 acre-ft	=	1,233 metric tons or cu m
1 acre-ft	=	43,560 cu ft
1 imperial gal	=	1.20 U.S. gal
1 metric ton	=	1,000 kg
	=	2,204 lb
	=	264 U.S. gal
	=	220 imperial gal
1 U.S. ton	=	240 U.S. gal
1,000,000 U.S. gal	=	3.07 acre-ft

For stream flow and hydraulic purposes, water is measured in cubic feet per second.

1,000,000 U.S. gal per day = 1.55 cfs
= 1,120 acre-ft per year

Water **costs** are expressed in terms of price per 1,000 gal, per acre-foot, per cubic foot, or per metric ton.

10¢ per 1,000 gal = $32.59 per acre-ft
= 0.075¢ per cu ft
= 3.78¢ per metric ton

Water **quality** is measured in terms of the solids, of any character, which are dissolved in the water. The solids are usually expressed in parts per million or in grains per gallon. One grain equals 1/7000 lb. Therefore, 17.1 ppm = 1 grain per U.S. gal. In the metric system, 1 ppm = 1 g per cu meter = 1 mg per liter. Standards for drinking water, or **potable water,** have been established by the U.S. Public Health Service. The recommended limit is 500 ppm of total dissolved solids (see Table 2). Potable water must also be bacteriologically safe and relatively free of odor, turbidity, and radioactivity. For temporary use, the California State Board of Public Health has permitted usage of water with up to 1,500 ppm total solids but containing not more than 600 ppm sulphate, 600 ppm chloride, and 150 ppm magnesium.

Table 2. Potable-water-constituent Limitations

Maximum limits		Some recommended limits	
Constituent	Mg per liter	Constituent	Mg per liter
Arsenic	0.05	Alkyl benzene sulphonate	0.5
Barium	1.00	Chloride	250.0
Cadmium	0.01	Nitrate	45.0
Chromium (hexavalent)	0.05	Sulphate	250.0
Cyanide	0.20	Copper	1.
Fluoride	(See USPHS)	Zinc	5.0
Lead	0.05		
Selenium	0.01		
Silver	0.05		

For **agricultural water,** mineral content up to 700 ppm is considered excellent to good. However, certain elements are undesirable, particularly sodium and boron. The California State Water Resources Board limits Class I irrigation water to:

	Max ppm
Sodium, as % of total sodium, potassium, magnesium, and calcium equivalents	60
Boron	0.5
Chloride	177
Sulphate	960

Class II irrigation water may run as high as 2,100 ppm total dissolved solids, with higher limits on the specific elements, but whether such water is satisfactory or injurious depends on character of soil, climate, and agricultural practice.

Waters containing dissolved salts are called **saline waters,** and the lower concentrations are commonly called **brackish;** these waters are defined, in ppm, as follows:

Saline	All concentrations up to 42,000
Slightly brackish	1,000–3,000
Brackish	3,000–10,000
Seawaters, average	32,000–36,000
Brine	Over 42,000

Hardness of water refers to the content of calcium and magnesium salts, which may be bicarbonates, carbonates, sulphates, chlorides, or nitrates. Bicarbonate content is called **temporary hardness** as it may be removed by boiling. The salts in "hard water" increase the amount of soap needed to form a lather and also form deposits or "scale" as water is heated or evaporated.

Hardness is a measure of calcium and magnesium salts expressed as equivalent calcium carbonate content and is usually stated in ppm (or in grains per gal) as follows: very soft water, less than 15 ppm; soft water, 15 to 50 ppm; slightly hard water, 50 to 100 ppm; hard water, 100 to 220 ppm; very hard water, over 220 ppm.

Industrial Water

The use of water within a given industry varies widely because of conditions of price, availability, and process technology (see Table 3).

When a sufficient water supply of suitable quality is available at low cost, plants tend to use maximum volumes. When water is scarce and costly at an otherwise desirable plant site, improved processes and careful water management can reduce water usage to the minimum. Industrial water may be purchased from local public utilities or self-supplied. Figure 1 shows the distribution of water **sources** among 3,000 typical plants. Small industries usually buy water from local suppliers at costs ranging from 12¢ to 28¢ per 1,000 gal. Larger industries may provide their own water from sources available to the site. Costs run from 1¢ to 11¢ per 1,000 gal and include

Table 3. Variance in Industrial Water Withdrawals*

Product or user and unit	Withdrawal in gallons		
	Maximum	Typical	Minimum
Steam-electric power per kwh	170	80	1.32
Petroleum refining, per gal of crude oil	44.5	18.3	1.73
Steel, per finished ton	65,000	40,000	1,400
Soaps, edible oils, per lb	7.5	....	1.57
Glass containers, per ton	667	....	118
Automobiles, per car	16,000	....	12,000
Newsprint, per ton	26,000	....	6,000
Cannery, per ton	2,500	....	1,200

* From data by Wolman, AAAS.

collection, pumping, distribution, storage tanks, and fire-protection system (see Sec. 12). Treatment, where needed, may add materially to these costs.

About 94 percent on industrial water is used for cooling, mostly on a once-through system. An open recirculation system with cooling tower or spray pond (Fig. 2)

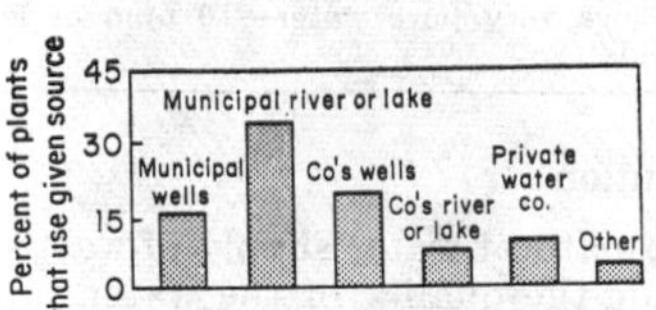

FIG. 1. Distribution of water sources among 3,000 typical plants. (*Chem. Eng., June* 10, 1963.)

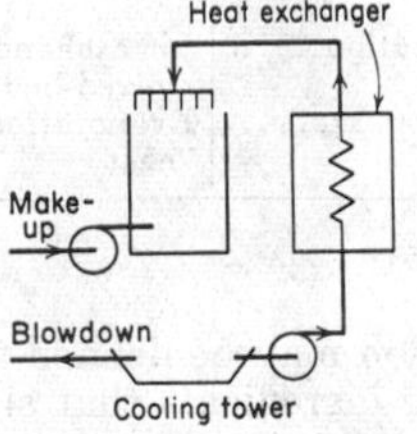

FIG. 2. Open recirculating system. (*Chem. Eng., June* 10, 1963.)

reduces withdrawal use of water by over 90 percent but increases consumptive use by 3 to 8 percent due to evaporation loss (see p. 9–93 *et seq.*). Even more effective reduction in water demand can be achieved by multiple reuse. An example is shown in Fig. 3.

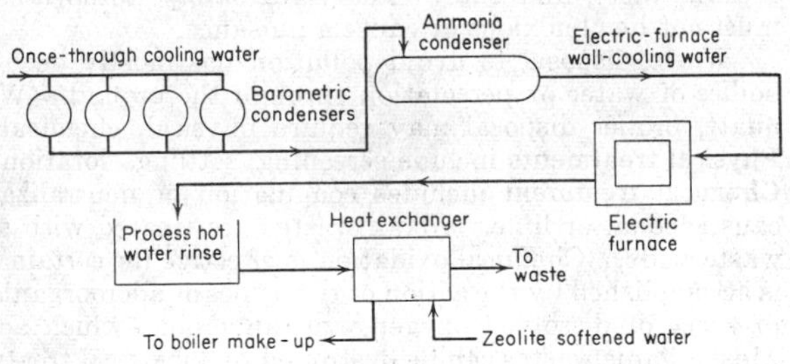

FIG. 3. Stepwise or cascade cooling system. (*Chem. Eng., June* 10, 1963.)

Quality requirements for general plant use (non-process) are that the water be low in suspended solids to prevent clogging, low in total dissolved solids to prevent depositions, free of organic growth and color, and free of iron and manganese salts. Where the water is also used for drinking, quality must meet the Public Health Service standards.

Cooling service requires that water be non-clogging. Reduction in suspended solids is made by settling or by using a coagulating agent such as alum and then settling. For recirculating-type cooling systems, corrosion inhibitors such as polyphosphates and chromates are added; algaecides and biocides may be needed to control microorganism growths; for cooling jackets on equipment, hardness may cause scaling and should be reduced by softening.

Process-water quality requirements are often more exacting than potable-water standards; *e.g.*, boiler-feed water must have less than 1 ppm of dissolved solids (see pp. 6–129 and 9–46). The required quality may be met by the general plant water as available or must be provided by treatment.

Table 4 shows methods and objectives for industrial-water treatment.

Table 4. Water Treatment

Treatment	Method	Objective
Clarification	Presedimentation Coagulation Settling Filtering	Remove suspended solids and reduce turbidity, color, organic matter.
Disinfection	Add chlorine, 5 to 6 ppm, or continuous-feed to maintain 0.2 to 0.3 ppm residual-free Cl_2	Prevent algae and slime growths.
Softening	Cold-lime process	Reduce temporary hardness to 85 ppm; also reduce iron and manganese.
	Hot-lime-soda process	Reduce total hardness to 25 ppm.
	Zeolite	Reduce total hardness to 5 ppm.
Electrodialysis	....	Partial removal of ions; can reduce 5,000 ppm brackish water to 500 ppm or less.
Demineralization	Ion exchange: two-stage or mixed-bed	Remove both negative and positive ions (cations and anions) to provide very pure water.
Distillation	Evaporation using steam heat	Produce very pure water—10 ppm or less total solids.

Water Pollution

Pollution may be defined as the return to a natural water supply of waste waters containing ingredients that significantly degrade the quality of the water supply to subsequent users. Most states have regulations to control pollution, and where waters are common to several states, interstate and international agencies have been established.

For the support of fish and aquatic life, water must contain a supply of **dissolved oxygen** (DO). Organic wastes consume oxygen by microbiological action, and this effect is measured by the **biochemical oxygen-demand** (BOD) test.

State **pollution ordinances** have standards to govern permissible plant effluents, setting limits for solids, turbidity, BOD, toxicity, color, pH, temperature, oils and greases, taste, and odor. Many regulatory authorities merely state that effluents must not be obnoxious or cause a nuisance.

Waste disposal to avoid pollution has mostly been done by dilution into large bodies of water or percolation through the ground. Where these means are inadequate, proper disposal may require physical, chemical, and biological treatments. **Physical treatments** include screening, settling, flotation, centrifuging, and filtration. **Chemical treatment** includes coagulation or neutralization of acids with soda ash, caustic soda, or lime. Alkali wastes are treated with sulphuric acid or inexpensive waste acids. Chemical oxidation is effective for certain waste. **Biological treatment** is accomplished by the action of two types of microorganisms: aerobic, which act in the presence of dissolved oxygen, and anaerobic, which act in the absence of oxygen. Most organic wastes can be destroyed by biological treatment. The principal aerobic treatment is by activated-sludge process, by trickling filters, or by lagoons.

Water Desalinization

An average seawater contains 35,000 ppm of dissolved solids, equal to $3\frac{1}{2}$ percent by weight of such solids, or 3.5 lb per 100 lb; in 1,000 gal, there are 300 lb of dissolved chemicals in 8,271 lb of pure water. The principal ingredient is sodium chloride (common salt), which accounts for about 80 percent of the total. Other salts are calcium sulphate (gypsum), calcium bicarbonate, magnesium sulphate, magnesium chloride, potassium chloride, and more complex salts. Because these dissolved chemicals are dissociated in solution, the composition of seawater is best expressed by the concentration of the major ions (*see* Table 5). Even when the content of total solids in seawater varies because of dilution or concentration, the proportion of the ions remains almost constant.

Table 5. Ions in Seawater*

Ions	Ppm	Lb per 1,000 gal
Chloride	19,350	165.6
Sodium	10,600	91.2
Sulphate	2,710	23.2
Magnesium	1,300	11.1
Calcium	405	3.48
Potassium	385	3.30
Carbonate and bicarbonate	122	1.05
Total principal ingredients	34,872	298.9
Others	128	1.1
Total dissolved solids	35,000	300.0

* Compiled from Spiegler, "Salt Water Purification," and Ellis, "Fresh Water from the Ocean."

The **composition of saline waters** varies so widely that no average analysis can be given. Common impurities in land waters are usually the calcium, magnesium, and bicarbonate ions. Some saline waters contain sodium chlorides or sulphates.

Purification of seawater requires reduction of 35,000 ppm of solids to less than 1,000 ppm, or a reduction of 35 to 1. For potable water, the sodium content must be further reduced; for agricultural water, the boron content may also have to be lowered. The oldest method of purification of seawater is **distillation.** This technique has been practiced for over a century on oceangoing steamships. Distillation is used in over 95 percent of all land-based conversion plants and is principally accomplished by submerged-surface evaporation, flash distillation, and vapor-compression distillation.

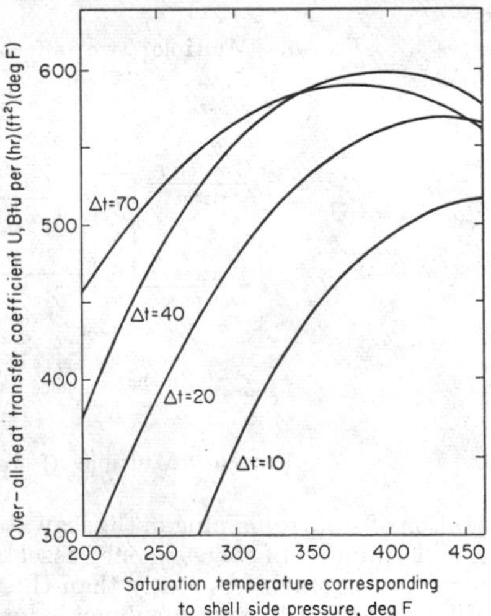

FIG. 4. Some heat-transfer rates, submerged-tube, single-effect, evaporators. These rates are approximately 65 percent of clean-tube rates.

In **submerged-surface distillation,** a heat-transfer surface, such as tubes or coils, is submerged in salt water in a suitable vessel. Steam is passed through the tubes, causing the brine to boil, and some water is evaporated. The vapors pass to a condenser cooled by incoming seawater and so yield a distillate of practically pure water. This is known as **single-effect** distillation. (See Fig. 4 for heat-transfer data.) **Multiple-effect** distillation (Fig. 5) uses several effects in series. While, in a single effect, 1 lb of steam will produce nearly 0.9 lb of distilled water, a double effect will yield 1.75 lb, and so on. The Freeport, Texas, plant uses 12 effects, producing nearly 10 lb of water per lb of steam. The evaporators in this plant employ long vertical tubes in which the seawater is heated and vaporized by steam surrounding the tubes. This is a variation of the submerged-coil evaporator and is commonly known as the **L.T.V.,** or long-tube vertical evaporator.

In **flash distillation,** the salt water is heated in a tubular heater and then passed to a separate chamber where a pressure lower than that in the heating tubes prevails. This causes some of the hot salt water to vaporize, or "flash," such vapor then being condensed by cooler incoming salt water to produce pure distilled water. A **single-stage flash evaporator** can produce nearly the same amount of distillate per heat unit as the submerged-surface type. Similarly, flash distillation can be carried on in a number of successive stages (Fig. 6) wherein the heated salt water flashes to vapor in a series of chambers, each at a lower pressure than the preceding one. The higher the number of stages in such a **multiflash system,** the better the over-all yield.

Flash distillation offers an advantage over submerged-surface distillation in that the separate heating of salt water without boiling causes less scale deposits. No scale occurs in the flash chambers as they contain no heated surfaces, the increased concen-

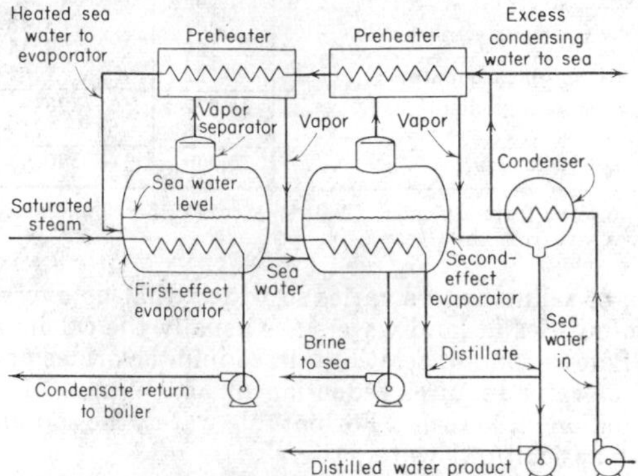

FIG. 5. Multiple (two) effect submerged-surface distillation process.

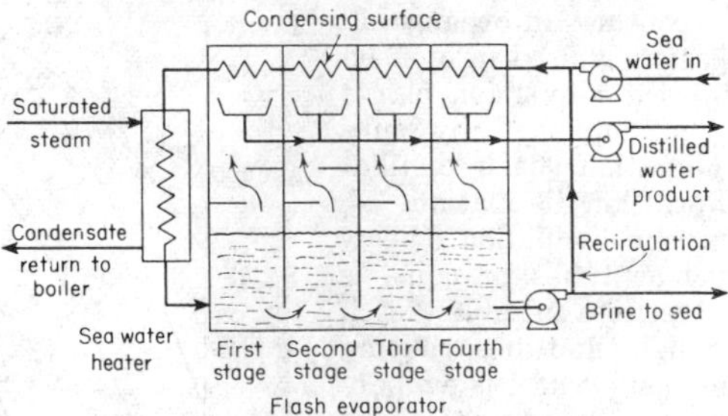

FIG. 6. Multiple (four) stage flash-distillation process.

tration of salts remaining in the seawater. Recent designs of flash evaporators provide a great number of stages in one vessel by simple divisions within the vessel. This construction is much less costly than the separate evaporators formerly used in flash distillation and still used in submerged-surface distillation. Therefore, in large modern plants, the multiflash system has practically replaced the heated-surface evaporators. The San Diego, California, OSW demonstration plant uses 36 stages of multiflash evaporation to produce 1 million gal of fresh water per day. Studies have been made of plants using more than 50 stages and producing yields as high as 15 to 18 lb of fresh water per lb of steam.

In vapor-compression distillation (Fig. 7), the energy is supplied by a compressor which takes the vapor from boiling salt water and compresses it to a higher pressure and temperature to furnish the heat for vaporization of more seawater. In so doing, the vapor is condensed to yield distilled water. Vapor compression is theoretically a more efficient method of desalinization than other distillation methods. The principle was widely applied during World War II in the form of small, portable units. The largest permanent installations are at Roswell, New Mexcio (1 million gpd); Dhahran, Saudi Arabia; and Kindley Field, Bermuda. The disadvantages of this process lie in the cost, mechanical operation, and maintenance of the compressors.

Other methods of purifying seawater include freezing, solar evaporation, electrodialysis, solvent extraction, reverse osmosis, and ion exchange.

The **freezing process** yields ice crystals of pure water, but a certain amount of salt water is trapped in the crystals and is mostly removed by washing. This process is promising because theoretically it takes less energy to freeze water than to distill it, but it is not yet in major commercial application.

Solar evaporation produces 0.1 gpd or more of water per sq ft of area, depending on climate conditions. Its capital and maintenance costs so far have not made it competitive for large plants, but it can be useful for small plants in favorable circumstances. (See also p. 9–216.)

Electrodialysis (Fig. 8) is a proven method of desalinization, but where used on ocean water, it is not competitive. The purification of brackish or low-saline waters lends itself most advantageously to the process. The ions of dissolved salts are pulled

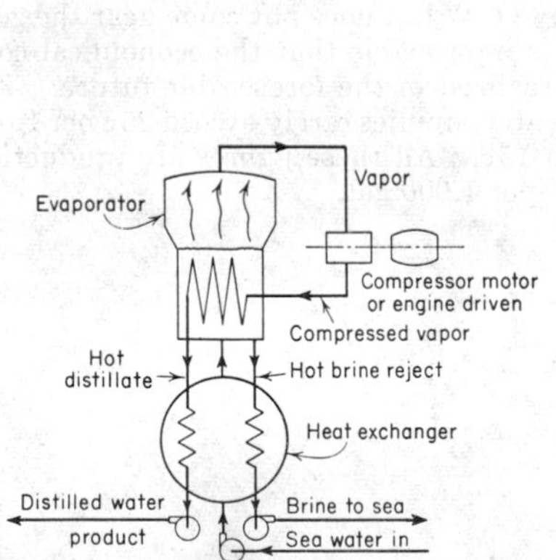
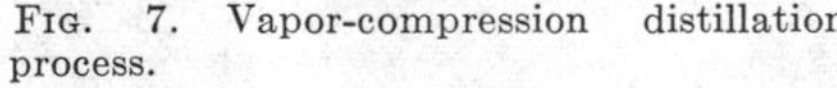

FIG. 7. Vapor-compression distillation process.

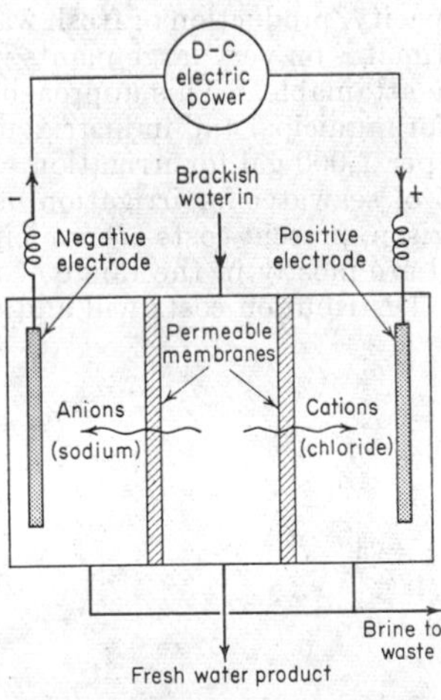

FIG. 8. Electrodialysis single-compartment process.

out of the saline water by electric forces and pass from the salt-water compartment into adjacent compartments through membranes which are permeable to positively charged ions or to negatively charged ions.

Electrodialysis equipment contains from 10 to 100 or more compartments between one set of electrodes. The number of cells and the amount of electric current required increase with the amount of purification to be done. A brackish water of 5,000 ppm max dissolved salts can be reduced to potable water with less than 500 ppm. A large plant in South Africa reduces 3 million gpd of a water having a salinity of 2,800 ppm.

A major problem in many desalting processes, especially distillation, is the concentration of dissolved salts. Heating seawater above 150 F causes **scale**, a deposition of insoluble salts on the heating surfaces, which rapidly reduces the heat transfer. For initial temperatures of 160 to 195 F, the addition of polyphosphates and organics forms a sludge rather than a hard scale. This practice is widely used in ships and present land-based plants but is limited to 195 F. Some plants use an acid or a sludge-recirculation treatment that permits boiling of seawater at 240 to 250 F. This improves the performance of the process and reduces costs. In electrodialysis, hard scale does not occur, but the concentration of salts does affect the performance of the unit by clogging the membranes. In the freezing process, there is no scale problem.

The theoretical **energy requirement** to convert seawater to fresh water is only 2.65 kwh (expressed as electrical energy) per 1,000 gal. Efficiencies of current methods are given in Table 6.

Table 6. Efficiencies of Processes*

Method	Efficiency, percent
6-effect evaporator	3.1
12-effect evaporator	7.2
Multistage flash	3.8–7.2
Vapor compression	4.6–7.2
Electrodialysis—seawater	2.7

* From Spiegler, "Salt Water Purification."

The **costs** of saline-water conversion are composed of energy costs, capital charges, and operation and maintenance costs. Current production costs of two seawater distillation demonstration plants are roughly $1 per 1,000 gal. For plants of 10 million gpd capacity, production of fresh water could now be done for 75¢ to 80¢ per 1,000 gal, and estimates on very large plants indicate that fresh-water costs of 50¢ per 1,000 gal may be attainable. This approaches the goal of 38¢ per 1,000 gal of converted seawater for municipal and industrial use as set by OSW but does not come near the goal of 12¢ per 1,000 gal for irrigation water. It is improbable that the economical conversion of seawater for irrigation use will be realized in the foreseeable future. For comparison, present costs of municipal fresh-water supplies rarely exceed 25¢ per 1,000 gal and are mostly in the range of from 3¢ to 15¢. All these figures are production costs. Distribution costs will add 10¢ to 20¢ per 1,000 gal.

LUBRICANTS AND LUBRICATION

BY

Fred J. Villforth, Jr.

(For a general discussion of friction see pp. 3–34 to 3–47; for viscosity p. 3–49; for bearings and coefficients of friction, pp. 8–156 to 8–187.)

REFERENCES: ASTM, Committee D-2, "Standards on Petroleum Products and Lubricants," "The Significance of Tests of Petroleum Products." ASLE, "Physical Properties of Lubricants," 2d ed. "Bearings, Lubricants, and Lubrication," ASME Digest of Literature. SAE Lubricants Handbook. Georgi, "Motor Oils and Engine Lubrication," Reinhold. Bondi, "Physical Chemistry of Lubricating Oils," Reinhold. Bauman, "Properties of Lubricating Oil and Engine Deposits," Macmillan. Bailey, "Industrial Oil and Fat Products," 2d ed., Interscience. Boner, "Manufacture and Application of Lubricating Greases," Reinhold. ASLE, "Fundamentals of Friction and Lubrication in Engineering." Shaw and Macks, "Analysis and Lubrication of Bearings," McGraw-Hill. Thomsen, "The Practice of Lubrication," 4th ed., McGraw-Hill. Slaymaker, "Bearing Lubrication Analysis," Wiley. Forbes, Pope, and Everitt, "Lubrication of Industrial and Marine Machinery," 2d ed., Wiley. Hobson, "Industrial Lubrication Practice," The Industrial Press. Brewer, "Basic Lubrication Practice," Reinhold.

LUBRICANTS

Lubrication is primarily concerned with reducing the frictional resistance occurring at the surfaces of two solids when one is moved relative to the other. Anything introduced on or between these surfaces to accomplish a reduction in friction or to change the frictional properties is called a **lubricant.**

Types and Properties. Although the substances most frequently used as lubricants have been oils or greases, many other materials, differing widely, may be suitable. Fluids (air or other gases as well as liquids) are finding application as lubricants. The lubricant frequently serves a multiple function; it may be a heat-transfer medium, a protection against rust and corrosion, a sealing medium, or a scavenger for contaminants.

The particular application, in its manifold aspects, determines the lubricant selected. Lubricants are manufactured and modified to have certain specific characteristics, which may be defined in terms of physical properties or by performance.

The concept of the lubricant as a design consideration has helped to place the proper emphasis on the lubrication aspects of the operation of mechanisms and has resulted in their much more satisfactory performance.

LIQUID-PETROLEUM LUBRICANTS

Liquid-petroleum lubricants are widely used because of their general suitability to much of existing equipment. Petroleum oils are variously prepared by fractionation and other refining processes from naturally occurring hydrocarbons. The three main crude-oil sources in the United States are characterized as pure paraffin, mainly from the Pennsylvania fields, semiparaffin from the Gulf Coast, and naphthene base from California fields. Other crude sources are located in scattered fields in both the Eastern and the Western hemispheres.

Physical tests are frequently used to characterize petroleum oils since the lubricant performance often depends upon or may be related to such physical properties. Usual physical tests include measurements of viscosity, density, pour, gravity, flash and fire, demulsibility, odor, and color. **Chemical tests** include tests for carbon residue, oxidation, corrosion, acidity, oiliness, extreme pressure, sulphur, ash, and precipitation number.

Viscosity is probably the single most important property of a lubricant and may be influenced by temperature, pressure, and shear (fluid motion). (See p. 3–49.)

The **Saybolt Standard Universal viscometer** is a standard instrument for determining viscosity of petroleum lubricants between 70 and 210 F (ASTM D88–56), with the results expressed as **Saybolt Universal seconds** (SUS or SSU). **Kinematic viscosity,** a fundamental and preferred determination, can be obtained in capillary-type instruments under Newtonian flow conditions. A large number of designs of commercially available capillaries are acceptable (ASTM D445–64).

The calculation of **absolute viscosity** (ASTM D1745–63) can be made from the determination of the kinematic viscosity and the density. A method of converting kinematic viscosity to Saybolt Universal or Saybolt Furol viscosity is available in the form of convenient tables (ASTM D2161–63T).

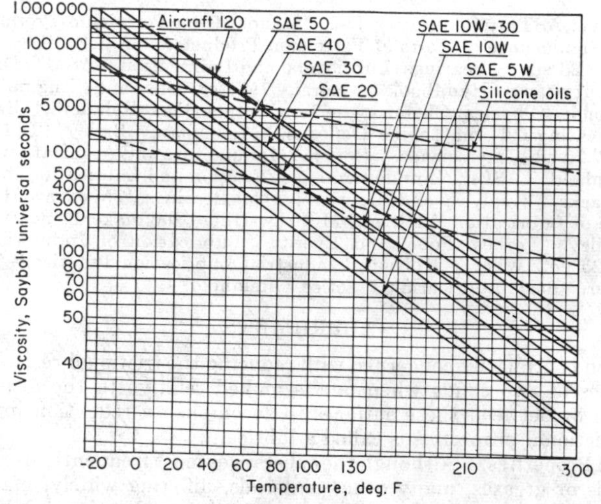

Fig. 1. Variation of viscosity with temperature for petroleum oils (ASTM viscosity chart). The broken lines are typical for silicone oils. The dot-dash line is for multigrade SAE 10W–30 motor oils.

The variation of viscosity with temperature of petroleum oils can be determined with considerable accuracy when the viscosities are known at any two temperatures. The ASTM D341–43 Standard Viscosity Temperature Charts are available for this purpose for both Saybolt and kinematic viscosities. The procedure states that the two known viscosity-temperature points are plotted on the appropriate chart; then with great accuracy, a straight line is drawn through these points. Any point on the line, within the explicit range, indicates the viscosity corresponding to the temperature, or vice versa. A typical chart is shown on Fig. 1; the solid lines are representative of the grades indicated, and the broken lines are for silicone fluids, illustrating their typically smaller change in viscosity with temperature.

The ASTM Viscosity-Temperature Chart can be used very conveniently **to predict the required composition of a two-component lubricating-oil blend** or to estimate the composition of an existing oil blend when the viscosities of the blend and of the two components are known. The vertical scale is almost linearly related to the composition of a two-component oil blend and can be used without change. The horizontal scale between 0 and 100 F is relabeled 0 to 100 percent and is used to represent the percentage by volume of the high-viscosity oil in the blend. To use the chart, plot the viscosity of the low-viscosity oil on the zero percent line and the viscosity of the high-viscosity component on the 100 percent line. If the two points are connected by a straight line, the volumetric composition of any blend of intermediate viscosity can be read. Conversely, the composition of a blend can be estimated when the viscosities of the two components and of the blend are known.

SAE Viscosity Number. The SAE viscosity numbers for crankcase oils constitute a classification in terms of viscosity only. They are as follows:

SAE Viscosity Values for Crankcase Oils

SAE viscosity number	Viscosity range, Saybolt Universal sec			
	at 0 F		at 210 F	
	Min	Max	Min	Max
5W	.....	4,000	39	
10W	6,000*	< 12,000	39	
20W	12,000†	48,000		
20	.....	.....	45	< 58
30	.....	.....	58	< 70
40	.....	.....	70	< 85
50	.....	.....	85	110

* Minimum viscosity at 0 F can be waived provided viscosity at 210 F is not below 40 sec, Saybolt Universal.

† Minimum viscosity at 0 F can be waived provided viscosity at 210 F is not below 45 sec, Saybolt Universal.

Viscosity of oils in this classification should not be less than 39 sec at 210 F; Saybolt Universal viscosity numbers without the letter W are based on the Saybolt viscosity at 210 F. Viscosity numbers with the letter W are based on the Saybolt viscosity at 0 F. A multiple-viscosity oil is one whose viscosity at 0 F falls within the prescribed viscosity range of the W-numbered oil (or oils) and whose viscosity at 210 F falls within the prescribed viscosity range of the designated oil whose viscosity number does not include the letter W.

Because of the importance of viscosity, the selection of a winter crankcase oil must be based on the lowest anticipated atmospheric temperature, while the selection of a summer lubricant should be based on the highest expected daytime temperatures.

Temperatures for Recommending Crankcase Oils, SAE J301*

Anticipated min temp, deg F				Daytime temp, deg F
Less than −10	−10	+10	+32	Above 90

* *SAE Inf. Rep.*, app. 1939, reaffirmed 1956.

Experience indicates that for satisfactory gear shifting of manually operated transmissions, the viscosity of the gear lubricant should not exceed 100,000 sec at the shifting temperature. This information should be of interest to manufacturers of SAE 80 or other grades recommended for winter service.

Transmission and Axle-lubricant Classification, SAE J306*
(Viscosity values in Saybolt Universal seconds for transmission and axle lubricants, MIL-L-2105.)

SAE viscosity no.	0 F		210 F		Must not channel in service at
	Minimum	Maximum	Minimum	Maximum	
75	....	15,000	...	....	−50 F
80	15,000†	100,000	...	....	−30 F
90	....	....	75	120‡	0 F
140	....	....	120	200	
250	....	....	200		

* *SAE Recommended Practice*, app. 1924, rev. 1953.

† The minimum viscosity at 0 F may be waived if the viscosity is not less than 48 SSU at 210 F.

‡ The maximum viscosity at 210 F may be waived if the viscosity is not greater than 750,000 SSU at 0 F (extrapolated).

In connection with axle lubrication, field experience indicates that lubricants with viscosities above 750,000 sec at the starting temperature may cause undesirable resistance to gear motion during the starting and warmup interval. This information is particularly important in connection with the SAE 90 and 140 grades.

The **basis for the design of journal bearings** is that the lubricant will form a fluid film separating two surfaces which slide relative to each other. For this to occur, the combination of speed, load, and lubricant viscosity must be within a rather broad but definite range. Increasing speed or lubricant viscosity results in a thicker film, and increasing load reduces film thickness as long as bearing geometry is not changed. Bearings are designed to permit the maintaining of a fluid film under most of the encountered operating conditions. However, when the movement between the bearing surfaces approaches zero (during start and stop), when high shock loads are imposed, or when high temperatures reduce viscosity to too low a level, the complete oil film cannot be maintained between journal and bearing and metal-to-metal contact occurs. Under these conditions, mild extreme-pressure (EP) additives are used to provide a margin of safety. The EP agents or components may be in the form of (1) polar material such as lard oil or tallow, or (2) sulphurized fat.

Filtration systems for the removal of foreign matter in the circulating lubricant may be necessary, particularly where devices having accurately machined and closely fitting parts are used.

The **load-carrying capacity of a bearing** may be limited by the physical properties of the bearing metal. Babbitts lose their strength at elevated temperatures. Other bearing materials, such as cadmium, copper, silver, nickel, copper-lead, aluminum, bronze, non-metallics, and various platings, may be used to impart special strengths, properties, or frictional characteristics for specific applications. Oxidation products in the oils may attack some of these bearing materials and weaken or destroy the bearing surface; oils used in such applications should be inhibited to reduce oxidation and corrosion. (See also p. 6–106.)

Viscosity index (VI) is an empirical system for expressing the rate of change of viscosity of an oil with change in temperature. It is based upon comparison of viscosity measurements of fractions from crude oils "L" and "H," which were chosen because they seemed to possess the maximum and minimum limits of viscosity-temperature sensitivity and were accordingly assigned viscosity indices of 0 and 100 as the presumed end points of a 100-point viscosity-index scale. While all other oils were expected to fall between these limits, the subsequent advent of solvent refining, the use of modifiers such as the polymers, and the manufacture of synthetics have all produced lubricants that are far outside the viscosity-index scale in both directions.

The **procedure for calculating the VI of an oil** is to determine its viscosity at 100 and 210 F. The Standard Methods (ASTM D567–53 and D2270–64) and ASTM Viscosity Tables (*ASTM Spec. Tech. Publ.* 4312) are used for viscosity-index calculations. Either Saybolt Universal or kinematic viscosities can be used, but the latter are preferred because of their greater accuracy.

Values of VI may be obtained from Fig. 2. As shown by the broken lines, the VI of an oil with Saybolt viscosities of 55 at 210 F and 400 at 100 F is 80. It should be noted that the VI may be negative or may be greater than 100. In the range above 125 VI, anomalous results are possible since two oils having the same viscosity at 100 F but with different viscosities at 210 F may have the same VI.

Oils with viscosity indices above 100 can be made from a wide variety of crude oils by solvent refining, by selective blending of paraffin-base oils, by the addition of relatively small amounts of high-molecular-weight polymeric additives to base oils, or by combinations of these methods.

When lubricating oils are subjected to high pressure, there is a marked increase in viscosity. Paraffinic oils of high viscosity index vary less with pressure than do naphthenic oils, and fixed oils vary least.

Lubricants with good temperature-viscosity curves (high viscosity index) are desirable. In cold starting, the flatter the temperature-viscosity curve, the less the energy required and the better the fluidity. In normal operation and at high temperatures and at high pressures, the flatter temperature-viscosity curve oils have less friction and higher load-carrying capacity.

Cloud and Pour Points. Petroleum oils, when cooled, may become plastic solids as a result either of partial separation of wax or of congealing of the hydrocarbons composing the oil. With some oils, the separation of wax becomes visible at temperatures slightly above the solidification point, and when that temperature is reached under prescribed conditions, it is known as the **cloud point** (ASTM D97–57). With oils in which wax does not separate prior to solidification, or in which the separation is invisible, the cloud point cannot be determined. That temperature at which the oil will just flow under prescribed conditions is known as the **pour point** (ASTM D97–57).

The pour point indicates the lowest temperature at which an oil will flow to the pump, bearings, or cylinder walls. It is particularly important for immediate oil circulation in connection with cold starting of engines, or with gravity lubricating systems, as the fluidity is a factor of pour point and viscosity of the cold oil. Pour-point depressants may be added to wax-containing oils to lower the pour points instead of dewaxing the oils.

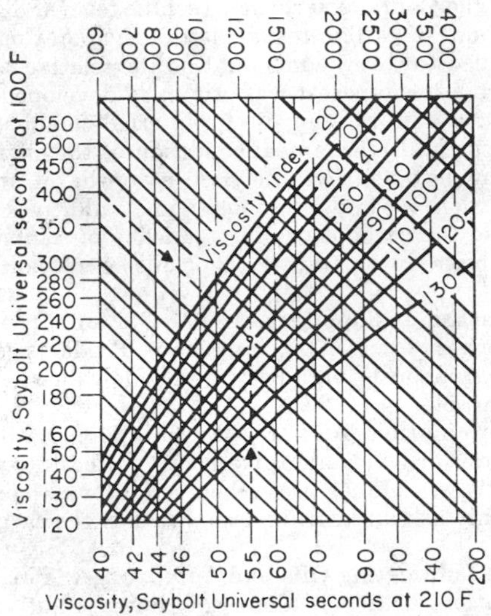

FIG. 2. Viscosity-index chart (ASTM D567–53 method).

Gravity. Lubricating-oil gravities are expressed either in specific gravity ASTM D1298–55 or API gravity (D287–64) (see p. 1–88). Low-viscosity oils have higher API gravities than the higher viscosity oils of the same crude-oil series. Paraffinic oils are the lightest or highest API gravities, naphthenic are intermediate, and animal and vegetable oils are the heaviest or low API gravity. The specific gravity of an oil is the ratio of its weight to that of an equal volume of water, both measured at 60 F. The gravity of lubricating oils is of no value in predicting quality although it gives a clue to the source of the crude-oil base.

Flash and Fire Points. The flash point of an oil is the temperature to which an oil has to be heated until sufficient flammable vapor is driven off to flash when brought into contact with a flame. The fire point is the higher temperature at which the oil vapors will continue to burn when ignited. The ASTM D92–57 standard method for flash and fire points by means of open cup tester is used for lubricating oils. In general, the open flash point is 30 F higher than the closed flash, and the fire point is some 50 to 70 F above the open flash point.

Flash and fire points depend upon the nature of the original crude oil, the viscosity, and the method of refining. For the same viscosities and degree of refinement, the paraffinic oils are higher than the naphthenic flash and fire points.

Steam Emulsion Test. ASTM D1401–64 Emulsion Characteristics of Steam-turbine Oil is used for measuring the ability of oil and water to separate. Although it is specifically intended for steam-turbine oils, this test may be used for other oils. When the oil is emulsified and separated under prescribed conditions, the time required for the emulsion to be reduced to 3 ml or less is recorded (at 5-min intervals).

Color. The color of a lubricating oil is obtained by reference to transmitted light; the color by reflected light is referred to as **bloom.** The color of an oil indicates the uniformity of a particular grade or brand and not its quality. ASTM D1500–64 is for the visual determination of color of lubricating oils, heating oils, Diesel fuels, and petroleum waxes using a standardized colorimeter. The method compares the samples with glass color standards and reports color in terms of the ASTM Color Scale; it also provides for comparison with the former ASTM Union Color. The color scale ranges from 0.5 to 8; oils darker than the 8 color are diluted with kerosine as prescribed by the test method and then observed in the same way as the lighter oils. For determining the color of petroleum products lighter than 0.5, ASTM D156–64 Test for Saybolt Color of Petroleum Products can be used.

Carbon Residue. The **Conradson carbon-residue test** (ASTM D189–65) is a means of determining the amount of carbon residue left on evaporating an oil under specified conditions and is intended to throw some light on the relative carbon-forming properties of an oil. The carbon-residue test was originally developed for comparison of the carbon-forming properties of lubricating oils for internal-combustion engines. The deposits vary with the type and mechanical condition of the engine, the service conditions, the time of continuous operation, the viscosity of the oil, and the character of the fuel. Modern refining methods and use of detergency additives tend to make this test less useful for predicting the carbon-forming tendency of a lubricating oil. The carbon-residue results are higher with additive-type oils because of the ash content of the additives.

The Ramsbottom carbon-residue test (ASTM D524–64) provides an indication of the coke-forming properties of petroleum products. Products containing ash-forming constituents will have erroneously high carbon-residue values. Results from the two methods are not comparable.

Ash. The ash determination (ASTM D482–63) of lubricating oil is used to measure undesirable impurities or contaminants and is limited to products which are free from ash-forming additives. Under prescribed conditions, the sample is ignited and allowed to burn until only ash and carbon remain; then the carbon residue is reduced to ash by heating.

Sulphated Ash from Lubricating Oils and Additives (ASTM D874–63). This test indicates the concentration of known metal-containing additives in unused oils and additive concentrates. Usually the additives contain one or more of the following metals: barium, calcium, magnesium, zinc, potassium, sodium, and tin. These may be in combination with one or more of the elements sulphur, phosphorus, and chlorine. Chemical analysis for metals in lubricating oils (ASTM D811–48) determines the barium, calcium, zinc, magnesium, tin, silica, sodium, aluminum, and potassium in new and used detergent-additive-type lubricating oils. Sulphur, phosphorus, and chlorine do not interfere in this method. These methods do not cover the determination of lead, copper, and iron.

Oxidation Testing Methods. Lubricating oils may be subjected to relatively high temperatures in the presence of air and catalytically active metals or metallic compounds. The process of oxidation becomes critical when oil is operating above 150 F. It is not uncommon to find lubricating oil sump temperatures in excess of 250 F. The rate of oxidation doubles for each 18 F rise in temperature of the oil above 150 F. The resultant oxidation of the oil develops increased viscosity, acids, carbon residue, sludge, and asphaltenes. There are numerous oxidation tests. The Navy work factor (U.S. Navy Bur. Ships, Federal Spec. VV-L-791, methods 345.12 and 3452) measures the stability of lubricating oils. The oxidation characteristics of inhibited steam-turbine oils are tested by method ASTM D943–54. The automotive industry uses the CRC L-38 high-temperature engine test for oxidation, bearing corrosion, and deposit service-performance ratings. To improve lubrication stability and engine performance by reducing oil oxidation effects such as thickening, formation of corrosive acids, varnish, and sludge deposits, antioxidant inhibitors are used. Additives that combat oxidation are usually complex organic chemical compounds containing phosphorus, zinc and/or sulphur.

Precipitation Number. Steam cylinder oils and black oils are checked by the (ASTM D91–61) precipitation number. This method is also applied to used crankcase oils of internal-combustion engines to check the oxidized products, carbonaceous matter, and asphaltenes formed through use.

Acid and Base Number and Corrosion. ASTM D664–58 method determines the acidic or basic constituents in lubricating oils. It also indicates the relative changes caused by oxidation during use. As an oil ages in service its acid number increases.

The acid number of used oil in no way indicates the corrosive action of the used oil in service. In some cases, an acid number of 1.0 may not attack the alloyed bearing metals; yet in other service tests of a different oil, 0.2 number will show high corrosive tendencies in short periods of operation.

Certain detergent additives used to counteract acidic bodies which cause deposits and corrosive wear are basic or alkaline. ASTM D664–58 is suitable to measure the basic constituents of many basic additive-type lubricating oils.

Certain phosphorus and sulphur additives are used to check corrosion in lubricating oils. The use of oiliness additives such as fatty oils in some instances may result in bearing corrosion especially where cadmium and certain alloy lead-base bearings are used.

Products, such as rust-proofing oils and similar compounds, which are used to protect metal surfaces from rusting or corrosion are generally required to pass special "weathering" tests. The tests measure the degree of protection afforded by the specimen under specified conditions such as salt-spray humidity cabinets, or immersion in water. Rust-preventing characteristics of steam-turbine oil in the presence of water is covered by ASTM D665–60.

Antifoam. The foam characteristics in crankcase, turbine, or circulating oils is checked by foaming test apparatus (ASTM D892–63). Certain additive oils tend to foam excessively in service. Only a minute quantity of antifoam inhibitor is required to break the air bubbles occurring in oil in service.

Oiliness. The property of lubrication known as oiliness is of considerable importance. It is a phenomenon that becomes strongly evident only when the oil film separating rubbing surfaces is exceedingly thin. In films of molecular dimensions, viscosity effects are negligible although oiliness has a marked bearing. Oiliness depends on both the lubricant and the surface to which it is attached. Oiliness is the property that causes a difference in the friction when lubricants of the same viscosity at the same temperature and pressure of the film are used with the same bearings.

Extreme-pressure Lubricants. The high tooth pressures and high rubbing velocities often encountered in hypoid and spur-type gearing have developed a class of lubricants called extreme-pressure or **hypoid-gear lubricants.** When mineral oils alone are used, metal-to-metal contact occurs which results in scoring, galling, and local seizure of the gear teeth. Most extreme-pressure lubricants are mineral oils containing active or passive held sulphur and/or chlorine or some highly reactive material. The important characteristics of extreme-pressure lubricants are ability to prevent galling or scoring; tendency to corrode; chemical stability; ability to reduce wear; ability to give low friction; and freedom from abrasive materials.

The SAE film-strength testing machine is used for checking extreme-pressure at high rubbing speeds and hypoid lubricants. This machine consists of a regular Timken bearing cup which rotates in contact with a second bearing cup at various speeds and rates of slippage. The passenger-car hypoid-gear lubricants have higher load-carrying capacity at high speeds. The truck-type hypoid lubricant is built for high torque. The API multipurpose gear lubricant is recommended for spiral-bevel and hypoid type differentials of passenger cars and trucks. U.S. Mil. Spec. MIL-L-2105 covers such a product.

ANIMAL, VEGETABLE, AND FISH OILS

Properties of Various Lubricating Fats and Fatty Oils. Fatty or fixed oils, such as animal, vegetable, and fish oils, are distinguished from mineral oils by being saponifiable with caustic alkalies. These organic oils oxidize, becoming rancid and setting free fatty acids. Oxidation also causes gumming, particularly with cottonseed and corn oil. Subjected to high temperatures they tend to decompose to corrosive acids.

Saponification Number. The saponification number (ASTM D94–62) is used to determine the percentage of fatty oil or fat in a compounded petroleum lubricant. When the sample contains appreciable amounts of sulphur, phosphorus, and halogens, the saponification number obtained will be greater for the amount of fatty matter actually present. The percentage of fatty oil (or fat) in a compounded petroleum product can be calculated from the saponification number when the fatty oil is known (see Table 1). Unless the saponification number is known, commercial practice uses a value 195 for calculation. The saponification number is the best obtainable index of the percentage of fat or fatty oil in a given lubricant.

The addition of fatty oils or fat to a petroleum mineral oil increases the adsorbed film on the working surface, which raises the load-carrying ability, or "oiliness," of the oil film, a property needed in special applications where boundary lubrication conditions are likely to be encountered. All animal, vegetable, and fish oils will support bacteria; care should be taken to see that such oils are sterile.

Table 1. Typical Properties of Some Animal, Vegetable, and Fish Oils

(Commonly used in compounded petroleum products)

	Free fatty acid or oleic, percent	Specific gravity at 60 F	Saponification number	ASTM pour point, deg F	Flash, open cup, deg F	Viscosity Saybolt sec @ 100 F	Price, cents per lb
Blown rapeseed	4–9	0.968	198–215	40	460	800–900	25
Castor, hydrogenated	0.15–2	0.963	178–181	15	505	1,485	21
Corn	1–10	0.922	189–192	14	480	180–190	17
Cottonseed	1–3	0.922	187–197	40	580	180–195	16
Degras, common	15–25	0.951	95–120	65	520	175–190*	11
Lard oil, prime	1.5–2	0.915	192–198	35	460	200–210	14
Lard No. 1	15–18	0.915	192–198	50	440	200–210	10
Neat's foot	10–12	0.915	193–204	40	440	200–210	16
Porpoise jaw	......	0.925	269–273	0	415	80–85	$15
Rosin, kidney	......	0.990	70–90	25	270	220–230	9
Sperm, 45 NW	1–2	0.880	120–140	45	550	95–105	15
Tallow, acidless	0.2–0.5	0.927	193–198	80	610	205–215	10
200 Vis. neutral, 95 VI	0	0.890	0.30	15	410	200–210	3

* At 210 F; it is semisolid at 100 F.

GREASES

The ASTM defines grease as ". . . a solid to semifluid product of dispersion of a thickening agent in a liquid lubricant. Other ingredients imparting special properties may be included." The majority of greases are soap-thickened. Soaps result from the chemical reaction of fats or fatty acids with alkali. The type of soap used plays an important role in determining the properties of the grease, as does the proportion of lubricant to thickener. The method of manufacture also influences the characteristics of the finished grease. Alkalies used in grease manufacture are usually calcium, sodium, lithium, barium, aluminum, and lead; fats may be of animal, vegetable, or fish source.

The **synthetic-type greases** contain synthetic oily materials in place of the usual petroleum oil. Because of their high cost, these are only used where their unique properties are required.

The **non-soap** or **solid-thickened greases** use finely divided solids such as graphite, clay, talc, asbestos, and molybdenum disulphide in place of soap as the thickening agent.

Additives may also be used to give improved characteristics, *e.g.*, extreme-pressure characteristics, better rust protection, and greater oxidation resistance.

The ASTM **dropping point** of grease is the temperature at which it changes from a semisolid to a liquid state when the determination is made according to the prescribed

ASTM D566–64. Calcium- or lime-soap greases have melting points below 200 F; for dropping points of 300 F or higher sodium-soap and for 400 F or less lithium greases.

The ASTM method (D217–65T) is used in measuring the worked or the unworked **consistency** of lubricating greases which have a worked consistency less than 400. In this test, a standardized double-pitch cone is allowed to drop in the product as a definite temperature. The depth of penetration is measured. The unworked (original) consistency of lubricating greases is affected by the soap content, the kind of fat used, the method of manufacture, the final water content, the rate of cooling, and the basic metallic constituent of the soap. It is impractical to control the consistency of a grease to narrow limits. Any working or remelting of a grease after it is in the container will change the consistency. Although many tests are based on the unworked consistency, this property bears no definite relationship to worked values. Final tests are usually based on worked consistency (ASTM) where possible although hard railroad greases and sodium-soap greases are tested for unworked consistency.

The texture of a grease refers to its structure such as smooth, fibrous, spongy, or rubbery. Calcium-base greases are smooth, soda-soap greases are fibrous or spongy, and aluminum-soap greases are stringy or rubbery.

Grease Numbers. Greases falling within certain consistency readings are classified in accordance with numbers of National Lubricating Grease Institute (NLGI) as follows:

Consistency No.	000	00	0	1	2	3	4	5	6
Appearance......	Semifluid	Semifluid	Semifluid	Soft	Medium	Medium hard	Hard	Very hard	Block type
Work penetration.	445–475	400–430	355–385	310–340	265–295	220–250	175–205	130–160	85–115

The ASTM methods (D128–64) of **analysis** permit determination of the constituents of grease likely to be covered by specifications. Such constituents are soap base and content, fat, water, fillers, ash, excess alkali or acid, unsaponifiable matter, and lubricating-oil content. Two greases showing the same analysis may show marked differences in lubricating performance and storage-stability properties. The sodium and lithium soap greases are more stable over much longer periods of service than calcium-base greases. The calcium base greases are water-resistant. The ASTM D942–50 method is used to determine the oxidation stability of lubrication greases (see Table 2).

Mineral additives such as graphite, talc, asbestos, carbon black, mica, lead naphthenate, and zinc powder are added to greases for special types of applications.

Synthetic Fluids. Synthetic lubricants are man-made, as opposed to naturally occurring petroleum fluids. Generally, the synthetics are organic chemicals. Certain groups have been found to have characteristics which make them suitable as lubricants. They often have outstanding properties, such as high viscosity index or thermal stability. The favorable characteristic is usually accompanied by one or more undesirable properties, such as low viscosity, high pour point, or low stability toward water. Some classes of synthetics are polyolefins, polyalkylene glycols, esters, silicones, polyphenol ethers, and halogenated hydrocarbons.

Synthetic lubricants, because of high cost, are only used where the particular property is essential, as in instruments, hydraulic systems, heat-transfer systems, and numerous speciality applications. The development of synthetics was initiated in the aircraft industry especially for the high speeds and high operating temperatures of jet aircraft. As with other lubricants, the basic synthetic fluid is often compounded with modifiers to improve or to impart special properties to the complete lubricant.

The **API Service Classification** includes three types for gasoline and three for Diesel engines. Aircraft engines are not included.

Service MS. Service typical of gasoline or other spark-ignition engines used under unfavorable or severe operating conditions, and where there are special lubrication requirements for deposit, wear, or bearing corrosion control, because of operating conditions, engine design, or fuel characteristics.

Service MM. Service typical of gasoline and other spark-ignition engines used under moderate to severe operating conditions, but presenting problems of deposit or bearing corrosion control when crankcase-oil temperatures are high.

Service ML. Service typical of gasoline and other spark-ignition engines used under light and favorable operating conditions, the engines having no special lubrication requirements and having no design characteristics sensitive to deposit formation.

Service DS. Service typical of Diesel engines operating under very severe conditions or having design characteristics or using fuel tending to produce excessive wear or deposits.

Service DM. Service typical of Diesel engines operating under severe conditions or using fuel of a type normally tending to promote deposits and wear, but where there are design characteristics or operating conditions which may make the engine either less sensitive to fuel effects or more sensitive to residues from lubricating oil.

Service DG. Service typical of Diesel engines in any operation where there are no severe requirements for wear or deposit control because of fuel, lubricating oil, or engine design characteristics.

Table 2. General Characteristics of Greases

Soap base	Texture	Dropping point (approx)	Maximum continuous usable temperature	Effect of water	Primary uses
Calcium	Buttery to smooth	200–225 F	175 F	Resistant	General purpose industrial lubricant for plain bearing and line shafting.
Sodium	Fibrous or smooth	350–450 F	260 F	Susceptible	Ball and roller bearings over wide speed and temperature range, automobile wheel bearings, universal joints, spring shackles.
Mixed base, sodium-calcium	Fairly buttery to fibrous	345 F	250 F	Susceptible	All types of ball and roller bearings, and special applications at both high and low temperatures, depending upon composition.
Lithium	Buttery to stringy	375 F	300 F	Resistant	Aircraft lubrication at temperatures from −100 to +300 F, and many applications in automotive and industrial use.
Aluminum	Some buttery, some stringy, but never fibrous	200 F	150 F	Resistant	Special applications where resistance to centrifugal force or adhesiveness is desired.

LUBRICATION

Internal-combustion-engine oils are required to carry out numerous functions in order to provide adequate lubrication. Crankcase oils, in addition to reducing friction and wear, may keep the engine clean and free from rust and corrosion, may act as a coolant and sealant, and may serve as a hydraulic oil in an engine with hydraulic valve lifters. The lubricant may function under high temperatures and in the presence of dust, water, and other adverse atmospheric conditions as well as with materials formed as a result of incomplete combustion; it must be resistant to oxidation and sludge formation.

Therefore, crankcase oils are compounded and may contain one or more necessary agents and additives, such as **dispersants** to keep insoluble materials suspended; **detergents** to clean mildly or deter deposit formation; **viscosity-index improvers** to increase the viscosity so that it is more, in proportion, at 210 F than at 100 F; **oxidation inhibitors** to decompose peroxides, inhibit free radical formation, and passivate exposed metal; **corrosion inhibitors** to neutralize acid materials and form protective films on metal surfaces; **metal deactivators** to form inactive protective films; **antiwear, extreme-pressure, oiliness, film-strength agents** to form film of lower shear strength than the base metals to reduce friction and prevent welding and seizure if and when the oil film is ruptured; **rust inhibitors** to provide protective, water-repellent films; **pour-point dispersants** to prevent or inhibit growth of wax crystals at reduced temperatures; **foam inhibitors** to reduce surface tension and allow air bubbles to separate more readily.

Gasoline-engine operational severity depends upon design and running conditions. Over a long period, the trend has been toward higher compression, increased displacement, and higher power with decreased engine size, and operating conditions may vary from prolonged high speed and high load under high-temperature conditions to excessive idling at low load and low temperatures. As a result, there is a trend toward increased service severity.

Diesel-engine service severity depends first upon power requirements. High continuous power output and overload at high temperature and intermittent power demands at low temperature represent severe conditions. Continuous or intermittent operation at rated load and normal temperatures is considered normal Diesel operation. Diesel engines normally operate at lower speeds but higher temperatures than gasoline engines; hence conditions are more conducive to oil oxidation, deposit formation, and corrosion of bearing metals. Engine design, including degree of supercharging, influences susceptibility to deposits, ring sticking, wear, and bearing corrosion. Harmful products of incomplete combustion promote wear and deposit formation; the situation is greatly magnified by low-temperature operation. The oils which perform most satisfactorily in a given engine under each service classification can be selected with certainty only after a series of performance tests.

Aircraft-engine oils, because of the necessity of starting at low temperatures, require a low-viscosity, low-pour-point oil. However, the same oil must also provide satisfactory lubrication at warmed-up engine conditions. Oils for aircraft **reciprocating engines** usually have a minimum viscosity index of 95 and viscosities of 90 to 100 SSU at 210 F. For operation at extremely low temperatures, oils having viscosities down to 65 SSU at 210 F are used. Aircraft **turbine engines,** because of their high operating temperatures and low-temperature starting requirements, employ synthetic-type fluids, usually considered to be operable at bulk temperatures of 300 F, or even as high as 450 F. The fluids must be pumpable at −65 F, have low volatility, good oxidation, and thermal stability at elevated temperatures, be non-corrosive to engine metals, and have adequate gear-load-carrying ability. Specifications require these lubricants to pass stringent static turbine-engine tests and also in-flight tests prior to approval.

Marine internal-combustion engines are generally run at high speed for sustained periods and are exposed to salt-water spray which introduces rust-corrosion problems more severe than those encountered in land vehicles. Heavy-duty oils having detergent, dispersant, and rust-protective qualities are desirable.

Steam turbines are usually lubricated with oils of 150 to 250 SSU viscosity at 100 F. In high-speed turbines with reduction gearing, because of the gearing, the entire system—turbine, reduction gears, and generator—is lubricated with oil having viscosity in the range of 250 to 350 SSU.

Usually turbine and generator bearings, the governor, and other auxiliaries are lubricated with the same oil which serves as the fluid in the control system. To accomplish adequately its numerous functions over an extended period, the lubricant usually contains additives which provide oxidation stability, rust and corrosion protection, and foam resistance. Equipment may also be provided to maintain the lubricant in a clean condition by removing water, sludge, and foreign materials. This purification may be accomplished with settling tanks, centrifuging, or filtering. Where filters are employed, they should be of such a nature as not to remove oil additives. The lubricating system should be designed to reduce all possible contamination, especially water.

In **steam-cylinder lubrication,** the lubricant is distributed to the cylinder walls or valve surfaces by the steam, which has been impregnated with oil from a lubricator. Every sliding surface in direct contact with steam or subject to its pressure and temperature must be lubricated. Steam-cylinder oil must be of comparatively heavy body and good wettability so that the lubricant will cling to the surfaces and resist washing off by the steam. Generally, the oils used have a viscosity between 100 and 220 SSU at 210 F, depending upon the steam pressure and temperature involved, the type of valving, and the method of lubricant application. The more complete the atomization and the more thorough the oil dispersion in the steam, the better the lubrication and the more economical the oil consumption.

The choice of lubricant and the amount of oil are influenced by the use to which the exhaust steam is put. In marine service, where condensate is recovered for boiler feed, straight mineral oils are usually selected.

Gears are of so many different designs and are used in such a variety of applications with so many different operating conditions that many diverse lubricants have been developed. The gear lubricant may serve a multiple function, such as removing heat and lubricating other machine elements. Selection of the gear lubricant is influenced by the gear type and materials, speed and corresponding sliding velocities, tooth contact and load, environment, temperatures, method of lubricant application, seals, and type of service.

Under moderate-speed and light-load conditions, straight mineral oils may be satisfactory. As operating severity in particular loads increases, extreme-pressure additives are required. Also, one or more modifiers may be employed to improve oxidation stability and service life or to impart other particular qualities. (See p. 8–154.)

Lubricants for open gears will have special adhesive properties to keep the lubricant on the tooth contact surfaces. In such service, the lubricant may be applied by brush or paddle or by spraying.

Where fluid lubricants would be vaporized or where the heat-transport properties are not essential, dry lubricants may be effective. Where leakage from the gear case could be a factor or with a self-contained sealed unit, greases may be employed.

Aircraft applications often impose severe restrictions, especially where a wide range of operating temperatures may be involved. Aircraft turbine oils of low viscosity because of starting or power requirements at low temperatures may also be required to lubricate high-speed, heavily loaded gears.

Enclosed gears use splash or pressure systems and must be kept free of grit or dust. The viscosities usually used range from 300 to 2,500 SSU at 100 F. The oil must flow at the lowest temperatures encountered.

Refrigeration-machinery lubricant selection must take into consideration the effect on parts not requiring lubrication as well as on the bearing surfaces. Oil, when miscible with the refrigerant, will coat the heat-transfer surfaces, restrict refrigerant flow, and impair performance. It is important that the lubricant remain fluid at the lowest operating temperatures; a low pour point, usually −35 F max, is indicated. Wax separation, referred to as **floc,** must be avoided. In any system operating below 32 F, the presence of water is objectionable because of ice formation in critical areas. Presence of water may also contribute to corrosion with certain refrigerants. High dielectric constant of the oil is indicative of low water content; care in handling and storage and delivery in sealed containers reduce the possibilities of moisture. The presence of unstable materials in the lubricant leads to sludge formation. To prevent undue carry-over into the refrigeration circuit, the lubricant should neither vaporize excessively nor foam unduly. Where refrigeration systems operate below 5 F, a viscosity of 150 SSU at 100 F is recommended; for systems operating above 5 F, 200 to 300 SSU. Compressor design, refrigerant type, and other factors influence lubricant choice. (See also Sec. 18.)

Compressors, particularly air compressors, are essential in many industries, and numerous types and special designs are used. All compressors have bearings—journal, sleeve, or rolling-element—which may be operated at high speeds and high temperatures in the presence of the compressor gas. Most frequently, oil is used as the bearing lubricant, but where atmospheric contaminants can reach the bearings, greases may be more effective in sealing the bearing elements.

In **reciprocating compressors,** valving and porting are exposed to hot gases. Excessive cylinder lubrication may lead to carbon formation at the valves or ports. Accumulation of oil in intercoolers, lines, and receivers where oxygen-containing gases are being compressed enhances the opportunity for explosion and severe damage.

Viscosity at the compression conditions is probably the most important property for the lubricants of reciprocating-compressor piston rings and cylinders. Effective air-filtration systems are essential in keeping contaminants and moisture from causing excessive wear and disrupted lubrication.

Lubricating oils for compressors include straight mineral oils, turbine oils with oxidation and corrosion additives, and heavy-duty engine oils containing oxidation and detergent-dispersant additives. Where gearing is involved, compounded gear oils may be required. (See also Sec. 14.)

Textile machinery has a wide variety of lubrication requirements—even within the same unit, which may have many different mechanisms. A unit may operate with plain bearings (*e.g.*, metal or plastic), rolling-element bearings, cams, gears, worms, spindles, sleeves, and chains. Often these parts operate at high speeds and high temperatures, with different methods of application, in dusty or moist atmospheres, with seals, and with intermittent or rapidly changing loads and motions. Some of the elements may require low-viscosity lubricants for low power consumption and small clearances. Other parts of the same machine may require high-viscosity lubricants with special properties such as adhesive and load-carrying abilities. Precision parts, very accurately finished, may require special corrosion and oxidation resistance. One lubricant property unique to the textile industry is that where the possibility of the lubricant's contacting the fabric exists, the lubricant must not stain or should at least be readily removable.

Electric-motor and generator bearings, plain or rolling-element type, are either oil- or grease-lubricated. The oils used either are straight mineral or have antirust, antioxidant inhibitors, with viscosities in the range from 150 to 360 SSU at 100 F. Grease-lubricated units use either sodium or lithium of No. 1 or No. 2 grade. The trend in lubricating electric motors is to grease-lubricate the bearing at manufacture for the life of the motor. The prelubrication is often done by the bearing manufacturer. Relubrication, if required, is done by disassembling the motor, washing the bearing, and repacking. Lubricating these bearings with a grease gun is not good practice since the quantity applied to the bearing, which is often shielded, is not controllable and overlubrication may result.

Pivot and Jewel Bearings. Oils used for pivot bearings in instruments are of low volatility and are usually synthetic-base oils with additive materials to impart oxidation-stability and corrosion-protective properties. The viscosity range is 52 to 60 SSU at 130 F and of very high VI and sub-zero pour point when used in aircraft instruments. The jewel-instrument bearing lubricant is a non-spreading oil and is for use at normal and sub-zero temperatures. Its chemical composition is best described by Navy Bur. of Aeronautics Spec. 14L16 (Aer).

Ball and Roller Bearings. (See also p. 8–186 *et seq.*) The term **antifriction bearings** has become synonymous with rolling-element (ball and roller) bearings. Types include tapered and spherical roller bearings, needle bearings, muliple-row roller and ball bearings, deep-groove bearings. Sizes range from miniature, 0.059 in. O.D., to diameters measured in feet. The wide acceptance of these bearings is partially attributable to their low friction; and friction is little affected by speed, load, and temperature. Their low static friction recommends their selection where low starting torque is sought. They are well suited for heavy loads at low speeds.

The primary motion is rolling, but sliding occurs, in assemblies employing separators, between (1) the rolling elements and the separator, and (2) the separator and races. Shearing of the lubricant film also contributes to the over-all friction. The lubricant consequently serves several functions: (1) to lubricate the sliding contacts, (2) to provide cooling, (3) to prevent rusting of highly finished surfaces, (4) to prevent scuffing and wear, and (5) to serve as a seal against moisture and dirt.

A general rule is to use the lowest-viscosity lubricant which can be retained in the bearing, of course taking into account operating speeds and temperature. The choice of grease or oil as a lubricant is influenced by (1) temperature, (2) speed, (3) load, (4) method of application, (5) sealing, (6) bearing size, and (7) type of service.

Oil lubrication is generally recommended where high-temperature, high-speed operation requires cooling and circulation. Greases permit the use of simplified lubrication and "sealed-for-life" designs, with accompanying reduced maintenance. Grease applications are used successfully in many places where oil previously had been considered essential.

Oil for ball- and roller-bearing lubrication must be resistant to degradation. If conditions indicate, additives may be used for rust protection, oxidation inhibition, extreme pressure, detergency, and other special properties. The viscosity of the oil depends upon the seals, the speed, and the operating temperatures. Methods of oil supply include spray or mist, oil jet, or more commonly, bath, drip, or pressure feed. The oil level in a bearing should be maintained as low as possible to reduce lubricant churning.

The selection of a suitable grease depends upon load, speed, temperature, method of application, presence of moisture, and bearing-housing design. The mineral-oil, soap-type greases most frequently used are sodium, calcium, sodium and calcium mixed, and lithium. Sodium-soap greases find wide use in automotive wheel bearings, home appliances, and industrial machinery. Calcium greases generally have excellent resistance to water and are favored as industrial and steel-mill greases. Sodium-calcium greases vary greatly in their characteristics, depending upon composition, but they generally have good water resistance and are widely used.

Lubrication Systems. There are many positive methods of applying products to ensure proper lubrication. Bath and circulating systems may be automatic to provide steady or intermittent but positive application as required. There are constant-level lubricators, bottle oilers, gravity-feed oilers, multiple-sight feeds, grease cups, forced-feed lubricators, centralized lubrication systems, and air-mist lubricators (to name a few). The selection of the method of application of lubricant is as important as the lubricant itself. The choice of device and the complexity of the system depend upon many factors, including the type and quantity of the lubricant, the reliability and value of the machine elements, maintenance schedules, accessibility of the lubrication points, and labor costs and other economic considerations, as well as the operating conditions.

Additives. Many industrial oils are enhanced or modified with additives, usually chemical compounds which will improve some inherent property or impart new characteristics. In general, lubricant modifiers fall in two general classes: (1) those that affect a physical characteristic, such as viscosity index or pour point; and (2) those whose ultimate influence is chemical in nature, such as oxidation and corrosion inhibitors or detergents. Additives do not transform poor-quality lubricants into high-quality products; it is necessary to start with quality lubricants. Additives in industrial oils are similar to those used in automotive and other engine oils, taking into account generally different levels of temperature and other operating conditions. Table 3 lists some of the common industrial applications and the additives used in the formulation of lubricants.

Metal-cutting fluids have two basic functions: (1) as coolants, and (2) as lubricants. They cool the tool to reduce abrasive wear and loss of hardness, and they cool the work to prevent distortion and dimensional inaccuracies. They lubricate the chip-tool interface to reduce frictional heat, tool wear, and power consumption and to improve surface finish. They prevent welding of metal to the tool point, causing rough surfaces on the work piece by the repeated sloughing off of built-up edge. The cutting fluids also serve to flush away chips and debris from the work and to protect the machined surfaces, tools, and machines from rusting.

Cutting fluids are either (1) cutting oils or (2) soluble oil emulsions. The former are the more effective lubricants; the latter are primarily coolants.

The selection of the most appropriate cutting fluid is complicated and should consider many factors. The motion of the chip over the tool face is essentially that of any surface moving over another at high velocity under high pressure. The type of metal and the sliding conditions determine the type of lubricant best suited to reducing friction. In the machining operation, many combinations of tools and workpieces and operating conditions may exist, resulting in many lubrication and lubricant requirements. In some cases, a straight mineral oil will suffice; in others, mildly compounded oils are used; while in most severe conditions, highly compounded oils are needed.

The effectiveness of compounds depends mainly on chemical activity, and the freshly formed, highly reactive surfaces combined with high temperatures and pressures at contact points are ideal for chemical reactions. Compounding agents include fatty oils, sulphur, sulphurized fatty oils, and sulphurized and chlorinated additives. These agents act to form metallic compounds, metal chlorides, or sulphides, or to form metallic soaps which reduce friction and impart penetrating and wettability qualities, oiliness, or strong or tacky films.

In all aspects, cutting fluids have been improved over the years, but possibly most progress has been in the development of transparent cutting oils. The transparent oil allows the operator to observe the machining operation, allows easy inspection of parts, and has a favorable psychological effect because of the apparent general cleanliness. It is now possible to incorporate high compounding and still retain transparency.

Water is a most effective coolant, while mineral oils are not among the best fluids in this respect. Since straight water can seldom, if ever, be employed as an effective cutting fluid, the combination of **oil and water in a stable emulsion** utilizes the effective cooling of the water with some of the benefits of the oil. Various combinations of

Table 3. Industrial Applications and Their Additive Requirements

Additives	Turbines	Hydraulics	Gear boxes			General purpose no drip	Electric motor	Spindles Machine tools	Ways	Internal-combustion engines	Steam engines and pumps	Circulating systems	Air compressors
			Worm	Hypoid	Other								
Antirust	x	x		x	x		x	x		x		x	x
Anticorrosion	x	x	x	x	x		x	x	x	x	x	x	x
Antioxidant	x	x					x			x		x	
Pour depressant		x	x	x	x		x			x			
Antifoam	x	x	x	x	x		x	x		x		x	
Detergent										x			
Fatty oils			x								x		
Extreme pressure			x	x					x				
Tackiness						x							

lubricating and cooling properties can be imparted by varying the ratio of water to soluble oil.

For two non-soluble liquids to form a mixture, an **emulsifier** must be added. In addition to their effectiveness as coolants, soluble oils may provide rust protection, detergency, and extreme-pressure properties. Water hardness is an important consideration in the forming of an emulsion, and protection against bacteria growth must be provided. A certain amount of care in handling will also ensure more satisfactory performance. Overheating and excessive air mixing, contamination, and continued freezing and thawing should all be avoided. (See also Sec. 13.)

Specifications. Gravity, flash point, carbon residue, and neutralization number (see p. 6–247) are of little value for indicating the performance of an oil, although in the past they were used in the selection of the type or source of the oil. The introduction of new refining methods and additives permits the manufacture of high-quality oils from low-grade crudes. Functional tests have taken the place of the earlier tests. The U.S. Army and Navy and many equipment manufacturers have set up specifications incorporating service performance tests. Basic requirements of some of the U.S. military specifications are listed in Table 4. The work-factor test is conducted in a bearing wherein the rating depends on the change in properties of the oil during the test. In case other functional test data are required the fact is noted under Special Provisions in which case the specification in question should be consulted for further details.

Table 4. Basic Requirements of Some U.S. Military Oil Specifications

	Military symbol	Saybolt Viscosity seconds 130 F	Saybolt Viscosity seconds 210 F	Pour point, deg F max	Fixed oil, per-cent	Work fac-tor	Special provisions
Aircraft reciprocating (piston) engine oils (MIL-L-6082C)...	1065	....	62–68	0	None	Yes	100 VI min
	1100	....	93–103	+10	None	Yes	95 VI min
General-purpose oils (engine and machine and general-purpose industrial oils) (MIL-L-15106A)...	2075	70–90	....	−10	None	Yes	No
	2110	90–120	....	0	None	Yes	No
	2135	120–145	....	0	None	Yes	No
	2190	185–205	....	35	None	Yes	No
	2250	245–280	....	35	None	Yes	No
Hydraulic and light turbine oils (non-corrosive) (MIL-L-17672B)...	2075TH	....	40–43	−20	None	No	Yes
	2110TH	....	43–48	−10	None	No	Yes
	2135TH	120–145	48–51	0	None	No	Yes
Turbine oil (non-corrosive) (MIL-L-17331D)...	2190T	53 min	....	20	None	Yes	Yes
Force-feed oils for general-purpose (MIL-L-15016A)...	3042	....	40–44	0	None	Yes	100 VI min
	3050	....	45–55	0	None	Yes	75 VI min
	3065	....	60–70	5	None	Yes	75 VI min
	3080	....	75–90	15	None	Yes	65 VI min
	3100	....	90–105	25	None	Yes	65 VI min
	3120	....	115–125	30	None	Yes	65 VI min
	3150	....	140–160	30	None	Yes	95 VI min
Compounded marine-engine oil (MIL-L-15019C)...	4065	....	65–80	10	10–20	No	Wick test emulsion
Mineral steam-engine cylinder oils (MIL-L-15018B)...	5150	....	135–165	60	None	Yes	No
	5190	....	180–220	60	None	Yes	No
	5230	....	220–240	60	None	Yes	90 VI min
Compounded steam cylinder oils (MIL-L-15019C)...	6135	....	120–150	60	5–7	No	Tallow
	7105	....	95–110	40	9–10	No	Lard or tallow
	8190	....	180–200	35	2–4	No	Lard or tallow
Navy Diesel-engine oils (heavy-duty or DM) detergent and inhibitor additive-type (MIL-L-9000E)...	9110	....	44 min	−20	None	No	Yes
	9170	....	50–58	0	None	No	Yes
	9250	....	66–72	10	None	No	Yes
	9500	....	85–110	15	None	No	Yes
Performance-tested army motor oils (heavy-duty for MS or DM service) (MIL-L-2104B)...	OE10	....	44–50	−20	None	No	Yes
	OE30	....	58–70	0	None	No	Yes
	OE50	....	85–110	15	None	No	Yes

SECTION 7

FUELS AND FURNACES

BY

L. L. NEWMAN, Chief Coal Technologist, Bureau of Mines.
W. A. LEECH, JR., Consulting Engineer, Swindell-Dresser Company.
M. H. MAWHINNEY, Consulting Engineer, Salem, Ohio.
C. R. VELZY, President, Charles R. Velzy Associates, New York.
C. O. VELZY, Secretary-Treasurer, Charles R. Velzy Associates.
A. J. TIGGES, Consultant, General Public Utilities Corporation.
HILMER KARLSSON, Consultant, The Air Preheater Company, Inc.
W. E. LEWIS, Manager-Field Sales, Lectromelt Furnace Division, McGraw-Edison Company.

CONTENTS

FUELS

BY

Staff, Bureau of Mines
U.S. Department of the Interior
Prepared under the direction of L. L. Newman

COAL

By W. H. Ode

REFERENCES: Bibliography of Bureau of Mines Investigations of Coal and Its Products, 1910–1960, *B of M Inf. Circ.* 8049. ASTM, "Standards on Gaseous Fuels, Coal and Coke." Lowry, "Chemistry of Coal Utilization," Wiley. "Steam—Its Generation and Use," Babcock & Wilcox Co. deLorenzi, "Combustion Engineering," Combustion-Engineering, Inc. Johnson and Auth, "Fuel and Combustion Handbook," McGraw-Hill.

Coal is a complex substance consisting of the metamorphosed remains of ancient vegetation, with an origin similar to the peat deposits of today. During past geological ages, these deposits of vegetation were changed by biochemical action, submersion, pressure, and heat into various ranks of coal. Because of variations in the degree of metamorphic change from the original plant material, coal is not a uniform substance, and no two coals are ever absolutely the same in every respect.

Classification

Coal may be classified in various ways: by rank, by variety, by size, and sometimes by use.

Coals are classified by **rank,** *i.e.*, according to their degree of metamorphism, or progressive alteration, in the natural series from lignite to anthracite. Table 1 shows the classification of coals by rank adopted as standard by the ASTM. The basic scheme of classification by this system is according to fixed carbon and heating value calculated to the *mineral-matter-free* (mm-free) basis. The higher-rank coals are classified according to fixed carbon on the dry basis, and the lower-rank coals according to heating value (Btu) on the moist basis. **Agglomerating** character is used to differentiate between certain adjacent groups. Coals are considered agglomerating if, in a test to determine the amount of volatile matter, they produce either a coherent button that will support a 500-g weight without pulverizing or a button that shows swelling or cell structure.

For classifying coals according to rank, fixed carbon and Btu are calculated to the mm-free basis by using either the Parr formulas, Eqs. (**1**) to (**3**), or the approximation formulas, Eqs. (**4**) to (**6**). In case of litigation, the appropriate Parr formula is used.

Parr formulas:

$$\text{Dry, mm-free F.C.} = \frac{\text{F.C.} - 0.15S}{100 - (M + 1.08A + 0.55S)} \times 100 \tag{1}$$

$$\text{Dry, mm-free V.M.} = 100 - \text{dry, mm-free F.C.} \tag{2}$$

$$\text{Moist, mm-free Btu} = \frac{\text{Btu} - 50S}{100 - (1.08A + 0.55S)} \times 100 \tag{3}$$

Approximation formulas:

$$\text{Dry, mm-free F.C.} = \frac{\text{F.C.}}{100 - (M + 1.1A + 0.1S)} \times 100 \tag{4}$$

$$\text{Dry, mm-free V.M.} = 100 - \text{dry, mm-free F.C.} \tag{5}$$

$$\text{Moist, mm-free Btu} = \frac{\text{Btu}}{100 - (1.1A + 0.1S)} \times 100 \tag{6}$$

Table 1. Classification of Coals by Rank (ASTM D388)[a]

Class	Group	Fixed-carbon limits, percent (dry, mineral-matter-free basis)		Volatile-matter limits, percent (dry, mineral-matter-free basis)		Calorific value limits, Btu per pound (moist,[b] mineral-matter-free basis)		Agglomerating character
		Equal or greater than	Less than	Greater than	Equal or less than	Equal or greater than	Less than	
I. Anthracitic	1. Meta-anthracite	98	...	...	2			Non-agglomerating[c]
	2. Anthracite	92	98	2	8			
	3. Semianthracite	86	92	8	14	....	......	
II. Bituminous	1. Low-volatile bituminous coal	78	86	14	22	......	......	Commonly agglomerating[e]
	2. Medium volatile bituminous coal	69	78	22	31	......	......	
	3. High-volatile A bituminous coal	...	69	31	...	14,000[d]	......	
	4. High-volatile B bituminous coal	...	...	...	...	13,000[d]	14,000	
	5. High-volatile C bituminous coal	...	...	...	...	{ 11,500	13,000	
						10,500	11,500	Agglomerating
III. Subbituminous	1. Subbituminous A coal	...	...	...	...	10,500	11,500	Non-agglomerating
	2. Subbituminous B coal	...	...	...	...	9,500	10,500	
	3. Subbituminous C coal	...	...	...	...	8,300	9,500	
IV. Lignitic	1. Lignite A	...	...	...	...	6,300	8,300	
	2. Lignite B	...	...	...	...	....	6,300	

[a] This classification does not include a few coals, principally non-banded varieties, which have unusual physical and chemical properties and which come within the limits of fixed-carbon or calorific value of the high-volatile bituminous and subbituminous ranks. All of these coals either contain less than 48 percent dry, mineral-matter-free fixed carbon or have more than 15,500 moist, mineral-matter-free British thermal units per pound.

[b] Moist refers to coal containing its natural inherent moisture but not including visible water on the surface of the coal.

[c] If agglomerating, classify in low-volatile group of the bituminous class.

[d] Coals having 69 percent or more fixed carbon on the dry, mineral-matter-free basis shall be classified according to fixed carbon, regardless of calorific value.

[e] It is recognized that there may be non-agglomerating varieties in these groups of the bituminous class, and there are notable exceptions in high-volatile C bituminous group.

Table 2. Sources and Analyses of Various Ranks of Coal

Classification by rank	State	County	Bed	Condition*	Proximate, percent				Ultimate, percent					Calorific value, Btu per lb
					Moisture	Volatile matter	Fixed carbon	Ash	Sulfur	Hydrogen	Carbon	Nitrogen	Oxygen	
Meta-anthracite	Rhode Island	Newport	Middle	1	13.2	2.6	65.3	18.9	0.3	1.9	64.2	0.2	14.5	9,310
				2		2.9	75.3	21.8	0.3	0.5	74.1	0.2	3.1	10,740
				3		3.8	96.2		0.4	0.6	94.7	0.3	4.0	13,720
Anthracite	Pennsylvania	Lackawanna	Clark	1	4.3	5.1	81.0	9.6	0.8	2.9	79.7	0.9	6.1	12,880
				2		5.3	84.6	10.1	0.8	2.5	83.3	0.9	2.4	13,470
				3		5.9	94.1		0.9	2.8	92.5	1.0	2.8	14,980
Semianthracite	Arkansas	Johnson	Lower Hartshorne	1	2.6	10.6	79.3	7.5	1.7	3.8	81.4	1.6	4.0	13,880
				2		10.8	81.5	7.7	1.8	3.6	83.6	1.6	1.7	14,240
				3		11.7	88.3		1.9	3.9	90.6	1.8	1.8	15,430
Low-volatile bituminous coal	West Virginia	Wyoming	Pocahontas No. 3	1	2.9	17.7	74.0	5.4	0.8	4.6	83.2	1.3	4.7	14,400
				2		18.2	76.3	5.5	0.8	4.4	85.7	1.3	2.3	14,830
				3		19.3	80.7		0.8	4.6	90.7	1.4	2.5	15,690
Medium-volatile bituminous coal	Pennsylvania	Clearfield	Upper Kittanning	1	2.1	24.4	67.4	6.1	1.0	5.0	81.6	1.4	4.9	14,310
				2		24.9	68.8	6.3	1.1	4.8	83.3	1.5	3.0	14,610
				3		26.5	73.5		1.1	5.2	88.9	1.6	3.2	15,590
High-volatile A bituminous coal	West Virginia	Marion	Pittsburgh	1	2.3	36.5	56.0	5.2	0.8	5.5	78.4	1.6	8.5	14,040
				2		37.4	57.2	5.4	0.8	5.4	80.2	1.6	6.6	14,370
				3		39.5	60.5		0.8	5.7	84.8	1.7	7.0	15,180
High-volatile B bituminous coal	Kentucky, western field	Muhlenburg	No. 9	1	8.5	36.4	44.3	10.8	2.8	5.4	65.1	1.3	14.6	11,680
				2		39.8	48.5	11.7	3.0	4.9	71.2	1.5	7.7	12,760
				3		45.0	55.0		3.4	5.5	80.6	1.7	8.8	14,460
High-volatile C bituminous coal	Illinois	Sangamon	No. 5	1	14.4	35.4	40.6	9.6	3.8	5.8	59.7	1.0	20.1	10,810
				2		41.4	47.4	11.2	4.4	4.9	69.8	1.2	8.5	12,630
				3		46.6	53.4		5.0	5.6	78.6	1.3	9.5	14,230
Subbituminous A coal	Wyoming	Sweetwater	No. 3	1	16.9	34.8	44.7	3.6	1.4	6.0	60.4	1.2	27.4	10,650
				2		41.8	53.8	4.4	1.7	4.9	72.7	1.5	14.8	12,810
				3		43.7	56.3		1.8	5.2	76.0	1.5	15.5	13,390

Table 2. Sources and Analyses of Various Ranks of Coal—*(Continued)*

Classification by rank	State	County	Bed	Condition*	Proximate, percent				Ultimate, percent					Calorific value, Btu per lb
					Moisture	Volatile matter	Fixed carbon	Ash	Sulfur	Hydrogen	Carbon	Nitrogen	Oxygen	
Subbituminous B coal	Wyoming	Sheridan	Monarch	1	22.2	33.2	40.3	4.3	0.5	6.9	53.9	1.0	33.4	9,610
				2		42.7	51.7	5.6	0.6	5.6	69.3	1.2	17.7	12,350
				3		45.2	54.8		0.6	6.0	73.4	1.3	18.7	13,080
Subbituminous C coal	Colorado	El Paso	Fox Hill	1	25.1	30.4	37.7	6.8	0.3	6.2	50.5	0.7	35.5	8,560
				2		40.6	50.3	9.1	0.4	4.6	67.4	1.0	17.5	11,430
				3		44.6	55.4		0.5	5.0	74.1	1.1	19.3	12,560
Lignite	North Dakota	McLean	Unnamed	1	36.8	27.8	29.5	5.9	0.9	6.9	40.6	0.6	45.1	7,000
				2		43.9	46.7	9.4	1.4	4.5	64.3	1.0	19.4	11,080
				3		48.4	51.6		1.6	5.0	70.9	1.1	21.4	12,230

* 1, sample as received; 2, moisture-free; 3, moisture- and ash-free.

where F.C. = percentage of fixed carbon, V.M. = percentage of volatile matter, M = percentage of moisture, A = percentage of ash, S = percentage of sulphur, all on a "moist" basis. "Moist" coal is coal that contains natural bed moisture but that does not have any visible water on its surface.

Figure 1 shows **representative proximate analyses and heating values** of various ranks of coal in the United States. The sources and analyses of the coals selected to represent the various ranks are given in Table 2. The analyses selected for the chart are calculated to an ash-free basis because ash in coal varies without regard to rank. The moisture contents of the coals represent the natural bed moisture. Figure 1 shows that the percentages of fixed carbon and the heating values, except for anthracite, increase from the lowest to the highest rank of coal as the percentages of volatile matter and bed moisture decrease.

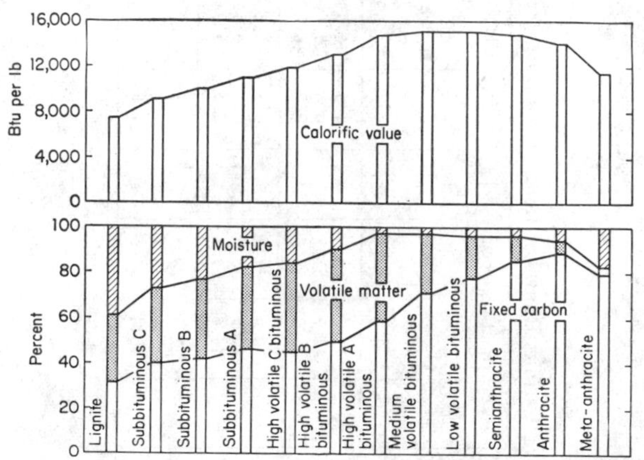

FIG. 1. Proximate analyses and heating values of various ranks of coal (ash-free basis).

Commercial varieties of coal, as defined by the ASTM (see ASTM "Standards on Coal and Coke"), are:

Common banded coal—the common variety of bituminous and subbituminous coal. It consists of a sequence of irregularly alternating layers or lenses of (1) homogenous black material having a brilliant vitreous luster; (2) grayish-black, less brilliant, striated material, usually of silky luster; and (3) generally thinner bands or lenses of soft, powdery, and fibrous particles of mineral charcoal. The difference in luster of the bands is greater in bituminous than in subbituminous coal.

Splint coal—a variety of bituminous or subbituminous coal, commonly having a dull luster and grayish-black color, of compact structure, often containing a few thin, irregular bands with vitreous luster. When struck, it is resonant. It is hard and tough and breaks with an irregular, rough, sometimes splintery fracture. It is free-burning and does not swell on heating.

Cannel coal—a variety of bituminous or subbituminous coal of uniform and compact, fine-grained texture with a general absence of banded structure. It is dark gray to black in color, has a greasy luster, and is noticeably of conchoidal or shell-like fracture. It is non-caking, yields a high percentage of volatile matter, ignites easily, and burns with a luminous, smoky flame.

Boghead coal—a variety of bituminous or subbituminous coal resembling cannel coal in appearance and behavior during combustion. It is characterized by a high percentage of algal remains and volatile matter. Upon distillation, it gives exceptionally high yields of tar and oil.

Size (see Designating the Size of Coal from Its Screen Analysis, ASTM "Standards on Coal and Coke"). **Anthracite** is sized and named as shown in Table 3. Names for the sizes of the lower-rank coals have not been standardized. **Semianthracite** is often sold in about the same sizes as anthracite. Coal as broken in the mine without any screening is called **run of mine.** Bituminous and subbituminous coal and lignite are screened to various sizes and called lump, egg, stove, nut, pea, stoker, slack, etc. **Stoker size** may mean, in one area, a slack coal but, in another area, a screened coal passed through one small-sized screen and retained on another of still smaller size. Slack coal is all the coal passing through a screen of a given mesh; it usually is named for the screen size, such as 3/4- or 2-in. slack. A slack 1 in. or larger is sometimes called **nut-and-slack.** The dimensions of the other grade sizes also vary according to the area in which the coal is produced. Standard screening methods for determining size of coal have been adopted by the ASTM ("Standards on Coal and Coke").

Table 3. Standard Anthracite Specifications

Size	Size of mesh (round)		Over-size max, percent	Undersize		Max impurities		
	Through, in.	Over, in.		Max,† percent	Min, percent	Slate,* percent	Bone,* percent	or Ash† (dry basis)
Broken	4 3/8	3 1/4–3		15	7 1/2	1 1/2	2	11
Egg	3 3/4–3	2 7/16	5	15	7 1/2	1 1/2	2	11
Stove	2 7/16	1 5/8	7 1/2	15	7 1/2	2	3	11
Nut	1 5/8	13/16	7 1/2	15	7 1/2	3	4	11
Pea	13/16	9/16	10	15	7 1/2	4	5	12
Buckwheat	9/16	5/16	10	15	7 1/2	...	...	13
Rice	5/16	3/16	10	17	7 1/2	...	...	13
Barley	3/16	3/32	10	20	10	...	...	15
No. 4	3/32	3/64	20	30	10	...	...	15
No. 5	3/64	...	30	No limit				16

* When slate content in Broken to Nut, inclusive, is less than the above standards, bone content may be increased by one and one-half times the decrease in the slate content under the allowable limits; but slate content specified above shall not be exceeded in any event.

"Slate" is any material which has less than 40 percent of fixed carbon.

"Bone" is any material which has 40 percent or more but less than 75 percent of fixed carbon.

Anthracite that conforms either to the above ash content, or the slate and bone content, is considered "standard" as to impurities.

† A tolerance of 1 percent is allowed on the maximum percentage of undersize and maximum percentage of ash. The maximum percentage of undersize is applicable only to anthracite as it is produced at the preparation plant.

Briquetting. The production of briquettes in the United States amounts to about 360,000 tons per year. Much of the raw fuel used is low-volatile bituminous coal that is mixed with a binding material and compressed into solid shapes. Other fuels used include petroleum coke, lignite char, anthracite, semianthracite, and high-volatile bituminous coal. Asphalt is the principal binder; about 135 lb of binder is used for each ton of briquettes produced.

Paper-wrapped cubes of coal, prepared by compressing raw screenings with a small amount of binder, usually starch and water, are marketed as packaged fuel. The fuel is produced as 3- or 4-in. cubes, six or eight of which are wrapped together in heavy kraft paper to form an 8- to 10-lb package that is burned as a unit without removing the paper. Packaged-fuel plants use an average of 12 lb of binder per ton of output.

Description, Uses, and Sources

Meta-anthracite is a high-carbon coal that approaches graphite in structure and composition. It usually is slow to ignite and difficult to burn. At the present time it has little commercial importance.

Anthracite, sometimes called **hard coal,** is hard, compact, and shiny black, with a generally conchoidal fracture. It ignites with some difficulty and burns with a short, smokeless, blue flame. Anthracite is used primarily for space heating and as a source of carbon. The largest market is for domestic and industrial heating. Electric-power-generating plants in or close to the anthracite-producing area also are important users. The iron and steel industry uses some anthracite in blends with bituminous coal to make coke, sintering iron-ore fines, lining pots and molds, for heating, and as a substitute for coke in foundries. It is used in making briquettes; for heating in bakery ovens; in burning cement, lime, and brick; in curing tobacco and hay; and wherever a clean, steady heat is required. As a source of carbon, limited amounts of anthracite are used, for example, in manufacturing electrodes, in water and chemical filters and purifiers, and in telephones.

Semianthracite is dense, but softer than anthracite. It burns with a short, clean, bluish flame and is somewhat more easily ignited than anthracite. The uses are about the same as for anthracite.

Low-volatile bituminous coal is grayish black, granular in structure, and friable on handling. It cakes in a fire and burns with a short flame that is usually considered smokeless under all burning conditions. It is used for space heating and steam raising and as a constituent of blends for improving the coke strength of higher-volatile bituminous coals. Low-volatile bituminous coals cannot be carbonized alone in slot-type ovens because they expand on coking and damage the walls of the ovens.

Medium-volatile bituminous coal is an intermediate stage between high-volatile and low-volatile bituminous coal and, therefore, has some of the characteristics of both. Some are fairly soft and friable, but others are hard and do not disintegrate on handling. They cake in a fuel bed and smoke when improperly fired. Cokes made from medium-volatile bituminous coals have excellent strength and are either carbonized alone or blended with other bituminous coals. When carbonized alone, only those coals that do not expand appreciably can be used without damaging oven walls.

High-volatile A bituminous coal is mostly homogeneous in structure with bands of varying luster. It is hard and handles well with little breakage. It includes some of the best steam and coking coal. On burning in a fuel bed, it cakes and gives off smoke

Table 4. Principal Ranks of Coal Mined in Various States*

State	Anthracite	Semianthracite	Low-volatile bituminous	Medium-vol. bituminous	High-vol. A bituminous	High-vol. B bituminous	High-vol. C bituminous	Subbituminous A	Subbituminous B	Subbituminous C	Lignite
Alabama				x	x						
Alaska						x	x	x	x	x	x
Arkansas		x	x	x	x						x
Colorado					x	x	x	x	x	x	x
Illinois					x	x	x				
Indiana						x	x				
Iowa							x				
Kansas					x	x					
Kentucky											
Eastern					x	x					
Western					x	x	x				
Maryland			x	x	x						
Missouri							x				
Montana						x	x	x	x	x	x
New Mexico					x	x	x		x		
North Dakota											x
Ohio					x	x	x				
Oklahoma			x	x	x	x	x				
Pennsylvania	x	x	x	x	x						
South Dakota											x
Tennessee				x	x						
Texas							x	x			x
Utah					x	x	x	x	x		
Virginia		x	x	x	x						
Washington					x	x	x		x		x
West Virginia			x	x	x						
Wyoming						x	x	x	x	x	

* Compiled largely from Typical Analyses of Coals of the United States, *B of M Bull.* 446, and Coal Reserves of the United States, *Geol. Survey Bull.* 1136.

if improperly fired. The coking property is often improved by blending with more strongly coking medium- and low-volatile bituminous coal.

High-volatile B bituminous coal is somewhat similar to high-volatile A bituminous but has slightly higher bed moisture and oxygen content and is less strongly coking. It is good coal for steam raising and space heating. Some of it is blended with more strongly coking coals for making metallurgical coke.

High-volatile C bituminous coal is a stage lower in rank than the B bituminous coal and therefore has a progressively higher bed moisture and oxygen content. It is used primarily for steam raising and space heating. At the present time it is not used in blends for making metallurgical coke.

Subbituminous coals usually are homogeneous in structure with less evidence of banding than higher-rank coals. They have a high moisture content, and on exposure to air, they disintegrate or "slack" because of shrinkage from loss of moisture. They are non-caking and non-coking, and their primary use is for steam raising and space heating.

Lignites are brown to black in color and have a bed moisture content of 30 to 45 percent with a resulting lower heating value than higher-rank coals. Like subbituminous coals, they have a tendency to "slack" or disintegrate during air drying. They are non-caking and non-coking. Lignite can be burned on traveling or spreader stokers and in pulverized form.

The principal ranks of coal mined in the major coal-producing states are shown in Table 4. Their analyses depend on several factors, *i.e.*, source, size of coal, and method of preparation. The *Information Circulars* published annually by the Bureau of Mines, Analyses of Tipple and Delivered Samples of Coal (Collected during the Fiscal Year 19—), are an excellent source of information on proximate and ultimate analyses, heating values, free-swelling indices, grindability, and ash-softening temperatures of various coals mined in the United States.

Composition and Characteristics

Proximate analysis, sulphur content, and heating value are the analytical determinations most commonly used for industrial characterization of coal. The **proximate analysis** is the simplest means for determining the distribution of products obtained during heating. It separates the products into four groups: (1) water or moisture, (2) volatile matter consisting of gases and vapors, (3) fixed carbon consisting of the carbonized residue less ash, and (4) ash derived from the mineral impurities in the coal. For standardized laboratory methods of making these determinations, refer to the latest edition of ASTM "Standards on Coal and Coke."

Moisture is the loss in weight obtained by drying the coal at a temperature between 104 and 110 C (219 to 230 F) under prescribed conditions. Further heating at higher temperatures may remove more water, but this moisture usually is considered part of the coal substance. The moisture obtained by the standard method consists of (1) surface or extraneous moisture that may come from external sources such as percolating waters in the mine, rain, condensation from the air, or water from a coal washery; (2) inherent moisture, sometimes called **bed moisture,** which is so closely held by the coal substance that it does not produce wetness. The laboratory determination does not separate these two types of moisture. A coal may be air-dried at room temperature or somewhat above, thereby determining an "air-drying loss," but this result is not the extraneous moisture because part of the inherent moisture also vaporizes during air drying.

Mine samples taken at freshly exposed faces in the mine, which are free from visible surface moisture, give the best information as to inherent, or bed-moisture, content. Such moisture content ranges in value from about 2 to 4 percent for anthracite and for bituminous coals of the eastern Appalachian field, such as the Pocahontas, Sewell, Pittsburgh, Freeport, and Kittanning beds. In the western part of this field, especially in Ohio, the inherent moisture ranges from 4 to 10 percent. In the interior fields of Indiana, Illinois, western Kentucky, Iowa, and Missouri, the range is from 8 to 17 percent. In subbituminous coals the inherent moisture ranges from 15 to 30 percent, and in lignites from 30 to 45 percent. The total amount of moisture in commercial coal may be greater or less than that of the coal in the mine. Freshly mined subbituminous coal and lignite lose moisture rapidly when exposed to the air. The extraneous or surface moisture in coal is a function of the surface exposed, each surface being able to hold a film of moisture. Fine sizes hold more moisture than lump. Coal which in the mine does not contain more than 4 percent moisture may in slack sizes hold as much as 15 percent; the same coal in lump sizes, even after underwater storage, may contain but little more moisture than originally in the mine.

In the standard method of analysis, the **volatile matter** is taken as the loss in weight, less moisture, obtained by heating the coal for 7 min in a covered crucible at about 950 C (1742 F) under specified conditions. Volatile matter does not exist in coal as such but is produced by decomposition of the coal when heated. It consists chiefly of the combustible gases, hydrogen, carbon monoxide, methane and other hydrocarbons, tar vapors, volatile sulphur compounds, and some non-combustible gases such as carbon dioxide and water vapor. The composition of the volatile matter varies greatly with different coals. The inert or non-combustible matter may range from 4 percent of the total volatile matter in low-volatile coals to 40 percent in subbituminous coals.

The standard method of determining the **fixed carbon** is to subtract from 100 the sum of the percentages of the moisture, volatile matter, and ash of the proximate analysis. It is the carbonaceous residue less ash remaining in the test crucible in the determination of the volatile matter. It does not represent the total carbon in the coal because a considerable part of the carbon is expelled as volatile matter in combination with hydrogen as hydrocarbons and with oxygen as carbon monoxide and carbon dioxide. It also is not pure carbon because it may contain several tenths percent of hydrogen and oxygen, 0.4 to 1.0 percent of nitrogen, and about half of the sulphur that was in the coal.

In the standard method, the **ash** is the inorganic residue that remains after burning the coal in a muffle furnace to a final temperature of 700 to 750 C (1292 to 1382 F). It is composed largely of compounds of silicon, aluminum, iron, and calcium, with smaller quantities of compounds of magnesium, titanium, sodium, and potassium. Although the constituents are reported as oxides by the analyst, they occur in the ash largely as a mixture of silicates, oxides, and sulphates, with smaller quantities of other compounds. The silicates have their origin in the shale and clay minerals. The principal source of the iron oxide is pyrite, which burns to form ferric oxide and sulphur oxides. The calcium and magnesium oxides result from decomposition of the carbonate minerals. The sulphates are formed largely from interaction among carbonate minerals, pyrite, and oxygen. These ash-forming constituents consist of (1) "inherent" or "intrinsic" impurities that are present in an intimate mixture with the coal substance and are derived either from the original vegetable material or from external sources by sedimentation or precipitation during the process of accumulation of coal-forming vegetation; (2) impurities deposited either during the laying down of the coal bed or subsequently, that occur in the form of partings, veins and nodules of clay, shale, pyrite, and calcite; and (3) impurities that become mechanically mixed with the coal in the process of mining, such as fragments of roof and floor.

The ash as determined is usually less than the inorganic mineral matter originally present in the coal. During incineration, various weight changes take place, such as loss of water of constitution of the silicate minerals, loss of carbon dioxide from carbonate minerals, oxidation of iron pyrites to iron oxide, and fixation of a part of the oxides of sulphur by bases such as calcium and magnesium.

The chemical composition of coal ash varies widely depending on the mineral constituents associated with the coal. Typical limits of ash composition of U.S. bituminous coals are:

Constituent	Percent	Constituent	Percent
Silica, SiO_2	20–60	Magnesium oxide, MgO	0.3–4
Alumina, Al_2O_3	10–35	Titanium dioxide, TiO_2	0.5–2.5
Ferric oxide, Fe_2O_3	5–35	Alkalies, Na_2O and K_2O	1–4
Calcium oxide, CaO	1–20	Sulphur trioxide, SO_3	0.1–12

(See Analyses of Ash from United States Coals, *B of M Bull.* 567.)

The ash of subbituminous coals may have more CaO, MgO, and SO_3 than the ash of bituminous coals; the trend may even be more pronounced for lignite ash.

Ultimate analysis expresses the composition of coal as sampled in percentages of carbon, hydrogen, nitrogen, sulphur, oxygen, and ash. The carbon includes that present in the organic coal substance as well as a minor amount that may be present as mineral carbonates. In ASTM practice, the hydrogen and oxygen values include those of the organic coal substance as well as those present in the form of moisture and the water of constitution of the silicate minerals. In certain other countries, the values for hydrogen and oxygen are corrected for the moisture in the coal and are reported separately. The ash is the same as reported in the proximate analysis; the sulphur, carbon, hydrogen, and nitrogen are determined chemically (see ASTM "Standards on Coal and Coke"). Because of the lack of a simple, direct method for determining oxygen in coal, it usually is estimated by subtracting the sum of carbon, hydrogen, nitrogen, sulphur, and ash from 100. If suitable corrections are made for the carbon, hydrogen, and sulphur derived from the inorganic material and for conversion of ash to mineral matter, the ultimate analysis represents the elemental composition of the organic coal substance in terms of carbon, hydrogen, nitrogen, sulphur, and oxygen.

Sulphur occurs in three forms in coal: (1) pyritic sulphur or sulphur combined with iron as pyrite or marcasite, (2) organic sulphur or sulphur combined with coal substance, (3) sulphate sulphur or sulphur combined mainly with iron or calcium together with oxygen as iron sulphate or calcium sulphate. Pyrite and marcasite are recognized by their metallic luster and pale brass-yellowish color, although some marcasite is almost white. Organic sulphur may comprise from about 20 to 85 percent of the total sulphur in the coal. Sulphate sulphur is usually found in greater amounts in weathered coal; most freshly mined coal contains only very small quantities. The total sulphur content of coal mined in the United States varies from about 0.4 to 5.5 percent by weight on a dry-coal basis.

The **gross or high heating value** (hhv) of a fuel (also called **calorific value**) expressed in Btu per lb of fuel is the heat produced by complete combustion of a unit quantity, at constant volume, in an oxygen-bomb calorimeter under standard conditions (see ASTM "Standards on Coal and Coke"). It includes the latent heat of the water vapor in the products of combustion. Since the latent heat is not available for making steam in actual operation of boilers, a **net** or **lower heating value** (lhv) is sometimes determined, although not in usual U.S. practice, by the following formula:

Net heating value, Btu per lb = gross heating value, Btu per lb − (92.70 × total hydrogen, percent in coal).

The gross heating value also may be approximated by **Dulong's formula,** as follows:

$$\text{Btu per lb} = 14{,}544C + 62{,}028\left(H - \frac{O}{8}\right) + 4{,}050S$$

where *C*, *H*, *O*, and *S* are weight fractions from the ultimate analysis. For anthracites, semianthracites, and bituminous coals, the calculated values are usually within 1½ percent of those determined by the bomb calorimeter. For subbituminous and lignitic coals, the calculated values show deviations often reaching 4 and 5 percent.

The proximate and ultimate analysis and heating value of a coal may be expressed on the *as-received, moisture-free,* and *moisture- and ash-free* basis, as shown in Table 2.

Because coal ash is a mixture of various components, it does not have a definite melting point; the gradual softening and fusion of the ash is not merely the successive melting of the various ash constituents, but it is a more complicated process in which reactions involving the formation of new and more fusible compounds take place.

The **fusibility of coal ash** is determined by heating a triangular pyramid (cone), ¾ in. high and ¼ in. wide at each side of the base, made up of the ash held together with a small amount of organic binder (ASTM "Standards on Coal and Coke"). As the cone is heated, three temperatures are noted: (1) the *initial deformation temperature,* or the temperature at which the first rounding of the apex or the edges of the cone occurs; (2) the *softening temperature,* or the temperature at which the cone has fused down to a spherical lump; and (3) the *fluid temperature,* or the temperature at which the cone has spread out in a nearly flat layer. The softening interval is the degrees of temperature difference between (2) and (1), the flowing interval the difference between (3) and (2). Of the three, the softening temperature is most widely used. (See Table 5 and p. 9–15.)

Table 5. Fusibility of Ash from Coals of the United States*

State	County	Bed	Number of samples	Softening temperature, deg F			Average analysis of dry coal, percent	
				Lowest	Highest	Average	Ash	Sulphur
				Anthracitic				
Arkansas	Pope	Shinn Basin	2	2180	2370	2280	10.4	2.2
Pennsylvania	Lackawanna	Diamond	1	....	......	+2970	7.9	0.8
	Luzerne	Top Red Ash (bottom bench)	1	....	......	+2990	12.1	0.6
	Schuylkill	Mammoth (middle bench)	1	....	......	2660	18.0	1.0
	Carbon	Buck Mountain	1	....	......	2910	11.1	0.5
Virginia	Montgomery	Merrimac	4	2590	+2910	+2800	18.5	0.5
				Bituminous and Subbituminous				
Colorado	Huerfano	Cameron	8	2280	2520	2360	9.8	0.8
Illinois	Williamson	No. 6	12	1950	2430	2230	9.3	1.1
Kentucky	Letcher	Elkhorn	20	2300	2730	2510	4.0	0.7
	Harlan	Harlan	8	2510	+3010	+2720	4.0	0.8
	Muhlenberg	No. 9	13	1870	2230	1990	9.6	3.6
Maryland	Allegany	Tyson (Sewickley)	8	2580	+3010	+2810	7.4	1.2
Missouri	Randolph	Bevier	11	1830	1990	1940	13.0	5.4
	Bates	Mulberry	5	1940	2070	1980	14.9	3.6
	Barton	Weir-Pittsburg	6	1900	1980	1940	10.8	4.4
Montana	Carbon	No. 3	11	1930	2190	2080	11.5	1.8
	Musselshell	Roundup	8	2070	2420	2280	8.6	0.8
New Mexico	Colfax	Raton	16	2530	+3000	+2880	13.0	0.7
	McKinley	Black Diamond	1	....	......	2490	7.4	0.9
Ohio	Columbiana	Middle Kittanning (No. 6)	5	2220	2600	2450	7.3	1.8
Oklahoma	Le Flore	Hartshorne	8	1870	2300	2060	7.6	0.9
Pennsylvania	Allegheny	Pittsburgh	7	2280	2580	2420	6.5	1.1
	Cambria	Lower Kittanning	88	2080	+3010	+2650	6.4	1.4
Utah	Carbon	Castle Gate	3	2110	2150	2140	6.0	0.5
Virginia	Dickenson	Upper Banner	2	2430	2630	2530	7.0	1.1
Washington	Kittitas	Roslyn	4	2320	2590	2410	12.7	0.4
West Virginia	Logan	Cedar Grove	14	2390	+3010	+2700	5.7	1.0
	Marion	Pittsburgh	44	2000	2410	2200	6.8	1.7
	Raleigh	Sewell	40	2090	+3010	+2530	5.4	1.0
	McDowell	Pocahontas No. 3	158	2120	3070	2370	5.0	0.6

* See also Fusibility of Ash of United States Coals, *B of M Inf. Circ.* 7923.

Most bituminous coals, when heated at uniformly increasing temperatures in the absence or partial absence of air, fuse and become plastic. These coals may be designated as either **caking or coking coals**; different coals possess this property of caking or coking in different degrees. Caking usually refers to the fusion process in a boiler furnace. Coking coals are those that make good coke, suitable for metallurgical purposes. Coals that are caking in a fuel bed do not necessarily make good coke in a coke oven. Subbituminous coal, lignite, and anthracite are non-caking.

The **free-swelling index** test measures the free-swelling properties of coal and gives an indication of the caking characteristics of the coal when burned on fuel beds. It is not intended to determine the expansion of coals in coke ovens. The test consists in heating 1 g of pulverized coal in a silica crucible over a gas flame under prescribed conditions to form a coke button, the size and shape of which are then compared with a series of standard profiles numbered 1 to 9 in increasing order of swelling. For details of the test and its significance, see ASTM "Standards on Coal and Coke" and

An Investigation of a Laboratory Test for Determination of the Free-swelling Index of Coal, *B of M Rept. of Inv.* 3989. See also Free-swelling and Grindability Indexes of United States Coals, *B of M Inf. Circ.* 8025.

The **specific gravity** of coal is the ratio of the weight of solid coal to the weight of an equal volume of water. It is useful in calculating the weight of solid coal as it occurs in the ground for estimating the tonnage of coal per acre of surface. For average specific gravities, see p. 6–8. An increase in ash-forming mineral matter increases the specific gravity; *e.g.*, bituminous coals of Alabama, ranging from 2 to 15 percent ash and from 2 to 4.5 percent moisture, vary in specific gravity from 1.26 to 1.37.

Bulk density is the weight per cubic foot of broken coal. It varies according to the specific gravity of the coal, its size distribution, its moisture content, and the amount of settling or shaking when piled. The range of weight from subbituminous coal to anthracite is from 44 to 59 lb per cu ft when loosely piled; when piled in layers and compacted, the weight per cubic foot may increase as much as 25 percent. The weight of fuel in a pile can usually be determined to within 10 to 15 percent by measuring its volume. Typical weights of coal "as received," as determined by shoveling loosely into a box of 8-cu-ft capacity, are as follows: anthracite 50 to 58 lb per cu ft; low- and medium-volatile bituminous coal, 49 to 47 lb per cu ft; high-volatile bituminous and subbituminous coal, 42 to 57 lb per cu ft.

The **grindability** of coal, or the ease with which it can be ground fine enough for use as a pulverized fuel, is a composite of several specific physical properties such as hardness, tensile strength, and fracture. A laboratory procedure adopted by ASTM for evaluating grindability, known as the **Hardgrove** machine method, uses a specially designed grinding apparatus to determine the relative grindability or ease of pulverizing coal in comparison with a standard coal, chosen as 100 grindability. Primarily, the ASTM Hardgrove grindability test is used for estimating how various coals affect the capacity of commercial pulverizers. A general relationship exists between grindability of coal and its rank. Coals that are easiest to grind (highest grindability index) are those of about 14 to 30 percent volatile matter on a dry, ash-free basis. Coals of either lower or higher volatile-matter content usually are more difficult to grind. The relationship of grindability and rank, however, is not sufficiently precise for grindability to be estimated from the chemical analysis, partly because of the variation in grindability of the various petrographic and mineral components. Table 6 lists the grindability index of some typical U.S. coals.

Table 6. Grindability of Some Typical Coals of the United States*

Source			Size	Proximate analysis, moisture-free basis, percent			Grindability index
State	County	Bed		Volatile matter	Fixed carbon	Ash	
Pa.	Clinton	Lower Kittanning (B)	R/M	24.2	62.4	13.4	117
Pa.	Somerset	Upper Kittanning (C′)	R/M	17.8	70.5	11.7	100
W. Va.	Greenbrier	Sewell	1¼ × 0	26.5	68.1	5.4	88
W. Va.	Randolph	Lower Kittanning	2 × 0	28.8	60.7	10.5	78
Okla.	McIntosh	Secor	5 × 2½	34.4	55.7	9.9	71
Ohio	Coshocton	Middle Kittanning	¾ × 0	37.8	55.4	6.8	66
Ind.	Vigo	III	½ × 0	43.5	46.4	10.1	63
Ill.	Williamson	No. 5	1½ × 28 mesh	36.1	54.6	9.3	60
Kan.	Bourbon	Bevier	¾ × 0	40.2	49.4	10.4	59
N. Dak.	Divide	....	2 × ¼	42.5	47.8	9.7	53
Ky.	McCreary	No. 2	2 × 0	40.5	46.2	13.3	49
Pa.	Northumberland	(Anthracite)	No. 4 (Buckwheat)	5.9	85.8	8.3	44
Utah	Carbon	Castlegate D	1 × 3⁄16	43.5	50.2	6.3	43
Ala.	Marion	Black Creek	2¾ × 0	39.6	57.7	2.7	37
Pa.	Luzerne	(Anthracite)	Nut	5.9	87.5	6.6	21

* See also Free-swelling and Grindability Indexes of United States Coals, *B of M Inf. Circ.* 8025.

Mining and Preparation

Coal is mined by either underground or surface methods. In underground mining, the coal beds are made accessible by slope, drift, or vertical shafts, depending on the location of the bed relative to the terrain. In recent years, underground coal mining has become highly mechanized, and cutting, loading, and conveying are virtually no longer manual. When coal occurs near the surface, strip or open-pit mining may be more economical than underground mining. In flat country, where the coal bed is nearly horizontal and of normal thickness, the overburden is removed with large power shovels. The coal is then scooped up by smaller shovels and loaded into trucks.

About two-thirds of all coal mined in the United States is mechanically cleaned. The introduction of mechanized mining that does not differentiate between coal and impurities during operations has given great impetus to coal preparation or cleaning. **Cleaning** consists of removing sulphur-bearing components and high-ash material such as rock and partings. The separation of impurities is based primarily on differences in density, the separable impurities being heavier than an equal volume of coal. Either wet or pneumatic methods may be used.

Storage

Coal may heat spontaneously, with the liability of self-heating greatest among coals of lowest rank. The heating begins as soon as the freshly broken coal is exposed to the air. The process accelerates with increase in temperature, and active burning will result if the heat from the oxidation is not dissipated as fast as it is produced. The finer sizes of coal, having more surface area per unit weight than the larger sizes, are more susceptible to spontaneous heating.

The **prevention of spontaneous heating** in storage is a problem of minimizing oxidation and of dissipating any heat produced. Air may carry away heat, but it also brings oxygen to create more heat. Spontaneous heating can be prevented or lessened by (1) storing coal under water; (2) compressing the pile in layers, as with a road roller, to prevent access of air; (3) storing large-size coal; (4) preventing any segregation of sizes in the pile (it is usually best to pile in layers); (5) storing in small piles; (6) keeping the storage pile as low as possible (6 ft is the limit for many coals); (7) keeping storage away from any external sources of heat; (8) avoiding any draft of air through the coal; (9) using older portions of the storage first and avoiding accumulations of old coal in corners. It is desirable to watch the temperature of the pile. A thermometer inserted in an iron tube driven into the coal will reveal the temperature encountered. When the coal reaches a temperature of 120 F, it should be moved. Using water to put out a fire, although effective for the moment, may only delay the necessity of moving the coal. (See The Storage of Coal, *B of M Inf. Circ.* 7235).

Sampling

Because coal is a heterogeneous material, collection and handling of samples that adequately represent the bulk lot of coal are required if the analytical and test data are to be meaningful. Coal is best sampled when in motion, as it is being loaded or unloaded from belt conveyors or other coal-handling equipment, by collecting increments of uniform weight evenly distributed over the entire lot. Each increment should be sufficiently large and so taken as to represent properly the various sizes of *size consist* of the coal. The standard methods of the ASTM cover sampling procedures for coals classed according to ash content as follows: under 8 percent, 8.0 to 9.9 percent, 10.0 to 14.9 percent, and 15 percent ash and over. For each ash classification, there are eight size groups; and for each size group, the methods prescribe a minimum number of increments, each of a minimum weight that results in a specified minimum of gross sample.

Two procedures are recognized in this method: (1) commercial sampling and (2) special-purpose sampling, such as classification by rank or performance. The **commercial-sampling** procedure is intended for an accuracy such that if a large number of samples were taken from a large lot of coal, the test results in 95 out of 100 cases would fall within ±10 percent of the ash content of these samples. For commercial sampling of lots up to 1,000 tons, it is recommended that one gross sample represent the lot taken, in accordance with the requirements in Table 7. For lots over 1,000 tons, the following alternatives may be used: (1) Separate gross samples may be taken for each 1,000 tons of coal or fraction thereof, and a weighted average of the analytical determinations of these prepared samples may be used to represent the lot. (2) Separate gross samples may be taken for each 1,000 tons or fraction thereof, and the −20- or −60-mesh samples taken from the gross samples may be mixed together in proportion to the tonnage represented by each sample and one analysis carried out on the composite sample. (3) One gross sample may be used to represent the lot, provided that at least four times the minimum number of increments prescribed in Table 7 are taken.

Table 7. Requirements for Commercial-sampling Procedure for Coals Classified according to Ash Content (ASTM D492–48)

	Group 1	Group 2	Group 3	Group 4	Group 5	Group 6	Group 7	Group 8
Top Size Range*...............	⅝ in. and under	Over ⅝ to 1¼ in., incl	Over 1¼ to 2 in., incl	Over 2 to 6 in., incl	Over 2 to 4 in., incl	Over 4 to 6 in., incl	*	*
UNDER 8 PERCENT ASH								
Min number of increments......	15	15	15	15	15	15	35	35
Min wt of increment, lb........	2	4	6	10	10	15	30	20
Min wt of gross sample, lb......	30	60	90	150	150	225	1,050	700
8.0 TO 9.9 PERCENT ASH								
Min number of increments......	20	20	20	20	20	20	35	35
Min wt of increment, lb........	2	4	6	10	10	15	30	20
Min wt of gross sample, lb......	40	80	120	200	200	300	1,050	700
10.0 TO 14.9 PERCENT ASH								
Min number of increments......	35	35	35	35	35	35	35	50
Min wt of increment, lb........	2	4	6	10	10	15	30	20
Min wt of gross sample, lb......	70	140	210	350	350	525	1,050	1,000
15.0 PERCENT ASH AND OVER								
Min number of increments......	35	35	35	35	35	35	35	50
Min wt of increment, lb........	2	4	6	10	10	15	30	20
Min wt of gross sample, lb......	70	140	210	350	350	525	1,050	1,000

* See Section 3 of ASTM D492-48.

In **special-purpose sampling,** the increment requirements prescribed in Table 7 are increased according to the following rules:

To increase accuracy in the collection of gross sample (in 95 cases out of 100)	Increase min number of increments given in Table 7
±5% of the ash content of the coal sampled........	4 times
±3.33% of the ash content of the coal sampled......	9 times

For details of sampling procedures and the preparation of coal samples for analysis, see the latest edition of ASTM "Standards on Coal and Coke."

Specifications

Specifications for the purchase of coal vary widely. In general, a specification drawn up as simply as the individual case under consideration will permit is recommended. Many characteristics of coal cannot be adequately stated or even tested in the laboratory. The United States government, purchasing coal on a guaranteed-analysis basis, specifies (1) delivery point, (2) size, (3) analytical constituents (limits), and (4) tonnages. For example: (1) Capitol Power Plant, Washington, D.C., Pennsylvania RR.; (2) nut-and-slack through not less than 1½-in. screen; (3) moisture (as received) maximum, 4 percent; volatile maximum, 29 percent; ash maximum, 10 percent; gross heating-value minimum, 13,900 Btu per lb, all on dry basis; ash-softening temperature for ash content up to 8 percent inclusive, 2500 F, and for ash content 8 to 10 percent, 2650 F; (4) 70,000 short tons. The bidder must state the name of the mine, its location, shipping point, the railroad at point of shipment, the coal seam, mine operator, and guaranteed analysis.

All bids offering coal that does not meet the analytical-specifications limits, that is known from previous experience to have characteristics that make it unsuitable for the purpose, or that is shown to be unsuitable by actual trial are rejected. Award is made to the bidder offering coal, the use of which results in the lowest yearly total operating cost at the plant. This determination includes consideration of the price of the coal, the efficiency of its use, the maintenance of the equipment, the labor involved in its use, and the handling of ash. This cannot be expressed by any universal formula.

Wage clauses are usually included in government coal contracts to take care of any change in wage scales, and clauses are also included that cover deliveries of unsatisfactory coal and that spell out the penalties involved.

COKE

By D. E. Wolfson

REFERENCES: ASTM, vol. 30, part I, 1930, p. 1147; also, "Book of ASTM Tentative Standards," 1933, p. 471. ASTM, Specification for Foundry Coke (D-17-16), *Standards for* 1939, *part* III, *Nonmetallic Materials*, pp. 59–61. Advance Data on Coke and Coal Chemicals in 1962, *B of M Minerals Industry Surveys*, U.S. Dept. of the Interior. Davis, Selection of Coals for Coke Making, *B of M Rept. of Inv.* 3601, 1942. Wolfson, Birge, and Walters, Relation of Properties of Coke Produced by BM-AGA and Industrial Methods, *Blast Furnace, Coke Oven and Raw Materials Proc.*, AIME, 1961, pp. 387–403.

Coke is the infusible, cellular, coherent, solid material obtained from coal, pitch, petroleum, and petroleum residues and from some other carbonaceous materials as the residue of destructive distillation. This residue has a characteristic structure resulting from the decomposition and hardening of a fused or semiliquid mass. At present, specific varieties of coke other than those from coal are distinguished by prefixing a qualifying word to indicate their source, as "Petroleum coke" and "pitch coke." A word may also be prefixed to indicate the process by which coke is manufactured, *e.g.*, in the case of coke from coal, "beehive coke" and "gashouse coke." See Table 8.

High-temperature coke is the type of coke most commonly used in the United States. In 1962, slot-type recovery ovens produced 98 percent of the total output of

Table 8. Analyses of Cokes

Kind of process	"As received" basis									
	Proximate, percent			Ultimate, percent						High heat value, Btu per lb
	Moisture	Volatile matter	Fixed carbon	Ash	Hydrogen	Carbon	Nitrogen	Oxygen	Sulphur	
By-product coke	0.8	1.4	87.1	10.7	0.8	85.0	1.3	1.2	1.0	12,690
Beehive coke	0.5	1.8	86.0	11.7	0.8	84.4	1.2	0.9	1.0	12,527
Low-temperature coke	0.0	9.8	83.5	6.7	3.2	84.2	1.9	3.2	0.8	14,030
Low-temperature coke	2.8	15.1	72.1	10.0	3.5	74.5	1.6	8.6	1.8	12,600
Pitch coke	0.3	1.1	97.6	1.0	0.6	96.6	0.7	0.6	0.5	14,097
Petroleum coke	1.1	7.0	90.7	1.2	3.3	90.8	0.8	3.1	0.8	15,060

high-temperature coke, with the remainder accounted for by non-recovery beehive and other types of ovens. Blast furnaces utilized 90 percent of the production, with the other 10 percent variously used by foundries, gas plants, residential heating, and other industries. **Low- and medium-temperature cokes** have limited production in the United States because of the absence of the open fireplaces common to European homes and because of the limited market for low-temperature tar.

A recent (1959) survey of **blast-furnace coke** plants whose capacity is 30 percent of the total in the United States is indicative of the chemical and physical properties of blast-furnace coke presently used. The volatile matter of the coke ranged from 0.6 to 1.4 percent; ash, 7.5 to 10.7 percent; sulphur, 0.6 to 1.1 percent; 2-in. shatter index, 59 to 82; 1½-in. shatter index, 83 to 91; 1-in. tumbler (stability factor), 35 to 57; and ¼-in. tumbler (hardness factor), 61 to 68. The quality of blast-furnace coke has improved during the last decade. Comparison of this survey with a previous survey made in 1949 shows that ash and sulphur contents of the coke have been reduced and that the average tumbler stability, which is the principal strength index for evaluating the physical properties of blast-furnace coke, has increased from 39 to 52.

The requirements for **foundry coke** are somewhat different from those for blast-furnace coke. Chemically, in the cupola the only function of the coke is to furnish heat to melt the iron, whereas in the blast furnace the function is twofold—to supply carbon monoxide for reducing ore and to supply heat to melt the iron. Usually, it should be of large size (more than 3 in.) and strong enough to prevent excessive degradation by impact of the massive iron charged into the cupola shaft. The ASTM states that the following chemical characteristics are desired in foundry coke: volatile matter, not over 2.0 percent; fixed carbon, not under 86.0 percent; ash, not over 12.0 percent; and sulphur, not over 1.0 percent. In the 1959 survey, coke from two plants showed the following properties: volatile matter, 0.6 and 1.4 percent; fixed carbon, 89.6 and 91.4 percent; ash, 8.7 and 7.5 percent; and sulphur, 0.6 percent. The 1½- and 2-in. shatter indices, which measure the ability of coke to withstand breakage by impact, were 98 and 97, respectively, for both cokes.

There appear to be no rigid specifications for the physical and chemical properties of **domestic coke** (coke for residential heating). The main chemical requirements are that the ash content be as low as possible, preferably below 12 percent, and that the softening temperature of the ash be as high as possible, preferably above 2300 F. Low- and medium-temperature cokes are preferred for some domestic heating purposes. The main chemical characteristics distinguishing them from high-temperature cokes are a higher volatile-matter content (3 to 18 percent) and higher reactivity or combustibility, with consequent greater ease of ignition.

The most serious operating problems encountered with **water-gas manufacture** are due to the presence of clinker and its removal. The ash content of water-gas coke should be low (8 to 9 percent), and best results are obtained with a softening temperature of about 2500 F. Very high- or low-fusion ash can be troublesome in this application. A low sulphur content is desirable because if the sulphur is high, more of it will pass into the gas and thus increase the cost of purification. The coke should be larger than 2 in.

Pitch coke is made from coal-tar pitch, whereas **petroleum coke** is made from residues from refining petroleum. Both are characterized by high carbon and low ash content and are used mainly for the production of electrode carbon.

PEAT, WOOD, AND MISCELLANEOUS SOLID FUELS

By L. L. Newman and W. H. Ode

REFERENCES: Odell and Hood, Possibilities for the Commercial Utilization of Peat, *B of M Bull.* 253, 1926, p. 56. Johnson and Auth, "Fuels and Combustion Handbook," McGraw-Hill. Cronin and Lang, Peat-fired Power Stations, *Jour. Inst. Fuel*, Nov., 1954. Cullen, The Use of Milled Peat in Large Boilers for the Generation of Electricity, *Jour. Inst. Fuel*, July, 1960.

Peat—the first stage in the metamorphism of vegetable matter to coal—is the product of partial decomposition and disintegration of mosses, sedges, trees, and other plant life. Like all material of vegetable origin, it consists of complex chemical compounds made up of carbon, hydrogen, oxygen, nitrogen, sulphur, and other elements in small amounts. About three-fourths of the total reserves of peat in the United States are in Minnesota, Wisconsin, and Michigan; the remainder is in some 27 other states, with more than half in Florida.

Peat is used as a fuel in many countries, but the abundance of higher-rank fuels has kept it out of the fuel and energy markets in the United States. In the United States, peat is used primarily for soil improvement; it also has been used as a conditioner and filler in mixed fertilizers, as mull or litter for domestic animals, as packaging material, and in chemical applications such as filtering and tanning.

Peat is usually found on waterlogged sites or swampy tracts generally referred to as *bogs*.

The **moisture content** of an undrained peat bog, usually between 92 and 95 percent, is associated with the raw peat as (1) free water, (2) capillary water, (3) colloidal water, (4) occluded water or water held by adsorption, (5) chemically combined water, and (6) water retained osmotically. Where peat is used as a commercial fuel (as in Ireland), the moisture content is reduced to between 10 and 55 percent, depending on the method of winning and the utilization. Normally, peat is harvested from a drained bog and dried naturally by the sun and wind. For the production of briquettes, further drying of the peat is done artificially by thermal methods.

The **chemical and physical properties of peat** vary considerably, depending on the nature of the bog and the method of harvesting.

The range of **moisture content** in percent is as follows: air-dried machine-cut sod peat, 25 to 40; air-dried hand-cut sod peat, 25 to 50; milled peat, 50 to 55; briquettes, 10 to 12.

The range of **bulk densities** in lb per cu ft is: air-dried machine-cut sod peat, 20 to 25; air-dried hand-cut sod peat, 15 to 20; briquettes (stacked), 50 to 60; briquettes (loose), 30 to 40.

On a dry basis, the **proximate analysis** of peat varies within the following limits: fixed carbon, 30 to 40 percent; volatile matter, 55 to 70 percent; and ash, 2 to 10 percent. On a dry, ash-free basis, the ultimate analysis ranges as follows (percent): Carbon, 53 to 63; hydrogen, 5.5 to 7.0; oxygen, 30 to 40; sulphur, 0.3 to 0.5; and nitrogen, 1.2 to 1.5.

Dry, ash-free peat has a **calorific value** ranging between 9500 and 11000 Btu per lb. Air-dried machine-cut sod peat at 30 percent moisture content has a calorific value of 6200 Btu per lb. Milled peat, with moisture content of 40 to 60 percent, has a range of calorific values of 5300 to 3700 Btu per lb. Briquettes, used principally for domestic heating, have a calorific value of approximately 8000 Btu per lb at 12 percent moisture content.

Wood. The approximate chemical composition (percent) of moisture-free wood is: carbon, 49; hydrogen, 6; oxygen, 44; and ash, 1. This composition corresponds to $C_6H_{10}O_5$ approx. The average hhv of moisture- and resin-free wood is 8300 Btu per lb, and the hhv of resin is about 16900 Btu per lb. Among woods, the heat value of which is influenced by varying contents of resin, are longleaf pine, shortleaf pine, loblolly pine, western yellow pine, piñon pine, cedar, juniper, and cypress. Green wood contains approximately 50 percent moisture, air-dried or seasoned wood contains 15 to 25 percent moisture, and kiln-dried about 8 percent. Analyses of typical wood fuels are given in Table 9.

Wood is sold by the cord. The **standard cord** is 8 ft long, 4 ft high, and 4 ft wide, or 128 cu ft as piled, but the actual solid content of a cord is only about 70 percent of this volume, or 90 cu ft for wood of average size. A **cord run,** sometimes called a *cord,* is 8 ft long and 4 ft high, with a width equal to that length to which the pieces of wood are cut. Wood is sold in various lengths; 16-in. wood is called **stovewood** or **blockwood,** and 4-ft wood is called **cordwood.** Table 10 gives the approximate weights and heat values per cord of various woods.

Charcoal is made by heating wood to the charring temperature in the absence of air. Wood loses up to 75 percent in weight and 50 percent in volume in charring, depending on the temperature of charring and the moisture content of the wood.

Charcoal has a higher heating value per cubic foot than wood and is cheaper to transport because of its light weight. It is sold in the form of lumps, screenings, powder, and briquettes. Its fuel uses include tobacco curing and restaurant and picnic fuels. Its non-fuel uses, particularly in the chemical industry, are mainly as filter media for purifying gas and water and as a decolorizing agent.

Table 9. Analyses of Wood Fuels, as Fired
(Percent)

Constituent	Wood, typical nonresinous, seasoned	Charcoal, willow	Wood waste: California redwood	Wood waste: Western hemlock	Wood waste: Douglas fir	Hogged fuel, Douglas fir	Sawdust, green, Douglas fir	Sawdust briquets, Douglas fir	Tanbark
Proximate analysis									
Moisture	24.0	3.2	50.4	57.9	35.9	47.2	44.9	10.3	71.8
Volatile matter	65.5	14.7	40.9	31.3	52.5	42.9	44.9	78.3	22.4
Fixed carbon	9.5	80.2	8.6	9.9	11.1	8.9	9.5	11.2	4.5
Ash	1.0	1.9	0.1	0.9	0.5	1.0	0.7	0.2	1.3
Ultimate analysis									
Hydrogen	7.2	2.7	8.5	8.9	8.0	....	....	....	9.6
Carbon	37.9	85.0	26.5	21.2	33.5	....	....	....	14.2
Nitrogen	0.1	0.2	0.1	0	0.1	....	....	....	0
Oxygen	53.8	10.1	64.8	69.0	57.9	....	....	....	74.9
Sulphur	0	0.1	0	0	0	....	....	....	0
Ash	1.0	1.9	0.1	0.9	0.5	....	....	....	1.3
High heat value, Btu per lb	6300	13,530	4570	3630	5800	4670	4910	8130	2600

Table 10. Approximate Weights and Heat Values per Cord of Fuel Woods[a]

Variety of wood	Weight per cord containing 90 cu ft of solid wood, lb		High heat value per cord, million Btu		Equivalent in heat value to tons of coal[b]	
	Green wood	Wood with 12 percent moisture	Green wood	Wood with 12 percent moisture	Green wood	Wood with 12 percent moisture
Ash, white	4,320	3,690	26.0	28.3	1.00	1.09
Beech	4,860	4,050	27.1	31.1	1.04	1.20
Birch, yellow	5,130	3,960	27.2	30.4	1.05	1.17
Chestnut	4,950	2,700	19.2	20.7	0.75	0.80
Cottonwood	4,410	2,520	18.0	19.4	0.69	0.75
Elm, white	4,860	3,150	22.2	24.2	0.85	0.93
Hickory	5,670	4,590	29.0	35.3	1.12	1.36
Maple, sugar	5,040	3,960	27.4	30.4	1.05	1.17
Maple, red	4,500	3,420	23.7	26.3	0.91	1.01
Oak, red	5,760	3,960	27.5	30.4	1.06	1.17
Oak, white	5,670	4,230	28.7	32.5	1.10	1.25
Pine, yellow	4,770	3,240	23.7	26.0	0.91	1.00
Pine, white	3,240	2,250	17.3	18.1	0.67	0.70
Walnut, black	5,220	3,420	24.8	26.3	0.95	1.01

[a] Compiled from Use of Wood for Fuel, *U.S. Dept. Agr. Bull.* 753.
[b] Based on high heat values; 2,000 lb of coal with a heat value of 13,000 Btu per lb.

In addition to peat and wood, other **lesser-known fuels** are in common use for production of process steam and power. They are mainly the waste or by-product materials of manufacturing processes. Aside from their value as a fuel, their utilization minimizes what otherwise would be a disposal problem. The combustible material in nearly all these waste fuels is cellulose. The heating value is almost entirely that of the carbon present because the hydrogen and oxygen are present in the same proportions as in water. The ash content is usually very low, but the moisture content may be as high as 50 to 60 percent, depending on the material. The heating value generally is about 8000 Btu per lb on a moisture- and ash-free basis. Resinous materials add to the heating value and may increase the figure to 9000 Btu or more.

Wood-waste fuel is refuse material from lumber mills and paper mills and consists of sawdust, shavings, bark, and chopped-up trimmings. It contains pieces varying in size from sawdust to pieces 6 in. long and 2 in. across. It contains on the average 50 percent moisture as fired. The ash is usually less than 1 percent.

Hogged fuel is sawmill refuse that has been fed through a disintegrator, or **hog,** by which the various sizes and forms are reduced to a practically uniform size of chips or shreds.

Sawdust briquettes. Sawdust pressed into briquettes is a convenient domestic fuel. The density of such briquettes is 75 to 80 lb per cu ft, the moisture is low, and the hhv is approximately 8100 Btu per lb.

Tanbark, or spent tan, is the fibrous portion of ground oak or hemlock bark used in tanning leather. As fired, it is a pulpy mass containing 65 to 80 percent moisture. The moisture may be reduced somewhat by pressing, but the bark is commonly burned in mixture with other fuels in order to maintain combustion, about 55 percent moisture being the upper limit at which tanbark can maintain its own combustion.

Bagasse is sugar cane from which the juice has been extracted by pressure between the rolls of a mill. Its moisture content ranges from 40 to 55 percent. Dry bagasse has the following percentage composition: C, 43 to 47; H, 5.4 to 6.6; O, 45 to 49; ash, 1.5 to 3. Its hhv ranges from 8000 to 8700 Btu per lb. Bagasse will usually supply all the fuel requirements of raw-sugar mills.

Miscellaneous By-product Fuels. Other industrial by-products or wastes used as fuels include "black liquor" from the pulp-and-paper industry, guayule fiber, grain hulls, cottonseed and linseed cake, straw, furfural waste, lampblack, and spent coffee grounds. Also, some grains (*e.g.*, corn), although not classed as a by-product fuel, have been used as an emergency fuel. The moisture content and the ash and heating values on a dry basis for many of the by-product fuels are given in Table 11.

Table 11. Heating Values of Miscellaneous By-product Fuels*

	Moisture, percent	Ash,† percent	Heat value,† Btu per lb
Black liquor			
Soda	20–25	45	6200
Sulfate	35	40–45	6500
Sulfite (Ca)	45	10	8000
Guayule fiber	.....	12.0	9000
Bark (spruce)	60	5	9000
Bark (pine)	40–50	5–10	9500
Rice hulls	3–5	25	6000
Tung-oil hulls	6.0	3–4	8000
Cottonseed cake	8–10	8	9500
Linseed cake	10	12–14	8750
Flax straw	10	2.0	8250
Furfural waste	20–25	3–4	8200
Lampblack	3.0	0.5	14800
Wheat straw	10	4	8500
Spent coffee	65	1.5	10000
Corn on cob	15–18	1–1.5	8200
Shelled corn	10–12	1–1.5	9300

* Compiled from *Combustion*, Jan., 1951, p. 35.
† Dry basis.

PETROLEUM AND OTHER LIQUID FUELS

By R. M. Gooding

REFERENCES: Guthrie, "Petroleum Products Handbook," McGraw-Hill. Nelson, "Petroleum Refinery Engineering," McGraw-Hill. Bell, "American Petroleum Refining," Van Nostrand. Institute of Petroleum, "Modern Petroleum Technology." Shell International Petroleum, "The Petroleum Handbook." Gruse and Stevens, "Chemical Technology of Petroleum," McGraw-Hill. Publications of ASTM and API.

Detailed information on sampling of petroleum and petroleum products is given in *Federal Test Method Standard* 791 or in ASTM D270. Brief descriptions of methods of analysis and testing, with their ASTM designations, are given in this section. For complete descriptions, see *Standards on Petroleum Products and Lubricants*, issued annually by the ASTM, or ASTM *Book of Standards*, parts 17 and 18, issued annually in January.

Crude Oils and Petroleum Products

Petroleum products are derived from **crude oil** recovered from the earth through wells. This material is a mineral oil containing many hydrocarbons, and its specific characteristics vary considerably. Crudes from the Pennsylvania–New York producing fields deposit a waxy material, paraffin, when chilled and are known as "paraffin-base" oils. California and Gulf Coast oils sometimes contain asphaltic materials and are often called "asphalt-base" oils, but the term "naphthene base" is preferable because the better grade oils of this type contain little if any asphalt. "Intermediate-base" oils, produced in the mid-continent fields, have some characteristics of both paraffin- and naphthene-base oils. About 85 percent of the crude oils of the world belong in the three preceding classes.

The **specific gravity** of crude oils is generally between 0.80 and 0.97, and the API gravity is from 45 to 15 deg. The flash point is usually below 90 F, and the ultimate composition by weight is 84 to 88 percent carbon and 11.5 to 14.5 percent hydrogen, with small percentages of impurities, such as water, sulphur, oxygen, and nitrogen. Sulphur is often less than 1 percent, but it may be as high as 4 to 5 percent. Table 12 gives data on crude oils from various fields and on their distillates.

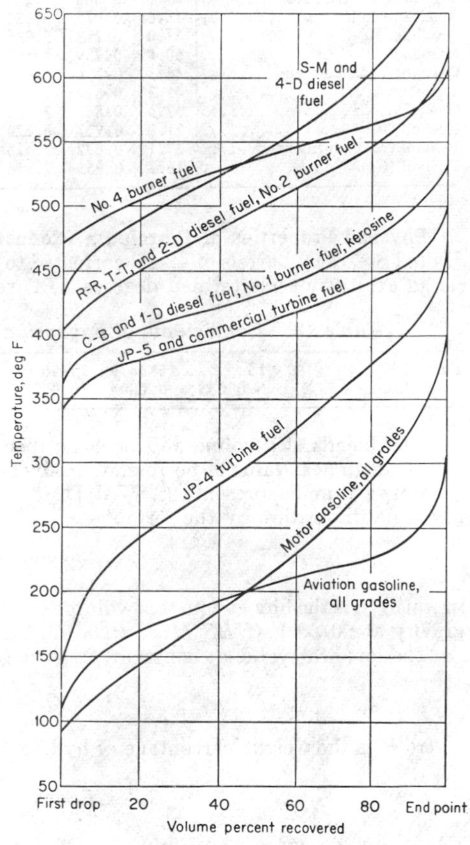

FIG. 2. Typical distillation curves.

Refining Crude Oil. Crude oils are seldom used as fuel because they are more valuable when refined to petroleum products. Distillation separates the crude oil into fractions equivalent in boiling range to gasoline, kerosine, gas oil, lubricating oil, and a residual. Thermal or catalytic cracking is used to convert kerosine, gas oil, or residual to gasoline, lower-boiling fractions, and a residual coke. Catalytic reforming, isomerization, alkylation, polymerization, hydrogenation, and combinations of these catalytic processes are used to upgrade the various refinery intermediates into improved gasoline stocks or distillates. The major finished products are usually blends of a number of stocks, plus additives. Distillation curves for these products are shown in Fig. 2.

Table 12. Analyses and High Heat Values of Crude Petroleum, Typical Distillates, and Fuel Oils

Product	Gravity, deg API	Specific gravity at 60 F	Wt per gal, lb	High heat value, Btu per lb	Ultimate analysis, percent				
					C	H	S	N	O
California crude	22.8	0.917	7.636	18,910	84.00	12.70	0.75	1.70	1.20
Kansas crude	22.1	0.921	7.670	19,130	84.15	13.00	1.90	0.45	
Oklahoma crude	31.3	0.869	7.236	19,502	85.70	13.11	0.40	0.30	
Oklahoma crude	31.0	0.871	7.253	19,486	85.00	12.90	0.76		
Pennsylvania crude	42.6	0.813	6.769	19,505	86.06	13.88	0.06	0.00	0.00
Texas crude	30.2	0.875	7.286	19,460	85.05	12.30	1.75	0.70	0.00
Wyoming crude	31.5	0.868	7.228	19,510					
Mexican crude	13.6	0.975	8.120	18,755	83.70	10.20	4.15		
Gasoline	67.0	0.713	5.935	....	84.3	15.7			
Gasoline	60.0	0.739	6.152	20,750	84.90	14.76	0.08		
Gasoline-benzene blend	46.3	0.796	6.627	....	88.3	11.7			
Kerosene	41.3	0.819	6.819	19,810					
Gas oil	32.5	0.863	7.186	19,200					
Fuel oil (Mex.)	11.9	0.987	8.220	18,510	84.02	10.06	4.93		
Fuel oil (mid-continent)	27.1	0.892	7.428	19,376	85.62	11.98	0.35	0.50	0.60
Fuel oil (Calif.)	16.7	0.9554	7.956	18,835	84.67	12.36	1.16		

Physical Properties of Petroleum Products. Petroleum products are sold in the United States by barrels of 42 gal corrected to 60 F. Their *specific gravity* is expressed on an arbitrary scale termed degrees API (see p. 1–88).

Table 13. Coefficients of Expansion of Petroleum Products at 60 F

Deg API	<15	15–34.9	35–50.9	51–63.9	64–78.9	79–88.9	89–93.9	94–100
Coef of expansion, F	0.00035	0.0004	0.0005	0.0006	0.0007	0.0008	0.00085	0.0009

Fuel blends of gasoline and benzene (benzol) have a coefficient of 0.0006.

The **high heat value** of petroleum products is determined by combustion in a bomb with oxygen under pressure (ASTM D240). It may also be calculated, in products free from impurities, by the formula

$$Q_v = 22{,}320 - 3{,}780d^2$$

in which Q_v is the hhv at constant volume (see p. 4–70) in Btu per lb and d is the specific gravity at 60/60 F (*NBS Misc. Pub.* 97, 1929).

The low heat value at constant pressure Q_p may be calculated by the relation

$$Q_p = Q_v - 90.8H$$

where H is the weight percentage of hydrogen and can be obtained from the relation

$$H = 26 - 15d$$

For the slight difference between heat values at constant volume and at constant pressure see p. 4–70ff.

Typical heats of combustion of petroleum oils free from water, ash, and sulphur are given in Table 14 with an estimated accuracy of 1 percent for normal products.

The heat value should be corrected for appreciable percentages of non-combustible material present. When the oil contains much sulphur, the results may be corrected by using a hhv of 4050 Btu per lb for sulphur. Calculation of net heat of combustion for aviation gasolines and aircraft turbine fuels is detailed in ASTM D1405. The calculation is based on the correlation of determined values with the aniline-gravity products for these types of fuels.

Table 14. Heat Values of Petroleum Oils

Deg API at 60 F	Density, lb per gal[a]	High heat value at constant volume Q_v, Btu		Low heat value at constant pressure Q_p, Btu	
		Per lb	Per gal	Per lb	Per gal
10	8.337	18,540	154,600	17,540	146,200
20	7.787	19,020	148,100	17,930	139,600
30	7.305	19,420	141,800	18,250	133,300
40	6.879	19,750	135,800	18,510	127,300
50	6.500	20,020	130,100	18,720	121,700
60	6.160	20,260	124,800	18,900	116,400
70	5.855	20,460	119,800	19,020	112,500
80	5.578	20,630	115,100	19,180	107,000

[a] The values in this column are true values obtained by correcting all weights for the buoyancy of air. The values given on p 1-88 are for weights in standard air.

The **specific heat** c of petroleum products at temperature t (deg F) is given by the equation

$$c = (0.388 + 0.00045t)/\sqrt{d}$$

Values from this equation are in good agreement for oils from intermediate-base crude oils, about 2 percent high for oils from paraffin crudes, and about 2 percent low for oils from naphthene-base crudes. Values are not more than 4 percent high for highly cracked oils. The values are probably too low for pressures much above 100 psi.

The **heat of vaporization** L (Btu per lb) may be calculated from the equation

$$L = (110.9 - 0.09t)/d$$

The heat of vaporization per gallon (measured at 60 F) is

$$8.34Ld = 925 - 0.75t$$

indicating that the heat of vaporization per gallon is dependent only on the temperature of vaporization, t. Typical data for petroleum products are given in Table 15 (*NBS Misc. Pub.* 97, 1929, p. 34).

The estimated accuracy of the preceding data is 10 percent, when the vaporization is at sensibly constant temperature and at pressures below 50 psi, without chemical change. The values are too high for vaporization at high pressures and too low by more than 10 percent for products containing large quantities of lower members of the aromatic series (benzol).

Table 15. Latent Heat of Vaporization of Petroleum Products

Product	Gravity, deg API	Average boiling temp, deg F	Heat of vaporization	
			Btu per lb	Btu per gal
Gasoline........	60	280	116	715
Naphtha........	50	340	103	670
Kerosine........	40	440	86	595
Fuel oil.........	30	580	67	490

Gasoline is a complex mixture of hydrocarbons which distills within the range 100 to 400 F. Commercial gasolines are blends of straight-run, cracked, reformed, and natural gasolines.

Straight-run gasoline is recovered from crude petroleum by simple distillation and contains a large proportion of normal hydrocarbons of the paraffin series. Its octane number (see p. 9-125) is often too low for use in modern engines, and it is blended with other products to improve its properties.

Cracked gasoline is manufactured by heating crude petroleum distillation fractions or residues under pressure, or by heating with or without pressure in the presence of a catalyst. Heavier hydrocarbons are broken into others, some of which distill in the gasoline range. The octane number is usually above that of straight-run gasoline.

Reformed gasoline is made by passing gasoline fractions over catalysts in such a manner that the low-octane-number hydrocarbons are molecularly rearranged to high-octane-number components. Many of the catalysts use platinum as the active material.

Natural gasoline is obtained from natural gas by liquefying those constituents which boil in the gasoline range either by compression and cooling or by absorption in oil. Natural gasoline is too volatile for general use, but proper characteristics can be secured by distillation or by blending. It is often blended with less volatile gasolines to improve their characteristics.

Hydrogenation now is used extensively to upgrade gasoline and cracking stocks and, in combination with catalysts, as a cracking process. Hydrogenation improves octane number, removes sulphur and nitrogen, and increases storage stability.

Properties and Specifications for Motor Gasoline. The tentative specifications of the ASTM (D439) provide for three types of gasoline: Type A, for use under normal conditions; Type B, for use where a gasoline of greater over-all volatility than Type A is desired; Type C, for use where a relatively non-volatile fuel is desired. The detailed requirements of these types are given in Table 16. The test methods for motor gasolines are described in detail in the annual ASTM publication *Standards on Petroleum Products and Lubricants.* The significance of these tests is discussed in the appendix of ASTM D439, "Significance of ASTM Specifications for Motor Gasolines." Military and Federal specifications for motor gasolines are set forth in MIL-G-3056B, VV-G-76a, and VV-G-109. The latter is for an unleaded gasoline for use in appliances and for special purposes. MIL-G-3056B and VV-G-76a differ in some particulars from ASTM D439, including lower maximum vapor pressures and higher octane-number minimums.

Table 16. Gasoline Specifications (ASTM D439)

Test	ASTM method	Type A	Type B	Type C
Distillation, min				
% evaporation at specified temp........	D86			
10%, F..........	......	W—140 F—149 S—158	W—140 F—149 S—158	167
50%, F..........	......	284	257	284
90%, F..........	......	392	356	392
Residue, max, %..........	......	2	2	2
Vapor pressure, max,				
psi at 100 F..........	D323	W—15.0 F—11.5 S—10.0	W—15.0 F—11.5 S—10.0	W—15.0 F—11.5 S—10.0
Octane number, min..........	D908	87 or 96*	87 or 96*	*
Corrosion, max..........	D130	No. 1	No. 1	No. 1
Gum, max, mg per 100 ml..........	D381	5†	5†	5†
Sulphur..........	D1266	‡	‡	‡

W, F, S: seasonal variations, approximately winter, fall, and summer. Vapor pressure specified depends upon atmospheric temperature expected.

* Octane number to be agreed upon between purchaser and seller. In 1963, 96 octane number was minimum for premium-priced gasolines; 87 octane number was minimum for regular-priced gasolines. There was no minimum specified for third-grade or super-premium gasolines.

† Gum requirement applies to base stock if gasoline contains added non-volatile material.

‡ Technical data not adequate for general specifications. In 1963, gasolines contained up to 0.25 percent sulphur.

The API gravity of gasoline at 60 F ranges from 54 to 72 deg, and the specific gravity ranges from 0.70 to 0.76. The composition of refined gasoline is approximately 84 to 86 percent carbon, 16 to 14 percent hydrogen, less than 0.3 percent sulphur, and negligible percentages of oxygen and nitrogen. The hhv is between 20000 and 20750 Btu per lb.

Knock characteristics (detonation) of motor fuels and aviation gasolines are most important because engine power output and economy are limited by the octane number of the fuel consumed. For knock rating of fuels, see p. 9–125. Octane numbers are a function of hydrocarbon type and of additives. Paraffinic hydrocarbons have low octane numbers, naphthenes have intermediate values, and isoparaffins and aromatics have high octane values. Characteristics *of* motor gasolines are shown in semiannual surveys of marketed products (*B of M PPS* 30). In 1963, average research-method octane numbers for motor gasolines were: regular, 92.4; premium, 99.5; and super-premium, 102.1.

Motor-gasoline Additives. Tetraethyl lead (TEL), $Pb(C_2H_5)_4$, has been added to motor fuels for 40 years to improve combustion characteristics by limiting knock, or detonation. Today tetramethyl lead, $Pb(CH_3)_4$, and the methylethyl lead alkyls are quite effective in some gasolines, as are mixtures of these with TEL. In 1963, the average lead content of regular gasoline was 1.8 g per gal; premium gasoline contained 2.6 g per gal. The lead compounds are added in the form of ethyl fluid, containing ethylene dibromide or ethylene dichloride, or both, as scavengers that cause the resultant lead compounds to volatilize and pass out the engine exhaust. Certain manganese compounds can also be added as a supplement to the lead compounds to improve octane number.

To minimize some of the harmful effects of lead additives, phosphorus compounds are used to control sparkplug fouling. Phosphorus and boron compounds are added to modify deposit formations in combustion chambers and to eliminate surface-ignition problems.

As TEL and the other lead compounds are poisonous and the use of leaded gasolines for purposes other than engine fuel can be hazardous all leaded gasolines must be dyed. The concentration required is small—4 to 5 ppm.

Oxidation and corrosion inhibitors and metal deactivators have been added to motor fuels for years to prevent gum formation and retard corrosion. Metal deactivators inhibit gum formation caused by copper in gasolines and are effective in concentrations not exceeding 1 ppm. Maximum concentration of the usual oxidation and corrosion inhibitors does not exceed 20 ppm.

Surface active materials are now used in gasolines to **prevent icing** in carburetors. Other materials are blended into the fuel to control freezing of water in fuel lines. Some refiners have added light lubricating oils to their gasolines as **upper-cylinder lubricants** in order to provide lubrication in cold engines during warm-up. **Carburetor detergents** also are helpful in dispersing solids such as dust, that enter the engine. Concentrations of these additives range up to 2,000 ppm.

Aviation Gasolines. Most aircraft piston engines require a gasoline of greater over-all volatility to secure even distribution to the cylinders, but low-boiling constituents are undesirable because of their tendency to cause vapor lock and icing of the carburetor. The military specifications (MIL-G-5572C, June, 1960) for four grades of aviation gasoline differ in some details from the ASTM D910 specifications for commercial aviation fuels. Grade 108/135, described in ASTM D910, is no longer in demand. The four grades are indicated in Table 17. Specifications applicable to all four grades are given in Table 18.

Table 17. Aviation Gasoline Grades (MIL-G-5572C)

Grade	Color	Tetraethyl lead content, ml per gal, max	Knock rating, min*	
			Lean mixture	Rich mixture
80/87	Red	0.50	80.0	
91/96	Blue	4.50	91.0	96.0
100/130	Green	4.50	100.0	130.0
115/145	Purple	4.50	115.0	145.0

* Knock ratings above 100.0 reported as performance numbers.

High-octane fuels are available in quantity. Two types of performance are required: (1) good antiknock characteristics at cruising speeds when lean mixtures are used, and (2) good antiknock characteristics under take-off or acceleration conditions when rich mixtures are used. Two test methods, **aviation,** or lean mixture (ASTM D614), and **supercharge,** or rich mixture (ASTM D909), have been developed to measure these characteristics. It is permissible to determine the lean-mixture rating alternatively by the motor method (ASTM D357).

Table 18. Aviation Gasoline Specifications—All Grades (MIL-G-5572C)

Test	Test limit	Test method
Distillation:		
Fuel evaporated, 10% min at	167 F	ASTM D86
Fuel evaporated, 40% max at	167 F	
Fuel evaporated, 50% min at	221 F	
Fuel evaporated, 90% min at	275 F	
End point, max	338 F	
Sum of 10% and 50% evaporated temp, min	307 F	
Residue, vol percent, max	1.5	
Distillation loss, vol percent, max	1.5	
Existent gum, max, mg/100 ml	3.0	ASTM D381
Potential gum, 16-hr aging, max, mg/100 ml	6.0	ASTM D873
Precipitate, max, mg/100 ml	2.0	ASTM D873
Sulphur, total, wt percent, max	0.05	ASTM D1266
Reid vapor press, min, psi at 100 F	5.5	ASTM D323
Reid vapor press, max, psi at 100 F	7.0	ASTM D323
Freezing point, max, F	−76	ASTM D1477
Copper-strip corrosion, ASTM class, max	No. 1	ASTM D130
Water reaction:		
Vol change, max, ml	2	FS 3251
Interface rating, max	2	FS 3251
Heat of combustion (lower or net), min, Btu/lb	18700*	ASTM D240
or		
Aniline-gravity product, min	7500*	ASTM D611 and ASTM D287

* For grade 115/145, the minimums are 18900 and 10000.

Special high-octane blending agents are essential components of aviation gasolines. These include alkylates, primarily the butane type; aromatics, principally toluene; catalytic-base stocks; isopentane; neohexane; and reformates. In addition to the required dyes and the tetraethyl lead added to these gasolines, MIL-G-5572C also specifies the types and quantities of oxidation and corrosion inhibitors to be included in the delivered products.

Jet or aviation turbine fuels are not limited by antiknock requirements and can have wider boiling ranges. Military specification MIL-J-5624F, Sept., 1962, covers two grades of jet fuel. Fuel JP-4 is a relatively wide-boiling-range distillate produced by blending gasoline and kerosine stocks, with an average initial boiling point of 140 F and an end point of 470 F. Fuel JP-5 is a high-flash-point kerosine-type fuel, initial boiling point of 355 F and end point of 490 F. Military procurement in 1963 was 90 percent JP-4 and 10 percent JP-5.

ASTM D1655 covers three grades of jet fuel: Type A is similar to JP-5, Type B is similar to JP-4, and Type A-1 is similar to Type A except for special low-temperature operational characteristics. Commercial purchases are primarily Types A and A-1.

Military specifications MIL-J-25656B and MIL-F-23188 cover fuel JP-6 for land-based supersonic craft and fuel MP-1 for multipurpose use in the Antarctic. There is limited production of both types. A thermally stable jet fuel is under development (1964) for military use. Requirements for the two major military jet fuels are shown in part in Table 19.

The conformance of aviation gasolines and jet fuels to current specifications is shown by data in the annual surveys of such fuels (*B of M PPS* 29). Antioxidants, corrosion inhibitors, and metal deactivators are used in jet fuels, and an icing inhibitor is specified for JP-4 (MIL-1-27686).

Kerosine. Kerosine is less volatile and is obtained by continuing the distillation of crude oil after gasoline has been recovered. Light hydrogenation or treatment with sulphuric acid can be used to improve quality. Most kerosine is used for illuminating purposes or as fuel in wick-fed burners. Small quantities are used as tractor or motor fuel. General properties are: API gravity, 50 to 35 deg at 60 F; sp gr, 0.78 to 0.85 at 60/60 F; flash point, 100 to 160 F; hhv, 19400 to 20200 Btu per lb; distillation range, 200 to 600 F; not over 0.5 wt percent sulphur, and negligible amounts of nitrogen and oxygen. The essential property of kerosine is that it burns satisfactorily in a wick burner (ASTM D187). Detailed requirements are given in Federal specification VV-K-211.

Table 19. Jet or Aviation Turbine Fuels (MIL-J-5624F)

Test	Test limits		Test method
	JP-4	JP-5	
Distillation:			D86
Fuel evaporated, 10% min at		400 F	
Fuel evaporated, 20% min at	290 F		
Fuel evaporated, 50% min at	370 F		
Fuel evaporated, 90% min at	470 F		
End point, max		550 F	
Residue, vol percent, max	1.5	1.5	
Distillation loss, vol percent, max	1.5	1.5	
Gravity, deg API, min (sp gr, max)	45.0 (0.802)	36.0 (0.845)	D287
Gravity, deg API, max (sp gr, min)	57.0 (0.751)	48.0 (0.788)	D287
Existent gum, mg/100 ml, max	7	7	D381
Total potential residue, 16-hr aging, mg/100 ml, max	14	14	D873
Sulfur, total, wt percent, max	0.4	0.4	D1266
Mercaptan sulphur, wt percent, max	0.001	0.001	D1219 or D1323
Reid vapor press, min, psi at 100 F	2.0		D323
Reid vapor press, max, psi at 100 F	3.0		D323
Freezing point, max	−76 F	−55 F	D1477
Heat of combustion (lower or net) min, Btu per lb	18400	18300	D240
or			
Aniline-gravity product, min	5250	4500	D611 and D287
Viscosity, centistokes at −30 F, max		16.5	D445
Aromatics, vol percent, max	25.0	25.0	D1319
Olefins, vol percent, max	5.0	5.0	D1319

Refer to MIL-J-5624F and ASTM D1655 for full details.

Gas oil is recovered in the distillation of petroleum between kerosine and light lubricating oil. Its name was derived from its once extensive use in making illuminating gas. This distillate now is used as cracking stock, Diesel fuel, and burner fuel.

Diesel fuel varies in its characteristics, ranging from light distillates to residual fuels, depending on the engines to be fueled. API gravity ranges from 47 to 11 deg at 60 F; sp gr, from 0.80 to 0.99 at 60/60 F; hhv from 18500 to 20000 Btu per lb; distillation range from 310 to over 600 F; and sulphur, up to 2.3 wt percent in the heavy grades. ASTM D975 provides for three grades of Diesel fuel, as shown in Table 20. Also shown in Table 20 are the requirements for a high-quality marine Diesel fuel as detailed in MIL-F-16884D, as amended April, 1963. The ASTM grades indicate fuels suitable for different classes of engines and service. (See also p. 9–124 *et seq.*)

GRADE 1-D. A volatile distillate fuel oil for engines in service requiring frequent speed and load changes.

GRADE 2-D. A distillate fuel oil of lower volatility, for engines in industrial and heavy mobile service.

GRADE 4-D. A fuel oil for low- and medium-speed engines.

The requirements of Diesel fuels, particularly those for high-speed engines, are still being developed. This is especially true for fuels used by the railroads, where fuel costs are a major expense. Engine speed and design are important, and these are related to viscosity and cleanliness. Ignition quality as measured by **cetane number** (see p. 9–127) is significant but is not now felt to be as important as in past years. To accommodate the special and changing requirements of the railroads, the refiners now offer four grades of Diesel fuel not covered by industrywide specifications. These four grades are described, as follows, in the annual surveys of commercial Diesel fuels (*B of M PPS* 32).

TYPE C-B. Diesel fuel oils for city-bus and similar operations.

TYPE T-T. Fuels for Diesel engines in trucks, tractors, and similar service.

TYPE R-R. Fuel for railroad Diesel engines.

TYPE S-M. Heavy-distillate and residual fuels for large stationary and marine Diesel engines.

In 1963, the average cetane number for Type C-B fuel was 51; for Type T-T, 50; for Type R-R, 47; and for Type S-M, 41. Cetane number is determined by engine

Table 20. Specifications for Diesel Fuels (ASTM D975)

Test	ASTM method	Grade of Diesel fuel 1-D	2-D	4-D	U.S. Military spec. MIL-F-16884D
		Limit			
Flash point, min, deg F	D93	100 or legal	125 or legal	130 or legal	150
Water and sediment, vol percent, max	D1796	Trace	0.10	0.50	0.01
Viscosity, kinematic, centistokes, 100 F	D445				
Min		1.4	2.0	5.8	2.1
Max		2.5	5.8	26.4	6.0
Carbon residue, wt percent, max	D524	0.15	0.35		0.20
Ash, wt percent, max	D482	0.01	0.02	0.10	0.005
Sulphur, wt percent, max	D129	0.50	1.0	2.0	1.00
Ignition quality, cetane number, min	D613	40	40	30	47
Distillation temp, deg F	D86				
90 % evaporated:					
Min			540		
Max		550	576		675

See ASTM D975 and MIL-F-16884D for full details.

test (ASTM D613), or a **cetane index** can be calculated for most fuels without additives for raising the cetane number. The calculation is based on specific gravity and the midboiling point of the fuel. (See Appendix II of ASTM D975.) The significance of the ASTM classification of Diesel fuel oils is discussed in Appendix I of ASTM D975.

The test for **water and sediment** is used to ensure clean fuels, and the **ash-content** test indicates fuel cleanliness and freedom from abrasive material. **Carbon-residue** determinations give a measure of possible carbon deposits that might form in the engine. The minimum-**viscosity** limits provide for fuels that will lubricate closely fitted engine parts, and the maximum limits ensure proper fuel atomization. Fuel Grades 1-D and 2-D and Types C-B, T-T, and R-R almost universally meet the necessary requirements. Type S-M fuels practically all meet the requirements tabulated above for Grade 4-D and for the intended service. Limitations on **distillation characteristics** are set to exclude too much residual material that might form cylinder deposits or might cause erratic fuel combustion.

The list of **additives** incorporated in Diesel fuels has grown in recent years because of problems associated with cracked stocks used in these fuels. Cetane-number improvers have been used successfully for many years, with amyl nitrate the principal additive. Metal deactivators, corrosion inhibitors, antioxidants, rust inhibitors and dispersants all are used in many fuels. Dispersants have been added in recent years to prevent agglomeration of gum or sludge deposits and thus allow these sludges to pass through filters and engine parts without plugging them. The dispersed solids burn with the fuel.

Fuel Oils. The characteristics of the several ASTM grades of distillate fuel oils are similar to those of like grades or types of Diesel fuels. Many refiners produce only one product to meet the requirements of the individual grades of Diesel and burner fuels. Six grades of fuel oil are described in ASTM D396. Military specification MIL-F-859D details requirements of two grades of heavy fuel oil for steam-powered vessels and shore installations: **Navy special** and **heavy.** The ASTM grades are:

No. 1. A distillate oil intended for vaporizing pot-type burners and other burners requiring this grade of fuel. (Similar to Grade 1-D and Type C-B Diesel fuel.)

No. 2. A distillate oil for general-purpose domestic heating in burners not requiring No. 1 fuel oil. (Similar to Grade 2-D and Types T-T and R-R Diesel fuel.)

No. 4. Preheating not usually required for handling or burning. (Similar to Grade 4-D and Type S-M Diesel fuel.)

No. 5 (Light). Preheating may be required, depending on climate and equipment.

No. 5. (Heavy). Preheating required for burning; in cold climates, it may be required for handling.

No. 6. Preheating required for burning and handling.

The only difference in the specifications for No. 5 (light) and No. 5 (heavy) fuels is in the viscosity requirements. For No. 5 (light), the Saybolt viscosity, universal at 100 F, must be 150 sec and not over 300 sec. For No. 5 (heavy), the lower limit is 350 sec and the upper is 750 sec.

Burner fuels have no cetane-number requirements, and no additives are needed to improve the cetane number. In addition to metal deactivators, corrosion inhibitors, antioxidants, rust inhibitors, and dispersants, some fuel oils contain combustion improvers.

Properties of burner fuel oils marketed in the United States in 1963 are detailed in the annual survey (*B of M PPS* 31).

Miscellaneous Liquid Fuels

Coal tar is recovered as a by-product from the carbonization of coal; its specific characteristics vary with the temperature to which the coal has been heated during carbonization and the duration of the process. Changes in characteristics are gradual as the temperature of carbonization increases and have the following limits for the range 932 to 2012 F: sp gr, 0.95 to 1.25 at 60/60 F; hhv, 17,300 to 16,000 Btu per lb; distillate to 662 F, 60 to 35 percent; pitch (residue), 40 to 65 percent; ultimate analysis in percent, carbon 84 to 91, hydrogen, 9 to 5, oxygen 7 to 2 (Fieldner and Davis, Gas-, Coke-, and Byproduct-making Properties of American Coals and Their Determination, *B of M, Monograph* 5, 1934). Oxygen in tars is affected by the rank of the coal carbonized; nitrogen (0.6 to 1.3 percent) and sulphur (0.3 to 1.0 percent) are influenced by characteristics of the coal.

Tars consist principally of aromatic compounds. The distillate (up to 662 F) contains tar bases, tar acids, and neutral oils. The neutral oils predominate in quantity, but their characteristics change as the temperature of coal carbonization is increased. In the above-mentioned temperature range, the aromatic constituents increase from 45 to 85 percent; paraffins decrease from 45 to 5 percent; olefins (unsaturated compounds) remain essentially constant (10 percent).

Coal tar can be burned with equipment suitable for heavy fuel oils if it is preheated to reduce its viscosity and aid atomization. Such use in the United States is limited. In Europe, tar distillates, particularly the neutral oils, are used as fuel for internal-combustion engines, primarily those of the Diesel type. Results are fairly satisfactory with low-speed engines, but high-speed engines give better results if these oils are improved by blending with better fuels. In either instance starting the engine is likely to be difficult.

Benzene, C_6H_6, is a by-product of high-temperature coal carbonization, and a product now derived in large quantities from petroleum. Benzene was used in past years as a blending component of gasolines to increase octane number, but demand for benzene as a solvent and as a starting material for synthetic rubber components, for plastics, and for petrochemicals precludes its addition to motor gasolines to any extent. Most gasolines do contain significant percentages of both benzene and toluene.

Ethyl alcohol, C_2H_5OH (grain alcohol), has been used for many years as a motor fuel when blended with gasoline, particularly in Europe. From 5 to 25 percent of anhydrous alcohol is used in commercial blends. Technical advantages are claimed owing to the high octane number of alcohol, 99, and the high latent heat of vaporization, 368 Btu per lb. The hhv, 12,810 Btu per lb, is relatively low when compared with gasoline so that the specific fuel consumption for maximum power is greater. The specific gravity is 0.794 at 60/60 F.

Alcohol-gasoline blends tend to separate in the presence of water. Their stability can be improved by suitable blending agents (benzene, toluene, and higher alcohols). The performance of blends in the range cited is essentially equivalent to that of gasoline alone except that cold starting may be more difficult. Troubles from increased corrosion and solvent action have been reported. (For further considerations see Symposium on Motor Fuels, *Ind. Eng. Chem.*, **28,** Sept., 1936, pp. 1080–1112.)

Methyl alcohol, CH_3OH (wood alcohol), is occasionally used in special fuel blends. Its octane number is 98; hhv, 9600 Btu per lb; and sp gr, 0.797 at 60/60 F.

Coal-in-oil suspensions, sometimes referred to as **colloidal fuels,** are fluid mixtures of pulverized coal dispersed in either fuel oil or coal-tar oil. Tests indicate a practical fuel can be prepared by dispersing 40 percent by weight of pulverized coal (98 to 99 percent through 230 mesh sieve) in heavy fuel oil (Barkley, Hersberger, and Burdick, *Trans. ASME,* **66,** 1944, p. 185). The best opportunity for the successful use of coal-in-oil suspensions is in large installations.

Synthetic Liquid Fuels. The two major processes for producing synthetic liquid fuels are (1) hydrogenation of coal, based on the Bergius process, and (2) synthesis by the catalytic reduction of carbon monoxide with hydrogen, using the Fischer-Tropsch type of reaction. Both processes have operated commercially outside the Western Hemisphere, and research continues in the United States on the adaptation of the methods to the resources and economy of the United States.

Shale oil is produced by heating or retorting solid oil shale. At high temperatures, the organic matter in shale, commonly called **kerogen,** changes into oil, gas, and carbon. From crude shale oil, products closely resembling those produced from petroleum can be prepared by distillation and refining processes similar to those used in refining petroleum. The equivalent of 1 trillion barrels of shale oil is contained in deposits in Colorado, Utah, and Wyoming. Commercial operations have been in use in Europe, Africa, and Asia. Experimental production has been demonstrated in Colorado. Commercial units can be expected in the United States in a few years, to supplement crude-oil and natural-gas supplies. In addition to conventional retorting processes, research has been proposed for *in situ* production, or retorting of oil shale in place without mining. Typically, raw Colorado oil shale has a specific gravity of 2.1, a total heat value of 2780 Btu per lb, and an ash content of 68 wt percent. Upon retorting by the Fischer assay method, the shale oil produced—about 30 gal per ton of shale—has a specific gravity of 0.92, a pour point of 80 F, a carbon-hydrogen ratio of 7.3, and a total heat value of 18400 Btu per lb.

GASEOUS FUELS

By R. M. Gooding

REFERENCES: Lewis and von Elbe, "Combustion, Flames and Explosions of Gases," Academic Press. Katz et al., "Handbook of Natural Gas Engineering," McGraw-Hill. AGA, "Natural Gas Handbook." Publications of AGA, API, ASTM, B of M, and IGT.

Natural gas, the primary gaseous fuel in the United States, accounts for 98 percent of all gas deliveries to ultimate consumers by gas utilities and pipelines. Natural gas occurs in underground reservoirs separately or in association with crude petroleum. Annual marketed production exceeds 14 trillion cu ft.

Manufactured gas is a fuel gas made from other solid, liquid, or gaseous materials, such as coal, coke, oil, or natural gas. The principal types of manufactured gas are retort coal gas, coke-oven gas, water gas, carbureted water gas, producer gas, oil gas, reformed natural gas, and reformed propane or liquefied petroleum gas.

Mixed gas is a gas prepared by adding natural gas or liquefied petroleum gas to a manufactured gas, giving a product of better utility and higher heat content or Btu value.

Liquefied petroleum gas (LP gas) is a hydrocarbon mixture of propane, butane, isobutane, propylene, or butylene. The most common commercial products are propane, butane, or some mixture of the two. The propane and the butanes generally are extracted from natural gas or crude petroleum. Propylene and butylenes result from cracking other hydrocarbons in a petroleum refinery. Liquefied petroleum gas is used in some special industrial applications, is supplied directly to consumers by a few gas utilities, and is sold widely as bottled gas for use in homes, trailers, and other establishments where natural gas is not available. It is the major supplement now used during periods of peak demand.

The use of other fuels and equipment to supplement the regular supply of gas during periods of peak demand or in emergencies is known as **peak shaving.** Most gas utilities, particularly natural-gas utilities at the end of long-distance transmission lines, maintain peak-shaving or standby equipment. Also, gas utilities in many cases have established natural-gas storage facilities close to their distribution systems. This allows gas to be stored underground near the point of consumption during periods of low demand, as in summer, and then produced to supply peak or emergency demands, as in winter. Propane-air mixtures are the major supplements to natural gas for peak-shaving use. Gas manufactured from various grades of petroleum distillates supplies most of the remaining peak requirements.

Composition of Gaseous Fuels. The principal constituent of natural gas is the paraffinic hydrocarbon methane (CH_4). Other constituents are the heavier paraffinic hydrocarbons such as ethane, propane, and the butanes. Many natural gases contain from 5 to 20 percent of nitrogen, and some contain appreciable quantities of carbon dioxide and hydrogen sulphide. Trace quantities of argon, hydrogen, and helium usually are present. A portion of the heavier hydrocarbons, carbon dioxide, and hydrogen sulphide are removed from natural gas prior to its use as a fuel. Typical natural-gas analyses are given in Table 21 (for additional analyses, see *B of M Bull.* 617, 576, and 486). Manufactured gases contain methane, ethane, ethylene, propylene, hydrogen, carbon monoxide, carbon dioxide, and nitrogen, with low concentrations of water vapor, oxygen, and other gases. For descriptions of individual gas-manufacturing processes and analyses of the produced gases, see pp. 7-52 to 7-63. When natural gas or LP gases are mixed with air to modify the performance characteristics or the heat value, the resulting mixtures contain nitrogen and oxygen.

Table 21. Composition of Typical Natural Gases*

	Natural gas from oil or gas wells						Natural gas from pipelines				
Sample No.	299	318	393	522	732	1177	1214	1225	1249	1276	1358
Composition, mole percent:											
Methane	92.1	96.3	67.7	63.2	43.6	96.9	94.3	72.3	88.9	75.4	85.6
Ethane	3.8	0.1	5.6	3.1	18.3	1.7	2.1	5.9	6.3	6.4	7.8
Propane	1.0	0.0	3.1	1.7	14.2	0.3	0.4	2.7	1.8	3.6	1.4
Normal butane	0.3	0.0	1.5	0.5	8.6	0.1	0.2	0.3	0.2	1.0	0.0
Isobutane	0.3	0.0	1.2	0.4	2.3	0.0	0.0	0.2	0.1	0.6	0.1
Normal pentane	0.1	0.0	0.6	0.1	2.7	0.3	Tr	Tr	0.0	0.1	0.0
Isopentane	Tr	0.0	0.4	0.2	3.3	0.0	Tr	0.2	Tr	0.2	0.1
Cyclopentane	Tr	0.0	0.2	Tr	0.9	Tr	Tr	0.0	Tr	Tr	0.0
Hexanes plus	0.2	0.0	0.7	0.1	2.0	0.1	Tr	Tr	Tr	0.1	Tr
Nitrogen	0.9	1.0	17.4	27.9	3.0	0.6	0.0	17.8	2.2	12.0	4.7
Oxygen	0.2	0.0	Tr	0.1	0.5	Tr	Tr	Tr	Tr	Tr	Tr
Argon	Tr	Tr	0.1	0.1	Tr	0.0	0.0	Tr	0.0	Tr	Tr
Hydrogen	0.0	0.2	0.0	0.0	0.1	0.0	Tr	0.1	0.1	0.0	0.0
Carbon dioxide	1.1	2.3	0.1	0.4	0.5	0.0	2.8	0.1	0.1	0.1	0.2
Helium	Tr	Tr	1.4	2.1	Tr	Tr	Tr	0.4	0.1	0.4	0.1
Heating value†	1062	978	1044	788	1899	1041	1010	934	1071	1044	1051
Origin of sample	La.	Miss.	N. Mex.	Okla.	Tex.	W. Va.	Colo.	Kan.	Kan.	Okla.	Tex.

* Analyses from *B of M Bull.* 617 (Tr = trace).

† Calculated total (gross) Btu per cu ft, dry, at 60 F and 30 in. Hg.

Specifications. Since the compositions of natural, manufactured, and mixed gases can vary so widely, no single set of specifications could cover all situations. The requirements are usually based on performance in burners and equipment, on minimum heat content, and on maximum sulphur content. Gas utilities in most states come under the supervision of state commissions or regulatory bodies. Some of these commissions set standards for the gas to be delivered to the consumer. Additionally, local authorities have set requirements, and in the case of natural gas, pipelines set certain requirements for gas before it is delivered to the pipeline. The utilities must provide a gas that is acceptable to all types of consumers and that will give satisfactory performance in all kinds of consuming equipment. The Federal Power Commission has not promulgated quality requirements for natural gas in interstate commerce.

As an example, the Public Service Commission of the State of New York requires in part that the monthy average Btu content of delivered gas shall not be less than 1000 and that the average for any three days shall not be less than 980. For a particular group of distribution systems, the minimum monthy average Btu values are set at 537 for mixed gas and propane-air, at 650 for propane-air, at 900 for mixed gas and propane-air, and at 950 for mixed gas. The gas as distributed shall not contain hydrogen sulphide, the total sulphur content shall not exceed 30 grains per 100 cu ft, and the ammonia content shall not exceed 5 grains per 100 cu ft. The average specific gravity shall be determined and reported.

Odorization. Since natural gas as delivered to pipelines has practically no odor, an odorant is required by most regulations in order that the presence of the gas can be detected readily in case of accidents and leaks. This odorization is provided by the addition of trace amounts of some organic sulphur compounds to the gas before it reaches the consumer. The standard requirement is that a normal person will be able to detect the presence of the gas by odor when the concentration reaches 1 percent of gas in air. Since the lower limit of flammability of natural gas is approximately 5 percent, this 1 percent requirement is essentially equivalent to one-fifth the lower limit of flammability. The combustion of these trace amounts of odorant does not create any serious problems.

Specifications for liquefied petroleum gases are set forth in ASTM D1835, as shown in Table 22. Commercial propane is a product for use in applications where high volatility is required, commercial butane is a product for use in applications where low volatility is needed, and commercial PB mixtures cover a broad range of intermediate products. Special-duty propane for use as engine fuel and for various other special purposes is described in ASTM D2154.

Table 22. Liquefied-petroleum-gas Specifications (ASTM D1835)

Test	Commercial test limits			Test method
	Propane	Butane	PB mixtures	
Vapor pressure at 100 F, max, psig	210	70	....	D1267
Evaporated temperature, 95% max, deg F	−37	36	36	D1837
Residue (end-point index), max	To be reported			D2158
Specific gravity at 60/60 F	To be reported			D1657
Corrosion, copper strip, max	No. 1	No. 1	No. 1	D1838
Sulphur content, grains per 100 cu ft, max	15	15	15	D1266
Moisture content	To be reported			
Free-water content	....	None	None	D1657

Refer to ASTM D1835 for full details.

Analysis. The different methods for gas analysis include absorption, distillation, combustion, mass spectroscopy, infrared spectroscopy, and gas chromatography. Absorption methods, such as the Orsat and Hempel, involve the absorbing of individual constituents one at a time in suitable solvents and the recording of the contraction in volume measured. Distillation methods, such as the Podbielniak, depend on the separation of constituents by fractional distillation and the measurement of the volumes distilled. In combustion methods, certain combustible elements are caused to burn to CO_2 and H_2O, and the volume changes are used to calculate composition. These combine absorption techniques in many cases. Infrared spectroscopy is useful in particular applications. For the most accurate analyses, mass spectroscopy and gas chromatography are the preferred methods.

ASTM has adopted a number of methods for gas analysis, including ASTM D1302 "Analysis of Carbureted Water Gas by the Mass Spectrometer." The mass spectrometer is the instrument used in D1137 for the analysis of natural gases and related mixtures. Gas chromatography is used in ASTM D1945 and D1946 for analyzing natural gas and reformed gas. ASTM D1136 covers a volumetric-chemical method for natural gas that is limited in accuracy. Gas chromatography is specified in ASTM D2163 for analysis of LP gases, and D1717 covers commercial butane-butylene mixtures. Recent developments are typified by the complete gas-chromatographic analysis of fixed gases using argon as gas carrier (Manka, *Anal. Chem.*, **36**, 1964, pp. 480–482).

Physical Constants. The specific gravity of gases, including LP gases, may be determined conveniently by a number of methods and a variety of instruments. An accurate (±2 percent) direct-weighing procedure and the use of two commercial instruments are detailed in ASTM D1070. An evaluation of a number of commercial instruments was made by the National Bureau of Standards in 1941(*NBS, Misc. Publ.* 177).

The heat value of gases is generally determined at constant pressure in a flow calorimeter in which the heat released by the combustion of a definite quantity of gas is absorbed by a measured quantity of water or air. The heat value is determined from the rise in temperature of the water or air (ASTM D900). A continuous-recording calorimeter is available for measuring heat values of natural gases (ASTM D1826). See p. 4–69 *et seq.* for a discussion of the combustion of fuels and for physical constants of gases and gas mixtures. More extensive data for gases have been published in "Handbook of Chemistry and Physics," The Chemical Rubber Publishing Co., Cleveland; Selected Values of Properties of Hydrocarbons and Related Compounds, *API Research Project* 44, Carnegie Institute of Technology, Pittsburgh; and *Bull.* 521, Phillips Petroleum Co., Bartlesville, Okla.

Flammability. The lower and upper limits of flammability indicate the percentage of combustible gas in air below which and above which flame will not propagate. When flame is initiated in mixtures having compositions within these limits, it will propagate and therefore the mixtures are flammable. A knowledge of flammable limits and their use in establishing safe practices in handling gaseous fuels is important, *e.g.*, when purging equipment used in gas service, in controlling factory or mine atmospheres, or in handling liquefied gases.

Many factors enter into the experimental determination of flammable limits of gas mixtures, including the diameter and length of the tube or vessel used for the test, the temperature and pressure of the gases, and the direction of flame propagation—upward or downward. For these and other reasons, great care must be used in the application of the data. In monitoring closed spaces where small amounts of gases enter the atmosphere, often the maximum concentration of the combustible gas is limited to one-fifth of the concentration of the gas at the lower limit of flammability of the gas-air mixture.

Table 23 lists the limits of flammability in air of a number of individual fuel gases and gas mixtures. Because the composition of natural and manufactured gases varies, the limits shown in Table 23 for these gases are illustrative. For further details and tabulations of other flammable limits, refer to *B of M Bull.* 503.

The calculation of flammable limits is accomplished by Le Chatelier's modification of the mixture law, which is expressed in its simplest form as

$$L = \frac{100}{(p_1/N_1 + p_2/N_2) + \cdots + p_n/N_n}$$

Table 23. Limits of Flammability of Gases in Air

Gas	Flammable limits in air, vol percent		Gas	Flammable limits in air, vol percent	
	Lower	Upper		Lower	Upper
Methane	5.3	14.0	Hydrogen	4.0	74.2
Ethane	3.0	12.5	Carbon monoxide	12.5	74.2
Propane	2.2	9.5	Ammonia	16.0	27.0
Butane	1.9	8.5	Hydrogen sulphide	4.3	45.5
Isobutane	1.8	8.4	Natural	4.8	13.5
Pentane	1.5	7.8	Producer	20.2	71.8
Isopentane	1.4	7.6	Blast-furnace	35.0	73.5
Hexane	1.2	7.5	Water	6.9	70.5
Ethylene	3.1	32.0	Carbureted-water	5.3	40.7
Propylene	2.4	10.3	Coal	4.8	33.5
Butylene	2.0	9.6	Coke-oven	4.4	34.0
Acetylene	2.5	80.0	High-Btu oil	3.9	20.1

L is the volume percentage of fuel gas in a limit mixture of air and gas; $p_1, p_2, \cdots p_n$ are the volume percentages of each combustible gas present in the fuel gas, calculated on an air- and inert-free basis so that $p_1 + p_2 \cdots + p_n = 100$; and $N_1, N_2, \cdots N_n$ are the volume percentages of each combustible gas in a limit mixture of the individual gas and air. The foregoing relation may be applied to gases with inert content of 10 percent or less without introducing an absolute error of more than 1 or 2 percent in the calculated limits. However, when the inert content exceeds 10 percent, the calculation must be modified as shown in the *B of M Tech. Paper* 450 and *Bull.* 503.

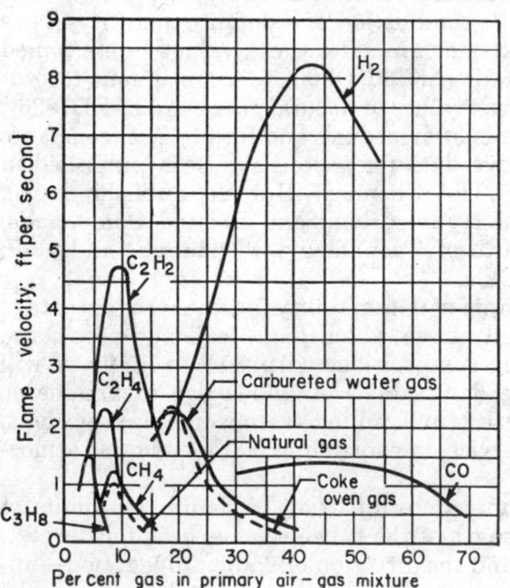

FIG. 3. Variation of flame velocities in air-gas mixtures with variation of gas content, at atmospheric pressure.

The **rate of flame propagation or burning velocity** in gas-air mixtures is of importance in utilization problems, including those dealing with burner design and rate of energy release. There are several methods that have been used for measuring such burning velocities, in both laminar and turbulent flames. Results by the various methods do not agree, but any one method does give relative values of utility. Maximum burning velocities for turbulent flames are greater than those for laminar flames. The Bunsen flame method gives results that have significance in gas-utilization problems. In this method, the burning velocity is determined by dividing the volume rate of gas flow from the Bunsen burner by the area of the inner cone of the flame. Changes in gas composition, in the ratio of fuel to air, and in temperature of the gas affect burning velocities. The burning velocity of some individual gases and gaseous fuels is shown in Fig. 3; all measurements are made at atmospheric temperature and pressure. A study of laminar Bunsen flames is reported in S. A. Weil, Burning Velocities of Hydrocarbon Flames, *IGT Research Bull.* 30, Chicago, 1961; and a study of turbulent Bunsen flames is included in *B of M Bull.* 604.

Underground Gasification. The gasification of coal in place underground was pioneered in Russia in 1931 and was used on a commercial scale in Russia for some years after 1938. Experiments were conducted in other countries, including Belgium, Great Britain, France, and the United States. The feasibility of underground gasification was shown, but economic problems and plentiful supplies of crude oil and natural gas curtailed further development efforts. The heating value of the produced gas seldom exceeded 100 Btu per cu ft. A bibliography with 800 abstracts covers the literature on underground gasification from 1945 to 1960 (*B of M Inf. Circ.* 8193).

EXPLOSIVES

By Robert W. Van Dolah

REFERENCES: Cook, "The Science of High Explosives," Reinhold. Davis, "The Chemistry of Powder and Explosives," Wiley. "Blasters Handbook," E. I. Du Pont de Nemours. "Manual on Rock Blasting," Aktiebolaget Atlas Diesel, Stockholm. Safety Recommendations for Sensitized Ammonium Nitrate Blasting Agents, *B of M Inf. Circ.* 8179, 1963.

The technology of commercial blasting has undergone revolutionary changes in recent years. Until the mid-1950s, most blasting was done using dynamites and blasting agents, the latter known in the trade as **nitrocarbonitrates (NCN). Liquid-oxygen explosives** accounted for a few percent of the total explosives consumed, and **black powder** was used for only a very small amount of blasting. The availability of low-cost, fertilizer-grade **ammonium nitrate** (AN) in convenient form—usually prilled roughly into spheres of 6- to 8-mesh size—led first to the development of a simple **AN-carbon-black** mixture (Lee and Akre, U.S. patent 2,703,528) and subsequently to **AN-fuel-oil (FO) mixtures.** The AN-FO could be readily prepared at the blasting site, leading to reduced transportation costs, and as it gave surprisingly good results when properly used, it was widely adopted, first in open-pit mines and quarries and subsequently in a wide variety of underground mines. Currently, AN-FO accounts for more than 50 percent of the explosives used in the United States. More recently still, new types of blasting agents—**a water slurry of ammonium nitrate,** either with explosive sensitizers such as TNT or smokeless powder or with non-explosive sensitizers such as aluminum powder and organic fuels—have been developed. The use of these slurries has been rapidly increasing, currently amounting to nearly 10 percent, because of their water compatibility and good performance in difficult blasting operations, such as those in taconite ores.

AN-FO blasting agents usually contain 5.5 to 6 percent fuel oil, typically No. 2 Diesel fuel. If used underground, the oil content must be carefully regulated to minimize the production of toxic fumes. Premixed AN-FO is usually shipped in 50- to 100-lb bags, although bulk shipment and storage are practiced in certain operations. The mixed product is poured into vertical boreholes or blown with air into other boreholes. Some AN-FO is packaged in 2- to 6-in. polyethylene bags for use in vertical boreholes. AN-FO has a density of 0.85 to 1.0 g per cc and a detonation velocity in the range of 10,000 to 14,000 fps. Under most conditions of blasting, AN-FO cannot be initiated simply by a blasting cap; primers are required. Commonly used **primers** are cartridges of ordinary dynamite or specially cast charges of ¼ to ¾ lb of military-type explosives such as **Composition B or pentolite.** The efficiency of AN-FO lies in the method of loading, which fills the borehole completely and provides good coupling with the burden.

Nitrocarbonitrate blasting agents consist of non-cap-sensitive mixtures of fuel and oxidizer, containing no ingredient in itself classed as an explosive. Besides AN-FO, other NCN compositions have been widely used for many years because of their lower cost and decreased hazards in storage and handling, particularly when packaged in metal cans. Density may vary from 0.9 to 1.5 g per cc; detonation velocity may range from 10,000 to 16,000 fps. Again, powerful primers must be used because of the low sensitivity of all these materials.

The **water-based slurries** fall into two classes. The most common type uses an explosive sensitizer such as **TNT or nitrostarch.** By virtue of availability, surplus Composition B and smokeless powders have been used in many compositions. The second type of slurry relies on the very energetic **aluminum-ammonium nitrate** reaction, no explosive sensitizer being used although in some cases other organic fuels may be incorporated. Both types of slurries contain a thickening agent to prevent segregation of suspended solids. A recent development has been a mobile mixing truck capable of high-speed mixing and loading of the composition directly into the large-diameter vertical boreholes. The density of the explosive-sensitized slurries is usually about 1.4 g per cc but may be as high as 1.7 g per cc for the aluminum-sensitized slurry; detonation velocities vary from 10,000 to 17,000 fps.

Dynamite is a generic term covering a multitude of nitroglycerin-sensitized mixtures of carbonaceous materials (wood flour, starch) and oxygen-supplying salts. The nitroglycerin contains ethylene glycol dinitrate or other nitrated compounds to lower its freezing point, and antacids, such as chalk or zinc oxide, are added to dynamites for improved storage life. Dynamites are divided into non-gelatinous and gelatinous types, the latter containing nitrocellulose.

Straight dynamites are graded by the percentage of explosive oil they contain; this may be as low as 15 percent and as high as 60 percent. A typical percentage formulation for a 40 percent straight dynamite is: nitroglycerin, 40; sodium nitrate, 44; antacid, 2; carbonaceous material, 14. The rate of detonation increases with grade from 9,000 to 19,000 fps. Straight dynamites now find common use only in ditching where propagation by influence is practiced.

Ammonia dynamites differ from straight dynamites in that some of the sodium nitrate and much of the explosive oil have been replaced by ammonium nitrate. Strength of ammonia dynamites ranges from 15 to 60 percent, each grade having the same weight strength as the corresponding straight dynamite when compared in the ballistic mortar. A typical percentage formula for a 40 percent ammonia dynamite is: explosive oil, 14; ammonium nitrate, 36; sodium nitrate, 33; antacid, 1; carbonaceous material, 16. The rate of detonation, 4,000 to 17,000 fps, again increases with grade. Low-density, high-weight-strength compositions are popular in many applications.

Blasting gelatin is the strongest and highest-velocity explosive used in industrial operations. It consists essentially of explosive oil (nitroglycerin plus ethylene glycol dinitrate) colloided with about 7 percent nitrocellulose. It is completely water-resistant but has a poor fume rating and consequently finds only limited use.

Gelatin dynamites correspond to straight dynamites except that the explosive oil has been gelatinized by nitrocellulose; this results in a cohesive mixture having improved water resistance. Under confinement, the gelatins develop high velocity, ranging from 8,500 to 22,000 fps and increasing between the grades of 20 and 90 percent. An approximate percentage composition for a 40 percent grade is: explosive oil, 32; nitrocellulose, 0.7; sulphur, 2; sodium nitrate, 52; antacid, 1.5; and carbonaceous material, 11. In the common grades of 40 and 60 percent, fume characteristics are good, making these types useful for underground hard-rock blasting.

Ammonia gelatin dynamites are similar to the ammonia dynamites except for their nitrocellulose content. These used to be popular in quarrying and hard-rock mining. Their excellent fume characteristics make them suitable for use underground, but they have been displaced by AN-FO in many operations. The rates of detonation are somewhat less than the straight gelatins (7,000 to 20,000 fps). A typical percentage composition for the 40 percent grade is: gelatinized explosive oil, 21; ammonium nitrate, 14; sodium nitrate, 49; with antacid and combustible making up the remainder.

The **semigels** are important variants of the ammonia gels; these contain less explosive oil, sodium nitrate, and nitrocellulose and more ammonium nitrate than the corresponding grade of ammonia gel. Rates of detonation fall in the limited range of 10,000 to 13,000 fps. These powders are cohesive and have good water resistance and good fume characteristics.

Permissible explosives are powders especially designed for use in underground coal mines, which have passed a series of tests established by the Bureau of Mines. The most important of these tests concern incendivity of the explosives—their tendency to ignite methane-air mixtures. Permissible explosives are either granular or gelatinous; the granular type makes up the bulk of the powders used today. Typically, a granular permissible contains (percentages): explosive oil, 9; ammonium nitrate,

65; sodium nitrate, 5; sodium chloride, 10; carbonaceous material, 10; and antacid, 1. Gels contain nitrocellulose for improved water resistance and more explosive oil. Detonation velocities for the granular grades vary from 4,500 to 11,000 fps, and for the gels, from 10,500 to 18,500 fps.

Liquid-oxygen explosives (LOX) once saw considerable use in coal strip mines but have been almost completely displaced by AN-FO. LOX consists of bags of pressed carbon black or specially processed char that are saturated with liquid oxygen just before loading into the borehole. The rate of detonation ranges from 12,000 to 18,000 fps.

Military explosives, originally developed for such uses as bomb, shell, and mine loads and demolition work, have been adapted to many industrial explosive applications. The more common military explosives are listed in Table 24, with their compositions, ballistic mortar strengths, and detonation velocities.

Table 24. Physical Characteristics of Military Explosives

Explosive	Composition, percent	Ballistic mortar strength (TNT = 100)	Density, g per cc	Rate of detonation, m per sec
80/20 amatol	Ammonium nitrate, 80; TNT, 20	117	Cast	4,500
50/50 amatol	Ammonium nitrate, 50; TNT, 50	122	Cast	5,600
Composition A (pressed)	RDX, 91; wax, 9	134	0.80	4,560
			1.20	6,340
			1.50	7,680
			1.60	8,130
Composition B (cast)	RDX, 59.5; TNT, 39.5; wax, 1	130	1.65	7,660
Composition C-3 (plastic)	RDX, 77; tetryl, 3; mononitrotoluene, 5; dinitrotoluene, 10; TNT, 4; nitrocellulose, 1	145	1.55	8,460
Composition C-4 (plastic)	RDX, 91; dioctyl sebacate, 5.3; polyisobutylene, 2.1; oil, 1.6	...	1.59	8,000
Explosive D	Ammonium picrate	97	0.80	4,000
			1.20	5,520
			1.50	6,660
			1.60	7,040
HBX-1	RDX, 40; TNT, 38; aluminum, 17; densensitizer, 5	130	1.70	7,310
Lead azide*	Lead azide	...	2.0	4,070
			3.0	4,630
			4.0	5,180
PETN	Pentaerythritol tetranitrate	145	0.80	4,760
			1.20	6,340
			1.50	7,520
			1.60	7,920
50/50 Pentolite	PETN, 50; TNT, 50	120	1.20	5,410
			1.50	7,020
			1.60	7,360
			Cast	7,510
Picric acid	Trinitrophenol	108	1.20	5,840
			1.50	6,800
			Cast	7,350
RDX (cyclonite)	Cyclotrimethylene trinitramine	150	0.80	5,110
			1.20	6,550
			1.50	7,650
			1.60	8,000
			1.65	8,180
Tetryl	Trinitrophenylmethylnitramine	121	0.80	4,730
			1.20	6,110
			1.50	7,160
			1.60	7,510
75/25 tetrytol	Tetryl, 75; TNT, 25	113	1.60	7,400
TNT	Trinitrotoluene	100	0.80	4,170
			1.20	5,560
			1.50	6,620
			1.60	6,970
			Cast	6,790

* Primary compound for blasting caps.

Amatol was used early in World War II, largely because of the short supply of TNT. Modifications of amatol have been used as industrial blasting agents. **Explosive D,** or ammonium picrate, by virtue of its extreme insensitivity, was used in explosive-filled armor-piercing shells and bombs.

RDX, a very powerful explosive compound, was widely used during World War II in many compositions, of which Compositions A, B, and C were typical. **Composition A** was used as a shell loading; **B** was used as a bomb and shaped-charge filling; **C,** being plastic enough to allow molding to desired shapes, was developed for demolition work. Compositions that also contained aluminum powder were developed for improved underwater performance (**Torpex, HBX**). RDX has found limited commercial application as the base charge in some detonators, the filling for special-purpose detonating fuses or cordeau detonants, and the explosive in small shaped charges used as oil-well perforators and tappers for open-hearth steel furnaces.

PETN has never found wide military application because of its sensitivity and relative instability. It is used extensively, however, as the core of detonating fuses and in caps and boosters.

Tetryl, once widely used by the military as a booster loading and commercially as a base charge in detonators, has been displaced by other compositions. **Tetrytol** found limited application as a demolition charge.

TNT is a very widely used military explosive. Its stability, insensitivity, convenient melting point (81 C), and relatively low cost have made it the explosive of choice either alone or in admixture with other materials for loadings which are to be cast. A free-flowing pelletized form has found application in certain types of blasting requiring high loading density, where it is used to fill the cavity formed in sprung holes or the free space around the column of other explosives in the borehole.

DUST EXPLOSIONS IN BUILDINGS

By Henry G. Dorsett, Jr.

REFERENCES: Combustible Solids, Dusts, Chemicals, and Explosives, *National Fire Codes*, vol. II, National Fire Protection Assoc.; *B of M Rept. of Invest.* 5624, 5753, 5971.

A potential dust-explosion hazard exists whenever combustible dusts accumulate, are handled, or are processed. Expanding industrialization, combined with development of new products, has increased the variety and quantity of materials used in dust form. The number of severe dust explosions, excluding mine disasters, in the United States averages about 20 per year, with about 10 fatalities and a property loss of approximately $2 million.

A dust explosion is a rapid combustion of a cloud of particulate matter in a confined space where heat is generated at a much higher rate than it is dissipated. The explosion is characterized by a relatively rapid development of pressure. The condition necessary for a dust explosion is the simultaneous presence of a dust cloud of proper concentration in air or some other gas that will support combustion and a source of ignition.

Explosibility Factors

Dust explosibility is affected by so many chemical and physical factors that a mathematical theory has yet to be developed. Empirical and experimental results are the chief guides in evaluating relative dust-explosion hazards.

Composition of Dust. (See p. 7-40 *et seq.*) Many industrial dusts are not pure compounds. High percentages of incombustibles such as mineral matter or moisture reduce the hazards of ignition and explosion. The heat of combustion, ease of oxidation, oxygen requirements, and specific heat influence the explosibility of dusts. Volatile combustibles in dusts, such as coals or pitches, increase explosibility. Although the pressure produced by a dust enplosion in an enclosure is chiefly due to the rapid heating of air and other gases, formation of gaseous combustion products may add to pressure development. The formation of gaseous products is related to the dust composition. Combustion of organic dusts generally produces gaseous products, whereas in some metal-powder explosions, the volume of gas after combustion is less than the initial volume of air.

Fineness and Structure of Dusts. Explosibility of dusts generally increases with a decrease in particle size. A pound of fine dust particles has a greater surface area, mixes better with air, and oxidizes more rapidly than a pound of coarse material. A decrease of particle size in dusts generally results in a lower ignition temperature, lower igniting energy, lower minimum explosive concentration, and higher pressure and rates of pressure rise. Some metals such as chromium become explosive only at very fine particle sizes, and almost all metal powders become pyrophoric if particle degradation is extreme. In a dust explosion, relatively coarse particles (20 to 30 mesh) may burn and add energy to the reaction.

Concentration of Dust Cloud. The concentration of dust in suspension must be between certain lower and upper limits, just as in a gas-air mixture (see p. 7–33), for flame to propagate rapidly and for an explosion to develop. Most combustible dusts have a well-defined lower limit, but the upper limit is not so definite. An optimum concentration exists at which maximum pressure develops; the optimum concentration is somewhat higher than the stoichiometric ratio. A typical example of the effect of dust concentration on pressure and rate of pressure rise is shown in Fig. 4. The range of explosive dust concentration is from about 0.02 to greater than 10 oz per cu ft. The optimum concentration for producing the strongest explosions is about 0.5 oz per cu ft for most dusts. In Table 25, which gives explosion characteristics of a number of dusts, data on the pressure and rates are given for this concentration.

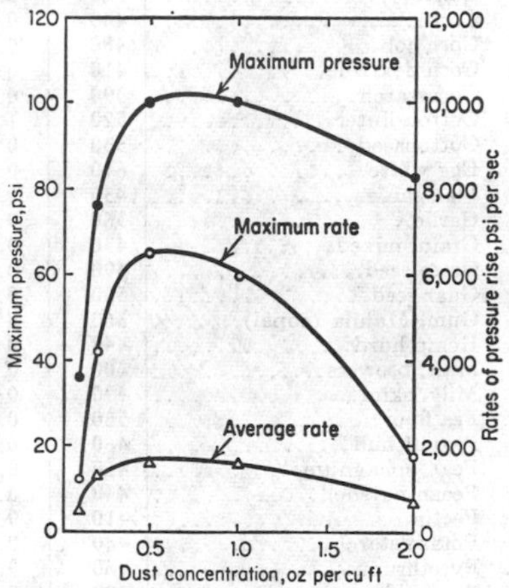

FIG. 4. Maximum pressures and rates of pressure rise produced by explosions of clouds of dried wheat starch.

Effects of Inerts. Dust is usually handled in an air atmosphere containing approximately 21 percent oxygen by volume. If the percentage of oxygen in the atmosphere is reduced, ignition and explosion may be inhibited or prevented. Carbon dioxide, nitrogen, argon, helium, and water vapor are effective gaseous diluents, but for highly reactive metal powders, only argon and helium are chemically inert. Terminal oxygen concentrations using carbon dioxide as a diluent are given in Table 25 for many dusts. With carbon dioxide as a diluent, a reduction of oxygen in the atmosphere to 11 percent is sufficient to prevent ignition by spark of all dust samples tested except the metallic powders. Values for other dusts may be found in the references. The other inert gases are usually not so efficient as carbon dioxide in inhibiting dust explosions. With nitrogen as the diluent, ignition of the non-metallic dusts is prevented by diluting the atmosphere to 8 percent oxygen. In some experiments with a wheat-flour gluten, water vapor and carbon dioxide were about equally effective as diluents in preventing ignition by spark. Some metal dusts, such as magnesium, magnesium-aluminum, titanium, thorium, uranium, and zirconium, ignite by spark in a pure carbon dioxide atmosphere. Freon is sometimes used as a diluent gas, but if metal dusts are involved, it can intensify rather than quench ignition. Values of limiting oxygen concentration decrease for dust of finer particle size. The limiting oxygen concentration varies slightly with dust concentration and is lowest at concentrations two to five times the stoichiometric mixture. Water or inert powder added in sufficient quantity to a combustible dust prevents ignition.

Ignition Source. A voluminous flame or a hot surface is a more potent source of ignition for most dusts than a point source such as a spark. Ignition sources known to have initiated dust explosions include electric sparks and arcs in fuses, faulty wiring,

Table 25. Explosive Characteristics of Various Dusts*

Type of dust	Ignition temperature of dust cloud, deg C	Minimum igniting energy, joules	Minimum explosive concentration, oz per cu ft	Maximum explosion pressure, psig	Maximum rate of pressure rise, psi per sec	Terminal oxygen concentration, percent†	Relative explosion hazard
Agricultural:							
Alfalfa	530	0.320	0.105	92	2,200	...	Moderate
Cereal grass	550	0.800	0.250	52	500	...	Weak
Cinnamon	440	0.030	0.060	114	3,900	...	Strong
Citrus peel	730	0.045	0.065	71	2,000	...	Moderate
Cocoa	500	0.120	0.065	55	900	...	Moderate
Coffee	720	0.160	0.085	53	300	...	Weak
Corn	400	0.040	0.055	95	6,000	...	Strong
Corn cob	480	0.080	0.040	110	3,100	...	Strong
Corn dextrine	410	0.040	0.040	105	7,000	...	Severe
Cornstarch	390	0.030	0.040	115	9,000	...	Severe
Cotton linters	520	1.920	0.500	48	150	...	Moderate
Cottonseed	530	0.120	0.055	96	3,000	...	Moderate
Egg white	610	0.640	0.140	58	500	...	Weak
Flax shive	430	0.080	0.080	81	800	...	Moderate
Garlic	360	0.240	0.100	80	2,600	...	Moderate
Grain, mixed	430	0.030	0.055	115	5,500	...	Strong
Grass seed	490	0.260	0.290	34	400	...	Weak
Guar seed	500	0.060	0.040	98	2,400	...	Strong
Gum, Manila (copal)	360	0.030	0.030	88	5,600	...	Severe
Hemp hurd	440	0.035	0.040	103	10,000	...	Severe
Malt, brewers	400	0.035	0.055	92	4,400	...	Strong
Milk, skim	490	0.050	0.050	83	2,100	...	Strong
Pea flour	560	0.040	0.050	95	3,800	...	Strong
Peanut hull	460	0.050	0.045	82	4,700	...	Strong
Peat, sphagnum	460	0.050	0.045	84	2,200	...	Strong
Pecan nutshell	440	0.050	0.030	106	4,400	...	Strong
Pectin	410	0.035	0.075	112	8,000	...	Severe
Potato starch	440	0.025	0.045	97	8,000	...	Severe
Pyrethrum	460	0.080	0.100	82	1,500	...	Moderate
Rauwolfia vomitoria root	420	0.045	0.055	106	7,500	...	Strong
Rice	440	0.050	0.050	93	2,600	...	Strong
Safflower	460	0.025	0.055	84	2,900	...	Strong
Soy flour	550	0.100	0.060	111	1,600	15	Moderate
Sugar, powdered	370	0.030	0.045	91	1,700	...	Strong
Walnut shell, black	450	0.050	0.030	97	3,300	...	Strong
Wheat flour	440	0.060	0.050	104	4,400	...	Strong
Wheat, untreated	500	0.060	0.065	98	4,400	...	Strong
Wheat starch	430	0.025	0.045	100	6,500	...	Severe
Wheat straw	470	0.050	0.055	99	6,000	...	Strong
Yeast, torula	520	0.050	0.050	105	2,500	...	Strong
Carbonaceous:							
Asphalt, resin, volatile content 57.5%	510	0.025	0.025	94	4,600	...	Severe
Charcoal, hardwood mix, volatile content 27.1%	530	0.020	0.140	100	1,800	18	Strong
Coal, Colo., Brookside, volatile content, 38.7%	530	0.060	0.045	88	3,200	...	Strong
Coal, Ill., No. 7, volatile content 48.6%	600	0.050	0.040	84	1,800	15	Strong
Coal, Ky., Breek, volatile content 40.6%	610	0.030	0.050	88	4,000	...	Strong
Coal, Pa., Pittsburgh, volatile content 37.0%	610	0.060	0.055	83	2,300	17	Strong
Coal, Pa., Thick Freeport, volatile content 35.6%	595	0.060	0.060	77	2,200	...	Moderate
Coal, W. Va., No. 2 Gas, volatile content 37.1%	600	0.060	0.060	82	1,600	...	Moderate
Coal, Wyo., Laramie No. 3, volatile content 43.3%	575	0.050	0.050	92	2,000	...	Strong

Table 25. Explosive Characteristics of Various Dusts*—(*Continued*)

Type of dust	Ignition temperature of dust cloud, deg C	Minimum igniting energy, joules	Minimum explosive concentration, oz per cu ft	Maximum explosion pressure, psig	Maximum rate of pressure rise, psi per sec	Terminal oxygen concentration, percent†	Relative explosion hazard
Gilsonite, Utah, volatile content 86.5%	580	0.025	0.020	78	3,700	...	Severe
Lignite, Calif., volatile content 60.4%	450	0.030	0.030	90	8,000	...	Severe
Pitch, coal tar, volatile content 58.1%	710	0.020	0.035	88	6,000	...	Severe
Metals:							
Aluminum	650	0.015	0.045	100	10,000+	2	Severe
Antimony	420	1.920	0.420	8	100	16	Weak
Boron	470	0.060	0.100	90	2,400	...	Moderate
Cadmium	570	4.000					
Chromium	580	0.140	0.230	56	5,000	14	Moderate
Cobalt	760				....	...	Fire
Copper	900	.....	.....	...	....		Fire
Iron	420	0.020	0.100	46	6,000	10	Strong
Lead	710						
Magnesium	520	0.020	0.020	94	10,000+	0	Severe
Molybdenum	720	.....	.....	...	....		Fire
Nickel	950+						
Selenium	950+						
Silicon	780	0.080	0.100	106	10,000+	12	Severe
Tantalum	630	0.120	0.200	51	3,700	...	Moderate
Tellurium	550						
Thorium	270	0.005	0.075	48	3,300	0	Severe
Tin	630	0.080	0.190	37	1,300	15	Moderate
Titanium	460	0.010	0.045	80	10,000+	0	Severe
Tungsten	950+						
Uranium	20	0.045	0.060	53	3,400	0	Severe
Vanadium, 86 percent	500	0.060	0.220	48	600	13	Weak
Zinc	600	0.640	0.480	48	1,800	9	Weak
Zirconium	20	0.005	0.045	65	9,000	0	Severe
Alloys and compounds:							
Aluminum-cobalt	950	0.100	0.180	78	8,500		Moderate
Aluminum-copper	930	1.920	0.280	27	500	...	Weak
Aluminum-iron	550	0.720	0.500	21	100	...	Weak
Aluminum-magnesium	430	0.020	0.020	90	10,000	0	Severe
Aluminum-nickel	940	0.080	0.190	79	10,000	14	Moderate
Aluminum-silicon, 12 percent Si	670	0.060	0.040	74	7,500	...	Strong
Calcium silicide	540	0.130	0.060	73	10,000+	8	Strong
Ferrochromium, high-carbon	790	.....	2.000	...	....	19	
Ferromanganese, medium-carbon	450	0.080	0.130	47	4,200	...	Moderate
Ferrosilicon, 75 percent Si	860	0.400	0.420	87	3,600	16	Weak
Ferrotitanium, low-carbon	370	0.080	0.140	53	9,500	13	Strong
Ferrovanadium	440	0.400	1.300	...	....	17	
Thorium hydride	260	0.003	0.080	60	6,500	6	Severe
Titanium hydride	440	0.060	0.070	96	10,000+	13	Strong
Uranium hydride	20	0.005	0.060	43	6,500	0	Severe
Zirconium hydride	350	0.060	0.085	69	9,000	8	Strong
Plastics:							
Acetal resin (polyformaldehyde)	440	0.020	0.035	89	4,100	11	Severe
Acrylic polymer resin							
Methyl methacrylate-ethyl acrylate	480	0.010	0.030	85	6,000	11	Severe
Alkyd resin							
Alkyd molding compound	500	0.120	0.155	15	150	15	Weak

Table 25. Explosive Characteristics of Various Dusts*—(*Continued*)

Type of dust	Ignition temperature of dust cloud, deg C	Minimum igniting energy, joules	Minimum explosive concentration, oz per cu ft	Maximum explosion pressure, psig	Maximum rate of pressure rise, psi per sec	Terminal oxygen concentration, percent†	Relative explosion hazard
Allyl resin							
Allyl alcohol derivative, CR-39	500	0.020	0.035	106	10,000+	13	Severe
Amino resin							
Urea-formaldehyde molding compound	450	0.080	0.075	89	3,600	17	Strong
Cellulosic fillers							
Wood flour	430	0.020	0.035	110	5,500	17	Severe
Cellulosic resin							
Ethyl cellulose molding compound	320	0.010	0.025	102	6,000	11	Severe
Chlorinated polyether resin							
Chlorinated polyether alcohol	460	0.160	0.045	66	1,000	...	Moderate
Cold-molded resin							
Petroleum resin	510	0.030	0.025	94	4,600	...	Severe
Coumarone-indene resin	520	0.010	0.015	93	10,000+	14	Severe
Epoxy resin	530	0.020	0.020	86	6,000	12	Severe
Fluorocarbon resin							
Fluoroethylene polymer	600	.....	.....	...	....	...	Fire
Furane resin							
Phenol furfural	520	0.010	0.025	90	8,500	14	Severe
Ingredients							
Hexamethylenetetramine	410	0.010	0.015	98	10,000+	14	Severe
Miscellaneous resins							
Petrin acrylate monomer	220	0.020	0.045	104	10,000+	...	Severe
Natural resin							
Rosin, DK	390	0.010	0.015	87	10,000+	14	Severe
Nylon polymer resin	500	0.020	0.030	89	7,000	13	Severe
Phenolic resin							
Phenol-formaldehyde molding compound	500	0.020	0.030	92	10,000+	14	Severe
Polycarbonate resin	710	0.020	0.025	78	4,700	15	Severe
Polyester resin							
Polyethylene terephthalate	500	0.040	0.040	91	5,500	13	Strong
Polyethylene resin	410	0.010	0.020	83	5,000	12	Severe
Polymethylene resin							
Carboxypolymethylene	520	0.640	0.115	70	5,500	...	Moderate
Polypropylene resin	420	0.030	0.020	76	5,000	...	Severe
Polyurethane resin							
Polyurethane foam	510	0.020	0.025	88	3,700	...	Severe
Rayon							
Rayon (viscose) flock	520	0.240	0.055	88	1,700	...	Moderate
Rubber							
Rubber, synthetic	320	0.030	0.030	93	3,100	15	Severe
Styrene polymer resin							
Polystyrene latex	500	0.020	0.020	91	7,000	13	Severe
Vinyl polymer resin							
Polyvinyl butyral	390	0.010	0.020	84	2,000	14	Severe

* Data taken from B of M Rept. of Invest. 5753, Explosibility of Agricultural Dusts; RI 5971, Explosibility of Dusts Used in the Plastics Industry; RI 6516, Explosibility of Metal Powders; and a forthcoming publication on Chemical Dusts. The information was obtained in the equipment described in RI 5624, Laboratory Equipment and Test Procedures for Evaluating Explosibility of Dusts.

† The terminal oxygen concentration is the limiting oxygen concentration in air-CO_2 atmosphere required to prevent ignition of dust clouds by electric spark.

motors, and other appliances; static electrical discharges; open flames; frictional or metallic sparks; glowing particles; overheated bearings and other machine parts; hot electric bulbs, hot driers, and other hot surfaces; spontaneous ignition and other exothermic chemical reactions. Ignition temperatures of several dust clouds are given in Table 25. In general, ignition temperatures of dust layers are considerably lower than for dust clouds. The ignition temperature of a dust cloud is increased by a decrease of the initial oxygen concentration.

Relative Explosion Hazards of Dusts

Table 25 gives the results of tests of selected dust samples whose explosive characteristics have been evaluated by the Bureau of Mines. The data were determined for dust passing a No. 200 sieve and represent the most hazardous of the specific materials tested. The values are relative rather than absolute because the test apparatus and experimental procedures affect the results to some degree. Different samples of the same substance frequently exhibit somewhat varying explosibilities. The samples were dried before testing only if the moisture content exceeded 5 percent. The ignition temperature was determined by dispersing a small quantity (usually 0.1 g) through a cylindrical furnace with stepped (5 C) changes in temperature until flame from the bottom of the furnace indicated ignition. The minimum electric-spark energy required to ignite a dust cloud was measured by discharge of a condenser through a luminous-tube transformer. The minimum explosive concentration is the least amount of dust that will ignite with a continuous-spark igniting source. The maximum pressure and rates of pressure rise were determined by explosion in a closed bomb. The terminal oxygen concentration is the least amount of oxygen necessary to prevent flame propagation. Detailed description of the equipment and procedures are given in *B of M Rept. of Invest.* 5624.

The ignition sensitivity of a dust cloud depends on the ignition temperature, the minimum energy required for ignition, and the minimum concentration. The violence of a dust explosion is determined by the maximum pressure and the rate of pressure development. The hazard of a dust explosion is related to its ease of ignition and to the severity of the ensuing explosion. To facilitate evaluation of the explosibility of dusts and to give a numerical rating for the relative hazard, empirical indices have been developed, comparing values obtained for these parameters with similar values for a standard Pittsburgh coal dust. The ignition sensitivity and explosion severity of a dust are defined as:

$$\text{Ignition sensitivity} = \frac{(\text{ign temp} \times \text{min energy} \times \text{min conc})\ \text{Pgh coal dust}}{(\text{ign temp} \times \text{min energy} \times \text{min conc})\ \text{sample dust}}$$

$$\text{Explosion severity} = \frac{(\text{max explosive press} \times \text{max rate of press rise})\ \text{sample dust}}{(\text{max explosive press} \times \text{max rate of press rise})\ \text{Pgh coal dust}}$$

The over-all index of explosibility is the product of the ignition sensitivity and the explosion severity and has a numerical value of 1 for a dust equivalent to the standard Pittsburgh coal. The relative hazard of dusts is further classified by adjective ratings of **fire, weak, moderate, strong,** or **severe.** Those materials igniting by the heated surface but not by the electric-spark source are considered to present primarily a fire hazard. These ratings, correlated with the empirical indices as follows, are used in classifying the dusts listed in Table 25.

Type of explosion	Ignition sensitivity	Explosion severity	Index of explosibility
Fire	....	....	≪0.1
Weak	<0.2	<0.5	<0.1
Moderate	0.2–1.0	0.5–1.0	0.1–1.0
Strong	1.0–5.0	1.0–2.0	1.0–10
Severe	>5.0	>2.0	>10

Prevention of Dust Explosions

(See also Sec. 12.)

Recommendations for several dust-producing industries are embodied in a series of safety codes prepared by committees of the National Fire Protection Assoc. The following pertinent codes have been published so far:

Aluminum-bronze Powder, Aluminum and Aluminum-alloy Processing and Finishing; Magnesium Powder or Dust; Coal Pneumatic-cleaning Plants; Plastics Plants; Flour and Feed Mills; Pulverized-coal Systems; Confectionery Plants; Spice-grinding Plants; Starch Factories; Sugar and Cocoa Plants; Sulphur Dust; Terminal Grain Elevators; Grain Elevators and Storage Units; Country Grain Elevators; Wood-flour Manufacturing; Woodworking Plants; Guide for Explosion Venting; Standards for Inerting for Fire and Explosion Prevention; Spontaneous Ignition of Coal and Other Products; Magnesium Storage, Handling and Processing; Pamphlet on Static Electricity; National Electrical Code.

Safeguards against explosions include the following:

Elimination of all sources of ignition from equipment containing flammable dust and from adjacent areas. This calls for prohibition of open flames or lights and of smoking; avoidance of the use of electric- or gas-cutting and welding equipment for repairs unless dust-producing machinery is shut down and all dust has been removed from the machines and their vicinity; grounding and bonding of all equipment to prevent the accumulation of static electrical charges; strict adherence in installation of electrical equipment and wiring to the provisions of the National Electrical Code for hazardous locations; use of magnetic separators to prevent entrance of ferrous materials into dust-grinding mills; use of non-ferrous blades in fans through which dust passes; avoidance of the use of spark-producing tools in certain industries; and avoidance of the use of high-speed shafting and belts.

Buildings should be constructed to minimize the collection of dust on beams, ledges, and other surfaces, particularly overhead. In removal of dust, vacuum cleaning is preferable to other methods, but soft push brooms may be used without serious hazard. Buildings in which highly flammable dusts are produced or stored should be detached units of incombustible construction, including inside partitions. Hazardous units within buildings should be separated by substantial fire walls.

Grinders, conveyors, elevators, collectors, and other equipment in which dust clouds might be produced should be as dust-tight as possible; they should have the smallest practical interior volume and should be constructed strong enough to withstand explosion pressures from dust.

Dust collectors preferably should be located outside of buildings or in detached rooms. They should be near the dust source. The type of collector best suited for a given installation depends on the particle size, dryness, flammability, and other characteristics of the dust; on the dust concentration; on the gas velocity and temperature; on efficiency requirements; on space requirements; and on economic considerations. (See also p. 7-88.)

Grinding and conveying equipment can frequently be protected by using an **inerted atmosphere,** reducing the normal oxygen content to a point at which the dust will not explode. The inert gas for this purpose may be obtained by dilution of air with flue gases from boilers, internal-combustion engines, or other sources, or by dilution with nitrogen, carbon dioxide, helium from high-pressure cylinders, or gas from inert-gas generators. Sometimes it is feasible to prevent the formation of explosive dust-air mixtures in grinding equipment by the addition of inert dusts to the flammable dust; this is similar to the rock-dusting procedure employed in coal mines for preventing the propagation of explosions.

To reduce structural damage from dust explosions, dust collectors and other equipment and the rooms in which dust-producing machinery is located should be provided with relief vents through which the pressure of an incipient dust explosion can be relieved quickly to the outside. The vents may be unrestricted or free openings; hinged or pivoted sash that swing outward at a low internal pressure; fixed sash with light wall anchorages; scored glass panes; light wall panels; monitors or skylights; paper, metal foil, or other diaphragms that burst at low pressures; poppet-type vent closures; pullout diaphragms; or other similar arrangements. The recommended areas of relief vents range from 1 sq ft per 15 cu ft to 1 sq ft per 80 cu ft or more of volume of the enclosure (see Hartman, Pressure Release for Dust Explosions, *Nat. Fire Protect. Assoc. Quar.*, **40**, July, 1946, pp. 47–53; Nagy, Zeilinger, and Hartmann, Pressure-relieving Capacities of Various Diaphragm Materials, *B of M Rept. of Invest.* 4636, 1950; and Hartmann and Nagy, Venting Dust Explosions, *Ind. Eng. Chem.*, **49**, Oct., 1957, pp. 1734–1740).

Pressures produced by explosion of dusts in a vented laboratory chamber are shown in Fig. 5. For the range indicated, pressure decreases exponentially with the area of the vent. The explosion pressures produced under controlled laboratory conditions are generally higher than those developed under operating conditions.

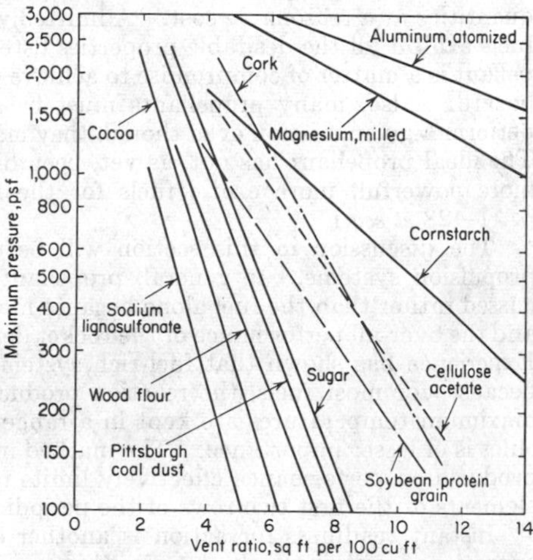

FIG. 5. Effect of unrestricted vents on pressures produced by strong explosions of various dusts.

In dealing with fires in combustible dusts, in addition to the usual recommendations for fire prevention and fire fighting, including sprinkler protection, the following points should be observed (see also p. 12–194 *et seq.*):

1. Attention should be directed to the possible hazard of spontaneous heating of powdered products, particularly soon after grinding.

2. First-aid and fire-fighting equipment should be installed. Small hoses with spray-type nozzles are particularly satisfactory. The fine spray wets the dust and is not so apt to raise a dust cloud as a solid stream does.

3. Large hose of fire-department sizes giving solid water streams should be used with caution, as dust may be thrown into suspension in this way, with consequent risk of an explosion. Plant employees and the fire department should be advised of this in advance of trouble. Hose equipped with spray or fog nozzles should be provided and kept ready for an emergency.

4. Small fires in magnesium, aluminum, and some other metal powders are best extinguished with sand, talc, or other dry inert materials applied gently to smother the fire or by use of materials, such as hard pitch, that completely seal the powder from the air.

ROCKET FUELS

By Glenn H. Damon

REFERENCES: Anon, World Missile/Space Encyclopedia, *Missiles and Rockets*, July 29, 1963. De Rieux, Solid-hybrid Propulsion, *Astronautics*, 1962, **7**, No. 3, p. 30. Myers, Solid Propellent Rockets, *Astronautics*, 1962, **7**, No. 11, p. 81. Penner, Propellants and Combustion, *Astronautics*, 1962, **7**, No. 11, p. 97. Cohen, Evolving Solid Boosters for Space Missions, *Astronautics*, 1963, **8**, No. 1, p. 60. Hendel, Chemical Rocket Propulsion Systems, *Chem. Eng.*, **68**, No. 5, 1961, p. 99. Hendel, Advanced Rocket Propulsion, *Chem. Eng.*, **68**, No. 7, 1961, p. 131. Kit and Evered, "Rocket Propellant Handbook," Macmillan. Warren, "Rocket Propellants," Reinhold. Hurden, Monopropellants, *Jour. Inst. of Fuels*, Feb., 1963, p. 50. Robinson, Ethylene Oxide as a Monopropellant, *Jet Propulsion*, 1954, p. 111. Brewer, Currie, and Knechthi, Ionic and Plasma Propulsion for Space Vehicles, *Proc. IRE*, 1961, p. 1789. Coar and King, Hydrogen for the Space Age, *Astronautics*, March, 1960, p. 26. Anon, Slush Hydrogen, *Chem. Week*, Aug. 24, 1963, p. 69. Gordon and Lee, Metals as Fuels in Multicomponent Propellants, *ARS Jour.*, April, 1962, p. 600. Anon, "Propellant Performance Data," Callery Chemical Co., 1961.

Col. Tosti (USAF), Titan III—A Pioneer, *Ordnance*, May–June, 1963, p. 663. (See also references under Jet Propulsion, Sec. 11.)

One of the **prime requirements** of a good rocket propellant is a high specific impulse. A successful rocket propellant should also exhibit most of the following characteristics: high heat of combustion; high density (high heat release per unit volume); low-molecular-weight combustion products; rapid conversion of chemical to thermal energy; high heat capacity of combustion products; combustion products that are mostly in gaseous form; chemical and physical stability to permit moderate-to-prolonged storage; relative insensitivity to shock; insignificant reactivity with common materials of construction below 150 F; low toxicity; and availability in large quantities at a reasonable cost. Admittedly, few if any of the more successful rocket fuels exhibit all the desirable properties listed. Consequently, the selection of a propellant is a matter of compromise to achieve the maximum performance at a minimum hazard. Also, many propellants must be selected on the basis of their ability to perform a given mission even though they may have many undesirable characteristics. The ideal propellant has not, as yet, been discovered, but research continues toward more powerful, more exotic fuels for the rocket engines of tomorrow. (See also p. 11–128 *et seq.*)

The discussion in this section will be confined essentially to chemical rocket-propulsion systems. In general, propellant systems (fuel and oxidant) will be discussed rather than the fuel alone because most rocket fuels require an oxidizing agent and the over-all performance of the rocket depends both upon the fuel and the oxidant. Experience has shown that fuel-rich systems generally give higher specific impulses because, for most fuels, the reaction products have lower molecular weight and the maximum temperatures are kept in a range where dissociation of the product molecules is of lesser importance. The marked influence of low-molecular-weight reaction products on performance effectively limits rocket fuels to those containing the light elements of the first two rows of the periodic chart.

Instant readiness for action is another essential requirement for many military operations involving rockets. For this reason, cryogenic fuels and oxidizers are more suitable for space operations than for military operations. To meet military needs, attention has been focused on storable or prepackaged liquid propellants. Thus, the Titan II missile is fueled with a mixture of hydrazine and unsymmetrical dimethyl hydrazine (UDMH), and the oxidizer is nitrogen tetroxide; fuel and oxidizer are stored in separate tanks. Some prepackaged propellant components have been stored for two to three years with no deleterious effect on the propellant performance. Some of of the most common storable liquid propellants are inhibited red fuming nitric acid (IRFNA), UDMH and its mixtures with hydrazine, monomethylhydrazine, UDMH + diethylenetriamine (DETA), chlorine trifluoride, and other halogen combinations.

Rapid advances in propellant technology in the last few years make it difficult to give a meaningful comparison between the performance of **solid- and liquid-fueled** rocket engines. The main advantages of solid-fueled rockets are simplicity, reliability, ease of handling and storage, high density, high mass ratio, and relatively lower cost. Liquid propellants, on the other hand, have many advantages, such as: combustion of large units can be more readily programmed; thrust control and termination are relatively simple; the fuels are relatively insensitive to temperature variations; engines can be cut off and restarted on command; and liquid-fuel systems are known that have higher specific impulse than that available in solid-fuel systems. A comparison of the advantages and disadvantages of each system indicates that the choice of propellant largely depends upon the mission to be accomplished.

Classification of Propellants

Rocket fuels can be classified according to their physical state and the method of furnishing the oxidant.

Physical State. The physical state of the fuel is an important factor in rocket-motor design. **Gaseous fuels** have never been considered suitable for rockets because of their low density. **Liquid propellants** are generally used for relatively long-range rockets only; **solid propellants** are used for most short-range rockets and increasingly for certain long-range missiles such as the Minuteman. Hybrid rockets, which use both liquid and solid fuels, are being developed.

There are many combinations of **liquid propellants** that function satisfactorily in a rocket engine. By definition, a liquid propellant is one in which the reacting material or materials are introduced into the combustion chamber in liquid form. These materials may serve as the fuel, oxidizer, or inert additive, and they may be in the form of a single compound or a mixture of two or more compounds. The number of potential organic and inorganic liquid fuels is virtually limitless, but a really successful fuel should maintain relatively constant viscosity over a wide range of conditions, undergo handling without excessive loss or decomposition, be sufficiently stable to be used for regenerative cooling, and have a low freezing point. These relatively rigid specifications eliminate many otherwise promising liquid fuels. Some of the most promising fuel types at the present time are jet fuels, hydrogen, amines, hydrazine and hydrazine derivatives, hydrides of light metals (such as boron hydrides), alcohols, acetylenic derivatives, ammonia, ethylene oxide, normal propyl nitrate, and hydrogen peroxide. Nitric acid, liquid oxygen, and nitrogen tetroxide are the most common oxidizers; hydrogen peroxide, fluorine, chlorine trifluoride, ozone, and oxides of fluorine have potentially great importance.

Oxygen, fluorine, and hydrogen are the principal **cryogenic liquids being used in liquid-propulsion systems.** The extremely low boiling points of these liquids present many difficulties in handling, storage, and use; liquid oxygen is the only one that has been used extensively to date. However, the extremely high specific impulse obtainable when using liquid hydrogen and liquid fluorine in propellant combinations has resulted in broad research-and-development programs that have solved many of the most baffling problems. The principal disadvantage of liquid hydrogen as a rocket fuel is its unusually low density (4.43 lb per cu ft).

Solid propellants have been developed to a relatively high degree of perfection and can now be manufactured in grains weighing over 50 tons. Solid-propellant grains measuring as much as 156 in. in diameter are now under development, and sizes as large as 260 in. are receiving consideration. The rapid advance in solid-propellant technology in the last few years has produced fuel systems that are now competitive with most liquid propellants both in specific impulse and in total thrust. The most commonly used solid propellants can be divided into two general groups: (1) **double-base or homogeneous,** essentially nitrocellulose and nitroglycerin or other nitroplasticizers; and (2) **composite or heterogeneous,** essentially an inorganic oxidizer in which the crystals are bonded together with a rubber or plasticlike material that serves as the fuel. Composite propellants can be subdivided into (1) rubberlike propellant compositions that bond to the case of the rocket motor, and (2) rigid propellant compositions that form a separate assembly inside the motor. The **binders** (fuels) most commonly used are asphalt, polysulphide, polyurethane, polyvinyl chloride + plasticizer, gums, and other resins. The most common **oxidizers** in use are ammonium perchlorate, potassium perchlorate, lithium perchlorate, and ammonium nitrate. Higher specific impulses are obtained from solid propellants by the addition of light metals such as aluminum, magnesium, and beryllium in place of some of the fuel.

The development of a practical hybrid (**liquid-solid**) rocket engine appears both possible and practical. Possibly this fuel system will combine the reliability and handling characteristics of the solid rocket with the controllability of the liquid-propellant engine.

Method of Furnishing Oxidant. Most liquid rocket-propellant combinations can be classified as monopropellants or bipropellants, depending upon how the combustible and the oxidant are mixed or combined. Although solid propellants have many of the characteristics of a monopropellant, they are sufficiently different to warrant restricting this discussion of monopropellants to liquid systems only.

Monopropellants are liquids containing both the fuel and the oxidizer in the same system. They decompose or react at a controllable rate, liberating heat and relatively simple gases. The propellant may or may not be a single compound, and only one storage space is required. Also, a monopropellant does not ignite at ambient temperatures but will ignite reliably with a short ignition delay when in contact with a catalyst or an ignition source.

Since monopropellants contain both the fuel and the oxidant, combustion or decomposition is initiated by a temperature rise or contact with a catalytic agent. Theoretically there are many fuel-oxidant systems that can function as monopropellants, but the number is limited because of two conflicting requirements, namely, that they be stable for storage and handling and yet readily combustible without the addition of an oxidant. Many otherwise good monopropellants cannot be used because of the hazard of sudden, uncontrolled decomposition (even detonation). Unfortunately, the specific impulse of most stable monopropellants is lower than many common bipropellant (fuel and oxidant separate) combinations. Although considerable improvement in the performance of this class of propellants has been achieved in the last few years, they still find their principal use in the auxiliary power systems of missiles and space vehicles. The most commonly employed monopropellants at the present time are hydrogen peroxide, N-propyl nitrate, ethylene oxide, propyne or methylacetylene, and hydrazine. A comparatively new family of monopropellants with relatively high specific impulses consists of quaternary ammonia salts dissolved in fuming nitric acid. One of these monopropellants, Cavea-B, has a relatively high density and is said to have a performance comparable with many bipropellant systems.

A large number of **bipropellant** systems have been proposed for rocket use, but factors such as safety in handling, shipping and storage, corrosive properties, freezing point, boiling point, toxicity, availability, and physical characteristics materially limit the number of practical fuel combinations. However, continuing research is providing the rocket industry with new and better propellants to power the ever-larger rockets for military and space operations. For the most part, bipropellant systems provide a degree of flexibility that cannot be obtained with solids or monopropellants. However, the complexity of the feed system required for the accurate transfer of huge volumes of fuel and oxidant from the storage tanks to the combustion chamber in a matter of seconds is a decided disadvantage because it increases cost and decreases reliability.

With **liquid bipropellants,** the combustible and the oxidant are mixed at the moment of use and the rate of energy release is relatively controllable. The combining materials are stored in separate tanks in the rocket and transferred to the combustion chamber by pressurizing the tanks or by separate metering pumps. Because the total combustion period for a rocket fuel is normally measured in seconds, the fuel-handling system must work with great precision.

Bipropellants are classed as **hypergolic** if they ignite spontaneously on mixing and **non-hypergolic** if an external ignition source is required. Hypergolic-propellant combinations are advantageous if the ignition delay is relatively short.

Composition and Characteristics of Rocket Propellants

It is impossible to describe all the promising propellant systems now under investigation in this short résumé. Some of the newer propellants are security classified, but on many propellants, only limited information can be obtained by reference to the literature. Strictly comparable performance data are difficult to obtain.

Solid Propellants. Double-base solid propellants, similar to smokeless gunpowder and made from nitrocellulose and nitroglycerin, were the principal fuels for military rockets in weapons such as the bazooka. A new process for manufacture, perfected during World War II, made it possible to produce relatively large rocket grains. While still suitable for some small, tactical military rockets, these propellants perform below many others developed for use in large rockets. A typical stabilized ballistite propellant may produce a specific impulse I of approximately 210 lb-sec per lb.

Most composite propellants consist of an inorganic oxidizer with an organic fuel binder. The most commonly used oxidizers in composite propellants are ammonium, potassium, and lithium perchlorate. The original JATO units used ammonium or potassium perchlorate with a special grade of asphalt as the fuel. This propellant, although surprisingly successful for its intended use, produced large volumes of smoke, and it has been completely replaced by plastic-binder fuels such as polysulphides, synthetic rubber, polyurethane, and hydrocarbon rubbers. The addition of light metals such as aluminum, magnesium, and beryllium to solid propellants improves the performance appreciably; such combinations are competitive with many liquid propellants. More energetic and faster-burning fuels using new nitroplasticizers are under investigation and will doubtless power the rockets of the future. The actual performance of solid-fuel rockets is not generally revealed in the literature, but theoretical values of specific impulse I are reported up to 289 lb-sec per lb; more advanced propellants are under consideration which will have even higher specific impulses.

Solids always require an external source of ignition. The principal problem is to obtain uniform, rapid ignition over the large surface areas where combustion is to occur without a violent pressure surge that may fracture the propellant grain. Areas where burning is not desired must be protected or inhibited. Igniters for solid-propellant rocket units are almost always pyrotechnics. The pyrotechnic igniters are initiated electrically with a hot wire surrounded by a small amount of a temperature sensitive starter. Recent investigations indicate that hypergolic ignition of solids using a liquid oxidant may prove feasible for certain operations.

Some of the best-known missiles using solid propellants are Nike-Hercules, Nike-Zeus, Minuteman, Polaris, Honest John, Scout, and Sergeant. The Titan III, which is now under development, will use the Titan II liquid rocket engine with two 120-in.-diam solid-propellant boosters. Each of these boosters reportedly weighs 500,000 lb and produces 1,000,000 lb of thrust.

Liquid Propellants. As stated previously, the number of liquid-propellant combinations is almost unlimited, but practical considerations tend to limit the field. Table 26 gives the characteristics of several well-known propellant combinations.

Table 26. Characteristics of Some Liquid Rocket Propellants

Oxidizer	Fuel	Bulk density g per cm³	Specific impulse I,* lb(f)-sec per lb(m)
M†	Ethylene oxide	0.87	175
	Hydrogen peroxide (100%)	1.44	166
	N-propyl nitrate	1.06	190
Oxygen	UDMH	0.96	295
	50-50 UDMH-hydrazine	1.02	312
	Hydrogen	0.28	390
	RP-1 (kerosine)	1.02	286
	Ammonia	0.89	294
Fluorine	Hydrogen	0.45	410
	Ammonia	1.18	357
Red fuming nitric acid (RFNA)	50-50 UDMH-hydrazine	1.28	283
	RP-1	1.35	268
Nitrogen tetroxide	50-50 UDMH-hydrazine	1.21	288
	RP-1	1.25	276
Hydrogen peroxide	JP-4	1.28	270
	50-50 UDMH-hydrazine	1.25	280

* Specific impulse measured at 1,000 psia expanded to 14.7 psia.
† M = monopropellant.

Concentrated Hydrogen Peroxide. With a solid catalyst such as calcium or sodium permanganate, this was used by the Germans in World War II as a monopropellant. Although the specific impulse is moderately low, high-strength hydrogen peroxide (90 to 100 percent) is very useful for driving small auxiliary equipment used in the space program. When used as an oxidant with a suitable fuel, a relatively high I is attained. Hydrogen peroxide is more easily stored than cryogenic oxidants, but concentrated hydrogen peroxide is an extremely active oxidizing agent and must be handled with utmost care. Suitable container materials are aluminum, tin, borosilicate glass, and polyethylene. Highly purified hydrogen peroxide is moderately stable to both heat and shock; handling offers no serious problems provided the fuel is protected from all impurities.

NORMAL PROPYL NITRATE (NPN). Normal propyl nitrate is a promising monopropellant for specific usage. Its performance is superior to that of hydrogen peroxide, but it is considered by some as hazardous to handle and use. NPN could probably be developed into a useful monopropellant if there were a demand for a propellant with its proven properties.

LIQUID OXYGEN WITH HYDROCARBONS. Kerosine and the JP fuels with liquid oxygen form successful bipropellant systems for which the components are cheap and available in large quantities. The principal disadvantage from a military standpoint is the use of a cryogenic component. The system is used as the power source for the Thor, Jupiter, and Atlas missiles as well as the first stage of the Saturn.

LIQUID HYDROGEN AND LIQUID OXYGEN. The combination of liquid hydrogen and liquid oxygen gives one of the highest specific impulses (on a weight basis) of any propellant system now under development. Although these propellants are generally difficult to handle, most of the major problems have been solved. The upper stages of space rockets such as the Saturn, Centaur, and Nova are expected to employ this fuel system. The relatively low-bulk density is a decided disadvantage for the lower stages of a rocket because of the large storage space required to hold a given weight of the propellant.

ALCOHOL AND LIQUID OXYGEN. This was one of the first successful liquid propellants and was used to power the German V-2 rockets. Methyl, ethyl, and isopropyl alcohol can be used, but ethyl alcohol is preferred. Although the performance of this fuel is average, other propellants have largely replaced alcohol.

HYDRAZINE AND UDMH. Hydrazine and unsymmetrical dimethylhydrazine (UDMH) have great potential as rocket fuels. Liquid oxygen, hydrogen peroxide, fluorine, chlorine trifluoride, inhibited fuming nitric acid (IRFNA), and nitrogen tetroxide are all suitable oxidants, but the last two are the ones presently in use. The performance of anhydrous hydrazine is slightly superior to UDMH, but the relatively high freezing point (34.5 F) of hydrazine is a decided disadvantage. UDMH has a satisfactory freezing point (−61.6 F), but its density is appreciably lower than anhydrous hydrazine. A 50-50 mixture of hydrazine and UDMH, known as **Aerozene 50,** has satisfactory physical properties and is used with nitrogen tetroxide as the propellant for the Titan II missile. This fuel system appears very satisfactory; both the fuel and the oxidant are storable, and the system is hypergolic. Other well-known rocket systems using UDMH and nitric acid are the Agena and Delta.

BORON HYDRIDES. The hydrides of boron have a high heat release when used with oxidants. The most important compounds are diborane (B_2H_6) and pentaborane (B_5H_9). Both hydrides give high theoretical performance with oxidants such as oxygen and fluorine, but diborane, in particular, is very difficult to handle and use. The boron hydrides were once considered the most promising of the high-energy fuels, but their future usefulness is now uncertain. No missile system presently uses the hydrides of boron as a fuel.

AMMONIA. The theoretically high specific impulse of ammonia when reacted with liquid oxygen or liquid fluorine gives it great potential as a rocket fuel. The performance of ammonia is only slightly less than that of hydrazine with the same oxidizers, and the cost and availability are most attractive. Mixtures of ammonia and hydrazine have been proposed for use because they have physical properties superior to either fuel alone. The X-15 is the only vehicle known to have employed ammonia as a propellant.

Multicomponent Propellant Systems. The addition of finely divided, low-molecular-weight metals such as boron, beryllium, lithium, and aluminum to some high-energy bipropellant systems results in a significant increase in the theoretical impulse. These multicomponent systems will doubtless be the subject of considerable research in the immediate future.

Future Developments

The rapidly changing character of the chemical-propellant field makes it difficult to predict anything other than trends for the future. The performance of solid propellants should continue to be improved both by the development of new, higher-energy components and by the use of better combinations of presently known ingredients. A mixture of solid hydrogen and solid oxygen (or solid hydrogen and solid ozone) has been suggested as a superpropellant of the future. Unfortunately, more energetic propellant combinations generally tend to be less stable, and thereby the hazard in handling and use is increased.

It seems safe to predict that rocket systems will increasingly employ high-energy fuels such as liquid hydrogen, hydrazine derivatives, boron derivatives, ammonia, and acetylene. Liquid fluorine, liquid ozone, oxygen difluoride, chlorine trifluoride, nitrogen trifluoride, perchloryl fluoride, and other similar oxidants will doubtless become increasingly more important. The use of a mixture of liquid and solid hydrogen at its triple point—the point of temperature and pressure at which liquid, vapor, and solid are in equilibrium (−259.3 C and 1.04 psi)—has been suggested recently as a means of improving the properties of liquid hydrogen. This slush hydrogen is reported to have a higher heat capacity and a higher density than liquid hydrogen, but it can still be handled by pumps.

Without a doubt, the specific impulse of purely chemical propellant systems is limited. Most authorities believe that a specific impulse of 500 is near the maximum limit. Several other systems are under consideration, *e.g.*, the use of the energy from nuclear fission to heat a jet of a stable gas such as hydrogen. Other possible systems involve the energy of charged colloids, free radicals, ions, arc jets, and plasma jets. (See also pp. 11–176.)

CARBONIZATION OF COAL AND GAS MAKING

BY

W. A. Leech, Jr.

REFERENCES: National Research Council, "Chemistry of Coal Utilization," Wiley. Porter, "Coal Carbonization," Reinhold. Morgan, "Manufactured Gas," J. J. Morgan, New York. AGA Committee Reports and Papers (Committees on Gas Production, Carbonization, Water Gas). *B of M, Monograph* 5 and other papers. "Gas Engineers' Handbook," McGraw-Hill. Powell, "Future Possibilities in Methods of Gas Manufacture," and Russell, "The Selection of Coals for the Manufacture of Coke," papers presented to the AGA Production and Chemical Conference. Wilson and Wells, "Coal, Coke and Coal Chemicals," McGraw-Hill. Walter, Gasification of Low-grade Coal, *Coal Utilization*, Mar., 1959. Coal Gasification, Sumitomo Process, *Chem. Eng. Progress*, Aug., 1960. Elliott, High-Btu Gas from Coal, *Coal Utilization*, Dec., 1961. Arne, Manufactured Gas. *Chem. Eng.*, Mar. 24, 1958. Osthaus, Town Gas Production from Coal by the Koppers-Totzek Process, *Gas and Coke*, Aug., 1962.

Carbonization of coal, or the breaking down of its constituent substances by heat in the absence of air, is carried on for the production of *coke* for metallurgical, gas making, and general fuel purposes; and *gas* for industrial and public-utility use. Coal chemicals recovered in this country include *tar* from which are produced crude chemicals and materials for creosoting, road paving, roofing, and waterproofing; *light oils,* mostly benzene and its homologues, used for motor fuels and chemical synthesis; *ammonia,* usually as ammonium sulphate, used mostly for fertilizer; to a lesser extent tar acids (phenol), tar bases (pyridine), and various other chemicals.

Gas making, as discussed here, includes gas from coal carbonization, water gas, and oil gas.

CARBONIZATION OF COAL

High-temperature carbonization is carried on in ovens or retorts with innerwall temperatures of from 1850 to 2100 F. A typical yield from 2,000 lb of high-grade dry coal of 30 to 31 percent volatile matter when carbonized in a modern oven is: coke, 1,440 lb; gas, 348 lb (11,200 cu ft); tar, 96 lb (10 gal); water, 87 lb; light oil, 24 lb (3.3 gal); ammonia, 4.9 lb.

Coal Characteristics. Most high-rank bituminous coals can be used to make coke and gas. Those well adapted to that purpose are not numerous. The coal must form a strong coherent coke and must not swell enough during coking to damage the oven walls. Coal for the best metallurgical coke should preferably have a low ash and sulphur content (ash below 7.5 and sulphur below 1.0 percent is good). Most coking coals now exceed these figures. The coke produced should be strong and blocky. Coal for water-gas coke should have a high ash-fusion temperature (2300 to 2700 F). Coal for the production of gas should have a high volatile-matter content (30 to 40 percent). In general, the higher the volatile-matter content, the greater the yield of gas and coal chemicals; the lower the volatile-matter content, the stronger the coke.

The **coking quality** in bituminous coals is limited by the oxygen content. Coals of over 10.0 percent oxygen content (on the dry, ash-free coal basis) generally do not coke appreciably. A high-oxygen content (7 to 10 percent) usually denotes a poor coke.

It is common practice in coal-chemical–recovery coking to mix two or more coals to make a better grade of coke or to avoid excessive expansion in the oven. One coal is usually of high (31 to 40 percent) volatile-content and the other of low (15 to 22 percent). Many medium-volatile (22 to 31 percent) coals are used. The low-volatile coal in the mix is generally in the range of 15 to 25 percent, with as much as 50 percent used in coal mixtures for producing foundry coke. High-volatile coals tend to shrink on coking while low-volatile coals tend to expand. Preliminary examination of the plastic properties, when heated, is of value in choosing the best types for blending, the high-volatile coals tending to be more fluid, the low-volatiles less so. The rate of heating influences the coke quality obtained.

Laboratory tests forecast imperfectly the quality of coke producible in commercial practice. Gas and coal-chemical yields can be forecast fairly well. The small-scale **free-swelling index test** of ASTM, Committee D-5, is sometimes used to estimate the coking properties. The **BM-AGA test,** developed jointly by the Bureau of Mines and a committee of the AGA (*B of M, Monograph* 5), gives yields close to those of commercial practice. It is useful for comparison of coals, effect of heating rates, densities of charge, and other conditions, on products and coke quality. The Geological Survey of Illinois (*Ind. Eng. Chem.,* **37,** 1945, 560–566), has an electrically heated oven for a 500 lb charge, the quality of whose resulting coke closely approximates that in commercial practice. **Box coking tests** (*Trans. AIME,* **74,** 1926, 600–639), made by placing a specially designed sheet-steel box containing about 60 lb of coal in a commercial oven, give the best small-scale information on coke quality. Accurate coke-quality determination is best had from a large-scale test in a commercial oven. Certain rapid small-scale tests for coal-chemical yields such as the **U.S. Steel Corp. tube test,** heating 20 g of coal in a glass tube under closely prescribed conditions, and the British **Gray-King assay** are useful for comparisons when checked against a standard coal of known industrial performance. The approximate estimation of coking properties of coals can be had from several plastometric methods, such as the **Giesler** (*Proc. ASTM,* **43,** 1943, 1176–1193), **Davis plastometer** (*Ind. Eng. Chem.,* **3,** 1931, 43–45), and **Agde-Damm** (*B of M, Bull.* 445, 1942). Petrographic analysis can also be used to predict the coking properties of a coal or coal mixture. For the **agglomerating index** and the **agglutination test** see p. 7–2 *et seq.*

Expansion tests are made to indicate whether or not the expansion pressure of the coal or mixture of coals is sufficient to damage the oven walls during the coking process. The **Russell movable-wall oven** (*Proc. AGA,* 1928) cokes a 400 lb charge of coal in a horizontal, 12 in. wide oven, heated from both sides, but with one wall floating and balanced against scales. As pressure is developed in the chamber, it is counteracted and measured by continually rebalancing the scales, thus recording the expansion pressure on the whole wall. The results are correlated comparatively with the behavior of coals in commercial ovens. Coals that yield expansion pressures of over 1.5 to 2.0 psi in the Russell oven are considered dangerous in commercial ovens. The Altieri tester (*Proc. ASTM,* **43,** 1943, 317–325) cokes under a constant pressure of 11 lb in a 4½ in. wide rectangular oven heated from both sides with one floating wall and measures lateral pressure and vertical expansion. The Bethlehem tester (*Proc. ASTM,* **43,** 1943, 314–316), developed by W. T. Brown, cokes under a constant pressure of 40 lb in a flat, rectangular oven heated from the bottom, and measures vertical expansion. The Bureau of Mines test oven developed at the Tuscaloosa, Ala., experimental station merits study in connection with this subject.

Coking Process. The constituents of coal begin to soften at 670 to 750 F in consequence of molecular readjustments that convert some of the material into viscous oils or tars, which merge or dissolve any solid or semisolid residues. It is not a true fusion, since decompositions play a part, but probably nearly all the coal materials change from the solid state. Gas is formed, increasing in amount as the temperature rises and producing swelling by the imprisoned bubbles proportional to its rate of formation and to the coal's fluidity. Further decomposition causes hardening into coherent porous coke, a material chiefly made up of compounds of carbon with H, O, and S in highly polymerized carbon-ring structures and a varying smaller content of graphitic carbon. Measurement of electrical conductivity of the coke indicates, in parallel relationship, the degree of coking and the temperature used.

As a result of the low thermal conductivity of coal (less than one-sixth of that of fire clay), and also of semicoke, heat penetrates slowly into the pieces and through the plastic layer; uniform plasticity or complete coalescence does not appear until the temperature (at the heated side of a softening layer) is considerably higher than the softening point of the coal. (See Fig. 1.)

The **plastic zone** moves slowly from the hot wall of the oven toward the center, at a rate first decreasing with the distance from the wall and then increasing again at the middle of the oven. For several hours after charging a red-hot oven, the center of the charge remains cool. The plastic layer's temperature variation, from one border to the other, is from 700 to 875 F and its thickness is 3/8 to 3/4 in. depending on the coal, the charge density, and the oven temperature.

In the modern coal-chemical–recovery coke oven the average rate of travel of the plastic zone is about 0.70 in. per hr, and the average **coking rate,** to finished coke in the center, is 0.50 to 0.53 in.; *i.e.*, a 17 in. oven may be run on a net coking time of 16 to 17 hr. (See Fig. 2.)

The gases and tar vapors travel chiefly outward toward the wall from the plastic layer and from the intermediate partly coked material, finding exit upward through coke and semicoke. Exit through the center core of uncoked coal, except for a very small fraction of the early formed gases, is barred by the relative impermeability of the plastic layer. The final chemical products, including gas, are the resultant of secondary decompositions and interreactions in the course of this travel.

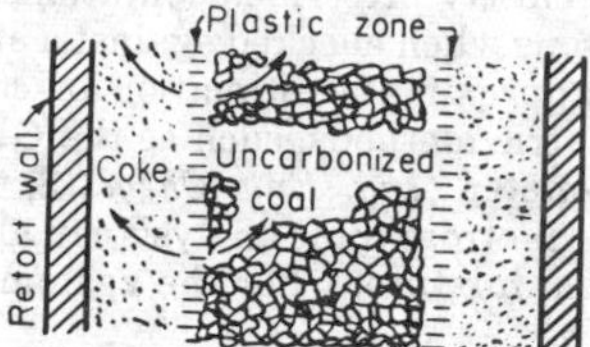

FIG. 1. Diagrammatic illustration of the progress of carbonization and of the position of the plastic zone.

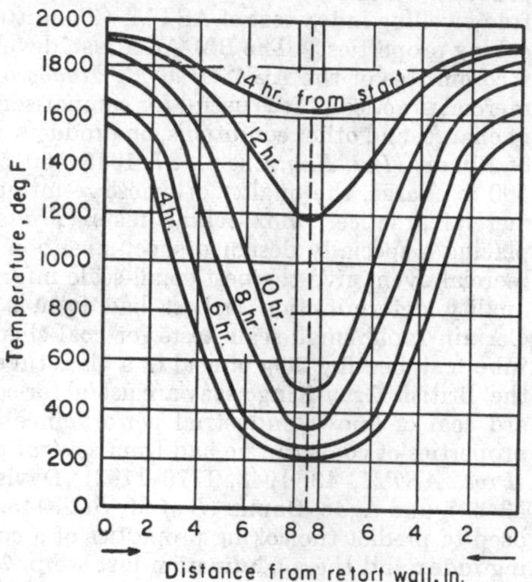

FIG. 2. Temperature gradients in a cross section of a coal-chemical–recovery coke oven, 17 in. wide, at about mid-depth on 17 hr coking time.

Average temperatures in various parts of the carbonizing system, for modern rapid coal-chemical–recovery oven operation, are about as follows: heating flues, at bottom, 2500 to 2600 F; heating flues, upper part, 2150 to 2450 F; oven wall, inner side (average final), 1850 to 2100 F; in coke, average throughout charge, 1600 to 2050 F; gases leaving ovens, 1000 to 1400 F; gases in collecting main, 180 to 212 F.

Temperature Effects during Carbonization. In industrial carbonizing, higher temperatures at the oven wall and in the outer layers of the charge produce higher gas yield and less tar. The gases and tar vapors change in quality and quantity continually during the carbonizing period. The percentage content of hydrocarbons and condensables in the oven gases decreases and that of hydrogen increases. Passage through the highly heated free space above the charge has the effect of increasing the yield of gas and light oil (reducing, however, the toluene and xylenes) and lowering tar yield, with increase of naphthalene, anthracene, and free carbon. Modern ovens tend to exercise control of the temperature in this free space. The rate of decomposition of ammonia increases above 1450 F.

The progressive change in gas yield and composition during the carbonizing period for a good gas-making coal is about as in Table 1.

The **over-all thermal efficiency** of industrial coal carbonization (useful recovery of heat from total input of heat) is between 86 and 92 percent approx. External sensible-heat efficiencies are between 65 and 80 percent approx. Heat efficiencies are complicated by the fact that the carbonization process yields an amount of exothermic heat equal to 10 to 20 percent of the heat of the combustion of the fuel gas. Three typical heat balances on coal-chemical–recovery ovens are shown in Table 3.

Heat Used for Carbonization. The total heating value of the gas burned in the flues to heat the ovens varies from 950 to 1250 Btu per lb of wet coal carbonized in efficient installations. Coke used in producers may be from 230 to 320 lb per ton of coal carbonized or 1150 to 1600 Btu per lb of coal, the difference between this and the

Table 1. Variation in Gas Yield during Carbonization

Period	Volume, cu ft per ton	Btu per cu ft	Approx composition, percent		
			Hydrocarbons	Hydrogen	Oxides of carbon
First quarter	3,630	651	41	46	7
Second quarter	3,190	610	37	53	7
Third quarter	3,250	567	32	59	6
Fourth quarter	1,875	363	8	82	5

Table 2. Gas Yields and Composition from Various Coal Types with High-temperature Carbonization

Coal	Temp, F, on inner wall	Gas yield, cu ft per ton	Gas composition, percent						
			Carbon dioxide	Carbon monoxide	Unsat'd hydrocarbons	Methane	Ethane, etc.	Hydrogen	Nitrogen
Pittsburgh bed, Fayette Co., Pa., V.M. 33.6	1950	11,700	1.3	6.8	3.2	31.1	0	56.5	1.1
Elkhorn bed, Letcher Co., Ky., V.M. 36.6	1950	11,500	1.1	7.7	4.0	31.0	0.2	55.0	1.0
Sewell bed, W. Va., V.M. 26.5	1950	12,000	0.7	5.5	2.5	26.5	0	64.8	1.0
Pocahontas No. 4, W. Va., V.M. 16.4	1950	11,900	0.4	5.0	1.1	18.0	0	75.0	0.5
Illinois, Franklin Co., V.M. 32.1	1950	12,000	3.8	14.5	2.8	21.0	0	56.9	1.0
Utah, Sunnyside, V.M. 38.8	1950	12,600	3.0	14.5	3.7	26.0	0.5	51.3	1.0

V.M. = percentage of volatile matter.

smaller figure being the losses in the producer plant. Gas producers are almost nonexistent in the United States today but are still in general use in Europe. Coke ovens are heated usually by coke-oven gas, producer gas, or blast-furnace gas. They are occasionally heated by blue water gas, natural gas, refinery gas, or liquid-petroleum gas (called L.P. gas and composed of commercial propane or butane), the last being diluted with air or lean gas. Producer and blast-furnace gases are called "lean" gases. When underfiring with lean gas, both air and gas are regenerated in order to get sufficient flame temperature for the flues. Coke-oven, natural, refinery, and L.P. gases are rich gases and are not regenerated as their flame temperatures are sufficiently high and regeneration would crack their hydrocarbons. Blue water gas produces a high flame temperature without regeneration. Air is regenerated in all cases.

Table 3. Heat Balances of Coal-chemical–recovery Ovens
(Including heats of combustion)

	Modern oven				Heated by coke-oven gas, 1923	
	Heated by blast-furnace gas, 1938		Heated by coke-oven gas, 1942			
	Btu per lb of coal	Percent of total heat introduced	Btu per lb of coal	Percent of total heat introduced	Btu per lb of coal	Percent of total heat introduced
Total Heat Balance (Including heats of combustion)						
Total heat introduced						
Coal: heat of combustion	13,880	93.0	......	.....	13,600	91.0
sensible heat	1	.....	......	.....	1	
Fuel gas: heat of combustion	1,038	7.0	......	.....	1,340	9.0
sensible heat	1	.....	......	.....	1	
Air: sensible heat	0	.....	......	.....	0	
Total	14,920	100.0	......	.....	14,942	100.0
Total heat in products						
Coke: heat of combustion	9,380	62.8	......	.....	9,620	64.4
sensible heat	485	3.2	......	.....	552	3.7
Gas and coal chemicals						
heat of combustion	4,344	29.0	......	.....	3,762	25.2
sensible heat	329	2.2	......	.....	333	2.2
Stack gases: sensible heat	227	1.5	......	.....	490	3.3
Radiation and convection losses	195	1.3	......	.....	179	1.2
Total	14,960	100.0	......	.....	14,936	100.0
Sensible Heat Balance						
Sensible heat introduced						
Coal	1	0.1	5	0.4	2	0.2
Air	.....	.....	3	0.3		
Fuel gas	1	0.1	7	0.7	1	0.1
Combustion of fuel gas	1,038	99.8	1,041	98.6	1,345	99.7
Total	1,040	100.0	1,056	100.0	1,348	100.0
Sensible heat in products						
Coke	485	46.7	468	44.3	552	41.0
Gas and coal chemicals	328	31.5	330	31.4	334	24.8
Stack gases	227	21.8	287	27.1	490	36.3
Radiation and convection losses	195	18.7	179	16.9	178	13.2
Total	1,235	118.7	1,264	119.7	1,554	115.3
Diff. between heat out and heat in = internal exothermic heat of carbonization	195	18.7	208	19.7	206	15.3
Efficiencies						
Over-all heat eff = $\frac{\text{heat of combustion in products}}{\text{total heat in}}$	91.8		....		89.6	
External sensible heat eff = $\frac{\text{sensible heat in products}}{\text{external heat in}}$	78.2		75.7		65.8	

Carbonizing Apparatus

The **beehive oven,** used now only to a minor extent, is 12 to 15 ft in diameter (or it may be rectangular to permit pushing out the coke and quenching outside) and cokes 6 to 8 tons of coal in a flat layer—usually 18 to 20 in. deep, although sometimes deeper, particularly when making 72-hr coke on weekends—by the heat of combustion of gases and of a small part of the coke in the oven tops. The coking time for a charge is usually 48 to 72 hr. It recovers no coal chemicals except, sometimes, waste heat from the oven gases. The waste heat may generate 500 to 600 lb of steam per hr per oven charge.

Coal-chemical-recovery coke ovens are usually built 39 to 42 ft long, 10 to 15 ft high, and 14 to 20 in. (most frequently, 16 to 18 in.) in average width, with a taper of 1.5 to 4.0 in. (usually, 2.5 to 4.0 in.) from end to end. They hold a charge of 12 to 22 tons of coal. Various types are in use, distinguished chiefly by their arrangements of heating flues. Modern ovens in this country have vertical flues. A widely used vertical-flued type avoids the horizontal collecting flue over the row of verticals by passing the hot gases from groups of flues on one side of the oven to groups on the other side in crossover flues above the oven roof. To give even, vertical heat-distribution in high ovens when burning rich gas (which tends to burn with a short flame), one design recirculates waste combustion gas from the adjacent heating wall through a duct underneath the oven and regenerator by the jet action of the fuel gas through a specially designed nozzle. This makes a leaner gas at the place where combustion takes place.

Coal-chemical–recovery coke ovens are built in batteries of from 15 to 106, modern ovens being arranged so that each row of heating flues, or *wall*, heats half of two adjacent ovens. Blast-furnace gas must be clean to avoid plugging of the regenerator checker-brick. Coal is charged through the top by machine. After coking, doors are removed at both ends of the oven by machine, and coke is pushed out of the oven horizontally by a ram operated by a pusher machine. Gas is removed continuously at constant pressure, in the oven, of a few millimeters of water column.

In America all modern coal-chemical–recovery ovens use regenerators for the air and lean gas. Average stack temperatures run from 450 to 700 F. Recuperators have poorer efficiencies and leakage problems, and are not used.

Oven chambers and heating flues are built on top of the regenerators. Silica brick is used for oven walls, flues, and regenerator walls because of its rigidity under load at high temperatures. Tightness of joints is of utmost importance to prevent leakage in the system. Pressure differentials between the oven chamber and the combustion system are carefully balanced to minimize leakage.

Coal-chemical Recovery. The gas is first cooled in indirect coolers or in direct scrubbers which condense out most of the tar and water, and some of the ammonia in the form of weak ammonia liquor. The tar is decanted and either sold as such or refined. Exhausters (usually centrifugal) follow and operate from 6 to 12 in. water column suction at inlet to 50 to 80 in. pressure discharge. Electrical precipitators, detarrers, or other tar extractors then remove the last traces of tar fog. The gas then passes through dilute sulphuric acid in ammonia saturators or scrubbers which recover the ammonia as ammonium sulphate. Ammonia washers sometimes recover aqua ammonia instead. Some plants recover ammonia as monoammonium phosphate or as diammonium phosphate. After a direct-water cooling, the gas is scrubbed of light oil (benzol, toluol, xylol, and *solvents*) with a petroleum oil. The enriched petroleum oil is stripped of the light oil by steam distillation and the resulting light oil refined into its constituents by fractionation and acid washing. Phenols and tar acids are recovered from the ammonia liquor and from tar. Pyridine and tar bases are recovered from the ammonia saturator bath and from tar. Creosote, naphthalene, and roofing and paving pitch are recovered from tar. Hydrogen sulphide, sulphur, and cyanogen compounds are sometimes recovered from the gas.

GAS MAKING

Water gas, or **blue gas** consists chiefly of carbon monoxide and hydrogen, formed by the action of steam upon hot coke. Some carbon dioxide is present, resulting from the primary reaction, and a small amount of methane, formed principally by a secondary reaction between carbon monoxide and hydrogen. **Carbureted water gas** contains, in addition, the hydrocarbon gases resulting from the cracking of enriching oils. Its composition varies with the quality of oil and fuel used and with the operating cycle in the manufacturing process. Typical percentage volumetric compositions are as follows:

Gas	CO_2	O_2	Illuminants	CO	H_2	CH_4	N_2	Sp gr	Btu per cu ft
Blue gas	5.0	0.6	...	38.0	48.0	1.2	7.2	0.56	290
Carbureted water gas	4.2	0.3	8.8	33.5	37.0	12.5	3.7	0.64	530

Coke, is almost exclusively used as **fuel** in the generator with the fine sizes, first removed, by screening.

The blue-gas process consists of alternate **blows** (with air) and **runs** (with steam) in a vertical cylindrical generator with mechanical (rotating) grate; the blow gases are passed to a waste-heat boiler, often mixing with more air to burn the CO content.

Typical **results in the manufacture of uncarbureted blue gas** are as follows (Morgan, "Manufactured Gas"):

Material per Mcf: coke as charged, 36.2 lb; air for blast, 2,230 cu ft; steam used, 51.9 lb; moisture in coke, 1.5 lb; steam decomposed, 23.85 lb; steam undecomposed, 29.55 lb.

For **carbureted water gas** the apparatus used consists of (1) the generator (7 to 12 ft I.D.) containing the fuel, alternately blown with air and steam; (2) the carburetor, usually containing heated checker-brick over which oil is sprayed for enrichment; (3) the superheater, containing heated checker-brick for cracking and fixing the vapors derived from the oil; and (4) waste-heat boilers for recovering heat from the blow gases, as air is passed through the generator, and sometimes also from the make gas, when steam is passed.

Average capacity of 9-ft set: gas made per hour (550 Btu), 100,000 to 250,000 cu ft; fuel gasified per hour per square foot of grate, 80 to 90 lb; depth of fuel bed, 4 to 7 ft; blast pressure, 25 to 35 in. water; oil efficiency, 90,000 to 110,000 Btu per gal; average tar yield, 20 to 26 percent of oil used.

Average quantities of materials required per Mcf of 550 Btu carbureted water gas: coke for generator fuel, 15 to 30 lb; boiler fuel, without waste-heat boiler, 8 to 14; with waste-heat boiler, 4 to 10 lb; air with coke, 1,400 to 1,800 cu ft at 60 F and 30 in.; total steam used in generator 25 to 35 lb; gas oil, 2.8 to 3.8 gal; percent of total heat in fuel, oil, and steam recovered in heat value of the gas alone, 60 to 66.

Operating Cycles. For **blue gas** the average cycle is: **air blow,** 1 to 2 min, passing the blast gases to a waste-heat boiler at 1300 to 1500 F after adding some air in a combustion chamber; **steam run,** 3 to 4 min, splitting into **uprun** and **downrun** if desired for improving fuel-bed conditions and thermal efficiency. Blue gas is also usually passed through a waste-heat boiler to recover the sensible heat of the gas and of the undecomposed steam.

The average operating cycle for **carbureted water gas,** regular system, is **air blow,** 2 to 3 min, passing the blast gases, with secondary air, through the carbureter and superheater and thence to the waste-heat boiler; **steam run,** 3 to 4 min (splitting into up and down runs if desired), with or without use of waste-heat boiler; **air-blow purge,** fraction of a minute, to recover gas left in the apparatus. If any downrun is used, a few seconds of uprun must always follow it, preceding the blow. The tendency is toward shorter cycles to approximate continuous operation.

In the **backrun process,** part of the run is made down, passing steam through the superheater, thence up through the carburetor, down through the generator, and direct to the scrubbers. The steam is thus preheated before entering the generator, and exhaust steam or even water or waste wash liquor may be used. The advantages are: (1) the gases leave the set at a lower temperature, with resulting increase in thermal efficiency; (2) increase of capacity by permitting larger ratio of run to blow; (3) longer life of checker-brick due to cleaning action of backrun steam; (4) more economical use of low-grade oils and coals. The backrun is standard practice in most large installations.

In the **reversed air-blast process,** after a short period of the ordinary blow, the air blast is reversed so as to enter the top of the superheater and passes back to the top of the generator and down. This blow gas, being richer than that of the upblast, passes into the make. The advantages are: (1) more even heat in the generator and less clinkering difficulty, (2) increased capacity and reduction of fuel used.

Gas Oils. In the carburetor, the action is largely one of **vaporizing** the oil, and in the superheater it is **cracking** or fixing of the vapors into simpler forms having vapor tensions high enough to carry them along in the gas. These oils vary considerably in composition, gravity, Btu value, and in coke (obtained by the "Conradson" carbonizing test). Such properties affect the carbureting and gas-making efficiencies, but the latter can be satisfactorily determined only by a plant trial.

Heavy oil (Bunker C fuel oil or other grade), cheaper than gas oil, has come into successful use in carbureting blue gas through modified methods, chiefly the use of a checkerless carburetor, marginal blasting, and spraying the oil to the top and sides in both generator and carburetor.

Table 4. Typical Backrun Operating Results[a]

Item	Diameter of generator, ft			
	6	11	11	11
Fuel	Coke	Coke	Coke	Coke
Cycle, blow, min	4.2	1.83		
Uprun, min	2.0	1.95		
Backrun, min	2.0	1.88		
Blow-run min	0.0	0.00		
Temp, top of superheater, deg F	......	1100		
base of carburetor	......	1350		
Oil used, field	Okla.	Tex.	Gas oil	Bunker C
gravity, Baumé	34–36	35	24	15.3
gal per Mcf	2.88	2.78	2.90	4.18
Carbureted blue gas, Btu per cu ft	570	530	535	535
Generator fuel, lb per Mcf	30.83	27.0	26.2	15.8
Period covered, months	6	5		
Oil efficiency, Btu per gal	111,700	100,700		
Capacity per day, Mcf	......	....	4500	5700

[a] Morgan, "Manufactured Gas," p. 308; Lowry, "Chemistry of Coal Utilization," p. 1745.

Steam production in waste-heat boilers per Mcf of gas made amounts to 20 to 35 lb when only the blow gases are used, and 10 to 20 lb more when the make gas is used.

The use of **exhaust steam,** by the aid of the **steam accumulator,** is increasing. The principal source of exhaust steam is from the blower engines, which operate at a time when steam for the make run is not required. The accumulator is necessary unless a number of sets, in one plant, can be operated alternately so as to send exhaust steam from one to the other.

The **heat balance of the carbureted water-gas process** in modern practice using heavy oil is as follows. **Input,** percent; hhv of combustion of coke, 19.7; oil, 77.0; total heat in steam, 2.7; sensible heat in air, 0.6. **Output,** percent; hhv of gas made, combustion, 63.5, sensible, 2.9; tar, combustion 16.0, sensible, 0.8; drip oil, combustion, 1.3; blast products, combustion 0.3, sensible, 2.2; waste-heat boiler, total heat of steam, 2.9; undecomposed steam, 1.6; water vapor, 0.1; refuse, 0.3; radiation and unaccounted for, 8.1.

Other Manufactured-gas Processes

In the United States, the use of manufactured gas as a domestic fuel is presently confined to (1) providing peak-load gas to supplement the capacity of natural-gas transmission lines and adjacent underground storage, and (2) making an alternate source of supply available to replace possible future depletion of the natural-gas reserves.

In the first category, there are three quick-starting processes which require comparatively low capital investment. One, the UGI catalytic reforming process, is cyclic and makes use of charging stocks ranging from natural gas and liquefied petroleum gas to kerosine. The other two are continuous—the Koppers-Hasche furnace, using feeds of propane, butane, or natural gasoline, and the IGT pressure hydrogasification process, using natural gasoline, light naphthas, or kerosine stocks. All these stocks are comparatively expensive and unsuitable for base-load gas production.

The second category contains two groups, one using cheaper charging stocks composed of the various heavy liquid hydrocarbons and other comprising those processes making use of coal as the basic raw material. Plants for both types of processes require comparatively higher capital investment than the light-liquid-hydrocarbon plants, but cheaper feedstocks and raw materials make them available as large-sized, base-load gas producers.

Among the heavy-liquid-hydrocarbon processes, two are cyclic: the Hall cyclic thermal-reforming process, using components of carbureted-water-gas sets modified for the purpose and feedstocks ranging from naphtha to Bunker C, and the UGI modified cyclic catalytic reforming process for heavy residual oil. Two others, the surface-combustion thermofor process and the IGT two-stage continuous catalytic methane process, are continuous, requiring high capital investment.

Base-load plants for the gasification of bituminous coal are of either the fixed-bed or the fluidized-bed type; both types are suitable for the purpose but require high capital investment. Demag has a fixed-bed process in which the fuel bed is automatically renewed, using no oxygen. Lurgi is developing a commercial fixed-bed plant to use coking coals, which is basically more efficient than the pulverized-coal gasification processes. IGT has two processes using suspended beds, one for direct hydrogenation to methane and one for oxygen-steam gasification followed by methanation. The Koppers-Totzek process has long been successful as a synthesis-gas producer using a fluidized bed.

At present in the United States, the various processes are rated as (1) the light-hydrocarbon reforming processes, (2) the heavy-oil processes, and (3) the coal-gasification processes. Economic changes such as the increased cost of petroleum and natural gas resulting from the depletion of the oil and natural-gas reserves or improved, more efficient, and cheaper mining and transportation of coal may be expected to bring the coal-gasification processes into use in the future with justifiable long-range development.

The **UGI catalytic reforming process** can utilize the carburetor and superheater of conventional carbureted-water-gas sets, or a specially designed two-shell plant may be provided. Using hydrocarbon fuels and charging stocks ranging from natural gas and liquified petroleum gas to kerosine, a peak-load gas of low heating value and high hydrogen content is produced at high rates. The converted carburetor or first shell of the set is used for the generation of heat by the combustion of liquid or gaseous hydrocarbon fuel to raise the temperature of the nickel-impregnated alumina catalyst in the second shell or catalyst chamber. Excess heat from the combustion gases is recovered in a waste-heat boiler as process steam, which is also admitted to the combustion chamber. An automatic control operates the unit on a fixed cycle. During the gas-reforming period, the charging stock is admitted to the catalyst chamber, where the conversion is performed. The cyclic combustion of fuel with some excess air keeps the catalyst free of carbon deposits, and substantial sulphur contents of the feedstock can be accepted without a damaging catalyst contamination. The equipment can be kept hot and ready for use by burning heating fuel in the combustion chamber for a few minutes each 24 hr. Many plants in the United States use this process.

The **Koppers-Hasche furnace** is a comparatively long, square, refractory-lined shell containing three chambers. In the center is an open combustion chamber flanked on each end by a cracking chamber filled with specially designed high-purity alumina checkers. Feedstock, together with insufficient air for complete combustion, is admitted to the central combustion chamber, where, by partial combustion, it generates sufficient heat to maintain a temperature of 3000 F in the cracking chambers. There the thermal decomposition of the unburned portion of the feedstock is performed. The gas produced is stabilized before leaving the furnace for cleaning and cooling. Gases of a wide range of heating value can be made from charging stocks of propane, butane, or natural gasoline. The composition and heating value of the gas produced can be regulated by controlling the air-gas mix to the combustion chamber. A furnace may be put into full operation in 1 hr from a cold start, or it may be held at operating temperature automatically by an economical use of fuel gas. The furnace makes gas at high rates per sq ft of plant area, per man-hour of operating labor, and per dollar of investment. Plants have been built for peak-load production and for some smaller base-load use in several countries.

In the **IGT pressure hydrogasification process,** steam and a feedstock of natural gas, vaporized natural gasoline, or recycled product gas are fed to alloy-steel catalytic cracking tubes operating at 1700 F and 70 psi approx. This produces a gas high in hydrogen but containing unwanted concentrations of carbon monoxide and carbon dioxide. A shift reaction is used for conversion of the carbon monoxide to hydrogen and more carbon dioxide; the latter is absorbed in monoethanolamine. The product at this point contains about 90 percent hydrogen, which in turn is fed with natural gasoline or some other selected feedstock to the alloy-steel tubes of a thermal cracking furnace operating at 1300 F and 60 psi approx. The final product gases are interchangeable with natural gas, require no scrubbing, and can be distributed directly by a high-pressure system. Low investment, operating, and labor costs are claimed.

The **Hall cyclic thermal-reforming process** uses component parts of carbureted-water-gas apparatus to generate high-Btu gas from feedstocks ranging from naphtha to Bunker C. Two pairs of checker-brick chambers are provided from two water-gas sets by cross-connecting the tops of the carburetors to serve as a pair of generators and by using the original superheaters and wash boxes. Other connections are added so that the superheaters can be used alternately for preheating air, superheating steam, and gas making. The automatic control is rearranged to operate the equipment on the new cycle.

In the first heating cycle, air for combustion is admitted at the top of one superheater, is preheated while passing downward through the hot checker-brick, passes upward through the companion generator, and meets the fuel oil at the burner at the top of the second generator. Combustion takes place downward, and the hot gases pass upward through the checker-brick of the second superheater, raising them to the desired cracking temperature. In the gas-making cycle, the blast air is shut off and steam is admitted at the same point at the top of the first superheater. The steam follows the original path of the air and meets the charging stock at the top of the second generator. The charging stock is vaporized in this generator and passes, with the superheated steam, through the second (hot) superheater, where it is cracked to product gas and stabilized for removal from the set through the wash box. The automatic control reverses the flow sequence for the next heating and gas-making cycles, which continue, using the alternate pairs of chambers in the same way. Gas handling, cooling, and cleaning may be by the original water-gas equipment. Tar and light oil are made as coproducts.

Many larger-sized water-gas plants have converted to this process. It is probably the most successful manufactured-gas process offered since the advent of high-pressure, long-range, natural-gas transmission lines. Using a specially designed plant which provides for hydrogen input with the feedstock, the IGT has projected an improvement on the Hall process to increase the yield and reduce the unsaturates in the product gas. In the suggested plant, the superheaters are used only for air and steam, thus keeping the coke and pitch confined to the generators, where they can be burned off on the succeeding heating cycle.

The **UGI modified cyclic catalytic reforming process for heavy oil** is a development of the original UGI catalytic reforming process to provide for the use of high-sulphur, high-Conradson-carbon oils as feedstocks. A specially developed nickel catalyst is regenerated in each cycle to eliminate sulphur contamination. The feedstock is volatilized before it comes in contact with the catalyst to reduce ash glazing.

The **Surface Combustion thermofor pyrolytic continuous cracking process** utilizes two circulating-coke-pebble heat exchangers. The primary pebble circulation is through a heater to a cracking chamber, where the pebbles meet and crack the feedstock, and thence to a drying zone where final coking takes place. A gas lift elevates the pebbles to the top of the unit for recirculation. Here the coldest pebbles are removed from stream to constitute the secondary circulation system, which goes to a heater where the pebble temperature is raised to some 700 F for use in cooling the hot gases released from the cracking chamber. These comparatively cool gases are then quenched and released as product. The circulating coke pebbles grow in size by collecting a deposit of carbon, and excess quantities of pebbles are continuously removed. With this method for carbon removal, there is practically no limitation on the Conradson-carbon content of the feedstock. The equipment for this process requires a high capital expenditure, making it prohibitive for use as a standby or peak-load producer. The process could become useful when oil gas is competitive with natural gas.

The **IGT two-stage continuous catalytic methane process** first treats the heavy residual-oil charge stock in a fixed bed of molybdenum catalyst in the liquid phase at high pressure. The second stage, performed in the vapor phase, converts the oil to methane. Oil and hydrogen are passed through the first catalyst bed continuously to the high-pressure, high-temperature, second-stage reactor, where the methanation is completed. The advantage is the removal of Conradson carbon in the first stage, freeing the second-stage of catalyst contamination. Capital investment is too high for peak-load use.

The **Flesch-Demag process** uses a type of cyclic water-gas apparatus for feeding and charring the coal charge and for gas generation with periodic automatic removal of the resultant ash. Two generators with rotary grates, similar to gas-producer grates, are connected together by appropriate gas offtakes and valves at their tops and are operated by an automatic control like that used for water-gas sets. The cycle is downblast, with removal of the blast gas through the grates, followed by an upblast of air or steam on one generator, fluidizing the bed and clinkering the ash to drop on the grate for removal. The gas generated crosses to the top of the second generator, flows down through the fixed bed and out through the grate. Pulverized coal is added to the fluidized bed for rapid devolatilization. The top blast is then resumed, followed by a fluidizing of the second fuel bed to complete the cycle. Cost is influenced favorably by requiring no oxygen and unfavorably by high gas-exit temperature and high investment.

The **Lurgi-process** fixed bed can be of low-grade, strip-mined, non-coking coal which may contain as much as 25 percent ash and 15 percent moisture. Gasification is completed in the generator in a continuous stream of superheated steam and oxygen at some 350 psi. Surplus heat in the crude gas is recovered by waste-heat boilers, and the gas is then cooled and scrubbed to remove the light oils and benzol. Ammonia recovered at this point is concentrated to a 20 percent solution for sale. The carbon monoxide is converted to hydrogen in a conventional shift plant, and the resultant carbon dioxide and most of the hydrogen sulphide are removed by scrubbing with a hot solution of potassium carbonate. At this point, the gas has a heating value of about 400 Btu per cu ft. The next step, hydrogenation, increases the heating value to some 700 Btu per cu ft and specific gravity of 0.45 approx. Benzene is recovered from the product stream, and final traces of hydrogen sulphide are removed in high-pressure iron-oxide purification chambers. The waste-heat boilers produce sufficient steam for all process purposes and for generation of sufficient power to operate the entire plant. Full-scale Lurgi plants are in regular commercial operation.

The **IGT direct hydrogenation process** requires a feedstock of coal pulverized to a particle size of −75, +200 mesh and pretreated at high temperature with inert gas or steam to provide a non-coking char. Hydrogen is produced from the char by reaction with steam and oxygen at 250 psi and 2700 F approx. More steam is added in a shift reactor to convert the resultant carbon monoxide to hydrogen and carbon dioxide; the latter is removed by chemical absorption and discarded, leaving substantially pure hydrogen for the hydrogenation step. Pretreated coal and hydrogen are then fed to the reactor, operating at 1,250 psi and 1300 F, where the coal bed is kept fluidized by the incoming hydrogen. The reaction produces a gas of some 70 percent methane as the final product. The process is said to eliminate all difficulty in the hydrogenation of coking coals.

Slagging Oxygen-steam Coal Gasification. In another IGT process, low-grade coal is crushed and charged with a carrier stream of high-pressure air and steam into a chamber in which the air and steam penetrate the coal particles. The coal stream is next discharged into a cyclone chamber where the coal particle size is still further reduced by rupture and attrition. A second cyclone chamber then receives the coal stream plus the air and steam and additional superheated steam. Here the fine coal is softened and partially devolatilized by incomplete combustion. The resultant char is then mixed with compressed oxygen and charged into the main reaction chamber, operating at 90 psi approx; over 90 percent of the carbon is gasified, and the ash is withdrawn as slag. The synthesis gas is washed, cooled, and reacted in contact with a nickel catalyst to form an intermediate product containing methane, carbon dioxide, and water vapor. The carbon dioxide, hydrogen sulphide, and water are removed by absorption. The end-product gas is high in methane concentration and has a heating value of 930 Btu per cu ft approx. It is a practical substitute for compression and addition to high-pressure natural-gas distribution systems.

Koppers-Totzek Process. This gasifier is adapted to the use of low-grade coals containing up to 35 percent ash. The raw coal is pulverized and dried before injection into the gasifier in a concurrent stream of 96 percent oxygen and 2750 F superheated steam. Under these conditions, gasification is practically instantaneous, liberating sufficient excess heat to maintain the required high temperature of the gasifier and also to provide, through the waste-heat boiler, steam and power for the entire operation, including the oxygen plant. Ashes with fusion points as high as 2820 F have been successfully slagged and removed by holding the temperature of the refractory lining above the fusion point of the ash. The waste-heat boiler cools the synthesis-gas stream and produces steam at 500 psi and 850 F. In order to keep the slagged ash dust in the boiler from solidifying, the temperature of the gas stream is reduced by a jet of steam at the boiler inlet. The slag then drops out, to be drawn off in a rather deep stream to a granulating bath, from which it is removed by a scraper for use in road building or in concrete aggregate.

The next step is the chemical removal of hydrogen sulphide, which can be separated by any one of several well-known processes as feed for a catalytic sulphuric acid plant or for the production of brimstone sulphur. After the removal of the hydrogen sulphide, the analysis of the gas will be, in percent, about $CO_2 = 11$, $CO = 58$, $H_2 = 29$, $N_2 = 2$; gross heating value = 250 Btu per cu ft.

A variation of the usual hydrogenation process has been demonstrated by Osthaus and Merkel in which the catalytic conversion of the carbon monoxide is performed at some 150 psi and 840 F on a magnesite or dolomite catalyst impregnated with nickel. Under proper control, the reaction is $4CO + 2H_2O \rightarrow CH_4 + 3CO_2$. By this method, the gasification efficiency from low-grade coal to domestic gas at 480 Btu per cu ft approx is about 60 percent, comparing closely with the efficiency obtained when making water gas from coke. The final product analyzes, in percent, about $CO_2 = 15$, $CO = 5$, $CH_4 = 28$, $H_2 = 48$, $N_2 = 4$; gross heating value = 480 Btu per cu ft.

The Koppers-Totzek gasifier has been widely used as a synthesis-gas producer since 1940, mostly in Europe and Japan in ammonia manufacturing plants. Using the process for production of 480-Btu gas and calculating on a heating-value basis, a substitute for 1000-Btu natural gas could be made for 96 cents per Mcf approx under conditions estimated to obtain on capital costs of equipment in the United States.

COMBUSTION FURNACES

BY

M. H. Mawhinney

REFERENCES: Trinks-Mawhinney, "Industrial Furnaces," Vols. I and II, Wiley.

FUELS

The selection of the best fuel should be based upon a study of the comparative prepared costs, cleanliness of operation, adaptability to temperature control, labor required, and the effect of each fuel upon the material to be heated and upon the furnace lining. Attention must be paid to the quantity to be burned in each burner, the atmosphere (fuel-to-air ratio) desired in the furnace, and the uniformity of temperature distribution required, which determines the number and the location of the burners. Common methods of burning furnace fuels are as follows.

Solid Fuels (almost entirely bituminous coals)

HAND-FIRED. Not frequently used, on account of the high labor costs, except in sheet mill furnaces, where the combustion of coal on the grate produces a soft nonoxidizing flame which is well suited to the heating of thin sheets to permit rolling without sticking.

STOKER-FIRED. Adaptable for mill furnaces, forging furnaces, and other applications where refined heating is not necessary.

POWDERED COAL. Not adaptable where the furnace atmosphere must be free from ash particles. Good efficiency and temperature control may be obtained, but the combustion space must be large. Commonly used in malleable-iron anealing furnaces, melting furnaces, and cement kilns, and sometimes in forging, reheating, and sheet furnaces.

Liquid Fuels (fuel oil and tar)

HIGH-PRESSURE BURNERS include all burners utilizing atomizing air or steam at pressures above 2 psig and are most common in high-capacity sizes. With 60 psig, 90 percent of the air needed for combustion is induced from the atmosphere.

INTERMEDIATE-PRESSURE BURNERS utilize atomizing air at 1 to 2 psig. Between 30 and 40 percent of the required combustion air is supplied mechanically, and the remainder induced.

FAN-BLAST BURNERS utilize atomizing air at 8 to 16 oz per sq in., and induce about 50 percent of the combustion air.

Gaseous Fuels

Burners for refined gases (natural gas, city gas, clean producer gas, propane, butane, and oil gas):

TWO-PIPE SYSTEMS. Comprise a simple mixing tee with separate control of gas and air, or, nozzle mixing burners with separated internal baffles for retarding the mixing of gas and air, or, luminous or radiant flame burners with parallel gas and air streams at low velocity.

PREMIX SYSTEMS. Air and gas mixed in a blower and supplied through one pipe.

PROPORTIONING LOW-PRESSURE MIXERS. Air and gas supplied under pressure and proportioned automatically.

HIGH-PRESSURE SYSTEMS. Gas at pressure of 5 to 25 psig induces air for combustion, or high-pressure air induces gas.

Burners for crude gases (raw producer-gas, blast-furnace gas, or coke-oven gas):

SIMPLE MIXING SYSTEMS with large orifices and simple mechanisms which cannot become clogged by tar and dirt contained in these gases.

SEPARATE GAS AND AIR SUPPLIES to the furnace, with all mixture taking place within the furnace.

INDUSTRIAL HEATING FURNACES

Heating furnaces are usually classified according to (1) the purpose for which the material is heated, (2) the nature of the transfer of heat to the material, (3) the method of firing the furnace, or (4) the method of handling material through the furnace.

Purpose. Primarily a metallurgical distinction, according as the furnace is intended for tempering, annealing, carburizing, cyaniding, case-hardening, forging, heating for forming or rolling, enameling, or for some other purpose.

Transfer of Heat. The principal varieties are **oven furnaces,** in which the heat is transferred from the products of combustion of the fuel, in direct contact with the heated material, by convection and direct radiation from the hot gases or by reradiation from the hot walls of the furnace; **muffle furnaces,** in which the heat is conducted through a metal or refractory muffle which protects the heated material from contact with the gases, and is then transferred from the interior of the muffle by radiation to the heated material, which is sometimes surrounded by inert gases to exclude air; or **liquid-bath furnaces,** in which a metal pot is heated on the outside or by immersion. This pot contains a liquid heating or processing medium which transfers heat to the material contained in it. This type includes low-temperature tempering furnaces with oil as the heating medium, hardening furnaces using a bath of lead, hardening and cyaniding furnaces with baths of special salts, and galvanizing or tinning furnaces for coating the heating material with zinc or tin. The generally accepted form of muffle is the **radiant-tube** fired furnace, in which the fuel is burned in metal or refractory tubes which radiate heat to the charge. An important form of furnace for temperatures below 1300 F is the **recirculating** type, in which the atmosphere (products of combustion, air, or protective gases) is recirculated rapidly through the heating chamber. A recent development is **forced convection** heating by a large number of jets of hot gas at high velocity. In **high-speed** heating (or **patterned combustion**), premixed burners are arranged for close application of heat, and with a high-temperature head, very rapid heating is accomplished.

Method of Firing. This classification applies principally to the oven type of furnaces, and it indicates whether the furnace is direct-fired, overfired, side-fired, or underfired. Figure 1 shows diagrammatically the principles of each of these types.

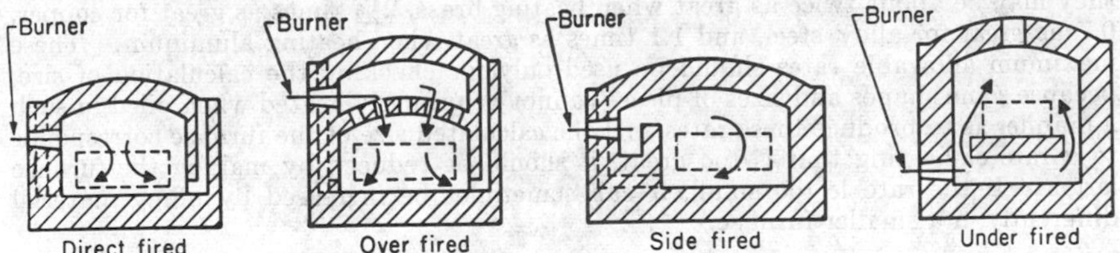

FIG. 1. Methods of firing oven furnaces.

The **underfired furnace** is excellent for low temperatures, because the heating material is best protected from the high temperatures of the burning fuel. The temperature and atmosphere can be more readily controlled than in the other types, but the temperature is limited, by the life of the refractories, to an upper value of about 1800 F. The **overfired** design is similar in characteristics to the underfired but is limited in width to about 6 ft by the strength of the perforated arch, and in height to about 4 ft by the difficulty in obtaining temperature uniformity, owing to the tendency of heat to rise. The **side-fired** design is used where the temperature is too high for underfiring (above 1800 F) or where under-firing interferes with the best handling method, and where better atmosphere is required than can be obtained with direct firing. The **direct-fired** principle is used almost entirely above 2000 F.

Method of Material Handling. In the **batch** type, the heated material charged into the furnace remains in the same position until it is withdrawn after sufficient heating. In a **continuous furnace,** the material is moved through the furnace by mechanical means which include pushers, chain conveyors, reciprocating hearths, rotating circular hearths, cars, walking beams, and roller hearths. Continuous furnaces are principally labor-saving devices and may or may not save fuel.

Size and Economy of Furnaces

The size of furnace required depends upon the amount of material to be heated per hour, the heating time required, the size of the pieces to be heated, and the amount of heat that can be liberated without excessive damage to the furnace. The efficiency and refractory life obtained depend upon the correctness of furnace size.

Heating Time. For the usual relation of refractory area to stock area, time to heat steel plate from one side for each ⅛ in. of thickness varies from 3 min for high-speed heating and 6 to 12 min for heating for forming by usual methods to 20 min. for heat-treating. Steel cylinders will be heated in one-half these times per ⅛-in diam. Below 800 F, the time may be two to three times these values. Brass requires about one-half as long as steel to heat, copper 40 percent as long, and aluminum 85 percent as long. The preceding heating times are based on a furnace temperature 50 to 100 deg higher than the final temperature of the heated material. It is assumed that the material is fully exposed to the heat of the furnace. Piling of material in a furnace lengthens the heating time by an amount that must be determined by actual trial. In addition to simple heating, there is frequently additional **time required for soaking** (holding at furnace temperature) to cause metallurgical changes in the material or for some other reason.

The **weight of material in the furnace** at any time is the product of weight of material per hour multiplied by the heating time in hours. If the weight and sizes of pieces involved are known, the **area of the furnace** can then be fixed. The width and length of the furnace to produce this hearth are fixed by the method of firing to be used and by the method of handling material.

The life of a furnace at given temperature depends upon the rate of heating, which may be expressed in pounds per square foot of hearth area per hour. The maximum allowable **rate of heating steel** is about 35 lb per sq ft per hr for heat-treating, 70 lb for in-and-out rolling-mill furnaces, 100 lb for single-zone continuous furnaces, and 150 lb for multiple-zone furnaces. These are upper limits which should not be used if long life of furnace refractories is expected. These rates are for heating mild steel; they may be about twice as great when heating brass, 2½ times as great for copper, 0.7 as great for alloy steel, and 1.1 times as great when heating aluminum. These maximum allowable rates should be used only for checking the calculation of size, because some shapes and sizes of pieces cannot be properly heated when piled in such a manner as to produce these rates. If the calculated size of the furnace corresponds to a rate of heating that is too great, it should be reduced by making the furnace larger. If the rate is too small, it can sometimes be increased by piling material differently in a smaller furnace.

EXAMPLE. To determine furnace size. If a furnace is required to heat 20 pieces per hr weighing 30 lb each and requiring a heating time of ½ hr, the furnace must be large enough to hold $\frac{1}{2} \times 20 = 10$ pieces. If each piece requires an area of 2 sq ft, the area of the hearth will be $2 \times 10 = 20$ sq ft for a single layer of pieces in the furnace. If the furnace is of the batch type, a size of 4 ft wide × 5 ft deep would probably be about right for convenient handling. Upon checking, the rate of heating is 20 pieces per hr × 30 lb/20 sq ft = 30 lb per sq ft per hr. For this rate an underfired furnace would be satisfactory, although for other methods of firing, a smaller furnace could be used if the pieces could be more densely piled without seriously interfering with the circulation in the furnace.

The heat released by the fuel in a furnace (heat input) is equal to the sum of the heat required in the heating process (useful heat) plus the heat losses from the furnace. **Heat input** includes the heat of combustion of the fuel, sensible heat in preheated air or fuel, and heat in the material charged. Low-heat values of the fuel are used, and the sensible heat can be calculated from the specific heats of the preheated air, fuel, or material. **Useful heat** includes the heat absorbed by the material in the furnace. Figure 2 gives heat contents for different metals. In the simple heating of metals, the useful heat applied to the metal includes only the heat absorption, as given in Fig. 2; but there are many processes that include other requirements, such as drying, where moisture must be heated and evaporated, heating of chemical products where heat is utilized to cause chemical changes, and other special cases.

Heat losses in a heating furnace include heat lost in waste gases, radiation from and heat absorbed by refractories, heat carried out of the furnace by containers or conveyors, heat lost through openings, and heat in unburned fuel escaping with the products of combustion. The **heat contained in waste gases** depends upon the temperature of these gases as they leave the heating chamber. Table 1 gives the approximate percentage of heat contained in the flue gases from perfect combustion at different temperatures. These values are about the same for most fuels except producer gas and blast-furnace gas, the losses with which are higher than those given in the table.

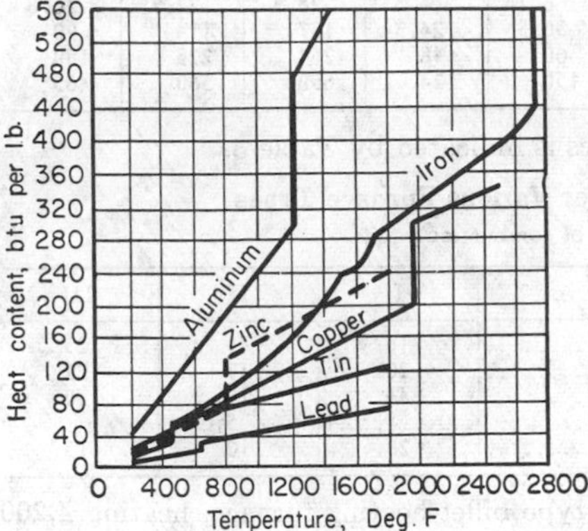

FIG. 2. Heat content of metals.

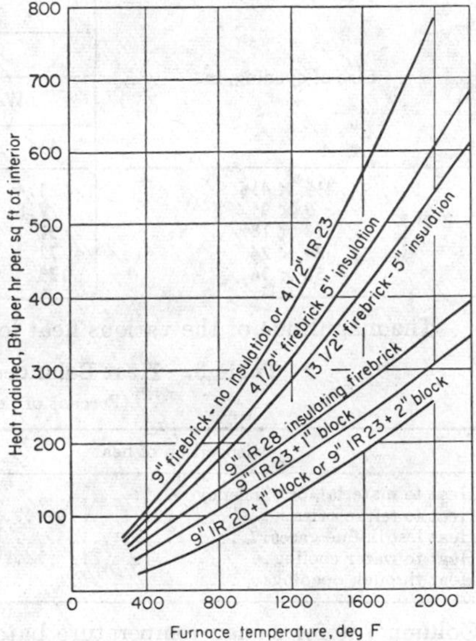

FIG. 3. Heat lost from thoroughly heated walls, based on interior area.

Table 1. Average Heat in Waste Products of Combustion at Various Temperatures, Percent of Low Heat Value of the Fuel

Temperature of gases, deg F	1000	1200	1400	1600	1800	2000	2200
Percent of low heat value in gases	24	28	34	38	45	50	55

Radiation and heat absorption by refractories depend also upon the rate of heating (which determines the interior temperature of the refractories) and upon the refractory area and thickness. Figure 3 shows the heat radiated through walls of different thickness at various furnace temperatures, for equilibrium conditions, when the wall has reached steady temperatures throughout (see also references at the beginning of this section and Keller, "Flow of Heat through Furnace Hearths," ASME, May, 1928). The **heat carried out by containers and conveyors** is the sensible heat content of these items as they leave the heating chamber. Such losses include the heat in carburizing boxes, pans, chain conveyors, and furnace cars. **Radiation from furnace openings** depends upon the size and shape of the opening and the thickness of the walls in which they are located, as well as upon the temperature of the furnace. Some idea of the magnitude of these losses is given by the values in Table 2.

The **heat lost in unburned fuel** escaping with the flue gases is small in most furnaces because the fuel can be almost completely consumed.

The **efficiency of an industrial furnace** is the ratio of the heat absorbed by the heated material to the heat of combustion of the fuel burned.

Table 2. Radiation through Openings in Furnace Walls, Thousands of Btu per Hour

Size of opening, in.	Furnace temperature, deg F					
	1400			2200		
	Wall thickness, in.			Wall thickness, in.		
	4½	9	18	4½	9	18
4½ × 4½	1.4	1.1	0.8	5.1	4.1	2.8
9 × 9	7.8	6.1	4.5	28.5	22.7	16.8
18 × 18	37	30.5	24.3	137	114	90
24 × 24	71	60	48	264	225	180
36 × 36	173	150	124	650	560	465

The magnitude of the various heat losses is indicated by Table 3.

Table 3. Heat Balances for Various Furnace Types

(Percent of heat of combustion)

Disposition of heat	I	II	III
Heat to material, or efficiency	16	49	23
Heat to refractories	20	17	22
Heat lost in flue gases	44	19	40
Heat to water cooling	....	5	
Heat through openings	20	10	15

Column I is for a high-temperature batch-type billet-heating furnace, heating 4,200 lb of billets per hour, a furnace load at a time, to 2300 F, at a rate of 25 lb per sq ft per hr, averaged over 10 hr of operation, and with a fuel consumption of 30 gal of oil per ton of steel heated. Column II is for a large continuous billet-heating furnace of the usual pusher type with a flow of gases opposite to that of the steel, and operating at a rate of 60 lb of steel heated to 2300 deg per sq ft of hearth area per hour. Column III is for an underfired batch-type furnace, heating steel to 1600 F for annealing, at a rate of 30 lb per sq ft per hr.

Table 4. Average Net Efficiencies and Fuel Requirements of Various Furnace Types with Good Operation

Type	Temp, deg F	Average efficiency, percent	Average heat required from fuel, Btu per lb of steel
Ingot heating, soaking pits, recuperative	2000–2400	20	500
Billet heating for forming			
Batch, in-and-out	2000–2400	20	1750
Continuous	2000–2400	32	1100
Wire annealing of coils, hood type	1300–1500	16	1350
Wire annealing of strands, in lead	1300–1500	19	1100
Wire patenting, strands	1650	21	1250
Wire baking, coils, continuous	450	20	250
Tube annealing, continuous, bright	1300–1500	35	600
Skelp heating, butt weld, continuous	2900	25	1500
Slab heating, continuous, recuperative	2400	42	800
Strip coil annealing, hood type	1250–1400	30	600
Hardening, continuous conveyor	1650	21	1250
Drawing, continuous conveyor	900–1100	20	750
Carburizing, gas, continuous	1750	19	1500

Table 4 gives average requirements in fuel of typical industrial heating furnaces. The values are for furnaces without heat-saving appliances (recuperators, regenerators, of waste-heat boilers) except as noted and show the efficiency and the Btu required in the fuel per net pound of steel heated. To obtain the average amount of any fuel required, this latter figure is divided by the low heat value of the fuel. The values are for average rates of heating. Fuel economy is of small importance as compared with the quality of the product.

Furnace Construction

Furnace refractories are made up largely of standard bricks and shapes, and it is advisable to specify furnace dimensions that can be built with a minimum of cutting. Horizontal flues are made a multiple of 2½ or 3 in. in height, and most other flue dimensions are multiples of 4½ in. to correspond to the width and length of standard bricks. The area of furnace flues must be large enough to avoid excessive pressures at maximum fuel rates. Flues should be located so as to promote the circulation of gases in all parts of the furnace. Average allowable **velocities in flues** for furnaces **without stacks are:**

Furnace temperature, deg F	200	1000	1500	2000
Allowable velocity (hot gases), fps	9	13	15	17

The total **flue areas required** in sq in. per cu ft of fuel per hr (or per gal per hr for fuel oil) at temperatures of the products of combustion of 1000 and 2000 F are as follows:

Temp F	Fuel oil	Natural gas	Artificial gas	Coke-oven gas	Raw producer gas
1000	14.0	0.11	0.06	0.05	0.02
2000	19.0	0.15	0.08	0.06	0.02

The **metal parts of a furnace** consist of the steel and cast-iron binding and of alloy parts exposed to the direct heat of the furnace. These alloy parts are of nickel or chromium alloys and must be made heavy enough to offset the loss of strength at high temperatures. They are resistant to oxidation at temperatures below 2000 F.

Heat-saving Methods

Methods of conserving heat include the use of recuperators or regenerators, waste-heat boilers (see Sec. 9), insulation of refractories, automatic control of temperature and atmosphere, and special attention to the construction and operation of the furnace.

Recuperators and regenerators extract some heat from the escaping flue gases and return it to the furnace by preheating the combustion air or the entering fuel. In **recuperators,** continuous flow of hot gases and cold entering air or gas is maintained through metal or refractory ducts which keep the two gas streams apart but which conduct heat from the hotter stream to the colder. Recuperators are built in the form of self-enclosed units set above the ground or in pits below floor level, and are made of fire-clay tile, silicon carbide, or heat-resisting metal. Over-all coefficients of heat transfer in metallic recuperators are between 2.5 and 6.0 Btu per sq ft per hr per deg F, and in silicon carbide recuperators about the same; the coefficient for fire-clay recuperators is considerably less than these values. Usual velocities of hot air in recuperators do not exceed 12 fps, in order to keep pressure drop to a reasonable value.

Regenerators are used where high temperature of air preheat is required to maintain high furnace temperature. They are usually constructed of firebrick and consist of two chambers completely filled with a checkerwork. The flow of flue gases and that of air or gas to be heated are periodically reversed, so that the hot gases and cold gases alternately flow through the two sets of chambers. The checkerwork retains the heat of the hot gases and gives it up to the cold gases with each reversal. Another regenerator design employs metal plates. Regenerators are more expensive than recuperators in most cases and are not frequently used with heating furnaces, but their use with open-hearth furnaces is almost universal. Over-all coefficient of heat transfer in regenerators is from 1.5 to 2.5 Btu per sq ft of checkerbrick surface per hr per deg F temperature difference, and the usual mass velocity of hot gas through the openings of the checker is about 0.065 lb per sq ft per sec.

The **saving effected by recuperators or regenerators** depends upon the temperature to which the incoming air or gas is preheated. With a flue gas temperature of 1600 F, the theoretical saving in fuel with 200 deg preheat of combustion air is about 4 percent; with 400 deg, 11 percent; with 600 deg, 15 percent; and with 800 deg, 19 percent. A recuperator or regenerator installation, to be a good investment, must show a satisfactory net saving after all costs of repairs and shutdown time lost by such repairs are subtracted from the savings in fuel used.

Automatic control prevents the waste of heat by unnecessarily high temperatures, preventable cold periods, and excessive air or unburned fuel from poor combustion. Of even greater importance is the prevention of damage to the heated product from overheating, excessive oxidation, and objectionable chemical reaction between furnace atmosphere and the product (principally decarburization and recarburization). Automatic **temperature** controllers are actuated by thermocouples in the furnace. The thermocouple must not be located in the direct path of the flames, which are not only several hundred degrees hotter than the furnace temperature but are also of extremely variable temperature and not an indication of the average temperature. Automatic control of **atmosphere** for the consistent maintainance of good combustion is accomplished by properly proportioning the fuel and combustion air as they enter the furnace. This is accomplished by the utilization of some characteristic of the flow of one fluid to regulate the flow of the other fluid. Automatic **pressure** control operates the flue dampers of a furnace to maintain a constant predetermined pressure (usually about 0.01 to 0.05 in. water) in the heating chamber, which excludes free oxygen from the surrounding atmosphere.

Care in furnace construction and operation is the simplest but most frequently neglected of all methods of heat saving. A large quantity of fuel can be saved by care in the construction of furnace refractories so that they will remain tight, by attention to the sealing of doors, and by taking care that the doors and other openings are kept closed when not in use.

Special Atmospheres

(See also p. 7-92)

In an increasing number of heat-treating operations the necessity for improved quality has created a demand for clean- or bright-heating furnaces, in which the heating material is surrounded by a suitable protective gas while it is heated by radiation from electric resistors, radiant tubes, or the walls of a muffle. Table 5 gives the chemical analysis of common protective gases used in the heat-treating industry.

Table 5. Protective Gas Atmospheres

Type	Typical analysis					Dew point, deg F
	CO_2	CO	CH_4	H_2	N_2	
I. Hydrogen, purified	....	....	...	100.0	....	Minus 60
II. Dissociated ammonia	....	....	...	75.0–5.0	25.0–95.0	
III. Rich hydrocarbon gas, not conditioned	5.5	9.0	0.8	15.0	69.7	Plus 50
IV. Lean hydrocarbon gas, not conditioned	11.5	0.7	...	0.7	87.1	Plus 50
V. Rich hydrocarbon gas, completely conditioned	0.1	9.5	0.8	15.8	73.8	Minus 60
VI. Lean hydrocarbon gas, completely conditioned	0.1	2.8	...	3.9	93.2	Minus 60
VII. Endothermic generator gas	0.5	20.0	1.0	38.0	40.5	Plus 50
VIII. Charcoal gas	0.5	30.0	...	2.0	67.5	Plus 50

Type I. Purified hydrogen is used for annealing, brazing, and other treatment of low-carbon steel; for the sintering of low-carbon ferrous powders; for the treatment of silicon iron (electrical sheets and strip); for the bright annealing of stainless steels, and the sintering of molybdenum, tungsten, and other metals.

Type II. Ammonia is dissociated by steam or electric heat, and is dried by chemical driers. By partial combustion the relative percentages of hydrogen and nitrogen may be varied as shown in Table 5. The resulting gases from this treatment are cheaper and are used for brazing and sintering copper alloys, and for annealing low-carbon steels. Dissociated ammonia without combustion is used for annealing stainless steels containing nickel, short-cycle heating of all carbon and alloy steels, treatment of silicon iron, and the treatment of cuprous products.

Type III. Rich hydrocarbon gas is produced by combustion with about 60 percent of theoretical air (6:1 air-gas ratio when using natural gas) in the presence of a nickel catalyst, followed by cooling to reduce the moisture content. It is used for the annealing of low-carbon steels, for short-cycle hardening of low-carbon steels, for clean annealing of chrome-type stainless steels, for treatment of silicon iron, and for brazing of copper alloys.

Type IV. This gas is similar to type III except that about 90 percent of theoretical air is used for combustion. It is used for bright annealing of copper (straight N_2 and CO_2 can also be used for this purpose) and for clean heating of brass and bronze.

Type V. This gas is the same as type III but is conditioned by chemical removal of carbon dioxide by monoethanolamine and by drying in chemical driers. It is used for short-cycle treatment of all carbon, alloy, and high-speed steels; for sintering of all ferrous powders; and as a carrier gas for carburizing and carbon restoration with the addition of natural gas or propane.

Type VI. This gas is similar to type V except that about 90 percent of theoretical air is used in the combustion. The resulting gas is used for long-cycle treatment of all ferrous materials except stainless steels containing nickel, and is effective in controlling decarburization in all carbon and alloy steels. It is also used for the annealing of brass and bronze.

Type VII. This endothermic gas is made in an externally heated generator with only 25 percent of theoretical air and is cooled to reduce moisture. It is used for short-cycle (under 2 hr) heat-treating and brazing, usually with small furnace installations. It is also used for dry cyaniding and as a carrier gas for carburizing and carbon restoration.

Type VIII. By passing air over heated charcoal, a gas is produced which may also be used for short-cycle heat-treating with small furnaces.

INCINERATION

BY

Charles R. Velzy and Charles O. Velzy

REFERENCES: *Proc. ASME National Incinerator Conference,* 1964. APWA, "Municipal Refuse Disposal," Research Foundation Project 104. *Proc. APWA National Conference on Solid-waste Research,* 1963.

Incineration is a method for disposing of solid wastes by the burning of the combustible portions. It reduces the volume of solid wastes and eliminates the possibility of pollution of ground water and the nuisance from dumping putrescible organic waste, and the residue may serve as satisfactory fill.

Nature of the Fuel

The refuse which is received at an incinerator today will contain a high proportion of paper, both plain and waxed; some wood; vegetable and animal waste; and varying amounts of cloth, leather, rubber, and plastics—together with metal cans, glass, and other non-combustible matter. Collections may also include metal appliances, furniture, tree limbs, waste building material, broken concrete, and other coarse waste matter, commonly classified as *rubbish.* With little or no regulation of the handling of refuse by the home owner, there may be a wide variation in moisture content of refuse depending on the weather. Thus, after a storm, the moisture content may be high and the burning difficult.

Types of Furnaces

The type of furnace for incinerators is dictated largely by the type of grate around which the furnace is built. With a stationary grate requiring hand stoking, the furnace must be proportioned so that the grate area can be reached with a stoking iron of reasonable length. On the other hand, a mechanically operated grate allows more freedom in the layout of the furnace. Except in small plants, the modern furnace is equipped with a mechanical grate.

The Circular Furnace. An early development in mechanical stoking was the monohearth circular furnace. The grate is stationary, with outer sections hinged for dumping of residue. At the center is a cone-shaped casting, and extending from the base of the cone is a pair of slowly revolving arms to gently stir the refuse during burning. The refuse is received through a gated opening in the roof, and the feeding of the material is a batching operation.

The Rectangular Furnace. The more recent grates are rectangular in shape, with movement provided by travel of the grate or by a reciprocating or rocking action of the grate sections. Little or no hand stoking is required; refuse is fed through a vertical chute or similar arrangement.

Plant Design

Capacity. The capacity to be provided is a function of (1) the area and population to be served; (2) the number of shifts (one, two, or three) the plant is to operate; and (3) the rate of refuse production for the population served. If records of collections have been kept, the capacity can be determined and forecasts made; lacking records, the quantity of refuse may be estimated as 4 lb per capita per day approx. A small plant (100 tons per day) will probably operate one shift per day; for capacities above 400 tons per day, economic considerations usually dictate three-shift operation.

Location. An isolated site may be preferred to avoid the possible objections of neighbors to the proximity of a waste-disposal plant. However, well-designed and well-operated incinerators which do not represent a nuisance are installed in many residential and commercial areas, thereby avoiding the economic burden of extended truck routes. Since there is considerable vertical distance involved in passing refuse through an incinerator, there is an advantage in a **sloping** or **hillside site.** Collection trucks can then deliver refuse at the higher elevation while the residue trucks operate at the lower elevation with a minimum of site grading.

Refuse-handling Facilities. Scales should be provided for the weighing and recording of weights delivered by the collection trucks. Trucks should proceed to the tipping floor, which is at the edge of the storage pit. The area, which may be open or enclosed, must be large enough to permit more than one truck at a time to maneuver to and from the dumping position.

Since collections may be limited to one 8-hr daily shift (with partial weekend operation) while burning proceeds during 24 hr, ample storage must be provided. Seasonal and cyclic variations must be considered in defining the requisite storage.

A single pit extending along the front end of the furnace or two pits, one extending from each side of the front end of the furnace, prevail. Pits are relatively long, narrow, and deep and are limited to some 25 ft in width to avoid rehandling of the refuse dumped from the trucks.

Feeding the Furnaces. The large incinerator (pit-and-crane type), burning continuously, transfers the refuse from the storage pit to the furnace hopper by a crane equipped with a grapple. (See Sec. 10.) With the hand-stoked furnace and with recent circular furnaces, there is a power-operated gate at the bottom of the hopper separating it from the furnace. As more fuel is needed, the gate is opened and the charge drops into the furnace. This is a batch-feed operation with the objectional features of dumping a large quantity of fuel into the furnace at one time and exposing the hot refractory to a blast of cold air.

For the more modern furnace using highly mechanized grates, a vertical charging chute, 12 to 14 ft long, leads from the hopper to the front end of the furnace. This chute is kept full of refuse; feeding is accomplished by the operation of the mechanical grate; the front of the furnace is sealed from cold air; and the fuel is spread over the grate in a relatively thin bed.

The **flues and chambers** beyond the furnace convey the gases to the stack and house the facilities for removal of fly ash. With limited furnace volume, the first chamber beyond the furnace is the combustion space in which the volatile gases escaping from the refuse are burned to completion. Next is the expansion chamber, with a large cross section for reduction of gas velocity and settlement of fly ash. In the modern rectangular furnace, the necessary combustion volume may be provided in the furnace and the space formerly utilized as an expansion chamber may be used as a **spray chamber** where the floor may be covered with water to trap the larger particles of fly ash. Sprays and baffle walls remove the finer particles of fly ash and reduce the temperature of the gas as required by fans or other downstream equipment.

The **draft** for an incinerator furnace may be provided by a stack of adequate diameter and height or by an induced draft fan. (See Secs. 4 and 14.) If the plant does not include heat-recovery equipment and if the flues and chambers are relatively short and simple, a stack of reasonable height will produce sufficient draft. Even with a spray chamber and wet baffle walls, and the consequent reduction of flue-gas temperature, a stack is usually adequate. With maximum fly-ash removal, the draft losses are higher and an induced draft fan is essential.

Air-pollution Control. A commonly accepted standard for air-pollution control is to limit the emission of fly ash to 0.85 lb per 1,000 lb of flue gas, corrected to 50 percent excess air. There is a trend toward more stringent regulations, and in some locations the emission is limited to less than half that amount. The designer should be alert to the possible emission of obnoxious gases if certain wastes, such as some plastics, are burned in any quantity. The dry expansion chamber, used in early designs, is generally inadequate for fly-ash removal. Surfaces, such as baffle walls, which are continually wetted by sprays will trap the fly ash by impingement. A further development is the wetted refractory baffle built across the gas path with openings offset so that the gas changes direction at least twice in passing through the baffle.

The dry cyclone has been successful in removals better than required by some standards. The wet scrubber accomplishes good removal but produces a visible white plume at the stack, and corrosion may be a problem. Electrostatic precipitation gives good removal but is expensive in first cost. (See also p. 7–80 *et seq.*)

Residue Discharge and Disposal. The residue from refuse burning consists of relatively fine, light ash mixed with items such as burned tin cans, partly melted glass, and small metal parts. Discharge from furnaces may be through manually operated dump grates or from mechanically operated grates to a hopper, where it is quenched and delivered, through a gate at the bottom, to a truck. The residue may be discharged through a chute into a conveyor trough filled with water for quenching and then carried by flight conveyor to an elevated storage hopper for truck delivery. Usually there are two conveyor troughs, so arranged that the residue can be discharged to either, one trough being used at a time.

The lower end of the discharge chute leading to the trough is submerged in a water seal to prevent entrance of cold air to the furnace. In design of the conveyor mechanism, the proportions should be large because of the nature of the material handled; the metal used should be selected to meet the severe, abrasive service. The final disposal of the residue is by dumping at a suitable location; volume required for disposal is 5 to 15 percent of that required for the dumping of raw refuse.

Miscellaneous Facilities. Good working environment and reasonable comfort for the staff should be provided. Since handling refuse releases dust, a vacuum system with inlets well distributed about the plant will help keep the building clean.

Furnace Design

Capacity. The basic design factors which determine furnace capacity are grate area and furnace volume. Provision for and quantity of underfire air, and provision for quantity and method of applying overfire air influence capacity. The required grate area depends upon the selected burning rate, which varies between 60 and 90 lb of refuse per sq ft per hr in practice. Conservative design, with reasonable reserve capacity and reasonable refractory maintenance, calls for a burning rate between 60 and 70 lb per sq ft.

The volume of a furnace is a function of the rate of heat release from the fuel. A commonly accepted minimum volume is that which results from a heat release of 20000 Btu per cu ft per hr. Thus, at this rate, if the fuel has a heat content of 5000 Btu per lb, the burning rate would be 4 lb per hr per cu ft of furnace volume. A conservative design, allowing for some overload and possible quantities of refuse of high heat content, would be from 25 to 30 cu ft per ton of rated capacity.

Grates. The primary objective of a mechanical grate is automatically to convey the refuse from the point of feed through the burning zone to the point of residue discharge with a proper depth of fuel and in a period of time to accomplish complete combustion. The rate of movement of the grate or its parts is adjustable to meet varying conditions.

A secondary, but important, objective is to gently stir or tumble the refuse to aid in completeness of combustion. With the traveling grate, this is accomplished by building the grate in two or more sections with a drop between sections to tumble the material. The reciprocating and rocking grates tumble the material by movement of the grate elements. In the United States, there are three types of mechanical grates: (1) traveling, (2) rocking, and (3) reciprocating. In Europe, variations of these designs as well as other types have been developed. The Volund incinerator (Danish) uses a slowly rotating, refractory-lined cylinder or kiln through which the fuel passes as it is burned; the so-called *Düsseldorf incinerator* uses a series of rotating cylindrical grates in an inclined arrangement. (See Stabenow, ASME, 1964.)

Configuration. The configuration of the furnace is largely dictated by the type of grate used. Thus the monohearth furnace uses a circular grate, and the furnace is a vertical cylinder. For the more recent mechanical grate, the furnace is rectangular in plan and the height is dependent upon the volume required by the limiting rate of heat release. Some grate designs, particularly those developed in Europe, require special shapes in furnace enclosures.

Air Supply. The total air capacity provided in an incinerator must be more than the theoretical amount required for combustion in order to obtain complete combustion and to control temperatures—particularly with dry, high-heat-content refuse. The total combustion-air requirements may range to 10 lb of air per lb of refuse. For the modern mechanical-grate furnace chamber, two blower systems should be provided to supply combustion air to the furnace. Blower capacities can be divided, with approximately half from the underfire blower and half from the overfire blower and with dampers on fan inlets and air-distribution ducts for control. The pressure on the underfire system approximates 3 in. of water. The pressure on the overfire air should be high enough so that the jet effect on passage through properly proportioned and distributed nozzles in the furnace roof and walls produces sufficient turbulence and retains the gases in the primary furnace chamber long enough to ensure complete combustion.

Heat Calculations. Among the factors directly affecting design are moisture and combustible content of refuse as received, heat released by combustion, temperature control, and water requirements. The design of furnaces, chambers, flues, and other plant elements should be based on characteristics which result in large sizes. Controls should provide satisfactory operation for loads below the maximum. The computations which follow are for relatively high heat releases. (See also Kaiser, ASME, 1964.)

The prime factors in **heat calculations** are the moisture and combustible content of the refuse, and the heat released by the burning of the combustible portion of the refuse. The moisture content may vary from 20 to 50 percent by weight, and the combustible content may range from 25 to 70 percent. The combustible portion is composed largely of cellulose and similar materials, mixed with appreciable amounts of proteins, fats, oils, waxes, rubber, and plastics. The heat released by burning cellulose is 7500 Btu per lb approx, while that released by the fats, oils, etc., is 17000 Btu per lb approx. If the cellulose and oil and fat material exist in the refuse in the ratio of 9 to 1, the heat content of the combustible matter will be 8500 Btu per lb and the heat content per lb of the refuse as received, for varying proportions of moisture and non-combustible, will be as given in the following table and in Fig. 1.

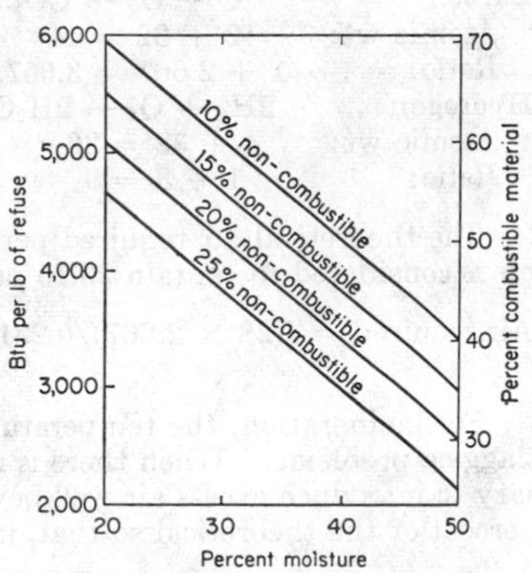

Fig. 1. Moisture–heat-content relation with 8500 Btu per lb combustible material.

Non-comb., %	10		15		20		25	
Moisture, %	Comb., %	Heat content*	Comb., %	Heat content*	Comb., %	Heat content*	Comb., %	Heat content*
50	40	3400	35	2975	30	2550	25	2125
40	50	4250	45	3825	40	3400	35	2975
30	60	5100	55	4675	50	4250	45	3825
20	70	5950	65	5525	60	5100	55	4675

* Btu per lb.

The determination of the **air requirement** is illustrated by computation with refuse of 5000 Btu per lb heat content where (from Fig. 1) the composition is: combustible, 58.6 percent; moisture, 22.4 percent; non-combustible, 19.0 percent.

Carbon and hydrogen are the essential fuel elements in the combustion of refuse; sulphur and other elements which oxidize during combustion are present in trace amounts and do not contribute significantly to the heat of combustion. The carbon and hydrogen content can be determined from a complete analysis of the refuse, but such an analysis is of questionable value because of the variable character of refuse and the difficulty of obtaining representative samples. For the purpose of this computation, a typical analysis is used in which the total carbon is 28 lb and the hydrogen 0.6 lb per 100 lb of refuse. It is probable that 1 to 3 lb of combustible material per 100 lb of refuse will escape unburned with the residue. For the sake of clarity in the illustrated computations, complete combustion is assumed.

The oxygen requirements and the products of combustion can be determined from the reactions as follows:

Cellulose $C_6H_{10}O_5 + 6O_2 \rightarrow 6CO_2 + 5H_2O$

Atomic wt: $72 + 10 + 80 + 192 = 264 + 90$

$162 + 192 = 264 + 90$

Ratios:

Referred to carbon, $1 + 0.14 + 1.11 + 2.667 = 3.667 + 1.25$

Referred to cellulose, $1 + 1.185 = 1.63 + 0.555$

Carbon $C + O_2 \rightarrow CO_2$

Atomic wt: $12 + 32 = 44$

Ratio: $1 + 2.667 = 3.667$

Hydrogen $2H_2 + O_2 \rightarrow 2H_2O$

Atomic wt: $4 + 32 = 36$

Ratio: $1 + 8 = 9$

The theoretical air required per 100 lb of refuse follows from these figures where air is considered to contain 23.15 percent oxygen.

$$\text{Air required} = [(28 \times 2.667)/0.2315] + [(0.6 \times 8)/0.2315] = 343.3 \text{ lb per 100 lb refuse}$$

For incineration, the temperature in the furnace must be controlled to minimize slagging problems. When there is no other provision for heat absorption, it is necessary to introduce excess air well beyond the needs for complete combustion, *e.g.*, 140 percent of the theoretical so that, in the example cited,

$$\text{Total air} = 2.4 \times 343.3 = 824 \text{ lb per 100 lb refuse}$$

To summarize the quantities for a computation of furnace temperature, a **materials balance** is given in Table 1, equating the input to the furnace and output for 100 lb of refuse. In this tabulation, allowance is made for the moisture taken in with the air at a commonly accepted rate of 0.0132 lb per lb of dry air. Some residue quench water will be evaporated, and the moisture added to the flue gases is estimated at the rate of 5 lb for each 100 lb of refuse burned. Since the assumed analyses are not precise, an exact balance is not obtained, but the indicated computations are sufficiently accurate for incinerator design.

In this tabulation, the total air is broken down into oxygen and nitrogen on the basis that 23.15 percent of the air is oxygen. To compute the air in the "output," or flue gas, the nitrogen is the same as the "input." The oxygen is diminished by the amount consumed in combustion. Since the elements carbon and hydrogen unite with oxygen during combustion, the oxygen consumed per 100 lb of refuse is:

For carbon, $28 \times 2.667 = 74.68$ lb

For hydrogen, $0.6 \times 8 = 4.8$ lb

Total.............. 79.48, say 80 lb

The moisture from burning cellulose and hydrogen is, for cellulose, $0.555 \times 52.74 = 29.3$ lb; for hydrogen, $9 \times 0.6 = 5.4$ lb.

The **heat-balance computation,** Table 2, is predicated on base temperature = 80F; vapor enthalpy = 1048 Btu per lb; fly-ash temperature leaving furnace = 1680 F;

Table 1. Materials Balance for Furnace
(In lb per 100 lb of refuse)

Input:			
Refuse			
Combustible material			
Cellulose	52.74		
Oils, fats, etc	5.86	58.6	
Moisture		22.4	
Non-combustible		19.0	100.0
Total air, at 140 % excess air			
Oxygen	191.0		
Nitrogen	633.0		824.0
Moisture in air			11.0
Residue quench water			5.0
Total			940.0
Output:			
CO_2 (28 × 3.667)			102.7
Air—Oxygen (191 − 80)	111.0		
Nitrogen	633.0		744.0
Moisture			
In refuse		22.4	
From burning cellulose		29.3	
From burning hydrogen		5.4	
In air		11.0	
In residue quench water		5.0	73.1
Non-combustible material			19.0
Unaccounted for			1.2
Total			940.0

fly ash = 2 percent of total refuse burned; residue is non-combustible introduced with the refuse; specific heat of fly ash and residue = 0.25. The total moisture in the flue gas is the sum of the moisture in the refuse, the bound water in the fuel, the moisture in the air at 0.0132 lb per lb of air, and the water evaporated in quenching the residue. The heat loss through the furnace enclosure depends largely on furnace construction and is estimated as 3 percent of the total heat input.

Table 2. Heat Balance for Furnace
(In Btu per 100 lb of refuse)

Heat input:		
Refuse, 100 × 5000		500000
Air Moisture, 11 × 1048		11530
Total		511530
Heat output:		
Heat of dry gas at 1680 F, 847 × 424 (Fig. 2)	359128	
Heat in water vapor, 73.1 × (1900 − 48) (from steam tables)	135381	
Heat in fly ash, assuming 2 lb per 100 lb of refuse and specific heat of 0.25, 2 × 0.25 × (1680 − 80)	800	
Heat in residue, 19 × 0.25 × (180 − 80)	475	
Loss through furnace enclosure at 3 % of total input	15346	
Unaccounted for	400	
Total		511530

The **temperature of the flue gas** is calculated from the data of Tables 1 and 2 and the enthalpy data of Fig. 2 as follows:

Input at 1680 F (Table 2)			511530 Btu
Losses:			
Vaporization at 80 F (lb)			
Moisture in refuse	22.4		
Bound water (Table 1)	34.7		
Air moisture	11.0		
Residue quenching	5.0		
	73.1		
73.1 × 1048		76609	
Fly-ash carry-over (Table 2)		800	
Residue (Table 2)		475	
Through furnace walls (Table 2)		15346	
Unaccounted for (Table 2)		400	
Total loss			93630
Balance to heat flue gas			417900 Btu

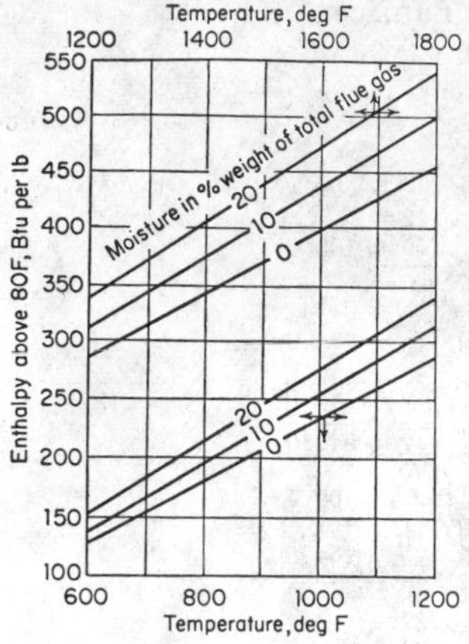

Fig. 2. Enthalpy of flue gas above 80 F.

Enthalpy = 417900/(846.7 + 73.1) = 455 Btu per lb. The percentage of moisture, for use with Fig. 2, = (73.1 × 100)/(846.7 + 73.1) = 7.95.

From the chart, the gas temperature is 1680 F. This is satisfactory and indicates that the assumed excess air of 140 percent is reasonable.

Flue-gas Treatment

In the design of an incinerator, consideration must be given to the condition of the gas discharged to atmosphere. The flue gas leaving the furnace carries an appreciable amount of fly ash, a portion of which must be removed in order to meet the requirements of air-pollution-control regulations. The equipment for fly-ash removal may be (1) the wet type, with a wet baffle wall and water supplied through sprays, or the so-called *wet scrubber;* or (2) the dry type, using cyclones or electrostatic precipitators, requiring gas temperatures below 600 F approx. With either type of equipment, gas temperatures are reduced by evaporation of water and a computation of water quantity is indicated.

Table 3 gives the requisite heat-balance calculations for a **spray chamber** where the flue gas is cooled to 600 F by water evaporating from sprays. There will be some air leakage into the chamber, estimated as 10 percent of the dry flue gas, or 85 lb of dry air. With this air, there will be 1.12 lb of moisture. Some minor losses will occur in the sluicing of the fly ash.

Table 3. Heat Balance for Spray Chamber
(In Btu)

Input at 1680 F (from Table 2):		
Heat of dry gas	359128	
Heat in water vapor	135381	
Heat in fly-ash carry-over	800	
Heat unaccounted for	400	
Total		495709
Output at 600 F:		
Heat in dry gas, (847 + 85) × 128	119296	
Heat in air-leakage moisture, 1.12 × (1335 − 48)	1441	
Heat loss through walls at 3% input	14871	
Minor losses from sluicing at 1% of 119296	1193	
Heat in vapor from furnace and spray water	358908	
Total		495709

The computation in Table 3 shows that there will be total heat of 358908 Btu to be absorbed by the moisture in the flue gas leaving the furnace and the moisture evaporated from the cooling sprays, or total moisture = 358908/(1335 − 48) = 278.9 lb. The spray water added = 278.9 − 73.1 = 205.8 lb.

The selection of equipment for **fly-ash removal** is dependent upon local circumstances, particularly the degree of removal required by ordinance or other regulation. A common requirement at present is that the stack effluent shall not carry more than 0.85 lb of fly ash per 1,000 lb of flue gas, corrected to 50 percent excess air. In some localities, the requirement is as low as 0.35 lb, and the trend is toward cleaner stack effluents. Of the various types of fly-ash removal equipment, the electrostatic precipitator is the most effective. In general, the wet scrubber is next in order of effectiveness, followed by cyclones and wet baffles. (See also p. 7–80 *et seq.*)

Recovery

Salvage. A number of attempts have been made to salvage salable portions of the refuse received at disposal plants to help offset operating costs. With favorable conditions, those efforts have met with some success. In general, the lack of a stable market and the cost of labor and equipment involved have made salvage unattractive.

Fly Ash and Residue. Fly ash has been used to a limited extent as a concrete additive and as a base for fertilizer. Incinerator residue is widely used for land reclamation in low areas and, in some cases, as a road-base material.

Heat Recovery. In a number of installations, the recovery of waste heat in the form of steam or power has been partially successful. Steam production has averaged

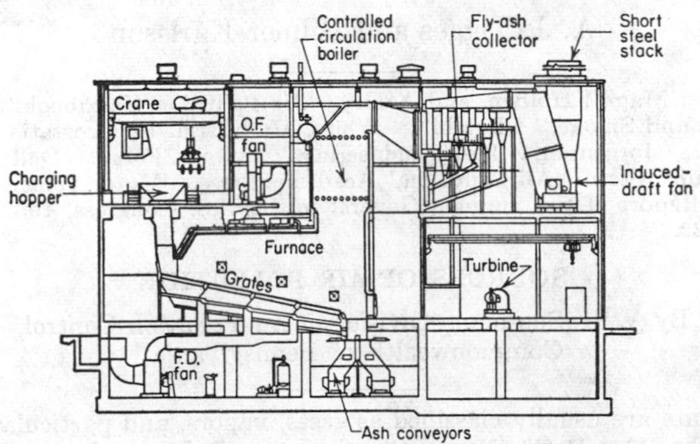

Fig. 3. Longitudinal section of the Oceanside (Hempstead, N.Y.) incinerator plant, equipped with fly-ash cyclones.

1.5 lb per lb of refuse, with a maximum of approximately 1.8 lb. This low steam production, together with troublesome operating problems, has discouraged efforts at waste-heat recovery.

With the rise in heat content of refuse during recent years and with increasing knowledge of the technical problems of incinerator design, the recovery of waste heat becomes attractive. Current developments indicate that problems of slag formation, temperature control, removal of fly ash, reduction of maintenance, etc., can be solved and that steam production can be increased to at least 3.0 lb per lb of refuse. Figure 3 illustrates a plant with power recovery.

ATMOSPHERIC POLLUTION AND GAS CLEANING

BY

A. J. Tigges and Hilmer Karlsson

References: Magill, Holden, and Ackley, "Air Pollution Handbook," McGraw-Hill. Gibbs, "Clouds and Smoke," Churchill. White, "Industrial Electrostatic Precipitation," Addison-Wesley. Jorgensen, "Fan Engineering," Buffalo Forge. Dallavalle, "Micrometrics," Pitman. Stern, "Air Pollution," Academic Press. Motor Vehicles, Air Pollution and Health, a Report of the Surgeon General to the U.S. Congress, 1962, *Public Health Service Pub.* 1022.

SOURCES OF AIR POLLUTION

By V. H. Sussman (Division of Air Pollution Control, Commonwealth of Pennsylvania)

Air pollutants are usually classified as gases, vapors, and particulate matter (see Table 1 and Fig. 1). **Particulate matter** includes: **Dusts**—a loose term applied to solid particles predominantly larger than colloidal and capable of temporary gas suspension. Dusts do not tend to flocculate except under electrostatic forces; they do not diffuse but settle under the influence of gravity. Dusts result from such operations as crushing, grinding, drilling, screening, and blasting. **Fumes**—the solid particles generated by condensation from the gaseous state, generally after volatilization from melted substances, and often accompanied by a chemical reaction such as oxidation. For example, zinc vapor will evaporate from the surface of heated liquid metal and will then condense upon contact with room or outdoor air and form small, fluffy particles of zinc oxide. Fumes are usually less than 1 micron in size, although they may coalesce or flocculate to form larger particles. **Smokes**—gasborne particles (usually less than 0.5 micron) resulting from incomplete combustion of materials such as wood, coal, and oil. **Mists**—a loose term applied to dispersions of liquid particles (0.1 to 2.5 microns), the dispersion being of low concentration and the particles of large size.

Table 1. Principal Air Pollutants

Gases	Vapors	Particulate matter			
		Dusts	Fumes	Smokes	Mists
Acid gases	Alcohols	Alumina	Metallic halogens	Ash	Acid
Carbon monoxide	Esters	Calcium fluoride	Metallic oxides	Cinders	Chromic
Hydrogen chloride	Hydrocarbons	Cement	Silicon tetrafluoride	Organic compounds	Phosphoric
Hydrogen fluoride	Ketones	Coal		Soot	Sulphuric
Hydrogen sulphide	Mercaptans	Grain			Organic chemicals
Nitrogen oxides		Limestone			Oil
Sulphur dioxide		Metal			
Alkaline gases		Ore			
Ammonia		Rock			
		Wood			

Sources of Air Pollution

(See Tables 2 and 3.)

Domestic and Municipal Sources. It has recently been recognized that the automobile is a major source of air pollution and a significant contributor to **photochemical**

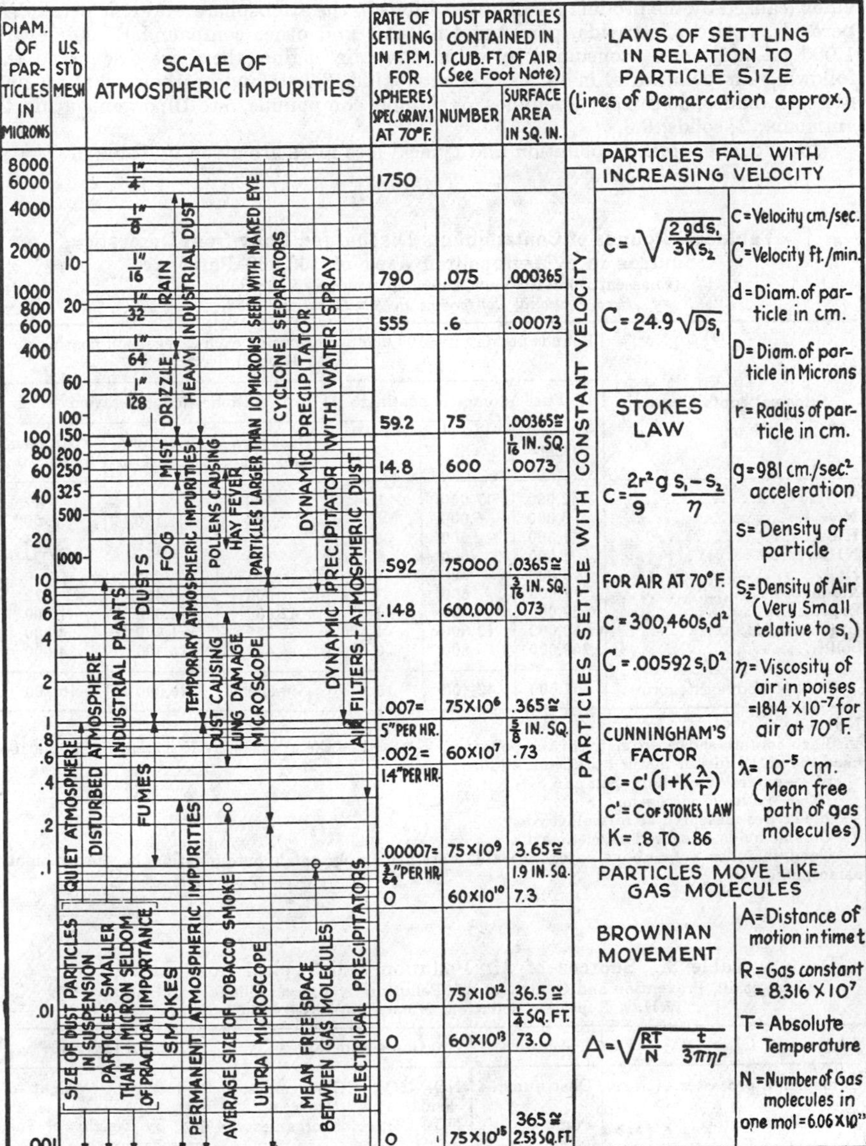

FIG. 1. Sizes and characteristics of airborne solids. (*Compiled by W. G. Frank. Copyrighted by American Air Filter Co., Louisville, Ky. Reproduced by permission.*) NOTE: It is assumed that the particles are of uniform spherical shape of specific gravity 1 and that the dust concentration is 0.6 grain per 1,000 cu ft of air, the average of metropolitan districts.

smog (caused by the products of photoreactions in the atmosphere—organic peroxides, peracids, hydroxy peracids, perozyacyl nitrate, and other compounds). For every 1,000 gal of gasoline consumed by an automobile engine, there are discharged the following air pollutants, in lb: carbon monoxide, 3,000; hydrocarbons, 200 to 400; nitrogen oxides, 50 to 150; aldehydes, 5; sulphur compounds, 5 to 10; organic acids, 2; ammonia, 2; solids, 0.3.

Industrial sources of pollution and typical loss rates are given in Table 3.

Table 2. Pounds of Contaminants Discharged Daily from Domestic Sources in a Metropolitan Area of 100,000 Persons

(Eliassen, Domestic and Municipal Sources of Air Pollution, *Proc. National Conference on Air Pollution*, 1958)

Principal contaminants	Pounds per day per 100,000 persons using each category of heating and refuse disposal					
	Fuel—domestic heating			Domestic incineration		
	Coal	Oil	Gas	Backyard burning	Household incinerator	Apartment incinerator
SO_x	42,000	17,000	0.4	180	1	12
NO_x	8,000	6,000	6	90	1,150	30
H_2S	1,000	500	0.1	......	......	24
NH_3	2,000	800	0.3	345	......	24
HCl	2,000	500	0.3			
Aldehydes	2,000	800	1	600	8,400	72
Organics	20,000	4,000	1	42,000	12,000	1,800
Organic acids	30,000	12,000	1	225	1,900	4,800
Solids	200,000	800	0.1	3,400	16,500	4,000
Total of above categories	307,000	42,400	10	46,800	40,000	10,700

NOTES:

Each column shows estimates of the pollutants released to the atmosphere if the entire population used the noted fuel or method of incineration.

SO_x—oxides of sulphur—SO_2 and SO_3.

NO_x—oxides of nitrogen.

Aldehydes measured as formaldehyde.

Organic acids measured as acetic acid.

Total includes only above categories and does not imply total contamination in the ambient atmosphere.

Table 3. Sources of Air Pollution and Typical Loss Rates

(Rose et al., Prevention and Control of Air Pollution by Process Changes and Equipment, W.H.O. Rept. Air Pollution, *Monograph Series* 46-307-343)

Class	Aerosols	Gases and vapors	Typical loss rates
Combustion processes	Dust, fume	NO_2, SO_2, CO, organics, acids	0.05–1.5% by weight of fuel
Automotive engines	Fume	NO_2, CO, acids, organics	4–7% by weight of fuel (hydrocarbons)
Petroleum operations	Dust, mist	SO_2, H_2S, NH_3, CO, hydrocarbons, mercaptans	0.25–1.5% by weight of material processed
Chemical processes	Dust, mist, fume, spray	Process-dependent (SO_2, CO, NH_3, acids, organics, solvents, odours, sulphides)	0.5–2% by weight of material processed
Pyro- and electro-metallurgical processes	Dust, fume	SO_2, CO, fluorides, organics	0.5–2% by weight of material processed
Mineral processing	Dust, fume	Process-dependent (SO_2, CO, fluorides, organics)	1–3% by weight of material processed
Food and feed operations	Dust, mist	Odorous materials	0.25–1% by weight of material processed

CLASSIFICATION OF SOLID POLLUTANTS

By A. J. Tigges and Hilmer Karlsson

The **micron** (0.001 mm) is the customary unit for measuring the dimensions of fine particles. Particles over 10 microns (10^{-3} cm) are classified by Gibbs as **dusts;** between 0.1 and 10 microns, **clouds;** between 0.001 and 0.1 micron, **smokes;** below 0.001, molecular dimensions. The law governing the **terminal velocity of the settling of particles** under the influence of gravity varies with the size of the particle. In the turbulent region (above 2,000 microns), the law is

$$V_t = Ks^{1/2}p^{1/2}D^{1/2} = k_1\sqrt{sD}$$

In the intermediate region (between 1,000 and 100 microns), the law is

$$V_n = K's^{2/3}\rho^{-1/3}\eta^{-1/3}D = k_2s^{2/3}D$$

In the streamline region (2 to 50 microns), Stokes' law holds:

$$V_s = K''sD^2\eta^{-1} = k_3sD^2$$

From 0.1 to 1.0 micron, Cunningham's correction must be applied to Stokes' law:

$$V_c = V_s\left(1 + \frac{1.72\lambda}{D}\right) = V_s\left(1 + \frac{0.172}{D}\right)$$

Below 0.1 micron, the velocity due to molecular shock (Brownian motion) exceeds that due to velocity. In these equations, V is the terminal velocity, fpm; D, particle diameter, microns; p, gas pressure, atm; s, specific gravity; ρ, density of the gas, g per cc; η, viscosity of the gas, poises; λ, the mean free path of the gas molecules, microns. The values of the constants in the equations for falling in normal air are given below, the velocities being in fpm. For irregular shapes, $k_1 = 28$, $k_2 = 0.51$, $k_3 = 0.0039$. For spheres, $k_1 = 48$, $k_2 = 0.81$, $k_3 = 0.0059$.

The **Tyler standard screen scale** is related to particle size as below:

Meshes per in.........	10	20	35	48	65	100	150	200	325
Micron scale..........	1650	830	420	300	220	150	110	74	44

The diameters of the commoner gas molecules range from about 0.0003 to 0.00045 micron; their mean free path is from 0.06 to 0.2 micron at atmospheric pressure.

The size ranges of particles in typical aerosols and industrial dusts are, in microns: raindrops, 500 to 5,000; mist, 40 to 500; fog, 1 to 40; tobacco smoke, 0.01 to 0.15; oil smoke, 0.03 to 1.0; pigments 1 to 7; fly ash, 3 to 70; carbon black, 0.04 to 0.2; pulverized coal, 10 to 400; foundry dusts, 1 to 200; cement, 10 to 150; metallurgical fumes, 0.1 to 100; sprayed zinc dust (condensed), 2 to 15; normal impurities in quiet outdoor air, less than 1; dust particles causing silicosis, below 10; pollens, 20 to 60; plant spores, 10 to 30; bacteria, 1 to 15.

Normal city air carries around 0.0006 grain of suspended matter per cu ft, which is a practical limit for most industrial operations for cleaning of gases; the amount of dust in the normal air of manufacturing plants frequently is as high as 0.002 grain per cu ft. The amount of dust in blast-furnace gas after passing the first dust catcher is of the order of 10 grains per cu ft, which is also that of raw hot producer gas. (All dust-content figures are based on cubic feet at 60 F and 30 in.)

EFFECT OF SULPHUR GASES AND PARTICULATES ON VEGETATION

By John B. Middleton (Pennsylvania Electric Company)

Vegetation is damaged by relatively low concentrations of sulphur gases in the atmosphere at ground level. Users of sulphur-bearing fuels may become involved

Table 4. Susceptibility of Vegetation to Injury by Sulphur Dioxide (from Field Observations)

Maximum susceptibility	Moderate susceptibility	Resistant
	WEEDS	
Plantain Ragweed Smartweed Dewberry Greenbriar Dandelion Galinsoga Pigweed (redroot)	Bracken fern Wild carrot Wild grape Sweet clover	Goldenrod Small-leaved milkweed Knotweed Milkweed
	WILDFLOWERS	
Greenbriar Galinsoga Dandelion	Blackberry Witch hazel Huckleberry Blueberry Bracken fern Viburnum Wild carrot Sweet clover	Goldenrod Small-leaved milkweed Elderberry Mountain laurel Yarrow Knotweed Joe-Pye weed Milkweed
	FARM CROPS	
Alfalfa Oats Buckwheat Barley	Alsike clover Corn Cabbage	Potato
	GARDEN VEGETABLES	
Beet Endive Bean Peas Brussels sprouts Sunflower	Huckleberry Blueberry Tomato Parsley Cauliflower Cabbage	Onion Cucumber Corn Potato
	LANDSCAPE MATERIALS	
Hawthorn Sunflower Cosmos Sweet William	Huckleberry Blueberry Nasturtium Dahlia Gladiolus Willow	Hazelnut Mountain laurel
	TREES	
White pine Hemlock Hawthorn Black birch Yellow birch	Larch Scotch pine Norway spruce Sumac Ash Wild cherry Domestic apple Willow	Red pine Blue spruce Black locust Black oak Red oak White oak Sugar maple Swamp red maple Norway maple

with damage claims where ground-level concentrations of sulphur gases are high. Tolerable ground-level concentrations are of consequent increasing importance. The contaminants causing damage to vegetation are sulphur trioxide (SO_3), sulphur dioxide (SO_2), and particulate materials.

Sulphur trioxide is hygroscopic and occurs at ground level as sulphuric acid mist. Plant damage by sulphuric acid aerosol has been achieved in the laboratory but has not been observed in the field. Sulphur trioxide, therefore, is not a consideration under field conditions.

Sulphur dioxide is the contaminant that has the greatest effect on plants. Concentrations greater than 0.3 ppm will damage the leaves of sensitive vegetation. Concentrations above 0.5 to 2.0 ppm are recognizable by smell and taste. The concentration and the duration of the fumigation determine the degree of injury. (See Table 4.) Environmental conditions of temperature, humidity, soil moisture, soil fertility, nutrient supply, light intensity, age of plants, and moist-leaf conditions have a marked influence on the susceptibility of vegetation.

Particulate materials on leaf surfaces have no harmful effect to the leaves other than to exclude the sunlight and to that extent reduce food manufacturing.

Atmospheric Dispersion of Pollutants from Stacks

By W. A. Verrochi (Pennsylvania Electric Company)

Stacks can provide effective atmospheric dispersion of gaseous and particulate pollutants with acceptable ground-level concentrations. Theoretical and empirical formulas are available for estimating the dispersion of airborne pollutants continuously emitted from stacks.

Notation

Symbol	Definition	System of consistent units
b	Atmospheric-dispersal parameter	Dimensionless
d	Stack-exit diameter	m
H	Effective stack height	m
h_r	Rise of plume	m
h_s	Stack height	m
p	Atmospheric-dispersal parameter	Dimensionless
Q	Emission rate of pollutant	cu m per sec
Q_h	Heat emission rate	cal per sec
q	Atmospheric-dispersal parameter	Dimensionless
u	Mean wind speed	m per sec
v	Stack-exit velocity	m per sec
X_g	Ground-level concentration of pollutant at a distance, x, from base of stack	ppm by vol
X_{mg}	Maximum ground-level concentration of pollutant at a distance, x_m, from base of stack	ppm by vol
x	Downwind distance from emission source in direction of mean wind	m
x_m	Distance from base of stack to maximum ground-level concentration	m
σ_A	Basic diffusion parameter related to azimuth plume angle in radians	m^{1-q}
σ_B	Basic diffusion parameter related to elevation plume angle in radians	m^{1-p}

Effective stack height of a plume is given by $H = h_s + h_r$. The **Holland formula,** recommended for calculating h_r, is

$$h_r = (1.5vd + 4.09 \times 10^{-5}Q_h)/u$$

A ratio of stack height h_s to building height of 2½ to 1 or more is commonly used to avoid entrapment of the plume in the vortex of adjacent buildings and the associated high values of ground-level concentration X_g. Stack-exit velocity v should be 14 to 28 m per sec (45 to 90 fps) to minimize plume entrapment in the stack vortices. The lower the ratio of stack inside to outside diameter at its top, the higher the necessary v.

The **Cramer equation**, recommended for calculating X_g, is

$$X_g = 10^6 Q/\pi u x^b \sigma_A \sigma_E \exp [H^2/2\sigma_E{}^2 X^{2p}]$$

The equation is for sampling intervals of 20 min approx, with X_g varying about inversely as the one-fifth power of the interval.

Simplified approximate formulas for X_{mg} and x_m are

$$X_{mg} = 2Q10^6\sigma_E/\pi e u H^{1.9}\sigma_A$$
$$x_m = H/1.35\sigma_E$$

The atmospheric-dispersal characteristics and, hence, the values of X_g, X_{mg}, and x_m are influenced by thermal stratification and turbulence in the atmosphere. A superadiabatic (adiabatic) [subadiabatic] lapse rate, *i.e.*, a drop in temperature with altitude greater than (equal to) [less than] 37.5 F per 1,000 ft, results in an unstable (neutral) [stable] atmosphere with much (moderate) [very little] vertical mixing.

The recommended parameters for use in the Cramer equations under the above conditions of thermal stratification are:

Thermal stratification	σ_A, radians	σ_E, radians	b	p	q
Unstable.......	0.39	0.13	2	1.1	0.9
Neutral........	0.21	0.07	1.85	1.0	0.85
Stable..........	0.12	0.04	1.6	0.8	0.8

The above formulas deal only with steady-state conditions. There are transient meteorological conditions which can result in significant ground-level concentrations of pollutants and which cannot readily be analyzed by computations. These conditions include the breakup of a temperature inversion and the slow, steady buildup of pollutants during stagnations accompanied by deep ground fogs in a valley. For large power plants, high stacks (400 ft and more), high stack-exit velocities (45 to 90 fps), and adequate exit temperatures (250 to 300 F) are usually effective in avoiding such fumigations.

STACK EMISSIONS

By A. J. Tigges and Hilmer Karlsson

Emission of sulphur-bearing gases and solids from a 1,000,000-kw fossil-fuel-fired power station is shown in Table 5. (See also Tables 6 and 7 for supplementary data.) Reducing the remaining solids in stack emissions from bituminous-coal-fired (excluding stoker firing) power boilers to 0.02 grain per scf and less results in a clear stack discharge. This requires collection efficiencies of 99+ percent, attainable with commercial equipment. These high collection-efficiency requirements demonstrate the need for optical instruments which will readily determine stack-emission quality. While the **Ringelman Chart** is frequently used to evaluate stack emission, it is a crude and inaccurate method. *A good indicator is a stack emission invisible to the naked human eye.* With oil firing, present practice is to control stack emissions by furnace design, combustion control, use of additives, and multiple cyclone-type collectors located in the low- or high-temperature zones of the flue-gas system; while for future plants of 1,000,000-kw capacity and larger, the use of high-temperature electrostatic precipitators located ahead of the air preheater may be considered.

Table 5. Emission of Sulphur-bearing Gases and Solids from a 1,000,000-kw Fossil-fuel-fired Power Station

Fuel	Mid-Western bit coal	Eastern bit coal	Central Ill. bit coal	High-sulphur fuel oil	Low-sulphur fuel oil
Firing method	Pulv.-coal round burners	Pulv.-coal round burners	Cyclone burners	Round burners	Round burners
Sulphur content of fuel, %	4.14	1.15	4.65	2.41	0.40
Ash content of fuel, %	18.16	7.59	15.00	0.10	0.10
Sulphur-bearing gases leaving boiler:					
Sulphur dioxide, lb per hr	69,000	15,100	97,500	23,200	3,620
Sulphur trioxide, lb per hr	3,450	755	4,875	1,160	180
Total sulphur-bearing gases, lb per hr	72,450	15,855	102,375	24,360	3,800
Solids in flue gas leaving boiler:					
Sulphur compounds, lb per hr	4,600	920	920	2,520	420
Carbon, lb per hr	8,280	2,760	1,190	4,200	4,200
Fly ash, lb per hr	118,680	38,640	20,250	420	420
Total solids, lb per hr	131,560	42,320	22,360	7,140	5,040
Collection efficiency,* %	99+‡	99+‡	99+‡	†	†
Solids in flue gas leaving stack, lb per hr	360	360	15	†	†

* Based on clear stack.
† See text.
‡ Total efficiency whether combination mechanical and electrostatic units or electrostatic alone.

Table 6. Common Applications of Industrial Precipitators
(From Holden and Ackley, "Air Pollution Handbook," McGraw-Hill.)

Industry	Application	Gas-flow range, cfm	Temp range, deg F	Dust-conc. range, grains cu ft	Per-cent weight of dust (below 10)	Usual effi-ciencies, %
Electric power	Fly ash from pulverized-coal-fired boilers	50,000–750,000	270–600	0.4–5.0	25–75	95–99+
Portland cement	Dust from kilns	50,000–1,000,000	300–750	0.5–15.0	35–75	85–99+
	Dust from dryers	30,000–100,000	125–350	1.0–15.0	10–60	95–99
	Mill ventilation	2,000–10,000	50–125	5.0–25.0	35–75	95–99
Steel	Cleaning blast-furnace gas for fuel	20,000–100,000	90–110	0.02–0.5	100	95–99
	Collecting tars from coke-oven gases	50,000–200,000	80–120	0.1–1.0	100	95–99
	Collecting fume from open-hearth and electric furnaces	30,000–400,000	300–700	0.05–3.0	95	90–99
Non-ferrous metals	Fume from kilns, roasters, sintering machines, aluminum potlines, etc.	5,000–1,000,000	150–1100	0.05–50.0	10–100	90–98
Pulp and paper	Soda-fume recovery in kraft pulp mills	50,000–200,000	275–350	0.5–4.0	99	90–95
Chemical	Acid mist	2,500–20,000	100–200	0.02–1.0	100	95–99
	Cleaning hydrogen, CO_2, SO_2, etc.	5,000–20,000	70–200	0.01–1.0	100	90–99
	Separate dust from vaporized phosphorus	2,500–7,500	500–600	0.01–1.0	30–85	99+
Petroleum	Powdered catalyst recovery	50,000–150,000	350–550	0.1–25.0	50–75	90–99.9
Rock products	Roofing, magnesite, dolomite, etc.	5,000–200,000	100–700	0.5–25.0	30–45	90–98
Gas	Tar from gas	2,000–50,000	50–150	0.01–2.0	100	90–98
Carbon black	Collecting and agglomerating carbon black	20,000–150,000	300–700	0.03–5.0	100	10–35
Gypsum	Dust from kettles, conveyors, etc.	5,000–20,000	250–350	1.5–5.0	95	90–98

Table 7. Characteristics of Air- and Gas-cleaning Devices
(From Jorgensen, "Fan Engineering," Buffalo Forge Co. Used by permission.)

Name of device		Device most suitable for	Removable contaminants	Optimum size particle	Optimum concentration	Limits of gas temperature
General class	Specific type			microns	grains per cu ft	deg F
Odor adsorbers	Shallow bed			(Molecular)	<0.001	0–100
Air washers	Spray chamber		Malodors, gases	>20	<0.005	40–700
	Wet cell			>5	<0.005	40–700
Electro. precip., low-voltage	Two-stage, plate	Atmospheric air cleaning	Lints, dusts, pollens, tobacco smoke	<1	<0.001	0–250
	Two-stage, filter			<1	<0.001	0–180
Air filters, viscous-coated	Throwaway			>5	<0.002	0–180
	Washable			>5	<0.002	0–250
Air filters, dry-fiber	5–10 micron			>3	<0.001	0–180
	2–5 micron			>0.5	<0.001	0–180
Absolute filters	Paper		Special*	<1	<0.001	0–1800
Industrial filters	Cloth bag			>0.3	>0.1	0–180†
	Cloth envelope			>0.3	>0.1	0–180†
Electro. precip., high-voltage	Single-stage, plate			<2	>0.1	0–700
	Single-stage, pipe			<2	>0.1	0–700
Dry inertial collectors	Settling chamber		Dusts, fumes, smokes, mists	>50	>5	0–700
	Baffled chamber			>50	>5	0–700
	Skimming chamber			>20	>1	0–700
	Cyclone			>10	>1	0–700
	Multiple-cyclone			>5	>1	0–700
	Impingement			>10	>1	0–700
	Dynamic	Stack gas cleaning		>10	>1	0–700
Scrubbers	Cyclone			>10	>1	40–700
	Impingement			>5	>1	40–700
	Dynamic			>10	>1	40–700
	Fog			<2	>0.1	40–700
	Pebble bed			>5	>0.1	40–700
	Multidynamic			<1	>0.1	40–700
	Venturi			<2	>0.1	40–700
	Submerged nozzle			>2	>0.1	40–700
	Jet			<5	>0.1	40–700
Incinerators	Direct		Gases, vapors, malodors	Any	(Combustible)	2000
	Catalytic			(Molecular)	Any	1000
Gas absorbers	Spray tower			(Molecular)	>0.001	40–100
	Packed column			(Molecular)	>0.001	40–100
	Fiber cell			(Molecular)	>0.001	40–100
Gas adsorbers	Deep bed			(Molecular)	>0.001	0–100

* Bacteria, radioactive, or highly toxic fumes.
† 500 F for glass.

AIR-POLLUTION CONTROL IN VARIOUS INDUSTRIES

By L. M. Roberts (Research-Cottrell, Inc.)

(See Tables 6 and 7)

Non-ferrous-metal smelting (*e.g.*, copper, zinc, lead) and **thermal operations** (*e.g.*, blast furnace, sintering machine, converters) are sources of air pollution and of potentially recoverable metallic values. A large variety of types of collection equipment has been tried. Experience has proved that precipitators, cloth filters, and gas washers are best.

Paper industry sources of air pollution are (1) recovery-furnace gases and (2) lime kiln exhaust gases. **Recovery-furnace gases** in the sulphate and soda processes of manufacture emit solids (2 to 6 grains per scf) which are mainly sodium salts. The small size of the particles is particularly bothersome because of the large, obscuring power in the stack tail. Chemically, the solids are destructive of painted and finished surfaces (*e.g.*, automobiles, structures). Valuable constituents are also recovered for return to the cycle. Electrostatic precipitators with 95 to 99 percent efficiency are favored for collection and return of the solids. Corrosion-resistant materials (glazed tile, special cements) must be used to reduce maintenance. **Limekilns** are used to calcine calcium carbonate and recover it as CaO for use in the process. The consequent air pollutant is recovered by gas washers and mechanical collectors.

Cement-industry sources of air pollutants are (1) clinker kilns, and (2) bagging and other mechanical operations. The **kilns** are the major source of air pollution, with large, unattractive exhaust plumes depositing cement-making solids on the landscape and on painted surfaces. Damages are reduced by the use of electrostatic precipitators with the wet process and cloth filters with the dry process. **Bagging and other mechanical losses** are reduced by use of cloth filters or cyclone separators.

Carbon-black production utilizes electrostatic precipitators, cloth filters, and scrubbers to collect the black from the gas stream and to control air pollution.

Iron-and-steel-industry sources of air pollution are open-hearth, oxygen-furnace, electric-furnace, and sintering operations. The dispersoids in these operations are mostly oxides of iron in particle sizes below 10 microns and with loadings ranging to 15 grains per scf. Dust emittance is acceptably controlled generally by use of precipitators and scrubbers for open-hearth and basic oxygen processes, of cloth filters and scrubbers for electric furnaces, and of precipitators, scrubbers, and filters for sintering.

Petroleum-refining sources of air pollution are mainly gaseous in nature. Solid dispersoids from the fluid-cracking processes are removed by electrostatic precipitators and/or cyclone-type collectors.

CONTROLLING AIR POLLUTION FROM INCINERATORS

By Leo P. Flood (New York City Department of Air Pollution Control)

Nature of Pollutants. Air pollution from large central incineration plants includes odors, noxious gases, and particulates (smoke). Odors are caused by decaying refuse, incomplete combustion of the gases volatilized in the furnace, and rotting, incompletely burned residue. Noxious gases result from the partial burning of volatiles and from the introduction of a large excess of air into a hot furnace. Particulates are generated by careless handling of dust-bearing refuse, by traffic on dusty roadways around the incinerator, by char of fly ash in the combustion gases, and by careless handling and disposal of incinerator residue and fly ash. Smoke made up of very small particulates is caused by incomplete combustion (see Fig. 1).

Means of Controlling Air Pollution. Process control is the most effective means. Dust will not be stirred up or blown around if clean, covered trucks operate on a clean, hard-surfaced roadway. Odors can be abated by burning putrescible refuse first. Dust and odors from the receiving pit can be controlled by closures between the tipping floor and the pit and by combustion air supply from the pit area. Correct management of the burning prevents generation of air pollutants. Complete burning of the refuse to a non-putrescible residue requires sufficient air and residence in a furnace hot enough completely to oxidize the combustibles; furnace temperature between 1600 and 2200 F; auxiliary heat for starting and for maintenance of temperature when refuse is wet or of low heating value; means for furnishing from 50 to 150 percent excess air and for adjusting its distribution both over and under the fire one-third to two-third of total air. Be thrifty with air; provide enough for combustion but introduce it to minimize lifting ash from the fuel bed and maximize turbulence above the fire. The underfire air should be provided at a pressure about 4 in. of water. In continuous incinerators, this pressure should decrease from a maximum where the bed is thickest. In batch-type incinerators, the wind-box pressure cannot be varied during the cycle, so the optimum value must be determined in operation. Overfire combustion air, to produce the greatest effects, should be introduced about 18 in. above the firebed. The pressure needed depends upon the dimensions of the furnace and the diameter of the air tubes, but usually 4 in. is ample. Diluting air, to limit furnace temperature, should be directed downward from the arch across the gas stream. The formation of nitrogen oxides, a dangerous pollutant, is avoided by using no more air than necessary.

Conditioning and Cleaning the Gas Stream. Fly ash is the principal pollutant removed by control equipment, although wet scrubbers may also remove some gaseous pollutants. Control equipment is rated on the volume of gas handled. Many types are limited by the temperature and moisture content of the gas. It is necessary, therefore, to cool the gas prior to cleaning. Cold air may be mixed with the furnace gas to reduce the temperature. This has the disadvantage of increasing the volume, thereby requiring equipment with a greater capacity and larger flues. Generation of oxides of nitrogen may also result. Water may be mixed with the hot gas through spray nozzles. This also increases the total volume of gas to be cleaned, but not so much as air cooling. If done so that all the water is evaporated and the resulting steam superheated, the mixture will be dry and cool enough for the collector. This, however, requires precise control of water introduced. Under adverse weather conditions, visible condensed water vapor in the stack plume may make it objectionable. Transferring the heat in the furnace gas to another fluid through a heat exchanger, such as a boiler or air preheater, decreases the temperature and volume without dilution or increase in moisture. The residual pollution passing the control equipment must be dispersed high enough to minimize its ground effects. (See p. 7-85.) Do not overlook the effects of topography and local meteorology.

Performance Criteria. A satisfactory large central incinerator should reduce the refuse burned to a non-putrescible residue without creation of a nuisance and with minimum air pollution. It is reasonable to specify that an incinerator burn refuse to a residue containing less than 10 percent combustible with a maximinum emission of 0.60 lb of dust per 1,000 lb of flue gas (0.32 grain per scf), adjusted to 50 percent excess air for combustion. If a nearly clear stack is required, this should be reduced to 0.21 lb per 1,000 lb of flue gas (0.11 grain scf). Smoke should be limited to No. 1 Ringelman except when starting from a cold condition.

ELECTRIC FURNACES AND OVENS

BY

William E. Lewis

REFERENCES: Robiette, "Electric Melting and Smelting Practice," Griffin. Campbell, "High-temperature Technology," Wiley. "Electric-furnace Steel Proceedings," Annual, AIME. Paschkis, "Industrial Electric Furnaces and Appliances," Interscience. Stansel, "Induction Heating," McGraw-Hill. Ess, The Modern Arc Furnace, *Iron Steel Eng.*, Feb., 1944.

CLASSIFICATION AND SERVICE

In **resistor furnaces and ovens** heat is developed by the passage of current through distributed resistors (heating units) mounted apart from the charge. Alternating current of a standard power frequency is used. The furnace service is for heat applications to solids such as heat-treatment of metals, annealing glass, and firing of vitreous enamel. Oven service is limited to drying and baking processes usually below 500 F.

In **induction heaters** heat is developed by currents induced in the charge. The service is heating metals to temperatures below the melting points.

In **induction furnaces** heat is developed by currents induced in the charge. The service is melting metals and alloys.

In **arc furnaces** heat is developed by an arc, or arcs, drawn either to the charge or above the charge. Direct-arc furnaces are those in which the arcs are drawn to the charge itself. In indirect-arc furnaces the arc is drawn between the electrodes and above the charge. A standard power frequency is used in either case. The general service is melting and refining metals and alloys.

In **resistance furnaces** of the submerged-arc type, heat is developed by the passage of current from electrode to electrode through the charge. The manufacture of basic products, such as ferro-alloys, graphite, calcium carbide, and silicon carbide, is the general service. Alternating current at a standard power frequency is used. An exception is the use of direct current where the product is obtained by electrolytic action in a molten bath, *e.g.*, in the production of aluminum.

The **characteristics of electric heat** are:

1. Precision of the control of the development of heat and of its distribution.

2. The heat development is independent of the nature of the gases surrounding the charge. This atmosphere can be selected at will with reference to the nature of the charge and the chemistry of the heat process. This freedom is often a primary reason for the use of electric heat.

3. The maximum temperature is limited only by the nature of the material of the charge.

The first two characteristics underlie the design of all electric heating apparatus. The third is utilized in thermal processes for the production of certain materials not obtainable in any other way.

Resistor Furnaces

Resistor furnaces may be either the batch or the continuous type. Batch furnaces include box furnaces, elevator furnaces, car-bottom furnaces, and bell furnaces. Continuous furnaces include belt-conveyor furnaces, chain-conveyor furnaces, rotary-hearth furnaces, and roller-hearth furnaces.

Standard resistor furnaces are designed to operate at temperatures within the range 1000 to 2000 F. For higher heating chamber temperatures, see Resistors, p. 7-94.

The **heating chamber** of a standard furnace is an enclosure with a refractory lining, a surrounding layer of heat insulation, and an outer casing of steel plate, or for large furnaces an outer layer of brick or tile, as indicated by Figs. 1 and 2. The hearth of a batch furnace often is constructed of a heat-resisting alloy, made in sections to prevent warping. In some continuous furnaces the conveyor forms the hearth; in others a separate hearth is required.

Insulating firebrick—a semirefractory material—is commonly used for the inner lining of the heating chamber. This material has thermal and physical properties intermediate between those of fire-clay brick and heat-insulating materials. A lining of this kind has less heat-storage capacity than a fire-clay brick lining, and its use accordingly decreases the time periods of heating and cooling the chamber and also decreases the stored-heat loss for a given cycle of operation. Other advantages are its high heat-insulating value and light weight.

The maximum temperature of the inner face of the layer of heat insulation determines the character of material required for the insulation. Practically all resistor furnaces have insulation made of diatomite. Composite wall structures with a 4½ in. semirefractory lining and a 9 to 13 in. layer of heat insulation represent general practice for standard furnaces.

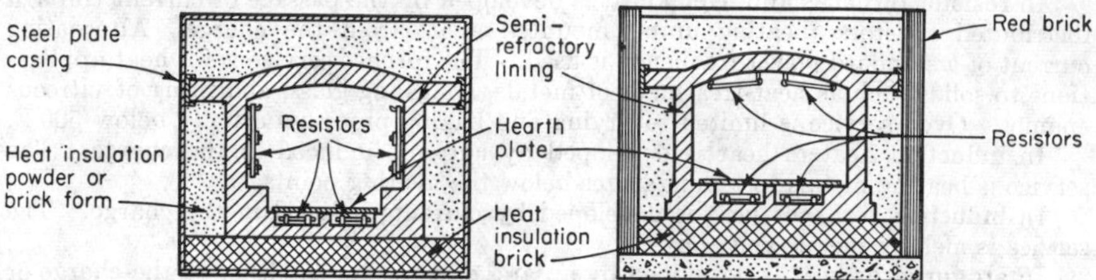

Fig. 1. Heating chamber with side-wall and hearth resistors.

Fig. 2. Heating chamber with roof and hearth resistors.

Atmospheres. A mixture of air and the gases evolved from the charge constitutes a **natural atmosphere** in the heating chamber of a resistor furnace. The composition of such an atmosphere in a batch furnace is variable during a heating cycle. A natural atmosphere in the heating chamber of a continuous furnace is mainly air. Natural atmospheres are used where the extent of the action of oxygen on the charge during the heating cycle is not objectionable and for processes where that chemical action is desired.

The basis of an **artificial atmosphere** is the exclusion of oxygen (air) from the heating chamber by the substitution of some other gas or mixture of gases. This gas or mixture of gases is selected with reference to the chemical activity of that atmosphere on the charge at the temperature of the heat application. A definite chemical action may be desired, for example, the reduction of any metallic oxide present on the charge, or it may be required that the artificial atmosphere be chemically inactive. Thus artificial atmospheres are divided into (1) active or process atmospheres and (2) inactive or protective atmospheres. The term "controlled" atmosphere refers generally to a protective atmosphere, but it also includes artificial atmospheres of some degree of chemical activity. An example of a process atmosphere is the use of a hydrocarbon gas to carburize steel. Examples of controlled atmospheres are: the bright annealing of metals, the prevention of decarburization of steel during a heat application, the use of a reducing gas (hydrogen or carbon monoxide) in a copper brazing furnace, etc. In this last example the reducing gas serves to clean the faces of the joint to be made (by removal of any oxide present) and to maintain that cleanliness during the operation. The primary gases for controlled atmospheres are hydrogen and carbon monoxide and nitrogen. See also p. **7-70**.

The main uses of controlled atmospheres are (1) the prevention of the formation of oxides on the material of the charge, or conversely the reduction of any oxides present, and (2) the prevention of a change in the carbon content of a steel undergoing a heat-treatment. Each of these uses denotes a chemical system in which the reactions are reversible.

The chemical systems relating to metallic oxides are:

A. Oxide + hydrogen ⇄ metal + water vapor
B. Oxide + carbon monoxide ⇄ metal + carbon dioxide

The chemical systems relating to carbon in steel are:

E. Methane ⇄ hydrogen + carbon
F. Carbon monoxide ⇄ carbon dioxide + carbon

In artificial atmospheres the volume ratio of the two gases in the heating chamber should be so maintained as to correspond to the desired direction of the chemical activity of the system, or, if no chemical action is desired, to maintain that volume ratio at (or near) its equilibrium value for the temperature of the heat application. The equilibrium volume ratios for each of the four chemical systems *A*, *B*, *E*, and *F* for carbon steel over the usual range of temperature of heat-treatment processes and for atmospheric pressure are shown in Fig. 3. There is but little tendency toward a change in the carbon content of a steel below the critical range. Oxidation is active down to about 1100 F.

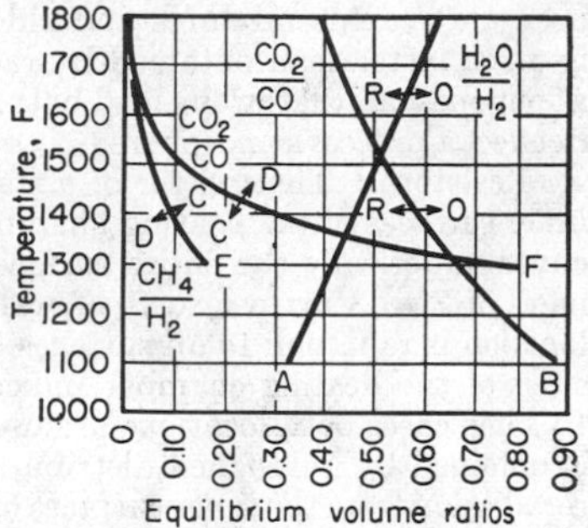

FIG. 3. Equilibrium volume ratios of the chemical systems *A*, *B*, *E*, and *F* for steel. *C* = carburizing condition; *O* = oxidizing; *D* = decarburizing; *R* = reducing.

Curves *E* and *F* of Fig. 3 show the volume ratios of systems *E* and *F* for equilibriums with graphite. The equilibrium volume-ratios of these two chemical systems for carbon in solid solution in steel (austenite) depend in each case on the carbon content of the steel. For the methane-hydrogen-carbon system (*E*) the volume ratio of the two gases at equilibrium with carbon in an unsaturated steel at a given temperature is less than the value shown by curve *E*. For the carbon monoxide-carbon dioxide-carbon system (*F*) the volume ratio of the two gases at equilibrium with the carbon in low- and medium-carbon steel at a given temperature is somewhat greater than the value shown by curve *F*; for high-carbon steels the equilibrium volume-ratios approach the values of curve *F*.

In the case of the hydrogen-iron oxide reaction, curve *A*, the water-vapor content of the mixture of gases at equilibrium decreases with decrease of temperature. Hence if a steel is to be cooled in a controlled atmosphere of this kind the permissible water-vapor content of the controlled atmosphere is dictated by the lowest temperature of the operation. The reverse is true of the carbon monoxide-iron oxide reaction, curve *B*. Thus if at a given temperature the carbon dioxide content of the mixture of carbon monoxide and carbon dioxide is less than the volume for equilibrium at that temperature it will be less than the volume for equilibrium at any lower temperatures and the steel can be cooled in that atmosphere without oxidation.

In the use of mixtures of the gases of the chemical systems noted to form controlled atmospheres for the heat-treatment of steel, the interactions of the gases at elevated temperatures must be controlled by removal of all or nearly all the carbon dioxide and water vapor from the heating chamber.

The available data concerning controlled atmospheres for the protection of alloy steels during heat-treatment processes indicate that the technique for alloy steels is much the same as for carbon steels; *i.e.*, a controlled atmosphere suitable for a carbon steel would, in general, be suitable for an alloy steel of the same carbon content.

In the heat-treatment of non-ferrous metals and alloys the use of either chemical system *A* or *B* requires for each oxide a knowledge of the equilibrium volume-ratios of the chemical system used over the range of the operating temperature. Individual problems may arise. For example, copper can be bright-annealed in an atmosphere of dry steam—an inactive gas for this application—but the resultant staining of the copper during cooling may be objectionable. Copper usually contains a small percentage of oxide, and when annealing such copper in an atmosphere containing a reducing gas the temperature of the metal must be kept below about 750 F otherwise the oxide will be reduced and the copper made brittle.

The foregoing discussion of atmosphere in heating chambers is intended to indicate the principles involved in the use of gases at elevated temperatures. The terms oxidation, reduction, carburization, and decarburization refer here to the chemical condition of a particular atmosphere and not to the extent of its effect on a charge. In all cases the concentration of the active gas or gases, time, temperature, in case of steel the carbon content and the gas pressure, and the catalytic action of hot surfaces within the chamber are important factors in the result obtained.

Bath Heating. Heating for local hardening of edge tools is the most general service. The lead-bath furnace has a working temperature range of 650 to 1700 F. The salt-bath furnace can be adapted to working temperature ranges within a total range of 300 to 2350 F by the selection of suitable mixture of salts. The two salt baths most generally used are cyanide mixtures and chloride mixtures. The rate of heating by immersion is much faster than obtained by radiation. The rate of heat transfer in a salt bath is about one-half that in the lead bath. An additional use of the salt bath is for cyaniding, in effect a process atmosphere.

Resistors. The resistor of a standard furnace is a sinuous winding mounted on the inner surfaces of the heating chamber as shown in Figs. 1 and 2. The resistor winding covers practically the entire surface of the space chosen. Resistors are applied on the basis of 2 to 3 kw per sq ft of wall surface in general practice. The basis of resistor location is radiation to all surfaces of the charge. Hence, the height and width dimensions of the heating chamber indicate the choice between side-wall and roof resistors. In some cases both locations are used. Uniform distribution of heat flow to the charge is obtained by a designed distribution of the surfaces of the resistors supplemented by reradiation from the inner surfaces of the chamber.

Resistors for the majority of standard furnaces are made of 80 Ni, 20 Cr alloy. A nickel-chromium-iron alloy is used in some furnaces for operation only over the lower portion of the furnace temperature range. Both ribbon and cast shapes are in use. The effort in each case is to obtain the maximum surface area per unit length of resistor and at the same time retain sufficient mechanical strength in the resistor winding.

The 80 Ni, 20 Cr alloy is self-protecting against oxidation, but this protection decreases with rise of temperature. The operating temperature of a resistor should be no higher than is needed in each case and should always be at a safe margin below the softening point of the alloy, which is about 2500 F. This corresponds to a maximum furnace temperature of about 2100 F. The life of a resistor is also affected by the frequency of heating and cooling. Barring accidents, the resistor of a standard furnace under average conditions of operation has a long life, usually measured in years of service.

The nickel-chromium alloy resistor is used in artificial atmospheres as well as in natural atmospheres. This alloy is not resistant to compounds of sulphur and is affected to some extent by carbon monoxide.

The electric insulation of the resistor circuit is that of its refractory supports at elevated temperatures. This limits the voltage of the circuit to about 600 volts. Small furnaces are usually designed for 110 volts, medium sizes for 220 volts, and the larger units for 440 volts. Single phase up to 25 or 30 kw and three phase for higher ratings is general practice.

The resistivity-temperature coefficient of the nickel-chromium alloy permits the operation of resistors of this material on constant-voltage circuits. The rate of heat development in a resistor is proportional to the square of the applied voltage; hence maintenance of normal voltage is desirable. Voltage regulation is not as important as for other types of electrical apparatus because of the heat-storage capacity of the structure of the heating chamber. The power factor of the resistor circuit is practically unity.

High-temperature Furnaces. **Silicon carbide** is the basis of a type of a non-metallic resistor for heating-chamber temperatures up to about 2800 F. The material is formed into rods. Resistors of this material do not require protection against oxidation and are operated on constant-voltage circuits.

Molybdenum resistors are suitable for temperatures up to 3000 F. Above that temperature the metal begins to vaporize. A molybdenum resistor cannot be operated in a natural atmosphere, and also it must be protected from reactions with silica and carbon. The metal is immune from reactions with sulphur compounds, nitrogen, and water vapor. Hydrogen is the most common artificial atmosphere used with molybdenum resistors. The difference between the cold and hot resistances of the circuit makes a starting device necessary.

Other materials used to some extent for resistors are iron, tungsten, and graphite. These require protection against oxidation.

Temperature Regulation. The temperature of the heating chamber of a resistor furnace is in most cases regulated by a more or less intermittent application of current —the on-and-off method—which is made automatic by instrument control. This method utilizes the heat-storage capacity of the inner lining of the heating chamber as a temperature equalizer. The variation from the normal temperature of the chamber can be kept within less than 7 deg F, plus and minus, without undue wear of the temperature-control equipment. Temperature regulation by voltage control is equally applicable to resistor furnaces, and the trend is toward the use of this more accurate method particularly for the more important installations.

Temperature protection for resistor furnaces is obtained by means of a temperature fuse mounted in the heating chamber and connected in the control circuit of the power supply to the furnace.

Multiple-temperature Control. The resistors of the larger furnaces are divided into two or more circuits. Each circuit can be equipped with individual temperature control. That arrangement provides temperature regulation at more than one location in the heating chamber and is an aid toward maintaining uniform temperature distribution within the chamber.

The subdivision of resistor circuits is used also for zone heating—and zone cooling where needed—in continuous furnaces.

Melting Pots. Resistor heating is applied to melting pots for the soft metals and alloys and for lead baths and for salt baths. The immersion heating unit is used for temperatures up to 950 F. For higher temperatures the metal pot is heated by resistors mounted outside and around the pot. The assembly in each case includes a heat-insulating wall similar to that of a resistor furnace. Another method of heating applicable only to salt baths is the passage of alternating current (of any frequency) between electrodes immersed in the bath.

Tempering Furnaces. The temperature is comparatively low—below 1300 F. Electrically heated oil baths and salt baths are used for tempering many kinds of small parts. Another form of tempering furnace is a vertical resistor furnace with the addition of a removable metal cylinder (or basket) to contain the charge and to provide an annular passageway for the circulation of air (by a fan mounted on the furnace) over the resistors and thence through the charge—an application of forced convection heating.

Sizes. The electrical rating is the general method of expressing the size of a resistor furnace. Sizes up to 100 kw predominate, 100 to 500 kw furnaces are common, and others within the range 500 to 1,000 kw are in service. The data of Table 1 refer to common sizes of so-called box furnaces for general service.

The **losses** from a resistor furnace for a given heating chamber temperature are as follows: The open-door loss is a variable depending on the area of the door (or doors) and the percentage of the time that the door is open—from a continuous furnace this loss also varies with the type and speed of the conveyor; with artificial atmospheres, the loss of heat in the gases discharged for atmosphere control; the stored-heat loss, a variable that depends on the extent and frequency of the cooling of the furnace within a given period of operation; the heat dissipated from the outer surfaces of the furnace.

The **operating efficiency** is expressed either as pounds of material treated per kwh or kwh per ton. Representative values for average service for the heat-treatment of steel range from 7 to 12 lb per kwh. Corresponding values for non-ferrous metals and alloys are within the range 12 to 22 lb per kwh.

Table 1. Box Resistor Furnaces, 1850 F Class

Connected load, kw	Power supply, 200 volts	Lb of steel per hr at 1500 F	Time in min to heat to 1500 F when used previous day	Radiation in kwh per hr at 1500 F	Approx dimensions, in. Inside			Over-all			
					Width	Depth	Height	Width	Depth	Height, door closed	Height, door open
29	1-phase	300	35	4.9	18	36	18	55	89	86	97
45	3-phase	500	35	6.9	24	54	20	61	108	90	101
60	3-phase	650	25	7.8	30	63	23	78	125	90	98
72	3-phase	750	25	9.1	36	72	23	84	135	90	98

The general field of the batch furnace is defined by the following conditions: (1) intermittent and varied production; (2) long periods of heating (and in some cases slow cooling); (3) heating service beyond the range of the handling capacity of furnace conveyors; and (4) supplementary heating service. A continuous furnace is indicated where the flow of material to be heated is reasonably uniform and continuous, *i.e.*, mass-production conditions. In some cases, batch furnaces with automatic charging and discharging equipment are essentially continuous furnaces.

Resistor Ovens

The resistor oven is a modification of the resistor furnace to correspond to the low temperatures of drying and baking processes. The heating chamber is an insulated metal structure with a fresh-air inlet and an exhaust fan for ventilation (the removal of vapors and gases evolved from the charge). A refractory lining is not required. Ovens may be of the batch type with conventional methods of handling the charge or of the continuous type, usually with chain conveyors.

The most common type of electric oven is heated by resistors mounted in a separate compartment of the heating chamber enclosure. The heat transfer is by forced convection which is accomplished by recirculation of the chamber atmosphere by a motor-driven fan.

A resistor oven with filament-type lamps as heating units provides what is generally known as infrared heating. The lamps, usually with self-contained reflectors, surround the charge, and the heat transfer is by radiation, mainly in the infrared portion of the spectrum. This type of oven is best adapted to the continuous heating of charges which present a large surface area in proportion to the mass and which require only surface heating, *e.g.*, baking finishes on sheet products.

Ventilation. The vapors and gases evolved from the charge during baking processes are often flammable, and the continuous discharge of these products from the oven chamber is essential for protection against explosions. For detailed recommendations, see *Pamphlet* 74 of the Assoc. Factory Mutual Fire Ins. Cos., Boston.

Dielectric Heating

The term relates to the heat developed in dielectric materials, such as rubber, glue, textiles, paper, and plastics, when exposed to an alternating electric field. The material to be heated is placed between plate-form electrodes, as indicated in Fig. 4. It is not necessary that the electrodes be in contact with the charge; hence continuous heating is often practicable.

If the material of the charge is homogeneous and the electric field uniform, heat is developed uniformly and simultaneously throughout the mass of the charge. The thermal conductivity of the material is a negligible factor in the rate of heating. The temperatures and services are within the oven classification.

The frequency and voltage for this class of service depend in each case on the electrical properties of the material of the charge at the temperature specified for the heat application. The frequencies in use range from 2 to 40 megacycles; the most common frequencies are from 10 to 30 megacycles. It is advisable to select the frequency for heating by trial.

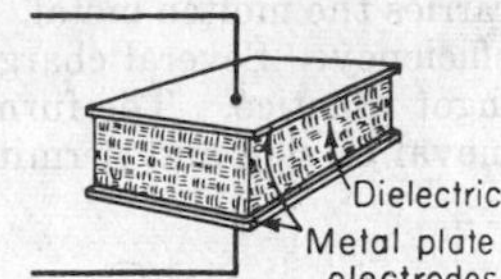

Fig. 4. Assembly for dielectric heating.

The upper limit of voltage across the electrodes is fixed by the spark-over value and by corona. The permissible voltage gradient depends on the nature of the material of the charge. Values within the range 2,000 to 6,000 volts per in. are found in practice; the voltage across the electrodes should not exceed 15,000 volts.

Applications of dielectric heating include setting glue as in plywood manufacture, curing rubber, drying textiles, and the heat-treatment of plastics.

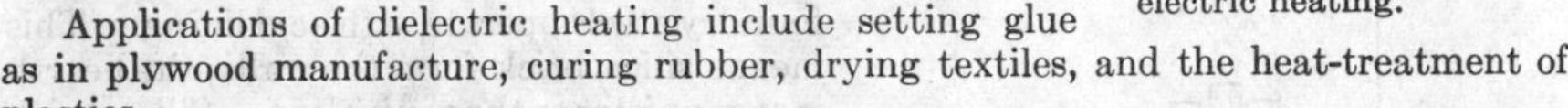

Induction Heating

In induction heating, the lateral surface of the charge is exposed to an alternating magnetic flux. The currents thus induced in the charge flow wholly within its mass. The term "eddy-current heating" is sometimes applied to the method.

A common assembly, if the charge is to be heated to a temperature below its melting point, is to place the charge within a coil as indicated in Fig. 5. An alternating current in the coil establishes the required alternating magnetic flux around the charge.

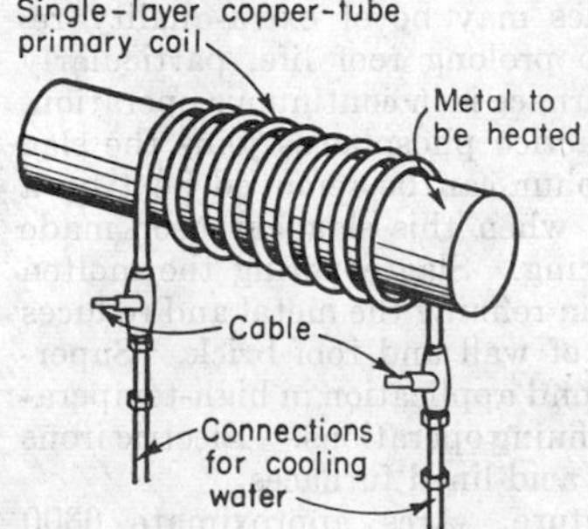

Fig. 5. Assembly for induction heating.

A peculiar feature of such assemblies, termed "induction heaters," is the absence of heat insulation; the coil is water-cooled. Thus, the charge is heated in the open air, or an artificial atmosphere can be used, if the assembly is enclosed. This requires rapid heating with heat cycles measured in minutes or seconds.

The frequency required is a function of the electric and magnetic properties of the charge at the temperature specified for the heat application and of the radius, or one-half the thickness, of the charge. This frequency for a given material increases with decrease of the dimension noted. The frequency in any case is not critical. In practice 480, 960, 3,000, 9,600 cycles and around 450 kilocycles suffice for the entire range of induction heating. The highest frequencies needed are those for heating steel charges to temperatures above the Curie point. About ½ in. diam in this case is the lower limit for 9,600 cycles. This limit dimension is decreased for steel heated to temperatures below the Curie point and for all charges of non-ferrous materials.

The operation can be either batch heating or continuous heating as required. Applications include heating for forging, for annealing, for hardening steel, for brazing, soldering, and strain relief. As most of the heat is developed within the annular zone of the charge, the method is particularly well adapted to heating steel parts for surface hardening. A recent application of induction heating is the raising in temperature of billet-size ingots for rolling into merchant bars.

Arc Furnaces

Two types of arc furnace are in common use: (1) the three-phase furnace and (2) the single-phase furnace. The general field of the three-phase furnace is the melting and refining of carbon and alloy steels; that of the single-phase furnace is the melting of non-ferrous alloys. There is an increasing amount of arc-furnace capacity used for melting and refining various types of iron.

Three-Phase Arc Furnaces. The general design of this type of furnace is shown in Fig. 6. In operation, each heat is started by swinging the furnace roof aside and then loading the refractory-lined furnace body with scrap dropped from a crane-handled clamshell charging bucket. Arcs next are drawn between the lower ends of the graphite electrodes and the scrap; melting proceeds under automatic control until the hearth carries the molten metal. This fluidizing stage is effected at about 85 percent thermal efficiency. Several charges usually are needed to build up the bath—particularly in ingot practice. The furnace tilts forward for pouring; the back tilt serves in the removal of slag and permits the furnace hearth to be kept in proper condition. The working door is opposite to the pouring spout. Large furnaces frequently also have a side door.

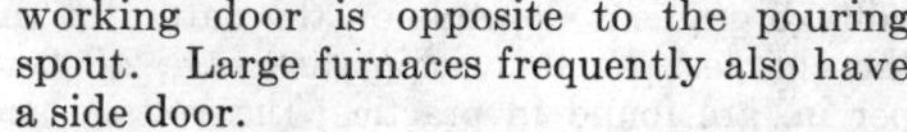

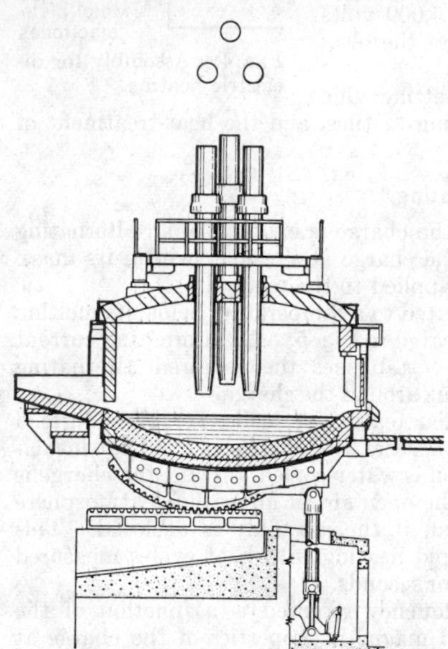

Fig. 6. Three-phase arc furnace with basic lining.

Refractories. Furnaces that produce foundry steels operate with acid lining. This means silica brick form the walls; the hearth is of gannister or the equivalent. Silica-brick roofs are the more widely used although, for intermittent operation, clay brick may be preferred. The slags of acid-lining practice remove no phosphorus or sulphur. Essentially all ingot operations are carried on with basic linings. This means magnesite bottom and sidewalls, so that the limey slags employed will not erode them. Entry ports for the electrodes may be of extra-quality refractories to prolong roof life, particularly where the furnace is in continuous operation. In basic practice phosphorus joins the slag readily; sulphur can be removed next by a second slag, when this slag has been made highly reducing. Slag covering the molten bath serves in refining the metal and reduces the heating of wall and roof brick. Super-refractories find application in high-temperature, long-refining operations. Electric irons are made in acid-lined furnaces.

Temperature. Arcs approximate 6300 F; hence operation must be carried out so as to protect the refractories as much as possible. As the top-charge furnace now has supplanted the door-charge furnace in nearly all cold-melt work, the conditions for shielding the refractories during the melt-down stage of each heat are good. With the furnace filled to the top with scrap, the electrodes bore down through that scrap, and the heat of the arcs is liberated right in the metallic charge itself. When the charge, and any back charges made, approach the fluid stage it is customary to reduce both the power input and the length of arcs employed. During the finishing stages, roof and sidewalls are protected both by the slag and by the "umbrella" effect of the electrodes themselves. Deserving mention is the expanding use of oxygen to gain speed in production, which makes for increasing furnace temperatures. The higher sidewalls of modern furnaces aid in obtaining good roof life.

Charges. The three-phase arc furnace is primarily a unit for converting scrap charges into steel for pouring into ingots and castings. This type of equipment finds increasing use also in the cold melting and duplexing of gray and white irons. Hand and chute charging have practically disappeared, at least in so far as furnaces of a ton charge size upward are concerned. One of the main advantages of the top-charge furnace is that the scrap used does not need to be cut to door size, as was the case formerly.

Although first employed only for the more expensive grades of steel, the arc furnace now is used widely in making ingots for rolling into merchant bars and similar grades. The speed of production on this type of working—termed single-slag dephosphorizing basic practice—can be double that obtained with the same furnace used to make two-slag dephosphorized and desulphurized basic alloy steels. Acid working on foundry steels generally approximates the same speed as single-slag dephosphorizing basic practice, and some alloy steels require about half again as much time. While most carbon steel for castings is made on an acid hearth, a basic bottom is regularly used for making manganese steels, for refining nickel and copper, and for the furnacing of many heat-resistant alloys. Sec. 6 discusses steel foundry practice.

In general, approximately 320 kwh at 100 percent thermal efficiency will be needed to melt 1 ton of cold steel scrap. This means about 400 kwh will be needed to fluidize each ton. Additionally, about 100 kwh per ton will be needed to finish the heat and superheat the bath—this in the case of ordinary plain carbon steels made on single-slag acid or basic practice. Double-slag steel heats will require no more power than others for fluidizing the scrap charge, but the additional power needed for melting new slag, refining, melting added alloys, etc., may require as much as 250 kwh per ton of bath, or even more.

Three-phase arc furnaces are usually given an hourly productive rating in terms of acid foundry steels when these equipments are supplied in sizes up to and including the 11 ft diam unit. However, with many furnaces extra-powered, quite a few shops exceed the normal hourly rating considerably—in some cases by essentially 100 percent. Representative sizes of furnaces are listed in Table 2.

Table 2. Sizes of Three-phase Arc Furnaces

Diam of shell, ft	Normal charge, tons	Normal powering, kva	Normal productive rate, single-slag steels, tons per hr*
5	1½	600	½
7	3½	1,500	1½
9	8	3,000	3
11	16	6,000	6
12½	27	9,000	9
15	50	12,500	13
20	115	25,000	27
24	225	36,000	40

* Many users exceed these outputs, particularly those using burners and oxygen to speed operations.

Arcs. The arc in each phase is maintained between the lower end of the electrode and the top of the charge (or bath, after the molten state is reached). Higher voltages can serve for melting as the size of the furnace increases; thus, where a 7 ft diam furnace employs 215 volts as its highest melting potential, a 15 ft furnace would use 290 volts or higher as the top tap. The furnace transformer is universally of the motor-operated tap-changer type, and in the case of, say, a 10,000 kva at 55 C rise substation, a secondary voltage variation of more than 150 volts is customary. The range of lower voltages used for refining the molten metal is obtained by changing the primary of the main transformer from delta to star connection; this reduces both voltage and capacity to 58 percent of their values with delta primary connection. If, say, 12 tons of steel scrap are to be melted down to fluid in 1 hr, then the electrical energy needed will approximate 5,000 kwh. With 245 volts used as the principal melt-down voltage, the current per phase will have to average close to 12,000 amp. A 12 in. diam graphite electrode would amply carry this current. Small furnaces operate with 600 kva and even higher powering per ton of charge, whereas in the case of the larger equipments the electrical backing of the furnace normally does not exceed 300 kva per ton of charge.

Reactance is required in the circuits of an arc furnace to give stability and to limit the current when an electrode makes contact with the metallic charge. The inherent reactance (impedance) in the instance of 10,000 kva installations and above normally is sufficient. The total stabilizing reactance provided in the case of a 1,000 kva load normally approximates 30 percent.

Regulation. The characteristics of an arc furnace circuit for a given applied voltage are shown in Fig. 7. For each voltage there is a value of current that gives maximum power in the furnace. This optimum current is the basis of the regulation of the circuit.

The control of the power input into direct-arc electric furnaces is effected by the adjustment of the arc length. To accomplish this, the electrode arms are positioned in the "raise" or in the "lower" direction by an automatic regulator. This regulator, which responds within a few cycles, causes the electrode arms to be lowered by extra-fast motor-driven winches when voltage is obtained by closing the circuit breaker. As soon as contact between electrode and scrap charge is established, melting current flows, and this current, whenever excessive, functions immediately through the medium of the winch motor to elevate that particular electrode arm and electrode by the distance corresponding to the diminution in power input needed just at that instant.

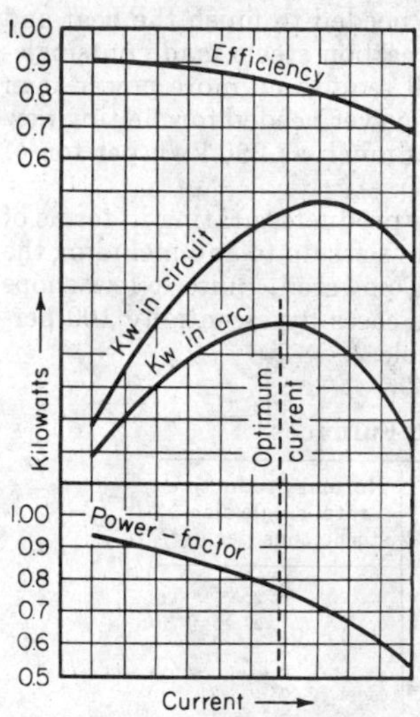

Fig. 7. Characteristics of an arc-furnace circuit.

Formerly, the so-called contactor regulator was used universally to energize the winch motors. More recently the rotary regulator—this, in effect, being a particularly responsive motor generator set for each of the three phases—has forged to the forefront by reason of giving more precise control with minimized maintenance. Currently, even faster response and electrode-travel speed are provided by low-inertia static-regulating equipment.

Single-phase Arc Furnaces. Single-phase arc furnaces usually are manufactured in the two-electrode type. When the electrodes operate vertically the furnace melts much as a three-phase direct-arc furnace does. However, most vertical-electrode single-phase furnaces are of laboratory size—that is, up to 150 kva in powering.

When two electrodes are mounted horizontally in a rocking furnace an indirect-arc unit is obtained. Many rocking furnaces serve well in the melting of brasses, bronzes, and in similar work. Volatiles are reincorporated in the metal since the bath washes over much of the interior of a rocking furnace. The oscillation approximates 200 deg.

Rocking furnaces usually do not exceed 500 kw in powering. A single operating voltage can suffice. In regulating a rocking furnace, only one electrode need be movable, on a carriage under automatic control, to maintain the requisite amperage by varying the length, and therefore the resistance, of the arc gap.

Induction Furnaces

There are two basic types of metal-melting induction furnaces: (1) coreless and (2) core-type. Both types utilize the principle of a transformer. The high-voltage circuit is coupled with that of the low voltage without directly connecting the two circuits. The element responsible for this coupling effect is the magnetic field. Induction heating utilizes the property of the magnetic field, which enables heat to be transferred without direct contact. By correctly disposing the high-voltage winding, which in the case of the induction furnace would be an induction coil or inductor, the magnetic field is directed so that the metal to be heated or melted is made to absorb energy. The temperature attainable is limited solely by the resistance to heat of the surrounding lining material. Induction heating enables any temperature to be achieved while providing for excellent regulation of temperature and metallurgical properties. Any metal which will conduct electric current can be melted in an induction furnace.

Coreless Induction Furnaces. (See Fig. 8.) This type of furnace consists of a crucible, copper coil, and framework on supports arranged for tilting and pouring. The specially designed induction coil acts as the primary of the transformer. The crucible conforms to conventional refractory practice. A rammed crucible is used for furnaces above 50 kw, and preformed crucibles are used on smaller furnaces such as laboratory units.

The principle of operation is essentially the same as that of the induction heater previously described. The initial charge in the furnace is cold scrap metal—pieces of assorted dimensions and shapes and a large percentage of voids. As the power is applied and the heat cycle progresses, the charge changes to a body of molten metal; additional cold metal is added until the molten-metal level is brought to the desired temperature and metallurgical chemistry. The furnace then is tapped.

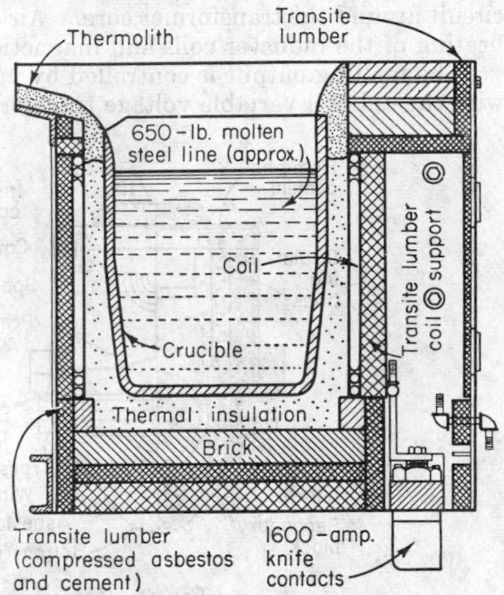

Fig. 8. Coreless induction furnace.

When the metal in the furnace becomes fluid, depending on whether a line frequency or medium-frequency supply by means of convertors is used, a certain electromagnetic stirring action will occur. This stirring action is peculiar to the induction furnace and aids in the production of certain types of alloys. The stirring action increases as the frequency is reduced.

Line-frequency applications are generally reserved to furnaces having a metal-holding capacity of 800 lb and above. There is always an ideal relationship between the size of a coreless furnace and its operating frequency. As a general rule, a small furnace gives best results at high to medium frequencies and large furnaces work best at the lower frequencies. A frequency is suited to a given furnace when it yields good, fast melting with a gentle stirring action. Too high or too low frequencies are accompanied by undesirable side effects. The tabulation below gives the charge weights and frequencies generally to be used:

Charge weight, lb	Frequency, cps
2–50	9,600
12–500	3,000
200–15,000	960
800–75,000	60

The coreless induction furnace is usually charged full and tapped empty, although at line frequencies, it may be necessary to retain a certain amount of metal in the furnace to continue the operation, since it is difficult to start the furnace with small metal particles, such as turnings and borings, in a cold crucible. As a result, it is general practice to retain a heel in the furnace of about one-third its molten-metal volume. This problem can be avoided in furnaces of higher frequencies, where start-up can be performed with small-size metal charges without carrying the heel.

Coreless induction furnaces are particularly attractive for melting charges and alloys of known analysis; in essence, the operation becomes one of metal melting with rapidly absorbed electric heat without disturbing the metallurgical properties of the initial charge.

These furnaces are supplied from a single-phase source. In order to obtain a balanced three-phase input, it is necessary specifically to design the electrical equipment for the inclusion of capacitors and suitable reactors, which are generally automatically switched (by inductance changes) during the operation in order to provide a reasonably high power factor. Power factors on such furnaces can be kept at or near unity. In high-frequency coreless induction furnaces, high power factors are necessary to prevent overburdening the motor-generator equipment.

Core-type Induction Furnaces. (See Fig. 9.) The transformer is actually wound to conform to a typical transformer design having an iron core and layers of wire acting as a primary circuit. The melting channel acts as a ring short circuit around this transformer in the melting chamber. According to the desired melting capacity, one, two, or three such transformers (or **inductors,** as they are called) may be added to the furnace shell. At all times, the channel must hold sufficient metal to maintain a short circuit around the transformer core. Air cooling is used as required to prevent undue heating of the inductor coils and magnetic cores.

The melting output is controlled by varying the voltage supplied to the inductors with the aid of a variable voltage transformer connected to the primary circuit of the

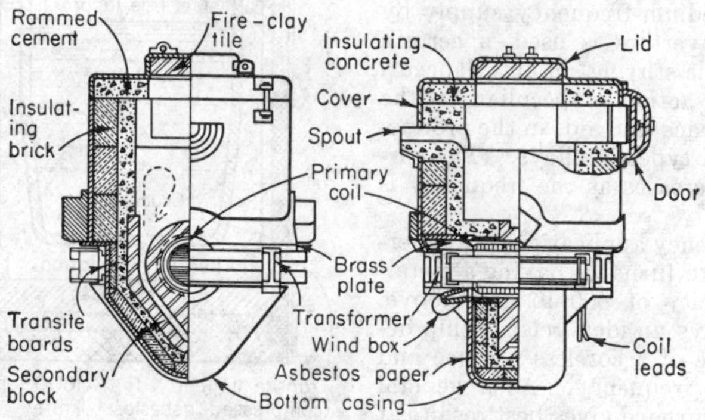

FIG. 9. Core-type induction furnace.

supply. Core-type furnaces always use line frequencies. Voltage or power-input regulation, therefore, can be performed by adjusting the tap setting of the transformer feeding the furnace transformer attached to the furnace shell. These transformers are single-phase units, and by using three such units, a balanced three-phase input can be obtained. The current flowing through the primary inductors by transformation causes a much larger current in the metal loop, whose resistance creates heat for melting.

The core-type furnace is the most efficient type of induction furnace because its iron core concentrates magnetic flux in the area of the magnetic loop, ensuring maximum power transfer from primary to secondary. Efficiency in the use of power can be as high as 95 to 98 percent.

The essential loop of metal must always be maintained in the core-type furnace. If this loop is allowed to freeze by cooling, extreme care is necessary in remelting because the loop may rupture and disrupt the circuit. This could require extensive work in dismantling the coil and restoring the loop. Consequently, core-type furnaces rarely are permitted to cool. This makes alloy changes difficult because a heel of molten metal always is required.

The relatively narrow melting channels must be kept as clean as possible since a high metal temperature exists in this loop. Non-metallics or tramps in the charge metal tend to accumulate on the walls in the channel area, restricting the free flow of metal and ultimately closing the passage.

This furnace is particularly useful for melting of non-ferrous metals such as aluminum, copper, copper alloys, and zinc.

Power Requirements for Electric Furnaces

The **energy required for melting metals** in electric furnaces varies for a given metal or alloy with the size of the furnace, the thickness of the refractory lining, the temperature of the molten metal, the rate of melting, and with the degree of the continuity of the operation of the furnace. An estimated efficiency of 50 to 60 percent is often used for preliminary purposes. As is well known, 3 to 6 ton direct-arc furnaces often are used to tap acid foundry steels with the consumption of less than 500 kwh to the ton, and large ingot furnaces of this same type, operating basic-lined on common steels for ingots, give even better results despite the call for several more charges of scrap per heat.

Average values in kwh per ton of molten metal are as follows: yellow brass, 200 to 350; red brass, 250 to 400; copper, 250 to 400; lead, 30 to 50; steel melting, when making high-quality double-slag basic heats, 650 to 800.

Electrode consumption varies considerably in arc furnaces because of their different constructions and operations. Average values in pounds of electrode per ton of molten metal are: steel melting, with graphite electrodes, 5 to 10; brass melting, with graphite electrodes, 3 to 5. Graphite electrodes have largely superseded carbon electrodes.

Table 3. Energy Consumption of Electric Furnaces

Process	Type of furnace	Lb per kwh
Baking finishes on sheet metal	Batch oven	10–18
Baking finishes on sheet metal	Continuous oven	25–30
Baking bread	Continuous oven	10–12
Annealing brass and copper	Batch furnace	10–25
Annealing steel	Batch furnace	5–15
Hardening steel	Batch furnace	7–11
Tempering steel	Batch furnace	15–25
Annealing glass	Continuous furnace	40–100
Vitreous enameling, single coat	Batch furnace	5–8
Vitreous enameling, single coat	Continuous furnace	10–15
Galvanizing	Batch furnace	12–20
Melting metals	**Type of furnace**	**Kwh per ton (2,000 lb)**
Lead	Resistor	40–50
Solder 50–50	Resistor	40–50
Tin	Resistor	35–50
Zinc	Induction	80–100
Brass	Arc and induction	250–400
Steel, melting only	Arc and induction	450–700
Steel, melting and refining	Arc	600–750
Gray iron	Arc and induction	450–600
Furnace products	**Type of furnace**	**Kwh per ton (2,000 lb)**
Aluminum	Electrolytic	22,000–27,000
Calcium carbide	Resistance	3,000–6,000
Ferroalloys	Resistance	4,000–8,000
Graphite	Resistance	3,000–8,000
Phosphoric acid	Resistance	5,000–6,000
Silicon carbide	Resistance	8,500–10,000
Smelting iron ore	Resistance	1,650–2,400

Submerged-arc and Resistance Furnaces

The resistance furnace is essentially a refractory-lined chamber with electrodes—movable or fixed—buried in the charge. This simplicity permits a wide range of designs and much latitude in dimensions. The general service is heating charges of a refractory nature to bring about chemical reactions or changes in the physical structure of the material of the charge. The energy requirement of each of such processes is a large item in the cost of production. Large units and a favorable power location are the rule. Resistance furnaces also are termed submerged-arc furnaces and/or, in quite a few instances, smelting-type furnaces.

The only limit on the temperature to which a charge can be heated by this method is the temperature at which the materials of the charge are vaporized. For temperatures beyond the limit of refractory linings, the materials of the charge are used to form a protective layer between the core of the charge (through which the current passes) and the walls of the furnace.

Resistance furnaces with movable electrodes may be either single phase or polyphase. The materials of the charge are fed more or less continuously, and the product is discharged intermittently or continuously as required. In some cases the product is in the molten state, in others the product is a vapor. The usual method of operation is the use of a single operating voltage and a constant power input. The power is regulated by adjustment of the depths of the electrodes in the charge. The load is fairly uniform and, if polyphase, is kept reasonably well balanced.

The **resistance furnace with fixed electrodes** is designed for heating materials in batches and is usually rectangular in shape with an electrode at each end for single-phase operation. The length and cross-sectional area of the path of the current are proportioned to suit the power characteristics of the charge. Refractory materials have negative temperature-resistance coefficients, and hence to maintain constant power in the furnace circuit the applied voltage must be reduced as the temperature of the charge rises in proportion to the square root of the ratio of the initial resistance of the furnace circuit to the resistance of the furnace circuit at the end of the heat cycle. If the materials of the charge are non-conductors at room temperature, a starting circuit is provided by means of a core of carbon—usually coke—placed in the charge. The heat cycles of furnaces of this class generally extend over a period of several days.

Some of the more common **uses of the resistance furnace** are:

Calcium carbide furnaces are charged continuously with lime and coke. These equipments can be either open or closed top. This type of furnace has been built up to 70,000 kva in electrical powering—covered and sealed for gas collection.

Ferroalloy furnaces for the production of ferrochrome, ferrosilicon, ferromanganese, etc., are usually three-phase furnaces with movable electrodes and are similar in construction to the three-phase arc furnace. The charge is a mixture of the ore (oxide) of the selected metal, scrap iron, and a reducing agent, generally carbon except for very low carbon content alloys, for which some other reducing agent such as aluminum or silicon is required. Six-electrode furnaces often are used for power inputs of 15,000 kva and more.

The **graphitizing furnace** is of the single-phase batch type. Artificial graphite is made by heating amorphous carbon (coal or coke) while shielded from air to a high temperature—around 4500 F. The presence of some metallic impurity, such as iron oxide, in the charge appears to be necessary for the conversion of amorphous carbon to graphitic carbon. The raw material for making bulk graphite constitutes both the charge and the protective layer around the core of the charge. Graphite shapes are made from the corresponding shapes of amorphous carbon which are embedded—between the electrodes—in raw material as noted for the manufacture of bulk graphite.

The **silicon carbide furnace** is similar to the graphitizing furnace. The charge is a mixture of sand (silica), coke, sawdust, and a small amount of salt. This mixture is packed around a core of granulated coke to form the initial circuit between the electrodes. The sand and coke are the reacting materials. The sawdust serves to make the charge porous so that the gases formed during the heating of the charge can escape freely. The salt vaporizes and removes impurities, such as iron, in the form of chlorides. The temperature of the process is 2700 to 3400 F.

SECTION 8

MACHINE ELEMENTS

BY

HEARD K. BAUMEISTER, Senior Engineer, Systems Development Division, International Business Machines Corporation.

EUGENE A. AVALLONE, Professor and Chairman, Department of Mechanical Engineering, The City University of New York.

GEORGE W. MICHALEC, Engineering Consultant, GPL Division, General Precision, Inc.; Associate Professor of Mechanical Engineering, Stevens Institute of Technology.

DUDLEY D. FULLER, Professor of Mechanical Engineering, Columbia University.

CHARLES L. POPE, Engineering Supervisor, Eastman Kodak Company.

CORT L. MILLER, Engineer, Eastman Kodak Company.

EDWARD W. FISHER, Chief Product Engineer, Garlock, Inc.

RENO C. KING, Professor of Mechanical Engineering, New York University.

C. H. BERRY, late Gordon McKay Professor of Mechanical Engineering, Emeritus, Harvard University; and late Professor of Mechanical Engineering, Northeastern University.

CONTENTS

PIPE AND PIPE FITTINGS

By RENO C. KING

PREFERRED NUMBERS

By C. H. BERRY

MECHANISM

BY

Heard K. Baumeister

REFERENCES: Reuleaux, "Kinematics of Machinery," Macmillan. Unwin, "Elements of Machine Design," Longmans. Schwamb and Merrill, "Elements of Mechanism," Wiley. Sloane, "Engineering Kinematics," Macmillan. Beggs, "Mechanism," McGraw-Hill.

Definition. A mechanism is that part of a machine which contains two or more pieces so arranged that the motion of one compels the motion of the others according to a definite law depending upon the nature of the combination.

LINKAGES

Links may be of any form so long as they do not interfere with the desired motion. The simplest form is that of four bars, A, B, C, D, fastened together at their ends by

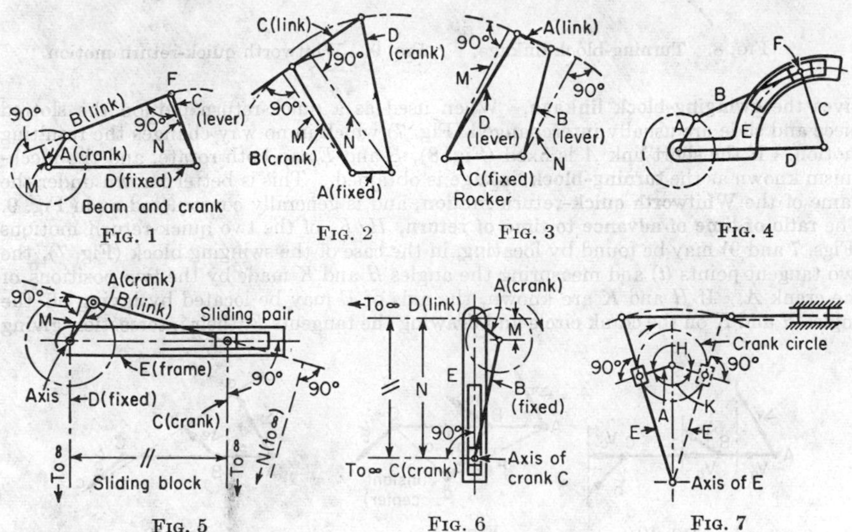

FIG. 1. Beam and crank mechanism.
FIG. 2. Drag-link mechanism.
FIG. 3. Rocker mechanism.
FIGS. 4 and 5. Sliding-block linkage.
FIG. 6. Swinging-block linkage.

cylindrical pins, and which are all movable in parallel planes. If the links are of different lengths and each is fixed in turn, there will be four possible combinations; but as two of these are similar there will be produced three mechanisms having distinctly different motions. Thus, in Fig. 1, if D is fixed A can rotate and C oscillate, giving the **beam-and-crank** mechanism, as used on side-wheel steamers. If B is fixed, the same motion will result; if A is fixed (Fig. 2), links B and D can rotate, giving the **drag-link** mechanism used to feather the floats on paddle wheels. Fixing link C (Fig. 3), D and B can only oscillate, and a **rocker** mechanism sometimes used in straight-line motions is produced. It is customary to call a rotating link a **crank;** an oscillating link a **lever,** or beam; and the connecting link a **connecting rod.** The fixed link is often enlarged and used as the supporting frame.

If in the linkage (Fig. 1) the pin joint F is replaced by a slotted piece E (Fig. 4), no change will be produced in the resulting motion, and if the length of links C and D is made infinite, the slotted piece E will become straight and the motion of the slide will be that of pure translation, thus obtaining the engine, or **sliding-block, linkage** (Fig. 5).

If in the sliding-block linkage (Fig. 5) the long link B is fixed (Fig. 6), A will rotate and E will oscillate and the infinite links C and D may be indicated as shown. This

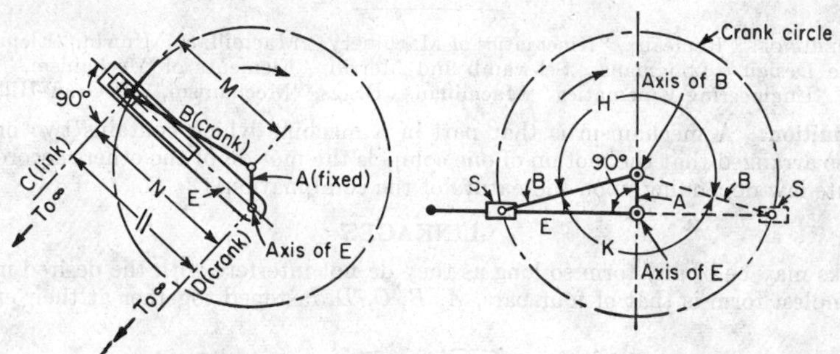

FIG. 8. Turning-block linkage. FIG. 9. Whitworth quick-return motion.

gives the **swinging-block linkage.** When used as a quick-return motion the slotted piece and slide are usually interchanged (Fig. 7) which in no way changes the resulting motion. If the short link A is fixed (Fig. 8), B and E can both rotate, and the mechanism known as the **turning-block linkage** is obtained. This is better known under the name of the **Whitworth quick-return motion,** and is generally constructed as in Fig. 9. The **ratio of time of advance to time of return,** H/K, of the two quick-return motions (Figs. 7 and 9) may be found by locating, in the case of the swinging block (Fig. 7), the two tangent points (t) and measuring the angles H and K made by the two positions of the crank A. If H and K are known, the axis of E may be located by laying off the angles H and K on the crank circle and drawing the tangents E, their intersection giving

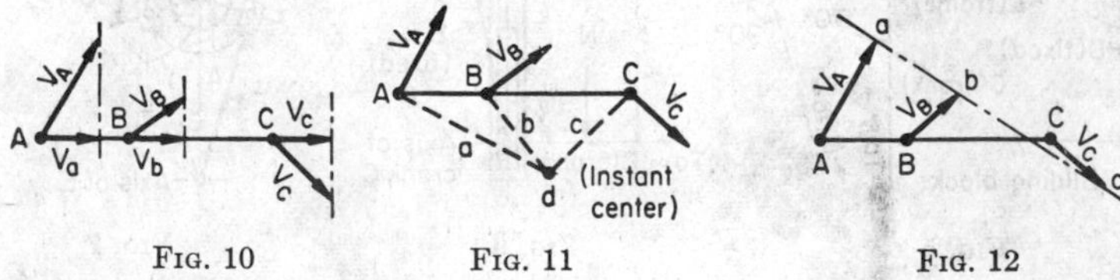

FIG. 10 FIG. 11 FIG. 12

the desired point. For the turning-block linkage (Fig. 9), determine the angles H and K made by the crank B when E is in the horizontal position; or, if the angles are known, the axis of E may be determined by drawing a horizontal line through the two crank-pin positions (S) for the given angle, and the point where a line through the axis of B cuts E perpendicularly will be the axis of E.

Velocities of any two or more points on a link must fulfill the following conditions (see p. 3-21): (1) Components along the link must be equal and in the same direction (Fig. 10): $V_a = V_b = V_c$. (2) Perpendiculars to V_A, V_B, V_C from the points A, B, C must intersect at a common point d, the **instant center** (or instantaneous axis). (3) The velocities of points A, B, and C are directly proportional to their distances from this center (Fig. 11): $V_A/a = V_B/b = V_C/c$. For a straight link the tips of the vectors representing the velocities of any number of points on the link will be on a straight line (Fig. 12): abc = a straight line. To find the velocity of any point when the velocity and direction of any two other points are known, condition (2) may be used, or a combination of (1) and (3). The **linear velocity ratio** of any two points on a linkage may be found by determining the distances e and f to the instant center (Fig. 13); then $V_c/V_b = e/f$. This may often be simplified by noting that a line drawn parallel to e and cutting B produced forms two similar triangles efB and sAy, which gives $V_c/V_b = e/f = s/A$. The **angular velocity ratio** for any position of two oscillating or rotating links A and C (Fig. 1), connected by a movable link B, may be determined by scaling the length of the perpendiculars M and N from the axes of rotation to the center line of the movable link. The angular velocity ratio is inversely proportional to these perpendiculars, or $O_C/O_A = M/N$. This method may be applied directly to a linkage

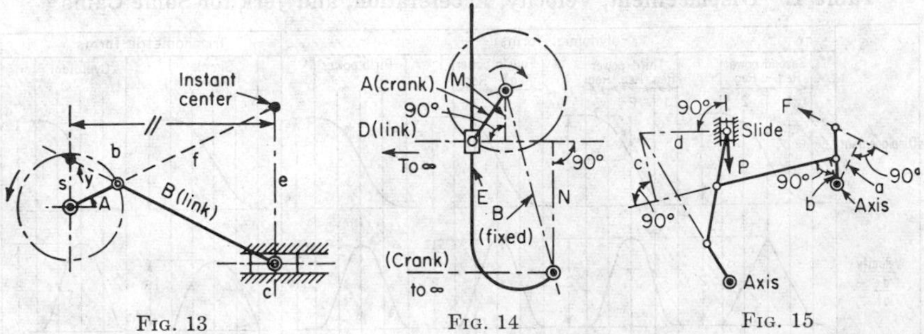

FIG. 13 FIG. 14 FIG. 15

having a sliding pair if the two infinite links are redrawn perpendicular to the sliding pair, as indicated in Fig. 14. M and N are also shown in Figs. 1, 2, 3, 5, 6, 8. In Fig. 5 one of the axes is at infinity, therefore N is infinite, or the slide has pure translation.

Forces. A mechanism must deliver as much work as it receives, neglecting friction; therefore the force at any point F multiplied by the velocity V_F in the direction of the force at that point must equal the force at some other point P multiplied by the velocity V_P at that point; or the forces are inversely as their velocities and $F/P = V_P/V_F$. It is at times more convenient to equate the moments of the forces acting around each axis of rotation (sometimes using the instant center) to determine the force acting at some other point. In Fig. 15, $(F \times a \times c)/(b \times d) = P$.

CAMS

Cam Diagram. A cam is usually a plate or cylinder which communicates motion to a follower by means of its edge or a groove cut in its surface. In the practical design of cams the follower (1) must assume a definite series of positions while the driver occupies a corresponding series of positions or (2) must arrive at a definite location by the time the driver arrives at a particular position. The former design may be severely limited in speed because the interrelationship between the follower and cam positions may yield a follower displacement versus time function that involves large values for the successive time derivatives indicating large accelerations and forces and large impacts and noise. The second design centers about finding that particular interrelationship between the follower and cam positions that results in the minimum forces and impacts so that the speed may be made quite large. In either case, the desired interrelationship must be put into hardware as discussed below. In the case of high-speed machines, small irregularities in the cam surface or geometry may be severely detrimental.

A step-wise displacement in time for the follower running on a cam driven at constant speed is, of course, impossible because the follower would require infinite velocities. A step in velocity for the follower would result in infinite accelerations; these in turn would bring into being forces that approach infinite magnitudes which would tend to destroy the machine. A step in acceleration causes a large jerk and large shock waves to be transmitted and reflected throughout the parts that generate noise and would tend to limit the life of the machine. A step in jerk, the third derivative of the follower displacement with respect to time, seems altogether acceptable. In those designs requiring or exhibiting clearance between the follower and cam (usually at the bottom of the stroke), as gentle and slow a ramp portion as can be tolerated must be inserted on either side of the clearance region to limit the magnitude of the acceleration and jerk to a minimum. The tolerance on the clearance adjustment must be small enough to assure that the follower will be left behind and picked up gradually by the gentle ramp portions of the cam.

Table 1 shows the comparable and relative magnitudes of velocity, acceleration, and jerk for several high-speed cams where the displacements are all taken as 1 at time 1 without any overshoot in any of the derivatives.

Table 1. Displacement, Velocity, Acceleration, and Jerk for Some Cams*

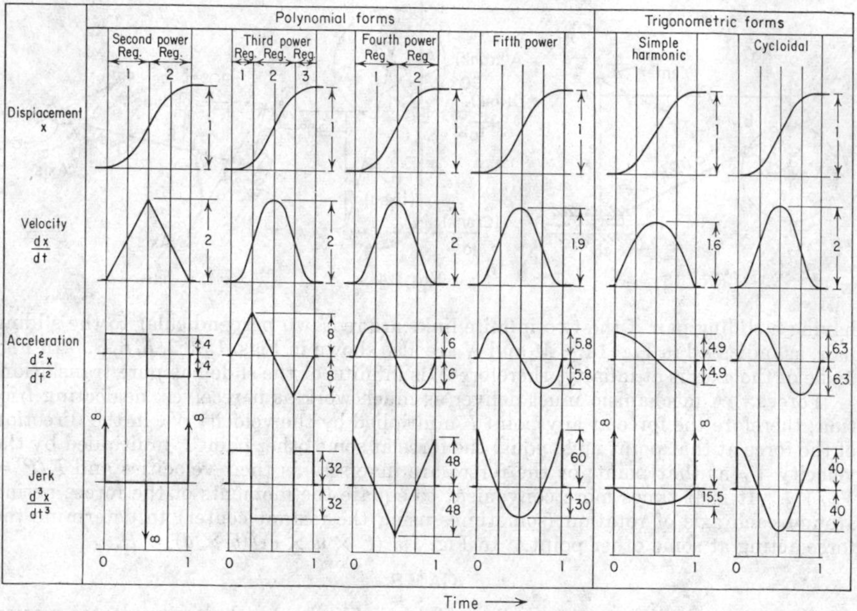

* Adapted from Gutman, *Machine Design*, March, 1951.

The three most common forms of motion used are uniform motion (Fig. 16), harmonic motion (Fig. 17), and uniformly accelerated and retarded motion (Fig. 18). In plotting the diagrams (Fig. 18) for this last motion, divide *ac* into an even number of equal parts and *bc* into the same number of parts with lengths increasing by a constant increment to a maximum and then decreasing by the same decrement, as, for example, 1, 3, 5, 5, 3, 1, or 1, 3, 5, 7, 9, 9, 7, 5, 3, 1. In order to prevent shock when the direction of motion changes, as at *a* and *b* in the uniform motion, the harmonic motion may be used; if the cam is to be operated at high speed, the uniformly accelerated and retarded motion should preferably be employed; in either case there is a very gradual change of velocity.

Pitch Line. The actual pitch line of a cam varies with the type of motion and with the position of the follower relative to the cam's axis. Most cams as ordinarily constructed are covered by the following four cases.

Follower on Line of Axis (Fig. 19). To draw the pitch line, subdivide the motion *bc* of the follower in the manner indicated in Figs. 16, 17, 18. Draw a circle with a radius equal to the smallest radius of the cam *a*0 and subdivide it into angles 0*a*1′, 0*a*2′, 0*a*3′, etc., corresponding with angular displacements of the cam for positions

1, 2, 3, etc., of the follower. With a as a center and radii $a1$, $a2$, $a3$, etc., strike arcs cutting radial lines at d, e, f, etc. Draw a smooth curve through points d, e, f, etc.

OFFSET FOLLOWER (Fig. 20). Divide bc as indicated in Figs. 16, 17, and 18. Draw a circle of radius ac (highest point of rise of follower) and one tangent to cb produced. Divide the outer circle into parts 1′, 2′, 3′, etc., corresponding with the angular displacement of the cam for positions 1, 2, 3, etc., of the follower, and draw tangents from points 1′, 2′, 3′, etc., to the small circle. With a as a center and radii $a1$, $a2$, $a3$, etc., strike arcs cutting tangents at d, e, f, etc. Draw a smooth curve through d, e, f, etc.

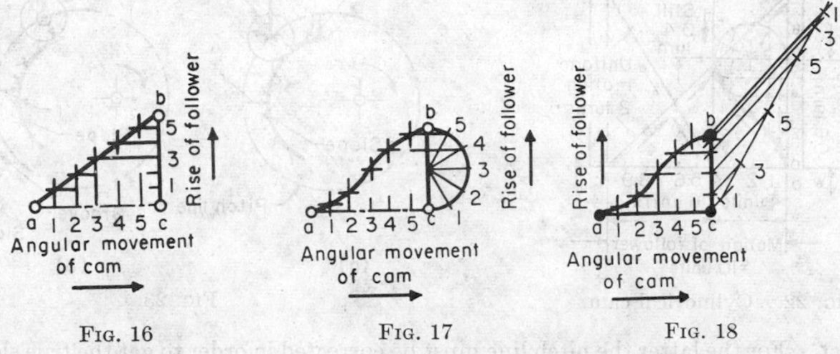

FIG. 16 FIG. 17 FIG. 18

ROCKER FOLLOWER (Fig. 21). Divide the stroke of the slide S in the manner indicated in Figs. 16, 17, and 18, and transfer these points to the arc bc as points 1, 2, 3, etc. Draw a circle of radius ak and divide it into parts 1′, 2′, 3′, etc., corresponding with angular displacements of the cam for positions 1, 2, 3, etc., of the follower. With k, 1′, 2′, 3′, etc., as centers and radius bk, strike arcs kb, $1'd$, $2'e$, $3'f$, etc., cutting at $bdef$ arcs struck with a as a center and radii ab, $a1$, $a2$, $a3$, etc. Draw a smooth curve through b, d, e, f, etc.

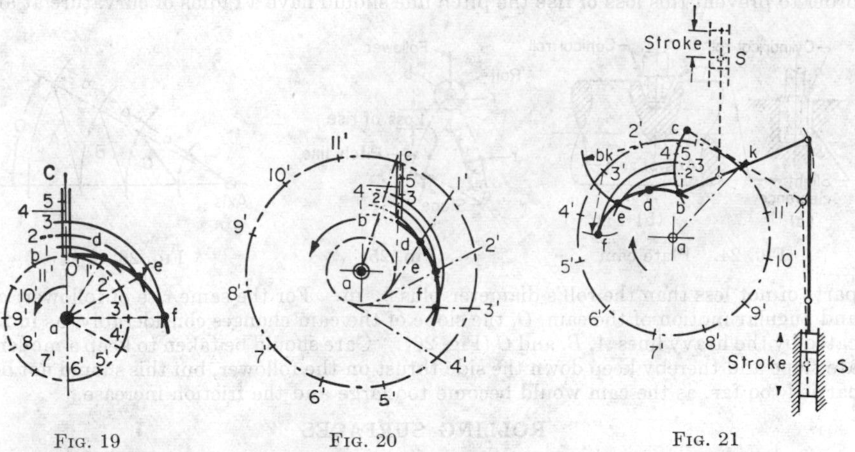

FIG. 19 FIG. 20 FIG. 21

CYLINDRICAL CAM (Fig. 22). In this type of cam more than one complete turn may be obtained, provided in all cases the follower returns to its starting point. Draw rectangle $wxyz$ (Fig. 22) representing the development of cylindrical surface of the cam. Subdivide the desired motion of the follower bc horizontally in the manner indicated in Figs. 16, 17, and 18, and plot the corresponding angular displacements 1′, 2′, 3′, etc., of the cam vertically; then through the intersection of lines from these points draw a smooth curve. This may best be shown by an example, assuming the following data for the diagram in Fig. 22: Total motion of follower $= bc$; circumference of cam $= 2\pi r$. Follower moves harmonically 4 units to right in 0.6 turn, then rests (or "dwells") 0.4 turn, and finishes with uniform motion 6 units to right and 10 units to left in two turns.

Cam Design. In the practical design of cams the following points must be noted. If only a small force is to be transmitted, sliding contact may be used, otherwise **rolling**

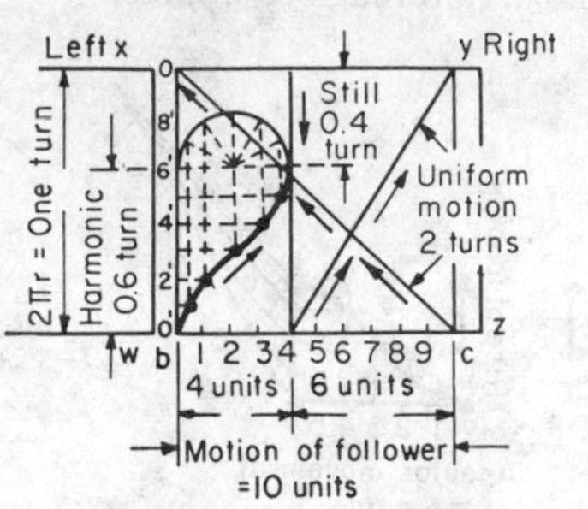

FIG. 22. Cylindrical cam.

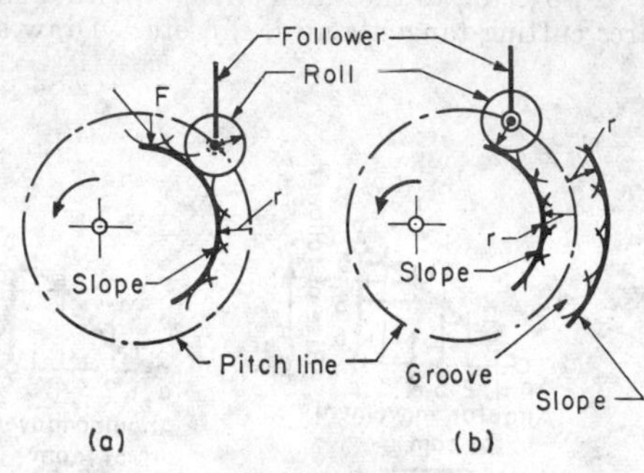

FIG. 23

contact. For the latter the pitch line must be corrected in order to get the true slope of the cam. An approximate construction (Fig. 23) may be employed by using the pitch line as the center of a series of arcs the radii of which are equal to that of the follower roll to be used; then a smooth curve drawn tangent to the arcs will give the slope desired for a roll working on the periphery of the cam [Fig. 23(*a*)] or in a groove [Fig. 23(*b*)]. For plate cams the roll should be a small cylinder, as in Fig. 24(*a*). In cylindrical cams it is usually sufficiently accurate to make the roll conical, as in Fig. 24(*b*), in which case the taper of the roll produced should intersect the axis of the cam. If the pitch line *abc* is made too sharp (Fig. 25) the follower will not rise the full amount. In order to prevent this **loss of rise** the pitch line should have a radius of curvature at all

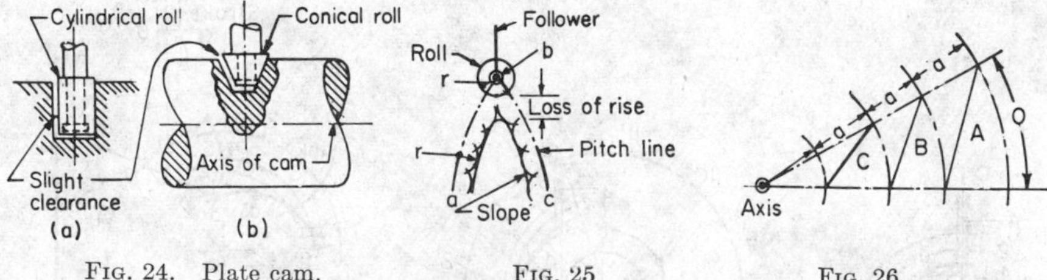

FIG. 24. Plate cam. FIG. 25 FIG. 26

parts of not less than the roll's diameter plus ⅛ in. For the same rise of follower, *a*, and angular motion of the cam, *O*, the slope of the cam changes considerably, as indicated by the heavy lines *A*, *B*, and *C* (Fig. 26). Care should be taken to keep a moderate slope and thereby keep down the side thrust on the follower, but this should not be carried too far, as the cam would become too large and the friction increase.

ROLLING SURFACES

In order to connect two shafts so that they shall have a definite angular velocity ratio, rolling surfaces are often used; and in order to have no slipping between the surfaces they must fulfill the following two conditions: the line of centers must pass through the point of contact, and the arcs of contact must be of equal length. The angular velocities, expressed usually in rpm, will be inversely proportional to the radii: $N/n = r/R$. The two surfaces most commonly used in practice, and the only ones having a constant angular velocity ratio, are cylinders where the shafts are parallel, and cones where the shafts (produced) intersect at an angle. In either case there are two possible directions of rotation, depending upon whether the surfaces roll in opposite directions (external contact) or in the same direction (internal contact). In Fig. 27,

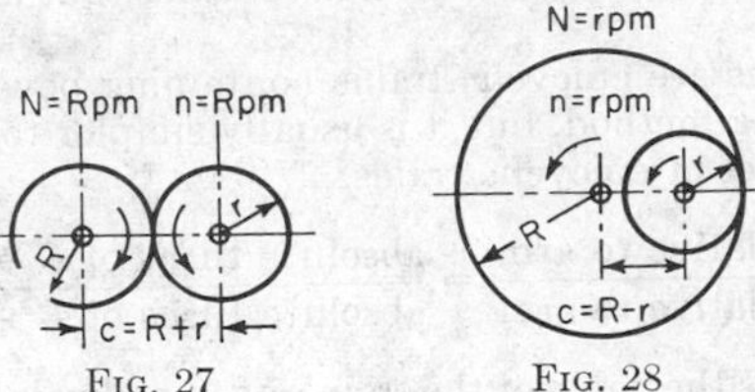

FIG. 27　FIG. 28

$R = nc/(N + n)$ and $r = Nc/(N + n)$; in Fig. 28, $R = nc/(N - n)$ and $r = Nc/(N - n)$. In Fig. 29, $\tan B = \sin A/[(n/N) + \cos A]$, and $\tan C = \sin A/[(N/n) + \cos A]$; in Fig. 30, $\tan B = \sin A/[(N/n) - \cos A]$, and $\tan C = \sin A/[(n/N) - \cos A]$. With the above values for the angles B and C, and the length d or e of one of the cones, R and r may be calculated.

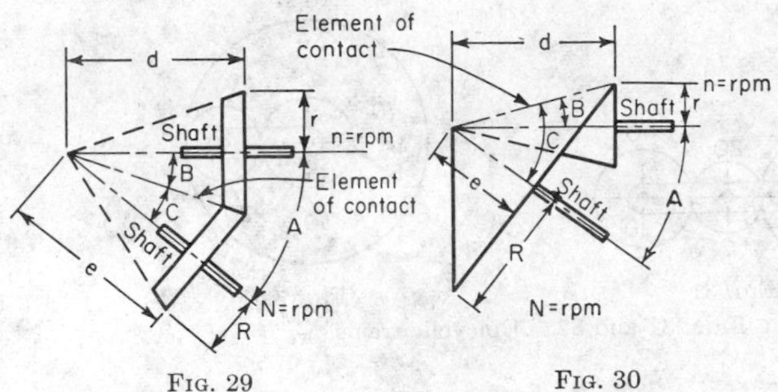

FIG. 29　FIG. 30

EPICYCLIC TRAINS

Epicyclic trains are combinations of gears in which some or all of the gears have a motion compounded of rotation about an axis and a translation or revolution of that axis. The gears are usually connected by a link called an arm, which often rotates about the axis of the first gear. Such trains may be calculated by first considering all gears locked and the arm turned; then the arm locked and the gears rotated. The algebraic sum of the separate motions will give the desired result. The following examples and method of tabulation will illustrate this. The figures on each gear refer to the number of teeth for that gear.

	A	*B*	*C*	*D*
Gear locked, Fig. 31	+1	+1	+1	+1
Arm locked, Fig. 31	0	−1	$+1 \times 50/20$	$-1 \times 50/20 \times 20/40$
Addition, Fig. 31	+1	0	+3½	−¼
Gears locked, Fig. 32	+1	+1	+1	+1
Arm locked, Fig. 32	0	−1	$+1 \times 30/20$	$+1 \times 30/20 \times 20/70$
Addition, Fig. 32	+1	0	+2½	+1 3/7

In Figs. 31 and 32 lock the gears and turn the arm A right-handed through 1 revolution (+1), then lock the arm and turn the gear B back to where it started (−1); gears C and D will have rotated the amount indicated in the tabulation. Then the algebraic sum will give the relative turns of each gear. That is, in Fig. 31, for one turn of the arm, B does not move and C turns in the same direction 3½ rev, and D in the opposite direction ¼ rev; whereas in Fig. 32, for one turn of the arm, B does not turn, but C and D turn in the same direction as the arm, respectively, 2½ and 1³⁄₇ rev. (NOTE. The arm in the above case was turned +1 for convenience, but any other value might be used.)

Bevel epicyclic trains are epicyclic trains containing bevel gears and may be calculated by the preceding method, but it is usually simpler to use the general formula which applies to all cases of epicyclic trains:

$$\frac{\text{Turns of } C \text{ relative to arm}}{\text{Turns of } B \text{ relative to arm}} = \frac{\text{absolute turns of } C - \text{turns of arm}}{\text{absolute turns of } B - \text{turns of arm}}$$

The left-hand term gives the value of the train and can always be expressed in terms of the number of teeth (T) on the gears. Care must be used, however, to express it as either plus (+) or minus (−), depending upon whether the gears turn in the same or opposite directions.

$$\frac{\text{Relative turns of } C}{\text{Relative turns of } B} = \frac{C - A}{B - A} = -1 \text{ (in Fig. 33)} = +\frac{T_E}{T_C} \times \frac{T_B}{T_D} \text{ (in Fig. 34)}$$

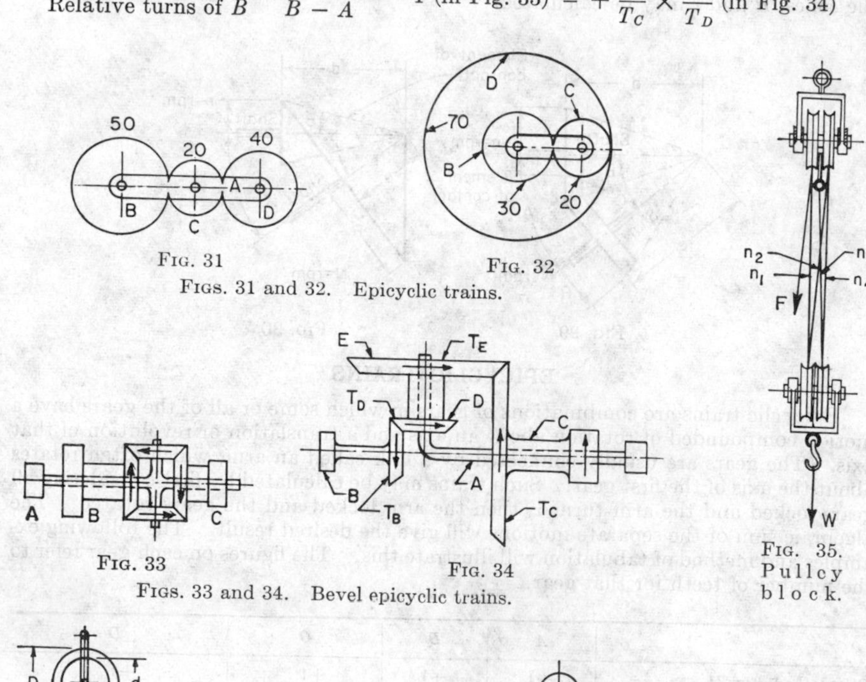

FIG. 31 FIG. 32

FIGS. 31 and 32. Epicyclic trains.

FIG. 33 FIG. 34

FIGS. 33 and 34. Bevel epicyclic trains.

FIG. 35. Pulley block.

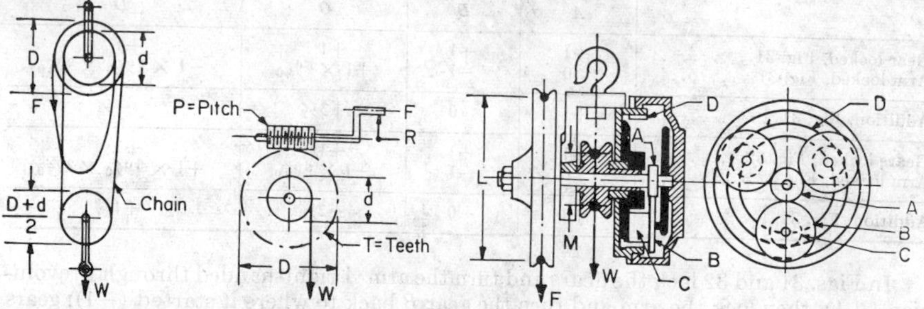

FIG. 36. Differential chain block.

FIG. 37. Worm and wheel.

FIG. 38. Triplex chain block.

HOISTING MECHANISMS

Pulley Block (Fig. 35). Given the weight W to be raised, the force F necessary is $F = V_W \times W/V_F = W/n$ = load/number of ropes; V_W and V_F being the respective velocities of W and F.

Differential Chain Block (Fig. 36). $F = V_W \times W/V_F = W(D - d)/2D$.

Worm and Wheel (Fig. 37). $F = \pi d(n/T)W/2\pi R = WP(d/D)/2\pi R$, where n = number of threads, single, double, triple, etc.

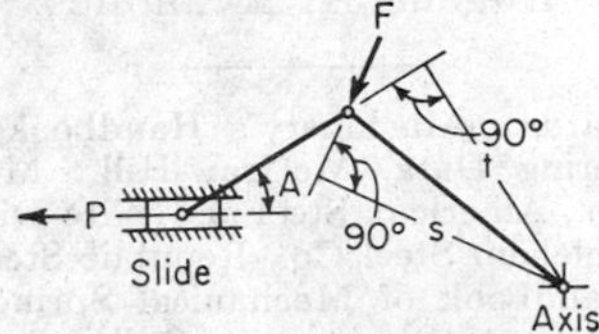

FIG. 39. Toggle joint.

The triplex chain block (Fig. 38) is a geared hoist making use of the epicyclic train. $W = F \times L/M\{1 + [(T_D/T_C) \times (T_B/T_A)]\}$, where T = number of teeth on gears.

Toggle Joint (Fig. 39). $P = F \times s \cos A/t$.

NEWTONIAN MECHANICS

For application of Newtonian mechanics, see "Vector Analysis," p. 2–97.

MACHINE ELEMENTS

BY

Eugene A. Avallone

References: ASA Standards. Machinery's Handbook, Industrial Press. Power's Manual of Practical Engineering Data, McGraw-Hill. Manufacturers' bulletins, *e.g.*, American Chain and Cable Co., American Steel and Wire Division of United States Steel Corp., Atlas Tack Corp., Bethlehem Steel Co., Republic Steel Corp., John A. Roebling's Sons Co., Townsend Co. Handbook of Mechanical Spring Design, Associated Spring Corp., Industrial Fasteners Institute Standards. Roller and Silent Chain Drives Assn. Design Manual. SAE Standards. French, "Engineering Drawing," McGraw-Hill. Maleev, "Machine Design," International Textbook. Kimball and Barr, "Elements of Machine Design," Wiley. Reuleaux, "The Constructor." Bach, "Die Maschinen Elemente," Kroener. Spotts, "Design of Machine Elements," Prentice-Hall. Peterson, "Stress Concentration Design Factors," Wiley.

SCREW FASTENINGS

By an accord signed in Washington, D.C., on Nov. 18, 1948, the screw-thread standardization committees of Canada, the United Kingdom, and the United States accepted a common standardization of screw threads for their respective countries and called it the **Unified Thread Standard.** This new standard is additional to and is not a substitute for the earlier American standards. It is based on the earlier standards and incorporates changes suggested from experience in the manufacture, assembly, and use of screw threads.

It is expected that the Unified screw threads will, in time, replace the American standard threads; to achieve this it is proposed that the Unified threads should be used wherever possible.

Unified and American Screw Threads for Bolts, Nuts, and Machine Screws

The new **Unified screw-thread standards** are published by the ASA as American Standard Unified and American Screw Thread Publication B1.1, 1949. The thread series referred to in this standard are groups of diameter-pitch combinations distinguished from each other by the number of threads used with each diameter in the series. There are six Standard series and three Special series. The latter should not be employed until use of the Standard series is proved impossible. Threads in the Unified and American standard which are common to the British and Canadian standards are known as Unified and carry the prefix letter "U" in the thread series symbol. Those without this prefix are American standard only. The Standard series and their suggested uses are as follows:

1. Coarse-thread Series (UNC and NC). For general use, especially where rapid assembly is required and for gray iron, soft metals, and plastics.

2. Fine-thread Series (UNF and NF). For applications requiring greater strength or where the length of engagement is limited.

3. Extra-fine-thread Series (UNEF and NEF). For highly stressed parts and where internal threads are required in thin-walled fasteners.

4. 8 Thread Series (8N). A substitute for the coarse-thread series for diameters larger than 1 in.

5. 12 Thread Series (12 UN and 12N). A continuation of the fine-thread series for diameters larger than 1½ in.

6. 16 Thread Series (16 UN and 16N). A continuation of the extra-fine-thread series for diameters larger than 2 in.

There are three **Special series: 8UN, UNS, and NS.**

The Unified and American screw-thread standard recognizes eight **thread classes** distinguished from each other by the amount of allowance and/or tolerance. **Classes 1A, 2A, and 3A** apply to external threads only, **Classes 1B, 2B, and 3B** apply to internal threads only, and **Classes 2 and 3,** which are used with American standard threads only, apply to both external and internal threads.

1. **Classes 1A and 1B** provided liberal allowance for ease of assembly even when threads are dirty or slightly damaged.
2. **Classes 2A and 2B.** For production of bolts, screws, nuts, and other commercial fasteners. Permits external threads to be plated.
3. **Classes 3A and 3B.** For close tolerance work where no allowance is required.
4. **Classes 2 and 3.** Retained as American standard, pending industry transition to the Unified classes.

The tolerances specified by each of these classes are based on a length of engagement equal to the nominal thread diameter.

The designation for a screw thread consists of a set of numbers and letter symbols which denote the diameter, pitch, thread series, class of fit, and hand as follows: **¼″-20 UNC-2A-LH**

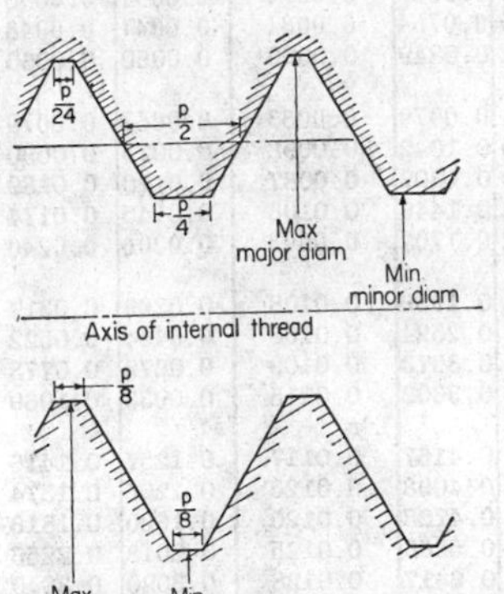

Fig. 1. Unified and American screw-thread forms.

¼″ = nominal size (fractional diameter or screw number)
20 = number of threads per inch
UNC = thread series symbol
2A = thread class symbol
LH = left hand (no symbol required for right-hand threads)

Tables 1 through 6 give the screw diameters, allowances, tolerances, and important areas for the six Standard series. The largest diameter of a screw thread is called the **major diameter,** and the smallest diameter is called the **minor diameter.** The **pitch diameter** is the diameter to an imaginary line drawn through the thread profile such that the widths of the thread and groove are equal. These terms apply to both internal and external threads. The maximum diameters of an external thread are equal to the basic diameters minus the allowance. For Class 3A threads the allowance is zero. The minimum diameters of an internal thread are equal to the basic diameters.

The minimum minor diameters of an external thread and the maximum major diameter of an internal thread are not specified, being determined by the crest of an unworn tool. The Unified and American screw-thread proportions are shown in Fig. 1.

American Standard Screw Threads for Bolts, Nuts, and Machine Screws

The **American standard thread** for machine screws, shown in Fig. 2, is proportioned by the formulas p = pitch = 1/number of threads per inch, and f = flat = $p/8$. The dimensions of American standard screw threads are published by the ASA as B1.1, 1935, and are based upon the earlier National screw-thread standard. The screw-thread profile is that previously known as the Sellers or U.S. standard. There are four thread series, as follows: coarse-thread, fine-thread, special-pitch, and 8, 12, and 16 pitch series. Four classes of fit are given, numbered **1 through 4.**

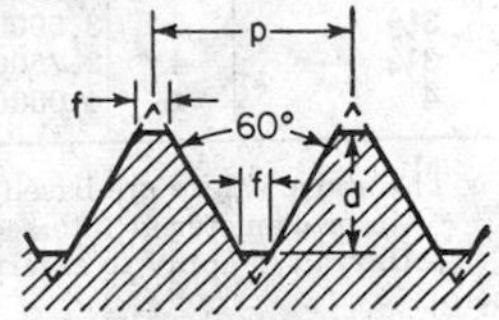

Fig. 2. American Standard screw threads.

Table 1. Coarse-thread Series—UNC and NC

(All dimensions in inches. Bold type indicates Unified threads.)

Identification		Screw basic diameters		External threads				Internal threads		Areas of sections	
Size	Threads per in., n	Major diam D* max	Pitch diam, E max	Basic minor diam, K_s	Allowances†, classes 1A and 2A	Class 1A, major diam tolerances‡	Class 2A and 3A, major diam tolerances‡	Minor diam, K_n min	Minor diam tolerances, classes 1B, 2B, and 3B§	Basic min minor diam, sq in.	Stress area, sq in.
1 (0.073)	64	0.0730	0.0629	0.0538	0.0006	......	0.0038	0.0561	0.0062	0.0022	0.0026
2 (0.086)	56	0.0860	0.0744	0.0641	0.0006	......	0.0041	0.0667	0.0070	0.0031	0.0036
3 (0.099)	48	0.0990	0.0855	0.0734	0.0007	......	0.0045	0.0764	0.0081	0.0041	0.0048
4 (0.112)	40	0.1120	0.0958	0.0813	0.0008	......	0.0051	0.0849	0.0090	0.0050	0.0060
5 (0.125)	40	0.1250	0.1088	0.0943	0.0008	......	0.0051	0.0979	0.0083	0.0067	0.0079
6 (0.138)	32	0.1380	0.1177	0.0997	0.0008	......	0.0060	0.1042	0.0098	0.0075	0.0090
8 (0.164)	32	0.1640	0.1437	0.1257	0.0009	......	0.0060	0.1302	0.0087	0.0120	0.0139
10 (0.190)	24	0.1900	0.1629	0.1389	0.0010	......	0.0072	0.1449	0.0106	0.0145	0.0174
12 (0.216)	24	0.2160	0.1889	0.1649	0.0010	......	0.0072	0.1709	0.0098	0.0206	0.0240
¼	20	0.2500	0.2175	0.1887	0.0011	0.0122	0.0081	0.1959	0.0108	0.0269	0.0317
5⁄16	18	0.3125	0.2764	0.2443	0.0012	0.0131	0.0087	0.2524	0.0106	0.0454	0.0522
⅜	16	0.3750	0.3344	0.2983	0.0013	0.0142	0.0094	0.3073	0.0109	0.0678	0.0773
7⁄16	14	0.4375	0.3911	0.3499	0.0014	0.0155	0.0103	0.3602	0.0115	0.0933	0.1060
½	13	0.5000	0.4500	0.4056	0.0015	0.0163	0.0109	0.4167	0.0117	0.1257	0.1416
½	12	0.5000	0.4459	0.3978	0.0015	0.0172	0.0114	0.4098	0.0125	0.1205	0.1374
9⁄16	12	0.5625	0.5084	0.4603	0.0016	0.0172	0.0114	0.4723	0.0120	0.1620	0.1816
⅝	11	0.6250	0.5660	0.5135	0.0016	0.0182	0.0121	0.5266	0.0125	0.2018	0.2256
¾	10	0.7500	0.6850	0.6273	0.0018	0.0194	0.0129	0.6417	0.0128	0.3020	0.3340
⅞	9	0.8750	0.8028	0.7387	0.0019	0.0208	0.0139	0.7547	0.0134	0.4193	0.4612
1	8	1.0000	0.9188	0.8466	0.0020	0.0225	0.0150	0.8647	0.0150	0.5510	0.6051
1⅛	7	1.1250	1.0322	0.9497	0.0022	0.0246	0.0164	0.9704	0.0171	0.6931	0.7627
1¼	7	1.2500	1.1572	1.0747	0.0022	0.0246	0.0164	1.0954	0.0171	0.8898	0.9684
1⅜	6	1.3750	1.2667	1.1705	0.0024	0.0273	0.0182	1.1946	0.0200	1.0541	1.1538
1½	6	1.5000	1.3917	1.2955	0.0024	0.0273	0.0182	1.3196	0.0200	1.2938	1.4041
1¾	5	1.7500	1.6201	1.5046	0.0027	0.0308	0.0205	1.5335	0.0240	1.7441	1.8983
2	4½	2.0000	1.8557	1.7274	0.0029	0.0330	0.0220	1.7594	0.0267	2.3001	2.4971
2¼	4½	2.2500	2.1057	1.9774	0.0029	0.0330	0.0220	2.0094	0.0267	3.0212	3.2464
2½	4	2.5000	2.3376	2.1933	0.0031	0.0357	0.0238	2.2294	0.0300	3.7161	3.9976
2¾	4	2.7500	2.5876	2.4433	0.0032	0.0357	0.0238	2.4794	0.0300	4.6194	4.9326
3	4	3.0000	2.8376	2.6933	0.0032	0.0357	0.0238	2.7294	0.0300	5.6209	5.9659
3¼	4	3.2500	3.0876	2.9433	0.0033	0.0357	0.0238	2.9794	0.0300	6.7205	7.0992
3½	4	3.5000	3.3376	3.1933	0.0033	0.0357	0.0238	3.2294	0.0300	7.9183	8.3268
3¾	4	3.7500	3.5876	3.4433	0.0034	0.0357	0.0238	3.4794	0.0300	9.2143	9.6546
4	4	4.0000	3.8376	3.6933	0.0034	0.0357	0.0238	3.7294	0.0300	10.6084	11.0805

The above values are based on a length of engagement equal to the nominal diameter.

* Major diameter at intersection of rounded root with flanks of threads.

† Allowances apply to external threads, Classes 1A and 2A only. The allowance for Class 3A threads is zero.

‡ Major diameter of internal threads may extend to a $P/24$ flat.

§ Minor diameter of external threads may extend to a $P/8$ flat.

Table 2. Fine-thread Series—UNF and NF

(All dimensions in inches. **Bold type indicates Unified threads.**)

Identification		Screw basic diameters		External threads				Internal threads		Areas of sections	
Size	Threads per in., n	Major diam, D* max	Pitch diam, E max	Basic minor diam, K_s	Allowances†, classes 1A and 2A	Class 1A, major diam tolerances‡	Class 2A and 3A, major diam tolerances‡	Minor diam, K_n min	Minor diam tolerances, classes 1B, 2B, and 3B§	Basic min minor diam, sq in.	Stress area, sq in.
0 (0.060)	80	0.0600	0.0519	0.0447	0.0005	......	0.0032	0.0465	0.0049	0.0015	0.0018
1 (0.073)	72	0.0730	0.0640	0.0560	0.0006	......	0.0035	0.0580	0.0055	0.0024	0.0027
2 (0.086)	64	0.0860	0.0759	0.0668	0.0006	......	0.0038	0.0691	0.0062	0.0034	0.0039
3 (0.099)	56	0.0990	0.0874	0.0771	0.0007	......	0.0041	0.0797	0.0068	0.0045	0.0052
4 (0.112)	48	0.1120	0.0985	0.0864	0.0007	......	0.0045	0.0894	0.0074	0.0057	0.0065
5 (0.125)	44	0.1250	0.1102	0.0971	0.0007	......	0.0048	0.1004	0.0075	0.0072	0.0082
6 (0.138)	40	0.1380	0.1218	0.1073	0.0008	......	0.0051	0.1109	0.0077	0.0087	0.0101
8 (0.164)	36	0.1640	0.1460	0.1299	0.0008	......	0.0055	0.1339	0.0077	0.0128	0.0146
10 (0.190)	**32**	**0.1900**	**0.1697**	**0.1517**	**0.0009**	......	**0.0060**	**0.1562**	**0.0079**	**0.0175**	**0.0199**
12 (0.216)	28	0.2160	0.1928	0.1722	0.0010	......	0.0065	0.1773	0.0084	0.0026	0.0257
¼	**28**	**0.2500**	**0.2268**	**0.2062**	**0.0010**	**0.0098**	**0.0065**	**0.2113**	**0.0077**	**0.0326**	**0.0362**
5/16	**24**	**0.3125**	**0.2854**	**0.2614**	**0.0011**	**0.0108**	**0.0072**	**0.2674**	**0.0080**	**0.0524**	**0.0579**
⅜	**24**	**0.3750**	**0.3479**	**0.3239**	**0.0011**	**0.0108**	**0.0072**	**0.3299**	**0.0073**	**0.0809**	**0.0876**
7/16	**20**	**0.4375**	**0.4050**	**0.3762**	**0.0013**	**0.0122**	**0.0081**	**0.3834**	**0.0082**	**0.1090**	**0.1185**
½	**20**	**0.5000**	**0.4675**	**0.4387**	**0.0013**	**0.0122**	**0.0081**	**0.4459**	**0.0078**	**0.1486**	**0.1597**
9/16	**18**	**0.5625**	**0.5264**	**0.4943**	**0.0014**	**0.0131**	**0.0087**	**0.5024**	**0.0082**	**0.1888**	**0.2026**
⅝	**18**	**0.6250**	**0.5889**	**0.5568**	**0.0014**	**0.0131**	**0.0087**	**0.5649**	**0.0081**	**0.2400**	**0.2555**
¾	**16**	**0.7500**	**0.7094**	**0.6733**	**0.0015**	**0.0142**	**0.0094**	**0.6823**	**0.0085**	**0.3513**	**0.3724**
⅞	**14**	**0.8750**	**0.8286**	**0.7874**	**0.0016**	**0.0155**	**0.0103**	**0.7977**	**0.0091**	**0.4805**	**0.5088**
1	**12**	**1.0000**	**0.9459**	**0.8978**	**0.0018**	**0.0172**	**0.0114**	**0.9098**	**0.0100**	**0.6245**	**0.6624**
1⅛	**12**	**1.1250**	**1.0709**	**1.0228**	**0.0018**	**0.0172**	**0.0114**	**1.0348**	**0.0100**	**0.8118**	**0.8549**
1¼	**12**	**1.2500**	**1.1959**	**1.1478**	**0.0018**	**0.0172**	**0.0114**	**1.1598**	**0.0100**	**1.0237**	**1.0721**
1⅜	**12**	**1.3750**	**1.3209**	**1.2728**	**0.0019**	**0.0172**	**0.0114**	**1.2848**	**0.0100**	**1.2602**	**1.3137**
1½	**12**	**1.5000**	**1.4459**	**1.3978**	**0.0019**	**0.0172**	**0.0114**	**1.4098**	**0.0100**	**1.5212**	**1.5799**

The above values are based on a length of engagement equal to the nominal diameter.

* Major diameter at intersection of rounded root with flanks of threads.

† Allowances apply to external threads, Classes 1A and 2A only. The allowance for Class 3A threads is zero.

‡ Major diameter of internal threads may extend to a $P/24$ flat.

§ Minor diameter of external threads may extend to a $P/8$ flat.

Table 3. Extra-fine-thread Series—UNEF and NEF

(All dimensions in inches. **Bold type indicates Unified threads.**)

Identification		Screw basic diameters		External threads				Internal threads		Areas of sections	
Size	Threads per in., *n*	Major diam, *D** max	Pitch diam, *E* max	Basic minor diam, K_s	Allowances†, classes 1A and 2A	Class 1A, major diam tolerances‡	Class 2A and 3A, major diam tolerances‡	Minor diam, K_n min	Minor diam tolerances, classes 1B, 2B, and 3B§	Basic min minor diam, sq in.	Stress area, sq in.
12 (0.216)	32	0.2160	0.1957	0.1777	0.0009	.....	0.0060	0.1822	0.0073	0.0242	0.2269
1/4	32	0.2500	0.2297	0.2117	0.0010	.....	0.0060	0.2162	0.0067	0.0344	0.0377
5/16	32	0.3125	0.2922	0.2742	0.0010	.....	0.0060	0.2787	0.0060	0.0581	0.0622
3/8	32	0.3750	0.3547	0.3367	0.0010	.....	0.0060	0.3412	0.0057	0.0878	0.0929
7/16	**28**	**0.4375**	**0.4143**	**0.3937**	**0.0011**	.....	**0.0065**	**0.3988**	**0.0063**	**0.1201**	**0.1270**
1/2	**28**	**0.5000**	**0.4768**	**0.4562**	**0.0011**	.....	**0.0065**	**0.4613**	**0.0063**	**0.1616**	**0.1695**
9/16	24	0.5625	0.5354	0.5114	0.0012	.....	0.0072	0.5174	0.0070	0.2030	0.2134
5/8	24	0.6250	0.5979	0.5739	0.0012	.....	0.0072	0.5799	0.0070	0.2560	0.2676
11/16	24	0.6875	0.6604	0.6364	0.0012	.....	0.0072	0.6424	0.0070	0.3151	0.3280
3/4	**20**	**0.7500**	**0.7175**	**0.6887**	**0.0013**	.....	**0.0081**	**0.6959**	**0.0078**	**0.3685**	**0.3855**
13/16	**20**	**0.8125**	**0.7800**	**0.7512**	**0.0013**	.....	**0.0081**	**0.7584**	**0.0078**	**0.4388**	**0.4573**
7/8	**20**	**0.8750**	**0.8425**	**0.8137**	**0.0013**	.....	**0.0081**	**0.8209**	**0.0078**	**0.5153**	**0.5352**
15/16	**20**	**0.9375**	**0.9050**	**0.8762**	**0.0014**	.....	**0.0081**	**0.8834**	**0.0078**	**0.5979**	**0.6194**
1	**20**	**1.0000**	**0.9675**	**0.9387**	**0.0014**	.....	**0.0081**	**0.9459**	**0.0078**	**0.6866**	**0.7095**
1 1/16	**18**	**1.0625**	**1.0264**	**0.9943**	**0.0014**	.....	**0.0087**	**1.0024**	**0.0081**	**0.7702**	**0.7973**
1 1/8	18	1.1250	1.0889	1.0568	0.0014	.....	0.0087	1.0649	0.0081	0.8705	0.8993
1 3/16	18	1.1875	1.1514	1.1193	0.0015	.....	0.0087	1.1274	0.0081	0.9770	1.0074
1 1/4	18	1.2500	1.2139	1.1818	0.0015	.....	0.0087	1.1899	0.0081	1.0895	1.1216
1 5/16	18	1.3125	1.2764	1.2443	0.0015	.....	0.0087	1.2524	0.0081	1.2082	1.2420
1 3/8	18	1.3750	1.3389	1.3068	0.0015	.....	0.0087	1.3149	0.0081	1.3330	1.3684
1 7/16	18	1.4375	1.4014	1.3693	0.0015	.....	0.0087	1.3774	0.0081	1.4640	1.5010
1 1/2	18	1.5000	1.4639	1.4318	0.0015	.....	0.0087	1.4399	0.0081	1.6011	1.6397
1 9/16	18	1.5625	1.5264	1.4943	0.0015	.....	0.0087	1.5024	0.0081	1.7444	1.7846
1 5/8	18	1.6250	1.5889	1.5568	0.0015	.....	0.0087	1.5649	0.0081	1.8937	1.9357
1 11/16	18	1.6875	1.6514	1.6193	0.0015	.....	0.0087	1.6274	0.0081	2.0493	2.0929
1 3/4	**16**	**1.7500**	**1.7094**	**1.6733**	**0.0016**	.....	**0.0094**	**1.6823**	**0.0085**	**2.2873**	**2.2382**
2	**16**	**2.000**	**1.9594**	**1.9233**	**0.0016**	.....	**0.0094**	**1.9323**	**0.0085**	**2.8917**	**2.9501**

The above values are based on a length of engagement equal to the nominal diameter.

* Major diameter at intersection of rounded root with flanks of threads.

† Allowances apply to external threads, Classes 1A and 2A only. The allowance for Class 3A threads is zero.

‡ Major diameter of internal threads may extend to a $P/24$ flat.

§ Minor diameter of external threads may extend to a $P/8$ flat.

Table 4. 8 Thread Series—8N

(All dimensions given in inches.)

Identification		Screw basic diameters		External threads				Internal threads		Areas of sections	
Size	Threads per in., n	Major diam, D* max	Pitch diam, E max	Basic minor diam, K_s	Allowances†, classes 1A and 2A	Class 1A, major diam tolerances‡	Class 2A and 3A, major diam tolerances‡	Minor diam, K_n min	Minor diam tolerances, classes 1B, 2B, and 3B§	Basic min minor diam, sq in.	Stress area, sq in.
1⅛	8	1.1250	1.0438	0.9716	0.0021	......	0.0150	0.9897	0.0150	0.7277	0.7896
1¼	8	1.2500	1.1688	1.0966	0.0021	......	0.0150	1.1147	0.0150	0.9290	0.9985
1⅜	8	1.3750	1.2938	1.2216	0.0022	......	0.0150	1.2397	0.0150	1.1548	1.2319
1½	8	1.5000	1.4188	1.3466	0.0022	......	0.0150	1.3647	0.0150	1.4052	1.4899
1⅝	8	1.6250	1.5438	1.4716	0.0022	......	0.0150	1.4897	0.0150	1.6801	1.7723
1¾	8	1.7500	1.6688	1.5966	0.0023	......	0.0150	1.6147	0.0150	1.9796	2.0792
1⅞	8	1.8750	1.7938	1.7216	0.0023	......	0.0150	1.7397	0.0150	2.3036	2.4107
2	8	2.0000	1.9188	1.8466	0.0023	......	0.0150	1.8647	0.0150	2.6521	2.7665
2⅛	8	2.1250	2.0438	1.9716	0.0024	......	0.0150	1.9897	0.0150	3.0252	3.1469
2¼	8	2.2500	2.1688	2.0966	0.0024	......	0.0150	2.1147	0.0150	3.4228	3.5519
2½	8	2.5000	2.4188	2.3466	0.0024	......	0.0150	2.3647	0.0150	4.2917	4.4352
2¾	8	2.7500	2.6688	2.5966	0.0025	......	0.0150	2.6147	0.0150	5.2588	5.4164
3	8	3.0000	2.9188	2.8466	0.0026	......	0.0150	2.8647	0.0150	6.3240	6.4957
3¼	8	3.2500	3.1688	3.0966	0.0026	......	0.0150	3.1147	0.0150	7.4874	7.6738
3½	8	3.5000	3.4188	3.3466	0.0026	......	0.0150	3.3647	0.0150	8.7490	8.9504
3¾	8	3.7500	3.6688	3.5966	0.0027	......	0.0150	3.6147	0.0150	10.1088	10.3249
4	8	4.0000	3.9188	3.8466	0.0027	......	0.0150	3.8647	0.0150	11.5667	11.7995
4¼	8	4.2500	4.1688	4.0966	0.0028	......	0.0150	4.1147	0.0150	13.1228	13.3683
4½	8	4.5000	4.4188	3.3466	0.0028	......	0.0150	4.3647	0.0150	14.7771	15.0372
4¾	8	4.7500	4.6688	4.5966	0.0029	......	0.0150	4.6147	0.0150	16.5295	16.8042
5	8	5.0000	4.9188	4.8466	0.0029	......	0.0150	4.8647	0.0150	18.3802	18.6694
5¼	8	5.2500	5.1688	5.0966	0.0029	......	0.0150	5.1147	0.0150	20.3290	20.6330
5½	8	5.5000	5.4188	5.3466	0.0030	......	0.0150	5.3647	0.0150	22.3760	22.6945
5¾	8	5.7500	5.6688	5.5966	0.0030	......	0.0150	5.6147	0.0150	24.5211	24.8541
6	8	6.0000	5.9188	5.8466	0.0030	......	0.0150	5.8647	0.0150	26.7645	27.1118

The above values are based on a length of engagement equal to the nominal diameter.

* Major diameter at intersection of rounded root with flanks of threads.

† Allowances apply to external threads, Classes 1A and 2A only. The allowance for Class 3A threads is zero.

‡ Major diameter of internal threads may extend to a $P/24$ flat.

§ Minor diameter of external threads may extend to a $P/8$ flat.

Table 5. 12 Thread Series—12UN and 12N

(All dimensions in inches. **Bold type indicates Unified threads.**)

Identification		Screw basic diameters		External threads				Internal threads		Areas of sections	
Size	Threads per in., n	Major diam, D* max	Pitch diam, E max	Basic minor diam, K_s	Allowances†, classes 1A and 2A	Class 1A, major diam tolerances‡	Class 2A and 3A, major diam tolerances‡	Minor diam, K_n, min	Minor diam tolerances, classes 1B, 2B, and 3B§	Basic min minor diam, sq in.	Stress area, sq in.
½	12	0.5000	0.4459	0.3978	0.0016	......	0.0114	0.4098	0.0127	0.1205	0.1374
⅝	12	0.6250	0.5709	0.5228	0.0016	......	0.0114	0.5348	0.0115	0.2097	0.2319
11/16	12	0.6875	0.6334	0.5853	0.0016	......	0.0114	0.5973	0.0112	0.2635	0.2883
¾	12	0.7500	0.6959	0.6478	0.0017	......	0.0114	0.6598	0.0109	0.3234	0.3508
13/16	12	0.8125	0.7584	0.7103	0.0017	......	0.0114	0.7223	0.0106	0.3895	0.4195
⅞	12	0.8750	0.8209	0.7728	0.0017	......	0.0114	0.7848	0.0108	0.4617	0.4943
15/16	12	0.9375	0.8834	0.8353	0.0017	......	0.0114	0.8743	0.0090	0.5000	0.5753
1 1/16	12	1.0625	1.0084	0.9603	0.0017	......	0.0114	0.9723	0.0100	0.7151	0.7556
1 3/16	12	1.1875	1.1334	1.0853	0.0017	......	0.0114	1.0973	0.0100	0.9147	0.9604
1 5/16	12	1.3125	1.2584	1.2103	0.0017	......	0.0114	1.2223	0.0100	1.1389	1.1898
1 7/16	12	1.4375	1.3834	1.3353	0.0018	......	0.0114	1.3473	0.0100	1.3876	1.4438
1⅝	12	1.6250	1.5709	1.5228	0.0018	......	0.0114	1.5348	0.0100	1.8067	1.8701
1¾	12	1.7500	1.6959	1.6418	0.0018	......	0.0114	1.6598	0.0100	2.1168	2.1853
1⅞	12	1.8750	1.8209	1.7728	0.0018	......	0.0114	1.7848	0.0100	2.4514	2.5250
2	12	2.0000	1.9459	1.8978	0.0018	......	0.0114	1.9098	0.0100	2.8106	2.8892
2⅛	12	2.1250	2.0709	2.0228	0.0018	......	0.0114	2.0348	0.0100	3.1943	3.2779
2¼	12	2.2500	2.1959	2.1478	0.0018	......	0.0114	2.1598	0.0100	3.6025	3.6914
2⅜	12	2.3750	2.3209	2.2728	0.0019	......	0.0114	2.2848	0.0100	4.0353	4.1291
2½	12	2.5000	2.4459	2.3978	0.0019	......	0.0114	2.4098	0.0100	4.4927	4.5916
2⅝	12	2.6250	2.5709	2.5228	0.0019	......	0.0114	2.5348	0.0100	4.9745	5.0784
2¾	12	2.7500	2.6959	2.6478	0.0019	......	0.0114	2.6598	0.0100	5.4810	5.5900
2⅞	12	2.8750	2.8209	2.7728	0.0019	......	0.0114	2.7848	0.0100	6.0119	6.1259
3	12	3.0000	2.9459	2.8978	0.0019	......	0.0114	2.9098	0.0100	6.5674	6.6865
3⅛	12	3.1250	3.0709	3.0228	0.0019	......	0.0114	3.0348	0.0100	7.1475	7.2714
3¼	12	3.2500	3.1959	3.1478	0.0019	......	0.0114	3.1598	0.0100	7.7521	7.8812
3⅜	12	3.3750	3.3209	3.2728	0.0019	......	0.0114	3.2848	0.0100	8.3812	8.5152
3½	12	3.5000	3.4459	3.3978	0.0019	......	0.0114	3.4098	0.0100	9.0349	9.1740
3⅝	12	3.6250	3.5709	5.5228	0.0019	......	0.0114	3.5348	0.0100	9.7132	9.8570
3¾	12	3.7500	3.6959	3.6478	0.0019	......	0.0114	3.6598	0.1000	10.4159	10.4649
3⅞	12	3.8750	3.8209	3.7728	0.0020	......	0.0114	3.7848	0.0100	11.1433	11.2970
4	12	4.0000	3.9459	3.8978	0.0020	......	0.0114	3.9098	0.0100	11.8951	12.0540
4¼	12	4.2500	4.1959	4.1478	0.0020	......	0.0114	4.1598	0.0100	13.4725	13.6411
4½	12	4.5000	4.4459	4.3918	0.0020	......	0.0114	4.4098	0.0100	15.1480	15.3265
4¾	12	4.7500	4.6959	4.6478	0.0020	......	0.0114	4.6598	0.0100	16.9217	17.1099
5	12	5.0000	4.9459	4.8978	0.0020	......	0.0114	4.9098	0.0100	18.7936	18.9916
5¼	12	5.2500	5.1959	5.1478	0.0020	......	0.0114	5.1598	0.0100	20.7636	20.9717
5½	12	5.5000	5.4459	5.3978	0.0020	......	0.0114	5.4098	0.0100	22.8319	23.0496
5¾	12	5.7500	5.6959	5.6478	0.0021	......	0.0114	5.6598	0.0100	24.9983	25.2257
6	12	6.0000	5.9459	5.8978	0.0021	......	0.0014	5.9098	0.0100	27.2628	27.4988

The above values are based on a length of engagement equal to the nominal diameter.

* Major diameter at intersection of rounded root with flanks of threads.

† Allowances apply to external threads, Classes 1A and 2A only. The allowance for Class 3A threads is zero.

‡ Major diameter of internal threads may extend to a $P/24$ flat.

§ Minor diameter of external threads may extend to a $P/8$ flat.

Table 6. 16 Thread Series—16UN and 16N

(All dimensions in inches. **Bold type indicates Unified threads.**)

Identification		Screw basic diameters		External threads				Internal threads		Areas of sections	
Size	Threads per in., n	Major diam, D* max	Pitch diam, E max	Basic minor diam, K_s	Allowances†, classes 1A and 2A	Class 1A, major diam tolerances‡	Class 2A and 3A, major diam tolerances‡	Minor diam, K_n min	Minor diam tolerances, classes 1B, 2B, and 3B§	Basic min minor diam, sq in.	Stress area, sq in.
13/16	**16**	**0.8125**	**0.7719**	**0.7358**	**0.0015**	......	**0.0094**	**0.7448**	**0.0085**	**0.4200**	**0.4429**
7/8	**16**	**0.8750**	**0.8344**	**0.7983**	**0.0015**	......	**0.0094**	**0.8073**	**0.0085**	**0.4949**	**0.5197**
15/16	**16**	**0.9375**	**0.8969**	**0.8608**	**0.0015**	......	**0.0094**	**0.8698**	**0.0085**	**0.5759**	**0.6025**
1	**16**	**1.0000**	**0.9594**	**0.9233**	**0.0015**	......	**0.0094**	**0.9323**	**0.0085**	**0.6630**	**0.6916**
1 1/16	**16**	**1.0625**	**1.0219**	**0.0958**	**0.0015**	......	**0.0094**	**0.9948**	**0.0085**	**0.7563**	**0.7867**
1 1/8	**16**	**1.1250**	**1.0844**	**1.0483**	**0.0015**	......	**0.0094**	**1.0573**	**0.0085**	**0.8557**	**0.8880**
1 3/16	**16**	**1.1875**	**1.1469**	**1.1108**	**0.0015**	......	**0.0094**	**1.1198**	**0.0085**	**0.9612**	**0.9955**
1 1/4	**16**	**1.2500**	**1.2094**	**1.1733**	**0.0015**	......	**0.0094**	**1.1823**	**0.0085**	**1.0729**	**1.1090**
1 5/16	**16**	**1.3125**	**1.2719**	**1.2358**	**0.0015**	......	**0.0094**	**1.2448**	**0.0085**	**1.1907**	**1.2287**
1 3/8	**16**	**1.3750**	**1.3344**	**1.2983**	**0.0015**	......	**0.0094**	**1.3073**	**0.0085**	**1.3147**	**1.3545**
1 7/16	**16**	**1.4375**	**1.3969**	**1.3608**	**0.0016**	......	**0.0094**	**1.3698**	**0.0085**	**1.4448**	**1.4865**
1 1/2	**16**	**1.5000**	**1.4594**	**1.4233**	**0.0016**	......	**0.0094**	**1.4323**	**0.0085**	**1.5810**	**1.6246**
1 9/16	16	1.5625	1.5219	1.4858	0.0016	......	0.0094	1.4948	0.0085	1.7234	1.7687
1 5/8	16	1.6250	1.5844	1.5483	0.0016	......	0.0094	1.5573	0.0085	1.8719	1.9191
1 11/16	16	1.6875	1.6469	1.6108	0.0016	......	0.0094	1.6198	0.0085	2.0265	2.0757
1 13/16	16	1.8125	1.7719	1.7358	0.0016	......	0.0094	1.7448	0.0085	2.3542	2.4070
1 7/8	16	1.8750	1.8344	1.7983	0.0016	......	0.0094	1.8073	0.0085	2.5272	2.5819
1 15/16	16	1.9375	1.8969	1.8608	0.0016	......	0.0094	1.8698	0.0085	2.7062	2.7269
2 1/16	16	2.0625	2.0219	1.9858	0.0016	......	0.0094	1.9948	0.0085	3.0831	3.1434
2 1/8	16	2.1250	2.0844	2.0483	0.0016	......	0.0094	2.0573	0.0085	3.2807	3.3427
2 3/16	16	2.1875	2.1469	2.1108	0.0016	......	0.0094	2.1198	0.0085	3.4844	3.5483
2 1/4	**16**	**2.2500**	**2.2094**	**2.1733**	**0.0016**	......	**0.0094**	**2.1823**	**0.0085**	**3.6943**	**3.7601**
2 5/16	16	2.3125	2.2719	2.2358	0.0017	......	0.0094	2.2448	0.0085	3.9103	3.9708
2 3/8	16	2.3750	2.3344	2.2983	0.0017	......	0.0094	2.3073	0.0085	4.1324	4.2018
2 7/16	16	2.4375	2.3969	2.3608	0.0017	......	0.0094	2.3696	0.0085	4.3606	4.4319
2 1/2	**16**	**2.5000**	**2.4594**	**2.4233**	**0.0017**	......	**0.0094**	**2.4323**	**0.0085**	**4.4950**	**4.6682**
2 5/8	16	2.6250	2.5844	2.5483	0.0017	......	0.0094	2.5573	0.0085	5.0822	5.1790
2 3/4	**16**	**2.7500**	**2.7094**	**2.6733**	**0.0017**	......	**0.0094**	**2.6823**	**0.0085**	**5.5940**	**5.6745**
2 7/8	16	2.8750	2.8344	2.7983	0.0017	......	0.0094	2.8073	0.0085	6.1303	6.2143
3	**16**	**3.0000**	**2.9594**	**2.9233**	**0.0017**	......	**0.0094**	**2.9323**	**0.0085**	**6.6911**	**6.7789**
3 1/8	16	3.1250	3.0844	3.0483	0.0017	......	0.0094	3.0573	0.0085	7.2765	7.3678
3 1/4	**16**	**3.2500**	**3.2094**	**3.1733**	**0.0017**	......	**0.0094**	**3.1823**	**0.0085**	**7.8864**	**7.9814**
3 3/8	16	3.3750	3.3344	3.2983	0.0017	......	0.0094	3.3073	0.0085	8.5209	8.6194
3 1/2	**16**	**3.5000**	**3.4594**	**3.4233**	**0.0017**	......	**0.0094**	**3.4323**	**0.0085**	**9.1799**	**9.2821**
3 5/8	16	3.6250	3.5844	3.5483	0.0017	......	0.0094	3.5573	0.0085	9.8634	9.9691
3 3/4	**16**	**3.7500**	**3.7094**	**3.6733**	**0.0017**	......	**0.0094**	**3.6823**	**0.0085**	**10.5715**	**10.6809**
3 7/8	16	3.8750	3.8344	3.7983	0.0018	......	0.0094	3.8073	0.0085	11.3042	11.4170
4	**16**	**4.0000**	**3.9594**	**3.9233**	**0.0018**	......	**0.0094**	**3.9323**	**0.0085**	**12.0614**	**12.1779**
4 1/4	**16**	**4.2500**	**4.2094**	**4.1733**	**0.0018**	......	**0.0094**	**4.1823**	**0.0085**	**13.6494**	**13.7730**
4 1/2	**16**	**4.5000**	**4.4594**	**4.4233**	**0.0018**	......	**0.0094**	**4.4323**	**0.0085**	**15.3355**	**15.4662**
4 3/4	**16**	**4.7500**	**4.7094**	**4.6733**	**0.0018**	......	**0.0094**	**4.6823**	**0.0085**	**17.1199**	**12.2575**
5	**16**	**5.0000**	**4.9594**	**4.9233**	**0.0018**	......	**0.0094**	**4.9323**	**0.0085**	**19.0024**	**19.1470**
5 1/4	**16**	**5.2500**	**5.2094**	**5.1733**	**0.0018**	......	**0.0094**	**5.1823**	**0.0085**	**20.9831**	**31.1350**
5 1/2	**16**	**5.5000**	**5.4538**	**5.4233**	**0.0018**	......	**0.0094**	**5.4323**	**0.0085**	**23.0620**	**23.2208**
5 3/4	**16**	**5.7500**	**5.7094**	**5.6733**	**0.0019**	......	**0.0094**	**5.6823**	**0.0085**	**25.2390**	**25.4047**
6	**16**	**6.0000**	**5.9594**	**5.9233**	**0.0019**	......	**0.0094**	**5.9323**	**0.0085**	**27.5142**	**27.6868**

The above values are based on a length of engagement equal to the nominal diameter.

* Major diameter at intersection of rounded root with flanks of threads.

† Allowances apply to external threads, Classes 1A and 2A only. The allowance for Class 3A threads is zero.

‡ Major diameter of internal threads may extend to a $P/24$ flat.

§ Minor diameter of external threads may extend to a $P/8$ flat.

Foreign Standard Screw Threads for Bolts, Nuts, and Machine Screws; Forms and Proportions

The **Whitworth Standard Thread** (Fig. 3) is used in Great Britain and is based on the formulas $d = 0.6403p$, $r = \text{radius} = 0.1373p$ (see Table 7).

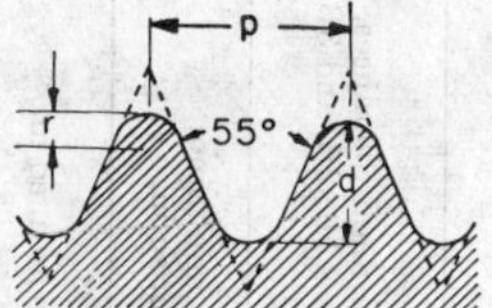

FIG. 3. Whitworth screw thread.

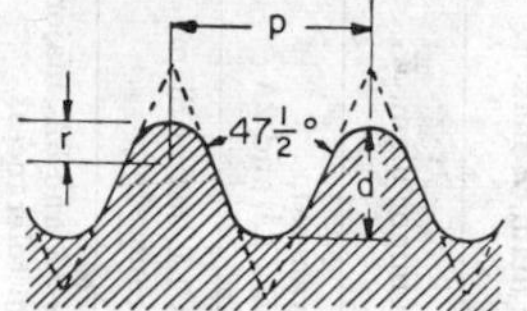

FIG. 4. British Association screw thread.

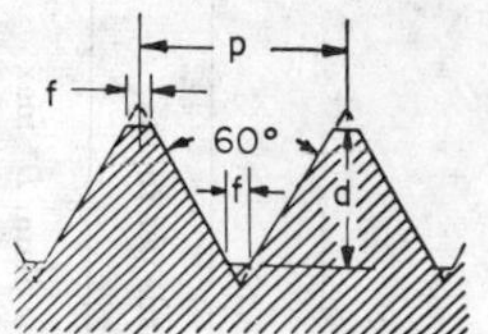

FIG. 5. Metric screw thread.

Table 7. Whitworth Standard Screw Threads

(See Fig. 3)

Diam of screw, in.	Threads per in.	Depth of thread, in.	Diam at root of thread, in.	Diam of screw, in.	Threads per in.	Depth of thread, in.	Diam at root of thread, in.
¼	20	0.0320	0.1860	1⅝	5	0.1281	1.3689
5⁄16	18	0.0356	0.2414	1¾	5	0.1281	1.4939
⅜	16	0.0400	0.2950	2	4½	0.1423	1.7154
7⁄16	14	0.0457	0.3460	2¼	4	0.1601	1.9298
½	12	0.0534	0.3933	2½	4	0.1601	2.1798
9⁄16	12	0.0534	0.4558	2¾	3½	0.1830	2.3841
⅝	11	0.0582	0.5086	3	3½	0.1830	2.6341
11⁄16	11	0.0582	0.5711	3¼	3¼	0.1970	2.8560
¾	10	0.0640	0.6219	3½	3¼	0.1970	3.1060
13⁄16	10	0.0640	0.6844	3¾	3	0.2134	3.3231
⅞	9	0.0711	0.7327	4	3	0.2134	3.5731
1	8	0.0800	0.8399	4½	2⅞	0.2227	4.0546
1⅛	7	0.0915	0.9420	5	2¾	0.2328	4.5343
1¼	7	0.0915	1.0670	5½	2⅝	0.2439	5.0121
1⅜	6	0.1067	1.1616	6	2½	0.2561	5.4877
1½	6	0.1067	1.2866				

The **British Association screw-thread** (Fig. 4) dimensions are given in Table 8.

Table 8. British Association Screw Threads

(See Fig. 4)

Number	Diam of screw, mm	Approx diam, in.	Pitch, mm	Approx pitch, in.	Diam at root of thread, mm	Number	Diam of screw, mm	Approx diam, in.	Pitch, mm	Approx pitch, in.	Diam at root of thread, mm
0	6.0	0.236	1.00	0.0394	4.8	13	1.20	0.047	0.25	0.0098	0.90
1	5.3	0.209	0.90	0.0354	4.22	14	1.00	0.039	0.23	0.0091	0.72
2	4.7	0.185	0.81	0.0319	3.73	15	0.90	0.035	0.21	0.0083	0.65
3	4.1	0.161	0.73	0.0287	3.22	16	0.79	0.031	0.19	0.0075	0.56
4	3.6	0.142	0.66	0.0260	2.81	17	0.70	0.028	0.17	0.0067	0.50
5	3.2	0.126	0.59	0.0232	2.49	18	0.62	0.024	0.15	0.0059	0.44
6	2.8	0.110	0.53	0.0209	2.16	19	0.54	0.021	0.14	0.0055	0.37
7	2.5	0.098	0.48	0.0189	1.92	20	0.48	0.019	0.12	0.0047	0.34
8	2.2	0.087	0.43	0.0169	1.68	21	0.42	0.017	0.11	0.0043	0.29
9	1.9	0.075	0.39	0.0154	1.43	22	0.37	0.015	0.10	0.0039	0.25
10	1.7	0.067	0.35	0.0138	1.28	23	0.33	0.013	0.09	0.0035	0.22
11	1.5	0.059	0.31	0.0122	1.13	24	0.29	0.011	0.08	0.0031	0.19
12	1.3	0.051	0.28	0.0110	0.96	25	0.25	0.10	0.07	0.0028	0.17

The **French (metric) screw thread** (Fig. 5) is based on the formulas p = pitch, mm, $d = 0.6495p$, and $f = p/8$ (see Table 9).

Table 9. Metric Standard Screw Threads
(See Fig. 5)

Nominal diam, mm	Pitch, mm: French std	Pitch, mm: German and Swiss std	Pitch diam, mm	Root diam, mm	Nominal diam, mm	Pitch, mm: French std	Pitch, mm: German and Swiss std	Pitch diam, mm	Root diam, mm
2	0.40	0.40	1.740	1.48	24	3.00	3.00	22.051	20.10
3	....	0.50	2.675	2.35	26	3.00	....	24.051	22.10
3	0.60	....	2.610	2.22	28	3.00	....	26.051	24.10
4	....	0.70	3.545	3.09	30	3.50	3.50	27.727	25.45
4	0.75	....	3.513	3.03	32	3.50	....	29.727	27.45
5	....	0.80	4.480	3.96	34	3.50	....	31.727	29.45
5	0.90	....	4.415	3.83	36	4.00	4.00	33.402	30.80
10	1.50	1.50	9.026	8.05	38	4.00	....	35.402	32.80
12	1.50	....	11.026	10.05	40	4.00	....	37.402	34.80
12	....	1.75	10.863	9.73	42	4.50	4.50	39.077	36.15
14	2.00	2.00	12.701	11.40	44	4.50	....	41.077	38.15
16	2.00	2.00	14.701	13.40	46	4.50	....	43.077	40.15
18	2.50	2.50	16.376	14.75	48	5.00	....	44.752	41.50
20	2.50	2.50	18.376	16.75	50	5.00	....	46.752	43.50
22	2.50	2.50	20.376	18.75					

International (metric) standard screw thread, as adopted by the "Congrés internationale pour l'unification des filetages," in Zurich, Oct. 24, 1898, is shown in Fig. 6, in which $d = 0.7036p$ and $t = 0.866p$ (see Table 10).

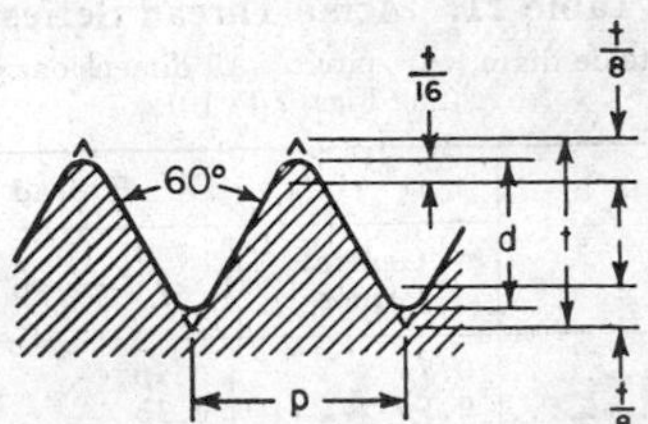

Fig. 6. International screw thread.

Table 10. International Standard Metric Screw Threads
(See Fig. 6)

Diam of screw, mm	Pitch, mm	Diam of screw, mm	Pitch, mm	Diam of screw, mm	Pitch, mm	Diam of screw, mm	Pitch, mm	Diam of screw, mm	Pitch, mm	Diam of screw, mm	Pitch, mm
6	1.00	12	1.75	24	3.00	42	4.50	64	6.00	96	8.00
7	1.00	14	2.00	27	3.00	45	4.50	68	6.00	116	9.00
8	1.25	16	2.00	30	3.50	48	5.00	72	6.50	136	10.00
9	1.25	18	2.50	33	3.50	52	5.00	76	6.50		
10	1.50	20	2.50	36	4.00	56	5.50	80	7.00		
11	1.50	22	2.50	39	4.00	60	5.50	88	7.50		

Power-transmission Screw Threads: Forms and Proportions

The **Acme thread** is obtained in four series (ASA B1.5 and B1.8):

The **general-purpose thread** (Fig. 7) is used for all Acme thread applications except in special design cases. The general dimensions are given in Table 11.

The **29 deg stub thread** (Fig. 8) is used where heavy loads are encountered and where space limitations or other economic considerations make a shallow thread desirable (see Table 11).

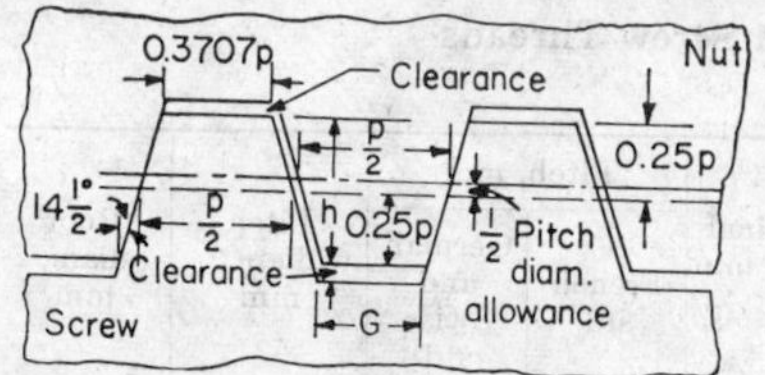

FIG. 7. General-purpose thread.

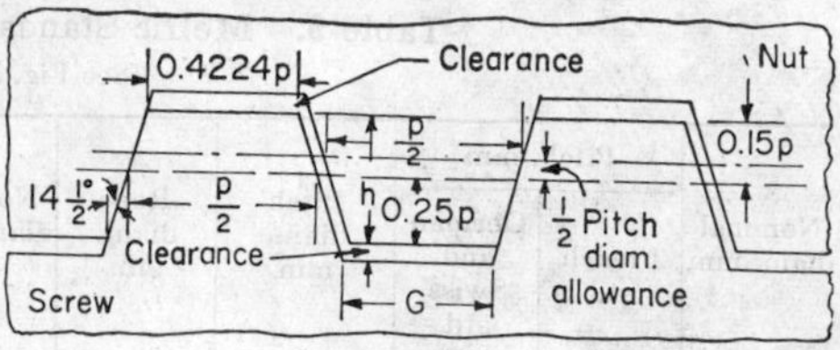

FIG. 8. 29 deg stub thread.

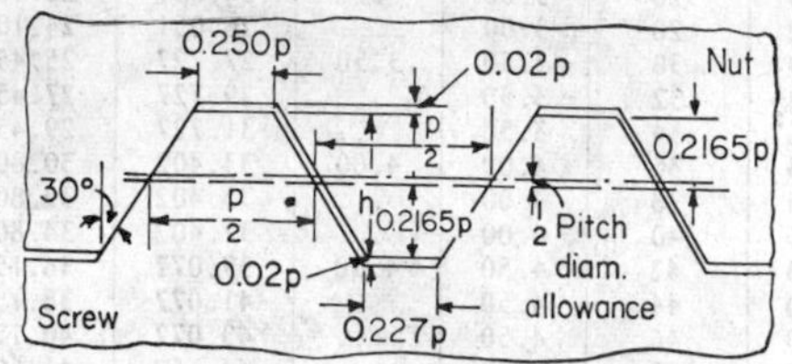

FIG. 9. 60 deg stub thread.

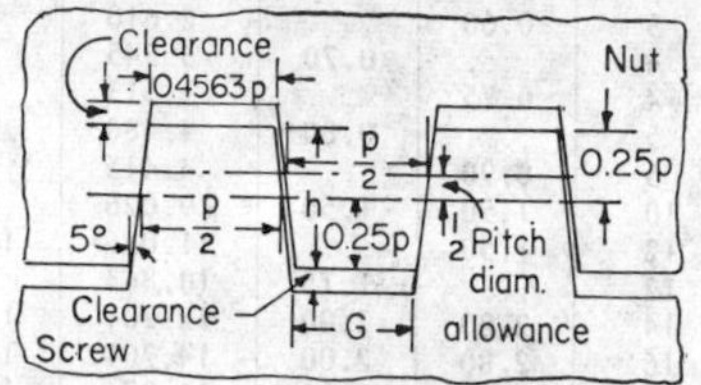

FIG. 10. 10 deg modified square thread.

Standard Acme Threads

The **60 deg stub thread** (Fig. 9) is used in special applications in the machine-tool industry (see Table 11).

The **10 deg modified square thread** (Fig. 10) is equivalent to a "square thread" for all practical purposes.

Table 11. Acme Thread Series

(D = outside diam, p = pitch. All dimensions in inches)
(See Figs. 7 to 10)

Symbols	Thread dimensions			
	General purpose	29 deg stub	60 deg stub	10 deg modified
t = thickness of thread	$0.5p$	$0.5p$	$0.5p$	$0.5p$
R = basic depth of thread	$0.5p$	$0.3p$	$0.433p$	$0.5p$*
F = basic width of flat	$0.3707p$	$0.4224p$	$0.250p$	$0.4563p$†
G = (see Figs. 7, 8, 10)	$F - (0.52 \times$ clearance)	$F - (0.52 \times$ clearance)	$0.227p$	$F - (0.17 \times$ clearance)
E = basic pitch diam	$D - 0.5p$	$D - 0.3p$	$D - 0.433p$	$D - 0.5p$
K = basic minor diam	$D - p$	$D - 0.6p$	$D - 0.866p$	$D - p$

* A clearance of at least 0.010 in. is added to h on threads of 10-pitch and coarser, and 0.005 in. on finer pitches, to produce extra depth, thus avoiding interference with threads of mating parts at minor or major diameters.

† Measured at crest of screw thread.

The range of threads per inch is as follows: general-purpose threads, 16 to 1; 29 deg stub thread, 16 to 2; 60 deg stub thread, 16 to 4.

The number of threads per inch diameter is not standardized. The usual values are given in Table 12.

Table 12. Acme Thread Diameter-pitch Combinations

(See Figs. 7 to 10)

Size	Threads per in.	Size	Threads per in.	Size	Threads per in.	Size	Threads per in.	Size	Threads per in.
1/4	16	5/8	8	1 1/4	5	2 1/4	3	4	2
5/16	14	3/4	6	1 3/8	4	2 1/2	3	4 1/2	2
3/8	12	7/8	6	1 1/2	4	2 3/4	3	5	2
7/16	12	1	5	1 3/4	4	3	2		
1/2	10	1 1/8	5	2	4	3 1/2	2		

American Standard Screw Threads for High-strength Bolting. These threads are used with pressure vessels, steel pipe flanges, fittings, valves, and other services. They can be applied to either hot or cold surfaces where high tensile stresses are produced when the joints are made up. For sizes 1 in. and smaller, the ASA coarse-thread series is used. For larger sizes, ASA 8 pitch thread series is used (see Table 13).

Table 13. Screw Threads for High-strength Bolting

(All dimensions in inches)

Size	Threads per in.	Allowance (minus)	Major diam	Major diam tolerance	Max pitch diam*	Max pitch diam tolerance	Minor diam max	Nut max minor diam	Nut max minor diam tolerance	Nut max pitch diam*	Nut max pitch diam tolerance
1/4	20	0.0010	0.2490	0.0072	0.2165	0.0026	0.1877	0.2060	0.0101	0.2211	0.0036
5/16	18	0.0011	0.3114	0.0082	0.2753	0.0030	0.2432	0.2630	0.0106	0.2805	0.0041
3/8	16	0.0013	0.3737	0.0090	0.3331	0.0032	0.2990	0.3184	0.0111	0.3389	0.0045
7/16	14	0.0013	0.4362	0.0098	0.3898	0.0036	0.3486	0.3721	0.0119	0.3960	0.0049
1/2	13	0.0015	0.4985	0.0104	0.4485	0.0037	0.4041	0.4290	0.0123	0.4552	0.0052
9/16	12	0.0016	0.5609	0.0112	0.5068	0.0040	0.4587	0.4850	0.0127	0.5140	0.0056
5/8	11	0.0017	0.6233	0.0118	0.5643	0.0042	0.5118	0.5397	0.0131	0.5719	0.0059
3/4	10	0.0019	0.7481	0.0128	0.6831	0.0045	0.6254	0.6553	0.0136	0.6914	0.0064
7/8	9	0.0021	0.8729	0.0140	0.8007	0.0049	0.7366	0.7689	0.0142	0.8098	0.0070
1	8	0.0022	0.9978	0.0152	0.9166	0.0054	0.8444	0.8795	0.0148	0.9264	0.0076
1 1/8	8	0.0024	1.1226	0.0152	1.0414	0.0055	0.9692	1.0045	0.0148	1.0517	0.0079
1 1/4	8	0.0025	1.2475	0.0152	1.1663	0.0058	1.0941	1.1295	0.0148	1.1771	0.0083
1 3/8	8	0.0025	1.3725	0.0152	1.2913	0.0061	1.2191	1.2545	0.0148	1.3024	0.0086
1 1/2	8	0.0027	1.4973	0.0152	1.4161	0.0063	1.3439	1.3795	0.0148	1.4278	0.0090
1 5/8	8	0.0028	1.6222	0.0152	1.5410	0.0065	1.4688	1.5045	0.0148	1.5531	0.0093
1 3/4	8	0.0029	1.7471	0.0152	1.6659	0.0068	1.5937	1.6295	0.0148	1.6785	0.0097
1 7/8	8	0.0030	1.8720	0.0152	1.7908	0.0070	1.7186	1.7545	0.0148	1.8038	0.0100
2	8	0.0031	1.9969	0.0152	1.9157	0.0073	1.8435	1.8795	0.0148	1.9294	0.0104
2 1/8	8	0.0032	2.1218	0.0152	2.0406	0.0075	1.9682	2.0045	0.0148	2.0545	0.0107
2 1/4	8	0.0033	2.2467	0.0152	2.1655	0.0077	2.0933	2.1295	0.0148	2.1798	0.0110
2 1/2	8	0.0035	2.4965	0.0152	2.4153	0.0082	2.3431	2.3795	0.0148	2.4305	0.0117
2 3/4	8	0.0037	2.7463	0.0152	2.6651	0.0087	2.5929	2.6295	0.0148	2.6812	0.0124
3	8	0.0038	2.9962	0.0152	2.9150	0.0092	2.8428	2.8795	0.0148	2.9318	0.0130
3 1/4	8	0.0039	3.2461	0.0152	3.1649	0.0093	3.0927	3.1295	0.0148	3.1820	0.0132
3 1/2	8	0.0040	3.4960	0.0152	3.4148	0.0093	3.3426	3.3795	0.0148	3.4321	0.0133

The American standard form of thread shall be used. Pitch diameter tolerances include errors of lead and angle.

* The maximum pitch diameters of screws are smaller than the minimum pitch diameters of nuts by these amounts.

Screw Threads for Pipes

American Standard Taper Pipe Thread, ASA B2.1, is shown in Fig. 11 and is made to the following specifications: The taper is 1 in. in 16 or 0.75 in. per ft. The basic length of the effective external taper thread is determined by $L_2 = p(0.8D + 6.8)$ where D is the basic outside diameter of the pipe (see Table 14).

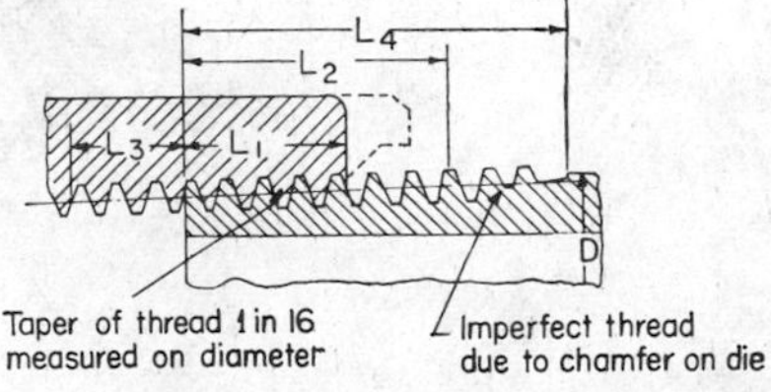

Fig. 11. American standard taper pipe thread.

Table 14. ASA Taper Pipe Thread

(All dimensions in inches)
(See Fig. 11)

Nominal pipe size	O.D. of pipe	Threads per in.	Pitch of thread	Hand-tight engagement length, L_1	Effective thread external length, L_2	Wrench make-up length for internal thread length, L_3	Over-all length external thread, L_4
1/16	0.3125	27	0.03704	0.160	0.2611	0.1111	0.3896
1/8	0.405	27	0.03704	0.180	0.2639	0.1111	0.3924
1/4	0.540	18	0.05556	0.200	0.4018	0.1667	0.5946
3/8	0.675	18	0.05556	0.240	0.4078	0.1667	0.6006
1/2	0.840	14	0.07143	0.320	0.5337	0.2143	0.7815
3/4	1.050	14	0.07143	0.339	0.5457	0.2143	0.7935
1	1.315	11½	0.08696	0.400	0.6828	0.2609	0.9845
1¼	1.660	11½	0.08696	0.420	0.7068	0.2609	1.0085
1½	1.900	11½	0.08696	0.420	0.7235	0.2609	1.0252
2	2.375	11½	0.08696	0.436	0.7565	0.2609	1.0582
2½	2.875	8	0.12500	0.682	1.1375	0.2500	1.5712
3	3.500	8	0.12500	0.766	1.2000	0.2500	1.6337
3½	4.000	8	0.12500	0.821	1.2500	0.2500	1.6837
4	4.500	8	0.12500	0.844	1.3000	0.2500	1.7337
5	5.563	8	0.12500	0.937	1.4063	0.2500	1.8400
6	6.625	8	0.12500	0.958	1.5125	0.2500	1.9462
8	8.625	8	0.12500	1.063	1.7125	0.2500	2.1462
10	10.750	8	0.12500	1.210	1.9250	0.2500	2.3587
12	12.750	8	0.12500	1.360	2.1250	0.2500	2.5587
14 O.D.	14.000	8	0.12500	1.562	2.2500	0.2500	2.6837
16 O.D.	16.000	8	0.12500	1.812	2.4500	0.2500	2.8837
18 O.D.	18.000	8	0.12500	2.000	2.6500	0.2500	3.0837
20 O.D.	20.000	8	0.12500	2.125	2.8500	0.2500	3.2837
24 O.D.	24.000	8	0.12500	2.375	3.2500	0.2500	3.6837

American Standard Straight Pipe Thread. There are certain types of joints where straight pipe threads can be used to advantage. The ASA has adopted five types of joints, the pertinent dimensions of which are shown in Table 15: (1) pressuretight joints with sealer, for pipe couplings, Cols. 3 and 4; (2) pressuretight joints without sealer, for drain plugs, filler plugs, etc., Cols. 5 and 6; (3) free-fitting mechanical joints for fixtures, Cols. 7 to 10; (4) loose-fitting mechanical joints with lock nuts, Cols. 11 to 14; (5) loose-fitting mechanical joints for hose couplings, Cols. 11 to 14.

Table 15. American Standard Straight Pipe Threads

(All dimensions in inches)

Nominal pipe size	Threads per in.	Pressure-tight with seals		Pressure-tight without seals		Free-fitting				Loose-fitting			
						External		Internal		External		Internal	
		Pitch diam, max	Minor diam, min	Pitch diam, max	Minor diam, min	Pitch diam, max	Major diam, max	Pitch diam, max	Minor diam, min	Pitch diam, max	Major diam, max	Pitch diam, max	Minor diam, min
(1)	(2)	(3)	(4)	(5)	(6)	(7)	(8)	(9)	(10)	(11)	(12)	(13)	(14)
1/16	27	......	......	0.2812	0.2491								
1/8	27	0.3782	0.342	0.3736	0.3415	0.3748	0.399	0.3783	0.350	0.3840	0.409	0.3898	0.362
1/4	18	0.4951	0.440	0.4916	0.4435	0.4899	0.527	0.4951	0.453	0.5038	0.541	0.5125	0.470
3/8	18	0.6322	0.577	0.6270	0.5789	0.6270	0.664	0.6322	0.590	0.6409	0.678	0.6496	0.607
1/2	14	0.7851	0.715	0.7784	0.7150	0.7784	0.826	0.7851	0.731	0.7963	0.844	0.8075	0.753
3/4	14	0.9956	0.925	0.9889	0.9255	0.9889	1.036	0.9956	0.941	1.0067	1.054	1.0179	0.964
1	11½	1.2468	1.161	1.2386	1.1621	1.2386	1.296	1.2468	1.181	1.2604	1.318	1.2739	1.208
1¼	11½	1.5915	1.506	......	......	1.5834	1.641	1.5916	1.526	1.6051	1.663	1.6187	1.553
1½	11½	1.8305	1.745	......	......	1.8223	1.880	1.8305	1.764	1.8441	1.902	1.8576	1.692
2	11½	2.3044	2.219	......	......	2.2963	2.354	2.3044	2.238	2.3180	2.376	2.3315	2.265
2½	8	2.7739	2.650	......	......	2.7622	2.846	2.7739	2.679	2.7934	2.877	2.8129	2.718
3	8	3.4002	3.277	......	......	3.3885	3.472	3.4002	3.305	3.4198	3.503	3.4393	3.344
3½	8	3.9005	3.777	......	......	3.8888	3.972	3.9005	3.806	3.9201	4.003	3.9396	3.845
4	8	4.3988	4.275	......	......	4.3871	4.470	4.3988	4.304	4.4184	4.502	4.4379	4.343
5	8	......	......	......	......	5.4493	5.533	5.4610	5.366	5.4805	5.564	5.5001	5.405
6	8	......	......	......	......	6.5060	6.589	6.5177	6.423	6.5372	6.620	6.5567	6.462
8	8	......	......	......	......	......	......	......	......	8.5313	8.615	8.5508	8.456
10	8	......	......	......	......	......	......	......	......	10.6522	10.735	10.6717	10.577
12	8	......	......	......	......	......	......	......	......	12.6491	12.732	12.6686	12.574

American Standard Dryseal Pipe Threads. In some instances, especially in automotive work, pipe threads which can be made up without lubricant or sealer are desirable. This series fills that requirement and has the same general form as the Standard Taper threads, except that the form is truncated as shown in Fig. 12, and further that, in Fig. 11, $L_4 = L_2 + 1$. There is no clearance between external and internal threads when the joint is made up; thus the flanks and flats meet, forming a metal-to-metal joint. A lubricant may be used to prevent galling (see Table 16).

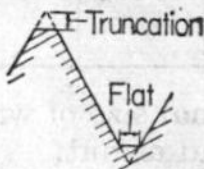

FIG. 12. American standard dryseal pipe threads.

Table 16. American Standard Dryseal Pipe Threads

(See Fig. 12)

Threads per in., n	Truncation, in.		Width of flat	
	Min	Max	Min	Max
27 Crest	$0.047p$	$0.094p$	$0.054p$	$0.108p$
Root	$0.094p$	$0.140p$	$0.108p$	$0.162p$
18 C	$0.047p$	$0.078p$	$0.054p$	$0.090p$
R	$0.078p$	$0.109p$	$0.090p$	$0.126p$
14 C	$0.036p$	$0.060p$	$0.042p$	$0.070p$
R	$0.060p$	$0.085p$	$0.070p$	$0.098p$
11½ C	$0.040p$	$0.060p$	$0.046p$	$0.069p$
R	$0.060p$	$0.090p$	$0.069p$	$0.103p$
8 C	$0.042p$	$0.055p$	$0.048p$	$0.064p$
R	$0.055p$	$0.076p$	$0.064p$	$0.088p$

Table 17. Pipe-thread Tap-drill Sizes, In.

Nominal pipe size	Taper thread	Straight thread
1/16	0.250	0.250
1/8	21/64	11/32
1/4	27/64	7/16
3/8	9/16	37/64
1/2	11/16	23/32
3/4	57/64	59/64
1	1 1/8	1 5/32
1 1/4	1 15/32	1 1/2
1 1/2	1 23/32	1 3/4
2	2 3/16	2 7/32
2 1/2	2 19/32	2 21/32

Wrench boltheads, nuts, and wrench openings have been standardized by the ASA B18.2. The wrench openings are given in Table 18.

Table 18. Wrench Boltheads, Nuts, and Wrench Openings

(All dimensions in inches)

Basic or max width across flats, boltheads and nuts	Wrench openings		Basic or max width across flats, boltheads, and nuts	Wrench openings		Basic or max width across flats, boltheads, and nuts	Wrench openings		Basic or max width across flats, boltheads, and nuts	Wrench openings	
	Max	Min		Max	Min		Max	Min		Max	Min
5/32	0.163	0.158	13/16	0.826	0.818	1 13/16	1.835	1.822	3	3.035	3.016
3/16	0.195	0.190	7/8	0.888	0.880	1 7/8	1.898	1.885	3 1/8	3.162	3.142
1/4	0.257	0.252	15/16	0.953	0.944	2	2.025	2.011	3 3/8	3.414	3.393
5/16	0.322	0.316	1	1.015	1.006	2 1/16	2.088	2.074	3 1/2	3.540	3.518
11/32	0.353	0.347	1 1/16	1.077	1.068	2 3/16	2.225	2.200	3 3/4	3.793	3.770
3/8	0.384	0.378	1 1/8	1.142	1.132	2 1/4	2.277	2.262	3 7/8	3.918	3.895
7/16	0.446	0.440	1 1/4	1.267	1.257	2 3/8	2.404	2.388	4 1/8	4.172	4.147
1/2	0.510	0.504	1 5/16	1.331	1.320	2 7/16	2.466	2.450	4 1/4	4.297	4.272
9/16	0.573	0.566	1 3/8	1.394	1.383	2 9/16	2.593	2.576	4 1/2	4.550	4.524
19/32	0.605	0.598	1 7/16	1.457	1.446	2 5/8	2.656	2.639	4 5/8	4.676	4.649
5/8	0.636	0.629	1 1/2	1.520	1.508	2 3/4	2.783	2.766	5	5.055	5.026
11/16	0.699	0.692	1 5/8	1.646	1.634	2 13/16	2.845	2.827	5 3/8	5.434	5.403
3/4	0.763	0.755	1 11/16	1.708	1.696	2 15/16	2.973	2.954	5 3/4	5.813	5.780
25/32	0.794	0.786							6 1/8	6.192	6.157

Wrenches shall be marked with the "nominal size of wrench" which is equal to the basic or maximum width across flats of the corresponding bolthead or nut.

Allowance (min clearance) between maximum width across flats of nut or bolthead and jaws of wrench equals $(1.005W + 0.001)$. Tolerance on wrench opening equals plus $(0.005W + 0.004)$ from minimum (W equals nominal size of wrench).

Boltheads and nuts have been standardized so as to fit the wrench sizes. These standards are given in ASA B18.2. The pertinent information is given in Table 19.

Table 19. Width across Flats of Boltheads and Nuts

(All dimensions in inches)

Nominal size or basic major diam of thread	Dimensions of regular boltheads unfinished, square, and hexagon		Dimensions of heavy boltheads unfinished, square, and hexagon		Dimensions of cap-screw heads hexagon		Dimensions of setscrew heads		Dimensions of regular nuts and regular jam nuts, unfinished, square, and hexagon (jam nuts, hexagon only)		Dimensions of machine-screw and stove-bolt nuts, square and hexagon		Dimensions of heavy nuts and heavy jam nuts, unfinished, square, and hexagon (jam nuts, hexagon only)	
	Max	Min	Max	Min	Max	Min	Max	Min	Max	Min	Max	Min	Max	Min
No. 0	.....	.....	.....	.....	.....	.....	.....	.....	.....	.....	0.1562	0.150		
No. 1	.....	.....	.....	.....	.....	.....	.....	.....	.....	.....	0.1562	0.150		
No. 2	.....	.....	.....	.....	.....	.....	.....	.....	.....	.....	0.1875	0.180		
No. 3	.....	.....	.....	.....	.....	.....	.....	.....	.....	.....	0.1875	0.180		
No. 4	.....	.....	.....	.....	.....	.....	.....	.....	.....	.....	0.2500	0.241		
No. 5	.....	.....	.....	.....	.....	.....	.....	.....	.....	.....	0.3125	0.302		
No. 6	.....	.....	.....	.....	.....	.....	.....	.....	.....	.....	0.3125	0.302		
No. 8	.....	.....	.....	.....	.....	.....	.....	.....	.....	.....	0.3438	0.332		
No. 10	.....	.....	.....	.....	.....	.....	.....	.....	.....	.....	0.3750	0.362		
No. 12	.....	.....	.....	.....	.....	.....	.....	.....	.....	.....	0.4375	0.423		
1/4	0.3750	0.362	.....	.....	0.4375	0.428	0.2500	0.241	0.4375	0.425	0.4375	0.423	0.5000	0.488
5/16	0.5000	0.484	.....	.....	0.5000	0.489	0.3125	0.302	0.5625	0.547	0.5625	0.545	0.5938	0.578
3/8	0.5625	0.544	.....	.....	0.5625	0.551	0.3750	0.362	0.6250	0.606	0.6250	0.607	0.6875	0.669
7/16	0.6250	0.603	.....	.....	0.6250	0.612	0.4375	0.423	0.7500	0.728	.....	.....	0.7812	0.759
1/2	0.7500	0.725	0.8750	0.850	0.7500	0.736	0.5000	0.484	0.8125	0.788	.....	.....	0.8750	0.850
9/16	0.8750	0.847	0.9375	0.909	0.8125	0.798	0.5625	0.545	0.8750	0.847	.....	.....	0.9375	0.909
5/8	0.9375	0.906	1.0625	1.031	0.8750	0.860	0.6250	0.606	1.0000	0.969	.....	.....	1.0625	1.031
3/4	1.1250	1.088	1.2500	1.212	1.0000	0.983	0.7500	0.729	1.1250	1.088	.....	.....	1.2500	1.212
7/8	1.3125	1.269	1.4375	1.394	1.1250	1.106	0.8750	0.852	1.3125	1.269	.....	.....	1.4375	1.394
1	1.5000	1.450	1.6250	1.575	1.3125	1.292	1.0000	0.974	1.5000	1.450	.....	.....	1.6250	1.575
1 1/8	1.6875	1.631	1.8125	1.756	1.5000	1.477	1.1250	1.096	1.6875	1.631	.....	.....	1.8125	1.756
1 1/4	1.8750	1.812	2.0000	1.938	1.6875	1.663	1.2500	1.219	1.8750	1.812	.....	.....	2.0000	1.938
1 3/8	2.0625	1.994	2.1857	2.119	.....	.....	1.3750	1.342	2.0625	1.994	.....	.....	2.1875	2.119
1 1/2	2.2500	2.175	2.3750	2.300	.....	.....	1.5000	1.464	2.2500	2.175	.....	.....	2.3750	2.300
1 5/8	2.4375	2.356	2.5625	2.481	.....	.....	.....	.....	2.4375	2.356	.....	.....	2.5625	2.481
1 3/4	2.6250	2.538	2.7500	2.662	.....	.....	.....	.....	2.6250	2.538	.....	.....	2.7500	2.662
1 7/8	2.8125	2.719	2.9375	2.844	.....	.....	.....	.....	2.8125	2.719	.....	.....	2.9375	2.844
2	3.0000	2.900	3.1250	3.025	.....	.....	.....	.....	3.0000	2.900	.....	.....	3.1250	3.025
2 1/4	3.3750	3.262	3.5000	3.388	.....	.....	.....	.....	3.3750	3.262	.....	.....	3.5000	3.388
2 1/2	3.7500	3.625	3.8750	3.750	.....	.....	.....	.....	3.7500	3.625	.....	.....	3.8750	3.750
2 3/4	4.1250	3.988	4.2500	4.112	.....	.....	.....	.....	4.1250	3.988	.....	.....	4.2500	4.112
3	4.5000	4.350	4.6250	4.475	.....	.....	.....	.....	4.5000	4.350	.....	.....	4.6250	4.475
3 1/4	.....	.....	.....	.....	.....	.....	.....	.....	.....	.....	.....	.....	5.0000	4.838
3 1/2	.....	.....	.....	.....	.....	.....	.....	.....	.....	.....	.....	.....	5.3750	5.200
3 3/4	.....	.....	.....	.....	.....	.....	.....	.....	.....	.....	.....	.....	5.7500	5.562
4	.....	.....	.....	.....	.....	.....	.....	.....	.....	.....	.....	.....	6.1250	5.925

Regular boltheads are for general use. Unfinished boltheads are not finished on any surface. Semifinished boltheads are finished under head.

Regular nuts are for general use. Semifinished nuts are finished on bearing surface and threaded. Unfinished nuts are not finished on any surface but are threaded.

Machine Screws

Machine screws are defined according to head types as follows:

Flat Head. This screw has a flat surface for the top of the head with a countersink angle of 82 deg. It is standard for machine screws, cap screws, and wood screws.

Round Head. This screw has a semielliptical-shaped head and is standard for machine screws, cap screws, and wood screws except that for the cap screw it is called *button head.*

Fillister Head. This screw has a rounded surface for the top of the head, the remainder being cylindrical. This type of head is standard for machine screws and cap screws.

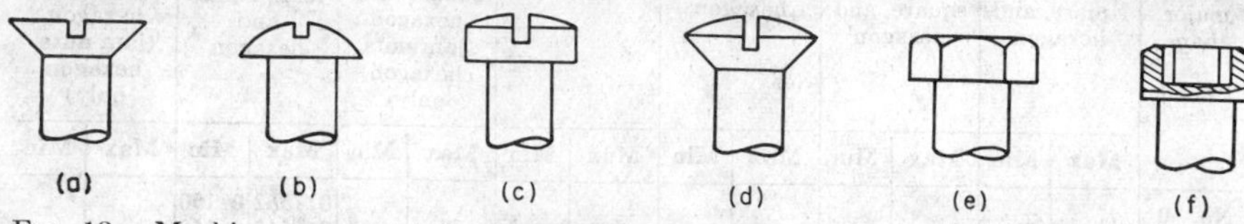

FIG. 13. Machine screws: (*a*) flat head; (*b*) round head; (*c*) fillister head; (*d*) oval head; (*e*) hexagon head; (*f*) socket head.

Oval Head. This screw has a rounded surface for the top of the head and a countersink angle of 82 deg. It is standard for machine screws and wood screws.

Hexagon Head. This screw has a hexagon-shaped head for use with external wrenches. It is standard for machine screws.

Socket Head. This screw has an internal hexagon-shaped socket in the head for internal wrenching. It is standard for cap screws.

These screws are shown in Fig. 13 and the pertinent dimensions in Table 20.

Table 20. Head Diameters (Maximum) in Inches

MACHINE SCREWS

Nominal size	Screw diam	Flat head	Round head	Fillister head	Oval head	Hexagon head across flats
2	0.086	0.172	0.162	0.140	0.172	0.125
3	0.099	0.199	0.187	0.161	0.199	0.187
4	0.112	0.225	0.211	0.183	0.225	0.187
5	0.125	0.252	0.236	0.205	0.252	0.187
6	0.138	0.279	0.260	0.226	0.279	0.250
8	0.164	0.332	0.309	0.270	0.332	0.250
10	0.190	0.385	0.359	0.313	0.385	0.312
12	0.216	0.438	0.408	0.357	0.438	0.312
1/4	0.250	0.507	0.472	0.414	0.507	0.375
5/16	0.3125	0.636	0.591	0.519	0.636	0.500
3/8	0.375	0.762	0.708	0.622	0.762	0.562

CAP SCREWS

Nominal size	Screw diam	Flat head	Button head	Fillister head	Socket head
1/4	0.250	1/2	7/16	3/8	3/8
5/16	0.3125	5/8	9/16	7/16	7/16
3/8	0.375	3/4	5/8	9/16	9/16
7/16	0.4375	13/16	3/4	5/8	5/8
1/2	0.500	7/8	13/16	3/4	3/4
9/16	0.5625	1	15/16	13/16	13/16
5/8	0.625	1 1/8	1	7/8	7/8
3/4	0.750	1 3/8	1 1/4	1	1
7/8	.....	.....	.....	1 1/8	1 1/8
1	.....	.....	.....	1 5/16	1 5/16

Eyebolts

Eyebolts are classified as rivet, nut, or screw, and can be had on a swivel. The proportions are given in Tables 21 and 22. The safe working load may be obtained for each application by applying an appropriate factor of safety.

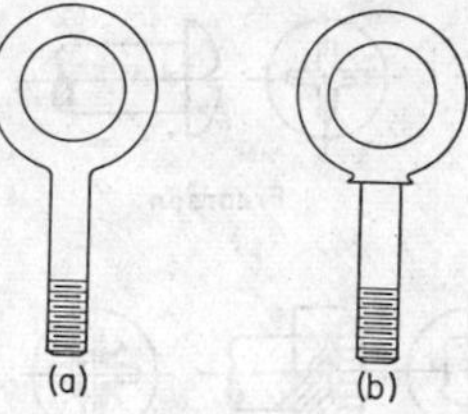

FIG. 14. (*a*) Regular nut and (*b*) shoulder nut eyebolts.

Table 21. Regular Nut Eyebolts—Selected Sizes
(Thomas Laughlin Co., Portland, Me.)
(All dimensions in inches)
(See Fig. 14)

Diam and shank length	Thread length	Eye dimension		Approx breaking strength, lb	Diam and shank length	Thread length	Eye dimension		Approx breaking strength, lb
		I.D.	O.D.				I.D.	O.D.	
¼ × 2	1½	½	1	2,200	¾ × 6	3	1½	3	23,400
5/16 × 2¼	1½	⅝	1¼	3,600	¾ × 10	3	1½	3	23,400
⅜ × 4½	2½	¾	1½	5,200	¾ × 15	5	1½	3	23,400
½ × 3¼	1½	1	2	9,800	⅞ × 8	4	1¾	3½	32,400
½ × 6	3	1	2	9,800	1 × 6	3	2	4	42,400
½ × 10	3	1	2	9,800	1 × 9	4	2	4	42,400
⅝ × 4	2	1¼	2½	15,800	1 × 18	7	2	4	42,400
⅝ × 6	3	1¼	2½	15,800	1¼ × 8	4	2½	5	67,800
⅝ × 10	3	1¼	2½	15,800	1¼ × 20	6	2½	5	67,800

Table 22. Shoulder Nut Eyebolts—Selected Sizes
(Thomas Laughlin Co., Portland, Me.)
(All dimensions in inches)
(See Fig. 14)

Diam and shank length	Thread length	Eye dimension		Approx breaking strength, lb	Diam and shank length	Thread length	Eye dimension		Approx breaking strength, lb
		I.D.	O.D.				I.D.	O.D.	
¼ × 2	1½	½	⅞	2,200	¾ × 6	3	1½	2¾	23,400
5/16 × 2¼	1½	⅝	1⅛	3,600	⅞ × 5	2½	1¾	3¼	32,400
⅜ × 4½	2½	¾	1⅜	5,200	1 × 9	4	2	3¾	42,400
½ × 6	3	1	1¾	9,800	1¼ × 8	4	2½	4½	67,800
⅝ × 4	2	1¼	2¼	15,800	1½ × 15	6	3	5½	98,400

Driving Recesses

Driving recesses for screws used in modern practice are shown in Fig. 15.

Setscrews

Setscrews are used for fastening collars, sheaves, gears, etc. to shafts to prevent relative rotation or translation. They are available in a variety of head and point styles, as shown in Fig. 16. A complete tabulation of dimensions is found in ASA B18.3 and B18.6.2. Holding power for various sizes is given in Table 23.

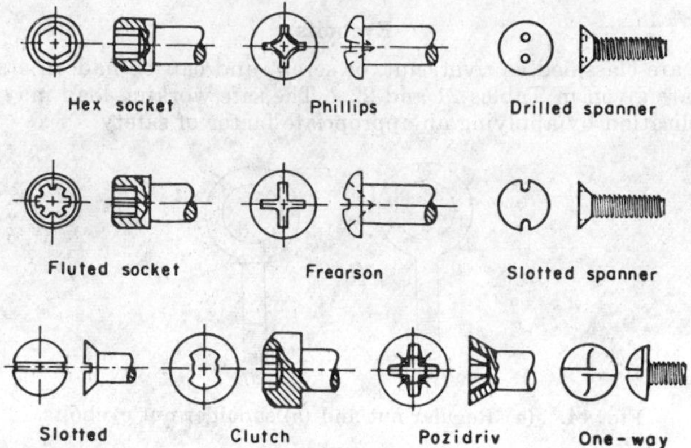

FIG. 15. Driving recesses. (*Adapted, with permission from "Machine Design," Mar. 11, 1965.*)

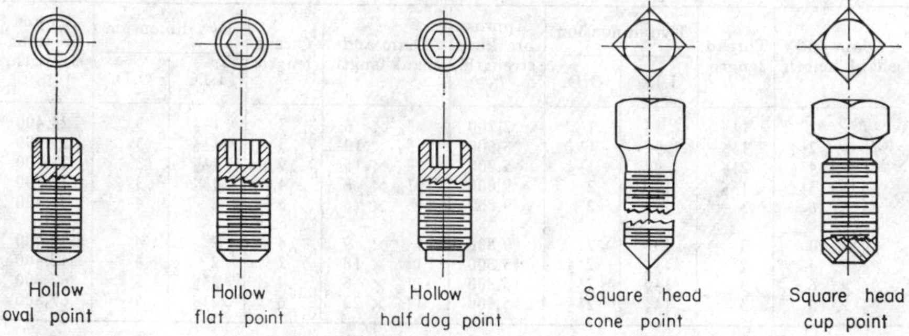

FIG. 16. Setscrews.

Locking Fasteners

Locking fasteners are used to prevent loosening of a threaded fastener in service and are available in a wide variety differing vastly in design, performance, and function. Since each has special features which may make it of particular value in the solution of a given machine problem, it is important that great care be exercised in the selection of a particular design in order that its properties may be fully utilized. These fasteners may be divided into six groups, as follows: seating lock, spring stop nut, interference, wedge, blind, and quick-release. The **seating-lock type** locks only when firmly seated and is therefore free-running on the bolt. The **spring stop-nut type** of fastener functions by a spring action clamping down upon the bolt. The **prevailing torque type** locks by elastic or plastic flow of a portion of the fastener material. The **wedge type** locks by relative wedging of either elements or nut and bolt. The **blind type** usually utilizes spring action of the fastener, and the **quick-release type** utilizes a quarter-turn release device. An example of each is shown in Fig. 17.

There is a continuing effort to develop industry-wide standards for these fasteners. One such specification developed for prevailing torque fasteners by the Industrial Fasteners Institute is based on locking torque and may form a precedent for other types of fasteners as well.

Coach and lag screws as shown in Fig. 18 are made in the proportions given in Table 24.

Wood screws are made in lengths from ¼ to 5 in. for steel and from ¼ to 3½ in. for brass screws, increasing by ⅛ in. up to 1 in., by ¼ in. up to 3 in., and by ½ in. up to 5 in. The **American standard** sizes are given in Table 25. Screws are made with flat, round, or oval heads. Figure 19 shows a flathead screw.

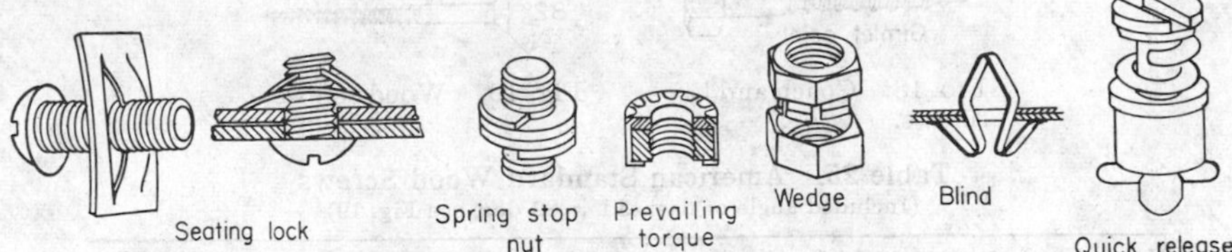

FIG. 17

Table 23. Cup-point Setscrew Holding Power[1]

Nominal screw size	Seating torque, lb-in.	Axial holding power, lb
No. 0	0.5	50
No. 1	1.5	65
No. 2	1.5	85
No. 3	5	120
No. 4	5	160
No. 5	9	200
No. 6	9	250
No. 8	20	385
No. 10	33	540
¼ in.	87	1,000
5⁄16 in.	165	1,500
⅜ in.	290	2,000
7⁄16 in.	430	2,500
½ in.	620	3,000
9⁄16 in.	620	3,500
⅝ in.	1,225	4,000
¾ in.	2,125	5,000
⅞ in.	5,000	6,000
1 in.	7,000	7,000

1. Torsional holding power in inch-pounds is equal to one-half of the axial holding power times the shaft diameter in inches.
2. Experimental data were obtained by seating an alloy-steel cup-point setscrew against a steel shaft with a hardness of Rockwell C 15. Screw threads were Class 3A, tapped holes were Class 2B. Holding power was defined as the minimum load necessary to produce 0.01 in. of relative movement between the shaft and the collar.
3. Cone points will develop a slightly greater holding power; flat, dog, and oval points, slightly less.
4. Shaft hardness should be at least 10 Rockwell C points less than the setscrew point.
5. Holding power is proportional to seating torque. Torsional holding power is increased about 6% by use of a flat on the shaft.
6. Data by F. R. Kull, Fasteners Book Issue, *Machine Design*, Mar. 11, 1965.

Table 24. Coach and Lag Screws

Diam of screw, in.	¼	5⁄16	⅜	7⁄16	½	⅝	¾	⅞	1
No. of threads per in.	10	9	7	7	6	5	4½	4	3½
Across flats of hexagon and square heads, in.	⅜	15⁄32	9⁄16	21⁄32	¾	15⁄16	1⅛	15⁄16	1½
Thickness of hexagon and square heads, in.	3⁄16	¼	5⁄16	⅜	7⁄16	17⁄32	⅝	¾	⅞

LENGTH OF THREADS FOR SCREWS OF ALL DIAMETERS

Length of screw, in.	1½	2	2½	3	3½	4	4½
Length of thread, in.	To head	1½	2	2¼	2½	3	3½
Length of screw, in.	5	5½	6	7	8	9	10–12
Length of thread, in.	4	4	4½	5	6	6	7

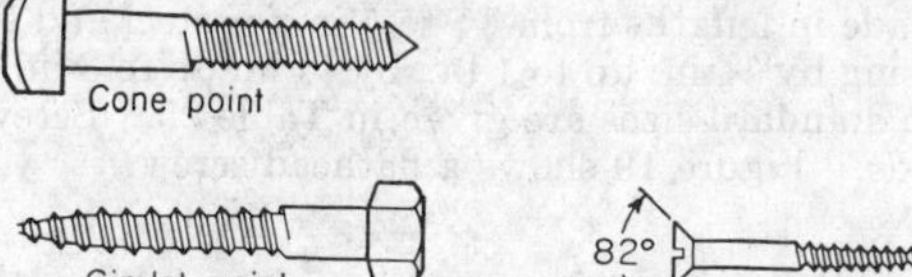

Fig. 18. Coach and lag screws.

Fig. 19. Wood screws.

Table 25. American Standard Wood Screws
(Included angle of flathead = 82 deg, see Fig. 19)

Number	0	1	2	3	4	5	6	7	8
Threads per in.	32	28	26	24	22	20	18	16	15
Diameter, in.	0.060	0.073	0.086	0.099	0.112	0.125	0.138	0.151	0.164
Number	9	10	11	12	14	16	18	20	24
Threads per in.	14	13	12	11	10	9	8	8	7
Diameter, in.	0.177	0.190	0.203	0.216	0.242	0.268	0.294	0.320	0.372

Washers for bolts and lag screws, either round or square, are made to the dimensions given in Table 26.

Table 26. Dimensions of Steel Washers, In.

Bolt size	Plain washer		Thickness	Lock washer		Thickness
	Hole diam	O.D.		Hole diam	O.D.	
3/16	1/4	9/16	3/64	0.194	0.337	0.047
1/4	5/16	3/4	1/16	0.255	0.493	0.062
5/16	3/8	7/8	1/16	0.319	0.591	0.078
3/8	7/16	1	5/64	0.382	0.688	0.094
7/16	1/2	1 1/4	5/64	0.446	0.784	0.109
1/2	9/16	1 3/8	3/32	0.509	0.879	0.125
9/16	5/8	1 1/2	3/32	0.573	0.979	0.141
5/8	11/16	1 3/4	1/8	0.636	1.086	0.156
3/4	13/16	2	1/8	0.763	1.279	0.188
7/8	15/16	2 1/4	5/32	0.890	1.474	0.219
1	1 1/16	2 1/2	5/32	1.017	1.672	0.250
1 1/8	1 1/4	2 3/4	5/32	1.144	1.865	0.281
1 1/4	1 3/8	3	5/32	1.271	2.058	0.312
1 3/8	1 1/2	3 1/4	11/64	1.398	2.253	0.344
1 1/2	1 5/8	3 1/2	11/64	1.525	2.446	0.375
1 5/8	1 3/4	3 3/4	11/64			
1 3/4	1 7/8	4	11/64			
1 7/8	2	4 1/4	11/64			
2	2 1/8	4 1/2	11/64			
2 1/4	2 3/8	4 3/4	3/16			
2 1/2	2 5/8	5	7/32			

Self-tapping screws are available in three types. **Thread-forming** tapping screws plastically displace material adjacent to the pilot hole. **Thread-cutting** tapping screws have cutting edges and chip cavities (flutes) and form a mating thread by removing material adjacent to the pilot hole. Thread-cutting screws are generally used to join thicker and harder materials and require a lower driving torque than thread-forming screws. **Metallic drive** screws are forced into the material by pressure and are intended for making permanent fastenings. These three types are further classified on the basis of thread and point form as shown in Table 27. In addition to these body forms, a number of different head types are available. Basic dimensional data are given in Table 28.

Table 27. Tapping Screw Forms

(Adapted, with permission, from *Machine Design*, Mar. 11, 1965.)

ASA type and thread form	Description and recommendations
AB	Spaced thread, with gimlet point, designed for use in sheet metal, resin-impregnated plywood, wood, and asbestos compositions. Used in pierced or punched holes where a sharp point for starting is needed.
B	Type B is a blunt-point spaced-thread screw, used in heavy-gage sheet metal and non-ferrous castings.
BP	Same as Type B, but has a 45 deg included angle unthreaded cone point. Used for locating and aligning holes or piercing soft materials.
C	Blunt point with threads approximating machine-screw threads. For applications where a machine-screw thread is preferable to the spaced-thread form. Unlike thread-cutting screws, the Type C makes a chip-free assembly.
U	Multiple-threaded drive screw with steep helix angle and a blunt, unthreaded starting pilot. Intended for making permanent fastenings in metals and plastics. Hammered or mechanically forced into work. Should not be used in materials less than one screw diameter thick.
D	Blunt point with single narrow flute and threads approximating machine-screw threads. Flute is designed to produce a cutting edge which is radial to screw center. For low-strength metals and plastics; for high-strength brittle metals; and for rethreading clogged pretapped holes.
F	Approximate machine-screw thread and blunt point.
G	Approximate machine-screw thread with single through slot which forms two cutting edges. For low-strength metals and plastics.
T	Same as Type D with single wide flute for more chip clearance.
BF	Spaced thread with blunt point and five evenly spaced cutting grooves and chip cavities. Wall thickness should be 1½ times major diameter of screw. Reduces stripping in brittle plastics and die castings.
BT	Same as Type BF except for single wide flute which provides room for twisted, curly chips.
TT	Thread-rolling screws roll-form clean, screw threads. The plastic movement of the material it is driven into locks it in place. The "Taptite"® form is shown here.

Table 28. Self-tapping Screws
(Threads per inch)

Screw size	Basic major diam, in.	AB	B, BP	C	D, F, G, T	BF, BT	Type U: Max outside diam, in.	Type U: Number of thread starts
00	......	...	...	....	....	...	0.060	6
0	0.060	40	48	....	....	48	0.075	6
1	0.073	32	42	....	....	42		
2	0.086	32	32	56 and 64	56 and 64	32	0.100	8
3	0.099	28	28	48 and 56	48 and 56	28		
4	0.112	24	24	40 and 48	40 and 48	24	0.116	7
5	0.125	20	20	40 and 44	40 and 44	20		
6	0.138	18	20	32 and 40	32 and 40	20	0.140	7
7	0.151	16	19	....	....	19	0.154	8
8	0.164	15	18	32 and 36	32 and 36	18	0.167	8
10	0.190	12	16	24 and 32	24 and 32	16	0.182	8
12	0.216	11	14	24 and 28	24 and 28	14	0.212	8
14	0.242	10	...	....	....	...	0.242	9
¼	0.250	...	14	20 and 28	20 and 28	14		
16	0.268	10						
18	0.294	9						
5/16	0.3125	...	12	18 and 24	18 and 24	12	0.315	11
20	0.320	9						
24	0.372	9						
⅜	0.375	...	12	16 and 24	16 and 24	12	0.378	12
7/16	0.4375	...	10	....	....	10		
½	0.500	...	10	....	....	10		

Carriage bolts have been standardized in ASA B18.5. They come in the styles as shown in Fig. 20. The range of bolt diameters is No. 10 (=0.19 in.) to 1 in., No. 10 to ¾ in., No. 10 to ½ in., and No. 10 to ¾ in., respectively.

Stove bolts (Fig. 21) are made in the sizes given in Table 29.

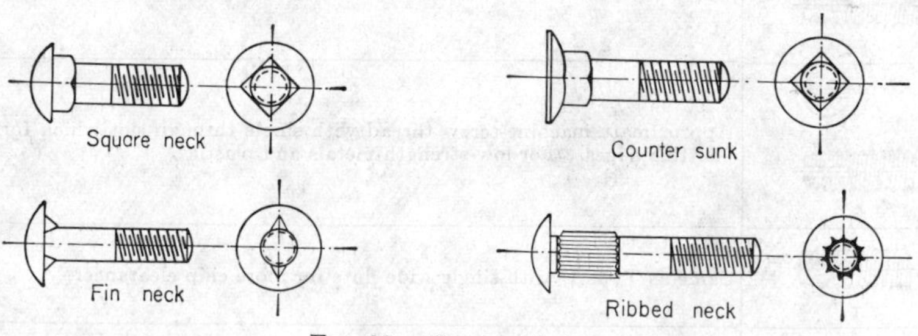

FIG. 20. Carriage bolts.

FIG. 21. Stove bolts.

Table 29. Stove Bolts

Diam of bolt, in.	⅛	5/32	3/16	7/32	¼	5/16	⅜
No. of threads per in.	32	28	24	22	18	18	16

Materials, Strength, and Service Adaptability of Machine Bolts and Screws

The **materials** to be used for bolts, screws, and nuts depend on service conditions and relative costs. The stresses to be allowed in determining the proportions in any case depend on the nature of the loading and the material. Table 30 will serve as a guide to the selection of **bolts and nuts for fastenings.**

Table 30. Physical Requirements for Threaded Fasteners (Bolts and Capscrews)

(Adapted with permission from *Machine Design*, Mar. 11, 1965.)

SAE grade	Bolt size, diam, in.	Proof load, psi	Min tensile strength, psi	Hardness	
				Brinell	Rockwell
0	All sizes				
1	All sizes	....	55,000	207 max	95 B max
2	Up to ½ incl	55,000	69,000	241 max	100 B max
	Over ½ to ¾ incl	52,000	64,000		
	Over ¾ to 1½ incl	28,000	55,000	207 max	
3	Up to ½ incl	85,000	110,000	207–269	95–104 B
	Over ½ to ⅝ incl	80,000	100,000		
5	Up to ¾ incl	85,000	120,000	241–302	23–32 C
	Over ¾ to 1 incl	78,000	115,000	235–302	22–32 C
	Over 1 to 1½ incl	74,000	105,000	223–285	19–30 C
5.1	Up to ⅜ incl	85,000	120,000	241–375	23–40 C
7	Up to 1½ incl	105,000	133,000	269–321	28–34 C
8	Up to 1½ incl	120,000	150,000	302–352	32–38 C

Table 31. Safe Loads for American Standard Bolts

Nominal diam, in.	No. of threads per in.	Ultimate strength, psi						
		20,000	40,000	50,000	60,000	65,000	80,000	95,000
¼	20	57	115	143	172	186	229	272
5⁄16	18	99	198	247	297	322	396	470
⅜	16	150	301	376	451	488	601	714
7⁄16	14	207	415	519	623	675	830	986
½	13	282	564	704	845	915	1,125	1,340
9⁄16	12	365	730	912	1,095	1,186	1,460	1,730
⅝	11	456	913	1,140	1,370	1,480	1,820	2,170
¾	10	690	1,380	1,725	2,070	2,240	2,760	3,280
⅞	9	964	1,930	2,410	2,900	3,140	3,860	4,580
1	8	1,265	2,530	3,170	3,800	4,120	5,060	6,010
1⅛	7	1,595	3,190	3,990	4,790	5,180	6,380	7,570
1¼	7	2,070	4,140	5,180	6,210	6,730	8,280	9,830
1⅜	6	2,440	4,890	6,110	7,330	7,940	9,780	11,600
1½	6	3,020	6,040	7540	9,060	9,800	12,050	14,300
1⅝	5½	3,530	7,060	8,820	10,600	11,500	14,100	16,750
1¾	5	4,060	8,120	10,150	12,200	13,200	16,200	19,250
1⅞	5	4,800	9,600	12,000	14,400	15,600	19,200	22,800
2	4½	5,360	10,750	13,400	16,100	17,400	21,500	25,500
2¼	4½	7,120	14,200	17,800	21,400	23,100	28,500	33,800
2½	4	8,750	17,500	21,900	26,300	28,400	35,000	41,500
2¾	4	11,000	22,000	27,500	33,000	35,700	44,000	52,200
3	4	13,400	26,800	33,500	40,200	43,600	53,600	63,600
3¼	4	16,100	32,200	40,200	48,400	52,400	64,400	76,400
3½	4	19,000	38,100	47,600	57,200	61,900	76,200	90,400
3¾	4	22,200	44,500	55,600	66,700	72,300	89,000	105,500
4	4	25,700	51,400	64,200	77,000	83,400	102,800	122,000
4¼	4	29,350	58,700	73,400	88,100	95,400	117,400	139,300
4½	4	33,300	66,600	83,200	100,000	108,000	133,000	158,000
4¾	4	37,400	75,000	93,700	112,000	122,000	150,000	178,000
5	4	41,900	83,800	105,000	126,000	136,000	167,500	199,000
5¼	4	46,600	93,200	116,500	140,000	151,000	186,000	221,000
5½	4	51,500	103,000	129,000	154,500	167,900	206,000	244,500
5¾	4	56,700	113,500	142,000	170,000	184,000	227,000	269,000
6	4	62,000	124,000	155,000	186,000	202,000	248,000	295,000

Safe loads in tension for American standard bolts, as determined by Harvey D. Williams, Bureau of Ships, U.S. Navy, are given in Table 31. Colvin and Stanley ("American Machinists' Handbook") compute the tensile and shearing strengths given in Table 32.

Table 32. Strength of American Standard Bolts

Bolt		Areas		Tensile strength, lb			Shearing strength, lb			
							Full bolt		Bottom of thread	
Diam of bolt, in.	No. of threads per in.	Full bolt sq in.	Bottom of thread, sq in.	At 10,000 psi	At 12,500 psi	At 17,500 psi	At 7,500 psi	At 10,000 psi	At 7,500 psi	At 10,000 psi
1/4	20	0.049	0.027	270	340	470	380	490	200	270
5/16	18	0.077	0.045	450	570	790	580	770	340	450
3/8	16	0.110	0.068	680	850	1,190	830	1,100	510	680
7/16	14	0.150	0.093	930	1,170	1,630	1,130	1,500	700	930
1/2	13	0.196	0.126	1,260	1,570	2,200	1,470	1,960	940	1,260
9/16	12	0.248	0.162	1,620	2,030	2,840	1,860	2,480	1,220	1,620
5/8	11	0.307	0.202	2,020	2,520	3,530	2,300	3,070	1,510	2,020
3/4	10	0.442	0.302	3,020	3,770	5,290	3,310	4,420	2,270	3,020
7/8	9	0.601	0.419	4,190	5,240	7,340	4,510	6,010	3,150	4,190
1	8	0.785	0.551	5,510	6,890	9,640	5,890	7,850	4,130	5,510
1 1/8	7	0.994	0.693	6,990	8,660	12,130	7,450	9,940	5,200	6,930
1 1/4	7	1.227	0.890	8,890	11,120	15,570	9,200	12,270	6,670	8,900
1 3/8	6	1.485	1.054	10,540	13,180	18,450	11,140	14,850	7,910	10,540
1 1/2	6	1.767	1.294	12,940	16,170	22,640	13,250	17,670	9,700	12,940
1 5/8	5 1/2	2.074	1.515	15,150	18,940	26,510	15,550	20,740	11,360	15,150
1 3/4	5	2.405	1.745	17,450	21,800	30,520	18,040	24,050	13,080	17,440
1 7/8	5	2.761	2.049	20,490	25,610	35,860	20,710	27,610	15,370	20,490
2	4 1/2	3.142	2.300	23,000	28,750	40,250	23,560	31,420	17,250	23,000
2 1/4	4 1/2	3.976	3.021	30,210	37,770	52,870	29,820	39,760	22,660	30,210
2 1/2	4	4.909	3.716	37,160	46,450	65,040	36,820	49,090	27,870	37,160
2 3/4	4	5.940	4.620	46,200	57,750	80,840	44,580	59,400	34,650	46,200
3	3 1/2	7.069	5.428	54,280	67,850	94,990	53,020	70,690	40,710	54,280

General Notes on the Design of Bolted Joints

Bolts subjected to shock and sudden change in load are found to be more serviceable when the unthreaded portion of the bolt is turned down or drilled to the area of the root of the thread. The drilled bolt is stronger in torsion than the turned down bolt.

When a **number of bolts** are **employed in fastening** together two parts of a machine, such as a cylinder and cylinder head, the load carried by each bolt depends on its relative tightness, the tighter bolts carrying the greater loads. When the conditions of assembly result in differences in tightness, lower working stresses must be used in designing the bolts than otherwise are necessary. On the other hand, it may be desirable to have the bolts the weakest part of the machine, since their breakage from overload in the machine will result in a minimum cost of replacement. In such cases, the breaking load of the bolts may well be equal to the load which causes the weakest member of the machine connected to be stressed up to the elastic limit.

Bolts screwed up tight have an initial stress due to the tightening before any external load is applied to the machine member. The initial tensile load due to screwing up for a tight joint varies about as the diameter of the bolt, and may be estimated at 16,000 lb per in. of diameter. The actual value depends upon the applied torque and the efficiency of the screw threads. Applying this rule to bolts of 1 in. diam or less results in excessively high stresses, thus demonstrating why bolts of small diameter are frequently fractured during assembly. It is advisable to use as large diameter bolts as possible in pressuretight joints requiring high tightening loads.

In pressuretight joints without a gasket the force on the bolt under load is essentially never greater than the initial tightening load. When a gasket is used the total bolt force is approximately equal to the initial tightening load plus the external load. In the first case, deviations from the rule are a result of elastic behavior of the joint faces without a gasket, and inelastic behavior of the gasket in the latter case. The following generalization will serve as a guide. If the bolt is more yielding than the connecting members, it should be designed simply to resist the initial tension or the external load, whichever is greater. If the probable yielding of the bolt is 50 to 100 percent of that of the connected members, take the resultant bolt load as the initial tension plus one-half the external load. If the yielding of the connected members is probably four to five times that of the bolt (as when certain packings are used), take the resultant bolt load as the initial tension plus three-fourths the external load.

In cases where bolts are subjected to cyclic loading, an increase in the initial tightening load decreases the operating stress range. In certain applications it is customary to fix the tightening load as a fraction of the yield-point load of the bolt.

In order to avoid the possibility of bolt fracture in pressuretight joints and to obtain uniformity in bolt loads, some means of determining initial bolt load is desirable. Calibrated torque wrenches are available for this purpose, reading directly in inch-pounds or inch-ounces. Inaccuracies in initial bolt load are possible even when using a torque wrench, due to variations in the coefficient of friction between the nut and the bolt and, further, between the nut or bolthead and the abutting surface.

In **drilling and tapping cast iron for steel studs,** it is necessary to tap to a depth equal to 1½ times the stud diameter in order that the strength of the cast-iron threads in shear may equal the tensile strength of the stud. Drill sizes and depths of hole and thread are given in Table 33.

Table 33. Depths to Drill and Tap Cast Iron for Studs

Diam of stud, in.	1/4	5/16	3/8	7/16	1/2	9/16	5/8	3/4	7/8	1
Diam of drill, in.	13/64	17/64	5/16	3/8	27/64	31/64	17/32	41/64	3/4	55/64
Depth of thread, in.	3/8	15/32	9/16	21/32	3/4	27/32	15/16	1 1/8	1 5/16	1 1/2
Depth to drill, in.	7/16	17/32	5/8	23/32	27/32	15/16	1 1/32	1 1/4	1 7/16	1 5/8

It is not good practice to drill holes to be tapped through the metal into pressure spaces for even though the bolt fits tightly, leakage will result that is difficult to eliminate.

Screw thread inserts, made of high-strength material, Fig. 22, are useful in many cases to provide increased thread strength and life. Soft or ductile materials tapped to receive thread inserts exhibit improved load carrying capacity under static and dynamic loading conditions. Holes in which threads have been stripped or otherwise damaged can be restored through the use of thread inserts.

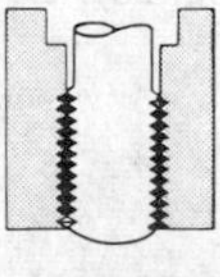

Fig. 22. Screw thread insert.

Holes for thread inserts are drilled oversize and specially tapped to receive the insert selected to mate with the threaded fastener used. The standard material for inserts is 18-8 stainless steel, but other materials are available, such as phosphor bronze and Inconel.® Recommended insert lengths are given in Table 34.

Table 34. Screw-thread Insert Lengths

(Heli-Coil® Corp.)

Shear strength of parent material, psi	Bolt material ultimate tensile strength, psi				
	60,000	90,000	125,000	170,000	220,000
	Length in terms of nominal insert diameter				
15,000	1½	2	2½	3	
20,000	1	1½	2	2½	3
25,000	1	1½	2	2	2½
30,000	1	1	1½	2	2
40,000	1	1	1½	1½	2
50,000	1	1	1	1½	1½

Drill Sizes for American Standard Thread Taps. Diameter of drills equals outside diameter of stud *minus* pitch of thread. Table 35 gives tap-drill sizes for taps with American Standard, V, and Whitworth threads.

Table 35. Tap-drill Sizes for American Standard Screw Threads
(The sizes listed are the commercial tap drills to produce approx 75 percent full thread)

Size	Coarse-thread series		Fine-thread series		Size	Coarse-thread series		Fine-thread series	
	Threads per in.	Tap drill size	Threads per in.	Tap drill size		Threads per in.	Tap drill size	Threads per in.	Tap drill size
No. 0	..	......	80	3/64	3/4	10	21/32	16	11/16
No. 1	64	No. 53	72	No. 53	7/8	9	49/64	14	13/16
No. 2	56	No. 50	64	No. 50	1	8	7/8	14	15/16
No. 3	48	No. 47	56	No. 45	1 1/8	7	63/64	12	1 3/64
No. 4	40	No. 43	48	No. 42	1 1/4	7	1 7/64	12	1 11/64
No. 5	40	No. 38	44	No. 37	1 3/8	6	1 7/32	12	1 19/64
No. 6	32	No. 36	40	No. 33	1 1/2	6	1 21/64	12	1 27/64
No. 8	32	No. 29	36	No. 29	1 3/4	5	1 35/64		
No. 10	24	No. 25	32	No. 21	2	4 1/2	1 25/32		
No. 12	24	No. 16	28	No. 14	2 1/4	4 1/2	2 1/32		
1/4	20	No. 7	28	No. 3	2 1/2	4	2 1/4		
5/16	18	F	24	I	2 3/4	4	2 1/2		
3/8	16	5/16	24	Q	3	4	2 3/4		
7/16	14	U	20	25/64	3 1/4	4	3		
1/2	13	27/64	20	29/64	3 1/2	4	3 1/4		
9/16	12	31/64	18	33/64	3 3/4	4	3 1/2		
5/8	11	17/32	18	37/64	4	4	3 3/4		

RIVET FASTENINGS

Forms and Proportion of Rivets. The forms and proportions of small and large rivets have been standardized by the ASA, and conform to ASA B18.1 and B18.4 (Fig. 23).

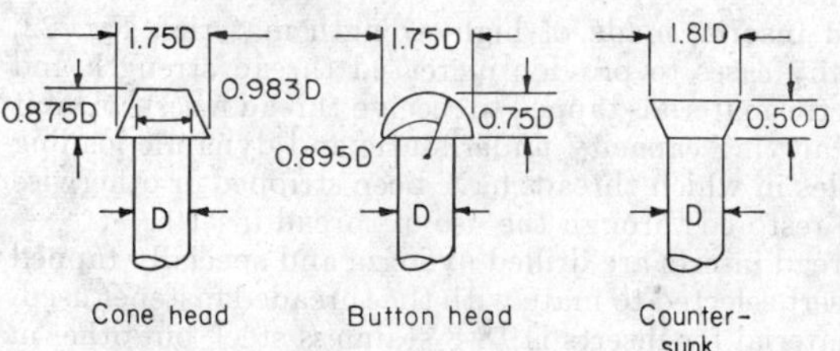

Fig. 23. Rivet heads.

Table 36. Weights of 100 Structural Rivets with Buttonheads, Lb

Length under head, in.	Diameter of rivet, in.							
	3/8	1/2	5/8	3/4	7/8	1	1 1/8	1 1/4
1 1/2	7	13	23	35	50	68	91	130
1 5/8	7	14	24	36	52	71	95	134
1 3/4	8	15	25	37	54	74	98	139
1 7/8	8	15	26	39	56	77	102	143
2	9	16	27	41	58	80	105	148
2 1/8	9	17	28	43	60	82	109	152
2 1/4	9	18	29	44	62	85	112	156
2 3/8	10	18	30	46	64	88	116	161
Lb per in. additional	3.0	5.6	8.7	12.5	17.0	22.2	28.2	34.7
	Weights of 100 buttonheads, lb							
On rivets..................	2.4	5.0	9.7	16.0	24.0	35.0	49.0	78.0
As driven..................	1.9	4.0	7.5	12.5	18.5	27.0	37.5	51.0

Forms and Proportions of Riveted Joints for Boilers and Tanks. Riveted joints for steam boilers and tanks may have the forms and proportions recommended by the Hartford Steam Boiler Inspection and Insurance Co., as given in Figs. 24 to 27 and Tables 37 to 40.

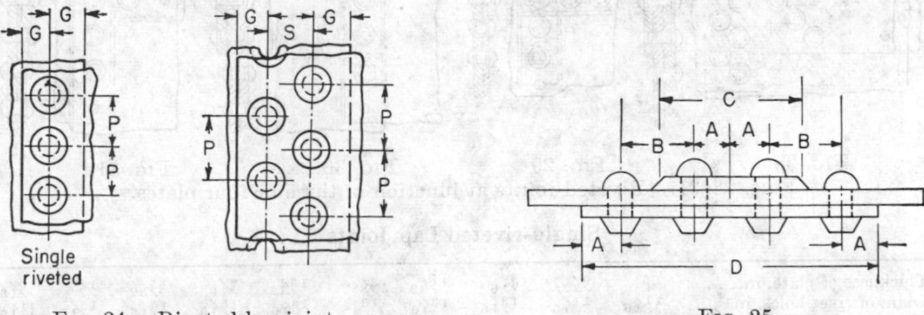

FIG. 24. Riveted lap joint.

FIG. 25

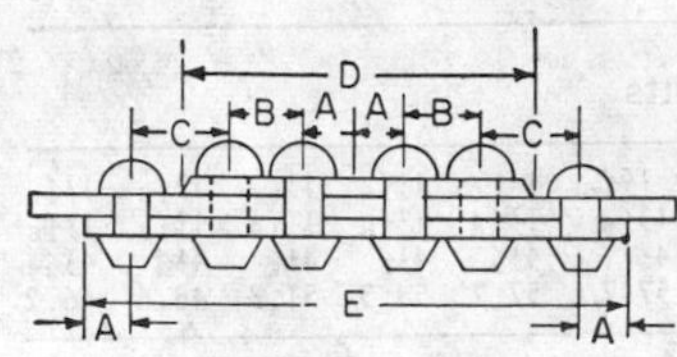

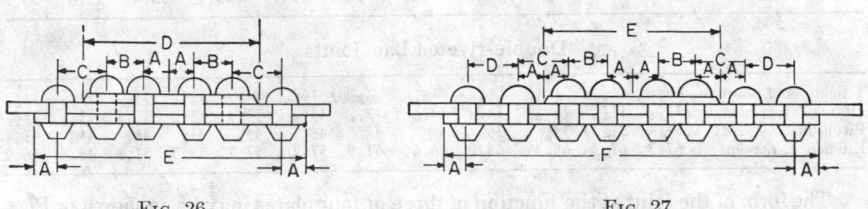

FIG. 26

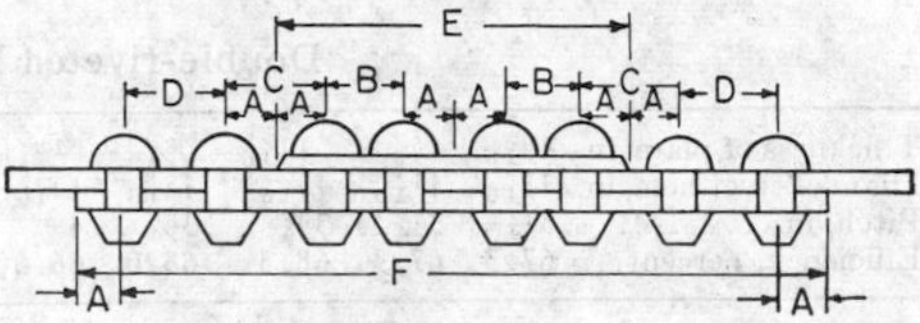

FIG. 27

FIGS. 24–27. Butt joints.

Table 37. Dimensions of Riveted Lap Joints

(All dimensions in inches. Letters refer to Fig. 24. E = percent efficiency of joint. Dimensions based on a tensile strength of 55,000 psi for the plate and a shearing strength of 44,000 psi for the rivets.)

Thickness of plate	Diam of rivet holes	Single riveted				Double riveted			
		E	*P*	*G*	Method of failure	*E*	*P*	*G*	*S*
¼	11⁄16	60.7	1¾	11⁄16	T.P.	69.5	2¼	11⁄16	1¾
9⁄32	11⁄16	60.3	1¾	11⁄16	S.R.	69.5	2¼	11⁄16	1¾
5⁄16	13⁄16	59.4	2	1¼	T.P.	69.5	2⅝	1¼	1⅞
11⁄32	13⁄16	59.4	2	1¼	T.P.	69.1	2⅝	1¼	1⅞
⅜	15⁄16	58.3	2¼	17⁄16	T.P.	68.9	3	17⁄16	2
13⁄32	15⁄16	58.3	2¼	17⁄16	T.P.	68.9	3	17⁄16	2
7⁄16	11⁄16	57.5	2½	1⅝	T.P.	68.5	3⅜	1⅝	2⅛
15⁄32	11⁄16	57.5	2½	1⅝	T.P.	68.5	3⅜	1⅝	2⅛
½	11⁄16	56.7	2½	1⅝	S.R.	68.5	3⅜	1⅝	2⅛

Lap-riveted Joints for Girth Seams of Cylindrical Vessels with Unstayed Heads

In horizontal tubular boilers, tanks, and similar vessels, it is customary for the sake of convenience to use the same size of rivets in the girth seams as in the longitudinal seams. Where the heads of such vessels are not stayed by tubes or through braces, the strength of the circumferential joints should be at least 50 percent of that required for the logitudinal joints of the vessel. The joints in the table below are designed to meet the above requirements, and it should be understood that a higher efficiency could be obtained in some instances by using different size rivets. It is assumed in each case that the efficiency of the corresponding longitudinal joint is not greater than that of the quadruple-riveted butt joints of Table 40.

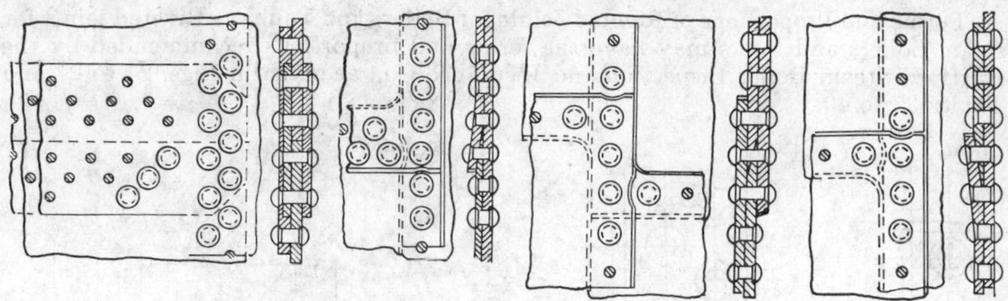

FIG. 28 FIG. 29 FIG. 30 FIG. 31

FIGS. 28–31. Riveted joints at junction of three or four plates.

Single-riveted Lap Joints

Thickness of plate, in.	1/4	9/32	5/16	11/32	3/8	13/32	7/16	15/32	1/2	9/16
Diam of rivet holes, in.	11/16	11/16	13/16	13/16	13/16	13/16	15/16	15/16	15/16	1 1/16
Pitch, in.	1 3/4	1 3/4	1 7/8	1 7/8	1 7/8	1 7/8	2 1/8	2 1/8	2 1/8	2 3/8
Efficiency, percent	60.7	60.3	56.7	56.7	56.7	54.5	55.9	55.4	52.0	53.3

Double-riveted Lap Joints

Thickness of plate, in.	9/16	5/8	11/16	3/4	13/16	7/8	15/16	1	1 1/16	1 1/8	1 3/16	1 1/4
Diam of rivet hole, in.	1 1/16	1 1/16	1 3/16	1 3/16	1 5/16	1 5/16	1 5/16	1 7/16	1 7/16	1 7/16	1 7/16	1 7/16
Pitch, in.	3 1/4	3 1/4	3 3/4	3 3/4	4	4	4	4 1/2	4 1/2	4 1/2	4 1/2	4 1/2
Efficiency, percent	67.3	67.3	68.3	63.0	66.6	61.9	57.7	57.7	54.3	51.3	48.6	46.2

The form of the **joint at the junction of three or four plates** may be as shown in Figs. 28 to 31.

Table 38. Dimensions of Double-riveted Butt Joints (**Steel Rivets in Steel Plates**)

(All dimensions in inches. Letters refer to Fig. 25. Dimensions based on a tensile strength of 55,000 psi for plates and straps and a shearing strength of 44,000 psi for rivets in single shear and 88,000 psi for rivets in double shear.)

Thickness of plate	Thickness of straps	Diam of rivet hole	Efficiency, percent	Long pitch	Short pitch	*D*	*C*	*A*	*B*
1/4	1/4	11/16	82.8	4	2	8 1/2	4 1/4	1 1/16	2 1/8
9/32	1/4	11/16	82.8	4	2	8 1/2	4 1/4	1 1/16	2 1/8
5/16	9/32	13/16	81.9	4 1/2	2 1/4	9 7/8	5	1 1/4	2 7/16
11/32	9/32	13/16	81.9	4 1/2	2 1/4	9 7/8	5	1 1/4	2 7/16
3/8	5/16	13/16	81.9	4 1/2	2 1/4	9 7/8	5	1 1/4	2 7/16
13/32	5/16	13/16	81.9	4 1/2	2 1/4	9 7/8	5	1 1/4	2 7/16
7/16	3/8	15/16	81.3	5	2 1/2	11 1/4	5 3/4	1 7/16	2 3/4
15/32	3/8	15/16	81.3	5	2 1/2	11 1/4	5 3/4	1 7/16	2 3/4
1/2	7/16	15/16	81.3	5	2 1/2	11 1/4	5 3/4	1 7/16	2 3/4

When **plates** are to be **joined at right angles** and riveted, the joint may have the form shown in Fig. 32. With such joints, the outer radius of curvature of the plate should be at least four times the plate thickness. The overlap should be three times the rivet diameter. Frequently, angle connections such as shown in Fig. 33 are used.

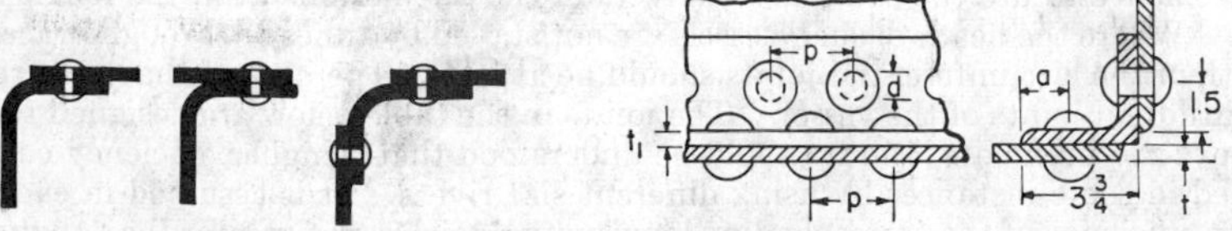

FIGS. 32 and 33. Turning plates at right angles.

Table 39. Dimensions of Triple-riveted Butt Joints (Steel Rivets in Steel Plates)
(All dimensions in inches. Letters refer to Fig. 26. Dimensions based on the tensile and shearing strengths given for Table 38.)

Thickness of plate	Thickness of straps	Diam of rivet hole	Efficiency, per cent	Long pitch	Short pitch	*E*	*D*	*A*	*B*	*C*
1/4	1/4	11/16	87.5	5 1/2	2 3/4	12	7 3/4	1 1/16	1 3/4	2 1/8
9/32	1/4	11/16	87.5	5 1/2	2 3/4	12	7 3/4	1 1/16	1 3/4	2 1/8
5/16	9/32	13/16	87.5	6 1/2	3 1/4	13 5/8	8 3/4	1 1/4	1 7/8	2 7/16
11/32	9/32	13/16	87.5	6 1/2	3 1/4	13 5/8	8 3/4	1 1/4	1 7/8	2 7/16
3/8	5/16	13/16	88.4	7	3 1/2	13 5/8	8 3/4	1 1/4	1 7/8	2 7/16
13/32	5/16	13/16	88.4	7	3 1/2	13 5/8	8 3/4	1 1/4	1 7/8	2 7/16
7/16	3/8	15/16	87.9	7 3/4	3 7/8	15 1/4	9 3/4	1 7/16	2	2 3/4
15/32	3/8	15/16	87.9	7 3/4	3 7/8	15 1/4	9 3/4	1 7/16	2	2 3/4
1/2	7/16	15/16	88.3	8	4	15 1/4	9 3/4	1 7/16	2	2 3/4
17/32	7/16	15/16	88.3	8	4	15 1/4	9 3/4	1 7/16	2	2 3/4
9/16	7/16	1 1/16	86.7	8	4	17	11	1 5/8	2 1/4	3
19/32	1/2	1 1/16	86.7	8	4	17	11	1 5/8	2 1/4	3
5/8	1/2	1 1/16	86.7	8	4	17	11	1 5/8	2 1/4	3
21/32	1/2	1 1/16	86.7	8	4	17	11	1 5/8	2 1/4	3
11/16	1/2	1 3/16	85.6	8 1/4	4 1/8	18 1/2	12	1 13/16	2 3/8	3 1/4
23/32	1/2	1 3/16	85.6	8 1/4	4 1/8	18 1/2	12	1 13/16	2 3/8	3 1/4
3/4	1/2	1 3/16	85.5	8 1/4	4 1/8	18 1/2	12	1 13/16	2 3/8	3 1/4
25/32	9/16	1 5/16	84.6	8 1/2	4 1/4	20 1/4	13 1/4	2	2 5/8	3 1/2
13/16	9/16	1 5/16	84.6	8 1/2	4 1/4	20 1/4	13 1/4	2	2 5/8	3 1/2
27/32	9/16	1 5/16	84.2	8 1/2	4 1/4	20 1/4	13 1/4	2	2 5/8	3 1/2
7/8	5/8	1 5/16	84.1	8 3/4	4 3/8	20 1/4	13 1/4	2	2 5/8	3 1/2
29/32	5/8	1 5/16	83.6	8 3/4	4 3/8	20 1/4	13 1/4	2	2 5/8	3 1/2
15/16	11/16	1 5/16	83.7	9	4 1/2	20 1/4	13 1/4	2	2 5/8	3 1/2
31/32	11/16	1 5/16	83.2	9	4 1/2	20 1/4	13 1/4	2	2 5/8	3 1/2
	3/4	1 7/16	83.4	9 1/2	4 3/4	22	14 1/2	2 3/16	2 7/8	3 3/4

In such construction, it is good practice to have the rivet diameter $d = 2 \times$ plate thickness t and the dimension $a = \frac{1}{2}(w - t_1)$, in which w = width of angle leg and t_1 = thickness of leg $= t + \frac{1}{16}$ in. The other dimensions in the figure are in terms of t.

Straining Actions in Riveted Joints. The straining actions to which the several elements of a riveted joint are subjected are easily determined as to kind, but are most difficult to evaluate. This is particularly true when the joint is one of several in a structure such as a boiler and receives its load according to the elasticity of the parts through which these loads are transmitted. Without regard to the friction between the plates and assuming all rivets in the joint to be equally well fitted and consequently sharing equally in taking up load, the accepted method of analyzing the stresses in the joint is as follows:

Let t = thickness of plate, in.; d = diameter of rivet, in.; p = pitch of rivets, in.; n = number of rivets per pitch width of plate, in single shear; m = same, in double shear; f_t = intensity of stress in tension, psi; f_c = intensity of stress in crushing, psi, single shear; f_s = intensity of stress in shearing, psi, single shear (f_c' and f_s' for double shear); P = pressure existing in the tank or boiler, psi; D = internal diam of tank, in.; S = capacity of joint per pitch width to resist shearing with a given intensity of shearing stress, lb; C = capacity of joint per pitch width to resist crushing with a given intensity of crushing stress, lb; T = capacity of joint per pitch width to resist tearing of plate between the last or outside row of rivets with a given intensity of tensile stress, lb; U = capacity of unpunched plate per pitch width to resist tearing with a given intensity of tensile stress, lb. Then

$$S = \pi d^2(nf_s + 2mf_s')/4 \qquad C = dt(nf_c + mf_c')$$

$$T = (p - d)tf_t \qquad U = p \times t \times f_t$$

and

$$E_s = \text{efficiency in shearing} = S/U = \pi d^2(nf_s + 2mf_s')/4ptf$$

$$E_c = \text{efficiency in crushing} = C/U = d(nf_c < mf_c')/pf_t$$

$$E_t = \text{efficiency in tearing} = T/U = (p - d)/p$$

Table 40. Dimensions of Quadruple-riveted Butt Joints (Steel Rivets in Steel Plates)
(All dimensions in inches. Letters refer to Fig. 27. Dimensions based on the tensile and shearing strengths given for Table 38.)

Thickness of plate	Thickness of straps	Diam of rivet hole	Efficiency, percent	Long pitch	Middle pitch	Short pitch	*F*	*E*	*A*	*B*	*C*	*D*
1/4	1/4	11/16	93.8	11	5 1/2	2 3/4	16 1/2	7 3/4	1 1/16	1 3/4	2 1/8	2 1/4
9/32	1/4	11/16	93.8	11	5 1/2	2 3/4	16 1/2	7 3/4	1 1/16	1 3/4	2 1/8	2 1/4
5/16	9/32	13/16	93.8	13	6 1/2	3 1/4	18 7/8	8 3/4	1 1/4	1 7/8	2 7/16	2 5/8
11/32	9/32	13/16	93.8	13	6 1/2	3 1/4	18 7/8	8 3/4	1 1/4	1 7/8	2 7/16	2 5/8
3/8	5/16	13/16	94.2	14	7	3 1/2	19 1/8	8 3/4	1 1/4	1 7/8	2 7/16	2 3/4
13/32	5/16	13/16	94.2	14	7	3 1/2	19 1/8	8 3/4	1 1/4	1 7/8	2 7/16	2 3/4
7/16	3/8	15/16	94.0	15 1/2	7 3/4	3 7/8	21 3/8	9 3/4	1 7/16	2	2 3/4	3 1/16
15/32	3/8	15/16	94.0	15 1/2	7 3/4	3 7/8	21 3/8	9 3/4	1 7/16	2	2 3/4	3 1/16
1/2	7/16	15/16	94.1	16	8	4	21 1/2	9 3/4	1 7/16	2	2 3/4	3 1/8
17/32	7/16	15/16	94.1	16	8	4	21 1/2	9 3/4	1 7/16	2	2 3/4	3 1/8
9/16	7/16	15/16	94.1	16	8	4	21 1/2	9 3/4	1 7/16	2	2 3/4	3 1/8
9/16	7/16	1 1/16	93.4	16	8	4	23 5/8	11	1 5/8	2 1/4	3	3 5/16
19/32	1/2	1 1/16	93.4	16	8	4	23 5/8	11	1 5/8	2 1/4	3	3 5/16
5/8	1/2	1 1/16	93.4	16	8	4	23 5/8	11	1 5/8	2 1/4	3	3 5/16
21/32	1/2	1 1/16	93.4	16	8	4	23 5/8	11	1 5/8	2 1/4	3	3 5/16
11/16	1/2	1 3/16	92.8	16 1/2	8 1/4	4 1/8	25 5/8	12	1 13/16	2 3/8	3 1/4	3 9/16
23/32	1/2	1 3/16	92.8	16 1/2	8 1/4	4 1/8	25 5/8	12	1 13/16	2 3/8	3 1/4	3 9/16
3/4	1/2	1 3/16	92.7	16 1/2	8 1/4	4 1/8	25 5/8	12	1 13/16	2 3/8	3 1/4	3 9/16
25/32	9/16	1 5/16	92.3	17	8 1/2	4 1/4	27 7/8	13 1/4	2	2 5/8	3 1/2	3 13/16
13/16	9/16	1 5/16	92.3	17	8 1/2	4 1/4	27 7/8	13 1/4	2	2 5/8	3 1/2	3 13/16
27/32	9/16	1 5/16	91.8	17	8 1/2	4 1/4	27 7/8	13 1/4	2	2 5/8	3 1/2	3 13/16
7/8	5/8	1 5/16	91.2	17 1/2	8 3/4	4 3/8	28	13 1/4	2	2 5/8	3 1/2	3 7/8
29/32	5/8	1 5/16	90.5	17 1/2	8 3/4	4 3/8	28	13 1/4	2	2 5/8	3 1/2	3 7/8
15/16	11/16	1 5/16	90.1	18	9	4 1/2	28 1/8	13 1/4	2	2 5/8	3 1/2	3 15/16
31/32	11/16	1 5/16	89.5	18	9	4 1/2	28 1/8	13 1/4	2	2 5/8	3 1/2	3 15/16
1	3/4	1 7/16	90.2	19	9 1/2	4 3/4	30 1/2	14 1/2	2 3/16	2 7/8	3 3/4	4 1/4
1 1/32	3/4	1 7/16	89.6	19	9 1/2	4 3/4	30 1/2	14 1/2	2 3/16	2 7/8	3 3/4	4 1/4
1 1/16	3/4	1 7/16	89.0	19	9 1/2	4 3/4	30 1/2	14 1/2	2 3/16	2 7/8	3 3/4	4 1/4
1 3/32	3/4	1 7/16	88.5	19	9 1/2	4 3/4	30 1/2	14 1/2	2 3/16	2 7/8	3 3/4	4 1/4
1 1/8	3/4	1 7/16	88.0	19	9 1/2	4 3/4	30 1/2	14 1/2	2 3/16	2 7/8	3 3/4	4 1/4
1 5/32	3/4	1 7/16	87.5	19	9 1/2	4 3/4	30 1/2	14 1/2	2 3/16	2 7/8	3 3/4	4 1/4
1 3/16	13/16	1 7/16	87.7	20	10	5	30 5/8	14 1/2	2 3/16	2 7/8	3 3/4	4 5/16
1 7/32	13/16	1 7/16	87.2	20	10	5	30 5/8	14 1/2	2 3/16	2 7/8	3 3/4	4 5/16
1 1/4	7/8	1 7/16	86.8	20	10	5	30 5/8	14 1/2	2 3/16	2 7/8	3 3/4	4 5/16

The preceding equations may be used to determine the **efficiency** of any form of riveted joint of known dimensions. When designing, the most economic relations between the pitch and diameter of rivet and the thickness of plate obtain when the three efficiencies are equal. If then these be equated and solved for p, d, and t, it will be found that, for the **longitudinal seams** of boilers and tanks,

$$t = PD(nf_c + mf_c' + f_t)/2(nf_c + mf_c')f_t$$
$$d = 4(nf_c + mf_c')t/\pi(nf_s + 2mf_s')$$
$$p = [\pi d^2(nf_s + 2mf_s')/4tf_t] + d$$

A factor of safety of 4½ or 5 is used in determining the value of t.

For iron plates and rivets, $f_s = 38{,}000$, $f_c = 65{,}000$, $f_s' = 35{,}500$, $f_c' = 80{,}000$; for steel plates and rivets, $f_s = 44{,}000$, $f_c = 90{,}000$, $f_s' = 45{,}000$, $f_c' = 110{,}000$; $f_t =$ 40,000 for iron and 55,000 for steel.

For the **girth seam** of single- or double-riveted lap joints, since the thickness of plate and diameter of rivets are established (all holes being of the same diameter for economy in fabrication), the pitch is determined such that a sufficient number of rivets may be placed to take up the total load on the joint with the proper limits of stress in shear and compression. The total load on the rivets in a girth seam is equal to $\pi D^2P/4$. The equations for t, d, and p will be found to give proportions ensuring steamtightness up to pressures of 200 psi when joints are properly calked.

The following **general practice rules** will be also found to be serviceable:

1. Butt joints are to be preferred to lap joints, since the latter occasion severe bending stresses in the rivet, which is a most frequent cause for failure.
2. The distance from the center line of the row of rivet holes nearest the edge of plate to edge of plate should be 1½ to 2 times rivet diameter.
3. The rivet diameter should be $d = 1.2\sqrt{t}$ to $1.4\sqrt{t}$.
4. In multiple-riveted joints, the minimum distance between rows of rivets is $1.7d$ or 0.6 to 0.8 pitch for staggered riveting. For chain riveting, this should be at least $2d$ and preferably $2\frac{1}{2}d$.

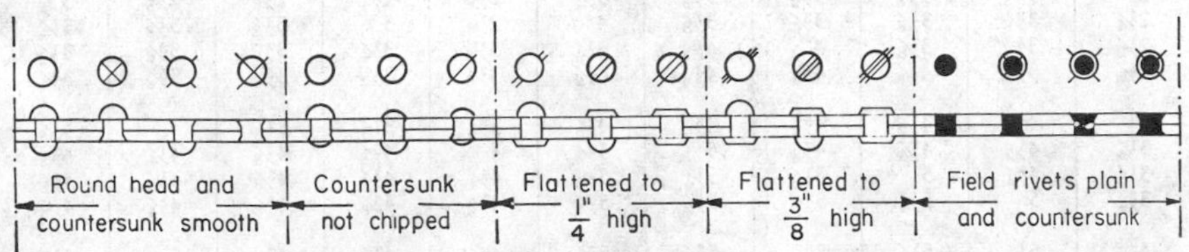

FIG. 34. Conventional signs for rivets.

Materials Specifications for Rivets and Plates. See p. 6-46.

Conventional signs to indicate the form of the head to be used and whether the rivet is to be driven in the shop or the field at the time of erection are given in Fig. 34. The **lengths of rivets for various grips** are given in Table 41 (see also Fig. 35).

For **structural riveting,** see Sec. 12.

Punched vs. Drilled Plates. Holes in plates forming parts of riveted structures are punched, punched and reamed, or drilled. Punching, while cheaper, is objectionable. The holes in different plates cannot be spaced with sufficient accuracy to register perfectly on being assembled. If the hole is punched out, say ¹⁄₁₆ in. smaller than is required and then reamed to size, the metal injury by cold flow during punching will be removed. Annealing after punching also largely obviates the injury. Drilling, while more expensive, is more accurate and does not injure the metal. The Massachusetts Boiler Inspection Law states:

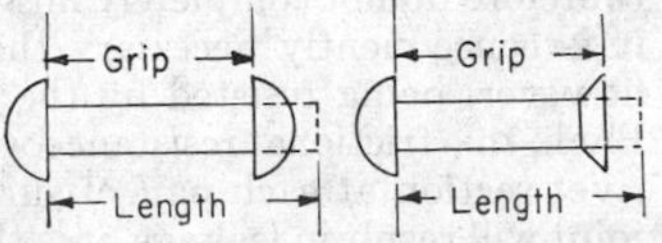

FIG. 35. Rivet length and grip.

> Rivet holes, excepting for attaching stays or angle bars to heads, shall be drilled full size with plates, butt straps, and heads bolted up in position; or they may be punched not to exceed ¼ in. less than full size for plates over ⁵⁄₁₆ in. in thickness, and ⅛ in. less than full size for plates not exceeding ⁵⁄₁₆ in. in thickness, and then drilled or reamed to full size with plates, butt straps and heads bolted up in position.

The U.S. Navy Department specifies that all holes in boiler plates must be drilled with the plates in place. In structural work, the holes are generally punched for shop riveting, while for field riveting it is usual to drill them to a template, or, if punched, to ream them with the parts to be connected bolted in place.

The **tensile strength** of the metal between holes drilled in a plate has been found to be greater than that of an undrilled plate. For the spacings usual in riveted work, the increase in strength as shown by experiment is 10 to 12 percent. Punching, on the other hand, results in a loss of tensile strength, experiments showing the strength of the metal between the holes to be 5 to 20 percent under that of unpunched plates in the case of iron, and 8 to 35 percent in the case of steel plates. With the latter, the loss increases with the thickness of the plate.

Hand-riveted joints are of practically the same strength as those machine-riveted, but the load at which visible slip occurs is much greater with machine riveting. In hot

Table 41. Lengths of Rivets for Various Grips for Boilers

Grip, in. (see Fig. 35)	Round-head rivets					Countersunk-head rivets				
	Diam, in.					Diam, in.				
	½	⅝	¾	⅞	1	½	⅝	¾	⅞	1
	Length, in.					Length, in.				
1	2	2¼	2⅜	2½	2⅝	1⅝	1¾	1¾	1⅞	1⅞
1¼	2¼	2½	2⅝	2¾	2⅞	1⅞	2	2	2⅛	2⅛
1½	2⅝	2⅞	3	3⅛	3¼	2⅛	2¼	2⅜	2⅜	2½
1¾	2⅞	3⅛	3¼	3⅜	3½	2⅜	2½	2⅝	2⅝	2¾
2	3⅛	3⅜	3½	3⅝	3¾	2⅝	2¾	2⅞	2⅞	3
2¼	3⅜	3⅝	3¾	3⅞	4	2⅞	3	3⅛	3⅛	3¼
2½	3⅝	3⅞	4	4⅛	4¼	3⅛	3¼	3⅜	3⅜	3½
2¾	3⅞	4⅛	4¼	4⅜	4½	3⅜	3½	3⅝	3⅝	3¾
3	4¼	4½	4⅝	4¾	4⅞	3¾	3⅞	3⅞	4	4⅛
3¼	4½	4¾	4⅞	5	5⅛	4	4⅛	4⅛	4¼	4⅜
3½	4¾	5	5⅛	5¼	5⅜	4¼	4⅜	4⅜	4½	4⅝
3¾	5	5¼	5⅜	5½	5⅝	4½	4⅝	4⅝	4¾	4⅞
4	5¼	5½	5⅝	5¾	5⅞	4¾	4⅞	4⅞	5	5⅛
4½	5¾	6	6¼	6⅜	6½	5¼	5⅜	5½	5½	5⅝
5	6⅜	6⅝	6¾	6⅞	7	5⅞	6	6	6	6⅛

riveting, pressures up to 150,000 psi and even higher are used, and in cold riveting the pressure required is about 300,000 psi of rivet section. Where the pressure exceeds 225,000 to 270,000 psi, however, there is danger that the lateral pressure of the rivet may crack the plate.

Frictional Resistance of Riveted Joints. Rivets in cooling contract longitudinally and draw the plates together with considerable force. They also contract laterally and therefore do not completely fill their holes when cold. Before shearing can take place, it is consequently necessary that the plates shall slip on each other, such slipping, however, being resisted by the friction of the surfaces in contact. According to C. Bach, this frictional resistance when slipping begins ranges from 14,000 to 30,000 psi of rivet section at each pair of surfaces in contact. As any appreciable slip of a boiler joint will result in leakage, it is the practice of European engineers to design such joints according to rules based by Bach on the resistance to slipping. The proportions specified in these rules, however, do not differ greatly from those based on a consideration of shearing strength.

KEYS, PINS, AND COTTERS

Keys have been standardized by the ASA and are given in their Standard B17.1. Descriptions of the principal type keys follows.

Woodruff keys are made to facilitate removal of pulleys from shafts. They should not be used as sliding keys. SAE Standards should be consulted. Cutters for milling out the key seats, as well as special machines for using the cutters, are to be had from the manufacturer. Where the hub of the gear or pulley is relatively long, two keys should be used. Slightly rounding the corners or ends of these keys will obviate any difficulty met with in removing pulleys from shafts. The key is shown in Fig. 36 and the dimensions in Table 42.

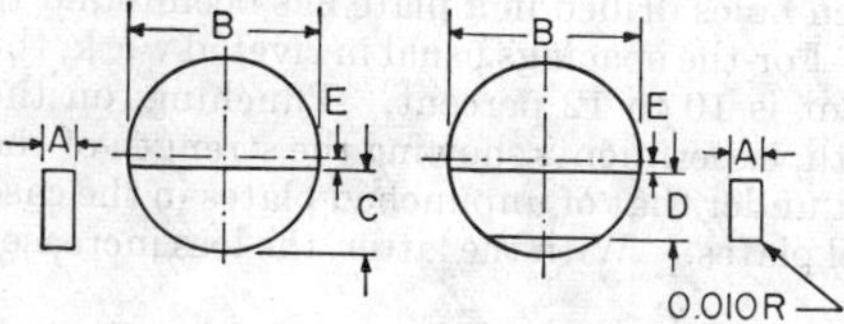

FIG. 36. Woodruff key.

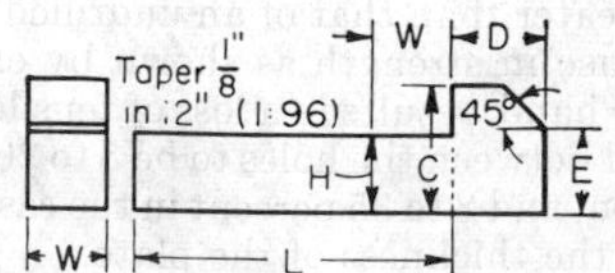

FIG. 37. Gib-head taper stock key.

Table 42. Woodruff Key Dimensions

(All dimensions in inches)

Key No.	Nominal key size, $A \times B$	Width of key, A		Diam of key, B		Height of key				Distance below E
						C		D		
		Max	Min	Max	Min	Max	Min	Max	Min	
204	1/16 × 1/2	0.0635	0.0625	0.500	0.490	0.203	0.198	0.194	0.188	3/64
304	3/32 × 1/2	0.0948	0.0928	0.500	0.490	0.203	0.198	0.194	0.188	3/64
305	3/32 × 5/8	0.0948	0.0938	0.625	0.615	0.250	0.245	0.240	0.234	1/16
404	1/8 × 1/2	0.1260	0.1250	0.500	0.490	0.203	0.198	0.194	0.188	3/64
405	1/8 × 5/8	0.1260	0.1250	0.625	0.615	0.250	0.245	0.240	0.234	1/16
406	1/8 × 3/4	0.1260	0.1250	0.750	0.740	0.313	0.308	0.303	0.297	1/16
505	5/32 × 5/8	0.1573	0.1563	0.625	0.615	0.250	0.245	0.240	0.234	1/16
506	5/32 × 3/4	0.1573	0.1563	0.750	0.740	0.313	0.308	0.303	0.297	1/16
507	5/32 × 7/8	0.1573	0.1563	0.875	0.865	0.375	0.370	0.365	0.359	1/16
606	3/16 × 3/4	0.1885	0.1875	0.750	0.740	0.313	0.308	0.303	0.297	1/16
607	3/16 × 7/8	0.1885	0.1875	0.875	0.865	0.375	0.370	0.365	0.359	1/16
608	3/16 × 1	0.1885	0.1875	1.000	0.990	0.438	0.433	0.428	0.422	1/16
609	3/16 × 1 1/8	0.1885	0.1875	1.125	1.115	0.484	0.479	0.475	0.469	5/64
807	1/4 × 7/8	0.2510	0.2500	0.875	0.865	0.375	0.370	0.365	0.359	1/16
808	1/4 × 1	0.2510	0.2500	1.000	0.990	0.438	0.433	0.428	0.422	1/16
809	1/4 × 1 1/8	0.2510	0.2500	1.125	1.115	0.484	0.479	0.475	0.469	5/64
810	1/4 × 1 1/4	0.2510	0.2500	1.250	1.240	0.547	0.542	0.537	0.531	5/64
811	1/4 × 1 3/8	0.2510	0.2500	1.375	1.365	0.594	0.589	0.584	0.578	3/32
812	1/4 × 1 1/2	0.2510	0.2500	1.500	1.490	0.641	0.636	0.631	0.625	7/64
1008	5/16 × 1	0.3135	0.3125	1.000	0.990	0.438	0.433	0.428	0.422	1/16
1009	5/16 × 1 1/8	0.3135	0.3125	1.125	1.115	0.484	0.479	0.475	0.469	5/64
1010	5/16 × 1 1/4	0.3135	0.3125	1.250	1.240	0.547	0.542	0.537	0.531	5/64
1011	5/16 × 1 3/8	0.3135	0.3125	1.375	1.365	0.594	0.589	0.584	0.578	3/32
1012	5/16 × 1 1/2	0.3135	0.3125	1.500	1.490	0.641	0.636	0.631	0.625	7/64
1210	3/8 × 1 1/4	0.3760	0.3750	1.250	1.240	0.547	0.542	0.537	0.531	5/64
1211	3/8 × 1 3/8	0.3760	0.3750	1.375	1.365	0.594	0.589	0.584	0.578	3/32
1212	3/8 × 1 1/2	0.3760	0.3750	1.500	1.490	0.641	0.636	0.631	0.625	7/64

Numbers indicate the nominal key dimensions. The last two digits give the nominal diameter (B) in eighths of an inch and the digits preceding the last two give the nominal width (A) in thirty-seconds of an inch. Thus, 204 indicates a key 2/32 × 4/8 or 1/16 × 1/2 in.; 1210 indicates a key 12/32 × 10/8 or 3/8 × 1 1/4 in.

Square and flat plain taper keys have the same dimensions as gib-head keys (Table 43) up to the dotted line of Fig. 37. **Gib-head keys** (Fig. 37) are necessary when the smaller end is inaccessible for drifting out and the larger end is accessible. It can be used, with care, with all sizes of shafts. Its use is forbidden in certain jobs and places for safety reasons. Proportions are given in Table 43.

The minimum stock length of keys is four times the key width, and the maximum stock length of keys is sixteen times the key width. The increments of increase of length are two times the width.

Sunk keys are made to the form and dimensions given in Fig. 38 and Table 44. These keys are adapted particularly to the case of hubs fittlng adjacent parts with neither end of the key accessible. **Feather keys** to prevent parts from turning on a shaft while allowing them to move in a lengthwise direction. They are of the forms shown in Fig. 39 with dimensions as given in Table 44. **Saddle keys and flat keys** (Fig. 40) are used only for the transmission of small torques that are never liable to sudden changes in magnitude. Under excessive stresses, they turn around the shaft and damage it.

In **transmitting large torques,** it is customary to use two or more keys, as shown in Figs. 41 and 42. The arrangement shown in Fig. 41 permits more ready cutting

Table 43. Dimensions of Square and Flat Gib-head Taper Stock Keys*

(All dimensions in inches)

Shaft diam	Square type: Key: Max width, W	Square type: Key: Height at large end,† H	Square type: Gib-head: Height, C	Square type: Gib-head: Length, D	Square type: Gib-head: Height edge of chamfer, E	Flat type: Key: Max width, W	Flat type: Key: Height at large end,† H	Flat type: Gib-head: Height, C	Flat type: Gib-head: Length, D	Flat type: Gib-head: Height edge of chamfer, E	Tolerance: On width (−)	Tolerance: On height (+)
1/2 – 9/16	1/8	1/8	1/4	7/32	5/32	1/8	3/32	3/16	1/8	1/8	0.0020	0.0020
5/8 – 7/8	3/16	3/16	5/16	9/32	7/32	3/16	1/8	1/4	3/16	5/32	0.0020	0.0020
15/16 – 1 1/4	1/4	1/4	7/16	11/32	11/32	1/4	3/16	5/16	1/4	3/16	0.0020	0.0020
1 5/16 – 1 3/8	5/16	5/16	9/16	13/32	13/32	5/16	1/4	3/8	5/16	1/4	0.0020	0.0020
1 7/16 – 1 3/4	3/8	3/8	11/16	15/32	15/32	3/8	1/4	7/16	3/8	5/16	0.0020	0.0020
1 13/16 – 2 1/4	1/2	1/2	7/8	19/32	5/8	1/2	3/8	5/8	1/2	7/16	0.0025	0.0025
2 5/16 – 2 3/4	5/8	5/8	1 1/16	23/32	3/4	5/8	7/16	3/4	5/8	1/2	0.0025	0.0025
2 7/8 – 3 1/4	3/4	3/4	1 1/4	7/8	7/8	3/4	1/2	7/8	3/4	5/8	0.0025	0.0025
3 3/8 – 3 3/4	7/8	7/8	1 1/2	1	1	7/8	5/8	1 1/16	7/8	3/4	0.0030	0.0030
3 7/8 – 4 1/2	1	1	1 3/4	1 3/16	1 3/16	1	3/4	1 1/4	1	1 3/16	0.0030	0.0030
4 3/4 – 5 1/2	1 1/4	1 1/4	2	1 7/16	1 7/16	1 1/4	7/8	1 1/2	1 1/4	1	0.0030	0.0030
5 3/4 – 6	1 1/2	1 1/2	2 1/2	1 3/4	1 3/4	1 1/2	1	1 3/4	1 1/2	1 1/4	0.0030	0.0030

* Stock keys are applicable to the general run of work and the tolerances have been set accordingly. They are not intended to cover the finer applications where a closer fit may be required.

† This height of the key is measured at the distance W equal to the width of the key, from the gib head.

of the keyway. If but one key is used with the arrangement shown in Fig. 42, torque can be taken in only one direction.

Another means for fastening gears, pulleys flanges, etc., to shafts is through the use of mating pairs of tapered sleeves known as **Grip-springs.** A set of sleeves is shown in Fig. 43. For further references see data issued by the U.S. Automatic Corp.

Tapered pins (Fig. 44) can be used to transmit very small torques or for positioning. They should be fitted so that the parts are drawn together when the pin is driven home to prevent their working loose. Table 45 gives dimensions of Morse tapered pins.

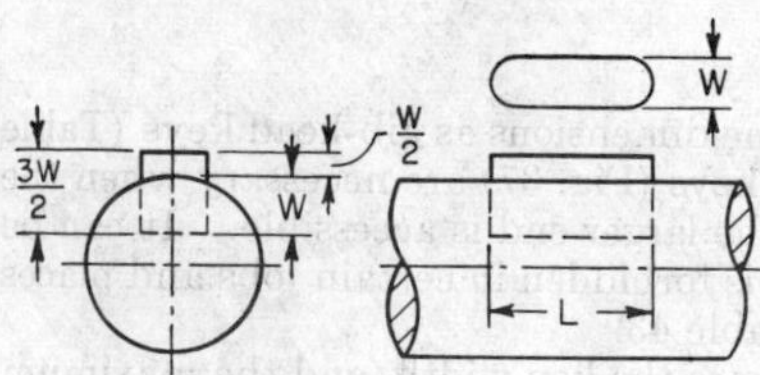

Fig. 38. Sunk key.

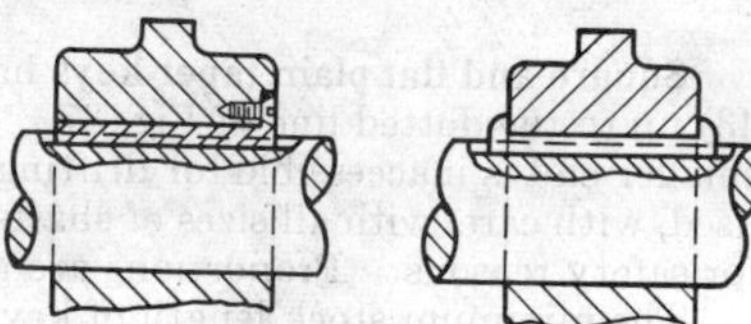
Fig. 39. Feather key.

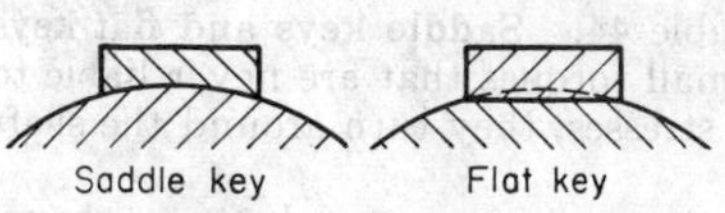

Fig. 40

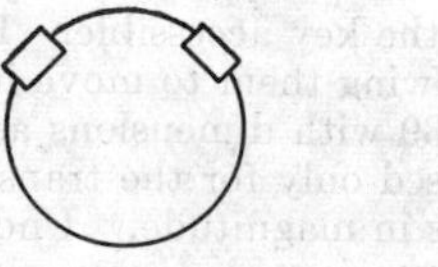
Double keying of shafts.

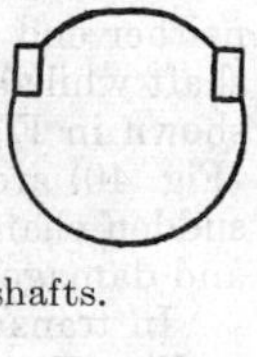

Fig. 41

Fig. 42

Table 44. Dimensions of Sunk Keys
(All dimensions in inches. Letters refer to Fig. 38)

Key No.	*L*	*W*	Key No.	*L*	*W*	Key No.	*L*	*W*	Key No.	*L*	*W*
1	1/2	1/16	13	1	3/16	22	1 3/8	1/4	54	2 1/4	1/4
2	1/2	3/32	14	1	7/32	23	1 3/8	5/16	55	2 1/4	5/16
3	1/2	1/8	15	1	1/4	F	1 3/8	3/8	56	2 1/4	3/8
4	5/8	3/32	B	1	5/16	24	1 1/2	1/4	57	2 1/4	7/16
5	5/8	1/8	16	1 1/8	3/16	25	1 1/2	5/16	58	2 1/2	5/16
6	5/8	5/32	17	1 1/8	7/32	G	1 1/2	3/8	59	2 1/2	3/8
7	3/4	1/8	18	1 1/8	1/4	51	1 3/4	1/4	60	2 1/2	7/16
8	3/4	5/32	C	1 1/8	5/16	52	1 3/4	5/16	61	2 1/2	1/2
9	3/4	3/16	19	1 1/4	3/16	53	1 3/4	3/8	30	3	3/8
10	7/8	5/32	20	1 1/4	7/32	26	2	3/16	31	3	7/16
11	7/8	3/16	21	1 1/4	1/4	27	2	1/4	32	3	1/2
12	7/8	7/32	D	1 1/4	5/16	28	2	5/16	33	3	9/16
A	7/8	1/4	E	1 1/4	3/8	29	2	3/8	34	3	5/8

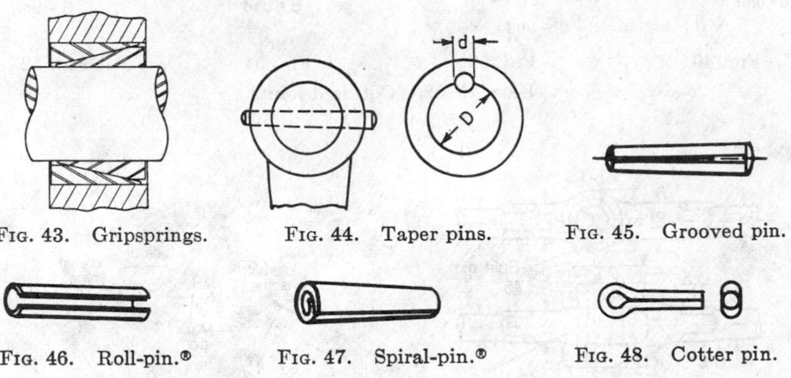

FIG. 43. Gripsprings. FIG. 44. Taper pins. FIG. 45. Grooved pin.

FIG. 46. Roll-pin.® FIG. 47. Spiral-pin.® FIG. 48. Cotter pin.

Table 45. Morse Standard Taper Pins
(Taper, 1/4 in. per ft. Lengths increase by 1/4 in. Dimensions in inches)

Size No.	0	1	2	3	4	5	6	7	8	9	10
Diam at large end	0.156	0.172	0.193	0.219	0.250	0.289	0.341	0.409	0.492	0.591	0.706
Length	0.5–3	0.5–3	0.75–3.5	0.75–3.5	0.75–4	0.75–4	0.75–5	1–5	1.25–5	1.5–6	1.5–6

The Groov-Pin Corp., New Jersey, has developed a special **grooved pin** (Fig. 45) which may be used instead of smooth taper pins in certain cases.

Straight pins, likewise, are used for transmission of light torques or for positioning. **Spring pins** have come into wide use recently. Two types shown in Figs. 46 and 47 deform elastically in the radial direction when driven; the resiliency of the pin material locks the pin in place. They can replace straight and taper pins and combine the advantages of both, *i.e.*, simple tooling, ease of removal, reuseability, ability to be driven from either side.

Cotter pins (Fig. 48) are used to secure or lock nuts, clevises, etc. Driven into holes in the shaft, the eye prevents complete passage, and the split ends, deformed after insertion, prevent withdrawal.

Cottered joints may be employed for fastening rods to other rods, rods to pistons and crossheads, yokes to rods (as in the case of connecting rods), and for services of similar kinds. Some forms of such joints and proportions recommended are shown in Figs. 49 to 52.

When two rods are to be joined so as to permit movement at the joint, a round pin is used in place of a cotter. In such cases, the proportions may be as shown in Fig. 53.

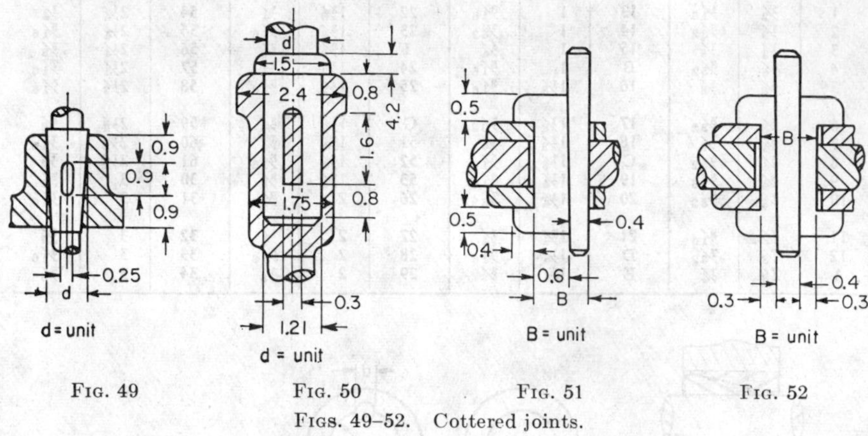

FIG. 49 FIG. 50 FIG. 51 FIG. 52

FIGS. 49–52. Cottered joints.

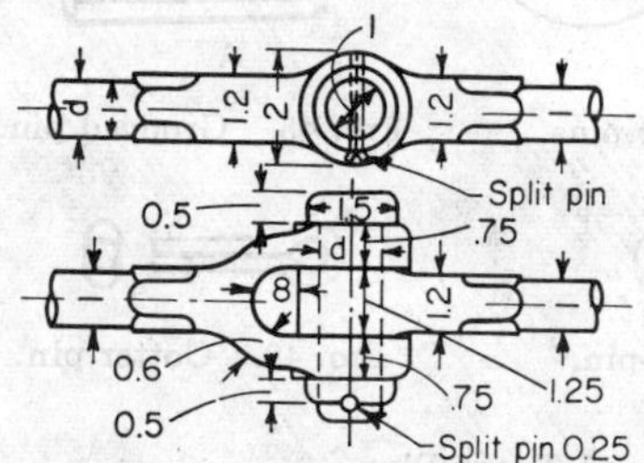

FIG. 53. Knuckle joint.

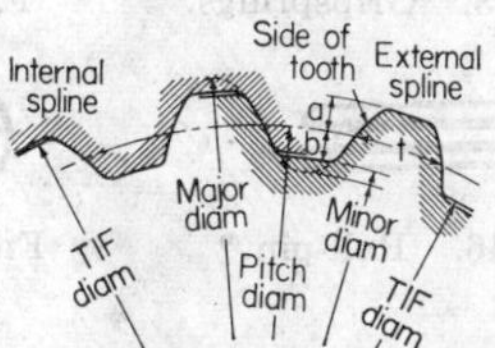

FIG. 54. Involute spline.

SPLINES

Involute spline proportions, dimensions, fits and tolerances are given in detail in ASA publication Involute Splines B5.15, 1950. External and internal involute splines (Fig. 54) have the same general form as involute gear teeth, except that the teeth are one-half the depth of standard gear teeth and the pressure angle is 30 deg. The spline is designated by a fraction in which the numerator is the diametral pitch and the denominator is always twice the numerator.

There are 15 series, as follows: 1/2, 2.5/5, 3/6, 4/8, 5/10, 6/12, 8/16, 10/20, 12/24, 16/32, 20/40, 24/48, 32/64, 40/80, 48/96. The number of teeth within each series varies from 6 to 50. Both a flat-root and a fillet-root type are provided. There are three **types of fits**: (1) **major diameter**—fit controlled by varying the major diameter of the external spline; (2) **sides of teeth**—fit controlled by varying tooth thickness and customarily used for fillet-root splines; (3) **minor diameter**—fit controlled by varying the minor diameter of the internal spline. Each type of fit is further divided into three classes: (*a*) **sliding**—clearance at all points; (*b*) **close**—close on either major diameter, sides of teeth, or minor diameter; (*c*) **press**—interference on either the major diameter sides of teeth, or minor diameter. Important basic formulas for tooth proportions are as follows:

D = pitch diam	a = addendum
N = number of teeth	b = dedendum
P = diametral pitch	D_O = major diam
p = circular pitch	TIF = true involute form diam
t = circular tooth thickness	D_R = minor diam

Flat and fillet roots

$$D = N/P \qquad D_O \text{ (external)} = \frac{N+1}{P}$$

$$p = \pi/P \qquad TIF \text{ (internal)} = \frac{N+1}{P}$$

$$t = p/2 \qquad D_R = \frac{N+1}{P} \text{ (minor diameter fits only)}$$

$$a = 0.5000/P \qquad TIF \text{ (external)} = \frac{N-1}{P}$$

$b = 0.600/P + 0.002$ (For major diameter fits, the internal spline dedendum is the same as the addendum; for minor diameter fits, the dedendum of the external spline is the same as the addendum.)

Fillet root only

½ through ¹²⁄₂₄	¹⁶⁄₃₂ through ⁴⁸⁄₉₆
$D_O \text{ (internal)} = \frac{N+1.8}{P}$	$D_O \text{ (internal)} = \frac{N+1.8}{P}$
$D_R \text{ (external)} = \frac{N-1.8}{P}$	$D_R \text{ (external)} = \frac{N-2}{P}$
b (internal) $= 0.900/P$	b (internal) $= 0.900/P$
b (external) $= 0.900/P$	b (external) $= 1.000/P$

Internal spline dimensions are basic while external spline dimensions are varied to control fit.

The advantages of involute splines are: (1) maximum strength at the minor diameter, (2) self-centering equalizes bearing and stresses among all teeth, and (3) ease of manufacture through the use of standard gear-cutting tools and methods.

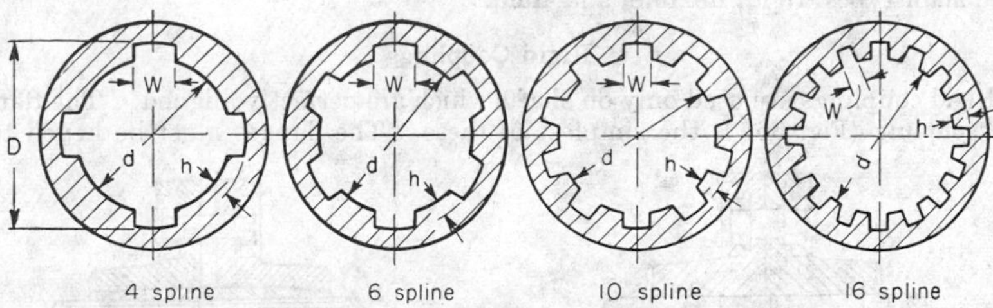

Fig. 55. Parallel-side splines.

The design of involute splines is critical in shear. The torque capacity may be determined by the formula $T = LD^2S_s/1.2732$, where L = the spline length, D = the pitch diam, S_s = allowable shear stress.

Parallel-side splines have been standardized by the SAE for 4, 6, 10, and 16 spline fittings. They are shown in Fig. 55; pertinent data is in Tables 46 and 47.

Table 46. Dimensions of Spline Fittings

(SAE Standard. All dimensions in inches)

Nominal diam	4-spline for all fits		6-spline for all fits		10-spline for all fits		16-spline for all fits	
	D max*	*W* max†	*D* max*	*W* max†	*D* max*	*W* max†	*D* max*	*W* max†
¾	0.750	0.181	0.750	0.188	0.750	0.117		
⅞	0.875	0.211	0.875	0.219	0.875	0.137		
1	1.000	0.241	1.000	0.250	1.000	0.156		
1⅛	1.125	0.271	1.125	0.281	1.125	0.176		
1¼	1.250	0.301	1.250	0.313	1.250	0.195		
1⅜	1.375	0.331	1.375	0.344	1.375	0.215		
1½	1.500	0.361	1.500	0.375	1.500	0.234		
1⅝	1.625	0.391	1.625	0.406	1.625	0.254		
1¾	1.750	0.422	1.750	0.438	1.750	0.273		
2	2.000	0.482	2.000	0.500	2.000	0.312	2.000	0.196
2¼	2.250	0.542	2.250	0.563	2.250	0.351		
2½	2.500	0.602	2.500	0.625	2.500	0.390	2.500	0.245
3	3.000	0.723	3.000	0.750	3.000	0.468	3.000	0.294
3½	.....	.....	.....	.....	3.500	0.546	3.500	0.343
4	.....	.....	.....	.....	4.000	0.624	4.000	0.392
4½	.....	.....	.....	.....	4.500	0.702	4.500	0.441
5	.....	.....	.....	.....	5.000	0.780	5.000	0.490
5½	.....	.....	.....	.....	5.500	0.858	5.500	0.539
6	.....	.....	.....	.....	6.000	0.936	6.000	0.588

* Tolerance allowed of −0.001 in. for shafts ¾ to 1¾ in., inclusive; of −0.002 for shafts 2 to 3 in., inclusive; −0.003 in. for shafts 3½ to 6-in., inclusive, for 4-, 6-, and 10-spline fittings; tolerance of −0.003 in. allowed for all sizes of 16-spline fittings.

† Tolerance allowed of −0.002 in. for shafts ¾ in., to 1¾ in., inclusive; of −0.003 in. for shafts 2 to 6 in., inclusive, for 4-, 6-, and 10-spline fittings; tolerance of −0.003 allowed for all sizes of 16-spline fittings.

Table 47. Spline Proportions

No. of splines	*W* for all fits	Permanent fit		To slide when not under load		To slide under load	
		h	*d*	*h*	*d*	*h*	*d*
4	0.241*D*	0.075*D*	0.850*D*	0.125*D*	0.750*D*		
6	0.250*D*	0.050*D*	0.900*D*	0.075*D*	0.850*D*	0.100*D*	0.800*D*
10	0.156*D*	0.045*D*	0.910*D*	0.070*D*	0.860*D*	0.095*D*	0.810*D*
16	0.098*D*	0.045*D*	0.910*D*	0.070*D*	0.860*D*	0.095*D*	0.810*D*

COUPLINGS

A **coupling** makes a semipermanent connection between two shafts. They are of three main types: **rigid, flexible, and fluid.**

Rigid Couplings

Rigid couplings are used only on shafts which are perfectly aligned. The **flanged-face coupling** (Fig. 56) is the simplest of these. The flanges must be keyed to the

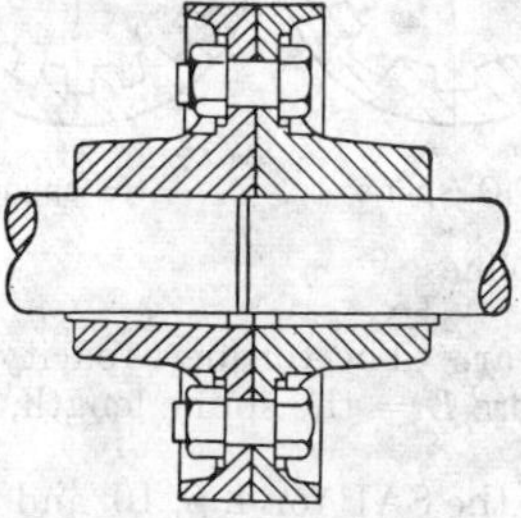

Fig. 56. Flanged face coupling.

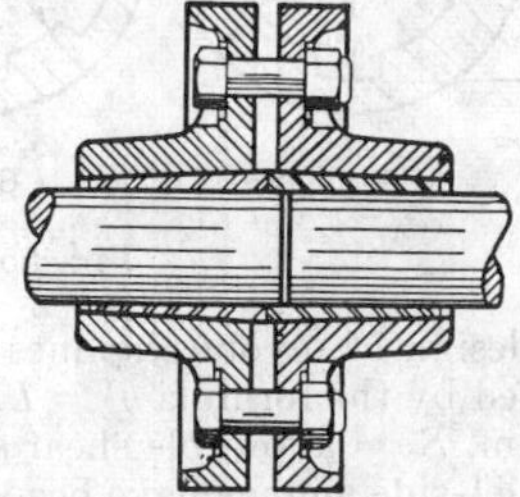

Fig. 57. Keyless compression coupling.

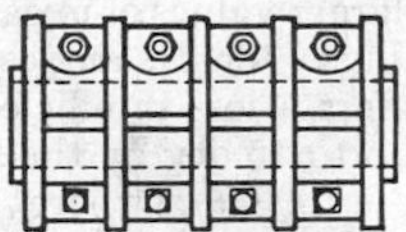

Fig. 58. Ribbed-clamp coupling

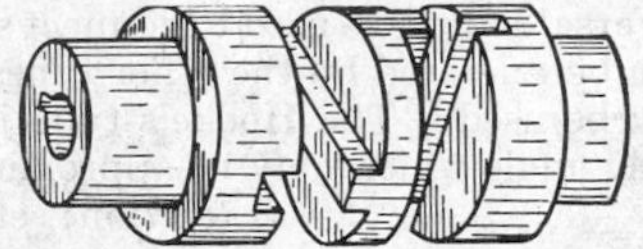

Fig. 59. Double-slider coupling.

shafts. The **keyless compression coupling** (Fig. 57) affords a simple means for connecting abutting shafts without the necessity of key seats on the shafts. The two flanges when drawn over the slotted tapered sleeve automatically center the shafts and provide sufficient contact pressure to transmit medium or light loads. **Ribbed-clamp couplings** (Fig. 58) are split longitudinally and are bored to the shaft diameter with a shim separating the two halves. It is necessary to key the shafts to the coupling.

Flexible Couplings

Flexible couplings are designed to connect shafts which are misaligned either laterally or angularly. A secondary benefit is the absorption of impacts due to fluctuations in shaft torque or angular speed. The **Oldham, or double-slider, coupling** (Fig. 59) may be used to connect shafts which have only lateral misalignment. The

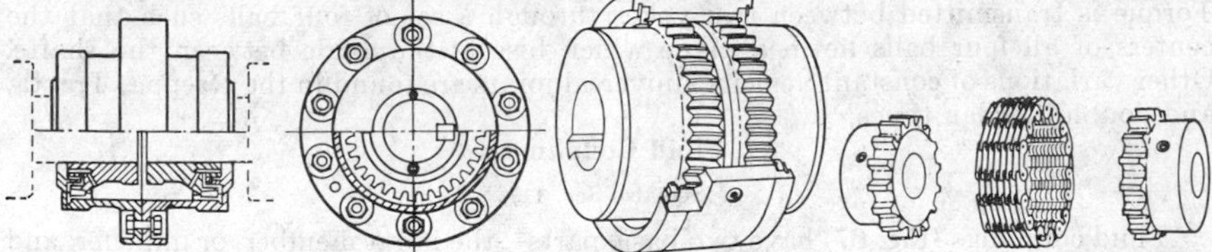

Fig. 60. "Fast" flexible coupling. Fig. 61. Waldron coupling. Fig. 62. Chain coupling.

"Fast" flexible coupling (Fig. 60) consists of two hubs each keyed to its respective shaft. Each hub has generated splines cut at the maximum possible distance from the shaft end. Surrounding the hubs is a casing or sleeve which is split transversely and bolted by means of flanges. Each half of this sleeve has generated internal splines cut on its bore at the end opposite to the flange. These internal splines permit a definite error of alignment between the two shafts.

Another type, the Waldron coupling (Midland-Ross Corp.), is shown in Fig. 61.

The chain coupling shown in Fig. 62 uses silent chain, but standard roller chain can be used with the proper mating sprockets. Nylon links enveloping the sprockets are another variation of the chain coupling.

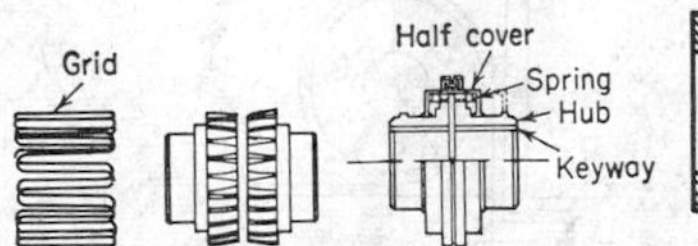

Fig. 63. Falk Steelflex® coupling.

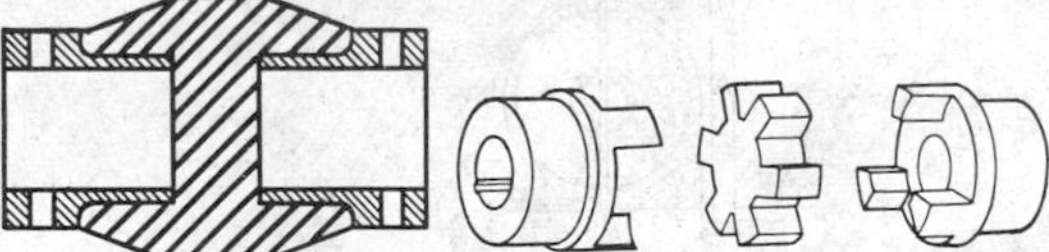

Fig. 64. Rubber flexible coupling, shear type. Fig. 65. Rubber flexible coupling, compression type.

Steelflex® couplings (Fig. 63) are made with two grooved steel hubs keyed to their respective shafts. Connection between the two halves is secured by a specially tempered alloy-steel member called the "grid."

In the rubber flexible coupling shown in Fig. 64, the torque is transmitted through a comparatively soft rubber section acting in shear. The type in Fig. 65 loads the intermediate rubber member in compression. Both types permit reasonable shaft misalignment and are recommended for light loads only.

Universal joints are used to connect shafts with much larger values of misalignment than can be tolerated by the other types of flexible couplings. Shafts angles up to 30 deg may be used. The Hooke's-type joint (Fig. 66) suffers a loss in efficiency with increasing angle which may be approximated for angles up to 15 deg by the following relation: efficiency $= 100(1 - 0.003\theta)$, where θ is the angle between the shafts. The velocity ratio between input and output shafts with a single universal joint is equal to

$$\omega_2/\omega_1 = \cos\theta/1 - \sin^2\theta \sin^2(\alpha + 90°)$$

where ω_2 and ω_1 are the angular velocities of the driven and driving shafts respectively, θ is the angle between the shafts, and α is the angular displacement of the driving shaft from the position where the pins on the drive shaft yoke lie in the plane of the two shafts. A velocity ratio of 1 may be obtained at any angle using two Hooke's-type joints and an intermediate shaft. The intermediate shaft must make equal angles with the main shafts, and the driving pins on the yokes attached to the intermediate shaft must be set parallel to each other.

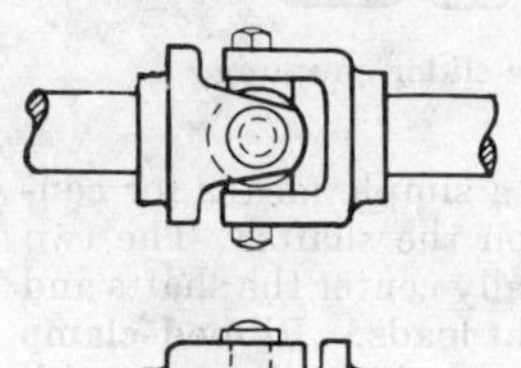

Fig. 66. Hooke's universal joint.

The Bendix-Weiss "rolling-ball" universal joint provides constant angular velocity. Torque is transmitted between two yokes through a set of four balls such that the centers of all four balls lie in a plane which bisects the angle between the shafts. Other variations of constant velocity universal joints are found in the Rzeppa, Tracta, and double Cardan types.

Fluid Couplings

(See also Sec. 11)

Fluid couplings (Fig. 67) have two basic parts—the input member, or impeller, and the output member, or runner. There is no mechanical connection between the two shafts, power being transmitted by kinetic energy in the operating fluid. The impeller B is fastened to the flywheel A and turns at engine speed. As this speed increases, fluid within the impeller moves toward the outer periphery because of centrifugal force. The circular shape of the impeller directs the fluid toward the runner C, where its kinetic energy is absorbed as torque delivered by shaft D. The positive pressure behind the fluid causes flow to continue toward the hub and back through the impeller. The toroidal space in both the impeller and runner is divided into compartments by a series of flat radial vanes.

The torque capacity of a fluid coupling with a full-load slip of about 2.5 percent is $T = 0.09n^2D^5$, where n is the impeller speed, hundreds of rpm, and D is the outside diameter, ft. The output torque is equal to the input torque over the entire range of

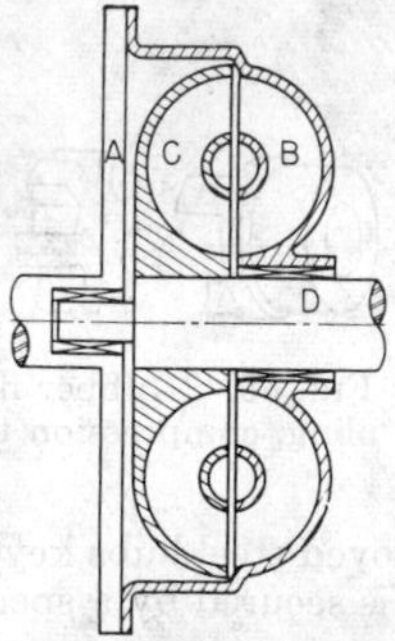

Fig. 67. Fluid coupling: (*A*) flywheel; (*B*) impeller; (*C*) runner; (*D*) output shaft.

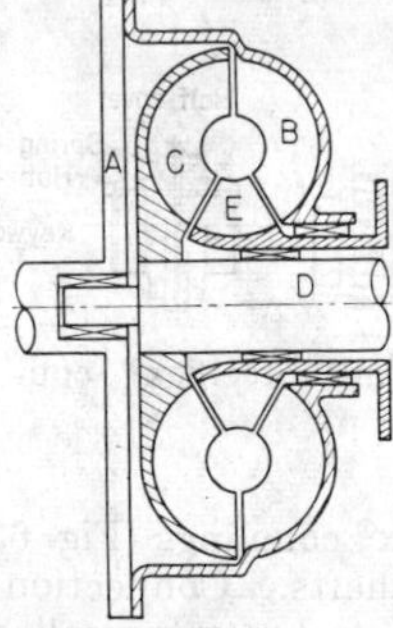

Fig. 68. Hydraulic torque converter: (*A*) flywheel; (*B*) impeller; (*C*) runner; (*D*) output shaft; (*E*) reactor.

input-output speed ratios. Thus the prime mover can be operated at its most effective speed regardless of the speed of the output shaft. Other advantages are that the prime mover cannot be stalled by application of load and that there is no transmission of shock loads or torsional vibration between the connected shafts.

An **hydraulic torque converter** (Fig. 68) is similar in form to the hydraulic coupling, with the addition of a set of stationary guide vans, the reactor, interposed between the runner and the impeller. All blades in a converter have compound curvature. This curvature is designed to control the direction of fluid flow. Kinetic energy is therefore transferred as a result of both a scalar and vectorial change in fluid velocity. The blades are designed such that the fluid will be moving in a direction parallel to the blade surface at the entrance (Fig. 69) to each section. With a design having fixed

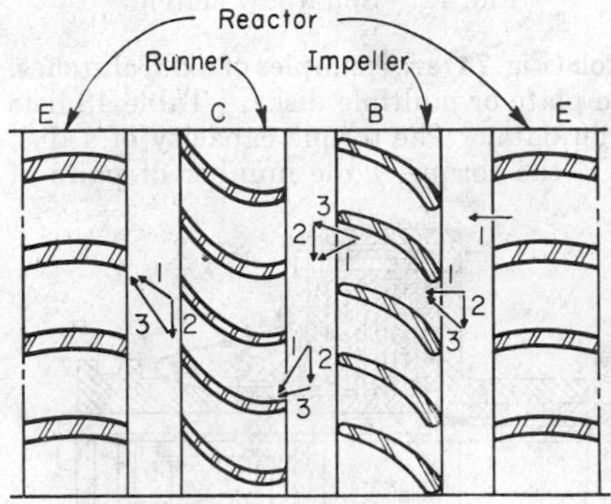

Fig. 69. Schematic of converter blading: (1) absolute fluid velocity; (2) velocity vector-converter elements; (3) fluid velocity relative to converter elements.

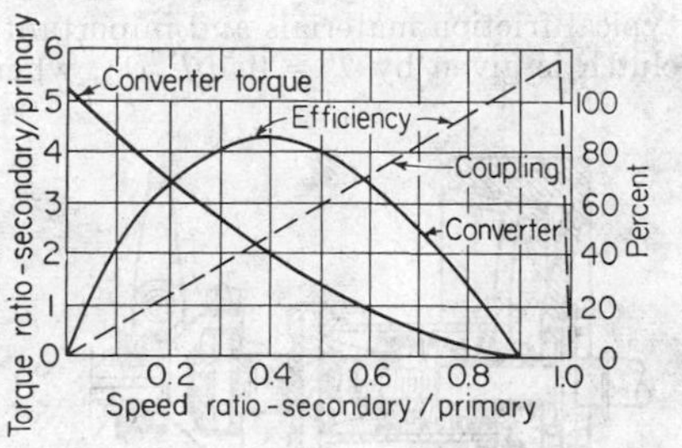

Fig. 70. Hydraulic coupling characteristic curves. (*Heldt, "Torque Converters and Transmissions," Chilton.*)

blading, this can be true at only one value of runner and impeller velocity, called the design point. Several design modifications are possible to overcome this difficulty. The angle of the blades can be made adjustable, and the elements can be divided into sections operating independently of each other according to the load requirements. Other refinements include the addition of multiple stages in the runner and reactor stages as in steam reaction turbines (see Sec. 9). The advantages of a torque converter are the ability to multiply starting torque five to six times and to serve as a stepless transmission. As in the coupling, torque varies as the square of speed and the fifth power of diameter.

Optimum efficiency (Fig. 70) over the range of input-output speed ratios is obtained by a combination converter coupling. When the output speed rises to the point where the torque multiplication factor is 1.0, the clutch point, the torque reaction on the reactor element reverses direction. If the reactor is mounted to freewheel in this opposite direction, the unit will act as a coupling over the higher speed ranges. An automatic friction clutch (see Clutches, below) set to engage at or near the clutch point will also eliminate the poor efficiency of the converter at high output speeds.

CLUTCHES

Clutches are couplings which permit the disengagement of the coupled shafts during rotation.

Positive clutches are designed to transmit torque without slip. The **jaw clutch** is the most common type of positive clutch. These are made with **square jaws** (Fig. 71) for driving in both directions or **spiral jaws** (Fig. 72) for unidirectional drive. Engagement speed should be limited to 10 rpm for square jaws and 150 rpm for spiral jaws. If disengagement under load is required, the jaws should be finish-machined and lubricated.

Friction clutches are designed to reduce coupling shock by slipping during the engagement period. They also serve as safety devices by slipping when the torque exceeds their maximum rating. They may be divided into two main groups, **axial** and **rim clutches**, according to the direction of contact pressure.

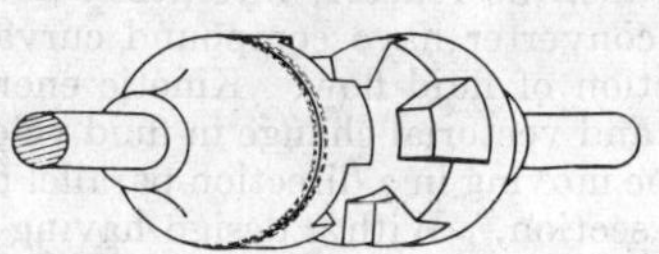

FIG. 71. Square-jaw clutch.

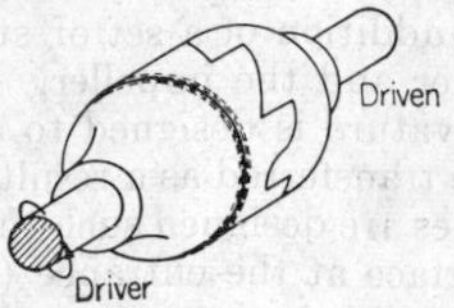

FIG. 72. Spiral-jaw clutch.

The **cone clutch** (Fig. 73) and the **disk clutch** (Fig. 74) are examples of axial clutches. The disk clutch may consist of either a single plate or multiple disks. Table 48 lists typical friction materials and important design data. The torque capacity of a disk clutch is given by $T = 0.5ifF_aD_m$, where T is the torque, i the number of pairs of

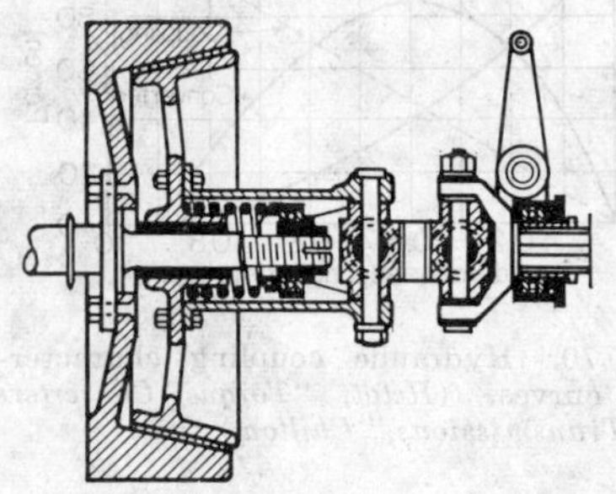

FIG. 73. Cone clutch.

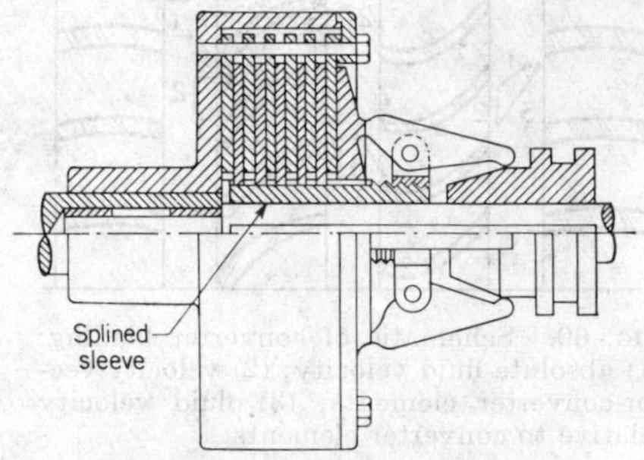

FIG. 74. Multidisk clutch.

contact surfaces, f the applicable coefficient of friction, F_a the axial engaging force, and D_m the mean diameter of the clutch facing. The spring forces holding a disk clutch in engagement are usually of relatively high value, as given by the allowable contact pressures. In order to lower the force required at the operating lever, elaborate linkages are required, usually having lever ratios in the range of 10 to 12. As these linkages must rotate with the clutch, they must be adequately balanced and the effect of centrifugal forces must be considered. Disk clutches are often run wet, either immersed in oil or in a spray. The advantages are reduced wear, smoother action, and lower operating temperatures. Disk clutches are often operated automati-

Table 48. Friction Coefficients and Allowable Pressures

(From Maleev, *Machine Design*, International Textbook, by permission)

Materials in contact	Friction coefficient f			Allowable pressure, psi
	Dry	Greasy	Lubricated	
Cast iron on cast iron	0.2–0.15	0.10–0.06	0.10–0.05	150–250
Bronze on cast iron	....	0.10–0.05	0.10–0.05	80–120
Steel on cast iron	0.30–0.20	0.12–0.07	0.10–0.06	120–200
Wood on cast iron	0.25–0.20	0.12–0.08	....	60–90
Fiber on metal	....	0.20–0.10	....	10–30
Cork on metal	0.35	0.30–0.25	0.25–0.22	8–15
Leather on metal	0.5–0.3	0.20–0.15	0.15–0.12	10–30
Wire asbestos on metal	0.5–0.35	0.30–0.25	0.25–0.20	40–80
Asbestos blocks on metal	0.48–0.40	0.30–0.25	....	40–160
Asbestos on metal, short action	....	....	0.25–0.20	200–300
Metal on cast iron, short action	....	....	0.10–0.05	200–300

cally by either air or hydraulic cylinders as, for example, in automobile automatic transmissions.

Rim clutches may be subdivided into two groups: (1) those employing either a band or block (Fig. 75) in contact with the rim and (2) overrunning clutches (Fig. 76) employing the wedging action of a roller or sprag. Clutches in the second category will automatically engage in one direction and freewheel in the other.

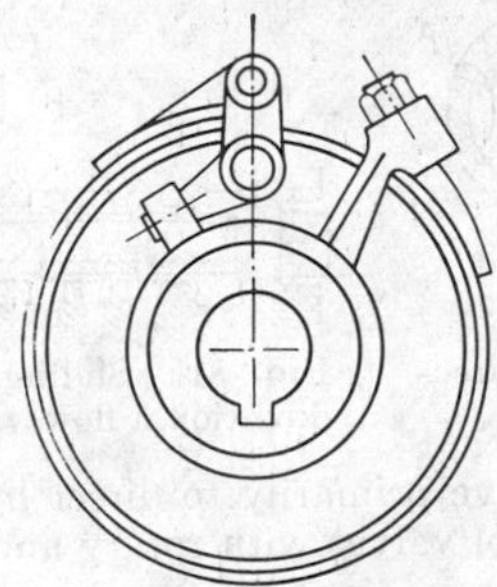

Fig. 75. Band clutch.

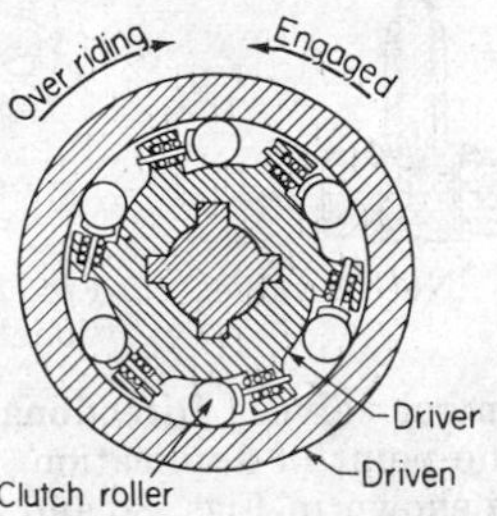

Fig. 76. Overrunning clutch. (*Fig. 198, Vallance and Doughtie, "Design of Machine Elements," 3d ed., McGraw-Hill, p. 262.*)

HYDRAULIC POWER TRANSMISSION

Hydraulic power transmission systems comprise machinery and auxiliary components which function to generate, transmit, control, and utilize hydraulic power. The **working fluid,** a pressurized incompressible liquid, is usually either a petroleum base or a fire-resistant type. The latter are water and oil emulsions, glycol-water mixtures, or synthetic liquids such as silicones or phosphate esters.

Liquid is pressurized in a **pump** by virtue of its resistance to flow; the pressure difference between pump inlet and outlet results in flow. Most hydraulic applications employ positive displacement pumps of the gear, vane, screw, or piston type; piston pumps are axial, radial, or reciprocating (see pp. 14-2 to 14-17).

Power is transmitted from pump to controls and point of application through a combination of **conduit and fittings** appropriate to the particular application. Flow characteristics of hydraulic circuits take into account fluid properties, pressure drop, flow rate, and pressure surging tendencies. Conduit systems must be designed to minimize changes in flow velocity, velocity distribution, and random fluid eddies, all of which dissipate energy and result in pressure drops in the circuit (see p. 3-55 *et seq.*). Pipe, tubing, and flexible hose are used as hydraulic power conduits; suitable fittings are available for all types and for transition from one type to another.

Controls are generally interposed along the conduit between the pump and point of application (*i.e.*, an actuator or motor), and act to control pressure, volume, or flow direction.

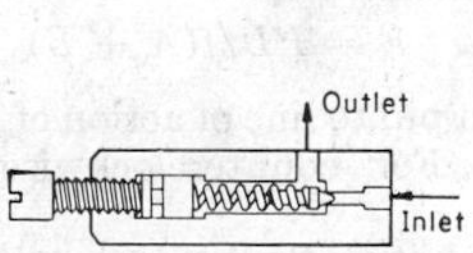

Fig. 77. Relief valve.

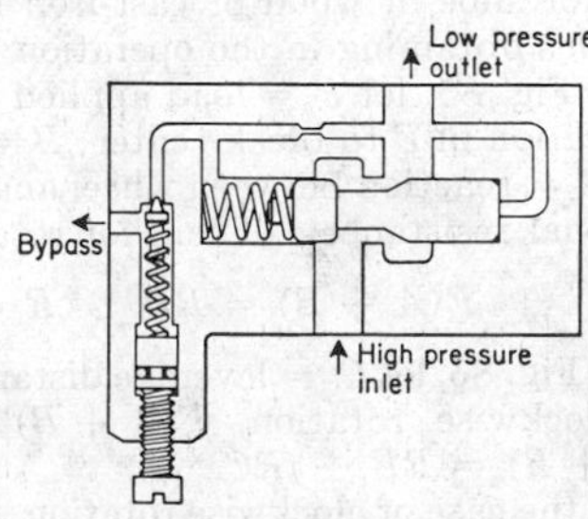

Fig. 78. Reducing valve.

Pressure control valves, of which an ordinary safety valve is a common type (normally closed), include relief and reducing valves and pressure switches (Figs. 77, 78). Pressure valves, normally closed, can be used to control sequential operations in a hydraulic circuit. **Flow control valves** throttle flow to or bypass flow around the unit being controlled, resulting in pressure drop and temperature increase as pressure energy is dissipated. Figure 79 shows a simple needle valve with variable orifice useable as a flow control valve. **Directional control valves** serve primarily to direct hydraulic fluid to the point of application. Directional control valves with rotary and sliding spools are shown in Figs. 80 and 81.

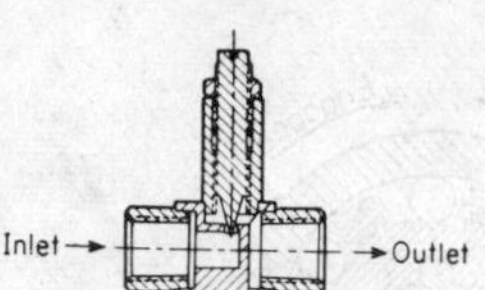

FIG. 79. Needle valve.

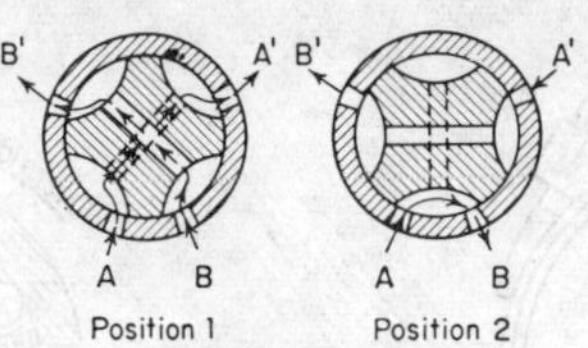

FIG. 80. Rotary-spool directional flow valve.

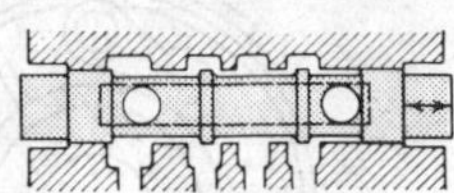
FIG. 81. Sliding-spool directional flow valve.

Accumulators are effectively "hydraulic flywheels" which store potential energy by accumulating a quantity of pressurized hydraulic fluid in a suitable enclosed vessel. The bag type shown in Fig. 82 uses pressurized gas inside the bag working against the hydraulic fluid outside the bag.

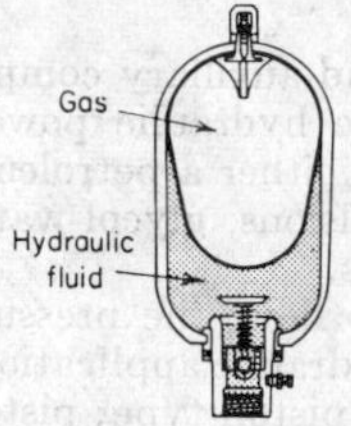

FIG. 82. Bag-type accumulator.

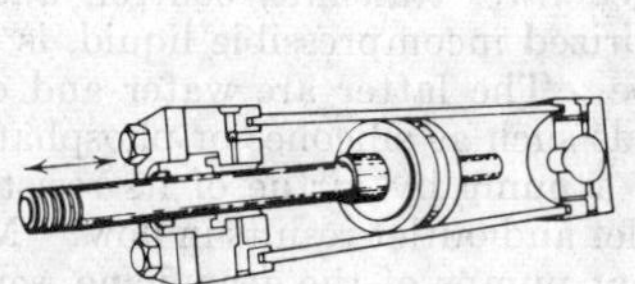
FIG. 83. Linear actuator or hydraulic cylinder.

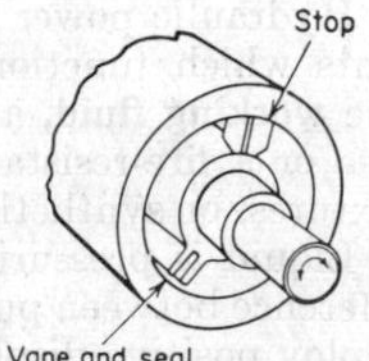

FIG. 84. Rotary actuator.

Pressurized hydraulic fluid acting against an **actuator** or motor converts fluid pressure energy into mechanical energy. Motors providing continuous rotation have operating characteristics closely related to their pump counterparts. A linear actuator, or cylinder (Fig. 83) provides straight line reciprocating motion; a rotary actuator (Fig. 84) provides arcuate oscillatory motion.

BRAKES

(See also Secs. 10 and 11)

Block brakes are shown diagrammatically in Figs. 85 to 89. They consist of a block or shoe of wood or cast-iron bearing upon an iron or steel wheel. The force relations obtaining in the operation of these brakes may be formulated as follows:

In Fig. 85, let F = load applied at end of lever arm; A = distance from point of application of F to block center; B = distance from block center to center of fulcrum pin; R = reaction between wheel and block; f = coefficient of friction; P = tangential frictional resistance. Then, for rotation in either direction.

$$F(A + B) = RB \qquad R = P/f \qquad \text{and} \qquad F = PB/f(A + B)$$

In Fig. 86, let C = leverage distance from fulcrum pin to line of action of P. Then, for clockwise rotation, $F(A + B) = RB - fRC$. For counterclockwise rotation, $F(A + B) = RB + fRC$.

In the case of clockwise rotation, it will be noted that C/B must be less than $1/f$, or the brake will be self-acting, *i.e.*, will bind.

In the arrangement shown in Fig. 87, for clockwise rotation, $F(A + B) = RB + fRC$ and for counterclockwise rotation, $F(A + B) = RB - fRC$.

In the latter case (for counterclockwise rotation), C/B must be less than $1/f$, or the brake will be self-acting, *i.e.*, will bind.

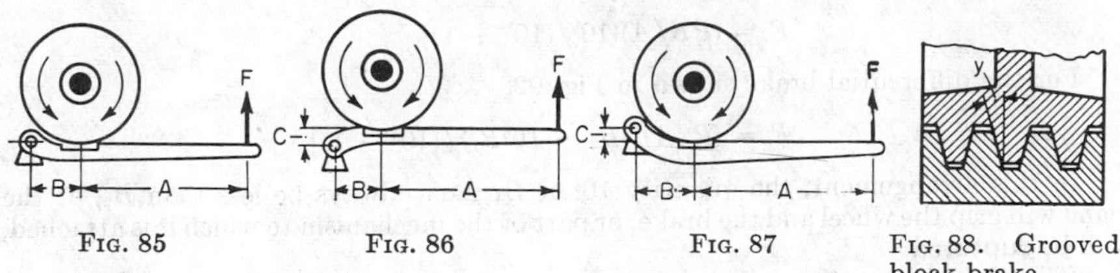

FIG. 85 FIG. 86 FIG. 87 FIG. 88. Grooved block brake.

FIGS. 85–87. Block brakes.

Double blocks are used to eliminate bending of the shaft. Figure 89 illustrates one way in which such brakes may be rigged. The force relations are as follows:

Let F = load applied at end of lever, lb; R = reaction between wheel and *each* block, lb; P = tangential frictional resistance on each block surface, lb; f = coefficient of friction of materials in contact for a given condition of surface; r = drum radius, in.; T = torque on drum shaft, in.-lb; other notations as in the figure. Then,

$$R = FA(c + d)/\cos(x/2)2Bc; \qquad P = Rf; \qquad T = 2Rfr$$

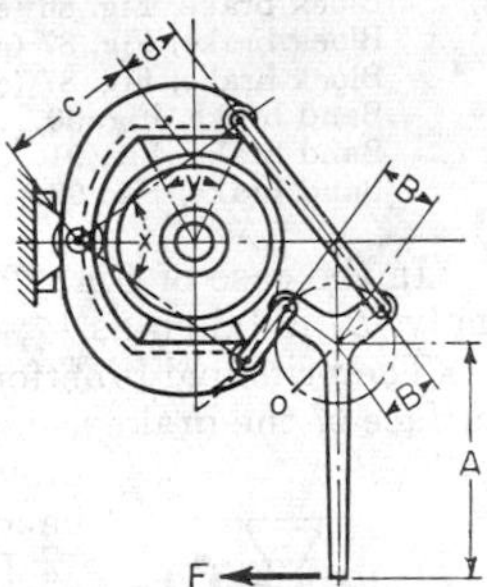

FIG. 89. Double block brake.

The point o should be a floating pivot to permit adjustment as the blocks wear.

Should the **face** of the brake wheel and blocks be **grooved,** as shown in Fig. 88, $f/(\sin y + f \cos y)$ must be substituted for f in the foregoing equations, y being equal to half the angle included by the faces of the grooves and not less than 23 deg, to prevent binding; y may have any value up to 30 deg.

Band brakes are shown diagrammatically in Figs. 90 to 92. The bands are usually of an asbestos fabric, sometimes reinforced with copper wire and impregnated with asphalt. The force relations obtaining in their operations are as follows:

In Fig. 90, let F = force at end of brake handle; P = tangential force at rim of wheel; f = coefficient of friction of materials in contact; a = angle of wrap of band, deg; T_1 = total tension in band on tight side; T_2 = total tension in band on slack side. Then $T_1 - T_2 = P$ and $T_1/T_2 = 10^{0.0076fa} = 10^b$ where $b = 0.0076fa$. Also, $T_2 = P/(10^b - 1)$ and $T_1 = P \times 10^b/(10^b - 1)$. The values of $10^{0.0076fa}$ are given in Fig. 114, p. 8–72, and Table 3, p. 3–46, (for a in radians).

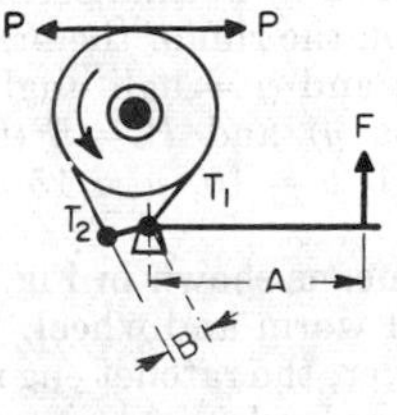

FIG. 90

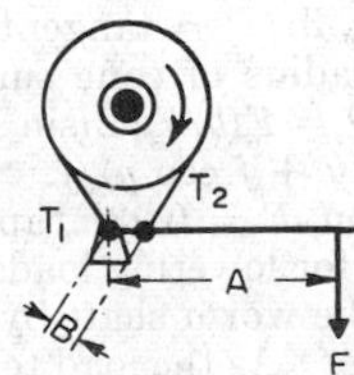

FIG. 91

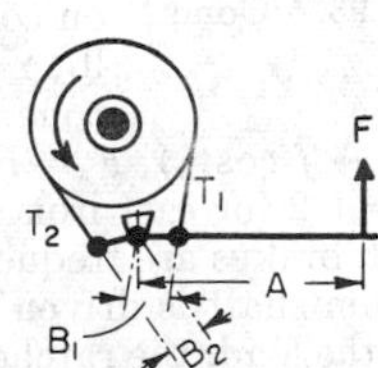

FIG. 92

FIGS. 90–92. Band brakes.

For the arrangement shown in Fig. 90,

$$FA = T_2B = PB/(10^b - 1)$$

and

$$F = PB/A(10^b - 1)$$

For the construction illustrated in Fig. 91,

$$F = (PB/A)[10^b/(10^b - 1)]$$

For the differential brake shown in Fig. 92,

$$F = (P/A)[(B_2 - 10^b B_1)/(10^b - 1)]$$

In this arrangement, the quantity $10^b \times B_1$ must always be less than B_2, or the band will grip the wheel and the brake, or part of the mechanism to which it is attached, will be ruptured.

It is usual in practice to have the leverage ratio A/B for block brakes about 5:1, and for band brakes about 10:1. The bands are faced with maple blocks.

If f for wood on iron be taken at 0.3 and the angle of wrap for the band be 270 deg, *i.e.*, subtends ¾ of the circumference, then, $10^b = 4$ approx, and C/B be taken equal to $1/0.5 = 2$, the loads required for a given torque will be as follows for the cases just considered and for the leverage ratios stated above:

Block brake, Fig. 85	$F = 0.55P$
Block brake, Fig. 86 (clockwise rotation)	$F = 0.22P$
Block brake, Fig. 86 (counterclockwise rotation)	$F = 0.90P$
Block brake, Fig. 87 (clockwise rotation)	$F = 0.90P$
Block brake, Fig. 87 (counterclockwise rotation)	$F = 0.22P$
Band brake, Fig. 90	$F = 0.033P$
Band brake, Fig. 91	$F = 0.133P$
Band brake, Fig. 92	$F = 0.016P$

In the case of Fig. 92, the dimension B_2 must be greater than $B_1 \times 10^b$. Accordingly, B_1 is taken as ¼, A as 10, and, since $10^b = 4$, B_2 is taken as 1½.

The principal function of a brake is to absorb energy. This energy appears at the surface of the brake as heat, which must be carried away at a sufficiently rapid rate to prevent burning of the wooden blocks. Suitable proportions may be arrived at as follows:

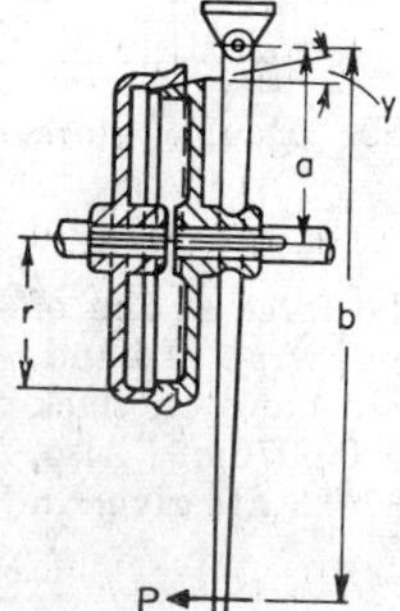

Fig. 93. Cone brake.

Let p = unit pressure on brake surface, psi = R (reaction against block)/area of block; v = velocity of brake rim surface, fps = $2\pi rn/60$, where n = rpm of brake wheel. Then pv = work absorbed per sq in. of brake surface per sec, and $pv \leqq 1{,}000$ for intermittent applications of load with comparatively long periods of rest and poor means for carrying away heat (wooden blocks); $pv \leqq 500$ for continuous application of load and poor means for carrying away heat (wooden blocks); $pv \leqq 1{,}400$ for continuous application of load with effective means for carrying away heat (oil bath).

Cone brakes, may be made to the form shown in Fig. 93. The force relations are as follows:

Let F = load applied at end of lever, lb; Q = normal pressure on cone surface, lb; P = tangential force on the rim of the brake, lb; r = mean radius of cone surface, in.; and y = half angle of cone. Then $Q = F(b/a)/2(\sin y + f \cos y)$ and $P = fF(b/a)/(\sin y + f \cos y)$; $F = P(a/b)(\sin y + f \cos y)/f$. For $a = 1$, $b = 10$, $y = 15$ deg, and $f = 0.2$ for cast iron on cast iron, $F = 0.23P$, approx.

Such brakes are frequently used for lowering loads by the means shown in Fig. 94. The drum shaft is driven through the worm shaft by means of worm and wheel. In raising the load, the ratchet runs free. As the load tends to lower, the ratchet engages and the worm thrusts the cone surfaces together. Lowering of the load must be accomplished by the application of torque to the worm shaft. In the case of worms of small pitch, no brake is required, for the wheel cannot turn the worm. This brake is therefore adapted to worms of large pitch, and the reason for employing a large pitch is that a more efficient drive is obtained (see p. 8–142). The force relations are approximately as follows:

Let R = mean radius of cone surface, in.; Q = force normal to cone surface, lb; P = tangential force at cone surface, acting with the leverage R; F = axial force, lb; f = coefficient of friction between cone surfaces; a = angle between shaft axis and element of cone surface, deg; b = angle of pitch of worm on worm wheel, deg; f_1 = coefficient of friction of worm and wheel teeth; r = pitch radius of worm, in.; r_3 = pitch radius of ratchet wheel, in.; L = load on ratchet teeth, lb. Let $x = f \cos a + \sin a$, and $y = (\tan b - f_1)$; then Lr_3 = torque on worm shaft (in.-lb) due to F, where F is the axial force due to load on drum $= Fry$ approximately.

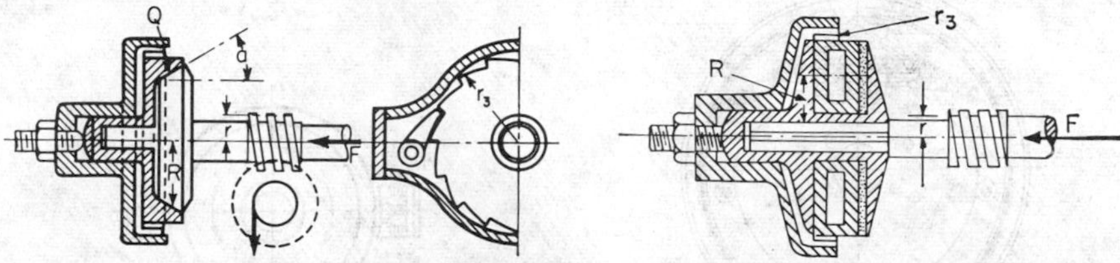

FIG. 94. Cone brake for lowering loads.

FIG. 95. Disk brake.

The resisting moment of the clutch is $PR = QfR = RFf/x$. To hold the load and prevent its lowering, the actuating torque Fry must be less than the reacting torque RFf/x. Accordingly, $Rf/x \geqq ry$, or $R \geqq ryx/f$. The angles a and b may be assumed 22 deg, f at 0.08, and f_1 at 0.10, depending on the lubrication, whence $x = 0.45$ and $y = 0.30$. Then for the above assumptions $R \geqq 1.7r$. If $a = 30$ deg, $b = 35$ deg, then, for f and f_1 as before, $x = 0.57$, $y = 0.60$, and $R \geqq 4.3r$.

Disk brakes of the same general type of construction but using a flat face instead of a cone are shown in Fig. 95. There are two faces to be moved against friction.

The force relations are $Lr_3 \leqq 2fFR = 2PR$, where $fF = P$. Also $R \geqq ry/2f$.

Frequently disk brakes are made as shown in Fig. 96. The pinion Q engages the gear in the drum (not shown). When the load is to be raised, power is applied through the gear and the connection between B and C is accomplished by the advancing of B along A and the clamping of the friction disks D and D and the ratchet wheel E. The

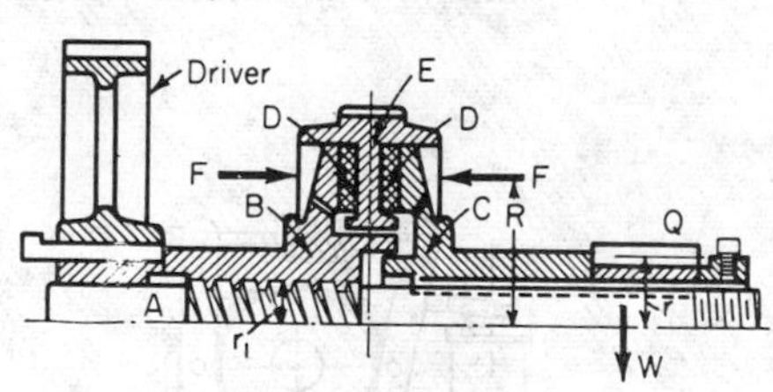

FIG. 96. Disk brake.

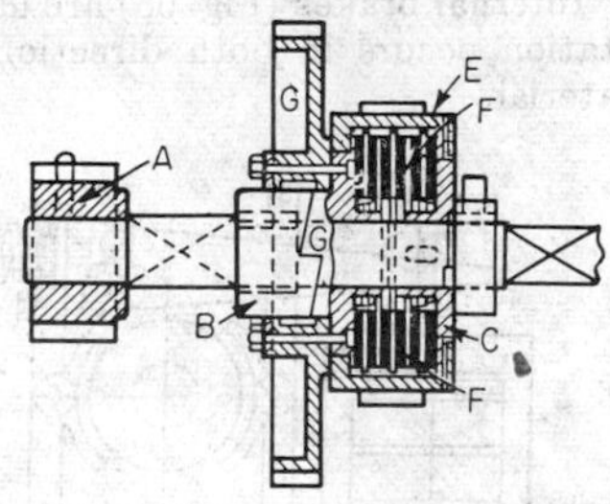

FIG. 97. Multidisk brake.

reversal of the motor disconnects B and C. In lowering the load, only as much reversal of rotation of the gear is given as is needed to reduce the force in the friction disks so that the load may be lowered under control.

The force relations are as follows:

Let R = mean radius of friction plates, in.; f = coefficient of friction between plates; F = axial force along the screw = force in friction plates, lb; P = tangential force on friction plates at mean radius R, lb, $= fF$; W = load on pinion teeth, lb; r = radius of pinion pitch circle, in.; r_1 = radius of pitch circle of screw, in.; a = angle of screw thread, deg; f_1 = coefficient of friction in thread; $z = (\tan a + f_1)$.

Then the load in lowering causes a moment $Wr = fFR + Fr_1z$, approx. To sustain the load, $Wr \leqq 2fFR$ and $fR \geqq r_1z$.

Acceptable values of the several factors are: $a = 10$ deg; $f = 0.08$; $f_1 = 0.10$; $R = 9$ in. Substituting these in the last equation, $r_1 \leqq 2.5$ in.+. Any radius of screw less than 2½ in. consistent with strength will be satisfactory for the above conditions.

A multidisk brake is shown in Fig. 97. This type of construction results in an increase in the number of friction faces. The drum shaft is geared to the pinion A, while the motive power for driving comes through the gear G. In raising the load, direct connection is had between G, B, and A. In lowering, B moves relatively to G and forces the friction plates together, those plates fast to E being held stationary by the pawl on E. In the figure, there are three plates fast to E, one fast to G, and one fast to C.

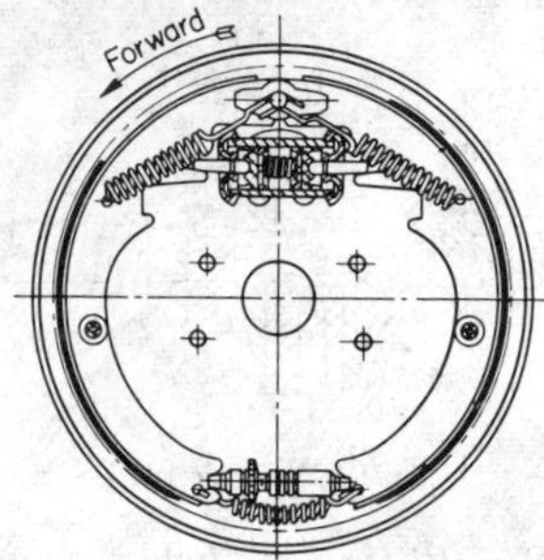

Fig. 98. Internal brake.

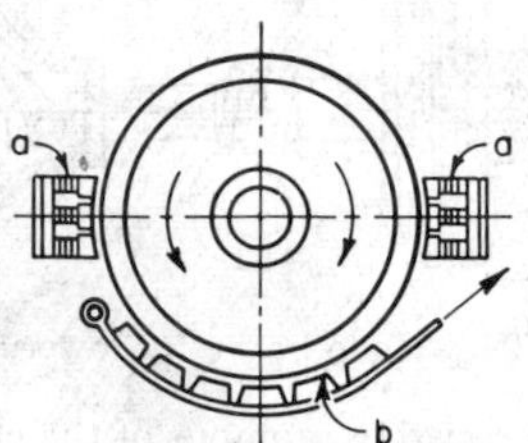

Fig. 99. Eddy-current brake.

In addition to the notation given in the previous case, let n = number of faces in sliding contact when the part C is moved relatively to part E which carries the ratchet. This condition obtains upon the load beginning to lower, and n_1 = number of faces in sliding contact when the parts G and C both move relatively to E. This obtains when full gripping of the plates takes place. The load in beginning to lower occasions the following force relation: $Wr = nfFR + Fr_1z$. To sustain the load, it is necessary that $Wr \leqq fFR$. Hence, to prevent the load from dropping, $r_1z \leqq fR(n_1 - n)$.

Internal brakes (Fig. 98) are used extensively on motor vehicles (see Sec. 11) where rotation occurs in both directions. The blocks are lined with a suitable friction material.

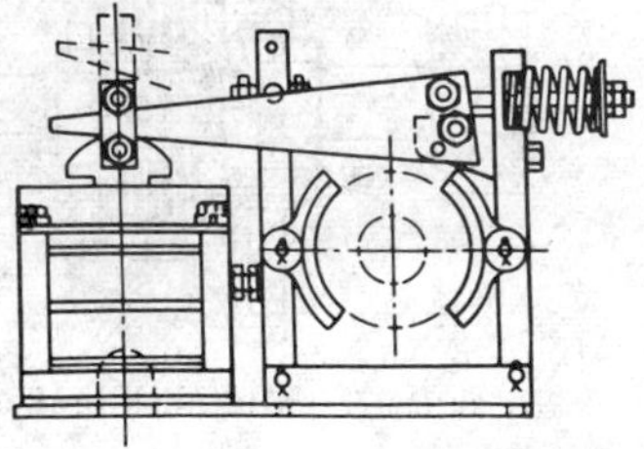

Fig. 100. Solenoid-type electric brake.

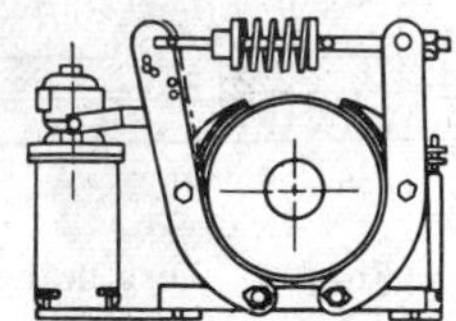

Fig. 101. Thrustor-type electric brake.

Brakes of the type illustrated are self-energizing; that is to say friction makes the shoe tend to follow the rotating brake drum, wedging itself between the drum and the point at which it is anchored. This type of action builds up a tremendous amount of friction, and for this reason gives a great deal of braking power without the use of excessive pedal pressure.

Eddy-current brakes (Fig. 99) are used with flywheels where quick braking is essential, and where large kinetic energy of the rotating masses precludes the use of block brakes due to excessive heating, as in reversible rolling mills. A number of poles *a* are electrically excited (north and south in turn) and create a magnetic flux which permeates the gap and the iron of the rim, causing eddy currents. The flywheel energy is converted through these currents into heat. The hand brake *b* may be used for quicker stopping when the speed of the wheel is considerably decreased; *i.e.*, when the eddy-current brake is inefficient. Two brakes are provided to avoid bending forces on the shaft.

Electric brakes are often used in cranes, bridges, turntables, and machine tools, where an automatic application of the brake is important as soon as power is cut off. The brake force is supplied by an adjustable spring which is counteracted by the force of a solenoid or a centrifugal thruster. Interruption of current automatically applies the spring-activated brake shoes. Figures 100 and 101 show these types of electric brake.

SHRINK, PRESS, DRIVE, AND RUNNING FITS

The American Standards Association (ASA B4.1, 1955) has made recommendations regarding preferred sizes, allowances, and tolerances for fits between plain cylindrical parts. Such fits include bearings, shrink and drive fits, etc. Terms used in describing fits are defined as follows: **Allowance:** minimum clearance (positive allowance) or maximum interference (negative allowance) between mating parts. **Tolerance:** total permissible variation of size. **Limits of size:** applicable maximum and minimum sizes. **Clearance fit:** one having limits of size so prescribed that a clearance always results when mating parts are assembled. **Interference fit:** in this case, limits are so prescribed that interference always results on assembly. **Transition fit:** this may have either a clearance or an interference on assembly. **Basic size:** one from which limits of size are derived by the application of allowances and tolerances. **Unilateral tolerance:** in this case a variation in size is permitted in only one direction from the basic size.

Fits are divided by the ASA into the following general classifications: (1) running and sliding fits, (2) locational clearance fits, (3) trasition fits, (4) locational interference fits, and (5) force or shrink fits.

1. Running and Sliding Fits. These are intended to provide similar running performance with suitable lubrication allowance throughout the range of sizes. These fits are further subdivided into the following classes:

Class RC1. Close-sliding Fits. Intended for accurate location of parts which must assemble without perceptible play.

Class RC2. Sliding Fits. Parts made with this fit move and turn easily but are not intended to run freely; also, in larger sizes they may seize under small temperature changes.

Class RC3. Precision-running Fits. These are intended for precision work at slow speeds and light journal pressures but are not suitable where appreciable temperature differences are encountered.

Class RC4. Close-running Fits. For running fits on accurate machinery with moderate surface speeds and journal pressures, where accurate location and minimum play is desired.

Classes RC5 and RC6. Medium-running Fits. For higher running speeds or heavy journal pressures, or both.

Class RC7. Free-running Fits. For use where accuracy is not essential, or where large temperature variations are likely to be present, or both.

Classes RC8 and RC9. Loose-running Fits. For use with materials such as cold-rolled shafting or tubing made to commercial tolerances.

Limits of clearance as given in ASA B4.1, 1955, for each of these classes are given in Table 49. Hole and shaft tolerances are listed on a unilateral tolerance basis in this reference to give the clearance limits of Table 49, the hole size being the basic size.

2. Locational Clearance Fits. These are intended for normally stationary parts which can, however, be freely assembled or disassembled. These are subdivided by the ASA into various classes which run from snug fits for parts requiring accuracy of location, through medium clearance fits (spigots) to the looser fastener fits where freedom of assembly is of prime importance.

Table 49. Limits of Clearance for Running and Sliding Fits
(Limits are in thousandths of an inch on diameter)

Nominal size range, in.		Class								
Over	To	RC1	RC2	RC3	RC4	RC5	RC6	RC7	RC8	RC9
0.04	0.12	0.1	0.1	0.3	0.3	0.6	0.6	1.0	2.5	4.0
		0.45	0.55	0.8	1.1	1.4	1.8	2.6	5.1	8.1
0.12	0.24	0.15	0.15	0.4	0.4	0.8	0.8	1.2	2.8	4.5
		0.5	0.65	1.0	1.4	1.8	2.2	3.1	5.8	9.3
0.24	0.40	0.2	0.2	0.5	0.5	1.0	1.0	1.6	3.0	5.0
		0.6	0.85	1.3	1.7	2.2	2.8	3.9	6.6	10.7
0.40	0.71	0.25	0.25	0.6	0.6	1.2	1.2	2.0	3.5	6.0
		0.75	0.95	1.4	2.0	2.6	3.2	4.6	7.9	12.8
0.71	1.19	0.3	0.3	0.8	0.8	1.6	1.6	2.5	4.5	7.0
		0.95	1.2	1.8	2.4	3.2	4.0	5.7	10.0	15.5
1.19	1.97	0.4	0.4	1.0	1.0	2.0	2.0	3.0	5.0	8.0
		1.1	1.4	2.2	3.0	4.0	5.2	7.1	11.5	18.0
1.97	3.15	0.4	0.4	1.2	1.2	2.5	2.5	4.0	6.0	9.0
		1.2	1.6	2.6	3.6	4.9	6.1	8.8	13.5	20.5
3.15	4.73	0.5	0.5	1.4	1.4	3.0	3.0	5.0	7.0	10.0
		1.5	2.0	3.2	4.2	5.8	7.4	10.7	15.5	24.0
4.73	7.09	0.6	0.6	1.6	1.6	3.5	3.5	6.0	8.0	12.0
		1.8	2.3	3.6	4.8	6.7	8.5	12.5	18.0	28.0
7.09	9.85	0.6	0.6	2.0	2.0	4.0	4.0	7.0	10.0	15.0
		2.0	2.6	4.4	5.6	7.6	9.6	14.3	21.5	34.0
9.85	12.41	0.8	0.8	2.5	2.5	5.0	5.0	8.0	12.0	18.0
		2.3	2.9	4.9	6.5	9.0	11.0	16.0	25.0	38.0
12.41	15.75	1.0	1.0	3.0	3.0	6.0	6.0	10.0	14.0	22.0
		2.7	3.4	5.8	7.4	10.4	13.0	19.5	29.0	45.0
15.75	19.69	1.2	1.2	4.0	4.0	8.0	8.0	12.0	16.0	25.0
		3.0	3.8	7.2	9.0	13.0	16.0	22.0	32.0	51.0

3. Transition Fits. These are for applications where accuracy of location is important, but a small amount of either clearance or interference is permissible.

4. Locational Interference Fits. Used where accuracy of location is of prime importance and for parts requiring rigidity and alignment with no special requirements for bore pressure.

Data on clearance limits, interference limits, and hole and shaft diameter tolerances for locational clearance fits, transition fits, and locational interference fits are given in ASA B4.1, 1955.

5. Force or Shrink Fits. These are characterized by approximately constant bore pressures throughout the range of sizes; interference varies almost directly as the diameter, and the differences between maximum and minimum values of interference are small. These are divided into the following classes:

Class FN1. Light-drive Fits. For applications requiring light assembly pressures (thin sections, long fits, cast-iron external members).

Class FN2. Medium-drive Fits. Suitable for ordinary steel parts or for shrink fits on light sections. These are about the tightest fits that can be used on high-grade cast-iron external members.

Class FN3. Heavy-drive Fits. For heavier steel parts or shrink fits in medium sections.

Classes FN4 and FN5. Force Fits. These are suitable for parts which can be highly stressed. Shrink fits are used instead of press fits in cases where the heavy pressing forces required for mounting are impractical.

In Table 50 are listed the limits of interference (maximum and minimum values) for the above classes of force or shrink fits for various diameters, as given in ASA B4.1, 1955. Hole and shaft tolerances to give these interference limits are also listed in this reference.

Stresses Produced by Shrink or Press Fit. STEEL HUB ON STEEL SHAFT. The maximum equivalent stress, pounds per square inch, set up by a given press-fit allowance (in inches per inch of shaft diameter) is equal to $3x \times 10^7$, where x is the allowance per inch of shaft diameter (Baugher, *Trans. ASME*, 1931, p. 85). The press-fit pres-

Table 50. Limits of Interference for Force and Shrink Fits
(Limits are in thousandths of an inch on diameter)

Nominal size range, in. Over	To	Class FN1	FN2	FN3	FN4	FN5
0.04	0.12	0.05	0.2	....	0.3	0.5
		0.5	0.85	....	0.95	1.3
0.12	0.24	0.1	0.2	....	0.4	0.7
		0.6	1.0	....	1.2	1.7
0.24	0.40	0.1	0.4	....	0.6	0.8
		0.75	1.4	....	1.6	2.0
0.40	0.56	0.1	0.5	....	0.7	0.9
		0.8	1.6	....	1.8	2.3
0.56	0.71	0.2	0.5	....	0.7	1.1
		0.9	1.6	....	1.8	2.5
0.71	0.95	0.2	0.6	....	0.8	1.4
		1.1	1.9	....	2.1	3.0
0.95	1.19	0.3	0.6	0.8	1.0	1.7
		1.2	1.9	2.1	2.3	3.3
1.19	1.58	0.3	0.8	0.8	1.5	2.0
		1.3	2.4	2.4	3.1	4.0
1.58	1.97	0.4	0.8	1.2	1.8	3.0
		1.4	2.4	2.8	3.4	5.0
1.97	2.56	0.6	0.8	1.3	2.3	3.8
		1.8	2.7	3.2	4.2	6.2
2.56	3.15	0.7	1.0	1.8	2.8	4.8
		1.9	2.9	3.7	4.7	7.2
3.15	3.94	0.9	1.4	2.1	3.6	5.6
		2.4	3.7	4.4	5.9	8.4
3.94	4.73	1.1	1.6	2.6	4.6	6.6
		2.6	3.9	4.9	6.9	9.4
4.73	5.52	1.2	1.9	3.4	5.4	8.4
		2.9	4.5	6.0	8.0	11.6
5.52	6.30	1.5	2.4	3.4	5.4	10.4
		3.2	5.0	6.0	8.0	13.6
6.30	7.09	1.8	2.9	4.4	6.4	10.4
		3.5	5.5	7.0	9.0	13.6
7.09	7.88	1.8	3.2	5.2	7.2	12.2
		3.8	6.2	8.2	10.2	15.8
7.88	8.86	2.3	3.2	5.2	8.2	14.2
		4.3	6.2	8.2	11.2	17.8
8.86	9.85	2.3	4.2	6.2	10.2	14.2
		4.3	7.2	9.2	13.2	17.8
9.85	11.03	2.8	4.0	7.0	10.0	16.0
		4.9	7.2	10.2	13.2	20.0
11.03	12.41	2.8	5.0	7.0	12.0	18.0
		4.9	8.2	10.2	15.2	22.0
12.41	13.98	3.1	5.8	7.8	13.8	19.8
		5.5	9.4	11.4	17.4	24.2
13.98	15.75	3.6	5.8	9.8	15.8	22.8
		6.1	9.4	13.4	19.4	27.2
15.75	17.72	4.4	6.5	9.5	17.5	25.5
		7.0	10.6	13.6	21.6	30.5
17.72	19.69	4.4	7.5	11.5	19.5	27.5
		7.0	11.6	15.6	23.6	32.5

sures set up between a steel hub and shaft, for various ratios d/D between shaft and hub outside diameters, are given in Fig. 102. These curves are accurate to 5 percent even if the shaft is hollow, provided the inside shaft diameter is not over 25 percent of the outside. The equivalent stress given above is based on the maximum shear theory and is numerically equal to the radial fit-pressure added to the tangential tension in the hub. Where the shaft is hollow, with an inside diameter equal to more than about 25 percent of the outside diameter, the allowance in inches per inch to obtain an equivalent hub stress of 30,000 psi may be determined by using Lamé's thick cylinder formulas (*Jour. Applied Mechanics*, Dec., 1937, p. A-185). It should be noted that these curves hold only when the maximum equivalent stress is below the yield point; above the yield point, plastic flow occurs and the stresses are less than calculated.

Cast-Iron Hub on Steel Shaft. Where the shaft is solid, or hollow with an inside diameter not over 25 percent of the outside diameter, Fig. 103 may be used to determine maximum tensile stresses in the cast-iron hub, resulting from the press-fit allowance;

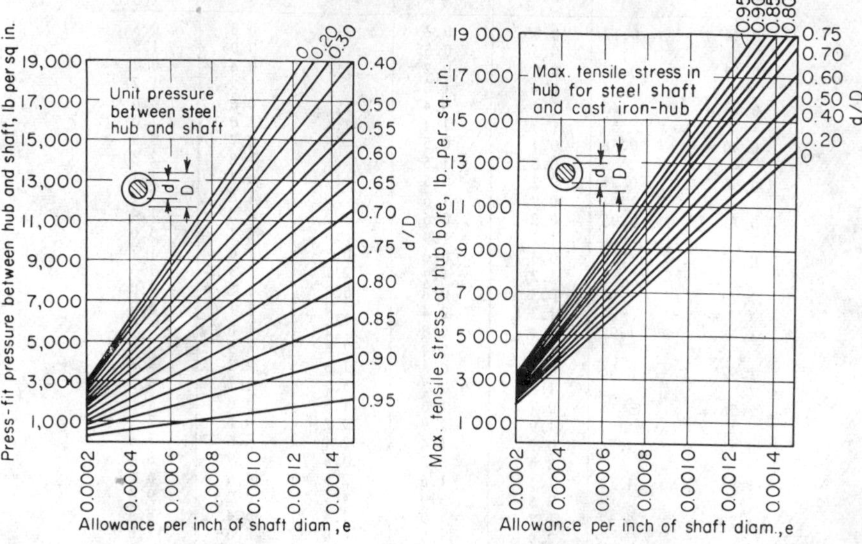

Fig. 102. Press-fit pressures between steel hub and shaft.

Fig. 103. Variation in tensile stress in cast-iron hub in press-fit allowance.

for various ratios d/D, Fig. 104 gives the press-fit pressures. These curves are based on a modulus of elasticity of 30×10^6 psi for steel and 15×10^6 for cast iron. For a hollow shaft with an inside diameter more than about ¼ the outside, the Lamé formulas may be used.

Pressure Required in Making Press Fits. The force required to press a hub on the shaft is given by $\pi fpdl$ where l is length of fit, p the unit press-fit pressure between shaft and hub, f the coefficient of friction, and d the shaft diameter. Values of f varying from 0.03 to 0.33 have been reported, the lower values being due to yielding of the hub as a consequence of too high a fit allowance; the average is around 0.10 to 0.15. (For additional data see Horger and Nelson, "Design Data and Methods," ASME, 1953, pp. 87–91.)

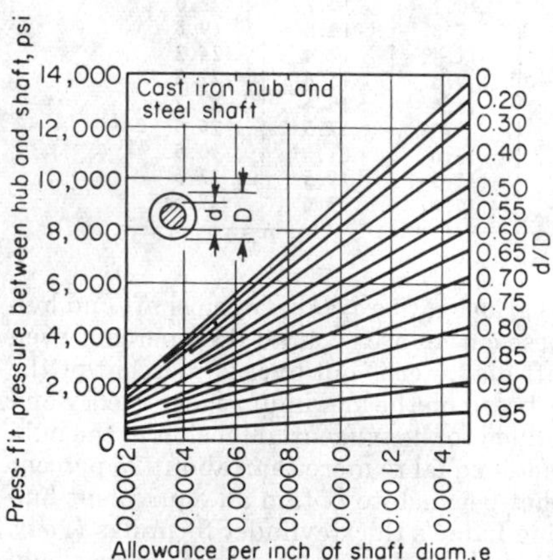

Fig. 104. Press-fit pressures between cast-iron hub and shaft.

Torsional Holding Ability. The torque required to cause complete slippage of a press fit is given by $T = \frac{1}{2}\pi fpld^2$. Local slippage will usually occur near the end of the fit at much lower torques. If the torque is alternating, stress concentration and rubbing corrosion will occur at the hub face so that, eventually, fatigue failure may occur at considerably lower torques. Only in cases of static torque application is it justifiable to use ultimate torque as a basis for design.

SHAFTS, AXLES, AND CRANKS

(For critical speeds and torsion of shafts see Sec. 5.)

Most shafts are subject to combined bending and torsion stresses. These in turn may be steady, variable, or a combination of the two. For example, in operation, an electric motor shaft may be subject to a steady torque on which is superimposed variations due to load fluctuations. An overhung pinion shaft may be subject to essentially constant torsion and completely reversed bending stress. In addition, shafts may be subject to repeated impact loading, as when electric motors are frequently started or plugged. In such cases the peak transient torques may reach several times the nominal values of the starting or plugging torques, depending on load inertia. An example of the latter is the roll-table drive used in steel-strip mills. (For calculating torques in such cases see Wahl, *Jour. Applied Mechanics*, March, 1941, p. A-17.)

In the past, the design of shafts has frequently been based on the use of relatively low working stresses, to cover up unknown factors of ignorance. At present there is a trend toward more accurate evaluation of the fatigue strength of shafts under various operating conditions, but it is still necessary to use a factor of safety to cover various uncertainties in our knowledge of action of materials under various operating conditions and in knowledge of the applied loading. The formulas given under Cases 1 to 4 below for calculating the factors of safety of shafts under operating conditions are based on equations developed by R. E. Peterson, utilizing the Mises criterion of strength as basis (see Peterson, "Stress Concentration Design Factors," Wiley). This book also gives methods for calculating factors of safety for shafts under a limited number of cycles of alternating or shock loading.

Assuming a solid shaft of diameter d inches, the nominal torsional stress τ and bending stress σ are

$$\tau = \frac{16T}{\pi d^3} = 5.1\,\frac{T}{d^3} \tag{1}$$

$$\sigma = \frac{32M}{\pi d^3} = 10.2\,\frac{M}{d^3} \tag{2}$$

where T and M are the torque and bending moments, in.-lb; and τ and σ are stresses, psi.

Case 1. A shaft is subject to a **pure torque** consisting of a **steady torque** T_0, on which is superimposed an **alternating torque** T_v (no bending being present). This loading imposes a steady torsional stress τ_0, combined with an alternating torsional stress τ_v. The stresses τ_0 and τ_v are calculated from Eq. (**1**), using T_0 and T_v, respectively. In this case, the factor of safety n is given by

$$n = \frac{1}{\sqrt{3}\,[\tau_0/(1.33\sigma_y) + K_{tfs}\tau_v/\sigma_e]} \tag{3}$$

where σ_y is the yield stress of the shaft material in tension and σ_e the endurance limit in reversed bending. (Typical σ_y and σ_e values for various materials are given on pages (5-5 and 5-11.) The factor 1.33 in the denominator of Eq. (**3**) is based on a limit design method (taking the redistribution of stress into account), while K_{tfs} is the **fatigue-notch** factor in torsion. The factor K_{tfs} where fillets or grooves are present is given by

$$K_{tfs} = q(K_{ts} - 1) + 1 \tag{4}$$

where K_{ts} = stress-concentration factor for grooved or filleted shaft in torsion (Figs. 13, 14, p. 5-10) and q = notch-sensitivity factor, which depends on the notch or fillet radius and on the material. Average values of q for quenched and tempered steels, and for annealed or normalized steels for various notch or fillet radii, as given by Peterson (*ibid.*), are listed in Table 51. The values in Table 51 are average and may vary considerably in individual cases, depending on the material and on the shape of the notch; in doubtful cases, $q = 1$ should be assumed; *i.e.*, K_{tfs} should be taken equal to K_{ts}.

Table 51. Values* of Notch-sensitivity Factor q

Notch or fillet radius r, in.	0.01	0.03	0.05	0.10	0.20
q (for quenched and tempered steels)	0.70	0.90	0.95	0.98	1.00
q (for annealed or normalized steels)	0.40	0.62	0.73	0.86	0.93

* These values apply where the ratio $t/r < 3$ and t = depth of notch or height of shoulder.

The choice of the factor of safety n for any given application is the prerogative of the designer and depends on such things as seriousness of failure, uncertainty in knowledge of applied loads or material properties, and other factors. Values of n in the range 2 to 3 have been used frequently in the past.

If a value of n is chosen and T_0 and T_v are given, the shaft diameter d can be calcucated from

$$d = 2.17 \sqrt[3]{n\left(\frac{K_{tfs}T_v}{\sigma_e} + \frac{T_0}{1.33\sigma_y}\right)} \tag{5}$$

Case 2. A round shaft is subject to a **steady bending moment** M_0 on which is superimposed an **alternating bending moment** M_v (no torsion being present). These moments give a steady stress σ_0, superimposed on a variable stress σ_v calculated from Eq. (**2**). In this case the equations for factor of safety n and diameter d are

$$n = \frac{1}{\sigma_0/(\sigma_u) + K_{tf}\sigma_v/\sigma_e} \tag{6}$$

$$d = 2.17 \sqrt[3]{n\left(\frac{M_0}{\sigma_u} + \frac{K_{tf}M_v}{\sigma_e}\right)} \tag{7}$$

where σ_u = ultimate strength or $1.7\sigma_y$, whichever is smaller. The fatigue-notch factor K_{tf} in Eqs. (**6**) and (**7**) is

$$K_{tf} = q(K - 1) + 1 \tag{8}$$

where the sensitivity index q may be estimated from Table 51 or, in case of doubt, may be taken as unity. K_t is the theoretical stress concentration factor in bending; approximate values are given on Figs. 10 and 11, p. 5–9 for fillets or grooves. (For more accurate values, see Peterson. *ibid.*) For press fits, the latter reference gives the values for fatigue-notch factor K_f listed in Table 52. These may be used for estimating K_{tf} in Eqs. (**6**) and (**7**). In general the K_f values increase with shaft size. (For further details, see Peterson, *ibid.*)

Table 52. K_f Values for Plain Press Fits
(Obtained from fatigue tests in bending)

Shaft material	Shaft diam, in.	Collar or hub material	K_f	Remarks
0.42 percent carbon steel	1⅝	0.42 percent carbon steel	2.0	No external reaction through collar
0.45 percent carbon axle steel	2	Ni-Cr-Mo steel (casehardened)	2.3	No external reaction through collar
0.45 percent carbon axle steel	2	Ni-Cr-Mo steel (casehardened)	2.9	External reaction taken through collar
Cr-Ni-Mo steel (310 Brinell)	2	Ni-Cr-Mo steel (casehardened)	3.9	External reaction taken through collar
2.6 percent Ni steel (57,000 psi fatigue limit)	2	Ni-Cr-Mo steel (casehardened)	3.3–3.8	External reaction taken through collar
Same, heat-treated to 253 Brinell	2	Ni-Cr-Mo steel (casehardened)	3.0	External reaction taken through collar

Case 3. A case frequently encountered in practice is that of a shaft subject to a **steady torque** T_0 and a completely **reversed bending moment** M_v, giving a steady shear

stress τ_0 and an alternating bending stress σ_v. The corresponding expression for n and d are

$$n = \frac{1}{\sqrt{3(\tau_0/1.33\sigma_y)_2 + (K_{tf}\sigma_v/\sigma_e)_2}} \tag{9}$$

$$d = 2.17 \sqrt[3]{n \sqrt{0.422 \left(\frac{T_0}{\sigma_y}\right)^2 + \left(\frac{K_{tf}M_v}{\sigma_e}\right)^2}} \tag{10}$$

Case 4. In the general case where a shaft is subject to a combination of a **steady** plus **alternating torsion stress** and a **steady** plus **alternating bending stress,** the factor of safety n and shaft diameter d are given by

$$n = \frac{1}{\sqrt{(\sigma_0/\sigma_u + K_{tf}\sigma_v/\sigma_e)^2 + 3(\tau_0/1.33\sigma_y + K_{tfs}\tau_v/\sigma_e)^2}} \tag{11}$$

$$d = 2.17\,(\sqrt[3]{n}) \sqrt[3]{\sqrt{\left(\frac{M_0}{\sigma_u} + \frac{K_{tf}M_v}{\sigma_e}\right)^2 + \frac{3}{4}\left(\frac{T_0}{1.33\sigma_y} + \frac{K_{tfs}T_v}{\sigma_e}\right)^2}} \tag{12}$$

where the symbols have the same meaning as for Cases 1 to 3 and σ_u is taken as the ultimate strength or $1.7\sigma_y$, whichever is smaller. Case 4 corresponds for example to the case of a motor which is started and stopped frequently.

EXAMPLE. A shaft is subject to an alternating bending moment M_v of 12,000 in.-lb and a constant torque T_0 of 7,000 in.-lb. Assume that at the point of maximum bending moment there is a press fit having a K_{tf} value of 2.5. The material is a medium-carbon axle steel with a yield strength σ_y of 70,000 psi and an endurance limit σ_e of 50,000 psi. The value of the factor of safety n is to be taken as 2. These are the conditions of Case 3. Substituting these values in Eq. (**10**), the required diameter d becomes

$$d = 2.17 \sqrt[3]{2\sqrt{\left(\frac{2.5(12{,}000)}{50{,}000}\right)^2 + 0.422\left(\frac{7{,}000}{70{,}000}\right)^2}} = 2.31 \text{ in.}$$

For data on heat-treatments, tensile strength, yield strength, and endurance limits of carbon and alloy steels commonly used in axles and shafts see Lessells, "Strength and Resistance of Metals," Wiley, pp. 393–395.

Stiffness of shafting may become important where critical speeds, vibration, etc., may occur. Also, the lack of sufficient stiffness in shafts may give rise to bearing troubles. Critical speeds of shafts in torsion or bending and shaft deflections may be calculated using the methods of Sec. 5. For shafts of variable diameter see Spotts, "Design of Machine Elements," Prentice-Hall. In order to avoid trouble where sleeve bearings are used, the angular deflections at the bearings in general must be kept within certain limits. One rule is to make the shaft deflection over the bearing width equal to a small fraction of the oil-film thickness. Note that since shaft stiffness is proportional to the modulus of elasticity, alloy-steel shafts are no stiffer than carbon-steel shafts of the same diameter.

Crankshafts. For calculating the torsional stiffness of crankshafts, the formulas given on pp. 5–95 *et seq.* may be used.

Marine-engine shafts and **Diesel-engine crankshafts** (see Sec. 11) should be designed not only for strength but for avoidance of critical speed. (See *Trans. ASME*, Applied Mechanics, Vol. 50, No. 8, for methods of calculating critical speeds of Diesel engines.)

PULLEYS, SHEAVES, AND FLYWHEELS

Arms of pulleys, sheaves, and flywheels are subjected to stresses due to condition of founding, to details of construction (such as split or solid), and to conditions of service, which are difficult to analyze. For these reasons, no accurate stress relations can be established, and the following formulas must be understood to be only approximately correct. It has been established experimentally by Benjamin (*Am. Mach.*, Sept. 22,

1898) that thin-rim pulleys do not distribute equal loads to the several pulley arms. For these, it will be safe to assume the tangential force on the pulley rim as acting on half the number of arms. Pulleys with comparatively thick rims, such as engine band wheels, have all the arms taking the load. Furthermore, while the stress action in the arms is similar to that in a beam fixed at both ends, the amount of restraint at the rim depending on the rim's elasticity; it may, nevertheless, be assumed for purposes of design that cantilever action is predominant. The bending moment at the hub in arms of thin-rim pulleys will be $M = PL/\frac{1}{2}N$, where M = bending moment, in.-lb; P = tangential load on the rim, lb; L = length of the arm, in.; and N = number of arms. For thick-rim pulleys and flywheels, $M = PL/N$.

For arms of elliptical section having a width of two times the thickness, where E = **width of arm section** at the rim, in., and s_t = intensity of tensile stress, psi,

$$E = \sqrt[3]{40PL/s_tN} \text{ (thin rim)} = \sqrt[3]{20PL/s_tN} \text{ (thick rim)}$$

For single-thickness belts, P may be taken as $50B$ lb and for double-thickness belts $P = 75B$ lb, where B is the width of pulley face, in. Then $E = k \times \sqrt[3]{BL/s_tN}$, where k has the following values: for thin rim, single belt, 13; thin rim, double belt, 15; thick rim, single belt, 10; thick rim, double belt, 12. For cast iron of good quality, s_t due to bending may be taken at 1,500 to 2,000. The arm section at the rim may be made from ⅔ to ¾ the dimensions at the hub.

For high-speed pulleys and flywheels, it becomes necessary to check the arm for tension due to rim expansion. It will be safe to assume that each arm is in tension due to one-half the centrifugal force of that portion of the rim which it supports. That is, $T = As_t = Wv^2/2NgR$, lb, where T = tension in arm, lb; N = number of arms; v = speed of rim, fps; R = radius of pulley, ft; A = area of arm section, sq in.; W = weight of pulley rim in lb and s_t = intensity of tensile stress in arm section, psi. Whence $s_t = WRn^2/5{,}800NA$, where n = rpm of pulley.

Arms of flywheels having heavy rims may be subjected to severe stress action due to the inertia of the rim at sudden load changes. There being no means of predicting the probable maximum to which the inertia may rise, it will be safe to make the arms equal in strength to ¾ of the shaft strength in torsion. Accordingly, for elliptical arm sections,

$$N \times 0.5E^3s_t = \tfrac{3}{4} \times 2s_sd^3 \qquad \text{or} \qquad E = 1.4d\sqrt[3]{s_s/s_tN}$$

For steel shafts with $s_s = 8{,}000$ and cast-iron arms with $s = 1{,}500$,

$$E = 2.4d/\sqrt[3]{N} = 1.3d \text{ (for 6 arms)} = 1.2d \text{ (for 8 arms)}$$

where $2E$ = width of elliptical arm section at hub, in. (thickness = E), and d = shaft diameter, in.

Rims of belted pulleys cast whole may have the following proportions (see Fig. 105):

$$t_2 = \tfrac{3}{4}h + 0.005D \qquad t_1 = 2t_2 + C \qquad W = \tfrac{9}{8}B \text{ to } \tfrac{5}{4}B$$

where h = belt thickness, $C = \frac{1}{24}\,W$, and B = belt width, all in inches.

Engine band wheels, flywheels, and pulleys run at **high speeds** are subjected to the following stress actions in the rim:

Considering the rim as a free ring *i.e.*, without arm restraint, and made of cast iron or steel, $s_t = v^2/10$ (approx), where s_t = intensity of tensile stress, psi, and v = rim speed, fps. For beam action between the arms of a solid rim, $M = Pl/12$ (approx), where M = bending moment in rim, in.-lb; P = centrifugal force of that portion of rim between arms, lb, and l = length of rim between arms, in.; from which $s_t = WR^2n^2/450N^2Z$, where W = weight of entire rim, lb; R = radius of wheel, ft; n = rpm of wheel; and Z = section modulus of rim section, in.³ In case the rim section is of the forms shown in Fig. 105, care must be taken that the flanges do not reduce the section modulus from that of the rectangular section. For **split rims** fastened with bolts as shown in Fig. 106, the stress analysis is as follows:

Let w = weight of rim portion L in. in length, lb; w_1 = weight of lug, lb; L_1 = lever arm of lug, in.; and s_t = intensity of tensile stress in rim section joining arm. Then $s_t = 0.00034n^2R(w_1L_1 + wL/2)/Z$, where n = rpm of wheel; R = wheel radius, ft; and Z = section modulus of rim section. The above equation gives the value of s_t for bending when the bolts are loose, which is the worst possible condition that may arise. On this basis of analysis, s_t should not be greater than 8,000. The stress due to bending in addition to the stress due to rim expansion as analyzed previously will be the probable maximum intensity of stress for which the rim should be checked for strength.

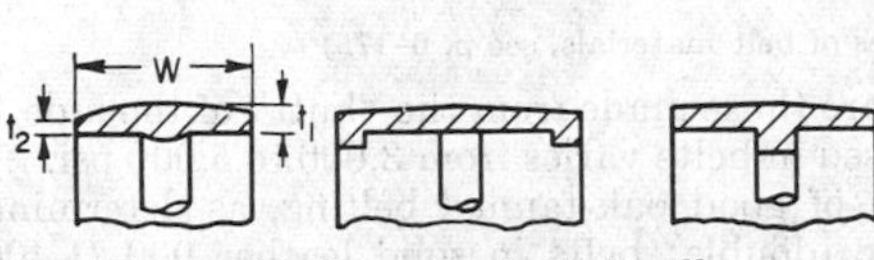

Fig. 105. Rims for belted pulleys.

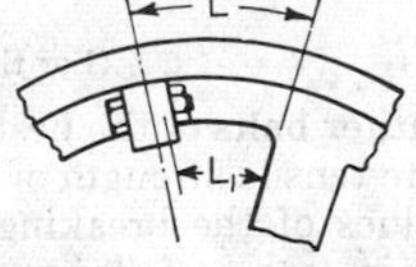

Fig. 106. Split rim.

The flange bolts, because of their position, do not materially relieve the bending action. In case a tie rod leads from the flange to the hub, it will be *safe* to consider it as an additional factor of safety. When the tie rod is kept tight, it very materially strengthens the rim.

A more accurate method for calculating maximum stresses due to centrifugal force in flywheels with arms cast integral with the rim is given by Timoshenko, "Strength of Materials," Part II, 1941, p. 98. More exact equations for calculating stresses in the arms of flywheels and pulleys due to a combination of belt pull, centrifugal force,

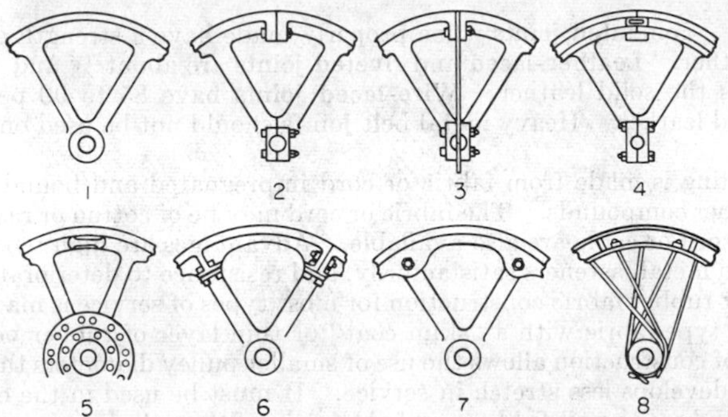

Fig. 107. Types of flywheel construction (see Table 53).

and changes in velocity are given by Heusinger, *Forschung*, 1938, p. 197. In both treatments, shrinkage stresses in the arms due to casting are neglected.

The relative strength of different types of wheel construction are shown by the results of Benjamin's experiments on the bursting of flywheels (*Trans. ASME*, 1899, 1902). The types of wheels experimented with and the speeds at which they burst are shown in Fig. 107, and Table 53.

Table 53. Test Data on the Flywheels of Fig. 107

Number*	1	2	3	4	5	6	7	8
Number of arms	6	6	6	6	8	6	6	24
Rim speed at failure, fps = v	395	194	225	305	256	223	393	424
Comparative rim speeds at failure	100	49	57	77	65	56.5	100	107
Apparent rim tension at failure psi = $v^2/10$	15,625	3,764	5,062	9,302	6,502	4,973	15,445	17,978
Efficiency† of construction	0.85	0.19	0.265	0.49	0.34	0.26	0.84	0.94

* Construction of flywheels: No. 1, solid wheel; No. 2, in halves, with flange joints; No. 3, in halves, with reinforced joints; No. 4, in halves, with link joints; No. 5, segmental, with link joints; No. 6, in halves, with pad joints; No. 7, solid rim, separate spider; No. 8, solid rim, with tangent spokes.

† Efficiency assuming tensile strength at 19,000 psi.

Large flywheels for high rim speeds and severe working conditions (as for rolling mill service) have been made from flat-rolled steel plates with holes bored for the shaft. A group of such plates may be welded together by circumferential welds to form a large flywheel. By this means, the welds do not carry direct centrifugal loads, but serve merely to hold the parts in position. Flywheels up to 15 ft diam for rolling mill service have been constructed in this way.

BELT DRIVES

(For the properties of belt materials, see p. 6-175)

Leather belts of the best quality are those made from the "butt" of the hide. The ultimate tensile **strength** of leather used in belts varies from 3,000 to 5,000 psi. Average values of the breaking strength of good oak-tanned belting, as determined by Benjamin, are as follows: For single (double) belts in solid leather 900 (1,400), at riveted joint 600 (1,200) at laced joint 350 lb. per in. of width.

The **weight** of leather belting is about 0.035 lb per cu in. For thickness of single-, double-, and triple-leather belts as specified by National Industrial Leather Assoc., see Table 54 below. Rawhide, semirawhide (*i.e.*, surface-tanned rawhide), and chrome-tanned (green) belts are not as serviceable in dry places as oak-tanned belts. Rawhide and chrome-tanned belts give good service in damp places, such as dye houses.

Certain special **mineral-tanned leather belts** are now available, while for application where excessive moisture exists, special waterproofed leather belts can be had. Common leather belts are not suitable where exposed to steam, dampness, or dripping oil.

Belt Joints. Cemented joints when properly made have a strength equal to that of the solid leather. **Leather-laced** and **riveted joints** are about ⅓ and ⅔ as strong, respectively, as the solid leather. **Wire-laced joints** have 85 to 90 percent of the strength of solid leather. Heavy metal belt joints should not be used on belts run at high speeds.

Rubber belting is made from fabric or cord impregnated and bound together by vulcanized rubber compounds. The fabric or cord may be of cotton or rayon. Nylon cord and steel cord or cable are also available. Advantages are high tensile strength, strength to hold metal fasteners satisfactorily, and resistance to deterioration by moisture. The best rubber fabric construction for most types of service is made from hard or tight-woven type fabric with a "skim coat" or thin layer of rubber between plies. The cord type of construction allows the use of smaller pulley diameters than the fabric type, and also develops less stretch in service. It must be used in the endless form, except in cases where the oil-field type of clamp may be used.

Initial tensions in rubber belts run from 15 to 25 lb per ply per in. width. A common rule is to cut belts 1 percent less than the minimum tape-line measurement around the pulleys. For heavy loads, a 1½ percent allowance is usually required, although, because of shrinkage, less initial tension is required for wet or damp conditions. Initial tensions of 25 lb per ply per in. may overload shafts or bearings. Maximum safe tight-side tensions for rubber belts are as follows:

Duck weight, oz	28	32	32.66	34.66	36
Tension, lb per ply per in. width	25	28	30	32	35

Centrifugal forces at high speeds require higher tight-side tensions to carry rated horsepower.

Rubber belting may be bought in endless form or made endless in the field by means of a vulcanized splice produced by a portable electric vulcanizer. For endless belts the drive should provide take-up of 2 to 4 percent to allow for length variation as received and for stretch in service. The amount of take-up will vary with the type of belt used. For certain drives, it is possible to use endless belts with no provision for take-up, but this involves a heavier belt and a higher initial unit tension than would be the case otherwise. Ultimate tensile strength of rubber belting varies from 280 to 600 lb or more per in. width per ply. The weight varies from 0.02 to 0.03 or more lb per in. width per ply. Belts with steel reinforcement are considerably heavier. For horsepower ratings of rubber belts, see Table 58.

Arrangements for Belt Drives. In belt drives, the center line of the belt advancing on the pulley should lie in a plane passing through the midsection of the pulley at right angles to the shaft. Shafts inclined to each other require connections as shown in Fig. 108. In case guide pulleys are needed, their positions can be determined as shown in Figs. 109 to 111. In Fig. 110 the center circles of the two pulleys to be connected are set in correct relative position in two planes, a being the angle between the planes

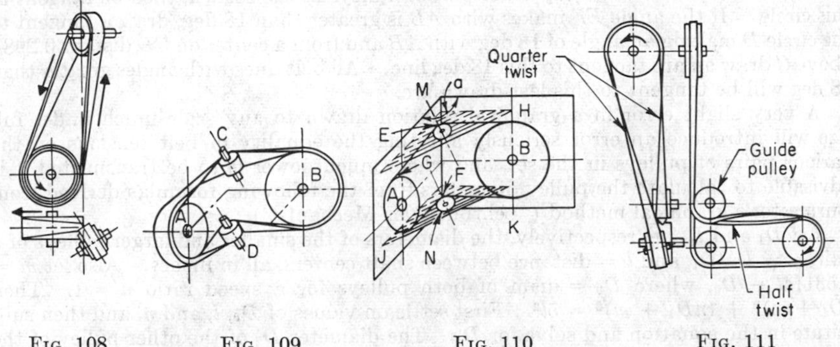

Fig. 108 Fig. 109 Fig. 110 Fig. 111

Figs. 108–111. Arrangements for belt drives.

(= supplement of angle between shafts). If any two points as E and F be assumed on the line of intersection MN of the planes, and tangents EG, EH, FJ, and FK be drawn from them to the circles, the center circles of the guide pulleys must be so arranged that these tangents are also tangents to them, as shown. In other words, the middle planes of the guide pulleys must lie in the planes GEH and JFK. When these conditions are met, the belts will run in either direction on the pulleys.

To avoid the necessity of taking up the **slack** in belts which have become stretched and permanently lengthened, a **belt tightener** such as shown in Fig. 112 may be employed. It should be placed on the slack side of the belt and nearer the driving pulley than the driven pulley. Pivoted motor drives may also be used to maintain belt tightness with minimum initial tension.

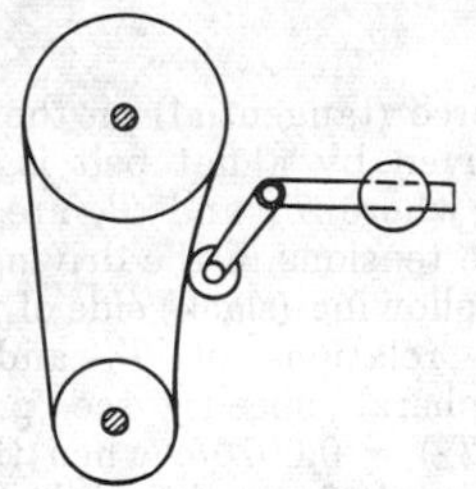

Fig. 112. Belt tightener.

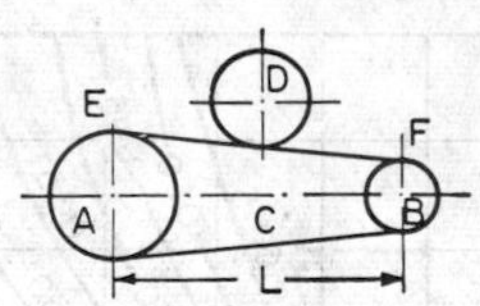

Fig. 113

Length of Belt for a Given Drive. The length of an **open belt** for a given drive is equal to $L = 2C + 1.57(D + d) + (D - d)^2/4C$, where L = length of belt, in.; D = diam of large pulley, in.; d = diam of small pulley, in.; and C = distance between pulley centers, in. Center distance C is given by $C = 0.25b + 0.25\sqrt{b^2 - 2(D - d)^2}$, where $b = L - 1.57(D + d)$. When a **crossed belt** is used, the length in $L = 2C + 1.57(D + d) + (D + d)^2/4C$.

Step or Cone Pulleys. For belts operating on step pulleys, the pulley diameters must be such that the belt will fit over any pair with equal tightness. With **crossed belts,** it will be apparent from the equation for length of belt that the sum of the pulley diameters need only be constant in order that the belt may fit with equal tightness on each pair of pulleys. With open belts, the length is a function of both the sum and the difference of the pulley diameters, hence no direct solution of the problem is possible.

A **graphical method** devised by C. A. Smith (*Trans. ASME*, **10**) is shown in Fig. 113. Let A and B be the centers of any pair of pulleys in the set, the diameters of which are known or assumed. Bisect AB in C, and draw CD at right angles to AB. Take $CD = 0.314$ times the center distance L, and draw a circle tangent to the belt line EF. The belt line of any other pair of pulleys in the set will then be tangent to this circle. If the angle EF makes with AB is greater than 18 deg, draw a tangent to the circle D making an angle of 18 deg with AB and from a center on CD distant $0.298L$ above C draw an arc tangent to this 18 deg line. All belt lines with angles greater than 18 deg will be tangent to this last-drawn arc.

A very slight error in a graphical solution drawn to any scale much under full size will introduce an error seriously affecting the equality of belt tensions on the various pairs of pulleys in the set, and where much power is to be transmitted it is advisable to calculate the pulley diameters from the following **formulas** derived from Burmester's graphical method ("Lehrbuch der Mechanik").

Let D_1 and D_2 be, respectively, the diameters of the smaller and larger pulleys of a pair, $n = D_2/D_1$, and l = distance between shaft centers, all in inches. Also let $m = 1.58114l - D_0$, where D_0 = diam of both pulleys for a speed ratio $n = 1$. Then $(D_1 + m)^2 + (nD_1 + m)^2 = 5l^2$. First settle on values of D_0, l, and n, and then substitute in the equation and solve for D_1. The diameter D_2 of the other pulley of the pair will then be nD_1. The values are correct to the fourth decimal place.

The speeds given by cone pulleys should increase in a **geometrical ratio**; *i.e.*, each speed should be multiplied by a constant a in order to obtain the next higher speed. Let n_1 and n_2 be, respectively, the lowest and highest speeds (rpm) desired and k the number of speed changes. Then $a = \sqrt[k-1]{n_2/n_1}$. In practice, a ranges from 1.25 up to 1.75 and even 2. The ideal value for a in machine-tool practice, according to Carl G. Barth, would be 1.189. In the example below, this would mean the use of 18 speeds instead of 8.

Example. Let $n_1 = 16$, $n_2 = 400$, and $k = 8$, to be obtained with four pairs of pulleys and a back gear. From formula, $a = \sqrt[7]{25} = 1.584$, whence speeds will be 16, ($16 \times 1.584 =$) 25.34, ($25.34 \times 1.584 =$) 40.14, and similarly 63.57, 100.7, 159.5, 252.6, and 400. The first four speeds are with the back gear in, hence the back-gear ratio must be $100.7 \div 16 = 6.29$.

Transmission of Power by Belts. The turning force (tangential) on the rim of a pulley driven by a flat belt is equal to $T_1 - T_2$, where T_1 and T_2 are, respectively, the tensions in the driving (tight) side and following (slack) side of the belt. (For the relations of T_1 and T_2 at low peripheral speeds, see p. 3–45.) Log $(T_1/T_2) = 0.0076fa$ when the effect of centrifugal force is neglected and $T_1/T_2 = 10^{0.0076fa}$. Figure 114 gives values of this function. When the speeds are high, however, the relations of T_1 to T_2 are modified by centrifugal stresses in the belt, in which case log $(T_1/T_2) = 0.0076f(1 - x)a$, where f = coefficient of friction between the belt and pulley surface, a = angle of wrap, and $x = 12wv^2/gt$, in which w = weight of 1 cu in. of belt material, lb; v = belt speed, fps; $g = 32.2$ and t = allowable working

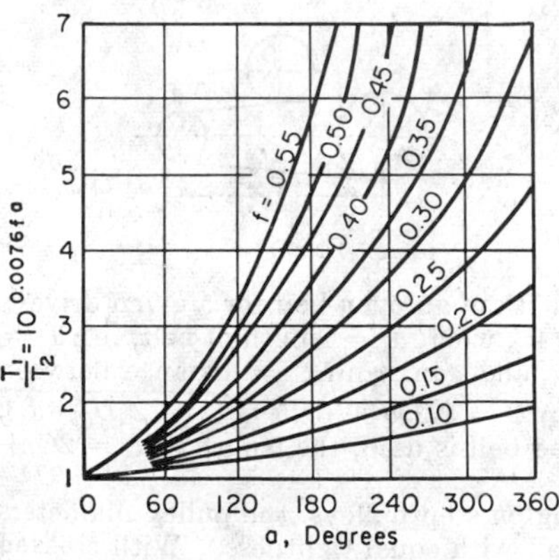

Fig. 114. Values of $10^{0.0076fa}$.

tension, psi. Values of x for leather belting (with $w = 0.035$ and $t = 300$) are as follows:

v	30	40	50	60	70	80	90	100	110	120	130
x	0.039	0.070	0.118	0.157	0.214	0.279	0.352	0.435	0.526	0.626	0.735

Researches by Barth (*Trans. ASME*, 1909) seem to show that f is a function of the belt velocity, varying according to the formula $f = 0.54 - 140/(500 + V)$ for leather belts on iron pulleys, where V = belt velocity in fpm. For practical design, however, the following values of f may be used: for leather belts on cast-iron pulleys, $f = 0.30$; on wooden pulleys, $f = 0.45$; on paper pulleys, $f = 0.55$. The treatment of belts with belt dressing, pulleys with cork inserts, and dampness are all factors which greatly modify these values, tending to make them higher.

The **arc of contact** on the smaller of two pulleys connected by an open belt, in degrees, is approximately equal to $180 - [60(D - d)/l]$, where D and d are the larger and smaller pulley diameters and l the distance between their shaft centers, all in inches. This formula gives an error not exceeding 0.5 percent.

Design of Leather Belts. The National Industrial Leather Assoc. gives the following formulas for calculating the belt width or horsepower rating of oak-tanned flat leather belt drives.

For **electric-motor drives,** $W = RM/KP$ and $H = WKP/M$, where W = width of belt, in.; R = name-plate horsepower rating of electric motor; H = horsepower rating of belt; K = theoretical belt capacity factor, Table 54; M = motor-load correction factor, Table 55; P = pulley correction factor, Table 56. Values of minimum pulley diameters for various belt speeds are indicated in Table 54. Where special operating conditions are present, multiply belt width by a factor F given in Table 57.

For **drives other than electric motors** the formulas are $W = HF/KP$ and $H = WKP/F$, where H = horsepower rating of belt and W = belt width. The factors K, P, and F are given in Tables 54, 56, and 57, respectively.

For belt speeds over 6,000 fpm or for pulley sizes less than those indicated, the supplier should be consulted.

Example. A squirrel-cage induction-motor drive rated at 15 hp, 1,750 rpm, has the following operating conditions: across-the-line starting; motor pulley 8 in. diam; driven pulley 16 in. diam; belt speed = $1750 \times \pi \times 8/12 = 3{,}665$ fpm. Belt thickness is "medium double" for 8 in. pulley diam, from bottom of Table 54. From this table, belt capacity factor K is 10.2 for medium double belt at 3,665 fpm. Factor M from Table 55 is 2.0, for line-start squirrel-cage motor, and P from Table 56 is 0.6 for 8 in. diam pulley. Required belt width from equation above is $W = RM/KP = 15 \times 2.0/10.2 \times 0.6 = 4.9$ in. Use a 5 in. width medium double leather belt. If the motor were used on a vertical drive without special motor base, the above belt width should be multiplied by the factor $F = 1.2$ from Table 57, giving a 6 in. wide medium double belt.

Horsepower Ratings of Rubber Transmission Belts. For calculating horsepower rating of rubber transmission belts, the following formula is used by B. F. Goodrich Co.: HP = (hp $\times$ S)/($W \times K$) where hp = actual horsepower transmitted or, if not known, rated horsepower of driver unit as shown on name plate; W = belt width, in. Values of HP (horsepower per inch of width for 180 deg arc of contact for various belt speeds and various materials) are given in Table 58. The ratings of Table 58 have been corrected for effects of centrifugal force and are based on a coefficient of friction of 0.3. S = service factor (Table 59). K = arc of contact factor (Table 60). Minimum pulley diameters are given in Table 61.

Example. Assume a normal-torque squirrel-cage a-c motor for a centrifugal-fan drive. Motor speed is 1,725 rpm and pulley diameter is 5 in. Horsepower transmitted at 1,725 rpm is 4.0. Arc of contact is 160 deg. From Table 59 factor $S = 1.2$ and, from Table 60, factor $K = 0.93$. Belt speed is $1{,}725 \times \pi \times 5/12 = 2{,}250$ fpm. For a 5 in. pulley diameter, choose from Table 61 a 3-ply, 32-oz fabric belt, giving HP = 3.0 at 2,250 fpm from Table 58. Required belt width from above equation is $W = (\text{hp} \times S)/(\text{HP} \times K) = (4 \times 1.2)/(3 \times 0.93) = 1.73$ in.

Table 54. Theoretical Belt Capacity Factors—*K* (Leather Belts)

Belt speed, fpm	Single ply		Double ply			Triple ply	
	11⁄64 in.	13⁄64 in.	18⁄64 in.	20⁄64 in.	23⁄64 in.	30⁄64 in.	34⁄64 in.
	Med.	Heavy	Light	Med.	Heavy	Med.	Heavy
600	1.1	1.2	1.5	1.8	2.2	2.5	2.8
800	1.4	1.7	2.0	2.4	2.9	3.3	3.6
1,000	1.8	2.1	2.6	3.1	3.6	4.1	4.5
1,200	2.1	2.5	3.1	3.7	4.3	4.9	5.4
1,400	2.5	2.9	3.5	4.3	4.9	5.7	6.3
1,600	2.8	3.3	4.0	4.9	5.6	6.5	7.1
1,800	3.2	3.7	4.5	5.4	6.2	7.3	8.0
2,000	3.5	4.1	4.9	6.0	6.9	8.1	8.9
2,200	3.9	4.5	5.4	6.6	7.6	8.8	9.7
2,400	4.2	4.9	5.9	7.1	8.2	9.5	10.5
2,600	4.5	5.3	6.3	7.7	8.9	10.3	11.4
2,800	4.9	5.6	6.8	8.2	9.5	11.0	12.1
3,000	5.2	5.9	7.2	8.7	10.0	11.6	12.8
3,200	5.4	6.3	7.6	9.2	10.6	12.3	13.5
3,400	5.7	6.6	7.9	9.7	11.2	12.9	14.2
3,600	5.9	6.9	8.3	10.1	11.7	13.4	14.8
3,800	6.2	7.1	8.7	10.5	12.2	14.0	15.4
4,000	6.4	7.4	9.0	10.9	12.6	14.5	16.0
4,200	6.7	7.7	9.3	11.3	13.0	15.0	16.5
4,400	6.9	7.9	9.6	11.7	13.4	15.4	16.9
4,600	7.1	8.1	9.8	12.0	13.8	15.8	17.4
4,800	7.2	8.3	10.1	12.3	14.1	16.2	17.8
5,000	7.4	8.4	10.3	12.5	14.3	16.5	18.2
5,200	7.5	8.6	10.5	12.8	14.6	16.8	18.5
5,400	7.6	8.7	10.6	12.9	14.8	17.1	18.8
5,600	7.7	8.8	10.8	13.1	15.0	17.3	19.0
5,800	7.7	8.9	10.9	13.2	15.1	17.5	19.2
6,000	7.8	8.9	10.9	13.2	15.2	17.6	19.3
	Minimum pulley diameters for belt speeds, in.						
Up to 2,500 fpm	2½	3	4	5*	8*	16†	20†
2,500–4,000 fpm	3	3½	4½	6*	9*	18†	22†
4,000–6,000 fpm	3½	4	5	7*	10*	20†	24†

* For belts 8 in. and over add 2 in. to minimum pulley diameter shown.
† For belts 8 in. and over add 4 in. to minimum pulley diameter shown.

Table 55. Correction Factors *M* for Type of Motor and Starting Method Used—Leather Belts

Motor type and starting method	Correction factor, *M*
Squirrel cage, compensator starting......	1.5
Squirrel cage, line starting..........	2.0
Slip ring and high starting torque.....	2.5

Table 56. Correction Factors *P* for Diameter of Smaller Pulley—Leather Belts

Diameter of small pulley, in.	Correction factor, *P*
4 and under.........	0.5
4½–8..........	0.6
9–12..........	0.7
13–16..........	0.8
17–30..........	0.9
Over 30............	1.0

Table 57. Correction Factors *F* for Special Operating Conditions—Leather Belts

Operating conditions	Correction factor, *F*
Oily, wet, or dusty atmosphere.........	1.35
Vertical drives.......	1.2
Jerky loads.........	1.2
Shock and reversing loads.............	1.4

V-belt Drives

V-belt drives are widely used in power transmission. Such drives consist essentially of endless belts of trapezoidal cross section which ride in V-shaped pulley grooves. The belts are formed of cord and fabric, impregnated with rubber, the cord material being cotton, rayon, synthetic, or steel. V-belt drives are quiet, able to absorb shock and operate at low bearing pressures. A V-belt should ride with the top surface approximately flush with the top of the pulley groove; clearance should be present between the belt base and the base of the groove so that the belt rides on the groove walls.

Table 58. Horsepower Ratings of Rubber Belts
(HP = horsepower per inch of belt width for 180 deg wrap)

	Ply	Belt speed, fpm										
		500	1,000	1,500	2,000	2,500	3,000	4,000	5,000	6,000	7,000	8,000
32-oz fabric	3	0.7	1.4	2.1	2.7	3.3	3.9	4.9	5.6	6.0		
	4	0.9	1.9	2.8	3.6	4.4	5.2	6.5	7.4	7.9		
	5	1.2	2.3	3.4	4.5	5.5	6.5	8.1	9.2	9.8		
	6	1.4	2.8	4.1	5.4	6.6	7.8	9.6	11.0	11.7		
	7	1.6	3.2	4.7	6.2	7.7	9.0	11.2	12.8	13.6		
	8	1.8	3.6	5.3	7.0	8.7	10.2	12.7	14.6	15.5		
32-oz hard fabric	3	0.7	1.5	2.2	2.9	3.5	4.1	5.1	5.8	6.2	6.1	5.5
	4	1.0	2.0	3.0	3.9	4.7	5.5	6.8	7.8	8.3	8.1	7.3
	5	1.3	2.5	3.7	4.9	5.9	6.9	8.5	9.8	10.3	9.1	9.0
	6	1.5	3.0	4.5	5.9	7.1	8.3	10.2	11.7	12.3	12.1	10.7
	7	1.7	3.5	5.2	6.9	8.3	9.7	11.9	13.6	14.3	14.1	12.4
	8	1.9	4.0	5.9	7.9	9.5	11.1	13.6	15.5	16.3	16.0	14.1
	9	2.1	4.5	6.6	8.9	10.6	12.4	15.3	17.4	18.3	17.9	15.8
	10	2.3	5.0	7.3	9.8	11.7	13.7	17.0	19.3	20.3	19.8	17.5
No. 70 rayon cord	3	1.6	3.1	4.6	6.0	7.3	8.6	10.6	12.0	12.7	12.3	10.7
	4	2.1	4.1	6.1	8.0	9.8	11.5	14.5	16.6	17.8	17.8	16.4
	5	2.6	5.1	7.6	10.1	12.3	14.5	18.3	21.1	23.0	23.5	22.2
	6	3.1	6.2	9.2	12.1	14.8	17.5	22.1	25.7	28.1	28.9	27.9
	7	3.6	7.2	10.7	14.1	17.4	20.4	26.0	30.3	33.2	34.5	33.7
	8	4.1	8.2	12.2	16.2	19.9	23.4	29.8	34.8	38.4	40.0	39.4

Table 59. Service Factors S

Application	Squirrel-cage a-c motor		Wound rotor a-c motor (slip ring)	Single-phase capacitor motor	d-c shunt-wound motor	Diesel engine, 4 or more cyl, above 700 rpm
	Normal torque, line start	High torque				
Agitators	1.0–1.2	1.2–1.4	1.2			
Compressors	1.2–1.4		1.4	1.2	1.2	1.2
Belt conveyors (ore, coal, sand)	...	1.4	...	...	1.2	
Screw conveyors	...	1.8	...	...	1.6	
Crushing machinery	...	1.6	1.4	...	...	1.4–1.6
Fans, centrifugal	1.2	...	1.4	...	1.4	1.4
Fans, propeller	1.4	2.0	1.6	...	1.6	1.6
Generators and exciters	1.2	...	...	...	1.2	2.0
Line shafts	1.4	...	1.4	1.4	1.4	1.6
Machine tools	1.0–1.2	...	1.2–1.4	1.0	1.0–1.2	
Pumps, centrifugal	1.2	1.4	1.4	1.2	1.2	
Pumps, reciprocating	1.2–1.4	...	1.4–1.6	...	...	1.8–2.0

Table 60. Arc of Contact Factor K—Rubber Belts

Arc of contact, deg	140	160	180	200	220
Factor K	0.82	0.93	1.00	1.06	1.12

Table 61. Minimum Pulley Diameters—Rubber Belts

	Ply	Belt speed, fpm										
		500	1,000	1,500	2,000	2,500	3,000	4,000	5,000	6,000	7,000	8,000
32-oz fabric....	3	4	4	4	4	5	5	5	6	6		
	4	4	5	6	6	7	7	8	9	10		
	5	6	7	9	10	10	11	12	13	14		
	6	9	10	11	13	14	14	16	18	19		
	7	13	14	16	17	18	19	21	22	24		
	8	18	19	21	22	23	24	25	27	29		
32-oz hard fabric..........	3	3	3	3	4	4	4	4	5	5	6	7
	4	4	4	5	5	6	6	7	7	8	9	12
	5	5	6	7	8	8	9	10	11	12	13	16
	6	6	8	10	11	11	12	13	15	16	18	21
	7	10	12	14	15	15	16	17	19	20	22	26
	8	14	16	17	18	19	20	21	23	24	27	31
	9	18	20	21	22	23	24	25	27	28	31	36
	10	22	24	25	26	27	28	29	31	33	35	41
No. 70 rayon cord........	3	5	6	7	7	8	8	9	10	11	12	13
	4	7	8	9	9	10	11	12	12	14	15	17
	5	9	10	11	12	13	13	15	16	17	19	21
	6	13	14	15	16	16	17	18	19	21	23	25
	7	16	17	18	19	20	21	22	23	24	26	29
	8	19	20	22	23	23	24	25	26	28	30	33

Light-duty or fractional-horsepower V-belt drives are widley used on fractional-horsepower motors or engines. Also, they are intended for use on small-diameter pulleys and on drives in which only one belt is required. Typical applications are washing machines, domestic ironers, small fans and blowers, centrifugal pumps and stokers. The data given for light-duty V-belt drives in Tables 62 to 68 are based on information given in "Standards for Light-duty or Fractional-horsepower V-Belts," Rubber Manufacturers Assoc. (RMA).

Nominal dimensions of light-duty V-belts are given in Table 62. To calculate speed ratio and belt speed use the effective O.D. minus $2X$ (Table 63) as a basis.

For calculating belt lengths and center distances use the equations given above, taking D and d as the effective outside diameters of large and small pulleys, respectively (Fig. 115). In case of a V-flat drive, the O.D. values are to be taken as the O.D. of the pulley plus twice the nominal belt thickness. The RMA recommends that if the center distance C is not dictated by other considerations, the following values be used: (1) for speed ratios less than 3, $C = (D + d)/2 + d$; (2) for speed ratios of 3 or more, $C = D$.

The basic horsepower ratings of the 3L, 4L, and 5L cross-section V-belts are given in Tables 64 to 66. These are nominal ratings based on 180 deg arc of contact on small pulley; for smaller arcs of contact these should be reduced by the correction factors of Table 67. In applying Tables 64 to 67, the nominal horsepower ratings of V-belt drives should be increased by the factors given in Table 68 depending on the type of service.

Table 62. Nominal Dimensions and Recommended Minimum Sheave Diameters—Light-duty V-belts

Cross section	Nominal top width, in.	Nominal thickness, in.	Min sheave O.D., in.
2L*	$\frac{1}{4}$	$\frac{5}{32}$	0.8
3L	$\frac{3}{8}$	$\frac{7}{32}$	1.5
4L	$\frac{1}{2}$	$\frac{5}{16}$	2.5
5L	$\frac{21}{32}$	$\frac{3}{8}$	3.5

* The 2L section is in limited usage and is not made by all manufacturers.

Table 63. Sheave Dimensions—Light-duty V-belts
(See Fig. 115)

Belt cross section	Sheave effective O.D., in.	Groove angle, deg	*W*, in.	*D*, in.	2*X*, in.
2L	Under 1.5	32	0.240	0.250	0.10
	1.5–1.99	34	0.243		
	2.0–2.5	36	0.246		
	Over 2.5	38	0.250		
3L	Under 2.2	32	0.360	0.406	0.15
	2.2–3.19	34	0.364		
	3.2–4.2	36	0.368		
	Over 4.20	38	0.372		
4L	Under 2.65	30	0.485	0.490	0.20
	2.65–3.24	32	0.490		
	3.25–5.65	34	0.494		
	Over 5.65	38	0.504		
5L	Under 3.95	30	0.624	0.580	0.30
	3.95–4.94	32	0.630		
	4.95–7.35	34	0.637		
	Over 7.35	38	0.650		

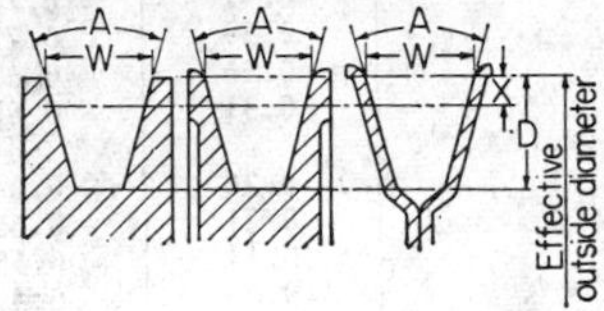

FIG. 115. Standard sheave groove dimensions—light-duty V-belts.

Table 64. Horsepower Ratings of 3L Cross-section V-belts

(Based on 180 deg arc of contact on small sheave)

Belt speed, fpm	Effective O.D. of small sheave, in.			
	1½	2	2½	3 and larger
200	0.05	0.08	0.10	0.11
400	0.08	0.14	0.18	0.20
600	0.11	0.20	0.25	0.29
800	0.12	0.24	0.31	0.36
1,000	0.13	0.28	0.37	0.43
1,200	0.14	0.32	0.43	0.50
1,400	0.15	0.35	0.48	0.56
1,600	0.15	0.38	0.52	0.62
1,800	0.14	0.41	0.57	0.67
2,000	0.13	0.43	0.60	0.72
2,200	0.12	0.44	0.64	0.77
2,400	0.10	0.45	0.66	0.81
2,600	0.07	0.46	0.69	0.84
2,800	0.04	0.46	0.70	0.87
3,000	0.01	0.45	0.72	0.89
3,200	....	0.44	0.72	0.91
3,400	....	0.42	0.72	0.92
3,600	....	0.39	0.71	0.92
3,800	....	0.36	0.69	0.92
4,000	....	0.31	0.67	0.91
4,200	....	0.26	0.64	0.89
4,400	....	0.21	0.60	0.86
4,600	....	0.14	0.55	0.82
4,800	....	0.06	0.49	0.77
5,000	....	....	0.42	0.72
5,200	....	....	0.34	0.65
5,400	....	....	0.26	0.58
5,600	....	....	0.16	0.49
5,800	....	....	0.05	0.39
6,000	....	....	....	0.29

Table 65. Horsepower Ratings of 4L Cross-section V-belts

(Based on 180 deg arc of contact on small sheave)

Belt speed, fpm	Effective O.D. of small sheave, in.				
	2	2½	3	3½	4 and larger
200	0.07	0.13	0.16	0.18	0.21
400	0.12	0.23	0.31	0.36	0.40
600	0.15	0.32	0.43	0.51	0.57
800	0.17	0.40	0.54	0.64	0.73
1,000	0.18	0.46	0.65	0.78	0.88
1,200	0.17	0.51	0.74	0.89	1.01
1,400	0.16	0.56	0.82	1.01	1.14
1,600	0.14	0.60	0.90	1.11	1.26
1,800	0.11	0.62	0.96	1.19	1.37
2,000	0.08	0.64	1.02	1.28	1.47
2,200	0.04	0.67	1.08	1.37	1.58
2,400	....	0.68	1.12	1.43	1.66
2,600	....	0.66	1.16	1.50	1.75
2,800	....	0.65	1.18	1.54	1.81
3,000	....	0.63	1.19	1.58	1.87
3,200	....	0.60	1.20	1.61	1.92
3,400	....	0.55	1.19	1.63	1.96
3,600	....	0.50	1.16	1.64	1.98
3,800	....	0.43	1.13	1.63	2.00
4,000	....	0.35	1.09	1.61	2.00
4,200	....	0.24	1.03	1.58	1.98
4,400	....	0.14	0.96	1.53	1.95
4,600	....	0.01	0.87	1.46	1.91
4,800	....	....	0.76	1.39	1.85
5,000	....	....	0.65	1.30	1.78
5,200	....	....	0.51	1.19	1.70
5,400	....	....	0.36	1.07	1.59
5,600	....	....	0.18	0.91	1.46
5,800	....	....	....	0.72	1.29
6,000	....	....	....	0.54	1.11

Table 66. Horsepower Ratings of 5L Cross-section V-belts

(Based on 180 deg arc of contact small sheave)

Belt speed, fpm	Effective O.D. of small sheave, in.				
	3	3½	4	4½	5 and larger
200	0.13	0.19	0.24	0.27	0.30
400	0.23	0.35	0.45	0.52	0.58
600	0.30	0.49	0.64	0.75	0.83
800	0.36	0.62	0.80	0.95	1.07
1,000	0.40	0.72	0.95	1.14	1.28
1,200	0.42	0.80	1.09	1.31	1.48
1,400	0.43	0.87	1.20	1.46	1.67
1,600	0.42	0.93	1.31	1.60	1.84
1,800	0.40	0.97	1.40	1.73	1.99
2,000	0.36	1.00	1.47	1.84	2.13
2,200	0.31	1.01	1.54	1.94	2.26
2,400	0.25	1.01	1.58	2.02	2.37
2,600	0.17	1.00	1.62	2.09	2.47
2,800	0.08	0.97	1.63	2.15	2.56
3,000	....	0.93	1.64	2.19	2.63
3,200	....	0.87	1.63	2.21	2.68
3,400	....	0.79	1.60	2.22	2.72
3,600	....	0.69	1.54	2.20	2.73
3,800	....	0.57	1.47	2.17	2.72
4,000	....	0.43	1.37	2.11	2.69
4,200	....	0.26	1.26	2.03	2.64
4,400	....	0.08	1.12	1.93	2.57
4,600	....	....	0.97	1.81	2.48
4,800	....	....	0.78	1.66	2.36
5,000	....	....	0.58	1.49	2.22
5,200	....	....	0.34	1.30	2.06
5,400	....	....	0.08	1.07	1.86
5,600	....	....	....	0.82	1.64
5,800	....	....	....	0.54	1.39
6,000	....	....	....	0.23	1.11

Table 67. Correction Factors for Arc of Contact—V-belt Drives

Arc of contact, deg	Correction factor		Arc of contact, deg	Correction factor	
	V to V	V to flat*		V to V	V to flat*
180	1.00	0.75	130	0.86	0.86
170	0.98	0.77	120	0.82	0.82
160	0.95	0.80	110	0.78	0.78
150	0.92	0.82	100	0.74	0.74
140	0.89	0.84	90	0.69	0.69

* A V-to-flat drive is one comprised of a small sheave and a larger diameter flat pulley.

Table 68. Service Factors for V-belt Drives

Typical machines	Type of service	Service factors
Domestic washing machines Domestic ironers Advertising display fixtures Small fans and blowers	Light	1.0–1.2
Fans and blowers (heavy rotors) Centrifugal pumps Oil burners Home workshop machines	Medium	1.2–1.4
Stokers Reciprocating pumps and compressors Refrigerators Drill presses, grinders Lathes Meat slicers Machines for industrial use	Heavy	1.4–1.6

Heavy service consists of heavy starting, shock, or reciprocating loads; frequent starting and stopping; industrial production service; or a combination of these. In the case of **light service** none of these factors is present to any degree.

EXAMPLE. A reciprocating pump is to be driven at approximately 550 rpm by a 1/2 hp motor having a speed of 1,725 rpm. From Table 68, the service factor taken as 1.6 gives a value of design horsepower equal to 0.8. Center distance $C = 12$ in.; outside diameter of large and small sheaves are 12 and 4 in., respectively. Belt speed is $1{,}725 \times \pi \times 3.8/12 = 1{,}715$ fpm. Arc of contact is $180 - (12 - 4)\,60/12 = 140$ deg. From Table 67, correction factor for V-to-V belt and 140 deg arc of contact is 0.89. From Table 65, rating for a 4L cross-section belt at 1,600 fpm is 1.26 hp for 180 deg arc of contact. For 140 deg arc of contact, the horsepower rating is $0.89(1.26) = 1.12$ hp. Since the belt needs to transmit only 0.8 hp, this size should be ample. The length of belt is given by $L = 2C + 1.57(D + d) + (D - d)^2/4C = 24 + 1.57(12 + 4) + (12 - 4)^2/48 = 50.4$ in. A standard 4L belt with an outside length of 51 in. may be used, with appropriate adjustment of center distance.

Multiple V-belt drives are customarily used for the transmission of power in heavy-duty applications. For such drives, the **Multiple V-belt Drive and Mechanical Power Transmission Assoc.**, in cooperation with the **Rubber Manufacturers Assoc.**, has published a booklet, "Engineering Standards—Multiple V-belt Drives," 1955. The data of Tables 69 to 77 and Figs. 116 to 118 are based on this booklet.

The standard V-belt cross sections and nominal dimensions for multiple V-belt drives are given in Table 69; standard groove dimensions and minimum sheave diameters, in Table 70. The face width of stock standard sheaves is equal to $S(N - 1) + 2E$, where N = number of grooves; S and E are taken from Table 70. V-belt cross sections as recommended for various rpm values of the small sheave and various horsepower ratings of the drive are indicated in Fig. 118. Where a drive falls near the dividing line it is desirable to investigate both cross sections.

Maximum horsepower ratings for multiple V belts of premium quality at various speeds are listed in Tables 73 to 77 (lower ratings for standard-quality belts are listed in the above-mentioned publication). These ratings are based on 180 deg arc of contact and assume belts of average length. For other lengths and arcs of contact these ratings must be corrected by the factors given in Tables 67 and 71. The belt speeds are figured using the pitch diameter (Table 70). The equivalent diameters d_e are obtained by multiplying the pitch diameter in inches of the small sheave by a "small-diameter factor" obtained from Table 72, depending on the speed ratio. Applications with belt speeds over 5,000 fpm may require special material or construction as well as balancing; these should be referred to the manufacturer. In using Tables 73 to 77, the rated horsepower of the drive (name-plate rating) should be multiplied by a service factor, Table 59, depending on the severity of service. Service factors for additional applications are given in the above-mentioned booklet.

Table 69. Nominal V-belt Cross Sections

(See Fig. 116)

Belt	Width, w, in.	Thickness, t, in.
A	½	5⁄16
B	21⁄32	13⁄32
C	⅞	17⁄32
D	1¼	¾
E	1½	29⁄32

Fig. 116. V-belt cross sections.

Table 70. Standard Groove Dimensions for Multiple V-belt Sheaves

(See Fig. 117)

Belt	Pitch diameter, in.		Groove angle, deg	Standard groove dimensions, in.				
	Min recommended	Range		W	D	X	S	E
A	3.0	2.6–5.4 Over 5.4	34 38	0.494 0.504	0.490	0.125	⅝	⅜
B	5.4	4.6–7.0 Over 7.0	34 38	0.637 0.650	0.580	0.175	¾	½
C	9.0	7.0–7.99 8.0–12.0 Over 12.0	34 36 38	0.879 0.887 0.895	0.780	0.200	1	1⅟16
D	13.0	12.0–12.99 13.0–17.0 Over 17.0	34 36 38	1.259 1.271 1.283	1.050	0.300	1⁷⁄16	⅞
E	21.0	18.0–24.0 Over 24.0	36 38	1.527 1.542	1.300	0.400	1¾	1⅛

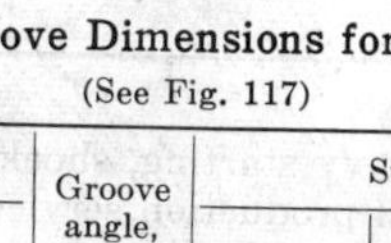

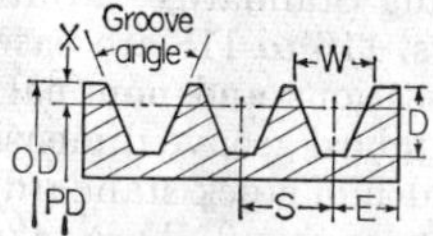

Fig. 117. Standard groove dimensions for multiple V-belt sheaves.

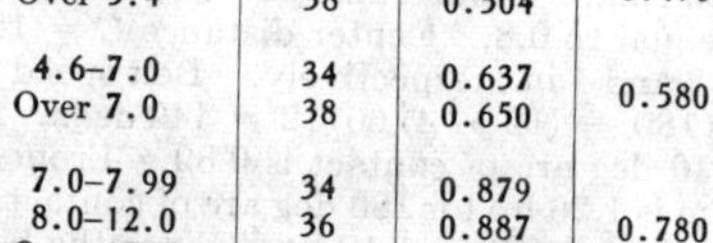

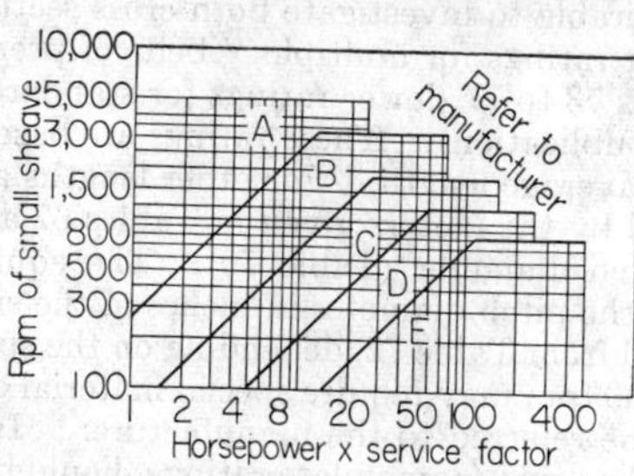

Fig. 118. V-belt cross section for required horsepower rating. Letters A, B, C, D, E refer to belt cross section (see Table 59 for service factor).

Table 71. Length Correction Factors—Multiple V-belts

Std length designation	Belt cross section				
	A	*B*	*C*	*D*	*E*
26	0.81				
33	0.86				
38	0.88	0.83			
46	0.92	0.87			
51	0.94	0.89	0.80		
55	0.96	0.90			
62	0.99	0.93			
66	1.00	0.94			
71	1.01	0.95			
78	1.03	0.98			
81	....	0.98	0.89		
85	1.05	0.99	0.90		
96	1.08	....	0.92		
105	1.10	1.04	0.94		
120	1.13	1.07	0.97	0.86	
136	....	1.09	0.99		
158	....	1.13	1.02	0.92	
173	....	1.15	1.04	0.93	
195	....	1.18	1.07	0.96	0.92
240	....	1.22	1.11	1.00	0.96
300	....	1.27	1.16	1.05	1.01
360	....	....	1.21	1.09	1.05
420	....	....	1.24	1.12	1.09
540	....	....	....	1.18	1.14
660	....	....	....	1.23	1.19

Table 72. Small-diameter Factors—Multiple V-belts

Speed ratio range	Small-diameter factor
1.000–1.019	1.00
1.020–1.032	1.01
1.033–1.055	1.02
1.056–1.081	1.03
1.082–1.109	1.04
1.110–1.142	1.05
1.143–1.178	1.06
1.179–1.222	1.07
1.223–1.274	1.08
1.275–1.340	1.09
1.341–1.429	1.10
1.430–1.562	1.11
1.563–1.814	1.12
1.815–2.948	1.13
2.949 and over	1.14

Table 73. Horsepower Ratings for Premium-quality A-section V-belts

Belt speed, fpm	Equivalent diameter d_e						
	2.6	3.0	3.4	3.8	4.2	4.6	5.0 and over
1,200	0.69	1.02	1.27	1.46	1.62	1.76	1.87
1,400	0.74	1.12	1.42	1.65	1.83	1.99	2.12
1,600	0.78	1.22	1.56	1.82	2.03	2.21	2.36
1,800	0.82	1.31	1.68	1.98	2.22	2.42	2.59
2,000	0.84	1.38	1.80	2.13	2.40	2.62	2.80
2,200	0.85	1.45	1.91	2.27	2.57	2.81	3.01
2,400	0.85	1.51	2.01	2.40	2.72	2.99	3.21
2,600	0.84	1.55	2.09	2.52	2.87	3.15	3.40
2,800	0.82	1.58	2.17	2.63	3.00	3.31	3.57
3,000	0.78	1.60	2.23	2.72	3.12	3.45	3.73
3,200	0.74	1.61	2.28	2.81	3.23	3.59	3.88
3,400	0.68	1.60	2.31	2.88	3.33	3.70	4.02
3,600	0.60	1.59	2.34	2.93	3.41	3.81	4.14
3,800	0.52	1.55	2.35	2.97	3.48	3.90	4.25
4,000	0.41	1.51	2.34	3.00	3.54	3.98	4.35
4,200	0.30	1.44	2.32	3.01	3.57	4.04	4.43
4,400	0.17	1.37	2.29	3.01	3.60	4.09	4.49
4,600	0.02	1.27	2.23	2.99	3.61	4.11	4.54
4,800	....	1.16	2.17	2.96	3.60	4.13	4.57
5,000	....	1.04	2.08	2.90	3.57	4.12	4.59
5,200	....	0.89	1.98	2.83	3.53	4.10	4.58
5,400	....	0.73	1.85	2.74	3.47	4.06	4.56
5,600	....	0.54	1.71	2.64	3.38	4.00	4.52
5,800	....	0.34	1.55	2.51	3.28	3.92	4.46
6,000	....	0.12	1.37	2.36	3.16	3.82	4.38

Table 74. Horsepower Ratings for Premium-quality B-section V-belts

Belt speed, fpm	Equivalent diameter d_e						
	4.6	5.0	5.4	5.8	6.2	6.6	7.0 and over
1,200	1.91	2.20	2.45	2.66	2.85	3.01	3.16
1,400	2.12	2.46	2.75	3.00	3.22	3.41	3.58
1,600	2.31	2.70	3.03	3.32	3.57	3.78	3.98
1,800	2.49	2.93	3.30	3.62	3.90	4.14	4.36
2,000	2.64	3.13	3.54	3.90	4.21	4.48	4.72
2,200	2.78	3.32	3.77	4.17	4.51	4.81	5.07
2,400	2.90	3.48	3.98	4.41	4.78	5.11	5.40
2,600	3.00	3.63	4.17	4.63	5.04	5.39	5.70
2,800	3.08	3.76	4.34	4.84	5.27	5.65	5.99
3,000	3.14	3.86	4.49	5.02	5.49	5.90	6.26
3,200	3.17	3.95	4.61	5.18	5.68	6.12	6.50
3,400	3.19	4.01	4.72	5.32	5.85	6.31	6.73
3,600	3.18	4.05	4.80	5.44	6.00	6.49	6.92
3,800	3.15	4.07	4.85	5.53	6.12	6.64	7.10
4,000	3.09	4.06	4.89	5.60	6.22	6.77	7.25
4,200	3.00	4.02	4.89	5.64	6.29	6.87	7.37
4,400	2.90	3.97	4.88	5.66	6.34	6.94	7.48
4,600	2.75	3.87	4.82	5.64	6.36	6.99	7.54
4,800	2.59	3.75	4.75	5.60	6.35	7.00	7.58
5,000	2.39	3.60	4.64	5.53	6.31	6.99	7.59
5,200	2.16	3.43	4.50	5.43	6.24	6.95	7.57
5,400	1.90	3.21	4.33	5.29	6.13	6.87	7.52
5,600	1.61	2.97	4.13	5.13	6.00	6.76	7.44
5,800	1.28	2.69	3.89	4.93	5.83	6.62	7.32
6,000	0.92	2.38	3.62	4.69	5.62	6.44	7.17

Table 75. Horsepower Ratings for Premium-quality C-section V-belts

Belt speed, fpm	Equivalent diameter d_e					
	7.0	8.0	9.0	10.0	11.0	12.0 and over
1,200	3.65	4.48	5.13	5.65	6.07	6.43
1,400	4.06	5.03	5.79	6.39	6.89	7.30
1,600	4.44	5.55	6.41	7.10	7.67	8.14
1,800	4.79	6.03	7.00	7.78	8.42	8.95
2,000	5.10	6.48	7.56	8.42	9.13	9.72
2,200	5.38	6.90	8.09	9.04	9.82	10.5
2,400	5.62	7.28	8.58	9.61	10.5	11.2
2,600	5.83	7.63	9.03	10.2	11.1	11.8
2,800	6.00	7.94	9.45	10.7	11.6	12.5
3,000	6.13	8.21	9.83	11.1	12.2	13.1
3,200	6.23	8.45	10.2	11.5	12.7	13.6
3,400	6.29	8.64	10.5	11.9	13.1	14.1
3,600	6.30	8.80	10.7	12.3	13.6	14.6
3,800	6.27	8.91	11.0	12.6	13.9	15.1
4,000	6.20	8.97	11.1	12.9	14.3	15.4
4,200	6.08	8.99	11.3	13.1	14.5	15.8
4,400	5.92	8.97	11.3	13.2	14.8	16.1
4,600	5.70	8.88	11.4	13.3	15.0	16.3
4,800	5.43	8.75	11.3	13.4	15.1	16.5
5,000	5.10	8.57	11.3	13.4	15.2	16.7
5,200	4.73	8.33	11.1	13.4	15.2	16.7
5,400	4.30	8.04	11.0	13.3	15.2	16.8
5,600	3.80	7.69	10.7	13.1	15.1	16.7
5,800	3.25	7.27	10.4	12.9	14.9	16.7
6,000	2.64	6.80	10.0	12.6	14.7	16.5

Table 76. Horsepower Ratings for Premium-quality D-section V-belts

Belt speed, fpm	Equivalent diameter d_e					
	12.0	13.0	14.0	15.0	16.0	17.0 and over
1,200	8.26	9.32	10.2	11.0	11.7	12.3
1,400	9.22	10.5	11.5	12.4	13.2	13.9
1,600	10.1	11.5	12.7	13.8	14.7	15.5
1,800	10.9	12.5	13.9	15.1	16.1	17.0
2,000	11.7	13.4	15.0	16.3	17.4	18.4
2,200	12.4	14.3	16.0	17.4	18.7	19.8
2,400	13.0	15.1	16.9	18.5	19.8	21.1
2,600	13.5	15.8	17.8	19.5	21.0	22.3
2,800	14.0	16.4	18.6	20.4	22.0	23.4
3,000	14.3	17.0	19.3	21.2	23.0	24.5
3,200	14.6	17.5	19.9	22.0	23.8	25.4
3,400	14.9	17.9	20.4	22.7	24.6	26.3
3,600	15.0	18.2	20.9	23.3	25.3	27.2
3,800	15.1	18.4	21.3	23.8	26.0	27.9
4,000	15.0	18.5	21.6	24.2	26.5	28.5
4,200	14.9	18.6	21.8	24.5	26.9	29.0
4,400	14.6	18.5	21.9	24.7	27.3	29.5
4,600	14.3	18.4	21.8	24.9	27.5	29.8
4,800	13.9	18.1	21.7	24.9	27.6	30.1
5,000	13.3	17.7	21.5	24.8	27.6	30.2
5,200	12.6	17.2	21.2	24.6	27.6	30.2
5,400	11.9	16.6	20.7	24.2	27.3	30.1
5,600	10.9	15.9	20.1	23.8	27.0	29.8
5,800	9.93	15.0	19.4	23.2	26.6	29.5
6,000	8.77	14.1	18.6	22.5	26.0	29.0

Table 77. Horsepower Ratings for Premium-quality E-section V-belts

Belt speed, fpm	Equivalent diameter d_e					
	18.0	20.0	22.0	24.0	26.0	28.0 and over
1,200	14.7	16.4	17.9	19.1	20.1	21.0
1,400	16.5	18.6	20.2	21.6	22.8	23.8
1,600	18.3	20.6	22.5	24.1	25.5	26.6
1,800	19.9	22.5	24.7	26.5	28.0	29.3
2,000	21.4	24.4	26.7	28.7	30.4	31.9
2,200	22.9	26.1	28.7	30.9	32.8	34.4
2,400	24.2	27.7	30.6	33.0	35.0	36.7
2,600	25.4	29.2	32.3	34.9	37.1	39.0
2,800	26.5	30.6	34.0	36.8	39.1	41.1
3,000	27.5	31.9	35.5	38.5	41.0	43.2
3,200	28.4	33.1	36.9	40.1	42.8	45.1
3,400	29.2	34.2	38.2	41.6	44.5	46.9
3,600	29.8	35.1	39.4	43.0	46.0	48.6
3,800	30.4	35.9	40.5	44.2	47.4	50.2
4,000	30.7	36.6	41.4	45.4	48.7	51.6
4,200	31.0	37.1	42.2	46.3	49.9	52.9
4,400	31.1	37.6	42.8	47.2	50.9	54.1
4,600	31.1	37.8	43.3	47.9	51.8	55.1
4,800	30.9	37.9	43.6	48.4	52.5	55.9
5,000	30.5	37.8	43.8	48.8	53.0	56.6
5,200	30.0	37.6	43.8	49.0	53.4	57.2
5,400	29.3	37.2	43.7	49.1	53.6	57.5
5,600	28.5	36.7	43.4	48.9	53.7	57.7
5,800	27.5	35.9	42.9	48.6	53.5	57.7
6,000	26.2	35.0	42.2	48.2	53.2	57.6

EXAMPLE. The following example (due to B. F. Goodrich Co.) illustrates the use of the tables in designing a multiple V-belt drive. Assume a 25 hp squirrel-cage normal-torque line-start motor with a speed of 1,160 rpm to drive a centrifugal fan at 400 rpm. Center distance $C = 39.2$ in. Sheave diameter = 24 in. PD. From Table 59, service factor = 1.2; hence design horsepower = $1.2 \times 25 = 30$ and, from Fig. 118, a C-section V-belt is indicated. Speed ratio = $1,160/400 = 2.90$. Size of small sheave = $24/2.9 = 8.3$ PD. From above, belt pitch length is 130.7 in. From Table 72 the small-diameter factor is 1.13, giving $d_e = 8.3 \times 1.13 = 9.4$ in. Belt speed = $1,160 \times 8.3 \times \pi/12 = 2,520$ fpm. From Table 75 for a C-section, premium-quality belt at 2,520 fpm and $d_e = 9.4$ in., by interpolation we obtain 9.3 hp per belt. From Table 67 the arc factor is 0.94 and from Table 71 the length factor is 0.98 (using interpolation). Hence the hp per belt is $9.3 \times 0.94 \times 0.98 = 8.6$ hp, and four premium-quality belts are required for 30 hp. If standard-quality belts are used, five belts would be required.

Narrow V-belts with cross sections designated 3V, 5V, and 8V overlap applications of the A, B, C, D and E sizes.

V-flat drives. These consist of a grooved small pulley driving a large flat pulley and are practical when (1) the speed ratio is over 3 to 1 and (2) the center distance is equal to or slightly less than the diameter of the larger pulley.

Quarter-turn Drives. V belts can also be used with quarter-turn drives, in which case special deep-groove sheaves are used. For further details, see the "Engineering Standards" booklet mentioned previously.

Cogged V-belts have cogs molded integrally on the underside of the belt, Fig. 119. Sheaves can be up to 25 percent smaller in diameter with cogged belts because of the greater flexibility inherent in the cogged construction. An extension of the cogged belt mating with a sheave or pulley notched at the same pitch as the cogs leads to a drive particularly useful for timing purposes.

Ribbed V-belts are really flat belts molded integrally with longitudinal ribbing on the underside, Fig. 120. Traction is provided principally by friction between the ribs and sheave grooves rather than by wedging action between the two, as in conventional

V-belt operation. The flat upper portion transmits the tensile belt loads. Ribbed belts serve well when substituted for multiple V-belt drives and for all practical purposes eliminate the necessity for belt-matching in multiple V-belt drives.

Adjustable Motor Bases

To maintain proper belt tensions on short center distances, an adjustable motor base is often used. Figure 121 shows an embodiment of such a base made by the Automatic Motor Base Co., in which adjustment for proper belt tension is made by turning

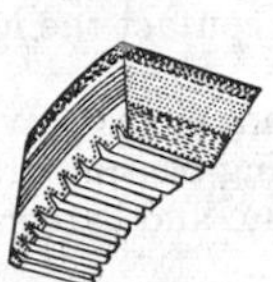

FIG. 119. Cogged V-belt.

FIG. 120. Ribbed V-belt.

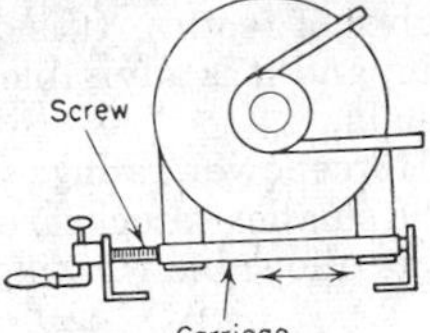

FIG. 121. Adjustable motor base.

a screw which opens or closes the center distance between pulleys, as required. The carriage portion of the base is spring loaded so that after the initial adjustment for belt tension has been made by the screw, the spring will compensate for a normal amount of stretch in the belts. When there is more stretch than can be accommodated by the spring, the screw is turned to provide the necessary belt tensions. The carriage can be moved while the unit is in operation, and the motor base is provided for vertical as well as horizontal mounting.

CHAIN DRIVES

Roller-chain Drives

The advantages of finished steel roller chains are high efficiency (around 98 to 99 percent), no slippage, no initial tension required, chains may travel in either direction. The basic construction of roller chain is shown in Fig. 122 and Table 78.

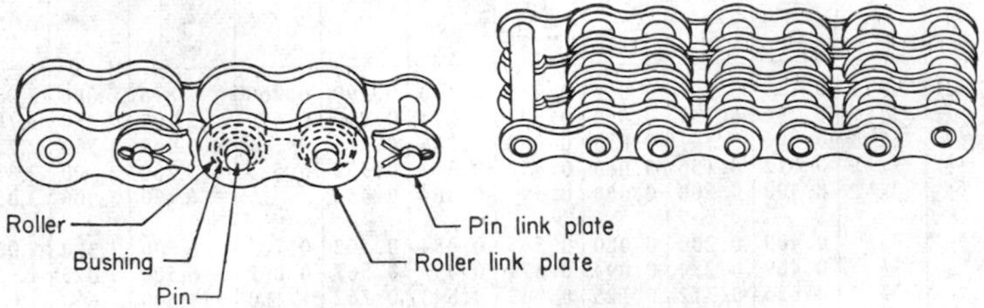

FIG. 122. Roller-chain construction.

The shorter the pitch, the higher the permissible operating speed of roller chain. Horsepower capacity in excess of that provided by a single chain may be had by the use of multiple chains which are essentially parallel single chains assembled on pins common to all strands. Because of its lightness in relation to tensile strength, the effect of centrifugal pull does not need to be considered; even at the unusual speed of 6,000 fpm, this pull is only 3 percent of the ultimate tensile strength.

Sprocket wheels with fewer than 16 teeth may be used for relatively slow speeds, but 18 to 24 teeth are desirable for high speed service. Sprockets with fewer than 25 teeth, running at speeds above 500 or 600 rpm, should be heat-treated to give a tough wear-resistant surface testing between 35 and 45 on the Rockwell C hardness scale.

If the speed ratio requires the larger sprocket to have as many as 128 teeth, or more than eight times the number on the smaller sprocket, it is usually better, with few exceptions, to make the desired reduction in two or more steps. The American Standard tooth form (ASA B29.1) allows roller chain to adjust itself to a larger pitch circle as the pitch of the chain elongates owing to natural wear in the pin-bushing joints. The greater the number of teeth, the sooner the chain will ride out too near the ends of the teeth.

Idler sprockets may be used on either side of the standard roller chain, to take up slack, to guide the chain around obstructions, to change the direction of rotation of a driven shaft, or to provide more wrap on another sprocket. Idlers should not run faster than the speeds recommended as maximum for other sprockets with the same number of teeth. It is desirable that idlers have at least two teeth in mesh with the chain, and it is advisable, though not necessary, to have an idler contact the idle span of chain.

Horsepower ratings are based upon the number of teeth and the rotative speed of the smaller sprocket, either driver or follower. The pin-bushing bearing area, as it affects allowable working load, is the important factor for medium and higher speeds.

Table 78. Roller-chain Data and Dimensions

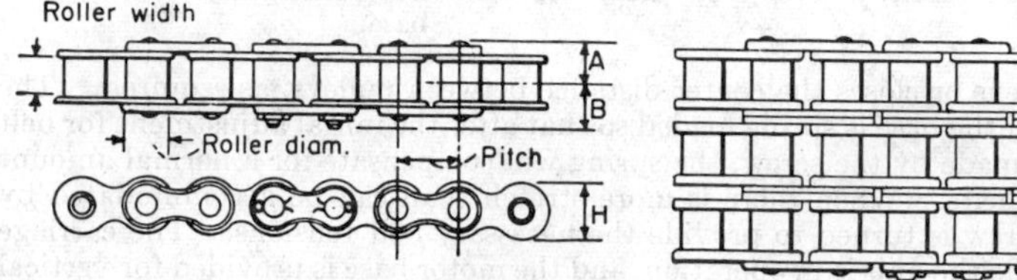

ASA chain number	Roller Pitch, in.	Roller Width, in.	Roller Diam, in.	Pin diam, in.	Roller link plate Thickness, in.	Roller link plate Height H, in.	Dimensions, in. A	Dimensions, in. B	Dimensions, in. C	Tensile strength per strand, lb	Recommended max rpm, Teeth 12	18	24
25	1/4	1/8	0.130	0.091	0.030	0.230	0.150	0.190	0.260	875	5,000	7,000	7,000
35	3/8	3/16	0.200	0.141	0.050	0.344	0.224	0.290	0.400	2,100	2,380	3,780	4,200
41	1/2	1/4	0.306	0.141	0.050	0.383	0.256	0.315	.....	2,000	1,750	2,725	2,850
40	1/2	5/16	0.312	0.156	0.060	0.452	0.313	0.358	0.563	3,700	1,800	2,830	3,000
50	5/8	3/8	0.400	0.200	0.080	0.594	0.384	0.462	......	6,100	1,300	2,030	2,200
50	5/8	3/8	0.400	0.200	0.080	0.545	0.384	0.462	0.707	6,600	1,300	2,030	2,200
60	3/4	1/2	0.469	0.234	0.094	0.679	0.493	0.567	0.892	8,500	1,025	1,615	1,700
80	1	5/8	0.625	0.312	0.125	0.903	0.643	0.762	1.160	14,500	650	1,015	1,100
100	1 1/4	3/4	0.750	0.375	0.156	1.128	0.780	0.910	1.411	24,000	450	730	850
120	1 1/2	1	0.875	0.437	0.187	1.354	0.977	1.123	1.796	34,000	350	565	650
140	1 3/4	1	1.000	0.500	0.220	1.647	1.054	1.219	1.929	46,000	260	415	500
160	2	1 1/4	1.125	0.562	0.250	1.900	1.250	1.433	2.301	58,000	225	360	420
180	2 1/4	1 13/32	1.406	0.687	0.281	2.140	1.421	1.770	2.530	76,000	180	290	330
200	2 1/2	1 1/2	1.562	0.781	0.312	2.275	1.533	1.850	2.800	95,000	170	260	300
240	3	1 7/8	1.875	0.937	0.375	2.850	1.722	2.200	3.375	135,000	120	190	210

[a] Not made in multiple strands.

For extremely slow speeds, the chain selection may be based upon the ultimate tensile strength of the chain. For chain speeds of 25 fpm and less, the chain pull should be not more than 1/5 of the ultimate tensile strength; for 50 fpm, 1/6; for 100 fpm, 1/7; for 150 fpm, 1/8; for 200 fpm, 1/9; and for 250 fpm, 1/10 of the ultimate tensile strength.

Ratings for **multiple strand chains** are proportional to the number of strands. The

Table 79. Horsepower Ratings for Single-strand, Roller-chain Drives

ASA No. 25 — ¼-in. pitch

Teeth	Rpm of sprocket											
	200	400	800	1,200	1,600	2,000	2,400	3,000	4,000	5,000	6,000	7,000
12	0.09	0.18	0.33	0.45	0.54	0.62	0.67	0.73	0.78	0.73		
15	0.12	0.24	0.44	0.60	0.73	0.85	0.94	1.03	1.14	1.20	1.14	
18	0.15	0.29	0.54	0.74	0.92	1.05	1.16	1.31	1.48	1.56	1.55	1.48
21	0.18	0.34	0.63	0.88	1.09	1.26	1.39	1.57	1.77	1.86	1.88	1.81
24	0.21	0.39	0.72	0.99	1.21	1.40	1.57	1.77	2.01	2.11	2.14	2.07

ASA No. 35 — ⅜-in. pitch

Teeth	Rpm of sprocket											
	200	400	800	1,200	1,600	2,000	2,400	2,800	3,200	3,600	4,000	4,500
12	0.34	0.60	1.01	1.31	1.53	1.66	1.72	1.73				
15	0.43	0.78	1.35	1.78	2.12	2.37	2.54	2.65	2.70	2.69		
18	0.52	0.96	1.65	2.21	2.65	2.98	3.24	3.43	3.52	3.57	3.55	
21	0.61	1.12	1.95	2.61	3.14	3.53	3.86	4.08	4.22	4.28	4.28	
24	0.70	1.28	2.22	2.98	3.57	4.04	4.38	4.65	4.81	4.86	4.87	4.75

ASA No. 40 — ½-in. pitch

Teeth	Rpm of sprocket											
	200	400	600	800	1,000	1,200	1,600	1,800	2,000	2,400	2,800	3,200
12	0.77	1.34	1.81	2.16	2.46	2.71	2.99	3.07	3.10			
15	0.99	1.76	2.40	2.93	3.38	3.77	4.32	4.52	4.67	4.81		
18	1.20	2.15	2.94	3.63	4.21	4.71	5.48	5.76	5.97	6.27	6.35	
21	1.41	2.52	3.47	4.27	4.97	5.57	6.50	6.86	7.13	7.50	7.63	
24	1.60	2.88	3.96	4.87	5.67	6.35	7.40	7.80	8.12	8.51	8.68	8.57

ASA No. 50 — ⅝-in. pitch

Teeth	Rpm of sprocket											
	100	200	300	400	600	800	1,000	1,200	1,400	1,600	1,800	2,200
12	0.80	1.44	1.99	2.48	3.26	3.86	4.3	4.6	4.8			
15	1.02	1.87	2.61	3.27	4.39	5.31	6.0	6.8	7.0	7.3	7.5	
18	1.23	2.27	3.19	4.01	5.41	6.58	7.5	8.3	8.9	9.4	9.7	
21	1.45	2.66	3.75	4.70	6.38	7.77	8.9	9.8	10.6	11.1	11.6	11.9
24	1.65	3.05	4.27	5.37	7.28	8.85	10.2	11.2	12.1	12.6	12.1	13.6

ASA No. 60 — ¾-in. pitch

Teeth	Rpm of sprocket											
	50	100	200	300	400	600	800	1,000	1,200	1,400	1,600	1,800
12	0.73	1.34	2.41	3.30	4.05	5.2	6.1	6.6	6.9			
15	0.92	1.72	3.14	4.34	5.39	7.1	8.5	9.5	10.2	10.6		
18	1.12	2.10	3.82	5.31	6.63	8.9	10.6	12.0	13.0	13.7	14.1	
21	1.31	2.46	4.49	6.24	7.80	10.4	12.5	14.1	15.4	16.3	16.9	
24	1.50	2.80	5.11	7.12	8.90	11.9	14.3	16.1	17.6	18.6	19.2	19.5

ASA No. 80 — 1-in. pitch

Teeth	Rpm of sprocket											
	50	100	150	200	300	400	500	600	700	800	1,000	1,160
12	1.68	3.07	4.28	5.3	7.2	8.7	9.8	10.7	11.4			
15	2.14	3.95	5.57	7.0	9.6	11.8	13.6	15.1	16.3	17.3		
18	2.59	4.81	6.79	8.6	11.8	14.5	16.9	18.9	20.5	21.9	24.0	
21	3.03	5.62	7.96	10.1	13.9	17.1	19.9	22.3	24.3	26.0	28.5	
24	3.46	6.43	9.10	11.5	15.8	19.5	22.7	25.4	27.7	29.6	32.5	33.9

Table 79. Horsepower Ratings for Single-strand, Roller-chain Drives—(*Continued*)

ASA No. 100 — 1¼-in. pitch

Teeth	Rpm of sprocket											
	25	50	100	200	300	400	500	650	700	750	800	870
12	1.72	3.19	5.8	9.9	13.0	15.6	17.2					
15	2.19	4.10	7.5	13.1	17.5	21.3	24.0	27.2	28.1			
18	2.55	4.97	9.1	16.0	21.6	26.6	30.2	34.5	35.7	36.8		
21	3.08	5.80	10.7	18.9	25.5	31.4	35.7	40.9	42.3	43.5	44.6	
24	3.52	6.62	12.2	21.5	29.2	35.4	40.5	46.5	48.1	49.5	50.6	52.0

ASA No. 120 — 1½-in. pitch

Teeth	Rpm of sprocket											
	25	50	75	100	150	200	250	300	350	400	500	600
12	2.90	5.4	7.6	9.6	13.2	16.2	18.7	21.0	22.8	24.3		
15	3.71	6.9	9.8	12.5	17.3	21.6	25.3	28.6	31.4	33.9	38.0	
18	4.74	8.4	12.0	15.3	21.3	26.6	31.3	35.4	39.2	42.4	47.9	
21	5.24	9.9	14.0	17.9	24.9	31.2	36.8	41.7	46.2	50.0	56.7	61.7
24	5.99	11.3	16.0	20.4	28.5	35.7	41.9	47.6	52.6	57.1	64.6	70.3

ASA No. 140 — 1¾-in. pitch

Teeth	Rpm of sprocket											
	20	30	50	100	150	200	250	300	350	400	450	475
12	3.72	5.4	8.4	14.8	20.1	24.5	28.1	31.0				
15	4.73	6.9	10.8	19.3	26.6	32.8	38.2	42.8	46.7			
18	5.73	8.3	13.1	23.7	32.7	40.5	47.3	53.2	58.4	62.9		
21	6.70	9.7	15.3	27.7	38.4	47.6	55.7	62.8	69.0	74.5	79.0	
24	7.65	11.1	17.5	31.7	43.7	54.3	63.6	71.6	78.7	84.8	89.9	92.4

ASA No. 160 — 2-in. pitch

Teeth	Rpm of sprocket											
	10	20	40	80	120	160	200	240	280	320	360	400
12	2.9	5.5	10.1	18.0	24.6	30.1	34.8	38.6				
15	3.7	7.0	13.0	23.5	32.4	40.2	47.0	52.9	58.0	62.4		
18	4.4	8.5	15.8	28.7	39.7	49.5	58.1	65.7	72.4	78.3		
21	5.2	9.9	18.5	33.6	46.7	58.1	68.3	77.5	85.5	92.5	99	
24	5.9	11.3	21.1	38.4	53.5	66.5	78.0	88.3	97.4	105.4	112	118

ASA No. 180 — 2¼-in. pitch

Teeth	Rpm of sprocket											
	10	20	40	60	80	100	140	180	220	260	300	330
12	4.09	7.72	14.2	19.9	25.0	29.7	33.7	44.4				
15	5.19	9.84	18.3	25.8	32.7	39.0	50.2	59.8	68.1			
18	6.27	11.9	22.1	31.4	39.9	47.7	61.8	73.9	84.5	93.7		
21	7.33	14.0	26.0	36.9	47.0	56.3	73.0	87.6	100.3	111.4	121.1	
24	8.38	15.9	29.7	42.1	53.6	64.7	83.2	99.7	114.2	126.9	137.7	145.0

ASA No. 220 — 2½-in. pitch

Teeth	Rpm of sprocket											
	10	20	40	60	80	100	120	160	200	240	260	280
12	5.6	10.5	19.1	26.8	33.6	39.6	45.1	54.4				
15	7.1	13.4	24.7	34.8	43.9	52.2	59.8	73.4	85			
18	8.6	16.2	30.0	42.4	53.7	64.1	73.7	90.7	105	118		
21	10.0	18.9	35.1	49.7	63.1	75.3	86.6	106.9	124	139	146	
24	11.4	21.6	40.2	56.8	71.9	86.0	98.8	121.8	142	159	166	173

Table 79. Horsepower Ratings for Single-strand, Roller-chain Drives—(*Continued*)

Teeth	ASA No. 240					3-in. pitch						
	Rpm of sprocket											
	10	20	30	40	60	80	100	120	140	160	180	200
12	9.5	17.7	25.1	32.0	44.4	55.1	64.7	73.0				
15	12.2	22.6	32.4	41.5	58.0	72.7	86.9	97.9	108.0	118.5		
18	14.6	27.7	39.3	50.5	70.8	87.1	105.7	120.7	134.5	147.0	158.0	
21	17.0	32.1	46.0	59.1	83.1	104.7	124.2	142.2	158.7	173.5	187.2	199.4
24	19.4	36.7	52.5	67.5	94.8	119.4	141.8	162.3	180.8	197.6	212.9	226.9

recommended numbers of strands for multiple chains are 2, 3, 4, 6, 8, 10, 12, 16, 20, and 24, with the maximum over-all width in any case limited to 24 in.

The **horsepower ratings** in Table 79 are modified by the **service factors** in Table 80. Thus for a drive having a nominal rating of 3 hp, subject to heavy shock, abnormal conditions, 24 hr day operation, the chain rating obtained from Table 79 should be at least $3 \times 1.7 = 5.1$ hp.

Table 80. Service Factors for Roller-chain Drives

Type load	Service factor	
	10-hr day	24-hr day
Uniform	1.0	1.2
Moderate shock	1.2	1.4
Heavy shock	1.4	1.7

Chain Length Calculations. Referring to Fig. 123 L = length of chain, in.; P = pitch of chain, in.; R and r = pitch radii of large and small sprockets, respectively, in.; D = center distance, in.; A = tangent length, in.; a = angle between tangent and

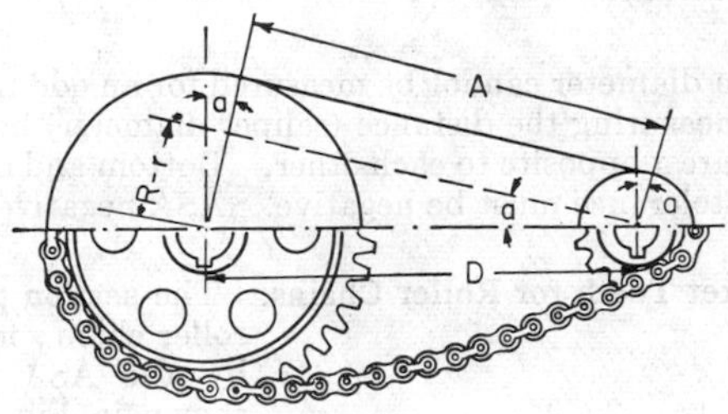

Fig. 123

center line; N and n = number of teeth on larger and smaller sprockets, respectively; $(180 + 2a)$ and $(180 - 2a)$ = angles of contact on larger and smaller sprockets, respectively, deg.

$$a = \sin^{-1}[(R - r)/D] \qquad A = D\cos a$$
$$L = NP(180 + 2a)/360 + nP(180 - 2a)/360 + 2D\cos a$$

If L_p = length of chain in pitches, and D_p = center distance in pitches,

$$L_p = (N + n)/2 + a(N - n)/180 + 2D_p \cos a$$

Avoiding the use of trigonometrical tables,

$$L_p = 2C + (N + n)/2 + K(N - n)^2/C$$

where C is the center distance in pitches and K is a variable depending upon the value of $(N - n)/C$. Values of K are as follows:

$(N - n)/C$	0.1	1.0	2.0	3.0	4.0	5.0	6.0
K	0.02533	0.02538	0.02555	0.02584	0.02631	0.02704	0.02828

Formulas for chain length on multisprocket drives are cumbersome except when all sprockets are the same size and on the same side of the chain. For this condition, the chain length in pitches is equal to the sum of the consecutive center distances in pitches plus the number of teeth on one sprocket.

Actual chain lengths should be in even numbers of pitches. When necessary, an odd number of pitches may be secured by the use of an offset link, but such links should be avoided if possible. An offset link is one pitch; half roller link at one end and half pin link at the other end. If center distances are to be non-adjustable, they should be selected to give an initial snug fit for an even number of pitches of chain. For the average application, a center distance equal to 40 ± 10 pitches of chain represents good practice.

There should be at least 120 deg of wrap in the arc of contact on a power sprocket. For ratios of 3:1 or less, the wrap will be 120 deg or more for any center distance or number of teeth. To secure a wrap of 120 deg or more, for ratios greater than 3:1, the center distance must be not less than the difference between the pitch diameters of the two sprockets.

Sprocket Diameters. N = number of teeth; P = pitch of chain, in.; D = diameter of roller, in. The pitch of a standard roller chain is measured from the center of a pin to the center of an adjacent pin.

$$\text{Pitch diam} = P/\sin \frac{180}{N}$$

$$\text{Bottom diam} = \text{pitch diam} - D$$

$$\text{Outside diam} = P\left(0.6 + \cot \frac{180}{N}\right)$$

$$\text{Caliper diam} = \left(\text{pitch diam} \times \cos \frac{90}{N}\right) - D$$

The exact bottom diameter cannot be measured for an odd number of teeth, but it can be checked by measuring the distance (caliper diameter) between bottoms of the two tooth spaces nearest opposite to each other. Bottom and caliper diameters must not be oversize—all tolerance must be negative. ASA negative tolerance = $0.003 + (0.001 \times P\sqrt{N})$ in.

Design of Sprocket Teeth for Roller Chains. The **section profile** for the teeth of roller chain sprockets, recommended by the ASA, has the proportions shown in Fig. 124. Let P = chain pitch; W = chain width (length of roller); n = number of strands of multiple chain; M = over-all width of tooth profile section; H = nominal thickness of link plate, all in inches. Referring to Fig. 124, $T = 0.93W - 0.006$, for single-strand chain; $= 0.90W - 0.006$, for double- and triple-strand chains; $= 0.88W - 0.006$, for quadruple or quintuple-strand chains; and $= 0.86W - 0.006$, for sextuple-strand chain and over. $C = 0.5P$. $E = \frac{1}{8}P$. $R(\min) = 1.063P$. $Q = 0.5P$. $A = W + 4.15H + 0.003$. $M = A(n - 1) + T$. Tolerance on sprocket thickness $= \pm(0.02W + 0.002)$. For further data, see ASA B29.1.

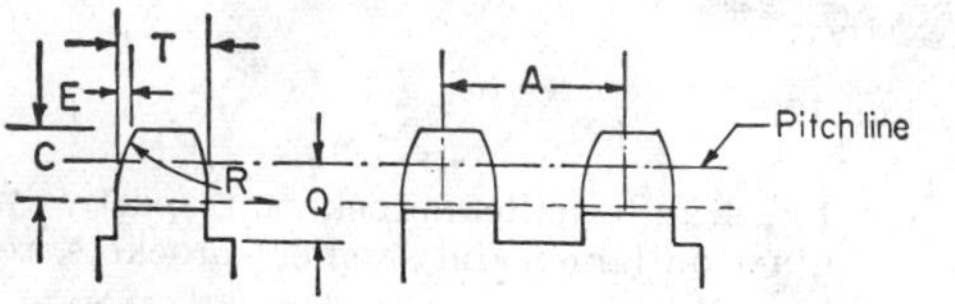

FIG. 124. Sprocket-tooth sections.

One of the most important requirements of a sprocket for roller chain is that the tooth space, or roller seat, should not be undersize. The size and shape of new straddle cutters, space cutters, or hobs should be checked carefully by cutting and testing a sample sprocket.

The method of laying out a standard sprocket tooth for roller chains is illustrated by Fig. 125. This form of tooth is recommended by the ASA and is designed for maximum efficiency throughout the life of the drive. Because of the large pressure angle, the tendency of the teeth to wear hook-shaped is reduced, while the chain rides higher on the teeth as it elongates, thus accommodating itself to a larger pitch circle.

In Fig. 125, let P = pitch; D = nominal roller diameter, in.; N = number of teeth; $D' = 1.005D + 0.003$; $A = 35 + 60/N$ deg; $B = 18 - 56/N$, deg; $C = 180/N$ deg.

In laying out the tooth, first draw line XY. Locate point a, and with that as a center and radius ax equal to $\frac{1}{2}D'$, draw a circular arc for the "seating curve" xx'.

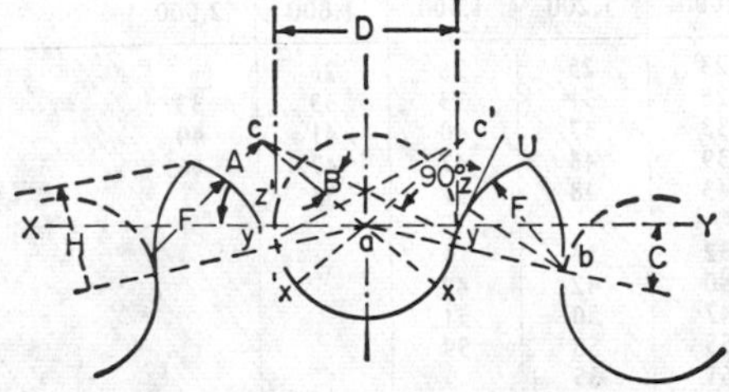

FIG. 125. Laying out a standard sprocket tooth.

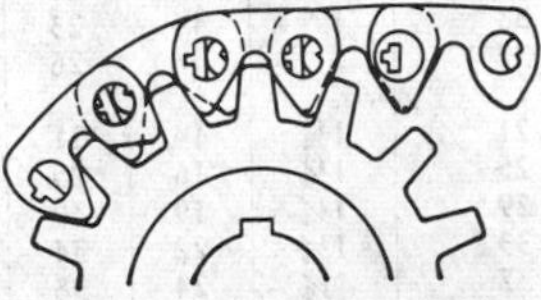
FIG. 126. Inverted-tooth (silent chain) drive.

Draw line xac making angle A with line XY, and locate point c so that $ac = 0.8D$. Draw line cy making angle B with line cx. With center at c and radius cx, draw arc xy for the "working curve."

Draw line yz perpendicular to line cy. Draw line ab making angle C with line XY, and locate point b so that $ab = 1.24D$. Draw line bz parallel to line yc. With b as center and radius bz, draw the "topping curve," arc zu tangent to line zy.

Table 81. Horsepower Ratings per Inch Width—Silent-chain Drives

No. of teeth in smaller sprocket	Pitch, in.	Rpm of small sprocket						
		500	1,000	1,500	2,000	3,000	4,000	5,000
21	⅜	2.2	4.1	5.8	7.2	9.1	9.9	9.5
25	⅜	2.6	4.9	7.0	8.8	11.0	12.0	12.0
29	⅜	3.0	5.8	8.2	10.3	13.0	15.0	15.0
33	⅜	3.5	6.6	9.4	12.0	15.0	17.0	17.0
37	⅜	3.9	7.3	11.0	13.0	17.0	19.0	19.0
21	½	4	7	....	11	13		
25	½	4	8	....	14	17	16	
29	½	5	10	....	17	20	20	
33	½	6	11	....	19	23	23	
37	½	7	13	....	21	26		

No. of teeth in smaller sprocket	Pitch, in.	Rpm of small sprocket							
		500	1,000	1,200	1,800	2,000	2,500	3,000	3,500
21	⅝	6	10	12	15	16	16	16	
25	⅝	7	13	15	19	20	21	21	19
29	⅝	8	15	17	22	24	25	25	23
33	⅝	9	17	20	26	27	29	29	27
37	⅝	10	19	22	29	31	34	33	
21	¾	8	14	16	19	20	19		
25	¾	10	17	20	25	25	24		
29	¾	12	21	24	29	30	30		
33	¾	13	24	27	34	35	35		
37	¾	15	27	31	38	39	39		

A similar construction for the other half will complete the tooth outline.

Outside diameter of sprocket when tooth is pointed $= P \cot (180/N) + 2H$.

The recommended value for H is $0.3P$; and when this value is chosen, the outside diameter of the sprocket will be $P[0.6 + \cot (180/N)]$.

Inverted-tooth (silent) chain drives have a typical tooth form shown in Fig. 126. Such chains should be operated in an oil-retaining casing with provisions for lubrication. The use of offset links and chains with an uneven number of pitches should be avoided.

Table 82. Horsepower Ratings per Inch Width—Silent-chain Drives

No. of teeth in smaller sprocket	Pitch, in.	Rpm of small sprocket								
		300	500	700	1,000	1,200	1,500	1,800	2,000	
21	1	9	14	18	23	25	26	26		
25	1	11	17	22	28	31	33	33	33	
29	1	13	20	26	33	37	40	41	40	
33	1	14	23	30	39	43	47	47	46	
37	1	16	26	34	43	48	52	53		
21	1¼	14	21	26	32	33				
25	1¼	16	25	32	40	42	42			
29	1¼	19	30	38	47	50	51			
33	1¼	22	34	44	55	58	59			
37	1¼	24	38	50	61	65				
		Rpm of small sprocket								
		200	300	400	500	600	700	800	900	1,000
21	1½	13	19	24	29	32	35	37	39	39
25	1½	16	23	30	35	40	44	47	49	52
29	1½	19	27	35	41	47	52	56	59	60
33	1½	22	31	40	47	54	60	64	68	70
37	1½	24	35	47	53	61	67	72	77	79
45	1½	30	43	54	65	74	81	86	90	
21	2	23	32	40	42	50	52			
25	2	28	39	49	56	62	66	68	68	
29	2	33	46	58	67	74	79	82	82	
33	2	37	53	66	77	85	91	94	94	
37	2	42	60	74	88	99	102	105		
45	2	51	72	90	105	115	121			

Horsepower ratings per inch of silent chain width, given in ASA B29.2, 1950, for various chain pitches and speeds, are shown in Tables 81 and 82. These ratings are based on ideal drive conditions with relatively little shock or load variation, an average life of 20,000 hr being assumed. In utilizing the horsepower ratings of the tables, the nominal horsepower of the drive should be multiplied by a service factor depending on the application. These service factors are listed in Table 83.

Table 83. Service Factors for Silent-chain Drives

Type load	Service factor	
	10-hr day	24-hr day
Uniform....................	1.0	1.3
Moderate shock...........	1.4	1.7
Heavy shock..............	1.7	2.0

For further details on service factors for a large number of specific applications, see ASA B29.2. This pamphlet also gives additional data on lubrication, sprocket dimensions, etc. In utilizing Tables 81 and 82 the required chain width is obtained by dividing the design horsepower by the horsepower ratings given. For calculating silent-chain lengths, the procedure for roller-chain drives may be used.

ROTARY AND RECIPROCATING ELEMENTS

Analysis of the Motion of the Reciprocating Parts. Let r = crank radius, in.; R = crank radius, ft; $s = 2r$ = stroke, in.; l = length of connecting rod, in.; x = displacement of piston from head end dead center, in.; a = crank angle corresponding to x; b = connecting-rod angle corresponding to x; v = crankpin velocity, fps; c = piston velocity, fps; N = rpm of the crank. Then, when the center lines of the piston rod and crankshaft lie in the same plane,

$$x = r(1 - \cos a) + l(1 - \cos b) = r\left(1 - \cos a + \frac{r}{2l}\sin^2 a\right) \qquad \text{(approx)}$$

Table 84 gives correct piston positions corresponding to various crank angles. Table 85 gives crank angles corresponding to various piston positions.

Table 84. Piston Positions for Various Crank Angles

(From beginning of stroke toward crankshaft. To find distance of piston from beginning of stroke, multiply tabular value by length of stroke)

Calculated from $\frac{x}{2r} = \frac{1}{2}(1 - \cos a) + \frac{l}{2r}\left(1 - \sqrt{1 - \frac{r^2}{l^2}\sin^2 a}\right)$

Crank angles, deg a	Ratio of length of connecting rod to length of crank										
	$\frac{l}{r}$ = 2.5	3	3.5	4	4.5	5	5.5	6	7	8	∞
5	0.0027	0.0025	0.0024	0.0023	0.0023	0.0022	0.0022	0.0022	0.0022	0.0021	0.0019
10	0.0106	0.0101	0.0098	0.0095	0.0093	0.0091	0.0090	0.0089	0.0087	0.0085	0.0076
15	0.0238	0.0226	0.0218	0.0212	0.0208	0.0204	0.0210	0.0198	0.0194	0.0191	0.0170
20	0.0419	0.0399	0.0385	0.0375	0.0367	0.0360	0.0355	0.0350	0.0343	0.0338	0.0302
25	0.0648	0.0618	0.0597	0.0580	0.0568	0.0558	0.0550	0.0543	0.0532	0.0524	0.0468
30	0.0922	0.0880	0.0849	0.0827	0.0809	0.0795	0.0784	0.0774	0.0759	0.0748	0.0670
35	0.1238	0.1181	0.1141	0.1111	0.1088	0.1069	0.1054	0.1042	0.1022	0.1007	0.0904
40	0.1590	0.1518	0.1467	0.1430	0.1401	0.1377	0.1358	0.1342	0.1318	0.1299	0.1170
45	0.1975	0.1887	0.1825	0.1779	0.1774	0.1716	0.1693	0.1674	0.1643	0.1621	0.1464
50	0.2387	0.2283	0.2210	0.2156	0.2114	0.2081	0.2054	0.2032	0.1996	0.1970	0.1786
55	0.2822	0.2702	0.2618	0.2556	0.2508	0.2470	0.2439	0.2413	0.2373	0.2342	0.2132
60	0.3274	0.3139	0.3044	0.2974	0.2921	0.2878	0.2843	0.2814	0.2769	0.2735	0.2500
65	0.3737	0.3588	0.3484	0.3407	0.3348	0.3301	0.3263	0.3231	0.3182	0.3144	0.2887
70	0.4207	0.4045	0.3932	0.3850	0.3786	0.3735	0.3694	0.3660	0.3607	0.3567	0.3290
75	0.4677	0.4505	0.4386	0.4298	0.4230	0.4177	0.4133	0.4097	0.4041	0.3999	0.3706
80	0.5142	0.4963	0.4839	0.4747	0.4777	0.4621	0.4576	0.4539	0.4480	0.4436	0.4132
85	0.5599	0.5415	0.5288	0.5194	0.5122	0.5065	0.5019	0.4981	0.4920	0.4876	0.4564
90	0.6044	0.5858	0.5729	0.5635	0.5563	0.5505	0.5458	0.5420	0.5359	0.5314	0.5000
95	0.6471	0.6287	0.6160	0.6066	0.5994	0.5937	0.5891	0.5852	0.5792	0.5747	0.5436
100	0.6879	0.6699	0.6575	0.6484	0.6414	0.6358	0.6313	0.6275	0.6216	0.6172	0.5868
105	0.7265	0.7093	0.6974	0.6886	0.6819	0.6765	0.6722	0.6685	0.6629	0.6587	0.6294
110	0.7627	0.7465	0.7353	0.7270	0.7206	0.7156	0.7114	0.7080	0.7027	0.6987	0.6710
115	0.7963	0.7814	0.7710	0.7633	0.7574	0.7527	0.7489	0.7457	0.7408	0.7371	0.7113
120	0.8274	0.8139	0.8044	0.7974	0.7921	0.7878	0.7843	0.7814	0.7776	0.7735	0.7500
125	0.8558	0.8438	0.8354	0.8292	0.8244	0.8206	0.8175	0.8149	0.8108	0.8078	0.7868
130	0.8815	0.8711	0.8638	0.8584	0.8542	0.8509	0.8482	0.8459	0.8424	0.8398	0.8214
135	0.9046	0.8958	0.8896	0.8851	0.8815	0.8787	0.8764	0.8745	0.8715	0.8692	0.8536
140	0.9250	0.9179	0.9128	0.9090	0.9061	0.9038	0.9019	0.9003	0.8978	0.8960	0.8830
145	0.9429	0.9372	0.9332	0.9302	0.9279	0.9261	0.9246	0.9233	0.9213	0.9199	0.9096
150	0.9583	0.9540	0.9510	0.9487	0.9469	0.9455	0.9444	0.9434	0.9420	0.9408	0.9330
155	0.9711	0.9681	0.9660	0.9643	0.9631	0.9621	0.9613	0.9606	0.9595	0.9587	0.9532
160	0.9816	0.9796	0.9782	0.9772	0.9764	0.9757	0.9752	0.9747	0.9740	0.9735	0.9698
165	0.9897	0.9886	0.9878	0.9872	0.9867	0.9863	0.9860	0.9858	0.9854	0.9851	0.9830
170	0.9954	0.9949	0.9946	0.9943	0.9941	0.9939	0.9938	0.9937	0.9935	0.9933	0.9924
175	0.9989	0.9987	0.9986	0.9986	0.9985	0.9984	0.9984	0.9984	0.9984	0.9983	0.9981
180	1.0000	1.0000	1.0000	1.0000	1.0000	1.0000	1.0000	1.0000	1.0000	1.0000	1.0000

Table 85. Crank Angles and Piston Positions for Connecting Rods of Different Lengths

Calculated from $\cos^{-1}\left(\dfrac{1 - x_1}{1 - 2x_1 \Big/ \left(1 + \dfrac{l}{r}\right)} - x_1\right)$, where $x_1 = \dfrac{x}{2r}$

Fraction of stroke from commencement, $\frac{x}{2r}$	Ratio of length of connecting rod to length of crank										
	2.5	3	3.5	4	4.5	5	5.5	6	7	8	∞
	Angle through which crank has advanced from dead center, deg										
0.005	6.86	7.02	7.15	7.25	7.34	7.40	7.46	7.51	7.59	7.65	8.11
0.01	9.70	9.94	10.13	10.27	10.39	10.48	10.56	10.63	10.74	10.83	11.48
0.02	13.75	14.09	14.35	14.56	14.72	14.86	14.97	15.06	15.22	15.34	16.26
0.03	16.88	17.30	17.62	17.87	18.07	18.23	18.37	18.49	18.68	18.82	19.95
0.04	19.53	20.02	20.38	20.67	20.91	21.10	21.26	21.39	21.61	21.78	23.07
0.05	21.88	22.43	22.84	23.16	23.42	23.64	23.82	23.97	24.21	24.40	25.84
0.06	24.02	24.62	25.08	25.43	25.71	25.95	26.15	26.31	26.58	26.79	28.36
0.07	26.01	26.65	27.14	27.53	27.84	28.09	28.30	28.48	28.77	28.99	30.68
0.08	27.86	28.56	29.08	29.49	29.82	30.09	30.32	30.51	30.82	31.06	32.86
0.09	29.62	30.36	30.92	31.35	31.70	31.99	32.23	32.43	32.76	33.01	34.92
0.10	31.29	32.07	32.66	33.12	33.49	33.79	34.05	34.26	34.61	34.87	36.87
0.15	38.77	39.74	40.47	41.04	41.49	41.86	42.17	42.43	42.85	43.17	45.57
0.20	45.31	46.46	47.31	47.97	48.49	48.92	49.27	49.57	50.05	50.42	53.13
0.25	51.32	52.62	53.58	54.31	54.90	55.38	55.77	56.10	56.63	57.04	60.00
0.30	56.99	58.43	59.49	60.30	50.94	61.46	61.89	62.25	62.82	63.26	66.42
0.35	62.45	64.03	65.18	66.06	66.75	67.30	67.76	68.15	68.76	69.22	72.54
0.40	67.80	69.51	70.75	71.68	72.41	73.00	73.49	73.89	74.53	75.02	78.46
0.45	73.12	74.95	76.26	77.25	78.02	78.63	79.14	79.56	80.23	80.73	84.26
0.50	78.46	80.41	81.79	82.82	83.62	84.26	84.78	85.22	85.90	86.42	90.00
0.55	83.90	85.95	87.39	88.46	89.28	89.94	90.48	90.92	91.62	92.14	95.74
0.60	89.50	91.64	93.13	94.23	95.07	95.74	96.28	96.73	97.44	97.96	101.54
0.65	95.35	97.56	99.08	100.20	101.05	101.72	102.27	102.72	103.42	103.94	107.46
0.70	101.54	103.80	105.34	106.46	107.31	107.98	108.52	108.97	109.66	110.17	113.58
0.75	108.21	110.49	112.02	113.13	113.97	114.62	115.15	115.58	116.25	116.74	120.00
0.80	115.57	117.82	119.32	120.39	121.19	121.82	122.32	122.73	123.37	123.83	126.87
0.85	123.94	126.10	127.51	128.52	129.26	129.84	130.31	130.68	131.26	131.69	134.43
0.90	133.96	135.90	137.17	138.05	138.71	139.21	139.61	139.94	140.44	140.81	143.13
0.91	136.26	138.15	139.37	140.22	140.85	141.34	141.72	142.03	142.51	142.86	145.08
0.92	138.71	140.52	141.69	142.51	143.11	143.57	143.94	144.24	144.70	145.03	147.14
0.93	141.32	143.05	144.16	144.94	145.51	145.95	146.30	146.58	147.01	147.33	149.32
0.94	144.13	145.77	146.82	147.55	148.09	148.50	148.82	149.09	149.49	149.79	151.64
0.95	147.21	148.73	149.71	150.38	150.88	151.26	151.56	151.81	152.18	152.45	154.16
0.96	152.62	152.02	152.90	153.52	153.97	154.31	154.59	154.81	155.14	155.39	156.93
0.97	154.51	155.75	156.53	157.07	157.47	157.77	158.01	158.20	158.50	158.71	160.05
0.98	159.15	160.18	160.83	161.28	161.61	161.86	162.06	162.22	162.46	162.46	163.74
0.99	165.23	165.98	166.44	166.77	167.00	167.18	167.32	167.44	167.61	167.74	168.52
0.995	169.55	170.08	170.41	170.64	170.81	170.94	171.04	171.12	171.24	171.33	171.89
1.00	180.00	180.00	180.00	180.00	180.00	180.00	180.00	180.00	180.00	180.00	180.00

When, however, the center line of motion of the reciprocating masses is located a distance h from the center of rotation of the crank, as shown in Fig. 127, the dead centers are unsymmetrical and the stroke is greater than $2r$, having the value

$$s = \sqrt{(l + r)^2 - h^2} - \sqrt{(l - r)^2 - h^2}$$

Determination of the Velocity of the Reciprocating Parts. The velocity of the reciprocating parts is

$$c = v\left(\sin a + r \sin 2a/2l \sqrt{1 - \frac{r^2}{l^2}\sin^2 a}\right) = v(\sin a + r \sin 2a/2l) \qquad \text{(approx)}$$

when the center lines of the piston rod and crankshaft lie in the same plane. The ratio

Table 86. Tangential Factors and Piston Velocities

Crank angles forward, deg a	Ratio of connecting-rod length to crank length										
	$\frac{l}{r} = 2.5$	3	3.5	4	4.5	5	5.5	6	7	8	∞
5	0.1219	0.1161	0.1120	0.1089	0.1065	0.1045	0.1029	0.1016	0.0996	0.0980	0.0872
10	0.2442	0.2307	0.2226	0.2164	0.2117	0.2079	0.2048	0.2022	0.1981	0.1950	0.1736
15	0.3594	0.3425	0.3304	0.3215	0.3145	0.3089	0.3043	0.3005	0.2946	0.2901	0.2588
20	0.4718	0.4499	0.4343	0.4227	0.4136	0.4064	0.4006	0.3957	0.3880	0.3822	0.3420
25	0.5781	0.5516	0.5329	0.5189	0.5081	0.4995	0.4925	0.4866	0.4770	0.4706	0.4226
30	0.6768	0.6464	0.6250	0.6091	0.5968	0.5870	0.5791	0.5724	0.5620	0.5542	0.5000
35	0.7667	0.7331	0.7097	0.6923	0.6788	0.6682	0.6595	0.6522	0.6409	0.6325	0.5736
40	0.8466	0.8108	0.7859	0.7675	0.7533	0.7421	0.7329	0.7253	0.7134	0.7045	0.6428
45	0.9156	0.8786	0.8530	0.8341	0.8196	0.8081	0.7988	0.7910	0.7789	0.7699	0.7071
50	0.9730	0.9358	0.9102	0.8915	0.8771	0.8657	0.8565	0.8488	0.8368	0.8279	0.7660
55	1.0181	0.9820	0.9572	0.9392	0.9253	0.9144	0.9055	0.8982	0.8867	0.8782	0.8192
60	1.0507	1.0168	0.9937	0.9769	0.9641	0.9540	0.9457	0.9390	0.9284	0.9205	0.8660
65	1.0707	1.0402	1.0196	1.0046	0.9932	0.9842	0.9769	0.9709	0.9615	0.9545	0.9063
70	1.0784	1.0525	1.0350	1.0224	1.0127	1.0051	0.9990	0.9939	0.9860	0.9801	0.9397
75	1.0743	1.0539	1.0402	1.0303	1.0228	1.0169	1.0121	1.0081	1.0020	0.9974	0.9659
80	1.0592	1.0452	1.0357	1.0289	1.0238	1.0197	1.0164	1.0137	1.0095	1.0063	0.9848
85	1.0341	1.0269	1.0221	1.0186	1.0160	1.0139	1.0122	1.0109	1.0087	1.0071	0.9962
90	1.0000	1.0000	1.0000	1.0000	1.0000	1.0000	1.0000	1.0000	1.0000	1.0000	1.0000
95	0.9583	1.9655	0.9703	0.9738	0.9764	0.9785	0.9801	0.9815	0.9837	0.9853	0.9962
100	0.9104	0.9245	0.9339	0.9407	0.9459	0.9499	0.9532	0.9559	0.9601	0.9633	0.9848
105	0.8575	0.8779	0.8916	0.9015	0.9090	0.9150	0.9198	0.9237	0.9299	0.9344	0.9659
110	0.8010	0.8269	0.8444	0.8570	0.8667	0.8742	0.8804	0.8855	0.8934	0.8992	0.9397
115	0.7419	0.7724	0.7930	0.8080	0.8194	0.8284	0.8357	0.8417	0.8511	0.8581	0.9063
120	0.6814	0.7153	0.7383	0.7551	0.7680	0.7781	0.7863	0.7931	0.8037	0.8116	0.8660
125	0.6202	0.6564	0.6811	0.6991	0.7130	0.7239	0.7328	0.7401	0.7516	0.7601	0.8192
130	0.5591	0.5963	0.6219	0.6406	0.6550	0.6664	0.6756	0.6833	0.6953	0.7042	0.7660
135	0.4986	0.5356	0.5612	0.5801	0.5946	0.6061	0.6154	0.6232	0.6353	0.6444	0.7071
140	0.4390	0.4748	0.4997	0.5181	0.5322	0.5435	0.5526	0.5602	0.5721	0.5810	0.6428
145	0.3805	0.4140	0.4375	0.4549	0.4683	0.4790	0.4877	0.4949	0.5062	0.5147	0.5736
150	0.3232	0.3536	0.3750	0.3909	0.4032	0.4130	0.4209	0.4276	0.4380	0.4458	0.5000
155	0.2672	0.2937	0.3124	0.3263	0.3371	0.3457	0.3528	0.3586	0.3678	0.3747	0.4226
160	0.2122	0.2342	0.2498	0.2614	0.2704	0.2776	0.2835	0.2884	0.2961	0.3018	0.3420
165	0.1583	0.1752	0.1872	0.1962	0.2032	0.2088	0.2133	0.2171	0.2231	0.2276	0.2588
170	0.1051	0.1165	0.1247	0.1309	0.1356	0.1394	0.1425	0.1451	0.1492	0.1523	0.1736
175	0.0524	0.0582	0.0623	0.0654	0.0679	0.0698	0.0714	0.0727	0.0748	0.0763	0.0872
180	0.0000	0.0000	0.0000	0.0000	0.0000	0.0000	0.0000	0.0000	0.0000	0.0000	0.0000

Tangential pressure on crank = resultant horizontal pressure times tabular quantity. Forward stroke is toward crankshaft. Wrist-pin velocity = crankpin velocity times tabular quantity. Calculated from

$$\sin a + r \sin 2a/2l \sqrt{1 - \frac{r^2}{l^2} \sin^2 a}$$

c/v is the tangential factor; Table 86 gives the values of velocities corresponding to various crank angles. When, however, the crank rotates about a center off the center line, as in Fig. 127 (**offset cylinder**), the above formula does not hold, and the graphical solution of Fig. 128 may be resorted to. AH is the center line of the piston rod pro-

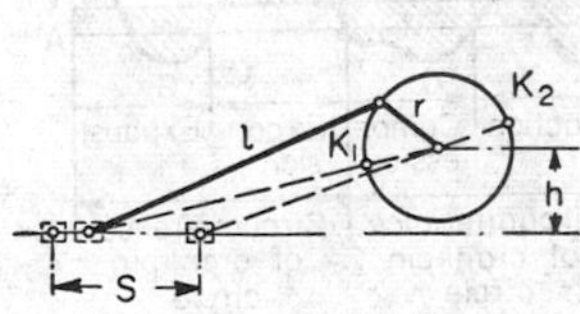

FIG. 127

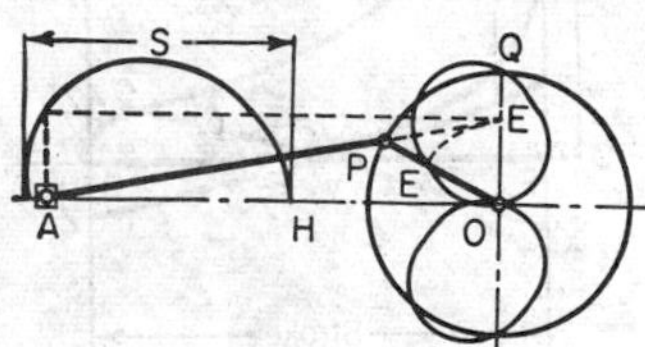

FIG. 128

duced, AP is the connecting rod, OP the crank with center at O. Draw OQ at right angles to AH. For any position AP of the connecting rod cutting OQ in E, the length OE represents the velocity of the reciprocating parts to the same scale to which OP represents the crankpin velocity. The graphical construction of Fig. 128 shows how to construct velocity ellipses for the whole revolution.

Determination of the Acceleration of the Reciprocating Parts. The acceleration p of the reciprocating parts is given by

$$p = v^2(\cos a + r \cos 2a/l)/R \qquad \text{(approx)}$$

when the center lines of the pistons and crankshaft lie in the same plane.

Table 87 gives accurate values of the acceleration for different crank angles.

If the cylinder is offset, as in Fig. 127, the acceleration of the reciprocating parts may be found by the approximate formula

$$p = (v^2/R)[\cos a + (r/l) \cos 2a + h/l \sin a]$$

The **inertia force** in pounds per sq in. of piston is $f = Mp/A = Wv^2(\cos a + r \cos 2a/l)/AgR = 0.00034WN^2R(\cos a + r \cos 2a/l)/A$, where W = total weight of reciprocating masses, lb; A = piston area, sq in. The value of W for any given engine is to be taken as the weight of the piston, piston rod, crosshead, and a portion of the connecting rod. It is usual to include ½ to ⅔ the connecting-rod weight as part of the reciprocating masses.

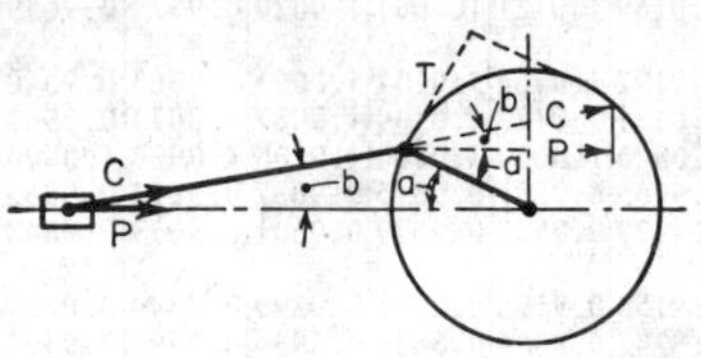

Fig. 129

Relation between the Force in the Line of Piston Travel and the Tangential Reaction at the Crankpin. In Fig. 129, if P is the force in the line of piston travel, the force acting along the connecting rod is $C = P/\cos b$, and that on the guides $N = P \tan b$. The force tangent to the crankpin circle at the crankpin is $T = C \sin (a + b) = P \sec b \sin (b + a) = P \sin a(1 + r \cos a/\sqrt{l^2 - r^2 \sin^2 a})$. Table 86 gives values of $\sec b \sin (b + a)$ for various values of l/r. They are equal to the tangential factors of piston velocities for different crank angles.

Determination of Flywheel Weight

Tangential Effort Curves. The total force on the piston at each instant is obtained from an indicator card or other suitable instrumentation providing a pressure or force measurement during the stroke. In the case of a double-acting engine, this force is obtained by subtracting from the pressure on one face the corresponding pressure on the other face of the piston. In Fig. 130 the indicator card $ABCDEF$ of a single-cylinder, single-acting, four-cycle Diesel engine is shown. The **inertia force** of the reciprocating parts per square inch of piston area is obtained by multiplying the mass

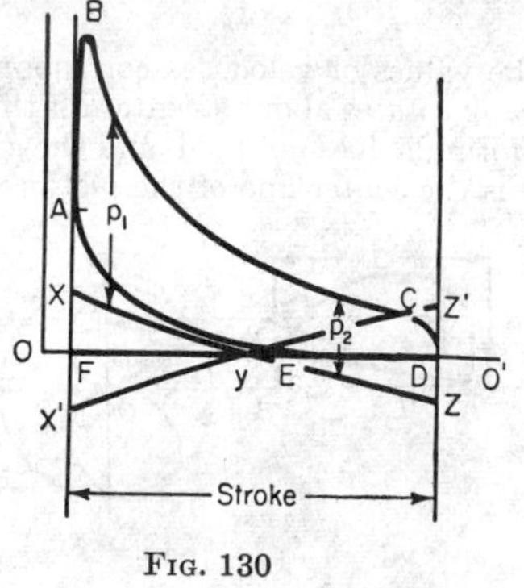

Fig. 130

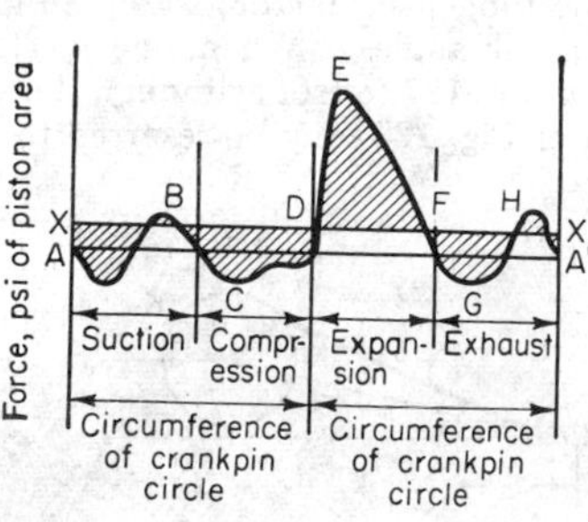

Fig. 131

of the parts per square inch of piston area (piston, piston-rod, crosshead, and 0.35 to 0.45 of the connecting rod) by the acceleration of the piston (see Table 87). It is represented by the ordinates of the curves xyz and $x'yz'$ for the forward and return strokes, respectively. The ordinates between the total gas pressure and the inertia curves (p_1, p_2) give the resultant pressures acting on the piston along the center line of the engine.

The tangential reactions at the crankpin can be obtained by multiplying the resultant pressure on the piston by the tangential factors for the various crank angles (see Table 86). Figure 131 shows the tangential reaction for the Diesel engine of Fig. 130 plotted against the travel of the crank.

In engine design, it is usual to construct the tangential effort curve from data obtained at normal or rated engine load and to assume that the engine is working against a constant and uniform torque. The uniform resisting torque is represented in Fig. 131 by XX, which is so located that the shaded areas above and below it are equal

Table 87. Inertia Factors and Piston Accelerations

(Values of $\cos a + r \cos 2a/ly + r^3 \sin^2 2a/4l^3y^3$, where $y = \sqrt{1 - \frac{r^2}{l^2} \sin^2 a}$. Algebraic signs relate to forward stroke; use opposite signs for return stroke)

Crank angles forward deg, a	Ratio of connecting-rod length to crank length										
	$\frac{l}{r} = 2.5$	3	3.5	4	4.5	5	5.5	6	7	8	∞
0	1.4000	1.3333	1.2857	1.2500	1.2222	1.2000	1.1818	1.1667	1.1429	1.1250	1.0000
5	1.3908	1.3249	1.2778	1.2426	1.2152	1.1932	1.1753	1.1604	1.1369	1.1193	0.9962
10	1.3635	1.2997	1.2543	1.2204	1.1941	1.1731	1.1559	1.1416	1.1192	1.1024	0.9848
15	1.3183	1.2580	1.2155	1.1839	1.1594	1.1399	1.1239	1.1107	1.0899	1.0744	0.9659
20	1.2558	1.2006	1.1621	1.1335	1.1116	1.0941	1.0799	1.0682	1.0496	1.0357	0.9397
25	1.1770	1.1283	1.0948	1.0702	1.0514	1.0365	1.0244	1.0144	0.9987	0.9871	0.9063
30	1.0829	1.0423	1.0149	0.9950	0.9779	0.9681	0.9585	0.9505	0.9382	0.9290	0.8660
35	0.9750	0.9439	0.9236	0.9091	0.8983	0.8898	0.8830	0.8775	0.8688	0.8624	0.8192
40	0.8551	0.8349	0.8225	0.8140	0.8078	0.8031	0.7993	0.7963	0.7917	0.7883	0.7660
45	0.7252	0.7172	0.7133	0.7112	0.7100	0.7092	0.7086	0.7083	0.7078	0.7076	0.7071
50	0.5878	0.5929	0.5980	0.6026	0.6064	0.6097	0.6124	0.6148	0.6186	0.6215	0.6428
55	0.4455	0.4643	0.4787	0.4899	0.4988	0.5061	0.5121	0.5171	0.5250	0.5310	0.5736
60	0.3013	0.3338	0.3574	0.3751	0.3889	0.4000	0.4091	0.4167	0.4286	0.4375	0.5000
65	0.1583	0.2041	0.2363	0.2601	0.2785	0.2931	0.3050	0.3149	0.3305	0.3420	0.4226
70	0.0197	0.0776	0.1175	0.1468	0.1692	0.1869	0.2013	0.2132	0.2319	0.2458	0.3420
75	−0.1117	−0.0434	0.0030	0.0368	0.0625	0.0828	0.0993	0.1129	0.1341	0.1499	0.2588
80	−0.2329	−0.1567	−0.1054	−0.0682	−0.0400	−0.0178	0.0002	0.0150	0.0381	0.0553	0.1736
85	−0.3417	−0.2605	−0.2062	−0.1669	−0.1372	−0.1138	−0.0949	−0.0793	−0.0550	−0.0369	0.0872
90	−0.4364	−0.3536	−0.2981	−0.2582	−0.2279	−0.2041	−0.1849	−0.1690	−0.1443	−0.1260	0.0000
95	−0.5160	−0.4348	−0.3805	−0.3412	−0.3115	−0.2881	−0.2692	−0.2536	−0.2293	−0.1212	−0.0872
100	−0.5802	−0.5040	−0.4527	−0.4155	−0.3873	−0.3651	−0.3471	−0.3323	−0.3092	−0.2920	−0.1736
105	−0.6292	−0.5610	−0.5146	−0.4809	−0.4551	−0.4348	−0.4184	−0.4048	−0.3835	−0.3677	−0.2588
110	−0.6644	−0.6064	−0.5665	−0.5373	−0.5149	−0.4971	−0.4827	−0.4708	−0.4521	−0.4382	−0.3420
115	−0.6869	−0.6411	−0.6090	−0.5851	−0.5667	−0.5521	−0.5402	−0.5303	−0.5148	−0.5032	−0.4226
120	−0.6987	−0.6662	−0.6426	−0.6249	−0.6111	−0.6000	−0.5909	−0.5833	−0.5714	−0.5625	−0.5000
125	−0.7016	−0.6829	−0.6685	−0.6573	−0.6483	−0.6411	−0.6351	−0.6301	−0.6221	−0.6161	−0.5736
130	−0.6978	−0.6927	−0.6875	−0.6830	−0.6792	−0.6759	−0.6732	−0.6708	−0.6670	−0.6641	−0.6428
135	−0.6890	−0.6970	−0.7009	−0.7030	−0.7043	−0.7050	−0.7056	−0.7059	−0.7064	−0.7066	−0.7071
140	−0.6770	−0.6971	−0.7096	−0.7181	−0.7243	−0.7290	−0.7328	−0.7358	−0.7404	−0.7438	−0.7660
145	−0.6633	−0.6944	−0.7147	−0.7292	−0.7400	−0.7485	−0.7553	−0.7609	−0.7695	−0.7759	−0.8192
150	−0.6491	−0.6898	−0.7172	−0.7370	−0.7521	−0.7640	−0.7736	−0.7815	−0.7939	−0.8030	−0.8660
155	−0.6356	−0.6843	−0.7178	−0.7424	−0.7612	−0.7761	−0.7882	−0.7982	−0.8139	−0.8256	−0.9063
160	−0.6236	−0.6788	−0.7173	−0.7458	−0.7678	−0.7853	−0.7995	−0.8113	−0.8298	−0.8436	−0.9397
165	−0.6136	−0.6738	−0.7163	−0.7480	−0.7725	−0.7920	−0.8079	−0.8212	−0.8419	−0.8575	−0.9659
170	−0.6061	−0.6700	−0.7153	−0.7492	−0.7755	−0.7965	−0.8137	−0.8280	−0.8504	−0.8673	−0.9848
175	−0.6015	−0.6675	−0.7146	−0.7498	−0.7772	−0.7991	−0.8171	−0.8320	−0.8555	−0.8731	−0.9962
180	−0.6000	−0.6667	−0.7143	−0.7500	−0.7778	−0.8000	−0.8182	−0.8333	−0.8571	−0.8750	−1.0000

to one another. The areas above XX represent in footpounds per square inch of piston area the amount of energy which is effective in increasing the kinetic energy of the moving masses; and the areas below XX represent the energy per square inch of piston area liberated in the retardation of the moving masses for the production of useful work in the driven unit.

In the case of multicylinder engines, the tangential effort curves for each cylinder are superimposed, properly shifted with respect to each other, corresponding to the angular location of their respective cranks.

Determination of Flywheel Weight. Let M = mass of wheel rim; W = weight of wheel rim, lb; v_1 = max linear rim velocity, fps; v_2 = min rim velocity, fps; $v = \frac{1}{2}(v_1 + v_2)$ = average rim velocity, fps; $k = (v_1 - v_2)/v$ = coefficient of velocity fluctuation; D = mean diam of rim, ft; N = rpm; A = piston area, sq in.; E_m = max energy in ft-lb per sq in. of piston area which must be absorbed or liberated by the wheel rim with velocity variation between v_1 and v_2. Then

$$E_m \times A = M\frac{v_1^2}{2} - M\frac{v_2^2}{2} = \frac{W}{g}kv^2 = \frac{kWD^2N^2}{11{,}744} \quad \text{or} \quad W = \frac{11{,}744E_mA}{kD^2N^2}$$

About $\frac{9}{10}$ W may be placed in the rim to account for the flywheel effect of the arms and other rotating masses. Some acceptable values of k are: pumps, 0.03–0.05; machine shops, 0.025–0.03; looms and paper mills, 0.025; spinning mills, 0.015; crushers, 0.2; electric generators, a-c, 0.003; d-c, 0.002.

Wittenbauer's Analysis for Flywheel Performance. The method does not involve more computation work than the one described above, but it is more accurate where the reciprocating parts are comparatively heavy. Wittenbauer's method avoids the inaccuracy resulting from the evaluation of the inertia forces on the reciprocating parts on the basis of the uniform nominal speed of rotation for the engine.

Let the crankpin velocity be represented by v_r and the velocity of any moving masses (m_1, m_2, m_3, etc.) at any instant or phase be represented, respectively, by v_1, v_2, v_3, etc. The kinetic energy of the entire engine system of moving masses may then be expressed as

$$E = \tfrac{1}{2}(m_1v_1^2 + m_2v_2^2 + m_3v_3^2 + \cdots) = \tfrac{1}{2}M_rv_r^2$$

or, the single reduced mass M_r at the crankpin which possesses the equivalent kinetic energy is

$$M_r = [m_1(v_1/v_r)^2 + m_2(v_2/v_r)^2 + m_3(v_3/v_r)^2 + \cdots]$$

In an engine mechanism, sufficiently accurate values of M_r can be obtained if the weight of the connecting rod is divided between the crankpin and the wrist pin so as to retain the center of gravity of the rod in its true position; usually 0.55 to 0.65 of the weight of the connecting rod should be placed on the crankpin, and 0.45 to 0.35 of the weight on the wrist pin. M_r is a variable in engine mechanisms on account of the reciprocating parts and should be found for a number of crank positions. It should include all moving masses except the flywheel.

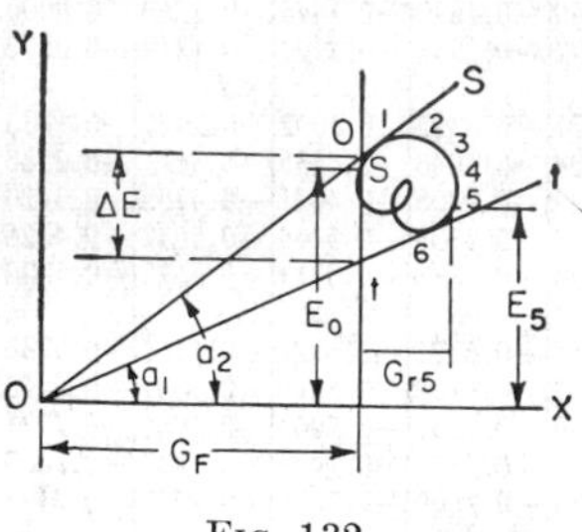

FIG. 132

The total energy E used in accelerating reciprocating parts from the beginning of the forward stroke up to any crank position can be obtained by finding from the indicator cards the total work done in the cylinder (on both sides of the piston) up to that time and subtracting from it the work done in overcoming the resisting torque, which may usually be assumed constant. The mean energy of the moving masses is $E_0 = \frac{1}{2}M_rv_r^2$.

In Fig. 132, the reduced weights of the moving masses $G_F + G_{r5}$ are plotted on the X axis corresponding to different crank positions. $G_F = gM_F$ is the reduced flywheel weight and $G_{r5} = gM_{r5}$ is the sum of the other reduced weights. Against each of these abscissas is plotted the energy E available for acceleration measured from the beginning of the forward stroke. The curve 0123456 is the locus of these plotted points.

The diagram possesses the following property: Any straight line drawn from the origin O to any point in the curve is a measure of the velocity of the moving masses; tangents bounding the diagram measure the limits of velocity between which the crank-pin will operate. The maximum linear velocity of the crankpin in feet per second is $v_2 = \sqrt{2g} \tan a_2$, and the minimum velocity is $v_1 = \sqrt{2g} \tan a_1$. Any desired change in v_1 and v_2 may be accomplished by changing the value of G_F, which means a change in the flywheel weight or a change in the flywheel weight reduced to the crank pin. As G_F is very large compared with G_r and the point 0 cannot be located on the diagram unless a very large drawing is made, the tangents are best formed by direct calculation:

$$\tan \alpha_2 = \frac{v_r^2}{2g}(1 + k) \qquad \tan \alpha_1 = \frac{v_r^2}{2g}(1 - k)$$

where k is the coefficient of velocity fluctuation. The two tangents ss and tt to the curve 0123456, thus drawn, cut a distance ΔE on the ordinate E_0. The reduced fly-wheel weight is then found to be

$$G_F(\Delta E)g/v_r^2k$$

SPRINGS

It is assumed in the following formulas that the springs are in no case stressed beyond the elastic limit (*i.e.*, that they are perfectly elastic) and that they are subject to Hooke's law.

Notation:

P = safe load, lb
f = deflection for a given load, P, in.
l = length of spring, in.
V = volume of spring, cu in.
S_s = safe stress (due to bending), psi
S_v = safe shearing stress, psi
U = resilence, in.-lb

The **work** in inch-pounds performed **in deflecting a spring** from 0 to f (spring duty) is $U = Pf/2 = s_s^2V/CE$. This is based upon the assumption that the deflection is proportional to the load. C is a constant dependent upon the shape of the springs.

The **time of vibration** T (in seconds) **of a spring** (weight not considered) is equal to that of a simple circular pendulum whose length l_0 equals the deflection f (in ft) that is produced in the spring by the load P. $T = \pi\sqrt{l_0/g}$, where g = acceleration of gravity, ft per sec/per sec.

Springs Subjected to Bending

1. Rectangular Plate Spring (Fig. 133)

$$P = bh^2S_s/6l \qquad I = bh^3/12 \qquad U = Pf/2 = VS_s^2/18E$$
$$f = Pl^3/3EI = 4Pl^3/bh^3E = 2l^2S_s/3hE$$

2. Triangular Plate Spring (Fig. 134). The elastic curve is a circular arc.

$$P = bh^2S_s/6l \qquad I = bh^3/12 \qquad U = Pf/2 = S_s^2V/6E$$
$$f = Pl^3/2EI = 6Pl^3/bh^3E = l^2S_s/hE$$

3. Rectangular plate spring with end tapered in the form of a cubical parabola (Fig. 135). The elastic curve is a circular arc. P, I, and f same as for triangular plate spring (Fig. 134). $U = Pf/2 = S_s^2V/9E$.

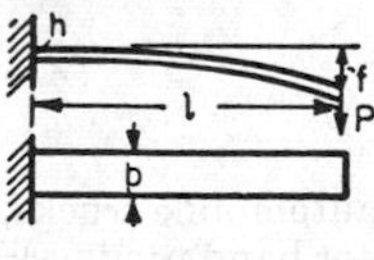

FIG. 133

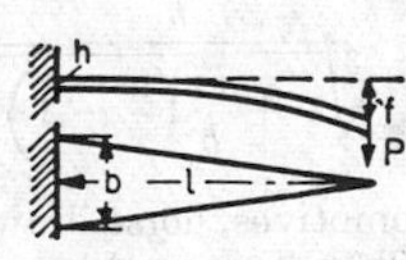

FIG. 134

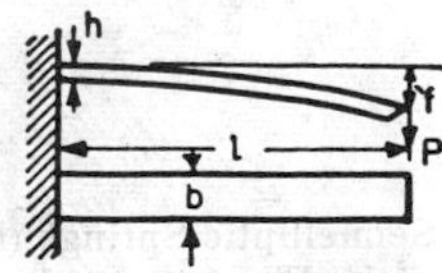

FIG. 135

Table 88. Strength and Deflection of Single-leaf Flat Springs

Load applied at end of spring; $c = 6/S_s$				Load applied at center of spring; $c = 6/4S_s$			
Plans and elevations of springs	a	U	v	Plans and elevations of springs	a	U	v
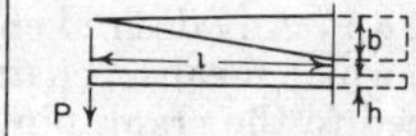	$\frac{S_s}{E}$	$\frac{S_s^2}{6E}$	$\frac{1}{2}$	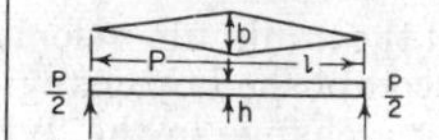	$\frac{S_s}{4E}$	$\frac{S_s^2}{6E}$	$\frac{1}{2}$
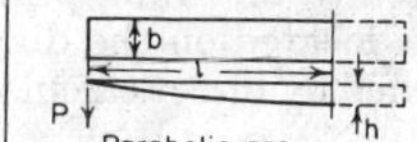 Parabolic arc	$\frac{4S_s}{3E}$	$\frac{S_s^2}{6E}$	$\frac{2}{3}$	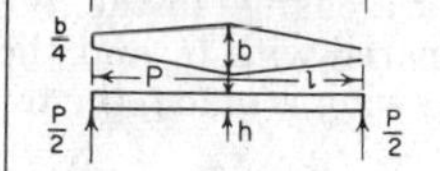	$\frac{0.87S_s}{4E}$	$\frac{0.70S_s^2}{6E}$	$\frac{5}{8}$
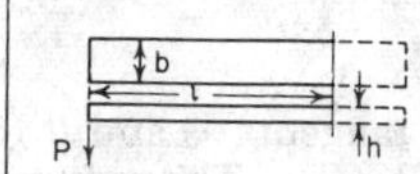	$\frac{2S_s}{3E}$	$\frac{0.33S_s^2}{6E}$	1	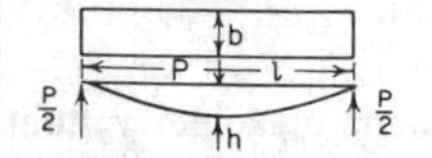 Parabolic arcs	$\frac{S_s}{3E}$	$\frac{S_s^2}{6E}$	$\frac{2}{3}$
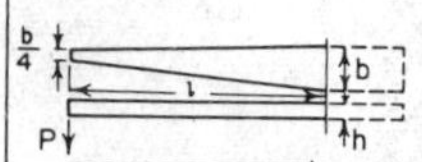	$\frac{0.87S_s}{E}$	$\frac{0.70S_s^2}{6E}$	$\frac{5}{8}$	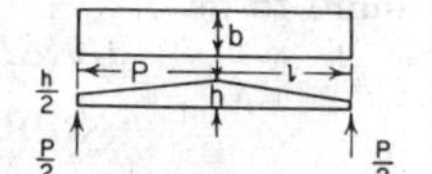	$\frac{1.09S_s}{4E}$	$\frac{0.725S_s^2}{6E}$	$\frac{3}{4}$
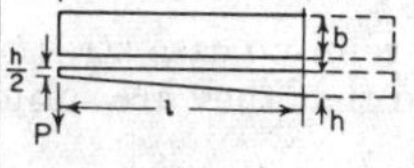	$\frac{1.09S_s}{E}$	$\frac{0.725S_s^2}{6E}$	$\frac{3}{4}$	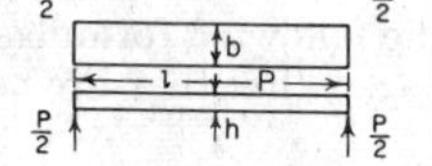	$\frac{S_s}{6E}$	$\frac{0.33S_s^2}{6E}$	1

The strength and deflection of **single-leaf flat springs** of various forms are given (Bruce, *Am. Mach.*, July 19, 1900) by the formulas $h = al^2/f$ and $b = cPl/h^2$. The volume of the spring is given by $V = vlbh$. The values of the constants a and c and the resilience in inch-pounds per cubic inch are given in Table 88, in terms of the safe stress S_s. Values of v are given also.

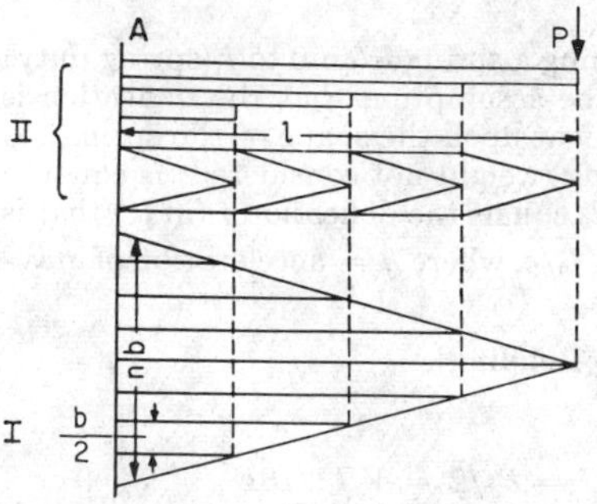

Fig. 136

4. Compound (Leaf or Laminated) Springs. If several springs of rectangular section are combined, the resulting compound spring should (1) form a beam of uniform strength that (2) does not open between the joints while bending (*i.e.*, elastic curve must be a circular arc). Only the type immediately following meets both requirements, the others meeting only the second requirement.

5. Laminated Triangular Plate Spring (Fig. 136). If the triangular plate spring shown at I be cut into an even number ($= 2n$) of strips of equal width (in this case eight strips of width $b/2$), and these strips be combined, a laminated spring will be formed whose carrying capacity will equal that of the original uncut spring; or $P = nbh^2S_s/6l$; $n = 6Pl/bh^2S_s$.

6. Laminated rectangular plate spring with leaf ends tapered in the form of a cubical parabola (Fig. 137); see Case 3.

7. Laminated Trapezoidal Plate Spring with Leaf Ends Tapered. (Fig. 138.) The ends of the leaves are trapezoidal in form and are tapered according to the formula

$$z = \frac{h}{\sqrt[3]{1 + \frac{b_1}{b}\left(\frac{a}{x} - 1\right)}}$$

8. Semielliptic Springs (for locomotives, horse-drawn and automobile trucks, etc.). Referring to Fig. 139, the load $2P$ (lb) acting on the spring center band produces a tensional stress $P/\cos a$ in each of the inclined shackle links. This is resolved into the vertical force P and the horizontal force $P \tan a$, which together produce a bending moment $M = P(l + p \tan a)$. The equations given in (1), (2), and (3) apply to curved

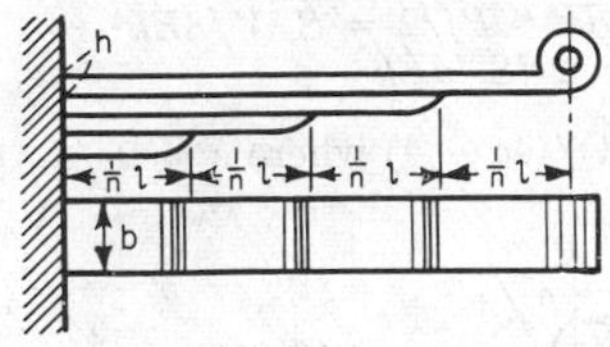

FIG. 137

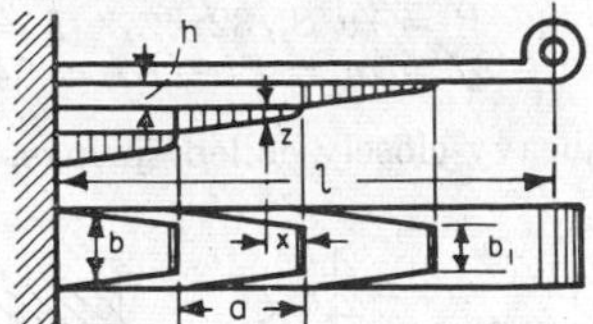

FIG. 138

as well as straight springs. The bearing force $= 2P = (2nbh^2/6)[S_s/(l + p \tan a)]$, and the deflection $= (6l^2/nbh^3)P(l + p \tan a)/E = l^2S_s/hE$.

In addition to the bending moment, the leaves are subjected to the tension force $P \tan a$ and the transverse force P, which produce in the upper leaf an additional stress $S = P \tan a/bh$, as well as a transverse shearing stress.

In determining the number of leaves n in a given spring, allowance should be made for an excess load on the spring caused by the vibration. This is usually made by decreasing the allowable stress about 15 percent.

The foregoing does not take account of initial stresses caused by the band. For more detailed information, see Wahl, "Mechanical Springs," Penton.

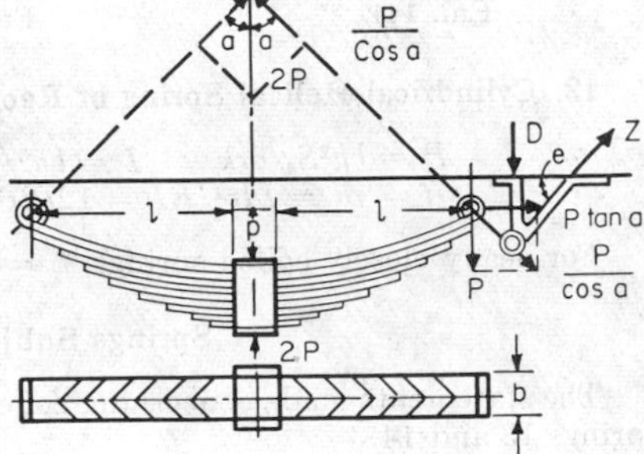

FIG. 139

9. Elliptic Springs. Safe load $P = nbh^2S_s/6l$, where $l = \frac{1}{2}$ distance between bolt eyes (less $\frac{1}{2}$ length of center band, where used); deflection $f = 4l^2S_sK/hE$, where

$$K = \frac{1}{(1-r)^3}\left[\frac{1-r^2}{2} - 2r(1-r) - r^2 \ln r\right]$$

r being the number of full-length leaves ÷ total number (n) of leaves in the spring. All dimensions in inches. For semielliptic springs, the deflection is only half as great. Safe load $= nbh^2S_s/3l$. (Peddle, *Am. Mach.*, Apr. 17, 1913.)

Coiled Springs. In these, the load is applied as a couple Pr which turns the spring while winding or holds it in place when wound up. If the spindle is not to be subjected to bending moment, P must be replaced by two equal and opposite forces ($P/2$) acting at the circumference of a circle of radius r. The formulas are the same in both cases. The springs are assumed to be fixed at one end and free at the other. The bending moment acting on the section of least resistance is always Pr. The length of the straightened spring $= l$. See Benjamin and French, Experiments on Helical Springs, *Trans. ASME*, **23**, p. 298.

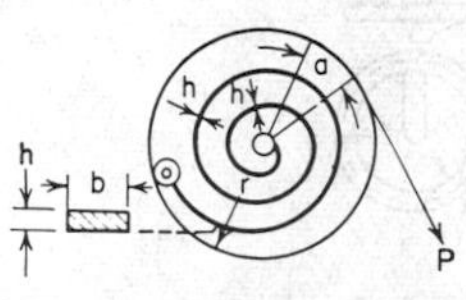

FIG. 140

For **heavy closely coiled helical springs** the usual formulas are inaccurate and result in stresses greatly in excess of those assumed. See Wahl, Stresses in Heavy Closely-coiled Helical Springs, *Trans. ASME*, 1929. In springs 10 to 12 and 15 to 18, the quantity k is unity for lighter springs and has the stated values (supplied by Wahl) for heavy closely coiled springs.

10. Spiral Coiled Springs of Rectangular Cross Section (Fig. 140)

$$P = bh^2S_s/6rk \qquad I = bh^3/12 \qquad U = Pf/2 = S_s^2V/6Ek^2$$
$$f = ra = Plr^2/EI = 12Plr^2/Ebh^3 = 2rlS_s/hEk$$

For heavy closely coiled springs $k = (3c - 1)/(3c - 3)$, where $c = 2R/h$ and R is the minimum radius of curvature at the center of the spiral.

11. Cylindrical Helical Spring of Circular Cross Section (Fig. 141)

$$P = \pi d^3 S_s/32rk \qquad I = \pi d^4/64 \qquad U = Pf/2 = S_s^2 V/8Ek^2$$
$$f = ra = Plr^2/EI = 64Plr^2/\pi Ed^4 = 2rlS_s/dEk$$

For heavy closely coiled springs, $k = (4c - 1)/(4c - 4)$ where $c = 2r/d$.

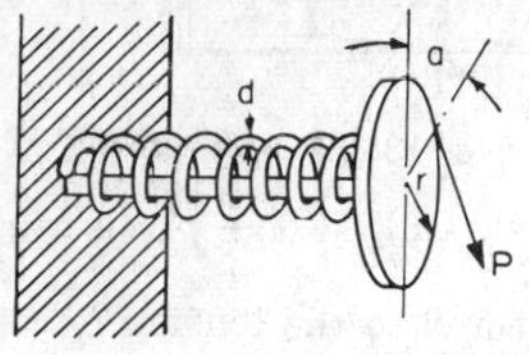

Fig. 141

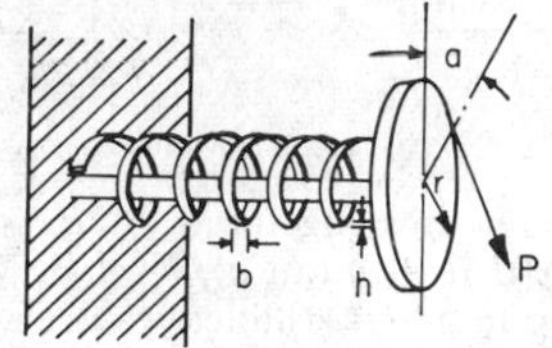

Fig. 142

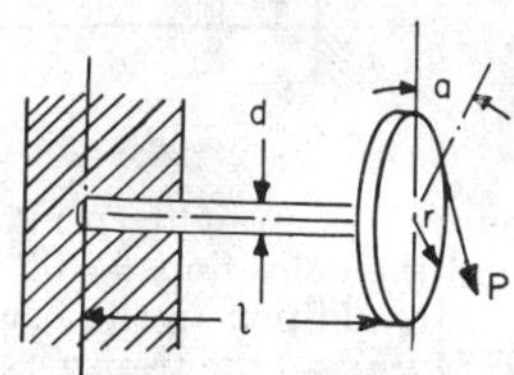

Fig. 143

12. Cylindrical Helical Spring of Rectangular Cross Section (Fig. 142)

$$P = bh^2 S_s/6rk \qquad I = bh^3/12 \qquad U = Pf/2 = S_s^2 V/6Ek^2$$
$$f = ra = Plr^2/EI = 12Plr^2/Ebh^3 = 2rlS_s/hEk$$

For heavy closely coiled springs, $k = (3c - 1)/(3c - 3)$, where $c = 2r/h$.

Springs Subjected to Torsion

The statements made concerning coiled springs subjected to bending apply also to springs 13 and 14.

13. Straight Bar Spring of Circular Cross Section (Fig. 143)

$$P = \pi d^3 S_v/16r = 0.1963d^3 S_v/r \qquad U = Pf/2 = S_v^2 V/4G$$
$$f = ra = 32r^2 lP/\pi d^4 G = 2rlS_v/dG$$

14. Straight Bar Spring of Rectangular Cross Section (Fig. 144)

$$P = 2b^2 hS_v/9r \qquad K = b/h \qquad U = Pf/2 = 4S_v^2 V(K^2 + 1)/45G \text{ (max when } K = 1)$$
$$f = ra = 3.6r^2 lP(b^2 + h^2)/b^3 h^3 G = 0.8rlS_v(b^2 + h^2)/bh^2 G$$

Springs Loaded Axially Either in Tension or Compression

Note. For springs 15 to 18, r = mean radius of coil; n = number of coils

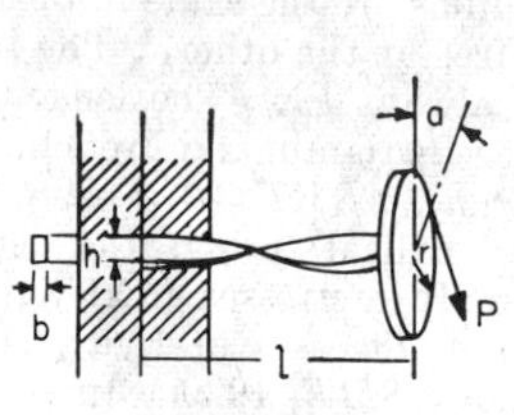

Fig. 144

Fig. 145

15. Cylindrical Helical Spring of Circular Cross Section (Fig. 145)

$$P = \pi d^3 S_v/16rk = 0.1963d^3 S_v/rk \qquad U = Pf/2 = S_v^2 V/4Gk^2$$
$$f = 64nr^3 P/d^4 G = 4\pi nr^2 S_v/dGk$$

For heavy closely coiled springs, $k = [(4c - 1)/(4c - 4)] + 0.615/c$, where $c = 2r/d$.

16. Cylindrical Helical Spring of Rectangular Cross Section (Fig. 146).

$$P = 2b^2hS_v/9rk;\ K = b/h \qquad U = Pf/2 = 4S_v^2V(K^2 + 1)/45Gk^2 \text{ (max when } K = 1)$$
$$f = 7.2\pi nr^3P(b^2 + h^2)/b^3h^3G = 1.6\pi nr^2S_v(b^2 + h^2)/bh^2Gk$$

For heavy closely coiled springs, $k = [(4c - 1)/(4c - 4)] + 0.615/c$, where $c = 2r/b$.

17. Conical Helical Spring of Circular Cross Section (Fig. 147)

l = length of developed spring, d = diameter of wire, r = maximum mean radius of coil

$$P = \pi d^3S_v/16rk = 0.1963d^3S_v/rk \qquad U = Pf/2 = S_v^2V/8Gk^2$$
$$f = 16r^2lP/\pi d^4G = 16nr^3P/d^4G = rlS_v/dGk = \pi nr^2S_v/dGk$$

For heavy closely coiled springs, $k = [(4c - 1)/(4c - 4)] + 0.615/c$, where $c = 2r/d$.

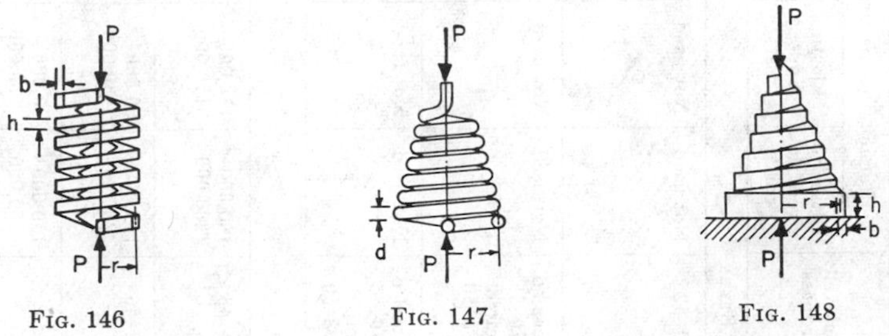

Fig. 146 Fig. 147 Fig. 148

18. Conical Helical Spring of Rectangular Cross Section (Fig. 148)

$$K = b/h;\ P = 2b^2hS_v/9rk \qquad U = Pf/2 = 2S_v^2V(K^2 + 1)/45Gk^2 \text{ (max when } K = 1)$$
$$f = 1.8r^2lP(b^2 + h^2)/b^3h^3G = 1.8\pi nr^3P(b^2 + h^2)/b^3h^3G$$
$$= 0.4rlS_v(b^2 + h^2)/bh^2Gk = 0.4\pi nr^2S_v(b^2 + h^2)/bh^2Gk$$

For heavy closely coiled springs, $k = [(4c - 1)/(4c - 4)] + 0.615/c$, where $c = 2r/b$.

19. Truncated Conical Springs (17 and 18). The formulas under 17 and 18 apply for truncated springs. In calculating deflection f, however, it is necessary to substitute $(r_1^2 + r_2^2)$ for r^2, and $\pi n(r_1 + r_2)$ for πnr, r_1 and r_2 being respectively the greatest and least mean radii of the coils.

Note. The preceding formulas for various forms of coiled springs are sufficiently accurate when the cross-section dimensions are small in comparison with the radius of the coil, and for small pitch. Springs 15 to 19 are for either tension or compression but formulas for springs 17 and 18 are good for compression only until the largest spring flattens out; then r becomes a variable, depending on the load.

Allowable Working Stresses for Springs. Allowable working stresses depend upon the type of spring, the atmosphere, temperature, ratio of spring diameter to wire diameter, rapidity and regularity of deflections, shock loads, wire size, and stress range. The values given in Table 89 are for **compression springs** not subjected to shock loads.

The fatigue life of a spring is considered "infinite" if it will withstand 10,000,000 cycles of deflections; "long" if between 1,000,000 and 10,000,000; "average" if between 100,000 and 1,000,000; "short" if between 10,000 and 100,000. **Severe service** comprises those applications in which springs are subjected to rapid deflections over long periods of time, such as in automobile valves, engine valves, or pneumatic hammers; **average service,** if subjected to normal operating deflections such as in brakes, motors, machine tools, or switches; **light service** if the springs are statically loaded or are subjected to less than 10,000 slow intermittent deflections during their lifetime, as in safety devices, emergency equipment, and springs used infrequently.

In Table 89, E is used for springs subjected to tensile stresses due to bending, such as torsion, flat, cantilever, clock, and power springs. G is used for springs subjected to torsional stresses, such as compression and extension helical springs.

Table 89. Physical Properties of Commonly Used Spring Materials

(From *Handbook of Mechanical Spring Design*, Associated Spring Corp., by permission.)

Material	Analysis	Tensile properties: Ultimate strength, psi	Tensile properties: Elastic limit, psi	Tensile properties: Modulus of elasticity (E)	Rockwell hardness	Torsional properties of wire: Ultimate strength, psi	Torsional properties of wire: Elastic limit, psi	Torsional properties of wire: Modulus in torsion (G)	Process of manufacture, chief uses, special properties
Flat Cold-rolled Spring Steel									
Clock spring steel AS 100 SAE 1095	C 0.90–1.05 % Mn 0.30–0.50 %	180,000–340,000	150,000–310,000	30,000,000	C40–52	Not used	Not used	Not used	Cold-rolled and heat-treated before forming. Clock and motor springs, miscellaneous flat springs
Flat spring steel AS 101 SAE 1074	C 0.70–0.80 % Mn 0.50–0.80 %	160,000–320,000	125,000–280,000	30,000,000	Annealed B70–85 temp'd C38–50	Not used	Not used	Not used	Cold-rolled, annealed, or tempered. Miscellaneous flat springs. Most popular spring steel
Flat spring steel AS 102 SAE 1060	C 0.50–0.65 % Mn 0.60–0.90 % P and S 0.04 % max	160,000–280,000	120,000–180,000	30,000,000	Annealed B70–85 temp'd C38–50	Not used	Not used	11,500,000	Use cold-rolled and annealed. Miscellaneous flat springs, static loads
Carbon Steel Wires									
High-carbon wire AS 8	C 0.85–0.95 % Mn 0.25–0.60 %	200,000–250,000	160,000–210,000	30,000,000	C44–48	160,000–200,000	110,000–150,000	11,500,000	Cold-rolled or drawn. High-grade helical springs or wire forms
Oil-tempered wire AS 10 ASTM A229–41	C 0.60–0.70 % Mn 0.60–0.90 %	155,000–300,000	120,000–250,000	30,000,000	C42–46	115,000–200,000	80,000–130,000	11,500,000	Cold-drawn and heat-treated before coiling. General spring use
Music wire AS 5 ASTM A228–47	C 0.70–1.00 % Mn 0.30–0.60 %	250,000–500,000	150,000–350,000	30,000,000		150,000–300,000	90,000–180,000	11,500,000–12,000,000, depending on size	Patented and cold-drawn. Miscellaneous small springs of various types—high quality

Hard-drawn spring wire AS 20 ASTM A227–47	C 0.60–0.70 % Mn 0.90–1.20 %	150,000– 300,000	100,000– 200,000	30,000,000		120,000– 220,000	75,000– 130,000	11,500,000	Patented and cold-drawn. Same uses as music wire but lower-quality wire
Hot-rolled Alloy Steel									
Silico-manganese alloy steel AS 70 SAE 9260	C 0.55–0.65 % Mn 0.60–0.90 % Si 1.80–2.20 %	200,000– 250,000	180,000– 230,000	30,000,000	C42–52	140,000– 175,000	100,000– 130,000	11,500,000	Hot- or cold-rolled or drawn. Better heat resistance than Cr. Va
Alloy and Stainless Spring Materials									
Chrome-vanadium alloy steel AS 32 SAE 6150	C 0.48–0.53 % Mn 0.70–0.90 % P 0.04 max S 0.04 max Si 0.20–0.35 % Cr 0.80–1.10 % V 0.15 min Subject to standard tolerances	200,000– 250,000	180,000– 230,000	30,000,000	C42–48	140,000– 175,000	100,000– 130,000	11,500,000	Cold-rolled or drawn. Special applications
Chrome-silicon alloy steel AS 33 SAE 9254	C 0.50–0.60 % Mn 0.50–0.80 % Si 1.20–1.60 % Cr 0.50–0.80 %	250,000– 325,000	220,000– 300,000	30,000,000	C47–51	160,000– 200,000	130,000– 160,000	11,500,000	Hot- or cold-rolled or drawn. Used at high stresses. Resists heat well to 450 F
18–8 type stainless AS 35 SAE 30302	C 17–20 % Ni 6–10 % C 0.08–0.15 % Mn 2 % max Si 0.30–0.75 %	160,000– 330,000	60,000– 260,000	28,000,000	C35–45	120,000– 240,000	45,000– 140,000	10,000,000	Cold-rolled or drawn. Best corrosion resistance. Fair temperature resistance
Type 316 stainless SAE 30316	C 16–18 % Ni 10–14 % Mo 2–3 % Mn 2 % max C 0.08 % max Si 1 % max P 0.04 % max S 0.03 % max	170,000– 250,000	130,000– 200,000	28,000,000	C35–45	120,000– 220,000	80,000– 130,000	11,000,000	Cold-rolled or drawn. Heat-treated after forming. Resists corrosion when polished. Good temperature resistance

Table 89. Physical Properties of Commonly Used Spring Materials—(*Continued*)

Material	Analysis	Tensile properties: Ultimate strength, psi	Tensile properties: Elastic limit, psi	Tensile properties: Modulus of elasticity (*E*)	Rockwell hardness	Torsional properties of wire: Ultimate strength, psi	Torsional properties of wire: Elastic limit, psi	Torsional properties of wire: Modulus in torsion (*G*)	Process of manufacture, chief uses, special properties
				Non-ferrous Spring Materials					
Spring brass AS 55 AS 155	Cu 64–72% Z remainder	100,000–130,000	40,000–60,000	15,000,000	B90	45,000–90,000	30,000–60,000	5,500,000	Cold-rolled or drawn. For electrical conductivity at low stresses. For corrosion resistance
Nickel silver	Cu 56% Z 25% Ni 18%	135,000–150,000	80,000–110,000	16,000,000	B95–100	85,000–100,000	60,000–70,000	5,500,000	Cold-rolled or drawn. Better quality than brass. Also used for its color. Corrosion resistant
Phosphor-bronze AS 60 AS 160	Cu 91–93% Sn 7–9% or Cu 94–96% Sn 4–6%	100,000–150,000	60,000–110,000	15,000,000	B90–100	80,000–105,000	50,000–85,000	6,250,000	Cold-rolled or drawn. Used for corrosion resistance and electrical conductivity
Silicon bronze AS 46 AS 146 (Made under various trade names)	Si 2–3% small amounts of tin or mn balance copper	100,000–150,000	60,000–110,000	15,000,000	B90–100	80,000–105,000	50,000–85,000	6,250,000	Cold-rolled or drawn. Used as substitute for phosphor-bronze where lower cost is necessary
Monel AS 40 AS 140	Ni (+Co) 63.0–70.0 Cu remainder Mg 2.00 max Fe 2.50 max Si 0.50 max C 0.30 max S 0.024 max	120,000–165,000	85,000–125,000	26,000,000	C23–32	85,000–110,500	50,000–70,000	9,500,000	Cold-rolled or drawn. Resists corrosion. Moderate stresses to 400 F
"K" monel AS 40 AS 140	Ni (+Co) 63.0–70.0 Cu remainder Mg 1.50 max Fe 2.00 max Si 1.00 max Al 2.0–4.0 S 0.01 max C 0.25 max Ti 0.25–1.00	120,000–180,000	85,000–140,000	26,000,000	C23–35	85,000–130,000	50,000–75,000	9,500,000	Same as monel except higher operational stresses can be employed to 450 F. Precipitation hardened by thermal treatment

Inconel AS 40 AS 140	Ni (+Co) 72.00 min Cu 0.50 max Mg 1.00 max Fe 6.0–10.0 Si 0.50 max Cr 14.0–17.0 S 0.015 max C 0.15 max	140,000–185,000	110,000–140,000	31,000,000	C25–37	95,000–130,000	55,000–80,000	11,000,000	Cold-rolled or drawn. Resists corrosion. High stresses to 650 F
Inconel "X" AS 40 AS 140	Ni (+Co) 70.00 min Cu 0.50 max Mg 1.00 max Fe 5.0–9.0 Si 0.50 max Cr 14.0–17.0 S 0.01 max Al 0.40–1.0 Ti 2.00–2.50 C 0.08 max Cb (+Ti) 0.70–1.20	130,000–220,000	90,000–150,000	31,000,000	C24–46	90,000–155,000	50,000–90,000	12,000,000	Resists corrosion and oxidation. Can be used to 1000 F for prolonged periods of service; up to 1200 F for short periods of intermittent temperature exposure
Duranickel AS 40 AS 140	Ni (+Co) 93.00 min Cu 0.25 max Mg 0.50 max Fe 0.60 max Si 1.00 max Al 4.00–4.75 S 0.01 max C 0.30 max Ti 0.25–1.00	125,000–205,000	80,000–140,000	30,000,000	C25–43	85,000–145,000	50,000–85,000	11,000,000	Cold-rolled or drawn. Precipitation hardened by heat-treatment. Resists corrosion. High stresses to 600 F
Beryllium copper AS 45 AS 145	Cu 98% Be 2%	160,000–200,000	100,000–150,000	16,000,000–18,500,000 subject to heat-treatment	C35–42	100.000–130,000	65,000–95,000	6,000,000–7,000,000 subject to heat-treatment	Cold-rolled or drawn Corrosion resistance like copper. High physicals for electrical work. Low hysteresis

Table 90. Safe Working Loads and Deflections of Cylindrical Helical Steel Springs of Circular Cross Section

(For closely coiled springs divide given load and deflection values by the curvature factor k)

Allowable unit stress, psi	Wire gage W. & M.	Diam, in.	Pitch diameter, D in.																				
			D	5⁄32	3⁄16	1⁄4	5⁄16	3⁄8	7⁄16	1⁄2	5⁄8	3⁄4	7⁄8	1	1 1⁄8	1 1⁄4	1 3⁄8	1 1⁄2	1 5⁄8	1 3⁄4	1 7⁄8	2	2 1⁄4
150,000	20	.035	P	16.2	13.4	10.0	8.10	6.66	5.75	4.96	4.05	3.39											
			f	.026	.037	.067	.105	.149	.200	.276	.420	.608											
	19	.041	P	26.2	21.6	16.2	13.0	10.8	9.27	8.10	6.52	5.35	4.57										
			f	.023	.032	.057	.089	.128	.175	.229	.362	.512	.697										
	18	.047	P	39.1	32.6	24.5	19.6	16.4	13.9	12.3	9.80	8.10	6.92	6.14									
			f	.019	.028	.049	.078	.112	.153	.200	.311	.449	.610	.800									
	17	.054	P	59.4	49.6	37.2	29.7	24.6	21.2	18.5	14.7	12.4	10.5	9.25	8.23								
			f	.016	.024	.043	.067	.098	.133	.174	.273	.390	.532	.695	.878								
	1⁄16″	.062	P	....	74.9	56.1	44.9	37.3	32.0	28.0	22.4	18.6	16.1	13.9	12.5	11.2							
			f	....	.021	.037	.058	.084	.115	.151	.235	.340	.460	.605	.760	.947							
	16	.063	P	....	78.2	58.7	46.9	39.2	33.9	29.4	23.5	19.6	16.8	14.7	13.2	11.9	10.7						
			f	....	.020	.037	.057	.083	.113	.148	.233	.335	.445	.591	.748	.930	1.12						
	15	.072	P	....	117.	80.7	70.0	58.7	50.2	43.6	35.2	29.0	25.0	21.9	19.5	17.5	16.0						
			f	....	.018	.032	.050	.077	.100	.130	.203	.294	.405	.521	.652	.802	.986						
	14	.080	P	....	....	121	96.6	80.5	69.1	60.4	48.2	40.1	34.6	30.1	26.7	24.2	22.1	20.2					
			f	....	....	.029	.045	.065	.090	.117	.183	.262	.359	.470	.593	.735	.886	1.105					
140,000	13	.092	P	....	....	171	136	113	97.6	85.5	68.9	57.3	48.8	42.6	37.8	34.5	31.3	28.6					
			f	....	....	.023	.037	.053	.072	.098	.148	.214	.291	.388	.481	.596	.720	.854					
	3⁄32″	.093	P	....	....	178	142	118	99.5	89.0	71.2	59.1	50.9	44.3	39.6	35.7	32.3	29.6	27.3				
			f	....	....	.023	.036	.052	.071	.093	.146	.211	.286	.376	.473	.585	.707	.841	.986				
	12	.105	P	....	....	....	204	170	147	127	102	85.4	73.0	63.4	56.6	51.1	46.3	42.6	38.9				
			f	....	....	....	.032	.047	.064	.083	.122	.188	.256	.336	.425	.512	.632	.755	.880				
	11	.120	P	....	....	....	303	253	217	190	152	126	108	95.2	84.2	76.2	69.2	63.5	58.5	54.3			
			f	....	....	....	.028	.041	.055	.073	.114	.174	.223	.296	.368	.449	.551	.657	.768	.893			
	1⁄8″	.125	P	....	....	....	....	286	245	214	171	143	121	107	95.5	85.2	78.0	71.5	65.8	60.8	57.2		
			f	....	....	....	....	.039	.053	.069	.109	.169	.213	.278	.353	.437	.528	.626	.731	.855	.981		
	10	.135	P	....	....	....	....	359	309	270	217	171	154	135	120	108	98.7	90.2	82.7	72.2	71.8	67.5	
			f	....	....	....	....	.036	.049	.064	.106	.145	.198	.260	.327	.399	.486	.581	.680	.791	.908	1.04	
	9	.148	P	....	....	....	....	....	408	356	285	237	207	178	158	142	130	118	109	102	95.0	89.0	
			f	....	....	....	....	....	.045	.059	.092	.132	.180	.236	.293	.370	.448	.530	.620	.723	.828	.945	
	5⁄32″	.156	P	....	....	....	....	....	480	418	330	270	234	208	185	167	152	139	128	119	111	104	92.7
			f	....	....	....	....	....	.042	.056	.087	.125	.171	.223	.282	.350	.422	.509	.588	.685	.785	.896	1.12
	8	.162	P	....	....	....	....	....	....	468	376	311	276	234	207	187	170	156	143	134	125	117	103
			f	....	....	....	....	....	....	.054	.084	.121	.165	.216	.273	.338	.409	.488	.566	.663	.757	.863	1.09

Table 90. Safe Working Loads and Deflections of Cylindrical Helical Steel Springs of Circular Cross Section—(*Continued*)

(For closely coiled springs divide given load and deflection values by the curvature factor k)

Allowable unit stress, psi	Wire gage W. & M.	Diam, in.	D	½	⅝	¾	⅞	1	1⅛	1¼	1⅜	1½	1⅝	1¾	1⅞	2	2¼	2½	2¾	3	3½	4	4½
				Pitch diameter, D in.																			
140,000	7	.177	P	608	487	406	347	305	270	243	223	205	187	174	163	152	135	122					
			f	.049	.077	.115	.151	.198	.251	.311	.375	.447	.522	.606	.695	.793	1.00	1.24					
125,000	3/16″	.187	P	642	522	426	367	320	284	256	233	213	197	183	170	160	142	128					
			f	.041	.065	.093	.127	.166	.210	.260	.314	.373	.487	.510	.584	.665	.832	1.04					
	6	.192	P	696	556	465	396	348	309	278	254	233	214	199	186	174	154	139	126				
			f	.040	.063	.091	.124	.160	.205	.252	.308	.366	.428	.499	.571	.652	.825	1.02	1.23				
	5	.207	P	....	694	579	495	432	385	346	315	288	266	247	232	216	192	173	158	144			
			f	....	.059	.085	.115	.151	.191	.236	.286	.342	.396	.462	.570	.607	.757	.943	1.11	1.36			
	7/32″	.218	P	....	812	678	580	509	452	408	360	339	310	291	270	255	225	204	185	169			
			f	....	.055	.080	.109	.142	.180	.223	.269	.321	.374	.437	.488	.570	.710	.891	1.08	1.28			
	4	.225	P	....	895	746	640	560	498	447	407	372	345	320	299	280	248	224	203	187			
			f	....	.054	.078	.106	.138	.175	.213	.262	.312	.372	.425	.486	.565	.691	.866	1.05	1.24			
	3	.244	P	....	1120	950	811	711	632	570	527	475	438	406	381	356	316	284	259	237			
			f	....	.049	.071	.098	.138	.161	.200	.240	.287	.336	.391	.449	.537	.646	.800	.965	1.14			
	¼″	.250	P	....	....	1027	880	760	685	617	560	513	476	440	410	385	342	308	281	266	222		
			f	....	....	.070	.095	.131	.157	.191	.236	.281	.328	.385	.439	.524	.624	.780	.946	1.12	1.53		
	2	.263	P	....	....	1195	1125	895	795	717	652	598	551	501	478	448	400	359	326	298	256		
			f	....	....	.066	.089	.118	.149	.183	.224	.266	.312	.363	.416	.475	.592	.740	.896	1.06	1.44		
	9/32″	.281	P	....	....	1450	1240	1087	969	863	794	724	665	620	580	543	482	437	395	362	310		
			f	....	....	.062	.085	.111	.140	.172	.209	.250	.292	.340	.390	.443	.562	.692	.840	1.02	1.36		
	1	.283	P	....	....	....	1264	1110	985	886	805	740	682	634	592	564	492	439	402	370	317		
			f	....	....	....	.084	.111	.139	.169	.207	.246	.289	.338	.386	.440	.559	.690	.883	.990	1.35		
115,000	5/16″	.312	P	....	....	....	1575	1376	1220	1100	1000	915	845	775	733	687	610	550	500	460	392	343	
			f	....	....	....	.070	.092	.116	.144	.174	.207	.242	.283	.322	.368	.467	.577	.697	.829	1.12	1.47	
	00	.331	P	....	....	....	....	1636	1455	1316	1187	1090	1000	932	870	818	725	653	594	545	468	410	
			f	....	....	....	....	.088	.109	.135	.163	.194	.227	.264	.343	.346	.437	.541	.654	.770	1.05	1.30	
	11/32	.341	P	....	....	....	....	1820	1620	1452	1325	1214	1120	1040	970	910	808	728	661	608	520	454	
			f	....	....	....	....	.082	.105	.127	.156	.186	.218	.256	.293	.330	.413	.522	.625	.745	1.02	1.32	
	000	.362	P	....	....	....	....	2140	1910	1714	1560	1430	1318	1220	1147	1070	950	858	778	714	612	535	
			f	....	....	....	....	.079	.100	.123	.149	.177	.207	.243	.273	.317	.400	.495	.598	.713	.965	.126	
	⅜″	.375	P	....	....	....	....	....	2110	1940	1780	1580	1458	1354	1265	1185	1058	950	860	790	678	592	528
			f	....	....	....	....	....	.079	.117	.144	.172	.201	.234	.268	.308	.382	.478	.579	.688	.938	1.22	1.54
	0000	.393	P	....	....	....	....	....	2430	2180	1984	182C	1680	1560	1458	1365	1212	1092	990	910	780	682	670
			f	....	....	....	....	....	.092	.114	.137	.164	.195	.223	.256	.292	.369	.457	.550	.657	.890	1.16	1.47

Table 90. Safe Working Loads and Deflections of Cylindrical Helical Steel Springs of Circular Cross Section—(*Continued*)

(For closely coiled springs divide given load and deflection values by the curvature factor k)

Allowable unit stress, psi	Wire gage W. & M.	Diam, in.	Pitch diameter, D in.																	
			D	1¼	1⅜	1½	1⅝	1¾	1⅞	2	2¼	2½	2¾	3	3½	4	4½	5	5½	6
115,000	13/32″	.406	P	2400	2170	2000	1840	1710	1600	1500	1330	1200	1090	1000	855	750	666			
			f	.108	.134	.159	.168	.217	.248	.284	.353	.444	.525	.640	.867	1.13	1.43			
	00000	.430	P	2875	2610	2400	2210	2050	1918	1798	1598	1440	1308	1200	1028	900	800			
			f	.104	.126	.150	.175	.204	.234	.267	.338	.418	.503	.600	.815	1.06	1.35			
	7/16″	.437	P	3000	2730	2500	2310	2140	2000	1800	1665	1500	1365	1250	1074	940	835	750		
			f	.100	.124	.148	.173	.201	.231	.264	.327	.412	.490	.593	.810	1.05	1.33	1.64		
110,000	000000	.460	P	....	3065	2800	2580	2400	2230	2100	1865	1680	1530	1400	1200	1058	952	840		
			f	....	.112	.134	.157	.183	.209	.239	.303	.374	.447	.536	.729	.956	1.21	1.49		
	15/32″	.468	P	....	3265	2940	2725	2530	2375	2210	1970	1770	1610	1472	1265	1110	935	885		
			f	....	.111	.132	.154	.182	.206	.235	.295	.368	.444	.530	.720	.943	1.19	1.47		
	0000000	.490	P	....	3675	3270	3115	2890	2710	2535	2245	2025	1840	1690	1445	1268	1125	1015	920	
			f	....	.106	.126	.148	.172	.196	.225	.284	.351	.424	.506	.688	.900	1.13	1.40	1.70	
	½″	.500	P	....	....	3610	3320	3090	2890	2710	2410	2160	1970	1810	1550	1352	1205	1082	985	
			f	....	....	.123	.144	.168	.192	.220	.274	.347	.415	.495	.672	.880	1.11	1.37	1.65	
	9/16″	.562	P	....	....	....	4700	4390	4090	3830	3420	3080	2790	2565	2190	1913	1710	1535	1395	1280
			f	....	....	....	.128	.149	.175	.195	.248	.306	.372	.440	.596	.782	.990	1.22	1.47	1.75
	⅝″	.625	P	....	....	....	....	6100	5600	5260	4660	4210	3825	3505	3000	2630	2340	2110	1913	1750
			f	....	....	....	....	.134	.154	.176	.218	.275	.328	.397	.538	.705	.875	1.05	1.33	1.58
100,000	11/16″	.687	P	....	....	....	....	....	....	6325	5660	5090	4630	4250	3625	3195	2825	2560	2330	2125
			f	....	....	....	....	....	....	.145	.183	.228	.274	.327	.443	.580	.733	.908	1.00	1.30
	¾″	.750	P	....	....	....	....	....	....	....	7400	6640	6030	5540	4745	4150	3690	3325	3025	2770
			f	....	....	....	....	....	....	....	.178	.218	.252	.299	.402	.532	.671	.832	1.00	1.19
	13/16″	.812	P	....	....	....	....	....	....	....	....	8420	7660	7000	6000	5260	4675	4200	3825	3500
			f	....	....	....	....	....	....	....	....	.192	.232	.276	.376	.490	.620	.766	.880	1.10
	⅞″	.875	P	....	....	....	....	....	....	....	....	10830	9550	8700	7500	6560	5740	5250	4770	4730
			f	....	....	....	....	....	....	....	....	.179	.218	.257	.348	.456	.577	.712	.860	1.02
90,000	15/16″	.937	P	....	....	....	....	....	....	....	....	....	10600	9700	8400	7160	6470	5810	5290	4850
			f	....	....	....	....	....	....	....	....	....	.179	.217	.290	.383	.480	.591	.715	.855
	1″	1.000	P	....	....	....	....	....	....	....	....	....	....	11780	10100	8800	7850	7050	6330	5870
			f	....	....	....	....	....	....	....	....	....	....	.206	.276	.360	.454	.561	.680	.803
	1⅛″	1.125	P	....	....	....	....	....	....	....	....	....	....	....	14400	12600	11230	10100	9200	8400
			f	....	....	....	....	....	....	....	....	....	....	....	.244	.320	.405	.496	.600	.718
	1¼″	1.250	P	....	....	....	....	....	....	....	....	....	....	....	24700	18200	15300	13250	12540	11500
			f	....	....	....	....	....	....	....	....	....	....	....	.260	.287	.364	.442	.545	.648
80,000	1⅜″	1.375	P	....	....	....	....	....	....	....	....	....	....	....	....	20400	18100	16150	14850	13600
			f	....	....	....	....	....	....	....	....	....	....	....	....	.280	.294	.364	.440	.522

Safe working loads and deflections of cylindrical helical springs of round steel wire in tension or compression are given in Table 90. The table is based on the formulas given for spring 15. d = diameter of steel wire, in.; D = pitch diameter (center to center of wire), in.; P = safe working load for given unit stress, lb; f = deflection of 1 coil for safe working load, in.

The table is based on the values of unit stress indicated, and G = 12,500,000. For any other value of unit stress, divide the tabular value by the unit stress used in the table and multiply by the unit stress to be used in the design. For any other value of G, multiply the value of f in the table by 12,500,000 and divide by the value of G chosen. For **square steel wire,** multiply values of P by 1.06, and values of f by 0.75. For **round brass wire,** take S_s = 10,000 to 20,000, and multiply values of f by 2 (Howe).

Examples of Use of Table 90. 1. Required the safe load (P) for a spring of ⅜ in. round steel with a pitch diameter (D) of 3½ in. In the line headed D, under 3½, is given the value of P, or 678 lb. This is for a unit stress of 115,000 psi. The load, P, for any other unit stress may be found by dividing the 678 by 115,000 and multiplying by the unit stress to be used in the design. To determine the number of coils this spring would need to compress (say) 6 in. under a load of (say) 678 lb, take the value of f under 678, or 0.938, which is the deflection of one coil under the given load. Therefore 6/0.938 = 6.4, say 7, equals the number of coils required. The spring will therefore be 2⅝ in. long when closed (7 × ⅜), counting the working coils only, and must be 8⅝ in. long when unloaded. Whether there is an extra coil at one end which does not deflect will depend upon the details of the particular design. The deflection in the above example is for a unit stress of 115,000 psi. The rule is, divide the deflection by 115,000 and multiply by the unit stress to be used in the design.

2. A 7⁄16 in. steel spring of 3½ in. O.D. has its coils in close contact. How much can it be extended without exceeding the limit of safety? The maximum safe load for this spring is found to be 1,074 lb and the deflection of one coil under this load is 0.810 in. This is for a unit stress of 115,000 psi. Therefore 0.810 is the greatest admissible opening between any two coils. In this way, it is possible to ascertain whether or not a spring is overloaded, without knowledge of the load carried.

WIRE ROPE

Wire ropes are built up of **strands** of wires laid together, the numbers of wires commonly used being 4, 7, 12, 19, and 37. Ordinarily the wires are laid into strands in the direction opposite to the twist of the strands into rope. When wires and strands are laid in the same direction, the rope is known as **lang-lay rope. Standard wire rope** is made of six wire strands and a sisal core. Wire strands are laid around the core, either to the right or to the left, and the resulting rope is designated as **right lay** or **left lay.** The lay may be long or short, the shorter lay forming the more flexible rope. The **core** of a wire rope is, as a rule, sisal saturated with a lubricant. It provides little additional strength but acts as a cushion to preserve the shape of the rope and helps to lubricate the wires. A wire-strand or wire-rope core adds 7 to 10 percent to the strength of the rope, but will wear from the friction between it and the outer strands as rapidly as the outside of the rope. This does not apply to stationary ropes.

For great flexibility, the strands of a wire rope sometimes consist of wire ropes, which in turn are made of strands composed of wires, as in tiller rope. Running ropes and one construction of ship's hawsers are made with strands composed of 12 or 18 wires each, laid about a fiber core. Ropes so made are very pliable and present good resistance to outside friction. Individual strands of wires are employed as smokestack guys, span wires for trolley roads, and wherever only moderate flexibility is needed.

Sizes of Ropes. The diameter of wire rope is the circle which will just contain the rope. In a rope classification the first number is the number of strands in the rope; the last number is the number of wires in a strand; and the middle number, if any, is the number of minor strands in a major strand. If there is a wire core, the rope is labeled IWRC (Independent Wire Rope Core), or if the core is the same as the main strands, it is counted as a strand.

Strength and Working Loads. The test **strength of wire ropes** seldom exceeds 90 percent of the aggregate strength of all of the wires, the average being about 82.5 percent.

The working load should never exceed ⅕ of the breaking strength and for many conditions should not be greater than 1/6 to 1/8. The proper factor of safety for a wire rope demands consideration of all loads; acceleration; deceleration; rope speed; rope attachments; the number, size, and arrangements of sheaves and drums; conditions producing corrosion and abrasion; length of rope; etc. The desirable factor of safety for given conditions can best be obtained by consulting the manufacturers of the wire rope.

Sizes of Drums or Sheaves. Tread diameters for 6 × 7 (6 × 19) [6 × 37] {8 × 19} rope should be approximately 72 (45) [27] {31} times the rope diameters, for average conditions. For economical service, these should often be increased; *e.g.*, on larger hoisting installations with the 6 × 7 (6 × 19) rope, the diameters may be 96 (90) times the rope diameter. In certain cases, the tread diameters may be less but should not be below 42 (30) [18] {21} times the rope diameters. Larger tread diameters give increased rope life and more economical service.

The size and condition of the sheave grooves are most important in determining rope life. The clearances for new or remachined grooves and the minimum clearances before sheave replacement or remachining grooves should be as follows:

Nominal rope diam, in.	1/4–5/16	3/8–3/4	13/16–1 1/8	1 3/16–1 1/2	1 9/16–2 1/4	2 5/16 and larger
Recommended clearance, in.	1/64	1/32	3/64	1/16	3/32	1/8

If a wire rope is operated over grooves that are too small, the rope will be abraded rapidly; in addition, a tight or corrugated sheave groove may disturb the strand relationship of the rope and necessitate its premature removal. The pressure of wire rope against a sheave groove is calculated by dividing the rope tension in pounds by the product of the radius to the bottom of the sheave groove and the diameter of the rope, both in inches. This quantity should not have a value greater than 450 psi for cast iron, or 850 psi for cast steel. For greater pressures, a material of greater wear resistance, such as manganese steel, should be used.

Handling. Wire rope must not be coiled or uncoiled like hemp rope. When it is received upon a reel, the latter should be mounted upon a spindle or turntable and the rope then run off. When shipped in a coil, it should be rolled along the ground like a

Table 91. Standard Hoisting Rope

Composed of 6 strands and a fiber core, 19 wires to the strand. (John A. Roebling's Sons Co.)

Diam, in.	Approx weight per ft, lb	Breaking strength, tons		
		Blue center steel	Plow steel	Mild plow steel
2 3/4	12.10	292.0	254.0	
2 1/2	10.00	244.0	212.0	
2 1/4	8.10	200.0	174.0	
2 1/8	7.23	179.0	156.0	
2	6.40	160.0	139.0	121.0
1 7/8	5.63	141.0	123.0	107.0
1 3/4	4.90	124.0	108.0	93.6
1 5/8	4.23	107.0	93.4	81.2
1 1/2	3.60	92.0	80.0	69.6
1 3/8	3.03	77.7	67.5	58.8
1 1/4	2.50	64.6	56.2	48.8
1 1/8	2.03	52.6	45.7	39.8
1	1.60	41.8	36.4	31.6
7/8	1.23	32.2	28.0	24.3
3/4	0.90	23.8	20.7	18.0
5/8	0.63	16.7	14.5	12.6
9/16	0.51	13.5	11.8	10.2
1/2	0.40	10.7	9.35	8.13
7/16	0.31	8.27	7.19	6.25
3/8	0.23	6.10	5.31	4.62
5/16	0.16	4.26	3.71	3.22
1/4	0.10	2.74	2.39	2.07

wheel. All untwisting and kinking must be avoided. When a wire rope is to be cut, soft iron wire should be served on each side of the place where the division is to be made to keep the rope from untwisting. (See *Seizing.*)

Materials. Rope made from iron wire is now used only for passenger elevators and similar service where the tendency to abrasion is comparatively slight, the speed is high, and the loads are moderate. The three grades of steel commonly used for the

Fig. 149

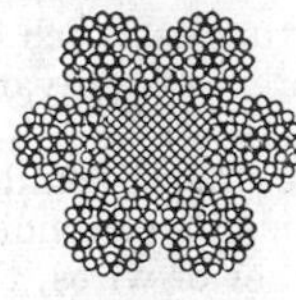

Fig. 150

Fig. 151

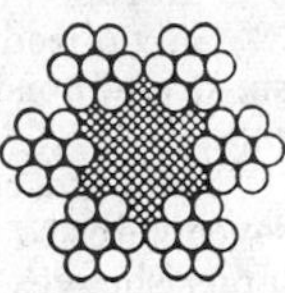

Fig. 152

Fig. 149. Standard hoisting rope.
Fig. 150. Extra-pliable hoisting rope.
Fig. 151. Extra-pliable hoisting rope.
Fig. 152. Standard coarse-laid rope.

manufacture of wire rope are designated "blue center," or "improved plow steel," "plow steel," and "mild plow steel." These grades were established in the *NBS Bull.* R 198–43.

Standard hoisting rope (Fig. 149) is made of 6 strands, each of 19 wires, the strands being laid around a fiber core.

Table 92. Extra-pliable Hoisting Rope
(Six 37-wire strands and fiber core)

Diam, in.	Approx weight per ft, lb	Breaking strength, tons	
		Blue center steel	Plow steel
3½	19.00	449.0	390.0
3¼	16.37	390.0	339.0
3	13.95	335.0	291.0
2¾	11.72	284.0	247.0
2½	9.69	236.0	205.0
2¼	7.85	193.0	168.0
2⅛	7.00	173.0	150.0
2	6.20	154.0	134.0
1⅞	5.45	136.0	118.0
1¾	4.75	119.0	103.0
1⅝	4.09	103.0	89.3
1½	3.49	87.9	76.4
1⅜	2.93	74.1	64.5
1¼	2.42	61.5	53.5
1⅛	1.96	50.1	43.5
1	1.55	39.8	34.6
⅞	1.19	30.6	26.6
¾	0.87	22.6	19.6
⅝	0.61	15.8	13.7
9/16	0.49	12.9	11.2
½	0.39	10.2	8.85
7/16	0.30	7.82	6.80
⅜	0.22	5.77	5.02
5/16	0.16	4.03	3.50
¼	0.10	2.59	2.25

Table 93. Extra-pliable Hoisting Rope
(Eight 19-wire strands and fiber core)

Diam, in.	Approx weight per ft, lb	Breaking strength, tons	
		Blue center steel	Plow steel
1½	3.26	79.4	69.1
1⅜	2.74	67.1	58.3
1¼	2.27	55.7	48.4
1⅛	1.84	45.3	39.4
1	1.45	36.0	31.3
⅞	1.11	27.7	24.1
¾	0.82	20.5	17.8
⅝	0.57	14.3	12.4
9/16	0.46	11.6	10.1
½	0.36	9.23	8.02
7/16	0.28	7.09	6.17
⅜	0.20	5.24	4.55
5/16	0.14	3.65	3.18
¼	0.09	2.35	2.04

Extra-pliable Hoisting Rope. Made of 6 strands of 37 wires each and a fiber core (Fig. 150). The wires in this rope are much finer than those used in the standard hoisting rope and consequently not as suitable to withstand abrasion. These ropes are used on electric cranes, dredges, and for similar service requiring a strong tough rope that will operate successfully over small sheaves.

Extra-pliable hoisting rope of 8 strands of 19 wires and a fiber core (Fig. 151) is much more pliable than the standard construction of 6 strands of 19 wires. The metallic area of an eight-strand rope is not as great as that of a six-strand rope, and the wires are smaller, but under severe bending stresses the decrease in strength is largely offset by the great pliability. It can be used over comparatively small sheaves and drums such as are frequently found on derricks. It is not good practice to use it except for comparatively light loads or where there is much overwinding, because it would flatten or lose shape more quickly than 6 × 19 rope. Moreover it stretches more than a 6 × 19 rope.

Galvanized extra-pliable cast-steel hoisting rope is much more flexible than the six-strand hoisting rope and is often used in preference to galvanized cast-steel running rope.

Standard coarse-laid rope (Fig. 152) is made of six strands and a fiber core with seven wires to the strand. It is much stiffer than standard hoisting rope and requires larger sheaves. On account of the smaller number of wires, this rope should also be used with a higher factor of safety, as the breaking of one or two wires materially reduces the strength of the rope. The wires used are considerably larger in diameter than in hoisting rope, and consequently will stand greater wear. **Iron rope** of this

Table 94. Standard Coarse-laid Rope for Haulages and Transmissions
(Composed of six 7-wire strands and a fiber core)

Diam, in.	Approx weight per ft, lb	Breaking strength, tons			Diam, in.	Approx weight per ft, lb	Breaking strength, tons		
		Blue center steel	Plow steel	Mild plow steel			Blue center steel	Plow steel	Mild plow steel
1½	3.38	86.2	75.0	65.2	⅝	0.59	15.9	13.9	12.0
1⅜	2.84	73.1	63.6	55.3	9/16	0.48	13.0	11.3	9.82
1¼	2.34	61.0	53.0	46.1	½	0.38	10.3	8.96	7.79
1⅛	1.90	49.8	43.3	37.7	7/16	0.29	7.93	6.90	6.00
1	1.50	39.7	34.5	30.0	⅜	0.21	5.86	5.10	4.43
⅞	1.15	30.7	26.7	23.2	5/16	0.15	4.10	3.56	3.10
¾	0.84	22.7	19.8	17.2	¼	0.094	2.64	2.30	2.00

Tables 95. Flat Rope

Width and thickness, in.	Approx weight per ft, lb	No. of ropes	Breaking strength, tons		Width and thickness, in.	Approx weight per ft, lb	No. of ropes	Breaking strength, tons	
			Plow steel	Mild plow steel				Plow steel	Mild plow steel
⅞ × 8	10.69	10	271.0	236.0	½ × 3½	2.82	8	72.7	63.3
⅞ × 7	9.63	9	244.0	212.0	½ × 3	2.47	7	63.6	55.4
⅞ × 6	8.56	8	217.0	188.0	½ × 2½	2.13	6	54.5	47.4
⅞ × 5	7.50	7	190.0	165.0					
					⅜ × 6	3.63	18	94.1	81.9
¾ × 8	9.70	11	227.0	197.0	⅜ × 5½	3.42	17	88.9	77.3
¾ × 7	8.13	10	206.0	179.0	⅜ × 5	3.03	15	78.4	68.2
¾ × 6	7.31	9	185.0	161.0	⅜ × 4½	2.83	14	73.2	63.7
¾ × 5	6.50	8	165.0	143.0	⅜ × 4	2.44	12	62.7	54.6
					⅜ × 3½	2.23	11	57.5	50.0
⅝ × 8	8.32	15	214.0	186.0	⅜ × 3	1.84	9	47.1	40.9
⅝ × 7	7.23	13	186.0	162.0	⅜ × 2½	1.64	8	41.8	36.4
⅝ × 6	6.14	11	157.0	137.0	⅜ × 2	1.25	6	31.4	27.3
⅝ × 5½	5.59	10	143.0	124.0					
⅝ × 5	5.04	9	129.0	112.0	5/16 × 4	2.17	15	55.3	48.1
⅝ × 4½	4.50	8	114.0	99.5	5/16 × 3½	1.89	13	47.9	41.7
⅝ × 4	3.95	7	100.0	87.1	5/16 × 3	1.61	11	40.5	35.3
⅝ × 3½	3.40	6	85.8	74.6	5/16 × 2½	1.33	9	33.2	28.8
					5/16 × 2	1.05	7	25.8	22.4
½ × 7	5.85	16	145.0	126.0	5/16 × 1½	0.77	5	18.5	16.0
½ × 6	4.85	14	127.0	111.0					
½ × 5½	4.50	13	118.0	103.0	¼ × 3	1.34	13	31.3	27.2
½ × 5	4.16	12	109.0	94.9	¼ × 2½	1.15	11	26.5	23.0
½ × 4½	3.82	10	90.9	79.1	¼ × 2	0.88	9	21.7	18.8
½ × 4	3.16	9	81.8	71.2	¼ × 1½	0.69	7	16.8	14.6

construction is recommended for power transmissions equipped with large sheaves. **Cast-steel** and **extra-strong cast-steel rope** are recommended for mine haulages, tramways, sand lines, and similar service where conditions tend to severe abrasion. **Plow-steel** and **improved plow-steel ropes** are recommended in place of cast steel when it is desirable to reduce the dead weight of the rope itself, or where, by reason of increased loads, it is necessary to use a stronger rope without increasing its diameter. This rope is particularly adapted for very long mine haulages.

Flat rope is composed of a number of wire ropes called "flat rope strands," of alternate right and left lay, placed side by side, then secured or sewed together with soft Swedish iron or steel wire (Fig. 153). The flat-rope strands consist of four 7-wire strands laid together with a center or core. The sewing or filling wire is much softer than the steel wires composing the strands of the rope, acts as a cushion or soft bed for the strands, and wears out much faster than the harder wires composing the latter. When the sewing wires are worn out, the flat rope can be resewed with new wire, and if any of the rope strands are also worn or damaged, these can be replaced by new portions. Flat rope is used principally for hoisting purposes. When large and long rope is used in hoisting heavy loads out of deep shafts, round rope requires large and heavy drums on which to wind, while flat rope, winding on itself, needs a reel but little wider than the width of the rope. Furthermore, flat rope does not spin or twist in the shaft. Flat rope is obtainable from 1¾ to 8 in. in width, and from ¼ to ⅞ in. in thickness, the length varying from 20 to 3,000 ft. Flat rope is particularly applicable to the operating of spouts on coal and ore docks, also for raising and lowering emergency gates on canals and similar machinery. It combines flexibility and great strength, thus making possible the use of simple and compact hoisting machinery.

Fig. 153. Flat rope.

The diameters of **drums and sheaves** for flat rope should be as large as possible, particularly for mine hoisting work. For average continuous duty of 4 × 7 flat rope, *i.e.*, 4 strands with 7 wires to the strand, sheaves (drums) should be at least 96 (80) times the nominal thickness of the rope: for intermittent duty such as flood gate hoists 60 (48): for shaft hoists with long lengths of rope, best economy requires about 200 (120).

Table 96. Flattened-strand Hoisting Rope, Type A

(Five 28-wire strands and a fiber core)

Diam, in.	Approx wt per ft, lb	Breaking strength, tons			
		Improved plow steel	Plow steel	Extra-strong cast steel	Cast steel
⅜	0.22	5.6	4.8	4.4	4.
½	0.39	9.5	8.2	7.5	6.8
9/16	0.49	11.9	10.3	9.4	8.5
⅝	0.61	14.6	12.7	11.6	10.4
¾	0.87	20.9	18.2	16.5	14.8
⅞	1.19	28.5	24.8	22.4	20.1
1	1.55	37.	32.	29.	26.
1⅛	1.96	47.	41.	37.	33.
1¼	2.42	57.	50.	45.	41.

Table 97. Flattened-strand Hoisting Rope, Type B

(Six 25-wire strands and a fiber core)

Diam, in.	Approx wt per ft, lb	Breaking strength, tons			
		Improved plow steel	Plow steel	Extra-strong cast steel	Cast steel
⅜	0.25	6.9	6.	5.5	4.9
½	0.45	11.8	10.3	9.3	8.4
9/16	0.57	14.8	12.8	11.6	10.5
⅝	0.70	18.2	15.8	14.4	12.9
¾	1.01	26.	22.6	20.5	18.4
⅞	1.39	35.4	30.	27.9	25.
1	1.80	46.	40.	36.	32.
1⅛	2.28	58.	50.5	45.5	40.
1¼	2.81	71.5	62.	56.	50.5
1⅜	3.40	86.	74.	67.	60.
1½	4.05	101.	88.	79.	71.
1⅝	4.75	118.	103.	93.	83.
1¾	5.51	136.	118.	107.	96.
2	7.2	177.	154.	139.	125.
2¼	9.1	222.	193.	176.	158.
2½	11.2	270.	.....	214.	193.
2¾	13.6	323.	.....	257.	233.

Sheaves should be slightly crowned in the center and have deep flanges to guide the rope.

Flattened-strand wire rope is designed to give increased contact or wearing surface. The wear is consequently lessened upon any one individual wire and the necessity of the use of heavier wire diminished, which results in greater flexibility. The wearing surface is approximately 150 percent greater than that of a round-strand rope. Another feature of this type of rope is that, the interstices between the strands being lessened, a greater number of wires are used for the same diameter. It is always made lang-lay. Flattened-strand rope has little tendency to kink, and, owing to its smooth wearing surface, saves wear on pulleys, sheaves, and drums. It is not so flexible or so fatigue-resistant as round-strand rope of the same general classification. The strength is greater than that of round-strand ropes, but the weight is proportionately greater than the increase in strength. These ropes are made in "blue center" steel grade only and are available in three styles: D, B, and G (Fig. 154). Style D is used on haulages and consists of six strands, each containing seven outside wires laid around a triangular-shaped center wire. Styles B and G, used for hoisting purposes, consist of six strands, each strand of which is made up of two layers of 12 wires each.

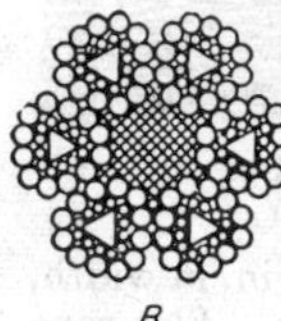

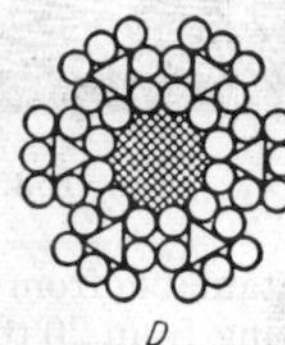

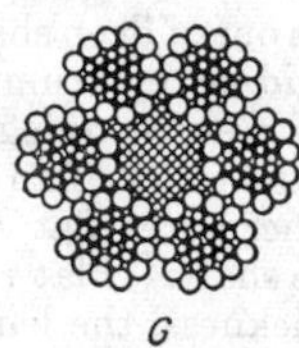

Fig. 154. Flattened-strand wire rope.

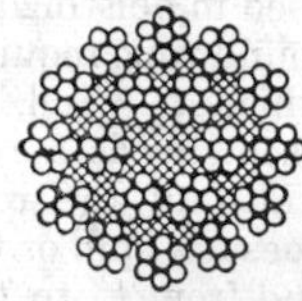

Fig. 155. Non-spinning hoisting rope.

Non-spinning hoisting rope (Fig. 155) is constructed of 6 strands of 7 wires each, lang-lay (wires in the strands and strands themselves laid to the left), laid around a fiber core, and covered with an outer layer composed of 12 strands, 7 wires, regular lay (wires in the strands laid to the left and strands themselves laid to the right). The object of this combination of lays is to prevent a free load suspended on the end of a single line from rotating. This type of rope is recommended for "back-haul" or single-line derricks; also for shaft sinking and mine hoisting where the bucket or cage swings free without guides. It works best where it does not overwind on the drum.

Table 98. Non-rotating Hoisting Rope

(Composed of 18 strands and a fiber core, 7 wires to the strand)

Diam, in.	Approx weight per ft, lb	Breaking strength, tons		Diam, in.	Approx weight per ft, lb	Breaking strength, tons	
		Blue center steel	Plow steel			Blue center steel	Plow steel
1¾	5.30	114.0	98.8	⅞	1.32	29.5	25.7
1⅝	4.57	98.4	85.6	¾	0.97	21.8	19.0
1½	3.89	84.4	73.4	⅝	0.68	15.3	13.3
1⅜	3.27	71.3	62.0	9/16	0.55	12.4	10.8
1¼	2.70	59.2	51.5	½	0.43	9.85	8.57
1⅛	2.19	48.2	41.9	7/16	0.33	7.58	6.59
1	1.73	38.3	33.3	⅜	0.24	5.59	4.86

Either a closed or an open socket makes the best fastening on the end of non-spinning rope. These may be fastened in the same manner as any rope socket, but great care must be taken in attaching the socket to the rope to see that the strands do not untwist or allow any slack to work back into the rope. It is best to seize the end of the rope tightly for a distance of 4 or 5 in. just outside of the socket until the socketing is completed, when it may be taken off.

Steel-clad ropes (Fig. 156) are made in three constructions for the purpose of securing different degrees of flexibility: the 6 × 19, 6 × 37, and 6 × 61 types, respectively. Flat strips of steel wound spirally around each of the six strands composing the rope give additional wearing surface without sacrificing flexibility. When the outer flat-steel winding is worn through, a complete hoisting rope remains, with unimpaired strength. These ropes are designed to meet very severe conditions of service. The increased life obtained by the use of steel-clad rope is, in places where conditions are suitable, from 50 to 100 percent. It is recommended particularly for such service as dredging. The breaking strength of these ropes is less than that of a round strand rope of the same diameter and grade.

FIG. 156. Steel-clad rope.

Galvanized wire rope has almost entirely superseded manila rope for shrouds and stays aboard ship. It is cheaper in first cost, is relatively unaffected by the weather, does not stretch and contract with changes in atmospheric conditions, and thus saves a great deal of labor in setting up. There is great reduction in bulk and weight by its use, as it is only one-fifth or one-sixth as large as a manila rope of equal strength. Consequently, it offers only half as much surface to the wind. It is much less liable to accidents by being cut or chafed, and does not rot and give way suddenly without warning. Galvanized rope is better suited for guys for derricks than hemp rope or rods linked together.

Table 99. Galvanized Common Steel Wire Strand
(Composed of 7 wires laid together)

Diam, in.	Approx weight per 1,000 ft, lb	Approx strength, lb	Diam, in.	Approx weight per 1,000 ft, lb	Approx strength, lb	Diam, in.	Approx weight per 1,000 ft, lb	Approx strength, lb
5/8	813	11,600	3/8	273	4,250	7/32	98.3	1,540
9/16	671	9,600	5/16	205	3,200	3/16	72.9	1,150
1/2	517	7,400	9/32	164	2,570	5/32	51.3	870
7/16	399	5,700	1/4	121	1,900	1/8	31.8	540

Galvanized steel wire strand (Fig. 157) is used chiefly for guying poles and smokestacks, for supporting trolley wire, and for operating railroad signals. For overhead catenary construction of suspending trolley wire, the special grades of strand are preferable because they possess greater strength and toughness. The smallest sizes (sometimes called "galvanized seizing strand") are used for seizing or binding the ends of wire rope and thimble splices, and for tying rope into coils.

FIG. 157. Galvanized steel wire strand.

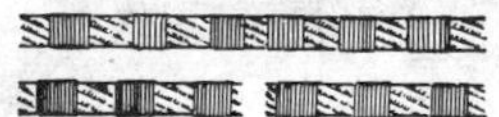

FIG. 158. Wire rope with three seizings, before and after cutting.

Seizing. When wire rope is cut to make attachment to fittings or for splicing, it is mportant that it be properly seized. The wires and strands are laid under uniform tension, and the tension is maintained (Fig. 158). The seizing required will vary with the rope diameter; annealed iron, plain or galvanized, is used for seizing according to the recommendations in Tables 100 through 102.

Wire Rope Fittings. Attachment to a socket is made by separating and straightening the wires, cutting out the hemp center, cleansing with kerosene, dipping in one-half muriatic acid and one-half water (which must be cleaned from the wires after dipping), distributing the wires uniformly in the socket, and pouring in molten zinc after plugging up the lower end of the socket with fire clay. Such an attachment will

Table 100. Number of Seizings on Each Side of Cut

(Bethlehem Steel Co.)

Steel wire ropes, form-set (preformed)	1
Steel wire ropes, non-preformed:	
Ropes 7/8 in. diam and smaller	2
Ropes 15/16–1 1/16 in. diam	3
Ropes 1 1/8 in. diam and larger	4
Lang-lay ropes 1 1/2 in. diam and larger	4
Iron wire ropes, non-preformed	2

Table 101. Recommended Lengths of Seizings

(Bethlehem Steel Co.)

Rope diameter, in.	Length of seizings, in.
1/2 and smaller	1/2
9/16–7/8	1
1–1 1/4	1 1/2
1 3/8–1 5/8	2
1 3/4–2	3
2 1/8 and larger	4

Table 102. Seizing Wire Diameters

(Bethlehem Steel Co.)

Diam of rope, in.	Approx diam of seizing wire, in.
1/4	0.063
3/8–5/8	0.080
3/4–1 1/8	0.104
1 1/4–1 1/2	0.124
1 5/8 and larger	0.138

develop the full strength of the rope (Fig. 159). Spliced eye connections when properly made will not pull out and will develop from 60 percent of the full strength of a 2 1/2 in.-diameter rope up to 95 percent for a 1/2-in. rope. Clip and clamp connections are not desirable as permanent fastenings on hoisting ropes and will develop 75 to 85 percent of the strength of the rope. Clips should be installed so that the U-bolt part is around the short, or dead, end of the rope, Table 103.

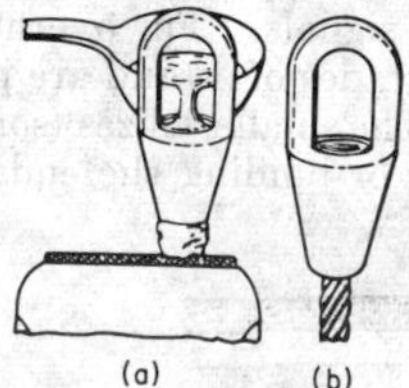

FIG. 159. Wire rope socket. (*a*) Pouring molten zinc into basket of socket; (*b*) finished socket.

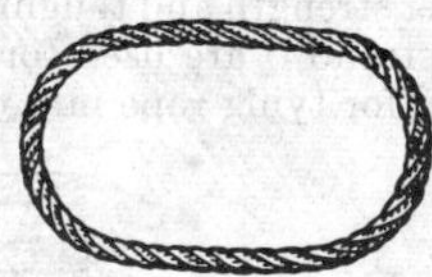

FIG. 160. Grommet sling.

FIG. 161. Single-leg sling.

Wire rope slings are made up in numerous styles, some of which are manufactured endless in grommet construction and develop the full strength of the rope, Figs. 160 and 161.

Examples of **end attachments** and miscellaneous wire-rope fittings are shown in Fig. 162.

The **efficiency of an end attachment** is measured by its ability to hold the wire rope. If the assembly reaches catalog strength of the rope before the end attachment loosens or gives way, the efficiency of the attachment is 100 percent. Table 104 shows approximate efficiencies developed by the various types of end attachments when properly applied.

Table 103. Number of Clips and Spacing for Safe Application

(Bethlehem Steel Co.)

Rope diam, in.	Diam of U-bolt, in.	Approx weight, lb	Minimum no. clips for each rope end	Spacing of clips, in.
3/16	11/32	0.09	2	2
1/4	7/16	0.18	2	2
5/16	1/2	0.30	2	2
3/8	9/16	0.47	2	2 1/4
7/16	5/8	0.71	2	2 5/8
1/2	11/16	0.73	3	3
5/8	3/4	1.01	3	3 3/4
3/4	7/8	1.57	4	4 1/2
7/8	1	2.42	4	5 1/4
1	1 1/8	2.64	4	6
1 1/8	1 1/4	3.32	5	6 3/4
1 1/4	1 7/16	4.48	5	7 1/2
1 3/8	1 1/2	4.88	6	8 1/4
1 1/2	1 23/32	5.44	6	9
1 5/8	1 3/4	7.02	6	9 3/4
1 3/4	1 15/16	9.28	7	10 1/2
2	2 1/8	12.04	8	12
2 1/4	2 5/8	14.81	8	12
2 1/2	2 7/8	16.60	8	13

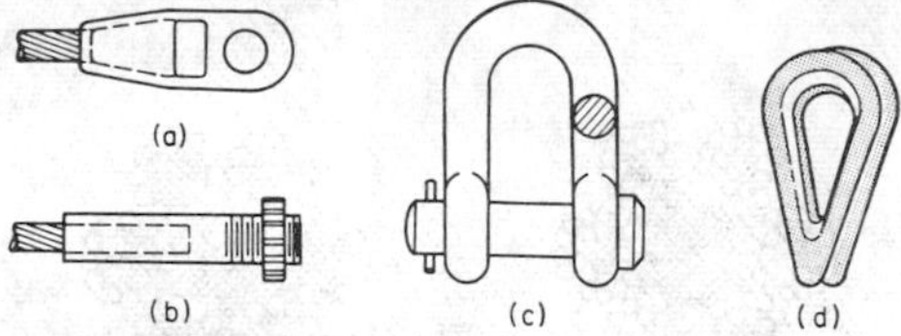

Fig. 162. Wire-rope fittings. (*a*) Zinced-type socket; (*b*) swaged-type socket; (*c*) pin-type shackle; (*d*) standard thimble.

Table 104. End-attachment Efficiencies

(Bethlehem Steel Co.)

Fitting	Nominal efficiency, %
Wire rope sockets zinced attachments	Catalog rated strength of rope
Fittings (swaged or pressed)	Catalog rated strength of rope
Open wedge sockets	80–90
Clips (U-bolt type)	80
Spliced-in thimbles:	
1/4 in. diam and smaller	90
5/16 in. diam	89
3/8 in. diam	88
1/2 in. diam	86
5/8 in. diam	84
3/4 in. diam	82
7/8 in., and up	80

Table 105. Tensile Strength of Galvanized Steel Wire Strands, Lb

(7-wire strand)

Diam, in.	5/8	9/16	1/2	7/16	3/8	5/16	9/32	1/4	7/32	3/16	5/32	1/8
Wt of 1,000 ft, lb	813	671	517	399	273	205	164	121	98.3	72.9	51.3	31.8
Siemens-Martin	19,100	15,700	12,100	9,350	6,950	5,350	4,250	3,150	2,560	1,900	1,470	910
High-strength	29,600	24,500	18,800	14,500	10,800	8,000	6,400	4,750	3,850	2,850	2,140	1,330
Extra-high strength	42,400	35,000	26,900	20,800	15,400	11,200	8,950	6,650	5,400	3,990	2,940	1,830

Minimum elongation, percent, in 24 in.: S.M., 8; H.S., 5; E.H.S., 4.

Table 106. Properties of Special Grades of Extra Galvanized Special Strands

Approx diam, in.	No. of wires in strand	Approx breaking strength, lb				Approx wt per 1,000 ft, lb	Approx diam, in.	No. of wires in strand	Approx breaking strength, lb				Approx wt per 1,000 ft, lb
		Extra high strength	High strength	Siemens-Martin	Common soft strand				Extra high strength	High strength	Siemens-Martin	Common soft strand	
1	19	104,500	73,200	47,000	28,700	2073	1¼	37	162,200	113,600	73,000	44,600	3,248
⅞	19	79,700	55,800	35,900	21,900	1581	1⅛	37	130,800	91,600	58,900	36,000	2,691
¾	19	58,300	40,800	26,200	16,000	1155	1	37	102,700	71,900	46,200	28,300	2,057
⅝	19	40,200	28,100	18,100	11,000	796	1¾	61	315,000	220,600	141,800	86,600	6,346
9/16	19	33,700	24,100	16,100	9,640	637	1⅝	61	271,300	189,900	122,100	74,600	5,497
½	19	26,700	19,100	12,700	7,620	504	1½	61	229,600	160,700	103,300	63,100	4,665
							1⅜	61	192,000	134,400	86,400	52,800	3,901

Minimum elongation, percent, in 24 in.: E.H.S., 4; H.S., 5; S.M., 8.

Table 107. Galvanized Mast-arm Rope
(Composed of nine 4-wire strands and a cotton center)

Diam, in.	⅜	5/16	¼
Weight per ft, lb	0.158	0.107	0.070
Approx breaking stress, lb	2200	1530	1100

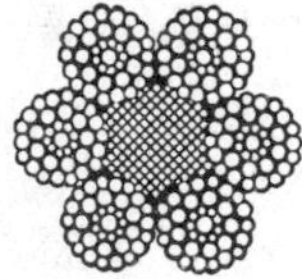
Fig. 163

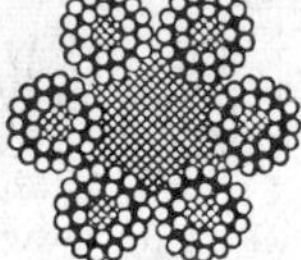
Fig. 164

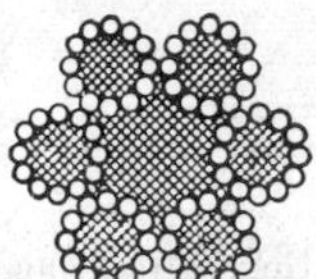
Fig. 165

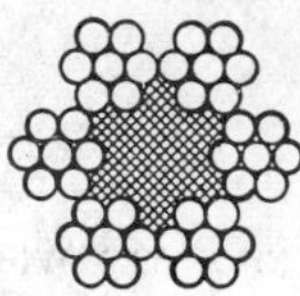
Fig. 166

Fig. 163. Galvanized steel hawsers.
Fig. 164. Galvanized steel mooring lines and hawsers.
Fig. 165. Standard 6 × 12 galvanized running rope and hawsers.
Fig. 166. Galvanized iron rigging and guy rope.

Galvanized mast-arm rope is used for arc lights, mast arms, or other purposes where exposed to moisture. This rope is more durable than manila rope and does not shrink.

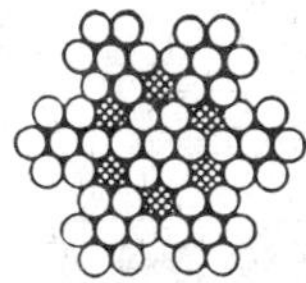
Fig. 167

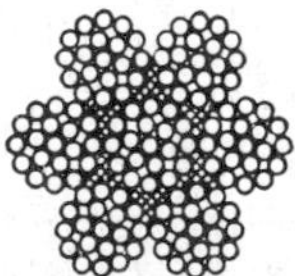
Fig. 168

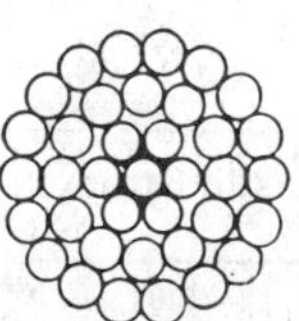
Fig. 169

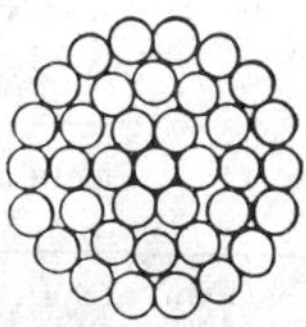
Fig. 170

Figs. 167 and 168. Galvanized steel bridge rope.
Fig. 169. Galvanized steel bridge strand.
Fig. 170. Smooth coil track strand.

Table 108. Galvanized Steel Hawsers
(Fig. 163. Composed of 6 strands and a fiber core, 37 wires to the strand)

Diam, in.	Approx weight per ft, lb	Breaking strength, tons	
		Blue center	Plow steel
2 3/8	8.74	199.0	173.0
2 5/16	8.29	189.0	164.0
2 1/4	7.85	179.0	156.0
2 1/8	7.00	160.0	139.0
2 1/16	6.59	151.0	132.0
2	6.20	143.0	124.0
1 15/16	5.82	134.0	117.0
1 13/16	5.09	118.0	102.0
1 3/4	4.75	110.0	95.7
1 11/16	4.41	103.0	89.2
1 5/8	4.09	95.3	82.9
1 1/2	3.49	81.5	70.9
1 7/16	3.20	75.0	65.3
1 3/8	2.93	68.8	59.8
1 1/4	2.42	57.1	49.7
1 3/16	2.19	51.7	44.9
1 1/8	1.96	46.5	40.4
1 1/16	1.75	41.6	36.1
1	1.55	36.9	32.1
7/8	1.19	28.4	24.7
13/16	1.02	24.5	21.3
3/4	0.87	21.0	18.2

Table 110. Standard 6 × 12 Galvanized Running Rope and Hawsers
(Fig. 165. Composed of 6 strands and a fiber core, each strand consisting of 12 wires and a fiber center)

Diam, in.	Approx weight per ft, lb	Breaking strength, tons		
		Blue center	Plow steel	Iron
2 1/16	4.47	93.6	81.4	
2	4.20	88.2	76.7	
1 15/16	3.94	83.0	72.2	
1 13/16	3.45	73.0	63.5	
1 3/4	3.22	68.3	59.4	
1 11/16	2.99	63.6	55.3	
1 5/8	2.77	59.2	51.4	
1 1/2	2.36	50.7	44.1	
1 7/16	2.17	46.7	40.6	
1 3/8	1.99	42.8	37.2	
1 1/4	1.64	35.6	30.9	
1 3/16	1.48	32.2	28.0	
1 1/8	1.33	29.0	25.2	
1 1/16	1.19	25.9	22.5	10.0
1	1.05	23.0	20.0	8.89
7/8	0.80	17.7	15.4	6.85
13/16	0.69	15.3	13.3	5.92
3/4	0.59	13.1	11.4	5.06
5/8	0.41	9.16	7.97	3.54
9/16	0.33	7.45	6.48	2.88
1/2	0.26	5.91	5.14	2.28
7/16	0.20	4.55	3.95	1.76
3/8	0.15	3.36	2.92	1.30
5/16	0.10	2.34	2.04	0.905

Table 109. Galvanized Steel Mooring Lines and Hawsers
(Fig. 164. Composed of 6 strands and a fiber core, each strand composed of 24 wires and a fiber center)

Diam, in.	Approx weight per ft, lb	Breaking strength, tons	
		Blue center	Plow steel
2 1/16	5.87	134.0	116.0
2	5.52	126.0	110.0
1 15/16	5.18	119.0	103.0
1 13/16	4.53	104.0	90.8
1 3/4	4.23	97.5	84.8
1 11/16	3.93	90.9	79.0
1 5/8	3.64	84.5	73.4
1 1/2	3.11	72.3	62.9
1 7/16	2.85	66.5	57.9
1 3/8	2.61	61.0	53.1
1 1/4	2.16	50.7	44.1
1 3/16	1.95	45.9	39.9
1 1/8	1.75	41.2	35.9
1 1/16	1.56	36.9	32.1
1	1.38	32.8	28.5
7/8	1.06	25.2	21.9
13/16	0.91	21.8	19.0
3/4	0.78	18.6	16.2
5/8	0.54	13.0	11.3
1/2	0.35	8.40	7.30
3/8	0.194	4.77	4.14

Table 111. Galvanized Iron Rigging and Guy Rope
(Fig. 166. Composed of 6 strands and a fibercore, 7 wires to the strand)

Diam, in.	Approx weight per ft, lb	Breaking strength, tons	Circum of good-grade three-strand manila rope of nearest strength, in.
1 1/4	2.34	21.2	7
1 3/16	2.12	19.2	6 1/2
1 1/8	1.90	17.3	6
1 1/16	1.70	15.5	5 1/2
1	1.50	13.8	5 1/4
7/8	1.15	10.7	4 3/4
13/16	0.99	9.23	4 1/4
3/4	0.84	7.90	3 3/4
5/8	0.59	5.54	3 1/4
9/16	0.48	4.51	3
1/2	0.38	3.58	2 1/2
7/16	0.29	2.76	2 1/4
3/8	0.21	2.04	2
5/16	0.15	1.42	1 1/2
1/4	0.094	0.918	1 1/4

When made with wire strand core add 10 percent to weights and 7 1/2 percent to breaking strengths.

Table 112. Galvanized Steel Bridge Rope

(Figs. 167 and 168. All ropes contain 7 strands)

Diam, in.	No. of wires per strand	Approx weight per ft, lb	Gross metallic area, sq in.	Min ultimate strength, tons	Diam, in.	No. of wires per strand	Approx weight per ft, lb	Gross metallic area, sq in.	Min ultimate strength, tons
1	7	1.67	0.471	45.7	2⅛	19	7.73	2.17	210
1⅛	7	2.11	0.596	57.8	2¼	19	8.66	2.42	235
1¼	7	2.64	0.745	72.2	2⅜	19	9.61	2.69	261
1⅜	7	3.21	0.906	87.8	2½	19	10.60	2.97	288
1½	7	3.82	1.076	104	2⅝	19	11.62	3.27	317
1⅝	19	4.51	1.27	123	2¾	19	12.74	3.58	347
1¾	19	5.24	1.47	143	2⅞	*	13.90	3.91	379
1⅞	19	6.03	1.69	164	3	28	15.11	4.25	412
2	19	6.85	1.92	186					

* Center strand, 28 wires; outside strand, 19 wires.

Table 113. Galvanized Steel Bridge Strand

(See Fig. 169)

Diam, in.	Approx weight per ft, lb	Approx area, sq in.	Min ultimate strength, tons
1	2.00	0.577	61
1¹⁄₁₆	2.30	0.663	69
1⅛	2.61	0.751	78
1³⁄₁₆	2.92	0.843	86
1¼	3.22	0.931	96
1⁵⁄₁₆	3.58	1.04	106
1⅜	3.89	1.12	116
1⁷⁄₁₆	4.29	1.24	126
1½	4.70	1.36	138
1⁹⁄₁₆	5.11	1.48	150
1⅝	5.52	1.60	162
1¹¹⁄₁₆	5.98	1.73	176
1¾	6.45	1.87	188

Table 114. Smooth Coil Track Strand

(See Fig. 170)

Diam, in.	No. of wires in strand	Approx weight per 100 ft, lb	Breaking strength, tons	
			Extra-high-strength steel	High-strength steel
½	19	55	15.3	12.6
⁹⁄₁₆	19	70	18.0	15.0
⅝	19	86	22.3	19.2
¾	19	124	32.5	27.6
⅞	19	169	44.4	37.6
1	19	220	58.0	49.2
1⅛	37	270	70.7	60.0
1¼	37	323	84.6	71.8
1⅜	37	401	105.0	88.8
1½	37	488	127.5	108.4
1⅝	61	563	146.0	124.0
1¾	61	659	171.0	145.8
1⅞	61	728	189.0	161.0
2	91	840	218.0	185.0
2⅛	91	935	240.0	204.0
2¼	91	1,036	266.0	233.0
2½	91	1,310	335.0	285.0

Table 115. Copper, Iron, Tinned, and Galvanized Sash Cords

(Six 7-wire strands and cotton core)

Diam, in.	¼	⁷⁄₃₂	³⁄₁₆	⁵⁄₃₂	⅛	³⁄₃₂	¹⁄₁₆
Weight per ft, lb							
Copper	0.108	0.083	0.061	0.044	0.026	0.015	0.007
Iron	0.094	0.072	0.053	0.038	0.023	0.013	0.006
Breaking strength, lb							
Bright copper	1,225	940	688	478	306	172	77
Annealed copper	760	580	425	295	190	105	48
Galvanized iron	1,836	1,413	1,035	756	504	283	126
Bright iron	2,040	1,570	1,150	840	560	315	140
Annealed iron	1,225	940	688	478	306	172	77

Table 116. Tiller Rope or Hand Rope

(6 strands of 42 wires each, 252 wires in all, 7 fiber cores)

Diam, in.	5/8	9/16	1/2	7/16	3/8	5/16	1/4
Approx weight per ft, lb	0.43	0.35	0.28	0.21	0.16	0.11	0.07
Breaking strength, tons							
Plow steel	8.04	6.53	5.18	3.98	2.93	2.05	1.31
Iron	3.57	2.90	2.30	1.77	1.30	0.908	0.584

FIBER LINES

The breaking strength of various fiber lines is given in Table 117.

Knots, Hitches, and Bends

No two parts of a knot which would move in the same direction if the rope were to slip should lie alongside of and touching each other. The knots shown in Fig. 171 are known by the following names:

A, bight of a rope; *B*, simple or overhand knot; *C*, figure 8 knot; *D*, double knot; *E*, boat knot; *F*, bowline, first step; *G*, bowline, second step; *H*, bowline, completed; *I*, square or reef knot; *J*, sheet bend or weaver's knot; *K*, sheet bend with a toggle; *L*, carrick bend; *M*, "stevedore" knot completed; *N*, "stevedore" knot commenced; *O*, slip knot; *P*, Flemish loop; *Q*, chain knot with toggle; *R*, half hitch; *S*, timber hitch; *T*, clove hitch; *U*, rolling hitch; *V*, timber hitch and half hitch; *W*, blackwall hitch; *X*, fisherman's bend; *Y*, round turn and half hitch; *Z*, wall knot commenced; *AA*, wall knot completed; *BB*, wall-knot crown commenced; *CC*, wall-knot crown completed.

The bowline *H*, one of the most useful knots, will not slip, and after being strained is easily untied. Knots *H*, *K*, and *M* are easily untied after being under strain. The

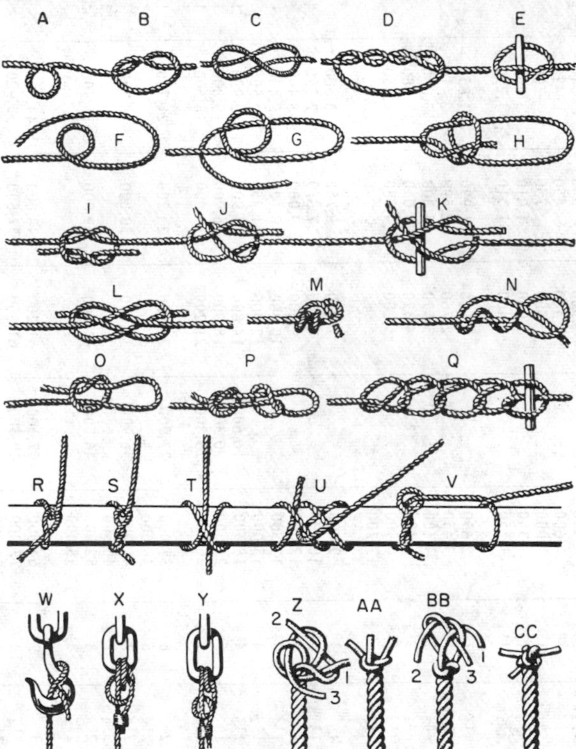

Fig. 171. Rope knots, hitches, and bends.

Table 117. Breaking Strength of Fiber Lines, Lb

(Adapted, by permission of the U.S. Naval Institute, Annapolis, Md., and Wall Rope Works, Inc., New York, N.Y.)

Size, in.		Manila	Composite	Sisal	Sisal mixed	Sisal hemp	Agave or jute	Nylon	Dacron	Poly-ethylene	Poly-propylene (mono-filament)	Esterlon (polyester)
Diam	Cir.											
3/16	5/8	450	......	360	340	310	270	1,000	850	700	800	720
1/4	3/4	600	......	480	450	420	360	1,500	1,380	1,200	1,200	1,150
5/16	1	1,000	......	800	750	700	600	2,500	2,150	1,750	2,100	1,750
3/8	1 1/8	1,350	......	1,080	1,010	950	810	3,500	3,000	2,500	3,100	2,450
7/16	1 1/4	1,750	......	1,400	1,310	1,230	1,050	4,800	4,500	3,400	3,700	3,400
1/2	1 1/2	2,650	......	2,120	1,990	1,850	1,590	6,200	5,500	4,100	4,200	4,400
9/16	1 3/4	3,450	......	2,760	2,590	2,410	2,070	8,300	7,300	4,600	5,100	5,700
5/8	2	4,400	......	3,520	3,300	3,080	2,640	10,500	9,500	5,200	5,800	7,300
3/4	2 1/4	5,400	......	4,320	4,050	3,780	3,240	14,000	12,500	7,400	8,200	9,500
13/16	2 1/2	6,500	......	5,200	4,880	4,550	3,900	17,000	15,000	8,900	9,800	11,500
7/8	2 3/4	7,700	......	......	......	......	......	20,000	17,500	10,400	11,500	13,500
1	3	9,000	......	7,200	6,750	6,300	5,400	24,000	20,000	12,600	14,000	16,500
1 1/16	3 1/4	10,500	......	8,400	7,870	7,350	6,300	28,000	22,500	14,500	16,100	19,000
1 1/8	3 1/2	12,000	......	9,600	9,000	8,400	7,200	32,000	25,000	16,500	18,300	21,500
1 1/4	3 3/4	13,500	......	10,800	10,120	9,450	8,100	36,500	28,500	18,600	21,000	24,300
1 5/16	4	15,000	......	12,000	11,250	10,500	9,000	42,000	32,000	21,200	24,000	28,000
1 1/2	4 1/2	18,500	16,600	14,800	13,900	12,950	11,100	51,000	41,000	26,700	30,000	34,500
1 5/8	5	22,500	20,300	18,000	16,900	15,800	13,500	62,000	50,000	32,700	36,500	41,500
1 3/4	5 1/2	26,500	23,800	21,200	19,900	18,500	15,900	77,500	61,000	39,500	44,000	51,000
2	6	31,000	27,900	24,800	23,200	21,700	18,600	90,000	72,000	47,700	53,000	61,000
2 1/8	6 1/2	36,000	......	......	......	......	......	105,000	81,000	55,800	62,000	70,200
2 1/4	7	41,000	36,900	32,800	30,800	28,700	......	125,000	96,000	63,000	70,000	81,000
2 1/2	7 1/2	46,500	......	......	......	......	......	138,000	110,000	72,500	80,500	92,000
2 5/8	8	52,000	46,800	41,600	39,000	36,400	......	154,000	125,000	81,000	90,000	103,000
2 7/8	8 1/2	58,000	......	......	......	......	......	173,000	140,000	92,000	100,000	116,000
3	9	64,000	57,500	51,200	48,000	44,800	......	195,000	155,000	103,000	116,000	130,000
3 1/4	10	77,000	69,300	61,600	57,800	53,900	......	238,000	190,000	123,000	137,000	160,000
3 1/2	11	91,000	......	......	......	......	......	288,000	230,000	146,000	162,000	195,000
4	12	105,000	94,500	84,000	78,800	73,500	......	342,000	275,000	171,000	190,000	230,000

Breaking strength is the maximum load the line will hold at the time of breaking. The working load of a line is one-fourth to one-fifth the breaking strength.

knot M is useful when the rope passes through an eye and is held by the knot, as it will not slip, and is easily untied after being strained. The wall knot is made as follows: Form a bight with strand 1 and pass the strand 2 around the end of it, and the strand 3 around the end of 2, and then through the bight of 1, as shown at Z in the figure. Haul the ends taut when the appearance is as shown at AA. The end of the strand 1 is now laid over the center of the knot, strand 2 laid over 1, and 3 over 2, when the end of 3 is passed through the bight of 1, as shown at BB. Haul all the strands taut, as shown at CC. The "stevedore" knot (M, N) is used to hold the end of a rope from passing through a hole. When the rope is strained, the knot draws up tight, but it can be easily untied when the strain is removed. If a knot or hitch of any kind is tied in a rope, its failure under stress is sure to occur at that place. The shorter the bend in the standing rope, the weaker is the knot. The approximate strength of knots compared with the full strength of (dry) rope (= 100), based on Miller's experiments (*Mach.*, 1900, p. 198), is as follows: eye splice over iron thimble, 90; short splice in rope, 80; S and Y, 65; H, O, and T, 60; I and J, 50; B and P, 45.

NAILS AND SPIKES

Nails are either **wire nails** of circular cross section and constant diameter or **cut nails** of rectangular cross section with taper from head to point. The larger sizes are called **spikes.** The length of the nail is expressed in the **"penny"** system, the equivalents in inches being given in the following tables. The letter "d" is the accepted

Table 118. Wire Nails for Special Purposes
(Steel wire gage)

Length, in.	Barrel nails		Barbed roofing nails		Barbed dowel nails	
	Gage	No. per lb	Gage	No. per lb	Gage	No. per lb
5/8	15½	1,570	..	...	8	394
3/4	15½	1,315	13	729	8	306
7/8	14½	854	12	478	8	250
1	14½	750	12	416	8	212
1 1/8	14½	607	12	368	8	183
1 1/4	14	539	11	250	8	162
1 3/8	13	386	11	228	8	145
1 1/2	13	355	10	167	8	131
1 3/4	....	.....	10	143		
2	....	.....	9	104		

Length, in.	Clout nails		Slating nails		Fine nails		
	Gage	No. per lb	Gage	No. per lb	Length, in.	Gage	No. per lb
3/4	15	999					
7/8	14	733					
1	14	648	12	425	1	16½	1,280
1 1/8	14	580	10½	229			
1 1/4	13	398	....	...	1	17	1,492
1 3/8	13	365					
1 1/2	13	336	10½	190	1 1/8	15	757
1 3/4	..	...	10	144	1 1/8	16	984
2	..	...	9	104			

Table 119. Approximate Number of Boat Spikes to a Keg of 200 Lb

Size of spike, sq in.	Length, in.									
	4	5	6	7	8	9	10	11	12	14
5/8	.....	.....	.....	.....	214	190	176	...	144	122
1/2	.....	.....	.....	.....	324	286	258	244	220	192
7/16	.....	.....	.....	480	438	...	378			
3/8	1,114	930	816	690	622	532	492	...	434	
5/16	1,776	1,342	1,124	978	858	776	706			
1/4	2,576	2,134	1,778	1,488	1,382					

symbol for penny. A keg of nails weighs 100 lb. **Heavy hinge nails** or **track nails** with countersunk heads have chisel points unless diamond points are specified. **Plasterboard nails** are smooth with diamond points. **Spikes** are made either with flat heads and diamond points or with oval heads and chisel points.

Table 120. Wire Nails and Spikes

(Steel wire gage)

Size of nail	Length, in.	Casing nails		Finishing nails		Clinch nails		Shingle nails	
		Gage	No. per lb	Gage	No. per lb	Gage	No. per lb	Gage	No. per lb
2d	1	15½	940	16½	1,473	14	723	13	434
3d	1¼	14½	588	15½	880	13	432	12	271
4d	1½	14	453	15	634	12	273	12	233
5d	1¾	14	389	15	535	12	234	12	203
6d	2	12½	223	13	288	11	158		
7d	2¼	12½	200	13	254	11	140		
8d	2½	11½	136	12½	196	10	101		
9d	2¾	11½	124	12½	178	10	91.4		
10d	3	10½	90	11½	124	9	70		
12d	3¼	10½	83	11½	113	9	64.1		
16d	3½	10	69	11	93	8	50		
20d	4	9	51	10	65	7	36.4		
30d	4½	9	45						
40d	5	8	37						

Size of nail	Length, in.	Boat nails				Hinge nails				Flooring nails	
		Heavy		Light		Heavy		Light			
		Diam, in.	No. per lb	Diam, in.	No. per lb	Diam, in.	No. per lb	Diam, in.	No. per lb	Gage	No. per lb
4d	1½	¼	47	3/16	82	¼	53	3/16	90		
6d	2	¼	36	3/16	62	¼	39	3/16	66	11	168
8d	2½	¼	29	3/16	50	¼	31	3/16	53	10	105
10d	3	⅜	11	¼	24	⅜	12	¼	25	9	72
12d	3¼	⅜	10.4	¼	22	⅜	11	¼	23	8	56
16d	3½	⅜	9.6	¼	20	⅜	10	¼	22	7	44
20d	4	⅜	8	¼	18	⅜	8	¼	19	6	32

Size of nail	Length, in.	Common wire nails and brads		Barbed car nails				Spikes			
				Heavy		Light					
		Gage	No. per lb	Gage	No. per lb	Gage	No. per lb	Size	Length, in.	Gage	Approx No. per lb
2d	1	15	847	..	...	..	...	10d	3	6	43
3d	1¼	14	548	..	...	..	...	12d	3¼	6	39
4d	1½	12½	294	10	179	12	284	16d	3½	5	31
5d	1¾	12½	254	9	124	10	152	20d	4	4	23
6d	2	11½	167	9	108	10	132	30d	4½	3	18
7d	2¼	11½	150	8	80	9	95	40d	5	2	14
8d	2½	10¼	101	8	72	9	88	50d	5½	1	11
9d	2¾	10¼	92	7	55	8	65	50d	6	1	10
10d	3	9	66	7	50	8	59	...	7	5/16 in.	7
12d	3¼	9	61	6	39	7	46	...	8	⅜	4.1
16d	3½	8	47	6	36	7	43	...	9	⅜	3.7
20d	4	6	30	5	27	6	32	...	10	⅜	3.3
30d	4½	5	23	5	24	6	28	...	12	⅜	2.7
40d	5	4	18	4	18	5	22				
50d	5½	3	14	3	14	4	17				
60d	6	2	11	3	13	4	15				

Table 121. Cut Steel Nails and Spikes

(Sizes, lengths, and approximate number per lb)

Sizes	Length, inches	Common	Clinch	Finishing	Casing and box	Fencing	Spikes	Barrel	Slating	Tobacco	Brads	Shingle
2d	1	740	400	1,100	....	....	.....	450	340			
3d	1¼	460	260	880	....	....	.....	280	280			
4d	1½	280	180	530	420	....	.....	190	220			
5d	1¾	210	125	350	300	100	.....	....	180	130		
6d	2	160	100	300	210	80	.....	....	....	97	120	
7d	2¼	120	80	210	180	60	.....	....	....	85	94	
8d	2½	88	68	168	130	52	.....	....	....	68	74	90
9d	2¾	73	52	130	107	38	.....	....	....	58	62	72
10d	3	60	48	104	88	26	.....	....	....	48	50	60
12d	3¼	46	40	96	70	20	.....	....	....	....	40	
16d	3½	33	34	86	52	18	17	....	....	....	27	
20d	4	23	24	76	38	16	14					
25d	4¼	20	....	....	....	....	.....					
30d	4½	16½	....	....	30	....	11					
40d	5	12	....	....	26	....	9					
50d	5½	10	....	....	20	....	7½					
60d	6	8	....	....	16	....	6					
....	6½	....	....	....	....	....	5½					
....	7	....	....	....	....	....	5					

Table 122. Sizes of American Wire Tacks

Oz	Length, in.	Size of wire, steel wire gage			Oz	Length, in.	Size of wire, steel wire gage		
		Upholsterers	Carpet	Bill posters			Upholsterers	Carpet	Bill posters
1	3⁄16	18	18	....	10	⅝	14½	15	12
1½	7⁄32	18	18	....	12	11⁄16	14½	15	12
2	¼	17	17	15	14	¾	14	14½	11½
2½	5⁄16	17	17	15	16	13⁄16	14	14½	11½
3	⅜	16	16	14	18	⅞	13½	13½	11
4	7⁄16	16	16	13½	20	15⁄16	13½	13½	11
6	½	15	15	13	22	1	13½	13½	10½
8	9⁄16	15	15	12½	24	1⅛	13	13	10½

STANDARD CROSS-SECTION SYMBOLS

Figures 172 and 173 are abstracted from American Drafting Standards Manual (ASA Y14.2, 1957) published as ASME. Subdivisions of any of the materials may be made by taking one of these standard cross sections as a basis and making minor changes or by writing on the standard cross section the name of the material.

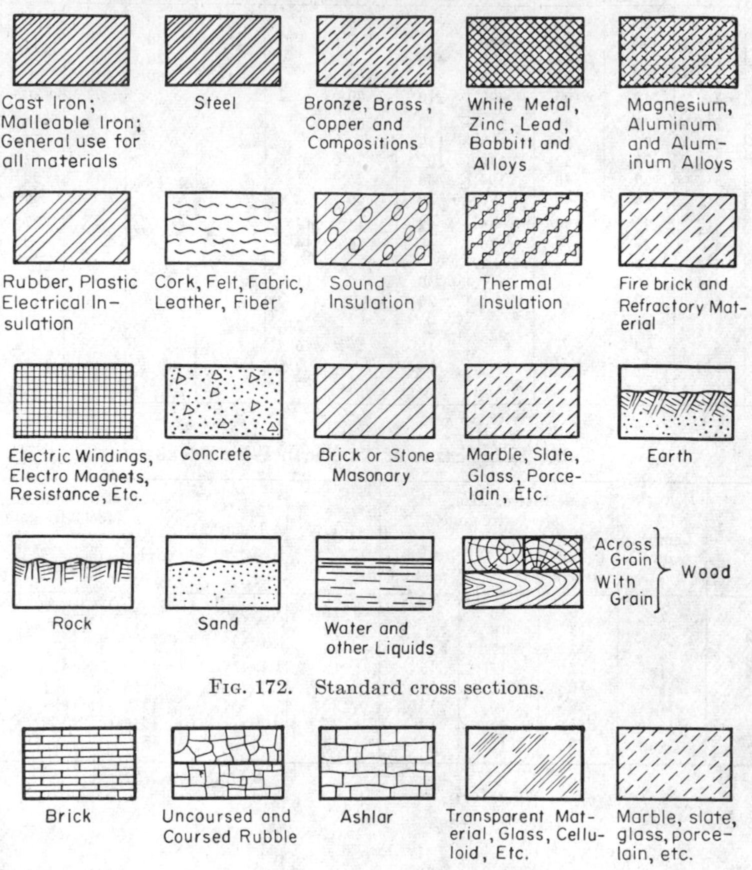

FIG. 172. Standard cross sections.

FIG. 173. Standard outside views.

GEARING

BY

George W. Michalec

REFERENCES: AMGA Standards Books 1 to 3. ASA, "Letter Symbols for Gear Engineering." Buckingham, "Manual of Gear Design," Industrial Press. Dudley, "Gear Handbook," McGraw-Hill. Dudley, "Practical Gear Design," McGraw-Hill. "Gleason Bevel and Hypoid Gear Design," Gleason Works, Rochester. "Van Keuren Precision Measuring Tools, Handbook No. 36," The Van Keuren Co., Watertown, Mass. Michalec, "Precision Gearing: Theory and Practice," Wiley.

Notation

a = addendum
b = dedendum
B = backlash, linear measure along pitch circle
c = clearance
C = center distance
d_b = base diam of pinion
d_o = outside diam of pinion
d_r = root diam of pinion
D = pitch diameter
D_P = pitch diam of pinion
D_G = pitch diam of gear
D_O = outside diam of gear
D_b = base diam of gear
D_t = throat diam of worm gear
F = face width
h_k = working depth
h_t = whole depth
inv ϕ = involute function ($\tan \phi - \phi$)
l = lead (advance of worm or helical gear in 1 rev)
$l_P(l_G)$ = lead of pinion (gear) in helical gears
L = gear face width
m_G = gear ratio ($m_G = N_G/N_P$)
m_p = contact ratio (of profiles)
M = measurement over-pins
$n_p(n_G)$ = speed of pinion (gear), rpm
$N_P(N_G)$ = number of teeth in pinion (gear)
N_W = number of threads in worm
p = circular pitch
p_b = base pitch (= normal pitch for helical gears)
p_n = normal circular pitch of helical gear
P_d = diametral pitch
P_{dn} = normal diametral pitch
R = pitch radius
R_c = radial distance from center of gear to center of measuring pin
$R_P(R_G)$ = pitch radius of pinion (gear)
R_T = testing radius when rolled on a variable center distance inspection fixture
s = stress
t = tooth thickness
t_n = normal circular tooth thickness
$T_P(T_G)$ = formative number of teeth in pinion (gear) (in bevel gears)
U = width of worm thread at tip
v = pitch line velocity
V = width of worm thread space at root
x = distance from center line to tip of worm tooth
X = correction factor for profile shift
α = addendum angle
γ = pitch angle of bevel pinion
γ_R = face angle at root of pinion tooth
γ_o = face angle at tip of pinion tooth
Γ = pitch angle of bevel gear
Γ_R = face angle at root of gear tooth
Γ_o = face angle at tip of gear tooth
δ = dedendum angle
$\overline{\Delta C}$ = relatively small change in center distance C
ϕ = pressure angle
ψ = helix or spiral angle
$\psi_P(\psi_G)$ = helix angle of teeth in pinion (gear)
Σ = shaft angle

Basic Gear Data

Gear types. Gears are grouped in accordance with tooth forms, shaft arrangement, pitch, and quality. Tooth forms and shaft arrangements are:

Tooth form	Shaft arrangement
Spur	Parallel
Helical	Parallel or skew
Worm	Skew
Bevel	Intersecting
Hypoid	Skew

Pitch divisions are: coarse (below $20P_d$) and fine ($20P_d$ and finer). Quality types are: commercial, precision, and ultra-precision.

Pitch definitions (see Fig. 1). **Diametral pitch** P_d is the ratio of number of teeth in the gear to the diameter of the pitch circle D measured in inches, $P_d = N/D$.

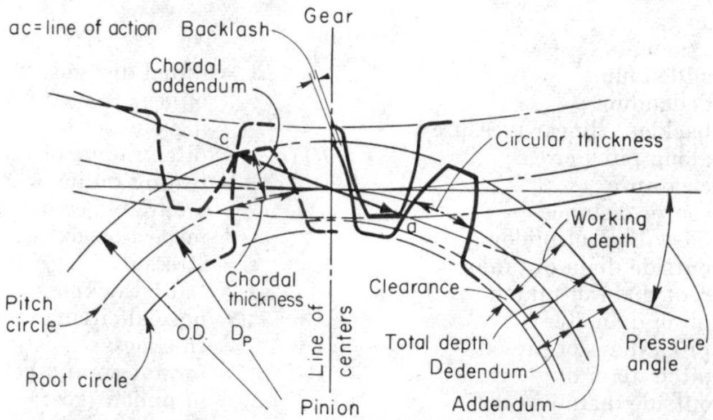

FIG. 1. Gear-tooth nomenclature.

Circular pitch p is the linear measure in inches along the pitch circle between corresponding points of adjacent teeth. From these definitions, $P_dp = \pi$. The **base pitch** P_b is the distance along the line of action between successive involute tooth surfaces. The base and circular pitches are related as $p_b = p \cos \phi$, where ϕ = the pressure angle.

Pitch circle is the imaginary circle that rolls without slippage with a pitch circle of a mating gear. The pitch (circle) diameter equals $D = N/P_d = Np/\pi$.

Pressure angle ϕ for all gear types is the acute angle between the common normal to the profiles at the contact point and the common pitch plane. For spur gears it is simply the acute angle formed by the common tangent between base circles of mating gears and a normal to the line of centers. For standard gears pressure angles of 14½ deg and 20 deg have been adopted by the ASA and the gear industry (see Fig. 1).

The **base circle** (or **base cylinder**) is the circle from which the involute tooth profiles are generated. The relationship between the base-circle and pitch-circle diameter is $D_b = D \cos \phi$.

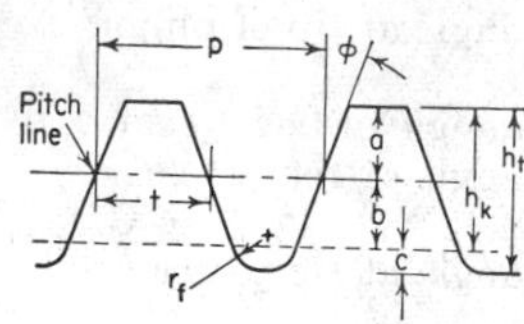

FIG. 2. Basic rack for involute gear systems. a = addendum, b = dedendum, c = clearance, h_k = working depth, h_t = whole depth, p = circular pitch, r_f = fillet radius, t = tooth thickness, ϕ = pressure angle.

Tooth proportions are established by the addendum, dedendum, working depth, clearance, tooth circular thickness, and pressure angle (see Fig. 1). In addition, gear face width L establishes thickness of the gear measured parallel to the gear axis.

For involute teeth, proportions have been standardized by ASA and AGMA into a limited number of systems using a basic rack for specification (see Fig. 2, Table 1). For non-spur and non-involute types see Table 2.

Table 1. Tooth Proportions of Basic Rack for Standard Involute Gear Systems

Tooth parameter (of basic rack)	Symbol, Fig. 1	Tooth proportions for various standard systems					
		1	2	3	4	5	6
		Full depth involute, 14½ deg	Full depth involute, 20 deg	Stub involute, 20 deg	Coarse pitch involute spur gears, 20 deg	Coarse pitch involute spur gears, 25 deg	Fine pitch involute, 20 deg
1 System sponsors	...	ASA and AGMA	ASA	ASA and AGMA	AGMA	AGMA	ASA and AGMA
2 Pressure angle.	ϕ	14½ deg	20 deg	20 deg	20 deg	25 deg	20 deg
3 Addendum....	a	$1/P_d$	$1/P_d$	$0.8/P_d$	$1.000/P_d$	$1.000/P_d$	$1.000/P_d$
4 Min dedendum	b	$1.157/P_d$	$1.157/P_d$	$1/P_d$	$1.250/P_d$	$1.250/P_d$	$1.200/P_d +$ 0.002 in.
5 Min whole depth	h_t	$2.157/P_d$	$2.157/P_d$	$1.8/P_d$	$2.250/P_d$	$2.250/P_d$	$2.200/P_d +$ 0.002 in.
6 Working depth	h_k	$2/P_d$	$2/P_d$	$1.6/P_d$	$2.000/P_d$	$2.000/P_d$	$2.000/P_d$
7 Min clearance.	c	$0.157/P_d$	$0.157/P_d$	$0.200/P_d$	$0.250/P_d$	$0.250/P_d$	$0.200/P_d +$ 0.002 in.
8 Basic circular tooth thickness on pitch line	t	$1.5708/P_d$	$1.5708/P_d$	$1.5708/P_d$	$\pi/2P_d$	$\pi/2P_d$	$1.5708/P_d$
9 Fillet radius in basic rack	r_f	1⅓ × clearance	1½ × clearance	Not standardized	$0.300/P_d$	$0.300/P_d$	Not standardized
10 Diametral pitch range	...	Not specified	Not specified	Not specified	19.99 and coarser	19.99 and coarser	20 and finer
11 Governing standard:							
ASA........	...	B6.1	B6.1	B6.1	....	....	B6.7
AGMA.....	...	201.02A	....	201.02A	201.02	201.02	207.05

Table 2. Non-spur Gear System Standards

Gear type	ASA no.	AGMA no.	Title
Straight bevel.......	B6.13	208.02	System for Straight Bevel Gears
Spiral bevel.........	......	209.03	System for Spiral Bevel Gears
Zerol bevel..........	......	202.03	Zerol Bevel Gear System
Face...............	......	203.02	Fine-pitch On-center Face Gears for 20 Deg Involute Spur Pinions
Wormgearing........	B6.9	374.03	Design for Fine-pitch Wormgearing

Gear ratio (or **mesh ratio**) m_G is the ratio of number of teeth in a meshed pair, expressed as a number greater than 1; $m_G = N_G/N_P$, where the pinion is the member having the lesser number of teeth. For spur and parallel shaft helical gears, the base circle ratio must be identical to the gear ratio. The speed ratio of gears is inversely proportionate to their numbers of teeth. Only for standard spur and parallel shaft helical gears is the pitch diameter ratio equal to the gear ratio and inversely proportionate to the speed ratio.

Fundamental Relationships of Spur and Helical Gears

Center distance is the distance between axes of mating gears and is determined from $C = (N_G + N_P)/2P_d$, or $C = (D_G + D_P)/2$. Deviation from ideal center distance of involute gears is not detrimental to proper (conjugate) gear action which is one of the prime superiority features of the involute tooth form.

Contact ratio. Referring to the top part of Fig. 3 and assuming no tip relief, the pinion engages the gear at *a*, where the outside circle of the gear tooth intersects the line of action *ac*. For the usual spur gear and pinion combination there will be two pairs of teeth theoretically in contact at engagement (a gear tooth and its mating pinion tooth considered as a pair). This will continue until the pair ahead (bottom part of Fig. 3) disengages at *c*, where the outside circle of the pinion intersects the line

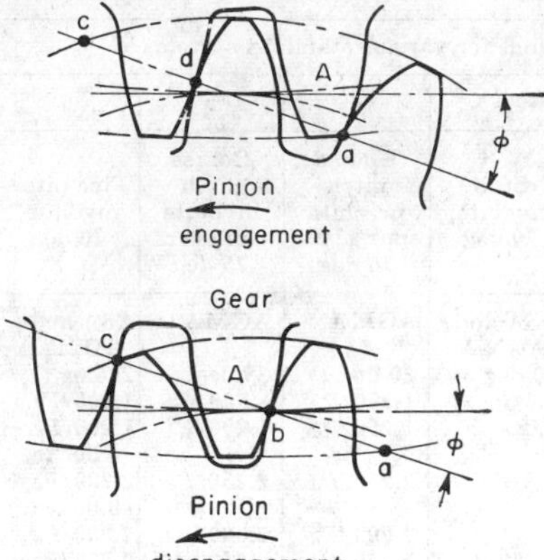

FIG. 3. Contact conditions at engagement and disengagement.

of action *ac*, the movement along the line of action being *ab*. After disengagement the pair behind will be the only pair in contact until another pair engages, the movement along the line of action for single-pair contact being *bd*. Two pairs are theoretically in contact during the remaining intervals, $ab + dc$.

Contact ratio expresses the average number of pairs of teeth theoretically in contact and is obtained numerically by dividing the length of the line of action by the normal pitch. For full depth teeth, without undercutting, the contact ratio is $m_p = (\sqrt{D_o^2 - D_b^2} + \sqrt{d_o^2 - d_b^2} - 2C \sin \phi)/2p \cos \phi$.

In Figs. 4 and 5 contact ratios are given for standard generated gears, the lower part of the charts representing the effect of undercutting. Contact-ratio numbers given on the charts may be interpreted as follows:

For $m_p = 1$, the load is carried by one pair of teeth all the time.

For m_p between 1 and 2: load is carried by one pair, $\left(\frac{2}{m_p} - 1\right)$ of the time; load is carried by two pairs, $\left(2 - \frac{2}{m_p}\right)$ of the time.

For $m_p = 2$, load is carried by two pairs all the time.

For m_p between 2 and 3: load is carried by two pairs, $2\left(\frac{3}{m_p} - 1\right)$ of the time; load is carried by three pairs, $3\left(1 - \frac{2}{m_p}\right)$ of the time.

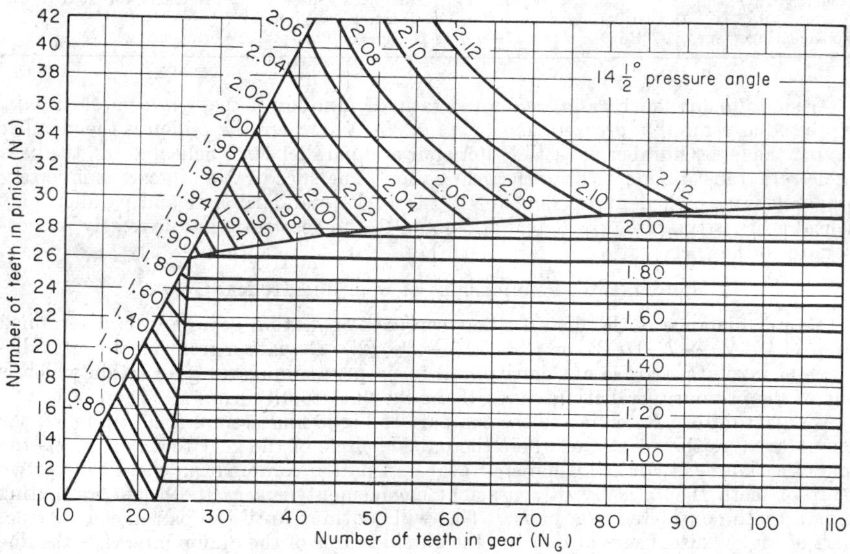

FIG. 4. Contact-ratio—full-depth standard generated teeth, 14½ deg pressure angle.

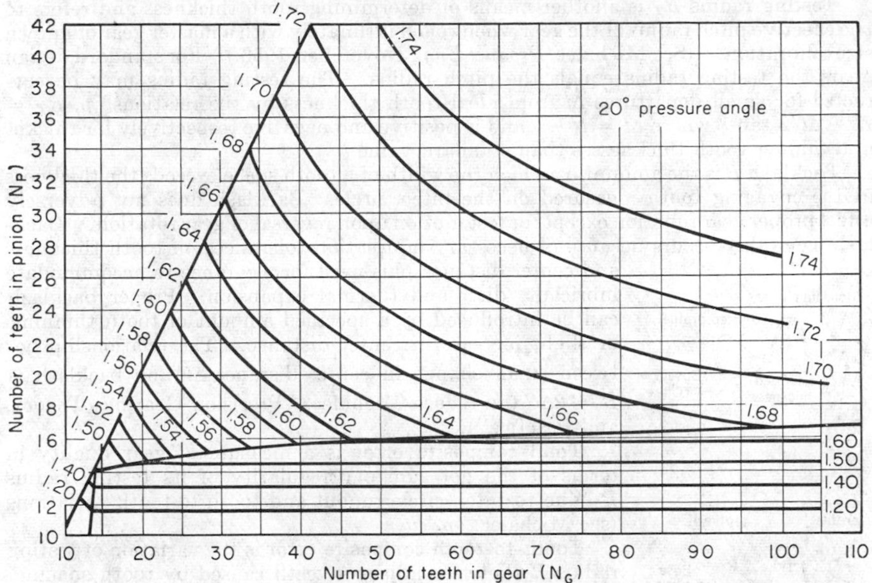

FIG. 5. Contact-ratio—full-depth standard generated teeth, 20 deg pressure angle.

Tooth thickness. For standard gears, the tooth thickness t of mating gears is equal, where $t = p/2 = \pi/2P_d$ measured linearly along the arc of the pitch circle. The tooth thickness t_1 at any radial point of the tooth (at diameter D_1) can be calculated from the known thickness t at the pitch radius ($D/2$) by the relationship $t_1 = t(D_1/D) - D_1$ (inv ϕ_1 − inv ϕ), where inv $\phi = \tan \phi - \phi$ (see Buckingham and Dudley for detail values).

Over-pins measurements (spur gears) are another means of deriving tooth thickness. If cylindrical pins are inserted in tooth spaces diametrically opposite one another (or nearest space for odd number teeth), Fig. 6, the tooth thickness can be derived from the measurement M by $t = D(\pi/N + \text{inv}\ \phi_1 - \text{inv}\ \phi - d_w/D_b)$, $\cos \phi_1 = (D \cos \phi)/2R_c$, $R_c = (M - dw)/2$ (for even number of teeth), $R_c = (M - dw)/[2 \cos (180/2N)]$ (for odd number of teeth), where d_w = pin diameter, R_c = distance from gear center to center of pin, and M = measurement over-pins.

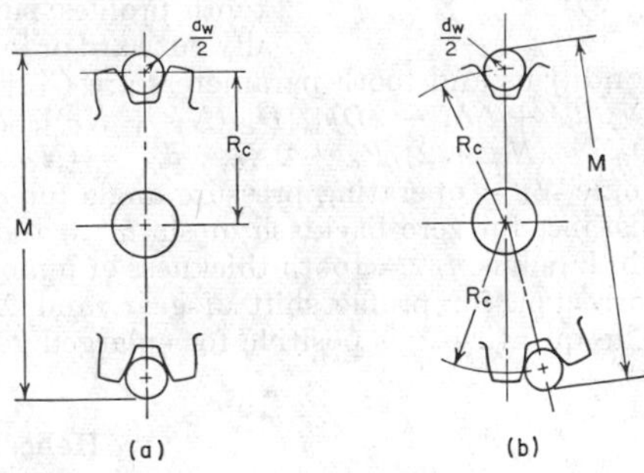

FIG. 6. Geometry of over-pins measurements, (*a*) for even number of teeth; (*b*) for odd number of teeth.

For the reverse situation, the over-pins measurement M can be found for a given tooth thickness t at diameter D and pressure angle ϕ by the following: inv $\phi_1 = t/D +$ inv $\phi + d_w/(D \cos \phi) - \pi/N$, $M = (D \cos \phi)/\cos \phi_1 + d_w$ (for even number of teeth), $M = (D \cos \phi)/\cos \phi_1 \cos (90°/N) + d_w$ (for odd number of teeth).

Table values of over-pins measures (see Dudley and Van Keuren) facilitate measurements for all standard gears including those with slight departures from standard. (For correlation with tooth thickness and testing radius, see Michalec, *Product Eng.*, May, 1957.)

Testing radius R_T is another means of determining tooth thickness and refers to the effective pitch radius of the gear when rolled intimately with a master gear of known size calibration. (See Michalec, *Product Eng.*, November, 1956.) For standard design gears the testing radius equals the pitch radius. The testing radius may be corrected for small departures Δt from ideal tooth thickness by the relationship, $R_T = R + \Delta t/2 \tan \phi$ where $\Delta t = t_1 - t$ and is positive and negative respectively for thicker and thinner tooth thicknesses than standard value t.

Backlash B is the amount by which the width of a tooth space exceeds the thickness of the engaging tooth measured on the pitch circle. Backlash does not adversely affect proper gear function except for lost motion upon reversal of gear rotation. Backlash inevitably occurs because of necessary fabrication tolerances on tooth thickness and center distance plus need for clearance to accommodate lubricant, dirt, and thermal expansion. Proper backlash can be introduced by a specified amount of tooth thinning or slight increase in center distance. The relationship between small change in center distance $\overline{\Delta C}$ and backlash is $B = 2\overline{\Delta C} \tan \phi$ (see Michalec, "Precision Gearing: Theory and Practice").

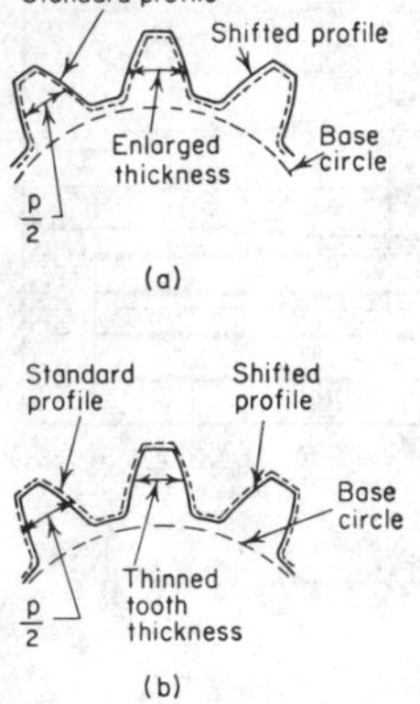

FIG. 7. Geometry of profile-shifted teeth, (*a*) enlarged case; (*b*) thinned tooth thickness case.

Total composite error is a measure of gear quality in terms of the net sum of irregularity of its testing radius R_T due to pitch-circle runout and tooth-to-tooth variations (see Michalec, *op. cit.*).

Tooth-to-tooth composite error is the variation of testing radius R_T between adjacent teeth caused by tooth spacing, thickness, and profile deviations (see Michalec, *op. cit.*).

Profile shifted gears have tooth thicknesses that are significantly different from nominal standard value; excluded are deviations caused by normal allowances and tolerances. They are also known as **modified gears, long and short addendum gears,** and **enlarged gears.** They are produced by cutting the teeth to standard depth with standard cutters at enlarged or reduced outside diameters. The result is a relative shift of the two families of involutes forming the tooth profiles, simultaneously with a shift of the tooth radially outward or inward (see Fig. 7). Calculation of operating conditions and tooth parameters are $C_1 = (C \cos \phi)/\cos \phi_1$, where $\text{inv}\, \phi_1 = \text{inv}\, \phi + [N_P(t_G' + t_P') - \pi D_P]/[D_P\,(N_P + N_G)]$, $t_G' = t + 2X_G \tan \phi$, $t_P' = t + 2X_P \tan \phi$, $D_O' = (N_G + 2)/P_d + 2X_G$, $d_O' = (N_P + 2)/P_d + 2X_P$, ϕ = standard pressure angle, ϕ_1 = operating pressure angle for profile shifted gears, C_1 = operating center distance for zero backlash mesh, t_G' = tooth thickness of gear measured at standard pitch radius, t_P' = tooth thickness of pinion measured at standard pitch radius, X_G = correction for profile shift of gear, and X_P = correction for profile shift of pinion. The quantity X is positive for enlarged gears and negative for thinned gears.

Helical Gears

Helical gears divide into two general applications: (1) for driving parallel shafts and (2) for driving skew shafts (mostly at right angles) in which case they are referred to as *crossed-axis* helical gears. The helical tooth form may be imagined as consisting of an infinite number of staggered laminar spur gears, resulting in the curved cylindrical helix shape.

Pitch of helical gears is definable in two planes. The diametral and circular pitches measured in the plane of rotation (transverse) are defined as for spur gears. However, pitches measured normal to the tooth are related by the cosine of the helix angle; thus, normal diametral pitch $= P_{dn} = P_d/\cos \psi$, normal circular pitch $= p_n = p \cos \psi$, and $P_{dn}p_n = \pi$. **Axial pitch** is the distance between corresponding sides of adjacent teeth measured parallel to the gear axis and is calculated as $p_a = p \cot \psi$.

Pressure angle of helical gears is definable in the normal and transverse planes by $\tan \phi_n = \tan \phi \cos \psi$. The transverse pressure angle, which is effectively the real pressure angle, is always greater than the normal pressure angle.

Tooth thickness t of helical gears can be measured in the plane of rotation, as with spur gears, or normal to the tooth surface t_n. The relationship of the two thicknesses is $t_n = t \cos \psi$.

Over-pins Measurement of Helical Gears. Tooth thicknesses, t at diameter d can be found from a known over-pins measurement M at known pressure angle ϕ, corresponding to diameter D, by $R_c = (M - d_w)/2$ (for even number of teeth), $R_c = (M - d_w)/[2 \cos (180/2N)]$ (for odd number of teeth), $\cos \phi_1 = (D \cos \phi)/2R_c$, $\tan \phi_n = \tan \phi \cos \psi$, $\cos \psi_b = \sin \phi_n / \sin \phi$, and $t = D[\pi/N + \text{inv } \phi_1 - \text{inv } \phi - d_w/(D \cos \phi \cos \psi_b)]$.

Parallel shaft helical gears must conform to the same conditions and requirements as spur gears with parameters (pressure angle and pitch) consistently defined in the transverse plane. Since standard spur gear cutting tools are usually used, normal plane values are standard, resulting in nonstandard transverse pitches and nonstandard pitch diameters and center distances. For parallel shafts meshing, helical gears must have identical helix angles but must be of opposite hand (left and right helix directions). The commonly used helix angles range from 15 to 35 deg. To make most advantage of the helical form, the advance of a tooth should be greater than the circular pitch; recommended ratio is 1.5 to 2 with 1.1 minimum. This overlap provides two or more teeth in continual contact with resulting greater smoothness and quietness than spur gears. Because of the helix, the normal component of the tangential pressure on the teeth produces end thrust of the shafts. To remove this objection, gears are made with opposite handed helixes on each half of the face and are then known as herringbone gears (see Fig. 8).

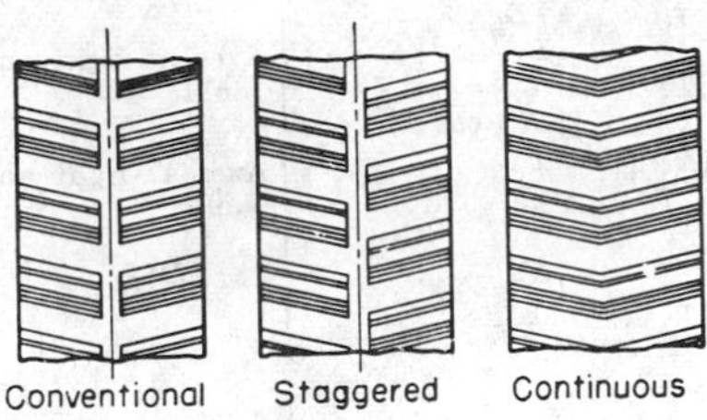

FIG. 8. Herringbone gears.

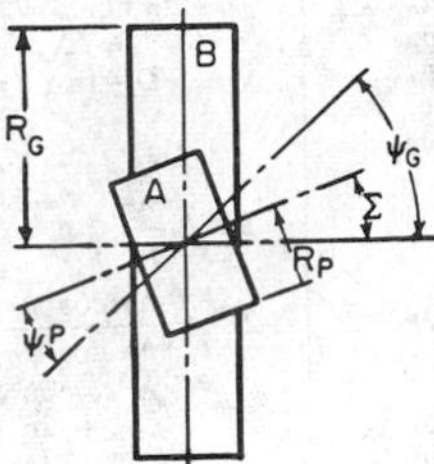

FIG. 9. Crossed-axis helical gears.

Crossed-axis helical gears, also called *spiral* or *screw gears,* (Fig. 9) are a simple type of involute gear used for connecting non-parallel, non-intersecting shafts. Contact is point and there is considerably more sliding than with parallel axis helicals, which limits the load capacity. The individual gear of this mesh is identical in form and specification to a parallel-shaft helical gear. Crossed-axis helicals can connect any shaft angle Σ although 90 deg is prevalent. Usually, the helix angles will be of the same hand, although for some extreme cases it is possible to have opposite hands, particularly if the shaft angle is small.

Helical Gear Calculations. For parallel shafts the center distance is a function of the helix angle as well as the number of teeth, that is, $C = (N_G + N_P)/2P_{dn} \cos \psi$. This offers a powerful method of gearing shafts at any specified center distance to a specified velocity ratio. For crossed-axis helicals the problem of connecting a pair of shafts for any velocity ratio admits of a number of solutions, since both the pitch radii and the helix angles contribute to establishing the velocity ratio. The formulas given in Table 3 are of assistance in calculations. The notation used in this table is as follows:

$N_P(N_G)$ = number of teeth in pinion (gear)
$D_P(D_G)$ = pitch diam of pinion (gear)
$p_P(p_G)$ = circular pitch of pinion (gear)
p_n = normal circular pitch for both gears
P_{d_n} = normal diametral pitch for both gears
$d_O(D_O)$ = outside diam of driver (follower)
a = addendum of normal pitch
ψ_G = tooth helix angle of gear
ψ_P = tooth helix angle of pinion
$l_P(l_G)$ = lead of pinion (gear) = lead of tooth helix
$n_P(n_G)$ = rpm of pinion (gear)
Σ = angle between shafts in plan
C = center distance

Table 3. Formulas for Helical-gear Calculations

Pinion		Gear		
To find	Formula	To find	Formula	Remarks
ψ_P	$\tan \psi_P = D_P n_P / D_G n_G$	ψ_G	$90 \text{ deg} - \psi_P$	Axes at right angles only
ψ_P	$\cos \psi_P = p_n / p_G$	ψ_G	$\Sigma - \psi_P$	
ψ_P	$\tan \psi_P = \pi D_P / l_P$	ψ_G	$\Sigma - \psi_P$	
p_n	$\pi D_P \cos \psi_P / N_P$	p_n	$\pi D_G \cos \psi_G / N_G$	Same in both gears
p_P	D_P / N_P	p_G	$\pi D_G / N_G$	
l_P	$\pi D_P / \tan \psi_P$	l_G	$\pi D_G / \tan \psi_G$	Axes at right angles only
N_P	$D_P P_d \cos \psi_P$	N_G	$D_G P_d \cos \psi_G$	
D_P	$2C \Big/ \frac{n_P}{n_G} \tan \psi_G + 1$	D_G	$2C \Big/ \left(\frac{n_P}{n_G} \tan \psi_P + 1\right)$	Axes at right angles only
D_P	$2C \Big/ \frac{n_P \cos \psi_P}{n_G \cos \psi_G} + 1$	D_G	$2C - D_P$	
D_P	$N_P / P_{d_n} \cos \psi_P$	D_G	$N_G / P_{d_n} \cos \psi_G$	
d_O	$D_P + 2a$	D_O	$D_G + 2a$	
d_O	$D_P + (2/P_d)$	D_O	$D_G + (2/P_d)$	
Cutter*	$N_P / \cos^3 \psi_P$		$N_G / \cos^3 \psi_G$	

Center distance $C = (N_P / 2P_d \cos \psi_P) + (N_G / 2P_d \cos \psi_G)$.
* Spur-gear cutter to be used which is correct for the number of teeth given by the formulas.

Non-spur Gear Types

Bevel gears are used to connect two intersecting shafts in any given speed ratio. The tooth shapes may be designed in any of the shapes shown in Fig. 10. Bevels connecting non-intersecting shafts are called **skew bevel gears.** A special type developed by the Gleason Works and used widely in automotive products is known as **hypoid gearing** (see *Jour. SAE* 18, no. 6), although this is not a true bevel gear. The "spherical involute" or, more accurately, **octoid** tooth form is almost universally used for bevel gears. This has a basic crown tooth with a straight-sided form.

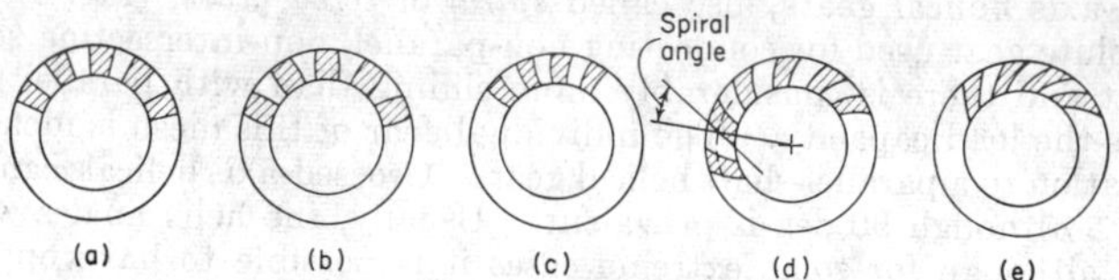

FIG. 10. Bevel gear types, (*a*) old type straight teeth; (*b*) modern coniflex straight teeth with exaggerated crowning; (*c*) Zerol teeth; (*d*) spiral teeth; (*e*) hypoid teeth.

Referring to Fig. 11, we see that the pitch surfaces of bevel gears are frustrums of cones whose vertices are at the intersection of the axes; the essential elements and definitions are as follows.

Addendum Angle, α. The angle between elements of the face cone and pitch cone.

Back Angle. The angle between an element of the back cone and a plane of rotation. It is equal to the pitch angle.

Back Cone. The angle of a cone whose elements are tangent to a sphere containing a trace of the pitch circle.

Back-cone Distance. The distance along an element of the back cone from the apex to the pitch circle.

Cone Distance, A_o. The distance from the end of the tooth (heel) to the pitch apex.

Crown. The sharp corner forming the outside diameter.

Crown-to-back. The distance from the outside diameter edge (crown) to the rear of the gear.

Dedendum Angle, δ. The angle between elements of the root cone and pitch cone.

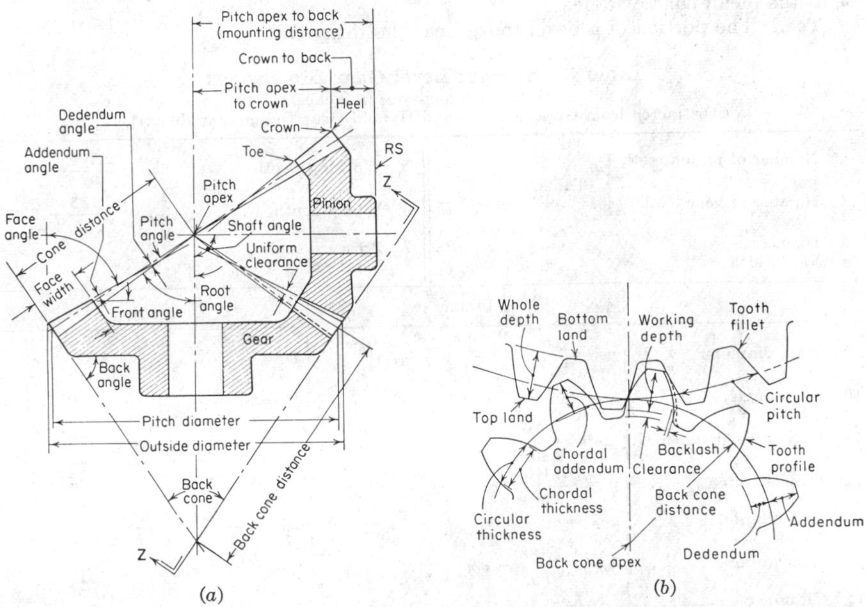

Fig. 11. Geometry of bevel gear nomenclature, (*a*) section through axes; (*b*) view along section Z-Z.

Face Angle, γ_o. The angle between an element of the face cone and its axis. It is equal to pitch angle.

Face Width, F. The length of teeth along the cone distance.

Front Angle. The angle between an element of the front cone and a plane of rotation.

Generating Mounting Surface, GMS. The diameter and/or plane of rotation surface or shaft center which is used for locating the gear blank during fabrication of the gear teeth.

Heel. The portion of a bevel gear tooth near the outer end.

Mounting Distance, MD. For assembled bevel gears, the distance from the crossing point of the axes to the registering surface, measured along the gear axis. Ideally, it should be identical to the pitch apex to back.

Mounting Surface, MS. The diameter and/or plane of rotation surface which is used for locating the gear in the application assembly.

Octoid. The mathematical form of the bevel tooth profile. Closely resembles a spherical involute but is fundamentally different.

Pitch Angle, Γ. The angle formed between an element of the pitch cone and the bevel-gear axis. It is the half angle of the pitch cone.

Pitch Apex to Back. The distance along the axis from apex of pitch cone to a locating registering surface on back.

Registering Surface, RS. The surface in the plane of rotation which locates the gear blank axially in the generating machine and the gear in application. These are usually identical surfaces, but not necessarily so.

Root Angle, γ_R. The angle formed between a tooth root element and the axis of the bevel gear.

Shaft Angle, Σ. The angle between mating bevel gear axes; also, the sum of the two pitch angles.

Spiral Angle, ψ. The angle between the tooth trace and an element of the pitch cone, corresponding to helix angle in helical gears. The spiral angle is understood to be at the mean cone distance.

Toe. The portion of a bevel tooth near the inner end.

Table 4. Straight Bevel Gear Dimensions

(All linear dimensions in inches)

(Abstracted from Gleason Bevel and Hypoid Gear Design Handbook)†

1 Number of pinion teeth	(Table 1)	n	5 Working depth	$h_k = \frac{2.000}{P_d}$
2 Number of gear teeth	(Table 1)	N	6 Whole depth	$h_t = \frac{2.188}{P_d} + 0.002$
3 Diametral pitch		P_d	7 Pressure angle	ϕ
4 Face width		F	8 Shaft angle	Σ

	Pinion	Gear
9 Pitch diameter	$d = \frac{n}{P_d}$	$D = \frac{N}{P_d}$
10 Pitch angle	$\gamma = \tan^{-1} \frac{n}{N}$	$\Gamma = 90° - \gamma$
11 Outer cone distance	$A_O = \frac{D}{2 \sin \Gamma}$	
12 Circular pitch	$p = \frac{3.1416}{P_d}$	
13 Addendum	$a_{OP} = h_k - a_{OG}$	$a_{OG} = \frac{0.540}{P_d} + \frac{0.460}{P_d(N/n)^2}$
14 Dedendum*	$b_{OP} = \frac{2.188}{P_d} - a_{OP}$	$b_{OG} = \frac{2.188}{P_d} a_{OG}$
15 Clearance	$c = h_t - h_k$	
16 Dedendum angle	$\delta_P = \tan^{-1} \frac{b_{OP}}{A_O}$	$\delta_G = \tan^{-1} \frac{b_{OG}}{A_O}$
17 Face angle of blank	$\gamma_O = \gamma + \delta_G$	$\Gamma_O = \Gamma + \delta_P$
18 Root angle	$\gamma_R = \gamma - \delta_P$	$\Gamma_R = \Gamma - \delta_G$
19 Outside diameter	$d_O = d + 2a_{OP} \cos \gamma$	$D_O = D + 2a_{OG} \cos \Gamma$
20 Pitch apex to crown	$x_O = \frac{D}{2} - a_{OP} \sin \gamma$	$X_O = \frac{d}{2} - 4a_{OG} \sin \Gamma$
21 Circular thickness	$t = p - T$	$T = \frac{p}{2} - 4(a_{OP} - a_{OG}) \tan \phi - \frac{K \text{ (see Fig. 12)}}{P_d}$
22 Backlash	B (see Table 5)	
23 Chordal thickness	$t_C = t - \frac{t^3}{6d^2} - \frac{B}{2}$	$T_C = T - \frac{T^3}{6D^2} - \frac{B}{2}$
24 Chordal addendum	$a_{CP} = a_{OP} + \frac{t^2 \cos \gamma}{4d}$	$a_{CG} = a_{OG} + \frac{T^2 \cos \Gamma}{4D}$
25 Tooth angle	$\frac{3438}{A_O}\left(\frac{t}{2} + b_{OP} \tan \phi\right)$ minutes	$\frac{3438}{A_O}\left(\frac{T}{2} + b_{OG} \tan \phi\right)$ minutes
26 Limit point width (L.E.)	$W_{LOP} = (T - 2b_{OP} \tan \phi) - 0.0015$	$W_{LOG} = (t - 2b_{OG} \tan \phi) - 0.0015$
27 Limit point width (S.E.)	$W_{LiP} = \frac{A_O - F}{A_O}(T - 2b_{OP} \tan \phi)$	$W_{LiG} = \frac{A_O - F}{A_O}(t - 2b_{OG} \tan \phi)$
28 Tool point width	$W = W_{LiP}$ − stock allowance	$W = W_{LiG}$ − stock allowance

* The actual dedendum will be 0.002 in. greater than calculated.

† Tables 4 to 8 and Figs. 12 and 13, courtesy of Gleason Works, Inc.

Bevel gears are described by the parameter dimensions at the large end (heel) of the teeth. Pitch, pitch diameter, and tooth dimensions, such as, addendum are measurements at this point. At the large end of the gear, the tooth profiles will approximate those generated on a spur gear pitch circle of radius equal to the back-cone distance. The formative number of teeth is equal to that contained by a complete spur gear. For pinion and gear, respectively, this is: $T_P = N_P/\cos\gamma$; $T_G = N_G/\cos\Gamma$, where T_P and T_G = formative number teeth, and N_P and N_G = actual number teeth.

Although bevel gears can connect intersecting shafts at any angle, most application is for right angles. When such bevels are in a 1:1 ratio, they are called **mitre gears.** Bevels connecting shafts other than 90 deg are called **angular bevel gears.** The speeds of the shafts of bevel gears are determined by $n_P/n_G = \sin\Gamma/\sin\gamma$, where $n_P(n_G)$ = rpm of pinion (gear), and $\gamma(\Gamma)$ = pitch angle of pinion (gear).

All standard bevel gear designs in the United States are in accordance with the **Gleason Bevel Gear System.** This employs a basic pressure angle of 20 deg with long and short addendums for ratios other than 1:1 to avoid undercut pinions and to increase strength.

Table 5. Recommended Backlash for Bevel Gear Meshes
(Abstracts from Gleason Bevel and Hypoid Gear Design Handbook)

Diametral pitch	Backlash	
1.00–1.25	0.020–0.030	For general-purpose bevel gears assembled ready to run. In case of choice, use the smaller backlash tolerances. In many instances these limits require modification to suit the special conditions of operation. For the finer pitches, such as precision instrument gears, it may be necessary to reduce the backlash values to a minimum.
1.25–1.50	0.018–0.026	
1.50–1.75	0.016–0.022	
1.75–2.00	0.014–0.018	
2.00–2.50	0.012–0.016	
2.50–3.00	0.010–0.013	
3.00–3.50	0.008–0.011	
3.50–4.00	0.007–0.009	
4–5	0.006–0.008	
5–6	0.005–0.007	
6–8	0.004–0.006	
8–10	0.003–0.005	
10–20	0.002–0.004	
20 and finer	0.001–0.003	

20 Deg Straight Bevel Gears for 90 Deg Shaft Angle. Since straight bevel gears are the easiest to produce and offer maximum precision, they are frequently a first choice. Modern straight-bevel-gear generators produce a tooth with localized tooth bearing designated by the Gleason registered tradename "Coniflex." These gears have a slightly crowned tooth form (see Fig. 10*b*). Because of the superiority of Coniflex bevel gears over the earlier "true-straight bevels" and because of their faster production, they are preferred. The older straight bevel is now largely restricted to existing replacement applications. The design parameters of Fig. 11 are calculated by the formulas of Table 4. Backlash data are given in Table 5.

Angular straight bevel gears connect shaft angles other than 90 deg (larger or smaller), and the formulas of Table 4 are not entirely applicable, as shown in the following:

Item 8, Shaft angle, is the specified non-90 deg shaft angle.
Item 10, Pitch angles. Shaft angle Σ less than 90 deg, $\tan\gamma = \sin\Sigma/(N/n + \cos\Sigma)$; shaft angle Σ greater than 90 deg, $\tan\gamma = \sin(180 - \Sigma)/[N/n - \cos(180° - \Sigma)]$. For all shaft angles, $\sin\gamma/\sin\Gamma = n/N$.
Item 13, Addendum, requires calculation of the equivalent 90 deg bevel gear ratio m_{90}, $m_{90} = [N\cos\gamma/n\cos\Gamma]^{1/2}$. The value m_{90} is used as the ratio N/n when applying the formula for addendum.
Item 20, Pitch apex to crown, $x_o = A_0\cos\gamma - a_{op}\sin\gamma$, $X_o = A_0\cos\Gamma - a_{oG}\sin\Gamma$.
Item 21, Circular thickness, except for high ratios, K may be zero.

Spiral Bevel Gears for 90 Deg Shaft Angle. The spiral curved teeth produce additional overlapping tooth action which results in smoother gear action, lower noise,

Table 6. Spiral Bevel Gear Dimensions

(All dimensions in inches)
(Abstracted from Gleason Bevel and Hypoid Gear Design Handbook)

1	Number of pinion teeth	n	5	Working depth	$h_k = \dfrac{1.700}{P_d}$
2	Number of gear teeth	N	6	Whole depth	$h_t = \dfrac{1.888}{P_d}$
3	Diametral pitch	P_d	7	Pressure angle	ϕ
4	Face width	F	8	Shaft angle	Σ

		Pinion	Gear
9	Pitch diameter............	$d = \dfrac{n}{P_d}$	$D = \dfrac{N}{P_d}$
10	Pitch angle...............	$\gamma = \tan^{-1} \dfrac{n}{N}$	$\Gamma = 90° - \gamma$
11	Outer cone distance........	$A_O = \dfrac{D}{2 \sin \Gamma}$	
12	Circular pitch............	$p = \dfrac{3.1416}{P_d}$	
13	Addendum...............	$a_{OP} = h_k - a_{OG}$	$a_{OG} = \dfrac{0.460}{P_d} + \dfrac{0.390}{P_d \left(\dfrac{N}{n}\right)^2}$
14	Dedendum...............	$b_{OP} = h_t - a_{OP}$	$b_{OG} = h_t - a_{OG}$
15	Clearance...............	$c = h_t - h_k$	
16	Dedendum angle...........	$\delta_P = \tan^{-1} \dfrac{b_{OP}}{A_O}$	$\delta_G = \tan^{-1} \dfrac{b_{OG}}{A_O}$
17	Face angle of blank........	$\gamma_O = \gamma + \delta_G$	$\Gamma_O = \Gamma + \delta_P$
18	Root angle...............	$\gamma_R = \gamma - \delta_P$	$\Gamma_R = \Gamma - \delta_G$
19	Outside diameter...........	$d_O = d + 2a_{OP} \cos \gamma$	$D_O = D + 2a_{OG} \cos \Gamma$
20	Pitch apex to crown.......	$x_O = \dfrac{D}{2} - a_{OP} \sin \gamma$	$X_O = \dfrac{d}{2} - a_{OG} \sin \Gamma$
21	Circular thickness.........	$t = p - T$	$T = \dfrac{p}{2} (a_{OP} - a_{OG}) \dfrac{\tan \phi}{\cos \phi} - \dfrac{K\text{(Fig. 13)}}{P_d}$
22	Backlash................	See Table 5	

and higher load capacity. The spiral angle has been standardized by Gleason at 35 deg. Design parameters are calculated by the formulas of Table 6.

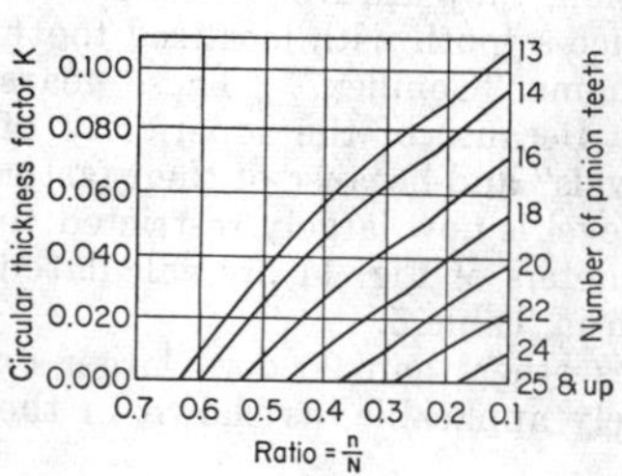

FIG. 12. Circular thickness factor for straight and Zerol bevel gears.

Angular Spiral Bevel Gears. Several items deviate from the formulas of Table 6 in the same manner as angular straight bevel gears. Therefore the same formulas apply for the deviating items with only the following exception:

Item 21, Circular thickness, the value of K in Fig. 13 must be determined from the equivalent 90° bevel ratio (m_{90}) and the equivalent 90° bevel pinion. The latter is computed as $n_{90} = (n \sin \Gamma_{90})/\cos \gamma$, where $\tan \Gamma_{90} = m_{90}$.

Zerol Bevel Gears for 90 Deg Shaft Angle. The Zerol bevel is essentially equivalent to the straight bevel in function. It is produced by the same equipment used for spiral bevels. Design parameters are calculated by the formulas of Table 7.

Angular Zerol Bevel Gears. The formulas of Table 7 apply with the same deviations as for angular straight bevel gears.

Worm Gears and Worms

Worm gearing is used for obtaining large speed reductions between non-intersecting shafts making an angle of 90 deg with each other. If a gear such as shown in Fig. 14

Table 7. Zerol Bevel Gear Dimensions

(All linear dimensions in inches)

(Abstracted from Gleason Bevel and Hypoid Gear Design Handbook)

1	Number of pinion teeth	n	5	Working depth	$h_k = \dfrac{2.000}{P_d}$
2	Number of gear teeth	N	6	Whole depth	$h_t = \dfrac{2.188}{P_d} + 0.002$
3	Diametral pitch	P_d	7	Pressure angle	ϕ
4	Face width	F	8	Shaft angle	Σ

		Pinion	Gear
9	Pitch diameter	$d = \dfrac{n}{P_d}$	$D = \dfrac{N}{P_d}$
10	Pitch angle	$\gamma = \tan^{-1}\dfrac{n}{N}$	$\Gamma = 90° - \gamma$
11	Outer cone distance	$A_o = \dfrac{D}{2 \sin \Gamma}$	
12	Circular pitch	$p = \dfrac{3.1416}{P_d}$	
13	Addendum	$a_{OP} = h_k - a_{OG}$	$a_{OG} = \dfrac{0.540}{P_d} + \dfrac{0.460}{P_d(N/n)^2}$
14	Dedendum	$b_{OP} = h_t - a_{OP}$	$b_{OG} = h_t - a_{OG}$
15	Clearance	$c = h_t - h_k$	
16	Dedendum angle	$\delta_P = \tan^{-1}\dfrac{b_{OP}}{A_o} + \Delta\delta$ (see Table 8)	$\delta_G = \tan^{-1}\dfrac{b_{OG}}{A_o} + \Delta\delta$ (see Table 8)
17	Face angle of blank	$\gamma_O = \gamma + \delta_G$	$\Gamma_o = \Gamma + \delta_P$
18	Root angle	$\gamma_R = \gamma - \delta_P$	$\Gamma_R = \Gamma - \delta_G$
19	Outside diameter	$d_o = d + 2a_{OP} \cos \gamma$	$D_o = D + 2a_{OG} \cos \Gamma$
20	Pitch apex to crown	$x_o = \dfrac{D}{2} - a_{OP} \sin \gamma$	$X_o = \dfrac{d}{2} - a_{OG} \sin \Gamma$
21	Circular thickness	$t = p - T$	$T = \dfrac{p}{2} - (a_{OP} - a_{OG}) \tan \phi - \dfrac{K}{P_d}$ (see Fig. 12)

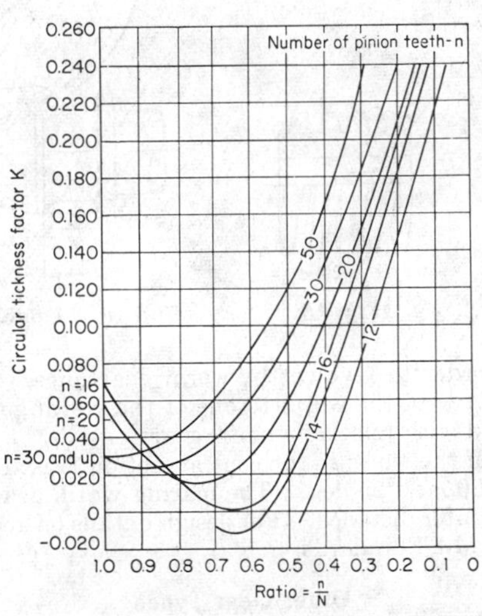

FIG. 13. Circular thickness factors for spiral bevel gears with 20 deg pressure angle and 35 deg spiral angle. L.H. pinion driving clockwise or R.H. pinion driving counterclockwise.

Table 8. Dedendum Formula for Zerol Bevel Gears
(Abstracted from Gleason Bevel and Hypoid Gear Design Handbook)

Pressure angle, deg	Change in dedendum angle = $\Delta\delta$ (min)
20	$\Delta\delta = \frac{6{,}668}{N_c} - \frac{300\sqrt{d \sin \Gamma}}{N_c F} - \frac{14P_d}{N_c}$
22½	$\Delta\delta = \frac{4{,}868}{N_c} - \frac{300\sqrt{d \sin \Gamma}}{N_c F} - \frac{14P_d}{N_c}$
25	$\Delta\delta = \frac{3{,}412}{N_c} - \frac{300\sqrt{d \sin \Gamma}}{N_c F} - \frac{14P_d}{N_c}$

N_c = number of teeth in crown gear − $2P_dA_o$
F = face width
d = pinion pitch diameter
A_o = outer cone distance
P_d = diametral pitch
Γ = gear pitch angle

engages a straight worm, as shown in Fig. 15, the combination is known as **single enveloping worm gearing.** If a gear of the kind shown in Fig. 14 engages a worm as shown in Fig. 16, the combination is known as **double enveloping worm gearing.**

With worm gearing, the **velocity ratio** is the ratio between the number of teeth on the gear and the number of threads on the worm. Thus, a 30-tooth worm gear meshing with a single-threaded worm will have a velocity ratio of 1 to 30; *i.e.*, the worm

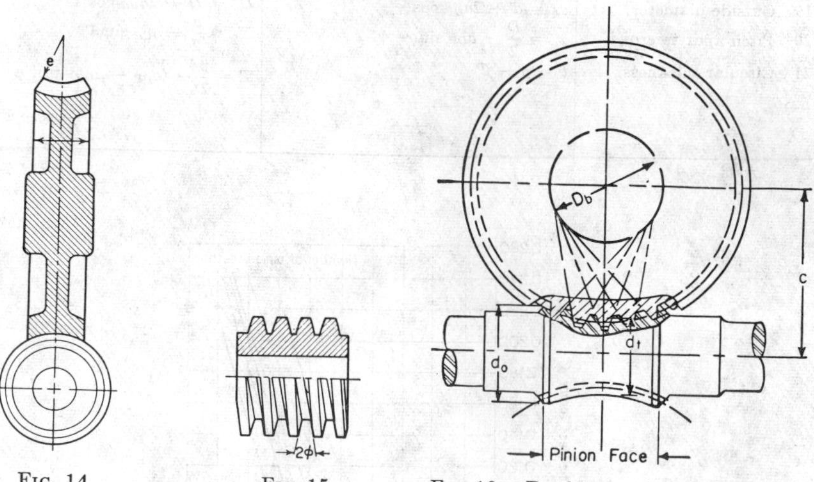

FIG. 14 FIG. 15 FIG. 16. Double enveloping worm gear.

must make 30 rev in order to revolve the worm gear once. For a double-threaded worm, there will be 15 rev of the worm to one of the worm gear, etc. High velocity ratios are thus obtained with relatively small gears.

Tooth proportions of the worm in the central section (Fig. 15) follow standard rack designs, such as 14½, 20, and 25 deg. The mating worm gear is cut conjugate for a unique worm size and center distance. For design details on geometry, tooth strength, and durability, see AGMA Standards.

Other Gear Types

Gears for special purposes include the following (details are to be found in the references).

Spiroid® (Illinois Tool Works) gears, used to connect skew shafts, resemble a hypoid-type bevel gear but in performance are more like worm meshes. They offer very high ratios and a large contact ratio resulting in high strength. The **Helicon®** (Illinois Tool Works) gear is a variation in which the pinion is not tapered, and ratios under 10:1 are feasible.

Beveloid® (Vinco Corp.) gears are tapered involute gears which can couple intersecting shafts, skew shafts, and parallel shafts.

Face gears have teeth cut on the rotating face plane of the gear and mate with standard involute spur gears. They can connect intersecting or non-parallel non-intersecting shafts.

Non-circular gears or **function gears** are used for special motions or as elements of analog computers. They can be made with elliptical, logarithmic, spiral, and other functions.

Design Standards

In addition to the ASA and AGMA standards on basic tooth proportions, the AGMA sponsors a large number of national standards dealing with gear design, specification, and inspection. (Consult AGMA, 330 Massachusetts Ave., Washington, D.C. for details.) A helpful item is the AGMA Gear Classification Manual 390.02 which establishes a system of quality classes for all gear sizes and pitches, ranging from crude commercial gears to the highest order of ultra-precision gear. Tables 9 and 10 list design parameter tolerances for the various quality grades. These are divided into two groupings: coarse pitch (up to $20P_d$) and fine pitch ($20P_d$ and finer). Backlash tolerances are given in Tables 11 and 12. A comparison of AGMA 390.02 quality tolerances for fine-pitch gears to an earlier AGMA Standard 236.04, which is still in wide use, is given in Table 13.

Strength and Durability

The capacity of a gear is measured in terms of its tooth strength and surface durability. There have been many attempts to derive expressions for calculating safe beam strength and surface stress, starting with the original Lewis-Buckingham formulas and extending to the latest AGMA equations.

The **Lewis formula** is an old method that is still useful in the analysis of tooth beam strength. It is based upon a tooth layout (Fig. 17) where the load is assumed

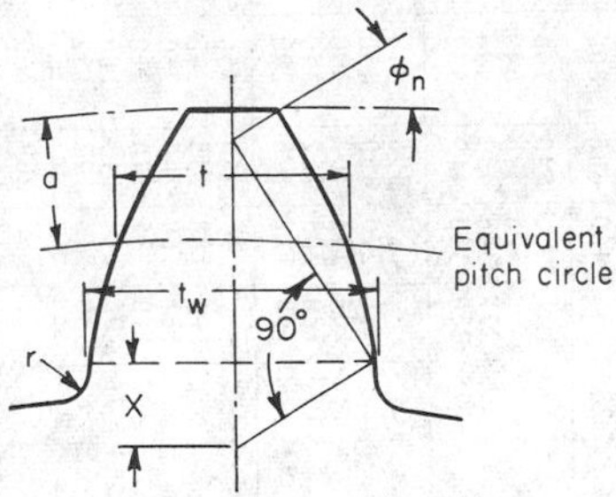

FIG. 17. Layout for beam strength.

to be at the tip. By Lewis' formula, $W_b = FSY/P_d$, or, in circular pitch, $W_t = SFp_cy_c$, and $y_c = Y/\pi$. The factor Y is derived from the layout as $Y = 2XP_d/3$.

For a given tooth design this value is constant with pitch and varies only with number of teeth (see Table 14). The transmitted load is calculated from horsepower by $W_t = 126{,}000P_t/[d\ (\text{rpm})_p]$, where P_t = transmitted horsepower and $(\text{rpm})_p$ = pinion speed, rpm. For safe design, $W_b \geq W_t$.

Table 9. Coarse-pitch Gear Tolerances for AGMA Quality Classes (Applicable to Spur, Helical, and Herringbone Gears)

(Tolerances in ten-thousandths of an inch. Abstracted from AGMA 390.02)

AGMA quality No.	Normal diametral pitch	Runout tolerance									Tooth-to-tooth spacing tolerance									Profile tolerance						
		Pitch diam, in.									Pitch diam, in.									Pitch diam, in.						
		¾	1½	3	6	12	25	50	100	200	¾	1½	3	6	12	25	50	100	200	¾	1½	3	6	12	25	50
3	½	...	...	...	...	...	770	1010	1360																	
	1	...	...	...	...	540	710	930	1250																	
	2	...	...	...	382	498	660	860	1150																	
	4	...	...	280	355	460	608	800																		
4	½	...	...	...	...	...	540	700	940																	
	1	...	...	...	...	378	496	640	860																	
	2	...	...	...	272	348	452	590	790																	
	4	...	...	198	250	320	419	542	720																	
5	½	...	...	...	...	...	396	510	665	880																
	1	...	...	...	...	270	350	450	582	775																
	2	...	...	...	184	233	302	390	510	680																
	4	...	...	130	160	203	262	340	440	590																
	8	...	91	112	140	177	228	290	380																	
6	½	...	...	...	...	...	280	350	450	600	...	...	...	...	...	50	55	62	70							
	1	...	...	...	...	188	235	295	378	508	...	...	...	...	31	33	38	42	50							
	2	...	...	...	131	160	200	250	322	425	...	...	...	26	27	29	33	37	42							
	4	...	...	92	110	135	170	210	270	360	...	...	22	22	24	26	28	32	37							
	8	...	64	76	93	114	143	180	230	...	...	18	18	19	21	23	25	28								
	16–19.99	46	55	66	80	98	122	152	193	...	16	16	16	17	18	19	21	23								
7	½	...	...	...	...	...	209	260	335	445	...	...	...	...	...	37	40	45	50	...	...	...	...	...	160	168
	1	...	...	...	...	132	165	205	261	350	...	...	...	...	23	25	28	32	37	...	...	...	...	100	106	111
	2	...	...	...	84	103	130	163	210	280	...	...	...	19	20	22	24	27	31	...	...	...	66	69	71	75
	4	...	...	55	67	82	103	130	167	225	...	...	16	16	17	19	21	24	28	...	...	44	45	48	50	52
	8	...	37	44	54	66	82	103	132	...	...	13½	14	14½	15½	17	19	21	...	...	28	30	32	33	35	37
	16–19.99	26	31	37	45	55	69	86	110	...	11	11½	12	12½	13	14	15½	17½	...	22	22	22	23	24	25	28

1. Values for sizes other than shown can be found through direct interpolation.

2. Values shown are average. The gear manufacturer will make every effort to deliver gears that comply with tolerances shown. Therefore, minor variations from any tolerance that do not affect satisfactory operational use shall not be cause for rejection.

3. Runout tolerance measurement may include the effects of: eccentricity, out of roundness, axial runout, lead variation, profile variation, spacing, and tooth thickness.

4. Tooth-to-tooth spacing tolerance is given for the plane of rotation. If measured in the normal plane, the measured values should be divided by the cosine of the helical angle.

5. Profile tolerance is exclusive of root and tip modification. Values are to be interpreted as maximum total deviation from high point to low point.

6. Unusual conditions may require that one or more of the individual quality tolerances be of a higher or lower number. In such cases it is possible to designate the quality number for each individual element. This should be done when it results in a more satisfactory gear. See Table 2 for examples.

Table 9. Coarse-pitch Gear Tolerances for AGMA Quality Classes—*(Continued)*
(Tolerances in ten-thousandths of an inch)

AGMA quality number	Normal diametral pitch	Runout tolerance, Pitch diam, in. ¾	1½	3	6	12	25	50	100	200	Tooth-to-tooth spacing tolerance, Pitch diam, in. ¾	1½	3	6	12	25	50	100	200
8	½	...	...	...	...	...	160	200	255	350	...	...	...	...	...	26	28	31	35
	1	...	...	...	...	95	115	140	180	235	...	...	...	...	16	18	19	22	26
	2	...	...	...	58	68	82	100	125	160	...	...	...	14	14	15	17	19	22
	4	...	...	36	41	47	56	67	83	110	...	...	11	11	12	13	15	17	19
	8	...	25	28	32	36	42	50	60	...	...	9	10	10	11	12	13	14	...
	16–19.99	19	21	23	26	30	35	42	51	...	8	8	8	9	9	10	11	12	...
9	½	...	...	...	...	...	113	140	180	250	...	...	...	...	...	19	20	22	25
	1	...	...	...	...	68	81	100	125	165	...	...	...	...	11	12	14	16	19
	2	...	...	...	40	48	58	70	88	113	...	...	...	10	10	11	12	14	15½
	4	...	...	26	29	34	40	48	58	78	...	...	8	8	9	9½	11	12	14
	8	...	18	20	22	26	30	35	42	...	...	7	7	7½	8	8½	9½	10½	...
	16–19.99	14	15	16	18	21	25	30	37	...	6	6	6	6¼	6¾	7¼	8	8¾	...
10	½	...	...	...	...	...	82	100	130	175	...	...	...	...	...	13	14	15	18
	1	...	...	...	...	50	58	70	87	125	...	...	...	...	8¼	8¾	9¾	11	13
	2	...	...	...	30	34	40	50	63	82	...	...	...	7	7¼	8	8¾	10	11
	4	...	...	18	21	24	28	34	42	56	...	...	5¾	5¾	6¼	7	7½	8½	9¾
	8	...	13	14	16	18	21	25	30	...	...	5	5	5¼	5¾	6¼	7	7½	...
	16–19.99	10	11	12	13	15	18	22	26	...	4¼	4¼	4½	4½	4¾	5	5½	6¼	...
11	½	...	...	...	...	...	58	70	90	120	...	...	...	...	...	9½	10	11	13
	1	...	...	...	...	34	41	50	64	84	...	...	...	...	6	6	7	8	10
	2	...	...	...	21	24	28	35	44	57	...	...	...	5	5	6	6	7	8
	4	...	...	13	15	17	20	24	30	40	...	...	4	4	4½	5	5½	6	7
	8	...	9	10	11	13	15	18	22	...	...	3½	3½	4	4	4½	5	5½	...
	16–19.99	7	8	8	9	11	13	15	18	...	3	3	3	3½	3½	3¾	4	4½	...
12	2	...	...	...	15	18	21	25	32	42	...	...	...	3½	3¾	4	4½	5	6
	4	...	...	9	11	12	14	17	21	28	...	...	3	3	3¼	3½	3¾	4½	5
	8	...	6½	7	8	9	11	13	15	...	...	2½	2½	2¾	3	3¼	3½	3¾	...
	16–19.99	5	5½	6	7	8	9	11	13	...	2¼	2¼	2¼	2¼	2½	2½	2¾	3¼	...

AGMA quality number	Normal diametral pitch	Profile tolerance, Pitch diam, in. ¾	1½	3	6	12	25	50	100	200	Total composite tolerance, Pitch diam, in. 1	3	6	12	25	50	100	Lead tolerance, Face width, in. 1 and less	2	3	4	5
8	½	...	...	...	...	...	110	118	123	130												
	1	...	...	...	...	70	75	78	81	85												
	2	...	...	...	46	48	50	52	55	58	..	..	..	80	94	111	135					
	4	...	...	30	32	34	35	37	39	41	..	46	52	58	68	79	93	7	12	17	19	24
	8	...	20	21	22	23	25	26	27	...	35	38	42	46	52	60	70					
	16–19.99	15	15	16	17	18	19	20	21	...	27	30	34	37	44	50	58					
9	½	...	...	...	...	...	80	83	88	90												
	1	...	...	...	...	50	52	56	59	60												
	2	...	...	...	32	33	35	37	39	40	..	..	..	57	66	78	95					
	4	...	...	21	22	23	25	25	27	29	..	33	37	42	48	54	66	6	10	14	16	20
	8	...	14½	15	16	17	17½	18	19	...	..	27	30	33	38	43	50					
	16–19.99	10¾	11	11½	12	12¾	13	14	15	...	19	22	24	27	31	36	42					
10	½	...	...	...	...	...	57	60	62	65												
	1	...	...	...	...	36	38	40	42	44												
	2	...	...	...	23	24	25	26	28	29	..	..	..	40	48	58	69					
	4	...	...	15	16	17	17½	18	19	20	..	23	26	29	34	39	47	5	8	11	13	16
	8	...	10½	11	11½	12	12½	13	14	...	..	19	21	24	26	30	35					
	16–19.99	7¾	8	8½	9	9¼	9½	10	10½	...	14	15	17	19	22	26	30					
11	½	...	...	...	...	...	40	42	46	48												
	1	...	...	...	...	25	27	28	30	31												
	2	...	...	...	17	18	18	19	20	21												
	4	...	...	11	11½	12	13	13½	14	15	..	17	18	21	24	28	34	4	6	9	10	12
	8	...	7½	8	8	8½	9	9½	9¾	...	..	14	15	17	19	22	26					
	16–19.99	5½	5½	6	6¼	6½	7	7¼	7½	...	10	11	12	14	16	18	21					
12	2	...	...	...	12	12½	13	14	14½	15												
	4	...	...	8	8¼	8½	9	9½	10	10½	..	12	13	15	17	20	25	3	5	7	8	10
	8	...	5¼	5½	6	6¼	6½	6¾	7	...	..	10	11	12	13	15	18					
	16–19.99	4	4	4¼	4½	4½	5	5¼	5½	...	7	8	9	10	11	13	16					

1. Values for sizes other than shown can be found through direct interpolation. 2. If total composite tolerance is specified, it should be in lieu of runout, pitch, and profile checks. 3. If runout, pitch, and profile tolerances are specified, they should be in lieu of total composite check. 4. Values shown are average. The gear manufacturer will make every effort to deliver gears that comply with the tolerances shown. Therefore, minor variations from any tolerance that do not affect satisfactory operational use shall not be cause for rejection. 5. Runout tolerance measurement may include the effects of: eccentricity, out of roundness, axial runout, lead variation, profile variation, spacing, and tooth thickness. 6. Tooth-to-tooth spacing tolerance is given for the plane of rotation. If measured in the normal plane, the measured values should be divided by the cosine of the helical angle. 7. Profile tolerance is exclusive of root and tip modification. Values are to be interpreted as maximum total deviation from high point to low point. 8. Lead tolerance is limited to 5 in. face and is measured normal to axis of tooth. Values are to be interpreted as maximum total deviation from high point to low point. 9. Applications requiring high-accuracy gearing necessitate the matching of pinion and gear profiles and pinion and gear leads so that the mismatch in a set does not exceed the tolerance on profile or the tolerance on lead for the applicable quality number. Matched sets can be provided but usually involves extra cost. In such a case, the manufacturer and user must agree on the details of the additional specifications covering how the matching is to be done and checked. 10. Unusual conditions may require that one or more of the individual quality tolerances be of a higher or lower number. In such cases it is possible to designate the quality number for each individual element. This should be done only when it results in a more satisfactory gear.

Table 9. Coarse-pitch Gear Tolerances for AGMA Quality Classes—(*Continued*)

(Tolerances in ten-thousandths of an inch)

AGMA quality number	Normal diametral pitch	Runout tolerance, Pitch diam, in.									Tooth-to-tooth spacing tolerance, Pitch diam, in.									Profile tolerance, Pitch diam, in.									Lead tolerance, Face width, in.				
		¾	1½	3	6	12	25	50	100	200	¾	1½	3	6	12	25	50	100	200	¾	1½	3	6	12	25	50	100	200	1 and less	2	3	4	5
	2	..	...	...	11	12¾	15	18	23	30	...	...	...	2½	2¾	2¾	3¼	3½	4	..	...	...	8½	9	9¼	9¾	10¼	11					
13	4	..	...	6¾	7½	9	10½	12½	15½	20	...	...	2	2	2½	2½	2¾	3	3½	..	...	5¾	6	6	6½	6¾	7	7¼					
	8	..	5	5¼	5¾	6¾	7¾	9¼	11	...	...	1¾	1¾	2	2	2¼	2½	2¾	...	..	3¾	4	4¼	4¼	4½	4¾	5		2½	3½	5	6	7
	16–19.99	5	5	5	5	5½	6½	7¾	9¾	...	1½	1½	1½	1¾	1¾	1¾	2	2¼	...	3	3	3	3¼	3¼	3½	3½	3¾						
	2	..	...	...	7¾	9	10½	13	16	20	...	...	...	1¾	1¾	2	2¼	2½	3	..	...	...	6	6½	6¾	7	7¼	7¾					
14	4	..	...	5	5½	6¼	7½	9	11	14	...	...	1½	1½	1½	1¾	2	2¼	2½	..	...	4	4¼	4¼	4½	4¾	5	5¼	2	3	3½	4	5
	8	..	5	5	5	5	5½	6½	7¾	...	...	1½	1½	1½	1½	1½	1¾	2	...	..	3	3	3	3¼	3¼	3½	3¾						
	16–19.99	5	5	5	5	5	5	5¾	6¾	...	1½	1½	1½	1½	1½	1½	1½	1¾	...	3	3	3	3	3	3	3	3						
	2	..	...	...	5½	6½	7½	9	11½	15	...	...	...	1½	1½	1½	1½	1¾	2	..	...	...	4½	4½	4¾	5	5¼	5½					
15	4	..	...	5	5	5	5½	6½	8	10	...	...	1½	1½	1½	1½	1½	1½	1¾	..	...	3	3	3¼	3¼	3½	3½	3¾	1½	2½	3	3½	4
	8	..	5	5	5	5	5	5	5½	...	...	1½	1½	1½	1½	1½	1½	1½	...	..	3	3	3	3	3	3	3						
	16–19.99	5	5	5	5	5	5	5	5	...	1½	1½	1½	1½	1½	1½	1½	1½	...	3	3	3	3	3	3	3	3						

1. The critical accuracy requirements of quality numbers 13, 14, and 15 require agreement between the manufacturer and user as to method of inspection.
2. Values for sizes other than shown can be found through direct interpolation.
3. Values shown are average. The gear manufacturer will make every effort to deliver gears that comply with the tolerances shown. Therefore, minor variations from any tolerance that do not affect satisfactory operational use shall not be cause for rejection.
4. Runout tolerance measurement may include the effects of: eccentricity, out of roundness, axial runout, lead variation, profile variation, spacing, and tooth thickness.
5. Tooth-to-tooth spacing tolerance is given for the plane of rotation. If measured in the normal plane, the measured values should be divided by the cosine of the helical angle.
6. Profile tolerance is exclusive of root and tip modifications. Values are to be interpreted as maximum total deviation from high point to low point.
7. Lead tolerance is limited to 5 in. face and is measured normal to axis of tooth. Values are to be interpreted as maximum total deviation from high point to low point.
8. Applications requiring high-accuracy gearing necessitate the matching of pinion and gear profiles and pinion and gear leads so that the mismatch in a set does not exceed the tolerance on profile or the tolerance on lead for the applicable quality number. Matched sets can be provided but usually involve extra cost. In such a case, the manufacturer and user must agree on the details of the additional specifications covering how the matching is to be done and checked.

Table 10. Fine Pitch Gear Tolerances for AGMA Quality Classes
(Abstracted from AGMA 390.02, September, 1964)
(For spur, helical, and herringbone gears)

AGMA quality No.	No. of teeth and pitch diameter	Diametral-pitch range	Tooth-to-tooth composite tolerance	Total composite tolerance
5	Up to 20 teeth incl	20–80	0.0037	0.0052
	Over 20 teeth up to 1.999 in.	20–32	0.0027	0.0052
	Over 20 teeth 2 to 3.999 in.	20–24	0.0027	0.0061
	Over 20 teeth 4 in. and over	20–24	0.0027	0.0072
6	Up to 20 teeth incl	20–200	0.0027	0.0037
	Over 20 teeth up to 1.999 in.	20–48	0.0019	0.0037
	Over 20 teeth 2 to 3.999 in.	20–32	0.0019	0.0044
	Over 20 teeth 4 in. and over	20–24	0.0019	0.0052
7	Up to 20 teeth incl	20–200	0.0019	0.0027
	Over 20 teeth up to 1.999 in.	20–100	0.0014	0.0027
	Over 20 teeth 2 to 3.999 in.	20–48	0.0014	0.0032
	Over 20 teeth 4 in. and over	20–40	0.0014	0.0037
8	Up to 20 teeth incl	20–200	0.0014	0.0019
	Over 20 teeth up to 1.999 in.	20–200	0.0010	0.0019
	Over 20 teeth 2 to 3.999 in.	20–100	0.0010	0.0023
	Over 20 teeth 4 in. and over	20–64	0.0010	0.0027
9	Up to 20 teeth incl	20–200	0.0010	0.0014
	Over 20 teeth up to 1.999 in.	20–200	0.0007	0.0014
	Over 20 teeth 2 to 3.999 in.	20–200	0.0007	0.0016
	Over 20 teeth 4 in. and over	20–120	0.0007	0.0019
10	Up to 20 teeth incl	20–200	0.0007	0.0010
	Over 20 teeth up to 1.999 in.	20–200	0.0005	0.0010
	Over 20 teeth 2 to 3.999 in.	20–200	0.0005	0.0012
	Over 20 teeth 4 in. and over	20–200	0.0005	0.0014
11	Up to 20 teeth incl	20–200	0.0005	0.0007
	Over 20 teeth up to 1.999 in.	20–200	0.0004	0.0007
	Over 20 teeth 2 to 3.999 in.	20–200	0.0004	0.0009
	Over 20 teeth 4 in. and over	20–200	0.0004	0.0010
12	Up to 20 teeth incl	20–200	0.0004	0.0005
	Over 20 teeth up to 1.999 in.	20–200	0.0003	0.0005
	Over 20 teeth 2 to 3.999 in.	20–200	0.0003	0.0006
	Over 20 teeth 4 in. and over	20–200	0.0003	0.0007
13	Up to 20 teeth incl	20–200	0.0003	0.0004
	Over 20 teeth up to 1.999 in.	20–200	0.0002	0.0004
	Over 20 teeth 2 to 3.999 in.	20–200	0.0002	0.0004
	Over 20 teeth 4 in. and over	20–200	0.0002	0.0005
14	Up to 20 teeth incl	20–200	0.00019	0.00027
	Over 20 teeth up to 1.999 in.	20–200	0.00014	0.00027
	Over 20 teeth 2 to 3.999 in.	20–200	0.00014	0.00032
	Over 20 teeth 4 in. and over	20–200	0.00014	0.00037
15	Up to 20 teeth incl	20–200	0.00014	0.00019
	Over 20 teeth up to 1.999 in.	20–200	0.00010	0.00019
	Over 20 teeth 2 to 3.999 in.	20–200	0.00010	0.00023
	Over 20 teeth 4 in. and over	20–200	0.00010	0.00027
16	Up to 20 teeth incl	20–200	0.00010	0.00014
	Over 20 teeth up to 1.999 in.	20–200	0.00007	0.00014
	Over 20 teeth 2 to 3.999 in.	20–200	0.00007	0.00016
	Over 20 teeth 4 in. and over	20–200	0.00007	0.00019

Table 11. AGMA Backlash Allowance and Tolerance for Coarse-pitch Gears
(Abstracted from AMGA 390.02)

Center distance, in.	Normal diametral pitches				
	0.5–1.99	2–3.49	3.5–5.99	6–9.99	10–19.99
Up to 5	....	....	....	....	0.005–0.015
Over 5–10	....	....	....	0.010–0.020	0.010–0.020
Over 10–20	....	....	0.020–0.030	0.015–0.025	0.010–0.020
Over 20–30	....	0.030–0.040	0.025–0.030	0.020–0.030	
Over 30–40	0.040–0.060	0.035–0.045	0.030–0.040	0.025–0.035	
Over 40–50	0.050–0.070	0.040–0.055	0.035–0.050	0.030–0.040	
Over 50–80	0.060–0.080	0.045–0.065	0.040–0.060		
Over 80–100	0.070–0.095	0.050–0.080			
Over 100–120	0.080–0.110				

Table 12. AGMA Backlash Allowance and Tolerance for Fine-pitch Gears
(Abstracted from AMGA 390.02)

Backlash designation	Normal diametral pitch range	Tooth thinning to obtain backlash		Resulting approximate backlash (per mesh) normal plane
		Allowance (per gear)	Tolerance (per gear)	
A	20–45	0.002	0–0.002	0.004–0.008
	46–70	0.0015	0–0.002	0.003–0.007
	71–90	0.001	0–0.00175	0.002–0.0055
	91–200	0.00075	0–0.00075	0.0015–0.003
B	20–60	0.001	0–0.001	0.002–0.004
	61–120	0.00075	0–0.00075	0.0015–0.003
	121–200	0.0005	0–0.0005	0.001–0.002
C	20–60	0.0005	0–0.0005	0.001–0.002
	61–120	0.00035	0–0.0004	0.0007–0.0015
	121–200	0.0002	0–0.0003	0.0004–0.001
D	20–60	0.00025	0–0.00025	0.0005–0.001
	61–120	0.0002	0–0.0002	0.0004–0.0008
	121–200	0.0001	0–0.0001	0.0002–0.0004
E	20–60	zero	0–0.00025	0–0.0005
	60–120		0–0.0002	0–0.0004
	121–200		0–0.0001	0–0.0002

Table 13. Comparison of New and Previous Fine-pitch AGMA Quality Classes

Previous fine-pitch system, AGMA 236.04			New fine-pitch system, AGMA 390.02		
AGMA quality No.	Tooth-to-tooth composite error	Total composite error	AGMA quality No.	Tooth-to-tooth composite (error) tolerance	Total composite (error) tolerance
Commercial 1	0.0020	0.0060	5 or 6	0.0027 or 0.0019	0.0052 or 0.0037
Commercial 2	0.0015	0.0040	6 or 7	0.0019 or 0.0014	0.0037 or 0.0027
Commercial 3	0.0010	0.0020	8	0.0010	0.0019
Commercial 4	0.0007	0.0015	9	0.0007	0.0014
Precision 1	0.0004	0.0010	10 or 11	0.0005 or 0.0004	0.0010 or 0.0007
Precision 2	0.0003	0.0005	12	0.0003	0.0005
Precision 3	0.0002	0.00025	13 or 14	0.0002 or 0.00014	0.0004 or 0.00027

Table 14. Values of Form Factor y in Lewis Formula for Spur Gears

No. of teeth	*Full depth, composite 14½ deg	Full depth involute 20 deg	†Stub involute 20 deg	No. of teeth	*Full depth, composite 14½ deg	Full depth involute 20 deg	†Stub involute 20 deg
12	0.210	0.245	0.311	30	0.320	0.358	0.437
14	0.226	0.276	0.339	43	0.346	0.396	0.464
16	0.242	0.295	0.361	60	0.358	0.421	0.484
18	0.261	0.308	0.377	100	0.371	0.446	0.506
20	0.283	0.320	0.393	150	0.377	0.459	0.518
25	0.305	0.339	0.418	Rack	0.390	0.484	0.550

* Use these values also for Brown and Sharpe full-depth teeth.

† Use these values also for Nuttall stub, AGMA stub, and Fellows stub, 4 or 8 pitch. For Fellows stub, 5, 6, and 7 pitch, values are slightly greater; for 9, 10, and 12 pitch, slightly less.

The values of S for various BHN are:

BHN	Cast iron	160	210	245	270	315	335	360	440
Allowable stress, kpsi	14	40	50	60	65	70	77	83	90

Refinement of Lewis' formula is necessary because the worse-load condition is not at the tip owing to multiple-tooth pairs in contact, and the stress concentration at the root fillet is neglected. The modified formula is $W_b = K_r m_p FSY/P_d$, where m_p = contact ratio and K_r = stress concentration factor (K = 1 for precision gears, 0.75 for high commercial grade, and 0.5 for commercial grade).

Dynamic Tooth Strength takes into consideration dynamic forces in a gear train not accounted for by the Lewis formula. This requires the beam strength to be sufficiently large to accommodate an increased transmitted load, termed dynamic load W_d. For safe design, $W_b \geq W_d$; approximate values of dynamic load can be obtained by modifying the transmitted load with an appropriate factor: $W_d = W_t \cdot \overline{DF}$, where $\overline{DF} = (600 + V)/600$ for general commercial-quality gears operating at a velocity less than 3,000 fpm; $DF = (1{,}200 + V)/1{,}200$ for high commercial-quality gears operating at a velocity less than 6,000 fpm; $DF = (250 + V)/150 + 0.25$ for non-metallic gears, 600 to 5,000 fpm, where V = pitch line velocity, fpm.

Buckingham's dynamic equation is an attempt to be more accurate through combination of profile error magnitude, elastic properties, and empirical data, where $W_d = W_t + [0.05V(FC + W_t)]/[0.05V + (FC + W_t)^{1/2}]$ (for spur gears), and $W_d = W_t + [0.05V(FC \cos^2 \psi + W_t) \cos \psi]/[0.05V + (FC \cos^2 \psi + W_t)^{1/2}]$ (for helical gears). The constant C is a deformation factor, values of which can be derived from Buckingham's special equations or taken from Table 15.

Table 15. Values of Deformation Factor C

Materials, pinion and gear	Tooth form	Error in action, in.					
		0.0005	0.001	0.002	0.003	0.004	0.005
Cast iron and cast iron	14½ deg	400	800	1,600	2,400	3,200	4,000
Steel and cast iron	14½ deg	550	1,100	2,200	3,300	4,400	5,500
Steel and steel	14½ deg	800	1,600	3,200	4,800	6,400	8,000
Cast iron and cast iron	20 deg full depth	415	830	1,660	2,490	3,320	4,150
Steel and cast iron	20 deg full depth	570	1,140	2,280	3,420	4,560	5,700
Steel and steel	20 deg full depth	830	1,660	3,320	4,980	6,640	8,300
Cast iron and cast iron	20 deg stub tooth	430	860	1,720	2,580	3,440	4,300
Steel and cast iron	20 deg stub tooth	590	1,180	2,360	3,540	4,720	5,900
Steel and steel	20 deg stub tooth	860	1,720	3,440	5,160	6,880	8,600

Durability. Stresses generated in the surface layers of the teeth by the crushing action of the forces can exceed material limits and result in a failure in the form of pitting, scoring, scuffing, seizing, and plastic deformation. Based upon Hertz contact stresses, Buckingham developed the following durability equations, modified by a contact ratio factor, $W_w = D_pQKFm_p$ (for spur gears), and $W_w = D_pQKFm_p/\cos^2\psi$ (for helical gears), where Q = ratio factor = $2N_G/(N_G + N_p)$, and K = Buckingham's durability factor as shown in Table 16. For safe design, $W_w \geq W_d$.

Other modifications of the strength and durability equations come from kinds of service. See Table 17 for useful service factors.

New AGMA Strength and Durability Ratings. The AGMA Gear Rating committee has developed new strength and durability rating equations suitable for modern gearing and arranged to enable expansion or contraction of governing parameters and details in accordance with available data and needs of the application. The following new AGMA formulas are intended for all sizes of spur, helical, and bevel gears (see Table 18). (Reference should be made to AGMA Standards for details.)

Tooth Strength (bending stress). Stress = $S_t = f$ (load, size, stress distribution) = $(W_tK_o/K_v)(P_d/F)(K_sK_m/J)$, and in terms of allowable bending stress, $S_t \leq S_{at}K_L/K_eK_T$, and the tooth strength power rating is $P_{at} = [(\text{rpm})_pF/126{,}000](JK_v/K_sK_nK_o)(S_{at}d/K_FK_R)^2$.

Table 16. Values of K for Buckingham's Durability Equation

(Abstracted from Buckingham, "Manual of Gear Design," Industrial Press; and Slaymaker, "Mechanical Design and Analysis," Wiley)

Material in pinion	Brinell hardness number	Material in gear	Brinell hardness number	S_c, surface endurance limit, psi	K, 14½ deg	K, 20 deg
Steel	150	Steel	150	50,000	30	41
Steel	200	Steel	150	60,000	43	38
Steel	250	Steel	150	70,000	58	79
Steel	200	Steel	200	70,000	58	79
Steel	250	Steel	200	80,000	76	103
Steel	300	Steel	200	90,000	96	131
Steel	250	Steel	250	90,000	96	131
Steel	300	Steel	250	100,000	119	162
Steel	350	Steel	250	110,000	144	196
Steel	300	Steel	300	110,000	144	196
Steel	350	Steel	300	120,000	171	233
Steel	400	Steel	300	125,000	186	254
Steel	350	Steel	350	130,000	201	275
Steel	400	Steel	350	140,000	233	318
Steel	500	Steel	350	145,000	250	342
Steel	400	Steel	400	150,000	268	366
Steel	500	Steel	400	175,000	364	497
Steel	600	Steel	400	180,000	385	526
Steel	500	Steel	500	190,000	430	588
Steel	600	Steel	600	230,000	630	861
Steel	150	Cast iron	180	50,000	44	60
Steel	200	Cast iron	180	70,000	87	119
Steel	250	Cast iron	180	90,000	144	196
Steel	and higher	Cast iron	180	90,000	144	196
Steel	150	Ph. bronze	100	50,000	46	62
Steel	200	Ph. bronze	100	70,000	91	124
Steel	250	Ph. bronze	100	85,000	135	204
Steel	and higher	Ph. bronze	100	85,000	135	204
Cast iron	180	Cast iron	180	90,000	193	284
Ga Meehanite	....	GA Meehanite	...	80,000	105	144
Steel	....	GA Meehanite	...	80,000	90	123

Table 17. Service Factors for Enclosed Gear Drives
(Abstracted from AGMA 420.03, "Standard Practice for Helical and Herringbone Gear Speed Reducers and Increasers")

Prime mover	Duration of service	Driven machine load classifications: Uniform	Moderate shock	Heavy shock
Electric motor	Occasional ½ hr per day	0.50	0.80	1.25
	Intermittent 3 hr per day	0.80	1.00	1.50
	Up to 10 hr per day	1.00	1.25	1.75
	24 hr per day	1.25	1.50	2.00
Multi-cylinder internal combustion engine	Occasional ½ hr per day	0.80	1.00	1.50
	Intermittent 3 hr per day	1.00	1.25	1.75
	Up to 10 hr per day	1.25	1.50	2.00
	24 hr per day	1.50	1.75	2.25
Single cylinder internal combustion engine	Occasional ½ hr per day	1.00	1.25	1.75
	Intermittent 3 hr per day	1.25	1.50	2.00
	Up to 10 hr per day	1.50	1.75	2.25
	24 hr per day	1.75	2.00	2.50

Table 18. Definitions of Terms

Term	Strength	Durability
Load:		
Transmitted load	W_t	W_t
Dynamic factor	K_v	C_v
Overload factor	K_o	C_o
Size:		
Pinion pitch diameter	...	d
Net face width	F	F
Transverse diametral pitch	P_d	
Size factor	K_s	C_s
Stress distribution:		
Load distribution factor	K_m	C_m
Geometry factor	J	I
Surface condition factor	...	C_f
Stress:		
Calculated stress	s_t	s_c
Allowable stress	s_{at}	s_{ac}
Elastic coefficient	...	C_P
Hardness-ratio factor	...	C_H
Life factor	K_L	C_L
Temperature factor	K_T	C_T
Factor of safety	K_R	C_R

Surface Durability. Stress $= S_c = f$(load, size, stress distribution) $= C_p(W_tC_0/C_v)(C_s/dF)(C_fC_m/I)^{1/2}$, and in terms of allowable surface durability stress, $S_c = S_{ac}(C_LC_H/C_RC_T)$, while the durability power rating is $P_{ac} = [(\text{rpm})_pF/126{,}000](IC_v/C_sC_mC_0)[(S_{ac}d/C_p)C_LH_L/C_TC_R]$.

It is beyond the scope of this introductory treatment to include details concerning the terms used in the above equations. Users should refer to Shigley, "Engineering Design," Chaps. 11 and 12, McGraw-Hill, for a concise treatment and the numerous AGMA Standards for details.

Gear Materials (See Table 19)

Plain carbon steels are most widely used as the most economical; similarly, cast iron is used for large units or intricate body shapes. Heat-treated carbon and alloy steels are used for the more severe load and wear resistant applications. Pinions are usually made harder to equalize wear. Bronze is particularly recommended for worm gears and crossed-helical gears. Stainless steels are limited to special corrosion-resistant environment applications. Aluminum alloys are used for light-duty instrument gears and airborne light-weight requirements. Non-metallic materials are for noise reduction, vibration damping, and economical large quantity production (see also Sec. 6).

Gear Lubricants (See Table 20)

Proper lubrication is important to prevention of premature wear of tooth surfaces. Choice of lubricant is a function of gear load, speed, temperature, and type of lubricating system (see also Secs. 6 and 8).

Table 19. Typical Gear Materials

Material and designation	Tensile strength, psi	Yield strength, psi	Hardness, BHN	Condition
Cast irons:				
ASTM 20	22,000	....	156	As cast
30	31,000	....	201	As cast
60	62,500	....	262	As cast
Plain carbon steels:				
AISI 1020	55,000	30,000	110	Hot-rolled
1020	78,000	66,000	155	Cold-worked
1040	76,000	42,000	150	Hot-rolled
1040	123,000	93,000	350	Cold-worked
1080	112,000	61,000	230	Hot-rolled
1080	189,000	142,000	385	Cold-worked
1117	62,000	34,000	120	Hot-rolled
1117	80,000	68,000	163	Cold-worked
Alloy steels:				
AISI 3140	105,000	90,000	280	Heat-treated
3140	228,000	209,000	450	Heat-treated
4140	145,000	120,000	290	Normalized
4140	215,000	190,000	440	Heat-treated
4820	150,000	125,000	325	Heat-treated
4820	206,000	166,000	415	Heat-treated
6120	125,000	94,000	......	Heat-treated
8620	122,000	98,000	245	Normalized
8620	173,000	142,000	375	Heat-treated
9310	152,000	120,000	350	Heat-treated
9310	180,000	140,000	375	Heat-treated
Stainless steels:				
AISI 303	90,000	35,000	160	Annealed
303	110,000	75,000	240	Cold-worked
416	75,000	40,000	155	Annealed
416	160,000	140,000	350	Heat-treated
Bronzes:				
Aluminum bronze ASTM-B139	105,000	60,000	B100*	
Phosphor bronze ASTM-B1397	60,000	45,000	B70*	
Silicon bronze ASTM-B99	58,000	25,000	B100*	
Aluminum alloys:				
2024-T4	68,000	47,000	120	Heat-treated ½ hard
7075-T6	83,000	73,000	150	Heat-treated ¾ hard
Non-metallics:				
Phenolic laminate				
NEMA, Grade C....................	11,000	....	M-103*	
NEMA, Grade L....................	14,000	....	M-105*	
Nylon				
ASTM-6	8,700	6,000	M-100*	2.5% moisture
ASTM-66	11,000	8,500	M-108*	2.5% moisture

* Rockwell.

Table 20. Typical Gear Lubricants

Lubricant type	Military specification	Useful temp range (deg F)	Commercial source and specification (a partial listing)		Remarks and applications
			Source	Identification	
Oils:					
Petroleum	MIL-L-644B	−10 to 250	Esso Standard Oil Co.	#4035 or Unvis P-48	Good general-purpose lubricant for all quality gears having a narrow range of operating temperature
			Franklin Oil and Gas Co.	L-499B	
			Royal Lubricants Co.	Royco 380	
			Texaco	1692 Low Temp. Oil	
Diester	MIL-L-6085A	−67 to 350	Anderson Oil Co.	Windsor Lube I-245X	General-purpose, low-starting torque, and stable over a wide temperature range. Particularly suited for precision instrument gears and small machinery gears
			Eclipse Pioneer Div., Bendix	Pioneer P-10	
			Shell Oil Co.	AeroShell Fluid 12	
			E. F. Houghton and Co.	Cosmolubric 270	
Diester	MIL-L-7808C	−67 to 400	Sinclair Refining Co.	Aircraft Turbo S Oil	Suitable for oil spay or mist system at high temperature. Particularly suitable for high-speed power gears
			Socony Mobil Oil Co.	Avrex S Turbo 251	
			Bray Oil Co.	Brayco 880	
			Esso Standard Oil Co.	Esso Turbine Oil 15	
Silicone		−75 to 350	Dow-Corning Corp.	DC200	Rated for low-starting torque and lightly loaded instrument gears
Silicone		−100 to 600	General Electric Co.	Versilube 81644	Best load carrier of silicone oils with widest temperature range. Applicable to power gears requiring wide temperature ranges
Greases:					
Diester oil-lithium soap	MIL-G-7421A	−100 to 200	Royal Lubricants Co.	Royco 21	For moderately loaded gears requiring starting torques at low temperatures
			Texaco	Low Temp. No. 1888	
Diester oil-lithium soap	MIL-G-3278A	−67 to 250	Esso Standard Oil Co.	Beacon 325	General-purpose light grease for precision instrument gears, and generally lightly loaded gears
			Shell Oil Co.	AeroShell Grease 11	
			Sinclair Refining Co.	Sinclair 3278 Grease	
			Bray Oil Co.	Braycote 678	
Petroleum oil-sodium soap	MIL-L-3545	−20 to 300	Esso Standard Oil Co.	Andok 260	A high-temperature lubricant for high speed and high loads
			Standard Oil Co. of Calif.	RPM Aviation Grease #2	
Mineral oil-sodium soap	....	−25 to 250	Esso Standard Oil Co.	Andok C	Stiff grease that channels readily. Suitable for high speeds and highly loaded gears

FLUID FILM BEARINGS

BY

Dudley D. Fuller

REFERENCES: "General Conference on Lubrication and Lubricants," ASME, 1957. Shaw and Macks, "Analysis and Lubrication of Bearings," McGraw-Hill. Forbes, Pope, and Everitt, "Lubrication of Industrial and Marine Machinery," Wiley. Fuller, "Theory and Practice of Lubrication for Engineers," Wiley.

Plain bearings, according to their function, may be

Journal bearings, cylindrical in shape, carrying a rotating shaft.

Thrust bearings, the function of which is to prevent lengthwise motion of a rotating shaft.

Guide bearings, to guide a machine element in its lengthwise motion, usually without rotation of the element.

In exceptional cases of design, or with a complete **failure of lubrication,** a bearing may run dry. The coefficient of friction is then between 0.25 and 0.40, depending on the materials of the rubbing surfaces. With the **bearing barely greasy,** or when the bearing is well lubricated but the speed of rotation is very slow, boundary lubrication takes place. The coefficient of friction may vary from 0.08 to 0.14. This condition occurs also in any bearing when the shaft is starting from rest if the bearing is not equipped with an oil lift.

Semifluid, or **mixed,** lubrication exists between the journal and bearing when the conditions are not such as to form a load-carrying fluid film and thus separate the surfaces. Semifluid lubrication takes place at comparatively low speed, with intermittent or oscillating motion, heavy load, insufficient oil supply to the bearing (wick or waste lubrication, drop-feed lubrication). Semifluid lubrication may also exist in thrust bearings with fixed parallel-thrust collars, in guide bearings of machine tools, in bearings with copious lubrication where the shaft is bent or the bearing is misaligned, or where the bearing surface is interrupted by improperly arranged oil grooves. The coefficient of friction in such bearings may range from 0.02 to 0.08 (Fuller, Mixed Friction Conditions in Lubrication, *Lubrication Eng.* 1954).

Fluid or **complete lubrication,** when the rubbing surfaces are completely separated by a fluid film, provides the lowest friction losses and prevents wear. A certain amount of oil must be fed to the oil film in order to compensate for end leakage and maintain its carrying capacity. Pressure lubrication, from a pump or gravity tank, is used, or automatic lubricating devices are provided in self-contained bearings (oil rings or oil disks), or the bearing is submerged in an oil bath (thrust bearings for vertical shafts).

PLAIN CYLINDRICAL JOURNAL BEARINGS

Notation

R = radius of bearing, in.
r = radius of journal, in.
$mr = R - r$ = radial clearance, in.
W = load on a bearing, lb
μ = viscosity, lb-sec per sq in.
Z = viscosity, centipoises
β = angle between load and entering edge of oil film
η = coefficient for side leakage of oil
ν = kinematic viscosity, in.^{2} per sec
Λ = compressibility number (gas bearings)
R_e = Reynolds number, $\frac{umr}{\nu}$
P_a = ambient pressure, psia
$P = W/ld$ = unit pressure, psi
N = rpm of a shaft

m = clearance ratio (diametral clearance/diameter)
F = friction force, lb
A = operating characteristic of a plain cylindrical bearing (see below)
P' = alternate operating characteristic of a plain cylindrical bearing
h_0 = min film thickness
ϵ = eccentricity ratio or ratio of eccentricity to radial clearance
f = coefficient of friction
f' = friction factor
l = length of bearing, in.
$d = 2r$ = diam of journal, in.
K_f = friction factor of a plain cylindrical bearing (see p. 8–160)
t_w = temp of bearing wall, deg F
t_0 = temp of air, deg F
t_1 = temp of oil film, deg F
u = surface speed, in./sec
ω = angular velocity, radians/sec
ρ = mass density, lb-sec²/in.⁴

Fluid lubrication in plain cylindrical bearings depends on the viscosity of the lubricant and on its adhesion to the surfaces of the journal and the bearing. The radial clearance provided in the bearing forms, automatically, a wedge-shaped film between the journal and the bearing. The oil is entrained by the journal into the film. A hydrodynamic pressure is created in the film, sufficient to float the journal and carry the load applied to it.

The **minimum film thickness** h_0 determines the closest approach of the journal and bearing surfaces with complete lubrication (Fig. 1). The allowable closest approach depends on the degree of finish of these surfaces and on the rigidity of the journal and bearing structures. In practice, $h_0 = 0.00075$ in. is common in electric motors and generators of medium speed, with steel shafts in babbitted bearings; $h_0 = 0.003$ to 0.005 in. for large steel shafts running at high speed in babbitted bearings (turbogenerators, fans), with pressure oil-supply for lubrication; $h_0 = 0.0001$ to 0.0002 in. in automotive and aviation engines, with very fine finish of the surfaces.

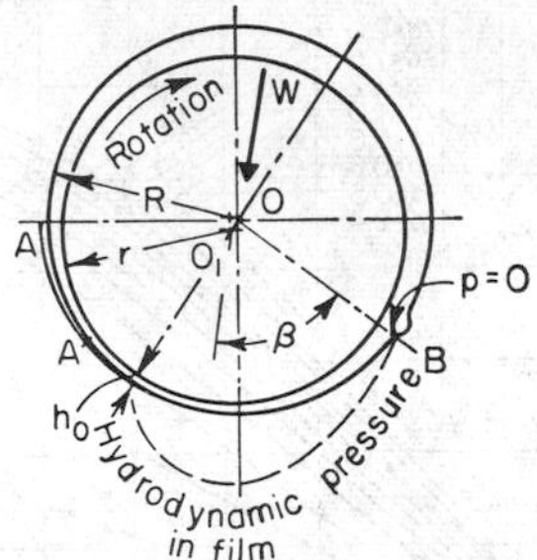

FIG. 1. Journal bearing with perfect lubrication.

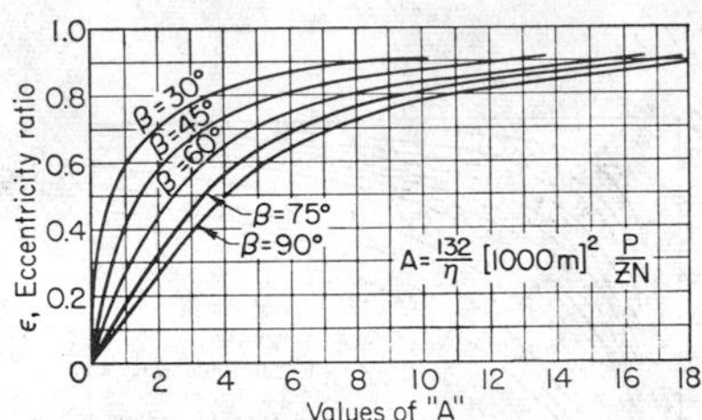

FIG. 2. Eccentricity ratio for a plain cylindrical journal.

Figure 2 gives the relationship between ϵ and the load-carrying coefficient A for a plain cylindrical journal. The operating characteristic of the bearing is

$$A = \frac{132}{\eta}(1{,}000m)^2\frac{P}{ZN}$$

In Fig. 1, β is the angle between the direction of the load W and the entering edge of the load-carrying oil film, in degrees. The entering edge is at the place where the hydrodynamic pressure is equal or nearly equal to the atmospheric pressure and may be at the location of the oil-distributing groove B, or at the end of a machined recess pocket as at AA. For **complete bearings,** *i.e.*, when the inner surface of the bearing is not interrupted by grooves, β may be taken as 90 deg. For a 120 deg bearing with a central load, β may be taken as 60 deg.

The coefficient η corrects for side leakage. There is a loss of load-carrying capacity caused by the drop in the hydrodynamic gage pressure p in the oil film from the midsection of the bearing toward its ends; $p = 0$ at the ends. The value of η depends on the length to diameter ratio l/d and ϵ, the eccentricity ratio. Values of η are given in Fig. 3.

EXAMPLE 1. A generator bearing, 6 in. diam by 9 in. long, carries a vertical downward load of 8,650 lb; $N = 720$ rpm. The diametral clearance of the bearing is 0.012 in.; the bearing is split on its horizontal diameter, and the lower half is relieved 40 deg down on each side, for oil distribution along journal; the bearing arc is therefore 100 deg; with the load vertical, $\beta = 50$ deg; bearing temperature 160 F. The absolute viscosity of the oil in the film is 12 centipoises (medium turbine oil). $P = W/ld = 160$ psi; $\mu = 12 \times 1.45 \times 10^{-7} = 17.4 \times 10^{-7}$ lb-sec per sq in. The solution is one of trial and error. By using Fig. 3 in conjunction with Fig. 2, only a few trials are necessary to obtain the answer. As a first trial assume $\epsilon = 0.85$. For an l/d ratio of 1.5 in Fig. 3, η, the end-leakage factor, will be 0.77. Compute A using this value of η. $m = 0.012/6 = 0.002$.

$$A = \frac{132}{0.77}\left(2\right)^2 \frac{160}{12 \times 720} = 12.7$$

Enter Fig. 2 with this value of A and at $\beta = 50$ deg, and find that $\epsilon = 0.9$. This value is larger than the initial assumption for ϵ. As a second trial, $\epsilon = 0.88$. Then $\eta = 0.8$, $A = 12.2$, and $\epsilon = 0.89$. This is a sufficiently close check. The minimum film thickness is $h_0 = mr(1 - \epsilon) = 0.002 \times 3 \times 0.12 = 0.0007$ in.

For severe operating conditions the value of A may exceed 18, the limit of Fig. 2. For complete journal bearings under extreme operating conditions, Fig. 4 should be used. The ordinate is P'. The curves are drawn for various values of l/d instead of values of β as in Fig. 2. Values of ϵ may thus be obtained directly (Dennison, Film-lubrication Theory and Engine-bearing Design, *Trans. ASME*, **58,** 1936).

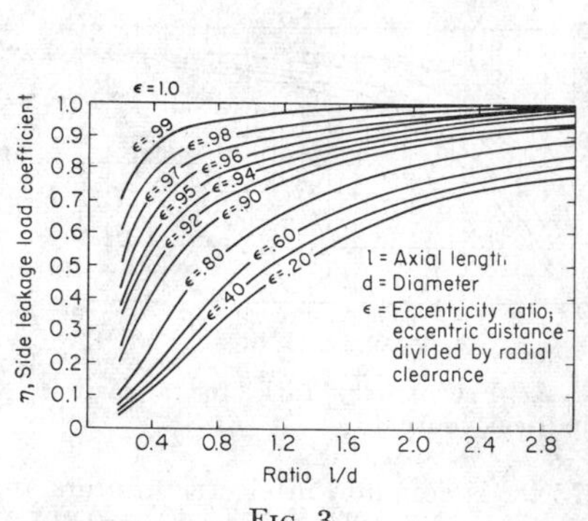

FIG. 3

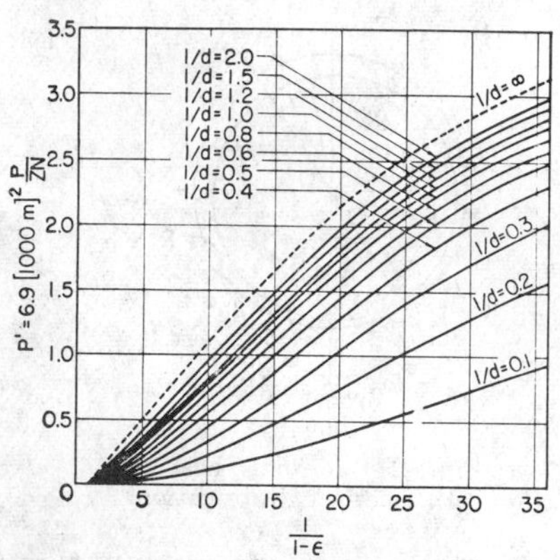

FIG. 4. Load-carrying parameter in terms of eccentricity.

EXAMPLE 2. A 360 deg journal bearing $2\frac{1}{2}$ in. diam and $3\frac{7}{8}$ in. long carries a steady load of 3,875 lb. Speed $N = 500$ rpm; diametral clearance, 0.0064 in.; average viscosity of the oil in the film, 23.4 centipoises (SAE 20 light motor oil at 105 F). $P = 3875/(2.5 \times 3.875) = 400$ psi. Value of $m = 0.0064/2.5 = 0.00256$. Value of $l/d = 1.55$. First, attempt to use Figs. 2 and 3 in this solution. Assume eccentricity ratio ϵ is 0.9. Then, in Fig. 3, with $l/d = 1.55$, value of η is determined as 0.8. A is calculated as 37. This is completely off scale in Fig. 2. Consider instead Fig. 4. Value of P' is computed as

$$P' = 6.9\left(2.56\right)^2 \frac{400}{23.4 \times 500} = 1.54$$

In Fig. 4, enter the curves with $P' = 1.54$, and move left to intersect the curve for $l/d = 1.5$. Drop downward to read a value for $1/(1 - \epsilon)$ of 16. Then $1/16 = 1 - \epsilon$, or the eccentricity ratio $\epsilon = 15/16$, or 0.94. The minimum film thickness, as in Example 1 $= h_0 = mr(1 - \epsilon)$, or

$$h_0 = 0.00256 \times 1.25\ (1 - 0.94) = 0.0002 \text{ in.}$$

Allowable mean bearing pressures in bearings with fluid film lubrication are given in Table 1. If the load maintains the same magnitude and direction when the journal is at rest (heavily loaded shafts, heavy gears), the mean bearing pressure should be somewhat less than when bearings are loaded only when running.

Table 1. Current Practice in Mean Bearing Pressures

Type of bearing	Permissible pressure, psi, of projected area	Type of bearing	Permissible pressure, psi, of projected area
Diesel engines, main bearings	800–1,500	Automotive gasoline engines, main bearings	500–1,000
Crankpin	1,000–2,000	Crankpin	1,500–2,500
Wrist pin	1,800–2,000	Air compressors, main bearings	120– 240
Electric motor bearings	100– 200	Crankpin	240– 400
Marine Diesel engines, main bearings	400– 600	Crosshead pin	400– 800
Crankpin	1,000–1,400	Aircraft engine crankpin	700–2,000
Marine line-shaft bearings	25– 35	Centrifugal pumps	80– 100
Steam engines, main bearings	150– 500	Generators, low or medium speed	90– 140
Crankpin	800–1,500	Roll-neck bearings	1,500–2,500
Crosshead pin	1,000–1,800	Locomotive crankpins	1,500–1,900
Flywheel bearings	200– 250	Railway-car axle bearings	300– 350
Marine steam engine, main bearings	275– 500	Miscellaneous ordinary bearings	80– 150
Crankpin	400– 600	Light line shaft	15– 25
Steam turbines and reduction gears	100– 220	Heavy line shaft	100– 150

For internal-combustion-engine bearing design, Etchells and Underwood (*Machine Design*, Sept. 1942) list the following maximum design pressures for bearing alloys, pounds per square inch of projected area. Lead-base babbitt (75 to 85 percent lead, 4 to 10 percent tin, 9 to 15 percent antimony) 600 to 800; tin-base babbitt (0.35 to 0.6 percent lead, 86 to 90 percent tin, 4 to 9 percent antimony, 4 to 6 percent copper) 800 to 1,000; cadmium-base alloy (0.4 to 0.75 percent copper, 97 percent cadmium, 1 to 1.5 percent nickel, 0.5 to 1.0 percent silver) 1,200 to 1,500; copper-lead alloy (45 percent lead, 55 percent copper) 2,000 to 3,000; copper-lead (25 percent lead, 3 percent tin, 72 percent copper) 3,000 to 4,000; silver (0.5 to 1.0 percent lead on surface, 99 percent silver) 5,000 up. The above pressures are based on fatigue life of 500 hr at 300 F bearing temperature, and a bearing metal thickness 0.01 to 0.015 in. for lead, tin, and cadmium base metals and 0.025 in. for copper, lead, and silver. At lower temperatures the life will be greatly extended.

Length-diameter ratios are usually chosen between $l/d = 1$ and $l/d = 2$, although many engine bearings are designed with $l/d = 0.5$, or even less. In shorter bearings, the carrying capacity of the oil film is greatly impaired by the effect of side leakage. Longer bearings are used to restrain the shaft from vibration, as in line shafts, or to position the shaft accurately, as in machine tools. In power machines, the tendency is toward shorter bearings. Typical values are as follows: turbogenerators, 0.8 to 1.5; gasoline and Diesel engines for main and crankpin bearings, 0.4 to 1.0, with most values between 0.5 and 0.8; generators and motors, 1.5 to 2.0; ordinary shafting, heavy, with fixed bearings, 2 to 3; light, with self-aligning bearings, 3 to 4; machine tool bearings, 2 to 4; railroad journal bearings, 1.2 to 1.8.

For the **clearance between journal and bearing** see Fits, p. 8–61. Medium fits may be used for journals running at speeds under 600 rpm, and free fits for speeds over 600 rpm. Kingsbury suggests for these journals a diametral clearance $= 0.002 + 0.001d$ in. In journals running at high speed, diametral clearance $= 0.002d$ should be used in order to lower the friction losses in the bearing. The most satisfactory clearance should, of course, be based on a complete bearing analysis which includes both load-carrying capacity and heat generation due to friction. For example, a bearing designed to run at the extremely high speed of 50,000 rpm uses a diametral clearance of 0.0025 in. for a journal 0.8 in. in diameter.

For high-speed internal-combustion-engine bearings using forced-feed lubrication, medium fits are used. Federal-Mogul recommends the following diametral clearances in inches per inch of shaft diameter for insert-type bearings. Tin-base and high-lead babbitts, 0.0005; cadmium-silver-copper, 0.0008; copper-lead, 0.001.

The dependence of the **coefficient of friction** for journal bearings on the bearing clearance, lubricant viscosity, rotational speed, and loading pressure, as reported by McKee and others, is shown in Fig. 11, p. 3–44. A plot of the coefficient of friction against the parameter ZN/P is a convenient method for showing this relationship. Z is the viscosity in centipoises, N is rpm, P is the mean pressure on the bearing due to the load, pounds per square inch of projected area, and m is the clearance ratio. Values of ZN/P greater than about 30 indicate fluid-film conditions in the bearings. If the viscosity of the lubricant becomes lower or if there is a reduction in rotational speed or an increase in load, the value of ZN/P will become smaller until the coefficient of friction reaches a minimum value. Any further reduction in ZN/P will produce breakdown of the oil film, marking the transition from fluid-film lubrication with complete separation of the moving surfaces to semifluid or mixed lubrication, where there is partial contact. As soon as semifluid conditions are initiated, there will be a sharp increase in the coefficient of friction. The critical value of ZN/P, where this transition takes place, will be lowest for a rigid bearing and shaft with finely finished surfaces.

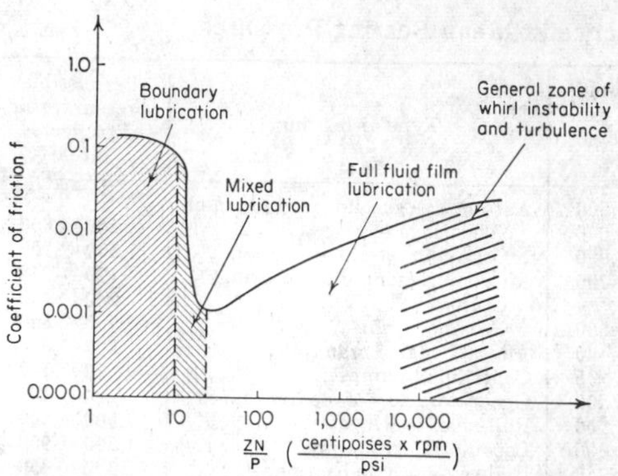

Fig. 5. Various zones of possible lubrication for a journal bearing.

Figure 5 shows a generalization of the relationship between the coefficient of friction for a journal bearing and the parameter ZN/P, indicating the various possible lubrication regimes that may be expected. For optimum design, a value of ZN/P somewhere between 30 and 300 would be recommended, but, in any case, the determination of minimum film thickness h_0 should be the deciding parameter. For extremely large values of ZN/P, whirl instability may be developed or a condition of turbulence may be established in the fluid film.

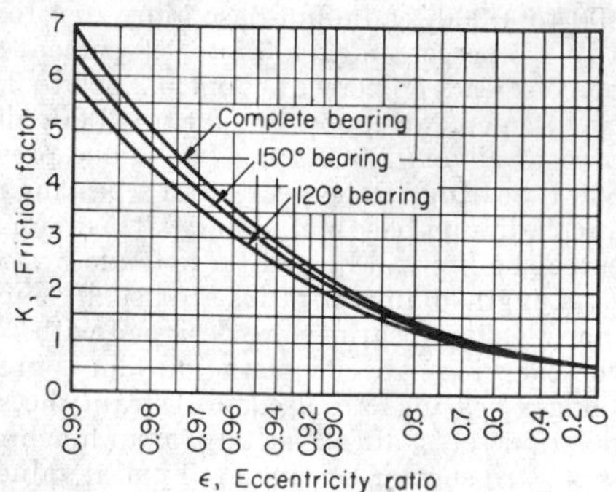

Fig. 6. Variation of the coefficient of friction of a bearing with the eccentricity ratio.

The friction force in plain journal bearings may be estimated by the use of the expression $F = K_f \mu Nrl/m$, where μ is in lb-sec per sq in. units. The value of K_f depends upon the magnitude of ϵ and the type of bearing. Figure 6 shows values of K_f for a complete bearing, a 150 deg partial bearing, and a 120 deg partial bearing, assuming that the clearance space is at all times filled with lubricant.

Example 3. As an illustration of the use of Fig. 6, determine the friction force in the bearing of Example 2. This is a complete journal bearing 2½ in. diam by 3⅞ in. The value of ϵ was determined as 0.94. From Fig. 6 $K_f = 2.8$. Then

$$F = \frac{2.8 \times 23.4 \times 1.45 \times 10^{-7} \times 500 \times 1.25 \times 3.875}{0.00256} = 8.97 \text{ lb}$$

The coefficient of friction $F/W = 8.97/3875 = 0.00231$. The mechanical loss in the bearing is $FV/33{,}000$ hp, where V is the peripheral velocity of the journal, fpm.

$$\text{Friction hp} = (8.97 \times 500 \times \pi \times 2.5)/(33{,}000 \times 12) = 0.089 \text{ hp}$$

Turbulence in the fluid film of a journal bearing will increase the friction loss. Figure 7 (Smith and Fuller, Journal Bearing Operation at Super-laminar Speeds, *Trans. ASME*, **78,** 1956) shows test results for such bearings, expressed in terms of a Reynolds number for the fluid film, $R_e = umr/\nu$. Laminar conditions hold up to a R_e of about 1,000. Friction may be calculated for laminar flow by using Fig. 6 or the first branch of the curve in Fig. 7, where $f' = 2/R_e$. The values from Fig. 7 may be converted to friction torque T by the use of the expression $T = f'\pi\rho U^2r^2l$, where ρ is the mass density of the lubricant, lb-sec²/in.⁴. From R_e of 1,000 to about 1,600, there is a transition zone, and at R_e of 1,600, fully turbulent flow may be expected. Values of f' are then obtained from $f' = 0.078/R_e^{0.43}$.

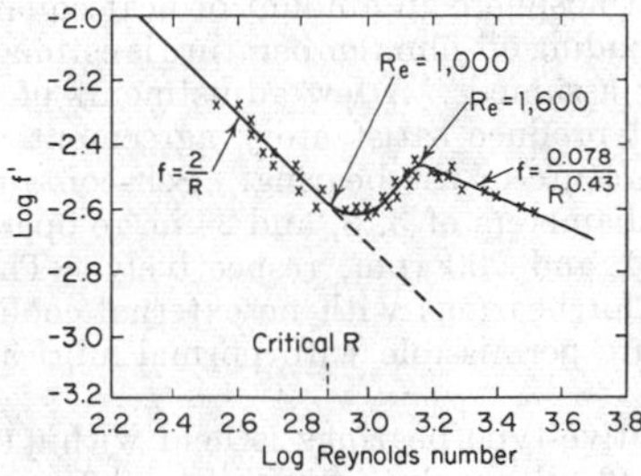

FIG. 7. Friction factor f' as a function of Reynolds number for an unloaded journal bearing with $l/d = 1$. (*Smith and Fuller.*)

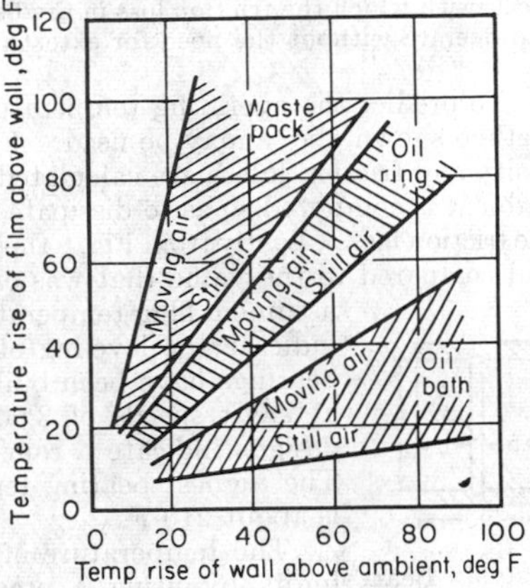

FIG. 8. Temperature rise of the film.

EXAMPLE 4. A journal bearing is 4.5 in. diameter by 4.5 in. long. Speed 22,000 rpm. $mr = 0.002$ in. Viscosity μ, 1 centipoise (water) $= 1.45 \times 10^{-7}$ lb-sec/in.²; mass density $\rho = 62.4/1{,}728 \times 386 = 9.35 \times 10^{-5}$ lb-sec²/in.⁴; $\nu = \mu/\rho = 1.45 \times 10^{-7}/9.35 \times 10^{-5} = 0.155 \times 10^{-2}$ in.²/sec; $U = 22{,}000 \times 2\pi \times 2.25/60 = 5{,}180$ in./sec; $R_e = 5{,}180 \times 0.002/0.155 \times 10^{-2} = 6{,}680$. This would indicate turbulence in the film. Value of f' is then $0.078/6{,}680^{0.43} = 0.078/44.2 = 1.765 \times 10^{-3}$. Friction torque $T = 1.765 \times 10^{-3} \times \pi \times 9.35 \times 10^{-5} \times 5{,}180^2 \times 2.25^2 \times 4.5$, $T = 317.5$ in. lbs. Friction horsepower $= 2\pi TN/12 \times 33{,}000 = 2\pi \times 317.5 \times 22{,}000/12 \times 33{,}000$, FHP = 111.

In self-contained bearings (electric motor, line shaft, etc.) without external oil or water cooling, the **heat dissipation** is equal to the heat generated by friction in the bearing.

The heat dissipated from the outside bearing wall to the surrounding air, according to Karelitz (*Trans. ASME*, **52,** 1930), is $L = 2.2S(t_w - t_0)$ Btu per hr for *quiet air*, where S is the surface area of the bearing wall, sq ft, and t_w and t_0 are the temperatures of the wall and ambient air, respectively, deg F. With *moving air* having a velocity of 500 fpm, the heat dissipation is $L = 6.5S(t_w - t_0)$. The surface area S = (10 to 15) $dl/144$ for pillow blocks carrying bushings, and S = (18 to 25) $dl/144$ for larger bearing pedestals carrying cast-iron or steel bearing shells.

The temperature of the oil film will be higher than the temperature of the bearing wall. Typical ranges of values according to Karelitz (*Trans. ASME*, **64,** 1942), Pearce (*Trans. ASME*, **62,** 1940), and Needs (*Trans. ASME*, **68,** 1948) for self-contained bearings with oil-bath, oil ring, and wastepacked lubrication are shown in Fig. 8.

EXAMPLE 5. The frictional loss for the generator bearing of Example 1, computed by the method outlined in Example 3 is 0.925 hp with $\epsilon = 0.88$, $K_f = 1.6$, and $F = 27$ lb. Operating in moving air the heat dissipated by the bearing housing will be $L = 6.5S(t_w - t_0)$. Since this is a self-contained bearing, the heat dissipated is also equal to the heat generated by friction in the oil film, or $L = 0.925 \times 2{,}545 = 2{,}355$ Btu per hr. With $S = 25 \times 6 \times 9/144 = 9.4$ sq ft, $t_w = t_0 = 2{,}355/6.5 \times 9.4 = 38.5$ F. This is the temperature rise of the bearing wall above the ambient room temperature. For an 80 F room, the wall temperature of the bearing would be about 118 F. In Fig. 8 an oil-ring bearing in moving air with a temperature rise of wall over ambient of 38 F should have a film temperature 50 F higher than that of the wall. The film temperature on the basis of Fig. 8 will then be 80 + 38 + 50, or 168 F. This is close enough to the value of the film temperature of 160 F from Example 1, with which the friction loss in the bearing was computed, to indicate that this bearing can operate without the need for external cooling.

To predict the operating temperature of a self-contained bearing the cut-and-try method shown above may be used. First, an oil-film temperature is assumed. Viscosity and friction losses are calculated. Then the temperature rise of the wall over ambient is computed so as to dissipate to the atmosphere an amount of heat equal to the friction loss. Lastly from Fig. 8 the corresponding oil-film temperature is estimated and compared to the value that was originally assumed. A few adjustments of the assumed film temperature will produce satisfactory agreement and indicate the leveling off temperature of the bearing. Self-contained bearings have been built with diameters of 3, 8, and 24 in. to operate at shaft speeds of 3,600, 1,000, and 200 rpm, respectively. These designs indicate a rough limit for bearings with no external cooling. The highest bearing temperature permissible with normal lubricants is about 210 F.

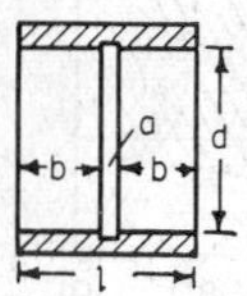

FIG. 9. Bearing with central circumferential groove.

The temperature of automotive-type bearings is held within safe limits by using a **pressure-feed oil supply.** Sufficient lubricant is forced through the bearing to act as a coolant and prevent overheating. One widely used practice is to place a circumferential groove at the center of the bearing to which the oil supply is fed. This is effective as far as cooling is concerned but has the disadvantage of interrupting the active length of the bearing and lowering its l/d ratio (see Fig. 9). The axial flow through the bearing, in cubic inches per second, one side only, is given by

$$Q_1 = \frac{\Delta P m^3 r^4 \pi}{6\mu b}\left(1 + \frac{3}{2}\epsilon^2\right)$$

where b is the effective axial length of the half bearing and ΔP is the difference between the oil pressure in the circumferential groove and the pressure at the ends of the bearing. The total flow will be twice this quantity. The value of the last term in this equation will vary between 1.0 for a concentric shaft and bearing indicated by $\epsilon = 0$ to a value of 2.5 for the extreme case of the shaft touching the bearing wall, indicated when $\epsilon = 1$. Most of the heat caused by friction in the bearing is carried away by the circulating oil. Permissible temperature rises for this type bearing may range from 15 to 50 F. In extreme cases a rise of 100 F can be tolerated for high-strength bearing materials. The lower values of temperature rise usually indicate needlessly large oil flow. Such a condition will result in an excessive friction loss in the bearing.

EXAMPLE 6. The bearing of Examples 2 and 3 is lubricated by a circumferential groove with an oil-supply pressure of 30 psi and, as before, $\epsilon = 0.94$, $m = 0.0026$, and $\mu = 23.4 \times 1.45 \times 10^{-7}$ lb-sec per sq in. Length b is about 1.93 in.

$$Q_1 \text{ flow out one side} = \frac{30 \times 0.0026^3 \times 1.25^4 \times \pi}{6 \times 23.4 \times 1.45 \times 10^{-7} \times 1.93}[1 + \tfrac{3}{2}(0.94)^2]$$
$$= 0.240 \text{ cu in. per sec}$$

Total flow (two sides) = 0.48 cu in. per sec = 53 lb per hr for sp gr = 0.85. The friction loss from Example 3 = 0.089 hp = 226 Btu per hr. With a specific heat of 0.5 Btu per lb deg F, and assuming that all the friction energy is given up to the oil in the form of heat, the temperature rise $\Delta t = 226/0.5 \times 53 = 8.5$ F.

A definite **minimum rate of oil feed** is required to maintain a fluid film in journal bearings. This makes no allowance for the additional flow that may be needed to cool the bearings. However, many industrial bearings run at relatively low speeds with light loads and, as a consequence, additional oil flow to provide cooling is not necessary. But if a fluid film is desired, a definite minimum amount of lubricant is required. If the volume of lubricant fed to the bearing is less than this minimum requirement, there will not be a complete fluid film in the bearing. Friction will rise, wear will become greater, and the satisfactory service life of such a bearing will be reduced. This minimum lubricant supply can be evaluated by using the equation

$$Q_M = K_M urml$$

where Q_M is in drops per min; K_M is approximately 2.2; u is the surface velocity of the shaft, in. per min; r, m, and l as before.

EXAMPLE 7. The minimum feed rate for a journal bearing 2⅛ in. diam by 2⅛ in. long will be determined. Diametral clearance is 0.0045 in.; speed, 1,230 rpm; load, 40 psi based on projected area. $u = 1230 \times \pi \times 2.125 = 10{,}220$ in. per min, $r = 1.062$ in., $m = 0.0045/2.125 = 0.00212$, $l = 2.125$ in. Substituting,

$$Q_M = 2.2 \times 10{,}220 \times 1.062 \times 0.00212 \times 2.125$$
$$= 108 \text{ drops per min}$$

This would be equivalent to about 0.28 cu in. per min. (Fuller and Sternlicht, Preliminary Investigation of Minimum Lubricant Requirements of Journal Bearings, *Trans. ASME*, **78,** 1956.)

Many bearings are supplied with oil at low rates of feed by **felts, wicks,** and **drop-feed oilers.** Wicks can supply substantial rates of feed if they are properly designed. The two basic types of wick feed are siphon wicks, as shown in Fig. 10, and bottom wicks, as shown in Fig. 11. Data on oil delivery for these wicks are shown in Figs. 12 and 13. The data, from the American Felt Co., are for SAE F1 felts, based on a cross-sectional area of 0.1 sq in. The flow rate is indicated in drops per minute.

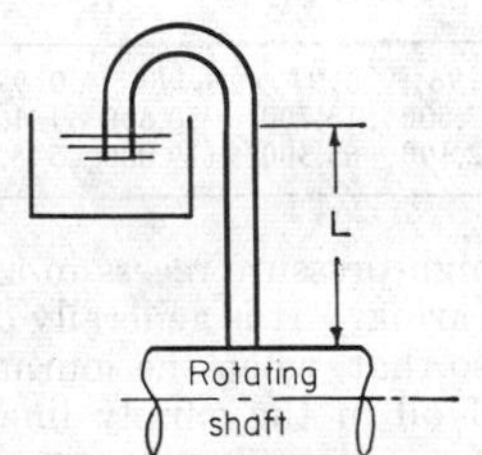

FIG. 10. Siphon wick.

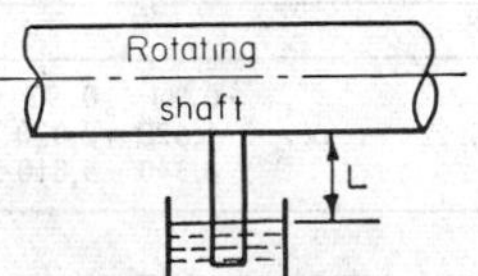

FIG. 11. Bottom wick.

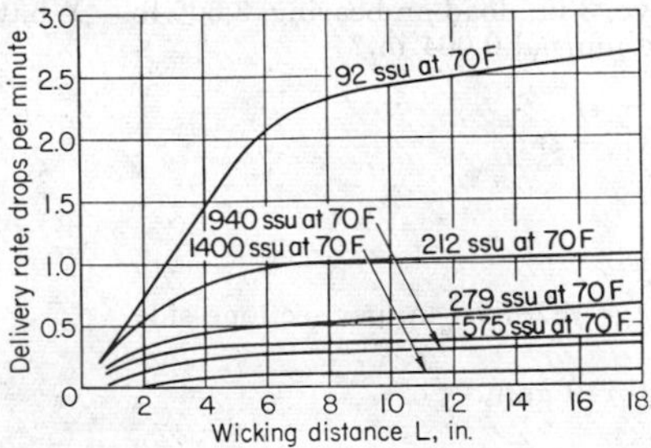

FIG. 12. Oil delivery with siphon wick (Fig. 10).

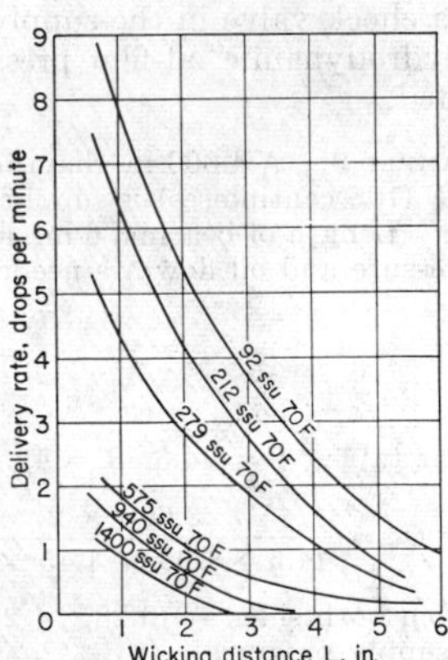

FIG. 13. Oil delivery with bottom wick (Fig. 11).

EXAMPLE 8. If it is desired to deliver 12.5 drops per min to a journal bearing and if the viscosity of the oil is 212 sec Saybolt Universal at 70 F, and if L, Fig. 10, is 5 in., what size of round wick would be required? From Fig. 12, for the stated conditions the delivery rate would be 0.9 drops per min for an area of 0.1 sq in. If 12.5 drops per min is needed, this would mean an area of 12.5 divided by 0.9 and multiplied by 0.1, or 1.4 sq in. For a round wick this would mean a diameter of 1⅜ in.

If a **bottom wick** is considered with $L = 4$ in., Fig. 11, then in Fig. 13 the delivery rate using the same oil would be 1.6 drops per min; and if 12.5 drops per min is required, the area would be 12.5 divided by 1.6 and multiplied by 0.1 or 0.78 sq in. This would mean a bottom wick of 1 in. diam if it is round.

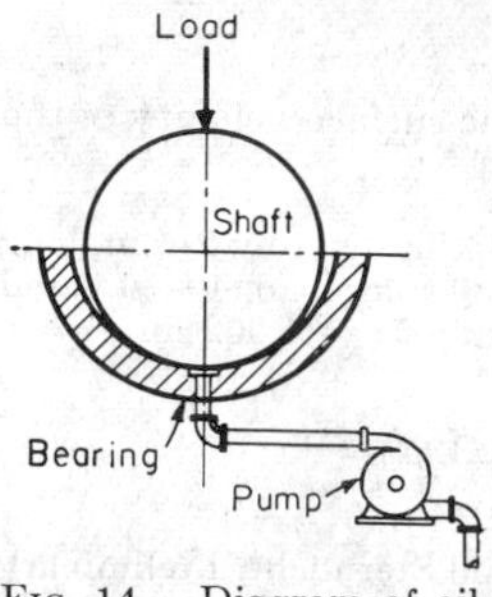

FIG. 14. Diagram of oil lift.

When journal **bearings** are **started, stopped,** or **reversed,** or whenever conditions are such that the operating value of ZN/P falls below the critical value for that bearing, the oil film will be ruptured and metal-to-metal contact will increase friction and cause wear. This condition can be eliminated by using a **hydrostatic oil lift.** High-pressure oil is introduced to the area between the bottom of the journal and the bearing (Fig. 14). If the pressure and quantity of flow are great enough, the shaft, whether it is rotating or not, will be raised and supported by an oil film. Neglecting axial flow, which is small, the flow up one side is

$$Q_1 = \frac{Wr}{A\mu}(m)^3 \text{ cu in. per sec}$$

and the inlet pressure required, $P_o = \mu Q_1 B / br^2(m)^3$, where b is the axial length of the high-pressure recess. Values of A and B are given in the following table as a function of ϵ.

ϵ	0	0.1	0.2	0.3	0.4	0.5	0.6	0.7	0.75	0.8	0.85	0.9
A	24.0	28.1	33.8	41.6	53.3	72.0	105	173	237	360	613	1,320
B	18.9	23.2	29.0	38.2	52.7	77.9	128	246	344	634	1,260	3,360

ϵ	0.91	0.92	0.93	0.94	0.95	0.96	0.97	0.98	0.99
A	1,620	2,070	2,620	3,530	5,040	7,800	13,700	30,600	121,000
B	4,340	5,810	8,040	11,800	18,400	32,100	65,300	179,000	348,000

Current practice is to make the total area of the high-pressure recess in a bearing 2½ to 5 percent of the projected area ($l \times d$) of the bearing. It is generally desirable to use a check valve in the supply line to the oil lift so that, when the journal builds up a hydrodynamic oil-film pressure, reverse flow of oil in the supply line will be prevented.

EXAMPLE 9. A 4.000 in. diam journal rests in a bearing of 4.012 in. diam. SAE 30 oil at 100 F (105 centipoises) is supplied under pressure to a groove at the lowest point in the bearing. Length of bearing, 6 in., length of groove, 3 in., load on bearing, 3,600 lb. What inlet pressure and oil flow are needed to raise the journal 0.004 in.?

$$h_o = mr(1 - \epsilon)$$
$$0.004 = 0.006(1 - \epsilon)$$
$$\epsilon = 0.333$$

From the table, $A = 44.5$, $B = 42$.

$$Q_1 = \frac{3{,}600 \times 2}{44.5 \times 105 \times 1.45 \times 10^{-7}}(0.003)^3 = 0.287 \text{ cu in. per sec, one side}$$

Flow from both sides = $(0.287 \times 2) \times {}^{60}\!/_{231} = 0.149$ gpm.

Oil-supply pressure,

$$P_o = \frac{105 \times 1.45 \times 10^{-7} \times 0.287 \times 42}{3 \times 4} \times \frac{1}{0.003^3} = 566 \text{ psi}$$

An adjustable constant-volume pump or a spur-gear pump with a capacity of about 1,000 psi should be used to allow for pressure that may be built up in the line before the journal begins to rise.

Other configurations for hydrostatically lubricated journal bearings are shown in Fig. 15. These were obtained by means of electric analog solutions (Loeb, "Determination of Flow, Film Thickness and Load-carrying Capacity of Hydrostatic Bearings Through the Use of the Electric Analog Field Plotter," *Trans. ASLE*, vol. 1, 1958).

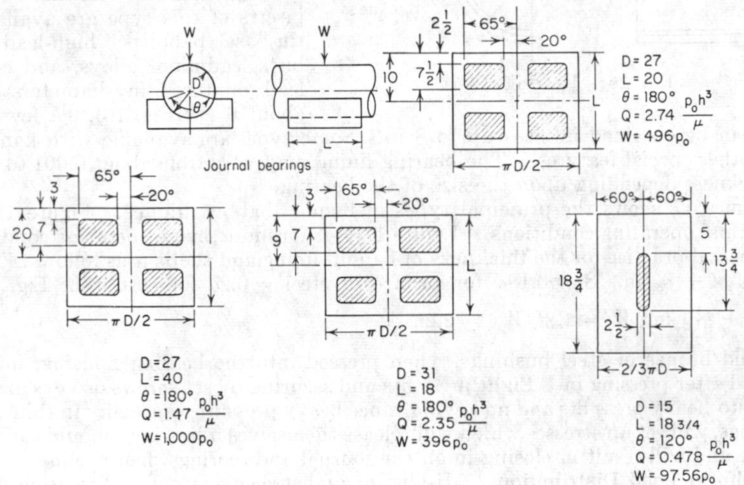

Fig. 15. Electric analog solutions for load-carrying capacity and flow for journal bearings (Loeb).

The data from Fig. 15 are exact for a uniform film thickness corresponding to $\epsilon = 0$ but may be used with discretion for other values of ϵ.

ELEMENTS OF JOURNAL BEARINGS

Typical dimensions of solid and split **bronze bushings** are given in Table 2.

Table 2. Wall Thickness of Bronze Bushings, Inches

Diam of journal, in.	<¼	¼–½	½–1	1–1½	1½–2½	2½–4	4–5½
Solid bushing, normal	1/16	3/32	1/8	3/16	1/4	3/8	1/2
Split bushing, normal	3/32	1/8	5/32	7/32	5/16	15/32	5/8
Solid bushing, thin	1/16	3/32	3/32	1/8	3/16	1/4	3/8
Split bushing, thin	1/16	3/32	1/8	3/16	1/4	3/8	1/2

Bronze bushings made from hard-drawn bronze sheets and rolled into cylindrical shape are made with a wall thickness of only 1/32 in. for bearings up to ½ in. diam and with a wall thickness of 1/16 in. for bearings from 1 in. diam up. The wall thickness of these bearings depends chiefly upon the strength of the material which supports them. Bushings of this type are pressed into place, and the bearing surface is finished by burnishing with a slightly tapered bar to a mirror finish. The allowable bearing pressures may exceed those of cast bronze shown in Table 1 by 10 to 20 percent.

Babbitt linings in larger bearings are generally employed in thickness of ⅛ in. or over and must be provided with sufficient anchorage in the supporting shell. The anchors take the form of dovetailed grooves or holes drilled in the shell and counterbored from the outside.

Improved conditions are obtained by sweating or bonding the babbitt to the shell by tinning the latter, using potassium chlorate as flux. Tin-base babbitts and other

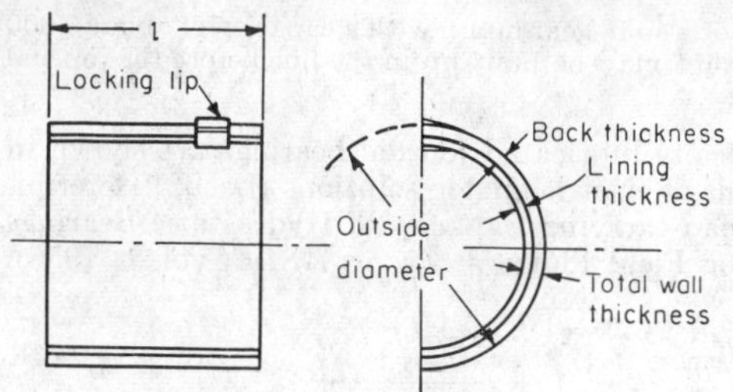

FIG. 16. Bearing insert.

low-strength materials evidence some yielding when subjected to heavy pressures. This tendency may be alleviated by the use of a thinner layer of the bearing material, fused either to a bronze or to a steel shell. This improves the fatigue life of the bearing material. Standard bearing inserts of this type are available in tin-base babbitts, high-lead babbitts, cadmium alloys, and copper-lead mixtures in diameters up to about 6 in. (Fig. 16). A few materials can be obtained in sizes up to 8 in. Some types are available with flanges or with other special features. The bearing lining may vary from about 0.001 to 0.1 in. in thickness depending upon the size of the bearing.

Figure 17 shows the principal types of bonded babbitt linings. Figure 17(*a*) is for normal operating conditions. Figure 17(*b*) is for more severe operating conditions.

General practice for the **thickness of babbitt lining and shells** is as follows: Fig. 18, $b = \frac{1}{32}d + \frac{1}{8}$ in., $S = 0.18d$ for bronze or steel $= 0.2d$ for cast iron; Fig. 18(*a*), $t = \frac{b}{2} + \frac{1}{16}$ in., $W = 1.8t$, $W_1 = 2.2t$.

Solid bronze or steel bushings, when pressed into the bearing housing, must be finished after pressing in. Light press fits and securing by set-screws or keys are preferable to heavy press fits and no keying, since heavy pressure, especially in thin-walled bushings, will set up stresses which will release themselves if bearings should run hot in service and will result in closing in on the journal and scoring when cooling.

Uniform Load Distribution. Misalignment between journal and bearing should never be so great as to cause metallic contact. The maximum allowable inclination α of the shaft to the bearing is given by $\tan \alpha = md/l$.

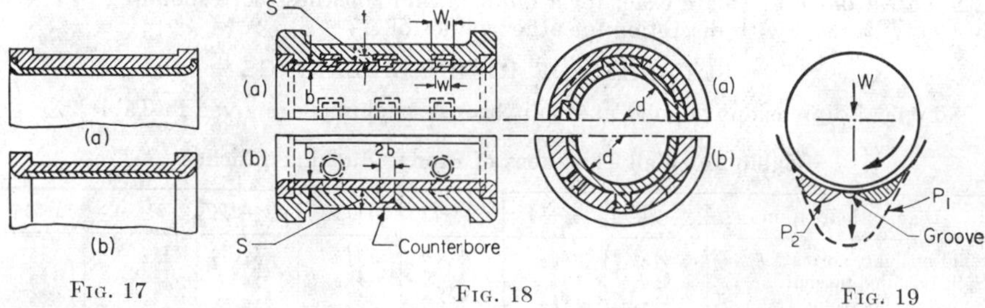

FIG. 17 FIG. 18 FIG. 19

Whenever the deflection angle of the bearing installation is greater than α, either the bearing length should be reduced or, if that is not feasible, the bearing should be mounted on a spherical seat to permit self-alignment.

Oil grooves are of two kinds, axial and circumferential; the former distribute the oil lengthwise in the bearing; the latter distribute it around the shaft at the oilhole, and also collect and return oil which would otherwise be forced out at the ends of the bearing. Grooves have often been put into bearings indiscriminatingly, with the result that they scrape off the oil and interrupt the film.

In Fig. 19, W is the resultant force or load, pounds, on the bearing or journal. The radial ordinates P_1, to the dotted curve, show the pressures, psi, of the journal on the oil film due to the load when there is no axial groove, while the ordinates P_2, to the solid curve, show the pressures with an incorrectly located groove. Since there is no oil pressure near the groove, the permissible load W must be reduced or the film will be ruptured.

Groove dimensions (Fig. 20) are given by the following relations: $a = \frac{1}{3}$ wall thickness; $W_o = 2.5a$; $W_d = 3a$; $c = 0.5W_d$; $f = \frac{1}{16}$ in. to $0.5W_d$.

In order to maintain the oil film, **the axial distributing groove should be placed in the unloaded sector** of the bearing. The location of grooves in a variety of cases is shown in Figs. 21 to 30.

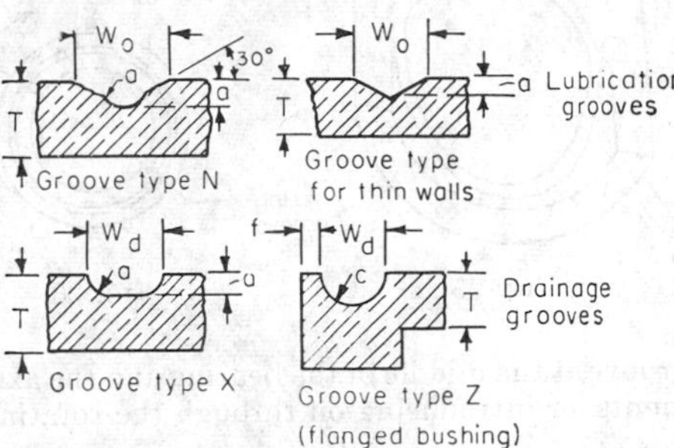

FIG. 20. Lubrication and drainage grooves.

Horizontal Bearings, Rotational Motion

Direction of Load Known and Constant

Load downward or inside the lower 60 deg segment as in the case of ring-oiling bearings (Fig. 21).

Load at an angle more than 45 deg to the vertical center line (Fig. 22).

Force- or drop-feed oiling. The oil inlet may be anywhere within the no-load sector (Fig. 23).

Oil introduced through the center of the revolving shaft (Fig. 24).

Where oil-ring electric-motor bearings will be subjected by the purchaser to belt loads varying from vertical downward to horizontal, a continuous type of oil groove developed by the General Electric Co. has proved very successful (Fig. 25). There are no critical spots with this groove because only a small percentage of the babbitt surface is removed along any axial line.

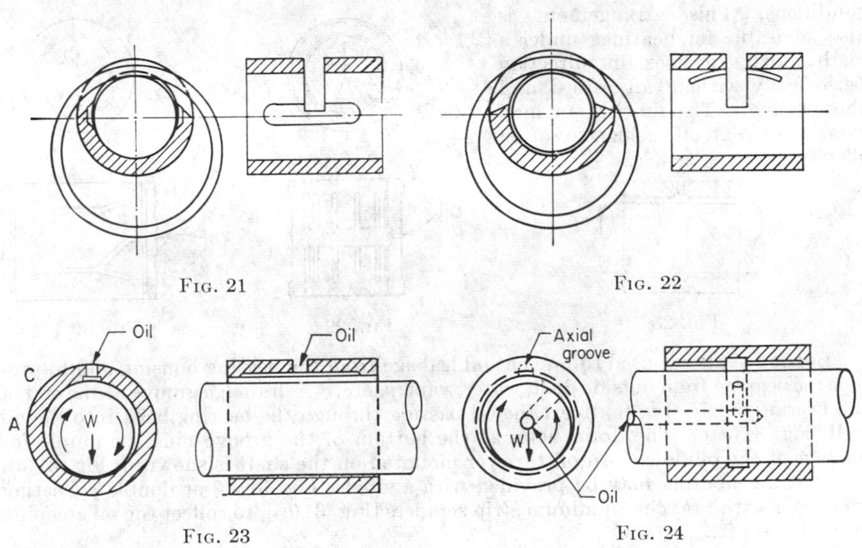

FIG. 21 FIG. 22

FIG. 23 FIG. 24

Rotating Load

For rotating shafts, a circumferential groove at the middle of the bearing and an axial groove on the no-load side (Fig. 26).

For stationary shafts and rotating bearings, a circumferential groove in the bearing and an axial groove on the no-load side. The oilhole is in the shaft at the mid-length of the bearing (Fig. 27).

Load Direction Uncertain

Oil-ring bearings (Figs. 21 and 22) may be used although they have defects under certain load directions. With forced or drop feed, the oilhole enters a circumferential

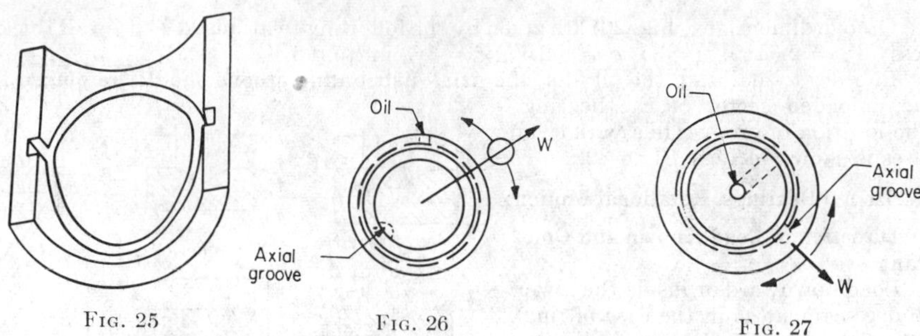

FIG. 25 FIG. 26 FIG. 27

groove at the middle of the bearing and the axial groove is omitted (Fig. 28). Arrangements for introducing oil through the rotating shaft can be made.

Bearings with Oscillatory Motion

Direction of Load Constant

No oil film can be built up due to the small sliding velocity, and boundary lubrication will exist. Axial grooves in the loaded sector distribute the lubricant to all parts of the bearing and avoid dry spots (Fig. 29).

Load Direction Reversed during Oscillation. Fluid film lubrication is possible, at least during part of the motion, due to the vacuum caused by shaft moving back and forth. Figure 30 shows grooving which may be modified to suit local conditions. This arrangement is also advisable for bearings under a load which reverses in direction periodically without any rotation of the bearing. The lubrication may then provide an oil cushion to soften shocks.

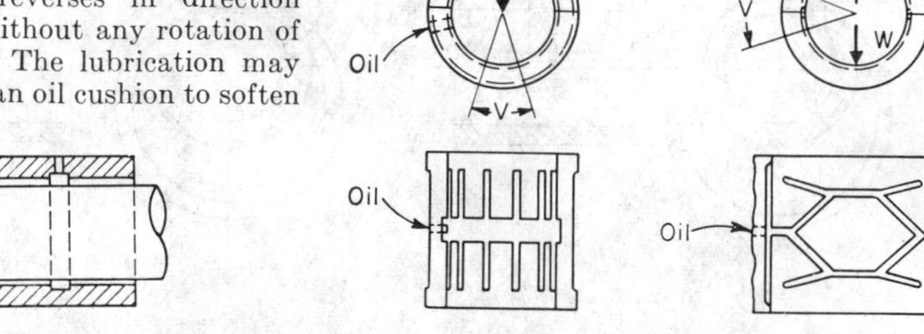

FIG. 28 FIG. 29 FIG. 30

Bearing seals are used to prevent oil leakage from the bearing housing and to protect the bearing from outside dust, water, vapors, etc. A drainage groove at the end of the bearing is effective to divert the oil passing through the bearing back into the oil well [Fig. 31(*a*)]. The drain holes at the bottom of the groove must be ample for passage of the oil flow. An oil thrower mounted on the shaft is shown in Fig. 31(*b*). The bearing housing may be provided with a single [Fig. 31(*c*)] or double collecting groove, or with brass or aluminum strip scrapers [Fig. 31(*d*)], to collect the oil creeping along the shaft.

For protection from dust, etc., felt packing rings are often used [Fig. 31(*e*)]. The

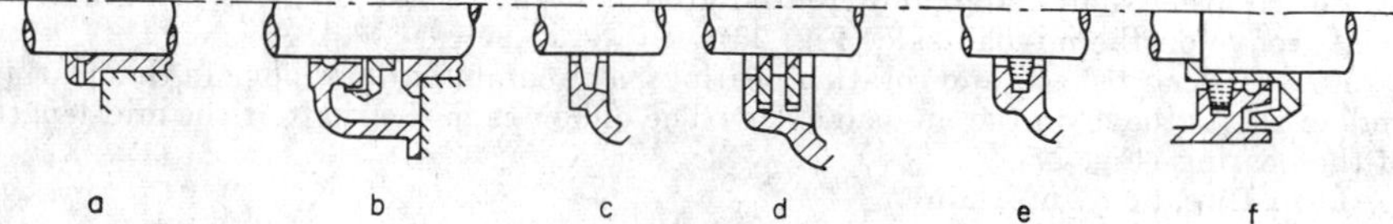

FIG. 31. Sealing end grooves.

felt ring is soaked in oil to prevent charring by friction heat. In severe cases, additional protection by a labyrinth runner is very effective [Fig. 31(*f*)].

Standard seals are available for oil and grease retention as shown in Fig. 32(*a*), (*b*), and (*c*). The seal material that is pressed against the rotating shaft may be leather or a synthetic rubber. Oak-tanned leather is suitable up to temperatures of 140 F and rubbing speeds of 750 fpm. Chrome-tanned leather may be used for temperatures up to approximately 180 F and speeds of 2,000 fpm. Synthetic rubber is satisfactory for temperatures as high as about 250 F and for faster rubbing speeds. Figure 32(*a*) shows the seal material pressed against the shaft by a series of flexible fingers or leaf

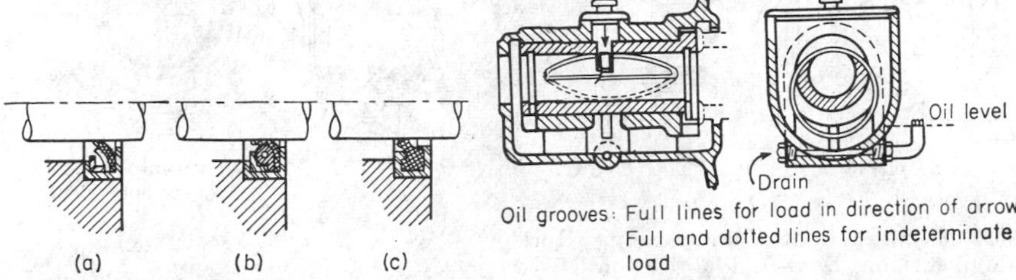

FIG. 32. Seals for oil and grease retention. FIG. 33. Ring-oiled bearing solid bushing.

springs. In Fig. 32(*b*) a helical garter spring provides the gripping force. In Fig. 32(*c*) a rubber spring is used for the same purpose.

Line-shaft bearings are purchasable in standard sizes by steps of ¼ in. for the smaller diameters, and by steps of ½ in. for the larger sizes. **Hangers** for line-shaft bearings may be purchased in types permitting ceiling, floor, or wall suspension.

Types of bearings are shown in Figs. 33 to 38. They include the principal methods of lubrication and types of construction.

Oilless bearings is the accepted term for self-lubricating bearings containing lubricants in solid or liquid form in their material. Graphite, molybdenum disulphide and Teflon are used as solid lubricants in one group, and another group consists of porous structures (wood, metal), containing oil, grease, or wax.

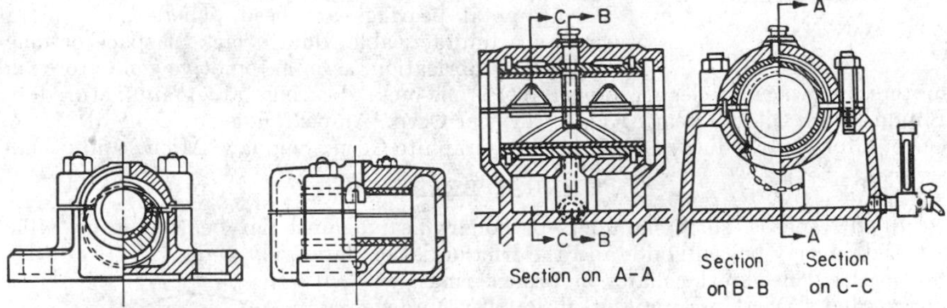

FIG. 34. Rigid ring-oiling pillow block. (*Link-Belt Co.*) FIG. 35. Split bearing with one chain. Main crankshaft bearing. Vertical oil engine.

Graphite-lubricated bearings (bridge bearings, sheaves, trolley wheels, high-temperature applications) consist generally of cast bearing bronze as a supporting structure containing various overlapping designs of grooves which are filled with graphite. The graphite is mixed with a binder, and the plastic mass is pressed into the cavities to the hardness of a lead pencil; 45 percent of the bearing area may be graphite. Drilled holes are also used for filling the bronze bearings with graphite in plastic form or with preformed graphite plugs. Strip bronze with indentations or grooves filled with graphite is used in sheet form or rolled to a butted cylindrical bushing. These bearings are manufactured by Bound Brook Oil-less Bearing Co., Johnson Bronze Co., Merriman Bros., Boston, and others.

Hardwood bearings containing lubricants are of lignum vitae which has a natural gum or hard maple which is impregnated with oil, grease, or wax. Lignum-vitae

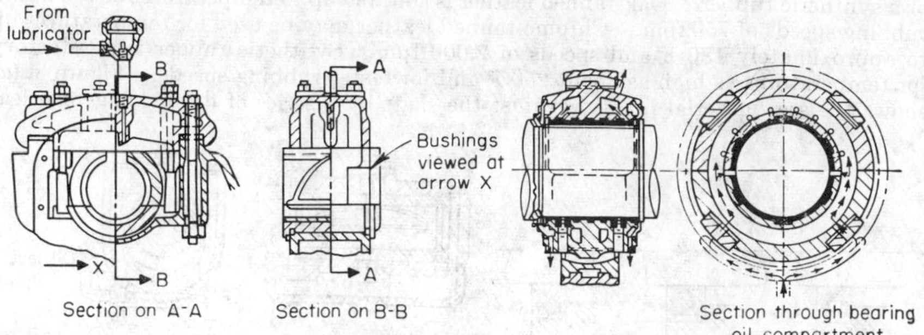

FIG. 36. Crankshaft main bearing. Horizontal engine. Drop-feed lubrication.

FIG. 37

propeller bearings are used for ships and for bearings in the chemical industry, hard-maple bearings are used for loose pulleys, in textile machinery, wringer blocks, and the like.

Porous-metal bearings, compressed from metal powders and sintered, contain up to 35 percent of liquid lubricant. See ASTM specification B-202-45T for sintered bronze and iron bearings, and also Army and Navy Specification AN-B-7G. The porous metal generally consists of a 90–10 copper-tin bronze with 1½ percent graphite. These bearings do not require oil grooves since capillarity distributes the oil and maintains an oil film. If additional lubrication from an oil well should be provided, oil will be absorbed through the porous wall as required. For high temperatures where oil will carburize, a higher percentage of graphite (6 to 15 percent) is used.

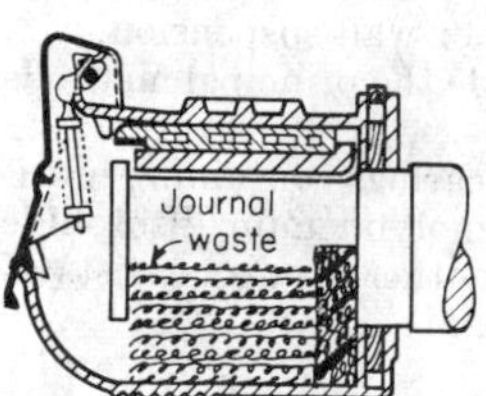

FIG. 38

Porous-metal bearings are used, where plain metal bearings are impracticable, due to lack of space or inaccessibility for lubrication, as in automotive generators and motors and vacuum-cleaner motors. Porous-metal bearings are manufactured by Bound Brook Oil-less Bearing Co.; Chrysler Corp., Ampex Division; General Motors Corp., Moraine Products Division; U.S. Graphite Corp., Saginaw, Mich., and others.

THRUST BEARINGS

At low speeds, shaft shoulders or collars bear against flat bearing rings. The lubrication may be semifluid, and the friction is comparatively high.

For hardened-steel collars on bronze rings, with interrupted service, pressures up to 2,000 psi are permissible; for continuous low-speed operation, 1,500 psi; for steel collars on babbitted rings, 200 psi. In multicollar thrust bearings, the values are reduced considerably because of the difficulty in distributing the load evenly between the several collars.

The performance of the bearing thrust rings is much improved by the introduction of **grooves** with tapered lands as shown in Fig. 39. The lands extend on either side of the groove. The taper angle of the lands is very slight, so that a pressure oil film is formed between the bearing ring and the collar of the

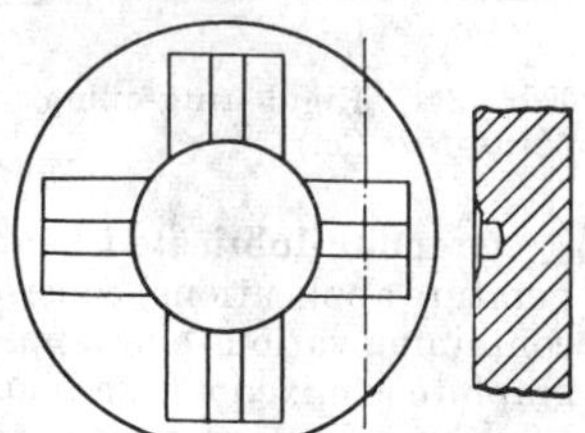

FIG. 39. Thrust collar with grooves fitted with tapered lands.

shaft. It is generally known that slightly tapered radial grooves will develop a hydrodynamic load-carrying film, when formed in the manner of Fig. 39. Leloup (Report on Investigations of Thrust Bearings, *Rev. universelle mines*, **5**, 1949) has evaluated in a quantitative manner, the build-up of pressure associated with placing a radius on the edge of such a groove. Leloup gives the test results below for a flat steel thrust washer 2.36 in. O.D. and 1.65 in. I.D., with a unit load of about 100 psi.

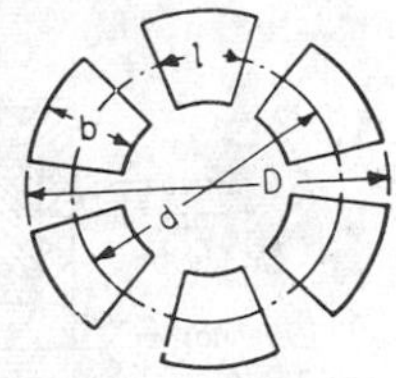

Fig. 40. Kingsbury thrust bearing with six shoes.

For high speeds or where low friction losses and a low wear rate are essential, **pivoted segmental thrust bearings** are used (Kingsbury thrust bearing, or Mitchell bearing in Europe). The bearing members in this type are tiltable shoes which rest on hard steel buttons mounted on the bearing housing. The shoes are free to form automatically a wedge-shaped oil film between the shoe surface and the collar of the shaft (Figs. 40 to 42).

N, rpm	Coef of friction, flat washer	Coef of friction, grooved washer
260	0.011	0.0065
520	0.0099	0.0067
900	0.015	0.0067

The **minimum oil-film thickness** h_o, in., between the shoe and the collar, at the trailing edge of the shoe, is approximately

$$h_o = 0.0341\sqrt{\mu u l / P_{avg}}$$

where μ is the viscosity in lb-sec per sq in.; u is the velocity of the collar, on the mean diam, in. per min; l is the length of a shoe, at the mean diam of the collar, in the direction of sliding motion; P_{avg} is the average load on the shoes, psi. As indicated in Fig. 40, $b = l$, approximately. The standard thrust bearings have six shoes. Load-carrying capacities of Kingsbury thrust bearings are given in Table 3.

Table 3. Capacities of Six-shoe Standard-duty Horizontal and Vertical Thrust Bearings

(Based on viscosity of 150 sec Saybolt at operating temperatures. Capacities given may be increased from 10 to 25% if viscosity is increased in same proportion)

Bearing size	Area, sq in.	Rpm: 100	200	400	800	1,800	3,600	Bearing size	Area, sq in.	Rpm: 100	150	200	300	500	700
		Safe load, thousands of pounds								Safe load, thousands of pounds					
5	12.5	1.44	1.7	2.0	2.4	2.9	3.5	19	180	40.00	44.0	48.0	53.0	60.0	65.0
6	18.0	2.30	2.7	3.2	3.8	4.6	5.5	21	220	51.00	57.0	61.0	68.0	77.0	84.0
7	24.5	3.30	3.9	4.7	5.6	6.8	8.0	23	264	65.00	72.0	77.0	85.0	97.0	105.0
8	32.0	4.60	5.5	6.6	7.8	9.6	11.4	25	312	80.00	88.0	95.0	105.0	119.0	123.0
9	40.5	6.20	7.4	8.8	10.4	13.0	15.0	27	364	97.00	107.0	115.0	127.0	144.0	146.0
10½	55.1	9.20	10.8	13.0	15.4	19.0	22.0	29	420	116.00	128.0	137.0	152.0	168.0	168.0
12	72.0	12.80	15.2	18.0	21.0	26.0	29.0	31	480	137.00	151.0	162.0	180.0	192.0	192.0
13½	91.1	17.20	20.0	24.0	29.0	35.0	36.0	33	544	160.00	177.0	189.0	210.0	220.0	220.0
15	112.5	22.00	26.0	32.0	37.0	45.0		37	684	215.00	235.0	250.0	275.0	275.0	
17	144.5	30.00	36.0	43.0	51.0	58.0		41	840	275.00	305.0	325.0	335.0	335.0	
								45	1012	345.00	385.0	405.0	405.0		

The coefficient of friction in Kingsbury thrust bearings, referred to the mean diameter of the shoes, is approximately $f = 11.7h_o/l$, where h_o is computed as shown above. Figures 41 and 42 show typical pivoted segmental thrust bearings. They usually

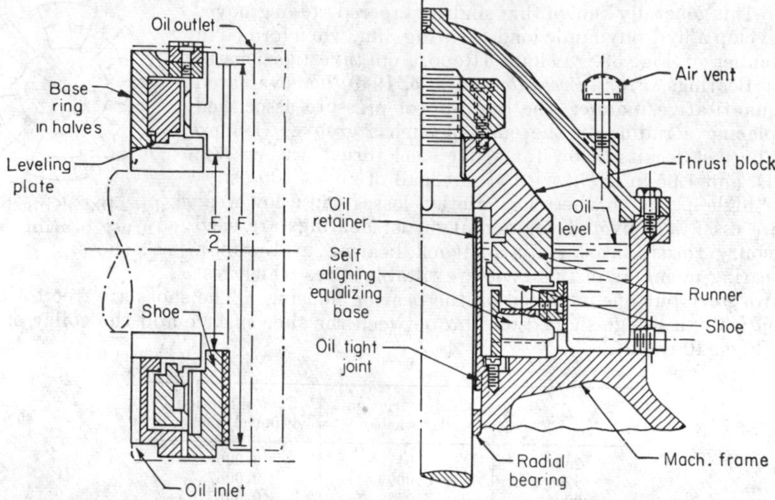

Fig. 41. Left half of six-shoe self-aligning equalizing horizontal thrust bearing for load in either axial direction.

Fig. 42. Half section of mounting for vertical thrust bearing.

embody a system of rocking levers which are used for alignment and equalization of load on the several shoes (Fig. 43).

Thrust may be carried on a hydrostatic step bearing as shown schematically in Fig. 44, where high-pressure oil at P_o psi is supplied at the center of the bearing from an external pump. The lubricant flows radially outward through the annulus of depth h_o and escapes at the periphery of the shaft at some pressure P_1 which is usually about atmospheric pressure. An oil film will be present whether the shaft rotates or not. Friction in these bearings can be made

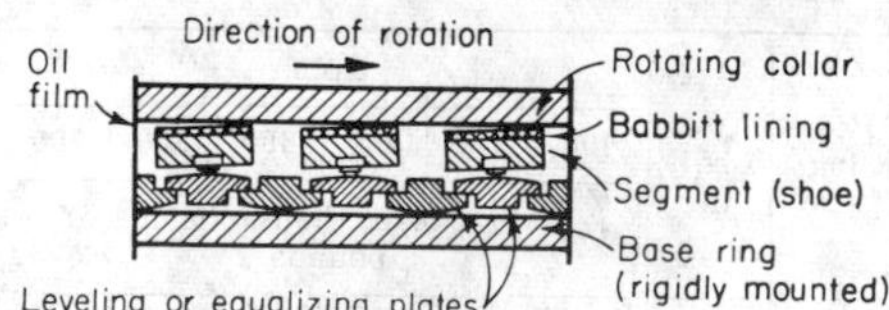

Fig. 43. Kingsbury thrust bearings. (Developed cylindrical sections.)

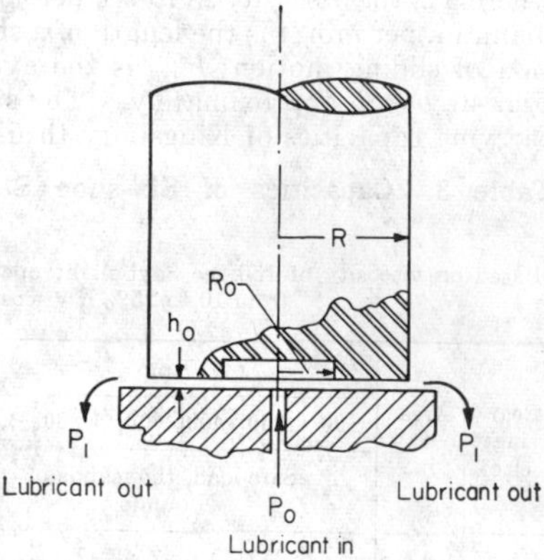

Fig. 44. Hydrostatic step bearing.

to approach zero, depending upon the rotational velocity and the viscosity of the lubricant film. Figure 45 shows the step bearing of a vertical turbogenerator. The load-carrying capacity

$$W = \frac{P_o \pi}{2} \left[\frac{R^2 - R_o^2}{\ln (R/R_o)} \right]$$

This equation is valid even when the recess is eliminated, in which case R_o becomes the radius of the inlet oil-supply pipe. The flow of lubricant in cubic inch per second is

$$Q = P_o \pi h_o^3 / 6\mu \ln (R/R_o)$$

The friction horsepower loss in the bearing is $H_f = N^2\mu(R^4 - R_o^4)/383{,}000h_o$, where N is rpm.

The pumping horsepower loss in forcing the lubricant through the bearing is $H_p = Q(P_o - P_1)/6{,}600\eta$, where η is the efficiency of the pump and Q the volume in cu in. per sec.

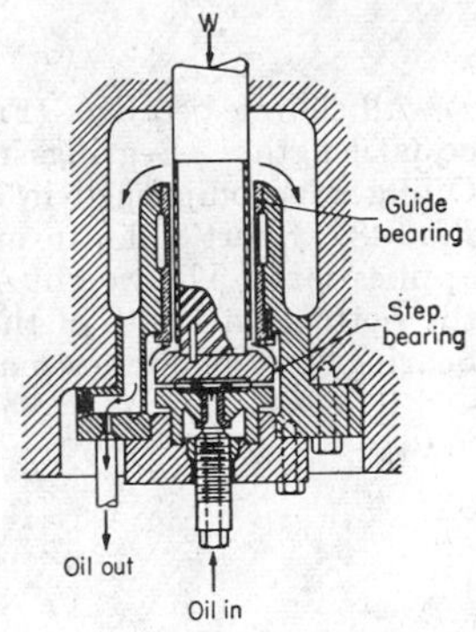

FIG. 45. Step bearing of a vertical turbogenerator.

EXAMPLE 10. A typical 5,000-kw vertical turbogenerator has a thrust load of about 101,000 lb; outside diameter of bearing, 16 in.; diam of recess, 10 in.; pump efficiency, 0.5; speed, 750 rpm. Substituting these values, $101{,}000 = \frac{P_o\pi}{2}\left[\frac{8^2 - 5^2}{\ln (8/5)}\right]$, or $P_o = 774$ psi. In practice about 825 psi is used on this step bearing to provide some margin of safety. Film thickness in the bearing should be from 0.001 to 0.01 in. to protect the surfaces from metal-to-metal contact and allow passage of harmful grit that may find its way into the system. The film thickness determines the oil flow for a given viscosity and pressure. With $h_o = 0.006$ in. and SAE 20 oil at 130 F (29 centipoises), $Q = 825 \times \pi \times (0.006)^3/6 \times 29 \times 1.45 \times 10^{-7} \times 0.470 = 46.8$ cu in. per sec. Flow $= 46.8 \times 60/231 = 12.15$ gpm. The horsepower lost due to friction, $H_f = 750^2 \times 29 \times 1.45(8^4 - 5^4)/383{,}000 \times 0.006 = 3.58$ hp. The horsepower lost due to pumping with pump efficiency of 0.5, $H_p = 46.8 \times 825/6{,}600 \times 0.5 = 11.7$ hp. The total energy lost $= 11.7 + 3.58 = 15.28$ hp.

Evaluation of these equations for other film thicknesses will show that the minimum lost energy will occur between $h_o = 0.004$ and $h_o = 0.006$ in. The coefficient of friction corresponding to an energy loss of 15.28 hp in the above example is 0.002.

Other configurations for hydrostatically lubricated thrust bearings are shown in Fig. 46 from Loeb. They may be used directly to obtain value of load-carrying capacity W and flow Q.

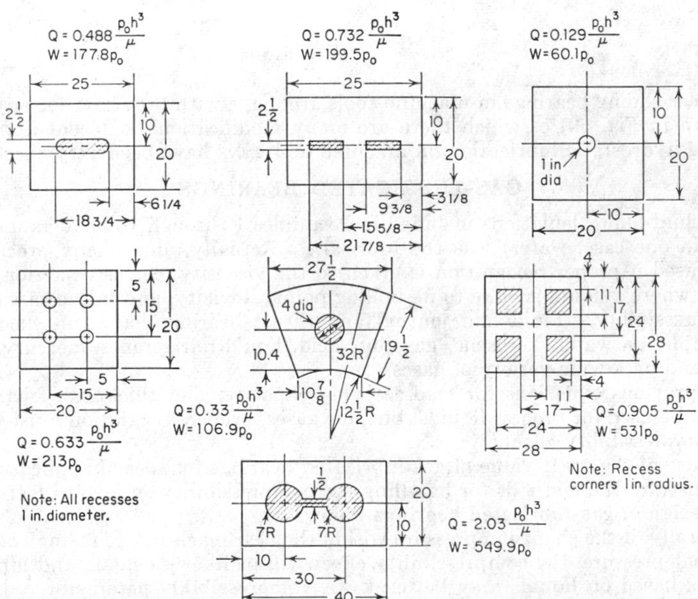

FIG. 46. Electric analog solutions for load-carrying several flat thrust bearings (Loeb).

SLIDING BEARINGS

All sliding bearings (Fig. 47) to wear true must have the sliding parts of nearly equal lengths. Bearings made in this way will be found not to wear out of true. Oiling is accomplished in several ways, an acceptable method being that shown in Fig. 48. Short slides in many machine tools are lubricated by oil pads or direct oil application. The weight of the table and work and thrust of the tool cause wear on the bottom and sides of the guides. To compensate for the wear in both directions, bearings are sometimes made V-shaped, as shown in Fig. 49.

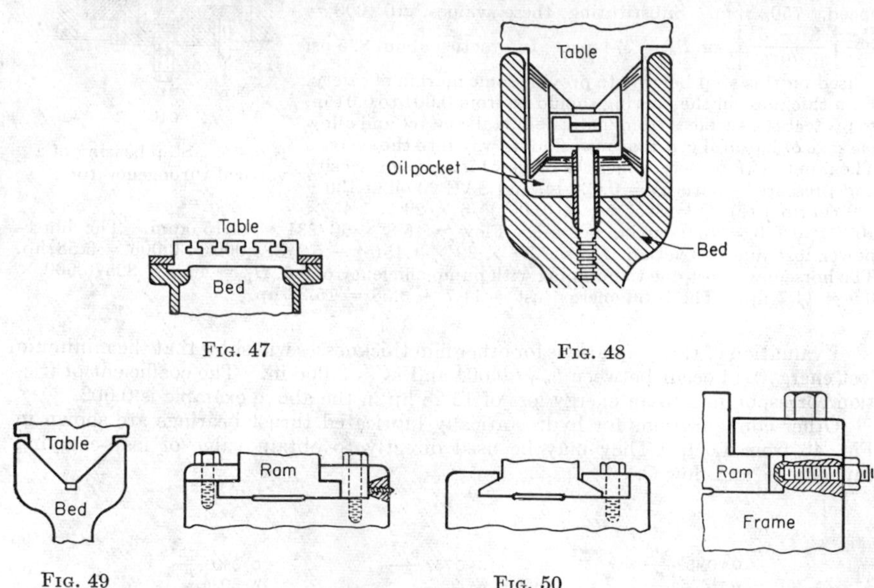

FIG. 47 FIG. 48

FIG. 49 FIG. 50

Simpler sliding bearings in machine tools are made with provision for adjustment (as shown in Fig. 50) of which there are many modifications. Recent applications involving hydrostatic lubrication on machine tool ways have been very successful.

GAS-LUBRICATED BEARINGS

The fluid film calculations included in Examples 1 through 10 have assumed that oil (or, in one case, water) was the lubricant. Actually, almost any **process fluid** may be used if proper recognition is given to the viscosity, corrosive action, change in state (where a liquid is close to its boiling point), toxicity, and in the case of a gas, its compressibility. Fluid film journal and thrust bearings have run successfully, for example, on water, kerosene, gasoline, acid, liquid refrigerants, mercury, molten metals, and on a wide variety of gases.

The previous equations for load-carrying capacity, film thickness, friction, and flow may be used for process liquids, but, for gases, proper recognition must be made of the compressibility effects.

Because of the great value of gas-lubricated bearings for special applications, and to demonstrate the methods for handling the compressibility action, an introduction to the **design of gas-lubricated bearings** follows.

Naturally, if the change in pressure within the bearing clearance is small compared to ambient pressure, the compressibility effect will be likewise small, and lubrication equations based on liquids may be used. A **compressibility parameter Λ** indicates the extent of this action. For hydrodynamic journal bearings it has the form $\Lambda = 6\mu\omega/P_a m^2$. For values of Λ less than one, the previous equations of this section for journal bearings may be used. For values of $\mathbf{\Lambda}$ greater than one, compressibility effects are included through the use of Figs. 51, 52, 53 and 54. (Data from Elrod and Burgdorfer, Proceedings First International Symposium on Gas-lubricated Bearings, 1959 and Raimondi, *Trans. ASLE*, vol. IV, 1961.)

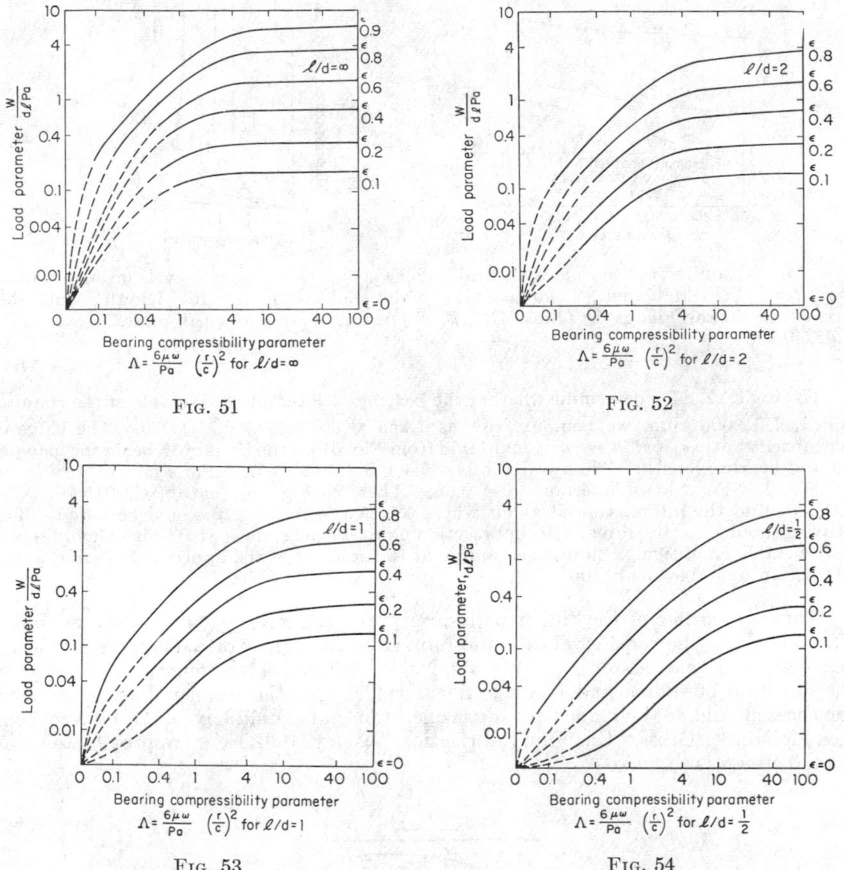

FIG. 51

FIG. 52

FIG. 53

FIG. 54

FIGS. 51–54. Theoretical load-carrying parameter vs. compressibility parameter for full journal bearing for $l/d = \infty$ (Fig. 51); $l/d = 2$ (Fig. 52); $l/d = 1$ (Fig. 53); $l/d = 0.5$ (Fig. 54) (*Elrod & Raimondi*).

EXAMPLE 11. Determine the minimum film thickness for a journal bearing 0.5 in. diameter by 0.5 in. long. Ambient pressure 14.7 psia. Speed 12,000 rpm. Load 0.4 lb. Diametral clearance 0.0005 in. Lubricant, air at 100 F and 14.7 psia (2.68×10^{-9} lb-sec/in.^{2} from Fig. 55). $m = 0.0005/0.5 = 0.001$ in./in. $\omega = 12{,}000 \times 2\pi/60 = 1{,}256$ radians/sec, $\mathbf{\Lambda} = (6 \times 2.68 \times 10^{-9} \times 1{,}256)/14.7 \times 0.001^2 = 1.37$, and $W/dlP_a = 0.4/0.5 \times 0.5 \times 14.7 = 0.109$. Then, in Fig. 53 ($l/d = 1$), we find that $\epsilon = 0.22$, and the minimum film thickness $h_0 = 0.00025(1 - 0.22) = 0.000195$ in.

Gas-lubricated journal bearings should be checked for **whirl stability.** Figure 56 is applicable with sufficient accuracy to bearings where l/d is equal to or greater than one. It is used in conjunction with Fig. 51 for $l/d = \infty$. The stability parameter is $\omega_1{}^*$ which, for a bearing having only gravity loading, has the value $\omega_1{}^* = \omega\sqrt{mr/g}$.

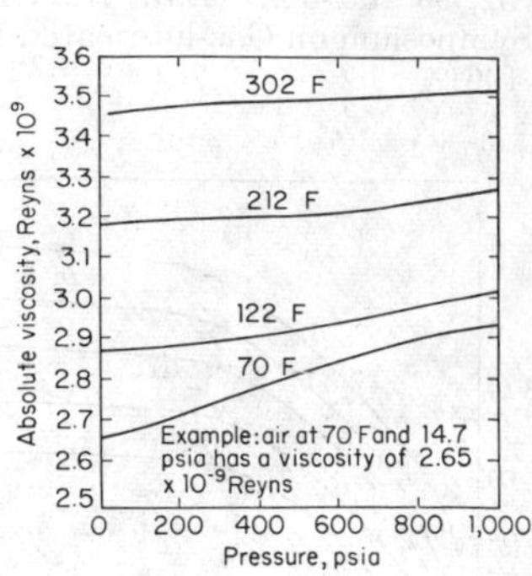

FIG. 55. Absolute viscosity of air (Iwasaki, *Sci. Repts.*, Research Inst., Tohoku Univ., Ser. A; Kestin and Pilarczyk, *Trans. ASME*, vol. 56, 1954).

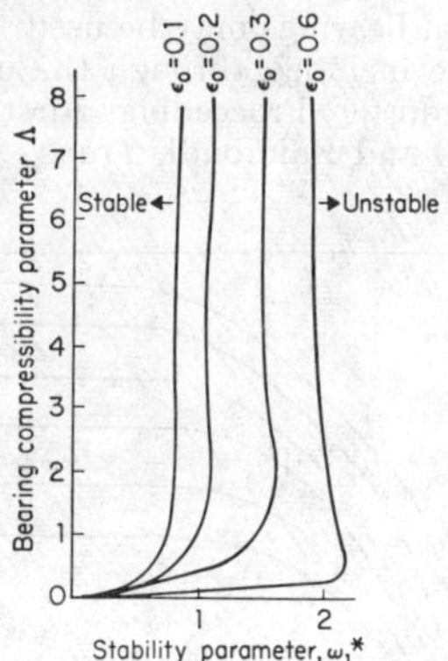

FIG. 56. Half-frequency translatory whirl threshold for infinite length, 360 deg journal bearing (*Castelli and Elrod*).

EXAMPLE 12. To determine whether the bearing of Example 11 is stable at the running speed of 12,000 rpm, we compute ω_1^* as $1{,}256\sqrt{0.00025/386} = 1.015$. The value of eccentricity ratio ϵ_0 for $l/d = \infty$ is computed from Fig. 51 on the basis of W being the load per inch of bearing length. Thus W(lb/in.) $= 0.4/0.5 = 0.8$ lb/in. For Fig. 51, $W/dlP_a = 0.218$ and in Fig. 51, we determine $\epsilon_0 = 0.18$. Then (in Fig. 56), for $\omega_1^* = 1.015$ and $\mathbf{\Lambda} = 1.37$, we find the intersection at about where a curve for $\epsilon_0 = 0.18$ would be found. The bearing should just be stable. An intersection point on the ϵ_0 line or to the left should represent a stable condition. An intersection point to the right of the appropriate ϵ_0 line would predict an unstable condition.

Thrust bearings of the tilting pad variety are less susceptible to compressibility effects and may be considered as liquid-lubricated for values of $\mathbf{\Lambda}$ (suitable for thrust bearings) less than about 30. $\mathbf{\Lambda} = 6u\mu l/h_0{}^2P_a$ where l is the length of the shoe in the direction of sliding and U is the linear velocity at the mean radius. However, the shoes should not be made flat for gas operation but should have a crowned contour (see Fig. 57). (Gross, "Gas Film Lubrication," Wiley, 1962.) An approximate value for the crown is to make $\delta = \frac{3}{4}h_0$.

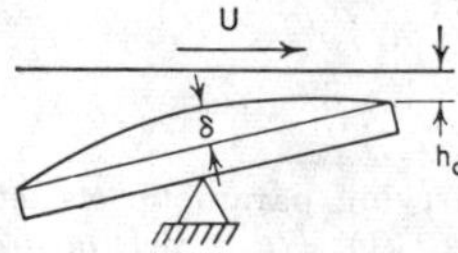

FIG. 57. Schematic of tilting-pad shoe, showing crown height δ.

Gas-lubricated hydrostatic bearings unlike liquid-lubricated bearings cannot be designed on the basis of constant flow volume. They are designed instead to have a pressure loss produced by an **orifice restrictor** in the supply line. Such throttling enables the bearing to have load-carrying capacity and stiffness. For maximum stiffness the pressure drop in the orifice may be about one-half of the manifold supply pressure. For a circular thrust bearing with a single circular orifice, the load-carrying capacity is given with sufficient accuracy by the equation previously used for liquids (see Fig. 44). $W = (P_R - P_a/2)[R^2 - R_0{}^2/\ln (R/R_0)]$, where P_R is the recess pressure, psia. The flow volume, however, is given by $Q_0 = \pi h_0{}^3/[6\mu \ln (R/R_0)](P_0{}^2 - P_1{}^2)/2P_0$. Q_0 and P_0 refer to recess conditions, and Q_1 and P_1 refer to ambient conditions. Pressures are absolute.

EXAMPLE 13. A circular thrust bearing 6 in. diameter with a recess 2 in. diameter has a film thickness of $h_0 = 0.0015$ in. $P_0 = 30$ psig or 44.7 psia. P_1 is room pressure, 14.7 psia. Depth of recess is 0.02 in. Applied load is 375 lb. $Q_0 = (\pi \times 0.0015^3)/(6 \times 2.68 \times 10^{-9} \ln 3)(44.7^2 - 14.7^2)/(2 \times 44.7)$, $Q_0 = 12.3$ in.^{3}/sec at recess pressure. Converted to free air, $Q_1 = Q_0(P_0/P_1)$ with isothermal expansion, $Q_1 = 12.3(44.7/14.7) = 37.4$ in.^{3}/sec, or $Q_1 = 37.4 \times 60 = 2{,}244$ in.^{3}/min. Actual measured flow $= 2{,}440$ in.^{3}/min.

The recess depth in Fig. 44 should be as shallow as possible, and the orifice restrictor in the supply line should be close to the entrance to the recess in order to avoid pneumatic instability. (Licht, Sternlicht and Fuller, Self-excited Vibrations of an Air-lubricated Thrust Bearing, *ASME Trans*, 1958, Vol. 80.) It is good practice to limit the manifold pressure to less than 100 psig and the recess pressure to less than 50 psig in order to avoid the formation of shocks in the bearing film with extreme pressure losses.

A review of gas-bearing lubrication may also be found in the Proceedings of the First International Symposium on Gas-lubricated Bearings, as well as in the book by Gross.

BEARINGS WITH ROLLING CONTACT

BY

C. L. Pope and C. L. Miller

REFERENCES: AFMBA, Method of Evaluating Load Ratings of Ball Bearings. ASA, Load Ratings for Ball and Roller Bearings. Lundberg and Palmgren, Dynamic Capacity of Rolling Bearings, Paper 48 A19, *Trans. ASME*, 1948. Lieblein and Zelen, Statistical Investigation of the Fatigue Life of Deep-groove Ball Bearings, Paper 2719, Jour. of Research at the NBS. Palmgren, Investigations Regarding the Static Capacity of Ball Bearings, DISS. Stockholm, 1930.

Rolling-contact Bearings

Rolling-contact bearings are designed to support and locate rotating shafts or parts in machines, to transfer loads between the rotating and stationary members, and to permit free rotation with a minimum of friction. They are composed of rolling elements interposed between an **outer** and **inner ring. Separators,** sometimes called **cages or retainers,** are used to space the rolling elements from each other. (See Fig. 1.)

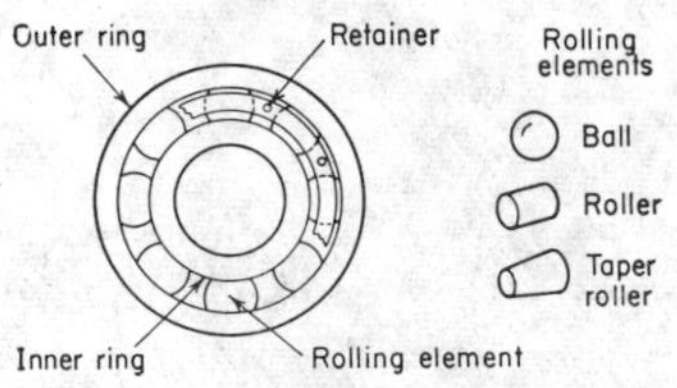

FIG. 1

A wide variety of rolling element bearings are normally manufactured to standard boundary dimensions (O.D., Bore, W.D.) and tolerances which have been standardized by the AFBMA. The ASA has for the most part adapted these **standards** and published them as follows:

Gaging practices	B3.4	Mounting accessories	B3.9
Tolerances	B3.5	Instrument bearings	B3.10
Boundary dimensions	B3.6	Load ratings	B3.11
Terminology	B3.7	Ball standards	B3.12
Mounting dimensions	B3.8	Identification code	B54.1

The first phase of **selecting** a rolling-contact bearing necessitates determining the type and style of bearing and then determining the size based on load speed and life.

1. **Ball bearings** are generally the less expensive choice for the smaller sizes and lighter loads. Since they function on theoretical point contact, they are suited for higher speeds and lighter loads than roller bearings.

2. **Roller bearings** are generally more expensive except in larger sizes. Since they function theoretically on line contact, they are more rugged and will carry heavy loads, including shock, more satisfactorily, but they are limited in speed.

3. Alignment problems are sometimes encountered and can be accounted for by using an internal **self-aligning bearing.** Self-aligning ball bearings are satisfactory only under light, pure radial loads. A single-row, deep-groove radial ball with extra loose internal clearance may be used for modest misalignment. Self-aligning roller

bearings (spherical roller bearings) are satisfactory for radial and thrust load under moderate misalignment.

4. **Thrust ball or roller bearings** should be subjected to pure thrust loads. Many times a deep-groove, conrad-type ball bearing will suffice for a thrust bearing.

5. **Precision angular contact ball bearings** are extensively used for precision application where both axial control and run-out are important. They are also recommended for higher speed.

6. **Deep-groove, conrad-type bearings** are furnished in a wide variety of types such as shielded, sealed, adapter, mounted, etc.

7. Owing to the large variety of standard bearings there is very little need for bearings of special design. **Special bearings** should be avoided and used only upon the advice of a bearing manufacturer.

Load Capacity

An accurate knowledge of the load-carrying capacity and expected life is essential in the proper selection of ball and roller bearings.

The **"life"** of an individual bearing is the number of revolutions (or hours) which the bearings run before the first evidence of fatigue develops in the material of either ring or any of the rolling elements.

The **"rating life"** of a group of apparently identical ball bearings is defined as the number of revolutions (or hours) at some given constant speed that 90 percent of a group of bearings will complete or exceed before the first evidence of fatigue develops. As presently determined for ball bearings, this rating life is approximately one-fifth of the life which 50 percent of the group of bearings will complete or exceed.

The **"basic load rating"** is that constant stationary load which a group of apparently identical ball bearings with stationary outer rings can endure for a rating life of one million revolutions of the inner ring.

"Equivalent load" is defined as that constant stationary radial load which, if applied to a bearing with rotating inner ring and stationary outer ring, would give the same life as that which the bearing will attain under the actual conditions of load and rotation.

Calculations of Basic Load Rating, Rating Life, and Equivalent Load

Basic Load Rating. The magnitude of the basic load rating C for radial and angular contact ball bearings, except filling slot bearings with balls not larger than 25.4 mm (1 inch), is $C = f_c(i \cos \alpha)^{0.7}Z^{2/3}D^{1.8}$ lb. With balls larger than 1 in., $C = f_c(i \cos \alpha)^{0.7}Z^{2/3}D^{1.4}$ lb. For thrust ball bearings, $C = f_cZ^{2/3}D^{1.8}$ lb ($\alpha = 90°$), and $C = f_c(\cos \alpha)^{0.7} \tan \alpha\, Z^{2/3}D^{1.8}$ ($\alpha \neq 90°$). For spherical, cylindrical, and tapered roller bearings, $C = f_c(il_{\text{eff}} \cos \alpha)^{7/9}Z^{3/4}D^{29/27}$ lb. For thrust roller bearings, $C = f_cl_{\text{eff}}^{7/9}Z^{3/4} D^{29/27}$ lb ($\alpha = 90°$), and $C = f_c(l_{\text{eff}} \cos \alpha)^{7/9} \tan \alpha Z^{3/4}D^{29/27}$ lb ($\alpha \neq 90°$), where i = the number of rows of balls or rollers in any one bearing, α = the nominal angle of contact = the nominal angle between the line of action of the ball or roller resultant load and a plane perpendicular to the bearing axis, Z = the number of balls or rollers per row; D = the ball or roller diameter (mean diameter of tapered roller bearings in index), l_{eff} = the effective length of contact between one roller and that ring where the contact is the shortest (over all roller length minus roller chamfers or grinding undercuts) in index, and f_c = a factor which depends on the geometry of the bearing components, the exact shape of the load-carrying surfaces of rollers and rings, and the accuracy to which the various bearing parts are made and the material. f_c is obtained by multiplying f_c/f from Table 1 by f. f = a material factor, f = 7,450 for ball bearings, and f = 49,500 for roller bearings

Rating Life. Rating life, L, for ball bearings except filling notch bearing is $L = (C/P)^3$ million revolutions. Rating life, L, for roller bearings is $L = (C/P)^{10/3}$ million revolutions. (Divide by revolutions per hour to obtain life in hours.) C is calculated from basic load rating as above. P is equivalent load.

Equivalent Load. $P = XVF_r + YF_a$, where X = radial factor, Y = thrust factor, F_r = radial load, F_a = thrust load. Values of X and Y are given in Table 2.

Table 1. Factor f_c/f

$\frac{D \cos \alpha}{d_m}$	Single-row and angular contact ball bearings	Double-row self-align	Spherical roller bearings	Cylindrical roller bearings	Ball thrust bearings	Roller thrust bearings	Tapered-roller bearings
0.01	.....	.....	0.077	0.095	0.374	0.185	0.069
0.02	.....	.....	0.090	0.111	0.461	0.215	0.081
0.03	.....	.....	0.099	0.120	0.521	0.235	0.088
0.04	.....	.....	0.105	0.128	0.568	0.250	0.094
0.05	0.476	0.176	0.110	0.134	0.607	0.262	0.099
0.06	0.500	0.190	0.114	0.139	0.641	0.271	0.102
0.07	0.521	0.203	0.118	0.144	0.671	0.279	0.105
0.08	0.539	0.215	0.121	0.147	0.699	0.286	0.108
0.09	0.554	0.227	0.123	0.150	0.724	0.291	0.110
0.10	0.566	0.238	0.125	0.152	0.747	0.296	0.112
0.12	0.586	0.261	0.128	0.156	0.789	0.303	0.115
0.14	0.600	0.282	0.130	0.159	0.827	0.307	0.117
0.16	0.608	0.303	0.131	0.161	0.860	0.310	0.118
0.18	0.611	0.323	0.132	0.161	0.891	0.310	0.118
0.20	0.611	0.342	0.132	0.161	0.920	0.310	0.118
0.22	0.608	0.359	0.131	0.160	0.947	0.308	0.117
0.24	0.601	0.375	0.130	0.159	0.972	0.305	0.116
0.26	0.593	0.390	0.128	0.156	0.995	0.301	0.115
0.28	0.583	0.402	0.126	0.154	1.02	0.297	0.113
0.30	0.571	0.411	0.124	0.152	1.04	0.292	0.112
0.32	0.558	0.418	.....	.....	1.06		
0.34	0.543	0.420	.....	.....	1.08		
0.36	0.527	0.421					
0.38	0.510	0.418					
0.40	0.492	0.412					

Table 2. Factors X and Y

Bearing type	Single-row bearings		Double-row bearings				e
	$\frac{F_a}{VF} > e$		$\frac{F_a}{VF} \leqq e$		$\frac{F_a}{VF} > e$		
Radial-contact ball bearings $\frac{F_a}{iZD} 2$	X	Y	X	Y	X	Y	
25	0.56	2.30	1	0	0.56	2.30	0.19
150	....	1.55	....	....	....	1.55	0.28
500	....	1.15	....	....	....	1.15	0.38
1,000	....	1.00	....	....	....	1.00	0.44
Angular-contact ball bearings							
20°	0.43	1.00		1.09	0.70	1.63	0.57
30°	0.39	0.76	1	0.78	0.63	1.24	0.80
40°	0.35	0.57		0.55	0.57	0.93	1.14
Self-align ball bearings	0.40	0.4 cot	1	0.42 cot	0.65	0.65 cot	1.5 tan
Roller bearing self-align and taper	0.40	0.4 cot	1	0.45 cot	0.67	0.67 cot	1.5 tan
Thrust ball bearings							
45	0.66	1	1.18	0.59	0.66	1	1.25
75	1.66		3.89	0.52	1.66		4.67
Thrust roller bearings	tan	1	1.5 tan	0.67	tan	1	1.5 tan

Data, such as those shown in Table 3, serve to check the **adequacy** of the rating life calculations.

Table 3. Guide for Design Life

Type of service	Rating life, hr
Occasional use, such as demonstration	500
Aircraft engines and most accessories	500–2,000
Short operation; household appliances and cranes	4,000–8,000
Machines for intermittent services (dependable operation)	8,000–14,000
Machines for:	
8-hr service, not always used	14,000–20,000
8-hr service, fully utilized	20,000–30,000
24-hr service	50,000–60,000
24-hr service max dependability	100,000–200,000

Basic Static Load Ratings

Static load is defined as a load acting on a non-rotating bearing.

Basic Static Load Rating. Permanent deformations occur in rolling elements and races under static load increasing with load. The permissible static load is therefore dependent upon the permissible magnitude of permanent deformation. Experience indicates that a total permanent deformation of 0.0001 times the ball or roller diameter can be tolerated in most bearing applications without impairment of bearing operation. Basic static load rating is defined as that static radial load which corresponds to a total permanent deformation of ball and race at the most heavily stressed contact of 0.0001 times the ball diameter.

The magnitude of the basic static load rating C_0 is $C_0 = f_0 iZD^2$ ball bearings, and $C_0 = f_0 iZl_{\text{eff}}D \cos \alpha$ roller bearings, where i = number of rows of balls or rollers in any one bearing, α = the nominal angle of contact = the nominal angle between the line of action of the ball (roller) load and a plane perpendicular to the bearing axis, Z = the number of balls (rollers) per row, D = the ball (roller) diameter, l_{eff} = the effective length of contact between one roller and ring where contact is shortest, and f_0 = factor for different kinds of bearings (Table 4).

Table 4.

Self-align ball bearings	484 lb-in.
Radial- and angular-contact bearings	1,780 lb-in.
Roller bearings	3,130 lb-in.

Static equivalent load is defined as the static radial load which, if applied, would cause the same total permanent deformation at the most heavily stressed roller and race contact as that which occurs under the actual condition of loading.

The magnitude of the static equivalent load P_0 under combined radial and thrust loads is the greater of $P_0 = X_0F_r + Y_0F_a$, and $P_0 = F_r$, where X_0 = radial factor (Table 5), Y_0 = thrust factor (Table 5), F_r = radial load, and F_a = thrust load.

Table 5.

Bearing type	Single row		Double row	
	X_0	Y_0	X_0	Y_0
Radial ball bearings	0.6	0.5	0.6	0.5
Self-align ball	0.5	0.22 cos α	1	0.04 cos α
		20 deg 40 deg		20 deg 40 deg
Angular contact	0.5	0.26–0.42	1	0.52–0.84
Roller	0.5	0.22 cos α	1	0.94 cos α

If a load higher than the basic static load rating is imposed while rotating, the deformation is distributed evenly, and no practical impairment occurs until the deformation becomes quite large. Some equipment operates with loads greatly exceeding the static capacity, such as bearings supporting artillery (twice static capacity), or bearings in aircraft control pulleys (four times static capacity). The load which will fracture a bearing is approximately eight times the basic static load rating.

Oscillating loads, where the motion is such that the rolling element rotates less than half a revolution, approach static load condition. This type of load is conducive to rapid false brinnelling and requires special lubrication techniques (see Lubrication, page 8–186).

Speed Ratings. The speed of any bearing is measured in surface feet per minute (sfm) calculated from the center of the bore to the center of the rolling element. Low speeds may be considered below 2,000 sfm, medium speeds between 2,000 and 3,000 sfm, and high speeds from 3,000 to 6,000 sfm. A convenient check on speed limits can be made from a **(dn) value.** The (dn) value is calculated by multiplying the bore diameter in millimeters by the rpm. The (dn) value is a direct function of size and speed and is dependent on type of lubrication. A guide for (dn) values is as follows:

	dn
Grease-lubricated:	
Ball bearings	200,000
Roller bearings	150,000
Oil-lubricated:	
Ball bearings	300,000
Roller bearings	200,000

As these values are approached, bearing life is shortened and care in bearing selection and application should be exercised. These values are only a guide to approaching difficulties and can be exceeded by special bearings, lubrication, and application. However, it is advisable to consult a bearing manufacturer for these special features.

Friction. One of the assets of rolling-contact bearings is their low friction. The coefficient of friction varies appreciably with the type of bearing, load, speed, lubrication, and sealing element. For rough calculations the following coefficients can be used for normal operating conditions and favorable lubrication:

Single-row ball bearings	0.0015
Roller bearings	0.0018

Items such as excess grease and contact seals will increase these values, and allowances should be made.

Components of Rolling-contact Bearings

Rings. The inner and outer rings of a rolling-contact bearing are normally made of SAE52100 steel, hardened to 59-63 Rockwell C. The rolling element raceways are accurately ground in the rings and often honed to a very fine finish. The life and operating characteristics depend on the quality of the surface finish and accuracy of the component parts. Recently, vacuum-processed steel has been introduced for bearing rings. Steel produced by this process has less gas content and reduced inclusions. Thus, fatigue life has been increased. Depending on the processing methods, an increase of fatigue life from three to six times may be achieved. Consult the bearing manufacturer for life formula and further information. Rings are available for special purposes in such materials as stainless steel, ceramics, and plastics. These materials are used to combat corrosion problems. Their life is normally less than standard steel bearings unless corrosion is a factor.

Rolling Elements. Normally the rolling elements, balls, or rollers are made of the same material as the rings. They are hardened, ground, and lapped to close tolerances and a very fine finish. Other ball materials such as stainless steel, ceramics, monel, and plastics are used in conjunction with various ring materials where corrosion is a factor.

Separators, sometimes called cages or retainers, are used to space the rolling elements from each other. Some rolling-contact bearings do not use separators. Separators are furnished in a wide variety of materials and construction. Pressed-steel separators, riveted or clinched, prevail. Solid-machined separators are used where greater strength or higher speeds are required. They are fabricated from bronze or synthetic plastic-type materials. The synthetic types operate quietly at high speeds with a minimum of friction.

PRINCIPAL STANDARD BEARING TYPES

The selection of the type of rolling-contact bearing depends upon many considerations, as evidenced by the numerous types available. Only the most broad general characteristics can be indicated. Some of the more common bearings are illustrated and described briefly. The load may be radial, thrust, or a combination thereof.

Ball Bearings

Figure 2 shows a separable, or magneto-type, bearing. This type of bearing is useful where disassembly is frequent. The outer race is pressed firmly in the removable housing, and the inner race may be pressed against a shoulder on the shaft.

A standard ball bearing (**Fig. 3**) is recommended for heavy radial loads and moderate thrust loads.

A bearing with filling slot (**Fig. 4**) allows more balls in the complement and thus will carry heavier radial loads but, because of the filling slot, should be used only for light thrust loads. If the thrust is in one direction, the bearing should be mounted with the slot away from the thrust direction.

The double-row radial bearing (**Fig. 5**) provides for heavy radial and thrust loads without increasing the O.D. of the bearing.

Internal self-aligning double-row bearings (**Fig. 6**) may be used for heavy radial loads where self-alignment (0.003 to 0.005 in.) is required. The self-aligning feature should not be abused, as excessive misalignment causes early failure. Thrust loads must be light, as any thrust loads only one row of balls.

The external self-aligning bearing (**Fig. 7**) requires a larger O.D. but has the advantage of being able to carry thrust in either direction where self-aligning features are required.

Angular-contact bearings (**Fig. 8**) provide for maximum thrust and modest radial loads. They may be mounted as duplex bearings, back to back, to carry thrust in either direction. These bearings may be preloaded to minimize axial movement of the shaft.

A ball bushing (Thompson) (**Fig. 9**) is useful for translational motions. Any rotational motion should be at very low speed and under light loads. The balls run through the load area to a non-loaded area by means of passages in the ball retainer as the shaft moves in and out of the bushing.

Roller Bearings

Roller bearings with short straight rollers (**Fig. 10**) permit free axial movement when the guide lips are on either the outer or inner race. They may also be procured with three and four lips.

Needle bearings (**Fig. 11**) have rollers whose length is at least four times the diameter. They may be furnished with a retainer, but have their maximum load capacity when they have a full complement of rollers. They are available with or without an inner race and are most useful where space must be saved. The shaft should be hardened when used as an inner race. They are useful for oscillating and slow-speed motions.

The tapered-roller bearings (**Fig. 12**) will permit heavy radial and thrust loads. These may be procured as double-tapered rollers with two inner and one outer race, or two outer and one inner race. The race cones intersect at the axis of the bearing.

Figure 13 is a self-aligning bearing with two rows of short barrel rollers (SKF type). The spherical outer race is one piece or in two parts for preloading. The thrust is taken on the spherical surfaces of the center flange on the inner race.

Figure 14 is a barrel roller (Hyatt type) with spherical outer race.

Figure 15 is a self-aligning bearing with hourglass rollers. This bearing is also built as a two-row bearing with a one-piece inner race.

Figure 16 is a split-type roller bearing with the feature of being split to the shaft. This feature allows the use of roller bearings where it would be difficult to replace or install solid roller bearings.

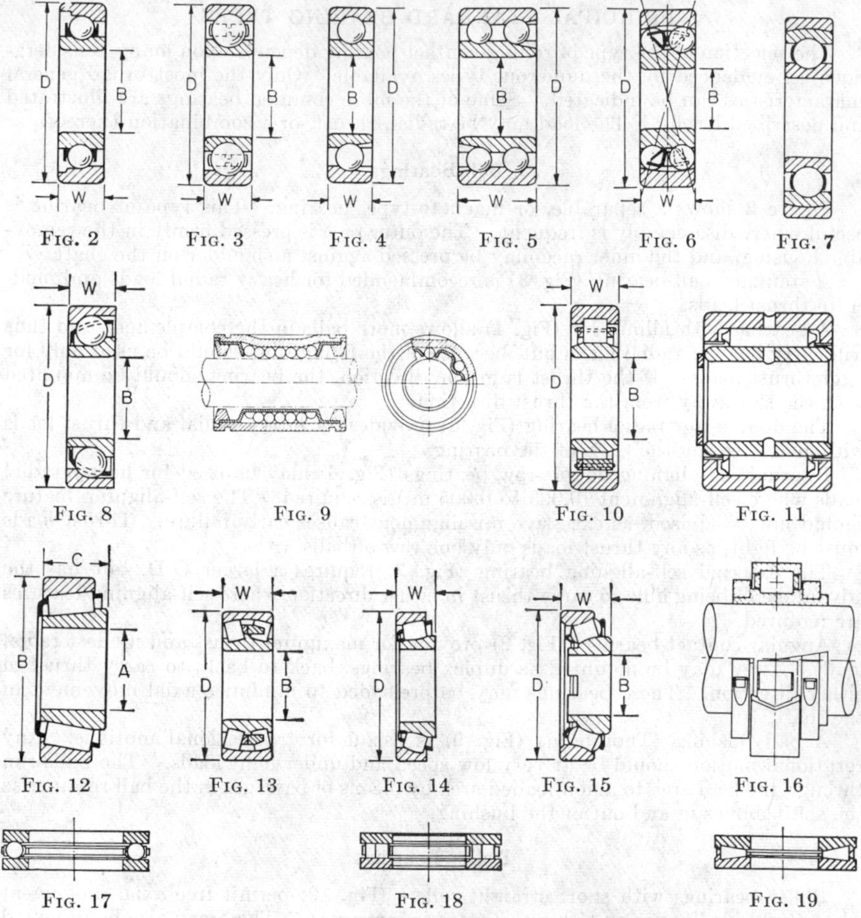

Figs. 2 to 19. Bearings and their mountings.

Thrust Bearings

The ball thrust bearing (**Fig. 17**) may be used for low-speed applications where other bearings carry the radial load. These bearings are made with shields, as well as the open type.

Straight-roller thrust bearings (**Fig. 18**) are made of a series of short rollers to minimize the twisting of the rollers. They may be used for moderate speeds and loads.

The tapered-roller thrust bearing (**Fig. 19**) eliminates the twisting that takes place with straight rollers, but causes a thrust load between the ends of the rollers and the shoulder on the race. They therefore should be used for moderate speeds and loads.

Bearing Closures

Ball bearings are made with shields on one side or on both sides (**Fig. 20**). There is no significant change in the frictional characteristics because of the fixed clearance between the stationary shield and the rotating race. A labyrinth formed when one shield is pressed into the non-rotating outer race and a shield pressed into the inner race is an effective seal. The shield rotating with the inner race acts as a slinger.

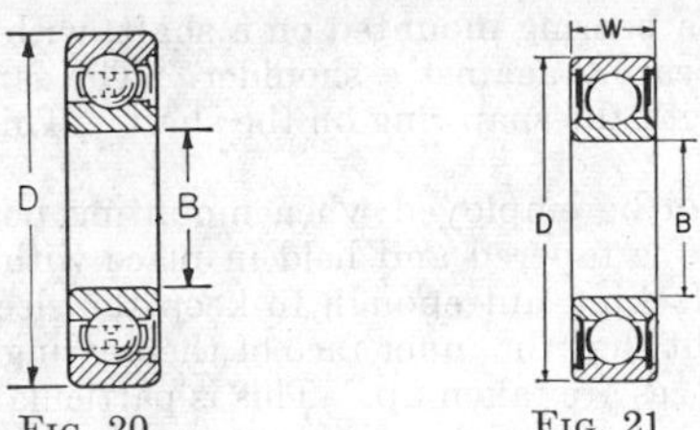

FIG. 20 FIG. 21

The sealed bearing (**Fig. 21**) has a flexible lip, usually of synthetic rubber, in contact with the inner race. Maximum sealing is provided with only a slight increase in the friction of the bearing. They should not be used for high speeds, as heating is likely to occur.

Bearing Mountings

The precision of the rolling-contact bearing should be reflected in the mounting, for the maximum success of the application. Many types of mountings are available to cover the variety of service conditions encountered.

Some factors which will determine the type of mounting are (1) the accuracy required, such as in a precision spindle; (2) the speed, because fast travel requires rigid and accurate mounting; (3) the load requirements, because the greater the loading or shock the better must be the mounting; (4) the desired bearing life; and (5) the economics of construction and the ease of maintenance.

The preferred method of mounting is shown in **Fig. 22.** Both the inner and outer races are held securely in place; this prevents creeping or spinning of the races in the housing or on the shaft. The compression of the inner race against the shoulder by the locking nut eliminates distortion.

In rigid mountings, provision must be made for expansion, either by building slip clearance into one mount or by using a straight roller bearing on the free end of the mechanism. Care must be exercised when designing the slip fit, as too loose a fit will encourage spinning of the bearing on the shaft or in the housing.

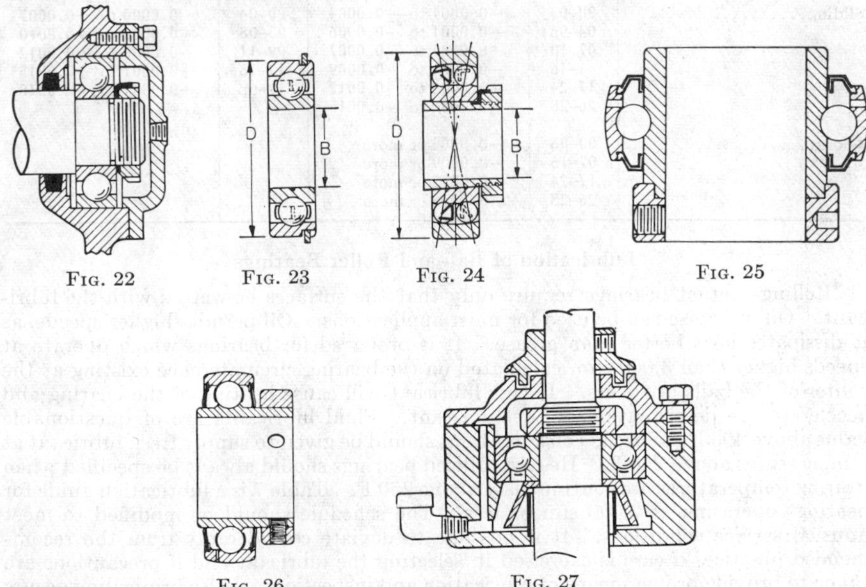

FIG. 22 FIG. 23 FIG. 24 FIG. 25

FIG. 26 FIG. 27

Figure 23 illustrates a bearing mounted on a shaft, with a snap ring on the outer race which locates the bearing against a shoulder. The same construction could be used for the inner race with the snap ring on the shaft. This method is prevalent for securing small bearings.

An adapter sleeve can be employed when mounting bearings on shafting, as in **Fig. 24,** where the sleeve is tapered and held in place with a locking unit. Skill is required to tighten the locking nut enough to keep the sleeve from spinning on the shaft, and yet not so tight that the inner race of the bearing is expanded to the point where all internal clearances are taken up. This is particularly true of the light series of bearings.

Bearings are mounted on shafts by means of an eccentric ring, cut on the side of the extended inner race (**Fig. 25**). A set screw holds the bearing in place.

Bearings with an extended inner race can be mounted on line shafting (**Fig. 26**), with a set screw securing the race to the shaft. This design should be used only where the service requirements are very light.

Figure 27 illustrates a vertical high-speed spindle mounting with oil circulation by means of a flinger and external-labyrinth dirt protector.

Table 6 is a suggested guide for the various fits for the more common sizes of ball and roller bearings. These dimensions should be followed rigidly for a successful bearing mounting. The table does not apply to precision bearings, where the shaft must be fitted to the bore and the O.D. of the bearing to the housing with 0.0001 in. tolerance.

Table 6. Guide for Shaft and Housing Clearance Where Shaft Is Turning

Type of fit	Shaft		Housing	
	Basic bearing No.	Tolerance, in.	Basic bearing No.	Tolerance, in.
Press or interference	All bearings	+0.0003 to 0.0000	00–04	−0.0002 to 0.0000
			05–up	−0.0003 to 0.0000
Push	All bearings	0.0000 to −0.0002	00–04	0.0000 to +0.0002
			05–up	0.0000 to +0.0003
Sliding	00–03	−0.0001 to −0.0004	00–04	0.0000 to +0.0007
	04–06	−0.0001 to −0.0006	05–08	0.0000 to +0.0010
	07–10	−0.0001 to −0.0007	09–11	0.0000 to +0.0012
	11–16	−0.0001 to −0.0009	12–18	+0.0001 to +0.0015
	17–24	−0.0002 to −0.0012	19–up	+0.0001 to +0.0018
	26–28	−0.0002 to −0.0015		
Loose	00–06	−0.0006 or more		
	07–16	−0.0009 or more		
	17–24	−0.0012 or more		
	26–28	−0.0015 or more		

Lubrication of Ball and Roller Bearings

Rolling-contact bearings require only that the surfaces be wetted with the lubricant. Oil or grease can be used for most applications. Oil permits higher speeds, as it dissipates heat better than grease. It is preferred for bearings which operate at speeds higher than 3,000 sfm, calculated on the bearing circumference existing at the center of the balls or rollers. Excess lubricant will cause heating of the bearing and accelerate the deterioration of the lubricant. Fluid lubricants are of questionable value above 400 F. Special considerations should be given to supply fresh lubricant at temperatures above 250 F. Heat-stabilized bearings should always be specified when bearing temperatures are continuously above 250 F. Table 7 is a lubrication guide for bearings operating at 2,000 sfm or less. The schedule should be modified to meet unusual service conditions. It is possible to deviate considerably from the recommended practices if care is exercised in selecting the lubricant and if precautions are taken to provide proper means of lubrication and inspection. False brinnelling occurs when the motion of a bearing is such that movement is less than half the circumference of the ball or roller. A viscous oil or very soft grease minimizes this effect and should be used under these operating conditions. (See also pp. 6-243 to 6-258.)

Table 7. Lubrication Guide

Facilities for adding grease	175 F(max) operating temp intermittent duty, or 150 F (max) operating temp 3,000 hr per yr	175 F operating temp 3,000 hr per yr, 150 F 8,000 hr per yr	175 F operating temp 8,000 hr per yr
None	Repack every 4 yr	Repack every 2 yr	Repack yearly
Facilities for inflow only	Add every 2 yr Repack every 8 yr	Add yearly Repack every 4 yr	Add every 6 months Repack every 2 yr
Facilities for inflow and relief of grease	Add every 3 yr Repack every 12 yr	Add yearly Repack every 8 yr	Add every 6 months Repack every 4 yr

External seals to the bearing may be used to retain the lubricant and to exclude dirt and foreign material. Two of the more common types are the lip seal, and the rotary, or mechanical, seal.

Lip-type seals may be mounted with the lip inward to retain lubricant or with the lip outward to exclude dirt. They are sometimes mounted back to back to retain lubricant and exclude dirt. In this latter mounting, provisions must be made to furnish lubricant between the seals to prevent wear and early failure. Figure 28 illustrates a lip-type seal.

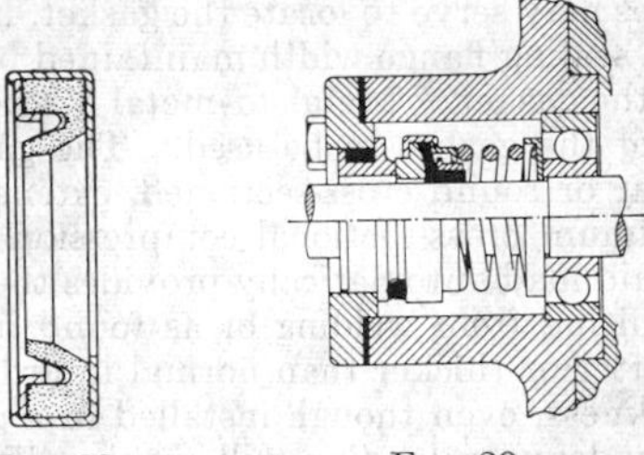

FIG. 28 FIG. 29

Mechanical seals are more effective in preventing leakage and are capable of operating at higher speeds and loads than are the lip-type seals. Figure 29 shows a spring-loaded collar rotating with the shaft, pressed against a stationary shaft in the housing. The faces may be carbon against a variety of hardened steels and alloys. Ceramics and other materials are used in corrosive solutions or where long life is imperative.

Interchangeability of Bearings

All American bearing manufacturers conform to the standards of the AFBMA as a minimum for manufacturing tolerances. This permits interchangeability of many standard rolling-contact bearings. The manufacturers' literature should be consulted for engineering data and unusual bearing applications.

PACKINGS

BY

Edward W. Fisher

REFERENCES: Staniar, "Plant Engineering Handbook," McGraw-Hill. Thorn, Rubber and Plastic Packings, *Rubber Age*, January, 1956. Roberts, Gaskets and Bolted Joints, *Jour. Applied Mechanics*, June, 1950. Non-metallic Gaskets, *Machine Design*, November, 1954. Elonka, "Basic Data on Seals," a *Power* reprint, McGraw-Hill.

Packings include those means used to prevent or minimize leakage of a fluid through mechanical clearances in either the static or dynamic state.

Gaskets are installed in static clearances which normally exist between parallel flanges or concentric cylinders. Sealing of flat flange gaskets is effected by compressive loading achieved through bolting or other mechanical means. The full face gasket (Fig. 1) is not recommended because the material outside the bolt holes is ineffective. The simple ring gasket (Fig. 2) is more efficient and economical. With irregularly contoured flanges, bolt holes may serve to locate the gasket, in which case they should be placed in lobes with full sealing flange width maintained between the inner edge of the holes and the inside of the gasket. **Metal-to-metal** fits require a recess whose volume is greater than that of the gasket to be used. The gasket, such as an O ring (Fig. 13), either rectangular or round cross-sectioned, extends above the groove sufficiently to provide a minimum cross-sectional compression of 15 percent for initial seating. In service, the fluid load automatically provides the sealing force. **Warped or wavy** flanges, often resulting from welding or as found in glass-lined equipment, require gaskets that are softer or thicker than normal in order to adjust to high and low areas. Excessive thickness, even though installed in a groove, must be avoided or "mushrooming" and inadequate loading will result. Tongue-and-groove joints (Fig. 4) confine the gasket and thus are well adapted to accommodating such extra thickness.

In addition to the types (Figs. 5, 6 and 7) shown, as defined in the table (Fig. 37), there are the machined metal-profile gasket (Fig. 8) and solid metal designs in flat, round, and either octagonal or oval API ring joint gaskets for extreme pressures and temperatures against steam, oil, and gases. Compressibilities are very low and depend on cross section. The envelope gasket (Fig. 3), usually polytetrafluorethylene with a variety of cores, is particularly useful for extremely corrosive or non-contaminating service under average pressure conditions.

Cylindrical or **concentric** gasketing involves the use of a gland to provide retention and mechanical loading, as in the standard mechanical joint for cast-iron pipe (Fig. 10) or the condenser tube-sheet ferrule (Fig. 11). There are also gaskets shaped like cups and designed to be self-tightening under pressure (Fig. 12). The O ring, Fig. 13, located in an annular groove and precompressed as in the grooved flange, is a self-energized gasket. A cylindrical ring with internal single or double lips, also automatic in action, is quite common in pipe joints.

Beyond these types are many specialty gaskets designed for specific or proprietary use; for example, a seal for a removable drumhead.

The compressibility of various gasketing materials is shown in Fig. 37, and their common usage is listed in the accompanying table. Beyond rubber are many elastomeric materials generally similar in mechanical behavior but varying in temperature limits and fluid compatibility (see pp. 6–197 *et seq.*).

The **proper design** of a gasketed joint requires flange rigidity to avoid bowing, surface finish commensurate with gasket type and fluid pressure, and adequate bolt loading. The load must seat the gasket, i.e., cause the material to flow into and fill flange irregularities. It must also carry the fluid load with sufficient excess so that the residual pressure on the gasket exceeds the fluid pressure. These values, known respectively as the seating load "y" in psi and the gasket factor "m," vary with gasket material and thickness. The *ASME* Code for Unfired Pressure Vessels, Section VIII, gives sufficient detail for typical joint design and tabulates values for y and m for various gasketing materials.

While high bolt loading is desirable for tight and enduring joints, it must not crush the gasket material. Crushing strength values, which will vary with thickness and temperature, can be obtained from the gasket manufacturers. Consistent with condition of the flanges, the thinner the gasket the more efficient the joint.

Data on the design of **O-ring joints** are available from suppliers. The nominal pressure limit for O rings, based on typical mechanical clearances, is 1,500 psi without backup rings and 3,000 with backup rings. If clearances can be eliminated, as in a flanged joint with close metal-to-metal contact, no limit can be set. Other self-energizing joints, such as the boiler hand-hole plate (Fig. 9), need only sufficient load to effect an initial seal.

Valve disks are specialized gaskets designed for joints that are frequently broken and restored. Disks for globe valves (Fig. 14) are usually encased in a disk holder with a swivel mounting so that they do not rotate while closing. They are made of firm rubber for bib washers to hard rubber and phenolics for more severe service. Plastics such as nylon and polytetrafluorethylene are also used. Pump valves (Fig. 15) are described on p. 14–11. **Valve seats** of rubber are used with metal valve disks on some pumps, *e.g.*, the rotary drilling pump (Fig. 16). Plastics are also used for seats, notably in ball valves.

Dynamic packings include all packings that operate on moving surfaces. In functioning, to retain fluid under pressure, they carry the hydraulic load. Where no pressure exists, as in many oil-seal applications, the packing is mechanically loaded as by a spring (Fig. 28) or by its own resiliency. Dynamic packings therefore operate as bearings, thereby indicating the need for lubrication to serve as both a separating film and a coolant. The presence of a film is vital for satisfactory service life, but it also means that leakage will occur. Low-viscosity fluids and high pressures add to leakage problems, as both require thin films to minimize leakage. This causes higher friction and results in heat, which is the one most detrimental factor in packing life. Deep packings reduce leakage but seriously increase frictional heat, particularly at high speeds. Normally the fluid being sealed serves as the lubricant. Thus, where oils are involved, maximum efficiency is obtained. Next in order are clean water, solvents, and fluids containing solids which progressively yield more unsatisfactory results unless supplemental lubrication is provided. Lubrication may be provided by using a lantern ring in the center of the set through which the more satisfactory lubricant is fed to the packing (Fig. 27). The preferred method of introducing the medium is to supply it at a slightly higher pressure, 5 to 10 psi, than the material being sealed. The choice of fluid is governed by the media involved, since the two should be compatible. In cases of extreme contamination, the lantern is moved to the bottom of the box and is used as a means to introduce a flushing fluid. The lantern is also effective in excluding air from a device operating at negative heads. In centrifugal pumps equipped in this manner, it is called a **water seal.**

Dynamic packings are classified in three ways:

1. On the basis of shape of the surfaces: cylindrical, conical, spherical, or flat. Cylindrical packings are in turn classified according to whether they pack on the outside perimeter, as in piston packings (Figs. 17 to 20) or inside perimeter, as on rods or shafts (Figs. 21 to 28). Other examples are: conical, the plug-cock lining (Fig. 29); spherical, the ball joint (Fig. 30); and flat, the mechanical seals (Figs. 31 and 32).

2. On the basis of the type of motion: rotary, oscillating, reciprocating, or helical (as in a rising stem valve packing).

3. On the basis of non-automatic: soft or jamb packings (tightened by external

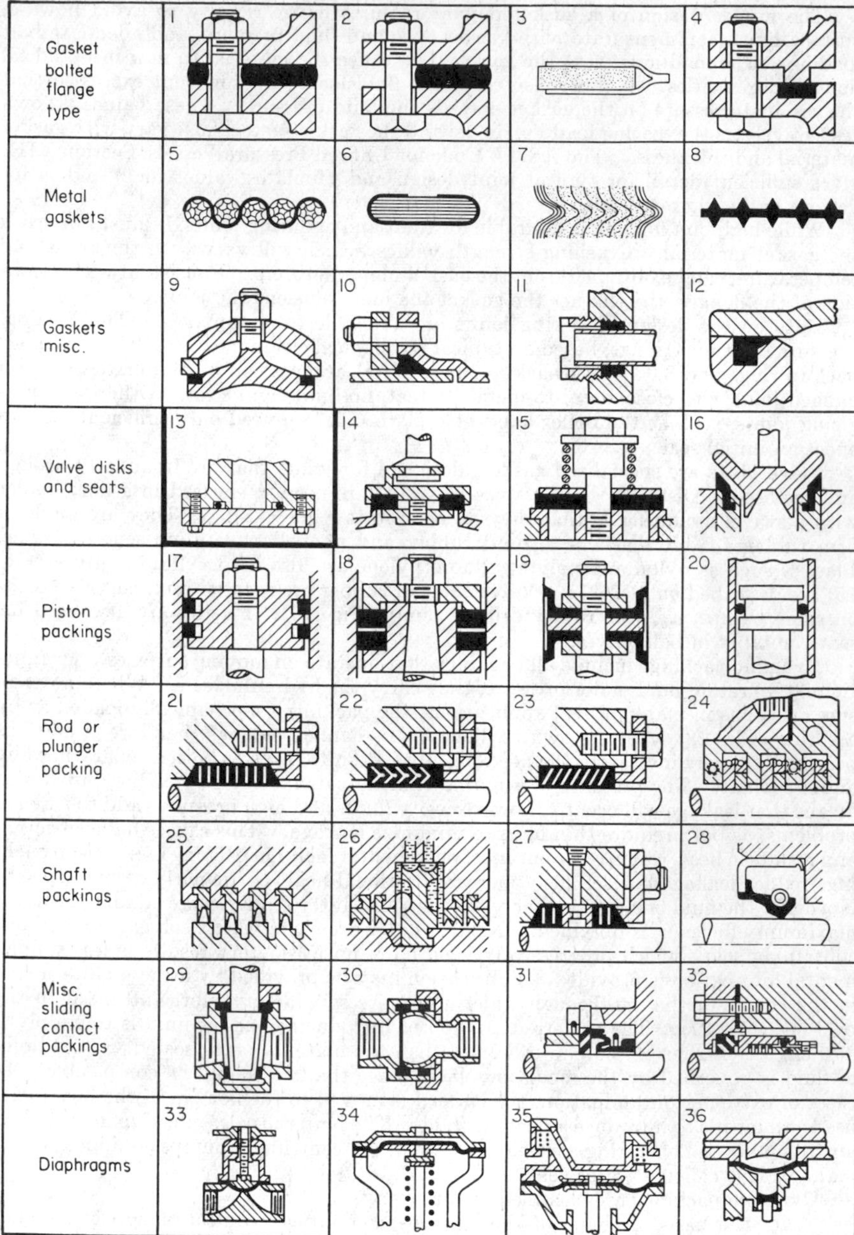

FIGS. 1 through 36. Packings.

means, generally a gland); or automatic-preformed, molded shapes (self-tightening under pressure).

The **selection of a packing** is a matter of economics. In most cases several types are available, some of which, though expensive in the first place, yield exceptional service. A less costly choice might yield degraded service.

For **reciprocating elements,** the **O ring** (Fig. 20) is extremely simple; however, suppliers' data reveal it is a precision part requiring close tolerances. As an elastomeric material completely exposed to the operating fluid, it is subject to attack. Careful choice of elastomer is necessary to insure compatibility or else either shrinkage

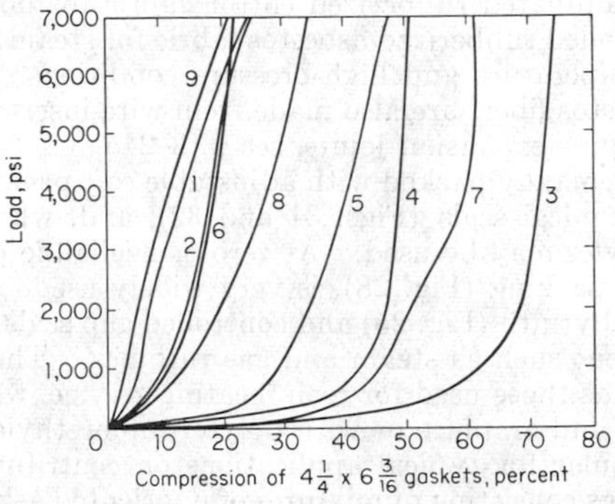

Fig. 37. Compressibility of gaskets.

No.	Type	Service principally for	Thickness tested, in.
1	Sheet rubber	Water	1/16
2	Cloth inserted sheet	Water	1/16
3	Cork composition	Oil, low pressure	1/8
4	Gasket paper	Oil, low pressure	1/16
5	Rubberized asbestos cloth (Fig. 9)	Hot water (boiler manholes, etc.)	1/4
6	Compressed asbestos sheet	All services up to 750 F	1/16
7	Corrugated sheet metal with filling (Fig. 5)	Steam, oil at high temperatures	1/4
8	Metal jacket over asbestos center (Fig. 6)	Steam, oil at high temperatures	1/8
9	Spirally wound steel strip with intervening asbestos layers (Fig. 7)	Steam, oil at high temperatures	3/16

or swelling may occur, causing early failure. It is best suited to medium pressure service from 1,500 to 3,000 psi with backup rings and intermittent movement, as in hydraulic cylinder or valve stem service. It is not a good choice for pump service. Backup rings are preferably of the heavy blocklike cross section in either leather or tetrafluorethylene, avoiding the thin spiral type. The split **piston ring** (Fig. 17), generally of cast iron, is widely used in gas, oil, and steam engines. Large pistons frequently employ segmental rings similar to floating metal rod packings (Fig. 24) but facing outward. **Floating metal packing rings** are made of numerous radial or tangential segments, making it possible for them to contract on the shaft; they are assembled, generally, in sets of two to break the joints and are held together with garter springs. They are used for steam, gas, or air, in either engines or compressors under the most severe conditions of operation and pressure up to 35,000 psi. Normally oil lubrication is provided; however, for less severe service, filled polytetrafluorethylene rings perform very well in dry gases without auxiliary lubrication. Step-, scarf-, or butt-cut rings of laminated cotton fabric, bonded with an elastomer or phenolic resin, are employed in water pumps, gasoline pumps, etc. They may float as cast-iron piston rings or be retained by a gland as in Fig. 18. **Cups** (Fig. 19) or their inverted form with the lip on the I.D., known as **flange packings,** are fully automatic and very tight. They are used principally for slow-speed applications such as air hoists. **Nested V and conical**

rings (Figs. 22 and 23) are automatic, though often provided with a gland to effect initial fit. They are made of a wide range of materials from homogeneous elastomers through cotton or asbestos fabric reinforcement for severe duty. They range in hardness from soft and flexible to semirigid. Use of multiple rings allows them to be cut open for ease of installation and replacement. **Soft or jamb packings** are best suited for rod or plunger service, since an adjustable gland (Fig. 21) is required. They are normally formed in rectangular section with a butt joint staggered from ring to ring at installation. Many materials are employed, such as braided flax saturated with wax or viscous lubricants for water and aqueous solutions; braided asbestos similarly treated or often impregnated with polytetrafluorethylene suspensoid for superior and more severe service; laminated rubberized cotton fabric for hot water, low-pressure steam and ammonia; rolled rubberized asbestos fabric for steam; and rolled or twisted metal foil for high-temperature and high-pressure conditions. Packings containing woven or braided asbestos fibers are also made from wire-inserted yarns to gain additional strength. For pipe expansion joints, see p. 8–245.

Rotary shafts are generally packed with adjustable soft packings, with the notable exception of the mechanical seals (Figs. 31 and 32), and, where pressures are low, nested V or conical styles may be used. At zero or negligible pressures, the oil seal, a spring-loaded flange packing (Fig. 28), is very widely used. Where some leakage can be tolerated, the labyrinth (Fig. 25) and controlled gap seals are used, particularly on high-speed equipment such as steam and gas turbines. The **soft packings** are of the same general type as those used for reciprocating service, with the asbestos braid lubricated with grease and graphite or with polytetrafluorethylene suspensoid. The latter is the most popular for typical applications on centrifugal pumps and valve stems. **Plastic packings** consisting of mixtures of unoriented asbestos fibers, graphite, soft metal particles, and a binder furnished either in bulk or formed rings are also popular. To prevent loss of plastic from the stuffing box, end rings of metal foil, braid, or laminated fabric and rubber are generally used. For continuous rotary service, **automatic packings** are best restricted to low pressure because their tightness under high pressure tends to cause overheating. However, for intermittent service, as on valve stems, they are excellent.

Oil seals (Fig. 28) are unique flange packings having an elastomer lip generally bonded to a metal cup which is press-fitted into a smooth cylindrical bore. Basically, an oil seal is a flange packing with a flexible lip and a narrow contact area about $\frac{1}{16}$ in. wide which, under pressure, causes extreme local heating and wear. They can therefore be recommended only for non-pressure service and are best against good lubricating media. To accommodate shaft run-out up to 0.020 in., depending on rpm, the lip is spring-loaded. Since the lip is completely exposed to the media, particular care should be taken to insure compatibility between the elastomer and the fluid. Temperature is another element important in this area.

Mechanical, rotary, or end-face seals (Figs. 31 and 32) consist of radial planar surfaces, normal to the shaft axis, cooperating as a thrust bearing. One face is generally resiliently gasketed to the housing, and the shaft-driven face is sealed thereon with a bellows (Fig. 31) or automatic-type packing (Fig. 32), permitting axial movement to compensate for end-play and wear. Bearing contact between the faces is accomplished by spring-loading. Wide choice of face materials, one of which is usually carbon, offers an extreme range of pressures and service conditions with very high efficiency. Probably one of the simplest designs is the bellows-supported phenolic-cotton washer bearing against a machined face of the cast-iron pump body of an automotive water pump (Fig. 31). A more refined, flexible design is shown in Fig. 32, and detailed in part in Fig. 38, which illustrates unbalanced and balanced constructions and how they are respectively suitable for pressures up to 250 and 3,000 psi. The purpose of balancing is to reduce the unit face load to approximately 60 to 70 percent of the unit fluid load. A complete balance is not practical.

For extremely high speeds, where it is desirable to eliminate all rubbing contact, the **labyrinth** seal (Fig. 25) is chosen. This seal is not fluid-tight but restricts a serious flow by means of a torturous path and induced turbulence. It is widely used on steam turbines (see p. 9–68). Where no leakage is permissible, a liquid seal based on the

U-tube principle (Fig. 26) may be used. The natural weight of the liquid is amplified by centrifugal force so that under high rpm a fair pressure differential can be sealed. Another non-contacting seal is the **controlled gap seal** which is being used on gas turbines where pressure differentials are not excessive and a small amount of leakage can be tolerated. The seal consists of a ring with a shaft clearance in the range of 0.0005 in. to 0.0015 in. and is made of such materials that this clearance is maintained at all operating temperatures. Usually one end of the ring is faced to form an axial seal against the inside of its housing.

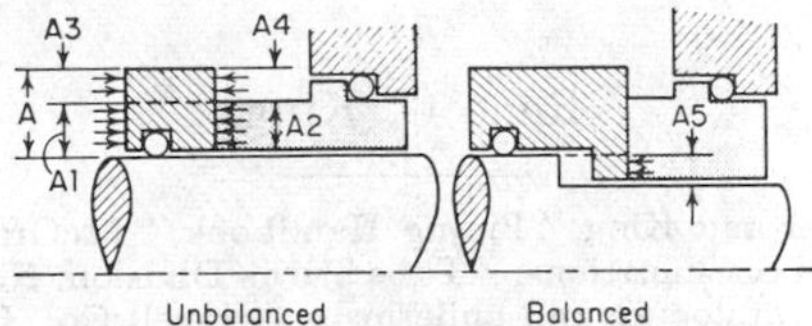

FIG. 38. Mechanical seal face loading. A = gross area under fluid load; A_1 = effective fluid load area for closing the seal; A_2 = pressure gradient area where average unit load equals that of the fluid on A_1 (shaft clearance ignored); A_3, A_4 = fluid load areas which balance each other; A_5 = balancing area, normally such that $A_2 + A_5$ will reduce the average unit load on this face to 60 to 70 percent of the unit fluid load on A_1.

Diaphragms are a form of dynamic packing but include the requirements of a gasket where they are gripped or held in position. In service they are leakless, although generally limited in travel. By literally rolling one cylinder inside another, considerable increase in travel is possible. This latter type is often called a bellows, and a simple application is the mechanical seal suspension shown in Fig. 31. In the diaphragm valve (Fig. 33) the diaphragm replaces both the conventional stem packing and valve disk. **Diaphragms** of fabric such as cotton or nylon (except friable materials such as glass) covered with an elastomer suitable for the media and temperatures involved are used in pumps (fuel pump, Fig. 35) and in motors (Fig. 34) to operate valves, switches, and other controls. Correctly designed diaphragms are made with slack to permit a natural rolling action. Flat sheet stock should be used only where limited travel is desired. An unusual application is found in the Pulsa-feeder pump (Fig. 36) in that the diaphragm is under balanced fluid pressure on both sides and is therefore unstressed. Thin sheet metal, usually with concentric corrugations, is used where movement is limited and long life is desired. However, where considerable movement is involved, the possibility of fatigue must be considered.

PIPE AND PIPE FITTINGS

BY

Reno C. King

REFERENCES: Crocker and King, "Piping Handbook," McGraw-Hill. ASA Code for Pressure Piping. ASTM Specifications. Tube Turns Division, Natural Cylinder Gas Co., catalogues. Crane Co., catalogues and bulletins. Grinnell Co., Inc., "Piping Design and Engineering." M. W. Kellogg Co., "Design of Piping Systems," Wiley.

PIPING STANDARDS

Standardization in the piping industry is the function of many groups, among whom are the American Society for Testing Materials (ASTM), the American Standards Association (ASA), the American Water Works Association (AWWA), and the Pipe Fabrication Institute (PFI); in addition, specifications have been issued by several governmental agencies to cover work on Federal installations.

The ASTM has as its aim the "Promotion of Knowledge of Materials of Engineering, and Standardization of Specifications and Methods of Testing." It is concerned with chemical and physical properties of piping (and other materials or products) as delivered from the fabricating mill.

The ASA deals with over-all piping systems. It standardizes dimensions, sets permissible stress values as functions of temperature, establishes working formulas for determination of wall thickness as determined by pressure and material at a given temperature, specifies general character of construction of valves and fittings, deals with the support, anchoring, and flexibility of a piping system and, in general, sets up a code of minimum requirements for the safety and reliability of a system. The work done by this organization has culminated in hundreds of standards for individual materials, published in several issues of its Code for Pressure Piping and its more recent Gas Transmission and Distribution Piping Systems.

The AWWA was one of the first groups to realize the importance and advantage of standardization of cast-iron pipe and fittings. Its standard, first published in 1908, has been superseded by ASA publications in all respects except for cast-iron fittings of a size larger than 12 in.

PFI has been active in preparation of standards dealing with shop fabrication, particularly in standardizing the technique for preparation of pipe ends prior to welding.

The Manufacturers' Standardization Society of the Valve and Fittings Industry engages in preparation of standards for both valves and fittings, generally in the lower range of pressures and temperatures.

Piping is available in both ferrous and non-ferrous materials. Cast iron and steel represent the ferrous class; brass, copper, aluminum, and lead are non-ferrous metals which have wide application as piping materials. Concrete, wood, tile, and plastic have found general acceptance for specific usages.

STEEL PIPE AND TUBING

There is no definite rule for distinguishing between the use of the general terms pipe, tube, and tubing; the proper designation has been determined by trade usage. The word **pipe** is generally used to apply to tubular products commonly used for pipelines and connections for conveying fluid from point to point. The word **tube** (or **tubing**) is generally used to apply to tubular products used in heat exchangers and boilers and in the machine and aircraft industries.

Piping Fabrication Methods. Piping is commercially available as manufactured by the following techniques: electric-fusion welding, electric-resistance welding, submerged-arc electric welding, seamless piercing and rolling, forging, turning, and boring, and hollow forging. In addition, some mills are prepared to extrude small-diameter pipe and tubing in a variety of geometric shapes or to cast large-diameter steel pipe.

Electric-fusion Welding. Flat plate, known as **skelp,** is prepared in proper width and thickness for the desired pipe inside and outside diameters. It is then charged into an electric furnace and, when the proper welding temperature has been reached, is drawn through a funnel-shaped die so shaped that the plate is gradually formed into the shape of a tube, with the edges of the plate being forced squarely together and fused. The formed pipe then passes through a series of rolls in which it is sized or drawn to final dimensions.

Electric-resistance Welding. For pipes or tubes sized 4 in. O.D. and under, strip is fed onto a set of forming rolls which consists of horizontal and vertical rollers so placed as to gradually form the flat strip into a tube. The tube form then passes to the welding electrodes. The electrodes are copper disks connected to the secondary of a revolving transformer assembly. The copper-disk electrodes make contact on each side of the seam of the tube form; a flow of current takes place across the seam, and temperature is raised to the welding point. Outside flash is removed by a cutting tool as the tube leaves the electrodes; inside flash is removed either by an air hammer or by passing a mandrel through the welded tube after the tube has been cooled.

Submerged-arc Electric Welding. This process is used for pipes from 24 to 36 in. O.D. Flat plate is first pressed unto a U and later into an O shape. The O shape is placed in an automatic welder and backed up on the inside by a water-cooled copper shoe. Two electrodes in close proximity are used. The electrodes are not in actual contact with the pipe. The current passes from one electrode through a granular flux and across the gap in the pipe to the second electrode. The high temperature of the arc heats the edges of the plate; a welding rod placed just over the seam is thereby melted and metal is deposited in the groove. After the outside weld has been made, the pipe is conveyed to an inside welder where a similar operation is carried on, except that no back-up shoe is needed.

Seamless Tubing and Pipe. A heated billet is brought into contact with tapered revolving rolls in such a way that the billet is pulled into the space allowed between the rolls. A piercing mandrel is placed in this space; the soft center of the billet makes it possible for the rolls to draw the billet over the mandrel, producing a hollow shell. When the billet has entirely passed over the mandrel, it is in the form of a thick-walled seamless tube. The heavy-walled tube is then passed to a rolling mill which reduces the tube to piping of proper outside diameter and wall thickness.

The method of fabrication described above is limited as to diameter and thickness. For seamless alloy tubes and for heavy-walled carbon-steel tubes or piping, a process known as **cupping and drawing** is frequently used. A circular flat plate of proper diameter and thickness is heated, placed in a hydraulic press, and pressed by a ram through a die. The cup so formed is reheated and pressed through a smaller die, thus elongating the cup so that it becomes a short cylinder with one closed end. This short cylinder is then placed in a horizontal drawbench, and with reheating as necessary, is pushed by a ram through dies of successively smaller diameters until the desired outer diameter is reached.

Forged, Turned, and Bored Tubing. In this process, the ingot is heated and forged to a rough cylindrical shape, oversize in both diameter and length. The forging is then placed in a lathe and the outside turned down to the desired outer diameter. Rough ends are then removed so that the finally desired length is obtained. The cylinder is then placed in a boring mill, and the inside bored out until the desired wall thickness is secured.

Hollow-forged Pipe and Tubing. In this process, ingots are cast and their ends cropped; then they are placed in a furnace and heated to a specified temperature. The heated ingot is placed in a press where it is pierced. This hollow cylinder, open at one end, is then descaled and drawn over a mandrel on a horizontal drawbench. The closed end is then burned off, and the hollow forging is chemically descaled. Following

Table 1. Allowable Stresses for Pipe in Power Piping Systems
(ASA Code for Pressure Piping, 1963)

Material*	ASTM specification	Grade	Minimum ultimate tensile strength	Values of S, psi, for temperatures in degrees F not to exceed†							
				−20 to 100	200	300	400§	450	500	600	650
Welded material:											
Furnace welded carbon steel											
Lap welded	A120	....	......	8,800	8,600	8,200	7,600	7,600			
Butt welded	A120	....	......	6,500	6,350	6,100	5,850	5,700			
Automatically welded austenitic stainless steel											
18% Cr–8% Ni-Ti	A312	TP321									
18% Cr–8% Ni-Cb	A312	TP347	75,000	15,950	15,950	14,450	13,450	.....	12,900	12,650	12,600
Seamless material:											
Carbon steel	A120	....	......	10,800	10,600	10,200	9,800	9,600			
5% Cr–½% Mo	A335	P5									
	A335	P5b	60,000	15,000	15,000	15,000	15,000	.....	14,500	14,000	13,700
	A369	FP5									
18% Cr–8% Ni-Ti	A312										
	A376	TP321									
18% Cr–8% Ni-Cb	A312	TP347	75,000	18,750	18,750	17,000	15,800	.....	15,200	14,900	14,850
	A376										
Seamless:											
Red brass	B43	....	......	8,000	8,000	7,000	3,000				
Copper 2 in. and smaller	B42	....	......	6,000	5,500	4,750	3,000				
Copper, over 2 in.	B42	....	......	6,000	5,500	4,750	3,000				
Copper tubing	B75	....	......	6,000	5,500	4,750	3,000				
Annealed	B88	....	30,000	6,000	5,500	4,750	3,000				
Bright annealed	B68	....	30,000	6,000	5,500	4,750	3,000				
Copper brazed steel	A254	Class 1	42,000	6,000	5,500	4,750	3,000				
		Class 2	42,000	3,600	3,300	2,850	1,800				
Cast iron‡											
Centrifugally cast	FSB WW-P-421	Types 1 & 2	......	6,000	6,000	6,000	6,000	6,000			
Metal molds	ASA A21.6										
Sand-lined molds	ASA B21.8	....	......	6,000	6,000	6,000	6,000	6,000			
Pit cast	ASA A21.2	....	......	4,000	4,000	4,000	4,000	4,000			

* Pipe in accordance with API specification 5L may be used.

† The several types and grades of pipe tabulated above shall not be used at temperatures in excess of the maximum temperatures for which the S values are indicated. (See also specific requirements for service conditions contemplated.) Allowable S values for intermediate temperatures may be obtained by interpolation.

‡ Cast-iron pipe shall not be used for lubricating oil lines for machinery and in any case not for oil having a temperature above 300 F.

§ For steam at 250 psi (406 F) the values given may be used.

Table 2. Allowable Stresses for Pipe in Power Piping Systems

(ASA Code for Pressure Piping, 1963)

[Where welded construction is used, consideration should be given to the possibility of graphite formation in the following steels: carbon steel above 775 F; carbon-molybdenum steel above 800 F; chrome-molybdenum steel (with chromium under 0.60) above 975 F.]

Material[a]	ASTM specification	Grade	Identification symbol	Minimum ultimate tensile strength	Values of S psi for temperatures in deg F not to exceed[b]											
					−20 to 650	700	750	800	850	900	950	1000	1050	1100	1150	1200
Welded material																
Furnace welded:																
Lap welded																
Carbon steel..........	A53	....	......	45,000	9,000											
Wrought iron..........	A72	....	......	40,000	8,000											
Butt welded																
Carbon steel..........	A53	....	......	45,000	6,750											
Wrought iron..........	A72	....	......	40,000	6,000											
Electric fusion welded:																
Carbon steel..........	A134	A245 A	......	48,000	8,000											
		A245 B	......	52,000	9,600											
		A245 C	......	55,000	10,100											
		A283 A	......	45,000	8,300											
		A283 B	......	50,000	9,200											
		A283 C	......	55,000	10,100											
		A283 D	......	60,000	10,100											
	A139	A[d]	......	48,000	9,600	9,250	8,300									
		B[d]	......	60,000	12,000	11,350	9,950									
	A155[c]	A285 A	C45	45,000	10,100	9,800	8,700	7,500	5,950							
		A285 B	C50	50,000	11,250	10,900	9,900	8,450	6,550							
		A285 C	C55	55,000	12,400	11,900	10,850	9,200	7,000							
Killed carbon steel..........	.....	A201 A	KC55	55,000	12,400	11,900	10,850	9,200	7,000							
		A201 B	KC60	60,000	13,500	12,900	11,650	9,700	7,000							
		A212 A	KC65	65,000	14,600	13,950	12,450	10,250	7,000							
		A212 B	KC70	70,000	15,750	14,950	13,250	10,800	7,000							
Carbon-molybdenum steel..	.....	A204 A	CM65	65,000	14,600	14,600	14,600	14,100	12,950	11,250						
		A204 B	CM70	70,000	15,750	15,750	15,750	15,200	13,500	11,450						
		A204 C	CM75	75,000	16,850	16,850	16,850	16,200	14,300	11,700						
½% Cr–½% Mo steel.....	.....	A301 A	½CR	65,000	14,600	14,600	14,600	14,100	12,950	11,250	9,000	5,600				
1% Cr–½% Mo steel.....	.....	A301 B	1 CR	60,000	13,500	13,500	13,500	13,250	12,750	11,800	9,900	6,750	4,500	2,500		
1¼% Cr–½% Mo steel....	.....	A335 P11	1¼CR	60,000	13,500	13,500	13,500	13,500	12,950	11,800	9,900	7,000	4,950	3,600		
2¼% Cr–1% Mo steel.....	.....	A335 P22	2¼CR	60,000	13,500	13,500	13,500	13,500	12,950	11,800	9,900	7,000	5,200	3,750	2,700	

Table 2. Allowable Stresses for Pipe in Power Piping Systems—(*Continued*)
(ASA Code for Pressure Piping, 1963)

[Where welded construction is used, consideration should be given to the possibility of graphite formation in the following steels: carbon steel above 775 F; carbon-molybdenum steel above 800 F; chrome-molybdenum steel (with chromium under 0.60) above 975 F.]

Material[a]	ASTM specification	Grade	Identification symbol	Minimum ultimate tensile strength	Values of S psi for temperatures in deg F not to exceed[b]											
					−20 to 650	700	750	800	850	900	950	1000	1050	1100	1150	1200
Electric resistance welded:																
Carbon steel..........	A53	A[e]	......	48,000	10,200	9,900	9,100									
		B[e]	......	60,000	12,750	12,200	11,000									
	A135	A[e]	......	48,000	10,200	9,900	9,100									
		B[e]	......	60,000	12,750	12,200	11,000									
Automatically welded stainless steel:																
18% Cr–8% Ni-Ti......... / 18% Cr–8% Ni-Cb	A312	TP321 / TP347	......	75,000	Note *f*	12,550	12,500	12,350	12,150	12,000	11,750	11,500	11,150	8,750	6,450	4,250
Seamless material																
Carbon steel..............	A53	A	......	48,000	12,000	11,650	10,700	9,000	7,100	5,000						
	A53	B	......	60,000	15,000	14,350	12,950	10,800	7,800	5,000						
	A106	A	......	48,000	12,000	11,650	10,700	9,000	7,100	5,000						
	A106	B	......	60,000	15,000	14,350	12,950	10,000	7,800	5,000						
	A83	Type A	......	(47,000)												
	A179	Low carbon	......	....	10,750	11,450	10,550	9,000	7,100	5,000						
	A192	....	......	(47,000)												
	A210	....	......	60,000	15,000	14,350	12,950	10,800	7,800	5,000						
Carbon molybdenum.........	A335 / A369	P 1 / FP 1	......	55,000	13,750	13,750	13,750	13,450	13,150	12,500						
Cr Mo																
½% Cr–½% Mo..........	A335 / A369	P 2 / FP 2	......	55,000	13,750	13,750	13,750	13,450	13,150	12,500	10,000	6,250				
1% Cr–½% Mo...........	A335 / A369	P12 / FP12	......	60,000	15,000	15,000	15,000	14,750	14,200	13,100	11,000	7,500	5,000	2,800		
1¼% Cr–½% Mo.........	A335 / A369	P11 / FP11	......	60,000	15,000	15,000	15,000	15,000	14,400	13,100	11,000	7,800	5,500	4,000		

2¼% Cr–1% Mo.	A213 A335 A369	T22 P22 FP22	. . . . . .	60,000	15,000	15,000	15,000	15,000	14,400	13,100	11,000	7,800	5,800	4,200	3,000	
3% Cr–1% Mo.	A213 A335 A369	T21 P21 FP21	. . . . . .	60,000	15,000	14,800	14,500	13,900	13,200	12,000	9,000	7,000	5,500	4,000	2,700	
5% Cr–½% Mo.	A335 A369	P 5 FP 5	. . . . . .	60,000	Note[f]	13,400	13,100	12,800	12,400	11,500	10,000	7,300	5,200	3,300	2,200	1,500
	A335	P 5b		60,000	Note[f]	13,400	13,100	12,800	12,400	10,900	9,000	5,500	3,500	2,500	1,800	1,200
Stainless steel: 18% Cr–8% Ni-Ti.	A213 A312 A376	TP321	. . . . . .	75,000	Note[f]	14,800	14,700	14,550	14,300	14,100	13,850	13,500	13,100	10,300	7,600	5,000
18% Cr–8% Ni-Cb.	A213 A312 A376	TP347	. . . . . .	75,000	Note[f]	14,800	14,700	14,550	14,300	14,100	13,850	13,500	13,100	10,300	7,600	5,000

[a] Pipe in accordance with API specification 5L may be used as specified.

[b] The several types and grades of pipe tabulated above shall not be used at temperatures in excess of the maximum temperatures for which the S values are indicated. (See also specific requirements for service conditions contemplated.) Allowable S values for intermediate temperatures may be obtained by interpolation.

[c] The values tabulated are for Class 2 pipe. For Class 1 pipe which is heat treated and radiographed, these stresses may be increased by the ratio of 0.95 divided by 0.90.

[d] If plate material having physical properties other than stated in Sec. 6 of the ASTM specification A139 is used in the manufacture of ordinary electric-fusion-welded steel pipe, the allowable stress shall be taken as 0.20 times the tensile strength for temperatures of 450 F and below.

[e] For electric-resistance-welded pipe for applications where the temperature is below 650 F, and where pipe furnished under this classification is subjected to supplemental tests and/or heat treatments as agreed to by the supplier and the purchaser, and whereby such supplemental tests and/or heat treatments demonstrate the strength characteristics of the weld to be equal to the minimum tensile strength specified for the pipe, the S values equal to the corresponding seamless grades may be used.

[f] See Table 1 for values from −20 to 650 F.

Table 3. Physical Properties of Pipe*

(Grinnell Co., Inc.)

Nominal pipe size, O.D., in.	Schedule number†			Wall thickness, in.	I.D., in.	Inside area, sq in.	Metal area, sq in.	Sq ft outside surface, per ft	Sq ft inside surface, per ft	Weight per ft, lb	Weight of water per ft, lb	Moment of inertia, in.⁴	Section modulus, in.³	Radius gyration, in.
	a	*b*	*c*											
⅛ *0.405*	...	.....	10S	0.049	0.307	0.0740	0.0548	0.106	0.0804	0.186	0.0321	0.00088	0.00437	0.1271
	40	Std	40S	0.068	0.269	0.0568	0.0720	0.106	0.0705	0.245	0.0246	0.00106	0.00525	0.1215
	80	XS	80S	0.095	0.215	0.0364	0.0925	0.106	0.0563	0.315	0.0157	0.00122	0.00600	0.1146
¼ *0.540*	...	.....	10S	0.065	0.410	0.1320	0.0970	0.141	0.1073	0.330	0.0572	0.00279	0.01032	0.1694
	40	Std	40S	0.088	0.364	0.1041	0.1250	0.141	0.0955	0.425	0.0451	0.00331	0.01230	0.1628
	80	XS	80S	0.119	0.302	0.0716	0.1574	0.141	0.0794	0.535	0.0310	0.00378	0.01395	0.1547
⅜ *0.675*	...	.....	10S	0.065	0.545	0.2333	0.1246	0.177	0.1427	0.423	0.1011	0.00586	0.01737	0.2169
	40	Std	40S	0.091	0.493	0.1910	0.1670	0.177	0.1295	0.568	0.0827	0.00730	0.02160	0.2090
	80	XS	80S	0.126	0.423	0.1405	0.2173	0.177	0.1106	0.739	0.0609	0.00862	0.02554	0.1991
½ *0.840*	...	.....	10S	0.083	0.674	0.357	0.1974	0.220	0.1765	0.671	0.1547	0.01431	0.0341	0.2692
	40	Std	40S	0.109	0.622	0.304	0.2503	0.220	0.1628	0.851	0.1316	0.01710	0.0407	0.2613
	80	XS	80S	0.147	0.546	0.2340	0.320	0.220	0.1433	1.088	0.1013	0.02010	0.0478	0.2505
	160	.....	...	0.187	0.466	0.1706	0.383	0.220	0.1220	1.304	0.0740	0.02213	0.0527	0.2402
	...	XXS	...	0.294	0.252	0.0499	0.504	0.220	0.0660	1.714	0.0216	0.02425	0.0577	0.2192
¾ *1.050*	...	.....	5S	0.065	0.920	0.665	0.2011	0.275	0.2409	0.684	0.2882	0.02451	0.0467	0.349
	...	.....	10S	0.083	0.884	0.614	0.2521	0.275	0.2314	0.857	0.2661	0.02970	0.0566	0.343
	40	Std	40S	0.113	0.824	0.533	0.333	0.275	0.2157	1.131	0.2301	0.0370	0.0706	0.334
	80	XS	80S	0.154	0.742	0.432	0.435	0.275	0.1943	1.474	0.1875	0.0448	0.0853	0.321
	160	.....	...	0.218	0.614	0.2961	0.570	0.275	0.1607	1.937	0.1284	0.0527	0.1004	0.304
	...	XXS	...	0.308	0.434	0.1479	0.718	0.275	0.1137	2.441	0.0641	0.0579	0.1104	0.284
1 *1.315*	...	.....	5S	0.065	1.185	1.103	0.2553	0.344	0.310	0.868	0.478	0.0500	0.0760	0.443
	...	.....	10S	0.109	1.097	0.945	0.413	0.344	0.2872	1.404	0.409	0.0757	0.1151	0.428
	40	Std	40S	0.133	1.049	0.864	0.494	0.344	0.2746	1.679	0.374	0.0874	0.1329	0.421
	80	XS	80S	0.179	0.957	0.719	0.639	0.344	0.2520	2.172	0.311	0.1056	0.1606	0.407
	160	.....	...	0.250	0.815	0.522	0.836	0.344	0.2134	2.844	0.2261	0.1252	0.1903	0.387
	...	XXS	...	0.358	0.599	0.2818	1.076	0.344	0.1570	3.659	0.1221	0.1405	0.2137	0.361
1¼ *1.660*	...	.....	5S	0.065	1.530	1.839	0.326	0.434	0.401	1.107	0.797	0.1038	0.1250	0.564
	...	.....	10S	0.109	1.442	1.633	0.531	0.434	0.378	1.805	0.707	0.1605	0.1934	0.550
	40	Std	40S	0.140	1.380	1.496	0.669	0.434	0.361	2.273	0.648	0.1948	0.2346	0.540
	80	XS	80S	0.191	1.278	1.283	0.881	0.434	0.335	2.997	0.555	0.2418	0.2913	0.524

1¼ *1.066*	160	.....	...	0.250	1.160	1.057	1.107	0.434	0.304	3.765	0.458	0.2839	0.342	0.506
	...	XXS	...	0.382	0.896	0.631	1.534	0.434	0.2346	5.214	0.2732	0.341	0.411	0.472
1½ *1.900*	...	.....	5S	0.065	1.770	2.461	0.375	0.497	0.463	1.274	1.067	0.1580	0.1663	0.649
	...	.....	10S	0.109	1.682	2.222	0.613	0.497	0.440	2.085	0.962	0.2469	0.2599	0.634
	40	Std	40S	0.145	1.610	2.036	0.799	0.497	0.421	2.718	0.882	0.310	0.326	0.623
	80	XS	80S	0.200	1.500	1.767	1.068	0.497	0.393	3.631	0.765	0.391	0.412	0.605
	160	.....	...	0.281	1.338	1.406	1.429	0.497	0.350	4.859	0.608	0.483	0.508	0.581
	...	XXS	...	0.400	1.100	0.950	1.885	0.497	0.288	6.408	0.412	0.568	0.598	0.549
2 *2.375*	...	.....	5S	0.065	2.245	3.96	0.472	0.622	0.588	1.604	1.716	0.315	0.2652	0.817
	...	.....	10S	0.109	2.157	3.65	0.776	0.622	0.565	2.638	1.582	0.499	0.420	0.802
	40	Std	40S	0.154	2.067	3.36	1.075	0.622	0.541	3.653	1.455	0.666	0.561	0.787
	80	XS	80S	0.218	1.939	2.953	1.477	0.622	0.508	5.022	1.280	0.868	0.731	0.766
	160	.....	...	0.343	1.689	2.240	2.190	0.622	0.442	7.444	0.971	1.163	0.979	0.729
	...	XXS	...	0.436	1.503	1.774	2.656	0.622	0.393	9.029	0.769	1.312	1.104	0.703
2½ *2.875*	...	.....	5S	0.083	2.709	5.76	0.728	0.753	0.709	2.475	2.499	0.710	0.494	0.988
	...	.....	10S	0.120	2.635	5.45	1.039	0.753	0.690	3.531	2.361	0.988	0.687	0.975
	40	Std	40S	0.203	2.469	4.79	1.704	0.753	0.646	5.793	2.076	1.530	1.064	0.947
	80	XS	80S	0.276	2.323	4.24	2.254	0.753	0.608	7.661	1.837	1.925	1.339	0.924
	160	.....	...	0.375	2.125	3.55	2.945	0.753	0.556	10.01	1.535	2.353	1.637	0.894
	...	XXS	...	0.552	1.771	2.464	4.03	0.753	0.464	13.70	1.067	2.872	1.998	0.844
3 *3.500*	...	.....	5S	0.083	3.334	8.73	0.891	0.916	0.873	3.03	3.78	1.301	0.744	1.208
	...	.....	10S	0.120	3.260	8.35	1.274	0.916	0.853	4.33	3.61	1.822	1.041	1.196
	40	Std	40S	0.216	3.068	7.39	2.228	0.916	0.803	7.58	3.20	3.02	1.724	1.164
	80	XS	80S	0.300	2.900	6.61	3.02	0.916	0.759	10.25	2.864	3.90	2.226	1.136
	160	.....	...	0.437	2.626	5.42	4.21	0.916	0.687	14.32	2.348	5.03	2.876	1.094
	...	XXS	...	0.600	2.300	4.15	5.47	0.916	0.602	18.58	1.801	5.99	3.43	1.047
3½ *4.000*	...	.....	5S	0.083	3.834	11.55	1.021	1.047	1.004	3.47	5.01	1.960	0.980	1.385
	...	.....	10S	0.120	3.760	11.10	1.463	1.047	0.984	4.97	4.81	2.756	1.378	1.372
	40	Std	40S	0.226	3.548	9.89	2.680	1.047	0.929	9.11	4.28	4.79	2.394	1.337
	80	XS	80S	0.318	3.364	8.89	3.68	1.047	0.881	12.51	3.85	6.28	3.14	1.307
4 *4.500*	...	.....	5S	0.083	4.334	14.75	1.152	1.178	1.135	3.92	6.40	2.811	1.249	1.562
	...	.....	10S	0.120	4.260	14.25	1.651	1.178	1.115	5.61	6.17	3.96	1.762	1.549
	40	Std	40S	0.237	4.026	12.73	3.17	1.178	1.054	10.79	5.51	7.23	3.21	1.510
	80	XS	80S	0.337	3.826	11.50	4.41	1.178	1.002	14.98	4.98	9.61	4.27	1.477
	120	.....	...	0.437	3.626	10.33	5.58	1.178	0.949	18.96	4.48	11.65	5.18	1.445
	160	.....	...	0.531	3.438	9.28	6.62	1.178	0.900	22.51	4.02	13.27	5.90	1.416
	...	XXS	...	0.674	3.152	7.80	8.10	1.178	0.825	27.54	3.38	15.29	6.79	1.374

* See footnote at end of table.
† See footnote at end of table.

Table 3. Physical Properties of Pipe*—(*Continued*)

Nominal pipe size, O.D., in.	Schedule number¶ a	Schedule number¶ b	Schedule number¶ c	Wall thickness, in.	I.D., in.	Inside area, sq in.	Metal area, sq in.	Sq ft outside surface, per ft	Sq ft inside surface, per ft	Weight per ft, lb	Weight of water per ft, lb	Moment of inertia, in.^{4}	Section modulus, in.^{3}	Radius gyration, in.
	...	.....	5S	0.109	5.345	22.44	1.868	1.456	1.399	6.35	9.73	6.95	2.498	1.929
	...	.....	10S	0.134	5.295	22.02	2.285	1.456	1.386	7.77	9.53	8.43	3.03	1.920
5	40	Std	40S	0.258	5.047	20.01	4.30	1.456	1.321	14.62	8.66	15.17	5.45	1.878
5.563	80	XS	80S	0.375	4.813	18.19	6.11	1.456	1.260	20.78	7.89	20.68	7.43	1.839
	120	.....	...	0.500	4.563	16.35	7.95	1.456	1.195	27.04	7.09	25.74	9.25	1.799
	160	.....	...	0.625	4.313	14.61	9.70	1.456	1.129	32.96	6.33	30.0	10.80	1.760
	...	XXS	...	0.750	4.063	12.97	11.34	1.456	1.064	38.55	5.62	33.6	12.10	1.722
	...	.....	5S	0.109	6.407	32.2	2.231	1.734	1.677	5.37	13.98	11.85	3.58	2.304
	...	.....	10S	0.134	6.357	31.7	2.733	1.734	1.664	9.29	13.74	14.40	4.35	2.295
6	40	Std	40S	0.280	6.065	28.89	5.58	1.734	1.588	18.97	12.51	28.14	8.50	2.245
6.625	80	XS	80S	0.432	5.761	26.07	8.40	1.734	1.508	28.57	11.29	40.5	12.23	2.195
	120	.....	...	0.562	5.501	23.77	10.70	1.734	1.440	36.39	10.30	49.6	14.98	2.153
	160	.....	...	0.718	5.189	21.15	13.33	1.734	1.358	45.30	9.16	59.0	17.81	2.104
	...	XXS	...	0.864	4.897	18.83	15.64	1.734	1.282	53.16	8.17	66.3	20.03	2.060
	...	.....	5S	0.109	8.407	55.5	2.916	2.258	2.201	9.91	24.07	26.45	6.13	3.01
	...	.....	10S	0.148	8.329	54.5	3.94	2.258	2.180	13.40	23.59	35.4	8.21	3.00
	20	.....	...	0.250	8.125	51.8	6.58	2.258	2.127	22.36	22.48	57.7	13.39	2.962
	30	.....	...	0.277	8.071	51.2	7.26	2.258	2.113	24.70	22.18	63.4	14.69	2.953
8	40	Std	40S	0.322	7.981	50.0	8.40	2.258	2.089	28.55	21.69	72.5	16.81	2.938
8.625	60	.....	...	0.406	7.813	47.9	10.48	2.258	2.045	35.64	20.79	88.8	20.58	2.909
	80	XS	80S	0.500	7.625	45.7	12.76	2.258	1.996	43.39	19.80	105.7	24.52	2.878
	100	.....	...	0.593	7.439	43.5	14.96	2.258	1.948	50.87	18.84	121.4	28.14	2.847
	120	.....	...	0.718	7.189	40.6	17.84	2.258	1.882	60.63	17.60	140.6	32.6	2.807
	140	.....	...	0.812	7.001	38.5	19.93	2.258	1.833	67.76	16.69	153.8	35.7	2.777
	...	XXS	...	0.875	6.875	37.1	21.30	2.258	1.800	72.42	16.09	162.0	37.6	2.757
	160	.....	...	0.906	6.813	36.5	21.97	2.258	1.784	74.69	15.80	165.9	38.5	2.748
	...	.....	5S	0.134	10.482	86.3	4.52	2.815	2.744	15.15	37.4	63.7	11.85	3.75
	...	.....	10S	0.165	10.420	85.3	5.49	2.815	2.728	18.70	36.9	76.9	14.30	3.74
	20	.....	...	0.250	10.250	82.5	8.26	2.815	2.683	28.04	35.8	113.7	21.16	3.71
10	...	.....	...	0.279	10.192	81.6	9.18	2.815	2.668	31.20	35.3	125.9	23.42	3.70
10.750	30	.....	...	0.307	10.136	80.7	10.07	2.815	2.654	34.24	35.0	137.5	25.57	3.69
	40	Std	40S	0.365	10.020	78.9	11.91	2.815	2.623	40.48	34.1	160.8	29.90	3.67
	60	XS	80S	0.500	9.750	74.7	16.10	2.815	2.553	54.74	32.3	212.0	39.4	3.63
	80	.....	...	0.593	9.564	71.8	18.92	2.815	2.504	64.33	31.1	244.9	45.6	3.60
	100	.....	...	0.718	9.314	68.1	22.63	2.815	2.438	76.93	29.5	286.2	53.2	3.56

10 *10.750*	120	.....	...	0.843	9.064	64.5	26.24	2.815	2.373	89.20	28.0	324	60.3	3.52
	140	.....	...	1.000	8.750	60.1	30.6	2.815	2.291	104.13	26.1	368	68.4	3.47
	160	.....	...	1.125	8.500	56.7	34.0	2.815	2.225	115.65	24.6	399	74.3	3.43
12 *12.750*	...	.....	5S	0.165	12.420	121.2	6.52	3.34	3.25	19.56	52.5	129.2	20.27	4.45
	...	.....	10S	0.180	12.390	120.6	7.11	3.34	3.24	24.20	52.2	140.5	22.03	4.44
	20	.....	...	0.250	12.250	117.9	9.84	3.34	3.21	33.38	51.1	191.9	30.1	4.42
	30	.....	...	0.330	12.090	114.8	12.88	3.34	3.17	43.77	49.7	248.5	39.0	4.39
	...	Std	40S	0.375	12.000	113.1	14.58	3.34	3.14	49.56	49.0	279.3	43.8	4.38
	40	.....	...	0.406	11.938	111.9	15.74	3.34	3.13	53.53	48.5	300	47.1	4.37
	...	XS	80S	0.500	11.750	108.4	19.24	3.34	3.08	65.42	47.0	362	56.7	4.33
	60	.....	...	0.562	11.626	106.2	21.52	3.34	3.04	73.16	46.0	401	62.8	4.31
	80	.....	...	0.687	11.376	101.6	26.04	3.34	2.978	88.51	44.0	475	74.5	4.27
	100	.....	...	0.843	11.064	96.1	31.5	3.34	2.897	107.20	41.6	562	88.1	4.22
	120	.....	...	1.000	10.750	90.8	36.9	3.34	2.814	125.49	39.3	642	100.7	4.17
	140	.....	...	1.125	10.500	86.6	41.1	3.34	2.749	139.68	37.5	701	109.9	4.13
	160	.....	...	1.312	10.126	80.5	47.1	3.34	2.651	160.27	34.9	781	122.6	4.07
14 *14.000*	10	.....	...	0.250	13.500	143.1	10.80	3.67	3.53	36.71	62.1	255.4	36.5	4.86
	20	.....	...	0.312	13.376	140.5	13.42	3.67	3.50	45.68	60.9	314	44.9	4.84
	30	Std	...	0.375	13.250	137.9	16.05	3.67	3.47	54.57	59.7	373	53.3	4.82
	40	.....	...	0.437	13.126	135.3	18.62	3.67	3.44	63.37	58.7	429	61.2	4.80
	...	XS	...	0.500	13.000	132.7	21.21	3.67	3.40	72.09	57.5	484	69.1	4.78
	...	.....	...	0.562	12.876	130.2	23.73	3.67	3.37	80.66	56.5	537	76.7	4.76
	60	.....	...	0.593	12.814	129.0	24.98	3.67	3.35	84.91	55.9	562	80.3	4.74
	...	.....	...	0.625	12.750	127.7	26.26	3.67	3.34	89.28	55.3	589	84.1	4.73
	...	.....	...	0.687	12.626	125.2	28.73	3.67	3.31	97.68	54.3	638	91.2	4.71
	80	.....	...	0.750	12.500	122.7	31.2	3.67	3.27	106.13	53.2	687	98.2	4.69
	...	.....	...	0.875	12.250	117.9	36.1	3.67	3.21	122.66	51.1	781	111.5	4.65
	100	.....	...	0.937	12.126	115.5	38.5	3.67	3.17	130.73	50.0	825	117.8	4.63
	120	.....	...	1.093	11.814	109.6	44.3	3.67	3.09	150.67	47.5	930	132.8	4.58
	140	.....	...	1.250	11.500	103.9	50.1	3.67	3.01	170.22	45.0	1,127	146.8	4.53
	160	.....	...	1.406	11.188	98.3	55.6	3.67	2.929	189.12	42.6	1,017	159.6	4.48
16 *16.000*	10	.....	...	0.250	15.500	188.7	12.37	4.19	4.06	42.05	81.8	384	48.0	5.57
	20	.....	...	0.312	15.376	185.7	15.38	4.19	4.03	52.36	80.5	473	59.2	5.55
	30	Std	...	0.375	15.250	182.6	18.41	4.19	3.99	62.58	79.1	562	70.3	5.53
	...	.....	...	0.437	15.126	179.7	21.37	4.19	3.96	72.64	77.9	648	80.9	5.50
	40	XS	...	0.500	15.000	176.7	24.35	4.19	3.93	82.77	76.5	732	91.5	5.48
	...	.....	...	0.562	14.876	173.8	27.26	4.19	3.89	92.66	75.4	813	106.6	5.46
	...	.....	...	0.625	14.750	170.9	30.2	4.19	3.86	102.63	74.1	894	112.2	5.44
	60	.....	...	0.656	14.688	169.4	31.6	4.19	3.85	107.50	73.4	933	116.6	5.43
	...	.....	...	0.687	14.626	168.0	33.0	4.19	3.83	112.36	72.7	971	121.4	5.42

* See footnote at end of table.
† See footnote at end of table.

Table 3. Physical Properties of Pipe*—(*Continued*)

Nominal pipe size, O.D., in.	Schedule number†			Wall thick-ness, in.	I.D., in.	Inside area, sq in.	Metal area, sq in.	Sq ft outside surface, per ft	Sq ft inside surface, per ft	Weight per ft, lb	Weight of water per ft, lb	Moment of inertia, in.[4]	Section modulus, in.[3]	Radius gyra-tion, in.
	a	*b*	*c*											
16 *16.000*	...	....	...	0.750	14.500	165.1	35.9	4.19	3.80	122.15	71.5	1,047	130.9	5.40
	80	....	...	0.842	14.314	160.9	40.1	4.19	3.75	136.46	69.7	1,157	144.6	5.37
	...	....	...	0.875	14.250	159.5	41.6	4.19	3.73	141.35	69.1	1,193	154.1	5.36
	100	....	...	1.031	13.938	152.6	48.5	4.19	3.65	164.83	66.1	1,365	170.6	5.30
	120	....	...	1.218	13.564	144.5	56.6	4.19	3.55	192.29	62.6	1,556	194.5	5.24
	140	....	...	1.437	13.126	135.3	65.7	4.19	3.44	223.50	58.6	1,760	220.0	5.17
	160	....	...	1.593	12.814	129.0	72.1	4.19	3.35	245.11	55.9	1,894	236.7	5.12
18 *18.000*	10	....	...	0.250	17.500	240.5	13.94	4.71	4.58	47.39	104.3	549	61.0	6.28
	20	....	...	0.312	17.376	237.1	17.34	4.71	4.55	59.03	102.8	678	75.5	6.25
	...	Std	...	0.375	17.250	233.7	20.76	4.71	4.52	70.59	101.2	807	89.6	6.23
	30	....	...	0.437	17.126	230.4	24.11	4.71	4.48	82.06	99.9	931	103.4	6.21
	...	XS	...	0.500	17.000	227.0	27.49	4.71	4.45	93.45	98.4	1,053	117.0	6.19
	40	....	...	0.562	16.876	223.7	30.8	4.71	4.42	104.75	97.0	1,172	130.2	6.17
	...	....	...	0.625	16.750	220.5	34.1	4.71	4.39	115.98	95.5	1,289	143.3	6.15
	...	....	...	0.687	16.626	217.1	37.4	4.71	4.35	127.03	94.1	1,403	156.3	6.13
	60	....	...	0.750	16.500	213.8	40.6	4.71	4.32	138.17	92.7	1,515	168.3	6.10
	...	....	...	0.875	16.250	207.4	47.1	4.71	4.25	160.04	89.9	1,731	192.8	6.06
	80	....	...	0.937	16.126	204.2	50.2	4.71	4.22	170.75	88.5	1,834	203.8	6.04
	100	....	...	1.156	15.688	193.3	61.2	4.71	4.11	207.96	83.7	2,180	242.2	5.97
	120	....	...	1.375	15.250	182.6	71.8	4.71	3.99	244.14	79.2	2,499	277.6	5.90
	140	....	...	1.562	14.876	173.8	80.7	4.71	3.89	274.23	75.3	2,750	306	5.84
	160	....	...	1.781	14.438	163.7	90.7	4.71	3.78	308.51	71.0	3,020	336	5.77
20 *20.000*	10	....	...	0.250	19.500	298.6	15.51	5.24	5.11	52.73	129.5	757	75.7	6.98
	...	....	...	0.312	19.376	294.9	19.30	5.24	5.07	65.40	128.1	935	93.5	6.96
	20	Std	...	0.375	19.250	291.0	23.12	5.24	5.04	78.60	126.0	1,114	111.4	6.94
	...	....	...	0.437	19.126	287.3	26.86	5.24	5.01	91.31	124.6	1,286	128.6	6.92
	30	XS	...	0.500	19.000	283.5	30.6	5.24	4.97	104.13	122.8	1,457	145.7	6.90
	...	....	...	0.562	18.876	279.8	34.3	5.24	4.94	116.67	121.3	1,624	162.4	6.88
	40	....	...	0.593	18.814	278.0	36.2	5.24	4.93	122.91	120.4	1,704	170.4	6.86
	...	....	...	0.625	18.750	276.1	38.0	5.24	4.91	129.33	119.7	1,787	178.7	6.85
	...	....	...	0.687	18.626	272.5	41.7	5.24	4.88	141.71	118.1	1,946	194.6	6.83
	...	....	...	0.750	18.500	268.8	45.4	5.24	4.84	154.20	116.5	2,105	210.5	6.81
	60	....	...	0.812	18.376	265.2	48.9	5.24	4.81	166.40	115.0	2,257	225.7	6.79
	...	....	...	0.875	18.250	261.6	52.6	5.24	4.78	178.73	113.4	2,409	240.9	6.77
	80	....	...	1.031	17.938	252.7	61.4	5.24	4.70	208.87	109.4	2,772	277.2	6.72
	100	....	...	1.281	17.438	238.8	75.3	5.24	4.57	256.10	103.4	3,320	332	6.63

20 20.000	120	....	...	1.500	17.000	227.0	87.2	5.24	4.45	296.37	98.3	3,760	376	6.56
	140	....	...	1.750	16.500	213.8	100.3	5.24	4.32	341.10	92.6	4,220	422	6.48
	160	....	...	1.968	16.064	202.7	111.5	5.24	4.21	379.01	87.9	4,590	459	6.41
24 24.000	10	....	...	0.250	23.500	434	18.65	6.28	6.15	63.41	188.0	1,316	109.6	8.40
	...	....	...	0.312	23.376	430	23.20	6.28	6.12	78.93	186.1	1,629	135.8	8.38
	20	Std	...	0.375	23.250	425	27.83	6.28	6.09	94.62	183.8	1,943	161.9	8.35
	...	....	...	0.437	23.126	420	32.4	6.28	6.05	109.97	182.1	2,246	187.4	8.33
	...	XS	...	0.500	23.000	415	36.9	6.28	6.02	125.49	180.1	2,550	212.5	8.31
	30	....	...	0.562	22.876	411	41.4	6.28	5.99	140.80	178.1	2,840	237.0	8.29
	...	....	...	0.625	22.750	406	45.9	6.28	5.96	156.03	176.2	3,140	261.4	8.27
	40	....	...	0.687	22.626	402	50.3	6.28	5.92	171.17	174.3	3,420	285.2	8.25
	...	....	...	0.750	22.500	398	54.8	6.28	5.89	186.24	172.4	3,710	309	8.22
	60	....	...	0.968	22.064	382	70.0	6.28	5.78	238.11	165.8	4,650	388	8.15
	80	....	...	1.218	21.564	365	87.2	6.28	5.65	296.36	158.3	5,670	473	8.07
	100	....	...	1.531	20.938	344	108.1	6.28	5.48	367.40	149.3	6,850	571	7.96
	120	....	...	1.812	20.376	326	126.3	6.28	5.33	429.39	141.4	7,830	652	7.87
	140	....	...	2.062	19.876	310	142.1	6.28	5.20	483.13	134.5	8,630	719	7.79
	160	....	...	2.343	19.314	293	159.4	6.28	5.06	541.94	127.0	9,460	788	7.70
30 30.000	10	....	...	0.312	29.376	678	29.1	7.85	7.69	98.93	293.8	3,210	214	10.50
	20	....	...	0.500	29.000	661	46.3	7.85	7.59	157.53	286.3	5,040	336	10.43
	30	....	...	0.625	28.750	649	57.6	7.85	7.53	196.08	281.5	6,220	415	10.39

* The ferritic stainless steels may be about 5 percent less, and the austenitic stainless steels about 2 percent greater than the values shown in this table, which are based on weights for carbon steel. The following formulas were used in the computation of the values shown in the table:

Weight of pipe per ft, lb $= 10.6802t(D - t)$
Weight of water per ft, lb $= 0.3405d^2$
Sq ft outside surface, per ft $= 0.2618D$
Sq ft inside surface, per ft $= 0.2618d$
Inside area, sq in. $= 0.785d^2$
Area of metal, sq in. $= 0.785(D^2 - d^2)$
Moment of inertia, in.[4] $= 0.0491(D^4 - d^4) = A_M R_g^2$
Section modulus, in.[3] $= \dfrac{0.0982(D^4 - d^4)}{D}$
Radius of gyration, in. $= 0.25\sqrt{D^2 + d^2}$

A_M = Area of metal, sq in.
d = I.D., in.
D = O.D., in.
R_g = Radius of gyration, in.
t = Pipe wall thickness, in.

† *a.* ASA B36.10 steel-pipe schedule numbers.
b. ASA B36.10 steel-pipe nominal wall-thickness designations.
c. ASA B36.19 stainless-steel–pipe schedule numbers (5S is not an approved standard).

this, the forging is straightened, placed in a lathe, and the outer diameter machined to a true dimension. The inside is dressed to remove scale, but no machining is done on the inside.

Code Designations. Appropriate ASTM specifications list the physical and chemical properties of materials used in piping systems. The complete compilation of "Steel Piping Materials" (July, 1963) can be purchased from the ASTM, 1916 Race St., Philadelphia 3, Pa. The treatment in this section is a brief outline of frequently encountered materials.

Carbon-steel piping is most frequently used as manufactured in accordance with ASTM specifications A106 and A53. The chemical composition of these two materials is identical; both are subjected to physical tests, but those for A106 are more rigorous. For example, the Code for Pressure Piping permits the use of A53 for pressures of 600 psig and less but excludes its use for higher pressures; A106 can be used for pressures not above 2,500 psig. A53 and A106 are made in Grades A and B; Grade B has higher strength properties but is less ductile and, for this reason, Grade A only is permitted for cold bending or close coiling. When carbon steel is intended for use in welded construction at temperatures in excess of 775 F, consideration should be given to the possibility of graphite formation.

Carbon-molybdenum steel piping may be obtained as A204 (electric-fusion-welded), A335 (seamless) or A369 (forged, turned, and bored). This material was developed in past years when steam temperatures were approaching, but not reaching, 1000 F, under which conditions carbon steel was both unsatisfactory and uneconomical. It has been found that there is a tendency for carbon-molybdenum to show graphitization at temperatures in excess of 800 F, and its use in welded construction above this value should be with caution.[1]

Chromium-molybdenum steel has been used for temperatures up to 1100 F. In the small diameters, the material is usually available in the seamless construction; because of the inability of the seamless mills to fabricate large-diameter and heavy-walled pipe, it may be necessary to resort to the more expensive hollow-forged or forged-and-bored piping for higher pressures and temperatures. The material for a high-temperature piping system should be selected after a careful review of technical and economic considerations; the following is intended only as being indicative of recent and current practice. For temperatures up to 950 F, ½ percent Cr–½ percent Mo (A335, Grade P2) is used; for temperatures 950 to 1000 F, 1 percent Cr–½ percent Mo (A335, Grade P12) is used; for temperatures 1000 to 1050 F, 1¼ percent Cr–½ percent Mo (A335, Grade P11) may be used; for temperatures 1050 to 1100 F, 2¼ percent Cr–1 percent Mo (A335, Grade P22) is frequently used. When there is a combination of high temperatures and erosive action, 5 percent Cr–½ percent Mo (A335, Grade 5) has been found desirable.

Stainless-steel piping is available in a variety of compositions, most popular of which are ASTM A213, Grade TP321 (16 percent Cr–8 percent Ni, stabilized with titanium) and ASTM A213, Grade TP347 (18 percent Cr–8 percent Ni, stabilized with columbium). Either of these two materials may be used up to 1200 F; particular care must be given to choice of welding rod to avoid brittleness in the welds.

Refer to Tables 1 and 2 respectively for permissible stress values for piping materials at low and elevated temperatures.

Schedule Designations. Piping was formerly designated as standard, extra-strong, and double extra-strong. There was no provision for thin-walled pipe, and no intervening standard thicknesses between the three schedules, which covered too great a spread to be economical without intermediate weights. Table 3 lists piping as a function of the more recent schedule number which is given, approximately, by the following relationship: Schedule no. $= 1{,}000 \times P/S$, where P is operating pressure, psig, and S is allowable stress value, psi.

EXAMPLE: Find the required schedule of ASTM A106 Grade B pipe operating at 1,150 psig and 600 F.

Table 2 lists S value as 15,000 psi. Substituting, 1,000 (1150/15,000) = 76.6. Use schedule no. 80, tentatively, but check with Eq. (1), p. 8–207.

[1] Modern steel-making practices have reduced significantly the problem of graphitization. However, in pipe installed in the 1940s and early 1950s, there have been many failures.

Commercial sizes of wrought-iron and steel pipe are known by their nominal inside diameter (I.D.) from ⅛ to 12 in. Above 12 in. I.D., pipe is usually known by its outside diameter (O.D.). All classes of pipe of a given nominal size have the same O.D., the extra thickness for different weights being on the inside.

Thickness of Pipe. The following notes, covering power piping systems, have been abstracted from Sec. I of the Code for Pressure Piping (ASA B31.1).

For inspection purposes, the minimum thickness of pipe wall to be used for piping at different pressures and for temperatures not exceeding those for the various materials listed in Tables 1 and 2 shall be determined by the formula

$$t_m = \frac{PD}{2S + yP} + C \tag{1}$$

where t_m = minimum pipe-wall thickness, in. allowable on inspection; P = maximum internal service pressure, psig (plus water-hammer allowance in case of cast iron conveying liquids); D = O.D. of pipe, in.; S = allowable stress in material (taken from Tables 1 and 2 at service temperature); y = a coefficient, values for which are listed in Table 4; C = allowance for threading, mechanical strength, and corrosion, in., with values of C listed in Table 5.

Table 4. Values of y
(Interpolate for intermediate values)
(ASA Code for Pressure Piping, 1963)

	Temperature, deg F					
	900 and below	950	1000	1050	1100	1150 and above
Ferritic steels........	0.4	0.5	0.7	0.7	0.7	0.7
Austenitic steels......	0.4	0.4	0.4	0.4	0.5	0.7

Table 5. Values of C
(ASA Code for Pressure Piping, 1963)

Type of pipe	Value of C, in.
Cast-iron pipe, centrifugally cast..........................	0.14
Cast-iron, pit cast..........................	0.18
Threaded-steel, wrought-iron, or non-ferrous pipe............	
⅜ in. and smaller..........................	0.05
½ in. and larger..........................	Depth of thread
Grooved-steel, wrought-iron or non-ferrous pipe..............	Depth of groove
Plain-end steel, wrought-iron or tube	
1 in. and smaller..........................	0.05
1¼ in. and larger..........................	0.065
Plain-end non-ferrous pipe or tube..........................	0.000

The thickness of cast-iron pipe conveying liquid may be taken from Table 14, using the pressure class next higher than the maximum internal service pressure in pounds per square inch. Where cast-iron pipe is used for steam service, the thickness shall be calculated by Eq. (1), using S values listed in Table 1.

Plain-end pipe includes pipe joined by flared compression couplings, lapped joints, and by welding, *i.e.*, by any method that does not reduce the wall thickness of the pipe at the joint.

Physical and Chemical Properties of Pipes, Tubes, Etc. The design of piping for operation above 750 F presents many problems not encountered at lower temperatures. For the properties of steel applicable to high-temperature service (as well as to

Table 6. Specifications for Tensile Strength of Pipe
(ASTM—July, 1963)

ASA designation	ASTM designation	Style of pipe	Tensile strength, min, psi	Scope
B36.1	A53	Welded and seamless steel	Welded: Bessemer, 50,000; O.H. 45,000. Seamless: Grade A, 48,000; Grade B, 60,000	*a*
B36.2	A72	Welded wrought iron	40,000	*b*
B36.3	A106	Lap-welded and seamless steel for high temperatures	Seamless: Grade A, 48,000; Grade B, 60,000	*c*
B36.4	A134	Electric-fusion-welded steel, sizes 16 in. and over	See ASTM Standard A134	*d*
B36.5	A135	Electric-resistance-welded steel	Grade A, 48,000. Grade B, 60,000	*e*
B36.9	A139	Electric-fusion-welded steel, sizes 4 in. and over	Grade A, 48,000. Grade B, 60,000	*f*
B36.11	A155	Electric-fusion-welded steel pipe for high-temperature high-pressure service	Varies with material. See Spec. ASTM A155	*g*
G8.7	A120	Black and hot-dipped galvanized welded and seamless steel	Same as B36.1	*h*

a Commercial steel pipe for general uses, also for coiling, bending, flanging, and similar forming operations when so specified.

b Commercial wrought-iron pipe for general uses, also for coiling, bending, flanging, and other special purposes.

c Lap-welded and seamless steel pipe for high-temperature service. Suitable for bending, flanging, and similar forming operations.

d Cover pipe 16 in. diam and over in wall thicknesses up to ¾ in., fabricated from steel plates by electric-fusion welding.

e Pipe up to 30 in. intended for conveying liquids, gas, or vapor at temperatures below 450 F. Adapted for flanging, bending, and similar forming operations in Grade A class.

f Covers sizes 4 to <16 in. in wall thicknesses not over ⅝ in., fabricated from steel plates by electric-fusion welding. Intended for conveying liquids, gas, or vapor at temperatures below 450 F. Adapted for flanging and bending.

g Electric-fusion-welded steel pipe having an outside diameter of 18 in. and over for high-temperature and high-pressure service. Suitable for bending, flanging, corrugating, and similar forming operations. Welding in accordance with Par. U-68 of the ASME code for unfired pressure vessels.

h Commercial steel pipe for ordinary uses such as low-pressure steam, liquid, or gas lines. Not intended for coiling or close bending, nor for high-temperature service.

ordinary service) for pipes, tubes, fittings, bolting material, etc., see p. 6–39. For a discussion of creep properties, see p. 5–13. The following notes have been abstracted from the Code for Pressure Piping, ASA B31.1, 1955 issue reaffirmed in 1963. Quantities in parentheses are ASTM specification numbers.

Steam Pressures above 250 and Not above 2,500 psi, Temperatures Not above 1100 F. For pressures in excess of 100 psi, the pipe may be seamless steel (A106), (A312), (A335), or (A376); or electric-fusion-welded steel (A155); or forged-and-bored steel (A369); or automatic-welded steel (A312). For pressures between 250 and 600 psi the pipe may be seamless steel (A106) or (A53); electric-fusion-welded steel (A155); electric-resistance-welded steel (A135) or (A53). For pressures of 250 psi and lower and for service up to 750 F, any of the following may be used: electric-fusion-welded steel (A134) or (A139); electric-resistance-welded steel (A135); seamless or welded steel (A53); or wrought-iron pipe (A72). Grade A seamless pipe (A106) or (A53); or Grade A electric-welded pipe (A53), (A135), or (A139); or Grade A wrought-iron pipe (A72) shall be used for close coiling or cold bending. Pipe permissible for services specified may be used for temperatures higher than 750 F, unless otherwise prohibited, if the *S* values of Tables 1 and 2 are used when calculating the required wall thickness.

Valves and fittings must have flange openings or welded ends, and valves must have external stem threads. Valves must be of cast or forged steel or of forged or cast non-ferrous

Table 7. Dimensions of Welded and Seamless Steel Pipe
(ASTM "Steel Piping Materials": July, 1963)

Nominal pipe size, in.	Outside diam, in.	Nominal wall thickness, in., for stated schedule numbers									
		10	20	30	40	60	80	100	120	140	160
1/8	0.405	.....	.....	.....	**0.068**	.....	**0.095**				
1/4	0.540	.....	.....	.....	**0.088**	.....	**0.119**				
3/8	0.675	.....	.....	.....	**0.091**	.....	**0.126**				
1/2	0.840	.....	.....	.....	**0.109**	.....	**0.147**	.....	.....	.....	
3/4	1.050	.....	.....	.....	**0.113**	.....	**0.154**	.....	.....	.....	
1	1.315	.....	.....	.....	**0.133**	.....	**0.179**	.....	.....	.....	
1 1/4	1.660	.....	.....	.....	**0.140**	.....	**0.191**	.....	.....	.....	
1 1/2	1.900	.....	.....	.....	**0.145**	.....	**0.200**	.....	.....	.....	
2	2.375	.....	.....	.....	**0.154**	.....	**0.218**	.....	.....	.....	0.344
2 1/2	2.875	.....	.....	.....	**0.203**	.....	**0.276**	.....	.....	.....	0.375
3	3.5	.....	.....	.....	**0.216**	.....	**0.300**	.....	.....	.....	0.438
3 1/2	4.0	.....	.....	.....	**0.226**	.....	**0.318**				
4	4.5	.....	.....	.....	**0.237**	.....	**0.337**	.....	0.437	.....	0.531
5	5.563	.....	.....	.....	**0.258**	.....	**0.375**	.....	0.500	.....	0.625
6	6.625	.....	.....	.....	**0.280**	.....	**0.432**	.....	0.562	.....	0.719
8	8.625	.....	0.250	**0.277**	**0.322**	**0.406**	**0.500**	0.593	0.718	0.812_2	0.906
10	10.75	.....	0.250	**0.307**	**0.365**	**0.500**	0.593	0.718	0.843	1.000	1.125
12	12.75	.....	0.250	**0.330**	0.406	0.562	0.687	0.843	1.000	1.125	1.312
14 O.D.	14.0	0.250	0.312	0.375	0.437	0.593	0.750	0.937	1.062	1.250	1.406
16 O.D.	16.0	0.250	0.312	0.375	0.500	0.656	0.843	1.031	1.218	1.437	1.594
18 O.D.	18.0	0.250	0.312	0.437	0.562	0.718	0.937	1.156	1.343	1.562	1.781
20 O.D.	20.0	0.250	0.375	0.500	0.593	0.812	1.031	1.250	1.500	1.750	1.969
24 O.D.	24.0	0.250	0.375	0.562	0.687	0.937	1.218	1.500	1.750	2.062	2.344

The schedule numbers are approximate values of $1{,}000P/S$ (see p. 8–206 for the symbols). Thicknesses include a mill tolerance of 12.5 percent. Thicknesses in black type in schedules 30 and 40 agree with those of standard-weight pipe, those in schedules 60 and 80 with extra-strong pipe.

Table 8. Dimensions of Welded Wrought-iron Pipe
(ASTM "Steel Piping Materials": July, 1963)

Nominal pipe size, in.	Outside diam, in.	Nominal wall thickness, in.	
		Standard weight pipe	Extra-strong pipe
1/4	0.540	**0.090**	**0.122**
3/8	0.675	**0.093**	**0.129**
1/2	0.840	**0.111**	**0.151**
3/4	1.050	**0.115**	**0.157**
1	1.315	**0.136**	**0.183**
1 1/4	1.660	**0.143**	**0.195**
1 1/2	1.900	**0.148**	**0.204**
2	2.375	**0.158**	**0.223**
2 1/2	2.875	**0.208**	**0.282**
3	3.5	**0.221**	**0.306**
3 1/2	4.0	**0.231**	**0.325**
4	4.5	**0.242**	**0.344**
5	5.563	**0.263**	**0.383**
6	6.625	**0.286**	**0.441**
8	8.625	**0.329**	**0.510**
10	10.75	**0.372**	0.510
12	12.75	0.383	0.510

Wrought-iron pipe contains about 3 percent of slag, 0.5 percent C, and other impurities. It is more resistant to corrosion than is steel pipe.

Table 9. API Standard Line Pipe, Threaded

(All weights and dimensions are nominal. National Tube Division, United States Steel Corp.)

Size, in.	Weight per ft, lb		Thickness, in.	Diameter, in.		Threads per in.	Couplings			Test pressure,* psi		
	Threads and coupling	Plain end		O.D.	I.D.		Length, in.	O.D., in.	Weight, lb	Lap-welded or Grade A seamless	Grade B seamless	Grade C seamless
⅛	0.25	0.24	0.068	0.405	0.269	27	1 1/16	0.563	0.04	700	700	700
¼	0.43	0.42	0.088	0.540	0.364	18	1⅝	0.719	0.09	700	700	700
⅜	0.57	0.57	0.091	0.675	0.493	18	1⅝	0.875	0.13	700	700	700
½	0.86	0.85	0.109	0.840	0.622	14	2⅛	1.063	0.24	700	700	700
¾	1.14	1.13	0.113	1.050	0.824	14	2⅛	1.313	0.34	700	700	700
1	1.70	1.68	0.133	1.315	1.049	11½	2⅝	1.576	0.54	700	700	700
1¼	2.30	2.27	0.140	1.660	1.380	11½	2¾	2.054	1.03	1,000	1,100	1,300
1½	2.75	2.72	0.145	1.900	1.610	11½	2¾	2.200	1.17	1,000	1,100	1,300
2	3.75	3.65	0.154	2.375	2.067	11½	3¼	2.875	2.13	1,000	1,100	1,300
2½	5.90	5.79	0.203	2.875	2.469	8	4⅛	3.375	3.27	1,000	1,100	1,300
3	7.70	7.58	0.216	3.500	3.068	8	4¼	4.000	4.09	1,000	1,100	1,300
3½	9.25	9.11	0.226	4.000	3.548	8	4⅜	4.625	5.92	1,200	1,300	1,600
4	11.00	10.79	0.237	4.500	4.026	8	4½	5.200	7.59	1,200	1,300	1,600
5	15.00	14.62	0.258	5.563	5.047	8	4⅝	6.296	9.98	1,200	1,300	1,600
6	19.45	18.97	0.280	6.625	6.065	8	4⅞	7.390	12.92	1,200	1,300	1,600
8	25.55	24.70	0.277	8.625	8.071	8	5¼	9.625	23.18	1,200	1,300	1,600
8	29.35	28.55	0.322	8.625	7.981	8	5¼	9.625	23.18	1,200	1,300	1,600
10	32.75	31.20	0.279	10.750	10.192	8	5¾	11.750	31.55	1,000	1,200	1,400
10	35.75	34.24	0.307	10.750	10.136	8	5¾	11.750	31.55	1,000	1,200	1,400
10	41.85	40.48	0.365	10.750	10.020	8	5¾	11.750	31.55	1,000	1,200	1,400
12	45.45	43.77	0.330	12.750	12.090	8	6⅛	14.000	49.27	1,000	1,200	1,400
12	51.15	49.56	0.375	12.750	12.000	8	6⅛	14.000	49.27	1,000	1,200	1,400
14 O.D.	57.00	54.57	0.375	14.000	13.250	8	6⅜	15.000	45.83	950	1,100	1,400
15 O.D.	61.15	58.57	0.375	15.000	14.250	8	6⅝	16.000	51.26	900	1,000	1,400
16 O.D.	65.30	62.58	0.375	16.000	15.250	8	6¾	17.000	55.83	850	1,000	1,300
17 O.D.	73.20	69.70	0.393	17.000	16.214	8	7	18.000	61.67	850	950	1,200
18 O.D.	81.20	76.84	0.409	18.000	17.182	8	7⅛	19.000	66.53	800	950	1,200
20 O.D.	90.00	85.58	0.409	20.000	19.182	8	7⅝	21.000	79.37	750	850	1,100

The permissible variation in weight for any length of pipe is 10 percent above and 3½ percent below; but the carload weight shall not be more than 1¾ percent under the calculated weight.

Furnished with threads and couplings and in random lengths, unless otherwise ordered.

The weight per foot of pipe with threads and couplings is based on a length of 20 ft, including the coupling.

* Test pressure butt-welded pipe ⅛ to 1 in. = 700 psi; 1¼ to 3 in. = 800 psi.

material. Malleable iron may be used up to 300 psi and 500 F for 3 (2) [1½] in. pipe, and pressure from 250 to 400 (400 to 600) [600 to 2,500] psi, forged and cast-steel screwed valves and fittings may be substituted. Malleable-iron screwed fittings (300 lb MSS SP-31) may be used for pressures not greater than 300 psi and temperatures not over 500 F. Valves 8 in. and larger should have the by-pass of at least ¾ in., commercial size.[1] Welded fittings may be used of the same material and thickness as the pipe with which they are to be used.

Steam Pressures from 125 to 250 psi, Temperature not above 450 F. Pipe may be electric-fusion-welded steel (A134 or A139), electric-resistance-welded steel (A135), seamless or welded steel (A53), or wrought iron (A72). Copper and brass may be used if the temperature does not exceed 406 F. Cast iron may also be used. For close coiling or cold bending, Grade A seamless steel (A)53; or Grade A electric-welded steel (A53), (A135), or (A139); or wrought iron (A72) is suitable. Pipe permissible for this service may be used for temperatures above 450 F if the proper S is used in calculating the pipe-wall thickness.

Valves below 3 in. may have inside stem screws. Stop valves 8 in. and over must be by-passed. Bodies, bonnets, and yokes shall be of cast iron, malleable iron, steel, bronze, brass, or Monel. Flanged-steel fittings must conform to the 300 lb American Standard B16e; if of cast iron, to the 250 lb American Standard B16b or, for screwed fittings, B16d. Malleable-

[1] See Manufacturere Standardization Society Mss SP–31 for recommended size of bypass valves.

iron screwed fittings shall conform to the 300 lb MSS SP-31, except that the 150 lb American Standard B16.3 may be used for pressures not greater than 150 lb. Welded fittings may be used.

Steam Pressures from 25 to 125 psi, Temperatures not above 450 F. Pipe may be of steel, wrought iron, cast iron, copper, or brass; valve bodies of cast iron, malleable iron, steel, or brass. Fittings shall be of 125 lb or 150 lb American Standard cast iron with screwed or flanged ends, or of malleable iron with screwed ends.

Steam Pressures 25 psi and less, Temperature up to 450 F. Pipe may be of steel, wrought iron, spiral-riveted steel, brass, copper, or cast iron. Flanged fittings shall conform to the 25 lb American Standard B16.2. Screwed fittings shall be of the 125 lb American Standard B16.4 or of the 150 lb American Standard B16.3 for cast iron or malleable iron, respectively, or the B16.15 for bronze. Welded fittings may be used.

Pipe coils are made from any of the commercial sizes of iron, steel, brass, and copper pipe and tubing. Limiting center-to-center dimensions, to which pipe coils can be fabricated in sizes ¾ to 2 in. are given in Table 10. Steel tubing cannot be bent to the absolute limits of brass or copper.

Table 10. Center-to-center Dimensions of Pipe Coils

(Crane Co.)

Size of pipe, in.	Recommended and advisable minimum, in.		Shortest possible, in.	
	Standard	Extra strong	Standard	Extra strong
¾	3½	2½	3½	2½
1	4	3	4	3
1¼	5	4	4½	3½
1½	6	5	5	4
2	8	6	6	5

Seamless mechanical tubing is obtainable in outside diameters ranging from ¼ to 10¾ in. in wall thicknesses from 20 gage to 2 in., and in standard pipe weights and dimensions up to 24 in. Oval, square, rectangular, and other special shapes can be obtained in various sizes and wall thicknesses. Mechanical tubing is available either hot-finished or cold-drawn, but is furnished principally cold-drawn. It is readily adaptable to varied treatment by expansion, cupping, tapering, swaging, flanging, coiling, welding, and similar manipulations. Typical of the many uses are aircraft tubing, automobile axle housings, drive shafts, drive-shaft housings, tie rods, steering columns, piston rods and pins, gear rings, roller bearing cases and cones, cylinders for various purposes, machine parts, sleeves, bushings, spacers, surgical instruments, and hypodermic needles. Table 11 gives weights and dimensions of round seamless-steel tubing for sizes that have by common usage become standard. Detailed information on mechanical tubing for any particular applications can be obtained from manufacturers.

Dimensions and weights of **condenser** and **heat-exchanger tubes** are given in Table 12 and of boiler tubes in Table 13.

Spiral Pipe. Spiral pipe is strong lightweight steel pipe with a single continuous welded helical seam from end to end stiffening it throughout. It is listed in sizes 6 to 42 in. I.D., in various thicknesses, and in lengths up to 40 ft. It is used for high- and low-pressure water lines, vacuum lines, exhaust-steam lines, low-pressure air lines, sand and gravel conveying and similar services. It is also used extensively by the petroleum industry, for oil and gas lines, for low-pressure steam lines, etc.

Spiral pipe may be asphalt coated or galvanized. The pipe is designed for special joints, flanges, and lightweight fittings, but the American Standard flanges and fittings can be furnished, if desired. For further details, refer to catalogue of Taylor Forge and Pipe Works, Chicago.

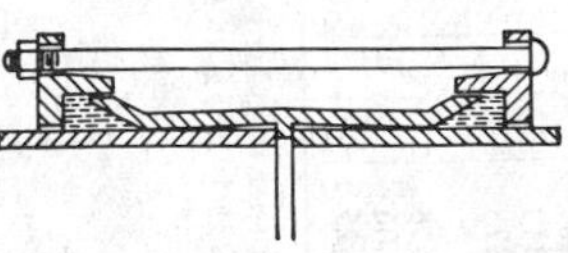

Fig. 1. Sleeve-type, plain-end coupling.

The **sleeve-type coupling** illustrated in Fig. 1 is particularly suitable for plain-end pipe and is widely used. A gasket is used to make a tight joint. Advantages of this coupling are low cost, the use of un-

Table 11. Approx Weight of Round Seamless Cold-finished Carbon-steel Mechanical Tubing, Lb per Ft*

(Carbon, 0.25 % max. Standard sizes for warehouse stocks random lengths. National Tube Division, United States Steel Corp.)

Wall thickness		O.D., in.																	
In.	G or in.	3/8	1/2	5/8	3/4	7/8	1	1 1/8	1 1/4	1 3/8	1 1/2	1 5/8	1 3/4	1 7/8	2	2 1/8	2 1/4	2 3/8	2 1/2
0.035	20 G	0.127	0.174	0.221	0.267	0.314	0.361	0.407	0.454	.....	0.548								
0.049	18 G	0.171	0.236	0.301	0.367	0.432	0.498	0.563	0.629	0.694	0.759	0.825	0.890	....	1.02				
0.058	17 G	.....	0.274	0.351	0.429	.....	0.584												
0.065	16 G	0.215	0.302	0.389	0.476	0.562	0.649	0.736	0.823	0.909	0.996	1.08	1.17	1.26	1.34	1.43	1.52	1.60	1.69
0.083	14 G	.....	0.370	0.480	0.591	0.702	0.813	0.924	1.03	1.15	1.26	....	.....	....	1.70				
0.095	13 G	.....	0.411	0.538	0.665	0.791	0.918	1.05	1.17	1.30	1.43	1.55	1.68	1.81	1.93	2.06	2.19	2.31	2.44
0.109	12 G	.....	0.455	0.601	0.746	0.892	1.04	1.18	1.33	.....	1.62								
0.120	11 G	.....	0.487	0.647	0.807	0.968	1.13	1.29	1.45	1.61	1.77	1.93	2.09	2.25	2.41	2.57	2.73	2.89	3.05
0.134	10 G	.....	.....	0.703	0.882	.....	1.24	1.42	1.60	1.78	1.96	2.13	2.31	....	2.67				
0.156	5/32	.....	.....	0.781	0.990	1.20	1.41	1.61	1.82	2.03	2.24	2.45	2.66	2.86	3.07	3.28	3.49	3.70	3.91
0.188	3/16	.....	.....	.....	1.13	1.38	1.63	1.88	2.13	2.38	2.63	2.89	3.14	3.39	3.64	3.89	4.14	4.39	4.64
0.219	7/32	.....	.....	.....	.....	1.53	1.83	2.12	2.41	2.70	3.00	3.29	3.58	3.87	4.17	4.46	4.75	5.04	5.34
0.250	1/4	.....	.....	.....	1.34	1.67	2.00	2.34	2.67	3.00	3.34	3.67	4.01	4.34	4.67	5.01	5.34	5.67	6.01
0.281	9/32	.....	.....	.....	.....	.....	.....	.....	2.91	.....	3.66	4.03	4.41	4.78	5.16	....	5.91	6.28	6.66
0.313	5/16	.....	.....	.....	.....	.....	.....	.....	3.13	3.55	3.97	4.39	4.80	5.22	5.64	6.06	6.48	6.89	7.31
0.375	3/8	.....	.....	.....	.....	.....	.....	.....	3.50	4.01	4.51	5.01	5.51	6.01	6.51	7.01	7.51	8.01	8.51
0.438	7/16	.....	.....	.....	.....	.....	.....	.....	.....	.....	4.97	5.53	6.14	6.72	7.31	7.89	8.48	9.06	9.65
0.500	1/2	.....	.....	.....	.....	.....	.....	.....	.....	.....	5.34	6.01	6.68	7.34	8.01	8.68	9.35	10.0	10.7
0.625	5/8	.....	.....	.....	.....	.....	.....	.....	.....	.....	.....	.....	.....	....	9.18	....	10.8	11.7	12.5

* Other standard sizes, in certain standard wall thicknesses, vary by 1/8 in. increments from 2 1/2 to 3 1/2 in.; by 1/4 in. increments from 3 1/2 to 7 1/2 in.; 1/2 in. increments from 7 1/2 to 10 1/2 in. O.D. There are also standard sizes for every 1/16 in. from 3/8 to 1 5/8 in. O.D.

Table 12. Condenser and Heat-exchanger Tubes

(Dimensions and weights. National Tube Division, United States Steel Corp.)

O.D., in.	Thickness, in.	Avg wall			Min wall		
		I.D., in.	Area of metal, sq in.	Weight per ft, lb	I.D., in.	Area of metal, sq in.	Weight per ft, lb
½	0.035	0.430	0.0511	0.1738	0.423	0.0558	0.1898
	0.050	0.400	0.0707	0.2403	0.390	0.0769	0.2614
	0.065	0.370	0.0888	0.3020	0.357	0.0963	0.3272
⅝	0.035	0.555	0.0649	0.2205	0.548	0.0709	0.2412
	0.050	0.525	0.0903	0.3071	0.515	0.0985	0.3348
	0.065	0.495	0.1144	0.3888	0.482	0.1243	0.4227
	0.085	0.455	0.1442	0.4902	0.438	0.1561	0.5308
¾	0.050	0.650	0.1100	0.3738	0.640	0.1201	0.4082
	0.065	0.620	0.1399	0.4755	0.607	0.1524	0.5181
	0.085	0.580	0.1776	0.6037	0.563	0.1928	0.6556
	0.095	0.560	0.1955	0.6646	0.541	0.2119	0.7204
⅞	0.050	0.775	0.1296	0.4406	0.765	0.1417	0.4817
	0.065	0.745	0.1654	0.5623	0.732	0.1805	0.6136
	0.085	0.705	0.2110	0.7172	0.688	0.2296	0.7804
	0.095	0.685	0.2328	0.7914	0.666	0.2530	0.8599
1	0.050	0.900	0.1492	0.5073	0.890	0.1633	0.5551
	0.065	0.870	0.1909	0.6491	0.857	0.2086	0.7090
	0.085	0.830	0.2443	0.8306	0.813	0.2663	0.9052
	0.095	0.810	0.2701	0.9182	0.791	0.2940	0.9994
1¼	0.050	1.150	0.1885	0.6408	1.140	0.2065	0.7020
	0.065	1.120	0.2420	0.8226	1.107	0.2647	0.8999
	0.085	1.080	0.3111	1.058	1.163	0.3397	1.155
	0.095	1.060	0.3447	1.172	1.041	0.3761	1.278
	0.105	1.040	0.3777	1.284	1.019	0.4117	1.399
1½	0.050	1.400	0.2278	0.7743	1.390	0.2497	0.8488
	0.065	1.370	0.2930	0.9962	1.357	0.3209	1.091
	0.085	1.330	0.3779	1.285	1.313	0.4053	1.378
	0.095	1.310	0.4193	1.426	1.291	0.4581	1.557
	0.105	1.290	0.4602	1.564	1.269	0.5024	1.708
1¾	0.065	1.620	0.3441	1.170	1.606	0.3803	1.293
	0.085	1.580	0.4446	1.512	1.561	0.4907	1.668
	0.095	1.560	0.4939	1.679	1.539	0.5448	1.852
	0.105	1.540	0.5426	1.845	1.517	0.5902	2.007
	0.120	1.510	0.6145	2.089	1.484	0.6766	2.300
2	0.065	1.870	0.3951	1.343	1.856	0.4370	1.486
	0.085	1.830	0.5114	1.738	1.811	0.5649	1.920
	0.095	1.810	0.5685	1.933	1.789	0.6275	2.133
	0.105	1.790	0.6251	2.125	1.767	0.6896	2.344
	0.120	1.760	0.7087	2.409	1.734	0.7812	2.656

skilled labor in making the connections, and the fact that small changes in alignment and grade can be made with regular straight lengths of pipe by a movement in the coupling. This type of coupling is used extensively in long oil lines.

Table 13. Seamless-steel Boiler Tubes

(National Tube Division, United States, Steel Corp.)

Outside diam, in.	Thickness BWG	Thickness In.	Mfg. wt, lb per ft	Outside diam, in.	Thickness BWG	Thickness In.	Mfg. wt, lb per ft	Outside diam, in.	Thickness BWG	Thickness In.	Mfg. wt, lb per ft
1	13	0.095	1.037	2½	12	0.109	3.171	4½	10	0.134	7.103
	12	0.109	1.168		11	0.120	3.457		9	0.148	7.817
	11	0.120	1.263		10	0.134	3.835		8	0.165	8.702
	10	0.134	1.384		9	0.148	4.207		7	0.180	9.447
1¼	13	0.095	1.323	2¾	12	0.109	3.504	5	9	0.148	8.720
	12	0.109	1.502		11	0.120	3.823		8	0.165	9.711
	11	0.120	1.628		10	0.134	4.244		7	0.180	10.550
	10	0.134	1.793		9	0.148	4.658		6	0.203	11.810
1½	13	0.095	1.619	3	12	0.109	3.838	5½	9	0.148	9.622
	12	0.109	1.836		11	0.120	4.189		8	0.165	10.720
	11	0.120	1.994		10	0.134	4.652		7	0.180	11.650
	10	0.134	2.201		9	0.148	5.110		6	0.203	13.050
1¾	13	0.095	1.910	3¼	11	0.120	4.555	6	7	0.180	12.750
	12	0.109	2.169		10	0.134	5.061		6	0.203	14.290
	11	0.120	2.360		9	0.148	5.561		5	0.220	15.410
	10	0.134	2.610		8	0.165	6.179		4	0.238	16.640
2	13	0.095	2.201	3½	11	0.120	4.921				
	12	0.109	2.503		10	0.134	5.469				
	11	0.120	2.726		9	0.148	6.012				
	10	0.034	3.018		8	0.065	6.683				
2¼	13	0.095	2.492	4	10	0.134	6.286				
	12	0.109	2.837		9	0.148	6.915				
	11	0.120	3.092		8	0.165	7.693				
	10	0.134	3.427		7	0.180	8.347				

CAST-IRON PIPE

Cast-iron pipe is extensively used for water, gas, sewage, culverts, drains, etc., in a wide range of sizes and for varying pressures, and is particularly adapted to underground and submerged service because of its comparatively high corrosion-resistance qualities. It is more durable than bare wrought-iron and steel pipe; however, steel pipe, when properly coated and wrapped, has been found to be resistant to corrosion when placed in certain soils. For any particular installation, relative cost figures for cast iron *vs.* coated-and-wrapped steel must be obtained to determine the most economical material. The tensile strength of commercial cast-iron pipe is uncertain, and, because of its low elasticity, it is not suitable for lines subject to the strains of expansion, contraction, and vibration. This pipe may be obtained in various thicknesses and weights with (1) flanges cast on, (2) ends threaded for screwed-on flanges, (3) ends prepared for mechanical joint, (4) ends grooved or shouldered for patented coupling, (5) one end bell, other end spigot, and (6) one end hub, other end spigot. **Bell-and-spigot** ends are most popular for underground work; hub-and-spigot ends are most frequently used for sewage systems in enclosed spaces. Spigot-end joints are prepared by tightly tamping in hemp or jute at the bottom of the recess with a yarning iron and then pouring in molten lead; the lead, when cooled, is calked in tightly with a calking iron and makes a gastight joint. For exposed piping, flanged ends are used, the joints being made up with gaskets. Flanged pipe has superior strength and tightness of the joint and is used where pipelines can be well supported. The bell-and-spigot joint possesses greater flexibility and provides for expansion and contraction. It is therefore suitable for water pipe and is largely used for that purpose. Figure 2 shows a typical form of this joint for ordinary pressures. Figure 3 shows one form of **mechanical joint** suitable for water, gas, or oil. Other forms of joint, plain-end pipe with couplings, and threaded pipe also are manufactured. Cast-iron pipe, fittings, and valves have been found unsuitable for superheated steam service. The Code for Pressure Piping, ASA B31.1, 1963, states that cast iron may be used for steam service not over 450 F provided that it meets the requirements as dictated by Eq. (1), p. 8–207.

Wall thicknesses for the various conditions which cast-iron pipe is designed to meet are determined in accordance with the American Recommended Practice Manual for the Computation of Strength and Thickness of Cast-iron Pipe, ASA A21.1, 1957.

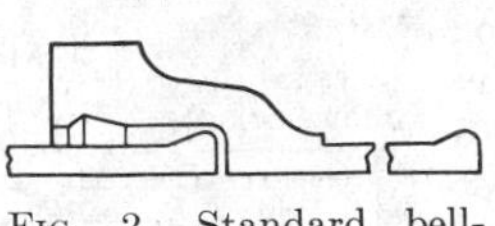

FIG. 2. Standard bell-and-spigot joint.

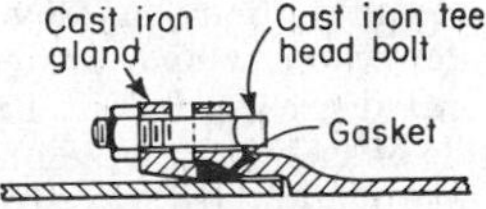

FIG. 3. Mechanical joint.

Cast-iron pipe is made by two methods—pit cast and centrifugally cast. **Pit-cast pipe** is cast vertically with dry-sand molds and cores; in **centrifugal casting,** molten iron is admitted to the interior of a sand-lined or metal-lined cast-iron flask, and the mold is rotated at high speeds so that the molten metal is thrown by centrifugal force against the lining. ASA specifications have been prepared for the various combinations of fabrication procedure and intended end use: pit-cast pipe for water or other liquids (ASA A21.2, 1953); pit-cast pipe for gas (ASA A21.3, 1953); centrifugally cast, sand molds, water (ASA A21.8, 1962); centrifugally cast, metal molds, water (ASA A21.6, 1962); centrifugally cast, sand molds, gas (ASA A21.9, 1962); centrifugally cast, metal molds, gas (ASA A21.7, 1962).

Table 14 lists thicknesses and weight data for pipe centrifugally cast in sand-lined molds and intended for use with water or other liquids. For pit-cast pipe, or for centrifugally cast pipe with metal molds or intended for gas service, consult the appropriate ASA specification as listed above.

The employment of cast-iron pipe for gas supply and distribution is second in importance only to its use for carrying water. Bell-and-spigot gas pipe is similar in design

Table 14. Standard Weights and Thicknesses of Cast-iron Bell-and-spigot Pipe for Water *

(Data from ASA A21.8, 1962)

Nominal size, in.	Class 50, 50 psi, 115 ft head			Class 100, 100 psi, 231 ft head			Class 150, 150 psi, 346 ft head			Approx lb lead per joint 2 in. thick	Approx lb hemp or jute per joint
	Thickness, in.	O.D., in.	Wt, lb per avg ft	Thickness, in.	O.D., in.	Wt, lb per avg ft	Thickness, in.	O.D., in.	Wt, lb per avg ft		
3	0.32	3.96	12.4	0.32	3.96	12.4	0.32	3.96	12.4	6.2	0.17
4	0.35	4.80	16.5	0.35	4.80	16.5	0.35	4.80	16.5	7.5	0.21
6	0.38	6.90	25.9	0.38	6.90	25.9	0.38	6.90	25.9	10.3	0.31
8	0.41	9.05	37.0	0.41	9.05	37.0	0.41	9.05	37.0	13.3	0.44
10	0.44	11.10	49.1	0.44	11.10	49.1	0.44	11.10	49.1	16.0	0.53
12	0.48	13.20	63.7	0.48	13.20	63.7	0.48	13.20	63.7	19.0	0.61
14	0.48	15.30	74.6	0.51	15.30	78.8	0.51	15.65	80.7	22.0	0.81
16	0.54	17.40	95.2	0.54	17.40	95.2	0.54	17.80	97.5	30.0	0.94
18	0.54	19.50	107.6	0.58	19.50	114.8	0.58	19.92	117.2	33.8	1.00
20	0.57	21.60	125.9	0.62	21.60	135.9	0.62	22.06	138.9	37.0	1.25
24	0.63	25.80	166.0	0.68	25.80	178.1	0.73	26.32	194.0	44.0	1.50
30	0.79	32.00	257.6	0.79	32.00	257.6	0.85	32.00	275.4	54.3	2.06
36	0.87	38.30	340.9	0.87	38.30	340.9	0.94	38.30	365.9	64.8	3.00
42	0.97	44.50	442.0	0.97	44.50	442.0	1.05	44.50	475.3	75.3	3.62
48	1.06	50.80	551.6	1.06	50.80	551.6	1.14	50.80	589.6	85.5	4.37

* Pipe weights indicated are approximate and include allowance for bell based on a 16 ft laying length. Calculations are for pipe laid without blocks, on flat-bottom trench, with tamped backfill under 5 ft of cover. For other conditions, see ASA A21.1. Thicknesses given above include allowance for water hammer and factory tolerance.

to bell-and-spigot water pipe (Fig. 2). For flanged gas pipe, the 25 lb ASA standard flanges are approved for maximum gas pressures of 25 psi. The 125 lb ASA standard flanges are approved for gas pressures of 125 psi, up to 4 in. nominal pipe size; 100 psi, 6 to 12 in.; and 80 psi, 16 to 48 in. The type of joint shown in Fig. 2 is also widely used for gas.

Flexible-joint Pipe. The necessity for crossing streams and other waterways and of laying pipelines into them has developed various forms of flexible-joint pipe adapted to laying under water, which are capable of motion through several degrees without leakage. Figure 4 shows one style of such joint which has an adjustment of about 15 deg in standard sizes.

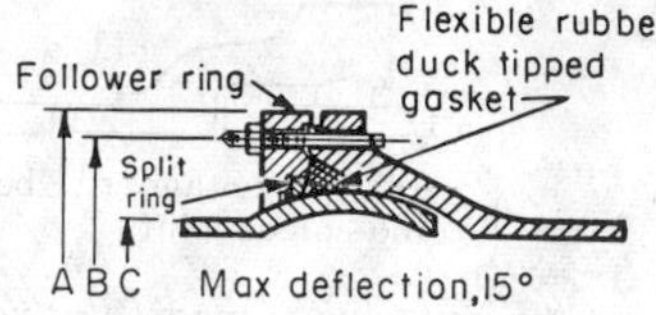

FIG. 4. Flexible joint.

In selecting the thickness of a pipe for a submerged line, the internal-service pressure is seldom the determining factor, as ample allowance should be made to minimize the risk of breakage in laying and to withstand external shocks from floating ice or other objects. The dimensions and weights given in Table 15 are typical of those listed by several manufacturers.

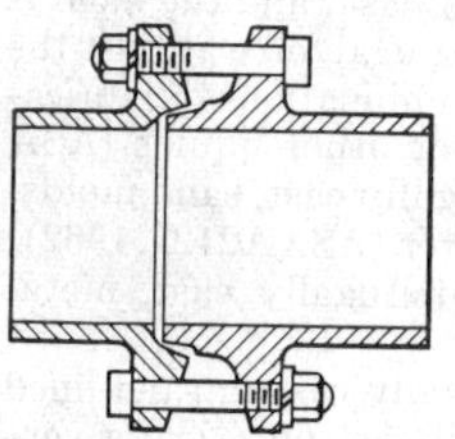

FIG. 5. "Universal" cast-iron pipe.

"Universal" pipe (Fig. 5) is cast-iron pipe with hub-and-spigot ends, the contact surfaces of which are machined on a taper, giving an iron-to-iron joint. By making the tapers of slightly different pitch, the joint provides for flexibility while remaining tight. Two bolts to the joint are sufficient, except for pressures above 175 psi. Universal cast-iron pipe is used largely for carrying gas and water and is suitable for all pressures and services. The pipe is tested with hydrostatic pressure of 300 to 500 psi. All universal pipe and special castings of a given diameter and of any class are interchangeable with those of a different class. Standard laying lengths, 6 ft. Thicknesses and weights of standard types up to 16 in. are given in Table 17. Information on other types and sizes and on fittings may be obtained from Central Foundry Co.

Table 15. Dimensions and Weights of Flexible-joint Pipe
(United States Pipe and Foundry Co.)
(Dimensions refer to Fig. 4)

Nominal diam, in.	Class	Dimensions, in.			Bolts			Average metal thickness, in.	Weight* of pipe, incl. bell, lb per 12 ft length
		A	B	C	No. required	Size, in.	Length, in.		
4	B	12.13	9.75	5.00	8	0.75	4.50	0.45	290
4	C	12.13	9.75	5.00	8	0.75	4.50	0.48	305
4	D	12.13	9.75	5.00	8	0.75	4.50	0.52	325
6	B	14.25	11.75	7.10	12	0.75	4.50	0.48	440
6	C	14.25	11.75	7.10	12	0.75	4.50	0.51	460
6	D	14.25	11.75	7.10	12	0.75	4.50	0.55	490
8	B	17.25	14.75	9.30	12	0.75	5.25	0.51	635
8	C	17.25	14.75	9.30	12	0.75	5.25	0.56	680
8	D	17.25	14.75	9.30	12	0.75	5.25	0.60	720
10	B	20.56	18.00	11.40	16	0.75	5.25	0.57	905
10	C	20.56	18.00	11.40	16	0.75	5.25	0.62	965
10	D	20.56	18.00	11.40	16	0.75	5.25	0.68	1035
12	B	23.75	21.00	13.50	16	0.75	6.25	0.62	1200
12	C	23.75	21.00	13.50	16	0.75	6.25	0.68	1280
12	D	23.75	21.00	13.50	16	0.75	6.25	0.75	1375

* Weights do not include follower rings, bolts, or gaskets. For sizes above 12 in., see manufacturers' catalogues.

Table 16. Cast-iron Flanged Pipe for Water
(ASA B16.1 Class 125 or ASA B16.2 Class 250)

Size	Actual O.D., in.	Diam of flange, in.	Diam of raised face, in.	Diam of bolt circle, in.	No. of bolts	Diam of bolts, in.	Thickness of flange, in.	Max working pressure, psi	Wall thickness, in.	Wt per ft plain end, lb	Wt of one flange, lb	Wt 16 ft. length with 2 flanges, lb
3	3.96	7.50		6.00	4	⅝	0.75	150	0.38	13.3	7	225
3	3.96	7.50		6.00	4	⅝	0.75	250	0.38	13.3	7	225
3	3.96	8.25	5.69	6.62	8	¾	1.12	250	0.38	13.3	12	235
4	4.80	9.00		7.50	8	⅝	0.94	150	0.38	16.5	13	290
4	4.80	9.00		7.50	8	⅝	0.94	250	0.38	16.5	13	290
4	4.80	10.00	6.94	7.88	8	¾	1.25	250	0.38	16.5	20	305
6	6.90	11.00		9.50	8	¾	1.00	150	0.38	24.3	17	425
6	6.90	11.00		9.50	8	¾	1.00	250	0.38	24.3	17	425
6	6.90	12.50	9.69	10.62	12	¾	1.44	250	0.38	24.3	34	455
8	9.05	13.50		11.75	8	¾	1.12	150	0.41	34.7	27	610
8	9.05	13.50		11.75	8	¾	1.12	250	0.41	34.7	27	610
8	9.05	15.00	11.94	13.00	12	⅞	1.62	250	0.41	34.7	50	655
10	11.10	16.00		14.25	12	⅞	1.19	150	0.44	46.0	38	810
10	11.10	16.00		14.25	12	⅞	1.19	250	0.44	46.0	38	810
10	11.10	17.50	14.06	15.25	16	1	1.88	250	0.44	46.0	70	875
12	13.20	19.00		17.00	12	⅞	1.25	150	0.48	59.8	58	1,075
12	13.20	19.00		17.00	12	⅞	1.25	250	0.52	64.6	58	1,150
12	13.20	20.50	16.44	17.75	16	1⅛	2.00	250	0.52	64.6	102	1,240
14	15.30	21.00		18.75	12	1	1.38	150	0.51	73.9	72	1,325
14	15.30	21.00		18.75	12	1	1.38	250	0.59	85.1	72	1,505
14	15.30	23.00	18.94	20.25	20	1⅛	2.12	250	0.59	85.1	130	1,620
16	17.40	23.50		21.25	16	1	1.44	150	0.54	89.2	90	1,605
16	17.40	23.50		21.25	16	1	1.44	250	0.63	103.6	90	1,840
16	17.40	25.50	21.06	22.50	20	1¼	2.25	250	0.63	103.6	162	1,980
18	19.50	25.00		22.75	16	1⅛	1.56	150	0.58	107.6	90	1,900
18	19.50	25.00		22.75	16	1⅛	1.56	250	0.68	125.4	90	2,185
18	19.50	28.00	23.31	24.75	24	1¼	2.38	250	0.68	125.4	200	2,405
20	21.60	27.50		25.00	20	1⅛	1.69	150	0.62	127.5	115	2,270
20	21.60	27.50		25.00	20	1⅛	1.69	250	0.72	147.4	115	2,590
20	21.60	30.50	25.56	27.00	24	1¼	2.50	250	0.72	147.4	245	2,850
24	25.80	32.00		29.50	20	1¼	1.88	150	0.73	179.4	160	3,190
24	25.80	32.00		29.50	20	1¼	1.88	250	0.79	193.7	160	3,420
24	25.80	36.00	30.25	32.00	24	1½	2.75	250	0.79	193.7	370	3,840
30	32.00	38.75		36.0	28	1¼	2.12	150	0.85	259.5	240	4,630
30	32.00	38.75		36.0	28	1¼	2.12	250	0.99	300.9	240	5,295
30	32.00	43.0	37.19	39.25	28	1¾	3.00	250	0.99	300.9	530	5,875
36	38.30	46.00		42.75	32	1½	2.38	150	0.94	344.2	350	6,205
36	38.30	46.00		42.75	32	1½	2.38	250	1.10	401.1	350	7,120
36	38.30	50.0	43.69	46.0	32	2	3.38	250	1.10	401.1	710	7,840
42	44.50	53.00		49.5	36	1½	2.62	150	1.05	447.2	500	8,155
42	44.50	53.0		49.5	36	1½	2.62	250	1.22	517.6	500	9,280
42	44.50	57.0	50.44	52.75	36	2	3.69	250	1.22	517.6	900	10,080
48	50.80	59.50		56.0	44	1½	2.75	150	1.14	554.9	625	10,130
48	50.80	59.50		56.0	44	1½	2.75	250	1.33	644.9	625	11,570
48	50.80	65.0	58.44	60.75	40	2	4.00	250	1.33	644.9	1350	13,020

Fittings for Cast-iron Water Pipe. Flanged fittings of the dimensions of the American standard for steam are not often used with cast-iron water pipe. The longer fittings of the AWWA are generally preferred because of low friction loss. The dimensions of the flanged fittings of this class conform very closely to the dimensions of the bell-and-spigot fittings of the AWWA. The flange thicknesses conform to those of the American standard (see pp. 8–228, 8–229) and are drilled to American standard templates. These fittings, both flange, and bell-and-spigot type, are made in a great variety of forms known as "standard special fittings." For dimensions and weights, see manufacturers' catalogues or standard specifications of the AWWA.

Table 17. Standard Weights and Thicknesses of Universal Cast-iron Pipe
(Central Foundry Co.)

Nominal I.D., in.	Class 150, 150 psi			Class 250, 250 psi		
	Approx thickness, in.	Estimated wt, lb per		Approx thickness, in.	Estimated wt, lb per	
		Ft	6 ft length		Ft	6 ft length
2	0.25	7	42	0.31	8	48
3	0.30	11¼	67½	0.34	12½	75
4	0.32	16½	99	0.37	18	108
6	0.36	26.6	160	0.43	30	180
8	0.39	38½	231	0.47	44¼	265½
10	0.43	53½	321	0.50	60½	363
12	0.47	69	414	0.53	77½	465
14	0.50	87	522	0.565	98½	591
16	0.53	106	636	0.60	121	726

I.D., in.	2	3	4	6	8	10	12	14	16
Bolt sizes, in.	½ × 4	½ × 4¼	⅝ × 5	¾ × 6	⅞ × 6¾	1 × 7½	1 × 8	1⅛ × 9	1¼ × 9½

Table 18. Cast-iron Soil Pipe and Fittings
(ASA A40.1, 1935)
(Approximate weights, in pounds[b])

Fittings	Size of fitting, in.														
	2	3	4	5	6	3 × 2	4 × 2	4 × 3	5 × 2	5 × 3	5 × 4	6 × 2	6 × 3	6 × 4	6 × 5
Pipe, per ft	5	9	12	15	19										
¼ bends, regular	5	10	15	19	24										
¼ bends, short sweep	6	13	18	23	28										
¼ bends, long sweep	8	16	22	28	34										
⅕ bends	5	10	14	18	22										
⅙ bends	5	9	13	17	20										
⅛ bends	4	8	12	15	18										
1/16 bends	4	8	11	13	16										
Return bends	7	14	21	27	34										
T branches	8	15	21	26	32	13	16	19	19	22	24	22	25	27	30
Tapped T branches[a]	7	..	..	..	..	12	15	..	18	..	..	20			
Sanitary T branch	8	16	22	28	34	14	17	20	20	23	26	23	26	29	32
Tapped sanitary T branch[a]	8	..	..	..	..	12	15	..	18	..	..	21			
Y branch	8	17	24	32	40	14	17	20	20	24	27	23	27	31	35
Inverted Y branch	9	18	25	33	41	15	18	22	22	25	29	25	29	33	37
Combination Y and ⅛ bend	10	20	29	38	50	15	18	24	21	27	33	24	30	36	42
Upright Y branch	10	20	28	37	47	16	19	23	22	27	32	25	30	35	40
Vent branch	9	18	25	32	41	14	18	21	21	24	28	22	27	31	36
Double hubs	5	8	11	13	15										
Reducers	..	..	..	..	..	6	7	9	8	10	11	9	11	12	13
Increasers	..	..	..	..	..	9	10	12	12	14	15	13	15	16	18
Tapped increasers	..	..	..	..	..	9	11	..	12	..	..	14			

[a] Tapped up to 2 in.

[b] Weights of pipe include the hub. Laying lengths of pipe are 5 ft. From the data given for staple fittings, weights of other fittings may be estimated. For data on pipe sizes 8, 10, and 15 in. and other data, see ASA A40.1, 1935.

Cast-iron soil pipe and fittings are of the hub-and-spigot form, similar in design to the cast-iron water pipe shown in Fig. 2. Tapped openings and pipe plugs are threaded in accordance with the American standard taper pipe thread, ASA B2.1, 1960.

American standard "Threaded Cast-iron Pipe for Drainage, Vent, and Waste Services," ASA A40.5, 1943, covers two types of pipe having threaded joints in nominal pipe sizes 1¼ to 12 in. and in lengths 5 to 27 ft. One type has external threads on both ends; the other type has external threads on one end and an internal threaded drainage hub on the other end.

PIPES AND TUBES OF NON-FERROUS MATERIALS

Brass tubing is commercially available in the form known as yellow brass, an alloy consisting of approximately 65 percent copper and 35 percent zinc, and is used principally for ornamental work and handrailings. It has a density of approximately 0.3 lb per cu in., the exact density being dependent upon the specific chemical composition. **Brass piping** is most frequently encountered as red brass, an alloy consisting of approximately 85 percent copper and 15 percent zinc. This alloy, having a density of about 0.32 lb per cu in., has been found to be structurally superior to the yellow brasses and is used where the fluid being conveyed has corrosive properties.

Copper is available either as pipe or as tubing. In the form of piping, it has the same outer diameter as that of standard steel pipe. As tubing, it is used for a variety of purposes, such as for compressed-air instrumentation lines, hydraulic control lines around machinery, domestic oil-burner and heating systems, and for general plumbing purposes. **Copper tubing** is furnished in 12 ft and 20 ft straight lengths or in coils of 100 ft length. **Type K** tubing, in coils, is used for underground work where the minimum number of joints, combined with greater thickness of type K tubing, is of distinct advantage. **Type L** tubing, usually in straight lengths, is being used to an increasing degree as the principal piping material for plumbing systems in homes and buildings; this is largely due to the economy of installation made possible by the use of soldered fittings. Copper deteriorates rapidly under high temperatures and repeated stresses. At a temperature of 360 F, its strength is reduced 15 percent, and on this account it should never be used for high steam pressures and temperatures.

Table 19. Sizes and Weights of S.P.S. Copper and 85 Red Brass Pipe*

(American Brass Co.)

Standard pipe size (S. P. S.), in.	O.D., in.	I.D., in.	Wall thickness, in.	Weight, lb per ft	
				85 Red brass	Copper
⅛	0.405	0.281	0.0620	0.2533	0.2590
¼	0.540	0.375	0.0825	0.4496	0.4596
⅜	0.675	0.494	0.0905	0.6302	0.6441
½	0.840	0.625	0.1075	0.9381	0.9588
¾	1.050	0.822	0.1140	1.271	1.299
1	1.315	1.062	0.1265	1.791	1.831
1¼	1.660	1.368	0.1460	2.633	2.692
1½	1.900	1.600	0.1500	3.127	3.196
2	2.375	2.062	0.1565	4.136	4.228
2½	2.875	2.500	0.1875	6.003	6.136
3	3.500	3.062	0.2190	8.560	8.750
3½	4.000	3.500	0.2500	11.17	11.42
4	4.500	4.000	0.2500	12.66	12.94
5	5.563	5.062	0.2505	15.85	16.20
6	6.625	6.125	0.2500	18.99	19.41
8	8.625	8.000	0.3125	30.95	31.63
10	10.750	10.019	0.3655	45.22	46.22
11	11.750	11.000	0.3750	50.82	51.94
12	12.750	12.000	0.3750	55.28	56.51

***85 % copper, 15 % zinc.**

Commercial sizes of **aluminum tubing** are listed by the manufacturers in even outside diameters and in wall thicknesses conforming to stubs gage. Aluminum pipe is available

Table 20. Sizes and Weights of Copper Tubes

(American Brass Co.)

Nominal size, in.	O.D., in., Types* K, L	I.D., in.		Wall thickness, in.		Permissible variation of mean O.D., in.		Weight, lb per ft	
						Types K, L			
		Type K	Type L	Type K	Type L	Annealed	Hard-drawn	Type K	Type L
⅜	0.500	0.402	0.430	0.049	0.035	0.0025	0.001	0.269	0.198
½	0.625	0.527	0.545	0.049	0.040	0.0025	0.001	0.344	0.285
⅝	0.750	0.652	0.666	0.049	0.042	0.0025	0.001	0.418	0.362
¾	0.875	0.745	0.785	0.065	0.045	0.003	0.001	0.641	0.455
1	1.125	0.995	1.025	0.065	0.050	0.0035	0.0015	0.839	0.655
1¼	1.375	1.245	1.265	0.065	0.055	0.004	0.0015	1.04	0.884
1½	1.625	1.481	1.505	0.072	0.060	0.0045	0.002	1.36	1.14
2	2.125	1.959	1.985	0.083	0.070	0.005	0.002	2.06	1.75
2½	2.625	2.435	2.465	0.095	0.080	0.005	0.002	2.93	2.48
3	3.125	2.907	2.945	0.109	0.090	0.005	0.002	4.00	3.33
3½	3.625	3.385	3.425	0.120	0.100	0.005	0.002	5.12	4.29
4	4.125	3.857	3.905	0.134	0.110	0.005	0.002	6.51	5.38
5	5.125	4.805	4.875	0.160	0.125	0.005	0.002	9.67	7.61
6	6.125	5.741	5.845	0.192	0.140	0.005	0.002	13.9	10.2
8	8.125	7.583	7.725	0.271	0.200	0.006	0.003	25.9	19.3
10	10.125	9.449	9.625	0.338	0.250	0.008	0.004	40.3	30.1
12	12.125	11.315	11.565	0.405	0.280	0.008	0.004	57.8	40.4

* Type K recommended for underground service and general plumbing. Type L suitable for interior plumbing and other services.

Table 21. Aluminum Piping

(Aluminum Co. of America)

Nominal pipe size, in.	Schedule number*	O.D., in.	I.D., in.	Wall thickness, in.	Weight per linear foot, lb, plain ends†	Cross-sectional wall area, sq in.	Inside cross-sectional area, sq in.	Moment of inertia, $in.^4$	Section modulus, $in.^3$	Radius of gyration, in.
⅛	40‡	0.405	0.269	0.068	0.085	0.0720	0.0568	0.0011	0.0053	0.1215
	80§	0.405	0.215	0.095	0.109	0.0925	0.0363	0.0012	0.0060	0.1146
¼	40‡	0.540	0.364	0.088	0.147	0.1250	0.1041	0.0033	0.0123	0.1628
	80§	0.540	0.302	0.119	0.185	0.1574	0.0716	0.0038	0.0139	0.1547
⅜	40‡	0.675	0.493	0.091	0.196	0.1670	0.1909	0.0073	0.0216	0.2090
	80§	0.675	0.423	0.126	0.256	0.2173	0.1405	0.0086	0.0255	0.1991
½	40‡	0.840	0.622	0.109	0.294	0.2503	0.3039	0.0171	0.0407	0.2613
	80§	0.840	0.546	0.147	0.376	0.3200	0.2341	0.0201	0.0478	0.2505
¾	10	1.050	0.884	0.083	0.297	0.2521	0.6138	0.0297	0.0566	0.3432
	40‡	1.050	0.824	0.113	0.391	0.3326	0.5333	0.0370	0.0705	0.3337
	80§	1.050	0.742	0.154	0.510	0.4335	0.4324	0.0448	0.0853	0.3214
1	5	1.315	1.185	0.065	0.300	0.2553	1.103	0.0500	0.0760	0.4425
	10	1.315	1.097	0.109	0.486	0.4130	0.9452	0.0757	0.1151	0.4382
	40‡	1.315	1.049	0.133	0.581	0.4939	0.8643	0.0873	0.1328	0.4205
	80§	1.315	0.957	0.179	0.751	0.6388	0.7193	0.1056	0.1606	0.4066
1¼	5	1.660	1.530	0.065	0.383	0.3257	1.839	0.1037	0.1250	0.5644
	10	1.660	1.442	0.109	0.625	0.5311	1.633	0.1605	0.1934	0.5497
	40‡	1.660	1.380	0.140	0.786	0.6685	1.496	0.1947	0.2346	0.5397
	80§	1.660	1.278	0.191	1.037	0.8815	1.283	0.2418	0.2913	0.5238

* See footnotes at end of table.

Table 21. Aluminum Piping—(*Continued*)

(Aluminum Co. of America)

Nominal pipe size, in.	Schedule number*	O.D., in.	I.D., in.	Wall thickness, in.	Weight per linear foot, lb, plain ends†	Cross-sectional wall area, sq in.	Inside cross-sectional area, sq in.	Moment of inertia, in.[4]	Section modulus, in.[3]	Radius of gyration, in.
1½	5	1.900	1.770	0.065	0.441	0.3747	2.461	0.1579	0.1662	0.6492
	10	1.900	1.682	0.109	0.721	0.6133	2.222	0.2468	0.2598	0.6344
	40‡	1.900	1.610	0.145	0.940	0.7995	2.036	0.3099	0.3262	0.6226
	80§	1.900	1.500	0.200	1.256	1.068	1.767	0.3912	0.4118	0.6052
2	5	2.375	2.245	0.065	0.555	0.4717	3.958	0.3149	0.2652	0.8170
	10	2.375	2.157	0.109	0.913	0.7760	3.654	0.4992	0.4204	0.8021
	40‡	2.375	2.067	0.154	1.264	1.074	3.356	0.6657	0.5606	0.7871
	80§	2.375	1.939	0.218	1.737	1.477	2.953	0.8679	0.7309	0.7665
2½	5	2.875	2.709	0.083	0.856	0.7280	5.764	0.7100	0.4939	0.9876
	10	2.875	2.635	0.120	1.221	1.039	5.453	0.9873	0.6868	0.9750
	40‡	2.875	2.469	0.203	2.004	1.704	4.788	1.530	1.064	0.9474
	80§	2.875	2.323	0.276	2.650	2.254	4.238	1.924	1.339	0.9241
3	5	3.500	3.334	0.083	1.048	0.8910	8.730	1.301	0.7435	1.208
	10	3.500	3.260	0.120	1.498	1.274	8.346	1.822	1.041	1.196
	40‡	3.500	3.068	0.216	2.621	2.228	7.393	3.017	1.724	1.164
	80§	3.500	2.900	0.300	3.547	3.016	6.605	3.894	2.225	1.136
3½	5	4.000	3.834	0.083	1.201	1.021	11.55	1.960	0.9799	1.385
	10	4.000	3.760	0.120	1.720	1.463	11.10	2.755	1.378	1.372
	40‡	4.000	3.548	0.226	3.151	2.680	9.887	4.788	2.394	1.337
	80§	4.000	3.364	0.318	4.326	3.678	8.888	6.281	3.140	1.307
4	5	4.500	4.334	0.083	1.354	1.152	14.75	2.810	1.249	1.562
	10	4.500	4.260	0.120	1.942	1.651	14.25	3.963	1.761	1.549
	40‡	4.500	4.026	0.237	3.733	3.174	12.73	7.232	3.214	1.510
	80§	4.500	3.826	0.337	5.183	4.407	11.50	9.611	4.272	1.477
5	40‡	5.563	5.047	0.258	5.057	4.300	20.01	15.16	5.451	1.878
	80§	5.563	4.813	0.375	7.188	6.112	18.19	20.67	7.432	1.839
6	40‡	6.625	6.065	0.280	6.564	5.581	28.89	28.14	8.496	2.246
	80§	6.625	5.761	0.432	9.884	8.405	26.07	40.49	12.22	2.195
8	30	8.625	8.071	0.277	8.543	7.265	51.16	63.35	14.69	2.953
	40‡	8.625	7.981	0.322	9.878	8.399	50.03	72.49	16.81	2.938
	80§	8.625	7.625	0.500	15.01	12.76	45.66	105.7	24.51	2.878
10	...	10.750	10.192	0.279	10.79	9.178	81.59	125.9	23.42	3.704
	30	10.750	10.136	0.307	11.84	10.07	80.69	137.4	25.57	3.694
	40‡	10.750	10.020	0.365	14.00	11.91	78.85	160.7	29.90	3.674
	80§	10.750	9.750	0.500	18.93	16.10	74.66	211.9	39.43	3.628
12	30	12.750	12.090	0.330	15.14	12.88	114.8	248.5	38.97	4.393
	..‡	12.750	12.000	0.375	17.14	14.58	113.1	279.3	43.81	4.377
	..§	12.750	11.750	0.500	22.63	19.24	108.4	361.5	56.71	4.335
Construction Pipe										
		2.00	1.900	0.050	0.3602	0.3063	2.835	0.1457	0.1457	0.6897
		3.00	2.900	0.050	0.5449	0.4634	6.605	0.5042	0.3361	1.043
		4.00	3.900	0.050	0.7297	0.6205	11.95	1.210	0.6051	1.397
		5.00	4.896	0.052	0.9506	0.8083	18.83	2.474	0.9896	1.749
		6.00	5.876	0.062	1.360	1.157	27.12	5.098	1.699	2.100
		7.00	6.856	0.072	1.843	1.567	36.92	9.403	2.687	2.450
		8.00	7.812	0.094	2.745	2.335	47.93	18.24	4.561	2.795

* Schedule numbers conform to American Standard for Wrought-iron and Wrought-steel Pipe, ASA B36.10.

† Weights calculated for 6061 and 6063. For 3003 multiply by 1.010.

‡ Also designated as standard pipe.

§ Also designated as extra-heavy or extra-strong pipe. All calculations based on nominal dimensions.

as listed in Table 21. To obtain the approximate weight per foot of aluminum pipe or tubing, a weight of 0.098 lb per cu in. may be used.

Lead pipe is supplied in straight lengths, in coils, or in reels. Sizes and weights are given in Tables 22 and 23. The data in Table 23 conform to the standards advocated by the Lead Industries Assoc. for water service and plumbing.

Table 22. Weights and Dimensions of Lead Tubing*
(National Lead Co.)

I.D., in.	O.D., in.	Weight per ft, oz	I.D., in.	O.D., in.	Weight per ft, oz	I.D., in.	O.D., in.	Weight per ft, oz
1/16	1/8	0.75	3/16	5/16	3.00	1/4	1/2	12.00
1/8	13/64	1.00	1/4	11/32	4.00	5/16	3/8	2.00
1/8	3/16	1.50	1/4	3/8	5.00	3/8	7/16	2.00
1/8	1/4	2.00	1/4	13/32	6.00	3/8	1/2	7.00
3/16	1/4	2.00	1/4	7/16	8.00	7/16	1/2	4.00

* Furnished in coils of approx 25 lb, or on reels carrying approx 50 or 100 lb.

Table 23. Weights and Dimensions of Lead Pipe
(National Lead Co.)

I.D., in.	Classification East	Classification West	O.D., in.	Weight per ft, lb	I.D., in.	Classification East	Classification West	O.D., in.	Weight per ft, lb
3/8	E	AQ	0.520	0.50	1	E	AQ	1.192	1.63
	D	XL	0.549	0.63		D	XL	1.232	2.00
	C	L	0.577	0.75		C	L	1.284	2.50
	B	M	0.631	1.00		B	M	1.356	3.25
	A	S	0.725	1.50		A	S	1.428	4.00
	AA	XS	0.811	2.00		AA	XS	1.492	4.75
	AAA	XXS	0.888	2.50		AAA	XXS	1.596	6.00
1/2	E	AQ	0.628	0.56	1 1/4	E	AQ	1.442	2.00
	D	XL	0.666	0.75		D	XL	1.486	2.50
	C	L	0.712	1.00		C	L	1.528	3.00
	B	M	0.756	1.25		B	M	1.592	3.75
	A	S	0.798	1.50		A	S	1.670	4.75
	AA	XS	0.876	2.00		AA	XS	1.765	6.00
	AAA	XXS	1.012	3.00		AAA	XXS	1.889	7.75
5/8	E	AQ	0.765	0.75	1 1/2	E	AQ	1.740	3.00
	D	XL	0.803	1.00		D	XL	1.776	3.50
	C	L	0.881	1.50		C	L	1.830	4.25
	B	M	0.953	2.00		B	M	1.882	5.00
	A	S	1.019	2.50		A	S	1.984	6.50
	AA	XS	1.082	3.00		AA	XS	2.076	8.00
	AAA	XXS	1.137	3.50		AAA	XXS	2.272	11.25
3/4	E	AQ	0.906	1.00	1 3/4				
	D	XL	0.940	1.25		D	XL	2.024	4.00
	C	L	1.006	1.75		C	L	2.086	5.00
	B	M	1.068	2.25		B	M	2.146	6.00
	A	S	1.156	3.00		A	S	2.193	6.75
	AA	XS	1.212	3.50		AA	XS	2.404	10.50
	AAA	XXS	1.336	4.75		AAA	XXS	2.624	14.75

Additional standard sizes are 2, 2 1/2, 3, 4, 5, and 6 in.

Block tin is a term used in the metal trade to refer to products made wholly from strictly pure high-grade tin. While tin pipe has many and varied uses, its most important applications are in types of equipment handling liquids intended for human consumption. Tin pipe does not rust, tarnish, or corrode, and therefore does not contaminate most of the liquids passing through it.

Table 24. Sizes and Weights of Block-tin Pipe

I.D., in.	O.D., in.	Weight per ft, oz	I.D., in.	O.D., in.	Weight per ft, oz	I.D., in.	O.D., in.	Weight per ft, oz
3/16	1/4	1½	3/8	9/16	7½	5/8	3/4	7
3/16	5/16	2½	3/8	19/32	8½	5/8	25/32	9
1/4	3/8	3	3/8	5/8	9½	5/8	13/16	10½
1/4	13/32	4	3/8	5/8	10½	5/8	7/8	15
1/4	7/16	5	3/8	21/32	12	3/4	7/8	8
1/4	15/32	6	7/16	9/16	4½	3/4	29/32	10
1/4	1/2	7	7/16	5/8	8	3/4	29/32	11
1/4	1/2	8	1/2	19/32	4	3/4	15/16	12½
5/16	7/16	4	1/2	5/8	5	3/4	1	17
5/16	1/2	5½	1/2	5/8	5½	3/4	1 1/32	20
5/16	17/32	7½	1/2	21/32	7	3/4	1 1/16	22½
3/8	1/2	4½	1/2	21/32	7½	1	1 3/16	16
3/8	1/2	5	1/2	11/16	9	1	1 3/16	17
3/8	17/32	5½	1/2	23/32	10½	1	1 7/32	19½
3/8	9/16	6½	1/2	3/4	12½			

Plastic pipes and **tubes** are available in a wide range of diameters and thicknesses, with Table 25 generally representative. The plastic used is resistant to attack by many

Table 25. Polyethylene Plastic Pipe Dimensions
(National Tube Division, United States Steel Corp.)

Nominal size, in.	O.D., in.	I.D., in.	Wall thickness, in.	Max operating press at 75 F, psi	Wt per ft, lb	Shipping length, ft
½	0.782	0.622	0.080	75	0.0704	100 and 400 (coiled)
	0.842	0.622	0.110	100	0.101	100 and 400 (coiled)
¾	1.024	0.824	0.100	75	0.1157	100 and 400 (coiled)
	1.114	0.824	0.145	100	0.176	100 and 400 (coiled)
1	1.300	1.050	0.125	75	0.1838	100 and 400 (coiled)
	1.410	1.050	0.180	100	0.277	100 and 400 (coiled)
1¼	1.660	1.380	0.140	70	0.266	100 and 400 (coiled)
	1.710	1.380	0.165	75	0.3190	100 and 400 (coiled)
	1.860	1.380	0.240	100	0.487	100 and 400 (coiled)
1½	1.900	1.610	0.145	60	0.318	100 and 400 (coiled)
	2.000	1.610	0.195	75	0.441	100 and 400 (coiled)
	2.170	1.610	0.280	100	0.662	100 and 400 (coiled)
2	2.375	2.067	0.154	50	0.428	100 and 400 (coiled)
	2.567	2.067	0.250	75	0.725	100 and 400 (coiled)
	2.777	2.067	0.355	100	1.077	100 and 400 (coiled)
3	3.500	3.068	0.216	50	0.888	100 (coiled)
	3.670	3.068	0.301	75	1.280	100 (coiled)
	4.068	3.068	0.500	100	2.230	100 (coiled)
4	4.500	4.026	0.237	40	1.265	25 (straight)
	4.820	4.026	0.397	75	2.200	25 (straight)
	5.386	4.026	0.680	100	4.000	25 (straight)
6	6.625	6.065	0.280	35	2.200	25 (straight)

chemicals, light in weight, flexible, and available in coiled form so that installation time is low. It is used for a variety of purposes including drainage, irrigation, sewage, and for conveying chemical solutions or waters that would attack metal piping. Caution should be used in selection of plastic piping in so far as service temperature is concerned: *e.g.*, polyethylene is suitable for a maximum temperature of 120 F. Table 26 lists corrosion-resistance data for polyethylene plastic piping.

Table 26. Corrosion-resistance Data, Polyethylene Pipe

(National Tube Division, United States Steel Corp.)

Reagent	Performance at 75 F	Performance at 120 F
Acetic acid, glacial*	F	NG
Acetic acid, 10 percent*	E	E
Acetone	NG	NG
Ammonia, dry gas	E	E
Ammonium hydroxide, 10 percent	E	E
Ammonium hydroxide, 28 percent	E	E
Amyl acetate	NG	NG
Aniline	E	F
Benzene	NG	NG
Bromine	NG	NG
Butyraldehyde	E	G
Calcium chloride, saturated	E	E
Calcium hydroxide	E	E
Calcium hypochlorite	E	E
Carbon disulphide	NG	NG
Carbon tetrachloride	NG	NG
Carbonic acid	E	E
Chlorine, dry gas	F	NG
Chlorine, liquid	NG	NG
Chlorosulphonic acid	NG	NG
Citric acid, saturated	E	E
Copper sulphate	E	E
Cyclohexanone	NG	NG
Diethylene glycol	E	E
Dioxane	E	G
Ethyl acetate	F	NG
Ethyl alcohol, 35 percent	NG	NG
Ethyl butyrate	F	NG
Ethylene dichloride	NG	NG
Ferric chloride	E	E
Ferrous sulphate, 15 percent aq	E	E
Fluorine	E	NG
Fluosilicic acid, concentrated	E	F
Formaldehyde, 40 percent	E	E
Formic acid, 50 percent	E	E
Furfuryl alcohol	NG	NG
Gasoline	NG	NG
Hydrobromic acid	E	E
Hydrochloric acid, 10 percent	E	E
Hydrochloric acid, 37 percent	E	E
Hydrofluoric acid, 48 percent	E	E
Hydrofluoric acid, 75 percent	E	F
Hydrogen peroxide, 30 percent	E	G
Hydrogen peroxide, 90 percent	G	NG
Lactic acid, 90 percent	E	E
Linseed oil	E	E
Lubricating oil	NG	NG
Magnesium chloride	E	E
Magnesium sulphate	E	E
Methyl bromide	NG	
Methyl isobutyl ketone	F	NG
Nitric acid, 10 percent	E	E
Nitric acid, 30–50 percent	E	E
Nitric acid, 70 percent	E	E
Oleic acid	F	NG
Phosphoric acid, 30 percent	E	E
Phosphoric acid, 90 percent	E	NG
Photographic developer	E	E
Potassium borate	E	E
Potassium carbonate	E	E
Potassium chloride, saturated	E	E
Potassium dichromate	E	E
Potassium hydroxide	E	E
Potassium nitrate	E	E
Potassium permanganate	E	E
Silicic acid	E	E
Silver nitrate	E	E
Sodium benzoate	E	E
Sodium bisulphite	E	E
Sodium carbonate, concentrated	E	E
Sodium chloride, saturated solution	E	E
Sodium hydroxide, 10 percent	E	E
Sodium hydroxide, 50 percent	E	E
Sodium sulphate	E	E
Stannic chloride, saturated	E	E
Stearic acid, 100 percent	E	E
Sulphuric acid, 10 percent	E	E
Sulphuric acid, 30 percent	E	E
Sulphuric acid, 60 percent	E	F
Sulphuric acid, 98 percent	F	NG
Tannic acid	E	E
Toluene	NG	NG
Trichlorobenzene	F	NG
Trichloroethylene	NG	NG
Vinegar	E	E
Xylene	NG	NG
Zinc chloride	E	E
Zinc sulphate	E	E

Corrosion resistance data given in this table are based on laboratory tests conducted by the manufacturers of the materials covered, and are indicative only of the conditions under which the tests were made. This information may be considered as a basis for recommendation, but not as a guarantee. Materials should be tested under actual service to determine suitability for a particular purpose.

E = excellent, G = good, F = fair, NG = not good.

* Polyethylene is permeable to acetic acid.

Pipes with Special Linings. For use in lines through which are passed solutions containing more or less free acid or other corrosive agents, standard pipe, valves, and fittings may be **lead-lined, tin-lined,** or **rubber-lined,** to resist corrosive action. This lining prolongs the life of the pipe and also gives it additional strength. For mine service in coal districts where the drainage water is more or less impregnated with sulphur or free sulphuric acid, **wood-lined pipe** and fittings are sometimes used. For special service, **seamless-copper-lined pipe** is also used. The **cement lining** of cast-iron and steel pipe for water and other services is regarded with increasing favor because of its protection against unusual destructive agencies and its ability to prevent tuberculation. Standard **hard-rubber pipe** and fittings have been developed for working pressures of 50 psi at normal temperatures. Standard sizes run from ¼ to 4 in. diam, in 10 ft lengths. For temperature above 120 F, the use of hard-rubber-lined steel pipe is recommended. This pipe is suitable for conveying strong acids and chemicals.

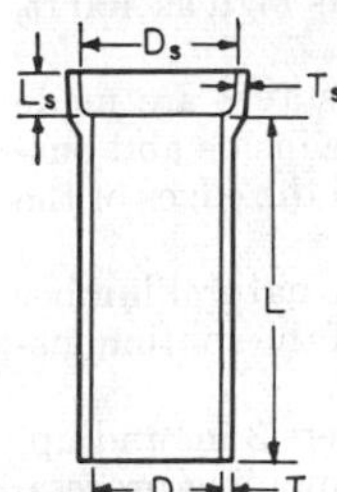

FIG. 6. Joint for vitrified pipe.

VITRIFIED, WOODEN-STAVE, AND CONCRETE PIPE

Vitrified pipe is used extensively for drains and sewerage systems. Burnt-clay tile, being rendered impervious to water by glazing, is by far the best material for sewage purposes as it is not attacked by acids. Dimensions are given in Table 27. For sizes larger than 36 in. and other data, refer to the publications of the Clay Products Assoc., Chicago (see ASTM Standard C13).

Table 27. Standard-strength Vitrified Clay Pipe
(Dimensions refer to Fig. 6)

Size, D, in.	Laying length, L		Max difference in length of two opposite sides, in.	O.D. of barrel, in.		I.D. of socket ½ in. above base, D_s, in.		Depth of socket, L_s, in.		Thickness of barrel, T, in.		Thickness of socket at ½ in. from outer end, T_s, in.	
	Nominal, ft	Limit of minus variation,* in. per ft length		Min	Max	Min	Max	Nominal	Min	Nominal	Min	Nominal	Min
4	2, 2½, 3	¼	5/16	4⅞	5⅛	5¾	6⅛	1¾	1½	½	7/16	7/16	⅜
6	2, 2½, 3	¼	⅜	7 1/16	7 7/16	8 3/16	8⅝	2½	2	⅝	9/16	½	7/16
8	2, 2½, 3	¼	7/16	9¼	9¾	10½	11	2½	2¼	¾	11/16	9/16	½
10	2, 2½, 3	¼	7/16	11½	12	12¾	13¼	2⅝	2⅜	⅞	13/16	⅝	9/16
12	2, 2½, 3	¼	7/16	13¾	14 5/16	15⅛	15¾	2¾	2½	1	15/16	¾	11/16
15	3, 4	¼	½	17 3/16	17 13/16	18⅝	19¼	2⅞	2⅝	1¼	1⅛	15/16	⅞
18	3, 4	¼	½	20⅝	21 7/16	22¼	23	3	2¾	1½	1⅜	1⅛	1 1/16
21	3, 4	¼	9/16	24⅛	25	25⅞	26¾	3¼	3	1¾	1⅝	1 5/16	1 3/16
24	3, 4	⅜	9/16	27½	28½	29⅜	30⅜	3⅜	3⅛	2	1⅞	1½	1⅜
27	3, 4	⅜	9/16	31	32⅛	33	34⅛	3½	3¼	2¼	2⅛	1 11/16	1 9/16
30	3, 4	⅜	⅝	34⅜	35⅝	36½	37¾	3⅝	3⅜	2½	2⅜	1⅞	1¾
33	3, 4	⅜	⅝	37⅝	38 15/16	39⅞	41¼	3¾	3½	2⅝	2½	2	1 13/16
36	3, 4	⅜	1 1/16	40¾	42¼	43¼	44¾	4	3¾	2¾	2⅝	2 1/16	1⅞

* There is no limit for plus variation.

When ordering standard-strength vitrified-clay pipe, give the size of pipe (I.D.) and the laying strength wanted, and refer to ASTM Specification C-13. Standard lengths of pipe shown meet normal practice in various sections of the country. Manufacturers' stocks include those lengths conforming to local practice.

Wood-stave pipe (Fig. 7) is used to a large extent for municipal water supply, outfall sewers, mining, irrigation, and various other uses providing for the transportation of water. The water carried may be hot, cold, or acid. It is made either untreated or creosoted by a vacuum and pressure process. This process uses 8 lb of creosote per cubic foot of wood treated. The untreated pipe is most used where the pipe is constantly full of water, and the wood therefore completely saturated, although in many such instances the creosoted wood is used to give assurance of permanence. (See also p. 6–167).

Wood-stave pipe is made in two types: machine-banded pipe and continuous-stave pipe. **Machine-banded pipe** is banded with wire and is made with wood or metal collars, or with inserted joints. **Continuous-stave pipe** is manufactured in units consisting of staves, bands, and shoes, shipped in knocked-down form, and constructed in the trench. In building this type of pipe, the staves are laid so as to break joints and the completed pipe is without joints. Continuous-stave pipe is banded with individual bands, ranging in size from ⅜ to 1 in., depending upon the size of the pipe. A factor of safety of 4 is maintained in the band, based on an ultimate strength of 60,000 psi of cross section. The maximum pressure to which a continuous-stave pipe may be subjected depends upon the size of the pipe. The head for small pipes may run as high as 400 ft, while in the largest sizes the head would be less than 200 ft.

Machine-banded pipe is made for pressures of 50 to 400 ft. The staves are made from redwood or Douglas fir lumber, dried and carefully selected. The inside and outside of the staves are dressed to conform to the circumferential lines, and the edges of the staves to conform to the radial lines.

Wooden pipe is most largely built in the West where it is close to the natural lumber market. The sizes of machine-banded pipe range from 2 to 24 in., and of the continuous-stave pipe from 6 in. to 20 ft inside diameter.

Pipe made from **plywood** is molded in lengths up to 11 ft, in diameters 3 in. and up, and in wall thicknesses to specifications. Tubes made from fiber, by a molding process, are obtainable in a variety of sizes and lengths.

Concrete pipe is an important factor in sewer, conduit, railroad, culvert, and water-pipe construction. The pipe, as usually made, is constructed of concrete reinforced longitudinally with bars and transversely with wire mesh or steel bands. It is made in sections of definite length, with the longitudinal reinforcement so disposed as to provide for the interlocking of one section with another, and so formed that when these are locked together and cemented they form a continuous line of pipe free from leakage or seepage. Various forms of joints are used, all capable of taking care of expansion. Figure 8 shows one type of construction. Concrete pipe is manufactured in a great variety of diameters, thicknesses, and lengths to suit almost any requirement arising in practice. (See also p. 6–230).

Asbestos-cement pipe, known by the trade name **Transite** pipe in this country, was developed initially in Europe. It has had a rapidly increasing use in this country for a wide variety of services. Made of a mixture of cement and asbestos fiber, it has great resistance to corrosion and is used in mine drainage systems, waterworks systems, gas lines, sewerage systems, etc. It is manufactured in diameters 3 to 36 in., in 13 ft lengths, and in pressure classes of 50,

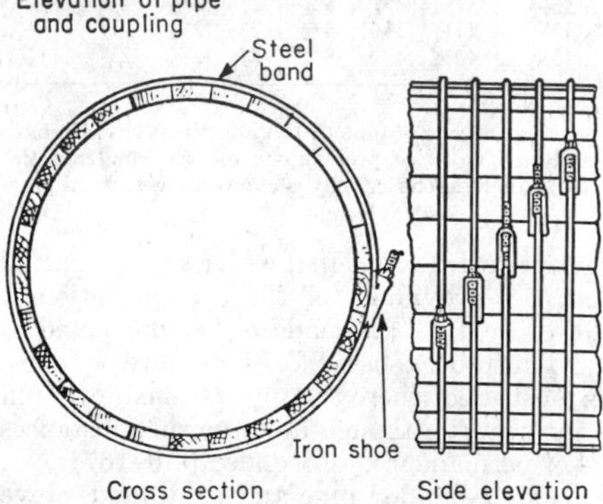

Fig. 7. Wood-stave pipes.

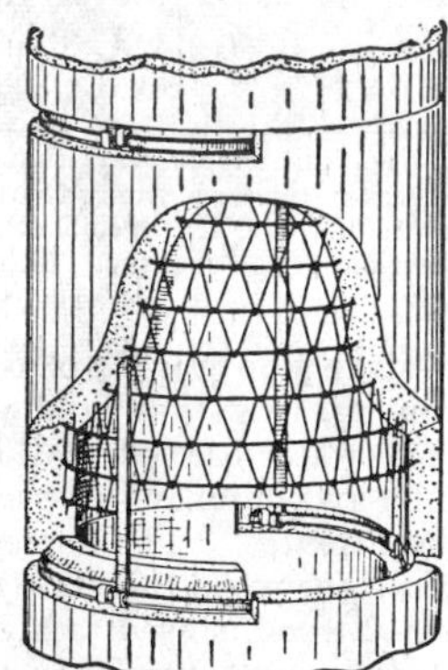

Fig. 8. Reinforced-concrete pipe.

100, 150, and 200 psi. Complete information as to specifications and recommended uses can be obtained from the Johns-Manville Co.

FITTINGS FOR WROUGHT-IRON AND STEEL PIPE

American Standard Cast-iron Pipe Flanges and Flanged Fittings for Max Working Saturated Steam Pressure of 25, 125, and 250 Psig

INTRODUCTORY NOTES

Sizes. The sizes of the fittings in the following tables are nominal pipe sizes. In the 25 lb standard, the nominal pipe size is the same as the port diameter of the fittings for *all* sizes. In the 125 and 250 lb standards the nominal pipe size is the same as the port diameter of fittings for pipe having inside diameters of 12 in. and smaller. For pipe 14 in. and larger, the corresponding outside diameter of the pipe is given, and consequently the fittings will have a smaller port diameter.

Pressure Rating. In the 25 lb standard (B16b2, 1931),[1] the sizes 36 in. and smaller may also be used for maximum non-shock working hydraulic pressures of 43 psig or a maximum gas pressure of 25 psig, at or near the ordinary range of air temperatures. In the 125 lb standard (B16.1, 1960), the sizes 12 in. and smaller may also be used for maximum non-shock working hydraulic pressure of 175 psig, at or near the ordinary range of air temperatures. In the 250 lb standard (B16.2, 1960), the sizes 12 in. and smaller may be used for maximum non-shock working hydraulic pressures of 400 psig at or near the ordinary range of air temperatures.

Facing. All 25 and 125 lb cast-iron flanges and flanged fittings shall be plain faced, *i.e.*, without projection or raised face. All 250 lb cast-iron flanges and flanged fittings shall have a raised face $\frac{1}{16}$ in. high, of the diameters given in Table 28. The raised face is included in the minimum flange thickness and center-to-face dimensions.

An **inspection limit** of $\pm\frac{1}{32}$ in. shall be allowed on all center-to-contact-surface dimensions for sizes up to and including 10 in. and $\pm\frac{1}{16}$ in. on sizes larger than 10 in. An inspection limit of $\pm\frac{1}{16}$ in. shall be allowed on all contact-surface to contact-surface dimensions for sizes up to and including 10 in. and $\pm\frac{1}{8}$ in. on sizes larger than 10 in.

Dimensions. In the 25 lb standard, the flange diameters, bolt circles, and number of bolts are the same as in the 125 lb American Standard (ASA B16.1, 1960), with a reduction in the thickness of flanges and bolt diameters, thereby maintaining interchangeability between the two standards.

The center-to-face and face-to-face dimensions of 25 lb standard fittings are the same as for the 125 lb standard.

Bolting. Drilling templates are in multiples of four, so that fittings may be made to face in any quarter. **Boltholes** shall straddle the center line. For bolts smaller than 1¾ in., the boltholes shall be drilled ⅛ in. larger in diameter than the nominal size of the bolt. Holes for bolts 1¾ in. and larger shall be drilled ¼ in. larger than nominal diameter of bolts. **Bolts** shall be of steel with standard "rough square heads" and the nuts shall be of steel with standard "rough hexagonal" dimensions; all as given in the American Standard on Wrench Head Bolts and Nuts and Wrench Openings of the National Screw Thread Commission (see p. 8–26). For bolts, 1¾ in. diam and larger, bolt-studs with a nut on each end are recommended.

Hexagonal nuts for pipe sizes 1 to 48 in. in the 125 lb standard and 1 to 16 in. in the 250 lb standard can be conveniently pulled up with open wrenches of minimum design of heads. Hexagonal nuts for pipe sizes 48 to 96 in. in the 125 lb standard and 18 to 48 in. in the 250 lb standard can be conveniently pulled up with box wrenches.

Spot Facing. The boltholes of 25, 125, and 250 lb cast-iron flanges and flanged fittings shall not be spot-faced for ordinary service. When required, the flanges and fitting in sizes 30 in. and larger may be spot-faced or back-faced to the minimum thickness of flange with a plus tolerance of ⅛ in.

Reducing Fittings. Reducing elbows and side-outlet elbows carry same dimensions center to face as straight-size elbows corresponding to the size of the larger opening.

Tees, side-outlet tees, crosses, and laterals sizes 16 in. and smaller, reducing on the outlet or branch, have the same dimension center to face and face to face as straight-size fittings corresponding to the size of the larger opening. Sizes 18 in. and larger,

[1] Revised 1952.

Table 28. Templates for Drilling Cast-iron Pipe Flanges, Flanged Valves, and Fittings (ASA)

Nominal pipe size, in.	Diameter of flange, in.	Thickness of flange (minimum), in.	Diameter of raised face, in.	Diameter of bolt circle, in.	Number of bolts	Diameter of bolts, in.	Diameter of drilled boltholes, in.	Length of bolts, in.	Length of bolt stud with two nuts, in.	Total effective area bolt metal, sq in.	Stress in bolt metal, lb per sq in.[a]	Size of ring gasket, in.
25 Lb Standard (ASA B16b2, 1931 Rev. 1952)												
4	9	3/4	......	7 1/2	8	5/8	3/4	2 1/4	......	1.616	570	4 × 6 7/8
5	10	3/4	......	8 1/2	8	5/8	3/4	2 1/4	......	1.616	750	5 × 7 7/8
6	11	3/4	......	9 1/2	8	5/8	3/4	2 1/4	......	1.616	930	6 × 8 3/4
8	13 1/2	3/4	......	11 3/4	8	5/8	3/4	2 1/4	......	1.616	1470	8 × 11
10	16	7/8	......	14 1/4	12	5/8	3/4	2 1/2	......	2.424	1440	10 × 13 3/8
12	19	1	......	17	12	5/8	3/4	2 3/4	......	2.424	2195	12 × 16 1/8
14	21	1 1/8	......	18 3/4	12	3/4	7/8	3 1/4	......	3.620	1750	14 × 18
16	23 1/2	1 1/8	......	21 1/4	16	3/4	7/8	3 1/4	......	4.830	1710	16 × 20 1/2
18	25	1 1/4	......	22 3/4	16	3/4	7/8	3 1/2	......	4.830	1965	18 × 22
20	27 1/2	1 1/4	......	25	20	3/4	7/8	3 1/2	......	6.040	1920	20 × 24 1/2
24	32	1 3/8	......	29 1/2	20	3/4	7/8	3 3/4	......	6.040	2690	24 × 28 3/4
30	38 3/4	1 1/2	......	36	28	7/8	1	4 1/4	......	11.760	2030	30 × 35 1/8
36	46	1 5/8	......	42 3/4	32	7/8	1	5	......	13.440	2610	36 × 41 7/8
42	53	1 3/4	......	49 1/2	36	1	1 1/8	5 1/4	......	19.800	2315	42 × 48 1/2
48	59 1/2	2	......	56	44	1	1 1/8	5 1/2	......	24.200	2475	48 × 55
54	66 1/4	2 1/4	......	62 3/4	44	1	1 1/8	5 3/4	......	24.200	3195	54 × 61 3/4
60	73	2 1/4	......	69 1/4	52	1 1/8	1 1/4	6	......	36.020	2515	60 × 68 1/8
72	86 1/2	2 1/2	......	82 1/2	60	1 1/8	1 1/4	6 1/4	......	41.570	3120	72 × 81 3/8
84	99 3/4	2 3/4	......	95 1/2	64	1 1/4	1 3/8	7 1/4	......	57.140	3005	84 × 94 1/4
96	113 1/4	3	......	108 1/2	68	1 1/4	1 3/8	7 3/4	......	60.570	3705	96 × 107 1/4
125 Lb Standard (B16.1, 1960)												
1	4 1/4	7/16	......	3 1/8	4	1/2	5/8	1 3/4	......	......	......	1 × 2 5/8
1 1/4	4 5/8	1/2	......	3 1/2	4	1/2	5/8	2	......	......	......	1 1/4 × 3
1 1/2	5	9/16	......	3 7/8	4	1/2	5/8	2	......	......	......	1 1/2 × 3 3/8
2	6	5/8	......	4 3/4	4	5/8	3/4	2 1/4	......	......	......	2 × 4 1/8
2 1/2	7	11/16	......	5 1/2	4	5/8	3/4	2 1/2	......	......	......	2 1/2 × 4 7/8
3	7 1/2	3/4	......	6	4	5/8	3/4	2 1/2	......	......	......	3 × 5 3/8
3 1/2	8 1/2	13/16	......	7	8	5/8	3/4	2 3/4	......	......	......	3 1/2 × 6 3/8
4	9	15/16	......	7 1/2	8	5/8	3/4	3	......	......	......	4 × 6 7/8
5	10	15/16	......	8 1/2	8	3/4	7/8	3	......	......	......	5 × 7 3/4
6	11	1	......	9 1/2	8	3/4	7/8	3 1/4	......	......	......	6 × 8 3/4
8	13 1/2	1 1/8	......	11 3/4	8	3/4	7/8	3 1/2	......	......	......	8 × 11
10	16	1 3/16	......	14 1/4	12	7/8	1	3 3/4	......	......	......	10 × 13 3/8
12	19	1 1/4	......	17	12	7/8	1	3 3/4	......	......	......	12 × 16 1/8
14 O.D.	21	1 3/8	......	18 3/4	12	1	1 1/8	4 1/4	......	......	......	14 × 17 3/4
16 O.D.	23 1/2	1 7/16	......	21 1/4	16	1	1 1/8	4 1/2	......	......	......	16 × 20 1/4
18 O.D.	25	1 9/16	......	22 3/4	16	1 1/8	1 1/4	4 3/4	......	......	......	18 × 21 5/8
20 O.D.	27 1/2	1 11/16	......	25	20	1 1/8	1 1/4	5	......	......	......	20 × 23 7/8
24 O.D.	32	1 7/8	......	29 1/2	20	1 1/4	1 3/8	5 1/2	......	......	......	24 × 28 1/4
30 O.D.	38 3/4	2 1/8	......	36	28	1 1/4	1 3/8	6 1/4	......	......	......	30 × 34 5/8
36 O.D.	46	2 3/8	......	42 3/4	32	1 1/2	1 5/8	7	......	......	......	36 × 41 1/4
42 O.D.	53	2 5/8	......	49 1/2	36	1 1/2	1 5/8	7 1/2	......	......	......	42 × 48
48 O.D.	59 1/2	2 3/4	......	56	44	1 1/2	1 5/8	7 3/4	......	......	......	48 × 54 1/2
54 O.D.	66 1/4	3	......	62 3/4	44	1 3/4	2	8 1/2	10 1/2	......	......	54 × 61
60 O.D.	73	3 1/8	......	69 1/4	52	1 3/4	2	8 3/4	11	......	......	60 × 67 1/2
72 O.D.	86 1/2	3 1/2	......	82 1/2	60	1 3/4	2	9 1/2	12	......	......	72 × 80 3/4
84 O.D.	99 3/4	3 7/8	......	95 1/2	64	2	2 1/4	10 1/2	13	......	......	84 × 93 1/2
96 O.D.	113 1/4	4 1/4	......	108 1/2	68	2 1/4	2 1/2	11 1/2	14 1/2	......	......	96 × 106 1/4

See Introductory Notes, p. 8–227.

[a] The stress shown is that of internal pressure assumed to act only on a circular area equal in diameter to the outside diameter of the ring gasket covering the flange to the inside of the bolts for the 25 lb standard.

Table 28. Templates for Drilling Cast-iron Pipe Flanges, Flanged Valves, and Fittings (ASA) *(Continued)*

Nominal pipe size, in.	Diameter of flange, in.	Thickness of flange (minimum), in.	Diameter of raised face, in.	Diameter of bolt circle, in.	Number of bolts	Diameter of bolts, in.	Diameter of drilled boltholes, in.	Length of bolts, in.	Length of bolt stud with two nuts, in.	Size of ring gasket, in.
250 Lb Standard (B16.2, 1960)										
1	4 7/8	1 1/16	2 11/16	3 1/2	4	5/8	3/4	2 1/4	......	1 × 2 7/8
1 1/4	5 1/4	3/4	3 1/16	3 7/8	4	5/8	3/4	2 1/2	......	1 1/4 × 3 1/4
1 1/2	6 1/8	13/16	3 9/16	4 1/2	4	3/4	7/8	2 1/2	......	1 1/2 × 3 3/4
2	6 1/2	7/8	4 3/16	5	8	5/8	3/4	2 1/2	......	2 × 4 3/8
2 1/2	7 1/2	1	4 15/16	5 7/8	8	3/4	7/8	3	......	2 1/2 × 5 1/8
3	8 1/4	1 1/8	5 11/16	6 5/8	8	3/4	7/8	3 1/4	......	3 × 5 7/8
3 1/2	9	1 3/16	6 5/16	7 1/4	8	3/4	7/8	3 1/4	......	3 1/2 × 6 1/2
4	10	1 1/4	6 15/16	7 7/8	8	3/4	7/8	3 1/2	......	4 × 7 1/8
5	11	1 3/8	8 5/16	9 1/4	8	3/4	7/8	3 3/4	......	5 × 8 1/2
6	12 1/2	1 7/16	9 11/16	10 5/8	12	3/4	7/8	3 3/4	......	6 × 9 7/8
8	15	1 5/8	11 15/16	13	12	7/8	1	4 1/4	......	8 × 12 1/8
10	17 1/2	1 7/8	14 1/16	15 1/4	16	1	1 1/8	5	......	10 × 14 1/4
12	20 1/2	2	16 7/16	17 3/4	16	1 1/8	1 1/4	5 1/2	......	12 × 16 5/8
14 O.D.	23	2 1/8	18 15/16	20 1/4	20	1 1/8	1 1/4	5 3/4	......	13 1/4 × 19 1/8
16 O.D.	25 1/2	2 1/4	21 1/16	22 1/2	20	1 1/4	1 3/8	6	......	15 1/4 × 21 1/4
18 O.D.	28	2 3/8	23 5/16	24 3/4	24	1 1/4	1 3/8	6 1/4	......	17 × 23 1/2
20 O.D.	30 1/2	2 1/2	25 9/16	27	24	1 1/4	1 3/8	6 1/2	......	19 × 25 3/4
24 O.D.	36	2 3/4	30 5/16	32	24	1 1/2	1 5/8	7 1/2	9 1/2	23 × 30 1/2
30 O.D.	43	3	37 3/16	39 1/4	28	1 3/4	2	8 1/4	10 1/2	29 × 37 1/2
36 O.D.	50	3 3/8	43 11/16	46	32	2	2 1/4	9 1/4	11 1/2	34 1/2 × 44
42 O.D.	57	3 11/16	50 7/16	52 3/4	36	2	2 1/4	9 3/4	12	40 1/4 × 50 3/4
48 O.D.	65	4	58 7/16	60 3/4	40	2	2 1/4	10 1/2	13	46 × 58 3/4

reducing on the outlet or branch, are made in two lengths depending on the size of the outlet as given in the tables of dimensions.

Tees, crosses, and laterals, reducing on the run only, have the same dimensions center to face and face to face as straight-size fittings corresponding to the size of the larger opening.

Reducers and eccentric reducers for all reductions have the same face-to-face dimensions for the larger opening.

Special double-branch elbows whether straight or reducing have the same dimension center to face as straight-size elbows corresponding to the size of the larger opening.

Side-outlet elbows and side-outlet tees shall have all openings on intersecting center lines.

Elbows. Special degree elbows ranging from 1 to 45 deg have the same center-to-face dimension given for 45 deg elbows, and those over 45 and up to 90 deg shall have the same center-to-face dimensions given for 90 deg elbows. The angle designation of an elbow is its deflection from straight-line flow and is the angle between its flange faces.

Screwed Companion Flanges. Screwed companion flanges in the 25 lb standard shall not be thinner than those in the 125 lb standard on sizes 24 in. and smaller. Other types of flanges may have thicknesses as given in Table 28.

Laterals. Laterals (Y branches) both straight and reducing sizes 8 in. and larger shall be reinforced to compensate for the inherent weakness in the casting design.

The American Standard covers also dimensions (not included in the tables) of base elbows and base tees and anchorage bases for straight tees and reducing tees.

American standard cast-iron pipe flanges and flanged fittings (ASA B16b1,[1] 1931)

[1] Revised 1952.

are available for maximum non-shock working hydraulic pressure of 800 psig at ordinary air temperatures.

Assembly of Flanged Joints. The optimum degree of tightening occurs when a stress of 30,000 psi is uniformly reached in each flange stud or bolt. For a modulus of elasticity of 30,000,000 psi, a stress of 30,000 psi occurs when the elongation, determined with a dial indicator or micrometer, is 0.001 in. per inch of stud length measured between centers of nuts. Uniform tension in flange bolts may also be obtained by use of a torque wrench; bearing surfaces of nuts must have a good machine finish, and threads must be properly lubricated for reliable results with a torque wrench. Torque values below have been found to give 30,000 psi stress in studs:

Stud diam, in.	Threads per in.	Torque, lb-ft
5/8	11	89
3/4	10	107
7/8	9	162
1	8	244
1 1/8	8	322
1 1/4	8	410
1 3/8	8	510
1 1/2	8	615

American Standard Steel Pipe Flanges and Flanged Fittings

Introductory Notes

Pressure Ratings and Tests. These standards shall be known as "American 150, 300, 400, 600, 900, 1,500, and 2,500 lb Steel Flange Standards" (ASA B16.5, 1961), said pressure designation being the recommended rating at the temperatures given in Table 29. This table shows recommended ratings for various temperatures, together with hydrostatic shell test pressures for one set of conditions. For similar tables for other conditions, refer to ASA B16.5, 1961.

Sizes. The size of the fittings and companion flanges in the tables is identified by the corresponding nominal pipe size. For pipe 14 in. and larger, the corresponding outside diameter of the pipe is given.

Materials. The flanged fittings and flanges should be either steel castings or steel forgings of the grade complying with the ASTM specifications recommended under these standards for the various pressure-temperature ratings for which these standards are designed. A few of these characteristics selected from ASA B16.5, 1961, are given in Table 30.

Bolting material including nuts and washers are based on a high-grade product equal to that given in ASTM Standard Specifications for Alloy-steel Bolting Material for High Temperature Service No. A193-62T and with physical and chemical requirements in accordance with the tables given under ASA B16.5, 1961. **Commercial steel bolts should not be used at steam pressures over 250 psi and temperatures over 450 F.** Nuts should be of carbon or alloy steel. Washers when used under nuts should be of forged or rolled carbon steel.

Bolting. Drilling templates are in multiples of four, so that fittings may be made to face in any quarter. Boltholes straddle the center lines. Boltholes are drilled 1/8 in. larger in diameter than the nominal size of bolt. Bolts or bolt studs threaded at both ends may be used and shall be equipped with cold-punched or cold-pressed semifinished nuts of American Standard rough dimensions, chamfered and trimmed.

All bolts and bolt studs having diameters 1 in. and smaller, and the corresponding nuts shall be threaded with the American (National) Standard Screw Thread, Coarse Thread Series, Medium Fit, Class 3 (see p. 8–12). Bolts and bolt studs whose diameters are 1 1/8 in. and larger shall have special threads of the American (National) form whose pitch is 1/8 in. (8 threads per in.). It is recommended that these special threads be allowed a pitch diameter tolerance of -0.006 in. and a lead tolerance of ± 0.002 in.

Bolt studs with a nut at each end are recommended for high-temperature service.

Table 29. Steam, Water, and Oil Pressure and Temperature Ratings* for Carbon Steel Flanges and Flanged Fittings (ASA)

(Other than ring joints)

Steam and water pressure rating (primary) psig...	150	300	400	600	900	1500
Hydrostatic shell test at 125 F, psig...	350	750	1000	1500	2000	3500
Service temperature, F	Max steam, water, and oil pressures, psig (non-shock)					
100	230	500	670	1000	1500	2500
150	220	480	640	960	1440	2400
200	210	465	620	930	1395	2325
250	200	450	600	900	1350	2250
300	190	435	580	870	1305	2175
350	180	420	560	840	1260	2100
400	170	405	540	810	1215	2025
450	160	390	520	780	1170	1950
500	150[a]	375	500	750	1125	1875
550	140	360	480	720	1080	1800
600	130	345	460	690	1035	1725
650	120	330	440	660	990	1650
700	110	315	420	630	945	1575
750	100	300[a]	400[a]	600[a]	900[a]	1500[a]
	Maximum steam and water pressure, psig					
800	85	250	335	500	750	1250
850	70	300	270	400	600	1000
	Maximum oil pressures, psig					
800	92	275	370	550	830	1380
850	82	245	330	490	740	1230
900	70	210	280	420	630	1050
950	55	165	220	330	495	825
1000	40	120	160	240	360	600

*** For temperature ratings for 2,500 psig, see ASA B16.5, 1961.**
[a] **Primary service pressure rating.**

The allowable working fiber stress, considering internal allowable working pressure only, in bolting material for valve bonnet flanges, cleanout flanges, etc., shall not exceed 9,000 psi assuming the pressure to act upon an area circumscribed by the periphery of the outside of the contact surface.

All flanges shall be spot-faced or back-faced parallel to the flange face. Metal removed in spot facing or back facing shall not reduce the thickness of the flange below the minimum given in the tables. Spot facing does not apply to forged steel flanges if the back of the flange is parallel to the flange face.

Table 30. Physical Characteristics of Steels for Flanges and Fittings

(ASTM Spec. A193–63T)

	Steel castings[a]	Alloy-steel bolt material[b]			Forged-steel flanges[c]	
		Class A	Class B	Class C	Class I	Class II
Tensile strength, psi	70,000	95,000	105,000	125,000	60,000	70,000
Yield point, min, psi	36,000	70,000	80,000	105,000	30,000	36,000
Elongation in 2 in., min, percent	22	20	20	16	22	18
Reduction of area, min, percent	30	50	50	50	35	24

[a] Carbon steel (ASTM A216–60T).
[b] ASTM A193–62T.
[c] ASTM A181–61T.
Phosphorus max, 0.05 percent; sulphur max, 0.05 percent.

Table 31. Facing Dimensions for the American 150, 300, 400, 600, 900, 1,500, and 2,500 Lb Steel Flanges (ASA B16.5, 1961)

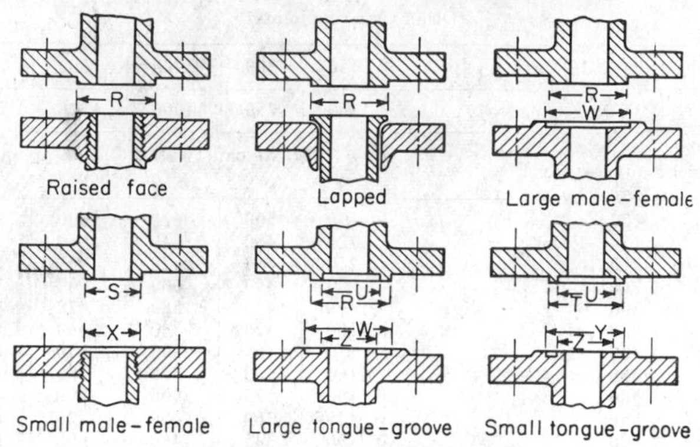

Nominal pipe size, in.	Outside diameter, in.				Outside diameter, in.				Height, in.		
	Raised face, lapped, large male, and large tongue, *R*	Small male, *S*	Small tongue, *T*	I.D. of large and small tongue, *U*	Large female and large groove, *W*	Small female, *X*	Small groove, *Y*	I.D. of large and small groove, *Z*	Raised face, 150 and 300 lb std*	Raised face, large and small male and tongue 400, 600, 900, 1500 and 2500 lb stds	Depth of groove or female companion flanges
1/2	1 3/8	23/32	1 3/8	1	1 7/16	25/32	1 7/16	15/16	1/16	1/4	3/16
3/4	1 11/16	15/16	1 11/16	1 5/16	1 3/4	1	1 3/4	1 1/4	1/16	1/4	3/16
1	2	1 3/16	1 7/8	1 1/2	2 1/16	1 1/4	1 15/16	1 7/16	1/16	1/4	3/16
1 1/4	2 1/2	1 1/2	2 1/4	1 7/8	2 9/16	1 9/16	2 5/16	1 13/16	1/16	1/4	3/16
1 1/2	2 7/8	1 3/4	2 1/2	2 1/8	2 15/16	1 13/16	2 9/16	2 1/16	1/16	1/4	3/16
2	3 5/8	2 1/4	3 1/4	2 7/8	3 11/16	2 5/16	3 5/16	2 13/16	1/16	1/4	3/12
2 1/2	4 1/8	2 11/16	3 3/4	3 3/8	4 3/16	2 3/4	3 13/12	3 5/16	1/16	1/4	3/16
3	5	3 5/16	4 5/8	4 1/4	5 1/16	3 3/8	4 11/16	4 3/16	1/16	1/4	3/16
3 1/2	5 1/2	3 13/16	5 1/8	4 3/4	5 9/16	3 7/8	5 3/16	4 11/16	1/16	1/4	3/16
4	6 3/16	4 5/16	5 11/16	5 3/16	6 1/4	4 3/8	5 3/4	5 1/8	1/16	1/4	3/16
5	7 5/16	5 3/8	6 13/16	6 5/16	7 3/8	5 7/16	6 7/8	6 1/4	1/16	1/4	3/16
6	8 1/2	6 3/8	8	7 1/2	8 9/16	6 7/16	8 1/16	7 7/16	1/16	1/4	3/16
8	10 5/8	8 3/8	10	9 3/8	10 11/16	8 7/16	10 1/16	9 5/16	1/16	1/4	3/16
10	12 3/4	10 1/2	12	11 1/4	12 13/16	10 9/16	12 1/16	11 3/16	1/16	1/4	3/16
12	15	12 1/2	14 1/4	13 1/2	15 1/16	12 9/16	14 5/16	13 7/16	1/16	1/4	3/16
14 O.D.	16 1/4	13 3/4	15 1/2	14 3/4	16 5/16	13 13/16	15 9/16	14 11/16	1/16	1/4	3/16
16 O.D.	18 1/2	15 3/4	17 5/8	16 3/4	18 9/16	15 13/16	17 11/16	16 11/16	1/16	1/4	3/16
18 O.D.	21	17 3/4	20 1/8	19 1/4	21 1/16	17 13/16	20 3/16	19 3/16	1/16	1/4	3/16
20 O.D.	23	19 3/4	22	21	23 1/16	19 13/16	22 1/16	20 15/16	1/16	1/4	3/16
24 O.D.	27 1/4	23 3/4	26 1/4	25 1/4	27 5/16	23 13/16	26 5/16	25 3/16	1/16	1/4	3/16

* Included in the minimum flange thickness dimensions. A 1/16 in. raised face is also permitted on the 400, 600, 900, 1,500, and 2,500 lb flange standards, but it must be added to the minimum flange thicknesses. Regular facing for 400, 600, 900, 1,500, and 2,500 lb flange standards is a 1/4 in. raised face not included in minimum flange thickness dimensions.

A tolerance of 1/64 in. is allowed on the inside and outside diameters of all facings.

Gaskets for male-female and tongue-groove joints shall cover the bottom of the recess with minimum clearances taking into account the tolerances stated above.

Metal Thickness. Minimum metal thicknesses specified in the tables are based on an allowable fiber stress of 7,000 psi, using the modified Barlow formula of the ASME

Boiler Construction Code for cylindrical sections and adding 50 percent to the thickness thus determined to compensate for the shape of the fittings. The minimum commercial casting thickness is considered to be ¼ in., therefore the standards do not show thicknesses less than this. The minimum thickness in these standards means the minimum thickness in any part of the finished casting.

The modified Barlow formula is as follows: For pipes having nominal diameters of ¼ to 5 in., $P + 125 = 2S(t - 0.065)/D$. For pipes of nominal diameters over 5 in., $P = 2S(t - 0.1)/D$, where P is the working pressure, psi, t is the thickness of wall of pipe, in.; D is the actual outside diameter of pipe, in.; and S is 7,000 psi.

Ring Joints. The dimensions used for ring and groove joint facings were developed by a committee of the API. The corresponding dimensions and ring numbers incorporated in this standard (B16.5, 1961) are identical with those given in API Std No.

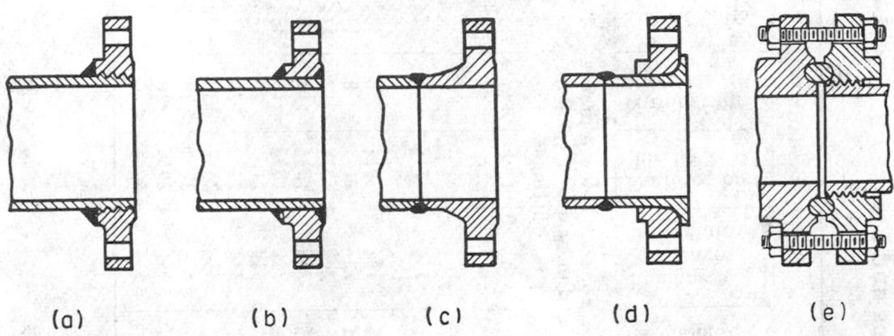

FIG. 9. Welded flange joints and ring joint: (*a*) forged steel, screwed flange, back welded and refaced; (*b*) forged steel, slip-on welding flange, welded front and back and refaced; (*c*) forged steel, welding neck flange, butt-welded to pipe; (*d*) lap welding nipple, butt-welded to pipe; (*e*) ring joint.

5-G-3-1937. The dimension for the depth of groove is added to the basic flange thickness which makes it necessary to include separate tables of dimensions for fittings having the ring joint facing.

Fitting Dimensions. An inspection limit of ±1⁄32 in. shall be allowed on all center-to-contact surface dimensions for sizes up to and including 10 in., and ±1⁄16 in. on sizes larger than 10 in. An inspection limit of ±1⁄16 in. shall be allowed on all contact-surface to contact-surface dimensions for sizes up to and including 10 in., and ±⅛ in., on sizes larger than 10 in.

When elbows having longer radii than specified in the standards are required, the use of pipe bends is recommended.

Laterals. The 45 deg laterals of the larger sizes may require additional reinforcement to compensate for the inherent weakness in this shape of casting.

Valve Dimensions. The center to contact-surface and contact-surface to contact-surface dimensions of valves for the various pressures shall be in accordance with the proposed American Standard dimensions for ferrous flanged valves.

Reducing Fittings. Reducing fittings shall have the same center-to-flange edge dimensions as those of straight-size fittings of the largest opening.

Side Outlet Fittings. All side-outlet fittings shall have all openings on the intersecting center lines.

Welding Neck Flanges. The materials, facings, spot facings, etc., conform to the requirements given for other flanges, with the additional provision that the carbon content of the steel shall not exceed 0.35 percent.

Templates for drilling and center to contact-surface dimensions of the American Standard 150 lb steel flanges and flanged fittings are the same as for the American Standard 125 lb cast-iron flanged fitting standard.

Templates for drilling and center to contact-surface dimensions of the American Standard 300 lb steel flanges and flanged fittings are the same as for the American 600 lb steel flanged fitting standard for sizes ½ to 1½ in. (Table 33); and the same as for the American 250 lb cast-iron flanged fitting standard for sizes 2 to 24 in.

Table 32. Templates for Drilling, American Standard Steel Pipe Flanges and Flanged Fittings* (ASA Spec. B16.5, 1961)

(All dimensions in inches)

Nominal pipe size	400 lb standard					600 lb standard					900 lb standard					1,500 lb standard				
	Outside diam of flange	Thickness of flange, minimum	Diam of bolt circle	Number of bolts	Size of bolts	Outside diam of flange	Thickness of flange, minimum	Diam of bolt circle	Number of bolts	Size of bolts	Outside diam of flange	Thickness of flange, minimum	Diam of bolt circle	Number of bolts	Size of bolts	Outside diam of flange	Thickness of flange, minimum	Diam of bolt circle	Number of bolts	Size of bolts
1/2	For sizes below 4 in. use dimensions of 600 lb fittings					3 3/4	9/16	2 5/8	4	1/2	For sizes below 3 in. use dimensions of 1,500 lb fittings					4 3/4	7/8	3 1/4	4	3/4
3/4						4 5/8	5/8	3 1/4	4	5/8						5 1/8	1	3 1/2	4	3/4
1						4 7/8	11/16	3 1/2	4	5/8						5 7/8	1 1/8	4	4	7/8
1 1/4	......	......	......	......	......	5 1/4	13/16	3 7/8	4	5/8	......	......	......	......	......	6 1/4	1 1/8	4 3/8	4	7/8
1 1/2	......	......	......	......	......	6 1/8	7/8	4 1/2	4	3/4	......	......	......	......	......	7	1 1/4	4 7/8	4	1
2	......	......	......	......	......	6 1/2	1	5	8	5/8	......	......	......	......	......	8 1/2	1 1/2	6 1/2	8	7/8
2 1/2	......	......	......	......	......	7 1/2	1 1/8	5 7/8	8	3/4	......	......	......	......	......	9 5/8	1 5/8	7 1/2	8	1
3	......	......	......	......	......	8 1/4	1 1/4	6 5/8	8	3/4	9 1/2	1 1/2	7 1/2	8	7/8	10 1/2	1 7/8	8	8	1 1/8
3 1/2	......	......	......	......	......	9	1 3/8	7 1/4	8	7/8										
4	10	1 3/8	7 7/8	8	7/8	10 3/4	1 1/2	8 1/2	8	7/8	11 1/2	1 3/4	9 1/4	8	1 1/8	12 1/4	2 1/8	9 1/2	8	1 1/4
5	11	1 1/2	9 1/4	8	7/8	13	1 3/4	10 1/2	8	1	13 3/4	2	11	8	1 1/4	14 3/4	2 7/8	11 1/2	8	1 1/2
6	12 1/2	1 5/8	10 5/8	12	7/8	14	1 7/8	11 1/2	12	1	15	2 3/16	12 1/2	12	1 1/8	15 1/2	3 1/4	12 1/2	12	1 3/8
8	15	1 7/8	13	12	1	16 1/2	2 3/16	13 3/4	12	1 1/8	18 1/2	2 1/2	15 1/2	12	1 3/8	19	3 5/8	15 1/2	12	1 5/8
10	17 1/2	2 1/8	15 1/4	16	1 1/8	20	2 1/2	17	16	1 1/4	21 1/2	2 3/4	18 1/2	16	1 3/8	23	4 1/4	19	12	1 7/8
12	20 1/2	2 1/4	17 3/4	16	1 1/4	22	2 5/8	19 1/4	20	1 1/4	24	3 1/8	21	20	1 3/8	26 1/2	4 7/8	22 1/2	16	2
14 O.D.	23	2 3/8	20 1/4	20	1 1/4	23 3/4	2 3/4	20 3/4	20	1 3/8	25 1/4	3 3/8	22	20	1 1/2	29 1/2	5 1/4	25	16	2 1/4
16 O.D.	25 1/2	2 1/2	22 1/2	20	1 3/8	27	3	23 3/4	20	1 1/2	27 3/4	3 1/2	24 1/4	20	1 5/8	32 1/2	5 3/4	27 3/4	16	2 1/2
18 O.D.	28	2 5/8	24 3/4	24	1 3/8	29 1/4	3 1/4	25 3/4	20	1 5/8	31	4	27	20	1 7/8	36	6 3/8	30 1/2	16	2 3/4
20 O.D.	30 1/2	2 3/4	27	24	1 1/2	32	3 1/2	28 1/2	24	1 5/8	33 3/4	4 1/4	29 1/2	20	2	38 3/4	7	32 3/4	16	3
24 O.D.	36	3	32	24	1 3/4	37	4	33	24	1 7/8	41	5 1/2	35 1/2	20	2 1/2	46	8	39	16	3 1/2

* See Introductory Notes, p. 8–230.

Table 33. Dimensions of American Standard Companion Flanges* (ASA Spec. 16.5, 1961)

(All dimensions in inches)

X Y Threaded — X Z Lapped

Nom pipe size	150 lb			300 lb			400 lb			600 lb			900 lb			1,500 lb		
	X	Y	Z	X	Y	Z	X	Y	Z	X	Y	Z	X	Y	Z	X	Y	Z
1/2	1 3/16	5/8	5/8	1 1/2	7/8	7/8	For sizes below 4 in., use dimensions of the 600 lb flanges			1 1/2	7/8	7/8	For sizes below 3 in., use dimensions of 1,500 lb flanges			1 1/2	1 1/4	1 1/4
3/4	1 1/2	5/8	5/8	1 7/8	1	1				1 7/8	1	1				1 3/4	1 3/8	1 3/8
1	1 15/16	11/16	11/16	2 1/8	1 1/16	1 1/16				2 1/8	1 1/16	1 1/16				2 1/16	1 5/8	1 5/8
1 1/4	2 5/16	13/16	13/16	2 1/2	1 1/16	1 1/16	....	.....	.....	2 1/2	1 1/8	1 1/8				2 1/2	1 5/8	1 5/8
1 1/2	2 9/16	7/8	7/8	2 3/4	1 3/16	1 3/16	....	.....	.....	2 3/4	1 1/4	1 1/4	....	...	....	2 3/4	1 3/4	1 3/4
2	3 1/16	1	1	3 5/16	1 5/16	1 5/16	....	.....	.....	3 5/16	1 7/16	1 7/16	....	...	....	4 1/8	2 1/4	2 1/4
2 1/2	3 9/16	1 1/8	1 1/8	3 15/16	1 1/2	1 1/2	....	.....	.....	3 15/16	1 5/8	1 5/8	....	...	....	4 7/8	2 1/2	2 1/2
3	4 1/4	1 3/16	1 3/16	4 5/8	1 11/16	1 11/16	....	.....	.....	4 5/8	1 13/16	1 13/16	5	2 1/8	2 1/8	5 1/4	2 7/8	2 7/8
3 1/2	4 13/16	1 1/4	1 1/4	5 1/4	1 3/4	1 3/4	....	.....	.....	5 1/4	1 15/16	1 15/16						
4	5 5/16	1 5/16	1 5/16	5 3/4	1 7/8	1 7/8	5 3/4	2	2	6	2 1/8	2 1/8	6 1/4	2 3/4	2 3/4	6 3/8	3 9/16	3 9/16
5	6 7/16	1 7/16	1 7/16	7	2	2	7	2 1/8	2 1/8	7 7/16	2 3/8	2 3/8	7 1/2	3 1/8	3 1/8	7 3/4	4 1/8	4 1/8
6	7 9/16	1 9/16	1 9/16	8 1/8	2 1/16	2 1/16	8 1/8	2 1/4	2 1/4	8 3/4	2 5/8	2 5/8	9 1/4	3 3/8	3 3/8	9	4 11/16	4 11/16
8	9 11/16	1 3/4	1 3/4	10 1/4	2 7/16	2 7/16	10 1/4	2 11/16	2 11/16	10 3/4	3	3	11 3/4	4	4 1/2	11 1/2	5 5/8	5 5/8
10	12	1 15/16	1 15/16	12 5/8	2 5/8	3 3/4	12 5/8	2 7/8	4	13 1/2	3 3/8	4 3/8	14 1/2	4 1/4	5	14 1/2	6 1/4	7
12	14 3/8	2 3/16	2 3/16	14 3/4	2 7/8	4	14 3/4	3 1/8	4 1/4	15 3/4	3 5/8	4 5/8	16 1/2	4 5/8	5 5/8	17 3/4	7 1/8	8 5/8
14 O.D.	15 3/4	2 1/4	3 1/8	16 3/4	3	4 3/8	16 3/4	3 5/16	4 5/8	17	3 11/16	5	17 3/4	5 1/8	6 1/8	19 1/2	.....	9 1/2
16 O.D.	18	2 1/2	3 7/16	19	3 1/4	4 3/4	19	3 11/16	5	19 1/2	4 3/16	5 1/2	20	5 1/4	6 1/2	21 3/4	.....	10 1/4
18 O.D.	19 7/8	2 11/16	3 13/16	21	3 1/2	5 1/8	21	3 7/8	5 3/8	21 1/2	4 5/8	6	22 1/4	6	7 1/2	23 1/2	.....	10 7/8
20 O.D.	22	2 7/8	4 1/16	23 1/8	3 3/4	5 1/2	23 1/8	4	5 3/4	24	5	6 1/4	24 1/2	6 1/2	8 1/4	25 1/4	.....	11 1/2
24 O.D.	26 1/8	3 1/4	4 3/8	27 5/8	4 3/16	6	27 5/8	4 1/2	6 1/4	28 1/4	5 1/2	7 1/4	29 1/2	8	10 1/2	30	.....	13

* Other dimensions are given in Tables 31 and 32. Finished bore on lapped flange to be such as method of attachment of pipe requires.

Flanged Pipe Joints

The usual form of pipe joint is that made up by bolting together flanges cast or forged integral with the pipe or fitting, threaded flanges, loose flanges on pipes with lapped ends, and flanges arranged for welding. These forms are illustrated above Table 31 and in Fig. 9. The threaded joint is satisfactory for low and medium steam pressures. The lapped joint is permitted in the same sizes and service ratings as for joints with integral flanges. It is extensively used in high-class work. With the ring joint a higher pressure can be maintained with the same total bolt stress than is possible with the flat gasket type of joint. The welded joint eliminates possibility of leakage between flange and pipe. It is very successful in lines subject to high temperatures and pressures and heavy expansion strains. The welding-neck flange is available in the various pipe sizes. Specific requirements covering the application of all the types of joints in common use are outlined in the Code for Pressure Piping (ASA B31.1).

Facing of Flanges. Various styles of finish are used on the faces of flanges, having for their purpose the retention of the gasket used to make a tight joint. Those in general use are as follows: (see Table 31) plain straight face, plain face corrugated or scored, male and female, tongue and groove, and raised face (see pp. 8–190, 8–232).

The **plain straight face** has the entire face of the flange faced straight across and may be used with either a full face or ring gasket. The **plain face, serrated or V-grooved,** is a plain face upon which concentric grooves have been cut with either a round-nose or V-shaped tool. This finish is sometimes of advantage when the service demands an exceptionally thick, loosely woven fibrous or soft metallic gasket, because the roughening of the faces of the flanges tends to keep the gasket from blowing out. The **male-and-female** facing consists of a recess in one flange and a corresponding raised face or projection on the other, extending from the inside of the pipe nearly to the inside of the boltholes. In the **tongue-and-groove** facing, the tongue or raised face and the groove or recess are narrow rings located between the boltholes and the port. The male-and-female and the tongue-and-groove facing have been extensively used, particularly on hydraulic lines, and to a more limited extent on high-pressure steam lines. Both of these types, however, have in common several objectionable features from the standpoint of manufacture, erection, and maintenance. These objections are removed by the use of the **raised-face** facing, which consists of a high narrow raised ring on each of the mating flanges, whose inside diameter is the same as that of the pipe or port. It is particularly recommended for high-pressure steam and hydraulic lines. **Gaskets** used in this type of joint are either soft fibrous material or soft metal and extend from the inside of the pipe to the boltholes, and only the small portion in contact with the narrow raised face is subjected to the compressive effect of the bolts. The following advantages are claimed for the raised-face type of facing: all mating of flanges has been eliminated; any valve or fitting may be removed from the line without springing the line apart; the gasket is automatically centered by its outer edge coming in contact with the bolts; the outside edges of the flanges are far enough apart to make it possible to determine whether the joint has been properly made.

Unions may be classified as **screw** and **flange.** Typical designs are shown in **Fig. 10,** where at the left is represented a female screw union of the gasket type, at the center a female screw union having a brass to iron seat that is non-corrosive and a ground joint

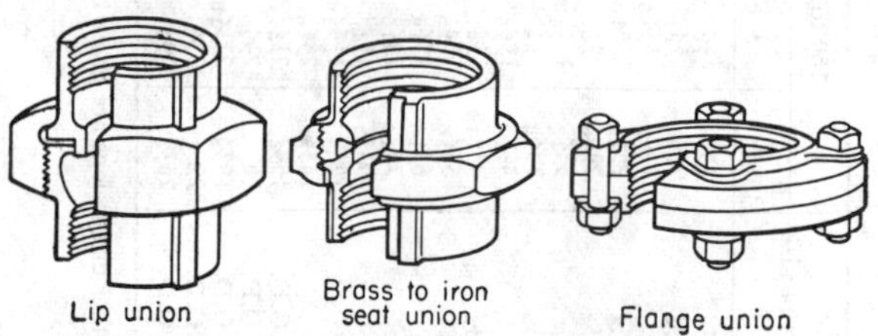

FIG. 10. Types of pipe unions.

that eliminates the need for a gasket, and at the right a flange union of the gasket type. As in the case of other pipe fittings, unions and union fittings are available in the various pipe sizes and in materials and designs suitable for any service conditions. Very large flange unions can be made by bolting together two screwed companion flanges.

Screwed Fittings

Screwed fittings are made in cast iron, malleable iron, cast steel, forged steel, and brass. Plain standard fittings are generally used for low-pressure gas and water, as in house plumbing and railing work, while the beaded fitting is the standard steam, air, gas, or oil fitting. Screwed fittings are supplied with a large factor of safety. The questions of strength involve much more than the pressure from within the pipe which induces a comparatively low stress in the material. The greater strains come from expansion, contraction, weight of piping, settling, water hammer, etc. Dimensions of cast-iron and malleable-iron screwed fittings of the American Standard are given in Tables 34 and 35.

The dimensions of ferrous plugs, bushings, locknuts, and caps with pipe threads are covered by American Standard ASA B16.14, 1949. The dimensions of pipe plugs from this standard are given in Table 42.

Table 34. Dimensions of American 150 Lb Standard Malleable-iron Screwed Fittings (Straight Sizes)*

(All dimensions in inches)

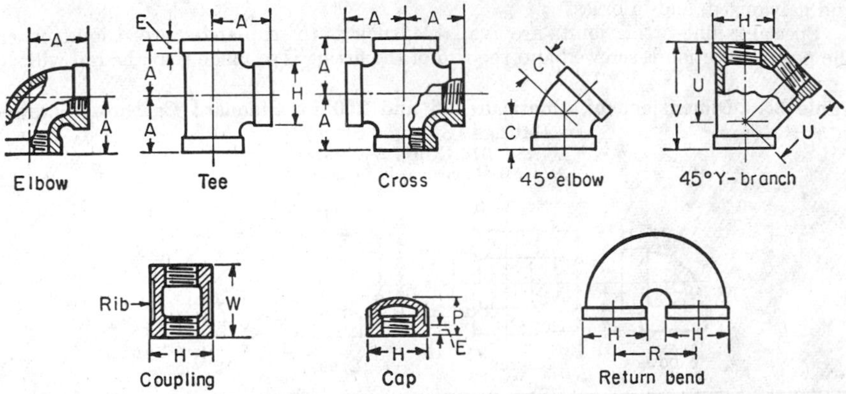

Elbow Tee Cross 45° elbow 45° Y-branch

Coupling Cap Return bend

Size	*A*	*H*	*E*	*C*	*V*	*U*	*W*	*P*	*R*		
									Close	Medium	Open
⅛	0.69	0.693	0.200	......	......	......	0.96				
¼	0.81	0.844	0.215	0.73	......	......	1.06				
⅜	0.95	1.015	0.230	0.80	1.93	1.43	1.16				
½	1.12	1.197	0.249	0.88	2.32	1.71	1.34	0.87	1.000	1.25	1.50
¾	1.31	1.458	0.273	0.98	2.77	2.05	1.52	0.97	1.250	1.50	2.00
1	1.50	1.771	0.302	1.12	3.28	2.43	1.67	1.16	1.500	1.875	2.50
1¼	1.75	2.153	0.341	1.29	3.94	2.92	1.93	1.28	1.750	2.25	3.00
1½	1.94	2.427	0.368	1.43	4.38	3.28	2.15	1.33	2.188	2.50	3.50
2	2.25	2.963	0.422	1.68	5.17	3.93	2.53	1.45	2.625	3.00	4.00
2½	2.70	3.589	0.478	1.95	6.25	4.73	2.88	1.70	....	....	4.50
3	3.08	4.285	0.548	2.17	7.26	5.55	3.18	1.80	....	....	5.00
3½	3.42	4.843	0.604	2.39	......	......	3.43	1.90			
4	3.79	5.401	0.661	2.61	8.98	6.97	3.69	2.08			
5	4.50	6.583	0.780	3.05	......	......	......	2.32			
6	5.13	7.767	0.900	3.46	......	......	......	2.55			

* The complete standard (ASA B16.3, 1951) covers also reducing couplings, elbows, tees, crosses, and service or street elbows and tees.

The normal amount of thread engagement necessary to make a tight joint for American Standard Pipe Thread joints as recommended by Crane Co. is as follows:

Size of pipe, in.	⅛	¼	⅜	½	¾	1	1¼	1½	2
Length of thread, in.	¼	⅜	⅜	½	9/16	11/16	11/16	11/16	¾

Size of pipe, in.	2½	3	3½	4	5	6	8	10	12
Length of thread, in.	15/16	1	11/16	1⅛	1¼	15/16	17/16	1⅝	1¾

The Manufacturers' Standardization Society of Valve and Fitting Industry (MSS) has standardized malleable-iron and bronze screw fittings for several pressures.

Brass screwed fittings are made in both the 125 and 250 lb standards. They are used for any water pipe where bad water makes steel pipe undesirable. Brass fittings may be had in iron pipe sizes. Forged-steel screwed fittings are made for cold water or oil-working pressures up to 6,000 psi hydrostatic. The ASA has approved a standard (ASA B16.26, 1958) for brass fittings for flared copper tubes for maximum cold-water service pressure of 175 psi.

Railing Fittings. Fittings of special construction and of lighter weight than standard steam, gas, and water pipe fittings are widely used for hand railings around areaways, on stairs, for office enclosures with gates, and for permanent ladders. Railing fittings are made in various styles, generally globe-shaped in body, with ends reduced to take thread and recessed to cover all threads. They are furnished in malleable iron, black and galvanized, and in brass.

Special railing-fitting joints are available, such as the slip-and-screwed joint, where the post connection is screwed and the rim of the fitting is so made that the rail will slip

Table 35. Dimensions of American 125 and 250 Lb Standard Cast-iron Screwed Fittings (Straight Sizes)*

(ASA B16.4, 1949 Rev. 1953)

(All dimensions in inches)

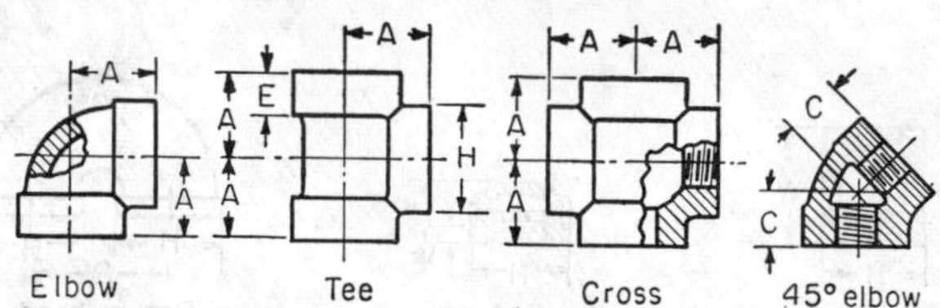

	125 lb				250 lb			
Size	*A*	*H*	*E*	*C*	*A*	*H*	*E*	*C*
¼	0.81	0.93	0.38	0.73	0.94	1.17	0.49	0.81
⅜	0.95	1.12	0.44	0.80	1.06	1.36	0.55	0.88
½	1.12	1.34	0.50	0.88	1.25	1.59	0.60	1.00
¾	1.13	1.63	0.56	0.98	1.44	1.88	0.68	1.13
1	1.50	1.95	0.62	1.12	1.63	2.24	0.76	1.31
1¼	1.75	2.39	0.69	1.29	1.94	2.73	0.88	1.50
1½	1.94	2.68	0.75	1.43	2.13	3.07	0.97	1.69
2	2.25	3.28	0.84	1.68	2.50	3.74	1.12	2.00
2½	2.70	3.86	0.94	1.95	2.94	4.60	1.30	2.25
3	3.08	4.62	1.00	2.17	3.38	5.36	1.40	2.50
3½	3.42	5.20	1.06	2.39	3.75	5.98	1.49	2.63
4	3.79	5.79	1.12	2.61	4.13	6.61	1.57	2.81
5	4.50	7.05	1.18	3.05	4.88	7.92	1.74	3.19
6	5.13	8.28	1.28	3.46	5.63	9.24	1.91	3.50
8	6.56	10.63	1.47	4.28	7.00	11.73	2.24	4.31
10	8.08	13.12	1.68	5.16	8.63	14.37	2.58	5.19
12	9.50	15.47	1.88	5.97	10.00	16.84	2.91	6.00

* This applies to elbows and tees only.

The 125 lb standard covers also reducing elbows and tees. The 250 lb standard covers only the straight sizes.

into the fitting and allow for an angular variation of several degrees, being fastened by pins which are riveted over and filed smooth. The flush-joint stair-rail fitting is another special style of fitting which provides a hand rail with even surfaces at the joints.

Drainage fittings, as shown in the figures accompanying Table 36, have no pockets for the lodgment of solids, and the length of the thread chamber is such that when the pipe is threaded to the American Standard dimensions, the end of the pipe will practically touch the shoulder when screwed in. They are especially adapted to plumbing work and vacuum-cleaning pipe installations. Dimensions in Table 36 conform to American Standard Cast-iron Screwed Drainage Fittings, ASA B16.12, 1953.

Table 36. Dimensions of American Standard Cast-iron Screwed Drainage Fittings
(ASA B16.4, 1949 Rev. 1953)
(All dimensions in inches)

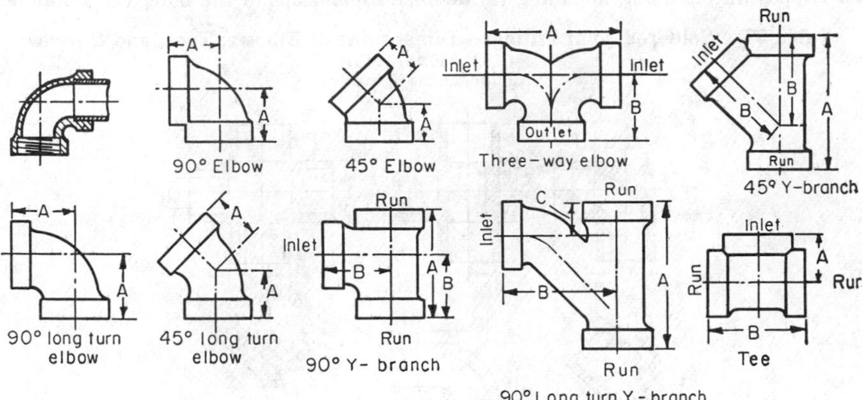

Size, in.	90 deg el-bows*	45 deg el-bows*	90 deg long-turn elbows	45 deg long-turn elbows	Three-way elbows†		Tees*		90 deg Y branches		90 deg long-turn Y branches			45 deg Y branches	
	A	*A*	*A*	*A*	*A*	*B*	*A*	*B*	*A*	*B*	*A*	*B*	*C*	*A*	*B*
1¼	1¾	1⁵⁄₁₆	2¼	1¾	4½	2¼	1¾	3½	3¾	2¼	4¾	3⅝	1⅛	5	3¼
1½	1¹⁵⁄₁₆	1⁷⁄₁₆	2½	1⅞	5	2½	1¹⁵⁄₁₆	3⅞	4¼	2½	5⅜	4⅛	1¼	5½	3⅝
2	2¼	1¹¹⁄₁₆	3¹⁄₁₆	2¼	6⅛	3¹⁄₁₆	2¼	4½	5³⁄₁₆	3¹⁄₁₆	7	5¼	1¾	6½	4⅜
2½	2¹¹⁄₁₆	1¹⁵⁄₁₆	3¹¹⁄₁₆	2⅝	7⅝	3¹¹⁄₁₆	2¹¹⁄₁₆	5⅜	6⁵⁄₁₆	3¹¹⁄₁₆	8¼	6¼	2	7⅞	5⅜
3	3¹⁄₁₆	2³⁄₁₆	4¼	2¹⁵⁄₁₆	8½	4¼	3¹⁄₁₆	6⅛	7¼	4¼	9⅞	7½	2⅜	9	6³⁄₁₆
4	3¹³⁄₁₆	2⅝	5³⁄₁₆	3½	10⅜	5³⁄₁₆	3¹³⁄₁₆	7⅝	8¾	5³⁄₁₆	13	9⅞	3⅛	10⅞	7¹¹⁄₁₆
5	4½	3¹⁄₁₆	6⅛	4⅛	12¼	6⅛	4½	9	10⁵⁄₁₆	6⅛	15¾	12¼	3½	12¹⁵⁄₁₆	9¾
6	5⅛	3⁷⁄₁₆	7⅛	4⅞	14¼	7⅛	5⅛	10¼	11¹⁵⁄₁₆	7⅛	18¾	14⅝	4⅛	14⅞	10¾

*** Same as adopted for 125 lb Cast-iron Screwed Fittings, ASA B16.4, 1949 (Rev. 1953).**
† Three-way elbows have same dimensions as 90 deg long-radius elbows.
Double Y branches have the same dimensions as single Y branches.
Other fittings which are available are as follows: 5⅝, 11¼, and 60 deg elbows; basin tees and crosses; double 90 deg Y branches; double 90 deg long-turn Y branches; 45 deg double Y branches; S traps; half S traps; offsets, couplings, increasers, and reducing sizes.

The development of standards for **cast-iron long-turn sprinkler fittings** was begun by the National Fire Protection Assoc. in 1914 with a study of the peculiar needs of fittings intended for fire-protection purposes. These fittings (screwed and flanged) are rated at 175 and 250 lb.

American Standard Air Gaps and Backflow Preventers in Plumbing Systems, ASA A40.4, 1942 and A40.6, 1943, was set up to establish minimum requirements for plumbing, including water-supply distributing systems, drainage and venting systems, fixtures, apparatus, and devices, and the standardization of plumbing equipment in general.

Ammonia valves and fittings must provide a high margin of safety against accidents. Flanged valves and fittings have tongue and groove faces to assure tightness at the joints and against blowing out gaskets. Gaskets are of lead or compressed asbestos sheet. Screwed valves and fittings have long threads and are recessed so that the joints may be soldered. These valves and fittings are made of malleable iron, ferrosteel, or forged steel, depending on the size and style. Valves are all iron, with steel stems, and have special lead disk faces or steel disks. No copper or brass must be used in their construction. Flanged valves are generally interchangeable with flanged fittings. All valves and fittings for ammonia are tested to 300 lb air pressure under water. For dimensions of valves, fittings, and specialties for ammonia, refer to manufacturers' catalogues.

Soldered-joint Fittings. The American standard for these fittings (ASA B16.18, 1963) covers certain dimensions of soldered-joint wrought metal and cast brass fittings for copper water tubing including (1) detailed dimensions of the bore, (2) minimum

Table 37. Soldered-joint Fittings—Dimensions of Elbows, Tees, and Crosses
(ASA B16.18, 1963)
(All dimensions in inches)

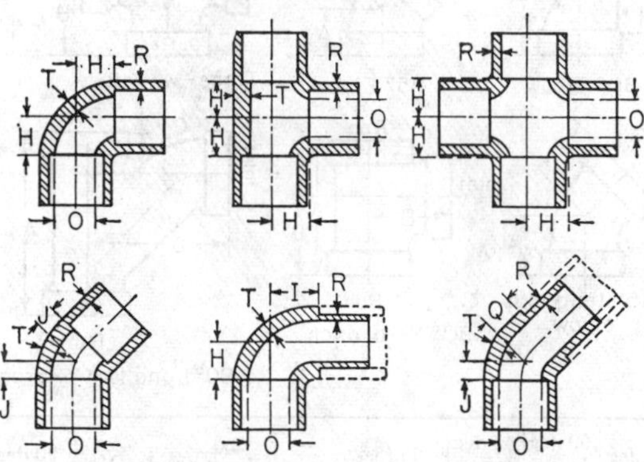

Nominal size	Cast brass[b]							Wrought metal
	H[a]	*I*	*J*	*Q*	*O*[c]	*T*	*R*	(*T* and *R*)[d,e]
¼	¼	⅜	3⁄16	¼	0.31	0.08	0.048	0.030
⅜	5⁄16	7⁄16	3⁄16	5⁄16	0.43	0.08	0.048	0.035
½	7⁄16	9⁄16	3⁄16	5⁄16	0.54	0.09	0.054	0.040
¾	9⁄16	11⁄16	¼	⅜	0.78	0.10	0.060	0.045
1	¾	⅞	5⁄16	7⁄16	1.02	0.11	0.066	0.050
1¼	⅞	1	7⁄16	9⁄16	1.26	0.12	0.072	0.055
1½	1	1⅛	½	⅝	1.50	0.13	0.078	0.060
2	1¼	1⅜	9⁄16	¾	1.98	0.15	0.090	0.070
2½	1½	1⅝	⅝	⅞	2.46	0.17	0.102	0.080
3	1¾	1⅞	¾	1	2.94	0.19	0.114	0.090
3½	2	2⅛	⅞	1⅛	3.42	0.20	0.120	0.100
4	2¼	2⅜	15⁄16	1¼	3.90	0.22	0.132	0.110
5	3⅛	....	17⁄16	....	4.87	0.28	0.168	0.125
6	3⅝	....	1⅝	....	5.84	0.34	0.204	0.140

[a] Dimensions for reducing elbows, reducing crosses, reducing tees, couplings, caps, bushings, adapters, and fittings with pipe thread on one end are also included in this standard.

[b] These dimensions may be used for wrought metal fittings as well as for cast brass fittings at manufacturer's option.

[c] This dimension is the same as the inside diameter Class L tubing, ASA H23.1, 1963 (ASTM B88).

[d] This dimension has the same thickness as Class L tubing.

[e] These dimensions are minimum, but in every case the thickness of wrought fittings should be at least as heavy as the tubing with which it is to be used.

Wrought fittings, as well as cast fittings, must be provided with a shoulder or stop at the bottom end of socket.

specifications for materials, (3) minimum inside diameter of the fitting, (4) metal thickness for both wrought metal and cast brass fittings, and (5) general dimensions for cast brass fittings including center-to-shoulder dimensions for both straight and reducing cast fittings. Pressure and temperature ratings also are given. Sizes of the fittings are

Table 38. Dimensions of Long Radius 90 Deg Butt-welding Elbows

(Standard weight—ASA B16.9, ASTM A234)
(Tube Turns Division, National Cylinder Gas Co.)

Nominal pipe size	O.D.	I.D.	Wall thickness	Center to face	Pipe schedule numbers	Approx wt, lb
2½	2.875	2.469	0.203	3¾	40	2.92
3	3.500	3.068	0.216	4½	40	4.58
3½	4.000	3.548	0.226	5¼	40	6.43
4	4.500	4.026	0.237	6	40	8.70
5	5.563	5.047	0.258	7½	40	14.7
6	6.625	6.065	0.280	9	40	22.9
8	8.625	7.981	0.322	12	40	46.0
10	10.750	10.020	0.365	15	40	81.5
12	12.750	12.000	0.375	18	ST*	119
14	14.000	13.250	0.375	21	30	154
16	16.000	15.250	0.375	24	30	201
18	18.000	17.250	0.375	27	ST*	256
20	20.000	19.250	0.375	30	20	317
22	22.000	21.250	0.375	33	ST*	385
24	24.000	23.250	0.375	36	20	458
26	26.000	25.250	0.375	39	ST*	539
30	30.000	29.250	0.375	45	ST*	720
34	34.000	33.250	0.375	51	ST*	926
36	36.000	35.250	0.375	54	ST*	1,040
42	42.000	41.250	0.375	63	ST*	1,420

All dimensions are in inches. * Standard weight.

Table 39. Dimensions of Straight Butt-welding Tees

(Standard weight—ASA B16.9, ASTM A234)
(Tube Turns Division, National Cylinder Gas Co.)

Nominal pipe size	O.D.	I.D.	Wall thickness	Center to end	Center to end	Pipe schedule numbers	Approx wt, lb
2½	2.875	2.469	0.203	3	3	40	5.21
3	3.500	3.068	0.216	3⅜	3⅜	40	7.44
3½	4.000	3.548	0.226	3¾	3¾	40	9.85
4	4.500	4.026	0.237	4⅛	4⅛	40	12.6
5	5.563	5.047	0.258	4⅞	4⅞	40	19.8
6	6.625	6.065	0.280	5⅝	5⅝	40	29.3
8	8.625	7.981	0.322	7	7	40	53.7
10	10.750	10.020	0.365	8½	8½	40	91.2
12	12.750	12.000	0.375	10	10	ST*	132
14	14.000	13.250	0.375	11	11	30	172
16	16.000	15.250	0.375	12	12	30	219
18	18.000	17.250	0.375	13½	13½	ST*	282
20	20.000	19.250	0.375	15	15	20	354
22	22.000	21.250	0.375	16½	16½	ST*	437
24	24.000	23.250	0.375	17	17	20	493
26	26.000	25.250	0.375	19½	19½	ST*	634
30	30.000	29.250	0.375	22	22	ST*	855
34	34.000	33.250	0.375	25	25	ST*	1,136
36	36.000	35.250	0.375	26½	26½	ST*	1,294

All dimensions are in inches. * Standard weight.

Table 40. Dimensions of Long Radius 45 Deg Butt-welding Elbows

(Standard weight—ASA B16.9, ASTM A234)
(Tube Turns Division, National Cylinder Gas Co.)

Nominal pipe size	O.D.	I.D.	Wall thickness	Center to face	Radius	Pipe schedule numbers	Approx wt, lb
2½	2.875	2.469	0.203	1¾	3¾	40	1.64
3	3.500	3.068	0.216	2	4½	40	2.43
3½	4.000	3.548	0.226	2¼	5¼	40	3.29
4	4.500	4.026	0.237	2½	6	40	4.31
5	5.563	5.047	0.258	3⅛	7½	40	7.30
6	6.625	6.065	0.280	3¾	9	40	11.3
8	8.625	7.981	0.322	5	12	40	22.8
10	10.750	10.020	0.365	6¼	15	40	40.4
12	12.750	12.000	0.375	7½	18	ST*	59.5
14	14.000	13.250	0.375	8¾	21	30	76.5
16	16.000	15.250	0.375	10	24	30	100
18	18.000	17.250	0.375	11¼	27	ST*	128
20	20.000	19.250	0.375	12½	30	20	158
22	22.000	21.250	0.375	13½	33	ST*	192
24	24.000	23.250	0.375	15	36	20	229
26	26.000	25.250	0.375	16	39	ST*	269
30	30.000	29.250	0.375	18½	45	ST*	358
34	34.000	33.250	0.375	21	51	ST*	463
36	36.000	35.250	0.375	22¼	54	ST*	518
42	42.000	41.250	0.375	26	63	ST*	707

All dimensions are in inches. * Standard weight.

Table 41. Dimensions of Concentric and Eccentric Butt-welding Reducers

(Standard weight—ASA B16.9, ASA A234)
(Tube Turns Division, National Cylinder Gas Co.)

Nominal pipe size	Length	Approx wt, lb	Nominal pipe size	Length	Approx wt, lb	Nominal pipe size	Length	Approx wt, lb
2½ × 1	3½	1.30	8 × 6	6	13.4	22 × 20	20	157
2½ × 1¼	3½	1.47	8 × 6	6	13.9	24 × 16	20	160
2½ × 1½	3½	1.51	10 × 4	7	21.1	24 × 18	20	163
2½ × 2	3½	1.60	10 × 5	7	21.8	24 × 20	20	167
3 × 1¼	3½	1.70	10 × 6	7	22.3	26 × 18	24	200
3 × 1½	3½	1.89	10 × 8	7	23.2	26 × 20	24	200
3 × 2	3½	2.00	12 × 5	8	30.5	26 × 22	24	200
3 × 2½	3½	2.16	12 × 6	8	31.1	26 × 24	24	200
3½ × 1¼	4	2.35	12 × 8	8	32.1	30 × 20	24	220
3½ × 1½	4	2.52	12 × 10	8	33.4	30 × 24	24	220
3½ × 2	4	2.71	14 × 6	13	55.8	30 × 26	24	220
3½ × 2½	4	2.96	14 × 8	13	57.2	30 × 28	24	220
3½ × 3	4	3.05	14 × 10	13	60.4			
4 × 1½	4	2.73	14 × 12	13	63.4			Conc. Ecc.
4 × 2	4	3.17	16 × 8	14	70.2	34 × 24	24	270 229
4 × 2½	4	3.34	16 × 10	14	72.9	34 × 26	24	270 237
4 × 3	4	3.50	16 × 12	14	75.6	34 × 30	24	270 253
4 × 3½	4	3.61	16 × 14	14	77.5	34 × 32	24	270 261
5 × 2	5	5.05	18 × 10	15	86.9	36 × 24	24	340 237
5 × 2½	5	5.52	18 × 12	15	89.2	36 × 26	24	340 245
5 × 3	5	5.73	18 × 14	15	90.9	36 × 30	24	340 261
5 × 3½	5	5.86	18 × 16	15	94.0	36 × 32	24	340 269
5 × 4	5	5.99	20 × 12	20	134	36 × 34	24	340 277
6 × 2½	5½	7.61	20 × 14	20	135	42 × 24	24	260
6 × 3	5½	8.00	20 × 16	20	138	42 × 26	24	270
6 × 3½	5½	8.14	20 × 18	20	142	42 × 30	24	285
6 × 4	5½	8.19	22 × 14	20	148	42 × 32	24	295
6 × 5	5½	8.65	22 × 16	20	151	42 × 34	24	300
8 × 3½	6	12.8	22 × 18	20	154	42 × 36	24	310
8 × 4	6	13.1						

All dimensions are in inches.

identified by the nominal tubing size as covered by the American Standard Specifications for Copper Water Tube, ASA H23.1, 1963 (ASTM B88). Dimensions of some of the fittings from this standard are given in Table 37.

Table 42. Dimensions of 125, 150, and 250 Lb Pipe Plugs*
(ASA B16.14, 1949)
(All dimensions in inches)

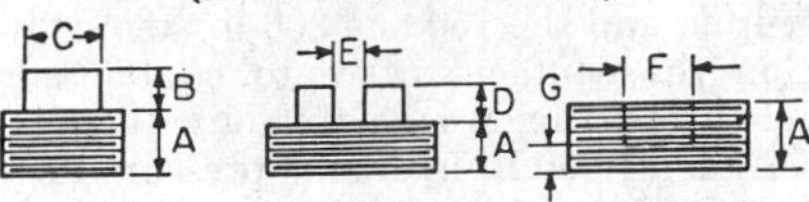

Nominal pipe size	Square-head pattern			Slotted pattern			Countersunk pattern† (square sockets)		
	A	*B*	*C*	*A*	*D*	*E*	*A*	*F*	*G*
1/8	0.37	0.24	9/32						
1/4	0.44	0.28	3/8						
3/8	0.48	0.31	7/16						
1/2	0.56	0.38	9/16	....	....	....	0.56	3/8	0.16
3/4	0.63	0.44	5/8	....	....	....	0.63	1/2	0.18
1	0.75	0.50	13/16	....	....	....	0.75	1/2	0.20
1 1/4	0.80	0.56	15/16	....	....	....	0.80	3/4	0.22
1 1/2	0.83	0.62	1 1/8	....	....	....	0.83	3/4	0.24
2	0.88	0.68	1 5/16	....	....	....	0.88	7/8	0.26
2 1/2	1.07	0.74	1 1/2	....	....	....	1.07	1 1/8	0.29
3	1.13	0.80	1 11/16	....	....	....	1.13	1 3/8	0.31
3 1/2	1.18	0.86	1 7/8	....	....	....	1.18	1 1/2	0.34
4	....	....	.....	1.22	1.00	0.88	1.22	2	0.37
5	....	....	.....	1.31	1.00	0.88	1.31	2 1/4	0.46
6	....	....	.....	1.40	1.25	1.25	1.40	2 1/2	0.52
8	....	....	.....	1.57	1.38	1.50			

* The material of this standard (ASA B16.14, 1949) to be cast iron, malleable iron, or steel, for use in connection with fittings covered by the American Standard 125 lb cast-iron screwed fittings (ASA B16.4) and the American Standard 150 lb malleable-iron screwed fittings (ASA B16.3).

† Hexagon sockets (sizes 1/8 to 1 in.) have dimensions to fit regular wrenches used with hexagon socket setscrews.

Valves

The face-to-face dimensions of ferrous flanged and welding end valves are given in ASA B16.10, 1957. The types covered are

Wedge-gate Valves. Cast iron, for 125, 175, and 250 lb steam service pressure and 800 lb hydraulic pressure, and steel, for 150, 300, 400, 600, 900, and 1,500 lb steam service pressures (see Fig. 11).

Double-disk Gate Valves. Cast iron, for 125, 175, and 250 lb steam service pressure and 800 lb hydraulic pressure (see ASA B16.10, 1957).

Globe and Angle Valves. Cast iron, for 125 and 250 lb steam service pressure, and steel, for 150, 300, 400, 600, 900, and 1500 lb steam service pressures (see Fig. 12).

Swing-check Valves. Cast iron, for 125 and 250 lb steam service pressure and 800 lb

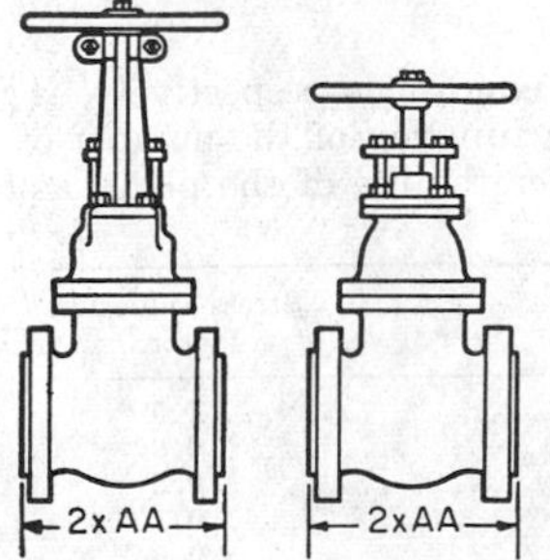

Fig. 11. Wedge-gate valves.

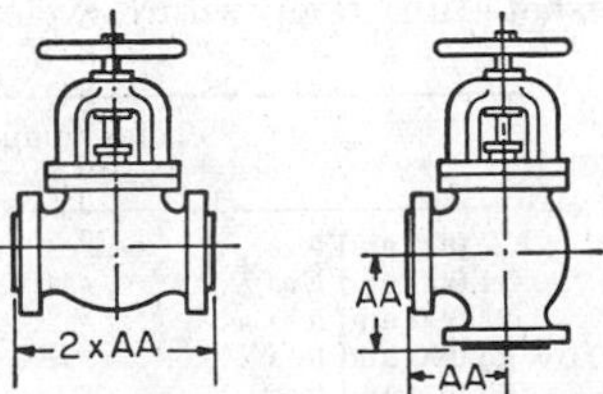

Fig. 12. Globe valve and angle valve.

hydraulic pressure, and steel, for 150, 300, 400, and 600 lb steam service pressures (see ASA B16.10, 1957).

Except for ring-joint facings the face-to-face dimension for flanged valves is the distance between the faces of the connecting end flanges upon which the gaskets are actually compressed, *i.e.*, the "contact surfaces."

All flanges for 125 lb cast-iron valves are plain-faced. The facings of the 175 lb cast-iron, the 250 lb cast-iron, and the 150 and 300 lb steel valves have a 1/16 in. raised face which is included in the contact-surface to contact-surface dimensions. The contact-surface to contact-surface dimensions of steel valves for 400 lb and higher pressures and for cast-iron valves for 800 lb hydraulic pressure include a 1/4 in. raised face.

The end-to-end dimensions for **welding-end** valves for sizes 1 to 8 in. are the same as the contact-surface to contact-surface dimensions given in the tables for steel valves. For details of welding bevel see ASA B16.10, 1957 and Fig. 15.

A plus or minus **tolerance** of 1/16 in. shall be allowed on all face-to-face dimensions of valves 10 in. and smaller, and a tolerance of 1/8 in. on sizes 12 in. and larger. This standard agrees with MSS SP32, 1937, API 5G2-36 for pipelines, and API 600A-38 for steel-flanged wedge-gate valves wherever valves of similar type, size, pressure, and material appear.

Cocks. The ordinary plug cock operated by a handle or wrench is a form of valve in comparatively small sizes suitable for ordinary service only. The Code for Pressure Piping requires that where cocks are used for high-temperature service they shall be so designed as to prevent galling, either by making the plugs of different material from the body of the cock or by treating the plugs to ensure different physical properties. By means of special design features that eliminate the tendency to leak and stick, the plug-cock type of valve has become available in large sizes and for severe service conditions. Sizes are listed as high as 30 in. and are gear-operated in the larger sizes. For further details, refer to manufacturers' catalogues.

Expansion and Flexibility

Piping systems must be designed so that they (1) will not fail because of excessive stresses, (2) will not produce excessive thrusts or moments at connected equipment, or (3) will not leak at joints because of expansion of the pipe. Flexibility is provided by changes of direction in the piping through the use of bends or loops, or provision may be made to absorb thermal strains by use of expansion joints. All, or portions, of the pipe may be corrugated to improve flexibility; in many systems, however, sufficient change is provided by the geometry of the layout to make unnecessary the use of either expansion joints or corrugated sections of piping. Judicious cold springing is beneficial in assisting the piping system to attain its most favorable condition. Because of plastic flow of the piping material, hot stresses tend to decrease with time while cold stresses tend to increase with time; their sum, called the stress range, remains substantially constant. For this reason no credit is warranted with regard to stresses; for calculation of forces and moments, the effect of cold spring is recognized by use of a cold-spring factor varying from 0 to 1 for cold spring varying from 0 to 100 percent.

The allowable stress range, S_A, is calculated by

$$S_A = f\,(1.25\,S_c + 0.25\,S_h)$$

where S_c and S_h are the S values for the cold and hot conditions, respectively, as given in Tables 1 and 2. The stress-reduction factor, f, is a function of the number of hot-to-cold-to-hot (full) temperature cycles anticipated over the life of the plant, as follows:

Total number of full temp cycles over expected life	Stress-reduction factor, f
7,000 and less	1.0
14,000 and less	0.9
22,000 and less	0.8
45,000 and less	0.7
100,000 and less	0.6
250,000 and more	0.5

The bending and torsional stresses calculated (see "Pipeline Flexure Stresses," p. 5–82) are used to determine the maximum computed expansion stress, $S_E = \sqrt{S_b^2 + 4 S_t^2}$, where S_b and S_t are bending and torsional stresses, respectively. S_E must not exceed the allowable stress range, S_A.

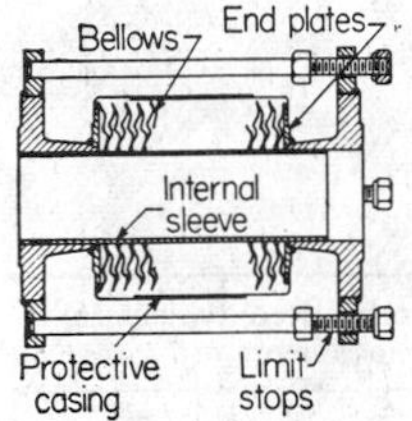

FIG. 13. Expansion joint for steam line. (*Croll-Reynolds, Inc.*)

In recent years, many principal high-temperature steam lines have either been analyzed, tested in a model-testing machine, or both. No rigid rule is stipulated for the requirement of analysis or model test; however, the Code for Pressure Piping suggests that when the following criterion is not satisfied, need for an analysis is indicated: $DY/(L-U)^2 \leqq 0.03$ where D is the nominal pipe size, in., Y is the resultant of movements to be absorbed by pipeline, in., U is the length of straight line joining the anchor points, ft, and L is the length of the developed line axis, ft.

Expansion Joints for Steam Pipelines. In many instances it may be economical to care for thermal expansion by use of expansion joints. For low-pressure steam lines, the use of packed expansion joints may be feasible; experience has indicated that packed joints are difficult to maintain when used on high-pressure lines. Figure 13 shows a type of joint that has been successfully used for high-pressure, high-temperature service. The bellows is designed to take either axial, lateral, or combined axial and lateral deflections. The internal sleeve guides movement of the joint and also protects the flexible bellows from direct contact with the fluid being handled. Face-to-face dimensions, as well as permissible axial and lateral deflections, are indicated in Table 43.

Where large lateral deflections are to be absorbed, two expansion joints separated by a length of pipe as shown in Fig. 14 may be used. With such an arrangement, the lateral deflection permissible with one joint only may be increased many times. Tierods, as shown, should always be installed to protect the joint against overtravel and externally to guide movement of the joint.

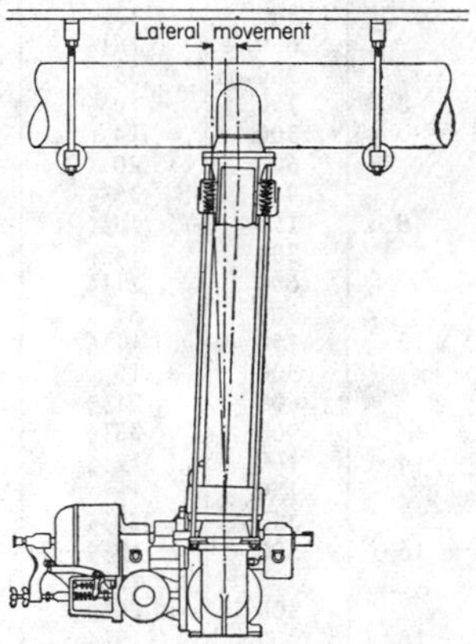

FIG. 14. Arrangement of expansion joints for large lateral deflection. (*Croll-Reynolds, Inc.*)

Table 44, extracted from the Code for Pressure Piping, lists thermal-expansion data for both ferrous and non-ferrous piping. For expansion at temperatures intermediate between those shown, straight-line interpolation is permitted.

The **rubber expansion joint** has become an established part of pipe-line equipment. Its special field of application is on low-pressure and vacuum lines in condenser applications, etc., and is recommended for pressures up to 25 psig where the maximum temperature does not exceed 250 F. Standard joints for pressure installations are reinforced to withstand working pressures up to 125 psig and temperatures up to 200 F. Joints are available in all standard pipe sizes.

Welding in Power-plant Piping

(For dimensions of welding fittings see Tables 38–41, pp. 8–241 and 8–242: for welding techniques see also pp. 13–39 to 13–68)

The majority of main-cycle and service steel piping in modern steam power plants is of welded construction. Steel pipe of 2 in. size and smaller is generally socket-welded; larger-size piping is usually butt-welded. Frequently, depending on location and scheduling, piping larger than 2 in. size is prefabricated; smaller piping is shipped to the construction site in random lengths and is fabricated concurrently with installation. Small-sized chromium-molybdenum piping requiring bending is frequently also shop-fabricated so as to avoid higher field preheat, welding, and stress-relieving costs. It is desirable to schedule shipment of hangers so that they will be available at the job site upon arrival of the prefabricated piping; this avoids the expense of providing, installing, and later removing temporary hangers and supports. Aside from the economy of welded construction, it is a virtual necessity in high-pressure, high-temperature work because of danger of leakage if joints are flanged.

Table 43. Dimensions of Expansion Joints

(Croll-Reynolds, Inc.)

Pipe size	Pressure series, psig	Face-to-face dimensions,* axial movements of			Lateral movements† equivalent to axial movements of		
		1 in.	2 in.	3 in.	1 in.	2 in.	3 in.
4	150	8½	11	15½	1/16	¼	9/16
	300	12	17	24	⅛	½	1
	600	17½	26½	....	¼	1	
	900	31½	....	....	11/16		
6	150	9½	12	16½	1/16	3/16	⅜
	300	13	18	25	3/32	13/32	15/16
	600	18½	27½	....	7/32	27/32	
	900	33½	....	....	½		
8	150	10½	13	17½	1/32	3/16	⅜
	300	14	19	26	3/32	⅜	27/32
	600	20	29	....	3/16	¾	
	900	35½	....	....	15/32		
10	150	10½	13	17½	1/32	⅛	5/16
	300	14	19	26	1/16	5/16	23/32
	600	21½	30½	....	5/32	⅝	
	900	37	....	....	⅜		
12	150	11½	14	18½	1/32	⅛	¼
	300	15	20	27	1/16	¼	19/32
	600	21½	30½	....	⅛	½	
	900	38½	....	....	5/16		
14	100	12½	15½		1/32	⅛	
	150	15	20		1/16	7/32	
	300	20½	....		3/32		
16	100	12½	15½		1/32	3/32	
	150	15	20		1/32	3/16	
	300	20½	....		3/32		
18	100	13½	16½		1/32	3/32	
	150	16	21		1/32	3/16	
	300	21½	....		3/32		
20	100	14½	16½			3/32	
	150	16	21		1/32	3/16	
	300	21½	...		3/32		
24	100	14½	17½			1/16	
	150	17	22		1/32	5/32	
	300	22½	....		1/16		
30	100	9½	12½			1/16	
	150	12	17		1/32	⅛	
	300	19½	....		1/16		

* For welding ends, add 4 in. to face-to-face dimension shown.
† Consult manufacturer for permissible combined axial and lateral deflection.

Shop welds are frequently made by automatic or semiautomatic submerged-arc or inert-gas shielded-arc processes; field welds are generally of the manual type and may be done by the shielded metal-arc, inert-gas metal-arc, or gas-welding processes. Welding in power piping systems, whether in the shop or at the job site, must be done by welders who have qualified under provisions of the Code for Pressure Piping or the ASME Boiler and Pressure Vessel Code.

End Preparation for Butt Welds. Figure 15 shows the end preparation recommended (not required) for piping whose wall thickness is ¾ in. or less, and Fig. 16

Table 44. Thermal-expansion Data

(ASA Code for Pressure Piping)

A = Mean coefficient of thermal expansion × 10^6, in. per in. per deg F } in going from 70 F to indicated temperature
B = Linear thermal expansion, in. per 100 ft }

Material	Coefficient	70	200	300	400	500	600	700	800	900	1000	1100	1200	1300	1400
		Temperature range: 70 F to													
Carbon steel; carbon-moly steel low-chrome steels (through 37 Cr)	*A*	...	6.38	6.60	6.82	7.02	7.23	7.44	7.65	7.84	7.97	8.12	8.19	8.28	8.36
	B	0	0.99	1.82	2.70	3.62	4.60	5.63	6.70	7.81	8.89	10.04	11.10	12.22	13.34
Intermediate alloy steels 5 Cr Mo–9 Cr Mo	*A*	...	6.04	6.19	6.34	6.50	6.66	6.80	6.96	7.10	7.22	7.32	7.41	7.49	7.55
	B	0	0.94	1.71	2.50	3.35	4.24	5.14	6.10	7.07	8.06	9.05	10.00	11.06	12.05
Austenitic stainless steels	*A*	...	9.34	9.47	9.59	9.70	9.82	9.92	10.05	10.16	10.29	10.39	10.48	10.54	10.60
	B	0	1.46	2.61	3.80	5.01	6.24	7.50	8.80	10.12	11.48	12.84	14.20	15.56	16.92
Straight chromium stainless steels: 12 Cr, 17 Cr, and 27 Cr	*A*	...	5.50	5.66	5.81	5.96	6.13	6.26	6.39	6.52	6.63	6.72	6.78	6.85	6.90
	B	0	0.86	1.56	2.30	3.08	3.90	4.73	5.60	6.49	7.40	8.31	9.20	10.11	11.01
25 Cr–20 Ni	*A*	...	7.76	7.92	8.08	8.22	8.38	8.52	8.68	8.81	8.92	9.00	9.08	9.12	9.18
	B	0	1.21	2.18	3.20	4.24	5.33	6.44	7.60	8.78	9.95	11.12	12.31	13.46	14.65
Monel 67 Ni–30 Cu	*A*	...	7.84	8.02	8.20	8.40	8.58	8.78	8.96	9.16	9.34	9.52	9.70	9.88	10.04
	B	0	1.22	2.21	3.25	4.33	5.46	6.64	7.85	9.12	10.42	11.77	13.15	14.58	16.02
Monel 66 Ni–29 CuAl	*A*	...	7.48	7.68	7.90	8.09	8.30	8.50	8.70	8.90	9.10	9.30	9.50	9.70	9.89
	B	0	1.17	2.12	3.13	4.17	5.28	6.43	7.62	8.86	10.16	11.50	13.00	14.32	15.78
Aluminum	*A*	...	12.95	13.28	13.60	13.90	14.20								
	B	0	2.00	3.66	5.39	7.17	9.03								
Gray cast iron	*A*	...	5.75	5.93	6.10	6.28	6.47	6.65	6.83	7.00	7.19				
	B	0	0.90	1.64	2.42	3.24	4.11	5.03	5.98	6.97	8.02				
Bronze	*A*	...	10.03	10.12	10.23	10.32	10.44	10.52	10.62	10.72	10.80	10.90	11.00		
	B	0	1.56	2.79	4.05	5.33	6.64	7.95	9.30	10.68	12.05	13.47	14.92		
Brass	*A*	...	9.76	10.00	10.23	10.47	10.69	10.92	11.16	11.40	11.63	11.85	12.09		
	B	0	1.52	2.76	4.05	5.40	6.80	8.26	9.78	11.35	12.98	14.65	16.39		
Wrought iron	*A*	...	7.32	7.48	7.61	7.73	7.88	8.01	8.13	8.29	8.39				
	B	0	1.14	2.06	3.01	3.99	5.01	6.06	7.12	8.26	9.36				
Copper-nickel (70/30)	*A*	...	8.54	8.71	8.90										
	B	0	1.33	2.40	3.52										

shows that required for piping with wall thickness above ¾ in. During the welding process, to avoid entrance of welding material into the pipe, backing rings may be used as shown in Figs. 17 (*a*), (*b*), and (*c*).[1] Note that thick-walled pipes (over ¾ in.) are taper-bored on the inside in order that they may receive a tapered, machined backing ring.

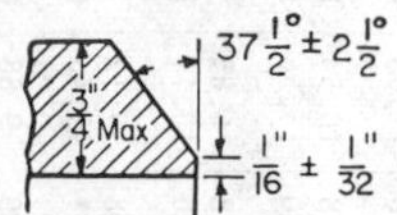

FIG. 15. Recommended end preparation for pipe wall thickness, ¾ in. or less.

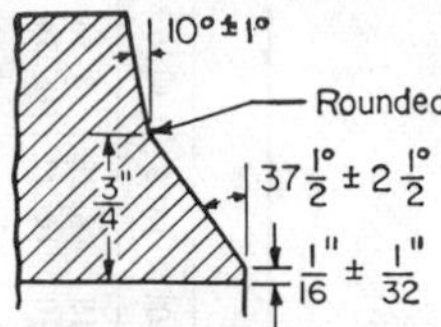

FIG. 16. Recommended end preparation for pipe wall thickness greater than ¾ in.

Preheating. Prior to start of welding, many materials require preheat to a specified temperature; preheat may be done by electrical-resistance or induction heating or by ring-type gas burners placed concentrically with the pipe. The preheat temperature is measured by indicating crayons or by thermocouple pyrometers and must be maintained during the welding operation. Table 1, Appendix D, of the Code for Pressure Piping lists materials used in piping systems and the appropriate temperatures for preheat. In general, the following is indicative of the intent only; for specific instances, the code must be consulted.

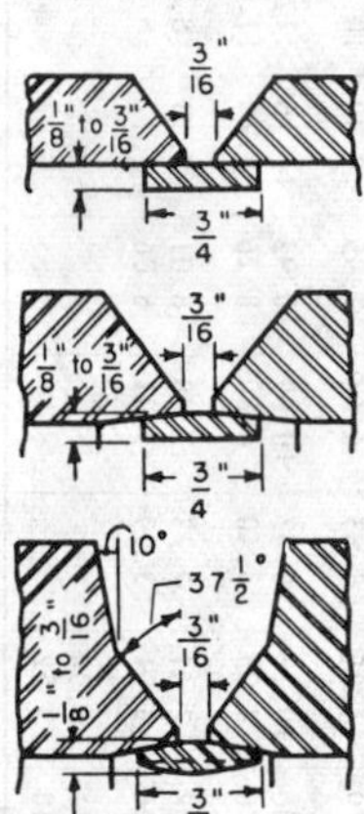

FIG. 17. Recommended backing-ring types: (*a*) butt joint with split backing ring; (*b*) butt joint with bored pipe ends and solid machined or split backing ring; (*c*) butt joint with taper-bored ends and machined backing ring.

Carbon steel and **wrought iron** should be preheated to a "hand-hot" condition if the ambient temperature at time of field installation is 32 F or less; carbon steels which have minimum tensile properties of 70,000 psi or higher should be preheated to 250 F; under other conditions, preheat is not mandatory, but some purchasers insist that the contractor preheat heavy-walled piping such as boiler feed.

Low-alloy steels with a chromium content not exceeding ¾ percent and low-alloy steels with a total alloy content not exceeding 2 percent are required to be preheated to a minimum temperature of 300 F.

Alloy steels with a chromium content between ¾ percent and 2 percent and low-alloy steels with a total alloy content not exceeding 2¾ percent require preheating to 375 F minimum. Those with a total alloy content greater than 2¾ percent but not exceeding 10 percent require preheating to a temperature of 450 F minimum.

High-alloy steels containing the martensitic phase require preheating to 450 F minimum; preheating shall be a matter of agreement between the purchaser and contractor in the case of welding high-alloy ferritic steels (A240, A268). The possible advantages of preheat have not been established in the case of welding high-alloy austenitic steels, and for this reason the Code for Pressure Piping states that preheat is optional for these materials.

Welding procedure varies with material and welding process. In general, the pipe ends must be cleaned of oil or grease, and excessive amounts of scale or rust should be removed. The size and type of welding rod must be stated; the number of layers or passes is determined by the thickness of the pieces being joined. All slag or flux remaining on any bead of welding must be removed before laying down the next successive bead; any cracks or blowholes that appear on the surface of any bead must be chipped or ground away before the next bead of weld material is deposited. Throughout the welding process, it is essential that the minimum specified preheat temperature be maintained.

Stress Relieving. Welded joints in all carbon-steel material whose thickness is **¾ in. or** greater must be stress-relieved at a temperature of 1100 F or over for a period

[1] **Consumable inserts are also available. They are recommended for installation in piping systems which require a smooth, unobstructed interior surface.**

of time proportioned on the basis of at least 1 hr per inch of pipe-wall thickness (but in no case less than ½ hr) and then allowed to cool slowly (generally under a blanket) and uniformly. No stress relief is required for joints in carbon-steel piping whose wall thickness is less than ¾ in.

Welded joints in wrought-iron piping require stress relief only as may be agreed upon between the purchaser and contractor. Welded joints in alloy steels with a wall thickness of ½ in. or greater, having a chromium content not exceeding ¾ percent, and low-alloy steels with a total alloy content not exceeding 2 percent require stress-relieving at a temperature of 1200 F or over for a period of time proportioned on the basis of at least 1 hr per in. of wall thickness, but in no case less than ½ hr.

Welded joints in alloy steels having a chromium content exceeding ¾ percent, or a total alloy content exceeding 2 percent, except high-alloy ferritic (A240, A268) and austenitic steels, regardless of wall thickness, require stress relief at a temperature of 1200 F or over for a period of time proportioned on the basis of at least 1 hr per in. of wall thickness, but in no case less than ½ hr. Stress relief of high-alloy ferritic steel (A240, A268) and austenitic steels is not required but may be performed as agreed upon by purchaser and contractor. In welds between austenitic and ferritic materials, stress-relieving is optional and, if used, shall be a matter of agreement between the purchaser and contractor. Because of the difference between the coefficients of thermal expansion of the two dissimilar materials, careful consideration should be given to the selection of a heat-treatment, if any, that will be beneficial to the welded joint.

Graphitization is precipitation of carbon at the grain boundaries in the heat-affected zone during the welding process. Such a phenomenon occurs when some metals operate at high temperatures for extended periods of time. It has been observed particularly in carbon-molybdenum steels that operate at 900 F or higher. Recent practice indicates that chromium in both the parent metal and welding rod reduces, or perhaps eliminates entirely, the possibility of graphitization. Graphitization can be corrected by (1) replacing the carbon or carbon-molybdenum installation with the properly selected chromium-molybdenum alloy, or (2) removing the various graphitized welded joints and replacing with chrome-bearing alloy spool pieces, or (3) chipping and grinding away that material at the welded joints which has become graphitized and subsequently rewelding with the proper chrome-bearing electrode, or (4) heat-treating the graphitized joints at a specified temperature for a specified time (a temporary cure); this will redissolve the graphite in the parent metal and in the weld metal. Since graphitization has been most usually observed at the joints, method 1 is perhaps more drastic than necessary. Method 3 does not give assurance that all graphitized material has been removed because it is necessary to avoid cutting through the backing ring. Method 4 will give short relief (measured in months or years) but is not a permanent remedy.

Pipe Supports

The Code for Pressure Piping (ASA B31.1, 1955) includes many types of supports and gives directions for their application. A proper pipe support must have a strong rigid base properly supported, and an adjustable roll construction which will maintain the alignment in any direction. It is important to avoid friction caused by the movement of the pipe in the support and to have all parts of sufficient strength to maintain alignment at all times. Wire hangers, band iron hangers, wooden hangers, hangers made from small pipe and hangers having one vertical pipe support do not maintain alignment.

The direction of expansion in a pipe run can be predetermined by anchoring one end, both ends, or the middle. **Anchors** must be firmly fastened to a rigid and heavy part of the power plant structure, and must also be securely fastened to the pipe, otherwise, the equipment for absorbing expansion is useless, and severe stresses may be thrown on parts of the piping system. Some methods of support are shown in Figs. 18 and 19. Welded steel brackets, Fig. 18 (*a*), are available in light, medium, and heavy weights. Many types of supports can be mounted on these brackets, such as the anchor chair shown on the bracket at (*a*), pipe roller supports of the type at (*c*), pipe roll stands of various types such as shown in Fig. 19, pipe seats, etc. Figure 18 (*b*) illustrates one of the many types of adjustable ring hangers in use. The split ring hanger can be applied after the pipeline is in place. At (*c*) in Fig. 18 is shown a spring cushion pipe roll hanger recommended for service where constant support[1] is

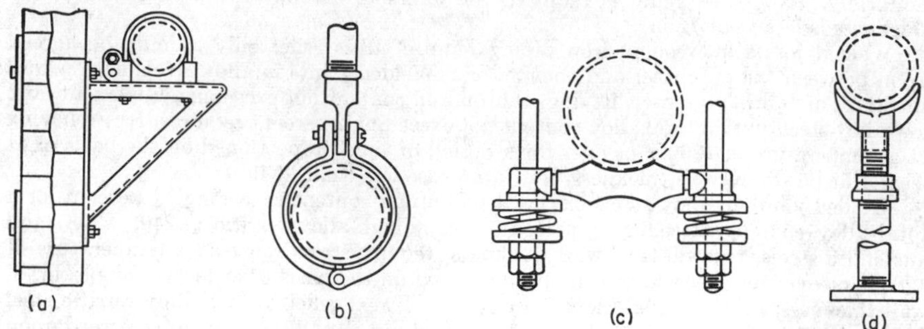

FIG. 18. Methods of supporting pipes.

required and compensation must be made for movement of the piping. The springs provide an efficient means of absorbing the vibration. Figure 18 (*d*) shows one of the many types of pipe saddle supports available. Figure 19 shows a cast-iron pipe roll stand designed for cases where vertical adjustment is not necessary but where provision must be made for expansion and contraction of the pipeline. Several designs of such stands with provision for vertical adjustment and of the same general dimensions are also available. One type of cast-iron roll and plate, illustrated in Fig. 19, provides for expansion and contraction where vertical adjustment is not necessary. If necessary, the base plate can be raised or lowered by use of shims. Detailed information and dimensions of a great variety of pipe supports can be found in manufacturers' catalogues.

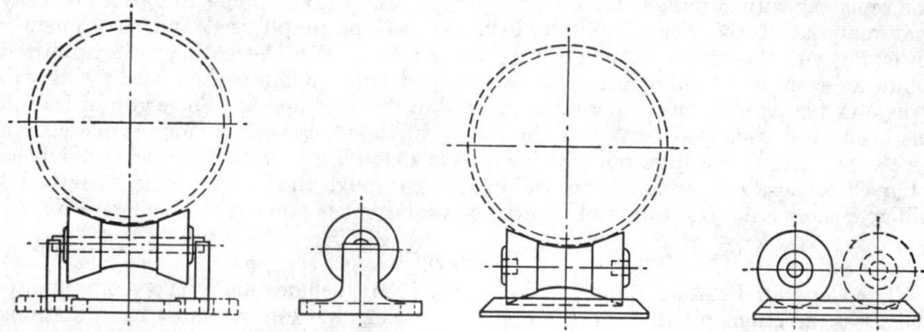

FIG. 19. Pipe supports on cast-iron rolls.

In supporting a high-temperature piping system, it is necessary to provide for expansion and contraction due to cyclic changes. It is often possible to find a point of zero movement along the run of a long line and to support a considerable portion of the total load by a rigid hanger or support of the type shown in Figs. 18 and 19. However, for other portions of the run, some form of spring support is often indicated. For relatively light lines, which are not subjected to excessive movements from hot to cold positions, a variable spring hanger will frequently suffice; for heavy lines, or those in which expansion movements are great, it is advisable to use constant support or counterweighted hangers so that transfer of weight to other hangers or equipment connections is prevented. Parts (*a*) and (*b*) of Fig. 20 indicate, respectively, a horizontal and vertical run of piping supported by a **constant-support hanger.** Figures 20 (*c*) and 21 (*a*) indicate horizontal runs supported by **variable-spring hangers.** Figure 21 (*b*) shows a riser supported by a variable spring beneath a base elbow. Figure 21 (*c*)

[1] The support afforded by the hanger of Fig. 18(*c*) is constant only in the sense that some degree of support is always present. It might be more appropriately termed a variable-support device.

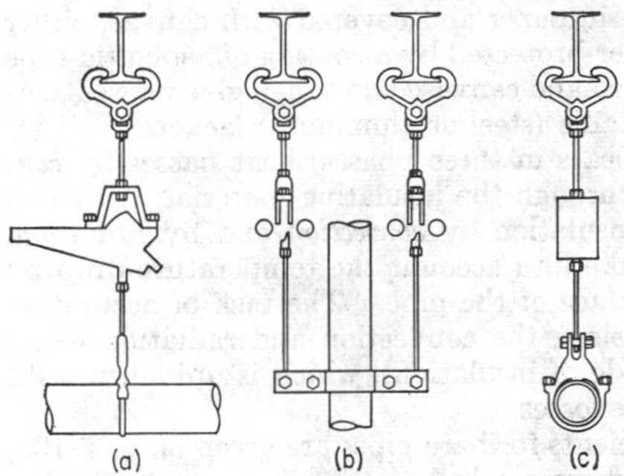

FIG. 20. Spring hangers.

indicates a **sway brace** that is used to control vibration and undesirable movement in a piping system.

The **distance between supports** will vary with the kind of piping and the number of valves and fittings. Supports should be provided near changes in direction, branch lines, and particularly near valves. The weight of piping must not be carried through valve bodies. In establishing the location of pipe supports, the designer should be guided by two requirements: (1) the horizontal span must not be so long that sag in the pipe will impose an excessive stress in the pipe wall and (2) the pipeline must be pitched downward so that the outlet of each span is lower than maximum sag in the span. Table 45 lists spacing for standard-weight pipe supports.

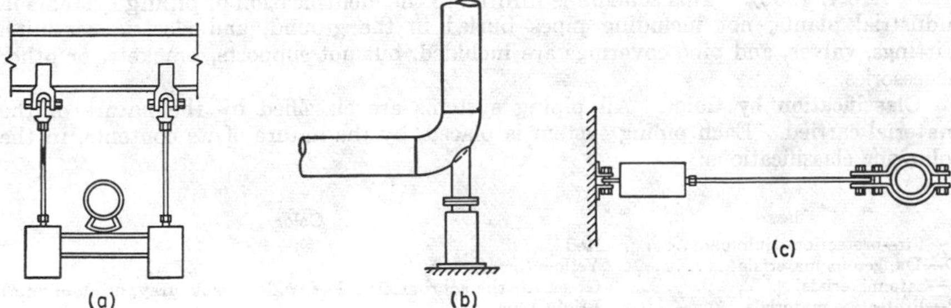

FIG. 21. Spring hangers and sway brace.

Table 45. Maximum Spacing of Pipe Supports at 750 F*

Nominal pipe size, in.	1	1½	2	3	4	6	8	10	12	14	16	18	20	24
Maximum span, ft	7	9	10	12	14	17	19	22	23	25	27	28	30	32

* This tabulation assumes that concentrated loads, such as valves and flanges, are separately supported. Spacing is based on a combined bending and shear stress of 1,500 psi when pipe is filled with water; under this condition, sag in pipeline between supports will be approximately 0.1 in.

Pipe Insulation

(See Secs. 4 and 6 for heat-transmission data)

The value of a steam-pipe covering is measured by its ability to reduce heat losses. This might range from 50 percent for small, low-temperature lines to 90 percent for large, high-temperature lines. Many **pipe-insulating materials** are available: 85 percent magnesia, foam glass, calcium silicate, and various forms of diatomaceous earths. Some of these materials are suited for relatively low temperatures only; others are best suited for high temperatures, and still others are suitable over a considerable temperature range.

Pipe insulation is applied in molded sections 3 ft long. For high-temperature work, the insulation is applied in at least two layers with the joints staggered so as to prevent a direct channel for heat loss. Because of its maximum temperature limitation of about 600 F, 85 percent magnesia is used as the second layer with a high-temperature-resistant material placed in direct contact with the pipe. The molded insulation is fastened securely in place with copper or galvanized wire and is then given a surface finish; indoor pipes are first sheathed with resin paper and covered with canvas, either pasted or sewed; outdoor pipes may be weather-protected by a coating of asphaltic-type waterproofing compound, they may be sheathed and canvased and then given a weatherproof surface, or they may be encased in metallic (steel or aluminum) jackets.

The heat loss from an insulated pipe appears in three phases: heat passes by *conduction* through the metallic pipe walls and through the insulating material; it then is dissipated from the outside surface of the insulation by *convection* and by *radiation*. Extremely accurate calculations must also take into account the temperature drop by convection through the film on the inside surface of the pipe. The task of accurately calculating heat losses is somewhat tedious since the convection and radiation losses are related to the surface temperature (outside of insulation), which is unknown until conduction losses are balanced against surface losses.

Combined convection and radiation coefficients for bare pipes are given on p. 4–106, and all necessary formulas to permit trial-and-error calculations are given, starting on p. 4–106. Insulation manufacturers publish data which give heat losses for wide ranges of pipe size and temperature.

Identification of Piping

The ASA has approved a **Scheme for the Identification of Piping Systems** (ASA A13.1, 1956). This scheme is limited to the identification of piping systems in industrial plants, not including pipes buried in the ground, and electric conduits. Fittings, valves, and pipe coverings are included, but not supports, brackets, or other accessories.

Classification by Color. All piping systems are classified by the nature of the material carried. Each piping system is placed, by the nature of its contents, in the following classifications:

Class	Color
F—Fire-protection equipment.......	Red
D—Dangerous materials...........	Yellow (or orange)
S—Safe materials..................	Green (or the achromatic colors, white, black, gray, or aluminum)
P—Protective materials............	Bright blue
V—Extra valuable materials........	Deep purple

Method of Identification. At conspicuous places throughout a piping system, color bands shall be painted on the pipes to designate to which one of the five main classes it belongs. If desired, the entire length of the piping system may be painted the main classification color.

Further, the actual contents of a piping system may be indicated by, preferably, a stenciled legend of standard size giving the name of the contents in full or abbreviated form. These legends shall be placed on the color bands. The identification scheme may be extended by the use of colored stripes placed at the edges of the colored bands.

The bands, legends, and stripes should be placed at intervals throughout the piping system, preferably adjacent to valves and fittings to insure ready recognition during operation, repairs, and at times of emergency.

A recommended classification, under this color scheme of materials carried in pipes, includes, as dangerous, combustible gases and oils, hot water and steam above atmospheric pressure; as safe, compressed air, cold water, and steam under vacuum.

Pressure Hose

Hose with durable rubber lining may be obtained to withstand any needed pressure. If the rubber compound is properly made, the life of a hose will be 7 to 10 years, while a cheaper hose, lined with inferior material, will probably not last more than 3 or 4 years. See also Secs. 3 and 12.

American National Fire-hose Coupling Screw Thread (ASA B26,[1] 1925). This standard is intended to cover the threaded part of fire-hose couplings, hydrant outlets, stand-pipe connections, and all other special fittings on fire lines, where fittings of the nominal diameters given in Table 46 are used. It also includes the limiting dimensions of the field inspection gages. The American National form of thread must be used.

[1] Revised 1953.

Table 46. Dimensions of Standard Fire-hose Couplings
(ASA B33.1, 1935 Rev. 1947)
(All dimensions in inches. Letters refer to Fig. 22)

Inside diam, *C*	Diam of thread, *D*	No. of threads per in.	*L*	*I*	*H*	*J*	*T*
2½	3 1/16	7½	1	¼	1 5/16	3/16	1 1/16
3	3⅝	6	1⅛	5/16	1 1/16	¼	1 3/16
3½	4¼	6	1⅛	5/16	1 1/16	¼	1 3/16
4½	5¾	4	1¼	7/16	1 3/16	⅜	1 5/16

American Standard Hose Coupling Screw Threads. (ASA B33.1, 1935).[1] These standards apply to the threaded parts of hose couplings, valves, nozzles, and all other fittings used in direct connection with hose intended for fire protection or for domestic, industrial, or general service in nominal sizes given in Table 47. The American National Standard thread form is used. This coupling is similar in design to the fire-hose couplings illustrated in Fig. 22.

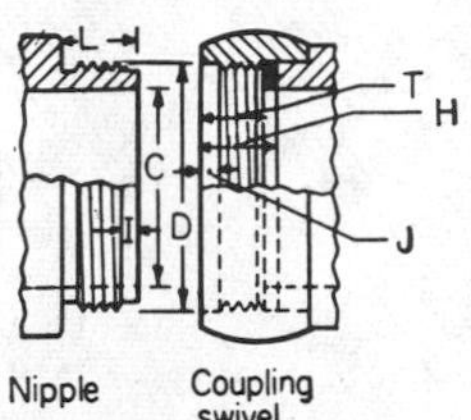

FIG. 22. Typical form of standard coupling.

Flexible metal hose and tubing are available for a wide range of conditions of temperature, pressure, vibration, and corrosion, and are made in two basic constructions, corrugated or interlocked, and in either bronze or steel.

The corrugated type (Fig. 23) may have either annular or helical corrugated formations, usually covered with metal braid and is adapted to high-pressure high-temperature leakproof service. Some typical applications include Diesel-engine exhaust hose, reciprocating flexible connections, loading and unloading hose, saturated and superheated steam lines, lubricating lines, gas and oil lines, vibration connections, etc.

Table 47. Dimensions of Standard Hose Couplings
(ASA B33.1, 1935 Rev. 1947)
(All dimensions in inches. Letters refer to Fig. 22)

Service and nominal size	Inside diam, *C*	Diam of thread, *D*	No. of threads per in.	*L*	*I*	*H*	*T*
Garden:							
½, ⅝, ¾	25/32	1 1/16	11½	9/16	⅛	17/32	⅜
Chemical:							
¾, 1	1 1/32	1⅜	8	⅝	5/32	19/32	15/32
Fire:							
1½	1 17/32	2	9	⅝	5/32	19/32	15/32
Other connections:							
½	17/32	13/16	14	½	⅛	15/32	5/16
¾	25/32	1 1/32	14	9/16	⅛	17/32	⅜
1	1 1/32	1 9/32	11½	9/16	5/32	17/32	⅜
1¼	1 9/32	1⅝	11½	⅝	5/32	19/32	15/32
1½	1 17/32	1⅞	11½	⅝	5/32	19/32	15/32
2	2 1/32	2 11/32	11½	¾	3/16	23/32	19/32

The interlocked type is made in several ways; the fully interlocked type is illustrated in Fig. 24. Typical applications include wiring conduit, cable armor, decorative wiring covering, dust-collective tubing, grease and oil connections, flexible spouts, moderate pressure oil lines, etc.

Standard couplings and fittings can be attached to flexible metal hose or tubing by various methods such as brazing or welding. Each type of hose construction has limits of service use and proved application usages. Information and recommendations as to

[1] Revised 1947.

the type and size to use under any given conditions should be obtained from the manufacturers.

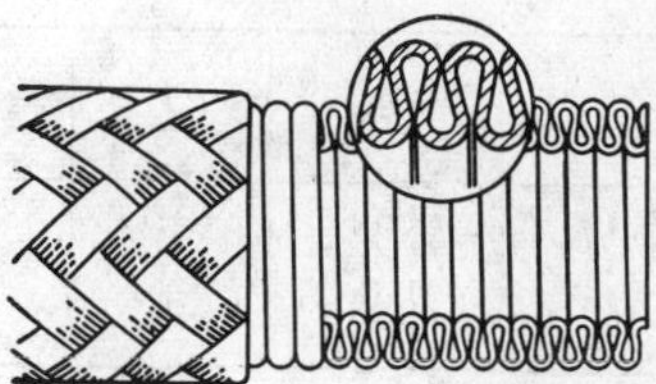

FIG. 23. Flexible metal hose.

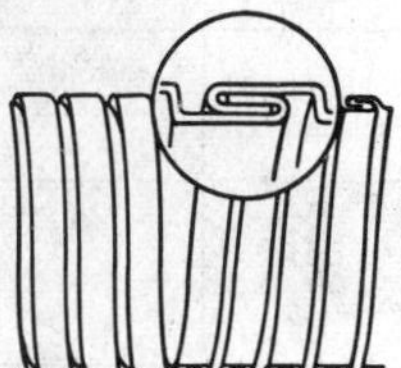

FIG. 24. Interlocked flexible metal hose.

PREFERRED NUMBERS

BY

C. H. Berry

REFERENCES: Hirshfeld and Berry, Size Standardization by Preferred Numbers, *Mech. Eng.*, Dec., 1922. Schlink, A New Tool for Standardizers, *Am. Mach.*, July 12, 1923. Tornebohm, The Development and Importance of Preferred Number Series, *Mech. Eng.*, Oct., 1923. Schlink, Use of Preferred Numbers, *Jour. SAE*, Feb., 1925. Table of Preferred Numbers, *ASA Standard* Z17.1, 1936. Steczynski, Preferred Numbers for American Practice, *Mech. Eng.*, Nov., 1928. Von Dobbeler, Preferred Numbers, *Mech. Eng.*, March, 1929.

Many manufactured articles are made in several sizes which may be designated by some dimension, speed, capacity, or other feature. Each such series of products may be paralleled by a series of numbers.

It is generally agreed that such number series should be **geometric progressions;** *i.e.*, each term should be a fixed percentage larger than the preceding. A geometric series provides small steps for small numbers, large steps for large numbers, and this best meets most requirements. The small steps in the diameter of the numbered twist drills would be absurd in drills of 1 in. diameter and larger.

In the case of sized objects that are used principally as raw material, *e.g.*, steel rod, an arithmetic progression may be preferable because it tends to reduce the cost of machining. It is desirable to be able to buy raw material a fixed amount (rather than a fixed percentage) larger than the finished article.

Preferred numbers is the name given to various series proposed for general use. These are either geometric progressions or approximations thereto. A geometric series is defined by one term and the ratio of each term to the preceding. On the choice of these elements for a preferred number series, there is as yet no general agreement. The same value would hardly be satisfactory for all cases. The idea of preferred numbers is to provide a master series from which terms can be chosen to suit any needs. This would ultimately lead to a comprehensive plan in all fields of manufacture, so that, for example, the sizes of shafting would be in accord with the sizes of bearings, and indeed with all manner of cylindrical machine elements.

An advantage of a geometric series is that if linear dimensions are chosen in the series, areas, volumes, and other functions of powers of dimensions are also members of the same series.

In one of the most carefully considered systems of preferred numbers the base term is 1, and the ratio is $\sqrt[80]{10}$. In this series, the 81st term is 10, and accordingly the series from 10 to 100 or from 0.01 to 0.1, or, in general, from 10^n to 10^{n+1} is identical with the series from 1 to 10 with the decimal point shifted. This series will rarely be used in full; some will choose alternate terms, some every fourth, fifth, tenth, or twentieth term. The index of the root, 80, has as factors 2^4 and 5, so that the series readily yields subseries having as ratios the roots of 10 with indices 2, 4, 8, 16, 5, 10, 20, 40, thus giving a wide range of choice.

The strict logic of this series has been somewhat impaired by the adoption of rounded values that are slightly different in the 1 to 10 and 10 to 100 intervals. For the United States, the ASA has adopted a Table of Preferred Numbers (ASA Z17.1, 1936) which differs slightly from the system described in the preceding paragraph.

Another type of series is the **semigeometric series** (Steczynski, *loc. cit.*) consisting of a basic geometric series with 1 as the base term, and a ratio of 2, giving a series . . . 1/8, 1/4, 1/2, 1, 2, 4, . . . Between consecutive terms are inserted arithmetic series of 2, 4, 8, or 16 terms, in general using different numbers of terms in different intervals.

SECTION 9

POWER GENERATION

BY

EUGENE AYRES, Consulting Chemical Engineer, South Wellfleet, Mass.

ELISHA N. FALES, Aerodynamics Engineer, Atlantic Research Corporation, Alexandria, Va.

G. W. KESSLER, Vice President, Engineering, Boiler Division, The Babcock and Wilcox Company.

P. H. KNOWLTON, JR., Advance Systems Engineer, Large Steam Turbine-Generator Department, General Electric Company.

WALTER J. KLEPONIS, Senior Negotiations Engineer, Steam Divisions, Westinghouse Electric Corporation.

RICHARD M. STEPHANI, Senior Design Engineer, Steam Divisions, Westinghouse Electric Corporation.

LESTER C. LICHTY, Robert Higgin Professor of Mechanical Engineering, Yale University.

NEIL MacCOULL, Consulting Automotive Engineer, Lecturer in Mechanical Engineering, Columbia University.

REEVES MORRISSON, Assistant to the Chief Scientist, United Aircraft Corporation.

LOUIS H. RODDIS, JR., President, Pennsylvania Electric Company.

ZALMAN M. SHAPIRO, President, Nuclear Materials and Equipment Corporation.

NUNZIO J. PALLADINO, Professor and Head, Nuclear Engineering Department, The Pennsylvania State University.

JOHN E. GRAY, President, Nuclear Utility Services, Inc.

BENJAMIN S. LOEB, Division of Technical Information, U.S. Atomic Energy Commission.

DAN K. PARK, Assistant to the President, Pennsylvania Electric Company.

WM. J. RHEINGANS, Consulting Engineer, Hydraulic Products Division, Allis-Chalmers Manufacturing Co.

PHILIP E. BENNER, Senior Application Engineer Retired, General Electric Company; Engineering Consultant.

E. S. KRENDEL, Professor of Operations Research and Statistics, University of Pennsylvania.

V. F. ESTCOURT, Consulting Engineer, Bechtel Corporation.

JOHN I. YELLOTT, Director, Yellott Solar Energy Laboratory, Phoenix, Ariz.

PHILIP C. WAGNER, Principal Engineer, Jackson and Moreland Division, United Engineers and Constructors.

ERICH A. FARBER, Professor and Research Professor of Mechanical Engineering, Director of the Solar Energy Laboratory, University of Florida.

CONTENTS

SOURCES OF ENERGY
By EUGENE AYRES

WINDMILLS
By ELISHA N. FALES

STEAM BOILERS
G. W. KESSLER

STEAM ENGINES

STEAM TURBINES
By P. H. KNOWLTON, JR.

POWER-PLANT HEAT EXCHANGERS
By WALTER J. KLEPONIS and RICHARD M. STEPHANI

INTERNAL-COMBUSTION ENGINES
By LESTER C. LICHTY and NEIL MacCOULL

GAS TURBINES
By REEVES MORRISSON

NUCLEAR (ATOMIC) POWER
By LOUIS H. RODDIS, JR., *et al.*

HYDRAULIC TURBINES
By WM. J. RHEINGANS

DIRECT-ENERGY CONVERSION
By PHILIP E. BENNER

POWER MISCELLANY

SOURCES OF ENERGY

BY

Eugene Ayres

REFERENCES: Proved Reserves of Crude Oil, Natural Gas Liquid, and Natural Gas, *Proc. API*, Dec. 31 of each year. Zapp, Future Petroleum Producing Capacity of the United States, *USGS Survey Bull.* 1142*H*, 1962. Schurr *et al.*, "Energy in the American Economy, 1850–1975," Johns Hopkins Press. Schurr, Energy, *Scientific American*, Sept., 1963. Searl, "Fossil Fuels in the Future," AEC, 1960. "Civilian Nuclear Power: A Report to the President," AEC, 1962. Science, Technology and Development, Vol. 1: Natural Resources—Energy, Water, and River Basin Development, *U.S. Papers Prepared for the United Nations Conference on the Application of Science and Technology for the Benefit of the Less Developed Areas*, GPO, 1963. Struth, World Petroleum Statistical Yearbook, *World Petroleum*, each year. Putnam, "Energy in the Future," Van Nostrand. Ayres and Scarlott, "Energy Sources, The Wealth of the World," McGraw-Hill. Landsberg *et al.*, "Resources in America's Future: Patterns of Requirements and Availabilities, 1960–2000," Johns Hopkins Press.

PRIMARY IRREPLACEABLE SOURCES OF ENERGY

Reserves

Petroleum. Reserves of petroleum are taken as the sum of two figures: (1) proved reserves, which are based upon reasonably trustworthy calculations from physical data; and (2) remaining undiscovered oil which is believed to be producible under present technology and economics. Proved reserves are computed each year by the American Petroleum Institute. Undiscovered producible reserves are estimated at various times by geological specialists.

API figures for proved reserves in the United States include liquified petroleum gases (LPG). World estimates take into account the LPG likely to be ultimately producible in the rest of the world.

United States	Billions of barrels
Proved reserves	40
Estimated reserves remaining to be discovered	100
Total	140
Rest of the world	
Proved reserves	300
Estimated reserves remaining to be discovered	950
Total	1,250

Natural Gas. Proved reserves of natural gas in the United States are estimated annually by the American Gas Assoc., but because of various technical factors, the figures are believed to have less validity than corresponding petroleum figures. No basis exists for estimates of reserves of gas outside the United States, except for a few countries like Canada, which is believed to have about 5 percent as much as the United States.

United States	Trillions of cubic feet
Proved reserves	250
Estimated reserves remaining to be discovered	350
Total	600

Coal. Estimates of United States reserves are made periodically by the U.S. Geological Survey. The 1960 survey indicates about 600 billion tons of recoverable coal (bituminous, subbituminous, lignite, and anthracite) disposed approximately as follows:

United States	Billions of tons
Beds 28 in. or more thick and not over 1,000 ft deep	95
Beds 28 in. or more thick and between 1,000 and 2,000 ft deep	380
Reserves inferred or in thin beds or more than 2,000 ft deep	1,425
Total	1,900

More than half the 1,425 billion tons is in beds less than 28 in. thick. For purposes of approximation, the USGS assumes that one-half the reserves can actually be produced. Thus it appears that the United States has about 48 billion tons that could be produced within the present economic framework, an additional 190 billion tons that could be produced at higher cost, and perhaps 350 billion tons (assuming lower recovery of less accessible coal) that we are not sure about. About 55 percent of the 48 billion tons of "most available" coal is bituminous. Most of the remainder is subbituminous and lignite. Thus it can be assumed that the United States has about 30 billion tons of bituminous coal that can be produced at anything like present costs.

Information on the coal reserves of the rest of the world is merely qualitative. It is believed that most of the coal of the Americas (at least 75 percent) is in the United States. Asia may have almost as much coal as the United States, and most of it is believed to be in China. Europe may have about a quarter as much as the United States, and all other parts of the world put together may have about a tenth as much. But most reserves outside the United States have not been carefully studied for grade and physical disposition, and any quantitative information is of doubtful value. An assumption that the United States contains nearly half the world's coal would be fairly accurate.

Shale Oil. Estimates have been made from time to time by the U.S. Bureau of Mines and by the corresponding agencies of some other governments. Most of the rich oil shale of the United States is in Colorado. The B of M believes that about 1,000 sq miles there is amenable to commercial development and could produce about 494 billion bbl of shale oil, but the larger part of this material probably assays about 15 gal of oil per ton, and recovery would, therefore, be relatively costly. The part of the 1,000 sq miles that appears to assay around 30 gal per ton contains a potential of around 126 billion bbl of oil.

Oil shales are widely distributed throughout the world, but it is believed that about 55 percent of the total is in the United States, with 43 percent in Brazil. This leaves only about 2 percent of the total for other countries. The proportions may change markedly with further exploration.

Tar Sands. Estimates have come largely from the Canadian government, for Canada contains the only known large deposits of tar sand. The ultimately recoverable oil from the Athabasca tar sands of northern Alberta has been variously estimated at 100 to 300 billion bbl. This does not include all tar sands that have not been exposed to erosion. Mining of underground tar sands is expensive. There may not be more than 1 billion bbl accessible to surface mining.

The total minable reserves of the United States may exceed 10 billion bbl, but present information is scanty.

Nuclear Fuels. The total recoverable uranium and thorium of the earth has been variously estimated as corresponding to between 10^{21} and 10^{19} Btu of potential energy. But this potential energy corresponds to a much smaller amount of net energy—just how much smaller is not yet known. Nuclear fuel for generation of heat must be manufactured, and the process of manufacture is a prolific consumer of energy. All that is certain in 1963 is that nuclear fuel will produce more energy than is required for its manufacture, especially when the "breeder" reactors successfully convert uranium 238 (the abundant isotope) into fissionable uranium 235, and thorium 232 into fissionable thorium 233.

The "fusion" of low-atomic-weight elements (as in so-called hydrogen bombs and in the sun itself) is capable of generating fantastic amounts of energy from almost limitless sources (such as water), but in 1963 it was not known how to achieve this fusion under controlled conditions without the expenditure of far more energy than was generated.

It is too early to assess the magnitude of nuclear sources of energy.

Demand

Petroleum. The average rate of increase in demand for petroleum in the United States has been about 5 percent per annum since 1940. The rate of increase is expected to average about 3 percent from 1965 to 1975.

The average rate of increase in demand for petroleum in the rest of the world has been about 10 percent per annum since 1940.

Natural Gas. The average rate of increase in demand for natural gas in the United States has been about 8 percent per annum since 1940. Demand figures for the rest of the world are unknown.

Coal. Consumption of coal in the United States and the rest of the world has been highly variable from year to year. Since 1910, the trend has been slightly upward for the rest of the world but not for the United States.

Dates of Peaks of Production

Petroleum. Assuming a reserve of 140 billion bbl of petroleum yet to be produced in the United States and assuming 3 percent per annum increase in demand, the peak of production in the United States should come about 1970.

Assuming a reserve of 1,250 billion bbl of petroleum yet to be produced in the rest of the world and assuming 5 percent per annum increase in demand, the peak of production in the rest of the world should come about 1980.

Natural Gas. Assuming a reserve of 600 trillion cu ft of gas yet to be produced in the United States and assuming a continuation for a few years of at least 4 percent per annum increase in demand, the peak of production should come between 1965 and 1970.

Coal. Assuming that the United States has 30 billion tons of "most available" bituminous coal yet to be produced and assuming that the major part of electric-power generation will utilize this coal, the peak of production of this type of coal should come about 1975.

Total World Fossil Fuels. Taking Palmer C. Putnam's figures for total world reserves and for rate of increase in world's energy demands and assuming that nuclear fuels will not take over more than electric-power generation (about 12 percent of total energy demand), the world peak of production of all fossil fuels should come before the year 2000. At the peak, the world would probably want about 4×10^{16} Btu per annum more than fossil fuels will provide, and world shortage would be noticeable around 1975.

PRIMARY REPLACEABLE SOURCES OF ENERGY

Waterfalls. The best estimate of potential waterpower that seems to be practically possible of development throughout the world is 6.42 trillion kwh per yr. This assumes an average mean stream flow three times the minimum flow and a use factor of 0.5. The capacity of waterpower plants installed throughout the world at the end of 1960 was about 135 million hp. Assuming a worldwide use factor of 0.5 and an over-all efficiency (from lake level to the station electrical bus) of 80 percent, hydraulic plants produced about 335 billion kwh of energy. This is little more than 4 percent of the estimated world potential. It is also about 4 percent of world energy consumption from all sources.

While hydroelectric-power requirements have been fairly constant (about 4 percent) since 1920 in relation to total energy requirements, hydroelectric power has declined in relation to total electric power generated. The reason for this trend is that demand for electric power has been rising more rapidly than capital has been attracted for development of decreasingly suitable waterpower sites.

Some idea of the distribution of potential and installed waterpower may be gained from the following approximate figures:

Area	Waterpower	
	Potential, percent	Installed, percent
North America	13	40
Europe	10	40
Africa	40	1
Rest of the world	37	19
Total	100	100

Waterpower sites in the United States are most abundant in the least populated areas. The 11 Western states (Pacific and Mountain), with 14 percent of United States population, have 58 percent of the nation's potential waterpower. The Northern states, from the Atlantic through Wisconsin, with almost half the United States population, have only 15 percent of the potential waterpower.

Vegetation. About 7 percent of the world's energy requirements are met by combustion of wood fuel. It is estimated that about 40 percent of the total energy requirements of the world (in 1960) could have been satisfied by utilizing, with good forest management, all the economically accessible productive forests of the earth. This estimate is based on the following assumptions: (1) that about 27 percent of the land area of the earth (or 15 million sq miles) is forested, (2) that two-thirds of the forested area is productive, (3) that somewhat more than half the productive area is economically accessible, (4) that the average balanced production of the world's forests is 1 cord of wood per acre per annum, (5) that Btu losses would be taken by conversion of wood to liquid fuel, (6) that abnormal energy would be required for transportation of fuel from remote regions to centers of energy consumption.

In the United States, wood provides almost as much energy as that derived from waterpower and more than twice as much energy as that derived from combustion of anthracite coal. Consumption of wood as fuel reached a peak in the United States about 1875, and consumption of wood for all purposes reached a peak in 1907.

Tide Power. The potential power obtainable from the earth's tides has been estimated at about 20 trillion hp-hr per annum, but the maximum amount of tide power that is practicable to develop in the seven locations in the world where the tide range is as much as 25 ft—the minimum required to generate power—is estimated at only 60 billion hp-hr per annum. This is less than one-half of 1 percent of the energy needs of the United States alone.

Wind Power. It has been estimated that the maximum energy practically obtainable from the wind is less than 5 percent of the world's 1960 requirements of energy, and the amount actually obtained in 1960 was probably not more than 0.03 percent of the potential.

Solar Energy. About one two-billionth of the sun's radiation impinges on the earth, but about half of this is radiated into interstellar space by our atmosphere. We receive at the earth's surface about 10^{18} hp-hr per annum.

About 30 percent (or 3×10^{17} hp-hr per annum) of the energy that reaches the earth's surface from the sun is reflected from the earth's surface into interstellar space during daylight hours. Most of the reflection of sunshine during the day is from vegetation, which rejects 1,000 quanta of light for every quantum that it usefully employs.

The disposition of the 7×10^{17} hp-hr per annum that is retained by the earth during the day is approximately as follows:

	Hp-hr per annum
Radiated away at night	1×10^{17}
Evaporation of water	6×10^{17}

Consumption of solar energy by vegetation is about as follows:

	Hp-hr per annum
Land vegetation	5.5×10^{13}
Marine vegetation	44.5×10^{13}
Total	5×10^{14}

On the average, each horsepower-hour of utilized solar energy leads to the production of 0.05 lb of vegetation and the same amount of oxygen.

It has been estimated that the amount of power that might reasonably be generated in Arizona from solar energy is about 440,000 hp-hr per annum per acre. The best photosynthetic production of power from combustion of land vegetation would be about 60,000 hp-hr per annum per fertile acre.

Solar energy is important for the generation of electric power in space vehicles through photovoltaic energy converters.

WINDMILLS

BY

E. N. Fales

REFERENCES: Eiffel, "Etudes sur L'Helice Aerienne," Paris. Tests on Windmills, *Ergebnisse der Aerodynamischen Versuchsanstalt zu Göttingen*, Berlin, 1927, pp. 19, 139. Glauert, Windmills and Fans (in Durand, "Aerodynamic Theory," **4**). Fales, A New Propeller-type High-speed Windmill, *Trans. ASME*, **50**, AER-50-6, 1928. Putnam, "Power from the Wind," Van Nostrand. Golding, "Generation of Electricity by Wind Power," Spon. Fales, Propeller Design as Applied to Windmills, *Jour. IAeS*, **50,** June, 1936, p. 278. Food & Agriculture Organization of the UN, "Windmills for Water Lifting & the Generation of Electricity on the Farm," *Informal Working Bull.* 17, Rome, 1959. Food & Agriculture Organization of the UN, "New Sources of Energy (Solar, Wind & Geothermal)," *Conference Proc.*, Rome, 1961. Fateev, "Wind Power Installations—Present Position & Possible Lines of Development" (in Russian), USSR Acad. of Sciences, Moscow, 1959.

Windmill performance may be investigated theoretically under the Betz momentum theory which concerns the decelerations in the air traversing the windmill disk, and under the Drzwiecki blade-element theory which concerns the air forces produced on an element of the blade. It may be investigated empirically by models in a wind tunnel or on a moving vehicle.

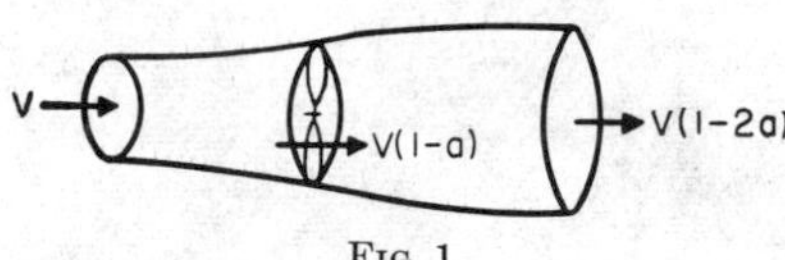

FIG. 1

The column of air arriving at the windmill with a velocity V is slowed down; its boundary is an expanding envelope as shown in Fig. 1. The diminution of velocity at the windmill disk may be expressed by the use of an interference factor a. From energy and momentum considerations, it can be shown that, behind the windmill, the diminution factor increases to an ultimate value of $2a$.

Energy is obtained from the wind by the slowing down of the air. Disregarding rotational and drag losses, the work obtainable from it per unit of time, P, is

$$P = 2\pi R^2 \cdot \rho V^3 \cdot a(1 - a)^2 \tag{1}$$

where R is the disk radius and ρ is the mass density of the air.

The power originally contained in a cylinder of air of radius R is given by

$$P = \tfrac{1}{2}\pi R^2 \cdot \rho V^3 \tag{2}$$

From Eq. (**1**) it may be seen that the power obtained is a maximum when $a = \tfrac{1}{3}$, in which case P is 59.2 percent of the power originally in the air. This may never be exceeded.

The **axial thrust,** representing the force tending to overturn a stationary windmill, or the "drag" on an airplane generator, is given by

$$T = 2\pi R^2 \rho V^2 a(1 - a) \tag{3}$$

This is a maximum at $a = \tfrac{1}{2}$ and grows smaller with smaller values of a. The thrust may be kept low by using a small a and a large diameter, thus taking a smaller percentage of power from the air.

The percentage of power removed from the air is proportional to the **power coefficient**

$$P_c = P/(\rho \cdot R^2 V^3) \tag{4}$$

It is a function of a, or of the geometric arrangement of the windmill, and of the **tip speed ratio** $2\pi nR/V$, where n is revolutions per second. P_c has been determined in wind-tunnel tests for various blade arrangements (Fig. 2). The higher the tip-speed ratio, the higher will be the power coefficient for a perfectly designed windmill.

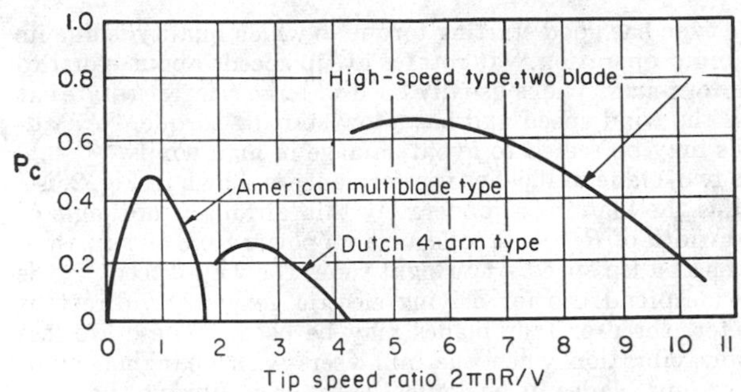

FIG. 2. Power coefficients of windmills.

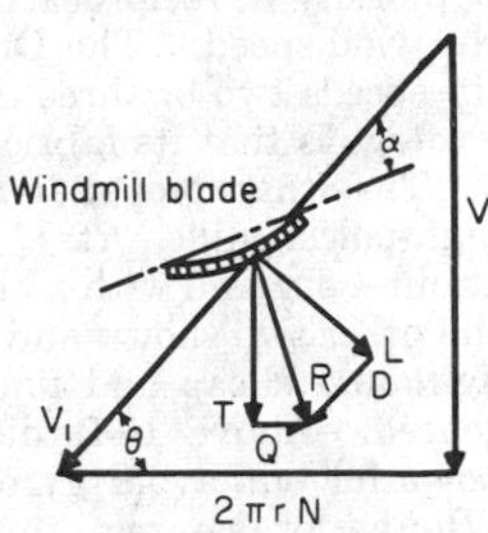

FIG. 3. Forces on windmill blade element.

Blade Elements. The **action of the blade** of a windmill is similar to that of a blade of an airplane propeller (see p. 11-78). A velocity, torque-force, and resistance-force diagram for a section of a windmill blade is given in Fig. 3. In this figure, V is the absolute wind velocity, V_1 the wind velocity relative to the blade element, α the angle of attack, R the force normal to the blade, L the lift, D the drag, T the thrust, and Q the torque-force. The following relations hold:

$$L = C_L \cdot \tfrac{1}{2}\rho V_1^2 S \qquad D = C_D \cdot \tfrac{1}{2}\rho V_1^2 S$$
$$Q = L \sin\theta - D\cos\theta \qquad T = L\cos\theta + D\sin\theta$$

where S is the elementary blade area, C_L and C_D are the lift and drag coefficients, respectively, and ρ is the mass density.

The conditions for maximum power output demand that at every radius r

$$(Bc)/(2\pi r) \cdot C_L = 4(1 - \cos\theta) \tag{5}$$

where B is the number of blades and c is the chord of the airfoil.

The angle θ is also an implicit function of the radius given by

$$\frac{2\pi nR}{V} \cdot \frac{r}{R} = \frac{\sin\theta(2\cos\theta - 1)}{(1 + 2\cos\theta)(1 - \cos\theta)} \tag{6}$$

Combining Eqs. (**5**) and (**6**), a plot as in Fig. 4 may be obtained giving the product $B \cdot c \cdot C_L$ for every tip-speed ratio and radius.

The angle of attack α corresponding to a given value of C_L is immediately obtainable from the known airfoil characteristics of the blade. The pitch of the blade is then fixed at $(\theta - \alpha)$.

The number of blades B for maximum power decreases as $2\pi nR/V$ increases for usual values of $c \cdot C_L$, as indicated in the test results in Fig. 2. A windmill with one or two blades has maximum efficiency at high tip speeds, a multiblade windmill at low speeds.

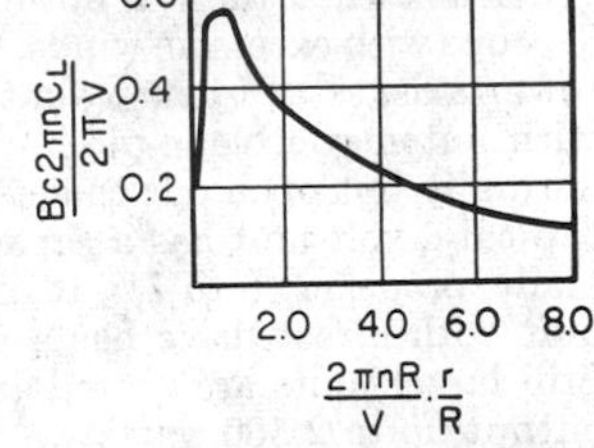

FIG. 4. (*From Glauert.*)

The preceding theory ignores frictional drag of the blades, and flow distortion due to blade interference. These result in a loss of power roughly proportional to the tip-speed ratio. At high ratios, errors can be reduced by working backward from empirical tests (Fig. 2).

The **American multiblade type,** as used for pumping water on American farms, utilizes about 30 percent of the kinetic energy of the wind. The **Dutch four-arm type** utilizes about 16 percent. The **high-speed propeller type** utilizes about 42 percent. Other types include the **Savonius,** composed of two semicylindrical offset cups rotating about a vertical axis, and the **Flettner,** with four arms each consisting of a rotating cylinder actuated by a Savonius rotor (see *Mech. Eng.*, Nov., 1925, and Mar., 1927). Neither of these is efficient.

The American multiblade type has good starting torque to which quality is due its popularity in reciprocating-pump operation. It rotates at tip speeds about equal to the wind speed. The Dutch four-arm type is usually built in large sizes; it rotates at tip speeds two or three times the wind speed and has a low starting torque. An advantage is that its fabric sails may be reefed to avoid damage in high winds.

The **Stuart propeller-type two-blade mill,** whose performance is shown in Fig. 2, is a high-power mill. At ¾ radius the blade is a moderately thin airfoil, at an angle of about 4 deg and with a chord width of $R/6$. It collects more power from the air than the other two shown and turns at a tip speed six to eight times the wind speed. It is light and cheap and finds widespread use for driving electric generators, direct or geared. Above 10-ft diameter, three or four blades may be used. These are less powerful but avoid gyroscopic vibration when the mill veers with changing wind. Whether of one, two, three, or four blades, it has much less starting torque than the multiblade slow-speed type and requires an unloading clutch when applied to a reciprocating-pump drive. Very large windmills are vulnerable when stopped during a tempest because the wind creates, at the blade roots, bending moments which increase with the cube of the diameter. A single-blade propeller when stopped overcomes this difficulty by floating downwind like a weathervane.

The power coefficients P_c of Fig. 2 may be used for performance prediction of the three types of windmills.

$$\text{Horsepower} = P_c \rho \frac{(2R)^2 V^3}{2{,}200}$$

The mass density ρ has the following standard values, in fps units: at sea level and 59 F, 0.002378; at 2,000 ft, 0.00224; at 4,000 ft, 0.00211.

For two-blade propeller windmills of diameter D ft, geared to electric generators of 70 percent efficiency, the maximum kilowatt output in winds of velocity V fps is expressed approximately by the formula

$$\text{kw} = 0.376 \times 10^{-6} D^2 V^3$$

and the corresponding rpm is $105V/D$.

Since 1935, **propeller-windmill electric-generating** units of small capacity have been available, first in the form of 6-volt "wind chargers" for charging radio batteries, and later as 32-volt and 110-volt "farm-lighting" plants operating in conjunction with a suitable storage battery and sometimes with an auxiliary gasoline-engine-driven generator. A simple automatic reverse-current relay disconnects the battery from the generator when there is not enough wind to produce the minimum charging current. To cope with excessive winds, the propeller is in some cases mounted off center from the tower axis, so as to swing out of the wind. In other cases, the propeller is provided with automatic blade-pitch change, or with paddles that rotate edgewise to the air normally but open out to act as countertorque paddles above the critical rpm. The typical 6 volt unit has a capacity of 120 to 200 watts, and is driven direct by a two-blade propeller, 6 to 7½ ft diameter, mounted on the armature shaft. The 32-volt unit with direct drive has a 6- to 8-ft two-blade propeller and a 600-watt generator. Still larger units are geared and have three or four blades, 10- to 14-ft diameter, and output up to 2,500 watts.

Hundreds of thousands of these small-capacity windmills were successfully used in the United States prior to the spread of rural electrification in the 1950s, but they have now disappeared from the U.S. market. They were simple to operate by anyone familiar with the lighting circuit of an automobile.

Outside the United States, large plants, up to 200-kw output and 112-ft diam, continue to be of interest. Serious experiments have been made showing that self-regulating wind-electric plants can be built to feed a-c into a public power network. The design problems are much more difficult than for the small plants. For example, vibration while running and destruction by tempest while not running must be prevented, and constant a-c frequency must be maintained in varying wind. The great problem in a large windmill project is to appraise the wind energy available at the selected site. Continuous wind records should be taken at the site for at least 1 year, and preferably for 3 years. While nearby Weather Bureau Station records may indicate expected daily and monthly rates of change of average wind, they are not a substitute for on-the-spot measurements. The latter should be insisted upon at the start, even though they are time-consuming and expensive.

Thorough experimentation has been made in England under the Electrical Research Assoc. A representative plant on the Isle of Man is rated at 100 kw in a 45-mph wind, using a 50-ft three-blade rotor. In non-rotating condition, it has withstood 80-mph winds. In a period of 1,000 hr running time, it has fed 25,000 kwh in a public power network. Estimates in 1959 set the production cost as £50 to £100 per kw. A representative plant in Denmark has a 43-ft three-blade rotor with output 50 kw at 32 mph feeding a-c to a public power network (S. E. Zealand Elec. Supply Co.). In 5 months of winter 1952–1953, it produced 26,092 kwh. In Germany since the war, the Studiengesellschaft Windkraft e.V. at Stuttgart has been developing a 100-kw plant having a 112-ft diam three-blade rotor at the top of a 72-ft mast. In France, Électricité de France has experimented with plants of 130 kw and larger. Neyrpic in Grenoble has built a 42-ft three-blade plant using controllable pitch and a small pair of pilot windmills to hold the rotor into the wind. In Russia, two 25-kw plants of 59-ft diam are under experimentation by the G. M. Krzhizhanooski Power Inst. of the USSR Academy of Sciences, Moscow; the plants are designed not for feeding into networks but for remote locations. One hundred and fifty 10-kw plants with 39-ft rotors were formerly built; many were damaged by tempests, but 50 were still running in 1960. In Vermont, the Smith-Putnam plant, rated at 1,250 kw and with a 175-ft two-blade rotor, cost $1¼ million. In 22½ days of March, 1945, it fed a-c electricity into the local power network at the rate 805 kwh per kw per year.

Power in the Wind. Since only 59.2 percent of the kinetic energy of the wind is theoretically recoverable, it appears that, with a windmill of 70 percent aerodynamic efficiency and 90 percent gearing efficiency, 37 percent of the wind kinetic energy is the top limit to be expected in any practical application. Weather Bureau records of seven years (1918 to 1924) at Dayton, Ohio, were analyzed to characterize wind variation over a flat agricultural region. (Anemometer was located on tower above office building at center of the city.) The results showed the following general characteristics, which are typical of ordinary winds:

In each month, there is a well-defined group of wind velocities which predominate, and may be called the **prevalent** or frequent **winds.** There is also a well-defined group of winds which contain the bulk of the energy of each month called **energy winds.**

The energy winds produce about three-fourths of the total energy of a given month. Even in a calm summer month, 70 percent of the energy comes from winds which blow only 42 percent of the time.

Energy winds blow 2 out of 7 days; prevalent winds 5 out of 7 days.

The mean prevalent wind velocity is 2 mph less than the average monthly velocity.

The energy winds blow at velocities of about 2.3 times those of the prevalent winds.

The wind of highest energy has about 10 mph higher velocity than the most frequent wind.

For each month the energy of all the varying winds adds up to double the amount that would be computed from the average hourly velocity of that month.

Comparing the windiest month with the calmest month of the year, the average velocity in the former is 1¾ times as great as in the latter and the kwh energy 4½ times greater. Any regulating device which aims to hold the power output of a windmill constant throughout the year must be able to spill three times as much energy as is normally used.

Figure 5 shows the wind-velocity distribution, averaged for the 7 years, on which the above relationships are based.

In estimating the power content of winds, gustiness must be allowed for. At Dayton, Ohio, the true velocity varied ±28 percent in 10 sec and ±45 percent in 38 sec from the average velocity.

In the greater part of the United States, 8 mph yearly average is the minimum wind velocity practical for propeller-type wheels. For very light multiblade wheels, which swing out of the wind above 15 mph, an operating range of 6 to 15 mph affords a

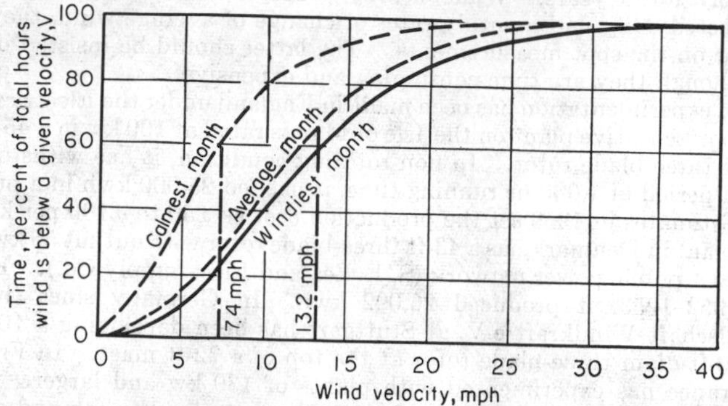

FIG. 5. Average hourly wind-velocity distribution at Dayton. (The average wind velocity for a whole month varies from 7.4 mph in the calmest month to 13.2 mph in the windiest month.)

monthly power output 14 percent greater than if the range were 8 to 15 mph. The high-wind regions of the United States, having 10 mph or more average yearly wind velocity, are a north-and-south strip 350 miles wide midway between the Atlantic and Pacific Oceans, the littoral of the Great Lakes, the Atlantic Seaboard, the Gulf Coast, and the Pacific Ocean near San Francisco and at the state of Washington. See Tables 1 and 2.

Table 1. Wind Velocities in the United States

Station	Avg velocity, mph	Prevailing direction	Fastest mile	Station	Avg velocity, mph	Prevailing direction	Fastest mile
Albany, N.Y.	9.0	S	71	Louisville, Ky.	8.7	S	68
Albuquerque, N.M.	8.8	SE	90	Memphis, Tenn.	9.9	S	57
Atlanta, Ga.	9.8	NW	70	Miami, Fla.	12.6	......	132
Boise, Idaho	9.6	SE	61	Minneapolis, Minn.	11.2	SE	92
Boston, Mass.	11.8	SW	87	Mt. Washington, N.H.	36.9	W	150
Bismarck, N.Dak.	10.8	NW	72	New Orleans, La.	7.7	......	98
Buffalo, N.Y.	14.6	SW	91	New York, N.Y.	14.6	NW	113
Burlington, Vt.	10.1	S	72	Oklahoma City, Okla.	14.6	SSE	87
Chattanooga, Tenn.	6.7	....	82	Omaha, Neb.	9.5	SSE	109
Cheyenne, Wyo.	11.5	W	75	Pensacola, Fla.	10.1	NE	114
Chicago, Ill.	10.7	SSW	87	Philadelphia, Pa.	10.1	NW	88
Cincinnati, Ohio	7.5	SW	49	Pittsburgh, Pa.	10.4	WSW	73
Cleveland, Ohio	12.7	S	78	Portland, Maine	8.4	N	76
Denver, Colo.	7.5	S	65	Portland, Ore.	6.8	NW	57
Des Moines, Iowa	10.1	NW	76	Rochester, N.Y.	9.1	SW	73
Detroit, Mich.	10.6	NW	95	St. Louis, Mo.	11.0	S	91
Duluth, Minn.	12.4	NW	75	Salt Lake City, Utah	8.8	SE	71
El Paso, Tex.	9.3	N	70	San Diego, Calif.	6.4	WNW	53
Galveston, Tex.	10.8	....	91	San Francisco, Calif.	10.5	WNW	62
Helena, Mont.	7.9	W	73	Savannah, Ga.	9.0	NNE	90
Kansas City, Mo.	10.0	SSW	72	Spokane, Wash.	6.7	SSW	56
Knoxville, Tenn.	6.7	NE	71	Washington, D.C.	7.1	NW	62

U.S. Weather Bureau records of the average wind velocity, and fastest mile, at selected stations. The period of record ranges from 6 to 84 years, ending 1954. No correction for height of station above ground.

Table 2. Beaufort Scale of Wind Force
(Compiled by U.S. Weather Bureau, 1955)

Beaufort number	Miles per hour	Knots	Wind effects observed on land	Terms used in USWB forecasts
0	Less than 1	Less than 1	Calm; smoke rises vertically	Light
1	1-3	1-3	Direction of wind shown by smoke drift; but not by wind vanes	Light
2	4-7	4-6	Wind felt on face; leaves rustle; ordinary vane moved by wind	Light
3	8-12	7-10	Leaves and small twigs in constant motion; wind extends light flag	Gentle
4	13-18	11-16	Raises dust, loose paper; small branches are moved	Moderate
5	19-24	17-21	Small trees in leaf begin to sway; crested wavelets form on inland waters	Fresh
6	25-31	22-27	Large branches in motion; whistling heard in telegraph wires; umbrellas used with difficulty	Strong
7	32-38	28-33	Whole trees in motion; inconvenience felt walking against wind	Strong
8	39-46	34-40	Breaks twigs off trees; generally impedes progress	Gale
9	47-54	41-47	Slight structural damage occurs; (chimney pots, slates removed)	Gale
10	55-63	48-55	Seldom experienced inland; trees uprooted; considerable structural damage occurs	Whole gale
11	64-72	56-63	Very rarely experienced; accompanied by widespread damage	Whole gale
12 or more	73 or more	64 or more	Very rarely experienced; accompanied by widespread damage	Hurricane

Over an unobstructed plain, the wind velocity V at height H may be estimated from velocity V_0, measured at height H_0, from the relationship

$$V/V_0 = (H/H_0)^n$$

where $n = 1/2$ for wind under 5 mph, $n = 1/5$ from 5 to 35 mph, and $n = 1/7$ above 35 mph. Over irregular terrain having obstructions, only those velocities recorded at the site are valid for energy prediction.

STEAM BOILERS

BY

G. W. Kessler

REFERENCES: The Babcock & Wilcox Co., "Steam—Its Generation and Use." De Lorenzi, "Combustion Engineering," Combustion Engineering, Inc. Staniar, "Plant Engineering Handbook," McGraw-Hill. Powell, "Conditioning of Water for Industrial Uses," McGraw-Hill. "Boiler and Pressure Vessel Code," "Power Test Code for Steam Boilers," ASME. *Proc. ASTM*. "1958 Manual, Steam Generating Equipment—Industry Standards and Engineering Information," ABAI.

FUELS AVAILABLE FOR BOILER FIRING

(See also Sec. 7)

Boilers in the United States are usually fired by the most economical fuel available. Natural gas is used in the Southwest. Natural gas and residual oil are burned on the West Coast. Residual oil is used in the Southeast and, with favorable prices, on the East Coast. Solid fuels serve most of the boiler needs on the East Coast and in the

Table 1. Burning Equipment for Solid Fuels*

		Stokers					PC		Crushed	
Fuel	Source	Underfeed	Traveling grate	Chain grate	Chain grate, jet ignition	Spreader	U flame, pulverized fuel	Horizontal burners, pulverized fuel	Cyclone (where fusion temp is suitable)	Cell furnaces
Coke breeze	....	...	✓	✓						
Anthracite	E. Pa.	...	✓	✓c†	...	...	✓			
Bituminous coal:										
17–27 % volatile	W.Va., Cent. Pa.	✓	...	...	...	✓	✓	✓	✓	
27–35 % volatile										
Strongly coking	W. Pa., W.Va., Ky., Ohio, Utah	✓	✓	✓	✓	✓	✓	✓	✓	
Weakly coking	Ind., Iowa, Ill., Colo., W. Ky.	...	✓	✓	✓	✓	✓	✓	✓	
Pipeline slurry	....	...	...	...	...	...	✓	✓	✓	
Lignite	N.Dak., S.Dak., Mont., Wyo., Tex.	...	✓	✓	✓	✓	✓	✓	✓	
Low-temp fluid-coal char	....	...	...	...	...	...	✓	✓ Aux†	✓	
Petroleum coke, 9–14 % volatile	....	...	...	...	...	...	✓	✓	✓	
Fluid petroleum coke, 4–5 % volatile	....	...	...	...	...	...	✓	✓ Aux†	✓	
Wood and bark‡	....	...	...	...	...	✓	...	......	✓ Aux†	✓
Bagasse	....	...	...	...	...	✓	...	......	......	✓

* Equipment indicated will usually result in a good application, but there are many factors affecting the burning of fuel, and variations of fuel properties that guide the individual selection of burning equipment.

†c = coarse sizes only. Aux = auxiliary fuel—coal, oil, or gas.

‡ Bark and wood are also burned on inclined grates and in Dutch-oven pile furnaces.

central section of the country. However, the development of pipelines and unitrains may change this usage of fuels. Table 1 lists the equipment used to burn different types of solid fuels.

Black liquor from the cooking of wood pulp is burned in many paper mills. Blast-furnace and coke-oven gases are available and used in steel-mill boilers. Lean CO gas, a waste product from oil-refinery operation, is burned in special furnaces in combination with a richer gas.

ASH AND SLAG

Ash and slag from solid and liquid fuels cause many problems in boiler operation. The ash, when sintered or fused, forms clinkers in fuel beds and deposits on the furnace walls, superheaters, and boiler surfaces, thus reducing heat absorption and increasing draft loss. Fly-ash collectors are required to decrease atmospheric pollution, and the disposal of slag and fly ash is costly.

Pulverized-coal dry-ash-type furnaces are usually provided with water-cooled wall surfaces to keep the ash relatively dry, although some ash may adhere to the furnace walls or may deposit on the superheater surfaces. Pulverized-coal **slag-tap-type furnaces** have the burners located so as to maintain a high-gas-temperature zone near the floor and to keep the ash molten for tapping. The suitability of a coal ash for slag-tap operation is indicated by its fluid, or flow temperature. The cone-fusion method of determining the fluid temperature of the ash (see p. 7–12) is widely used, but ash viscosity is a better guide.

The **viscosity** of the ash can be determined by a viscometer, but the test requires considerable time and special equipment. The approximate viscosity can be calculated from the chemical or spectrographic analysis of the ash after establishing the ratio of the silica to the sum of the silicon, iron, calcium, and magnesium oxides (Reid and Cohen, *Trans. ASME*, 1944). Figure 1 shows, in full lines, the viscosity, the temperature, and the silica ratio of slags from two coals derived from viscometer cooling tests. The dashed lines are the corresponding values calculated from spectrographic analyses. At the **critical viscosity** (where some constituents start to freeze), the viscosity curve rises steeply and the upper portion of the dashed line is drawn from a point on the ratio curve at a temperature 300 F higher than the cone softening temperature and at a slope of 10 deg from the vertical for the coordinates shown. For satisfactory slag tapping, a viscosity of 250 poises should be obtained at a temperature less than 2600 F. Thus, in Fig. 1, coal A is satisfactory but coal B is questionable. More than 50 percent of the coals available in the United States are satisfactory for slag-tap furnaces. The viscosity and the fusing temperature are greatly affected by silica and, to a lesser degree, by ferric oxide (Fig. 2). **A low ash fluid temperature** facilitates ash tapping as slag but may lead to slag deposits on the furnace walls and **superheaters.**

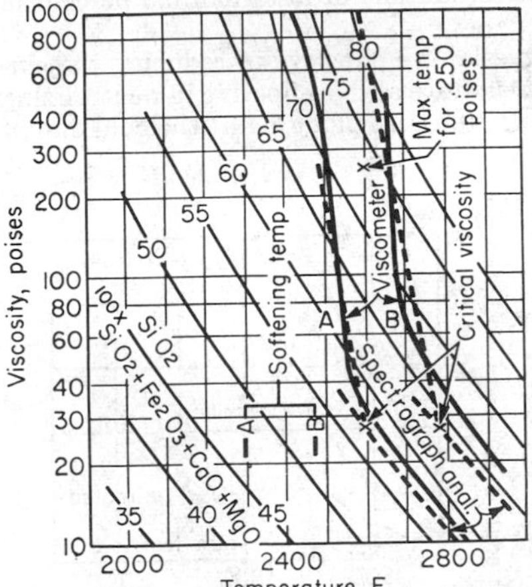

FIG. 1. Viscosity of slags by viscometer and as calculated from analysis.

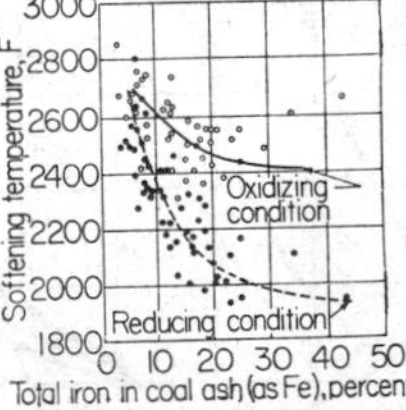

FIG. 2. Influence of iron on ash-softening temperature.

Some of the sodium and potassium in coal ash vaporizes in the furnace and later condenses on the superheater tubes, forming a cementlike accumulation of slag and fly ash. The outer layer of this deposit is similar to fly ash, but the inner layer contains a much greater amount of Na_2O, K_2O, and SO_3. The SO_3 content usually is so large that part of the sulphur exists as complex sulphates of sodium or potassium and iron or alumina, all of which have lower melting temperatures than the normal sulphates.

The temperature at which **sintering of fly ash** starts may be much lower than the initial deformation temperature determined for ash from coal samples using conventional laboratory methods. However, with a special laboratory furnace, fly ash may be produced from coal samples with sintered strength comparable to fly ash from an operating boiler. The **sintering strength** of slag deposits can be established by crushing cylinders of fly ash previously heated for 10 hr at temperatures ranging from 1400 to 2000 F (Barnhart and Williams, *Trans. ASME*, 1956). Figure 3 shows the widely differing sintering strengths of the fly ash from two coals whose initial deformation temperatures are identical and whose fusing temperatures are almost the same. Figure 4 illustrates the varying of sintered strength with the sodium oxide content of the coal, and experience indicates that slagging is reduced when firing coals having a sodium oxide content of less than 0.3 percent of the dry coal weight.

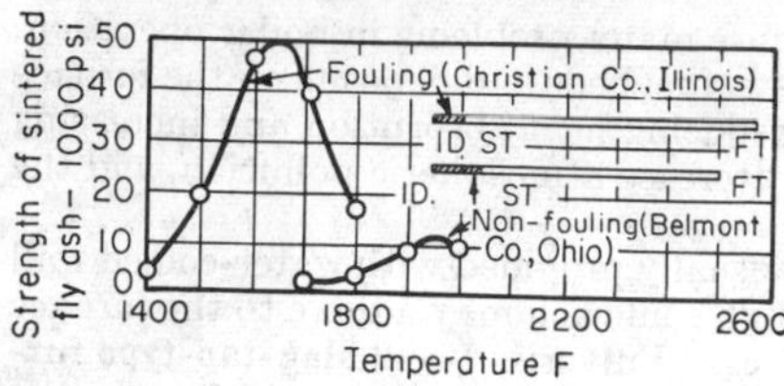

FIG. 3. Comparative sintered strengths and temperatures of initial deformation (ID), start of sintering (ST), and ash fusion (FT) for a fouling and a non-fouling coal.

Additives, such as dolomite, lime, and magnesia, are effective in reducing the sintering strength of fly ash, as shown in Fig. 5. Dolomite also is effective in neutralizing the acid in flue gases and in eliminating condensation and plugging at the cold end of air heaters.

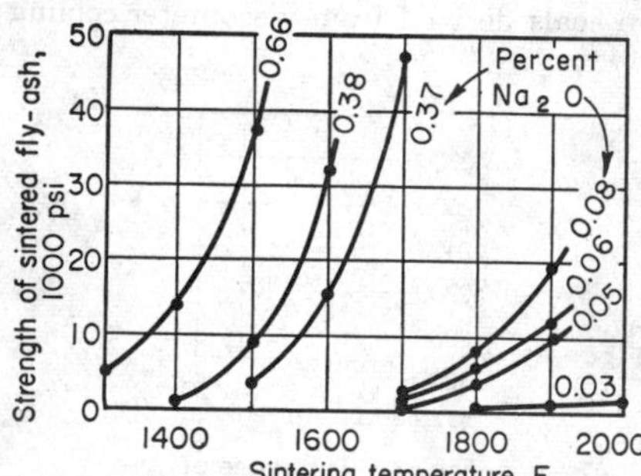

FIG. 4. Effect of sodium oxide content of coal on sintered strength of fly ash.

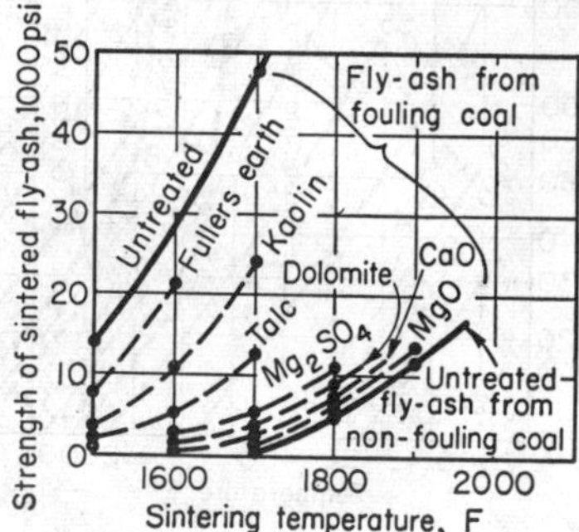

FIG. 5. Effect of additives on sintered strength of fly ash (1 part additive to 4 parts fly ash).

Although **fuel oils** have a low ash content (0.05 to 0.20 percent), slagging and high-temperature corrosion are experienced in oil-fired units. The analyses listed in Table 2 indicate that high-alkali fuel-oil ash, with or without vanadium, can cause trouble. Thus, dolomite, added in quantities equal to the ash weight, is used in many oil-fired boilers to produce a softer slag, which can be removed easily by soot blowing (McIlroy, Holler, and Lee, *Trans. ASME*, 1954). In some installations, air-heater corrosion and pluggage and acid stack discharge also are minimized by the use of dolomite additives (Huge and Piotter, *Trans. ASME*, 1955).

Soot-blower systems are used to maintain boiler efficiency and capacity by the periodic removal of ash and slag from the heat-absorbing surfaces. Steam or air jets from the soot-blower nozzles dislodge the dry or sintered ash or slag, which then falls into hoppers or travels along with the gases to the removal equipment. Types of soot blowers vary with location in the boiler unit, severity of ash or slag conditions, and arrangement of the heat-absorbing surfaces.

Table 2. Analyses of Ash from Heavy Fuel Oil

	Analysis, percent		
	Trouble-free fuel oil	Troublesome fuel oils	
Ferric oxide, Fe_2O_3	54	8	6
Silica, SiO_2	24	9	5
Alumina, Al_2O_3	6	4	1
Lime, CaO	3	10	1
Magnesia, MgO	9	3	2
Vanadium pentoxide, V_2O_5	...	1	35
Alkali sulphates	1	67	37

Constituent	Melting point in air, deg F
V_2O_5	1274
$NaSO_4$	1625
$MgSO_4$	2165
$CaSO_4$	2640
Fe_2O_3	2850

Cleaning of furnace walls is generally done with **wall blowers** (Fig. 6*a*), which project a nozzle assembly into the furnace for blowing and retract it behind the wall tubes for protection after operation.

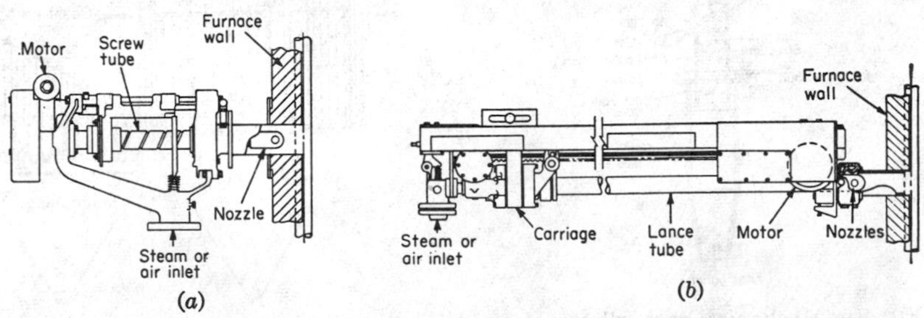

Fig. 6. Retracting soot blowers; (*a*) furnace wall blower, (*b*) long-lance blower.

Tube banks in high-gas-temperature sections, such as slag screens, superheaters, and reheaters, where slag or sintered ash may accumulate, are generally cleaned by **long-lance retracting blowers** (Fig. 6*b*). The lance, which rotates or oscillates as it advances, has large nozzles to supply more powerful cleaning action and is retracted out of the boiler for protection when not operating.

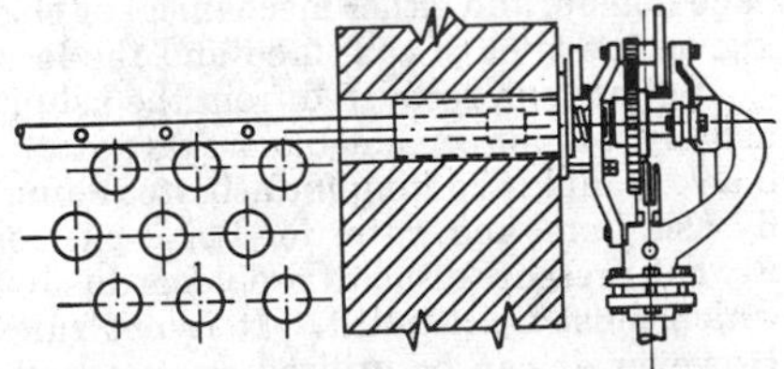

Fig. 7. Rotating soot blower with multiple nozzles.

Tube banks located in lower gas temperatures, including the economizer and boiler sections, where uncooled metal will have satisfactory life and ash removal is easier, often can be cleaned by **multiple-nozzle rotating soot blowers** (Fig. 7). However, long-lance retracting blowers may be necessary for very wide boilers, for long cleaning ranges, or where the ash tends to pack or cake.

Air-heater blowers are arranged to blow through plate or tube assemblies with single- or multiple-nozzle elements moved in an arc or straight-line motion by a suitable mechanism. These blowers are sometimes arranged so they also can supply water for washing the air-heater surface.

Shot cleaning is effective in removing dry ash from the heat-absorbing surfaces by raining steel or iron shot over a horizontal area where the shot can fall by gravity through or over the tubes. The shot is collected in hoppers and then recycled for further use. Where applicable, excellent cleaning can be obtained with this method.

Additives to soften oil slag for easier removal by soot blowers, to protect against high-temperature slag attack, to reduce the bond strength of slag to tubes, or to overcome low-end-temperature corrosion may be introduced as a **slurry spray** through suitably equipped long-lance retractable blowers or through separate spraying equipment.

Automatic controls for soot-blower systems often are used and can be arranged to operate the blowers in a prescribed sequence at time intervals adjusted to the boiler-cleaning problem or to receive signals from the boiler unit's instruments and controls so as to operate the soot blowers selectively in the various heat-absorbing sections to maintain the required cleanliness and heat absorption.

Dust collectors (see also Sec. 7) are required on all large coal-burning boiler units to reduce atmospheric pollution. The amount of ash entrained in the flue gas varies from about 80 percent of the ash in the coal for dry-ash pulverized-coal firing to approximately 50 percent for slag-tap pulverized-coal firing and from 15 to 30 percent for cyclone-furnace firing. Both **mechanical separators** (Fig. 8) and **electrostatic dust collectors** (Fig. 9) may be used in series, but most pulverized-coal-fired units use only electrostatic collectors. In spreader-stoker-fired units, the fly ash is coarse and mechanical separators generally are used. The gas-dust loading is low in cyclone-furnace boilers, and either mechanical or electrostatic dust collectors can be used, depending on the type of coal fired and the local air-pollution codes.

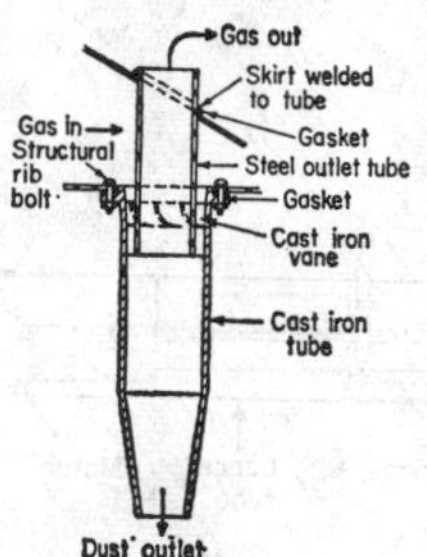

Fig. 8. Mechanical dust collector element.

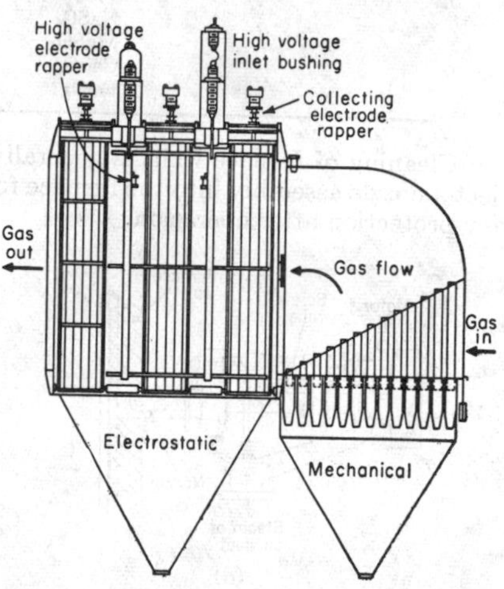

Fig. 9. Mechanical and electrostatic dust collectors in series.

Bottom ash recovered from the ashpits of chain-grate and spreader-type stokers is usually sold for cement-block aggregate. **Slag** from slag-tap furnaces can be used as a black granular coating for asbestos shingles and roofing, as a mixture containing slag, fly ash, lime, and water for Poz-o-pac roads, or as an antiskid material for icy roads. **Fly ash** presents disposal problems due to its low density and, consequently, the volume which must be handled. It is not suitable for fill material unless quickly covered. However, it can be utilized as an admixture, replacing 20 to 30 percent of portland cement, and as a lightweight aggregate, after sintering.

STOKERS

Chain- and traveling-grate stokers have been extensively used to burn non-coking coals, but only a few installations have been made in recent years because of their slow response to load changes, loss of ignition on swinging loads, high ashpit heat losses, high excess air requirements, and limitations on size. However, by a unique arrangement of **air jets** in the front wall (Fig. 10), the ignition on chain-grate stokers can be maintained close to the feed gate during wide changes in load, thus obtaining quick response to varying firing rates. Further, by maintaining higher air-blast pressures in the forward compartments of the stoker, coking coals can be burned.

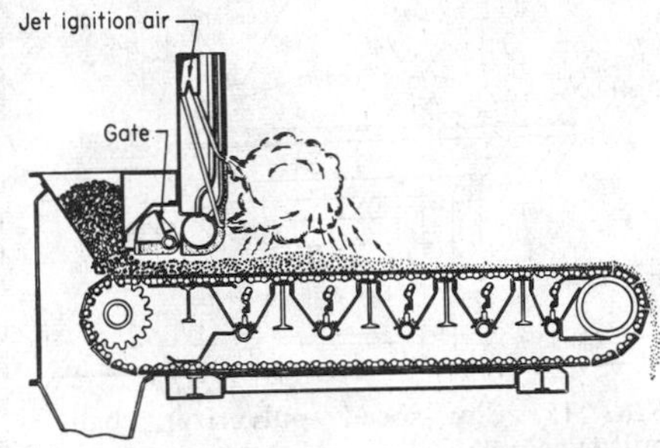

Fig. 10. Chain-grate stoker with jet ignition.

Spreader stokers with continuous-ash-discharge traveling grates (Fig. 11), intermittent-cleaning dump grates, or reciprocating continuous-cleaning grates (Fig. 26) are capable of burning all types of bituminous and lignite coals. The fines are burned in suspension, and the larger fuel particles are burned on the grate. The use of a thin, fast-burning fuel bed provides rapid response to variations in load. Rotating mechanical feeding and distributing devices are generally used with spreader stokers. These stokers operate with low excess air and high efficiencies when the carbon in the fly ash is reinjected above the grate. However, relatively low gas velocities through the boiler are necessary to prevent fly-ash erosion, and fly-ash collectors should be used to reduce air pollution.

Oscillating, or pulsating, continuous-cleaning grates also are used with spreader-type feeds. The water-cooled vibrating-grate, hopper-fed, bed-burning stoker with a continuous ash discharge reduces ash carry-over as well as grate maintenance.

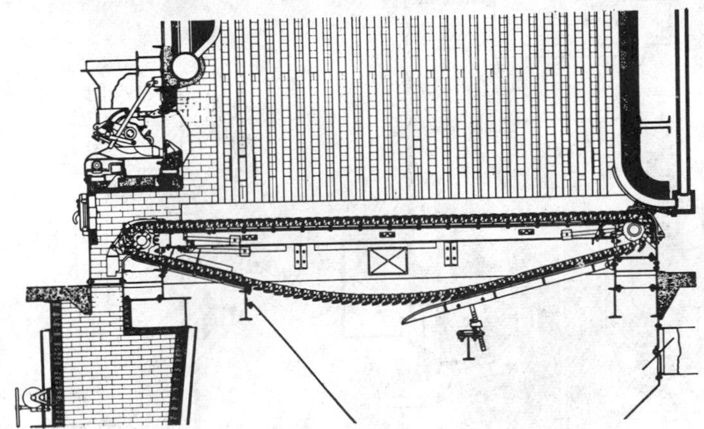

Fig. 11. Spreader stoker with traveling grate.

Single- or double-retort **underfeed stokers** with side ash dump and multiple-retort underfeed stokers with rear ash discharge are well suited for the burning of coking coals. These stokers operate best at steady loads. The ashpit heat loss and maintenance are high, while capacity is limited.

PULVERIZERS

Coal for the firing of boilers is taken from the pulverizers in a stream of air which is supplied to the pulverizer at a temperature of 300 to 750 F, depending upon the amount of moisture in the coal. The pulverizer provides the active mixing needed for drying, and the temperature of the coal and air mixture in and leaving the pulverizer ranges from 130 to 180 F. In **bin-storage systems,** the coal and air (or flue gas) from the pulverizers are separated in cyclones and the coal is then stored in bins and fed to the burners as needed. In **direct-fired systems,** the coal and the air pass directly from the pulverizer to the burners and the desired firing rate is regulated by the rate of pulverizing. Practically all recent installations utilize the direct-fired system.

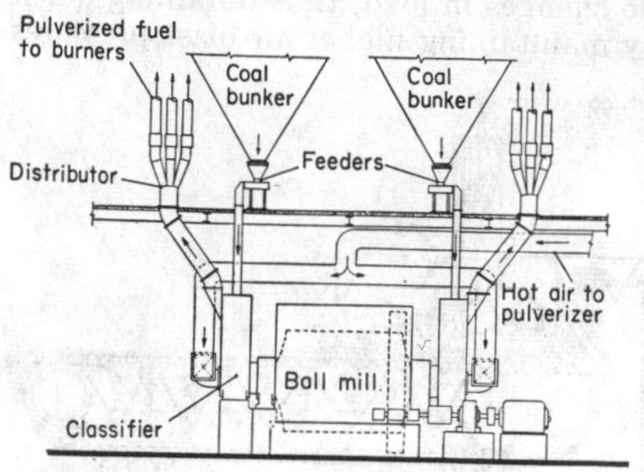

FIG. 12. Slow-speed pulverizer, ball-mill type.

Three general types of pulverizers are used with coal: The **slow-speed pulverizer** (Fig. 12) consists of a rotating drum with a tumbling charge of steel balls. It is used for all types of coal but is particularly adaptable to abrasive materials such as anthracite. **Medium-speed pulverizers** are used for all grades of bituminous coal; and their low power requirements, consistently high fineness, and quick response to load change are well suited to large industrial and central-station boiler applications. Figure 13 shows a ball-race type, and Fig. 14 a bowl and roller type. **High-speed pulverizers** also are used for all grades of bituminous coal. This type of pulverizer (Fig. 15) uses a preliminary stage consisting of two rows of hammers and a second stage of intermeshing rotating and stationary pegs, which is followed by the exhauster.

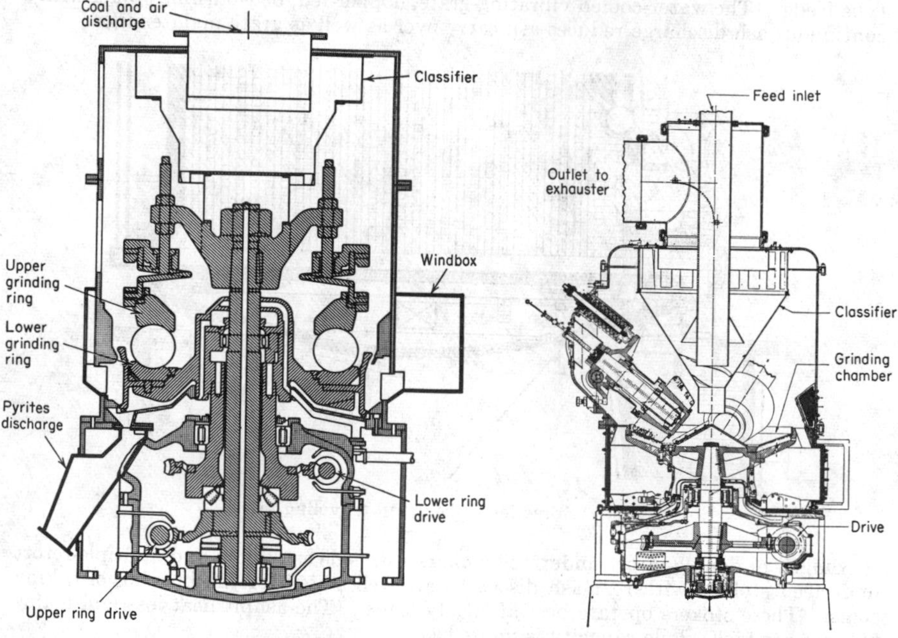

FIG. 13. Medium-speed pulverizer, contra-rotation ball-race type.

FIG. 14. Medium-speed pulverizer, roller type.

The **fineness** of pulverization required varies with the type of coal and with the size and kind of furnace; it usually ranges from 65 to 80 percent through a 200-mesh screen. (The USS Sieve 200-mesh screen has 200 openings per linear in., giving a nominal aperture of 0.0029 in. The ASTM equivalent is 74 microns. (See also pp. 6–220 and 7–81). The **capacity** of a pulverizer is affected by the **grindability** of the coal and the fineness produced (Fig. 16), and capacities are established by testing with coals of different grindability. (See also p. 7–13.)

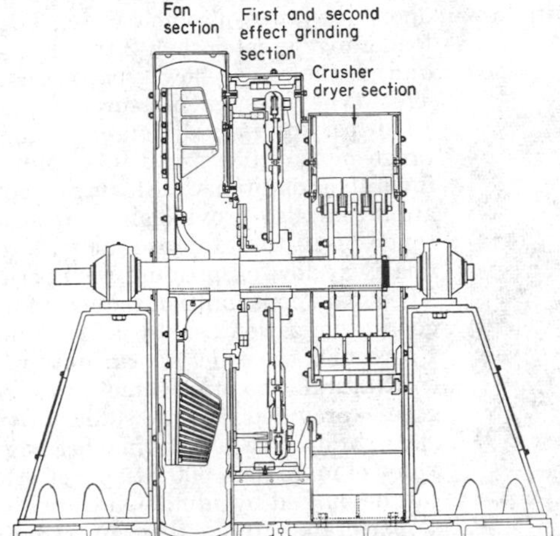

Fig. 15. High-speed pulverizer, attrition type.

Pulverized-coal firing is rarely used on boilers of less than 100,000 lb of steam per hr capacity, since the use of stokers is more economical. Direct-fired pulverizers for large boilers have been designed for capacities up to 50 tons per hr, and one large storage-system pulverizer delivers approximately 53 tons per hr of bituminous coal.

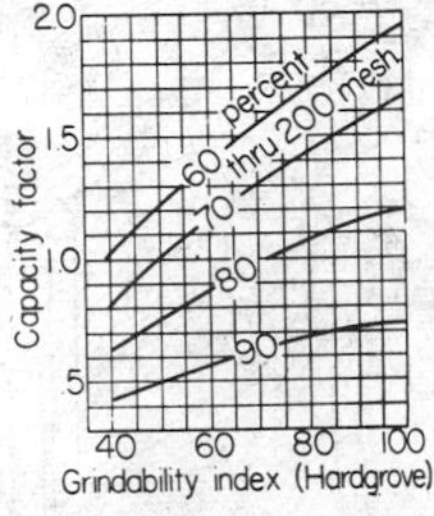

Fig. 16. Pulverizer capacity factor for varying fineness and grindability; medium-speed, ball-race pulverizer.

BURNERS

The primary purpose of a fuel burner is to mix and direct the flow of fuel and air so as to ensure rapid ignition and complete combustion. In pulverized-coal burners, only a part (15 to 25 percent) of the air, called **primary air,** is initially mixed with the fuel to obtain rapid ignition and to act as a conveyor for the fuel. The remaining portion, or **secondary air,** is introduced to the burner outside of the primary-air ports.

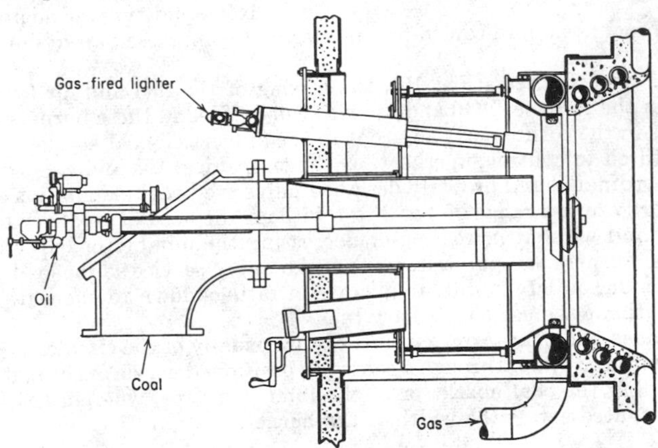

Fig. 17. Circular burner for pulverized coal, oil, or gas.

Circular-type burners (Fig. 17) may be used for firing coal, oil, or gas. They are built in capacities as high as 165 million Btu per hr.

Oil, when fired, can be atomized by the fuel pressure or by a compressed gas, usually steam or air. Atomizers utilizing fuel pressure generally are of the **uniflow** or **return-flow mechanical** types. The uniflow type uses an oil pressure of 300 to 600 psi at the maximum flow rate and is limited to an operating range of some 2 to 1. If a load range greater than 2 to 1 is required, the return-flow type is used. This type uses oil pressures up to 1,000 psi and provides an operating range of as much as 10 to 1 under favorable conditions. **Steam** and **air atomizers** also provide an operating range of 10 to 1 approx but with a relatively low oil pressure (100 psi). The steam consumption required for good atomization usually is less than 1 percent of the boiler's steam output.

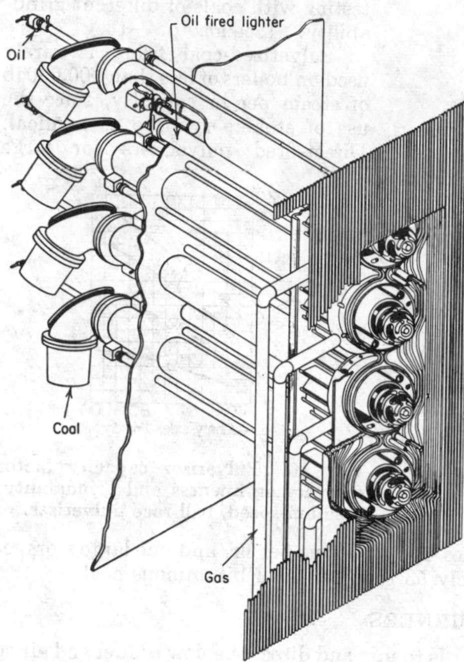

FIG. 18. Cell-type burner for pulverized coal, oil, or gas.

Natural gas and some process gases (provided they are sufficiently clean and have a calorific heating value of more than 500 Btu per cu ft) can be burned by admission through a **perforated ring,** through **radial spuds** (Fig. 17), or through a centrally located **center-fire** type of fuel element. Since the center-fire fuel element is removable for cleaning, restrictions on gas cleanliness are less severe for this type of burner.

The **cell-type pulverized-coal burner** (Fig. 18) uses two to four fuel nozzles and provides the excellent ignition characteristics of the circular burner. Gas, when fired in these burners, is introduced through fixed-spud-type elements located in the burner throat; standard return-flow or steam or compressed-air atomizers are used for firing oil.

In corner-fired burners (Fig. 19), the mixing of the fuel and air for combustion takes place in the furnace. Oil and gas also can be fired in these burners by inserting fuel elements in the corner ports adjacent to the pulverized-coal nozzles. The burner tips can be tilted to control superheat, as shown in Figs. 19*b* and *c*.

A well-coordinated and properly designed pulverized-coal installation should operate satisfactorily over a range of 2 or 3 to 1 without the need of auxiliary fuel to maintain ignition and without increasing or decreasing the number of burners in service. If some of the burners and pulverizers are taken out of service as the load decreases, it is not uncommon, on large units, to operate at ratings down to one-sixth of full-load steam flow without the use of auxiliary fuel.

Blast-furnace and **coke-oven gas burners** are usually of the **circular** type, in which the gas is introduced either through a centrally positioned nozzle or through an annular port surrounding the coal nozzle, or of the **intertube** type, wherein the fuel and air ports are alternated across the width of the burner.

CYCLONE FURNACES

The cyclone furnace is designed to burn all low-ash-fusion coals and to retain most of the ash in the slag, which is then tapped from the furnace, thus preventing the passage of the ash through the heat-absorbing surfaces. The coal, crushed to 4-mesh size, is admitted with the primary air in a tangential manner to the primary burner (Fig. 20). The finer particles burn in suspension while the coarser particles are thrown by centrifugal force to the outer wall of the cyclone furnace. The wall surface, sticky from the coating of molten slag, retains most of the coal particles until they burn and leave their molten ash on the wall. From the wall, the molten ash drains into the boiler furnace and then through an opening in the boiler furnace floor into the slag-collecting tank.

The secondary air, which is admitted tangentially at the top of the cyclone, vigorously scrubs the coal particles on the wall, and combustion is completed at a firing rate of about ½ million Btu per cu ft per hr.

Figure 30 shows a boiler fired with twenty-three 10-ft-diam cyclone furnaces. The primary-furnace walls (consisting of fully studded tubes) also are wetted with molten ash and help to catch any ash particles that are not retained in the cyclone furnaces. Gas, when available, can be burned by injection through openings at the bottom of the secondary-air ports. Oil is burned by spraying it axially into the cyclone through the primary burner or by firing tangentially through an oil element located in the secondary-air port.

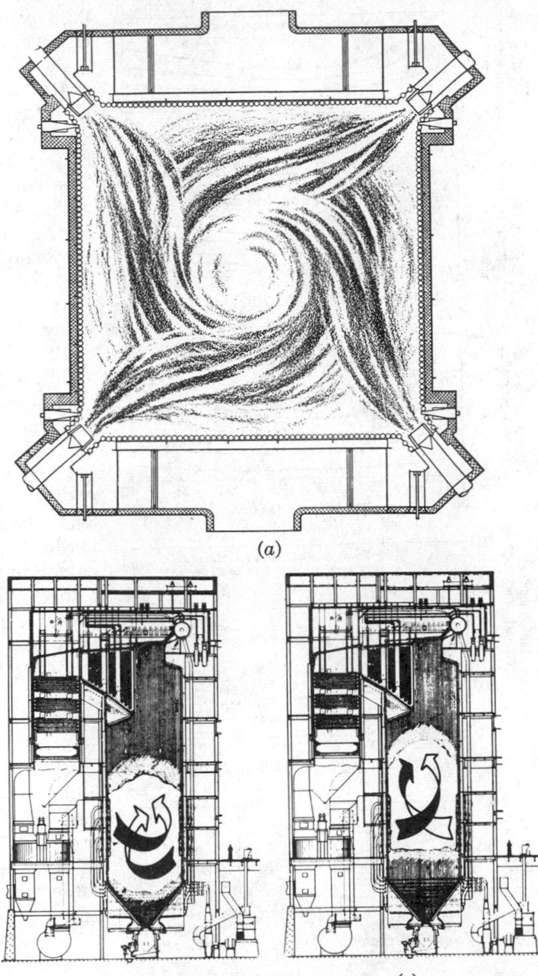

FIG. 19. Corner-fired tangential tilting burners for pulverized coal, oil, or gas; (a) plan section, (b) burners tilted down, (c) burners tilted up.

UNBURNED COMBUSTIBLE LOSS

The unburned combustible loss in the fly ash from **pulverized-coal firing** varies with the furnace-heat liberation, the type of furnace cooling, the use of slag-tap or dry-ash removal, the volatility and fineness of the coal, the excess air, and the type of burner (see Fig. 21). There is practically no combustible in the fluid slag from **slag-tap furnaces.** Although the hopper refuse from **dry-ash furnaces** usually is low in combustible, the combustible may be appreciable in some cases. The fly ash from **cyclone-furnace boilers** has a very low combustible content, varying from an equivalent

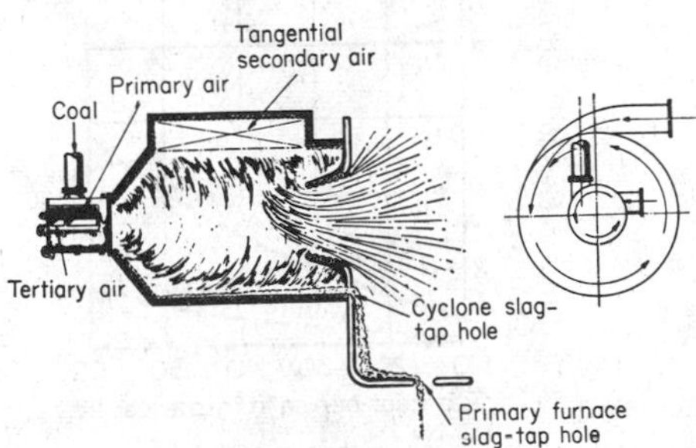

FIG. 20. Cyclone furnace.

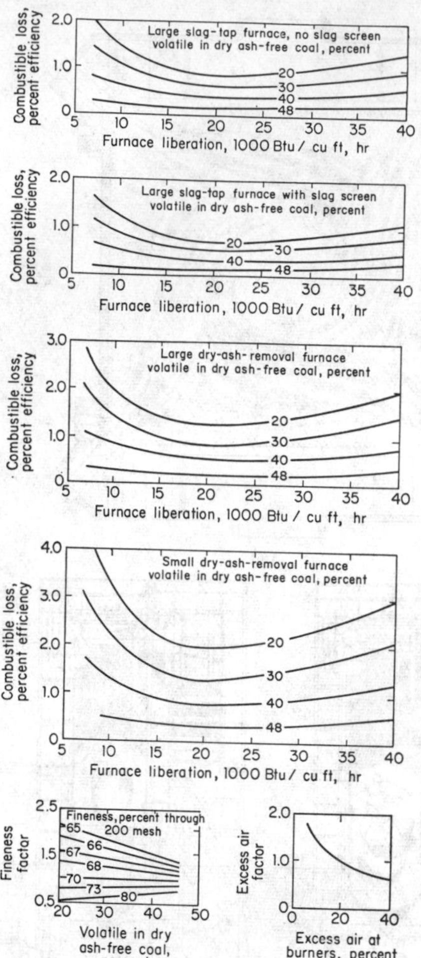

FIG. 21. Principal factors affecting combustible loss for pulverized-coal firing in various types of furnaces.

0.03 percent efficiency loss when burning Illinois coal to 0.15 percent for Ohio coal.

The combustible fly-ash losses of **chain-grate stokers** with **jet ignition** are shown in Fig. 22. Fly-ash combustible from **spreader stokers** varies widely with the rating, the size, and the type of coal burned. The combustible carry-over at high rates of firing is relatively large, but reinjection of the fly ash is common, and the loss in efficiency can be reduced as shown in Fig. 23.

Combustible losses are negligible when firing **oil.**

The combustible loss in the fly ash from solid fuels is determined by withdrawing a representative sample of fly ash and flue gas from the boiler outlet flue, or stack, at the same velocity in the sampling tip as the gas velocity in the flue (see ASME Test Code). The rates of flue-gas flow and fly-ash collection are measured, and the dust loading (in lb per 1,000 lb of flue gas) is calculated. The combustible in the fly ash also can be measured. Figure 24 can be used for rapid determination of the efficiency loss when the dust loading and the amount of combustible are known.

BOILER TYPES

The greater safety of **water-tube-type** boilers was recognized over 100 years ago, and these have generally superseded the fire-tube type except in special cases, such as some small package-boiler designs and some waste-heat boiler designs for medium- and low-pressure applications.

In the **package-boiler** field (5,000 to 200,000 lb of steam per hr), water-tube boilers are very popular, particularly in the larger sizes. These boilers are oil- or gas-fired and generally utilize two drums with

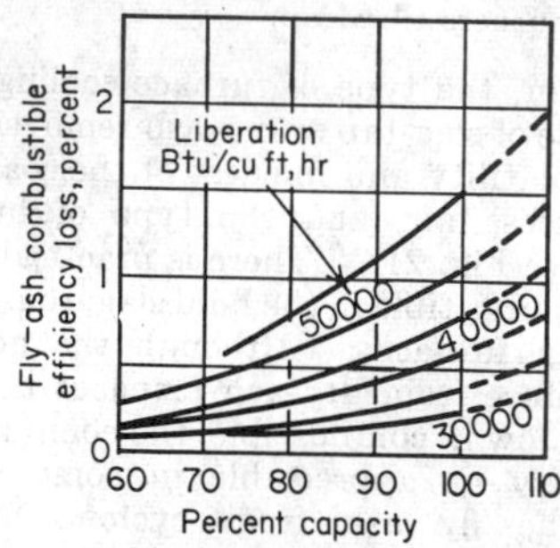

FIG. 22. Combustible efficiency loss, chain-grate stoker with jet ignition.

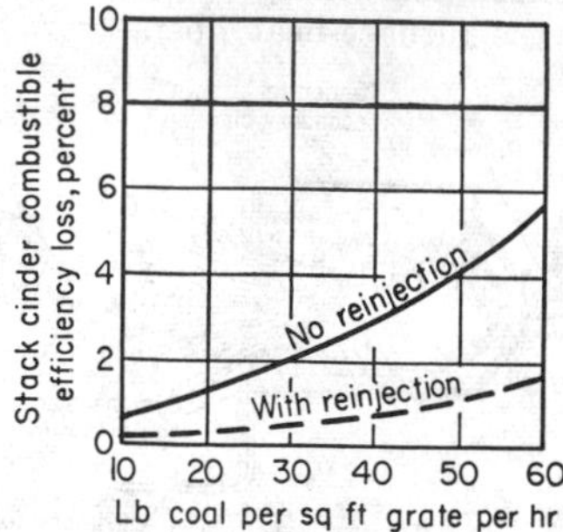

FIG. 23. Combustible efficiency loss, spreader stoker.

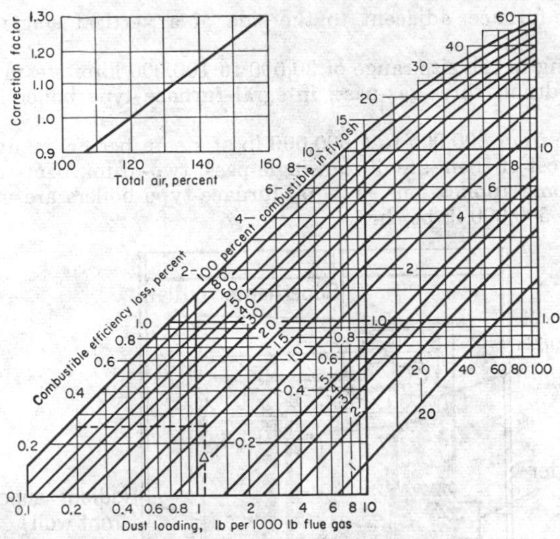

FIG. 24. Chart for determining combustible efficiency loss in fly ash. Heat loss in percent from combustible in fly ash =

$$\left[\frac{DL \times C/100 \times 14{,}600}{\dfrac{10{,}000{,}000}{(7.6 \times TA/100 + 0.9)} \times (DL \times C/100 \times 14{,}600)}\right] + 100$$

where DL = dust loading, lb per 1,000 lb flue gas; C = combustible in fly ash, percent; TA = total air, percent.

FIG. 25. Water-tube, package boiler; single-gas pass.

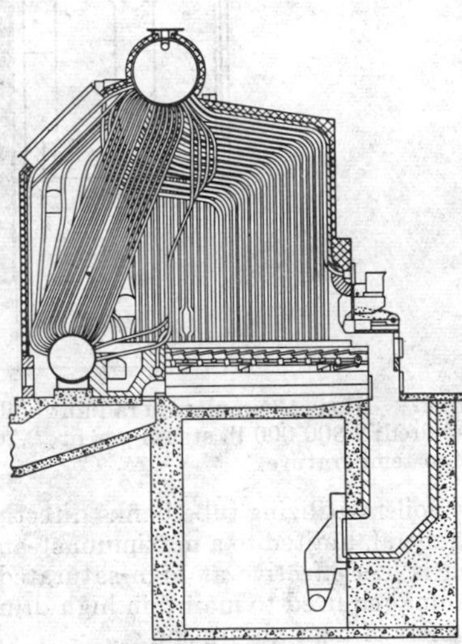

FIG. 26. Integral-furnace boiler; three-gas pass; reciprocating-grate, spreader-stoker-fired.

a water-cooled furnace adjacent to the side of a vertical single-pass tube bank (Fig. 25).

For coal firing in the size range of 30,000 to 100,000 lb of steam per hr, the field-assembled two-drum, three-gas-pass, **integral-furnace-type** boiler is generally used (Fig. 26).

In the range from 100,000 to 1,000,000 lb of steam per hr, many types of boilers are used, but most of them are of the single-pass, two-drum, bent-tube construction. However, for some applications, integral-furnace-type boilers are used for steaming capacities up to 500,000 lb per hr.

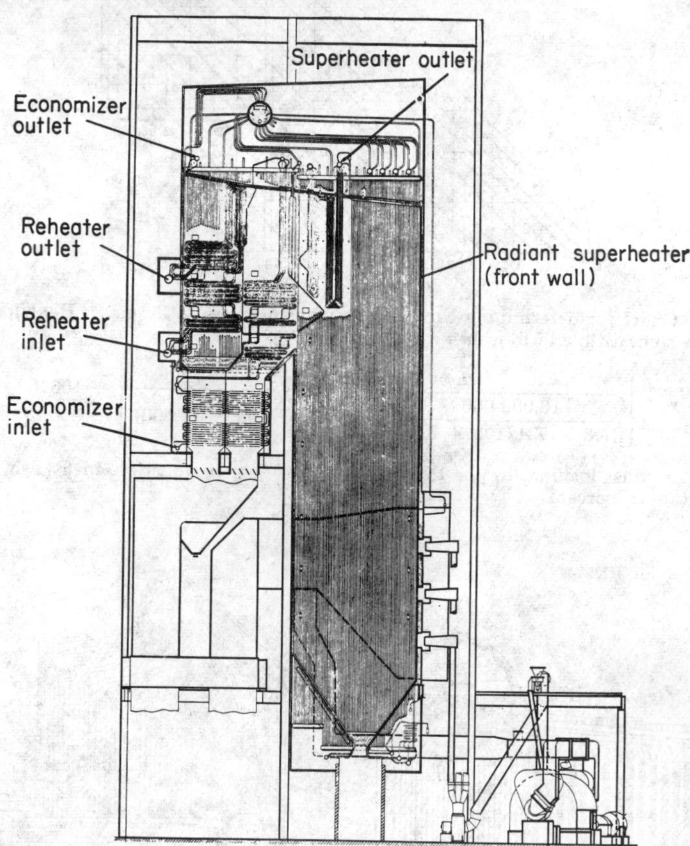

Fig. 27. Natural circulation radiant boiler with radiant superheater front wall; pulverized-coal-fired; 2,300,000 lb steam per hr; 2,200 psi; 1010 F steam temperature; 1010 F reheat-steam temperature.

Boilers utilizing tube banks directly connected to the steam and water drums are, in general, limited to a maximum steam pressure of 1,650 psi since the convection surface is less effective at high saturated-steam temperatures and since the wide tube spacing required to maintain high drum-ligament efficiency further reduces the effectiveness of heat absorption.

For the large, high-pressure, utility-type boilers, ranging from 300,000 to 8,000,000 lb of steam per hr, many designs are used, but they can all be classed as **radiant-type boilers.** In radiant boilers, little or no steam is generated by convection heat-absorbing surfaces since virtually all the steam is generated in the tubes forming the furnace enclosure walls by the heat radiated to these tubes from the flame and the hot combustion gases. Figure 27 illustrates a large radiant-boiler unit which also incorporates a radiant-type superheater in the front wall of the furnace. Figure 28 shows a **turbo-furnace** design utilizing opposed burners. In both of these designs, the primary superheater and the reheater are located in separate gas passes and the quantity of flue gas flowing through each pass can be varied to control steam temperature (see p. 9–32). The two boilers illustrated in Figs. 27 and 28 also are of the **natural-circulation** type. Figure 29 shows a tangentially fired, **supercritical-pressure, combined-circulation**

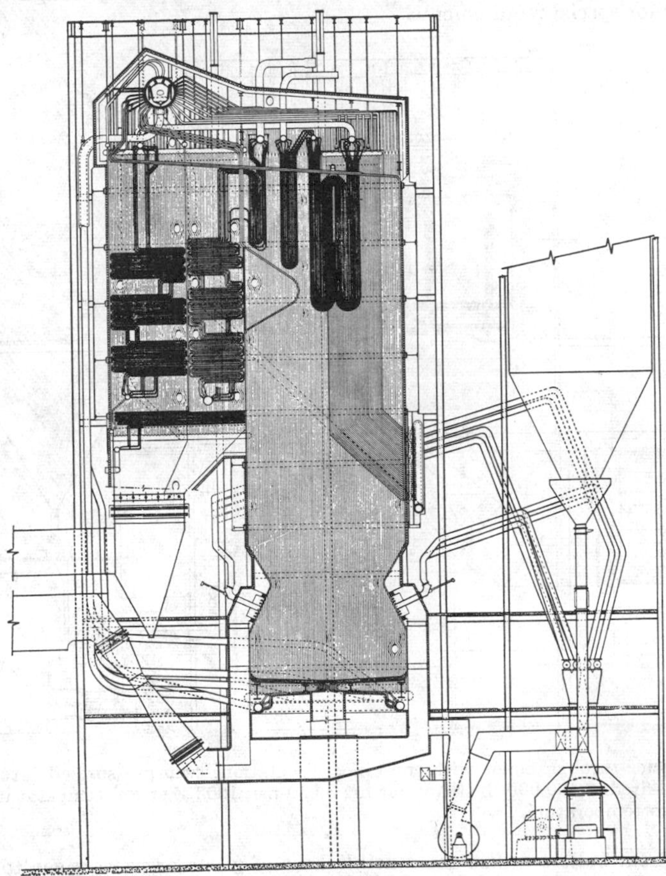

FIG. 28. Natural-circulation radiant boiler with pressurized turbo furnace; pulverized-coal-fired; 1,820,000 lb steam per hr; 2,000 psi; 1000 F steam temperature; 1000 F reheat-steam temperature.

type of boiler. The unit shown in Fig. 30 is known as a **universal pressure boiler** since it can be designed for operation at pressures either above or below the critical pressure (3,206 psi).

Due to circulation and steam-separation limits, **drum-type** natural- or controlled-circulation boilers are restricted to a pressure of about 2,600 psi at the superheater outlet. The once-through forced-flow-type boilers are not restricted to any pressure plateau by these limits.

In **once-through forced-flow boilers,** the water generally flows from the economizer to the furnace-wall tubes, then to the convection-pass enclosure tubes and the primary superheater. Usually, the transition to the vapor phase (if below critical pressure) begins in the furnace circuits and, depending upon the operating conditions and the design, is completed either in the convection pass enclosure or in the primary superheater. The steam from the primary superheater passes to the secondary (and possibly to a tertiary) superheater. One or more reheaters are provided to reheat the low-pressure steam.

In addition to boilers for the conversion of energy in the conventional fuels (coal, oil, and gas) to steam for power, heating, or process use, many designs have been developed for special requirements.

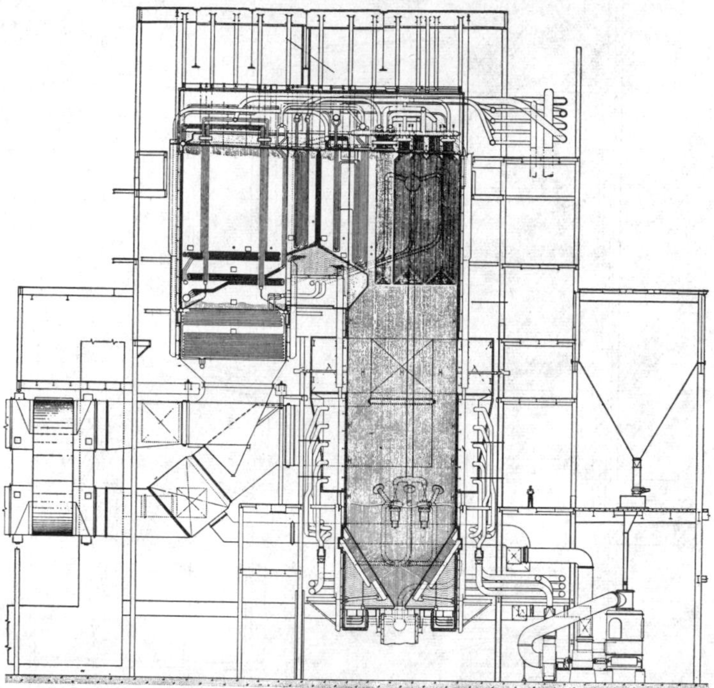

FIG. 29. Once-through boiler with combined circulation; twin pressurized furnaces; pulverized-coal-fired; 6,400,000 lb steam per hr; 3,650 psi; 1003 F steam temperature; 1003 F reheat-steam temperature.

Waste-heat boilers utilize the sensible heat of waste or process gas to generate steam. In the recovery of heat from exhaust gas, water-tube boilers, often in conjunction with economizers, are generally used, but fire-tube boilers are frequently used for cooling process gas when the containment of pressurized gas is a factor.

High-temperature-water boilers provide hot water, under pressure, for space heating of large areas. Water is circulated at pressures up to 450 psi through the generator and heating system. The water leaves the generator at subsaturated temperatures ranging up to 400 F. The boilers usually incorporate a water-cooled furnace and convection enclosure, with the convection surface arranged in sections similar to those of an economizer. Sizes range up to 60 million Btu per hr for package units, and field-erected units can be designed for much higher capacities.

Carbon monoxide boilers use as fuel the CO gas exhausted from oil-refinery fluid catalytic cracking units. Generally, a cylindrical furnace is used to contain the pressurized gas, and the CO burners are arranged tangentially to obtain long residence time for the gas in the furnace. The walls are water-cooled but are refractory-covered to promote ignition. Conventional-type gas and/or oil burners are provided for start-up, for continuous pilots, and for steam generation when the cracker is out of service.

Recovery boilers are designed specifically for the recovery of chemicals in the spent cooking liquors from kraft, sulphite, soda, and other papermaking processes. The liquor is fired in a water-cooled furnace, either in suspension or in a smelt bed on the

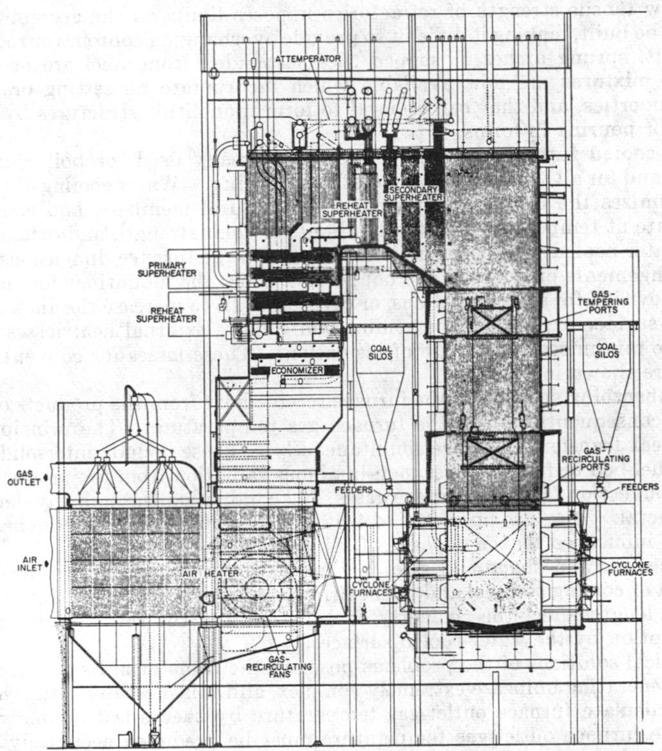

Fig. 30. Universal pressure boiler; pressurized cyclone furnace coal-fired; 8,000,000 lb steam per hr; 3,650 psi; 1003 F steam temperature; 1003 F reheat-steam temperature.

furnace floor. Depending upon the process, the chemicals are recovered from the smelt, or from the flue gas, in a form which permits economical conversion for reuse.

FURNACES

A furnace is an enclosed space provided for the combustion of fuel. The enclosure confines the products of combustion and must be capable of withstanding the high temperatures developed and the pressures used. Its dimensions and geometry must be adapted to the rate of heat release, to the type of fuel, and to the method of firing so as to promote complete burning of the combustible and suitable disposal of ash. In **water-cooled furnaces,** the heat absorbed materially affects the temperature of gases at the furnace outlet and contributes directly to the generation of steam.

Prior to 1925, most furnaces were constructed of **firebrick** (see pp. 6–206 to 6–215). As the capacities and the physical sizes of boiler units increased and as the suspension burning of pulverized coal was developed, limits were reached in the heights of refractory walls that could be made self-supporting at high temperatures. Limits also were reached due to the inability of refractories to resist the fluxing action of molten fuel ash.

These limits can be extended by cooling the brickwork with air flowing through channels in the structure or by sectionalizing the wall into panels and transferring the load to external air-cooled steel or cast-iron supporting members. The heat absorbed can be recovered by using the cooling air for combustion, and the low rate of heat transfer through the refractory helps to maintain high furnace temperature, thus accelerating ignition and the burning of the fuel.

The low tensile strength of refractories imposes limits on the geometrical shapes which can be built, making it difficult to provide overhanging contours or roof closures. As a result, sprung arches or shaped tiles suspended from steel are used. Many **refractory mixtures** are now available which incorporate air-setting or hydraulic-setting properties, and they can be used to form monolithic structures by ramming, guniting, or pouring in forms.

Water-cooled furnaces are now almost universally used for boiler units of all capacities and for all types of fuel and methods of firing. Water cooling of the furnace walls minimizes the transfer of heat to the structural members, and consequently, they operate at temperatures within the limits of their strength and oxidation resistance. Water-cooled tube constructions facilitate large furnace dimensions and optimum arrangements of the roof, the hopper, the arch, the mountings for the burners, and the provision for screens, platens, or division walls to increase the amount of heat-absorbing surface exposed in the combustion zone. External heat losses are small and can be minimized by the use of insulation. These losses for conventional-type furnaces are shown in Fig. 43.

Heat-absorbing surfaces in the furnace receive heat from the products of combustion and, consequently, lower the furnace gas temperature. The principal mechanisms of heat transfer take place simultaneously. These include intersolid radiation from the fuel bed or fuel particles, non-luminous radiation from the products of combustion, convection from the furnace gases, and conduction through any deposits and the tube metal. (See also pp. 4–121 to 4–123.) The absorption effectiveness of these surfaces is influenced by the deposits of ash or slag.

Furnaces vary in **shape** and **size,** in the location and spacing of burners, in the disposition of cooling surface, and in the arrangement of arches and hoppers. Flame shape and length affect the geometry of radiation and the rate and distribution of heat absorption by the water-cooled surfaces.

Analytical solutions of the problems posed in the **transfer of heat** in the furnaces of steam-generating units are extremely complex, and it is most difficult, if not impossible, to calculate furnace outlet-gas temperature by theoretical methods. Nevertheless, the furnace outlet-gas temperature must be predicted accurately since this temperature determines the design of the remainder of the unit, particularly that of the superheater. Calculations must, therefore, be based upon test results supplemented by data accumulated from operating experience and by judgments predicated

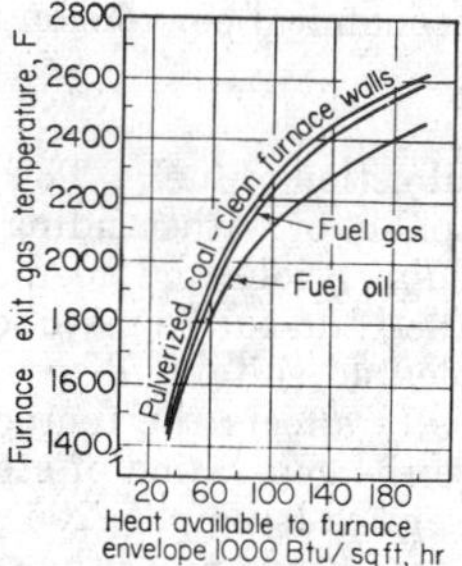

FIG. 31. Approximate gas temperature at water-cooled furnace outlet with different fuels.

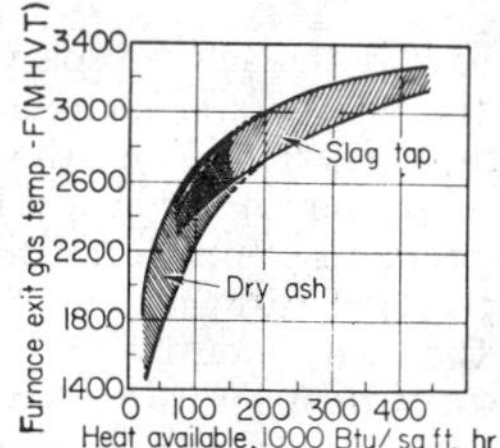

FIG. 32. General range of furnace exit-gas temperature, pulverized-coal firing ($MHVT$ = multiple-shield high-velocity thermocouple).

upon knowledge of the principles of heat transfer and the characteristics of fuels and slags.

The curves of Figs. 31 and 32 show typical gas temperatures at the furnace outlet for the three common fuels—coal, oil, and gas. Temperatures vary considerably with coal firing because of the insulating effect of ash and slag deposits on the heat-absorb-

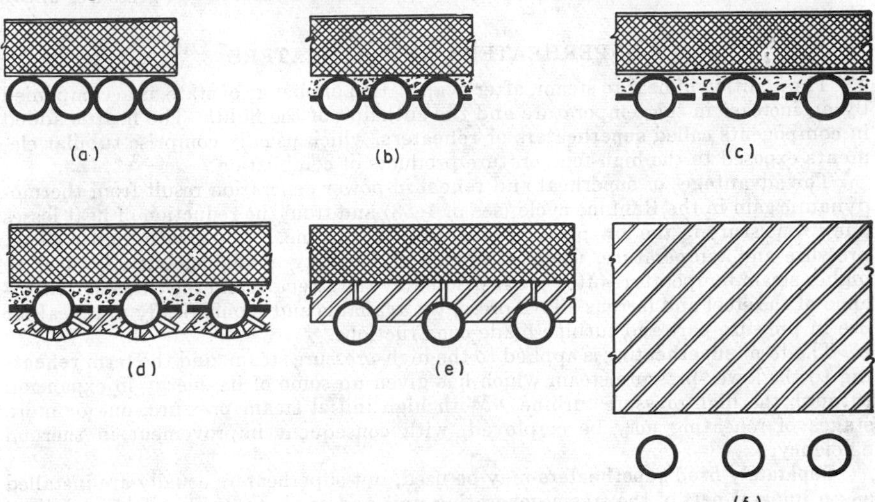

Fig. 33. Water-cooled furnace-wall construction types. (*a*) Tangent-tube wall; (*b*) welded membrane panel wall; (*c*) flat studs welded to sides of tubes; (*d*) full stud wall, refractory covered; (*e*) tube and tile wall; (*f*) tubes spaced from refractory wall.

ing surfaces. Since the amount of surface is the major factor in over-all furnace heat absorption, the **heat released and available** for absorption per hr per sq ft of effective surface is a satisfactory basis for correlation. The heat available is the sum of the calorific heat content of the fuel fired and the sensible heat of the combustion air, less the sum of the unavailable heat due to any unburned portion of the fuel and the latent heat of the water vapor formed from the moisture in the fuel and the combustion of hydrogen.

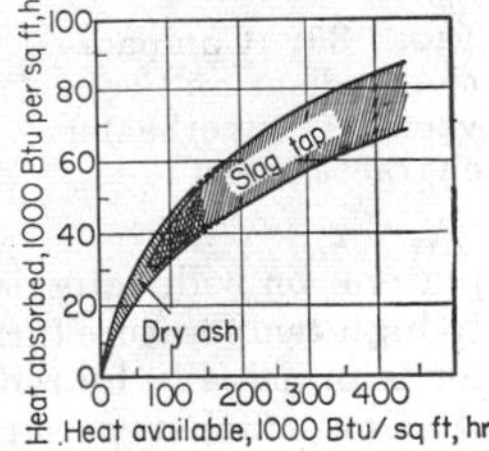

Fig. 34. General range of average heat absorption rate in water-cooled pulverized-coal-fired furnaces.

Furnace-wall tubes are pitched on close centers to obtain maximum heat absorption and to facilitate ease of ash removal. The arrangement may take the form of the so-called **tangent-tube** construction (Fig. 33), wherein the adjacent tubes are almost touching, with only a small clearance provided for erection purposes. However, many units now use **membrane tube walls,** in which a steel bar or membrane is welded between adjacent tubes. This construction facilitates the fabrication of water-cooled walls in large shop-assembled tube panels. Less effective cooling is obtained at a lower cost by placing the tubes on wider spacing and using **extended metal surface** in the form of flat studs, welded to the tubes. If even less cooling is desired, the tube spacing can be increased and refractory can be installed between or behind the tubes to form the wall enclosure.

Additional furnace cooling, in the form of tubular **platens, division walls,** or **wide-spaced screens** often is used, and in high-heat input zones, the tubes may be protected by refractory coverings anchored to the tubes by studs. Peak heat-absorption rates for furnace-wall tubes in the combustion zone may, in some designs, approximate 200,000 Btu per hr per sq ft of projected surface, but the average heat-absorption rate for the furnace is considerably lower (Fig. 34).

Furnace walls must be adequately supported, with provision for **thermal expansion** and with reinforcing **buckstays** to withstand the lateral forces caused by the difference between the furnace pressure and the surrounding atmosphere. The furnace enclosure walls must prevent air infiltration when the furnace is operated under suction, and they must prevent gas leakage when the furnace is operated at pressures above atmospheric.

SUPERHEATERS AND REHEATERS

The addition of heat to steam, after evaporation or change of state, is accompanied by an increase in the temperature and the enthalpy of the fluid. The heat is added in components called **superheaters** or **reheaters,** which usually comprise tubular elements exposed to the high-temperature products of combustion.

The advantages of **superheat** and **reheat** in power generation result from thermodynamic gain in the Rankine cycle (see p. 4–58) and from the reduction of heat losses due to moisture in the low-pressure stages of the turbine. Thus, with higher steam pressure and temperature, there is more useful energy available, but advances to higher steam temperature often are restricted by the strength and the oxidation resistance of the steel and ferrous alloys presently available and economically practical for use in pressure-part and turbine-blade constructions.

The term **superheating** is applied to the high-pressure steam, and the term **reheating** to the lower-pressure steam which has given up some of its energy in expansion through the high-pressure turbine. With high initial steam pressure, one or more stages of reheating may be employed, with consequent improvement in thermal efficiency.

Separately fired superheaters may be used, but superheaters usually are installed as an **integral part** of the steam-generating unit and are broadly classified as **radiant** or **convection** types, depending upon the predominant method of heat transfer to the heat-absorbing surfaces.

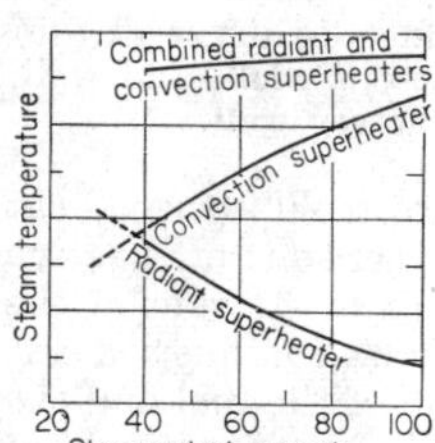

Fig. 35. Comparative radiant and convection superheater characteristics.

The quantity of heat absorbed and the superheat attained are dependent upon the size, location, and arrangement of the heat-absorbing surfaces; the temperature differentials between the gas, the tube metal, and the steam; and the heat-transfer coefficients, which are affected by the gas and steam flow rates and the surface cleanliness. **Steam-temperature characteristics** of radiant and convection superheaters are shown in Fig. 35, which also indicates the effect of combining these types to produce a more uniform steam temperature over a wide operating range.

Superheaters of the predominantly **radiant** type usually are arranged for direct exposure to the furnace gases and, in some designs, form a part of the furnace enclosure, while in other designs, the surface is arranged in the form of loops or

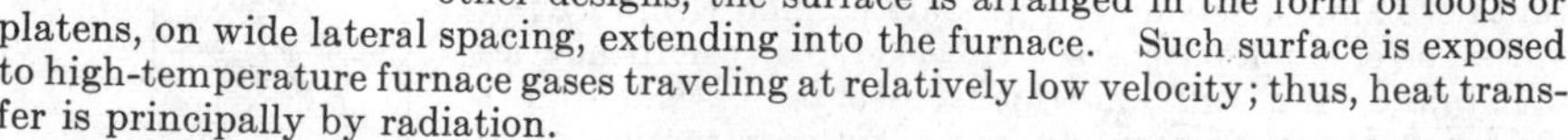

platens, on wide lateral spacing, extending into the furnace. Such surface is exposed to high-temperature furnace gases traveling at relatively low velocity; thus, heat transfer is principally by radiation.

Convection-type superheaters are installed beyond the furnace exit in zones where the gas temperatures are generally much lower than those in the zones where radiant-type superheaters are used. The tubes are usually arranged in the form of parallel elements on close lateral spacing and in tube banks extending partially or completely across the width of the gas stream, with the gas flowing through the relatively narrow spaces between the tubes. High rates of gas flow and, thus, high convection heat-transfer rates are maintained at the expense of gas-pressure drop through the tube bank.

Characteristics of both radiant- and convection-type superheaters can be obtained from superheaters which are shielded from the furnace combustion zone by arches or wide-spaced screens of generating tubes but which receive heat by radiation from the high-temperature gases in the cavity or intertube spaces and also by convection due to the relatively high rate of gas flow through the bank.

Superheaters may utilize tubes arranged in the form of **hairpin loops** connected, in parallel, to inlet and outlet headers, or they may be of the **continuous-tube** type, wherein each element has a number of tube loops in series between the inlet and outlet headers. The latter arrangement permits the use of large tube banks, thus increasing the amount of heat-absorbing surface which can be installed and providing economy of space and reduction of cost. Either type may be designed for the **drainage** of the condensate which forms within the tubes during outages of the unit, or they may be in **pendent** arrangements which are not drainable but usually have simpler and better supports. **Non-drainable** superheaters require additional care during start-up so as to remove the condensate by evaporation; thus, the gas temperature entering the superheater must be kept below 1000 F to prevent overheating of the tube metal before steam flow is established in all elements of the tube bank.

The heat transferred from high-temperature gases by radiation and convection is conducted through the metal tube wall and imparted by convection to the high-velocity steam in the tubes. The removal of heat by the steam is necessary to keep the tube metals within a safe temperature range consistent with the limits of oxidation and the creep or rupture strength of the materials (see Sec. 5). Allowable **design stresses** for various steels and alloys, as established by the ASME Code, are shown in Table 3. (See also Sec. 6.) The practical **use limit** for each material also is indicated. For economic reasons, it is customary to use low-carbon steel in the steam inlet sections of the superheater and progressively higher-limit, more costly alloys as the metal temperatures increase.

The **rate of steam flow** through the superheater tubes must be sufficiently high to keep the metal temperatures within a safe operating range and to ensure good distribution of flow through all the elements connected in parallel circuits. This can be accomplished in hairpin-tube-type superheaters by the use of diaphragmed or sectionalized headers to produce multiple passes for the steam flow through the tube bank. Excessive steam-flow rates, while providing lower tube-metal temperatures, result in high **pressure drop,** with consequent loss of thermodynamic efficiency and higher initial cost of equipment. As a general guide, the range of the steam-flow rates required for various steam and gas temperature conditions is shown in Table 4.

Table 3. Superheater and Reheater Tubes—Maximum Allowable Design Stresses, psi

Material	ASME spec No. and type	Temperature, deg F								
		900	950	1000	1050	1100	1150	1200	1350	1500
Carbon steel..	SA210	5,000	3,000							
Carbon moly..	SA209, T1a	12,500	8,500							
Croloy 1¼ ...	SA213, T11	13,100	11,000	6,550	4,050					
Croloy 2¼....	SA213, T22	......	11,000	7,800	5,800	4,200				
Croloy 5.....	SA213, T5	......	......	.....	5,200	3,300	2,200			
Croloy 9.....	SA213, T9	......	......	.....	5,500	3,300	2,200	1,500		
Croloy 304H..	SA213, TP304H	......	......	.....	10,000	7,500	5,750	4,500	1,500	750
Croloy 321H..	SA213, TP321H	......	......	.....	13,100	10,300	7,600	5,000	1,500	750

Table 4. Range of Steam-mass-flow Values for Convection Superheaters

Temperature, deg F		Steam mass flow, lb per hr per sq ft flow area
Steam	Gas	
Less than 750	1200	75,000–150,000
700–800	1600	250,000–350,000
800–900	2400	400,000–500,000
900–1000	2400	500,000–600,000
1000–1100	2400	700,000 and higher

The **spacing** of the tubular elements in the tube bank and, consequently, the rate of gas flow and convection heat transfer are governed primarily by **draft-loss** considerations and the **fouling** and **erosive** characteristics of fuel ash carried in the gas stream. With clean gases, or in the low-temperature zones of coal-fired units, a gas-flow rate of about 6,000 lb per hr per sq ft of free-flow area is generally within economic limits. In the higher-gas-temperature zones, 1600 to 2300 F, the adherence and the accumulation of ash deposits can reduce the gas-flow area and, in some cases, may completely bridge the space between tubes. Thus, as gas temperature is increased, it is customary to increase the tube spacings in the tube banks to avoid excessive draft loss and to facilitate ash removal. The tube spacings also are dependent upon the type of fuel fired. As tube spacings increase, rates of gas mass flow decrease, although the gas velocities may remain fairly constant due to the higher gas temperatures in the wider-spaced tube zones.

ECONOMIZERS

Economizers remove heat from the moderately low-temperature flue gases after the gases leave the steam-generating and superheating sections of the unit. The name, accepted through common usage, is indicative of savings in the fuel required. Economizers are, in effect, feedwater heaters, receiving water from the boiler feed pumps and delivering it at a higher temperature to the steam generator. Economizers are used instead of additional steam-generating surface since the feedwater, and consequently the heat-receiving surface, is at a temperature below the saturated-steam temperature and thus the gases can be cooled to lower temperature levels for greater heat recovery.

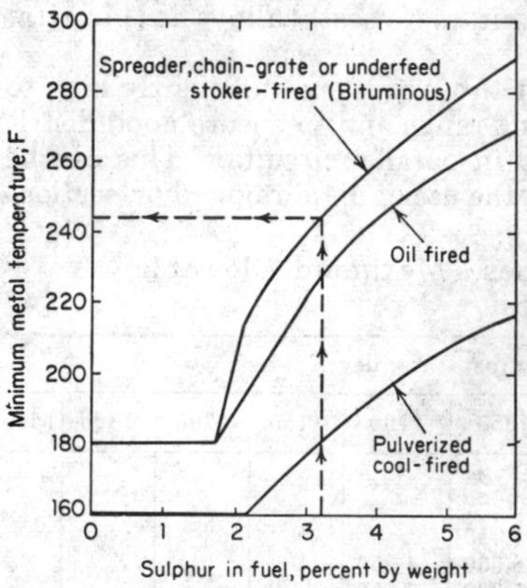

FIG. 36. Limiting metal temperatures to avoid external corrosion in economizers or air heaters when burning coal, fuel oil (grades 1 to 6), and natural gas containing sulfur. For anthracite coal or natural gas without sulfur, minimum metal temperature is 160 F. To avoid internal corrosion of economizer tubes, the temperature of the feedwater entering should not be less than 212 F.

An economizer is a forced-flow, once-through, convection heat-transfer device, usually consisting of steel tubes, to which feedwater is supplied at a pressure above that in the steam-generating section and at a rate corresponding to the steam output of the unit. In early practice, economizers often were installed to serve more than one boiler, but it is now customary to employ individual economizers coordinated with the generating section and placed within the setting of the unit.

Economizers are usually classed as **horizontal-** or **vertical-tube types,** according to geometrical arrangement; as **longitudinal** or **crossflow,** depending upon the direction of gas flow with respect to the tubes; as **parallel** or **counterflow,** with respect to the relative direction of gas and water flow; as **steaming** or **nonsteaming,** depending on the thermal performance; as **return-bend** or **continuous-tube,** depending upon the details of design; and as **plain-tube** or **extended-surface,** according to the type of heat-absorbing surface. Further, **staggered** or **in-line** tube arrangements can be used; the arrangement affects the gas flow through the tube bank, the draft loss, the heat-transfer characteristics, and the ease of cleaning.

The **size** of an economizer is governed by economic considerations involving the cost of fuel, the comparative cost and thermal performance of alternate steam-generating or air-heater surface, the feedwater temperature, and the desired exit-gas temperature. In many cases, it is more economical to use both an economizer and an air heater.

The temperature of the economizer tube metal is very close to that of the water flowing within the tubes, and thus, with low feedwater temperatures, condensation and **external corrosion** are encountered at those locations where the tube-metal temperature is below that of the acid or water dew point of the gas (see Fig. 36). **Internal corrosion** and **pitting** also may be experienced if the feedwater contains more than 0.007 ppm of dissolved oxygen. Therefore, it is imperative to maintain feedwater temperatures above the dew-point temperature of the gas and to provide suitable deaeration of the feedwater for the removal of oxygen (see p. 9-46).

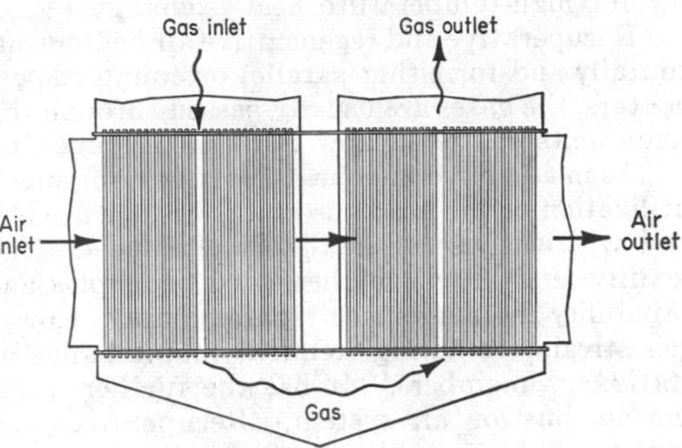

FIG. 37. Tubular air heater, two-gas-pass, single-air-pass.

AIR HEATERS

Air heaters, like economizers, remove heat from the relatively low-temperature flue gases. Since the temperature of the inlet air is less than that of the water to the economizer, it is possible to reduce further the temperature of flue gas before it is discharged to the stack.

The heat recovered from the gas is recycled to the furnace by the combustion air and, added to the thermal energy released from the fuel, is made available for absorption by the steam-generating unit, with a resultant gain in over-all thermal efficiency. Additional benefits accrue from the use of preheated combustion air through accelerated ignition and more rapid burning of the fuel.

Air heaters are usually classed as **recuperative** or **regenerative types**. Both types depend upon the convection transfer of heat from the gas stream to a metal or other

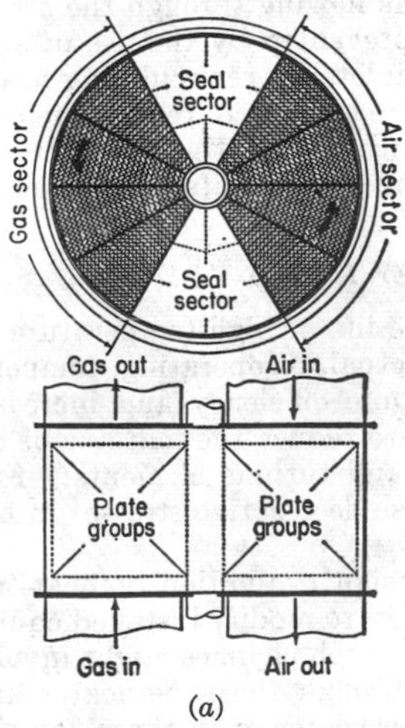

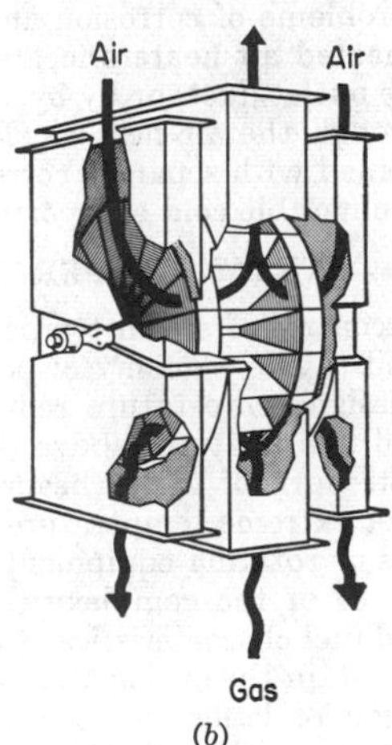

FIG. 38. Two designs of rotary regenerative air heaters.

solid surface and the convection transfer of heat from this surface to the air. In the recuperative type, exemplified by **tubular**- or **plate**-type heaters (Fig. 37), the metal parts are stationary and form a separating boundary between the heating and cooling fluids, with the heat passing by conduction through the metal wall. In the **rotary** regenerative type, illustrated in Fig. 38, the heat-transferring members are moved alternately through the gas and air streams, undergoing successive heating and cooling cycles and transferring heat by the thermal storage capacity of the members. Other regenerative-type air heaters have stationary elements, with the alternate flow of gas and air controlled by rotating inlet and outlet connections or by dampers, as in the refractory stoves of blast furnaces; or they may employ a flow of solid particles which are alternately heated and cooled, as in the pebble heaters used in the petroleum industry for high-temperature heat exchange.

Recuperative and regenerative air heaters may be arranged either **vertically** or **horizontally** and for either **parallel** or **counterflow** of the gas and air. With tubular air heaters, the gases are usually passed through the tubes to facilitate cleaning, although some units utilize air flow through the tubes, particularly in marine installations.

As in all convection heat-transfer equipment, better heat-transfer rates and better utilization of the heat-absorbing surface are obtained with a counterflow of the gases and with the use of small flow channels. The rotary regenerative-type air heater readily lends itself to these two principles and offers relatively large performance capability in small space requirements. However, it permits leakage of air into the gas stream, requiring frequent maintenance of the seals between the moving and stationary members. It has the further disadvantage of transporting fly ash into the combustion air system. Recuperative air heaters of the tubular type do not encounter these problems.

Since the products of combustion from most fuels contain a high percentage of water vapor, **condensation** will occur in the air heater if the exposed metal surfaces are cooled below the gas dew point. Minute concentrations of sulphur trioxide in the gases, originating from the combustion of sulphur and varying with the sulphur content of the fuel and the method of firing, combine with the water vapor to form sulphuric acid, which may condense on the metal surfaces at **acid-dew-point** temperatures as high as 250 to 300 F, well above the water dew point (Huge and Piotter, *Trans. ASME*, 1955). This condensation leads to **corrosion** and/or **plugging** of the gas-flow area. It is most likely to occur in the winter season, when the entering-air temperature is lowest, and at low operating loads or in localized sections at the cold-air inlet if there is poor distribution of the air or gas flowing through the air heater. These problems of corrosion and pluggage can be prevented by the use of auxiliary **steam-heated air heaters** located ahead of the air inlet, by **recirculating** heated air from the outlet duct, or by **bypassing** a portion of the cold air to reduce the air-mass flow through the air heater. Both recuperative and regenerative air heaters often are designed with separate **corrosion sections,** arranged to facilitate the replacement of the vulnerable cold-end portions.

STEAM TEMPERATURE, ADJUSTMENT AND CONTROL

The control of steam temperature is vital to the life of high-temperature equipment and to the economy of power generation. Actual, or operating, temperatures below design temperature reduce the thermodynamic efficiency and increase fuel cost, and temperatures above the design temperature reduce the margins of reserve in the strength of tubes, headers, piping, valves, and turbine elements. Further, sudden or extreme temperature variations may cause destructive stresses in tubular members or rotating equipment.

Because of the complexities involved in the design evaluation of heat-transfer rates and fuel characteristics, it is sometimes necessary to modify installed equipment so as to obtain the anticipated steam temperature. Such changes might involve the installation of baffles for the distribution of gas through the superheater and the removal or addition of tubular elements in the superheater or in those components preceding the superheater which affect the temperature of the gas to the superheater.

It is desirable, and usually essential, to provide some **means of controlling** steam temperature so as to compensate for the variations in load and surface-cleanliness conditions encountered during normal operation. These include (1) damper control of the gases to the superheater and the reheater; (2) recirculation of low-temperature flue gas to the furnace to change the relative amounts of heat absorbed in the furnace and in the superheater and/or reheater; (3) selective use of burners at different elevations in the furnace, or the use of tilting burners, to change the location of the combustion zone with respect to furnace heat-absorbing surface; (4) attemperation, or controlled cooling, of the steam at superheater inlet, at superheater outlet, or between the primary and secondary stages of the superheater; (5) control of the firing rate in divided furnaces; (6) control of the firing rate relative to the pumping rate in forced-flow once-through boilers.

The **speed of response** differs for the various methods, the control of steam temperature by gas bypass or flame position being slower than that by spray-water attemperation. Operating controls for these methods can be arranged for **manual, automatic,** or **combination** adjustment; the use of more than one method often permits holding the steam temperature constant over a wider range of boiler load (Fig. 39).

The **attemperation** of superheated steam by direct-contact water spray (Fig. 40) results in an equivalent increase in high-pressure steam generation without thermal loss. It requires the use of essentially pure water, such as condensate, to avoid imparting impurities to the steam. **Submerged-type attemperators,** when used, are generally restricted to relatively low-pressure units operating with steam temperatures of 850 F or less. Usually, attemperators are not used for the control of reheat-steam temperature since their use reduces the over-all cycle efficiency. They are, however, often installed for the emergency control of reheat-steam temperature.

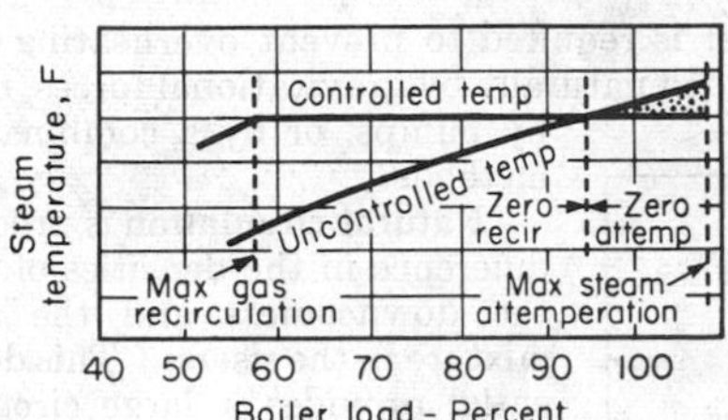

FIG. 39. Steam temperature control by flue-gas recirculation and attemperation.

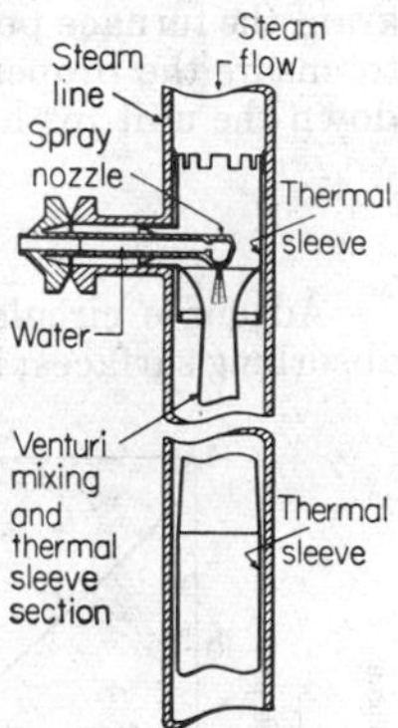

FIG. 40. Spray-type direct-contact attemperator.

Ash and **slag deposits** on superheater and reheater surfaces reduce heat transfer and tend to lower steam temperature. Similar deposits on the furnace walls and steam-generating surface ahead of the superheater and/or reheater also reduce heat transfer to those surfaces, resulting in higher-temperature gas to the superheater and reheater and increased steam temperature. Thus, the control of surface cleanliness is an important factor in the control of steam temperature.

Increased **excess air** results in higher steam temperature due to the reduction in furnace radiant-heat absorption, the greater amount of gas, and the increased convection heat transfer in the superheater and reheater. Operation with **feedwater temperature** below that anticipated also results in increased steam temperature due to the increased firing rate required to maintain steam generation.

OPERATING CONTROLS

(See also Sec. 16)

The need for operating instruments and manual or automatic controls varies with the size and type of equipment, the method of firing, and the proficiency of the operating personnel. For **safe operation** and **efficient performance,** information is required relative to the (1) water level in the boiler drum; (2) burner performance; (3) pressures of the steam and the feedwater; (4) temperatures of the superheated and reheated steam; (5) drafts or pressures of the gas and air entering and leaving principal components; (6) feedwater and boiler-water chemical conditions and particle carry-over; (7) operation of feed pumps, fans, and fuel-burning and fuel-preparation equipment; (8) relationship of the actual combustion air passing through the furnace to that theoretically required for the fuel fired, as indicated by flue-gas analyses; (9) temperatures of the water, gas, fuel, and air entering and leaving the principal component parts of the unit; (10) feedwater, steam, fuel, and air flows.

Control of the various functions to maintain the desired operating conditions may be accomplished on small-capacity boilers by the **manual adjustment** of valves, dampers, and motor speeds, although most of the oil- and gas-fired package-type boilers are equipped with **automatic controls** to purge the furnace, to start and stop the burner, and to maintain the required steam pressure and water level. The operational requirements of large industrial and utility boilers dictate the use of automatic controls for the major variables, such as feedwater flow, firing rate, and steam temperature. The type of boiler, and its components, establishes the basic mode of control, and **analog controls** of either the **pneumatic** or the **electric** type are available.

Sequence controls often are applied to the start-up of utility boilers. These program the furnace purge, burner light-off, and burner control. **Interlocks** are essential to ensure the proper starting and firing sequence and to alarm or automatically shut down the unit in the event of the failure of essential auxiliaries.

BOILER CIRCULATION

Adequate circulation in a boiler is required to prevent overheating of the heat-absorbing surfaces; it may be provided naturally by gravitational forces, mechanically by pumps, or by a combination of both methods.

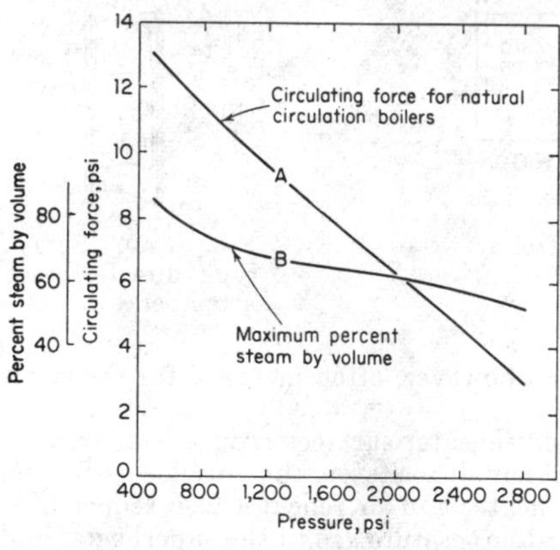

Fig. 41. Maximum percent steam by volume and circulating force for natural circulation boilers.

Natural circulation is produced by the difference in the densities of the water in the downcomers and the steam-water mixture in the risers. This density differential provides a large circulating force (curve *A*, Fig. 41). The downcomers and risers are so designed that the friction through the system balances the circulating force at the desired total circulating flow.

In **dual-circulation** units, the feedwater enters the first of two steam drums, which supplies only the downcomers to the furnace walls. Thus, the concentration of solids is lowest in the furnace walls where the heat input is greatest. From the first steam drum, the partly concentrated water flows to the second steam drum, which supplies water to those heating surfaces subjected to lower rates of heat input and where higher concentration can be used.

The **forced-recirculation** type of boiler requires a pump but uses a steam drum similar to that used with natural-circulation boilers. The water supply to the furnace walls and the boiler surface flows from this drum to a circulating pump, which supplies the pressure necessary to force it through the water-steam–mixture circuits and then back to the drum, where the steam and water are separated. The quantity of water pumped usually is four to six times the amount of steam evaporated, as shown in Fig. 42. The recirculating pump produces a differential pressure of 30 to 40 psi, and the power required is equivalent to about 0.5 percent of the heat input to the boiler. Resistor orifices are required at the entrance to each tube, or circuit, to control flow distribution.

In this design, the velocities, or flows, are independent of boiler rating, thus facilitating the use of smaller connecting piping and, sometimes, smaller furnace-wall tubing than is used in natural-circulation-type units. Both drum-type natural-circulation and forced-recirculation boilers maintain essentially saturated-steam temperatures in all parts of the steam-evaporating sections, and they can be used for drum pressures ranging up to approximately 2,800 psi.

In natural-circulation, dual-circulation, and forced-recirculation boilers, it is essential that the inside surfaces be continually wetted by the water phase of the two-phase mixture to prevent the overheating of these heat-absorbing surfaces. Operating experience indicates that the maximum **percentage of steam by volume** is a significant design criterion, and a typical limit curve is shown in Fig. 41, curve *B*.

As boiler output is increased, the percentage of steam by volume and the **circulating force** also increase. However, friction, or resistance to flow, increases at a faster rate, and thus, beyond a certain heat input, the rate of circulation tends to level off, as shown in Fig. 42. At partial loads, circulation is more than adequate since the circulating flow is always greater than that determined by a straight-line relationship between circulating flow and steam output.

In **forced-flow once-through boilers,** the water from the feed supply is pumped to the inlet of the heat-absorbing circuits. Evaporation, or change of state, takes place along the length of the circuit; when evaporation is completed, the steam is super-heated. These units do not require steam or water drums and, in most cases, use small-diameter tubes. The boilers can be started rapidly due to the elimination of the drums and the reduced weight of metal. The water flow through the unit is the same as the steam output (Fig. 42), and fluid velocities greater than those needed for natural-circulation or forced-recirculation units must be used at full load so as to maintain adequate velocities at the low loads and satisfactory tube-metal temperatures at all loads.

For operation at or above the **critical steam pressure,** 3,206 psi, the transition from liquid to vapor is dependent upon temperature and takes place without a change in density. Thus, separation of steam and water is impossible, and forced-flow once-through boilers must be used.

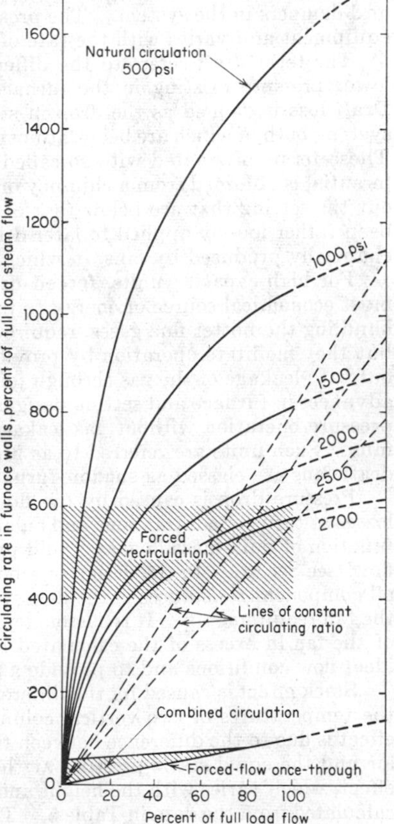

FIG. 42. Circulating flow for natural and forced-circulation systems.

To maintain adequate water velocities in the furnace-wall tubes, forced-flow once-through boilers must be operated above a specified minimum flow—usually one-quarter to one-third of full-load flow. However, the turbogenerator can be operated at any load by the use of a **bypass system** to divert the excess flow to a flash tank for heat recovery. The bypass system also can be used as a pressure-relieving system, as the source of low-pressure steam to the turbine during start-up, and as a means of controlling steam temperature to the turbine during hot restarts.

Combined circulation utilizes forced once-through flow with flow recirculation in the furnace walls to provide satisfactory water velocities during start-up and low-load operations. In this design, some of the water at the exit of the furnace circuits is mixed with the incoming feedwater, flows to and through a circulating pump, and then passes to the furnace-wall inlet headers. The use of combined circulation increases the water velocities in the furnace tubes at low loads, and since recirculation is not used at the higher loads, there is no increase in velocity or in the resistance to flow at these higher loads.

FLOW OF GAS THROUGH BOILER UNIT

For the combustion of fuel and the transfer of heat to the heat-absorbing surfaces, it is necessary to maintain pressure differentials to overcome the **flow resistance** imposed by such elements as burning equipment, tube banks, direction turns, and flues and dampers in the system. The pressure drop depends upon the arrangement of the equipment and varies with the rate of flow and the temperature of the fluid.

The term **draft** refers to the difference between atmospheric pressure and some lower pressure existing in the furnace or gas passages of a steam-generating unit. **Draft loss** is defined as the drop in static pressure of a gas between two points in a system, both of which are below atmospheric pressure; it is caused by resistance to flow. These terms originated with so-called **natural-draft** units, in which the pressure differential is obtained from a chimney or stack which produces static pressures throughout the setting that are below that of the atmosphere (see p. 9–41). The terms have been rather loosely applied to later designs using **induced draft** and **forced draft,** mechanically produced by fans, in which pressures may be above atmospheric pressure.

For high-capacity units, **forced-draft fans,** handling cold, clean air, provide the most economical source of energy to produce flow (see Sec. 14). **Induced-draft fans,** handling the hotter flue gases, require more power and are subject to fly-ash erosion, but they facilitate operation by providing a draft in the setting and thus preventing outward leakage of the gas through joints or crevices in the structure. As a result of advances in furnace and setting designs, present-day units often are built for positive-pressure operation without gas leakage, thus eliminating the need for induced-draft fans. Such units are referred to as **pressure-furnace units,** and those using induced-draft fans are classed as **suction-furnace units.**

Pressure drop is caused by the fluid friction in the gas stream and by the shock losses at turns or contractions and enlargements of sections. It can be calculated as a function of fluid-mass flow and fluid properties, in accordance with principles of fluid flow (see Sec. 3). In the design of a boiler unit, it is essential to determine the sum of all component resistances in the flow system at the maximum load in order to establish the fan requirements. It is customary to specify a **test-block static head** and **capacity** of the fan in excess of the calculated requirements so as to allow for departure from ideal flow conditions and to provide a suitable margin of reserve.

Stack effect is caused by the difference in densities resulting from the difference in the temperatures of two vertical columns of gas. In a chimney, or stack, the stack effect is due to the difference between the confined hot gas and the cooler surrounding air and the equal static pressure at the top, or free outlet, of the stack. The stack effect, which varies with the height and the mean temperature of the columns, can be calculated from the data in Table 5. The result is the static draft produced by a stack, at sea level, with no gas flow. When flow occurs, a portion of the stack effect, or differential, is used to establish gas velocity and the remainder is used to overcome the resistance of the connected system, including the damper, and of the stack. The limit of natural-draft capacity is reached when these forces are in balance with the damper in a wide-open position. **Stack performance** may be affected, favorably or adversely, by external factors such as the wind and the atmospheric conditions. For altitudes other than sea level, the draft available varies directly with the barometric pressure.

Stack effects also exist within the boiler setting, being most pronounced in tall units with vertical gas passes. Individual gas columns within the setting may aid the head produced by the fan or chimney if the flow is upward or may oppose it if the flow is downward. The **net stack effect,** and its over-all influence on the performance of the fan, may be calculated from the data in Table 5, taking into account the positive or negative sign. The relation between local static pressures and the atmospheric pressure is most important, since gas may blow out into the room through an open inspection door at the top of a furnace, even though a strong draft, or negative pressure, exists at a lower elevation.

Table 5. Stack Effect or Pressure Difference, In. of Water, for Each Foot of Vertical Height

(Barometer = 29.92 in. Hg)

Avg temp in flue, deg F	Temp of air outside flue, deg F			
	40	60	80	100
250	0.0045	0.0039	0.0034	0.0029
500	0.0073	0.0067	0.0061	0.0056
1000	0.0101	0.0095	0.0089	0.0084
1500	0.0114	0.0108	0.0102	0.0097
2000	0.0122	0.0116	0.0110	0.0105
2500	0.0127	0.0121	0.0115	0.0110

PERFORMANCE

Steam-generating units are designed for specific operating conditions and are generally sold with a **guarantee** of performance. The **boiler rating** is usually specified and guaranteed in terms of steam output (lb per hr) at a given pressure and temperature at full load or maximum continuous operation. When the steam is reheated, the rating includes this requirement in terms of the quantity of reheat steam at stated inlet and outlet steam pressures and temperatures.

Generally, either the **efficiency** or the **gas temperature leaving the unit** is guaranteed at a specified rate of operation, and the **draft loss** and the **quality,** or **purity, of the steam** also may be guaranteed at this rate. When component equipment such as stokers, pulverizers, burners, and air heaters are supplied by different manufacturers, the performance of the individual components is usually guaranteed by the various manufacturers and then, in turn, guaranteed by the prime contractor.

Expected-performance data for several rates of operation may be given to the purchaser, in addition to the guaranteed-performance data. Guarantees may be demonstrated by **acceptance tests,** conducted in accordance with established codes, as agreed upon by the parties to the contract. However, as unit size and capacity increase, acceptance tests are more difficult to perform and over-all performance usually is determined from operating data. Guarantees of such items as materials and quality of manufacture and erection are usually considered separately from those pertaining to operating performance.

The **heat balance** is a means of accounting for the thermal energy entering the system in terms of its ultimate useful heat absorption or thermal loss. Methods of measuring and calculating the quantities involved in heat balances are presented in the ASME Power Test Code for Stationary Steam Generating Units.

The **heat input** is predicated upon the hourly firing rate, the calorific heating value of the fuel, and any additional heat supplied from an outside source. Heat in the preheated combustion air, which is obtained from an air heater integral with the boiler unit, is not considered in the determination of heat input since this heat is recycled within the system.

The **heat absorption** in a boiler is calculated from the rate of steam output and the increase in fluid enthalpy from feedwater conditions to that at the superheater outlet. To this is added the quantity of heat absorbed by the steam passing through the reheater, if used. The total heat absorption also must take into account any steam generated but not superheated. Usually the heat absorption is determined on an hourly basis.

In its simplest form,

Efficiency (percent) = heat absorbed, Btu per hr/heat input, Btu per hr × 100

Both terms may be very large. Therefore, unless elaborate precautions are taken in the sampling and the measurement of fuel and steam quantities, it is difficult to obtain test data having the degree of accuracy required to determine the actual efficiency of the unit. For this reason, boiler efficiency usually is established by determining the

heat losses, since each of the thermal losses is a relatively small percentage of the heat entering the system and reasonable errors in measurement will not appreciably effect the final result.

The principal **thermal losses** are those due to the sensible heat in the gases leaving the unit, to the latent heat losses associated with the evaporation of fuel moisture and with the formation of water vapor resulting from the burning of the hydrogen in the fuel, to the unburned-combustible loss, to the loss from the boiler setting or enclosure due to external convection and radiation, and to the ashpit loss. The first two losses can be determined from the fuel analysis, the exit-gas temperature, and the analysis of the flue gas (see p. 4-77). The unburned-combustible loss can be determined by a qualitative and quantitative sampling of the refuse and the fly ash. Radiation from the boiler setting can be estimated in detail, but it also can be approximated from Fig. 43. For large units, the heat loss to the ashpit can be determined by measuring

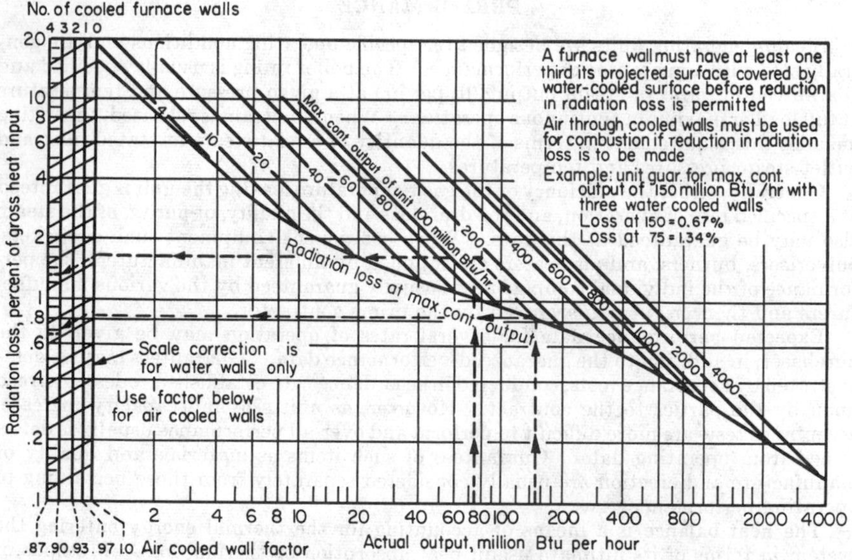

Fig. 43. External heat loss from boiler setting (ABAI).

the quantity of quenching water evaporated from the furnace ash-hopper or the slag tank; for small units, the ashpit loss is included in the loss from the boiler setting. The sum of these heat losses, expressed as a percentage of the total heat input, accounts for the measurable losses. Usually the anticipated- or guaranteed-performance data include a tolerance for the **manufacturer's margin** in the order of 0.5 to 0.75 percent, depending upon the fuel fired. The thermal efficiency of the unit is then established by subtracting the sum of all losses from 100 percent.

Form sheets, designating the specific items of measurement and the procedures for reporting data and the results of boiler tests, can be procured from the ASME at a nominal price.

Tests of the individual components of the unit, such as the furnace, superheater, economizer, or air heater, may be desired for the determination of heat-transfer and gas-flow characteristics, for comparisons with other units, or for possible changes in operating procedures or equipment; ASME codes are available for such tests. (The techniques and special equipment required for measurements in the high-temperature furnace and superheaters are described by Cohen, Corey, and Myers, *Trans. ASME*, Nov. 1949).

STEAM PURIFICATION

In drum-type boilers, using either natural or assisted circulation in the steam-generating circuits, a mixture of steam and water is delivered to the upper or steam drum, where separation takes place and a water level is maintained. The water is recycled through downcomers to the heat-absorbing circuits, and the steam is discharged from the top of the drum for use as saturated steam or as the supply for the superheater.

Separation of the **steam** and **water** by buoyant or gravitational force requires a relatively large cross-sectional area and, consequently, a low fluid velocity within the drum, as well as an effective difference in the fluid densities, which decreases as pressure is increased. Steam entrainment in the recycled water retards circulation, and water entrainment in the outlet steam transports dissolved or suspended particulate matter into the superheater, steam piping, and turbine, where particle deposition can cause overheating of the tubes or flow obstruction in the turbine blading, with subsequent loss of capacity and efficiency or dynamic unbalance. However, in low-pressure, low-duty boilers, **gravity separation** of steam and water may be satisfactory. This type of separation can be augmented by the use of **baffles** utilizing a change in direction to

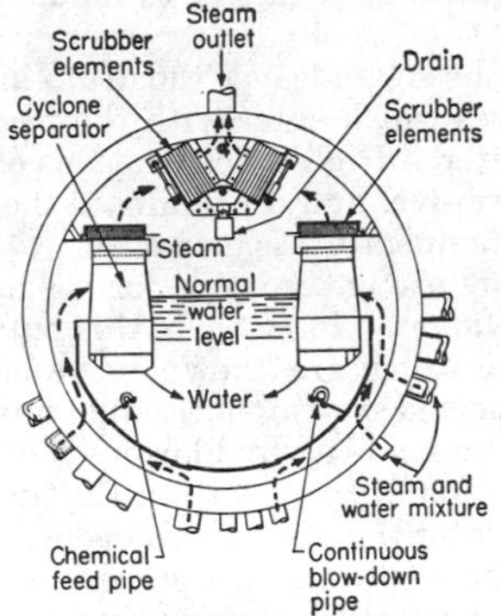

FIG. 44. Drum internal arrangement with cyclone steam separators and scrubber elements.

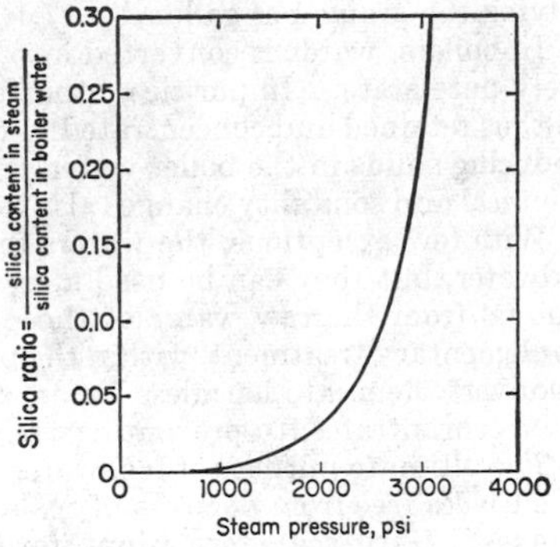

FIG. 45. Equilibrium relationship of silica ratio and operating pressure for a given concentration of silica in boiler water.

throw out water droplets or by **dry pipes** which impose a pressure drop that promotes evaporation of the moisture and reduces the tendency of solids to deposit in the superheater.

For higher-pressure units, particularly those employing high evaporative ratings, a part of the circulating head can be utilized to provide a separating force, many times greater than that of gravity, in centrifugal separating devices such as the **cyclone steam separators** shown in Fig. 44. These separators deliver steam-free water to the drum and downcomers and discharge steam with a minimum of water entrainment. Secondary steam-and-water separation is accomplished by passing the steam at a low velocity through sinuously shaped passages between closely spaced **corrugated plates,** which provide a large surface area for intercepting entrained boiler-water particles. In modern high-capacity boilers, the steam leaving the steam drum contains less than 1 ppm of total solids.

Mechanical steam separators do not prevent the transport of **silica** in a vapor solution. The amount of silica dissolved in the steam is dependent upon its concentration in the boiler water, and for a given concentration, the ratio of silica in the steam to the silica in the water increases rapidly with an increase in the operating pressure (see Fig. 45). Silica can be removed by **steam washers,** which provide a large surface area for contact with the relatively pure feedwater and which reabsorb the silica and return it to the boiler-water system. Turbine deposits can be practically eliminated, and the requirements of boiler blowdown materially reduced by this method of steam purification.

WATER TREATMENT

(See also pp. 6-129 to 6-134 and 6-234 *et seq.*)

All natural waters contain impurities which may be harmful in boiler operation. These impurities originate from the earth and the atmosphere (or from municipal and industrial wastes) and are broadly classified as suspended or dissolved organic and inorganic matter or as dissolved gases. They vary greatly due to seasonal changes, distribution of rainfall, and other causes.

The **concentration** of the **impurities** is customarily expressed in terms of the parts by weight of the constituent per million parts of water (ppm). This is equivalent to the percentage of concentration multiplied by 10^4 and has the advantage of using positive whole numbers for small concentrations; for exceedingly small concentrations, especially those involving gases, the quantities are sometimes expressed as parts per billion (ppb). For some years, concentrations were expressed in terms of the grains per gallon, but in boiler practice, this has, in general, been superseded by the gravimetric relation, ppm. Conversion of grains per gallon to ppm can be made by multiplying the grains per gallon by 17.1.

In boilers, water is converted into steam, and the steam leaves the drum in a relatively pure state. Impurities, other than the gases which enter with the feedwater, are thus retained and concentrated in the boiler water. High concentrations of **foam-producing solids** in the boiler water aggravate **carry-over** and contaminate the steam. Chemical and solubility changes also take place as temperature is increased.

With few exceptions, the waters found in nature are not suitable for use as boiler feedwater, but they can be used after **proper treatment.** In essence, this entails the removal from the raw water of those constituents which are known to be harmful; supplementary treatment, within the boiler or connected system, of residual impurities to convert them into harmless forms; and systematic removal, by blowdown of boiler-water concentrates, to prevent excessive accumulation of solids within the unit.

The ultimate purpose of feedwater and boiler-water treatment is to keep the internal surfaces free from deposits of scale or sludge and to prevent the corrosion of these surfaces. **Hard-scale formations,** formed by certain constituents in the zones of high-heat input, retard the flow of heat and raise the metal to higher-than-normal temperatures. This can cause overheating and the failure of pressure parts. **Sludge,** or solid particles normally carried in suspension, may settle locally and restrict the flow of cooling water or, in some cases, may deposit in the form of insulating layers, with an effect similar to that of hard scale. **Oil** and **grease** prevent adequate wetting of the internal surfaces and, in areas of high-heat input, cause overheating; they also may carbonize and form a tightly adherent insulating coating. **Corrosion** (see also Sec. 6), due to acidic conditions or to dissolved gases, can weaken the boiler by the removal of metal, but it usually occurs in localized areas as cavities and pits which may result in complete penetration and leakage. Certain chemical reactions produce an intergranular attack of the metal, leading to **embrittlement** and fracture.

When **condensate** is used as the feedwater to a boiler, the water treatment is minimized since it is required only for the small amounts of raw-water leakage into the system and the **makeup** water needed (normally ½ to 3 percent) to replace the loss of steam and condensate from the system. In industrial plants using a large portion of the steam generated for process work, the makeup-water requirements may be 90 to 100 percent of the total feedwater flow. Such plants require considerable equipment for water treatment.

The treatment best suited, or economically justified, for any given plant depends upon the characteristics of the water supply, the amount of makeup, and the design of the steam-generating and related equipment. Usually, the feedwater and boiler-water treatment is supervised by a chemist, and often it is desirable to engage a reputable feedwater specialist to prescribe specific procedures. However, the results obtained will depend upon the diligence and integrity of routine sampling and the control carried out by plant personnel.

Raw Water

The treatment of raw water for makeup and boiler feedwater involves one or more of the following procedures:

1. **Removal of suspended solids.** Large particles are removed by **settling** and decantation or by **filtering** through screens, fabrics, or beds of granular material. Small particles which settle slowly or colloidal particles which do not settle can be removed by **coagulation** using floc-forming chemicals, such as alum or ferrous sulphate, which trap the particles in the floc. The floc is then removed by settling or filtration. The removal of solids can be conducted on either an intermittent or a continuous basis.

2. **Chemical treatment for removal of hardness.** Calcium, magnesium, and silica are the principal **scale-forming** impurities in water and, if present in the boiler water, may form compounds whose solubility decreases with an increase in temperature.

In the **lime-soda process** for **softening** water, lime (calcium hydroxide) reacts with the soluble calcium and magnesium bicarbonates to form precipitates of calcium carbonate and magnesium hydroxide, and these can be removed as sludge. The soda ash (sodium carbonate) reacts with the scale-forming calcium sulphate and magnesium sulphate, which precipitates the calcium and magnesium as insoluble carbonates, and both reactions produce sodium sulphate, a soluble and non-scale-forming compound. When the **hot lime-soda process** is carried out at temperatures of 200 to 250 F, the reaction rates are accelerated and some of the silica may be removed.

The reactions, as in all chemical processes, tend to approach equilibrium, but they are affected by time, the completeness of mixing, and the removal of the products. Therefore, in either the intermittent batch or the continuous process, some unreacted hardness is left in the treated water.

3. **Cation exchange for removal of hardness.** Certain naturally occurring minerals, such as sodium aluminum silicate, or synthetic resins, such as the polystyrenes or phenolic-type materials, have the ability to exchange sodium ions for calcium and magnesium ions if present in water solution. Thus, softening can be accomplished by passing raw or filtered water through beds of granulated **zeolite** particles. The calcium and magnesium ions are retained by the zeolite material, while their equivalents of non-scale-forming sodium ions are released to the water solution. Before complete exhaustion of the sodium is reached, the softening equipment must be isolated from the system and **regenerated** by the passage of a strong brine of sodium chloride through the softener. Sodium ions are thus restored to the zeolite, and calcium or magnesium is removed as soluble chloride and drained to waste. After the regenerating cycle, the equipment is purged of the brine by flushing with filtered water and then returned to softening service.

The most popular system today combines methods 2 and 3, utilizing hot lime (with or without Mg for SiO_2 removal) and followed by hot sodium-cation exchange.

4. **Demineralization for complete removal of dissolved solids.** Several types of synthetic organic resins are capable of selectively removing undesirable cations or anions from water solutions by their exchange for hydrogen or hydroxyl ions. When used in combination, as **separate** or **mixed beds** of small-sized beads or particles through which the water flows, they can produce an effluent that is virtually free of mineral solutes and, therefore, satisfactory for boiler feedwater. The cation exchanger is regenerated by acid, which restores hydrogen ions to the resin in exchange for the calcium, sodium, or other metallic cations removed from the water. The anion exchanger is regenerated by the use of caustic soda or another appropriate base, which restores the hydroxyl ions in exchange for the chloride, sulphate, or other negative chemical radicals previously removed from the water. The hydrogen and hydroxyl ions, released from the resins during the treating process, combine to form pure water. The **greatest effectiveness** is attained by a mixed-bed arrangement of resins since the interchange of cation and anion components proceeds in minute increments and with less probability of the escape of unexchanged ions. With individual regeneration, the mixed resins are separated hydraulically due to differences in specific gravity. The resins must then be remixed before the demineralizer is returned to service.

5. **Evaporation.** Essentially pure water can be obtained by the evaporation of raw water and the collection of the **distillate.** This leaves the soluble constituents as concentrates in the residual water, which can be removed by blowdown, or as scale deposited on the heat-absorbing surfaces, which can be mechanically removed. Some contamination may be encountered in the distillate due to the carry-over of water particles with the vapor and the reabsorption of non-condensable gases. **Multiple-effect-type evaporators** are used to improve the thermal economy (see also Sec. 6).

Feedwater

Boiler feedwater may consist of condensate, treated water, or a mixture of both. The amount of **dissolved** and **suspended solids** is usually low as a result of the previous treatment, and generally, removal of additional solids is not required. However, any **dissolved gases** present must be removed to prevent corrosion in the boiler and in the preboiler system (see also p. 6–129).

Dissolved oxygen is, perhaps, the greatest factor in the corrosion of steel surfaces in contact with water. It may be in the makeup or in the feedwater as a result of previous contacts with atmospheric air, or it may be added to the water by the leakage of air into the system, *e.g.*, through low-pressure-pump seals and storage tanks.

Oxygen may be partially removed (to a residual of 0.2 to 0.3 ppm) by heating the water to its boiling temperature in **open-type feedwater heaters.** Removal is more effective (to residuals of 0.02 to 0.04 ppm) in the **tray-** or **spray-type deaerating heaters,** and the oxygen content can be reduced to 0.007 ppm or less by the use of **multistage deaerators** arranged for the countercurrent scavenging of non-condensable gases. (See p. 9–101.)

In plants using high-purity feedwater, corrosion may be experienced in the **condensate piping** and the **preboiler system** due to dissolved gases such as carbon dioxide, sulphur dioxide, or hydrogen sulphide in the water. These gases may originate from the atmosphere or from constituents in the boiler water. Although released as gases in the steam generators, they are intimately mixed with the outgoing steam and return to solution in the condenser, except for those partially removed by the vacuum pumps. These gases in the condensate produce an acidic reaction leading to corrosion, even in the absence of dissolved oxygen. The corrosion products in the preboiler cycle often are carried into the boiler, increasing the amount of sludge and, possibly, the amount of deposits on the heat-absorbing surfaces.

A small amount of **alkaline** boiler water is sometimes **recirculated** to the feedwater heaters to raise the **pH** of the feedwater and, thus prevent corrosion in the preboiler system. However, this may cause precipitation of sludge in the feedwater piping if appreciable hardness is present.

The pH of the water can be raised by the addition of **ammonia** or **volatile amines,** such as morpholine or cyclohexylamine, to the boiler or to the steam lines for mixture with the steam. This provides a protection against corrosion in the early stages of moisture formation in the turbine and the condenser as well as in the entire condensate-return system.

Filming amines also can be used and are generally introduced to the system through small chemical pumps in the feedwater or steam line. These materials do not change the pH of the fluid but give protection by forming a monomolecular coating on the metal surfaces. Caution must be exercised, however, since filming amines used in excess have been known to agglomerate boiler sludge and produce strongly adherent internal deposits.

Boiler Water

Boiler water is **treated internally** to prevent corrosion, the fouling of heat-absorbing surfaces, and the contamination of steam. This requires the introduction of chemicals, in suitable amounts, to react with the residual impurities in the feedwater. Internal treatment also aids in the maintenance of water conditions within satisfactory limits.

Corrosion is minimized by maintaining an alkaline boiler water. This condition may be expressed in terms of **pH** or as **total alkalinity.**

Acid or alkaline reactions of aqueous solutions are due to the presence of free or excess hydrogen (H^+) or hydroxyl (OH^-) ions, and the strength of the reaction varies with the concentration or activity of the excess ions.

Some compounds enter into solution without dissociation; others **dissociate** partially or completely into ions carrying positive or negative electrical charges. If such ionizable compounds contribute hydrogen (H^+) ions to the solution (*e.g.*, HCl), they add to the strength of its acid reaction; if they contribute hydroxyl (OH^-) ions (*e.g.*, NaOH), they add to its alkaline or basic reaction. When the ions of many different compounds are present, as is the usual case with boiler waters, their interaction or **buffering effect** modifies the resulting concentration of the specific ions, and the solution tends to approach a balance or equilibrium in accordance with the principles of chemical mass action. It is, therefore, possible, by the addition of some compounds which in themselves contain neither hydrogen nor hydroxyl components, to suppress or release these ions from other constituent solutes and, thereby, change the acidity or alkalinity of the solution.

The pH value of a solution, which designates its acidity or alkalinity, refers to a logarithmic scale proposed by Sorenson in 1909. The symbol *p* is derived from the German word *potenz*, meaning power or exponent. By definition, the **pH value** is equal to the logarithm of the reciprocal of the hydrogen ion concentration, measured in gram mols per liter.

Pure water, which may be considered as composed primarily of molecular H_2O, exhibits a slight degree of dissociation to hydrogen (+) and hydroxyl (−) ions in the equilibrium amounts, at room temperature, of 0.0000001 gram mol each per liter of water. It thus has the somewhat unusual capability of reacting, under proper conditions, as a weak acid or as a weak base and is said to be **amphoteric.** The H^+ and OH^- ions are in exact balance, however, and the water is electrically neutral.

The equation which expresses the **equilibrium dissociation** of water and also applies to water solutions is

$$H^+OH^- = K_{H_2O} = 10^{-14} \qquad \text{at 25 C}$$

H^+ and OH^- represent the respective concentrations of the ionized hydrogen and hydroxyl groups, and the **dissociation product** K_{H_2O} is found by experimental methods to be $1/10^{14}$ at 25 C.

Since the product of the two concentrations is a constant, some OH^- ions are present even in a highly acidic solution and some H^+ ions are present in a basic solution; the relationship of these factors can be determined from measurement of either term. Thus, in the case of neutral water, the value of each is 10^{-7}, or 0.0000001, gram mol per liter.

In a solution having a hydrogen ion concentration of 10^{-3} (0.001 gram mol per liter), the corresponding hydroxyl ion concentration is 10^{-11}, as a result of the dominating influence of the solvent, which is present in great excess and maintains the product equilibrium. Although either factor in the equation can be used, the **conventional scale** is based upon the measurement of the **hydrogen ion.**

Numerical values of this relationship extend over an extremely wide range and can best be expressed in terms of logarithms or exponents; thus,

$$\log H^+ + \log OH^- = -14$$
$$-\log H^+ - \log OH^- = 14$$
$$\log 1/H^+ = 14 - \log 1/OH^- = \text{pH}$$

The term **pH** is used to represent $\log 1/H^+$ and is, therefore, the logarithm of the reciprocal of the hydrogen ion concentration (more properly, the hydrogen ion activity, which is equal to the concentration multiplied by an activity factor that approaches unity in dilute solutions).

For **neutral water,** the pH $= \log 1/H^+ = \log 1/0.0000001 = \log 1/10^{-7} = 7.0$.

For an **acid solution** in which H^+ exceeds OH^-, say $H^+ = 10^{-3}$, the pH $= \log 1/10^{-3} = 3.0$.

For an **alkaline solution** in which OH^- exceeds H^+, say $OH^- = 10^{-3}$, the pH $= \log 1/10^{-11} = 11.0$.

In practical terms, the pH scale extends from 0 to 14, as shown in Table 6. The value 7.0, corresponding to pure water, is considered as the neutral point; values below 7.0 are increasingly acidic, and values above 7.0 are increasingly alkaline. Since this

Table 6. Relationship of pH and Hydrogen Ion Concentration

	pH	Hydrogen ion concentration, gram mols per liter	
	0	1.0	10^{0}
	1	0.1	10^{-1}
Acid	2	0.01	10^{-2}
range	3	0.001	10^{-3}
	4	0.000,1	10^{-4}
	5	0.000,01	10^{-5}
	6	0.000,001	10^{-6}
Neutral	7	0.000,000,1	10^{-7}
	8	0.000,000,01	10^{-8}
	9	0.000,000,001	10^{-9}
Alka-	10	0.000,000,000,1	10^{-10}
line	11	0.000,000,000,01	10^{-11}
range	12	0.000,000,000,001	10^{-12}
	13	0.000,000,000,000,1	10^{-13}
	14	0.000,000,000,000,01	10^{-14}

is a logarithmic scale, a change from one number to the next in series is equivalent to a ten times change in activity. Beyond the range of the scale, the strength of acid or alkaline solutions is expressed in terms of **normality or percentage of concentration.**

The pH of a water sample can be determined accurately by the measurement of its **electrical potential.** It also can be approximated by means of **indicators** that change color in certain pH ranges by reaction with the solution. The pH of boiler water usually is maintained within the range of 10.2 to 11.5, except that in forced-flow once-through units, the normal range is 8.5 to 9.2 (see also p. 6-125).

Total alkalinity (expressed in ppm) is a measure of all reactives that have the ability to neutralize acids. It is determined by titrating a water sample with a standard acid, and it is frequently expressed as **equivalent calcium carbonate,** which has a molecular weight of 100. Total alkalinity, as determined in this manner, is not exactly the same as the pH measurement of alkalinity due to the buffering action which occurs in complex solutions. However, it is widely used as a reference and, in the case of low-pressure boilers where higher concentrations or greater diversity of solids can be tolerated, often is more satisfactory than the measurement of pH as an index of boiler-water conditions.

Complete removal of **dissolved oxygen** is desirable and, for high-pressure boiler units, a necessary requirement. For oxygen removal, it is customary to supplement feedwater deaeration by internal chemical treatment of the boiler water, using a **scavenging agent** such as **sodium sulphite,** which combines with the oxygen to form a stable sodium sulphate. **Hydrazine** also is used for this purpose, yielding end products of water and inert nitrogen. Such chemicals safeguard against the entrance or the retention of dissolved oxygen and are maintained at a small marginal excess in the boiler water.

Elimination of **hardness** in the boiler water is necessary to prevent scale. Hardness can be removed by introducing one of the forms of **sodium** or **potassium phosphate** and thoroughly mixing it with the boiler water. The residual calcium ions entering with the feedwater are precipitated as an insoluble phosphate sludge, and the magnesium is precipitated as a non-adherent magnesium hydroxide if the alkalinity is maintained at a pH of 10 or higher. A lower pH may permit the formation of magnesium phosphate, an adherent type of sludge. Routine control requires the adjustment of the pH by the addition of sodium hydroxide or its equivalent and the maintenance of a moderate excess of phosphate ions in the boiler water.

Early methods of internal treatment employed **soda ash** for hardness removal.

However, the hydrolysis of soda ash at the temperatures encountered with high operating pressures releases carbon dioxide into the steam, making it difficult to maintain an excess of carbonate and promoting corrosion in the condensate system. In some services, **sodium carbonate,** in combination with the hydroxides and phosphates of sodium, is used for hardness removal. A phosphate sludge is preferred since it is less adherent and more easily kept in suspension.

Silica may enter the system in the form of soluble compounds or as finely divided particles which are not removed by filtration. It dissolves in alkaline boiler waters and will, with unreacted calcium or magnesium hardness in the water, form an adherent scale. Under some conditions, it may produce complex scale-forming silicates with soluble or colloidal iron oxide (acmite) or alumina (analcite). On heated surfaces, the crystalline matrix of these deposits traps sludge particles, further contributing to scale formation.

Silica also is **soluble in steam,** and its solubility increases rapidly at temperatures above 500 F. Thus, it can be transported in a vapor phase into the turbine and deposited on the turbine blading. This characteristic dictates limits of silica concentration in the boiler water to avoid **turbine deposits,** the limits varying with operating pressure from about 10 ppm at 1,000 psi to 0.5 ppm at 2,500 psi.

Silica is partially removed from raw water by the hot lime-soda softening process and can be completely removed by the evaporation of the makeup water. Soluble silica can be removed by demineralization, but in colloidal forms, it may pass through the treating beds. The silica concentration in the boiler water can be controlled by blowdown.

The recommended **limits** of **boiler-water concentration,** as defined in the ABAI manual, are listed in Table 7. These data are not applicable to forced-flow once-through boilers. The **total solids content** can be determined by weighing the residue of a water sample which has been evaporated to dryness. The **dissolved-solids content** can be determined in a similar manner from a filtered sample, but for immediate determinations and control purposes, it can be quickly approximated by an **electrical-conductivity** measurement and the use of conversion factors previously established by comparisons with gravimetric determinations.

Table 7. Recommended Limits of Boiler-water Concentration (ABAI)

Pressure at outlet of steam-generating unit, psig	Total solids, ppm	Total alkalinity, ppm	Suspended solids, ppm
0–300	3,500	700	300
301–450	3,000	600	250
451–600	2,500	500	150
601–750	2,000	400	100
751–900	1,500	300	60
901–1,000	1,250	250	40
1,001–1,500	1,000	200	20
1,501–2,000	750	150	10
2,001 and higher	500	100	5

Solids concentration also can be controlled by **blowdown,** either intermittent or continuous. The amount of blowdown and the time interval between blows should be coordinated with operation and should consider or anticipate load changes, water conditioning, and chemical treatment.

In **forced-flow once-through boilers,** the impurities entering with the feedwater must either leave with the steam or be deposited within the unit. Thus, such units require high-purity feedwater and the control of corrosion by **volatile bases,** such as ammonia, which will not result in deposits in the boiler or the turbine. Raw-water leakage into the system must be prevented, and the makeup must be evaporated or demineralized water.

When **sampling** water from high-pressure, high-temperature sources, cooling is required to prevent the flashing or selective loss of water vapor at atmospheric pressure.

The approved methods for sampling and analysis are given in the ASTM "Manual on Industrial Water and Industrial Waste Water," 2d ed., 1960.

CARE OF BOILERS

The care of boilers is delineated in Section VII of the ASME Boiler and Pressure Vessel Code, titled "Suggested Rules for Care of Power Boilers." Principal considerations include the initial preparation of new equipment for service; normal operation, including routine start-up and shutdown; emergency operations; inspection and maintenance; and idle storage. In all these phases, the handling of equipment is the responsibility of the operator, but recommendations and operating instructions supplied by the manufacturer should be thoroughly understood and followed.

The **initial preparation** of new units for service, or of old equipment after completing major alterations or repairs, involves the removal of construction or foreign material from the setting and from the interior of pressure parts, **hydrostatic testing** and inspection for leaks, and the boiling out of the unit with a caustic solution for the removal of grease and other deposits in the economizer and generating pressure parts. During **boil-out,** the unit is fired at a low rate and the pressure is maintained at about 50 percent of the design operating pressure. This procedure also facilitates the desired slow drying of any refractories used in the setting. During the boil-out period of 12 to 36 hr, the unit is blown down periodically through all the blowdown connections so as to eliminate any sediment removed from the surfaces. The boil-out often is supplemented, particularly on high-pressure boilers, by **inhibited-acid cleaning** for the removal of mill scale.

It is general practice, following the boil-out, to reduce the concentration of boil-out chemicals to a satisfactory level for operation by blowing down and replenishing the amount of water blown down with fresh water. The pressure is then raised to **test** and to **set** the **safety valves** to Code requirements; the superheater and the steam piping are **blown out** to remove any foreign material, and the boiler is placed on the line for a period of low-load operation, during which the auxiliary equipment, controls, and interlocks are test-operated. After this, it is advisable to shut down, cool, and drain the unit for a thorough internal and external inspection and for any adjustments or modifications required to the equipment.

Normal operation covers the orderly start-up and shutdown of equipment and the operation, under controlled conditions, to meet plant requirements. Statistics show that about 80 percent of the recorded furnace explosions occur during start-up and low-load operation, and particular care must be taken during such operations to prevent furnace explosions. The National Fire Protection Assoc. Committee on Boiler Furnace Explosions has prepared standards for the prevention of furnace explosions. These standards delineate the preferred sequence of starting fuel-burning equipment, the recommended minimum flame-monitoring equipment and safety interlocks, the recommended fuel-transport piping systems, the recommended purging procedures, and the procedures to be taken in the event of burner or furnace flameout.

Normal operation also entails the **maintenance** of specified feedwater and boiler-water conditioning to avoid internal scales or corrosion, of designed steam and metal temperatures, of clean gas passages and heat-absorbing surfaces, and of fuel-ash removal.

The rate of firing during **start-up** is limited by the superheater and reheater metal temperatures to prevent overheating and by the temperature differentials in thick-walled pressure parts to avoid excessive thermal stress. Such considerations govern the time required for start-up and for cooling after shutdown.

Emergency operations are usually the direct result of abnormal conditions such as the failure of the feedwater supply, the rupture of a pressure part, the interruption of the fuel supply, the loss of air, or a burner flameout. **Automatic safety interlocks** are usually installed which trip the fuel supply and shut down the unit if these or other hazardous conditions develop. Other abnormal operating conditions which might become hazardous if allowed to persist, such as low (fuel-rich) or high (air-rich) air-fuel ratios or the failure of essential auxiliaries, require the operator to take the necessary appropriate action to correct operating conditions. If the **operator** cannot correct an abnormal condition, he must determine whether operation can continue, and if not, he must **shut down** the unit in the proper manner or activate the **emergency trip** through the automatic interlock system.

Inspection and **maintenance** should be performed during outages regularly scheduled for this purpose. A list of the known items requiring repair or maintenance should be prepared before the outage and should be supplemented by any additional items noted in a thorough inspection of the boiler and auxiliary equipment during the outage. A major item on this work list should be the maintenance of internal and external cleanliness. **External cleaning** is usually accomplished by water washing or air-lancing. Although mechanical cleaning of **internal surfaces** often is done on smaller units, **chemical cleaning** is generally used as a practical necessity on the large-capacity units. Under competent supervision, which can be obtained from several firms specializing in chemical cleaning, this method can be used with complete confidence for boilers of all sizes and is usually more rapid, thorough, and economical. The chemical cleaning solution normally is composed of a 3 to 5 percent solution of hydrochloric acid, wetting and complexing agents for the removal of silica or other hard-to-remove deposits, such as iron and copper oxides, and a suitable inhibitor to prevent excessive chemical attack upon the pressure parts of the boiler. Hydrochloric acid, however, should not be used for cleaning stainless-steel surfaces since it causes stress-corrosion cracking; thus, other organic or inorganic acids are used, depending upon the type of material to be cleaned and the composition of the deposit to be removed.

For **drum-type boilers,** chemical cleaning involves filling the boiler (which has previously been heated uniformly to about 175 F) with the cleaning solution at 150 to 160 F and allowing it to soak for 6 to 8 hr, or until samples of the solution show no appreciable further reduction in acid strength. The boiler should never be fired while it contains the acid solution, and open lights or other ignition sources must be prohibited in the area to avoid the ignition of the explosive gases (usually hydrogen) evolved during the cleaning operation. The unit is then drained and flushed several times, preferably under a nitrogen blanket, with neutral or slightly acidic water to remove the loosened deposits and to displace the acid solution and any corrosive gases. This is followed by boil-out with an alkaline solution to neutralize any residual acid and to passivate the surfaces. The unit is then flushed with clean water (any sloping tubes are flushed individually) to remove any remaining loose deposits and is inspected before being returned to service.

Essentially the same procedure is followed in the chemical cleaning of **forced-flow once-through** units, with the exception that the cleaning solution is circulated continuously through the equipment.

Units removed from service for long periods of time may be protected against damage from corrosion by **dry-storage** methods, which require the thorough cleaning, drying, and closure of all openings so as to exclude moisture and air. Low humidity within the pressure parts and setting is maintained by trays of moisture-absorbing materials, such as silica gel or lime, replenished at intervals to retain effectiveness and to prevent the overflow of collected liquid. For **standby storage,** where service may be required on short notice, internal corrosion may be minimized by completely filling the pressure parts, including the superheater, with water treated to a hydrate alkalinity of at least 400 ppm and to a sodium sulphite concentration of 100 ppm.

CODES

The ASME Boiler and Pressure Vessel Code, initiated in 1914 and supplemented by continuing revisions, contains the basic rules for the safe design, the construction, and the materials for steam-generating units. Its legal status depends upon its adoption by state or municipal authority. The Code is administered by the National Board of Boiler and Pressure Vessel Inspectors, and this organization also has formulated rules for the repair of boiler equipment, known as the "Recommended Rules for Repairs by Fusion Welding to Power Boilers and Unfired Pressure Vessels." The adoption of both codes has been widespread, and they form the basis for the pertinent legal requirements in all but a few localities throughout the country. The National Bureau of Casualty and Surety Underwriters, New York, has prepared a booklet titled "Synopsis of Boiler Rules and Regulations," which lists the states and the communities having laws which govern the installation and the operation of steam boilers.

NUCLEAR BOILERS

(See also p. 9–171 *et seq.*)

Nuclear-power boilers are usually identified by the **primary fluid** used as reactor coolant. A number of coolants and system-design concepts have been studied, but only four basic coolants have been used in U.S. power plants—liquid metals, helium, organic fluids, and water.

Most of the reactor power systems built for commercial power production have used water in some form as the primary coolant, principally the **pressurized-water-reactor (PWR)** and **boiling-water-reactor (BWR)** systems. This preference for water as the coolant is due to the fact that its physical, chemical, and thermodynamic characteristics are well known and that materials and equipment for its handling and containment are available; to its relative safety; and to its low cost.

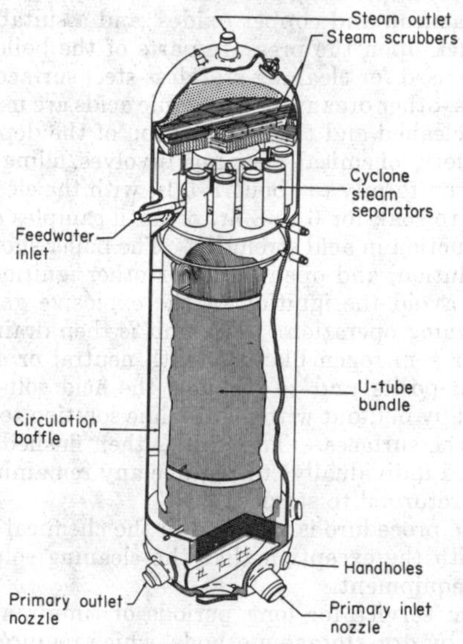

Fig. 46. Nuclear power boiler.

The boiler unit shown in Fig. 46 is typical of those used in PWR and BWR installations, and the data in Table 8 are typical of boiler operating requirements. In the design shown, hot primary fluid enters one side of the divided primary head, passes through the U-type tubes, and leaves through the primary outlet nozzle. Boiling takes place on the outside, or secondary side, of the tubes; the steam-water mixture passes through the riser section and through the steam-and-water separators, and the steam is discharged through the scrubbers into the outlet connection. The separated water flows downward, mixes with the incoming feedwater, and is then circulated downward through the annulus around the tube bundle to enter the tube bundle at the bottom.

Generally, in units of this type, stainless-steel or Inconel® tubes are used to minimize corrosion, all structural components are of carbon or low-alloy steel, and the primary head and primary tube-sheet faces are completely clad with stainless steel or Inconel®.

There are three **major design considerations:**

1. **Hazards.** In the design of nuclear components, consideration must be given not only to the actual damage and loss of life which could result from an accident but also to the psychological effect of an accident. Safeguards against possible nuclear

Table 8. Typical Reactor-boiler Design Data

Steam side:	
Flow, lb per hr	1,300,000
Pressure, psi	500
Temperature, F (saturated)	470
Feedwater temperature, F	340
Primary side:	
Transport fluid	Pressurized light water
Flow, lb per hr	17,750,000
Pressure drop, psi	40
Inlet temperature, F	547
Outlet temperature, F	493
Operating pressure, psi	2,200
Heat transferred:	
Thermal megawatts	341
Btu per hr	1,164,000,000

incidents are the responsibility of the core designer, but other potential dangers must be considered by the boiler designer. These include the hazards of:

Radioactivity. The primary fluid, and any materials transported in the primary passages, may become radioactive from neutron bombardment. This radioactivity can hold at a high level for varying lengths of time, and since radioactive products may be deposited anywhere in the primary system, the boiler designer must design the equipment for minimum exposure of personnel to radiation.

Chemical Poisons. Some fission products are lethal, not only because they are radioactive but because they are chemically poisonous by both ingestion and inhalation. Personnel must be protected against exposure to these poisons.

Chemical Reactions. In some reactor systems, contact between the primary and secondary fluids causes strong chemical reactions. Sodium and water, for example, react violently, yet sodium has been selected as the primary fluid in some systems because of excellent nuclear properties and because of good heat-transfer and heat-transport characteristics. Therefore, steam generators in which sodium is used for the primary fluid must be designed so that direct contact between the sodium and the water is unlikely and so that the effects of such a reaction, if one should occur, are minimized.

2. **Codes and Specifications.** The requirements for safe design and fabrication are delineated in the ASME Boiler and Pressure Vessel Code, augmented by Special Code Cases. These special cases, which apply specifically to nuclear components, establish design, inspection, and fabrication rules which are more stringent than those required for other types of equipment. The construction of commercial nuclear components is governed by the ASME Code, Section III, "Rules for Construction of Nuclear Vessels," while that of equipment for military use is governed by special military specifications. Each requires comprehensive stress and fatigue analyses.

3. **Economics.** Several basic considerations, common to both the PWR and the BWR systems, differ greatly from those of fossil-fuel systems. The temperature difference that produces heat transfer between the primary and secondary water is dependent upon an appreciable difference in pressure between the two fluids, and the hotter primary fluid is at the higher pressure. Therefore, an optimized boiler design, using a minimum amount of heat-absorbing surface, should have the boiling secondary fluid outside of the tubes since a tube, or cylinder, can withstand greater internal pressures. This is the opposite of modern fossil-fuel-fired water-tube boiler designs, wherein the boiling fluid is contained in the tubes.

Both internal and external heat-transfer coefficients are high, and consequently, in most cases, the tube-wall and the fouling-film coefficients control the over-all rate of heat transfer. Thus, the tube diameter should be small, and the tube wall as thin as practical. Further, the water must be conditioned to minimize scale and sludge formations. Primary systems are designed for relatively high pressures, 1,200 to 2,500 psi, and extremely compact systems are economically justified in the efforts to minimize the size and the weight of the pressure vessels. Temperature differences are necessarily small in order to achieve the highest practical secondary-steam pressure. This tends to increase surface requirements and, consequently, size.

STEAM ENGINES

(Staff Contribution)

REFERENCES: Ewing, "The Steam Engine and Other Heat Engines," Cambridge. Ripper, "Steam Engine Theory and Practice," Longmans. Heck, "The Steam Engine and Turbine," Van Nostrand. Allen, "Uniflow, Back Pressure, and Steam Extraction Engines," Pitman. Peabody, "Valve Gears for Steam Engines," Wiley. Zeuner, "Treatise on Valve Gears," Spon. Spangler, "Valve Gears," Wiley. Dalby, "Valves and Valve Gear Mechanisms," Longmans.

For more than a hundred years the steam engine was the only practical heat-power prime mover. It was built in sizes from children's toys to 25,000 hp. Until the introduction of the steam turbine it generated the major part of electric power; it propelled all large ships, naval and merchant; as the steam locomotive it hauled railroad trains; it drove rolling mills and mine hoists; and it pumped drinking water for cities. Most of the machine elements, as known today, like cylinders, piston rings, valves, crankshafts, connecting rods, crossheads, governors, and indicators were developed in connection with steam engines. These engines utilize the expansive power of steam. Theoretically, the more the steam can be expanded in the engine cylinder, the higher the economy. Certain losses, which occur in every steam engine, limit the expansion ratio and result in a minimum steam rate for a definite degree of expansion.

Work and Dimensions of the Steam Engine

(See also Sec. 4)

A typical steam-engine indicator card is shown in Fig. 1, which also lists the established nomenclature for the different events of the cycle. Superimposed is a theoretical diagram, with expansion and without clearance or compression. The terminal pressure controls the steam rate. The term "back pressure" is used for pressures either atmospheric or higher, while "condenser pressure" is used when engines operate with negative exhaust pressure. The volume ratio $v_j \div v_h = R$ is called the **ratio of expansion.**

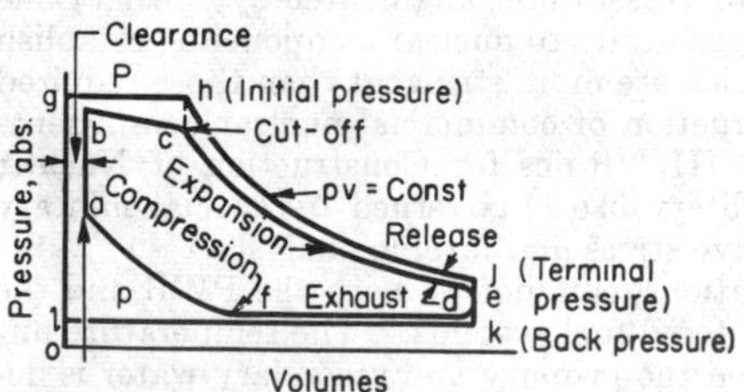

FIG. 1. Typical steam-engine indicator diagram.

The average ordinate or **mean effective pressure** of the diagram *ghjkl* is

$$p_m = P[(1 + \ln R)/R] - p \tag{1}$$

Table 1 gives the ratio p_m/P for zero back pressure ($p = 0$) for various values of R.

Pressures and Expansion Ratios [for Eq. (**1**)]. In ordinary practice, P ranges from 75 to 400 maximum value up to 1,800 psi. Common values for simple engines are from 95 to 115 psia. For non-condensing engines exhausting to the atmosphere at sea level, p is between 15 and 17 psia. For condensing engines, p is between 1 and 2½ psia. If the exhaust steam from an engine is used for heating buildings or in manufacturing processes, p may have any value from 15 psia upward.

The value of R is commonly around 4 in simple engines. It should increase as P increases and as p decreases, being usually between 3 and 5. It should be higher in jacketed than in unjacketed engines. The efficiency of the engine depends largely on the value chosen for R. High values of R will be adopted for an engine to be used where

Table 1. Ratio of Mean Effective Pressure to Initial Pressure for Various Ratios of Expansion (Zero Back Pressure)

Ratio of expansion, R	Ratio of mean to initial pressure (p_m/P)	Ratio of expansion, R	Ratio of mean to initial pressure (p_m/P)	Ratio of expansion, R	Ratio of mean to initial pressure (p_m/P)	Ratio of expansion, R	Ratio of mean to initial pressure (p_m/P)
1.67	0.907	3.33	0.662	6.67	0.435	18	0.216
1.82	0.874	3.64	0.631	7.00	0.421	20	0.200
2.00	0.847	4.00	0.597	8.00	0.385	22	0.186
2.22	0.810	4.44	0.561	10.00	0.330	24	0.174
2.50	0.766	5.00	0.522	12.00	0.290	26	0.164
2.67	0.744	5.71	0.481	14.00	0.260	28	0.155
2.86	0.717	6.00	0.465	16.00	0.236	30	0.147

fuel is costly or the load steady. The overload capacity is similarly influenced: low values of R lead to high mep—and hence to large output from a cylinder of given size—but also to low overload capacities.

Figure 1 shows that the theoretical card has a larger area than the actual card. The values of p_m obtained from Table 1 must be multiplied by the **diagram factor** to obtain the actual p_m for the assumed conditions. This factor may have values from 0.70 to 0.95.

Power Developed by the Steam Engine. The ihp, or indicated horsepower, of an engine is proportional to p_m and to the mean piston speed. The latter is defined as

$$S = 2Ln/12\text{fpm}$$

where L is the stroke, in., and n the rpm. The usual range of S is from 400 to 800 fpm. If A is the net piston area in sq in., then ihp $= Ap_mS/33{,}000$ for a double-acting engine, and ihp $= Ap_mS/66{,}000$ for a single-acting engine. The piston area always refers to net area. For a double-acting engine with piston rod at the crank end only, the net area equals the area of the cylinder bore minus one-half the area of the rod section.

Losses in steam engine cylinders are (1) incomplete expansion; (2) initial condensation; (3) throttling, affected by valve and port area; and (4) radiation, which can be considered constant. The point of best economy occurs with the p_m at which the total of all losses is a minimum.

Brake horsepower (bhp) = ihp × mechanical efficiency. Friction horsepower = ihp − bhp and is substantially constant over the load range, so that the mechanical efficiency may be calculated for the whole load range if the *friction hp* is known for one load point. Representative values for mechanical efficiency (at full load) vary from 0.80 to 0.94 as follows:

Bhp	25	50	75	100
Friction hp	6	6	6	6
Ihp	31	56	81	106
Mech eff, percent	81	89.5	92.5	94

Figure 2 shows the effect of mechanical efficiency and generator efficiency on the steam rate of an engine-generator set, both as to relative magnitude and as to location of the minimum values.

Means of improving engine economy are as follows: (1) **Separation of inlet and outlet ports.** (2) **Steam jackets,** which are applied to cylinders and heads to keep the surfaces hot and dry. (3) **Compounding.** Condensation losses are related to the total temperature difference existing in the cylinder. By placing two cylinders in series this temperature difference is halved. Three or four cylinders in series, as with triple and quadruple expansion, carries this idea further, but the successive improvement is smaller and smaller. (4) **Superheating,** which gives steam vapor the properties of a gas. Its introduction effected decisive changes in engine design and gave a sharp reduction in steam rates. While, theoretically, the improvement in the Rankine-cycle rate due to superheat is not large, the improvement obtained in practice is such that superheat is prevalent. (5) **Uniflow** arrangement was the last great improvement in engine design. Its high economy is explained by the high temperature of the residual steam at the end of compression. This temperature, aided by the jackets, is much higher than the live steam temperature, so that initial condensation is reduced to a negligible amount.

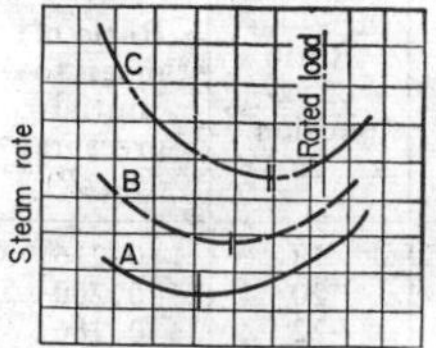

FIG. 2. Engine steam rate curves, (*A*) at the steam cylinder, lb per ihp-hr, (*B*) at the engine shaft, lb per bhp-hr, (*C*) at the generator terminals, lb per kwh.

Engine Steam Rates. The basis of comparison for steam-engine performance is the Rankine cycle with adiabatic expansion from initial to back pressure. The Rankine-cycle steam rate N_r is given by

$$N_r = 2{,}544/(h_1 - h_2)\text{lb per hp hr}$$

where h_1 is initial enthalpy and h_2 is exhaust enthalpy. The lowest point of the actual steam-rate curve (see Figs. 3 and 4) is usually referred to as the Rankine rate, and the ratio Rankine rate/actual rate is the Rankine efficiency ratio. This ratio may vary from 0.5 to 0.9, depending on the type of engine. For incomplete expansion (Fig. 5) the theoretical steam rates are higher.

When clearance and compression are also introduced (Fig. 6), the methods of Sec. 4 should be used to evaluate the steam rate. This involves the use of steam tables and charts to find the net work of the indicator card from the positive and negative areas of

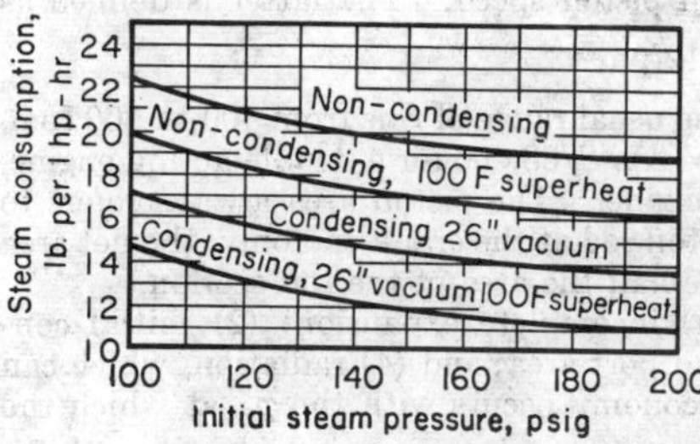

FIG. 3. Steam consumption of 400 hp uniflow engine.

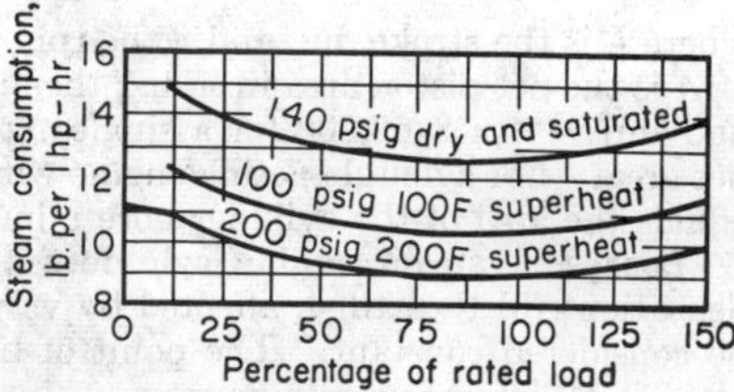

FIG. 4. Steam consumption of uniflow engine with 27.5 in. vacuum.

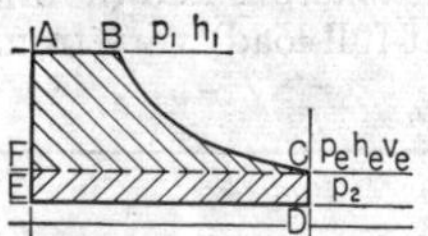

FIG. 5. Theoretical card, no clearance or compression.

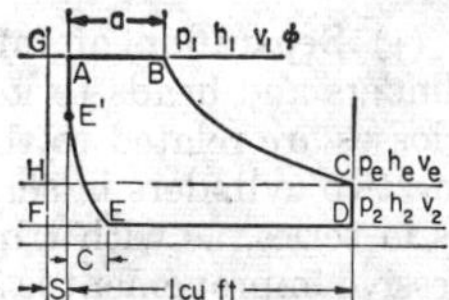

FIG. 6. Theoretical card, with clearance and compression.

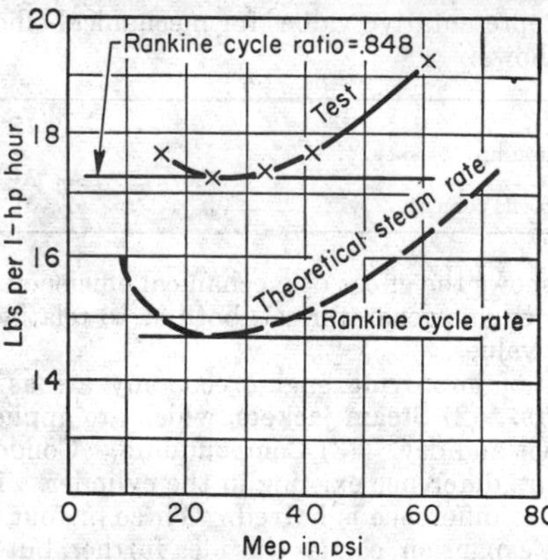

FIG. 7. Theoretical and test steam rate curves. Uniflow engine 20 × 24 at 200 rpm; throttle conditions 150 psi saturated; exhaust to atmosphere.

the several component phases. Figure 7 shows a theoretical steam-rate curve, computed by such methods, together with the actual test curve on the engine.

Single-expansion Engines. This is the simplest type of steam engine and has been built with every form of valve and valve gear. Valve types are plain D slide, gridiron, double slide (Meyer or Rider), rocking, piston, releasing and non-releasing Corliss, and poppet. The following are important design details.

1. Volumetric clearance. This should be made as small as possible. Figure 8 shows the effect of large clearance on p_m with the same terminal pressure in each case. Slide valves and piston valves bring clearance volumes to 12 or 15 percent, Corliss valves 6 to 10 percent, and poppet valves 4 to 8 percent.

2. Valve and port sizes. Flow area of valves and cross section of ports are usually determined by port area $= AS/C$ sq in. where A is net piston area, sq in., S is mean piston speed, fpm, and C is a constant, fpm. Values for C are 9,000 to 15,000 fpm for inlet and 6,000 to 7,500 fpm for outlet. Small outlet valves and ports cause sloping exhaust lines (see Fig. 9), the shaded area representing lost work.

3. Superheated steam. With high-temperature steam, the cylinder and parts design must allow for free expansion. Poppet- or piston-valve cylinders can easily meet these requirements. The orthodox type of Corliss cylinder, however, is not suitable for highly superheated steam.

Compound Engines. These are built either as tandem compound, with the two cylinders arranged coaxially and both connected to one frame, or cross compound, with two frames and cranks usually set at 90 deg. The Woolf-type tandem engine omits the receiver and the low-pressure steam valve, and the high-pressure exhaust valve controls low-pressure admission. While this valve is open, expansion takes place in both cylinders simultaneously. A combined indicator card of a compound engine is shown in Fig. 10. Initial condensation in the low-pressure cylinder is indicated as well as the pressure drop between high-pressure exhaust and low-pressure admission lines. The total referred mean effective pressure is used to calculate the size of the low-pressure cylinder. The high-pressure cylinder does not enter into the calculation.

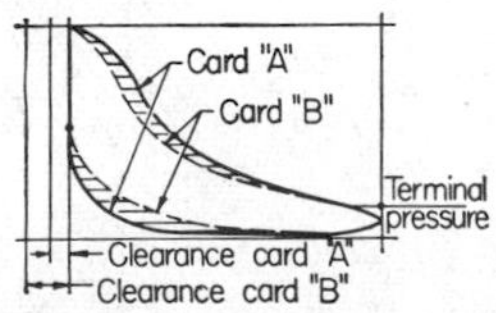

Fig. 8. Indicator card showing effect of clearance.

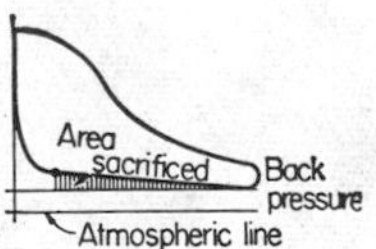

Fig. 9. Indicator card showing effect of small exhaust valves.

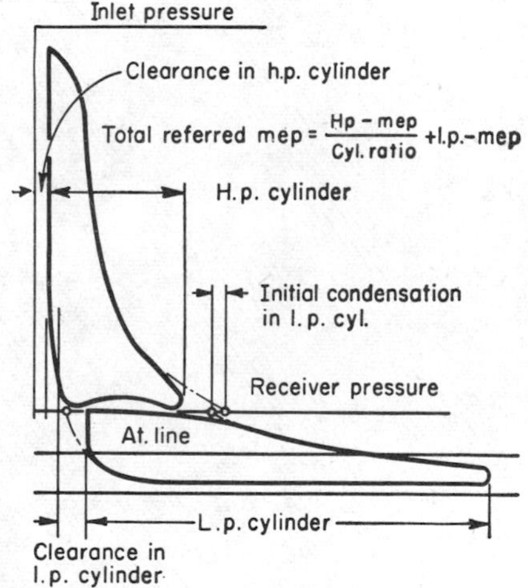

Fig. 10. Combined compound-engine indicator card.

Cylinder ratios of compound engines range from 3.5 to 5, for condensing types, and from 2 to 3.5, for non-condensing and back-pressure engines. When process steam is to be extracted from the receiver, the cylinder ratio is based on a receiver pressure equal to the process-steam pressure. In such cases the cutoff control of the low-pressure cylinder is made partly responsive to process-steam demands. Adjustment of the receiver pressure is effected by a change of the low-pressure cutoff. Lengthening this cutoff will lower the receiver pressure and vice versa.

Uniflow Engines. For condensing operations, uniflow engines are built with steam valves only (two-valve type). Clearance pockets are provided, with either hand-operated or automatic valves to permit operation with atmospheric exhaust or against back pressure (see Fig. 11).

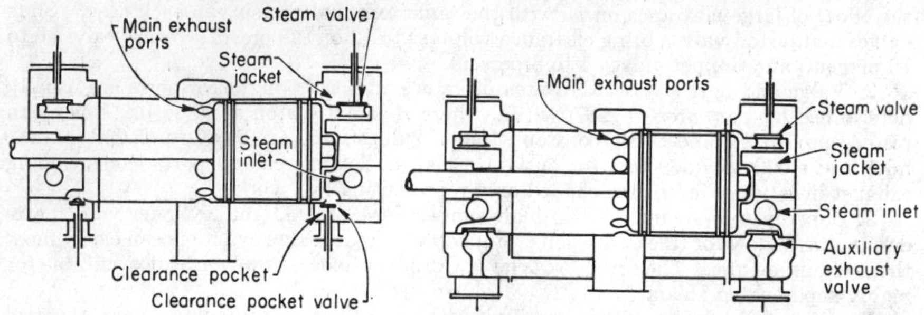

Fig. 11. Condensing uniflow engine cylinder, with clearance pockets.

Fig. 12. Non-condensing uniflow engine cylinder, with auxiliary exhaust valves.

Non-condensing uniflow engines have in addition auxiliary exhaust valves to reduce the otherwise large clearance required (four-valve type). If the back pressure is variable, exhaust-valve *gears* are designed to change the length of compression while the engine is in operation (see Fig. 12).

STEAM TURBINES

BY

P. H. Knowlton, Jr.

REFERENCES: Stodola, "Steam and Gas Turbines," trans. by L. C. Loewenstein, McGraw-Hill. Elston and Knowlton, Comparative Efficiencies of Central Station Reheat and Non-reheat Steam Turbine-generator Units, *Trans. ASME*, **74**, No. 8. Campbell, Trends in Steam-turbine Development, *Westinghouse Eng.*, **7**, 1947, pp. 79–83. Warren, Development of Steam Turbines for Main Propulsion of High-powered Combatant Ships, *Trans. Soc. Naval Architects Marine Engrs.*, 1946. Newman, Modern Extraction Turbines, *Power Plant Eng.* Jan.-Apr., 1945. Salisbury, "Steam Turbines and Their Cycles," Wiley. Downs, Margins for Improvement of the Steam Cycle, *Paper* 55–SA–76, *ASME*, June, 1955. Franck, Superpressure Steam Turbines, *Combustion*, Nov. 1955. Campbell and Heckman, Tangential Vibration of Steam Turbine Buckets, *Trans. ASME*, **47,** 1925, pp. 643–671. Campbell, Protection of Steam Turbine Disk Wheels from Axial Vibration, *Trans. ASME*, **46,** 1924, pp. 31–139. Spencer, Cotton, and Cannon, Method for Predicting the Performance of Steam Turbine Generators, *Trans. ASME*, **85,** series A, Oct. 1963. Deák and Baird, A Procedure for Calculating the Packet Frequencies of Steam Turbine Exhaust Blades, *Trans. ASME*, **85,** series A, Oct. 1963.

Steam turbines have established a wide usefulness as prime movers, and are manufactured in many different forms and arrangements. They are used to drive many different types of apparatus, *e.g.*, electric generators, pumps, compressors, and for driving ship propellers, through suitable gears. When designed for variable-speed operation, a turbine may be operated over a considerable speed range, which may be of advantage in many applications. Steam turbines range in output capacity from a few horsepower to as much as 1,000,000 kw; still larger machines can no doubt be built. The largest ones are used for generator drive in central power stations.

Turbines are classified descriptively in various ways:

1. By steam supply and exhaust conditions, *e.g.*, condensing, non-condensing, automatic extraction, mixed pressure (in which steam is supplied from more than one source at more than one pressure), regenerative extraction, reheat.

2. By casing or shaft arrangement, *e.g.*, single casing, tandem compound (two or more casings with the shaft coupled together in line), cross compound (two or more shafts not in line, often at different rpm).

3. By number of exhaust stages in parallel as regards steam flow, *e.g.*, double flow, triple flow.

4. By details of stage design, *e.g.*, **impulse** or **reaction.**

5. By direction of steam flow in the turbine, *e.g.*, axial flow, radial flow, tangential flow. In this country, radial-flow steam turbines have not been used; there are quite a few such machines abroad. Axial-flow units predominate; some small turbines in this country operate on the tangential-flow principle.

6. Whether single stage or multistage. Small turbines, or those designed for small energy drop, may have only one stage; larger units are always multistage.

7. By type of driven apparatus, *e.g.*, generator drive or mechanical drive.

Any particular turbine unit may be described under one or more of these classifications, *e.g.*, a single-casing condensing regenerative-extraction unit, or a tandem-compound three-casing triple-flow reheat regenerative unit.

Turbine-stage Design. A turbine stage consists of a **stationary set of blades,** often called **nozzles,** and a moving set adjacent thereto, called **buckets,** or **rotor blades.** These stationary and rotating blades act together to allow the steam flow to do work on the rotor, which can be transmitted to the **load** through the **shaft** on which the rotor assembly is carried. Classical turbine-stage design recognized two distinct designs of turbine stage, "impulse" and "reaction" (see classification 4 above). In the **impulse** stage, the total pressure drop for the stage is taken across the nozzles or stationary element, the flow through the buckets or rotor blades then being substantially at constant static pressure. This may be extended to include flow through an additional set of stationary "intermediate" blades and another row of buckets, or rotor blades (Curtis or two-row stages). See velocity diagrams (Figs. 1 and 2).

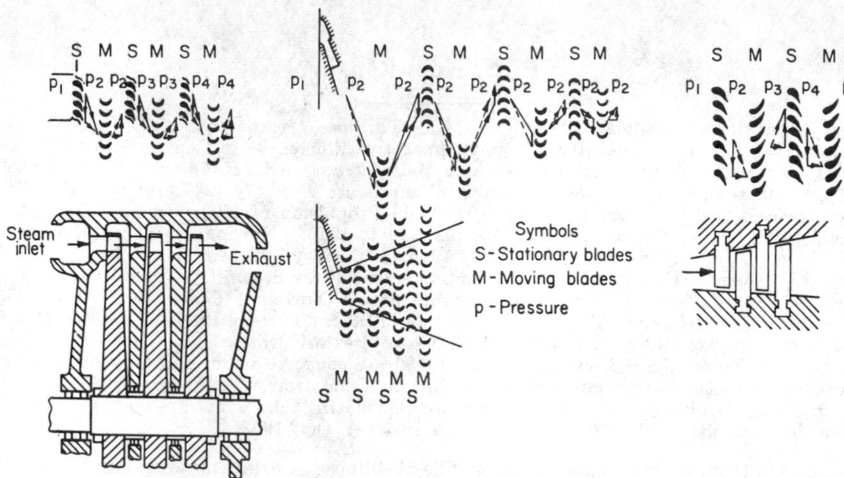

FIG. 1. Impulse turbine with single-velocity stages.

FIG. 2. Impulse turbine with multi-velocity stages.

FIG. 3. Reaction turbine.

FIGS. 1 to 3. Diagrammatic illustrations of turbine elements and corresponding bucket-velocity diagrams.

In the **reaction** stage, the total pressure drop assigned to the stage is divided equally between the stationary blades and the rotor blades, giving rise to a velocity diagram, as shown in Fig. 3. As can be seen, there arises a marked difference in the shapes of the rotor blades in the two classical designs; the impulse buckets do much more turning of the stream; the reaction-bucket shape is more nearly the same as the nozzle-blade shape.

Modern fluid-flow theory recognizes that only in rare cases can an axial-flow turbine stage be either pure impulse or pure reaction. The annulus following the nozzle exit is filled with steam flowing with a high tangential velocity, *i.e.*, a vortex, confined between inner and outer boundaries, and for equilibrium to exist, there must be a gradient in static pressure from a lower-than-average value at the inner boundary to a higher-than-average value at the outer boundary. The amount of this depends upon the boundary **radius ratio,** $R_{\text{outer}}/R_{\text{inner}}$. Thus it can be seen that only for radius ratio near 1.0 (small-height blades) can it be said that any one pressure condition exists for the stage. All axial-flow turbine stages of larger radius ratios tend to be more nearly impulse at the inner diameter and more nearly reaction at the outer diameter.

Differences in basic mechanical construction of axial-flow turbine stages exist. Generally, the reaction type of turbine has continued as in the past with a "drum rotor" and stationary blades fixed in the casing, while the impulse type continues as a "diaphragm-and-wheel" construction. However, the mechanical construction bears no fixed relation to the degree of impulse or reaction adopted in the blading design. Designers employ the mechanical construction which they deem suitable for best reliability and efficiency.

The impulse element, when employed for the first expansion, permits nozzle-group control, *i.e.*, steam admission to each group, opening and closing, successively, in response to load changes. This improves the efficiency at low loads through the reduction of the loss due to throttling. With reaction elements, a somewhat similar effect may be obtained by bypassing certain stages as the load increases. The same practice is also employed in impulse elements, for the purpose of sustaining overload.

A greater enthalpy drop can be employed per stage with the impulse element, particularly in the case of multivelocity elements, thus reducing the number of stages in a turbine. This is of special importance in the first expansion if the nozzle chamber is not integral with the turbine casing, so that the casing is not subjected to the initial steam conditions. If turbine elements of equal blade speed could have equal efficiency, one 2 row impulse element would equal four 1 row impulse elements or 16 rows (8 pairs) of reaction elements.

General Advantages of Steam Turbines. Compared with other prime movers, steam turbines require less floor space, lighter foundations, and less attendance; have a lower lubricating oil consumption, with no internal lubrication, the exhaust steam being free from oil; have no reciprocating masses with their resulting vibrations; have uniform torque; have no rubbing parts excepting the bearings; have great overload capacity, great reliability, low maintenance cost, and excellent regulation; are capable of operating with higher steam temperature and of expanding to lower exhaust pressure than the reciprocating engine. Their efficiencies may be as good as steam engines for small powers, and much better in ranges of greater capacities. Single units can be built of greater capacity than can any other type of prime mover. Small turbines cost about the same as reciprocating engines, but large-capacity turbines cost much less than corresponding sizes of reciprocating engines, and they can be built in capacities never reached by reciprocating engines.

STEAM FLOW THROUGH NOZZLES AND BUCKETS IN IMPULSE TURBINES

Nozzles. For the general treatment of the flow of steam, see p. 4–60; for maximum weight of flow of saturated steam, see p. 4–63.

The **theoretical work** obtainable from the expansion of 1 lb of steam is equal to the enthalpy drop in isentropic expansion $h_1 - h_{s2}$, and the spouting velocity is $223.8\sqrt{h_1 - h_{s2}}$ fps. The actual expansion is not isentropic but follows a path such as h_1h_2 on the enthalpy-entropy diagram (Fig. 4), and the available work becomes $h_1 - h_2$.

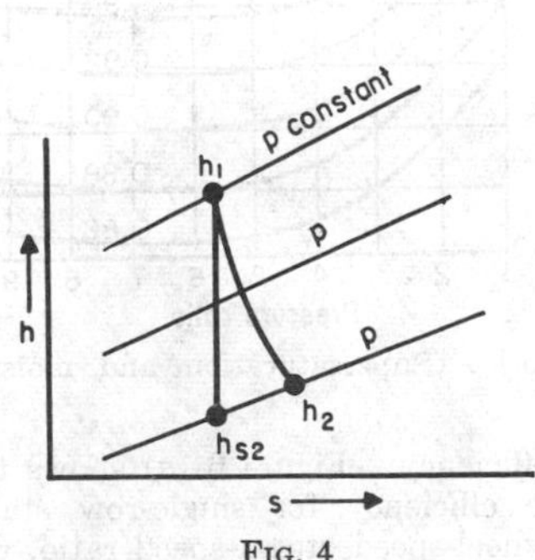

Fig. 4

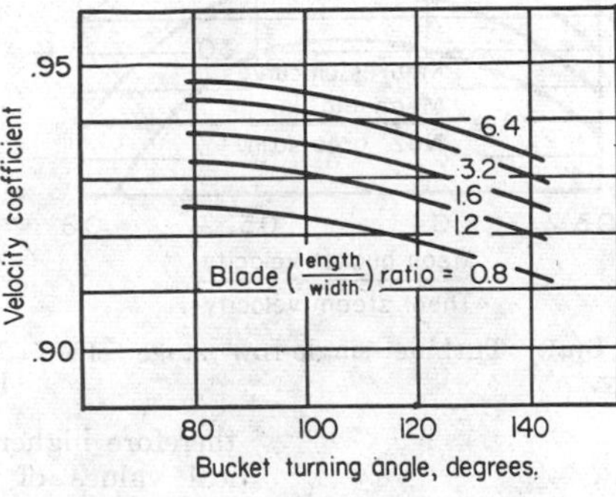

Fig. 5. Impulse bucket-velocity coefficients.

The **nozzle efficiency** is $(h_1 - h_2)/(h_1 - h_{s2})$.

The required **throat area** of the nozzle is $A_t = Wv_t/V_t$ and the **mouth area** is $A_m = Wv_m/V_m$, where v is specific volume, V is velocity, and the subscripts relate to throat and mouth, respectively.

In the case of a subcritical pressure ratio, throat and mouth conditions will coincide; with a supercritical pressure ratio, the mouth area will be larger than the throat area. For **nozzle velocity coefficients** based on tests, see Keenan and Kraft, *Trans. ASME*, **71,** 1949, pp. 773–787. The **bucket-velocity coefficient** is the ratio of the average exit velocity from the bucket divided by the velocity equivalent of the total energy available to the bucket, *i.e.*, the sum of inlet-velocity energy and pressure-drop energy. Typical values of tests on impulse buckets are shown in Fig. 5, when the bucket inlet angle is 3 to 5 deg larger than the exit angle. These are for subsonic flow. Reaction buckets can have the same coefficients as nozzles. For intermediate cases between pure impulse and pure reaction, interpolate between the values for these limiting cases.

If, in the velocity diagram for a usual turbine stage, V_1 = actual nozzle exit velocity, V_2 = bucket relative entrance velocity, V_3 = bucket relative exit velocity, V_4 = absolute leaving velocity, V_0 = velocity corresponding to total state available energy, then the **diagram efficiency** is $(V_1^2 - V_2^2 + V_3^2 - V_4^2)/V_0^2$.

Diagram efficiencies calculated with nozzle and bucket coefficients given above will be higher than efficiencies derived by turbine tests, due to losses not existing in stationary tests of nozzles and buckets.

For supersonic bucket velocities, the impulse bucket-velocity coefficient is lower by the factors in Table 1.

Table 1. Impulse Bucket-velocity Coefficient Factors

Mach No.	< 1.0	1.2	1.3	1.5	1.75	2.0
Factor	1.0	0.997	0.995	0.978	0.928	0.816

Turbine-stage Efficiency. Single-row stages of short blade length have relatively lower efficiency, due to inner and outer side-wall losses; stages with longer blades are therefore higher in efficiency. Figure 6 (*a*) shows typical values of stage efficiency for single-row stages, plotted against the wheel-speed–steam-speed ratio, with pitch diam, inches/noz area, square inches, as a parameter. These curves reflect the net total of losses: (1) friction losses in nozzles (stationary blades); (2) friction losses in buckets (rotor blades); (3) rotation loss of rotor; (4) leakage loss between inner circumference of stationary element and rotor; (5) leakage loss between tip of rotor blades and casing; (6) moisture and supersaturation losses, if steam is wet; [not included in curves of Fig. 6 (*a*)].

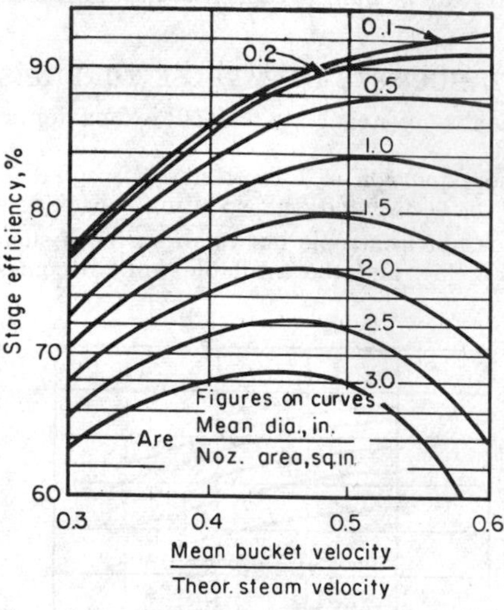

FIG. 6(*a*). Turbine single-row stage efficiency.

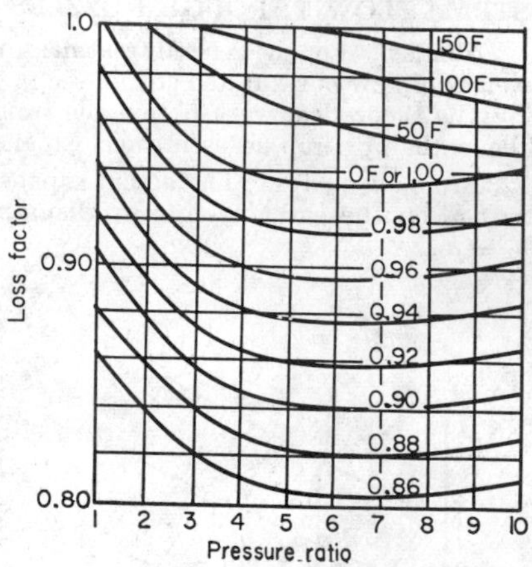

FIG. 6(*b*). Supersaturation and moisture loss.

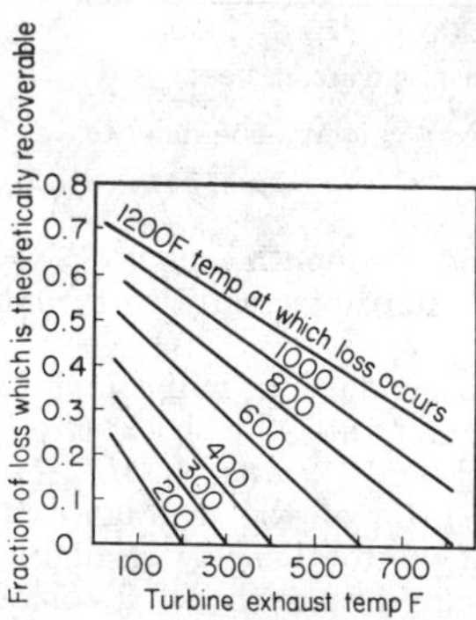

FIG. 6(*c*). Energy-regain chart.

Nozzle and bucket friction losses are minimized by good aerodynamic design and by increasing aspect ratio (blade length/steam passage width). Rotation losses depend upon disk or rotor dimensions and surrounding stationary parts. Exact values for rotation loss depend on several factors; the following formulas may be relied upon for all usual purposes:

$$L_d = 0.042D^2w \times (U/100)^{2.9}$$
$$L_b = 0.187Dwh^{1.25} \times (U/100)^{2.9}$$

where L_d = rotation loss of disk carrying buckets, kw
L_b = rotation loss of one row of buckets, kw
U = wheel speed at pitch diameter, fps
D = pitch diameter (at center line of nozzle), ft
w = density of steam, lb per cu ft
h = mean bucket height, in.

L_b must be figured for each row of buckets. L_d plus the sum of the values of L_b gives the total rotation loss in kilowatts for dry saturated steam. The formula for L_b is approximate.

Leakage loss of steam between inner circumference of stationary element and rotor is minimized by maintaining minimum practical clearance and by use of labyrinth packings (see Figs. 12 and 13 and accompanying text). Leakage loss of steam between tip of rotor blades and casing is similar to that through labyrinths between shaft and stationary parts; the magnitude depends upon the clearance area and the amount of reaction; other things being equal, the larger the percentage of reaction, the larger the leakage (see Fig. 7). Thus designers often employ considerable amounts of reaction in stages with long blades where such losses are small; this improves the net efficiency. In stages with short blades, the best net efficiency obtains with near impulse design. The curves in Fig. 6(*a*) reflect the effects of these practices.

The presence of moisture in the steam causes extra losses. These are probably mainly due to three factors:

1. Effect of supersaturation; that is, the steam in expanding rapidly does not remain in equilibrium but tends to be more or less supercooled; thus less than theoretical equilibrium energy is available.
2. The presence of water drops increases friction losses in the steam itself.
3. Water drops tend to move more slowly than the vapor; they strike the rotor blades at unfavorable velocities and exert a braking effect.

Figure 6(*b*) gives correction factors which may be applied to the values from Fig. 6(*a*) to arrive at stage efficiencies in the "wet" region.

Two- or three-row stages, with one set of nozzles, have lower basic efficiency than single-row stages; they are useful in smaller turbines, and for the first, or governing, stage in larger units. Approximate relative efficiency level of these stages is shown in Fig. 7.

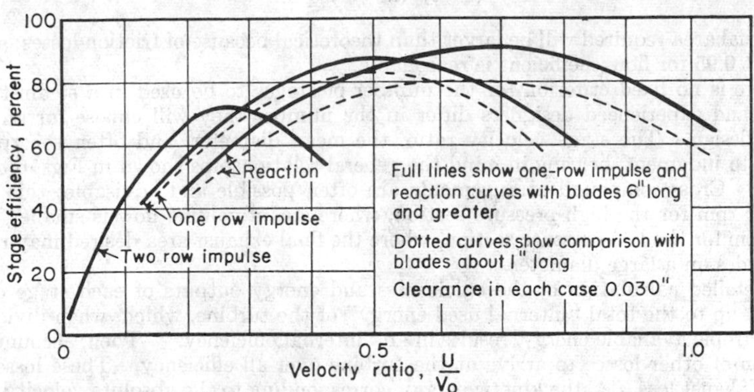

FIG. 7. Variation of the efficiency of turbine elements with the velocity ratio.

The losses occurring in a turbine stage are partially recoverable in succeeding stages in a multistage turbine because the energy available to succeeding stages is increased above that resulting from isentropic expansion. The amount of this factor depends upon the temperature at which the loss takes place, and the turbine exhaust temperature. Values for this factor are shown in Fig. 6(*c*).

Turbine Steam-flow Requirements. The steam flow required by a turbine is related to its power output and steam conditions by the following expressions:

Flow, lb per hr = (TSR/efficiency) × power output, hp or kw
where TSR = theoretical steam rate, lb per hp-hr = 2,545/available energy, Btu per lb,
or, TSR, lb per kwh = 3,413/available energy, Btu per lb.

Values of TSR are given in tables or may be calculated. In case of mixed-pressure or extraction turbines, the various sections of the turbine where flows are added or subtracted must be treated separately.

Turbine Steam-path Design. The basic quantities required for this are the steam conditions (*i.e.*, inlet pressure and temperature and exhaust pressure), the required flow (see above), and the turbine rpm. The latter is often fixed by the requirements of the driven machine; if not, then the choice of rpm by the designer is based upon his experience, and factors such as space or weight limitations, efficiency requirements, stress limits, or required exhaust area. Often several preliminary layouts are needed to arrive at the best design. If it appears that a single stage will suffice, the problem is simple, since the entire available energy is allotted to the one stage. If a multistage machine is required, the total available energy must be divided properly between the various stages.

For a given wheel-speed–steam-speed ratio, the energy to be allotted to the stage is directly proportional to the square of the product (rpm × D), D being the rotor mean diameter. If available energy AE is in Btu per lb, D, in., and velocity ratio, 0.50, then

$$AE = (D/10)^2 \times (\text{rpm}/100)^2 \times 1/657$$

The sum of the AE's per stage for all the stages must equal the total energy on the turbine, which is greater than the isentropic available energy by the amount of the reheat factor.

Having determined the energy to be assigned to each stage, the steam pressure in each stage is fixed, and this, together with the enthalpy determined from the efficiency of the machine from inlet, determines the steam specific volume. The velocity ratio and the degree of reaction decided upon fix the velocity diagram, from which the velocities through the stationary and rotating blades are determined. With the flow Q, lbs per hr, the velocity V, fps, and the volume v, cu ft per lb, determined, then theoretical areas required are given by

$$A = (Q \cdot v)/(25 \cdot V) \text{sq in.}$$

The actual area required will be larger than theoretical because of friction losses; a value of about 0.95 for flow coefficient is reasonable.

There is no fixed criterion for the number of stages to be used in a steam-turbine design, and experienced designers differ in the number they will choose for any particular design. The stage velocity ratio, the mean diameter, and often the rpm are subject to judgment, bearing in mind the general relationships shown in Figs. 6(*a*), (*b*), and (*c*). Cross-compound arrangements are often possible and advisable; this allows a higher rpm for the high-pressure section, where steam volume flow is smaller, and a lower rpm for the low-pressure section, where the final exhaust area desired may require long blades on a large diameter.

A detailed calculation of the efficiencies and energy outputs of each stage can be summed up to the total "internal used energy" of the turbine, which, when divided by the isentropic available energy, results in an "internal efficiency." Then, account must be taken of other losses to arrive at the turbine over-all efficiency. These losses are:

1. Exhaust loss, *i.e.*, the kinetic energy corresponding to the absolute velocity of the steam leaving the last stage, plus the pressure drop through the exhaust connection to the turbine outlet flange, where exhaust pressure is by custom measured as a static pressure
2. Pressure drops through crossover connections if turbine has more than one casing
3. Shaft end-packing leakages

4. Valve-stem leakages, if any
5. Inlet-valve pressure-drop losses
6. Bearing and oil-pump power losses
7. If the turbine drives a generator or gear, the losses of these elements.

LOW-PRESSURE ELEMENTS OF TURBINES

In single-case single-flow turbines (see Fig. 8) designed to expand to high vacuum and to give high efficiency at full rating, difficulty is experienced either (1) in providing the desired areas of low-pressure blades because of the great steam volume in the large machines, or (2) in devising high-pressure elements of the desired efficiency because of the small steam volume, particularly on small machines or machines for high initial pressure. Low-pressure elements are frequently proportioned so as to obtain the maximum advantage from the specified exhaust pressure at some output less than the maximum continuous rating, *i.e.*, to tolerate some congestion and leaving loss in the last rows of blades at the higher outputs.

The ratio of the permissible height of blades to the mean diameter of the steam path may be as high as 0.35. With such a ratio, there is a variation in blade velocity between the inner and the outer radius of the steam path that cannot be properly satisfied with any one steam velocity. Losses incidental to this may be minimized or eliminated by providing blades with warped surfaces, the sections at the inner radius partaking of impulse form with relatively small inlet angles, and those at the outer radius of reaction form with large inlet angles.

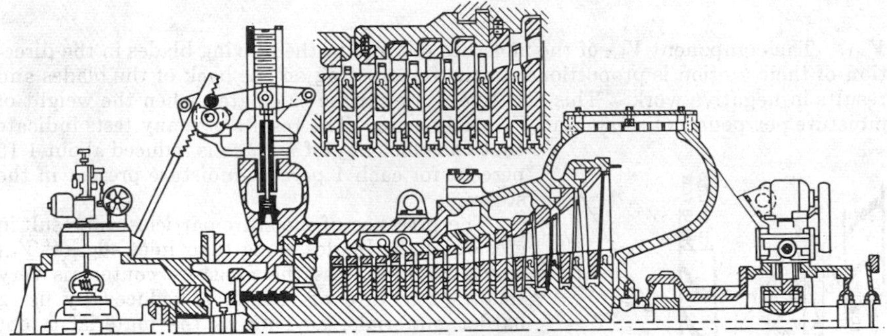

FIG. 8. Half-section of a multistage impulse condensing turbine.

Increased low-pressure blade areas may be obtained by arranging the last expansions in multiple flow thus obtaining greater output with improved efficiency at a given rpm. Some methods of accomplishing this are as follows:

1. A single-case turbine with the last elements arranged for double flow.
2. The steam expansion divided between two casings, coupled in tandem, and driving a single main generator, the low-pressure casing being arranged for double flow.
3. Cross-compound turbines, in which the steam expansion is divided between two or more separate casings driving separate generators electrically tied together. The low-pressure casings are usually double flow. This system permits the turbine elements to be operated at different speeds, selected as appropriate to the respective steam volumes. It lends itself to geared applications, such as marine-propelling machinery, when two or more pinions of different diameters and speeds drive a single gear wheel.
4. Divided-flow turbines in which steam expands in a series of elements in single flow to a point where the flow is divided, with, perhaps, one-third continuing expansion within the same casing to condenser pressure, the remaining two-thirds expanding to condenser pressure in a separate casing containing double-flow elements. This provides triple-flow low-pressure elements. Some four- and six-flow turbines have been built.

Figure 9 represents a tandem compound double-flow 3,600 rpm turbine.

The **leaving loss** at the exit from the last row of blades is $V_{c2}^2/50{,}100$ Btu per lb of steam, where V_{c2} is the absolute terminal velocity in feet per second. The presence of moisture in the steam causes a further loss. The acceleration of moisture particles is less as the density of the steam decreases; hence the difference between the velocities of the particles and the steam increases. As indicated in Fig. 10, with steam velocity V_{s1} and moisture velocity V_m leaving the stationary blades and with bucket velocity V_b, the velocities relative to the moving blades of the steam are V_{c1} and of the moisture V_{m1}. The component V_{m2} of the moisture relative to the moving blades in the direction of their motion is proportional to the force acting on the back of the blades and results in negative work. This negative work can be calculated when the weight of moisture per pound of steam and V_m are known. The results of many tests indicate that the efficiency of a stage is reduced about 1.15 percent for each 1 percent moisture present in the steam.

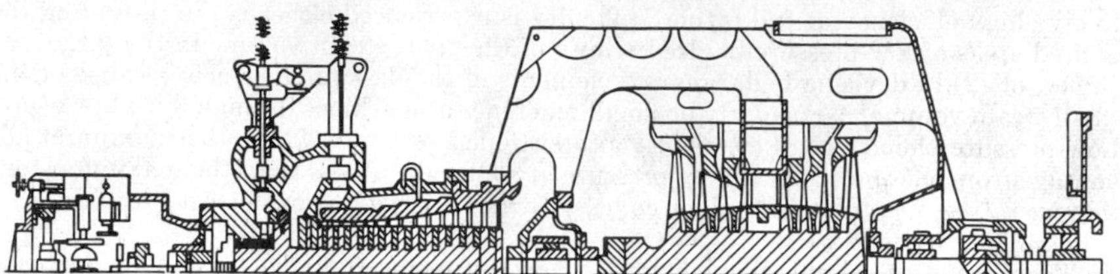

FIG. 9. 60,000-kw, 3,600-rpm, 21-stage impulse turbine with reaction in the later stages. Low-pressure double-flow element.

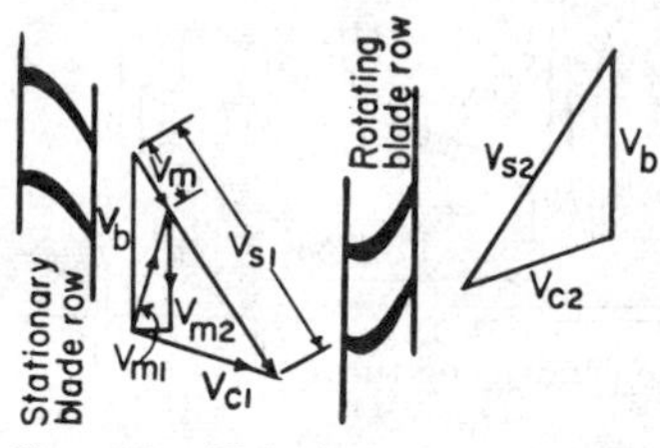

FIG. 10. Velocity of steam and of the moisture in steam.

The presence of moisture particles will result in erosion of the blades along their inlet edges if V_{m1} is too large—unless the moisture content is very small. The rate of erosion is reduced by using harder materials, as long as the material is not affected by corrosion. With blades of 13 percent chrome iron, experience shows that erosion will be small, with V_b of 1,000 fps or less and moisture content not over 12 percent. With a harder material, such as stellite, applied as a shield to the entrance side of the blades, the erosion has been found to be well within practical limits up to V_b of 1,800 fps with moisture of 6 percent. The rate of erosion seems to be roughly proportional to the amount of moisture present and to the third or fourth power of V_{m1} and seems to vary inversely with hardness of the material.

Rotative Speed. The rpm selected greatly influences weight and cost. With two geometrically similar turbines, one having twice the linear dimensions of the other, the steam path areas of the larger, and hence its capacity, would be four times and its weight eight times as great as the smaller. The weight per unit of capacity with similar machines increases inversely as the speed with strict geometrical similarity. For this reason, the highest possible low-pressure blade speeds and rpm are selected. Machines of different speeds are not usually made strictly geometrically similar, and the reduction of specific weight is not so rapid as the above rule would indicate. With large-capacity turbines, blade speeds, at the outer radius, have reached 1,500 fps. With high speeds and small dimensions, the turbine can operate with higher steam temperature and greater temperature fluctuations because of lighter casing walls and less mass of rotor; the amount of distortion is less with more uniform heating; the turbine can be heated and put in service more quickly; space requirements are less; and dynamic loadings on foundations are less.

Balancing (see Secs. 3 and 5). With a rotor, or a component of a rotor, of relatively short axial length (such as a disk), static balancing may suffice. Single bodies of more than half the diameter in axial length are usually dynamically balanced by the use of balancing machines. The balancing is usually done at less than the running speed since a bladed turbine rotor cannot be conveniently rotated in the air at a speed approaching the running speed. The balance at full speed may not be satisfactory unless the balance weights are applied at points diametrically opposite the errors in balance. For this reason balance corrections must sometimes be provided along the length of the rotor.

Unsatisfactory operation of turbine rotors in service, resembling an unbalance, may be caused by non-uniform material or non-uniform heating of a stationary rotor. Care must be taken to see that non-uniformity of material which would cause rotor distortion with heat is eliminated. Turning gears are generally used to keep the rotor turning at low speed when the turbine is shut down, or for a prolonged period before starting.

TURBINE BUCKETS, BLADING, AND PARTS

Figure 11 shows various blade fastenings. Blades are subject to vibration and possible fatigue fracture if their natural frequency is resonant with some applied vibration force. Forced vibrations may arise from the following causes (see p. 5-90):

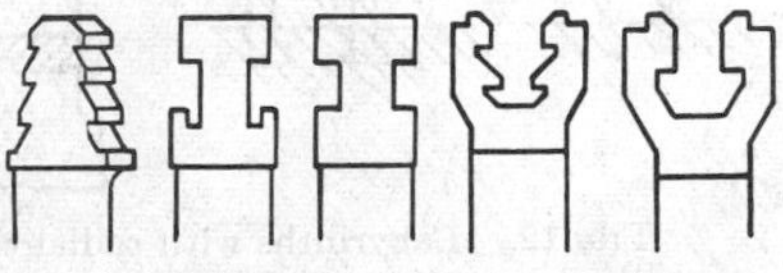

1. Variations in steam forces. The blade frequencies should not be even multiples of the running speed, nor should they be resonant with the frequency of passing nozzle partitions or exhaust hood struts.

Fig. 11. Turbine blade fastenings.

2. Shock, the result of blades being subjected to discontinuous steam flow, such as may be caused by incomplete peripheral steam admission or extraction.

3. Torsional vibrations of the rotor, which may arise in a driven machine.

High-speed, low-pressure blades of condensing turbines are usually of tapering section and have a warped surface in order to provide appropriate blade angles throughout the length of the blade. Long blades of this type frequently have their natural frequency between three and four times the running speed or even lower. Such buckets should always be specially tuned to have a margin in frequency away from running-speed stimuli.

Margins from running speed to assure freedom from fatigue due to resonant vibration whether within or transverse to the plane of the wheel are as follows:

Frequency, cycles per rev	2	3	4	5
Margin between critical and running speeds, percent	20	10	10	5

Higher-frequency buckets whose frequencies cannot assuredly be made nonresonant should be designed with adequate strength to resist such stimuli as may occur under service conditions.

Blade Materials. The material in most general use is a low-carbon stainless steel of the following composition: Cr, 12 to 14 percent; C, 0.10 to 0.12; Mn, 0.08 max; P, 0.03 max; S, 0.05 max; Si, 0.25 max. Its physical characteristics in the heat-treated condition at room temperature may be tensile strength, 100,000 psi; yield point, 80,000 psi; elongation, 21; reduction of area, 60 percent. For the higher-temperature blades, particularly on large machines, it is practice to use this 12 percent chrome steel alloyed with W, Mo, and Va; the superalloys developed for gas turbines are gradually being introduced to permit design for the highest steam temperatures. For the longest last-stage blades required for very large machines, lighter materials such as aluminum alloys and titanium are being seriously considered and may prove useful.

Rotor Materials. Since steam turbines operate at high speeds, rotor materials must be of very high integrity and of basically high strength. In addition, the material should be "tough" at the temperatures at which it is to be highly stressed. This toughness can be measured by laboratory Charpy impact tests at various temperatures (see p. 5-8) or by spinning sample test disks to destruction. In general, the best combination of qualities for both low and high temperatures cannot be obtained in a single forging. Turbine rotor forgings are usually made with small amounts of alloying elements such as Ni, Cr, Va, and/or Mo. For higher temperatures, alloyed 12-Cr steels or austenitic materials are stronger for long-time high-stress conditions but are considerably more expensive.

Casing and Bolting Materials. Casing materials follow the same patterns as rotor materials in general, except that they are almost always used as castings rather than forgings, and the alloy compositions may be biased in favor of those resulting in the best casting practice. Bolts are made of forged or rolled materials.

The practical use of higher steam pressures and temperatures is limited by the available strength and the cost of the best materials.

Leakage. To prevent steam leakage from stage to stage or to the atmosphere, either carbon packings or metallic labyrinth packings are employed. Carbon packings consist of one or more rings of pure carbon made in sections of 90 or 120 deg and held toward the shaft with small clearances by means of springs. The springs should have an axial component of force to hold the rings against the side of the box. To reduce steam leakage from the high-pressure end to the atmosphere, and air from the atmosphere to the vacuum end of the turbine, the packing is arranged in multiple rings. On the high-pressure end, the leakage of steam past the first few rings may be carried to some of the low-pressure stages of the turbine, so that the outer rings need only prevent the leakage of this low-pressure steam to atmosphere. On the vacuum end, water glands are used, or low-pressure steam is introduced between the packing rings in just sufficient quantity to supply the leakage toward the vacuum end of the turbine, and again the outer rings are employed to reduce the leakage of this low-pressure steam to the atmosphere.

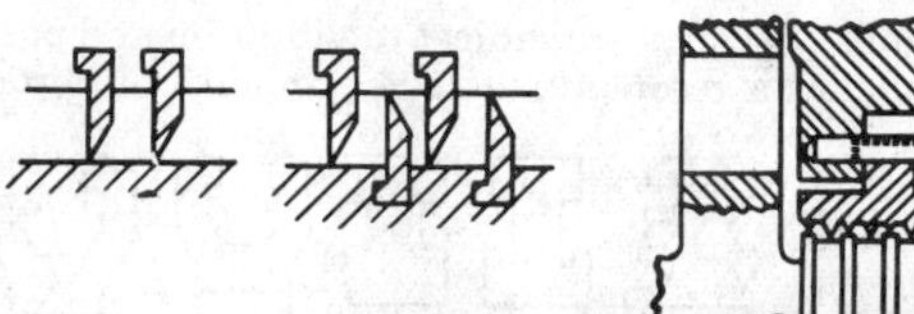

Fig. 12. Labyrinths with radial clearance.

Labyrinths dependent upon radial clearances are shown in Fig. 12. In the design with "high-and-low" teeth, heavy teeth are cut on the turbine shaft, and thin teeth are part of a renewable packing ring which is made in segments backed and held inward by flat springs. The key indicated in the figure prevents turning of the segments. These types require that the rotor remain sensibly concentric with the stator but do not require a close axial adjustment.

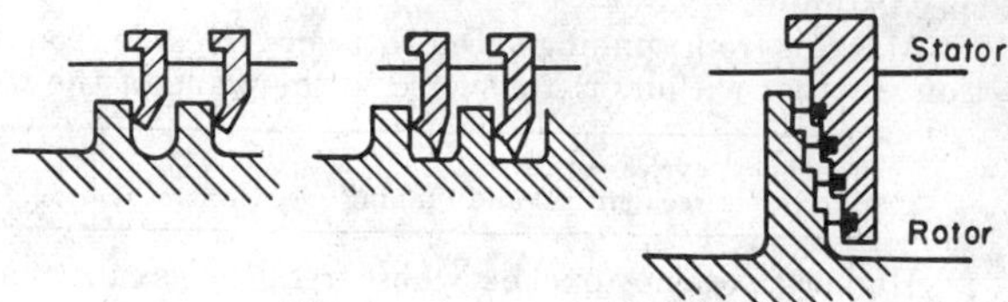

Fig. 13. Labyrinths with axial clearance.

Labyrinths dependent upon axial clearances are shown in Fig. 13. These require the maintenance of a close axial adjustment of the rotor.

The flow through a labyrinth may be approximately determined by the formula:

$$W = 25KA \sqrt{\frac{P_1}{V_1}\left[1 - \left(\frac{P_2}{P_1}\right)^2\right] \Big/ \left[N - \ln \frac{P_2}{P_1}\right]}$$

where W = weight flow of steam, lb per hr
K = experimentally determined coef
A = area through packing clearance space, sq in.
P_1 = initial pressure, psia
V_1 = initial specific volume of steam, cu ft per lb
P_2 = final pressure, psia
N = number of throttlings

The value of K for interlocking labyrinths where the flow velocity is effectively destroyed between throttlings is approximately 55 and is independent of clearance for usual clearance values.

For non-interlocking labyrinths, *i.e.*, stationary teeth against a straight cylindrical shaft, the value of K varies with the ratio of tooth spacing to radial clearance, being about 100 for tooth spacing of five times the radial clearance, reducing to about 60 for a tooth spacing fifty times the clearance.

Turning Gears. Large turbines are equipped with turning gears to rotate the rotors slowly during warming up, cooling off, and particularly during shutdown periods of several days when it may be necessary to start the turbine again at short notice. The object is to maintain the shaft or rotor at an approximately uniform temperature circumferentially, so as to maintain straightness and preserve the balance. Turning gears permit an appreciable reduction in starting time, particularly following a relatively short shutdown.

It is not necessary to use high-pressure oil to lift the journals off their bearings when using a turning gear. A low-pressure motor-driven oil pump is used which floods the bearings with about half their usual flow of oil. The turning gear is made powerful enough to start the rotor and rotate it at from 1½ to 3 rpm.

High-temperature Bolting. The bolting of high-pressure high-temperature joints, particularly turbine-shell or valve-bonnet joints, is very exacting. It is worth while to taper the threads of either the male or the female element so that the engagement of the threads throughout the length of the engaged threaded portion will give approximately uniform bearing. The reliability of taper-threaded bolts is superior to that of parallel-threaded bolts.

Thrust bearings must usually be designed to carry axial rotor thrust in either direction, with sufficient margin to take care of unusual operating conditions. The thrust runner on small turbines may be machined solid on the shaft, but more usually it is a separate piece shrunk on and secured from endwise motion. The stationary bearing surfaces may be of the pivoted-shoe type, or made in solid plates with babbitt or other bearing-material facing, with grooves for oil supply and "lands" to carry the thrust load.

Axial thrust on the turbine rotor is caused by pressure and velocity differences across the rotor blades, pressure differences from one side to the other on wheels or rotor bodies, and pressure differences across shaft labyrinths which have steps in diameter. The net thrust is the sum of all of these effects, some of which may be in one direction, and some in the opposite direction. Rotor-blade and wheel or body thrust are usually in the direction of steam flow. It is usual to balance this thrust either partially or completely by proper choice of shaft packing diameters and pressure differences, so that the net thrust may not be too large. The thrust bearing must be made large enough so that it is not overloaded by the net thrust. In this respect it is necessary to foresee all operating conditions which may influence the net thrust and allow for these; in addition some margin must be allowed for abnormal or unforeseen circumstances which may occur in service. (See also p. 8–170.)

Governors. Steam turbines are nearly always equipped with speed-control governors and with separate overspeed governors. The only exceptions are special cases where it is judged that the possibility of overspeed due to loss of load is exceedingly remote. The speed-control governor may be arranged for a wide range of speed setting, in the case of a variable-speed turbine. The steam flow-controlling valve or valves are operated by this governor, usually through a hydraulic relay mechanism. The overspeed governor is usually of an overisochronous type, arranged to trip at 10 percent over normal full speed (on some small turbines, 15 percent), actuating a quick-closing stop valve to shut off the steam supply to the turbine. Speed-control governing systems are usually designed so that the overspeed-governing system is not brought into action on sudden loss of full load.

On automatic extraction machines, the speed governor must be correlated with the extraction-pressure controlling-valve system.

On reheat turbines, because of the large stored steam volume in the reheater and piping, it is necessary to protect the turbine from overspeed on sudden loss of load by shutting off this stored steam from the low-pressure stages. This is done by intercept valves, actuated by a governor set slightly higher than the speed governor. In some cases, a stop valve is added in series for greater certainty of operation. Alternately, a relief valve can be actuated to blow the reheater steam down to the condenser or to atmosphere.

Speed-governing systems can be supplied of various sensitivities and speed ranges, to suit the requirements of the driven apparatus. (See also Sec. 16.)

TURBINES FOR SPECIAL CONDITIONS

Low-capacity and **low-speed turbines** are employed for engine-room auxiliaries, portable generating sets, etc. Usually, they comprise a single turbine element. Their efficiency may be less than that of a corresponding reciprocating engine, but they are employed because of their compactness and because they require no internal lubrication. The exhaust steam is free from oil or grease and is available for heating purposes. They are frequently coupled to the driven machine by means of speed-reducing gears.

In **back-pressure turbines,** the exhaust steam is employed for some heating process, and the turbine work is a by-product. If all the exhaust steam is condensed in heat-absorbing apparatus and returned to the system, the thermal efficiency of the system may be over 90 percent. One application is the **superposition** of a high-pressure system on lower-pressure power units, with the exhaust from the high-pressure turbine going to the low-pressure steam mains. By this device, an old power station can be rehabilitated and its capacity increased. Two methods of operation are in use: (1) with constant intermediate pressure, as when the lower-pressure power units operate also with steam from lower-pressure boilers such as older existing boilers, and (2) with variable intermediate pressure as when the low-pressure units receive steam only from the back-pressure turbine.

Boiler feed-pump drive turbines have been used extensively as part of the power plant system, especially for large, high-pressure plants where the required feed-pump power may amount to 4 percent of the gross plant output. The turbine and pump can be matched as to rotative speed. These turbines are integrated into the main cycle in one way or another, usually by taking their inlet steam from the reheater inlet line and exhausting to one or more feedwater heaters or to a condenser after extractions for feedwater heating. These turbines often have a connection to the main steam header for starting and low-load operation.

With **extraction turbines,** partly expanded steam is extracted at one or more points; the turbines may be either condensing or non-condensing. Extraction turbines are usually designed to sustain full rated output, with or without extraction, and are provided with automatic regulating mechanisms to deliver steam from the extraction points at constant pressure, as long as there is sufficient power load to provide the necessary flow. The use of such extraction turbines, particularly with high initial pressures in connection with many industrial processes requiring moderate- or low-pressure steam, results frequently in a high efficiency of power production; *i.e.,* the only heat required in such a plant over and above that to provide the required process steam is the heat equivalent of the power generated by the steam before extraction. This means that such power can be produced at nearly 100 percent thermal efficiency.

Figure 14 illustrates a typical extraction turbine. In this case, the unit is equipped with internal valves (grid valves) at the lower extraction point shown. The valves at higher extraction points are usually of the internal "poppet-valve" type. The extraction-stage valves are under the control of an extraction-pressure-actuated governor; they determine the flow to the subsequent stages of the turbine and maintain the pressure in the extraction stage. The operation of the valves is by means of a diaphragm or piston controlling the admission of high-pressure steam or oil to an actuating cylinder, which, in turn, opens or closes the valves to the nozzle ports to the succeeding stage. Extractions of this kind are called pressure-controlled extractions, and the pressure is maintained practically constant over a wide range if the load is sufficient to provide the required steam flow. These are to be differentiated from the reducing-valve extractions.

In the reducing-valve type of extraction, a simple opening into a given stage is provided, the pressure in the stage varies with the load, and the flow of extracted steam is regulated by a valve external to the turbine.

Turbines that heat their own feed water only are regenerative.

A house turbine is a turbine that generates power for service within the plant, driving auxiliaries, etc. Certain house turbines, in addition, heat the feed water for the whole station, the main units not being used for this purpose. Such turbines are extraction turbines. With this type of house turbine the exhaust is condensed in the lowest temperature feed-water heater and the turbine is provided with points of extraction for further feedwater heating. If pressure-regulating valves are used at the extraction, the feedwater temperature can be maintained constant regardless of load variations of the main unit and the station auxiliaries. Even without such valves the extraction pressures may be kept higher than on the main unit by regulating the load on the extraction turbine. Such turbines are frequently used to drive the large auxiliaries and also in conjunction with superposed turbines to give a regenerative cycle effect when the older main units being superposed upon do not have adequate provision for steam extraction.

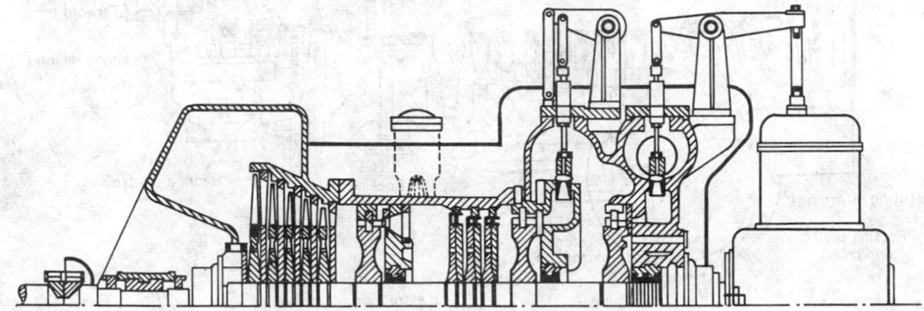

FIG. 14. Extraction turbine.

Special Turbine Types

Although a large majority of turbines built are of the axial-flow type, of which typical examples are shown in the various illustrations, several other types are manufactured. Most important among these are:

1. The **tangential helical-flow** turbine, in which the steam is directed tangentially and radially inward by nozzles against buckets milled in the wheel rim and made to flow in a helical path reentering the buckets one or more times. Such machines have been limited to smaller single-stage designs, and are very simple and rugged.

2. The radial outward-flow turbines of the **Ljungström** type, having two opposed-rotation rotors. Such machines are not built in the United States, but there are at least two manufacturers in Europe using this design with success. These turbines are shorter axially than axial-flow units of similar capacity, but require two generators, one for each rotating shaft.

Single-rotation radial-flow machines are also built in Europe. Other special types include the axial reentry single-stage machine, now generally outmoded, and the radially inward-flow type as described by Birmann (*Trans. ASME*, **76,** No. 2, 1954, p. 173), which, while not available as a standard steam-turbine type, has found use in a number of special design cases.

Main Propulsion Marine Turbines. (See also p. 11–48.) The main propulsion marine turbines are basically the same as central-station or industrial turbines except that usually the turbine is divided into a high-pressure and a low-pressure element, each geared through a common low-speed gear to the propeller shaft. The advantages of this compound arrangement are that two high-speed pinions divide the load on a common low-speed gear, thus reducing gear weight as compared to a single turbine. The high-pressure turbine can be made higher speed than the low-pressure turbine and

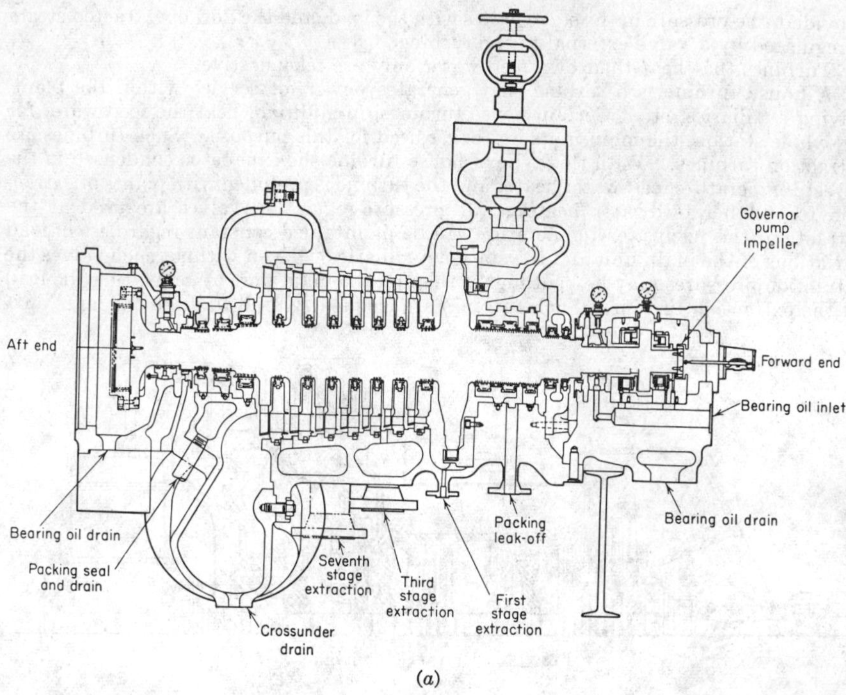

(*a*)

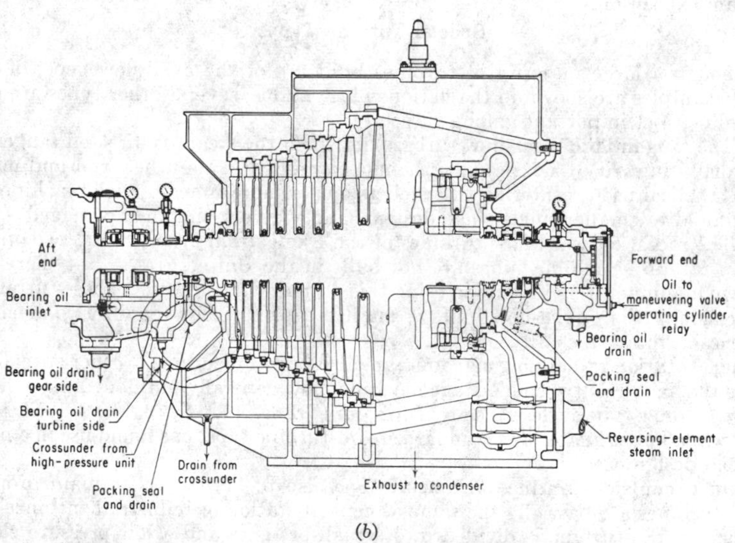

(*b*)

FIG. 15. 16,000-hp cross-compound marine turbine designed for steam conditions of 600 psig, 850 F, 1½ in. Hg. (*a*) High-pressure section for 6,550 rpm normal speed; (*b*) low-pressure section for 3,750 rpm normal speed. Low-pressure section contains 2-stage reversing element. (*General Electric Co.*)

so better adapted to the low volume flow; and each turbine can have a short rugged shaft.

Such turbines usually require a reversing element for operating the vessel astern. This is usually a two- or three-row velocity-stage impulse turbine arranged in the exhaust space of the low-pressure ahead turbine so as to operate under vacuum under normal ahead conditions. The rotation loss of such an astern turbine varies from 1 to 2 percent depending upon the vacuum and the percentage of ahead power which is put into the astern turbine.

Being directly geared to the propeller shaft, marine turbines must work at variable speeds. Overspeed governors are not required but are sometimes applied as precautionary measures. Control is effected in most cases by nozzle valves supplemented by a throttle valve. A typical marine turbine is shown in Fig. 15.

Mechanical-drive Turbines. So many sizes and types are available from manufacturers, and they have been adapted to so many applications, that it is impossible to

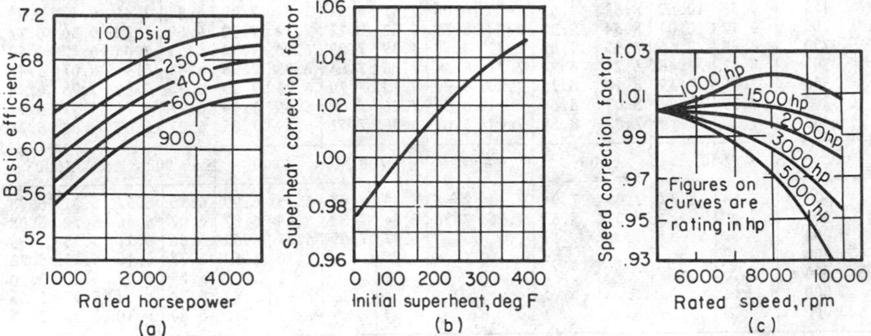

Fig. 16. Mechanical-drive turbine efficiencies. (*a*) Curve applies for speed of 5,000 rpm. Figures on curves are main pressure in psig. (*b*) Superheat correction factor. (*c*) Rated load speed correction factor.

give here more than a general description. These turbines are commonly built in sizes from a few horsepower to several thousand horsepower; for marine propulsion, machines of 70,000 hp or more have been built, and there is no real upper limit. If the speed of the driven machine is low, a reduction gear should be used in order to reduce size and cost of the turbine and improve its efficiency. Mechanical-drive turbines have a wide range of application, being very adaptable to design for any steam conditions, and a wide variety of speeds. They can be equipped with speed governors suited to the requirements, *i.e.*, of very good stability and accuracy if this is desirable, and arranged for various constant-speed settings over a wide speed range (as much as 10:1), if required. Figure 16 shows approximate values of turbine efficiency to be expected in the medium-size ranges for the range of normal steam pressures encountered.

STEAM-TURBINE PERFORMANCE

The ideal **steam rate** (steam consumption in pounds per kwh) of a turbine is $3412.7/(h_1 - h_{s2})$. See Fig. 4 for symbols. See also p. 4–58.

The actual steam rate is $3412.7/\eta_t(h_1 - h_{s2})$, where η_t is the **engine efficiency** of the turbine only, inclusive of mechanical losses.

The actual steam rate of turbine and generator is $3412.7/\eta_e(h_1 - h_{s2})$, where η_e is the engine efficiency including all mechanical and electrical losses.

The enthalpy of the steam leaving the turbine elements h_2 is

$$h_2 = h_1 - \eta_s(h_1 - h_{s2}) = (Wh_1 - 3412.7P_g)/W$$

where η_s is the engine efficiency of the steam path, inclusive of leakages and losses but exclusive of mechanical and electrical losses; W is the steam flow, lb per hr; and the gross output P_g is the net output plus mechanical and electrical losses, kw.

Table 2 gives steam rates for the ideal turbine through a wide range of operating conditions. The performance of a turbine is usually expressed as a steam rate in the case of machines having no extraction or admission of steam between inlet and exhaust. This is generally true of small units and most non-condensing turbines.

Table 2. Theoretical Steam Rates, Pounds per Kwh
(From Keenan and Keyes, "Theoretical Steam Rate Tables," ASME, 1938.)

Pressure, psig	Initial temperature, deg F													
	Saturated		500		600		700		800		900		1000	
	Exhaust pressure, in. Hg abs													
	1	2	1	2	1	2	1	2	1	2	1	2	1	2
100	10.20	11.32	9.72	10.24	8.72	9.60	8.18	8.98	7.67	8.38	7.19	7.83	6.74	7.31
150	9.58	10.52	8.82	9.68	8.30	9.08	7.81	8.51	7.34	7.97	6.89	7.46	6.47	6.99
200	9.17	10.01	8.54	9.32	8.04	8.75	7.57	8.21	7.12	7.70	6.69	7.22	6.30	6.77
250	8.88	9.66	8.35	9.07	7.85	8.52	7.39	7.99	6.96	7.50	6.55	7.05	6.17	6.62
300	8.67	9.40	8.21	8.90	7.71	8.34	7.26	7.83	6.83	7.36	6.44	6.91	6.07	6.49
350	8.49	9.19	8.10	8.76	7.60	8.20	7.15	7.70	6.73	7.23	6.35	6.80	5.98	6.39
400	8.35	9.01	8.03	8.66	7.51	8.09	7.06	7.60	6.65	7.14	6.27	6.71	5.91	6.31
450	....	....	7.97	8.59	7.44	8.01	6.99	7.51	6.59	7.05	6.21	6.63	5.86	6.24
	550		600		650		700		800		900		1000	
500	7.64	8.22	7.39	7.94	7.15	7.68	6.94	7.43	6.53	6.99	6.15	6.57	5.81	6.18
600	....	....	7.31	7.83	7.06	7.56	6.84	7.32	6.44	6.87	6.07	6.46	5.72	6.08
1,000	....	....	....	....	....	....	6.67	7.09	6.23	6.62	5.86	6.21	5.53	5.86
1,400	....	....	....	....	....	....	....	....	6.16	6.53	5.77	6.10	5.43	5.73
1,600	....	....	....	....	....	....	....	....	....	....	5.75	6.07	5.40	5.70
2,000	....	....	....	....	....	....	....	....	....	....	5.73	6.04	5.37	5.65
3,000	....	....	....	....	....	....	....	....	....	....	5.80	6.10	5.36	5.63

Turbines having automatic pressure-controlled extractions or admissions of steam between inlet and exhaust usually have their performance expressed by a chart showing required throttle flow *vs.* load for varying amounts of steam extracted or admitted at specified conditions.

Turbines working on regenerative and/or reheat cycles, condensing, usually have performance expressed as a heat rate, based upon a carefully specified heat-cycle arrangement. This is usually illustrated by a diagram that defines all the surrounding conditions. See, for example, Fig. 21, actual cycle.

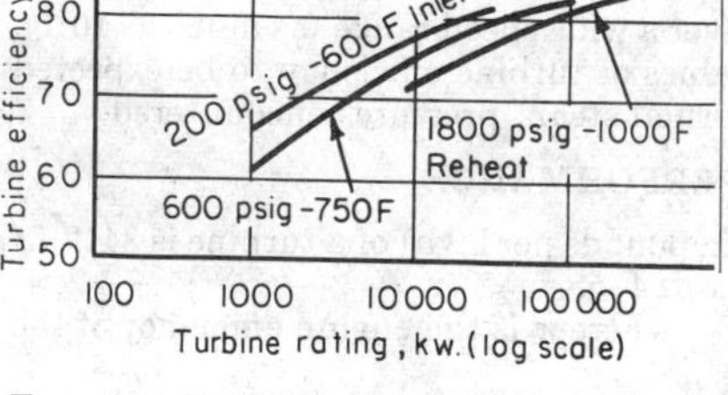

Fig. 17. Turbine efficiencies *vs.* capacity.

The above methods for expressing turbine performance are more satisfactory for most applications than the use of turbine "engine efficiencies." However, it is useful to know the general range of turbine efficiency realized in practice. The engine efficiency of a turbine depends mainly upon the flow areas and diameter of stages, the average velocity ratio, as can be deduced from Fig. 6, the number of turbine stages, and the steam conditions. With so many variables, it is not possible to do more than show a general picture of efficiency as a function of rating, as in Fig. 17, for multistage condensing turbines. Non-condensing turbines will usually have similar efficiency levels; automatic extraction turbines will generally be slightly lower because of extra losses in the control-stage sections.

Approximate steam rates for turbines operating without auxiliary admissions or extractions of steam between inlet and exhaust may be estimated for any turbine rating by dividing theoretical steam rate, corresponding to inlet steam pressure and temperature and exhaust pressure, by the appropriate turbine efficiency from Fig. 17.

A short method for calculating extraction-turbine performance is illustrated by the following example:

Assume a 12,500-kw automatic-extraction-condensing unit operating at 10,000 kw, with 175,000 lb per hr extraction for process at 150 psig with no extraction for feedwater heating, and throttle steam conditions of 850 psi, 825 F, exhaust at 2 in. Hg abs.

PROCEDURE. Find theoretical steam rates (TSR) from Table 2 or steam charts; TSR_1 for 850 psi, 825 F, 2 in. Hg is 6.58 lb per kwh; TSR_2 for 850 psi, 825 F to 150 psi is 18.6 lb per kwhr.

Turbine generator efficiency from Table 3, single auto extraction at 80 percent rating (10,000 kw on a 12,500-kw unit), is 78 percent. Efficiency correction for auto extraction (see Table 3) is 0.92. Then actual steam rate (ASR) is TSR/(efficiency × correction); $ASR_1 = 6.58/78\% \times 0.92 = 9.17$ lb per kwh; $ASR_2 = 18.6/78\% \times 0.92 = 25.9$ lb per kwh; Kw generation from extraction flow = extraction flow/ASR_2 = 175,000/25.9 = 6,760 kw.

Kw to be generated by condenser flow = 10,000 − 6,760 = 3,240.

Condenser steam flow required is 3,240 × 9.17 = 29,700 lb per hr, or (say) 30,000 lb per hr. Total steam flow to throttle then is 175,000 + 30,000 = 205,000 lb per hr.

Table 3. Basic Efficiency for Steam Turbines, Straight Condensing at Rated Load

Kw capacity	Equivalent mechanical drive, hp	Initial steam conditions				
		250 psi 500 F	400 psi 650 F	600 psi 750 F	800 psi 825 F	1,250 psi 900 F
875	1,200	63	63	62		
1,875	2,600	76	67	66		
2,500	3,500	69	69	68		
5,000	6,900	...	74	73	73	
7,500	10,300	...	76	75	75	
12,500	17,200	...	78	78	78	77
15,625	21,500	...	79	79	79	77
20,000	27,100	...	79	80	79	79

Efficiency correction factors, mechanical drive and auto-extraction-condensing turbines—multiply basic efficiencies by:

	At 80% rating	At 100% rating
Single auto-extraction-condensing..........	0.92	0.96
Double auto-extraction-condensing.........	0.88	0.92

Figure 18 gives correction factors for speeds which differ from 3,600 rpm.

Comparative heat rates of large turbine-generator units are shown in Fig. 19 as functions of unit capacity and steam pressure and temperature. In these charts the difference between the "gross" heat rate, *i.e.*, based on generator terminal output, and the "net" heat rate, based on generator terminal output minus power to drive the boiler feed pump, is clearly shown. Six feed-water heaters are assumed in each case.

Over-all plant heat rates for large modern steam electric-generating plants are now in the range of 8700 to 9000 Btu per kwh, based on the higher heating

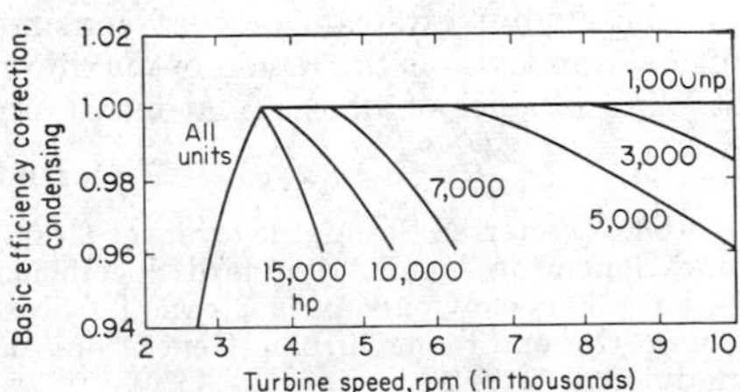

FIG. 18. Correction factor for condensing mechanical drive turbines.

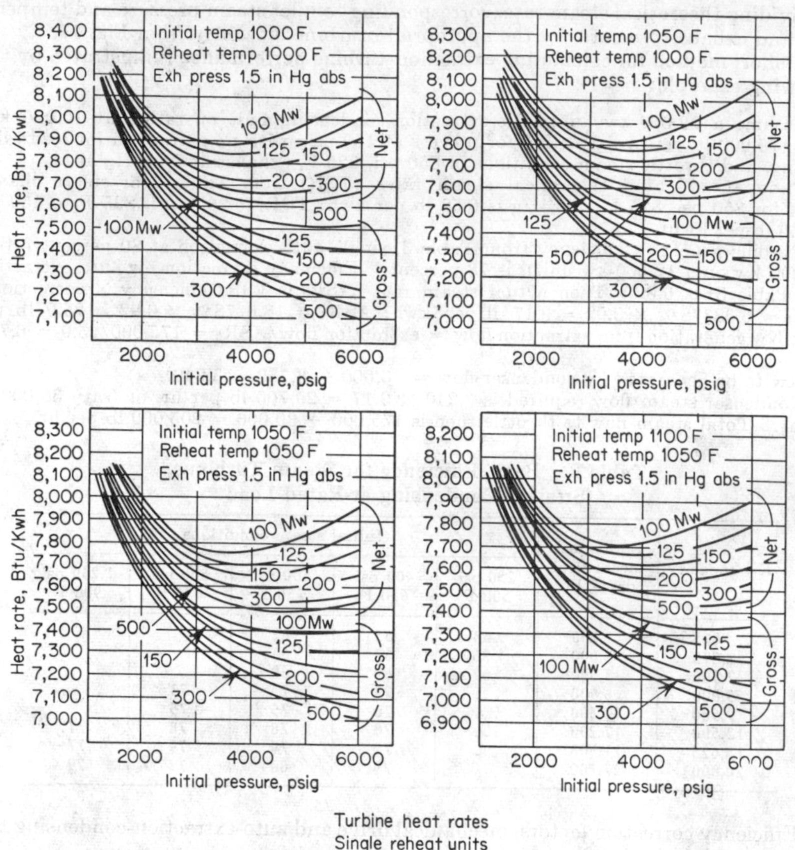

Fig. 19. Heat rates of large central-station turbine-generators. (*Courtesy Westinghouse Electric Corp., Southeastern Electric Exchange, and Combustion Magazine.*)

value of the fuel (38 to 39 percent thermal efficiency). Some new plants being designed may be expected to have 39 to 40 percent thermal efficiency.

Turbine Ratings

Turbine generating sets are usually rated at the maximum capability of the turbine under specified conditions of steam pressures and temperatures, and extraction, if any. The best point of steam or heat consumption is usually near rated capacity. For special applications the region of maximum efficiency can often be set at a lower load, at some sacrifice of efficiency at maximum capability.

Preferred Standards

(See "Preferred Standards for large 3,600 rpm 3-phase, 60-cycle Condensing Steam Turbine-Generators" and "Standard Specification Data for Generators for large 3,600 rpm 3-phase 60-cycle Condensing Steam Turbine Generators" prepared by Joint AIEE-ASME Committee on Steam Turbine-Generators, AIEE Publications 601 and 602, May, 1945, and modified Oct. 1948).

The preferred standard turbine-generator units have been established by a joint Committee of the AIEE and ASME for ratings shown in Table 4. In each case the unit is expected to develop its full rating at 3½ in. Hg abs exhaust pressure when steam is extracted for heating its own feedwater in a regenerative arrangement, with the specified number of feedwater heater extractions and with final feedwater temperatures as shown. The feedwater temperatures will vary a few degrees among different manufacturers.

Table 4. Preferred Standards for Large 3,600-rpm, Three-phase, 60-cycle Condensing Steam Turbine-generators

Rating, kw	Steam press, psig	Initial temp, deg F	Reheat temp, deg F	Std exhaust press, in. Hg abs	No. of extractions	Approx feed-water temp, deg F	Approx reheat press, psia	Approx heat rate, Btu per kwh*
12,650	600	825	....	1.5	4	348	...	10,370
16,500	850	900	....	1.5	4	347	...	9740
22,000	850	900	....	1.5	4	354	...	9650
33,000	850	900	....	1.5	5	415	...	9480
44,000	850	900	....	1.5	5	413	...	9350
44,000	1,250	950	....	1.5	5	404	...	8960
66,000	850	900	....	1.5	5	414	...	9320
66,000	1,250	950	....	1.5	5	408	...	8960
100,000	1,450	1000	....	1.5	5	442	...	8620
100,000	1,450	1000	1000	1.5	5	442	433	8150
150,000	1,800	1000	1000	1.5	7	450	445	7990

* These heat rates are based upon generator terminal output, and are values approximating those which would be quoted by manufacturers. They are given here to show typical performance to be expected from machines of these ratings and steam conditions.

Steam Pressure and Temperature

There has been a continual increase in turbine-inlet steam pressures and temperatures in fossil-fuel-fired plants because of improved thermal efficiency and greater capacity from a given physical machine size. For large units (over 100,000 kw), pressures of 1,800 to 2,400 psi are usual, with temperatures of 1000 to 1050 F, and 1100 F in a few instances. A 125,000-kw unit at 4,500 psi, 1150 F, with reheatings to 1050 and 1000 F, and a 325,000-kw unit at 5,000 psi, 1200 F, with two reheats to 1050 F, have been in service for some years; but these steam conditions are now judged too high for best over-all economy, and the newest large units are at the 3,500-psi level with initial temperature not above 1050 F and one or two reheats at 1000 or 1050 F.

Because of reactor limitations, turbines for **nuclear-fueled plants** have been designed for saturated steam at 1,000 psi maximum. These steam conditions, with relatively low available energy per pound of steam, require large throttle- and condenser-steam rates (nearly double the values attained in fossile-fired plants) and consequent larger passages. The moisture content must be limited, as expansion proceeds, by moisture-extraction devices and/or intermediate reheating. The low initial temperature and pressure and the high moisture content so reduce turbine efficiency that the heat rates of turbine generators in nuclear plants are appreciably higher than those of similar-sized machines in fossil-fuel plants utilizing higher steam conditions. The usual steam pressures delivered to the turbine are 965 psi for boiling-water reactors and 650 psia for pressurized-water reactors. Heat rates of large turbines are respectively about 10300 and 10900 Btu per kwh after deduction of pumping power from gross generator output. With steam reheat, these heat rates are lowered by about 4 to 5 percent.

Reheating with Regenerative Cycle

References: Reynolds, Reheating in Steam Turbines, *Trans. ASME*, **71,** 1949, p. 701. Harris and White, Developments in Resuperheating in Steam Power Plants, *Trans. ASME*, **71,** 1949, p. 685.

Reheating is currently used on almost all new large central-station turbines. It is accomplished by taking the steam from the turbine after partial expansion, reheating it, and returning it to the lower-pressure section of the turbine. Reheating results in lowering of the turbine heat rate by approximately 5 percent; the exact improvement is dependent on several factors. Roughly speaking, 40 percent of the improvement comes from having added heat to the cycle at a higher-than-average temperature (thermodynamic gain), and the remaining 60 percent comes from improvement in turbine efficiency due to reduced moisture loss, increased reheat factor, etc.

Fig. 20. Approximate gains due to reheating.

Reheating can theoretically be done any number of times, but because of extra cost of apparatus and piping, and the steam pressure drops required in practice (8 to 10 percent of the reheat pressure), the economic gains diminish rapidly with more than one reheating (see Fig. 20). In a few cases, two reheatings are employed. (See also p. 4–58).

The throttle and condenser steam-flow rates for a given turbine output are reduced approximately 17 percent and 13 percent, respectively, by reheating once to the initial temperature, as compared to no reheat with the same initial steam conditions.

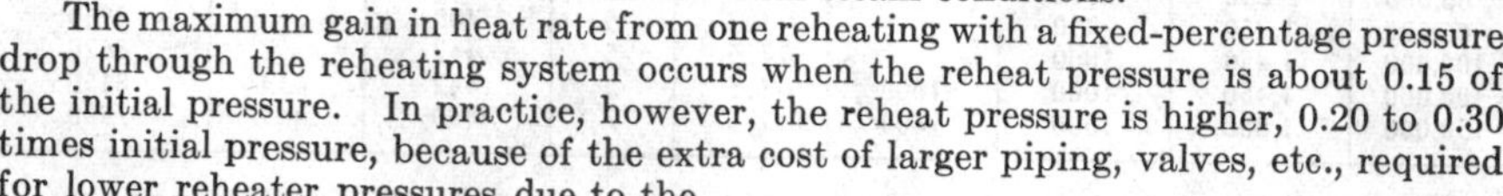

The maximum gain in heat rate from one reheating with a fixed-percentage pressure drop through the reheating system occurs when the reheat pressure is about 0.15 of the initial pressure. In practice, however, the reheat pressure is higher, 0.20 to 0.30 times initial pressure, because of the extra cost of larger piping, valves, etc., required for lower reheater pressures due to the larger steam volume.

Because the reheater and piping contain a relatively large volume of steam, it is necessary to provide quick-closing valves (intercept valves) to shut off this steam from the turbine in the event of sudden loss of load. These valves are operated by the turbine speed-governor system. In extreme cases of a combination of large stored volume and relatively low turbine and generator rotor inertia, another set of valves (reheater stop valves) is used to give added protection against overspeeding. Alternatively, governor-operated blowdown valves may be used to bypass this volume of steam to the condenser.

Regenerative Feedwater Heating

(See also p. 4–59)

The heat consumption of a turbine may be reduced by heating the condensate (feedwater) in stages by the condensation of steam extracted at various points from the turbine. This is shown diagrammatically for an ideal cycle and a more practical cycle in Fig. 21. The difference between the two is in the use of mixing heaters in the ideal cycle with each discharge pumped back while the practical cycle has closed heaters with cascaded drains in the upper and pumped drains in the lowest heater, together with some pressure drop between turbine and heaters and a terminal temperature difference between saturated-steam temperature in the heater and feedwater temperature coming out. Usually the difference between such an ideal and a practical cycle is

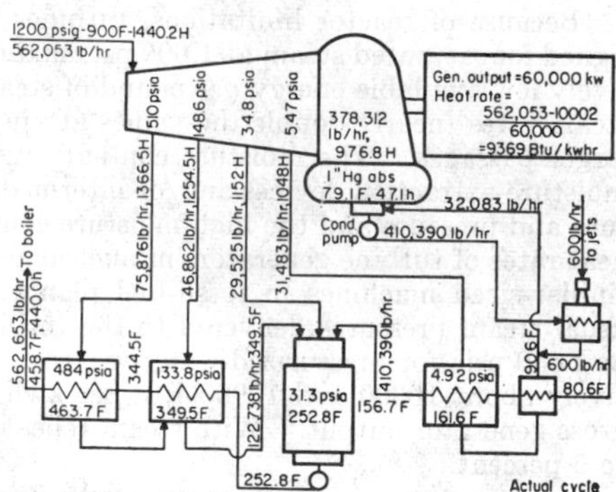

Fig. 21. Comparison of ideal and actual cycles for regenerative feedwater heating.

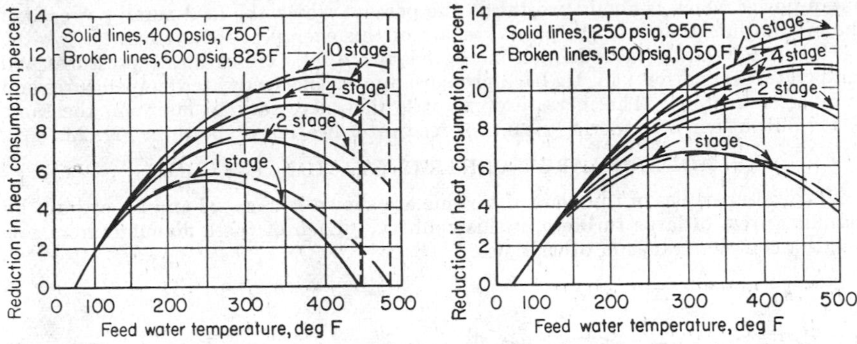

FIG. 22. Reduction in heat rate by use of ideal regenerative cycle, with 1 in. Hg back pressure.

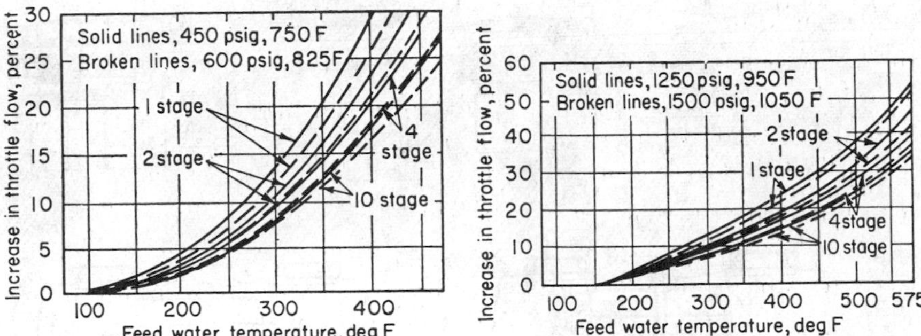

FIG. 23. Increase in steam flow necessary to maintain the same power output when using the ideal regenerative cycle, with 1 in. Hg back pressure.

about 1½ percent. A deaerating type of contact heater with no terminal difference may be substituted for one of the closed heaters as is shown in Fig. 21. Other variations are the use of (1) all open-contact heaters, or (2) drain coolers to reduce the loss due to cascading the drips, or (3) a desuperheating section on the top heater to get a higher final feed temperature, thereby approaching most closely to the ideal cycle. Figures 22 and 23 and Table 5 supply data on the results of regenerative heating based upon the ideal cycle of Fig. 21. No allowance is made for the loss due to the feed-

Table 5. Total Steam Bled, Percent of Throttle Flow

Final feed temp., deg F	Steam pressure and temperature							
	400 psig		600 psig, 825 F		1,250 psig, 950 F		1,500 psig, 1050 F	
	Stages of feedwater heating							
	2	10	2	10	2	10	2	10
150	7.0	7.1	6.9	7.0				
200	11.4	11.8	11.3	11.6	11.2	11.5	10.7	11.0
250	15.6	16.2	15.5	16.0	15.5	15.9	12.6	13.1
300	19.6	20.6	19.5	20.4	19.5	20.3	18.8	19.5
350	23.6	24.8	23.5	24.6	23.6	24.6	20.7	21.6
400	27.1	29.0	27.1	28.8	27.4	28.9	26.4	27.8
450	....	....	30.2	32.5	31.1	33.2	30.0	32.0
500	....	....	....	....	35.0	37.4	33.9	36.1

pump power which is about two-thirds the percent which the feed-pump power is of the net output because of the partial regain of this energy in the system.

Figure 22 shows the reduction in the heat rate for various initial pressures and temperatures, and for 1 in. Hg back pressure, for various feedwater temperatures and number of heaters. The increase of throttle flow necessary to maintain the same power output when extracting steam for feedwater heating is shown in Fig. 23.

MODERN LARGE CENTRAL-STATION TURBINES

Typical examples of this class of turbine are shown in Figs. 24 and 25, as built by manufacturers of large turbines in this country. Each of these manufacturers also builds a complete range of other types.

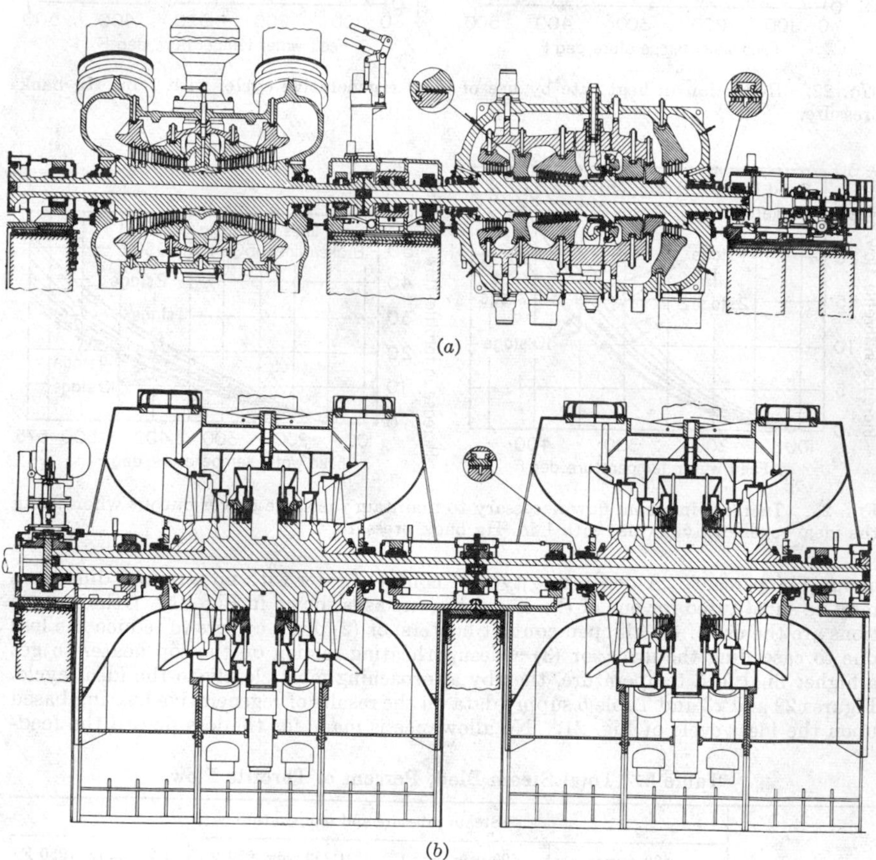

(a)

(b)

FIG. 24. 400,000-kw tandem-compound turbine, Westinghouse Electric Corp.

Figure 24 shows a 3,600-rpm tandem-compound four-flow unit for a rating of 400,000 kw as built by Westinghouse Electric Corp. It is a double-reheat unit for inlet-steam conditions of 3,500 psi, 1000 F, first reheat at 1025 F, second at 1050 F. Steam enters the very-high-pressure section in the right-hand casing and flows to the left and out to the first reheater, returning to the same casing near the left-hand end. After passing through this short group of stages, the steam is led to the second reheater and thence returns to the double-flow casing, from which it is led to the two double-flow low-pressure sections on the left end of the unit. The inlet and interceptor valves and the generator are not shown. The low-pressure-turbine last-stage rotor blades are 28.5 in. active length.

Figure 25 shows a 570,000-kw cross-compound 3,600/1,800-rpm turbine built by General Electric Co. for steam conditions of 2,400 psi, 1050 F, with reheat to 1050 F, with a four-flow exhaust on the low-pressure section. The left-hand casing in Fig. 25*a* is the high-pressure casing, with steam inlet at its right-hand end to a double-flow first stage, from both sides of which the steam then goes through a single-flow section of seven stages. This section exhausts to the reheater, and from the reheater the steam

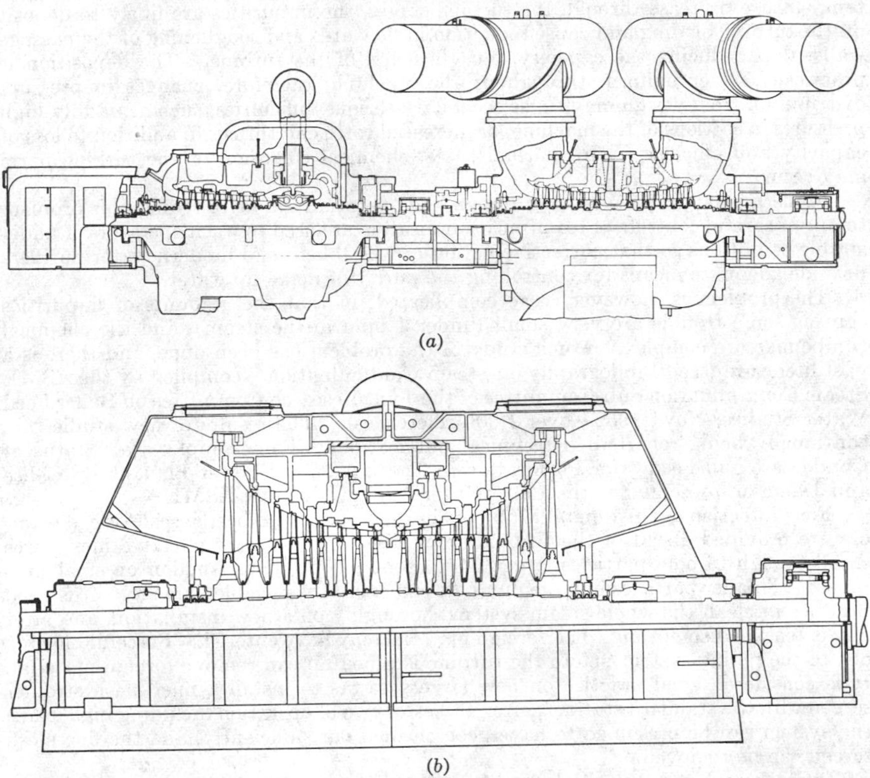

FIG. 25. 570,000-kw cross-compound turbine, General Electric Co. (*a*) High-pressure section; (*b*) low-pressure section (one of two elements).

enters the middle of the right-hand casing shown on Fig. 25*a*, flowing through the two 6-stage sections in this casing in parallel. From each end of this casing, a crossover pipe carries the steam to the low-pressure sections shown in Fig. 25*b*. The generators (not shown) are coupled to the right-hand ends of the two shafts. The low-pressure-turbine last-stage buckets are 38 in. active length.

Impurities in the Steam

(See also p. 9–43)

The steam supply to the turbine is never absolutely free from impurities in the form of various inorganic or organic compounds, the nature of which depends upon the compounds present in the water in the boiler. Some of these compounds are brought to the boiler as impurities in the feed water, and some may be deliberately added as protection against the effects on the boiler of free oxygen, etc. These impurities may then appear in the steam as a consequence of either droplet carry-over in the vapor space of the boiler drum or existence of the impurities in their gaseous form in the steam. Good boiler design includes the use of low vapor velocities and good separators, so that droplet carry-over is usually kept to a very low value. Carry-over of impurities in the gaseous form can only be minimized by keeping the troublesome impurities in the boiler water to the lowest practicable value. Silica in various complicated compound forms is the most troublesome. Copper compounds may appear as deposits in supercritical-pressure turbines.

The effect on the turbine is that as the steam expansion proceeds, and pressure and temperature decrease through the turbine stages, the impurities are likely to deposit on the turbine blading and cause reduction in flow area and roughening of the passage walls, thus reducing the capacity and efficiency of the turbine. The deposition is practically never uniform throughout the machine; therefore, changes in pressure distribution from design may cause secondary serious difficulties, such as unduly high pressures in sections of the machine, or increased rotor end thrust, in addition to loss of capacity and efficiency. In unusual cases, chemical corrosion of the turbine parts may occur.

Modern good practice in plant design and operation is able to reduce this problem to one of careful control. Steam-purity indicators are used to warn operators of undesirable conditions so that corrective action can be taken, and modern water purifiers provide adequate means for controlling the purity of make-up water.

The problem is, however, very complicated, in that the amounts of impurities causing some trouble are very small (under 1 ppm in the steam), and the chemical compounds are complex. Much study of the problem has been done, and there is a vast literature (see "Bibliography on Steam Contamination," compiled by the ASME Steam Contamination Sub-Committee of the Joint Research Committee on Boiler Feed Water Studies, Nov., 1952—over 1,000 references). The results of new studies are continually being reported in technical publications. For example, see "Status of Condensate and Feedwater Purification in Today's Utility Power Plants," by Calise and Dallman, presented at the 1963 Winter Annual Meeting, ASME.

For protection against metallic objects in the steam, weld beads, scale, etc., strainers are provided ahead of the turbine stop valve. These have effective mesh sizes small enough to hold particles larger than about $\frac{1}{10}$-in. diam (smaller on small turbines). Smaller particles in large numbers can cause appreciable damage. It is good practice to clean the whole steam system thoroughly on a new installation, and after any extensive dismantling when foreign material may have entered. Forceful blowing out of the piping system before the turbine is piped up can remove foreign material. It is considered good practice on new large systems to install a finer-mesh strainer screen with the standard strainer; after a week or two of operation including high loads, the system can be presumed to have been cleaned out sufficiently, and the fine mesh screen can be removed.

In large high-pressure, high-temperature systems, appreciable amounts of black iron oxide are formed in the boiler and piping, and this may become loosened and broken into small particles flowing with the steam. These particles can cause harmful erosion of turbine nozzles and buckets.

POWER-PLANT HEAT EXCHANGERS

BY

Walter J. Kleponis and
Richard M. Stephani

SURFACE CONDENSERS

REFERENCES: Heat Exchange Institute Standards for Surface Condensers. Archbold, Miholits, Leidner, and Peron, Economic Sizing of Condensers, through the Use of the Digital Computer, *Proc. Am. Power Conferences*, 1960.

Surface condensers are used in steam-power plants, refrigeration, and air-conditioning systems. (See Figs. 1 and 2.) Their **functions** are (1) to produce an economical back pressure or vacuum at the turbine exhaust for the improvement of heat rate, (2) to deaerate the condensate and decrease corrosion of the feedwater system, and (3) to conserve the condensate for reuse as boiler feed.

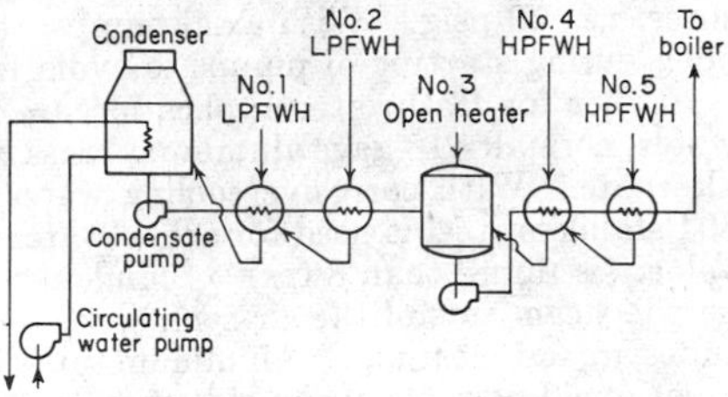

A condensing turbine usually operates at a pressure of 1.0 to 3.5 in. Hg abs. The low back pressure at the exhaust of a turbine improves the heat rate, but the lowest pressure is not necessarily the most economical vacuum.

FIG. 1. Equipment arrangement, schematic.

Deaeration is accomplished by raising the temperature to saturation and reducing the pressure. (See also p. 6–160.) Henry's law states that the concentration of the dissolved gas in a solution is directly proportional to the partial pressure of that gas in the free space above the liquid, with the exception of those gases, *e.g.*, CO_2 and NH_3, which unite chemically with the solvent. Removal of dissolved gas from water is effected by reduction of the partial pressure of the gas in the surrounding atmosphere, regardless of the total pressure. The most practical method of removing dissolved O_2

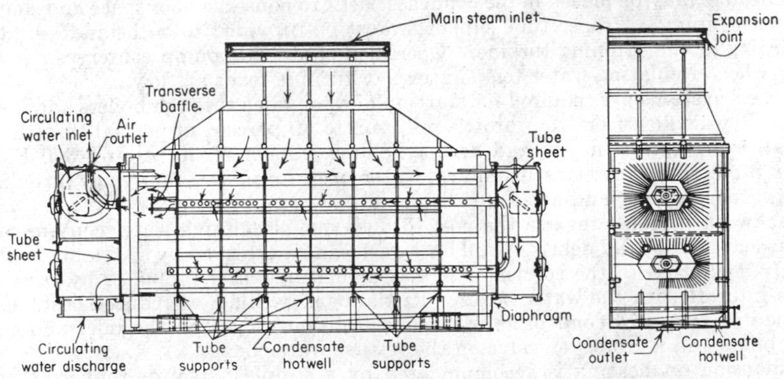

FIG. 2. Two-pass surface condenser. (*Westinghouse Electric Corp.*)

from condensate is to use steam as a scrubber, with a lower pressure at the point of exit from the condenser. The concentration of O_2 in the surrounding atmosphere is thus reduced by dilution with the steam, and by reheating the condensate rain as it falls through a steam belt at the bottom of the condenser, effective deaeration is accomplished. Normally the gas content in the effluent should not exceed 0.03 to 0.01 cc per liter, but condensers can deaerate to 0.005 cc per liter, if needed.

Various ammonia compounds are added to boiler feed makeup as water treatment (see p. 9–46) to reduce the last traces of O_2; free ammonia is liberated in the system and is difficult to remove. With an open tube-bundle design, any ammonia liquid or gas which tends to cling to and corrode the tubes is washed away by a constant stream of condensate. Connections for drains introduced to the condenser must ensure deaeration of the drains.

Tube-bundle design is important. Pressure drop from the outside tube to the air-removal section must be kept to a minimum and yet ensure that all surface is active. Venting of non-condensables must be given attention. The air is drawn from the bundle near the water inlet to the condenser with maximum subcooling of the exiting air-vapor mixture.

Water-box design should minimize turbulence and equalize the water velocities to the tubes to reduce erosion. Semicylindrical water boxes, with either vertical or horizontal axes, have generally superseded rectangular boxes. Design is for a pressure slightly above the shutoff head of the circulating pumps, normally 20 psig with 25 psig as the test pressure. Condensers used with cooling towers have higher water-box pressures, *i.e.*, 50 psig. With axial pumps, the valves at water-box outlets must be kept open during starting of pumps to avoid inherent high shutoff heads.

Tubes for freshwater application are normally 18-gage admiralty metal; for seawater, normally 18-gage aluminum brass, with 90-10 copper-nickel as a more expensive alternate. With corrosive cooling water, stainless steel may be substituted. Type 304 stainless steel is used for acidic water—normally 20- to 22-gage tubes with higher velocities (more than 8 fps). Stainless-steel tubes are resistant to ammonia corrosion on the steam side of the air-cooling section; a higher cleanliness factor can be used, as tubes are self-cleaning. Aluminum tubes frequently offer lower investment, but design must avoid possible steam-side erosion.

The **tube-to-tube-sheet joint** is usually rolled, but welding has found recent favor in minimizing condensate contamination. Silicon-bronze, rather than Muntz metal, tube sheets are preferred when welding with admiralty or aluminum-brass tubes.

Condenser configurations can be varied to the application. Small condensers have round, cylindrical shells, and large condensers have rectangular shells for better utilization of space. Since operation is below 15 psig, the ASME Pressure Vessel Code is not applicable. Steam normally flows down into the condenser, but side-exhaust and axial-flow turbines can be appropriately accommodated with suitable design. Feedwater heaters may be placed in the condenser neck to conserve floor space and simplify extraction piping. Proper tube supports must be provided to withstand vibrations originating in the spinning turbine. Operation of a single pump conserves auxiliary power when circulating-water temperatures or turbine loads are low.

Bypass systems are required for start-up of some once-through boilers and atomic units. Bypass flow from the throttle may run to 30 percent of normal throttle flow through a pressure-reducing and desuperheating station to 50 psi and 300 F with proper protective provisions in the condenser neck or sides. Spraying, turbulence, mixing time, contact, and noise are all problems.

Backwash systems reverse the flow to flush out circulating-water contaminants, such as leaves, fish, and debris. Full backwash can be achieved by a system of butterfly valves external to the condenser in the circulating-water piping or by backwash valves integral with the water boxes. Partial backwashing, at reduced cost, can be obtained on two-pass condensers with pass partition valves on the inlet and outlet water boxes and a crossover valve on the reverse water box.

Expansion on heating is accommodated by a stainless-steel or rubber-belt-type expansion joint between the condenser and turbine exhaust or by spring supports for a condenser directly connected to the turbine exhaust. A flexible diaphragm may be used to accommodate differential expansion between the shell and tube sheets.

Corrosion is minimized by proper selection of materials. Gases (O_2, CO_2, NH_3) causing corrosion are concentrated and deaerated in the air-cooler section, equipped with stainless-steel or 70-30 copper-nickel tubes. (See also p. 6–124 *et seq.*) **Galvanic corrosion,** which takes place between two dissimilar metals connected by a conducting liquid, is especially active when salt water is used for cooling. A protective coating on the steel water box will isolate the steel from the tube sheet and prevent corrosion of the box; wasting plates may serve to compensate for galvanic corrosion.

Erosion by water droplets in the steam is minimized by deflecting baffles or gratings of stainless or carbon steel and by a row or two of stainless-steel tubes on the outer end of the bundle. Tube life is extended by lowered velocities when water contains abrasive materials.

Syphon recovery (28 ft maximum) on the circulating-water systems requires tight piping and a water seal on the discharge pipe.

Performance Calculations, Sizing

Notation:

A = condenser-surface area, sq ft
C_c = cleanliness factor
C_1 = heat-transfer-rate constant
C_m = material and gage factor
C_t = temperature correction factor
c_p = specific heat, Btu per lb, deg F
G = circulating-water quantity, gpm
h = enthalpy, Btu per lb
h_r = heat rejected by steam, Btu per lb
k = tube diameter and gage factor, Table 12
L = length of water travel, ft
NPSH = net positive suction head, ft
O.D. = tube outside diameter, in.
Q = heat transferred, Btu per hr
R = temperature rise $(t_o - t_i)$, deg F
TDH = total dynamic head, ft
t = tube thickness, in.; temperature, deg F
ttd = terminal temperature difference = $t_v - t_o$
t_i = inlet-water temperature, deg F
t_o = outlet-water temperature, deg F
t_v = saturation temperature in condenser, deg F
U_o = over-all heat-transfer rate, Btu per sq ft, hr, deg F
V = water velocity, fps
W_s = steam to be condensed, lb per hr
Δt_m = logarithmic mean temperature difference, deg F
ϵ = effectiveness

In **sizing** a condenser, the steam flow and heat rejected to the condenser are obtained from the turbine heat balance. Table 1 gives representative steam flows; heat rejected to the condenser is approximately 950 Btu per lb of steam for non-reheat turbines and 975 Btu per lb for reheat machines. Figure 3 shows approximate average water temperatures for the United States; local water temperature should be used, when known. The number of passes is usually dictated by the plant arrangement, with total length of water travel and tube diameter dictated by economic considerations. Normally, small-diameter tubes, single-pass condensers are used where water is plentiful, and larger-diameter tubes, two-pass condensers when water is scarce. The vacuum, or back pressure, is determined by economic evaluation, but Table 2 gives normal recommended values for average water temperatures. Table 3 is a pressure-temperature conversion table.

A cleanliness factor is applied to the heat-transfer rate of new, clean tubes to allow

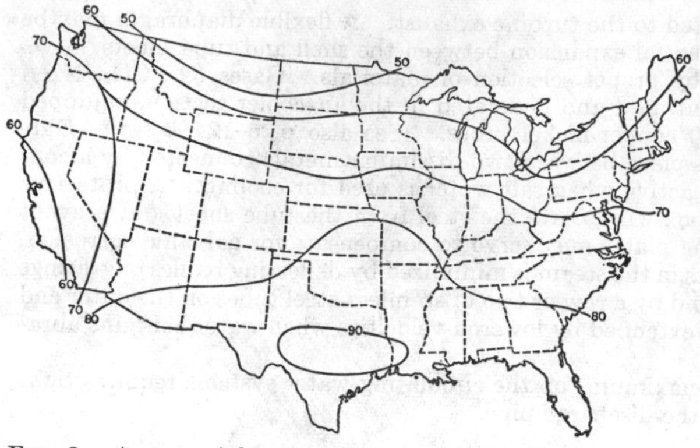

FIG. 3. Average inlet temperatures of circulating water, United States.

for gradual decrease by fouling. A standardized cleanliness factor of 85 percent is frequently used, but this can often be misleading and even erroneous. The fouling is attributable to (1) sedimentation, (2) scaling, (3) reaction, (4) corrosion, and (5) biological growth. The fouling is correctly determined by use; in some cases the cleanliness factor will be 90 percent, whereas in other cases it may never rise about 75 percent.

Velocities normally used are: for clean water, 7.0 fps; for very clean water with cooling towers, 8.0 fps; and for seawater, with entrained sand, as low as 6.0 fps to

Table 1. Steam Flow to Condensers*

Turbine throttle conditions	Weight flow, lb per kwh
600 psi, 825 F	7.08
850 psi, 900 F	6.45
1,250 psi, 950 F	5.80
1,450 psi, 1000 F	5.44
1,450 psi, 1000 F, 1000 F	4.70

* Approximate values for unit sizes to 100,000 kw and exhaust at 1.0 in. Hg abs.

Note: For exhaust pressures other than 1.0 in. Hg abs, multiply tabular values by 1.02 (1.04)[1.06] for 1.5 (2.0)[2.5] in.

Table 2. Normal Condenser Pressures and Circulating-water Temperatures

Water inlet temp, t_i, deg F	Normal back pressure, in. Hg abs
55	1.0
70	1.5
80	2.0
85	2.5
90	3.0
95	3.5

Table 3. Pressure-Temperature Conversion Table*

Abs press, psi	Sat temp, deg F	Abs press, psi	Sat temp, deg F	Abs press, psi	Sat temp, deg F	Abs press, psi	Sat temp, deg F
0.20	34.57	1.35	88.36	2.50	108.71	8.00	152.24
0.25	40.23	1.40	89.51	2.55	109.38	9.00	157.09
0.30	44.96	1.45	90.64	2.60	110.06	10.00	161.49
0.35	49.06	1.50	91.72	2.65	110.72	11.00	165.54
0.40	52.64	1.55	92.77	2.70	111.37	12.00	169.28
0.45	55.89	1.60	93.81	2.75	112.01	13.00	172.78
0.50	58.80	1.65	94.80	2.80	112.63	14.00	176.05
0.55	61.48	1.70	95.78	2.85	113.25	15.00	179.14
0.60	63.96	1.75	96.73	2.90	113.86	16.00	182.05
0.65	66.26	1.80	97.65	2.95	114.45	17.00	184.82
0.70	68.41	1.85	98.56	3.00	115.06	18.00	187.45
0.75	70.43	1.90	99.43	3.20	117.35	19.00	189.96
0.80	72.32	1.95	100.30	3.40	119.51	20.00	192.37
0.85	74.13	2.00	101.14	3.60	121.57	21.00	194.68
0.90	75.84	2.05	101.96	3.80	123.53	22.00	196.90
0.95	77.48	2.10	102.77	4.00	125.43	23.00	199.03
1.00	79.03	2.15	103.56	4.20	127.21	24.00	201.09
1.05	80.53	2.20	104.33	4.40	128.94	25.00	203.08
1.10	81.96	2.25	105.09	4.60	130.61	26.00	205.00
1.15	83.33	2.30	105.85	4.80	132.20	27.00	206.87
1.20	84.64	2.35	106.58	5.00	133.76	28.00	208.67
1.25	85.93	2.40	107.30	6.00	140.78	29.00	210.43
1.30	87.17	2.45	108.01	7.00	146.86	29.921	212.00

* See also Sec. 4 for further data.

minimize erosion. Prevalent velocities are 6.5 fps with aluminum-brass tubes, 7.0 fps with admiralty metal, and 8+ fps with stainless steel. **Water-temperature rise** is about 10 F for single-pass condensers and 15 F for two-pass condensers, with a minimum 5-deg terminal temperature difference (*ttd*).

Table 4. Condenser Proportions

Surface, area, sq ft	Effective tube lengths, ft		
	¾ in. O.D.	⅞ in. O.D.	1 in. O.D.
1,000–1,750	8, 10, 12, 14		
2,000–2,500	10, 12, 14, 16		
2,750–4,750	12, 14, 16, 18	12, 14, 16, 18	
5,000–7,000	14, 16, 18, 20	14, 16, 18, 20	14, 16, 18, 20
7,250–14,000	16, 18, 20, 22	16, 18, 20, 22	16, 18, 20, 22
15,000–19,000	....	18, 20, 22, 24	18, 20, 22, 24
20,000–27,500	....	20, 22, 24, 26	20, 22, 24, 26
30,000–47,500	....	22, 24, 26, 28	22, 24, 26, 28
50,000 and over	....	24, 26, 28, 30	24, 26, 28, 30

Approximate General Rules. The **surface area,** sq ft, is equal to the steam flow, lb per hr, divided by 10 for single-pass condensers and by 7.5 for two-pass condensers. **Circulating-water quantity,** gpm, is equal to the area, sq ft, for a two-pass condenser and is twice the area for a single condenser. Condenser **proportions** are given in Table 4. Empty **weight** of an installed condenser is 5 to 6 lb per sq ft of surface. (See Fig. 9 for relationships.)

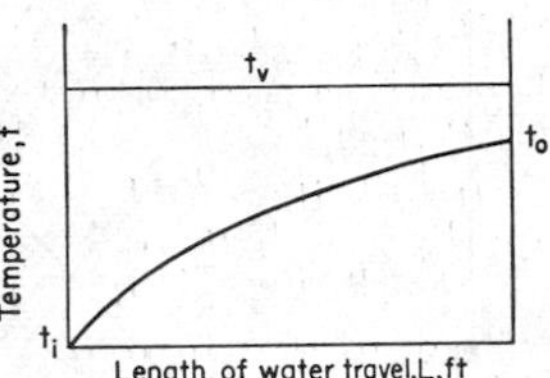

FIG. 4. Temperature versus water travel, surface condenser.

Condenser Calculations

It is normally a tedious process to calculate the size and performance by the use of the logarithmic mean temperature difference. With the use of several aids, the calculations can be simplified. (See Heat Exchange Institute Standards for details.)

The basic diagram is shown in Fig. 4, and the applicable equations are

$$Q = UA\,\Delta t_m \tag{1}$$
$$Q = 500Gc_p(t_o - t_i) \tag{2}$$
$$R = W_s h_r/500G \tag{3}$$
$$A = GkL/V \tag{4}$$
$$k = 0.107\,\text{O.D.}/(\text{O.D.} - 2t)^2 \tag{5}$$
$$\epsilon = (t_o - t_i)/(t_v - t_i) \tag{6}$$
$$\epsilon = 1 - e^{\frac{-R}{\Delta t_m}} \tag{7}$$
$$R/\Delta t_m = [kL(U_o C_t C_c C_m)]/500V \tag{8}$$

EXAMPLE. Calculate the surface and circulating-water requirements to condense 445,000 lb of steam per hr to an absolute pressure of 2.00 in. Hg abs. The heat rejected is 980 Btu per lb of steam and is absorbed by circulating seawater at an average inlet temperature of 75 F. The condenser is to be two-pass with ⅞-in. 18-gage 26-ft-active-length aluminum-brass tubes; cleanliness factor = 85 percent.

SOLUTION. Obtain the material and gage factor C_m from Table 5. Calculate the tube diameter and gage factor k by Eq. (**5**). Use a velocity of 7 fps; $(t_v - t_i) = 101.1 - 75.0 = 26.1$ deg.

To calculate the temperature rise R in Eq. (**3**), the quantities $R/\Delta t_m$ and ϵ must first be computed from Eqs. (**8**) and (**7**).

The heat-transfer rate U_o is a function of velocity and tube diameter; $U_o = C_1\sqrt{V}$, with velocity limits of 3.0 and 10.0 fps. In Eq. (**8**), reduce the quantity to U_o/V to $C_1/\sqrt{V}$. For ⅝- and ¾-in. tubes, $C_1 = 267$; for ⅞- and 1-in. tubes, $C_1 = 263$; and for 1⅛- and 1¼-in. tubes, $C_1 = 259$. Inlet-water-temperature correction factor C_t is obtained from

Table 5. Material and Gage Factor

Tube material	C_m						
	BWG No.						
	24	22	20	18	16	14	12
Admiralty metal	1.06	1.04	1.02	1.00	0.96	0.92	0.87
Arsenical copper	1.06	1.04	1.02	1.00	0.96	0.92	0.87
Aluminum	1.06	1.04	1.02	1.00	0.96	0.92	0.87
Aluminum brass	1.03	1.02	1.00	0.97	0.94	0.90	0.84
Aluminum bronze	1.03	1.02	1.00	0.97	0.94	0.90	0.84
Muntz metal	1.03	1.02	1.00	0.97	0.94	0.90	0.84
90-10 Cu-Ni	0.99	0.97	0.94	0.90	0.85	0.80	0.74
70-30 Cu-Ni	0.93	0.90	0.87	0.82	0.77	0.71	0.64
Cold-rolled, low-carbon steel	1.00	0.98	0.95	0.91	0.86	0.80	0.74
Stainless steels:							
Type 410/430	0.88	0.85	0.82	0.76	0.70	0.65	0.59
Type 304/316	0.83	0.79	0.75	0.69	0.63	0.56	0.49
Type 329	0.78	0.76	0.74	0.69	0.65	0.60	0.54
Titanium (tentative)	0.85	0.81	0.77	0.71			

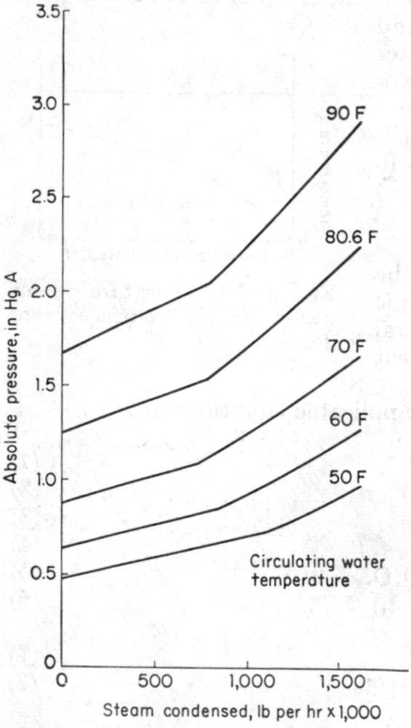

Table 6. By Eqs. (**8**) and (**7**),

$$\frac{R}{\Delta t_m} = \frac{0.1550 \times 52(263 \times 1.025 \times 0.85 \times 0.97)}{500 \times \sqrt{7.0}} = 1.35$$

and $\epsilon = 0.740$. In Eq. (**6**), multiply $(t_v - t_i)$ by ϵ to get a rise of 19.3 deg. By Eq. (**3**), $G = 1.96W_s/R$ = 45,200 gpm; and by Eq. (**4**), surface = 52,100 sq ft.

Table 6. Inlet-water-temperature Correction Factors

Inlet temp t_i, deg F	Correction factor, C_t
40	0.685
50	0.810
60	0.915
70	1.000
80	1.045
90	1.075
100	1.100

Since this is not a standard surface, it must be corrected with a corresponding change in circulating-water quantity. A rule of thumb is: For a change of 2 sq ft in surface area, there is a corresponding inverse change of 1 gpm of circulating-water quantity. With these corrections, rework the condenser performance to obtain the original back pressure; two or three trials, with adjustments in circulating-water quantity, should suffice.

FIG. 5. Representative performance curves for a large surface condenser. 157,500-sq ft one-pass surface condenser; 1-in. 18-gage, 37.8-ft active-length aluminum-brass tubes. Performance is based on 85 percent clean tubes, 221,400 gpm at a velocity of 7 fps, and 968 Btu per lb rejected to the circulating water.

Performance curves (Fig. 5) are drawn for a condenser to show the back pressure for various condenser steam loads and inlet-water temperatures maintaining a minimum ttd of 5 deg. The zero-load back pressure and the cutoff pressure are shown in Fig. 6, where the cutoff limitation is set by the air-removal equipment. A combined turbine-condenser performance curve is sometimes drawn in which heat rejected versus back pressure for a given turbine load is superimposed on the condenser performance.

Circulating-water pumps are usually half capacity, with 3 or 4 percent additional allowance on each pump for miscellaneous heat exchangers. The total dynamic head (TDH) is the sum of the condenser and water-box friction (Figs. 7 and 8), the pipe loss, and any unrecovered static head. Normal heads are about 20 ft; for cooling-tower installations, 60 ft max. (See also p. 14–21 *et seq*, and Fig. 9.)

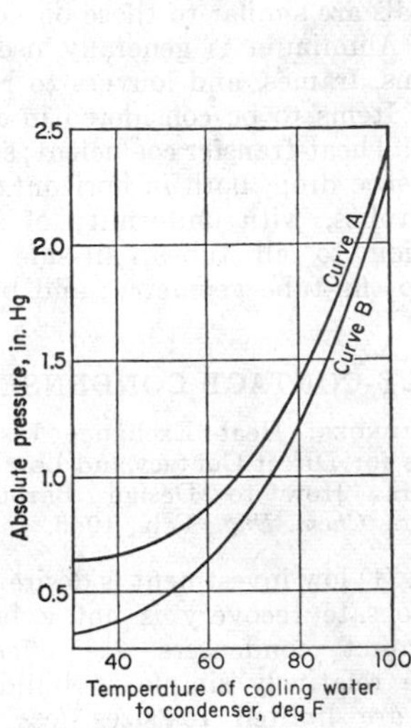

FIG. 6. Cutoff and zero-load vacuums. Curve *A*, cutoff (except where the absolute pressure is limited by 5 deg F TTD); curve *B*, zero load.

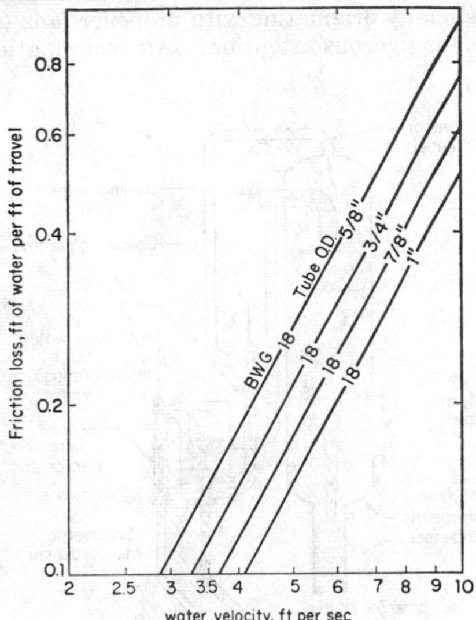

FIG. 7. Tube friction loss.

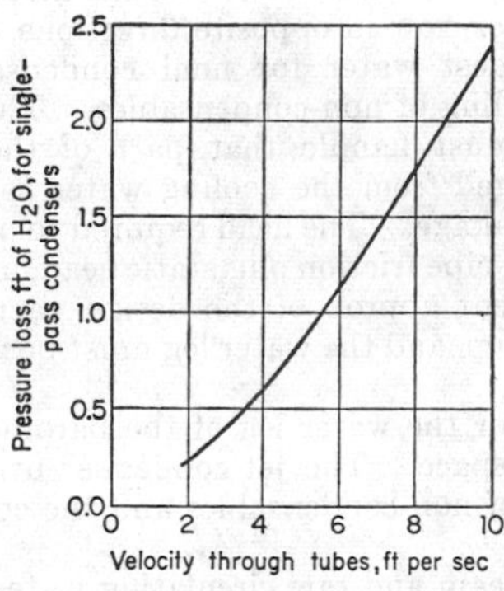

FIG. 8. Pressure drop in water boxes.

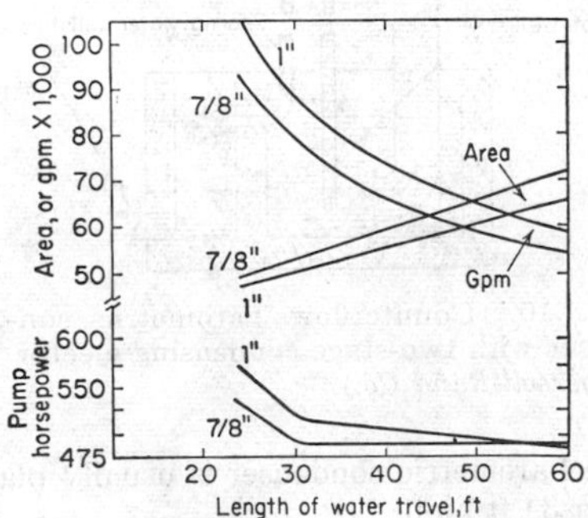

FIG. 9. Condenser configuration selection for a given heat load. W_s = 477,355 lb per hr; h = 975 Btu per lb; t_i = 70.0 F; 150 in. Hg abs; 18-gage admiralty-metal tubes; 7.0 fps water velocity; 85 percent cleanliness factor.

Condensate pumps are usually full capacity, determined by condenser flow plus any heater drains dumped into the condenser and 5 percent additional margin. Vertical-pit-type designs are commonly used because of low net-positive-suction-head (NPSH) requirements with water at the boiling point. TDH ranges from a normal value of 100 ft on small plants to 800 ft on some larger plants. (See also p. 14–21 *et seq.*)

AIR-COOLED CONDENSERS

The air-cooled condenser is used where adequate water is not available and to minimize the number of pieces of equipment. It is adaptable to power plants mounted on trains or made up in modules and transported to isolated locations. Installations have been limited to plant sizes below 1,000 kw. The steam condenses inside the tubes, and cooling air flows over the external finned surface; louvers control the airflow, generally originating with propeller fans (see p. 14–69). Freezing is a problem which needs rigorous attention. Air-recirculation potentials are similar to those on cooling towers. Aluminum is generally used for tubes, fins, frames, and louvers to reduce weight. Items to be considered in design are over-all heat-transfer coefficient; steam-side pressure drop, both in horizontal and vertical tubes, with uniformity of steam distribution to all tubes; air-side pressure drop; fin-tube geometry; and bundle geometry.

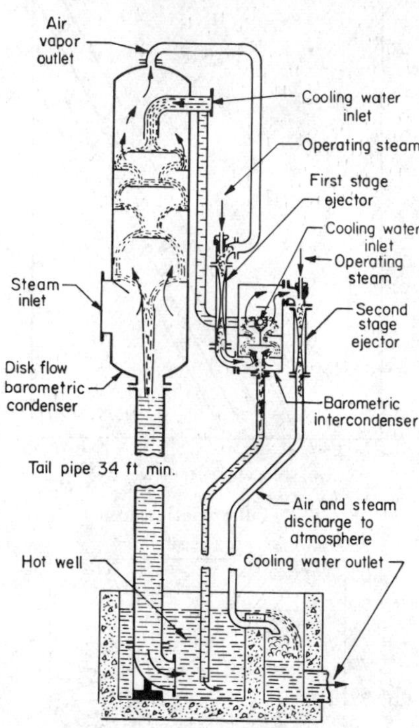

FIG. 10. Counterflow barometric condenser with two-stage condensing ejector. (*Ingersoll-Rand Co.*)

DIRECT-CONTACT CONDENSERS

REFERENCES: Heat Exchange Institute Standards for Direct Contact and Low Level Condensers. How to Design Barometric Condensers, *Chem. Eng.*, Feb., 1956.

When (1) low investment is desired and (2) condensate recovery is not a factor, direct-contact condensers are effective. They are relatively simple to build and operate, are limited to sizes less than 250,000 lb of steam per hr, and are built in three types: (1) barometric, (2) low-level, and (3) jet.

Figure 10 shows a self-supported counterflow **barometric condenser** with tail pipe, hot well, and air ejector. Steam and cooling water flow in opposite directions, with the coldest water for final condensation and cooling of non-condensables. The air pump must handle that part of the air disengaged from the cooling water as well as air leakage. The head required to pump water is pipe friction plus static head, minus 75 percent approx of the design vacuum. The barometric condenser is usually placed outdoors, and the water leg must be more than 34 ft high.

The **low-level condenser** substitutes a pump for the water leg of the barometric condenser to remove the liquid from the vacuum space. The **jet condenser** utilizes the aspirating effect of a jet for the entrainment of non-condensables and the consequent elimination of a separate air pump.

In the usual direct-contact condenser, where steam and raw circulating water are mixed, the recovery of pure condensate is precluded; greater feedwater makeup is necessary, and poorer vacuums are attained than with surface condensers. Direct-contact-condenser installations are not found in large plants, but there is some recent interest in their use with dry cooling towers.

Table 7 gives values of expected air content of cooling waters; Fig. 11 gives typical performance curves; Fig. 12 defines flows W, temperatures t, and enthalpies h needed for the basic heat-balance equation $W_s(h_s - h_2) = W_w(t_2 - t_1)$. The latent heat $(h_s - h_2)$ is frequently taken as 950 Btu per lb of steam.

Table 7. Air in Cooling Water

Water temp, deg F	Air, cfm per 1,000 gpm
35	4.0
40	3.78
50	3.35
60	2.97
70	2.68
80	2.41
90	2.21
100	2.0

Shell materials are usually steel plate; with dirty or corrosive water, bronze, stainless steel, or linings of ceramic, plastic, or rubber may be used (at increased cost).

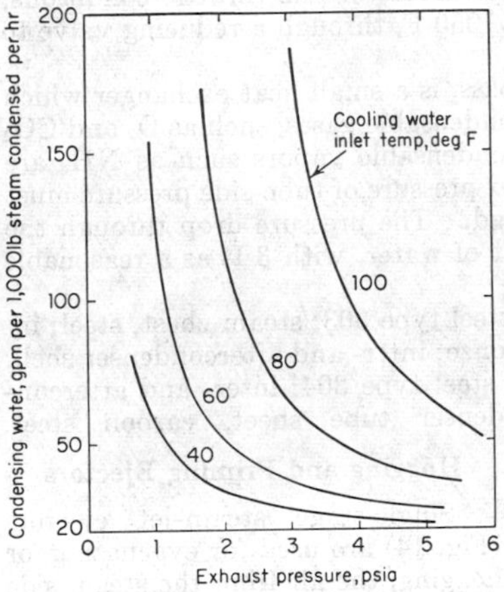

Fig. 11. Representative performance curves of a direct-contact condenser.

AIR EJECTORS

Reference: Heat Exchange Institute, Standards for Steam Jet Ejectors.

The steam-jet air ejector is used to remove non-condensable air and gases from condensers. It consists of a suction chamber, diffuser, and steam nozzle. The high-velocity jet of steam issuing from the nozzle entrains the gas, and the kinetic energy of the mixture is converted to pressure energy in the diffuser. Ratings are in lb per hr at a given suction pressure. Ejectors are operated in series or are staged for absolute suction pressures of 1 ± in. Hg abs. They will handle wet or dry mixtures, they are easy to operate, installation costs are low, and there are no moving parts—with consequent long life, high sustained efficiency, and low maintenance.

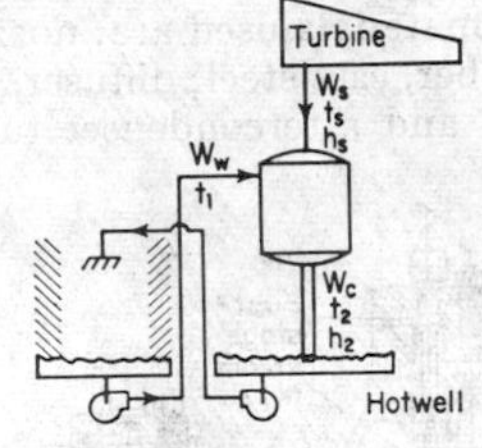

Fig. 12. Direct-contact-condenser performance terms.

Two-stage ejectors, with surface-type inter- and aftercondensers (Fig. 13), are common in steam-surface-condenser application. The main condensate serves as a coolant, returning heat regeneratively to the boiler feed system. Two-stage ejectors have a shutoff pressure of 0.4 in. Hg abs approx. Two elements are usually provided, one serving as a spare.

Computation of **ejector performance** requires application of Dalton's law of mixtures (see pp. 4–24 and 4–80 to 4–89), where basically the total pressure is the sum of the condensable vapor (steam) pressure and the non-condensable gas (air) pressure. In power-plant condensers, the mixture is saturated with steam so that the temperature of the mixture fixes the partial pressure of the vapor.

Air ejectors are usually rated with suction conditions of 1 in. Hg abs and 7.5 F subcooling. Since the saturation temperature of steam at 1 in. Hg abs is 79 F, the mixture entering the ejector is at 71.5 F. The partial pressure of the vapor at 71.5 F is 0.78 in. Hg abs, and the partial pressure of the air is $1 - 0.78 = 0.22$ in. Hg abs. Therefore, an ejector with a standard rating (see Table 8) of 12.5 cfm of free dry air at 30 in. Hg abs handles, by the gas laws, $12.5(30/0.22) = 1{,}704$ cfm at the ejector suction.

Table 8. Performance Data for Two-stage Air Ejectors
(Westinghouse Electric Corp.)

Steam to condenser, lb per hr	Capacity, free dry air, cfm 70 F	Ejector-frame size	Capacity, free dry air, lb per hr	Capacity, air and vapor mixture, lb per hr	Steam consumption, lb per hr
0–25,000	3.0	E-30	13.5	45.0	180
25,001–50,000	4.0	E-40	18.0	60.0	240
50,001–100,000	5.0	E-50	22.5	75.0	300
100,001–250,000	7.5	E-75	33.75	112.5	450
250,001–500,000	10.0	E-100	45.0	150.0	600
Over 500,000	12.5	E-125	56.25	187.5	750

Motive steam to the ejector is usually supplied from turbine throttle conditions, *e.g.*, 600 psi, 750 F; 1,500 psi, 1000 F; 2,500 psi, 1050 F, through a reducing valve to a pressure not higher than 600 psi.

The **inter- and aftercondenser,** one- or two-pass, is a small heat exchanger which condenses the motive steam and allows the noncondensable gases, such as O_2 and CO_2 to be expelled to the atmosphere. However, condensable vapors such as NH_3 are returned to the feedwater system. The water-box pressure of tube-side pressure must be designed for the condensate-pump shutoff head. The pressure drop through the inter- and aftercondensers varies from 1 to 10 ft of water, with 3 ft as a reasonable average.

Normal **materials** used are: nozzle, stainless steel type 303; steam chest, steel; inlet-air chamber, cast steel; diffuser, aluminum bronze; inter- and aftercondenser shell, steel; inter- and aftercondenser tubes, stainless steel type 304; inter- and aftercondenser tube sheet, carbon steel.

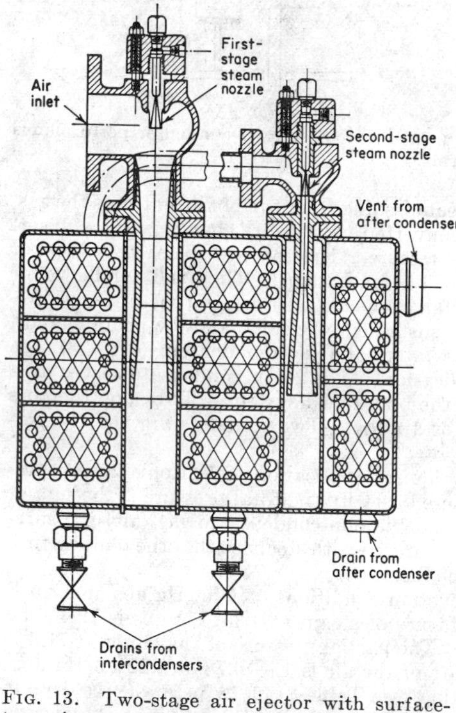

FIG. 13. Two-stage air ejector with surface-type inter- and aftercondensers. (*Westinghouse Electric Corp.*)

Hogging and Priming Ejectors

Single-stage steam-jet ejectors (Fig. 14) are used for evacuating, or **hogging,** the air from the steam side of a surface condenser, in 15 or 20 min time, so that steam flow can be established and the condenser brought on the line. These ejectors are usually non-condensing and exhaust to the atmosphere. Ratings (Table 9) are typically in lb per hr of free dry air at 70 F, suction conditions of 15 in. Hg abs, shutoff pres-

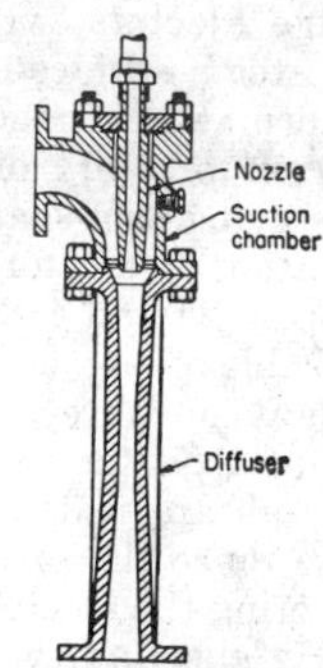

FIG. 14. Single-stage air ejector. (*Ingersoll-Rand Co.*)

sure about 2 in. Hg abs, motive steam pressures and temperatures as with multistage ejectors.

Priming ejectors are also single-stage non-condensing units and are used to withdraw air from the water side and to fill the condenser with circulating water during start-up periods. The hogging ejector may also serve this priming function by a suitable system of piping and valves.

Materials normally employed are: for the nozzle, stainless steel, 18-8 chrome nickel; steam chest, steel; air-inlet chamber and diffuser, cast steel.

Table 9. Hogging-ejector Data
(Westinghouse Electric Corp.)

Max steam condensed, lb per hr	Capacity, free dry air, cfm	Capacity, free dry air, lb per hr	Ejector-frame, size	Motive steam required, lb per hr
Up to 75,000	150	675	P-15	900
75,001–250,000	300	1,350	P-30	1,700
250,001–600,000	600	2,700	P-60	3,100
Over 600,000	900	4,050	P-90	4,300

VACUUM PUMPS

Reference: Woodman, Rotary or Steam-jet Air Pumps, *Power*, Aug., 1948.

Mechanical vacuum pumps, used for hogging, holding, and priming, are of several types for power-plant service: (1) reciprocating—piston, diaphragm; (2) rotary—sliding-vane, oval-water-seal, eccentric-rotor. (See Sec. 14 for details.) Multistage pumps usually need intercooling. A silencer is generally provided on the air discharge. Normally, two half-capacity pumps are installed, both operating during hogging and one adequate for holding service. The relative capabilities of a vacuum pump and hogging and holding ejectors are illustrated in Fig. 15 (note the considerable hogging capacity of the vacuum pump on start-up).

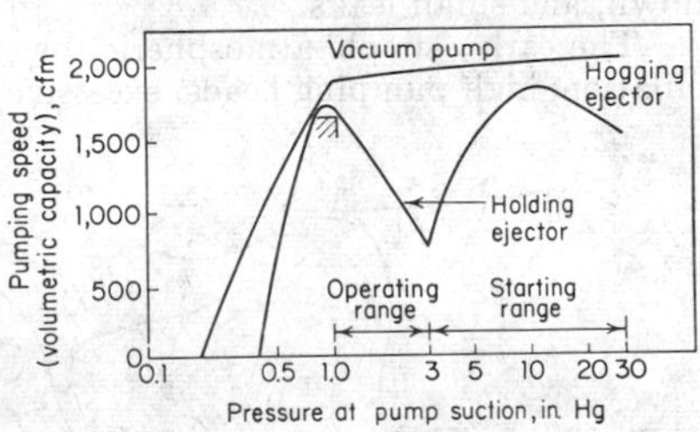

Fig. 15. Relative capabilities of air removal pumps.

Advantages of vacuum pumps compared to steam-jet air ejectors include (1) system independent of a steam supply; (2) start-up when steam is not available, as on a once-through boiler system; (3) system capable of completely automatic operation; (4) high-pressure steam piping eliminated; (5) recycling of non-condensables and ammonia eliminated; (6) quieter operation. Disadvantages include (1) damage by water entering the intake (except when pumps having a liquid rotating seal); (2) higher initial cost; (3) higher maintenance cost. Operating costs are approximately equal. Various combination arrangements are found in practice, *e.g.*, an air-operated air-ejector first stage followed by a vacuum-pump second stage, with consequent savings in motor-horsepower and space requirements.

COOLING TOWERS

References: "Evaluated Weather Data for Cooling Equipment Design," Fluor Products Co. Cooling Towers, *Power*, Mar., 1963. Baker and Shryock, A Comprehensive Approach to the Analysis of Cooling Tower Performance, *Trans. ASME*, 1961.

The prevalent type of cooling tower (see Figs. 16 and 19) dissipates heat by the evaporation of some of the water sprayed into the air circulated through the tower. It is used where water is in limited supply, where temperature pollution of natural water bodies is to be avoided, where water conservation is to be effected, or where otherwise polluted sources must be avoided. Figure 17 illustrates the functional cycle and the significant basic terms (see also p. 4–80 *et seq.*).

Wet-bulb temperature, for design purposes, should not exceed the maximum expected value more than 5 percent of the time during summer (June to September). (See Fig. 18.)

Approach is the difference in temperature between the cold water leaving the tower and the ambient wet bulb.

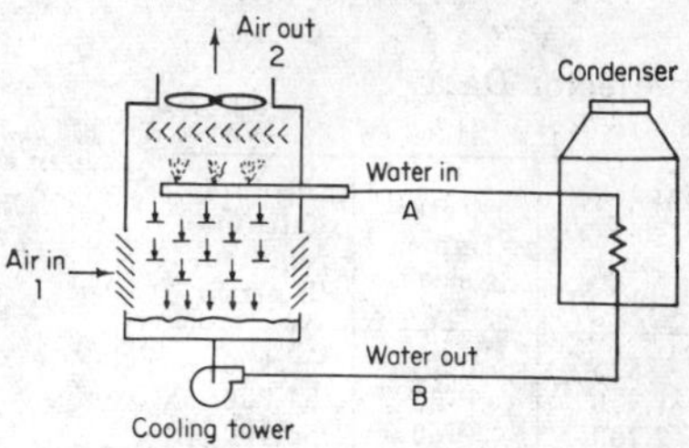

FIG. 16. Schematic for induced-draft, counterflow, cooling-tower installation.

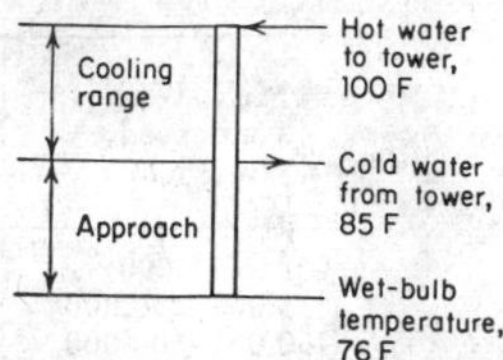

FIG. 17. Cooling-tower terms.

Cooling range is the difference in temperature between the hot water entering and the cold water leaving the tower.

Drift is the water lost as mist or droplets entrained by the circulating air and discharged to the atmosphere. It is in addition to the evaporative loss and is minimized by good design.

Makeup is the water required to replace total losses by evaporation, drift, blowdown, and small leaks.

The early, simple atmospheric towers have, because of reliance on natural air circulation, high pumping heads, excessive spray losses, and makeup, been largely superseded by three important types: (1) forced-draft, (2) induced-draft, and (3) hyperbolic (Fig. 19).

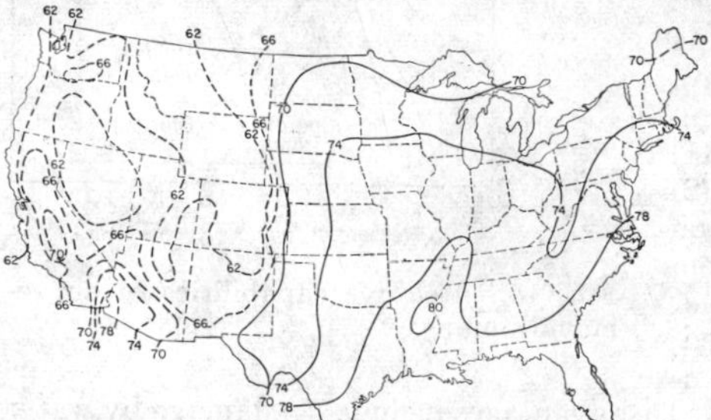

FIG. 18. Wet-bulb temperature isolines at the 5 percent level, United States. (*Adapted from Fluor Products Co., by permission.*)

The **mechanical forced-draft tower** (Fig. 19*a*) gives (1) a controllable air supply from fans conveniently located for inspection and maintenance at ground level, and (2) reduced water-pumping head. Non-uniform distribution of air over the ground area of the tower cell, recirculation of vapor from the tower discharge to the tower inlet, with its deleterious effects and fan icing in cold weather, and limitations on the physical diameter of fans are all problems with forced-draft towers.

The **induced-draft tower** (Fig. 19*b*) is prevalent in U.S. practice. The fan is mounted on the top (discharge) of the cell, with consequent improved air distribution within the cell; drift eliminators reduce makeup requirements; spray nozzles, downspouts, splash plates, and splash bars ensure ample evaporative surface for the water, with maximum volumetric heat-transfer rates. In the **counterflow** design, air is introduced beneath the cell fill, but in the **crossflow** design (Fig. 19*b*), air is introduced at the sides of the fill.

The **hyperbolic tower** (Fig. 19*c*) utilizes the chimney effect (height, 300 ± ft) for natural circulation. It has been favored in large European installations where the prevalent lower dry-bulb ambient temperature gives a greater difference in density between entrance to and exit from the tower. The wide approach keeps the unit size within practical bounds, and the savings in fan power support the higher investment. Recent installations in the Unites States attest to its attractiveness.

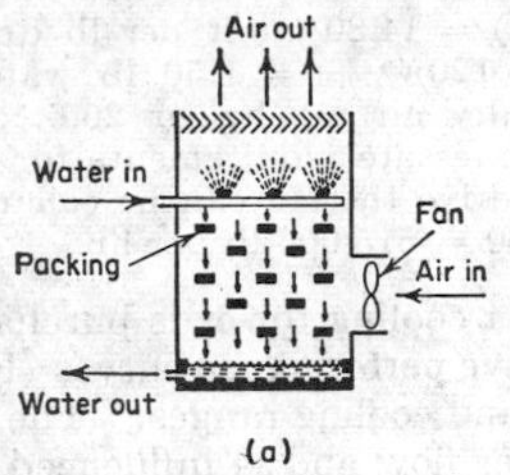

Precautions are necessary to avoid freezing troubles in cold weather, fire hazards with intermittent operations, corrosion, scale, and microbiological growth problems. **Location** must avoid recirculation: for tower lengths to 250 ft, the long-axis orientation should be parallel to the prevailing wind; towers longer than 250 ft should be arranged broadside to the prevailing wind. The tower should be isolated as much as possible; adjacent heat sources compel the specification of higher design wet-bulb temperatures.

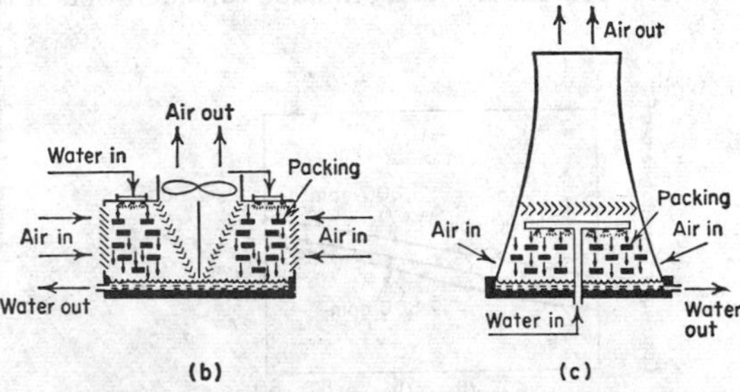

FIG. 19. Cooling-tower types; (*a*) forced-draft; (*b*) crossflow induced-draft; (*c*) hyperbolic.

Performance Calculations

(See Fig. 16)

Applicable equations are

$$W_{a1}h_{a1} + W_{v1}h_{v1} + W_{wA}h_{fA} = W_{a2}h_{a2} + W_{v2}h_{v2} + W_{wB}h_{fB} \tag{9}$$

$$W_{wB} = W_{wA} - (W_{v2} - W_{v1}); \qquad W_{a1} = W_{a2} \tag{10}$$

$$W_{wA}(h_{fA} - h_{fB}) = (W_{a2}h_{a2} + W_{v2}h_{v2}) - (W_{a1}h_{a1} + W_{v1}h_{v1}) - (W_{v2} - W_{v1})h_{fB} \tag{11}$$

$$h_{fA} - h_{fB} = t_{wA} - t_{wB} \tag{12}$$

and

$$W_ah_a + W_vh_v = \text{total heat, from psychrometric chart} \quad \text{(See p. 4–84)} \tag{13}$$

$$W_{wA}(t_{wA} - t_{wB}) = \text{total heat at 2} - \text{total heat at 1} - (W_{v2} - W_{v1})h_{fB} \tag{14}$$

where W = flow, lb per hr; a = air; w = water; v = vapor; h = enthalpy, Btu per lb; f = fluid; t = temperature, deg F; 1, 2, A, B = locations.

EXAMPLE. Given: flow = 80,000; wet bulb = 76 F; dry bulb = 86 F; range (also condenser rise) = 100 − 85 = 15 F; approach = 9 F. Find: economical tower size, circulating-pump power, fan capacity and power, and makeup water.

SOLUTION. (1) *Economical tower size:* A study must be made to tie in with condenser. Heat to be dissipated is constant. Vary rise (range), approach, and then compare capital costs of cooling tower, circulating pump, and condenser with operating costs for fan and pump power. (2) *Circulating-water-pump power:* bhp = gpm × TDH/3,960 × eff. TDH = condenser friction + pipe friction + static head. (3) *Fan capacity and power:* If air leaves tower saturated at 95 F, then from psychrometric charts (p. 4–84),

$$\text{Total heat} = 1 \text{ lb dry air } C_p(t_a - 0 \text{ deg}) + W_vh_g \text{ at } t_a \tag{15}$$

For air and vapor at 1, vapor = 120 grains per lb dry air. By Eqs. (**13**) and (**15**), total heat = 1 × 0.24(86 − 0) + (120/7000)1099.2 = 39.5 Btu per lb dry air. For air and vapor at 2, vapor = 256 grains per lb dry air. Total heat = 63.1 per lb dry air. Sp vol (air and vapor) = 14.80 cu ft per lb dry air. By Eq. (**14**), $W_{wA}(100 - 85) = 63.1 - 39.5 - (256 - 120)63/7000 = 1.50$ lb water per lb dry air. 80,000 gpm/1.50 × 500 = 26.6 × 10⁶ lb dry air per hr, or 26.6 × 10⁶ × 14.80/60 = 6.58 × 10⁶ cfm. With test data on static-pressure requirements for the tower and with the fan characteristics, the horsepower to drive the fan can be calculated. (4) *Makeup:* $W_{v2} - W_{v1} = (256 - 120)\ 26.6 \times 10^6/7000 = 515{,}000$ lb per hr.

Normally, a cooling tower is purchased for only one guarantee point. It is well, however, to have **performance** curves (Fig. 20) showing operation for various wet-bulb temperatures and cooling ranges. The **investment** for a cooling tower is essentially a matter of water flow and is influenced by approach, range, and wet bulb (Fig. 21). The **cost evaluation** should include consideration of tower frame and fill, fans, motors,

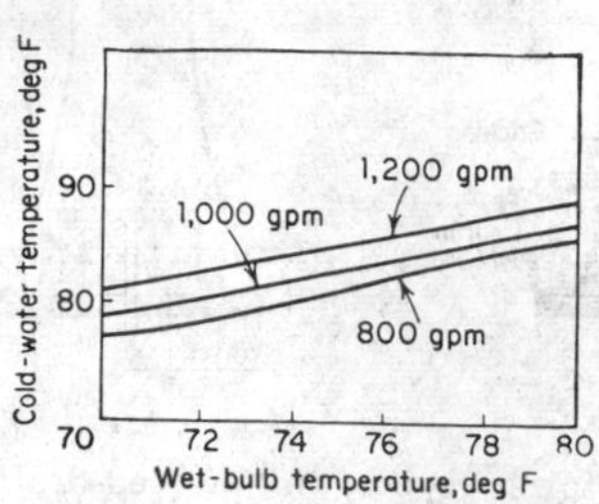

FIG. 20. Cooling-tower performance: design 85 F cold water, 95 F hot water; 78 F wet bulb; 10-deg range; 1,000-gpm cell.

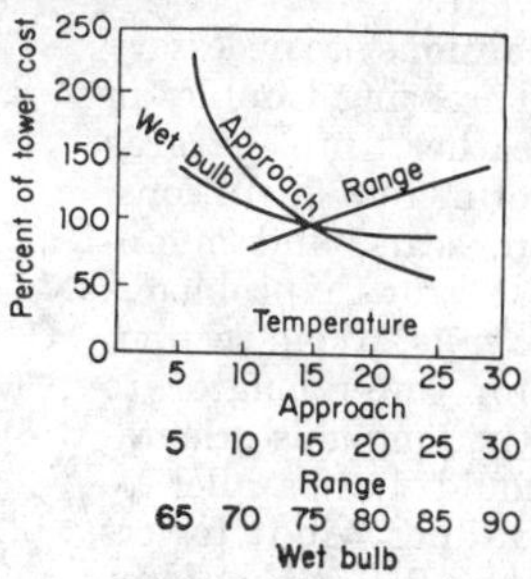

FIG. 21. Comparative cooling-tower costs. (*Foster Wheeler Corp.*)

basin and pump pit, pump head, fan horsepower, freight, labor, and erection. In the choice of a tower for a power plant, there should be coordinated study and evaluation of the turbine and condenser for best over-all economy.

The **height** of a field-erected induced-draft tower, from basin curb to fan deck, ranges from 8 to 50 ft; widths vary from 6 to 60 ft; lengths from 8 to 500 ft; fan-stack height between 2 and 15 ft.

Materials used are: frame—redwood (treated or untreated), Douglas fir (treated), steel (galvanized), concrete; fill—redwood, plastics (polyethylene, polypropylene), cement asbestos board (extruded); casing—cement asbestos board (corrugated, slat), redwood, fiber glass, aluminum, concrete; fan blades—aluminum, glass-reinforced polyester, stainless steel, monel; fan hubs—cast iron, galvanized steel, stainless steel; fan stack—redwood, steel, masonite; drift eliminators—redwood, cement, asbestos board; spray nozzles—ceramic, bakelite; louvers—redwood, cement asbestos board.

DRY COOLING TOWERS, WITH DIRECT-CONTACT CONDENSERS

REFERENCE: Ritchings and Lotz, Economics of Closed vs Open Cooling Water Cycles, *Power Eng.*, May and June, 1963.

The thermodynamic requirement for a heat sink can generally best be met with a natural body of water such as a river, lake, or ocean. When water supplies are limited, a **"wet" cooling tower** (water losses less than 2 or 3 percent) may be used for reclamation. A **"dry" cooling tower** will further reduce this loss. Figure 22 shows an application with a direct-contact condenser. The finned surfaces of the dry cooling tower are substituted for the tubes of a surface condenser. Heat-transfer rates (see p. 4–90 *et seq.*) are appreciably lower, but the extended surface, relatively low in cost, may be installed in an induced-draft tower or in an hyperbolic tower, as in England for a 125,000-kw unit. Problems of recirculation,

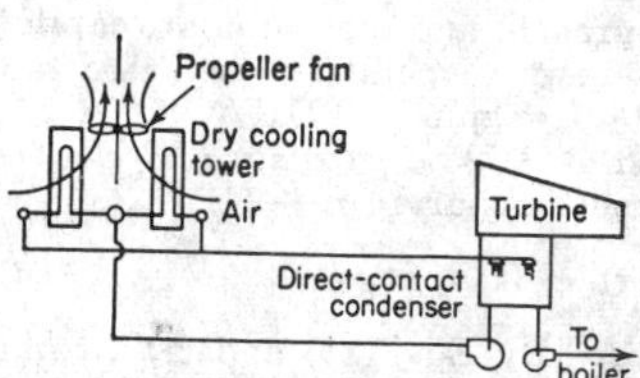

FIG. 22. Dry-cooling-tower system.

freezing, and air leakage must be solved. If a minor evaporative loss is permissible, peaking capacity is obtained by wetting the heat-exchange surface in the tower.

SPRAY PONDS

If land area is available, a spray pond may serve as an alternative reclamation system. Pipelines are typically arranged on 50-ft centers, with five nozzles (50± gpm each) every 12 ft of pipeline. Cooling is limited by the relatively short period of contact between spray and air. Drift, especially with adverse wind conditions, can make losses higher than on towers. Generally, if cooling efficiencies above 50 percent are required, a tower is favored, where efficiency = $(t_h - t_c) \times 100/(t_h - t_{wb})$, where the temperature t subscripts are h = hot water, c = cold water, wb = wet bulb of the ambient air. (See Wright and Kirsopp, Pond Surface Cooling of a Chemical Plant Cooling Water, *Proc. Am. Power Conference*, 1960.)

CLOSED FEEDWATER HEATERS

REFERENCE: Standards of Feedwater Heater Manufacturers Assoc.

Feedwater heaters are used (1) to effect the thermodynamic gains of the regenerative steam cycle (see pp. 4–59 and 9–78), and (2) to raise water temperatures to a sufficient value for the avoidance of thermal shock to the boiler metal. The **number and types of heaters** usually employed are: (1) plant sizes of 10 to 70 mw, two closed low-pressure heaters, one open heater, one closed high-pressure heater; (2) plant sizes of 75 to 200 mw, two or three closed low-pressure heaters, one open heater, two closed high-pressure heaters; (3) plant sizes above 200 mw, three or four closed low-pressure heaters, one open heater, two or three high-pressure heaters. In the largest plants, half-capacity heaters, in parallel, are generally preferred.

Minimum heater **cost** prevails with minimum restrictive specifications, *e.g.*, horizontal, two-pass, high water velocity (10 fps at 60 F), no length limits. Over-all heater **length** is limited by maximum available tube lengths of 100 ft for copper alloys,

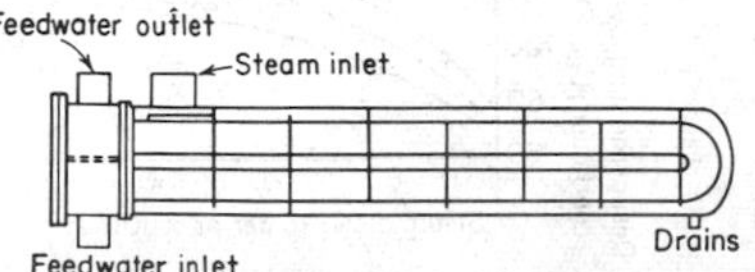

FIG. 23. Basic heater section for condensing heating.

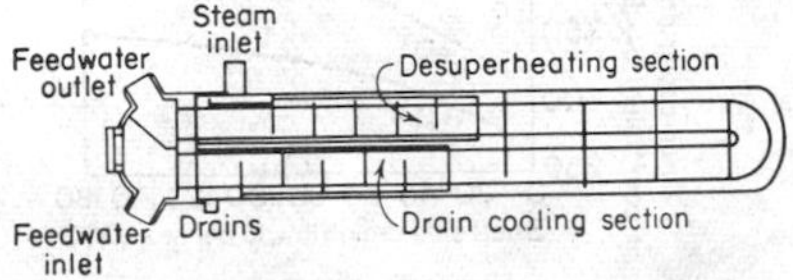

FIG. 24. Basic heater section with drain-cooling and desuperheating sections added.

admiralty metal, and copper-nickel and 85 ft for monel. With U-tube construction, this results in heater lengths of about 48 ft and 40 ft, respectively. A general rule, to ensure good steam distribution, is that the length in feet shall not exceed the shell diameter in inches plus 2; *i.e.*, with a 30-in.-diam shell, the length should not exceed 32 ft. **Pressure drop** through the tubes must be economically evaluated as it varies approximately with the square of the water velocity.

If a **length restriction** is imposed, the designer may have to substitute a four-pass arrangement for the two-pass design, with consequent large-diameter shell and water chamber, heavier walls, more tube holes to be drilled, more tubes to be installed, and a cost increase. If a **pressure-drop restriction** is imposed, a lower water velocity results, with more tubes, larger shell and chamber diameter, and more surface because of the lower heat-transfer rate. Vertical heaters, with appropriate construction details, are also higher in cost.

The **condensing heater** (Fig. 23), like a surface condenser, performs at constant saturation temperature outside the tubes with no condensate subcooling. Feedwater is generally heated to within 5 F of the saturation temperature. The addition of a **drain-cooling section** (Fig. 24), with a cover or enveloping baffle around the tubes of the inlet pass, can reduce the drip temperature to within 10 or 15 F of the incoming water. When superheated steam, *e.g.*, 200 F and 80 psi, is supplied, a **desuperheating section** (Fig. 24), using an enveloping baffle around the tubes at feedwater outlet, can raise the water temperature above the saturation temperature of the entering steam. Drain coolers and desuperheating sections improve over-all plant heat rate by reduction of energy degradation. Subcooling of drains reduces flashing, erosion, vibration, and noise when drains are dropped to a lower-pressure heater. Special attention should be given to drains flashed to the main condenser as this is a direct thermodynamic loss.

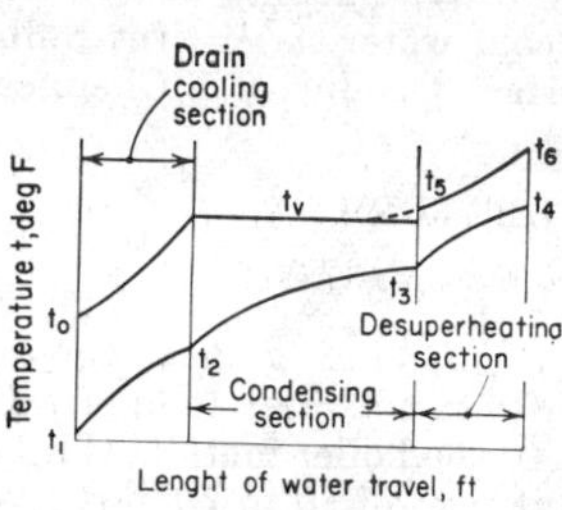

FIG. 25. Temperature versus water travel, closed-feed heater.

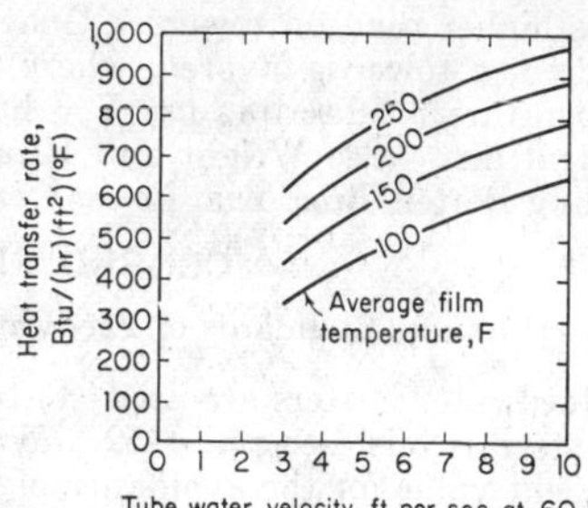

FIG. 26. Approximate condensing heat-transfer rates with 18 BWG admiralty-metal tubes. Average film temp = $t_v - 0.8\Delta t_m$.

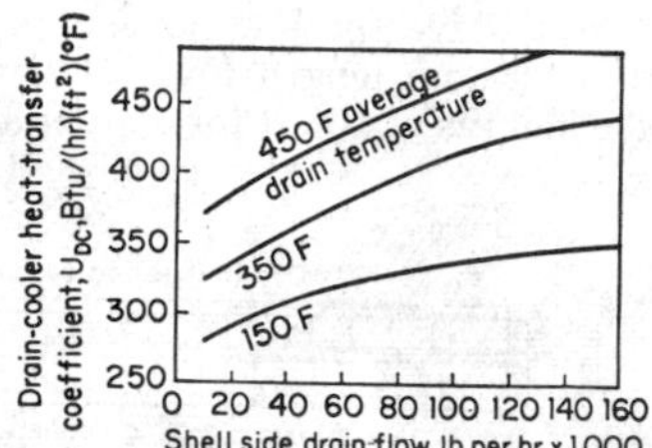

FIG. 27. Approximate drain-cooler heat-transfer rates.

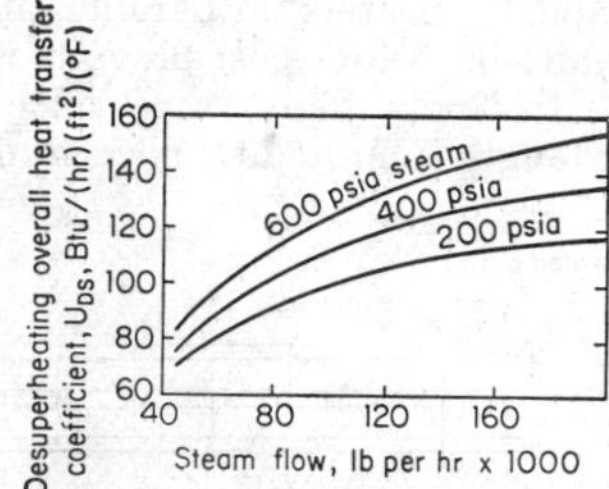

FIG. 28. Approximate desuperheating-section heat-transfer rates.

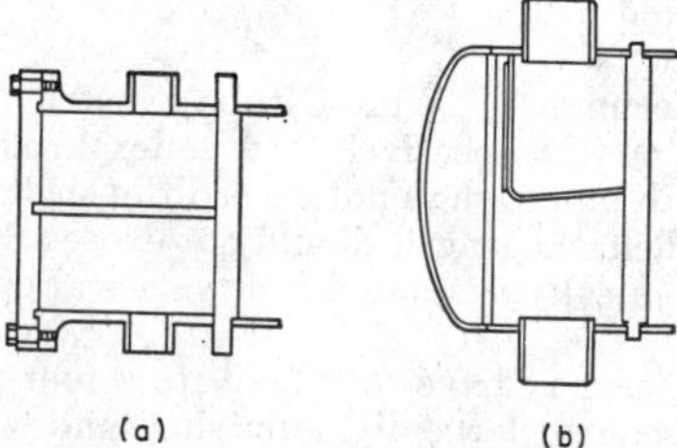

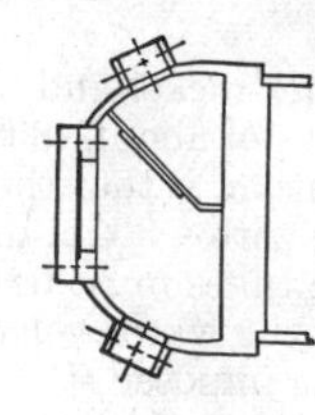

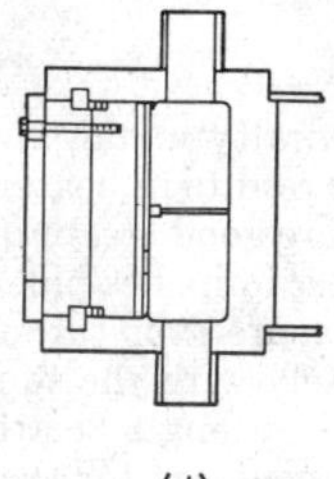

FIG. 29. Feedwater-heater channels: (*a*) bolted, (*b*) dished, (*c*) hemispherical, (*d*) single-piece, forged.

Heat-transfer rates for a condensing feedwater heater range, over-all, between 500 and 900 Btu per hr, sq ft, deg F. (See Figs. 25 and 26.) Heat-transfer rates for drain-cooling and desuperheating sections must be separately evaluated, with over-all ranges from 300 to 500 on the former and 80 to 140 on the latter. (See Figs. 27 and 28.) Normally, the three sections are included in the same shell (Fig. 24); when the cooler becomes too large, as with the lowest-pressure heater, a separate shell and tube exchanger may be justified.

Low-pressure heaters (less than 900 psi on the water side) usually use admiralty metal or steel tubes and a bolted head with flange and gasket for the channel (Fig. 29*a*). A welded, dished head (Fig. 29*b*) will eliminate gaskets.

High-pressure heaters (more than 900 psi on the water side) usually use monel, copper-nickel alloy, or carbon-steel tubes; chemistry, water pressure, and operating temperature dictate the choice. The tube cost represents the largest component of heater cost so that economy favors the stronger materials with thinner walls, No. 18 BWG being the accepted minimum. Water channels or heads may utilize completely welded construction (hemispherical head, Fig. 29*c*) or the forged steel barrel with pressure-sealing covers (Fig. 29*d*). Access to the tube sheet is through the manhole. Tubes are sealed into the tube sheet either by roller-expanding or by welding the end of the tube to the face of the sheet. With the hemispherical head, the tubes are welded to the sheet for a completely welded design. On the pressure-sealed lower-pressure units and on bolted-head designs, tube rolling prevails.

Performance Calculations

Notation:

A = heat-transfer surface, sq ft
C_m = material and gage correction factor, Table 11
D = tube I.D., in., Table 13
d = O.D. of tube, in. (5/8 in. is common)
F_1 = friction factor, Table 14
F_2 = water-temperature correction factor, Table 15
h = enthalpy, Btu per lb
k = tube diameter and gage factor, Table 12
L = active length of tubes per pass, ft
N = number of passes
n = number of tubes
P = design pressure, psi
p = pressure, psi
Q = total heat transferred, Btu per hr
S = allowable design stress at tube design temperature, psi, from ASME Code
t = wall thickness, in. (See Table 10.); temperature, deg F
U = over-all heat-transfer rate, Btu per hr, sq ft, deg F (The material correction factor, Table 11, must be applied to the over-all heat-transfer rate.)
V = water velocity, fps
W_s = steam flow, lb per hr
W_w = feedwater flow, lb per hr
Δp = pressure drop, psi
Δt_m = logarithmic mean temperature difference, deg F (Fig. 25) (See p. 4–98.)

Heat-balance data for the steam cycle and the choice of proper materials (see p. 9–101) are essential preliminary decisions. Design pressure should be 5 percent greater than the associated maximum pump pressure, rounded to the next higher 25 psi. Tube thickness is calculated by

$$t = Pd/(2S + 0.8P)$$

Test pressure is 1.5 times design pressure.

Condensing-heater-size equations are

$$Q = UA\,\Delta t_m = W_w(h_3 - h_2) = W_s(\Delta h_s)$$

(See Figs. 25 and 26.) The minimum terminal temperature difference is 2 F.

The active length of tubes is calculated from $L = 500AV/NW_wk$ where maximum velocity is 10 fps at 60 F; the number of tubes, from $n = 3.82A/Ld$; the pressure drop, from $\Delta p = (L + 5.5D)F_1 F_2 N/D^{1.24}$.

The shell design pressure is 20 percent greater than the maximum operating pressure, rounded to the higher 25 psi, with 50 psi as a minimum.

A drain-cooling section, when added, is treated as a separate heat exchanger where

Table 10. Tube-wall Thickness

Gauge, BWG	Thickness, in.
15	0.072
16	0.065
17	0.058
18	0.049
19	0.042
20	0.035
22	0.028

Table 11. Material and Gage Correction Factor, C_m
(For ⅝- to 1-in. tubes)

BWG	Tube material							
	Ars-Cu	Admiralty	90-10 Cu-Ni	80-20 Cu-Ni	70-30 Cu-Ni	Monel	18-8 SS	Carbon steel
18	1.00	1.00	0.97	0.95	0.92	0.89	0.85	0.96
17	1.00	1.00	0.94	0.91	0.87	0.85	0.80	0.92
16	1.00	1.00	0.91	0.88	0.84	0.82	0.77	0.89
15	1.00	0.99	0.89	0.86	0.82	0.79	0.74	0.87
14	1.00	0.96	0.85	0.82	0.77	0.75	0.70	0.83
13	0.98	0.93	0.81	0.78	0.73	0.70	0.65	0.79

Table 12. Tube Diameter and Gage Factor, k

Diam, in.	BWG				
	20	18	17	16	15
⅝	0.217	0.2407	0.2580	0.2728	0.289
¾	0.1732	0.1887	0.1995	0.2089	0.218
⅞	0.1445	0.1550	0.1624	0.1686	0.1748
1	0.1238	0.1314	0.1369	0.1413	0.1458

Table 13. Feedwater-heater Tube Constants

Tube BWG	⅝-in. O.D.		¾-in. O.D.		⅞-in. O.D.	
	D	$D^{1.24}$	D	$D^{1.24}$	D	$D^{1.24}$
18	0.527	0.452	0.652	0.589	0.777	0.731
17	0.509	0.433	0.634	0.567	0.759	0.710
16	0.495	0.418	0.620	0.554	0.745	0.695
15	0.481	0.404	0.606	0.538	0.731	0.678
14	0.458	0.380	0.584	0.514	0.709	0.652
13	.....	.....	0.560	0.488	0.685	0.625

Table 14. Friction Loss, Psi per ft of Straight Travel

Water velocity (at 60 F), fps	F_1
3.0	0.018
4.0	0.031
5.0	0.047
6.0	0.065
7.0	0.085
8.0	0.108
9.0	0.134
10.0	0.162

Table 15. Water-temperature Correction Factor*

Average water temp, deg F	F_2
100	0.905
150	0.840
200	0.795
250	0.770
300	0.755
350	0.750
400	0.755
450	0.757
500	0.795
550	0.830
600	0.885

* Average water temperature = $t_s - \Delta t_m$.

the quantities t_v, t_o, t_i, W_s, and W_w are known; t_2 is the only unknown and is to be calculated from a heat balance on the section or $Q = W_s(t_v - t_o) = W_w(t_2 - t_1)$. Compute Δt_m; find the area of the drain-cooler section, A_{dc}, from $Q = UA_{dc}\,\Delta t_m$, with over-all U from Fig. 27.

A **desuperheating section** is similarly calculated with t_v, t_6, t_4, p_6, h_6, h_4, W_s, and W_w known. Allow approximately 1 percent pressure drop through the section to get p_v, and 80 to 90 percent desuperheating (30 F superheat entering condensing section) to obtain t_5 and h_5. By a heat balance on section, calculate h_3 from $Q = W_s(h_6 - h_5) = W_w(h_4 - h_3)$. With equivalent t_3, calculate Δt_m and substitute in $Q = UA\,\Delta t_m$ for area of desuperheating section (over-all U from Fig. 28).

Materials

Heaters are designed to the Standards of the Feedwater Heater Manufacturers Assoc. and the ASME Code for Pressure Vessels, using the following materials:

Tubes:

Material	Maximum temp, deg F	
	Rolled joint	Welded joint
Admiralty metal, ASTM B111	350	
90-10 Cu-Ni, ASTM B111	400	450
80-20 Cu-Ni, ASTM B111	430	475
70-30 Cu-Ni, ASTM B111	460	525
70-30 Cu-Ni, stress-relieved, ASTM B111	460	525
Monel, ASTM B163	525	600
Carbon steel, ASTM A-179 and A-210	650	650

Shell, nozzles: carbon-steel pipe and plate, ASTM A-285 Gr. C and A-106 Gr. B.
Channels, or heads, channel covers: carbon-steel plate, forgings, and pipe, ASTM A-212 Gr. B and A-106 Gr. B.
Baffles and tube supports: steel plate, ASTM A-283 Gr. C.
Tube sheets: carbon-steel plate and forgings, ASTM A-212 Gr. B and A-266 Gr. II.

Carbon steel is used for temperatures up to 800 F. Carbon molybdenum or chrome molybdenum is used for higher temperatures.

OPEN, DEAERATING, AND DIRECT-CONTACT HEATERS

REFERENCE: Heat Exchange Institute Standards for Deaerators and Deaerating Heaters.

Deaerators or deaerating heaters serve (1) to degasify feedwater and thus reduce equipment corrosion (see p. 6–129), (2) to heat feedwater regeneratively and improve thermodynamic efficiency (see p. 9–78), and (3) to provide storage, positive submergence, and surge protection on the boiler feed-pump suction (see p. 14–38).

Removal of oxygen and carbon dioxide from boiler feedwater and process water at elevated temperature is essential for adequate conditioning. In some power-plant applications, a well-designed surface condenser gives adequate deaeration and the accompanying exclusive use of closed feedwater heaters.

A modern **deaerator** will, by mechanical action, reduce O_2 content of effluent to less than 0.005 cc per liter and CO_2 content to a negligible amount. Water must (1) be heated to and kept at saturation temperature, as the gas solubility is zero at the boiling point of the liquid, and (2) be mechanically agitated by spraying or cascading over trays for effective scrubbing, release, and removal of gases. Gases must be swept away by an adequate supply of steam. Since the water is heated to saturation conditions, the terminal temperature difference is zero with maximum improvement in associated turbine heat rate. Extremely low partial gas pressures, dictated by Henry's law, call for large volumes of scrubbing steam. **Vent condensers** of the shell-and-tube or direct-contact types, cooled by incoming feed, serve to recover heat and water before release of gases to the atmosphere.

The **tray-type deaerator** (Fig. 30) is prevalent. While it has some tendency to scale, it will operate at wide load conditions and is practically independent of water-inlet temperature. Trays can be loaded to some 10,000 lb per sq ft-hr, and the deaerator seldom exceeds 8 ft in height.

The **spray type** uses a high-velocity steam jet to atomize and scrub the preheated water. Applications are (1) marine service, where it is unaffected by ship roll and pitch, and (2) industrial plants where operating pressures are stable. It requires a

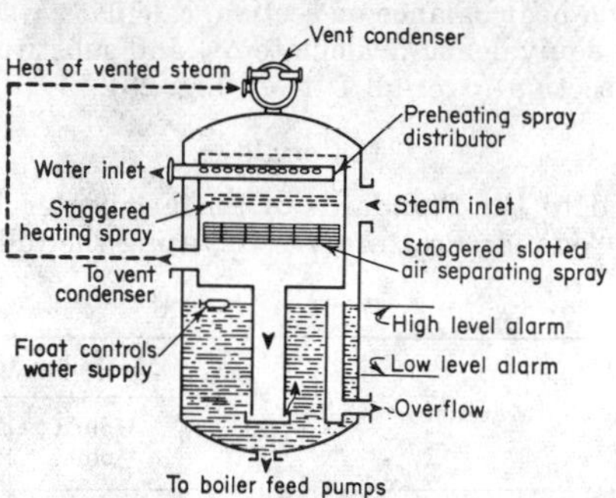

Fig. 30. Tray-type deaerating heater, section.

temperature gradient, *e.g.*, 50 F minimum, to produce the fine sprays and vacuums with the cold water required.

Materials

Open-feed heaters are designed to the ASME Unfired Pressure Vessel Code. Materials used are: shell—steel, ASTM A-285 Gr. C and A-212 Gr. B; trays—stainless steel, type 304; baffles in vent condenser—stainless steel, type 304; spray valves—bronze.

EVAPORATORS

For general treatment of evaporators used in the preparation of makeup water, see p. 6–239.

INTERNAL-COMBUSTION ENGINES

BY

L. C. Lichty and Neil MacCoull

REFERENCES: Dicksee, "The High-speed Compression-ignition Engine," Interscience. Heldt, "High-speed Diesel Engines," Heldt. Judge, "High-speed Diesel Engines," Van Nostrand. Lichty, "Internal-combustion Engines," McGraw-Hill. Maleev, "Internal-combustion Engines," McGraw-Hill. Obert, "Internal-combustion Engines," International Textbook. Pye, "The Internal-combustion Engine," Oxford. Ricardo, "The Internal-combustion Engine," Van Nostrand. Ricardo, "The High-speed Internal-combustion Engine," Blackie. Schweitzer, "Scavenging of Two-stroke-cycle Engines," Macmillan. Shepherd, "Diesel-engine Design," Wiley. Taylor and Taylor, "The Internal-combustion Engine," International Textbook. Vincent, "Supercharging the Internal-combustion Engine," McGraw-Hill. *Trans. ASME. Trans. SAE. Proc. I Mech E*, Automobile Division, *Automotive Inds.*

GENERAL FEATURES

Cycles

(See also p. 4–27)

In **internal-combustion engines,** the combustion process is assumed to occur at constant volume (Fig. 1), at constant pressure (Fig. 2), by a sequence of these two procedures (Fig. 3), or in various other ways. The constant-volume process is characteristic of the **spark-ignition or Otto cycle;** the constant-pressure is found only in the slow-speed **compression-ignition** or **Diesel cycle;** with both procedures, the cycle is sometimes called a **mixed, combination,** or **limited-pressure cycle** and occurs in high-speed compression-ignition engines. Actually, the indicator card obtained from a high-speed, mixed-cycle, compression-ignition engine may be similar to that obtained from a spark-ignition engine. The fundamental differences are the methods of mixing the air and fuel (before compression in the Otto cycle, and usually near the end of compression in the Diesel cycle) and the methods of ignition.

The nominal **compression ratio** (usually specified) is the displacement plus clearance volume divided by the clearance volume. The actual compression ratio is appreciably less than the nominal value because of late intake valve or port closing.

The **compression pressure** may be estimated from the relation $p = r_a^{1.33}\, p_m$, where p_m is the intake-manifold pressure and r_a is the actual compression ratio.

$$r_a = (r_{\text{nominal}} - 1)(\text{relative effective stroke}) + 1$$

The actual compression pressure can be determined with a compression-pressure gage that traps the gases by means of a check valve, thus indicating the maximum pressure under motoring conditions. The compression pressure will be a maximum at some engine speed, depending principally on intake-valve closing time.

Spark-ignition engines use volatile liquids or gases as fuel, have compression ratios between 4:1 and 12:1 (limited by combustion knock of the fuel-air mixture) and compression pressures from below 100 to above 300 psi, use carburetors, gas-mixing valves, or fuel-injection systems, and operate on the Otto cycle. Gasoline is the fuel commonly used in airplane, automobile, small marine, small stationary, and tractor engines. Kerosene also is used in small marine, small stationary, and tractor engines. Commercial gases such as blast-furnace gas, coal gas, coke-oven gas, carbureted water gas, producer gas, and natural gas are used almost exclusively in stationary engines. The mixtures used generally have little or no excess air, and the exhaust gases usually contain CO at full-load conditions for carbureted engines. The combustion pressures are usually 3.5 to 5 times the compression pressures. Load and speed are usually controlled by throttling the charge; high piston speeds (well above 3,000 fpm) are permissible.

Advantages are low first cost, low specific weight, low cranking effort required, wide variation obtainable in speed and load, high mechanical efficiency, and fairly low specific fuel consumption at high compression ratios and wide-open throttle.

Compression-ignition engines use liquid fuels of low volatility varying from low-grade kerosene and distillates to crude oil (see p. 7–27), have compression ratios between 11.5:1 and 22:1 and compression pressures 400 to 700 psi, and operate on the Diesel cycle. No ignition devices are used; load and speed are controlled by varying the fuel quantity injected.

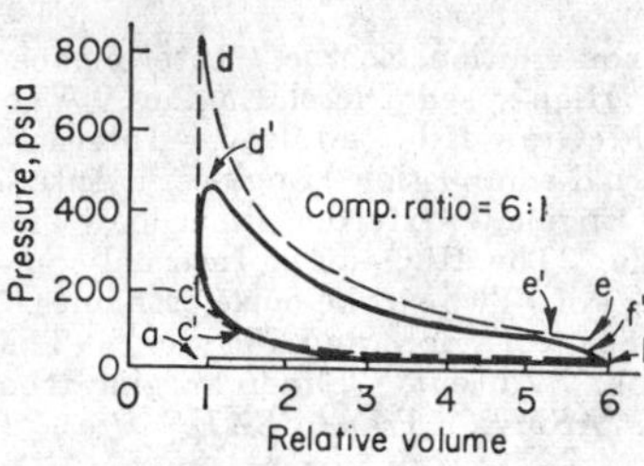

FIG. 1. Otto cycle (constant-volume combustion, no excess air).

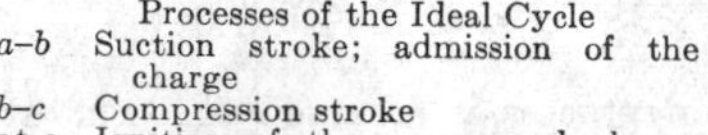

Processes of the Ideal Cycle

a–b Suction stroke; admission of the charge
b–c Compression stroke
at *c* Ignition of the compressed charge
c–d Combustion
d–e Expansion
at *e* Exhaust valve opens
b–a Exhaust stroke

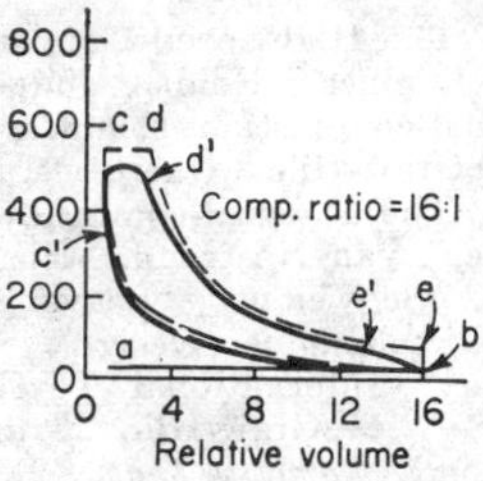

FIG. 2. Diesel cycle (constant-pressure combustion, 50 percent excess air).

Processes of the Ideal Cycle

a–b Suction stroke; admission of air
b–c Compression of air
c–d Injection and combustion of the fuel
d–e Expansion
at *e* Exhaust valve opens
b–a Exhaust stroke

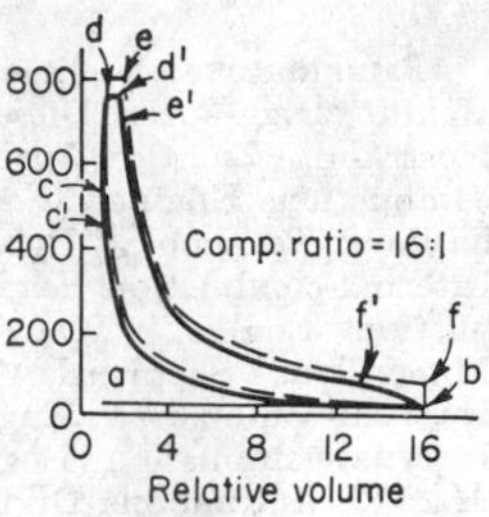

FIG. 3. Mixed cycle (constant-volume and constant-pressure combustion, 50 percent excess air).

Processes of the Ideal Cycle

a–b Suction stroke; admission of air
b–c Compression of air
c–d Ignition and constant-volume combustion
d–e Constant-pressure combustion
e–f Expansion
at *f* Exhaust begins
b–a Exhaust stroke

Broken lines represent the ideal cycle; solid lines show characteristics of the actual cycle. Primes attached to letters show actual locations of events.

The **dual-fuel engine** is a Diesel engine with a compression ratio which is too low to result in ignition, at the desired time, of the gas-air mixture inducted into the cylinder. A pilot (small) injection of liquid fuel with good ignition quality is used to initiate the combustion process. In Worthington four-cycle engines with valve overlap (both valves open at top dead center) and supercharging, the gas is usually admitted only after the exhaust valve has closed to eliminate any loss of gas into the exhaust manifold. In other cases the gas may be mixed and inducted with the air stream. In Nordberg two-cycle engines the gas and pilot fuel are injected for about 25 deg of crank travel on the compression stroke, the gas being compressed to a pressure usually above 1,000 psi before injection. The pilot fuel has about 5 to 7 percent of the total charge Btu.

Some compression-ignition engines (sometimes called semi-Diesel) have compression pressures of 100 to 300 psi, inject the fuel during the compression stroke, and require an electric glow plug or the heating of an uncooled portion of the combustion chamber for starting. The uncooled hot bulb or plate heats the mixture and causes compression ignition at low or moderate compression pressures.

Advantages are low specific fuel consumption, ability to maintain economy and thermal efficiency at part loads, low fuel cost, no preignition, practically no CO except near full-load or at over-load conditions, and suitability for two-stroke operation.

The lower compression engines require electric glow plugs or heating for starting, are of simpler construction (usually valveless two-stroke cycle), have less weight, lower first cost, lower operating expense, and higher mechanical efficiency than the higher-compression engines.

The **four-stroke cycle** (four-cycle) requires four piston strokes or two crankshaft revolutions per cycle (Figs. 1 and 2). This engine cycle is used almost exclusively in automobile, tractor, and aircraft engines in all types and sizes, and also in engines of other classifications with the exception of outboard engines. Small four-cycle engines are always single-acting (combustion on only one side of the piston), but large engines may be double-acting and necessitate water-cooled pistons. The pumping loss, indicated by the area between the exhaust and the induction curves (Fig. 69), is more than the negative loop of the indicator card and at wide-open throttle depends on valve openings and speed and amounts to 3 to 7 percent of the engine indicated power. Throttling increases the pumping loss and reduces the positive indicator card area.

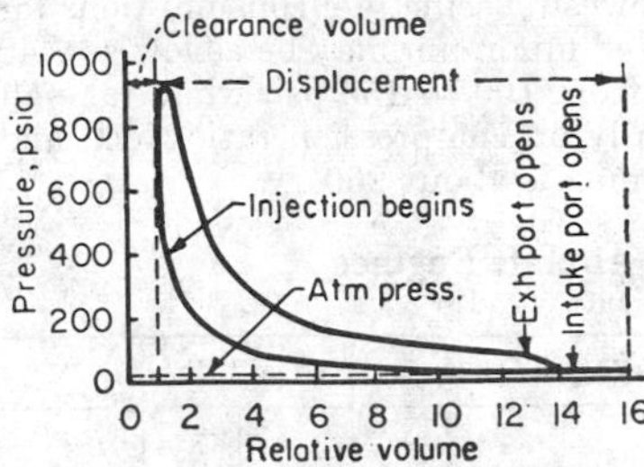

FIG. 4. Indicator card for two-cycle Diesel engine (16:1 compression ratio).

Advantages compared with two-cycle crankcase-compression spark-ignition engines: higher piston speed, wider variation in speed and load, cooler pistons, common crankcase in multicylinder engines, good lubrication secured more easily, no fuel loss during exhaust, higher mechanical efficiency, lower specific fuel consumption, lower pumping losses.

The **two-stroke cycle** (two-cycle) engine requires two piston strokes or only one revolution for each cycle. Exhaust ports in the cylinder wall are uncovered by the piston, or exhaust valves in the cylinder head are opened near the end (at 60 to 88 percent) of the expansion stroke, permitting the escape of exhaust gases and reducing the pressure in the cylinder (Fig. 4). The charge of air or combustible mixture flows into and is compressed in a separate crankcase compartment for each cylinder, a compressor, or a blower to a few pounds above atmospheric pressure. Intake ports are uncovered by the piston or intake valves, are opened soon after the opening of the exhaust, and the compressed charge flows into the cylinder, expelling most of the exhaust products, some charge escaping with the exhaust.

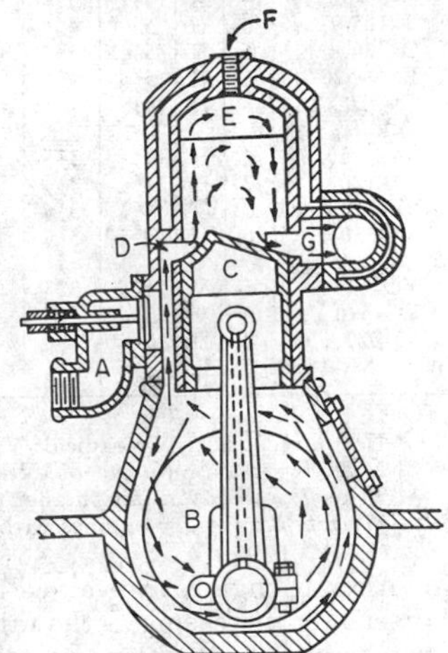

FIG. 5. Small two-cycle gasoline engine with crankcase compression.

Blowers or compressors, driven either mechanically or by an exhaust turbine, are often used to supply sufficient air to scavenge the cylinder and clearance space and, in some cases, to supercharge the engine. Although small engines use only ports and crankcase compression (Fig. 5), large engines usually have separate compressors or blowers and either ports, or both valves and ports. With crankcase compression, no scavenging of the cylinder is possible, the volumetric efficiency is low (30 to 50 percent), and the engine is limited to operation at low piston speed (usually less than 1,000 fpm) for economical operation. The crankcase compression work amounts to 7 to 12 percent of the total work, but scavenging blowers with displacements 20 to 80 percent greater than piston displacement may require as high as 30 percent of the indicated work in high-speed engines.

Advantages, compared with four-cycle engines, 50 to 80 percent greater power output per unit piston displacement and same speed, depending on scavenging, twice as many power impulses per cylinder per revolution, piston-pin and crankpin pressures in one direction up to the speed at which the piston inertia force exceeds the gas pressure, low cost for valveless designs, and crankcase compression.

Aircraft Engines

Aircraft piston engines use the Otto cycle, are air-cooled and invariably four-stroke. All types are normally aspirated or supercharged. These engines have the lowest specific weight (Table 1). Aircraft engines have two valves per cylinder and valve-in-head construction. Large ones have also the lowest specific fuel consumptions for the carbureted spark-ignition engine; the guaranteed minimum may be as low as 0.40 lb per bhp-hr. Maximum cruising bmep ranges from 100 to 150 psi, while take-off bmep ranges from 120 to 230, depending principally on compression ratio, fuel, and supercharge. With water injection the take-off bmep is about 260.

Table 1. Selected Piston-type Aircraft Engines
(*Automotive Inds.*, **132**, Nov. 6, 1965, p. 218)

Make and model	Cylinders						Ratings (METO)†				Weight, lb§		
	Number	Arrangements*	Bore, in.	Stroke, in.	Displacement, cu in.	Compression ratio	Bhp‡	Rpm	At sea level or altitude	Bmep at max bhp, psi	Engine, dry	Per max bhp (except takeoff)	Fuel octane no. required
Continental													
A-56-8F....	4	H	3⅞	3⅝	171.0	6.3	65	2,300	SL	131	170	2.62	80/87
C-85-8F....	4	H	4 1/16	3⅝	188.0	6.3	85	2,575	SL	139	179	2.14	80/87
E-185-9....	6	H	5	4	471.0	7.0	205	2,600	SL	133	352	1.73	80/87
O-300......	6	H	5 1/16	3⅞	301.0	7.0	145	2,700	SL	141	268	1.85	80/87
FSO-526...	6	H	5⅛	4¼	526.0	6.0	270	3,000	7,900	129	553	2.05	91/96
10-520.....	6	H	5¼	4	520.0	8.5	285	2,700	SL	161	454	1.59	100/130
Franklin													
6A4-150....	6	H	4½	3½	335	7.0	150	2,600	SL	136	277	1.85	80/87
2A-120.....	2	H	4⅝	3½	120	10.5	60	3,000	SL	134	130	2.17	100/130
6V-350.....	6	V	4⅝	3½	350	10.5	235	3,200	SL	166	319	1.36	100/130
6A-350.....	6	H	4⅝	3½	350	10.5	235	3,400	SL	...	319	1.36	100/130
Lycoming													
VO-435....	6	V	4⅞	3⅞	434	7.3	250	3,200	SL	140	392	1.57	80/87
VO-540....	6	V	5⅛	4⅜	541.5	8.7	305	3,200	3,000	139	442	1.45	100/130
10-720.....	8	H	5⅛	4⅜	722	8.7	400	2,650	SL	166	552	1.38	100/130
Wright R-1820	9	R	6⅛	6⅞	1,823	6.8	1,275	2,500	3,500	222	1,419	1.11	115/145

* H = horizontal; R = radical; V = vertical.
† METO = maximum except during takeoff.
‡ Takeoff power is usually higher than the recommended max continuous power.
§ Weights are for dry engines without hub or starter.

Aircraft engines are valved to obtain high mep at the rated speed, the full-throttle horsepower increasing as the rated speed is approached. High-output engines usually operate under conditions of compression ratio and supercharging that prohibit full-throttle operation at or near sea level with the specified fuel. Such engines can be operated at full throttle at or above a critical altitude beyond which the power decreases with an increase in altitude. Below the critical altitude, the power decreases with a decrease in altitude, with constant intake-manifold pressure, because of the increase in exhaust back pressure and ambient temperature.

The performance of an aircraft engine varies with speed, altitude, and manifold pressure. At any given speed and with a fixed supercharger or blower ratio (supercharger rpm to engine rpm) and wide-open throttle the bhp of an engine varies almost linearly with the density of the atmosphere. This characteristic makes possible the estimating of the power curves at altitude if the sea-level output is known. The power at 20,000 ft altitude is about 50 percent of the sea-level wide-open throttle output for any given speed.

Low specific fuel consumption is obtained by operating at the lowest rpm possible for the desired power with lean carburetor setting, the optimum output being about one-half to two-thirds of the normal rated output of the engine.

Power output for take-off or climb may be increased appreciably for engines having a surplus supercharger capacity by means of *water* (best coolant) or *water-methanol* (max output) *injection* into the engine intake manifold. The use of a 50–50 water-methanol mixture in amounts equal to 50 percent of the fuel permits an increase of about 40 percent in the knock-limited output for fuel-air ratios of about 0.10. More efficient results are obtained at lean fuel-air ratios.

Aircraft-engine cylinders are limited to a maximum diameter of about 6 in. because of the piston cooling and knocking difficulties that arise with large cylinders, desirable compression ratios, and high intake-manifold pressures. The stroke-bore ratio ranges from 0.76 to 1.12 including both Otto and Diesel engines, with the exception of the Junkers engine which has a ratio of 1.53.

Radial engines have an odd number of cylinders operating on each crankpin and permit the firing of the odd-numbered cylinders in one revolution and the even-numbered cylinders in the next revolution, and result in evenly spaced power impulses for equally spaced cylinders. The usual construction consists of a master connecting rod for one cylinder, the other rods being connected to the crank end of the master rod by means of knuckle pins. A solid crankshaft and a master rod with a detachable bearing cap or a solid master rod and a built-up crankshaft may be used.

Aircraft engines may be direct-connected to the propellers or be connected through gearing that reduces the propeller speed usually to about two-thirds of the crankshaft speed. The centrifugal supercharger runs seven to twelve times the crankshaft speed, two-speed gear mechanisms being used in some cases, the high-speed for use only above certain altitudes. Multistage superchargers (two rotors with intercooling) are required for high power at high altitudes. In some cases a turbosupercharger is used for the first stage, the second stage being integral with the engine. In other cases exhaust turbines are direct-connected to the engine shaft.

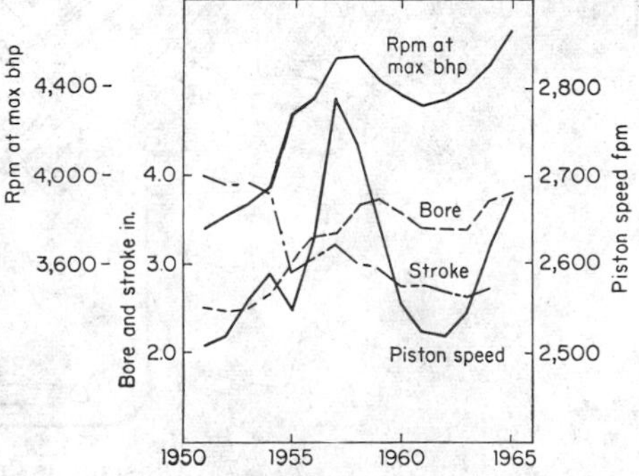

FIG. 6. Trend of average American automobile engine dimensions.

United States Automobile Engines

(See also p. 11-3)

The **size (displacement)** of the average U.S. automobile engine has remained substantially between 250 and 330 cu in. from 1927 through 1965, but the advertised **maximum power** has increased greatly, especially after 1953 (see Fig. 2, p. 11-4, and Fig. 6). This has been accomplished by (1) increased compression ratios; (2) more rigid bearing alignment, better bearing materials, and better lubrication; and (3) higher volumetric efficiencies (better "breathing" with reduced intake-system resistance). The advertised engine power is based on conditions not existing in cars, but it is generally comparable between makes. The conventional advertised power rating may be designated **gross horsepower,** measured (1) on the test stand at wide-open throttle, with the spark advance and carburetor adjusted for maximum power at each test speed; (2) with no mufflers and no heat supplied to the intake manifold; (3) with no auxiliaries, such as electric generators and pumps for power steering; and (4) with the power readings raised by calculation to the equivalent of 60 F carburetor air temperature.

Valve timing, particularly the closure of intake valves (varying from 35.5 to 105 deg crankshaft rotation after bottom dead center for 1965 cars, with 67.5 deg average), is selected to give a rising volumetric efficiency and torque as the rpm is increased from low speed until restrictions in the intake system, developed primarily by the carburetor Venturis and the intake valves, begin to throttle the engine. The 1965 engines developed maximum torque at 2,600 rpm approx. Despite torque falloff at higher speeds, the power peaked at 4,800 to 6,000 rpm. Still higher powers were optionally obtainable by such means as (1) higher compression ratios, and (2) four-barrel (compound) carburetors or additional carburetors, which improved the volumetric efficiency and raised the torque peaks to higher speeds.

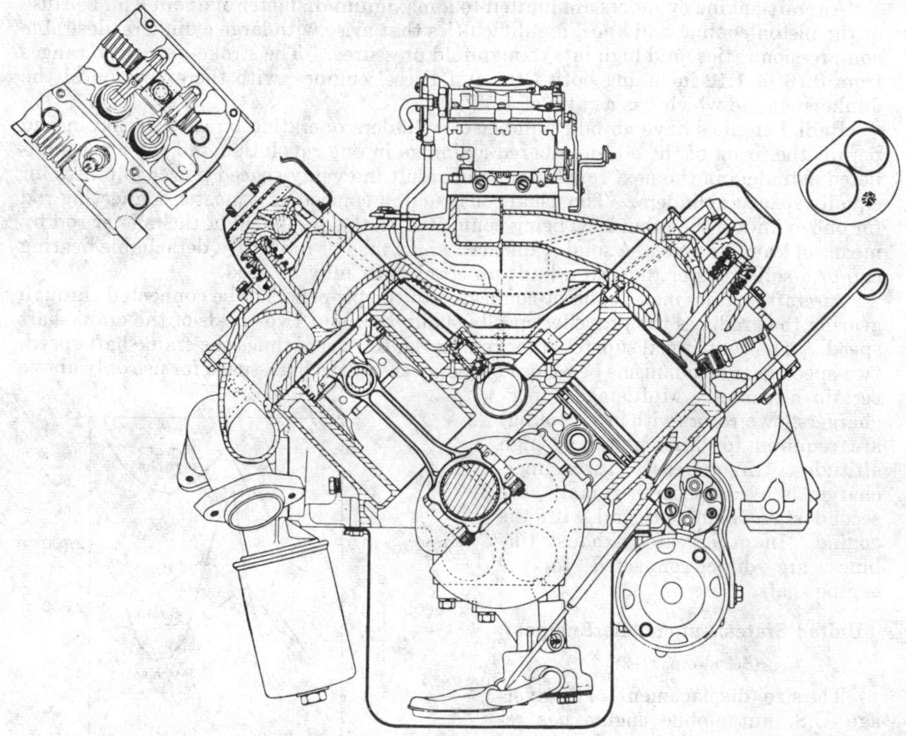

Fig. 7. Oldsmobile Jetfire rocket engine.

Engines have been supplied with various numbers of cylinders over the years (from 4 to 16 in a V), but the conventional engine has become the **V-8** (Fig. 7) for larger cars (60 percent of all 1965 car models), the remainder being predominantly 6-cylinder. Advantages of the V-8 arrangement include short length and low height with low-hood designs; rigid, compact construction, with carburetors located centrally in the V, giving short, symmetrical, intake-manifold designs; five-bearing crankshafts; cylinders and upper crankcase of integral construction; detachable cylinder heads; and overhead valves. Crankshafts are arranged with 90 deg between the front pair of crankpins, 90 deg between the rear pair, and 180 deg between the center pair. (Introduced by Cadillac in 1927, this arrangement results in excellent dynamic balance, previously lacking in V-8 engines with crankpins all in the same plane.) The connecting rods for corresponding cylinders on each side of the V are side by side on the same crankpin, with the right and left cylinder blocks suitably staggered.

While the average cylinder bore increased from 3.27 in. in 1946 to 3.91 in. in 1965, the stroke decreased from about 4.11 in. to 3.45 in. in the same period, with reduction in the width and weight of V-8 engines and the added rigidity necessary for satisfactory bearing life in high-speed engines.

Quiet operation is essential in automobile engines and requires close manufacturing control of clearances. The larger engines usually have hydraulic valve lifters and means of rotating the exhaust valves, at least, for prolonged life.

It is standard practice to provide pistons with three rings above the wrist pin—two narrow compression rings above one oil-scraper ring, with several drain holes from the back of the ring groove to return oil to the crankcase. All compression rings are narrow, of cast iron from 0.063 to 0.0787 in. wide, and have a wear-resistant coating, such as chromium (particularly for the top ring) and tin, or compounds (iron oxide, phosphates), which minimizes the running-in period without danger of scuffing or scoring the cylinders. Oil-scraper rings are of steel or cast iron, generally a little less than $\frac{3}{16}$ in. wide, and are provided with internal expander springs to increase pressure against the cylinder walls. One design uses two very narrow steel rings with a spring expander between them to maintain pressure against the sides of the ring groove. Many oil-scraper rings, especially those of steel, also use wear-resistant coatings.

Table 2. Selected United States Automobile Engines
(*Automotive Inds.*, **132,** Nov. 6, 1965, p. 123)

Make and model	Cylinders					Published maximums				Car weight, lb		Bhp per cu in.
	Number	Bore, in.	Stroke, in.	Displacement, cu in.	Std compression ratio	Bhp	at Rpm	Torque, lb-ft,	at Rpm	Per cu in.	Per bhp	
Rambler												
American 440	6	$3\frac{1}{8}$	$4\frac{1}{4}$	195.6	8.7	125	4,200	180	1,600	15.8	24.6	0.64
Ambassador	8	4	$3\frac{1}{4}$	327.0	9.7	270	4,700	360	2,600	11.4	13.8	0.83
Plymouth												
Valiant	6	$3\frac{13}{32}$	$3\frac{1}{8}$	170.0	8.5	101	4,400	155	2,400	18.3	30.5	0.59
Valiant	8	$3\frac{5}{8}$	$3\frac{5}{16}$	273.0	8.8	180	4,200	260	1,600	11.9	18.0	0.65
Belvedere	8	$4\frac{1}{4}$	$3\frac{3}{4}$	426.0	10.3	365	4,800	470	3,200	....	....	0.86
Dodge												
Dart	6	$3\frac{13}{32}$	$4\frac{1}{8}$	225.0	8.4	145	4,000	215	2,400	14.2	22.0	0.64
Coronet	8	$4\frac{1}{8}$	$3\frac{3}{8}$	361.0	9.0	265	4,400	380	2,400	10.7	14.6	0.73
Chrysler	8	$4\frac{1}{4}$	$3\frac{3}{8}$	383.0	9.2	270	4,400	390	2,800	11.6	16.5	0.70
Imperial	8	$4\frac{3}{16}$	$3\frac{3}{4}$	413.0	10.1	340	4,600	470	2,800	13.3	16.2	0.82
Ford												
Falcon	6	$3\frac{1}{2}$	$2\frac{5}{16}$	170.0	9.1	105	4,400	158	2,400	17.1	27.7	0.61
Mustang	8	4	$2\frac{7}{8}$	289.0	10.1	225	4,800	305	3,200			
Galaxie 500	8	4	$2\frac{7}{8}$	289.0	9.3	200	4,400	282	2,400	11.1	16.6	0.69
Thunderbird	8	$4\frac{3}{64}$	$3\frac{25}{32}$	390.0	10.1	300	4,600	427	2,800	12.7	16.5	0.77
Mercury												
Comet	6	$3\frac{11}{16}$	$3\frac{1}{8}$	200.0	9.2	120	4,400	190	2,400	15.6	26.0	0.60
Monterey	8	$4\frac{3}{64}$	$3\frac{25}{32}$	390.0	9.4	250	4,400	378	2,400	11.1	17.4	0.64
Lincoln Continental	8	$4\frac{19}{64}$	$3\frac{15}{64}$	430.0	10.10	320	4,600	465	2,600	12.9	17.4	0.74
Chevrolet												
Corvair 500	6	$3\frac{7}{16}$	$2\frac{15}{16}$	164.0	8.25	95	3,600	154	2,400	17.7	30.5	0.58
Biscayne	6	$3\frac{7}{8}$	$3\frac{1}{4}$	230.0	8.50	140	4,400	220	1,600	....	....	0.60
Biscayne	8	$3\frac{7}{8}$	3	283.0	9.25	195	4,800	285	2,800	11.6	16.9	0.69
Corvette	8	4	$3\frac{1}{4}$	327.0	10.50	250	4,400	350	2,800	10.6	17.9	0.77
Pontiac Tempest	8	$4\frac{1}{16}$	$3\frac{3}{4}$	389.0	10.75	335	5,000	431	3,200	10.1	11.7	0.87
Buick												
Special	8	$3\frac{3}{4}$	$3\frac{13}{32}$	300.0	9.00	210	4,600	310	2,400	12.0	17.2	0.70
Riviera	8	$4\frac{5}{16}$	$3\frac{41}{64}$	425.0	10.25	340	4,400	445	2,800	....	....	0.80
Oldsmobile Dynamic 88	8	$4\frac{1}{8}$	$3\frac{31}{32}$	425.0	10.25	310	4,400	450	2,400	10.3	14.2	0.72
Cadillac 68	8	$4\frac{1}{8}$	4	429.0	10.50	340	4,600	480	3,000	11.6	14.6	0.79
Studebaker Commander	8	$3\frac{7}{8}$	3	283.0	9.25	195	4,800	285	2,800	12.3	17.9	0.69

Water cooling under a pressure of 7 to 14 psi is standard for all U.S. cars except the 6-cylinder horizontally opposed Corvair, which is **air-cooled** (as are several smaller

European cars). Water-jacket temperatures are controlled by thermostats which open at 160 to 180 F, permitting water from the cylinder heads to flow to the radiator. With one exception, all engines are designed with water all around each cylinder (not "siamesed") and jackets the full length of the piston travel.

Manufacturers supply a range of engine sizes for the various car models. Many may be provided with optional features, such as higher compression ratios and multiple carburetors of the compound type to increase the "breathing" capacity of the engines and thus raise the peak torque and power to speeds where the valve areas are the principal limitation to volumetric efficiency.

Foreign Automobile Engines

Foreign automobile engines, Table 3, are principally of the four-stroke Otto-cycle type, with some two-stroke designs, and a few engines of the Diesel type. The engines are principally water-cooled, using both thermosiphon and pump systems, and combinations of both. All of the horizontal-opposed type of engines are air-cooled. The bhp values range from 10 to 335, compared to 50 to 365 in the United States. Most

Table 3. Selected Foreign Automobile Engines
(*Automotive Inds.*, **132,** Nov. 6, 1965, pp. 145–150)

Make and model	Cylinders				Maximum bhp at rpm		Compression ratio	Cylinder arrangement*	Valve location†
	Number	Bore, in.	Stroke, in.	Displacement, cu in.					
GREAT BRITAIN									
Austin Mini	4	2.48	2.69	51.7	34	5,500	8.3	IL	IH
A 110 MK11	6	3.28	3.50	177.7	120	4,750	8.3	IL	IH
Austin-Healey Sprite MK111	4	2.54	3.50	67.0	59	5,750	9.0	IL	IH
Bentley S3	8	4.10	3.60	380.2	...	.....	9.0	V	IH
Daimler Majestic Major Saloon	8	3.75	3.15	278.3	220	5,500	8.0	V	IH
Ford Anglia 2-door std	4	3.19	1.91	60.9	41	5,000	8.9	IL	IH
Consul Corsair 4-door std	4	3.19	2.87	91.5	65	4,800	9.0	IL	IH
Jaguar MKX 42 litre	6	3.63	4.17	258.0	265	5,400	9.0	IL	TO
MG Midget MK11	4	2.54	3.30	67.0	59	5,750	9.0	IL	IH
Morris Mini Minor MK11	4	2.48	2.69	51.7	37	5,500	8.3	IL	IH
Rolls Royce Silver Cloud 111	8	4.10	3.60	380.2	...	.....	9.0	V	IH
Rover 3-litre coupe	6	3.06	4.13	183.0	129	4,750	8.0	IL	F
FRANCE									
Citroen AZ2CV	2	2.59	2.44	25.8	18	5,000	7.5	Op	OC
Peugeot 403	4	3.13	2.87	89.6	65	4,750	7.5	IL	IH
Renault R-1094 Dauphine	4	2.28	3.15	51.6	32	4,500	8.0	IL	IH
GERMANY									
Mercedes-Benz 190	4	3.35	3.29	115.8	90	5,200	8.7	IL	OC
190D	4	3.43	3.29	121.3	60	4,200	21.0	IL	OC
Opel Kadett 2-door	4	2.83	2.40	60.6	46	5,200	7.8	IL	IH
Porsche 356C/2000GS	4	3.63	2.91	119.5	130	6,200	9.5	Op	IH
Volkswagen 1500-31N	4	3.27	2.72	91.1	54	4,000	7.8	Op	IH
ITALY									
Giulia 1600 Sprint	4	3.07	3.23	95.8	106	6,200	9.0	IL	OC
Ferrari Spydre 275/GTS	12	3.03	2.32	220.4	260	7,000	9.2	V	OC
Fiat 500-D Berlina	2	2.65	2.76	30.5	22	4,400	7.1	IL	IH

* IL = in line; V = V type; Op = opposed.
† IH = in head; TO = twin overhead camshafts; F = F Head, valves in head and side; OC = overhead camshaft.

engines are normally aspirated, but some are supercharged. The displacements, in cubic inches, range from 1 cylinder, 7.3; 2 cylinders, 15.4 to 42; 3 cylinders, 45.9; 4 cylinders, 38.6 to 183; 6 cylinders, 92 to 295; 8 cylinders, 143.5 to 244.7; to 12 cylinders (Ferrari), 180.1 to 302.3 cu in.; most of the engines being of the 4-cylinder inline type.

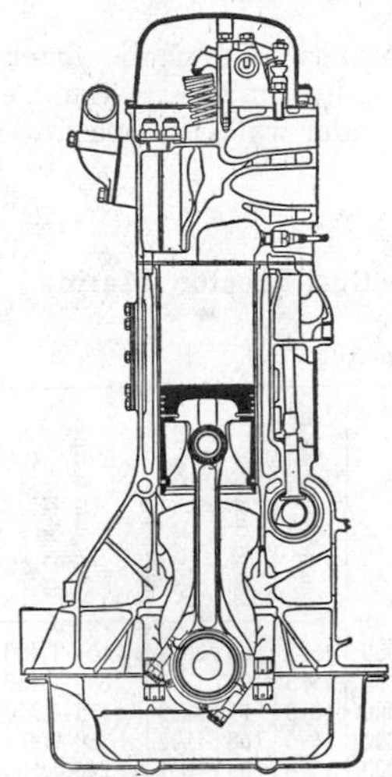

FIG. 8. Mack truck and bus gasoline engine.

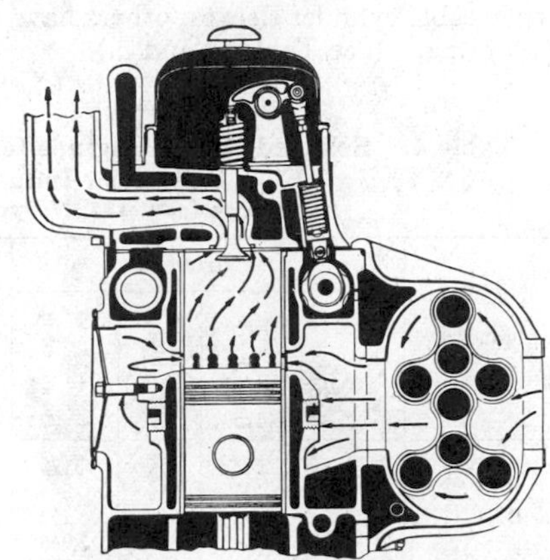

FIG. 9. General Motors two-cycle blower-scavenged Diesel engine.

The bmep psi at maximum power ranges from 61 to 120 for two-stroke engines, 88 to 180, compared to 101 to 146 in the United States, for four-stroke Otto-cycle carbureted engines, these performances being attained at 2,730 (Ford, Anglia) and 3,540 (Maserati) fpm mean piston speed, compared to 2,625 (Metropolitan) and 3,142 (Chrysler) fpm in the United States.

The stroke-bore ratio ranges from 0.77 (Ferrari) to 1.60 (Panhard), compared to 0.88 (Hudson 6) to 1.58 (Hudson 8).

Truck and Bus Engines

Truck and bus engines (Fig. 8) are similar to automobile engines but, in general, are larger, having 300- to 1,000-cu in. displacement, are more rugged, and run at lower speeds. Both Otto and Diesel cycles are used, and, in one case, a two-cycle blower-scavenged Diesel engine has been developed (Fig. 9). Water cooling is universally used, and the engines are normally aspirated. These engines have compression ratios slightly lower than automobile engines but are valved similarly, have similar performance curves, and attain maximum bhp (50 to above 300) at a piston speed ranging from 1,800 to 2,600 fpm, with an average about 2,600 fpm for the gasoline engines. Maximum torque is obtained at about 1,200 rpm, appreciably lower than for automobile engines. The Diesel engines have piston speeds ranging from 1,000 to 1,900 fpm, operating at somewhat lower speeds than the gasoline engines. Truck and bus engines do not operate at speeds much higher than those at which maximum power is attained. The two-cycle Diesel does not attain the maximum-power speed (Fig. 10).

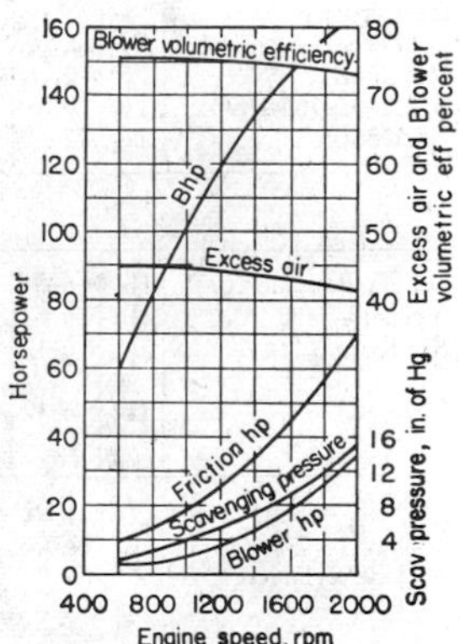

FIG. 10. Performance data of blower-scavenged General Motors two-cycle Diesel engine.

Truck and bus engines are usually built with four or six cylinders in line and with eight cylinders in V-type construction. The stroke-bore ratio ranges from about 0.76 to 1.47, the later engines having the smaller values. (See Tables 4 and 5.)

Tractor Engines

Both Otto and Diesel cycles are used in tractor engines. Particular attention is given to air cleaning because of the effect of atmospheric dust on wear. Some engines have replaceable cylinder sleeves; others have thick cylinder walls that permit considerable reboring. (See Tables 4 and 5.)

Table 4. Selected Diesel Engines for Truck, Bus, Tractor, Marine Railcar, or Industrial Use

(*Automotive Inds.*, **132,** Nov. 6, 1965, pp. 196–204)

Make and model	Type*	Cylinders			Displacement, cu in.	Continuous bhp at rpm		Compression ratio	Bmep, psi	Weight, lb per bhp	Maximum torque, lb-ft at rpm	Shipping weight, lb
		Number	Bore, in.	Stroke, in.								
Allis Chalmers D-175	EC	4	3 9/16	4 3/8	175	38	2,000	15.3	86	20	104–1,400	760
16000	DI	6	5 1/4	6 1/2	844	180	1,800	15.3	103	17.2	645–1,400	2,920
Caterpillar D311	PC	4	4	5	252	50	2,000	18.0	79	22.9	175–1,350	1,145
D398	PC	12	6 1/4	8	2,946	750	1,200	15.5	168	15.2	4,260–900	11,300
Cummins C105	DI	4	4 7/16	5	309	72	2,200	15.8	84	18.1	246–1,500	1,300
NH250	DI	6	5 1/2	5	855	174	1,800	14.9	90	14.3	685–1,500	2,490
LRT6	DI	6	7 1/4	10	2,477	325	1,000	13.5	107	23.7	2,250–850	7,690
Fairbanks Morse												
50A5T	DI	4	4 15/16	5 1/8	389	126	1,800	15.5	143	17.5	380–1,350	2,200
50A6T-12V	DI	12	6 1/4	6 1/2	2,392	695	1,800	14.5	135	12.4	2,375–1,320	8,650
GMC D478	DI	6	5 1/8	3 55/64	478	.....	.....	17.5	...	....	275–2,000	950
GM Diesel 2-71	DI	2	4 1/4	5	142	48	1,800	17.0	75	20.0	194–1,400	960
Twin 6-110	DI	12	5	5.6	1,320	454	1,800	18.0	76	25.2	2,820–685	11,440
Hercules D 2300	DI	4	4	4 1/2	226	59	2,200	17.5	94	10.1	182–1,400	600
International												
UDT817	DI	6	5 3/8	6	817	360	2,100	15.0	142	9.9	1,010–1,000	3,570
DU66D	PC	2	3 1/4	4	66	13	2,000	19.0	75	26.6	45–1,400	346
Waukesha 180-DLC	TC	4	3 1/2	3 3/4	144	31	2,000	17.0	71	18.3	102–1,800	475
L5788DS	TC	12	8 1/2	8 1/2	5,788	988	1,200	15.0	80	14.9	5,440–1,000	16,300
STATIONARY ENGINES (*Manufacturers' data*)												
Cooper-Bessemer	IL	6–8	10 1/2	13 1/2	1,169†	159†	720	13.1	150	23.8		
Ingersoll-Rand	IL	6	10 1/2	12	1,039†	120†	720	14.0	127	35.2		
Nordberg	IL	6–12	29	40	26,420† (2 cycle)	1,000†	200	12.0	75	95		
Sulzer RD-90	IL	4–12	35.4	61	60,038† (2 cycle)	2,000†	119	....	109			
						3,000†	130	....	130			

* EC = Lanova energy cell; DI = direct injection; PC = precombustion chamber; TC = turbulence chamber; IL = in line.

† Per cylinder.

Most tractor engines are of the valve-in-head type, and all are water-cooled (see Fig. 11). The low-compression Otto engines are designed to use kerosene or a distillate and the higher compression-ratio engines use either "third-grade" or "regular" gasoline. Some engines use liquefied petroleum gas (LPG).

Piston speeds at maximum rpm range from 1,000 to 1,300 fpm, these engines being in the comparatively slow-speed class. Fairly high torque is obtained throughout the speed range, and the power curve does not reach its maximum at the governed speed (Fig. 12). The cylinders are in line either vertically or horizontally, although some eight-cylinder engines are of the V-type construction.

Table 5. Selected Gasoline Engines for Truck, Bus, Tractor, Marine, and Industrial Use

(*Automotive Inds.*, March 15, 1965, pp. 186–195)

Make and model	Designed for*	Cylinders: Number	Cylinders: Bore, in.	Cylinders: Stroke, in.	Cylinders: Displacement, cu in.	Cylinders: Compression ratio	Rating, bhp at rpm		Max torque, lb-ft at rpm		Weight, lb	Over-all dimensions: Length, in.	Over-all dimensions: Height, in.
Allis-Chalmers G-138	Ind	4	3 3/8	3 7/8	138	7.75	39†	1,800	118	1,200	392	27 3/16	33 3/16
G-262	Tr	6	3 9/16	4 3/8	262	8.00	96	2,200	234	1,500	720	37 35/64	32 3/8
Brennan Imp	M	4	2 17/64	3 1/8	50	7.40	20	4,000	34	3,200	165	26	17 5/8
125	M	6	4 3/8	5 1/2	496	6.00	94	2,200	350	1,200	900	65	24 3/4
Case A251G	Tr, Ind	4	4	5	251	6.80	73	2,000	215	1,300	1,015	39 3/4	38 3/4
Chevrolet 230	T, B	6	3 7/8	3 1/4	230	8.50	140	4,400	220	1,600	465	39	32
Chrysler M225A	M	6	3 13/32	4 1/8	225	8.20	120	4,000	200	1,400	670	43 21/32	
M413B	M	8	4 3/16	3 3/4	413	8.00	280†	4,000	395	2,800	900	45 1/2	
Continental N-62	Ind	4	2 3/8	3 1/2	62.0	6.46	16	2,800	41.8	1,200	170	19	19
R-6602	T, B	6	4 7/8	5 3/8	602.0	6.00	232	2,800	482	1,200	1,525		
Ford 134	Tr	4	3 7/16	3 39/64	134	7.50	48	2,200	121	1,600	505‡	31 13/64	27 7/64
EFY-4V	T, B, Ind	8	4 3/64	3 25/32	391	7.60	235	4,000	372	2,000	596	34 7/8	35 17/64
GMC 702	T	12	4 9/16	3 37/64	702.1	7.50	275	2,400	630	1,600	......	58 13/16	37 1/4
153	T	4	3 7/8	3 1/4	153	8.50	90†	4,000	152	2,400	359		
Gray Marine Tour 112	M	4	3 3/16	3 1/2	401.0	9.00	31†	2,200	280	4,400	390	33	15
V8CH280	M	8	4 3/16	3 41/64	401	9.00	280†	4,000	396	2,800	925	47 3/8	21 3/4
Hercules OXLD	T, B, Tr, M, Ind	6	3 7/16	4 1/4	236.7	6.50	92	3,200	190	1,400	440	35 1/16	20 9/16
International UC-60	Tr, Ind	4	2 5/8	2 3/4	59.5	7.00	38	1,700	17	2,500	279‡	23 13/16	25 1/4
UV-401	Tr, Ind	8	4 1/8	3 3/4	401.0	7.69	335	1,650	206	3,600	1,310	41	41 3/16
Minneapolis-Moline 206L4	Tr	4	3 5/8	5	206.5	7.2	56	1,750	183	1,100	650‡	36	32
HD800-6A	Ind	6	5 5/16	5	799.9	8.3	250	2,000	718	1,100	2,425‡	76 1/2	43 3/4
REO 6-130	T, B	6	3 7/8	4 1/8	292	6.94	130	3,300	230	1,600	946	45 9/32	34 1/16
Waukesha 180GKB	T, Tr, Ind	4	3 5/8	3 3/4	155	7.50	50	2,400	131	1,400	450	30 7/8	27 3/4
L7040G	Ind	12	9 3/8	8 1/2	7,040	8.80	1,186	1,200	5,840	600	15,000	130	75 1/2

* B = bus; Ind = industrial; M = marine; T = truck; Tr = tractor.

† Hp with accessories.

‡ Weight complete with ignition and carburetor.

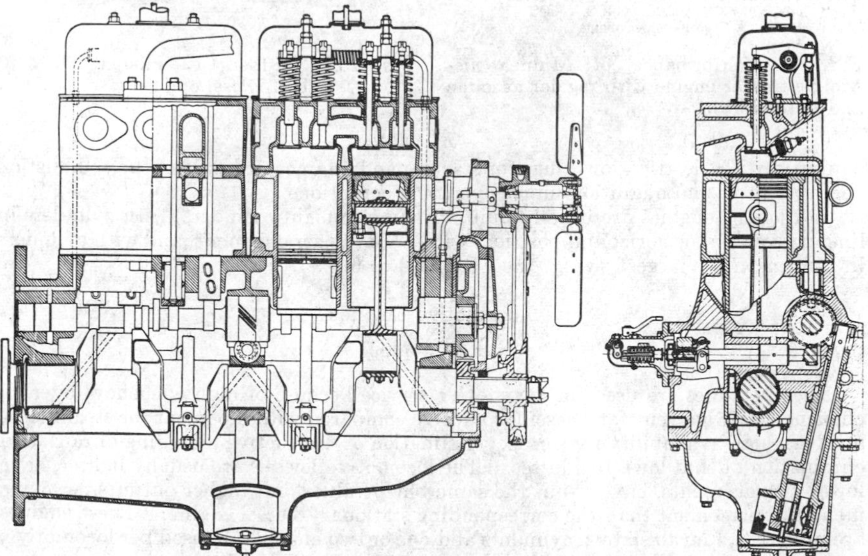

Fig. 11. Minneapolis-Moline tractor engine.

Stationary Engines

Stationary engines may be either Otto or Diesel cycle, use either liquid or gaseous fuel, and operate on the two- or four-stroke principle. The power output ranges up to about 18,000 bhp per engine. The smaller sizes are always single-acting, and the largest sizes are usually double-acting. In the larger sizes, cylinders may be built up of several parts, cylinder liners are used, long pistons for single-acting Diesel engines may have as many as eight piston rings. The valves are usually massive and in the largest sizes may be cooled. The exhaust pipe is sometimes water-cooled, and the pistons and rods for double-acting engines are always liquid-cooled. In general, there is much less integral construction (Fig. 13) in the large stationary engine than in the automotive type.

Stationary engines usually operate at constant speed and are governed by throttling the charge of the Otto engine and by varying the amount of fuel injected into the Diesel engine.

Compression ratios as low as 4:1 are used with spark-ignition engines and as low as 7:1 with fuel-injection engines equipped with electric glow plugs for starting and an uncooled part of the combustion chamber to promote ignition under operating conditions.

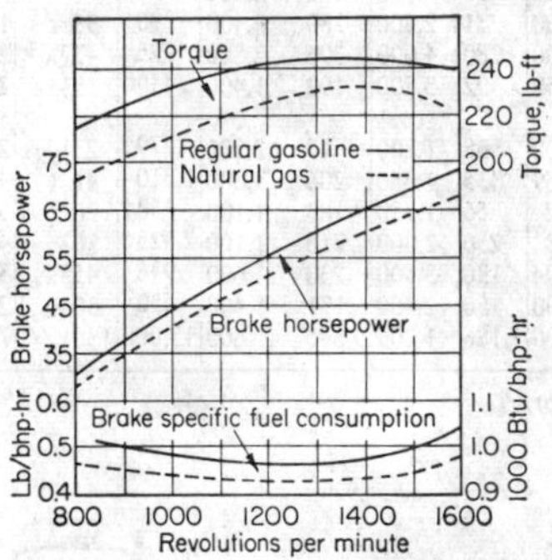

FIG. 12. Performance of Minneapolis-Moline tractor engine with regular gasoline and natural gas.

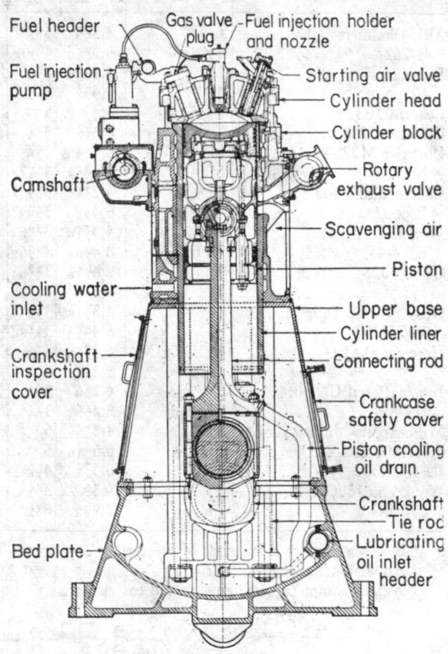

FIG. 13. Nordberg 12-cylinder, 29 × 40 in., 12,000-bhp Diesel engine.

Stationary engines are usually built with one to eight cylinders, with cylinders in line in a vertical or horizontal position, with a V-type arrangement, and with cylinders in tandem in the largest sizes. (See Tables 4 to 6.)

Locomotive Engines

(See also p. 11–28)

Diesel engines are used for locomotive service because of high efficiency (over-all efficiency of 25 percent for Diesel locomotive compared with 6 percent for steam locomotive), high availability for service, elimination of destructive pounding of rails, and elimination of shutdown fuel losses. The locomotive Diesels are usually lighter, have lower displacements, have about the same bmep values, but higher outputs per cubic inch of displacement than the corresponding stationary Diesel engine. These engines are built with four to sixteen cylinders and one or two engines are used per locomotive, but one or more locomotives are used per train. (See Table 7.)

Marine Engines

(See also p. 11-48)

Marine engines may be either Otto or Diesel cycle and are usually normally aspirated. Small outboard engines range in power from less than 1 to more than 60 bhp, generally of the two-cycle type. Other Otto-cycle engines range in power from below 1 to more than 900 bhp and are usually of the four-cycle type. Diesel engines range

Table 6. Selected Small Gasoline Engines

(*Automotive Inds.*, **132,** Nov. 6, 1965, pp. 206–207)

Make and model	Cycles	Type	Cylinders: Number	Bore, in.	Stroke, in.	Displacement, cu in.	Compression ratio	Valve location	Continuous rating, bhp	at rpm	Maximum torque, lb-ft	at rpm	Weight, lb
Air-cooled													
Briggs & Stratton													
60100, 61100....	4	Hor	1	2⅜	1½	6.65	5.4	L	1.7	3,600	3.14	3,000	23.25
80200, 81200....	4	Hor	1	2⅜	1¾	7.75	6.2	L	2.55	3,600	4.06	3,100	24
142300, 143300..	4	Hor	1	2¾	2⅛	14.00	6.6	L	5.10	3,600	9.30	3,000	44.75
Clinton 407-411-													
415-431......	4	Ver	1	2⅜	1⅞	8.30	....	L	2.80	3,600	5.30	2,800	30.5
414............	4	Hor	1	2$\frac{13}{16}$	2⅝	16.30	....	L	5.04	3,600	10.50	2,100	87
Gravely L........	4	Ver	1	3¼	3½	29.04	4.75	T	5.40	2,600	15.80	1,600	55
Onan AJ.........	4	Ver	1	2¾	2½	14.90	6.25	L	3.86	3,600	8.00	2,100	150
Wisconsin AENL..	4	Ver	1	3	3¼	23.00	6.24	L	7.40	3,600	16.50	2,300	110
Water-cooled													
Kohler L-161.....	4	Hor	1	2⅞	2½	16.22	6.20	L	4.54	3,000	11.50	2,300	100
Onan MJ-30......	4	Ver	1	3¼	3⅝	30.00	6.50	I	9.20	2,700	22.70	1,900	

Table 7. Selected Diesel Engines for Locomotive Use

(*Automotive Inds.*, **132,** Nov. 6, 1965, p. 204)

Make and model	Cylinder arrangement	Cycle	Cylinders: Number	Bore, in.	Stroke, in.	Displacement, cu in.	Compression ratio	Maximum rating bhp	at rpm	Supercharger	Weight, lb
Alco 251C.............	V	4	12	9	10½	8,016	13	2,155	1,025	Yes	32,300
Cooper Bessemer											
FVBL-12T..........	V	4	12	9	10½	8,016	12.7	2,000	1,200	Yes	31,500
Electro-Motive											
6-567C.............	V	2	6	8½	10	3,402	16.0	720	835	No	15,000
12-567D1...........	V	2	12	8½	10	6,804	20.0	1,500	835	No	25,000
Fairbanks Morse											
12-38D 8⅛..........	Op	2	12	8⅛	10	12,443	16.1	2,580	850	No	44,910

* Op = opposed piston; V = vee.

in power from below 50 to above 20,000 bhp and may be either two- or four-cycle engines. Both automotive and stationary types of engines are used in marine work and, consequently, wide variations in specific weights are found. (See Tables 4, 5, and 8.)

The outboard two-cycle engines (see Table 8) have crankcase compression (Fig. 14) and may have either two ports, three ports, or two ports with a rotary or reed crankcase inlet valve for the highest outputs (Fig. 15). The Otto four-cycle engines have either L-head or valve-in-head construction, and the Diesel four-cycle engines are invariably of valve-in-head construction.

Regular gasoline is required for the Otto-cycle engines, the fuel and lubricating oil being mixed for the outboard two-cycle engines. A comparison of a number of fuel-consumption curves for various types of engines shows the large low-speed marine Diesel engine as having the lowest specific fuel consumption (Fig. 16).

Table 8. Selected Outboard Engines
(*Automotive Inds.*, **132**, Nov. 6, 1965, pp. 208–209)

Make and model	Cylinders				Engine type*	Rating, bhp at rpm		Weight, lb
	Number	Bore, in.	Stroke, in.	Displacement, cu in.				
Evinrude								
Lightwin 3502	2	1 9/16	1 3/8	5.28	AF	3.0	4,000	35
Sportwin 9502	2	2 5/16	1 13/16	15.2	AF	9.5	4,500	60
Bigtwin 40502	2	3 3/16	2 3/4	43.9	AF	40.0	4,500	132
Sportfour	4	3	2 1/2	70.7	VT	60.0	4,500	225
Homelite								
Deluxe 460A101A	4	2 3/4	2 1/2	59.4	IL	55.0	5,500	224
Johnson								
FD	2	2 1/2	2 1/4	22.0	AF	18.0	4,500	78.5
RDS	2	3 3/16	2 3/4	43.9	AF	40.0	4,500	145
VX	4	3	2 1/2	70.7	VT	60.0	4,500	225
McCulloch								
4500X Electric	2	3 1/8	2 3/4	42.2	AF	45.0	5,200	165
Mercury								
500	4	2 9/16	2 1/8	44.0	AF	50.0		
1000	6	2 7/8	2 19/64	90.0	AF	100.0		
West Bend								
4553 Long Leg	2	3 1/8	2 3/4	42.18	AF	45.0	4,750	138
8056	4	3 1/8	2 3/4	84.36	AF	80.0	4,750	247

* AF = alternate firing; VT = V4 arrangement, two-cycle; IL = in line.

Low-speed engines are direct-connected to the propellers, and high-speed engines are connected through reduction gearing. Outboard engines have maximum speeds of 3,500 to 6,000 rpm, the piston speeds ranging from 1,000 to about 2,500 fpm.

Maximum engine speed is obtained at the intersection of the propeller-horse power and the maximum-horsepower curves (Fig. 17). This may occur well below the speed

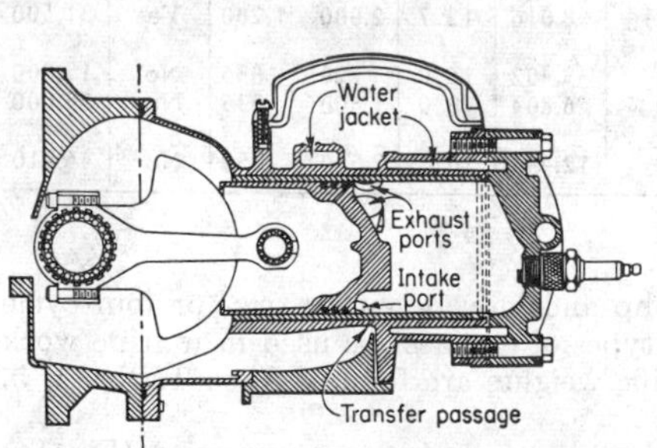

Fig. 14. Johnson two-cycle, 30-hp, outboard motor.

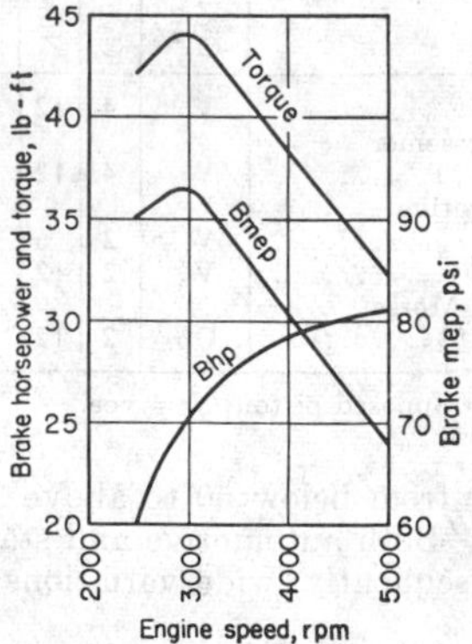

Fig. 15. Performance of Johnson outboard motor.

for maximum horsepower or beyond this speed. The effect of throttling to reduce speed is to increase the specific fuel consumption considerably.

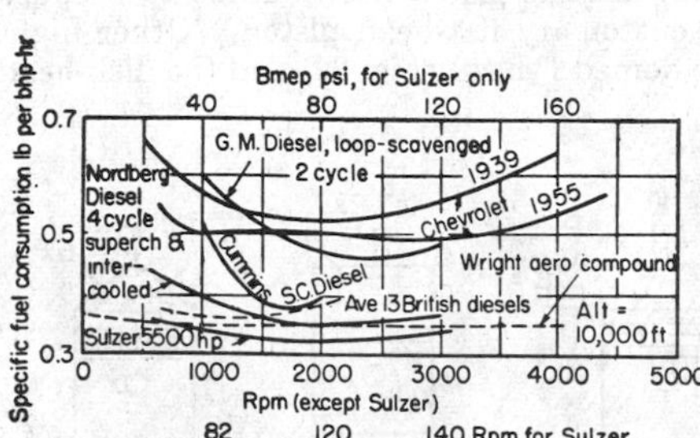

FIG. 16. Specific fuel-consumption curves.

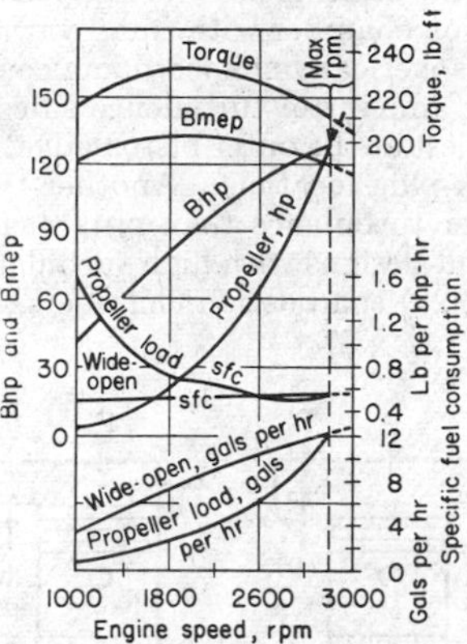

FIG. 17. Performance of 6-cylinder $3\frac{7}{16} \times 4\frac{3}{4}$ in. Chrysler Marine engine with 7 : 1 compression ratio.

COMBUSTION CHAMBERS

Spark-ignition Engines

Non-turbulent Heads. All combustion chambers for four-cycle engines may be classified according to valve arrangement and type of turbulence. The common types of so-called non-turbulent combustion chambers are T head, L head, F head, valve in head, and domed head (Fig. 18).

The **T-head** design is practically obsolete, does not permit the use of high compression ratios without combustion knock, requires two camshafts, has the longest flame travel when ignition occurs near the exhaust valve, but is unrestricted as to valve size.

The **L-head** design has a more compact combustion chamber, permits higher compression ratios than the T head, requires only one camshaft, but is restricted in valve size by the center-to-center distance between cylinders in a multicylinder engine.

The **F-head** design permits large valve sizes, requires one rocker-arm mechanism for the inlet valve, has a slightly more compact combustion chamber, and permits slightly higher compression ratios than the L-head design.

The **valve-in-head** design has a very compact combustion chamber, is restricted in valve size, permits higher compression ratios than the foregoing designs, but requires either valve rocker arms and push rods or an overhead camshaft mechanism.

The **domed-head** design is a modification of the valve-in-head design, permits large valves, has the most compact combustion chamber, and permits the highest compression ratios. It requires an overhead camshaft or otherwise complicated valve mechanism for cylinder-in-line engines. This design may have the spherical-shaped combustion chambers which are used in radial aircraft engines, Chrysler, and Jaguar automobiles.

High-turbulence Heads. Ricardo introduced high turbulence into combustion-chamber design by lowering part of the cylinder head (Fig. 19) so that the piston closely approaches this part at the top of its stroke. The charge is forced out of the thin space, greatly agitating the entire mixture and resulting in a faster and more complete combustion, there being a minimum "stagnant" wall film. This type of head tends to restrict the flow passage between the cylinder and the combustion space for high compression ratios (8 to 12), for which cases the trend is toward the valve-in-head combustion chamber.

One valve-in-head design (Fig. 20) has a wedge-shaped combustion chamber with inclined in-line valves. The small clearance between the part of the head and the piston when it is near its top position provides the high turbulence. This type of combustion chamber with small variations is used extensively in the automotive industry. The spherically shaped dome combustion chamber with a flat piston head has a moderate amount of turbulence since the vertical distance from the piston to the head is smallest at the outer piston edge. This type has the shortest flame travel with central spark-plug location. Another type (Fig. 21) has the piston head formed to produce higher turbulence than obtained with the customary flat-head piston. Other high-output designs with high turbulence are the domed F-head (Fig. 22) and the disk-head (Fig. 23) combustion chambers.

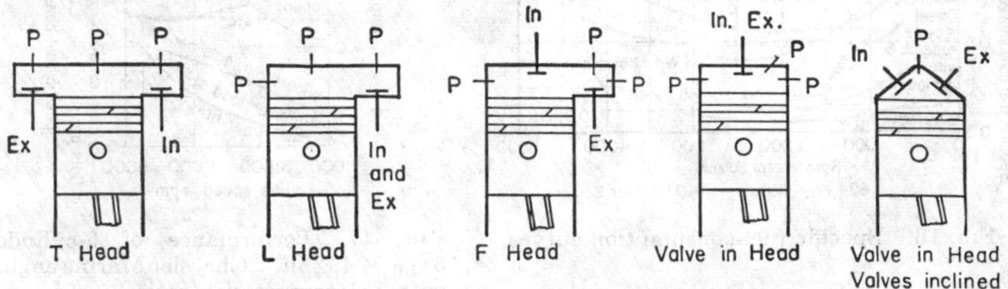

FIG. 18. Combustion chambers and valve locations (P = possible spark-plug locations).

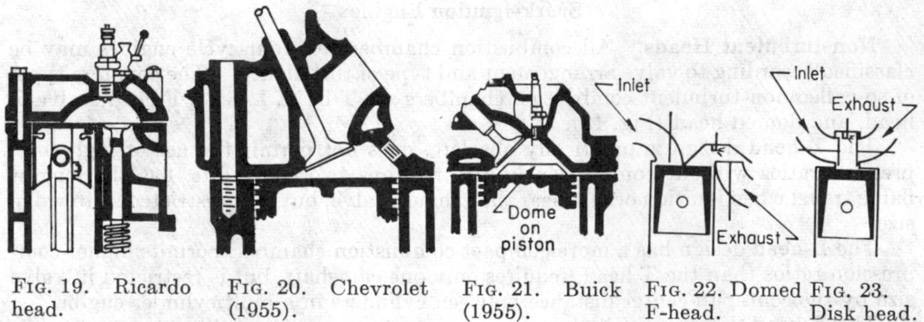

FIG. 19. Ricardo head. FIG. 20. Chevrolet (1955). FIG. 21. Buick (1955). FIG. 22. Domed F-head. FIG. 23. Disk head.

FIGS. 19 to 23. High-turbulence combustion chambers.

Combustion Roughness. The high rate of pressure rise during combustion at relatively low engine speeds (1,000 rpm) and the maximum combustion pressure at high engine speeds (3,500 rpm) subject the engine mechanism to severe stresses which may result in combustion roughness unless the process is controlled. Spark-plug location, combustion-chamber shape, and the degree of turbulence are the principal factors that can be varied to control combustion rate. The first two factors determine the flame-front area at various distances from the spark plug and are the basis of the so-called **volume control,** while the degree of turbulence affects the reaction rate. The maximum combustion pressure can be reduced by retarding the spark timing or by decreasing the volumetric efficiency.

Stone, Fry, and Withrow (*Trans. SAE Quart.*, **1**, 1947, p. 164) have found that combustion roughness associated with lateral flywheel vibration can be controlled more effectively by adding a suitable damping system to the flywheel than by altering combustion-chamber shape.

Ricardo has found that a rate of pressure rise of 30 psi per deg of crank travel results in maximum power and that higher rates of pressure rise usually result in combustion roughness. Increasing the rigidity of the crankshaft and crankcase increases the natural frequency of vibration and reduces the deflection of the structure caused by combustion and inertial forces.

Compression-ignition Engines

Most compression-ignition engines have valve-in-head construction if operating with a four-stroke cycle. The classification of these engines according to combustion-chamber design is based upon the method of controlling the combustion process.

Open Combustion Chambers (Direct Injection). Fuel is injected under high pressure usually through a multiple-orifice nozzle directly into the clearance space or chamber between the piston and the cylinder head. The piston head is usually conformed (Figs. 24 and 25) to fit the fuel spray, and **air swirl** moves the unsprayed air into the fuel spray. Air swirl is accomplished, by intake-port design, by shrouding the intake valve, or, in the two-cycle engine, by using tangential intake ports. High turbulence is accomplished by having the piston very closely approach part of the cylinder head. This forces the gases out of the small clearances and agitates the mixture.

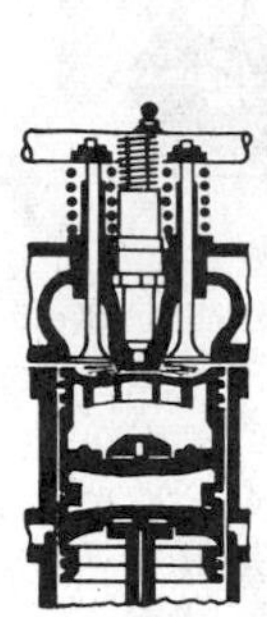

FIG. 24. General Motors combustion chamber (swirl produced by intake ports).

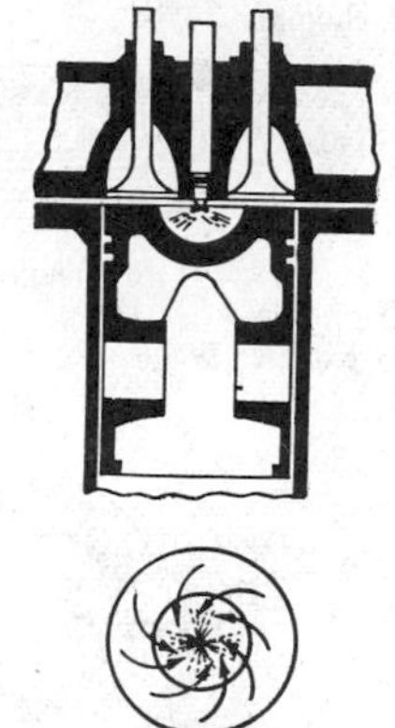

FIG. 25. Open combustion chamber with high turbulence and some swirl.

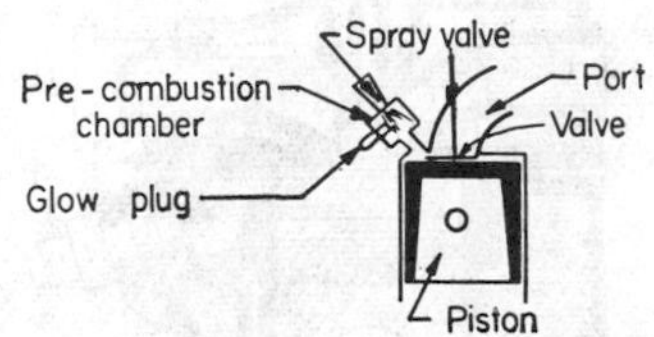

FIG. 26. Precombustion chamber.

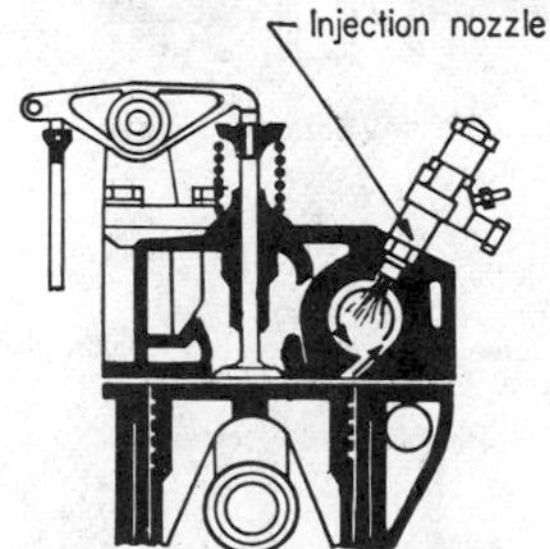

FIG. 27. Ricardo divided combustion chamber.

Precombustion chambers are divided into two parts, the major part being between the piston and the cylinder head and connected by a small passageway to the minor part located in the cylinder head (Fig. 26). Fuel is injected only into the smaller chamber and, except under light loads, partial combustion occurs and discharges the burning mixture into the larger chamber in which combustion is completed. This type of combustion chamber produces a smooth combustion process but has fairly high fluid-friction and heat-transfer losses.

Ante- or **divided combustion chambers** are modifications of the precombustion chamber, having the major chamber in the cylinder head and usually only a small clearance space between the piston and the cylinder head (Fig. 27). The passage between the two chambers is considerably larger than the passage in the precombustion chamber. Close piston clearance produces high turbulence in the antechamber and promotes rapid combustion. Part of the antechamber containing the transfer passage is usually not well cooled and provides a regenerative action from cycle to cycle.

The **Hercules design** (Fig. 28) restricts the transfer passage and tends to maintain high velocities in the passage as the piston approaches top center.

Air-cell combustion chambers are divided into two parts with a restricted connecting passage (Fig. 29). Fuel is injected into the major chamber at a position near the connecting passage and may or may not be directed at the air cell. Little if any fuel enters the air cell which discharges its air into the partly burned mixture during the expansion stroke. This results in a late but smooth combustion process which is less efficient than with combustion nearer top center position.

The **energy cell** is a modification of the air-cell combustion chamber. The fuel is injected at the air cell and some enters and promotes combustion. The Lanova design (Fig. 30) uses two air-cells connected by a restricted passage. The combustion in the first cell ejects the burning mixture and produces a double swirl in the usual construction. Closing the passage to the second cell increases the compression ratio and facilitates starting.

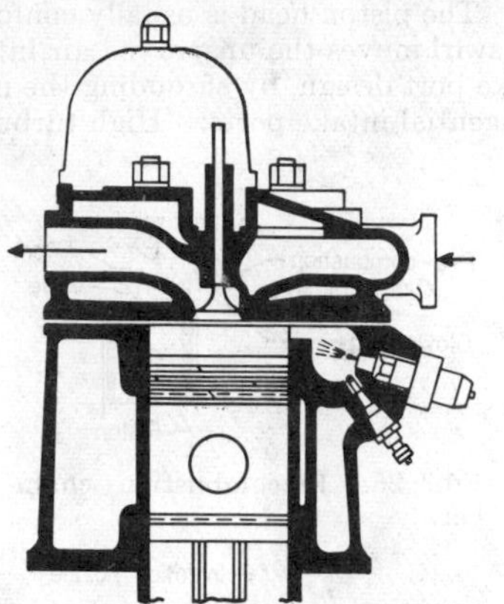

FIG. 28. Variable antechamber orifice.

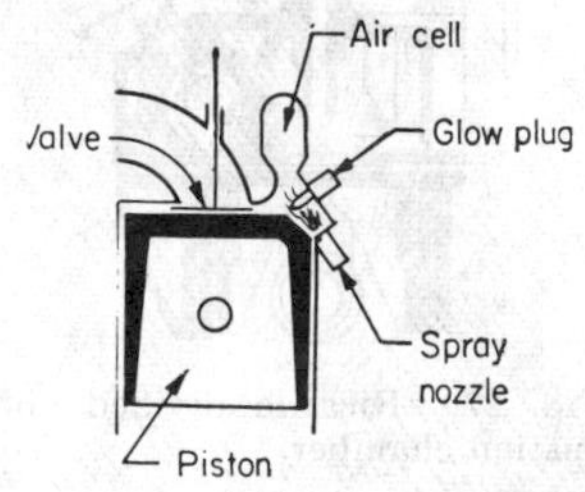

FIG. 29. Air-cell combustion chamber.

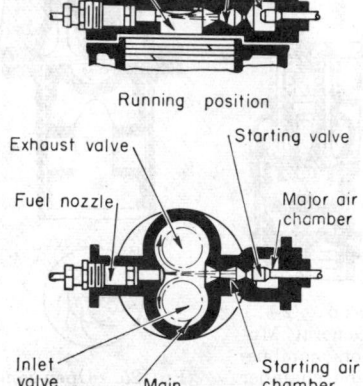

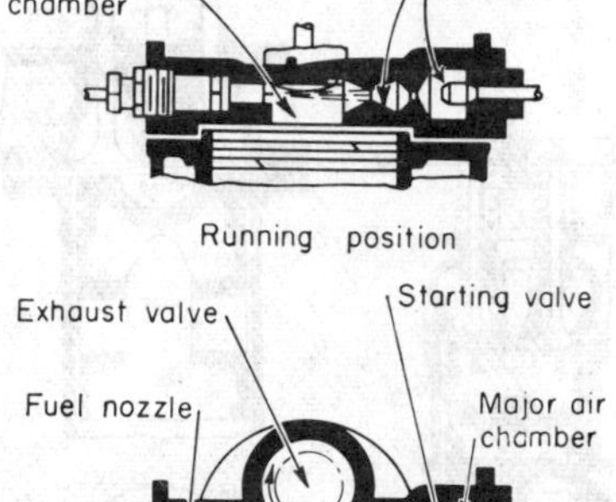

FIG. 30. Lanova air-cell combustion chamber.

In **low-compression chambers,** a glow plug or ignition device is required for starting. A part of the combustion chamber not in contact with the cooling water rises sufficiently in temperature to heat the air enough during the compression stroke to promote combustion during normal operating conditions, resulting in a low-compression Diesel engine.

FUELS

(See also Sec. 7)

Fuels for internal-combustion engines are usually petroleum products or natural and manufactured gases. Alcohols, alcohol-gasoline blends, and benzol are used to a small degree.

Gasoline consists of various amounts of many hydrocarbons, each having its vapor-pressure–temperature characteristic. The over-all **volatility** of a gasoline sample is specified in U.S. industry by the ASTM Distillation Test, which records the temperature of vapor in the neck of a flask in which 100 ml of the fuel is distilled as increasing percentages of the vapor are condensed after passing through a tube immersed in a bath of water and cracked ice. All dimensions of the apparatus and details of the test procedure are standardized. The B of M makes a survey of fuel samples sold each summer and winter in 17 geographical areas over the United States. Representative data for the average of 2,751 samples of regular-grade gasoline collected in the winter 1963–1964 (Petroleum Products Survey 35) are:

ASTM Distillation

Percent evaporated	5	10	20	30	50	70	90	95
Temp, deg F	103	116	137	158	207	259	347	375

Because of differences in climatic conditions, the petroleum industry has found it desirable to adjust the volatility of gasoline marketed in areas similar to those selected by the B of M (but adjusted to specific marketing requirements) at two or more seasons each year.

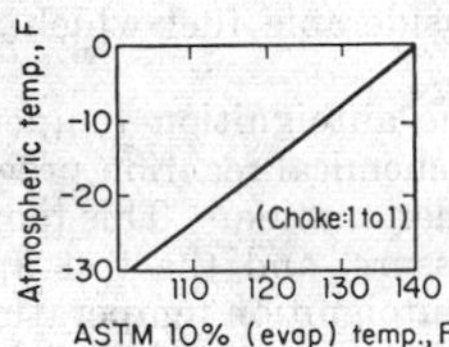

Fig. 31. ASTM 10 percent point and "satisfactory" engine starting at various temperatures.

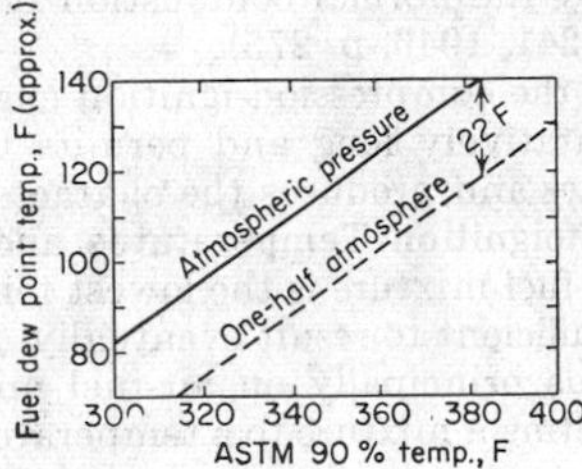

Fig. 32. Variation of fuel dew-point with ASTM 90 percent point for a 12.5 air-fuel ratio (0.08 fuel-air ratio).

Data from the ASTM distillation can be converted to indicate the effect of fuel volatility on engine performance, *e.g.*, ease of starting and freedom from **vapor lock** (boiling in the fuel system) (see Bridgeman, *Trans. SAE*, 1928 and 1929). Thus:

1. The temperature at which gasoline will boil in a fuel system at atmospheric pressure is close to the 10 percent point of the distillation curve.

2. The temperature at which a cold engine in good condition may be expected to start satisfactorily also can be estimated from the 10 percent point by means of Fig. 31 when the carburetor is "choked" to give a 1:1 fuel-air ratio. The volatility requirements for a gasoline to give easy starting and yet have relative freedom from vapor lock are contradictory. The tendency of an engine to vapor lock can be curtailed by variable-speed cooling fans to reduce under-hood temperatures when a car is standing after a run as well as by fuel-pump and carburetor design to dispose of the vapor without affecting the carburetor metering when gasoline boils in the fuel system.

3. The temperature to which the fuel-air mixture in the engine manifold must be heated to evaporate the fuel metered by the carburetor so that reasonably equal mixtures may be distributed to all cylinders can be estimated from the 90 percent point (Fig. 32). The desired temperature will be somewhat higher than the **dew point** of the gasoline mixture (the temperature at which liquid starts to condense from a dry fuel-air mixture as its temperature is reduced) because there is insufficient time for evaporation to equilibrium to be established—the dew point being understood to be the lowest temperature to which a "dry" mixture of fuel vapor and air can be reduced before liquid fuel starts to condense. A higher temperature than necessary (1) decreases the volumetric efficiency and power of the engine, and (2) increases the tendency to knock and to vapor lock. Nevertheless, some heat must be supplied to

the carburetor throttle to avoid the ice formation which, under certain conditions of atmospheric temperature and humidity, results from the refrigerating effect of that portion of the gasoline which evaporates.

Combustion Knock

Combustion knock in the internal-combustion engine is the spontaneous combustion of an appreciable portion of the charge (Rassweiler and Withrow, *Trans. SAE*, **31,** 1936, p. 297) which results in an extremely rapid local pressure rise and produces a sharp metallic knock. In the spark-ignition engine, the last fraction of the charge to burn is compressed appreciably above its autoignition temperature by the fraction that has burned. An appreciable lag in time (ignition lag) between the attainment of this temperature and the spontaneous appearance of flame permits the flame from the spark plug to travel through the unburned fraction before it can knock if the compression ratio is not too high. Thus, combustion knock depends principally on the autoignition temperature, ignition lag, and flame speed of the air-fuel mixture, all under the given engine conditions.

Combustion knock in the spark-ignition engine has been eliminated by coordinating the injection of the fuel into the cylinder with the air swirl and spark timing and location so that the fuel-air mixture is in the cylinder the minimum time before inflammation by the normal combustion process (Barber, Malin, and Mikita, *Jour. Franklin Inst.*, **241,** 1946, p. 275).

In the compression-ignition engine, combustion knock occurs when ignition lag is comparatively long and permits the injection of considerable fuel which suddenly inflames and produces the characteristic knock.

Autoignition Temperatures and Ignition Lag. The autoignition temperature of an air-fuel mixture is the lowest temperature at which chemical reaction proceeds at a rate sufficient to result eventually (long time lag) in inflammation. This temperature depends principally on air-fuel mixture, mixture pressure, and the test apparatus. Subjecting a mixture to a temperature higher than the autoignition temperature results in inflammation after a short-time lag, there being a temperature for each mixture which results in practically instantaneous inflammation (Table 9).

Table 9. Ignition Temperatures of Air-gas Mixtures at Atmospheric Pressure

Gas	Chemical symbol	With lag[a]		Instantaneous[b]	
		Percent gas in mixture	Avg temp, deg F	Percent gas in mixture	Deg F
Hydrogen	H_2	8–24	1130	10	1377
Carbon monoxide	CO	13–47	1204	50	1708
Methane	CH_4	5–38	1202[c]	25	>1832
Ethane	C_2H_6	[d]	968[c]		
Propane	C_3H_8	[d]	914[c]		
Acetylene	C_2H_2	4–22	804		
Ethylene	C_2H_4	6–19	1004	10	1832
Benzene	C_6H_6	.....	....	50	1943
Ether	$C_4H_{10}O$	.....	....	50	1892

[a] Dixon and Coward, *Trans. Chem. Soc.*, **95,** 1909, p. 514.
[b] David, *Trans. Chem. Soc.*, **111,** 1917, p. 1003.
[c] Minimum value, since spread in values was appreciable.
[d] Composition not reported.

An increase in pressure decreases the ignition temperature of an air-fuel mixture (Table 10). See CRC Report on Project CFD–37–53 (CRC, 30 Rockefeller Plaza, New York 20, N.Y.)

Flame Speed. Flame speeds in spark-ignition engines are low immediately after ignition, attain maximum values when about half the combustion chamber has been inflamed, and decrease toward the end of the process. Mean flame speeds are a maximum for mixtures usually 10 to 20 percent richer than the chemically correct air-fuel ratio, and vary with fuels, engine speed, and turbulence.

Table 10. Ignition Temperatures at Various Air Pressures, Deg F

Gas	Air pressure, atm								
	1	3	5	7	10	15	20	25	30
Hydrogen[a]	1134	1132	1112	1100					
Methane[a]	1343	1269	1215	1175					
Gasoline[b]	....	....	590	....	480	420			
Kerosene[b]	....	....	670	....	490	430	400	385	
Gas oil[b]	....	....	580	....	500	450	435	415	
Machine oil[b]	....	....	710	....	610	550	520		
Benzene[b]	....	....	685	....	585	545	530	515	500
Cylinder oil[b]	....	....	825	....	710	645	620	595	572
Benzol[b]	....	....	....	....	1095	970	930	905	880

[a] Bone and Townsend, "Flame and Combustion in Gases," p. 69.
[b] Tausz and Schulte: *ZVdI*, 1924, p. 574.

At 900 fpm mean piston speed, mean flame speeds with maximum-power gasoline-air mixtures and optimum spark advance range from about 50 to 100 fps. Mean flame speeds under the same mixture, spark, and speed conditions in the CFR Waukesha engine are estimated at 55 (70) [80] fps for a 4.6 (6.5) [8]: 1 compression ratio, while with ethyl alcohol-air mixtures the corresponding mean flame speeds are 50 (65) [75] fps.

The mean flame speed in an automotive engine (De Soto, 1937) under the foregoing conditions is estimated from the optimum spark advance (being approximately 5/9 of combustion time) to be 90 fps for a 6.5: 1 compression ratio. In the same engine, mean flame speeds with optimum conditions vary from about 60 fps at 500 fpm to about 170 fps at 3,000 fpm mean piston speed. The higher flame speeds at comparable piston speeds (De Soto) are due to greater turbulence obtained with Ricardo-type head compared with the usual flat valve-in-head (CFR) design. A value of about 140 fps at 2,420 fpm is indicated for the 1956 Chrysler 9: 1 engine.

Because of the time required for combustion, it is necessary, in order to develop maximum torque, to ignite the mixture in the cylinder before the piston reaches the end of its compression stroke. Spark advance is measured by the number of degrees the crankshaft rotates between the time of the spark and the end of the compression stroke. **Optimum spark advance** is the timing which develops maximum torque. The torque lost by a spark timing earlier or later than optimum is at first only slight but increases rapidly as the timing is further removed from optimum. The tendency of an engine to knock increases almost directly with spark advance (Fig. 33). General practice in automobile-engine design uses a spark advance a few degrees less than optimum at wide-open throttle. This materially reduces the tendency to knock with only a negligible loss of torque. At part-throttle operation, where combustion knock is not a problem, the spark is advanced to optimum by manifold vacuum acting through a diaphragm on the spark-timing mechanism.

Knock Suppression. The antiknock characteristics of a fuel can be improved by adding another fuel of better antiknock characteristics (Fig. 34). Tetraethyllead is the most effective knock suppressor (Table 11) and is used extensively in small amounts

Table 11. Relative Effect of Antiknock Compounds*

Compound	Chemical symbol	Weight for a given effect, gm
Tetraethyllead	$Pb(C_2H_5)_4$	0.0295
Aniline	$C_6H_5NH_2$	1.0000
Ethyl iodide	C_2H_5I	1.55
Ethyl alcohol	C_2H_5OH	4.75
Xylene	$C_6H_4(CH_3)_2$	8.0
Toluene	$C_6H_5CH_3$	8.8
Benzene	C_6H_6	9.8

* "International Critical Tables," Vol. 2, pp. 162-163.

(up to 3 cc per gal of automotive fuels) in many "Standard" gasolines and practically in all "Premium" gasolines. The continued addition of tetraethyllead to gasoline has progressively less effect on the antiknock characteristics.

Ethyl fluid is a liquid composed of tetraethyllead, ethylene dibromide, $C_2H_4Br_2$, and ethylene dichloride, $C_2H_4Cl_2$ (the latter combining with the lead during combustion to form volatile compounds which escape from the engine with the exhaust gases), and a small amount of oil-soluble dye used for identification purposes.

Alcohol-gasoline blends are used extensively in those foreign countries which have little or no petroleum reserves. A blend of 1 part of ethyl alcohol and 9 parts of gasoline by volume is usually equivalent in antiknock value to the same gasoline with less than 1 cc of tetraethyllead (Phelps and Lichty, *API*, May 18, 1939). Since the octane numbers of both regular and premium gasolines have been increased appreciably during the past few years there is little or no gain obtained in antiknock value

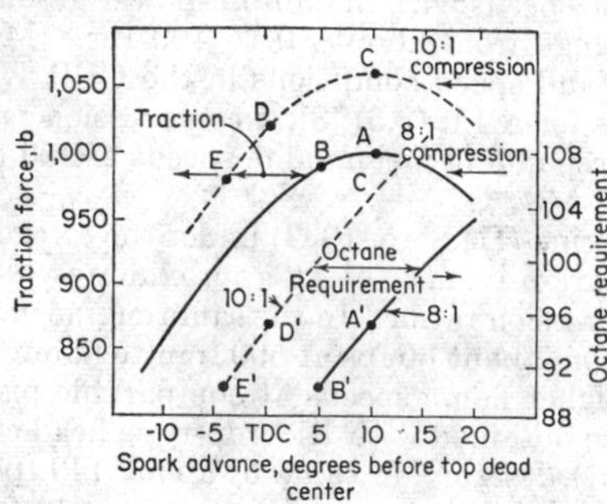

FIG. 33. Effects of shifting spark advance at a given speed, on the octane requirement and traction force developed by the rear wheels of a typical automobile at wide-open throttle.

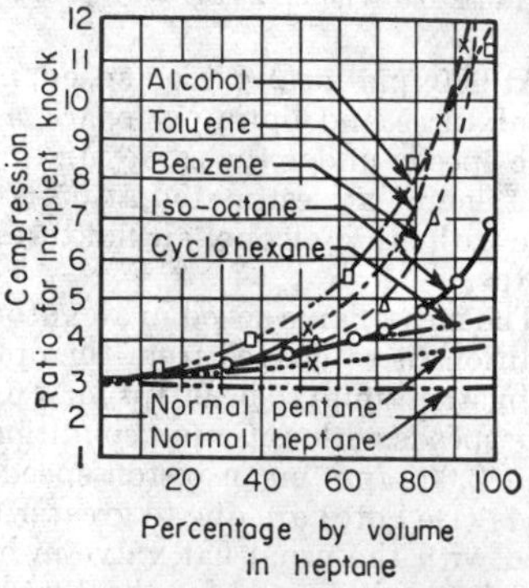

FIG. 34. Influence on the permissible compression ratio of the addition of certain fuels to *n*-heptane. (*Campbell, Lovell, and Boyd, Trans. SAE*, **25**, 1930, *p.* 126.)

by blending alcohol with gasoline in the United States. The relatively high cost of alcohol and its low heat value make its use uneconomical in this country at present.

Alcohol and water are injected into the intake manifold of high-output engines to cool internally and also to suppress combustion knock. Water is the best internal coolant while a water-methanol mixture is the best knock suppressor and power improver. (Rowe and Ladd, *Trans. SAE*, **54**, 1946, p. 26; Porter, Roth, and Wiebe, *Automotive Inds.*, May 1, 1948, p. 34.) A 50–50 mixture of water and alcohol is recommended. Tetraethyllead may be added to advantage if the fuel is susceptible to it.

Critical Compression Ratios. The compression ratio which results in incipient knock with maximum-power conditions in the spark-ignition engine is termed the critical compression ratio. This varies with engines but serves as a means of classifying fuels according to knocking tendency (Table 12). The knocking of an air-fuel mixture depends on the **molecular structure** of the fuel. Lovell and Campbell (*Chem. Rev.*, **22,** 1938, p. 159) state that the addition of methyl groups (CH_3), shortening the straight chain of a molecule and centralizing the molecule without changing the number of atoms, improve the antiknock characteristics. Thus, normal pentane has a critical compression ratio of 3.8 (Table 16); 2,2,4 trimethylpentane, commonly known as isooctane and consisting of three methyl groups added to normal pentane, has a critical compression ratio of 7.7; normal octane has a critical compression lower than normal pentane. For the molecular structure and the knocking tendency of other types of fuels, see the above reference.

In Diesel engines, the critical compression ratio is defined as the minimum compression ratio at which the engine will ignite the charge injected under specified oper-

Table 12. Critical Compression Ratios for Various Classes of Hydrocarbons in a Spark-ignition Engine*

Saturated paraffins	Crit comp ratio	Unsaturated paraffins	Crit comp ratio	Naphthenes	Crit comp ratio	Aromatics	Crit comp ratio
Methane	>15	Acetylene	4.6	Cyclopentene	7.9	Benzene	>15
Ethane	14	Ethylene	8.5	Cyclopentane	10.8	Toluene	13.6
Propane	12	Propylene	8.4	Cyclohexene	4.8	*o*-Xylene	9.6
n-Butane	6.4	1-Pentene	5.8	Cyclohexane	4.5	*m*-Xylene	13.6
n-Pentane	3.8	1-Hexene	4.6	Methylcyclohexane	4.6	*p*-Xylene	14.2
n-Hexane	3.3	1-Heptene	3.7	Ethylcyclohexane	3.8	*n*-Propylbenzene	10.1
n-Heptane	2.8	1-Octene	3.4	*n*-Butylcyclohexane	3.3	*n*-Butylbenzene	7.7
2,2,4 Iso-octane	7.7			*n*-Amylcyclohexane	3.1		
Triptane†	14.4						

* Lovell, Campbell, and Boyd, *Ind. Eng. Chem.*, **26**, 1934, p. 1105.
† Kettering, *Trans. SAE*, **53**, 1945, p. 352. Triptane is 2-2-3 trimethylbutane.

Table 13. Critical Compression Ratios for Various Fuels in a Compression-ignition Engine*

Fuel	Benzol	Octane 2,2,4 trimethylpentane	Gasoline, 80 O.N.	Gasoline, 60 O.N.	"Rough" Diesel fuel	Heptane, 0 O.N.	Good Diesel fuel	Kerosene
Crit comp ratio	>20	17.3	14.2	11.1	10.6	8.6	8.0	7.5
Comp press, psi	>520	455	355	260	240	190	175	160

* Pope and Murdock, *Trans. SAE*, **28**, p. 136.
O.N., octane number.

ating conditions. This has served as a means of rating Diesel fuels (Table 13). See Cetane Number, p. 9–127.

Permissible Compression Ratios. Data obtained on single-cylinder test engines and multicylinder automotive engines show wide variations in the compression ratios producing incipient knocking of fuels of various octane numbers. High compression ratios in engines using fuels of given octane number do not necessarily indicate excellent design and high performance, since valve timing, manifolding, and porting may act as throttling devices, or spark timing may be retarded. Average compression ratios vary considerably depending on design and fuel used. An increase in cylinder size usually necessitates a lower compression ratio (Fig. 35), which may be due in some cases to the use of a lower grade of fuels with the larger spark-ignition engines. The larger Diesel engines require less compression to obtain the desired temperatures since the heat-transfer effect is less than in the smaller engine.

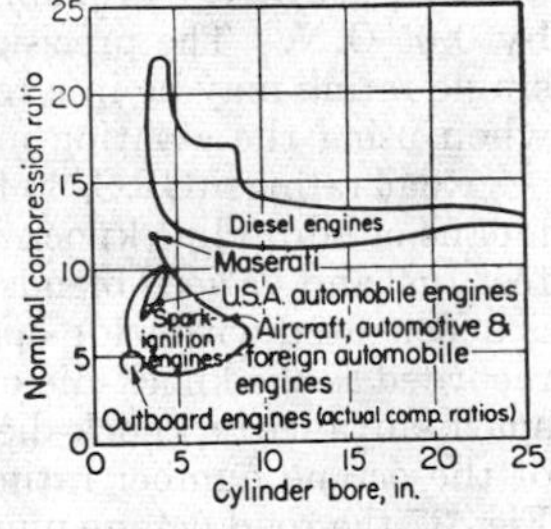

FIG. 35. Range of compression ratios as a function of cylinder bore (1956).

Knock Rating of Fuels

For detailed information regarding methods, apparatus, reference fuels, and suppliers of apparatus and reference fuels, see ASTM Manual of Engine Test Methods for Rating Fuels, 1952.

Octane Number. The octane number (O.N.) of a fuel is the percentage by volume of iso-octane (2,2,4 trimethylpentane) in a mixture of iso-octane and normal heptane which matches the unknown fuel in knock tendency when compared by a specified procedure in the ASTM-CFR knock-testing engine. A fuel that knocks less than iso-octane is rated by the amount of tetraethyllead in iso-octane required to match the knock of the unknown fuel. A tentative octane number scale has been proposed for the tetraethyllead content of gasoline which indicates antiknock quality of gasoline above 100 O.N. (Fig. 36).

The Army-Navy **performance number** scale for aviation gasolines (Fig. 36) is designed to relate fuel rating to average knock-limited performance (imep). A gasoline of the 100/130 grade indicates that in the aviation test (lean mixture, normally aspirated) the fuel is equivalent to iso-octane in imep while in the supercharge test (rich mixture) it permits an imep of 130 percent of that of iso-octane.

Secondary reference fuels calibrated against the primary reference fuels are seldom used.

There are four methods, **research, motor, aviation** (lean mixture), and **supercharge** (rich mixture) (ASTM D908, 357, 614, and 909, respectively) in general use in the rating of gasolines according to knocking tendency. These methods vary principally in the engine operating conditions and the means for indicating knock intensity (see ASTM Manual).

The engine conditions, as indicated by the air or mixture temperature and by the coolant temperature, are less severe in the **research method** than in the other methods. Thus, some fuels rate lower by the motor method than by the research method. The **sensitivity of a fuel** is defined quantitatively as the difference between the research and motor octane numbers. Although most gasolines rate lower by the motor method than by the research method, straight-run gasolines have about the same rating by both methods. The conditions of the motor method were designed to provide reasonable correlation with road ratings; however, with the present fuels and engines, the research method provides better correlation with the road ratings.

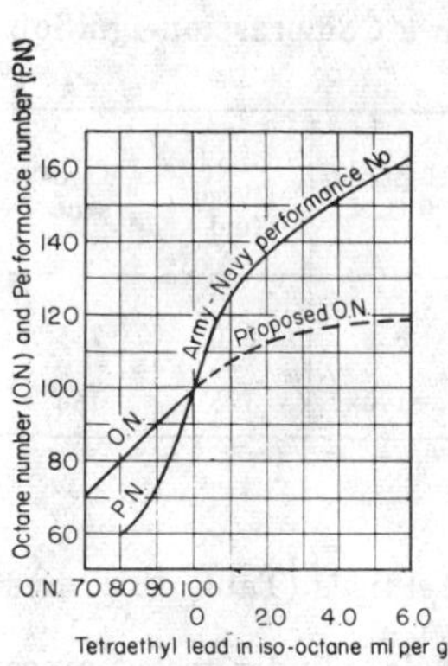

FIG. 36. Octane number and Army-Navy performance-number scales.

The use of the aviation and supercharge methods for grading aviation gasolines results in two performance numbers (such as 100/130) being assigned to commercial aviation fuel. This grading indicates that the commercial fuel is less sensitive than iso-octane to the difference in engine severity in the two test methods, since with the aviation method the performance (imep) with the commercial fuel is equal to that of iso-octane, while with the supercharge method its performance is better than that of iso-octane (see Fig. 36).

The **precision** of rating motor fuels by either the research or the motor method is about ± 0.4 O.N. Probability indicates once in 10 times a single rating may be in error by 0.65 O.N. The precision of rating aviation fuels is such that once in 10 times a single rating may be in error by 3 percent of the true performance number of the fuel when using the aviation method (see Brooks and Cleaton, *Jour. ASE*, June, 1948).

Road ratings (CRC, 30 Rockefeller Plaza, New York) of gasoline are determined by means of borderline knock (or given knock intensity above border line) curves for the test fuel and various blends of the reference fuels at various spark advances. The car is accelerated with wide-open throttle, and the speed at which steady knock ceases is recorded as the knock-die-out speed (CRC procedure, E-2). A plot of these data on a spark-advance *vs.* knock-die-out speed chart (Fig. 37) makes possible the determination of the octane number rating of the test fuel over the desired speed range. Thus, in Fig. 37 the road octane number of the test fuel at 15 mph (750 rpm) is 72 while at 50 mph (2,500 rpm) it is 60. Other CRC road-test procedures are described in the CRC Handbook.

The **road octane number requirement** of a motor vehicle is the octane number of the reference-fuel blend which produces the selected knock intensity at any desired speed while accelerating with wide-open throttle (see CRC E-1). The maximum octane number requirement is given if a single value is desired. The road octane values at low car speeds approximate the research ratings while those at high speeds approximate the motor ratings.

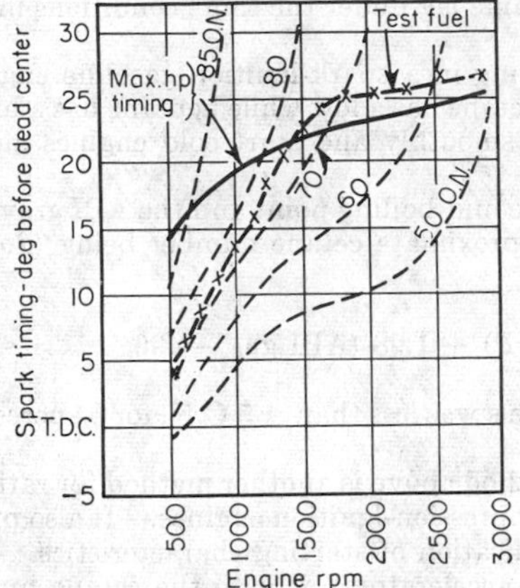

FIG. 37. Borderline knock curves for an automobile engine.

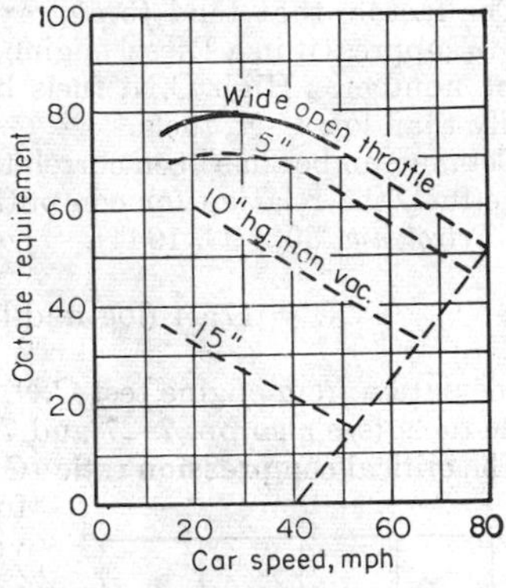

FIG. 38. Octane requirement of automobile engine at various speeds and loads in high gear.

The road octane number requirement decreases with **altitude** from 80 to 42 (high compression ratio) or from 70 to 62 (low compression ratio), in going from sea level to 10,000 ft altitude (see *NBS Jour. Research,* **28,** 1942, p. 727).

The road octane number requirement varies with engine speed and load, being very low (below zero O.N.) at low speeds and level-road conditions, and approaching full-throttle high-speed requirement at maximum level-road speed (Fig. 38). This has led to the development of devices that inject knock-suppressing liquids only at the higher manifold pressure conditions (Heldt, *Automotive Inds.,* 1948, p. 32) and to a dual-fuel carburetor that switches from regular or low octane fuel to a high octane fuel only at the higher manifold conditions (Mack, *Automotive Inds.,* 1948, p. 36).

Lead Susceptibility. Most gasolines have their antiknock characteristics appreciably improved by the addition of tetraethyllead. The susceptibility of the fuel to improved antiknock quality with lead additions varies with different fuels and decreases with the amount of lead added (Fig. 39).

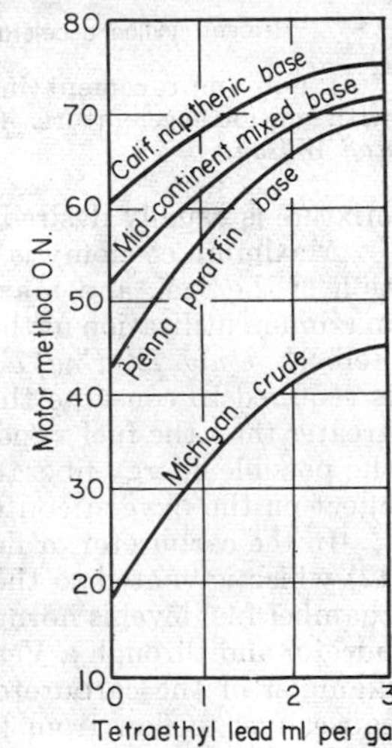

FIG. 39. O.N. and lead susceptibility of straight-run gasolines (380 F end point).

Cetane Number. The cetane number (C.N.) of a fuel is the percentage by volume of normal cetane in a mixture of cetane (E. I. du Pont de Nemours & Co.) and alpha-methylnaphthalene (Reilly Tar and Chemical Co.) which matches the unknown fuel in **ignition quality** when compared in an ASTM-CFR Diesel engine (Waukesha Motor Co.) by a specified procedure (ASTM-D613 or CRC-F-5). The C.N. scale ranges from 0 to 100 C.N. for fuels equivalent in ignition quality to alpha-methylnaphthalene and cetane, respectively. Two **secondary reference fuels** (Shell Petroleum Corp.) having cetane values of about 25 and 74 are blended in any desired proportion and used for routine testing.

The **ignition quality** of a fuel for a compression-ignition engine is indicated by the time lag between the beginning of injection and the rapid pressure rise caused by combustion. The compression ratio in the test engine is adjusted to result in a 13 deg crank-angle lag for the unknown fuel when injection begins at 13 deg before top center.

The mixture of reference fuels which has the same lag under the same conditions indicates the cetane number of the fuel.

The factors that tend to aggravate knocking in a spark-ignition gasoline engine tend to suppress it in a Diesel engine. Thus, octane has a low while heptane has a high cetane number. High C.N. fuels burn more smoothly and start cold engines more readily than low C.N. fuels.

Cetane number has been correlated with the mid-boiling point and the API gravity of the fuel, the relation for computing the approximate cetane number being (*Jour. Inst. Petroleum*, **30,** 193, 1944),

$$\text{C.N.} = 175.4\ (\log \text{mid-boiling pt, F}) + 1.98\ (\text{API gr}) - 496$$

The deviation from engine test C.N. for 579 fuels was less than ± 5 C.N. for 94 percent of the fuels (see also pp. 7–27 and 7–28).

The **critical compression ratio** (C.C.R.) **method** above is another method for rating fuels for compression-ignition engines. It also provides an indication of starting characteristics.

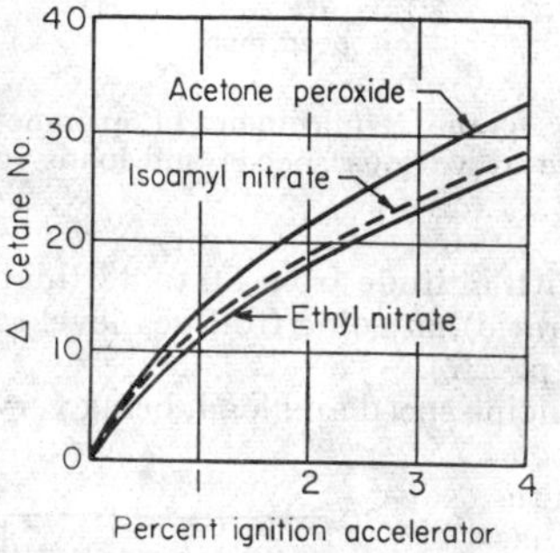

Ignition accelerators increase the cetane number of Diesel fuels but the susceptibility of the fuel to the accelerator decreases with an increase in the amount of the accelerator (Fig. 40). Commerical amyl nitrate is slightly less effective than the pure isoamyl nitrate (Bogen and Wilson, *Petroleum Refiner*, July, 1944).

FIG. 40. Improvement in C.N. with ignition accelerators. (*Bogen and Wilson.*)

Carburetion

The carburetor meters, atomizes (if liquid), and mixes the fuel with the air flowing to the engine. A rich **mixture** is required for idling and small throttle openings on account of the dilution of the small incoming charge with the exhaust gases in the clearance space. A maximum-economy mixture is desired at intermediate loads, and a maximum-power mixture is usually desired (automotive practice) at wide-open throttle (Fig. 41).

Maximum economy is obtained with lean mixtures which permit maximum utilization of the fuel, and maximum power is obtained with rich mixtures which permit maximum utilization of the oxygen with maximum energy liberation (Goodenough and Felbeck, *Univ. Ill. Eng. Exp. Sta. Bull.* 139). Also, since an excess of one constituent is required to consume the other, and since the required air volume is usually much greater than the fuel vapor or gas volume, a decrease in fuel (lean mixture) decreases the possible energy liberation while an increase in fuel (rich mixture) has a negligible effect on the oxygen content of the charge and permits maximum energy liberation.

In the carburetor, a float maintains a constant fuel level in a float chamber (Fig. 42) which is vented to the atmosphere or air entrance of the carburetor. The float-chamber fuel level is normally below the outlet of the fuel jet. Air flows into the carburetor and through a Venturi tube which has a throat diameter of 0.75 to 0.85 of the diameter of the carburetor bore. The reduction in pressure at the Venturi throat causes fuel to flow from the float chamber through the fuel jet into the air stream. Fuel atomization is accomplished by the difference between the air and fuel velocities at the jet. Vaporization of the fuel occurs while flowing to the engine cylinder, but is usually not completed in the intake manifold at wide-open throttle.

The **metering characteristic** of a carburetor is the ratio of fuel to air by weight, supplied over the operating range of airflow volumes. These values may be calculated for steady airflow rates, but such calculations usually are not made in carburetor design because on each cycle the airflow through a carburetor at wide-open throttle generally reverses through the metering system to some extent. This is due to **blow-back** through the intake valves, both when they are first opened (with higher gas pressure in the cylinder than in the intake manifold) and just before they close, which

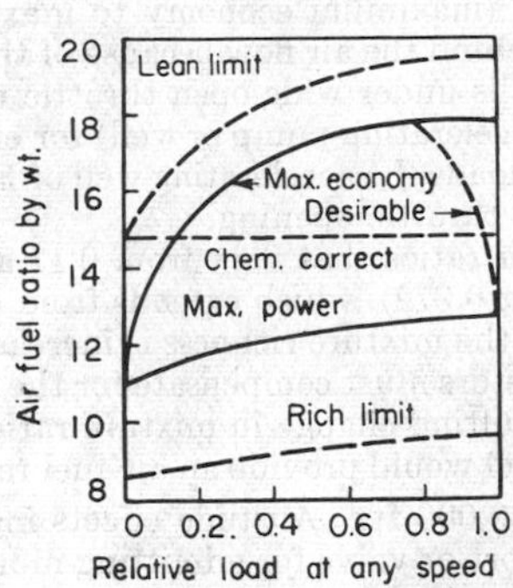

Fig. 41. Air-fuel ratios for gasoline.

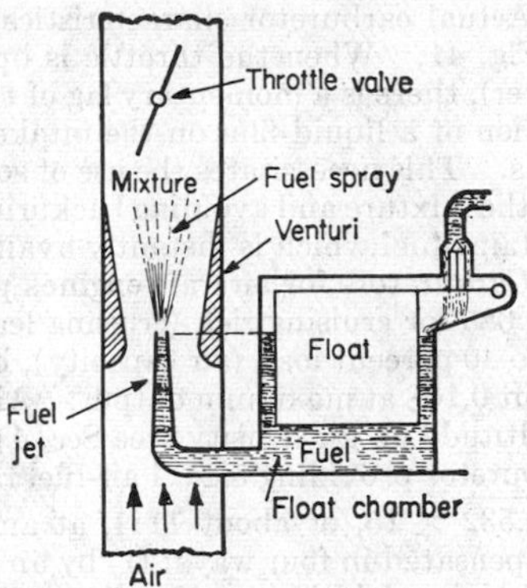

Fig. 42. Elementary updraft carburetor.

is always after the piston has traveled an appreciable distance on the compression stroke. Each passage of even a small portion of the mixture through the carburetor metering system picks up fuel. While blowback may well be averaged out at the carburetor when six or more cylinders are supplied by it through a single manifold, the resulting enrichment of the mixture may be 30 to 40 percent when four cylinders are supplied from a single metering system (as with V-8 engines equipped with dual carburetors), and it may be over 100 percent where a single cylinder receives its mixture from a single metering system (as when a 6-cylinder engine is equipped with three dual carburetors).

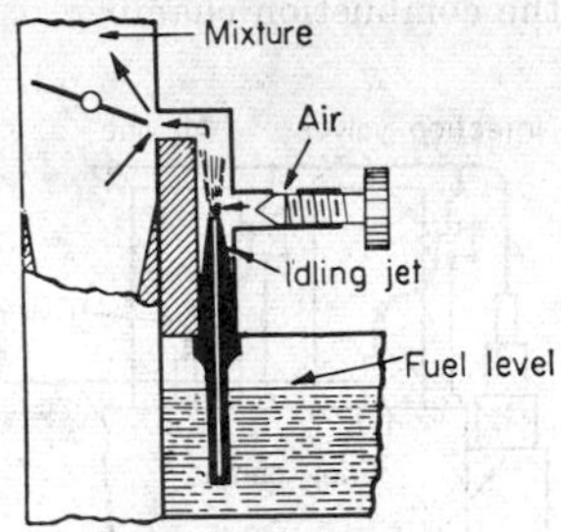

Fig. 43. The idling jet of an updraft carburetor.

The **idling jet** (Fig. 43) has maximum suction with the engine idling and the throttle closed. The main jet begins to operate at small throttle opening. The increasing richness accompanying increase in throttle opening is usually compensated (Fig. 44) by a restricted air-bled jet (Stromberg, Carter), an unrestricted air-bled jet (Zenith, Fig. 45), or an air valve (Schebler, Fig. 46). Bleeding air into a fuel jet reduces the effective head that causes fuel flow. The unrestricted air bleed eliminates the suction head due to Venturi action, and the compensating fuel-flow occurs only because of fuel head (h, Fig. 45). Restricted air bleeding only partly reduces the head on the fuel jet. At **wide-open throttle,** the main fuel-orifice area may be increased or another fuel orifice opened, either by throttle action or manifold pressure, to provide the maximum-power mixture.

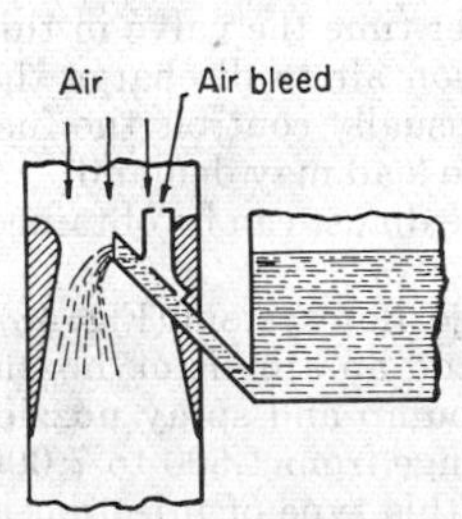

Fig. 44. Single-jet downdraft carburetor with restricted air bleeding.

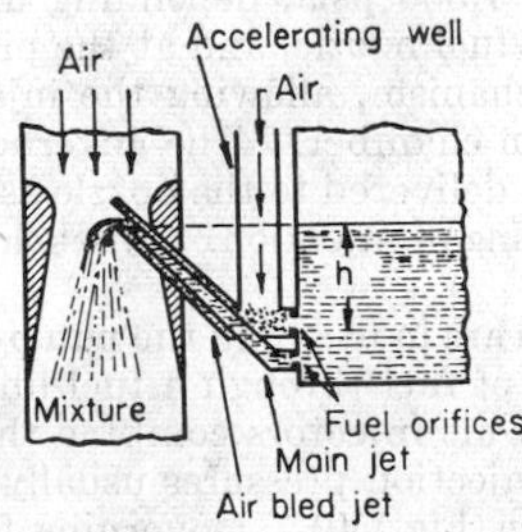

Fig. 45. Unrestricted air-bled jet and single-jet downdraft carburetor.

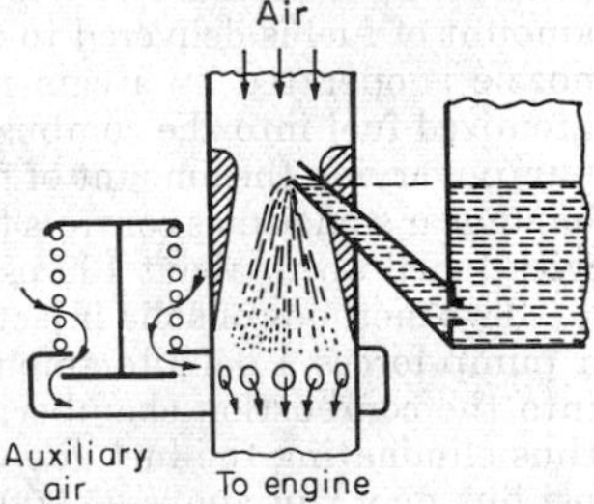

Fig. 46. Auxiliary air valve and single-jet downdraft carburetor.

Actual carburetor characteristics approach the desirable characteristics indicated in Fig. 41. When the throttle is opened quickly (maximum economy to maximum power), there is a momentary lag of the fuel flow behind the air flow because of the formation of a liquid film on the intake-manifold walls under wide-open throttle conditions. This necessitates the use of some device (accelerating pump or well) for enriching the mixture and avoiding backfiring. At light loads the accelerating well of Fig. 45 contains fuel which is instantly available on rapid throttle opening.

Carburetors for **aircraft engines** provide fuel-air ratios that vary from 0.11 at idle to 0.085 for cruising rich (cruising lean being about 0.072), which extends from about 20 to 40 percent load (air capacity), beyond which the mixture richness is increased to about 0.108 at maximum output. Aircraft carburetors must compensate for the effect of altitude on air density (see Sec. 11) and the resulting change in mixture ratio. A carburetor providing a 15:1 air-fuel ratio at sea level would provide an air-fuel ratio of $\sqrt{0.532} \times 15$, or about 11:1, at an altitude of 20,000 ft. Altitude effects may be compensated in four ways: (1) by an altitude air port or valve for admitting more air, (2) by a variable fuel orifice for restricting fuel flow, (3) by pressure reduction in the float chamber for restricting fuel flow, and (4) by throttling the air supply to maintain constant air density.

Fuel Injection

Diesel Engines. The fuel-injection system for Diesel engines consists of a pump, fuel line, and nozzle, the combination of which controls the beginning, rate, and duration of injection, meters the desired amount, and atomizes and distributes the fuel in the combustion chamber.

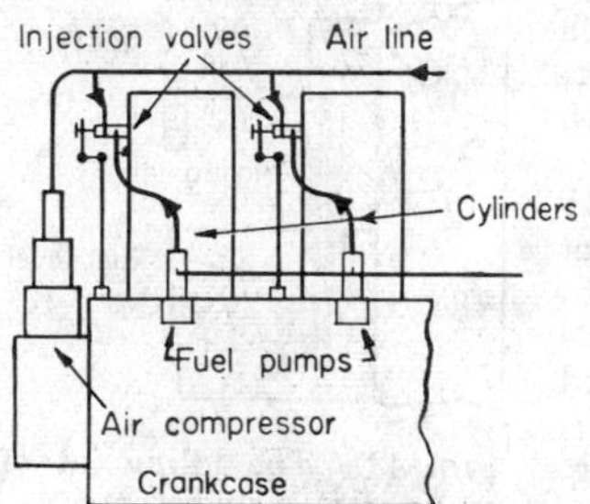

FIG. 47. Air injection.

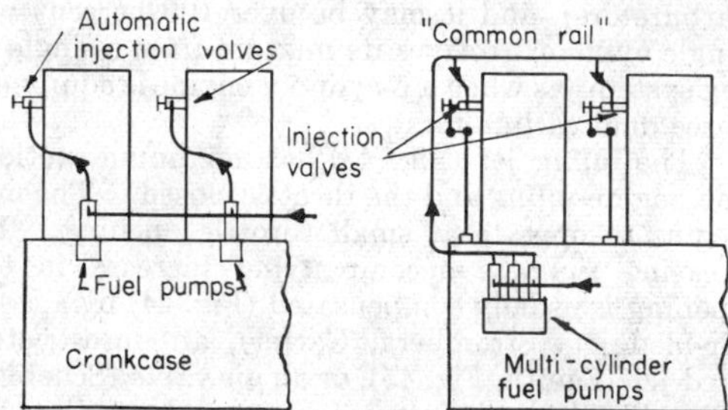

FIG. 48. Pump injection.

FIG. 49. Common rail.

Methods of Fuel Injection. There are two principal methods of injecting fuel into the combustion chamber: air injection and solid injection. In the **air-injection** system (Fig. 47), now being used only on a few large engines, a multistage air compressor supplies air at a pressure of 800 to 1,300 psia, depending upon the load. A metered amount of fuel is delivered to the fuel nozzle, and at the proper time the valve in this nozzle is operated by a cam mechanism, allowing the injection air to discharge the atomized fuel into the combustion chamber. The governor usually controls the fuel pump, varying the amount of fuel delivered to the nozzle as the load may demand. A hand gear sometimes controls timing of injection. Smokeless exhaust can be obtained with bmep up to about 130 psi.

Two methods of **solid injection** are in use. In the **pump-injection system** (Fig. 48), a pump forces a definite amount of fuel through a fuel line and an atomizing nozzle into the combustion chamber. Unit injectors combine the pump and spray nozzle, thus eliminating the fuel line. Injection pressures usually range from 1,500 to 7,000 psi but may run above 25,000 psi (Fig. 50). Governing for this type of injection is usually effected by controlling a bypass valve in the pump or the pump discharge line or by varying the time of closure of the fuel-pump inlet valve. A separate fuel pump is usually required for each cylinder, although rotating plunger pumps serving more than one cylinder per plunger are available. In the **common-rail system** (Fig. 49), a constant pressure is maintained in the fuel discharge line, and the discharge to the engine cylinder is controlled by the lift, timing, and duration of opening of the fuel valve. Considerable capacity of the discharge line is necessary in this case; the number of fuel pumps is not necessarily the same as the number of engine cylinders, a triplex pump being considered desirable to supply fuel at a constant rate.

Pumps. The volume of liquid fuel to be metered per cycle per cylinder is about 7×10^{-5} cu in. per cu in. of displacement at full load for a normal aspirated engine and only a fraction of this for idling conditions. Fuel pumps that only meter fuel usually operate at low pressures, have variable stroke, and require a maximum displacement only slightly larger than the required amount of fuel.

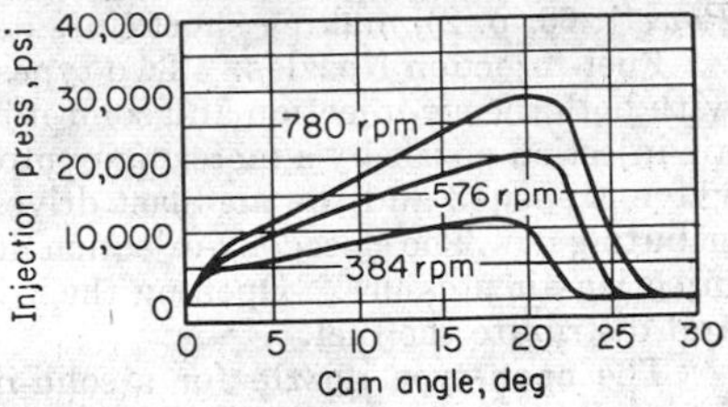

FIG. 50. Injection pressures, solid injection; plunger diameter 0.375 in., displacement, 501 cu mm, 6 spray holes 0.008 in. diam. (*Shoemaker*, *Trans. SAE*, 1938, *p.* 485.)

Fuel pumps for pump-injection systems require rugged construction, are usually operated by a cam or a swash-plate mechanism, and are of constant stroke. The pump plunger and barrel (Fig. 51) are a very close lapped fit to minimize leakage. The inlet port is uncovered at the bottom of the plunger stroke, the partial vacuum in the cylinder causing fuel flow into the barrel. On the upward plunger stroke, fuel flows past the discharge valve to the nozzle until the bypass port is uncovered. Then fuel flows out of the pump cylinder and through the line until the delivery valve closes and maintains a desired line residual pressure until the next injection. Turning the pump plunger in the barrel varies the time of uncovering the bypass port by the plunger helix which varies the duration of the effective plunger stroke and the amount of fuel injected. The high pressures in these systems and the relatively large volume of fuel in the line between the pump and the nozzle, except for unit injectors, result in considerable compression of the fuel which necessitates a pump displacement three to five times larger than the maximum volume of fuel injected per cycle. The coefficient of compressibility (see Secs. 3 and 6) is about 90×10^{-6} for fuel oil, from which the decreased volume of the fuel originally between the pump and the nozzle when subjected to injection pressure can be determined.

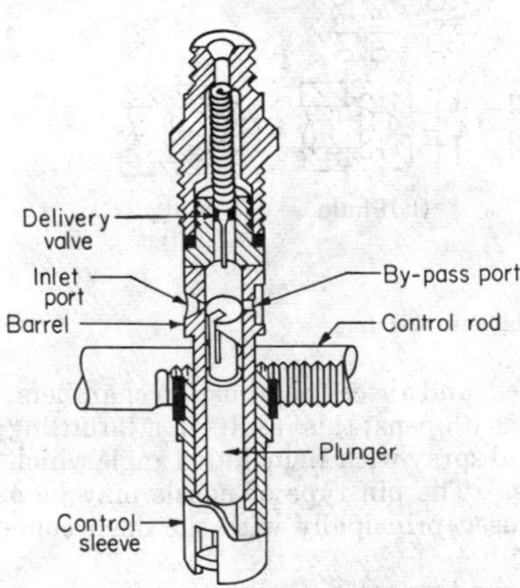

FIG. 51. Bosch plunger, barrel, and delivery-valve assembly.

The **air compressor** for air-injection systems is usually three-stage, built with a stepped piston, and supplies 15 to 20 cu ft of free air per bhp-hr. It uses 8 to 11 percent of the indicated power of the engine and is completely water-cooled with intercoolers between stages. The injection air should not exceed the amount required to atomize the fuel both on account of the work of compressing the air and also to minimize its cooling effect on the cylinder gases. The amount of air is controlled by throttling the suction to the air compressor, or by varying the duration and amount of the opening of the spray valves, or by spilling the discharge from the low-pressure compressor.

Fuel Lines. The tubing connecting the injection pump with the spray nozzle must be thick-walled, or smooth and uniform bore, and be made of very ductile material to permit bending. Bosch recommends SAE 1010 steel with a carbon content not exceeding 0.05 to 0.15 percent, a maximum tensile strength of 45,000 psi, and a maximum elongation of 35 percent in 2 in. Tubes range in size from ¼ in. O.D. and 1⁄16 in. I.D to ½ in. O.D. and 3⁄16 in. I.D.

Fuel lines should be of the same length for each cylinder to obtain the same hydraulic characteristics. Pressure waves due to plunger motion and nozzle efflux characteristics are developed, travel back and forth, and create disturbances during the injection process (Rothrock, *NACA Rept.* 396; De Juhasz, *Trans. ASME (Oil and Gas Power)*, **60,** p. 2), making short lines desirable.

Fuel-injection Nozzles. Two types of injection nozzles, open and closed, are used with both the air-injection and solid-injection systems. Fuel is pumped into the open air-injection nozzle by a metering pump. At the desired crank angle, the injection-air valve is opened and the air blast drives the fuel into the cylinder, atomizing and distributing it. The closed air-injection nozzle has fuel pumped into it while subjected to injection-air pressure. Opening the injection valve permits the air to inject, atomize, and distribute the fuel.

The **open-type nozzle** for a solid-injection system may have fuel delivered to it from a low-pressure metering pump (Cummins), a cam-operated plunger being used to inject the fuel. The open-type nozzle is also used with unit injectors (G.M.) which combine the injection pump and nozzle, eliminating the fuel line and its pressure-wave disturbances. During the pump discharge stroke, fuel flows past a number of check valves and through small holes (6 holes, 0.0008 in. diam for a 4¼ × 5 in. cyl) in the nozzle tip.

Closed solid-injection nozzles are usually hydraulically operated, having a differential-diameter valve (Fig. 52), held on its seat by a spring, which opens when the fuel-line pressure is increased by the injection pump. The valve closing pressure is always lower than the opening pressure, depending on the relative effective valve areas exposed to the fuel pressure. The valves may be either of pintle or pin type (Fig. 52). The former has a single orifice through which the end of the valve protrudes.

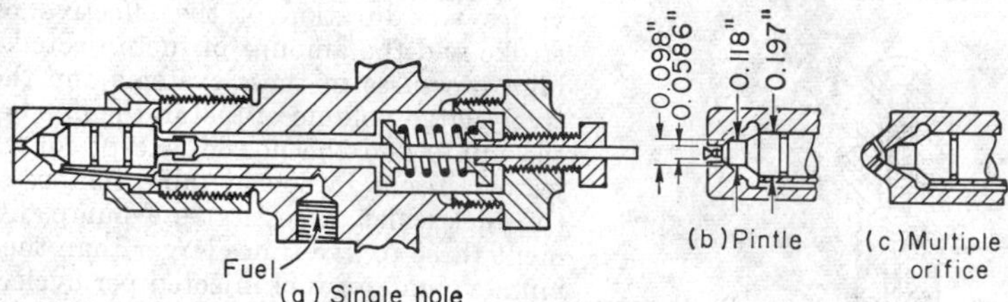

FIG. 52. Solid-injection closed nozzle.

It is used mostly with ante-, precombustion, divided, and air-cell combustion chambers. A pintle may be designed to restrict the fuel flow as it opens; this results in a **throttling nozzle.** The pintle nozzle provides a hollow conical spray with an included angle which varies from 4 to 60 deg with various pintle sizes. The pin type of nozzle may be a single- or multiple-hole nozzle, the latter being used principally with the open combustion chamber.

Injection nozzles should be mounted so that the tips are not subjected to intense heat effects. Water cooling and exposing only a small portion of the nozzle tip are desirable and reduce the tendency for carbon formation.

Fuel Sprays. The fuel spray may be a hollow cone or consist of a core and surrounding envelope of atomized fuel. Lee (*NACA Repts.* 425 and 438) found that the particle size in the spray could be classified into groups with mean diameters ranging from 0.0005 to above 0.007 in. Increasing the injection pressure increases the percentage of fuel particles of the smaller sizes. Orifice diameters of 0.02 and 0.03 in. showed little difference, but an orifice diameter of 0.008 in. improved atomization appreciably.

Fuel-spray penetration varies inversely with the spray angle. Helical grooves through which the fuel flows to the orifice increase the spray angle.

Pilot injection of the regular fuel or of a more readily ignitable fuel may be used to reduce ignition lag of some fuels. Two fuel pumps are required, the pilot pump injecting a small portion of the fuel charge ahead of the main injection. The pilot charge should have a low ignition temperature and a small ignition lag, and should raise the cylinder-gas temperature sufficiently to promote rapid ignition and combustion of the main charge (*Automotive Inds.*, **79,** 1938, p. 533).

Fuel-injection-system Characteristics. At any given setting the usual fuel-injection system delivers more fuel per cycle with an increase in speed. If speed decreases during idling or with increase in load, the fuel-injection system injects less fuel which causes the engine to run still slower, etc. Thus, the Diesel engine is usually unstable and requires a governor for idling as well as at other loads.

A declining delivery characteristic with an increase in speed is desirable.

Spark-ignition Engines. Fuel is injected into either the supercharger, the intake manifold, the intake valve ports, or the combustion chambers of spark-ignition engines. The advantages of fuel injection over carburetion are uniform distribution of fuel between the engine cylinders, the elimination of combustion knock because of non-uniform fuel distribution, or the suppression of combustion knock in any cylinder by increasing mixture richness for that cylinder only (see also Combustion Knock, p. 9–122), the elimination of heat to the intake manifold to obtain the desirable fuel vaporization thus obtaining higher power outputs because of higher charge density, and the use of less volatile fuel. Carburetor (automobiles) and induction-system (aircraft) icing are eliminated. Wright aircraft engines and some Mercedes (four-cycle) and Goliath (two-cycle) automobile engines use cylinder injection.

The principal disadvantages compared to carburetor systems are the added complications, weight, and increased cost, excepting the case of two 4-barrel carburetors.

Injection of fuel into the intake port occurs usually during the first half or first two-thirds of the induction stroke in order to provide good mixing with the air entering the engine cylinder.

Ignition and Spark Advance

(For details of ignition systems, see Sec. 15)

The ignition system consists usually of a 12-volt storage battery, contact breaker, induction coil, and high-tension distributor, or a high-tension magneto with a distributor. For aircraft the low-tension distribution system to transformer spark plugs or other apparatus for obtaining a high-tension spark at the plug appears to eliminate some of the troubles of the conventional ignition system in aircraft engines at high altitude.

The usual firing order for in-line engines is 1, 3, 4, 2 or 1, 2, 4, 3 for four cylinders; 1, 5, 3, 6, 2, 4 (United States automobile engines) or 1, 4, 2, 6, 3, 5, for six cylinders; in V-8 engines (all United States automobile engines) thirteen makes of cars use a firing order of 1, 8, 4, 3, 6, 5, 7, 2; four an order of 1, 5, 4, 8, 6, 3, 7, 2; and one an order of 1, 2, 7, 8, 4, 5, 6, 3.

Radial four-cycle engines have firing orders that skip every other cylinder. For a nine-cylinder single-row engine the order would be 1, 3, 5, 7, 9, 2, 4, 6, 8. **Spark-plug gaps** vary from 0.015 to 0.040 in. With 0 to 20 in. Hg manifold gage pressures, the smaller gaps require 4,000 to 6,000 volts while the larger gaps require 8,000 to 10,000 volts.

Spark plugs are usually located near the exhaust valve (hottest spot) so that the flame progresses toward the cooler part of the combustion chamber. This permits higher compression ratios without combustion knock. Part-throttle operation may require a slight change in location to provide a combustible mixture at the spark plug. Engines with lower than optimum compression ratios may have central spark-plug location which usually results in minimum combustion time. Dual ignition (two spark plugs located opposite each other) also reduces combustion time and results in a slight gain in efficiency (usually less than 1 percent) compared with single ignition with optimum spark advance.

Since combustion requires appreciable time, the spark advance should distribute the combustion process before and after top center in order to obtain maximum power.

Optimum spark advance depends principally on air-fuel mixture, combustion-chamber design, turbulence, engine speed, number of spark plugs, and spark plug location. Maximum power air-fuel ratios require the minimum spark advance. Low-speed engines require 10 to 20 deg (crank travel) spark advance, and high-speed automotive engines require 30 to 40 deg spark advance. Racing engines require still more. Full load requires less spark advance than part throttle. Spark advance in most automotive engines is controlled automatically by engine speed and manifold vacuum; increases in both of these independently increase the spark advance.

Air and Fuel Lines, Manifolds, Mixture Distribution, and Mufflers

Air lines, extending from the engine to the outside air, should be designed for air velocities of 50 to 100 fps. Air cleaners for the removal of dirt particles reduce piston, ring, and cylinder wear. Air silencers, used at the entrance to the air lines, are combined with cleaners for automotive purposes.

Gas lines should be designed for gas velocities of 30 to 60 fps. A pressure drop of 0.07 to 0.12 in. of water should be allowed per 100 ft of pipe. Close calculation of the **size of gas pipe** for industrial gas installations is undesirable, because of the reduction of the normal cross section of the pipe by tar and dust deposits. A storage chamber of large diameter should be located in the pipe near the engine. The gas line should be free from traps and as free as possible from changes in direction of flow, and should be pitched slightly (¼ in. to the foot) from both ends toward a low point in the center, where a sealed drain should be located. All water seals in the gas line should be as cool as possible to minimize evaporation and the breaking of the seal.

Gasoline and **fuel-oil lines** should be designed for maximum velocities under 1 fps for gravity feed. Gasoline lines should be in a cool location, as heating above 100 F may vaporize the lighter fractions and cause **vapor lock.** Sediment and water traps as well as strainers or filters should be located in the fuel line ahead of the carburetor, fuel pump, or injection pump.

Intake Manifolds. The intake manifold distributes the air (Diesel) or the air and fuel (Otto) to the various cylinders of a multicylinder engine. The **updraft** manifold (carburetor below manifold) should have a **riser velocity** of not less than 40 fps to entrain or lift the liquid fuel particles from the carburetor to the **distributor** section of the manifold. This determines the minimum wide-open throttle speed for satisfactory operation. The **downdraft** manifold permits larger areas and lower velocities between the carburetor and manifold, the average for automotive practice being about 50 fps for a mean piston speed of 700 fpm (500 to 900 rpm). The corresponding mean gas velocity of about 250 fps at a top speed of 3,500 fpm mean piston speed indicates a maximum loss of volumetric efficiency of about 3 percent due to pressure drop required to attain this velocity. Higher velocities are undesirable because of greater losses in volumetric efficiency, a drop in intake pressure of 1 psi below atmospheric reducing the volumetric efficiency about 7 percent.

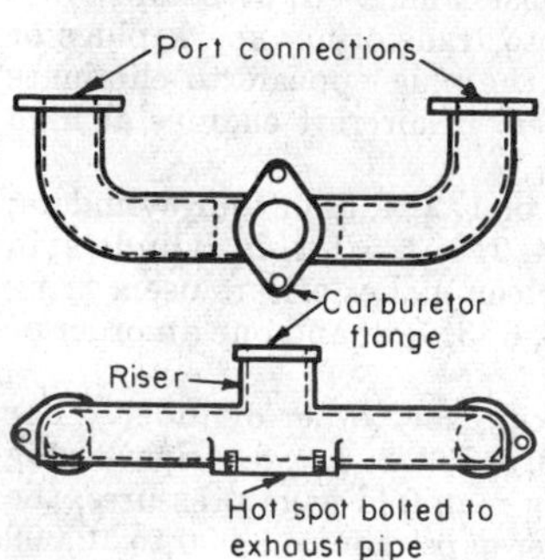

FIG. 53. Downdraft two-port intake manifold with flat floor and hot spot.

Intake manifolds are either **streamlined** (always with Diesel), of the **rake type,** or a combination of both. The sections may be either circular or rectangular. In some cases, the circular sections are combined with a flat **floor** or bottom to provide more surface on which the liquid fuel may spread and be vaporized. **Dams** are also used to prevent liquid fuel from flowing along the manifold floor.

The overlapping of the intake-valve periods produces complicated disturbances in the intake manifold and has resulted in the use of dual manifolds in some engines with six or more cylinders. In six-cylinder engines, the first three and the last three cylinders are fed with separate systems. V-8 automobile engines have complicated dual manifolds, integrally cast, each manifold feeding two cylinders of each bank.

Some heat must be supplied to vaporize the fuel. Preheating the air is undesirable since it heats the carburetor, evaporates fuel in the float chamber, and changes the air-fuel ratio with change in air temperature. Preheating the fuel is undesirable since the light fuel fractions will be lost by vaporization. Consequently, most intake manifolds for liquid fuels have a **hot spot** (Fig. 53), which receives heat from the exhaust (usually thermostatically controlled) and on which the fuel particles impinge upon leaving the manifold riser. The dew points or condensation temperatures for fuel in an air-fuel mixture depend on the fuel, air-fuel ratio, and total pressure (Table 14), and may be determined from the equilibrium air-distillation data (Fig. 32).

Table 14. Condensation Temperatures of Liquid Fuels

Fuel	Deg API	ASTM Distillation, deg F				Condensation temp, deg F			
						Atmospheric pressure		Pressure, ⅔ atmospheric	
						Air-fuel ratio		Air-fuel ratio	
		Initial point	50 percent	90 percent	End point	12:1	15:1	12:1	15:1
Gasoline....	60	100	249	354	400	118	114	111	107
Kerosene....	43	350	450	510	550	204	200	201	197

Mixture Distribution. Perfect distribution consists of equal distribution of both air and fuel to the various cylinders of a multicylinder engine. The compression pressure of each cylinder is an indication of the air distribution if all cylinders have identical valve timing and compression ratio and no leakage. The effect of unequal distribution of fuel or both air and fuel on the performance of each cylinder is shown by the performance of a single-cylinder engine with variations in air-fuel ratio (Fig. 54). Cylinders receiving lean mixtures develop less power than those receiving correspondingly rich mixtures. Increasing the carburetor richness of a multicylinder engine increases the power output of the lean cylinders more than it decreases the power of the rich cylinders unless the mixture is already too rich in some of the cylinders. Thus, poor distribution can be masked by enriching the mixture and high power output attained at the cost of high fuel-consumption rates.

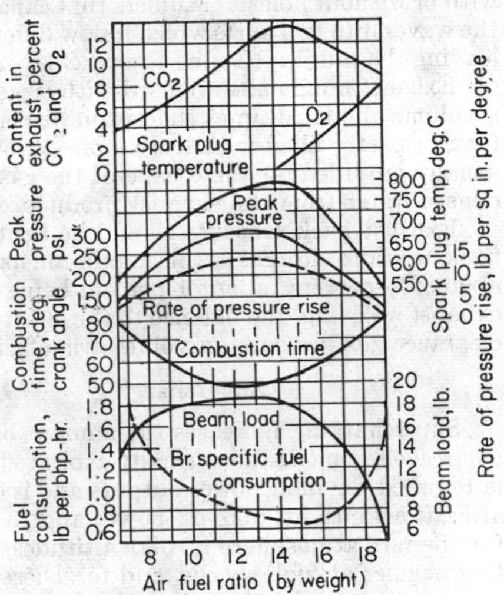

FIG. 54. Influence of air-fuel ratio in an overhead-valve engine with cylindrical combustion chamber. (*Rabezzana and Kalmar, Automotive Inds.*, **66,** 1932, *p.* 13.)

Figure 54 also shows that the CO_2 analysis of the exhaust gases from the individual cylinders and spark-plug temperatures (thermocouple in the center electrode) may be used for determination of mixture distribution. Typical mixture distribution with liquid fuel shows a variation of 10 to 25 percent in fuel supplied the various cylinders (Fig. 55). The use of a gaseous fuel in the same engine resulted in almost perfect distribution. Samples of exhaust gas taken near the exhaust valve of one cylinder may be contaminated by the exhaust gases from another cylinder. Bartholomew, Chalk, and Brewster (*Trans. SAE*, **33,** 1938, p. 141) developed a combination mixture-sampling valve and spark plug and found variations in air-fuel ratios as high as 5 while accelerating at wide-open throttle on the road.

Distribution of load (and fuel) and variation in injection timing between cylinders of a Diesel engine are indicated by the exhaust-gas temperature of the individual cylinders, the mixtures in the various cylinders usually being lean under all conditions.

Exhaust Manifolds. The cross-sectional area of the exhaust manifold and pipe should be 1.1 to 1.3 times the area of the intake manifold. Small multicylinder engines have the exhaust manifold cast in one piece. This is anchored at the center of the engine, and elongated holes are provided at other points to allow for expansion and growth. Large engines usually have water-jacketed exhaust manifolds to prevent strain and for safety measures, or must be provided with expansion joints.

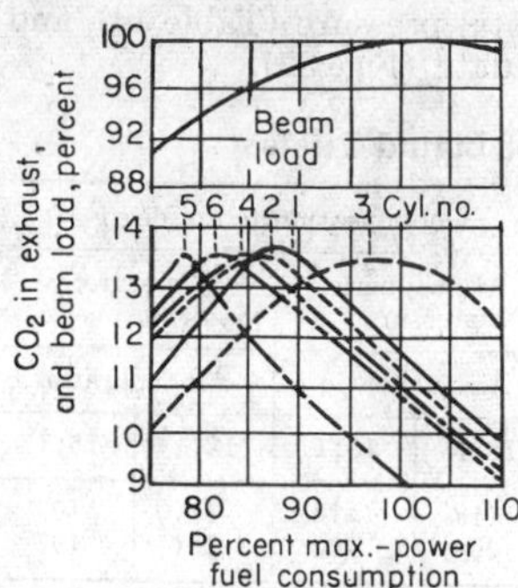

FIG. 55. Mixture distribution in a six-cylinder automobile engine. (*Rabezzana, Trans. SAE*, 1938, *p.* 511.)

The overlapping of the exhaust-valve periods in multicylinder engines makes multiple manifolding desirable. A desirable construction for a six-cylinder engine is one exhaust manifold for each group of three cylinders. Individual exhaust stacks or lines joined to a common exhaust line at some distance from the exhaust ports is considered good practice.

Long exhaust lines should have provision for expansion in the line, and drains should be located at the lowest points.

Mufflers (see Sec. 12). Exhaust mufflers, to be efficient as sound silencers, must decrease the exhaust-gas velocity and also **absorb** the sound waves or **cancel** them by interference with other waves from the same source. Mufflers should have volumes six to eight times the piston displacement and may contain baffles with or without holes. Mufflers that cancel sound waves by interference usually break the waves into two parts which follow different paths and meet again out of phase before leaving the muffler (Gunn, *Trans. SAE*, **29**, 1934, p. 107).

Exhaust **muffle pits** are used with large engines, are usually made of concrete, have a volume about 20 times the piston displacement, may be open or provided with baffling or partly filled with loose stone through which the gases must pass. A stack is usually provided for the escape of the gases and a drain for the discharge of the condensed water from the exhaust products.

Exhaust **back pressure** should be kept to a minimum since an increase of 1 psi in back pressure decreases the maximum power output about 2½ percent, about 1 percent being due to more exhaust work and the balance to the effect of increased clearance gas pressure on volumetric efficiency.

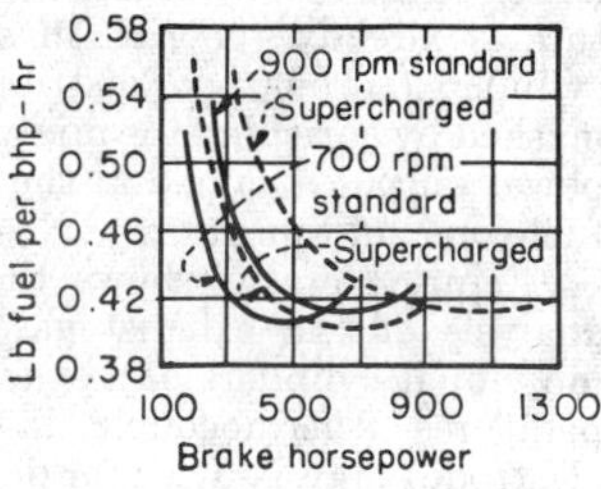

FIG. 56. Specific fuel consumption of a 12-cylinder, 9 × 12 in. Westinghouse engine, both with and without supercharging.

Supercharging

Supercharging increases the amount of charge per cycle above that of the normally aspirated engine. It is required for high power outputs and is desirable for aircraft engines for take-off power and to compensate for the rare atmosphere at high altitudes, for automotive engines at high speeds, and for Diesel engines for increased output. Supercharging a carbureted engine which has the optimum compression ratio for the available fuel causes combustion knock and necessitates lowering of the compression ratio, enriching the mixture, or increasing the octane number of the fuel. Supercharging a Diesel engine increases the maximum pressure and necessitates lowering the compression ratio or changing the fuel-injection timing, if the limiting pressure is already attained without supercharging. Thus in an engine with optimum compression ratio, gain in power by supercharging is obtained at the expense of fuel consumption if the compression ratio must be lowered.

The specific fuel consumption (Fig. 56) of a constant-speed Diesel engine, supercharged with a Roots blower, is higher at low loads than that of the unsupercharged engine. About the same minimum specific fuel consumption is attained in both cases but at 50 percent higher loads for the supercharged engine.

Intake manifold pressures of 40 to 48 in. Hg abs are used for take-off performance in aircraft engines, and pressures up to 40 in. Hg are used in stationary engines. The clearance space may be scavenged completely in the Diesel engine. Mucklow (*Brit. Air. Min. Repts. and Mem.*, 1460, 1931), in a single-cylinder spark-ignition engine with constant induction temperature, found that the percentage increases in imep and bmep were about 15 and 27 percent higher than the percentage increase in absolute induction pressure. DuBois (*Trans. SAE*, **34,** 1937, p. 231) obtained an imep of 310 psi with an absolute intake pressure of 55 in. Hg in a single-cylinder spark-ignition engine with 8:1 compression ratio, and 418 psi with a pressure of 85 in. Hg in a 6:1 compression ratio. Iso-octane with 4 cc of tetraethyllead was used as the fuel, and consequently these represent limiting outputs at these compression ratios until better fuels are available.

Sulzer Bros. Ltd., Switzerland, have developed and supercharged the two-cycle opposed-piston engines to 2, 3, and 6 atm abs and have obtained mean effective pressures of 170, 210, and 255 psi, respectively. The compression ratio was lowered for the highest supercharge in order to reduce the maximum cylinder pressures attained. In all cases considerable excess air was present and resulted in an invisible exhaust gas

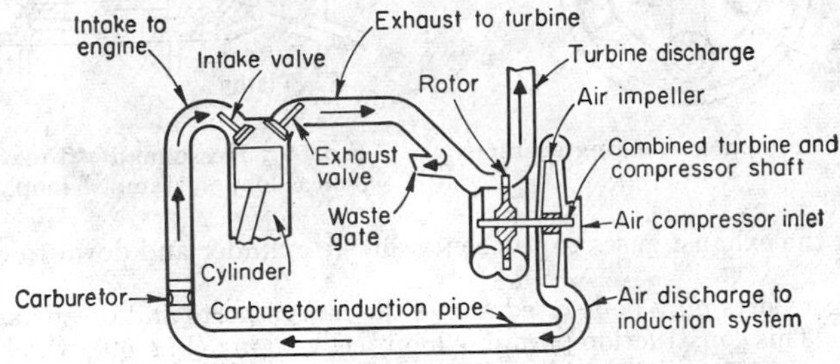

Fig. 57. Diagram of exhaust turbine supercharger.

(Oederlin, *Jour. ASME*, Nov., 1942, p. 779). Supercharged to 5 to 6 atm abs, the power output of the Diesel engine is all required for the supercharger, the engine-supercharger combination becoming a gas generator which can supply gas to a turbine from which useful work can be attained at 35 to 40 percent thermal efficiency, without regenerators, since none of the turbine work is required for an air compressor (see Gas Turbines, p. 9–150).

Two types of superchargers are in general use: the positive-displacement type (Roots blower) and the centrifugal type (see p. 14–55 *et seq.*). The positive type is desirable for variable-speed engines (Diesel rail car) where high torque is required at various speeds, since the pressure and capacity characteristics of this type do not decrease with speed. The centrifugal type is particularly adaptable to aircraft engines because of high capacity, small size, and low weight, and also to automotive engines for improving the volumetric efficiency at high speeds only. Centrifugal blowers may have one or two stages with cooling between stages or after the single or last stage. The rotors run at maximum speeds of 16,000 to 30,000 rpm, or seven to twelve times crankshaft speed for aircraft engines.

Superchargers may be geared directly to the engine, or driven through a gear box and clutches providing two speed ratios, or driven by an exhaust turbine (Fig. 57). The carburetor may be located before or after the supercharger but is usually between the two stages of a multistage supercharger.

Scavenging Two-cycle Engines

Either the crankcase compression for each cylinder or a blower may be used for scavenging and charging the cylinders of a two-cycle engine (Fig. 58). With crankcase compression, a third port uncovered by the piston at the top of the stroke, a rotary valve, or an automatic poppet valve may be used. The top of the piston may have a deflector fastened to it or may be shaped to deflect the gases entering the cylinder and prevent short-circuiting to the exhaust port. A "dead" spot of gases may remain in the lower center of the cylinder or in the upper corners.

The intake may be inclined and tangential, giving the entering charge an upward helical motion (Fig. 59). This motion keeps the entering charge near the cylinder

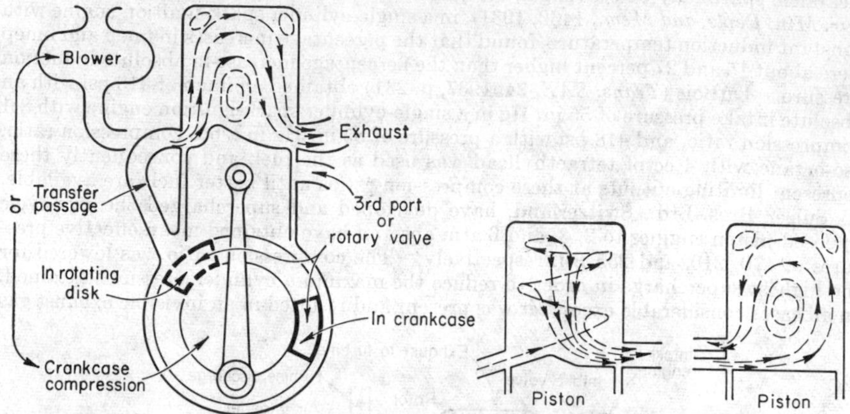

Fig. 58. Common scavenging systems.

Fig. 59. Hesselman helical loop system.

Fig. 60. M-A-N loop scavenging.

walls, forcing the exhaust gases to the center of the cylinder and down to the exhaust port.

The exhaust ports may be located above the intake ports and on the same side of the cylinder. This construction permits "loop" scavenging (Fig. 60), which may leave a dead spot in the center of the loop.

The **General Motors** engines have poppet exhaust valves in the cylinder head (Fig. 9), eliminating the hot exhaust ports from the cylinder walls. Intake ports are completely around the cylinder. The blower pressure ranges from 2 to 15 in. Hg for speeds of 600 to 2,000 rpm, respectively. Maximum imep and bmep obtained with this engine are 140 and 94 psi, respectively.

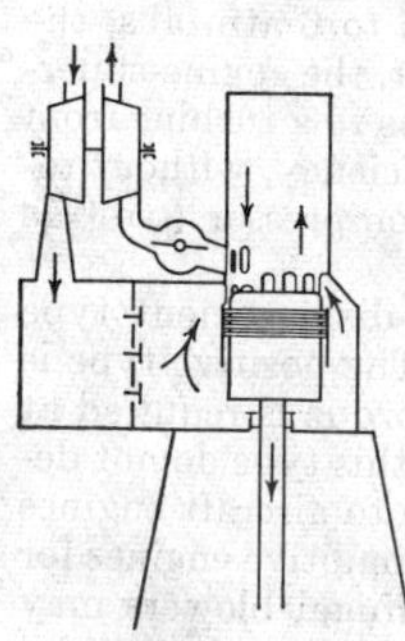

Fig. 61. Sulzer RD-90 two-cycle Diesel engine (schematic).

The **Junkers** engine has intake and exhaust ports located in the cylinder walls at the opposite ends of the cylinder. A blower forces the entering charge through the intake ports which extend around the entire circumference of the cylinder, the scavenging process being similar to that of the Fairbanks-Morse engines.

The conventional two-cycle **Sulzer Diesel engine** (Fig. 61) makes use of a cross-head and piston-rod design wherein air in the space between the piston and the diaphragm carrying the piston-rod stuffing box is displaced by the descending piston and forced into the cylinder through the intake ports as they are uncovered by the piston. This scavenges the cylinder of exhaust gases by the loop scavenging principle. As the piston rises, a rotary plate valve in the exhaust line is closed before the intake ports, allowing compression to start with whatever pressure is supplied by the intake system. After the engine is running, supercharging is provided by exhaust-gas-turbine-driven blowers. Air from these blowers passes through intercoolers and is admitted through flap valves to the scavenging chambers.

A short piston is possible with this design because the rotary valve in the exhaust lines prevents the escape of air from the scavenging chamber when the exhaust ports are uncovered by the piston on its compression stroke. The crosshead design, with its stuffing box, prevents any combustion products from contaminating the crankcase oil system.

The type RD 90 design is used for cylinder diameters up to 900 mm (35.4 in.). With 1,550-mm (61-in.) stroke and 1,200-fpm piston speed, such a cylinder has a continuous rating of 2,300 bhp at 119 rpm and fuel consumption of 0.33 lb per bhp hr. Overload tests developing 3,000 bhp per cylinder at 130 rpm are reported, with a specific fuel consumption of 0.34 lb per bhp hr and no smoke.

Cooling Systems

Engine cylinders must be cooled to maintain a lubricant film on the cylinder walls; the cylinder heads, pistons, and exhaust valves are cooled to prevent combustion knock or destruction of these parts due to overheating; and the lubricant must be cooled to maintain the desirable viscosity under operating conditions. Either water- or air-cooling systems are used, but pistons, exhaust valves, and lubricants in comparatively small or low-duty engines are sufficiently cooled by contact with other engine parts or the lubricant between them and do not require cooling systems.

Water Cooling. The heat removed by the cooling water from the cylinders and cylinder heads ranges from 15 to 20 percent of the energy input for large Diesel engines, 20 to 35 percent for automotive engines, and may run as high as 40 percent for automotive engines at one-third load. An increase in speed from 1,000 to 3,000 rpm decreases the heat loss to the cooling water about 20 to 30 percent. These values indicate a heat loss ranging from 40 to 50 percent of the brake output for large Diesel engines and 100 to 150 percent of the brake output for automotive engines.

Pistons in small engines are cooled by heat transfer to the cylinder walls and lubricant. In some cases, an appreciable quantity of oil is directed against the piston head to maintain desirable head temperatures.

Water is fed into and out of water-cooled pistons usually by means of swing joints or telescopic water connections. To keep the piston jackets of large engines filled, the cooling water must be under a pressure of 60 to 80 psi. For the other jackets, 10 to 15 psi is sufficient, and therefore two cooling systems at the different pressures may be used or the water may be throttled at the entrance to the other jackets. Valves on the discharge sides of the jackets should not be used. Even with the high pressure of the jacket water, there will be a water hammer in the piston jackets unless the area of the discharge is restricted to about 20 percent of the area of the inlet opening. The average percentage distribution of the water to the various jackets is approximately as follows: 60 to the cylinder jacket and 40 to the cylinder-head jacket with uncooled piston; 50 to the cylinder jacket, 25 to the cylinder-head jacket, and 25 to the piston and piston rod with water-cooled piston.

The cooling system may be non-circulating, in which case cold water is supplied, flows through the water jacket, and is wasted. With a temperature rise of 90 F, from 2 (in large engines) to 4 gal of water per bhp-hr must be supplied. In some engines, cooling-water outlet temperatures as low as 120 F must be maintained, which with high inlet temperatures may increase the required quantity of water to as much as 10 gal per bhp-hr. Water is circulated at a rate of 25 to 50 gal per bhp-hr with a temperature rise of 10 to 20 F while flowing through the water jacket.

Natural circulation (**thermosiphon**), with low velocities, requiring large connections, may be used if the water forms a complete circuit. In this case, hot water rises in the engine jacket, flows to the radiator, is cooled, descends, and flows to the engine jacket.

Small stationary engines are often **hopper-cooled.** This is an **evaporative cooling system** requiring about 4 to 6 lb of make-up water per bhp-hr. The ASTM-CFR knock-testing engines are cooled by evaporation, the vapor being condensed by a **reflex condenser** (copper coil with cold water flowing through) and returned to the cylinder jacket.

In high-output engines, the coolant is directed at the hottest spot, usually the exhaust-valve seat, either with an external or internal inlet manifold for a common cylinder-block jacket; otherwise vapor bubbles will form, cling to the surface, and cause overheating. In vertical engines, the water usually flows upward, around the cylinder barrel into the cylinder-head jacket, and to the outlet. Higher output and reduced knocking tendency have resulted from directing the entering coolant at the hot spots in the cylinder head and then flowing the coolant downward around the cylinders.

The **size of piping** required for the inlet to the jacket may be calculated for 3 fps water velocity, and for the discharge 2 fps for large engines. In engines with recirculation, these values are increased up to 10 or 15 fps, and the size of the inlet line to the circulating pump is usually larger than the outlet from the water jacket. It is desirable to have an open or visible outlet from each separately cooled part, showing the flow of cooling water.

Ethylene glycol is used as the cooling medium when high jacket temperatures are desired (see p. 6–187).

Air Cooling. Small industrial engines, motorcycle engines, and many aircraft engines are air-cooled. Air cooling eliminates the necessity of the water or other liquid cooling medium, water jackets, pumps, radiators, and water connections, but necessitates single-cylinder construction, finning, baffles, and, in some cases, blowers. The permissible compression ratio and output of air-cooled aircraft engines depend on the efficiency of the cooling of the cylinder head, exhaust valves, and seats. Long fins (1 to 2 in., depending on cylinder size), closely spaced (0.10 to 0.20 in.), with baffles directing the air at high velocity at the hot spots, have made high outputs of aircraft engines possible at the expense of considerable air resistance or drag. Properly designed cooling ducts may make use of the heat added to the cooling air to obtain a jet effect, thereby reducing the drag.

The heat dissipation for copper or aluminum fins in a parallel blast of air is $H = [0.0247 - 0.0054(l^{0.8}/p^{0.4})]v^{0.73}$ Btu per sq ft of fin surface per min per deg F difference between the mean fin temperature and the incoming air temperature, where l is the length of fins, in.; p is distance between fins, in.; and v is the air velocity, mph. For steel fins it is 5 to 10 percent greater [Gibson, *Inst. Automobile* (*London*), 1920].

Oil Cooling. The shearing of the various oil films by the moving parts and the contact with hot parts of an engine cause a rise in oil temperature until energy input to the oil equals the energy transferred by it to the cooler parts it contacts. Oil coolers are required for high-duty engines to maintain oil temperatures of 200 F or under. Temperatures of 250 F are not uncommon in automobile engines on hot days; 300 F is considered too high, particularly for those oils which decompose rapidly under conditions causing the high oil temperatures. The desired oil temperature is maintained by circulating the oil through a radiator or cooler to an oil sump and then through the engine.

LUBRICATION

(See pp. 6–243 *et seq.*)

Oil Circulation. The pressure loss in the oil-circulation duct system may be estimated from flow formulas (see Sec. 3), including the entrance loss and that due to sharp bends or corners. The centrifugal force on the oil in the crankshaft duct at the bearings must be considered in determining oil flow into the shaft and to the connecting rods of engines with high rotative speed.

Oil-system pressures range from a few pounds to above 100 psi, the maximum pressure usually being controlled by an adjustable spring-loaded relief valve.

Oil-pump capacities range from about 2 gpm for a 20 hp truck or passenger-car engine to about 9 gpm for a 140 hp engine. A capacity of 30 gpm per sq in. of *total bearing clearance area* is recommended by Eaton Mfg. Co.

Oil Consumption. Oil is thrown or fed onto the cylinder walls, and some is worked into the combustion chamber by the motion of the pistons and rings, and is either vaporized or burned and escapes with the exhaust gases. Oil mist or vapor in the crankcase escapes through the breather pipe. Contact with the hot piston head or blow-by gases causes decomposition of the oil. Oil leakage may occur from shafts extending from the crankcase, unless provided with **oil slingers,** and from any loose joints in contact with oil. The principal factors affecting oil consumption are speed, output, viscosity, quantity circulated, volatility, and any other factors affecting oil viscosity and quantity circulated. Everett and Stewart (*Penn. State Coll. Bull.* 44,

1935) determined the effect of various factors on the oil consumption of three 1933 Dodge engines (Fig. 62). Some unpublished data on a fleet of 1952 Chevrolets in a controlled road test at turnpike speeds limited to 70 mph showed an average consumption of SAE 20 grade oil of 1,100 miles per qt at the start, dropping as the piston rings wore in to a minimum of 2,700 miles per qt approx at 12,000 miles, after which it rose gradually to some 2,000 miles per qt at 20,000 miles. Inspection of these engines indicated that (1) cylinder lubrication was ample, and (2) a very small quantity of oil was needed to replace the loss due to combustion heat. To ensure replacement under all operating conditions, lubricating systems generally flood the cylinder walls, and the oil-scraper rings on the piston remove the excess. Enough, however, remains to be vaporized on the hot piston heads and burned with the gasoline mixture. An increase in speed, particularly at high speed, usually increases the oil consumption very appreciably. Higher speeds cause more oil to be thrown on the cylinder walls, and eventually a critical speed is reached (Sparrow, *Trans. SAE*, **30**, 1935, p. 58) when **ring flutter** occurs and cylinder lubrication as well as blow-by become uncontrolled.

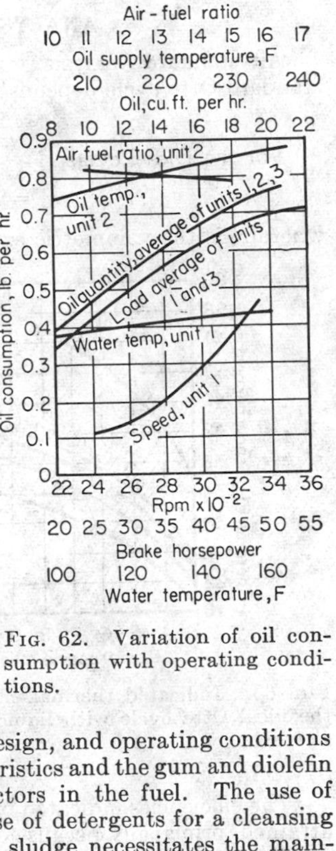

The effect of an increase in oil viscosity is to decrease oil consumption, tests by the Texas Co. (*Lubrication*, **24**, 1938, p. 55) indicating a minumum consumption with automobile engines for SAE 40 oil; higher viscosity oils result in higher consumption. Minimum oil consumption obtained in this manner causes higher friction losses and increased fuel consumption.

Automobile crankcase oils classified as SAE Nos. 10W and 20W provide easy winter starting, having viscosities at 0 F of 6,000 to 12,000 and 12,000 to 48,000 SSU, respectively. SAE Nos. 20, 30, 40, and 50 indicate desirable viscosities for summer operation (or for worn or larger engines), having viscosities at 210 F of 45 to 58, 58 to 70, 70 to 85, and 85 to 100 SSU, respectively. A cross-graded oil (10W-30) has desirable viscosities for both cold starting and summer operation, the SAE classification indicating that it is a high-viscosity-index oil. Crankcase oils labeled ML, MM, and MS indicate their desirability for light, moderate, and severe service, respectively. (See SAE Handbook for more detailed information.)

FIG. 62. Variation of oil consumption with operating conditions.

Sludge and Varnish Formation. Four principal factors control sludge and varnish formation: fuel characteristics, lubricating oil characteristics, engine design, and operating conditions (*Jour. SAE*, Sept., 1947, p. 54). The volatility characteristics and the gum and diolefin content of the fuel appear to be the responsible factors in the fuel. The use of antioxidants to prevent oxidation of the oil and the use of detergents for a cleansing action are beneficial. Prevention of low-temperature sludge necessitates the maintenance of coolant jacket temperatures of 160 to 180 F, oil temperatures of about 180 F, and high intake-manifold temperatures. Frequent oil and oil-filter element changes, adequate crankcase ventilation, good carburetor and air-filter adjustment and conditions, and minimum idling of engine are beneficial.

Regulation

Speed and load regulation are usually obtained in Otto-cycle engines by throttling the charge, or **quantitative** governing. The air-fuel ratio may vary depending on the carburetor characteristics. Throttling restricts the flow of charge into the cylinder, reduces the suction pressure, increases the pumping work, and consequently decreases the efficiency of the engine. It is the simplest means for regulation and the most satisfactory for this type of engine.

Qualitative governing is used in some cases with constant-speed gas engines. The fuel is throttled while the air is unrestricted. Qualitative governing is limited by the lean limit of flammability. In addition, lean mixtures burn slower than chemically correct mixtures and lower the thermal efficiency of the engine. Advancing the ignition timing, as the mixture is made leaner, reduces this loss of efficiency.

Governing by **variation of ignition timing** is undesirable since this is regulation by variation of thermal efficiency and may result in overheating the engine and burning the exhaust valves. Variation of ignition timing is required for each change in speed and load to obtain optimum results (see Ignition and Spark Advance, p. 9-133).

Diesel engines have qualitative governing by varying the amount of fuel injected into the engine cylinder. Theoretically, the highest indicated thermal efficiency is obtained with the smallest amount of fuel injected. Actually, maximum economy based on engine output usually occurs at about 80 percent of the rated load.

ANALYSIS OF THE ENGINE PROCESS

Air-standard Analysis. The theoretical indicated thermal efficiency η_a of the air-standard Otto cycle depends only on the volumetric compression ratio r_c (Sec. 4).

$$\eta_a = 1 - (1/r_c)^{0.4} \tag{1}$$

For the Diesel cycle,

$$\eta_a = 1 - (r_d^{1.4} - 1)/[1.4r_c^{0.4}(r_d - 1)] \tag{2}$$

where r_d is the volumetric expansion ratio during the constant-pressure combustion.

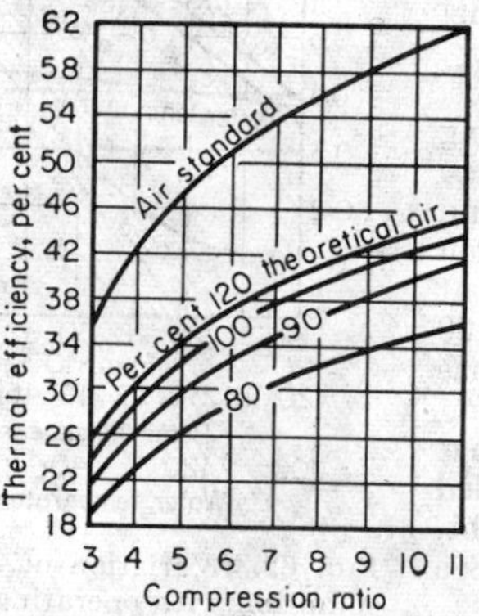

FIG. 63. Indicated thermal efficiencies of the ideal Otto cycle with liquid iso-octane as fuel.

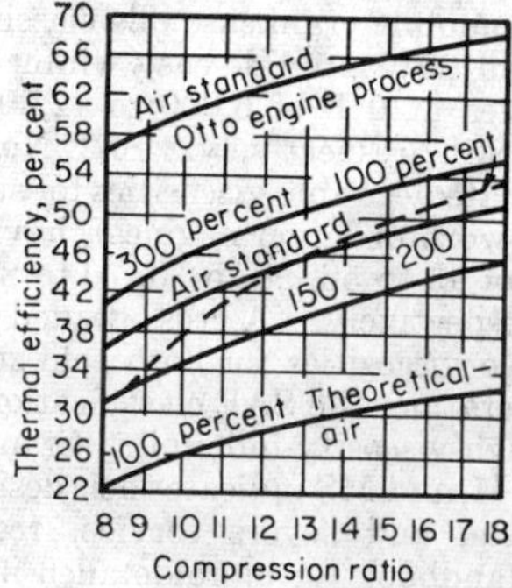

FIG. 64. Indicated thermal efficiencies of the ideal Diesel cycle with constant-pressure combustion and liquid dodecane as fuel.

The efficiencies indicated by the air-standard analysis are much higher than can be attained, principally because of variable specific heats, dissociation, and heat-loss.

The **mean effective pressure** is equal to net work divided by displacement. **Horsepower** follows from

$$\text{hp} = (\text{mep})Lan/33{,}000 \tag{3}$$

where mep = mean effective pressure, psi
L = stroke, ft
a = net piston area, sq in.
n = number of cycles completed per min

(See also p. 4-27 *et seq.*)

Increasing the compression ratio and the air-fuel ratio increases the thermal efficiency (Fig. 63). Liquid fuel was used in computing data for Fig. 63, it being assumed that no heat was supplied before the mixture entered the cylinder. This results in higher volumetric efficiencies than when supplying the engine with a vaporized fuel.

The thermal efficiency with maximum power mixture (90 percent theoretical air) is represented very closely by the equation

$$\eta_{\text{max power}} = 1 - (1/r_c)^{0.22}$$

and the thermal efficiency at maximum economy mixture (120 percent theoretical air) is represented very closely by the equation

$$\eta_{\text{max economy}} = 1 - (1/r_c)^{0.257}$$

Increasing the compression ratio and the air-fuel ratio also increases the thermal efficiency of the Diesel cycle with constant-pressure combustion (Fig. 64). Mean effective pressures depend on charge input and thermal efficiency, both of which depend on compression ratio and air and fuel supply (Figs. 65 and 66).

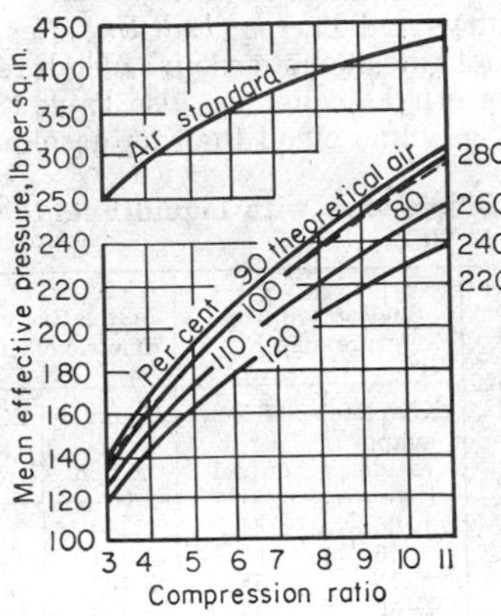

FIG. 65. Mep for Otto-cycle engine (air and liquid iso-octane supplied at 60 F).

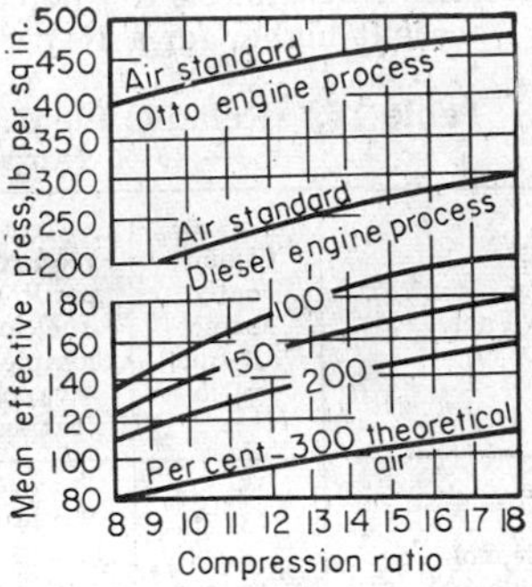

FIG. 66. Mep for Diesel-cycle engine (air and liquid dodecane supplied at 60 F).

Deviations from Ideal Processes

Changes in atmospheric pressure and temperature change power output although not appreciably affecting thermal efficiency. The standard correction formula adopted by the SAE for brake power output is

$$\text{Bhp}_s = \text{Bhp}_o\,(P_s/P_o)\,\sqrt{T_o/T_s}$$

where subscripts o and s indicate observed and standard conditions, respectively.

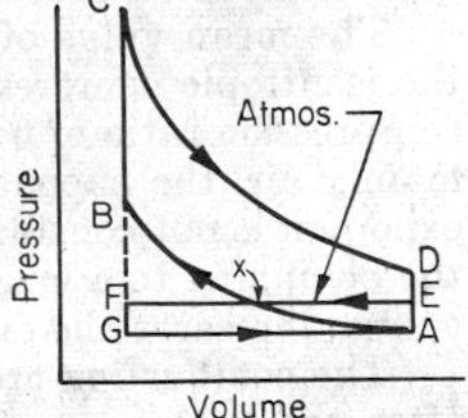

FIG. 67. Throttled Otto cycle.

Pumping work (area *EFGAE*, Fig. 67) is required to overcome the resistance to flow of fresh charge into and exhaust products out of the cylinder. It varies from almost 0 for an engine running at slow speed with wide-open throttle to about 3 psi mep at high speed, and to 10 psi with idle throttle position. The negative loop (area *AXFGA*, Fig. 67) in the normally aspirated engine is about 60 percent of the pumping work.

Volumetric efficiency is the ratio of the volume of air (for a liquid-fuel engine) and charge (for a gas engine) actually admitted, measured at atmospheric pressure and temperature, to the displacement volume. High manifold and cylinder temperatures and resistance to flow reduce volumetric efficiency. High-output aircraft engines have maximum volumetric efficiencies of 85 to 90 percent at rated speeds. Supercharged engines may have volumetric efficiencies well above 100 percent or may be designed to maintain high volumetric efficiencies with an increase in speed.

Volumetric efficiencies of automobile engines (Fig. 68) diminish appreciably as piston speeds exceed 1,200 to 1,600 fpm, decreasing to about 60 percent at top speeds of 2,500 to 3,200 fpm. These vary appreciably with valve timing.

Two-cycle crankcase compression engines have volumetric efficiencies of about 60 percent at low speeds and 50 percent or below at high speeds.

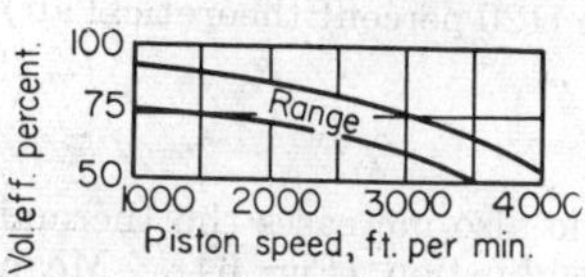

Fig. 68. Volumetric efficiencies of normally aspirated engines with poppet valves.

According to Ricardo ("The High-speed Internal-combustion Engine," p. 211, 1953) for poppet-valve engines, the volumetric efficiency, expressed as a function of mean gas velocity through inlet valves, is 70 (80) [60] percent at 40 (140) [240] fps.

Fuels with high latent heats and low boiling temperatures reduce the charge temperature and result in high volumetric efficiencies (Table 15).

Tests by Ziurys and Phelps (*Ind. Eng. Chem.*, **28,** 1936, p. 1094; **29,** 1937, p. 495) using ethyl alcohol and alcohol-gasoline blends resulted in volumetric efficiencies 5 to 7 percent higher for ethyl alcohol (see also Table 15), and about 1 percent higher for a 10 percent alcohol-gasoline blend than for gasoline.

Table 15. Relative Ideal Volumetric Efficiencies with Liquid Fuels

(Air and liquid fuel at 60 F)

Fuel	Chemically correct air-fuel ratio	Heat required per lb of fuel for complete evaporation	Percent evap with 200 Btu supplied per lb of fuel	Suction temperature, deg F		Relative volumetric efficiency	
				Complete evaporation	200 Btu per lb of fuel	Complete evaporation	200 Btu per lb of fuel
Gasoline	15.11	330	81	106	81	100	100
Benzene	13.26	149	100+	50	68	111	103
Ethyl alcohol	8.99	425	55	71	55	107	105
Methyl alcohol	6.46	519	49	68	45	108	107

Suction producers, air cleaners, governors, and carburetors increase the resistance to flow and decrease the volumetric efficiency.

The **compression stroke** begins with heat transfer from the cylinder walls to the charge but ends with heat transfer from the charge to the walls. The net result is a heat loss of about ½ to 1½ percent of the heat value of the charge. Heat loss during compression lowers the compression curve and work, but lowers the expansion work a greater amount, thus slightly reducing the net work output.

The mean value of the exponent in the approximate equation pv^k = constant for the isentropic compression of a correct mixture of octane and air is about 1.33 for a compression ratio of 6:1. For the Diesel cycle in which the gas under compression is mainly air, the exponent is about 1.38 for a 15:1 compression ratio. Actually, the exponent is not constant during the compression, but decreases from a higher value at the beginning to a lower value at the end of the compression. Heat transfer into the charge increases the exponent, but leakage lowers its value.

The **combustion process** begins before the end of the compression stroke and ends after the beginning of the expansion stroke. Rassweiler, Withrow, and Cornelius (*Trans. SAE*, **34,** 1939) found a maximum variation of 30 percent in combustion time for a single-cylinder engine, due probably to cyclic variation of air-fuel ratio, homogeneity of mixture, and turbulence. Poor distribution in multicylinder engines would cause greater variation in combustion time. Marvin (*NACA Rept.* 276, 1927) has shown that the loss due to the actual combustion time is 3 to 6 percent of the ideal efficiency with constant-volume combustion. Any energy liberated before or after top center piston position has an availability corresponding to the expansion ratio for the piston position at which the energy is liberated. Heat loss during the combustion process amounts to 5 to 7 percent of the heat supply of the charge at rated outputs and speeds for automotive engines.

Flame Travel. Flame begins at the spark plug in the spark-ignition engine or at various points in the combustion chamber of the compression-ignition engine and travels in all possible directions through the mixture. At the end of combustion, a temperature difference exists between the first and last part of the charge to burn except in the constant-pressure process. Rassweiler and Withrow (*Trans. SAE*, **30,** 1935, p. 125) observed temperature differences of over 400 F (non-knocking) and over 600 F (knocking) in a non-turbulent combustion chamber.

The combustion of part of the charge compresses the remainder. Thus with 30 percent of the mass burned, the volume of the unburned portion will be about 35 percent of the total volume. The temperature of the last fraction to burn in a constant-volume process will ordinarily be about 500 F above its temperature at the beginning of combustion.

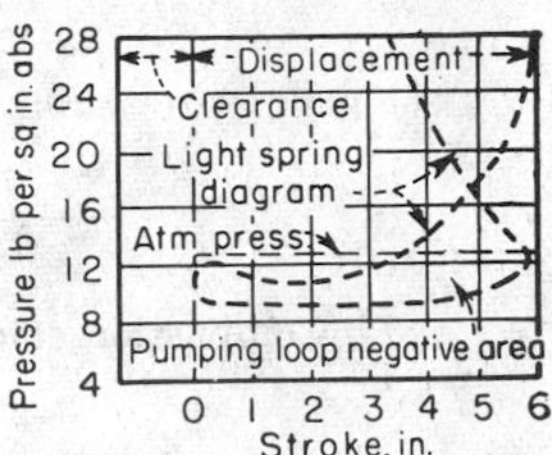

FIG. 69. Pumping loop of Otto-cycle engine.

The mean adiabatic exponent for the **expansion process** is about 1.22, varying from about 1.20 at the beginning to 1.25 at the end of the process. Heat transfer and leakage increase the exponent, an average value of 1.33 being found by Rassweiler and Withrow (*Trans. SAE*, **33,** 1938, p. 185) in an L-head 2⅞ in. by 4¾ in. cylinder. The heat transfer during the expansion stroke amounts to 8 to 12 percent of the heat value of the charge. Since heat loss occurs during the entire stroke, that part of the loss which could have been transformed into work is equal to about 40 percent of the ideal thermal efficiency of the engine.

Release begins at 80 to 90 percent of the expansion stroke. This reduces the work about 1 to 2 percent. High gas velocities (1,200 to 1,500 fps) are attained and heat transfer, including that through exhaust-port walls, amounts to 10 to 20 percent of the heat value of the charge but represents practically no loss of work or availability.

The **exhaust process** is the discharging of some of the gases from the cylinder by the piston. The exhaust pressure is usually above atmospheric (Fig. 69) but may run below atmospheric for part of the stroke. Heat loss during exhaust amounts to 3 to 5 percent of the heat value of the charge but does not represent any loss of work or

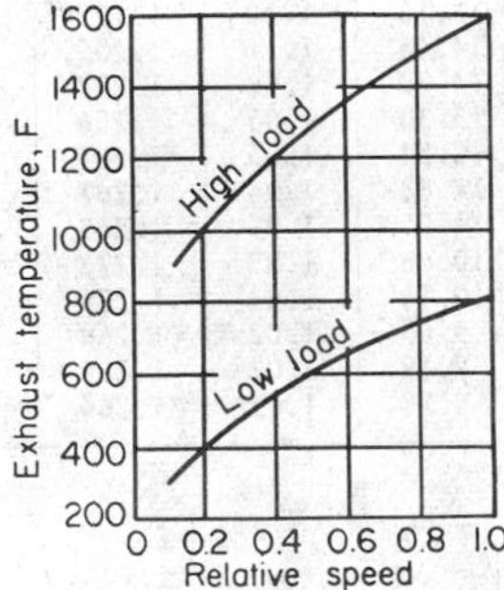

FIG. 70. Exhaust temperatures for Otto-cycle engines.

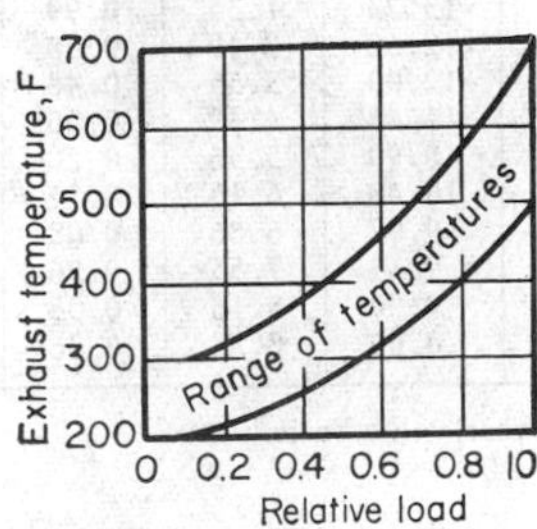

FIG. 71. Exhaust temperatures for Diesel-cycle engines.

availability. About 80 percent of the gases in the cylinder escape during release, and about 15 percent are pushed out of the cylinder during exhaust, the remainder being left in the clearance space at the end of the exhaust stroke.

Exhaust-gas temperatures vary with speed and load (Figs. 70 and 71), high loads and speeds resulting in the highest temperatures. The first gases escaping during release are at the highest temperature. The mean exhaust-gas temperature is obtained from the energy equation for the release and exhaust processes.

$$E_e + W_{exh} = H_{exh} + Q_{out}$$

where E, W, H, and Q are internal energy, work, enthalpy, and heat transfer, respectively, subscript e referring to Figs. 1 and 2.

Exhaust-gas temperatures are used for determining load distribution between the cylinders of a multi-cylinder Diesel engine.

Exhaust-gas Analysis. Gerrish and Tessmann (*NACA Rept.* 476, 1933) found $H_2 = 0.51CO$ and $CH_4 = 0.22$ percent in the exhaust gases when using several grades of aviation gasoline and Diesel fuels having an H/C value of 0.175. Gerrish and Voss (*NACA Rept.* 616, 1937) developed the following relationships which can be evaluated from Orsat determination of percentage of CO_2 and O_2 in the products.

$$\frac{\text{Air}}{\text{Fuel}} = 1.523\left(\frac{102.350 + O_2 + 2.056CO_2}{21.139 - O_2 - 0.491CO_2}\right)$$

$$\frac{\text{Water}}{\text{Fuel}} = 0.680\left(\frac{20.562 - O_2 + 0.391CO_2}{21.139 - O_2 - 0.491CO_2}\right)$$

$$\text{Combustion efficiency} = 0.370\left(\frac{20.74 - O_2 + 1.079CO_2}{21.11 - O_2 - 0.491CO_2}\right)$$

The relation for combustion efficiency (ratio of actual energy liberation to maximum possible energy liberation) does not include the heat of vaporization of the H_2O in the exhaust gases.

Table 16 gives a summary of the principal exhaust-gas constituents and combustion efficiency (see also D'Alleva and Lovell, *Trans. SAE,* **31,** 1936, p. 90; and Graf, Gleason, and Paul, *Ore. State Agr. Coll. Bull.* 4, 1934).

Table 16. Summary of Exhaust-gas Constituents and Combustion Efficiency
(Gerrish and Voss)

Air/Fuel	Percent by volume						H_2O/CO_2	H_2O/Fuel	Combustion[a] eff, percent
	CO_2	O_2	CO	H_2	N_2	H_2O			
11	8.76	0.15	9.14	4.66	77.08	13.78	1.57	0.972	66.7
12	10.18	0.44	6.65	3.39	79.13	13.93	1.37	1.043	73.8
13	11.60	0.59	4.31	2.20	81.09	14.16	1.22	1.122	81.5
14	13.02	0.63	2.09	1.07	82.99	14.46	1.11	1.205	89.6
15	13.23	1.35	0.99	0.50	83.72	14.09	1.06	1.247	93.8
16	12.62	2.49	0.68	0.35	83.65	13.30	1.05	1.256	94.8
17	12.00	3.55	0.48	0.25	83.51	12.54	1.05	1.261	95.5
18	11.45	4.49	0.30	0.16	83.39	11.88	1.04	1.267	96.2
19	10.90	5.36	0.20	0.10	83.23	11.25	1.03	1.269	96.5
20	10.40	6.15	0.11	0.06	83.07	10.68	1.03	1.272	96.9
21	9.92	6.86	0.08	0.04	82.90	10.16	1.03	1.271	96.9
22	9.44	7.55	0.06	0.03	82.71	9.65	1.02	1.268	96.8
23	9.00	8.18	0.05	0.03	82.53	9.19	1.02	1.266	96.7
24	8.60	8.74	0.06	0.03	82.37	8.78	1.02	1.264	96.6

[a] Low-heat-value basis.

Special Developments

Compounding the internal-combustion engine has been attempted at various times but without commercial success so far (see Sperry, *Trans. ASME,* 1921). Considerable heat loss occurs in transferring the gases from the high- to the low-pressure cylinder. This reduces appreciably the possible work output in the low-pressure cylinders. Compounding also increases the back pressure in the high-pressure cylinder and reduces its output.

Compounding by the use of an exhaust-gas turbine for the purpose of supercharging the engine (see p. 9–136) is practicable and is in use. More energy is available in the engine exhaust than is required for supercharging. Consequently, aircraft engines have been directly connected to gas turbines with a resulting gain in power output and increase in thermal efficiency. Optimum pressure between the engine and the turbine varies with altitude and other conditions but is much nearer the ambient pressure than the pressure in the cylinder when the exhaust port opens.

Waste heat is frequently recovered from the jacket water and exhaust gases by the use of exhaust-heat boilers. Cast iron is the best material for an exhaust-gas heat exchanger. Care must be taken to avoid restriction of the gas passage since each pound of back pressure decreases the engine output 1 to 2 percent. The area of the heating surface varies from 1 to 2 sq ft per hp, and the heat transfer is about 1100 Btu per sq ft per hr at rated load. The heat-transfer coefficient varies from 1 to above 2 Btu per sq ft per hr per deg F temperature difference. If the exhaust gas heater is used to evaporate water, about 2 lb of steam can be generated per bhp-hr at any moderate pressure.

The **Humphrey gas pump** is a combined internal-combustion engine and pump in which the metal piston has been replaced by a column of water. The inertia of the water takes the place of the flywheel and maintains the necessary cyclic periodicity. Both two- and four-cycle operation are used. Four-cycle Humphrey pumps are fitted with an interlocking gear arranged between the inlet and the exhaust valves so that when either one closes, it locks itself closed and releases the other one.

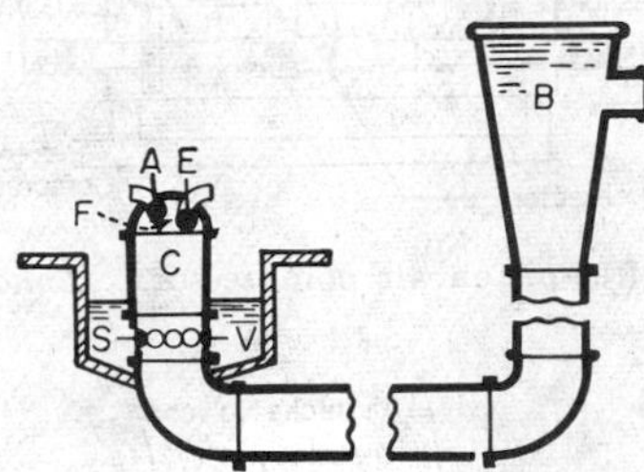

FIG. 72. Humphrey gas pump.

In the **four-cycle pump** (Fig. 72), water has to be raised from a suction tank S to an elevated tank B; the cycle of operations is as follows:

1. All valves are closed when an explosion of the compressed charge occurs, driving water out of the combustion chamber C and setting the whole water column in motion, raising the water into B. The inertia of the water column reduces the gas pressure below atmospheric, opening exhaust valves E and inducting water through valves V.

2. The column of water reverses its motion and the gases are exhausted through valves E which close when the water reaches them. The remaining gas is compressed in clearance space F and the column motion is reversed.

3. When the water level falls below valve E, the spring-loaded intake valve A opens and a fresh charge is admitted.

4. The return of the water column compresses the combustible charge which is ignited and the cycle is repeated.

The maximum lift of the simple pump is about 40 ft. Under this condition the compression pressure may equal the explosion pressure, depending on the fuel.

For information on the **Stirling-cycle** (Wankel) engine, see p. 4–29.

Free-piston Compressors and Gas Generators

Free-piston motion is controlled completely by the gas pressure in the cylinders, the pistons being connected only by a synchronizing mechanism which drives the fuel-injection pump and any other accessories. The power section is usually an opposed-piston (inherently vibrationless), two-stroke Diesel engine, each power piston being directly connected to a compressor piston. The power output of the engine section is absorbed directly by the compressor section.

The compressor section may supply compressed air from one side of the compressor piston and scavenging air for the Diesel cylinder on the other side (free-piston compressors, Fig. 73); or the compressed air is used only to scavenge and supercharge (60 psia) the engine which has an exhaust back pressure slightly below the scavenge pressure. The excess scavenge air is mixed with the Diesel exhaust to provide hot (900 F) gas under pressure (free-piston gas generators, Fig. 74) to a gas turbine which provides the power output (see also pp. 9–150 *et seq.*).

The frequency of oscillation of the free piston (cycles per second) is a function of (spring effect of gas pressure/mass of pistons)$^{1/2}$. Since the spring effect is proportional to compressor discharge pressures which range from >1 to about 4 atm, the idling frequency (about 400) will be greater than 50 percent of maximum frequency (about 600 for a Sigma Model GS-34), indicating relatively high idling friction losses. Also, since bounce, air-box, and engine exhaust pressures must be increased to increase the output, there is an appreciable lag (seconds) between increasing the fuel injected and obtaining the increased output because the compressor must increase all of the pressures indicated.

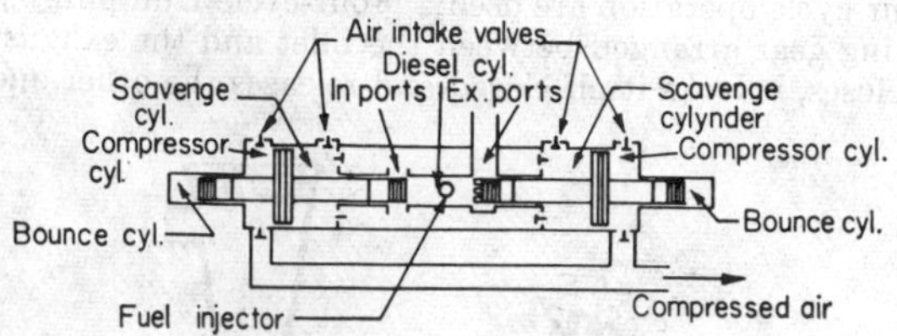

FIG. 73. Unsupercharged free-piston air compressor. (*London and Oppenheim, Trans. ASME*, **74**, 1952, *p.* 1349.)

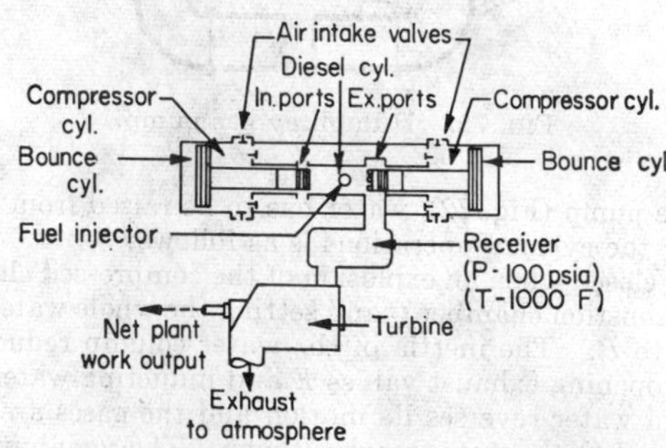

FIG. 74. Supercharged free-piston engine. (*London and Oppenheim.*)

The stroke of the GS-34 free-piston generator (about 18 in.) decreases with a decrease in load since the combustion process does not accelerate the piston as fast as at high load (high frequency). However, because of the effect of large clearance volume in the compressor cylinders, a relatively small decrease in stroke (10 to 20 percent) reduces the power appreciably (about 60 percent).

The actual volumetric compression ratio in the Diesel-engine cylinder at full load is usually less than 10:1 for the supercharged engine. However, the over-all compression ratio is usually between 20:1 and 25:1, the compressor volumetric compression ratio being less than 3:1. Since engine compression ratio is not fixed, appreciably higher compression ratios may be used for starting.

The gas horsepower of the generator is based on the ideal adiabatic isentropic enthalpy drop from generator supply conditions (about 60 psia and 900 F) to atmospheric pressure. This indicates ideally 106 Btu of work per lb of medium, based on air only. Turbine losses reduce this to about 90 Btu.

Cooling losses are lower or higher than 20 percent of the calorific value of the fuel for the larger and smaller engines, respectively. About 25 percent of the cooling loss appears in the piston cooling oil.

The high output of the supercharged free-piston Diesel (imep >200 psi) increases the heat load on the engine pistons, and, since only the lubricant consumed is fed to the cylinder walls, the lubrication of these pistons and rings is more difficult than that of the usual Diesel engine.

Specific fuel consumptions of 0.38 lb of fuel per shaft hp-hr (compared to 0.32, best Diesel performance) have been reported in Europe, while values for experimental engines in the United States range from 0.40 to 0.43 lb per shaft hp-hr. The high temperatures and pressures of the compression process in the Diesel cylinders make this engine less critical of fuel type and result in more complete combustion than obtained in other engines.

Pescara started the development of free-piston engines in France in 1922, and SIGMA (Société Industriale Générale de Méchanique Appliqué) has built about 1,500 Model P13 (5 in. power-piston bore) air-compressor units, and about 1,000 of Model GS-34 (13.4 in. power-piston bore) free-piston gas generators. The principal engine applications have been in the marine field and central power stations. Only one locomotive application has been reported, although others are planned. General Motors has built about eight of these gas generators and also has built a 200-hp experimental automobile free-piston engine. Ford Motor Co. has built a small free-piston engine.

GAS TURBINES

BY

Reeves Morrisson

REFERENCES: Vincent, "The Theory and Design of Gas Turbines and Jet Engines," McGraw-Hill. Zucrow, "Principles of Jet Propulsion and Gas Turbines," Wiley. Journal of Engineering for Power, *Trans. ASME*, series A, **81**, 1959. "Bibliography on Gas Turbines," ASME Gas Turbine Power Div., 1962. *The Gas Turbine Catalog*, Gas Turbine Publications, Inc., annual.

GAS-TURBINE CYCLES

The basic gas-turbine cycle (Fig. 1) is the Brayton, or Joule, cycle (see p. 4–28), consisting of adiabatic compression, constant-pressure heating, and adiabatic expansion. By adding a **regenerator** (Fig. 2) to recover heat from the turbine exhaust, the

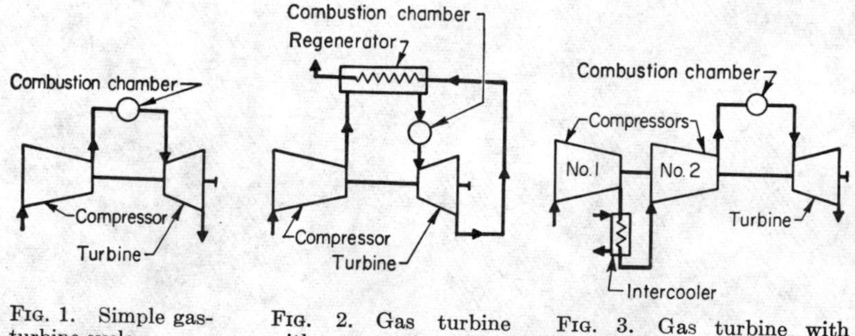

FIG. 1. Simple gas-turbine cycle.

FIG. 2. Gas turbine with regeneration.

FIG. 3. Gas turbine with intercooling.

efficiency is improved. The additions of **intercooling** (Fig. 3) in the compressor and **reheat** (Fig. 4) of the working fluid during expansion increase the output of a given-size gas turbine, and with the addition of a regenerator a further improvement is made in efficiency. The explosion or constant-volume combustion cycle was used in early gas turbines (Holzwarth) but is not suited to a continuous-flow turbine process and results in very complicated machinery.

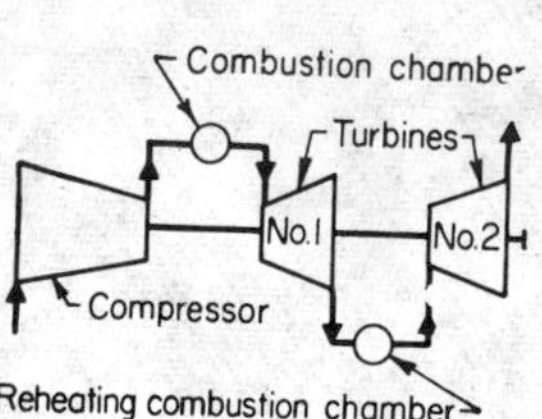

FIG. 4. Gas turbine with reheating.

Figure 5 shows the influence of the **pressure ratio** on the performance of the simple gas-turbine cycle for turbine inlet temperatures of 1200, 1500, and 1800 F. The curves are based on ambient inlet conditions of 80 F and 1,000 ft altitude, 85 percent compressor efficiency, 90 percent turbine efficiency, 95 percent combustion efficiency, and 5 percent combustor pressure loss.

Figure 6 shows the influence of pressure ratio on plant efficiency for various gas-turbine cycles. The gas-turbine cycles are (I) the simple Brayton gas-turbine cycle; which is combined (II) with 80 percent regeneration; (III) with intercooler; (IV) with reheat; (V) with intercooler and 80 percent regeneration; (VI) with reheat and 80 per-

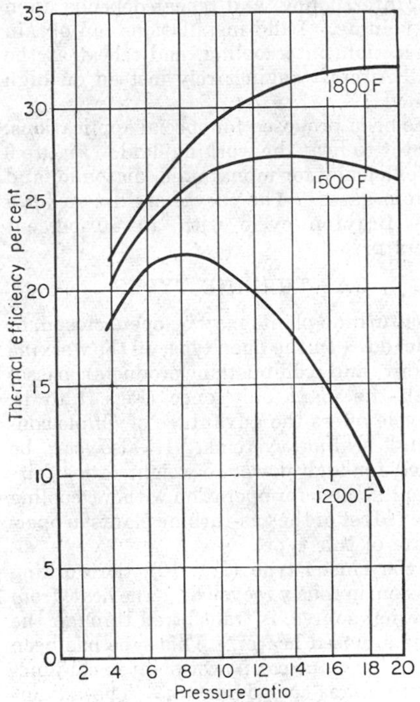

Fig. 5. Effect of pressure ratio on thermal efficiency for a simple gas-turbine cycle at various turbine inlet temperatures.

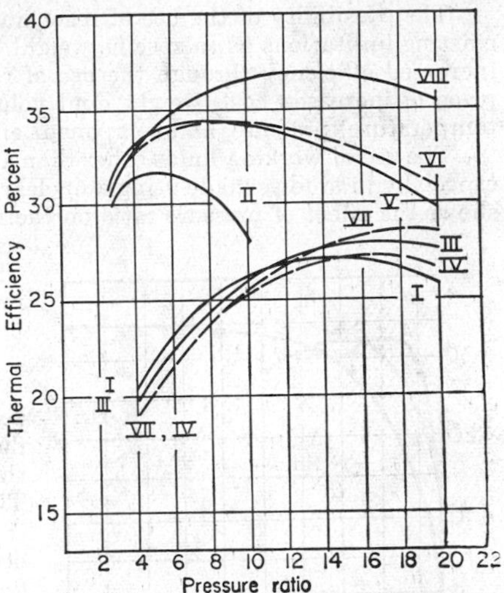

Fig. 6. Effect of pressure ratio on thermal efficiency for various gas-turbine cycles.

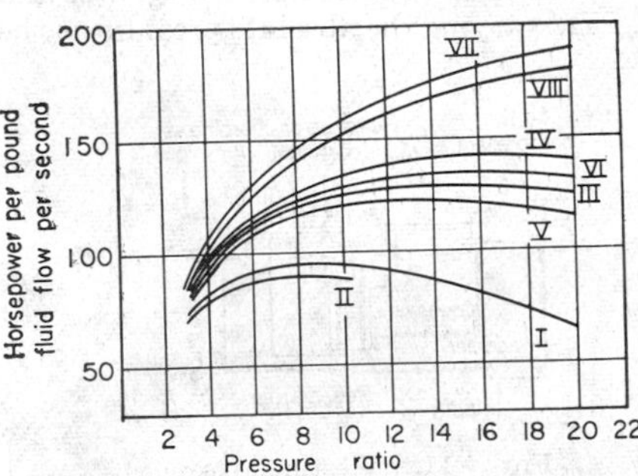

Fig. 7. Effect of pressure ratio on the net energy per pound of working fluid.

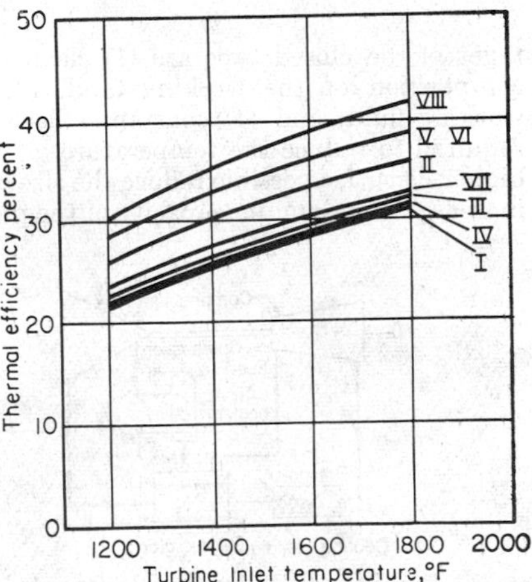

Fig. 8. Effect of turbine inlet temperature on thermal efficiency for various gas-turbine cycles.

cent regeneration; (VII) with intercooler and reheat; and (VIII) with intercooler, 80 percent regeneration, and reheat. The curves are drawn for turbine inlet temperatures of 1500 F, reheat to 1500 F, and 4 percent total pressure loss through the regenerator. The **horsepower** developed per pound of fluid flow per second is shown in Fig. 7. The effect of turbine **inlet temperature** on plant efficiency for the various gas-turbine cycles is shown in Fig. 8. The curves are drawn for the optimum pressure ratio for each cycle at the various turbine inlet temperatures.

The possibility of the use of regeneration, intercooling, and reheat depends upon existing limitations as to specific weight and volume. Land installations can obtain increased efficiency through the use of regeneration, intercooling, and reheat at the price of increased cost, weight, and volume. Aircraft engines rely instead on high temperature, pressure, and component efficiency.

The use of **working fluids** other than air has been proposed for special applications, especially in studies made using a nuclear reactor to heat the working fluid. Figure 9 shows the effect of pressure ratio on thermal efficiency for monatomic, diatomic, and triatomic gases. The curves are drawn for a simple Brayton cycle with an 80 percent regenerator.

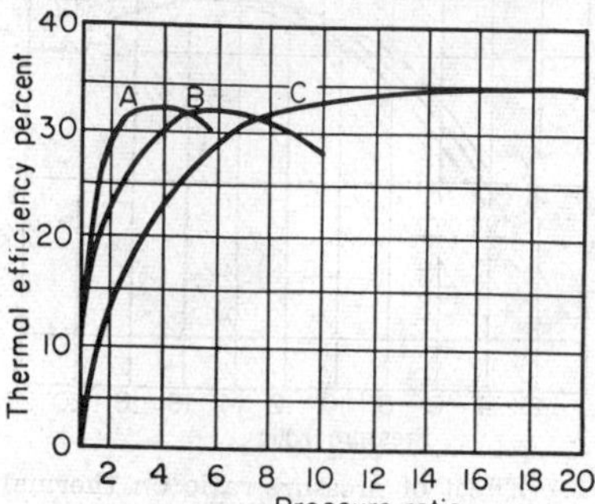

FIG. 9. Effect of pressure ratio on thermal efficiency for various working fluids: (*A*) monatomic gas, $k = 1.67$; (*B*) diatomic gas, $k = 1.40$; (*C*) triatomic gas, $k = 1.28$.

GAS-TURBINE TYPES

Gas-turbine plants may be **open, closed,** or **semiclo•ed.** In the **open type,** all the working fluid (air and combustion products) passes through the plant only once (Figs. 1 to 4). This cycle offers the advantage of simple control and sealing systems. It also can be designed for high power-to-weight ratios (aircraft units) and for operation without cooling water. Most of the gas-turbine plants in operation are of this type.

In the **closed type** (Fig. 10), the working fluid is continuously recycled. The heat, from an external source, is transferred through the walls of a closed heater. This type has been proposed for a nuclear power plant in conjunction with a gas-cooled reactor. The advantages of the closed type are (1) clean working fluid, (2) control of the pressure and composition of the working fluid, (3) high absolute pressure and density of the working fluid, and (4) constant efficiency over a wide load range. A precooler is required to reduce the temperature of the working fluid before recompression. The higher densities possible reduce the size of compressor and turbine per horsepower and increase the maximum capacity of the plant. By varying the absolute pressure at the compressor inlet, the weight of working fluid circulated may be varied at will without changing the compression ratio or the temperatures, so that a wide range of load can be carried at practically constant speed and efficiency. The major disadvantage of this cycle is the size and cost of the required high-temperature heater.

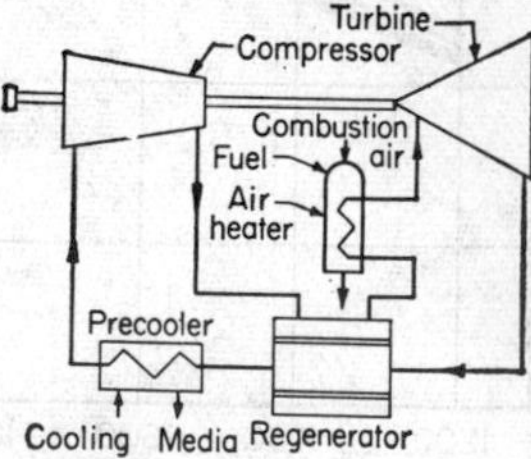

FIG. 10. Closed-cycle gas turbine.

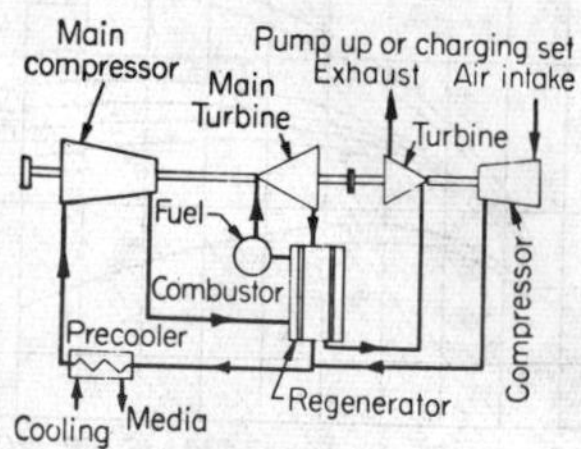

FIG. 11. Westinghouse semiclosed internally fired gas-turbine cycle.

In the **semiclosed type** (Fig. 11), approximately two-thirds of the working fluid is recirculated. This type requires a precooler for the recirculated gas, like the closed type, and a "charging" compressor to provide the necessary air for combustion. This "charging" compressor is driven by a turbine utilizing the working fluid from the cycle.

The semiclosed cycle similar to the closed type can be operated at high densities and approximately constant efficiency over a wide load range. The major disadvantage of this type is the corrosion and fouling problems which occur with the recirculation of the products of combustion, particularly when fuels are used having high sulphur or high ash content.

GAS-TURBINE COMPONENTS

Compressors may be of any high-efficiency type (see pp. 14–55 *et seq.*). The displacement varies from 8 to 20 cfm of working fluid per horsepower. The power absorbed by the compressor is two to four times the net output of the plant. Axial-flow compressors are used on all larger gas-turbine units because of their high efficiency and capacity. They have been constructed in sizes handling airflows up to 300,000 cfm. Axial compressors used in gas-turbine power plants must be designed to avoid operation in the instability (pumping) region. A number of high-pressure-ratio gas-turbine plants have compressors which are operated in this region during starting and low-load and low-speed operation. To avoid compressor instability under these conditions several methods are used: interstage bleed, discharge bleed, variable compressor inlet vanes, turbine variable vanes, and bypass. Centrifugal compressors are used mainly on the low-flow, low-pressure-ratio units. Centrifugals are more stable than axials but not as efficient.

Turbines used in the gas-turbine plant are almost all axial flow, except for a few smaller sizes which are radial inflow. Unlike most steam turbines, all the high-performance gas turbines have blading which varies in the degree of reaction from hub to tip so as to satisfy radial equilibrium conditions. This means that a gas-turbine blade will appear as an impulse section at the hub and as a reaction section at the tip. The average degree of reaction varies for different units. Gas turbines have been built using both air and liquid cooling, to permit higher operating temperature or the use of less critical materials.

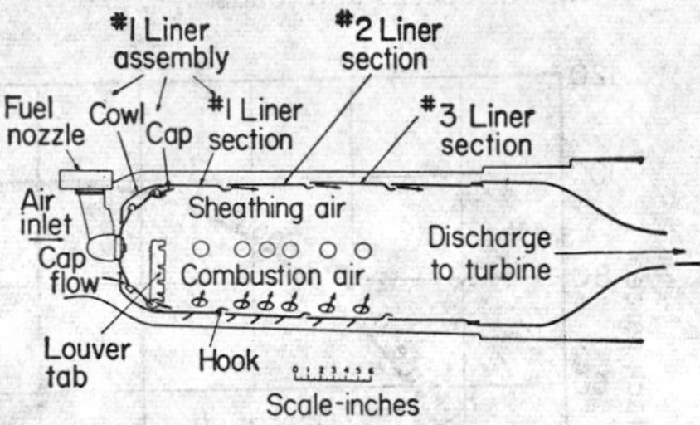

Fig. 12. Cross section of metal-cooled combustor arranged for residual oil firing.

The **combustion chamber,** or **combustor,** must bring the gas to a controlled uniform temperature with a minimum of impurities and a minimum loss of pressure. In the open-type gas turbine, the large excess of air must be controlled to avoid chilling the flame before complete combustion has taken place. Extremely high rates of combustion are common, the heat release being 1 to 5 million Btu per cu ft per hr per atm, or from 5 to 20 times that of high-output steam-boiler furnaces. The major problems of combustor design, in addition to clean combustion and proper mixing of the gases, are flame stabilization; elimination of pulsations and noise; reduction of pressure loss; and maintenance of steady, closely controlled outlet temperature. The high velocities and violent pulsations prevent the use of refractories in combustion chambers. Metal walls and baffles, cooled by the incoming air, are common practice. Gas-turbine power plants are arranged with either single or multiple combustors. The single-combustor design is easier to control but is larger and less compact than the multiple type. Figure 12 shows the cross section of a typical cooled metal-wall combustor.

Heat exchangers, or **regenerators,** for transferring heat from the turbine exhaust to the air leaving the compressors, are most useful in increasing efficiency but increase the weight, volume, and cost of a gas-turbine plant. They must withstand rapid large-temperature changes and must have low pressure drop. Their large size makes them unsuitable for aircraft. Compressor intercoolers are subject to the same limitations as regenerators and in addition require a supply of cooling fluid. In an effort to reduce the size of heat exchangers, extended surface designs have been used. Rotary regenerators offering high performance and low weight are under development.

GAS-TURBINE ARRANGEMENTS

The various gas-turbine cycles and types can be constructed for single- or multiple-shaft arrangements. The **single-shaft** machines are the simplest, with all rotating elements operating as a single assembly. Figures 1 to 4 show various cycle arrangements of single-shaft machines. This type is best suited for constant speed and load operation. Figure 13 shows a typical load-speed range for a single-shaft machine. The minimum operating speed is set by the stall (pumping-limit) characteristic of the compressor. The maximum power is set by the maximum allowable gas-turbine inlet temperature. The **multiple-shaft** machines may have a separate output turbine in

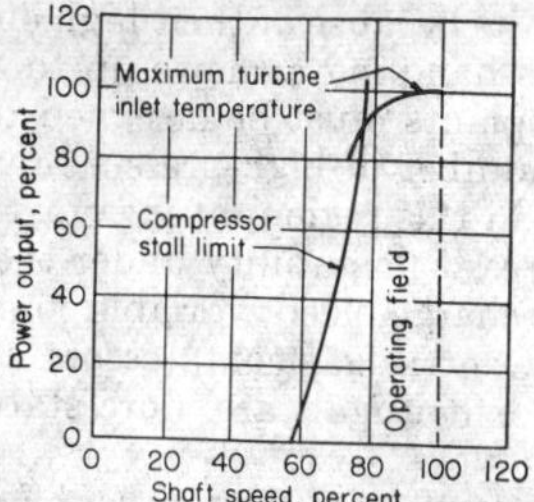

FIG. 13. Single-shaft gas-turbine operating range for various speeds and loads.

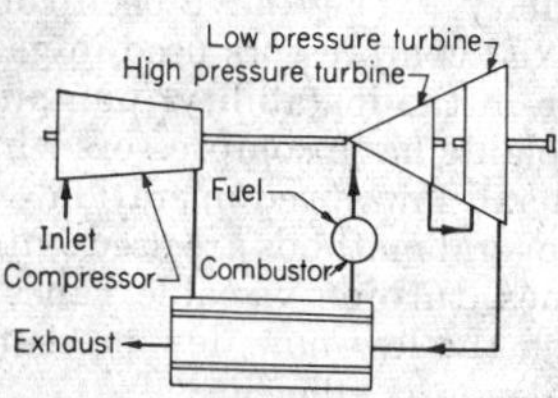

FIG. 14. Regenerative cycle gas turbine, two-shaft arrangement with separate power turbine in series.

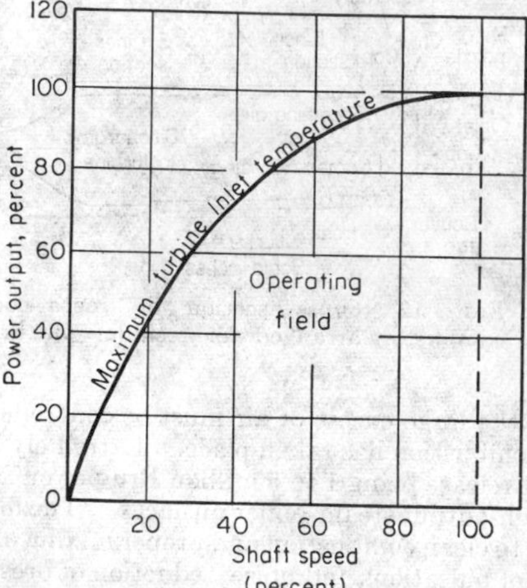

FIG. 15. Two-shaft gas-turbine operating range for various speeds and loads.

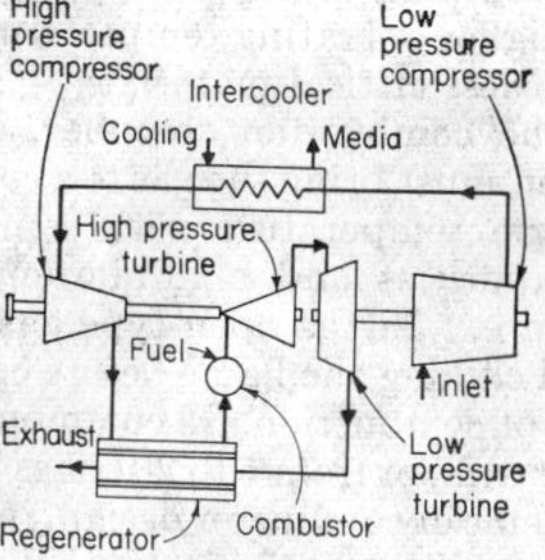

FIG. 16. Regenerative, intercooled gas turbine with two-shaft arrangement.

series or parallel, with one or more turbines driving the compressor. The latter may operate at any speed desired, independent of the output turbine. Figure 14 illustrates a two-shaft arrangement with the power turbine in series. The major advantage of the multiple-shaft arrangement is the wide load-speed range possible, as shown in Fig. 15. This makes it most suitable for mechanical-drive application where variable speed and load operation are required. Figure 16 shows a regenerative, intercooler gas turbine with a two-shaft arrangement. The high-pressure turbine drives both the load and the high-pressure compressor, while the low-pressure turbine drives the low-pressure compressor. Multiple-shaft units can be arranged for improved part-load thermal efficiency.

The **aircraft jet engine** is a compressor-combustor-turbine system whose output is in the form of a high-energy exhaust stream. With the addition of a separate power turbine in series, as in Fig. 14, it provides an extremely light and compact source of power. The availability of well-proved jet engines in a wide range of power has led to extensive use of this arrangement for industrial purposes.

The **fan engine** is a development of the simple jet engine in which a large-diameter-compressor stage is added to pump additional air for propulsion. The additional air does not go through the main engine. The turbine must be enlarged to provide power to drive the fan, and the thrust of the main jet is thereby reduced, but the net effect is increased thrust and improved efficiency (Figs. 17 and 18).

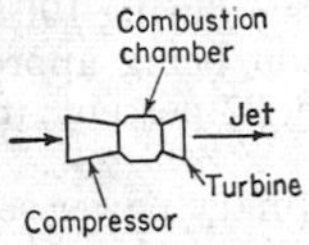

Combustion chamber
Jet
Turbine
Compressor

Fig. 17. Jet engine.

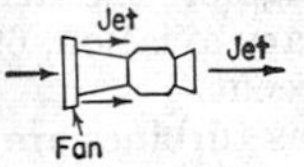

Jet
Jet
Fan

Fig. 18. Fan engine.

GENERAL CHARACTERISTICS

In its simplest form (Fig. 1), the gas turbine is small and light, requires only a modest foundation and building, does not require cooling water, runs unattended, and can be remotely controlled. It is capable of rapid start-up and loading, low standby losses, low maintenance, and long life. The simple-cycle gas turbine has good efficiency at full load when operating temperature and pressure ratio are high (Fig. 5); but as load is reduced, the efficiency falls. Efficiency can be maintained in a multiple engine installation by cutting out engines as the load is reduced. A relatively flat efficiency curve can be obtained at the cost of some complexity using regeneration and regulation of airflow by variable-area turbine nozzles or variable supercharging (Fig. 19).

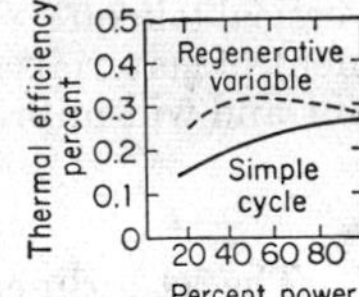

Fig. 19. Efficiency at part load.

Gas turbines can be arranged to supply power, high-pressure air, or hot exhaust gases either singly or in combination. They have been used in the Houdry process to charge the catalytic cracking reactor and in Velox boilers to pressurize the furnace. The exhaust gases are used in many installations to make steam for process use. This flexibility of application is a characteristic feature of the gas turbine.

FUELS

(See also Sec. 7)

The open-cycle gas turbine, where the products of combustion come in direct contact with the turbine blades, requires a fuel in which the products of combustion are free of high-temperature ash corrosion or deposition and the residual solids are small enough to avoid erosion. Natural gas, refinery gas, blast-furnace gas, and distillate oil have proved to be ideal fuels for gas turbines. Combustion-chamber and fuel-nozzle maintenance are negligible with these types of fuel. Residual fuel oil, treated to avoid hot-ash corrosion and deposition, is also satisfactory, although it requires frequent cleaning of fuel nozzles and higher combustor maintenance. Vanadium pentoxide and sodium sulphate are the principal ashes that cause corrosion and deposition in the 1250 to 1500 F temperature range. The most successful method of overcoming this problem is to eliminate the maximum amount of sodium by water washing and then to treat the oil with additives, such as magnesium oxide, magnesium sulphate, and aluminum silicate. Such treatment systems are in successful commercial operation and appear economically feasible. It should be pointed out that the corrosion-deposition problem in utilizing residual fuels is not unique to the gas turbine but is a function of operating temperatures. As temperatures are increased in other types of power plants to the present gas-turbine level, similar problems can be expected if present-day untreated residual fuels are used. (See also p. 9–16.)

The B of M is continuing work on using pulverized coal as fuel. Eliminating the solid ash to avoid erosion is the major problem. Other developments abroad are also directed toward utilization of coal. Escher-Wyss, Zurich, has placed in operation a series of closed-cycle units burning pulverized coal.

APPLICATIONS

About 85 manufacturers, concentrated in the principal industrial countries, but mainly in the United States and England, produce over 500 models of gas-turbine engines, covering the range from 50 to nearly 50,000 hp. Gas turbines have been used most successfully in rather large sizes and especially in aviation.

Worldwide sales of large gas turbines (5,000 hp and over) during 1964 totaled well over 3,000 engines, the distribution by field of application being approximately as follows: military aviation, 69 percent; commercial aviation, 27 percent; industrial and marine, 4 percent.

Smaller gas turbines are used in large numbers for auxiliary power services—electricity and compressed-air supply—predominantly in aviation.

Military Aviation

(See also Sec. 11)

New military aircraft are almost exclusively gas-turbine-powered. Simple-cycle engines producing shaft power are used for helicopters and to drive propellers in small or moderate-speed aircraft. Most combat types now in use have jet engines, often using afterburning (reheat ahead of the jet nozzle) to get up to 100 percent additional thrust for short periods. The fan engine is increasingly favored for both long-range and fighter aircraft. Future trends in military aircraft are toward higher speed and vertical takeoff. Both require the use of higher turbine-inlet temperature. Development of materials and design techniques for higher temperature will permit higher output and will improve thermal efficiency (Fig. 5).

Commercial Aviation

(See also Sec. 11)

The jet airliner has demonstrated exceptionally high utility and profitability due in large part to the good reliability record and low operating cost of the turbojet and turbofan engines. This in turn has contributed to very rapid growth of commercial aviation. Revenue passenger-miles were 50 billion in the United States in 1963, up 15 percent over the previous year.

Propeller, fan, and jet-type engines are in use, with the trend more and more to the fan engine and to higher power. Engines rated at 20,000 lb of thrust are in general use, and engines of twice this rating are planned. The fastest-growing segment of commercial aviation is **air cargo,** carried to a large extent in passenger aircraft. Specialized, very large cargo aircraft powered by very large gas turbines are forecast.

Electric Generation

Over half the large industrial gas turbines are in electric-generating use. Electric-utility companies in the United States use gas turbines for **peak-load** duty primarily. Installed and operating costs, even when using refined fuels, are favorable for such intermittent duty, and gas turbines are well suited to automation and remote control. Aircraft engines adapted for this service offer very rapid start-up—as short as 2 min from start to full load. Peak-load power plants up to 120 mW have been ordered, with a single generator driven by a battery of engines.

Gas turbines are used for **base-load** electric generating where additional capacity is needed quickly, where refined fuel, such as natural gas, is available at low cost, or where turbine-exhaust energy can be utilized. Combining the gas turbine with a steam power plant makes possible improved efficiency. Various combinations are possible, *e.g.*, (1) gas-turbine exhaust for feedwater heating; (2) turbine-exhaust heat-recovery boilers; (3) fuel-fired boilers, with gas-turbine exhaust as combustion air; and (4) supercharged boilers, in which the high-pressure boiler becomes the combustor of the gas-turbine unit. Figure 20 is a cycle diagram of a **combined steam and gas-turbine** plant where the gas turbine is used to supply preheated combustion air to the boiler. Figure 21 shows the possible gain in over-all plant heat rate over a conven-

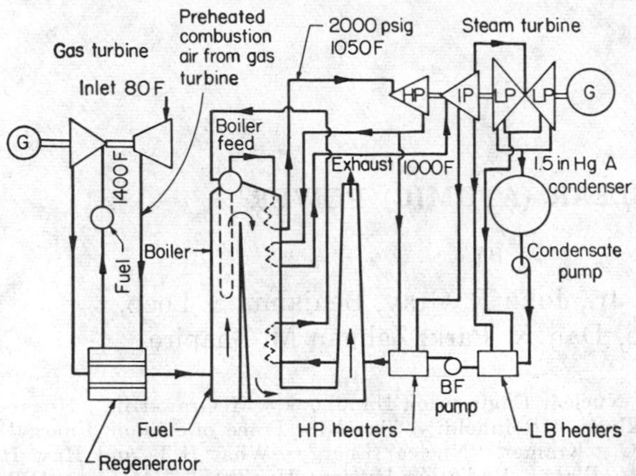

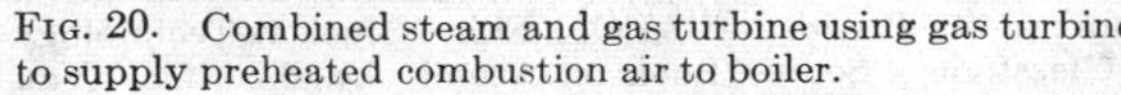

FIG. 20. Combined steam and gas turbine using gas turbine to supply preheated combustion air to boiler.

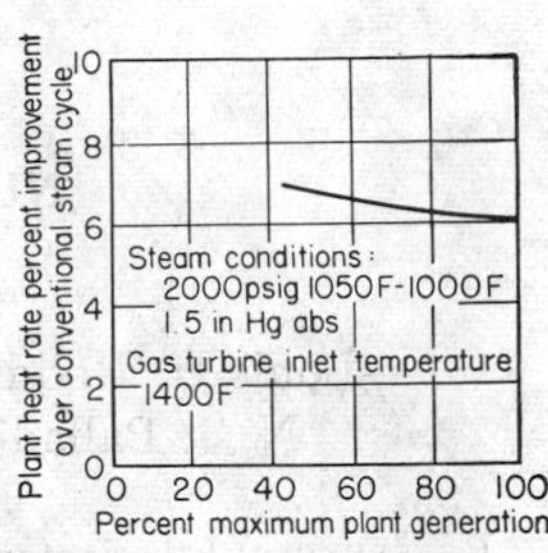

FIG. 21. Over-all plant efficiency improvement using combined steam and gas-turbine cycle as compared to conventional steam plant.

tional steam plant designed for 2,000 psi, 1050 F inlet temperature, with reheat to 1000 F and 1.5 in. Hg back pressure, when using a combined cycle as shown in Fig. 20.

Gas Pipeline Transmission

(See also p. 11–180 *et seq.*)

This industry is a major user of gas turbines—about one-third of all industrial units of large size. Gas turbines have been installed as compressor drives in sizes up to about 13,000 hp. This is an excellent application for the gas turbine since natural gas is an ideal fuel and large powers are required. Simple-cycle and regenerative engines are used about equally in this duty.

Transportation

(See also Sec. 11)

The Union Pacific Railroad operates a fleet of gas-turbine **freight locomotives** now totaling 55 units of 4,500 hp and 8,500 hp. These engines burn a selected grade of residual fuel. The Union Pacific has also operated, on an experimental basis, a locomotive burning powdered coal. **Railcars** powered by small gas turbines appear to be practical and are under study for passenger transportation.

The British Navy has pioneered in the use of gas turbines, used together with steam or Diesel power plants, in fast **motor-torpedo boats** and in larger warships. Problems of saltwater corrosion were encountered but now seem under control. A Danish **frigate,** a German **light cruiser,** and a U.S. **Coast Guard cutter** are also planned for gas-turbine-*cum*-Diesel power. The U.S. Navy is testing several sizes of modified aircraft engines preparatory to their use in ships.

There is great interest in the possibility of applying gas turbines to **automobiles.** The major auto companies have engines under development and vehicles under road test.

Other

The gas turbine is a key element in what have come to be known as **total-energy** units. In such systems, waste-heat recovery supplies heat or refrigeration which, together with electrical power from the engine itself, can furnish all the energy needs for a shopping center, institution, or factory.

In addition to pumping natural gas in pipelines, gas turbines are used extensively in the **petroleum industry** for such applications as compressor and pump drive in refineries and oil-well pressurization.

The **steel industry,** especially in Europe, uses, gas turbines burning blast-furnace gas for driving electric generators and compressors.

NUCLEAR (ATOMIC) POWER

BY

Louis H. Roddis, Jr., John E. Gray, Benjamin S. Loeb, N. J. Palladino, Dan K. Park, Zalman M. Shapiro

REFERENCES: Etherington, "Nuclear Engineering Handbook," McGraw-Hill. Hogerton, "The Atomic Energy Deskbook," Reinhold. "The New Force of Atomic Energy" and "Reactor Handbook," AEC. Kramer, "Nuclear Energy—What It Is and How It Acts," Technical Publishing Co. Blatz, "Radiation Hygiene Handbook," McGraw-Hill. "Civilian Nuclear Power—A Report to the President," AEC. Ellis, "Nuclear Technology for Engineers," McGraw-Hill. Glasstone, "Source Book on Atomic Engineering," Van Nostrand. Murray, "Nuclear Reactor Physics," Prentice-Hall. "Nuclear Terms—a Brief Glossary," AEC.

FISSION AND FUSION ENERGY

Nuclear power is the energy derived from the fission (or splitting) of the nuclei of heavy elements, such as uranium or thorium, or from the fusion (or combining) of the nuclei of light elements, such as deuterium or tritium. Particles set in motion by these processes yield heat energy virtually instantaneously. The amount of energy released per atom exceeds by a factor of several million the amount of energy obtainable per atom in a chemical reaction, such as the burning of fossil fuels. While control of the fusion process is still surrounded by tremendous technical problems, considerable success has been achieved in utilizing heat energy produced by fission for power generation, propulsion, industrial production, and scientific experiments.

NUCLEAR PHYSICS

A nuclear reaction occurs when the particles making up the nucleus of an atom are rearranged—as distinct from a chemical reaction, which is caused by changes in the electron structure surrounding the nucleus. To understand nuclear reactions fully requires some understanding of fundamental particles, of quantum mechanics, of the relationship between mass and energy, and of the processes involved in electricity, magnetism, light, and X rays.

Fundamental (elementary) particles are, theoretically, the irreducible constituents of the material world. All particles of each kind are identical to one another. There are 31 particles currently (1964) regarded as elementary, but with the advance of experimental techniques, more particles are discovered, and with the advance of theory, more particles can be understood as being compounds of particles. For example, atoms and atomic nuclei were at one time believed to be non-composite. Except for the electron and proton, all the fundamental particles are unstable.

An **electron** carries one unit of negatively charged electricity (defined as 1.6×10^{-19} coul) and has a mass at rest equal to $1/1836 \times$ the mass of the hydrogen atom. Electrons emitted by radioactive atoms are called **beta** (β) **rays** and have energies up to several mev (million electron volts).

A **proton** carries one unit of positively charged electricity equal in magnitude to that of the electron and has a mass, at rest, of 1.0075 atomic mass units (amu when 1 amu is defined as $\frac{1}{16} \times$ the mass of a neutral atom of the most abundant isotope of oxygen). It is identical to the nucleus of the hydrogen atom. Protons are not a constituent of radioactivity since these particles are not emitted spontaneously from atomic nuclei.

A **neutron** has a mass approximately equal to that of the proton but lacks an electric charge, a property which enables it to pass through matter with relative ease. It cannot be detected by the ordinary method of subjecting it to electric or magnetic fields, nor can its presence be shown by its passage through cloud chambers. The only way the presence of neutrons can be shown is by their interaction with other particles.

An **atom,** which is the basic unit of any chemical element, consists of a central nucleus surrounded by planetary electrons. The number of its electrons determines its chemical characteristics and also the positive charge on its nucleus (always equal to the sum of the negative charges of the surrounding electrons). The nuclei of all atoms except the hydrogen atom are composed of protons and neutrons. The nucleus of the hydrogen atom consists of a single proton, which gives it an atomic number of 1. This number is designated by the letter Z. The number of neutrons in the nucleus is represented by the letter N. From this it follows that the mass number A, which represents the atomic weight, is equal to $N + Z$. In writing the symbols for the various atoms, it is usual to write the atomic number (Z) as a subscript before the chemical symbol of the element and the atomic weight (A) as a superscript. There are 103 elements currently (1964) known. All with atomic numbers above 92 (uranium) must be produced artificially and have a short half-life.

Isotopes are elements which have identical chemical characteristics but varying atomic weights; *i.e.*, certain atoms of the same element have varying numbers of neutrons in their nuclei. There are considerably more than a thousand isotopes of the known elements. Only 320 of these exist in nature, of which approximately 40 are unstable and radioactive.

For example, hydrogen has three isotopes. One is ordinary hydrogen with a proton nucleus. Another is deuterium, whose nucleus consists of a proton and a neutron. The third is tritium, which consists of one proton and two neutrons. At the heavy end of the natural periodic table is uranium, with 92 protons. When it has 146 neutrons, it is ${}_{92}U^{238}$, which comprises 99.28 percent of natural uranium. The remainder of natural uranium consists of 0.006 percent U^{234} and 0.71 percent U^{235}. The latter isotope, with 92 protons and 143 neutrons, is the only one of the three which is readily fissionable and is the one utilized in most of the nuclear-power reactors operating in the United States. It is separated from the natural element in the enrichment desired by a gaseous diffusion process in government facilities.

Energy and mass are used interchangeably in nuclear physics, and the total energy of a nucleus can be determined by measurement of its exact mass m, which is related to its energy E by the Einstein equation $E = mc^2$, where c is the velocity of light, 3×10^{10} cm per sec. This law of equivalence of mass and energy unifies two long-accepted laws: the conservation of energy and the conservation of matter. Singly, the two older laws must be regarded as high-order approximations, adequate in all engineering fields except atomic energy. The exact mass m of a nucleus differs by only a few hundredths of a percent from an integral number A of proton masses. It is, however, just this small deviation which is of significance for nuclear theory since it measures the difference in energy between the nucleus and its separate components, *i.e.*, its binding energy. The energies of nuclides are recorded in the tables in terms of their masses.

Precision measurement of m is made by means of the mass spectograph. Physical atomic weights do not quite equal chemical atomic weights because the oxygen used in the chemical determinations is a mixture of isotopes, whereas in mass-spectographic measurements the single isotope O^{16} is used for reference. The relationship is: Physical atomic wt $= 1.000279 \times$ chemical atomic wt.

QUANTUM FIELD THEORY

The **nuclear cosmos** involves a number of fields which have no classical counterparts and which require, in description, an infinite set of variables. Since radiation has the properties of both waves and particles, it is theorized that in the emission or absorption of energy by atoms or molecules, the process takes place by steps, each step being the emission or absorption of an **indivisible quantity of electromagnetic energy,** which is considered the elementary quantum of action. It is known as **Planck's**

constant and has the value $h = 6.624 \times 10^{-27}$ erg-sec. It is used in virtually all quantum relationships, including Schrödinger's equation and Heisenberg's uncertainty principle, and in the formula for the energy levels of atomic hydrogen. The standard notation is $\hbar = h/2\pi$.

Relativistic Mass. When moving particles approach the speed of light, the classical formula for kinetic energy, $\frac{1}{2}m_0v^2$, fails; it then becomes necessary to use the equation $E = mc^2$ and to use the relativistic mass, a mass that increases with velocity according to the law $m = m_o/\sqrt{1 - (v/c)^2}$, where m_o is the rest mass (*i.e.*, the mass of Newtonian mechanics) and v is the velocity of the particle.

If the formula for m is substituted in $E = mc^2$ and the expression expanded by the binomial theorem, the first two terms of the series give

$$E = m_oc^2 + \frac{1}{2}m_ov^2$$

which expresses the total energy as the rest-mass equivalent plus the kinetic energy of classical mechanics. This is generally adequate up to about one-tenth the velocity of light.

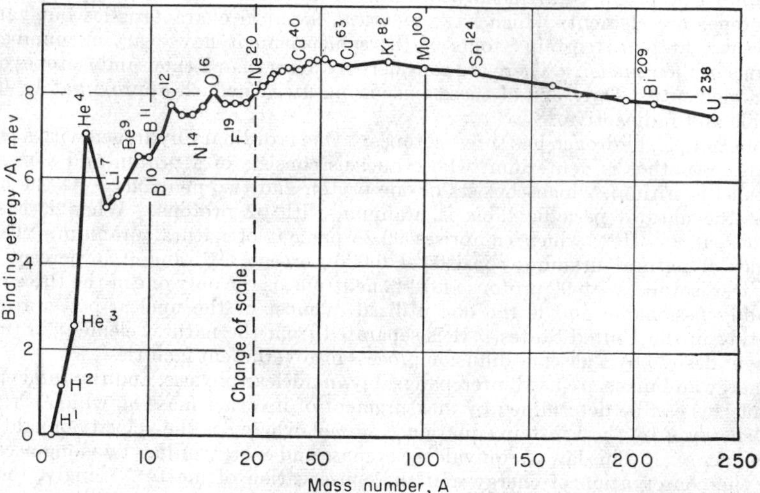

FIG. 1. Binding energy per nuclear particle for stable nuclei.

On the other hand, a 3.1-mev beta particle has a velocity of 0.99c; the two-term expansion gives $E \approx 1.5m_oc^2$, whereas the true expression gives $E \approx 7m_oc^2$.

Binding energy is the work required to disintegrate an atom completely into Z protons and A–Z neutrons. It is a measure of the total kinetic and potential energy of the nucleons in the nucleus and may be calculated from the equations

$$B = c^2\Delta$$
$$\Delta = Zm_H + (A - Z)m_n - m$$

where m is the mass of the nuclide, m_H the mass of the hydrogen atom, and m_n the mass of the neutron, all on the physical atomic-mass scale (amu). The quantity of Δ is known as the **mass defect.**

The energy involved is of such magnitude that it usually is stated in mev. It is 931 mev times the mass defect and, for all but the lightest nuclides, is approximately 8 mev, as indicated in Figure 1.

Fusion. Figure 1 shows that if two deuterium (H^2) nuclei react to produce one He^3 nucleus plus one neutron, the total binding energy of the four particles (two neutrons plus two protons) involved in the reaction is increased from approximately 4.4 mev to 7.6 mev, releasing 3.2 mev for the reaction. Such a process is called **fusion.**

The deuterium-deuterium fusion reaction may also produce an H^3 plus an H^1 nucleus, with a release of 4.0 mev.

For fusion to occur, the two nuclei must approach each other with exceptionally high kinetic energy in order to overcome their electrostatic repulsion; and since kinetic energy is proportional to absolute temperature, effective fusion can occur only at extremely high temperatures. For fusion to continue as a chain reaction, it is further necessary that nuclear collisions be sufficiently frequent to maintain the high temperature in spite of heat radiation. The condition necessary for frequent collisions is high pressure.

A light-element chain reaction is the principal source of heat in the sun, hydrogen being converted to helium as the net result of a multistage process. The temperature and pressure at which this reaction is sustained at the center of the sun are 35 million F and 1.5×10^{11} psi, respectively.

A deuterium-deuterium reaction can be sustained at temperatures and pressures which are considerably lower than those in the solar reactions but still fantastically high by terrestrial standards. Achievement of a controlled light-element chain reaction for power generation by fusion depends on producing high particle velocity and high density locally by electromagnetic means, without development of correspondingly high temperatures and pressures at the container walls.

Fission is the division of an atomic nucleus into parts of comparable mass, either naturally (spontaneously) or under bombardment (induced) with neutrons, α particles, γ rays, deutrons, or protons. While it can be induced in most elements with $Z > 30$, it is only for $Z > 90$ that fission is produced by neutrons of low or moderate energy and with appreciable cross sections.

The practical importance of fission lies in the fact that in the process neutrons are emitted that may, under certain conditions, be utilized to produce further fissions, thus leading to a self-sustaining, or "chain," reaction. It is thus possible to "burn" uranium to obtain an energy release per atom approximately 10^8 greater than from a chemical fuel. The energy release in the fission of U^{235} is:

	mev
Kinetic energy of fission products	168
Kinetic energy of fission neutrons	5
Energy of γ rays	10
Energy of β rays	5
Energy of neutrinos	11
Total	199

The total of 199 mev is equivalent to 3.2×10^{-11} watt-sec, which indicates that it requires the fissioning of 1.12×10^{17} atoms to release a kilowatt-hour of energy. Even though a hundred million billion atoms appear to be a large number, actually they would be only a speck of matter six-thousands of an inch in diameter.

Radioactivity occurs when an unstable nucleus undergoes atomic disintegration by emitting particles or electromagnetic radiation. There are three decay chains of primary interest for nuclear power. U^{238} is the first member of a chain which, after emitting eight β particles and six γ particles, terminates as a stable isotope of lead (Pb^{206}). Similar chains begin with U^{235} and Th^{232} and terminate as Pb^{206} and Pb^{208}, respectively.

The **alpha** (α) **particle** is identical with the nucleus of a helium atom. The emission of an α particle creates a new nucleus, with Z reduced by 2 and A decreased by 4 mass units.

Beta (β) **decay** involves emission of an electron from the nucleus of an atom, thereby increasing Z by unity.

The **gamma** (γ) **ray** is electromagnetic radiation originating in the nucleus—as differentiated from X rays, which usually are less energetic and arise from energy adjustments as electrons move between orbital shells outside the nucleus. Gamma rays are emitted instantaneously when a neutron is captured in a nucleus and are frequently emitted following ejection of a particle from a radioactive nucleus.

The **positron** ($\beta+$) is a particle whose mass is the same as that of an electron and whose charge is equal in magnitude but opposite in sign. Positron emission decreases Z by unity.

Electron capture (EC) results when an unstable atom decays by capturing an orbital electron in the nucleus, resulting also in a decrease of Z by unity. This capture produces a vacancy in the orbital shell which is filled by an electron moving from an outer shell, giving rise to X-ray characteristics.

Half-life is the time required for half the original nuclei in a sample of any isotope to decay; it is given as $0.693/\lambda$ sec. Half-lives of the radioactive nuclides vary from 10^{-7} sec to 10^{10} years.

NUCLEAR-REACTOR DESIGN

Neutron Balance. A nuclear reactor operates by means of the neutrons produced by fissioning. When the reactor is operating at steady state, the number of neutrons produced by fissioning is equal to the neutrons lost either by absorption or by leakage. If this neutron balance is disturbed, the density of neutrons in the reactor increases or decreases. The net rate of change of neutrons per unit volume n is given by

$$\partial n/\partial t = \text{production} - \text{absorption} - \text{leakage}$$

If $\partial n/\partial t$ is positive, the reactor is said to be **supercritical**; if it is negative, the reactor is said to be **subcritical**; if it is equal to zero, the reactor is at steady state and is said to be **critical.**

The terms on the right-hand side of the equation represent a number of competing processes: absorption of neutrons by uranium to produce fission, absorption of neutrons by uranium without producing fission, non-fission absorption by other materials or impurities in the reactor, and escape of neutrons from the reactor. All the absorption processes are evaluated in terms of cross sections for the different processes; the leakage is generally evaluated by diffusion theory.

Cross Section. The cross section for a particular nuclear process is the effective target area of the nucleus with which a neutron must interact to produce the given reaction. Cross sections are of two kinds: scattering and absorption. Scattering can be either elastic or inelastic; absorption can result either in fissioning (if the absorption takes place in a fissionable material) or in some other process of transformation such as radioactive decay.

Cross sections are generally measured in square centimeters or **barns.** A barn is 10^{-24} sq cm and represents the order of magnitude of the geometric cross section of a nucleus. Scattering cross sections are generally of the order of a few barns and do not vary greatly with the energy of the impinging neutron. Absorption cross sections, however, extend over a wide range of values and vary greatly with neutron energy. Aside from specific resonance peaks, absorption cross sections, including absorption cross sections for fission, usually have their highest values for slow-speed neutrons. Typical of slow-speed neutrons are those whose speed has been reduced to a value corresponding to the thermal activity of surrounding nuclei; they are called **thermal neutrons.** Absorption cross sections for thermal neutrons range from 0.00046 barns for deuterium to 3.2×10^6 barns for xenon^{135}. Table 1 gives thermal-neutron cross sections in barns for selected elements; these values are based on a thermal energy of 0.0253 ev (velocity 2200m per sec, or 1.4 miles per sec).

The values given in Table 1 are based upon the naturally occurring combinations of isotopes. Individual isotopes may have markedly different cross sections. The isotope U^{235}, for example, has an absorption cross section for all absorption processes

Table 1. Absorption (σ_α) and Scattering (σ_s) Cross Sections for Thermal Neutrons

Element	σ_α	σ_s	Element	σ_α	σ_s	Element	σ_α	σ_s
Aluminum	0.23	1.4	Helium	0.007	0.8	Potassium	1.97	1.5
Beryllium	0.01	7	Hydrogen	0.33	38	Plutonium^{239}	1.026	9.6
Bismuth	0.032	9	Iron	2.53	11	Sodium	0.505	4.0
Boron	755	4	Lead	0.17	11	Thorium	7.56	12.6
Cadmium	2,550	7	Magnesium	0.063	3.6	Tin	0.6	4
Carbon	0.0032	4.8	Molybdenum	2.7	7	Titanium	5.6	4
Chromium	2.9	3.0	Nickel	4.6	17.5	Uranium	7.68	8.3
Copper	3.7	7.2	Niobium	1.1	5	Zirconium	0.18	8
Hafnium	105	8	Oxygen	<0.0002	4.2			

of 682 barns. Its fission-absorption cross section is 580 barns. Natural uranium, which consists of 99.3 percent U^{238}, has, on the other hand, an over-all absorption cross section of 7.68 barns.

Materials such as natural cadmium and boron have such high absorption cross sections that they are called **nuclear poisons.** These particular nuclear poisons are useful as materials for controlling reactors.

Macroscopic Cross Sections. The probability of a neutron hitting a target depends on the number of targets as well as the size of each target. The total effective target area of all nuclei within 1 cc is called the macroscopic cross section. Thus the macroscopic cross section, Σ, is given by $\Sigma = N\sigma$, where N is the number of nuclei per cc and σ is the cross section in sq cm for the particular process involved. The units of Σ are cm^{-1}. On the basis that one interaction takes place per neutron, Σ can be considered as the number of interactions per cm of track length of the neutrons of a given speed.

Neutron Flux and Interaction Rate. The neutron flux is the total track length that all neutrons travel within a cubic centimeter. If all neutrons are going at the same speed, it is equal to nv, the product of neutron density and velocity. Neutron flux has the units: neutrons/sq cm sec. The interaction rate per cc between neutrons of a given speed and the flux, ϕ, of neutrons of that speed is given by $\Sigma\phi$.

Moderation. The neutrons released from fission have an energy spectrum ranging from 1 to 10 mev, with a peak between 2 and 2.5 mev. For a 2-mev neutron, U^{235} has a fission-absorption cross section of a little over 1 barn, which is only about 0.2 percent of the value at thermal energy. Because of the improved fissioning probability at thermal energy, a reactor that operates with neutrons that are slowed down to thermal energy requires less U^{235} than one which operates with neutrons that are not slowed down.

The neutrons are slowed down by colliding with nuclei of the atoms. The material used to slow down the neutrons is called a **moderator.** Light elements serve best as moderators because their nuclear masses are close to the mass of the neutrons. Heavy elements are not good moderators because the inertia of a heavy nucleus would cause the neutron to rebound without appreciable loss of its incident energy.

A good moderator, besides being light, should have a low absorption cross section to avoid parasitic loss of neutrons, and it should have a good scattering cross section with a sufficient density or compactness of atoms to provide the necessary moderation. This latter requirement of density eliminates the use of gases, particularly hydrogen and helium, as moderators except at extremely high pressures. Hydrogen and its isotope, heavy hydrogen, can be used, however, in the form of water and heavy water. Among the remaining light elements which might be used for moderating are lithium, beryllium, boron, and carbon. Lithium and boron have high absorption cross sections and, therefore, can be eliminated. This leaves as the moderators of practical importance water, heavy water, beryllium and its compounds, and carbon as graphite or as carbides.

Multiplication Factor. The number of neutrons produced in any one generation in a reactor for each neutron produced in a previous generation is called the multiplication factor, k. If $k = 1$, the reactor is critical; if $k > 1$, the reactor is supercritical; if $k < 1$, it is subcritical. The value of k for an infinite reactor (known as k^∞) is different from the value of k for a finite reactor (called k_{eff}) by the fast-neutron non-leakage probability P_f and the slow-neutron non-leakage probability P_s. Hence, $k_{eff} = k^\infty P_f P_s$.

The value k^∞ is determined by evaluating the four factors which comprise it. These are η, the number of neutrons produced by fissioning for each neutron absorbed in fuel; ϵ, the total number of neutrons produced by fissioning (including slow and fast neutrons) per neutron produced by thermal fission; f, the thermal utilization, which is the number of thermal neutrons absorbed in fuel per thermal neutron absorbed in any material of the reactor; and p, the resonance escape probability, which is the probability of a neutron escaping resonance capture by U^{238} during the process of slowing down. The relationship between these factors is $k^\infty = \eta\epsilon fp$.

Diffusion Theory. Diffusion theory is often used to estimate the size and characteristics of nuclear reactors. It assumes that neutrons follow Fick's law of diffusion, namely, that if J is the net current of neutrons and D the diffusion coefficient, then $J = -D\nabla\phi$.

On this basis, the neutron-balance equation for thermal neutrons becomes

$$D\nabla^2\phi - \Sigma_a\phi + S = \frac{\partial n}{\partial t} = \frac{1}{v}\frac{\partial \phi}{\partial t}$$

The source term S can be evaluated by a number of different models, each of which exchanges simplicity for more precise description. These include **one-group theory,** in which neutrons are assumed to be born, live, and die (leak or be absorbed) as thermal neutrons; **two-group theory,** in which neutrons are characterized as either fast or slow and are described by two equations coupled to each other so that the absorption from the fast group becomes the source of neutrons for the thermal group and the fissions caused by the thermal group serve as the source of neutrons for the fast group; **multi-group theory,** which extends the two-group theory to include intermediate groups of neutrons; the **Fermi age theory,** based on a continuous-slowing-down concept; and a **modified one-group theory,** in which parameters of the one-group equation are modified by Fermi age approximations.

Breeding Ratio. U^{235} is the only naturally occurring nuclide which fissions when it absorbs thermal neutrons. Yet it forms only 0.7 percent of the uranium found, the other 99.3 percent being U^{238}. While the U^{238} does not fission with thermal neutrons, it can be transformed, by a process known as **breeding,** to Pu^{239}, which is **fissionable;** in a similar manner, Th^{232} can be transformed to U^{233}, which is also fissionable. Th^{232} and U^{238} are called **fertile materials.** The processes of transformation are

$${}_{90}Th^{232} + {}_0n^1 \rightarrow {}_{90}Th^{233} \xrightarrow[\text{half-life}]{23.3\text{ min}} \beta^- + {}_{91}Pa^{233} \xrightarrow[\text{half-life}]{27.4\text{ days}} \beta^- + {}_{92}U^{233}$$

$${}_{92}U^{238} + {}_0n^1 \rightarrow {}_{92}U^{239} \xrightarrow[\text{half-life}]{23.5\text{ min}} \beta^- + {}_{93}Np^{239} \xrightarrow[\text{half-life}]{2.33\text{ days}} \beta^- + {}_{94}Pu^{239}$$

Since from each fission at least one neutron must be retained for sustaining the chain reaction, breeding requires the release of at least two neutrons per neutron absorbed in fuel in addition to neutrons lost by leakage and by absorption in materials other than fuel or fertile materials.

Control. A practical reactor must contain more fuel than that just required for criticality. Extra fuel is required for depletion to compensate for fuel lost in producing energy, for the poison effects of fission products produced, and for temperature effects. The effect of this extra fuel must be neutralized until needed. This is usually done by means of control rods which contain a strong neutron absorber such as boron, cadmium, or hafnium. Control can also be accomplished by movement of fuel, moderator, or reflector. These rods are inserted to shut down the reactor and are withdrawn slowly to bring the reactor to criticality. Once the reactor is critical, the power level can be increased by withdrawing the rods somewhat further to make the reactor slightly supercritical. The power level then rises until the rods are reinserted to make the reactor just critical at the new power level. To lower the power level, the rods are inserted to make the reactor slightly subcritical so that the power starts to drop. When the desired power level is established, the rods are withdrawn to make the reactor critical again. The term **reactivity** is used to indicate departure from criticality. If ρ is used to indicate reactivity, $\rho = (k_{eff} - 1)/k_{eff}$.

Control rods are sometimes given special names to indicate specific uses. A rod used to make small adjustments in reactivity is called a **regulating rod.** Rods used to compensate for large, slowly varying reactivity changes, such as those brought about by depletion, are called **shim rods.** Rods used to provide rapid shutdown (known as a **scram**) are sometimes called **safety rods.** In some reactors, the same rods may perform more than one function.

The neutron lifetimes are so small in nuclear reactors (10^{-5} to 10^{-3} sec) that many generations of neutrons are formed in a second. If each generation is multiplied by a number only slightly greater than 1, the neutron density (and, hence, power level) would increase by a factor of several thousand or greater in a second; however, due to the fact that a small fraction of the neutrons (0.0065) is delayed (because they are produced by decay of certain fission products), the effective lifetime is increased so that control is relatively easy, provided k does not exceed 1.0065 (prompt control).

Thermal Design

Sources of Heat. The energy produced by fissioning appears in several forms, each of which eventually degrades to heat. To provide for removal of this heat, the core, or active portion of the reactor, usually consists of uranium-bearing fuel elements with passages around these elements for flow of coolant. The rate of coolant flow and the temperature of the coolant must be such as to permit removal of all the heat generated in the elements without exceeding allowable materials properties.

Hot-spot and Hot-channel Factors. The problem of heat removal is complicated by the fact that heat is not generated uniformly throughout the core. The basic power-generation pattern follows the neutron-flux pattern (Table 2). In addition, the power generation is influenced by mechanical factors such as variations in fuel-element dimensions, fuel concentrations, and flow. These nuclear and mechanical factors are

Table 2. Geometric Characteristics of Critical Bare Homogeneous Reactors

Geometry	B_g^2	Thermal flux shape	Minimum critical volume of extrapolated core
Infinite slab of thickness t	$(\pi/t)^2$	$\phi = \phi_0 \cos \pi x/t$	
Rectangular parallelepiped with radius a, b, and c	$(\pi/a)^2 + (\pi/b)^2 + (\pi/c)^2$	$\phi = \phi_0 \cos \pi X/a \cos \pi y/b \cos \pi z/c$	$161/B^3$
Sphere of radius R	$(\pi/R)^2$	$\phi = \phi_0 R/\pi r \sin \pi r/R$	$130/B^3$
Finite cylinder of radius R and height H	$(2.405/R)^2 + (\pi/H)^2$	$\phi = \phi_0(\cos \pi z/H)[J_0(2.405r/R)]$	$148/B^3$*

* $H/R = 1.84$.

Practical Consideration: The foregoing computational techniques are based on assumptions of homogeneity and uniformity. No reflectors are considered present, yet the characteristics of reactors can be markedly improved by reflectors. These characteristics are also influenced by fine structure within the core. More inclusive computational techniques exist and are used for design work.

generally called **hot-spot factors.** Thus, the peak power density or heat flux in the core is greater than the average by an amount indicated by the hot-spot factor. In addition, **hot-channel factors** are identified which indicate how much greater the temperature rise of coolant is in the hot channel than in the average channel. As an example of how such factors are used, consider a reactor in which the axial heat-generation pattern is a cosine and the total flow passes uniformly once through all channels of the core; the maximum fuel-element surface temperature T_{sm} depends on the hot-channel and hot-spot factors $F_{\Delta T}$ and F_θ and on the three temperatures—the coolant temperature at the core inlet T_1, the coolant temperature rise in the core ΔT, and the average film-temperature drop in the core, θ_a. (F_θ includes the axial peak-to-average of $\pi/2$.)

$$T_{sm} = T_1 + \tfrac{1}{2}F_{\Delta T}\,\Delta T + \tfrac{1}{2}\sqrt{F_{\Delta T}{}^2\,\nabla T^2 + 4F_\theta{}^2\theta_a{}^2}$$

Design Criteria. The maximum fuel-element surface temperature T_{sm} is of interest because it may be limited by corrosion effects or, in a pressurized-water reactor, by a desire to avoid boiling. However, other limiting conditions also exist.

Internal fuel-element temperature is generally limited to a maximum value or to a maximum average value. In addition, fuel-cladding chemical reactions may limit the temperature of the fuel-cladding interface (except for short periods of time). In general, high fuel temperatures cause swelling owing to decrease in fuel strength and increased diffusion of gases.

Coolant-temperature rise generally is limited indirectly by fuel-temperature limits. Occasionally, however, thermal stresses within the fuel element may impose a direct limit. In pressurized-water reactors, the coolant temperature cannot rise above the saturation temperature of the fluid; thus it is more significant to speak of the **maximum enthalpy rise,** which is related directly to the steam quality of the fluid leaving the hot channel.

Density changes within the coolant may be limited to provide control stability in reactors that use boiling heat transfer.

Coolant velocity usually is limited to maximum value by erosion or by vibration resonances and sometimes is required to exceed a minimum value because of crud deposition. The burnout condition is reached in a given fuel-element geometry for a particular combination of fuel-element heat flux, primary coolant flow, and primary coolant enthalpy. Steady-state, local, or bulk boiling may have to be limited, even when burnout is not a danger, because of pitting of fuel-element surfaces or crud deposition on the fuel surfaces. The burnout problem is most acute during reactor transients; hence, steady-state burnout generally is not limiting.

Mechanical Design

The mechanical design of nuclear reactors is influenced by three factors not encountered with other apparatus: the need to control criticality, the effects of irradiation, and the high power density produced in the core.

Control of Criticality. The following requirements are introduced by the need to control criticality:

1. Not only must components perform reliably, but if they fail to function as designed, the reactor will shut down. Small parts located elsewhere in the core should be designed so that if they fail they do not interfere with the action of control rods in shutting down the reactor.
2. Emergency shutdown mechanisms must be fast-acting devices to reduce the time delay in initiating shutdown.
3. During normal operation, components of the core must be rigid enough so that deflections due to mechanical or thermal stresses do not introduce unpredicted criticality variations.

Effects of Irradiation. Neutron and gamma irradiations cause four effects which must be considered in the design of reactor systems and reactor components. These are:

1. Radiation effects on properties of materials—particularly on the brittle-fracture characteristics of the reactor vessel, on the relaxation characteristics of bolts, and on crevice corrosion.
2. Heat generation brought about by attenuation of radiation within components materials—particularly insofar as such heat influences heat-removal requirements, thermal stresses, and thermal distortions of parts.
3. Induced radioactivity in corrosion and wear products that could be carried by the coolant and deposited in such regions as pumps and valves.
4. Residual radioactivity which influences programs and facilities for refueling of the core and for periodic maintenance of components in the reactor system.

The foregoing effects greatly influence the selection of materials for parts, the stresses at which they operate, and the environment in which they must function. Moving parts may have to operate without benefit of organic lubricants because such lubricants tend to sludge under irradiation and, if deposited on heat-transfer surfaces, could interfere with removal of heat from the core.

High Power Density. A nuclear reactor requires a large amount of heat-transfer surface for removal of the high power which can be produced per unit volume. Thus the reactor consists of many small, closely packed fuel elements. Mechanical tolerances are often appreciable fractions of the dimensions and spacing of these elements and therefore influence thermal performance. The influence of such tolerances on performance must be evaluated. Parts also must be rigid and vibration-free in the face of the high fluid-flow rates required for power removal. The high power density may also lead to large thermal stresses in fuel elements.

Instrumentation

Neutron-level instruments, located adjacent to but outside of the core or core vessel, are used for the basic control of nuclear reactors. Thermocouples, flowmeters, pressure taps, and flux wires are used inside the core for power calibration of nuclear instruments and for determining the distribution of power and/or temperature within the core; in turn, the power distribution is used to compute heat fluxes and fuel temperatures for comparison with limiting values. (See also p. 16–29.)

Neutron-level instruments utilize the fact that neutrons can produce ionizing particles to indicate their presence. The two most common processes used for this purpose are the (n,α) reaction with boron and the fission reaction. The resulting ion pair is used to produce ionization of a gas in a tube containing a central anode and outer electrode. The electric discharge produced by the ionization is used for measurement purposes. The detailed design features vary widely with the range of the instrument and the type of reactor in which it is to be used.

Different neutron-level instruments are required during various stages of reactor operation because of the wide range of sensitivity required. During start-up of the reactor, the neutron level will be small and will be based on the strength of the neutron source. During power operation, the neutron level is many times greater. Generally a reactor must be supplied with at least five ranges of instrumentation to cover the entire range of operation.

The instrumentation used for measurement of internal core parameters is based on conventional techniques, except in the case of flux wires. Special considerations are required, however, in applying these techniques; these include adapting the instruments to the space limitations of the reactor, providing cooling and pressure integrity, and ensuring vibration-free operation.

The flux wires used in reactors depend upon induced activity to indicate the flux distribution in the core. These wires are usually inserted longitudinally into the core to measure the axial flux. After the wires have been exposed, they are removed and scanned by a radiation monitor to determine the distribution activity, which in turn represents the distribution of the flux to which the wire was exposed in the core. The wire may be full length or segmented. In pressurized systems, special automated means are used for getting wires in and out of the core expeditiously. A number of wires appropriately distributed across the cross section of the core will permit exploration of the regions expected to be operating at the highest power levels.

Shielding

Shielding is required around a nuclear reactor to protect personnel against damaging biological effects of neutrons and gamma rays. The neutron and gamma-ray fluxes in the core vary from one core to another, but values of 10^{13} and 10^{14} particles per sq cm per sec are not uncommon. These fluxes must be reduced to the order of 10^3 particles per sq cm per sec of each type at the outside of the shield to meet tolerance limits. While some of the reduction in flux is brought about by the inverse-square law, most of the reduction must be accomplished by massive shielding.

To attenuate gamma rays, which interact primarily with the orbital electrons of atoms, a material with high electron density is most useful; this generally means a high-atomic-number material: a metal such as lead, tungsten, or depleted uranium or a concrete which contains high-Z elements in the form of scrap or heavy ore.

To attenuate neutrons, they must first be slowed down and then absorbed. Neutrons are slowed down most efficiently by low-Z elements, particularly hydrogeneous materials such as water, concrete, or polyethylene. After being slowed down, the neutrons must be absorbed without appreciable production of high-energy-capture gammas. The most common and useful element for this purpose is boron, sometimes enriched in B^{10}. However, because some gamma rays accompany almost all neutron absorption, some gamma shielding is usually required outside the neutron shield.

Because of the conflicting requirements for low-Z and high-Z elements, a shield will contain a mixture of materials. Concrete containing heavy filter material is often used for this purpose.

PROPERTIES OF MATERIALS

Materials used in nuclear reactors can be divided into six basic categories: fuel, radiation, control, coolant, structural, and shielding. While the nature of the materials may be different, they must be physically and chemically stable and compatible with their environment for a sufficient period to enable the reactor to operate predictably, stably, and economically under the particular set of parameters imposed by the design. (See also Sec. 6.)

In addition to the environmental conditions to which materials may ordinarily be exposed, reactor materials must also sustain the extraordinary bombardment of X rays (photons) and other atomic particles which are products of nuclear fission. In their passage through matter, these photons and atomic particles may inflict severe damage since the energy of these particles is spent mainly in ejecting or pulling electrons from their orbits, *i.e.*, producing **ionization.** Gamma photons and neutrons are highly penetrating, whereas fission fragments have a path under 0.001 in. in solids and liquids (but cause intense ionization over that path).

The **behavior of materials** following breakage of a bond by ionization may differ markedly. The fragments of simple, highly stable molecules such as water (H_2O) or carbon dioxide (CO_2) will most probably recombine. However, it is highly probable that the parts of complex **organic compounds** such as lubricants and electrical insulation will suffer permanent fragmentation and/or recombination in a different manner to produce new molecules.

Metals, on the other hand, are essentially unaffected by ionization since the probability of displacement of excited atoms in a metal lattice is small and the atoms will merely revert to their original status on ridding themselves of their excess energy. The atoms of **non-conducting crystals** and glasses are similarly immobile, and most of their properties are insensitive to the ionization. However, since these crystals are non-conducting, some of the electrons displaced by ionization become trapped in lattice vacancies, producing changes of optical properties (such as darkening of glass by gamma irradiation) and change of electrical resistivity.

On direct collision, **fast neutrons** may displace atoms from a chemical compound without affording opportunity for immediate recombination. Similarly, **energetic neutrons** may displace atoms from their normal lattice positions in a metal or other crystalline material and push them into abnormal interstitial positions in the lattice, generally producing an effect on metals similar to work hardening. The hardness and tensile strength of the metal will increase, but the metal becomes more brittle. **Thermal neutrons** affect the properties of metals only in those cases where the probability of absorption is high enough to cause significant transmutation to other elements.

Most severe damage occurs when the atoms of a fuel material fission and produce two or more new atoms from each of the original fissioned atoms. Volumetric changes occur by the substitution of these additional atoms in the lattice for the original atom, and the lattice is further damaged by the intrusion of the high-velocity fission fragments.

Fuel Materials

Fuel materials are generally divided into two categories: fissionable and fertile. The **fissionable materials** are those isotopes of uranium and plutonium which fission upon interaction with thermal neutrons. These are the isotopes U^{233}, U^{235}, Pu^{239}, and Pu^{241}, which have odd atomic weights. The **fertile materials** are those isotopes of uranium and plutonium which have even atomic weights. These absorb neutrons under proper conditions and undergo a series of nuclear reactions, with the eventual formation of fissionable isotopes. Thus, U^{238} forms Pu^{239}, and Pu^{240} forms Pu^{241}. In addition, thorium^{232} forms the fissionable isotope U^{233}.

Both fissionable and fertile materials fall short of possessing the **properties considered ideal** for a nuclear fuel, namely, corrosion resistance, good thermal conductivity, strength, and ductility. To overcome these problems as well as to prevent fission products from entering the coolant, various techniques are used, including plating, cladding, and alloying.

Materials for this use must be corrosion resistant, be compatible with the fuel material, be physically stable under irradiation, have good heat-transfer characteristics, have good nuclear properties, and be reasonably fabricable. From a consideration of cross section alone, only aluminum, beryllium, magnesium, and zirconium are attractive for use in thermal reactors. Magnesium usually is ruled out on the basis of strength and corrosion resistance but has been widely used in some gas-cooled systems. In fast reactors, a number of other materials become attractive, the most important being stainless steel, which also is used under special conditions in thermal reactors. Consideration also is being given to ceramic materials, BeO, Be_2C, SiC, and $MoSi^2$, which are very attractive in all phases except resistance to thermal shock.

Moderating material must be capable of reducing neutron energy very rapidly and should have good strength at high temperatures, corrosion resistance, thermal and radiation stability, and reasonable cost. Such properties are not available in a single material. Graphite is the most widely used solid moderator. Attention also is being given to beryllium and its compounds, deuterium, oxygen, and hydrogen.

The nuclear and physical properties considered desirable for **fuel diluents and cladding** are, in general, desirable for structural materials. For the latter, however, more emphasis is placed on strength and corrosion resistance than on nuclear properties. Stainless steel, aluminum, zirconium, molybdenum, titanium, niobium, and their alloys are used. As operating temperatures continue to rise, ceramics and cermets will have to be developed for this purpose.

Materials used for **control purposes** must have a high cross section for absorption of neutrons, adequate strength, low mass to permit movement, good corrosion resistance, chemical and dimensional stability under heat and irradiation, and low cost. Boron, cadmium, and hafnium are given the most consideration in various metallic and ceramic forms and as compounds dissolved in the coolant.

Coolant Properties

The choice of a coolant also is a compromise since no known material possesses all the **desirable characteristics.** These are good heat-transfer coefficient and good heat capacity on a volume basis, low absorption cross section, low vapor pressure at the operating temperature, minimum of chemical reaction with the material contacted by the coolant, good resistance to forming γ emitters with long half-lives, stability under irradiation and high temperatures, and workable melting points.

Coolants are divided into three broad **classes:** aqueous and organic liquids, liquid metals, and gases. **Water** has found the widest application, largely because it is readily available and economical, has fairly good heat-transfer properties, and offers no corrosion problems which cannot be handled. Its most serious drawback is its high vapor pressure. **Heavy water** has superior qualifications except for cost, which is high. Diphenyl and other **organic liquids** have demonstrated an ability to stand up under irradiation but are handicapped by a tendency to deposit decomposition products on the fuel-element plates.

Liquid metals are attractive because they give high heat-transfer rates and do not require pressurizing to operate at high temperatures. Sodium is most attractive because of its high boiling point and high heat conductivity, but it reacts violently with water and has poor lubricating qualities. Lithium-7 better meets qualifications but is harder to obtain and is costly.

Gas coolants offset their advantage of being inert at elevated temperatures with poor heat-transfer qualities. They must be operated at high pressures to be useful in power reactors. Sodium hydroxide and yellow phosphorus are among other materials considered as coolants, but their acceptability has yet to be demonstrated.

Table 3. General Properties of Reactor Materials before Irradiation*

Materials	Density, g per cc	Melting point, deg C	Specific heat, cal per (mol)(deg C)	Thermal conductivity, cal per (sec)(cm)(deg C)	Coefficient of thermal expansion, 10^{-6} per deg C	Ultimate tensile strength, 10^2 psi	Modulus of elasticity, 10^6 psi	Capture cross sections, 0.025 ev (σ_α barns)
FUELS AND FERTILE MATERIALS								
Uranium, normal	19.3	1133 ± 1	6.649	100 C, 0.063	25–125 C, 45.8	56	24	7.68
Thorium, normal	11.71	1690 ± 10	100 C, 6.59	100 C, 0.090	30–100 C, 11.5	30.6	10.6	7.56
Plutonium^{239}	19.60	623 ± 7	....	100 C, 0.061	....	125	13–16	1,026
Uranium oxide (UO_2)	10.96	2500–2600	15.38	100 C, 0.022	22–363 C, 9.3–10.8	....	21	24.3
Al-16 weight % U alloy	....	~650	....	200 C, 0.42	20–100 C, 20	17.7	10.6	
Zr-4 weight % U alloy	6.72	1840 ± 25	....	100 C, 0.033	190–300 C, 6.66	63	14.4	
DILUENTS AND CLADDING MATERIALS								
Zirconium	6.50	1845 ± 25	6.31	50 C, 0.05	5.82	30–38	13.8	0.18
Zircaloy 2	6.55	1820 ± 25	....	<0.04	20–100 C, 5.2 ± 0.6	65	14	
Aluminum (2S)	2.694	600.2	100 C, 6.07	0.53	20–100 C, 23.8	13	10.3	0.26
Magnesium	1.74	650	25 C, 6.08	18 C, 0.376	49 C, 26	Annealed, 27	Annealed, 6.5	0.069
$MoSi_2$	6.24	1870	....	370 C, 0.088	0–1500 C, 5.1	27 C, 22		
SOLID MODERATORS								
Graphite	2.27	Sublimes at 3650 ± 25 C	2.066	100 C, 0.37–0.48	20–250 C, 1.9–4.0	0.500–2.4	0.5–1.2	0.0032
Be_2C	6.24	1870	....	30 C, 0.02	25–200 C, 7.7	....	400 C, 23	
Beryllium	1.847	1315	100 C, 13.69	100 C, 0.34	25–100 C, 11.54	29	44	0.01
Sintered BeO†	2.2–2.8	2550 ± 25	100 C, 7.7	200 C, 0.19	25–100 C, 5.5	400 C, 15	400 C, 39	0.000727
SiC	3.21	Decomposes at 2500 C	327 C, 10.06	400 C, 0.060	0-1700 C, 4.4	1700 C, 50		
STRUCTURAL MATERIALS								
Stainless steel (347)	8.027	1427	100 C, 0.12‡	100 C, 0.037	20–100 C, 16.5	85	29	3
Inconel X	8.51	1395–1425	25–100 C, 0.109‡	0–100 C, 0.036	20–100 C, 11.5	Annealed, 100–120	....	4.1
Molybdenum	10.2	2622 ± 10	100 C, 6.24	0 C, 0.32	5.1	67	48	2.7
Titanium (commercial purity)	4.507	1690	0–500 C, 6.61	25 C, 0.41	25 C, 8.5	85–100	15.5	5.8
Niobium	8.57	2415	0 C, 6.01	....	....	1200 C, 14.7	....	1.1
CONTROL MATERIALS								
Cadmium	8.694	321	25–321 C, 6.19	0.22	20–100 C, 31.8	10.3	7.1–10	2.450
Hafnium	13.36	2130 ± 15	25–2227 C, 6.16	....	0–100 C, 5.9	67.5	14	105

* All properties change with irradiation at room temperature except when specified.
† Thermal conductivity, strength, and the modulus of elasticity vary directly with the density; however, the coefficient of thermal expansion appears unaffected.
‡ Cal per (g)(deg C).
Sources: H. A. Saller, Properties of Reactor Materials, "Nuclear Engineering Handbook," McGraw-Hill, 1958; "Reactor Physics Constants," ANL 5800, 1963.

Table 4. Properties of Nuclear Coolants*

AQUEOUS AND ORGANIC LIQUIDS

	Water	Heavy water	Diphenyl	Dowtherm-A	Santowax R
Density, lb/ft³	42.4 (600 F)	46.2 (600 F)	46.4 (675 F)	46.6 (675 F)	52.29 (675 F)
Viscosity, lb/hr/ft	0.20 (600 F)	0.220 (600 F)	0.353 (675 F)	0.7986 (675 F)	0.630 (675 F)
Melting point, deg F	32	39	156	53.2	293
Boiling point, deg F	212	214	49	496	687–784
Heat capacity, Btu/lb/deg F	1.54 (600 F)	1.68 (600 F)	0.637 (675 F)	0.675 (675 F)	0.539 (675 F)
Thermal conductivity, Btu/hr/ft/deg F	0.294 (600 F)	0.294 (600 F)	0.0763 (675 F)	0.098 (675 F)	0.064 (675 F)
Capture cross section, σ_a 0.025 ev (barns)	0.66	0.0011	3.3	3.3	4.6
Cost, $/lb	....	28	0.16	0.30	0.17

GASES

	Hydrogen	Helium	CO_2	Air	Nitrogen	Steam	Neon
Density, lb/ft³	0.00185	0.00375	0.041	0.0275	0.026	0.0167	0.0190
Viscosity, lb/hr/ft	0.042	0.094	0.081	0.089	0.086	0.069	0.1445
Heat capacity, Btu/lb/deg F	3.625	1.245	0.283	0.263	0.268	0.518	0.246
Thermal conductivity, Btu/hr/ft deg F	0.224	0.159	0.0328	0.0337	0.0327	0.0341	0.0536
Prandtl No.	0.660	0.735	0.6988	0.6898	0.7097	1.048	0.6632
Cost, $/100 ft³	0.85	1.90	0.25	......	0.30	......	475

LIQUID METALS

	Gallium	Lithium	Potassium	Rubidium	Sodium	Tin	Na(56%) K(44%)	Pb(44.5%) Bi(55.5%)
Density, lb/ft³	359	29.9	44.6	84.4	51.2	421	48.8	625.5
Viscosity, lb/hr/ft	1.836	1.188	0.3816	0.415	0.5040	2.736	0.435	2.88
Melting point, deg F	85.86	354	147	102	208	449	66.2	257
Boiling point, deg F	3,601	2,403	1,400	1,270	1,621	4,118	1,518	3,038
Heat capacity, Btu/lb/deg F	0.082	1.0	0.180	0.0877	0.3005	0.0639	0.2484	0.035
Thermal conductivity, Btu/hr/ft/deg F	18.0	18.0	21.15	13.2	37.7	19.0	16.35	8.05
Capture cross section, σ_a 0.025 ev (barns)	2.77	71.0†	1.97	0.70	0.505	0.60	......	0.094
Cost, $/lb	680	1†	3.66	390	0.17	1.00	0.60	‡

* At 1,000 F unless otherwise specified. Adapted from L. Green, Reactor Coolant Properties, *Nucleonics*, vol. 19, No. 11, which contains a detailed bibliography.

† Li^7 cross section 0.033 barns; cost $54.50 per lb at 99.99 percent purity.

‡ $1.29 per lb computed from Pb and Bi prices.

UTILIZATION OF FISSION ENERGY

The Power Cycle. Although the energy of fission appears as kinetic energy (85 percent) and photon energy of γ rays, there is no practical method of converting this energy directly into useful work on a large scale. Therefore, a nuclear reactor must be treated as a heat source which differs from a chemical heat source in that no oxygen is required and the heat does not have to be removed from gaseous combustion products which possess poor heat-transfer properties.

The simplest possible cycle for heat-transfer devices is the **Brayton cycle** (Sec. 4), but for nuclear use, it presents problems of containment, contamination, high temperature, and high pressure. The **Carnot-cycle** (Sec. 4) efficiency is the maximum theoretically attainable for any heat engine, but this cycle has not been considered for a nuclear reactor because of a difficulty in transferring large amounts of heat isothermally. The **Otto cycle** (Sec. 4), with its constant-volume heat addition, isentropic expansion, and constant-volume heat rejection, might possibly be applied using either a solid or a gaseous fuel. However, very little work has been done on this type.

Processes in the **Rankine vapor cycle** (Sec. 4) are effective for handling power in large amounts and, therefore, are used for central-station generation even though the efficiency of the plant is lower than for internal-combustion-engine cycles. The Rankine cycle appears to be best suited for nuclear power because (1) the maximum practicable operating temperature for a reactor corresponds to or is lower than the temperature used in the conventional Rankine vapor cycle; (2) the problem of containment of radioactivity is better solved by this cycle than by other cycles; (3) reactors are most economical in large sizes, as are Rankine engines.

Three variations of the Rankine cycle (Fig. 2) are being used. The **direct cycle** is the least expensive and thermodynamically the most desirable. Its disadvantages are the facts that the boiling process does not permit the high power densities which are attainable with liquid cooling and that radioactive steam is carried into the turbine and condenser. The **indirect cycle** gives greater power density and eliminates radioactivity in the turbine, although it produces steam at lower pressures and temperatures than those considered most efficient for modern turbines. Both concepts are highly developed and commercially available. Plants utilizing sodium or other liquid metal as the heat-exchange medium use an **intermediate-link system** to isolate the water system from radioactive sodium.

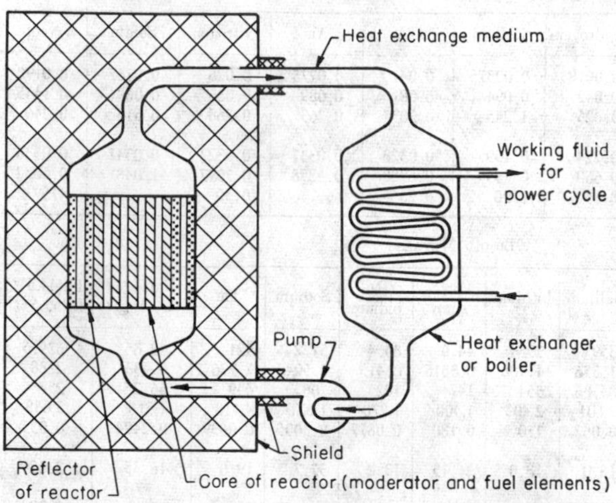

FIG. 2. Plant cycles—coupling with working fluid. (*A. Amorosi, Selection of Reactors "Nuclear Engineering Handbook," McGraw-Hill*, 1957.)

Essentially, there are five main **components in a reactor**: (1) atomic fuel, which must be sealed as protection against oxidation; (2) a moderator to slow down the neutrons so that the chain reaction can continue efficiently; (3) a control mechanism to maintain the chain reaction at desired levels; (4) a coolant to maintain temperatures below the melting point of materials and, in the case of power reactors, to convey the heat to a steam generator; and (5) a shield to contain radioactive by-products.

The arrangement of moderator and fuel provides one basis for classification. In a **heterogeneous** or **solid-fuel** reactor, the fuel is mixed in a regular pattern within the moderator. In a **homogeneous** reactor, the fuel and moderator are intimately mixed in the form of a solution, whether aqueous or liquid salts or metals.

A second basis of classification is coolants, which include light water (H_2O), heavy water (D_2O), liquid metal, gas, and organic liquids. A further classification is by the speed or energy of the neutrons that cause fission. Neutrons of about 0.025 ev are called **slow** or **thermal**; neutrons from 1 to 1,000 ev are known as **intermediate**; and neutrons with energies above 1,000 ev are called **fast.** A fast reactor does not use a moderator.

Finally, reactors may be classified according to application: **research** reactors, which are designed to provide neutrons and γ rays for physical research and radioisotope manufacture; **materials-testing** reactors, generally classified as research although they run at higher power to produce a very high neutron flux; **production** reactors, which manufacture fissionable material by conversion of non-fissionable material; and **power** reactors for generating electricity providing process heat and propelling ships and other vehicles.

Research and test reactors are an exceedingly useful source of neutrons for a variety of experiments in the study of neutron properties, radiation damage, detecting and counting of rays, critical behavior, energy of fission, distribution of fission fragments, and related technology.

Radioactive isotopes, obtained by irradiation of samples with neutrons in a reactor, are used for tracing the progress of foods and minerals in plants and animals; studying blood processes, gland functions, and animal metabolism; investigating the properties of various elements and compounds; and measuring and detecting flaws in industrial processes.

A research reactor utilizing natural uranium has a large critical mass of U^{235} and hence has a low neutron flux for a given power rating. It also is physically large, providing large working areas around the reactor. Reactors utilizing enriched uranium have a small critical mass which provides a high flux. All research reactors operate at low power and are relatively safe because they are designed to handle very little excess reactivity and have a strong negative temperature coefficient.

Technical details of **production reactors** are classified, although in constructing a dual-purpose (production-power) reactor, the NPR at Hanford, the AEC revealed that the reactor consists of a large block of graphite pierced horizontally by zirconium-alloy tubes containing the fuel elements and providing passage for coolant flow. This matrix is enveloped by thermal and biological shields. A primary cooling system transfers the heat from the reactor to a secondary cooling system, where it is utilized to generate steam for use in a turbine generator.

POWER REACTORS

A great variety of reactor types is conceptually possible. Although more than a score of combinations have gone through various stages of development, guidelines for selecting the maximum design have not been firmly established. In the United States, development of water-cooled reactors has outdistanced that of other types, while in England gas-cooled reactors hold the lead. It is not clear which, if either, of these two types eventually will prove to be the best power producer. There are indications that to meet future demands for energy, it will be necessary to obtain more efficient utilization of fuel than now appears possible in converter (burner) reactors.

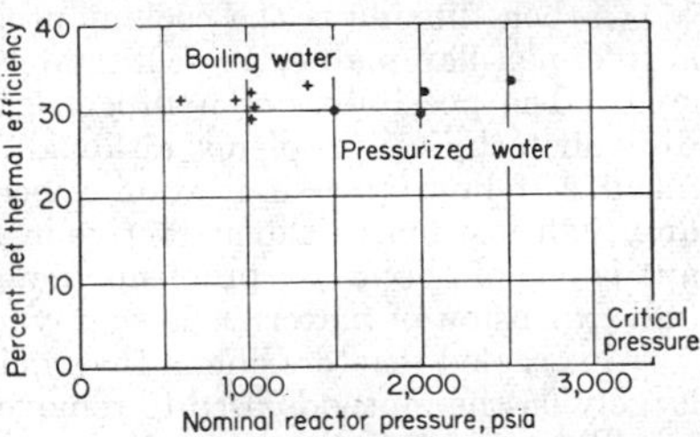

FIG. 3. Typical pressure requirements of water-cooled reactors. (*S. Untermyer, Water Cooled Reactor Systems, "Nuclear Engineering Handbook," McGraw-Hill,* 1958.)

Pressurized-water Reactors. Properties of water and steam which led to their predominance as general-purpose heat-transfer mediums have also caused their wide-spread application as a reactor coolant. A major disadvantage of water results from its relatively high vapor pressure. However, this can be partially overcome by allowing boiling in the reactor. Thermal efficiencies up to 36 percent are possible.

The use of H_2O as a coolant and moderator is based on well-developed technology which indicates that the ultimate size (or capacity) will be dictated primarily by heat-transfer requirements. The average heat flux q/A is around 300000 Btu per hr per sq ft, with a maximum of 600000 approx. The resonance absorption requires enriched fuel. However, the cost of enrichment is economically justified because the increased power density reduces inventory charges. To provide sufficient neutron moderation, the H_2O-U^{235} volume ratio is kept slightly above 2:1.

The use of oxide fuel minimizes corrosion. Design problems are reasonably well understood, although costly structural provisions must be made to load and unload fuel because of the high pressures. Fuel enrichment usually runs between 1.5 and 3.0 percent, depending on the alloy used for corrosion resistance. Because of the strong moderating property of H_2O, control rods must be placed on about 1-ft centers. To prevent the large number of these rods from interfering with the unloading of a large power reactor, they are often operated from the bottom.

For utilization of natural uranium as a fuel, D_2O is substituted for H_2O as the coolant-moderator. The reactor must be unloaded more frequently because the specific power is greater. The flux is higher, 5×10^{13} approx for 1,000 mw, and there is a problem in overriding xenon. The success of this type depends to a large extent on the availability and cost of D_2O.

Boiling-water reactors have a simpler design and can utilize relatively thin-walled vessels and pipes because they operate at moderate pressures compared with pressurized-water reactors. Fuel temperatures are only slightly higher than steam temperatures, and there is an inherent safety factor because the steam-void volume increases on a transient power increase. Some of the problems caused by radioactivity carry-over, such as maintenance on the turbine and condenser and the prevention of radioactive leakage, are offset by the cost of the boiler in pressurized-water reactors.

Limitations on the power density imposed by exit voids (*i.e.*, the vapor volume of the exiting steam-water mixture from the reactor core) is a disadvantage in that low power density contributes to high fuel-inventory charges. Load change must be accomplished by steam bypass control or rods since adjustment of the turbine throttle and consequent reduction in steam flow will cause an increase in pressure in the reactor, which in turn will collapse the steam bubbles and increase reactivity. The net decomposition of the water into O and H is much greater than in a pressurized-water reactor.

Gas-cooled reactors offer low fuel and operating costs because of their ability to utilize natural uranium as fuel. This advantage is offset by higher capital costs resulting from the larger facilities required by the low power densities which prevail. It is certain that the substitution of slightly enriched uranium would reduce capital expenditures, but it is not obvious as to how this change would affect economics associated with the fuel cycle itself.

Carbon dioxide is the coolant usually used as it is non-toxic, only mildly radioactive, non-flammable, non-contaminating in case of leakage, and relatively inexpensive. The possibility of hydrogen gas as a coolant has been ruled out because of difficult technical problems, although its potential for superior performance is recognized. Helium gives indication of being an ideal coolant, but its limited availability and high cost make it unattractive in a power reactor. Full containment of the coolant is one of the major problems in a gas-cooled reactor because the natural warping and expansion of materials is aggravated by high operating temperatures.

Gas-cooled reactors offer a thermodynamic problem for which the solution depends largely on the methods used to remove the heat from the core. Both convection and conduction come into play, and these two phenomena differ in their nature and methods of handling. Extensive studies are being made of the heat-transfer and pressure-drop characteristics of finned cans and cartridges. Although the power consumption of the blowers required to circulate the cooling gas is an appreciable fraction of the power output, efficiencies approaching 30 percent have been achieved.

An upper limit on gas temperatures is created by the fact that the oxidation of graphite by CO_2 increases with the temperature. Limitations of size also are provided by the practical consideration of how large a pressure vessel can be constructed, stress-relieved, and tested in the field. Prestress of concrete and all-steel construction have both been used. From the reactor-performance point of view, there always will be an incentive to increase the physical size or pressure level of a given reactor, thus permitting the extraction of more power. Accordingly, the capabilities of pressure-vessel fabricators play an important role in the final design of a gas-cooled system.

Liquid-metal advantages as reactor coolants include low vapor pressure, excellent heat-transfer characteristics, and the potential of producing steam conditions which are typical of modern generating station practice. Disadvantages stem from their chemical activity, neutron absorption, and induced radioactivity.

Choice of a liquid-metal coolant is based mainly on nuclear properties and on the engineering difficulties associated with melting temperatures and corrosion effects. Those of prime interest are sodium, sodium-potassium alloy, bismuth, lead, and lead-bismuth alloy. Separated Li^7 would be very attractive were it not for its high cost.

In general, ferrous alloys with low carbon content and high nickel and chromium content are preferred as materials containing liquid metals. Final choice is based on fabrication, initial cost, and corrosion resistance within the operating temperature range. Solubility of oxide in liquid sodium increases rapidly with temperature (by a factor of 40 between 150 and 500 C). Excessive oxide creates mass transport, plugging, and self-welding. Development of suitable pumps presents some difficult problems, and considerable research has been done on pumping by electromagnetic means.

Liquid-metal heat exchangers frequently are called upon to operate at much higher temperature differences than are common in water types. Therefore, extra precautions are necessary to avoid thermal shock or thermal cycling. Precautions against leaks must be intense as most liquid metals react with both water and air.

Fast breeder reactors operate at extremely high power densities (as they are unmoderated) and are liquid-metal-cooled. Their attractiveness stems from an ability to "breed," *i.e.*, produce more fuel than they consume. Aside from savings in fuel cost, this characteristic is believed necessary to conserve the world's supply of energy.

Two conflicting definitions of a breeder reactor are in common use: (1) a nuclear reactor that produces more fissionable material than it consumes, regardless of type of fuel used; (2) a nuclear reactor that produces the same species of material as it consumes, regardless of the net gain or loss. The first definition has wider acceptance in the United States.

Advantages of operating in the fast-neutron spectrum include: (1) structural material for the reactor core can be selected without consideration of neutron absorption; (2) very little excess reactivity is needed to compensate for fission-product buildup; and (3) reprocessed fuel in which fission-product removal may not be complete can be used. The last attribute has the potential of substantially reducing fuel costs.

Disadvantages are basically similar to those of moderated liquid-metal reactors, including the fact that sodium undergoes a violent exothermic chemical reaction on contact with water in the presence of air. The use of water and other, similar coolants is ruled out because thay also act as moderators. A critical problem is to develop a low-cost, high-burnup fuel element.

NUCLEAR-POWER-PLANT ECONOMICS

(See also p. 17–53 *et seq.*)

Decisions by electric utilities about whether to install nuclear or fossil-fueled plants are based largely, though not wholly, on a comparison of the costs for which the alternative plants can produce electricity over their lifetimes. It is customary to compare generating costs for nuclear and fossil-fueled plants in three broad categories: (1) fixed charges on capital investment, (2) fuel costs, and (3) operating, maintenance, and insurance costs.

Construction costs, when considered in the context of estimating power costs, include not only direct costs for site, materials, equipment, and installation, but also various indirect costs, such as costs for design, fees, and interest on capital during construction.

The total of these items tends to be higher for nuclear than for fossil-fueled plants largely because of (1) the need for containment shells, shielding, instrumentation, and other measures to contain radioactivity and assure safety; (2) the greater complexity, hence greater costs, of reactor equipment as compared with conventional boiler equipment; and (3) the lower steam temperatures, pressures, and thermal efficiencies of nuclear plants as compared with conventional plants, requiring the use of larger, hence costlier, turbines. The discrepancy is wider in warm climates, which permit fossil-fuel plants to utilize outdoor (unenclosed) construction.

Mitigating factors which prevent the construction-cost discrepancy between nuclear and coal plants, in particular, from being still larger are (1) the lesser cost of fuel-handling equipment in nuclear plants, and (2) the need in coal plants, but not in nuclear plants, for smoke-control and ash-removal equipment.

Unit construction costs (expressed in dollars per kilowatt) for both nuclear and fossil-fueled plants decrease with increases in plant size because of various economies of scale. The decreases are sharper in the case of nuclear plants, largely because of the prominence of certain minimum and relatively fixed costs of assuring safety. The existence of these inescapable costs places small nuclear plants at a particularly great economic disadvantage. It is not until unit sizes of 200 mwe or more are reached that the capital-cost disadvantage of nuclear plants narrows to the point where there is generally conceded to be a possibility of over-all economic competitiveness under conditions prevailing anywhere in the Continental United States. The economic contest in the remainder of this century is considered most likely to be waged initially at unit sizes ranging from 500 to 1,000 mwe or larger.

Construction costs of nuclear plants may be expected to diminish over time with the achievement of greater experience and a larger-scale industry. In particular, such cost reductions can result from design simplifications, standardization of systems and components, less stringent specifications, cheaper field assembly, and a larger sales volume over which to spread fixed costs of manufacture and various development and overhead costs.

Continued reductions in unit capital costs are to be expected for fossil-fuel plants also, but there is reason to believe that the reductions in capital costs of nuclear plants will be more rapid for some years to come.

The unit capital costs of nuclear plants often can be reduced substantially over their lifetimes by using improved fuel cores to achieve outputs higher than the original rating, which is usually conservative. To take advantage of this opportunity, allowance for higher output must be made at the outset in the capacity of turbine generators.

Generating costs (mills per kwh) can be obtained from construction costs (dollars per kw) by appling an annual fixed-charge rate and an annual plant-capacity factor.

The fixed-charge rate is made up of depreciation charges and the costs of money, interim replacements, insurance, and taxes. The annual capacity factor is calculated by dividing the kwh generated by the plant in a year by the kwh that would have been generated had the plant operated continuously at full capacity.

The conversion from construction to generating costs may be illustrated as follows: Assume a plant of 100,000-kw capacity costing $15 million, with annual fixed charges of 14 percent and operating at 80 percent capacity factor. The capital-cost contribution to generating costs would then be 3 mills per kwh, calculated as follows:

$$\frac{\$15{,}000{,}000 \times 14\%}{100{,}000 \text{ kw} \times 8760 \text{ hr} \times 80\%} = \frac{\$2{,}100{,}000}{700{,}800{,}000 \text{ kwh}} = \frac{3 \text{ mills}}{\text{kwh}}$$

Annual fixed-charge rates for investor-owned plants adopted in 1963 for use in the FPC's national power study were somewhat higher for nuclear than for fossil-fuel plants, as follows:

	Fixed-charge rate, percent	
	Nuclear	Fossil-fuel
Investor-owned	13	12
Government-owned	8	7

The slightly higher charges for nuclear relative to fossil-fueled plants were primarily in insurance and faster depreciation. The significantly higher charges for investor-owned relative to government-owned plants are ascribable principally to higher interest charges on debt and to taxes, principally real estate and income taxes, from which government-owned plants are generally exempt. Thus nuclear plants, because they have higher construction costs, are at a greater relative disadvantage when investor-financed than when government-financed.

Influence of Capacity Factor. Because they cost more, nuclear plants compete more favorably at relatively high capacity factors. Nuclear plants have demonstrated a capacity for sustained operation. Under circumstances where their operating (as opposed to fixed) costs are lower than those of fossil-fueled plants in the same system, they are likely to be assigned to base-load operation, making for high capacity factors. If nuclear plants replace fossil-fueled plants to the extent that their total capacity exceeds base load, however, their capacity factors must be expected to decrease.

Fuel Costs

The economic promise of nuclear power lies essentially in its potential for achieving fuel costs substantially lower than those of conventional stations, which would make it possible to more than offset the higher capital costs.

The potential is implicit in the compactness of nuclear fuel: 1 cu ft of uranium, **if fully consumed,** contains the energy equivalent of 1.7 million tons of coal, 7.2 million barrels of oil, or 32 billion cu ft of natural gas.

Net nuclear-fuel costs are made up of costs of fuel-element fabrication, net fuel-burnup costs, fuel-inventory charge, the costs for shipping and reprocessing irradiated fuel, and investment charges on fabricated fuel. The dollar amounts for these items, divided by the amount of energy generated, yields fuel costs in mills per kwh.

Fabrication. The cost of fuel-element fabrication is taken to include all the steps necessary to change a starting material (UF_6 in the case of enriched uranium elements) into a usable element. These steps involve chemical conversion to a powder or metal, metallurgical and mechanical processing to form and clad the elements, inspection, testing, scrap recovery, and fixed charges on material being processed.

Net Fuel-burnup Cost. The user of AEC-owned fuel must pay for any amounts lost or consumed, but he is currently (1964) compensated for any new fuel (*i.e.*, Pu or U^{233}) produced. Both charges and credits are determined by AEC schedules. The charges vary with enrichment and are based on full recovery of AEC costs. It is significant that AEC was able to reduce the charges 30 percent or more on July 1, 1962.

Use Charge. Nuclear fuel, under the 1954 Atomic Energy Act, is the property of the Federal government, which charges for its use 4.75 percent of the value of the material per annum (increased from 4 percent in July 1961). The charge is applied to the total fuel inventory of a plant, defined to include material being fabricated, in the reactor, in storage at the reactor site, undergoing decay cooling, and in transit to or undergoing reprocessing. The Atomic Energy Act of 1964 authorizes private ownership of fuel and requires it by Jan. 1. 1971. Enrichment services, for a fee, will be provided by the government after 1969. Although the change from government to private ownership raises some question concerning future nuclear-fuel costs, it is anticipated that, if a price increase occurs during the changeover, it will be short-lived. Uncertainties include fluctuations of U_3O_8 prices in an open market and the value of power-reactor-produced plutonium. Development of recycling techniques and of breeder reactors to more fully utilize plutonium as a fuel will increase its value and improve the economics of U^{235}-burning reactors. Development of a wider market for by-product isotopes could reduce over-all fuel costs.

Shipping Charge. The costs of transporting irradiated-fuel elements from a reactor site to a chemical-processing plant include charges for freight, shipping casks, handling, and insurance. The shape of the fuel element (having an effect on the size of cask required), the irradiation level, the cooling time required, the shipping distance, the route and type of transport, and the regulatory requirements are all factors which affect the cost.

Chemical Processing. Chemical processing (dissolving irradiated fuel, followed by separation and storing of fission products) and producing purified solutions of uranium and plutonium nitrates are performed at four AEC sites, pending the availability of such services at reasonable prices from private facilities. (A private processing plant began operations in 1966, and AEC has determined that its proposed charges will be reasonable for certain classes of fuel.) AEC chemical-processing charges are obtained by multiplying a fixed daily charge (based on current costs of operating a conceptual plant) by the estimated number of days required for processing a given batch of fuel. A charge is also made for estimated losses of uranium and plutonium incurred during processing.

Future Reductions in Fuel Costs. As indicated above, the economic promise of nuclear power depends importantly on the success of efforts to bring about lower fuel costs. Prominent among developments which may contribute to future cost reductions are those in the following areas:

BURNUP. The amount of heat that can be obtained from a given weight of nuclear fuel before it is discharged from the reactor is known as the fuel's **burnup.** Higher burnups are expected as a result of technological improvements. This would have the consequence of reducing the amount of fuel that must be fabricated, reprocessed, and shipped per unit of electrical output. Cost reductions should be acheived as a result, but they may be limited by the fact that fuel elements capable of achieving the higher burnups may be more expensive to fabricate and process and may require higher enrichment.

FABRICATION. Lower fuel-element fabrication costs may result from larger-scale production and from simplification and standardization of design.

REPROCESSING. Lower reprocessing charges may result from economies of scale, as the batches of fuel sent through reprocessing plants become larger, and also from improvements in technology.

Operating, Maintenance, and Insurance Costs

The main cost items included in this category are station labor, training of replacement personnel, expendable materials and supplies other than fuel, maintenance operations not accounted for by the aforementioned items, and insurance.

The novelty and complexity of nuclear plants, a conservative approach to health and safety problems, and the need for specialized knowledge are all factors requiring a more skilled staff in nuclear plants and a longer period of training. Problems of coal- and ash-handling and maintenance of tubes and related boiler components require a larger working force in conventional plants. While insurance costs have been higher for nuclear plants, it is expected that a continuance of safe-operating experience will eventually equalize this item.

From a functional standpoint, a nuclear reactor is easier to operate than a steam boiler, and inherently it is automated to a high degree.

Total Generating Costs

From the foregoing discussion, it should be clear that estimating nuclear-power costs requires that assumptions be made on a fairly large number of factors: technological, economic, even political. In the past, there have been periods when estimates of the relative economic position of nuclear power tended to be overly optimistic and other periods when the pendulum seemed to swing the other way.

Late in 1962, the AEC prepared its "Civilian Nuclear Power—A Report to the President," containing a series of nuclear-cost estimates extending to 1980. The report cited estimates by manufacturers that a large water-cooled nuclear plant could be initiated at once which could generate power at first at approximately 6 mills per kwh and over its lifetime at 5.5 or 5.4 mills per kwh. (The decreases in cost would be brought about chiefly by increases in fuel burnup and in the operating-power level.) It was estimated that such a plant would be competitive with conventional plants of equivalent size built at the same time in areas where fossil fuels cost 30¢ or 31¢ per million Btu. About one-third of the nation's electrical energy was at that time (1962) produced with fossil fuels costing this much or more.

The AEC report went on to predict further lowering in nuclear-power costs such that a 500-mwe nuclear plant placed in service in 1980 would, 5 years thereafter, be producing power for 3.6 mills per kwh. Conventional power plants offer a moving economic target for nuclear power since further technological improvements in them are to be expected and since some decreases in fossil-fuel costs are also possible, particularly in high-cost areas. Even allowing for these factors, however, the AEC's 1962 estimate was that the 500-mwe nuclear plant would be competitive in virtually all parts of the country in 1980.

Indications that cost competitiveness has been achieved at an earlier date were given in 1966 when 57 percent of central station capacity ordered by USA utilities was nuclear. Unit capacities ranged from 450 to 1,065 mwe.

There is general agreement that, as a consequence of the improving economic position of nuclear power, an increasing percentage of new power plants and of produced power will be nuclear. The AEC's 1962 Report to the President forecast that in the period 1980–2000, 66 percent of new steam-electric capacity would be nuclear; that after 2000, virtually all additions to capacity would be nuclear; and that in the year 2000, 50 percent of all utility generation would be from nuclear plants. The latter figure is close to estimates made by others. Resources for the Future, Inc., in 1963 estimated the nuclear proportion in the year 2000 at 51.1 percent of total generation.

BENEFITS FROM NUCLEAR POWER

Whatever the speed with which nuclear fuels replace fossil fuels, certain benefits are considered likely to result. These include:

1. **Equalizing Generating Costs.** Fuel costs of fossil-fuel-fired stations are greatly influenced by the cost of transportation. In some sections of the country, freight rates equal or exceed the purchase price of the fuel at source. As transportation is a minor factor in the delivered cost of nuclear fuel, expanding construction of nuclear plants will tend to equalize generating costs. Such equalization is likely to be at lower average costs. Thus nuclear techniques would enable utilities to maintain the trend toward lower generating costs (in constant dollars) which they have established in the past through continued improvements in the efficiency of steam plants.

2. **Extending Energy Resources.** The AEC calculated on the basis of various estimates of fuel reserves and energy demands that if nuclear power or some other substitute were not introduced, the United States "would exhaust our readily available, low-cost supplies of fossil fuels in from 75 to 100 years and our presently visualized total supplies in from 150 to 200 years." Moreover, there is need to conserve fossil fuels for certain uses for which there is no practical present substitute, *e.g.*, in transportation and as sources of industrial chemicals.

Nuclear power can be effective in extending energy resources because the energy potential in uranium and thorium reserves is considered to be many times that in remaining fossil-fuel reserves. How completely nuclear-fuel reserves are used depends on the course of future nuclear-power development, in particular on the relative degree of emphasis placed on breeder reactors (which produce more fissionable material than they consume) as opposed to the presently predominant converter reactors (which produce some fissionable material, but not as much as they consume).

If breeders are developed to an extent making possible utilization of all the fertile uranium and thorium, as well as the naturally fissionable U^{235} (0.7 percent of natural uranium), AEC estimated the fission-energy content of domestic nuclear resources as essentially limitless, over 300,000 Q, as opposed to estimates that the energy still available in fossil fuels is from 26 to 130 Q. (The energy unit Q equals 1 billion billion Btu. It is estimated that between 3 and 4 Q will be consumed in the United States between 1963 and the year 2000.) (See also p. 9–3 *et seq.*)

3. **Other Benefits.** The negligible transportation costs of nuclear fuel can greatly reduce the interarea differential in power-generation costs now existing, making possible increased economic development in areas where power costs are now relatively high. If reductions in the cost of electricity brought about by nuclear power are substantial, it would have the effect of stimulating wider use of electricity. Because they depend less on fuel-transportation systems, nuclear-power systems would be less vulnerable to interruption during war, thus improving the country's defense posture. Whereas coal-fueled plants can present a serious smoke-pollution problem, nuclear plants are free of this difficulty.

OTHER POWER APPLICATIONS

Nuclear Ships. Considerable development work is being directed to finding ways in which nuclear power can be used effectively in transportation on land, sea, and air. The most successful of these efforts have been those by the U.S. Navy, which launched the USN *Nautilus* in 1954 and followed with several score other submarines as well as a number of surface vessels. Nuclear submarines also are being operated by the British and Russian navies, and one is under construction by the French.

Although a ship can be propelled by Diesel engines, steam engines, gas turbines, and other devices, the steam turbine has emerged as the principal modern marine propulsion unit. When a nuclear reactor of a type developed for generating stations is used to produce the steam, the combustion process is eliminated. Such a propulsion plant is especially advantageous for a submarine since it is then completely free from dependence on the earth's atmosphere. The U.S. Navy's nuclear ships and submarines all employ the pressurized-water type of nuclear reactor.

On commercial ships, the advantages of nuclear power are related to higher-speed operation over long-run routes. Experience indicates that an increase in speed usually produces substantial increases in cargoes, thereby increasing a ship's load factor. In conventional ships, the power required for higher speed is increased by the third power of the speed ratio. This means larger engines and greater fuel-storage capacity. On the other hand, a nuclear ship can operate continuously at the maximum level of its hull form without penalty in pay load. Such advantages are especially desirable for icebreakers, large bulk-cargo vessels, and high-speed long-distance passenger service. In 1964, only two nuclear commercial vessels were operating: the U.S.S.R. icebreaker *Lenin* and the U.S. nuclear ship *Savannah*.

Other Vehicles. The use of nuclear power in airplanes, automobiles, and railroad trains has been deterred by the requirement for heavy shielding to protect against radioactivity and collisions.

Space Travel. In space and other difficult-to-reach regions, where a compact, dependable source of energy is required, nuclear power holds much promise. Under the **SNAP** (systems for nuclear auxiliary power) program, much research and development are being done to develop compact reactors, radioisotope heat-energy capsules, thermoelectric generators, and thermionic generators. Although development of these concepts has proved to be both difficult and time-consuming, by the beginning of 1964 four devices powered by radioisotopes had been placed in operation, two much larger fission-powered space reactors had been tested, and five radioisotope power units for terrestrial weather and navigational uses where operating.

Isotopic power generators take advantage of the fact that radiations of an appreciable amount of radioactive material sealed in a container are absorbed by the container. This action creates high temperatures, which are utilized to create an electric current by thermocouples or by direct-energy conversion—thermionic emission.

Plutonium^{238} and strontium^{90} were the radioisotopes first used. Eight radioisotopes are now being utilized in this work.

Table 5. Radioisotopic Materials

Radioisotope	Half-life, years	Typical power density, watts per cc*	Radiation present†	Shielding required
Strontium^{90}	28	1.4	Beta and bremsstrahlung	Heavy
Cesium^{137}	30	0.21	Beta and gamma	Heavy
Cerium^{144}	0.78	24.5	Beta and gamma	Heavy
Promethium^{147}	2.7	1.8	Beta	Minor
Polonium^{210}	0.38	1,210	Alpha	Minor
Plutonium^{238}	89	3.5	Alpha	Minor
Curium^{242}	0.45	1,150	Alpha	Minor
Curium^{244}	18	26.4	Alpha and neutron	Moderate

Source: AEC TID-20079.
* Reduced below theoretical maxima in order to account for expected isotopic impurities.
† Of dominant importance in heat generation and for consideration of radiation shielding.

Reactor power generators are being developed to meet the need for larger power sources than the isotopic sources can provide. Proposed is a compact reactor operating at a very high temperature (to minimize radiator area) and having ceramic fuel, such as uranium oxide, carbide, or nitride, with fuel elements of such temperature-resistant metals as niobium, tantalum, and tungsten. It would be unmoderated. Usable energy would be produced by an electric generator driven by a small turbine or by pumping the electrically conductive metal coolants through magnetic-field regions, thus inducing electric currents by so-called **magnetohydrodynamic** effects.

Work on a mercury-Rankine-cycle turboelectric system has indicated a potential capacity of 5 kwe, while a potassium-Rankine system is projected for capacity of 300 kwe. These systems have the unusual complications of a two-phase working fluid operating under zero-gravity conditions.

HEALTH PHYSICS

Radiation, which accompanies all nuclear reactions, can be advantageous or disadvantageous, depending generally on the manner in which contact is made and on the amount of energy involved. In its application to human beings, the common terminology is "radiation dose," which is measured in units of **roentgen (r), rad,** and **rem.** Each of these units is applicable to a different type of dose: (1) roentgen, to exposure dose; (2) rad, to absorbed dose; and (3) rem, to dose equivalent (DE), formerly called **RBE dose.** The roentgen is a physical unit, and it is applicable only to X and gamma radiation. A measurement in roentgens is a determination of the ionization produced in air under specified conditions. The rad is also a physical unit, and it is a measure of the energy absorbed from radiation per unit mass of irradiated material. Unlike the roentgen, the rad is applicable to all types of ionizing radiation. A roentgen (of X or gamma rays), however, is not biologically equivalent to a rad of other types of radiation; neither is a rad of one type of radiation biologically equivalent to a rad of a different type of radiation. Therefore, a dose in rads must have certain modifying factors applied to it in order to relate it to biological effect. For radiation-protection purposes, use is made of **dose equivalent,** which is defined as the product of absorbed dose (in rads), quality factor (QF), dose distribution factor (DF), and other necessary modifying factors. The unit of dose equivalent is the rem. For purposes of radiation protection, any of the following external doses may be considered to be equivalent to a dose of 1 rem: (1) 1 r of X or gamma radiation; (2) 1 rad of X, gamma, or beta radiation; (3) 0.1 rad of neutrons or high-energy protons; and (4) 0.05 rad of particles heavier than protons and with sufficient energy to reach the lens of the eye.

Exposure to radiation may be divided into two general types: (1) external exposure, which is that resulting from radiation sources external to the body; and (2) internal exposure, which is that resulting from radionuclides within the body. Radiation-protection standards are established for both types of exposure. Limits for external exposure are given in units of rem (or rad) per unit time. Basic limits are usually for a control period of ¼ year and for 1 year. Local operational rules may specify control limits for shorter exposure times (day, week, month), such limits being based on the basic limits. Radiation-protection standards for controlling internal exposures are based on the same basic limits as those for external exposures. Controls however, are effected by use of maximum-permissible-concentration (MPC) values established for each of the various radionuclides, for both air and water. Many factors (physical, chemical, biological, and physiological) are involved in determining the MPC of a radionuclide. As such, the MPC's of the radionuclides have a very wide range of values. MPC's are normally expressed in units of microcuries (μc) per cc of air (or water). Generally, MPC values are based on a 40-hr work week for radiation workers and on a 168-hr week for the general population.

Monitoring is the periodic or continuous determination of the presence and extent of ionizing radiation and radioactive contamination. It provides information for radiation protection and normally is assigned to a health physics group, which establishes schedules, executes or supervises the operations, and evaluates their results. It is divided into these special types: personnel, area, source, surface, air, and water.

Regulations governing exposure to radiation are promulgated in the form of AEC Regulations—Title 10, Chapter 1, Part 20. Reference to the current full statement of Part 20 is mandatory for a full understanding of the regulations. As a general guide, material and equipment must be shielded and the exposure time limited so that no worker will receive a radiation dose during a calendar quarter in excess of 1¼ rems on whole body, head and trunk, active blood-forming organs, lenses of eyes, or gonads; 18¾ rems on hands and forearms, feet and ankles; and 7½ rems on skin of whole body.

REACTOR SAFETY

It is physically impossible for a reactor to explode in the nuclear sense, but an uncontrolled increase in power or loss of coolant could cause the core to vaporize and release radioactive material. However, if a major amount of vaporized metal reacts with water suddenly, the energy release from the chemical reaction can be much more than that from the nuclear reaction.

The important feature in controlling a reactor is to be sure that the introduction of reactivity is slow enough so that control elements always can counteract the introduced reactivity with an appreciable safety factor. It is desirable to have more than one channel of control to reduce reactivity. Even better is to have a reactor design which inherently compensates itself without instruments or controls.

Design should provide against sudden changes in temperature to protect material against undue stresses, strains, warping, and breaking. Failures in auxiliary equipment, such as pumps and power supply, must be provided against with auxiliary units. It is especially important to plan against failure of the coolant system since all reactors require positive cooling to remove the heat from decay of fission products even after shutdown.

It is customary to design the control system so that it is mechanically impossible to remove control rods at a rate in excess of the safe rate and so that they will "fail safe." Careful training of operating personnel should be correlated with a positive system of interlocks on all vital parts of the control system.

As a final precaution, it is customary to contain the reactor in such a manner that, if an accident does occur, the results will be confined to the immediate area. This may take the form of a vaportight steel shell, a large pool of water, or a combination of both. As additional protection against the unlikely occurrence of an accident releasing large amounts of radioactivity, the container should be lined with high-density concrete, or the reactor should be located below grade. Actually, the distance over which accident hazards could exist is relatively short. The layer of air reducing the average fission-product γ-ray intensity to one-half is about 284 ft, and the inverse-square law reduces intensity still more rapidly.

If a nuclear reactor is of the proper design and is operated and supervised adequately, it will have a low accident probability. In addition, if properly contained, it can be located anywhere. The cost of excessive safety features and the frailties of human behavior must be factored in the design and location of a reactor, just as they must be in designing and engineering other equipment.

HYDRAULIC TURBINES

BY

Wm. J. Rheingans

REFERENCES: Daugherty, "Hydraulic Turbines," McGraw-Hill. Daugherty and Ingersoll, "Fluid Mechanics," McGraw-Hill. Barrows, "Water Power Engineering," McGraw-Hill. Creager and Justin, "Hydroelectric Handbook," Wiley.

GENERAL

Notation:

B = width of distributor or height of wicket gates, in.
D = diameter of runner, in.
D_1 = diameter of runner, at center line of guide case, in.
D_{th} = throat diameter of runner, in.
D_r = relative diameter of runner, in. (= entrance diameter for low-speed Francis turbines; throat diameter for high-speed Francis turbines; bore of throat ring at center line of blade for propeller turbines)
D_d = diameter top of draft tube, in.
D_p = pitch diameter of impulse turbine runner, in.
d = jet diameter of impulse turbine, in.
e = over-all efficiency of turbine = $e_h \times e_m$
e_h = hydraulic efficiency (including draft tube)
e_m = mechanical efficiency
g = acceleration of gravity
H = net effective head, ft
h = head change due to load change, ft
n = rpm
n_1 = rpm at 1 ft head = $n/\sqrt{H}$
n_s = specific speed = $n\sqrt{P}/H^{5/4} = n_1\sqrt{P_1}$
P = horsepower
P_1 = horsepower at 1 ft head = $P/H^{3/2}$
Q = discharge, cfs
Q_1 = discharge at 1 ft head = $Q/\sqrt{H}$, cfs
t = thickness, in., or time, sec
u = circumferential velocity of a point on runner, fps
V = absolute velocity of water, fps
V_u = tangential component of absolute velocity = $V \cos \alpha$
V_r = component of V in radial plane
v = velocity of water relative to runner, fps
w = weight of water per cu ft
z = number of runner buckets (blades for propeller turbines)
α = angle between V and u (measured between positive directions)
β = angle between v and u (measured between positive directions)
θ = angle of water deflection relative to bucket
ϕ = peripheral coefficient = $\pi Dn/720\sqrt{2gH}$
σ = cavitation coefficient

Fundamental Formulas. The theoretical horsepower P_T of a hydraulic turbine can be expressed as

$$P_T = HQw/550 = HQ/8.82$$

The actual horsepower of a hydraulic turbine is the theoretical horsepower multiplied by the turbine efficiency e,

$$P = eP_T = eHQ/8.82$$

The laws of proportionality for homologous turbines are:

For constant runner diam	For constant head	For variable diam and head
$P \propto H^{3/2}$	$P \propto D^2$	$P \propto D^2H^{3/2}$
$n \propto H^{1/2}$	$n \propto 1/D$	$n \propto H^{1/2}/D$
$Q \propto H^{1/2}$	$Q \propto D^2$	$Q \propto D^2H^{1/2}$

Nomenclature. The nomenclature used throughout this section is based on NEMA's standards publication HT1-1957, "Hydraulic Turbines, Governors and Accessory Equipment," which also contains definitions and purchase specifications.

Types of Turbines. There are three characteristic types of hydraulic turbines now in general use: the **impulse** type (Fig. 12); the **Francis reaction** type (Fig. 1); and the **propeller reaction** type (Fig. 3). The propeller type may be further divided into fixed- and adjustable-blade types. All three types have in common a stationary guide case (or nozzle in the case of the impulse type) in which the static head is transformed partly, or wholly, into velocity, and a revolving part, the runner.

In the guide case of the impulse turbine, the static head is completely transformed into velocity, so that air surrounds both the jet issuing from the nozzle and the runner.

In the guide case of the reaction types, the static head is only partly transformed into velocity, leaving an overpressure between the guide case and the runner. This overpressure causes an acceleration of the relative velocity of the water passing through the runner, the discharge area of which is smaller than the entrance area. Except when operating vented at low loads, the water passages are completely filled with water from the intake to the end of the draft tube.

The impulse type is of relatively low (specific) speed, suitable for the higher heads; the Francis type is of relatively medium speed, suitable for medium heads; while the propeller type is of relatively high speed, suitable for low heads.

For higher speeds, more than one runner may be employed on one shaft. This is limited to horizontal-shaft arrangements of small or medium-sized Francis turbines and to impulse turbines.

Selection of Turbine Type and Casing. Impulse turbines receive their water supply directly from a pipeline. Francis and propeller reaction types are set either in an open flume or in a case of concrete or metal. While the limits of head to which the impulse and reaction types are adopted may be fairly well defined in practice, as roughly outlined in Table 1, there is no definite line where the application of one type ends and the other begins. The limits given in the table should not be taken as representing absolute points beyond which the respective types are not suitable, but rather, as an indication of general practice. The choice between impulse and reaction types depends upon the size of the unit as well as upon the head and other considerations.

Specific Speed. The common basis of comparison between turbine runners of different types and between runners of the same type but different design and characteristics is termed *specific speed* n_s. This is the constant relationship between the speed of a runner at the point of highest efficiency and the maximum power output at this speed regardless of size. However, since both power and speed vary with head, specific speed is defined as the relationship between the speed n_1 and power P_1 at 1-ft head. Subscript 1 denotes that the value is reduced by the similarity law to a 1-ft-head basis. Since $n \propto 1/D$ and $P \propto D^2$, the product $n_1\sqrt{P_1}$ remains a constant regardless of the size of the runner and is designated the specific speed of the runner.

Table 1. General Arrangements of Turbine Installations and Usual Head Limits Employed

Type	Setting	Construction	Number of runners	Usual head limits for direct-connected units, ft
Reaction turbines, 5 to 1,300 ft head	Open flume, 5 to 40 ft head	Vertical	1	5–40
		Horizontal	1 2 4	12–40 16–40 16–30
	Encased, 15 to 1,300 ft head	Plate steel, vertical	1	40–300
		Plate steel, horizontal	1	30–100
		Plate steel, horizontal	2	30–100
		Concrete, vertical	1	15–50
		Concrete spiral, vertical	1	15–90
		Cast or welded-plate steel spiral, vertical	1	75–1,300
		Cast or welded-plate steel spiral, horizontal	1	50–600
		Cast or welded-plate steel spiral, horizontal	2	50–500
Impulse wheels, 500 to 5,500 ft head	Encased	Horizontal	1 2	500–5,500 500–1,500
		Vertical	1	500–5,500

The term *specific speed* for this relationship stems from the fact that $n_1 \sqrt{P_1}$ also is the value of the speed in rpm at best efficiency which the runner would have if operated under 1-ft head, the runner being of such size as to develop 1 hp ($P_1 = 1$).

Since $n \propto \sqrt{H}$ and $P \propto H^{3/2}$, the specific speed of any runner operating under head H will be $n_s = n \sqrt{P}/H^{5/4}$, where n is the best-efficiency speed and P the maximum power output at this speed, all at head H.

Selecting the Speed. Hydraulic turbines are usually connected to a-c generators. The turbine speed must agree with one of the synchronous speeds required for the system frequency. The prevailing frequency for most systems in America is 60 cps. Synchronous speeds are determined by the formula $n = 120 \times$ frequency/number of poles in generator. The number of poles must be even.

The speed should be as high as practicable as the higher the speed the less expensive will be the turbine and generator and the more efficient will be the generator.

A convenient way of determining the highest practicable speed is by the relation of the specific speed to the head. For Francis turbines this may be taken as $n_s = 675/\sqrt{H}$; for propeller-type turbines as $n_s = 500/(H)^{1/3}$. The adoption of these values of specific speed is predicated on the use of a reasonable setting of the unit with reference to tail-water level, *i.e.*, selection of proper cavitation coefficient (see p. 9–199.)

Number of Units. From the standpoint of reducing the number of auxiliaries and the amount of associated equipment and also reducing initial and maintenance costs for the entire plant, the number of units should be kept to a minimum. Also the larger the unit, the higher the efficiency. However, other considerations, such as flexibility of operation, higher-efficiency operation during low-load demands, and minimum loss of capacity during shutdown for repair or maintenance, might dictate the use of multiple units where one unit would be feasible in terms of physical size. For some projects, the physical size of the unit has been limited to the maximum-size runner that could be shipped in one piece; this is largely due to the extra manufacturing costs involved in furnishing split runners. However, since split runners present no serious mechanical difficulties, the tendency in recent years has been to disregard this limitation. Another limitation on size is the availability of machine tools for machining large turbine parts.

REACTION TURBINES

Francis. Figure 1 shows a Francis-type inward-flow reaction turbine for medium head. The runner consists of a relatively large number of shrouded buckets. Movable wicket gates with axes parallel to the turbine shaft control the flow. This type of turbine is normally used for heads ranging from 75 to 1,300 ft. Specific speeds vary from 15 to 100. Low-specific-speed runners have narrow inlet passages. For high-specific-speed runners, the width of the runner inlet is increased (Fig. 2).

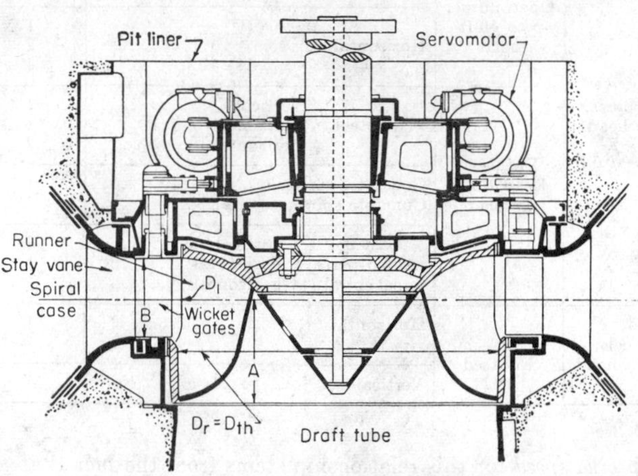

FIG. 1. Medium-head Francis turbine.

Propeller Turbines, Fixed and Adjustable Blade. The propeller turbine has a runner which is normally provided with from 3 to 8 unshrouded blades, either fixed or adjustable. This type of turbine usually is used for heads from 10 ft or even less up to 120 ft, although in a few cases they have been used for heads up to 200 ft. The higher the head, the greater the number of blades used. Specific speeds vary from 80 to 250. Propellers have very steep efficiency-versus-power curves (4 and 5, Fig. 5). Adjustable-blade propeller runners are used to produce a flat efficiency curve over a wide range of power (6, Fig. 5) and to produce considerably more power beyond the maximum-efficiency point than can be obtained with a fixed-blade runner of equal diameter. For fixed-blade runners the blade angle is usually set between 16 and 20 deg, where maximum efficiency occurs. For adjustable-blade runners, the blade angle may vary from 10 deg min to 32 deg max. The blades may be adjusted by hand or motor. However, these methods have been largely abandoned in favor of the automatically oil-pressure-operated blades commonly called a **Kaplan turbine** (Fig. 3). The blades are adjusted by means of an oil-operated piston located either within the main shaft or in the runner hub above or below the runner blades. The oil is admitted to and discharged from the piston by means of a distributor head either on top of the generator shaft or surrounding the main shaft below the generator. The oil pressure is supplied from the governor oil-pressure system. The controls are so arranged that the blade tilt varies automatically with the wicket-gate opening so as to produce a maxi-

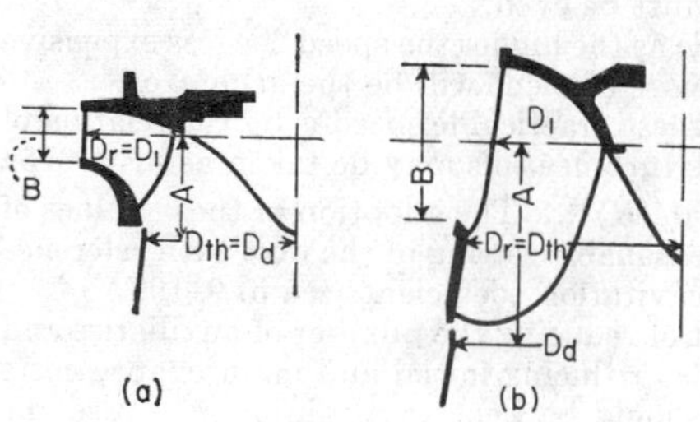

FIG. 2. Typical profiles of Francis-type runners: (*a*) low specific speed; (*b*) high specific speed.

mum-efficiency envelope curve (Fig. 9). A large operating-cylinder capacity is required. The S, ft-lb, may be approximated from the formula $S = 20Pn_s^{1/4}/\sqrt{H}$. If antifriction bearings are used in the hub instead of bronze bearings for the blade trunnions, this formula becomes $S = 4Pn_s^{1/4}/\sqrt{H}$. However, since the hydraulic unbalance on the blades varies with speed, gate opening, and the location of the blade pivot axis, the cylinder size should be calculated from model test data.

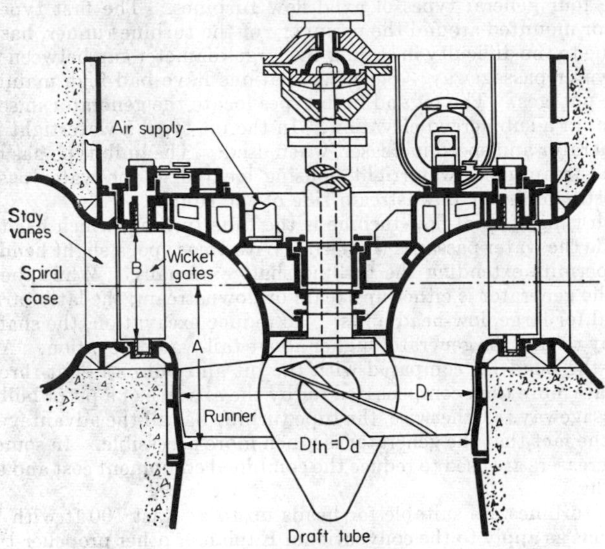

FIG. 3. Adjustable-blade Kaplan-type turbine.

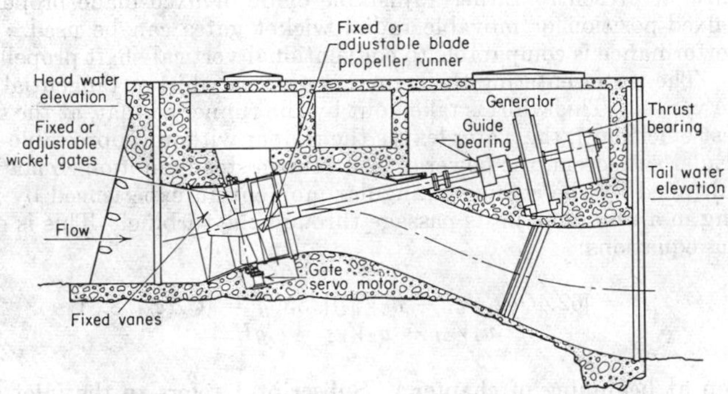

FIG. 4. Axial-flow tube-type turbine.

Axial-flow Turbines. Axial-flow turbines use the propeller-type runner with either fixed or adjustable blades. Their characteristic feature is the straight-through, or nearly straight-through, water passageway from intake to discharge. The shaft is, therefore, either horizontal or inclined (Fig. 4). The spiral or semispiral case and elbow draft tube, which require substantial widths and depth of excavation, are eliminated. Therefore, with a reduction in height and area of the powerhouse and the turbine's suitability for location directly within the dam, an over-all construction-cost savings of up to 35 percent can be obtained for the power-plant part of the project compared with conventional vertical units. This makes it possible to build or redevelop power plants for low heads or in small sizes that have previously been considered uneconomical.

In recent years, axial-flow turbines have been considered seriously for use with tidal power since they can be arranged to operate with water flowing in either direction and, when required, to pump with water flowing in either direction in addition to operating as turbines.

There are four general types of axial-flow turbines. The first type, having the generator rotor mounted around the periphery of the turbine runner, has been largely abandoned due to the difficulty in sealing the large-diameter gap between the rotor and the turbine water passageway. Such installations have had high maintenance costs and excessive outages. The **pit** and **bulb** types locate the generator in series with the turbine runner at a submerged elevation. In the pit type, a watertight pit is used to house the generator and speed increaser, when used. The bulb type has the generator enclosed in a streamlined, watertight housing located in the water passageway, on either the upstream or the downstream side of the runner.

The fourth type of axial-flow turbine is the **tube** turbine, which has the generator located outside the water passages (Fig. 4). With this type, a slight bend in the water passageway permits extending the turbine shaft externally. While the unit can be arranged so the generator is either upstream or downstream, the latter arrangement is more practical for large, low-head units. To reduce excavation, the shaft may be inclined, thereby raising the generator higher above tail-water elevation. Any hydraulic losses due to the bend (as compared with the pit and bulb straight-through flow arrangements) are more than compensated for by the absence of a pit or bulb obstructing the water passageway. Otherwise, the tube turbine has all the advantages of the bulb turbine plus the fact that the generator is much more accessible. In some cases, gear-type speed increasers are used to reduce the combined equipment cost and the generator size and weight.

Axial-flow turbines are suitable for heads up to at least 100 ft with basically the same limitations as apply to the conventional Kaplan or other propeller-type turbines. Maximum unit capacity is limited, however, by maximum practical speed-increaser torques and maximum practical horizontal-generator capacities. This appears to be approx 50 mw at present. Either adjustable-blade or fixed-blade propeller runners and either fixed-position or movable radial wicket gates can be used. Power and efficiency performance is comparable to conventional vertical-shaft propeller turbines.

Design. The water entering the runner is given a whirl or tangential component by the guide vanes. This whirl is taken out by the runner so that, at the design point (point of best efficiency), the water leaves the runner without appreciable whirl. According to Euler's theorem, the power of a turbine in steady motion equals the angular velocity multiplied by the change in angular momentum experienced by the mass of water flowing in a unit time in its passage through the turbine. This is expressed in the following equations:

$$P = [62.4Q(u_1V_{u1} - u_2V_{u2})]/550g = (QHe_h)/8.81 \quad (1)$$

and

$$u_1V_{u1} - u_2V_{u2} = e_hgH \quad (2)$$

(See notation at beginning of chapter.) Subscript 1 refers to the inlet edge of the bucket and 2 to the discharge edge.

In practice e_h may be taken as 0.92 to 0.94, and the term u_2V_{u2} may be omitted as it becomes zero for discharge in a radial plane, $\alpha_2 = 90$ deg.

The right-hand member of Eq. (**2**) may be regarded as a fixed value for a given head. Consequently, in order to have a high-speed-type runner (u_1, large) the whirl V_{u1} placed in the water by the guide case must be small. This means that for the best load, low-speed low-capacity (small n_s) runners will have relatively small gate openings and short wicket gates, whereas high-speed high-capacity (large n_s) runners will have relatively large gate openings and long wicket gates.

Equations (**1**) and (**2**) are used in designing the runner and guide case. The P and Q used in Eq. (**1**) are for the point of best efficiency and not for the rated values. For specific speeds up to about 60 the power at best efficiency may be taken as 85 percent of the rated power. Above that specific speed the point of best efficiency occurs at higher loads as indicated in Fig. 5. Adjustable-blade-propeller turbine-runner blades are laid out for an intermediate load of 75 to 80 percent of the rated load. The actual design of a runner should be worked out by an experienced designer on the basis of coordinated test data.

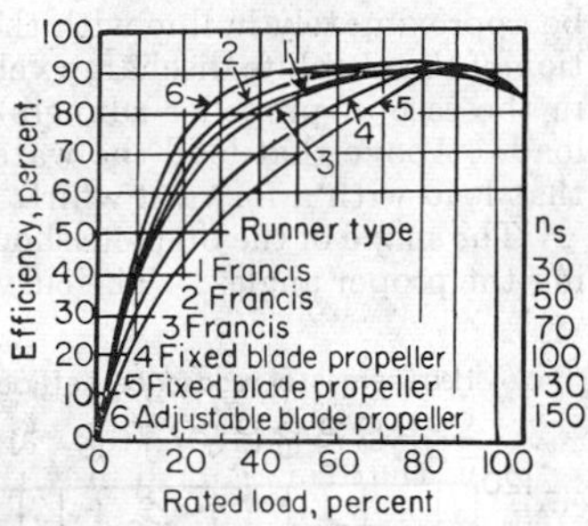

FIG. 5. Efficiency-load relations for reaction turbines.

The general proportions of a normal line of turbine runners may be determined as follows for any combination of net head H and rated horsepower P. (Rated horsepower is usually considered to be 95 percent of full gate power.)

First select the specific speed appropriate to the head (see page 9–185). Next calculate n from the formula $n_s = n\sqrt{P}/H^{5/4}$. If n is not a synchronous speed, select the nearest synchronous speed and calculate the corresponding n_s. This value of n_s may be used in Fig. 6 to determine the peripheral coefficient ϕ for D_r and D_1. Then the diameter may be determined from the formula $\phi = \pi D_n/720 \sqrt{2gH}$.

Other proportions of the runner may be determined from Fig. 7, which shows the ratio to D_r of width of distributor B; diameter at top of draft tube D_d; and center line of distributor to top of draft tube A. See Fig. 1 for D_r, B, and A.

The values of unit power P_1, and unit speed n_1, for $D_r = 100$, which correspond to the specific speed of the runner may be determined from Fig. 6. The following formulas may then be used: $P = P_1 H^{3/2}(D_r/100)^2$ and $n = n_1\sqrt{H}(100/D_r)$. These formulas may be used to verify the diameter calculated from the peripheral coefficient,

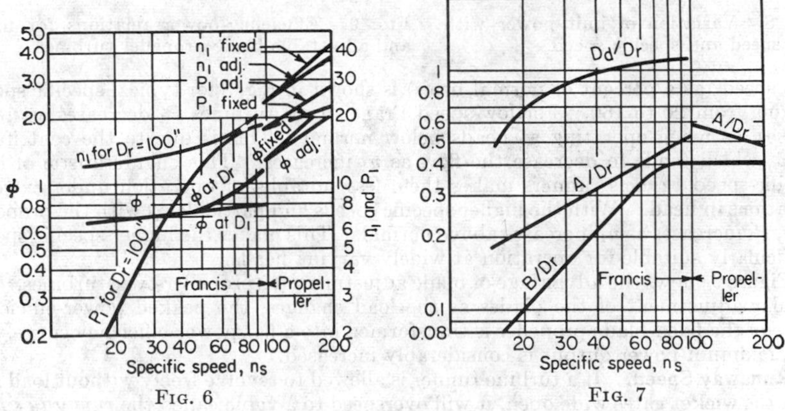

FIG. 6

FIG. 7

FIGS. 6 and 7. Turbine characteristics and specific speed.

and will prove useful in selecting runner sizes for units which must meet power requirements other than rated power at design head. In such cases the values of n_1 and P_1 from Fig. 6 should be used in conjunction with Fig. 8.

For preliminary powerhouse layouts these ratios of diameter to D_r may be used for all specific speeds: gate circle, 1.20; stay ring, 1.65; pit liner, 1.50; unit spacing, 3.5 to 4.5.

The clearance space between the discharge tips of the wicket gates and the entrance edge of the runner buckets is treated as a free vortex space in which the tangential component of the absolute velocity of discharge from the gates (V_u) increases in inverse proportion to the radius while the component in a radial plane (V_r) increases in inverse proportion to the area.

To obtain the best efficiency, the water must enter the runner without shock and leave it with as little velocity as possible; *i.e.*, the entrance angles of the buckets must be approximately in line with the relative direction of the entering flow and the direction of the absolute discharge velocity should be approximately in a radial plane (axial in the case of propeller runners). This condition prevails only at the most efficient load. Above that load the water enters the draft tube with reverse whirl and below that load with a forward whirl.

The shape of the buckets should be kept as simple as possible, consistent with meeting the proper angles. The curvature of the bucket along a flow line is made greatest near the entrance and reduces as the discharge edge is approached, somewhat the shape of a portion of a parabola.

Turbine Characteristics. Speed, power, and efficiency characteristics vary widely with specific speed as shown in Figs. 5 and 6. The variation of unit power P_1 with the unit speed (as a percent of normal basis) is shown in Fig. 8 for typical specific speeds ranging from 20 to 160. For low-speed Francis-type turbines P_1 decreases as n_1 increases, as when operating at heads below normal. This is due to the centrifugal effect, which tends to decrease the flow as n_1 increases. This characteristic of low-specific-speed Francis runners makes them less suitable for operation under extreme variations in head. With the higher specific speeds and particularly with the propeller type, P_1 increases as n_1 increases above normal. This makes the higher specific speeds particularly suitable for operation at widely varying heads.

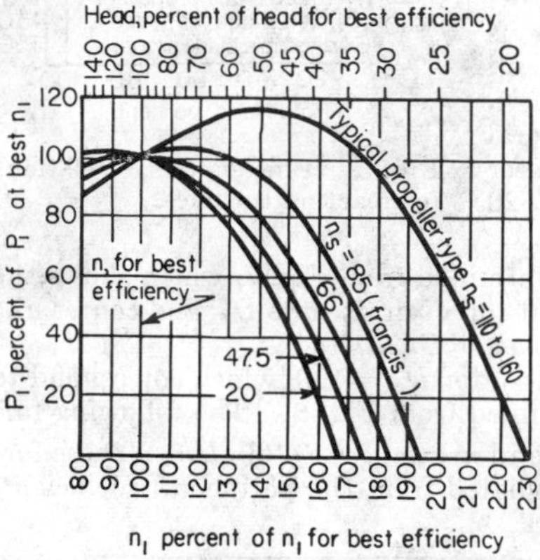

FIG. 8. Variation of unit power with unit speed and specific speed.

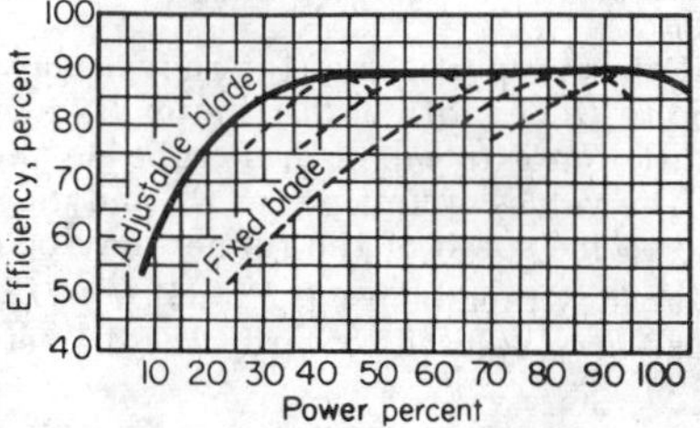

FIG. 9. Efficiency-power relations for fixed- and adjustable-blade propeller turbines.

Figure 9 shows the advantage of blade adjustment for propeller-type turbines. By angular adjustment of the blades as the load changes, the peaked power-efficiency curve of the fixed-blade propeller is transformed into a flat power-efficiency curve, and the maximum power output is considerably increased.

Runaway Speed. If a turbine runner is allowed to revolve freely without load and with the wicket gates wide open, it will overspeed to a value called the *runaway speed*. The runaway speed, at normal head, varies with the specific speed and for Francis turbines ranges from 170 percent (normal speed = 100 percent) at low specific speed (n_s = 20) to some 195 percent at high specific speed (n_s = 100). For propeller turbines, the runaway speed varies with blade angle—the steeper the blade angle, the lower the runaway speed. For fixed-blade propellers with the blades set from 16 to 20 deg, where maximum efficiency is usually obtained, the runaway speed ranges approx from 255 to 235 percent, respectively. For adjustable-blade turbines, where the minimum blade angle is sometimes as low as 10 to 12 deg in order to obtain high efficiency at part load, the maximum possible runaway speed will be about 290 to 270 percent, respectively. However, with adjustable-blade propeller turbines, there is from the standpoint of efficiency an optimum relationship between runner-blade angle and wicket-gate opening, usually controlled by a cam in the operating mechanism; the higher the gate opening, the steeper the blade angle. Thus the combination of wide-open gate and minimum-design blade angle can only occur in the so called "off-cam" position, which is an extremely rare possibility. In most units, this maximum possible off-cam runaway speed is reduced by limiting the minimum-design blade angle to 14 to 16 deg. Another method is the use of a runaway-speed limiter. There are several designs in use. One of the most reliable is a valve designed to open by centrifugal force at speeds of 130 percent approx. The open valve bypasses the runner-blade servomotor piston, thus equalizing the oil pressure on both sides of this piston. If the runner blades are designed to open because of hydraulic unbalance at overspeeds, they will then go to a higher blade angle under off-cam overspeed conditions. The off-cam runaway speed thus can be limited to some 185 percent if the runner is designed for a maximum blade angle of 28 to 32 deg.

For all turbines, if the maximum head is higher than the normal head, the runaway speed will be increased in proportion to the square root of the head. Therefore, runaway speeds should be based on the maximum operating head rather than on the normal head. Any runaway speed above 200 percent can increase appreciably the cost of the generator.

Turbine Thrust and WR^2. The turbine thrust is usually carried by a thrust bearing furnished with the generator. For vertical units the thrust, T, consists of the hydraulic thrust, T_h, plus the weight of the turbine runner and shaft, T_w, lb.

The hydraulic thrust is obtained by using a thrust coefficient K_t multiplied by the weight, lb, of a circular column of water whose diameter is the diameter of the runner D_r, in., and whose height is equal to the maximum head H_m, ft, under which the turbine must operate, or $T_h = K_t D_r^2 H_m / 2.94$.

The thrust coefficient for Francis turbines varies with the specific speed and may be taken as approximately $K_t = n_s/250$. In using this value of K_t it is assumed that the runner seals are properly arranged and that the crown of the runner inside the seals is properly drained, otherwise the thrust may be much higher.

For propeller turbines, with either fixed or adjustable blades, the thrust coefficient K_t may be taken as 0.90 for all specific speeds.

Reaction-turbine Elements

Runner and Wearing Rings. The number of buckets z for Francis runners ranges from about 21 for low specific speed to 12 for high specific speed. The approximate number may be taken as $z = 55/n_s^{1/3}$.

The number of blades for propeller-type turbines ranges from 8 for low specific speeds to 3 for high specific speeds.

Most runners are made of cast steel, which can readily be repaired by welding with either mild- or stainless-steel electrodes. Cast iron is sometimes used for low- and medium-head Francis turbines. Built-up runners with pressed-steel or cast-steel buckets welded to the crown and band are sometimes used for Francis turbines. The welded type is suitable for very large runners. Bronze may be used for smaller runners of all types and for medium-high heads. The use of cast stainless-steel runners is increasing, particularly for small and medium-sized runners for high heads and for conditions where pitting may be troublesome.

Propeller runners are practically always made of cast steel, and the surfaces over which pitting may be expected are overlaid with stainless-steel welding, before finishing to the final contour. In place of overlay welding, solid stainless-steel inserts are sometimes welded into the Francis buckets or propeller blades.

The functions of the runner seals for Francis turbines are to prevent excessive leakage loss and thus improve the efficiency; to reduce the hydraulic thrust; to prevent seizure in operation; and to prevent undue wear.

Rolled, forged, and cast steels make excellent wearing rings for low- and medium-head units. To prevent seizure in case of contact the rotating ring material should differ from that of the stationary rings, and any material which contains nickel, including stainless, should not be used for either ring. Stainless steel, bronze, or steel with bronze inserts make excellent wearing rings. For extremely high heads, stainless steel should be used to prevent undue wear and erosion. Wearing rings should be made renewable, or provision should be made for restoration of clearances by welding and remachining.

Seal clearances are made as small as practicable to reduce leakage, particularly on high-head units. Larger clearances are required with water-lubricated main bearings, subject to considerable wear before being readjusted.

Main-shaft Bearing. The main shaft must be rigid and is made of a medium grade of forged steel, with torsional stress ranging from 4,000 to 6,000 psi.

For water-lubricated bearings a bronze or, preferably, stainless-steel sleeve is installed on the bearing surface. Such a sleeve is also put on the shaft adjacent to the packing box.

Turbines are usually provided with one main bearing located in the head cover as near the runner as practicable. This is usually babbitted and in halves, with an independent low-pressure oiling system. Self-lubricated babbitted bearings, containing an oil reservoir and pumping grooves in the babbitt, are sometimes used.

Water-lubricated bearings of lignum vitae, rubber, or special composition materials are sometimes preferred, particularly for small and medium-sized propeller-type turbines where the bearing is located at the bottom of the head cover cone and where the packing box of an oil-lubricated bearing would be inaccessible and where it would be difficult to avoid water contamination. With the water-lubricated bearing the packing box is placed above the bearing.

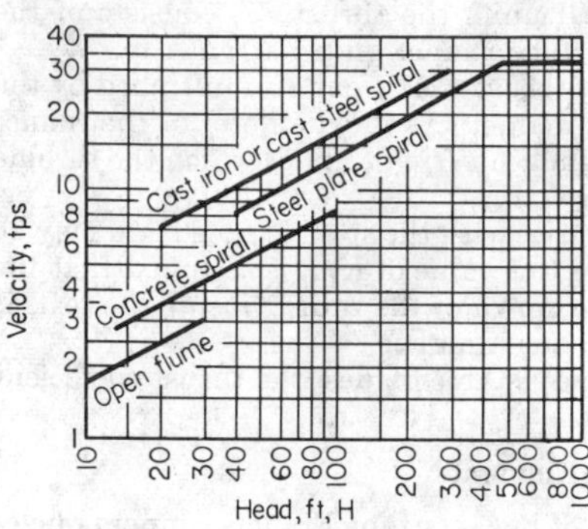

FIG. 10. Case velocities.

Spiral Case. The spiral case must be proportioned so as to cause relatively low friction losses, as well as to prevent eddying which would travel into the runner and affect its efficiency. The cases generally used are (1) metal case: cast steel, cast iron, or steel plate, and (2) concrete case. Metal cases are made as complete spirals, customarily with uniform or slightly increasing velocity from the throat to the small end. It is preferable that the water be accelerated as it approaches the case in order to suppress vortices. When a valve is used at the case entrance, the net area at the center line of the valve should be at least equal to the case entrance area.

Concrete cases may be complete spirals or semispirals, rectangular or oval in cross section. There should be no piers close to the turbine.

Rated load velocities for general practice for cases of various types are shown in Fig. 10. Higher velocities are sometimes used with the larger units to reduce size and cost.

Stay Ring. That part of the guide apparatus between the spiral case and the wicket gates, containing stationary stay vanes, is called the stay ring. The water is accelerated within this space as it approaches the gates. The number of stay vanes employed is usually made equal to or one-half the number of gates. They are placed at that angle which will cause the least obstruction to the flow.

The stay ring is cast integral with cast-steel and cast-iron cases and is made separately of cast iron or of welded or cast steel for concrete or steel-plate spiral cases. It should be a continuous ring to facilitate erection, and very rigid, because it serves as a foundation for the rest of the turbine.

Wicket Gates and Operating Mechanism. Wicket gates control the power and speed of the turbine. The number of gates m ranges from 12 for small units to 28 for large units. The over-all dimensions of the turbine decrease as the number of gates increase.

To prevent interference between the gates and the runner buckets, which may cause noise and vibration, the discharge tips of the fully open gates should be kept well away from the inlet edges of the runner buckets of Francis turbines, the radial clearance being large enough to prevent the gate tips from overhanging the curved part of the discharge ring.

The height and angular movement of the gates increase with the specific speed. The angular movement varies from 15 deg for low specific speed to 50 deg for high specific speed.

Most wicket gates are made of cast steel; a few, for higher heads, are made of forged steel; some, for lower heads, are weldments built from rolled materials and castings. To reduce wear, the gate tips and ends may be coated with stainless steel welded on before final finishing.

Each gate connection to the operating ring should be provided with a breaking element to protect the gate and other mechanism in case of an obstruction. Each gate should also be provided with stops to prevent it from striking the runner or reversing after the breaking element fails.

The capacity G, foot-pounds, of the oil-pressure cylinder or cylinders (sometimes known as governor capacity) may be computed from the formula

$$G = 18Pn_s^{1/4}/\sqrt{H}$$

One or more **vacuum breakers** or **air valves** are installed in the head cover to admit air to the runner or draft tube, to improve efficiency at low gate openings or to alleviate draft-tube vortex cavitation. An air valve is also necessary on propeller-type units to break the vacuum under the head cover and to help prevent the runner from "screwing up" in the water when the gates are suddenly closed. The air valve is piped to the outside of the power house above the flood-water level.

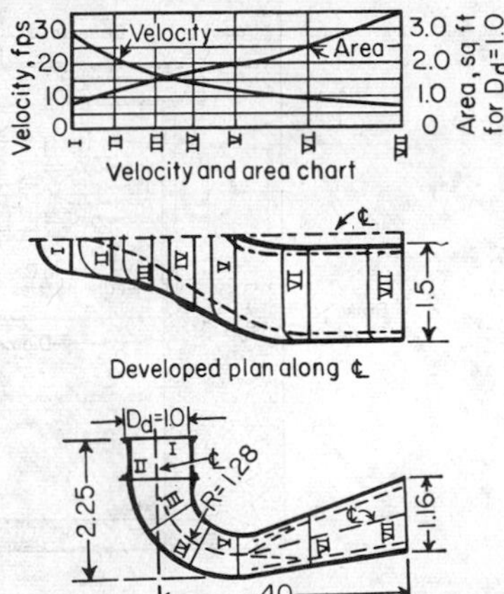

FIG. 11. Elbow draft-tube layout.

Draft Tubes. The draft tube serves the double purpose of (1) allowing the turbine to be set above tail-water level, without loss of head, to facilitate inspection and maintenance, and (2) regaining, by diffuser action, the major portion of the kinetic energy delivered to it from the runner.

At rated load the velocity at the upstream end of the tube for modern units ranges from 24 to 30 fps, representing from 9 to 16 ft head. As the specific speed is increased and the head reduced, it becomes increasingly more important to have an efficient draft tube. Good practice limits the velocity at the discharge end of the tube to 5 to 7 fps, representing less than 1 ft velocity head loss.

Two types of tubes are commonly used: (1) the straight conical or concentric tube and (2) the elbow type. Properly designed, the two types are about equally efficient, over 85 percent.

The **conical type** is generally used on low-powered units for all specific speeds and, frequently, on large high-head units. The side angle of flare ranges from 4 to 6 deg, the length from 3 to 4 D_d, and the discharge area from four to five times the throat area.

The **elbow type** of tube is now used with most turbine installations. With this type the vertical portion begins with a conical section which gradually flattens in the elbow section and then discharges horizontally through substantially rectangular sections to the tail race. Most of the regain of energy takes place in the vertical portion, very little in the elbow section which is shaped to deliver the water to the horizontal portion so that the regain may be efficiently completed. Figure 11 shows proportions of a good elbow tube, taken as the average proportions from a large number of recent installations. One or two vertical piers are placed in the horizontal portion of the tube for structural and hydraulic reasons.

Small conical tubes are sometimes made entirely of steel plate. Most tubes are made of concrete with a steel-plate lining extending from the upper end to a point where the velocity has been sufficiently reduced (say 15 fps) to prevent erosion of the concrete. Sometimes the liner is carried around the elbow. Pier noses are also lined where necessary to prevent erosion and for structural reasons.

IMPULSE TURBINES

Impulse turbines are utilized when the head is too high for the practical use of Francis turbines, which is normally any head exceeding 1,300 ft. Impulse turbines are also sometimes used for heads below 1,300 ft where excessive erosion due to foreign materials in the water presents a problem or to provide simplicity in operation and maintenance. The main disadvantage of impulse turbines, especially for low heads, is their low specific speed. In the past, this was overcome on conventional horizontal-shaft units by the use of two runners or two jets per runner. In recent years, the vertical-shaft multijet impulse turbine (Fig. 12) has become increasingly popular.

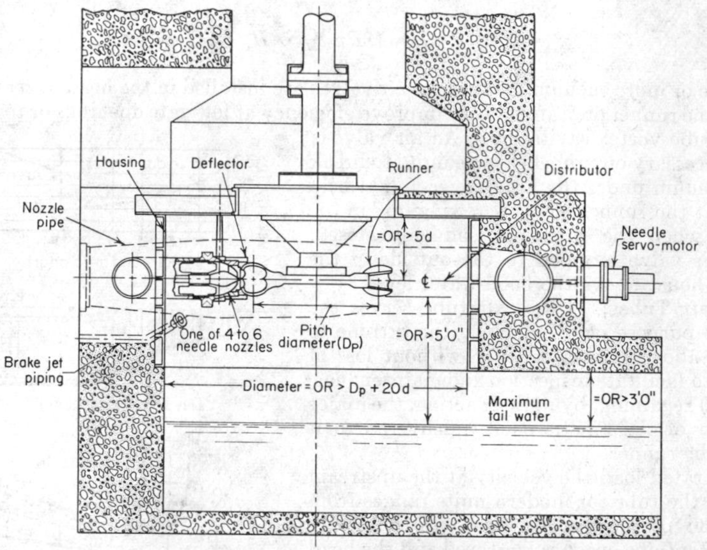

Fig. 12. Vertical-shaft multijet impulse-turbine installation.

The maximum efficiency obtainable from a horizontal-shaft impulse turbine under optimum conditions is about 90 percent. Field tests on multijet vertical units have shown efficiencies as high as 91.5 percent. This higher performance is due to the fact that on a properly designed vertical unit there is less tendency for the water to interfere with the buckets. In addition, the use of multiple jets on the vertical units reduces the percentage loss due to windage of the runner. Another advantage of multiple-jet turbines is that the unit can be operated with a reduced number of jets at part load, thus increasing part-load efficiency. Model tests have indicated that six jets are about the maximum number that can be used on one runner without jet interference.

The essential parts of an impulse turbine (Fig. 12) are a runner either integrally cast with the buckets or with bolted-on buckets, a nozzle pipe, a needle nozzle, a deflector, and a housing with a guide bearing.

Selection of Speed. The first consideration is the selection of a suitable n_s. As with reaction turbines, there is a relation which determines approximately the limiting value of specific speed n_s (per jet) for any head acting. For heads around 1,000 ft, $n_s = 5.0$ to 5.5 gives high efficiency. For heads around 2,000 ft, maximum efficiency is attained near $n_s = 4.0$ to 5.0. Care has to be exercised in selecting an n_s (per jet), especially for the higher heads, so that the proper number of buckets can be used on the wheel disk. The higher the n_s, the fewer the number of buckets required (Fig. 13) but the smaller the pitch circle. The latter can create stress problems in the attachment of the buckets to the disk. If the resulting speed n is quite low for the power to be developed, the n_s of the unit and consequently the speed n can be increased by increasing the number of runners or the number of jets per runner. The n_s of the unit will then be n_s (per jet) times the square root of the number of jets.

Basic Dimensions. The pitch diameter D_p of the runner is twice the distance from the center of the runner to the axial centerline of the jet and is determined by the value of the coefficient ϕ selected. $D_p = (1{,}840\phi\sqrt{H})/n$. The variation of ϕ with n_s is established by experience and model tests (Fig. 13).

The quantity of water Q discharged per jet is $8.82P/He$, where P is the horsepower developed by each jet.

The diameter of the jet is $4.95\sqrt{Q}/H^{1/4}$ in., using a velocity coefficient of 0.97 for the jet.

The **velocity** in the inlet should not exceed $0.09\sqrt{2gH}$ approx, and it is considered good practice not to exceed an absolute value of 30 ft per sec.

The **valve** employed in the inlet pipe should be of a type which, when open, permits a smooth, uninterrupted flow, free of eddies or obstructions. Modern preference is for rotary sphere valves for this purpose.

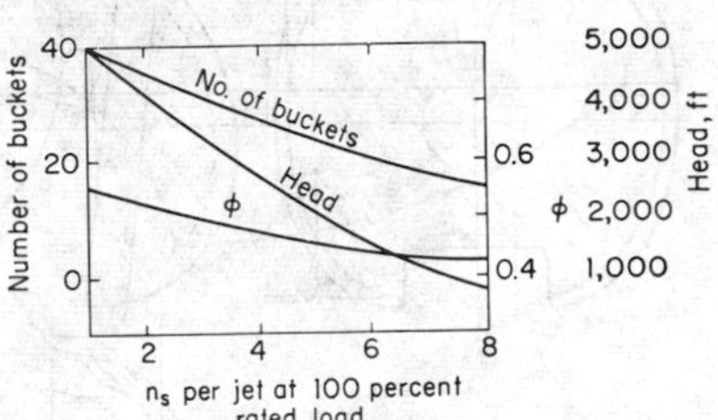

FIG. 13. Impulse-turbine characteristics and proportions.

The **housing** serves primarily to carry off the discharged water to the tail pit below and to support the nozzles. On horizontal-shaft units, at the place where the runner receives the discharge from the jet, the housing should be about 10 to 12 times the jet diameter. The more ample width results in higher efficiency. At the place where the runner has been cleared of the discharge, the housing should be as narrow as possible to decrease windage. Suitable baffling should be used to carry the discharge away from the buckets. The housing should be vented adequately near the center of the runner to permit the inflow of air to replace that entrained with the discharged water.

For vertical-shaft units, the housing should be of ample size to prevent discharge water from interfering with the buckets. The distance from the head cover to the centerline of the jet should not be less than 5 times the jet diameter (Fig. 12). The diameter of the housing should not be less than $D_p + 20d$, where D_p is the pitch diameter and d is the jet diameter. The housing should also be vented adequately near the center of the runner.

The **setting** of the horizontal-shaft unit should be such that the lower edges of the buckets are at least 3 ft above maximum tail-water elevation to ensure that the runner revolves in air at all times. For vertical-shaft units, this distance should be at least 5 ft. Any gain in head by setting the unit closer to tail water is more than offset by loss in performance. Impulse-turbine discharge entrains large amounts of air, and unless this is completely replaced, a vacuum will be produced in the housing which will draw the tail water up and drown out the runner. Thus the roof of the discharge tunnel or passageway, for both horizontal- and vertical-shaft units, should be at least 3 ft above the maximum operating tail-water elevation to permit the free circulation of air to the runner (Fig. 12).

In cases where extremely high tail water occurs for a short period, compressed air can be used to depress the tail water.

Experience has shown that the cfs of air (at the discharge pressure of the compressor) required to maintain the depressed tail water is about 15 percent of the cfs of water (Q) discharged by the turbine.

Runner. The force F exerted by a stream upon a stationary bucket (Fig. 14) is

$$F = MV(1 - \cos \theta) = wQV(1 - \cos \theta)/g$$

where M = mass per sec and θ = angle in deg through which the water is turned relative to the bucket (see section Y-Y, Fig. 14). If the bucket is moving in the direction of the stream with a velocity u, $F = wQ(V - u)(1 - \cos \theta)/g$. The work done by the stream $= Fu = wQn(V - u)(1 - \cos \theta)/g$. Work done is 0 when $u = 0$ and when $u = V$ and is a maximum when $u(V - u)$ is a maximum or when $u = V/2$. When θ is greater than 90 deg, the cosine becomes negative. Thus the closer the angle θ is to 180 deg, the greater the amount of work done with the same Q and V. However, in order to prevent the water from striking the succeeding bucket, θ should never be 180 deg (see section Y-Y, Fig. 14). Also, since the water discharged from the bucket must have some velocity, the value of u is made somewhat less than $V/2$.

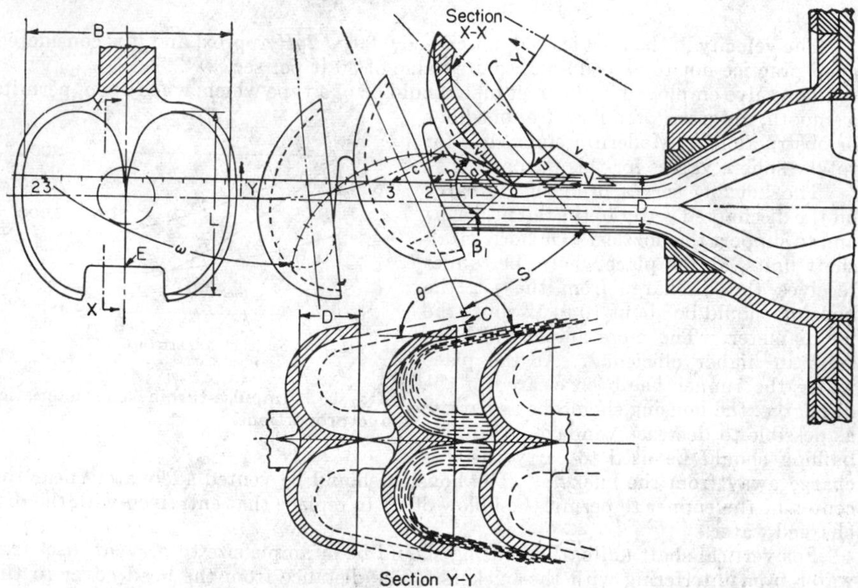

Fig. 14. Impulse-turbine bucket diagram.

The angle β_1, at the centerline of the bucket should be calculated from the velocity triangle (Fig. 14). The value of β_1, is greatest as the entrance lip E enters the jet. The angle of the underside of the bucket should be greater than β_1 to avoid pitting.

In terms of the jet diameter which will give maximum guaranteed or rated capacity, the approximate proportions of the buckets are $B = 3d$, $L = 2.6d$, $D = 0.85d$ (Fig. 14). These proportions depend on the bucket contour and may vary greatly. The contour of the entrance lip E is important since the manner in which this lip comes in contact with the jet affects the path of the water passing to the preceding bucket. The size of the bucket with relation to the jet diameter also determines the percentage of full load at which maximum efficiency occurs. The larger the bucket, the higher this percentage of load.

The number of buckets on a runner should be such that no water can pass through the buckets without being deflected by the buckets. Figure 13 indicated approximately the most efficient number. A more accurate determination necessitates drawing the path of the water in its relation to the rotating buckets. In Fig. 14, the line V of the velocity triangle representing the absolute path of the water has been extended far to the left, terminating in point 23. At point 0, this line intersects the entrance lip E of the bucket. To construct the curve of the relative path, various points on the absolute path 0–23 must be rotated in a direction opposite to that of the bucket. For instance, the arc a (drawn from the center of rotation of the runner) represents the distance that the bucket travels while the stream is traveling from 0 to 1. Similarly, the bucket travels the arc b while the stream travels from 0 to 2. In like manner, the arcs c and w correspond with 0 to 3 and 0 to 23, respectively.

The paths relative to the buckets should be determined for the outer, center, and inner filaments of water of the jet. For all the water to be acted upon by the buckets, the angle between the latter should be about 25 to 30 percent less than the angle subtended by the relative path of the outer filament through the buckets. This subtended angle actually tends to increase with increasing specific speed. Therefore, the number of buckets required decreases with increasing specific speed, as indicated in Fig. 13.

The **needle nozzle** should be placed as close to the buckets as possible, as the jet tends to lose its compactness of form shortly after emerging from the nozzle. The needle and the seat of the nozzle should be designed for easy replacement and should be of a material highly resistant to erosion. The needle should terminate in a cone of 42 to 48 deg. The nozzle tip should have a subtended angle of 60 to 64 deg and a diameter at discharge about 20 percent greater than the calculated diameter of the jet. The maximum diameter of the needle should be about 15 percent greater than the discharge diameter of the nozzle tip. The diameter of the upstream portion of the nozzle should be such that the velocity does not exceed $0.10\sqrt{2gH}$. (See Lowy, Efficiency Analysis of Pelton Wheels, *Trans. ASME*, Aug., 1944, for additional information on the design of impulse turbines.)

Regulation. The inertia of the water flowing through the long penstocks usually employed with impulse turbines prohibits rapid reduction in velocity because of the pressure rise which would occur. Therefore, to minimize the speed rise following a sudden load rejection, it is necessary to reduce the hydraulic power delivered to the runner without changing the flow in the penstock too rapidly. This is usually accomplished by placing a governor-controlled jet deflector between the needle nozzle and the runner. The governor moves this deflector rapidly into the jet, cutting off the load. It is not unusual for the deflector to cut off the entire jet in 1½ sec. Since the deflector acts on the jet after it leaves the nozzle, there is no change of flow in the penstock; hence, there is no pressure rise. The governor then moves the needle at a permissible rate (in terms of pressure rise), with simultaneous automatic withdrawal of the deflector. The jet is finally reduced the necessary amount to correspond to the reduced load. The needle must also move slowly in the opening direction for oncoming loads to avoid penstock collapse because of large pressure drops.

Runaway Speed. The runaway speed for impulse turbines ranges from 180 to 190 percent of normal speed, depending upon the specific speed of the runner; the higher the specific speed, the higher the runaway speed.

REVERSIBLE PUMP-TURBINES

There has been a trend in recent years toward the increased use of **pumped storage** hydro facilities for seasonal storage and peaking capacity. In this type of project, surplus low-value energy from either hydro or thermal plants is used to pump water during off-peak periods to an elevated reservoir, where it becomes available for generating high-value peaking energy. While separate pumps and hydraulic turbines of conventional design can and have been used for this purpose, the development of single reversible pump-turbines has made many pumped-storage projects economically feasible.

Figure 15 is a cross section of a reversible pump-turbine, showing that, with the exception of the runner, it is essentially a conventional turbine. It has a spiral case, stay ring, movable wicket gates, head cover, discharge ring, and draft tube. The wicket gates must be designed for flow in both directions. A few units have been built without movable wicket gates. The runner is essentially a pump runner modified for optimum performance while generating power. (See Sec. 14 for the design of centrifugal pumps and their characteristics.) Conventional turbine runners, because of their short blades, are not well suited for the pumping cavitation requirements.

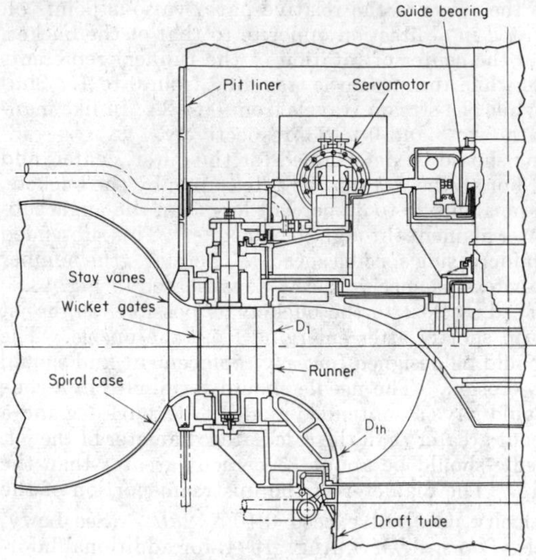

FIG. 15. Reversible pump-turbine.

The reversible pump-turbines have certain fundamental performance characteristics which are inherent in the design. The relationship between pumping and generating performance for a given specific speed is more or less fixed and can be modified only to a minor degree by alterations in the design. For example, if a certain generating capacity is desired, the pumping capacity will be fixed within limits. On the other hand, if a certain pumping capacity is desired, the maximum generating capacity is fixed. Figure 16 shows the expected generating performance, and Fig. 17 shows the expected pumping performance based on model tests of a reversible pump-turbine with a specific speed $n_s = 47.3$ generating and $n_s = 2{,}600$ pumping.

The best efficiency, with reversible pump-turbines, occurs at a lower speed when generating than when pumping. This can be compensated for by using a generator-motor capable of operating at two speeds with a constant frequency. Several units of this type have been built, but since two-speed generator-motors cost considerably more than those built for single speed, a careful study should be made of the advantages to be obtained in operating at two speeds.

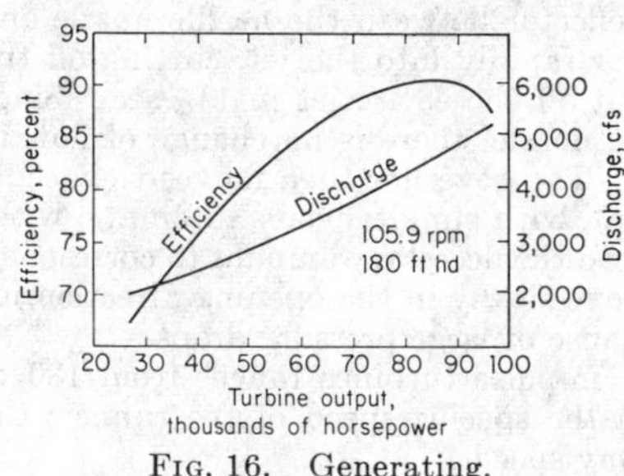

FIG. 16. Generating.

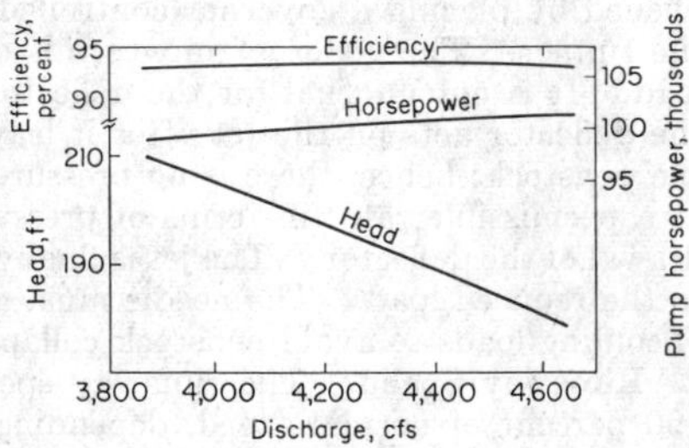

FIG. 17. Pumping.

FIGS. 16 and 17. Typical performance curves for a pump-turbine.

Single reversible pump-turbines can be built for any heads up to 1,200 ft. Beyond this, either multiple-stage reversible units or separate pumps and turbines should be used. Some of the more notable reversible pump-turbine installations in the United States are:

Plant	Generating		Pumping	
	Power, hp	Head, ft	Capacity, cfs	Head, ft
Flatiron*	13,000	290	370	240
Lewiston	28,000	75	3,400	85
Taum Sauk	340,000	835	2,650	764
Yards Creek	140,000	656	1,450	730
Cornwall	395,000	1,150	2,550	1,020

* Two-speed unit without movable wicket gates.

Runaway Speed. The runaway speed for pump-turbines is considerably lower than that for conventional turbines. It ranges from 150 percent of normal for low-specific-speed runners to 175 percent for high-specific-speed runners.

MODEL TESTS

Model tests serve several purposes. They are primarily used to check turbine runner, wicket-gate, draft-tube, casing, and (sometimes) inlet-works designs for optimum performance. Correctly interpreted, they may also be used as a reliable indication of the performance of the units in the field. In many cases, purchasers specify the performance of a homologous-model test, which is used as an acceptance test of the unit in lieu of field tests. In such cases, the field conditions, particularly the casing and draft tube, must be reproduced faithfully. Model tests should be run in accordance with the ASME Test Code for Hydraulic Turbines. The International Electrotechnical Commission is in the process of preparing an International Test Code for Hydraulic Turbines Using Laboratory Models for Acceptance Test. When completed, this Code will probably be adopted universally by all members, including the United States and Canada.

Figure 18 shows typical model-test results of a reaction-type turbine, in which the power P at 1-ft head and the efficiency are each plotted against the speed n at 1-ft head, for each of several gate openings.

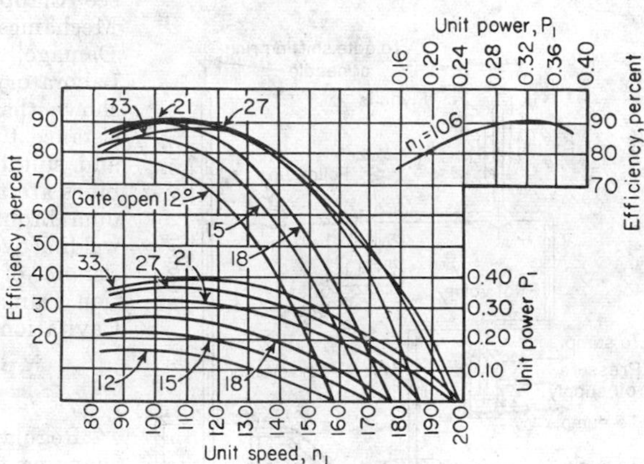

FIG. 18. Model-test curves for Francis runner ($D_r = D_{th} = 16.2$; n_s about 65.)

Laws of Proportionality for Homologous Turbines. The laws of proportionality shown on p. 9–184 are used to calculate from model tests the power, speed, and discharges of an homologous turbine of different diameter under a different head. Actually, the laws are employed only in computing the power and speed data for the field unit. The field unit will have a somewhat higher efficiency and power owing to proportionally smaller frictional and bearing losses. Expected field efficiency is customarily computed from the model efficiency by the Moody formula $e' = 1 - (1 - e)(D/D')^{1/5}$, in which the prime letters refer to the field installation. The step-up efficiency is computed for the point of best efficiency only, and the corresponding differential is applied as a constant value from, say, half load to full load.

CAVITATION

Cavitation occurs when the pressure at any point in the flowing water drops below the vapor pressure of the water, which varies with temperature.

The relationship which produces cavitation is between vapor pressure, barometric pressure, setting of the runner with respect to tail water, and net effective head on the turbine and is expressed by the **Thoma cavitation coefficient** $\sigma = (H_b - H_v - H_s)/H$, where H_b = barometric head, ft of water; H_v = vapor pressure of water, abs; H_s = elevation, ft, of the runner above tail water, measured at the throat of a Francis runner and at the centerline of the blades of a propeller runner (if the runner is submerged, H_s becomes negative); and H = total or net effective head, ft, on the turbine. From the above formula, $H_s = H_b - H_v - \sigma H$. Thus the setting of the runner depends upon the value of σ, which varies with specific speed n_s of the runner and the individual characteristics of a particular runner design. In practice, the model of the proposed runner is first tested with relatively high back pressure (H_s small or negative). Then the back pressure is reduced in increments until the breaking point, as indicated by a drop in power, efficiency, and discharge, is reached. This breaking point is designated as the critical σ and will vary with gate opening and speed and, on propeller turbines, with blade angle. Consequently, σ must be determined for a range of limiting conditions.

In the absence of cavitation tests, the value of σ should not be lower than $\sigma = n_s^{3/2}/2{,}000$ for Francis and propeller runners and $\sigma = n_s^2/25{,}000$ for adjustible-blade propeller runners.

The value of σ at which a plant operates, depending largely upon the setting of the runner with respect to tail water, is called the **plant** σ. To avoid excessive cavitation, the plant σ should exceed the critical σ. The greater this margin, the less possibility of cavitation during operation. For a general discussion of cavitation phenomena, see Knapp, Recent Investigations of the Mechanics of Cavitation and Cavitation Damage, *Trans. ASME*, Oct., 1955. Laboratory tests and experience have shown that materials having a high resistance to cavitation erosion (pitting) and suitable for use in hydraulic turbines are the stainless steels and aluminum bronzes, especially when used as welding overlays. (See Rheingans, "Resistance of Various Materials to Cavitation Damage," ASME Report of 1956 Cavitation Symposium.)

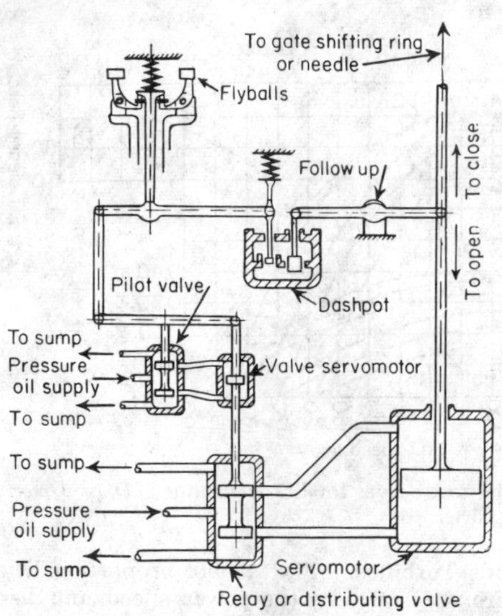

FIG. 19. Schematic diagram of governor.

SPEED REGULATION

(See also Sec. 16)

Regulation is accomplished by changing the flow of water to the turbine. The flow is controlled by the wicket gates of reaction turbines and by the needle valve or jet deflector of impulse turbines. The governor, usually supplied with the turbine, moves the gates or needle in response to speed changes resulting from load or head changes.

A schematic diagram of a governor is shown in Fig. 19. The parts consist of a speed-responsive device, a power element that changes the gates or needle position, and a follow-up or compensating device that prevents hunting.

The **speed-responsive device** is usually a pair of spring-loaded flyballs mounted directly on the turbine shaft, or driven from the shaft by belt or gears, or driven by an electric motor that receives its power either from the bus line or from an independent generator driven from the main turbine generator shaft.

The **power element** consists of one or two oil-operated power cylinders or servomotors which operate the turbine gates or needle. Oil pumps and a pressure tank or accumulator maintain a supply of oil under pressure. A valve operated by the flyballs controls the flow of oil to the servomotors or acts as a pilot valve controlling a larger relay valve, which in turn controls the oil to the servomotors. With a plant consisting of several units, a unit system may be used for each turbine, or there may be a central pumping unit for the turbines. The pump capacity is usually $3\frac{1}{3}$ servomotor volumes per minute. The capacity of the pressure tank is generally made 20 times the servomotor volume, allowing for 8 volumes of oil and 12 volumes of air. The velocity of oil in the pipelines is kept below 15 fps.

The **follow-up** or **compensating device** connects the power piston of the servomotor to the control valve, usually through a dashpot, and causes the motion of gates or needle to stop when they have moved sufficiently to compensate for the load change.

The time for a full stroke or traverse of the governor is controlled by the rate of flow of oil to the servomotors; most governors have provisions for varying this time. The gate opening changes at a uniform rate over the major portion of the stroke and at a somewhat slower rate at the ends of the stroke. The governor *dead time*, or the elapsed time from the initial speed change to the first movement of the gates, is usually less than 0.2 sec.

Electric Governor. In recent years, the functional requirements placed upon the hydraulic-turbine governor have increased to the point where electrical control of the hydraulic turbine is attractive in view of the simplicity with which electrical signals can be manipulated. The basic elements of an electric-hydraulic governing system are (1) permanent-magnet generator (PMG) or equivalent for measurement of turbine speed and the means for transmittal of such speed signals to the electrical portion of the governor; (2) an electric circuit sensitive to speed variations about some adjustable reference point; (3) amplifying circuits to convert speed-reference changes, speed-error signals, and auxiliary signals into a useful electric current; (4) an electrohydraulic transducer to transform the electric current into a hydraulic-output signal; (5) hydraulic-amplifying equipment to deliver suitable power and the desired signal to the gate servomotors as a function of the output of the electrohydraulic transducer; (6) power supplies for the electric and hydraulic portions of the control. For further particulars of the electric governor, see Leum, Electric Governors for Hydro Turbines, *ASME Paper* 62-WA165.

Speed-regulation Requirements. Usually, a sufficient measure of the regulation provided is the maximum speed rise resulting from sudden rejection of full load, as from the breaker tripping. A maximum speed rise of 35 percent of normal speed for this condition is a common limitation.

Speed Rise Following Load Reduction. For sudden load reductions, the approximate speed rise is

$$n_x/n = [1 + 1{,}620{,}000T_xP_x(1 + h/H)^{3/2}/WR^2n^2]^{1/2}$$

where n_x is the rpm at the end of time T_x; n is the speed before the load decrease; T_x is the time interval, sec, for the governor to adjust the flow to the new load; P_x is the reduction in load; h is the head rise caused by the retardation of the flow; H is the net effective head before the load change; WR^2 is the product of the revolving parts, lb, and the square of their radius of gyration, ft. For values of h, see below. Very rapid gate closure produces a reduction of pressure in the draft tube and the possibility of breaking the water column, with subsequent violent resurge which may damage the turbine.

Speed Drop Following Load Increase. For sudden load increases, the approximate speed drop is

$$n_x/n = [1 - 1{,}620{,}000T_xP_x/WR^2n^2(1 - h/H)^{3/2}]^{1/2}$$

where P_x is the actual load increase and h is the head drop caused by the increase of the flow. If the speed drop is to be determined for a given increase in gate opening, the governor time T_x for making this increase and the normal change in load for the change in gate opening, under constant head H, can be used in the following formula:

$$n_x/n = [1 - 1{,}620{,}000T_xP_x(1 - h/H)^{3/2}/WR^2n^2]^{1/2}$$

The actual change in load, however, will be $P_x(1 - h/H)^{3/2}$.

For derivation of the above speed-variation formulas and for a more accurate determination, see Strowger and Kerr, Speed Changes of Hydraulic Turbines for Sudden Changes of Load, *Trans. ASME*, 1926; and Rich, "Hydraulic Transients," McGraw-Hill.

Water Hammer in Penstocks. If a gate movement is considered as a series of instantaneous movements with a very small interval between each movement, the pressure variation in the penstock following the gate movement will be the effect of a series of pressure waves, each caused by one of the instantaneous small gate movements. For a steel penstock, the velocity of the pressure wave $a = 4{,}660/\sqrt{1 + (d/100t)}$, where d is the penstock diameter, in., and t is the penstock wall thickness, in. The pressure change at any point along the penstock at any time after the start of the gate movement may be calculated by summing up the effect of the individual pressure waves. See "Symposium on Water Hammer," ASME, 1933; and Parmakian, "Water Hammer Analysis," Prentice-Hall.

Approximate formulas (De Sparre) for the increase in pressure h, ft, following gate closure, are given below. They are quite accurate for pressure rises not exceeding 50 percent of the initial pressure, which includes most practical cases.

$$h = aV/g \qquad [\text{for } K < 1 \text{ and } N < 1]$$
$$h = aV/g[N + K(N - 1)] \qquad [\text{for } K < 1 \text{ and } N > 1]$$
$$h = aV/g(2N - K) \qquad [\text{for } K > 1 \text{ and } N > 1]$$

where $K = aV/2gH$; $N = aT/2L$; V and H are the penstock velocity, fps, and head, ft, prior to closure; L is the penstock length, ft; and T is the time of gate closure. For full-load rejection, T may be taken as 85 percent of the total gate traversing time to allow for non-uniform gate motion.

For pressure drop following a complete gate opening, the following formula (S. Logan Kerr) may be used with T not less than $2L/a$:

$$h = \frac{aV}{g}\left(\frac{-K + \sqrt{K^2 + N^2}}{N^2}\right) = \text{pressure drop, ft}$$

Pressure variations exceeding 40 percent rise and about 25 percent drop should be avoided. When the control, directly by the governor, causes undesirable pressure variations, a surge tank, a pressure regulator, or a jet deflector may be used. A **surge tank** is a standpipe with an atmospheric tank, attached to the penstock as close as possible to the casing inlet. The tank provides a reservoir and expansion chamber for the water demand or the water rejection following sudden gate movements, so that sudden accelerations or decelerations of the flow in the penstock are avoided.

Pressure regulators may be either of the water-wasting or water-saving type. The **water-wasting type** is a synchronous bypass, generally attached to the turbine casing. It is operated directly from the governor, or the gate mechanism of the turbine, and wastes such an amount as to keep the total water discharge equal at all times to the full-load discharge of the turbine. The bypass is a needle nozzle or a mushroom-shaped disk valve which opens and is partly balanced hydraulically by a piston under pipeline pressure. The **water-saving type** permits the regulator to open upon rapid closure of the turbine gates, and then close slowly, so that the total water discharge is gradually reduced and finally limited to that through the turbine, adjusted for the new load.

AUXILIARIES

Valves and head gates are provided for shutting off the water from each turbine for safety, for ease of maintenance, and to reduce water-leakage losses. Motor-operated steel head gates are generally used for low- and medium-head plants with concrete scroll cases, although a few still use stop logs. The butterfly type of valve placed close to the turbine casing is suitable for medium- and high-head units with metal casings of circular inlet diameter. Butterfly valves of 8-ft diameter for 1,000-ft head and 27-ft diameter for 100-ft head have been built. In recent years, rotary sphere valves have replaced gate valves for high heads and where the loss through the butterfly valve is excessive due to the obstruction to flow by the valve wicket.

TURBINE TESTS

Field testing of hydraulic turbines to determine the absolute efficiency and output involves careful and accurate measurement of the power available in the water supplied to the turbine (water hp) and the turbine output (developed hp); e = developed hp/

water hp $= 8.82P/QH$. The tests should be conducted in accordance with ASME Test Code for Hydraulic Prime Movers.

Because of the difficulties and costs involved in making accurate measurements of horsepower, net head, and discharge in the field, there has been a trend in recent years to dispense with the field test, especially where a laboratory test on an homologous-model turbine is available. Instead, an index test is made on the unit in the field, which measures the turbine output and relative discharge under various conditions. Index tests should be conducted in accordance with ASME Test Code for Hydraulic Prime Movers.

DIRECT-ENERGY CONVERSION

BY

Philip E. Benner

REFERENCES: Kaye and Welsh, "Direct Conversion of Heat to Electricity," Wiley. Mitchell, "Fuel Cells," Academic. Chang, "Energy Conversion," Prentice-Hall. Shive, "Properties, Physics and Design of Semiconductor Devices," Van Nostrand. Bredt, Thermoelectric Power Generation, *Power Eng.*, Feb.–Apr., 1963. Douglas, Fuel Cells, *Elec. Eng.*, Sept., 1959. Wilson, Conversion of Heat to Electricity by Thermionic Conversion, *Jour. Applied Physics*, Apr., 1959. Steg-Sutton, The Prospects of MHD Power Generation, *Astronautics*, Aug., 1960. Rappaport, The Photovoltaic Effect and Its Utilization, *RCA Rev.*, **20,** 1959.

In contrast to the conventional thermal cycle for the conversion of heat into electricity are several more direct methods of converting thermal and chemical energy into electrical power. The methods which seem to have the greatest potential possibilities are thermoelectric, thermionic, magnetohydrodynamic (MHD), fuel-cell, and photovoltaic. The principles of operation of these processes have long been known, but technological and economic obstacles have thwarted their use. New applications, materials, and technology are now providing increased impetus to the development of these processes.

Thermoelectric generation is based on the phenomenon, discovered by **Seebeck** in 1821, that current is produced in a closed circuit of two dissimilar metals if the two junctions are maintained at different temperatures, as in thermocouples for measuring temperature. Typical thermocouples produce potentials in the order of 50 to 70 microvolts per deg C and power at efficiencies in the order of 1 percent.

Certain semiconductors have thermoelectric properties superior to conductor materials, with resultant improved efficiency. The criterion for evaluating material characteristics for thermoelectric generation is the **figure of merit,** Z, measured in (deg C)$^{-1}$ and defined as $Z = S^2/PK$, where S = Seebeck coefficient, volts per deg C; P = electrical resistivity, ohms per cc; K = thermal conductivity, watts per deg C per cc.

An ideal thermoelectric material would have a high Seebeck coefficient, low electrical resistivity, and low thermal conductivity. Unfortunately, materials having a low electrical resistivity have a high thermal conductivity since both properties are dependent, to some extent, on the number of free electrons in the material. The maximum conversion efficiency of a thermoelectric generator is a function of the figure of merit, the hot-junction temperature, and the temperature difference between the hot and cold junctions. It is therefore Carnot-cycle-limited. (See p. 4-18.)

In some types of thermoelectric materials, the voltage difference between the hot and cold junctions results from the flow of negatively charged electrons ("n" type, hot-junction positive), whereas in other types, the voltage difference between the cold and hot junctions results from the flow of positively charged voids vacated by electrons ("p" type, cold-junction positive). Since the voltage output of a typical semiconductor thermoelectric couple is low (about 100 to 300 microvolts per deg C, temperature difference between the hot and cold junctions), it is advantageous to use both "p" and "n" type materials in constructing a thermoelectric generator. The two types of materials make it possible to connect the thermojunctions in series electrically and in parallel thermally (Fig. 1).

Typical semiconductor thermoelectric materials are compounds and alloys of lead, zinc, tellurium, antimony, bismuth, germanium, arsenic, manganese, cobalt, and silicon. Optimized designs of thermoelectric junctions using semiconductor materials have resulted in conversion efficiencies as high as 13 percent (Fig. 2); however, the efficiency of actual thermoelectric generators is lower, *e.g.*, 4 to 9 percent. Materials which have higher figures of merit (2 or 3 $\times 10^{-3}$) and which are capable of operating at higher temperatures (800 to 1000 C) are required for an appreciable improvement in efficiency. High-temperature operation increases the tendency of materials to sublimate, oxidize, or become poisoned. It also increases the problem of hot-junction fabrication and the differential expansion of components. Thermoelectric generation could be attractive for tactical and space applications and for other uses where efficiency is not important.

The **Peltier effect,** discovered in 1834, is the inverse of the Seebeck effect. It involves the heating or cooling of the junction of two thermoelectric materials by passing current through the junction. The effectiveness of thermojunction as a cooling device has been greatly increased by the application of semiconductor thermoelectric materials. Figure 3 shows the maximum temperature difference which a junction has produced under no-load conditions when the hot junction is at room temperature.

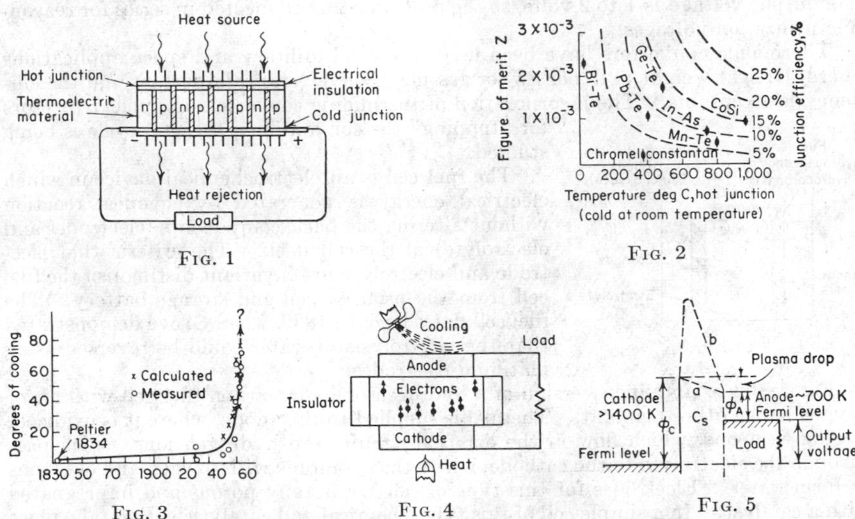

FIG. 1 FIG. 2

FIG. 3 FIG. 4 FIG. 5

When the cool junction is functioning as a refrigerating element, the temperature difference will be smaller.

Thermionic generation, proposed by **Schlicter** in 1915, uses a thermionic converter (Fig. 4), which is a vacuum or gas-filled device with a hot electron "emitter" (cathode) and a cold electron "collector" (anode) in or as part of a suitable gastight enclosure, with electrical connections to the anode and cathode, and with means for heating the cathode and cooling the anode.

Figure 5 is a plot of the electron energy at various places in the converter. The abscissa is cathode-anode spacing, and the ordinate is electron energy. The base line corresponds to the energy of the electrons in the cathode before heating. Heating the cathode imparts sufficient energy to some of the electrons to lift them over the **work-function barrier** (retaining force) at the surface of the cathode into the interelectrode space. (The lower the work function, the easier it is for an electron to escape from the surface of the cathode.) If it is assumed that the electrons can follow path *a* to the anode with only a small loss of energy, they will "drop down" the work-function barrier as they join the electrons in the anode still retaining some of their potential energy (**Fermi level**), which is available to cause an electric current to flow in the external circuit. The work function of the anode should be as small as possible. The anode should be maintained at a lower temperature to prevent anode emission or back current. This pattern presumes that the electrons could follow path *a* from the cathode to the anode with little interference. Since, however, electrons are charged particles, those in the space between the cathode and anode form a space-charge barrier, as shown by *b*. This space-charge barrier limits the electrons emitted from the cathode. Space-charge formation can be reduced by close spacing of the cathode and anode surfaces or by the introduction of a suitable gas atmosphere that can be ionized by heating and thus neutralize the space charge. In vacuum-type thermionic converters, the spacing between cathode and anode must be less than a thousandth of an inch to get as many as 10 percent of the electrons over to the cathode and to achieve an efficiency of 4 to 5 percent. In gas-filled converters, the negative-electron space-charge is neutralized by positive ions. Cesium vapor is used for this purpose. If operated at low pressure, it will also lower the work function of the anode, and if operated at high pressure, it can, in addition, be used to adjust the work function of the cathode. An anode work function of 1.0 volt has been achieved at 400 K for a surface cesium on silver oxide. Efficiencies as high as 17 percent have been obtained with gas-filled converters operating at a cathode temperature of 1900 C (2173 K). The output voltage is 1 to 2 volts, so the units must be connected in series for reasonable utilization voltages.

Thermionic converters have been used in special military and space applications where the light weight (4 lb per kw for gas-filled converters) is important and the efficiency is acceptable. The incorporation of thermionic converters in nuclear reactors for "topping" the conventional thermal cycle is being studied.

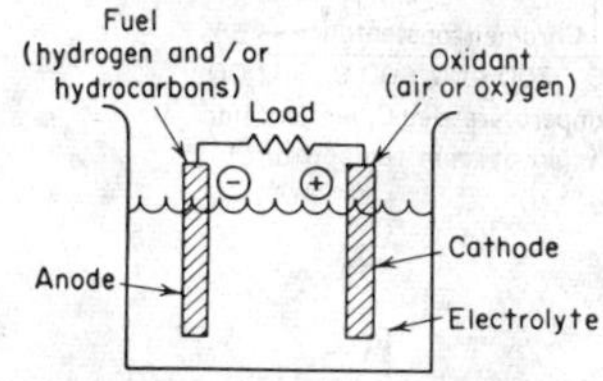

The **fuel cell** is an electrochemical device in which electrical energy is generated by chemical reaction without altering the basic components (electrodes and electrolyte) of the cell itself. The criteria that electrode and electrolyte are invariant distinguish the fuel cell from the primary cell and storage battery. The fuel cell dates back to 1839, when **Grove** demonstrated that the electrolysis of water could be reversed using platinum electrodes.

FIG. 6

Figure 6 is a simplified version of a hydrogen or hydrocarbon fuel cell with air or oxygen as the other reactant. The fuel is supplied to the anode, where it is oxidized, freeing electrons, which flow in the external circuit, and hydrogen ions, which pass through the electrolyte to the cathode, where they combine with oxygen and electrons to form water. Electrodes for this type of cell are usually porous and impregnated with a catalyst. In a simple cell of this type, chemical and catalytic action take place only at the line (**notable surface of action**) where the electrolyte, gas, and electrode meet. One of the objectives in designing a practical fuel cell is to increase the notable surface of the action. This has been accomplished in a number of ways, but usually by the creation of porous electrodes within which, in the case of gas-diffusion electrodes, the fuel and oxidant in gaseous state can come in contact with the electrolyte at many sites. If the electrolyte is a liquid, a delicate balance must be achieved in which surface tension and density of the liquid must be considered and gas pressure and electrode pore size must be chosen to hold their interface inside the electrode. If the gas pressure is too high, the electrolyte is excluded from the electrode, gas leaks into the electrolyte, and ion flow stops; if the gas pressure is too low, drowning of the electrode occurs and electron flow stops.

Fuel cells are often classified on the basis of the fuel used, *i.e.*, high-cost fuels, such as hydrogen; intermediate-cost fuels, such as alcohol; low-cost fuels, such as hydrocarbons. Hydrocarbon and carbonaceous fuels are inert and require high temperatures and/or special catalysts. An 800 C fuel cell, using molten alkali carbonate electrolyte and hydrocarbon fuel, has been intensively studied but not practically developed. Encouraging results (40 to 50 percent efficiency) have been attained at a more reasonable temperature (200 C) with a liquid phosphoric acid electrolyte and propane, methane, or octane fuel. The most highly developed fuel cells use hydrogen and oxygen (air) and are limited to applications which can justify the high-priced fuel. The ion-exchange-membrane fuel cell is of this type, operating at atmospheric pressure and room temperature, with a platinum catalyst. The absence of the Carnot-cycle limitation is most attractive, and conversion efficiencies as high as 70 percent have been achieved with hydrogen fuel. Initial application will be space and military services, with potential future mobile-power uses as economics will permit.

Magnetohydrodynamic (MHD) generation utilizes the movement of electrically conducting gas through a magnetic field. In the simple MHD generator (Fig. 7), hot, partially ionized, compressed gas is expanded in a duct and forced through a strong magnetic field. Electrodes in the sides of the duct pick up the potential generated in the gas, so that current flows through the circuit of gas, electrodes, and external load. Temperature in excess of 5000 F is necessary for the required ionization of gas. Ionization can be increased by the addition of a seeding material such as potassium or cesium. Even with seeding, it is necessary for the gas temperature entering the MHD generator to be in the order of 4500 to 5000 F and the temperature of the gas leaving the generator to be about 4000 F. The high exhaust-gas temperature suggests use of the MHD generator as the topping element of a more conventional thermal cycle. The exhaust gas from the MHD generator might be passed in turn through a boiler, a regenerator or air preheater, and the superheater, reheater, economizer, and stack gas cooler. Preheating of combustion air to some 2000 F is necessary if an initial gas temperature of 5000 is to be attained. The potential improvement in efficiency from the use of MHD in a combined-cycle plant is in the order of 15 to 30 percent, or it would raise an over-all plant efficiency of 38 percent to some 45 to 54 percent.

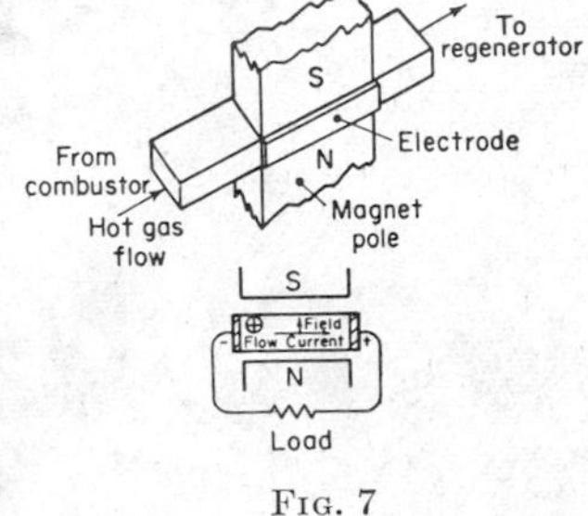

FIG. 7

Contrasted to other methods for direct conversion of heat into electrical energy, MHD appears best suited to the generation of large blocks of power. For instance, an MHD generator 20 ft long, with a field intensity of 100 kilogauss (attained by means of a cryogenic magnet), might have an estimated output of about 360,000 kw d-c at 5,000 volts.

Photovoltaic generation utilizes the direct conversion of light energy into electrical energy and stems from the discovery by **Becquerel** in 1839 that a voltage is generated when light is directed on one of the electrodes in an electrolyte solution. Subsequent work using selenium led to the development of the photoelectric cell and the exposure meter.

Photovoltaic effect is the generation of electric potential by the ionization by light energy (photons) of the area at or near the p-n junction of a semiconductor. The p-n junction constitutes a one-way potential barrier which permits the passage of photon-generated (−) electrons from the "p" to the "n" material and (+) "holes" from the "n" to the "p" material. The resulting excess of (−) electrons in the "n" material and (+) holes in the "p" material produces a voltage at the terminals comparable to the junction potential.

A commercially available solar cell consists of a silicon wafer of "n" material 1 cm by 2 cm by ½ mm thick and having a thin layer (several microns) of Boron ("p" material) diffused on the side to be exposed to light. Connections are made by nickel-plating and soldering. The nickel plating on the light-exposure side is restricted to a narrow strip so as not to interfere with the transmission of light.

The efficiency of a photovoltaic cell varies with the spectrum of the light. The maximum theoretical efficiency of a single-junction, single-transition cell with solar illumination is about 22 percent. The efficiency increases substantially with monochromatic light. The practical commercial efficiency of a silicon cell with sun illumination is about 10 percent; with tungsten-lamp illumination, it is about 12 percent.

The open-circuit voltage of a cell varies with the material used and the operating temperature. Open-circuit voltage of a silicon cell (10 percent efficiency) is about

0.6 volt at room temperature. This increases or decreases inversely with temperature at a rate of 2×10^{-3} volts per deg C approx.

The power output of a 1- by 2-cm, 10 percent efficiency, silicon cell is in the order of 2×10^{-2} watts at room temperature. The power output varies inversely as temperature at a rate of 2×10^{-5} watts per deg C approx. The cost of 1- by 2-cm silicon cells, even in large quantities, is such (about $4 each) as to limit use. The major use of photovoltaic cells is in satellites where long life and low weight (about 2 lb per sq meter of cells, plus mounting structure) are the important considerations.

POWER MISCELLANY

MAN- AND ANIMAL-GENERATED POWER

By E. S. Krendel

REFERENCES: Bink, The Physical Working Capacity in Relation to Working Time and Age, *Ergonomics*, June, 1962. Bonjer, Actual Energy Expenditure in Relation to the Physical Working Capacity, *Ergonomics*, June, 1962. Brody, "Bioenergetics and Growth," Reinhold. Krendel, Man Generated Power, *ASME Report* 59-A-190, 1959. Krendel, Design Requirements for Man Generated Power, *Ergonomics*, Oct., 1960. Ursinus, Mitteilungen des Muskelflug Institut, *Bericht* 1, **40,** 1935. Wilkie, The Work Output of Animals: Flight by Birds and by Man-power, *Nature*, May, 1959. Wilkie, Man as a Source of Mechanical Power, *Ergonomics*, Jan., 1960.

The **use of human muscles** to generate work has been examined from two points of view. The first is that of measuring the energy expended in gross, long-duration physical activities such as marching, forestry work, freight handling, and factory work. The second is that of determining the useful mechanical work which can be performed by specified muscle groups for brief or extended periods of time in well-defined work situations, such as pedaling or cranking.

Over an 8-hr day for a 48-hr week, a useful norm for a 35-year-old European laborer for **total power** expenditure, including basal-metabolism energy, is 0.49 hp. Of this total expenditure, approx 0.1 hp is available for **useful work.** A 20-year-old man can generate about 15 percent more power than this norm, and a 60-year-old man about 20 percent less. The **total** energy or power expenditure is needed for determining nutritional requirements for classes of labor. A rule of thumb for power developed by European males can be expressed as a function of age and duration of effort in minutes for work lasting from 4 to about 480 min, assuming that 20 percent of the total output is useful power.

Age of man	Useful horsepower (t in min)
20	$hp = 0.39 - 0.104 \log t$
35	$hp = 0.35 - 0.092 \log t$
60	$hp = 0.29 - 0.077 \log t$

Work scheduling, either as rhythmic work activity or with rest stops for recuperation, the temperature and humidity of the environment, and the detailed nature of the laborer's diet are factors which influence **ability to generate and maintain** the above nominal power values. These considerations should be factored in for specific work situations.

When man and a passive mechanism are working together to generate power the following conditions obtain: Energy is available both from stores residing in the muscles (a total **usefully** available energy of about 0.6 hp-min, usually applied in **transient** bursts of activity) and from the oxidation of foods (for producing **steady-state** power). For transient activity, energy production depends on the mass of muscle which can be brought into effective contact with the power-transmission mechanism. For example, bicycle pedaling is an effective use of a large muscle mass. For steady-state activity, assuming adequate food for fuel energy, production depends on the oxygen supply and the efficiency with which oxygenated blood can be transported to the muscles.

In **bursts of energy** emitted in under 1 sec, up to about 6 hp may be generated.

The difficulty of matching musculature to **useful** load in this type of activity limits the engineering applicability of this figure.

For a **well-trained man, useful power production** by pedaling, hand cranking, or a combination of the two for working durations of from 20 to 120 sec may be summarized as follows (t is in sec):

Arms and legs	$hp = 4.4t^{-0.40}$
Legs only	$hp = 2.8t^{-0.40}$
Arms only	$hp = 1.5t^{-0.40}$

There are examples of well-trained athletes generating between 1.5 and 2 hp for efforts of 5 to 10 sec, using both arms and legs to generate power.

For pedaling efforts of from 1 to about 100 min, the useful power generated may be expressed as $hp = 0.53 - 0.13 \log t$ (t is in min).

The **physiological limit,** determined by oxygen-respiration capacity, for steady-state **useful** mechanical-power generation is between 0.4 and 0.54 hp, depending on the man's physical condition.

In order to approach an optimal **conversion efficiency** (mechanical work/food energy) of 25 percent, a mechanism would be required to store and to transmit energy from the body muscle masses when they were operating at optimal efficiency. This condition occurs when the force exerted by the muscle is about one-half its maximum and the speed of muscle movement one-quarter its maximum. Data on both force and speed for a given set of muscles are best measured *in situ.* Optimal conversion efficiency and maximum output power do not occur together.

Brody has developed detailed nomograms for determining the energetic cost of muscular work by farm **animals**; these nomograms are useful for precise cost-effectiveness comparisons between animal and mechanical power-generation methods. A 1,500- to 1,900-lb horse can work continuously for up to 10 hr a day at a rate of 1 hp, or equivalently pull 10 percent of its body weight for a total of 20 miles per day, and retain its vigor to an advanced age. Brody's work allows the following approximations for estimating the useful power output of work animals of varying sizes: The ratio of the power exerted in maximal energy production for a few seconds to the maximum steady-state power maintained for 5 to 30 min to the power produced in sustained heavy work over a 6- to 10-hr day is approximately 25:4:1. For any one of these conditions, it has been found that, for healthy mature specimens,

$$hp_{animal} = hp_{man}(\text{mass of animal/mass of man})^{0.73}$$

Thus, from the previously given horsepower magnitudes for men, one can compute the power generated by ponies, horses, bullocks, or elephants under the specified working conditions.

GEOTHERMAL POWER

By V. F. Estcourt

References: McNitt, Exploration and Development of Geothermal Power in California, *Special Report* 75, Calif., Division of Mines and Geology. Kaufman, Geothermal Power, an Economic Evaluation, *Inf. Circ.* 8230, B of M. Haldane and Armstead, The Geothermal Power Development at Waraikei, New Zealand, *Proc. IMechE.*, 1962. Facca and Ten Dam, "Geothermal Power Economics," Worldwide Geothermal Exploration Co., Los Angeles, 1964. *Petroleum Management*, **33,** Oct., 1961.

Although the generation of electric power from geothermal heat sources is still in the pioneering stage, its practicality and economics have been demonstrated in installations in Italy, New Zealand, and the United States. Chemicals and minerals in the water or brine discharged with the steam are by-products which may enhance the over-all economy of the undertaking. In Italy, the Lardarello wells presently supply an installed generating capacity of over 300,000 kw. In California, the geysers supply steam for two 12,500-kw units and one 27,500-kw unit, and the owners of the wells presently estimate that there is an ultimate potential of roughly 600,000 kw in the area. The Waraikei installation in New Zealand involves nearly 300,000 kw. More recently, the Tasman Pulp and Paper Co. has been utilizing geothermal wells in Kamerau for electric power and process steam.

Geothermal steam sources in the United States, suitable for electric-power generation, are located in Hawaii, Alaska, Oregon, Idaho, Nevada, and California. Drilling has taken place in the Imperial Valley (near the Salton Sea), in Casa Diablo, California, and in Beowawe and Steamboat Springs, Nevada. A 15,000-kw generating plant will be constructed on the Casa Diablo site. An experimental plant is in operation in Pathe, Mexico. A large field is being explored in Mexicali, Mexico, and the installation of experimental units have been authorized by the Mexican government.

Geothermal steam is also being utilized in Reykjavik, Iceland, for the heating of homes and the necessary indoor growing of vegetables; construction of the first 17,000-kw power plant is under way in Hveragardi. Other potential sources of geothermal steam are known to exist in El Salvador, Venezuela, Chile, the Belgian Congo, Kenya, France, Japan, Russia, Burma, and Indonesia. Geothermal exploration and development programs are in progress in some of these locations, and it is reported that a 2,000-kw experimental unit will be installed in Chile. Two 30-kw pilot plants are under test in Japan, and a 3,500-kw plant is in operation in Katanga.

Meteoric water, or **ground water,** contacting hot rocks near the surface is commonly held responsible for geyser phenomena; but it is **magmatic water,** reckoned at some 10 percent of the superheated earth's core and released upon cooling and crystallization of magma into igneous rock, that makes up the bulk of the steam reserve. These phenomena occur in areas of magmatic formations, which are near the surface in volcanic regions or are at greater depths in non-volcanic regions such as Lardarello, where the wells are 1,200 to 2,000 ft deep. At such depths, the boiling point of water may be in excess of 400 F, and the temperature of the rocks will determine whether the medium is hot water, steam, or a mixture of both. (See McNitt and Kaufmann.)

Steam conditions in geothermal wells in different areas vary over a wide range as to pressure, temperature, relative amounts of water and steam, mineral content, and non-condensable gases. In some plants, the hot water is flashed into steam for additional power generation. However, the steam from the geysers in California is dry and slightly superheated, and one well in the Salton Sea area had a bottom-hole temperature of 800 F at a depth of 8,100 ft. This is believed to be the hottest geothermal steam discovered to date. The Lardarello wells yield minerals from the water which are an important by-product of the operation—principally boric acid, borax, ammonium bicarbonate, and boron carbide.

Construction costs per kilowatt are lower for a large fossil-fuel plant but increase significantly as the size of the unit is reduced. The economics probably will be less favorable for the construction of a small fossil-fuel plant as compared with a geothermal plant, which, with lower operating costs, can usually produce electric energy from relatively small units at a lower cost per kilowatt in spite of higher fixed costs for exploration and drilling. Obviously, this is only a broad generalization, and the feasibility and economics of each individual source must be carefully evaluated. Exploration methods have been improved as the result of experience, and costs for this work have been reduced accordingly. (See Kaufman, Facca and Ten Dam.)

In evaluating the engineering and economic factors in each particular instance, it is necessary to determine not only the **quality of the steam** and the **minerals** in the water or brine but the quantity of **non-condensable gases.** The latter is an important factor which must be taken into consideration in providing for sufficient gas-removal equipment in the plant cycle.

Some special alloys may be needed in certain parts of the turbine and other power-plant equipment to resist **corrosion.** Copper may be attacked by the hydrogen sulphide in the ambient air. In such cases, aluminum and tinned copper have been substituted for transmission lines and electrical contacts, respectively. **Atmospheric pollution** from hydrogen sulphide may be released through the gas ejectors in the plant cycle and from the cooling-tower vapor. It should be monitored to avoid reaching levels adverse to vegetation or health. Since there is **no need to recover the condensate** for feed purposes, barometric condensers are feasible in place of the conventional surface condenser. In the case of some small wells with relatively low pressure or when the gas content of the steam is high, a non-condensing unit may be the economic choice.

Because there are no boilers, with the related complications of fuel handling and combustion, a geothermal plant is relatively simple to operate. It is of interest to note that the Geysers Plant in California was designed for **unattended operation** for at least 16 hr of the day. This arrangement has proved to be entirely successful in actual practice. As far as is known, this plant is the first unattended thermal electric power plant in the world. It operates 7 days per week around the clock with a total of five regular employees, who are spread over the 7 day shifts on a 5-day-work-week basis for routine operation and maintenance. This means that there may be only two of these men on the job for 4 out of the 7 days. For 16 hr per day, the plant is normally unattended and the doors are locked. Should minor trouble occur during this period, a signal is sent over the transmission line by carrier wave to an attended substation 35 miles away. One of the plant operators is then notified by telephone at his home to investigate the trouble. Should more serious trouble occur, the plant will shut itself down automatically. It must be restarted manually.

Interest in the practical utilization of geothermal energy was expressed at the United Nations Conference on New Sources of Energy at Rome in 1961. Again, at a second conference in Geneva in 1963, emphasis was placed upon its potential benefits for less-developed countries. Hearings in the House and Senate of the United States have been held in connection with a proposed bill submitted in 1963 to permit leasing of government lands for commercial production of geothermal power. This would be applicable principally in the 11 Western states, where the Federal government owns roughly 50 percent of the land. No definite legislative action, however, has been taken up to the present time.

SOLAR ENERGY

By John I. Yellott

References: Zarem and Erway, "Introduction to Utilization of Solar Energy," McGraw-Hill. Yellott, Power from Solar Energy, *Trans. ASME*, Aug., 1957. Selective Reflectance Glass, *ASHRAE Jour.*, Jan., 1964. Moon, Standard Solar Radiation Curves, *Jour. Franklin Inst.*, Nov., 1940. Threlkeld and Jordan, Direct Solar Radiation Available on Clear Days, *Trans. ASHRAE*, 1958. Tables of Computed Altitude and Azimuth, *H. O. Pub.* 214, GPO, 1962. "Guide and Data Book," ASHRAE, 1963. Threlkeld, "Thermal Environmental Engineering," Prentice-Hall. Whillier, Plastic Covers for Solar Collectors, *Solar Energy*, July, 1963. Tabor, Selective Radiation, *Bull. Res. Council Israel*, vol. 5A, No. 2–3, 1956. Thomason, Solar Space Heating, *Solar Energy*, vol. 4, No. 4, 1960.

Notation

A, R, T = subscripts denoting absorbed, reflected, and transmitted solar radiation
Btu = Btu per hr per sq ft
C = concentration ratio
c = subscript denoting collector cover
c_p = specific heat of fluid, Btu per lb per deg F
I_{DN} = direct normal solar intensity, *Btu*
I_d = diffuse radiation, *Btu*
I_o = radiation intensity beyond earth's atmosphere, *Btu*
I_r = reflected solar radiation, *Btu*
I_{sc} = solar constant; normal incidence intensity at average earth-sun distance, *Btu*
I_t = total solar radiation, *Btu*
L = latitude, deg
o, i = subscripts denoting outgoing and incoming fluid conditions
q = rate of heat flux, *Btu*
q_I = heat flow through insulation, *Btu*
T_p = temperature of absorbing surface, deg R
U = over-all coefficient of heat transfer, *Btu* per deg F

w_f = flow rate of collecting fluid, lb per hr per sq ft
Z = solar azimuth, deg
α, ρ, τ = absorptance, reflectance, and transmittance for solar radiation
β = solar altitude, deg
δ = solar declination, deg
ϵ = emittance for long-wave radiation
γ = wall-solar azimuth, deg
μ = unit of wavelength, micron
ϕ = angle of tilt from vertical, deg
θ = incident angle, deg

Solar-energy Utilization. Solar energy reaches the earth as electromagnetic radiation in the wavelength band between 0.3 and 3.0 μ, with its peak spectral intensity near 0.5 μ (Fig. 1). On clear days, the total solar-radiation intensity on a horizontal surface varies from zero at sunrise and sunset to a maximum which can reach 350 *Btu*. Despite this variation, solar energy can be used in three processes: (1) **Heliothermal,** in which the incident radiation is absorbed and turned into heat for converting seawater into salt or to potable water, heating air and water to moderate temperatures for house heating and domestic hot water, cooking, attaining temperatures up to 6,500 F in solar furnaces, producing electricity by thermodynamic and thermoelectric devices. (2) **Heliochemical,** in which radiation between 0.3 and 1.0 μ can cause chemical reactions, sustain growth of plants and animals, and, through photosynthesis, convert exhaled carbon dioxide to breathable oxygen. (3) **Helioelectrical,** in which part of the radiation in the band between 0.33 and 1.2 μ can be converted directly into electricity by photovoltaic cells. Solar batteries, although still too expensive for most terrestrial uses, have become the standard power source for satellites and space probes.

Solar-radiation Intensity. In space, at the average earth-sun distance (92.9 million miles), solar radiation intensity is 445 ± 10 *Btu*. This quantity, called the solar constant I_{sc}, undergoes small (±2 percent) variations, which are apparently related to sunspot activity. The earth-sun distance varies throughout the year, causing the extra-atmospheric solar-radiation intensity to vary by ±3.3 percent (Table 1). The great seasonal variations in terrestrial solar intensity are caused by the variation in the solar declination δ from +23.5 deg on June 21 through 0 deg on Sept. 21 and Mar. 21 to −23.5 deg on Dec. 21.

Table 1. Annual Variation in Solar Declination and Extra-atmospheric Solar-radiation Intensity

Date	Jan. 1	Feb. 1 Nov. 10	Mar. 1 Oct. 13	Apr. 1 Sept. 12	May 1 Aug. 12	June 1 July 12	July 1
Declination, deg	−23.0	−17.1	−7.7	+4.4	+15.0	+22.0	+23.1
Ratio, I_o/I_{sc}	1.033	1.029	1.017	1.000	0.983	0.971	0.967
Intensity, *Btu*	459.4	457.6	452.3	444.9	437.1	43.81	430.0

In passing through the atmosphere, part of the sun's radiation is reflected, scattered, and absorbed by air molecules, dust, water vapor, and man-made pollution. The intensity of the direct normal radiation I_{DN} reaching the earth's surface depends upon the solar altitude β and upon the clarity and humidity of the atmosphere. Some of the scattered and reflected radiation reaches the earth as diffuse or sky radiation I_d.

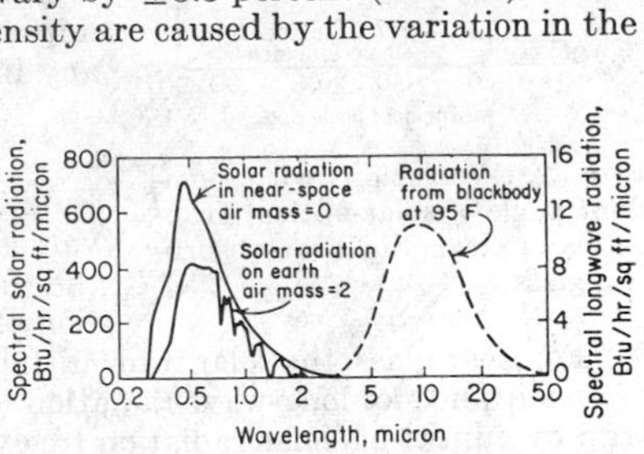

Figure 1 shows Moon's estimates (1940) of the spectral variation of solar radiation in space and at sea level for a solar altitude of 30 deg (air mass = 2). Table 2 shows (1) the variation of terrestrial direct solar radiation for clear winter and summer condi-

FIG. 1. Spectral distribution of solar radiation and radiation emitted by blackbody at 95 F.

Table 2. Intensity of Direct Solar Radiation at Sea Level; Diffuse Radiation on Horizontal and Vertical Surfaces*

Solar altitude, deg	10	20	30	40	60	80
Relative air mass	5.75	2.92	2.00	1.56	1.15	1.015
Direct normal radiation, I_{DN}						
Winter, max	175	247	280	300		
Summer, min	91	168	220	246	270	279
Diffuse radiation, I_d						
Horizontal, surface	14	23	28	31	34	36
Vertical, south	8	13	17	21	27	30
Vertical, east (A.M.)	20	31	36	36	28	24
Vertical, west (P.M.)	7	12	15	17	21	24

* Northern Hemisphere.

tions, as estimated by Jordan and Threlkeld (1958), and (2) typical values of diffuse radiation for various orientations.

The total radiation intensity reaching a terrestrial surface is the sum of the direct, diffuse, and reflected components: $I_t = I_{DN} \cos\theta + I_d + I_r$, where θ is the incident angle between the solar rays and a line perpendicular to the receiving surface and I_r is the shortwave radiation reflected from surrounding surfaces.

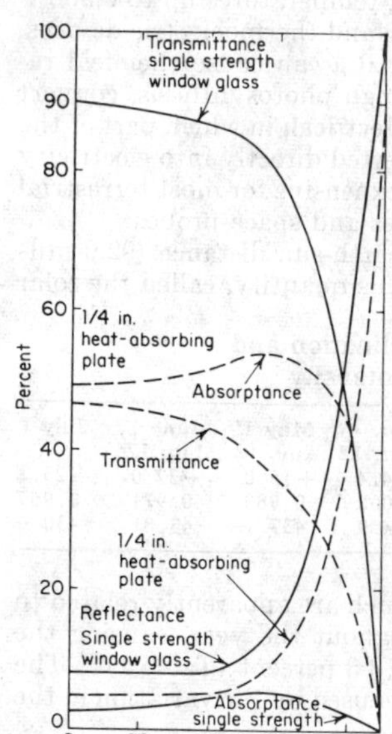

FIG. 2. Variation with incident angle of solar-optical properties of clear and heat-absorbing glass.

Direct-solar-radiation intensity is measured by **pyrheliometers,** which convert the radiation into heat and then use thermoelectric or calorimetric methods to determine the rate of energy absorption. The total radiation from sun and sky and the diffuse component alone are measured by similar but uncollimated instruments called **pyranometers.**

Incident-angle Determination. The incident angle θ controls both the direct solar intensity and the solar-optical properties of the irradiated surface. For any flat surface tilted at an angle ϕ from the vertical, $\cos\theta = \cos\beta\cos\gamma\cos\phi + \sin\beta\sin\phi$, where γ is the wall-solar azimuth. For vertical surfaces, $\phi = 0$ deg, so $\cos\theta = \cos\beta\cos\gamma$; for horizontal surfaces, $\theta = 90\text{ deg} - \beta$. (See Tables of Computed Altitude and Azimuth for solar positions throughout the year.)

Solar-optical Properties of Transparent Materials. When solar radiation with total intensity I_t falls on a transparent surface, part of the energy is transmitted, part is absorbed, and part is reflected. At any instant,

$$I_t = q_T + q_A + q_R = I_t(\tau + \alpha + \rho)$$

Evidently, $\tau + \alpha + \rho = 1.0$, but the individual values of these solar-optical properties depend upon the wavelength, the incident angle, and the composition of the material.

For clear glass, the solar transmittance at $\theta = 0$ deg (Fig. 2) is approx 0.90, but the transmittance for long-wave radiation (5μ) is virtually zero. Thus glass acts as a heat trap by admitting solar radiation freely but retaining most of the absorbed sunshine. This "greenhouse effect," which is also exhibited by some plastic films (see Whillier), is the basis for most heliothermal processes. Heat-absorbing glass (Fig. 2) usually transmits less than 50 percent of the incident solar radiation; it is widely used by architects to reduce the amount of solar radiation admitted through unshaded windows.

For all types of glass, the transmittance falls and the reflectance rises as the incident angle increases (Fig. 2). The absorptance increases slightly due to the increased path traversed by the rays and then drops off sharply as the incident angle exceeds 60 deg.

Absorptance and Emittance of Opaque Surfaces. Opaque materials absorb or reflect all the incident sunshine. The absorptance α for solar radiation and the emittance for long-wave radiation at the temperature of the receiving surface are particularly important in heliotechnology. For a true blackbody, the absorptance and emittance are equal and do not change with wavelength. Most real surfaces have reflectances and absorptances which vary with wavelength (Fig. 3). Aluminum foil has a consistently low absorptance and high reflectance over the entire spectrum from 0.25 to 25μ, while black paint has a high absorptance and low reflectance. White paint, however, has low shortwave (solar) absorptance, but beyond 3μ, its absorptance and reflectance are virtually the same as for black paint.

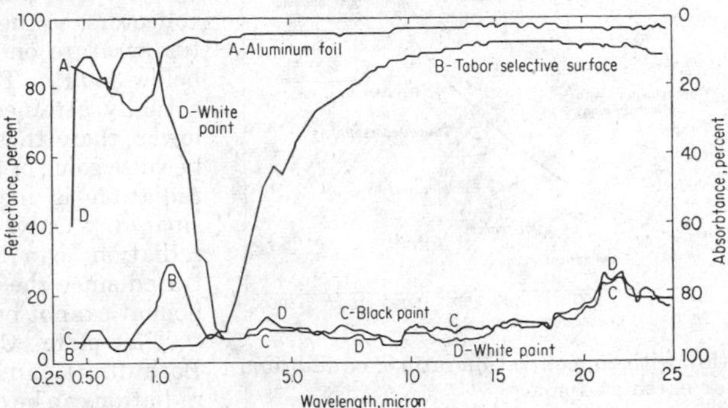

Fig. 3. Variation with wavelength of reflectance and absorptance for opaque surfaces.

Solar collectors require a high α/ϵ ratio, while surfaces which should remain cool, such as rooftops or space vehicles, should have low ratios since their objective usually is to absorb as little solar radiation and emit as much long-wave radiation as possible. Special surface treatments have been developed (see Tabor) for which the ratio α/ϵ is above 7.0, making them suitable for solar collectors; others with ratios as low as 0.15 are useful as heat rejectors for space applications (see Table 3).

Table 3. Solar Absorptance, Long-wave Emittance, and Radiation Ratio for Typical Surfaces

Surface or material	Shortwave (solar) absorptance, α	Long-wave emittance, ϵ	Radiation ratio, α/ϵ
Flat, oil-based paints:			
Black	0.90	0.90	1.00
Red	0.74	0.90	0.82
Green	0.50	0.90	0.55
Aluminum	0.45	0.90	0.50
White	0.25	0.90	0.28
Whitewash on galvanized iron	0.22	0.90	0.25
Building materials:			
Asbestos slate	0.81	0.96	0.84
Tar paper, black	0.93	0.93	1.00
Brick, red	0.55	0.92	0.59
Concrete	0.60	0.88	0.68
Sand, dry	0.82	0.90	0.92
Glass	0.04–0.70	0.84	
Metals:			
Copper, polished	0.18	0.04	4.50
Copper, oxidized	0.64	0.60–0.90	1.03–0.71
Aluminum, polished	0.30	0.05	6.00
Selective surfaces:			
Tabor, electrolytic	0.90	0.12	7.50
Silicon cell, uncoated	0.94	0.30	3.13
Black cupric oxide on copper	0.91	0.16	5.67

Equilibrium Temperatures. When a surface is irradiated, its temperature rises until the rate of solar-energy input balances the rate of heat dissipation. For the ideal case (no heat lost), $I_{DN}C\alpha = 1.723(T_p/1{,}000)^4$, where C is the concentration ratio and T_p is the absolute temperature of the surface. Figure 4 shows the variation of black-body surface temperature with concentration ratios for earth and space, with $I_{DN} = 320$ and 445 *Btu*. $C = 1.0$ for flat-plate solar collectors, so their maximum temperature on earth is well below 300 F. Temperatures actually attained are always lower than those in Fig. 4 because some of the absorbed radiation is inevitably dissipated. Only the direct radiation can be concentrated since the diffuse component cannot be collimated.

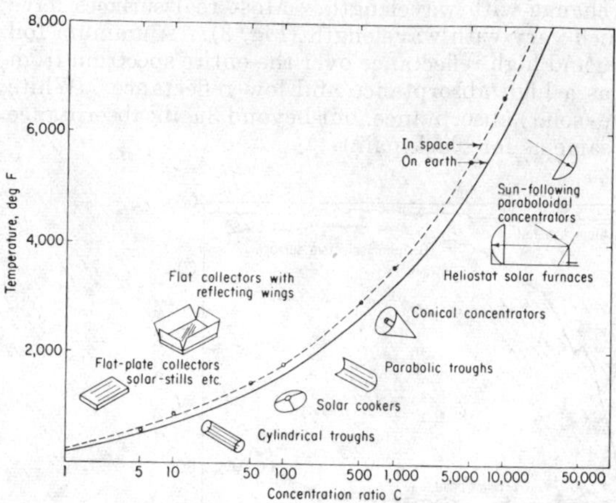

FIG. 4. Variation with concentration ratio of equilibrium temperatures for earth and space.

Flat-plate Collectors. Both direct and diffuse solar radiation can be collected and put to use by blackened flat plates which are insulated and finned or tubed (Fig. 5) so that the absorbed heat can be transferred to air or water. The heat balance for a unit area of collector surface is

$$q_A = I_t\tau_c\alpha_p = w_f c_p(t_o - t_i) + q_I + U(t_p - t_a)$$

For collectors with glass and plastic covers, approximate values of transmittance τ_c and over-all coefficient U are given in Table 4. (See Whillier.) The insulation heat leak q_I can be minimized, but some upper-surface loss is unavoidable; this loss increases with rising fluid temperature. Upper-surface loss can be reduced by a wavelength-selective coating with high solar-radiation absorptance and low long-wave emittance. (See Tabor, Zarem, and Erway.)

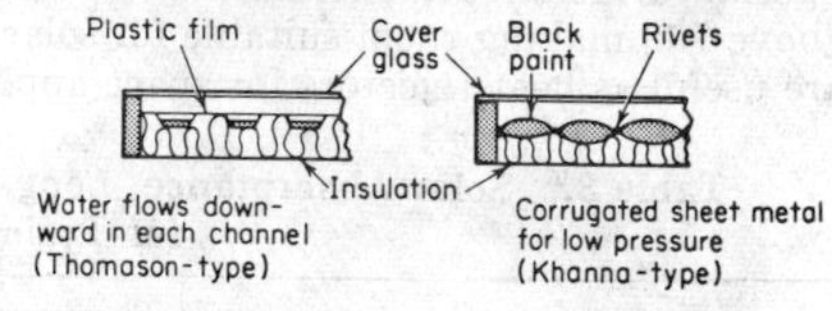

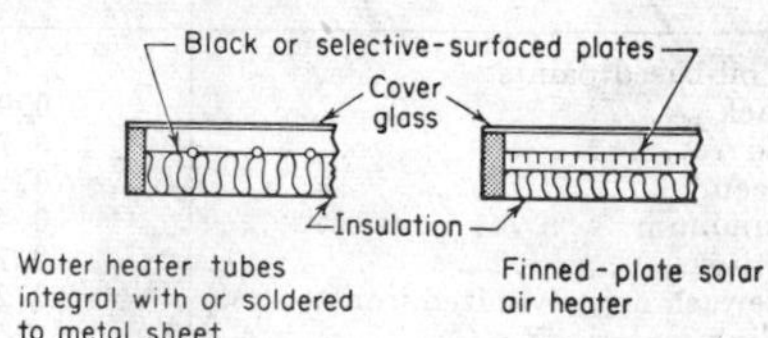

FIG. 5. Typical flat-plate solar-radiation collectors.

Applications of Heliotechnology

Solar Stills. The simplest roof-type solar still (Fig. 6*a*) uses a shallow blackened box covered by a tilted sheet of glass. The sun's rays enter through the glass cover and warm the water, producing vapor which condenses on the inner surface of the cover and flows downward into the troughs. The remaining brine is discharged at intervals, and more seawater is added. Yield ranges from 0.4 lb per day in winter to 1.0 lb per day in summer per

Table 4. Transmittance and Over-all Heat-transfer Coefficients for Collectors with Glass and Plastic Covers

Type and number of covers	None	One glass	One plastic	Two glass	Two plastic
Solar transmittance	1.00	0.90	0.92	0.81	0.85
Over-all coeff, U	3.90	1.12	1.30	0.71	0.87

sq ft of water surface. Tilted stills (Figs. 6*b* and *c*) produce twice as much as distillate as roof-type stills in winter when the solar altitude is low. Thus far, no solar-distillation process can produce water in quantities required for irrigation, but drinking water can be produced at competitive costs in many arid regions.

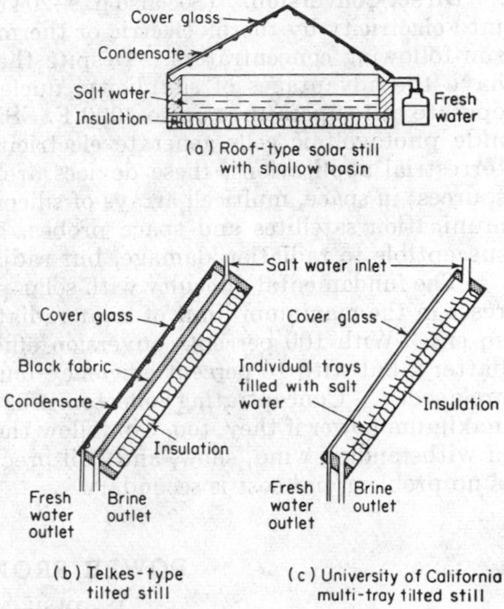

Solar Water Heaters. The simple natural-circulation flat-plate collector (Fig. 7) is used in thousands of domestic water heaters in Japan, Europe, and North Africa. Under favorable climatic conditions, they produce 30 to 50 gal of hot water during each clear or partially overcast day. Prevalent use is for locations where daily demands are below 50 gal at 140 F. Tested in Arizona, two absorbers (6 by 3 ft) with Tabor-type selective coatings heated about 40 gal of water per day to 160 F in summer and 120 F in winter.

(a) Roof-type solar still with shallow basin

(b) Telkes-type tilted still

(c) University of California multi-tray tilted still

FIG. 6. Solar stills: (*a*) roof type with shallow basin; (*b*) wick type inclined still (Telkesde sign); (*c*) tilted-tray type (University of California design).

Solar Househeating, Low-temperature Heat Storage. Roof-mounted collectors of the types shown in Fig. 6 can be used for househeating in temperate climates. The economics of solar househeating have not been favorable because of the high cost of the collectors and storage systems and the necessity for auxiliary fuel-burning equipment. Water heated during sunny days can be used to warm the house at night, but heat-storage capacity is limited to approximately 500 Btu per gal of water at 140 F max; 1,000 gal of stored hot water can heat a small, well-insulated house (25,000 Btu per hr heat loss) for about 1 day. Greater heat-storage capacity per unit of volume is possible with heat-of-fusion systems, *e.g.*, utilizing Glauber's salt, but there are attendant problems.

Solar refrigeration utilizing high-temperature collectors with an absorption system has a long history, but practical problems of economics and intermittent operation have limited application to experimental installations.

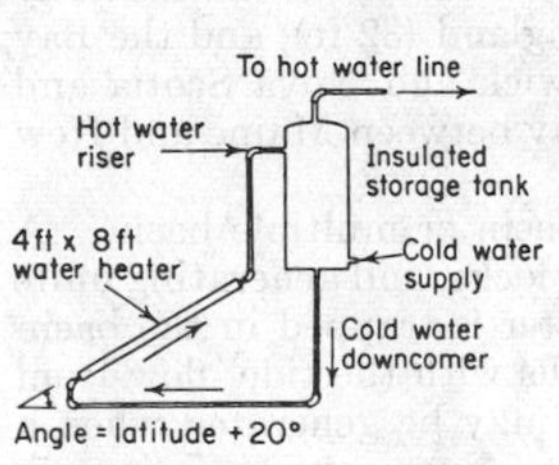

FIG. 7. Thermosyphon-type solar water heater.

Solar cooking utilizes (1) a sun-following broiler-type device with a metallized parabolic reflector and a grid in the focal area where cooking pots can be placed; (2) an oven-type cooker comprising an insulated box with glass covers over an open end which is pointed toward the sun. When reflecting wings are used to increase the solar input, midday temperatures as high as 400 F are reached.

Solar Furnaces. Precise paraboloidal concentrators can focus the sun's rays upon small areas, and if suitable receivers are used, temperatures up to 6500 F can be attained. The concentrator must be able to follow the sun, either through movement of the paraboloidal reflector itself (Fig. 4) or by the use of a heliostat which tracks the sun and reflects the rays along a horizontal or vertical axis into the concentrator.

Power from Solar Energy. During the past century, many attempts have been made to generate power from solar energy for terrestrial purposes using both flat-plate and concentrating collectors. Vapor cycles have been used with water, sulphur dioxide, and complex heavy molecules with low boiling points, but none has been commercially successful because of low conversion efficiency, intermittent operations, and high costs. For space applications, exotic thermal cycles are under development using liquid metals as the working fluid, with high-temperature heat storage by metallic hydrides. Problems of lubrication, weight reduction, and shaft sealing still await solution.

Direct Conversion. (See also p. 9–204 *et seq.*) Solar heat can be converted directly into electricity by thermoelectric or thermionic devices mounted at the focal areas of sun-following concentrators. Despite their low efficiency, direct-conversion devices have the advantages of simplicity, nuclear-radiation resistance, and the ability to operate at temperatures up to 4000 F. Silicon, cadmium sulphide, and gallium arsenide photovoltaic cells generate electricity directly from solar radiation. In most terrestrial applications, these devices are not competitive with conventional power sources; in space, multicell arrays of silicon solar batteries are in regular use for communication satellites and space probes. The first silicon cells (p-on-n type) were susceptible to radiation damage, but radiation-resistant n-on-p cells are now in use.

The fundamental difficulty with solar-power generation in the vicinity of the earth rests in the maximum limit of solar radiation at some 460 *Btu*, or 144 milliwatts per sq cm. With 100 percent conversion efficiency, 1 kw would require 9 sq ft of solar battery, but with 10 percent efficiency (current realization), 90 sq ft of collector area are needed. Concentrating collectors must track the sun, and flat devices will produce maximum power if they, too, can follow the sun. The cost of large structures capable of withstanding wind, snow, and hail precludes terrestrial use; but in space, weather is no problem and cost is secondary.

POWER FROM THE TIDES

By Philip C. Wagner

REFERENCES: Emil Mosonyi, "Water Power Development," vol. 1, Hungarian Academy of Sciences, Budapest, 1963; chap. 4, pp. 56–77, and bibliography, pp. 1020–1025. The Rance Estuary Tidal Power Project, *Public Utilities Fortnightly,* Dec. 3, 1964.

Tidal power is power derived from large periodic variations in water levels occurring in certain basins of oceanic coastal areas as a result of tidal flows. Suitable configurations of the continental shelves and of the coastal profiles result in reflection and resonance such as to amplify normally small tidal bulges to ranges of up to 50 ft.

The principal tidal power sites are the North Sea (12 ft average tidal range), the Irish Sea (22 ft), the west coast of India (23 ft), San José Bay on the east-central coast of Argentina (23 ft), St. Michel (including the Rance estuary) on the Brittany coast of France (26 ft), the Bristol Channel (Severn) in England (32 ft), and the Bay of Fundy, including Chignecto Bay between New Brunswick and Nova Scotia and Minas basin in Nova Scotia (40 ft) and Passamaquoddy Bay between Maine and New Brunswick (18 ft).

Developments take one of two general forms: single basin or multiple basin. A **single-basin project,** such as the Rance, has a dam, sluices, locks, and generating units in a structure separating a tidal basin from the sea. Water is trapped in the basin after a high tide. As the water level outside the basin falls with the tide, flow from the basin through turbines generates power. Power also may be generated when a basin emptied during a low tide is refilled on a rising tide. Numerous variations in operation are possible, depending on tide conditions and the relationship between the tide cycles and the load cycles. Pumping into or out of the basin increases the availability of the installed capacity for peak-load service.

A **multiple-basin development,** such as Chignecto or Passamaquoddy, generally has the power plant between two basins. Sluices between the sea and the basins are so arranged that one basin is filled twice a day on high tide and the other emptied twice a day on low tide. Power output can be made continuous.

The amount of **energy available** from a tidal development is proportional to the basin area and to the square of the tidal range. Head variations are large in tidal projects during generating cycles and on a daily, monthly, and annual basis due to various cosmic factors. Intermittent power, as from all single-basin plans and from two-basin plans with low-capacity factor, implies that the output can best be utilized as peaking capacity. Because of low heads, particularly toward the end of any generating cycle when pools have been drawn down, the cost of adding generating units only to tidal projects is well over the total installation cost of alternative peaking capacity. To be economically competitive with alternative capacity, the tidal projects must produce enough energy to pay the power-plant costs and also to pay for the dams and other costs, such as general site development, transmission, operation, and replacements.

The **risks and uncertainties** involved in designing, pricing, building, and operating capital-intensive tidal works and the technological developments in alternative types of generating capacity have tended to defeat tidal developments, with the notable exception of the Rance project. All the other sites noted above have not been authorized for development (1965) for a variety of reasons, *e.g.*, civil works are too extensive, transmission distances to load centers are too great, the required scale of development is too large for existing loads, a single basin limits flexibility, and/or the head is too low.

The Rance development of Électricité de France has been under construction since 1960 and is expected to be completed in 1967. It is a single-basin project with twenty-four 10-mw bulb units which will produce 2,270 kwh per kw per year net after deducting pumping energy. About 200 mw are firm on the winter peak load. The structure includes a navigation lock and will also serve as a highway bridge across the Rance Estuary. The construction cost will be $200 per kw for all equipment including the turbines and generators and $146 per kw for civil works, a total of $346 per installed kw.

UTILIZATION OF THE HEAT ENERGY OF THE SEA

(Staff Contribution)

Claude and Boucherot (*Compt. rend.*, **183**, 1926, pp. 929–933) suggest using the temperature difference between surface water and water from deep levels for the operation of steam turbines. An analysis of this proposal (*The Engineer*, 1926, p. 584) assumes surface temperature of 87 F, cold water at 30 F, and a fall of temperature to 78 F in the evaporator (boiler). The steam produced would be at 0.55 psia, the condenser pressure 0.117 psia. With turbine efficiency of 75 percent, the steam consumption would be 53 lb per kwh. It would require 116 lb of warm water to produce 1 lb of steam. For a 10,000 kw turbine, the steam-pipe diameter would be 23 ft for steam velocity of 200 fps and other dimensions would be equally enormous. The magnitudes of these physical dimensions, coupled with the problems of high vacuum in boiler and condenser, have prompted the proposal to substitute a thermodynamic fluid with positive pressures and high densities at the prevailing low temperatures, *e.g.*, propane (see Anderson and Anderson, *Power*, Jan. and Feb., 1965). New problems are introduced tending to offset the advantages despite recent progress in underwater technology, *e.g.*, (1) the sacrifice of availability by the thermodynamic irreversibility in the transfer of heat in both the boiler and the condenser, (2) materials selection, (3) corrosion, and (4) maintenance (see Anderson and Anderson, *Mech. Engg.*, Apr., 1966).

UTILIZATION OF THE ENERGY OF THE WAVES

(Staff Contribution)

According to Albert W. Stahl, USN (*Trans. ASME*, **13**, p. 438), the total energy of a series of **trochoidal deep-sea waves** may be expressed as follows: Hp per ft of breadth of wave $= 0.0329 \times H^2 \sqrt{L}[1 - 4.935\,(H^2/L^2)]$, where H = height of wave, ft, and L = length of wave between successive crests, ft. For example, with $L = 25$ ft and $L/H = 50$, hp $= 0.04$; with $L = 100$ ft and $L/H = 10$, hp $= 31.3$. Not much more than a quarter of the total energy of such waves would probably be available after reaching shallow water, and apparatus rugged enough for this purpose would doubtless be unable to utilize more than a third of this amount. **Wave motors** brought out from time to time have depended for their operation largely on the lifting power of the waves.

One installed at Atlantic City, N.J. (*Power*, Jan. 17, 1911), consisted of six 4-ft cylindrical floats 4 ft high. These, each weighing about 3,100 lb, were lifted 2 ft by the waves about 11 times per minute, and drove a horizontal shaft by means of chains and ratchets, developing but 12 hp, steadiness being obtained by the use of heavy flywheels. The fixed charges on the excess cost of wave motors thus far proposed, over steam-power plants of equal capacity, have been more than sufficient to care for the fuel and other additional costs necessitated by the use of the latter.

A wave motor employing a hydraulic ram for raising a portion of the water to a high level has been proposed by Smith (*Mech. Eng.*, Sept., 1927, p. 995). The waves enter a scoop which is connected to the ram by a long drive pipe. The apparatus is automatically adjusted for vertical level as the tide changes.

Gravity waves may be only a few feet high yet develop as much as 50 kw per ft of wave front. Most historical wave motors utilize (1) the kinetic energy of the waves by a device such as a paddle wheel, or (2) the potential energy by such a device as a series of floats. Few devices proposed utilize both forms of energy. Jacobs (*Power Eng.*, Sept., 1956) has analyzed the periodic fluctuation or **"seiching"** of the water level of harbors or basins where, with a resonant port, a 1,000-ft wave front might be used to achieve a liquid piston effect for the compression of air, the air to be subsequently used in an air turbine.

HOT-AIR ENGINES

By Erich A. Farber

Hot-air engines are heat engines in which air or other gases like H_2, He, and N_2, are used as the working fluid, operating on the Stirling or Ericsson cycles (see p. 4-29) or modifications of them. While the earlier engines of this type were bulky, slow in speed, and low in efficiency, a number of new developments have rectified these deficiencies. Hot-air engines are multifuel engines and have been driven by solid, liquid, and gaseous fuels and with concentrated solar energy. They are quiet-running, relatively simple in construction, and if used with solar energy, without waste products.

The Philips Hot-air Engine. (*Philips Tech. Rev.*, **8,** 1936, pp. 129–136; **9,** 1947, pp. 97–104 and 125–134; **20,** 1959, pp. 245–262.) The Philips Research Laboratory (in Holland) seems to have developed the first efficient, compact hot-air engine. It operates at 3,000 rpm, with hot-chamber temperature of 1200 F, maximum pressure of 50 atm, and mep of 14 atm. The regenerator consists of a porous coil of thin wires having 95 percent efficiency, saving about three-fourths of the heat required by the working fluid. The exhaust gases preheat the air, saving about 70 percent of this loss.

The Philips engine uses only one cylinder and piston for the cycle instead of the separate working and displacer cylinders of the older engines. The heater, cooler, and regenerator are located in an annular space around the cylinder for single-cylinder engines and in the passageways between cylinders for multicylinder engines. Mechanical efficiencies of 90 percent and thermal efficiencies of 40 percent have been obtained.

GMR Stirling Thermal Engine. (*Trans. SAE*, **68,** 1960, pp. 665–684.) A co-operative program, since 1958, between the Philips Research Laboratory and General Motors Corp., resulted in the development of two engines. The larger engine (bore 3.47 in., stroke 2.37 in.), weighing 450 lb and operating at a mean pressure of 1,500 psi, produces 30 hp at 1,500 rpm with 39 percent efficiency and 40 hp at 2,500 rpm with 33.3 percent efficiency. The smaller engine (bore 2.36 in., stroke 1.33 in.), weighing 127 lb and operating at a mean pressure of 1,000 psi, produces 6 hp at 2,400 rpm with 29.6 percent efficiency and 8.63 hp at 3,600 rpm with 26.4 percent efficiency.

Internally Focusing Regenerative Gas Engine. (*ASME Paper* 61-*WA*-297.) This type of engine, conceived at the Solar Energy Laboratory of the University of Wisconsin, uses solar energy concentrated by a parabolic reflector and directed through a quartz dome upon an internally located absorber. This reduces the heat losses since the engine has no external high-temperature heat-transfer surfaces. A small working model of this type of engine has been built at Battelle Memorial Inst. and was demonstrated driving a small fan.

Fractional-horsepower Solar Hot-air Engines. (*ASME Paper* 64-*WA*/*SOL*-5.) The Solar Energy Laboratory of the University of Florida has developed small (¼ to ⅓ hp) solar hot-air engines (converted lawn-mower engines). They operate at 500 rpm max and at a conversion efficiency of 9 percent max. They are simple, rugged, and primarily designed for possible use in underdeveloped countries. They can also be operated by other sources of heat.

The Stirling Engine for Space Power. (*SAE Paper* 594*C*, 1962.) The General Motors Corp., under contract to the USAF Aeronautical Systems Command, is working on the adaptation of the GMR Stirling engine to space applications. A 3-kw engine has been built utilizing NaK heated to 1250 F as heat source and water at 150 F as the cooling medium. The engine is pressurized to a mean pressure of 1,500 psi, giving an efficiency of 27 percent at 2,500 rpm or 24.4 percent at 3,000 rpm. The weight of this solar-energy conversion system is given as 555 lb. Chemical, nuclear, or other sources could also be used.

SECTION 10

MATERIALS HANDLING

BY

HAROLD V. HAWKINS, Manager Product Development and Engineering, Columbus McKinnon Corporation, Tonawanda, N.Y.

CONTENTS

METHODS OF MOVING MATERIALS

LIFTING

DRAGGING, PULLING, AND PUSHING

CARRYING AND LIFTING

CONVEYING AND CONTINUOUS FLOW

METHODS OF MOVING MATERIALS

BY

Harold V. Hawkins

MATERIALS-HANDLING SYSTEMS

Materials-handling systems often comprise many individual mechanisms integrated into a network which becomes a dominant factor in the design of the plant as well as in the manufacturing process involved. Individual motions may be required such as **lifting, translating,** or a complicated pattern of the two. The sequence of motions may be back and forth over the same path or may be unidirectional over a circulating or **continuous conveying system.** The type of commodity carried may be classified as liquid, solid, or a combination of the two; the solids may be granular, bulk material, or packaged. Liquids or granular solids may also be in containers, thus becoming packaged types. The motion needed, kind and consistency of item to be moved, quantity to be moved, and type of process to be accommodated all make for a complex of requirements that demands careful study to assure economic justification as well as technical sufficiency. The basic materials-handling elements available are outlined here to provide (1) the **lifting,** (2) the **dragging, towing,** and **pushing,** and (3) the **carrying and lifting** functions most often used in reciprocating motions, or (4) the **conveying systems** required for continuous movement of bulk or packaged materials.

SELECTION OF TYPE OF METHOD

When making a choice of the type of handling system to be used, ask:

1. Is the job to be done an isolated motion (lifting, dragging, towing, or pushing), or should it be integrated into a sequence (conveying)?

2. What is the rate of weight and volume to be moved? (See Table 1 or pp. 6–7 and 6–8.) Is the movement periodic (reciprocating), or can it be averaged out (continuous)?

3. What type of commodity is to be handled—bulk, granular, packaged, liquid? Its handling characteristics, such as **angle of repose** or **angle of slide,** will be important.

Table 1. Weights of Materials*

Material	Lb per cu ft	Material	Lb per cu ft	Material	Lb per cu ft
Barley	37–40	Earth	75–115	Ore	105–215
Charcoal	17–27	Lignite	31–47	Rye	44–50
Clay	95–169	Limestone	90–110	Slag, blast-furnace	37–63
Coke	26–30	Oats	28–31	Stone, broken	90–120
				Wheat	44–50

* See also Table 2.

The **angle of repose** of any material is the angle with the horizontal at which material will stand when piled. For anthracite coal, it is about 27 deg; for coke of the same size, about 40 deg. Moisture content is often the controlling factor. The percentage of fine material in the mass has a decided influence on the angle, as the fines carry the bulk of the moisture. Screened material has an angle of repose of 35 to 40 deg, depending on the shape, smoothness, and method of storing. The

Table 2. Preferred Types of Conveyors and Elevators for Bulk and Packaged Materials

Material	Physical condition	Avg wt per cu ft, lb	Reaction on conveyor	Preferred conveyors*	Preferred elevators*	Comment
Acid phosphate	Damp	90	Adheres	*a, e*	*h*	Sticky
Alum	Granular	60–65	Abrasive	*a, b, c, e*	*g, h*	
Aluminum oxide	Pulv.	60	Abrasive	*a, e*	*g*	
Ammonium nitrate	Pulv.	62	Hygroscopic	*b, c, e*	*g, h*	Explosive
Ammonium nitrate	Damp	65+	Adheres	*c, e*	*g, h*	Sticky
Arsenic salts	Pulv.	100	Heavy	*c, e*	*g, h*	Poisonous
Ashes: dry	Granular	35–40	Abrasive	*d, f*	*h*	Dusty
wet	Sticky	45–50	Abrasive	*f*	*h*	Corrosive
Bone meal	Pulv.	55–60	....	*a, b, c, d, e*	*g, h, c*	
Borax	Pulv.	50–70	Abrasive	*a, b, c, d, e*	*g, h*	
Bran	Granular	16–20	....	*a, b, c, d, e*	*g, h*	Sometimes sticky
Brewers grains, hot	Granular	55	Corrosive	*c, e*	*g, h*	
Carbon black (pellets)	Granular	40	....	*a, e*	*g, h*	Fragile
Cement, dry	Pulv.	90–118	....	*a, c, d, e*	*g, h*	Packs
Clays	Pulv.	35–60	Adheres	*a, b, c, e*	*g, h*	Sluggish
Coal: anthracite	Lumpy	50–54	....	*a, b, c, e*	*g, h*	
steam sizes	Granular	50–60	....	*a, b, c, d, e*	*g, h, c*	
bit., lump	Lumpy	50–60	....	*a, b, e*	*h*	
bit., slack	Granular	50–60	....	*a, b, c, d, e*	*g, h, c*	
Chalk	Pulv.	70–75	....	*a, b, c, d, e*	*g, h, c*	Sluggish
Coffee beans	Granular	40–45	....	*a, c, e*	*g, h*	Fragile
Copra, ground	Pulv.	40	May be abrasive	*a, b, c, e*	*g, h*	Sticky
Cork, ground	Pulv.	5–15	....	*a, b, c, d, e*	*g, h*	Sluggish
Corn, shelled	Granular	45	Abrasive shell	*a, c, e*	*g, h, c*	
Cottonseed	Granular	35–40	Sometimes sticky	*a, b, c, d, e*	*g, h*	
Cullet	Granular	80–100	Abrasive	*a, b, e*	*g, h*	Corrosive
Flaxseed	Granular	45	Shell abrasive	*a, b, c, d, e*	*g, h, c*	Free-flowing
Flue dirt	Pulv.	100	Abrasive	*b, d, e, f*	*g, h*	
Fly ash, clean	Pulv.	35–45	Mild abrasive	*a, b, c, d, e*	*g, h, c*	Free-flowing
Glass batch	Granular	80+	Abrasive	*a, b, e*	*g, h*	
Glue	Granular	45	....	*a, c, e*	*g, h. c*	Keep cool
Graphite (flour)	Pulv.	40	Lubricant	*a, b, c, d, e*	*g, h, c*	
Gravel	Granular	95–135	Abrasive	*a, e, f*	*g, h*	
Gypsum	Pulv.	60	....	*a, b, c, e*	*g, h*	
Heavy ores	Lumpy	100+	....	*a, b, f*	*g, h*	May be tough
Hog fuel	Stringy	15–30	May jam	*a, b, d, e*	*g*	
Lead salts	Pulv.	60–150	Sluggish	*a, b, c, e*	*g, h*	Poisonous
Lime, pebble	Granular	55–80	....	*a, b, c, e*	*g, h*	
Limestone dust	Pulv.	85–95	Abrasive	*a, b, e*	*g*	
Malt	Dry	45	May be sticky	*a, b, c, d, e*	*g, h*	
Manufactured products	Boxed	1–200	....	*a, i, j*		
Merchandise						
Packaged	Boxed	15	....	*a, b, i, j*		
Garments	Hanging	5	....	*i, j*		
Mica, pulv	Pulv.	20–30	Free-flowing	*a, b, c, d, e*	*g, h, c*	Dusty
Molybdenum conc'ts	Pulv.	110	Abrasive	*a, b, d*	*h*	Sticky
Metallic dusts	Pulv.	50–100	Abrasive	*a, b, c, d, e*	*g, h*	Sometimes difficult
Petroleum coke	Lumpy	42	Mild abrasive	*a, b, c, e*	*g, h*	
Pumice	Pulv.	45	Mild abrasive	*a, b, c, d, e*	*g, h, c*	Polisher
Quartz (ground)	Pulv.	110	Very abrasive	*a, b, c, d*	*g*	
Rubber scrap	Stringy	50	Sluggish	*a, b, e*	*g, h*	Difficult
Salt: coarse	Granular	50	Hygroscopic	*a, b, c, e*	*g, h*	Corrosive if wet
cake	Pulv.	75–95	Flows freely	*a, b, c, d, e*	*g, h*	
Sand: dry	Granular	90–110	Abrasive	*a, e, f*	*g, h*	
damp	Granular	90–110	Sticky	*a, e, f*	*g, h*	
Sawdust	Granular	15–20	....	*a, b, c, d, e*	*g, h, c*	
Sewage sludge	Pulv.	60	Sticky if wet	*a, b, e, f*	*g*	Abrasive
Silica flour	Pulv.	80	Sluggish	*a, d, e*	*g*	Abrasive
Soap flakes	Granular	10–20	Fragile	*a, c, e*	*g*	Sticky if hot
Soda ash: light	Pulv.	25–35	Flows freely	*a, b, c, d, e*	*g, c*	Caustic
heavy	Pulv.	55–65	Flows freely	*a, b, c, d, e*	*g, c*	Caustic
Soybean flour	Pulv.	30	Sticky	*a, b, c, e*	*g, c*	Explosive dust
Starch	Pulv.	30–40	....	*a, b, c, e*	*g, c*	Explosive dust
Sugar: raw	Granular	55–65	Sticky	*a, b, c, e*	*g*	
refined	Granular	50–55	....	*a, b, c, e*	*g*	Handle gently
Sulphur	Pulv.	55	Corrosive if wet	*a, b, c, e*	*g, h*	Explosion risk
Talc	Pulv.	50–60	Mild abrasive	*a, b, c, d, e*	*g, h*	Adheres to metal
Tobacco stems	Stringy	25	Sluggish	*a, b, d, e*	*g*	
Wheat	Granular	48	Free-flowing	*a, c, d, e*	*g, c*	Keep clean
Wood chips	Granular	18–20	May arch	*a, c, d, e*	*g, c*	Corrosive if wet
Zinc oxide	Pulv.	20–35	May pack	*a, b, c, d, e*	*g*	Avoid discoloration
Zinc sulphate	Pulv.	70	May pack	*a, b, c, d, e*	*g*	

* Explanation of letter symbols:
a—belt. *b*—flight. *c*—continuous flow. *d*—pneumatic. *e*—screw.
f—drag chain. *g*—belt and bucket. *h*—chain and bucket.
i—overhead straight power. *j*—overhead power and free.

average angle for crushed and screened limestone, iron and copper ore, and similar materials has been found to be 37 deg. Mine-run soft coal will stand at 35 to 37 deg.

The **angle of slide** is the angle at which material will flow on an inclined surface. Anthracite coal will flow on steel plate inclined at about 20 deg, coke at about 25 to 30 deg. Ore, stone, etc., will slide at about 30 deg where the fine material is removed and at 35 to 40 deg for mine-run material. It is customary to build chutes on an angle of 45 deg for such material as coal, stone, and ore, this angle being increased when there is a large percentage of fine, damp material. Where gentle handling is required to prevent breakage, special tests should be made to determine the minimum angle of slide. A chute found too steep may be provided with cross angles to retard the flow.

The answers to these questions, together with the experience in conveying materials included in Table 2, should provide a basis for choice of one or more mechanical devices to accomplish alternate methods of handling. A careful study of the economics of each to minimize capital investment, maintenance, and operating costs will determine the best method.

INFLUENCE OF CODES AND SPECIFICATIONS

A dominant factor in the choice of handling method or in the design of its parts may be the **local** or **national specifications** or **codes.** A review should be made of such general codes as "Safety Code for Cranes, Derricks, and Hoists," ASA B30.2; "Elevators, Dumbwaiters, and Escalators," ASA A17.1; "Conveyors, Cableways, and Related Equipment," ASA B20.1; "Manlifts," ASA A90.1. These all affect design parameters, kinds of acceptable mechanisms, acceptable safety factors, materials that can be transported, etc. Codes are especially restrictive if people are to be transported. In many instances, local or state codes will be even more restrictive than national codes. If safety is not jeopardized, deviations from codes can be requested in advance of usage.

LIFTING

BY

Harold V. Hawkins and Associates

CHAINS

By E. R. Behnke

Columbus McKinnon Corporation

Sling Chains

Until 1933, slings for use where failure could be dangerous to personnel or equipment were usually made from wrought iron. It had good shock-absorbing capability and was easily welded using forge-welding techniques.

However, wrought iron had serious disadvantages. Most important were its tendency to work harden in service and its inability to be welded electrically. Work hardening had to be corrected by frequent annealing to remove brittleness. The requirement for forge welding prevented the use of higher-quality and more consistent methods such as electric-resistance welding.

Research led to the introduction, in 1933, of the first alloy-steel, electrically welded link chain. Since then, alloy chain, which should **never** be annealed, has come into universal acceptance. Although iron is still specified for a handful of applications, it is no longer of commercial importance, and data have accordingly been omitted from this edition.

Most **alloy chains** are made from water-hardening grades of one of the constructional alloy steels such as 4615 or 8620 (see Sec. 6). Some work has been done on higher-carbon, higher-hardenability analyses, but these have not yet become available commercially.

Current commercial alloy sling chain varies among producers from 250 to 400 Brinell in hardness. This is equivalent to a material tensile-strength range of 125,000 to 200,000 psi. In terms of d^2 tons of breaking strength, where d is the chain wire diameter in inches, these material tensile strengths provide a breaking-strength range of $62d^2$ to $100d^2$ tons. For comparison, ASTM specifications for minimum breaking strengths average $60d^2$ tons based upon nominal wire sizes or $56d^2$ tons based upon actual wire diameters. Table 1 gives the ASTM specifications plus working-load limits for nominal and actual sizes. Link inside dimensions have not been standardized among manufacturers. Working-load limits recommended by the NACM (National Association of Chain Manufacturers) for alloy chains in simple, straight tension average about $20d^2$ tons (based upon the nominal size). Endurance limits are about 18 percent of breaking strengths. Thus, even for the highest-strength ($100d^2$ tons) chain available, the endurance limit is 10 percent less than the rated load capacity. For the weaker ones, it may be as much as 45 percent less. This fact should be taken into account where an application calls for many thousands of cycles of loading.

Present product specifications (NACM and ASTM) call for a minimum elongation of 15 percent at failure. This was established originally as a guarantee against brittle failure and to give visible warning of overloading and impending failure. For the soft chains (under 200 Brinell) in use before the advent of hardened alloy steel or even for some of the softer alloy chains sold today, the requirements provided a useful safety feature. Although sling-chain elongation is still important as an

Table 1. ASTM Specifications for Alloy-steel Chain

Nominal size of chain,* in.	Working-load limit, lb	Minimum proof-test load, lb	Minimum break-test load, lb	Maximum length, 100 links, in.	Maximum weight, 100 ft, lb
1/4	3,250	6,500	10,000	98	84
3/8	6,600	13,200	19,000	134	175
1/2	11,250	22,500	32,500	156	288
5/8	16,500	33,000	50,000	182	453
3/4	23,000	46,000	69,500	208	655
7/8	28,750	57,500	93,500	234	910
1	38,750	77,500	122,000	277	1,170
1 1/8	44,500	89,000	143,000	332	1,425
1 1/4	57,500	115,000	180,000	371	1,765
1 3/8	67,000	134,000	207,000	396	2,010
1 1/2	80,000	160,000	244,000	432	2,185
1 3/4	100,000	200,000	325,000	503	3,020

* Most manufacturers make their chains in sizes up to 7/8 in., from bars that are 1/32 in. larger than the nominal-size rating of the chain. Columbus McKinnon produces all sizes of its Herc-Alloy sling chain from wire which is the same as the nominal-size rating.

indicator of resistance to shock loading, it is no longer of use as an overload-warning signal when considering modern, high-quality chains of 300 Brinell or over. More than 50 percent of their total elongation at failure occurs during the final 10 percent of loading. It is unlikely, therefore, that the untrained eye will notice stretch from overloading until it reaches a hazardous amount. Promulgation of the philosophy of 15 percent elongation for overload detection can therefore instill a dangerously false sense of security.

High-test chain is made from heat-treatable plain-carbon steel, usually with a carbon content of 0.15 to 0.20 percent. It provides good reliability and is widely used for load binding, tie-downs, and similar applications where failures would be costly but the maximum security provided by alloy chain is not required. It may have a typical breaking strength as high as $60d^2$ tons, although NACM specifications require an average minimum of only $46d^2$ tons. Hardness is about 170 to 250 Brinell. Table 2 gives ASTM specifications plus working-load limits for different sizes.

General-purpose Chains

BBB and **Proof Coil chains** are quite similar. Both are made from non-heat-treatable, low-carbon steel containing about 0.08 percent carbon. They differ only in geometry, with BBB being somewhat shorter and narrower, which gives it greater flexibility and permits slightly higher proof-test and working-load limits than for Proof Coil chain. However, for most applications, the differences are negligible. Both have a breaking strength of about $35d^2$ tons at a hardness of 125 Brinell. These chains are generally selected for less-critical applications such as logging, agricultural-equipment hitching, tow chains, animal leashes, and boat mooring. They are not recommended for overhead lifting. Some manufacturers weld electrically through 5/8 in., others through 3/4 in., and some through 1 in. Larger sizes are fire-welded. Tables 3 and 4 give pertinent ASTM data plus working-load limits.

Chain Strength

Welded chain links are complex, statically indeterminate structures subjected to combinations of bending, shear, and tension under a normal axial load (see Seely and Smith, "Advanced Mechanics of Materials," Wiley). The maximum tensile stress occurs in the outside fiber at the intersection with the long axis (see Fig. 1). The maximum shear stress occurs approximately 45 deg away from this axis and on a radial line through the center of curvature of the link end.

For chains with low-to-medium hardness (under 400 Brinell), failure is typically due to shear. As chain hardness rises, there is a tendency for the typical mode of

Table 2. ASTM Specifications for High-test Steel Chain

Trade size, in.	Material size, in.		Nominal link inside dimension, in.		Maximum length, 100 links, in.	Maximum weight, 100 ft, lb	Working-load limit, lb	Minimum proof-test load, lb	Minimum break-test load, lb
	Fraction	Decimal	Length	Width					
1/4	9/32	0.281	0.82	0.39	86	80	2,500	4,100	7,750
5/16	11/32	0.343	1.01	0.48	105	123	4,000	6,700	11,500
3/8	13/32	0.406	1.15	0.56	121	175	5,100	8,500	16,200
7/16	15/32	0.468	1.29	0.65	135	235	6,600	11,200	20,700
1/2	17/32	0.531	1.43	0.75	150	300	8,200	13,700	26,000
5/8	21/32	0.656	1.79	0.90	186	450	11,500	19,500	36,900
3/4	25/32	0.781	1.96	1.06	205	655	16,200	27,000	50,400
7/8*	29/32	0.906	2.25	1.09	234	814	22,500	45,000	90,000
1*	1 1/32	1.031	2.63	1.25	273	1,064	26,500	53,000	106,000

* Specifications for these sizes have not yet been adopted by ASTM.

Table 3. ASTM Specifications for BBB Steel Chain

Trade size, in.	Material size, in.		Nominal link inside dimension, in.		Maximum length, 100 links, in.	Maximum weight, 100 ft, lb	Working-load limit, lb	Minimum proof-test load, lb	Minimum break-test load, lb
	Fraction	Decimal	Length	Width					
3/16	7/32	0.218	0.78	0.37	81	46	800	1,600	3,200
1/4	9/32	0.281	0.85	0.43	88	81	1,325	2,650	5,300
5/16	11/32	0.343	1.00	0.50	104	120	1,950	3,900	7,800
3/8	13/32	0.406	1.09	0.62	113	173	2,750	5,500	11,000
7/16	15/32	0.468	1.21	0.68	126	231	3,625	7,250	14,500
1/2	17/32	0.531	1.34	0.75	139	296	4,750	9,500	19,000
9/16	19/32	0.593	1.56	0.78	162	366	5,875	11,750	23,500
5/8	21/32	0.656	1.68	0.87	175	447	7,250	14,500	29,000
3/4	25/32	0.781	1.87	1.00	194	640	10,250	20,500	41,000
7/8	29/32	0.906	2.25	1.25	234	850	12,000	24,000	48,000
1	1 1/32	1.031	2.56	1.37	266	1,087	15,500	31,000	62,000
1 1/8	1 5/32	1.156	2.87	1.62	298	1,362	19,500	39,000	78,000
1 1/4	1 9/32	1.281	3.06	1.75	318	1,664	24,000	48,000	96,000

Table 4. ASTM Specifications for Proof Coil Steel Chain

Trade size, in.	Material size, in.		Nominal link inside dimensions, in.		Maximum length, 100 links, in.	Maximum weight, 100 ft, lb	Working-load limit, lb	Minimum proof-test load, lb	Minimum break-test load, lb
	Fraction	Decimal	Length	Width					
3/16	7/32	0.218	0.95	0.40	99	42	700	1,400	2,800
1/4	9/32	0.281	1.00	0.50	104	76	1,175	2,350	4,700
5/16	11/32	0.343	1.10	0.50	114	115	1,750	3,500	7,000
3/8	13/32	0.406	1.23	0.62	128	166	2,450	4,900	9,800
7/16	15/32	0.468	1.37	0.75	142	225	3,250	6,500	13,000
1/2	17/32	0.531	1.50	0.81	156	286	4,250	8,500	17,000
9/16	19/32	0.593	1.75	0.87	182	355	5,250	10,500	21,000
5/8	21/32	0.656	1.87	1.00	194	425	6,375	12,750	25,500
3/4	25/32	0.781	2.12	1.12	220	605	9,125	18,250	36,500
7/8	29/32	0.906	2.50	1.37	260	811	10,750	21,500	43,000
1	1 1/32	1.031	2.75	1.50	286	1,045	12,400	24,800	49,600
1 1/8	1 5/32	1.156	3.12	1.75	324	1,321	15,600	31,200	62,400
1 1/4	1 9/32	1.281	3.25	1.87	338	1,622	19,200	38,400	76,800

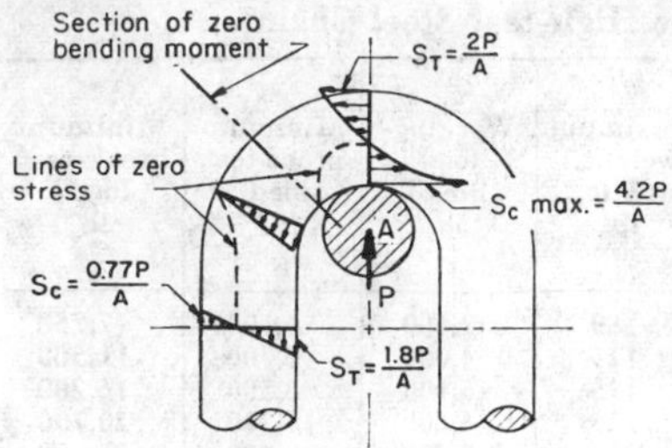

FIG. 1. Magnitude of tensile and compressive stresses in a chain link under load. (*Reprint from Product Engineering, Nov.* 25, 1963, *copyright* 1963 *by McGraw-Hill.*)

failure to shift from shear to tension due to bending. The failure location will simultaneously shift from the maximum-shear plane to a plane in the long axis of the link.

The effect of **combined stresses** is to reduce the breaking strength from that computed by considering the applied load as uniformly distributed in simple tension across the two circular areas of the straight sides of a link. The actual breaking strength is about two-thirds of the value that would be obtained from such computation.

Chain End Fittings

Most industrial chains must be equipped with some type of end fittings. These usually consist of oblong links or rings (called **masters**) on one end to fit over a crane hook and some variety of hook or enlarged link at the other end to engage the load. The hooks are normally drop-forged from heat-treated carbon or alloy steel. They are designed (using curved-beam theories) to be compatible in strength to the chain for which they are recommended. Master links or rings must fit over the rather large section thicknesses of crane hooks, and they therefore must have large inside dimensions. For this reason, they must be designed on the basis of bending strength, and their section diameters will consequently be much larger than would be required on a straight tensile-strength basis.

Columbus McKinnon Chain Division recommends that oblong master links be designed with an inside width of $3.5d$ and an inside length of $7.0d$, where d is the section diameter in inches. For this condition and assuming a material yield strength of 100,000 psi, d can be calculated from the relationship $d = \sqrt{WLL/20{,}000}$, where WLL is the working-load limit in pounds.

Rings require a somewhat greater section diameter than oblong links to withstand the same load without deforming. Master rings with an inside diameter of $4d$ can be sized from the relationship $d = \sqrt{WLL/15{,}000}$. Rings require a 15 percent larger section diameter and a 33 percent greater inside width than oblong links for the same load-carrying capacity, and the use of the less bulky oblong links is therefore preferred.

Pear-shaped master links were once the most commonly used design. However, they are less versatile than **oblong links** and can be inadvertently reversed, leading to bending of the narrow end due to jamming around the thick saddle of the crane hook. In recent years their use has declined greatly.

Hooks and **end links** are attached to sling chains by means of **coupling links,** either welded or mechanical. Welded couplers require special equipment and skill to produce quality and reliability compatible with the other components of a sling and, consequently, must be assembled by manufacturers in plants. Since these plants are usually distant from the place of need, undesirably long delays in obtaining new slings or repairs to existing ones often result. The advent of reliable mechanical couplers such as Hammerloks (Columbus McKinnon), made from high-strength alloy forgings, relieved this problem greatly. With such units, customized slings can be assembled by users from component parts carried in local-distributor stocks.

Welded-link Wheel Chains

These differ from sling chains and general-purpose chains in two principal respects: First, they are precisely calibrated to function in pocketwheels. Second, they are usually provided with considerably higher surface hardness to provide adequate wear life.

The most widely used variety is **Alloy Load wheel chain,** a short-link style used as the lifting chain in hand, electric, and air-powered hoists. Some roller chain is still used for this purpose, but its use is steadily declining because of the higher

Table 5. Pocketwheel Specifications for Flite Chain
(Columbus McKinnon Chain Division)

Chain size, in.	Number of pockets	Pitch diam, in.	Outside diam, in.	Thickness, in.	Maximum bore diam: With square key, in.	Maximum bore diam: No key, in.	Maximum key size, in.
3/8	4	4.777	5 5/8	1 7/8	2 1/4	2 3/4	1/2
3/8	5	5.971	6 13/16	1 7/8	2 15/16	3 11/16	3/4
3/8	6	7.165	7 5/8	1 7/8	3 3/4	4 5/8	7/8
1/2	4	5.095	5 5/8	2 1/4	2 1/4	2 3/4	1/2
1/2	5	6.369	7	2 1/4	3 1/8	3 7/8	3/4
1/2	6	7.643	8 1/4	2 1/4	3 15/16	4 15/16	1
5/8	4	6.369	7	2 3/4	2 3/4	3 3/8	5/8
5/8	5	7.961	8 3/4	2 3/4	3 3/4	4 5/8	7/8
5/8	6	9.554	10 1/4	2 3/4	4 15/16	6	1 1/4
3/4	4	8.117	9	3 1/8	3 5/8	4 1/2	7/8
3/4	5	10.149	11 1/8	3 1/8	5	6	1 1/4
3/4	6	12.170	13 1/16	3 1/8	6	6	1 1/2

strength/weight ratio and three-dimensional flexibility of welded-link chain. Wire rope is also sometimes used in hoist applications. However, it is much less flexible than either welded-link or roller chain and, consequently, requires a drum of thirty to fifty times the rope diameter to maintain bending stresses within safe limits. Welded-link chain can operate over a three-pocket wheel with a pitch diameter of only six times the chain wire diameter. This permits the use of much smaller gear reductions and thus reduces hoist weight, bulk, and cost.

To achieve maximum flexibility, Alloy Load wheel chain is made with link inside dimensions of pitch = $3d$ and width = $1.25d$. Breaking strength is $90d^2$ tons, and endurance limit is about $18d^2$ tons. In hand-operated hoists, it can be used safely at working loads providing a safety factor of 5 on ultimate strength. Some designers believe a factor of 4 is adequate. In powered hoists, the higher operating speeds and expectancy of more lifts during the life of the hoist require a somewhat higher design factor of safety. Columbus McKinnon Chain Division recommends a factor of 7 for such units where starting-up, stopping, and resonance effects do not cause dynamic loads to exceed the static chain load by more than 25 percent. For this condition, chain fatigue life will exceed 500,000 lifts, the normal maximum requirement for a powered hoist. Standard Alloy Load chains, now produced in sizes from 0.218- through 0.500-in. diameter, meet requirements for working-load limits up to 4.5 tons for hand-operated hoists and 3 tons for power-operated hoists. Current research indicates that an improved type of chain with 60 percent higher strength may become commercially available in the near future.

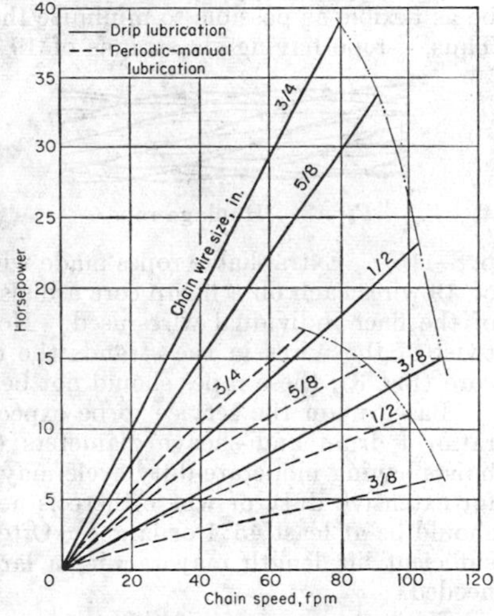

FIG. 2. Flite chain horsepower ratings. (*Reprint from Product Engineering, Nov. 25, 1963, copyright 1963 by McGraw-Hill.*)

Conveyor chains for use in high-load and/or high-speed applications are made to the same quality level as Alloy Load chain. However, they are usually designed with longer links, both for economy and to accommodate attachments such as flights. Columbus McKinnon Chain Division reports that its brand, Flite chain, is produced to inside-width/section-diameter and length/section-diameter ratios of 1.25 and 4, respectively. This chain has been designed to operate in pocketwheels having pitch diameters of 13*d* through 19*d*. Table 5 gives pertinent wheel dimensions, and Fig. 2 gives horsepower ratings for periodic-manual and drip lubrication.

Power Transmission

Power transmission, in the sense used to describe the transfer of power in machines from one shaft to another one close-by, is a relatively new field of application for welded-link chain. Roller chain and other pin-link chains have been widely used for this purpose for many years. However, recent studies have shown that welded-link chain can be operated at speeds to 3,000 fpm. Its three-dimensional flexibility, which can sometimes eliminate the need for direction-change components, and its high strength/weight ratio suggest the possibility for significant cost savings in some power-transmission applications.

Miscellaneous Special Chains

Special requirements calling for corrosion or heat resistance, non-magnetic properties, non-contamination of dyes and foodstuffs, and spark resistance have resulted in the development of many special chains. They have been produced from beryllium copper, bronze, monel, Inconel, Hadfield's manganese, and aluminum and from a wide variety of AISI analyses of stainless and non-stainless alloys. However, the need for such special chains, other than those of stainless steel, is so infrequent that they are seldom carried as stock items.

WIRE ROPE

By Harold V. Hawkins

Load Suspension and Haulage

Wire rope (see pp. 8–113 to 8–124) used for suspending loads is usually required to be as flexible as possible to minimize the diameters of the drums or sheaves involved. Thus, a rope having six strands of 19 wires each on a hemp core is used (Fig. 149,

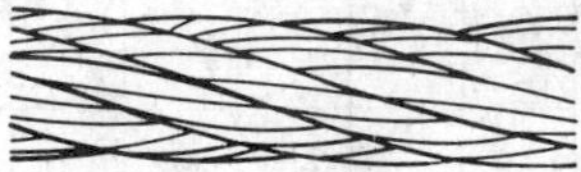

Fig. 3. Haulage rope.

Fig. 4. Lang-lay rope.

p. 8–115). Extrapliable ropes made with six strands of 37 wires each or eight strands of 19 wires each on a hemp core are also available but are much less durable because of the finer individual wires used. Hoisting ropes are constructed with the relative twist of the wires in the strands the reverse of the twist of the strands about the core (Fig. 3); these ropes should not be spliced.

Based upon the service to be expected, special attention should be given to the ratio of drum and sheave diameters (p. 8–117) to cable diameter. For example, hoists having moderate-duty cycle may have a ratio of diameters as low as 20:1, but for extensive duty or where there is need for great safety, such as in elevators, this should be at least 45:1 or larger. Often the need for storing enough cable to obtain sufficient lift length may require a larger drum diameter than would otherwise be needed.

Haulage ropes are of the same construction as **suspension ropes** or are of the **lang-lay** type shown in Fig. 4, with the twist of the wire and strand in the same direction. This lang-lay construction increases the wear resistance of the rope, but it tends to untwist and should not be used where the load is in free suspension. Lang-lay rope is difficult to splice. By preforming individual wires and strands before laying up, secondary stresses due to bending are reduced and longer life is obtained. Preformed ropes have less tendency to kink and are easier to handle.

Hoisting and haulage ropes should be frequently **greased** to minimize wear and to prevent corrosion; either a special commercial lubricant or boiled linseed oil may be used on ropes subjected to atmospheric action, and a tacky petroleum and **graphite** on hoisting ropes in wet places. Crude oil or other lubricants having an acid or basic characteristic should not be used because of corrosive action on both wire and sisal core. To ensure penetration, lubricant can be applied hot or a volatile solvent can be used. Though galvanized wire ropes are available, they are not recommended for applications requiring them to pass repetitively over drums and sheaves. Ropes should be inspected frequently for broken strands and excessive wear.

For **strength** and **working loads** of wire rope, see pp. 8–113 to 8–125.

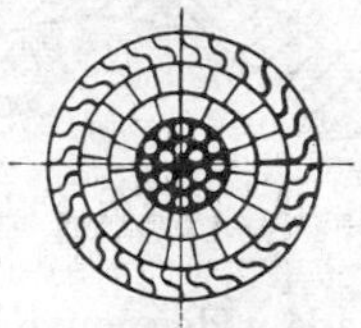

Fig. 5. Locked-coil track strand wire rope. (*United States Steel.*)

Track Cables

Cables used as **tracks to support loads suspended on trolleys** are either the locked-coil type for longest life (Fig. 5) or the round-wire track strand shown in Fig. 170, p. 8–122. The strength of the locked-coil type is given in Table 6, while that for the round-wire or smooth-coil type is given in Table 114, p. 8–124. This type of wire minimizes the impact loads on the outer wires which result from the rolling of the trolley.

Table 6. Locked-coil Track Strand Wire Rope
(United States Steel Corp.)

Diameter, in.	Breaking strength, tons		Weight per foot, lb
	Special grade	Standard grade	
¾	31.5	25	1.41
⅞	41.5	32	1.92
1	52.5	42	2.50
1⅛	66.0	54	3.16
1¼	81.0	65	3.91
1⅜	100.0	78	4.73
1½	120.5	93	5.63
1⅝	140.0	108	6.60
1¾	165.0	125	7.66
1⅞	187.5	138	8.79
2	215	158	10.00
2¼	280		12.50
2½	345		15.20
2¾	420		18.30
3	500		22.2
3¼	580		25.6
3½	690		29.9
3¾	785		33.9
4	880		38.4

End Fittings

Fittings for cables are attached at the ends by (1) passing the cable around a minimum-radius thimble and then splicing the end to the cable itself (80 to 90 percent efficient), (2) using zinc to embed the end of the cable in a fitting having a socket to receive it (100 percent efficient), or (3) using the thimble and some type of squeezed mechanical ring which gets its gripping action from bolts or from a permanent deformation such as crimping (100 percent efficient).

Drums

Drums are made with smooth surfaces on hand-powered hoists and on power hoists subject to light-duty operation. Medium- and heavy-duty drums are normally grooved. Drums can be welded or cast, depending upon the quantity to be manufactured, since cast drums are economical when mass-produced. Large drums frequently have separate shells welded to the spider or end plate. The normal practice, as adopted by McDowell-Wellman Engineering Company, is to build all drum shells of steel plates which are bent to a cylindrical shape and welded to the end plates with welded hubs before they are grooved for the rope. Steel-plate shells are stronger than cast shells, better balanced, and free from hidden initial defects. The thickness can be less, thus reducing the inertia of the rotating drum and the resulting acceleration-peak loads. Conical and cylindroconical drums are frequently used on large mine hoists (see p. 10–21). Faces of drums for medium and heavy duty are made wide enough to hold the rope in one layer plus two to four holding turns. The hole for attachment of the rope should be as shown in Fig. 6 to prevent excessive bending; this method of anchoring is normally done on cast drums which have a limited face width. Figure 7 shows an alternate, preferred method of anchoring the rope on welded and cast drums when space is not a problem.

FIG. 6

The pitch diameter of the drum should be at least twenty-four times the rope diameter in order to obtain reasonable life for both drum and rope. Long life requires forty-five to sixty times the rope diameter.

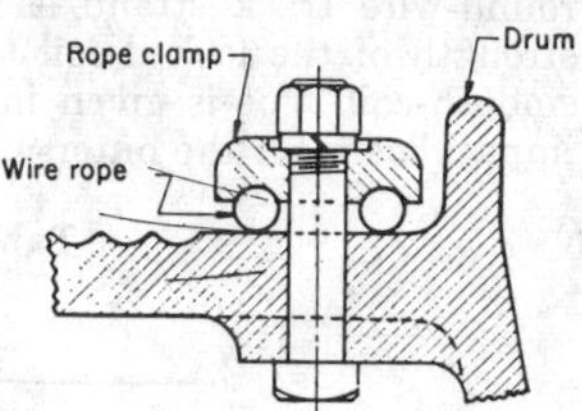

FIG. 7. Rope-anchoring attachment. (*McDowell Wellman.*)

Where there is side draft on the rope, movable **idlers** are provided to align the rope and groove. The idlers may be moved parallel to the face of the drum by the side pressure of the rope or may be driven positively sideways, thus eliminating friction and increasing the life of rope. In Fig. 8, idler sheave *c* revolves between fixed collars on shaft *a*, which is connected to the drum shaft by sprocket and chain. The shaft is prevented from rotating by a feather key. On sprocket *b*, a nut is held from moving sideways by flanges; the shaft *a* with sheave *c* moves in the direction of its axis. In an alternative construction, the idler shaft is threaded but held stationary and the sheave hub is a nut. The sheave is turned by the friction of the rope, which causes it to travel back and forth. Figure 9 shows a construction used when the side draft is excessive. The upright rollers *a* are moved sideways by screw *b*, which is driven by sprocket and chain *c* from the drum shaft. For winding the rope on the drum in several layers, a clutch is provided which reverses the direction at the end of travel.

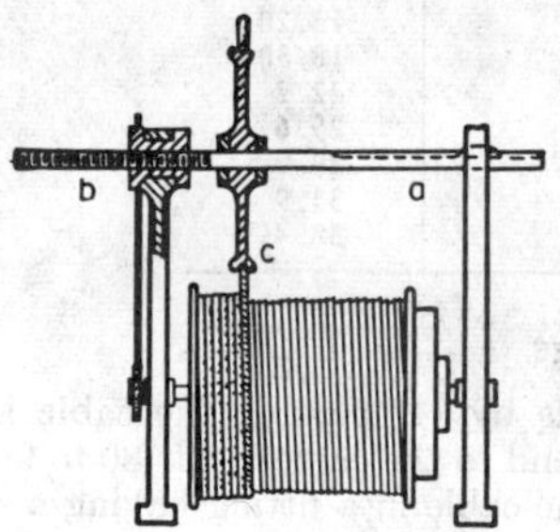

FIG. 8. Hoisting drum.

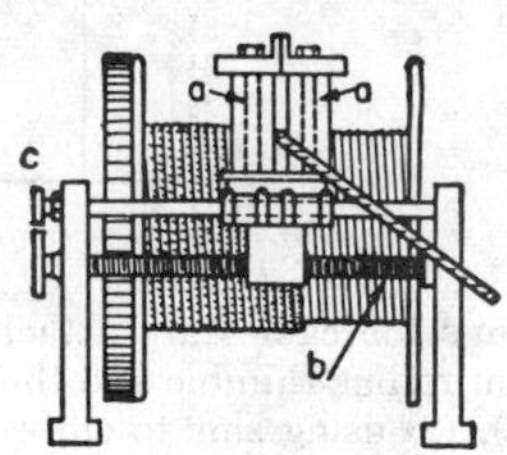

FIG. 9. Hoisting drum.

Sheaves

Sheaves should be grooved to fit the rope as closely as possible in order to prevent the rope from assuming an oval or elliptical shape under heavy load. They should be balanced and properly aligned to prevent swaying of the rope and abrasion against the sheave flanges. Sheaves and drums should be as large as possible to obtain maximum rope life, but factors such as weight of machinery for easy transport, minimizing headroom, and high-speed operation call for small sheaves. Hence rope life is sometimes sacrificed for over-all economy. Undue wear on sheaves is avoided by flame-hardening them and by properly aligning them with the drum. The fleet angle of the rope should not exceed 1½ deg, but sometimes with grooved drums up to 2 deg is acceptable. Sheaves of any diameter can be welded or cast; most manufacturers make cast sheaves since they are economical. To avoid rope damage, worn sheaves should be replaced or the grooves turned before the sheaves are used with a new rope. In some cases, especially in mines, the grooves are lined with renewable, well-seasoned hardwood blocks.

Tackle blocks (Fig. 35, p. 8–10) consist of one or two blocks, each carrying one or more sheaves. A single-sheave block (generally used to change the direction of a lead line and frequently arranged for easy removal of the loop of rope) is called a **snatch block.** Blocks are made for both manila and wire rope. Those for manila rope are usually made with wooden cheeks to prevent chafing of the rope and have sheaves of smaller diameter than wire-rope blocks for the same size of rope. Heavy hoisting is almost universally done with wire-rope blocks. Tests by the American Bridge Co. found the following approximate efficiencies for well-designed and properly maintained ¾-in. wire-rope tackle.

Number of ropes supporting load	1	2	3	4	5	6	7	8	9	10	11	12
Efficiency, percent	86	96	91	87	82	78	74	71	68	65	62	59

Each snatch block between the hoisting blocks and the hoist or winch will have an efficiency of about 86 percent.

Brakes

Small hoists are provided with hand-operated band brakes or electrically operated disk brakes; larger hoists have mechanically operated post brakes (see pp. 8–56 to 8–61). On electric hoists, it is usual to apply the brake with a weight or spring and to remove it by a solenoid. Where controlled rate of application of a brake is desirable, a **thrustor** is frequently used. This is a self-contained unit consisting of a vertical motor, a centrifugal pump in a piston, and a cylinder filled with oil. Starting the motor raises the piston and connected counterweight. Stopping the motor permits the weight to fall. An adjustable range of several seconds in falling sets the brake slowly. Thrustors are built with considerably greater load capacities and stroke lengths than solenoids. Should the current fail, the brakes are automatically applied. On steam hoists, the brake is taken off by a steam piston and cylinder instead of by a solenoid. On overhead cranes, load brakes are used to sustain the load automatically at any point and to regulate the speed when lowering.

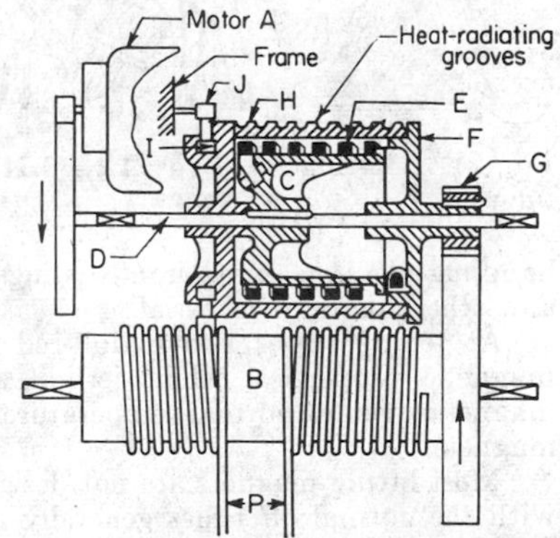

FIG. 10. Load brake.

In one type of **load brake** (Fig. 10), the motor *A* drives drum *B* through the load brake on intermediate shaft *D*. A spider *C* is keyed to shaft *D*, its inner end supporting one end of a coiled bronze spring of square section *E*. The opposite end of the spring is fixed in flange *F*, which is loosely fitted to shaft *D* and directly attached to pinion *G*. Any relative angular motion of flange *F* and spider *C* alters the closeness of the coiling of spring *E*, consequently altering its outside diameter (considered as a drum). This outer surface is one of the friction surfaces of the brake, the other being provided by the internal face of drum *H*, which revolves loosely on shaft *D* at one end and on flange *F* at the other. Drum *H* is restrained from moving in one direction by ratchet *I* and pawls *J*. The exterior of drum *H* is grooved for heat dissipation.

The action of the **load brake** in Fig. 10 is as follows: When hoisting, the brake revolves as shown by the arrow. Pawls *J* permit drum *H* to revolve; consequently, the whole mechanism is locked and revolved as one piece. When stopping the load, the downward pull of the load reacts to drive drum *H* against pawl *J*. Flange *F* therefore moves slightly in an angular direction relative to spider *C*, and spring *E* consequently untwists until it grips the interior of drum *H*, thus locking the load. The action is such that the grip is slightly more than necessary to hold the load. Reversing the motor for lowering the load drives the interior of the brake surface against drum *H* so that the power consumed is the amount necessary to overcome the excess holding power of the brake over the load reaction.

Load brakes of the **disk** and **cone** types (see pp. 8–58 and 8–59) are also used and embody the same principle of pawl locks and differential action. The choice of brake type should be based on considerations of smoothness of working and lack of chatter, as well as on the power requirements for lowering at different values of load within the range of the crane.

In regenerative braking, the motor, when overhauled, acts as a generator to pump current back into the line. (See also p. 11–30 *et seq.*)

HOLDING MECHANISMS

By Harold V. Hawkins

Lifting Tongs

Figure 11 shows the type of tongs used for lifting plates. The cams *a* grip the plate when the chains tighten, preventing slipping. They are safer than plain hooks. Self-closing tongs (Fig. 12) are used for handling logs, manure, straw, etc. The rope *a* is attached to and makes several turns around drum *b*; chains *c* are attached to the bucket head *e* and to drum *b*. When power is applied to rope *a*, drum *b* is revolved, winding itself upon chains *c* and closing the tongs. To open, slack off on rope *a*, holding tongs on rope *d*, attached to head *e*.

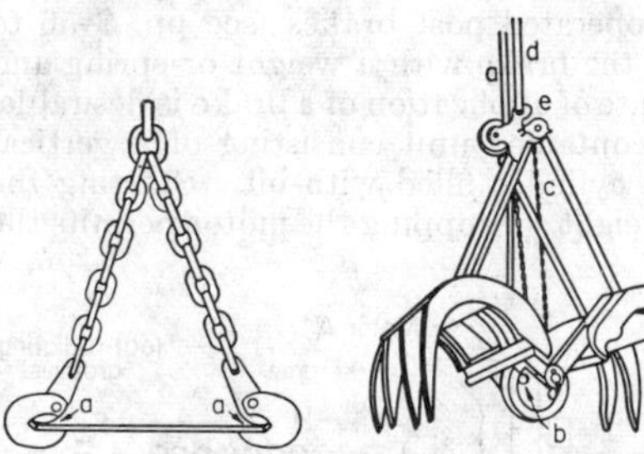

FIG. 11. Lifting tongs.

FIG. 12. Lifting tongs.

Lifting Magnets

Lifting magnets (see also p. 15–107) are materials-handling devices used for handling pig iron, scrap iron, castings, billets, tubes, rails, plates, skull-cracker balls, and other magnetic material.

At temperatures above dull-red heat, ordinary magnetic materials lose their magnetic properties, while certain stainless and high-manganese steels are nonmagnetic even at normal temperatures. Such materials cannot be handled by lifting magnets.

Most lifting magnets are not designed for continuous operation but for operation with the normal off times generally associated with materials-handling applications. In addition, attention should be given to operation of magnets on high-temperature loads so as to keep the magnet-coil temperature within the design limits of the insulation. Lifting magnets can be used for underwater operation when they are supplied with watertight cases and specially designed lead connections.

To obtain optimum magnet performance, a suitable **magnetic controller** should be used. It is necessary in most cases to provide means to reverse the current in the magnet in order to efficiently release the materials from the magnet. The controller should also have protective features to absorb the stored energy of the magnet during its discharge, especially when the d-c power requirements for a magnet are supplied from a **rectifier-type** power supply.

Lifting magnets can be classified as follows:

1. **Circular Magnets.** This configuration makes the most efficient use of materials, is extremely rugged, and is best suited for general lifting applications. Recently this category of magnets has been subdivided into two distinct types: a relatively large diameter magnet, which is especially efficient on low-permeability material such as scrap; and a magnet which, for equal weight, has a smaller diameter but a much deeper magnetic field, making it more suitable for high-permeability loads typically found in steel mills.

2. **Rectangular Magnets.** Many types of material such as rails, beams, and plates can be handled more efficiently with a rectangular magnet. The tendency of these materials to pull away from the face of the magnet because of deflection rather than total weight is a limiting factor when these magnets are applied. Two or more small rectangular magnets mounted on a spreader beam usually give a better lifting performance than a single large magnet of equal weight. This is especially true in the case of thin plates.

3. **Specialty Magnets.** Loads such as coiled steel present unique problems when lifted by a magnet. Special magnets are available for loads of this type, but the scope of this text does not permit detailed discussion.

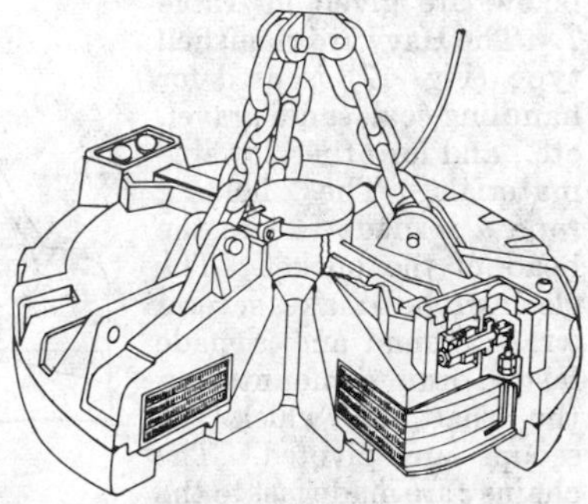

FIG. 13. Circular lifting magnet. (*Dings.*)

Construction features of a typical **circular magnet** are shown in Fig. 13. A winding of either strap aluminum or copper is located inside the cast-steel case. Strap material with insulating tape between turns, rather than insulated wire, is used for windings since it permits a greater number of turns in the same space. Recent advances in the processing of anodized aluminum have permitted the elimination of the turn-to-turn insulation, thereby allowing an increase in the number of turns, which results in increased lifting capacity. A nonmagnetic manganese-steel bottom plate is welded to the case to make the coil cavity watertight. The center and outer pole shoes are made so that they can be replaced since they will wear in severe service.

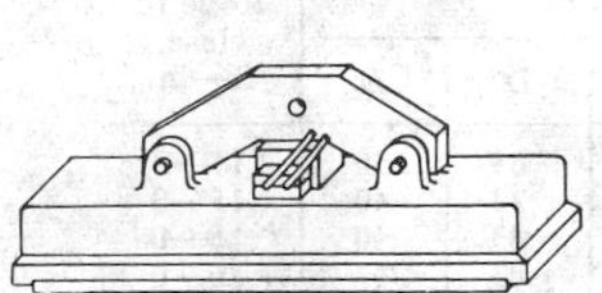

FIG. 14. Rectangular lifting magnet. (*Dings.*)

Rectangular-magnet construction features are shown in Fig. 14, which illustrates a typical plate-handling magnet. Coils for this type of magnet are generally wound with wire and formed to fit over the center pole. A manganese bottom plate is used to hold the coils in place and seal the coil cavity. The external flux path is from the center pole to each of the outer poles.

Buckets and Scrapers

One type of **Williams self-filling dragline bucket** (Fig. 15) consists of a bowl with the top and digging end open. The shackles at *c* are so attached that the cutting edge will penetrate the material. When filled, the bucket is raised by keeping the line *a* taut and lifting on the fall line *d*. In this position, the bucket is carried to the dumping position, where by slacking off on line *a*, it is dumped. Line *b* holds up line *a* and the

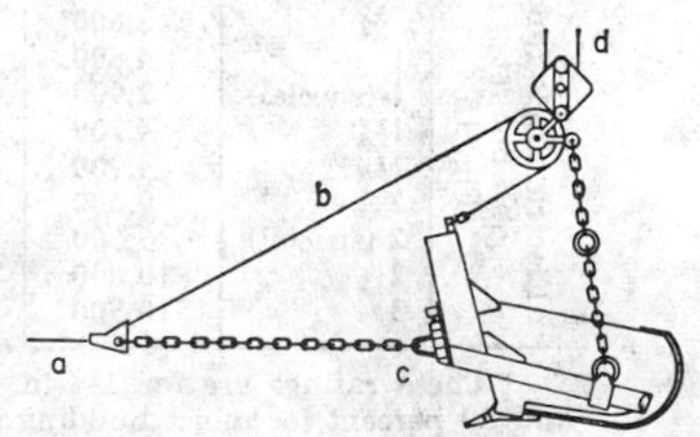

FIG. 15. Self-filling dragline bucket. (*Williams.*)

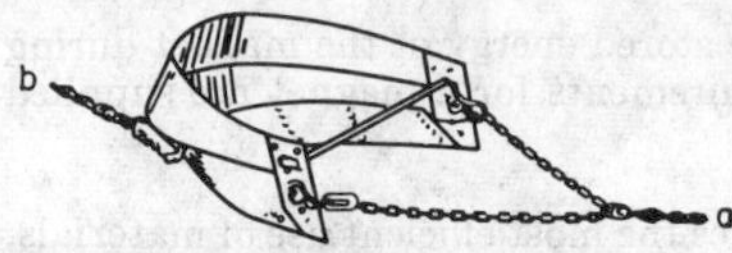

FIG. 16. Scraper bucket. (*Sauerman.*)

bridle chains while dumping. Such buckets are built in sizes from ¾ cu yd to as large as 85 cu yd, weighing 188,000 lb.

Figure 16 shows an **open-bottom-type scraper.** Inhauling on cable *a* causes the sloping bottom plate to dig and load until upward pressure of the material against the top prevents further loading. The scraper continues its forward haul to the dumping point. Pulling on cable *b* deposits the load and returns the scraper to the excavation point. Scrapers are made in sizes from ⅓- to 12-cu-yd capacity.

The approximate **weights, capacities, and dimensions** of the more important types of **grab buckets** described below are given in Table 7. The **Hayward clamshell** type (Fig. 17) is used for handling coal, sand, gravel, etc., and for other flowable materials. The holding rope *a* is made fast to the head of the bucket. The closing rope *b* makes several wraps around and is made fast to drum *d*, mounted on the shaft to which the scoops are pivoted. The chains *c* are made fast to the head of the bucket and to the small diameter of drum *d*. When power is applied to rope *b*, it causes the drum to wind itself up on chain *c*, raising the drum and closing the bucket. To dump, hold

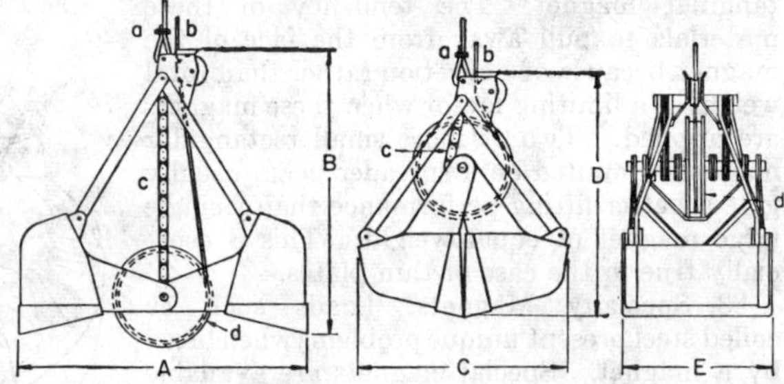

FIG. 17. Hayward grab bucket.

Table 7. Weights, Dimensions, and Capacities of Self-filling Grab Buckets
(Hayward Company)

Make	Capacity, cu yd*	Weight, lb	Dimensions, in. *A*	*B*	*C*	*D*	*E*	Rope to close, ft—in.
General-purpose bucket with ore bowl (Fig. 17)	½	1,750	71	69	49	63	36	11—3
	¾	2,600	83	84	61	73	40	15—0
	1	3,200	97	94	68	83	40	16—0
	1¼	3,400	97	94	68	83	47	16—0
	1½	4,600	106	104	74	91	50	18—0
	1¾	5,100	106	104	74	92	54	18—0
	2	5,750	106	107	76	94	62	20—0
	2½	7,500	117	120	84	105	63	21—0
	3	8,000	118	120	84	106	74	21—0
	4†	13,500	136	140	103	119	74	23—6
Electric single-rope grab bucket (Fig. 18)	0.288	1,200	51	65	40	57	33	
	¾	2,600	65	77	49	69	46	
	1	4,600	76	88	56	79	48	
	1 (special)	2,900	65	77	49	69	56	
	1¼	4,700	88	97	61	89	51	
	1½	4,900	88	97	61	89	59	
	2	9,000	105	120	73	108	67	
	2 (special)	5,500	88	97	61	89	72	
	2½	10,000	117	125	84	112	60	
	3	10,500	117	125	84	112	70	

* These ratings are for 1½-in. crushed stone; increase 25 percent for 1½-in. gravel and 50 percent for moist building sand. Those marked "special" are for coke or other light work.

† Larger buckets are more or less special.

rope *a* and slack off rope *b*. The digging power of the bucket is determined by its weight and by the ratio of the diameters of the large and small parts of the drum. Hayward also has an **orange-peel** bucket that operates like the clamshell type (Fig. 17) but has four blades pivoted to close.

The **Hayward electric** single-rope type (Fig. 18) listed in Table 7 is used not only for handling coal and sand in foundries but also where it is desirable to hook the bucket on a derrick or crane hook. The bucket requires only to be hung from the crane or derrick hook by the eye *a* and an electric line plugged in. No ropes are fed into the bucket and no time-consuming shifting of lines is required—thus facilitating changing from magnet to bucket. The four bucket arms are pivoted on the head, and suspended therefrom is a self-contained electric hoist *b*, consisting of an a-c or d-c motor, a gear-reduction box, and a drum. One end of the special Hayward chain *c* is made fast to the casing of the hoist, and the other end to the hoist drum. When current is turned on, the drum revolves, winding up the chain and thus raising roller *d* and closing the bucket. To dump the bucket, the hoist is reversed. The hoist is provided with a disk clutch, which is adjusted to slip should the bucket be prevented by a large lump from closing. This clutch also slips if the motor is not stopped when the bucket is entirely open or closed. This prevents overloading the motor. The ¾-cu-yd bucket is provided with a 4-hp motor. The 1-, 1¼-, and 1½-cu-yd buckets have motors of 6 to 10 hp, according to the duty.

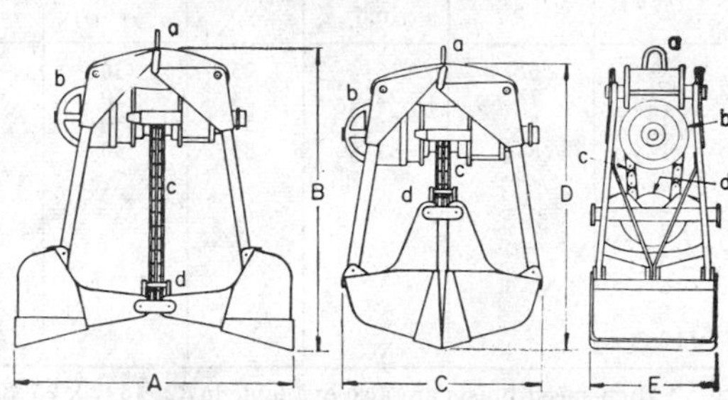

Fig. 18. Hayward electric single-rope grab bucket.

HOISTS

By C. J. Manney

Columbus McKinnon Corporation

Hand-chain Hoists

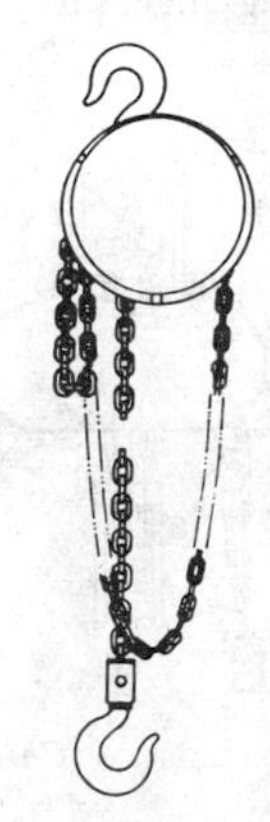

Fig. 19. High-speed hand hoist. (*Chisholm-Moore Hoist Division.*)

Hand-chain hoists are portable lifting devices suspended from a hook and operated by a hand chain. They are used in intermittent service, especially for erection and maintenance work, and are available to 40 tons capacity and with almost unlimited lift. Two types are in common use. The differential hoist (see Fig. 36, p. 8–10) consists of a dual upper sheave and single lower sheave connected by an endless chain for lifting and operating. The two upper sheaves differ by one link pocket, the difference in diameters being too small to overcome the friction of the parts. The load is thus automatically held at any point; effort must be applied either to raise or to lower the load hook. The **high-speed hoist** (Fig. 19) is relatively efficient and incorporates a brake to resist uncontrolled lowering of the load. The brake is usually of the **Weston self-energizing type** (see cone or disk brakes, p. 8–58), which provides a holding force proportional to the load. The separate hand and load chains operate over pocket wheels connected by a gear train. The brake is disengaged during hoisting by a one-way ratchet mechanism. To lower, the hand chain must be pulled continuously in the reverse direction to overcome the brake torque. Table 8 gives **typical data** for hand-chain hoists.

Table 8. Data on Chain Hoists
(From specification MIL-H-904E)

Capacity, tons*	Differential hoists: Standard lift, ft	Max distance between hooks, in.†	Net weight, lb	Minimum efficiency,‡ percent	High-speed hoists: Standard lift, ft	Max distance between hooks, in.†	Net weight, lb§	Minimum efficiency,‡ percent
¼	6	18½	25	30	8	14	40	80
½	7	22½	34	30	8	15	40	80
1	8	26½	54	30	8	18	44	80
1½	8½	32½	85	30	8	21	66	80
2					9	23	77	80
3					10	25½	115	70
4					10	37	138	70
5					12	45	172	70
6					12	45	195	70
8					12	49	305	65
10					12	54	322	65

* High-speed hoists are also available in 12, 16, 20, 25, 30, and 40 tons capacity.
† With load chain retracted to shortest length.
‡ Efficiency = (ft-lb output)(100)/(ft-lb input).
§ Class 2 (lightweight) hoists.

Pullers or Come-alongs

Pullers or come-alongs are lever-operated chain or wire-rope hoists (see Fig. 20) for lifting or pulling at any angle. A reversible ratchet mechanism in the lever permits short-stroke operation for both tensioning and relaxing. The load is held by a Weston-type friction brake or a releasable ratchet. Much smaller and lighter than chain hoists of equal capacities, pullers are used for short-travel distances where the lever is within reach of the operator (*e.g.*, tensioning wires, skidding machinery). Table 9 gives data for lever-operated hoists.

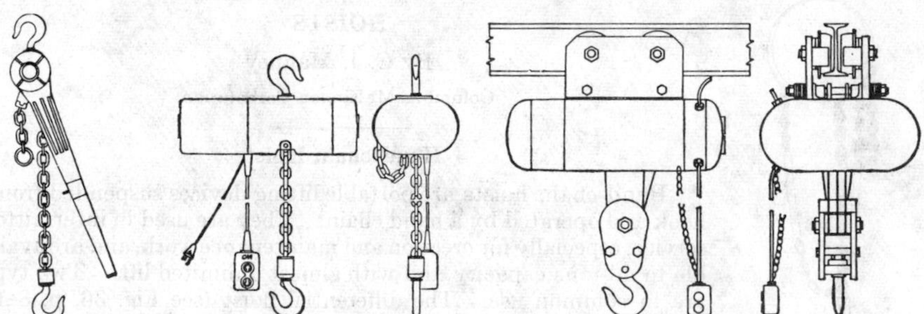

FIG. 20. Puller or come-along hoist. (*Chisholm-Moore Hoist Division.*)

FIG. 21. Electric chain hoist. (*Chisholm-Moore Hoist Division.*)

FIG. 22. Electric wire-rope hoist. (*Chisholm-Moore Hoist Division.*)

Electric Hoists

Electric hoists are used for repetitive or high-speed lifting. Two types are available: chain (see Fig. 21) (both link and roller), in capacities from ⅛ to 2 tons; wire rope (see Fig. 22), in ratings from ⅛ to 20 tons. The typical hoist has a drum or sprocket centered in the frame, with the motor and gearing at opposite ends, the motor shaft passing through or alongside the drum or sprocket.

Electric hoists are equipped with at least two independent braking means. An electrically released brake causes spring-loaded disk brake plates to engage when

Table 9. Data on Lever-operated Hoists
(From specification MIL-H-904E)

Capacity,* tons	Chain hoists: Standard lift, in.	Chain hoists: Retracted distance between hooks, max, in.	Chain hoists: Net weight,† lb	Chain hoists: Efficiency,‡ percent	Wire-rope hoists: Standard lift, in.	Wire-rope hoists: Retracted distance between hooks, max, in.	Wire-rope hoists: Net weight,† lb	Wire-rope hoists: Efficiency,‡ percent
¾	50	13	14	80	120	28	10	80
1½	50	16	25	80	60	28	10	80
3	50	18	36	80				
6	50	25	65	65				

* Chain hoists also available in 9, 11, 13, and 15 tons capacity, wire-rope hoists in 1 and 2 tons capacity.

† Class 2 (lightweight) hoists.

‡ Efficiency = (ft-lb output)(100)/(ft-lb input).

current is off. When the hoist motor is activated, a solenoid overcomes the springs to release the brake. In the lowering direction, the motor acts as a generator, putting current back into the line and controlling the lowering speed. Some electric hoists use the same type of Weston brake as is used in hand hoists, but with this type, the motor must drive the load downward so as to try to release the brake. This type of brake generates considerable heat that must be dissipated—usually through an oil bath. The heat generated may also lower the useful-duty cycle of the hoist. If the

Table 10. Data on Electric Chain Hoists
(Chisholm-Moore Hoist Division)

Capacity, tons	Lifting speed, fpm	Motor hp	Shortest distance between hooks, in.	Net weight, lb
⅛	32	¼	15	51
¼	16	¼	15	51
	32	½	15	59
½	8	¼	18	61
	16	½	15	60
	32	1	16¼	110
1	8	½	18	68
	16	1	16¼	110
2	8	1	24	128

Table 11. Data for Electric Wire-rope Hoists
(Chisholm-Moore Hoist Division)

Capacity, tons	Lifting speed, fpm	Motor hp	Beam to high hook, in.*	Net weight, lb*
½	60	2	22½	500
1	30	2	22	535
	37	3	22½	505
	60	4	22½	515
1½	18	2	22	535
	30	3	22	535
	37	4	22½	515
2	18	3	22	535
	30	4	22	550
3	18	4	22½	630
5	13	4½	28	780

* Hoist with plain trolley.

Weston brake is used, an additional auxiliary hand-released or electrically released friction brake must be provided since the Weston brake will not act in the raising direction. All electric hoists have upper-limit switches; lower-limit switches are standard on chain hoists, optional on wire-rope hoists. Control is usually by push button; pendant ropes from the controller are obsolescent. Control is "deadman" type, the hoist stopping instantly upon release. Modern multiple-speed a-c controls for larger units have made d-c hoists obsolete. Single-phase a-c hoists are available to 1 hp, polyphase in all sizes.

The hoist may be suspended by an integral hook or bolt-type lug or may be attached to a trolley rolling on an I beam or monorail. The trolley may be plain (push type), geared (operated by a hand chain), or motor-driven; the latter types are essential for heavier loads. Table 10 gives data for electric **chain hoists,** and Table 11 for **wire-rope hoists.**

Air Hoists

Air hoists are similar to electric hoists in construction, except that air motors are used. Hoists from ⅛- to 1-ton capacity are available in wire-rope, link-chain, and roller-chain models and utilize either rotary-vane or piston-type air motors. Wire-rope hoists with piston-type motors are built up to 15 tons rating. A brake, interlocked with the controls, automatically holds the load in neutral; moving the control valve releases the brake, either mechanically or by air pressure. Air hoists may be suspended from a hook, lug, or trolley; occasionally air-motor-driven trolleys are fitted. Horizontal movement is limited by the bulky air hose to about 25 ft.

Air hoists provide **infinitely variable speed,** according to the movement of the control valve. Very high speeds are possible with light loads. When severely overloaded, the air motor stalls without damage. Air hoists are smaller and lighter than electric hoists of equal capacity and can be operated in explosive atmospheres. They are more expensive than electric hoists, require mufflers for reasonably quiet operation, and normally are fitted with automatic lubricators in the air supply.

FIG. 23 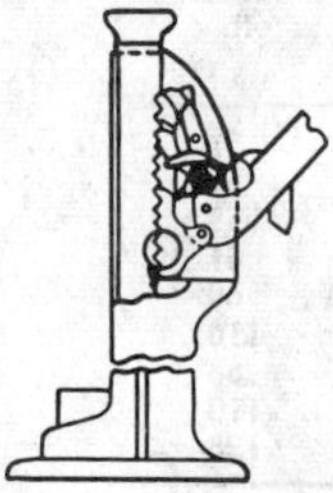 FIG. 24 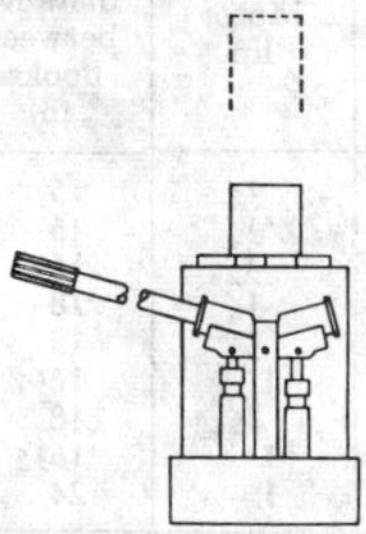 FIG. 25

FIG. 23. Bell-bottom screw jack.
FIG. 24. Rack-and-lever jack.
FIG. 25. Hydraulic jack.

Jacks

Jacks are portable, hand-operated devices for moving heavy loads through short distances. There are three types in common use: screw jacks, rack-and-lever jacks, and hydraulic jacks. Bell-bottom **screw jacks** (Fig. 23) are available in capacities to 24 tons and lifting ranges to 14 in. The screw is rotated by a bar inserted in holes in the screw head or by a ratchet lever fitted to the head. Geared bridge jacks will lift up to 50 tons. A lever ratchet mechanism turns a bevel pinion; an internal thread in the gear raises the non-rotating screw. **Rack-and-lever jacks** (Fig. 24) consist of a cast-steel or malleable-iron housing in which the lever pivots. The rack toothed bar passes through the hollow housing; the load may be lifted either on the top or on a toe extending from the bottom of the bar. The lever pawl may be biased either to raise or to lower the bar, the housing pawl holding the load on the return lever stroke. Rack-and-lever jacks to 20 tons are direct-acting. Lever-operated geared jacks range up to 35 tons. Lifting heights to 18 in. are provided. **Track jacks** are rack-and-lever jacks which may be tripped to release the load. They are used for railroad-track work but not for industrial service where the tripping feature might be hazardous. **Hydraulic jacks** (Fig. 25) consist of a cylinder, a piston, and a lever-operated pump. Capacities to 100 tons and lifting heights to 22 in. are available. Jacks 25 tons and larger may be provided with two pumps, the second pump being a high-speed unit for rapid travel at partial load.

MINE HOISTS, SKIPS

Large hoists for such uses as mines and blast-furnace skips were formerly steam-engine driven but are now almost entirely electrically driven. Such hoists are of either the single- or the double-drum type, with drums keyed or bushed on the shaft and driven through friction clutches. Drums are generally driven through single- or double-reduction gears, almost exclusively of the herringbone type and enclosed in oiltight casings. Each drum is equipped with a **post-type brake** (Fig. 26), usually operated by hand for small installations but on large machines applied by weights suspended from the operating lever and released through the action of an air- or oil-pressure cylinder. The clutches on large hoists are also equipped with air or oil cylinders. Large hoists operating at high rope speeds (drums more than 10 ft in diameter and rope speeds 2,500 to 3,000 fpm) are frequently connected directly to the driving-motor shaft; they are designated as **first-motion** hoists.

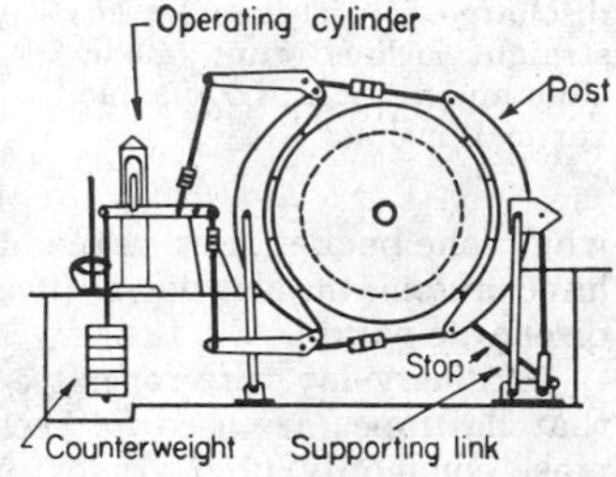

Fig. 26. Post-type brake.

Mine hoists are generally divided into (1) **metal-mine hoists** (e.g., iron, copper, zinc, salt, gypsum, silver, gold, ores) and (2) **coal-mine hoists.** These classes subdivide into main hoists (for handling ores or coal) and hoists for men, timbers, and supplies. They are designed for operating (1) mine shafts, vertical and inclined, balanced and unbalanced; and (2) slopes, balanced and unbalanced. When an empty cage or platform descends while the loaded cage or platform ascends, as when both cables are wound on a single drum, the machine is referred to as a **balanced hoist.** Most medium- and large-sized hoists normally operate in balance, as the tonnage obtained for a given load and rope speed is about double that for an unbalanced hoist and the power consumption per ton hoisted is lower. Balanced operation can also be obtained by a counterweight. The counterweight (approximately equal to all the dead loads plus one-half the live load) is usually installed in guides within a single shaft compartment. The average depth of ore mines is about 2,000 ft, and that of coal mines is close to 500 ft. Most ore-mine hoists are of the double-drum type, normally hoisting in balance, each drum being provided with a friction clutch for changing the relative positions of the two skips when operating from various levels.

Hoists for coal mines are principally of the keyed-drum type, for operating in balance from one level. For high rope speeds in shallow shafts, it is generally advantageous to use **combined cylindrical and conical drums.** The cylindroconical drum places the maximum rope pull (weight of rope and loaded skip) on the small diameter, so that during the acceleration period of the cycle, the weight of the opposing skip is offering the greatest counterbalance torque, reducing motor peak loads and slightly reducing the power consumption. The peak reduction obtained becomes greater when shafts are shallower and hoisting speeds are higher, provided that the proportion between the smaller and the large diameters is increased as these conditions increase. By varying the ratio of diameters and the distribution of rope on the drum profiles with respect to the periods of acceleration, retardation, and constant speed, static and dynamic torques can be modified to produce the most economical power consumption and the minimum size of motor. The conical drum is not applicable for multiple-level operation, and except in very special cases, only a single layer of rope can be used.

Skip hoists for industrial purposes such as power-plant fuel handling and blast-furnace charging are similar to shallow-lift slow-speed coal-mine hoists in that they operate from a single level. Speeds of 100 to 400 fpm are usual. For blast furnace charging with combined bucket and load weights up to 31,000 lb and a speed of 500 fpm, modern plants consist of straight-drum geared engines, frequently with Ward Leonard control (p. 15–51).

Industrial skip hoists may be specified where the lift is too high for a bucket elevator, where the lumps are too large for elevator buckets, or where the material is pulverized and extremely abrasive or actively corrosive. For high lifts having a vertical or nearly vertical path, the skip with supporting structure usually costs less than a bucket elevator or an inclined belt conveyor with bridge. Typical paths are shown in Fig. 27, paths *C* and *D* being suitable when the load is received through a track hopper.

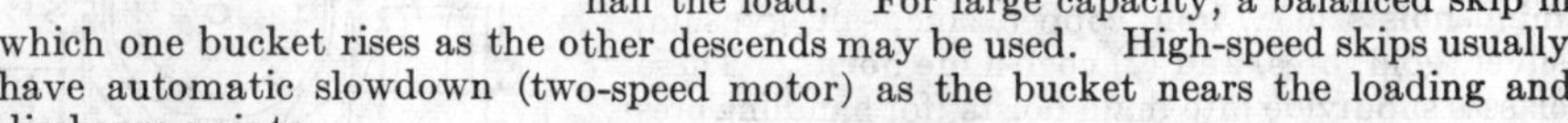

FIG. 27. Typical paths for skip hoists: (*A*) vertical, with discharge to either side; (*B*) straight inclined run; (*C*) incline and vertical; (*D*) incline, vertical, incline.

The skip may be **manually loaded** direct from a wheelbarrow or dump car or **automatically loaded** by a pivoted chute, which is actuated by the bucket and which, when upturned, serves as a cutoff gate (Fig. 28).

For small capacities, the skip can be manually loaded with semiautomatic control. When the bucket has been filled, the operator pushes the start button and the bucket ascends, dumps, and returns to loading position. With automatic loading and larger capacity, the skip may have full automatic control. For economy, the bucket is counterbalanced by a weight, usually equaling the weight of the empty bucket plus half the load. For large capacity, a balanced skip in which one bucket rises as the other descends may be used. High-speed skips usually have automatic slowdown (two-speed motor) as the bucket nears the loading and discharge points.

Ordinary-lay wire rope (see p. 8–113) is employed for mine-hoisting duty, except that flat ropes are used for reel hoists. Plow steel and improved plow steel are the most commonly used grades; the latter is used where the service is severe. Some state mining regulations require higher factors of safety than the usual hoisting requirements. The working capacity of new ropes is usually computed by using the minimum breaking strength given in the manufacturer's tables and the following factors of safety: rope lengths of 500 ft or less, minimum factor 8; 500 to 1,000 ft, 7; 1,000 to 2,000 ft, 6; 2,000 to 3,000 ft, 5; 3,000 ft or over, 4½. These are gross factors between the rated minimum breaking strength of the rope and the maximum static pull due to suspended load plus rope weight. The net factor, which should be used in dealing with large capacities and great depth, must take into consideration stresses due to acceleration and bending around the drum, together with suitable allowances for shock. With 6-by-19 wire construction, the pitch diameter of the drums is generally not less than sixty times the diameter of the rope. Drums are made of either cast iron or cast steel machine-grooved to suit the size of rope (see p. 10–12). In large hoists, a lifting device is installed at the free rope end of the drum to assist the rope in doubling back over the first layer.

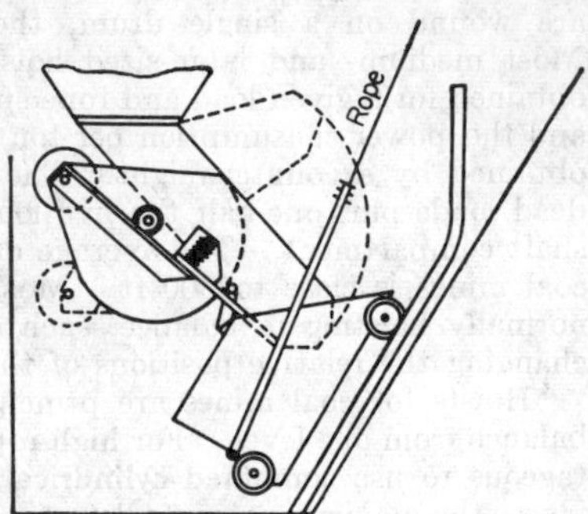

FIG. 28. Automatic loader (in loading position).

Brakes. The band-type brake is restricted to small hoists for light duty. Two types of post brakes are used: the parallel-acting type (Fig. 26) and the anchored type. The bottom ends of the beams on the latter type are anchored to hinge-pin castings secured to the foundation. Asbestos composition blocks are rapidly replacing wood. Their coefficient of friction is greater and more uniform, and considerably higher unit pressures can be used. They eliminate screeching and arrest motion quickly without jerking. Blocks vary from 2½ to 5 in. in thickness. The brake lining for medium-sized hoists consists of asbestos and cotton-fabric bands, varying in thickness from ½ to 1 in. and secured to the beam by copper rivets.

Hoist Motors. Determining the proper size of motor for driving a hoist calls for setting up a definite cycle of duty based upon the required daily or hourly tonnage.

The **permissible hoisting speed** for mine hoists largely depends upon the depth of the shaft; the greater the depth, the higher the allowable speed. Conservative maximum hoisting speeds, as recommended by *B of M Bull.* 75, are as follows:

Depth of shaft	Fpm
500 or less	1,200
500–1,000	1,600
1,000–2,000	2,000
2,000–3,000	3,000

High hoisting speeds call for rapid **acceleration** and **retardation.** For small hoists, the rate of acceleration may be made as low as 0.5 ft per sec. An average value of 3 ft per sec^2 is adopted for large hoists with fairly high speeds. Exceptional cases may require up to 6 ft per sec^2. The speed should also be considered with regard to the weight of the material to be hoisted per trip. The question of whether the load should be increased and the speed reduced or vice versa is controlled by local conditions, mining laws, and practical experience. The rest period assigned to the duty cycle, *i.e.*, the requisite time for loading at the bottom and unloading at the top, is dependent upon the equipment employed. With skips loaded from underground ore-storage hoppers, 5 to 6 sec is the minimum that can be assumed. Unless special or automatic provision is made, the loading time should be taken as 8 to 10 sec minimum. When the (1) hoisting speed, (2) weight of skip or cage, (3) weight of load, (4) periods of acceleration, (5) retardation, and (6) time for loading have been decided upon, the next step is to ascertain the "root-mean-square" equivalent continuous load-heating effect on the motor, taking into account rope and load weights, acceleration and deceleration of all hanging and rotating masses, and friction of sheaves, machines, etc. The friction load is usually taken as constant throughout the running period of the cycle. The over-all efficiency of the mechanical parts of a single-reduction-geared hoist averages 80 percent; that of a first-motion hoist is closer to 85 percent. The motor selected must have sufficient starting torque to meet the temporary peaks of any cycle, including, in the case of balanced hoists, the requirements of trips out of balance.

Electrical equipment for driving mine hoists is of four classes:

1. *Direct-current motors* with resistance control for small hoists, usually series-wound but occasionally compound-wound in conjunction with dynamic braking control.
2. *Alternating-current slip-ring-type motors* with secondary resistance.
3. *Ward Leonard system of control* (p. 15–51) for higher efficiency, particularly on short lifts at high rope speeds, where the rheostatic losses during acceleration and retardation represent a large proportion of the net work done during the cycle; for accuracy of speeds, with high-speed hoists; and for equalization of power demands. Complete control of the speed from standstill to maximum is obtained for all values of load from maximum positive to maximum negative. The lowering of unbalanced loads without the use of brakes is as readily accomplished as hoisting.
4. The *Ilgner Ward Leonard system* consists of a flywheel directly connected to a Ward Leonard motor-generator set and a device for automatically varying the speed through the secondary rheostatic control of the slip-ring induction motor driving the set. This form of equipment is used under conditions that prohibit the carrying of heavy loads or where power is purchased under heavy reservation charges for peak loads. It limits the power taken from the supply circuit to a certain predetermined value; whatever is required in excess of this value is produced by the energy given up by the flywheel as its speed is reduced.

ELEVATORS, DUMBWAITERS, ESCALATORS

All **hydraulic elevators** except the short-rise slow-speed plunger type are obsolete. Drum-type electric elevators have been superseded by **traction type** elevators, which are inherently safest because the reduction of tractive effort when the car or counterweight bottoms minimizes the possibility of these members being drawn into overhead work. The design of this type of equipment must follow closely the requirements of specification ASA 17.1 or applicable local codes, which impose specific safety requirements, including use of limit switches, type of braking means, and number of supporting cables.

Geared traction elevators are used for car speeds up to 250 to 300 fpm; above 300 fpm, gearless machines have decided advantages. **Gearless machines** (Fig. 29) have either 2:1 or 1:1 roping. With 2:1 machines, the car speed is one-half the rope speed, with 1:1 machines, the car speed is the same as the rope speed. The 2:1 machines are adapted to car speeds from 300 to 500 fpm; 1:1 machines are adapted to car speeds of 600 fpm and higher. Gearless machines are operating satisfactorily for car speeds of 1,000 fpm.

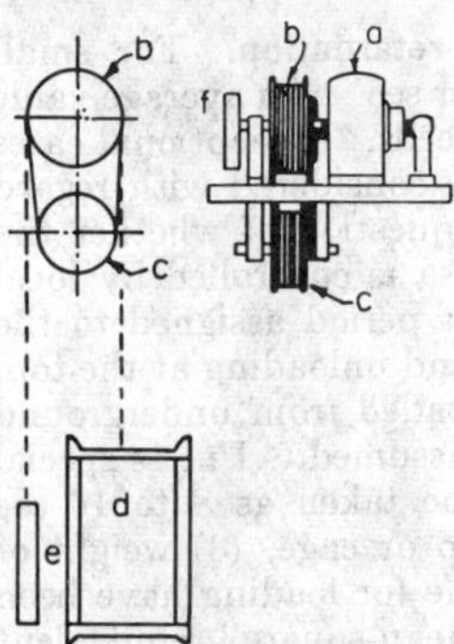

Fig. 29. Electric traction elevator.

Motors. Direct-current motors have the advantages of good starting torque and ease of speed control. Elevator motors are obliged to develop double rated torque at 125 percent rated current and have frequent starting, stopping, reversing, and running at constant speed. With sparkless commutation under all conditions, commercial motors cannot as a rule meet these requirements. For constant voltage, cumulative-compound motors with heavy series fields are used. The series fields are gradually short-circuited as the motor comes up to speed, after which the motor operates shunt. The shunt field is excited permanently, the current being reduced to a low value with increased resistance rather than the circuit opening when the motor is not in operation.

Squirrel-cage induction motors with high-resistance end rings to reduce starting current and increase starting torque are preferable to slip-ring motors because of their greater simplicity and ruggedness. For speeds greater than 150 fpm, two-speed squirrel-cage induction motors are preferable. Two separate stator windings having different numbers of poles and giving speed ratios of 3:1 and greater are in most common use.

Control. There are two types of control in use: resistance control and Ward Leonard, or voltage, control. With resistance control, reduced voltage for starting is obtained by resistance in series with the armature. With voltage control, an individual d-c generator is used for each elevator. The generator may be driven by either a d-c or an a-c motor (see Ward Leonard and Ilgner systems, p. 15–51). The generator voltage is controlled through its field current, which gives the highest rates of acceleration and retardation. This system is equally efficient with either d-c or a-c supply. When resistance control is used, sections of the resistance are short-circuited successively, usually by contactors, until the armature is directly across the line. The objection to this method is the large energy loss in the starting resistance. With several elevators in operation, starting energy loss is reduced by using a multivoltage supply obtained from balancer sets across the line. With several elevators in operation, the unbalanced current carried by the balancer set is small.

Resistance control is used with geared machines for car speeds up to about 400 fpm. For speeds up to 150 fpm, single-speed motors are usually used; for speeds above 150 fpm, two-speed motors are used. For speeds of 300 to 400 fpm, voltage control is frequently used instead of resistance control, particularly with a-c supply. For gearless machines, voltage control is used.

Counterweights are used with elevators, skip hoists, and mine hoists to equalize the engine load. The engine or motor can be smaller, since it must only drive against the unbalanced load and overcome friction. The brakes of a counterbalanced system retard greater masses and must be more powerful than for the same hoist without counterweights. Skip and mine hoists are counterbalanced by means of duplicate cars, one traveling up while the other goes down; the effective load is the difference between the weights of a full and an empty car, corrected for the weight of the rope. Elevators are usually overbalanced; *i.e.*, the counterweight exceeds the light weight of the car by the average expectation of load. With high lifts, the weight of rope is neutralized by compensating chains hung from the top of the shaft and looped to the bottom of car, producing no pull when the car is down and maximum pull when the car is at the top.

Loads. The rated load of passenger elevators is as follows:

Effective area of platform, sq ft.......	40	60	80	100	120
Total capacity, lb....................	3,400	5,600	7,700	9,800	12,000

Codes in various cities specify that provision made for loads shall not be less than 75 psf, based on an average person occupying 2 sq ft and weighing 150 lb. Practice shows that for department stores, roof gardens, and subway stations, large cars may be loaded as high as 120 psf effective area.

Efficiencies and power consumption per car mile of load of 2,500 lb for geared elevators are as follows:

Direct-current supply:

150 fpm, efficiency 45 percent, power consumption 3.6 kwh.
300 fpm, efficiency 55 percent, power consumption 5.0 kwh.

Alternating-current supply:

150 fpm, efficiency 40 percent, power consumption 5.0 kwh.
300 fpm (two-speed), efficiency 50 percent, power consumption 7.5 kwh.

Gearless elevators, resistance-control d-c supply:

600 fpm, efficiency 60 to 65 percent, power consumption 5.5 kwh.

Efficiencies are based upon net load, i.e., full load minus overbalance.

Car Mileage and Stops (per elevator—8-hr day). **Office buildings—local elevators,** intensive service 12 to 20 car miles, making about 150 regular stops per mile; **express elevators,** 20 to 40 car miles, making about 75 to 100 regular stops per mile. **Department store elevators,** 4 to 8 miles, make about 350 regular stops per mile.

Automatic push-button elevators without microdrive are limited to speeds of 100 to 150 fpm with moderate loads owing to the difficulty of making accurate stops at higher speeds. With microdrive, speeds of 250 to 300 fpm can be used.

Collective automatic control is adapted to higher car speeds than the ordinary push-button elevator and is capable of handling more passengers, as the car responds to all calls made in the direction in which it is traveling. Signal control, in combination with microdrive and voltage control, is adapted to intensive service and high car speeds and is as fully automatic as a high-speed elevator can be. With signal control, a car automatically stops at a floor and levels with the landing in response to the pressing of a hall button. Signal-control elevators have been installed for car speeds of 1,000 fpm. Manual control is limited to car speeds of 700 fpm.

Dumbwaiters follow the general design requirements of elevators except that code specifications are somewhat more relaxed. For example, roller-link chain can be used for support instead of wire rope. Moreover, a single strand can be used instead of the mandatory minimums of three for traction-type elevators and two for drum-type elevators.

Escalators have the advantages of continuity of motion, great capacity, and small amounts of space occupied and current consumed for each passenger carried. Escalators are built 2, 3, and 4 ft wide between balustrading geared to move at the same speed as the element. The angle of incline is 30 deg from the horizontal, and the speed is 90 fpm. The normal carrying capacity of 2- (3-) [4-] ft escalators is 4,000 (6,000) [8,000] passengers per hr.

DRAGGING, PULLING, AND PUSHING

BY

Harold V. Hawkins

HOISTS, PULLERS, AND WINCHES

Many of the fundamental portable lifting mechanisms such as hoists or pullers (see p. 10–17) can also be used to forcefully drag or pull materials. In addition, nonmobile versions, called **winches**, utilizing hoisting drums like that shown in Fig. 9 (p. 10–12) can also be used.

LOCOMOTIVE HAULAGE, COAL MINES

Rubber-tired haulage at the coal face was introduced in 1935 and received further impetus with the introduction of the rubber-tired shuttle car in 1938. Crawler-mounted loaders and rubber-tired universal coal cutters completed the equipment needed for complete off-track mining. This off-track mining caused a revolution in face haulage since it eliminated the expense of laying track in the rooms and advancing the track as the face of the coal advanced. It also made gathering locomotives of the cable-reel, crab-reel, and battery types obsolete. Practically all the gathering duty is now performed by rubber-tired shuttle cars, chain conveyors, extensible belt conveyors, and other methods involving off-track equipment. Some mines eliminated track completely by having belt conveyors carry the coal to the outside.

Most coal operators today employ a combination system, using conveyors on panel development and locomotives for the main-line haulage. A **track haulage system,** properly installed with 85- or 100-lb rail, well bonded, and carefully graded, ballasted, and drained, is still the safest and most dependable type of mine haulage. Grades in favor of or against the loads should not exceed 3½ percent and grades for long distances against the load should not exceed 2 percent. The trend in **main-line haulage** is toward heavier and faster locomotives since the hauls are becoming longer and longer. The sleek, streamlined, fast, and easy-riding **Jeffrey** eight-wheel four-motor locomotives, available in 27-, 37-, and 50-ton sizes, are ideally suited to these conditions. This type of locomotive has two four-wheel trucks, each having two motors. The trucks, having Pullman or longitudinal-type equalizers with snubbers, will go around a 50-ft radius curve, have short overhang, and provide a very easy ride. This construction is easy on the track, with consequent low track-maintenance cost. Speed at full load ranges from 10 to 12.5 mph, and the maximum safe speed is approximately 30 mph.

The **eight-wheel locomotive** usually has a box frame; series-wound motors with single-reduction spur gearing; 10 steps of straight parallel, full electropneumatic contactor control; dynamic braking; 32-volt battery-operated control and headlights, with the battery charged automatically from the trolley; straight air brakes; air-operated sanders; air horn; automatic couplers; one trolley pole; two headlights at each end; and blowers to ventilate the traction motors. The equipment is located so that it is easily accessible for repair and maintenance.

The eight-wheel type of locomotive has, to a great extent, superseded the tandem type, consisting of two four-wheel two-motor locomotives coupled together and controlled from the cab of one of the units of the tandem.

The older Jeffrey **four-wheel-type locomotive** is available in 11-, 15-, 20-, and 27-ton nominal weights. The 20- and 27-ton sizes have electrical equipment very much like that of the eight-wheel-type locomotive. Speeds are also comparable.

The 15-ton locomotive usually has semi-electropneumatic contactor control, rather than full electropneumatic control, and dynamic braking but usually does not have the 32-volt battery-operated control. The 11-ton locomotive has manual control, with manual brakes and sanders, although contactor control, air brakes, blowers, etc., are optional.

Locomotive motors have a horsepower rating on the basis of 1 hr at 75 C above an ambient temperature of 40 C. Sizes range from a total of 100 hp for the 11-ton to a total of 720 hp for the 50-ton.

The following formulas are recommended by the Jeffrey Manufacturing Co. to **determine the weight of a locomotive** required to haul a load. Table 1 gives haulage capacities of various weights of locomotives on grades up to 5 percent. The tabulation of haulage capacities shows how drastically the tons of trailing load decrease as the grade increases. For example, a 50-ton locomotive can haul 1,250 tons trailing load on the level but only 167 tons up a 5 percent grade.

Table 1. Haulage Capacities of Locomotives with Steel-tired or Rolled-steel Wheels
(Jeffrey Manufacturing Co.)

Grade		Weight of locomotive, tons*					
		11	15	20	27	37	50
Level	Drawbar pull, lb; Haulage capacity, gross tons	5,500 275	7,500 375	10,000 500	13,500 675	18,500 925	25,000 1,250
1%	Drawbar pull, lb; Haulage capacity, gross tons	5,280 132	7,200 180	9,600 240	12,960 324	17,760 444	24,000 600
2%	Drawbar pull, lb; Haulage capacity, gross tons	5,260 88	6,900 115	9,200 153	12,420 207	17,020 284	23,000 384
3%	Drawbar pull, lb; Haulage capacity, gross tons	4,840 67	6,600 82	8,800 110	11,880 149	16,280 204	22,000 275
4%	Drawbar pull, lb; Haulage capacity, gross tons	4,620 46	6,300 63	8,400 84	11,340 113	15,540 155	21,000 210
5%	Drawbar pull, lb; Haulage capacity, gross tons	4,400 31	6,000 50	8,000 67	10,800 90	14,800 123	20,000 167

* Haulage capacities are based on 20 lb per ton rolling friction, which is conservative for roller-bearing cars.

The following formulas are based on the use of steel-tired or rolled-steel wheels on clean, dry rail.

Weight of locomotive required on level track:

$$W = L(R + A)/(0.3 \times 2{,}000 - A)$$

Weight of locomotive required to haul train up the grade:

$$W = L(R + G)/(0.25 \times 2{,}000 - G)$$

Weight of locomotive necessary to start train on the grade:

$$W = L(R + G + A)/(0.30 \times 2{,}000 - G - A)$$

where W is the weight in tons of locomotive required; R is the frictional resistance of the cars in pounds per ton and is taken as 20 lb for cars with antifriction bearings and 30 lb for plain-bearing cars; L is the weight of the load in tons; A is the acceleration resistance (this is 100 for 1 mph per sec and is usually taked at 20 for less than 10 mph or at 30 from 10 to 12 mph, corresponding to an acceleration of 0.2 or 0.3 mph per sec); G is the grade resistance in pounds per ton or 20 lb per ton for each percent of grade (25 percent is the running adhesion of the locomotive, 30 percent is the starting adhesion using sand); 2,000 is the factor to give adhesion in pounds per ton.

Where the grade is in favor of the load:

$$W = L(G - R)/(0.20 \times 2{,}000 - G)$$

To brake the train to a stop on grade:

$$W = L(G + B - R)/(0.20 \times 2{,}000 - G - B)$$

where B is the braking (or decelerating) effort in pounds per ton and equals 100 lb per ton for a braking rate of 1 mph per sec or 20 lb per ton for a braking rate of 0.2 mph per sec or 30 lb for a braking rate of 0.3 mph per sec. The adhesion is taken from a safety standpoint as 20 percent. It is not advisable to rely on using sand to increase the adhesion since the sandboxes may be empty when sand is needed.

Time in seconds to brake the train to a stop:

$$\text{Sec} = \frac{\text{mph (start)} - \text{mph (finish)}}{\text{deceleration in mph/sec}}$$

Distance in feet to brake the train to a stop:

$$\text{Ft} = [\text{mph (start)} - \text{mph (finish)}] \times \text{sec} \times 1.46/2$$

Storage-battery locomotives are used for hauling muck cars in tunnel construction where it is inconvenient to install trolley wires and bond the track as the tunnel advances. They are also used to some extent in metal mines and in mines of foreign countries where trolley locomotives are not permitted. They are seldom used anymore in coal mines of the United States. Their first cost is frequently less than that for a trolley installation. They also possess many of the advantages of the trolley locomotive and eliminate the danger and obstruction of the trolley wire. Storage-battery locomotives are limited by the energy that is stored in the battery and should not be used on steep grades or where large, continuous overloads are required. Best results are obtained where light and medium loads are to be handled intermittently over short distances with a grade of not over 3 percent against the load.

The general construction and mechanical features are similar to those of the four-wheel trolley type, with battery boxes located either on top of the locomotive or between the side frames, according to the height available. The motors are rugged, with high efficiency. Storage-battery locomotives for coal mines are generally of the explosion-tested type approved by the B of M for use in gaseous mines.

The **battery** usually has sufficient capacity to last a single shift. For two- or three-shift operation, an extra battery box with battery is required so that one battery can be charging while the other is working on the locomotive. Motor-generator sets or rectifiers are used for charging the batteries. The over-all efficiency of the battery, motor, and gearing is approximately 63 percent. The speed varies from 3 to 7 mph, the average being 3½ to 4½ mph. Battery locomotives are available in sizes from 2 to 50 tons. They are usually manufactured to suit individual requirements since the sizes of motors and battery are determined by the amount of work that the locomotive has to do in an 8-hr shift.

INDUSTRIAL CARS

Various types of narrow-gage industrial cars are used for handling bulk and package materials inside and outside of buildings. Those used for bulk material are usually of the dumping type, the form of the car being determined by the duty. They are either pushed by men or drawn by mules, locomotives, or cable. **The rocker side-dump car** (Fig. 1) consists of a truck on which is mounted a V-shaped steel body supported on rockers so that it can be tipped to either side, discharging material. This type is mainly used on construction work. Capacities vary from ⅔ to 5 tons for track gages of 18, 20, 24, 30, 36, and 56½ in. In the **gable-bottom car** (Fig. 2), the side doors a are hinged at the top and controlled by levers b and c, which lock the doors when closed. Since this type of car discharges material close to the ground on both sides of the track simultaneously, it is used mainly on trestles. Capacities vary from 29 to 270 cu ft for track gages of 24, 36, 40, and 50 in. The **scoop dumping car**

(Fig. 3) consists of a scoop-shaped steel body pivoted at *a* on turntable *b*, which is carried by the truck. The latch *c* holds the body in a horizontal position, being released by chain *d* attached to handle *e*. Since the body is mounted on a turntable, the car is used for service where it is desirable to discharge material at any point in the circle. This car is made with capacities from 12 to 27 cu ft to suit local require-

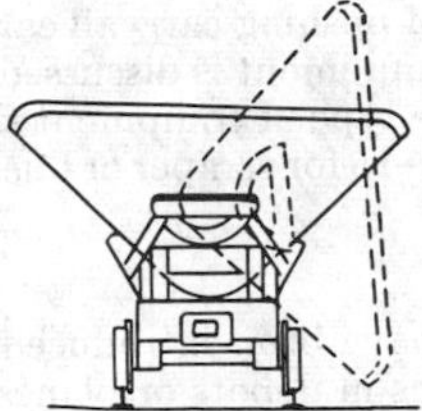

Fig. 1. Rocker side-dump car.

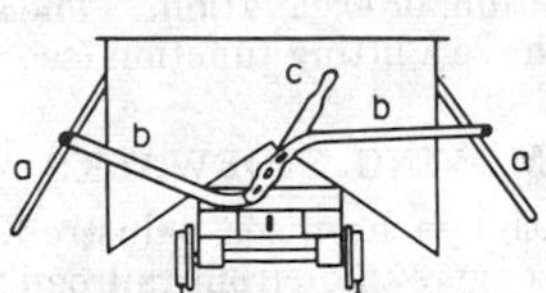

Fig. 2. Gable-bottom car.

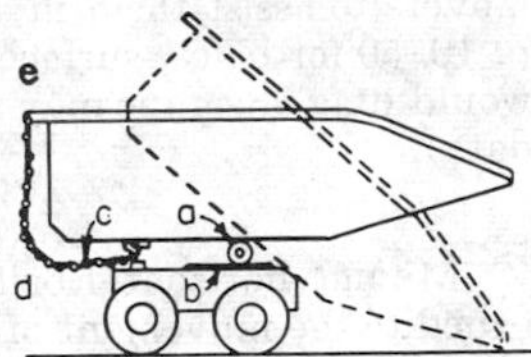

Fig. 3. Scoop dumping car.

ments. The **hopper-bottom car** (Fig. 4) consists of a hopper on wheels, the bottom opening being controlled by door *a*, which is operated by chain *b* winding on shaft *c*. The shaft is provided with handwheel and ratchet and pawl. The type of door or gate controlling the bottom opening varies with different materials.

The **box-body dump car** (Fig. 5) consists of a rectangular body pivoted on the trucks at *a* and held in horizontal position by chains *b*. The side doors of the car are attached to levers so that the door is automatically raised when the body of the car is tilted to its dumping position. The cars can be dumped to either side. On the large sizes, where rapid dumping is required, dumping is accomplished by compressed air. This type of car is primarily used in excavation and quarry work, being loaded by power shovels. The greater load is placed on the side on which the car will dump, so that dumping is automatic when the operator releases the chain or latch. The car bodies may be steel or steel-lined wood. **Mine cars** are usually of the four-wheel type, with low bodies, the doors being at one end, and pivoted at the top with latch at the bottom. Industrial **tracks** are made with rails from 12 to 45 lb per yd and gages from 24 in. to 4 ft 8½ in. Either steel or wooden ties are used. Owing to its lighter weight, the steel tie is preferred where tracks are frequently moved, the track being made up in sections. Industrial cars are frequently built with one wheel attached to the axle and the other wheel loose to enable the car to turn on short-radius tracks. Capacities vary from 4 to 50 cu yd for track gages of 36 to 56½ in., with cars having weights from 6,900 to 80,300 lb. The frictional resistance per ton (2,000 lb) for different types of mine-car bearings is as follows (see also pp. 11–37 to 11–39):

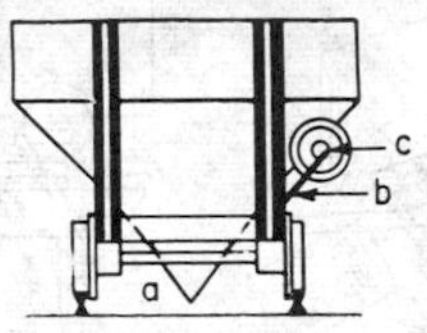

Fig. 4. Hopper-bottom car.

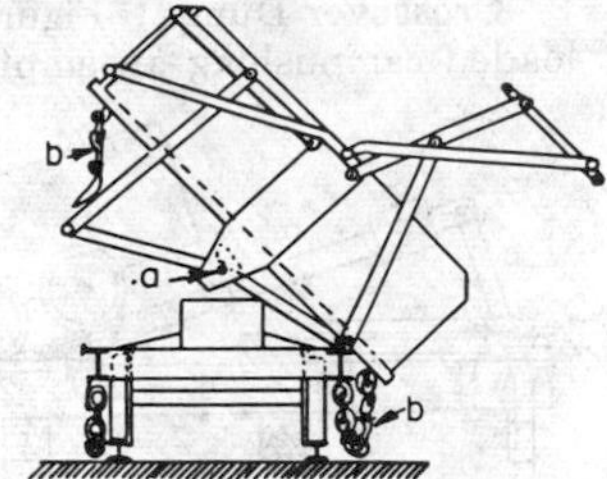

Fig. 5. Box-body dump car.

Type of bearing	Drawer pull, lb per ton		
	Level track	2% grade	4% grade
Spiral roller	13	15	46
Solid roller	14	18	53
Self-oiling	22	31	
Babbitted, old style	24	40	

DOZERS, DRAGLINES

The dual capability of some equipment, such as **dozers** and **draglines,** suggests that it should be mentioned as prime machinery in the area of materials handling by dragging, pulling, or pushing. Dozers are described in the discussion on earthmoving equipment (p. 10–33ff) since their basic frames are also used for power shovels and back-hoes. In addition, dozers form the auxiliary function of pushing carryall earthmovers to assist them in scraping up their load. Dragline equipment is discussed on p. 10–50 for below-surface handling or excavation. The same type of equipment that would drag or scrape may also have a lifting function (see p. 10–15 for scraper or bucket data).

MOVING SIDEWALKS

Moving horizontal belts with synchronized balustrading have been introduced to expedite the movement of passengers to or from railroad trains in depots or planes at airports (see belt conveyors, p. 10–71). A necessary feature is the need to prevent the clothing of anyone (*e.g.*, a child) sitting on the moving walk from being caught in the mechanism at the end of the walk. Use of a comblike stationary end fence protruding down into longitudinal slots in the belt is an effective preventative.

CAR-UNLOADING MACHINERY

Four types of devices are in common use for unloading material from all types of open-top cars: crossover and horn dumps, used to unload mine cars with swinging end doors; rotary car dumps, for mine cars without doors; and tipping car dumps, for unloading standard-gage cars where large unloading capacity is required.

Crossover Dump. Figure 6 shows a car in the act of dumping. Figure 7 shows a loaded car pushing an empty car off the dump. A section of track is carried by a

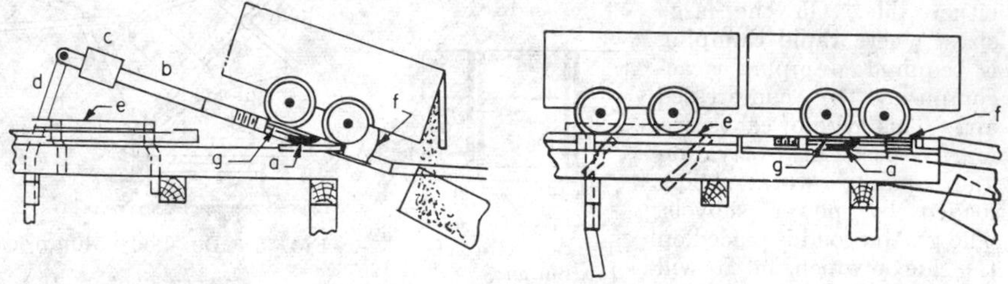

Fig. 6 Fig. 7

Figs. 6 and 7. Crossover dump.

platform supported on rockers *a*. An extension bar *b* carries the weight *c* and the brake friction bar *d*. A hand lever controls the brake, acting on the friction bar and placing the dumping under the control of the operator. A section of track *e* in front of the dump is pivoted on a parallel motion and counterbalanced so that it is normally raised. The loaded car depresses the rails *e* and, through levers, pivots the horns *f* around the shafts *g*, releasing the empty car. The load car strikes the empty car, starting it down the inclined track. After the loaded car has passed the rails *e*, the springs return the horns *f* so that they stop the loaded car in the position to dump. Buffer springs on the shaft *g* absorb the shock of stopping the car. Since the center of gravity of the loaded car is forward of the rockers, the car will dump automatically under control of the brake. No power is required for this dump, and one operator can dump three or four cars per minute.

Rotary Gravity Dump (Fig. 8). This consists of a steel cylinder supported by a shaft *a*, its three compartments carrying three tracks. The loaded car *b* is to one side of the center and causes the cylinder to rotate, the material rolling to the chute beneath. The band brake *c*, with counterweight *d*, is operated by lever *e*, putting the dumping under control of the operator. No power is required; one operator can dump two or three cars per minute.

Rotary power dumpers are also built to take any size of open-top railroad car and are frequently used in power plants, coke plants, ports, and ore mines to dump coal, coke, ore, bauxite, and other bulk material. They are mainly of two types: (1) single barrel, and (2) tandem.

The McDowell-Wellman Engineering Co. dumper consists of a revolving cradle supporting a platen (with rails in line with the approach and runoff car tracks in the upright position), which carries the car to be dumped. A blocking on the dumping side supports the side of the car as the cradle starts rotating. Normally, the platen is movable and the blocking is fixed, but in some cases the platen is fixed and the blocking movable. Where there is no variation in the car size, the platen and blocking are both fixed. The cradle is supported on two end rings, which are bound with a rail and a gear rack. The rail makes contact with rollers mounted in sills resting on the foundation. Power through the motor rotates the cradle by means of two pinions meshing with the gear racks. The angle of rotation for a complete dump is 155 deg for a normal operation, but occasionally, a dumper is designed for 180-deg rotation. The clamps, supported by the cradle, start moving down as the dumper starts to rotate. These clamps are lowered, locked, released, and raised either by a gravity-powered mechanism or by hydraulic cylinders.

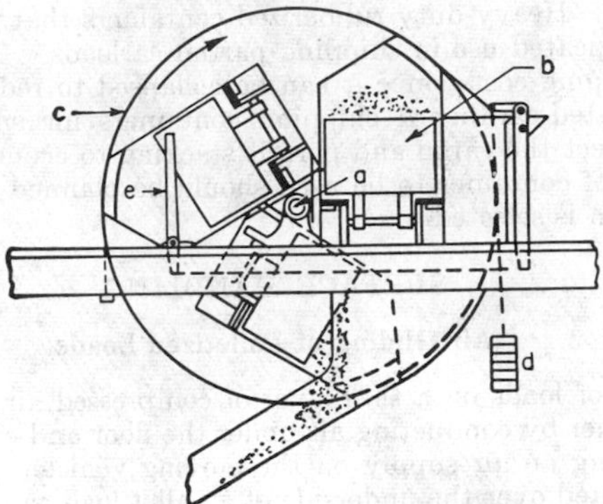

FIG. 8. Rotary gravity dump.

With the advent of the **unit-train system,** the investment and operating costs for a dumper have been reduced considerably. The design of dumpers for unit train has improved and results in fewer maintenance problems. The use of rotary couplers on unit train eliminates uncoupling of cars while dumping because the center of the rotary coupler is in line with the center of rotation of the dumper.

The McDowell-Wellman Engineering Co. will, when it is specified, provide an automatic electronic weighing system with a car dumper. The platen, car, and load are raised from the platen supports, and the weight is automatically recorded at the beginning and end of each dump cycle.

Car Shakers. As alternatives to rotating or tilting the car, several types of car shakers are used to hasten the discharge of the load. Usually the shaker is a heavy yoke equipped with an unbalanced pulley rotated at 2,000 rpm by a 20-hp motor. The yoke rests upon the car top sides, and the load is actively vibrated and rapidly discharged. While a car shaker provides a discharge rate about half that of a rotary dumper, the smaller investment is advantageous.

CARRYING AND LIFTING

BY

Harold V. Hawkins and Associates

CONTAINERIZATION

The proper packaging of material to assist in handling can significantly minimize the handling cost and can also have a marked influence on the type of handling equipment employed. For example, partial carload lots of liquid or granular material may be shipped in rigid or non-rigid containers equipped with proper lugs to facilitate in-transit handling. Heavy-duty rubberized containers that are inert to most cargo are available for repeated use in shipping partial carloads. The non-rigid container reduces return shipping costs since it can be collapsed to reduce space. Disposable lightweight corrugated-cardboard shipping containers for small and medium-sized packages both protect the cargo and permit stacking to economize on space requirements. The type of container to be used should be planned or considered when the handling mechanism is selected.

SURFACE HANDLING

Air Gliding of Palletized Loads

The movement of loads on a thin layer of compressed air over relatively smooth floors is feasible either by conducting air under the floor and ejecting it through small holes or by providing an air supply on the moving vehicle. Low-pressure air (say, 5 to 10 psi) distributed over the underside of a pallet load can lift the load slightly so that 5 lb can move a 1,000-lb load. Perforated floors in truck chassis or in factory aisles make possible the general movement of equipment. Also, by attaching an air hose to a pallet equipped with a perforated bottom, the pallet can be moved. Clark Equipment Co. economizes the amount of exhausted air by selectively porting air under the loads. The floor in a boxcar would require, at 12-psi pressure, 600 std cfm when simultaneously moving five pallets, each 36 by 40 in. and weighing 3,000 lb. In 35 min, 140,000 lb can be loaded manually.

Lift Trucks and Palletized Loads

The use of lift trucks is advantageous for movement of materials in industrial processing and warehousing where batches or unit quantities of materials of varying amounts are moved on schedules that are not well ordered to destinations that are quite varied. The most common type of lift truck is equipped with a fork on the front, which is projected under the load to be moved. The load is first lifted and then transported; the lifting action is either a direct lift or a direct lift coupled with a tilt to secure against quick stops. **Hand-powered vehicles** (Fig. 1) utilize a towing handle that operates both as a hydraulic pump for the lifting process and as a means of towing during the movement. Similar **electric-powered,** battery-energized units are available (Fig. 2). Loads to 6,000 lb can be moved in this fashion on pallets that have an initial clearance under them of about 3½ in., with the added lifting

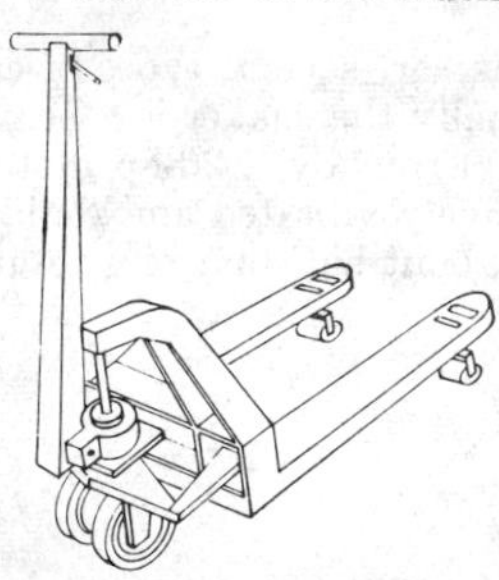

FIG. 1. Hand-powered pallet truck.

height 4 in. The lifting forks vary upward from 24 in. in length and from 21 in. in width.

Powered lift trucks provide for lifting loads from the floor to as high as 17 ft or more for stacking. Usual capacities are from 1,000 to 6,000 lb. With one type of lift truck, the operator walks beside the truck, commanding it through controls on a handle; another type provides a platform for a standing operator; a third type has a conventional driver's seat (Fig. 3). All types have extremely short turning radii for mobility in narrow aisles. Motive power is by electric motor and battery or by internal-combustion engine generally operating from liquid propane gas. In some units, the gas engine drives a d-c generator to provide current for an electric motor in order to retain the convenience of electric controls. Large forklift trucks are also available for yard work to lift loads as heavy as 40 tons to heights of 11 ft.

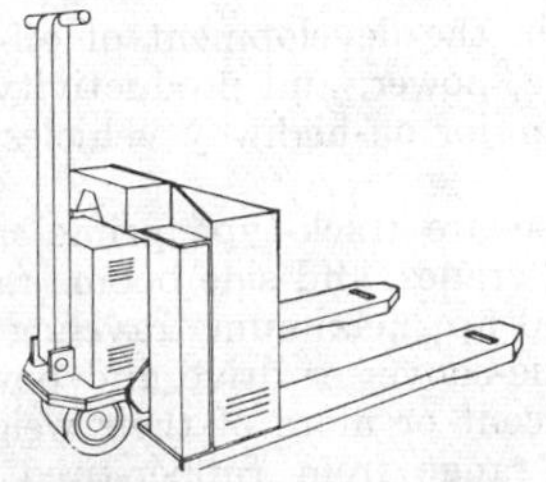

FIG. 2. Electric-powered, battery-energized hand truck.

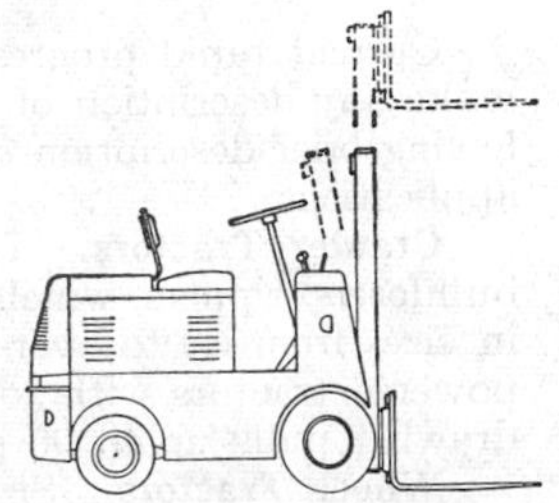

FIG. 3. Lift truck powered by an internal-combustion engine.

To facilitate the use of forklift trucks, the **load is generally piled on a pallet** (usually 36 by 42 in.), consisting of a low platform having sufficient clearance to the floor to permit the truck's lifting forks to protrude under the load. Some trucks are equipped with straddle forks, which also go under the load and press against the floor to take the overturning reaction as the load is lifted. This minimizes the need for a large counterbalance in the back of the lift truck, but it also makes movement with the load elevated somewhat more awkward. The pallet moves with the load and remains under it when the load is left at its destination. Pallets are so inexpensive as to be considered expendable.

Customized load-handling mechanisms are available in place of standard forks for lift trucks. One type provides a surface either curved (for rolls of newsprint) or flat (for large cardboard containers), depending upon the shape of the usual load, and is equipped with a vacuum pump, which sucks the load to the surface sufficiently to permit the load to be lifted. Special hooks are available for lifting 30- or 55-gal steel drums. The hydraulic lifting mechanism provides a source of power for manipulating many special clamps, pivots, etc. Hydraulically actuated clamps provide for squeezing rolls to permit lifting. Spindles or rams are available for inserting in steel coils to permit lifting.

Off-highway Vehicles and Earthmoving Equipment

(By H. V. Parsley and E. A. Braker, International Harvester Company)

The movement of large quantities of bulk materials, earth, gravel, and broken rock in road building, mining, construction, quarrying, and land clearing may be handled by **off-highway vehicles.** Such vehicles are mounted on large pneumatic tires or on crawler tracks if heavy pulling and pushing are required on poor or steep terrain. Width and weight of the rubber-tired equipment often exceed highway legal limits, and use of grouser tracks on highways is prohibited.

Proper selection of size and type of equipment depends on the amount, kind, and density of the material to be moved in a specified time and on the distances, direction, and steepness of grades, footing for traction, and altitude above sea level. Time cycles (see Table 1) and pay loads for production per hour can then be estimated from manufacturers' performance data and job experience. This production per hour, together with the corresponding owning, operating, and labor costs per hour, enables selection by favorable cost per cubic yard, ton, or other pay unit.

Table 1. Approximate Cycle Time of Power-shift Bulldozers and Scrapers—Level Haul

Hauling unit	Round-trip minutes for one-way haul distances, ft						
	50	150	300	500	1,000	2,500	5,000
Bulldozer, crawler....................	0.6	1.2	2.1				
Bulldozer, wheel-type..................		0.7	1.35	2.2			
Scraper, crawler-drawn.................			2.8	3.7	5.9		
Scraper, self-propelled (pusher-loaded)...					3.2	4.7	7.1

Production: 60-min time, hr = pay load × 60/cycle time, min.
50-min work, hr = pay load × 50/cycle time, min.

Current rapid progress in the development of off-highway equipment will soon make any description of size, power, and productivity obsolete. However, the following brief description of major off-highway vehicles will serve as a guide to their applications.

Crawler Tractors. These are track-type prime movers for use with mounted bulldozers, rippers, winches, cranes, and side booms rated by net engine horsepower in sizes from 30 to over 400 hp; maximum traveling speeds, 5 to 8 mph. Diesel-powered tractors with torque-converter drive and power-shift transmission develop drawbar pulls up to 90 percent or more of their weight with mounted equipment.

Wheel Tractors. Sizes range from rubber-tired industrial tractors for small scoops, loaders, and backhoes to large, Diesel-powered, two-wheel or four-wheel pneumatic-tired prime movers for propelling scrapers and wagons. Large, four-wheel-drive, articulated-steering types also power bulldozers.

Bulldozer—Crawler Type (Fig. 4). This is a crawler tractor with a front-mounted blade, which is lifted by hydraulic or cable power control. There are four basic types

Fig. 4. Bulldozer on crawler tractor. (*International Harvester.*)

Fig. 5. Bulldozer on four-wheel-drive tractor. (*International Harvester.*)

of moldboards: straight, semi-U and U (named by top-view shape), and angling. The angling type, often called **bullgrader or angledozer,** can be set for side casting 25 deg to the right or left of perpendicular to the tractor center line, while the other blades can be tipped forward or back through about 10 deg for different digging conditions. All blades can be tilted for ditching, with hydraulic-power tilt available for all but angling blades.

Application. This is the best machine for pioneering access roads, for boulder and tree removal, and for short-haul earthmoving to 300 ft in rough terrain. It push-loads self-propelled scrapers and is often used with a rear-mounted ripper to loosen firm or hard materials, including rock, for scraper loading. U blades drift 25 to 30 percent more loose material than straight blades but have poor digging ability. Angling blades expedite sidehill benching and backfilling of trenches. Loose-material capacity of straight blades varies approximately as the blade height squared, multiplied by length. Average capacity of digging blades is about 1 cu yd loose measure per 30 *net* hp rating of the crawler tractor. Payload is 60 to 90 percent of loose measure, depending on material swell variations.

Bulldozer—Wheel Type (Fig. 5). This is a four-wheel-drive, rubber-tired tractor, generally of the hydraulic articulated-steering type, with front-mounted blade that can be hydraulically raised, lowered, tipped, and tilted. Its operating weights range to 150,000 lb, with up to 700 hp, and its traveling speeds range from stall to about 20 mph for pushing and mobility.

Application. It is excellent for push-loading self-propelled scrapers, for grading the cut and spreading fill, and for drifting loose materials on firm or sandy ground for distances up to 500 ft. Useful tractive effort on firm earth surfaces is limited to about 60 percent of weight, as compared with 90 percent for crawler dozers.

Loader—Crawler Type (Fig. 6). This is a track-type prime mover with front-mounted bucket that can be raised, dumped, lowered, and tipped by power control. Figure 6 illustrates an optional 4-in-1, multipurpose bucket that can be used as a shovel, bulldozer, clamshell, or scraper. Capacities range from ¾ to 4 cu yd, SAE rated. It is also available with grapples for pulpwood, logs, and lumber.

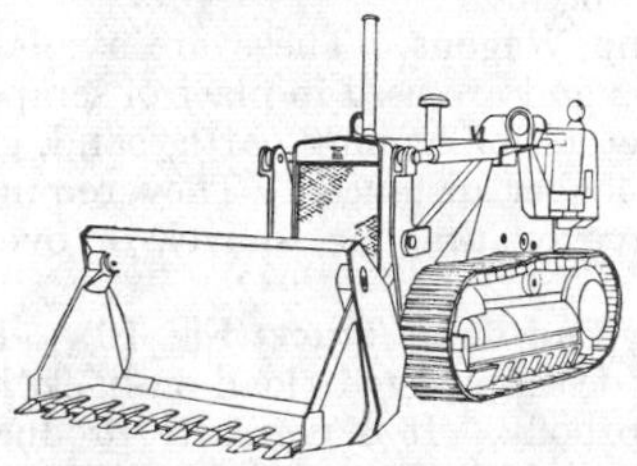

Fig. 6. Crawler-type loader with 4-in-1 bucket. (*International Harvester.*)

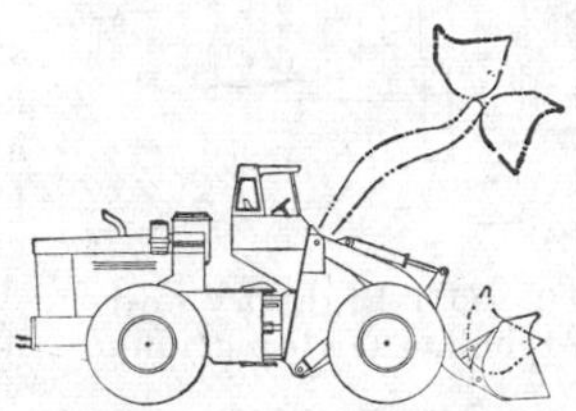

Fig. 7. Four-wheel-drive loader. (*International Harvester.*)

Application. It is used for digging basements, pools, ponds, and ditches; for loading trucks and hoppers; for placing, spreading, and compacting earth over garbage in sanitary fills; for stripping sod; for removing steel-mill slag; and for carrying and loading pulpwood and logs.

Loader—Wheel Type (Fig. 7). This is a four-wheel, rubber-tired prime mover with front-mounted hydraulic-operated shovel, often called a **Payloader.** It is available in SAE-rated capacities from ½ to 10 cu yd for materials weighing 3,000 lb per cu yd, with larger buckets available for lighter materials.

Application. This highly mobile equipment is used for handling and loading materials of all kinds on firm surfaces.

Scrapers—Tractor Drawn (Fig. 8). These are four-wheel, rubber-tired trailers for loading, hauling, dumping, and spreading earth and for bank-sloping and finishing. They are self-loading when matched to crawler tractors having at least 12 *net* hp per cu yd struck capacity and operating weights 10 to 20 percent more than scraper pay-load weight. Popular sizes range from 7 to 27 cu yd struck capacity, with 1:1 slope/heaped ratings to 35 cu yd.

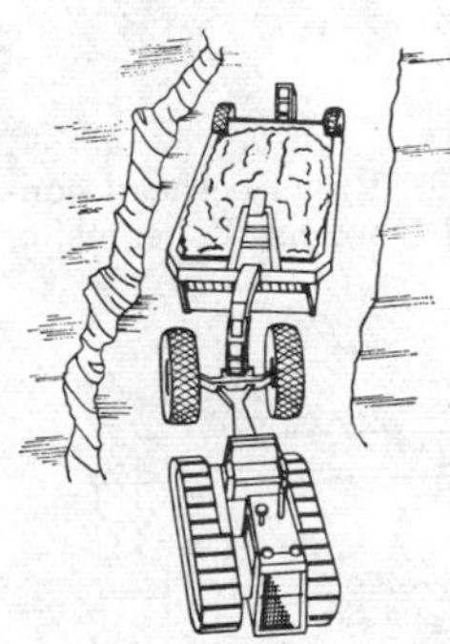

Fig. 8. Crawler tractor and drawn scraper. (*International Harvester.*)

Fig. 9. Two-axle self-propelled scraper. (*International Harvester.*)

Application. They are used for earthmoving for one-way distances up to 1,000 ft or under traction and terrain conditions unsuitable for faster, self-propelled scrapers.

Scrapers—Self-propelled (Fig. 9). These are similar to the tractor-drawn type but the front wheels are replaced by Diesel-powered, two-wheel or four-wheel tractors with 148 to 450+ hp and with numerous load-matching speeds to 30 mph and faster. Scraper rear wheels may also be driven by a separate rear-mounted engine. Ratings are given in cubic-yard struck/heaped capacities, such as 7/9, 14/18, 24/32, and 40/54. Pay-load capacities depend on loadability and swell of materials but approximate the struck capacity.

APPLICATION. They are used for high-speed earthmoving in road building and construction work, generally requiring pusher loading and smooth-haul roads for maximum production. However, some sizes are available with an elevator or with all-wheel drive for self-loading under favorable conditions. Two-axle, four-wheel types have best maneuverability, but the three-axle type is sometimes preferred for easier riding on long hauls at higher speed.

FIG. 10. Off-highway end-dump truck. (*International Harvester.*)

Bottom-dump Wagons. These are available in sizes to 100 tons and are used in place of scrapers on large-wheel tractors for hauling earth, sand, gravel, and coal over longer distances. They require top loading by conveyor, dragline, shovel, or overhead grizzly.

Off-highway End-dump Truck (Fig. 10). This is a heavy-duty, deisel-powered, load-on-back hauler with rear-dump body. It is regularly produced in rated capacities of 12 to 65 tons. The body cubic-yard struck capacity is about two-thirds tonnage rating. The all-wheel-drive, 45-ton-capacity, 475-hp Payhauler illustrated in Fig. 10 has power-shift transmission, with nine speeds to over 30 mph, and gross weight of 155,000 lb.

APPLICATION. It is used for hauling and dumping blasted rock, ore, and other hard and abrasive shovel-loaded materials in road and dam construction and in quarries and mines.

Owning and Operating Costs. These include depreciation; interest, insurance, taxes; parts, labor, repairs, and tires; fuel, lubricant, filters, hydraulic-system oil, and other operating supplies. This is reduced to cost per hour over a service life of 4 to 6 yr of 2,000 hr each—average 5 yr, 10,000 hr. Owning and operating costs of Diesel-powered bulldozers and scrapers, excluding operator's wages, average 2½ to 3 times the delivered price in 10,000 hr.

ABOVE-SURFACE HANDLING

Monorails

Materials can be carried on light, rigid trackage, as described for overhead conveyors (see p. 10–52ff). Trolleys are supported by structural I beams, H beams, or

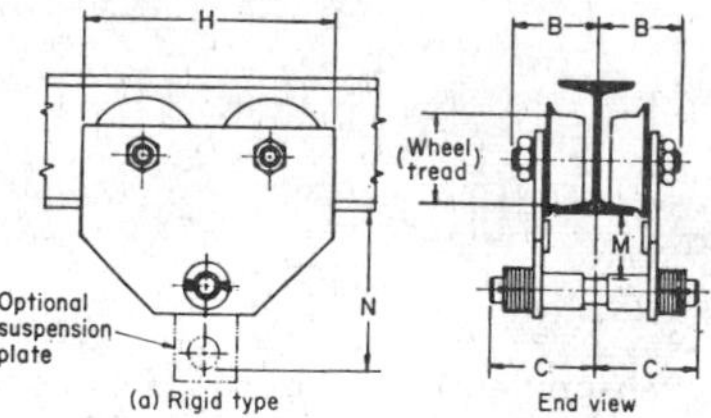

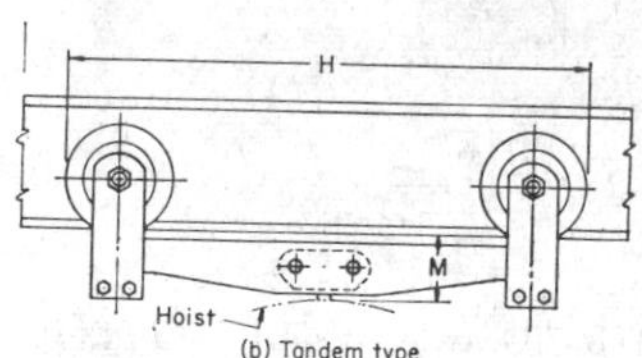

FIG. 11. Monorail trolleys. (*Chisholm-Moore Hoist Division.*)

I-beam-like rails with special flat flanges to improve rolling characteristics of the wheels. Size of wheels and smoothness of tread are important in reducing roller resistance. Figure 11*a* shows a typical rigid trolley. For traversing short-radius track curves or spreading the load along more track, a tandem trolley (Fig. 11*b*) is required. Typical dimensions for both types are given in Table 2. These trolleys

Table 2. Typical Monorail Trolley Dimensions
(Chisholm-Moore Hoist Division)

Capacity, tons	I-beam range (depth), in.	Wheel-tread diam, in.	Net weight, lb	*B*,* in.	*C*, in.	*H*, in.	*M*, in.	*N*, in.	Minimum beam* radius, in.
Rigid trolley (Fig. 11*a*)									
1/2	5–10	3 1/2	30	3 1/4	4	10	1 7/8	5 3/8	21
1	5–10	3 1/2	30	3 1/4	4	10	1 7/8	5 3/8	21
1 1/2	7–10	4	49	3 7/8	4 3/8	11 3/8	2 3/16	7 7/16	30
2	7–10	4	49	3 7/8	4 3/8	11 3/8	2 3/16	7 7/16	30
3	8–12	5	89	4 1/2	5	13 1/2	2 15/16	8 11/16	42
4	8–12	5	89	4 1/2	5	13 1/2	2 15/16	8 11/16	42
5	10–15	6	119	5	5 3/4	15 1/2	3 1/4	9 3/4	48
6	10–15	6	119	5	5 3/4	15 1/2	3 1/4	9 3/4	48
8	12–24	8	276	5 3/4	7	21 1/2	4 1/4	13 1/4	60
10	12–24	8	276	5 3/4	7	21 1/2	4 1/4	13 1/2	60
Tandem trolley (Fig. 11*b*)									
1	5–10	3 1/8	23	2 7/8	2 5/8	20	3 3/8	......	30
2	6–10	4	44	3 1/4	2 7/8	22 3/4	3 5/8	......	30

* These dimensions are given for minimum beam.

may be plain, with geared handwheel and hand chain, or motor driven. For very low headroom, the trolley can be built into the hoist; this is known as a **trolley hoist.**

Overhead Traveling Cranes

An **overhead traveling crane** is a vehicle for lifting, transporting, and lowering loads. It consists of a bridge supporting a hoisting unit and is equipped with wheels for operating on an elevated runway or track. The hoisting unit may be fixed relative to the bridge but is usually supported on wheels, permitting it to traverse the length of the bridge.

The motions of the crane—hoisting, trolley traversing, and bridging—may be powered by hand, electricity, air, hydraulics, or a combination of these. Hand-powered cranes are generally built in capacities under 50 tons and are used for infrequent service where slow speeds are acceptable. Pneumatic cranes are used where electricity would be hazardous or where advantage can be taken of existing air supply. Electric cranes are the most common overhead type and can be built to capacities of 500 tons or more and to spans of 150 ft and over.

Single-girder Cranes (Fig. 12). In its simplest form, this consists of an I beam *a* supported by four wheels *b*. The trolley *c* traveling on the lower flanges carries the

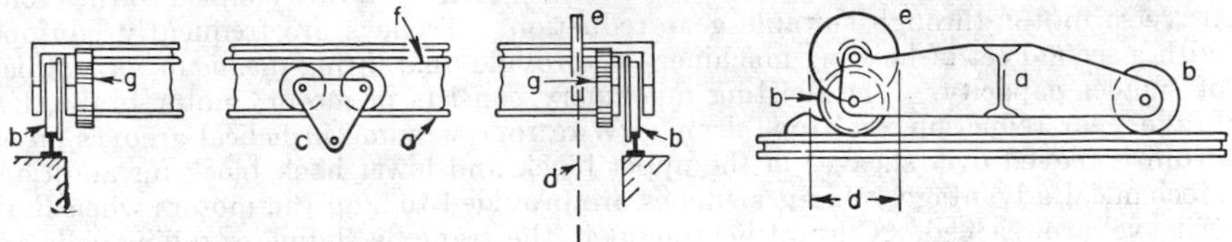

Fig. 12. Hand-powered crane.

chain hoist, forming the lifting unit. The crane is moved by hand chain *d* turning sprocket wheel *e*, which is keyed to shaft *f*. The pinions on shaft *f* mesh with gears *g*, keyed to the axles of two wheels. An underslung construction may also be used, with pairs of wheels at each corner which ride on the lower flange of I-beam rails. Single-girder cranes may be hand-powered by pendant hand chains or electric-powered as controlled by a pendant push-button station.

Electric Traveling Crane, Double-girder Type (Fig. 13). This consists of two bridge girders *a*, on the top of which are rails on which travels the self-contained hoisting unit *b*, called the **trolley.** The girders are supported at the ends by trucks with two or four wheels, according to the size of the crane. The crane is moved along the track by motor *c*, through shaft *d* and gearing to the truck wheels. Suspended from the girders on one side is the operator's cab *e*, containing the controller, or master switches, master hydraulic brake cylinder, warning device, etc. The bridge girders for small cranes are of the I-beam type, but on the longer spans, box girders are used to give torsional and lateral stiffness. The girders are rigidly attached to the truck end framing, which carries the double-flanged wheels for supporting the bridge. The end frames project over the rails so that in case of a broken wheel or axle, the frame will rest on the rail, preventing the crane from dropping. One wheel axle on each truck is fitted with gears for driving the crane or is coupled directly to the shaft which transmits power from the gear reducer. On a cab-operated bridge, a brake, usually hydraulic, is applied to the motor shaft to stop the crane. Floor-operated cranes generally utilize spring-engaged, electrically released brakes.

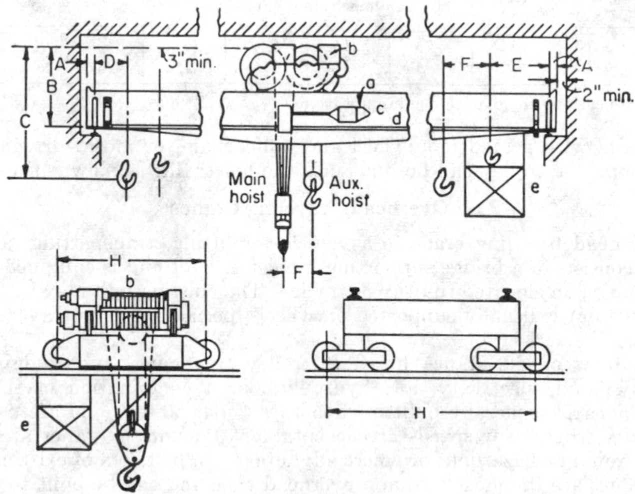

Fig. 13. Electric traveling crane.

The trolley consists of a frame which carries the hoisting machinery and is supported on wheels for movement along the bridge rails. The wheels are coupled to the trolley traverse motor through suitable gear reduction. Trolleys are frequently equipped with a second set of hoisting machinery to provide dual lifting means or an auxiliary of smaller capacity. The hoisting machinery consists of motor, motor brake, load brake, gear reduction, and rope drum. Wire rope winding in helical grooves on the drum is reeved over sheaves in the upper block and lower hook block for additional mechanical advantage. Limit switches are provided to stop the motors when limits of travel are reached. Current is brought to the crane by sliding or rolling collectors in contact with conductors attached to or parallel with the runway and preferably located at the cab end of the crane. Current from the runway conductors and cab is carried to the trolley in a like manner from conductors mounted parallel to the bridge girder.

Electric cranes are built for either alternating or direct current, with the former predominating. The motors for both kinds of current are designed particularly for crane service. Direct-current motors are usually series-wound, and a-c motors are generally of the wound-rotor or two-speed squirrel-cage type. The usual a-c voltages are 220 and 440, the most common being 440. The **capacities** and other dimensions

Table 3. Dimensions, Loads, and Speeds, Industrial-type Cranes
(Manning, Maxwell & Moore, Inc.)

Capacity main hoist, tons	Span, ft	Std lift main hoist, ft[b]	Std hoist speed, fpm	Dimensions refer to Fig. 13							Lb max load per wheel[d]	Runway rail, lb per yd	X, in.
				A	*B*	*C*	*D*	*E*[c]	*F*	*H*			
5	40	50	36	7½″	4′9″	4′2″	2′9″	2′9″	....	8′10″	13,600	60	6
	60	50	36	7½″	4′11″	4′2″	2′9″	2′9″	....	9′8″	17,000	60	6
	80	60	36	8½″	5′1″	4′2″	2′9″	2′9″	....	11′10″	21,000	60	6
	100	70	36	8½″	5′1″	4′2″	2′9″	2′9″	....	14′2″	25,000	60	6
10	40	40	24	7½″	5′1″	5′0″	3′0″	3′0″	....	8′10″	19,000	60	6
	60	40	24	8½″	5′7″	5′0″	3′0″	3′0″	....	9′8″	24,000	60	6
	80	55	24	8½″	5′7″	5′0″	3′0″	3′0″	....	11′10″	28,000	60	6
	100	60	24	8½″	6′0″	5′0″	3′0″	3′0″	....	14′2″	35,000	60	6
15	40	30	16	8½″	5′7″	6′3″	3′0″	3′0″	....	10′0″	25,500	60	12
	60	30	16	8½″	5′7″	6 3″	3′0″	3′0″	....	10′10″	27,500	60	12
	80	40	16	9″	5′11″	6′3″	3′0″	3′0″	....	11′8″	30,000	60	12
	100	40	16	10½″	6′2″	6′3″	3′0 ′	3′0″	....	14′2″	35,000	60	12
20, 5-ton auxiliary	40	40	17	9″	6′5″	7′9″	3′3″	2′9″	2′6″	10′6″	37,000	80	12
	60	45	17	10½″	6′8″	7′9″	3′3″	2′9″	2′6″	11′6″	42,000	80	12
	80	45	17	10½″	6′8″	7′9″	3′3″	2′9″	2′6″	12′4″	47,000	80	12
	100	50	17	10½″	6′8″	7′9″	3′3″	2′9″	2′6″	14′2″	54,000	80	12
30, 5-ton auxiliary	40	45	15	11½″	7′0″	9′9″	3′6″	3′0″	2′6″	11′4″	50,000	100	12
	60	45	15	11½″	7′0″	9′9″	3′6″	3′0″	2′6″	11′8″	54,000	100	12
	80	45	15	11½″	7′2″	9′9″	3′6″	3′0″	2′6″	13′0″	60,000	100	12
	100	45	15	11½″	7′2″	9′9″	3′6″	3′0″	2′6″	14′2″	68,000	100	12
40, 5-ton auxiliary	40	30	12	11½″	7′1″	9′11″	3′6″	3′0″	2′9″	11′4″	63,000	100	18
	60	30	12	11½″	7′1″	9′11″	3′6″	3′0″	2′9″	11′8″	69,000	100	18
	80	30	12	13″	7′5″	9′11″	3′6″	3′0″	2′9″	12′8″	77,000	135	18
	100	30	12	13″	7′5″	9′11″	3′6″	3′0″	2′9″	14′2″	87,000	175	18
50, 10-ton auxiliary	40	30	12	11½″	7′5″	10′3″	4′0″	3′6″	3′7″	13′0″	74,000	135	18
	60	30	12	13″	8′0″	10′3″	4′0″	3′6″	3′7″	13′5″	81,000	175	18
	80	30	12	13″	8′0″	10′3″	4′0″	3′6″	3′7″	13′11″	92,000	175	18
60, 10-ton auxiliary	40	40	12	13″	9′0″	9′0″	5′0″	3′6″	4′7″	14′6″	84,000	175	18
	60	40	12	14″	9′0″	9′0″	5′0″	3′6″	4′7″	14′10″	94,000	175	18
	80[a]	40	12	12″	9′0″	9′0″	5′0″	3′6″	4′7″	13′10″	52,500	100	18

[a] Up to 60-ton capacity, 60-ft span, all cranes have two-wheeled trucks; larger sizes, four-wheeled.
[b] For each 10-ft extra lift, increase *H* by *X*.
[c] Main hook where no auxiliary hoist.
[d] Direct loads, no impact.
For 30-ton and smaller cranes, standard trolley speed is 150 fpm, bridge speed 300 fpm; 40 to 60 ton, 100 and 250 fpm, respectively.
For steel-mill service, a heavier type of crane is generally used.

for standard electric cranes are given in Table 3. These figures should be used for preliminary work only, as the data vary with different manufacturers.

Gantry Cranes

Gantry cranes are modifications of traveling cranes and are generally used out of doors where it is not convenient to erect on overhead runway. The bridge (Fig. 14) is carried at the ends by the legs *a*, supported by trucks with wheels so that the crane can travel. As with the traveling crane, the bridge carries a hoisting unit; a cover to protect the machinery from the weather is often used. The crane is driven by motor *b* through a gear reduction to shaft *c*, which drives the vertical shafts *d* through bevel gears. Bevel- and spur-gear reductions connect the axles of the wheels with shafts *d*. Many gantry cranes are built without the cross shaft, employing separate motors, brakes, and gear reducers at each end of the crane. Gantry cranes are made in the same sizes as standard traveling cranes.

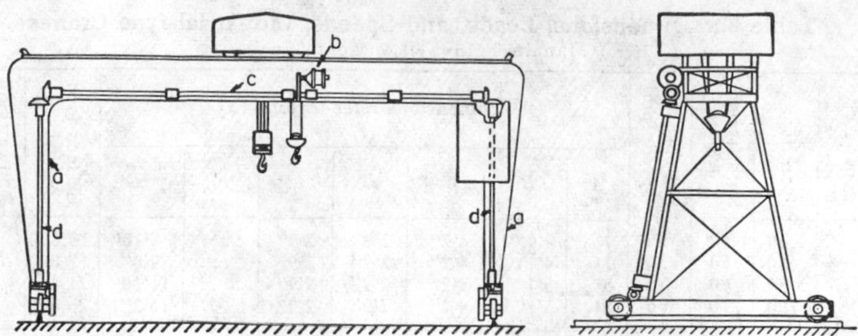

FIG. 14. Gantry crane.

Special-purpose Overhead Traveling Cranes

A wide variety can be built to meet special conditions or handling requirements; examples are stacker cranes to move material into and out of racks, wall cranes using a runway on only one side of a building, circular running or pivoting cranes, and semi-gantries. Load-weighing arrangements can be incorporated, as well as special load-handling devices such as lifting beams, grapples, buckets, forks, and vacuum grips.

Rotary Cranes and Derricks

Rotary cranes are used for lifting material and moving it to points covered by a boom pivoted to a fixed or movable structure. **Derricks** are used out of doors (e.g., in quarries and for construction work), being built so that they can be easily moved. Pillar cranes are always fixed and are used for light, infrequent service. Jib cranes are used in manufacturing plants. Locomotive cranes mounted on car wheels are used to handle loads by hook or bulk material by means of tubs, grab buckets, or magnets. Wrecking cranes are of the same general type as locomotive cranes and are used for handling heavy loads on railroads.

Derricks are made with either wood or steel masts and booms, are of the guyed or stiff-leg type, and are either hand-slewed or power-swung with a bull wheel. Figure 15 shows a guyed wooden derrick of the bull-wheel type. The mast a is carried at the

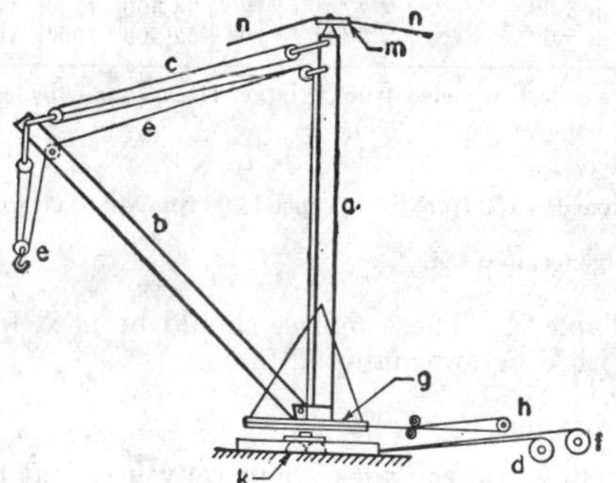

FIG. 15. Guyed wooden derrick.

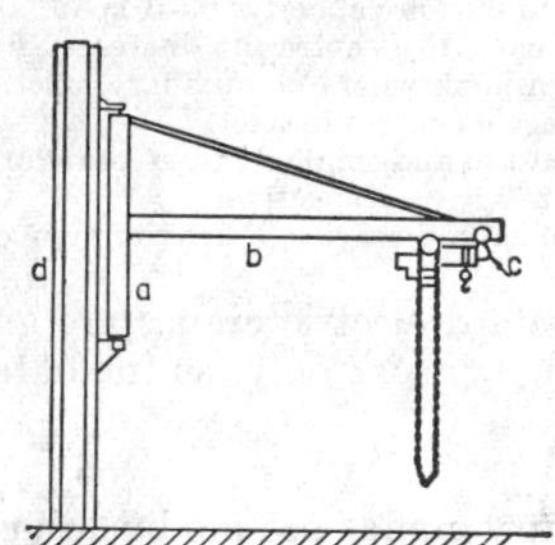

FIG. 16. Column jib crane.

foot by pivot k and at the top by pivot m, held by rope guys n. The boom b is pivoted at the lower end of the mast. The rope c, passing over sheaves at the top of the mast and at the end of the boom and through the pivot k, is made fast to drum d and varies the angle of the boom. The hoisting rope e, from which the load is suspended, is made fast to drum f. The bull wheel g is attached to the mast and swings the derrick by a rope made fast to the bull wheel and passing around the reversible drum h. In derricks of the self-slewing type, the engine is mounted on a platform attached to the mast and the derrick is swung by a pinion meshing with a gear attached to the foundation. Either the bull-wheel or the self-slewing type may be made of steel or wood construction and may be of the guyed or stiff-leg type. Figure 16 shows a **column jib crane,** consisting of pivoted post *a* and carrying boom *b*, on which travels either an electric or a hand hoist *c*. The post *a* is attached to building column *d* so that it can swing through approximately 270 deg. Cranes of this type are rapidly being replaced by such other methods of handling materials as the mobile lift truck (p. 10–42) or the automotive-type crane (p. 10–48). Column jib cranes are built with radii up to 20 ft and for loads up to 5 tons. Yard jib cranes are generally designed to meet special conditions.

Locomotive Cranes

The locomotive crane (Fig. 17) is self-propelled and provided with trucks, brakes, automatic couplers, fittings, and clearances which will permit it to be used or hauled in a train; it can function as a complete unit on any railroad. Locomotive cranes are of the rotating-deck type, consisting of a hinged boom attached to the machinery deck, which is turntable mounted and operated either by mechanical rotating clutches or by a separate electric swing motor. The boom is operated by powered topping line, with a direct-geared hoisting mechanism to raise and lower it. Power to operate the machinery is deck-mounted, and the machinery deck is completely housed. The crane may be powered by internal-combustion engine or electric motor. Steam engines were used in the past, but no one uses steam today. The combination of internal-combustion engine, generator, and electric motor make up the power arrangement for the Diesel-electric locomotive crane, which is the most popular today. The car body and machinery deck are ballasted, thereby adding stability to the crane when it is rotated under load. The basic boom is generally 50 ft in length (see Table 4); however, booms range to 130 ft in length. Locomotive cranes are so designed that power-shovel, pile-driver, hook, bucket, or magnet attachments can be installed and the crane used in such service. Locomotive cranes are used most extensively in railroad work, steel mills, and scrap yards. The cranes usually have sufficient propelling power not only for the crane itself, but also for switching service and hauling cars.

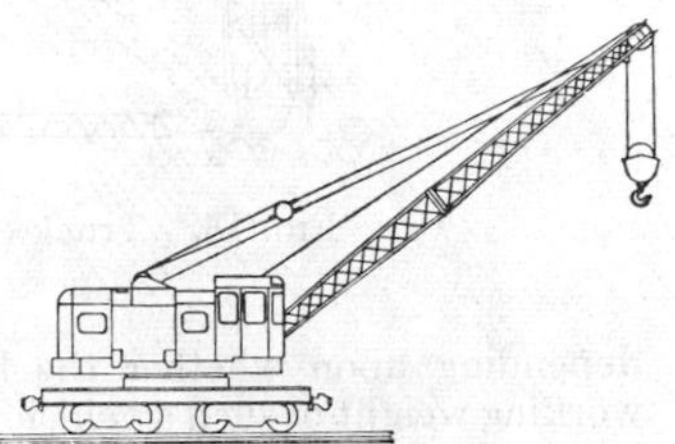

FIG. 17. Locomotive crane. (*American Hoist and Derrick.*)

Table 4. Data on Locomotive Cranes
(American Hoist & Derrick Co.)

Size, tons	Number of wheels	Min working radius, 50-ft boom			Max working radius, 50-ft boom			Approx working wt, lb	Wheelbase	Max on any wheel, lb
		Radius A, ft	Free capacity, lb	Outrigger capacity, lb	Radius A, ft	Free capacity, lb	Outrigger capacity, lb			
25	8	12	50,000	50,000	50	8,200	9,600	132,000	18′10″	44,250
30	8	12	60,000	60,000	50	9,800	11,500	156,000	18′10″	53,500
40	8	12	80,000	100,000	50	13,600	20,000	216,000	19′ 8″	70,000
50–60	8	12	100,000	120,000	50	16,100	24,000	261,000	21′ 8″	87,100
50–80	8	12	100,000	160,000	50	16,100	32,000	261,000	21′ 8″	87,100
60–110	8	20	65,000	136,000	50	20,700	43,000	312,500	21′ 8″	88,500

Truck Cranes

The advent of the truck crane shown in Figs. 18 and 19 has changed significantly the methods of lifting and placing heavy items such as concrete buckets, logs, pipe, and bridge or building members. Truck cranes can without assistance, be rapidly equipped with accessory booms to reach to 153 ft vertically—or 140 ft vertically with 69 ft of horizontal reach. Loads can be lifted to 45 tons at short-boom radius, with the size of load decreasing as the radius increases. The size and eccentricity of the allowed load are reduced by a factor of about 2 to 5 if outriggers are not used,

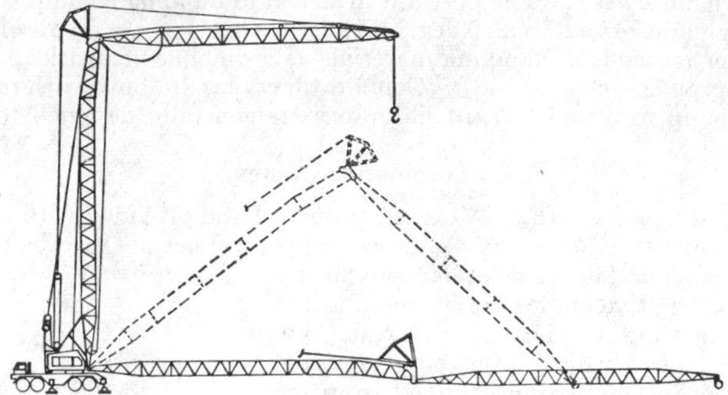

Fig. 18. Truck crane, showing self-erection. (*Link-Belt.*)

depending upon whether the boom points rearward or sideward (Table 5). The working weight of such a vehicle is upwards of 70,000 lb. The truck chassis is equipped with four driven wheels and either two or four additional supporting wheels, of which six wheels are hydraulically braked Twelve forward and three reverse speeds are provided for road speeds up to 36.7 mph. When the crane is in transit, counterweights and boom are conveyed on an accessory trailer to meet highway load requirements.

Table 5. Capacities of Truck-mounted Cranes (Fig. 18)
(Link-Belt Zephyrcrane)

Radius, ft	Angle, deg	Boom-point height, W	Lifting capacity, lb: With out-riggers, side or rear	Lifting capacity, lb: On tires, Side	Lifting capacity, lb: On tires, Rear	Angle, deg	Boom-point height, W	Lifting capacity, lb: Without out-riggers, side or rear	Lifting capacity, lb: On tires, Side	Lifting capacity, lb: On tires, Rear
	40-ft boom					60-ft boom				
10	80	46′1″	70,000	36,910	62,770					
12	77	45′8″	70,000	31,610	48,420					
15	73	44′10″	57,000	23,610	35,870	79	65′6″	56,060	22,990	35,270
20	65	43′0″	43,400	16,250	24,790	74	64′3″	42,460	15,640	24,190
30	48	36′4″	27,200	9,640	14,950	64	60′4″	26,460	9,030	14,350
40	23	22′4″	19,880	6,570	10,420	52	54′1″	19,390	5,970	9,830
50						39	44′4″	14,140	4,200	7,230
60						19	25′11″	10,930	3,050	5,540
	80-ft boom					100-ft boom				
20	78	84′11″	41,880	15,030	23,590	80	105′3″	41,120	14,200	22,990
30	70	82′0″	25,720	8,430	13,750	74	103′0″	24,980	7,820	13,150
40	63	77′8″	18,900	5,370	9,230	68	99′8″	18,400	4,770	8,630
50	54	71′7″	13,620	3,600	6,630	62	95′0″	13,110	3,000	6,030
60	45	63′0″	10,400	2,450	4,950	55	88′11″	9,870	1,850	4,350
70	33	50′8″	8,220	1,640	3,760	48	81′1″	7,680	1,050	3,170
80	16	29′1″	6,600	1,050	2,890	40	70′8″	6,110	450	2,290
90						30	56′3″	4,920		1,620
100						15	31′8″	3,990		1,080

Equipment such as this comes under Commercial Standard specification CS90-58, "Power Cranes and Shovels." Similar equipment, called **utility cranes,** without the highway-truck-type cabs, are also available.

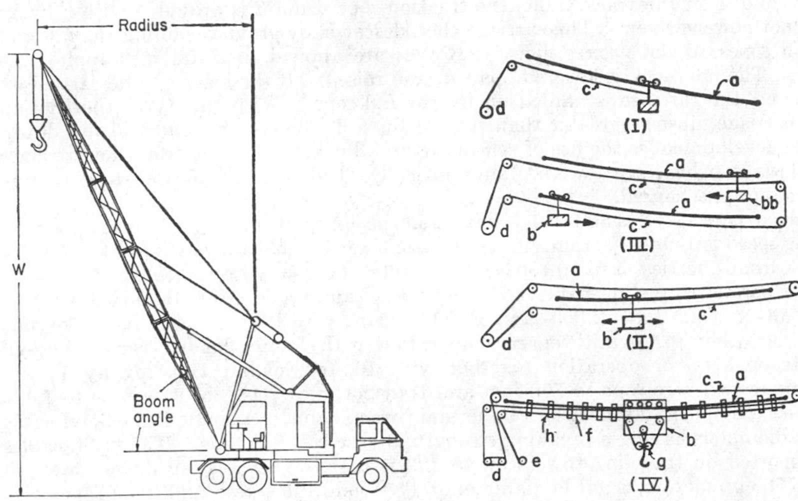

Fig. 19. Truck crane.

Fig. 20. Cableways.

Cableways

Cableways are **aerial hoisting and conveying devices** using suspended steel cable for track (see p. 10–11), the loads being suspended from carriages and moved by gravity or power. The most common uses are transporting material from open pits and quarries to the surface; handling construction material in the building of dams, docks, and other structures where the construction of tracks across rivers or valleys would be uneconomical; loading logs on cars; and coaling vessels at sea. The maximum clear *span* is 2,000 to 3,000 ft; the usual spans, 300 to 1,500 ft. The gravity type is limited to conditions where a grade of at least 20 percent is obtainable on the track cable. Transporting cableways move the load from one point to another. Hoisting transporting cableways hoist the load as well as transport it.

A **transporting cableway** may have one or two fixed track cables, inclined or horizontal, on which the carriage operates by gravity or power. The gravity transporting type (Fig. 20-I) will either raise or lower material. It consists of one track cable *a* on which travels the wheeled carriage *b* carrying the bucket. The traction rope *c* attached to the carriage is made fast to power drum *d*. The inclination must be sufficient for the carriage to coast down and pull the traction rope after it. The carriage is hauled up by traction rope *c*. Drum *d* is provided with a brake to control the lowering speed, and material may be either raised or lowered. When it is not possible to obtain sufficient fall to operate the load by gravity, traction rope *c* (Fig. 20-II) is made endless so that carriage *b* is drawn in either direction by power drum *d*. Another type of inclined cableway, shown in Fig. 20-III, consists of two track cables *aa*, with an endless traction rope *c*, driven and controlled by drum *d*. When material is being lowered, the loaded bucket *b* raises the empty carriage *bb*, the speed being controlled by the brake on the drum. When material is being raised, the drum is driven by power, the descending empty carriage assisting the engine in raising the loaded carriage. This type has twice the capacity of that shown in Fig. 20-I.

A **hoisting and conveying cableway** (Fig. 20-IV) hoists the material at any point under the track cable and transports it to any other point. It consists of a track cable *a* and carriage *b*, moved by the endless traction rope *c* and by power drum *d*.

The hoisting of the load is accomplished by power drum *e* through fall rope *f*, which raises the fall block *g* suspended from the carriage. The fall-rope carriers *h* support the fall rope; otherwise, the weight of this sagging rope would prevent fall block *g* from lowering when without load. Where it is possible to obtain a minimum inclination of 20 deg on the track cable, the traction-rope drum *d* is provided with a brake and is not power-driven. The carriage then descends by gravity, pulling the fall and traction ropes to the desired point. Brakes are applied to drum *d*, stopping the carrier. The fall block is lowered, loaded, and raised. If the load is to be carried up the incline, the carriage is hauled up by the fall rope. With this type, the friction of the carriage must be greater than that of the fall block or the load will run down. A novel development is the use of self-filling grab buckets operated from the carriages of cableways, which are lowered, automatically filled, hoisted, carried to dumping position, and discharged.

The **carriage speed** is 300 to 1,400 fpm (in special cases, up to 1,800 fpm); average hoisting speed is 100 to 700 fpm. The **average loads** for coal and earth are 1 to 5 tons; for rock from quarries, 5 to 20 tons; for concrete, to 12 cu yd at 50 tons.

Two parallel traveling cableways (built by Lidgerwood Manufacturing Co.) at Glen Canyon Dam have 2,050- and 1,800-ft spans with 910- and 810-ft tracks, one above the other to permit separate operation with 50-ton loads (using 12-cu-yd concrete buckets) or operation together with 100-ton loads. Hoisting by 1⅛-in. four-part-reeved wire rope to 700 fpm and transporting by 1½-in. wire rope to 1,400 fpm can be done simultaneously. The main track cable is a single locked-coil cable 4 in. in diameter, having a breaking strength in excess of 880 tons. The track cables are supported on traveling towers up to 189 ft high. The hoisting drum, powered by dual 500-hp motors, is 9 ft in diameter and 8 ft long and stores 2,200 ft of rope, with hoist action four-part-reeved (see Fig. 20-IV).

The **deflection of track cables** with their maximum gross loads at midspan is usually taken as 5½ to 6 percent of the span. Let S = span between supports, ft; L = one-half the span, ft; w = weight of rope, lb per ft; P = total concentrated load on rope, lb; h = deflection, ft; H = horizontal tension in rope, lb. Then $h = (wL + P)L/2H$; $P = (2h - wL^2)/L = (8hH - wS^2)/2S$.

For track cables, a **factor of safety** of at least 4 is advised, though this may be as low as 3 for locked smooth-coil strands that use outer wires of high ultimate strength. For traction and fall ropes, the sum of the load and bending stress should be well within the elastic limit of the rope or, for general hoisting, about two-thirds the elastic limit (which is taken at 65 percent of the breaking strength). Let P = load on the rope, lb; A = area of metal in rope section, sq in.; E = 29,500,000; R = radius of curvature of hoisting drum or sheave, whichever is smaller, in.; d = diameter of individual wires in rope, in. (for six-strand 19-wire rope, $d = 1/15$ rope diam; for six-strand 7-wire rope, $d = 1/9$ rope diam). Then load stress per sq in. = $T_1 = P/A$, and bending stress per sq in. = $T_b = Ed/2R$. The radius of curvature of saddles, sheaves, and driving drums is thus important to fatigue life of the cable (see p. 8–117). In determining the horsepower required, the load on the traction ropes or on the fall ropes will govern, depending upon the degree of inclination.

Cable Tramways

Cable tramways are aerial conveying devices using suspended cables, carriages, and buckets for transporting material over level or mountainous country or across rivers, valleys, or hills (they transport but do not hoist). They are used for handling small quantities over long distances, and their construction cost is insignificant compared with the construction costs of railroads and bridges. Five types are in use:

Monocable, or Single-rope, Saddle-clip Tramway. Operates on grades to 50 percent gravity grip or on higher grades with spring grip and has capacity of 250 tons per hr in each direction and speeds to 500 fpm. Single section lengths to 16 miles without intermediate stations or tension points. Can operate in multiple sections without transshipment to any desired length (monocables to 170 miles over jungle terrain are practical). Construction costs from $15,000 per mile. Loads automatically leave the carrying moving rope and travel by overhead rail at angle stations and transfer points between sections with no detaching or attaching device required. Main rope constantly passes through stations for inspection and oiling. Cars are light and safe for passenger transportation.

Single-rope Fixed-clip Tramway. Endless rope traveling at low speed, having buckets or carriers fixed to the rope at intervals. Rope passes around horizontal sheaves at each terminal and is provided with a driving gear and constant-tension device. Cost from $11,000 per mile.

Bicable, or Double-rope, Tramway. Standing track cable and a moving endless hauling or traction rope traveling up to 500 fpm. Used on excessively steep grades. A detacher and attacher is required to open and close the car grip on the traction rope at stations. Track cable is usually in sections of 6,000 to 7,000 ft and counterweighted because of friction of stiff cable over tower saddles.

Jigback, or Two-bucket, Reversing Tramway. Usually applied to hillside operations for mine workings so that on steep slopes loaded bucket will pull unloaded one up as loaded one descends under control of a brake. Loads to 10 tons are carried using a pair of track cables and an endless traction rope fixed to the buckets.

To-and-Fro, or Single-bucket, Reversing Tramway. A single track rope and a single traction rope operated on a winding or hoist drum. Suitable for light loads to 3 tons for intermittent working on a hillside, similar to a hoisting and conveying cableway without the hoisting feature.

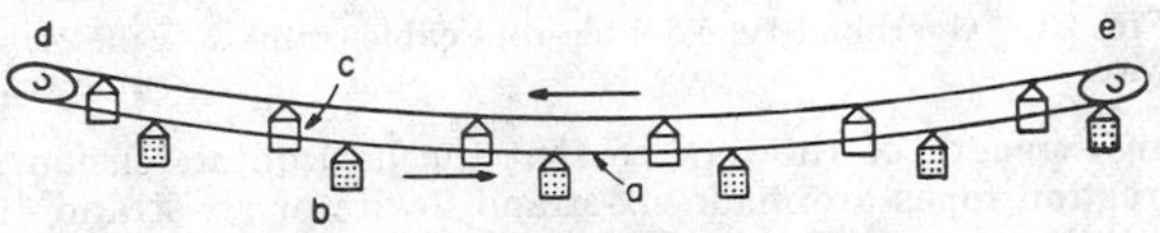

Fig. 21. Single-rope cable tramway.

The **monocable tramway** (Fig. 21) consists of an endless cable *a* passing over horizontal sheaves *d* and *e* at the ends and supported at intervals by towers. This cable is moved continuously, and it both supports and propels carriages *b* and *c*. The carriages either are attached permanently to the cable (as in the **single-rope fixed-clip tramway**), in which case they must be loaded and dumped while in motion, or are attached by friction grips so that they may be connected automatically or by hand at the loading and dumping points. When the tramway is lowering material from a higher to a lower level, the grade is frequently sufficient for the loaded buckets *b* to raise the empty buckets *c*, operating the tramway by gravity, the speed being controlled by a brake on grip wheel *d*.

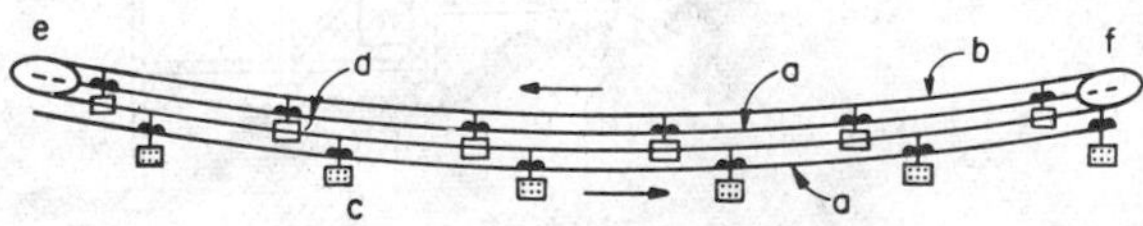

Fig. 22. Double-rope cable tramway.

The **bicable tramway** (Fig. 22) consists of two stationary track cables *a*, on which the wheeled carriages *c* and *d* travel. The endless traction rope *b* propels the carriages, being attached by friction grips. Figure 23 shows the arrangement of the **overhead type.** The track cable *a* is supported at intervals by towers *b*, which carry the saddles *c* in which the track cable rests. Each tower also carries the sheave *d* for supporting traction rope *e*. The self-dumping bucket *f* is suspended from carriage *g*. The grip *h*, which attaches the carriage to traction rope *e*, is controlled by lever *k*. In the **underhung type,** shown in Fig. 24, track cable *a* is carried above traction rope *e*. Saddle *c* on top of the tower supports the track cable, and sheave *d* supports the traction cable. The sheave is provided with a rope guard *m*. The lever *h*, with a roller on the end, automatically attaches and detaches the grip by coming in contact with guides at the loading and dumping points. The carriages move in only one direction on each track. On steep downgrades, special hydraulic speed controllers are used to fix the speed of the carriages.

The **track cables** are of the special locked-joint smooth-coil, or tramway, type. Nearly all wire rope is made of plow steel, and the old cast-steel type is no longer used (see p. 10–11). The track cable is usually provided with a smooth outer surface of

Z-shaped wires for full lock type or with a surface with half the wires *H*-shaped and the rest round. Special tramway couplers are attached in the shops with zinc or are attached in the field by driving little wedges into the strand end after inserting the end into the coupler. The second type of coupling is known as a **dry socket** and, though convenient for field installation, is not held in as high regard for developing full cable strength. The usual spans for level ground are 200 to 300 ft. One end of the track cable is anchored; the other end is counterweighted to one-quarter the break-

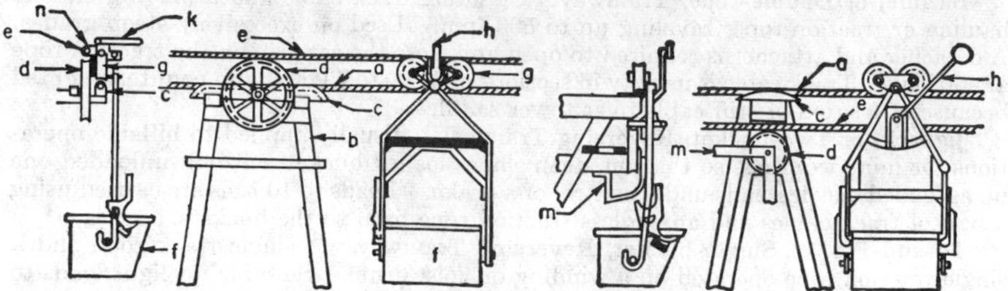

FIG. 23. Overhead-type double-rope cable tramway.

FIG. 24. Underhung-type double-rope cable tramway.

ing strength of the rope so that the horizontal tension is a known quantity. The **traction ropes** are made six-strand 7-wire or six-strand 19-wire, of cast or plow steel on hemp core. The maximum diameter is 1 in., which limits the length of the sections. The traction rope is endless and is driven by a drum at one end, passing over a counterweighted sheave at the other end.

Figure 25 shows a **loading terminal.** The track cables *a* are anchored at *b*. The carriage runs off the cable to the fixed track *c*, which makes a 180-deg bend at *d*.

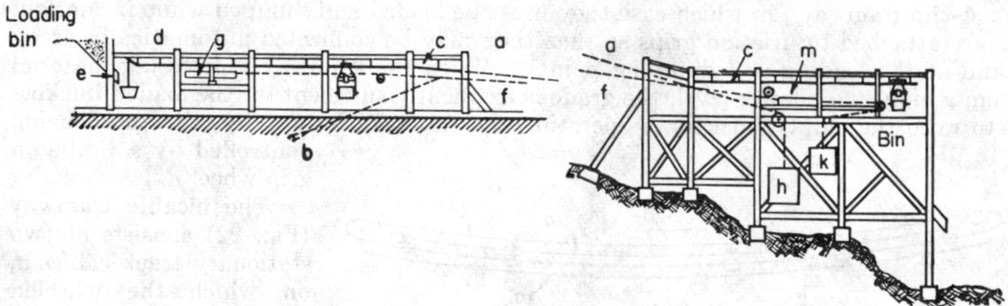

FIG. 25. Cable-tramway loading terminal.

FIG. 26. Cable-tramway discharge terminal.

The empty buckets are loaded by chute *e* from the loading bin, continue around track *c*, are automatically gripped to traction cable *f*, and pass on the track cable *a*. Traction cable *f* passes around and is driven by drum *g*. When the carriages are permanently attached to the traction cable, they are loaded by a moving hopper, which is automatically picked up by the carriage and carried with it a short distance while the bucket is being filled. Figure 26 shows a **discharge terminal.** The carriage rolls off from the track cable *a* to the fixed track *c*, being automatically ungripped. It is pushed around the 180-deg bend of track *c*, discharging into the bin underneath and continuing on track *c* until it is automatically gripped to traction cable *f*. The counterweights *h* are attached to track cables *a*, and the counterweight *k* is attached to the carriage of the traction-rope sheave *m*. The **supporting towers** are A frames of steel or wood. At abrupt vertical angles, the supports are placed close together and steel tracks installed in place of the cable. Spacing of towers will depend upon the capacity of the track cables and sheaves and upon the terrain as well as the bucket spacing.

Stress in Ropes (Roebling). The deflection for track cables of tramways is taken as one-fortieth to one-fiftieth of the span to reduce the grade at the towers. Let S = span between supports, ft; h = deflection, ft; P = gross weight of buckets and carriages, lb; Z = distance between buckets, ft; W_1 = total load per ft of rope, lb; H = horizontal tension of rope, lb. The formulas given for cableways (p. 10–44) then apply When several buckets come in the span at the same time, special treatment is required for each span. For large capacities, the buckets are spaced close together, the load may be assumed to be uniformly distributed, and the live load per linear foot of span $= P/Z$. Then $H = W_1S^2/8h$, where W_1 = (weight of rope per ft) + (P/Z). When the buckets are not spaced closely, the equilibrium curve can be plotted with known horizontal tension and vertical reactions at points of support.

For figuring the traction rope, t_0 = tension on counterweight rope, lb; t_1, t_2, t_3, t_4 = tensions, lb, at points shown in Fig. 27; n = number of carriers in motion; a = angle subtended between the line connecting the tower supports and the horizontal; W_1 = weight of each loaded carrier, lb; W_2 = weight of each empty carrier, lb; w = weight of traction rope, lb per ft; L = length of tramway of each grade a, ft; D = diameter of end sheave, ft; d = diameter of shaft of sheave, ft; f_1 = 0.015 = coefficient of friction of shaft; f_2 = 0.025 = rolling friction of carriage wheels. Then, if the loads descend, the maximum stress on the loaded side of the traction rope is

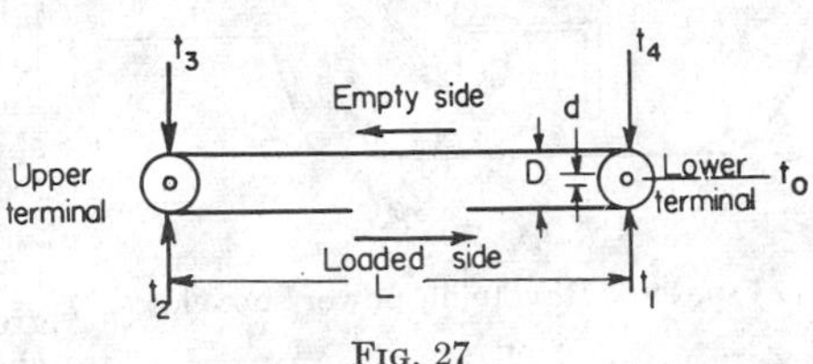

Fig. 27

$$t_2 = t_1 + \Sigma(Lw \sin a + \tfrac{1}{2}nW_1 \sin a) - f_2\Sigma(Lw \cos a + \tfrac{1}{2}nW_1 \cos a)$$

where $t_1 = \tfrac{1}{2}t_0[1 - f_1(d/D)]$. If the load ascends, there are two cases: (1) driving power located at the lower terminal, (2) driving power at the upper terminal. If the line has no reverse grades, it will operate by gravity at a 10 percent incline to 10 tons per hr capacity and at a 4 percent grade for 80 tons per hr. The preceding formula will determine whether it will operate by gravity.

The **power required** or developed by tramways is as follows: Let V = velocity of traction rope, fpm; P = gross weight of loaded carriage, lb; p = weight of empty carriage, lb; N = number of carriages on one track cable; $P/50$ = friction of loaded carriage; $p/50$ = friction of empty carriage; W = weight of moving parts lb; E = length of tramway divided by difference in levels between terminals, ft. Then, power required is

$$\text{Hp} = \frac{NV}{33{,}000}\left(\frac{P-p}{E} \pm \frac{P+p}{50}\right) \pm 0.0000001WV$$

Where power is developed by tramways, use 80 instead of 50 under $P + p$.

BELOW-SURFACE HANDLING (EXCAVATION)

Power Shovels

Power shovels stand upon the bottom of the pit being dug and dig above this level. Small machines are used for road grading, basement excavation, clay mining, and trench digging; larger sizes are used in quarries, mines, and heavy construction; and the largest are used for removing overburden in opencut mining of coal and ore. The uses for these machines may be divided into two groups: (1) **loading,** where sturdy machines with comparatively short working ranges are used to excavate material and load it for transportation; (2) **stripping,** where a machine of very great dumping and digging reaches is used to both excavate the material and transport it to the dump or wastepile. The **full-revolving shovel,** which is the only type built at the present (having entirely displaced the old railroad shovel), is usually composed of a crawler-mounted truck frame with a center pintle and roller track upon which the revolving frame can rotate. The revolving frame carries the swing and hoisting machinery and supports, by means of a socket at the lower end and cable guys at the upper end, a boom carrying guides for the dipper handles and machinery to thrust the dipper into the material being dug.

Figure 28 shows a full-revolving shovel. The dipper *a*, of cast or plate steel, is provided with special wear-resisting teeth. It is pulled through the material by a steel cable *b* wrapped on a main drum *c*. Gasoline engines are used almost exclusively in the small sizes, and Diesel, Diesel-electric, or electric power units, with Ward Leonard control, in the large machines. The commonly used sizes are from ½- to 5-yd capacity, but special machines for coal-mine stripping are built with buckets holding up to 33 yd or even more. The very large machines are not suited for quarry or heavy rock work. Sizes up to 5 yd are known as **quarry machines.** Stripping shovels are crawler-mounted, with double-tread crawlers under each of the four corners and with power means for keeping the turntable level when traveling over uneven ground. The crowd motion consists of a chain which, through the rack-and-pinion mechanism, forces the dipper into the material as the dipper is hoisted and withdraws it on its downward swing. On the larger sizes, a separate engine or motor is mounted on the boom for crowding. A separate engine working through a pinion and horizontal gear *g* swings the entire frame and machinery to bring the dipper into position for dumping and to return it to a new digging position. Dumping is accomplished by releasing the hinged dipper bottom, which drops upon the pulling of a latch. With gasoline-engine or Diesel-engine drives, there is only one prime mover, the power for all operations being taken off by means of clutches.

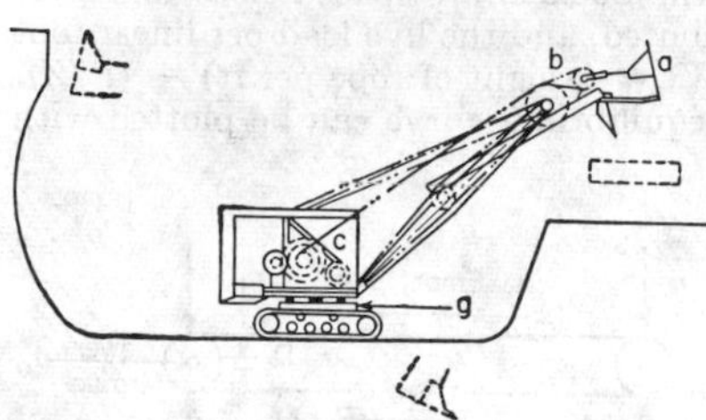

FIG. 28. Revolving power shovel.

Practically all **power shovels** are readily **converted** for operation **as dragline excavators, or cranes.** The changes necessary are very simple in the case of the small machines; in the case of the larger machines, the installation of extra drums, shafts, and gears is required, in addition to the boom and bucket change.

The **telescoping-boom,** hydraulically operated excavator shown in Fig. 29 is a versatile machine that can be quickly converted from the rotating-boom power shovel shown in Fig. 29*a* to one with a crane boom (Fig. 29*b*) or backhoe shovel boom (Fig. 29*c*). It can dig ditches reaching to 22 ft horizontally and 9 ft 6 in. below grade; it can cut slopes, rip, scrape, dig to a depth of 12 ft 6 in., and load to a height of 11 ft 2 in. It is completely hydraulic in all powerized functions.

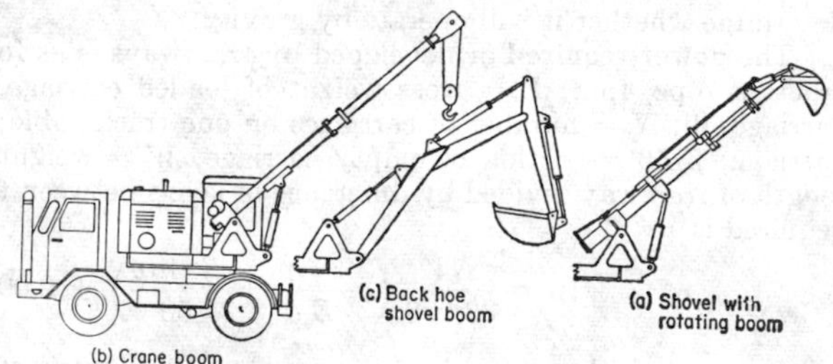

FIG. 29. Hydraulically operated excavator. (*Link-Belt.*)

Dredges

Placer dredges are used for the mining of gold, platinum, and tin from placer deposits. The usual maximum digging depth of most existing dredges is 65 to 70 ft, but one dredge is digging to 125 ft. The dredge usually works with a bank above the water of 8 to 20 ft. Sometimes hydraulic giants are employed to break down these banks ahead of the dredge. The excavated material is deposited astern, and as the dredge advances, the pond in which the dredge floats is carried along with it.

The digging element consists of a chain of closely connected buckets passing over an idler tumbler and an upper or driving tumbler. The chain is mounted on a structural-steel ladder which carries a series of rollers to provide a bearing track for the chain of buckets. The upper tumbler is placed 10 to 40 ft above the deck, depending upon the size of the dredge. Its fore-and-aft location is about 65 percent of the length of the ladder from the bow of the dredge. The ladder operates through a well in the hull, which extends from the bow practically to the upper-tumbler center. The material excavated by the buckets is dumped by the inversion of the buckets at the upper tumbler into a hopper, which feeds it to a revolving screen.

Placer dredges are made with buckets ranging in capacity from 2 to 20 cu ft. The usual speed of operation is 15 to 30 buckets per min, in the inverse order of size.

The digging reaction is taken by stern spuds, which act as pivots upon which the dredge, while digging, is swung from side to side of the cut by swinging lines which lead off the dredge near the bow and are anchored ashore or pass over shore sheaves and are dead-ended near the lower tumbler on the digging ladder. By using each spud alternately as a pivot, the dredge is fed forward into the bank. Table 6 gives average capacities for placer dredges of various sizes working under normal conditions 24 hr per day.

Table 6. Capacities of Placer Dredges

Size of buckets, cu ft	2	4	6	8
Capacity, thousands of cu yd per month	34	70	106	148
Size of buckets, cu ft	10	13	16	20
Capacity, thousands of cu yd per month	186	248	312	395

Elevator dredges, of which dredges are a special classification, are used principally for the excavation of sand and gravel beds from rivers, lakes, or ocean deposits. Since this type of dredge is not as a rule required to cut its own flotation, the bow corners of the hull may be made square and the digging ladder need not extend beyond the bow. The bucket chain may be of the close-connected placer-dredge type or of the open-connected type with one or more links between the buckets. The dredge is more of an elevator than a digging type, and for this reason the buckets may be flatter across the front and much lighter than the placer-dredge bucket.

The excavated material is usually fed to one or more revolving screens for classification and grading to the various commercial sizes of sand and gravel. Sometimes it is delivered to sumps or settling tanks in the hull, where the silt or mud is washed off by an overflow. Secondary elevators raise the material to a sufficient height to spout it by gravity or to load it by belt conveyors to the scows.

Hydraulic dredges are used most extensively in river and harbor work, where extremely heavy digging is not encountered and spoil areas are available within a reasonable radius of the dredge. This radius may vary from a few hundred feet to a mile or more, and with the aid of booster pumps in the pipeline, hydraulic dredges have pumped material through distances in excess of 2 miles, at the same time elevating it more than 100 ft. This type of dredge is also used for sand-and-gravel–plant operations and for land-reclamation work. Levees and dams can be built with hydraulic dredges. The usual maximum digging depth is about 50 ft. Hydraulic dredges are reclaiming copper stamp-mill tailings from a depth of 115 ft below the water, and a depth of 165 ft has been reached in a land reclamation job.

The usual type of hydraulic dredge has a **digging ladder** suspended from the bow at an angle of 45 deg for the maximum digging depth. This ladder carries the suction pipe and cutter, with its driving machinery, and the swinging-line sheaves. The cutter head may have applied to it 25 to 1,000 hp. The 20-in. dredge, which is the standard, general-purpose machine, has a cutter drive of about 300 hp. The usual operating speed of the cutter is 5 to 20 rpm.

The material excavated by the cutter enters the mouth of the suction pipe, which is located within and at the lower side of the cutter head. The material is sucked up by a centrifugal pump, which discharges it to the dump through a pipeline. The shore discharge pipe is usually of the telescopic type, made of No. 10 to 3⁄10-in. plates in lengths of 16 ft so that it can be readily handled by the shore crew. Floating pipelines are usually made of plates from 1⁄4 to 1⁄2 in. thick and in lengths of 40 to 100 ft, which are floated on pontoons and connected together through rubber sleeves or, preferably, ball joints. The floating discharge line is flexibly connected to the hull in order to permit the dredge to swing back and forth across the cut while working without disturbing the pipeline.

Pump efficiency is usually sacrificed to make an economical unit for the handling of material, which may run from 2 to 25 percent of the total volume of the mixture pumped. Most designs have generous clearances and will permit the passage of stone which is 70 percent of the pipeline diameter. The pump efficiencies vary widely but in general may run from 50 to 70 percent.

Commercial dredges vary in size and discharge-pipe diameters from 12 to 30 in. Smaller or larger dredges are usually special-purpose machines. A number of 36-in. dredges are used to maintain the channel of the Mississippi River. The power applied to pumps varies from 100 to 3,000 hp. The modern 20-in. commercial dredge has about 1,350 bhp applied to the pump.

Diesel dredges are built for direct-connected or electric drives, and modern steam dredges have direct-turbine or turboelectric drives. The steam-turbine and the d-c electric motor have the advantage that they are capable of developing full rating at reduced speeds.

The **hydraulic-dredge** installation (1938) used in the construction of the Fort Peck dam had four duplicate units. At maximum service, each unit (dredge, floating booster, and land booster), with five pumps in series, delivered 750,000 cu yd of fill per month against a lift of 240 ft and through 17,000 ft of 28-in. discharge line. The suction line between the cutter head and the first pump was 33 in. in diameter. The cutter head, 7 ft in diameter by 6 ft long, was carried by a 75-ft ladder. (*Eng. News-Rec.*, Dec. 12, 1935.)

Within its scope, the hydraulic dredge can work more economically than any other excavating machine or combination of machines.

Dragline Excavators

Dragline excavators are typically used for digging open cuts, drainage ditches, canals, sand, and gravel pits, where the material is to be moved 20 to 1,000 ft before dumping. They cannot handle rock unless the rock is blasted. Since they are provided with long booms and mounted on turntables, permitting them to swing through a full circle, these excavators can deposit material directly on the spoil bank farther from the point of excavation than any other type of machine. Whereas a shovel stands below the level of the material it is digging, a dragline excavator stands above and can be used to excavate material under water.

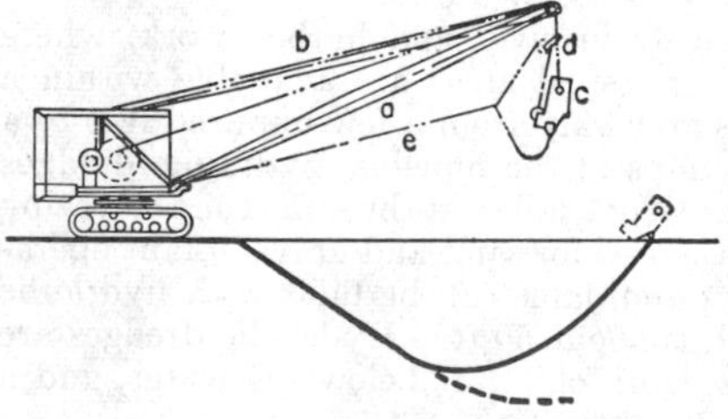

FIG. 30. Dragline excavator.

Figure 30 shows a self-contained dragline mounted on crawler treads. The drive is almost exclusively gasoline in the small sizes and Diesel, Diesel-electric, or electric, frequently with Ward Leonard control, in the large sizes. The boom *a* is pivoted at its lower end to the turntable, the outer end being supported by cables *b* so that it can be raised or lowered to the desired angle. The scraper bucket *c* is supported by cable *d*, which is attached to a bail on the bucket, passes over a sheave at the head of the boom, and is made fast to the engine. A second cable *e* is attached to the front of the bucket and made fast to the second drum of the engine. The bucket is dropped and dragged along the surface of the material by cable *e* until filled. It is then hoisted by cable *d*, drawn back to its dumping position, *e* being kept tight until the dumping point is reached, when *e* is slacked, allowing the bucket to dump by gravity. After the bucket is filled, the boom is swung to the dumping position while the bucket is being hauled out. A good operator can throw the bucket 10 to 40 ft beyond the end of the boom, depending on the size of machine and the working conditions. The depth of the cut varies from 12 to 75 ft, again depending on the size of machine and the working conditions. With the smaller machines and under favorable conditions, two or even three trips per minute are possible; but with the largest machines, even one trip per minute may not be attained. The more common sizes are for handling ¾- to 4-yd buckets with boom lengths up to 100 or 125 ft, but machines have been built to handle an 8-yd bucket with a boom length of 200 ft (the same machine can handle a 12-yd bucket with the boom shortened to 165 ft).

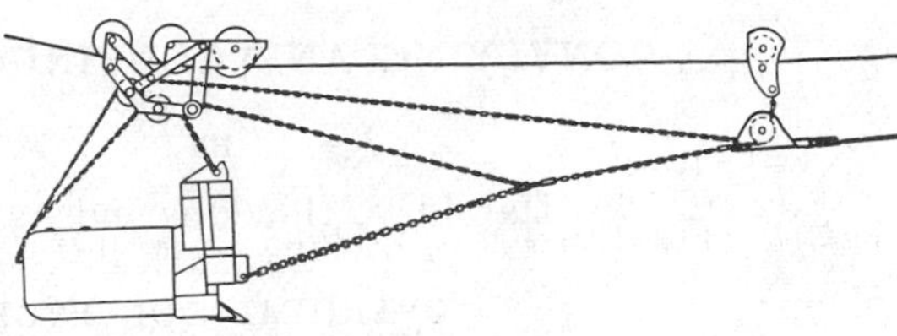

FIG. 31. Slackline-cable bucket and trolley.

Slackline Cableways

Used widely in sand-and-gravel plants, the **slackline cableway** employs an open ended dragline bucket suspended from a carrier (Fig. 31) which runs upon a track cable. It will dig, elevate, and convey materials in one continuous operation.

Figure 32 shows a typical slackline-cableway operation. The bucket and carrier is *a*; *b* is the track cable, inclined to return the bucket and carrier by gravity; *c* is a tension cable for raising or lowering the track cable; *d* is the load cable; and *e* is a power unit with two friction drums having variable speeds. A mast or tower *f* is used to support guide and tension blocks at the high end of the track cable; a movable tail tower *g* supports the lower end of the track cable. The bucket is raised and lowered by tensioning or slacking off the track cable. The bucket is loaded, after lowering, by pulling on the load cable. The loaded bucket, after raising, is conveyed at high speed to the dumping point and is returned at a still higher speed by gravity to the digging point. The cableway can be operated in radial lines from a mast or in parallel lines between two moving towers. It will not dig rock unless the rock is blasted. The depth of digging may vary from 5 to 100 ft. Capacities are shown in Table 7.

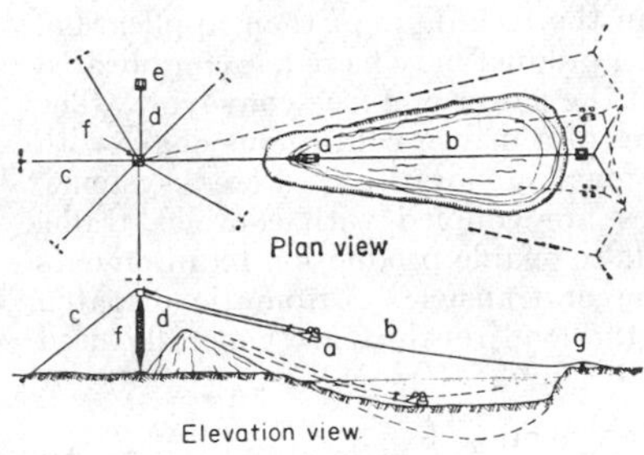

FIG. 32. Slackline-cable plant. (*Sauerman.*)

Table 7. Slackline Cableway
(Sauerman)

Kind of power	Approximate hp	Size of bucket, cu yd	Length of span, ft	Handling capacity in cu yd per hr when digging 30 ft below mast on an average haul of					
				150 ft	200 ft	250 ft	300 ft	400 ft	500 ft
Electric	20	½	400	25	22	20	17	...	...
Diesel	30	½	400	25	22	20	17	...	...
Electric	40	¾	500	39	37	36	33	...	...
Diesel	92	¾	500	57	54	51	46	...	...
Electric	60	1	600	51	50	46	43	37	...
Diesel	140	1	600	83	80	70	65	55	...
Electric	100	1½	700	...	79	76	73	66	57
Diesel	140	1½	700	...	97	91	84	72	61
Electric	150	2	800	...	...	94	90	80	70
Diesel	207	2	800	...	...	114	110	98	84
Electric	200	2½	900	...	...	113	112	105	95
Diesel	320	2½	900	...	...	150	147	125	107
Electric	250	3½	1,000	...	...	...	156	140	129
Diesel	410	3½	1,000	...	...	...	182	161	143

CONVEYING AND CONTINUOUS FLOW

BY

Harold V. Hawkins and Associates

OVERHEAD CONVEYORS

By Richard J. Foster

Columbus McKinnon Corporation

Mass-production, assembly-line, and warehousing requirements of most all-finished commodities and many semifinished products have caused considerable development in **overhead power conveyors** and in the technique of their application. The variety of style, color, and other options that a product may have has complicated overhead-conveyor application and brought about the **power and free conveyor.** The power-and-free conveyor combines the advantages of a driven continuous chain with the versatile traffic system exampled by traditional monorail unpowered systems. Thus, high-density-load-transmission capabilities are coupled with complex traffic patterns and process or work-station requirements to enable production requirements to be met with a minimum of manual handling or transfer. Automatic dispatch systems, to permit coding and programming of the load routing, are generally used with power-and-free conveyors.

Powered Overhead Conveyors

Overhead power conveyors, often referred to as *trolley conveyors* are utilized for **transmission or float** of loads on hangers over a fixed path. The power conveyor is constructed of some form of chain or cable (Fig. 1) fitted with wheels and guide

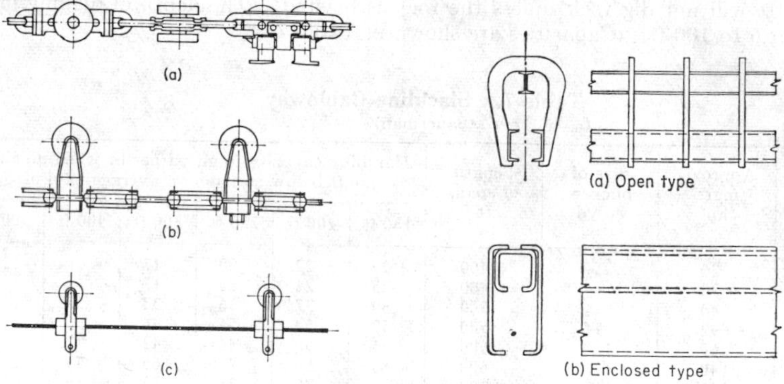

FIG. 1. Typical conveyor chains or cable.

FIG. 2. Conveyor tracks.

rollers and designed to ride in or on a structural member. Track sections (Fig. 2) range from lightweight angle members or tubular sections to medium- and heavy-duty box sections and I beams.

The load-carrying member of an overhead conveyor is the trolley, and it is spaced as a function of its load and the conveyor chain-supporting capability. The work hanger, or carrier, is attached to the trolley and generally remains attached unless manually removed. However, installations are made where the work hanger is transferred by a special device. In other cases, the work is transferred from the hanger while the conveyor is in motion.

The overhead power conveyor can employ any chain length consistent with allowable chain pull (lengths to 2000 ft are not uncommon). The track layout usually involves both horizontal turns and vertical displacement. In open-track systems (Fig. 2*a*), the chain is guided around horizontal turns by sprocket or traction wheels or by continuous roller turns. On enclosed-track systems (Fig. 2*b*), the chain is fitted with horizontal as well as vertical wheels, which guide the chain at all times in the track section.

Once dimensional layout, load spacing, weights of dead and live loads, and function (load and unload points) are determined, the chain pull can be calculated. Manufacturer's data should be used for frictional values. A classical point-to-point analysis should be made, using the most unfavorable instantaneous-loading condition.

In the absence of precise data, the following formulas can be used to find the approximate chain pull:

$$\text{Max chain pull} = A + B + C$$

$$\text{Net chain pull at drive} = A + B + C - D$$

where $A = fW$ (where W = total weight of chain, carriers, and live load, lb; and f = coefficient of friction); $B = wS$ (where w = average carrier load per ft of rail on *up* slopes, lb-ft; and S = total vertical rise); $C = 0.017f(A + B)N$ (where N = sum of all horizontal and vertical curves, deg); and $D = w'S$ (where w' = avg carrier load per ft of rail on *down* slopes, lb-ft). For a ball-bearing conveyer in clean operating condition, the coefficient of friction f can be taken as 0.013.

Where calculations indicate that the allowable chain pull may be exceeded, multiple-drive units are used. Drive units are sprocket, pocket, or caterpillar type and are available for fixed-speed or manual variable-speed control. Common variation is 3/1. Drive motors range from fractional to 10 hp.

When multiple drives are used for fixed-speed systems, either high-slip a-c motors or fluid couplings are used. If variable speed is required of a multiple-drive system, it is most common to use a variable-frequency generator with a-c motors or a d-c generator with compound-wound d-c motors. The common generator or alternator provides power to all drives. Special care must be given to drive-unit and take-up locations.

In addition to the major components mentioned above, the following devices or components are useful or necessary to overhead-conveyor applications:

Trolley Assembly. Standard wheels and carriage mechanism are usually adapted to a particular application, depending upon loading, duty cycle, and expected environment.

Trolley Brackets, Hanger Attachments, and Load Bars. Standard-size brackets, hangers, and load bars are adapted to suit specific application and load-bearing requirements.

Sprocket- or Traction-wheel Turns. Any arc of horizontal turn is available. Standards are in increments of 15 to 180 deg. On enclosed-track conveyor chains having horizontal wheels, this device is not required.

Roller Turns. Any arc of horizontal turn is available. Standards are in increments of 7½ to 180 deg.

Track-hanger Brackets, Supports, and Bracing. Standard to conform to track size and shape.

Track Expansion Joints. For operation in ovens or other nonambient applications.

Chain Take-up Unit. Required to compensate for chain wear. May be sprocket or telescoping-track type. Adjustment is maintained by screw, springs, counterweight, or air cylinders.

Chain Safety Devices. A chain backup device will ratchet into trolley or chain engagement in case of unexpected reversal. A chain runaway mechanism will sense abnormal chain or trolley velocity and engage a safety ratchet to stop chain or trolley. Overspeed sensing can be used to cut the power to the drive unit.

Drive-unit Overload. Overload is detected by a torque limiter which causes clutch to slip and, if overload is persistent, will cause disconnect of electric power. Shear pins can still be found but are not common.

Chain, Trolley, and Equipment Guards. Especially in processing applications, it is necessary to guard the conveyor chain and trolleys from hostile environment and the work from track contaminants. In other cases, personnel must be protected from accidental engagement with the conveyor or work. Special shrouding and guarding must be considered; in some cases, the shrouding must be pressurized to keep out undesirable airborne contaminants.

Transfer Devices. Although largely special to the application, these devices include stand-up and load devices, load or unload stations for trays, and automatic tilt or unload stations.

Power-and-Free Overhead Conveyers

The power-and-free conveyor has potential application wherever there is a requirement for other than a single fixed-path flow. This equipment can eliminate the numerous hand transfers required when using other types of conveyor equipment or floorborne vehicles. Systems of power-and-free conveyors can be linked together, and any number of automatic switch points can be used. The work carriers can be switched manually or automatically to the free rail. The power-and-free system permits scheduled transit and delivery of work to the next assigned station automatically. Accumulation and storage areas are designed to accommodate in-process inventory between operations.

The components and chain-pull calculation discussed above for powered overhead conveyors are applicable to the powered portion of the power-and free conveyor. Addition of a secondary free-track surface is provided for the work carrier to traverse. This free track is usually disposed directly below the power rail but is sometimes found alongside the power rail (this limits switching to only the free side). The power-and-free rails are joined by brackets or in a continuous fashion. The power chain is fitted with pushers to engage the work-carrier trolley.

Figure 3 shows the Columbus McKinnon combined power-and-free rail. In the cutaway portion, the pushers are shown engaged with the work-carrier trolley. The pushers are pivoted on an axis parallel to the chain path and swing aside to engage the pusher trolley. The pusher trolley remains engaged on level and sloped sections. At automatic or manual switching points, the leading dispatch-trolley head which is not engaged with the chain is propelled through the switch to the branch line. As the chain passes the switching point, the pusher trolley departs to the right or left from pusher engagement and arrives on a free line, where it is subject to manual or controlled gravity flow.

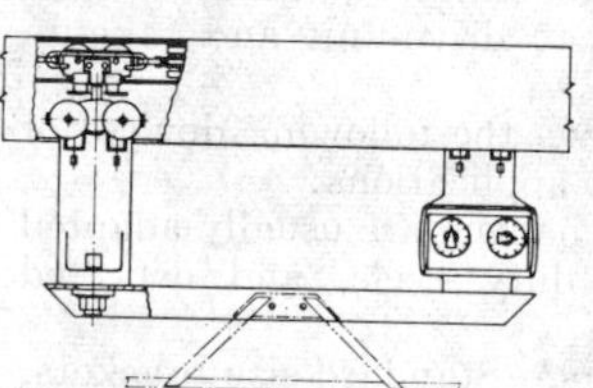

FIG. 3. Columbus McKinnon power-and-free conveyor rail and trolley heads.

The **distance between pushers** on the chain for power-and-free use is established in accordance with conventional practice, except that the minimum allowable pusher spacing must take into account the wheelbase of the trolley, the bumper length, the load size, the chain velocity, and the action of the carrier at automatic switching and reentry points. A switching headway must be allowed between work carriers. An approximation of the minimum allowable pusher spacing is that the pusher spacing will equal twice the work-carrier bumper length. Therefore a 4-ft work carrier would indicate a minimum pusher spacing of 8 ft.

The load-transmission capabilities are a function of velocity and pusher spacing. At the 8-ft pusher spacing and a velocity of 40 fpm, five pushers per min are made available. The load-transmission capability is 5 loads per min, or 300 loads per hr.

Method of Automatic Switching from a Powered Line to a Free Line. Power-and-free work carriers are usually switched automatically from a powered line to a free line.

To do this, it is necessary to have a code device on the work carrier and a decoding device along the track in advance of the track switch. Figure 4 shows the equipment relationship. On each carrier, the Telematic trolley head carries the code selection, manually or automatically introduced, which identifies it for a particular destination or routing. As the trolley head passes the readout station, the trolley intelligence is decoded and compared with a preset station code and its current knowledge of the switch position and branch-line condition; a decision is then reached which results in correct positioning of the rail switch.

In Fig. 4, the equipment illustrated includes a transistorized **readout station** *a*, which supplies 12 volts direct current at stainless-steel code brushes *b*. The code brushes are "matched" by contacts on the encoded trolley head *c*. When a trolley is in register and matches the code-brush positioning, it will be allowed to enter branch line *d*, if the line is not full. If carrier *e* is to be entered, the input signal is rectified and amplified so as to drive a power relay at junction box *f*, which in turn actuates solenoid *g* to operate track switch *h* to the branch-line position. A **memory circuit** is established in the station, indicating that a **full-line** condition exists. This condition is maintained until the pusher pin of the switched carrier clears reset switch *j*.

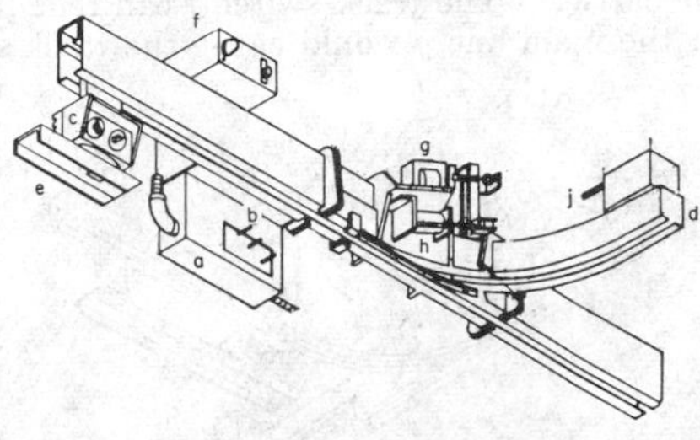

Fig. 4. Switch mechanism exiting trolley from power rail to free rail. (*Columbus McKinnon.*)

The **situations which can be handled** by the **decoding stations** are as follows: (1) A trolley with a matching code is in register; there is space in the branch line. The carrier is **allowed to enter** the branch line. (2) A trolley with a matching code is in register; there is no space in the branch line. The carrier is automatically **recirculated** on the powered system and will continue to test its assigned destination until it can be accommodated. (3) A trolley with a matching code is in register; there is no space in the branch line. The powered conveyor is automatically **stopped,** and visual and audible signals are started. The conveyor can be automatically restarted when the full-line condition is cleared, and the waiting carrier will be allowed to enter. (4) A trolley with a non-matching code is in register; in this case, the decoding station always returns the track switch to the main-line position, if necessary, and **bypasses** the carrier.

Use and Control of Carriers on Free and Gravity Lines. Free and gravity lines are used as follows: (1) To connect multiple power-and-free conveyors, thus making systems easily extensible and permitting different conveyor designs for particular use. (2) To connect to auxiliary devices such as vertical conveyors and drop-lift stations. (3) As manned or automatic work stations. In this case, the size of the station depends on the number of carriers processed at one time, with additional space provision for arriving and departing carriers. (Considerable knowledge of work-rate standards and production-schedule requirements are needed for accurate sizing.) (4) As manned or automatic storage lines, especially for handling production imbalance for later consumption.

Non-manned automatic free lines require that the carrier be controlled in conformance with desired conveyor function and with regard to the commodity being handled. The two principal ways to control carriers in non-manned free rails are (1) to slope the free rail so that all carriers will start from rest and use incremental spot retarders to check velocity, and (2) to install horizontal or slightly sloped rails and use auxiliary driving devices (often termed **spring pushers**) to consolidate carriers arriving in the line. In **manned free lines,** it is usual to have slope at the automatic-arrival and automatic-departure sections only. These sections are designed for automatic accumulation of a finite number of carriers, and retarding or feeding devices may be used. Throughout the remainder of the manned station, the carrier is propelled by hand.

Method of Automatic Switching from a Free Line to a Powered Line. Power-and-free work carriers can be **reentered** into the powered lines either manually or automatically. The carrier must be integrated with traffic already on the powered line and must be entered so that it will engage with a pusher on the powered chain. Figure 5 illustrates a typical method of automatic reentry. The carrier *a* is held at rest on a slope in the demand position by the electric trolley stop *b*. The demand to enter enables the sensing switches *c* and *d* mounted on the powered rail to test for the availability of a pusher. When a pusher that is not propelling a load is sensed, all conditions are met and the carrier is released by the electric trolley stop such that it arrives in the pickup position in advance of the pusher. A retarding or choke device *e* can be used to keep the entering carrier from overrunning the next switch position or another carrier in transit. The chain pusher engages the pusher trolley and departs the carrier. The track switch *f* can remain in the branch-line position until a carrier on the main line *g* would cause the track switch to reset. Automatic reentry control ensures that no opportunity to use a pusher is overlooked and does not require the time of an operator.

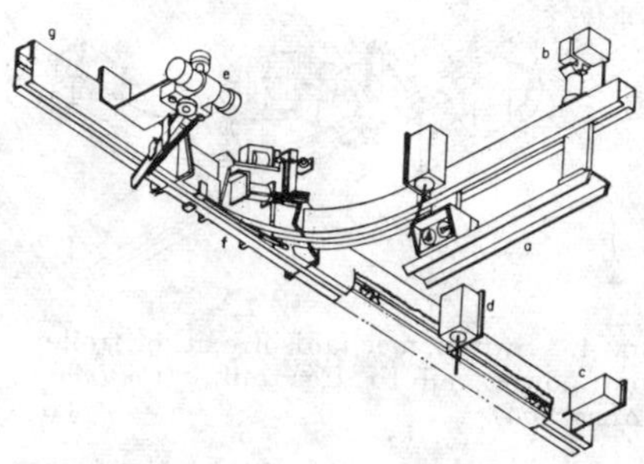

Fig. 5. Switch mechanism reentering trolley from free rail to power rail. (*Columbus McKinnon.*)

Power-and-free Conveyor Components. Listed below are the various devices and components basic to power-and-free systems and not described above for overhead power conveyors.

1. **Track Switches for Diversion of Work Carriers.** These may be manually, electrically, pneumatically, or trolley operated, depending upon the application and the type of system (power-and-free to free; free to power-and-free; free monorail system). Switching may be to right, to left, or to right or left. Not all types of conditions are possible (depending upon type of track, etc.)

2. **Trolley Stops.** Manual trolley stops are usually spring-loaded in the normally closed position. By use of a chain or rope, the stop is opened momentarily to permit moving a carrier past the stop. Latches to hold the stop open may be provided. **Electromechanical trolley stops** are similar in principle but are used in automatic situations and/or remote locations. The signal to release a carrier may be given to the operating mechanism by an operator, but often this is part of a feed-in or demand control.

3. **Retarding Devices and Powerized Storage Lines.** Incremental retarding devices or spot retarders used on gravity free-rail sections are essentially trolley stops which incorporate a cushioning device to check velocity partially or entirely and then rerelease the trolley to the next segment. Numerous devices are found which rely on friction between the free trolley and the retarder. More recent retarders employ air or hydraulic cylinders to dissipate the energy. Often a timing device signals the release of the carrier from the retarder to the next segment or position. Spot retarders may be used on short or long lines. The manufacturer's specifications must be followed closely as to rail slope, allowable loads, and spot-retarder spacing. On gravity lines 50 ft long or longer, the possibility of using a powerized storage line should be examined. The powerized storage line (sometimes called an **accumulation conveyor**) can be installed with little or no slope and will keep carriers consolidated at the lower end of the line. The spring-loaded pushers are overturned when stack resistance is met. The spring pusher may reset after engagement with each carrier or may be recocked periodically.

4. **Safety Devices.** In addition to chain safety devices (see above), antirunaway devices for free trolley are installed on major slopes. Abnormal trolley velocity is sensed, and a crash bar is fired across the path of the runaway trolley. Power to the conveyor is opened, so that additional carriers are not driven into the runaway unit.

The deformed crash bar is replaced, and the conveyor restarted. Runaways should be rare, and their cause should be immediately determined. In some applications, where the cargo load will vary widely in density, it is advisable to employ **weight-limiter** sections which will cause carriers weighing more than design weight to be stopped from entering powered sections or, if already entered, to be switched to a service station.

Vertical Conveyor Sections. Vertical conveyor sections are an often-used accessory to power-and-free mechanization. For practical purposes, the vertical conveyor can be divided into two classes of devices:

1. **Booster or Drop-lift Section.** This device is usually used at substations only or, if used on the main line, is usually in parallel, as the unit is a reciprocating device and generally cannot match the speed of the continuous power-and-free conveyor. The vertical unit may be powered by a cylinder or a hoist, depending on the stroke, speed, and load. When **used as a booster** in a free conveyor, the unit will accept a carrier at a low level and discharge at a higher level—matching at each extreme of travel with a section of free rail. This may constitute a vertical shunt between different conveyors or even the same chain where it is impractical or undesirable to run the carrier on an incline. **When used as a drop-lift section** in a free conveyor, the units will accept a carrier on a high level and lower the carrier to an operations level. The lower level may be a load-unload station or a processing station. Automatic safety stops are used to close rail ends.

2. **Interfloor Vertical Conveyor.** When used for interfloor service and long lifts, the vertical conveyor may be powered by high-speed hoists or elevating machines. In any case, the carriers are automatically transferred to and from the lift by power-and-free conveyors, and the dispatch control on the carrier instructs the machine to the destination of the carrier. This machine can be equipped with a variety of speeds and operating characteristics. Sometimes multiple carriers are handled and priority-call control systems can be fitted to suit individual requirements.

Load-bar and Carrier Design. The design of load bar, bumpers, swivel devices, index devices, hooks, or carriers with shelves or compartments should be carried on with the initial power-and-free investigation, as the system will see only the carrier and all detail system design is a function of carrier design. Therefore, how the commodity being handled is arranged on or in the carrier is carefully considered. Attention should be given to packaging or containerization, either to protect the commodity or to facilitate manual handling where required.

NON-CARRYING CONVEYORS

By Harold V. Hawkins

Flight Conveyors

Flight conveyors are used for moving granular, lumpy, or pulverized materials along a horizontal path or on an incline seldom greater than about 40 deg. Their principal application is in handling coal. The flight conveyor of usual construction should not be specified for a material that is actively abrasive, such as damp sand and ashes. The **drag-chain conveyor** (Fig. 6) has an open-link chain, which serves, instead of flights, to push the material along. With a hard-faced concrete or cast-iron trough, it serves well for handling ashes. The return run is, if possible, above the carrying run, so that the dribble will be back into the loaded run. A feeder must be provided unless the feed is otherwise controlled, as from a tandem elevator or conveyor. As the feeder is interlocked, either mechanically or electrically, the feed stops if the conveyor stops. Flight conveyors may be classified as **scraper type** (Fig. 7), in which the element (chain and flights) rests on the trough; **suspended-flight type** (Fig. 8), in which the flights are carried clear of the trough by shoes resting on guides; and **suspended-**

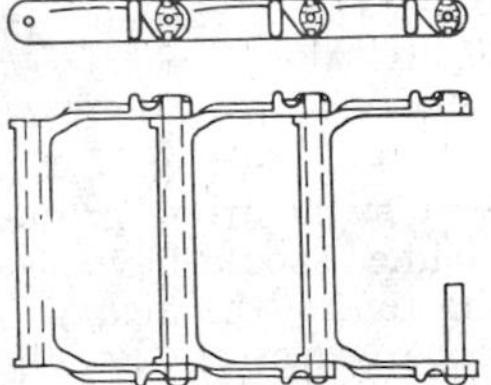

FIG. 6. Drag chain.

chain type (Fig. 9), in which the chain rests on guides, again carrying the flights clear of the trough. These types are further differentiated as **single strand** (Figs. 7 and 8) and **double strand** (Fig. 9). For lumpy material, the latter has the advantage since the lumps will enter the trough without interference. For heavy duty also, the double strand has the advantage, in that the pull is divided between two chains. A special type for simultaneous handling of several materials may have the trough divided by

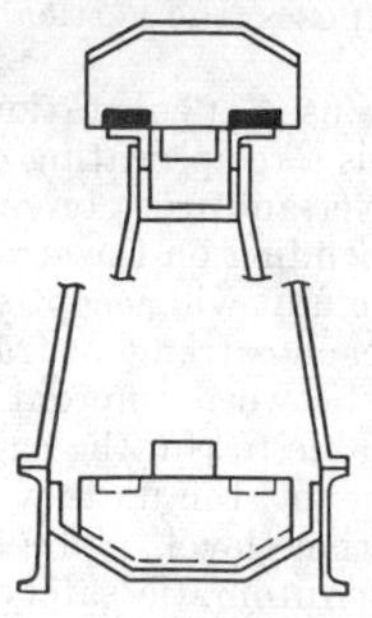

Fig. 7. Single-strand scraper-flight conveyor.

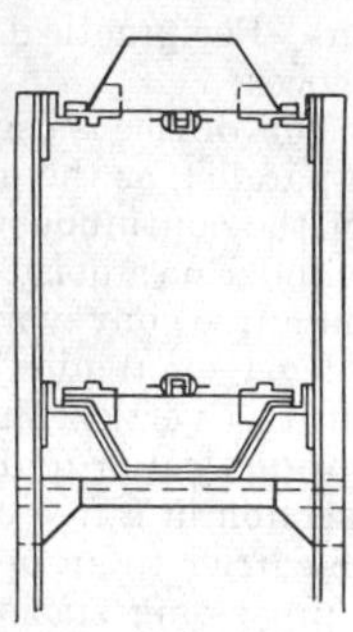

Fig. 8. Single-strand suspended-flight conveyor.

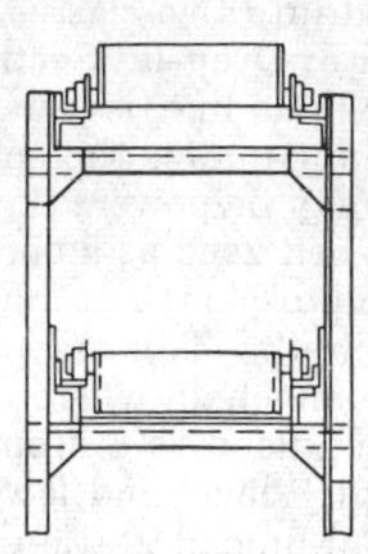

Fig. 9. Double-strand roller-chain flight conveyor.

longitudinal partitions. The material having the greatest coefficient of friction is then carried, if possible, in the central zone to equalize chain wear and stretch.

Improvements in the welding and carburizing of welded-link chain (see p. 10–9) have made possible its use in flight conveyors, offering several significant advantages, including economy and flexibility in all directions. Figures 10 and 47 show a typical scraper-type flight cast from malleable iron incorporated onto a slotted conveyor bed. The small amount of fines that fall through the slot are returned to the top of the bed by the returning flights. Figure 11 shows a double-chain scraper conveyor in which the ends of the flights ride in a restrictive channel. These types of flight conveyors are driven by pocketwheels (see p. 10–9).

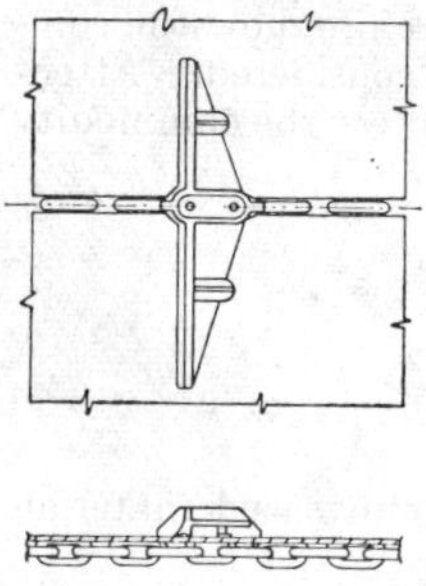

Fig. 10. Scraper flight with welded chain.

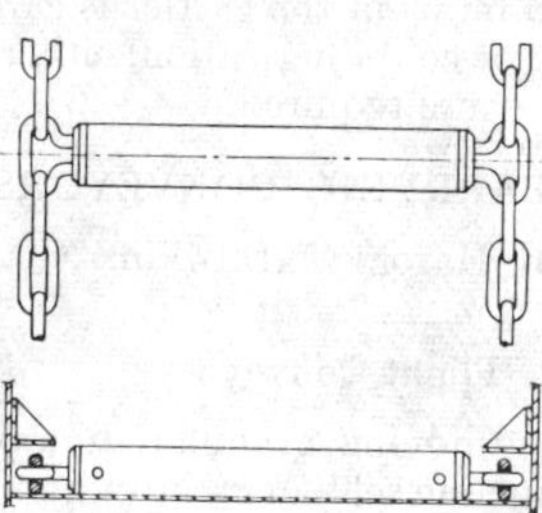

Fig. 11. Scraper flight using parallel welded chains.

Flight conveyors of small capacity operate usually at 100 to 150 fpm. Large-capacity conveyors operate at 100 fpm or slower; their long-pitch chains hammer heavily against the drive-sprocket teeth or pocketwheels at higher speeds. A conveyor steeply inclined should have closely spaced flights so that the material will not avalanche over the tops of the flights. The capacity of a given conveyor diminishes as the angle of slope increases. For the heaviest duty, hardened-face rollers at the articulations are essential.

The capacity of an inclined conveyor is found by multiplying the capacities in Table 1 by the following factors:

Inclination, deg	20	25	30	35
Factor	0.9	0.8	0.7	0.6

Table 1. Capacity and Size of Lumps of Flight Conveyors

Flight width and depth, in.	Cu ft of material per ft of conveyor	Approx capacity at 100 fpm with 50 lb material, tons per hr*	Lump size, in., not to exceed 10 percent of total volume	
			Single strand	Double strand
12 × 6	0.40	60	3½	4
15 × 6	0.49	73	4½	5
18 × 6	0.56	84	5	6
24 × 8	1.16	174	...	10
30 × 10	1.60	240	...	14
36 × 12	2.40	360	...	16

* For material weighing other than 50 lb per cu ft, the capacity is proportional to the weight.

For flight shoes or flights against guides (not lubricated) or trough, $F = 0.33$; if rollers are used instead of shoes, $F = 0.1$; for rollers with antifriction bearings, 0.05.

The chain pull for a horizontal conveyor $= 2WLF + W_1LF_1$, where W = weight per ft of element, lb; L = length of conveyor, ft; F = coefficient of friction of element; W_1 = weight of material per ft of conveyor, lb; F_1 = material coefficient from Table 2.

Table 2. Coefficients of Friction on Steel Plate

Anthracite	0.33	Coke	0.36	Hydrated lime	0.65
Bituminous coal	0.59	Copra	0.40	Limestone, pulv	0.53
Cement	0.93	Grains	0.30–0.40	Sawdust, wet	0.60
Clay	0.60–0.70	Hog fuel, dry	0.65	Soda ash	0.65

In an **inclined conveyor,** the power requirement is the sum of that required for the horizontal run plus that required to lift the load. The turning effort at the pitch line of the head sprocket for a conveyor inclined

$$\theta \text{ deg} = WL(F\cos\theta + \sin\theta) + W_1L(F_1\cos\theta + \sin\theta) + WL(F\cos\theta - \sin\theta), \text{ lb}$$

The third term may be a minus quantity, indicating that the return run then is assisting the turning effort.

For the motor horsepower, add 10 percent for friction in the terminal bearings, plus 10 percent for loss in the speed-reduction gearing, plus 10 percent for starting or surge loads.

EXAMPLE. Horizontal conveyor, 150-ft centers; capacity, 175 tons per hr of bituminous coal. Determine conveyor size, chain pull, speed, and motor.

From Table 1, use a 24- by 8-in. flight size at a speed of 100 fpm. Assume an engineering-type chain with sleeve-bearing rollers and weighing, with flights, 60 lb per running ft.

$$W \times L = 60 \times 150 = 9{,}000$$
$$W_1 \times L = 1.16 \times 50 \times 150 = 8{,}700$$
$$F = 0.10 \qquad F_1 = 0.59$$
$$\text{Chain pull} = (2 \times 9{,}000 \times 0.10) + (8{,}700 \times 0.59) = 6{,}933 \text{ lb}$$
$$HP = (6{,}933 \times 100)/33{,}000 = 21 \quad \text{Use 27.9-hp motor.}$$

Cautions in Flight-conveyor Selections. With abrasive material, the trough design should provide for renewal of the bottom plate without disturbing the side plates. If the conveyor is inclined and will reverse when halted under load, a solenoid brake or other automatic backstop should be provided. Chains may not wear or stretch equally. In a double-strand conveyor, it may be necessary to shift sections of chain from one side to the other to even up the lengths.

Intermediate slide gates should be set to open in the opposite direction to the movement of material in the conveyor.

The **continuous-flow conveyor** serves as a conveyor, as an elevator, or as a combination of the two. It is a slow-speed machine in which the material moves as a continuous core within a duct. Except with the **Redler** conveyor, the element is formed by a single strand of chain with closely spaced impellers, somewhat resembling the flights of a flight conveyor.

The **Bulk flo** (Fig. 12) has peaked flights designed to facilitate the outflow of the load at the point of discharge. The load, moved by a positive push of the flights, tends to provide self-clearing action at the end of a run, leaving only a slight residue.

The **Redler** (Fig. 13) has skeletonized or U-shaped impellers which move the material in which they are submerged because the resistance to slip through the element is greater than the drag against the walls of the duct.

Materials for which the continuous-flow conveyor is suited are listed below in groups of increasing difficulty. The constant C is used in the power equations below, and pp. 10–61, 10–62.

C = 1: clean coal, flaxseed, graphite, soybeans, copra, soap flakes
C = 1.2: beans, slack coal, sawdust, wheat, wood chips (dry), flour
C = 1.5: salt, wood chips (wet), starch
C = 2: clays, fly ash, lime (pebble), sugar (granular), soda ash, zinc oxide
C = 2.5: alum, borax, cork (ground), limestone (pulverized)

Among the materials for which special construction is advised are bauxite, brown sugar, hog fuel, wet coal, shelled corn, foundry dust, cement, bug dust, hot brewers' grains. The machine should not be specified for ashes, bagasse, carbon-black pellets, sand and gravel, sewage sludge, and crushed stone. Fabrication from corrosion-resistant materials such as brass, monel, or stainless steel may be necessary for use with some corrosive materials.

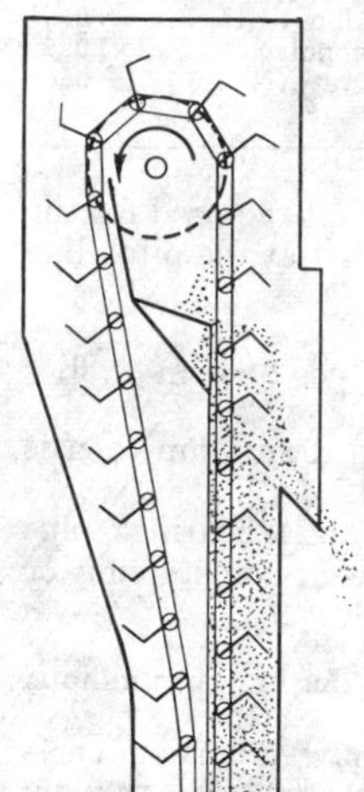

FIG. 12. Bulk flo continuous-flow elevator.

Where a single **runaround conveyor** is required with multiple feed points and some recirculation of excess load, the Redler serves. The U-frame flights do not squeeze the loads, as they resume parallelism after separating when rounding the terminal wheels. As an elevator, this machine will also handle sluggish materials that do not flow out readily. A pusher plate opposite the discharge chute can be employed to enter between the legs of the U flights to push out such material. When horizontal or inclined, continuous-flow elevators such as the Redler are normally self-cleaning. When vertical, the Redler type can be made self-cleaning (except with sticky materials) by use of special flights.

Continuous-flow conveyors and elevators do not require a feeder (Fig. 14). They are self-loading to capacity and will not overload, even though there are several open- or uncontrolled-feed openings, since the duct fills at the first opening and automatically prevents the entrance of additional material at subsequent openings. Some special care may be required with free-flowing material.

The duct is easily insulated by sheets of asbestos-cement or similar material to reduce cooling in transit. As the duct is completely sealed, there is no updraft where the lift is high. The material is protected from exposure and contamination or contact with lubricants. The handling capacity for horizontal or inclined lengths (nearly to the angle of repose of the material) approximates 100 percent of the volume swept through by the movement of the element. For steeper inclines or elevators, it is between 50 and 90 percent.

If the material is somewhat abrasive, as with wet bituminous coal, the duct should be of corrosion-resistant steel, of extra thickness, and the chain pins should be both extremely hard and of corrosion-resistant material.

A long horizontal run followed by an upturn is inadvisable because of radial thrust. Lumpy material is difficult to feed from a track hopper. An automatic brake is unnecessary as an elevator will reverse only a few inches when released.

The motor horsepower P required by continuous-flow conveyors for the five arrangements shown in Fig. 15 is given in the accompanying formulas in terms of the

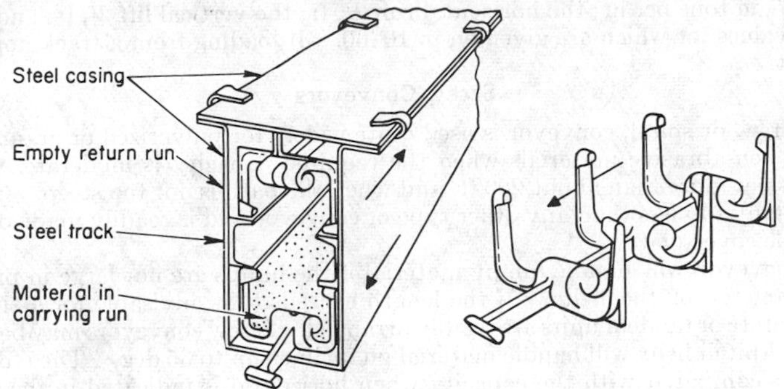

FIG. 13. Redler U-type continuous-flow conveyor.

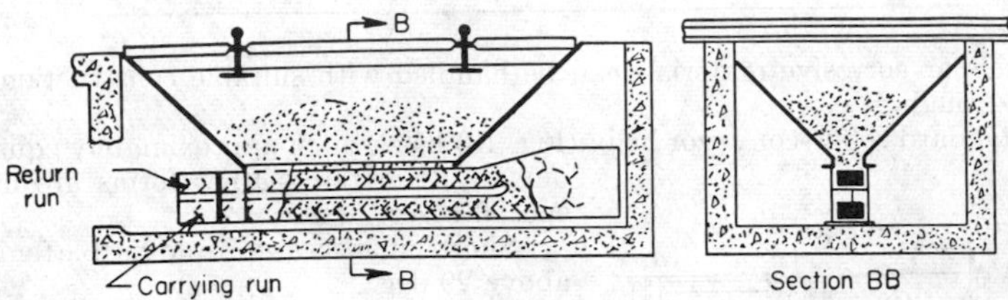

FIG. 14. Shallow-track hopper for continuous-flow conveyor with feed to return run.

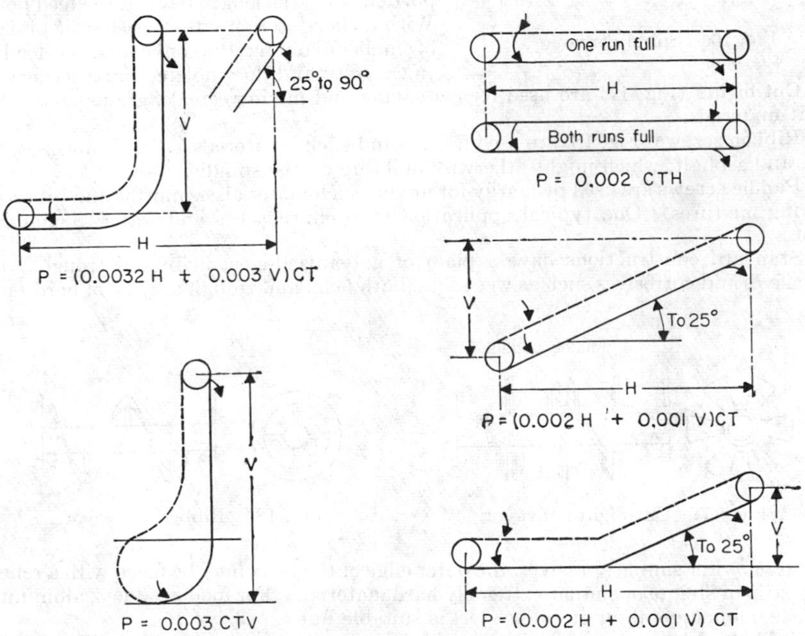

FIG. 15. Continuous-flow-conveyor arrangements.

capacity T, in tons per hr; the horizontal run H, ft; the vertical lift V, ft; and the constant C, values for which are given on p. 10–60. If loading from a track hopper, add 10 percent.

Screw Conveyors

The screw, or spiral, conveyor is used quite widely for pulverized or granular, noncorrosive, non-abrasive materials when the required capacity is moderate, when the distance is not more than about 200 ft, and when the path is not too steep. It usually costs substantially less than any other type of conveyor and is readily made dust-tight by a simple cover plate.

The conveyor will handle lumpy material if the lumps are not large in proportion to the diameter of the helix. If the length exceeds that advisable for a single conveyor, separate or tandem units are readily arranged. Screw conveyors may be inclined. A standard-pitch helix will handle material on inclines up to 35 deg. The reduction in capacity as compared with the capacity when horizontal is indicated in the following table:

Inclination, deg	10	15	20	25	30	35
Reduction in capacity, percent	10	26	45	58	70	78

Abrasive or corrosive materials can be handled with suitable construction of the helix and trough.

The standard screw-conveyor helix (Fig. 16) has a pitch approximately equal to its outside diameter. Other forms are used for special cases.

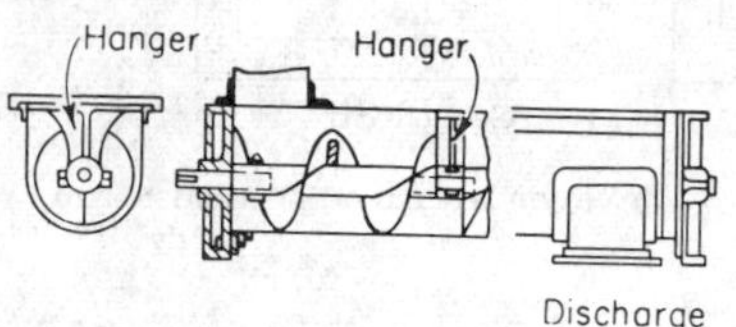

Fig. 16. Spiral conveyor.

Short-pitch screws are advisable for inclines above 29 deg.

Variable-pitch screws, with short pitch at the feed end, automatically control the flow to the conveyor so that the load is correctly proportioned for the length beyond the feed point. With a short section either of shorter pitch or of smaller diameter, the conveyor is self-loading to capacity and does not require a feeder.

Cut flights (Fig. 17) are used for conveying and mixing cereals, grains, and other light materials.

Ribbon screws (Fig. 18) are used for wet and sticky materials, such as molasses, hot tar, and asphalt, which might otherwise build up on the spindle.

Paddle screws are used primarily for mixing such materials as mortar and bitulithic paving mixtures. One typical application is to churn ashes and water to eliminate dust.

Standard constructions have a plain or galvanized-steel helix and trough. For abrasives and corrosives such as wet ashes, both helix and trough may be of hard-faced

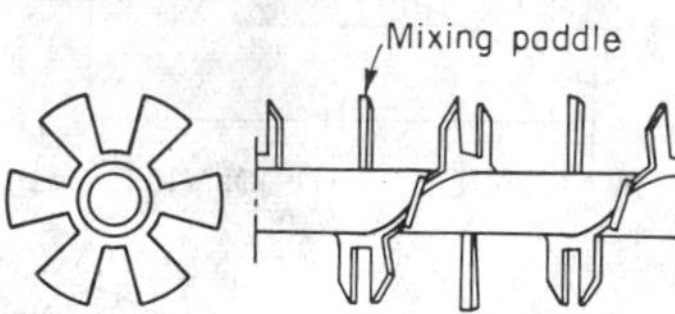

Fig. 17. Cut-flight conveyor.

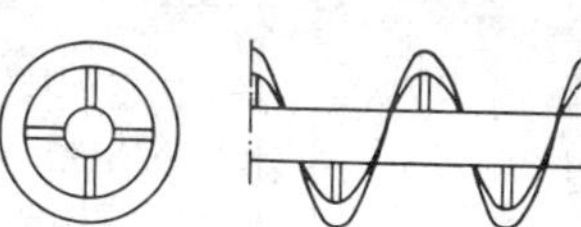

Fig. 18. Ribbon conveyor.

cast iron. For simple abrasives, the outer edge of the helix may be faced with a renewable strip of stellite or similar extremely hard material. For food products, aluminum, bronze, monel metal, or stainless steel is suitable but expensive.

Table 3 gives the capacities, allowable speeds, percentages of helix loading for five groups of materials, and the factor F used in estimating the power requirement.

Table 3. Capacities and Speeds of Spiral Conveyors

Group	Max percent of cross section occupied by the material	Max density of material, lb per cu ft	Max rpm for diameters	
			6 in.	20 in.
1	45	50	170	110
2	38	50	120	75
3	31	75	90	60
4	25	100	70	50
5	12½	...	30	25

NOTES. Group 1 includes light materials such as barley, beans, brewers grains (dry), coal (pulv.), corn meal, cottonseed meal, flaxseed, flour, malt, oats, rice, wheat. The value of the factor F is 0.5.

Group 2 includes fines and granular material. The values of F are alum (pulv.), 0.6; coal (slack or fines), 0.9; coffee beans, 0.4; sawdust, 0.7; soda ash (light), 0.7; soybeans, 0.5; fly ash, 0.4.

Group 3 includes materials with small lumps mixed with fines. Values of F are alum, 1.4; ashes (dry), 4.0; borax, 0.7; brewers grains (wet), 0.6; cottonseed, 0.9; salt, coarse or fine, 1.2; soda ash (heavy), 0.7.

Group 4 includes semiabrasive materials, fines, granular and small lumps. Values of F are acid phosphate (dry), 1.4; bauxite (dry), 1.8; cement (dry), 1.4; clay, 2.0; fuller's earth, 2.0; lead salts, 1.0; limestone screenings, 2.0; sugar (raw), 1.0; white lead, 1.0; sulphur (lumpy), 0.8; zinc oxide, 1.0.

Group 5 includes abrasive lumpy materials which must be kept from contact with hanger bearings. Values of F are wet ashes, 5.0; flue dirt, 4.0; quartz (pulv.) 2.5; silica sand, 2.0; sewage sludge (wet and sandy), 6.0.

Table 4 gives the handling capacities for standard-pitch screw conveyors in each of the five groups of materials when the conveyors are operating at the maximum advised speeds and in the horizontal position. The capacity at any lower speed is in the ratio of the speeds.

Table 4. Screw-conveyor Capacities
(Cu ft per hr)

Group	Conveyor size, in.							
	6	9	10	12	14	16	18	20
1	350	1,100	1,600	2,500	4,000	5,500	7,600	10,000
2	220	700	950	1,600	2,400	3,400	4,500	6,000
3	150	460	620	1,100	1,600	2,200	3,200	4,000
4	90	300	400	650	1,000	1,500	2,000	2,600
5	20	68	90	160	240	350	500	650

Power Requirements. The power requirements for horizontal screw conveyors of standard design and pitch are determined by the Link-Belt Co. by the formula that follows. Additional allowances should be made for inclined conveyors, for starting under load, and for materials that tend to stick or pack in the trough, as with cement.

$$H = \text{hp at conveyor head shaft} = (ALN + CWLF) \times 10^{-6}$$

where A = factor for size of conveyor (see Table 5); C = quantity of material, cu ft per hr; L = length of conveyor, ft; F = factor for material (see Table 3); N = rpm of conveyor; W = density of material, lb per cu ft.

The motor size depends on the efficiency E of the drive (usually close to 90 percent); a further allowance G, depending on the horsepower, is made:

H	1	1–2	2–4	4–5	5
G	2	1.5	1.25	1.1	1.0

$$\text{Motor hp} = HG/E$$

When the material is distributed into a bunker, the conveyor has an open-bottom trough to discharge progressively over the crest of the pile so formed. This trough reduces the capacity and increases the required power since the material drags over the material instead of over a polished trough.

Table 5. Factors A
(Self-lubricating bronze bearings assumed)

Diam of conveyor, in.	6	9	10	12	14	16	18	20	24
Factor, A	54	96	114	171	255	336	414	510	690

If the material contains unbreakable lumps, the helix should clear the trough by at least the diameter of the average lump. For a given capacity, a conveyor of larger size and slower speed is preferable to a conveyor of minimum size and maximum speed. For large capacities and lengths, the alternatives—a flight conveyor or a belt conveyor—should recieve consideration.

EXAMPLES:

1. Slack coal 50 lb per cu ft; desired capacity 50 tons per hr (2,000 cu ft per hr); conveyor length, 60 ft; 14-in. conveyor at 80 rpm. F for slack coal = 0.9 (group 2).

$$H = (255 \times 60 \times 80 + 2{,}000 \times 50 \times 60 \times 0.9)/1{,}000{,}000 = 6.6$$
$$\text{Motor hp} = (6.6 \times 1.0)/0.90 = 7.3$$

Use 7½-hp motor.

2. Limestone screenings, 90 lb per cu ft; desired capacity, 10 ton per hr (222 cu ft per hr); conveyor length, 50 ft; 9-in. conveyor at 50 rpm. F for limestone screenings = 2.0 (group 4).

$$H = (96 \times 50 \times 50 + 222 \times 90 \times 50 \times 2.0)/1{,}000{,}000 = 2.24$$
$$\text{Motor hp} = (2.24 \times 1.25)/0.90 = 2.8$$

Use 3-hp motor.

Chutes

Bulk Material. If the material is fragile and cannot be set through a simple **vertical chute, a retarding chute** may be specified. Figure 19 shows a ladder chute in which the material trickles over shelves instead of falling freely. If it is necessary to minimize breakage when material is fed from a bin, a vertical box chute with flap doors opening inward, as shown in Fig. 20, permits the material to flow downward only from the top surface and eliminates the degradation that results from a converging flow from the bottom of the mass.

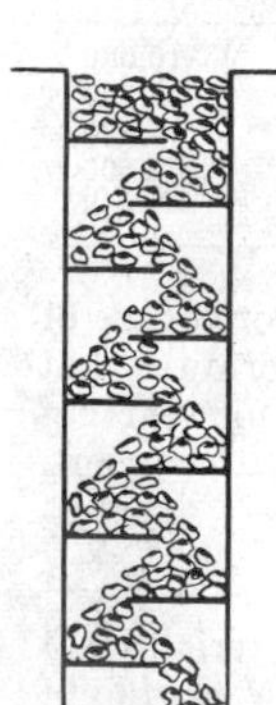

FIG. 19. Ladder chute.

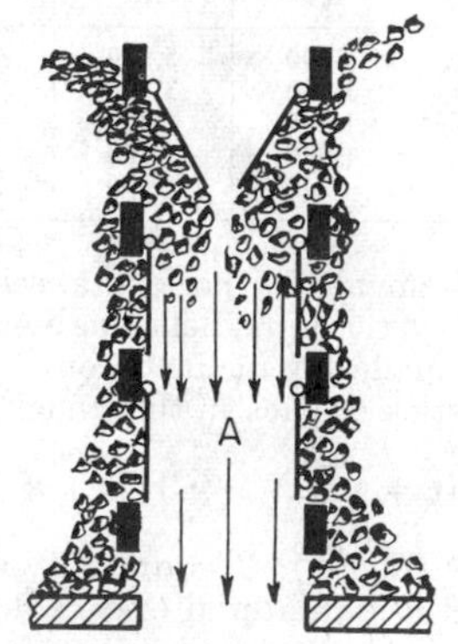

FIG. 20. Box chute with flap doors. Chute is always full up to discharging point.

Straight inclined chutes for coal should have a slope of 40 to 45 deg. If it is found that the coal accelerates objectionably, the chute may be provided with cross angles over which the material cascades at reduced speed (Fig. 21).

Lumpy material such as coke and large coal, difficult to control when flowing from a bin, can be handled by a **Ross feeder.** The Ross feeder chute has a screen of heavy endless chains hung on a sprocket shaft (Fig. 22). The weight of the chain curtain holds the material in the chute. When a feed is desired, the sprocket shaft is revolved slowly, either manually or by a motorized reducer.

Unit Loads. Mechanical handling of unit loads, such as boxes, barrels, packages, castings, crates, and palletized loads, calls for methods and mechanisms entirely different from those adapted to the movement of bulk materials.

Spiral chutes are adapted for the direct lowering of unit loads of various shapes, sizes, and weights, so long as their slide characteristics do not vary widely. If they do vary, care must be exercised to see that items accelerating on the selected helix pitch do not crush or damage those ahead.

A spiral chute may extend through several floors, *e.g.*, for lowering parcels in department stores to a basement shipping department. The opening at each floor must be provided with automatic closure doors, and the design must be approved by the Board of Fire Underwriters.

At the discharge end, it is usual to extend the chute plate horizontally to a length in which the loads can come to rest. A tandem gravity roll conveyor may be advisable for distribution of the loads.

The **sheet-metal spiral** (Fig. 23) has a fixed blade and can be furnished in varying diameters and pitches, both of which determine the maximum size of package that can be handled. These chutes may have receive and discharge points at any desired floors. There are certain kinds of commodities, such as those made of metal or bound with wire or metal bands, that cannot be handled satisfactorily unless the spiral chute is designed to handle only that particular commodity. Sheet-metal spirals can be built with double or triple blades, all mounted on the same standpipe. Another form of sheet-metal spiral is the open-core type, which is especially adaptable for handling long and narrow articles or bulky classes of merchandise or for use where the spiral must wind around an existing column or pass through floors in locations limited by beams or girders that cannot be conveniently cut or moved. For handling bread or other food products, it is customary to have the spiral tread made from monel metal or aluminum.

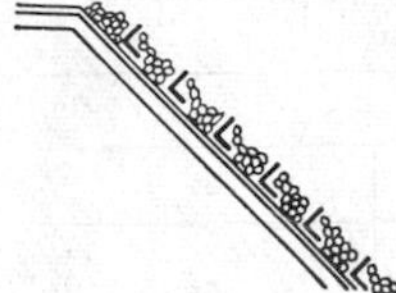
Fig. 21. Inclined chute with cross angles.

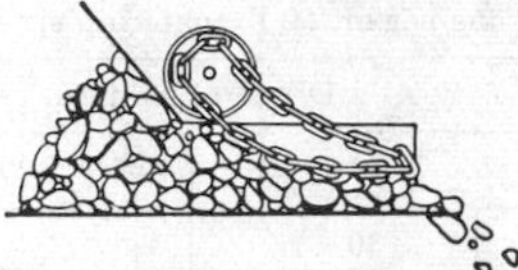
Fig. 22. Ross feeder chute.

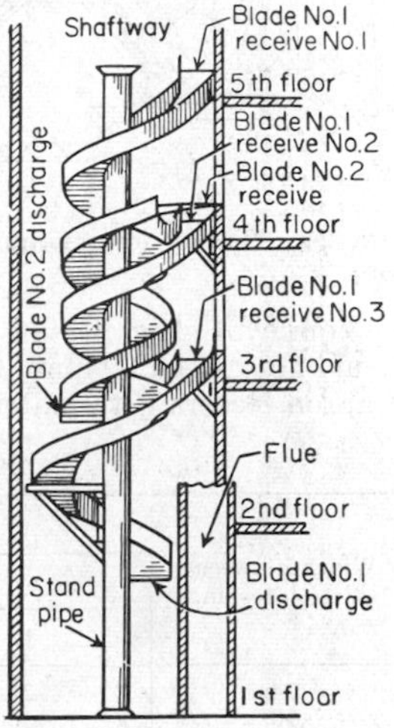

Fig. 23. Metal spiral chute.

CARRYING CONVEYORS

By Harold V. Hawkins

Apron Conveyors

Apron conveyors are specified for granular or lumpy materials. Since the load is carried and not dragged, less power is required than for screw or scraper conveyors. Apron conveyors may have stationary skirt or side plates to permit increased depth of material on the apron, *e.g.*, when used as a feeder for taking material from a track hopper (Fig. 24) with controlled rate of feed. They are not often specified if the length is great, since other types of conveyor are substantially lower in cost. Sizes of lumps are limited by the width of the pans and the ability of the conveyor to withstand the impact of loading. Only end discharge is possible. The apron conveyor (Fig. 25) consists of two strands of roller chain separated by overlapping apron plates, which form the carrying surface, with sides 2 to 6 in. high. The chains are driven by sprockets at one end, take-ups being provided at the other end. The conveyors always pull the material toward the driving end. For light duty, flangeless rollers on flat rails are used; for heavy duty, single-flanged rollers and T rails are used. Apron conveyors may be run without feeders, provided that the opening of the feeding hopper is made sufficiently narrow to prevent material from spilling over the sides of

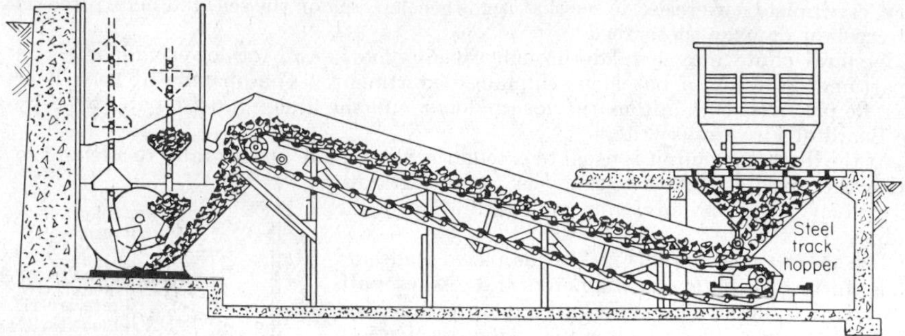

FIG. 24. Track hopper and apron feeder supplying a gravity-discharge bucket-elevator boot.

the conveyor after passing from the opening. When used as a conveyor, the **speed** should not exceed 60 fpm; when used as a feeder, 30 fpm. Table 6 gives the capacities of apron feeders with material weighing 50 lb per cu ft at a speed of 10 fpm.

Table 6. Capacities of Apron Conveyors

Width between skirt plates, in.	Tons per hr, 50 lb material, speed 10 fpm			
	Depth of load, in.			
	12	16	20	24
24	22	30		
30	26	37	47	56
36	34	45	56	67
42	39	52	65	79

Chain pull for horizontal apron conveyor:

$$2LF(W + W_1)$$

Chain pull for inclined apron conveyor:

$$L(W + W_1)(F \cos \theta + \sin \theta) + WL(F \cos \theta - \sin \theta)$$

where L = conveyor length, ft; W = weigth of chain and pans per ft, lb; W_1 = weight of material per ft of conveyor, lb; θ = angle of inclination, deg; F = coefficient of rolling friction, usually 0.1 for plain roller bearings or 0.05 for antifriction bearings.

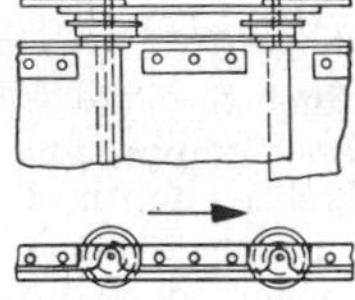

FIG. 25. Apron conveyor.

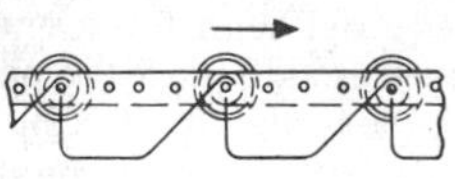

FIG. 26. Open-top carrier.

Bucket Conveyors and Elevators

Open-top bucket carriers (Fig. 26) are similar to apron conveyors, except that dished or bucket-shaped receptacles take the place of the flat or corrugated apron plates used on the apron conveyor. The carriers will operate on steeper inclines than apron conveyors (up to 70 deg), as the buckets prevent material from sliding back. Neither sides extending above the tops of buckets nor skirtboards are necessary. **Speed,** when loaded by a feeder, = 60 fpm (max) and when dragging the load from a hopper or bin, $\leq$ 30 fpm. The **capacity** should be calculated on the basis of the buckets being three-fourths full, the angle of inclination of the conveyor determining the loading condition of the bucket. For **power required,** see p. 10–69.

V-bucket carriers are used for elevating and conveying non-abrasive materials, principally coal when it must be elevated and conveyed with one piece of apparatus. The length and height lifted are limited by the strength of the chains and seldom exceed 75 ft. These carriers can operate on any incline and can discharge at any point on the horizontal run. The size of lumps carried is limited by the size and spacing of the buckets. The carrier consists of two strands of roller chain separated by V-shaped steel buckets. Figure 27 shows the most common form, where material is received on the lower horizontal run, elevated, and discharged through openings in the bottom of the trough of the upper horizontal run. The material is scraped along the horizontal trough of the conveyor, as in a flight conveyor. The steel guard plates *a* at the right prevent spillage at the bends. Figure 28 shows a different form, where material is dug by the elevator from a boot, elevated vertically, scraped along the horizontal run, and discharged through gates in the bottom of the trough. Figure 29 shows a variation of the type shown in Fig. 28, requiring one less bend in the conveyor. The troughs are of steel or steel-lined wood. When feeding material to the horizontal run, it is advisable to use an automatic feeder driven by power from one of the bend shafts to prevent overloading. Should the buckets of this type of conveyor be overloaded, they will spill on the vertical section. The drive is located at *b*, with take-up at *c*. The speed should not exceed 100 fpm when large material is being handled, but when material is small, speed may be increased to 125 fpm. The best results are obtained when speeds are kept low. Table 7 gives the **capacities** and **weights** based on an even and continuous feed.

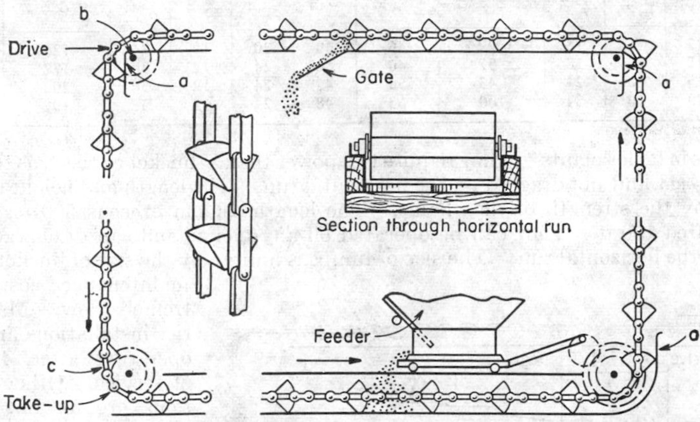

Fig. 27. V-bucket carrier.

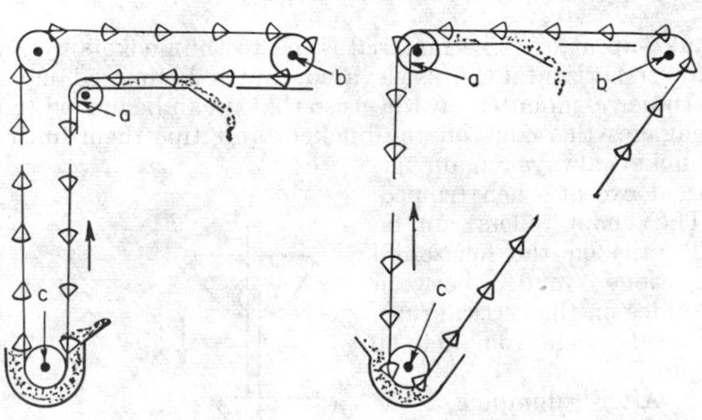

Fig. 28 Fig. 29

Figs. 28 and 29. V-bucket carriers.

Pivoted-bucket carriers are used primarily where the path is a runaround in a vertical plane. Their chief application has been for the dual duty of handling coal

Table 7. Capacities and Weights of V-bucket Carriers

Buckets				Capacity, tons of coal per hour at 100 fpm	Weight per ft of chains and buckets, lb	Buckets				Capacity, tons of coal per hour at 100 fpm	Weight per ft of chains and buckets, lb
Length, in.	Width, in.	Depth, in.	Spacing, in.			Length, in.	Width, in.	Depth, in.	Spacing, in.		
12	12	6	18	29	36	30	20	10	24	126	70
16	12	6	18	32	40	36	24	12	30	172	94
20	15	8	24	43	55	42	24	12	30	200	105
24	20	10	24	100	65	48	24	12	36	192	150

and ashes in boiler plants. They require less power than V-bucket carriers, as the material is carried and not dragged on the horizontal run. The length and height lifted are limited by the strength of the chains. The length seldom exceeds 500 ft, and the height lifted 100 ft. They can be operated on any incline and can discharge at any point on the horizontal run. The size of lumps is limited by the size of buckets. The maintenance cost is extremely low. Many carrier installations are still in operation after 40 years of service. Other applications are for hot clinker, granulated and pulverized chemicals, cement, and stone.

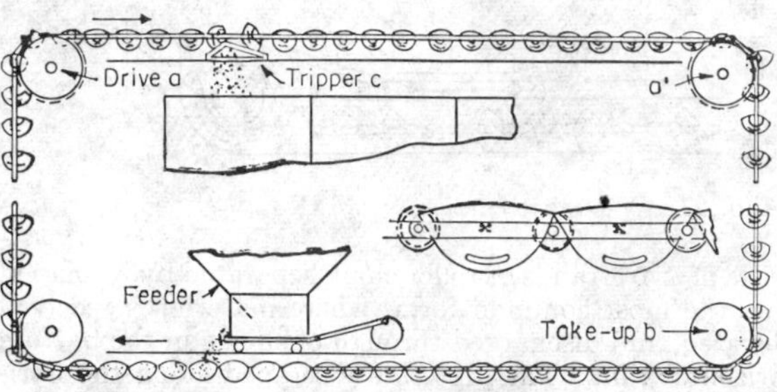

Fig. 30. Pivoted-bucket carrier.

The carrier consists of two strands of roller chain, with flanged rollers, between which are pivoted buckets, usually of malleable iron. The drive (Fig. 30) is located at *a* or *a′*, the take-up at *b*. The material is fed to the buckets by a feeder at any point along the lower horizontal run, is elevated, and is discharged on the upper horizontal run. The tripper *c*, mounted on wheels so that it can be moved to the desired dumping position, engages the cams on the buckets and tips them until the material runs out. The buckets always remain vertical except when tripped. The chain rollers run on T rails on the horizontal sections and between guides on the vertical runs. Speeds range from 30 to 60 fpm.

After dumping, the overlapping bucket lips are in the wrong position to round the far corner; after rounding the take-up wheels, the lap is wrong for making the upturn. The **Peck** carrier eliminates this by suspending the buckets from trunnions attached to rearward cantilever extensions of the inner links (Fig. 31). As the chain rounds the turns, the buckets swing in a larger-radius curve, automatically unlatch, and then lap correctly as they enter the straight run.

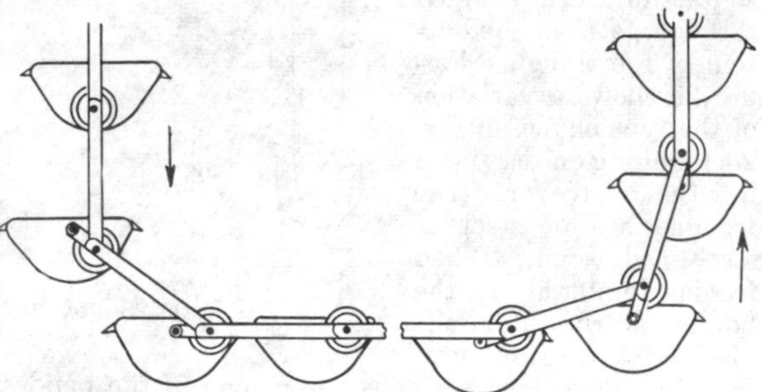

Fig. 31. Peck carrier buckets.

The pivoted-bucket carrier requires little attention beyond periodic lubrication

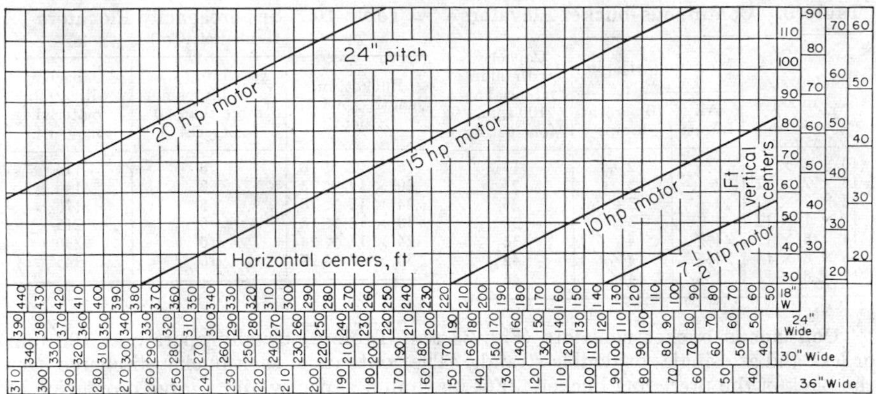

Fig. 32. Motor determinations for pivoted-bucket carriers. (*Link-Belt.*)

and adjustment of take-ups. For the dual service of coal and ash handling, its only competitor is the skip hoist.

Table 8 shows the **capacities** of pivoted-bucket carriers with materials weighing 50 lb per cu ft, with carriers operating at 40 to 50 fpm, and with buckets loaded to 80 percent capacity. Figure 32 gives the motor size for specified horizontal and vertical centers with material weighing 50 lb per cu ft and with speed 40 fpm.

Table 8. Capacities of Pivoted-bucket Carriers with Coal or Similar Materials Weighing 50 lb per cu ft at Speeds Noted

Bucket pitch × width, in.	Capacity, tons of coal per hr	Speed, fpm
24 × 18	35–45	40–50
24 × 24	50–60	40–50
24 × 30	60–75	40–50
24 × 36	70–90	40–50

Example. For a carrier with 240-ft horizontal and 50-ft vertical centers to handle 65 tons of coal per hr, select from Table 8 a 24- by 30-in. carrier at 40 fpm. By Fig. 32, the lines for the horizontal and vertical centers intersect between 15 and 20 hp. Specify a 20-hp motor.

Bucket elevators are of two types: (1) chain-and-bucket, where the buckets are attached to one or two chains; and (2) belt-and-bucket, where the buckets are attached to canvas or rubber belts. Either type may be vertical or inclined and may have continuous or non-continuous buckets. Bucket elevators are used to elevate any bulk material that will not adhere to the bucket. Belt-and-bucket elevators are particularly well adapted to handling abrasive materials which would produce excessive wear on chains. Chain-and-bucket elevators are frequently used with perforated buckets when handling wet material, to drain off surplus water. The length of elevators is limited by the strength of the chains or belts. They may be built up to 100 ft long, but they average 25 to 75 ft. Inclined-belt elevators operate best on an angle of about 30 deg to the vertical. At greater angles, the sag of the return belt is excessive, as it cannot be supported by rollers between the head and foot pulleys. This applies also to single-strand chain elevators. Double-strand chain elevators, however, if provided with roller chain, can run on an angle, as both the upper and return chains are supported by rails. The size of lumps is limited by the size and spacing of the buckets and by the speed of the elevator.

Table 9. Continuous-bucket Elevators

Bucket size in.	Max lump size, in. All lumps	Max lump size, in. 10 percent lumps	Capacity with 50 lb material at 100 fpm, tons per hr
10 × 5 × 8	¾	2½	17
10 × 7 × 12	1	3	21
12 × 7 × 12	1	3	25
14 × 7 × 12	1	3	30
14 × 8 × 12	1¼	4	36
16 × 8 × 12	1½	4½	42
18 × 8 × 12	1½	4½	46

Table 10. Supercapacity Elevators
(Link-Belt Co.)

Bucket, in. length × width × depth	Max lump size, large lumps not more than 20 percent	Capacity with 50 lb material tons per hr
16 × 12 × 18	8	115
20 × 12 × 18	8	145
24 × 12 × 18	8	175
30 × 12 × 18	8	215
24 × 17 × 24	10	230
36 × 17 × 24	10	345

Continuous-bucket elevators (Fig. 33 and Table 9) usually operate at 100 fpm or less and are single- or double-strand. The contents of each bucket discharge over the back of the preceding bucket. For maximum capacity and a large proportion of lumps, the buckets extend rearward behind the chain runs. The elevator is then called a **supercapacity elevator** (Fig. 34 and Table 10).

Gravity-discharge elevators operate at 100 fpm or less and are double-strand, with spaced V buckets. The path may be an L, an inverted L, or a runaround in a vertical plane (Fig. 27). Along the horizontal run, the buckets function as pushers within a trough. An elevator with a tandem flight conveyor costs less. For a runaround path, the pivoted-bucket carrier requires less power and has lower maintenance costs.

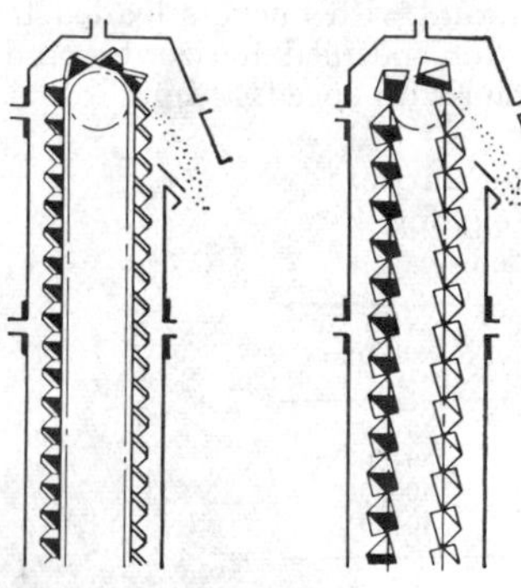

FIG. 33. Continuous bucket. FIG. 34. Supercapacity.

As bucket elevators have no **feed control,** an interlocked feeder is desirable for a gravity flow. Some types scoop up the load as the buckets round the foot end and can take care of momentary surges by spilling the excess back into the boot. The continuous-bucket elevator, however, must be loaded after the buckets line up for the lift, *i.e.*, when the gaps between buckets have closed.

Belt-and-bucket elevators are advantageous for grain, cereals, glass batch, clay, coke breeze, sand, and other abrasives if the temperature is not high enough to scorch the belt (below 250 F for natural rubber).

Elevator casings usually are sectional and dust-tight, either of $\frac{3}{16}$-in. sheet steel or, better, of aluminum. If the elevator has considerable height, its cross section must be sufficiently large to prevent sway contact between buckets and casing. Chain guides extending the length of both runs may be provided to control sway and to prevent piling up of the element, at the boot, should the chain break. **Caution:** Indoor high elevators may develop considerable updraft tending to sweep up light,

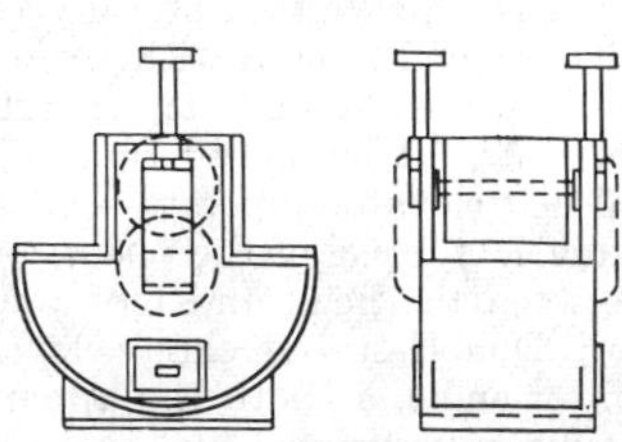

FIG. 35. Cast-iron boot.

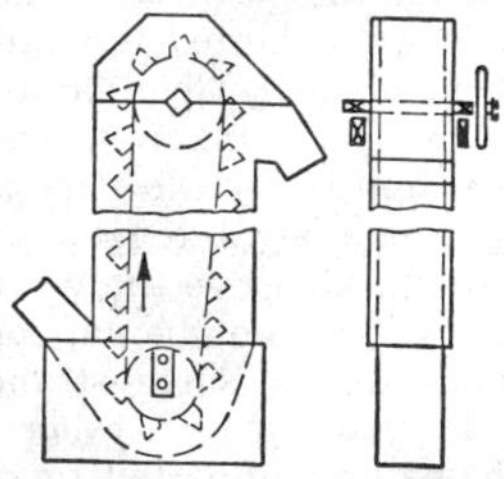

FIG. 36. Structural-steel boot and casing.

pulverized material. Provision to neutralize the pressure differential at the top and bottom may be essential. Figure 35 shows the **cast-iron boot** used with centrifugal-discharge and V-bucket chain elevators and belt elevators. Figure 36 shows the general form of a belt-and-bucket elevator with **structural-steel boot and casing.** Elevators of this type must be run at sufficient speed to throw the discharging material clear of the bucket ahead.

Capacity. Elevators are rated for capacity with the buckets 75 percent loaded. The buckets must be large enough to accommodate the lumps, even through the capacity is small. The bucket spacing and sizes given in Table 11 are standard with most manufacturers.

Table 11. Gravity-discharge Elevators
(Capacity with bituminous coal, at 100 fpm)

Bucket spacing, in.	Bucket length × width, in.				
	20 × 15	24 × 15	20 × 20	24 × 20	30 × 20
18	58	70	104	125	159
24	44	52			
36	29	35	52	63	79

Power Requirements. The motor horsepower for the continuous-bucket and supercapacity elevators can be approximated as

$$\text{Motor hp} = (2 \times \text{tons per hr} \times \text{lift, ft})/1{,}000$$

The motor horsepower of gravity-discharge elevators can be approximated by using the same formula for the lift and adding for the horsepower of the horizontal run the power as estimated for a flight conveyor. For a vertical runaround path, add a similar allowance for the lower horizontal run.

Belt Conveyors

The belt conveyor is a heavy-duty conveyor available for transporting large tonnages over paths beyond the range of any other type of mechanical conveyor. The capacity may be several thousand tons per hour, and the distance several miles. It may be horizontal or inclined upward or downward, or it may be a combination of these, as outlined in Fig. 37. The limit of incline is reached when the material tends to slip on the belt surface. There are special belts with molded designs to assist in keeping material from slipping on inclines. They will handle pulverized, granular, or lumpy material. Special compounds are available if material is hot or oily.

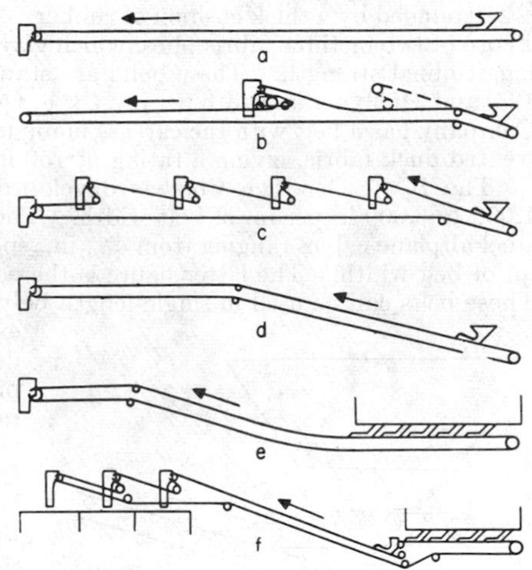

Fig. 37. Typical arrangements of belt conveyors.

In its simplest form, the conveyor consists of a head or drive pulley, a take-up pulley, an endless belt, and carrying and return idlers. The spacing of the carrying idlers varies with the width and loading of the belt and usually is 5 ft or less. Return idlers are spaced on 10-ft centers or slightly less with wide belts. Sealed antifriction idler bearings are used almost exclusively, with pressure-lubrication fittings requiring attention about once a year.

Belts. The belt width is governed by the capacity of the conveyor and the size of lumps. The standard construction of rubber belts (Fig. 38) has several plies of cotton duck or synthetic square-woven fabric such as rayon or nylon cemented together with a rubber compound called the **friction** and covered both top and bottom with rubber to resist abrasion and keep out moisture. The thickness of the top cover is determined by the severity of the job and ranges from 1/16 to 1/2 in. The bottom cover is usually 1/16 in. A layer of loosely woven fabric, called the **breaker strip,** is embedded in the top layer next to the duck to increase the adhesion of the cover to the carcass. Through the use of a breaker, it is often possible to double the adhesion of the cover

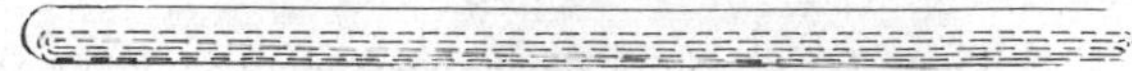

Fig. 38. Rubber-covered conveyor belt.

to the carcass. The belt is rated according to the tension to which it may be safely subjected, and this is a function of the length of the conveyor. The nominal weight of duck is based on a length of 36 in. and width of 44 in. The standard ratings for duck belt per inch of width per ply are as follows (see also Secs. 6 and 8):

Weight of duck, oz	28	32	36	42
Permissible pull, lb per in. of belt width per ply, vulcanized splice	30	35	43	50
Permissible pull, lb per in. of belt width per ply, mechanical splice	24	27	33	40

Thus, for a pull of 3,600 lb and a belt of 24 in., a five-ply belt of 28-oz duck could be used with a vulcanized splice or a five-ply belt of 36-oz duck could be used with a mechanical splice.

High-strength Belts. For belt conveyors of extreme length, a greater strength per inch of belt width is available. In the **cord belt,** a large part of the tension is taken by longitudinal cords embedded in the rubber to form the carcass. Each cord is surrounded by a thick cushion of rubber. The cord plies are placed above and below a core of two or three fabric plies, which give transverse strength as well as add to the longitudinal strength. These belts are standardized for 43, 50, 60, 70, 90, 120, 155, 195, and 240 lb per in. width per ply (B. F. Goodrich Co.). The United States Rubber Company has a belt with the carcass made up of a combination of nylon and specially treated duck fabric, giving a rating of 150 lb per in. width per ply.

The B. F. Goodrich Co. has developed a **wire-cable** reinforced belt rated for 1,000 to 3,000 lb per in. of belt width. The belt has parallel copper-plated braided-steel airplane cables ranging from 3/64 in., spaced 20 per in., up to 5/32 in., spaced 6 per in. of belt width. The latter figure is the equivalent of about 80 plies of 42-oz duck. These belts can be used in single-length belt conveyors for extremely heavy duty and extra length, e.g., for taking ore from deep open pits up to ground level, thus providing an alternative to a spiraling railway.

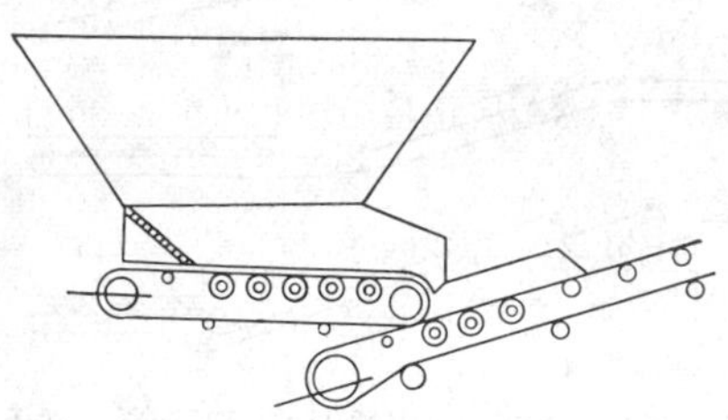

Fig. 39. Pneumatic-tired idlers applied to belt feeder at loading point of belt conveyor.

Synthetic rubber is in use for belts. Combinations of synthetic and natural rubbers have been found satisfactory. Synthetics are superior under special circumstances, e.g., neoprene for flame resistance and resistance to petroleum-based oils, Buna N for resistance to vegetable, animal, and petroleum oils, and butyl for resistance to heat (per RMA).

Belt Life. With lumpy material, the impact at the loading point may be destructive. Heavy lumps, such as ore and rock, cut through the protective cover and expose the carcass. The impact shock is reduced by making the belt supports flexible. This can be done by the use of idlers with cushion or pneumatic tires (Fig. 39) or by supporting the idlers on rubber mountings. Chuting the load vertically against the belt should be avoided. Where possible, the load should be given a movement in the direction of belt travel. When the material is a mixture of lumps and fines, the fines should be screened through to form a cushion for the lumps. Other destructive factors are belt overstressing, belts running out of line and rubbing against supports, broken idlers, and failure to clean the belt surface thoroughly before it comes in contact with the snub and tripper pulleys. Introduction of a 180-deg twist in the return belt (B. F. Goodrich Co.) at both head and tail ends can be used to keep the clean side of the belt against the return idlers and to prevent buildup. Using one 180-deg twist causes both sides of belt to wear evenly. For each twist, 1 ft of length per in. of belt width is required.

Idler Pulleys. Troughing idlers are usually of the three-pulley type (Fig. 40), with the troughing pulleys at 20 deg. There is a growing tendency toward the use of 35 and 45-deg idlers to increase the volume capacity of a belt; 35-deg idlers will increase the volume capacity of a given belt 25 to 35 percent over 20-deg idlers, and

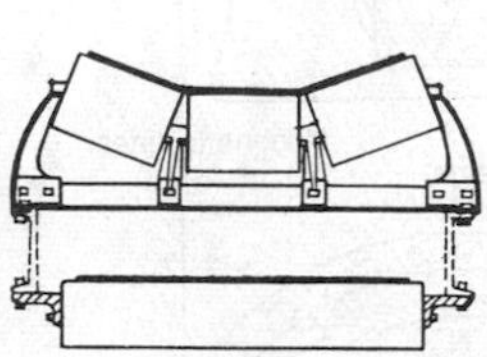

FIG. 40. Standard assembly of three-pulley troughing idler and return idler.

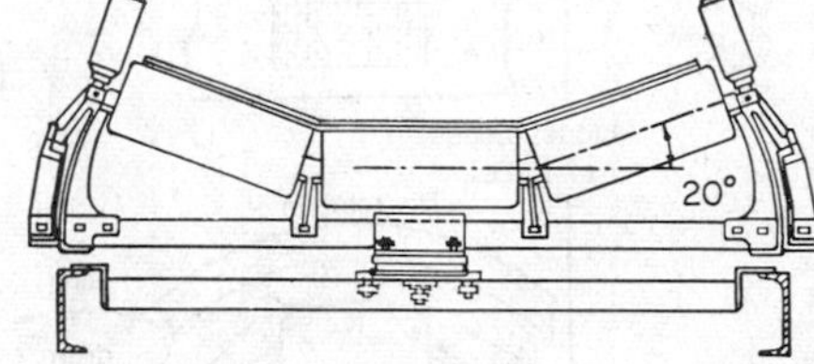

FIG. 41. Self-aligning idler.

45-deg idlers, 35 to 40 percent. The bearings, either roller or ball type, are protected by felt or labyrinth grease seals against the infiltration of abrasive dust. A belt running out of line may be brought into alignment by shifting slightly forward one end or the other with a few idler sets. **Self-aligning idlers** (Fig. 41) should be spaced not more than 75 ft apart. These call attention to the necessity of lining up the belt and should not serve as continuing correctives.

Drive. Belt slip on the conveyor-drive pulley is destructive. There is little difference in tendency to slip between a bare pulley and a rubber-lagged pulley when the belt is clean and dry A wet belt will adhere to a lagged pulley much better, especially if the lagging is grooved. Heavy-duty conveyors exposed to the possibility of wetting the belt are generally driven by a head pulley lagged with a ½-in. rubber belt and with ¼- by ¼-in. grooves spaced ½ in. apart and, preferably, diagonally as a herringbone gear. A snub pulley can be employed to increase the arc of contact on the head pulley, and since the pulley is in contact with the dirty side of the belt, a belt cleaner is essential. The belt cleaner may be a high-speed bristle brush, a spiral rubber wiper (resembling an elongated worm pinion), circular disks mounted slantwise on a shaft to give a wiping effect when rotated, or a scraper. Damp deposits such as clay or semifrozen coal dirt are best removed by multiple diagonal scrapers of stainless steel.

A belt conveyor should be emptied after each run to avoid a heavy starting strain. The motor should have high starting torque, moderate starting-current inrush, and good characteristics when operating under full load. The double-squirrel-cage a-c motor fulfills these requirements.

Heavy-duty Belt-conveyor Drives. For extremely heavy duty, it is essential that the drive torque be built up slowly, or serious belt damage will occur. The hydraulic clutch, derived from the hydraulic automobile clutch, serves nicely. The best drive developed to date is the **dynamatic clutch** (Fig. 42). This has a magnetized rotor on the extended motor shaft, revolving within an iron ring keyed to the reduction gearing of the conveyor. The energizing current is automatically built up over a period that may extend to 2 min, and the increasing magnetic pull on the ring builds up the belt speed.

Take-ups. For short conveyors, a screw take-up is satisfactory. For long conveyors, the expansion and contraction of the belt with temperature changes and the necessity of occasional cutting and resplicing make a weighted gravity take-up preferable, especially if a vulcanized splice is used. The take-up should, if possible, be located where the slack first occurs, usually just back of the drive except in a conveyor inclined downward (retarding conveyor), when the take-up is located at the downhill end.

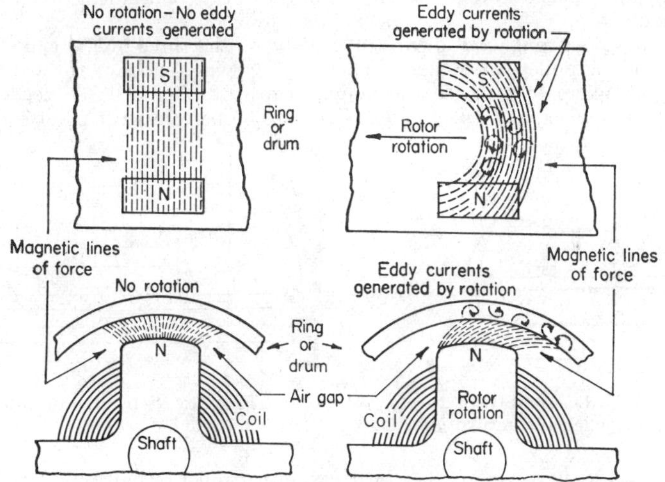

Fig. 42. Operating principle of the dynamatic clutch.

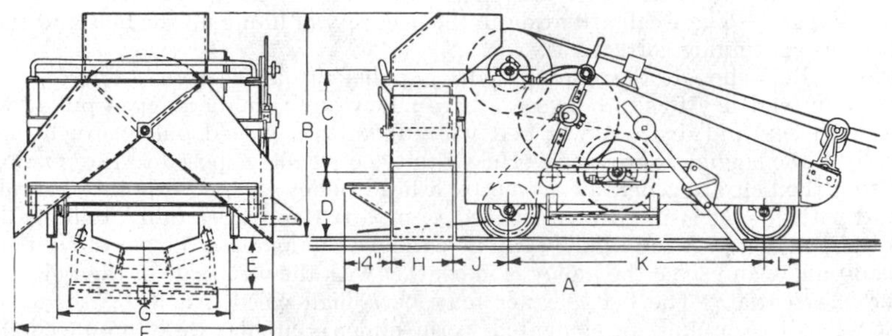

Fig. 43. Self-propelled tripper with automatic reverse and auxiliary hand control.

Trippers. The load may be removed from the belt by a diagonal or V plow, but a tripper that snubs the belt backward is standard equipment. Trippers may be (1) stationary, (2) manually propelled by crank, or (3) propelled by power from one of the snubbing pulleys (Fig. 43) or by an independent motor. The discharge may be chuted to either side or back to the belt by a deflector plate. When the tripper must move back to the load-receiving end of the conveyor, it is usual to incline the belt for about 15 ft to match the slope up to the tripper top pulley. As the lower tripper snub pulleys are in contact with the dirty side of the belt, a cleaner must be provided between the pulleys. A scraper in light contact with the face of the pulley may be advisable.

Belt Slope. The slopes (in degrees) given in Table 12 are the maximum permissible angles for various materials.

Table 12. Maximum Belt Slopes for Various Materials, Degrees

Material	Degrees	Material	Degrees	Material	Degrees
Coal, bituminous	20	Briquets	10	Ore, crushed	20
Coal, mine run	18	Gravel, bank	18	Sand, damp	20
Coke, screened	17	Gravel, washed	12	Sand, dry	15
Earth, loose	20	Grains	15	Wood chips	28

Determination of Motor Horsepower. The power required to drive a belt conveyor is the sum of the powers required (1) to move the empty belt, (2) to move the load horizontally, and (3) to lift the load if the conveyor is inclined upward. If (3) is larger than the other two, an automatic brake must be provided to hold the conveyor if the current fails. A solenoid brake is usual. The power required to move the empty belt is given by Fig. 44. The power to move 100 tons per hr horizontally is given by the formula hp $= 0.4 + 0.00325L$, where L is the distance between centers, ft. For other capacities the horsepower is proportional.

The capacity in tons per hour for materials of various weights per cubic foot is given by Table 13. For grains, use 0.85 of the listed figures. Table 14 gives minimum belt widths for lumps of various sizes. Table 15 gives advisable maximum belt speeds for various belt widths and materials. The speed should ensure full-capacity loading so that the entire belt width is utilized.

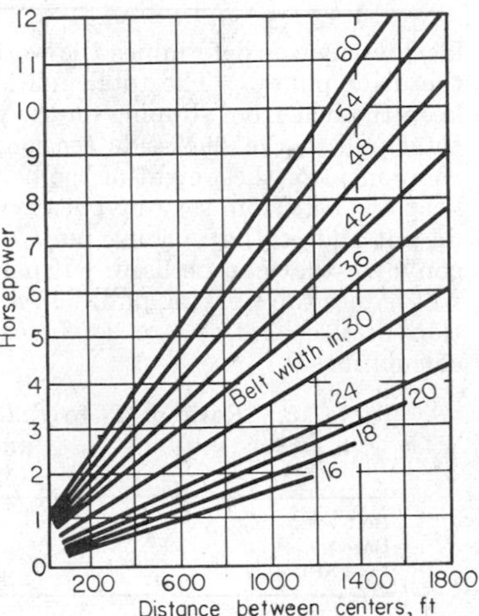

FIG. 44. Horsepower required to move belt conveyor empty at 100 fpm.

Drive Calculations. From the standpoint of the application of power to the belt, a conveyor is identical with a power belt (see pp. 3–45 to 3–47). The determining factors are the coefficient of friction between the drive pulley and the belt, the tension in the belt, and the arc of contact between the pulley and the belt. The arc of contact is increased up to about 240 deg by using a snub pulley and up to 410 deg by using two pulleys geared together or driven by separate motors and having the belt wrapped around them in the form of a letter S. The resistance to be overcome is the sum of all the frictional resistances throughout the length of the conveyor plus, in the case of a rising conveyor, the resistance due to lifting the load. The sum of the conveyor and

Table 13. Capacities of Troughed Belts
(United States Rubber Co.)
(Tons per hour with belt speed of 100 fpm)

Belt width, in.	Weight of material, lb per cu ft				Belt width, in.	Weight of material, lb per cu ft			
	30	50	100	150		30	50	100	150
14	10	17	34	51	30	47	79	158	237
16	13	22	44	66	36	69	114	228	342
18	17	28	56	84	42	97	162	324	486
20	20	34	68	102	48	130	215	430	645
24	30	50	100	150	60	207	345	690	1035

Table 14. Minimum Belt Width for Lumps

Belt width, in.	14	16	18	24	30	36	42	48	60
Sized material, in.	2	2½	3	4½	7	8	10	12	12
Unsized material, in.	3	4	5	8	12	14	20	24	28

Table 15. Maximum Belt Speeds, Fpm, for Various Materials

Width of belt, in.	Light or free-flowing materials, grains dry sand, etc.	Moderately free-flowing sand, gravel, fine stone, etc.	Lump coal, coarse stone, crushed ore	Heavy sharp lumpy materials, heavy ores, lump coke
12–14	400	250		
16–18	500	300	250	
20–24	600	400	350	250
30–36	750	500	400	300
42–60	850	550	450	350

load resistances determines the working pull that has to be transmitted to the belt at the drive pulley. The total pull is increased by the slack-side tension necessary to keep the belt from slipping on the pulley. (See Table 3, p. 3–46, for the ratio of the total pull to the slack-side tension.) Other factors adding to the belt pull are the component of the weight of the belt if the conveyor is inclined and a take-up pull to keep the belt from sagging between the idlers at the loading point. These, however, do not add to the working pull. The maximum belt pull determines the length of conveyor that can be used. If part of the conveyor runs downgrade, the load on it will reduce the working pull. In moderate-length conveyors, stresses due to acceleration or deceleration are safely carried by the factor of safety used for belt-life calculations.

Table 16. Ratio of T_1 to T_e for Various Arcs of Contact with Bare Pulleys and Lagged Pulleys

(Coefficients of friction 0.25 and 0.35, respectively)

Belt wrap, deg	180	200	210	215	220	240
Bare pulley	1.85	1.72	1.67	1.64	1.62	1.54
Lagged pulley	1.50	1.42	1.38	1.36	1.35	1.30

The total or maximum tension T_{max} must be known to specify a suitable belt. The effective tension T_e is the difference between tight-side tension and slack-side tension, or $T_e = T_1 - T_2$. The coefficient of friction between rubber and steel is 0.25; with a lagged pulley, between rubber and rubber, it is 0.55 for ideal conditions but should be taken as 0.35 to allow for loss due to dirty conditions.

Except for extremely heavy belt pulls, the tandem drive is seldom used since it is costly; the lagged-and-grooved drive pulley is used for most industrial installations.

For a belt with 6,000-lb max tension running on a bare pulley drive with 180-deg wrap (Table 16), $T = 1.85T_e = 6{,}000$ lb; $T_e = 3{,}200$ lb. Such a belt, 30 in. wide, might be a six-ply 36-oz duck, a four-ply cord belt rated at 70 lb per in. width per ply, or a steel-wire-cable belt with $\frac{3}{16}$-in. cables spaced six per inch. The last is the most costly.

In an inclined belt with single pulley drive, the T_{max} is lowest if the drive is at the head end and increases as the drive shifts toward the foot end.

Allowance for Tripper. The belt lifts about 5 ft to pass over the top snub pulley of the tripper (Fig. 43). Allowance should be made for this lift in determining the power requirement of the conveyor. If the tripper is propelled by the belt, an allowance of 1 hp for a 16-in. belt, 3 hp for a 36-in. belt, or 7 hp for a 60-in. belt is ample. If a rotary cleaning brush is driven from one of the snub shafts, an allowance should be made which is approximately the same as that for the propulsion of the tripper.

Magnetic pulleys are frequently used as head pulleys on belt conveyors to remove tramp iron, such as stray nuts or bolts, before crushing; to concentrate magnetic ores, such as magnetite or nickeliferous pyrrhotite, from non-magnetic material; and to reclaim iron from foundry refuse. A chute or hopper automatically receives the extracted material as it is drawn down through the other non-magnetic material, drawn around the end pulley on the belt, and finally released as the belt leaves the pulley. Light-duty permanent-magnet types (for pulleys 12 to 24 in. in diameter) will separate material through a 2-in. layer on the belt. Heavy-duty permanent-magnet units (12 to 24 in. in diameter) will separate material if the belt carries over

2 in. of material or if the magnetic content is very fine. Even larger units are available for special applications. So effective and powerful are the permanent-magnet types that **electromagnetic pulleys** are only available in the larger sizes, from 18 to 48 in. in diameter. The permanent-magnet type requires no slip rings, external power, or upkeep. Table 17 gives approximate performance data.

Table 17. Data on Magnetic Pulleys (Dings)

Diameter, in.	Shipping weight per ft width, lb			Light-duty permanent magnet—2-in. burden depth		Heavy-duty permanent or electromagnet, over 2-in. burden depth		Electromagnet, approx watts per ft belt width
	Permanent magnet		Electromagnet	Belt speed, fpm	Capacity, tons per hr per ft belt width*	Belt speed, fpm	Capacity, tons per hr per ft belt width*	
	Light	Heavy						
12	221	237	.....	135	23	175	28	.....
15	200	265	.....	165	28	200	33	.....
18	260	344	535	190	35	225	40	600
24	545	740	820	250	52	285	75	770
30	...	...	1,185	...	...	315	93	1,020
36	...	...	1,620	...	...	375	95	1,200
42	...	...	2,320	...	...	385	100	1,360
48	...	...	3,200	...	...	440	110	1,620

* Figures given are for level conveyors. Improvement factors vary from 4.5 percent at 5 deg to 18 percent at 20 deg of elevation of belt. Capacities shown are for coal at 50 lb per cu ft when computing volume conveyed. Volume of any other material will be reduced in proportion of its unit weight to that of coal.

Overhead electromagnetic separators (Dings) for suspension above a belt conveyor are also available to pull magnetic material from burden as thick as 40 in. and at belt speeds to 750 fpm. These may or may not be equipped with a separately encompassing belt to be self-cleaning. Wattages vary from 1,035 to cover an area of 16 in. wide by 21½ in. long to 12,870 for a 66-in. width by 82½-in. length.

Trippers of the fixed or movable type are used for discharging material between the ends of a belt conveyor. Figure 43 shows a **self-propelling tripper** which consists of two pulleys, over which the belt passes, the material being discharged into the chute as the belt bends around the upper pulley. The pulleys are mounted on a frame carried by four wheels and power driven. A lever on the frame and stops alongside the rails enable the tripper, taking power from the conveyor belt, to move automatically between the stops, thus distributing the material. Rail clamps are provided to hold the tripper in a fixed position when discharging. Motor-driven trippers are used when it is desirable to move the tripper independently of the conveyor belt. Fixed trippers have their pulleys mounted on the conveyor framework instead of on a movable carriage.

Shuttle conveyors are frequently used in place of trippers for distributing materials. They consist of a reversible belt conveyor mounted upon a movable frame and discharging over either end.

Belt-conveyor Arrangements. Figure 37 shows **typical arrangements of belt conveyors.** *a* is a level conveyor receiving material at one end and discharging at the other. *b* shows a level conveyor with traveling tripper. The receiving end of the conveyor is depressed so that the belt will not be lifted against the chute when the tripper is at its extreme loading end. *c* is a level conveyor with fixed trippers. *d* shows an inclined end combined with a level section. *e* is a combination of level conveyor, vertical curve, and horizontal section. The radius of the vertical curve depends upon the weight of the belt and the tension in the belt at the point of tangency. This must be figured in each case and is found by the formula: min radius, ft = belt tension at lowest point of curve divided by weight per ft of belt. The belt weight should be for the worn belt with not over ¹⁄₁₆-in. top cover. *f* is a combination of level conveyor receiving material from a bin, a fixed dump, an inclined section, and a series of fixed trippers.

Portable conveyors are widely used around retail coal yards, small power plants, and at coal mines for storing coal and reclaiming it for loading into trucks or cars. They are also used for handling other bulk materials. They consist of a short section of chain or belt conveyors mounted on large wheels or crawler treads and powered with a gasoline engine or electric motor. They vary in length from 20 to 90 ft and can handle up to 250 tons per hr of coal. For capacities greater than what two men can shovel onto a belt, some form of power loader is necessary.

Sectional belt conveyors have come into wide use in coal mines for bringing the coal from the face and loading it into cars in the entry. They consist of short sections (6 ft or more) of light frame of special low-type construction. The sections are designed for ease of connecting and disconnecting for transfer from one part of the mine to another. They are built in lengths up to 1,000 ft or more under favorable conditions and can handle 125 tons per hr of coal.

Sliding-belt conveyors use belts sliding on decks instead of troughed belts carried on rollers. Sliding belts are used in the shipping rooms of department stores for handling miscellaneous parcels, in post offices for handling mail bags, in chemical plants for miscellaneous light waste, etc. The decking preferably is of maple strips. If of steel, the deck should be perforated at intervals to relieve the vacuum effect between the bottom of the belt and the deck. Cotton or balata belts are best. The speed should be low. The return run may be carried on 4-in. straight-face idlers. The power requirement is greater than with idler rolls.

The **oscillating conveyor** is a horizontal trough varying in width from 12 to 48 in., mounted on rearward-inclined cantilever supports, and driven from an eccentric at 400 to 500 rpm. The effect is to "bounce" the material along at about 50 fpm with minimum wear on the trough. The conveyor is adapted to abrasive or hot fragmentary materials, such as scrap metals, castings, or metal chips. The trough bottom may be a screen plate to cull fine material, as when cleaning sand from castings, or the trough may have louvers and a ventilating hood to cool the moving material. These oscillating conveyors may have unit lengths up to 100 ft. Capacities range from a few tons to 100 tons per hr with high efficiency and low maintenance.

Feeders

When material is drawn from a hopper or bin to a conveyor, an **automatic feeder** should be used (unless the material is dry and free-running, *e.g.*, grain). The satisfactory operation of any conveyor depends on the material being fed to it in an even and continuous stream. The automatic feeder not only ensures a constant and controlled feed, irrespective of the size of material, but saves the expense of a man who would otherwise be required at the feeding point. Figure 45 shows a **reciprocating plate feeder,** consisting of a plate mounted on four wheels and forming the bottom of the hopper. When the plate is moved forward, it carries the material with it; when moved back, the plate is withdrawn from under the material, allowing it to fall into the chute. The plate is moved by connecting rods from cranks or eccentrics. The capacity of this feeder is determined by the length and number of strokes, width of plate, and location of the adjustable gate. The number of strokes should not exceed 60 to 70 per min. When used under a track hopper, the material remaining on the plate may freeze in winter, as this type of feeder is not self-clearing.

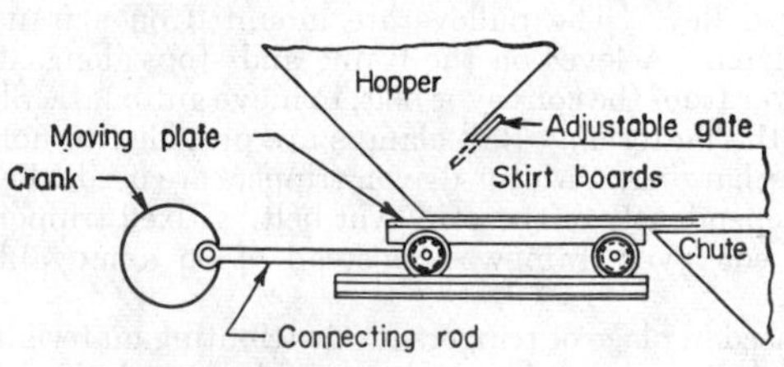

Fig. 45. Reciprocating plate feeder.

Vibrating Feeders. The vibrating feeder consists of a plate inclined downward slightly and vibrated (1) by a high-speed unbalanced pulley, (2) by electromagnetic vibrations from one or more solenoids, as in the Jeffrey Manufacturing Co. feeder, or (3) by the slower pulsations secured by mounting the plate on rearward-inclined leaf springs.

The **electric vibrating feeder** (Fig. 46) operates magnetically with a large number of short strokes (7,200 per min from an alternating current in the small sizes and 3,600 from a pulsating direct current in the larger sizes). It is built to feed from a few pounds per minute to 1,250 tons per hr and will handle any material that does not adhere to the pan. It is self-cleaning, instantaneously adjustable for capacity, and controllable from any point near or remote. It is usually supported from above with spring shock absorbers *a* in each hanger, but it may be supported from below with similar springs in the supports A modified form can be set to feed a weighed **constant amount** hourly for process control.

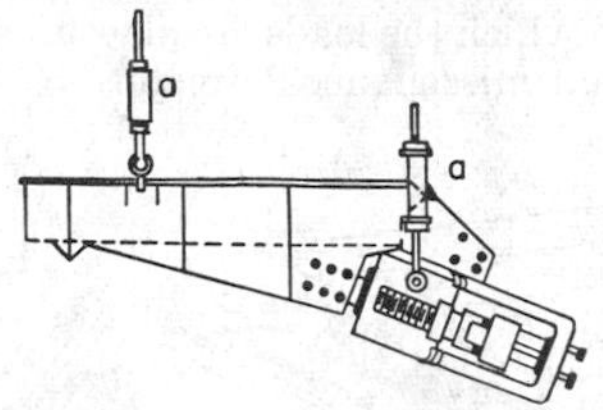

FIG. 46. Electric vibrating feeder.

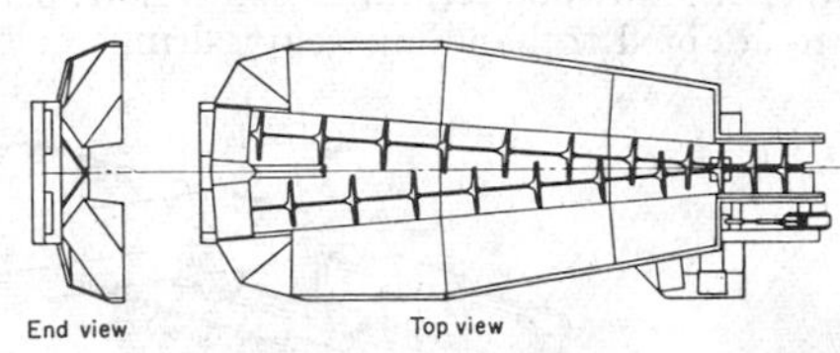

FIG. 47. Ratio feeder. (*Columbus McKinnon.*)

The **Ratio** (trademark of Columbus McKinnon) **feeder** is a flight-conveyor type of unit having two converging sets of flights moving lengthwise along its bed (see Fig. 47). At the inlet end, the flights provide a wide carrying surface, but as they approach the narrow outlet-throat section, they mesh together to reduce the carrying width. This construction is possible by the use of welded-link chain, which is flexible horizontally to permit the converging and flexible vertically to permit the driving over the pocket wheel that propels the chain. Such a feeder will accept a large, sudden surge of material, will carry it away from the delivery means (*e.g.*, a coal-mining shuttle car), and will then "ration" it out onto a belt at a uniform rate.

Roller Conveyors

The principle involved in **gravity roller conveyors** is the control of motion due to gravity by interposing an antifriction trackage set at a definite grade. Roller conveyors are used in the movement of all sorts of package goods with smooth surfaces

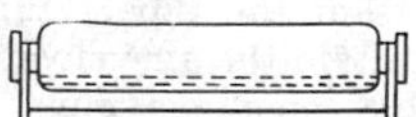

FIG. 48. Gravity roller conveyor.

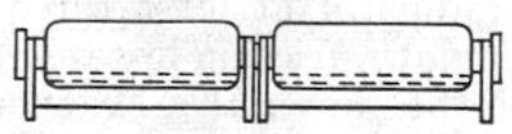

FIG. 49. Multiple-roller conveyor.

FIG. 50. Wheel-type conveyor.

which are sufficiently rigid to prevent sagging between rollers—in warehouses, brickyards, building-supply yards, department stores, post offices, and the manufacturing and shipping departments of industrial manufacturers.

The **rollers vary in diameter** and strength from 1 in., with a capacity of 5 lb per roller, up to 4 in., with a capacity of 1,800 lb per roller. The heavier rollers are generally used in foundries and steel mills for moving large molds, castings, or stacks of sheet steel. The small roller is used for handling small, light objects. The spacing of the rollers in the frames varies with the size and weight of the objects to be moved. Three rollers should be in contact with the package to prevent hobbling. The grade of fall required to move the object varies from 1½ to 7 percent, depending on the weight and character of the material in contact with the rollers.

Figure 48 shows a typical cross section of a roller conveyor. Curved sections are similar in construction to straight sections, except that in the majority of cases multiple rollers (Fig. 49) are used to keep the package properly lined up and in the center of conveyor.

Figure 50 illustrates a **wheel conveyor,** used for handling bundles of shingles, fruit boxes, bundles of fiber cartons, and large, light cases. The wheels are of ball-bearing type, bolted to flat-bar or angle-frame rails.

When an installation involves a **trunk line with several tributary runs,** a simple two-arm deflector at each junction point holds back the item on one run until the item on the other has cleared. **Power-operated** roller conveyors permit handling up an incline. Usually the rolls are driven by sprockets on the spindle ends. An alternative of a smooth deck and pusher flights should be considered as costing less and permitting steeper inclines.

Platform conveyors are single- or double-strand conveyors (Fig. 51) with plates of steel or hardwood forming a continuous platform on which the loads are placed. They are adapted to handling heavy drums or barrels and miscellaneous freight.

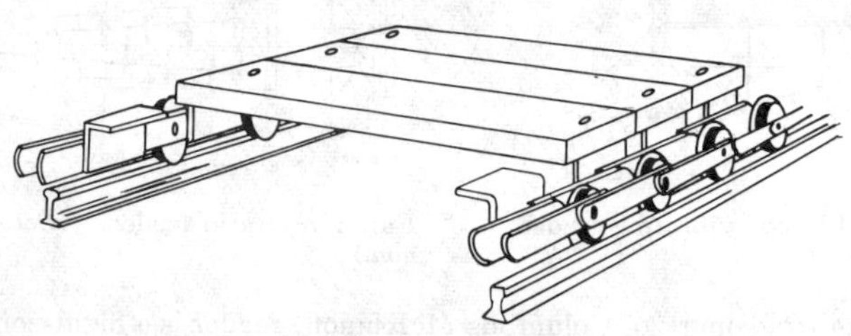

FIG. 51. Double-strand platform conveyor.

Pneumatic Conveyors

The pneumatic conveyor transports dry, free-flowing, granular material in suspension within a pipe or duct by means of a high-velocity airstream or by the energy of expanding compressed air within a comparatively dense column of fluidized or aerated material. Principal uses are (1) dust collection; (2) conveying soft materials, such as grain, dry foodstuff (flour and feeds), chemicals (soda ash, lime, salt cake), wood chips, carbon black, and sawdust; (3) conveying hard materials, such as fly ash, cement, silica metallic ores, and phosphate. The need in processing of bulk-transporting plastic pellets, powders, and flour under contaminationfree conditions has increased the use of pneumatic conveying.

Dust Collection. All pipes should be as straight and short as possible, and bends, if necessary, should have a radius of at least three diameters of the pipe. Pipes should be proportioned to keep down friction losses and yet maintain the air velocities that will prevent settling of the material. Frequent cleanout openings must be provided. Branch connections should go into the sides of the main and deliver the incoming stream as nearly as possible in the direction of flow of the main stream. Sudden changes in diameter should be avoided to prevent eddy losses. (See also p. 7–80 *et seq.*)

When **vertical runs** are short in proportion to the horizontal runs, the size of the riser is locally restricted, thereby increasing the air velocity and producing sufficient lifting power to elevate the material. If the vertical pipes are comparatively long, they are not restricted, but the necessary lifting power is secured by increased velocity and suction throughout the entire system.

The area of the main at any point should be 20 to 25 percent in excess of the sums of the branches entering it between the point in question and the dead end of the main. Floor sweepers, if equipped with efficient blast gates, need not be included in computing the main area. The diameter of the connecting pipe from machine to main and the suction required at each hood are determined by experience. The sum of the volumes of each branch gives the total volume to be handled by the fan.

Fan Suction. The maintained resistance at the fan is composed of (1) suctions of the various hoods, which must be chosen from experience (see p. 12–145), (2) collector loss, and (3) loss due to pipe friction.

The **pipe loss** for any machine is the sum of the losses in the corresponding branch and in the main from that branch to the fan. For each elbow, add a length equal to 10 diameters of straight pipe. The total loss in the system, or static pressure required at the fan, is equal to the sum of (1), (2), and (3).

For conveying soft materials, a fan is used to create a suction. The suspended material is collected at the terminal point by a separator upstream from the fan. The material may be moved from one location to another or may be unloaded from barge or rail car. Required conveying velocity ranges from 2,000 fpm for light materials, such as sawdust, to 3,000 to 4,000 fpm for medium-weight materials, such as grain. Since abrasion is no problem, steel pipe or galvanized-metal ducts are satisfactory. Unnecessary bends and fittings should be avoided to minimize power consumption.

For conveying hard materials, a water-jet exhauster or steam exhauster is used on suction systems, and a positive-displacement blower on pressure systems. A mechanical exhauster may also be used on suction systems if there is a bag filter or air washer ahead of the exhauster. The largest tonnage of hard material handled is fly ash. A single coal-fired, steam-electric plant may collect more than 1,000 tons of fly ash per day. Fly ash can be conveyed several miles pneumatically at 30 tons or more per hr using a pressure conveyor. Another high-tonnage material conveyed pneumatically is cement. Individual transfer conveyors may handle several hundred tons per hour. Hard materials are usually also heavy and abrasive. Required conveying velocities vary from 4,000 to 5,000 fpm. Heavy cast-iron or alloy pipe and fittings are required to prevent excessive wear.

Pneumatic ash-handling systems usually have the airstream maintained either by a stream-jet ejector-type fitting, located at the foot of the riser pipe that leads to a storage bin, or by the more efficient Argand type of jet between the receiver and air washer, as in the Nuveyor (Fig. 52). An airstream of 3,500 cu ft of free air per min

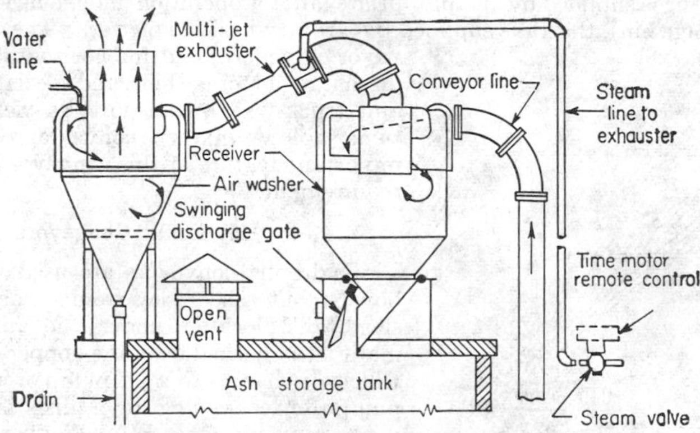

Fig. 52. Nuveyor pneumatic ash-handling system.

through an 8-in. pipe (United Conveyor) will provide a handling capacity of 300 lb of dry ash per min, which is about the rate at which a man can hoe the ashes from pit to intake.

The **power requirement** for pneumatic conveyors is much greater than for a mechanical conveyor of equal capacity, but the duct can be led along practically any path. There are no moving parts and no risk of injury to the attendant The vacuum-cleaner action provides dustless operation, sometimes important when pulverized material is unloaded from boxcars through flexible hose and nozzle. A few materials build up a static-electric charge which may introduce an explosion risk. Sulphur is an outstanding example. Sticky materials tend to pack at the elbows and are unsuitable for pneumatic handling.

The performance of a pneumatic conveyor cannot be predicted with the accuracy usual with the various types of mechanical conveyors and elevators. It is necessary to rely on the advice of experienced engineers.

The **Fuller-Kinyon system** for transporting dry pulverized material consists of a motor- or engine-driven pump, a source of compressed air for fluidizing the material, a conduit or pipeline, distributing valves (operated manually, electropneumatically, or by motor), and electric binlevel indicators (high-level, low-level, or both). The impeller is a specially designed differential-pitch screw normally turning at 1,200 rpm. The material enters the feed hopper and is compressed in the decreasing pitch of the screw flights. At the discharge end of the screw, the mass is introduced through a check valve to a mixing chamber, where it is aerated by the introduction of compressed air. The fluidized material is conveyed in the transport line by the continuing action of the impeller screw and the energy of expanding air. Practical distance of transportation by the system depends upon the material to be handled. Cement has been handled in this manner for distances up to a mile. The most important field of application is the handling of portland cement. For this material, the Fuller-Kinyon pump is used for such operations as moving both raw material and finished cement within the cement-manufacturing process; loading out; unloading ships, barges, and railway cars; and transferring from storage to mixer plant on large construction jobs.

The **Airslide** (registered trademark of the Fuller Company) **conveyor system** is an air-activated gravity-type conveyor using low-pressure air to aerate or fluidize pulverized material to a degree which will permit it to flow on a slight incline by the force of gravity. The conveyor comprises an enclosed trough, the bottom of which has an inclined air-permeable surface. Beneath this surface is a plenum chamber through which air is introduced at low pressure, the pressure depending upon the application. Various control devices for controlling and diverting material flow and for controlling air supply may be provided as part of complete systems. For normal conveying applications, the air is supplied by an appropriate fan; for operation under a head of material (as in a storage bin), the air is supplied by a rotary positive blower. The Airslide conveyor is widely used for horizontal conveying, discharge of storage bins, and special railway-car and truck-trailer transport, as well as in stationary blow-tank-type conveying systems. An important feature of this conveyor is low power requirement.

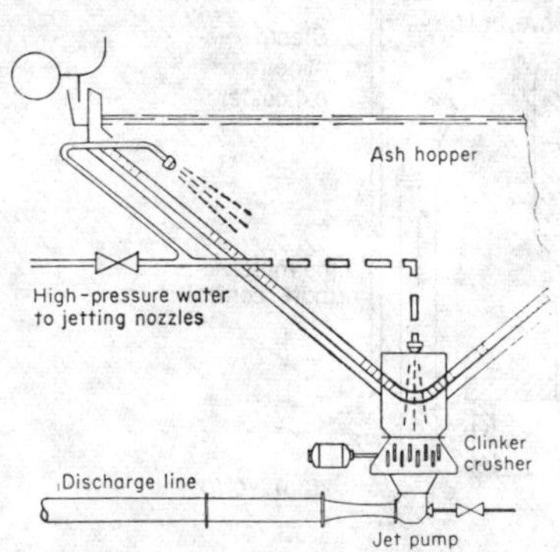

Fig. 53. Ash-sluicing system with jet pump. (*United Conveyor.*)

Hydraulic Conveyors

Hydraulic conveyors are used for handling boiler-plant ash or slag from an ash hopper or slag tank located under the furnace. The material is flushed from the hopper to a grinder, which discharges to a jet pump or a mechanical pump for conveying to a disposal area or a dewatering bin (Fig. 53). Water requirements average 1 gal per lb of ash.

Pipeline Transportation of Coal. (See p. 11–85 *et seq.*)

Pipeline Transportation of Concrete. The **Pumpcrete** method of handling concrete by Rex Chain Belt Equipment provides for the pumping of mixed concrete by positive-displacement hydraulic rams in either 6-in. or 8-in. steel pipes at heights up to 120 ft or horizontal distances to 1000 ft (or equivalent combinations at 1:8 ratio). Delivery rates are 15 to 65 cu yd per hr using 25 to 60 hp at the pump and up to 17 hp for the remixer at pump point. To ensure that no concrete is wasted and to simplify cleanout of the pipe, a "go-devil" plug is forced with water pressure (using the Pumpcrete ram) behind the concrete, cleaning the pipe and ejecting the last yard simultaneously. Sometimes air pressure is used if the disposal of the water is especially difficult.

AUTOMATIC METERING

By Harold V. Hawkins

Automatic scales are often used for **weighing** and **recording** the weight of material being carried by belt conveyors, apron conveyors, open-top carriers, or pivoted-bucket carriers. They may also be adapted to recording the gross weights of loaded cars, such as are used on industrial cable railways or overhead transporters, without stopping the cars on the weighing track. By returning the empty cars, the mechanism can be made to deduct automatically the tare weight from the gross weight, leaving the net weight of the material transported. The output from the scale can be used to control the processing of material carried. The scales may be either continuous or batch weighers. Some of the continuous weighers function through constant volume control, and others through constant weight control, and thus they are automatic feeders as well as weighers.

Figure 54 shows the **Merrick Weightometer** attached to a belt conveyor. A number of the supporting idlers *a* are carried by the steel framework, hung by the

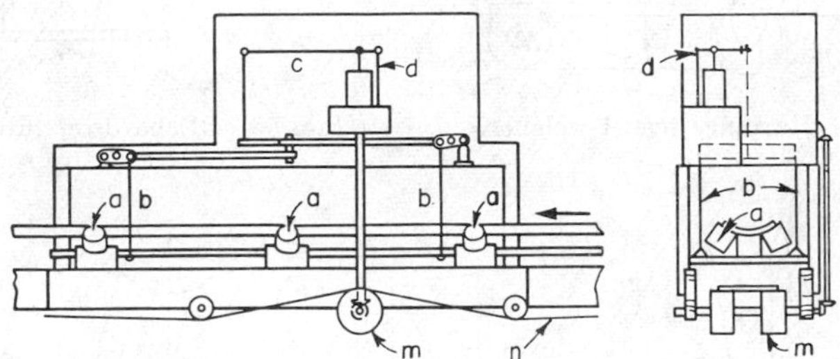

FIG. 54. Merrick Weightometer for belt conveyor.

rod *b* from the scale beams. These scale beams are attached by levers to the weighbeam *c*. The weight of the load on the suspended portion of the conveyor at any instant is automatically balanced by the buoyancy of the cylindrical steel float suspended from the long end of the weighing beam and partly immersed in a bath of mercury. An increase or decrease of the load on the levers will raise or lower the float in the mercury *d* until the loss or gain in buoyancy compensates for the variation in load. The function of the float is to ensure that the movement of the beam from its zero position, when the conveyor is empty, will be proportional to the weight of the material at any instant on the suspended portion of the conveyor. The extreme end of weighbeam *c* is connected by rod *d* to a totalizing mechanical integrator, which gets actual belt speed from idler wheel *m*, from return belt *n*, to give instantaneous flow rate on the belt. Models are also available which electrically weigh and integrate the load carried.

The **Hardinge feeder-weigher** (Fig. 55) is a pivoted short belt which controls the rate of flow from a hopper by weight per cubic foot. Any desired rate of feed is attained by adjusting the counterweight or by varying the speed. A constant-weight feed is maintained, and a revolution counter records the distance the belt travels and, when calibrated, records the weight. Its error should not exceed 0.5 percent.

The **Richardson automatic scale** (Fig. 56) weighs batches of from 200 to 1,000 lb and records the weight total on a counter. A counterweighted hopper is served by a belt feeder. When the beam is poised, the feed is stopped and the hopper empties. Then the cycle repeats. An accuracy within 0.5 percent is usual. Any flowable material without lumps larger than 3 in. can be handled.

Feeders for Automatic Batch Weighers. To ensure constant accuracy in automatic batch weighing, the scale must be fed in a steady stream. This becomes obvious when automatic batch weighing is viewed as "cutting up" the stream into equal batches by weight. Figure 57 indicates how this is accomplished by Richardson for various kinds of bulk materials: (*a*) Granular free-flowing materials can be fed directly from an overhead bin. For many ground, sluggish materials, an agitator assists the flow. (*b*) Powdered materials which tend to flush from supply bins should be fed by means of a screw feeder long enough to ensure uniform flow. A gate switch on the scale starts and stops the screw feeder. (*c*) Many materials such as large pellets and briquettes should be fed to the scale by a vibrator or belt feeder. The scale inlet cutoff gate will then act as a "catch gate." The scale control system starts and stops the feeding mechanism and controls the "catch-gate" operation automatically.

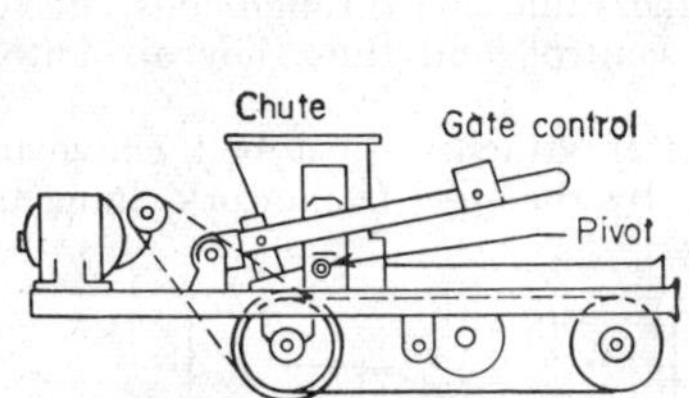

Fig. 55. Hardinge feeder-weigher.

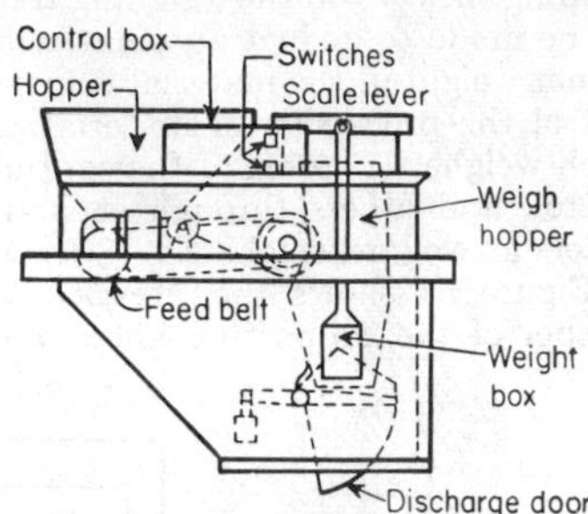

Fig. 56. Richardson automatic scale.

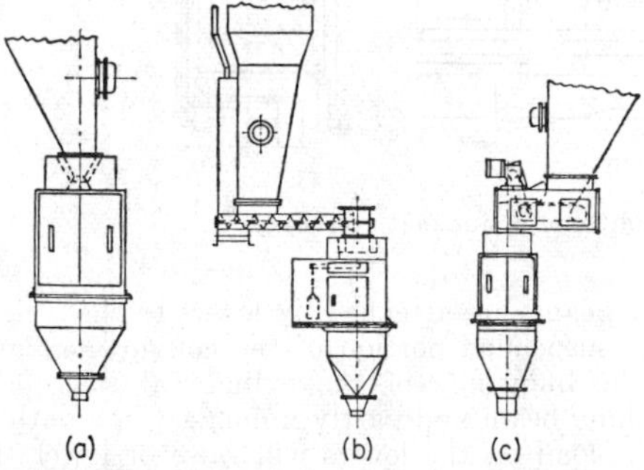

Fig. 57. Richardson steady feeders.

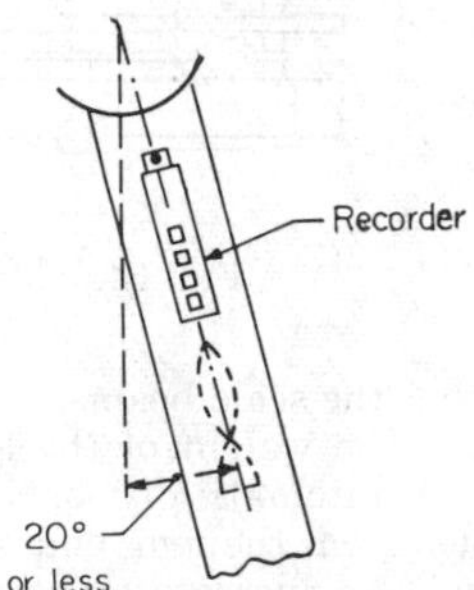

Fig. 58. Bailey meter for granular material.

The **Bailey solids flowmeter** (Fig. 58) consists of a helical quarter-turn vane which, by means of a flexible shaft and a set of change gears, operates either a direct mechanical counter or a remote electric-contact counter. It can be calibrated to record total weight of granular material flowing through vertical or near-vertical ducts, spouts, or pipes. It is typically applied to coal chutes or to spouts to pulverizers or stoker hoppers. Accuracy is within 3 percent of the actual weight of flowing material as long as the chute remains full.

SECTION 11

TRANSPORTATION

BY

NEIL MacCOULL, Consulting Automotive Engineer; Lecturer in Mechanical Engineering, Columbia University.

JOHN F. PARTRIDGE, District Industrial Engineer, New York Central System, Indianapolis.

GEORGE L. WEST, Jr., Professor of Marine and Nuclear Engineering, University of Michigan.

FINN C. MICHELSEN, Professor of Naval Architecture and Marine Engineering, University of Michigan.

LEWIS H. ABRAHAM, Senior Technical Staff, Product Development, Douglas Aircraft Company, Inc.

M. J. ZUCROW, Atkins Professor of Engineering, Purdue University.

S. N. B. MURTHY, Visiting Professor of Mechanical Engineering, Purdue University; Professor, Bangalore Institute of Technology, India.

E. A. HELLEBRAND, Deputy Director Propulsion and Vehicle Engineering Laboratory, NASA, George C. Marshall Space Flight Center.

GEORGE H. EWING, Vice President and Chief Engineer, Texas Eastern Transmission Corporation.

CONTENTS

PIPELINE TRANSMISSION

BY GEORGE H. EWING
WITH THE ASSISTANCE OF
ROLAND E. MOORE

AUTOMOBILES

BY

Neil MacCoull

REFERENCES: Lichty, "Internal Combustion Engines," McGraw-Hill. Heldt, "The Automotive Chassis," Heldt. Heldt, "The Gasoline Automobile," Heldt. Annual (March) specification number of *Automotive Inds.* Annual (November) specification and show number of *Motor*. Molloy, "Automobile Engineer's Reference Book," George Newnes, Ltd., London.

General

(See also p. 9–103 *et seq.*)

The use of automotive vehicles has increased to such an extent that by 1964 over 92 percent of all intercity traffic in passenger miles was carried by motor vehicles. Railroads carried only 2.1 percent and airways 5.6 percent. Intercity motor carriers of freight handled over half as many ton-miles as the railroads. In 1965 some 74 million automobiles and 14 million trucks and buses were **registered** in the United States, including over 9 million automobiles manufactured that year. The average **age** in use was slightly less than 6 years, which has changed but little during the preceding 10 years. If it can be assumed that the average of these vehicles, in good condition, can maintain 60 mph on modern highways, this represents a total of at least 2.5 billion horsepower available for use from the engines.

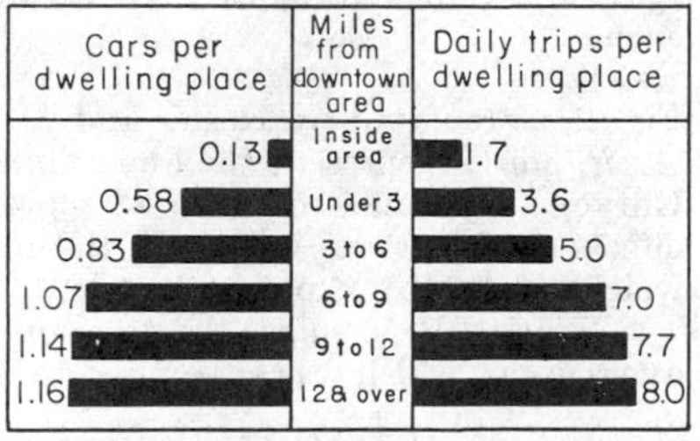

FIG. 1. Distribution of car use with distance from a large city. ("*Automobile Facts and Figures.*")

Characteristics of the cars purchased in 1965 are indicated by their optional and special equipment: Engines—six cylinders, 27 percent; eight-cylinders V, 73 percent. Automatic transmissions, 81 percent. Power brakes, 32 percent. Power steering, 60 percent. Heaters, 98 percent. Air conditioners, 23 percent. A representative distribution of **car use** is given in Fig. 1 for dwellings at various distances from downtown Detroit, as typical of large cities. Almost 60 percent of all car trips are less than 5 miles.

Vehicle Dimensions

The average dimensions of the three 1966 cars with the highest production were: length, bumper to bumper, 202 in.; wheelbase, 112 in.; width, 76 in., increasing to 152 in. with opposite doors open; height, 54 in.; ground clearance, 5.4 in. For the largest cars, these dimensions may be as great as 228 in. length and 133 in. wheelbase, the width and height being little different than for the large-production cars. Turning diameter, as measured to the outside of the outside front tire, is about 41 ft, although the largest cars may require 48 ft. The overhang of the front fenders requires about 3 ft more if the turn is made between walls.

Traction Required

The total resistance, or traction force, required for steady motion of a vehicle on a level road, is the sum of (1) air resistance and (2) friction resistance. The latter is dominated to such an extent by the rolling resistance of tires that the friction of bearings may be disregarded in a first approximation. **Tire resistance,** as reported by Billingsley, Evans, *et. al.*, *Trans. SAE*, 1942, was about 1 percent of the load carried at low speeds, increasing to about 1.5 percent at 60 mph. For modern passenger-car tires, with various percentages of synthetic rubbers, these values are about 1.2 to 1.4 percent at 30 mph, increasing to 1.6 to 2.0 percent at 70 mph. This is about nine times the rolling resistance reported for rail cars on steel rails (*see Univ. Illinois Exp. Sta. Bull.* 167). Greater **tire deflection,** by deviation from manufacturer's recommendations (see Table 1) on load and air pressure, increases tire resistance. Low temperatures do likewise, especially with high synthetic-rubber content. Lundstrom (*Trans. SAE*, 1957, p. 725) reports that a run of approximately 20 miles at 30 mph in 70 F air, was necessary to reach temperature equilibrium in the tires. The **total air-and-rolling resistance** for a 4,000 lb car fell approximately from 117 lb, after a 7 mile run, to 92 lb, after 20 miles.

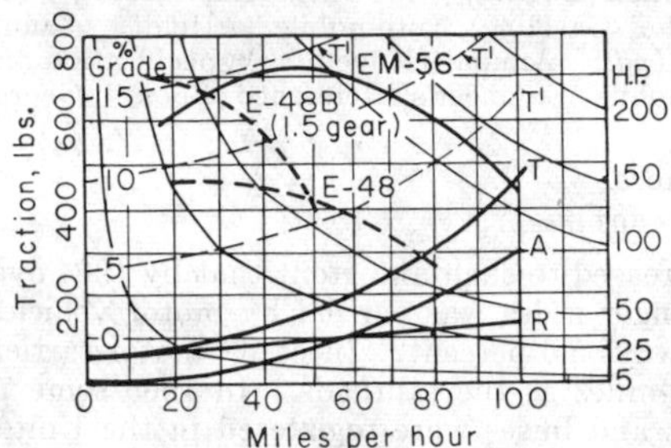

FIG. 2. Traction required for a typical car and traction available from different engines.

Air resistance varies closely with the square of the car speed and has a value between 120 and 170 lb at 60 mph, depending on the body size and design. The total car drag at 60 mph varies from 150 to 230 lb, with an average of about 200 lb (equivalent to 32 hp) for the majority of modern American cars. Rolling drag and air drag are about equal at 40 mph. (See also p. 11–74).

Average values for **traction requirements** of several high-production 1956 cars with an average weight of 4,000 lb (including two passengers) are shown in Fig. 2, as reported by Kosier and McConnell in *Trans. SAE*, 1957, p. 730. Curves *A*, *R*, and *T* represent the air, rolling, and total drag, respectively, on a level road. Curves *T'*, parallel to curve *T*, represent the displacement of the latter for gravity effects on the grades indicated, the additional traction required being equal to the car weight (4,000 lb) × percent grade.

Curves *EM*-56 shows the traction available in high gear from the engines in this average car, which was advertised to develop about 200 hp under laboratory test con-

Table 1. Passenger-car Tires (Four-ply, Tubeless)

Tire size	Recommended inflation pressure, psi	Max load, lb	Over-all diam, in.	Static load radius, in.	Rev per mile*
6.00–13	24	725	23.9	11.1	889
6.50–13	24	835	24.9	11.6	852
7.00–13	24	920	25.4	11.8	837
6.50–14	24	880	25.6	11.9	830
7.00–14	24	975	26.3	12.2	809
7.50–14	24	1085	27.1	12.5	790
8.00–14	24	1175	27.6	12.7	778
8.50–14	24	1265	28.2	13.0	760
9.00–14	24	1355	29.0	13.2	748
6.00–15	26	900	26.3	12.2	809
6.50–15	26	1000	26.8	12.4	796
6.70–15	26	1115	27.5	12.8	772
7.10–15	26	1195	28.1	13.0	760
7.60–15	26	1310	28.7	13.3	742
8.00–15	26	1395	29.2	13.4	737
8.20–15	24	1415	29.8	13.6	726

* Rev per mile (approx) at 35 mph = 9882/(static load radius, in.)

ditions. Curve *E*-48 gives corresponding data for 1948 engines. The intersection of such curves with any of the constant-gradient curves indicates the top speed which may be attained on the selected grade. For example, the 1956 car should negotiate a 12.5 percent grade in high gear at 60 mph, or a maximum grade of 14.5 percent at 40 mph, while the 1948 car could negotiate only an 8 percent grade at 40 mph and had a top speed of about 77 mph on a level road.

Effects of Transmission Gear Ratios. Constant-horsepower parabolas, which apply to any vehicle, are shown as light curves in Fig. 2. Except for small effects of friction losses, changes in gear ratio move points of a curve for traction available from an engine, such as *EM*-56 or *E*-48, along these constant-power parabolas to traction values multliplied by the change in gear reduction. In this way the curve *E*-48*B* was developed from the curve *E*-48 for an additional gear reduction of 1.5. Such shifting of the traction values available from engines follows gear changes in the rear axle as well as in the gear box.

Acceleration. The difference between the traction available from an engine and that required for a steady speed on a given grade may be used for acceleration [or acceleration, mph per sec = 21.9 × (surplus traction force/total effective car weight)]. Car weight should include a factor for the rotating parts of the engine, which may be of considerable magnitude when a high gear reduction is used. The effective mass of engine rotating parts increases as the square of the engine revolutions per mile and, for a typical example, may equal the car weight at a gear ratio giving about 15,000 engine rev per mile (Kosier and McDonnell, *Trans. SAE*, 1957, p. 730). This would result from a 5.33 gear ratio with a 3.6 axle ratio. Since the effective mass of engine rotating parts increases with the square of the gear reduction, while the traction force at the wheels increases directly, there is an optimum gear reduction for maximum acceleration (Fig. 3). For the hypothetical 1956 car under discussion, this maximum would be developed at a gear ratio of 4.2 with a 3.6 axle ratio. The maximum acceleration rate possible is limited by the friction between the driving tires and the road. For a dry roadway, the coefficient of friction is about 1.0; but when the roadway is wet, this drops to 0.6 or even 0.4, depending on the polish of the surface due to wear. (Stonex, *SAE Paper* 539A, 1962.) Thus for a car with 2,000 lb on the driving wheels, the limiting traction force would be about 2,000 lb on a dry pavement and less than half this value on a fairly wet pavement. The maximum accelerations possible under these two conditions for a car of 4,000 lb would be equivalent to a speed change of from 0 to 60 mph in about 5.5 sec and 11 sec, respectively.

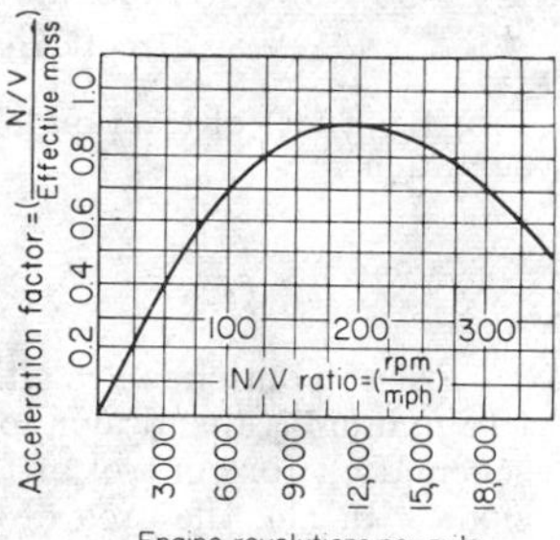

FIG. 3. Equivalent mass added to car by rotating engine parts at various gear ratios (*Trans. SAE*, 1957, *p.* 734).

Fuel Consumption. It is convenient to plot a modified "Willans line" with the fuel consumption of a car, gallons per mile, *vs.* rear-wheel traction, pounds (Fig. 4). A single straight line will generally represent the fuel consumption at a given fuel-air ratio over a wide range of loads and speeds. The points shown in Fig. 4 are for different speeds on two different cars. On such a plot the group of radial lines from the origin represent constant brake specific fuel-consumption (bsfc) values based on power available at the wheels. A fuel consumption of 0.10 gal per mile at a traction of 225 lb represents a bsfc of 1.0, with a fuel weight of 6 lb per gal. A study of the effects of gear changes may be approximated by displacing the fuel consumption line so that corresponding points, as their traction is changed by gear changes, will remain on the same bsfc lines. This is shown by the dotted line for an additional gear reduction of 1.5, and emphasizes the importance of axle ratio on fuel consumption. Such plots of fuel consumption may be combined with Fig. 2 by means of the traction scales which are common to both.

The fuel consumption obtainable from modern cars is indicated by the results of the annual **Mobilgas Economy Run** for stock cars, under AAA direction. In Fig. 5

the results are shown for the winners in the various classes plotted against over-all car weight. This race, over a distance of about 1,300 miles under a wide range of driving conditions, demonstrates that excellent fuel economy is possible when modern cars are driven at moderate speeds. The fuel-consumption rate rises at higher speeds and may be estimated from Figs. 2 and 4.

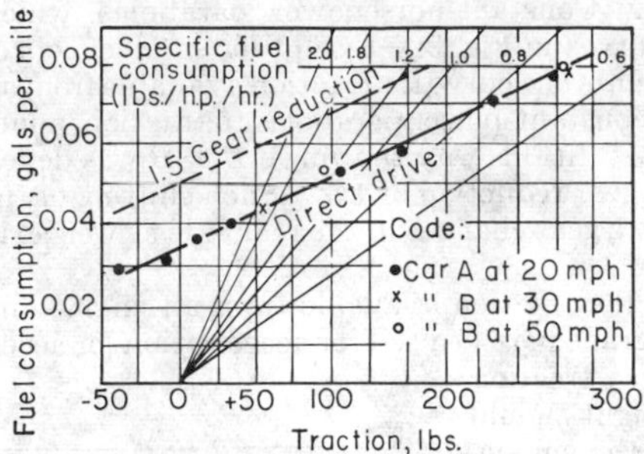

FIG. 4. Effect of traction load on fuel consumption.

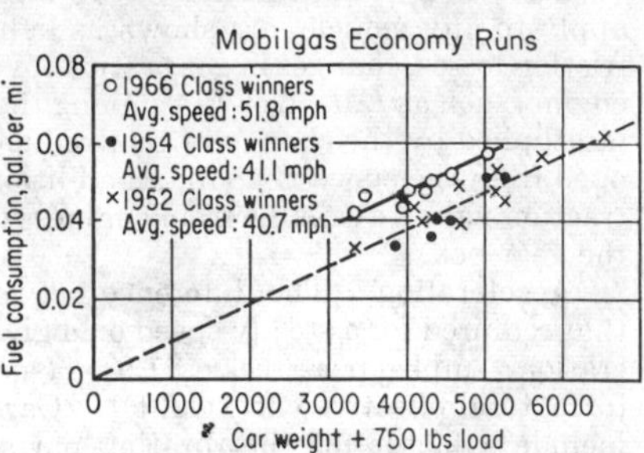

FIG. 5. Effect of car weight plus 750 lbs load on fuel consumption of American stock cars in Mobilgas Economy Run.

Transmission Mechanisms

Friction clutches are either (1) the single-disk type (Fig. 6), connecting the engine to a manual transmission, or (2) the hydraulically operated multiple-disk type (Fig. 7, schematic), for control of the various planetary-gear changes in automatic transmissions. In (1), the area of the friction facing is usually based on a pressure of 30 psi, and the torque rating on a friction coefficient of 0.25. The clutch is held in engagement

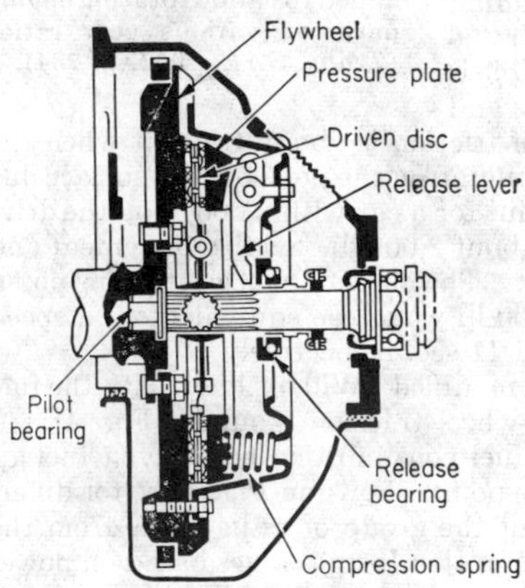

FIG. 6. Single-plate dry-disk friction clutch.

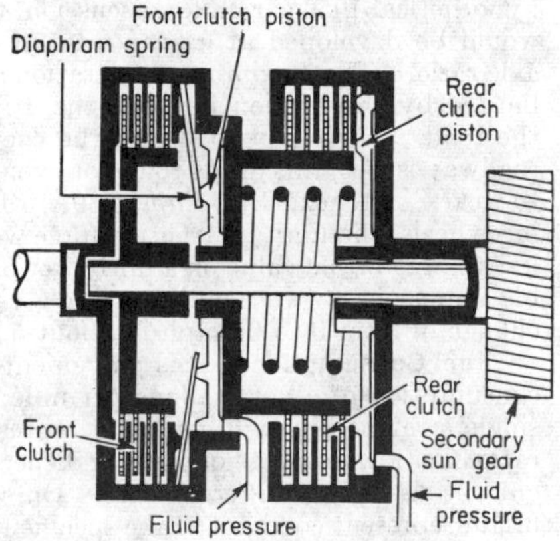

FIG. 7. Schematic of two hydraulically operated multiple-disk clutches in an automatic transmission. (*Ford Motor Co.*)

by several coiled springs or a diaphragm spring and is disengaged by means of a pedal with such leverage that 30 to 40 lb will overcome the clutch springs.

Fluid couplings between the engine and transmission provide a smooth drive by the flow of oil between the flat radial blades in two adjacent toroidal casings [Fig. 8(*a*), schematic]. The difference in centrifugal force between the mass of oil contained in each toroid, when either is running at a speed higher than the other, causes a flow of oil from the periphery of the faster one to the slower one. Since this mass of oil is also rotating around the shaft at the speed of the driving torus, its impact on the blades of the slower torus develops a torque on the latter. The developed torque is equal to, and cannot exceed, the torque of the driving torus. In this respect it is similar to a slipping friction clutch. The driven member must always run at a lower speed, though at high rotative speeds, and when the torque demand is small, the slip may be only 2 or 3 percent. The **stalled torque** increases with the square of the engine speed, so that very little is developed when idling. Since torque may be transmitted in either direction, depending only on which member is rotating at the higher speed, the engine may be used as a brake as with friction clutches, and the car may be started by pushing.

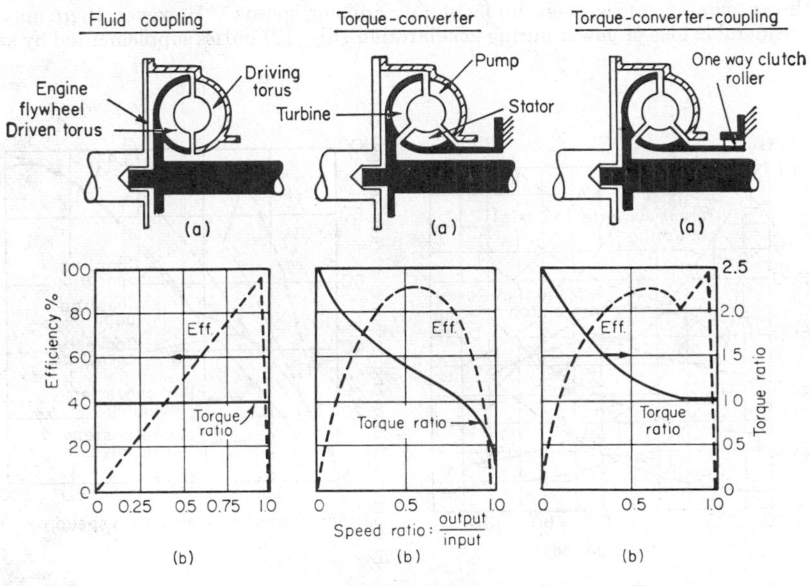

FIG. 8. Fluid coupling: (*a*) section; (*b*) characteristics.

FIG. 9. Torque converter: (*a*) section; (*b*) characteristics.

FIG. 10. Torque-converter coupling: (*a*) section: (*b*) characteristics.

Torque-converter couplings [Fig. 10(*a*)] have largely replaced fluid couplings because the torque transmitted can be increased at high slippage. The circulation of oil between the driving, or higher-speed, torus (the pump) and the driven, or lower-speed, torus (the turbine) results from the difference in centrifugal force developed in these two units, just as in the fluid coupling. With the torque converter, however, the turbine blades are given a curvature so that an additional torque is developed by the reaction of a backward-spinning mass of oil as it leaves the turbine. Stationary, or stator, blades, are interposed between the turbine and the pump to change the direction of the oil spin. The entrance angle of the stator blades required for tangential flow varies widely with the slip ratio. For a given blade angle there is a hydraulic shock loss at any slip ratio greater or less than that which provides tangential flow. This is reflected in the rapid fall of the efficiency curve in Fig. 9(*b*) on each side of the maximum. The essential parts of a torque converter with its stationary stator are shown in Fig. 9(*a*). A **stalled-torque** multiplication of 2.0 to 2.7 was developed in various 1964 cars. When the torque ratio is almost unity the slip is such that oil from the turbine starts to impinge on the back of the stator blades. By mounting the stator assembly on a **sprag,** or one-way clutch [Fig. 10(*a*)], it remains stationary while subject to the reversing action of the backward-spinning oil mass as it leaves the turbine. When the slip reaches the point where the oil flow from the turbine begins to spin forward, the stator is free to turn with it. When the slip is further reduced, the unit acts as a fluid coupling with improved efficiency [Fig. 10(*b*)]. Such a unit is a **fluid torque-converter coupling.** Some designs eliminate all slippage by the inclusion of a friction clutch which carries the load when a predetermined car speed is reached. These clutches are hydraulically operated, the engagement being controlled automatically by accelerator position and car speed.

Figure 11 compares a torque-converter coupling to a friction clutch on **car performance** in direct drive. The increase in traction available for acceleration from a standing start substantiates its public acceptance. An axle gear is generally used which gives a propeller shaft speed about 90 percent as great as with a manual transmission at the same car speed. The gain in engine efficiency compensates for the losses of the automatic transmissions under steady cruising speeds. However, there may be a considerable **loss of power during acceleration** (Fig. 12) unless supplemented by such

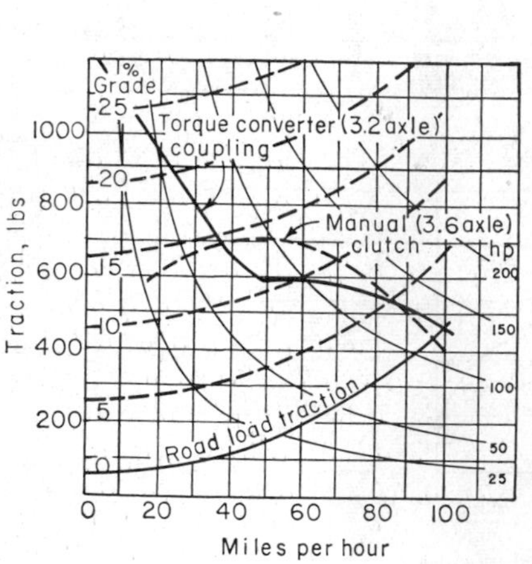

FIG. 11. Comparative traction available in performance of a fluid torque-converter coupling and a friction clutch (*Trans. SAE*, 1957, *p*. 724).

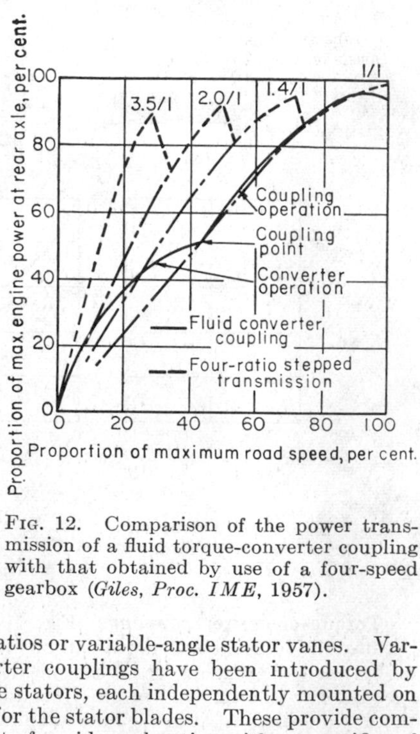

FIG. 12. Comparison of the power transmission of a fluid torque-converter coupling with that obtained by use of a four-speed gearbox (*Giles, Proc. IME*, 1957).

modifications as one or more auxiliary gear ratios or variable-angle stator vanes. Various design modifications of torque-converter couplings have been introduced by different manufacturers, such as two or more stators, each independently mounted on one-way clutches, and variable pitch angles for the stator blades. These provide compromises in blade angles for the development of rapid acceleration without sacrifice of high efficiency while cruising. Most manufacturers warn that **automatic transmissions may be damaged** if cars are towed a considerable distance with the rear wheels turning. Starting an engine by pushing a car with an automatic transmission should follow the manufacturer's directions.

All **manual transmissions** installed as standard equipment on American cars have three forward speeds, including direct drive, and one reverse. These speeds are obtained by sliding either one of two gears along a splined shaft to bring it into mesh with a corresponding gear on a countershaft which is, in turn, driven by a pair of gears in constant mesh. Helical gears are used to minimize noise. A **"synchromesh"** device (Fig. 13), acting as a friction clutch, brings the gears to be meshed approximately to the correct speed just before meshing and minimizes **"clashing,"** even with inexperienced drivers. Gear changes are generally in geometric ratios. Transmission ratios average about 2.76 in first gear, 1.64 in second, 1.0 in third or direct drive, and 3.24 in reverse. The shift lever is generally located on the steering column. Four-speed transmissions are offered as optional equipment at extra cost on most cars, with the shift lever on the floor. Average gear ratios are about 2.67 in first, 1.93 in second, 1.45 in third, and 1.0 in fourth or direct drive.

Overdrives have been available for some cars equipped with manual transmissions. These are supplemental planetary gear units with three planetary pinions driven around a stationary sun gear. The surrounding internal gear is coupled to the propeller shaft, which thus turns faster than the engine. The gear ratio is selected to permit the engine to slow down to about 70 percent of the propeller-shaft speed and operate with less noise and friction. These units automatically come into action when the driver momentarily releases the accelerator pedal at a car speed above 25 to 28 mph. It may be thrown out of action through a solenoid by pressing the accelerator pedal to the floor.

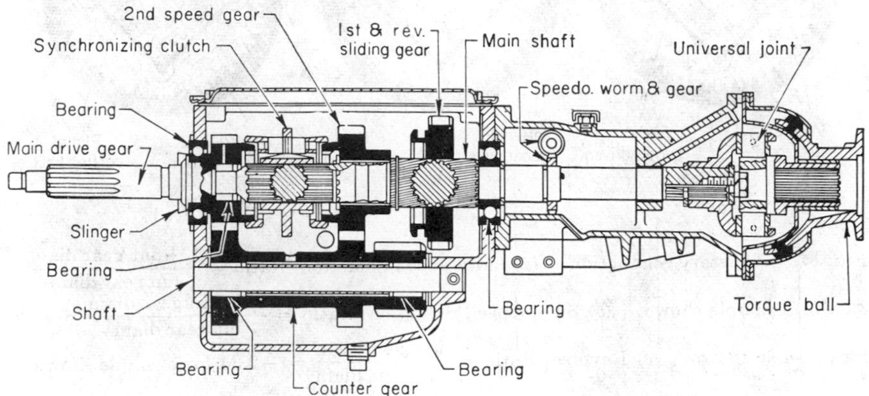

FIG. 13. Three-speed synchromesh transmission (Buick).

Automatic Transmissions

All automatic transmissions, except the Hydra-Matic, use torque-converter couplings with planetary-gear units which can supply one or two gear reductions and reverse, depending on the design, by simultaneously engaging or locking various elements of planetary systems (Fig. 14). Automatic control is provided by disk clutches or brake bands which lock the various elements, operated by oil pressure as regulated by governors at car speeds where shifts are made from one speed to another. Mechanical losses in these transmissions are sufficient to require water cooling of the oil on all the larger units. Oil from the pump for the control system, after passing through a pressure regulator and the converter, passes through a cooling tank submerged in the engine-jacket water radiator.

A schematic of a representative automatic transmission, combining a three-element torque converter and a compound planetary gear (as used on several of General Motors' larger cars in 1964), is given in Fig. 15. The speed reductions and reverse are provided by a compound planetary system consisting of two simple systems in series. The two sun gears are an integral unit with the same number of teeth, and the forward internal gear carries the planets of the rear unit. The internal gears of both systems are all of the same size, and consequently all planets are of equal size. This arrangement, together with three clutches, two brake bands, and suitable one-way sprags, makes possible three forward gear or torque ratios besides direct drive and reverse, all of which may be doubled by the slip, or difference in speed, of the torque-converter pump and turbine.

The **Hydra-Matic** transmission, installed in some 15 million cars prior to 1964, made use of a fluid coupling rather than a torque converter, with consequent lack of torque boost. Two separate planetary systems, with both planet carriers connected to the drive shaft, gave the desired gear reductions.

Automatic transmissions for many smaller cars provide a torque converter with only one speed reduction and reverse; this is accomplished with the simplicity of a single planetary system.

Manufacturing precision and the use of helical gears contribute greatly to the comparative quietness of planetary systems.

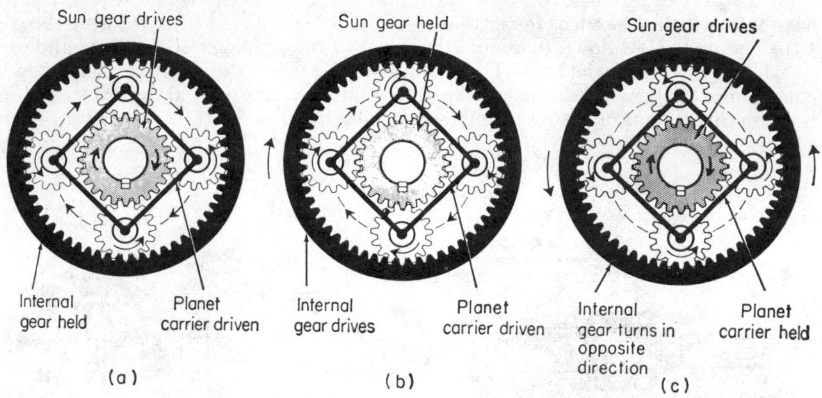

FIG. 14. Planetary gear action. (*a*) Large speed reduction: Ratio $= \dfrac{1 + \text{int gear diam}}{\text{sun gear diam}} =$ 3.33 for example shown. (*b*) Small speed reduction: Ratio $= \dfrac{1 + \text{sun gear diam}}{\text{int gear diam}} = 1.428$ for example shown. (*c*) Reverse: Ratio $= \dfrac{\text{int gear diam}}{\text{sun gear diam}} = -2.33$ for example shown.

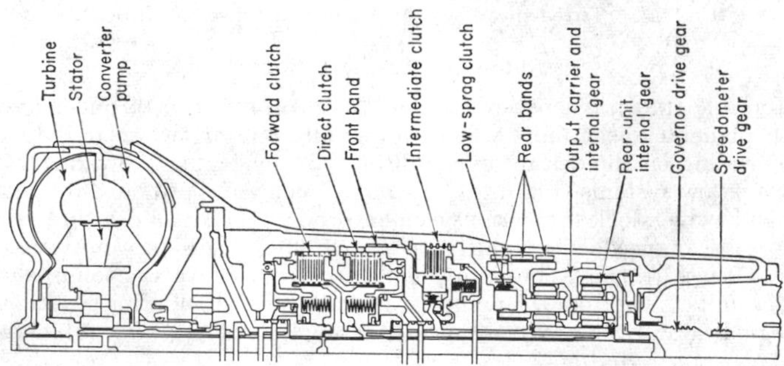

FIG. 15. Three-element torque converter and planetary gear (General Motors).

The **differential** is a unit attached to the ring gear (Fig. 16 and 18) which equalizes the traction of both wheels and permits one wheel to turn faster than the other, as needed on curves. Each axle is driven by a bevel gear meshing with pinions on a cross-shaft pinion pin secured to the differential case. The case also carries the ring gear. An undesirable feature of the conventional differential is that no more traction may be developed on one wheel than on the other. If one wheel slips on ice, there is no traction to move the car. **Limited-slip differentials** are offered as optional equipment on most cars. Figure 17 shows one design, in which four pinions are carried on two separate cross shafts at right angles to each other, each being driven by V-shaped notches in the carrier. As torque is developed to drive either axle, one pinion cross shaft or the other moves axially and locks the corresponding disk-clutch plates between that axle drive gear and the differential housing. In another design, similar disk clutches are locked by spring pressure, which prevents differential action until a differential torque greater than the limit established by the springs is developed.

The **semifloating rear axle** (Fig. 18) used on almost all cars has a bearing for each drive axle at the outer end of the housing as well as near the differential carrier, with the full load on each wheel taken by the drive axles in combined bending and shear. The **full-floating axle,** generally used on commercial vehicles, supports each wheel on two bearings carried by the axle housing or an extension to it. Each wheel is bolted to a flange on one of the axle shafts. The axle shafts carry none of the vehicle weight and may be withdrawn without jacking up the wheel.

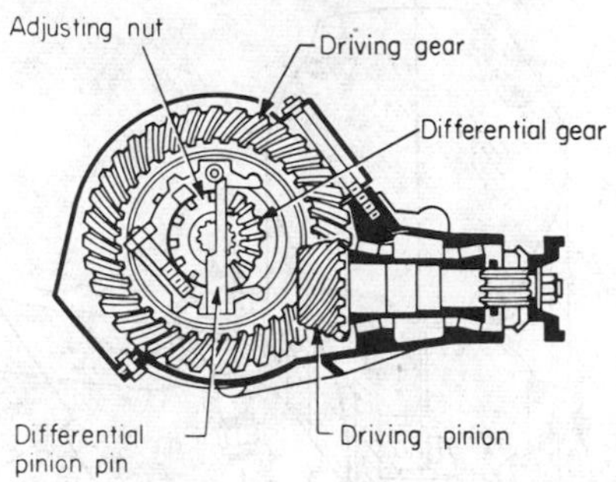

Fig. 16. Rear-axle hypoid gearing.

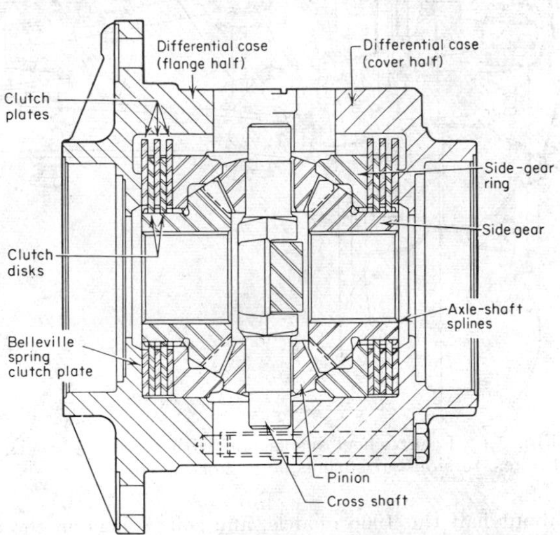

Fig. 17. Limited-slip differential (Buick).

Rear Suspensions

Torque reactions may be taken through longitudinal leaf springs, as in the **Hotchkiss drive,** or through radius rods when coil springs are used. Some designs in the past used a torque tube around the propeller shaft, bolted to the axle housing, with universal joints for both at the forward ends. **Leaf springs,** with one to nine leaves, were installed on

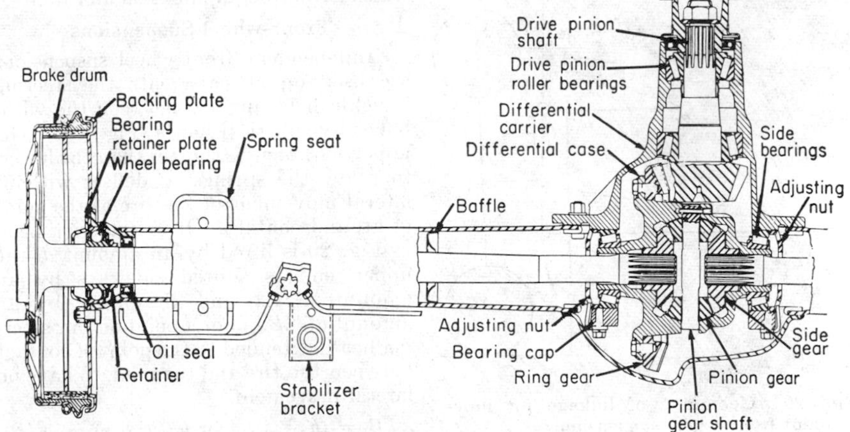

Fig. 18. Rear axle (Oldsmobile).

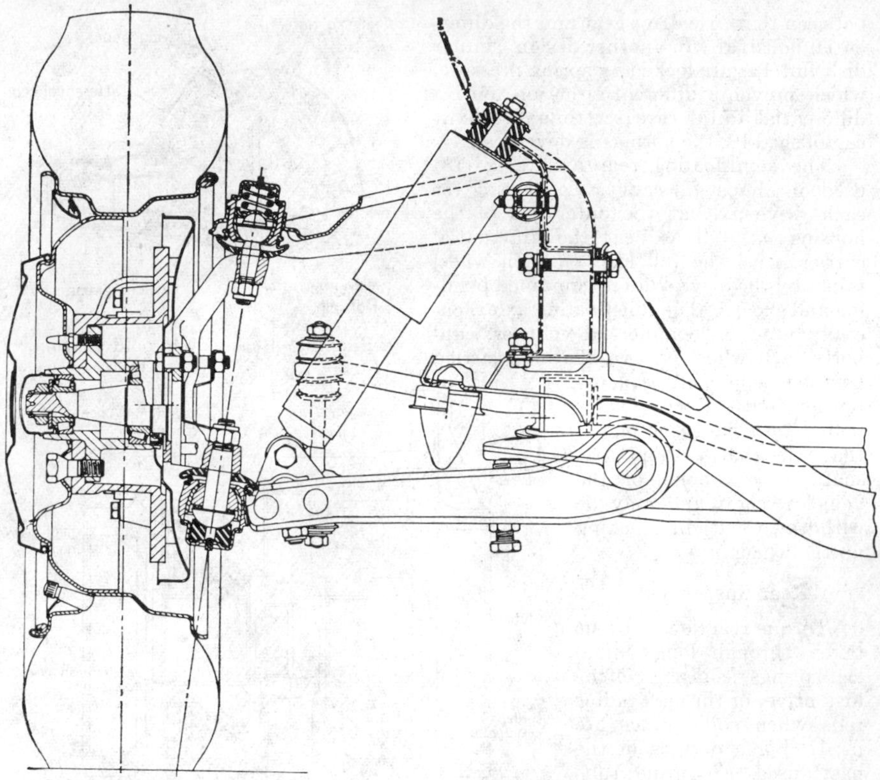

Fig. 19. Front-wheel suspension with spherical steering swivels. Design includes disk brakes, torsion-bar springs, and shock absorber.

about half the 1966 models, and coil springs on the other half. Spring stiffness (at the rear wheels) ranged from about 82 lb per in. deflection to some 160 lb. Shock absorbers, to dampen road vibrations, were standard equipment on all cars.

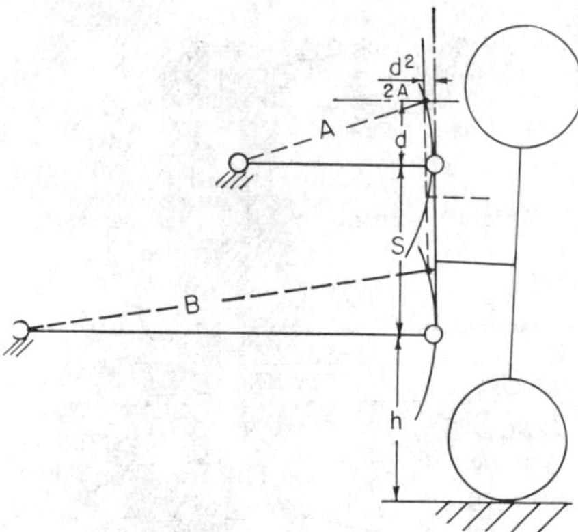

Fig. 20. Geometry of linkage for independent front-wheel suspension.

Front-wheel Suspensions

Independent front-wheel suspensions are used on all cars, with the steering knuckle held directly between the wishbones by spherical joints (Fig. 19). The upper wishbone is shorter than the lower, to allow the springs to deflect without lateral movement of the tire at the point of ground contact. If the steering head in Fig. 20 is lifted by an amount d, the upper end is shifted sideways by an amount $d^2/2A$ and the lower by an amount $d^2/2B$. For a point on this steering head, extended to the point of contact between the tire and the road, to have no lateral movement,

$$hB = (h + s)\,A \text{ or } h/(h + s) = A/B$$

A modification of the conventional suspension consists of sloping the upper wishbones down toward the rear, so that the steering spindle is given more "caster" when the front springs are compressed. This geometry causes the torque produced from braking at the front wheels to develop a couple on the inclined wishbones, which tends to raise the front of the car frame. By suitable proportioning of the parts it is possible by this means to reduce "nose diving" of the car when the brakes are applied (*Engineering*, Oct. 28, 1955, p. 611).

The load on these wishbones is generally taken by coil springs acting on the lower wishbone or by torsion-bar springs mounted longitudinally.

Wheel Alignment

Caster is the angle, in side elevation, between the steering axis and the vertical. It is considered positive when the upper end of the steering axis is inclined rearward. Manufacturers' specifications vary considerably, with the range for 1966 cars from 1½ to −2¼ deg. **Camber,** the inclination of the wheel plane from the vertical, is positive when the wheel leans outward, and varies from 2 to −½ deg, with many preferring 0 deg. **Toe-in** of a pair of wheels is the difference in transverse distance between the wheel planes taken at the extreme rear and front points of the tire treads. It is limited to ¼ in., with ⅛ in. or less generally preferred.

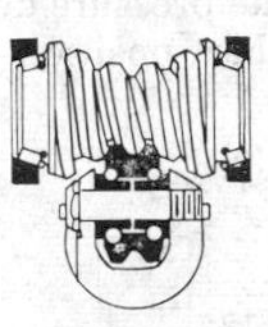

FIG. 21. Roller-cam steering gear.

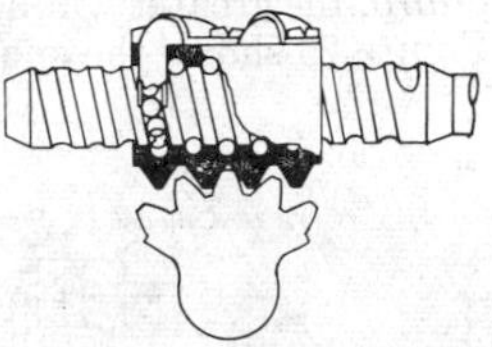

FIG. 22. Recirculating-ball steering gear.

Steering

The force applied to the steering wheel is generally multiplied through a **worm-and-roller** (Fig. 21) or a **recirculating-ball** (Fig. 22) type of steering gear. The over-all ratios are such that 20 to 33 deg rotation of the steering wheel results in 1 deg turn of the front wheels for manual steering and 17.6 to 25.0 for power steering. Figure 23 illustrates the geometry of the prevalent **Ackermann steering gear.** To avoid slippage of the wheels when turning a curve of radius *r*, the point of intersection *M* for the projected front-wheel axes must fall in a vertical plane through the center of the rear axle. The torque, in foot-pounds, required to turn the wheels of a vehicle standing on smooth concrete varies with the angle of turn, from about 6 percent of the weight on the front axle, in pounds, to start a turn, to 17 percent for a 30 deg turn (Davis, *Trans. SAE*, 1945, p. 241).

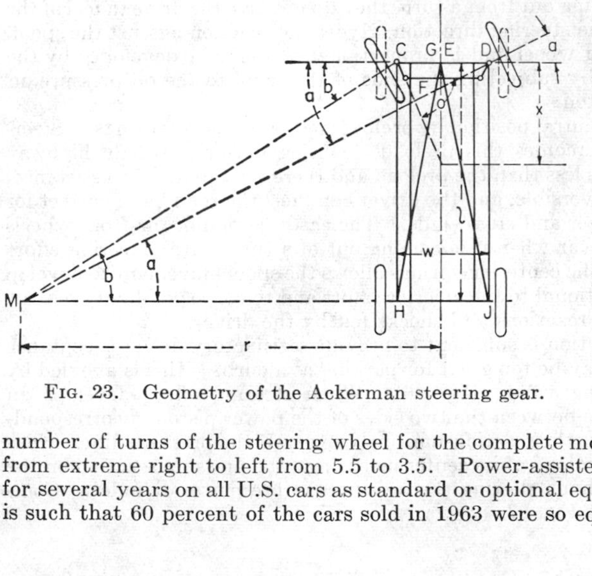

FIG. 23. Geometry of the Ackerman steering gear.

Power-assisted Steering

The physical effort required to steer an automobile, especially when parking, is appreciably lessened by the power-assisted steering device. This permits reduction in the gear ratio between the steering wheel and the car wheels from some 29 to 20, with consequent reduction in the number of turns of the steering wheel for the complete movement of the front wheels from extreme right to left from 5.5 to 3.5. Power-assisted steering has been offered for several years on all U.S. cars as standard or optional equipment; public acceptance is such that 60 percent of the cars sold in 1963 were so equipped.

All systems provide (1) steering control in case of failure of the hydraulic-power assistance, and (2) a "feel of the road," by which the driver's effort on the steering wheel is proportional to the force needed to turn the front wheels and by which the tendency of a car to straighten out from a turn or the drag of a soft front tire may be felt at the steering wheel.

Power assistance is effected by hydraulic pressure from an engine-driven pump, acting on a piston in the steering linkage. The piston and its cylinder may be incorporated in the steering-gear housing, Fig. 28*a*, or installed as a supplemental link between the car frame and the steering cross-link. Oil pressure on the piston is controlled by a valve, such as the balanced spool valve of Fig. 24.

When the spool is moved slightly to the right (Fig. 25), the lands on the spool restrict the return of oil from the pump through both return circuits, thus building up delivery pressure. Since the pump delivery is still open to the left end of the power cylinder while the right end is open to the pump suction, a force is developed to move the piston to the right. The greater the restriction imposed on the return of oil to the pump, the greater will be the pressure developed and the resulting force on the piston. Figure 25 shows the spool in a position where all flow of oil from the pump is cut off

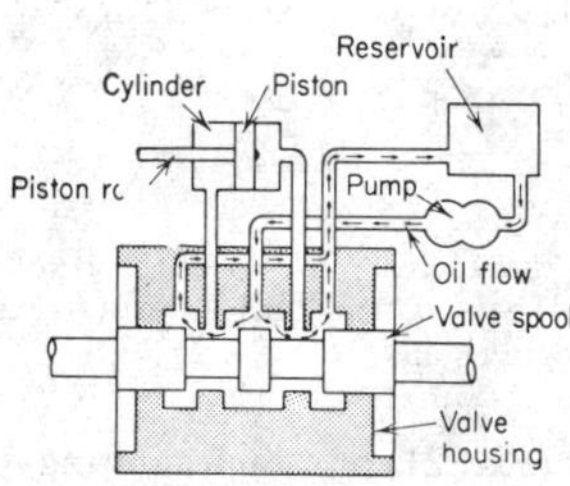

FIG. 24. Schematic of spool-type control valve in neutral position.

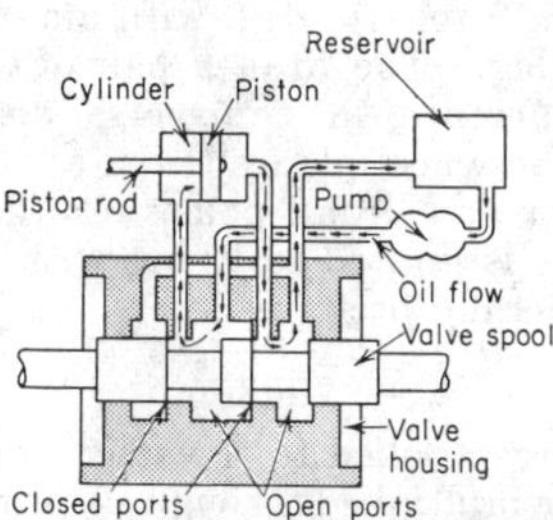

FIG. 25. Control valve positioned for full-turn power assistance.

from its return and where the oil pressure would be raised to the maximum delivery pressure of the pump.

The spool (Fig. 26) is centered to the neutral position by suitable **centering springs.** These provide an increasing effort on the steering wheel for increasing steering angle. While they aid in straightening out from a turn, they do not give the driver a feel of the force required to provide the steering direction. **Hydraulic reaction** against the spool, which is felt at the steering wheel and is proportional to the force developed by the steering gear, is developed by subjecting the ends of the spool to the oil pressure on either side of the power piston.

The valve is held in its neutral position by **preloading** the centering springs. Steering effort at the wheel overcomes this preload. During normal, straight-highway driving, the steering effort is less than the preload and there is no hydraulic assistance; the steering gear is freely reversible, and the driver can "feel the road" and correct for elements such as road camber and crosswinds. The caster action of the front wheels straightens the path of the car when it is coming out of a turn. Any steering effort greater than the preload of the centering springs allows the spool movement to develop a steering assistance proportional to the steering effort and to correspondingly reduce, but not eliminate, the road reactions and shocks felt by the driver.

When the hydraulic reaction is sufficient to provide satisfactory driver acceptance during normal driving, it may be too great for parking at a curb. This is avoided by the Bendix **reaction-limiting valve** (Fig. 26). When steering effort develops an hydraulic pressure difference between the two sides of the power piston, a corresponding pressure difference moves the reaction-limiting valve. If the pressure difference is sufficient to overcome the preload of its centering springs, the pressure reaction on the control valve is limited without altering the pressures in the power cylinder. Comparable results are shown in Fig. 27.

Other designs of power-assisted steering gears accomplish similar results. In the **Saginaw** system (General Motors), the steering column operates the steering worm through a torsion bar. A rotary three-way open-center valve (Fig. 28*b*) is incorporated, with its outer element or body attached to the lower end of the torsion bar and its inner element or spool attached to the upper, or steering-wheel, end. When driving with negligible steering effort on a straight, smooth road, the steering is accomplished manually through the torsion bar with no power assistance. When steering resistance develops, e.g., requiring a force of about 1 lb at the rim of the steering wheel, the torsion bar deflects to start power assistance. Increasing force and deflection give

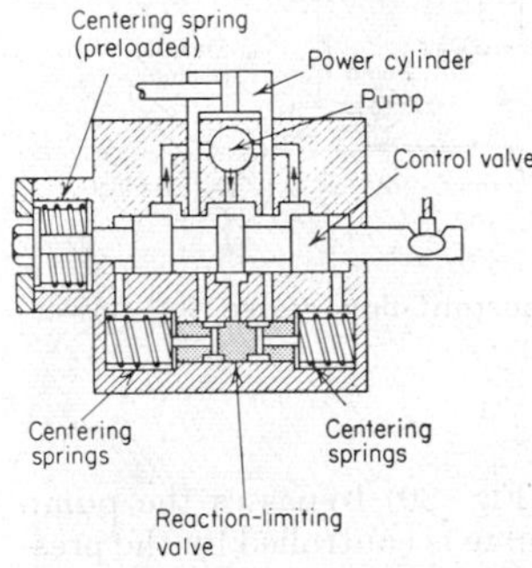

FIG. 26. Hydraulic reaction-limiting valve (schematic).

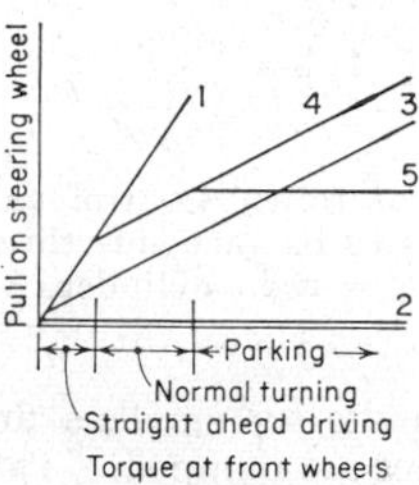

FIG. 27. Braking characteristics: (1) manual steering; (2) power steering without reaction; (3) power-assisted with hydraulic and spring reaction; (4) power-assisted with preloaded centering springs; (5) power-assisted with reaction-limiting valve.

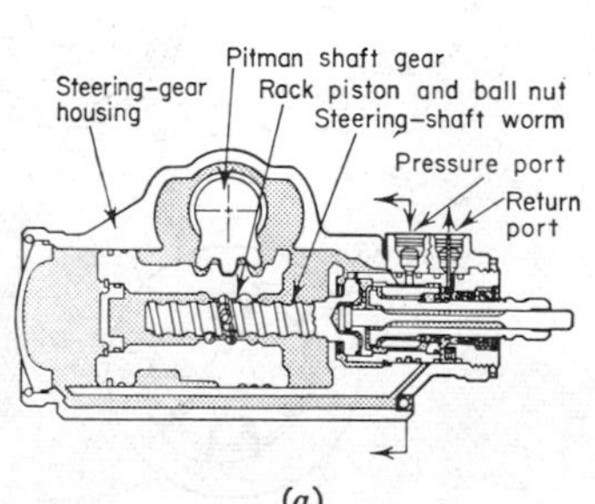

(*a*)

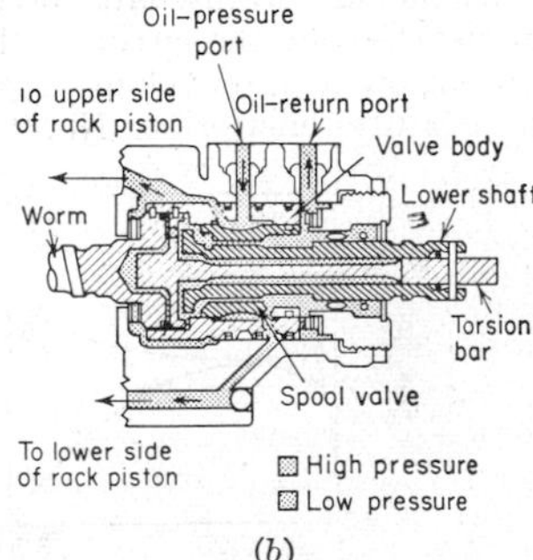

(*b*)

FIG. 28. (*a*) In-line power-steering gear with rotary control valve. (*b*) Rotary-valve assembly with torsion-bar drive (Saginaw).

increasing assistance; full power is developed at a rim pull of 3 lb approx, with a 4-deg twist. As the steering rack responds to the pressure on the power piston, the valve body rotates to bring the valve ports back to their neutral position. This "follow-up" motion is similar in principle to that of steering gears on ships.

If oil-supply pressure should fail, as by a stalled engine, manual steering is effected by stops on the valve elements, which engage when the torsion bar is deflected a few degrees. The power piston would then be driven so as to force oil back through the pump, but this resistance is avoided by a check valve which allows oil to flow freely from the suction side of the pump to the delivery side but not in the reverse direction. To minimize deflections of the valve elements and binding from high oil pressures, the valve is designed with four sets of lands at 90 deg around the circumference (Fig. 29).

Oil pumps for power-assisted steering gears are generally driven from the engine by V belts, though in some instances they have been driven at higher speeds directly from the electric generator. A typical unit delivers 1.75 gpm at engine idling speed, at any pressure up to 1,200 psi as may be required while parking. To avoid excessive power consumption and heating of the oil at high engine speeds where the volume and

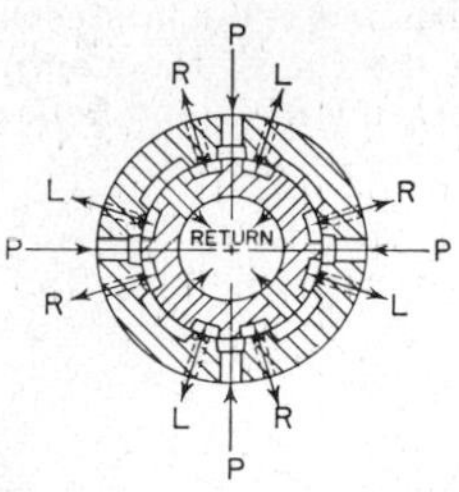

FIG. 29. Section of rotary control valve with multiple ports to balance side thrust; P = pressure in., R = right cylinder, L = left cylinder.

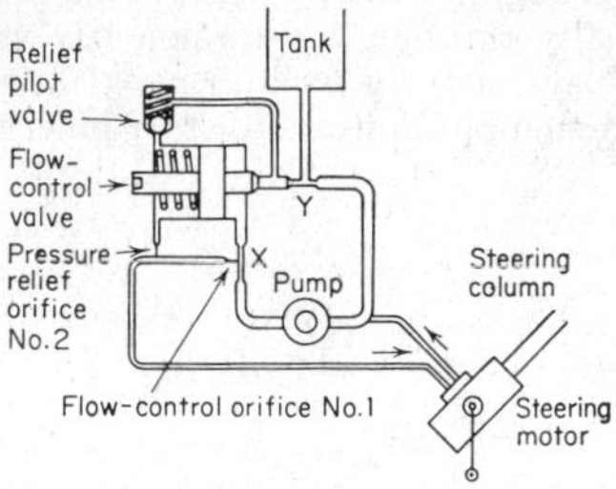

FIG. 30. Constant-flow valve for power-steering pump.

pressure requirements are small, a **flow-control valve** (Fig. 30) bypasses the pump when large volumes are pumped. The opening of this valve is controlled by the pressure drop across flow-control orifice No.1 while oil flows freely through the steering-control valve in its neutral position. This valve changes the oil-delivery characteristic from curve A to curve B in Fig. 31. When oil flow through the steering-control valve is interrupted by the steering-gear valve, the pressure drop across orifice No. 1 diminishes and allows the spring to close the flow-control valve, thus raising the discharge pressure. If the pressure rises beyond the setting of the relief pilot, the flow through it develops a pressure drop through pressure-relief orifice No. 2, also opening

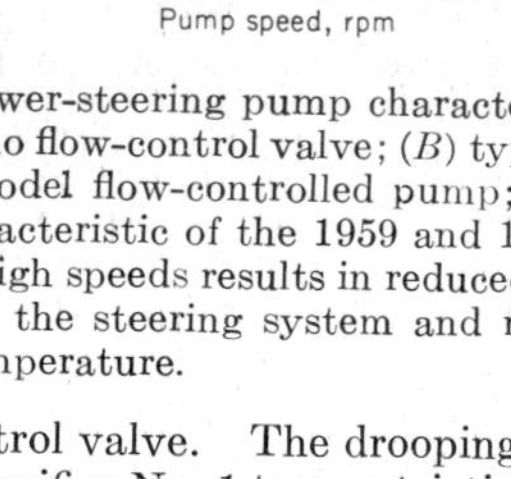

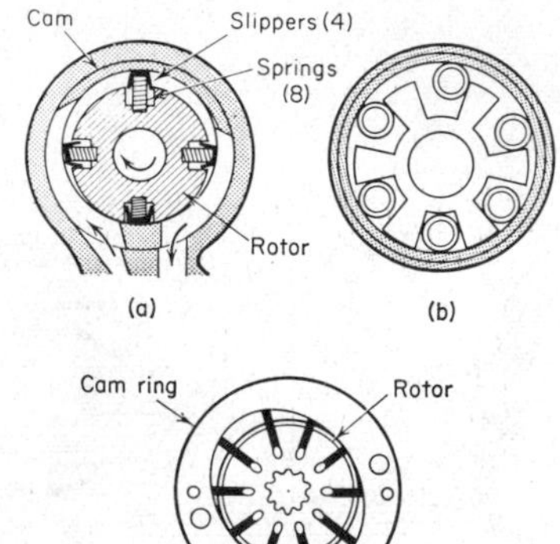

FIG. 31. Power-steering pump characteristics: (A) output with no flow-control valve; (B) typical output for a 1956-model flow-controlled pump; (C) drooping flow characteristic of the 1959 and 1960 pumps. Drop-off at high speeds results in reduced back pressure through the steering system and reduction in operating temperature.

FIG. 32. Rotary-pump types: (a) Chrysler, (b) Ford (Eaton), (c) General Motors (Saginaw).

the flow-control valve. The drooping curve C has been developed by connecting the flow-control orifice No. 1 to a restriction X, in the pump bypass circuit, which acts as a venturi.

Cavitation at the pump inlet when running at high speeds is minimized by connecting the oil reservoir to another restricted passage, Y, also equivalent to a venturi in the pump circuit, thus permitting the circuit to be "supercharged," or operated at a pressure correspondingly above atmospheric.

Three types of **rotary pumps** for the high pressures required are shown in **Fig.** 32 (see also Sec. 14). Centrifugal force holds the sliding elements against a cam-shaped or eccentric case at high speeds. At low speeds, the sliding elements are held against the case—in design *a* by springs and in design *c* by oil pressure admitted to the base of the vanes. The double cam of design *c*, in addition to doubling the normal volumetric displacement, provides for balancing the oil pressure on each side of the rotor and on the bearings. The cam is contoured for uniform acceleration.

Brakes

The maximum retarding force which can be applied to a vehicle though its wheels is limited by the friction between the tires and the road, equal to the coefficient of friction times the vehicle weight. With a coefficient of 1.0, which is about the maximum for *dry* pavements, this force can equal the car weight and can develop a retardation of $1.0g$ (32.2 ft per sec²), with a **stopping distance** $S = V^2/29.9$, where V is in miles per hour. Tests conducted by the U.S. Bureau of Public Roads on **dry pavements** with vehicles picked at random on the U.S. highways (*SAE Trans.*, 1957, pp. 403–426) indicated that some vehicles and trucks of all classes developed such a retarding rate for at least part of the stopping distance but that most vehicles did not. Fifteen percent of the automobiles failed to develop a retardation rate greater than $0.84g$, and a corresponding percentage of heavy trucks failed to exceed $0.53g$.

Table 2 presents maximum stopping distances permissible under the 1962 Revision of the Uniform Vehicle Code which has been adopted by several states as the basis

Table 2. Maximum Stopping Distances Permissible under Uniform Vehicle Code of 1962, on Level, Dry, and Smooth Highway Surfaces, Ft

Speed, mph	Distance for driver to react in ¾ sec, ft	Automobiles		Buses and trucks over 10,000 lb	
		Braking distance, ft	Total distance, ft	Braking distance, ft	Total distance, ft
20	22	25	47	40	62
30	33	55	88	92	125
40	44	105	149	165	209
50	55	188	243	255	310
60	66	300	366	370	436
70	77	453	530		
80	88	650	738		

of their vehicle braking-performance requirements. A column is included for distances traversed during the ¾ sec an average alert driver may require to start applying his brakes after perceiving the need to stop. This time interval varies widely for different drivers and under different conditions; many drivers' reactions may be considerably slower than this at least some of the time. Also, the braking distances will of course be greater on downhill slopes. This table is based on tests run by the Bureau of Public Roads (U.S. Department of Commerce) on more than 1,300 vehicles stopped from 20 mph. Suitable expansion factors were developed for the higher speeds shown. In the 1963 tests, 85 percent of the automobiles were stopped within 22.5 ft, and three-axle trucks weighing over 10,000 lb were stopped within 41 to 49 ft after the drivers started to apply the brake controls at 20 mph.

All automobiles have two independent systems of brakes for safety. One is generally a **parking brake** and is rarely used to stop a car from speed, though it should be able to. The brake manually operates on the rear wheels through cables or mechanical linkage from an auxiliary foot lever (or, less frequently, a hand pull) under the dash; it is held on by a ratchet until released by some means such as a push button or a foot pedal.

The main system, or **service brakes,** on all U.S. cars is hydraulically operated, with equalized pressure to all four wheels. Rubber seals preclude the use of petro-

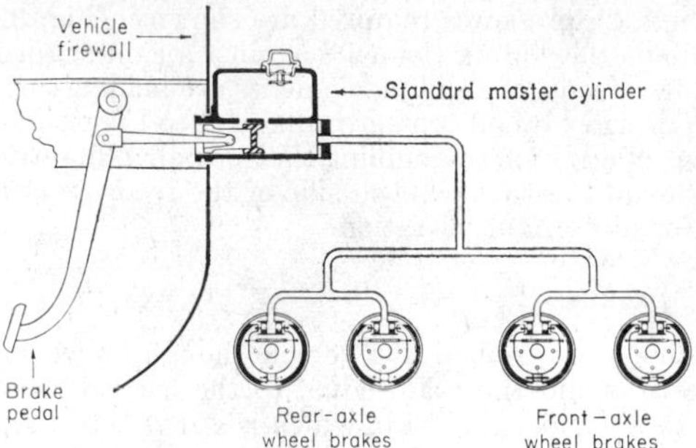

FIG. 33. Conventional hydraulic brake system.

leum products; hydraulic fluids are generally mixtures of glycols with inhibitors. Figure 33 shows the usual system, and Fig. 34 shows the **split system,** for improved safety, with two independent master cylinders in tandem, each actuating half the brakes, either front or rear or one front and the opposite rear. Failure of either hydraulic section allows stopping of the car by brakes on two wheels.

Figure 35 shows the customary design of a **brake master cylinder** and a **wheel-brake cylinder,** by which the brake shoes are applied in the conventional internal-expanding brakes, Fig. 36. When the brakes are released, a spring in the master cylinder returns the piston, with its flexible primary cup, to a stop plate. This uncovers the compensating port, permitting brake fluid to enter from the reservoir or to escape from the wheel cylinders after brake application. The check valve facilitates the maintenance of 8- to 16-psi line pressure to prevent the entrance of air into the system.

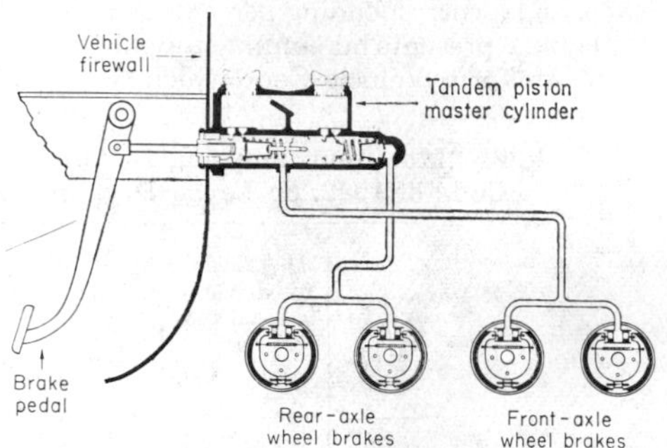

FIG. 34. "Split" hydraulic brake system.

Three **types of internal-expanding brakes,** Fig. 36, have been accepted in service. All are **self-energizing,** where the drum rotation increases the applying force supplied by the wheel cylinder. Huck (*Trans. SAE,* Pt. I, 1926, p. 455) has shown that self-energization, expressed as the percentage of change of effort required for a given braking effect because of the turning of the drum, is a product of the coefficient of friction and a design constant which depends on the location of the anchor pin, the arc subtended, and the location of the lining. Such a brake will self-lock if the friction coefficient exceeds a value also determined by this design constant. Burkhardt (*Trans. SAE,* Pt. II, 1925, p. 282) has shown that the brake lining should be limited to a 120-deg arc because the self-energization of increments near the ends (especially near the toe) is so great that squealing may develop.

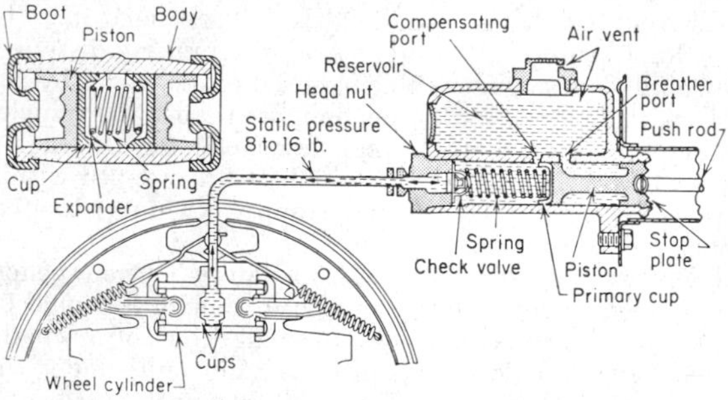

FIG. 35. Conventional master cylinder and, wheel cylinder, brakes released.

With the **trailing shoe** (Fig. 36*a*), friction is opposed to the actuating force. The resulting de-energization of this shoe causes it to do about one-third the work of the leading shoe. Its tendency to lock or squeal is much less, and the length and position of the lining are not so critical. The type of brake shown in Fig. 36*a*, with one leading and one trailing shoe, has been used by one U.S. manufacturer (Chrysler) for the rear wheels. The braking work and wear of the two shoes can be equalized by use of a larger bore for that half of the wheel cylinder which operates the trailing shoe.

The design shown in Fig. 36*b* has two leading shoes, each actuated by a single-piston wheel cylinder and each self-energizing. This design has been used for the front wheels where the Fig. 36*a* design was used for the rear wheels. A variation of this design has been used abroad, with two trailing shoes, and is equivalent to running Fig. 36*b* in reverse. It is less sensitive to changes in friction coefficient than other designs, and the required greater braking force is generally provided by a power booster.

Figure 36*c* shows the **Bendix Duo-Servo design,** used on most U.S. cars, in which the self-energizing action of **two leading shoes** is much increased by operating them **"in series";** the braking force developed by the primary shoe becomes the actuating force for the secondary shoe. The action reverses with rotation. This design is even more sensitive than that of Fig. 36*b* to variations in the coefficient of friction. The lowered coefficient resulting from the heating effects of operation on long grades or

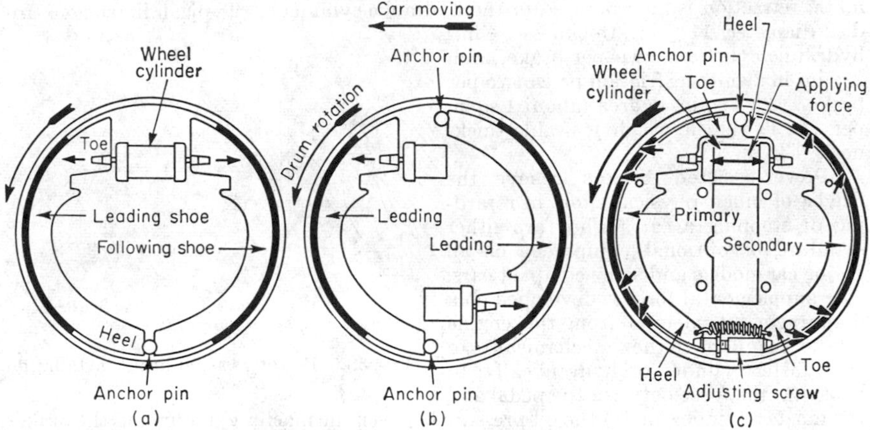

FIG. 36. Three types of internal-expanding brakes.

repeated severe stops tends to develop brake **"fade."** Conversely, a large increase in friction coefficient, *e.g.*, following standing with wet brakes, may develop a tendency to **"grab."**

Adjustment for lining wear is effected automatically on most cars. If sufficient wear has developed, a linkage may turn the notched wheel on the adjusting screw (Fig. 36*c*) by movement of the primary shoe relative to the anchor pin when the brake is applied with the car moving in reverse. On other designs, adjustment is by linkage between the hand brake and the adjusting wheel.

Brake drums are designed to be as large as practicable in order to develop the necessary torque with the minimum application effort and to limit the temperature developed in dissipating the heat of friction. The 14-in. wheel-rim diameters prevalent on standard cars since 1957 limit the drum diameters to 10 to 12 in., while the 13-in. rims of "compact" cars limit the diameters to 9 to 9½ in. Drum widths limit unit pressures between the linings and the drums to 16 to 23 lb of car weight per sq in. Drum **friction surfaces** are usually cast iron or iron alloy; **brake shoes** are lined with compounds or mixtures of asbestos, resin, and filler materials, formed into relatively hard blocks and riveted or thermally bonded to the shoes; friction coefficients range from 0.3 to 0.4. Where identical brakes are used on front and rear wheels, the rear-wheel cylinders are smaller, so that about 40 to 45 percent of the total braking force is developed at the rear wheels. With the split system, Fig. 34, a smaller master cylinder for the rear brakes gives a similar division. **Master cylinders** are about 1 in. in diameter, and other parts of the brake system are so proportioned that a 100-lb brake-pedal pressure develops 600- to 1200-psi fluid pressure. **Air** in an hydraulic system makes the brakes feel spongy, and it must be bled wherever it accumulates, as at each wheel cylinder. Air is introduced when the system is opened for servicing or when the reservoir-fluid level is allowed to fall too low.

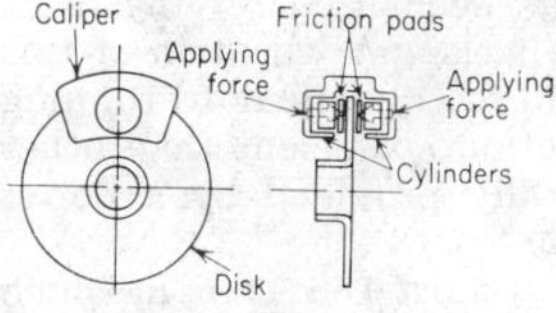

FIG. 37. Caliper disk brake, schematic.

Caliper disk brakes, Fig. 37, favored particularly on racing cars, are found also on passenger cars, especially in Europe. They offer better heat dissipation by direct contact with moving air; they are not self-energizing, so that there is less drop in the friction coefficient with temperature rise of the brake shoes. Contrarily, the absence of self-energization requires higher hydraulic-system pressures and consequent power boosters on heavier cars. **Wear** of the friction pads is normally greater because of the smaller area of contact and the greater exposure to road dirt. The pads are consequently made thicker than the linings of drum brakes, and automatic retraction is incorporated in the hydraulic cylinders. Typical dimensions are: disk diameter, 11½ in.; thickness, ⅜ in.; hydraulic cylinders, two per brake, each 2⅛ in. in diameter; friction pads, two per brake, each 4 sq in. in area (about 1 sq in. per 152 lb vehicle weight); usable thickness, 0.40 in.

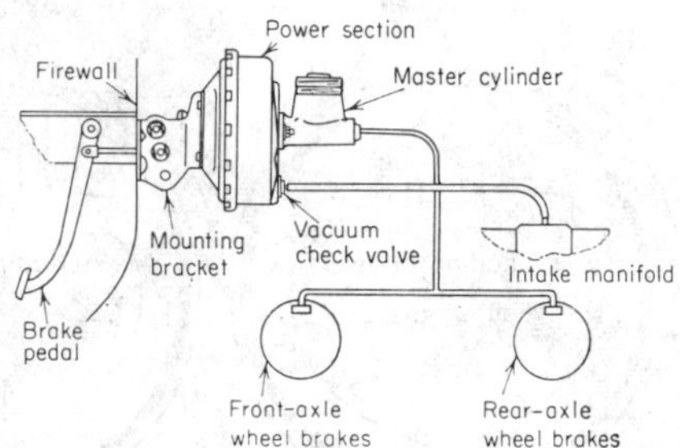

FIG. 38. Power-assisted brake installation.

Power-assisted brakes relieve the driver of much physical effort in retarding or stopping a car. They are either standard or optional equipment on all major car models and some compact cars. The supplemental force is developed on a diaphragm by vacuum from the engine intake manifold, either mechanically to the master cylinder or hydraulically, to boost (1) the force between the pedal and the master cylinder, or (2) the oil pressure between the master cylinder and the brakes. Common characteristics are (1) a braking force which is related to pedal pressure so that the driver can feel a pedal reaction proportional to the force applied, and (2) ability to apply the brakes in the absence of the supplemental power.

Figures 38 and 39 illustrate a passenger-car **vacuum-suspended type** of power

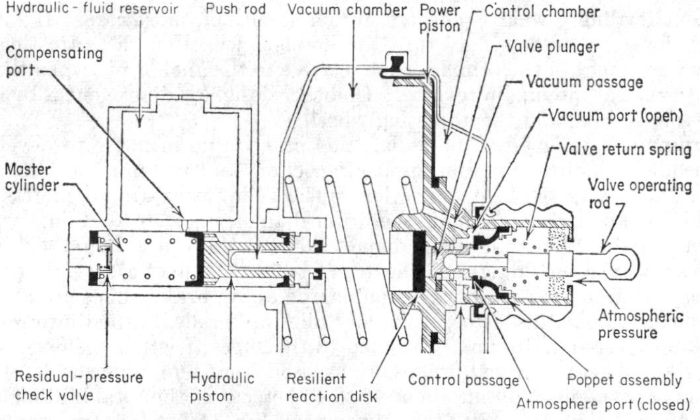

FIG. 39. Bendix Master Vac power brake, at rest position (schematic).

brake, where vacuum exists on both sides of the main power element when the brakes are released. In the released position, as shown, there is contact between the valve plunger and the poppet; thus the port is closed between the power cylinder and the atmosphere but there is clearance between the poppet and the piston hub, which provides a passage to equalize the pressure between both sides of the piston.

Physical effort applied to the brake pedal moves the valve operating rod toward the master-cylinder section. Initial movement of this rod, which carries with it both the valve plunger and the poppet (held in contact with each other by a spring), closes the port between the poppet and the power piston. This closes the vacuum passage and brings the valve plunger into contact with the resilient reaction disk. Additional movement of the valve rod then separates the valve plunger from the poppet, thus opening the atmospheric port and admitting air to the control chamber at the right of the piston. The air pressure in this chamber depends upon the amount of physical effort applied to the pedal. The pressure differences between the two sides of the power piston causes it to move toward the master cylinder, closing the vacuum port and transferring its force through the resilient reaction disk to the hydraulic piston of the master cylinder. This force tends to extrude the reaction disk against the valve plunger and react against the valve operating rod, thus reducing the pedal effort required.

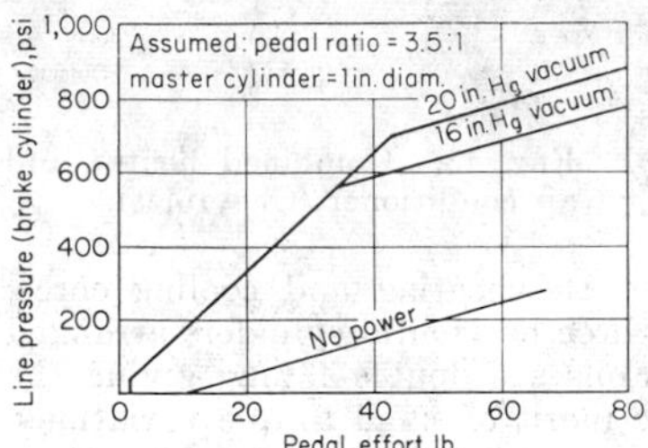

FIG. 40. Performance chart of a typical power-assisted brake.

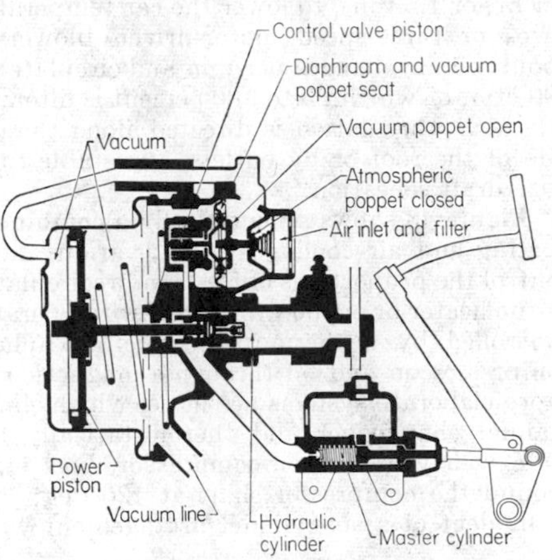

FIG. 41. Bendix "Hydra-Vac" in released position.

The hydraulic pressure is directly proportional to the effort applied by the driver, and so is the reaction force transmitted by the reaction disk, which reduces the pressure required on the brake pedal. The hydraulic pressure created by the master cylinder is the sum of the physical effort exerted on the brake pedal and the force developed by the power piston. When vacuum is not available, the unassisted effort on the pedal can still apply the brakes, though less effectively. An inherent feature of the vacuum-suspended type of power brake is the existence of vacuum, without an additional reservoir, for at least one brake stop after the engine is stopped. Figure 40 exemplifies the relationship between pedal effort and hydraulic line pressure.

The **booster-brake system,** Fig. 41, where the line pressure between the master cylinder and the brakes is boosted by a vacuum-operated hydraulic piston, has been largely superseded except for some large commercial vehicles and some foreign cars.

Air Conditioning

(See also Sec. 12)

Automobiles are generally **ventilated** through an opening near the windshield with a plenum chamber to separate rain from air. Airflow developed by car motion is augmented, especially at low speed, by a variable-speed, electrically driven blower. When **heat** is required, this air is passed through a finned core served by the engine-jacket water. Core design typically calls for delivery of 20000 Btu per hr (125 cfm approx at 130 F with 0 F ambient). Car **temperature** is controlled by (1) mixing ambient with heated air, (2) mixing heated with recirculated air, or (3) variation of blower speed. Provision is always made to direct heated air against the interior of the windshield to prevent formation of ice or fog. Figure 42 illustrates schematically a three-speed blower which drives fresh air through (1) a radiator core, or (2) a bypass. The degree and direction of air heating are further regulated by the doors.

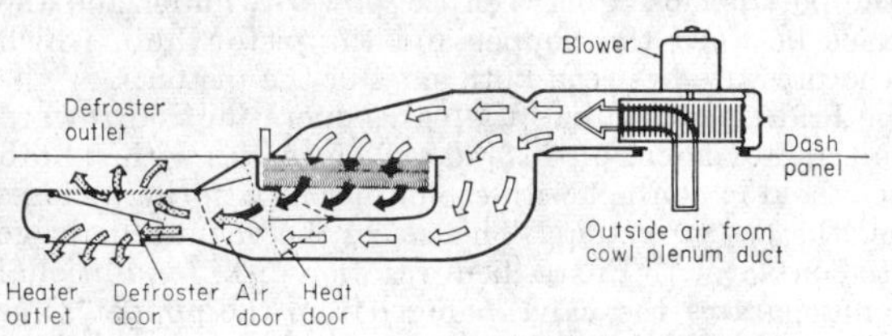

FIG. 42. Heater airflow.

Most higher-priced cars, particularly in the Southern states, are equipped with **air-cooling systems.** The **refrigeration capacity** of a typical installation is 20,000 Btu per hr, or 1.5 tons, to lower the car temperature 25 to 30 F at a car speed of 30 mph. Two- or three-speed motor-driven blowers give about 1.5 air changes per min and circulate 200 to 300 cfm, of which 25 to 100 percent is filtered outside air. Circulation is directed along the underside of the roof or by outlets, adjustable to minimize draft sensation.

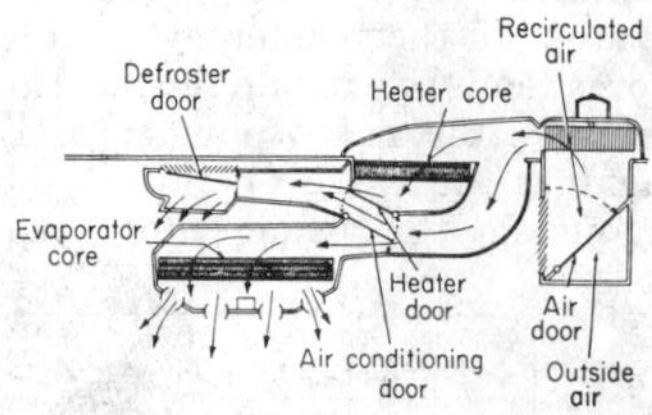

FIG. 43. Combined heater and air conditioner (Chevrolet).

Figure 43 shows schematically a **combined air-heating and air-cooling system;** various dampers control the proportions of fresh and recirculated air to the heater or evaporator core; air temperature is controlled by a thermostat, which switches the compressor on and off through a magnetic clutch. More elaborate systems are in use which eliminate manual changeover and thermostatically actuate the heating and cooling cores.

A widely used freon **compressor,** Fig. 44, has three horizontal cylinders arranged around the compressor shaft at 120 deg; the pistons are double-acting, giving the equivalent of a six-cylinder arrangement with the merit of small torque variations.

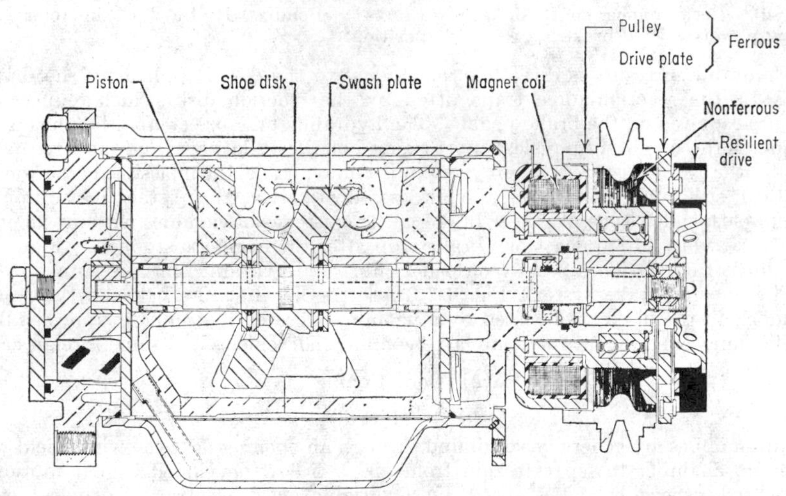

FIG. 44. Air-conditioning freon compressor with three parallel cylinders; double-acting pistons driven by swash plate; drive through a magnetic clutch with stationary coil (Frigidaire).

The pistons are driven by a swash plate of such thickness that its mass balances the reciprocating masses of the pistons. Pistons are 1½ in. in diameter with a 1$\frac{3}{16}$-in. stroke, giving a displacement of 12.6 cu in. per revolution. At 3,000 rpm, this unit can develop about 3 tons of refrigeration. For smaller cars, this capacity is reduced by counterboring the piston heads for sufficient reexpansion to reduce the equivalent displacement to 10.8 without altering other dimensions. The unit is driven through a magnetic clutch with no moving electrical contacts. Refrigeration capacity is controlled by intermittent operation or by continuous operation with suction throttling. To reduce the drain on the battery, the compressor is locked out while the car engine is started.

Automobile Engines

For details on engines, see Sec. 9. Table 3 gives antifreeze-protection data (see also pp. 6–186 and 9–139).

Table 3. Antifreeze (Permanent-type) Protection

Cooling-system capacity, qt	Antifreeze required, qt					
	2	4	6	8	10	12
	Deg F					
10	16	−12	−62			
12	19	0	−34			
14	..	6	−18	−54		
16	..	10	−8	−34		
18	..	14	0	−21	−50	
20	..	16	4	−12	−34	−62
22	..	18	8	−6	−23	−47
24	..	19	10	0	−15	−34
26	..	21	13	3	−9	−25
28	..	....	15	6	−5	−18

Antifreeze, %	20	25	33	40	50	60
Protection to, deg F	16	10	0	−12	−34	−62

RAILWAY ENGINEERING

BY

John F. Partridge

REFERENCES: *Proc. AAR*, Div. U, Mechanical. *Proc. AREA*. Bureau of Railway Economics. "Car Builder Cyclopedia," Simmons-Boardman. Sillcox, "Mastering Momentum," Simmons-Boardman. Schmidt, "High Horsepower Diesel-Hydraulic Locomotives in Heavy Duty Freight Service," *ASME Paper* 62-WA-245. Botzow, "Monorails," Simmons-Boardman. Pamphlet 1025A, Vol. I, Sec. K, General Railway Signal Co.

ELECTRIC TRACTION

(See also Sec. 15)

Electric and Diesel-electric locomotives are classified by wheel arrangement; letters represent the number of adjacent driving axles in a rigid truck (A for one axle, B for two axles, C for 3 axles, etc). Idler axles between drivers are designated by numerals. A plus sign indicates articulated trucks or motive power units. A minus sign indicates separated swivel trucks not articulated. For example, A1A − A1A + A1A − A1A represents a locomotive consisting of two articulated units mounted on six-wheel swivel trucks with motors on the end axles of each truck and one idler in each truck. This nomenclature has been adopted as standard by the AAR. (See Tables 1 and 2.)

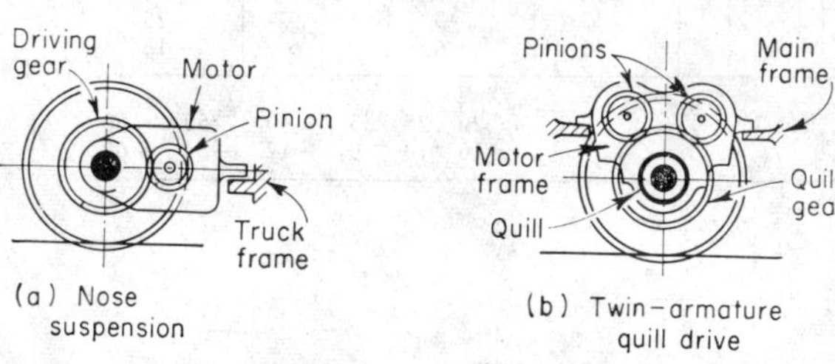

FIG. 1. Electric-locomotive drives.

Drives. The principal types of drives for electric locomotives are as follows (Fig. 1): (a) "nose suspension," one side of the motor being carried on the driving axle and one side on the truck frame, driving through pinion on armature shaft and gear on axle; (b) "quill," the pinion on the armature shaft (usually two armatures per motor are used) engaging a gear mounted on a sleeve, the latter normally concentric with the axle but capable of permitting the axle to move vertically to accommodate itself to the track surface and with the locomotive frame carrying the total weight of the motor and quill. The nose-suspension drive is used almost exclusively in new locomotives. Other forms of drives have been used, including a linkage drive, jack shaft and side rods, and a yoke drive, but have not been generally adopted by American designers. The characteristics of a satisfactory drive are: maximum proportion of weight carried on frame rather than on axle; motor weight well above axle center; freedom for driving axle to move vertically to accommodate variation in track surface; a connection with some flexibility between the armature shaft and the driving axle to absorb shocks.

Traction Motors. Fundamental relations for motors used in railway service take the forms shown in Fig. 2.

The **series motor,** either a-c or d-c, has the inherent advantage of the combination of low speed, large torque, and high starting current. At speeds below that at which maximum current can be imposed on the armature, the current is limited by controller

Table 1. Electric Locomotives

Road	Date built	Service	Arrangement	Starting tractive force, limited by motors or 25% adhesion	Weight 1,000 lb[a]		Wheelbase		Volts		Hp rating		Transformer or other equipment	Number of traction motors	Drive	Max speed, mph
					Total	On drivers	Rigid	Total	Supply	Motors	1 hr	Continuous				
Various....	.....	Sw	(1) b	25,000	100	100	6′6″	22′–25′	600–1,500 d-c	600–750 d-c	500	400	None	4	Nose susp	40–45
N.Y.C.	1930[c]	Pass.	(2) d	72,125	388.3	288.5	15′0″	69′0″	600 d-c	600 d-c	.....	4,750	[e]	6	Nose susp	70
P.R.R.	1951	Frt	2 unit	187,750[a]	751[a]	751	9′6″	43′2″	11,000 a-c	600 d-c	.....	5,984	Ign rectif	12	Nose susp	63
N.Y.N.H. &H.	1954	Pass.		87,000	348	348	15′0″	52′6″	11,000 a-c	600 d-c	.....	4,000	Ign rectif	6	Nose susp	90
N.Y.N.H. &H.	1938	Pass.		68,000	432	272	13′8″	66′0″	11,000 a-c 600 d-c	600 d-c[f] or a-c S.P.	.....	3,600	Transf	6 twin	Quill	90
P.R.R.	1935	Pass.		72,300	460	300	13′8″	69′0″	11,000 a-c	600 a-c S.P.	8,500[g]	4,620	Transf	6 twin	Quill	100
Great Northern	1947	P&F		180,000	735	735	16′9″	85′9″	11,000 a-c	600 d-c	.....	5,000	Motor-gen set	12	Nose susp	65
N.&W.	1948	Frt	2 units	260,000[a]	1,033.8[a]	1,033.8	9′0″	133′10″[a]	11,000 a-c	600 d-c	.....	6,800[a]	Motor-gen set	16	Nose susp	50
N.Y.N.H. &H.	1956	Frt		118,000	394	394	13′0″	52′9¾″	11,000 a-c	1,000 d-c approx	.....	3,300	Ign rectif	6	Nose susp	65
P.R.R.	1960–1963	Frt		89,000	386	386	13′0″	52′9¾″	11,000 a-c	1,000 d-c approx	.....	4,400	Ign rectif or sel rectif	6	Nose susp	70
Butte Anacon. & Pacific	1957	Frt		75,000	250	250	10′0″	30′3½″	2,400 d-c	1,200 d-c	.....	2,480	None	4	Nose susp	45

[a] For entire locomotive.
[b] ● = driving wheel.
[c] Rebuilt 1955.
[d] ○ = non-driving wheel.
[e] Three series—two parallel and full parallel.
[f] Motors operate both d-c and a-c.
[g] "Short-time rating."

Table 2. Diesel-Electric Locomotives

Builder	Service	Arrange-ment*	Weight, lb	Tractive force, lb		Engines					Engs per unit	No. of motors	Wheelbase	
				Starting	Continuous, at speed (mph)	Type	No. of cycles	Cyl per eng	Size of cyl, in.	Hp rating at (rpm)			Truck	Center plate
EMD...	Sw	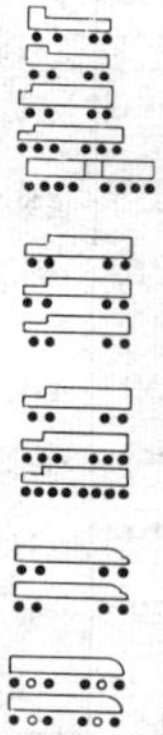	248,000	62,000	31,200 (12.0)	V	2	12	8½ × 10	1,200 (800)	1	4	8′0″	22′0″
Alco....	Sw		230,000	57,500	34,000 (8.0)	Inline	4	6	12½ × 13	1,000 (740)	1	4	8′0″	22′6″
EMD...	Rd sw		240,000	60,000	45,000 (12.0)	V	2	16	8½ × 10	1,800 (835)	1	4	9′0″	32′0″
EMD...	Rd sw		333,000	83,250		V	2	16	8½ × 10	2,500 (900)	1	6	13′7″	35′0″
EMD...	Rd sw†		488,000	122,000	102,800 (12.0)	V	2	16	8½ × 10	2,500 (900)	2	8	17′0¾″	55′0″
Alco....	Rd sw		240,000	60,000	53,000 (11.5)	V	4	12	9 × 10½	2,000 (1,025)	1	4	9′4″	34′5″
Alco....	Rd sw		246,000	61,500	53,000 (14.0)	V	4	16	9 × 10½	2,400 (1,025)	1	4	9′4″	32′6″
Alco....	Rd sw		340,000	85,000	79,500 (11.5)	V	4	16	9 × 10½	2,750 (1,050)	1	6	12′6″	41′6″
GE.....	Rd sw		252,000	63,000	53,000 (14.7)	V	4	16	9½ × 10	2,500 (1,000)	1	4	9′4″	36′2½″
GE.....	Rd sw		335,000	83,750	79,500 (9.0)	V	4	16	9½ × 10	2,500 (1,000)	1	6	13′0″	......
GE.....	Rd sw		556,000	139,000	106,000 (14.7)	V	4	16	9½ × 10	2,500 (1,000)	2	8	9′4″	......
EMD...	Frt		246,000	61,500	40,000 (11.5)	V	2	16	8½ × 10	1,750 (835)	1	4	9′0″	30′0″
Alco....	Frt		240,000	60,000	38,000 (12.0)	V	4	12	9 × 10½	1,600 (1,000)	1	4	9′4″	29′2″
EMD...	Pass.		331,800	55,300	‡	V	2	12	8½ × 10	1,200 (800)	2	4	14′1″	43′0″
Alco....	Pass.		303,000	50,500	33,600 (21.0)	V	4	16	9 × 10½	2,250 (1,000)	1	4	15′6″	34′2″

* ● = driving wheel; ○ = non-driving wheel.

† Has no operating cab; must be operated in road service in multiple with other units.

‡ In most cases, rating will be determined by adhesion.

resistance, which is cut out, step by step, as the motor speeds up. The normal motor connections do not permit a wide enough range of speeds. With the d-c motor, variable connections are provided through the controller to change from series or series parallel (at low speeds) to full parallel at high speed. Field shunting is also used in some cases. Characteristics of the series motor are more fully described in the section on Diesel locomotives. Curves shown in Fig. 3 afford a comparison of the types of motors used and show relations between speed, tractive force, and current. For the **a-c motor,** the motors are placed permanently in parallel, and speed control is obtained by "tapping" the transformer to secure desirable fractional voltages [Fig. 3(*b*)]. The **polyphase motor** has an important advantage in its lack of commutator and brushes, but being a constant-speed motor it has its principal application in slow freight service with infrequent stops. Speed variation, at considerable expense in efficiency, can be obtained for starting by the insertion of resistance in the short-circuited rotor circuit as shown in Fig. 3(*c*). Two (sometimes three) running speeds can be obtained by changing the number of poles, the speed varying inversely with the number operative, or by reconnection in concatenation, giving speeds half as great as the normal characteristic.

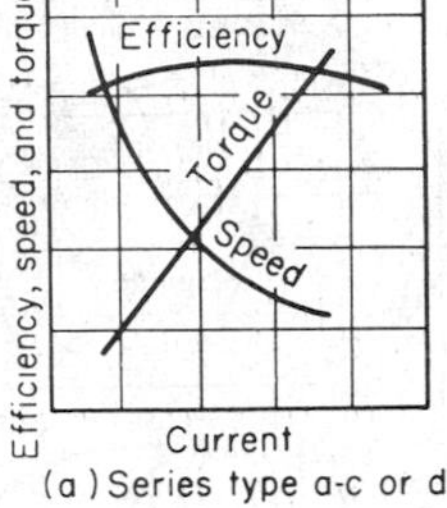

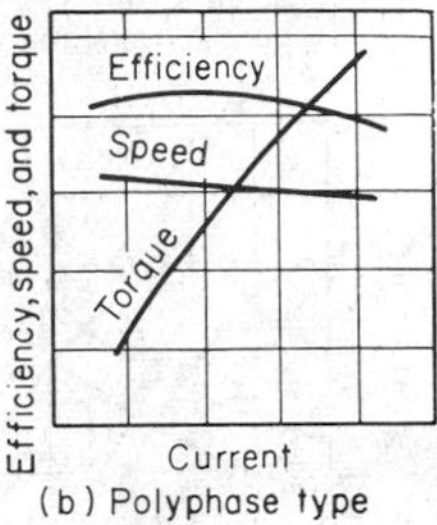

FIG. 2. Characteristics of electric-locomotive motors.

Ignitron Rectifier. As a result of improvements in the design of the mercury-pool ignitron rectifier, it has been adopted for use in electric locomotives. Its use permits combining the economic advantages of the high-voltage a-c overhead catenary and distribution systems with the efficiency of d-c traction motors and their desirable operating characteristics. The a-c voltage at the pantagraph is stepped down by a liquid-cooled transformer. Transformer output is fed through the rectifiers before going to the traction motors. Control of tractive effort is accomplished by cutting in accelerating resistors between rectifier and motors and by changing transformer taps. Motors are also reconnected at higher locomotive speeds (transition) to maintain proper level of armature current. (See also p. 15–117.)

Recently, ignitron locomotives, gas-turbine locomotives, and some Diesel-electric locomotives have been built with three-axle swing bolster trucks and three nose-suspension-type d-c traction motors. To provide room for the motor on the center axle the center plate is located between two adjacent axles. Two horizontal spring-loaded sliding plates on each side of the truck frame also carry underframe load and provide proper distribution of weight on the axles.

DIESEL-ELECTRIC LOCOMOTIVES

General. The high efficiency of the Diesel engine is an important factor in its selection as a prime mover for traction. It is a constant-torque machine that cannot be started under load and hence requires a variably coupled transmission arrangement. Being essentially a constant-horsepower machine it is ideally suited to switching service since it can make use of its full rated-power output at low track speeds. Examples of the various types and service designs are shown in Table 2.

Diesel-electric locomotives have a d-c generator coupled directly to the Diesel-engine crankshaft. The generator is electrically connected to series traction motors having a nose-suspension mounting. The tooth ratio of the axle-mounted gears to the motor-pinion gears which they engage determines the speed range and is related to the type of service. A high ratio is used where high tractive efforts and low speeds are required, whereas high-speed passenger locomotives have a low ratio.

Most locomotives have four traction motors per unit and either four or six axles.

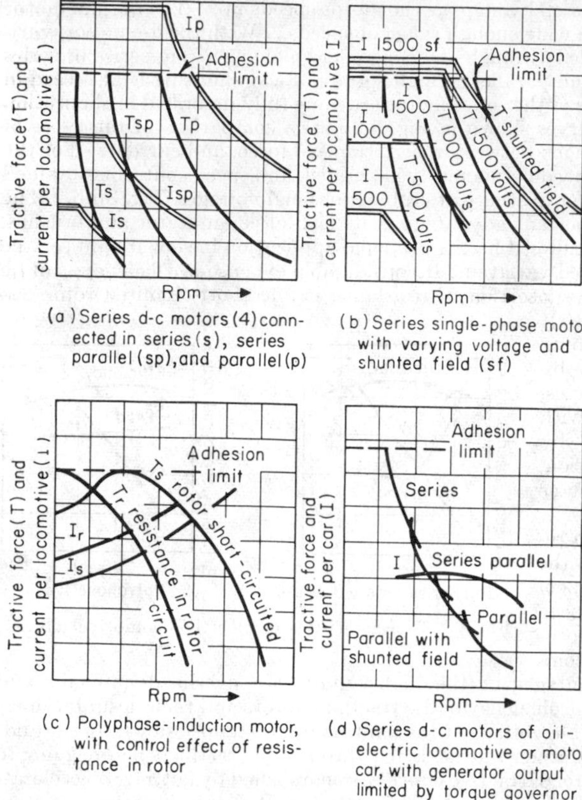

FIG. 3. Speed-tractive-force relations of electric locomotives.

Where high tractive efforts are required six motors may be used to advantage, especially where track conditions require low axle loading.

Diesel Engines

(See also p. 9-114)

Types. Diesel engines as developed for locomotive applications include the V type, 2 cycle; V type, 4 cycle; 6 or 8 cylinder in-line, 4 cycle; and 8, 10, or 12 cylinder opposed-piston, 2 cycle. Two-cycle engines are equipped with an air-intake blower or supercharger, gear-driven from the crankshaft. Four-cycle engines may be normally aspirated or supercharged. The supercharger turbine is driven by expansion of engine exhaust gases and usually accounts for 50 percent increase in the horsepower rating. In the V type, two-cycle engine, the fuel injector mounted in each cylinder head is used to meter the fuel as well as atomize it, whereas in four-cycle engines a separate injector pump for each cylinder delivers a metered amount of fuel per stroke under high pressure to the injector.

The **governor** is mounted on the engine and usually geared to the camshaft. It may, however, receive its engine-speed signal electrically in the form of a variable a-c frequency from a tachometer generator. It serves to maintain a constant engine speed with varying loads at a predetermined value of rpm between idle and full speed according to the position of the engineman's throttle. It may be actuated electrically to give any one of eight steps by energizing one or more of its four speed solenoids, or by varying air pressure to the spring-loaded diaphragm of a "receiver," giving an infinite number of steps. The former has been more widely used, especially where control of more than one unit from a single cab is involved. The governor power piston is connected through mechanical linkage to the fuel racks on the engine. If the load is sufficient for the governor to call for more fuel than should be required for the engine's full rated power at that particular rpm, it will act to reduce the generator output. This is usually accomplished through a hydraulic connection to a load regulator, which may or may not be an integral part of the governor itself. The load regulator consists of a rheostat in series with the main-generator excitation system, and thus is made to vary the main-generator voltage.

Electric Traction Equipment

The **main generator** has several field windings incorporated in the stator; *i.e.*, series, shunt, differential, battery (or separately excited from a smaller generator, or "exciter"), and starting. The last is employed when feeding power from the storage batteries into the main generator to start the engine.

Generator power output is controlled by (1) varying engine speed through movement of the engineman's controller, and (2) controlling the flow of current in the main-generator battery field or in the field of a separate exciter generator. The shunt and differential fields (if used) are designed to contribute toward a constant generator power output for a given engine speed as the armature current and voltage vary. They do not completely accomplish this. The battery or separately excited field is controlled by the load regulator to provide the final adjustment in excitation to load the engine properly. It is also automatically deenergized to reduce or remove the load, when certain undesirable conditions occur, to prevent damage to the power plant or other traction equipment.

Auxiliary Generating Apparatus. D-c power for battery charging, lighting, and control is furnished by a separate generator, geared or belt-driven from the main generator. Voltage output is regulated within 1 percent over the full range of engine speeds at 74 volts. A separate generator may be provided to supply power for motor driven blowers to ventilate the traction motors and for the radiator-fan motors. It may be a d-c machine or a three-phase alternator. The alternator is mounted on the end of the main generator and directly coupled to it.

Traction-motor blowers are mounted above the locomotive underframe. Air from the centrifugal-blower housings is carried through the underframe and into the motor housings through flexible ducts. (See also pp. 14–69 *et seq.*)

Traction motors employ series- and commutating-field poles. The current in the series fields is reversed to change locomotive direction and may be partially shunted through resistors to reduce counter emf as locomotive speed is increased. Armature shafts are equipped with grease-lubricated roller bearings. Axle bearings are of the friction type and have lubricant wells and wool waste or spring-loaded felt wicks which maintain constant contact with the axle surface.

Electrical Controls

Electropneumatic **contactors** are used to make and break the proper circuits between traction motors and the main generator. They are equipped with interlocks for various control-circuit functions. Magnetically operated contactors are used for other power and excitation circuits of lower amperage. An electropneumatic **cam switch,** consisting of a two-position drum with copper segments moving between spring-loaded fingers, is used to reverse traction-motor field current ("reverser") or to set up the circuits for dynamic braking. This switch is not designed to operate under load.

Electrically actuated **relays** are used frequently in control and alarm circuits. Their contacts usually handle 75 volts and 1 amp or less. Relay-operating coils may be energized by the 75 volt control system, or they may be preset to respond to a particular voltage level. The latter is sometimes used to activate transition and motor-shunting equipment in response to the level of main-generator voltage. Wheel-slip relays operate by sensing the difference in magnitude of the current in two traction-motor armatures paralleling each other or by sensing the difference in voltage drop across two motor armatures that are connected in series.

Propulsion control circuits transmit the engineman's movements of the throttle lever, reverse lever, and transition or dynamic brake control lever in the controlling unit to the power-producing equipment of each unit operating in multiple in the group. Before power is applied, all reversers must move to provide proper motor connections for the movement desired, taking into account the direction in which each individual unit is heading. Power contactors complete the proper circuits between generators and motors. Excitation circuits are then allowed to function to provide the proper main-generator field current while the engine speed increases to correspond to the engineman's controller position.

Wheel slip is detected by some form of speed-sensing equipment connected electrically to the motor circuits or connected mechanically to the axles. When slipping occurs, relays automatically reduce main-generator excitation or engine speed until slipping ceases, whereupon power is gradually reapplied. A warning light and buzzer in the operating cab inform the engineman, so that if the condition persists, he will notch back on the throttle.

Batteries

Lead-acid storage batteries of 280 or 420 amp-hr capacity are usually used for starting the Diesel engine. Thirty-two cells on each locomotive unit are used to provide the standard 64 volt system. (See also p. 15–16)

Braking

Air-brake System. The "independent" brake-valve handle at the engineman's position controls the air pressure supplied from the locomotive reservoirs to the brake cylinders on the locomotive itself. The "automatic" handle controls the air pressure in the brake pipe to the train.

Air for braking and for various pneumatic controls on the locomotive is supplied by a two-stage three-cylinder compressor, usually connected directly to the main-generator shaft. Since it is constantly moving with the rotation of the engine, a pressure-sensitive unloader is provided to maintain a pressure of approximately 130 to 140 psi in the main reservoirs. When charging an empty train line with the locomotive at standstill (maximum compressor demand), the engineman may increase engine (and compressor) rpm without feeding power to the traction motors.

Dynamic Braking. On some locomotives dynamic brakes supplement the air-brake system. The traction motors are used as generators to convert the kinetic energy of the locomotive and cars into electrical energy, which is dissipated through resistance grids located near the roof. Motor-driven blowers, designed to utilize some of this energy, force outside air over the grids and out the top of the roof. By directing a generous and evenly distributed air stream over the grids their physical size is reduced in keeping with the relatively small space available in the locomotive.

By means of a cam switch, the traction motors are connected to the resistance grids; their fields are usually connected in series across the main generator to supply the necessary high current excitation. By controlling the engine speed and/or main-generator excitation, the magnitude of the braking force is determined. Dynamic braking is not usually effective below 10 mph on most locomotives, but it is very useful at 20 to 30 mph, particularly on long grades, where brake-shoe wear would otherwise be considerable. Other advantages are relieving crews from setting up air-brake retainers on freight cars, smoother control of train speed, and reduction in the number of wheel-rim thermal cracks.

An automatic protective device may be incorporated in the excitation circuit which limits motor currents to a maximum safe value. A warning light is used at the engineman's position to inform him that he cannot obtain further braking effort and must depend on the air-brake system for additional retardation.

Performance

Engine Indicated Horsepower. The horsepower delivered at the Diesel-locomotive drawbar is the end result of a series of subtractions from the original indicated horsepower of the engine, in order to take into account efficiency of transmission equipment and losses due to the power requirements of various auxiliaries. The formula for the engine's indicated horsepower is ihp $= PLAN/33{,}000$, where P = mean effective pressure in the cylinder, psi; L = length of piston stroke, ft; A = piston area, sq in.; N = total number of cycles completed per min. The factor P is governed by the over-all condition of the engine, quality of fuel, rate of fuel injection, completeness of combustion, compression ratio, etc. Factors L and A are fixed with the design of the engine. Factor N is a function of engine speed, number of working chambers, and strokes needed to complete a cycle.

Engine Brake Horsepower. In order to obtain horsepower delivered to the crankshaft coupling (main-generator connection), frictional losses in bearings and gears must be subtracted from ihp. Also some power is used to drive lubricating-oil pumps, governor, water pump, and scavenging blower. The resultant horsepower at the coupling is brake horsepower (bhp).

Thermal efficiency of the Diesel engine at the crankshaft, or the ratio of bhp output to the rate at which energy of the fuel is delivered to the engine, is about 30 percent. Thermal efficiency at the rail is about 23 percent.

Rail Horsepower. A portion of the engine bhp is transmitted mechanically through the generator armature shaft via couplings or belts and pulleys to traction-motor blowers, air-brake compressor, auxiliary generator, and radiator cooling-fan generator or alternator. In some cases part of the generator electrical output is used to run some of the auxiliaries. The remainder of the engine bhp transmitted to the main generator for traction purposes must be multiplied by generator efficiency (usually about 91 percent), and the result again multiplied by the efficiency of the traction motors (including power circuits) and gears to arrive at rail horsepower. Power output of the main generator for traction may be expressed as $\text{Watts}_{\text{traction}} = E_g \times I_m$, where E_g = main-generator voltage, I_m = traction-motor current, amp, multiplied by the number of parallel paths. Rail horsepower may be expressed as $\text{hp}_{\text{rail}} = \text{mph} \times TE/375$; where TE = tractive effort at the rail, lb.

Drawbar horsepower represents power available at the rear of the locomotive to move the cars, and may be expressed as

$$\text{hp}_{\text{drawbar}} = \text{hp}_{\text{rail}} - \text{locomotive running resistance} \times \text{mph}/375$$

Running-resistance calculations are discussed below under Train Resistance. Theoretically, drawbar horsepower available, therefore, is power output of the Diesel engine less parasitic losses described above.

Speed-Tractive Effort. At full throttle the losses vary somewhat at different values of speed and tractive effort, but a curve of tractive effort plotted against speed is nearly hyperbolic. Figure 4 is a typical speed–tractive-effort curve for a 1,500 hp freight locomotive. The Diesel-electric has full horsepower available over the entire speed range (within limits described below).

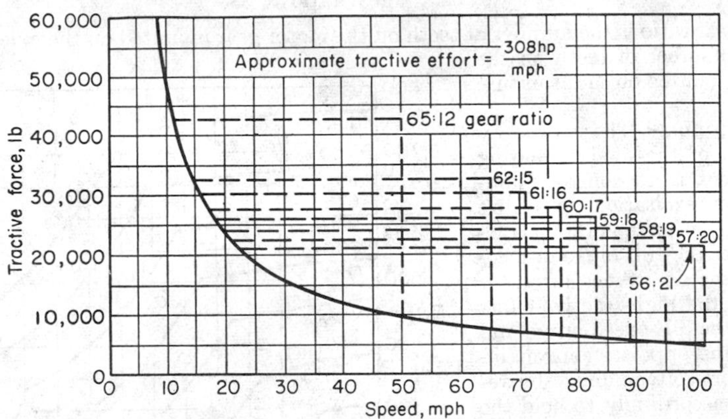

FIG. 4. Speed–tractive-force relations of a 1,500 hp Diesel-electric locomotive.

Adhesion. In Fig. 4 the maximum value of tractive effort represents the point of wheel slippage with average rail conditions. It is usually taken at 25 percent adhesion or 25 percent of total locomotive weight on drivers. Actually the point of wheel slip will vary considerably with rail conditions, being as low as 10 percent or as high as 35 percent. Adhesion is greatly reduced by lubricants which spread as thin films in the presence of moisture on running surfaces.

Traction-motor Characteristics. Motor torque is a function of armature current and field flux (which itself is a function of field current). Since traction motors are series-connected, armature and field current are the same (except when field-shunting circuits are introduced), and therefore tractive effort is a function solely of motor current. Figure 5 is a typical group of curves of tractive effort plotted against motor amperes. The indicated values of percent represent degrees of field shunting (see Saturation Curves). Wheel diameter and gear ratio must be specified when plotting torque in terms of tractive effort. (See also Sec. 15.)

Traction motors are usually rated in terms of maximum continuous current. This represents the current whose **heating effect** due to I^2R losses in the armature and field windings is sufficient to raise the temperature of the motor to its maximum safe limit when cooling air at maximum expected ambient temperature is forced through it by the blowers at the prescribed rate. Continuous operation at this current level results in the motor operating at its maximum safe level, heat generated just being equal to heat dissipated. The tractive effort corresponding to this current is usually somewhat lower than the adhesion limit above. Operation must be restricted by the engineman when hauling heavy trains up long grades. Somewhat higher current values may be permitted for short periods of time. These ratings are specified in terms of load-meter amperes and corresponding time intervals and are posted on or near the meter dial in the cab.

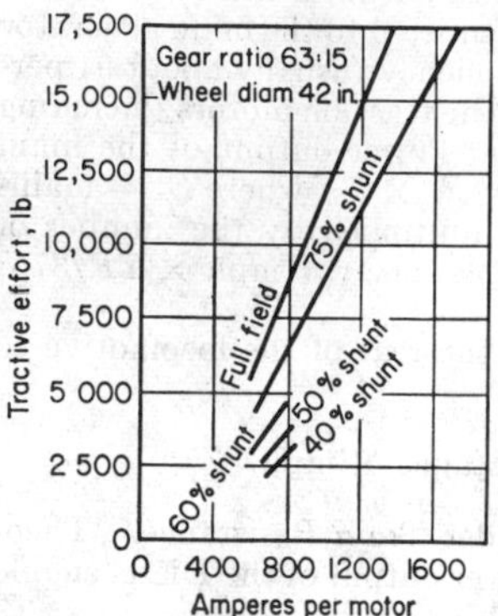

FIG. 5. Motor transmission.

Maximum Speed. Traction motors are also rated in terms of maximum safe rpm, which in turn limits locomotive speed. The gear ratio and wheel diameter also alter speed and tractive effort at which full horsepower is developed through the motors at their continuous rating. Maximum locomotive speed may be expressed as follows:

$$\text{mph}_{\text{max}} = \frac{\text{wheel diam (in.)} \times \text{motor rpm}_{\text{max}}}{\text{gear ratio} \times 336}$$

where gear ratio is the number of teeth on the motor gear mounted on the axle divided by the number of teeth on the pinion mounted on the armature shaft.

Transition. The primary function of the load-regulating equipment is to control main-generator excitation to utilize rated engine horsepower for traction over the full range of locomotive speeds. Since current is high at the high-tractive-effort end of the TE-speed curve and low at the opposite end, main-generator voltage must be regulated accordingly to hold the product of volts and amperes nearly constant. The design of generator and motors imposes practical limits in both directions. Figure 6 is a series of typical main-generator voltage-current curves for the eight throttle positions. To live within these limits and still accomplish the desired objective, two principle types of power circuits are employed: (1) transition and (2) field shunting. Sometimes they are used in combination. In Fig. 7, motors are connected in series when starting, by closing only contactor S-1. As current demand falls off, the S-1 contactor opens and P-1 and P-2 contactors close, providing a series-parallel connection.

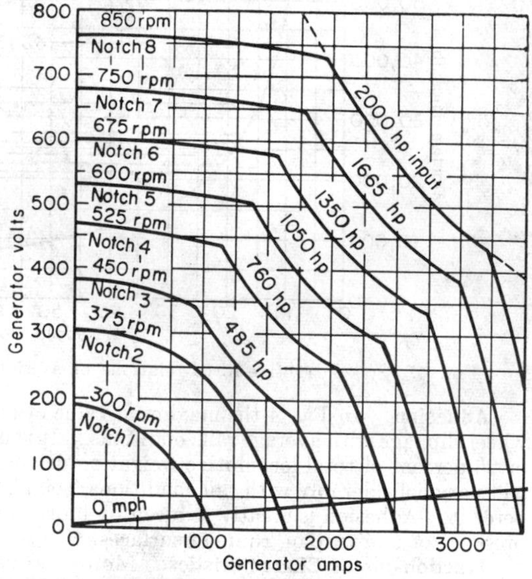

FIG. 6. Characteristic curves of a generator for a 2,000 hp Diesel-electric locomotive.

Field Shunting. In Fig. 8, motor connections are permanently in series parallel. As current demand decreases, shunting contactors M-1 and M-2 close at specific points on the generator voltage-current curve, reducing motor field current. For example, if M-1 and M-2 close at about 25 mph, motor-current demand suddenly increases to maintain the same tractive effort. The shunting effect also reduces required generator voltage at that speed and therefore permits a repositioning higher on the curve. As locomotive speed further increases, current demand is gradually reduced until a second set of contactors close (M-3 and M-4).

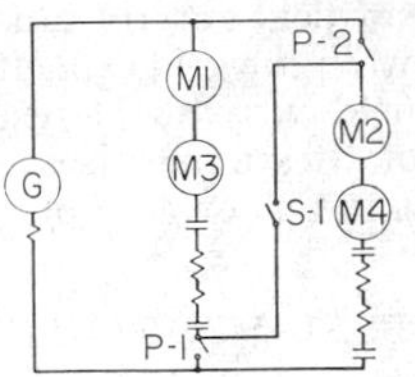

Fig. 7. Transition circuit.

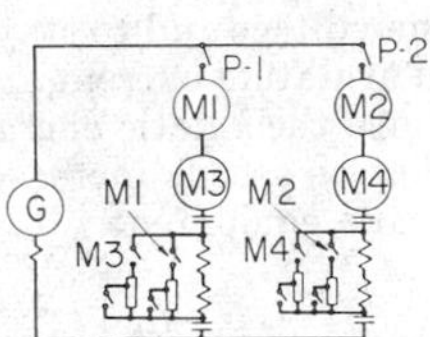

Fig. 8. Field shunting circuit.

Saturation Curves. Figure 9 shows a series of curves for a traction motor with internal voltage per rpm plotted against armature current. The uppermost curve represents equal field and armature currents (full field strength). Remaining curves are designated in terms of percent expressed as field current/armature current $\times$ 100%. The ratio may be expressed in terms of resistance values: $R_s/(R_f + R_s) \times 100\%$, where R_f = motor series field resistance, ohms, and R_s = shunting resistance in parallel with the field, ohms. The voltage-current relationship in a typical Diesel-locomotive power circuit may be expressed as

$$E_g = [(\text{emf/rpm}) \times \text{mph} \times C + I_m R_m] N + I_m R_c$$

or

$$\text{mph} = [E_g - I_m(R_c + R_m N)]/(\text{emf/rpm}) \times N \times C$$

where E_g = main-generator voltage; emf/rpm = motor internal volts per rev of the armature; mph = locomotive speed; I_m = motor-armature current, amp; R_m = motor-armature and field resistance, ohms; N = number of motors in series; R_c = other resistance in one path of the circuit through the motors, including cables, motor brushes, contactors, etc., ohms; C = constant represented by

$$\frac{336 \times \text{gear ratio (gear)/(pinion)}}{\text{wheel diam (in.)}}$$

Speed–tractive-effort curves may be determined by using this formula, together with the appropriate curves illustrated in Figs. 5, 6, and 9. When fields are shunted, the appropriate emf/rpm curve must be used, and the proper shunting resistance taken into account in determining R_m. By assuming values of motor current, main-generator voltage may be determined from Fig. 6. Emf/rpm is selected from Fig. 9, and the formula used to find speed. The curve in Fig. 5 is used to determine corresponding tractive effort for one motor and multiplied by the number of motors to obtain the total.

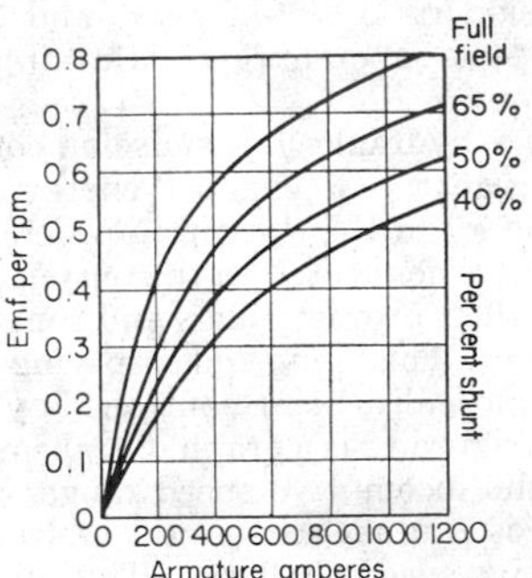

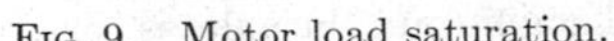
Fig. 9. Motor load saturation.

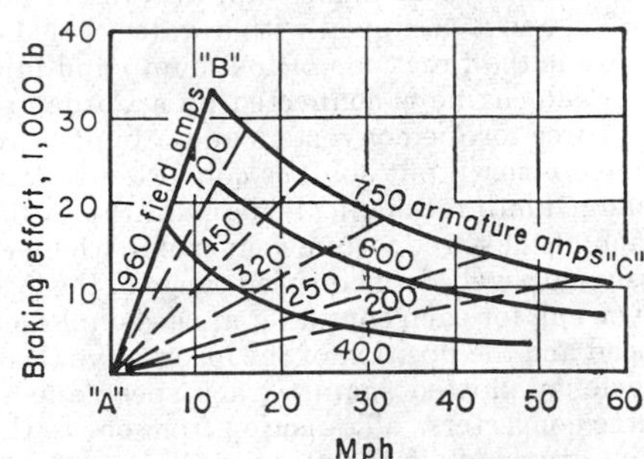

Fig. 10. Dynamic brake limits.

Dynamic Braking. Voltage generated by the traction motors is a function of rpm (locomotive speed) and field current. Since the resistance of the grids is fixed, the current output and torque, or braking force, are also functions of these variables. Therefore, at low speeds, braking effort is limited by the current that can be passed through the motor field coils. In Fig. 10 this limit is represented by the portion of the curve from A to B. At high locomotive speeds, the limit is set by the current-carrying capacity of the resistance grids, or the portion of the curve from B to C. At speeds above point B, the value of field current must be lowered as speed increases, to limit the voltage and to stay within the grid capacity. Since the braking effect is a function of armature current and field current, the result is a gradual decrease in braking force. Since the kinetic energy of a train increases as the square of the speed, it may be seen that as speeds increase above 35 or 40 mph the engineman depends more on the air-brake equipment.

DIESEL-HYDRAULIC LOCOMOTIVES

In 1961, some of the Western railroads in the United States began using 4,000-hp (engine bhp) locomotives of European manufacture and powered by two Diesel engines driving six axles through two hydraulic transmissions. Three of these units are commonly used at the head end of a train of 4,500 gross tons to negotiate a long 2 percent grade. For the same tonnage and grade, five Diesel-electric locomotives would be required, each rated at 1,750 hp (into main generator for traction). Each unit weighs 172 tons and is 67 ft long, with a maximum speed of 70 mph. Figure 11 is

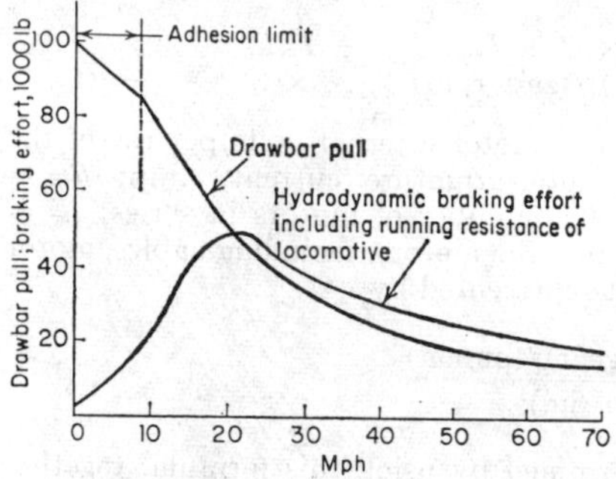

FIG. 11. Speed-drawbar pull relations of a 4,000-hp Diesel-hydraulic locomotive. (*Krauss-Maffel A. G. München-Allach.*)

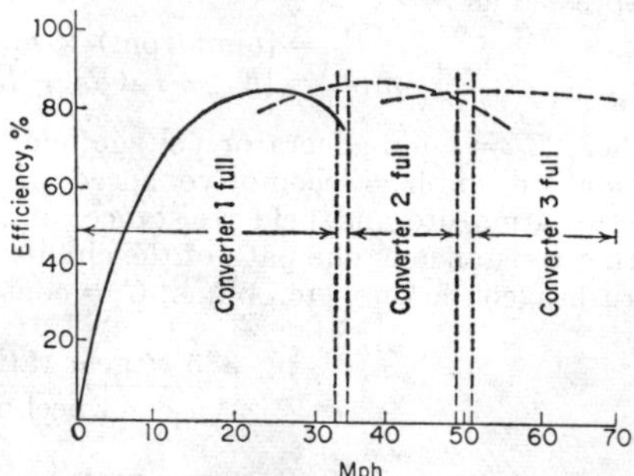

FIG. 12. Curve of transmission efficiency and track speed for a Diesel-hydraulic locomotive.

a graph of drawbar pull versus track speed. It also shows the braking effort of the hydrodynamic brake plotted against track speed.

The two **Diesel engines** are 16-cylinder V types, with four-stroke cycle; each engine is rated at 2,000 bhp, has 16.2:1 compression ratio, 7.3-in. bore, and 7.9-in. stroke, and is equipped with a water-cooled exhaust-gas supercharger. Unit injectors combine the functions of fuel pump and injection valve.

Each engine is connected by a Cardan shaft to a **hydraulic transmission** containing three torque converters and a built-in reversing gear. Mechanical energy at the transmission input shaft is converted to kinetic energy in the "pump impellers" and changed into mechanical energy in the turbine runners connected to the output shaft. Each of the three torque converters, which contain their own impellers and runners, is assigned a well-defined speed range of the locomotive. The filling and emptying of the oil circuit for each converter are accomplished automatically, being controlled by track speed and the position of the locomotive throttle. Figure 12 is a graph of transmission efficiency plotted against track speed and shows the locomotive speed ranges of the three converters. Transition from one to the other is gradual because the oil from one is emptying while the other is filling as the locomotive speed changes. The efficiency of the transmission and gearing between the Diesel engine and the axles is comparable to the efficiency of the generator–traction-motor transmission system in a Diesel-electric locomotive.

The output shaft of each transmission drives an **intermediate-gear assembly** mounted on the three-axle truck through a Cardan shaft. This assembly contains an encased spur gear which drives three double-reduction spur-bevel gears, one mounted on each axle.

The **hydrodynamic brake** operates on the principle of the Froude brake. One brake is mechanically connected to the output shaft of each transmission unit. With the engines idling, activation of the brake is accomplished by filling the hydraulic coupling circuit. Heat is dissipated in eddy formations, causing the temperature of the fluid in the circuit to increase. A heat exchanger is located in the circuit, which dissipates the heat through the locomotives water-cooling system. This system is also used to cool the engine-jacket, engine, and gear oil and the transmission oil.

Hydrostatically driven cooling fans, powered by multipistoned oil pumps and belt-connected to the engines, pull outside air through the radiators to maintain water temperature approximately constant. When the engines are idling down long mountain grades, the hydrodynamic braking heat helps keep the engines at the desired operating temperature.

GAS-TURBINE LOCOMOTIVES

(See also p. 9–150)

Design. Use of gas-turbine locomotives in the United States has been confined chiefly to one portion of one of the Western railroads. Locomotives constructed in 1956 are built in three sections, each with its own independent underframe. The first unit contains the operating cab and controls, auxiliary Diesel engine (also used for hostling and switching), auxiliary generators, air compressor (air brake), Diesel-fuel tank, miscellaneous auxiliaries, and one-half the total number of traction motors. The second portion contains d-c traction generators, the gas turbine, fuel-heating equipment, and the remaining traction motors. The third unit is used to carry bunker C fuel oil. The gas turbine is rated at 10,700 hp at 1,000 ft elevation and 80 F, and the locomotive rail horsepower rating is 8,500.

The Diesel engine supplies power through an auxiliary generator to one of the traction generators for cranking the turbine. When sufficient rpm is attained, Diesel fuel is fed into the combustion chambers. When all burners are firing properly and up to temperature, preheated, treated bunker C oil is fed to the burners, and Diesel fuel is cut off.

The **turbine** is the single-shaft type having the air compressor at one end, combustion chambers in the middle, and turbine on the opposite end. Filtered-air intake and exhaust are on the roof. The turbine is connected to the traction generators through gear-reduction units. The traction generators are housed in a positively ventilated, sealed compartment and deliver power to the traction motors on all axles of the first and second units. The fuel oil is preheated at the fueling station before being fed into the third section, which is insulated with glass wool.

The air-brake compressor is motor-driven, power being supplied from one of the Diesel-engine auxiliary generators. Lubricating oil for the gas turbine is filtered and pumped through cooling radiators. Dynamic-brake apparatus is housed in the first section. The first and second portions are each equipped with two 3-axle swing bolster trucks (see Ignitron Rectifier, p. 15–117).

Comparison with Diesel-electric. Full-load tractive-effort–speed characteristics are similar to those of Diesel-electric locomotives. The turbine is much more efficient at high values of power output than at the lower values and hence is best used where high-horsepower output is required over most of the run, as when hauling a non-stop freight train up a long sustained grade. Gas-turbine locomotives have fewer moving parts in the main power equipment than Diesel-electric locomotives. They also have more horsepower per foot of length. The above-described three-section turbine locomotive is 165 ft in over-all length, whereas Diesel units of the same total horsepower would measure about 260 ft. Gas-turbine locomotive weight per axle is 68,000 lb versus a Diesel-electric's fully loaded weight of about 60,000 lb. This turbine's weight on drivers does not decrease appreciably as the fuel supply is depleted, since bunker C oil is carried in the third section. The Diesel-electric's weight with an empty fuel tank is reduced to about 59,000 lb per axle. When fully loaded with supplies, the Diesel-electric locomotive's ratio of weight on drivers to horsepower would be 141 lb per hp against 96 lb per hp for the gas turbine.

FREIGHT AND PASSENGER CARS

Lightweight passenger cars have been built for service in Diesel-powered trains with weights as low as 60,000 lb by making use of special designs and articulating units to reduce the number of trucks. High strength steels, including cold-drawn stainless, are extensively used in welded construction. Until recently the use of aluminum alloys has been limited to riveted construction.

In freight-car construction the trend is to follow AAR specifications, although there are regional variances on account of special service requirements. Low-alloy high-strength steels are extensively used to reduce weight and corrosion losses and because of

Table 3. Dimensions of Freight Cars

Kind and description	Weight empty, lb	Capacity		Length over striking castings	Max width inside	Height	
		Lb	Cu ft			Rail to top of floor	Rail to run board or top of sides
Box, all steel*	53,500	100,000	4,882	51′10″	9′2″	3′7¾″	14′11 19/32″
Box, all steel (welded)†	43,300	100,000	4,136	41′7⅞″	9′6″	3′7″	15′1″
Stock, steel frame‡	54,700	80,000	2,670	41′10″	8′6″	3′7¾″	14′5 7/32″
Refrigerator	56,600	79,000	1,988 2,332	42′2¾″	8′3″	4′3⅛″	13′7 15/32″
Refrigerator	62,900	100,000	2,270	41′11¾″	8′6″	4′4⅛″	....
Refrigerator (pass. exp.)	95,000	40,000	2,737	53′5¾″	8′11″	....	....
Hopper, all steel	43,900	100,000	2,054	32′4″	9′9″	....	11′5″
Hopper, all steel	48,400	140,000	2,773	41′8″	10′4″	....	10′8″
Ore, all steel	54,600	190,000	1,283	....	9′7¼″	3′8 1/16″	8′8 1/16″
Gondola, all steel	42,300	100,000	1,980	41′9¾″	9′6″	3′5 9/16″	8′7¼″
Gondola, all steel	59,000	140,000	1,963	47′4½″	9′6″	3′6 15/16″	8′5/16″
Tank	45,700	10,000 gal	1,337	37′6″	7′4″ diam	....	14′1⅝″
Flat	50,400	100,000	....	54′1½″	10′6″	3′7¼″	....
Flat	52,500	140,000	....	50′0″	9′3″	3′5⅛″	....
Auto transport (tri-level)	99,800	12 std autos or 15 compacts		85′8¼″	8′6″	3′3″ first deck	16′9⅞″ 18′4″—top of load
Covered hopper	62,000	....	3,960	51′3″	10′7⅜″	....	14′4 27/32″
Trailer flat (piggy-back)	56,000	130,000	....	89′7″	8′2″	2′8½″	....

* T&G lining.
† Plywood-lined.
‡ Adjustable deck.

their weldability. Aluminum alloys are less extensively used but are being developed and adapted to freight-car structural requirements. Table 3 shows the dimensions of typical freight cars.

Wheels and Axles. Cast-steel and wrought-steel wheels are used on about 90 percent of the freight cars in the United States; data are given in Table 4. All passenger cars are equipped with wrought-steel wheels, except in Canada, where some steel-tired wheels are used.

Wrought-steel wheels are available in diameters from 28 to 42 in. for passenger cars and Diesel locomotives. Standard and temporary standards are shown in Sec. G of the AAR Manual of Standard and Recommended Practice (Div. V).

Axles have been standardized for freight-car interchange on the basis of load limit at the rail (Table 5), and a series of passenger-car axles with enlarged wheel fits has been designed for high-speed passenger service for use with conventional or roller bearings. A recent development is a forged tubular axle.

Dimensions, load limits, limits of wear, and inspection and shop practice as recommended by the AAR will be found in the AAR Wheel and Axle Manual (Div. V). The dimensions of conventional bearings are fixed by the same interchange requirements as the standard axles. Roller bearings are generally applied to all new passenger-train cars. Some applications of roller bearings have been made on special-service freight cars.

Table 4. One-wear Cast-steel and Wrought-steel Wheels for Freight Cars

Load limit, eight-wheeled car, lb	103,000	142,000	177,000	220,000	263,000
Size of journal, in	4¼ × 8	5 × 9	5½ × 10	6 × 11	6½ × 12
Nominal 33-in. wheel weight, cast steel, lb	660	660	650	670	
Nominal 36-in. wheel weight, cast steel, lb					760
Nominal 33-in. wheel weight, wrought steel, lb	612	577	575	640	

Table 5. Dimensions of Standard Freight-car Axles

Size of journals, in.	Carrying capacity of axle, lb	Load capacity of car, tons	Diameter, in.		Length, in.		Weight of rough-turned axle, lb
			At the wheel seat	Minimum (at mid-length)	Over-all	Center to center of journals	
4¼ × 8	25,750	30	5¾	4¾	84¼	75	520
5 × 9	35,500	40	6½	5⅜	86½	76	695
5½ × 10	44,250	50	7	5⅞	88½	77	825
6 × 11	55,000	70	7⅝	6⁷⁄₁₆	90¾	78	1,005
6½ × 12	65,750	100	8⅛	7⅜	92¾	79	1,185

Design Fundamentals. The Manual of the Mechanical Division of the AAR (Div. V) defines a large number of standards for the design of car details to which freight cars must conform on account of the universal interchange of cars on American railways. The manual is corrected annually by the AAR and many of the standards are reproduced in the "Car Builders Cyclopedia," which is revised about every four years. Safety appliances, end ladders, steps, uncoupling levers, running boards, and other similar items must comply with the Safety Appliance Act as administered by the Interstate Commerce Commission.

TRAIN RESISTANCE

(See Schmidt, *Bull.* 43, and Tuthill, *Bull.* 376, *Univ. Ill. Eng. Exp. Sta.*)

The resistance offered by a train to motion along the track could be expressed as a coefficient of friction, but it is more convenient to discuss it in terms of "pounds per ton" of weight. **Gross train resistance** is the force exerted by the locomotive at the rear drawbar. It overcomes two classes of resistances in producing and maintaining motion: "inherent," "true," "rolling," or "net" resistance, or merely "train" resistance, which is always present, and certain "incidental" or "accidental" resistances. The **inherent resistance** includes the resistance due to journal and flange friction, the action of the tread on the rail, and the resistance due to motion through still air. It may be defined as "the force necessary to maintain motion at constant speed on straight level track in still air." The **incidental resistances** include the resistances due to grade, curvature, acceleration, and wind resistance. Additional resistance due to extreme cold may well be considered an incidental effect.

Inherent Resistance. Of the elements of inherent resistance, at low speeds, journal friction is probably more than half the total, but at high speeds, air resistance is the predominant factor. Attempts to differentiate and evaluate the various elements through the speed range have not been very satisfactory, and it is more convenient to treat the total as a unit. At very high speeds, the effect of air resistance can be approximately determined; this is an aid to studies in its reduction by means of cowling and fairing. The resistance of a car moving in still air on straight level track at constant speed increases with the speed, but the resistance in pounds per ton decreases as the weight of the car increases. The total resistance of a 50 ton car is much less than twice as great as that of a 25 ton car under similar conditions. With known conditions of speed and car weight, inherent resistance can be predicted with reasonable accuracy; knowledge of track conditions will permit further refining of the estimate, but for very rough track or extreme cold, generous allowances must be made. Under such conditions, normal resistance may be doubled. A formula proposed by W. J. Davis, Jr. (*Gen. Elec. Rev.*, Oct., 1926) has been used extensively for inherent freight-train resistances at speeds up to 40 mph:

$$R = 1.3 + (29/w) + 0.045V + 0.0005AV^2/wn$$

where R = resistance, lb per ton; w = average weight per axle, tons; V = speed, mph; n = total number of axles; and A = cross-sectional area, sq ft. With the recent trend toward freight-train speeds of 50 to 70 mph, it has been found that actual resistance values fall considerably below calculations based on the above formula at these high speeds.

For passenger cars the Davis formula is satisfactory, giving good results at high speed with vestibuled passenger equipment (not streamlined). This formula is for coaches pulled by a locomotive and does not include head-end air resistance.

The introduction of the ultralightweight Talgo design, with the reduction in the number of axles, equipment cross section, and car unit length, has made it impossible to use the standard Davis formula. Actual road tests have indicated that the following modified Davis formula is quite reliable:

$$\text{Locomotive: } R_L = 1.3 + (29/w) + 0.03V + (0.002AV^2/wn)$$
$$\text{Cars: } R_C = 1.3 + (29/w) + 0.03V + (0.00034AV^2/wn^1)$$

where n^1 = number of axles per length of train equivalent to 80 ft passenger cars; A = height of unit, ft, divided by 14.9 and multiplied by 120.

For conventional streamlined Diesel and electric locomotives the Davis formula for vestibuled passenger-car equipment gives reasonable results, using a coefficient of 0.0016 for the last term in place of 0.00034 to include head-end air resistance. The resistance thus calculated may be subtracted from locomotive tractive effort available at the rail to obtain drawbar pull on tangent level track in still air at constant speed.

For **wind resistance** see p. 11–74 and Lipetz, *Trans. ASME*, Oct., 1937.

Curve Resistance. Resistance due to track curvature varies with speed and curvature; it is a minimum at the speed corresponding to the superelevation of the outer rail, for at this speed there would be the least flange contact. Curve resistance is also decreased by the practice of relieving (widening) the gage on curves from ⅛ to 1 in., in proportion to their sharpness. For general estimates of car resistance and locomotive hauling capacity, speed and gage relief may be ignored and a figure of 0.8 lb per ton per degree used.

Grade resistance depends only on the angle of ascent or descent. It is 20 lb per ton for each foot-in-one-hundred rise, or "percent of grade," or 0.379 lb for each foot-per-mile rise. A car cannot be left standing with brakes off on a grade of more than about 0.3 of 1 percent (15 ft per mile).

Acceleration Resistance. The force required to produce acceleration is the sum of the forces required to produce accelerated translation and that required to produce accelerated rotation of the wheels about their axle centers. A translatory acceleration of 1 mph per sec is produced by a force of 91.1 lb per ton. The rotary acceleration requirement adds 6 to 12 percent to this force, so that the total force is nearly 100 lb per ton (the figure commonly used) for each mph per sec. If greater accuracy is required,

$$R_a = A(91.05W + 36.36n)$$

where R_a is the total accelerating force, lb; A the acceleration in mph per sec; W the weight of train, tons; and n the number of axles.

Acceleration and Distance. If in a distance of S ft the speed of a car or train changes from V_1 to V_2 mph, the force required to produce the acceleration (or the braking force if the speed is reduced) is $R_a = 74(V_2^2 - V_1^2)/S$, the coefficient 74 corresponding to the use of 100 lb per ton above. This formula is useful in the calculation of climbing a grade with the assistance of stored energy. In any train-resistance calculation or analysis, assumptions with regard to acceleration will generally submerge all other variables; *e.g.*, an acceleration of 0.1 mph per sec requires a greater tractive force than that required to overcome inherent resistance for any car at moderate speeds.

Starting Resistance. The force required to produce an oil film on a journal is considerable, and if a train is fully stretched, so that all the wheels must be started rolling simultaneously (an unusual condition for freight trains, but approached in passenger trains), 35 to 45 lb per ton of weight of train will be required for starting. In practice, slack in couplers of draft gears results in more gradual starting which permits a freight train to move with a force of 15 to 20 lb; a passenger train requires 25 to 30 lb.

Roller Bearings. Little information is available on the resistance of roller-bearing freight cars. Only the journal friction is affected; hence the variation is important at starting, reducing the starting force to 5 or 6 lb per ton. The reduction at high speeds becomes relatively small. (See also pp. 8–178 *et seq.*)

BRAKING

(See also p. 8–56)

The forces effective in retarding the motion of a railway vehicle are (1) inherent resistance, (2) any incidental resistances effective at the time such as wind, curvature, or ascending grade, (3) friction of the brake shoes on the wheel rims. The brake-shoe pressure is the major factor in stopping and, aside from shoe friction and grade, other forces may be neglected. Brakes on American trains are operated by air pressure. A continuous pipe through the train (the train-line brake pipe) carries pressure from the compressors on the locomotive to a reservoir on each car through a "control valve." Reduction in the pressure in this pipe is effected by manipulation of the brake valve and results in the movement of a balanced piston in the control valve of each car. The piston movement carries with it a slide valve, through the ports of which compressed air flows from the "auxiliary reservoir" on each car into the brake cylinder, and the brakes are applied. The action thus initiated travels rapidly through the train. When the pressure in the train line is rebuilt, the balanced piston again moves into a position where the air in the brake cylinder is exhausted and the pressure in the auxiliary reservoir is returned to its normal value.

The foregoing describes briefly the functions of the fundamental automatic air brake based on the functions of the control valve. Brake equipment designed to specifications per ICC Docket 13528 is now required on all freight cars used in interchange service. The functions of the control valve have been refined to permit the handling of longer trains by more uniform brake performance. Important improvements in this design are (1) the time required to apply the brakes on the last car of a train has been reduced; (2) a more uniform and faster release of the brakes is possible; (3) emergency application is always available, irrespective of the state of brake application or release; this feature eliminates the possibility of trains being out of control on long grades.

In high-speed passenger service, a greater brake-shoe pressure may be applied at high speeds than at low speeds without the danger of sliding the wheels. This reduces stopping distances. It may be accomplished pneumatically, using a higher brake-pipe pressure, or by electropneumatic systems, using speed-governor control to proportion brake-shoe pressure according to train speed.

The total retarding force in pounds per ton may be taken as $F = (PLef/W) + 20G$, where P = total brake-cylinder piston pressure, lb; L = multiplying ratio of the leverage between cylinder pistons and wheel rims; ef = the product of the coefficient of brake-shoe friction and foundation-gear efficiency; W = loaded weight of vehicle, lb; G = grade, percent. Stopping distance in feet may be found from $h = 0.035WV^2p_n/W_1Rp_aef$, where W = loaded weight of vehicle, lb; V = speed, mph; p_n = basic brake-cylinder pressure on which R is selected, psi; W_1 = light weight of vehicle, lb; R = nominal braking ratio (expressed as a decimal), representing the ratio of total brake-shoe pressure at a stated brake-cylinder pressure (and with 100 percent brake foundation-gear efficiency) to vehicle light weight; p_a = actual maintained brake-cylinder pressure from point of equivalent instantaneous maximum pressure development, psi; e = brake foundation-gear efficiency (a decimal); f = coefficient of brake-shoe friction. To this value of h must be added the distance traveled at initial speed from the time the brake-valve handle is moved to application position until the point of maximum pressure development is reached.

The friction coefficient f varies with the speed (usually lower at high speed), unit pressure (lower at high pressure), and with the material of the wheel and shoe. For stops below 60 mph a conservative figure for an ordinary shoe on steel wheels is $ef = 0.15$. p_n is based on 50 psi air pressure in the cylinder for freight-car and locomotive brakes, and 60 psi for passenger cars. The braking ratios R commonly used are freight cars, 75 percent of empty weight with 50 psi cylinder pressure; passenger cars, 90 percent of the empty weight based on 60 psi cylinder pressure and full service application (150 percent based on 100 psi cylinder pressure and emergency application); Diesel locomotives, 60 to 80 percent. 70 psi is a typical value for the brake-pipe pressure of a fully charged freight train. This will give 50 psi brake-cylinder pressure during a full service application on AB equipment, and 60 psi brake-cylinder pressure with an emergency application. Total brake-shoe pressure at 60 psi cylinder pressure may be determined from the braking ratio R and p_a. Assuming R = 70 percent, and car light weight is 50,000 lb, brake-shoe pressure = RW_1p_a/p_n, or $0.70 \times 50{,}000 \times 60/50$, or 42,000 lb.

To prevent wheel sliding, $F \leqq \phi w$, where F = force at the wheel rims resisting rotation of any pair of connected wheels, lb; ϕ = coefficient of wheel-rail adhesion or friction (a decimal); and w = static weight upon a pair of wheels, lb. Actual or adhesive weight on wheels when the vehicle is in motion is affected by weight transfer (moment transmitted to the trucks by the inertia of the car body through the truck center plates) and vertical oscillation of body weight upon truck springs. The value of ϕ remains constant at its static value at all speeds, being about 0.25 for a dry or sanded moist rail. A value of 0.20 would provide reasonable assurance against sliding when used to include car-body oscillation and weight transfer.

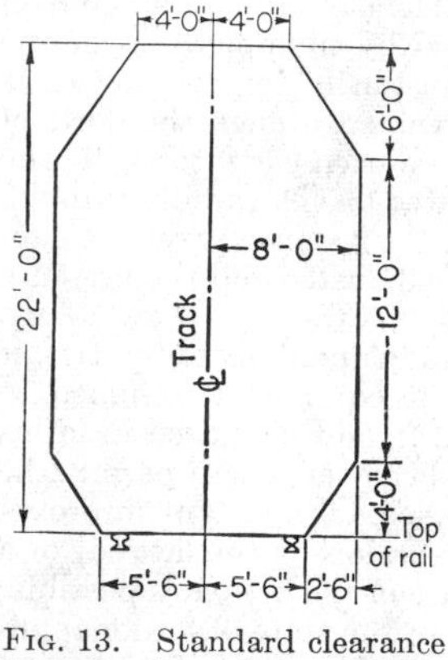

The relationship between required coefficient ϕ_1 of wheel-rail adhesion to prevent wheel sliding and rate of retardation in miles per hour per second A may be expressed by the equation $\phi_1 = 0.04555A$.

Fig. 13. Standard clearance diagram for railway bridges on tangent track.

TRACK

Mileage. For the year ending Dec. 31, 1962, the total point-to-point mileage operated by Class I railways (including fully electrified sections) was 215,300 miles. There were 377,200 miles of track operated, including yards and sidings.

Gage. The gage of railway track is the distance between the inner sides of the rail heads. Practically all American railways are laid with a gage of 4 ft 8½ in., which is known as **standard gage.** Rail wear causes an increase in gage; and on sharp curves, because of rail wear, it is usual practice to begin widening the gage on curves over 8 deg, the limiting value being ¾ in. In America the gage of **narrow-gage** track is usually 3 ft, the variations being 2½ and 3½ ft. In Europe, 1 m is the prevailing narrow gage.

Track Spacing. The distance between centers of main-line track varies between 12 and 14 ft. Twelve foot spacing has, however, become unusual. The prevailing spacing is 13 ft 0 in. and has the implied endorsement of the AREA.

Clearances. The AREA standard clearance diagrams provide for a clear height of 22 ft above the tops of the rail heads and for a width of 16 ft on bridges and 15 ft elsewhere. If obstructions are kept outside these limits, they will clear a man riding on the top or sides of the largest cars. Where it is certain that men will be kept off the cars, or where conditions require the minimum clearance, as in tunnels, these dimen-

Table 6. Radii of Steam Railway Curves

Degree of curve	Radius to track center line, ft	Degree of curve	Radius to track center line, ft	Degree of curve	Radius to track center line, ft
1	5,730	9	637.3	17	338.3
2	2,865	10	573.7	18	319.6
3	1,910	11	521.7	19	302.9
4	1,433	12	478.3	20	287.9
5	1,146	13	441.7	21	274.4
6	955.4	14	410.3	22	262.0
7	819.0	15	383.1		
8	716.8	16	359.3		

sions are much reduced. For tracks entering buildings an opening 12 ft wide and 17 ft high will ordinarily suffice to pass the largest locomotives and cars. A standard clearance diagram for railway bridges is Fig. 13. The diagram represents the AAR recommendation for new construction. For specific clearances limitations on a particular railroad refer to the official publication, "Railway Line Clearances," Railway Equipment and Publishing Co.

Curvature. The curvature of track is designated in terms of "degree of curve." **Degree of curve** is the number of degrees of central angle subtended by a chord of 100 ft length (measured on the track center line). Table 6 gives the radii for ordinary railway curves.

On important main lines where trains are operated at high speed, the curves are ordinarily not sharper than 6 or 8 deg. In

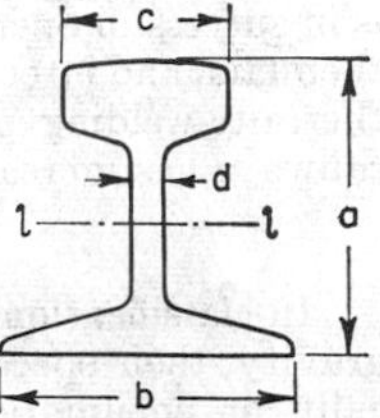

Fig. 14. Standard rail section.

Table 7. Dimensions of Standard Rails

(Letters refer to Fig. 14)

Standard and nominal weight		Weight per yd, lb	Dimensions, in.				Distribution of metal			Axis l–l	
			a	b	c	d	Percent head	Percent web	Percent base	I, in.^{4}	S, in.^{3}
P.S.	155	155.5	8	6 3/4	3	3/4	33.1	27.9	39.0	130.9	37.4
AREA	140	140.6	7 5/16	6	3	3/4	37.0	25.0	38.0	95.6	28.2
C.F. & I.	136	136.2	7 5/16	6	2 15/16	1 1/16	36.4	27.1	36.5	94.9	28.3
L.V.	136	137.363	7	6 1/2	2 15/16	1 1/16	34.8	24.5	40.7	86.7	28.3
AREA	133	133.4	7 1/16	6	3	1 1/16	36.3	26.5	37.2	86.0	27.0
AREA	132	132.1	7 1/8	6	3	21/32	34.1	28.3	37.6	88.2	27.6
H.F.	132	132.4	7 5/16	6	2 31/32	21/32	35.8	26.7	37.5	93.8	28.4
AREA	131	130.8	7 1/8	6	3	21/32	35.0	27.0	38.0	88.5	27.6
C.B. & Q.-T.R.	129	129.4	7 5/16	6	2 5/8	21/32	32.9	28.7	38.4	90.4	28.1
N.Y.C.	127	127.5	7	6 1/4	3	21/32	34.2	26.4	39.4	81.57	26.4
C.F. & I.	119	118.8	6 13/16	5 1/2	2 21/32	5/8	37.1	26.1	36.8	71.4	22.9
AREA	115	114.7	6 5/8	5 1/2	2 23/32	5/8	34.8	27.1	38.1	65.6	22.0
H.F.	113	113.2	6 13/16	5 1/2	2 11/16	19/32	36.4	25.0	38.6	69.8	22.8
C.B. & Q.-T.R.	112	112.3	6 3/4	5 1/2	2 1/2	5/8	34.3	26.7	39.0	67.0	22.3
AREA	112	112.3	6 5/8	5 1/2	2 23/32	19/32	35.9	25.1	39.0	65.5	21.8
N.Y.C.	105	104.7	6	5 1/2	3	5/8	40.9	24.0	35.1	49.9	17.3
AREA	100	101.5	6	5 3/8	2 11/16	9/16	38.2	22.6	39.2	49.0	17.8
A.R.A.-A.	100	100.4	6	5 1/2	2 3/4	9/16	36.9	23.4	39.7	48.9	17.8
A.R.A.-B.	100	100.5	5 41/64	5 9/64	2 21/32	9/16	40.2	19.2	40.6	41.3	15.7
ASCE	100	100.4	5 3/4	5 3/4	2 3/4	9/16	42.0	21.0	37.0	44.0	16.1
A.R.A.-A.	90	90.0	5 5/8	5 1/8	2 9/16	9/16	36.2	24.0	39.8	38.7	15.2
A.R.A.-B.	90	90.5	5 17/64	4 49/64	2 9/16	9/16	40.1	19.2	40.7	32.3	13.2
ASCE	90	90.1	5 3/8	5 3/8	2 5/8	9/16	42.0	21.0	37.0	34.4	13.5
ASCE	85	85.0	5 3/16	5 3/16	2 9/16	9/16	42.0	21.0	37.0	30.1	12.2
ASCE	80	80.2	5	5	2 1/2	35/64	42.0	21.0	37.0	26.38	11.08
ASCE	75	74.8	4 13/16	4 13/16	2 15/32	17/32	42.0	21.0	37.0	22.86	9.94

I = moment of inertia of section; S = section modulus; l–l = neutral axis.

P.S. = Pennsylvania Section (P.R.R.); C.F. & I. = Colorado Fuel & Iron; H.F. = Head Free; L.V. = Lehigh Valley; C.B. & Q.-T.R. = Chicago, Burlington & Quincy—Torsion-resisting; N.Y.C. = New York Central.

mountainous territory, in rare instances, main-line curves as sharp as 18 deg occur. Most Diesel and electric locomotives are designed to traverse curves of 21 deg. A car alone will pass considerably sharper curves, the limiting factor in this case being the flexibility of the brake connections to the trucks.

Rails. The ASCE and the AREA have defined standards for the cross section of rails of various weights per yard. The ASCE standards provide for rail weights up to 110 lb per yd; those of the AREA for weights varying from 90 to 140 lb. The dimensions of these standard rail sections are shown in Table 7. A few railroads use special sections of their own design for heavy rails.

The **length of rails** has been largely determined by the length of the cars available for their transportation. The standard length in use is 39 ft.

The prevailing weight of rails used in main-line track is 90 to 133 lb per yd; on lines with very heavy traffic, weights up to 155 lb are in use. Secondary and branch lines are generally laid with 75 to 100 lb rail which has been previously used and partly worn in main-line service. A considerable mileage of welded rail has recently been laid and is in successful operation. In general, rails are first welded into lengths up to 20 rails, then laid, and later welded into lengths up to 2 miles. Electric-flash-, gas-fusion-, and thermite-welding processes are used. Average weight per yard of rail on Class I railways has increased from 82.89 lb in 1921 to 107.4 lb in 1961.

CAR RETARDERS

In classification yards where cars roll from a "hump" into their assigned tracks by gravity, their speed is controlled by retarders. Each retarder is a rail brake electrically or pneumatically operated and equipped with heat-treated alloy-steel shoes

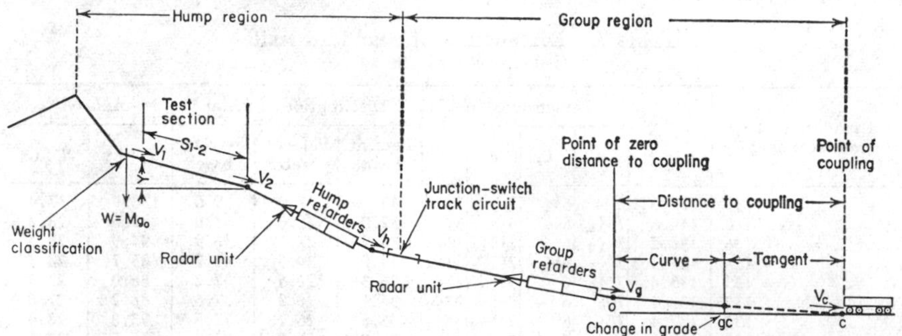

Fig. 15. Automatic car-retarder installation, elevation. (*General Railway Signal Co., Rochester, N.Y.*)

mounted on each side of the rail to provide a controlled pressure on the inner and outer surfaces of the car wheels.

Modern yards are equipped with **automatic retarder control,** which predicts the rolling resistance of each separate car or "cut" and determines the speed at which it must leave the retarders in order to couple to the next car in its assigned track at a safe speed (2 to 4 mph).

Figure 15 shows an elevation view of a typical installation with a hump region (single track) and a group region, which represents one of several tracks branching off at the junction switch. From the group retarders, each track branches into several classification tracks.

After leaving the crest of the hump, the cut passes over a weight-detecting device, which classifies it as "light," "medium," or "heavy." Next it passes through the **test section** of specified track length S_{1-2}, where its velocity is measured as it enters (V_1) and as it leaves (V_2). Y is the difference in elevation between the entrance and the exit points. The rolling resistance RR_{1-2} of the cut passing through the test section is calculated by an analog or digital computer on the basis of the formula

$$-RR_{1-2} = \frac{1}{S_{1-2}}\left[Y - \frac{1}{2g_o}(V_2{}^2 - V_1{}^2)\right]$$

where g_o is the acceleration of the cut due to gravity, modified by its weight classification and adjusted for the rotational energy of the car wheels.

The calculated value of RR_{1-2} is transmitted to a second part of the computer, which determines the desired speed V_h of the cut leaving the **hump retarders.** The positions of the track switches (junction-track-switch circuit) are also taken into account by the computer to allow for variations in curve and frog resistance, depending on the route selected between the hump and group retarders. As the cut enters the hump retarders, shoe pressure is at a maximum for the weight classification involved. A radar unit measures the speed of the cut while it moves through retarders and transmits the information continuously to the retarder-control discriminators. The latter compare the actual speed with the calculated value of the desired leaving speed and reduce the shoe pressure accordingly until the value of V_1 is attained, at which time shoe pressure is released completely.

Control of the **group retarders** is accomplished in the same way. The desired speed V_g for leaving the group retarders is calculated by a third part of the computer, using the formula

$$V_g = \sqrt{V_c{}^2 + 2g_o[C_{o-c} - (Y_{gc} - Y_c) + RR_{o-c}S_{o-c}]}$$

where V_c is the desired velocity of the cut at coupling. It is preset and is the same for each cut. C_{o-c} is the equivalent head loss due to curved-track rolling resistance, frog loss, and elevation difference between zero distance to coupling and the point-of-grade change. It depends on the route selected and is derived on the basis of measured past performance of a large number of cars through each specific route. $Y_{gc} - Y_c$ is the elevation difference between point-of-grade change and point of coupling. Y_{gc} is fixed, but Y_c is governed by the distance to coupling S_{o-c} and the route selected. S_{o-c} is measured by a track circuit whose electrical resistance is varied by the location of the next car ahead in the designated classification track. RR_{o-c} is the predicted rolling resistance of the cut after it leaves the retarder. It is derived by computer from the rolling resistance RR_{1-2} and is modified by the distance to coupling for light cars. It may also be modified slightly if desired by the retarder operator for unusual conditions.

MONORAIL SYSTEMS

The monorail has been developed for high-speed passenger service in heavily populated urban localities, where the land area for right-of-way is at a premium. Operating 16 ft or more above the ground level, it provides minimum interference with surface traffic. There are two general types: the "suspended" and the "supported."

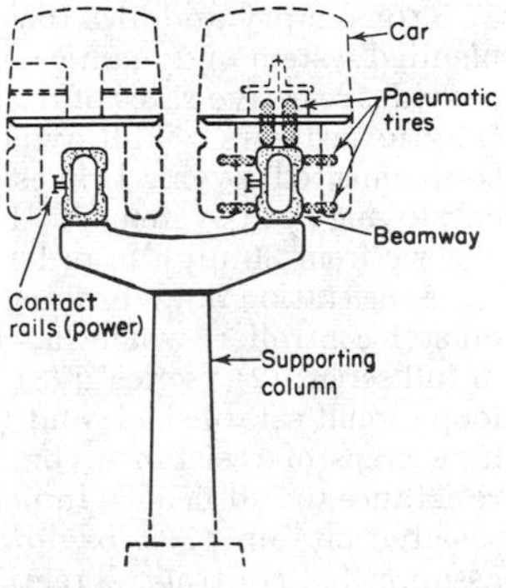

FIG. 16. Supported monorail system, sectional view.

The **suspended system** has been used successfully in Japan and Germany. The car body is suspended, pendulum fashion, from the running gear and rides below the beamway, which is supported 35 ft above the ground. The running gear, equipped with pneumatic tires (or flanged wheels), travels over the top surface of the beamway. Auxiliary guide wheels attached to the truck frame bear against the sides of the beamway to control sway. This type allows full use of the space within the car for pay load, but the car body must be designed to transmit the weight of car and passengers to the running gear above.

The **supported system,** as used at Disneyland and at the Seattle Fair, employs a prefabricated, prestressed, hollow concrete girder supported from below by reinforced-concrete T columns. A cross section of the beamway and car is shown in Fig. 16.

Since the center of gravity of the car is above the beamway, the guide wheels, which rotate in a horizontal plane, contact the beamway's vertical side to keep the car upright.

Trains of the design used at the Seattle Fair are composed of two 60-ft cars, each weighing 50,000 lb (empty), with a 62-passenger seating capacity. Each car is mounted on four axles equipped with dual pneumatic tires, and each axle is driven by a 600-volt 100-hp d-c motor through a double-reduction gearbox. Power is picked up by current-collector shoes from two contact rails mounted on one side of the beamway.

Maximum acceleration is automatically controlled at a rate of 2.5 mph per sec. Deceleration rates are 3.3 mph per sec at the service rate and 5.7 in emergency. A dynamic brake is effective above speeds of 10 mph and is used in conjunction with a pneumatic system.

Supported monorail cars generally are capable of negotiating curves of 100-ft radius at limited speed and curves of 1,000-ft radius at 60 mph. Grades steeper than 10 percent can be negotiated when pneumatic tires are used. Speeds of 90 mph have been attained with equipment under test. However, the Seattle installation was operated at 53 mph maximum over the 1.2-mile distance.

In comparison with subway equipment, the monorail car weighs 50 percent less per passenger (seating capacity). With pneumatic tires, it has almost double the rate of deceleration. Motor capacity and acceleration rates are similar.

SUBWAY TRAINS

Subway cars such as those used by the New York City Transit Authority are self-propelled. They are equipped with contact shoes which take 600-volt nominal d-c electric power from a third rail. The cars are designed to operate in multiple, with as many as 12 cars controlled from one position. Each car is 51 ft 4 in. long over drawbar faces and seats 44 passengers. It is designed to negotiate curves of 90-ft minimum radius and operate at speeds up to 55 mph on standard-gage track.

Acceleration is automatically controlled at 2.5 mph per sec between the limits of 37.5 tons empty and 51.5 tons fully loaded weight. Deceleration is accomplished by a blended system of dynamic and electropneumatic brake. Automatic dynamic braking provides selective rates of deceleration between 1.5 and 3.0 mph per sec for empty and fully loaded cars. Full dynamic braking is effective from 45 mph to 10 mph, being supplemented by air brakes for the final stop. The emergency-brake application, employing both systems, is designed to provide an average retardation rate of 3 mph per sec from 30 mph in order to stop a fully loaded car within 220 to 250 ft.

Acceleration and braking are both controlled by the motorman's five-position master controller, which has the following positions: (1) "minimum power"—motors in full series; (2) "series"; (3) "series-parallel"; (4) "coast"—no power, dynamic-brake loop circuit established; and (5) "braking." With the controller in positions 2 and 3, nine steps of resistance commutation are progressed automatically from maximum resistance to full field. In position 5, dynamic braking is effected, uniformly and at a selected rate, in 17 steps down to 10 mph before the air-brake system automatically assumes full control. Traction motors are the four-pole d-c commutating-pole type, rated at 100 shaft hp at 300 volts, 280 amp, and 1,175 rpm. Motor and axle are connected through a gear-drive unit equipped with a 123-tooth gear (mounted on the axle) and a 17-tooth pinion. Motor and drive unit are joined through a flexible coupling. Each car is equipped with four traction-motor and gear assemblies.

MARINE ENGINEERING

BY

George L. West, Jr.

References: Seward, "Marine Engineering," Soc. Naval Architects and Marine Engrs. Osborne, "Modern Marine Engineers Manual," Cornell. "Rules for Building and Classing Steel Vessels," Am. Bureau of Shipping. Baker, "Ship Design, Resistance, and Screw Propulsion," *Jour. Commerce Shipping Teleg.* (Liverpool). Van Lammeren, "Resistance, Propulsion, and Steering of Ships," Technical Publishing Co., Haarlem, Holland. Arnott, "Design and Construction of Steel Merchant Ships," Soc. Naval Architects and Marine Engrs. U.S. Coast Guard Regulations, engineering and electrical. *Jour. Am. Soc. of Naval Engrs., Trans. Inst. Marine Engrs.* (London). *Trans. Soc. Naval Architects and Marine Engrs.* (New York). *Trans. Inst. Naval Architects* (London). *Trans. North East Coast Inst. Engrs. & Shipbuilders* (Newcastle). Rossell and Chapman, "Principles of Naval Architecture," SNA&ME.

All self-propelled commercial vessels must comply with the published **rules** of the U.S. Coast Guard. These rules deal with lifesaving and fire-fighting equipment, navigation lights, and boiler construction. For passenger ships, certain minimum standards of stability, floodability, and fireproof construction are prescribed. Compliance with these rules is ensured through a yearly inspection.

The majority of American merchant ships are classified by the American Bureau, although another **classification** society, Lloyd's Register, is also used. (Lloyd's Register should not be confused with Lloyds of London, a group of British insurance underwriters.) Classification societies issue rules for the construction of steel merchant ships and their machinery, carry out periodical surveys at the time of construction and during the life of the vessel to see that it is maintained in insurable condition, and issue certificates of seaworthiness.

DIMENSIONS AND DEFINITIONS

The dimensions of a ship may refer to the molded body (or form defined by the outside of the frames), to general outside or over-all dimensions, and to dimensions on which the determination of tonnage or of classification is based. There are thus (1) molded dimensions, (2) over-all dimensions, (3) tonnage dimensions, and (4) classification dimensions. The published rules and regulations of the classification societies and the U.S. Coast Guard should be consulted for detailed information.

The **length on the load water line** (L.W.L.) is the length between the foreside of the stem and the aft side of the sternpost, or faired stern contour, measured at the designed load water line.

The **classification length** according to the American Bureau is the distance on the summer-load water line from the foreside of the stem to the after side of the rudder or sternpost. If no vertical rudder or sternpost is fitted, the after point of measurement is taken to the center line of the rudder stock. The classification society length is commonly noted as the length between perpendiculars (L.B.P.).

The **molded beam** is the extreme breadth of the molded form. With steel ships this is the only value ordinarily considered. The extreme or over-all breadth is occasionally used, referring to the extreme transverse dimension taken to the outside of the plating.

The **depth** is the vertical distance amidships from the upper surface of the flat plate keel to the underside of the deck plating at ship's side. Depth to freeboard deck, strength deck, or some erection deck is usually specified.

The **draft** (molded) is the distance from the top of the keel plate or bar keel to the load water line. It may refer to draft amidships, forward, or aft.

The amount of convex curvature or rise in the transverse or athwartship plane, which is often given to the weather deck and certain lower decks to free them more readily of water, is termed **camber.**

Many vessels have their weather decks "swept higher" at bow and stern than amidships in order to improve their seagoing abilities. The increase in such deck heights is known as **sheer.**

Midship section is the transverse plane located at the center of the classification length.

The **displacement** is the weight (in tons of 2,240 lb) of the water displaced by the immersed part of the ship and is equal to the weight of the ship and everything on board. The density of sea water averages about 64 lb per cu ft (1 ton = 35 cu ft); hence, the displacement in sea water is measured by the immersed volume, in cubic feet, divided by 35. In fresh water the corresponding divisor is taken as 35.9.

The **dead weight** of a ship is the weight of cargo, stores, fuel, water, personnel, and effects that the ship can carry when loaded to a specified load draft. Dead weight is equal to the load displacement minus the weight of the equipped ship, commonly expressed in long tons (2,240 lb).

The **tonnage** is an arbitrary measure of capacity used in estimating navigation charges of various kinds and is intended to be proportional to the earning capacity of the vessel. **Gross tonnage** is based on cubic capacity of the ship below the tonnage deck, plus allowances for certain compartments above, which are used for cargo, passengers, crew, and navigating gear. Deduction of spaces for propelling machinery, crew quarters, and other prescribed volumes from the gross tonnage will give the **net tonnage.** One ton is equal to 100 cu ft of volume. (For directions in detail, see bulletin, "Measurement of Vessels," issued by the Bureau of Customs, U.S. Treasury Department.)

The **center of buoyancy** (see p. 3–54) is the center of the molded volume of the vessel below the water line. Its vertical and fore-and-aft positions are computed from the lines. In preliminary work, the distance of the center of buoyancy above the keel can be approximated by the expression

$$\frac{5}{6}(\text{draft, ft}) - \frac{1}{3}\,\frac{\text{displacement, cu ft}}{\text{area of water line, sq ft}}$$

Coefficients of Form. Assume the following notation: L = length on water line, ft; B = beam, ft; H = draft, ft; D = displacement, tons of sea water; A = area of water plane at surface of water, sq ft; M = area of midship section below water plane, sq ft; V = speed in knots. Then,

b = block coefficient of fineness = $35D/LBH$
m = midship section coefficient = M/BH
l = mean length or prismatic coefficient = $35D/ML$
α = water plane coefficient = A/BL
$D/(L/100)^3$ = displacement length coefficient, the displacement in tons of a mechanically similar ship 100 ft in length

From the preceding definitions, $l = b/m$.

For a ship-shaped form, $\alpha = \frac{2}{3}b + \frac{1}{3}$ approximately (Riddlesworth).

The typical and usual values of these coefficients range as follows:

Table 1. Coefficients of Form

Type of vessel	$\frac{V}{\sqrt{L}}$	b	m	l	α	$\frac{D}{(L/100)^3}$
Great Lakes ore ships	0.39–0.43	0.85–0.87	0.99–0.995	0.86–0.88	0.89–0.92	70– 95
Slow ocean freighters	0.45–0.50	0.77–0.82	0.99–0.995	0.78–0.83	0.85–0.88	180–200
Moderate-speed freighters	0.55–0.75	0.67–0.76	0.98–0.99	0.68–0.78	0.78–0.84	165–195
Fast passenger liners	0.70–1.05	0.56–0.65	0.94–0.985	0.59–0.67	0.71–0.76	75–105
Fast cruisers	1.30–1.70	0.45–0.53				
Destroyers	1.8 –2.5	0.44–0.53	0.72–0.83	0.62–0.71	0.67–0.73	40– 65
Tugs	0.90–1.2	0.45–0.53	0.71–0.83	0.61–0.66	0.71–0.77	200–420

STABILITY

Problem of Stability. (See p. 3–53 for Buoyancy and Flotation.) A ship or other floating body is in vertical equilibrium under the action of two systems of forces: (1) gravity, acting down, and (2) buoyancy, acting up. The center, or point of application, of the gravity system considered as a whole is at the **center of gravity** of the ship and its contents. The corresponding center for the buoyancy system is the **center of buoyancy.** These two centers lie in the same vertical line, when the body is in vertical equilibrium.

If an external transverse couple acts on the ship, it will rotate about a longitudinal axis, *i.e.*, take a list. The center of gravity of the vessel will not change; on the other hand, the vertical buoyancy force will alter position owing to the change of the underwater form. Reference to Fig. 1 shows that the weight and buoyancy forces form a couple equal and opposite to the above external couple. A stability curve, consisting of value of the **gravity-buoyancy couple** plotted against angles of inclination, gives a graphic representation of the stability of the ship.

With the ship inclined at any angle the vertical line of action of the buoyancy force can be found by taking moments of transverse underwater sections about a longitudinal axis. These can be integrated for the underwater volume and its moment.

For inclinations up to 5 or 10 deg the lines of action of the buoyancy system will all pass near a single point M in the ship known as the **metacenter.** If this is taken as a fixed point for small inclinations, the expression for stability becomes simple. For positive stability the metacenter must lie above the center of gravity G. Let G_M denote the distance between these points. Then $G_M \sin c$ is the moment arm for a small inclination of c deg, and $DG_M \sin c$ is the **stability moment.**

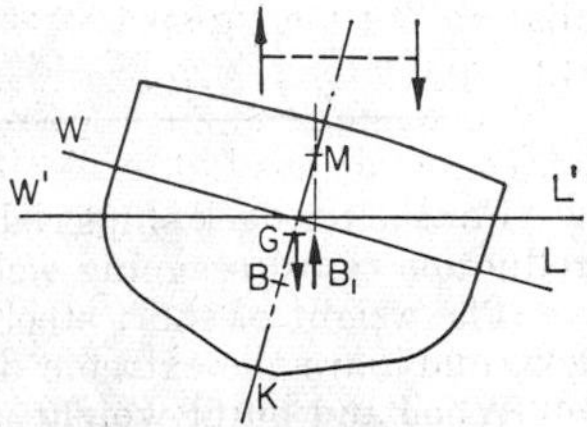

FIG. 1. Buoyancy of ships.

The distance BM of the center of buoyancy from the transverse metacenter = $I/35D$, where I is the moment of inertia of the water plane about its fore-and-aft center line. For water-plane coefficients α ranging from 0.65 to 0.8, the moment of inertia of the water plane about its center line can be approximated as $0.125(\alpha - 0.36)LB^3$. As the vertical location of the center of buoyancy is known from design data, the value of G_M can be found once KG the distance of the ship's center of gravity above the keel is known. Unfortunately, the vertical center of gravity of practically all commercial vessels varies with the condition of loading; its location may be determined either by a careful calculation or by the results of an inclining experiment.

Suitable minimum values of G_M, ranging from 1.5 to 3.5 ft, corresponding to small and large seagoing ships, respectively, have been accepted in the past. The G_M of passenger ships should be under $0.06B$ to ensure a reasonable (comfortable) rolling period. The curve of righting arms or moments *vs.* degrees inclination should be positive (*i.e.*, indicate a righting effect) from 0 to 65 deg for seagoing vessels. (See Vincent, "Principles of Naval Architecture.")

Starting with a ship in equilibrium in the upright position, suppose it to be heeled over continuously to any ultimate angle. The opposing moment of the statical stability must be overcome, and work will therefore be performed. The amount of such work is a measure of the so-called **dynamic stability** of the ship for any angle of inclination.

Trim. The problem of trim, or change of trim, is simply that of rotation about a transverse axis and hence of longitudinal stability. For all ordinary changes of trim the vertical through the center of buoyancy passes through a point practically fixed relative to the ship—the longitudinal metacenter. Let G_{M1} denote the distance of this point above the center of gravity. Then the moment of longitudinal stability = $G_{M1} \sin c \times D$. Also, if L = length of ship, ft, and h = change of trim, in., then for small angles, approximately, $\sin c = \tan c = h/12L$. Hence, moment = $G_{M1}hD/12L$ (ft-tons). In general, the moving of a weight of W tons a distance l ft in a fore-and-aft direction will produce a disturbing moment which must be balanced by the development of an equal trim moment. Hence, $Wl = G_{M1}hD/12L$. This equation serves to connect the moving of weights and the resulting change of trim. As an approximation, $Wl = L^2B\alpha^2/5{,}700$.

A **weight estimate** of the ship and her equipment is necessary for design and cost-estimating purposes previous to the completion of the detailed design. Weights are usually subdivided as follows: (1) steel hull and steel erections, (2) machinery, (3) wood outfit and equipment. Propelling-machinery weight will vary greatly with power, rpm, and type; it usually includes propulsion units, their auxiliaries, propellers, shafting, and bearings, and gratings and ladders in the machinery space.

Net steel weight up to and including the strength deck can be approximated as $C_sLBD_e/100$, units ft and long tons, where D_e is the depth to the strength deck. C_s for a cargo ship with no erections and of normal beam will range about as follows:

L/D_e	10	10	10	14	14	14
L	300	400	500	300	400	500
C_s	0.30	0.28	0.28	0.34	0.32	0.32

For shelter-deck ships reduce C_s by 0.02. Welded construction also calls for a 0.02 reduction (most seagoing welded hulls have several riveted seams).

The weight of short steel erections and houses will be about $klbd/100$ tons where l, b, and d are the extreme dimensions of such structures in ft and $k = 0.25$ to 0.35.

Wood and outfit weight usually includes all weights not classed as steel or as propelling machinery. Its value is dependent on the type of service, number of passengers, cargo-handling gear, etc.; for preliminary design this weight may be taken as $C_wLBD_e/100$. Provisional design values of C_w for ships 350 ft and over in length can be taken as follows: cargo ships, 0.06 to 0.09; colliers, 0.06; refrigerated ships, 0.12 to 0.19; passenger liners, 0.15 to 0.20; oil tankers, 0.04 to 0.08.

SHIP RESISTANCE AND POWERING

The resistance to motion is the aggregate of (1) **wave-making,** (2) **frictional,** (3) **pressure** or **form,** and (4) **air** resistances.

Wave-making resistance is primarily a function of **Froude's number** $Fr = v/\sqrt{gL}$, where v = ship speed, fps; g = acceleration of gravity; and L = ship length, ft. In many instances, the **speed-length ratio** $v/\sqrt{L}$ is used instead, where v is given in knots. A ship makes at least two distinct wave patterns, one from the bow and the other at the stern. There may be other patterns caused by abrupt changes in section. These patterns combine to form the total wave system for the ship. At various speeds there is mutual cancellation and reinforcement of these patterns. Thus the total-resistance curve of the ship is not smooth but shows humps and hollows which correspond to cancellation or reinforcement of the wave patterns. Normal design procedure is to cause the **normal** operating speed of the ship to fall at one of the **low points** in the resistance curve.

Frictional resistance is a function of **Reynolds number** (see p. 3–58ff). Because of the size of a ship, the Reynolds number is large and the **flow** is always **turbulent.**

Pressure or form resistance is a viscosity effect but is different from frictional resistance. The principal observed effects are boundary-layer separation and eddying near the stern.

It is usual practice to combine the wave-making and pressure resistances into one term, called the **residual resistance,** which is assumed to be a function of **Froude's number.** The combination, while not strictly legitimate, is practical because the pressure resistance is usually only 2 to 3 percent of the total resistance. The frictional resistance is then the only term which is considered to be a function of Reynolds number. By using measured friction coefficients and calculating the wetted surface of the ship, the frictional resistance can be calculated. Based on an analysis of the water resistance of flat, smooth planes, Schoenherr gives the formula $R = 0.5c_f\rho Av^2$, where R = resistance, lb; A = wetted surface, ft²; ρ = mass density, lb per sec² (ft⁴); v = velocity, fps; and c_f is as in table below.

Reynolds number/ $(10)^5$*.....	4	10	20	40	100	200	400	1,000	4,000	10,000
c_f..........	0.0053	0.0044	0.0038	0.00342	0.00293	0.00263	0.00236	0.00207	0.00172	0.00153

* Reynolds number = vL/ν (in any consistent units), L = length of plane, ft; ν = kinematic viscosity, ft² per sec.

If this formula is used for calculating ship frictional resistance, c_f should be increased to allow for roughness, e.g., by 0.0004.

The **wetted surface** A can be found by girthing the transverse stations below the waterline and then integrating these values. In consequence of obliquity, the actual wetted surface is increased about 1 percent. An approximate formula by Taylor is $A = K\sqrt{\Delta L}$, where K ranges from 15.0 to 16.3; Δ = ship displacement, long tons; and L = waterline length, ft.

The first function of a **model test** is to determine the residual resistance. The model is tested at the same Froude number, but not the same Reynolds number, as the ship. Therefore, the frictional resistance for the model must be determined by calculation and subtracted from the total to obtain the residual resistance and dimensionless plot. Froude's number is plotted as abscissa, and the residual resistance divided by the displacement (*i.e.*, weight of the ship) is plotted as ordinate.

Air Resistance. The end-on resistance is roughly 30 percent greater when the wind direction is about 30 deg with the keel, than when it is dead ahead. The end-on resistance can be approximated by $R_A = 0.002B^2V_R^2$ lb, where V_R is the ship speed relative to the air in knots in still air. It is usually less than 3 percent of the total resistance but in storm conditions may be ten times this value. (See also p. 11–74.)

Submarines. A deeply submerged submarine has only pressure and frictional resistance. At low speed, the wetted surface of the submarine means higher propulsive power than for a comparable surface ship. At high speeds, however, when the wave-making resistance of the surface ship is high, the submarine will require considerably less power than the surface ship. For a more complete discussion, see *International Shipbuilding Progress*, Vol. 3, Nos. 22 and 28, Vol. 4, No. 35, published by International Periodical Press, Rotterdam, Holland (in English).

Ayre Method for Calculation of Ehp. A. L. Ayre developed a method of calculating the ehp of ships based on a review of model tests. Volker has made some changes (see *North East Coast Inst. Engrs. & Shipbuilders*, 1932–1933; 1947–1948; Von Lammeren, "Resistance, Propulsion and Steering of Ships," Technical Publishing Co., Haarlem, Holland). According to Ayre, ehp $= D^{0.64}V^3/C_2$. This is the ehp for the hull, including the rudder but excluding bilge keels, twin-screw struts, and shaft bossing. C_2 is a coefficient depending on $V/\sqrt{L}$; $L/D^{1/3}$, a form of displacement-length ratio; the block coefficient, b; the beam-draft ratio, B/H; and the longitudinal location of the center of buoyancy.

Figure 2 gives C_2 uncorrected, based on Ayre and Volker, and follows the latter closer at $V/\sqrt{L} > 1$. The following corrections should be applied:

Correction for Fullness. The maximum block coefficient economical to use for a shipshaped form is dependent principally on the ship length and speed. Ayre's standard block coefficient b_2 is given in the upper scale below the curves of Fig. 2. The lower scale gives the correction coefficients for fullness as a function of $(b - b_2)/b_2$. If $b > b_2$, the vessel is "full" and the left-hand half of the scale applies; in this case the correction yC_2b is negative. If $b < b_2$, the vessel is "fine," the right-hand half of the scale applies, and the correction uC_2 is positive.

If the ratio of beam to draft B/H is greater than 2.0, the C_2 *correction for excess* $B/H = -0.1\left(\frac{B}{H} - 2.0\right)C_2$, where C_2 has already been corrected for variation from the standard block coefficient.

Table 2.

Ship	Type[o]	Year built	Length water line, L, ft[a]	Beam, molded, B, ft	Depth, molded, D_s, ft	Load, draft, H, ft	Displacement tons, D	Dead-weight capacity, tons	Tonnage, gross	Block, coefficient, b
America	P & C	1940	690	93.2	55.5	32.5	35,440	14,330	27,000	0.59
Queen Mary	P & C	1937	1,004	118	92.5	38.8	77,400	17,000	80,700	0.59
Nieuw Amsterdam	P & C	1938	700	88	55	31.5	36,240	10,260	36,290	0.63
Constitution	P & C	1951	650	89	70.8	30	30,090	12,309	.....	0.60
Olympia	P & C	1954	569	79	33.7	28.1	22,500	8,240	22,980	0.62
Mauretania	P & C	1939	772	89.5	51.7	30.8	....	....	35,700	.....
Edmund Fitzgerald	L	1958	711	75	39	26.8	35,005	27,250	13,362	0.864
Beaverglen	C	1946	481	64	42.7	29.6	....	11,000	.....	.....
Old Colony Mariner	C	1953	533	76	44.5	29.8	21,093	13,418	9,216	0.61
Barrett	M-T	1952	508	73.2	49	27	17,600	6,900	.....	0.62
Panama	P & C	1939	486	64	38.5	26.0	14,030	6,800	10,020	0.61
Canadian cruiser	Di.C	1946	410	59	36.5	25.0	11,400	7,500	.....	0.66
Victory class	C	1941	445	63	38	28.5	15,200	10,750	7,612	0.67
Schuyler Otis Bland	C	1951	450	66	41.5	28.5	15,900	10,516	8,918	0.66
Surat	C	1948	525	67	....	29.5	....	10,750	9,000	0.53
Prince Boudoin	CC	....	361	45.9	24.8	11.1	2,755	....	3,300	0.53
Red Jacket	C	1939	435	63	40.5	25.8	13,900	7,620	.....	0.69
Agwimonte	C	1941	395	60	37.5	27.5	12,860	9,100	.....	0.69
H. S. Dennison	Hydro-foil	1962	104	22.5	14.7	15.5	95	10	.....	.....
Ernest T. Weir	Ore	1954	670	70	37	25.5	28,830	21,950	12,746	0.86
Antrim	Di.C	1946	320	50	29	21	7,435	5,032	3,805	0.75
Manhattan	T	1962	892	132	67.5	49.3	137,068	106,568	65,740	0.793
Liberty class	C	1942	428	56.9	37.3	27.7	14,250	10,844	7,180	0.74
Ramb I	Di.Fr.	1937	354	47.9	....	18.2	5,200	2,300	3,500	0.57
Quaker	C	1939	280	48.5	32.2	18.5	4,215	2,050	.....	0.585
World Glory	T	1954	705	102	50	37.5	58,265	45,510	27,812	0.76
Esso Lima	T	1950	600	82.5	42.5	31.9	34,640	26,800	17,060	0.76
Atlantic Seaman	T	1951	625	85	45	34.3	39,664	30,155	.....	0.76
Joseph F. Merrell	F	1951	277.5	49	20	13.2	2,370	406	2,258	0.42
John Sergeant	C	1956	441	56.9	37.3	26.0	13,570	8,870	.....	0.72
Venore	Ore	1945	575	78	43.8	34.2	32,450	24,250	8,560	0.75
Esso Bayonne	T	1938	445	66.5	34.5	28.0	17,050	13,080	7,700	0.721
Destroyer	D	1935	320	31.2	18.0	10	....	....	.....	.....
Cruiser	Cr	1936	550	51.2	....	18	6,800	....	.....	0.47
Corsair	Y	1930	280	42.7	21.7	16.2[b]	2,590	....	.....	0.47
Alexander Hamilton	C.G.Cu	1937	308	41.0	....	12.7	2,350	....	.....	0.51
Itasca	C.G.Cu	....	239	42	....	12.9	1,662	....	.....	0.49
Walter Wyman	Cu	1932	92	23.2	14.2	9.3	270	....	.....	0.48
Patrol boat	C.G.Cu	....	70	12.8	....	3.6	31	....	.....	0.45
Motor gunboat 2009	......	1947	110	19.5	....	4.3	100	....	.....	0.38
Pennsylvania	T	1949	610	84	44	33.2	36,280	28,170	17,900	0.765

[a] Length between perpendiculars, if counter stern.
[b] Trial results.
[c] Indicated horsepower.
[d] Some Victory ships have 8,500 shp.
[e] Reheat cycle.
[f] Sulzer, two-stroke, single-acting.
[g] Nordberg, 21.5 × 29 in.
[h] Gasoline engine.
[k] Sun-Doxford, two-stroke.
[l] See *Trans. Soc. Naval Architects Marine Engrs.*, 1948.

Ship Data

Normal speed, knots, V	$V/\sqrt{L}$	Propellers	Propeller rpm	Total shp	Machinery[p] Engines	Boilers No.	Boilers Type	Boiler heating surface, sq ft[m]	Boiler press, psig	Steam temp, deg F	Machinery weight, lb per shp[l]	Admiralty coef
22	0.84	2	128	34,000	3 cyl s.r. d.r.	6	3 dr.	63,000	425	725		
29.0	0.92	4	180	158,000	4 cyl s.r.	24	4 dr.	.....	400	700		
20.5	0.77	2	131	34,000	4 cyl s.r.	6	4 dr.	51,000	550	740		
22.5	0.88	2	134	37,000	2 cyl d.r.	4	2 dr.	36,800	627	840		
.....	....	2	.....	24,000	2 cyl d.r.	4	2 dr.	24,120	525	800		
.....	....	2	140	......	3 cyl s.r.	6	3 dr.	64,500	425	725		
14	0.55	1	100	7,500	2 cyl d.r.	2	dr.	5,250	450	750		
16	0.73	1	108	9,000	1 m.t.g.[e]	1	Johnson	......	850	850	213	347
20.0	0.88	1	102	17,500	2 cyl d.r.	2	2 dr.	......	600	865	.....	433
19.2	0.85	2	92	12,500	2 cyl d.r.	2	cr. dr.	13,700	615	850	.....	435
16.5	0.75	2	90	9,000	2 cyl d.r.	2	3 dr.	18,400	445	750	.....	382
16.5	0.81	1	94	6,000	4 cyl Di.[k]							
15.5	0.74	1	100	6,000[d]	2 cyl d.r.	2	cr. dr.	8,600	440	740		
18.5	0.87	1	90	12,500	2 cyl d.r.	2	2 dr.	......	865	800	.....	405
20.1[b]	0.88	1	118	11,000	3 cyl	2	2 fur.	15,290	500	825		
22	1.16	2	258	15,000	12 cyl Di.[f]	..	....	......	....	....	105	
15.5	0.75	1	92	6,000	2 cyl d.r.	2	....	......	450	750	.....	448
14.0	0.70	1	90	4,000	2 cyl d.r.	2	cr. dr.	5,400	450	750		
60	....	1	2,045	8,700	gas turb.	..	....	......	....	....	2.5	
13.9	0.54	1	108	7,000	2 cyl d.r.	2	2 dr.	......	450	750		
11.0	0.61	1	180	1,700	6 cyl Di.[g]							
17.75	0.59	2	......	39,000	2 cyl d.r.	2	dr.	......	623	850		
11.5	0.56	1	76	2,300[c]	1 triple exp.	2	cr. dr.	4,850	220	450		
18.5[b]	0.98	2	......	5,000	9 cyl Di.[n]							
16.5	0.99	1	120	4,000	2 cyl d.r.	2	cr. dr.	9,360	400	715		
17.1[b]	0.64	1	100	15,000	2 cyl d.r.	2	2 dr.	......	600	850		
17.4	0.71	1	112	12,500	2 cyl d.r.	2	2 dr.	12,410	850	850	.....	415
17.0	0.68	1	100	16,500	2 cyl d.r.	2	cr. dr.	17,740	625	1020		
15.7[b]	0.94	1	165	4,000	uniflow	3	cr. dr.	......	275	614		
15.4	0.72	1	110	6,000	gas turb.[s]							
16	0.67	1	94	11,000	3 cyl d.r.[e]	2	2 dr.	7,800	1450	750	184	400
13.8[b]	0.65	1	102[b]	4,100[b]	2 cyl d.r.	2	2 dr.	4,570	400	750		
36.7[b]	2.05	2	446[b]	31,280[b]	2 cyl s.r.	3	4 dr.	17,970	386	660	28.5	
32	1.36	4	320	66,000	2 cyl s.r.	6	3 dr.	43,000	415	660		
16.0[b]	0.96	2	210	3,140[b]	2 m.t.g.	4	cr. dr.	13,290	300	620	.....	247
20[b]	1.14	2	241	5,250[b]	2 cyl d.r.	2	....	......	400	650	177	270
17[b]	1.10	1	163	3,350	1 m.t.g.	2	cr. dr.	6,330	265	586	216	206
11.7[b]	1.22	1	180	557	2–5 cyl Di. el.	..	....	......	....	....	500	120
30.4[b]	3.63	2	1,490	1,680	4–12 cyl V.[h]	..	....	......	....	....	9.4	
34	....	3	1,090	5,000	2–12 cyl[r]							
16.6	0.67	1	97	11,000	2 cyl d.r.	2	2 dr.	13,400	600	850	.....	465

[m] Boiler heating surface = steam generating surface.

[n] Fiat two-stroke, 20.5 × 32.2 in.

[o] P, Passenger; C, Cargo; CC, Cross channel; C.G., Coast Guard; Cr, Cruiser; Cu, Cutter; D, Destroyer; Di.C, Diesel Cargo; Di.Fr., Diesel Fruiter; L, Laker; T, Tanker; Y, Yacht; F, Ferry; M-T, Military Transport.

[p] cr. dr., cross drum; cyl, cylinder; Di, Diesel; Di. el., Diesel electric; dr., drum; d.r., double-reduction geared turbine; m.t.g., main turbogenerators; s.e. S., single-ended Scotch; s.r., single-reduction geared turbine.

[r] 12 cyl, 1,250 bhp Packard gas. Also a 2,500 hp Metropolitan Vickers geared gas turbine on the center propeller. The first gas-turbine plant to operate at sea.

[s] Converted and lengthened Liberty. Open-cycle gas-turbine with 14-stage compressor and h-p turbine drive; one stage l-p propulsion gas-turbine geared to reversible blade propeller.

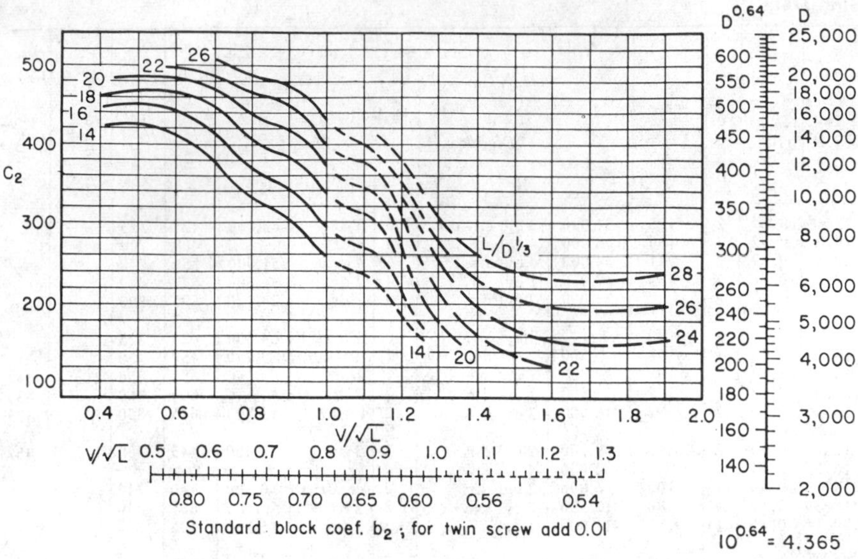

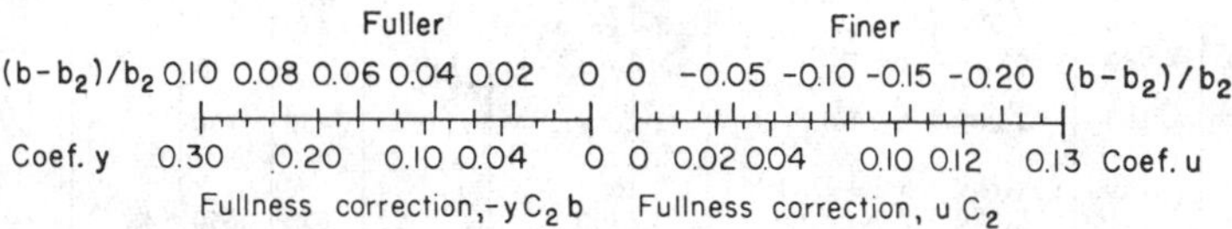

FIG. 2. Values of C_2 for use in Ayre's method of calculating effective horsepower.

Where information is available, a correction to C_2 for variation in longitudinal position of the center of buoyancy from the optimum location should also be subtracted from C_2 as corrected above (see Tables 3 and 4). If the correction for location of longitudinal center of buoyancy is less than the correction for fullness, neglect it; if greater, include only the excess. The correction (see Table 4) is $-kC_2$.

Table 3. Ideal Location of the Center of Buoyancy

$V/\sqrt{L}$	0.5	0.6	0.7	0.8	0.9	1.0	1.1	1.2
Single screw	0.02L	0.018L	0.013L	0.002L	0.012L	0.020L	0.024L	0.025L
	←Forward of midship→				←Aft of midship→			

Table 4. Correction Factors k for Position of Center of Buoyancy

$V/\sqrt{L}$	0.5	0.6	0.7	0.8	0.9	1.0	1.1	1.2
Center 0.01L too far forward	0.01	0.01	0.03	0.05	0.07	0.09	0.11	0.13
Center 0.02L too far forward	0.04	0.04	0.06	0.10	0.14	0.18	0.22	0.26
Center 0.01L too far aft	0.04	0.03	0.02	0.01	....	....	0.01	0.02
Center 0.02L too far aft	0.10	0.08	0.06	0.04	0.02	0.02	0.04	0.06

The ideal location of the center of buoyancy of twin-screw ships is 0.01L aft of the ideal location for single-screw vessels.

EXAMPLE. Find the ehp and shp of the following single-screw vessel by the Ayre method. Speed 14.1 knots, L.W.L. 400, displacement 11,200 tons, beam 54 ft, draft 24.3 ft, $b = 0.747$, $V/\sqrt{L} = 0.705$, $L/D^{1/3} = 17.9$, $B/H = 2.22$. Center of buoyancy 0.009L forward of amidships. Assume propulsive coefficient = 0.70.

C_2 uncorrected at $V/\sqrt{L} = 0.7$ and $L/D^{1/3} = 17.9 = 453$

Actual block of ship, $b_1 = 0.747$; Ayre's standard block b_2 (Fig. 2) $= 0.73$; $b - b_2 = 0.017$; $(b - b_2)/b_2 = 0.023$

Coefficient y, scale diagram, Fig. 2, $= 0.040$; correction $= yC_2b = -0.04 \times 453 \times 0.747 = -13$

C_2 corrected for difference in block coef $= 453 - 13 = 440$

Correction for beam, since $B/H > 2.0$, is $-0.1(B/H - 2.0)bC_2 = -7$

C_2 corrected for beam $= 440 - 7 = 433$

Correction for location of center of buoyancy; ideal location, $0.013L$. Actual location $0.004L$ too far aft. From Table 4, correction $= -0.008 \times 433 = -3$

C_2 corrected for location of center buoyancy $= 433 - 3 = 430$

ehp $= 11{,}200^{0.64} \times 14.1^3/430 = 2{,}550$

shp $=$ ehp/propulsive coef $= 2{,}550/0.70 = 3{,}643$

The determination of the bhp required for new power boats and yachts is complicated by the difficulty in accurately measuring the motor output developed. The method of finding the **power necessary for a motorboat,** proposed by Keith, is $V_m = C\sqrt[3]{LP/B}$, where V_m is the speed in statute miles per hr; L is the load-water-line length, ft; B is the maximum water-line beam, ft; and P is the bhp developed. Values of C (White, *Yachting,* Jan., 1933, p. 49) are as follows:

Heavy cruiser	8 – 9	Heavy runabout	11.7–14.3
Medium cruiser	8.4–10	Average runabout	14 –16.3
Light cruiser	9.2–11.3	Racing runabout	15.8–18.2
Express cruiser	9.8–12.6	Hydroplane	18 –20

SCREW PROPELLERS

A propeller of constant pitch on the face shows reasonable efficiency. The aft surface or face of the propeller blade is commonly constructed as a true helical surface of constant pitch. The blade back or forward surface is not a helical surface.

Pitch is often expressed as a ratio to the diameter or as p/d.

Diameter, ft $= d$
Pitch, ft $= p$
Projected blade area (sq ft) $= A$
Revolutions per minute $= N$
Speed, knots $= V$
Speed of advance of propeller relative to water at stern in which it is working, knots $= u$
Shaft horsepower $= P$
Number of blades $= n$

Projected area is the area of the projection of the propeller contour on a plane normal to the shaft. The projected-area ratio is the ratio of the projected area to $\pi d^2/4$. The ratio of the projected to the "actual" or helicoidal area (Taylor) is approximately $[1.067 - 0.229(p/d)]$ for blades of elliptical form; the relation holds less accurately for any blade which departs from an oval contour.

Apparent slip ratio S' is the propeller slip relative to the outlying body of still water divided by pN

$$S' = (pN - 101.3V)/pN$$

The wake or a frictional belt of water accompanies every hull in motion; its velocity varies as the ship's speed, the form of the ship, the distance from the ship's side and from the bow, together with the condition of the hull surface. For ordinary propeller design in America the wake velocity is a fraction w of the ship's speed

$$\text{Wake velocity} = wV$$

The wake factor w for a ship may be approximated by Taylor's equations of the following form:

$$w = 0.5b - 0.05, \text{ for single-screw ships}$$
$$w = 0.55b - 0.2, \text{ for twin-screw ships}$$

The velocity of the ship relative to the ship's wake at the stern $V_a = (1 - w)V$.

The **true slip ratio** S is the propeller slip relative to the moving wake at the stern divided by pN.

$$S = (pN - 101.3V_a)/pN$$
$$V_a = pN(1 - S)/101.3 \text{ knots}$$
$$V = pN(1 - S')/101.3 \text{ knots}$$
$$V_a/V = (1 - S)/(1 - S') = 1 - w$$

Propeller Design. For important installations, a self-propelled test of a ship model with propeller is commonly carried out, but propeller design is frequently based on systematic model tests of propellers that were run in the open, in other words, clear of any hull.

Coefficients of thrust C_T and torque C_Q derived from such tests may be plotted against propeller slip, but Taylor's power and diameter factors B_p and δ are more convenient for the practical design of propellers. They can be derived from dimensional analysis. As the water density is constant, it is omitted in the B_p factor.

$$B_p = \frac{NP^{1/2}}{V_a^{5/2}}, \text{ power factor} \qquad \delta = \frac{Nd}{V_a}, \text{ diameter factor}$$

$$C_T = \frac{T}{N^2p^2d^2} \qquad C_Q = \frac{Q}{N^2p^3d^2} \qquad e = \frac{C_T}{C_Q}\frac{(1 - S)}{2\pi}$$

T = thrust, lb $\qquad Q$ = torque, lb-ft $\qquad e$ = efficiency

Taylor's design diagram for three-blade propellers of an elliptical developed contour and with a blade thickness ratio $= t/d$ of 0.05 is given in Fig. 3. The dimension t

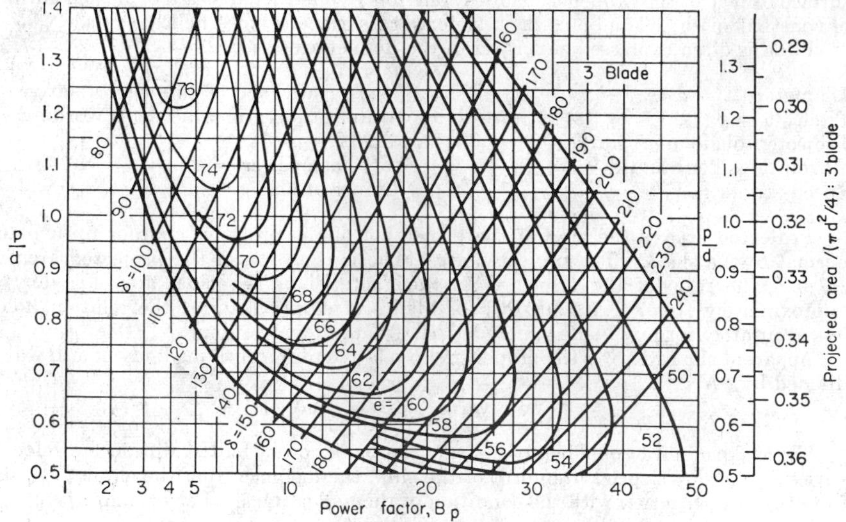

FIG. 3. Taylor design diagrams for three-blade propellers.

is the length intercepted on the shaft axis by the prolonged blade section lines of Fig. 4. The families of curves give δ and e, respectively.

The projected-area ratios of the model propellers from which the curves were developed varied with the pitch ratios, as shown by the scale to the right of Fig. 3. Except for the possibility of cavitation and a slight variation in slip, moderate variations in amount of projected area and alteration in blade contour have little effect on propeller performance. Appreciable change in the above or in thickness ratio will alter the propeller characteristics. These curves do not indicate propeller slip; it can readily be determined as shown by the example on p. 11–56. (For similar three- and four-blade charts by Laurens Troost, see Osborne, Vol. 11.)

A **four-blade propeller** of 0.97 × the diameter of the three blade, the same pitch ratio, and 1.33 × the area will absorb the same shp at the same rpm as the three-blade propeller. Similarly, a two-blade propeller of 5 percent greater diameter is approximately equivalent to a three-blade unit. Figure 3 shows that propeller efficiency increases with decrease in value of the power, or revolution, factor B_p. A low value of B_p in a slow-speed ship calls for a large-diameter (optimum) propeller. It is frequently necessary to limit the diameter of the propeller and accept the accompanying loss in efficiency. For an approximation of the **optimum diameter** use $d = 50\ \text{shp}^{0.2}/\text{rpm}^{0.6}$, where d is in ft.

The number of propeller blades is usually three or four. Four blades have been universal with single-screw merchant ships. Recently five, and even six blades have been used to reduce vibration. Highly loaded propellers of fast ships and naval vessels call for large blade area; preferably, three—blades to reduce blade interference.

Propeller fore-and-aft clearance from the stern frame of large single-screw ships at 70 percent of propeller radius should be greater than 18 in. The stern frame should be streamlined. The clearance from the propeller tips to the shell plating of twin-screw vessels ranges from about 20 in. in low-powered ships to 4 or 5 ft in high-powered steamships. Many high-speed motorboats have a tip clearance of only several inches. The immersion of the propeller tips should be sufficient to prevent the drawing in of air.

Propeller cavitation results in marked increase in rpm, propeller slip, and shp with little increase in ship speed and ehp and also in erosion of the propeller blade surface with service (at times so severe that propellers must be replaced after little service). It may occur either on the face or on the back of the propeller. Cavitation of the face has little effect on thrust and torque and can be prevented by cutting away the face of the leading edge and making the blade section at this point more symmetrical. Cavitation of the back of the propeller materially affects the propeller thrust and performance and cannot be eliminated by alterations to the propeller-blade cross section.

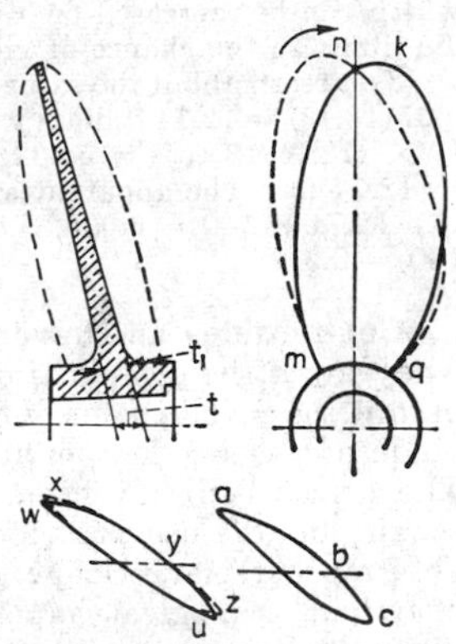

Fig. 4. Propeller-blade sections.

Commander Irish, on the basis of an analysis of propellers that have cavitated, suggests the following values of critical thrust at various tip speeds. The calculated thrust of a propeller should be about 10 percent below the table values to avoid cavitation.

Thrust $= 326P/VA$ psi; P = shp per screw; A = projected area, sq in.; V = speed, knots. According to Bowers (David Taylor Model Basin), cavitation begins at N rpm, where N is given by $N^2 = 37{,}500(1 - S)^2Shb/tpd$, where $h = 33.1 +$ submergence of propeller hub, ft; b is the mean width ratio which for elliptical propellers, according to Schonherr, is approximately $A/[(\pi/4)\ nd^2\ (0.612 - 0.133p/d)] + 0.009$; and t is the extrapolated blade thickness, ft, at the shaft center as shown in Fig. 4.

Table 5. Critical Thrust of Propellers

Tip speed, fpm	2,000	4,000	6,000	8,000	10,000	12,000	14,000
Thrust, psi	1.2	5.6	12.0	18.2	23.6	28.5	33.0

Consider a three-blade propeller for a single-screw ship with shp = 2,950, speed = 17 knots, and block coefficient = 0.47. Find the size and efficiency of propellers for rpm = 160 and for rpm = 140. The wake factor $w = 0.5b - 0.05 = 0.185$. $V_a =$

$V(1 - 0.185) = 13.85$. At 160 rpm $B_p = N(P)^{1/2}/(V_a)^{5/2} = 12.15$. At 140 rpm $B_p = 10.64$. From Fig. 3, the following may be obtained:

Rpm	B_p	p/d	Efficiency	δ	Diam, ft	Pitch, ft
160	12.15	0.9	0.682	146	12.85	11.56
160	12.15	1.0	0.682	139	12.23	12.23
140	10.64	0.9	0.696	140	13.83	12.45
140	10.64	1.0	0.70	133	13.13	13.13
140	10.64	1.1	0.692	127	12.55	13.81

The propeller of 13.13 ft diam and a pitch ratio of 1.0 at 140 rpm is most efficient. The optimum diameter $= 50\ \text{shp}^{0.2}/\text{rpm}^{0.6} = 12.8$ ft.

Find the projected area of this propeller, if designed with the area indicated by this table, and investigate the possibility of cavitation. The projected-area ratio for $p/d = 1.0$, according to Fig. 3, is 0.32. Projected area $= 0.32\ (\pi d^2/4) = 43.3$ sq ft. Thrust, by the Irish formula $= P(326)/V(A) = 2{,}950(326)/17(43.3)144 = 9.1$ psi. Tip speed $= \pi dN = 3.142 \times 13.13 \times 140 = 5{,}770$ fpm. According to the table, the maximum thrust at this tip speed is about 11.2 psi. If the margin of 2.1 psi is considered inadequate, the blade width can be increased or a four-blade propeller of larger projected area can be adopted. To diminish the chance of vibration a four-blade wheel is selected.

To absorb about the same power at the same revolutions, a four-blade propeller of about $0.97(13.13) = 12.74$ ft diam with the same blade shape would have a projected area of $43.3 \times \frac{4}{3} \times (12.74/13.13)^2 = 54.32$ sq ft, or about 25 percent increase. The pitch $= 0.97(13.13) = 12.74$ ft. The apparent and real slips are, respectively, $S_1 = (12.74 \times 140 - 101.3 \times 17)/12.74 \times 140 = 0.039$, *i.e.*, 4 percent; $S = (12.74 \times 140 - 101.3 \times 13.85)/12.74 \times 140 = 0.212$.

Controllable- and **reversible-pitch** propellers are being used up to 10,000 shp. They avoid the complications of a reverse gear. In direct-drive Diesel plants, they permit the development of full power when the ship resistance increases. With fixed-blade propellers, the rpm and engine output decrease with increase of ship resistance. The principal disadvantages of variable pitch are cost, difficulty of inspection and repair, and the necessity for a governor.

Propeller-blade Shape. Formerly, the sections of marine propeller blades were of symmetrical ogival shape as *wyu*, Fig. 4. A modern airfoil blade section such as *abc*, according to Baker, will improve the efficiency of a lightly loaded propeller several percent; further gain in efficiency can be made by the skewbacked shape of blade *mnq* constructed with, say, 10 to 20 percent reduced pitch toward the blade hub.

Thickness of Propeller Blades. The thickness of the blade at the tip depends on the material, type of propeller, etc.; an approximate value is $(0.04d + 0.10)$ in., where d is the propeller diam in ft.

Propeller-blade Strength. The blade intersection with the hub, neglecting fillets, is taken as the critical section. Tingey gives the center of (1) the blade thrust force parallel to the shaft, and (2) the application of the turning force in a plane normal to the shaft, as $0.33d$ and $0.30d$ from the shaft, respectively.

$$\text{Blade thrust} = 33{,}000(P.C.)P/[nV(1 - 0.7w)101.3]$$

where $P.C.$ is the propulsive coefficient; if unknown take approximately as e, the propeller efficiency.

$$\text{Turning force} = 33{,}000P/[2\pi Nn(0.30d)]$$

The above forces, together with the arms to blade-root sections, give corresponding bending moments and stresses.

Stresses due to centrifugal force should be combined with those due to thrust and torque at critical points of the blade-root section. Tingey suggests allowable stresses of 10,000 and 6,000 psi with manganese bronze for naval and merchant ships, respectively.

Weight of a propeller blade $= \rho[A(1.067 - 0.229p/d)]0.428t$, where ρ is density, A projected area, t maximum thickness of blade root, using consistent units.

Center of gravity of blade to shaft $= 0.24d$. Compute weight of hub for propeller mass inertia. Radius of gyration of entire propeller $= 0.20$ to $0.22d$.

The **Voith-Schneider propulsion system** consists of one or two vertical-axis rotors located underwater at the stern. Rotor disks are flush with the shell plating which is approximately horizontal at this point. Five to eight streamline spadelike vertical-impeller blades are fitted near the periphery of the disks and feather during the rotation of the disk so that a maximum lift or thrust effect is produced. The feathering action is under control; hence the propulsion equipment serves both as propeller and as rudder. Very effective steering action is claimed at low ship speed, together with propulsive efficiency comparable to that of a screw propeller. Propulsion sets of 20 to 1,200 shp per unit have been installed in a number of European craft for river and harbor service (see *Engg.*, Sept. 15, 1939). Kirsten (*Marine Eng. and Shipping Rev.*, pp. 108–110, 1946) has developed a similar system.

In the **Kort nozzle system** the screw propeller operates in a cylindrical tube or "nozzle." The walls of this tube, where clear of the ship's shell, are made of streamline form to reduce resistance. The Kort system decreases the tendency of the screw race to spread; tests show increased towing efficiency, particularly at high slips. It has been adopted in many river towboats.

The **outboard gasoline engine** (1 to 100 bhp), combining steering and propulsion, is popular for small pleasure craft. Higher-powered units are available with 40 to 400 bhp Diesel drive for commercial use (see pp. 9–115 and 116).

VIBRATION

(See also p. 5–90 *et seq.*)

Hull Vibration. A ship is an elastic structure subject to natural and forced vibrations. Natural vibrations may be (1) horizontal or vertical with two or more nodes or (2) torsional. The period of natural hull vibration depends on dimensions, displacement, fore-and-aft distribution of weights, elastic characteristics of hull girder, and mass of water entrained by the vibrating ship. Shallowness of the water influences the last. The following modified Schlick formula, based on one proposed by Burrill (*Trans. North East Coast Inst. Engrs. & Shipbuilders*, 1934–1935) gives the approximate natural two-node vertical frequency per minute of a ship in deep water as equal to

$$\frac{16{,}000}{\sqrt{(1 + B/2H)(2D_e/L + 0.93)}} \times \sqrt{\frac{I}{L^3D}}$$

where D_e is the depth to the strength deck, and I is the moment of inertia of the midship section taken to the uppermost continuous deck, in.^{4}; other symbols as on p. 11–46. The moment of inertia must include all continuous longitudinal members. The equation contains allowances for shear correction and entrained water.

Brown (*Trans. North East Coast Inst. Engrs. & Shipbuilders*, 1939) gives preliminary hull horizontal vibrations per minute $= \mu\sqrt{B^3D_e/DVL^3}$, where $\mu =$ 47,000 approx (range 42,000 to 62,000), and $V = 1.3 + 0.3H/B$.

The frequency of a freely supported uniform beam in three-node vibration is 2.8 times that for two-node vibration. A few ship tests show that three-node vertical frequency is about 1.9 to 2.3, say 2 times that for two-node frequency, *i.e.*, less than the ratio above.

Vibration Forces in Ships. Serious vibrations may be noticed when the frequency of the disturbing force agrees with the natural frequency of two- or three-node hull vibration. Such forces include:

1. Intermittent unbalanced **forces due to propeller action.** The causes for the unbalance may be variation in propeller pitch among different propeller blades; nonuniform wake velocity in way of the propeller; insufficient clearance between propeller blades and ship's hull in twin-screw ships, or between blades and propeller strut or propeller rudder post. Such intermittent forces cause vibrations of a frequency equal

to (1) the product of revolutions by the number of propeller blades or (2) the number of revolutions. A statically unbalanced propeller will likewise produce vibrations of this frequency.

2. The **engine torque reaction** produces an unbalanced athwartship or side thrust on the crosshead guide surface or on the cylinder wall of trunk piston engines.

3. **Vertical inertia forces** due to the acceleration of the reciprocating parts of an unbalanced reciprocating engine, whether Diesel or steam. These forces can be divided into a primary force with a frequency of once a revolution and a secondary force of twice that frequency.

4. Horizontal and vertical components of centrifugal forces developed by **unbalanced rotating parts.** Rotating parts can be balanced.

5. Unbalanced fore-and-aft **rocking moments** due to unbalanced inertia forces arising from the reciprocating parts or because of an unbalanced crankshaft.

Intermittent unbalanced forces on the hull due to propeller action can never be entirely eliminated. They can be greatly reduced by providing sufficient clearance between propeller and hull and by selecting the propeller revolutions or the number of blades to avoid synchronism.

The replacement of a four-blade propeller by a three- or five-blade, or vice versa, may bring about a reduction in vibration. Geared-turbine and turboelectric-drive vessels are free of disturbing forces aside from those due to propeller action except for vibration caused by unbalanced auxiliaries. Singing propellers are due to the vibration of the propeller blade edge about the blade body, producing a disagreeable noise or hum. Thinning the edge is sometimes useful.

Engine Torque Reaction. Vibrations due to variations in engine torque reaction are hard to overcome, particularly in twin-screw Diesel-engine ships where the torque reaction tends to produce an athwartship motion of the upper ends of the engines. The motion will be increased if the engine foundation strength is inadequate. Rigid athwartship tie rods between the upper framing of the port and starboard engines will often reduce such vibrations.

Synchronizing of twin-screw engines so as to maintain equal speeds and constant relative phase positions has been attempted by throttle control and also by a power-transfer method through the installation of special synchronous motor on each propeller shaft, tied in electrically.

Torsional vibration frequency of the main-unit–propulsion-shafting–propeller system should be carefully computed, and necessary steps taken to ensure that its natural frequency is clear of the frequency of the main-unit or propeller heavy-torque variations, as serious failures have occurred. With Diesel drive the engine manufacturer usually makes the necessary computations. Experience in calculations and tests has led to methods of good accuracy for frequency and amplitude. The propeller mass inertia is commonly increased by 25 percent to allow for water.

While more rare, a **longitudinal vibration** of the propulsion shafting has occurred when the natural frequency of the shafting agreed with that of a pulsating axial force, such as thrust variation.

Definitions of Power and Speed

The Society of Naval Architects and Marine Engineers sponsor the following definitions:

Shaft horsepower is the net power supplied to the propeller shafting after passing through all reduction gears or other transmission devices and after power for all attached auxiliaries has been taken off.

Brake horsepower is the power delivered by the output coupling of a Diesel or steam reciprocating engine before passing through speed-reducing and transmission devices and with all continuously operating engine-driven auxiliaries in use.

Normal shp or normal power is the power at which the ship is designed to run most of her service life.

Maximum shp is the highest power for which propulsion machinery is designed to operate continuously.

Service speed is the actual speed maintained by ship at load draft on her normal route and under average weather and sea conditions typical of that route and with average fouling of bottom.

Designed service speed is the speed expected on trials in fair weather at load draft, with clean bottom when machinery is developing a specified fraction of maximum shp. This fraction may vary, but is of order of 0.9.

Normal shaft rpm and **maximum shaft rpm** correspond to the preceding respective definitions.

MARINE SHAFTING

Line Shafts. The principal dimensions, kind of material, and material tests are specified by the classification societies for marine propulsion shafting. For ships fitted with turbine machinery the American Bureau of Shipping gives the following equation for the diameter of the line shaft:

$$d = c\sqrt[3]{K_1P/N} \text{ in.}$$

where P = shp at normal rating speed; N = rpm, normal; $K_1 = 64$ for ocean and coastwise service, 58 for river and harbor service; $c = 1.0$ for line shafts, 1.05 for thrust shafts at the bottom of collars when they transmit torque. The diameter of shafts for gears and rotors and for auxiliary units is based on $d = 0.1\sqrt[6]{(k_2T)^2 + 3.6M^2}$, where M and T are maximum moment and torque, respectively, at the section under consideration and at maximum power for continuous service, lb-in.; $k_2 = 0.182 + 24{,}500/Y$, where Y is the yield strength.

Tail or **propeller shafts** are made of larger diameter than the line or tunnel shafting because of bending moment from propeller weight; also inspection during service is possible only when the vessel is dry-docked. Propeller-shaft diameter $d_e = d + D_p/c$, in., where D_p = propeller diam, ft, $c = 12$ when a continuous bronze liner is fitted on the shaft, 8.3 if liners are fitted only at bearings.

Diesel-engine Crankshafts. The American Bureau and Lloyd's issue rules for the minimum diameter D_s of the crankshaft. An extract of Lloyd's Rules follows: $D_s = \sqrt[3]{D^2(AS + BL)}$, where D is the cylinder diam, in.; S is the length of stroke, in.; and L is the distance between inner edges of bearings, in.

The values of A and B for a mip of 100 psi are as follows:

No. of cylinders, four-cycle	1 to 4	5 or 6	7 or 8	9 or 10	11 or 12	
No. of cylinders, two-cycle	1 or 2	3	4	5	6	8
A	0.076	0.082	0.092	0.101	0.103	0.109
B	0.067	0.064	0.062	0.061	0.061	0.061

The preceding values are based on a maximum pressure of 500 to 700 psi in single-acting engines without firing in succession of adjacent cylinders. The published rules are extensive and should be referred to.

Propellers are **fitted to shafts** over 6 in. diam by a taper fit with a taper of 1:12. Aft of the propeller, the shaft is reduced to 0.58 to 0.68 of its specified diameter under the liner and is fitted with a relatively fine thread, nut, and keeper. Propeller torque is taken by a long flat key, the width and total depth of which are, respectively, about 0.21 and 0.11 times the shaft diameter under the liner. The forward end of the key slot in the shaft should be tapered off in depth and terminate well aft of large end of taper to avoid a high concentrated stress at the end of the keyway. Every effort is made to keep salt water out of contact with the steel tail shaft so as to prevent failure from corrosion fatigue.

A cast-iron, cast-steel, or wrought-steel–weldment stern tube is rigidly fastened to the hull. In single-screw ships it supports the propeller shaft and is normally provided with a packing gland at the forward end as sea water lubricates the stern-tube bearings. The aft stern-tube bearing is made four diameters in length; the forward stern-tube bearing is much shorter. A bronze liner, ¾ to 1 in. thick, is shrunk on the propeller shaft to protect it from corrosion and to give a good journal surface. Lignum-vitae inserts, arranged with the grain on end for medium and large shafts, are normally used for stern-tube bearings; the average bearing pressure is about 30 psi. Rubber and phenolic compound bearings, having longitudinal grooves, are also extensively used. White-metal oil-lubricated bearings and, in Germany, roller-type stern bearings have been fitted in a few installations.

The line or tunnel shafting is laid out, in long equal lengths, so that, in the case of a single-screw ship, withdrawal of the tail-shaft inboard for inspection every several years will require only the removal of the next inboard length of shafting. For large outboard or water-exposed shafts of twin-screw ships, a bearing spacing up to 30 shaft diameters has been used. A greater ratio prevails for steel shafts of power boats. Bearings inside the hull are spaced closer—normally under 15 diameters if shaft is more than 6 in. diameter. Usually, only the bottom half of the bearing is completely white-metaled; oil-wick lubrication is common, but oil-ring lubrication is used in high-class installations.

STRUCTURES

The structure of a ship is a complex assembly of small pieces of material. Common materials for small boats are wood, aluminum, and fiber glass. Large ships are nearly always constructed of steel, although current practice is to use an increasing amount of aluminum, especially in deckhouses and other superstructures. Structural analysis of small craft is at the discretion of the designers since there are no well-established practices in this regard.

The analysis of the structure of a large ship can be divided into two logical steps: first, determining the loads; and second, determining the strength and elastic stability. Many refined methods of structural analysis are available, especially from the aircraft industry, which has basically similar problems. These methods have been generally ignored by naval architects.

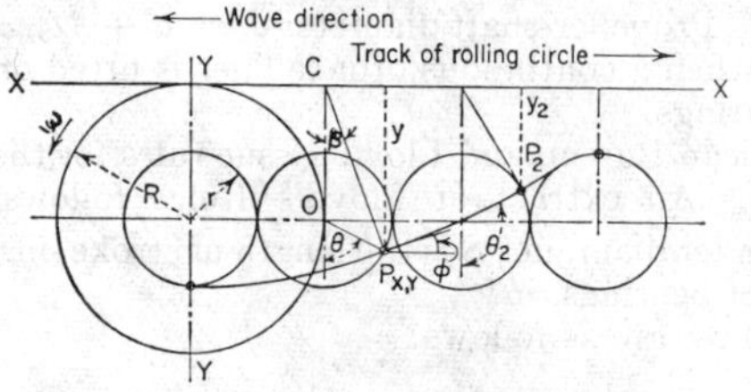

FIG. 5. Geometry of trochoid. (*Rossell and Chapman.*)

Method of Loading. The shear and bending of the hull are determined by assuming the ship supported on a trochoidal wave. Static shear and bending moments are then calculated. Numerous model and full-scale tests in waves have shown that this procedure usually gives higher stresses than the actual dynamic stresses in waves. This procedure is relatively simple; more through analyses will be found in Rossell and Chapman, "Principles of Naval Architecture," SNA&ME, and Wah, "A Guide for the Analysis of Ship Structures," OTS.

Trochoidal Wave. Until a water wave breaks, there is no net displacement of water as the wave travels. The water particles rotate in elliptical or circular orbits which decrease in magnitude with the depth of water. At the top of the orbit, the particles are traveling in the direction of the wave advance, and at the bottom, opposite to the wave advance. Trochoidal wave theory applies well to waves which are old and not sharp-crested. The parametric equations for the trochoid, Fig. 5, are $x = R\theta + r \sin \theta$ and $y = R + r \cos \theta$. If it is assumed that the trochoids are the loci of equal pressure, then the expressions for wave velocity V_w and period T are $V_w = \sqrt{g\lambda/2\pi}$ and $T = \lambda/V_w$, where V_w = wave velocity, fps; T = wave period, sec; λ = wave length (crest to crest), ft; g = gravitational constant, ft per sec^2. (See also Biglow and Edmondson, Wind Waves at Sea, Breakers and Surf, *Ho Publication* 62, U.S. Navy Oceanographic Office.) Figure 6 shows the distribution of buoyancy forces along the length of a vessel for two conditions. Table 6 gives the trochoidal coefficients (normalized wave height) for 10 intervals between the fore perpendicular, FP, and amidships.

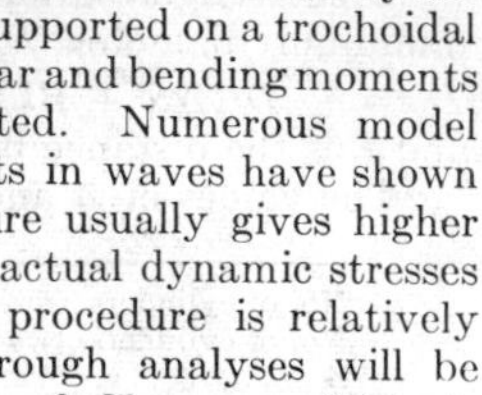

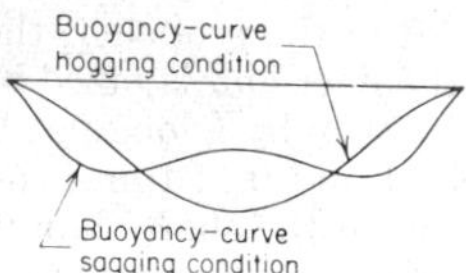

FIG. 6. Buoyancy curves for hogging and sagging conditions. (*Rossell and Chapman.*)

Table 6. Trochoidal Wave Coefficients *

Station No.	Hogging	Sagging
0 (FP)	1.000	0.000
1	0.982	0.034
2	0.927	0.128
3	0.839	0.266
4	0.720	0.421
5	0.577	0.577
6	0.421	0.720
7	0.266	0.839
8	0.128	0.927
9	0.034	0.982
10	0.000	1.000

* From Wah, "A Guide for the Analysis of Ship Structures," U.S. Dept. of Commerce, OTS.

Standard Bending Moment. The **standard-bending-moment procedure assumes** that all loads can be reduced to two static conditions, **hogging and sagging** (Fig. 7), with the ship supported by a trochoidal wave (1) of length equal to the length of the ship and (2) of height, trough to crest, of $\lambda/20$. In the hogging condition, Fig. 7*a*, the deck is in tension and the bottom shell in compression; in the sagging condition, Fig. 7*b*, the deck is in compression and the bottom in tension. For normal cargo ships with the machinery amidships, the hogging condition produces the highest bending moment, while for normal tankers and ore carriers with the machinery aft, the sagging condition gives the highest bending moment.

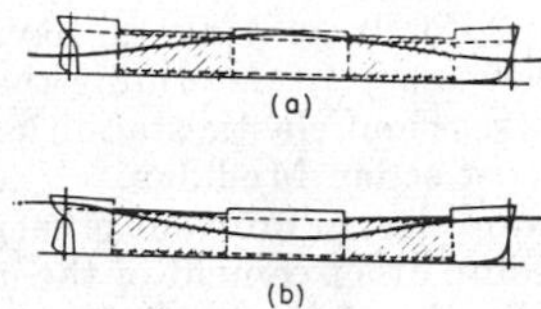

Fig. 7. Hogging (*a*) and sagging (*b*) conditions of a vessel. (*Rossell and Chapman.*)

Weight, buoyancy, and load curves (Figs. 8 and 9) are developed for the ship for the determination of shear and moment. The weight curves include the weights of the hull, superstructure, rudder, end castings, forgings, masts, booms, all machinery and accessories, solid ballast, anchors, chains, cargo, fuel, supplies, passengers, and baggage. Each individual weight is distributed over a length equal to the distance between frames at the location of that particular weight.

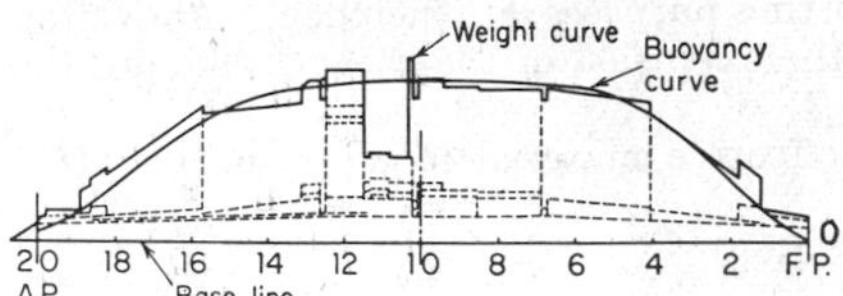

Fig. 8. Representative buoyancy and weight curves for a ship in still water. (*Rossell and Chapman.*)

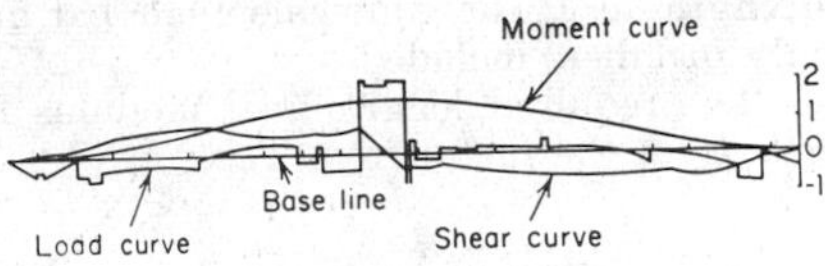

Fig. 9 Representative moment and net-load curves for a ship in still water. (*Rossell and Chapman.*)

Standard Approximations. The bending of the ship, as a beam, will vary approximately as the length and width, or $M = 0.75L^2Bd/(35)^2$, where B = maximum breadth, ft; d = mean draft in the loaded conditions, ft; and L = length between perpendiculars, ft. This equation gives the maximum hogging moment for normal merchant vessels with machinery amidships; it overestimates the moment for fine vessels and underestimates for full vessels.

Great Lakes ships require different treatment because of the shorter prevailing waves. The approximate moment is given by $M = 0.86L^2Bd/36K$, where K is as listed in Table 7.

Table 7*

L	K
340	41.2
360	42
380	43
400	44.3
420	46
440	48
460	50
480	52
500	54.3
520	56.6
540	59
560	61.5
580	64.1
600	67

* From "A Guide for the Analysis of Ship Structures."

The **scantlings** (dimensions required for strength) of a ships's hull can be found by the rules of the American Bureau of Shipping (ABS) if the ship is of the normal merchant type (see "Rules for the Classification and Construction of Steel Vessels," ABS, issued annually).

For large tankers, naval vessels, and unusual structures such as drill rigs, it is necessary to determine the loading by detailed analysis and by the investigation of stress and elastic stability.

Section Modulus. (See also Sec. 5.) Stress determination is based on the section modulus, or moment of inertia, of the hull assumed to be a beam in bending. There is some disagreement of the inclusion of certain structural members in this computation. For ships of the U.S. Navy, the calculation of longitudinal strength is governed by the special specifications for the particular ship and by the design data sheets. (Design Data Sheets, Code 415, BuShips, Dept. of the Navy). For non-military ships, the Load Line Regulations of the U.S. Coast Guard outline the requirements for the calculation of the section modulus. The following statements are abstracted from "Load Lines," USCG, Treasury Dept., 1961.

The **longitudinal modulus** I/Y is the moment of inertia I of the midship section about the neutral axis divided by the distance Y measured from the neutral axis to the top of the strength-deck beam at side, calculated in way of openings but without deductions for rivet holes. Areas are measured in square inches, and distances in feet. Below the strength deck, all continuous longitudinal members, other than parts of underdeck girders required entirely for supporting purposes, are included. Above the strength deck, the gunwhale angle bar and the extension of the shear strake are the only members included.

The required longitudinal modulus for effective material is expressed by fDB, where f is the factor from Table 8.

Table 8*

L	f	L	f
100	1.80	360	9.40
120	2.00	380	10.30
140	2.35	400	11.20
160	2.70	420	12.15
180	3.15	440	13.10
200	3.60	460	14.15
220	4.20	480	15.15
240	4.80	500	16.25
260	5.45	520	17.35
280	6.20	540	18.45
300	6.95	560	19.60
320	7.70	580	20.80
340	8.55	600	22.00

* From Table 43.15-17(c)(5)(ii), "Load Lines," USCG, Treasury Dept., 1961.

The formula applies where L does not exceed 600 ft, B is between $[(L/10) + 5]$ and $[(L/10) + 20]$, and L/D is between 10 and 13.

Before a section modulus and stresses can be determined, it is necessary to have at least a preliminary midship drawing, *i.e.*, a vertical transverse section at the longitudinal center which shows the size and location of the structural members forming the hull.

Box-girder Stress Analysis. In the hogging condition, it is necessary to investigate the stress in the deck and the elastic stability of the bottom structure. The following excerpts from "A Guide for the Analysis of Ship Structures" outline the box-girder analysis. With few exceptions, structures are designed to preclude buckling under normal operation. Thus, in ship-hull design, if the plating is determined to be insufficient to preclude buckling, stiffeners are added to increase the critical compressive strength of the shell. (See Timoshenko, "Elastic Stability," McGraw-Hill.) In the case of buckling, the effective width of plating is not a fixed value but decreases with increasing stress, as indicated by the Von Karman equation

$$\lambda = [\pi t/\sqrt{12(1 - \mu)^2}]\sqrt{E/\sigma}$$

where λ = effective width, ft; t = plating thickness, ft; E = Young's modulus, psi; μ = Poisson's ratio; and σ = maximum compressive stress, psi.

If it is assumed that the maximum compressive stress developed cannot exceed the compressive yield strength of the material and that $\mu = 0.3$, the above equation reduces to the widely used design formula for minimum effective width

$$\lambda = 0.94t\sqrt{E/\sigma_{cy}}$$

where σ_{cy} = compressive yield stress, psi. On the other hand, the effective width in the case of the shear-lag problem does not vary with stress so long as all stresses remain in the elastic range. Figure 10 shows a box girder which schematically represents a portion of the midship section, subject to shear and bending loads.

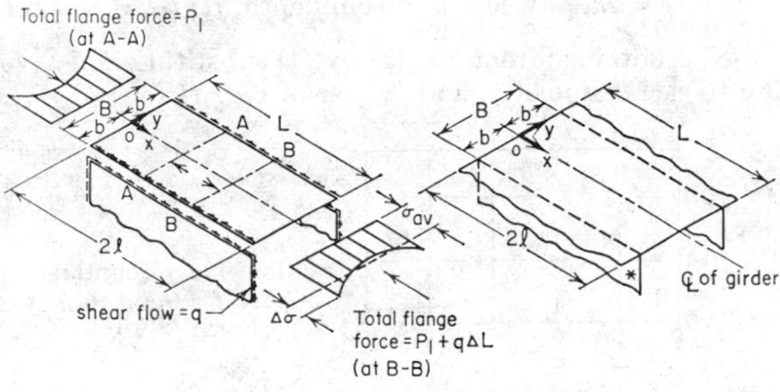

FIG. 10. Schematic representations—box-girder sections. (*Wah, "A Guide for the Analysis of Ship Structures," OTS.*)

Assumed boundary conditions:

$$v = \tau_{xy} = 0,\ 0 < x < L,\ y = 0$$
$$\sigma_y = 0,\ 0 < x < L,\ y = \pm b$$
$$\sigma_x = \sigma_y = 0,\ x = 0,\ L,\ (-b < y < +b)$$

NOTE: v = displacement in y-direction.

Assumed boundary conditions:

$$v = \tau_{xy} = 0,\ 0 < x < L,\ y = 0$$
$$\sigma_y = 0,\ 0 < x < L,\ y = \pm b$$
$$\sigma_x = \sigma_y = 0,\ x = 0,\ L,\ (-b < y < +b)$$

NOTE: All webs identical, equally spaced, and equally loaded.

The correct value of maximum stress is obtained from the elementary flexural formula by incorporating a modified or effective width of flange over which the total flange force is considered to be uniformily distributed at an intensity corresponding to the theoretical maximum stress. Since the resisting moment of the modified section is equal to that of the original section, the effective width of flange will be less than that of the actual flange.

Schade (*Trans. SNA&ME*, Vol. 59, 1951) presents means for calculating the effective widths of sections under various loadings, to wit:

$$\lambda = b\sum\left(\frac{\bar{\lambda}_n}{b}\bigg/S_n\right)K_n\bigg/\sum(K_n/S_n) \qquad \textbf{(1)}$$

where b = actual semiwidth of the flange, ft

λ_n = boundary functions, effective semiwidth of the flange, corresponding to a single value of n, ft (Fig. 11)

K_n = loading function (Table 9)

S_n = section modulus, ft³, of the assembly of flange or flanges and web or webs for a flange semiwidth $\bar{\lambda}_n$

An approximate expression developed by Schade for section modulus of a box girder consisting of two identical webs is

$$S = \frac{h}{3}\,\frac{12A_1A_2 + 4A_W(A_1 + A_2) + A_W^2}{2A_2 + A_W} \tag{2}$$

where S = section modulus, ft³

A_1 = total effective area of upper flange
$= 2\bar{\lambda}t_1$, ft²

A_2 = total effective area of bottom flange
$= 2\bar{\lambda}t_2$, ft²

A_W = total area of both webs
$= 2ht_W$ (where h = semidepth, ft; t_W = thickness of both webs, ft)

S_n is obtained from Eq. (**2**) by (1) substitution of $\bar{\lambda}_n$ for $\bar{\lambda}$ in A_1 and A_2 corresponding to each value of n, and (2) use of Fig. 11 for $\bar{\lambda}_n$. When $A_1 = A_2$ and t_1 or $t_2 \ll h$,

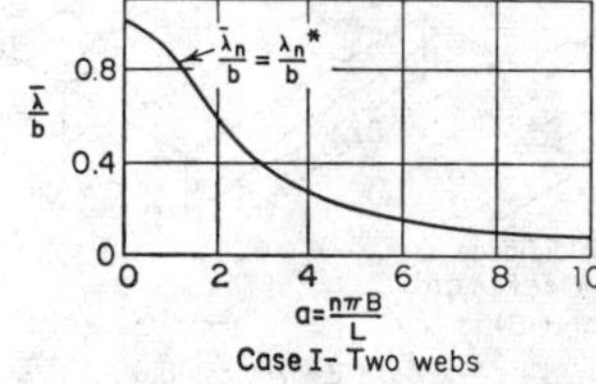

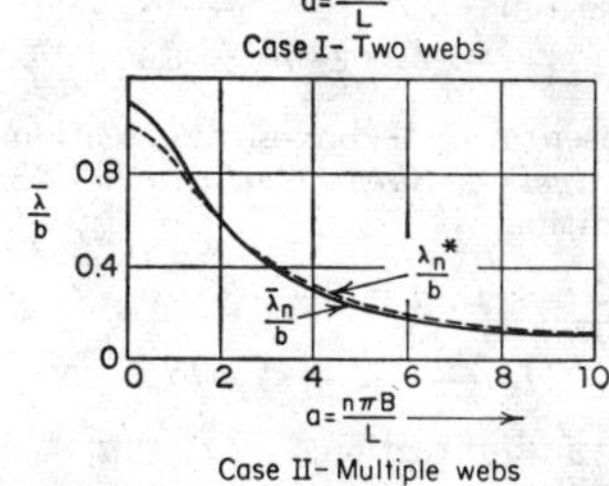

FIG. 11. Boundary functions, $\bar{\lambda}/b$. (*Wah*, "*A Guide for the Analysis of Ship Structures*," *OTS*.)
For $a > 10$

$$\frac{\bar{\lambda}_n}{b}\,\frac{\lambda_n{}^*}{b} = \frac{1.0}{a}$$

$$\frac{\bar{\lambda}_n}{b} = \frac{4}{(3-\mu)(1+\mu)}\,\frac{1}{a} = \frac{4}{(2.7)(1.3)}\,\frac{1}{a} = \frac{1.140}{a}$$

$$\frac{\lambda_n{}^*}{b} = \frac{4}{3+\mu}\,\frac{1}{a} = \frac{4}{3.3}\,\frac{1}{a} = \frac{1.212}{a}$$

the effective section modulus becomes

$$S_{\text{eff}} = 4hbt\left(\frac{\lambda}{b} + \beta\right) \tag{3}$$

where $\beta = 1ht_w/6bt$, and t = flange thickness. Substituting Eq. (**3**) in Eq. (**1**),

$$\frac{\lambda}{b} = \sum \frac{(\bar{\lambda}_n/b)K_n}{(\bar{\lambda}_n/b) + \beta} \Big/ \sum \frac{K_n}{(\bar{\lambda}_n/b) + \beta} \tag{4}$$

The influence of β on effective-width ratio is small; λ/b, for the case of a uniform load, is virtually independent of β. Figure 12 may be used with reasonable accuracy to obtain the effective-width ratio for doubly symmetric box girders. Since the effect of β is small, Fig. 12 may be used for box girders of unequal flange area, provided t/h is small and A_1/A_2 is less than 2. For a sinusoidal bending moment, Eq. (**5**) may be used. (Vedeler, "Grillage Beams in Ships and Similar Structures," Grondahl and Sons, Oslo.)

$$\frac{\lambda}{b} = \frac{1 + [\sinh(\pi B/L)/\pi b/L]}{1 - \cosh(\pi B/L)} \tag{5}$$

Table 9. Loading Functions K_n*

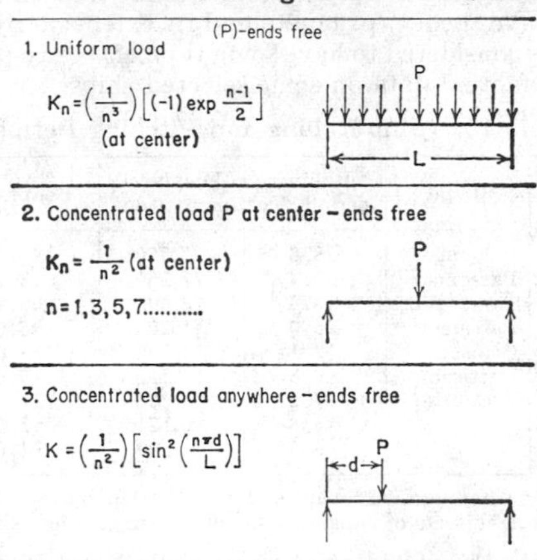

(P)-ends free

1. Uniform load

$K_n = \left(\frac{1}{n^3}\right)\left[(-1) \exp \frac{n-1}{2}\right]$ (at center)

2. Concentrated load P at center – ends free

$K_n = \frac{1}{n^2}$ (at center)

$n = 1, 3, 5, 7 \ldots\ldots$

3. Concentrated load anywhere – ends free

$K = \left(\frac{1}{n^2}\right)\left[\sin^2\left(\frac{n\pi d}{L}\right)\right]$

* From Wah, "A Guide for the Analysis of Ship Structures," OTS.

Since a uniform loading produces a bending moment not too different from a sinusoidal moment, the expression may be used directly to obtain an approximate value for

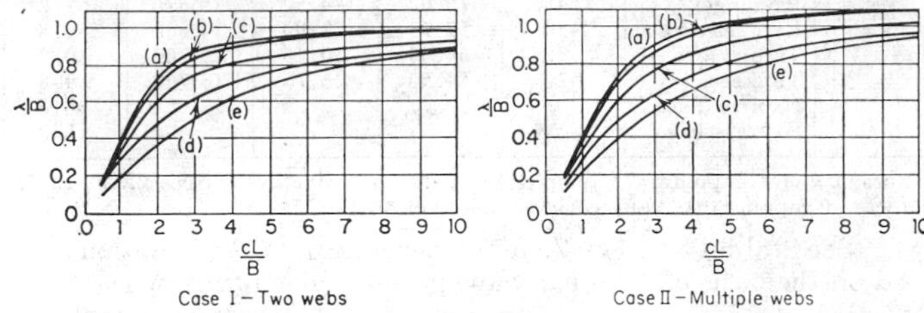

FIG. 12. Effective-width ratios λ/b: (*a*) uniform load; (*b*) sine load; (*c*) central load, $\beta \to \infty$; (*d*) central load, $\beta = 0.167$; (*e*) central load, $\beta \to 0$. Note: cL is distance between points of zero bending moment. (*Wah, "A Guide for the Analysis of Ship Structures," OTS.*)

effective width under a uniform load. For gross design estimates with a uniform loading, Schade recommends

$$\frac{\lambda}{b} = \frac{1.1}{1 + 2(cL/B)^2} \qquad \text{if } cL/B > 2 \tag{6}$$

EXAMPLE. For a box girder 16 ft deep, 40 ft wide, and 160 ft long, flange thickness = 1 in., web thickness = 0.5 in. uniformly loaded, $L = 160$ ft, $B = 40$ ft, $b = 8$ ft, $t_w = 1.0$ in., $t_1 = t_2 = 1.0$ in., $L/B = 4$, $c = 1$ (simply supported), and $cL/B = 4$

From Fig. 12, $\lambda/b = 0.91$, and the effective flange width is $0.91 \times 40 = 36.4$ ft. This flange width should be used in calculating maximum stress and deflection. In Eq. (**3**), substitute $\beta = (1 \times 8 \times 1)/(6 \times 20) = 0.066$ or $S_{\text{eff}} = (4 \times 8 \times 20/12)(0.91 + 0.066) = 52 \text{ ft}^3$.

SHIP MOTIONS

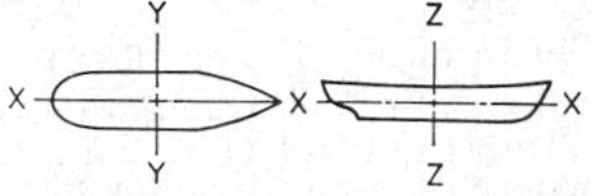

FIG. 13. Conventional ship coordinate axes.

The motion of any floating object has six degrees of freedom. Figure 13 shows the conventional coordinate axes for a ship. Oscillatory movement along axis xx is called **surge;** along axis yy, **side sway;** and along zz, **heave.** Rotation about xx is called **roll;** about yy, **pitch;** and about zz, **yaw.** Normally, the important motions are heave, pitch, and roll. Yaw is important in considering directional stability and steering.

Present methods of analysis of ship movements are limited by inadequate data to the use of trochoidal wave theory (p. 11–60) and its extension by a sine or cosine function. Thus, the ship is considered to have some type of steady-state harmonic motion. Tables 10 and 11 give factual data on some selected ships.

Table 10. Ship Rolling and Pitching Periods*

Ship	Type	Rolling period, sec	Displacement, tons	Beam, ft	*GM*, ft
America	Passenger	28.0	27,500	74.3	1.40
Mt. Vernon	Passenger	20.4	27,250	72.2	2.50
Covington.	Passenger	18.3	22,000	65.4	2.50
Conte di Savoia	Passenger	26.0	41,200	96.0	3.14
Salt Lake City	Cruiser	12.1	11,500	64.0	5.55
Revenge	Battleship	16.8	13,370	75.0	3.29
Yamato	Battleship	17.2	69,200	121.0	9.16
Kowa Maru		13.8	10,121	52.5	2.16
Akebono Maru		6.3	399	24.6	3.48

* From Rossell and Chapman, "Principles of Naval Architecture," SNA&ME, 1947, and Soc. of Naval Architects of Japan, 60th Anniversary Series, Vol. 6, 1960.

Table 11. Data on Periods of Roll and Pitch*

Ship	Type	Length, ft	Breadth, ft	Draft, ft	Displacement, tons	Period of pitch, sec	Period of roll, sec
Montcalm	Passenger	546	70.00	24.50	19,670	7.2	17.0
London Mariner	Express cargo	450	57.75	27.00	14,660	6.8	9.0
San Gerardo	Tanker	530	64.00	30.75	25,700	10.2	10.0
San Tirso	Tanker	420	54.50	26.75	13,700	9.8	9.0
Aquitania	Express Pass.	...	.....	.....	......	8.0	....
Lusitania	Express Pass.	...	.....	.....	......	8.0	....

* From Rossell and Chapman, "Principles of Naval Architecture," SNA&ME, 1947, and Soc. of Naval Architects of Japan, 60th Anniversary Series, Vol. 6, 1960.

Rolling. (See Stability, p. 11–47, for nomenclature.) An equation for rolling can be developed on the basis of a regular wave pattern (sine form), where Fig. 14 identifies the wave parameters; λ = wave length, ft; H = wave height, ft; T_1 = wave period, sec; t = time, sec; and θ_1 = instantaneous wave slope, radians. Figure 15 shows the ship in an arbitrary position on the wave when θ = angle of heel from the vertical. The equation of unresisted rolling in waves is

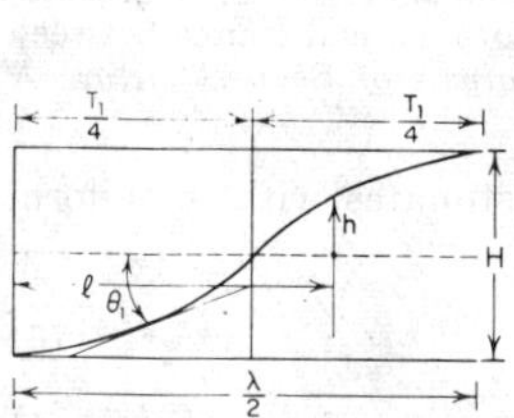

Fig. 14. Important wave parameters.

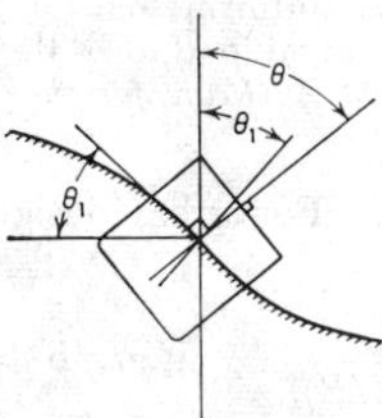

Fig. 15. Ship in an arbitrary rolling position in waves.

$$\frac{d^2\theta}{dt^2} + \frac{4\pi^2}{T^2}\left(\theta - \phi \sin \frac{\pi}{T_1} t\right) = 0$$

where T = ship's natural period of roll, sec; $\phi = \Pi(H/\lambda)$, radians; and t = time, sec.

The general solution of this equation is

$$\theta = \frac{1}{1 + (T^2/T_1{}^2)} \phi \sin\left(\frac{2\pi}{T_1} t\right) + \left(W_o \frac{T}{2\pi} \sin \frac{2\pi t}{T} + \gamma \cos \frac{2\pi t}{T}\right)$$

where W_o = initial angular velocity, radians per sec; and γ = initial angular displacement, radians.

The ship's period T can be found from

$$T = \frac{2\pi K}{\sqrt{g(GM)}} = \frac{1.108K}{\sqrt{GM}}$$

where GM is metacentric height, ft; and K is the radius of gyration, estimated from

$$\left(\frac{K}{B}\right)^2 = f\left[C_b \cdot C_u + 1.10C_u(1 - C_b)\left(\frac{H}{d} - 2.20\right) + \frac{H^2}{B^2}\right]$$

where K = virtual radius of gyration, ft
B = moulded breadth of the ship, ft
C_b = block coefficient (L_{pp} × beam at waterline × draft/volumetric displacement)
C_u = ratio of the total area of the upper deck to the area of its circumscribed rectangle
H = effective depth of the ship = $D + A/L_{pp}$, ft
D = moulded depth of the ship, ft
A = sum of the projected lateral areas of erections and deckhouses. When the breadth of a deckhouse is less than 0.7 × beam, the area must be multiplied by the ratio of the breadth of the deckhouse to the breadth of the ship.
L_{pp} = length between perpendiculars of the ship, ft
d = mean draft (moulded draft, in case the ship has block keel), ft
f = a constant dependent on ship type, to wit: 0.125 for passenger, intermediate passenger, and cargo ships; 0.133 for oil tankers; 0.200 for bonito fishers; 0.177 for whalers.

For warships, the formula is

$$\left(\frac{K}{B_u}\right)^2 = f\left[C_b \cdot C_e + 1.10C_u(1 - C_b)\left(\frac{H_n}{d} - 2.20\right) + \frac{H_n}{B_n{}^2}\right]$$

where B_u = maximum breadth under water, ft
C_e = exposed-deck-area coefficient
H_n = $D + A_n/L_{pp}$, ft
D = depth from top of keel to upper deck, ft
A_n = sum of the projected lateral areas between the upper or forecastle deck and the lower bridge deck, including the lateral area of the turrets, sq ft
f = 0.177 for battleships
= 0.172 for cruisers, destroyers, and torpedo boats

For all practical purposes, the unresisted-rolling equation is a sufficiently accurate approximation of the more complex resisted-rolling periods. However, the unresisted approximation gives poor results for the amplitude of rolling.

Pitching and heaving are presently evaluated on the assumption of a regular wave pattern (sine or cosine function of the period and amplitude) because of the inadequacy of data on longitudinal ship motions. Korvin-Kroukovsky and Jacobs (Pitching and Heaving Motions of a Ship in Regular Waves," SNA&ME, 1957) give the linear equations of pitching and heaving as

$$a\ddot{z} + b\dot{z} + cz + d\ddot{\theta} + e\dot{\theta} + g\theta = F_o \cos(\omega t + \sigma)$$
$$A\ddot{\theta} + B\dot{\theta} + C\theta + D\ddot{Z} + E\dot{Z} + GZ = M_o \cos(\omega t + \tau)$$

where F_o and M_o are, respectively, the amplitudes of the heaving force and the pitching moment; σ and τ are the phase angles at which the maximum force and moment occur; ω is the frequency of heaving and pitching; and t is the time. Estimates of the coefficients a to g and A to G are more easily made from Gerritsma, Shipmotions in Longitudinal Waves, *Netherland Research Center TNO for Shipbuilding and Navigation Report* 35*S*, Feb., 1960. Results are of doubtful validity for the comparison of the seaworthiness of alternate designs. The coefficients from this report are given in Table 12 for a typical cargo ship.

The equations account for the coupling which exists between the pitching and heaving motions of a ship. Figure 16 shows the results of the calculation for the Mariner, neglecting the coupling terms.

Table 12. Coefficients for Ship-motion Equations of a Mariner-type Cargo Ship*

$A = 1.605 \times 10^7$ ton-ft sec²
$B = 0.374 \times 10^7$ ton-ft sec
$C = 0.740 \times 10^7$ ton-ft
$D = 0$ ton sec
$E = 7.60 \times 10^3$ ton sec
$G = 2.52 \times 10^3$ ton
$a = 1.145 \times 10^3$ ton sec² per ft
$b = 0.333 \times 10^3$ ton sec per ft
$c = 0.833 \times 10^3$ ton per ft
$d = 0$ ton sec²
$e = -2.95 \times 10^4$ ton sec
$g = 2.52 \times 10^3$ ton
$F_o = 1.965 \times 10^3$ ton
$M_o = 5.10 \times 10^5$ ton-ft
$\sigma = 90$ deg
$\tau = 28$ deg

* See Arnott, "Design and Construction of Steel Merchant Ships," SNA&ME, 1955.

The natural pitching period can be found by the same expression as that used for the rolling period, where all the terms are the same except K, which is the longitudinal, K_L, rather than transverse radius of gyration. A good approximation is $K_L = L/4$, where L is the length of the ship. K_L should be increased by 80 percent approx to

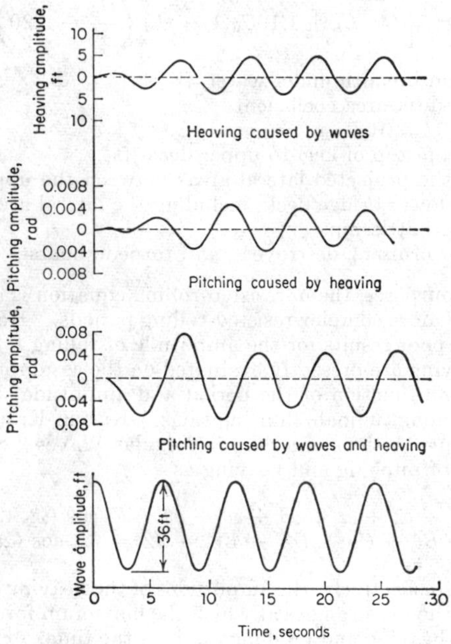

FIG. 16. Curves of a Mariner heaving and pitching in regular waves; $\lambda = 520$ ft, $H = 36$ ft. (*Panel on Nuclear Marine Propulsion, Jour. I Mar E, Oct.*, 1962.)

account for the added mass of entrained water, or $K_L = 1.8(L/4)$. Natural heaving periods can be estimated from the same equations because of the close correspondence between heaving and pitching periods. (For details on ship motions, see Vossers, "Resistance, Propulsion and Steering of Ships, Part C, Behavior of Ships in Waves," Technical Publishing Co., 1962.)

HYDROFOIL CRAFT AND AIR-CUSHION VEHICLES

BY

Finn C. Michelsen

REFERENCES: Hovering Craft and Hydrofoil, *International Review of Air Cushion Vehicles and Hydrofoils,* Kalerghi-McLeavy Publications, London. *Proc. of the National Meeting on Hydrofoils and Air Cushion Vehicles,* IAeS, Washington, 1962. "Third Symposium on Naval Hydrodynamics. High Performance Ships," U.S. Government Printing Office, 1960. "Study of Hydrofoil Seacraft," Vols. I and II, Grumman Aircraft Engineering Corp. Report to Maritime Administration, Dept. of Commerce.

Although the basic principles of the hydrofoil craft and the air-cushion vehicle (ground-effect machine, GEM) have been known for a long time, it was only during the 1950s that these devices were developed to an extent where they offered competition to other, established modes of transportation. Both types are faster than ships and slower than aircraft; they are less able to carry payload than a ship but will probably be better than aircraft in the future. Their chief commercial advantage over aircraft is their ease of access to and from any city or center located on the waterfront. Collectively, they are referred to as **interface vehicles.** Some forms of the air-cushion vehicle are amphibious, a feature which offers advantages where port facilities are limited. In addition, the amphibious type will operate over waters completely or partially covered with ice. The technology of interface vehicles is in a state of rapid development, and there is reason to believe that interface vehicles will revolutionize transportation in some areas. Figure 1 illustrates the comparative performance of several types of transportation vehicles.

HYDROFOIL CRAFT

Support System. Under foilborne conditions, the support of the hydrofoil craft is derived from the dynamic lift generated by the foil system. The craft itself is lifted clear from the water. The special problems pertaining to hydrofoil-craft operation and directly related to the conditions presented by water waves, high fluid density, surface piercing of foils and struts, stability, control, and cavitation and ventilation of foils have given rise to foil-system configurations defined as follows (see Fig. 2):

1. Longitudinal area distribution—(*a*) airplane, (*b*) tandem, (*c*) canard.
2. Lateral area distribution—(*a*) split, (*b*) non-split.
3. Vertical configuration—(*a*) surface-piercing, (*b*) fully submerged, (*c*) hybrid surface-piercing, (*d*) ladder.
4. Foil section—(*a*) subcavitating, (*b*) supercavitating, (*c*) ventilated.
5. Struts—(*a*) subcavitating, (*b*) base-vented.

The hydrofoil craft has actually three modes of operation: hullborne, takeoff, and foilborne. Design must be a compromise between the varied requirements of these operating conditions. This may be difficult, as with propeller design, where maximum thrust is often required at takeoff speed (normally about one-half the operating speed). A propeller designed for maximum efficiency at takeoff will have a smaller efficiency at design speeds, and vice versa. This is complicated by the need for supercavitating propellers at operating speeds over 50 knots. Two sets of propeller may be needed—in such a case, one for hullborne operation and the other for foilborne operation. The selection of a surface-piercing or a fully submerged foil design is determined from specified operating conditions and the permissible degree of complexity. A surface-piercing system is inherently stable, as a deviation from the equilibrium

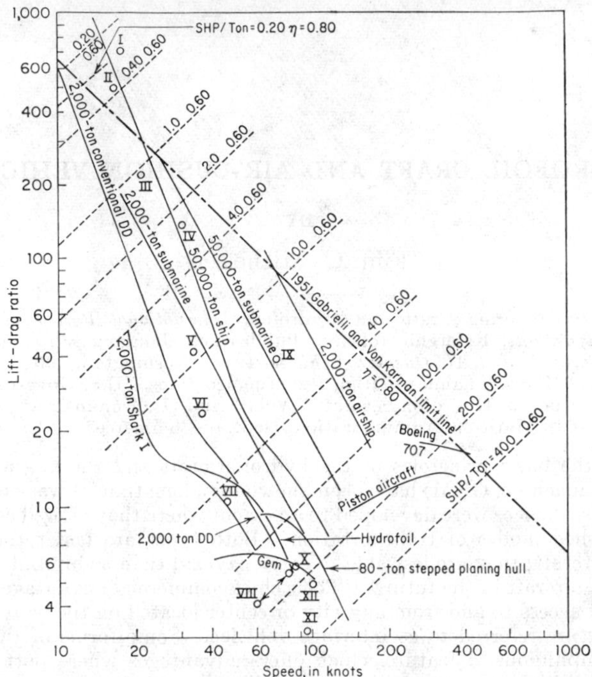

FIG. 1. Lift-drag ratio versus calm-weather speed for various vehicles. (*Mandel, Trans. SNA&ME*, 1962.)

No.	Vehicle	Weight, tons	Installed power, hp	Length, ft	η
		Waterborne vehicles			
I	Tanker	137,000	34,400	926	0.67
II	Tanker	36,500	11,000	575	0.75
III	Mariner cargo ship	22,500	19,250	520	0.75
IV	Passenger liner	68,500	160,000	962	0.61
V	Cruiser	10,500	84,000	560	0.59
VI	Destroyer	3,500	62,000	426	0.59
VII	Hydrofoil	100	5,500	...	0.55
VIII	Hydrofoil (Marad)	90	16,800	...	0.55
		Airborne vehicles			
IX	Airship	139	2,900	781	0.61
X	Helicopter S-58	6	900	...	0.65
XI	Helicopter S-64	17	5,400	...	0.65
XII	Gem (Marad)	100	22,000	140	0.65

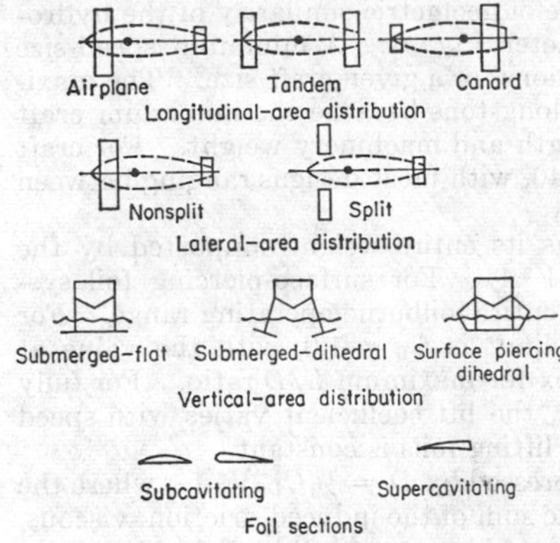

FIG. 2. Some foil arrangements and sections.

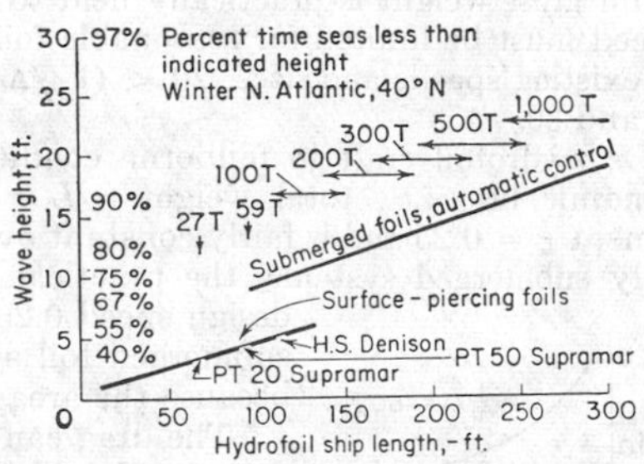

FIG. 3. Wave height versus length of hydrofoil craft. (*Proc. Nat. Meeting on Hydrofoils and Air Cushion Vehicles*, 1962.)

position of the craft results in corrective lift forces. Fully submerged foil designs, on the other hand, are not stable by themselves and require a depth-control system for satisfactory operation. Such a control system will, however, permit operation of the submerged-foil design in higher waves, as shown in Fig. 3.

Notation

a = length of jet curtain, ft
A_F = projected area of foils, sq ft
C_L, C_D = non-dimensional lift and drag coefficients
D = drag force, lb
D_e = equivalent diameter, ft
f_m = mass-flow coefficient
h = cushion height, ft
h_j = head at cushion nozzle, psf
Δh = head rise through lifting impeller, psf
k_p = non-dimensional correction factor to account for the pressure being zero outside the jet
L = lift force of foil system, lb
L/D = lift-drag ratio
$(L/D)_e$ = equivalent lift-drag ratio
m = mass flow, lb per sec
P_N = nozzle power, lb-ft per sec
p_o = air-cushion pressure, psf
S = cushion plan area, sq ft
sfc = specific fuel consumption, lb per hp-hr
T_j = total jet thrust, lb
t_o = thickness of jet curtain, ft
V = speed of craft, fps
V_j = mean jet velocity, fps
V_k = speed of craft, knots
W_E = empty weight of craft, lb
W_G = total gross weight of craft, lb
Δ_t = total weight of craft, long tons (2,240 lb)
θ = angle of jet with respect to the horizon
η_d = duct efficiency
η_i = efficiency of impeller
ρ = density of water or air, slugs per cu ft

General Design Formulas. A good measure of geometric similarity of the hydrofoil craft is provided by the speed-size parameter $V_k/\Delta_t^{1/6}$. A minimum speed-size parameter of 20 will avoid excessive foil dimensions for a given craft size. The maximum gross weight is practically held to 1,000 long tons because the maximum craft speed must be limited for reasonable foil strength and machinery weight. For craft of existing speeds and sizes, $20 < (V_k/\Delta_t^{1/6}) < 40$, with most designs ranging between 20 and 30.

A hydrofoil craft in foilborne condition has its entire weight supported by the dynamic lift; *i.e.*, total weight $= L = \frac{1}{2}C_L\rho V^2 A_F$. For surface-piercing foil systems, $C_L = 0.25$ and is fairly constant over the entire foilborne operating range. For fully submerged systems, the practical upper limit is $C_L = 1.0$, with the value at design speed 0.26 approx for maximum L/D ratio. For fully submerged foil systems, the lift coefficient varies with speed because the area of the lifting foils is constant.

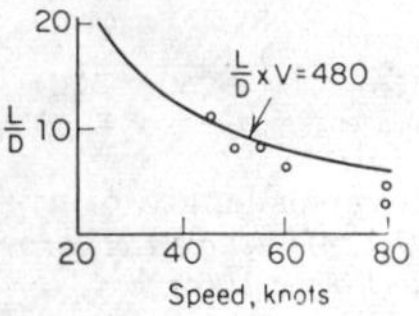

The drag can be expressed by $D = \frac{1}{2}C_D\rho V^2 A_F$, where the drag coefficient C_D is the sum of the induced, friction, viscous, form, wave, and parasitic components. The performance can most readily be judged by the lift-drag ratio L/D, which is a function of speed (Fig. 4).

FIG. 4. Vehicle lift-drag ratio versus speed. (*Proc. Nat. Meeting on Hydrofoils and Air Cushion Vehicles,* 1962.)

The operating range of a hydrofoil craft depends upon speed, size, and type of propulsion machinery. In common use are high-speed lightweight Diesel engines (specific weight = 4–8 lb per hp, sfc = 0.4 lb per hp-hr) and gas turbines (specific weight = 0.5–1.0 lb per hp, sfc = 0.55–0.75 lb per hp-hr). Maximum practical operating range of the hydrofoil craft is about 500 nm. The empty weight of a hydrofoil craft can be estimated by $W_E = 800(W_G/1000)^{0.97}$. Table 1 gives data on two existing designs of the surface-piercing type, each with several years of successful commercial operation.

Table 1

Length, over-all	68 ft	89 ft
Displacement, fully loaded	28 tons	60 tons
Payload	6.8 tons	15.0 tons
Number of passengers	75	140
Max power	1,350 hp	2,700 hp
Max speed	42 knots	40 knots
Cruising speed	38 knots	36 knots
Power at cruising speed	920 hp	1,000 hp
Range	300 nm	300 nm
Power per ton	48.2 hp per ton	45 hp per ton
Power at cruising, payload	135 hp per ton	134 hp per ton
Power at cruising, passengers	12.3 hp per pass.	14.3 hp per pass.

AIR-CUSHION VEHICLES (ACV)

Present ACV designs are primarily intended for use on lakes and sheltered coastal waters. These vehicles can operate over moderate waves, as well as over mudbanks and swamps, and can climb beaches that are not too steep. The basic concept of the ACV has been known for a great many years. The practical application of the principle of utilizing the ground effect is recent, with the first license to carry paying passengers issued in Great Britain in 1962.

Basically, the ACV rides on a cushion of compressed air generated and maintained in the space between the vehicle and the surface over which it moves or hovers. The cushion is produced in several different ways, as illustrated in Fig. 5. Within the existing technology, the peripheral jet configuration offers the simplest and most efficient means of obtaining and maintaining a stable cushion pressure. The basic principle of this craft is illustrated in Fig. 6 and shows that the cushion pressure acting on the curtain and the rate of change of momentum in a radial direction are equal; that is, $p_o h = \rho V_j^2 t_o(1 + \cos\theta)$. Since total jet thrust $T_j = \rho V_j^2 t_o a$, it follows that $(W/T_j) = (S/ah)(1 + \cos\theta)$ and $W_G = Sp_o$. If the air intake is facing forward, the total head at the cushion nozzle will be $h_j = \rho V^2/2 + \Delta h - k\rho V_j^2/2$, where the head rise through the lifting impeller is Δh and the duct loss is k times the dynamic head at the nozzle. With m the mass flow and P_i the impeller-shaft power, $\eta_i P_i = \frac{m}{\rho}[h_j(1 + k\rho V_j^2/2h_j) - \rho V_j^2/2] = \frac{m}{\rho}[h_j/\eta_d - \rho V_j^2/2]$. Defining available power at the nozzle as $P_N = mh_j/\rho$, then $\rho P_N/mp_o = h_j/p_o$.

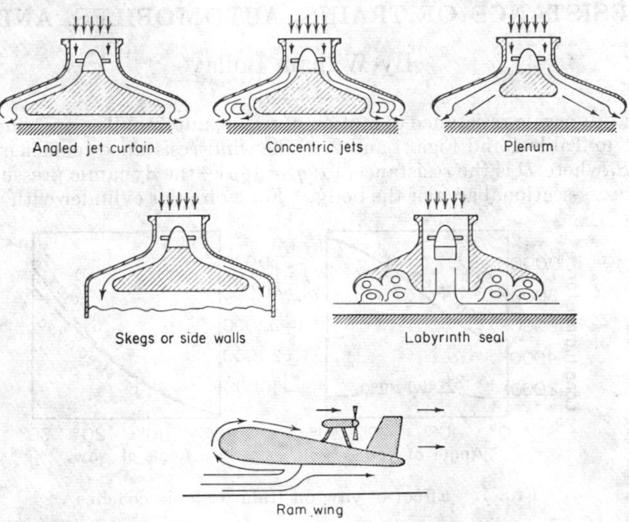

FIG. 5. Configurations of the air-cushion principle.

By the use of Bernoulli's equation, $h_j \simeq K_p p_o + \rho V_j^2/2$, or $h_j/p_o \simeq k_p + h/4t$, where $0.5 < k_p < 1$ and $t = (1 + \cos\theta)t_o/2$. The approximate mass flow is given by $m \simeq \rho V_j a t_o$ or by momentum equation $m = a[t_o h \rho p_o/(1 + \cos\theta)]^{0.5}$. Eliminating h, the mass-flow coefficient can be written

$$f_m = m/at_o(2\rho p_o)^{0.5} \simeq (h_j/p_o - k_p)^{0.5}$$

These formulas show that the peripheral-jet ACV derives a large part of its lift from the cushion pressure. For economical operation, the lift so derived should be at least five times the vertical jet thrust. This puts a practical limit on the cushion height. In general, $h/D_e < 0.1$, where $D_e = (4S/\pi)^{0.5}$. The cushion height will decrease with vehicle speed. Low cushion pressure will generally produce large structures for a given pay load, whereas high pressures will result in large power losses. A practical design range is $p_o = 30$ to 60 psf. Recently a large increase in the height of air cushion (4 to 5 ft operational heights) has been realized by the use of flexible rubber trunks and skirts.

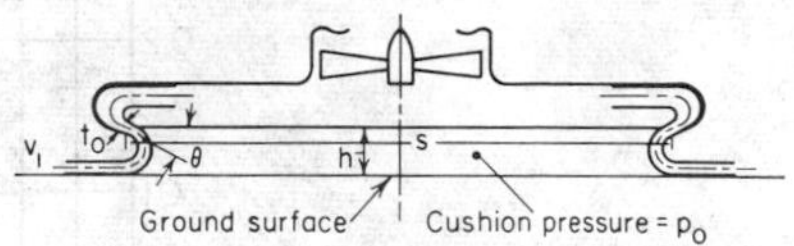

FIG. 6. Simple air-cushion configuration.

Because power is needed to support the vehicle, the equivalent L/D ratio is not so high as for the hydrofoil craft. A reasonable range of $(L/D)_e$ is 2.5 to 5, with $(L/D)_e$ defined by $(L/D)_e = W_G V_K/325.7(\text{hp})_{\text{total}}$.

Although the ACV can hover at zero speed, its principle of design favors high operational speed (practical range is 50 to 100 knots). To avoid impact damage, excessive structural weight prohibits speeds much above the upper value. Saving in weight is a key to economic success. Pay loads are in the order of 30 to 45 percent of all up weight. There seem to be no limiting factors as to size other than those resulting from structural considerations.

AIR RESISTANCE OF TRAINS, AUTOMOBILES, AND SHIPS

By William Bollay

The fluid-dynamic resistance to motion of trains, automobiles, and ships is reflected by the data in Table 1 and Figs. 1 and 2. The wind-resistance coefficient of a body is $C_D = D/qS$, where D is the resistance, lb; $q = \frac{1}{2}\rho V^2$ the dynamic pressure; and S the maximum cross-sectional area of the body. For a circular cylinder with wind blowing

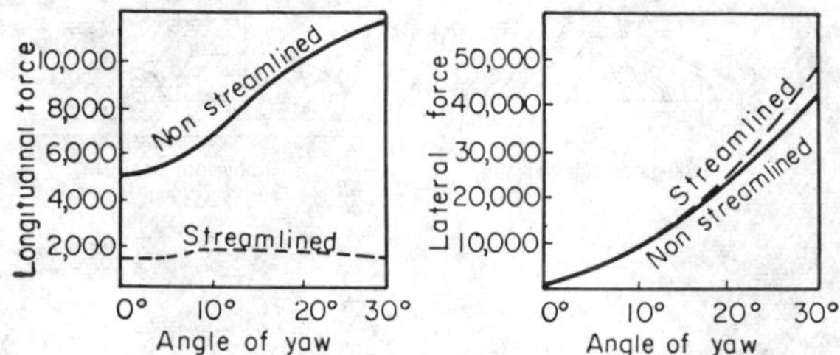

FIG. 1. Effect of yaw on train with six coaches.

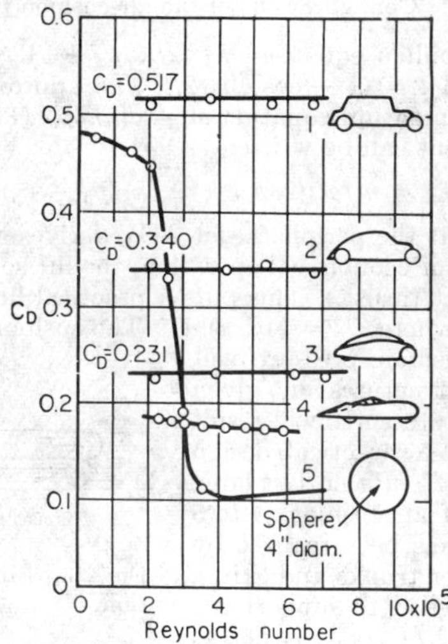

FIG. 2. Wind-resistance coefficients of various bodies.

along the axis, $C_D \approx 0.90$. For a streamlined body such as an airship shape, $C_D \approx 0.040$. The values of C_D for trains, automobiles, and ships lie in this range, as shown by Table 1.

Even though the air resistance due to the motion of a body such as a ship may be a negligibly small percentage of its total resistance, this may be magnified many times when a wind arises. For a ship with a speed of 10 knots, the air resistance is about

2½ percent of its total resistance. When the ship is proceeding against a 20 knot wind, the wind resistance becomes 22½ percent of the total resistance. Similarly, a small side wind may cause appreciable increase in the resistance of bodies such as ships or railroad trains. Figure 1 (Johansen, The Air-resistance of Passenger Trains, *Proc. I Mech E*, **134**, 1936, p. 111) shows that the resistance of a non-streamlined train may

Table 1. Wind-resistance Coefficient for Trains, Automobiles, and Ships

Non-streamlined locomotive* and tender (length 110–120 ft)	C_D = 0.80–1.05
Streamlined locomotive and tender (length 110–120 ft)	0.35–0.45
Non-streamlined railroad car	0.40
Streamlined railroad car	0.15
Conventional-type automobile (sedan)†	0.52
Moderately streamlined automobile† (rounded back)	0.34
Well-streamlined passenger automobile†	0.23
Streamlined racing-type automobile†	0.17
Passenger ship, non-streamlined‡	0.90

* Lipetz, Air Resistance of Railroad Equipment, *Trans. ASNE*, 1937.
† Schmidt, *ZVdI*, **82**, 1938, p. 188.
‡ Taylor, "The Speed and Power of Ships," chap. 10.2, 1933.

be doubled when the relative wind comes from an angle of yaw, although that of the streamlined train remains practically constant.

Figure 2 (Schmidt, *ZVdI*, **82**, 1938, p. 188) shows the variation of drag coefficient with Reynolds number for various automobile models compared with that of a sphere. Apparently there is no scale effect on the automobile tests except on the highly streamlined model whose resistance is largely skin friction.

AERONAUTICS

BY

Lewis H. Abraham

REFERENCES: National Advisory Committee for Aeronautics, *Technical Reports* (designated *NACA-TR* with number), *Technical Notes* (*NACA-TN* with number), and *Technical Memoranda* (*NACA-TM* with number). British Aeronautical Research Committee *Reports and Memoranda* (designated *Br. ARC-R & M* with number). *Ergeb. Aerodynamischen Versuchsanstalt zu Göttingen.* Diehl, "Engineering Aerodynamics," Ronald. Reid, "Applied Wing Theory," McGraw-Hill. Durand, "Aerodynamic Theory," Springer. Prandtl-Tietjens, "Fundamentals of Hydro- and Aeromechanics," and "Applied Hydro- and Aeromechanics," McGraw-Hill. Goldstein, "Modern Developments in Fluid Dynamics," Oxford. Millikan, "Aerodynamics of the Airplane," Wiley. Von Mises, "Theory of Flight," McGraw-Hill. Hoerner, "Aerodynamic Drag," Hoerner. Glauert, "The Elements of Airfoil and Airscrew Theory," Cambridge. Milne-Thompson, "Theoretical Hydrodynamics," Macmillan. Munk, "Fluid Dynamics for Aircraft Designers," and "Principles of Aerodynamics," Ronald. Abraham, "Structural Design of Missiles and Spacecraft," McGraw-Hill. "U.S. Standard Atmosphere, 1962," U.S. Government Printing Office.

Definitions

Aeronautics is the science and art of flight and includes aviation, the operation of aircraft heavier than air (airplanes). An **aircraft** is any weight-carrying device designed to be supported by the air, either by buoyancy or by dynamic action. An **airplane** is a mechanically driven fixed-wing aircraft, heavier than air, which is supported by the dynamic reaction of the air against its wings. A **helicopter** is a kind of aircraft lifted and moved by a large propeller mounted horizontally above the fuselage. It differs from the **autogiro** in that this propeller is turned by motor power and there is no auxiliary propeller for forward motion. A **ground-effect machine (GEM)** is a heavier-than-air surface vehicle which operates in close proximity to the earth's surface (over land or water), never touching except at rest, being separated from the surface by a cushion or film of air, however thin, and depending entirely upon aerodynamic forces for propulsion and control.

Aerodynamics is the branch of dynamics that treats of the motion of air and other gaseous fluids and of the forces acting on solids in motion relative to such fluids. Aerodynamics falls into velocity ranges, depending upon whether the velocity is below or above the local speed of sound in the fluid. The velocity range below the local speed of sound is called the **subsonic** regime. Where the velocity is above the local speed of sound, the flow is said to be **supersonic.** The term **transonic** refers to flows in which both subsonic and supersonic regions are present. The **hypersonic** regime is that speed range usually in excess of five times the speed of sound.

Standard Atmosphere

The standard atmosphere of Table 1 is a revised U.S. Standard Atmosphere, adapted by the United States Committee on Extension to the Standard Atmosphere (COESA) in 1962. For all practical purposes, the U.S. Standard Atmosphere, 1962, is in agreement with the ICAO Standard Atmosphere over their common altitude range.

The values given up to about 65,000 ft are designated as **standard.** The region from 65,000 to 105,000 ft is designated **proposed standard.** U.S. Standard Atmosphere, 1962, gives data out to 2,320,000 ft, however, the region from 105,000 to 295,000

Table 1. U.S. Standard Atmosphere, 1962

Altitude h, ft	Temp T, deg F	Pressure ratio, p/p_0	Density ratio, ρ/ρ_0	$(\rho_0/\rho)^{0.5}$	Speed of sound V_s, ft per sec^{-1}
0	59.00	1.0000	1.0000	1.000	1,116
5,000	41.17	0.8320	0.8617	1.077	1,097
10,000	23.34	0.6877	0.7385	1.164	1,077
15,000	5.51	0.5643	0.6292	1.261	1,057
20,000	−24.62	0.4595	0.5328	1.370	1,036
25,000	−30.15	0.3711	0.4481	1.494	1,015
30,000	−47.99	0.2970	0.3741	1.635	995
35,000	−65.82	0.2353	0.3099	1.796	973
36,089	−69.70	0.2234	0.2971	1.835	968
40,000	−69.70	0.1851	0.2462	2.016	968
45,000	−69.70	0.1455	0.1936	2.273	968
50,000	−69.70	0.1145	0.1522	2.563	968
55,000	−69.70	0.09001	0.1197	2.890	968
60,000	−69.70	0.07078	0.09414	3.259	968
65,000	−69.70	0.05566	0.07403	3.675	968
65,800	−69.70	0.05356	0.07123	3.747	968
70,000	−67.30	0.04380	0.05789	4.156	971
75,000	−64.55	0.03452	0.04532	4.697	974
80,000	−61.81	0.02725	0.03553	5.305	977
85,000	−59.07	0.02155	0.02790	5.986	981
90,000	−56.32	0.01707	0.02195	6.970	984
95,000	−53.58	0.01354	0.01730	7.600	988
100,000	−50.84	0.01076	0.01365	8.559	991

ft is designated **tentative,** and that portion of the atmosphere above 295,000 ft is termed **speculative.**

The assumed sea-level conditions are: pressure, p_0 = 29.91 in. (760 mm) Hg = 2,116.22 psf; mass density, ρ_0 = 0.002378 slugs per ft^3, (0.001225 g per cm^3); T_0 = 59 F (15 C).

Upper Atmosphere

High-altitude atmospheric data have been obtained directly from balloons, sounding rockets, and satellites and indirectly from observations of meteors, aurora, radio waves, light absorption, and sound effects. At relatively low altitudes, the earth's atmosphere is, for aerodynamic purposes, a uniform gas. Above 250,000 ft, day and night standards differ because of dissociation of oxygen by solar radiation. This difference in density is as high as 35 percent, but it is usually aerodynamically negligible above 250,000 ft since forces here will become less than 0.05 percent of their sea-level value for the same velocity.

Temperature profile of the COESA atmosphere is given in Fig. 1. From these data, other properties of the atmosphere can be calculated.

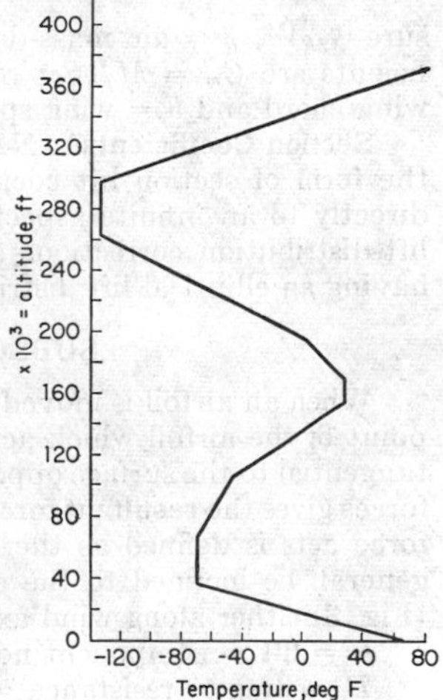

FIG. 1. Temperature as a function of altitude (*COESA*).

Pressure and Density. For all practical purposes, both decrease exponentially with altitude. The variations in T, Fig. 1, are accompanied by slight inflections in the curves of p and ρ, but the deviations from a mean curve are far less than the scatter in test data from various sources. For altitudes above 100,000 ft, pressure and density may be approximated by

$$\log p_0/p = 0.00001910h + 0.0140$$
$$\log \rho_0/\rho = 0.00001890h - 0.1000$$

where h is in ft. At h = 320,000 ft, or about 60 miles, p and ρ are about one-millionth of the sea-level values.

Speed in aeronautics may be given in knots (now standard for USAF, USN, and FAA), miles per hour, feet per second, or meters per second. The international standard mile = 6,076.1155 ft (1,852 m). The basic relations are: 1 knot = 0.5144 m per sec = 1.6877 fps = 1.1508 mph. For additional conversion factors see p. 1–80. High speeds are often given as **Mach number,** or the ratio of the particular speed to the speed of sound in the surrounding air. For additional data see p. 11–96.

Axes. The forces and moments acting on an airplane (and the resultant velocity components) are referred to a set of three mutually perpendicular axes having the origin at the airplane cg and moving with the airplane. At least three sets are in general use in aeronautics. The basic difference in these is in the direction taken for the longitudinal, or x, axis, as follows:

Wind axes: The x axis lies in the direction of the relative wind. This is the system most commonly used, and the one used in this section. It is shown on Fig. 2.

Body axes: The x axis is fixed in the body, usually parallel to the thrust line.

Stability axes: The x axis coincides with the principal inertial axis. This system eliminates the products of inertia in the equations of motion.

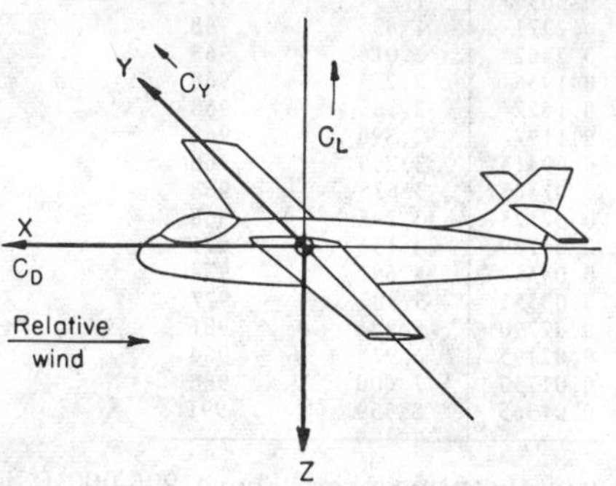

FIG. 2. Wind axes.

Absolute Coefficients. Aerodynamic force and moment data are usually presented in the form of absolute coefficients. Examples of force coefficients are lift $C_L = L/qS$; drag $C_D = D/qS$; side force $C_C = C/qS$; where q is the dynamic pressure $\frac{1}{2}\rho V^2$, ρ = air mass-density, and V = air speed. Examples of moment coefficients are $C_m = M/qSc$; roll $C_l = L/qSb$; and yaw $C_n = N/qSb$; where c = mean wing chord and b = wing span.

Section Coefficients. NACA basic test data on wing sections are usually given in the form of section lift coefficient C_l and section drag coefficient C_d. These apply directly to an infinite aspect ratio or to two-dimensional flow, but aspect-ratio and lift-distribution corrections are necessary in applying to a finite wing. For a wing having an elliptical lift distribution, $C_L = (\pi/4)C_l$.

SUBSONIC AERODYNAMIC FORCES

When an airfoil is moved through the air, the motion produces a pressure at every point of the airfoil which acts normal to the surface. In addition, a frictional force tangential to the surface opposes the motion. The sum of these pressure and frictional forces gives the **resultant force** R acting on the body. The point at which the resultant force acts is defined as the **center of pressure,** c.p. The resultant force R will, in general, be inclined to the airfoil and the relative wind velocity V. It is resolved (Fig. 3) either along wind axes into

L = **lift** = component normal to V

D = **drag** or resistance = component along V

or along body axes into

N = **normal force** = component perpendicular to airfoil chord

T = **tangential force** = component along the airfoil chord

The resolution along wind axes is generally used for aerodynamic calculations, the resolution along body axes, for the structural analysis.

Instead of specifying the center of pressure, it is convenient to specify the moment of the air forces about the so-called **aerodynamic center,** a.c. This point lies at a distance a (about a quarter-chord length) back of the leading edge of the airfoil and is defined as the point about which the moment of the air forces remains constant when the angle of attack α is changed. Such a point exists for every airfoil. The force R

acting at the c.p. is equivalent to the same force acting at the a.c. plus a moment equal to that force times the distance between the c.p. and the a.c. (see Fig. 3). The location of the aerodynamic center, in terms of the chord c and the section thickness t, is given approximately by

$$a/c = 0.25 - 0.40(t/c)^2$$

The distance C_p from the leading edge to the center of pressure expressed as a fraction of the chord is, in terms of the moment $M_{c/4}$ about the quarter-chord point,

$$M_{c/4} = (\tfrac{1}{4} - C_p) \cdot c \cdot N$$

$$C_p = \frac{1}{4} - \frac{M_{c/4}}{c \cdot N}$$

From dimensional analysis it can be seen that the **air force on a body** of length dimension l moving with velocity V through air of density ρ can be expressed as

$$F = \varphi \cdot \rho V^2 l^2$$

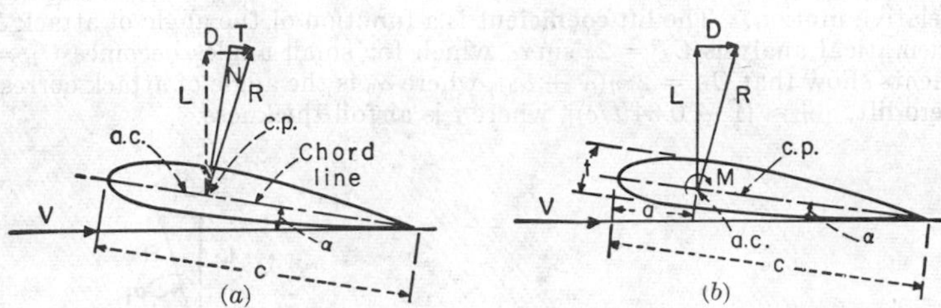

FIG. 3. Forces acting on an airfoil: (a) actual forces; (b) equivalent forces through the aerodynamic center plus a moment.

where φ is a coefficient that depends upon all the dimensionless factors of the problem. In the case of a wing these are:

1. **Angle of attack** α, the inclination between the chord line and the velocity V.
2. **Aspect ratio** $A = b/c$, where b is the span and c the mean chord of the wing.
3. **Reynolds number** $R = \rho Vl/\mu$, where μ is the coefficient of viscosity of air.
4. **Mach number** V/V_s, where V_s is the velocity of sound.
5. Relative surface roughness.
6. Relative turbulence.

The dependence of the force coefficient φ upon α and A can be theoretically determined; the variation of φ with the other parameters must be established experimentally, *i.e.*, by model tests.

AIRFOILS

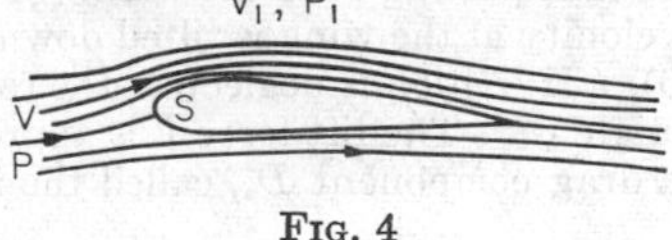

FIG. 4

Applying Bernoulli's equation to the flow around a body, if p represents the **static pressure,** *i.e.*, the atmospheric pressure in the undisturbed air, and if V is superposed as in Fig. 4 and if p_1, V_1 represent the pressure and velocity at any point 1 at the surface of the body,

$$p + \tfrac{1}{2}\rho V^2 = p_1 + \tfrac{1}{2}\rho V_1^2$$

The maximum pressure occurs at a point s on the body at which the velocity is zero. Such a point is defined as the **stagnation point.** The maximum pressure increase occurs at this point and is

$$p_s - p = \tfrac{1}{2}\rho V^2$$

This is called the stagnation pressure, or **dynamic pressure,** and is denoted by q. It is customary to express all aerodynamic forces in terms of $\frac{1}{2}\rho V^2$, hence

$$F = \tfrac{1}{2}\varphi\rho V^2 l^2 = q\varphi l^2$$

For the case of a wing, the forces and moments are expressed as

$$\textbf{Lift} = L = C_L \tfrac{1}{2}\rho V^2 S = C_L qS$$
$$\textbf{Drag} = D = C_D \tfrac{1}{2}\rho V^2 S = C_D qS$$
$$\textbf{Moment} = M = C_M \tfrac{1}{2}\rho V^2 Sc = C_M qSc$$

where S = the wing area and c = the wing chord.

The lift force is the algebraic sum of the normal components of the positive pressures on the lower surface and negative pressures on the upper surface of a wing. These are due to the fact that the wing has imparted a downward momentum to the air passing over it. The velocity distribution around a wing is equivalent to the superposition of a circulatory flow on a translatory (parallel) flow. The lift produced can be determined from the intensity of the circulatory flow or **circulation** Γ by the relation $L' = \rho V\Gamma$, where L' is the lift per unit width of wing. In a **wing of infinite aspect ratio**, the flow is two-dimensional and the lift reaction is at right angles to the line of relative motion. The **lift coefficient** is a function of the angle of attack α, and by mathematical analysis $C_L = 2\pi \sin \alpha$, which for small angles becomes $C_L = 2\pi\alpha$. Experiments show that $C_L = 2\pi\eta(\alpha + \alpha_0)$, where α_0 is the angle of attack corresponding to zero lift. $\eta \approx [1 - 0.64(t/c)]$, where t is airfoil thickness.

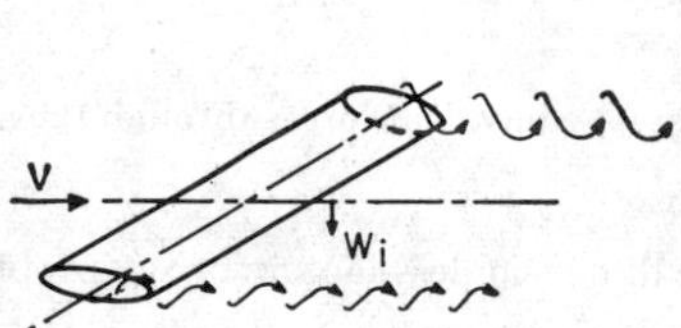

FIG. 5. Vortex formation at wing tips.

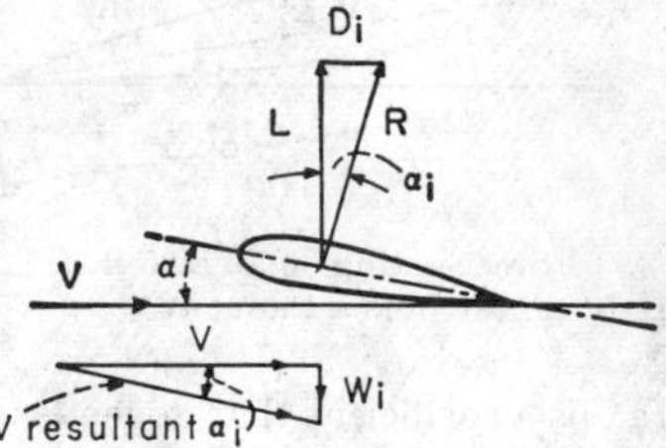

FIG. 6. Induced angle of attack.

In a **wing of finite aspect ratio,** the circulation flow around the wing creates a strong vortex trailing downstream from each wing tip (Fig. 5). Physically, this corresponds to a flow around the wing tips from the region of high pressure below the wing to the low-pressure region above. This causes a downflow, or downwash, w_i of the entire air stream passing over the wing. The effect of this is that the direction of the resultant velocity at the wing is tilted downward by an **induced angle of attack** $\alpha_i = w_i/V$ (Fig. 6). If friction is neglected, the resultant force R is now tilted to the rear by this same angle α_i. The lift force L is approximately the same as R. In addition, there is also a drag component D_i, called the **induced drag,** given by

$$D_i = L \tan \alpha_i = Lw_i/V$$

For a given geometrical angle of attack α the **effective angle of attack** has been reduced by α_i, and thus

$$C_L = 2\pi\eta(\alpha - \alpha_0 - \alpha_i)$$

According to the Lanchester-Prandtl theory, for **wings having an elliptical lift distribution,**

$$\alpha_i = w_i/V = C_L/\pi A \qquad \text{radians}$$
$$D_i = L^2/\pi b^2 q \qquad \text{and} \qquad C_{Di} = D_i/qS = C_L^2/\pi A$$

where b = span of wing and $A = b^2/S$ = aspect ratio of wing. These results also apply fairly well to wings not differing much from the elliptical shape. For **square tips,** correction factors are required:

$$\left.\begin{aligned} \alpha_i &= \frac{C_L}{\pi A}(1+\tau) \qquad \text{where } \tau = 0.05 + 0.02A \\ C_{Di} &= \frac{C_L{}^2}{\pi A}(1+\sigma) \qquad \text{where } \sigma = 0.01A - 0.01 \end{aligned}\right\} \text{for } A < 12$$

These formulas are the basis for transforming the characteristics of rectangular wings from an **aspect ratio** A_1 to an aspect ratio A_2

$$\alpha_2 = \alpha_1 + \frac{57.3C_L}{\pi}\left[\frac{(1+\tau_2)}{A_2} - \frac{(1+\tau_1)}{A_1}\right] \text{ deg}$$

$$C_{D2} = C_{D1} + \frac{C_L{}^2}{\pi}\left[\frac{(1+\sigma_2)}{A_2} - \frac{(1+\sigma_1)}{A_1}\right]$$

For elliptical wings the values of τ and σ are zero. Most wing-section data are given in terms of aspect ratios 6 and ∞. For other values, the preceding formulas must be used.

Characteristics of Airfoils. Airfoil characteristics are expressed in terms of the dimensionless coefficients C_L, C_D, and C_M and the angle of attack α. The NACA presents the results for wings of aspect ratio 6 and also corrected to aspect ratio ∞ (see Fig. 10).

The lift coefficient C_L is a linear function of the angle of attack up to a critical angle called the **stalling angle** (Fig. 7).

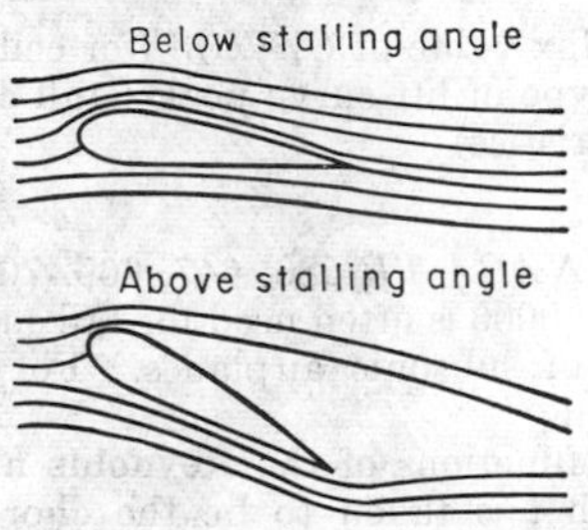

FIG. 7. Stalling angle of airfoil.

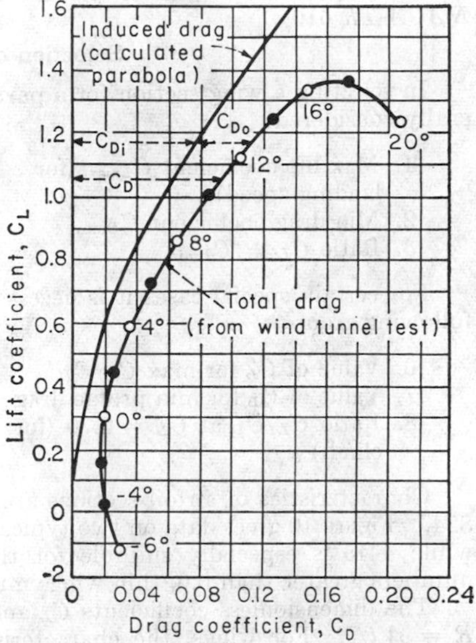

FIG. 8. Polar-diagram plot of airfoil data.

At this angle the flow which had been smooth over the upper surface of the wing breaks away, the lift decreases, and the drag increases. The **maximum lift coefficient** $C_{L\max}$ which can be reached is one of the important characteristics of a wing because it determines the landing speed of the airplane.

The **drag of a wing** is made up of two components: the **profile drag** D_0 and the **induced drag** D_i. The profile drag is due principally to surface friction. At aspect ratio ∞ or at zero lift the induced drag is zero, and thus the entire drag is profile drag. The drag characteristics are generally shown in the polar diagram of C_L *vs.* C_D. In Fig. 8 the coefficient of induced drag $C_{Di} = C_L{}^2/\pi A$ is also plotted. The difference $C_D - C_{Di} = C_{D0}$, the profile-drag coefficient. Among the desirable characteristics of an airfoil is a small value of the minimum profile-drag coefficient and a large value of C_L/C_D.

The moment characteristics of a wing are obtainable from the curve of the center of pressure as a function of α or by the **moment coefficient** taken **about the aero-**

dynamic center $C_{M\text{a.c.}}$ as a function of C_L. A forward motion of the c.p. as α is increased corresponds to an unstable wing section. The same fact is indicated by a negative value of the moment about the a.c. at zero lift. This instability is undesirable because it requires a large download on the tail to counteract it.

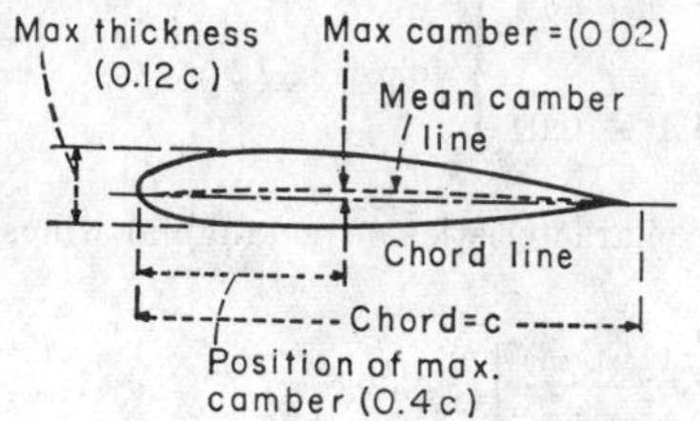

FIG. 9. Characteristics of a wing section.

The characteristics of a wing section (Fig. 9) are determined principally by its **mean camber line**, *i.e.*, the curvature of the median line of the profile, and secondly by the thickness distribution along the chord. In the NACA system of designation, when a four-digit number is used such as 2412, the significance is always first digit = maximum camber in percent of chord, second digit = location of position of maximum camber in tenths of chord measured from the leading edge (*i.e.*, 4 stands for 40 percent), and the last two figures indicate the maximum thickness in percent of chord. The NACA five-digit system is explained in *NACA-TR* 610.

Selection of Wing Section

In selecting a wing section for a particular airplane the following factors are generally considered:

1. Max lift coefficient $C_{L\max}$ (for landing speed)
2. Min drag coefficient $C_{D\min}$
3. Ratio $C_{L\max}/C_{D\min}$
4. Moment coefficient at zero lift C_{m0}
5. Max value of the ratio C_L/C_D (for range)

For certain special cases it is necessary to consider one or more factors from the following group:

6. Value of C_L for max C_L/C_D
7. Value of C_L for min profile drag
8. Ratio C_L/C_D at $C_L = 0.70$ (for climb)
9. Max value of C_L^3/C_D^2 (for ceiling)
10. Type of lift-curve peak (stall characteristics)

Characteristics of airfoil sections are given in *NACA-TR* 586, 647, 669, 708, and 824. Figure 10 gives data on two typical sections: 0006 is often used for tail surfaces, while 4415 is especially suitable for the wings of subsonic airplanes. For Mach numbers greater than 0.6, thin wings must be used.

The dimensionless coefficients C_L and C_D are functions of the **Reynolds number** $R = \rho Vl/\mu$. For wings, the characteristic length l is taken to be the chord. In standard air at sea level

$$R = 6{,}378V_{fps} \cdot l_{ft} = 9{,}354V_{\text{mph}} \cdot l_{ft}$$

For other heights, multiply by the coefficient $K = \dfrac{\rho/\mu}{\rho_0/\mu_0}$. Values of K are as follows:

Altitude, ft	0	5,000	10,000	15,000	20,000	25,000	30,000	40,000	50,000	60,000
K	1.000	0.884	0.779	0.682	0.595	0.515	0.443	0.300	0.186	0.116

The variation of C_L and C_D with the Reynolds number is known as **scale effect.** For any given airfoil the scale effect must be determined either directly or indirectly from wind-tunnel tests or a full-scale comparison. For practical purposes, the variations of $C_{L\max}$ and $C_{D0\min}$ with the Reynolds number are most important. These are shown in Figs. 11 and 12 for some typical airfoils. Figure 12 shows in dotted lines also the theoretical variation of the drag coefficient for a smooth flat plate for laminar and turbulent flow, respectively, and also for the transition region.

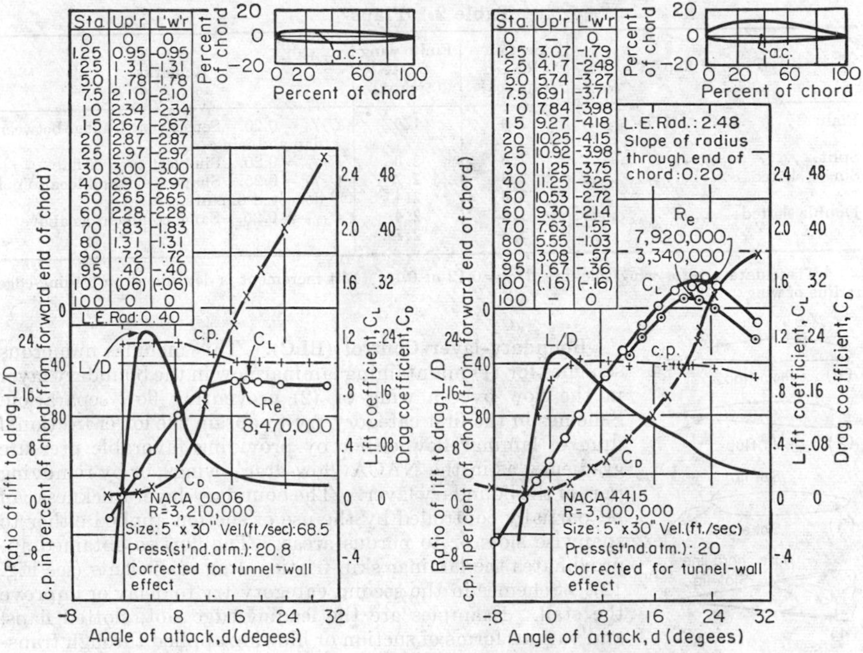

FIG. 10. Properties of an airfoil section.

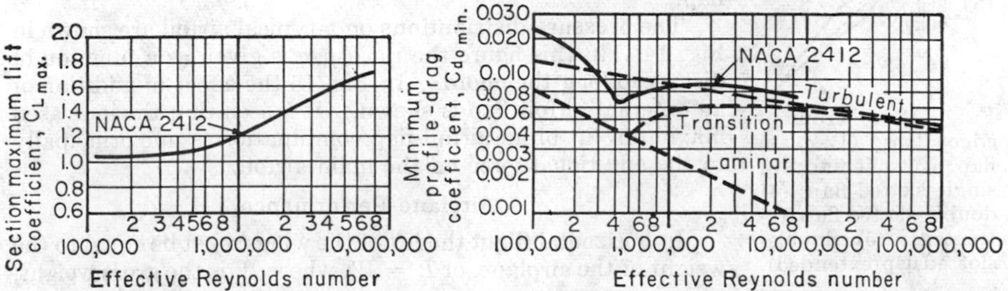

FIG. 11. Scale effect on section maximum lift coefficient.

FIG. 12. Scale effect on minimum profile-drag coefficient.

In addition to the Reynolds number, airfoil characteristics also depend upon the **Mach number** (see pp. 11–96 *et seq.*).

Flaps and Slots

The maximum lift of a wing can be increased by the use of **slots** on the leading edge or **flaps** on the trailing edge. **Fixed slots** are formed by rigidly attaching a curved sheet of metal or a small auxiliary airfoil to the leading edge of the wing to form a Venturisloped slot at the leading edge. The trailing-edge flap is used to give increased lift at moderate angles of attack and to increase $C_{L\max}$. Theoretical analyses of the effects are given in *NACA-TR* 938 and *Br. ARC-R&M* 1095. Flight experience indicates that the four types shown in Fig. 13 have special advantages over other known types. Values of $C_{L\max}$ for these types are shown in Table 2. All flaps cause a diving moment ($-C_m$) which must be trimmed out by a download on the tail, and this download reduces $C_{L\max}$. The correction is $\Delta C_{L\max}$ (trim) $= \Delta C_{mo}(l/c)$, where l/c is the tail length in mean chords.

Table 2. Flaps*

Type of flap	Section C_{max} (approx)	Finite wing C_{Lmax} (approx)	Remarks
Plain	2.4	1.9	$C_f/_c = 0.20$. Sensitive to leakage between flap and wing
Split	2.6	2.0	$C_f/_c = 0.20$. Simplest type of flap
Single slotted	2.8	2.2	$C_f/_c = 0.25$. Shape of slot and location of deflected flap are critical
	3.0	2.4	
Double slotted	3.0	2.4	$C_f/_c = 0.25$. Same comment as above
	3.4	2.7	

* These data are for wing thickness $t/c = 0.12$ or 0.15. Lift increment is dependent on leading-edge radius of wing.

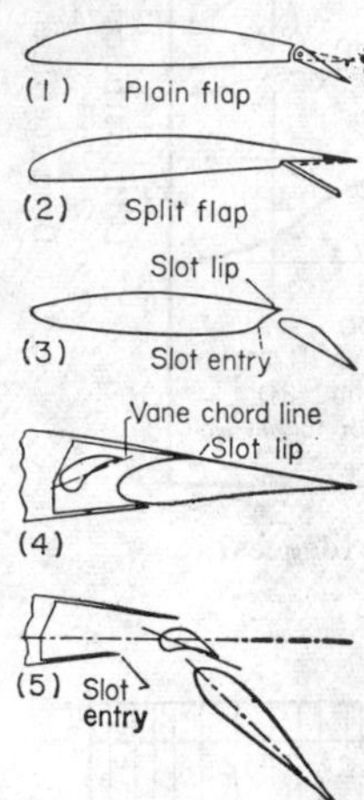

FIG. 13. Trailing-edge flaps: (1) plain flap; (2) split flap; (3) single-slotted flap; (4) double-slotted flap (retracted); (5) double-slotted flap (extended).

Boundary-layer Control (BLC). This includes numerous schemes for (1) maintaining laminar flow in the boundary layer in the flow over a wing or (2) preventing flow separation. Schemes in the first category try to obtain the lower frictional drag of laminar flow either by providing favorable pressure gradients, as in the NACA "low-drag" wings, or by removing part of the boundary layer. The boundary-layer thickness can be partially controlled by the use of suction applied either to spanwise slots or to porous areas. The flow so obtained approximates the laminar skin-friction drag coefficients (see Fig. 12). Schemes in the second category try to delay or improve the stall. Examples are the leading-edge slot, slotted flaps, and various forms of suction or blowing applied through transverse slots. The slotted flap is a highly effective form of boundary-layer control that delays flow separation on the flap.

The **pressure distributions** on a typical airfoil are shown in Fig. 14. In this figure the ratio p/q is given as a function of distance along the chord. In Fig. 15 the effect of addition of an external airfoil flap is shown. It is seen that the increased maximum lift of an airfoil-flap combination is due principally to the additional force on the main airfoil.

Airplane Performance

In **horizontal flight** the lift of the wings must be equal to the weight of the airplane, or $L = W$, where W is the gross weight,

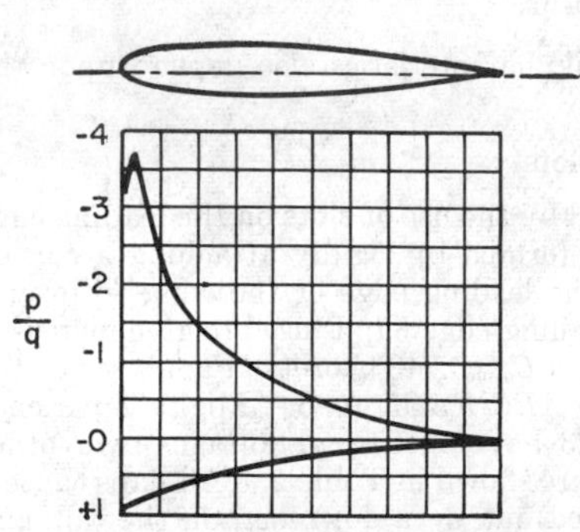

FIG. 14. Pressure distribution over a typical airfoil.

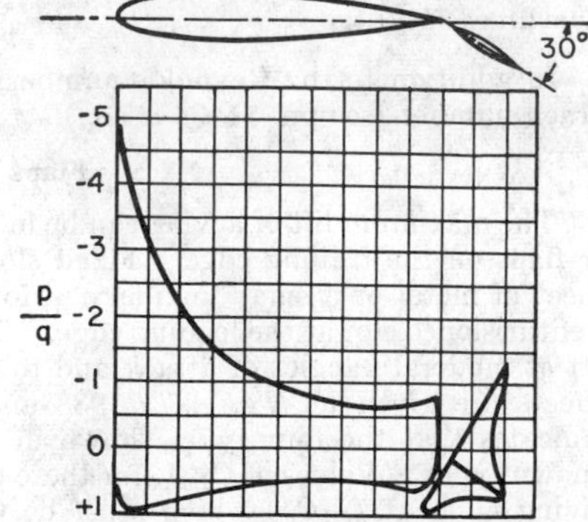

FIG. 15. Pressure distribution on airfoil-flap combination.

lb. This equation determines the minimum horizontal speed of an airplane since

$$W = C_{L\max}\tfrac{1}{2}\rho V^2_{\min}S \qquad \text{or} \qquad V_{\min} = \sqrt{2W/C_{L\max}\rho S}.$$

This corresponds to the **landing speed** without power, or the **stalling speed.**

In uniform horizontal flight the **propeller thrust** T must be exactly equal to the drag of the airplane, or $T = D$. (See p. 11–112). It is more convenient to discuss this as an energy equation. Then TV = power available from the propeller and DV = power required for overcoming the drag of the airplane; for horizontal flight $TV = DV$. If the airplane climbs at a rate dh/dt, where h = height, then an additional power $= W(dh/dt)$ is required to increase the potential energy of the airplane. The equilibrium condition becomes

$$TV = DV + W\,dh/dt$$

If the **thrust power available** P_{Ta} is measured in hp, D and W in lb, and V and dh/dt in fps,

$$P_{Ta} = \frac{1}{550}DV + \frac{1}{550}W(dh/dt) \qquad \textbf{(A)}$$

The thrust horsepower available $P_{Ta} = \eta P_a$, where P_a = **available engine horsepower** and η is the propeller efficiency. P_{Ta} is determined as a function of V from the engine and propeller characteristics. The **thrust horsepower required** to overcome the drag D is $P_{Tr} = DV/550$. The **drag** is the sum of the wing profile drag D_0, the wing induced drag D_i, and the parasite drag of the other airplane parts D_p. D_0 can be obtained from wing-profile tests corrected to full-scale Reynolds number, D_i from the induced drag formula $D_i = L^2/\pi q b^2$, and D_p by summation of the parasite drag components due to fuselage, tail surfaces, landing gear, etc.

From Eq. (**A**) the performance of an airplane can be obtained either graphically or analytically. In the graphical determination the curves of power available and power required are plotted for a fixed altitude (Fig. 16). If $P_{Ta} > P_{Tr}$, the excess horsepower can be used either for horizontal acceleration to a higher speed or for climbing. The **maximum speed** $V_{\max}$ occurs when $P_{Ta} = P_{Tr}$. The rate of climb is determined by the equation $dh/dt = 550/W(P_{Ta} - P_{Tr})$. To calculate the **maximum velocity and rate of climb for another altitude,** another set of curves of P_{Ta} and P_{Tr} *vs.* V is constructed. At any altitude at which the air density is ρ and for a given angle of attack (corresponding to an unchanged lift/drag ratio), $L/D = L_0/D_0$. As the lift is equal to the weight, $L = L_0 = W$, therefore $D = D_0$ and

$$P_{Tr}/P_{Tr0} = VD/V_0D_0 = V/V_0$$

But $C_L = C_{L0}$ and $C_L \cdot \tfrac{1}{2}\rho V^2 S = C_{L0}\tfrac{1}{2}\rho_0 V_0^2 S$. Therefore, $V/V_0 = \sqrt{\rho_0/\rho}$. From this relation, new curves of P_{Tr} *vs.* V may be constructed for various altitudes by multiplying both the ordinates and abscissas of the original curve by $\sqrt{\rho_0/\rho}$.

Figure 16 shows a performance chart for a 2,100 lb airplane. The maximum velocity at 10,000 ft altitude is 168.5 fps. At sea level $(P_{Ta} - P_{Tr})_{\max} = 71$ and the rate of climb is $71 \times 33{,}000/2{,}100 = 1{,}120$ fpm. At 10,000 ft altitude the rate is $30 \times 33{,}000/2{,}100 = 470$ fpm.

When the curves of power required and power available become tangent to each other, there is only one speed at which the airplane can fly level and the rate of climb is zero. The corresponding altitude is the **absolute ceiling** H. It can be determined from the curve of maximum rate of climb as a function of altitude when this is approximated by a straight line (Fig. 17). The **service ceiling** h_s is defined as the altitude at which the rate of climb is 100 fpm. For a linear decrease of rate of climb the following approximations hold:

Absolute ceiling: $\qquad H = r_0h/(r_0 - r)$

where r_0 is the rate of climb at sea level and r is the rate of climb at altitude h.

Service ceiling: $h_s = H(r_0 - 100)/r_0$

Altitude climbed in t min,

$$h = H(1 - e^k)$$

where $k = -r_0t/H$.

Time to climb to altitude h,

$$t = 2.303\left(\frac{H}{r_0}\right)\log\frac{H}{H-h}$$

The maximum distance that an airplane can fly is called its **range**, the length of time that it can remain flying, its **endurance.** If W_0 is the weight in pounds fully loaded

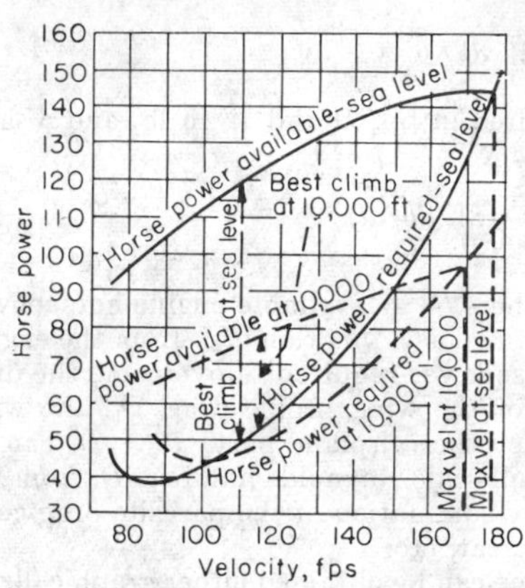

FIG. 16. Construction for determining airplane ceiling.

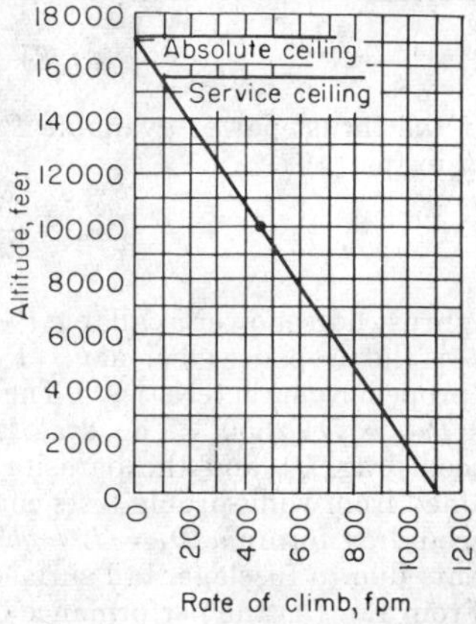

FIG. 17. Characteristic airplane curves.

and W_1 the weight after having consumed its fuel at the rate of C lb per bhp-hr, then

$$\text{Range} = 863.5\,\frac{\eta}{C}\cdot\frac{L}{D}\cdot\log\left(\frac{W_0}{W_1}\right)\quad\text{miles}$$

$$\text{Endurance} = 750\,\frac{\sqrt{W}}{V_c}\cdot\frac{\eta}{C}\cdot\frac{L}{D}\left(\frac{1}{\sqrt{W_1}}-\frac{1}{\sqrt{W_0}}\right)\quad\text{hr}$$

where η is the average propulsive efficiency and $L/D = C_L/C_D$ is the ratio of lift to drag. V_c is the cruising speed, mph, at any gross weight W, lb.

Power Available. The maximum efficiency η_m and the diameter of a propeller to absorb a given power at a given speed and rpm are found from a propeller-performance curve (see p. 11–136). The thrust horsepower at maximum speed P_{Tm} is found from $P_{Tm} = \eta_m P_m$. The **thrust horsepower at any speed** can be approximately determined from the ratios given in the following table:

V/V_{max}	20	30	40	50	60	70	80	90	1.00	1.10
P_T/P_{Tm} fixed-pitch propeller	0.29	0.44	0.57	0.68	0.77	0.84	0.90	0.96	1.00	1.03
P_T/P_{Tm} constant-rpm propeller	0.47	0.62	0.74	0.82	0.88	0.93	0.97	0.99	1.00	1.00

The **brake horsepower** of an engine decreases with increase of altitude. (See pp. 9–106 *et seq.*). The variation of P_T with altitude depends on engine and propeller characteristics with average values as follows:

h, ft	0	5,000	10,000	15,000	20,000	25,000
P_T/P_{T0} (fixed pitch)	1.00	0.82	0.66	0.52	0.41	0.30
P_T/P_{T0} (controllable pitch)	1.00	0.85	0.71	0.59	0.48	0.38

Table 3. Principal Dimensions and Performance of Typical Airplanes

	Aero Commander	BAC	Beech	Bell	Boeing	Boeing	Boeing	Convair	Douglas	Douglas	Lockheed	Piper	Sikorsky
Designation model No.	680F-P	One-Eleven	Bonanza S35	Ranger 47J2-A	707-320	720B	727	340	Liftmaster DC-6B	DC-8 Series 5D	Electra L-188	Super Cub PA 18-150	S-58
Type	Executive transport	Jet transport	Business plane	Executive helicopter	Jet transport	Jet transport	Jet transport	Transport	Transport	Jet transport	Transport	Utility plane	Helicopter
No. passengers	5–7	63	4–6	4	133–186	88–142	70–114	44	64–92	116–176	66–98	2	12–18
Cargo capacity, lb	2,815	N.A.	270	1,120	17,750	13,900	8,550	N.A.	—	20,850	—	50	—
Span, ft	49.5	83.5	33.4	37.0*	145.9	130.8	108.6	105.4	117.5	142.3	99.0	35.3	56.0*
Over-all length, ft	35.1	92.1	26.4	43.3	145.5	130.5	134.3	79.2	105.6	150.5	104.5	22.5	65.8
Over-all height, ft	14.5	23.8	6.5	9.3	42.6	41.5	34.0	28.2	28.4	42.3	33.0	6.7	14.3
Wing area, sq ft	255	980	181	Rotor	2,892	2,433	1,650	817	1,463	2,868	1,300	178.5	Rotor
Weight empty, lb†	5,185	58,000	1,885	1,730	181,000	156,000	86,000	32,359	54,148	124,529	59,308	930	7,900
Weight gross, lb	8,000	73,800	3,300	2,850	328,000	234,000	142,000	47,000	100,000	310,000	116,000	1,750	13,000
Power plant	(2) Lyc IGSO-540B1A	(2) RR Spey 2	Con IO-520-B	Lyc VO540	(4) PW JT3D-3	(4) PW JT3C-7	(3) PW JT8D-1	(2) R2800	(4) PW R2800-CB17	(4) PW JT3D-3	(4) All 501D-13	Lyc O-320	WR R1820
High speed, knots	252	469	184	91	524	534	539	273	313	521	0.64‡	113	106
Cruise speed, knots	220	441	178	81	500–525	517	513	247	270	472	0.615§	100	84
Landing speed, knots	91	N.A.	54	0	128	127	121	75	81	133	113	37	0
Range, miles	1,310	1,700	1,145	260	6,000	4,300	2,320	1,260	4,540	8,600	3,400	460	247

* Rotor diameter.
† Operating weight empty (includes trapped oil).
‡ Mach-number limit above 8,000 ft.
§ Mach-number limit above 12,000 ft.
N.A. Not available.

Performance with Jet Thrust. In all cases where jet thrust constitutes either a part or all of the power source, it is necessary to use graphical methods, plotting thrust and drag as functions of speed at each altitude to be investigated. The major thrust corrections as those due to losses in (1) the air intake, (2) the ducting system, and (3) the tailpipe. (See pp. 11–112 *et seq.*)

An excess thrust T, lb, at a speed V, mph, is equivalent to a thrust horsepower $P_T = TV/375$. The corresponding rate of climb is $dh/dt = 33{,}000P_T/W = 88TV/W$.

Parasite Drag

The drag of the non-lifting parts of an airplane is called the *parasite drag.* It consists of two components: the frictional and the eddy-making drag.

Frictional drag, or **skin friction,** is due to the viscosity of the fluid. It is the force produced by the viscous shear in the layers of fluid immediately adjacent to the body. It is always proportional to the wetted area, *i.e.*, the total surface exposed to the air.

Eddy-making drag, sometimes called **form drag,** is due to the disturbance or wake created by the body. It is a function of the shape of the body.

The total drag of a body may be composed of the two components in any proportion, varying from almost pure skin friction for a plate edgewise or a good streamline form to 100 percent form drag for a flat plate normal to the wind. A **streamline form** is a shape having very low form drag. Such a form creates little disturbance in moving through a fluid.

When air flows past a surface, the layer immediately adjacent to the surface adheres to it, or the tangential velocity at the surface is zero. In the transition region near the surface, which is called the **boundary layer,** the velocity increases from zero to the velocity of the stream. When the flow in the boundary layer proceeds as if it were made up of laminae sliding smoothly over each other, it is called a **laminar boundary layer.** If there are also irregular motions in the layers normal to the surface, it is a **turbulent boundary layer.** Under normal conditions the flow is laminar at low Reynolds numbers and turbulent at high R with a transition range of values of R extending between 5×10^5 and 5×10^7. The profile-drag coefficients corresponding to these conditions are shown in Fig. 12.

For laminar flow the friction-drag coefficient is practically independent of surface roughness and for a flat plate is given by the Blasius equation,

$$C_{DF} = 2.656/\sqrt{R}$$

The turbulent boundary layer is thicker and produces a greater frictional drag. For a smooth flat plate with a turbulent boundary layer

$$C_{DF} = 0.91/\log R^{2.58}$$

For rough surfaces the drag coefficients are increased (see von Kármán, *Jour. Aeronaut. Sci.*, **1,** No. 1, 1934). The drag coefficients as given above are based on *projected area* of a double-surfaced plane. If *wetted* area is used, the coefficients must be divided by 2. The frictional drag is $D_F = C_{DF}qS$, where S is the *projected area,* or $D_F = \frac{1}{2}C_{DF}qA$, where A is the wetted area.

Values of C_{DF} for double-surfaced planes may be estimated from the following tabulation:

Laminar flow (Blasius equation):

R	10	10^2	10^3	10^4	10^5	10^6
C_{DF}	0.838	0.265	0.0838	0.0265	0.0084	0.00265

Turbulent flow:

R	10^5	10^6	10^7	10^8	10^9	10^{10}
C_{DF}	0.0148	0.0089	0.0060	0.0043	0.00315	0.0024

These are double-surface values which facilitate direct comparison with wing-drag coefficients based on projected area. For calculations involving wetted area, use one-half of double-surface coefficients. Interpolations in the foregoing tables must allow for the logarithmic functions; *i.e.*, the variation in C_{DF} is not linear with R.

Laminar-flow Wings. NACA has developed a series of *low-drag wings* in which the distribution of thickness along the chord is so selected as to maintain *laminar* flow over as much of the wing surface as possible. Typical low-drag wings are shown in Fig. 18.

The low-drag wing under controlled conditions of surface smoothness may have drag coefficients about 30 percent lower than those obtained on normal conventional wings. Low-drag airfoils are so sensitive to roughness in any form that the full advantage of laminar flow is unobtainable.

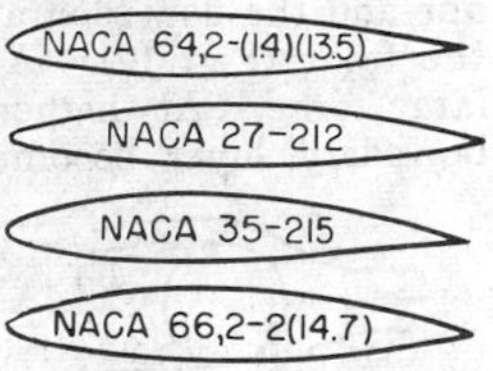

NACA 64,2-(14)(13.5)
NACA 27-212
NACA 35-215
NACA 66,2-2(14.7)

Fig. 18. Typical NACA low-drag airfoil sections.

Drag Coefficients of Various Bodies

For **bodies with sharp edges** the drag coefficients are almost independent of the Reynolds number, for most of the resistance is due to the difference in pressure on the front and rear surfaces. Table 4 gives $C_D = D/qS$, where S is the maximum cross section perpendicular to the wind.

For **rounded bodies** such as **spheres, cylinders,** and **ellipsoids** the drag coefficient depends markedly upon the Reynolds number, the surface roughness, and the degree of

Table 4. Drag Coefficients

Object	Proportions	Attitude	C_D
Rectangular plate, sides a and b	a = 1 4 8 12.5 25 50 ∞	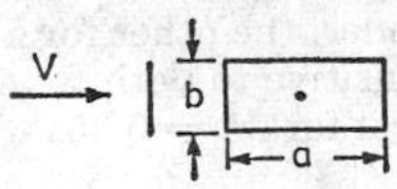 V → b, a	1.16 1.17 1.23 1.34 1.57 1.76 2.00
Two disks, spaced a distance l apart	$\frac{l}{d}$ = 1 1.5 2 3	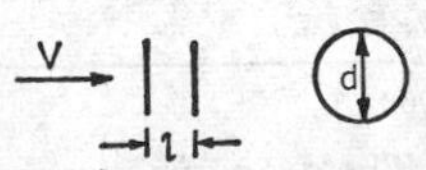 V → l, d	0.93 0.78 1.04 1.52
Cylinder	$\frac{l}{d}$ = 1 2 4 7	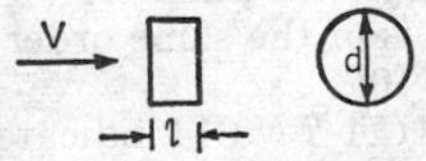 V → l, d	0.91 0.85 0.87 0.99
Circular disk		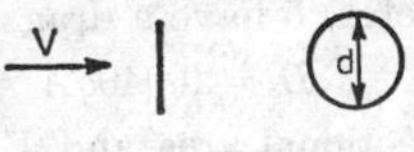 V → d	1.11
Hemispherical cup, open back		 V → d	0.41
Hemispherical cup, open front, parachute		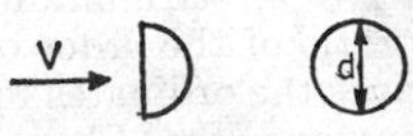 V → d	1.35
Cone, closed base		 V → d	α = 60°, 0.51 α = 30°, 0.34

turbulence in the air stream. A sphere and a cylinder, for instance, experience a sudden reduction in C_D as the Reynolds number exceeds a certain critical value. The reason is that at low speeds (small R) the flow in the boundary layer adjacent to the body is laminar and the flow separates at about 83 deg from the front (Fig. 19). A wide wake thus gives a large drag. At higher speeds (large R) the boundary layer becomes turbulent, gets additional energy from the outside flow, and does not separate on the front side of the sphere. The drag coefficient is reduced from about 0.47 to about 0.08 at a critical Reynolds number of about 400,000 in free air. Turbulence in the air stream reduces the value of the critical Reynolds number (Fig. 20). The Reynolds number at which the sphere drag $C_D = 0.3$ is taken as a criterion of the amount of turbulence in the air stream of wind tunnels.

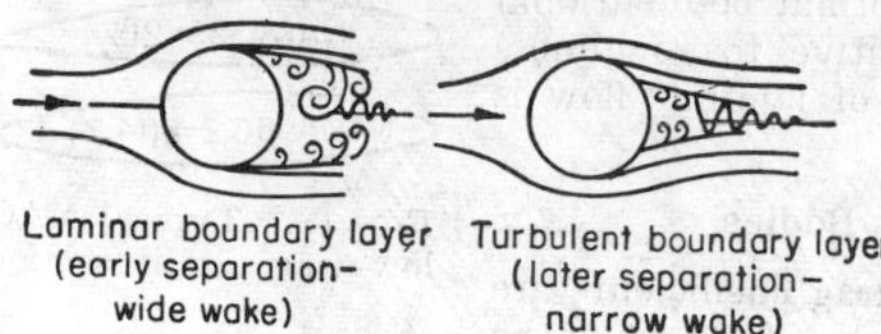

FIG. 19. Boundary layer of a sphere.

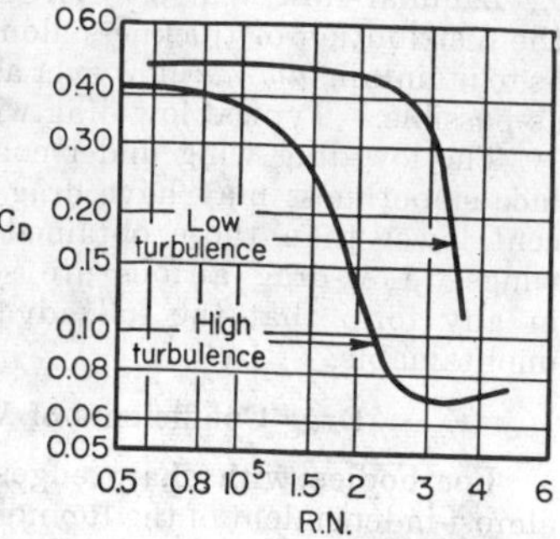

FIG. 20. Drag coefficient of a sphere as a function of Reynolds number and of turbulence.

Cylinders. The drag coefficient of a cylinder with its axis normal to the wind is given as a function of Reynolds number in Fig. 21. Two curves are given: one for a section of an infinite cylinder, the other for a finite cylinder having a length of 5 diameters. Cylinder drag is sensitive to both Reynolds and Mach number. Figure 21 gives the Reynolds number effect for $M = 0.35$. The increase in C_D because of Mach number is approximately:

M	0.35	0.4	0.6	0.8	1.0
C_D increase, percent	0	2	20	50	70

(See *NACA-TN* 2960)

Streamline Forms. The drag of a streamline body of revolution depends to a very marked extent on the Reynolds number. The difference between extreme types at a given Reynolds number is of the same order as the change in C_D for a given form for values of R from 10^6 to 10^7.

Tests reported in *NACA-TN* 614 indicate that the shape for minimum drag should have a fairly sharp nose and tail. At $R = 6.6 \times 10^6$ the best forms for a fineness ratio (ratio of length to diameter) 5 have a drag

$$D = 0.040qA = 0.0175qV^{2/3}$$

where A = max cross-sectional area and V = volume. This value is equivalent to about 1.0 lb per sq ft at 100 mph. For $R > 5 \times 10^6$, the drag coefficients vary approximately as $R^{0.15}$.

Minimum drag on the basis of cross-sectional or frontal area is obtained with a fineness ratio of the order of 2 to 3. Minimum drag on the basis of contained volume is obtained with a fineness ratio of the order of 4 to 6 (see *NACA-TR* 291).

The following table gives the ordinates for good streamline shapes: the **Navy strut,** a two-dimensional shape; and the Class C **airships,** a three-dimensional shape. Streamline shapes for high Mach numbers have a fine entry and high fineness ratio.

Percent length		1.25	2.50	4.00	7.50	10.0	12.50	20	40	60	80	90
Percent of max ordinate	Navy strut	26	37.1	52.50	63.00	72.0	78.50	91.1	99.5	86.1	56.2	33.8
	Class C airship	20	33.5	52.60	65.80	75.8	83.50	94.7	99.0	88.5	60.5	49.3

Test data on the *RM*-10 shape are given in *NACA-TR* 1160. This shape is a parabolic-arc type for which the coordinates are given by the equation $r_x = X/7.5(1.0 - X/L)$.

Struts. Drag coefficients for streamline struts are given in the form

$$C_D = D/qS_f = D/qdl$$

where S_f is the projected frontal area; d is the thickness, ft; and l is the length, ft. The variation of C_D with R for a Navy No. 1 strut of fineness ratio 3 is as follows:

$R \times 10^{-5}$	0.75	1.0	1.25	1.5	2.0	3.0	4.0
C_D	0.114	0.102	0.093	0.088	0.085	0.077	0.073

Wing Profile Drag. For accurate basic values of profile drag it is necessary to refer to test data on the wing section employed. In the absence of test data, the following approximate values may be used:

Average t/c		0.10	0.12	0.14	0.16
Basic	C_{D0}	0.0058	0.0060	0.0063	0.0067
	D_0/S	0.148	0.154	0.161	0.171
Best wing	C_{D0}	0.0078	0.0080	0.0083	0.0087
	D_0/S	0.20	0.205	0.212	0.223
Average roughness	C_{D0}	0.098	0.0100	0.0103	0.0107
	D_0/S	0.25	0.256	0.264	0.274

The "basic" values are for a perfectly smooth wing of infinite aspect ratio, "best-wing" values are for smooth full flush-riveted construction, and "average-roughness" values are for flush-riveted leading-edge with brazier head rivets back of the 20 percent

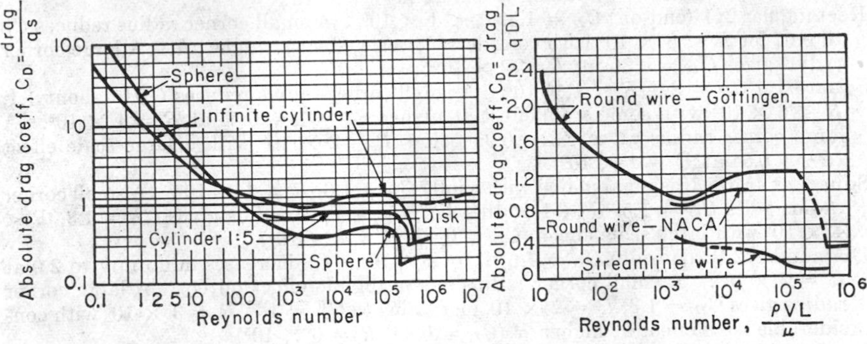

FIG. 21. Drag coefficients of cylinders and spheres.

FIG. 22. Drag coefficients of wires.

chord point. C_{D0} is the profile-drag coefficient ($D_0 = C_{D0}qS$). The values of D_0/S are drags in lb per sq ft of projected wing area at 100 mph in standard air ($q_0 = 25.58$ lb per sq ft). t/c is the maximum wing thickness as a fraction of the chord.

Faired values of NACA data on **symmetrical sections** at $R = 8 \times 10^6$ give the variation of minimum C_{D0} and C_{DA} with thickness as follows:

NACA section	0006	0009	0012	0015	0018	0021	0025	0030	0035
Min C_{D0}	0.0051	0.0056	0.0061	0.0067	0.0073	0.0080	0.0089	0.0103	0.0120
C_{DA} (see below)	0.085	0.062	0.050	0.045	0.041	0.038	0.036	0.034	0.034

NOTE: C_{DA} is the drag coefficient based on the frontal area. The 00 section is also suitable for use in struts or fairings. (See *NACA-TR* 628, 647, 669, 708.)

Drag of Tail Surfaces. Owing to joints, control balances, and interference effects, the drag of a control surface is much higher than that of the basic section. The average value is about 0.40 lb per sq ft at 100 mph in standard density.

Streamline Wire. The drag coefficient of a standard streamline wire of lenticular or elliptical cross section is given as a function of Reynolds number in Fig. 22.

The drag coefficients of wires and cables are also shown in Fig. 22.

Elliptic Cylinders

FR	C_D when *R* is			
	3×10^4	6×10^4	1×10^5	2×10^5
1:1	1.20	1.22	1.22	1.23
2:1	0.62	0.57	0.46	0.35
4:1	0.32	0.32	0.30	0.24
8:1	0.27	0.23	0.22	0.21

The above data are for $M < 0.4$. For additional data see *NACA-TR* 619.

C_L and C_D for **inclined wires** are as follows:

Angle of attack, deg.	0	15	30	45	60	75	90
C_L	0	0.09	0.25	0.39	0.42	0.27	0
C_D	0.01	0.05	0.17	0.46	0.77	1.01	1.12

C_L and C_D are based on the area $S = LD$, where L is the length and D the diam, ft.

Drag coefficients for **prismatic cylinders** of various cross sections:

Ellipse 1:2 (broadside) $C_D = 1.6$, $R < 6 \times 10^5$.

Rectangle 1:2 (broadside) $C_D = 2.2$, $R < 6 \times 10^5$. A small corner radius reduces C_D to 1.8. A large corner radius reduces C_D to 1.5 at $R < 2 \times 10^5$. At higher R there is a large scale effect, C_D falling to 0.5 at $R = 4 \times 10^5$.

Rectangular 2:1 (end-on) $C_D = 1.3$, $R < 1 \times 10^6$. A small corner radius reduces C_D to 0.67 for $R < 8 \times 10^5$ with considerable scale effect at higher R. A large corner radius gives $C_D = 0.30$ for $R < 2 \times 10^6$.

Square 1:1 $C_D = 2.0$, $R < 1 \times 10^6$. A small corner radius reduces C_D to about 1.1, $R < 6 \times 10^5$ with some scale effect at higher R. $C_D = 0.55$ at $R = 1 \times 10^6$. A large corner radius gives $C_D = 0.95$ below $R = 2 \times 10^5$ with a large scale effect ($C_D = 0.54$ at $R = 1 \times 10^6$).

Square at 45 deg (diagonal in line with wind) $C_D = 1.6$, $R < 1 \times 10^6$. A small corner radius gives $C_D = 1.5$, $R < 1 \times 10^6$. A large corner radius gives $C_D = 1.3$, $R < 4 \times 10^5$ with large scale effect ($C_D = 0.40$, $R = 7 \times 10^5$).

Diamond 1:2 (broadside) $C_D = 1.6$, $R = 2 \times 10^4$. C_D increases uniformly to 2.0 at $R = 7 \times 10^5$. A small corner radius has negligible effect on C_D. A large corner radius gives $C_D = 1.3$, $R = 2 \times 10$, increasing to $C_D = 1.7$, $R = 3 \times 10^5$ with considerable scale effect at higher R ($C_D = 0.44$, $R = 6 \times 10^5$).

Equilateral triangle (apex into wind) $C_D = 1.2 < 1 \times 10^6$. A small corner radius increased C_D to 1.4, $R < 1 \times 10^6$. A large corner radius gives $C_D = 1.2$, $R = 4 \times 10^5$ with considerable scale effect at higher R ($C_D = 0.35$, $R = 8 \times 10^5$).

Equilateral triangle (apex downstream) $C_D = 2.0$, $R < 1 \times 10^6$. A small corner radius had no appreciable effect. A large corner radius gives $C_D = 1.2$, $R < 3 \times 10^5$ with large scale effect at higher R ($C_D = 0.20$, $R = 6 \times 10^5$).

(Additional data on these and other prismatic cylinders are given in *NACA-TR* 619 and *NACA-TN* 3038.)

Engine Drag, Nacelle Drag. The drag of an uncowled air-cooled engine is approximately $D = 0.050d^2(V/100)^2$, where d is the over-all diameter of the engine, in., and V is the speed, mph. The average drag in pounds at 100 mph for a fixed-slot NACA type cowl is as follows:

Engine diam, in.	40	44	48	52	56
Drag, lb at 100 mph	28	34	40	47	54

If adjustable **cowl flaps** or controlled airflow are used, the engine drag need not vary as the square of the speed; it may remain substantially constant. Theoretically, it is possible to cool an engine by forced cooling at an expenditure of about 2 percent of the engine power.

The average drag coefficient of a nacelle is $C_D = 0.20$, based on frontal area. This is equivalent to about 5.0 lb per sq ft at 100 mph. A very clean form may be as low as 3 lb per sq ft at 100 mph. The drag of a pure streamline form would be of the order of 1 lb per sq ft at 100 mph (see *NACA-TR* 313, 314, and 415).

Fuselage Drag. Owing to various projections and irregularities in the surface, the drag of an average airplane fuselage is considerably greater than the drag of a pure streamline form. Since the increase is due in effect to a substantially constant drag increment, the drag per unit of cross-sectional area tends to decrease with increase in the size of the fuselage. At 100 mph the drag in lb per sq ft will be approximately as follows:

A, sq ft	10	15	20	40	60
D/A, average	5.5	4.5	4.0	3.3	3.0
D/A, lower limit	4.0	3.3	3.0	2.4	2.3

Cockpit enclosures, if properly designed and blended into fuselage lines, do not appreciably increase the fuselage drag coefficient. Sharp junctures must be avoided. The best fairing radius is approximately 25 percent of the enclosure height. Length of tail fairing should be 4 × height (see *NACA-TR* 730).

Seaplane Floats, Flying-boat Hulls. The drag of a seaplane float is between 3 and 6 lb per sq ft at 100 mph, depending on the lines. The step accounts for 5 to 10 percent of the drag.

The drag of a flying-boat hull is comparable to, but slightly higher than, the drag of a fuselage of the same cross-sectional area. Average values at 100 mph are as follows:

A, sq ft	40	60	80	100
D/A, lb per sq ft	4.5	4.3	4.1	4.0

Wire Mesh. Measurements on square pieces of exposed wire mesh have given the following results:

Percent area blocked	100	80	60	50	40	30	20
Percent flat plate, C_D	100	92	77	60	43	26	10

The pressure drop through a screen in a tube is given by

$$\Delta p = C_D q = \tfrac{1}{2} C_D \rho V^2$$

where C_D is a function of the percent area blocked as follows:

Percent area blocked	20	30	40	50	60	70
C_D	0.20	0.45	0.90	1.60	3.40	7.20

(See *Br. ARC-R&M* 1469.)

Interference Drag. The total drag of two objects in close proximity is generally greater than the sum of the individual free-flow drags. The increase (or decrease) is known as interference drag. It is especially important where the wing is one component and the fuselage or a nacelle the other component. In this case it may be reduced to a minimum by an appropriate fairing or "fillet" in the path of the expanding flow (see *NACA-TN* 460).

Fig. 23. Strut intersection with flat surface.

The interference drag of two parallel streamline struts is as follows:

Spacing/thickness	5	4	3	2	1.5	1.25
D/D_0	1.00	1.06	1.12	1.25	2.25	2.87

The interference drag of a strut intersection with a flat surface is a function of the intersection angle θ (see Fig. 23). The drag increase, expressed as an equivalent length increase ΔL in diameters, is as follows:

θ, deg	90	70	60	50	40	30	20
ΔL	0	1.5	2.5	4.0	6.0	9.5	14.0

STABILITY

Airplane Control. An airplane is controlled in flight by imposing yawing, pitching, and rolling moments by use of rudders, elevators, and ailerons. This is known as the **three-control** system and is in almost universal use, although it is possible to dispense with either the ailerons or the rudders and so obtain a two-control system.

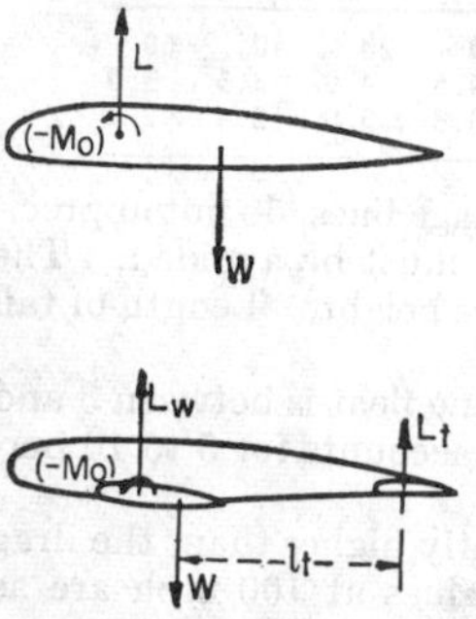

Fig. 24. Longitudinal stability of an airplane.

Controllability is separate and distinct from stability in physical significance, but not necessarily so in flight. An airplane may be made automatically stable by gyroscopic or other devices that actuate the controls mechanically; it is inherently stable if, on disturbance from any cause, the aerodynamic forces and moments induced always tend to return the airplane to its original attitude.

Stability may be either static or dynamic. An airplane is **statically stable** if the moments tend to return it to the original attitude. It is **dynamically stable** if the oscillations produced by the static stability are rapidly damped out. If it is **statically unstable,** any departure tends to increase, there being an upsetting moment instead of a restoring moment. If it is **dynamically unstable,** the oscillations due to static stability tend to increase in amplitude with time. Static stability or a condition of stable equilibrium is necessary to obtain dynamic stability, but static stability does not ensure dynamic stability. Too much static stability may cause dynamic instability if damping is inadequate.

The common method of getting **static longitudinal stability** is by means of a tail surface. A wing alone has a lift force L acting at the a.c. and a moment M_0 about the a.c. (Fig. 24). The moment is measured positively as a stalling moment. Most wings alone are "unstable" (positive lift-curve slope), though possessing a small negative moment (diving moment). If there were no other air forces acting, this could be balanced by putting the center of gravity of the airplane behind the a.c. a distance δ such that $W\delta = M_0$. This arrangement would be in equilibrium but would be unstable. Upon a small increase in the angle of attack such as by a gust, the lift force will be increased. This gives a moment tending to increase further the angle of attack. The curve of the moment of the air forces on a wing about the center of gravity thus starts from the value M_0 and becomes positive for larger angles of attack. The curve is shown in Fig. 25. The positive slope of M *vs.* α thus corresponds to an unstable moment. When a horizontal tail surface is added, a lift force also acts upon the tail. This gives a diving moment $M_t = -L_t \cdot l_t$. Upon an increase in the angle of attack α, the diving tail moment is increased more rapidly than the stalling moment of the wing. Thus, the combination is stable. The resultant curve of pitching moment against angle of attack has a small

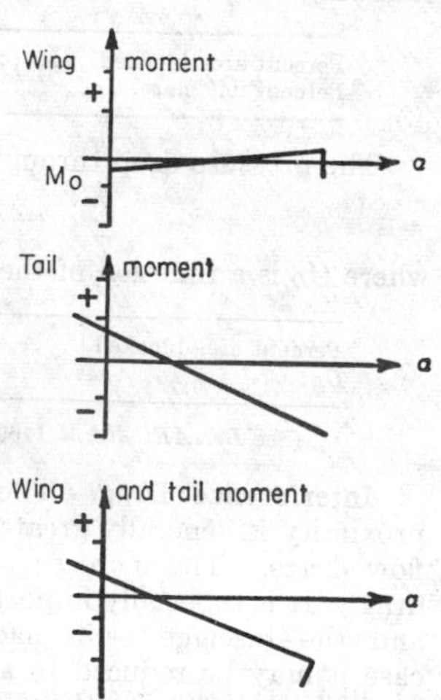

Fig. 25. Longitudinal stability. Wing and foil moments.

negative slope. Too steep a slope would indicate longitudinal stiffness and difficulty in control.

Rolling (or **banking**) does not produce any lateral shift in the center of the lift, so that there is no restoring moment as in pitch. However, when banked, the airplane **sideslips** toward the low wing. A fin placed above the center of gravity gives a lateral restoring moment that can correct the roll and stop the slip. The same effect can be obtained by **dihedral,** *i.e.*, by raising the wing tips to give a transverse V. An effective dihedral of 1 to 3 deg on each side is generally required to obtain stability in roll. In low-wing monoplanes, 2 deg effective dihedral may require 8 deg or more of geometrical dihedral owing to interference between the wing and fuselage.

In a **yaw** or **slip** the line of action of the lateral force depends on the size of the effective vertical fin area. Insufficient fin surface aft will allow the skid or slip to increase. Too much fin surface aft will swing the nose of the plane around into a tight spiral. Sound design demands sufficient vertical tail surface for adequate directional control and then enough dihedral to provide lateral stability.

When moderate positive effective dihedral is present, the airplane will possess **static lateral stability,** and a low wing will come up automatically with very little yaw. If the dihedral is too great, the airplane may roll considerably in gusts, but there is little danger of the amplitude ever becoming excessive. **Dynamic lateral stability** is not assured by static stability in roll and yaw but requires that these be properly proportioned to the damping in roll and yaw.

Spiral instability is the result of too much fin surface and insufficient dihedral.

HELICOPTERS

References: *Br.ARC-R & M* 1111, 1127, 1132, 1157, 1730, and 1859. *NACA-TM* 827, 836, 858. *NACA-TN* 626, 835, 1192, 3323, 3236. *NACA-TR* 434, 515, 905, 1078. *NACA Wartime Reports* L-97, L-101, L-110. NACA, "Conference on Helicopters," May, 1954. Gessow and Myers, "Aerodynamics of the Helicopter," Macmillan.

Helicopters derive lift, propulsion force, and control effect from adjustments in the blade angles of the rotor system. At least two rotors are required, and these may be arranged in any form that permits control over the reaction torque. The common arrangements are main lift rotor, auxiliary torque-control or tail rotor at 90 deg; two main rotors side by side; two main rotors fore and aft; and two main rotors, coaxial and oppositely rotating.

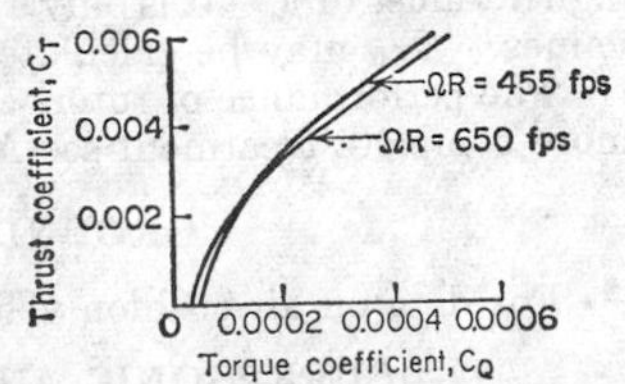

Fig. 26. Static thrust performance of NACA 8-H-12 blades.

The helicopter rotor is an actuator disk or momentum device that follows the same general laws as a propeller. In calculating the rotor performance, the major variables concerned are diameter D, ft (radius R); tip speed, $V_t = \Omega R$, fps; angular velocity of rotor $\Omega = 2\pi n$, rps; and rotor solidity q (= ratio of blade area/disk area). The rotor performance is usually stated in terms of coefficients similar to propeller coefficients. The rotor coefficients are:

$$\text{Thrust coefficient } C_T = T/\rho(\Omega R)^2\pi R^2$$
$$\text{Torque coefficient } C_Q = Q/\rho(\Omega R)^2\pi R^3$$
$$\text{Torque } Q = 5{,}250 \text{ bhp/rpm}$$

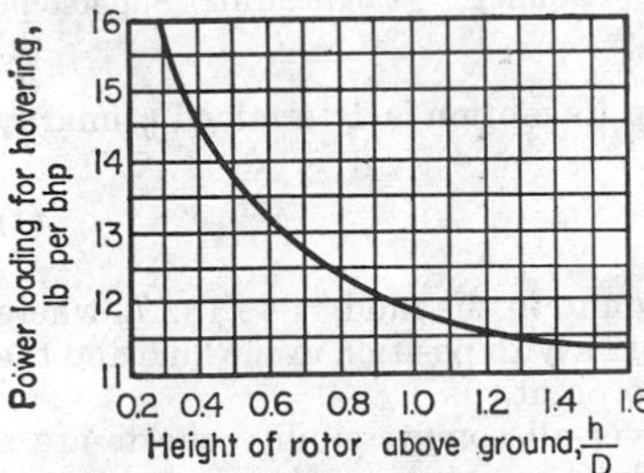

Fig. 27. Observed ground effect on Sikorsky-type helicopters.

Hovering. The **hovering flight** condition may be calculated from basic rotor data given in Fig. 26. These data are taken from full-scale rotor tests. Surface-contour accuracy can reduce the total torque coefficient 6 to 7 percent. The power required for hovering flight is greatly reduced near the ground. Observed flight-test data from various sources are plotted in Fig. 27. The ordinates are heights above the ground measured in rotor diameters.

Effect of Gross Weight on Rate of Climb. Figure 28 from Talkin (*NACA-TN* 1192) shows the rate of climb that can be obtained by reducing the load on a helicopter that will just hover. Conversely, given the rate of climb with a given load, the curves determine the increase in load that will reduce the rate of climb to zero; *i.e.*, they determine the maximum load for which hovering is possible.

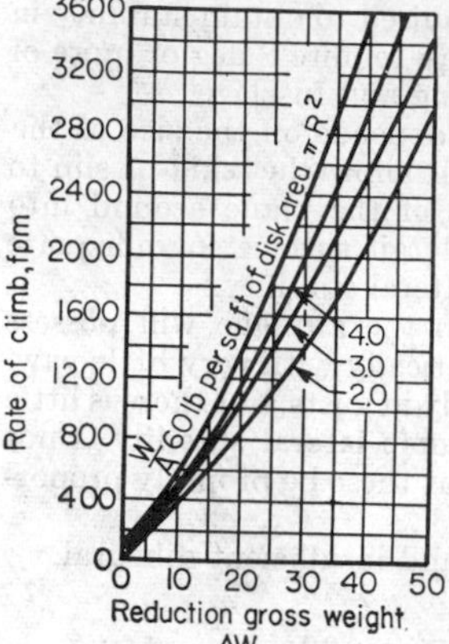

FIG. 28. Effect of gross weight on the rate of climb of a helicopter.

Performance with Forward Speed. The performance of a typical single-main-rotor-type helicopter may be shown by a curve of C_{TR}/C_{QR} plotted against $\mu = v/\pi nD$, where v is the speed of the helicopter, as in Fig. 29.

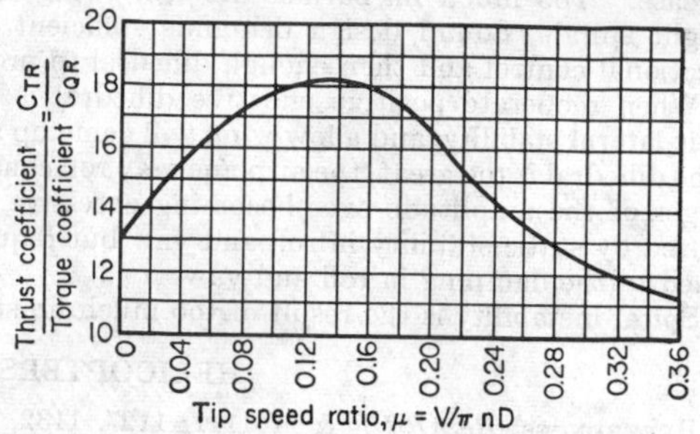

FIG. 29. Performance curve for a single-main-rotor-type helicopter.

This curve includes the parasite-drag effects which are appreciable at the higher values of μ. It is only a rough approximation to the experimentally determined values. C_{TR} may be calculated to determine C_{QR}, from which Q is obtained.

The performance of rotors at forward speeds involves a number of variables. For more complete treatment see *NACA-TN* 1192 and *NACA Wartime Report* L-110.

GROUND-EFFECT MACHINES (GEM)

For data on air-cushion vehicles and hydrofoil craft, see pp. 11–69 *et seq.*

SUPERSONIC AND HYPERSONIC AERODYNAMICS

REFERENCES: Liepmann and Roshko, "Elements of Gas Dynamics," Wiley. "High Speed Aerodynamics and Jet Propulsion," 12 vols., Princeton. Shapiro, "The Dynamics and Thermodynamics of Compressible Fluid Flow," Vols. I, II, Ronald. Howarth (Ed.), "Modern Developments in Fluid Mechanics—High Speed Flow," Vols. I, II, Oxford. Kuethe and Schetzer, "Foundations of Aerodynamics," Wiley. Ferri, "Elements of Aerodynamics of Supersonic Flows," Macmillan. Bonney, "Engineering Supersonic Aerodynamics," McGraw-Hill.

The effect of the compressibility of a fluid upon its motion is determined primarily by the **Mach number** M.

$$M = V/V_s \tag{1}$$

where V = speed of the fluid and V_s = speed of sound in the fluid $= 49.1\sqrt{T}$, where T is in deg R and V_s in fps. The Mach number varies with position in the fluid and the compressibility effect likewise varies from point to point.

If a *body moves through the atmosphere,* the over-all compressibility effects are a function of the Mach number $\bar{M}$ of the body, defined as

$$\bar{M} = \text{velocity of body/speed of sound in the atmosphere}$$

Table 5 lists the useful **gas dynamics relations** between velocity, Mach number, and various fluid properties for isentropic flow. (See also pp. 4–60 *et seq.*)

$$V^2 = 2(h_0 - h) = 2C_p(T_0 - T)$$

$$\frac{V^2}{V_{s0}^2} = \frac{M^2}{1 + \frac{\gamma - 1}{2} M^2}$$

$$\left(\frac{p}{p_0}\right)^{\frac{\gamma-1}{\gamma}} = \frac{T}{T_0} = \left(\frac{\rho}{\rho_0}\right)^{\gamma-1} = \left(\frac{V_s}{V_{s0}}\right)^2 = \frac{1}{1 + \frac{\gamma - 1}{2} M^2} \tag{2}$$

$$\frac{\frac{1}{2}\rho V^2}{p_0} = \frac{\frac{\gamma}{2} M^2}{\left(1 + \frac{\gamma - 1}{2} M^2\right)^{\gamma/(\gamma-1)}}$$

$$\left(\frac{A}{A^*}\right)^2 = \frac{1}{M^2}\left[\frac{2}{\gamma + 1}\left(1 + \frac{\gamma - 1}{2} M^2\right)\right]^{(\gamma+1)/(\gamma-1)}$$

where h = enthalpy of the fluid; A = stream-tube cross section normal to the velocity; and the subscript $_0$ denotes the isentropic stagnation condition reached by the stream when stopped frictionlessly and adiabatically (hence isentropically). V_{s0} denotes the speed of sound in that medium.

For a nozzle, the stagnation condition is the state of the fluid at rest in the chamber ahead of the nozzle. For a body moving through the atmosphere, the stagnation state occurs only at the stagnation point at the nose of the body and may be computed by the above formulas using the Mach number of the body, $\bar{M}$.

The superscript * denotes the conditions occurring when the speed of the fluid equals the speed of sound in the fluid. For $M = 1$, Eqs. (**2**) become:

$$\frac{T^*}{T_0} = \left(\frac{V_s^*}{V_{s0}}\right)^2 = \frac{2}{\gamma + 1} \qquad \frac{p^*}{p_0} = \left(\frac{2}{\gamma + 1}\right)^{\frac{\gamma}{\gamma-1}} \qquad \frac{\rho^*}{\rho_0} = \left(\frac{2}{\gamma + 1}\right)^{\frac{1}{\gamma-1}} \tag{3}$$

For air $p^* = 0.52828p_0$; $\rho^* = 0.63394\rho_0$; $T^* = 0.83333T_0$.

For **subsonic regions,** flow behaves similarly to the familiar hydraulics or incompressible aerodynamics; in particular, an increase of velocity is associated with a decrease of stream-tube area, while friction causes a pressure drop in a tube. For **supersonic regions,** an increase of velocity is associated with an increase of stream-tube area, while friction causes a pressure rise in a tube. $M = 1$ is the dividing line between these two regions.

The **hypersonic regime** is that range of very high supersonic speeds (usually taken as $\bar{M} > 5$) where even a very streamlined body causes disturbance velocities comparable to the speed of sound, and stagnation temperatures can become so high that the gas molecules dissociate and become ionized.

Shock waves may occur at supersonic speeds. At low velocities the fluctuations that occur in the motion of a body (at the start of the motion or during flight) propagate away from the body at essentially the speed of sound. At higher subsonic speeds, fluctuations still propagate at the speed of sound in the fluid away from the body in all directions, but now the waves cannot get so far ahead; therefore, the force coefficients increase with an increase in the Mach number. When the Mach number of a body exceeds unity, the fluctuations instead of traveling away from the body in all directions are actually left behind by the body. These cases are illustrated in Fig. 30. As the supersonic speed is increased, the fluctuations are left farther behind and the force coefficients again decrease.

Where, for any reason, waves form an envelope as at $M > 1$ in Fig. 30, a wave of finite pressure jump may result.

Table 5. Isentropic Gas Dynamics Relations

(Emmons, "Gas Dynamics Tables for Air," Dover Publications, Inc., 1947)

M	$\frac{p}{p_0}$	$\frac{V}{V_{s0}}$	$\frac{A}{A^*}$	$\frac{\frac{1}{2}\rho V^2}{p_0}$	$\frac{\rho V}{\rho_0 V_{s0}}$	$\frac{\rho}{\rho_0}$	$\frac{T}{T_0}$	$\frac{V_s}{V_{s0}}$
0.00	1.000	0.000	∞	0.000	0.000	1.000	1.000	1.000
0.05	0.998	0.050	11.59	0.002	0.050	0.999	0.999	1.000
0.10	0.993	0.100	5.82	0.007	0.099	0.995	0.998	0.999
0.15	0.984	0.150	3.91	0.016	0.148	0.989	0.996	0.998
0.20	0.972	0.199	2.964	0.027	0.195	0.980	0.992	0.996
0.25	0.957	0.248	2.403	0.042	0.241	0.969	0.988	0.994
0.30	0.939	0.297	2.035	0.059	0.284	0.956	0.982	0.991
0.35	0.919	0.346	1.778	0.079	0.325	0.941	0.976	0.988
0.40	0.896	0.394	1.590	0.100	0.364	0.924	0.969	0.984
0.45	0.870	0.441	1.449	0.123	0.399	0.906	0.961	0.980
0.50	0.843	0.488	1.340	0.148	0.432	0.885	0.952	0.976
0.55	0.814	0.534	1.255	0.172	0.461	0.863	0.943	0.971
0.60	0.784	0.580	1.188	0.198	0.487	0.840	0.933	0.966
0.65	0.753	0.624	1.136	0.223	0.510	0.816	0.922	0.960
0.70	0.721	0.668	1.094	0.247	0.529	0.792	0.911	0.954
0.75	0.689	0.711	1.062	0.271	0.545	0.766	0.899	0.948
0.80	0.656	0.753	1.038	0.294	0.557	0.740	0.887	0.942
0.85	0.624	0.795	1.021	0.315	0.567	0.714	0.874	0.935
0.90	0.591	0.835	1.009	0.335	0.574	0.687	0.861	0.928
0.95	0.559	0.874	1.002	0.353	0.577	0.660	0.847	0.920
1.00	0.528	0.913	1.000	0.370	0.579	0.634	0.833	0.913
1.05	0.498	0.950	1.002	0.384	0.578	0.608	0.819	0.905
1.10	0.468	0.987	1.008	0.397	0.574	0.582	0.805	0.897
1.15	0.440	1.023	1.018	0.407	0.569	0.556	0.791	0.889
1.20	0.412	1.057	1.030	0.416	0.562	0.531	0.776	0.881
1.25	0.386	1.091	1.047	0.422	0.553	0.507	0.762	0.873
1.30	0.361	1.124	1.066	0.427	0.543	0.483	0.747	0.865
1.35	0.337	1.156	1.089	0.430	0.531	0.460	0.733	0.856
1.40	0.314	1.187	1.115	0.431	0.519	0.437	0.718	0.848
1.45	0.293	1.217	1.144	0.431	0.506	0.416	0.704	0.839
1.50	0.272	1.246	1.176	0.429	0.492	0.395	0.690	0.830
1.55	0.253	1.274	1.212	0.426	0.478	0.375	0.675	0.822
1.60	0.235	1.301	1.250	0.422	0.463	0.356	0.661	0.813
1.65	0.218	1.328	1.292	0.416	0.443	0.337	0.647	0.805
1.70	0.203	1.353	1.338	0.410	0.433	0.320	0.634	0.796
1.75	0.188	1.378	1.387	0.403	0.417	0.303	0.620	0.788
1.80	0.174	1.402	1.439	0.395	0.402	0.287	0.607	0.779
1.85	1.161	1.425	1.495	0.386	0.387	0.272	0.594	0.770
1.90	0.149	1.448	1.555	0.377	0.372	0.257	0.581	0.762
1.95	0.138	1.470	1.619	0.368	0.357	0.243	0.568	0.754
2.00	0.128	1.491	1.688	0.358	0.343	0.230	0.556	0.745
2.50	0.059	1.667	2.637	0.256	0.219	0.132	0.444	0.667
3.00	0.027	1.793	4.235	0.172	0.137	0.076	0.357	0.598
3.50	0.013	1.884	6.790	0.112	0.085	0.045	0.290	0.538
4.00	0.007	1.952	10.72	0.074	0.054	0.028	0.238	0.488
4.50	0.003	2.003	16.56	0.049	0.035	0.017	0.198	0.445
5.00	0.002	2.041	25.00	0.033	0.023	0.011	0.167	0.408
10.00	0.00002	2.182	536.00	0.002	0.001	0.005	0.048	0.218

The speed of sound is higher in a higher temperature region. For a compression wave, disturbances in the compressed (hence high-temperature) fluid will propagate faster than and overtake disturbances in the lower temperature region. In this way shock waves are formed.

For a **stationary normal shock wave,** the fluid velocities V_1 before and V_2 after the shock are related by

$$V_1 V_2 = (V_s^*)^2 \tag{4}$$

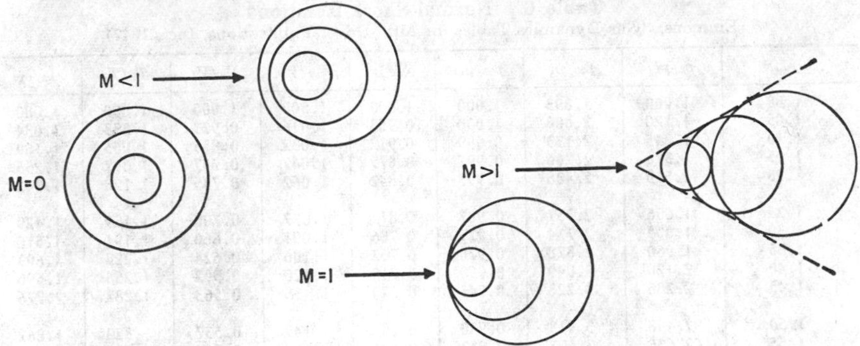

FIG. 30. Propagation of sound waves in moving streams.

Other properties are given by

$$p_2 - p_1 = \rho_1 V_1 (V_1 - V_2) \tag{5}$$

$$\frac{T_2}{T_1} = \left(\frac{V_{s2}}{V_{s1}}\right)^2 = \left(\frac{2}{\gamma + 1}\right)^2 \frac{1}{M_1{}^2}\left(1 + \frac{\gamma - 1}{2} M_1{}^2\right)\left(\gamma M_1{}^2 - \frac{\gamma - 1}{2}\right) \tag{6}$$

$$M_2{}^2 = \left(1 + \frac{\gamma - 1}{2} M_1{}^2\right)\left(\gamma M_1{}^2 - \frac{\gamma - 1}{2}\right)^{-1} \tag{7}$$

$$\frac{p_{20}}{p_1} = \left(\frac{\gamma + 1}{2}\right)^{\frac{\gamma+1}{\gamma-1}} M^2 \left(\gamma - \frac{\gamma - 1}{2M_1{}^2}\right)^{-1/(\gamma-1)} \tag{8}$$

$$\frac{p_{20}}{p_{10}} = \left(\frac{\gamma + 1}{2}\right)^{\frac{\gamma+1}{\gamma-1}} M^2 \left(1 + \frac{\gamma - 1}{2} M^2\right)^{-\frac{\gamma}{\gamma-1}} \left(\gamma - \frac{\gamma - 1}{2M^2}\right)^{-1/(\gamma-1)} \tag{9}$$

The subscript 20 refers to the stagnation condition after the shock, while the subscript 10 refers to the stagnation condition ahead of the shock.

In a normal shock M, V, and p_0 decrease; p, ρ, T, and s increase; while T_0 remains unchanged. These relations are given numerically in Table 6.

If the shock is moving, these same relations apply *relative to the shock*. In particular, if the shock advances into stationary fluid, it does so at the speed V_1 which is always greater than the speed of sound in the stationary fluid by an amount dependent upon the shock strength.

A **shock wave** may be **oblique** to a supersonic stream (see Fig. 31). If so, it behaves exactly like a normal shock to the normal component of the stream. The tangential component is left unchanged. Thus the resultant velocity not only drops abruptly in magnitude but also changes discontinuously in direction. Figure 32 gives the relations between M_1, M_2, θ_w, and δ.

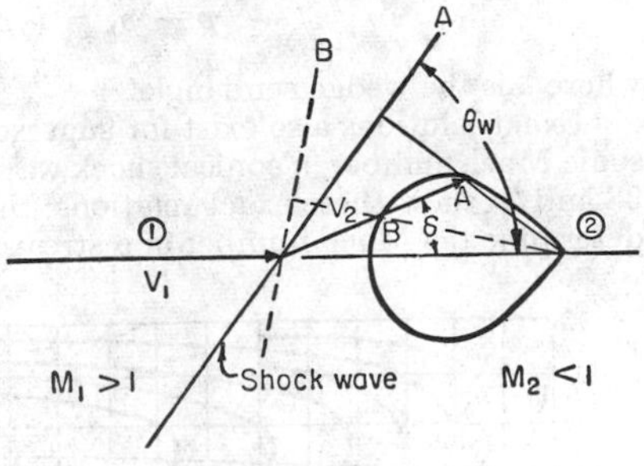

FIG. 31. Shock polar.

If, for a given supersonic stream, the velocities following all possible oblique shocks are plotted, a **shock polar** is obtained, as in Fig. 31. For any given stream deflection there are two possible shock angles. The **supersonic flow past a wedge** can, in principle, occur with either the strong shock B or the weak shock A attached to the leading edge; in practice only the weak shock occurs. The exact flow about the wedge may be computed by Eqs. (**4**) to (**9**) or more easily with the help of Fig. 32. For small wedge angles, the shock angle differs only slightly from $\sin^{-1}(1/M)$, the **Mach angle,** and the

Table 6. Normal Shock Relations
(Emmons, "Gas Dynamics Tables for Air," Dover Publications, Inc., 1947)

M	p_2/p_1	p_{20}/p_1	p_{20}/p_{10}	M_2	V_{s2}/V_{s1}	V_2/V_1	T_2/T_1	ρ_2/ρ_1
1.00	1.000	1.893	1.000	1.000	1.000	1.000	1.000	1.000
1.05	1.120	2.008	1.000	0.953	1.016	0.923	1.033	1.084
1.10	1.245	2.133	0.999	0.912	1.032	0.855	1.065	1.169
1.15	1.376	2.266	0.997	0.875	1.047	0.797	1.097	1.255
1.20	1.513	2.408	0.993	0.842	1.062	0.745	1.128	1.342
1.25	1.656	2.557	0.987	0.813	1.077	0.700	1.159	1.429
1.30	1.805	2.714	0.979	0.786	1.091	0.660	1.191	1.516
1.35	1.960	2.878	0.970	0.762	1.106	0.624	1.223	1.603
1.40	2.120	3.049	0.958	0.740	1.120	0.592	1.255	1.690
1.45	2.286	3.228	0.945	0.720	1.135	0.563	1.287	1.776
1.50	2.458	3.413	0.930	0.701	1.149	0.537	1.320	1.862
1.55	2.636	3.607	0.913	0.684	1.164	0.514	1.354	1.947
1.60	2.820	3.805	0.895	0.668	1.178	0.492	1.388	2.032
1.65	3.010	4.011	0.876	0.654	1.193	0.473	1.423	2.115
1.70	3.205	4.224	0.856	0.641	1.208	0.455	1.458	2.198
1.75	3.406	4.443	0.835	0.628	1.223	0.439	1.495	2.279
1.80	3.613	4.670	0.813	0.617	1.238	0.424	1.532	2.359
1.85	3.826	4.902	0.790	0.606	1.253	0.410	1.573	2.438
1.90	4.045	5.142	0.767	0.596	1.268	0.398	1.608	2.516
1.95	4.270	5.389	0.744	0.586	1.284	0.386	1.647	2.592
2.00	4.500	5.640	0.721	0.577	1.299	0.375	1.688	2.667
2.50	7.125	8.526	0.499	0.513	1.462	0.300	2.138	3.333
3.00	10.333	12.061	0.328	0.475	1.637	0.259	2.679	3.857
3.50	14.125	16.242	0.213	0.451	1.821	0.235	3.315	4.261
4.00	18.500	21.068	0.139	0.435	2.012	0.219	4.047	4.571
4.50	23.458	26.539	0.092	0.424	2.208	0.208	4.875	4.812
5.00	29.000	32.653	0.062	0.415	2.408	0.200	5.800	5.000
10.00	116.500	129.220	0.003	0.388	4.515	0.175	20.388	5.714

velocity component normal to this **Mach wave** is the speed of sound; the pressure jump is small and is given approximately by

$$p - p_1 = (\gamma p_1 \bar{M}_1^2/\sqrt{\bar{M}_1^2 - 1})\delta \qquad \textbf{(10)}$$

where δ is the wedge semiangle.

Exact solutions also exist for **supersonic flow past a cone.** Above a certain supersonic Mach number, a conical shock wave is attached to the apex of the cone. Figures 33 and 34 show these exact relations; they are so accurate that they are often used to determine the Mach number of a stream by measuring the shockwave angle on a cone of known angle. For small cone angles the shock differs only slightly from the **Mach cone,** *i.e.*, a cone whose semiapex angle is the Mach angle; the pressure on the cone is then given approximately by

$$p - p_1 = \gamma p_1 \bar{M}_1^2 \delta^2 (\ln 2/\delta \sqrt{\bar{M}_1^2 - 1}) \qquad \textbf{(11)}$$

where δ is the cone semiangle.

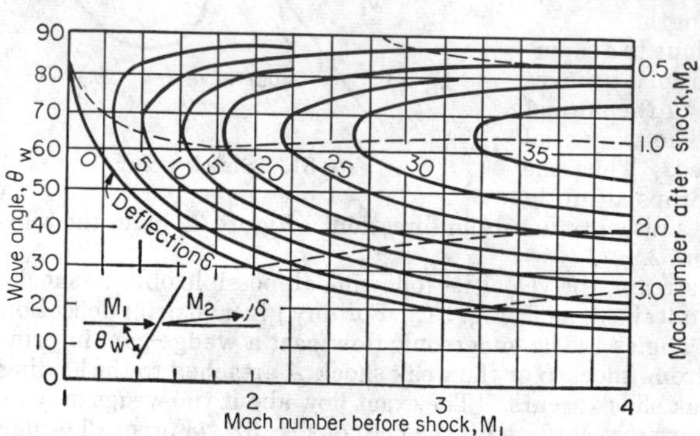

FIG. 32. Oblique-shock wave relations.

A nozzle consisting of a single contraction will

produce at its exit a jet of any velocity from $M = 0$ to $M = 1$ by a proper adjustment of the pressure ratio. For use as a subsonic wind-tunnel nozzle where a uniform parallel gas stream is desired, it is only necessary to connect the supply section to the parallel-walled, or open-jet, test section by a smooth gently curving wall. If the radius of curvature of the wall is nowhere less than the largest test-section cross-sectional dimension, no flow separation will occur and a good test gas stream will result.

When a **converging nozzle** connects two chambers with the pressure drop beyond the critical $[(p/p_0) < (p^*/p_0)]$, the Mach number at the exit of the nozzle will be 1; the pressure ratio from the supply section to the nozzle exit will be critical; and all additional expansion will take place outside the nozzle.

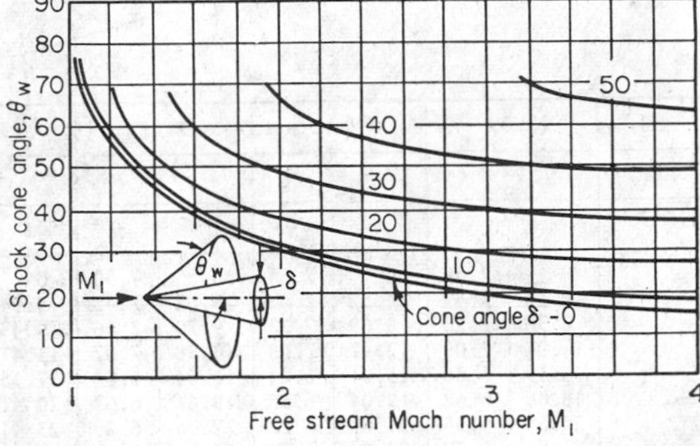

FIG. 33. Wave angles for supersonic flow around cones.

A nozzle designed to supply a supersonic jet at its exit must converge to a minimum section and diverge again. The area ratio from the minimum section to the exit is given in the column headed A/A^* in Table 5. A converging-diverging nozzle with a pressure ratio p/p_0 = (gas pressure)/(stagnation pressure), Table 5, gradually falling from unity to zero will produce shock-free flow for all exit Mach numbers from zero to the subsonic Mach number corresponding to its area ratio. From this Mach number to the supersonic Mach number corresponding to the given area ratio, there will be shock waves in the nozzle. For all smaller pressure ratios, the Mach number at the nozzle exit will not change, but additional expansion to higher velocities will occur outside of the nozzle.

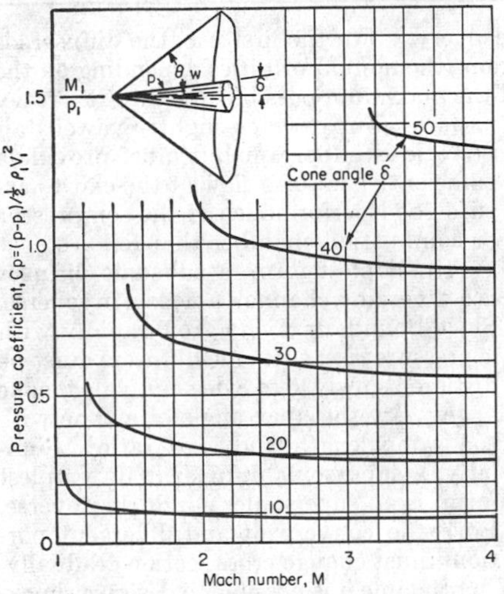

FIG. 34. Pressure coefficients for supersonic flow around cones.

To obtain a uniform parallel shock-free supersonic stream, the converging section of the nozzle can be designed as for a simple converging nozzle. The diverging or supersonic portion must be designed to produce and then cancel the expansion waves. A series of designs are given in Table 7. These nozzles would perform as designed if it were not for the growth of the boundary layer. Experience indicates that these nozzles give a good first approximation to a uniform parallel supersonic stream but at a somewhat lower Mach number.

For **rocket nozzles** and other thrust devices, the gain in thrust obtained by making the jet uniform and parallel at complete expansion must be balanced against the loss of thrust caused by the friction on the wall of the greater length of nozzle required. A simple conical diverging section, cut off experimentally for maximum thrust, is generally used (see also p. 11–126).

For transonic and supersonic flow, **diffusers** are used for the recovery of kinetic energy. They follow the test sections of supersonic wind tunnels and are used as inlets

Table 7. Typical Nozzle Ordinates

(Puckett, Supersonic Nozzle Design, *Jour. Applied Mechanics*, **13**, No. 4, 1948)

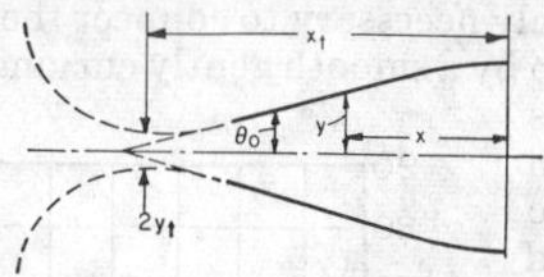

M	1.99		2.42		2.82		3.24		3.62		4.04	
θ_0	7°		9°		12°		13°		14°		15°	
	x	y	x	y	x	y	x	y	x	y	x	y
	0	7.50	0	7.50	0	7.50	0	7.50	0	7.50	0	7.50
	4.38	7.42	4.52	7.42	5.62	7.40	4.94	7.41	5.52	7.40	5.94	7.40
	8.36	7.28	8.69	7.28	9.70	7.26	9.43	7.26	10.39	7.23	11.20	7.21
	11.97	7.09	12.47	7.08	13.38	7.07	13.47	7.05	14.89	7.00	16.10	6.96
	15.19	6.88	15.91	6.84	16.64	6.84	17.15	6.79	18.75	6.73	20.22	6.67
	18.06	6.62	19.04	6.56	19.67	6.57	20 41	6.50	22.24	6.42	23.94	6.34
	20.65	6.35	21.80	6.27	22.35	6.29	23 41	6.19	25.39	6.09	27.17	6.00
	21.84	6.20	24.34	5.96	24.80	5.99	26.03	5.87	28.08	5.76	30.11	5.64
			26.57	5.65	26.95	5.69	28.42	5.53	30.56	5.41	32.69	5.28
	x_t	4.48	27.48	5.49	28.90	5.37	30.46	5.21	32.73	5.07	34.95	4.92
					30.70	5.07	32.35	4.87	34.66	4.73	36.96	4.57
			x_t	3.06	32.20	4.77	33.99	4.56	36.35	4.40	38.69	4.23
					32.90	4.62	35.44	4.25	37.87	4.08	40.26	3.90
							36.13	4.09	39.20	3.77	41.62	3.58
					x_t	2.10			39.80	3.62	42.79	3.29
							x_t	1.41			43.32	3.15
									x_t	0.988		
											x_t	0.673

on high-speed planes and missiles for ram recovery. For the first use, the diffusers is fed a non-uniform stream from the test section (the nonuniformities depending on the particular body under test) and should yield the maximum possible pressure-rise ratio. In missile use the inlet diffuser is fed by a uniform (but perhaps slightly yawed) air stream. The maximum possible pressure-rise ratio is important but must provide a sufficiently uniform flow at the exit to assure good performance of the compressor or combustion chamber that follows.

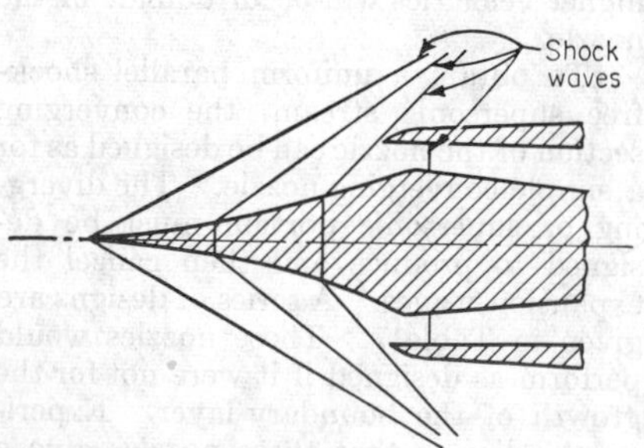

FIG. 35. Oblique-shock diffuser for ram recovery on a supersonic-plane air intake (Oswatitsch diffuser).

In simplest form, a **subsonic diffuser** is a diverging channel, a nozzle in reverse. Since boundary layers grow rapidly with a pressure rise, subsonic diffusers must be diverged slowly, 6 to 8 deg equivalent cone angle, *i.e.*, the apex angle of a cone with the same length and area ratio. Similarly, a **supersonic diffuser** in its simplest form is a supersonic nozzle in reverse. Both the convergent and divergent portions must change cross section gradually. In principle it is possible to design a shock-free diffuser. In practice shock-free flow is not attained, and the design is based upon minimizing the shock losses. Oblique shocks should be produced at the inlet and reflected a sufficient number of times to get compression nearly to $M = 1$. A short parallel section and a divergent section can now be added with the expectation that a weak normal shock will be formed near the throat of the diffuser.

An efficient diffuser for a supersonic inlet is illustrated in Fig. 35. The central body has stepped cones, each one of which produces an oblique conical shock wave. After two or three such weak shock compressions, the air flows at about $M = 1$ into an annular opening and is further compressed by an internal normal shock and by subsonic diffusion. *NACA-TM* 1140 describes this diffuser. A ratio of pressure after diffusion to the total pressure in the atmosphere of as high as 0.6 is obtained with such diffusers at a Mach number of 3. The indications are that higher efficiencies are obtainable by careful design.

For a **supersonic wind tunnel,** the best way to attain the maximum pressure recovery at a wide range of operating conditions is to make the diffuser throat variable. The ratio of diffuser-exit static pressure to the diffuser-inlet (test-section outlet) total pressure is given in the following table:

Table 8

M	1	1.5	2	3	4
p_e/p_0	0.83	0.69	0.50	0.23	0.10

These pressure recoveries are attained by the proper adjustment of the throat section of a variable diffuser on a supersonic wind-tunnel nozzle.

A **supersonic wind tunnel** consists of a compressor or compressor system including precoolers or aftercoolers, a supply section, a supersonic nozzle, a test section with balance and other measuring equipment, a diffuser, and sufficient ducting to connect the parts. The *minimum pressure ratio* required from supply section to diffuser exit is given in Table 8. Any pressure ratio greater than this is satisfactory. The extra pressure ratio is automatically wasted by additional shock waves that appear in the diffuser. The compression ratio required of the compressor system must be greater than that of Table 8 by at least an amount sufficient to take care of the pressure drop in the ducting and valves. The latter losses are estimated by the usual hydraulic formulas.

After selecting a compressor system capable of supplying the required maximum pressure ratio, the test section area is computed from

$$A = 1.73 \frac{Q}{V_{s0}} \frac{A}{A^*} \frac{p_e}{p_0} \quad \text{sq ft} \qquad \textbf{(12)}$$

where Q is the inlet volume capacity of the compressors, cfs; V_{s0} is the speed of sound in the supply section, fps; A/A^* is the area ratio given in Table 5 as a function of M; p_e/p_0 is the pressure ratio given in Table 8 as a function of M.

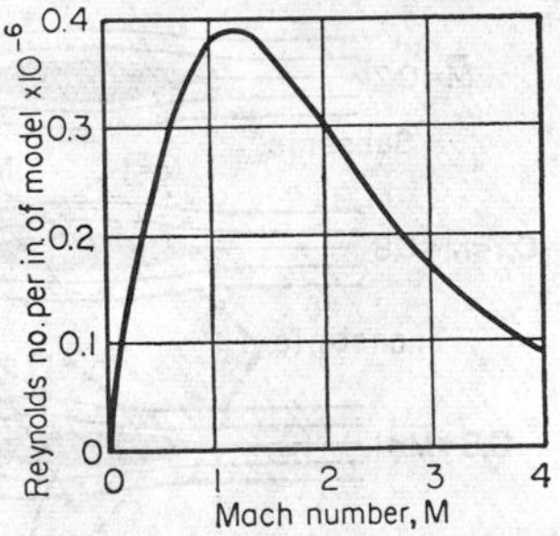

FIG. 36. Reynolds number–Mach number relation (for fixed model size and stagnation condition).

The nozzle itself is designed for uniform parallel air flow in the test section. Such designs are given in Table 7, which covers only the part of the nozzle between the exit section and the maximum expansion angle. Since for each Mach number a different nozzle is required, the nozzle must be flexible or the tunnel so arranged that fixed nozzles can be readily interchanged.

The Mach number of a test is set by the nozzle selection, while the Reynolds number is set by the inlet conditions and size of model. The Reynolds number is computed from

$$R = R_0 D\,(p_0/14.7)\,(540/T_0)^{1.268} \qquad \textbf{(13)}$$

where R_0 is the Reynolds number per inch of model size for atmospheric temperature and pressure, as given by Fig. 36; D is model diam, in.; p_0 is the stagnation pressure, psi; T_0 is the stagnation temperature, deg F abs.

For a closed-circuit tunnel, the Reynolds number can be varied independently of the Mach number by adjusting the mass of air in the system, thus changing p_0.

Intermittent-wind tunnels for testing at high speeds do not require the large and expensive compressors associated with continuous-flow tunnels. They use either a large vacuum tank or a large pressure tank (often in the form of a sphere) to produce a pressure differential across the test section. Such tunnels may have steady flow for only a few seconds, but by careful instrumentation, sufficient data may be obtained in this time. A **shock tube** may be used as an intermittent-wind tunnel as well as to study shock waves and their interactions; it is essentially a long tube of constant or varying cross section separated into two parts by a frangible diaphragm. High pressure exists on one side; by rupturing the diaphragm, a shock wave moves into the gas with the lower pressure. After the shock wave a region of steady flow exists for a few milliseconds. Very high stagnation temperatures can be created in a shock tube, which is not the case in a wind tunnel, so that it is useful for studying hypersonic flow phenomena.

Wind-tunnel force measurements are subject to errors caused by the model support strut. Wall interference is small at high Mach numbers for which the reflected model head wave returns well behind the model. Near $\bar{M} = 1$, the wall interference becomes very large. In fact the tunnel chokes at Mach numbers given in Table 5, at

$$\frac{A}{A^*} = \frac{1}{1 - \dfrac{\text{area of model projected on test-section cross section}}{\text{area of test-section cross section}}} \tag{14}$$

There are two choking points: one subsonic and one supersonic. Between these two Mach numbers, it is impossible to test in the tunnel. As these Mach numbers are approached, the tunnel wall interference becomes very large.

For tests in this range of Mach number, specially constructed **transonic wind tunnels** with perforated or slotted walls have been built. The object here is to produce a mean flow velocity through the walls that comes close to that which would have existed there had the body been moving at that speed in the open. Often auxiliary blowers are needed to produce the necessary suction on the walls and to reinject this air into the tunnel circuit in or after the diffuser section.

Drag is difficult to predict precisely from wind-tunnel measurements, especially in the transonic regime. **Flight tests** of rocket-boosted models which coast through the range of Mach number of interest are used to obtain better drag estimates; from telemetered data and radar or optical sighting the deceleration can be determined, which in turn yields the drag.

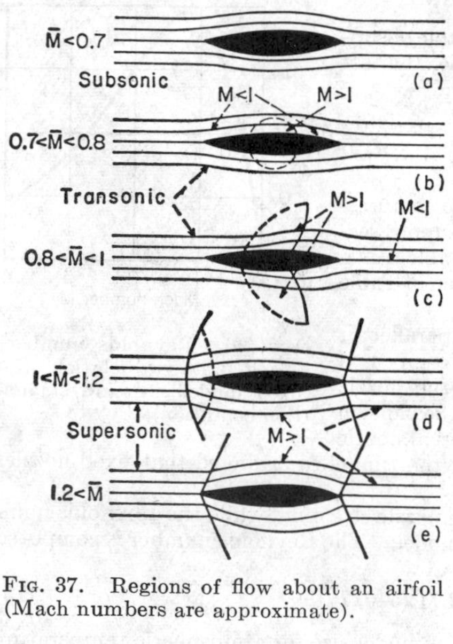

Fig. 37. Regions of flow about an airfoil (Mach numbers are approximate).

ACOUSTIC THEORY

As the speed of a body is increased from a low subsonic value [Fig. 37(*a*)], the local Mach number becomes unity somewhere in the fluid along the surface of the body, *i.e.*, the lower critical Mach number is reached. Above this there is a small range of transonic speed in which a supersonic region exists [Fig. 37(*b*)]. Shock waves appear in this region attached to the sides of the body [Fig. 37(*c*)] and grow with increasing speed. At still higher transonic speeds a detached shock wave appears ahead of the body, and the earlier side shocks either disappear or move to the rear [Fig. 37(*d*)]. Finally, for a sharp-nosed body, the head wave moves back and becomes attached [Fig. 37(*e*)]. The flow is now generally supersonic everywhere, and the transonic regime is replaced by the supersonic regime. With the appearance of shock waves there occurs a considerable alteration of the pressure distribution, and the center of pressure on airfoil sections moves from the one-fourth chord point back toward the one-half chord point. There is an associated increase of drag and, often, flow separation at the base of the shock.

The redistribution of pressures and the motion of shock waves over the wing surfaces through the transonic regime demands special consideration in the design of control surfaces so that they do not become ineffective by separation or inoperative by excessive loading.

If a body is slender (*i.e.*, planes tangent to its surface at any point make small angles with the flight direction), the disturbance velocities caused by this body will be small compared to the flight speed and, excluding the hypersonic regime, small compared to the speed of sound. This permits the use of **acoustic theory** (also called linearized small-disturbance theory) to predict the approximate flow past the body. This theory relates the steady flow past the body at subsonic speeds to the incompressible flow past a distorted version of this body (the "generalized Prandtl-Glauert rule").

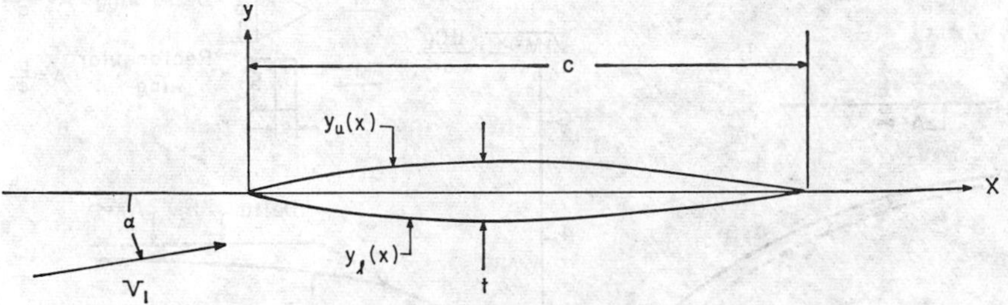

FIG. 38. Supersonic airfoil section.

To find the velocity components in the **subsonic** flow about any slender body, first determine the velocity components, u, v, w (in the x, y, z directions, respectively), in the incompressible flow, at the same stream speed, about a stretched shape whose streamwise (x-axis direction) dimensions are $1/\beta$ times as great ($\beta = \sqrt{1 - \bar{M}^2}$). The desired velocity components are then $\beta^{-2}u$, $\beta^{-1}v$, $\beta^{-1}w$ at corresponding points of the stretched and unstretched bodies. For **thin airfoil sections** this theory predicts

$$C_L = 2\pi\alpha/\sqrt{1 - \bar{M}^2} \quad \alpha \text{ in radians} \tag{15}$$

where $L = C_L qS$ and $q = (\gamma/2)p_0\bar{M}^2$. For finite-span wings and for bodies, no such simple relations exist. However, an approximation to the over-all **lift coefficient** for thin flat wings of rectangular platform is (see Fig. 39):

$$C_L = 2\pi A\alpha/[2 + \sqrt{4 + (\beta A)^2}] \tag{16}$$

and the drag is made up of the induced drag due to lift and the skin-friction drag (see p. 11–88).

$$C_D = (C_L/\pi A)(1 + 0.01\beta A) + C_{DF} \tag{17}$$

At supersonic speeds, the Prandtl-Glauert rule is also applicable if we replace β by $\lambda = \sqrt{\bar{M}^2 - 1}$ and relate flows to flow past a stretched (or compressed) body at $\bar{M} = \sqrt{2}$, where $\lambda = 1$. For **thin airfoil sections** (see Fig. 38) this theory predicts

$$C_L = 4\alpha/\sqrt{\bar{M}^2 - 1} \quad \alpha \text{ in radians} \tag{18}$$

$$C_D = \frac{2}{\lambda}\int_0^1 \left[\left(\frac{dy_u}{dx}\right)^2 + \left(\frac{dy_l}{dx}\right)^2\right] d\left(\frac{x}{c}\right) + \frac{4\alpha^2}{\lambda} + C_{DF} \tag{19}$$

where $\dfrac{dy_u}{dx}$ and $\dfrac{dy_l}{dx}$ are the slopes of the upper and lower surfaces of the airfoil, respectively, and C_{DF} is again the skin-friction drag coefficient. Note that there is a drag due to thickness and a drag due to lift at supersonic speeds for an airfoil section where there is none at subsonic speeds. For symmetric double-wedge airfoil sections, the thickness drag coefficient becomes $(4/\lambda)(t/c)^2$, while for symmetric biconvex airfoil sections it is $(16/3\lambda)(t/c)^2$, where t is the maximum thickness.

Within the acoustic approximation, a disturbance at a point in supersonic flow can affect only the points in the downstream **Mach cone,** *i.e.*, a conical region with apex at the point, axis parallel to the stream direction, and semicone angle equal to the Mach angle (see Fig. 30). Thus a rectangular wing with constant airfoil section has two-dimensional flow on all parts of the wing except the points within the tip Mach cones. At Mach numbers near unity these tip Mach cones cover nearly the entire wing, whereas at high Mach numbers they cover only a small part. Figure 39 shows the lift-curve

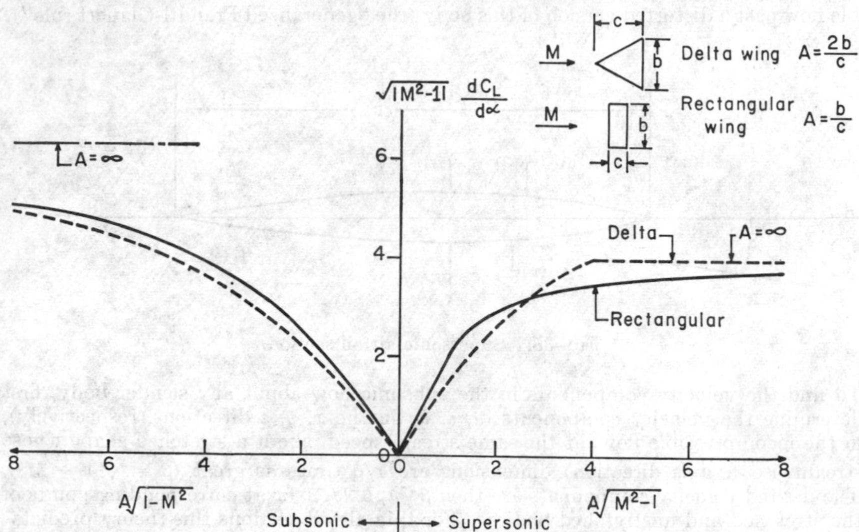

FIG. 39. Lift-coefficient curve slope for rectangular and delta wings (according to linearized theory).

coefficient slope for flat **rectangular** and **delta plan-form wings** at subsonic and supersonic speeds; these predictions of acoustic theory are inaccurate for high-aspect-ratio wings in the transonic regime, but elsewhere compare favorably with experiment. Figure 40 shows the drag due to lift for the same wings. The reduction in drag due to lift of the delta wing relative to the rectangular wing at moderate supersonic speeds, predicted by acoustic theory and shown in Fig. 40 is due to the fact that the delta-wing leading edge is **swept back,** and the component of velocity normal to the leading edge is subsonic. This creates a leading-edge suction which reduces the drag. This drag reduction is only partially realized in practice; a wing with a rounded leading edge realizes more of this reduction than a wing with a sharp leading edge. Figure 41 shows the thickness drag of the rectangular and delta wings, which occurs only at supersonic speeds. Note again that the leading-edge sweepback of the delta wing helps to reduce this drag at moderate supersonic speeds.

The lift of a slender **axially symmetric body** at small angle of attack is nearly independent of Mach number and is given approximately by

$$C_L = 2\alpha \tag{20}$$

where the lift coefficient is based on the cross-sectional area of the base. The drag for $\alpha = 0$ at subsonic speeds is made up of skin friction and **base drag;** a dead-air region exists just behind the blunt base, and the pressure here is below ambient, causing a rearward suction which is the base drag. At supersonic speeds a wave drag is added, which represents the energy dissipated in shock waves from the nose. Figure 42 shows a typical drag-coefficient curve for a body of revolution where the **fineness ratio** (ratio of length to diameter) is 12.2. The skin-friction drag coefficient based on wetted area is the same as that of a flat plate, within experimental error.

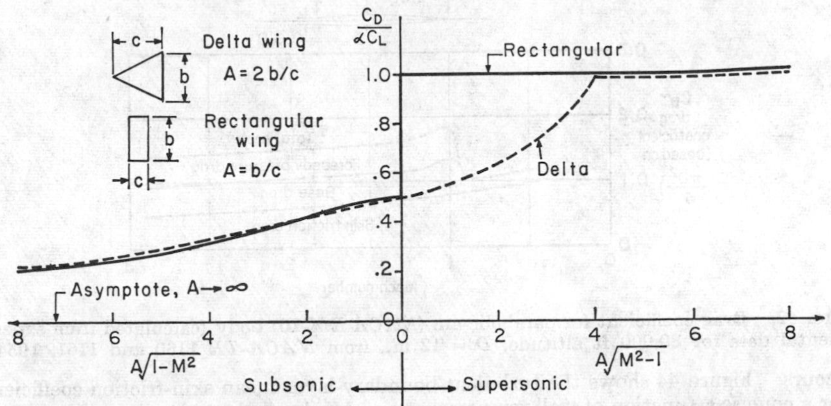

Fig. 40. Drag due to lift for rectangular and delta wings (according to linearized theory).

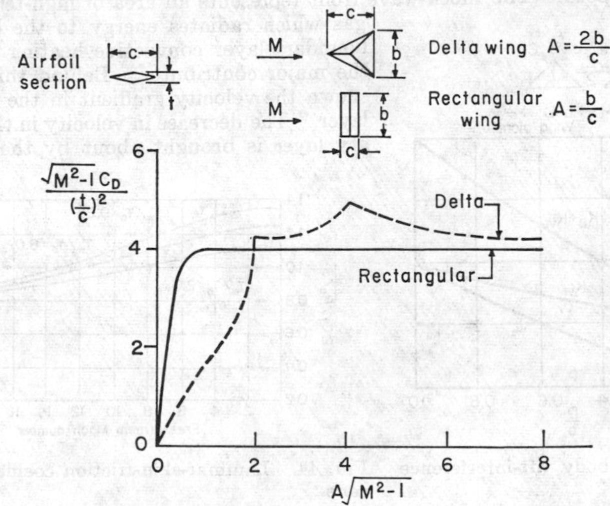

Fig. 41. Supersonic thickness drag coefficient for rectangular and delta wings with symmetrical double-wedge airfoil section (according to linearized theory).

At transonic and moderate supersonic speeds, the wave drag of a **wing-body combination** can be effectively reduced by making the cross-sectional area distribution (including wings) a smooth curve when plotted *vs.* fuselage station. This is the **area rule**; its application results in a decided indentation in the fuselage contour at the wing juncture. **Lift interference** effects also occur, especially when the body diameter is not small compared to the wing span. If the wing is attached to a cylindrical body, and if the wing-alone lift coefficient would have been C_L, then the lift carried on the body is $K_B C_L$, and the lift carried on the wing is $K_W C_L$. Figure 43 shows the variation of K_B and K_W with body diameter to wing-span ratio.

The **effect of compressibility on skin-friction drag** (see p. 11–88) is slight at subsonic speeds, but at supersonic speeds, a significant reduction in skin-friction coefficient occurs. Figure 44 shows the turbulent-boundary-layer mean skin-friction coefficient for a cone as a function of wall temperature and Mach number. An important effect at high speed is **aerodynamic heating.**

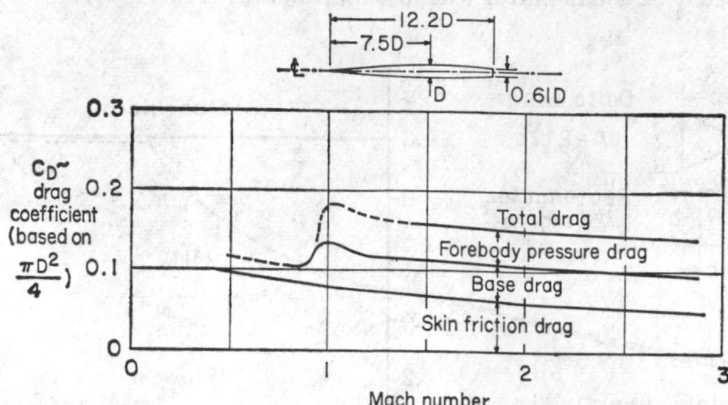

FIG. 42. Drag coefficient for parabolic-arc (*NACA RM*-10) body (calculated from experimental data for 30,000 ft altitude, $D = 12$ in., from *NACA-TR* 1160 and 1161, 1954).

Figure 45 illustrates the velocity profile behind the shock wave of a body traveling at hypersonic speed. The shock-wave front represents an area of high-temperature gas which radiates energy to the body, but boundary-layer convective heating is usually the major contributor. Behind this front is shown the velocity gradient in the boundary layer. The decrease in velocity in the boundary layer is brought about by the forces of interaction between fluid particles and the body (viscosity). This change in velocity is accompanied by a change in temperature and is dependent on the characteristics of the boundary layer. For example, heat transfer from a turbulent boundary layer may be of an order of magnitude greater than for laminar flow.

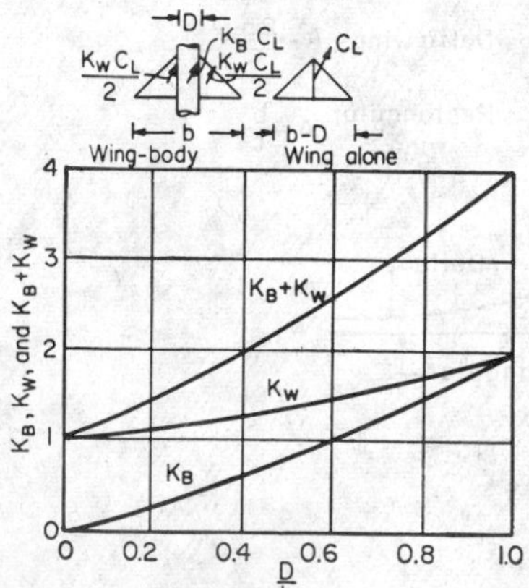

FIG. 43. Wing-body lift-interference factors.

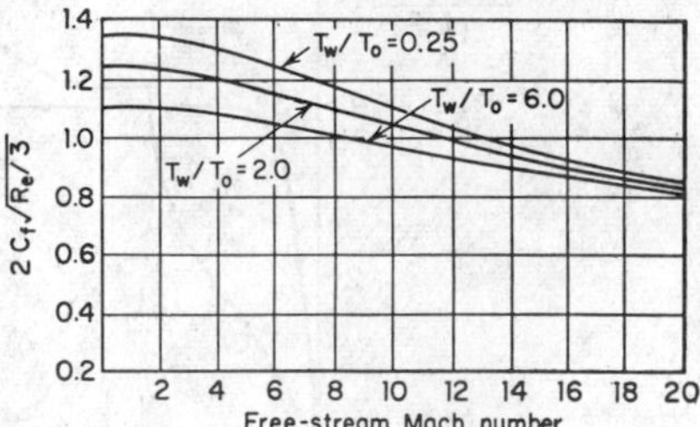

FIG. 44. Laminar-skin-friction coefficient for a cone.

If the gas is brought to rest instantaneously, the total energy in the flow is converted to heat and the temperature of the air will rise. The resulting temperature is known as the **stagnation temperature** (see stagnation point, Fig. 45).

$$T_S = T_\infty \left[1 + \left(\frac{\gamma - 1}{2} \right) M^2 \right] \tag{21}$$

T_∞ is the ambient temperature of the gas at infinity, and γ is the specific-heat ratio of the gas. For undissociated air, $\gamma = 1.4$.

In general, this simple, one-dimensional relationship between velocity and temperature does not hold for temperature in the boundary layer. The laminae of the boundary layer are not insulated from each other, and there is cross conduction. This is associated with the **Prandtl number** Pr, which is defined as

$$Pr = \frac{C_p \mu}{k_r} \tag{22}$$

where k_r = thermal conductivity of the fluid
C_p = specific heat of the fluid at constant pressure
μ = absolute viscosity of the fluid

Defining the **recovery factor** r as the ratio of the rise in the idealistic wall and stagnation temperature over the free-stream temperature,

$$r = (T_{aw} - T_\infty)/(T_s - T_\infty) = (Pr)^n \tag{23}$$

For laminar flow, $r = (Pr)^{1/2}$; and for turbulent flow, $r = (Pr)^{1/3}$.

Prandtl number Pr greatly complicates the thermal computations, but since it varies only over a small range of values, a recovery factor of 0.85 is generally used for laminar flow and 0.90 for turbulent flow.

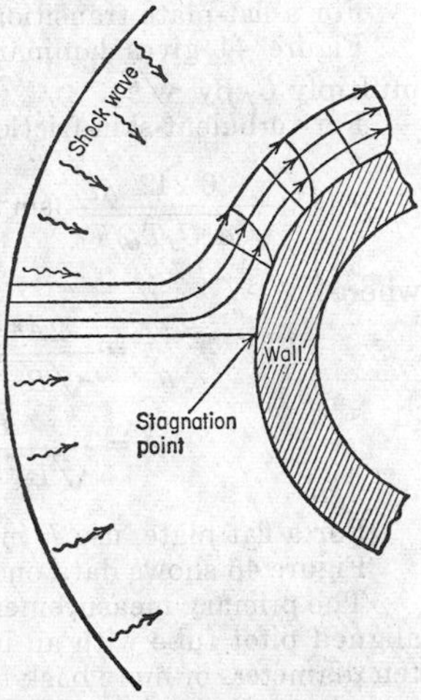

Fig. 45. Velocity profile behind a shock wave.

For a thermally thin wall, the rate of change of the surface temperature is a function of the rate of total heat input and the surface's ability to absorb the heat.

$$\frac{dT_w}{dt} = \frac{\dot{q}_T}{wcb} \tag{24}$$

where t = time
$\dot{q}_T$ = forced convective heating + radiation heating − heat radiation from the skin
w = density of skin material
c = specific heat of skin material
b = skin thickness
T_w = skin temperature

The heat balance may then be written

$$wcb\left(\frac{dT_w}{dt}\right) = k_c\left\{T_0\left[1 + r\left(\frac{\gamma_B - 1}{2}\right)M_0{}^2\right] - T_w\right\} + \alpha G_s A_p - \epsilon\sigma T_w{}^4 \tag{25}$$

where A_p = correction factor to account for area normal to radiation source; γ_B = specific heat ratio of boundary layer; ϵ = radiative emissivity of surface; σ = Stefan-Boltzmann constant [17.3×10^{-10} Btu per hr (ft²)(deg R⁴)]; α = surface absorptivity; G_S = solar irradiation Btu per hr (ft²)

For small time increments Δt,

$$\frac{dT_w}{dt} = \frac{T_{w2} - T_{w1}}{\Delta t}$$

Then

$$T_{w_2} = T_{w_1} + \frac{\Delta t}{wcb}\left(h_c\left\{T_0\left[1 + \left(\frac{\gamma_B - 1}{2}\right)M_0{}^2\right] - T_w\right\} + \alpha G_s A_p - T_w{}^4\right) \tag{26}$$

The local heat-transfer coefficient h_c is defined as

$$h_c = \frac{k_r}{r^4/3}\, C_p C_q \rho_0 V g \tag{27}$$

where C_p = specific heat of air; C_f = local skin-friction coefficient; ρ_0 = density outside of boundary layer; V = velocity outside of boundary layer; g = acceleration of gravity.

For a cone, $k_r = 1{,}800$ (laminar $R < 2 \times 10^6$) and $k_r = 1{,}800r^{4/3}$ (turbulent).

For a flat-plate transition, Reynolds number is 1×10^6.

Figure 44 gives laminar-skin-friction coefficient for a cone. For a flat plate, multiply C_f by $\sqrt{3/2}$.

For turbulent-skin-friction coefficient for a cone,

$$\frac{0.242}{\sqrt{A^2 C_f T_w/T_0}} (\sin^{-1} \psi + \sin^{-1} \theta) = 0.41 \log_{10} \frac{R}{2} C_f - 1.26 \log_{10} \frac{T_w}{T_0} \tag{28}$$

where

$$\psi = \frac{2A^2 - B}{\sqrt{B^2 + 4A^2}} \qquad A^2 = \frac{(\gamma_0 - 1/2)M_0^2}{T_w/T_0}$$

$$\theta = \frac{B}{\sqrt{B^2 + 4A^2}} \qquad B = \frac{1 + (\gamma_0 - 1/2)M_0^2}{T_w/T_0} - 1$$

For a flat plate, use R instead of $R/2$ in Eq. (**28**).

Figure 46 shows data on stagnation and adiabatic wall temperatures.

The primary **measurements in aerodynamics** are pressure measurements. A well-aligned pitot tube with an impact-pressure hole at its nose and static-pressure holes ten diameters or more back from the nose will accurately measure the **impact pressure** and the **static pressure** of a uniform gas stream. Up to sonic speed the impact pressure is identical with stagnation pressure, but at supersonic speeds, a detached shock wave forms ahead of the probe, through which there is drop in stagnation pressure; the portion of the shock wave just ahead of the probe is normal, so that Eq. (**9**) gives the relation of the measured impact pressure to the isentropic stagnation pressure.

Force measurements of total lift, drag, side force, pitching, moment, yawing moment, and rolling moment on models are made on wind-tunnel balances just as at

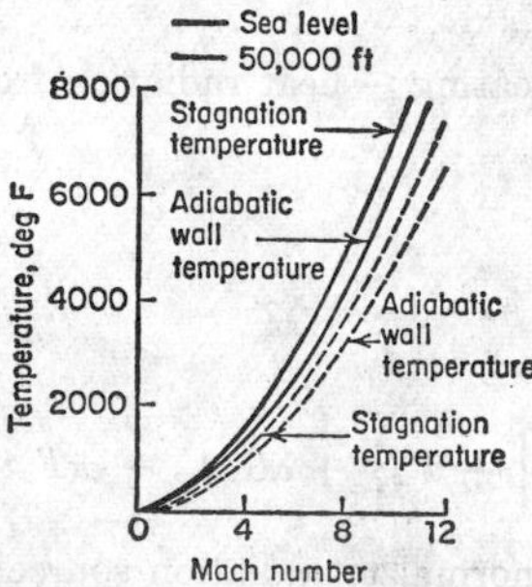

FIG. 46. Variation of stagnation and adiabatic wall temperature with Mach number.

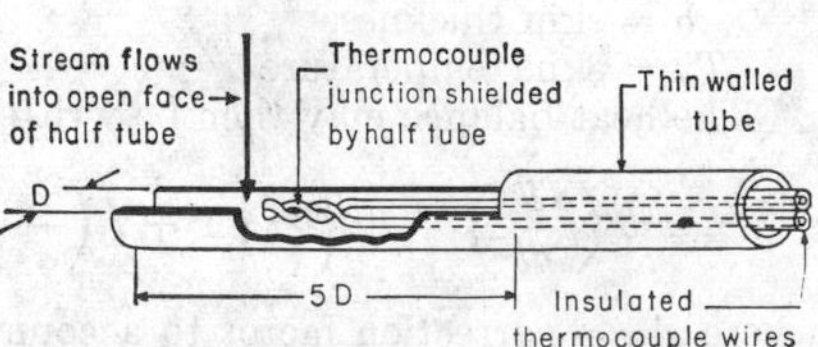

FIG. 47. Stagnation-temperature probe (recovery factor = 0.98).

low speed. Small internal-strain-gage balances are often used to minimize strut interference.

An open thermocouple is unreliable for determining **stagnation temperature** (see p. (4–101) if it is in a stream of high velocity. Figure 47 shows a simple temperature probe in which the fluid is decelerated adiabatically before its temperature is measured. The recovery factor used in Eq. (**9***c*), p. 4–101, for this probe, accurately aligned to the stream, is 0.98.

Optical measurements in high-speed flow depend on the variation of index of refraction with gas **density**. This variation is given by

$$n = 1 + k\rho \tag{29}$$

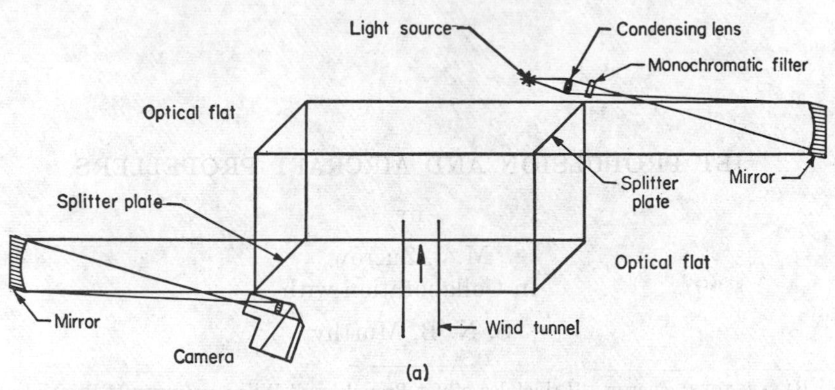

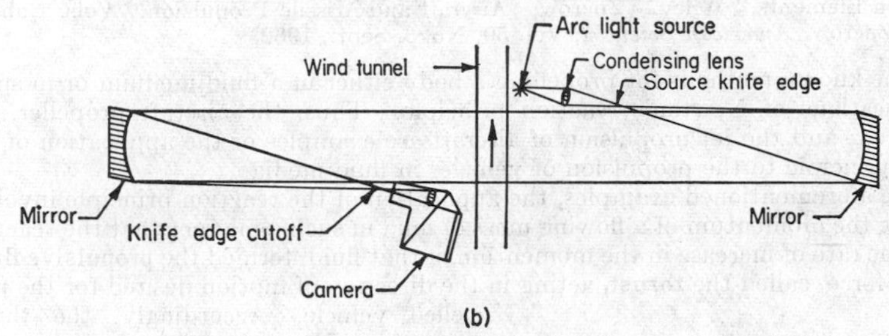

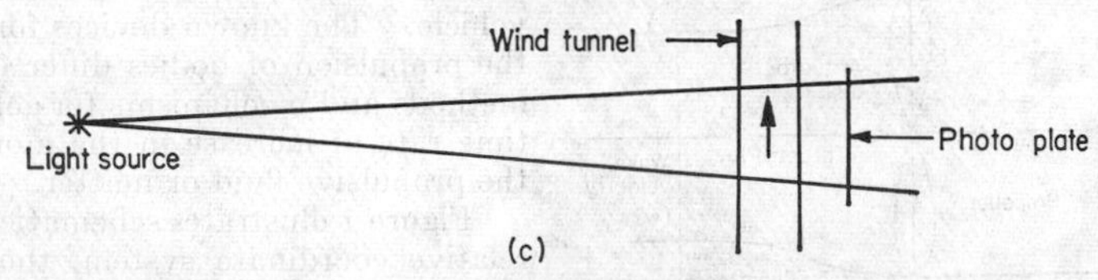

FIG. 48. Optical systems for observing high-speed flow phenomena: (*a*) interferometer; (*b*) Schlieren (two-mirror) system; (*c*) shadowgraph.

where $k = 0.116$ cu ft per slug for air. A Mach-Zehnder **interferometer** [Fig. 48(*a*)], is capable of giving accurate density information for two-dimensional and axially symmetric flows. The **Schlieren** optical system [Fig. 48(*b*)] is sensitive to density gradients and is the most commonly used system to determine location of shock waves and regions of compression or expansion. The **shadowgraph** optical system is the simplest system [Fig. 48(*c*)] and is sensitive to the second space derivative of the density.

JET PROPULSION AND AIRCRAFT PROPELLERS

BY

M. J. Zucrow
In Collaboration with

S. N. B. Murthy

REFERENCES: Zucrow, "Principles of Jet Propulsion," Wiley. Zucrow, "Principles of Guided Missile Design," (Propulsion Section), Vol. 2, Van Nostrand. Sutton, "Rocket Propulsion Elements," Wiley. Zucrow, "Aircraft and Missile Propulsion," Vols. 1 and 2, Wiley. Zucrow, *American Scientist*, Vol. 50, No. 3, Sept., 1962.

All the known methods for propelling a body either in a fluid medium or in space are applications of Newton's reaction principle. Thus, the aircraft propeller, the ship's screw, and the jet propulsion of aircraft are examples of the application of the reaction principle to the propulsion of vehicles in fluid media.

In the aforementioned examples, the application of the reaction principle involves increasing the momentum of a flowing mass of fluid in such a manner that the reaction to the time rate of increase in the momentum of that fluid, termed the **propulsive fluid,** creates a force, called the **thrust,** acting in the direction of motion desired for the propelled vehicle. Accordingly, the thrust arises from increasing the momentum flux of the propulsive fluid in the direction opposite to that desired for the propelled vehicle. The known devices for achieving the propulsion of bodies differ only in the methods and mechanisms for achieving the time rate of increase in the momentum of the propulsive fluid or matter.

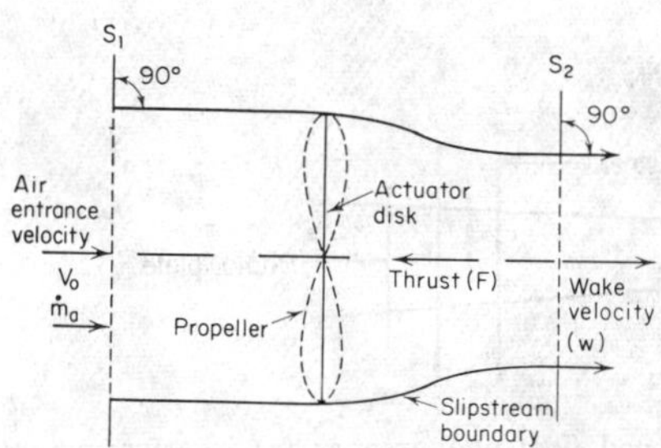

FIG. 1. Ideal propeller in relative coordinate system.

Figure 1 illustrates schematically, in the relative coordinate system, the operating principle of the **ideal aircraft propeller.** Power is supplied to the propeller, which is assumed to be equivalent to an **actuator disk,** which imparts only an axial acceleration to the air flowing through it. The rotation of the actuator disk produces a **slipstream** composed of the entire mass of air flowing in the axial direction through the actuator-disk area, *i.e.*, the area of the circle swept by the propeller blades. Atmospheric air enters the slipstream with the flight speed V_0 and mass flow rate $\dot{m}_a$. It leaves the slipstream with the **wake velocity** w, and the thrust is given by Eq. (**4**) (p. 11–122). Propulsion systems employing propellers will be termed **propeller propulsion.** (For detailed discussions of the airplane propeller, see p. 11–129 *et seq.*)

Jet propulsion differs from propeller and other methods of propulsion in that the propulsive fluid (or matter) is ejected from within the propelled body in the form of a high-speed jet of fluid or particles, instead of being caused to flow around the propelled body. In the abstract, at least, there are no restrictions upon either the type of matter, called the **propellant,** for forming the high-velocity exhaust jet or the means for producing the high-velocity exhaust jet. The selection of the most suitable **propellant** and the most appropriate jet-propulsion engine is dictated by the flight mission for the vehicle. For the practical propulsion of bodies, however, only two types of exhaust jets are suitable:

1. For propulsion within the atmosphere of the earth, there is the jet formed by expanding a highly heated, compressed gas containing atmospheric air as either a major or a sole constituent. Such an engine is called either an **airbreathing** or a **thermal-jet engine.** If the heating is accomplished by burning a fuel in the air, the engine is a **chemical thermal-jet engine.** If the air is heated by direct or indirect heat exchange with a nuclear-energy source, the engine is termed a **nuclear thermal-jet engine.**

2. For propulsion both within and beyond the atmosphere of earth, there is the exhaust jet containing no atmospheric air. Such an exhaust jet is termed a **rocket jet,** and any matter used for creating the jet is called a **propellant.** A rocket may consist of a stream of gases, solids, liquids, ions, electrons, or a plasma. The assembly of all the equipment required for producing the rocket jet constitutes a **rocket engine.**

Modern airbreathing engines may be segregated into two principal types: (1) **ramjet engines,** and (2) **turbojet engines.** The turbojet engines are of two types: (1) the **simple turbojet engine,** and (2) the **turbofan,** or **bypass engine.**

Rocket engines can be classified by the form of energy used for achieving the desired jet velocity. The three principal types of rocket engines are (1) **chemical rocket engines,** (2) **nuclear heat-transfer rocket engines,** and (3) **electric rocket engines.**

The propulsive element of a jet-propulsion engine, irrespective of type, is the **exhaust nozzle** or orifice. If the exhaust jet is gaseous, the assembly comprising all the other components of the jet-propulsion engine constitutes a gas generator for supplying highly heated, high-pressure gases to the exhaust nozzle.

These classifications of jet-propulsion engines apply to the basic types of engines. It is possible to have combinations of the different types of thermal-jet engines and also combinations of thermal-jet engines with rocket engines; only the principal types are discussed here.

ESSENTIAL FEATURES OF AIRBREATHING OR THERMAL-JET ENGINES

In the subsequent discussions a *relative coordinate system* is employed wherein the atmospheric air flows toward the propulsion system with the flight speed V_0, and the gases leave the propulsion system with the velocity w, *relative to the walls of the propulsion system.* Furthermore, steady-state operating conditions are assumed.

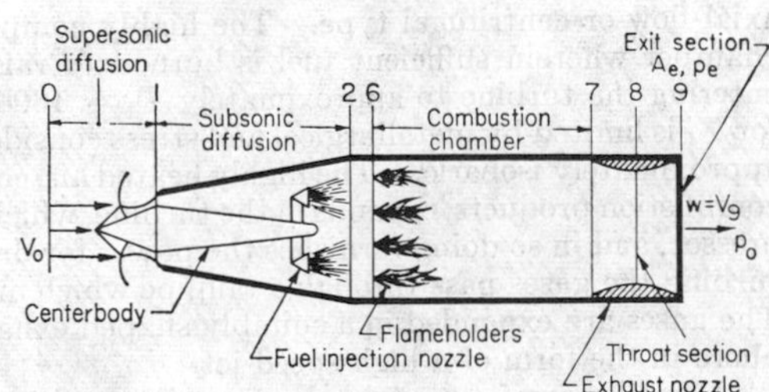

FIG. 2. The ramjet engine.

1. Ramjet Engine. Figure 2 illustrates schematically the essential features of a ramjet engine for propelling a vehicle at supersonic flight speeds. It comprises three major components: a diffusion system, consisting of a supersonic diffuser followed by a subsonic diffuser (0–2); a combustion chamber (6–7); and an exhaust nozzle (7–9). Apart from the necessary control devices the engine has no moving parts.

The operating principle of the ramjet engine is as follows. The free-stream air flowing toward the engine with the supersonic Mach number M_0 is decelerated by the supersonic diffuser to approximately unity Mach number at the entrance to the subsonic diffuser; the deceleration is accompanied by the formation of shock waves and by an increase in the pressure of the air (diffusion). In the subsonic diffuser the air is further diffused so that it arrives at the entrance to the combustion chamber with a low Mach number ($M_6 = 0.2$, approximately); the value of M_6 is dictated by the combustion requirements. If P_0 is the total pressure of the free-stream air having the Mach number M_0, and P_6 that for the air entering the combustion system with the Mach number M_6, then it is desirable that P_6/P_0 be as large as possible.

In the combustion chamber a fuel is burned in the air, thereby raising the total temperature of the gases entering the exhaust nozzle (see Sec. 7) to approximately $T_7 = 3800$ F. Most generally a liquid hydrocarbon fuel is used, but experiments have been conducted with solid fuels and "slurries" of solid fuels in a liquid fuel. The combustion process is not quite isobaric because of the pressure drops in the combustion chamber, because of the increase in the momentum of the working fluid by heat addition, and because of friction. The hot gases are discharged to the atmosphere, after expanding in the exhaust nozzle, with the relative velocity $w = V_9$.

Since the ramjet engine can function only if there is a ram pressure rise at the entrance to the combustion chamber, it is not self-operating at zèro flight speed. It must, therefore, be accelerated to a flight speed which permits the engine to develop sufficient thrust for accelerating the vehicle it propels to the design flight Mach number. Consequently, a ramjet-propelled missile, for example, must either be launched by dropping it from an airplane or be **boosted** to the required flight speed by means of **launching,** or **booster,** rockets. From our present knowledge it appears that the most appropriate flight regime for the ramjet engine is between $M_0 = 2$ and $M_0 = 4$, approximately; the upper limit is set by the problem of cooling the outer skin of the engine body. If the fuel can be employed for cooling the metal parts exposed to high stagnation temperatures, then the Mach number range can be raised. In the past 5 years it has been demonstrated that it is possible to achieve combustion in a supersonic air stream so that it appears to be feasible to develop a supersonic combustion ramjet engine (**Scramjet**). Its successful development offers the potential of airplane flights in the hypersonic regime, $M_0 = 7$ to 12.

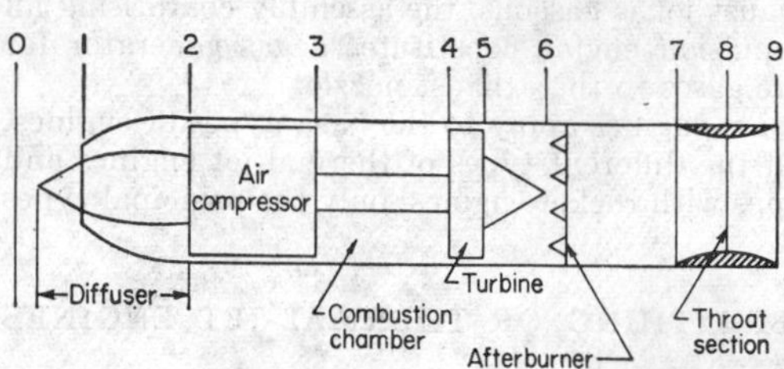

FIG. 3. The simple turbojet engine.

2. The Simple Turbojet Engine. Figure 3 illustrates schematically the principal features of a simple turbojet engine. Atmospheric air enters the engine and is partially compressed in the diffusion system, and further compressed to a much higher pressure by the air compressor, which may be of either the axial-flow or centrifugal type. The highly compressed air then flows to a combustion chamber wherein sufficient fuel is burned to raise the total temperature of the gases entering the turbine to approximately $T_4 = 1600$ F. The maximum allowable value for T_4 is limited by metallurgical and stress considerations. The combustion process is approximately isobaric. The highly heated air, containing approximately 25 percent of combustion products, expands in the turbine, which is directly connected to the air compressor, and in so doing furnishes the power for driving the air compressor. From the turbine the gases pass through a tailpipe which may be equipped with an **afterburner.** The gases are expanded in a suitably shaped exhaust nozzle and ejected to the atmosphere in the form of a high-speed jet.

Like the ramjet engine, the turbojet engine is a continuous-flow engine. It has an advantage over the ramjet engine in that its functioning does not depend upon the ram pressure of the entering air, although the amount of ram pressure recovered does affect its over-all economy and performance. The turbojet is the only airbreathing jet engine that has been applied in practice as the sole propulsion means for piloted aircraft. It appears to be eminently suited for propelling aircraft at speeds above 500 mph. As the design flight speed is increased, the ram pressure increases rapidly, and the characteristics of the turbojet engine tend to change over to those of the ramjet engine. Consequently, its top speed appears to be limited to that flight speed where it becomes more advantageous to employ the ramjet engine. No reliable figures can be given at this time, but estimates indicate that for speeds above approximately 1,800 mph it will be more advantageous to use some form of ramjet engine.

As in the case of any gas-turbine power plant, the efficiencies of the components of the turbojet engine have an influence on its performance characteristics, but its performance is not nearly as sensitive to changes in the efficiency of its component machines as is a gas turbine which delivers shaft power. (See p. 9–150 *et seq.*)

It has been indicated that two types of compressors are currently employed, the centrifugal compressor and the axial-flow compressor. Irrespective of the type, the objectives are similar. The compressor must be reliable, compact, easy to manufacture, and have a small frontal area. Because of the limited air induction capacity of centrifugal compressors, engines for developing thrusts above 7,000 lb approx at static sea level, employ axial-flow compressors (see p. 14–42 *et seq.*).

Because of its rather flat thrust *vs.* speed curve, the turbojet engine introduces certain operational problems at take-off because of the small ratio of take-off thrust to thrust in flight. Since the exhaust gases from the turbine contain considerable excess air, the jet velocity, and consequently the thrust, can be increased by burning additional fuel in the tailpipe upstream from the exhaust nozzle. By employing **"tailpipe burning,"** or **"afterburning,"** as it is called, the thrust can be increased by 35 percent, and at 500 mph, in a tactical emergency, by approximately 60 percent. With afterburning, the temperature of the gases entering the nozzle T_7 is of the order of 3800 R.

3. The Turbofan, or Bypass, Engine. For a fixed turbine inlet temperature, the jet velocity from a simple turbojet engine propelling an airplane at subsonic speed is relatively constant. The propulsive efficiency depends on the ratio of the flight speed to the jet velocity (see p. 11–122) and increases as the ratio increases. On the other hand, the thrust depends on the difference between the jet velocity and the flight speed; the larger the difference, the larger the thrust per unit mass of air induced into the engine. By reducing the jet velocity and simultaneously increasing the mass rate of airflow through the engine, the **propulsive efficiency** can be increased without decreasing the thrust. To do this, however, the engine must employ two or more airstreams (see Fig. 4 for a schematic illustration). A secondary stream of air is inducted through a **ducted fan,** which is driven from the turbine operating with the main hot-gas stream. Either the bypassed air can mix with the exhaust from the main turbine before being discharged through a single nozzle, or the bypassed air and the main gas stream can be ejected through separate nozzles (Fig. 4). Both of these systems provide a mean jet velocity which is smaller than that for a normal turbojet engine. Figure 4 also illustrates how afterburners can be incorporated into the primary and secondary fluid streams. In comparison with the simple turbojet engine, the takeoff thrust is larger for the turbofan engine. However, at low flight speeds, the gain in propulsive efficiency is smaller than at the design cruise speed.

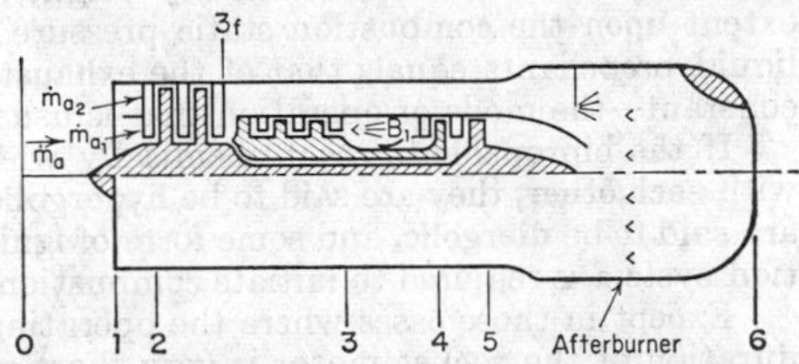

Fig. 4. The turbofan, or bypass, engine.

ESSENTIAL FEATURES OF ROCKET ENGINES

Figure 5 is a block-type diagram illustrating the essential features of a rocket engine, which comprises three main components: (1) a supply of propellant material contained in the rocket-propelled vehicle, (2) a propellant feed and metering system, and (3) a **thrust chamber,** also called a **rocket motor, thrustor,** or **accelerator.** In any rocket engine, energy must be added to the propellant as it flows through the thrustor. In Fig. 5, propellant material from the supply is metered and fed to the thrust chamber, where energy is added to it. As a consequence of the energy addition, the propellant is discharged from the thrustor with the jet velocity V_j. The thrust F acts in the direction opposite to that for the jet velocity V_j.

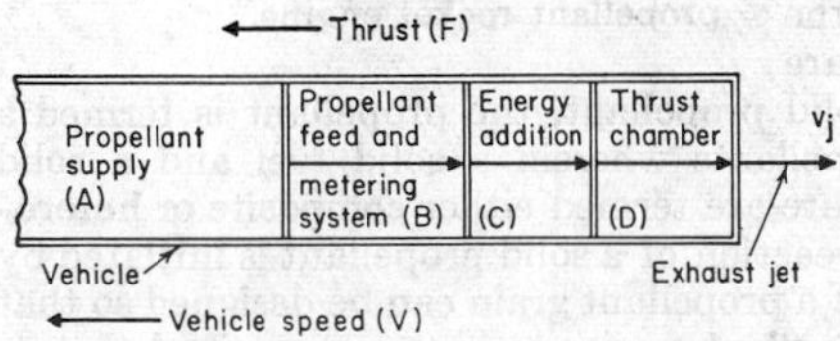

Fig. 5. Essential features of a rocket engine.

Chemical Rocket Engines

All chemical rocket engines have two common characteristics: (1) they utilize chemical reactions in a thrust chamber to produce a high-pressure, high-temperature gas at the entrance to a converging-diverging exhaust nozzle; (2) the hot propellant gas expands in flowing through the exhaust nozzle, and the expansion process converts a portion of the thermal energy, released by the chemical reaction, into the kinetic energy associated with a high-velocity gaseous-exhaust jet. Chemical rocket engines may be grouped into (1) liquid-bipropellant rocket engines, and (2) solid-propellant rocket engines.

Liquid-bipropellant Rocket Engine. Figure 6 illustrates the essential features of a liquid-bipropellant rocket engine employing **turbopumps** for feeding two propellants, an **oxidizer** and a **fuel,** to a rocket motor. The motor comprises (1) an injector, (2) a combustion chamber, and (3) a converging-diverging exhaust nozzle. The liquid propellants are fed under pressure, through the injector, into the combustion chamber, where they react chemically to produce large volumes of high-temperature, high-pressure gases. For a given propellant combination, the **combustion temperature** T_c depends primarily on the oxidizer-fuel **ratio** (by weight), termed the **mixture ratio,** and to a lesser extent upon the combustion static pressure p_c. When the mass rate of flow of the liquid propellants equals that of the exhaust gases, the combustion pressure remains constant—the mode of operation that is usually desired.

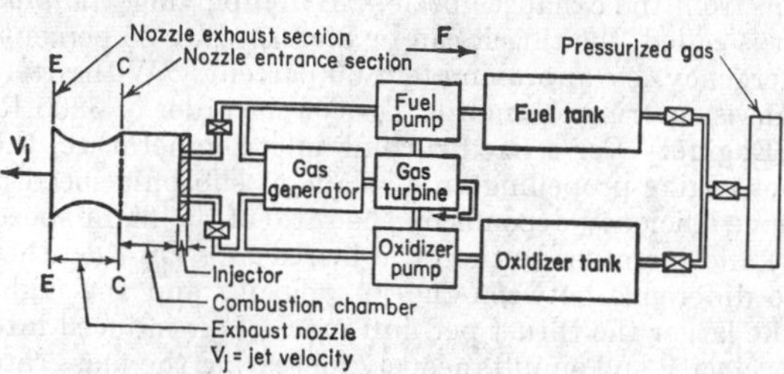

Fig. 6. Essential features of a liquid-bipropellant rocket engine.

If the bipropellants react chemically when their liquid streams come in contact with each other, they are said to be **hypergolic.** Propellants which are not hypergolic are said to be **diergolic,** and some form of ignition system is required to initiate combustion.

Except in those cases where the operating duration of the rocket motor is very short or where the combustion temperature is low, means must be provided for cooling the interior walls of the motor. In **regenerative cooling,** one of the propellants is circulated around the walls before injection into the motor. (See Table 2 (p. 11–128) for bipropellant combinations.)

Solid-propellant Rocket Engine. Figure 7 illustrates schematically a solid-propellant rocket engine employing an **internal-burning case-bonded grain;** the latter burns radially outward at a substantially constant rate. A solid propellant contains both its fuel and the requisite oxidizer. If the fuel and oxidizer are contained in the molecules forming the solid propellant, the propellant is termed a **double-base propellant.** Those solid propellants wherein a solid fuel and a solid oxidizer form an intimate mechanical mixture are termed either **composite or heterogeneous** solid propellants. The chemical reaction of a solid propellant is initiated by an igniter. In general, the configuration of a propellant grain can be designed so that the area of the burning surface of the propellant varies to give a prescribed thrust-versus-time curve.

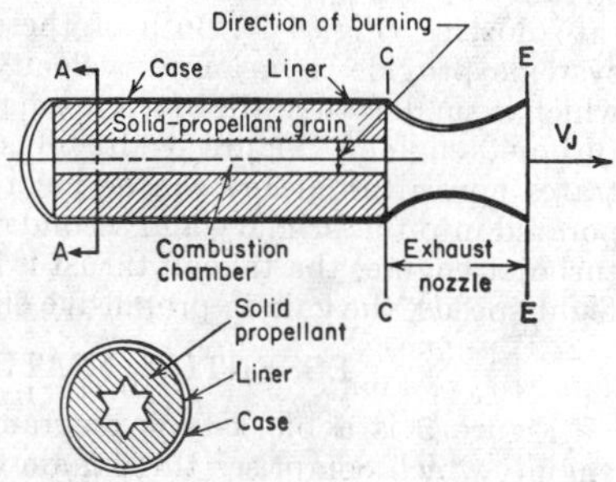

Fig. 7. Essential features of an internal-burning case-bonded solid-propellant rocket engine.

Nuclear Heat-transfer Rocket Engine

Figure 8 illustrates schematically a nuclear heat-transfer rocket engine employing a **solid-core reactor.** The heat generated by the fissions of the uranium nucleus is utilized for heating a gaseous propellant, such as hydrogen, to a high temperature of 4000 R (2200 K) approx at the entrance section of the exhaust nozzle. The hot gas is ejected to the surroundings after expansion in a converging-diverging exhaust nozzle. The basic difference between the operating principles of a nuclear heat-transfer and a chemical rocket engine is the substitution of nuclear fission for chemical reaction as the source of heat for the propellant gas. Since the exhaust nozzle is the propulsive element, the remaining components of the nuclear heat-transfer rocket engine constitute the hot-gas generator.

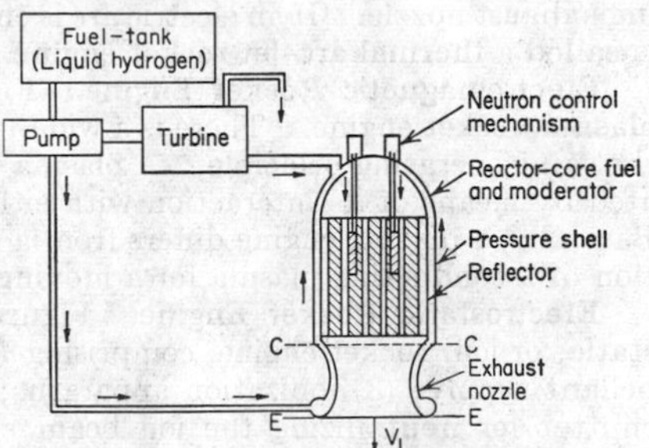

Fig. 8. Schematic arrangement of a nuclear heat-transfer rocket engine.

The propellant in a nuclear heat-transfer rocket engine functions basically as a fluid for cooling the solid-core nuclear reactor. Its selection is not based on energy considerations alone, but on such properties as specific heat, latent heat, molecular weight, and liquid density and on certain practical considerations.

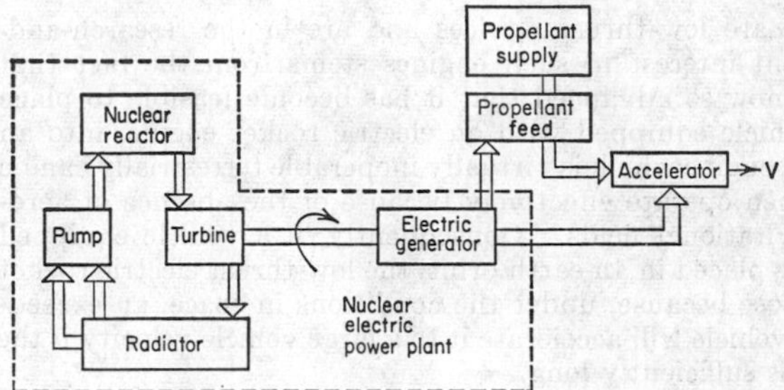

Fig. 9. Essential features of an electric rocket engine.

Electric Rocket Engines

Figure 9 illustrates diagrammatically an electric rocket engine, comprising (1) a **nuclear power source,** (2) an energy-conversion unit for obtaining the desired form of electrical energy, (3) a propellant feed and metering system, (4) an electrically operated thrustor, and (5) the requisite control devices. Electric rocket engines may be classified as (1) electrothermal, (2) electromagnetic, and (3) electrostatic.

Electrothermal Rocket Engine. Figure 10*a* illustrates the type of engine which uses electric power for heating a gaseous propellant to a high temperature before ejecting it through a converging-diverg-

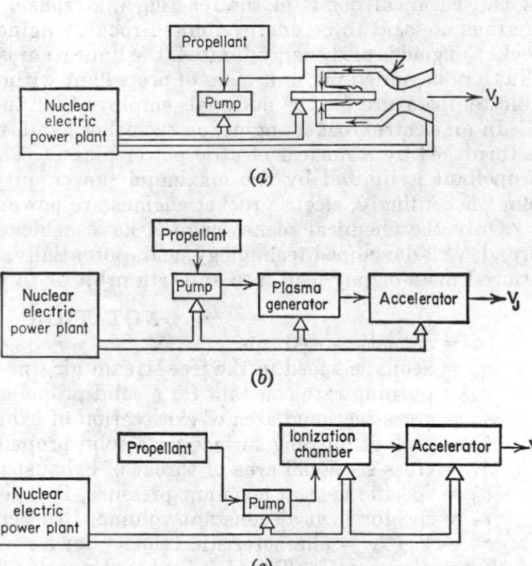

Fig. 10. Electric rocket engines. (*a*) Electrothermal rocket engine. (*b*) Electromagnetic rocket engine. (*c*) Electrostatic (ion) rocket engine.

ing exhaust nozzle. If an electric arc is employed for heating the propellant, the engine is called a **thermal arc-jet rocket engine.**

Electromagnetic Rocket Engine. Figure 10*b* illustrates an electromagnetic, or **plasma,** rocket engine. There is a wide variety of such engines, but all of them utilize the same operating principle. A plasma (a neutral ionized conducting gas) is accelerated by means of its interaction with either a stationary or a varying magnetic field. Basically, a plasma engine differs from a conventional electric motor by the substitution of a conducting plasma for a moving armature.

Electrostatic Rocket Engine. Figure 10*c* illustrates schematically the electrostatic, or ion, rocket engine, comprising (1) a nuclear electric power plant; (2) a propellant supply; (3) ionization apparatus; (4) an ion accelerator; and (5) an electron emitter for **neutralizing** the ion beam ejected from the accelerator. Its operating principle is based on utilizing electrostatic fields for accelerating and ejecting electrically charged particles with extremely large velocities. The over-all objective is to transform thermal (nuclear) energy into the kinetic energy associated with an extremely-high-velocity stream of electrically neutral particles ejected from one or more thrustors.

All electric rocket engines are low-thrust devices and are in the research-and-development stage. The recent interest in such engines stems from the fact that chemical-rocket technology is now so advanced that it has become feasible to place heavy *pay loads,* such as a vehicle equipped with an electric rocket engine, into an earth orbit. An electric rocket engine which is virtually inoperable terrestrially can be positioned in space and can then operate effectively because of the absence of aerodynamic drag and strong gravitational fields. Consequently, if a vehicle equipped with an electric rocket engine is placed in an earth orbit, the low-thrust electric rocket engine can serve a useful purpose because, under the conditions in space, an exceedingly small thrust applied to a vehicle will accelerate it to a large vehicle velocity if the operating time for the engine is sufficiently long.

In a chemical rocket engine, the energy for propulsion, as well as the mass ejected through the exhaust nozzle, is provided by the propellants, but the energy which can be added to a unit mass of the propellant gas is a fixed quantity, limited by the nature of the chemical bonds of the reacting materials. For that reason, chemical rocket engines are said to be **energy-limited rocket engines.** While a nuclear heat-transfer rocket engine is also energy-limited, the limitation is imposed by the amount of energy that can be added per unit mass of propellant without exceeding the maximum allowable temperature for the materials employed for the solid-core reactor.

In an electric rocket engine, on the other hand, the energy added to the propellant is furnished by a nuclear electric power plant. The power available for heating the propellant is limited by the maximum power output of the nuclear electric power plant accordingly, electric rocket engines are **power-limited.**

Only the chemical rocket engines have achieved operational realization, have a broad, well-developed technology, and, potentially, can be developed for boosting any desired mass or pay load into an earth orbit or to the escape velocity.

NOTATION

a = acoustic speed, fps
a_0 = acoustic speed in the free-stream air, fps
a_2 = burning rate constant for a solid propellant
A_e = cross-sectional area of exit section of exhaust nozzle
A_p = area of burning surface for a solid propellant, sq in.
A_t = cross-sectional area of throat of exhaust nozzle
c_p = specific heat at constant pressure, Btu per slug deg F
c_v = specific heat at constant volume, Btu per slug deg F
$c^* = V_j/C_F$ = characteristic velocity for a rocket motor, fps
C_d = discharge coefficient for exhaust nozzle
C_F = thrust coefficient
C_{Fg} = gross-thrust coefficient for a ramjet engine
C_{Fn} = net thrust coefficient
D or $\mathfrak{D}$ = drag
$D_i = \dot{m}_a V_0$ = ram drag for an airbreathing or thermal-jet engine, lb

d = diameter
d_p = diameter of propeller, ft
E_{in} = rate at which energy is supplied propulsion system, ft-lb per sec
E_f = calorific value of fuel, ft-lb per slug
E_p = calorific value of rocket propellants, ft-lb per slug
$f = \dot{m}_f/\dot{m}_a$ = fuel-air ratio
$f' = f/\eta_B$ = fuel-air ratio for an ideal combustion chamber
F = force or thrust, lb
$F_i = \dot{m}_e w - \dot{m}_i V_0 + (p_e - p_0)A_e$ = thrust due to internal flow, lb
$F_j = \dot{m}_e V_j$ = jet thrust, lb
$F_p = (p_e - p_0)A_e$ = pressure thrust, lb
$F_g = F_i$ = gross thrust for a ramjet engine, lb
F_gSFC = gross-thrust specific-fuel consumption for a ramjet engine, lb fuel per hr per lb gross thrust
g_c = gravitational conversion factor = lb_m ft per lb sec²
h = static specific enthalpy, Btu per slug
Δh_n = enthalpy change for exhaust nozzle, Btu per slug
H = total (stagnation) specific enthalpy, Btu per slug
ΔH_c = lower heating value of fuel, Btu per slug
I = specific impulse, lb-sec per lb
$I_a = F/g\dot{m}_a$ = air specific impulse, lb-sec per lb, or sec
J = 778 ft-lb per Btu = mechanical equivalent of heat; advance ratio, propeller
$k = c_p/c_v$ = specific heat ratio
L or $\mathfrak{L}$ = lift
m = mass, slug
$\dot{m}$ = mass rate of flow, slug per sec
$\dot{m}_a$ = mass rate of air consumption for a thermal-jet engine, slug per sec
$\dot{m}_e$ = mass rate of flow of gas leaving a propulsion system, slug per sec
$\dot{m}_f$ = mass rate of fuel consumption, slug per sec
$\dot{m}_i$ = mass rate of flow of gas into a propulsion system, slug per sec
$\dot{m}_o$ = mass rate of oxidizer consumption for a rocket engine, slug per sec
$\dot{m}_p = \dot{m}_o + \dot{m}_f$ = mass rate of propellant consumption for a rocket engine, slug per sec
$\bar{m}$ = 1,545/R = molecular weight of combustion gases
$\mathbf{M}_e$ = momentum of gases leaving a propulsion system in unit time
$\mathbf{M}_i$ = momentum of the gases entering a propulsion system in unit time, slug-ft per sec
$M_0 = V_0/a_0$ = Mach number of the free-stream air (flight speed), fps
n = revolutions per sec
p = static pressure, psia; pitch of propeller blade
p_c = static pressure of gases in combustion chamber, psia, or psf as needed
p_e = static pressure in exit section of exhaust nozzle, psia, or psf as needed
p_0 = static pressure of free-stream ambient air, psia, or psf as needed
P = total (stagnation) pressure, psia, or psf as needed
P_c = total pressure at entrance to exhaust nozzle
$P_0 = p_0\left(1 + \frac{k-1}{2} M_0^2\right)^{k/(k-1)}$ = total pressure of free-stream air, psia
$\mathcal{P}$ = propulsion power, ft-lb per sec, or Btu per sec as needed
$\mathcal{P}_L$ = leaving loss, ft-lb per sec, or Btu per sec as needed
$\mathcal{P}_T$ = thrust power, ft-lb per sec, or Btu per sec as needed
$q = \rho V^2/2$ = dynamic pressure, psf
$q_0 = \rho_0 V_0^2/2 = k_0 p_0 M_0^2/2$ = dynamic pressure of the free-stream air, psf
Q = torque
Q_i = heat supplied to an actual combustor
Q_i' = heat supplied to an ideal combustor (no losses)
r_0 = linear burning rate for a solid propellant, in. per sec
R = 1,545$\bar{m}$ = gas constant, ft-lb per lb deg F
t_p = temperature of solid propellant prior to ignition, deg F
T = absolute total (stagnation) temperature, deg R

T_c = total temperature of gas entering the exhaust nozzle of a rocket motor, deg R
T_2 = total temperature at entrance to air compressor (see Fig. 3), deg R
T_3 = total temperature at exit section of air compressor (see Fig. 3), deg R
T_3' = total temperature at exit section of an ideal compressor (see Fig. 3) operating between some pressure limits as actual compressor, deg R
T_4 = total temperature at entrance to turbine (see Fig. 3), deg R
T_5 = total temperature at exit from turbine (see Fig. 3), deg R
T_5' = total temperature at exit from an ideal turbine, deg R
$u = \pi n d_p$ = propeller tip speed, fps
V = velocity, fps
V_F = forward speed of the propeller, fps
V_j = effective jet velocity, fps
V_0 = velocity of free-stream air (flight speed), fps
w = velocity of exit gases relative to walls of the exhaust nozzle or velocity of air in ultimate wake of propeller fps
$\dot{W} = g\dot{m}$ = weight rate of flow, lb per sec
$\dot{W}_o = g\dot{m}_o$ = weight rate of flow of oxidizer, lb per sec
$\dot{W}_p = g\dot{m}_p$ = weight rate of flow of propellants, lb per sec

Greek

$\alpha = T_4/t_0 = \alpha_d\alpha_1$ = cycle temperature ratio; angle of attack
$\alpha_d = T_2/t_0$ = diffusion temperature ratio
$\alpha_1 = T_4/T_2$
β = helix angle for propeller blade
$\Delta = gI_a/\sqrt{2gJc_pt_0}$ = thrust parameter for turbojet engine
$\delta = P/14.7$ = corrected pressure
η = efficiency
$\eta_B = f'/f$ = efficiency of combustion for a thermal-jet engine
$\eta_c = (T_3' - T_2)/(T_3 - T_2)$ = isentropic efficiency of compressor
η_d = isentropic efficiency of diffuser
$\eta_n = \varphi^2$ = isentropic efficiency of exhaust nozzle
$\eta_o = \mathcal{P}_T/E_{in}$ = over-all efficiency of propulsion system
$\eta_P = \mathcal{P}_T/(\mathcal{P}_T + \mathcal{P}_L)$ = ideal propulsive efficiency
$\eta_t = (T_4 - T_5)/(T_4 - T_5')$ = isentropic efficiency of turbine
$\eta_{th} = \mathcal{P}/E_{in}$ = thermal efficiency of propulsion engine
γ = weight density, lb per cu ft
γ_p = density of propellant, lb per cu ft
$\lambda = \frac{1}{2} + \frac{1}{2}\cos\phi$ = divergence coefficient for exhaust nozzle
$\nu = V_0/w$ = speed ratio
$\Omega = \sqrt{k}\left(\frac{2}{k+1}\right)^{(k+1)/[(2k-1)]}$
ω = angular velocity of propeller shaft
ω' = rate of rotation of slipstream at the propeller
ω'' = rate of rotation of slipstream in the ultimate slipstream
Φ = fan velocity coefficient = V_F/u
ϕ = semiangle of exhaust-nozzle divergence; effective helix angle
$\varphi = \sqrt{\eta_n}$ = velocity coefficient for exhaust nozzle
ρ = density, slug per cu ft = γ/g
σ = solidity of propeller
$\Theta = (P_3/p_0)^{(k-1)/k} = \Theta_d\Theta_c$ = cycle pressure ratio parameter
$\Theta_c = (P_3/P_2)^{(k-1)/k}$ = compressor pressure-ratio parameter
$\Theta_d = (P_2/p_0)^{(k-1)/k}$ = diffuser pressure-ratio parameter
$\Theta_n = (P_7/p_0)^{(k-1)/k} = (P_7/p_9)^{(k-1)/k}$ = nozzle pressure-ratio parameter
$\Theta_t = (P_4/P_5)^{(k-1)/k}$ = turbine pressure-ratio parameter.
$\theta = T/519$ = corrected temperature

Subscripts

(a) numbered

0 = free stream

1 = entrance to subsonic diffuser
2 = exit from subsonic diffuser
3 = entrance to combustion chamber
4 = entrance to turbine of turbojet engine
5 = exit from turbine of turbojet engine
6 = tailpipe entrance
7 = entrance to exhaust nozzle
8 = throat section of exhaust nozzle
9 = exit section of exhaust nozzle

(*b*) *lettered*

a = air
B = burner or combustion chamber
b = blade
c = compressor
d = diffuser
e = exit section; effective
F = fan
f = fuel
n = nozzle
o = over-all or oxidizer
P = propulsive
t = turbine or throat, as specified in text

THRUST EQUATIONS FOR JET-PROPULSION ENGINES

Refer to Fig. 11, which illustrates schematically a rotationally symmetrical arbitrary propulsion engine immersed in a uniform flow field. Because of the reactions between the fluid flowing through the engine, called the **internal flow,** and the interior surfaces wetted by the internal flow a resultant **axial force** is produced; that is, a force colinear with the longitudinal axis of the engine. If an axial force acts in the **forward direction,** employing a relative coordinate system, it is called a **thrust,** and if it acts in the **backward direction** it is called a **drag.** Similarly, the resultant axial force due to the **external flow,** the flow passing over the external surfaces of the propulsion system, is a thrust or drag depending upon whether it acts in the forward direction or the backward direction.

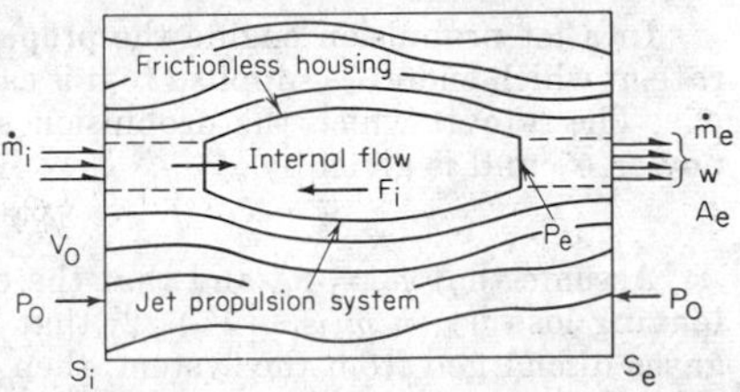

FIG. 11. Generalized jet-propulsion system.

Application of the momentum equation of fluid mechanics to the generalized propulsion system illustrated in Fig. 11 gives the following equation for the thrust F_i due to the **internal flow.** Thus

$$F_i = \dot{m}_e w - \dot{m}_i V_0 + (p_e - p_0)A_e \quad \textbf{(1)}$$

In Eq. (**1**), $\dot{m}_e w = F_j$ = the **jet thrust** $\dot{m}_i V_0 = D_i$ = **ram drag** and $(p_e - p_0)A_e = F_p$ = the **pressure thrust.** Hence,

$$F_i = F_j - D_i + F_p \quad \textbf{(2)}$$

For **thermal jet engines,** $\dot{m}_i = \dot{m}_a$ (see notation), and $\dot{m}_e = \dot{m}_a + \dot{m}_f$. Let $f = \dot{m}_f/\dot{m}_a$, $\nu = V_0/w$, then

$$F_i = \left(\frac{1+f}{\nu} - 1\right)\dot{m}_a V_0 + (p_e - p_o)A_e \quad \textbf{(3)}$$

In the case of a conventional turbojet engine, $\dot{m}_f$ is not significantly different from the fraction of $\dot{m}_a$ utilized for cooling the bearings and turbine disk. Consequently, no significant error is introduced by assuming that $\dot{m}_e = \dot{m}_a + \dot{m}_f \approx \dot{m}_a = \dot{m}$. Furthermore, no appreciable error is introduced by assuming that w is the velocity achieved by expanding the gases to p_0. Hence, for a **turbojet engine,** one may write

$$F_i = \dot{m}_a(w - V_0) = \dot{m}V_0[(1/\nu) - 1)] \tag{4}$$

Equation (**4**) is also the thrust equation for an **ideal propeller;** in that case w is the **wake velocity** for the air leaving its slipstream.

In the case of **rocket engines,** since they do not consume atmospheric air, $\dot{m}_a = 0$, and the flow of gas out of the rocket motor, under steady state conditions, is equal to $\dot{m}_p = \dot{m}_0 + \dot{m}_f$ (see notation). Hence, for a rocket engine,

$$F_i = \dot{m}_p w + (p_e - p_o)A_e \tag{5}$$

To eliminate the pressure thrust $(p_e - p_o)A_e$ from Eq. (**5**), let

$$F_i = \dot{m}_p V_j \tag{6}$$

where $$V_j = w + (p_e - p_o)A_e/\dot{m}_p = \textbf{effective jet velocity} \tag{7}$$

The effective jet velocity V_j is larger than $w = V_e$ = the **exit velocity** if $p_e > p_0$; that is, if the gases are **underexpanded.** The effective jet velocity is a useful criterion because it can be determined accurately from the measured values of F_i and $\dot{m}_p$ obtained from a static firing test of the rocket motor.

The ratio $F_i/g\dot{m}_p$ is denoted by I and called either the **specific thrust** or the **specific impulse.** Hence

$$I = F_i/g\dot{m}_p = V_j/g \tag{8}$$

Equation (**4**) for the thrust of a **turbojet engine,** when expressed in terms of the effective jet velocity, V_j, becomes

$$F_i = \dot{m}_a(V_j - V_0) \tag{9}$$

POWER AND EFFICIENCY RELATIONSHIPS

In a jet-propulsion engine the **propulsion element** is the **exhaust nozzle,** and the rate at which energy is supplied to it is called the **propulsion power,** which is denoted by $\mathcal{P}$. The rate at which the propulsion system does useful work is termed the **thrust power** $\mathcal{P}_T$ and is given by

$$\mathcal{P}_T = F_i V_0 \tag{10}$$

Assume that $p_e = p_0$, and that the only energy loss in a propulsion system is the **leaving loss** $\mathcal{P}_L = \dot{m}(w - V_0)^2/2$; that is, the kinetic energy associated with the jet gases discharged from the system, then the propulsive power is given by

$$\mathcal{P} = \mathcal{P}_L + \mathcal{P}_T \tag{11}$$

The **ideal propulsive efficiency** is defined, in general, by

$$\eta_P = \mathcal{P}_T/(\mathcal{P}_T + \mathcal{P}_L) = \text{thrust power/propulsion power} \tag{12}$$

For a turbojet engine,

$$\eta_P = 2\nu/(1 + \nu) \tag{13}$$

For a rocket engine,

$$\eta_P = 2\nu/(1 + \nu^2) \tag{14}$$

The propulsive efficiency η_P is of more or less academic interest. Of more importance is the over-all efficiency η_o, which is defined by

$$\eta_o = \eta_{th}\eta_P \tag{15}$$

where $$\eta_{th} = \mathcal{P}/E_{in} = \text{thermal efficiency of system} \tag{16}$$

and E_{in} is the rate at which energy is supplied to the propulsion system.

For an airbreathing jet engine, $E_{in} = \dot{m}_f(E_f + V_0^2/2)$, and

$$\eta_o = \frac{2\nu}{1 + \nu}\left[\frac{\mathcal{P}}{\dot{m}_f(E_f + V_0^2/2)}\right] \tag{17}$$

The ratio $g\dot{m}_f/F_i$ is called the **thrust specific-fuel consumption** (*TSFC*) and is measured in pounds of fuel per hour per pound of thrust. Hence,

$$TSFC = 3{,}600\, g\dot{m}_f/F_i \tag{18}$$

For a rocket engine $E_{in} = \dot{m}_p(E_p + V_0^2/2)$, so that

$$\eta_o = \frac{2\nu}{1 + \nu^2}\left[\frac{\mathcal{P}}{\dot{m}_p(E_p + V_0^2/2)}\right] \tag{19}$$

PERFORMANCE CHARACTERISTICS OF AIRBREATHING JET ENGINES

The Ramjet Engine. In ramjet technology the thrust due to the internal flow F_i is called the **gross thrust** and denoted by F_g. Refer to Fig. 2 and assume $\dot{m}_0 \approx \dot{m}_9 = \dot{m}_a$. Then

$$F_g = F_i \approx \dot{m}_a(V_j - V_0) \tag{20}$$

In level unaccelerated flight F_g is equal to the external drag of the propelled vehicle and the ramjet body.

It is customary to express the thrust capabilities of the engine in terms of the **gross-thrust coefficient** C_{Fg}. If A_m is the maximum cross-sectional area of the ramjet engine, $q_0 = \rho_0 V_0^2/2 = k_0 p_0 M_0^2/2 =$ the **dynamic pressure** of the free-stream air, then

$$C_{Fg} = \frac{F_g}{q_0 A_m} = \frac{2F_g}{A_m k_0 p_0 M_0^2} \tag{21}$$

In terms of the Mach numbers M_0 and M_9,

$$C_{Fg} = \frac{2A_9/A_m}{k_0 M_0^2}\left[\frac{P_9}{p_0}\left(\frac{1 + k_9 M_9^2}{P_9/p_9}\right) - 1\right] - 2\frac{A_0}{A_m} \tag{22}$$

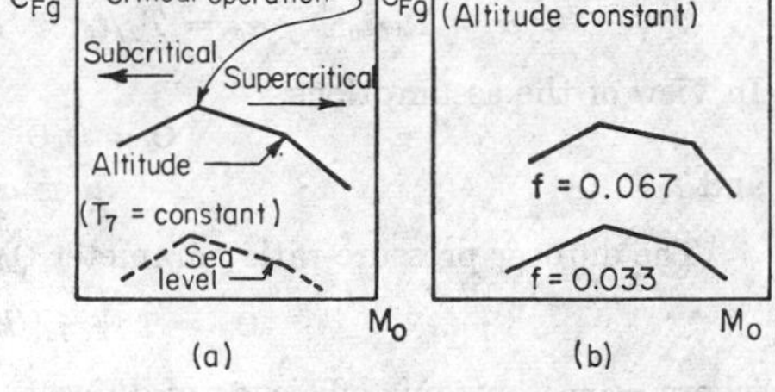

FIG. 12. Effect of altitude and fuel-air ratio on the gross thrust coefficient of a fixed-geometry ramjet engine: (*a*) effect of altitude; (*b*) effect of fuel-air ratio.

In a fixed-geometry engine, M_9 depends upon the total temperature T_7, the total pressure P_7, the fuel-air ratio f, the nozzle area ratio A_e/A_t, and the efficiency of the nozzle η_n. For estimating purposes, $k_0 = 1.4$ and $k_9 = 1.28$, when the engine burns a liquid-hydrocarbon fuel. The manner in which C_{Fg} varies with altitude M_0 and fuel-air ratio f is shown schematically in Fig. 12.

If, $\alpha = T_7/t_0 =$ cycle temperature ratio, and k_B is the mean value of k for the combustion gases, the rate at which heat is supplied to the engine is

$$Q_i = Q_i'/\eta_B = g\dot{m}_a c_{pB} t_0(\alpha - T_2)/\eta_B \tag{23}$$

It is readily shown that

$$Q_i = \frac{A_0 p_0 V_0}{\eta_B J}\left(\frac{k_B}{k_B - 1}\right)\left[d - \left(1 + \frac{(k_0 - 1}{2} M_0^2\right)\right] \tag{24}$$

The **gross-thrust specific-fuel consumption** (F_gSFC) is, by definition,

$$F_gSFC = g\dot{m}_f\left(\frac{3{,}600}{F_g}\right) = \frac{7{,}200g}{a_0 M_0}\left(\frac{A_0}{A_m}\right)\frac{f}{C_{Fg}} \tag{25}$$

The principal sources of loss are aero-thermodynamic in nature, and cause a decrease in total pressure between stations 0 and 7. For estimating purposes, assuming $M_0 =$

2.0 and $T_6 = 3800$ R, the total pressures across different sections of the engine may be assumed to be those tabulated below.

Part of Engine	Total Pressure Ratio
Supersonic diffuser (0–1)	$P_1/P_0 = 0.92$
Subsonic diffuser (1–2)	$P_2/P_1 = 0.90$
Flameholders (2–6)	$P_6/P_2 = 0.97$
Combustion chamber (6–7)	$P_7/P_6 = 0.92$
Exhaust nozzle (7–9)	$P_9/P_7 = 0.97$

The Simple Turbojet Engine. A good insight into the design performance characteristics of the turbojet engine is obtained conveniently by making the following assumptions: (1) the mass rate of flow of working fluid is identical at all stations in the engine; (2) the thermodynamic properties of the working fluid are those for air; (3) the air is a perfect gas and its specific heats are constants; (4) there are no pressure losses due to friction or heat addition; (5) the exhaust nozzle expands the working fluid completely so that $p_9 = p_0$; and (6) the auxiliary power requirements can be neglected. Refer to Fig. 3 and let

$$\Theta = \left(\frac{P_3}{p_0}\right)^{(k-1)/k} \qquad \Theta_d = \left(\frac{P_2}{p_0}\right)^{(k-1)/k} \qquad \Theta_c = \left(\frac{P_3}{P_2}\right)^{(k-1)/k}$$

$$\Theta_t = \left(\frac{P_4}{P_5}\right)^{(k-1)/k} \qquad \Theta_n = \left(\frac{P_7}{p_0}\right)^{(k-1)/k} = \left(\frac{P_7}{p_9}\right)^{(k-1)/k}$$

$$\alpha = T_4/t_0 \qquad \alpha_d = T_2/t_0 \qquad \alpha_1 = T_4/T_2$$

In view of the assumptions,

$$\Theta = \Theta_d\Theta_c = \Theta_t\Theta_n \tag{26}$$

and

$$\alpha = \alpha_d\alpha_1 \tag{27}$$

The diffuser pressure-ratio parameter Θ_d is given by

$$\Theta_d = 1 + \eta_d[(k-1)/2]M_0^2 \tag{28}$$

where η_d = isentropic efficiency of diffuser.
Heat supplied, in Btu per slug of air, is

$$Q_i = (c_p/\eta_B)(T_4 - T_3)$$

or

$$Q_i = \frac{c_p t_0}{\eta_B\eta_c}\,\alpha_d\left(\frac{\alpha}{\alpha_d} - \eta_c - \Theta_c + 1\right) \tag{29}$$

where η_c is the isentropic efficiency of the air compressor.

The turbine pressure-ratio parameter Θ_t is given by

$$1/\Theta_t = 1 - [(\Theta_c - 1)/\alpha_1\eta_c\eta_t \tag{30}$$

where η_t = the isentropic efficiency of the turbine.

The enthalpy change for the exhaust nozzle Δh_n is given by

$$\Delta h_n = c_p t_0 \frac{\eta_n}{\eta_c}\{\alpha\eta_c - \alpha_d(\Theta_c - 1)\}\left\{1 - \frac{\alpha_1\eta_c\eta_t}{\Theta_c[1 + \eta_d(\alpha_d - 1)][\alpha\eta_c\eta_t - (\Theta_c - 1)]}\right\} \tag{31}$$

The **specific thrust,** also called the **air specific impulse,** is

$$I_a = \frac{F_i}{\dot{m}_a g} = (\sqrt{2\Delta h_n} - V_0)g_c/\dot{m}_a \tag{32}$$

It should be noted that in turbojet technology the thrust F_i is called the **net thrust** and is frequently denoted by F_n, while the sum $F_j + F_p$ [see Eq (**2**)] is called the **gross thrust** of the **turbojet engine.**

The *TSFC* for a turbojet engine is given by

$$TSFC = 3{,}600\,\frac{g\dot{m}_f}{F_i} \tag{33}$$

It can be shown by dimensional analysis, if the effects of Reynolds numbers are neglected, that the variables entering into the performance of a given turbojet engine may be grouped as indicated in Table 1.

Table 1

Non-dimensional group	Uncorrected form	Corrected form
Flight speed	$V_0/\sqrt{t_0}$	$V_0/\sqrt{\theta}$
Rotational speed	$N/\sqrt{T}$	$N/\sqrt{\theta}$
Air flow rate	$\dot{W}_a\sqrt{T}/D^2P$	$\dot{W}_a\sqrt{\theta}/\delta$
Thrust	F/D^2P	F/δ
Fuel flow rate	$\dot{W}_f J\Delta H_c/D^2P\sqrt{T}$	$\dot{W}_f/\delta\sqrt{\theta}$

$\theta = T/T_{std} = T/519$ = corrected temperature (exact value for T_{std} is 518.699 R).
$\delta = P/p_{std} = P/14.7$ = corrected pressure.

Figure 13 presents the effects of engine rpm, flight speed, and altitude upon the performance of a turbojet engine.

Figure 14 presents the effect of flight speed upon the *design point* performance, at 30,000 ft altitude, for engines having the following characteristics: $\eta_c = 0.85$, $\eta_t = 0.90$, $\eta_B = 0.95$, $T_4 = 2000$ R, $\Delta H_c = 18{,}700$ Btu per lb. It is seen that the optimum

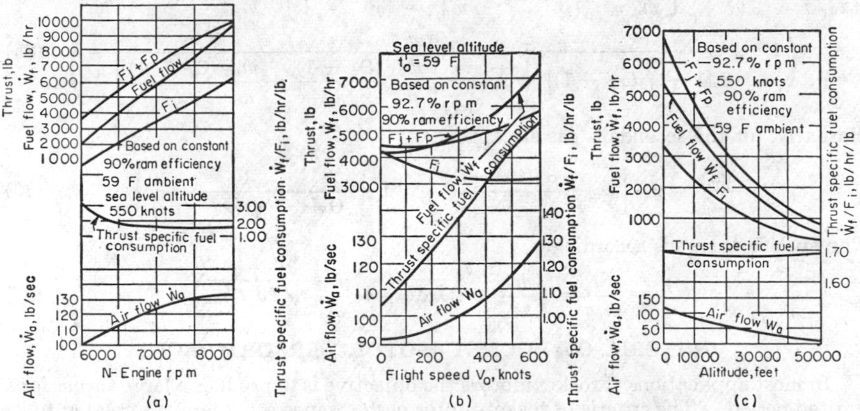

FIG. 13. Performance characteristics of a turbojet engine (General Electric Co.): (*a*) effect of engine speed; (*b*) effect of flight speed; (*c*) effect of altitude.

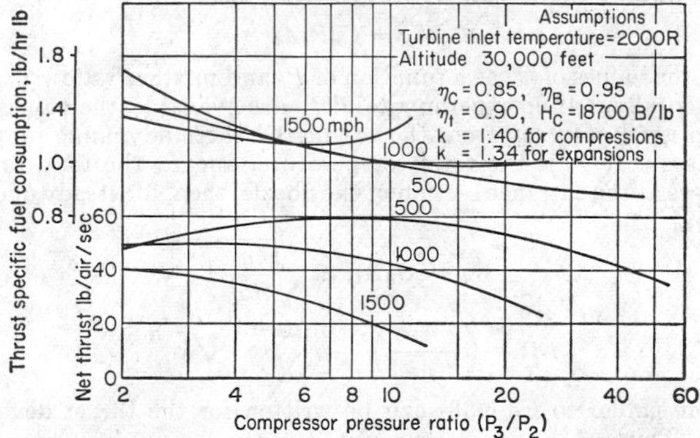

FIG. 14. Effect of flight speed on engine performance.

compressor pressure ratio P_3/P_2 approaches unity at flight speeds around 1,500 mph, indicating that at flights speeds above 1,500 mph, approximately, the compressor and turbine are superfluous; that is, the propulsion requirements would be met more adequately by a ramjet engine.

The Turbofan or the Ducted-fan Engine. In addition to the assumptions introduced in the analysis of the simple turbojet engine, assume, with reference to Fig. 4, that (1) the diffusers are identical for the ducted fan and the compressor, (2) there are no afterburners, and (3) the primary and secondary streams expand through separate exhaust nozzles to ambient pressure. Let

$$\Theta_F = \left(\frac{P_{3F}}{P_2}\right)^{k-1/k} \qquad \dot{m}_a = \dot{m}_{a1} + \dot{m}_{a2}$$

where the additional subscripts 1 and 2 refer to the primary and secondary streams.

The turbine pressure-ratio parameter Θ_t is given by

$$\frac{1}{\Theta_t} = 1 - \left[\frac{\dot{m}_{a1}}{\dot{m}_a}\frac{(\Theta_c - 1)}{\eta_c} + \frac{\dot{m}_{a2}}{\dot{m}_a}\frac{(\Theta_F - 1)}{\eta_F}\right]\frac{1}{\alpha_1\eta_t} \tag{34}$$

The enthalpy change in the exhaust nozzle for the primary air is given by

$$\frac{\Delta h_{n1}}{c_p t_0} = \eta_{n1}\left\{\alpha - \left[\frac{\dot{m}_{a1}}{\dot{m}_a}\frac{\alpha_d}{\eta_c}(\Theta_c - 1) + \frac{\dot{m}_{a2}}{\dot{m}_a}\frac{\alpha_d(\Theta_F - 1)}{\eta_F}\right]\right\}$$
$$\left(1 - \frac{\alpha_1\eta_t}{\Theta_c[1 + \eta_d(\alpha_d - 1)]\left\{\alpha_1\eta_t - \left[\frac{\dot{m}_{a1}}{\dot{m}_a}\frac{(\Theta_c - 1)}{\eta_c} + \frac{\dot{m}_{a2}}{\dot{m}_a}\frac{(\Theta_F - 1)}{\eta_F}\right]\right\}}\right) \tag{35}$$

Similarly, for the secondary gas stream

$$\frac{\Delta h_{n2}}{c_p t_0} = \eta_{n2}\left[\alpha_d + \frac{\alpha_d(\Theta_F - 1)}{\eta_F}\right]\left\{1 - \frac{1}{\Theta_F[1 + \eta_d(\alpha_d - 1)]}\right\} \tag{36}$$

The specific thrust is accordingly

$$I_a = \frac{F_i}{\dot{m}_a g} = \left(\frac{\dot{m}_{a1}}{\dot{m}_a}\sqrt{2J\,\Delta h_{n1}} + \frac{\dot{m}_{a2}}{\dot{m}_a}\sqrt{2J\,\Delta h_{n2}}\right) \tag{37}$$

CRITERIA OF ROCKET-MOTOR PERFORMANCE

In most applications of rocket motors the objective is to produce a large thrust for a limited period. The criteria of rocket-motor performance are, therefore, related to its thrust-producing capabilities and operating duration. If $\dot{W}_p$ denotes the rate at which the rocket motor consumes propellants, P_c the total pressure at the entrance to the exhaust nozzle, and C_w the **weight flow coefficient,** then

$$\dot{W}_p = C_w P_c A_t \tag{38}$$

Ordinarily, the values of C_w as a function of P_c and **mixture ratio** $\dot{W}_o/\dot{W}_f$ are determined experimentally. If no experimental data are available, the values of C_w can be calculated with good accuracy from the calculated thermodynamic properties of the combustion gases. If T_c is the total temperature, and P_c the total pressure of the combustion gases at the entrance section of the nozzle, then, for steady operating conditions, $\dot{W}_p = \dot{W}_g$,

$$\dot{W}_g = C_d A_t P_c \Omega \sqrt{\frac{g}{RT_c}} \tag{39}$$

where

$$\Omega = \left(\frac{2}{k+1}\right)^{(k+1)/[2(k-1)]}\sqrt{k} \tag{40}$$

An equation similar to Eq. (**38**) can be written for the thrust developed by the rocket motor. Thus

$$F = C_F P_c A_t \tag{41}$$

The values of the **thrust coefficient** C_F for specific propellant combinations are determined experimentally as functions of P_c and the ratio $\dot{W}_o/\dot{W}_f$. When no experimental values are available, C_F can be calculated from the following equation. Therefore

$$C_F = C_d\lambda\phi\Omega\sqrt{\frac{2k}{k-1}Z_t} + \left(\frac{p_e}{P_c} - \frac{p_0}{P_c}\right)\frac{A_e}{A_t} \tag{42}$$

where

$$Z_t = 1 - \left(\frac{p_e}{P_c}\right)^{(k-1)/k}$$

Equation (**42**) shows that C_F is independent of the combustion temperature T_c and the molecular weight of the combustion gases. The nozzle area ratio A_e/A_t is given by the formula

$$\frac{A_e}{A_t} = \frac{(P_c/p_e)^{1/k}}{\left(\frac{k+1}{2}\right)^{1/(k-1)}\sqrt{[(k+1)/(k-1)]Z_t}} \tag{43}$$

Figure 15 presents C_F calculated by means of the preceding equations, as a function of the area ratio A_e/A_t, with P_c/p_0 as a parameter, for gases having $k = 1.28$; the calculations assumed $\lambda = 0.983$ and $C_d = \varphi = 1.0$. The curves do not take into account the separation phenomena which occur when A_e/A_t is larger than that required to expand the gases to p_0.

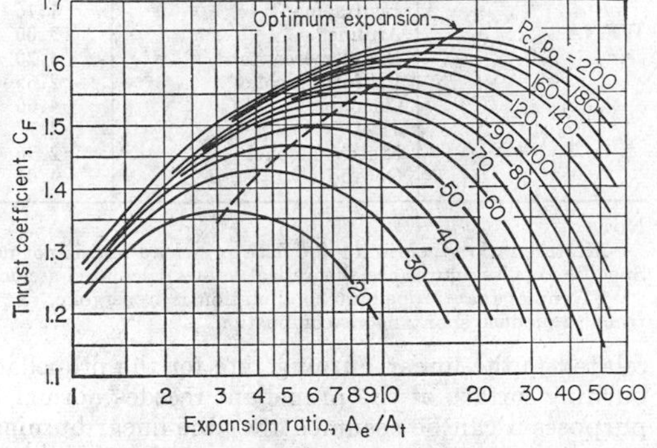

FIG. 15. Calculated thrust coefficient vs. expansion ratio for different pressure ratios (based on $k = 1.28$, $\lambda \doteq 0.9830$, $C_D = \phi = 1.0$).

The specific impulse I is defined by Eq. (**9**) and can be shown to be given by

$$I = \frac{F}{\dot{W}_o + \dot{W}_f} = \frac{C_F}{C_w} = 6.93\lambda\varphi\sqrt{\frac{T_c}{\bar{M}}\left(\frac{2k}{k-1}\right)Z_t} \tag{44}$$

A criterion which is employed quite frequently for stating the performance of rocket motor is the characteristic velocity c^*. By definition

$$c^* = V_j/C_F = P_cA_t\dot{W}_p/g_c = gI/C_F = g/C_w \tag{45}$$

The values for c^* for a given propellant combination are determined experimentally. It should be noted that the value of c^* is independent of the thrust. Basically, c^* measures the effectiveness with which the thermochemical energy of the propellants is converted into effective jet kinetic energy. When no experimental data are available the value of c^* can be estimated quite closely from

$$c^* = \sqrt{gRT_c}/\Omega \tag{46}$$

Table 2 presents values of specific impulse for some possible rocket-propellant combinations.

Solid propellant rocket motors may be segregated into (1) **double-base powders** and (2) **composite, or heterogeneous, propellants.** Double-base powders are gelatinized colloidal mixtures of nitroglycerin and cellulose to which certain stabilizers have been added. Heterogeneous, or composite, propellants are physical mixtures of a solid oxidizer in powder form and some form of solid fuel, such as a plastic or rubber-like material.

In the case of solid-propellant rockets the rate of propellant consumption $\dot{W}_p$ is

Table 2. Some Possible Propellant Combinations

Oxidizer	Fuel	Ratio (O/F)	Combustion temperature, deg F	I (300 → 14.7)	Bulk, sp gr
Fluorine	Ammonia	2.90	7512	205.5	1.017
	Hydrazine*	1.98	7692	300	1.070
	Hydrogen*	9.42	8072	371	0.457
		3.77	4469	356	0.269
	Lithium	2.19	7000	335.5	0.830
	Methyl alcohol*	2.37	7472	298	0.991
Hydrogen peroxide	Aluminum borohydride*	3.0	5772	200	0.82
	Hydrazine*	1.69	4200	240	1.22
	Methyl alcohol-hydrazine* hydrate-water (57–32–11)	2.54	3934	224	1.196
	Nitromethane	0.42	4719	232	1.200
	n-Octane	5.10	4095	230	1.205
Liquid oxygen	Acetylene	1.23	6012	266	0.828
	Ammonia	1.25	4834	250	0.969
	Ethyl alcohol	1.50	5297	242	0.970
	Hydrogen	2.89	3886	345	0.23
Ozone	Hydrogen	2.65	4280	373	0.23
RFNA (16% NO_2)	Aniline*	3.00	5067	221	1.39
	Hydrazine*	1.16	4728	242	1.25
WFNA	Aniline*	3.00	4942	222	1.355
	Butyl mercaptan*	4.20	5980	234	1.30
	Furfuryl alcohol*	2.65	4885	210	1.38
	Gasoline	4.60	4941	223	1.25
	JP-4	4.7	5000	229	1.30
	Methyl alcohol	2.36	4480	219	1.19
	Octane	4.00	4744	229	1.225

NOTE.
Mixture ratio given is for the data presented and is not necessarily optimum or stoichiometric value. Specific impulse figures are theoretical values calculated assuming frozen composition.
* Denotes that propellant combination is hypergolic, *i.e.*, the ability of propellants upon mixing to react to produce spontaneous combustion.

related to the **linear burning rate** for the propellant r_0; that is, the rate at which the burning surface of the propellant recedes normal to itself as it burns. For practical purposes it can be assumed that the linear burning rate r_0 is given by

$$r_0 = a_2 p_c^n \tag{47}$$

where a_2 and n are constants which are determined by experiment.

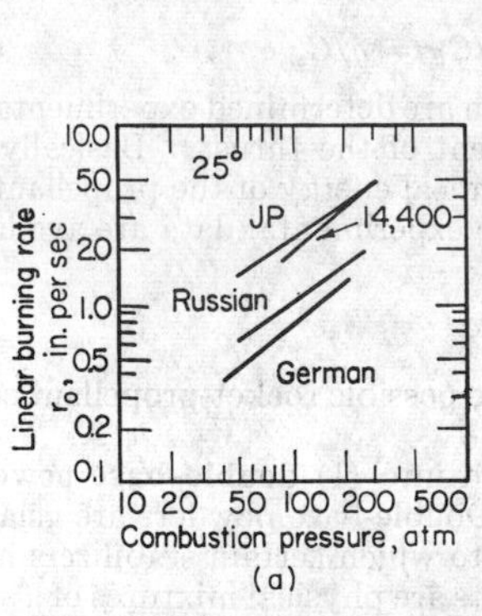

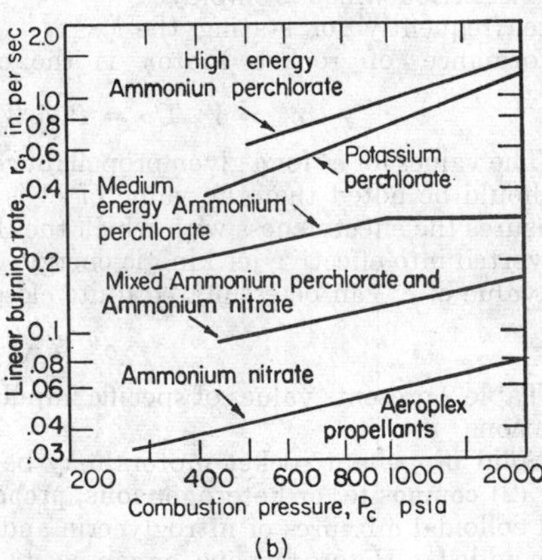

FIG. 16. (*a*) Linear burning rate as a function of combustion pressure for representative colloidal propellants. (*b*) Burning-rate characteristics of several heterogeneous propellants at 60 F. (*Aerojet-General Corp.*)

If γ_p denotes the specific weight of the solid propellant (lb per cu ft) and A_p the area of the burning surface, then the propellant consumption rate $\dot{W}$ is given by

$$\dot{W} = A_p\gamma_p r_0 = a_2 A_p \gamma_p p_c^n \text{ lb per sec} \quad \textbf{(48)}$$

Figure 16 presents the linear burning rate as a function of the combustion pressure for several double-base powder propellants.

The linear burning rate r_0 is influenced by the temperature of the solid propellant t_p prior to its ignition. Low values of t_p reduce the burning rate, and vice versa. Consequently, the temperature of the propellant must be given in presenting data on linear burning rates. Figure 17 presents r_0 as a function of p_c for $t_p = -40$, 60, and 140 F for a composite propellant manufactured by the Aerojet-General Corp., Azusa, Calif.

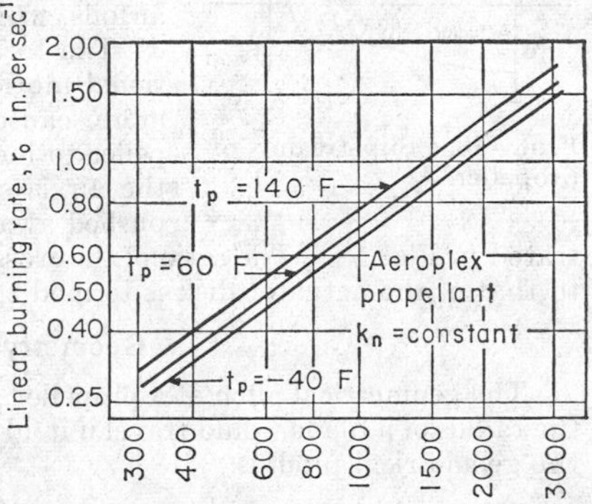

FIG. 17. Effect of propellant temperature upon the linear burning rate of a heterogeneous propellant. (*Aerojet-General Corp.*)

AIRCRAFT PROPELLERS

REFERENCES: Theodorsen, "Theory of Propellers," McGraw-Hill. Smith, "Propellers for High Speed Flight," Princeton. Webb and Willer, "Propeller Performance at Zero Forward Speed," Wright Air Development Center Report 52–152. Kuchemann and Weber, "Aerodynamics of Propulsion," McGraw-Hill. Gray and Nicholas, "Representative Operating Charts of Propellers," NACA Wartime Report. Gutin, "On the Sound Field of a Rotating Propeller," *NACA-TM* 1195, Oct., 1948. Garrick and Watkins, "A Theoretical Study of the Effect of Forward Speed on the Free Space Pressure Field around Propellers," NACA, Oct., 1953. Ribner, "Propellers in Yaw," *NACA-TR* 820, 1945. Zucrow, "Principles of Jet Propulsion," Wiley.

The function of the aircraft propeller (or airscrew) is to convert the torque delivered to it by an engine into the thrust for propelling an airplane. If the airplane is in steady, level flight, the propeller thrust and the airplane drag equal each other. If the airplane is climbing, the thrust must overcome the drag plus the weight component of the airplane.

The propeller may be the sole thrust-producing element, but it can also be employed in conjunction with another thrust-producing device, such as the exhaust jet of a **turboprop** or **gas-turbine engine.** It may also be employed as a **windmilling** device for producing power.

Propellers may be classified according to a variety of considerations, such as (1) location on the airframe, (2) subsonic or supersonic airstream or rotational velocities, and (3) ducted or open configurations. There is no standard system of propeller designation. Table 3 presents the NACA system, which is commonly employed in the literature.

Table 3. NACA Propeller Designation

EXAMPLE. NACA 10—(3) (066)—03

Number	Term definition	Units	Example
First	Diameter	Ft	10
Second	Design lift coefficient at 0.7R	Tenths	3
Third	Design thickness ratio at 0.7R	Tenths	066
Fourth	Solidity per blade at 0.7R	Tenths	03

The conventional propeller consists of two or more equally spaced radial blades, which are rotated at a substantially uniform angular velocity. At any arbitrary radius, the section of a blade has the shape of an airfoil, but as the hub is approached, the sections become more nearly circular because of considerations of strength rather than aerodynamic performance. The portions of the blades in the vicinity of the hub contribute, at best, only a small portion of the thrust developed by the propeller blades.

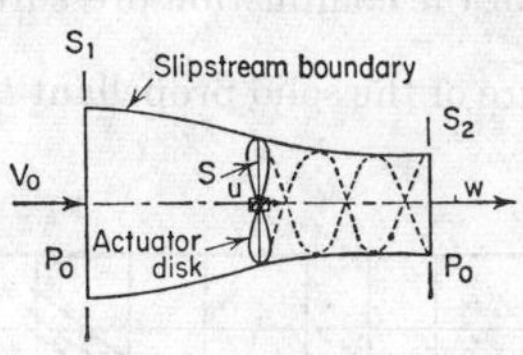

Fig. 18. Slipstream of propeller.

Each section of the propeller blade experiences the aerodynamic reactions of an airfoil of like shape moving through the air in a similar manner. Furthermore, at each radius, the section of one blade forms with the corresponding sections on the other blades a series of similar airfoils, which follow one another as the propeller rotates

The torque of the rotating propeller imparts a rotational motion to the air flowing through it and, furthermore, causes the pressure immediately behind the propeller to increase while that in front of it is reduced; *i.e.*, the air is sucked toward the front of the propeller and pushed away behind it. A slipstream is created as illustrated in Fig. 18. The ratio of the cross-sectional area of the slipstream at any station to that of the actuator disk is termed the **slipstream contraction.**

Geometry of Propellers

The **geometrical pitch** of a propeller, denoted by p, is the axial distance a point on the radius of a blade would travel if it advanced along the helix angle β. From Fig. 19, the geometrical pitch is

$$p = bc = \pi d \tan \beta \tag{49}$$

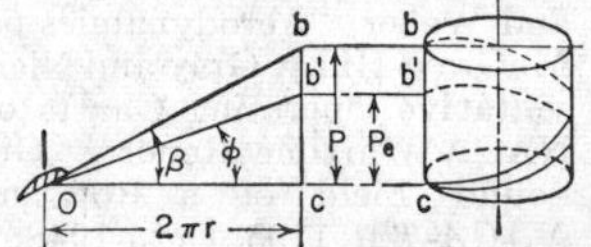

Fig. 19. Pitch and helix angles for a propeller element.

The actual advance of the same point (cb') is governed by the velocity of the airflow in the plane of the propeller. If n denotes the revolutions per second of the propeller, then

$$cb' = \frac{V_F \text{ (fps)}}{n \text{ (rps)}} \qquad \text{(ft per rev)} \tag{50}$$

The effective helix angle ϕ is determined by the ratio $cb'/\pi d$. The **effective pitch** p_e is given by

$$p_e = \pi d \tan \phi$$

The distance bb' is called the **slip** and measures the distance the propeller lags behind the distance that it would advance if the air were incompressible. Thus

$$\text{Slip} = 1 - \frac{p_e}{p} = 1 - \frac{V_F}{np} \tag{51}$$

Aerodynamic Theories

Axial-momentum Theory. The axial-momentum theory of the propeller is due to Rankine and Froude, and the conception arose in the studies of propellers for ships. It is basically a special case of the generalized jet-propulsion system presented in Fig. 11. The thrust is given by Eq. (4).

If V_0 is the forward speed of the airplane, w is the velocity of airflow in the ultimate wake (Fig. 18), and $\nu = V_0/w$, the velocity ratio, then

$$F = \dot{m}(w - V_0) = \rho A V_0(w - V_0) = \rho A V_0^2[(1/\nu) - 1] \tag{52}$$

$$\mathcal{P} = \mathcal{P}_T + \mathcal{P}_L = \tfrac{1}{2}\dot{m}(w^2 - V_0^2) = \tfrac{1}{2}\dot{m}w^2(1 - \nu^2) \tag{53}$$

$$\mathcal{P}_T = FV_0 = \dot{m}V_0(w - V_0) \tag{54}$$

$$\mathcal{P}_L = \tfrac{1}{2}\dot{m}(w - V_0)^2 \tag{55}$$

$$\eta_P = \mathcal{P}_T/\mathcal{P} = 2\nu/(1 + \nu) \tag{56}$$

The propulsive power $\mathcal{P}$, the thrust power $\mathcal{P}_T$, and the loss of kinetic energy in the wake $\mathcal{P}_L$, can be related to the propeller diameter d_p. Thus

$$\frac{\mathcal{P}}{\rho d_p{}^2 V^3} = \frac{\pi}{2}\frac{1 - \eta_P}{\eta_P{}^3} \tag{57}$$

also

$$\frac{F}{\rho d_p{}^2 V^2} = \frac{\pi}{2}\frac{1 - \eta_P}{\eta_P{}^2} \tag{58}$$

The axial-momentum theory is only a first approximation of the action of the propeller and cannot be employed for design purposes. It neglects such factors as the drag of the blades, energy losses due to slipstream rotation, blade interference, and compressibility effects. Because of those losses, an actual propeller requires power to rotate at zero thrust, and at zero thrust its propulsive efficiency is zero.

Modifications to the Axial-momentum Theory. One of the parameters neglected in the axial-momentum theory is the effect of the rotation in the slipstream. In order to take this into account, a solid-body rotation may be superimposed on the axial velocity distribution in the slipstream. Thus, if ω and ω' are the rotations of the propeller shaft and of the slipstream at the propeller, respectively, the propulsive efficiency taking into account the rotation losses is

$$\eta_P = \frac{2 - (\omega'/\omega)}{1 + (w/V_0)} \tag{59}$$

The angular rotation in the ultimate slipstream ω'' is given by

$$\frac{\omega''}{\omega'} = \left[2 - \eta_P\left(1 + \frac{w}{V_0}\right)\right]\frac{2w/V_0}{1 - (w/V_0)} \tag{60}$$

Blade-element Theory. This theory, sometimes called the **strip theory,** takes into account the profile losses of the blade sections. It is the theory most commonly employed in designing a propeller blade and for assessing the off-design performance characteristics of the propeller.

Each section of the propeller is considered to be a rotating airfoil. It is assumed that the radial flow of air may be neglected, so that the flow over a blade section is two-dimensional. Figure 20 illustrates diagrammatically the velocity vectors pertinent to a blade section of length dr, located at an arbitrary radius r. The projection of the axis of rotation is OO', the plane of rotation is OC, the blade angle is β, the angle of attack for the air flowing toward the blade (in the relative coordinate system) with the velocity V is α, the tangential velocity of the blade element is $u = 2\pi nr$, and the pitch or **advance angle** is ϕ. From Fig. 20,

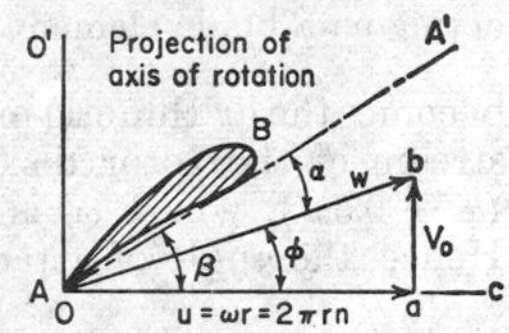

Fig. 20. Vector diagram for a blade element of a propeller.

$$\alpha = \beta - \phi \tag{61}$$

and

$$\phi = \tan^{-1}(V_0/\pi nd) \tag{62}$$

Figure 21 illustrates the forces acting on the blade element. If b denotes the width of the blade under consideration and C_L and C_D are the lift and drag coefficients of the blade (airfoil) section, then the thrust force dF acting on the blade element is given by

$$dF = \tfrac{1}{2}\rho V_F{}^2 b^2\, dr C_L \frac{\cos(\phi + \gamma)}{\cos\gamma \sin^2\phi} \tag{63}$$

The corresponding torque force dQ is given by

$$dQ = \tfrac{1}{2}\rho V_F{}^2 b\, dr C_L \frac{\sin(\phi + \gamma)}{\cos\gamma \sin^2\phi} \tag{64}$$

where

$$\tan\gamma = d\mathfrak{D}/d\mathfrak{L} = C_D/C_L = \mathfrak{D}/\mathfrak{L} \tag{65}$$

where $\mathfrak{D}$ and $\mathfrak{L}$ denote drag and lift, respectively.

The propulsion efficiency of the blade element, termed the **blading efficiency,** is defined by

$$\eta_b = \frac{V_F\, dF}{u\, dQ} = \frac{\tan \phi}{\tan (\phi + \gamma)} = \frac{(\mathcal{L}/\mathcal{D}) - \tan \phi}{(\mathcal{L}/\mathcal{D}) + \cot \phi} \tag{66}$$

The value of ϕ which makes η_b a maximum is termed the **optimum advance angle** ϕ_{opt}. Thus

$$\phi_{opt} = \frac{\pi}{4} - \frac{\gamma}{2} = 45° - \frac{57.3}{2(\mathcal{L}/\mathcal{D})} \tag{67}$$

The maximum blade efficiency is accordingly

$$(\eta_b)_{max} = \frac{2\gamma - 1}{2\gamma + 1} = \frac{2(\mathcal{L}/\mathcal{D}) - 1}{2(\mathcal{L}/\mathcal{D}) + 1} \tag{68}$$

A force diagram similar to Fig. 21 can be constructed for each element of the propeller blade, taking into account the variation in ϕ with the radius. The resultant forces acting on the propeller are obtained by summing (integrating) those forces acting on each blade element.

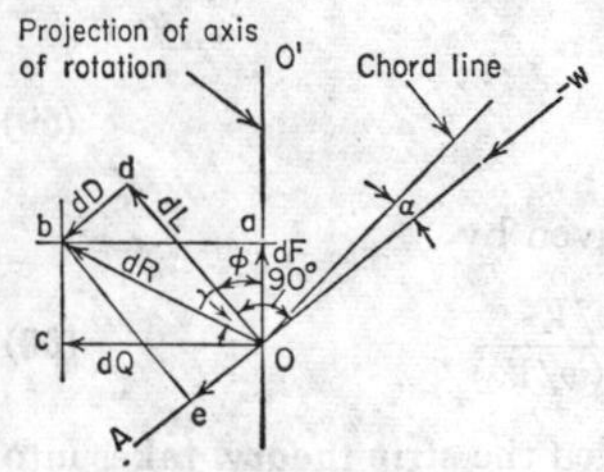

Fig. 21. Aerodynamic forces acting on a blade element.

Vortex Theory. The simple two-dimensional blade-element theory can be further improved by taking account of the actual velocity distribution in the slipstream and thus determining the actual loading on the blading by the so-called *vortex theory*. The blades are represented by bound vortex filaments sweeping out vortex sheets to infinity. The vortex sheets are distorted both by the slipstream contraction and by the profile drag of the blades. If such distortions are neglected, the induced velocity in the wake can be calculated by assuming the vortex sheets to be tubular. Thus, in Fig. 20, the induced axial velocity becomes the arithmetic mean of the axial velocities at far distances upstream and downstream of the rotor disk; and the induced rotational velocity at the disk becomes $(\omega - 0.5\omega')$, where ω' is the rotation of the slipstream in the plane of the propeller. Hence, the angle of attack α for a rotor element is given by

$$\alpha = \beta - \tan^{-1}[V_F/r(\omega - 0.5\omega')] \tag{69}$$

where V_F = the induced axial velocity in the plane of the propeller.

Performance Characteristics

The pitch and the angle ϕ (Fig. 20) have different values at different radii along a propeller blade. It is customary, therefore, to refer all parameters determining the over-all characteristics of a propeller to their values at $0.7r$.

For a given blade angle β, the angle of attack α at any blade section is a function of the **velocity coefficient** V_0/u, where $u = \pi n d_p$; it is customary, however, to replace V_0/u by its equivalent, the **advance ratio** $J = V_0/nd_p$.

For given values of β and n, the angle of attack α attains its maximum value when $V_0 = 0$, with $\phi = 0$. In other words, the propeller thrust F is maximum at takeoff. As V_0 increases, α decreases and so does the thrust. Finally, a forward speed is reached for which the thrust is zero.

Increasing $J = V_0/nd_p$, for a constant blade angle, causes the propeller to operate successively as a fan, brake, and windmill. Most of the operation, however, is conducted in the propeller state. At takeoff, the propeller is in the fan state. Windmilling must be avoided because it may overspeed the engine and damage it.

The lift coefficient C_L is a linear function of α up to the stalling angle, while C_D is a quadratic function of α. Furthermore, the lift L is zero at a negative value for α. Figure 22 presents the $\mathcal{L}/\mathcal{D}$ ratios of typical propeller sections. Figure 23 presents the blade (section) efficiency as a function of the pitch angle ϕ for different values of

$\mathcal{L}/\mathcal{D}$. Propellers normally operate at $\mathcal{L}/\mathcal{D}$ ratios of 20 or more. Supersonic propellers operate with $\mathcal{L}/\mathcal{D}$ ratios of approximately 10, and from Fig. 22 it is apparent that they must operate close to the optimum pitch angle ϕ to obtain usable blade efficiencies.

Propeller Coefficients. It can be shown, neglecting the compressibility of the air, that

$$f(V_0,n,d_p,\rho,F) = 0 \tag{70}$$

By dimensional analysis, the following coefficients are obtained for expressing the performances of propellers having the same geometry:

$$F = \rho n^2 d_p{}^4 C_F \qquad Q = \rho n^2 d_p{}^5 C_Q \qquad \mathcal{P} = \rho n^3 d_p{}^5 C_P \tag{71}$$

C_F, C_Q, and C_P are termed the **thrust, torque,** and **power coefficients,** respectively. They are independent of the size of the propeller. Consequently, tests of small-scale models can be employed for obtaining the values of F, Q, and $\mathcal{P}$ for geometrically similar full-scale propellers. Hence, the ideal propulsive efficiency of a propeller is given by

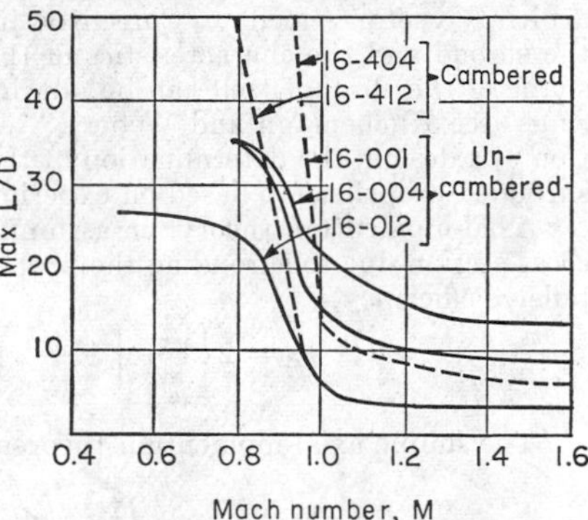

FIG. 22. Maximum lift-drag ratios for representative sections.

$$\eta_P = \frac{FV_0}{\mathcal{P}} = \frac{C_F}{C_P}\frac{V_0}{d_p n} = J\frac{C_F}{C_P} \tag{72}$$

Other useful coefficients are the **speed-power coefficient** C_S and the **torque-speed coefficient** C_{QS}. Thus,

$$C_S = V_0 5\sqrt{\rho/\mathcal{P}n^2} \qquad C_{QS} = V_0\sqrt{\rho d_p{}^3/Q} \tag{73}$$

A commonly employed factor related to the geometry of a propeller is the **solidity** σ. By definition,

$$\sigma = \frac{c}{p} \tag{74}$$

The solidity varies from radius to radius; at a given radius, σ is proportional to the power-absorption capacity of the annulus of blade elements.

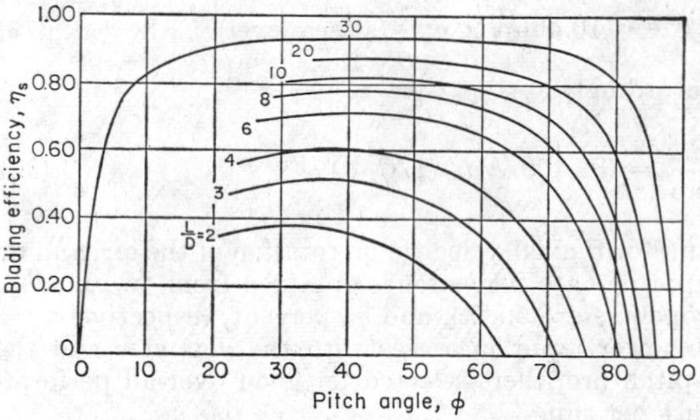

FIG. 23. Blade-element efficiency versus pitch angle.

Ducted Fan or Shrouded Propeller. In this arrangement, the propeller is located inside a ring which has airfoil cross section. The object of the configuration is to increase the thrust of the system for a given power input. If the lateral extent of the ring is much longer than the axial length of the propeller, the arrangement is termed a **fan-in-wing.**

The analysis of the ducted fan must take into account the conventional propeller variables and also such variables, pertaining to the design of the duct, as the chord-diameter ratio and the profile thickness distribution. In addition, the location of the propeller and the shape of the center body must be considered.

A ducted propeller is essentially a ring airfoil of specified camber line and thickness distribution, inside of which there is a propeller disk producing a pressure discontinuity normal to the axis of symmetry. To analyze the system, one must determine the flow field produced by the ducted fan in the presence of a uniform free stream having an arbitrary vector velocity. Currently, in designing a shrouded propeller, the shape of the shroud and the characteristics of the wake at its exit section are assumed. The shape of the shroud itself can be obtained in terms of a series of elementary vortex rings (see Kuchemann and Weber, "Aerodynamics of Propulsion"). The optimization of a design, the determination of the off-design performance, and the scaling of a shrouded propeller are based on experimental results.

Axial-momentum theory, on assuming an increment in velocity of ΔV at the disk cross section due to shrouding the propeller, gives the following equation for the propulsive efficiency:

$$\eta_P = 2\left\{1 + \left[1 + 2\left(1 + \frac{V_F}{2V_0} + \Delta V\right)\frac{V_F}{V_0}\right]^{1/2}\right\} \quad \textbf{(75)}$$

The simple axial-momentum theorem indicates that, for a shrouded propeller,

$$\frac{F_{\text{shrouded}}}{F_{\text{isolated}}} = 1.26\left(\frac{d_2}{d_p}\right)^{2/3} \quad \textbf{(76)}$$

where d_2 = the exit diameter of the shroud.

If $\Phi = V/u$ = the velocity coefficient, $\psi = \Delta p/(\frac{1}{2}\rho V^2)$ = the pressure coefficient, and A_F = the area of the actuator disk corresponding to the propeller, and if the effects of the compressibility of the air are neglected, then by definition

$$C_F = \frac{F}{\frac{1}{2}\rho V_F{}^2 A_F} = \frac{\rho V_F}{V_0}\left[\sqrt{1 + \frac{\psi}{\Phi^2} - \xi\left(\frac{V_F}{V_0}\right)^2} - 1\right] \quad \textbf{(77)}$$

where ξ = (frictional losses in the duct)/$(\frac{1}{2}\rho V_F{}^2)$.

For given values of V_F/V_0 and ξ, the maximum propulsive efficiency of the ducted propeller is obtained when

$$\left(\frac{\psi}{\Phi^2}\right)_{\text{opt}} = 2\left(\xi + \frac{\xi}{V_F/V_0}\right) \quad \textbf{(78)}$$

Performance

Static Thrust. From the simple axial-momentum theory, the static thrust F_0 of an actuator disk of diameter d_p is given by

$$F_0 = (\pi\rho/2)^{1/3}(\mathcal{P}d_p)^{2/3} = 10.4\text{bhp} \times d_p{}^{2/3} \text{ (at sea level)} \quad \textbf{(79)}$$

The **thrust horsepower** (thp) is accordingly

$$\text{thp} = \frac{F_0}{\text{bhp}} = (38{,}400/Nd_p)(1/C_P{}^{1/3}) \quad \textbf{(80)}$$

Equations (**79**) and (**80**) assume uniform axial velocity, no rotation of the air, and no profile losses. In practice, the approximate percentages obtained from two-bladed, four-bladed, and dual-rotation propellers are 50, 75, and 85 percent, respectively.

The static thrust for a given power input increases with the diameter and the number of blades. Controllable-pitch propellers selected for good over-all performance will develop 3 to 4 lb of thrust per shp.

Cruise Thrust. Cruise performance can be predicted with satisfactory accuracy either from blade-element theory or from wind-tunnel tests. In general, the approximate diameter for peak efficiency is given by

$$d_p = K\sqrt{\text{shp}/N^2V_0} \quad \textbf{(81)}$$

where V_0 = the flight speed, in miles per hour, and N = rpm. Approximate values of K are as follows:

Propeller type	Two blades	Three blades	Four blades
Wooden........	285	252	240
Metal..........	318	300	280

Figure 24 presents representative data for a three-bladed 10-ft propeller.

Reverse Thrust. By operating the propeller blades at large negative angles of attack, reversed thrust can be developed. In that condition, the blades are stalled, and as in the case of static thrust, the forces acting on the blades cannot be calculated. In practice, the reverse-pitch stop is set by trial and error so that the propeller can absorb the rated power at zero speed, *i.e.*, at $V_0 = 0$. With fixed-pitch reversing, the power absorbed when there is forward speed will be smaller than the rated value, but the reversed thrust is usually substantially larger than the static forward thrust corresponding to the rated power. The landing roll of an aircraft with reversed thrust plus brakes is approximately 45 percent of that with brakes alone.

Compressibility Effects. As the relative velocity between an airfoil and the free-stream air approaches the sonic speed, the lift coefficient C_L decreases rapidly, and simultaneously there is a large increase in the drag coefficient C_D. The propeller is subject to those effects. Since the acoustic speed decreases from sea level to the isothermal altitude, the effects appear at lower tip speeds at high altitude. Furthermore, the effect is more pronounced at higher tip speeds. Shock waves are formed at the leading edge of a propeller blade when its pitch-line velocity approaches the local sonic velocity of the air. As a consequence, the coefficient C_F is reduced and C_P is increased, thereby adversely affecting the propulsive efficiency of the propeller. Moreover, as the tip speed approaches the sonic speed, there is a large increase in the noise generated by the propeller.

Operation of a propeller in the transonic range requires that the blades be thin and have sweepback. Such designs present severe mechanical problems. Moreover, there is also the possibility of the propeller blades operating in the shock-stalled condition, which would cause serious losses if flow separation occurred. A propulsive efficiency of approximately 70 percent might be achieved with careful design for such a propeller.

Noise. The noise produced by a propeller arises from the rotation of the pressure fields associated with the aerodynamic pressures acting on the blades. The fundamental frequency of the rotating pressure pattern produced by the propeller is, to a stationary observer, equal to the blade-passage frequency. The noise level associated with a given tip speed can be estimated by Gutin's method (see References, p. 11–129). The noise intensity is determined by the number of blades, the tip speed, and the power input per unit of actuator-disk area. Increasing the number of blades, reducing the tip speed, and reducing the power loading reduce the noise. Reduction in noise level usually requires a compromise between performance and weight and is, therefore, not usually a factor in propeller selection. For high-subsonic-speed operation, see Garrick and Watkins (p. 11–129).

Mechanical Design

Blades. The principal blade loadings are (1) steady tensile, due to centrifugal forces, (2) steady bending, due to the aerodynamic thrust and torque forces, and (3) vibratory bending, due to cyclic variations in airloads and other excitations originating in the engine. The most serious and limiting stresses usually result from the vibratory loadings. The principal vibratory loading results from the cyclic variation in angle of attack of the blades when the axis of rotation is pitched or yawed relative to airstream. When the axis is pitched up, such as when the aircraft is in a high-angle-of-attack climb, the blades are at a higher angle of attack on the downstroke than when on the upstroke. This results in a once per revolution, $1 - P$, variation in aerodynamic loading on the blades, usually referred to as $1 - P$ aero-

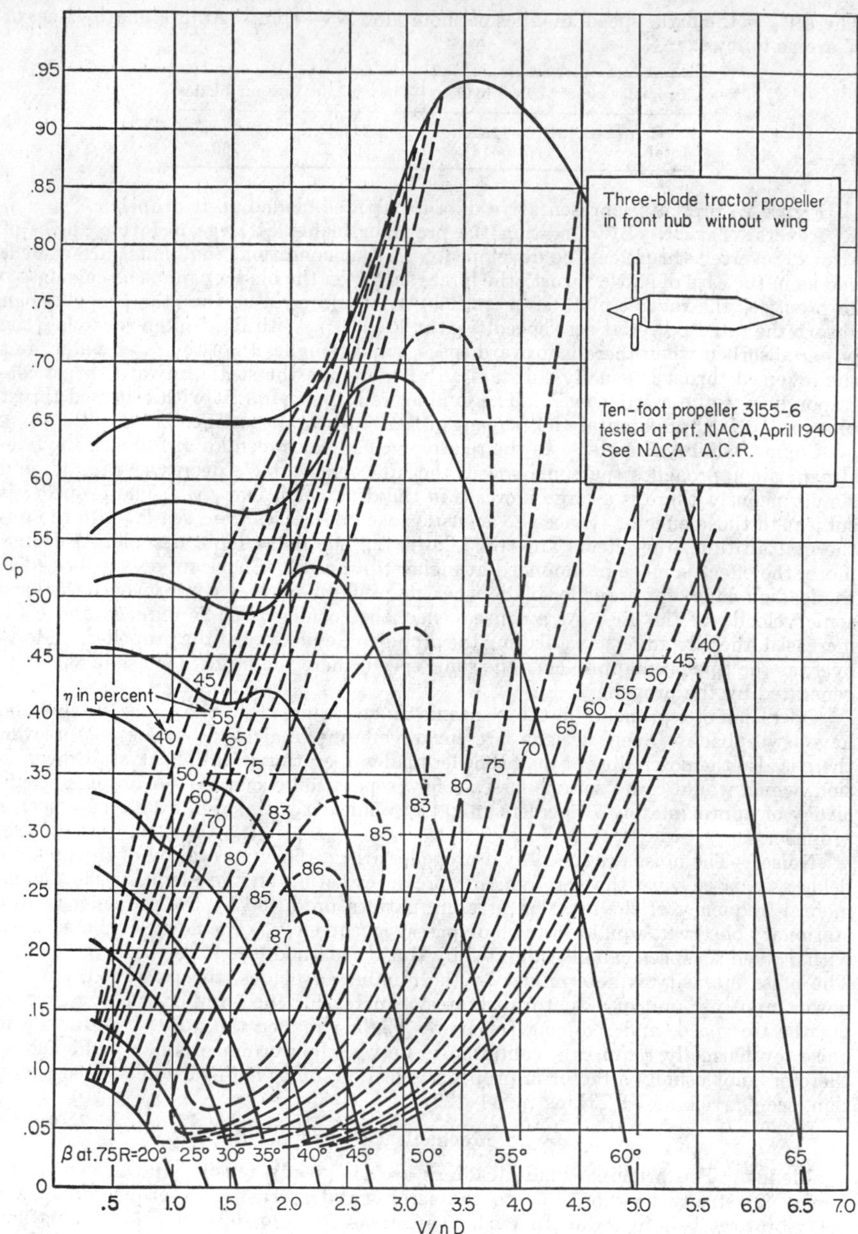

Fig. 24. Typical propeller characteristics.

dynamic excitation, and a steady **side force** and **yawing moment,** which are transmitted through the shaft to the aircraft.

The degree of pitch or yaw of the propeller axis is usually measured in terms of the **excitation factor,** defined as

$$\text{Excitation factor} = \psi(V_i/400)^2 \qquad \textbf{(82)}$$

where ψ = angle of pitch or yaw, deg; V_i = indicated flight velocity, mph. Another factor sometimes used is Aq, where $A = \psi°$, $q = 12\rho V_i^2$, Aq = excitation factor × 410. Ribner presents means of estimating the forces on inclined propellers.

Because of the restoring moment of the **centrifugal loads** on the blade elements when the blade deflects in bending, centrifugal forces have the effect of apparently stiffening the blade in **bending.** In Fig. 25, the bending natural frequency increases with rpm. At some rpm, the bending natural frequency will come into resonance with the $1 - P$ excitation, at which point small loadings will be greatly magnified (limited only by the damping present in the blade).

Propellers are designed so that the $1 - P$ resonant speed is above any expected operating speed. However, there will always be some magnification of the vibratory loads (due to proximity to resonant speed), resulting in disproportionately high vibratory stresses. As indicated in Fig. 25, blades normally pass through a $2 - P$ **resonance** in coming up to speed (usually not critical because it is a transient condition) and may pass through or be close to resonance with other modes.

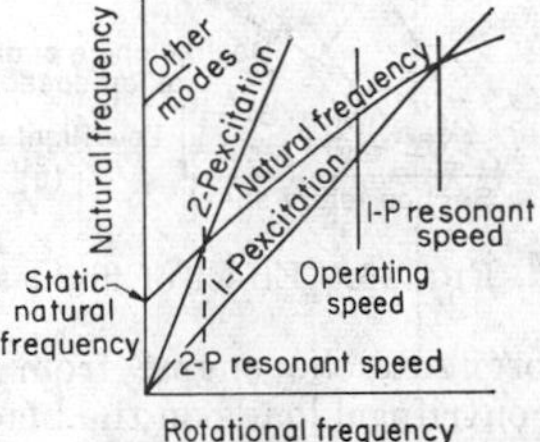

FIG. 25. Relation between blade natural frequency and major excitations.

The **natural frequencies** of the rotating propeller blade can be computed with good accuracy, but since the excitation varies from aircraft to aircraft and is usually not well defined, vibration surveys must be made of all new installations. These often result in the definition of ranges at which continuous operation should be avoided.

Allowable vibratory stresses are limited by the fatigue strength of the material. Unlike the steady-stress limits, **fatigue strength** is not a unique function of the material but is a function of surface finish as well. A sharp notch in the surface reduces the fatigue strength to a very low value. If propellers were designed to hold vibratory stresses below the lowest possible fatigue strength, the blades would be unacceptably heavy. Thus propellers are designed on the maintenance of a reasonably smooth surface finish. Since the blade surfaces are constantly subject to **store damage,** blades must be regularly inspected to make sure that the finish does not deteriorate below design standards.

Propeller blades are stalled when operating at low forward speeds, and when reversing (see Performance, above). Under these conditions **stall flutter** can occur. Stall flutter appears as a torsional oscillation caused by a lagging of the aerodynamic moment relative to the blade motion. This results in placing one component of the aerodynamic moment in phase with the twisting motions of the blade, thus feeding energy into said motions. This energy input increases with the magnitude of the aerodynamic forces *i.e.,* approximately as the square of the velocity, and with the degree of lag, *i.e.,* as the degree of stall. When this energy input exceeds that absorbed by mechanical and other damping, the motions become divergent. The ratio of aerodynamic to damping forces is, to a first approximation, proportional to $V/b\omega$, where V = velocity at $0.75R$, b = chord at $0.75R$, and ω = torsional frequency. Experience indicates that when this parameter is greater than 1.0, the blades will flutter when stalled. Increasing camber, chord, and rpm tend to unstall a blade at a given power. Increasing torsional stiffness increases ω and damping.

In general, $1 - P$ **considerations** control the design of the **inboard** portions of a blade, and **stall flutter** the **outboard** sections.

There are three types of **blade construction** in common use today, **solid aluminum, fabricated steel,** and **one-piece steel.** As in any beam designed on the basis of bending loads, it is desirable to concentrate the structural material at the maximum radii, as in the flanges of a simple I beam, and omit it from the center, where it carries no load. This is accomplished, with steel blades, by making them hollow. The structural material is concentrated in the outer fibers, or surface. In general, steel blades weigh about 80 to 85 percent of the equivalent solid aluminum blade. The advantage of steel increases with size. The blades normally constitute from one-third to one-half of the total propeller weight.

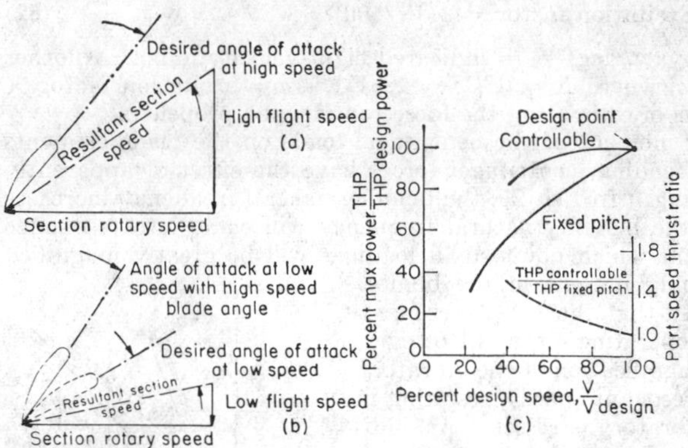

Fig. 26. Effect of flight speed on desired blade angle.

The **hub** retains the blades and contains the pitch-change motor. A **pitch-change mechanism** is provided so that the blades can be positioned at the proper angle of attack α to absorb the desired power at the desired rpm, regardless of flight speed. If the pitch is unchanged, as in Fig. 26, the angle of attack is excessive at low speed. This prevents the engine from reaching rated speed and delivering rated power. The centrifugal loads on the blade elements tend to rotate the blades toward flat pitch (see Fig. 27). The pitch-change motor acts against this moment by applying a pitch-increasing moment. The addition of **counterweights,** shown dotted in Fig. 27, reduces the moment and the size of the pitch-change motor. Counterweights, however, add to the radial centrifugal load of the blades, necessitating a heavier retention, and consequently do not necessarily reduce the net weight of the propeller.

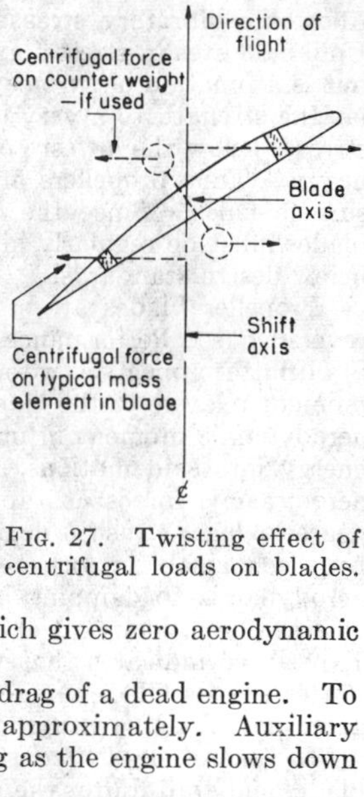

Most pitch-change mechanisms employ a **hydraulic piston,** mounted on the hub, with feed through the propeller shaft and with rotation of the blades by means of gears or links. **Electric motors** and **direct mechanical drives** have been used successfully. In the past, the weight of all systems, when fully developed, has turned out to be about the same.

Fig. 27. Twisting effect of centrifugal loads on blades.

Action of the pitch-change motor is limited by **low- and high-pitch stops.** These prevent the blades from assuming negative angles with reverse thrust. On reciprocating engines, the low-pitch stop is set to allow the propeller to absorb approximately rated power at zero forward speed. A lower setting results in higher windmilling drags in gliding flight, which could be dangerous if carried too far. In reversing propellers the low-pitch stop is automatically removed when the controls are set for reverse pitch. The high-pitch stop prevents the propeller from reversing through the positive range. In feathering propellers it is set at the angle which gives zero aerodynamic moment about the shaft.

Propeller feathering is provided in order to reduce the drag of a dead engine. To accomplish it, the blade-angle range is extended to 90 deg, approximately. Auxiliary pitch-change power is provided to complete the feathering as the engine slows down and to unfeather when the engine is stationary.

Reversing is provided in order to give propeller braking on the landing roll. It is accomplished by removing the flight low-pitch stop and driving the blades to a high negative **reverse-pitch angle.** The principal mechanical problem is to provide a mechanism which has the least possible chance of going into reverse inadvertently.

The **propeller control** is that portion of the system which regulates the blade angle. In light aircraft, this may consist merely of a mechanism which sets a given blade angle corresponding to a given position of the cockpit control. In such cases the propeller acts as a fixed-pitch propeller except when activated by the pilot. In most cases, the propeller control regulates blade angle so as to maintain a preset rotary rpm, irrespective of flight speed or shaft power. The **basic elements** of this system normally consist of a spring-balanced, engine-drive flyweight delivering an error signal which directs the servo, or pitch-change motor, to increase or decrease blade angle (Fig. 28). The control loop is closed by rpm feedback through the main engine. This basic system may be embellished with anticipating and delay devices to maintain speed in rapid throttle movements, synchronizing to coordinate two or more engines, and with overriding features to activate the reversing and feathering sequences. (See also Sec. 16.)

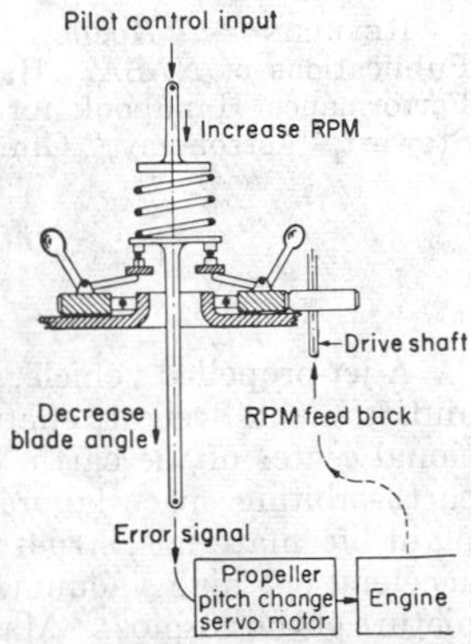

Fig. 28. Propeller-speed governor.

Propeller **controls** are fundamentally the same, with several added secondary features. First, because the engine is capable of a very rapid increase or decrease in torque and because of the high gear ratio between the propeller and engine shaft, anticipating features are necessary to prevent overspeeds in the propeller from producing large overspeeds and possible failure in the turbine. Second, because of the high idle rpm needed to maintain the pressure ratio in the compressor, the low-pitch stop of the turboprop engine propeller must be set substantially lower than for a piston engine. This is not true of a free-turbine drive and is only partially true of a split-compressor engine. In the event of an **engine failure,** the propeller, sensing the loss in rpm, will govern down to the low-pitch stop. This may lead to large, often uncontrollable, negative thrust. To avoid this possibility, an engine-shaft torque signal is put into the control, a negative torque automatically activating the feathering system. This portion of the system is known as **ENT (emergency negative-thrust)** system. Third, because of the high idle rpm characteristic of the turboprop engine, and the resulting low blade angles at low power in the ground-taxi regime, provision must be made to cut out the governing system and substitute direct blade-angle regulation (known as **beta control**). This is required because the propeller will not govern under these conditions as the torque-to-blade-angle relationship goes to zero. The propeller control of a turboprop engine is normally mechanically coordinated directly to the engine throttle, leaving only a single control, with so-called power lever, in the aircraft.

The shaft on which the propeller is mounted is subjected to the steady-thrust load, vibratory loads due to the propeller side, and **gyroscopic forces** (the $1 - P$ moment acting on the blades, is reactionless in propellers with three or more blades). In large aircraft, the shaft size is usually determined by the propeller side force (Ribner). In aircraft used for aerobatics, gyroscopic loads may become limiting. The **gyroscopic moment** on the propeller shaft is given by $2\omega_1 \cdot \omega_2(I_1 - I_2)$, where ω_1 = angular velocity of maneuver, ω_2 = angular velocity of shaft, I_1 = polar moment of inertia of propeller about shaft, I_2 = moment of inertia of propeller about diameter in plane of rotation. (See also p. 3–32.)

ASTRONAUTICS

BY

E. A. Hellebrand
and Associates at the NASA
George C. Marshall Space Flight Center

REFERENCES: Koelle, "Handbook of Astronautical Engineering," McGraw-Hill. Publications of NASA. Handbook of the British Astronautical Assoc. White, "Flight Performance Handbook for Powered Flight Operations," Wiley. Russell, Dugan, and Stewart, "Astronomy," Ginn. Ehricke, "Space Flight," Van Nostrand.

SPACE MISSIONS

By E. A. Hellebrand

A jet-propelled vehicle, not dependent upon an ambient gas to support combustion and to lift its weight, enables man to travel great distances away from the gravitational center of the earth. He can penetrate the dense air curtain and assemble an earth-orbiting space laboratory. Out in space, he may expose himself, animal and plant life, materials, structures, and mechanisms to the combined environment of zero acceleration, high vacuum, and uninhibited radiation and obtain an intensely clear picture of the cosmos. Man will learn to adjust to the artificial gravity created by the slow rotation of his space station and to the high gradients in this artificial gravitational field. He will also learn how earthly life processes—metabolism, cell division, and photosynthesis—change when removed from the 24-hr period of an earth day and how he can adapt himself to different rates of environmental changes that may not be periodic.

Satellites and Space Probes

(See Table 1)

Earth-orbiting satellites, manned and unmanned, serve the exploration of our earth and its surroundings, its weather, and its particle, magnetic, and radiation environment. Communication, navigation, and reconnaissance satellites are for immediate terrestrial uses such as improved live televised news around the globe, early wind and iceberg warnings for sea and air traffic, and timely warnings of impending inclement weather. High-resolution satellite borne cameras may reduce the element of surprise in future warfare. A military space force of inspector, interceptor, and earth-target attack satellites is also feasible. Satellites and space probes are being developed to explore our solar system in preparation for manned excursions and to gather information in many areas of modern science.

Lunar Base and Earth-orbiting Laboratory

A logical early step in space exploration is the approach to the earth's moon and a landing and stay thereon leading to a permanent lunar base. An earth-orbiting laboratory and a lunar base complement each other. The laboratory is dependent upon supplies from its mother planet. It would enable us to learn much about our immediate environment and to increase our experience in earth-orbital operations. An orbiting platform is better suited to optical telescopic observations, but a lunar station may be better for radio astronomy. The lunar base will be able to explore lunar materials to provide subsistence for its crew and fuel and nutrition for space travelers; it will function as a true relay station since there will be little gravity to hinder travel farther out into space, e.g., to Mars, Venus, and the more distant planets.

Table 1. Highlights of the History of Non-military Satellites and Space Probes

Name; launch date	Mission weight; lb	Results; time in orbit	Launch vehicle; origin
Sputnik 1; Oct., 1957	Earth orbit; 184	4 months	U.S.S.R.
Explorer 1; Feb., 1958	Earth orbit; 31	Radiation belt; 1958 to present	Jupiter C; U.S.
Pioneer 1; Oct., 1958	Lunar probe; 84	Radiation, magnetic micrometeorite data; 70,000 miles	Thor-Able; U.S.
Lunik 2; Sept., 1959	Lunar probe; 860	Impact on moon lunar ionosphere; flight time 34 hr	U.S.S.R.
Tiros 1; Apr., 1960	Weather; 270	23,000 cloud pictures; 3 months	Thor-Able; U.S.
Echo 1; Aug., 1960	Passive communications; 166	Relayed voice and TV signals; in orbit	Delta; U.S.
Vostok 1; Apr., 1961	Man in orbit; 10,400	Y. Gagarin recovered; 1 orbit	U.S.S.R.
Explorer 11; Apr., 1961	Earth orbit; 82	Gamma-ray counter; 4 months	Juno II; U.S.
Mercury-Atlas 6; Feb., 1962	Man in earth orbit; 3,000	J. Glenn landed; 3 orbits	Atlas D; U.S.
Telstar 1; July, 1962	Communications; 170	First active repeater; 8 months	Delta; U.S.
Vostok 3; Aug. 11, 1962	Man in earth orbit; 10,000	A. Nikoloyev landed; 48 orbits	U.S.S.R.
Vostok 4; Aug. 12, 1962	Man in earth orbit; 10,000	P. Popovich landed; 48 orbits	U.S.S.R.
Mariner 2; Aug., 1962	Venus probe; 450	Passed within 21,600 miles, reported surface temp 800 F	Atlas-Agena; U.S.
Relay 1; Dec., 1962	Communications; 170	Active repeater; in orbit	Delta; U.S.
Telstar 2; May, 1963	Communications; 180	Active repeater; in orbit	Delta; U.S.
Mercury-Atlas 9; May, 1963	Man in earth orbit; 3,000	G. Cooper landed; 22 orbits, 34 hr	Atlas D; U.S.
Atlas Centaur; Dec., 1963	Propulsion into earth orbit	First liquid-hydrogen stage; in orbit	Atlas; U.S.
Apollo; Jan., 1964	Preparatory to manned moon flights	38,000 lb in elliptical orbit; predicted—1½ years	Saturn 1; U.S.
Ranger 7; July, 1964	Moon-surface exploration; 800	Several thousand closeup pictures of moon surface details	Atlas-Agena; U.S.

Manned-space-flight Programs of the United States

The Mercury project proved man's capabilities in space and helped to develop the foundations for manned-space-flight technology; the launch vehicles were Redstone and Atlas. The Gemini project will provide a carrier for extended orbital crew operations and rendezvous; the launch vehicle is the Titan II. The Apollo project will accomplish manned exploration of the moon, by circumnavigation and landings; launch vehicle is Saturn V. Saturn V could be adapted to establish and support a small lunar base for a crew of 10 to 20. With perfected earth-orbital assembly and refueling techniques, the Saturn IB will provide economical operation of a lunar-base support system. The major requirements for large-scale lunar colonies and for planetary exploration are (1) nuclear propulsion to reduce transport time, and (2) nuclear power to support man during the extended journey. Chemical power is not efficient enough for these purposes.

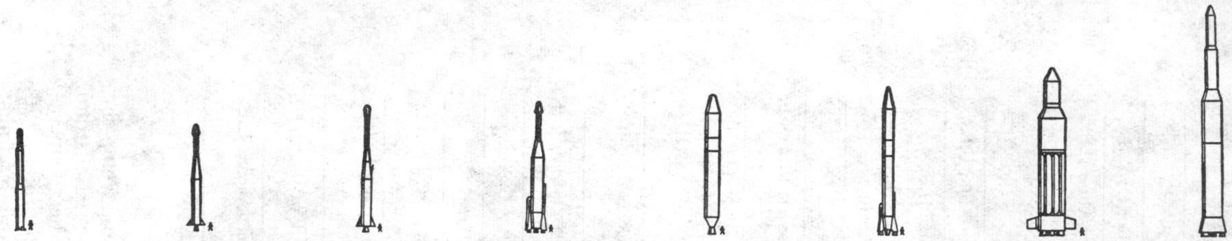

	Scout	Delta	Thor-Agena B	Atlas-Agena B	Titan II	Centaur	Saturn 1B	Saturn V
Stages	4	3	2	2	2	2	2	3
Propellants	Solid	1st stage, liquid oxygen and kerosine (LOX/RP); 2d stage, unsymmetrical dimethylhydrazine (UDMH) and inhibited red fuming nitric acid (IRFNA); 3d stage, solid	1st stage, liquid oxygen and kerosine (LOX/RP); 2d stage, unsymmetrical dimethylhydrazine (UDMH) and inhibited red fuming nitric acid (IRFNA)	1st stage, liquid oxygen and kerosine (LOX/RP); 2d stage, unsymmetrical dimethylhydrazine (UDMH) and inhibited red fuming nitric acid (IRFNA)	Sterable [a blend of unsymmetrical dimethylhydrazine (UDMH) and hydrazine as fuel; nitrogen tetroxide as oxidizer]	1st stage, liquid oxygen and kerosine (LOX/RP); 2d stage, liquid oxygen and liquid hydrogen (LOX/LM)	1st stage, liquid oxygen and kerosine (LOX/RP); 2d stage, liquid oxygen and hydrogen (LOX/LM)	1st stage, liquid oxygen and kerosine (LOX/RP); 2d and 3d stages, liquid oxygen and liquid hydrogen (LOX/LM)
Thrust	1st stage (Algel II-A), 86,000 lb at sea level; 2d stage (Caster), 64,000 lb; 3d stage (Antares), 23,000 lb; 4th stage (Altair), 3,000 lb	1st stage (Thor, DM-21), 170,000 lb at sea level; 2d stage (AJ10-118), 7,700 lb; 3d stage (Altair), 2,800 lb	1st stage (Thor, DM-21), 170,000 lb at sea level; 2d stage (Agena B), 16,000 lb	Atlas D, 367,000 lb at sea level; Atlas D sustainer, 80,000 lb; Agena B, 16,000 lb	1st stage (XLR-87), 430,000 lb at sea level; 2d stage (XLR-91), 100,000 lb	Atlas D, 367,000 lb at sea level; Atlas D sustainer, 80,000 lb; Centaur, 30,000 lb	1st stage (S-1), 1,600,000 lb at sea level; 2d stage (S-IVB), 200,000 lb in a vacuum	1st stage (S-IC), 7,500,000 lb at sea level; 2d stage (S-11), 1,000,000 lb in a vacuum; 3d stage (S-IVB), 200,000 lb in a vacuum
Max diameter	3.3 ft, excluding fins	8 ft, excluding fins	8 ft, excluding fins	10 ft (16 ft at base)	10 ft	10 ft, excluding fins	21.6 ft, excluding fins	33 ft, excluding fins
Height	65 ft, less spacecraft	88 ft, less spacecraft	76 ft, less spacecraft	91 ft, less spacecraft	90 ft, less spacecraft	100 ft, less spacecraft	Approximately 150 ft, less spacecraft	280 ft, less spacecraft
Payload	220 lb is 300-nm orbit	300 lb in 350-nm orbit; 130 lb escape	1,600 lb in 300-nm orbit	6,000 lb in 300-nm orbit; 750 lb escape; 425 lb to Mars or Venus	More than 6,000 lb in low earth orbit	8,500 lb in 300-nm orbit; 2,300 lb escape; 1,300 lb to Mars or Venus	34,000 lb in 100-nm orbit	240,000 lb in 300-nm orbit; 90,000 lb escape; 70,000 lb to Mars or Venus
Use	Launching of probes and satellites	Launching of scientific satellites and space probes	Launching of meteorological, communications, and scientific satellites	Lunar missions and launching of communications and scientific satellites	Launching of the two-man Gemini spacecraft	Launching of earth satellites and lunar and planetary exploration missions	Launching into earth orbit of the Apollo spacecraft with its Lunar Excursion Module (LEM), as well as the launching of unmanned pay loads in support of the manned lunar-landing program	Launching of circumlunar and lunar leading flights

FIG. 1. United States launch vehicles.

Launch Vehicles

(See also p. 11–163 *et seq.*)

Liquid Propellants. Economic efficiency and timely schedules dictate the use of available ballistic missiles for space missions involving pay loads up to 3,000 lb in circular earth orbits of 300 nm approx or equivalent energy requirements. More powerful vehicles are needed for larger pay loads and velocities (Fig. 1). The ratio of launch weight to pay load has decreased with recent larger launch vehicles utilizing improved technology, e.g., high specific impulses, high-pressure engines, nuclear propulsion, lower dry weight (better materials), more efficient designs, and better fabrication processes. The vehicle total volume, including pay load, increases approximately linearly with the launch weight, the vehicle specific density being 40 to 50 lb per ft^3 for liquid oxygen and kerosine and 15 to 20 lb per ft^3 for liquid oxygen and liquid hydrogen propellants. Low densities are attributable to incomplete utilization of space in engine and instrument compartments, around tank bulkheads, and in pay loads and interstages. Therefore, launch vehicles become bulky and difficult to handle. Fabrication, assembly, testing, and check-out are more efficiently performed on sites close to navigable waterways. It is mandatory to provide the lightest possible structural envelope for these large volumes commensurate with the vehicle strength and stiffness required to carry ground and flight loads. Thin-walled, integrally stiffened shells and corrugated or honeycomb panels must be used throughout. Lightweight, weldable, high-strength materials applicable over a wide temperature range, e.g., some aluminum alloys, are used for cryogenic propellant tanks (see Secs. 6 and 18). Titanium and steel for high-pressure tanks and fiber-reinforced plastics for honeycomb structures are needed. Cryogenic propellant tanks must be insulated with lightweight plastic foams to minimize boilover losses. A reduction of the vehicle structural weight is possible if insulation layers can be combined with the structural walls to form a stiff honeycomb or multilayer composite shell. A modern launch vehicle needs about 3 lb of propulsion hardware (engines, turbines, pumps, valves, and lines) and 4 to 5 lb of structure and instrumentation, and may carry up to 5 lb of orbital pay load and 2 lb of escape pay load for every 100 lb of liquid propellants.

Solid Propellants. Solid-propellant vehicles attain a higher over-all density and are, therefore, more compact and easier to handle. No turbines, pumps, or other complex machinery are required, as the propellant burns in place. The casing, the major portion of the vehicle's body, however, has to withstand higher internal pressure, *i.e.*, the combustion pressure, about fifteen to thirty times the liquid tank pressure. With liquid-propelled vehicles, the combustion pressure is confined to the small space of the engine's combustion chamber, and therefore, the ratio of launch to dry weight is larger than with vehicles using solid propellants. Solid propellants have a lower specific impulse than liquid propellants, but multiple-stage solid-propelled vehicles are applicable to boost a variety of ballistic, orbital, and escape pay loads. Solid motors are also useful for auxiliary power to separate stages, control the attitude, settle propellants in liquid boosters, and brake the speed of reentry bodies. Strap-on solids provide an effective means of increasing the versatility of launch vehicles when new missions become apparent.

ASTRONOMICAL CONSTANTS OF THE SOLAR SYSTEM

By Helmut G. L. Krause

REFERENCES: Handbook of the British Astronautical Assoc. Blanco and McCuskey, "Basic Physics of the Solar System," Addison-Wesley. Clarke, Constants and Related Data for Use in Trajectory Calculations, *Tech. Rep.* 32-604, Jet Propulsion Lab., Pasadena. Francis, Constants for an Earth-Moon Transit, *Lockheed Rep. LAC*/421571. Krause, On a Consistent System of Astrodynamic Constants, *NASA-TN* D-1642. Makemson, Baker, and Westrom, Analysis and Standardization of Astrodynamic Constants, *Jour. Astro. Sci.*, Spring, 1961. Middlehurst and Kuiper, "The Solar System," Vols. 1–4, Univ. of Chicago Press. Townsend, "Orbital Flight Handbook," Martin Co

A greater number of astronomical constants is used in astrodynamics and astronautics than in classical astronomy because astronautics is a kind of experimental

Table 2. General, Terrestrial, and Lunar Constants

1. Ephemeris second: 1 $\sec_E$ = 1/31,556,925.9747 of tropical year at 1900.0.
2. Mean solar day (culmination period of the mean sun):

$$1^d = 1^{d*}.002\ 737\ 909\ 265 + 0^{d*}.589 \times 10^{-10}T = 24^{h*}03^{m*}56^{s*}.555\ 360\ 50 + 0^{s*}.050\ 89 \times 10^{-4}T$$
$$= 1^{rot}.002\ 737\ 811\ 891 - 0^{rot}.001\ 4 \times 10^{-10}T = (1 \pm 10^{-8})^{d_E}$$

3. Mean siderial day or mean equinoctial day (culmination period of the vernal equinox):

$$1^{d*} = 0^d.997\ 269\ 566\ 414 - 0^d.587 \times 10^{-10}T = 23^h56^m04^s.090\ 538\ 17 - 0^s.050\ 716\ 8 \times 10^{-4}T$$
$$= 0^{rot}.999\ 999\ 902\ 892 - 0^{rot}.589 \times 10^{-10}T$$

4. Mean stellar day or mean period of the earth's rotation (culmination period of an equatorial star without proper motion):

$$1^d_{st} = 1^{rot} = 1^{d*}.000\ 000\ 097\ 108 + 0^{d*}.589 \times 10^{-10}T$$
$$= 24^{h*}00^{m*}0^{s*}.008\ 390\ 13 + 0^{s*}.050\ 89 \times 10^{-4}T$$
$$= 0^d.997\ 269\ 663\ 257 + 0^d.001\ 4 \times 10^{-10}T = 23^h56^m04^s.098\ 905\ 40 + 0^s.001\ 21 \times 10^{-5}T$$

5. Tropical year (equinox to equinox):

$$P_{trop} = (365.242\ 198\ 78 - 0.000\ 006\ 138T)^{d_E} = 365^{d_E}05^{h_E}48^{m_E}45^{s_E}.530T$$

6. Siderial year (fixed star to fixed star):

$$P_{sid} = (365.256\ 360\ 42 + 0.000\ 000\ 11T)^{d_E} = 365^{d_E}06^{h_E}09^{m_E}09^{s_E}.54 + 0^{s_E}.010T$$

7. Synodic month (new moon to new moon):

$$P_{syn} = (29.530\ 588\ 2 - 0.000\ 000\ 2T)^d = 29^d12^h44^m02^s.78 - 0^s.017T$$

8. Tropical month (equinox to equinox):

$$P_{trop} = (27.321\ 581\ 7 - 0.000\ 000\ 2T)^d = 27^d07^h43^m04^s.7 - 0^s.017T$$

9. Siderial month (fixed star to fixed star):

$$P_{sid} = (27.321\ 661\ 0 - 0.000\ 000\ 2T)^d = 27^d07^h43^m11^s.47 - 0^s.017T$$

10. Astronomical unit (mean earth-sun distance): au = 149,598,700 ± 400 km.
11. Light year: ly = (9.460 530 ± 0.000 003) × 10^{12} km = 63,239.39 ± 0.15 au.
12. Parsec: pc = 206,264.806 247 au = (3.085 695 ± 0.000 008) × 10^{13} km.
13. Semimajor axis of the earth's orbit: $a\oplus$ = 1.000 000 236 au = 149,598,700 ± 400 km.
14. Mean orbital speed: $v\oplus$ = 29,784.90 ± 0.08 m/sec.
15. Mass of the earth: $M\oplus$ = (5.9761 ± 0.004 3) × 10^{24} kg.
16. Equatorial radius of the earth: $R_e\oplus$ = 6,378,170 ± 20 m.
17. Flattening (oblateness, ellipticity): $f\oplus = (R_e - R_p)/R_e$ = 0.003 352 55 = 1:(298.28 ± 0.05).
18. Acceleration of gravity at the earth's surface:

$$g = g_e(1 + \beta \sin^2 \phi + \gamma \sin^2 2\phi) = 9.780\ 315(1 + 0.005\ 302\ 74 \sin^2 \phi - 0.000\ 005\ 9 \sin^2 2\phi)\ \text{m/sec}^2$$

19. Moments of inertia of the earth:

$$A = (0.329\ 681_4 \pm 0.000\ 11)M\oplus R_e^2 = (0.801\ 50 \pm 0.000\ 85) \times 10^{38}\ \text{kg-m}^2$$
$$C = (0.330\ 763_9 \pm 0.000\ 11)M\oplus R_e^2 = (0.804\ 13 \pm 0.000\ 85) \times 10^{38}\ \text{kg-m}^2$$

20. Circular and escape velocities from the earth's surface at the equator:

$$v_{cir} = 7{,}905.39 \pm 0.06\ \text{m/sec} \qquad v_{esc} = v_{cir}\,2^{1/2} = 11{,}179.91 \pm 0.08\ \text{m/sec}$$

21. Mean observed distance of the perturbed moon from the earth:

$$\bar{r}☾ = 384{,}401.0 \pm 1.0\ \text{km} = (60.268\ 23 \pm 0.000\ 35)R_e\oplus = 0.002\ 569\ 548 \pm 0.000\ 000\ 014\ \text{au}$$

22. Semimajor axis of the moon's orbit: $a☾ = 1.000\ 907\ 681\bar{r}☾$ = 384 749.9 ± 1.0 km.
23. Mean orbital velocity: $v☾$ = 1,024.089 ± 0.003 m/sec.
24. Mass of the moon: $M☾$ = (7.353 4 ± 0.007 5) × 10^{22} kg = $M\oplus$: (81.270 ± 0.024).
25. Semiaxes of the moon ellipsoid: a = 1,738,780 ± 186 m; b = 1,738,452 ± 209 m; c = 1,737,688 ± 188 m.

The time T is in Julian centuries of 36,525 days from 1900 Jan. 0.5 U.T. (universal time). The constants are given with probable errors (pe).

Table 3. Orbital Data of Planetary Orbits for Epoch 1960.0*

Name of planet	Symbol	Mean distance a (au)	Mean siderial motion n_{sid} (u/d)	Siderial period P_{sid} (d)	Mean synodical period P_{syn} (d)	Mean orbital velocity, m/sec
Mercury	☿	0.387	14,732.419	87.969	115.88	47,872
Venus	♀	0.723	5,767.669	224.700	583.92	35,020
Earth	⊕	1.000	3,548.192	365.256		29,784
Mars	♂	1.523	1,886.518	686.979	779.94	24,129
Jupiter	♃	5.202	299.128	4,332.588	398.88	13,064
Saturn	♄	9.538	120.455	10,759.205	378.09	9,645
Uranus	♅	19.181	42.235	30,685.5	369.66	6,800
Neptune	♆	30.057	21.532	60,189.5	367.49	5,432
Pluto	♇	39.517	14.283	90,737.2	366.74	4,738

* Epoch 1960.0 means 1960, Jan. 0, 12^h E.T. (ephemeris time) = J.D. 243,693.0 (Julian day No.).

Table 4. Physical Data of Sun, Moon, and Planets

Name		Radius R, km	Mass M ($\oplus = 1$)	Radius R ($\oplus = 1$)	Volume V ($\oplus = 1$)	Mean density $\bar{\rho}$ ($\oplus = 1$)	Visual albedo $\bar{A}_V$	Rotational period at equator P_{rot}	Inclination of equator to orbit I	Rotational velocity at equator V_{rot}, m/sec	Gravitational parameter $\mu = GM$, km³/sec²
Sun		695,995	332,948	109.121	1,303,735	0.2553		$25^d.035$	7°15′	2,021.73	132,714.6 × 10^6
Moon		1,738	0.0123	0.272	0.020	0.6058	0.067	27 .321	6°41′	4.62	4,904.70
Mercury		2,422	0.0544	0.379	0.054	0.9896	0.056	87 .969	7°(?)	2.00	21,684.1
Venus		6,114	0.8149	0.958	0.883	0.9221	0.76	30(?)	32°(?)	14.82	324,851
Earth	(e)	6,378	1.0000	1.000	1.000	1.0000	0.36	$23^h56^m4^s$	23°26′.7	465.10	398,604.6
Earth	(p)	6,356		0.996							
Mars	(e)	3,416	0.1078	0.535	0.153	0.7031	0.16	$24^h37^m22^s$	23°59′	242.13	42,977.5
Mars	(p)	3,398		0.532							
Jupiter	(e)	71,403	317.821	11.195	1,315.996	0.2415	0.73	9^h50^m	3°6′.9	12,673.3	126,684,900
Jupiter	(p)	66,749		10.465							
Saturn	(e)	60,502	95.112	9.485	772.552	0.1231	0.76	10^h14^m	26°44.7′	10,318.6	37,912,080
Saturn	(p)	54,577		8.556							
Uranus	(e)	24,848	14.516	3.895	55.619	0.2610	0.93	10^h49^m	97°53′	4,009.5	5,786,140
Uranus	(p)	23,295		3.652							
Neptune	(e)	25,000	17.140	3.919	59.217	0.2894	0.84	15^h40^m	28°48′	2,785	6,832,080
Neptune	(p)	24,500		3.841							
Pluto		2,966	0.1(?)	0.465	0.10	0.991(?)	0.14	$6^d.390$	(?)	33.75	40,000(?)

astronomy and its missions vary so greatly. A higher accuracy is also necessary because the astrodynamic missions include departure, landing, and flyby maneuvers. Some of the constants, given in relative and astronomical units in celestial mechanics, must be known in absolute units for astrodynamic purposes. Tables 2 to 4 provide the latest observed data for standardization of astrodynamic computations. See references for additional constants.

SPACE-VEHICLE ENVIRONMENTS

By J. H. Farrow and R. E. Jewell

REFERENCES: Harris and Crede, "Shock and Vibration Handbook," McGraw-Hill. Beranek, "Noise Reduction," McGraw-Hill. Crandall, "Random Vibration," Technology Press, MIT. Neugebauer, The Space Environment, *Tech. Rep.* 34-229, Jet Propulsion Lab., Pasadena, 1960. Hart, Effects of Outer Space Environment Important to Simulation of Space Vehicles, *ASD Tech. Rep.* 61-201, Cornell Aeronautical Lab. Barrett, Techniques for Predicting Localized Vibratory Environments of Rocket Vehicles, *NASA-TN D*-1836. Wilhold, Guest, and Jones, A Technique for Predicting Far Field Acoustic Environments Due to a Moving Rocket Sound Source, *NASA-TN D*-1832. Eldred, Roberts, and White, Structural Vibration in Space Vehicles, *WADD Tech. Rep.* 61–62. Bolt, Beranek, and Newman, Exterior Sound and Vibration Fields of a Saturn Vehicle during Static Firing and during Launching, *U.S.A. Ord. Rep.* 764.

Definitions. Space-vehicle environments are conditions or influences recognizable on and caused by the vehicle. Environments which are recognizable **on** the vehicle may be either **natural** or **induced.** Environments which are **caused by** the vehicle are **induced.** The natural environments exist in the absence of any operational influence of the space vehicle. The induced environments exist as a result of an outside agency, such as transportation, handling, and operation of the space vehicle.

At the time of launch, the total configuration which lifts from the launch pad is called the space vehicle. This configuration does not necessarily enter space in the sense of performing a space mission. The sequence of events is the burnout and separation of the various boost stages, followed by injection of a "spacecraft" into orbit or escape trajectory. The space-vehicle configuration differs for various phases of operation. The environments are changing due to a continuous interplay of natural and induced influences and to changes in configurations.

The basic concepts concerning natural and induced environments are equally applicable to aircraft, but the environments of space vehicles cover a broader spectrum of severity. The aircraft experiences heat and cold, dry desert air, salt spray, and humidity but always remains within a radiation-protective convective atmosphere. The induced environment for aircraft is also relatively moderate due to moderate speeds, relatively low thrust levels, and unchanging configurations. The space-vehicle environments are much more severe. The forces required to propel a space vehicle from the launch pad are tremendous. The dynamic pressures generated in the atmosphere by large rocket engines are exceeded only by nuclear blasts. Slow initial ascent from the launch pad is followed by rapid acceleration and high g loading, while acoustic and aerodynamic forces drive every point of the vehicle surface. The space-vehicle velocity quickly becomes supersonic and continues to hypersonic velocities. Gradually, as the space vehicle leaves the atmosphere, the aerodynamic forces recede. Then suddenly the rocket thrust decays and is followed by the ignition of another rocket, which quickly develops thrust and continues to accelerate the space vehicle. Finally, the space vehicle becomes weightless. While in space, the vehicle exists in a vacuum, is bombarded by solar radiation and micrometeorites, and experiences continuous cyclic variation of temperature. In completing a mission, a space vehicle is subjected to the additional environmental extremes of planetary landings, escape, and earth reentry (Fig. 2).

These environments represent basic criteria for space-vehicle design. For operational reliability, the most important are the shock, vibration, and acoustic environments which are present to varying magnitudes in all operational phases and which constitute a major engineering problem.

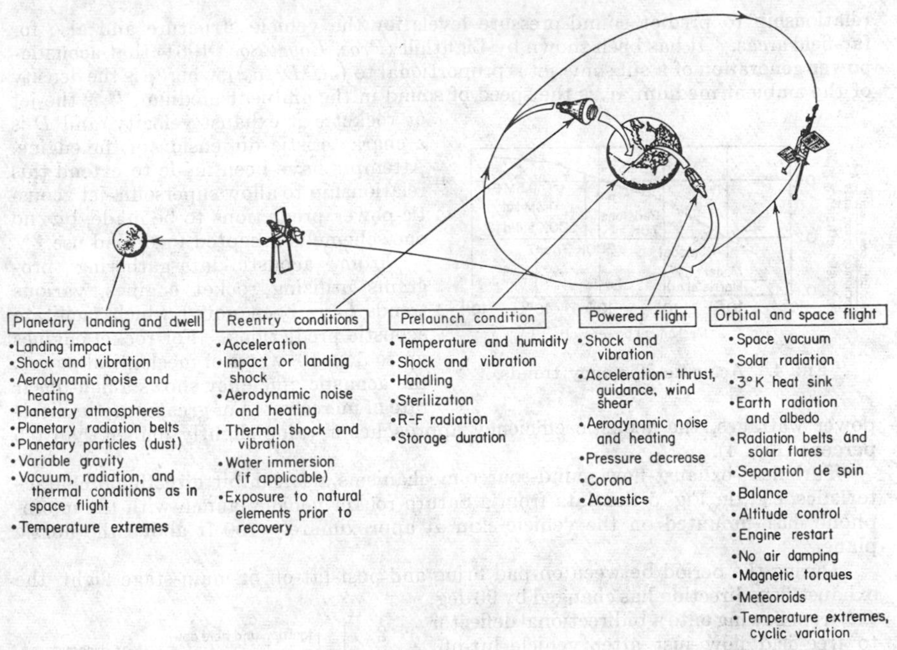

FIG. 2. Environmental conditions experienced by space vehicles.

Importance of Dynamic Environments. (See Fig. 3.) The problem is selection of the most practical point to enter the inner cycle. It is not possible to have original environmental data prior to fabrication and testing of a particular structure. Vibration, shock, and acoustic noise adversely affect structural integrity and vehicle reliability. These environments must be considered prior to design and fabrication and then again for design verification through ground testing. Precise vibration and acoustic environmental predictions are complicated due to structural non-linearities, random forcing functions, and multidegree-of-freedom systems. Current environmental-prediction techniques consist mainly of extrapolating measured data obtained from existing vehicles. Acoustic environments produced during ground operation are important factors in evaluating ground-facility locations and design, personnel safety, and public relations.

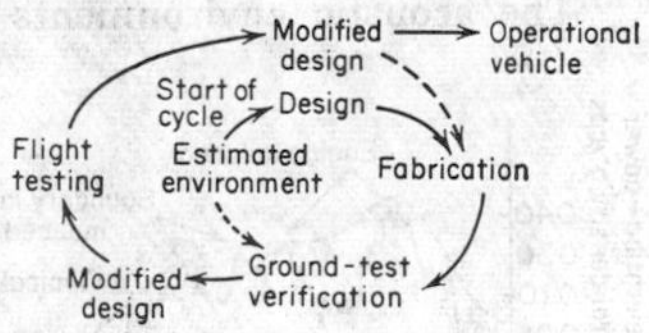

Modified design → Operational vehicle
Start of cycle
Design
Flight testing
Estimated environment
Fabrication
Modified design ← Ground-test verification

FIG. 3. Space vehicle development.

A **source of sound** common to all jet and rocket-engine propulsion systems is the turbulent exhaust flow. This high-velocity flow produces pressure fluctuations, referred to as **noise,** and has adverse effects on the vehicle and its operations. Also, far-field, uncontrolled areas may be subjected to intense acoustic-sound-pressure levels which may require personnel protection or sound-suppression devices. (See also Sec. 12.)

The sound source is the exhaust flow, where the viscous atmospheric fluid is subjected to high-shear forces between the region of high-velocity flow and the ambient medium. These shear forces produce random eddy motions to propagate randomly fluctuating pressures, which are numerically described in standard statistical form.

The **sound-generation mechanism** is presented in empirical and analytical form, utilizing measured sound pressures and the known engine operational parameters. This combination of empirical terms and analytical reasoning provides a generalized relationship to predict sound-pressure levels for the vehicle structure and also for far-field areas. It has been shown by Lighthill (*Proc. Royal Soc.*, 1961) that **acoustic-power generation** of a subsonic jet is proportional to $(\rho U^8 D^2/a_o^5)$, where ρ is the density of the ambient medium, a_o is the speed of sound in the ambient medium, U is the jet or rocket exit exhaust velocity, and D is a characteristic dimension of the engine. Attempts have been made to extend this relationship to allow supersonic-jet acoustic-power predictions to be made, but no one scheme is accepted for broad use.

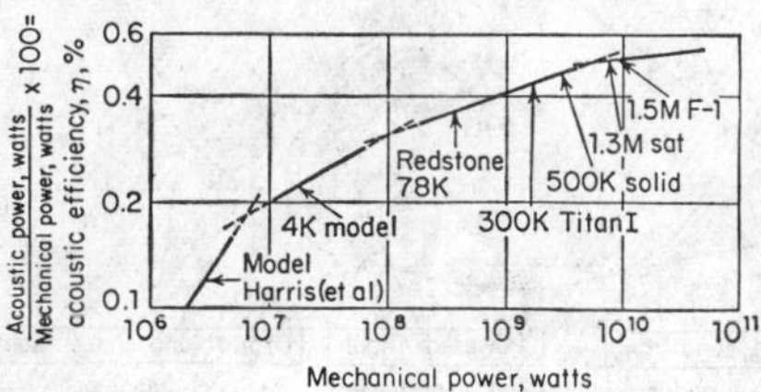

FIG. 4. Acoustic-efficiency trends.

From acoustic-data-gathering programs utilizing rocket engines, various trends have been noted which facilitate acoustic predictions. For rocket engines up to 5×10^9 watts of mechanical power, the **acoustic efficiency** shows a non-linear rate of increase. For greater mechanical-power wattages, the acoustic efficiency approaches a value slightly higher than 0.5 percent (Fig. 4).

Turbulent-exhaust-flow sound-source mechanisms also exhibit **directional characteristics,** e.g., in Fig. 5 the data from a Saturn rocket vehicle launch with the microphone flush-mounted on the vehicle skin at approximately 100 ft above the nozzle plane.

During the period between on-pad firing and post-lift-off or main-stage flight, the exhaust-flow direction has changed by 90 deg, *i.e.*, from flowing onto a bidirectional deflector to free-field flow just after vehicle lift-off. With exhaust-flow direction change, the directivity has also shifted 90 deg to retain its inherent relationship to the exhaust stream. The **sound-pressure-level** variation during a small time interval—between on-pad condition and shortly after lift-off—depends on the changes which have occurred in the directivity and the jet-exhaust-velocity vector (Fig. 5). This change in sound-pressure level is 20 db approx in this case and is indicative of the significance of a sound source's directional properties, which depend on velocity and temperature of the jet.

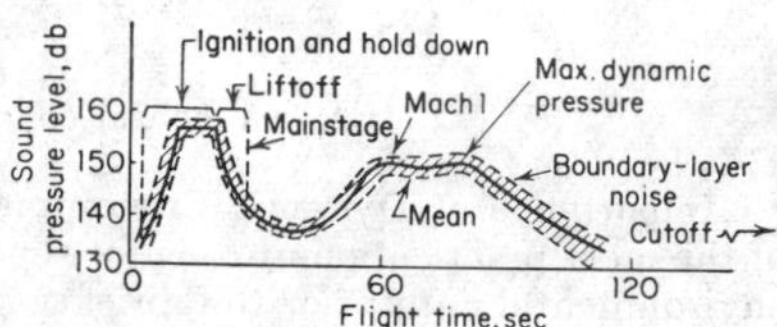

FIG. 5. Vehicle acoustic environment.

The **acoustic environments** produced by a given conventional engine can be empirically described by that engine's flow parameters and geometry. It is difficult to predict the acoustic environments for non-conventional engines such as the plug-nozzle and expansion-deflection engines.

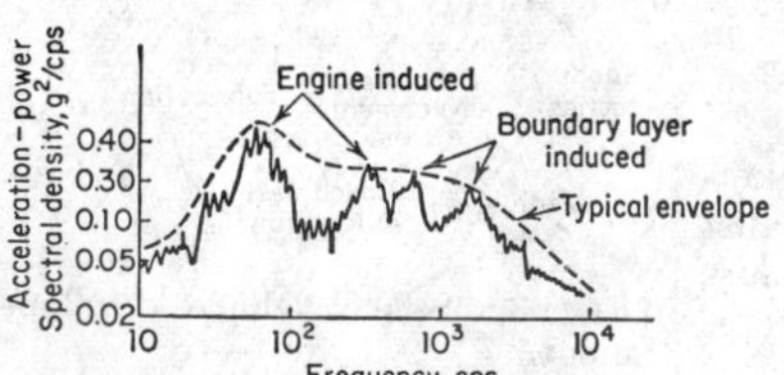

FIG. 6. Random-vibration spectrum of space-vehicle structure.

The **turbulent-boundary-layer** problem of high-velocity vehicle flights is difficult to evaluate in all but the simplest cases. Only for attached, homogeneous, subsonic flows can the boundary-layer noise be estimated with confidence.

Space-vehicle Vibration. (See also p. 5–90 *et seq.*) The vibratory environment on rocket vehicles consists of total-vehicle bending vibrations, in which the vehicle is considered a non-uniform beam, with low-frequency responses (0 to 20 cps) and localized vibrations with frequencies up to thousands of cycles per second.

The response of a simple structure to a dynamic forcing function may be described by the universal equation of motion given as $M\ddot{X} + C\dot{X} + KX = F(t)$ or $F(t)/X(t) = (M - K/\omega^2) + j(C/\omega)$ and is a complex function containing real and imaginary quantities. In the case of rocket-vehicle vibrations, $F(t)$ is a **random** forcing phenomenon. Thus, the motion responses must also be random. **Random vibration** may be described as vibration whose instantaneous magnitudes can be specified only by probability-distribution functions giving the probable fraction of the total time that the magnitude, or some sequence of magnitudes, lies within a specified range. In this type of vibration, many frequencies are present simultaneously in the wave form. (See Fig. 6.) **Power spectral density** (PSD; in units of g^2/cps) is defined as the limiting mean-square value of a random variable, in this case acceleration per unit bandwidth; *i.e.*,

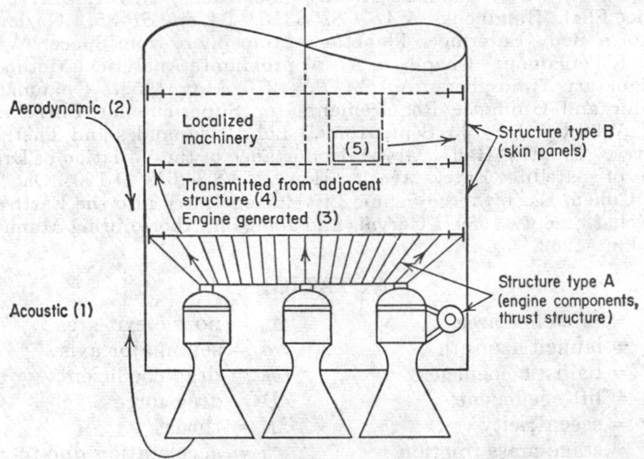

FIG. 7. Sources of vibration excitement.

$$\text{PSD} = \lim_{\Delta f \to 0} \overline{g^2}/\Delta f = d\overline{g^2}/df$$

The **sources of vibration excitation** are (1) acoustic pressures generated by rocket-engine operation, (2) aerodynamic pressures created by boundary layer fluctuations, (3) mechanically induced vibration from rocket-engine pulsation, which is transmitted throughout the vehicle structure, (4) vibration transmitted from adjacent structure, and (5) localized machinery. Since the mean-square acceleration is proportional to power, the total vibrational power at any point on the vehicle may be expressed as $Pv = Pv(1) + Pv(2) + Pv(3) + Pv(4) + Pv(5)$.

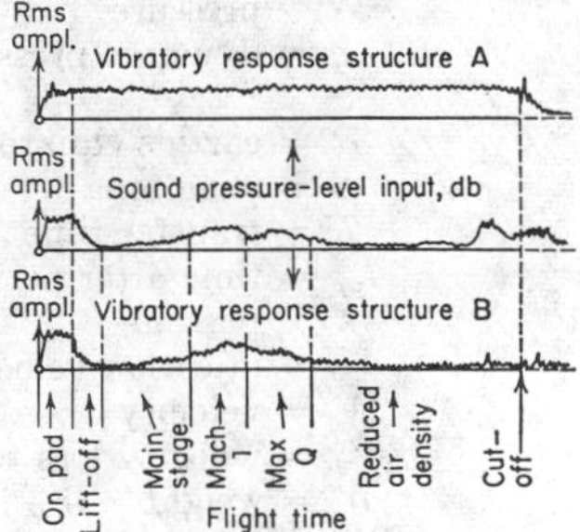

FIG. 8. Typical structural responses to random-vibration environment.

This is illustrated in Fig. 7 for an arbitrary vehicle. In many instances, the structure is principally excited by only one of these sources and the remaining can be considered negligible. (See Fig. 8.) The vibration characteristics of structure B, taken from a skin panel, closely correspond to the trends of the acoustic pressures during flight. However, structure A, taken from a rocket-engine component, exhibits stationary trends, indicating no susceptibility to the impinging acoustic field. Thus for this structure, it can be assumed that only $Pv(3)$ is significant; while for structure B, only $Pv(1)$ is the principal exciting source during the on-pad phase and only $Pv(2)$ is significant during the maximum dynamic-pressure phase. This also holds true for captive firings of the vehicle, in which only $Pv(1)$ is significant for structure B and $Pv(3)$ for structure A.

SPACE-VEHICLE TRAJECTORIES, FLIGHT MECHANICS, AND PERFORMANCE

By W. R. Perry, J. W. Russell, A. G. Kromis, and D. W. Fellenz

REFERENCES: Russell, Dugan, and Steward, "Astronomy," Ginn. Sutton, "Rocket Propulsion Elements," Wiley. White, "Flight Performance Handbook for Powered Flight Operations," Wiley. "U.S. Standard Atmosphere, 1962," NASA, USAF, U.S. Weather Bureau. Space Flight Handbooks, *NASA SP*-33, *SP*-34, and *SP*-35. Gazley, Deceleration and Heating of a Body Entering a Planetary Atmosphere from Space, "Vistas in Astronautics," Vol. I, Pergamon. Chapman, An Approximate Analytical Method for Studying Entry into Planetary Atmospheres, *NACA-TN* 4276, May, 1958. Chapman, An Analysis of the Corridor and Guidance Requirements for Super-circular Entry into Planetary Atmospheres, *NASA-TN D*-136, Sept., 1959. Loh, "Dynamics and Thermodynamics of Planetary Entry," Prentice-Hall. Grant, Importance of the Variation of Drag with Lift in Minimization of Satellite Entry Acceleration, *NASA-TN D*-120, Oct., 1959. Lees, Hartwig, and Cohen, Use of Aerodynamic Lift during Entry into the Earth's Atmosphere, *Jour. ARS*, Vol. 29, Sept., 1959. Gervais and Johnson, Abort during Manned Ascent into Space, *AAS*, Jan., 1962.

NOTATION

A = reference area
A_z = launch azimuth
B = ballistic coefficient
C_L = lift coefficient
e = eccentricity
f = stage-mass fraction (WP/W_A)
H = total energy
H_∞ = hyperbolic excess energy
I = specific impulse
Δ_i = plane-change angle
L = lift force
m = mass
p = ambient atmospheric pressure
q = dynamic pressure
R = earth's equatorial radius
S = wing area
T = transfer time
t_{pp} = time after perigee passage
V_c = injection velocity
V = velocity
V_g = velocity loss to gravity
W = weight
W_L = payload weight
W_P = propellant weight
Y = distance
$\alpha\Omega$ = right ascension of the ascending node
$\gamma = \vartheta - 90°$ = flight-path angle used in reentry analysis
ν = true anomaly
ω = earth's rotational velocity

A_e = nozzle exit area
a = semimajor axis
C_D = drag coefficient
D = drag force
F = thrust
g = acceleration due to gravity
H_{esc} = escape energy
h = altitude
i = inclination
J_2 = oblateness coefficient of the earth's potential (second-zonal harmonic)
M = molecular weight
nm = nautical miles
P = period of revolution
P_e = nozzle exit pressure
q_s = stagnation-point heat-transfer rate
r = radius
s = range
T = absolute temperature
t = time
V_∞ = hyperbolic excess velocity
V_{id} = ideal velocity
ΔV = impulsive velocity
W_A = stage weight ($W_o - W_L$)
W_o = gross weight
X = distance
α = angle of attack
β = exponent of density-altitude function
μ = gravitational constant
ω = argument of perigee
ϕ' = latitude

ψ = central angle
$\sigma = \rho/\rho_o$ = relative atmospheric density
γ = vernal equinox
ρ = atmospheric density
ϑ = flight-path angle

Subscripts

a = apogee
e = entry
f = final
o = sea level conditions at 45-deg latitude
s = space fixed
vac = vacuum
circ = circular orbital condition
esc = escape
i = initial
p = perigee
SL = sea level

ORBITAL MECHANICS

(By W. R. Perry)

The motion of the planets about the sun, as well as that of a satellite in its orbit about a planet, is governed by the inverse-square force law for attracting bodies. In those cases where the mass of the orbiting body is small relative to the central attracting body, it can be neglected. This simplifies the analysis of the orbital motion. The shape of the orbit is always a conic section, *i.e.*, ellipse, parabola, or hyperbola, with the central attracting body at one of the foci. Parabolic and hyperbolic orbits are open, terminate at infinity, and represent cases where the orbiting body escapes the central force field of the attracting body.

The **laws of Kepler** for satellite orbits are (1) the radius vector to the satellite from the central body sweeps over equal areas in equal times; (2) the orbit is an ellipse, with the central attracting body at one of its foci; and (3) the square of the period of the satellite is proportional to the cube of the semimajor axis of the orbit.

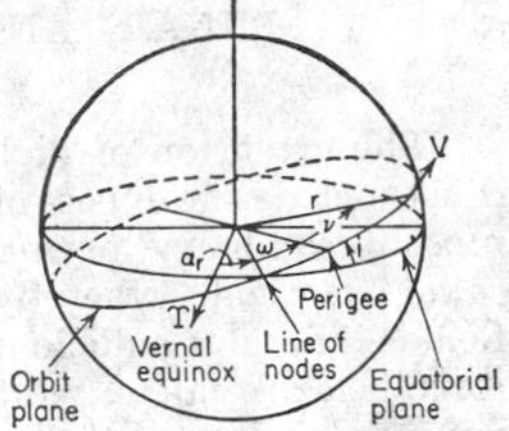

FIG. 9. Elements of satellite orbit around planet.

Six **orbital elements** are required to describe the orbit in the orbit plane and the orientation of the plane in inertial space. The three elements that define the orbit are the semimajor axis a, eccentricity e, and period of revolution P. The orientation of the orbit (Fig. 9) is defined by the right ascension of the ascending node α_Ω, inclination of the orbit plane to the earth's equatorial plane i, and the argument of perigee ω, which is the central angle measured in the orbit plane from ascending node to perigee. The following equations compute these orbital elements and other orbital parameters.

$$a = (r_a + r_p)/2 = \mu/V_aV_p = r_a/(1+e) = r_p/(1-e)$$
$$e = (r_a/a) - 1 = (V_p - V_a)/(V_p + V_a) = (r_pV_p{}^2/\mu) - 1$$
$$r = a(1-e^2)/(1 + e\cos\nu) \qquad r_a = a(1+e) = r_p(1+e)/(1-e)$$
$$r_p = a(1-e) = r_a(1-e)/(1+e) \qquad V = [\mu(2/r - 1/a)]^{0.5}$$
$$P = 2\pi(a^3/\mu)^{0.5} \qquad \text{[For circular orbits, } r = a.]$$
$$V_a = V_p(1-e)/(1+e) = [\mu(1-e)/a(1+e)]^{0.5}$$
$$V_p = V_a(1+e)/(1-e) = [\mu(1+e)/a(1-e)]^{0.5}$$
$$\nu = \cos^{-1}\{[2r_ar_p - r(r_a+r_p)]/r(r_a - r_p)\}$$
$$t_{pp} = (a^3/\mu)^{0.5}\{\cos^{-1}[(a-r)/ae] - e[1 - (a-r)^2/(ae)^2]^{0.5}\}$$

Hohmann Transfer. This is a maneuver between two coplanar orbits where the elliptical transfer orbit is tangent at its perigee to the lower orbit and tangent at its apogee to the higher orbit. To transfer from a low circular orbit to a higher one, the impulsive velocity required is the difference between the velocities in the circular orbits and the velocities in the corresponding points on the transfer orbit. Using the general velocity equation above, the transfer velocities are $\Delta V_i = \{\mu[2/r_i - 2/(r_i + r_f)]\}^{0.5} - (\mu/r_i)^{0.5}$ and $\Delta V_f = (\mu/r_f)^{0.5} - \{\mu[2/r_f - 2/(r_i + r_f)]\}^{0.5}$, where V_i is the orbiting velocity in low orbit and V_f is the orbiting velocity in the high orbit.

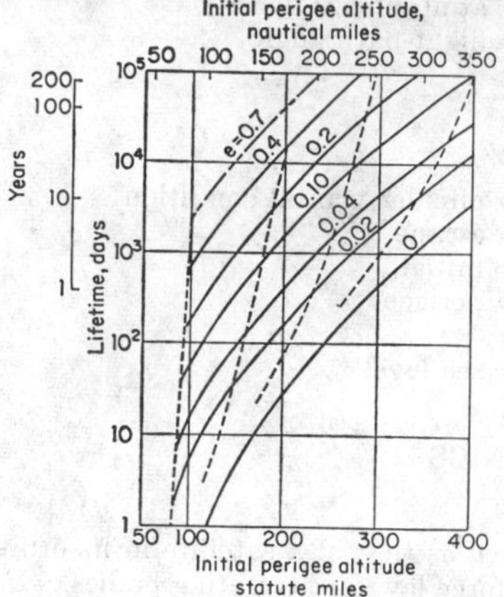

FIG. 10. Satellite lifetimes in elliptic orbits. ρ = ARDC, 1959; $B = C_DA/2m = 1.0$ ft² per slug; e = initial eccentricity; ---- = decay histories.

Orbital Lifetime. The satellite orbit will gradually decay to lower altitudes due to the drag effects of the atmosphere. This drag force has the form $D = \frac{1}{2}C_D A \rho V^2$, where values of the drag coefficient C_D may range from 2.0 to 2.5. The atmospheric density, as a function of altitude, can be used for computing an estimated orbital lifetime of a satellite (Fig. 10). (See NASA, "U.S. Standard Atmosphere" and "Space Flight Handbooks.")

Perturbations of Satellite Orbits. There are many secular and periodic perturbations of satellite orbits due to the effects of the sun, the moon, and some planets. The most significant perturbation on close-earth satellite orbits is caused by the oblateness of the earth. Its greatest effects are the precession of the orbit along the equator (nodal regression) and the rotation of the orbit in the orbit plane (advance of perigee). The nodal-regression rate is given to first-order approximation by

$$\dot{\alpha}_\Omega = -\tfrac{3}{2}(\mu/a^3)^{0.5}J_2[R/a(1 - e^2)]^2 \cos i$$

LUNAR- AND INTERPLANETARY-FLIGHT MECHANICS

(By J. W. Russell)

The extension of flight mechanics to the areas of lunar and interplanetary flight must include the effects of the sun, moon, and planets on the transfer trajectories. For most preliminary performance calculations, the "*sphere-of-influence,*" or "*patched-conic,*" method—whereby the multibody force field is treated as a series of central force fields—provides sufficient accuracy. By this method, the trajectories in the central force field are calculated to the "sphere of influence" of each body by standard Keplerian mechancis, and the velocity and position of the extremals are then matched to give a continuous trajectory. After the missions have been finalized, the precision trajectories are obtained by numerically integrating the equations of motion which include all the perturbative elements. It is necessary to know the exact positions of the sun, moon, and planets in their respective orbits.

Lunar-flight Mechanics. The moon moves about the earth in an orbit having an eccentricity of 0.055 and an inclination to the ecliptic of about 5.145 deg. The sun causes a precession of the lunar orbit about the ecliptic, making the inclination of the lunar plane to the earth's equatorial plane oscillate between 18.5 and 28.5 deg over a period of 18.5 years approx. To compute precision earth-moon trajectories, it is necessary to know the precise launch time to be able to include the perturbative effects of the sun, moon, and planets. The data presented are based on the moon being at its mean distance from earth and neglect the perturbation of the sun and planets; they are therefore only to be considered as representative data. The injection velocity (see Gazley) at 100 nm for earth-moon trajectories and the impulsive velocity for braking into a 100-nm orbit about the moon are shown in Fig. 11 as a function of transfer time. Additional energy is required to offset losses due to gravity and aerodynamic drag as well as to provide plane-change and launch-window capabilities.

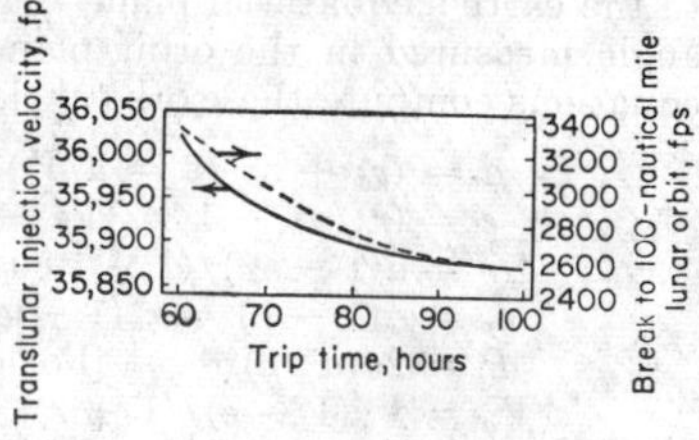

FIG. 11. Lunar-mission velocity requirements.

Interplanetary-flight Mechanics. The fact that planetary orbits about the sun are not coplanar greatly restricts the number of feasible interplanetary trajectories. The plane of the interplanetary trajectory must include the position of the departure planet at departure, the sun, and the position of the target planet at arrival. The necessary plane change can be prohibitive even though the relative inclinations of the planetary orbits are small. The impulsive velocity required to effect a plane change for a space-

Table 5. Hyperbolic-excess-velocity Requirements (fps) for Typical Mars Missions
(Gammal, "Space Flight Handbooks")

Trip time, days	Opposition year				
	1965	1967	1969	1971	1973
100	27,241	23,012	18,070	15,569	19,955
150	15,940	13,088	11,437	10,520	13,792
200	12,268	10,021	11,486	9,308	12,463
250	10,510	12,688	13,410	10,480	15,784

craft departing earth can be approximated by $\Delta V = 195{,}350 \sin (\Delta_i/2)$, where Δ_i is the amount of plane change required and ΔV is in fps.

For interplanetary flight, the "ideal" total energy that must be imparted to the spacecraft is the energy required to escape the gravitational field of the departure planet plus the energy required to change path about the sun so as to arrive at the tar-

Table 6. Hyperbolic-excess-velocity Requirements (fps) for Typical Venus Missions
(Gammal, "Space Flight Handbooks")

Trip time, days	Conjunction year				
	1964	1966	1967	1969	1970
60	21,615	21,225	22,220	20,746	20,219
80	15,403	15,628	15,970	14,309	14,456
100	12,649	12,932	12,424	10,930	10,266
120	12,063	12,814	10,334	9,240	11,213

get planet at the desired position and time. The energy required to escape the gravitational attraction of a planet can be determined by Keplerian mechanics to be $H_{esc} = \mu/r$, where μ is the Gaussian gravitational constant and r is the distance from the center of the planet. After escaping the departure planet, the velocity must be altered in both magnitude and direction—in order to arrive at the target planet at the chosen time—by supplying additional energy, $H_\infty = \frac{1}{2}V_\infty^2$.

For determination of vehicle size necessary to inject the spacecraft into the interplanetary trajectory, it is convenient to express the total energy $H = H_{esc} + H_\infty$ in in terms of the required injection velocity

$$V_c = \sqrt{2(H_{esc} + H_\infty)} \text{ or}$$

$$V_c = \sqrt{(2\mu/r) + V_\infty^2}$$

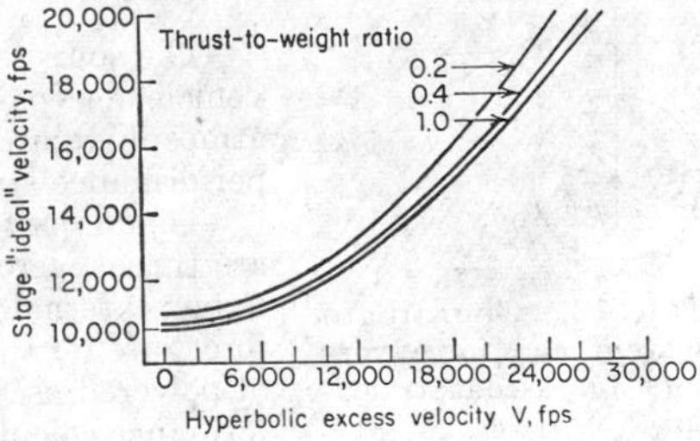

FIG. 12. Stage-velocity requirements for earth departure from a 100-nm parking orbit (specific impulse = 450 sec).

Hyperbolic excess velocities, V_∞**'s, for earth-to-Mars** missions are shown in Table 5. These velocities are near optimum for the trip time and year given but do not represent absolute-optimum trajectories. Mars has a cyclic period with respect to earth of 17 years approx; hence the energy requirements for Mars missions from earth also follow approximate 17-year cycles.

Hyperbolic-excess-velocity requirements for **earth-Venus** missions are shown in Table 6. Venus has a cyclic period of about 8 years with respect to earth; therefore these velocities follow an 8-year cycle.

In Tables 5 and 6, the energy requirements are a function of date as well as of trip time. Figure 12 shows how the hyperbolic excess velocities of Tables 5 and 6 can be converted to stage-characteristics velocities for a vehicle leaving a 100-nm earth parking orbit.

POWERED-FLIGHT-TRAJECTORY ANALYSIS

(By A. G. Kromis)

For the analysis of powered-flight trajectories, the equations of motion for the boost vehicle can be very simple (two degrees of freedom) or extremely complex (six degrees of freedom), depending on the degree of accuracy required in the final answers. For preliminary performance analysis of vehicles, it is adequate to simulate the vehicle as a point mass and restrict the ascent flight to two dimensions. If the object of the study is to analyze the stability and control of the vehicle, more elaborate equations are required to simulate the flexure of the vehicle structure and the angular rotations of the vehicle about its own axes. A simplified trajectory routine suitable for the analysis of preliminary-design vehicles is as follows: Considering the vehicle as a point mass, the equations of motion for flight over a spherical, non-rotating earth are (Fig. 13)

$$V = (F \cos \alpha)/m - D/m - g \cos \vartheta$$
$$\dot{\vartheta} = (F \sin \alpha)/m + L/mv + (g/v - v/r) \sin \vartheta$$

Upon numerical integration, the velocity v and flight-path angle ϑ are obtained as functions of time. $v = \int_{t_i}^{t} \dot{v}\, dt;\ \vartheta = \int_{t_i}^{t} \dot{\vartheta}\, dt.$

The altitude and ground range on a spherical earth, are found from

$$h = \int_{t_i}^{t} v \cos \vartheta \, dt$$

and $s = r_0 \int_{t_i}^{t} (v \sin \vartheta)/r \, dt.$

Addition of Earth's Rotational Velocity. The equations for $\dot{v}$ and $\dot{\vartheta}$ give the so-called *earth relative velocity* and path angle for flight over a non-rotating, spherical earth. To account for the effects of earth rotation on the velocity and flight-path angle, find

$$v_s = \sqrt{v^2 + 2\omega r v \cos \phi' \sin \vartheta \sin A_z + \omega^2 r^2 \cos^2 \phi'}$$
$$\vartheta_s = \text{arc cos } [(v \cos \vartheta)/v_s]$$

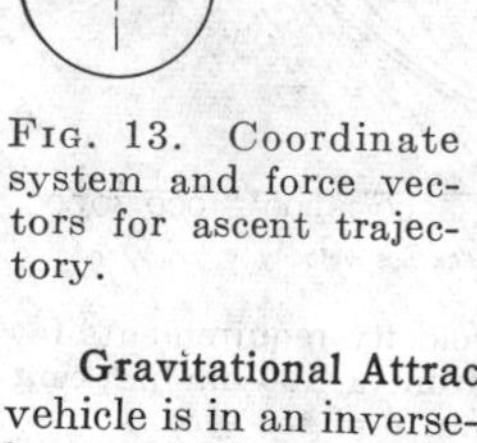

FIG. 13. Coordinate system and force vectors for ascent trajectory.

The conversion to space fixed quantities is made after the vehicle has passed through the more dense portion of the atmosphere; this approach is accurate enough for preliminary performance studies.

The **major forces acting on the vehicle** during ascent flight are thrust, aerodynamic forces, and gravitational attraction. Other external forces, such as centrifugal force and Coriolis force, are for the most part insignificant due to the short time of powered ascent and are generally neglected in simple performance calculations. (For thrust and aerodynamic forces, see pp. 11–78 *et seq.*)

Gravitational Attraction. With the assumption that during the ascent phase the vehicle is in an inverse-square gravitational field, the gravitational attraction is given by $g = g_o(r_o/r)^2$.

ESTIMATION OF VEHICLE PERFORMANCE. For a quick, fairly accurate estimate of vehicle performance, the tangential component of the equations of motion proves to be very valuable. This equation may be written as

$$\dot{v} = \int_{t_i}^{t} (F \cos \alpha)/m \, dt - \int_{t_i}^{t} (D/m) \, dt - \int_{t_i}^{t} g \cos \vartheta \, dt,$$

where the first integral gives the total or ideal velocity the vehicle would attain in field-free space, the second integral gives the velocity loss due to atmospheric effects, and the last integral gives the velocity loss incurred in overcoming the earth's gravitational attraction.

Evaluation of Velocity Integrals. If the ascent trajectory is assumed to be a gravity turn path with zero angle of attack, the ideal velocity integral reduces to $v_{id} = \int_{t_i}^{t} (F/m)\ dt = \bar{I}g \ln\ (m_i/m_f)$. Where $\bar{I}$ is an average value of specific impulse during first-stage flight and is given by $\bar{I} = (I_{SL} + 2I_{vac})/3$. Upper-stage flight is assumed to occur in vacuum conditions, and the ideal velocity for the upper stages is obtained by use of vacuum specific impulse I_{vac}. The velocity loss during ascent due to aerodynamic drag is relatively low for large, low-acceleration vehicles. For such a vehicle, the velocity loss due to drag is 300 to 500 fps approx. The gravity loss is not wholly a true loss in that, as the vehicle ascends, there is an increase in potential energy with increasing altitude. Typically, for large rocket vehicles taking off with low initial thrust-to-weight ratios, the gravitational loss is 3,000 to 4,000 fps approx. The gravitational loss of each stage during ascent can be approximated by $v_g = (g \cos \bar{\vartheta})t$, where $\bar{\vartheta}$ is an average value of the flight-path angle for a given stage (Fig. 14).

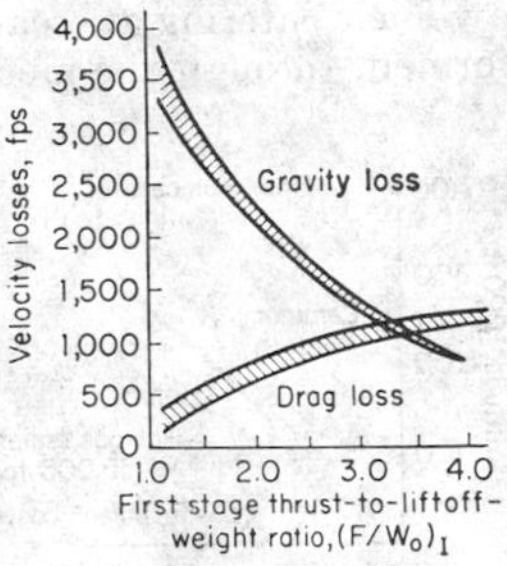

Fig. 14. Ascent velocity losses as a function of thrust-to-weight ratio.

ATMOSPHERIC ENTRY

(By D. W. Fellenz)

A vehicle approaching a planet possesses a considerable amount of energy. The entry vehicle must be designed to dissipate this energy without exceeding its limits with respect to maximum decelerations or heating.

The trajectory parameters of an entering vehicle are determined largely by its initial trajectory conditions (suborbital, orbital, superorbital), by the ratio of gas-dynamic forces acting upon it, and by its mass (ballistic factor, lift-drag ratio) and the type of atmosphere it is entering.

Planetary atmospheres (Table 7) can be assumed, as a first approximation, to have exponential density-altitude distributions: $\sigma = \rho/\rho_{SL} = e^{-\beta h}$, where

$$\beta = -(1/\rho)(d\rho/dh) = Mg/RT$$

For more exacting analyses, empirical atmospheric characteristics (e.g., U.S. Standard Atmosphere) have to be used.

The trajectory of the vehicle in flight-path fixed notation with the assumption of a non-rating atmosphere is described as $dV/dt = g \sin \gamma - (C_D A/m)(\rho/2)V^2$ and

Table 7. Planetary Atmospheres

Planet	V_{esc}, fps	Gases	M, gmmol^{-1}	T, deg K	β^{-1}, ft	βr	ρ_{SL}, lb per ft^3
Venus........	34,300	10% N_2 90% CO_2	40	250–350	2×10^4	1,006	1.0
Earth.........	36,800	79% N_2 20% O_2	29	240	2.35×10^4	880	0.0765
Mars..........	16,900	95% N_2 5% CO_2	30	200–300	6×10^4	132	0.0062
Jupiter........	195,000	H_2 CH_4	3	100–200	6×10^4	3,600	

$(V/\cos\gamma)(d\gamma/dt) = g - (V^2/r) - (C_LA/m)(\rho/2)(V^2/\cos\gamma)$. Solutions exist for direct ($\gamma > 5$ deg) ballistic entry and for equilibrium glide-lifting entry for $L/D > 1$. General solutions of the equations of motion have been obtained for shallow entry of both ballistic and lifting bodies. For a survey of analytical methods available, see Chapman, Loh, Grant, Lees, and Gervais.

The **energy of an earth satellite** at 200 miles altitude is about 13000 Btu per lb, and a vehicle entering at escape velocity possesses twice this energy. This energy is transformed, through the mechanism of gas-dynamic drag, into thermal energy in the air around the vehicle, of which only a fraction enters the vehicle surface as heat. This fraction depends on the characteristics of the boundary-layer flow, which is determined by shape, surface condition, and Reynolds number. Figure 15 illustrates the **energy conversion** where it is necessary to manage a given amount of energy in a way that minimizes structural and heat-protection weights, operational restraints, and cost. It would be most desirable if this energy could be dissipated at a constant rate, but with constant vehicle parameters, decelerations vary proportionally to ρV^2 and heating rates proportionally to ρV^3. The selection of a heat-protection system depends on the type of entry flown. Lifting entry from orbit results in relatively long flight times (in the order of ½ hr) as compared with 10 min in the case of a steep ballistic entry. **Radiative-heat-transfer systems** favor low heating rates over long time periods. **Ablative systems** favor short heat pulses. In fact, longer soaking periods may melt the ablation coating without getting the benefit of heat absorption through multiple-phase changes. A more uniform dissipation of energy can be achieved by modulation of vehicle parameters.

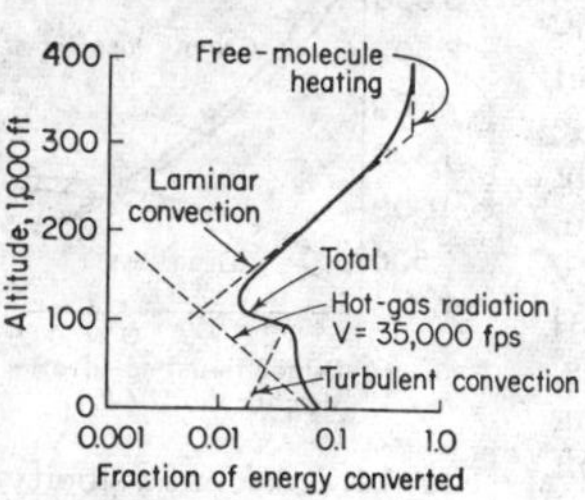

FIG. 15. Energy conversion during reentry (*after Gazley in Koelle Handbook*).

Determination of an **entry-vehicle configuration** is a process of iteration. The entry-flight profile and the entry and recovery procedures are mainly determined by

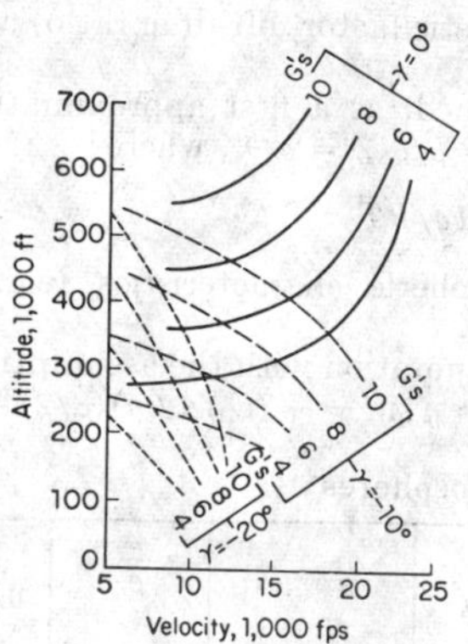

FIG. 16. Suborbital entry of a lifting vehicle. $W/C_DA = 28$ psf; $L/D = 0.7$.

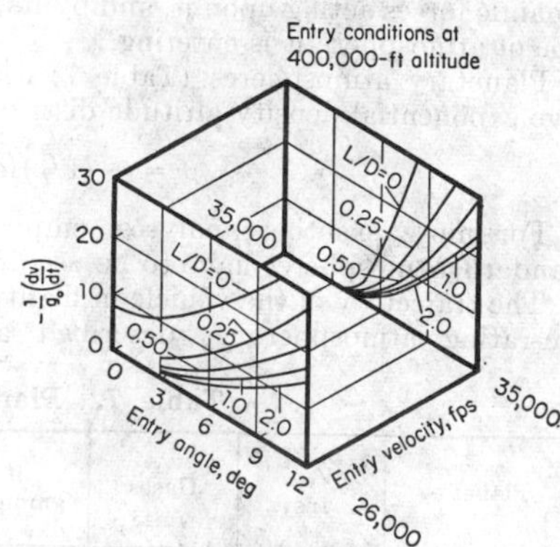

FIG. 17. Peak decelerations for entry at constant L/D.

whether experiments or passengers are carried. The external shape is determined by requirements for hypersonic glide capability and subsonic handling and landing characteristics and also by the relations between aerodynamic shape, heat input, and structural-materials characteristics. Intermediate results are fed back into the evaluation of performance and operational effectiveness of the total transportation system.

If reentry capability from any point of the ascent trajectory is desired for a manned vehicle, vehicle constraints and trajectory requirements must be compatible. **Per-**

formance-optimized trajectories encompass combinations of relatively small velocities and large flight-path angles, which would result in considerable decelerations. In such cases, either reshaping the ascent trajectory or adding velocity at the time of abort, resulting in lower entry-flight-path angles, is effective (see Fig. 16). Lower flight-path angles during ascent depress the trajectory and increase drag losses. **Atmospheric entry is initiated** by changing the vehicle-velocity vector such that the

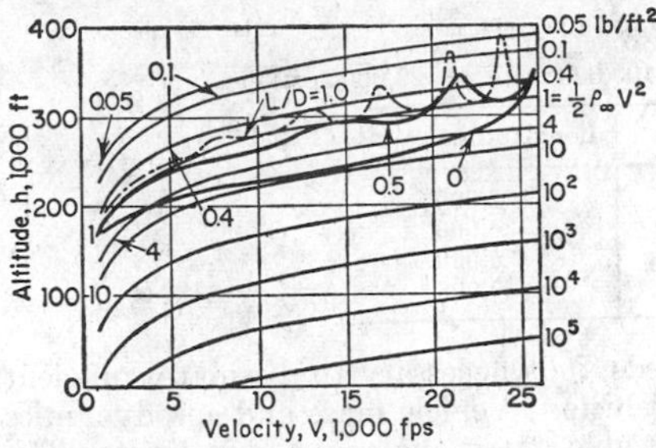

FIG. 18. Glide reentry, dynamic pressure. $W/C_DA = 1$ psf; $\gamma = 2$ deg; $\frac{1}{2}\rho_\infty V^2 = (W/C_DA)(\frac{1}{2}\rho_\infty V^2)_1$; $h = h_1 - 23{,}500 \ln (W/C_DA)$; $V = V_1$.

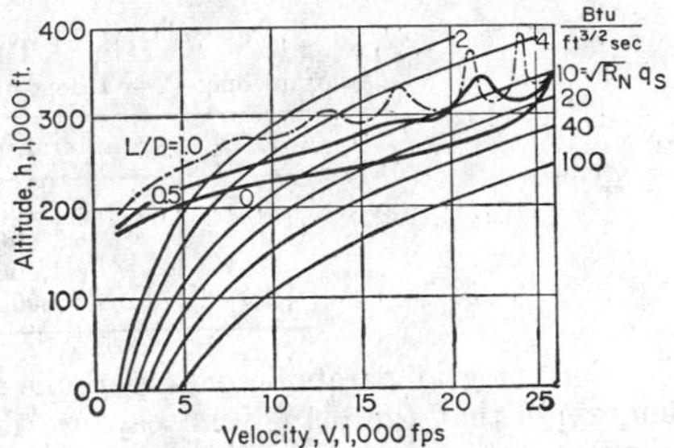

FIG. 19. Glide reentry, stagnation-heating rate. $W/C_DA = 1$ psf; $\gamma = 2$ deg; $q_s = q_{s_1}\sqrt{W/C_DA}$; $h = h_1 - 23{,}500 \ln (W/C_DA)$; $V = V_1$.

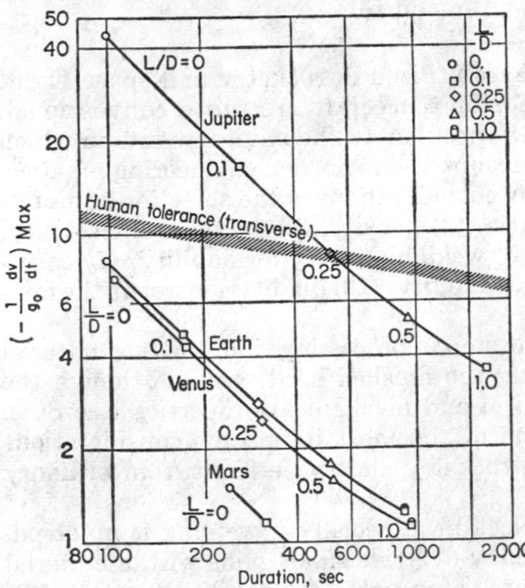

FIG. 20. Comparison of decelerations and duration for entry into various planetary atmospheres from decaying orbits (*after Chapman*).

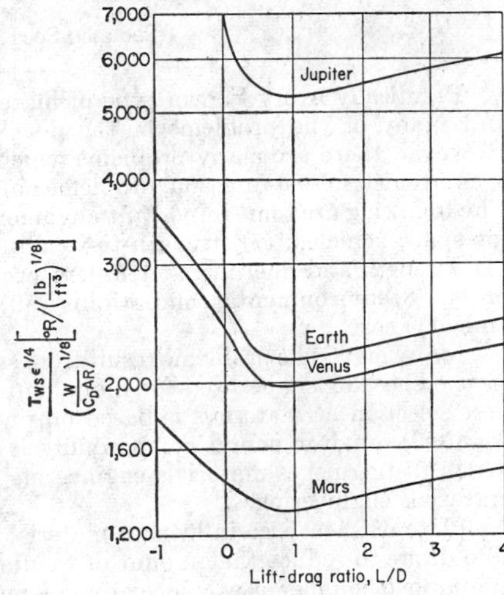

FIG. 21. Maximum surface temperature for entry into various planets from decaying orbits (*after Chapman*).

virtual perigee of the descent ellipse comes to lie inside the atmosphere. The retro-velocity requirement for entry from low orbit is between 250 and 500 fps, depending on the range desired from deorbit to landing. For non-lifting entry, maximum deceleration and heat input into the vehicle are largely a function of entry angle, with the ballistic factor W/C_DA determining the altitude at which the maximum decelerations and heating rates occur. Deceleration can be readily determined through the approximate relation $-(1/g)(dv/dt) \approx q/(W/C_DA)$. Decelerations and temperatures are drastically reduced with increasing lift-drag ratio (Fig. 17) and decreasing W/C_DA

(Figs. 18 and 19). This effect is particularly beneficial at steeper entry angles. The combination of longer flight times with lower heating rates, however, may actually result in a larger total heat input into the vehicle.

The **influence of lift** on the reduction of decelerations is greatest for the step up to $L/D \approx 1$. The influence of W/C_DA on decelerations disappears beyond $L/D \approx 0.6$. Higher, hypersonic L/D ratios serve to improve maneuverability. For entry from low orbit, the landing area selection (footprint) can be increased (see Table 8).

Table 8

(Assumptions: γ_e = 1 deg; h_e = 400,000 ft; V_e = 26,000 fps.)

L/D	Lateral, nm	Longitudinal, nm
0.5	≈ 200	≈2,000
1	≈ 600	≈4,000
1.5	≈1,200	≈6,000
2	≈2,000	≈9,000

For entry at parabolic or hyperbolic speeds, it is necessary to dissipate sufficient energy so that the planet can capture the vehicle. Vehicle mass and aerodynamics characteristics determine the minimum allowable entry angle, the skip limit. The vehicle must be steered between the skip limit and the angle for maximum tolerable deceleration and heating. (See Figs. 20 and 21.)

MATERIALS FOR ROCKET SYSTEMS AND SPACECRAFT

By William R. Lucas

(See also Secs. 5, 6, 13, and 18)

Practically every known type of material is utilized in rocketry and space flight, and many of the problems of the developer of spacecraft are quite conventional. However, there are many problems which are peculiar to the environments in which space vehicles must function, problems not encountered in normal engineering practice. The following are some important **engineering considerations in the selection of metals** for space vehicles: (1) strength-to-weight ratio, (2) density, (3) modulus of elasticity, (4) strength and ductility at temperature, (5) weldability, (6) formability, (7) castability, (8) environmental compatibility, (9) availability, (10) quality control at the mill, and (11) cost.

Many materials problems result from some step in processing from the raw material to the sheet or shape used for manufacturing the finished hardware. Although the first selection of materials is based on physical and mechanical properties (see Secs. 5 and 6), **environmental compatibility** is one of the most important considerations which distinguishes materials engineering in rocketry and space flight from ordinary materials engineering.

Plate or sheet size influences material selection, especially if welding is involved. The desire to reduce the amount of welding may override small gains with a material available in smaller sizes, especially in a material of marginal weldability (see Sec. 13). Quality control of the raw material is one of the most significant problems because often the mills are not accustomed to supplying the quality required for ultrareliable space-vehicle hardware. Cost must be judged in terms of its significance with respect to the total expenditure of putting a given pay load in orbit. The designer first considers the strength-to-weight ratio. However, some of the most favorable materials from this standpoint have deficiencies which preclude their use. Furthermore, if the design concept is based upon structural stability, it may not be possible to utilize the strongest material efficiently. Here the best way of achieving higher strength-to-weight ratios is by decreasing the density (see Sec. 5).

Low-temperature Applications

For rocket systems utilizing cryogenic propellants, no environmental consideration is more important than low temperature, because it may increase brittleness of materials. Furthermore, since one of the most common oxidizers, liquid oxygen, boils at a temperature of −297 F and liquid hydrogen, a very important fuel, boils at −423 F, the rocket designer's temperature problems are much more difficult than those ordinarily associated with operation of equipment in cold climates. (See also Sec. 18.)

Whether a brittle fracture or a tough fracture will occur depends mainly on the material, the temperature, the rate of load application, notches or surface discontinuities, and residual and multiaxial stresses. (See Sec. 5.) With the decrease in temperature, there is an increase in hardness, strength, and modulus of elasticity in most materials. The effect of low temperature on ductility and toughness varies considerably among the metals and alloys: the ductility of some metals increases with decrease in temperature; others increase in ductility to some limiting low temperature and then decrease at lower temperatures; still others decrease in toughness and ductility immediately as the temperature is decreased below normal. Face-centered-cubic (F.C.C.) alloys usually retain their ductility and toughness at low temperatures. The body-centered-cubic (B.C.C.) alloys tend to undergo a ductile-to-brittle transformation at below-normal temperature, and this transformation limits the usefulness for low-temperature applications. The hexagonal-close-packed alloys are usually brittle at low temperature, but there are important exceptions, such as some titanium and magnesium alloys (Figs. 22 and 23).

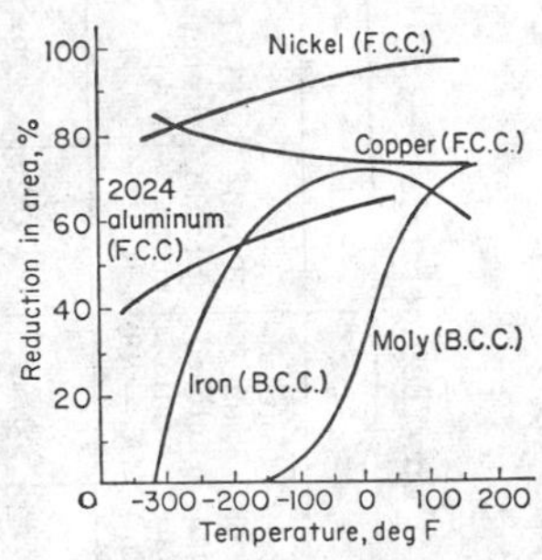

FIG. 22. Effect of temperature on reduction of area for tension-test specimens.

In **face-centered-cubic metals,** there is usually some increase in initial resistance to plastic deformation as the temperature is lowered, and the rate of work hardening which results in higher fracture strength is increased greatly by reducing the temperature. Thus, the ultimate, or fracture, strength increases at a rate equal to or greater than the rate at which the yield strength increases (Fig. 23). The increasing spread between yield and ultimate strengths as the temperature is reduced indicates more plastic deformation before fracture and, consequently, increased ductility.

Body-centered-cubic metals show a more rapid increase in yield strength than in ultimate strength as the temperature is lowered. Ductility decreases until the two curves coincide, at which point fracture occurs without plastic deformation (Fig. 23).

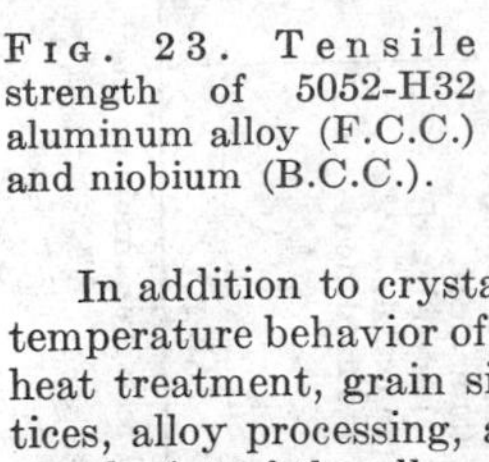

FIG. 23. Tensile strength of 5052-H32 aluminum alloy (F.C.C.) and niobium (B.C.C.).

In structural elements, there are often surface or internal discontinuities which act as **stress concentrators,** and these defects cause fracture at a higher temperature than would be predicted by a smooth tensile test. In order to evaluate the capacity of a material to flow locally and reduce the severity of stress concentration, notched tensile specimens are used. The tensile strength of the notched specimen is compared with that of the smooth specimen, and notched-unnotched strength ratios below 1.0 indicate decreasing "toughness" of the material. For aerospace applications, the notched-unnotched ratio of the material should be measured using a stress-concentration factor (K_t) approximating the anticipated conditions.

In addition to crystal structure, **other metallurgical factors** which affect the low-temperature behavior of metals are chemical composition, minor alloying constituents, heat treatment, grain size, precipitation phenomena, melting and deoxidation practices, alloy processing, and alloy stability. Small **inclusions,** insignificant from the standpoint of the alloy meeting normal specifications, have caused premature failure at cryogenic temperature of an otherwise suitable alloy. Higher-than-commercial quality is required in many alloys for optimum use at the temperature of liquid hydrogen. New alloys are being developed specifically for low-temperature service.

Most metals retain their original properties when returned to room temperature

Table 9. Mechanical Properties of Engineering Materials at Low Temperature

Alloy	80 F				−320 F				−423 F			
	Tensile strength, kpsi	Yield strength, kpsi	Percentage of elongation (2 in.)	Notched-unnotched ratio (K_t = 10)	Tensile strength, kpsi	Yield strength, kpsi	Percentage of elongation (2 in.)	Notched-unnotched ratio (K_t = 10)	Tensile strength, kpsi	Yield strength, kpsi	Percentage of elongation (2 in.)	Notched-unnotched ratio (K_t = 10)
Aluminum												
2014-T6	70	64	9.7	0.99	84	76	11.7	0.93	97	80	13.6	0.88
2020-T6	79	75	8.0	0.67	95	88	4.0	0.52	101	93	2.3	0.50
2219-T6	65	52	9.8	0.92	82	64	12.1	0.90	96	79	15.3	0.81
2219-T87	68	56	13.0	0.74	85	68	16.3	0.73	100	73	17.6	0.67
2119-T6	60	43	9.0	0.93	76	53	12.2	0.86	88	43	16.5	0.62
5052-H32	34	25	10.6	0.97	53	29	30.0	0.93	73	37	26.5	0.88
5086-H34	47	37	10.4	1.00	65	44	25.0	0.89	85	48	20.2	0.76
5456-H343	58	45	8.7	0.92	74	53	13.0	0.79	87	58	8.7	0.75
7002-T6	70	57	16.7	1.05	83	70	19.8	1.03	104	77	18.9	0.86
7075-T651	80	74	9.2	0.90	94	88	5.2	0.68	101	95	3.2	0.56
7079-T6	76	67	9.0	1.00	94	84	4.0	0.68	101	94	3.0	0.56
7178-T6	94	88	7.5	0.67	109	104	1.2	0.41	117	113	1.0	0.32
Maraging steel—18% Ni (annealed)	192	175	7.0	1.16	268	250	8.0	1.01	313	283	8.7	0.59
Maraging steel—18% Ni (aged)	254	245	2.8	1.09	321	309	2.5	0.90	365	355	3.2	0.41
Super alloys												
A-286 (annealed)	93	42	37.3	0.86	144	68	71.0	0.80	161	81	47.3	0.82
A-286 (age-hardened)	140	94	22.0	0.94	191	122	40.7	0.82	218	137	28.5	0.83
Inconel X (annealed)	111	48	50.7	0.82	150	65	58.3	0.79	160	70	51.3	0.82
Inconel X (age-hardened)	180	126	25.3	0.90	220	139	32.0	0.79	224	140	28.0	0.82
Waspaloy (annealed)	144	80	48.0	0.85	200	108	53.0	0.77	214	118	50.4	0.80
Waspaloy (age-hardened)	177	116	26.3	0.81	205	142	15.0	0.80	197	154	10.2	0.85
K-Monel (annealed)	95	46	38.8	0.95	133	65	48.0	0.91	152	75	43.3	0.86
K-Monel (age-hardened)	148	106	22.7	0.92	177	128	30.7	0.92	192	137	28.3	0.90
Titanium												
Ti-6Al-4V	139	133	11.0	1.02	218	214	13.0	0.82	240	240	1.7	0.61
Ti-5Al-2.5 Sn	134	128	12.8	1.20	213	207	14.0	0.81	234	234	5.0	0.66
Ti-13V-11Cr-3Al	137	137	13.3	1.20	285	282	2.5	0.54	289	289	0.7	0.40

Note: All tests were made on sheet.

after exposure to low temperatures; however, some metastable austenitic stainless steels transform to brittle martensite upon exposure to the temperature of liquid hydrogen (Table 9).

Although face-centered-cubic alloys are superior in low-temperature behavior to body-centered-cubic alloys, all face-centered-cubic alloys do not behave equally. The effects of various alloying elements upon phase relations and microstructure must be considered. Alloying elements which increase strength often lower ductility and toughness. Impurity elements which segregate and form a second phase in the grain boundaries have a marked effect on toughness. For example, interstitial impurities in titanium which do not cause embrittlement at room temperature may cause excessive embrittlement at the temperature of liquid hydrogen. The behavior of castings of face-centered-cubic alloys at low temperature usually is inferior to that of wrought alloys, primarily because of different alloying elements and different grain size.

Welding results in a cast structure in the fusion zone, larger grain size, concentration of impurities and defects such as porosity, modification of the microstructure in the adjacent heat-affected zones, and the formation of surface irregularities or notches which reduce ductility at room temperature. Low temperatures accentuate the problems associated with these factors. It is not acceptable to extrapolate the parent-metal behavior to that of the weldment. In weldments of castings or wrought material, tests are needed to simulate anticipated use conditions and to prove weld soundness (see also p. 13–39 *et seq.*).

Corrosion

(See also p. 6–124 *et seq.*)

Liquid fuels and oxidizers are highly active chemical substances and, in structures made of light, active metals, provide the elements for chemical corrosion. The active metals, if not properly protected, are also heavily corroded by the humid sea-coast environments in which rockets are usually launched. **Galvanic corrosion** is present when dissimilar metals are coupled, when differences in solution potential from point to point on a single metal surface result from impurities on the surface, from differences in surface structure, or from differences in crystal structure due to mechanical working of a portion of the metal, and when thermal treatment results in grain-boundary precipitation.

The use of higher-strength alloys and higher-strength conditions of a given alloy increases the danger of corrosion, which can result in sudden failure of hardware. Contributing to **stress corrosion** are separation of a phase, corrosive environment, temperature, stress, surface defects, and time. A phase, such as a carbide at the grain boundary, may be anodic to the primary phase, and this plus a corrosive environment may start a reaction, which is accelerated by residual tensile stresses at the surface. Design stresses seldom cause stress-corrosion cracking. Time is required for stress corrosion to develop, but cracking is usually sudden. A temperature rise of 10 deg may double the speed of the corrosion reaction. Prone to stress corrosion are aluminum alloys of the 2000 and 7000 series and the precipitation-hardening stainless steels. Stress corrosion may be minimized by proper heat treatment, by avoiding residual stresses, and by providing protection against corrosive attack. Alloys should be in the annealed temper when subjected to severe forming or should be heat-treated subsequent to forming. Quenching usually results in compressive stresses on the surface of a heat-treated part. Excessive machining following heat treatment causes a redistribution of stresses and usually leaves the machined surface in tension. Thus, heat treatment should follow excessive machining, or compressive stresses can be induced by shot-peening the surface. High residual stresses can be reduced by stress-relief treatments at temperatures lower than the recrystallization temperature, but this is not appropriate for heat-treated aluminum alloys. Special heat treatments such as overaging make some aluminum alloys less susceptible to stress corrosion. Random orientation of a precipitate in small, discrete particles improves the stress-corrosion resistance of any precipitation-hardening alloy.

Space Environment

The most adverse conditions in space for materials are vacuum, radiation, temperature extremes, meteoric bombardment, and possible synergistic effects of two or more environments. Where oxidation is involved as a degradation mechanism, *e.g.*, in the irradiation of Teflon and the fatigue of oxide-forming metals, the space environment is less severe than the earth environment.

Vacuum. The **vacuum of space** may cause the evaporation of a material, or a volatile component of the material, and of the adsorbed gases on the surfaces of all materials. The evaporation rate of a pure material can be calculated by

$$G = \sqrt{\frac{M}{T}}\,\frac{P}{17.14}$$

where G = evaporation rate, g per cm² (sec); M = molecular weight; T = absolute temperature, deg K; and P = vapor pressure, mm Hg at temperature T. (See Dushman, "Scientific Foundations of Vacuum Technique," Wiley.) This simple formula is not applicable to heterogeneous materials or even to a pure substance, such as a plasticizer in an elastomer, which is removed from a matrix of another substance. In this case, other factors such as migration rate influence the rate of the reaction. Although the evaporation of a component of a material may not reduce the effectiveness of the material, *e.g.*, the plasticizer in the insulation of an electrical conductor,

Table 10. Effects of Vacuum and Radiation on Elastomers

Material	Test	Pressure, mm Hg	Temp, deg F	Radiation ergs, g⁻¹/deg C	Tensile strength, psi	Elongation, percent
Neoprene	Air	760	80	0	3,135	426
	Vac	1×10^{-5}	80	0	3,350	405
	Air/Rad	760	80	1.9×10^{9}	2,769	265
	Vac/Rad	5×10^{-6}	80	1.9×10^{9}	191	218
Buna N	Air	760	80	0	2,630	685
	Vac	1×10^{-5}	80	0	2,640	700
	Air/Rad	760	80	1.9×10^{9}	2,175	390
	Vac/Rad	5×10^{-6}	80	1.7×10^{9}	203	450
Viton A	Air	760	80	0	1,343	172
	Vac	1×10^{-5}	80	0	1,168	238
	Air/Rad	760	80	2×10^{10}	2,629	36
	Vac/Rad	5×10^{-7}	109	1.6×10^{10}	1,830	31

the deposition of the vapor on a colder surface may be intolerable. Metals are not usually evaporated in space at modest temperatures, but organic materials, including elastomers, plastics, coatings, adhesives, and lubricants, must be of very high molecular weight to avoid evaporation.

Radiation. Spacecraft will be exposed to electromagnetic and particle radiation and to the radiation environment of nuclear reactors. Metals and ionic compounds are relatively resistant to space-indigenous radiation. However, semiconductors are sensitive to permanent radiation damage, and other electrical materials are subject to permanent or transient damage. Organic materials are highly susceptible to degradation by both electromagnetic and particle radiation, especially in vacuum. Organic polymers of high molecular weight may have such low vapor pressures that their evaporation in vacuum at reasonable temperatures will not be significant. However, radiation, which produces chain scission, yielding fragments of reduced molecular weight and increased vapor pressure, will result in the degradation of the mass at the same temperature which did not affect the non-irradiated material (Table 10). Note the almost complete degradation of the tensile strength of Neoprene and Buna N as a result of irradiation in vacuum. On the other hand, Viton A appears to be satisfactory for this environment on the basis of increased tensile strength; however, the decreased elongation would be an important consideration in the application of this material as a seal, particularly as a dynamic seal. Furthermore, Viton A is not suitable for very-low-temperature applications, another component sometimes encountered in the space environment.

Lubrication. (See also Secs. 6 and 8.) The better-known organic lubricants will be subject to evaporation in space, either with or without degradation by radiation. Gases which are normally absorbed to surfaces and reduce friction between mating surfaces will be removed. Mating metal parts of the same material or of materials forming a solid solution in one another may weld together when clean surfaces are exposed as a result of the degrading influence of the space environment. Thus, lubrication is one of the most significant space-related problems. The most effective lubricants for space are those based upon the heavy metal sulfides, such as MoS_2. A lubricant known as MLF-5, consisting of MoS_2, graphite, and gold in the ratio of 10:1:5, has a coefficient of friction which is less in vacuum than at 1 atm. Moving electrical-contact surfaces, such as brushes, slip rings, and make-break switches, require either reliable isolation from the vacuum environment or special selection of materials, especially where long-time operation is involved. Composites of heavy metal sulfides with silver or copper are promising possibilities for this application.

Meteoroids. Meteoroids are metallic or stony bodies of various sizes which travel through space at velocities up to 300,000 fps. Large meteoroids are rare, but the great number of small ones increases the probability of impacts on a spacecraft. These small meteoroids may be only a few thousandths of an inch in diameter, but their tremendous velocities make them destructive. Experimental studies of hypervelocity impact phenomena have been conducted in velocity ranges up to 30,000 fps, but extrapolation is not advisable. However, there is widespread acceptance of the dual-wall technique of protecting a craft against meteoroid damage. The outer wall, called the **bumper**, is detached from the load-carrying structural wall. The bumper dissipates some of the kinetic energy of the particle, but primarily it serves to fragment the particle into a fine spray so that the impact energy is spread over a larger area of the structural wall.

LAUNCH-VEHICLE DESIGN LOADS

By N. Showers

REFERENCES: Bonney, "Engineering Supersonic Aerodynamics," McGraw-Hill. Chin, "Missile Configuration Design," McGraw-Hill. Daniels, Natural Environment Climate Criteria Guidlines, *Marshall Space Flight Center MTP-AERO*-63-8. Scanlan and Rosenbaum, "Aircraft Vibration and Flutter," Macmillan.

Notation

A = reference area
C_D = drag coefficient
$C_{Z\alpha}$ = local lift coefficient per radian angle of attack
D = vehicle diameter
g = acceleration of gravity, ft per sec^2
L_α = total lift per radian angle of attack
M = Mach number
q = trajectory dynamic pressure, $\frac{1}{2}\rho V^2$
v_w, v_v = wind velocity, vehicle velocity
V = sheer
W_i = incremental weight at any station
α = angle of attack
ϵ = rotational acceleration/g
η = translation acceleration/g
λ = longitudinal acceleration/g
ρ = air density, 0.002378 slug per ft^3

Launch-vehicle loads occur during manufacture, assembly, transportation, static firing, launch preparations, launch, and flight. Static and dynamic loads imposed upon the main load-carrying members of the vehicle structure are external forces, like thrust, lift and drag, and thermal and inertia loads.

Manufacture, assembly, and transportation loads should not dictate the design of a stage or vehicle. Residual stresses from welding can be minimized by careful machine settings. Vertical assembly of large components and stages eliminates bending distortions and subsequent forcing together during the mating operation. Large space-vehicle stages are transported by road or water shipment. Adequate design acceleration for this mode of shipment is 1.5 g vertical, in combination with 0.5 g longitudinal and 0.5 g lateral. Rail shipment would import 5 to 10 g in all directions.

Static-firing loads originate under support conditions different from the launch pad. This gives rise to a different spring-mass system for calculations of dynamic loads in the vehicle due to rapid thrust buildup and decay rates, gimbaling of engines, and hold-down forces.

Launch Preparations

Erection. Methods of vehicle erection, such as free-hoisting at both ends or corseting for soft structures, are considered in order to design proper handling points and to avoid weight penalties.

Ground Winds. For this case, the vehicle is fully assembled and exposed along its full length to ground winds and to lateral loads due to von Karman vortex-shedding effects. The vehicle responds as a cantilever beam supported by longitudinal, lateral, or torsional springs at the base, depending on the vehicle and launch-pad design (Fig. 24). Mission requirements dictate the use of certain statistical ground winds, *e.g.*, the 99 percent probability-of-occurrence profile. The shear-load distribution over the vehicle is

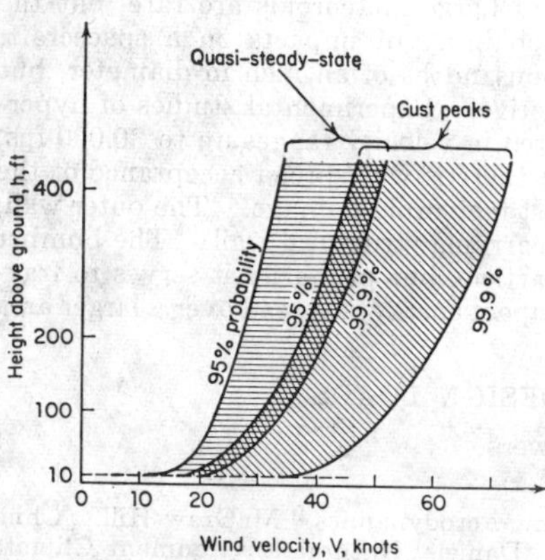

FIG. 24. Typical ground-wind profiles.

$$\text{Shear, } V = \int_0^L \tfrac{1}{2}\rho v_w(h)^2 C_D(h) D(h)\, dh$$

Here ρ is average air density, v_w is wind velocity as a function of height above ground, D is vehicle diameter, and C_D is a drag coefficient. For cylindrical surfaces, $C_D = 0.56$. For multicylindrical stages, scalloped bodies and fins, or other aerodynamic protrusions such as external conduits, $C_D = 1.2$. The wind-gust profile is assumed to be 1.4 times the steady state. To account for vortex shedding, gusts, and turbulence, a dynamic load factor of 1.5 is applied. Wind-tunnel models of the vehicle are checked for all operational conditions and include simulations of the launch pad, adjacent service and umbilical towers, and other ground equipment that may influence the airflow around the erected vehicle. Spoilers, fairings, and flow deflectors attached to the vehicle or the ground equipment are used to reduce ground-wind loads.

Transportation as an Assembled Vehicle. Some vehicle systems require the completely assembled vehicle to be transported vertically as a cantilever beam, tied to a structure mounted on wheels or treads. In this condition, the vehicle is subjected to wind loads as mentioned above and to vibratory forces at its base due to motions of the transport system.

Blast Effects. The effect of pressure waves from explosions of other vehicles in the vicinity must be determined by ground tests.

Launch

This phase is the time from engine ignition through vehicle release. Ground-wind and blast loads apply also for this phase. The vehicle responds as a system of longitudinal springs and masses, including launcher flexibilities, similar to the condition described for static firing. Rapid engine-thrust buildups and decay rates, for the case of abortive firing, are imposed on the vehicle, and longitudinal inertia forces are added to the static loads. The vehicle also undergoes lateral accelerations and shock loads immediately after vehicle-launch release, when it is deflected and loaded as a cantilever beam and the boundary conditions change to free flight.

Flight

Longitudinal force, shear, and bending moments are critical in the vicinity of maximum dynamic pressure and first-stage-boost cutoff. For computation of longitudinal loads, the summation of aerodynamic drag, engine forces, and steady-state vehicle-acceleration loads are sufficient. However, at cutoff of the engines of the various stages, dynamic forces must be included. These occur as a result of the rapid thrust decay of the engines and consequent springback of the compressed structure.

Vehicle stability during the powered part of the trajectory depends upon atmospheric disturbances, various control modes, vehicle structural and engine characteristics, and sloshing of liquid fuels.

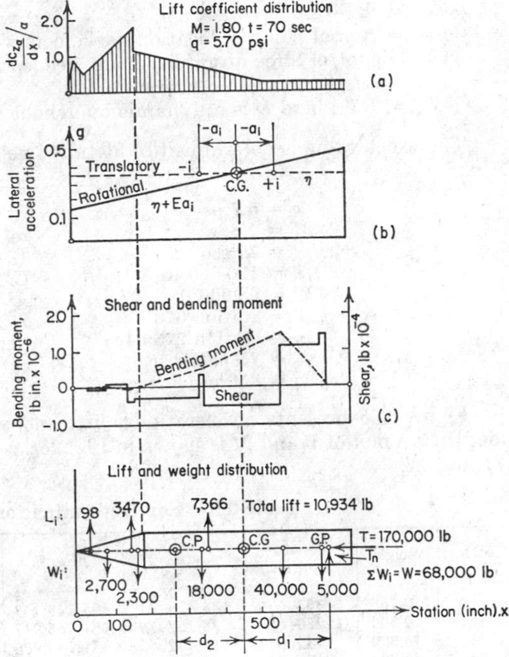

Fig. 25. Aerodynamic, control, and inertia forces on typical launch vehicle.

Rigid-body lateral structural loads are a combination of aerodynamic and inertia loads. They are caused by rigid-body motion plus elastic-body bending modes. They are maximum in flight near the time point of maximum dynamic pressure. The external forces are air forces due to angle of attack and that component of engine thrust required for control of the vehicle against winds at altitude. The total lift on a vehicle is given by $C_{z\alpha}qA\alpha$. The distribution of the total lift over the vehicle length is shown in Fig. 25*a* for a typical vehicle.

The equation for shear at station X is

$$V_x = \sum_{i=0}^{i=x} W_i(\eta + a_i\epsilon) + \sum_{i=0}^{i=x} L_i + T_n$$

The equation for moment at station X is

$$M_x = \sum_{i=0}^{i=x} W_i(\eta + a_i\epsilon)(d_i - d_x) + \sum_{i=0}^{i=x} L_i(d_i - d_x)$$

where W_i = weight increment at station i
a_i = distance from station i to cg of vehicle
d_i, d_x = distance from reference station
L_i = lift increment at station i
I_ω = moment of inertia about cg $= \Sigma W_i a_i^2$
$\eta = (\Sigma L_i + T_n)/\Sigma W_i$
$\epsilon = [L(\text{cg} - \text{cp}) + T_n(\text{cg} - \text{gimbal station})]/I_\omega$

$$\alpha_t = \frac{T\alpha_\omega}{T + L_\alpha[1 + (d_2/d_1)]}$$

where α_t = trim angle of attack due to wind, radians
T = total thrust available for vehicle control, lb
α_w = wind angle = $\tan^{-1} v_w/v_v$, radians
L_α = total lift per radian angle of attack, lb per radian
d_2 = c.p. − cg
d_1 = cg − g.p.
g.p. = gimbal point = location on vehicle where engine thrust is applied
T_e = control force at gimbal point needed to put $\Sigma M_{cg} = 0$
= Ld_2/d_1
$T_n = DT_e$; here D is a dynamic overshoot factor; $D \geq 1.25$

The exact value is determined by detailed vehicle-control analysis.

EXAMPLE:

q = 5.7 psi
M = 1.8
t = 70 sec
T = 170,000 lb
W = 68,000 lb
g.p. = station 670
c.p. = station 273.64
v_w = 75 m per sec
v_v = 450 m per sec

α_w = 0.165 radians
α_t = 2.283 deg
T_e = 10,379. lb
T_n = 12,974. lb
c.g. = station 466.656
I_ω = 1,338,835,514. psi
ϵ = −0.0003942 in.$^{-1}$
η = 0.35159

Figure 25*b* presents accelerations, lift, and weight increments over the vehicle length. A plot of V and M is shown in Fig. 25*c*. For detailed calculations, see Tables 11 and 12.

Table 11. For Determination of Input Data

Station	Weight	CG–station, a_i	a_i^2	$W_i a_i^2$	ϵa_i	$\eta + \epsilon a_i$	$W_i(\eta + \epsilon a_i)$
84	2,700	382.656	146,425.61	395,349,147	−0.15,084	0.20,075	542.03
186	2,300	280.656	78,767.79	181,165,917	−0.11,063	0.24,096	554.21
331	18,000	135.656	18,402.55	331,245,900	−0.05,348	0.29,811	5,365.98
546	40,000	−79.344	6,295.47	251,818,800	+0.03,128	0.38,287	15,314.80
656	5,000	−189.344	35,851.15	179,255,750	+0.07,464	0.42,623	2,131.15

Table 12. For Determination of Shear V and Moment M

Station	$-L_i$ and T_n	$W_i(\eta + \epsilon a_i)$	V	Δ station	M
49	−98	....	−98	0	0
84	....	542.03	+444.03	35	−3,430
154	−3,470	....	−3,025.97	70	+27,652
186	....	554.21	−2,471.76	32	−69,179
331	....	5,365.98	+2,894.22	145	−427,584
333	−7,366	....	−4,471.78	2	−421,796
546	....	15,314.80	+10,843.02	213	−1,374,285
656	....	2,131.15	−12,974.17	110	−181,553
670	−12,974	....	0	14	0

Longitudinal loads in flight are a maximum at cutoff of first-stage engines. The equation for determining longitudinal force is $F_x = \sum_0^x W_i\lambda + \sum_0^x D_i + \sum_0^x T_i$, where $\lambda = (T - D)/W$, $D = \sum_0^x D_i$, and D_i = drag increment at station i.

For vehicle fins and control surfaces, flutter analyses determine stability margins over the vehicle trajectory. Flutter of individual panels may occur at Mach 1 and maximum dynamic pressure, especially at increased temperatures. Buffeting or oscillating aerodynamic pressures and their distribution and effects on the vehicle are checked in wind-tunnel tests to determine if such loads need to be considered for gross vehicle loads or are only local effects. Separation of stages, docking maneuvers, and resultant impulses impose highly concentrated forces on a vehicle structure.

Reentry pay loads, such as manned capsules and recoverable stages, are exposed to very high thermal and deceleration loads and compressive stresses.

VEHICLE DESIGN

By E. A. Hellebrand

Vehicle Configurations

A space-vehicle structure consists of pressure tanks, unpressurized shells (serving as intertank and interstage adapters), shrouds around engine compartments, and thrust-distribution members such as conical shells, thrust columns, and beams. Aerodynamic fairings, fins, and control surfaces similar to aircraft designs are also used. Integration of propulsion, guidance, and control with the primary vehicle structure calls for support brackets, shear panels, flat plates, doors, and frames around cutouts. During flight, compression loads due to thrust, aerodynamic, and control forces are very effectively counteracted by the internal working pressure in propellant tanks. In all other regions, the vehicle shell must have stiffening rings and ribs and corrugations or honeycomb and sandwich designs and must be reinforced where concentrated loads are applied.

Figure 26 shows a hypothetical vehicle with typical configurations and some basic design details. The right half shows separate propellant tanks and one center engine. This arrangement will not yield minimum structural weights because large portions of the outer shell, not pressurized, are exposed to compressive forces from thrust and bending moments and only a small area in the upper tank region is supported by internal pressure. Relatively deep ellipsoidal bulkheads—with an axis ratio of $\sqrt{2}:1$ to avoid compressive hoop stresses at the equatorial region—and the long thrust cone contribute to the excessive length of the unpressurized shell areas.

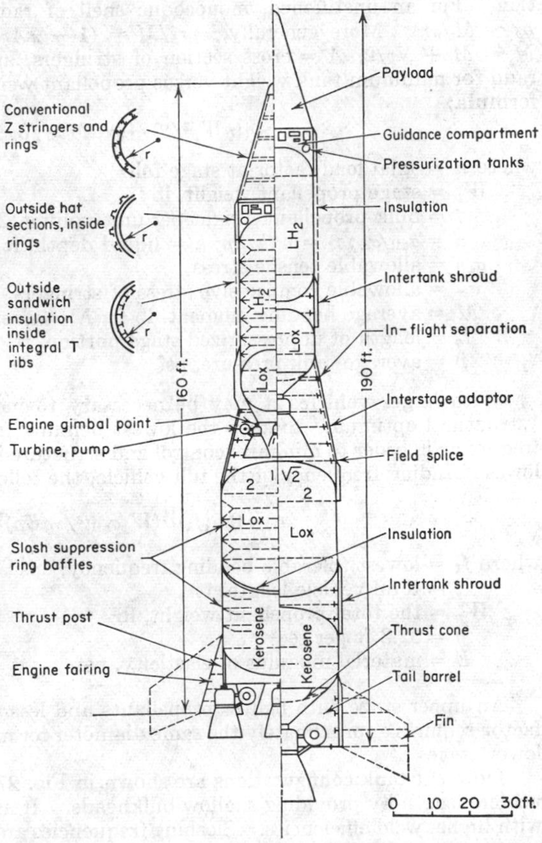

FIG. 26. Boost-vehicle configuration.

The left half shows a much shorter vehicle of equal performance capability. The length reduction is caused by a multiple-engine arrangement, common bulkheads, and ellipsoidal heads with an axis ratio of 2:1. Almost 60 percent of the outer shell is supported by internal pressure, compared with only 20 percent on the right. Internal pressure reduces compressive stresses in the shell from thrust and bending moments and increases the buckling stress itself by as much as 70 percent. The shorter vehicle also has higher bending-, torsional-, and longitudinal-vibration frequencies and is less susceptible to dynamic overshoots of bending moments due to sudden gust forces.

There are certain **penalties** to pay for this ideal configuration. The engines require fairings exposed to aerodynamic heating. The common bulkheads require insulation and must be reinforced to withstand possible pressure differences causing an unfavorable buckling condition. Shallower bulkheads must be reinforced at the equator.

Propellant tanks should be designed so that the cylindrical-wall thickness required to carry internal and dynamic head pressures coincides with the wall thickness required to withstand axial compressive forces from thrust and bending moments. Propulsion requirements, however, might necessitate pressures different from "optimum" condition. For an unstiffened, monocoque shell of radius r, the optimum pressure is $p_o \sim \bar{M}/\pi r^3$. More generally, $\pi p r^3/\bar{M} = (1 - \pi A r^2 \sigma_{cr}/\bar{M} b)/(0.5 + \alpha + \alpha\beta)$, where $\bar{M} = M + Nr/2$, A = cross section of stringers, and b = stringer spacing. Stage radii for minimum tank weight versus propellant weight are found from the following formula:

$$r_{\text{opt}} \sim [(nW_p{}^2/\bar{\gamma}) + \pi\alpha M l_o r/3\pi^2 p]^{0.20} \quad \text{ft}$$

where n = axial load factor at stage full
W_p = stage propellant weight, lb
$\bar{\gamma}$ = bulk propellant weight per unit volume, lb per ft³
$\alpha = \sigma_{\text{all}}/\sigma_{cr}$; $\beta = n\bar{\gamma}h/2p$; h = liquid depth, ft
σ_{all} = allowable tensile stress
σ_{cr} = allowable compressive stress of stringers
M = average bending moment, lb-ft; N = average axial load, lb
l_o = length of unpressurized stage portion, ft
p = average tank pressure, psf

With **larger vehicles** it may be necessary to increase the diameter beyond the "structural optimum" to keep the lowest bending frequency well above the control frequency in order to minimize control and structure interference. To stay above the lowest bending frequency of the full vehicle, the following radius is required:

$$r \sim 0.5(f_1)^{1/2}(W_p \sigma_{\text{all}} l^3/\pi g E p)^{1/2} \quad \text{ft}$$

where f_1 = lowest tolerable bending frequency, cps
l = total vehicle length, ft
W_p = the total propellant weight, lb
g = 32.3 ft per sec²
E = material modulus of elasticity, psf

An upper stage with lighter propellants and less pressure but a higher axial-load factor requires approximately the same diameter for minimum tank weight as does the lower stage.

Different **tank configurations** are shown in Fig. 27. A multicell tank reduces the vehicle length by providing shallow bulkheads. It also allows for thinner-skin gages with higher weld efficiencies. Sloshing frequencies are increased and effective sloshing masses are reduced. If engines can be arranged such that the thrust is led into longerons between cells, the weight of thrust-distribution members is minimized. A single engine attached to the center post counteracts the inertia forces of the center portion of the liquid; however, additional stability of the center portion of the tank has to be provided by reinforcing the radial walls to convert them into rigid shear webs. A multicell tank with radial walls is stable under internal pressure but unstable under inertia forces. This is also true for a toroidal tank or a cylindrical tank with semitoroidal bulkheads. Both tank configurations help reduce over-all vehicle length and weights: the toroidal tank, by utilizing areas around bulkheads of adjacent tanks; the semitoroidal bulkheads, by their shallowness. When studying minimum-

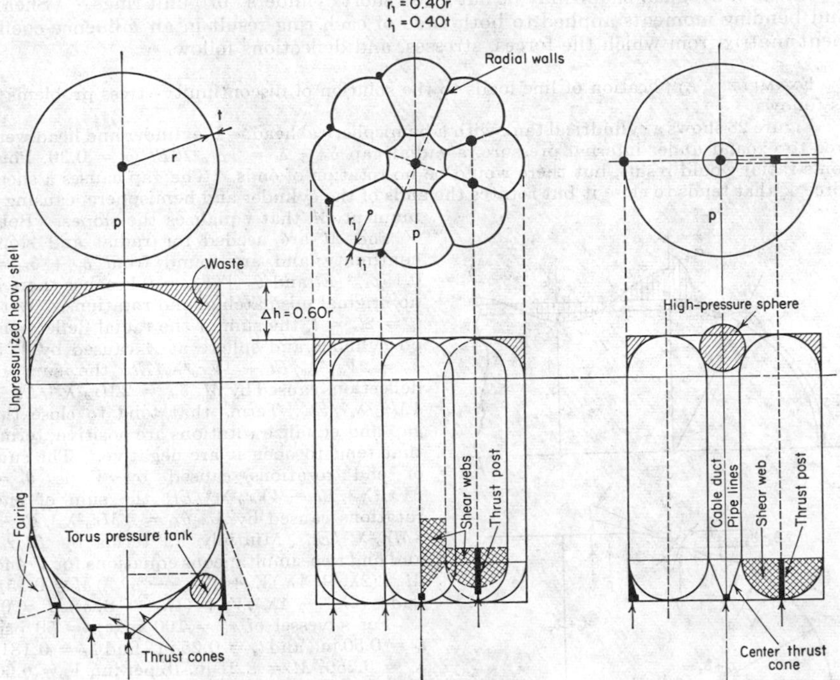

FIG. 27. Booster-tank configurations with different thrust distributions.

weight tank configurations, it is important to consider the whole vehicle and especially the number, types, and location of engines.

Structural-design Formulas for Vehicle Components

Analysis of stresses and experimental strain-gage readings often lead to very high "nominal" stress values if a linear stress-strain law is assumed. If a calculated stress exceeds the proportional limit (σ_p), a reduction formula is useful for preliminary adjustment. Multiply the nominal "elastic" stress with the plasticity factor: $\eta = \alpha(2 - \alpha)$, where $\alpha = \sigma_p/\sigma\epsilon$. $\sigma\epsilon$ is the elastic stress $= \epsilon E$, from a strain-gage reading of ϵ, or in buckling cases, is the theoretical buckling stress found from linear analysis.

Shells with Discontinuities Represented by Line Loads. Cylindrical shell with circumferential end shear V_o (lb per in.): longitudinal bending stress: $\sigma_{bx} = (\pm 6V_o e^{-\lambda x} \sin \lambda x)/\lambda t^2$, $\lambda = 1.28/\sqrt{r_o t}$, $\max \sigma_{bx} = \pm 1.93 V_o/\lambda t^2$, at $x = \pi/4\lambda$; shear stress at x: $\tau_x = V_o e^{-\lambda x}(\cos \lambda x - \sin \lambda_x)/t$; hoop stress: $\sigma_{hx} = 2V_o r \lambda e^{-\lambda x} \cos \lambda x/t \pm \nu\sigma_{bx}$. At load, $\delta = 2V_o r_o^2 \lambda/Et$, $\theta = 2V_o r_o^2 \lambda^2/Et$. For short cylinders ($\lambda l < 2$), $\sigma_{bx} \to o$, $\sigma_{h1} = 4V_o r_o/lt$ at load; $\sigma_{h2} = -2V_o r_o/lt$ at other end; $\delta_{1,2} = \sigma_{h1,2} r_o/E$, $\theta = 6V_o r_o^2/El^2 t$.

Cylindrical shell with circumferential end moment M_o (lb): $\sigma_{bx} = 6M_o e^{-\lambda x}(\cos \lambda x + \sin \lambda x)/t^2$, $\tau_x = (2\lambda M_o e^{-\lambda x} \sin \lambda x)/t$; $\sigma_{hx} = 2M_o r_o \lambda^2 e^{-\lambda x}(\cos \lambda x - \sin \lambda x)/t \pm \nu\sigma_{bx}$. At load $\delta = 2M_o r_o^2 \lambda^2/Et$, $\theta = 4M_o r_o^2 \lambda^3/Et$. For short cylinders ($\lambda l < 2$), $\sigma_{bx} \to o$, $\sigma_h = \pm 6M_o r_o/l^2 t$, $\delta = \sigma_h r_o/E$, $\theta = 2M_o r_o^2/Etl^3$.

Spherical segment or cone with half-angle ϕ: With end shear, if $\phi < 60$ deg and $r_o\lambda > 10$, σ_{bx} may be taken from the cylinder formula. At load, $\max \sigma_h \sim 2V_o r_o \lambda(1 - \sin \phi/2r_o\lambda)/t$, $\delta = \sigma_h r_o/E$, $\theta = 2V_o r_o^2 \lambda^2/Et \cos \phi$, with end moment, at load, $\max \sigma_h = 2M_o r_o \lambda^2/t$, $\delta = 2M_o r_o^2 \lambda^2/Et \cos \phi$, $\theta = 4M_o r_o^2 \lambda^3/Et \cos^2 \phi$

Shells of irregular shape may be cut into "short cylinders" or "unit rings." Shears and bending moments applied to both ends of each ring result in an influence-coefficient matrix from which the forces, stresses, and deflections follow.

EXAMPLE. Application of line loads to the solution of discontinuity-stress problems is as follows:

Figure 28 shows a cylindrical tank with a hemispherical head. If cylinder and head were free to expand under internal pressure, a radial gap $\delta_c - \delta_s = \nu p r_o^2/2Et$ ($\nu = 0.30$, Poisson's ratio) would result, but there would be no rotation of ends. The gap causes a shear force V that tends to close it but rotates the ends of the cylinder and hemisphere, causing a moment M that equalizes the slopes. Both V and M are needed for radial and slope continuity and are found from $\delta_v + \delta_m = 0.15 p r_o^2/Et$ and $\theta_v + \theta_m = 0$ because there is no original mismatch of end rotations. With $t_c = 2t_s = t$, the sum of the radial deflections on cylinder and sphere at A caused by V is $\delta_v = 2Vr_o^2\lambda_c/Et + 4Vr_o^2\lambda_s/Et$; the sum of deflections caused by M, $\delta_m = 2Mr_o^2\lambda_o^2/Et - 4Mr_o^2\lambda_s^2/Et$. Terms that tend to close the gap and equalize rotations are positive; terms that tend to open it are negative. The sum of end rotations caused by V is $\theta_v = 2Vr_o^2\lambda_e^2/Et - 4Vr_o^2\lambda_s^2/Et$; the sum of end rotations caused by M, $\theta_m = 4Mr_o^2\lambda_c^3/Et + 8Mr_o^2\lambda_s^3/Et$. Multiply all terms by Et/r_o^2 and find two simultaneous equations for V and M: $(2\lambda_c + 4\lambda_s)V + (2\lambda_c^2 - 4\lambda_s^2)M = 0.15p$ and $(2\lambda_c^2 - 4\lambda_s^2)V + (4\lambda_c^3 + 8\lambda_s^3)M = 0$.

For a vessel of $r_o = 100$ in., $p = 50$ psi, $t_c = 0.50$ in., and $t_s = 0.25$ in., find $\lambda_c = 0.181$, $\lambda_s = 0.256$, $M = 8.21$ in.-lb per in., $V = 6.60$ lb per in. The maximum total stress on the sphere occurs in hoop direction at the inner face and amounts to 11,158 psi, as compared with the membrane stress $pr_o/2t_s = 10{,}000$ psi.

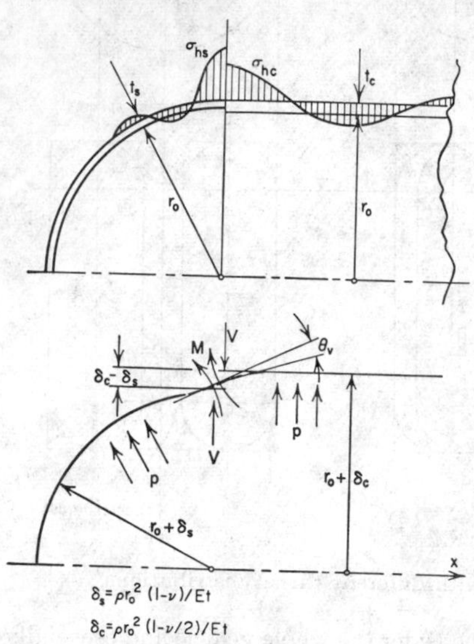

FIG. 28. Discontinuity stresses in cylindrical tank with hemispherical head.

Buckling of Shells and Rings under External Pressure. A cylindrical shell of length l or with rings at spacing l, radius r, and wall thickness t, buckles at $\sigma_{cr} \sim (0.87Et^{1.5})/l(r)^{0.5}$ if external radial pressure p causes hoop compression pr/t. The same formula also holds for a closed vessel with axial compression $pr/2t$ added, but in this case, axial instability must also be checked: $\bar{\sigma}_{cr} = (K + K_1)Et/r$; $K \sim 9(t/r)^{0.6} \leq 0.607$, $K_1 \sim 0.16rt^{0.3}/l^{1.3}$. K_1 considers the stiffening effect of rings at spacing l. In all cases, the rings must not buckle prematurely. Thus, the moment of inertia of rings $I_r > plr^3/3E$ if the rings are to carry the whole external load, after buckling of the shell, to avoid complete collapse. Less conservative is the assumption that rings provide lateral support but do not carry the full load if the shell buckles. In this case, $\rho^2 = I_r/A_r \geq (0.29r^2t^{1.5})/l(r)^{0.5}$. With C, Z, or hat section rings, the depth h needed to provide ρ is about $h = 3\rho$. From this it follows that, for average conditions, $h/r \sim (0.30)\,(t/l)^{0.5}$. The wall thickness of the ring should be $t_r \geq h/40$, and the width of a web-stabilizing flange, $b \sim 10t_r$.

Buckling of Integrally Ribbed or Sandwich Panels and Shells. (See Fig. 29.) They may be treated approximately like monocoque structures if t_e is used instead of t in the formulas of this and the preceding paragraph. In the case of a ribbed panel, the effective wall thickness $t_e = (12I_r/d)^{1/3}$, but only if ribs in both directions are provided, not farther apart than $d_x = d_y = d \leq 50t$, $h \leq 10t_r$. I_r = moment of inertia of one rib including adjacent panel or shell width d. If ribs in circumferential direction (rings) are spaced $d_x > 50t$, the formula for axial instability is $\sigma_{cr} = (K + K_1)Et_{ex}/r$; $K \sim 9(t_{ey}/r)^{0.6}$, $K \leq 0.607$. $K_1 \sim 0.16rt_{ex}^{0.3}1/l^{1.3}$ if extra ring frames are provided at spacing l, with $I_r \geq 10I_y$. For a shell with internal pressure stabilization, use $\bar{K} = K[1 + 0.23\beta(r/t_{ey})^{0.6}]/(1 + 3\beta) \leq 0.607$, instead of K, where $\beta = pr^2/Et^2$.

$t_{ex} = (12I_x/dy)^{1/3}$; $t_{ey} = (12Iy/d_x)^{1/3}$. For radial instability, $\sigma_{cr} \sim (0.87Et_{ey}{}^{1.5})/l(r)^{0.5}$.

If d_x and $d_y > 50t$, skin buckling may occur at stresses below the over-all instability stress. In this case, assume the shell is made up of discrete stringers and rings, integral or built-up. Calculate A_x, I_x for stringers with an effective shell width of $2e_x = 50t$ and I_y for rings with $2e_y = 2\sqrt{rt} < d_x/2$. For axial instability, assume a column term $\bar{\sigma}_{cr} = \pi^2EI_x/A_x\bar{l}^2$; $\bar{l} \sim 0.85r(I_xd_x/I_yr)^{1/4}$, $d_x \leq \bar{l} \leq l$. To this add a shell term $\sigma_{cr} = \alpha KEt_{ex}/r$, $K \sim 9(t_{ey}/r)^{0.6}$, $\alpha = (50t/d_y)^{1/2}$ = solidity factor. The total buckling load is $P_{cr} = 2\pi rt\sigma_{cr} + 2\pi rA_x\bar{\sigma}_{cr}/d_y$, and the equivalent buckling stress is $\sigma_{ecr} = \sigma_{cr} + A_x\bar{\sigma}_{cr}/d_yt$. Use $\bar{A}_x = A_x - 50t^2$ for integral ribs.

In the case of a flat or curved sandwich panel or shell, $t_c = (6\bar{\eta}t_fh^2)^{1/3}$; $h \geq 5t_f$. The reduction factor $\bar{\eta}$ depends on the module and shear strength of the core. $\bar{\eta} \sim 1/(1 + 3\alpha)$; $\alpha = \pi^2Et_fh/2G_cb^2$. For a full shell, use $\bar{\alpha} = Et_f/G_cr$ instead of α.

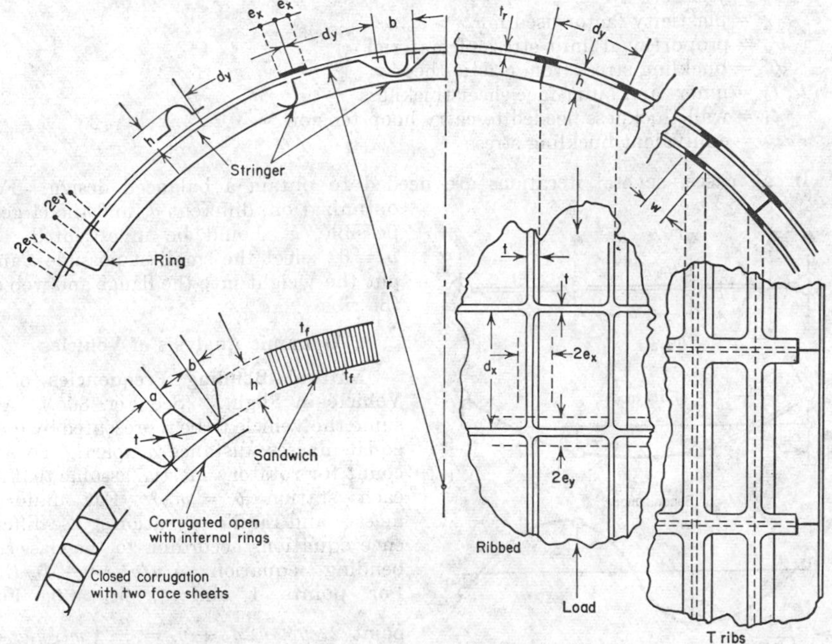

FIG. 29. Panel and shell types.

In the case of an open-corrugated panel or shell, I_x and A_x are the moment of inertia and the cross-sectional area of one pitch. If rings I_r are spaced a distance a apart, $\bar{l} \sim 0.85r(I_xa/I_rr)^{1/4} \geq a$; $\bar{\sigma}_{cr} = \pi^2EI_x/A_x\bar{l}^2$, and no shell term is used. The depth and width of corrugations must not be greater than $50t$. Corrugated panels with one or two face sheets may be treated like ribbed panels or sandwiches, including the shell-buckling term.

Over-all Vehicle-shell-design Formulas

If a monocoque vehicle shell has to carry a bending moment M, a longitudinal load N, and internal pressure p, find the required wall thickness from $M/\pi r^2t + N/2\pi rt - pr/2t = \eta\sigma_{cr}/Sf_u$ or $\eta\sigma_{ecr}/Sf$ in the compression zone or from $M/\pi r^2t - N/2\pi rt + pr/2t = \sigma_y/Sf_y$ in the tension zone, and check $t \leq t_1$ from $(p + ngh_1)r/t_1 = \sigma_y/Sf$ for hoop tension, whichever gives the highest value for t. For stringer-stiffened shell, integral or built-up and with or without ring frames, use $t_r = t + \bar{A}_x/d_y$ except for hoop tension. For σ_{cr} or σ_{ecr}, use the applicable t_e from preceding paragraphs. For sandwich shells, use $t_s = t_i + t_o$. For hoop tension, the inner face carries $\bar{p}(\alpha + \beta)/(1 - \alpha + \beta)$ and the outer face carries $\bar{p}/(1 + \alpha + \beta)$, where $\alpha = Eth/E_c r^2$, $\beta = t_i/t_o$, and $\bar{p} = p + n\gamma h$. For open-corrugated shells, use $t^* = (a + \sqrt{b^2 + h^2})\, t/(a + b)$. These shells can carry modest differential pressures if ring frames are closely spaced so that corrugations carry the pressure loads as beams in bending. Most efficient are integrally ribbed shells with T ribs.

These formulas use the following notation:

$Sf_{u,y}$ = ultimate and yield safety factors
n = axial-load factor a/g of vehicle
γ = density of liquid in tank, lb per unit volume
h_1 = depth of liquid
E = elastic module of face material
E_c = elastic module of core material
σ_y = yield stress
η = plasticity factor used if $\sigma_{cr} > \sigma_p$.
σ_p = proportional limit stress of material
σ_{cr} = buckling stress from elastic theory
t_i, t_o = inner- and outer-face sheet thickness
t_1 = wall thickness needed to carry hoop tension
σ_{ecr} = equivalent buckling stress

In all cases, several iterations are needed to obtain a balanced design. For optimization, different d_y and the largest possible h should be investigated. If $p = 0$, select the smallest possible t and put the weight into the flange and web of the ribs.

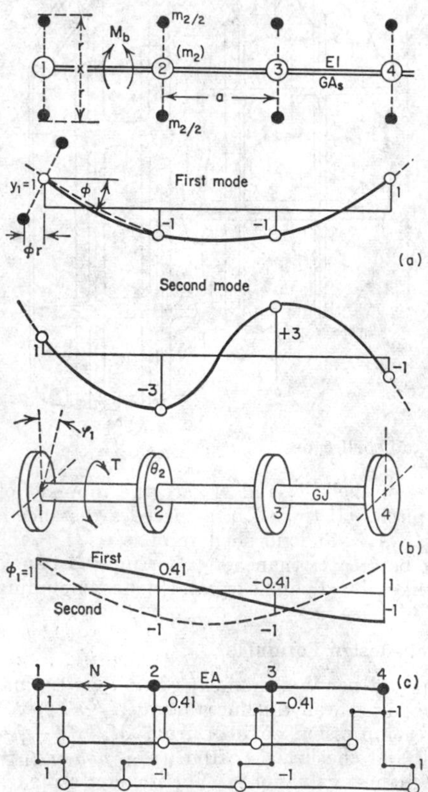

FIG. 30. Idealized space vehicle for vibration analysis.

Dynamic Analysis of Vehicles

Natural Bending Frequencies of a Vehicle in Flight. (See Fig. 30*a*.) Assume the vehicle to be represented by four equal masses, distance a apart. To account for rotatory inertia, assume that at each station $\theta_i = m_i r^2$. For uniform masses and radii of gyration r, use difference equations according to the classical bending equation $\Delta^2 y/a^2 = -M_b/EI$. For points 1 and 4, $M_b = 0$. For point 2, $y_1 - 2y_2 + y_3 = \dfrac{a^2}{EI}\left(m\omega^2 y_1 a + m\omega^2 r^2 \dfrac{y_1 - y_2}{a}\right)$; since by symmetry, $y_1 = y_4$ and $y_2 = y_3$, one equation describes the first mode: $y_1 - y_2 = \alpha[y_1 + (y_1 - y_2)\beta]$, where $\alpha = m\omega^2 a^3/EI$ and $\beta = (r/a)^2$. Also, for a free-free mode, $\Sigma y = y_1 + y_2 + y_3 + y_4 = 0$, to make the shear at both ends zero. This provides $-y_2 = y_1$ and $\alpha_1 = 2/(1 + 2\beta)$, the frequency of the first bending mode. To obtain the second bending mode, which is antisymmetric, take $y_1 = y_4$ and $y_2 = -y_3$. The boundary condition $\Sigma M_b = 0$ provides $y_2 = -(3 + \beta)y_1/(1 + \beta)$. The bending equation is $y_1 - 3y_2 = \alpha[y_1 + (y_1 - y_2)\beta]$ which, with the substitution of y_2, yields $\alpha_2 = (10 + 4\beta)/(1 + 5\beta + 2\beta^2)$.

With $\beta = 0$, $\alpha_1 = 2$ and $\alpha_2 = 10$. For comparison with uniform beam, put $m = M/4$ and $a = l/4$, and find $\omega_1 = 22.7\sqrt{EI/Ml^3}$ and $\omega_2 = 51\sqrt{EI/Ml^3}$. The correct coefficients are 22.4 and 61.6. For $\beta = 0.5$, find $\alpha_1 = 1$ and $\alpha_2 = 3$, which shows that higher modes are slowed down faster with increasing rotatory inertia. To include shear deformation, use $\gamma = EI/GA_s a^2$ and find $\alpha_1 = 2/(1 + 2\beta + \gamma)$ and $\alpha = (10 + 4\beta)/(1 + 5\beta + 2\beta^2 + 3\gamma + \beta\gamma)$. A_s = cross section of vehicle effective in shear.

Natural Torsional Frequencies of a Vehicle in Flight. (See Fig. 30*b*). Apply the difference equation of torsion, $\Delta\phi/a = -T/GJ$, to stations 2, 3, and 4: $\phi_1 - \phi_2 = a\theta\omega^2\phi_1/GJ$; $\phi_2 - \phi_3 = a\theta\omega^2(\phi_1 + \phi_2)/GJ$; $\phi_3 - \phi_4 = \alpha\theta\omega^2(\phi_1 + \phi_2 + \phi_3)/GJ$. The boundary condition $\Sigma T = 0$ gives $\phi_1 + \phi_2 + \phi_3 + \phi_4 = 0$. Put $\bar{\alpha} = a\theta\omega^2/GJ$ and obtain the determinant

$$\begin{vmatrix} 1 - \bar{\alpha} & -1 & 0 \\ -\bar{\alpha} & 1 - \bar{\alpha} & -1 \\ 1 - \bar{\alpha} & 1 - \bar{\alpha} & 2 - \bar{\alpha} \end{vmatrix} = 0$$

with the solution $\bar{\alpha}^3 - 6\bar{\alpha}^2 + 10\bar{\alpha} - 4 = 0$. Which yields $\bar{\alpha}_1 = 0.59$, $\bar{\alpha}_2 = 2.00$, and $\bar{\alpha}_3 = 3.41$. (ϕ = angle of twist, θ = torsional mass moment of inertia, and GJ = torsional rigidity, lb in.^{2})

Natural Longitudinal Frequencies of a Vehicle in Flight. (See Fig. 30*c*.) The difference equation of longitudinal tension or compression, $\Delta a/a = N/EA$, applied to stations 2, 3, and 4 yields $x_1 - x_2 = am\omega^2 x_1/EA$; $x_2 - x_3 = am\omega^2(x_1 + x_2)/EA$; $x_3 - x_4 = am\omega^2(x_1 + x_2 + x_3)/EA$. The boundary condition of ends free of external forces is $x_1 + x_2 + x_3 + x_4 = 0$. Put $\alpha^* = am\omega^2/EA$, and obtain determinant identical to that of preceding paragraph by substituting α^* for $\bar{\alpha}$. The roots are again $\alpha_1^* = 0.59$, $\alpha_2^* = 2.00$, and $\alpha_3^* = 3.41$.

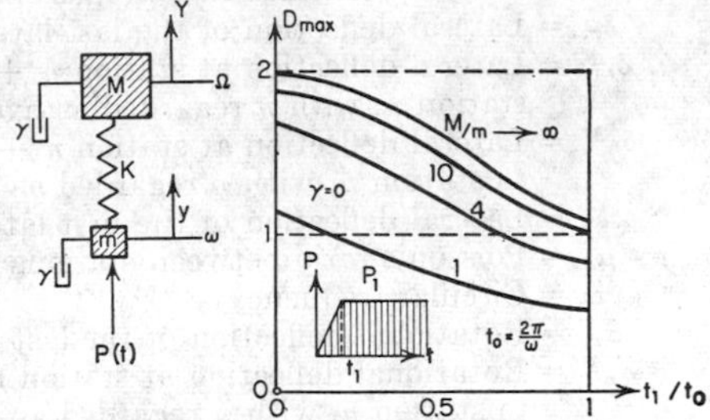

FIG. 31. Dynamic magnification factors for rapid thrust buildup.

Forced Longitudinal Vibrations, Dynamic-thrust Overshoot. Assume that a force $P(t)$, increasing to P_1 in a time t_1, acts on a mass m coupled to a mass M by spring K. Both masses are damped. The equations of dynamic equilibrium are $m\ddot{y} + K(y - Y) + c\dot{y} = P(t)$ and $M\ddot{Y} - K(y - Y) + C\dot{Y} = 0$ or $\ddot{y} + \omega^2(y - Y) + \gamma\omega/\dot{y} = P(t)/m$ and $\ddot{Y} - \Omega^2(y - Y) + \gamma\Omega\dot{Y} = 0$, where $\omega^2 = K/m$, $\Omega^2 = K/M$, and $\gamma = 2c/c_{cr} = 2C/C_{cr} = C/m\omega = C/M\Omega$. Substitute $\ddot{y}_n = (y_{n-1} - 2y_n + y_{n+1})/\Delta t^2$, $\dot{y}_n = (y_n - y_{n-1})/\Delta t$, and similar expressions for $\ddot{Y}_n$ and Y_n, and obtain two simultaneous difference equations for the motion of m and M:

$$y_n = P\,\Delta t^2/m - (1 - \gamma\omega\,\Delta t)y_{n-2} + (2 - \omega^2\,\Delta t^2 - \gamma\omega\,\Delta t)y_{n-1} + \omega^2\,\Delta^2 t\,Y_{n-1}$$
$$Y_n = -(1 - \gamma\Omega\,\Delta t)Y_{n-2} + (2 - \Omega^2\,\Delta t^2 - \gamma\Omega\,\Delta t)Y_{n-1} + \Omega^2\,\Delta t^2\,y_{n-1}$$

Select $\Delta t \leq 2\pi/10\omega$. If the static deflection of the system is expressed by P_1/K and the dynamic deflection by $y - Y$, which is directly proportional to the spring force, the dynamic magnification factor is $D = K(y - Y)_{\max}/P_1$. The force P_1 causes a load on the system equal to DP_1. Figure 31 indicates values of D for different force buildups times t_1 versus t_0, the uncoupled natural period of mass m on spring K, and for different mass ratios M/m. For practical applications, M would be the total vehicle mass at lift-off minus the mass of the engines and the adjacent thrust structure. The mass of engines and thrust structure is m. With $\gamma \neq 0$, the dynamic factor is reduced by $1/(1 + \gamma/2)$, for small γ, but more accurate values are found by stepwise, simultaneous integration of the above equations.

A METHOD FOR DETERMINING LATERAL BENDING MODES OF SPACE VEHICLES

By Tulon Bullock

(See also Sec. 5.)

REFERENCES: Myklestad, "Fundamentals of Vibration Analysis," McGraw-Hill. Bisplinghoff, Ashley, and Halfman, "Aeroelasticity," Addison-Wesley. Timoshenko and Goodier, "Theory of Elasticity," McGraw-Hill. Den Hartog, "Advanced Strength of Materials," McGraw-Hill.

Notation

A_n = Cross-section area between stations n and $n + 1$
E_n = Young's modulus between stations n and $n + 1$
I_n = Area moment of inertia between stations n and $n + 1$
J_n = Mass moment of inertia at station n in pitch direction
K_n = Lateral spring constant at station n
$\bar{K}_n$ = Shear-shape factor between stations n and $n + 1$
M_n = Moment to left of nth mass point
m_n = Mass at station n
Q_n = Shear force to left of nth mass point
R_n = Rotational spring constant at station n
Y_n = Lateral deflection at nth mass point
δ_m = Lateral deflection of the last lateral spring due to a unit force
δ_n^F = Lateral deflection at station $n + 1$ due to a unit force at $n + 1$ relative to station n, with n regarded as fixed
δ_n^M = Lateral deflection at station $n + 1$ due to a unit moment at $n + 1$ relative to station n, with n regarded as fixed
δ_1 = Lateral deflection of the first lateral spring due to a unit force
μ_n = Poisson's ratio between stations n and $n + 1$
ω = Circular frequency
σ_m = Rotational deflection of the last rotational spring due to a unit moment
σ_n^F = Rotational deflection at station $n + 1$ due to a unit force at $n + 1$ relative to station n, with n regarded as fixed
σ_n^M = Rotational deflection at station $n + 1$ due to a unit moment at $n + 1$ relative to station n, with n regarded as fixed
σ_1 = Rotational deflection of the first rotational spring due to a unit moment
θ_n = Rotational deflection at nth mass point

The **Myklestad method,** adapted to include secondary effects of shear and rotary inertia, is a practical approach to mode-shape and frequency analysis of space vehicles. The masses are concentrated at a finite number of points along the beam, with elastic properties remaining constant between consecutive mass points. One lateral and one rotational spring are located at each mass point. (See Fig. 32.) Values of K_n, for $n = 2, 3, \ldots, m - 1$, which cause the transfer matrices to be ill-conditioned should not be used.

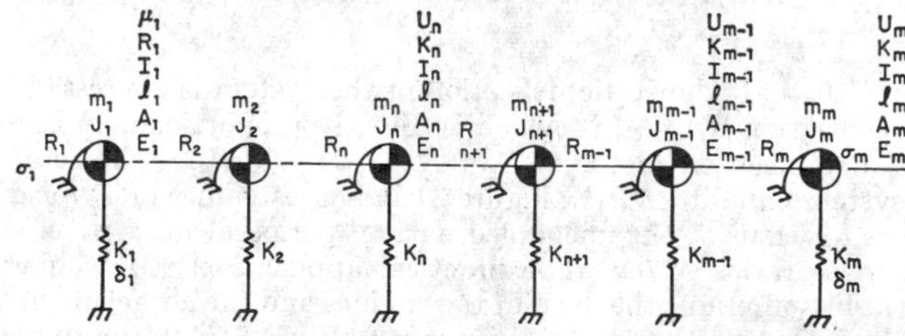

FIG. 32. Flexible space vehicle represented by beam with discrete masses and springs.

A segment of the beam between stations n and $n + 1$ is illustrated Fig. 33. The relative influence coefficients are expressed as

$$\delta_n{}^F = \frac{l_n{}^3}{3E_nI_n} + \frac{2(\mu_n + 1)}{\bar{K}_n} \frac{l_n}{A_nE_n} \tag{1}$$

$$\delta_n{}^M = \frac{l_n{}^2}{2E_nI_n} \tag{2}$$

$$\sigma_n{}^F = \frac{l_n{}^2}{2E_nI_n} \tag{3}$$

$$\sigma_n{}^M = \frac{l_n}{E_nI_n} \tag{4}$$

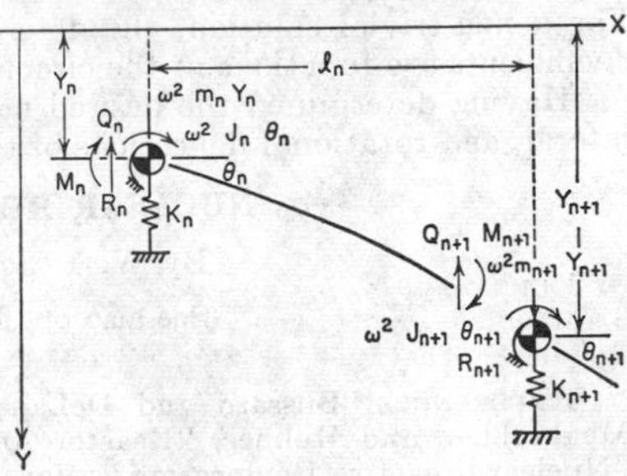

FIG. 33. Forces and deflections of beam segment during bending vibrations.

With the aid of Figure 33, the shear, moment, lateral, and rotational deflection at station $n + 1$ can be expressed in terms of the values at station n as follows:

$$\underbrace{\begin{bmatrix} Q_{n+1} \\ M_{n+1} \\ Y_{n+1} \\ \theta_{n+1} \end{bmatrix}}_{\{Z_{n+1}\}} = \underbrace{\begin{bmatrix} l & 0 & K_n - \omega^2 M_n & 0 \\ l_n & l & l_n(K_n - \omega^2 M_n) & \omega^2 J_n - R_n \\ -\delta_n{}^M l_n + \delta_n{}^F & -\delta_n{}^M & l + (\delta_n{}^F - l_n\delta_n{}^M)(K_n - \omega^2 M_n) & l_n - \delta_n{}^M(\omega^2 J_n - R_n) \\ -\sigma_n{}^M l_n + \sigma_n{}^F & -\sigma_n{}^M & (\sigma_n{}^F - \sigma_n{}^M l_n)(K_n - \omega^2 M_n) & l - \sigma_n{}^M(\omega^2 J_n - R_n) \end{bmatrix}}_{[\bar{A}_n]} \underbrace{\begin{bmatrix} Q_n \\ M_n \\ Y_n \\ \theta_n \end{bmatrix}}_{\{Z_n\}} \tag{5}$$

or $\{Z_{n+1}\} = [\bar{A}_n]\{Z_n\}$

For the last matrix, $\bar{A}_m$, it is necessary to set $l_m = 0$, since the last segment consists of only a mass.

The loads and deflections to the left of the first station can be related to the loads and deflections to the right of the last station by

$$\{Z_{m+1}\} = [A_m][A_{m-1}] \cdot \cdot \cdot [A_2][A_1]\{Z_1\} = [\bar{A}]\{Z_1\} \tag{6}$$

where $\bar{A}$ is the product of all $\bar{A}_n$'s.

The *frequency determinant* is obtained by using the $\bar{A}$ matrix and the boundary conditions of the beam. For the left end of the beam, they are expressed as

$$Q_1 = Y_1K_1 \tag{7}$$

$$M_1 = -\theta_1R_1 \tag{8}$$

$$Y_1 = Q_1\delta_1 \tag{9}$$

$$\theta_1 = -M_1\sigma_1 \tag{10}$$

For a given end condition, only two of the above equations are necessary to define the boundary conditions. Equations (**7**) to (**10**) can be expressed in matrix form as

$$\begin{bmatrix} Q_1 \\ M_1 \\ Y_1 \\ \theta_1 \end{bmatrix} = \begin{bmatrix} 1 & 0 & K_1 & 0 \\ 0 & 1 & 0 & -R_1 \\ \delta_1 & 0 & 1 & 0 \\ 0 & -\sigma_1 & 0 & 1 \end{bmatrix} \begin{bmatrix} Q_1 \\ M_1 \\ Y_1 \\ \theta_1 \end{bmatrix} = [\bar{E}_1] \begin{bmatrix} Q_1 \\ M_1 \\ Y_1 \\ \theta_1 \end{bmatrix} \quad \text{or} \quad \{\bar{Z}_1\} = [\bar{E}_1]\{\bar{Z}_1\} \tag{11}$$

In the matrix $\bar{E}_1$, only two columns are necessary, as required by the end conditions. The remaining columns are zero. A free end requires the last two columns, while a fixed end requires the first two columns. For all other cases, the two columns may be selected as is appropriate.

The boundary conditions for the right end of the beam can be expressed as

$$[\bar{E}_m]\{Z_m\} = 0 \tag{12}$$

A free end requires the first two rows; a fixed end, the last two rows.

From Eqs. (**6**), (**11**), and (**12**),

$$[\bar{E}_m][\bar{A}][\bar{E}_1]\{Z_1\} = \{0\} \tag{13}$$

Since $\bar{E}_m$ contains only two non-zero rows and $\bar{E}_1$ contains only two non-zero columns, Eq. (**13**) is a system of two linear homogeneous equations containing two unknowns.

For a non-trivial solution, the determinant of the coefficients must be zero. The coefficients are functions of the circular frequency ω.

Having determined the desired natural frequencies, all values of shear, moment, lateral, and rotational deflections of the beam can be computed using Eq. (**5**).

NUCLEAR ROCKET PROPULSION

By W. Y. Jordan and R. F. Nixon

(See also pp. 9–158 and 11–112 *et seq.*)

References: Bussard and DeLauer, "Nuclear Rocket Propulsion," McGraw-Hill. Meghreblian and Holmes, "Reactor Analysis," McGraw-Hill. Glasstone and Sesonske, "Nuclear Reactor Engineering," Van Nostrand. Koelle, "Handbook of Aeronautical Engineering," McGraw-Hill.

The **major components** of a nuclear rocket engine are shown in Figs. 34*a* and 34*b*. The **feed system** forces the propellant through regenerative cooling passages in the nozzle, reflector, pressure shell, and shield into the reactor heat exchanger, where the propellant is heated and expanded through the rocket nozzle. The flow path of the propellant required to drive the turbine is shown in the Figures for bleed and topping

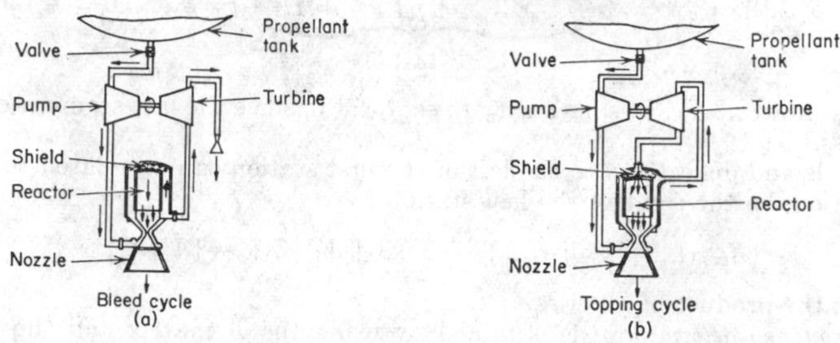

Fig. 34. Components of a nuclear rocket engine.

cycles. Liquid hydrogen is the best choice for the nuclear rocket's working fluid because its low molecular weight produces the highest exhaust velocity for a given nozzle-inlet temperature. The nuclear rocket engine is **started** by adjusting the reactor neutronic-control drums to increase neutron population. Propellant flow is initiated at a low reactor-power level and is increased in proportion to the increasing neutron population until the design steady-state reactor-power output is obtained. For **shutdown** of the engine, control drums are adjusted to poison the core and decrease the neutron population.

Nozzle Thermodynamics. If the nuclear reactor is operated in a temperature and pressure regime in which no appreciable hydrogen dissociation occurs, the following isentropic relationships yield good approximations of the rocket nozzle performance:

$$P/p = (T/t)^{\gamma/(\gamma-1)} = [1 + (\gamma - 1)M^2/2]^{\gamma/(\gamma-1)} \quad \textbf{(14)}$$
$$\dot{w}\sqrt{RT}/PA = M\sqrt{\gamma g}/[1 + (\gamma - 1)M^2/2]^{(\gamma+1)/2(\gamma-1)} \quad \textbf{(15)}$$
$$V = M\sqrt{\gamma g RT}/\sqrt{1 + (\gamma - 1)M^2/2} \quad \textbf{(16)}$$
$$A/A_* = (1/M)\{[1 + (\gamma - 1)M^2/2]/[(\gamma + 1)/2]\}^{(\gamma+1)/2(\gamma-1)} \quad \textbf{(17)}$$

where P = total pressure, p = static pressure, T = total temperature, t = static temperature, M = Mach number, γ = specific-heat ratio, $\dot{w}$ = flow rate, R = gas constant, g = acceleration due to gravity, V = velocity, A = flow area, and A_* = sonic-flow area. With the initial conditions in the chamber, the local conditions of state at any point in the nozzle plane can be determined. The **nozzle exhaust velocity** V_e, or velocity V at any plane, can be calculated from Eq. (**16**) and the appropriate local M, as determined from Eq. (**17**). The data in Figs. 35 to 37 can be used with good accuracy over the range of conditions shown. Nuclear rocket **nozzle thrust** is $F = \dot{w}V_e/g + (p_e - p_a)A_e$, and nozzle specific impulse is $I_s = F/\dot{w}$. Subscripts e and a refer to nozzle exit and ambient conditions. **Specific impulse** and **exhaust velocity** can be determined from Fig. 37 for a given chamber-temperature and nozzle-area ratio.

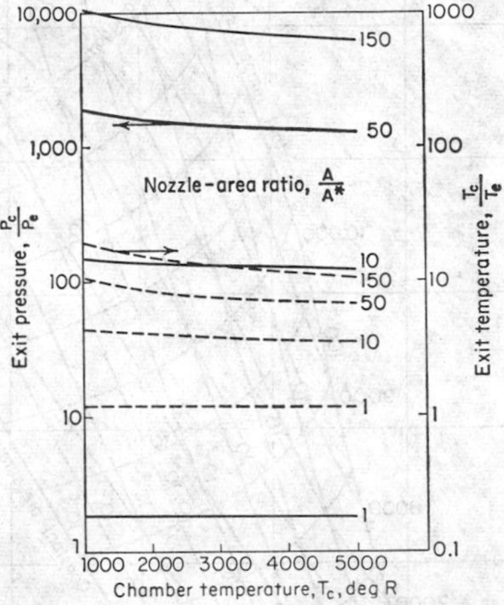

FIG. 35. Nozzle temperature and pressure ratios. Subscript c refers to chamber or stagnation conditions; subscript e to nozzle exit conditions.

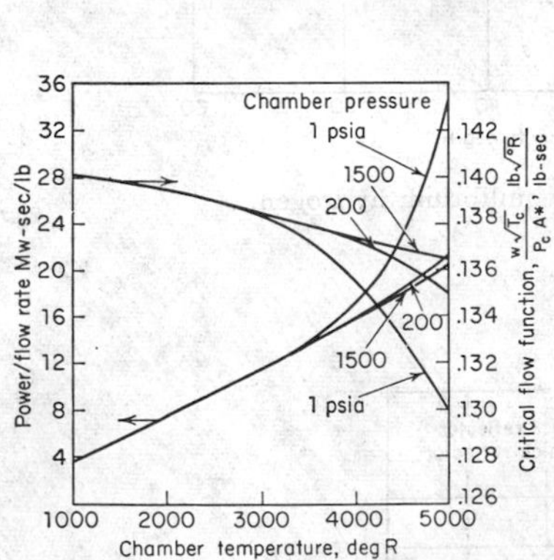

FIG. 36. Flow parameters, reactor and nozzle.

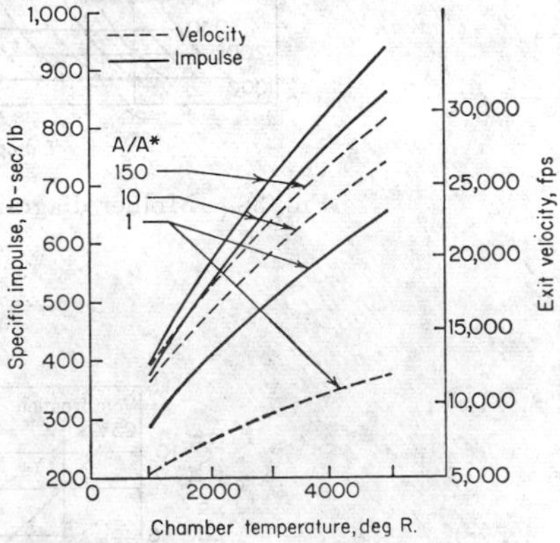

FIG. 37. Nozzle specific impulse and exit velocity.

Hydrogen Properties. (See Fig. 38 for an enthalpy-entropy (Mollier) diagram.) Ionization effects were not considered in the calculations. From the chart, the temperature and pressure regime in which molecular dissociation of hydrogen should be considered can be determined. The change in enthalpy during an isentropic expansion process can be read from the chart for given nozzle inlet and exit conditions. In actual practice, the dissociation and recombination of hydrogen requires a finite reaction time which does not result in an exact chemical equilibrium process. The "real" case would fall somewhere between the "frozen-flow" case and the "equilibrium" case.

Turbomachinery. A turbopump is required for the propellant feed system because of the high-pressure drop across the engine, the high-pressure level for high-power-

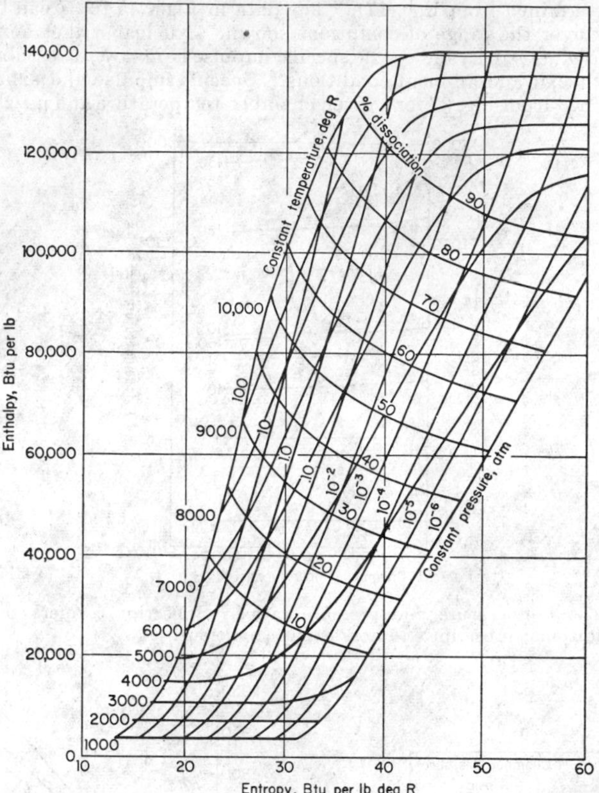

Fig. 38. Mollier diagram for equilibrium hydrogen.

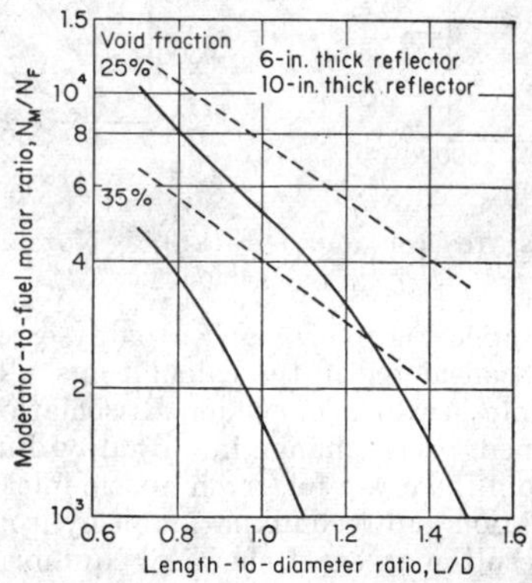

Fig. 39. Fuel requirements for a cylindrical core. Carbon moderator; beryllium reflector; enriched U-235; $K_{eff} = 1.05$; length = 50 in.; three-energy-group calculation.

density propulsion reactors, and long engine operating time. The turbopump is driven by a gas turbine, using gas extracted from the system, as shown in Fig. 34. (See also Secs. 9 and 14.)

Reactor Analysis. Steady-state reactor thermal power, in megawatts, is determined by the relation $P_r = K\dot{w}(h_{\text{out}} - h_{\text{in}})$. The conversion factor from Btu per second to megawatts is K, which is equal to 1.055×10^{-3}; $\dot{w}$ and h are core flow rate and enthalpy, respectively (Fig. 38). Reactor power can be determined from the reactor-power parameter $P_r/\dot{w}$ (Fig. 36).

The reactor is a high-power-density, self-energizing heat exchanger which elevates the temperature of the hydrogen propellant to the limit of component materials. Rigorous computations are necessary to obtain realistic solutions to the neutronic and thermodynamic equations for critical assembly data, uranium loadings, moderator and other material compositions, heat-transfer rates, and temperature and pressure gradients. See Fig. 39 for **critical loading data,** as a function of geometry.

A unique problem associated with the reuse or cyclic operation of nuclear rockets is the requirement to cool the engine after each power phase in order to prevent self-destruction from reactor **afterheating.** The nuclei of the fissionable material continue to give off high-energy particles, primarily delayed neutrons, gamma rays, and beta particles, after the fissioning process has been suppressed during engine shutdown. The quantity of heat produced after shutdown is proportional to the operating-power level and the duration of operation, while the amount of propellant required for aftercooling is dependent upon the heat produced, the average allowable temperature of critical engine components, and the nuclear and thermal radiative heat transfer away from the engine.

Space-vehicle Applications. The gamma and neutron radiation environment emitted from a nuclear rocket requires (1) reactor shielding to attenuate the energy deposition in structure, propellant, and components and to obtain a certain separation distance and interface geometry between stage and engine; (2) careful selection of radiation-insensitive materials for critical components; (3) biological shielding for manned flight; and (4) special flight safety measures. The nuclear rocket is characterized by a high engine weight per pound of thrust produced, large over-all engine dimensions, and bulky, low-density hydrogen tanks. The problems associated with nuclear space vehicles, however, must be weighed against the advantages derived from the very high nuclear performance potential. The high system specific impulse produces an increasingly advantageous pay-load fraction as the mission velocity requirement increases.

PIPELINE TRANSMISSION

BY

George H. Ewing

(With the assistance of Roland E. Moore)

REFERENCES: AGA, "Gas Facts." Huntington, "Natural Gas and Gasoline," McGraw-Hill. Leeston, Crichton, and Jacobs, "The Dynamic Natural Gas Industry," University of Oklahoma Press. Lester, "Hydraulics for Pipeliners," Oildom. Bell, "Petroleum Transportation Handbook," McGraw-Hill. Fuels, *Mineral Yearbook*, Vol. II, Bureau of Mines. "The Transportation of Solids in Steel Pipelines," Colorado School of Mines Research Foundation, Inc. Ellis, Redberger, and Bolt, Transporting Solids by Pipe Line, *Ind. and Eng. Chemistry*, Aug., 1963. Wasp, Regan, Withers, Cook, and Clancey, Cross Country Coal Pipe Line Hydraulics, *Pipe Line News*, July, 1963.

NATURAL GAS

General. According to AGA estimates for 1962, approximately 90 percent of the U.S. natural-gas reserves occur in five states (Tex., La., Okla., New Mex., and Kan.) and only about 40 percent of the total natural gas produced there is consumed within these states. In 1950, there were 314,000 miles of gas pipelines in this country, and by 1962, with natural gas supplying 25 percent of the nation's energy requirements, this mileage had increased to 664,000.

Transmission pipelines move the gas from the producing regions to consuming areas throughout the country. The trend for transmission lines has been toward the use of larger pipe diameters and pipe steel of greater tensile strength. Transmission lines of 36-in. diameter and pipe steel of 60,000-psi minimum specified yield are now in general use. Larger-diameter pipe, along with increasing pressure capabilities and growing pipeline mileage, brought forth a considerable rise in prime-mover and compressor requirements. Natural-gas pipelines in the United States have experienced an increase from about 4 million installed horsepower in 1953 to over 7 million by the end of 1962.

Gas engines, gas turbines, and electric motors are most generally employed as **prime movers on gas pipelines.** The gas engines generally drive reciprocating compressors, while gas turbines and electric-motor drivers are usually connected to centrifugal compressors. The industry trend is toward the use of larger compressor units because of inherent economic advantages. Prime movers in general use have increased in size from the early 1950s to the early 1960s as follows: gas engines from 2,500 to 5,500 hp, gas turbines from 5,000 to 13,000 hp, and electric-motor drives from 2,500 to 20,000 hp. Modified aircraft-type jet engines are now being employed as prime movers driving centrifugal compressors.

Much progress has been made in **automated operations** of all types of pipelines. Valves, measuring and regulating stations, and other facilities are operated remotely or automatically. Factory-packaged compressor-station assemblies most of which are highly automated, are now commonplace. Whole compressor stations with thousands of horsepower are operated unattended by the use of coded dispatching systems handled by high-speed communications.

Flow. From the thermodynamic-energy-balance equations for the flow of compressible fluids, Sec. 4, the general flow formula is derived and expressed in *B of M Monograph* 6 (1935) as

$$Q = K \frac{T_o}{P_o} \left[\frac{(P_1^2 - P_2^2)d^5}{GT_fLf} \right]^{1/2}$$

The gas industry has generally accepted the simplified form, known as the **Panhandle formula,**

$$Q = 435.87E\left(\frac{T_o}{P_o}\right)^{1.0788}\left(\frac{P_1 - P_2}{G^{0.8539}T_fL}\right)^{0.5394} d^{2.6182}$$

where d = I.D., in.; E = pipeline flow eff, dimensionless decimal fraction (design values of 0.88 to 0.94 are common); f = coef of friction, dimensionless; G = sp gr of

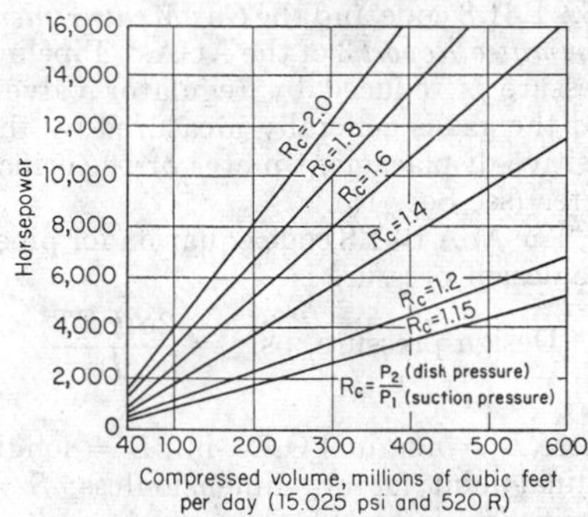

Fig. 1. Reciprocating-compressor horsepower graph. $R_c = P_2/P_1$ = discharge pressure, psia ÷ suction pressure, psia.

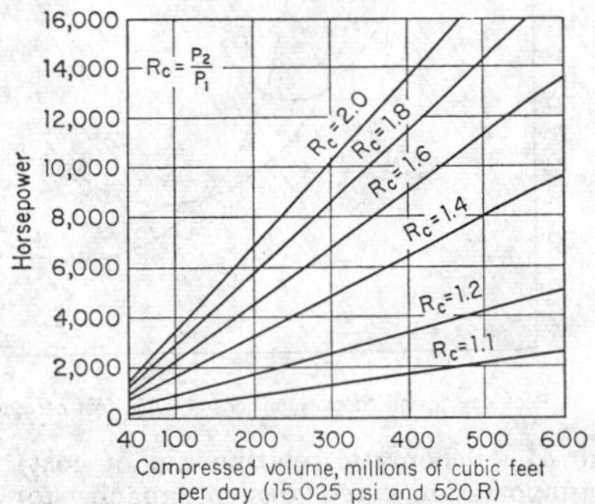

Fig. 2. Centrifugal-compressor horsepower graph. $R_c = P_2/P_1$ = discharge pressure, psia ÷ suction pressure, psia.

gas (air = 1.00); K = const; L = length of pipe, miles; P_o = pressure base, psia; P_1 = inlet pressure, psia; P_2 = outlet pressure, psia; Q = rate of flow, cu ft per day; T_o = temperature base, deg R; and T_f = avg flowing temperature, deg R.

This formula lends itself to rapid, accurate graphical solution, as described by Marvin, *Oil and Gas Jour.*, Sept. 20, 1954.

Compression. The theoretical horsepower requirements for a station compressing natural gas can be calculated by the polytropic compression formulas (see Sec. 4). The change of state that takes place in almost all reciprocating compressors is close to polytropic. Heat of compression is taken away by the jacket cooling and by radiation, and a small amount of heat is added by piston-ring friction. Compression by centrifugal compressors is even closer to polytropic.

For general design, the horsepower requirements for a station compressing natural gas with reciprocating compressors can be calculated as

$$\text{Reciprocating station horsepower} = HP\,Z_s\left(\frac{T_s}{520}\right)$$

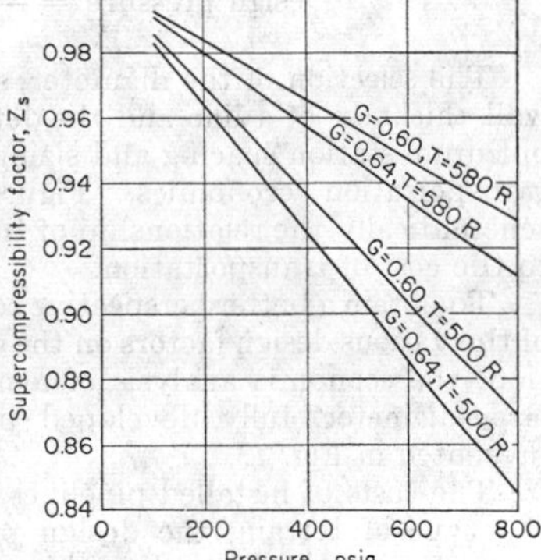

Fig. 3. Supercompressibility factor Z_s for natural gas. (Natural gas, 1 percent CO_2, 1 percent N_2.)

The value for HP can be taken from Fig. 1, a typical manufacturer's curve; T_s is suction temperature, deg R; and Z_s can be taken from Fig. 3.

Similarly, the horsepower requirements for a station compressing natural gas with centrifugal compressors can be calculated as

$$\text{Centrifugal station horsepower} = \frac{hp\,Z_s}{E_c}\left(\frac{T_s}{520}\right)$$

The value for hp can be taken from Fig. 2, a typical centrifugal horsepower curve; E_c

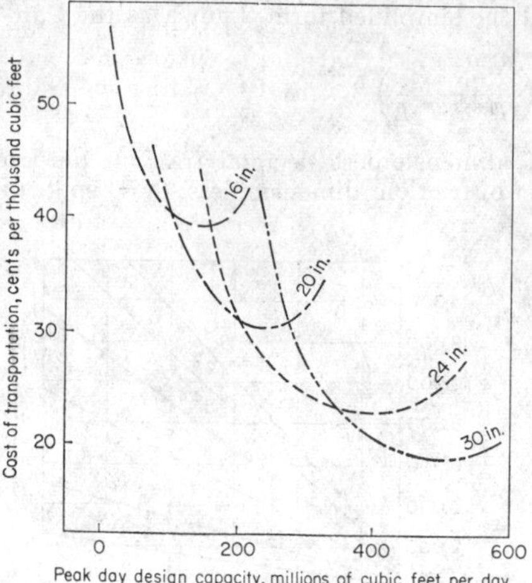

FIG. 4. Schematic relationship of cost of transportation versus design capacity for a given length of line with various pipeline diameters at equal design pressures.

is the centrifugal-compesssor shaft efficiency (design shaft efficiencies of 80 to 85 percent are common).

Design. The pipe and fittings for gas transmission lines are manufactured in accordance with the specifications of the API and are usually fabricated, installed, and operated in conformance with the ASA B31.8 code and the *Gas Measurement Committee Report* 3 of the AGA. Pipeline pressure is reduced by regulator valves, and the gas is generally measured by the positive-displacement meter or the orifice meter (see Sec. 16).

The ASA B31.8 code equation for pipeline design pressure is

$$\text{Design pressure, psig} = \frac{2StFET}{D}$$

where D = nominal O.D., in.; E = longitudinal joint factor, dimensionless; S = specified min yield strength, psi; t = nominal wall thickness, in.; T = temperature derating factor, deg F (applies above 250 F only); and F = factor based on population density in area through which the line passes, dimensionless.

For cross-country pipelines in which the population density is very low, the factor F is 0.72, and assuming seamless or electric-resistance-weld pipe with an E value of 1.00 and an operating temperature below 250F, the equation can be written as

$$\text{Design pressure} = \frac{1.44St}{D}$$

The selection of the diameter, steel strength, and wall thickness of a line and the determination of the optimum station spacing and sizing are based on the transportation economics. Figures 4 to 6 show schematically the relationship of these design factors to the cost of transportation.

To obtain a better perspective regarding the effect of the various design factors on the cost of transportation, the economic analysis of a new long-distance, large-diameter, fully developed pipeline system is presented in Fig. 7.

The costs of installed pipelines vary greatly with the type of terrain, the design pressure, the total length to be constructed, and many other factors. For general estimating purposes, a figure of \$4,000 per in. of O.D. can be used to obtain the approximate cost per mile of installed pipeline. In a like manner, compressor-station installed costs vary widely with the amount of horsepower to be installed, the location, and the construction and weather conditions. For rough estimating purposes, the installed cost of gas-turbine stations can be taken as \$200 to \$300 per installed hp; gas-engine stations, from \$275 to \$375; and electric-motor stations, from \$125 to \$200.

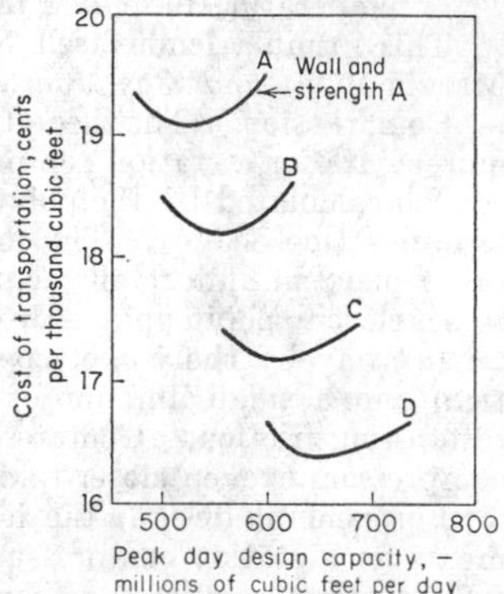

FIG. 5. Schematic relationship of cost of transportation versus pipeline steel strength and wall thickness. A = 30 in. × 0.312-in. WT × 52,000-psi min yield (779-psi operating pressure). B = 30 in. × 0.312-in. WT × 56,000-psi min yield (838-psi operating pressure). C = 30 in. × 0.375-in. WT × 52,000-psi min yield (935-psi operating pressure). D = 30 in. × 0.375-in. WT × 56,000-psi min yield (1,008-psi operating pressure).

After a pipeline system is constructed and fully utilized, expansion of delivery capacity can be accomplished by adding pipeline loops (installing segments of line parallel to the original line, with each loop connected at each end to the original line), by adding additional horsepower at compressor stations, or by adding loop and horsepower.

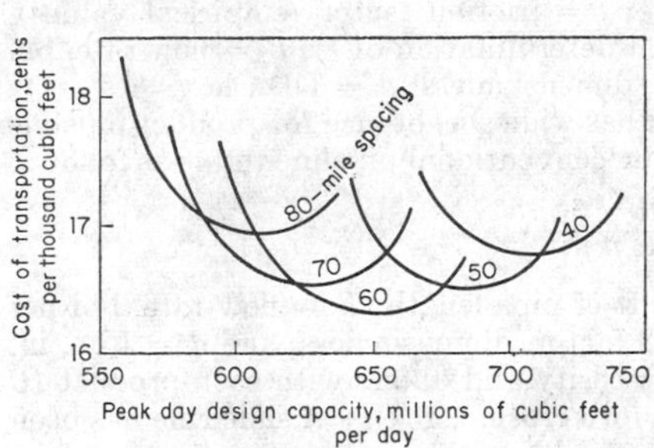

FIG. 6. Schematic relationship of cost of transportation versus design capacity for a given pipeline diameter and length, with various spacings of compressor stations.

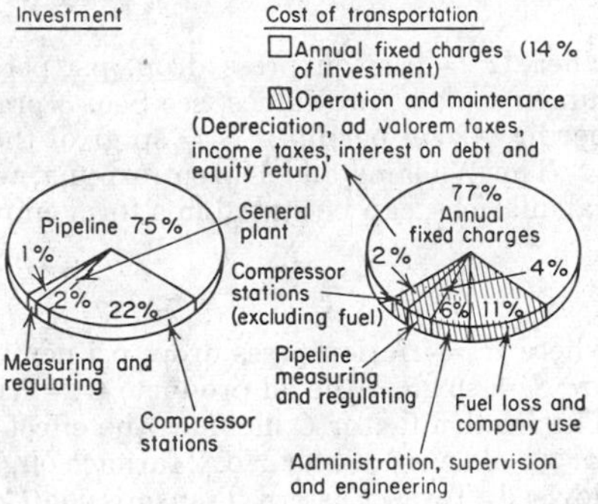

FIG. 7. Analysis of investment and cost of transportation.

CRUDE OIL AND OIL PRODUCTS

General. Approximately 75 percent of the U.S. liquid hydrocarbon reserves are situated in the five states of Tex., La., Okla., New Mex., and Kan. The markets which ultimately consume much of the oil products are remote from these five states. Oil transportation is in two successive operations: (1) the movement of the crude oil from the point of production to a refinery, and (2) the transportation of refined products to the consumer. About 75 percent of U.S. crude oil and 20 percent of the refined products are transported by pipeline, with the total oil trunk pipeline mileage exceeding 100,000 miles.

The industry trend for oil main-line design is toward larger pipe diameters and stronger pipe steels. The first transcontinental (Tex. to N. Car.) 36-in. diameter oil-products pipeline has recently been placed in operation.

Centrifugal pumps have been used extensively in recent years. Generally these units are of one- or two-stage design, with several units placed in series. This arrangement provides greater stability, efficiency, and flexibility than is obtained with multistage centrifugals installed in parallel. Reciprocating pumps are installed in parallel; *i.e.*, a common suction and a common discharge header are utilized by all pumps. There are instances where rotary, gear, and vane-type pumps have been employed to fulfill specific requirements (see Sec. 14).

Electric motors directly connected to centrifugal pumps have been widely employed because of their compactness, low initial cost, and ease of control. Slow-speed horizontal-type Diesel engines have been replaced by higher-speed vertical units, which are coupled directly to reciprocating pumps. Diesel engines generally require speed increasers to drive centrifugal pumps. Advantages are occasionally realized by the installation of crude-oil-burning engines, gas engines, or gas turbines.

Positive-displacement meters are in general use on product systems. Totalizers for multimeter installations and remote transmission of readings are becoming widely accepted. Greater application of meters with crude-oil-gathering facilities is being made as automatic-custody units are installed.

Flow. (See also Sec. 3.) The Darcy formula,

$$h_f = \frac{fLV^2}{D2g}$$

(where h_f = friction loss, ft; f = friction factor (empirical values), dimensionless; L = length of pipe, ft; D = I.D., ft; V = velocity of flow, fps; and g = 32.2 ft per sec²) is in general use by engineers making crude-oil pipeline calculations. The Darcy formula, when stated in a form utilizing conventional pipeline units, is

$$P = \frac{34.87fB^2S}{d^5}$$

where P = friction press drop, psi per mile; f = friction factor (empirical values), dimensionless (for values, see Sec. 3 practical determination of f); B = flow rate, bbl per hr (42 gal per bbl); S = sp gr of the oil, dimensionless; d = I.D., in.

The Williams and Hazen formula, which has wide acceptance for product pipeline calculations, can be stated in a form employing conventional pipeline terms as follows:

$$P = \frac{2340B^{1.852}S}{C^{1.852}d^{4.870}}$$

where P = friction press drop, psi per 1,000 ft of pipe length; B = flow rate, bbl per hr; S = sp gr of the oil product; C = friction factor, dimensionless; and d = I.D., in. The friction factor C includes the effect of viscosity and differs with each product (C for gasoline is 150; for No. 2 furnace oil, 130; for kerosine, 134). A slide rule has been devised (Texas Eastern Transmission Corp.) which provides a scale to adjust the friction factor C for viscosity.

The brake horsepower for pumping oil is $RSh/3960E$ or $BP/2450E$, where R = flow rate, gpm; S = sp gr of the oil; h = pump head, ft; E = pump eff, decimal fraction; B = flow rate, bbl per hr; and P = pump differential pressure, psi.

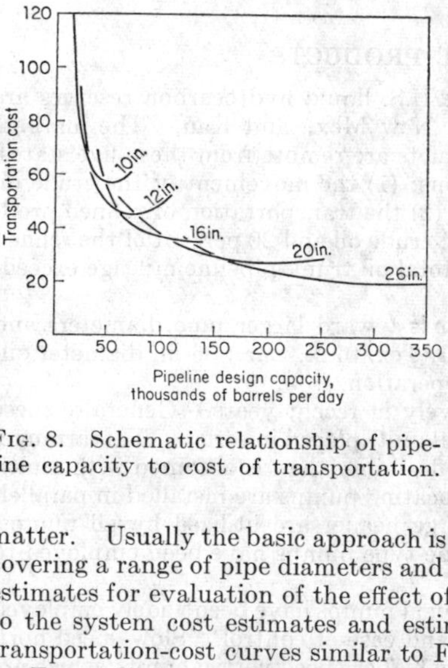

Design. The pipe and fittings for oil transmission lines are manufactured in accordance with the specifications of the API and are fabricated, installed, and operated in conformance with the ASA B31.1 and B31.4 codes for pressure piping. Many factors influence the working pressure of an oil line, and the ASA code serves as a national authority in these matters. A study of the hydraulic gradient, land profile, and static-head conditions is made in conjunction with the selection of the main-line pipe.

Fig. 8. Schematic relationship of pipeline capacity to cost of transportation.

Determining the pipe size and station spacing to transport a given oil or oil product at a specified rate of flow and provide the lowest cost of transportation is a complex matter. Usually the basic approach is to prepare (1) a series of pipeline cost estimates covering a range of pipe diameters and wall thicknesses, and (2) a series of station cost estimates for evaluation of the effect of station spacing. By applying capital charges to the system cost estimates and estimating the system operating costs, a series of transportation-cost curves similar to Fig. 8 can be drawn.

For preliminary purposes, an estimate of \$4,000 per in. of O.D., can be used to obtain the cost per mile of installed trunk pipeline. The tabulation of pump-station investment costs for automated electric-motor–centrifugal-type installations presented in Table 1 can be used for preliminary evaluations.

Table 1

Pump-station installed horsepower, total	Cost per installed horsepower
250–500	\$275–\$300
500–750	\$200–\$225
750–1,000	\$160–\$180
1,000–2,000	\$110–\$135
Above 2,000	\$100

Careful design and good operating practice must be followed to minimize contamination due to interface mixing in oil-product pipelines. When the throughput capacity of an oil line becomes fully utilized, additional capacity can be obtained by installing a parallel pipeline or a partial-loop line. A partial loop is a parallel line which runs for only part of the distance between stations. In the case of product lines, careful attention must be paid to the design of the facilities where the loop line is tied into the original pipeline to prevent commingling of products.

SOLIDS

General. Some of the **solids being transported** in slurry form considerable distances by pipeline are coal, coal refuse, gilsonite, phosphate rock, tin ore, nickel ore, copper ore, gold ore, kaolin, limestone, clay, borax, sand, and gravel. **Solids pipelines differ** from pipelines for oil, gas, and other true fluids in that the product to be transported must be designed and prepared for pipeline transportation.

Materials must satisfy the following conditions to be transported by long-distance pipelines: (1) the largest particle size must be limited to that which can readily pass through commercially available pumps, pipes, and other equipment; (2) solids must mix and separate easily from the carrying fluids; (3) material degradation must be negligible or beneficial to pipelining and utilization; (4) material must not react with the carrying fluid or become contaminated in the pipeline; (5) solids-liquid mixture must not be excessively corrosive to pipe, pumps, and equipment; (6) solids must not be so abrasive as to cause excessive wear at carrying velocities.

Coal Slurry. Uncleaned coal can be transported by pipeline, but a more stable and economic long-distance pipeline operation can be achieved with clean coal. The use of clean coal allows a variety of supply sources, produces a slurry with a lower, more uniform friction-head loss, reduces the pipe-wall wear, and increases the system capacity. Cleaning pipeline coal costs about 20 percent less than cleaning coals for other forms of transportation since drying can be eliminated after the cleaning operation. Coal-slurry preparation consists of reducing clean coal to the proper particle size and size-range distribution and mixing the particles with water in the desired concentration. A typical size-range distribution (size consist) for a coal slurry designed for 57 percent concentration (percentage of coal by weight) is given by the following screen analysis:[1]

Mesh (Tyler wet screen)	8	14	28	48	100	200	325	−325
Percent solids by weight	0.2	5.0	20.0	18.0	13.5	6.0	6.2	30.0

The cost of slurry preparation is only slightly affected by changes in concentration or size consist but is materially affected by plant capacity. For example, preparation-plant operating costs per ton of coal are nearly twice as high for a plant with a capacity of 1 million tons per year as for a plant of 4 million tons per year.

The normal slurry-preparation-plant practice is to hold the concentration within 1 percent of design to provide a slurry with a uniform pressure drop. Different slurry designs have been used, ranging from 45 to 58 percent concentration.

Optimum characteristics for a slurry are (1) maximum concentration, (2) low rate of settling, and (3) minimum friction-head loss. Variables which can be manipulated to control and optimize slurry design are particle shape, size distribution, concentration, and ash content.

Economics and Design. Because of the many slurry variations, there is no single formula available by which the friction-head loss can be readily determined for all slurry applications. A general approach is described by Wasp, Regan, Withers, Cook, and Clancey (Cross Country Coal Pipeline Hydraulics, *Pipeline News*, **7,** 1963, p. 20), giving calculation methods which have been developed for predicting slurry pressure drops. The described methods are quite accurate and can be used for preliminary design. Slurry hydraulics should be verified in pilot plant operations before constructing a full-scale long-distance pipeline.

[1] See Coal-and-Water Slurry Burned As Delivered by Pipeline, *Electrical World*, Nov. 20, 1961.

Slurry velocities are generally limited to a minimum velocity to prevent solids from settling to the bottom of the pipe and a maximum velocity to prevent excessive friction-head loss and pipe-wall wear. These velocity limitations and the throughput volume determine the diameter of the main-line pipe. The relationship of volume and velocity to the pipe diameter is expressed as I.D. $= 0.6392\sqrt{\text{gpm}/V}$, where the I.D. is in inches, gpm is the volume rate of slurry flow, and V is flow velocity, fps.

Pipe-wall thickness in inches is computed by the modified Barlow formula as $[(PD/2SF) + tc]/tm$, where P = maximum pressure, psi; D = pipe O.D., in.; S = minimum yield strength of the pipe, psi; F = a safety factor; tm = pipe mill tolerance, usually 0.875; and tc = internal erosion/corrosion allowances, in., for the life of the system. The internal metal loss results from the erosion of corrosion products from the pipe wall and thus can be controlled with chemical inhibitors and velocity control. This metal loss occurs in all pipeline steels and, according to Swan, Bomberger, and Barthauer, Corrosion Control Achieved on Coal Slurry Pipeline, *Materials Protection*, **9,** 1963, p. 26, ". . . can be controlled to a level of less than three mils per year with the addition of sufficient inhibitors." A minimum pipe wall of 0.250 in. is often used to provide mechanical strength for large lines even where pressures and wear permit the use of a thinner wall. Coal pipelines employ a graduated wall thickness to meet the demands of the hydraulic gradient which saves pipe costs.

Pump-station hydraulic horsepower is calculated as $(P_d - P_s)$ gpm/1716, where $(P_d - P_s)$ = pressure rise across the station, psi; gpm = maximum flow rate through

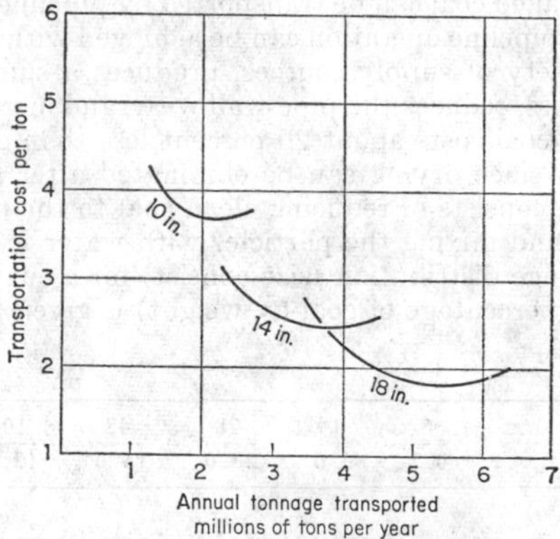

FIG. 9. System transportation-cost comparison for various main-line pipe sizes.

the station; and 1716 is a const, gal per ft in.[2] Stations employ positive-displacement reciprocating pumps of the type used for oil-field mud pumps (see Sec. 14), as they attain high pressures with low slurry velocities. This allows fewer stations and lower over-all costs than with centrifugal pumps. Stations are located where the friction-head loss and the effects of terrain have reduced the pressure head to 100 ft.

The annual tonnage **throughput** for any diameter line can be varied within the velocity limits or by intermittent operation near the low velocity limit. The optimum main-line size for a high-load-factor system is found by comparing the cost of transportation for a series of pipe sizes as in Fig. 9.

When a main-line size is selected, the **cost of transportation** for that line size at various rates of throughput is weighed against the projected system growth and compared with other line sizes to determine the size which gives the best over-all system economics. Coal pipelines cannot be expanded by line looping because of the velocity limitations. Some expansion can be attained by oversizing the line and operating it intermittently near the minimum velocity in the earlier years of life. The effect of system capacity on the cost of transportation per ton-mile and on the system investment cost is illustrated in Fig. 10.

The **cost of utilizing pipeline coal** includes (1) a cost of approximately 36 cents per ton to dewater it to about 17 percent moisture by centrifuge (see Hindenland, The Burning Question, *Coal Utilization*, Aug., 1962, or (2) an efficiency loss of about 4.5 percent when burned directly at 70 percent concentration (see Kelcec, Olivadoti, and

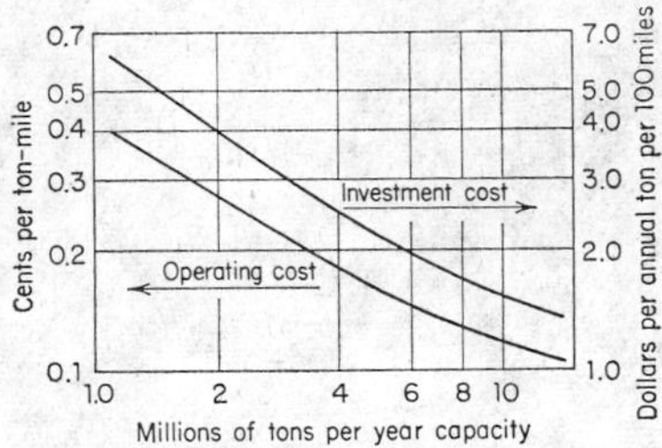

FIG. 10. Investment and operating costs of coal-slurry pipelines of various capacities. Basis: short tons of coal at 3 percent surface moisture; operating factor 90 percent. (From Reichl and Thagard, *National Power Conference Paper CPA* 62-5113, Sept., 1962.)

Duzy, Coal Slurry Firing at Werner Station, *ASME Paper* 62-PWR-3). A savings in new-plant investment of 5 percent or more can be realized at power stations by eliminating the usual coal-handling equipment when supplied by pipeline coal. Operating costs of conventional coal-handling equipment at either a new or an old plant can also be eliminated.

SECTION 12

BUILDING CONSTRUCTION AND EQUIPMENT

BY

JOHN R. IMMER, President, Work Saving International, Washington, D.C.

JOHN A. BLUME, Consulting Civil and Structural Engineer, San Francisco.

JOSEPH P. NICOLETTI, Vice President, John A. Blume and Associates, San Francisco.

CLYDE E. KESLER, Professor of Theoretical and Applied Mechanics and of Civil Engineering, University of Illinois.

JOHN O'KEEFE, Chief Mechanical and Electrical Engineer, Praeger-Kavanagh-Waterbury, Engineers-Architects, New York.

J. K. WHITTEKER, Specification Writer Praeger-Kavanagh-Waterbury, Engineers-Architects, New York.

RAYMOND J. RICE, Consulting Engineer, New York.

BENSON CARLIN, Director of Research and Development, Air-Shields, Inc., Hatboro, Pa.

RALPH R. MEIGS, Vice President and Manager, Loss Prevention Department, Liberty Mutual Insurance Company.

STEPHEN F. KIMBALL, General Liability Service, Loss Prevention Department, Liberty Mutual Insurance Company.

ARTHUR L. BROWN, Consultant in Fire Protection, Brookline, Mass.

CONTENTS

INDUSTRIAL PLANTS

BY

John R. Immer

REFERENCES: Muther, "Practical Plant Layout," McGraw-Hill. Immer, "Materials Handling," McGraw-Hill. "The Administrative Building Code (and Amendments) of the City of New York," Dept. of Housing and Buildings. "Building Code," Building Officials Conference of America.

GENERAL PLANNING OF INDUSTRIAL PLANTS

Top-management decisions relative to the planning of new industrial plants or a major addition to an existing plant require a study of the present and future manufacturing requirements of the company, its financial position, general economic conditions and the condition of the capital market, and a wide range of general policy matters affecting the most fundamental aspects of its operations. This planning should be preceded by detailed studies of manufacturing costs under various methods and processes, of equipment requirements, of various methods of handling materials, and of other considerations which affect these costs.

Basic data concerning the major factors must be assembled and coordinated. Preliminary comparative estimates of investment costs, maintenance costs, and operating costs for more than one desirable design should be prepared. Finally, all these data must be presented to top management in such form that the most important considerations will be noted first with appropriate supporting data available as needed. Cost summaries, artists' drawings, scale models, and flow charts should be utilized.

A **construction progress chart** should be prepared showing the sequence and time required for each major item of construction and for the installation of principal equipment. This progress chart must take into account the time required to prepare detail plans and specifications; to purchase, fabricate, and deliver major items of construction materials and process equipment; and to do the preliminary operation and make any necessary adjustment; the chart should be arranged to correlate and integrate each element of design and construction into an orderly sequence leading to a definite date for placing the plant in commercial operation. **Schedules** should then be prepared showing the sequence and date on which all drawings, structural, mechanical, and electrical, must be completed, specifications written, and contracts placed for the required materials and equipment, so that these elements may be fabricated and delivered to meet the requirements of the construction progress chart. Computerized analyses such as the "critical path method" should be considered to shorten total time (see p. 17-6). A complete cost estimate, covering all items required to complete the project, should be made as soon as the progress of the actual design will permit.

Factors Determining the General Location of a New Plant

Geographical distribution of present and potential sales and cost of transporting **finished products** must be compared with cost of transporting **raw materials** and components. **Labor** cost and supply, skilled and unskilled, and need of inducements to engineers and scientists may require an urban location. Some industries have special **power** requirements as to cost and availability. State and local **taxes** vary considerably from one state to another. Some processes require large quantities of water, sometimes with a particular chemical content, while others have special problems of disposal of waste products. Factors which **attract employees** to an area must be considered.

Existing communities, educational opportunities, recreational areas, mild climate, and convenience to plant are important.

Factors Controlling Selection of Site

Size of site must be adequate for present and future requirements and land values should be in relation to justifiable costs. The effect of **hazardous** or **objectionable features** of plant operations on surrounding countryside must be considered, and, conversely, the site must be of sufficient size to afford reasonable protection against objectionable features of future industrial neighbors. **Shipping facilities** and suitable rates, including rail, water, and truck, for raw materials and finished products are often important factors. **Public transportation** for employees or parking lots or both must be available. Provision for **disposal of plant waste** is becoming increasingly important in view of legislative trends. Do **zoning codes** permit all types of processing involved in operations of proposed plant? **Building code** requirements as to construction and setbacks may affect layout and cost of buildings.

Topography of the site, as regards clearing, leveling, drainage, and flood conditions, is especially important for large single-story plants. **Foundation conditions** should be investigated and, generally, one or more deep borings made before a site is purchased; unsuspected soft strata at considerable depths below the ground surface may add materially to the cost of adequate foundations, or if not detected and provided for, may cause serious damage from settlement of the completed plant. Special precautions must be taken if **large presses** are planned in the layout. Various **public services,** such as supplies of potable and process water, light and power, gas, and sewers must also be checked for availability.

Power may be either purchased or generated; studies based on present and expected future demand should determine the more economical procedure. **Process steam and heating requirements** have an important effect on this decision. In case of generated power, interconnection with public utilities for emergency service should be investigated. It is sometimes possible to sell excess power to public utilities in cases where steam requirements permit economical generation of power in excess of plant demand.

PROCESSING AND LAYOUT

Determine Process and Space Requirements

Determine the output required initially and at various stages of expansion for which space must be provided. Determine the specific processes to be employed and the specific operations which will be required. State these **space requirements** in broad terms, as for production centers, cost centers, or major manufacturing departments. Figure 1 shows the relationship of these departments and the way in which materials-in-process flow through the plant. Summary of area requirements will provide total space requirements for plant.

Special processes should be noted. Large machines with special foundation requirements should be indicated. Processes with objectionable fumes or noises should be segregated. Mezzanines and upper floors may be utilized for processes involving small and lightweight machines and for storage and assembly areas. Railroad requirements vary as to loadings, car-door height of loading docks, minimum radius of curvature, overhead clearance, and clearance to buildings and canopies.

Flow of Materials

Flow of material through the plant in a straight line and with a minimum of backtracking and recrossing of lines is desirable. The basic lines of flow may be a straight line, with the raw materials entering at one end of the plant and the finished product leaving at the other end, or they may be U shaped, with both receiving and shipping departments at the same end of the plant. More complicated processes may require modification of these basic forms (see Figs. 2 and 3).

Flow diagrams establish the relationship of processes and working areas. They are of two basic types: (1) those employing **continuous** operations, such as paper mills and sugar refineries; (2) those employing **intermittent** operations, such as the manufacture and assembly of parts. As the layout of the former type is determined by the process,

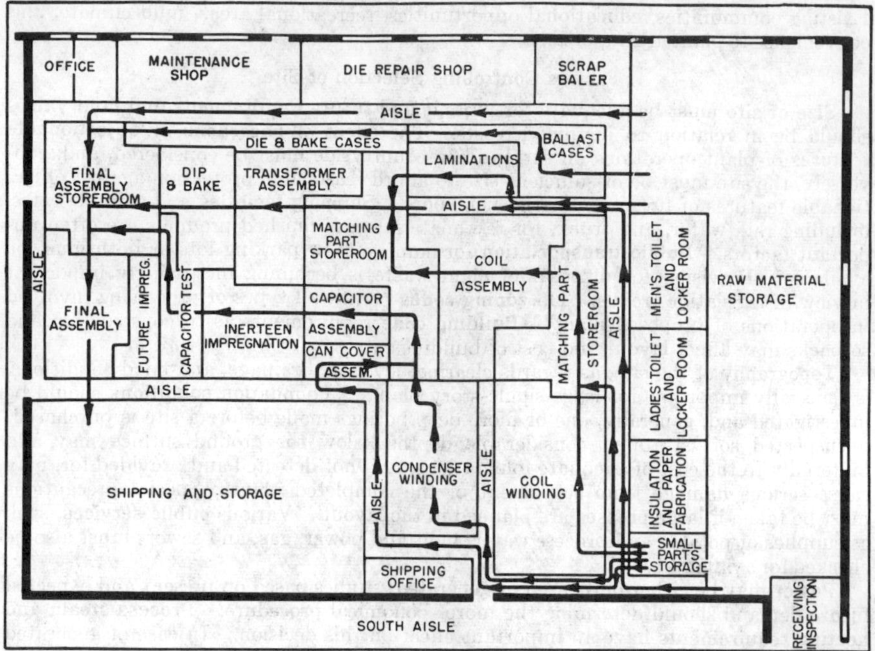

FIG. 1. Diagram of preliminary area allocation showing flow of materials.

they are often referred to as "process" industries. Most manufacturing plants involve the intermittent type in which the "flow" of materials is more difficult to establish. Flow diagram of operations in a foundry is shown in Fig. 4.

Lines of flow of materials are shown on layouts, as in Fig. 1, for the flow of materials through various departments. The layout of the machine shop in Fig. 5 shows the flow of materials from the machines to inspection and to finish stores.

Operation process charts help to visualize the relationship of numerous assembly operations in a complicated process by using standard symbols. The flow process chart uses the same symbols but includes more detail as to movement and delay of materials in process.

Materials Handling

(See also Sec. 10)

Materials-handling equipment must be selected to move materials into and out of machines, from one operation to the next, and from one department to another. In

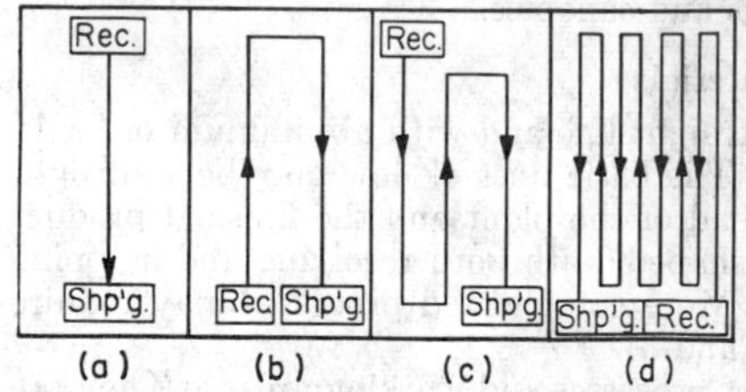

FIG. 2. Patterns of production lines: (*a*) straight-line; (*b*) U shape; (*c*) S shape; (*d*) convoluted.

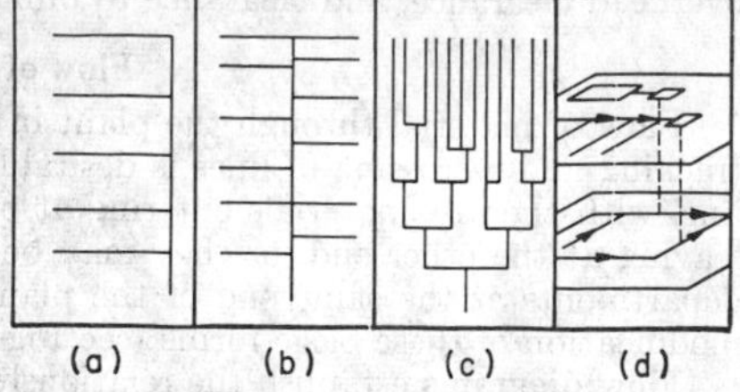

FIG. 3. Patterns of assembly lines: (*a*) comb; (*b*) tree; (*c*) dendritic; (*d*) overhead.

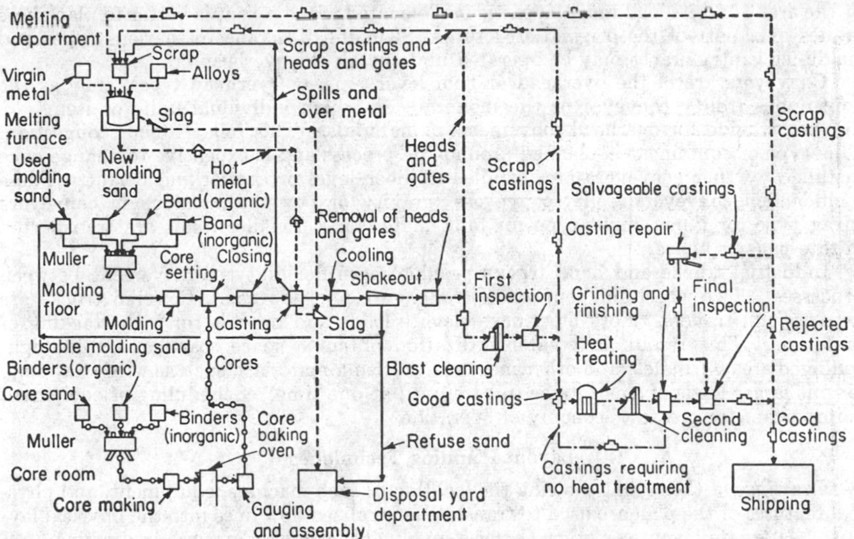

FIG. 4. Flow diagram of foundry operations.

many industries the cost of handling exceeds the cost of machine and assembly operations. Usually, several types of equipment must be used in the same plant, and it is important that all types of handling equipment used in a plant fit into the over-all plant handling system. In general, plants tend to rely on a system based predominantly on one type of equipment, such as conveyors or trucks, although other types will be used in connection with them.

Overhead traveling cranes are used for heavy lifts. They traverse production areas and provide for both horizontal and vertical movement of heavy items. As the weight

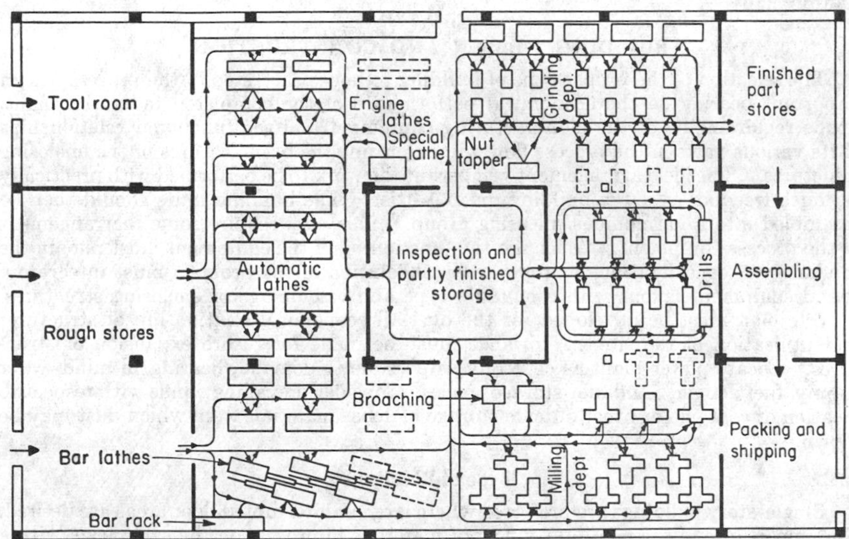

FIG. 5. Layout of a machine shop, providing for inspection of work after each operation, and showing the flow of materials in process.

of the crane and its load must be carried on elevated crane rails it is better to plan these cranes as a part of the original structure. Swinging jib cranes of various types and single-leg gantry cranes may be operated underneath the overhead crane.

Conveyors are of the overhead or floor-level types. **Overhead types,** such as the continuous trolley conveyor or the monorail, on which individual units or items are moved, provide for overhead movement of materials. This relieves floor congestion. This type of equipment is planned around the process and is expensive to change once installed. Other conveyors are installed at floor level or at working height. These include **belt conveyors, roller conveyors** (gravity or powered), and **chain conveyors** (drag type for items, flight type for bulk materials). Smaller items are transported in **tote pans** or **boxes.**

Industrial trucks and **hand trucks** provide more flexibility of movement between processes. Two-wheel and four-wheel trailers are non-powered. Powered trucks are used to pull trailers. Fork-lift trucks elevate loads and provide for high stacking of materials. This results in greater utilization of cubic space, particularly in high-ceilinged areas. **Pallets** and other means of unitizing materials, such as wire strapping, permit larger loads of small items to be moved at one time. **Scheduling of equipment** is important for greatest economy of operation.

Layout Planning Techniques

Drawings of the layout showing the location of each machine, equipment, and physical features of the plan are used to translate generalized flow lines into the physical layout. Alternate layouts or other changes involve considerable expense in drafting.

Templets are two-dimensional representations of machines and equipment which are easily moved around and changed. If negatives of templets are used the complete layout can be reproduced without any drafting. Scale commonly used is ¼ in. to the foot. Larger layouts may use a scale of ⅛ in. to the foot. Colored string or other lines may be used to indicate conveyors or to show flow of materials.

Scale models are used for better visualization of layout. Cost of models is often less than the cost of making drawings. Scale models provide the ultimate in visualization of layouts and frequently prevent serious mistakes in planning and location of machines and other facilities. Models vary from plain wooden blocks to cast-metal models complete to minute detail. Both templets and models are available commercially.

BUILDING DESIGN AND CONSTRUCTION

The selection of the proper type of building to house each step in the process has an important bearing on the economical performance of the completed industrial plant. **Space requirements** of the manufacturing equipment and the **functional relationships** of its various parts in the process flow will determine the basic features of the enclosing structures. The ideal arrangement will permit the work to be performed with practically as much freedom as if the building did not exist. The building units should then be assembled into a harmonious, pleasing group. This may require some rearrangement of the process equipment. Although the functioning of the equipment must remain the fundamental consideration, a proper over-all solution of the problem must integrate a sound equipment layout with a suitable type and assemblage of enclosing structures.

Site plan must be developed for the over-all economical relationship of structures and utilization of the site. Allowance must be made for future expansion of structures. Locate power plant as centrally as possible to demand, bearing in mind water supply, fuel delivery, and fuel storage space. Consider prevailing winds with respect to location of coal pile or other outside storage of loose materials from which dust may be blown.

Type of Buildings

Single-story buildings are preferred where large uninterrupted floor areas are desired. The importance of the continuous flow of materials in process on the same level with a minimum of obstruction favors single-story construction even in areas of high land value. Long-span construction can be adopted at reasonable cost thus providing working spaces with a minimum of columns and, by means of monitors of various types, skylights, and ventilators, afford overhead light and ventilation. One-story structures are well adapted to processes requiring crane runways. In determining the spacing of columns, a longitudinal span of 20 to 25 ft provides an economical purlin design for most lightweight roof construction. For the transverse span, the advantage to the process layout of unobstructed floor space must be balanced against the cost of long-span girders or trusses. In some cases for buildings more than one bay in width, the use of longitudinal trusses to support one or more transverse trusses, thereby eliminating a number of interior columns, is warranted (see Figs. 10 and 11). The general trend is for wider spans and fewer columns in order to obtain greater flexibility of layout on the factory floor.

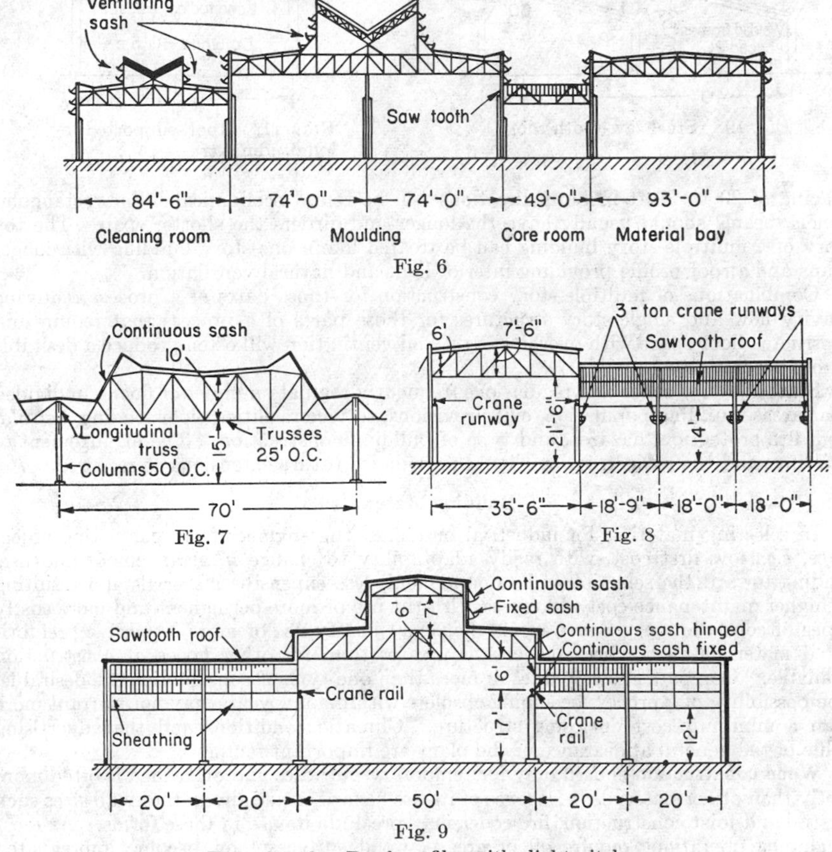

Figs. 6 to 9. Roof profiles with slight pitch.

A variety of **roof profiles** for one-story buildings, with many types of monitors, skylights, and ventilators, offer a wide choice to meet the requirements of a particular problem. The single longitudinal monitor elevated well above the working area does not provide good interior lighting especially for the longer spans, and this type of roof is not well adapted to buildings more than one bay in width. Figures 6 to 9 illustrate a few of the many combinations of roof profile available for roofs having only a slight pitch. Although these types of trusses because of their practically constant depth are somewhat more expensive for a given span and load than the familiar pitched roof they offer advantages in adapting the building outline to the requirements of the process layout and in providing good interior light. Extension is practicable in more than one direction in combinations such as those illustrated in Figs. 8 and 9. Figure 10 shows a typical saw-tooth roof profile, which with the face of the saw tooth toward the north affords excellent natural interior lighting over large areas.

Multiple-story buildings are advantageous where a gravity flow of the process is desired, where the site is restricted in area, or where high land values prevail. For the usual types of construction and for floor live loads up to about 200 lb per sq ft, a column

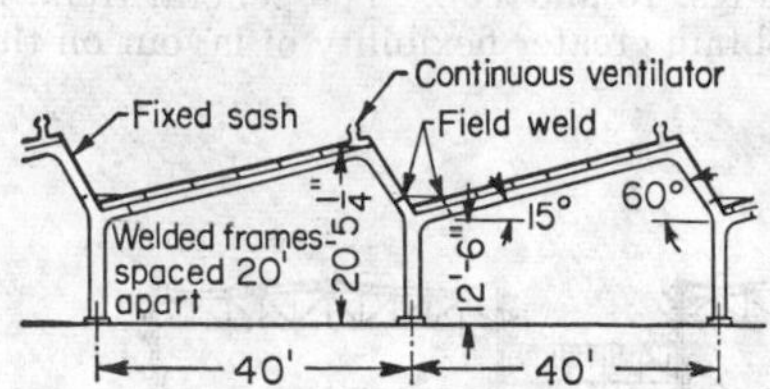

Fig. 10. Steel saw-tooth roof.

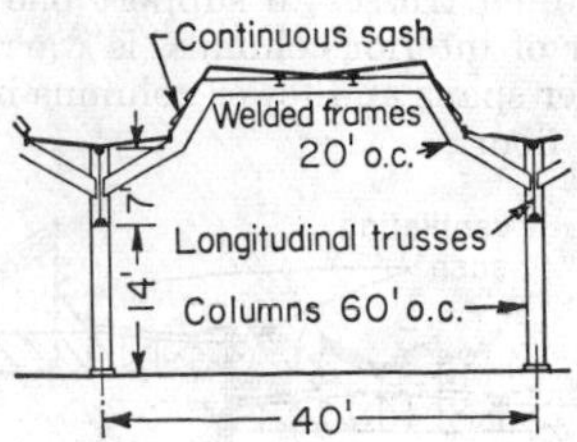

Fig. 11. Roof supported by longitudinal trusses.

spacing of 20 to 25 ft in both directions will be found economical. For rectangular panels, beams should usually have the longer and girders the shorter span. The top story of a multiple-story building can be treated like a one-story building with longer spans and a roof profile providing interior light and natural ventilation.

Combinations of multiple-story construction for those parts of a process requiring gravity flow and single-story structures for those parts of a process that require unobstructed floor space with overhead light and ventilation will often produce a desirable plant layout.

State and city codes and regulations frequently regulate number of floors, undivided floor areas, building population, exit provisions, service facilities, floor loading, ventilation, fire protection, hazards, and type of building construction. The arrangement of buildings and their construction should provide for future extensions as required.

Building Materials

In selecting materials for industrial buildings, the engineer faces conflicting objectives, *e.g.*, low first cost, with ready adaptability to change in arrangement and use, tending toward the selection of less permanent, less expensive materials and resulting in higher maintenance cost contrasted with the use of more permanent and more costly types of construction. **Speed of erection** may justify use of more expensive prefabricated materials even where the cost is greater than for other types of construction available. Comparative estimates of more than one type of construction are desirable. The possibility of a process becoming obsolete within a few years may not warrant more than a minimum-cost enclosing structure. Climatic conditions and the advertising value of the general appearance of the plant are important factors.

Wood construction is used only for temporary purposes and even then is often more costly than other materials. Because of its fire hazard, especially in the small sizes such as stud and joist construction, fire codes may preclude its use in these forms. As most machining operations require oil or grease, wood surfaces soon become impregnated and form a fire hazard. (See p. 12–194.)

The development of **laminated structural members** and of improved types of fastening devices has led to the use of wood for roof structures. Spans of 40 to 240 ft are used. These are made of **impregnated timbers,** which increase their fire resistance. They are also used in hangar construction, as they will not melt in flash fires, and they retain their structural strength long enough to permit evacuation of personnel and planes.

Steel-frame construction is used almost exclusively for long-span single-story structures, and is generally economical for short-span single- and multistory construction where fireproof structures are not required. Unprotected steel begins to lose its strength at about 700 F and may warp, twist, and fail in the event of a serious fire in the contents of a building. An adequate sprinkler system is desirable. Where steel structures must be fireproofed, reinforced concrete construction will generally be more economical except for long spans where steel framing, fireproofed with thin gunite or other light-weight material, may be lower in cost. Steel requires maintenance painting, the need for which depends on conditions of exposure (see p. 6–147).

Masonry construction is generally the most economical for single-story structures. Concrete block, with or without facing brick or other material, is constructed with supporting pillars built in at regular spaces to support roof girders. A waterproof surface can be provided by new silicon paints or by a plastered surface plain or sprayed with a quartz aggregate.

Precast concrete is used increasingly for structural members, walls, floors, and roofs. Structural sections are formed with conventional steel reinforcing, or wire or cable reinforcing, or may be prestressed or poststressed for additional strength and smaller sections. Units may be obtained commercially or cast at the site. In either case erection time is usually minimal.

Reinforced-concrete construction provides full fireproof construction. For approximately square panels and spans up to 25 ft, flat-slab construction is usually more economical than beam and girder construction, and its comparative economy increases with heavier live loads. Flat slabs are not well adapted to layouts requiring irregular column spacing or numerous floor openings after a building is completed. It is frequently desirable to provide inserts at regular intervals in all ceilings to allow for initial and future requirements in hanging piping, shafting, and the like. Concrete construction, because of its resistance to vibration, is especially adaptable to plants using high-speed machinery or having high floor-load requirements (see also p. 12–60).

Lift-slab construction is used for multistory construction. Floor slabs are poured at ground level, and after reaching the full strength of the poured concrete, slabs are elevated on supporting columns to the desired height by means of hydraulic jacks. Frequently, major items of mechanical equipment are loaded on the slab before it is elevated into place.

Walls may be constructed of metal panels (galvanized iron, steel, or aluminum); asbestos cement or cinder blocks; hollow clay tile, brick, concrete (poured-in-place, tilt-up, or precast), or stone. All the corrugated or thin panel materials can be erected quickly and are light in weight, but they require girt framing on the inside. Increased use of air conditioning in summer and desire to reduce heat loss in winter have resulted in an increased use of insulating materials. Clay tile of various kinds and new epoxy paints provide sanitary, easily cleaned interior surfaces where needed.

Windows may consist of factory-type sash built of rolled sections of steel or aluminum; wood windows; double-hung metal windows; glass-block windows; and other special construction, the cost increasing roughly in the order listed. Standard steel sash is usually the economical window for industrial buildings. Pivoted ventilators are awkward where shades or screens are required, but the use of projected ventilators at small increased cost avoids this difficulty. An entire side wall constructed of standard sash, located so as to run continuously past columns and floors, and glazed with steel plate at floor levels and glass elsewhere is frequently a low-first-cost construction. **Glass** may be rough, clear, or ribbed in various forms for light diffusion. Corrugated glass is frequently used for skylights and to some extent for certain types of windows. For large lights, as in skylights, it is less likely to crack from expansion and contraction than flat glass. Wired glass frequently justifies its added cost as protection against the hazard of falling broken glass, particularly for high side walls and windows in monitors over working spaces. It is generally desirable for the psychological effect on employees to provide one or more lights of clear glass at eye level in working spaces. In contrast to the low first cost of standard steel sash, consideration must be given to the maintenance cost of painting to protect the light metal sections. Glass-block windows provide excellent diffused light and relatively good insulation, which is particularly important where condensation is a factor, and they require no maintenance painting. **Translucent plastic panels** also admit light and can be obtained in various colors to diffuse glare.

Roofs having a pitch of 4 in. or more per foot can be economically constructed of corrugated materials, such as galvanized iron, zinc, asbestos-protected metal, and asbestos cement, the purlin span varying with the material selected but all light in weight and requiring no additional covering. Such roofs afford little insulation, and where conditions are such that condensation is likely to occur on the underside of the roof, an insulated roof deck is advisable. For roofs having a pitch less than 4 in. per ft, a membrane roof covering is desirable. The corrugated materials listed above can be used by applying insulating board over the corrugations as a base for membrane roofing, and this construction can also be used on the steeper pitches where insulation is desired. Flat interlocking steel sheets formed with ribs for strength and stiffness provide a lightweight deck on which membrane roofing is laid with or without insulation. For relatively flat pitches, lightweight precast concrete slabs, either flat or channel shaped, provide a low-cost fire-resistant deck. Wood plank, gypsum plank, precast concrete plank, and poured-in-place reinforced concrete, covered with membrane roofing, are suitable for either pitched or flat decks, and insulation can be applied when desired. As between the many types of roof decks available, the relative first cost depends not only on the erected cost of the material itself but also on its effect on the cost of the supporting framing, particularly in long-span construction. Proper selection, in a given case, can best be based on comparative estimates of the cost of the entire roof system, weighing also the maintenance cost, resistance to heat loss and condensation, light-reflecting qualities, fire resistance, appearance, and other similar factors. For **roof insulation,** fiber insulating boards, cork, and processed glass products are excellent, the latter usually being slightly higher in cost. For membrane roofing, a variety of good factory-finished composition roofings ready to lay are available at low cost, but in general this type of roofing will not have so long a life as roofing consisting of several plies of high-grade roofing felts, each layer mopped down in hot pitch or asphalt. On relatively flat pitches, a surface coating of small gravel or slag embedded in the final hot mopping is desirable. **Flashings** against parapet walls and curbs around roof openings are important in tight roof construction. Flashings may be galvanized iron, membrane, or copper. The life of galvanized iron is limited, and, where metal flashing is used, the additional first cost of copper is generally warranted in avoiding maintenance expense.

Floors in industrial plants are usually of concrete poured in place as a concrete slab on grade or on concrete or steel beams. In multistory construction it may be monolithic reinforced concrete, either flat slab or beam and girder. Floors may also be of precast concrete floor slabs or of sections resting on beams, or they may be cast with an integral beam construction such as T- or inverted U-shaped sections. Finished floors may be exposed concrete, hardened concrete topping, or a vinyl floor finish. Cellular-type steel floors merit special consideration for offices or other areas where underfloor telephone or signal systems are required, since the wiring may be run through the cells of the steel floor deck. Relative costs depend on floor loadings, column spacing, number and size of openings required, and other similar factors. Comparative estimates of alternative designs, based on a typical cross section of the building, one bay in length, which include the effect on columns and foundations of the relative dead weight and the adaptability of the construction to conditions of service, offer the best basis for proper selection for a given case. An ideal **floor finish** should be resistant to wear and to the action of process spillage, sanitary, comfortable, non-slip, easily cleaned, and low in maintenance cost. A properly laid cement-finish floor using hard aggregate such as trap rock, granite, or quartzite chips laid over a concrete slab has excellent wearing qualities. Best results are obtained when the finish is at least 1 in. thick, placed as a separate operation rather than monolithic with the slab. About 1 lb of carborundum grits per square foot worked into the cement finish provides a good non-slip surface and is especially desirable where floors are wet during working operations. For aisles, areas at elevators, and loading platforms subject to heavy-duty iron-wheel trucking, grids of **cast iron** bedded flush with the cement finish, although high in first cost, give excellent service with low maintenance cost. For floors subject to strong acid or alkali action from process spillage, an **asphalt mastic** finish floor usually gives best results. Hardwood-finish floors such as maple provide an excellent working surface but are generally quite high in first cost and in maintenance cost, especially in areas subject to trucking, unless rubber tires are used. End-grain **wood-block** floors provide a good working surface at reasonable cost for dry locations and wear well under moderate trucking, but are subject to buckling if wet accidentally as from sprinkler operation. Creosoted wood-block and asphalt-block floors give good service in heavy machine shops, foundries, and the like, but are not attractive in appearance and are hard to keep clean.

Partitions fall into two general classes: those likely to be relatively permanent and those likely to require moving owing to future changes in layout. For **permanent** partitions in steel or concrete buildings, masonry construction of cinder blocks, hollow clay tile, common brick, concrete, salt-glazed tile, and ceramic-glazed tile are generally desirable, the cost increasing about in the order listed. Except for glazed materials, plaster can be applied readily if desired. Subdividing fire walls should be provided to comply with building-code and insurance requirements. Gypsum block or metal studs with wire lath and plaster provide low-cost lightweight fire-resistant construction in semipermanent locations. For **movable** partitions, wood studs faced with fiberboard or plywood sheets afford minimum-first-cost construction but present some fire hazard. Filling all spaces between studs with rock wool adds to the cost but lessens the fire risk and improves the sound-insulating quality. Woven-wire grille partitions are frequently used for tool- and stock-room enclosures where the principal requirement is to prevent unauthorized access. Sectional steel or steel-and-glass partitions are widely used for shop offices, inspection rooms, and other similar enclosures, as they can be readily enlarged, taken down, and rearranged, but have little sound insulation in noisy locations. Double steel or asbestos cement sectional partitions with rock wool or other insulation and double glazing are readily moved, are effective against noise transmission, but are relatively high in first cost.

Stair arrangement, location, and construction is one of the most important problems in industrial-plant design, affecting, in the form of exits, the life and safety of all employees and, in the form of access to equipment, the safety and efficiency of operation. For exit stairways, a width of 22 in. accommodates one person, and the total stair width should be in multiples of this unit, with 3 ft a desirable minimum where only a single unit is required. Up to 66 in. width, a handrail should be provided on each side, and for wider stairs an additional center handrail is desirable. Handrails projecting not more than 3 in. do not encroach on the effective width of a stair, but beams, columns, and other obstructions should not project into the effective stair width. Not more than 15 risers should be permitted in a single run beyond which intermediate platforms should be provided. Winding treads at stair turns or straight runs of less than three risers should not be allowed. There should be at least two exits arranged so that, with a fire originating in any location, employees in any area can reach one of them. The maximum distance from any area to an exit should preferably not exceed 100 ft for hazardous occupancy or 150 ft in sprinklered fire-resistant construction. Stairs should be provided so that the total employee occupancy can be evacuated on one of three bases: (1) a safe total time depending on the hazards present based on 45 persons per 22 in. stair width, walking down in 1 min; (2) all occupants of the most densely populated floor above, on the stairs in any story below that floor, assuming one person per 22 in. width on every other tread and one person per 3½ sq ft of landing area; (3) divide the gross square-foot area of any one floor above the ground by 6,000 for low-hazardous and by 3,000 for high-hazardous conditions, and provide a 22 in. width of stair for each unit resulting from this division.

Exit stairways should be suitably enclosed with fire-resistant walls and doors, the latter equipped with self-closing devices and opening into the stair shaft without encroaching on the required effective landing width, except at ground level where doors should open out direct to safe open air or to a fireproof passage.

Stairs should be constructed of non-combustible materials with non-slip nosings. Steel stringers with pressed-metal treads filled with concrete, surfaced with carborundum grits, steel stringers with sheet steel risers and non-slip cast-iron treads, and grit-surfaced reinforced concrete are excellent constructions for exit stairs. Storage spaces under stairs should not be allowed.

The efficiency of convenient safe **access to working levels** around large equipment and to important operating valves justifies in most cases the cost of the necessary platforms and access stairs. Ship-ladder stairs, circular stairs, and ladders are inconvenient and somewhat hazardous. Grating platforms, with access stairs having a minimum width of 2 ft 2 in., grating treads with visible non-slip nosings and handrails are generally a desirable construction. **Non-skid surfaces** may also be obtained by the use of special tapes and by paints and other materials which prevent slipping even when the surface is wet or oily.

For stairs with open risers, plates about 2 in. high at the back of the tread will prevent tools laid on the stair from being kicked off onto employees below; similarly curbs are advisable around floor openings and elevated platforms.

Lighting

Natural lighting of building interiors is subject to wide variation in intensity due to fluctuations in outside brightness. Although it is practically impossible to design a building so as to provide uniform distribution of daylight over an interior area of appreciable size, the arrangement of windows in side walls and monitors affects to a marked degree the uniformity of daylight lighting of the interior and warrants careful study in planning a new building.

For the average factory, the normal accumulation of dirt on the glass of vertical windows will, in a 6 months' period, reduce the light transmission about one-half as compared with clean glass. Although there is not much difference in the rate of dirt accumulation on clear, rough, and ribbed glass, the last is more difficult to clean. Much more dirt collects on the inside than on the outside; therefore, the inside should be washed twice as often as the outside. Windows set on a slope increase the amount of light transmitted to the interior as compared with those set vertical, but the former collect dirt more rapidly and with a 6 months' washing period there is little actual difference.

Assuming a desirable minimum lighting intensity of 10 foot-candles on a working plane 3 ft above the floor and overcast sky conditions, side-wall windows without monitors limit the working area to a distance from the wall of about three times the height from the floor to the top of the window with clean glass and only about twice the height to the window head, with no washing for 6 months. For the same conditions, the total window area in side walls and monitors should be not less than 30 percent of the floor area, and the heads of the windows should be set close to the ceiling; the width of a monitor should be not less than twice its height, and the total width of monitors should be not less than one-half the width of the building.

Skylights provide high-intensity lighting in the areas immediately beneath them, but non-uniform conditions immediately adjacent. **A-frame monitors** of the same width as skylights provide comparable lighting and, with movable sash, some gravity ventilation.

For multistoried buildings constructed in U, E, or other court form, the **width of court** should preferably be equal to the height of the building, court walls should be faced with light-colored material to reflect light into the building, and for equal story heights the intensity of interior light decreases from the top story to the ground so that, considering daylight lighting only, each lower story should have a greater story height than the story next above.

Artificial lighting (see pp. 12–154 to 12–176) is essential in most modern industrial plants during dull natural-light periods at any time and to permit two- or three-shift operation when desired. Its influence on labor productivity in many industries may justify continuous operation of artificial lighting during the entire working day. A **windowless industrial building** has many advantages, including freedom from the maintenance cost of painting and glazing windows and from the transmission of heat through them. The major drawback is the shut-in psychological reaction of most employees where no natural light is provided. Designs embodying low windows at working levels for employees' vision only with complete dependence on artificial light for proper working conditions merit consideration.

Acoustics. Definite improvement in employee efficiency frequently results from reducing high-pitched objectionable sounds and creating an improved noise level by the application of sound-absorbing materials to the underside of roofs, ceilings, and frequently on walls and partitions. (See p. 12–177.)

Heating and Ventilating (see pp. 12–83 to 12–153). The heating and ventilating of industrial buildings are allied problems, each affecting the health and comfort of employees and, to a marked degree, their efficiency. Despite high initial and operating cost, complete air-conditioning systems, supplying an adequate quantity of clean properly humidified air at comfortable temperature throughout the entire seasonal cycle, have demonstrated their effectiveness in stores, offices, and to a limited extent in industry. The growing appreciation of the resulting efficiency, coupled with a continued downward trend in initial and operating costs, points the way to their wider application.

In many cases, the manufacturing equipment will furnish adequate heat during operation, and a heating system is necessary only to prevent freezing when the equipment is shut down. Quite frequently, the equipment will give off too much heat, and the problem then becomes one of ventilation.

Plumbing

Codes in most states specify the minimum number of plumbing fixtures required. For modern plants, employees' comfort and convenience are a consideration, and in many cases it is desirable to provide a greater number of fixtures than the prescribed legal minimum. The following ratios of fixtures to employees are recommended:

	Employees per shift			
	1–5	6–12	13–30	31 or more
Water closets, men	1	2	2	1 per 15
Water closets, women	1	2	3	1 per 12
Urinals			1	1 per 20–30
Individual lavatories	1	2	1 per 7	1 per 8

For washrooms serving 25 or more, **circular wash fountains** are often economical in floor space required and cost. In the preceding schedule, one 36 in. diam fountain is equivalent to four, and one 54 in. diam fountain to seven individual lavatories. Frequently, **showers** also should be provided, one to serve 6 to 15 employees, depending on conditions. Where a number of showers are required, a circular arrangement consisting of five stalls arranged around a common supply and drain connection is inexpensive and will often save space. **Lockers** should be provided for all employees, and in general individual lockers are desirable. In cases where damp work clothing is customarily stored, exhaust-fan ventilation connected direct to each locker is effective. Centrally located locker rooms with adjacent sanitary and wash-up facilities can be properly ventilated, maintained in a clean condition, and supervised more easily and are generally more satisfactory than a number of smaller scattered rooms. If central locker, toilet, and washrooms are used, it is advisable to provide, in addition, small toilet rooms containing a few sanitary fixtures located throughout the factory within one story and 200 ft walking distance of any appreciable number of employees. Traveling distance between male and female toilet-room entrances should be preferably not less than 20 ft. **Drinking-water** facilities should be provided on every floor, spaced not over 300 ft, and closer for large employee groups. For most locations, refrigerated drinking water is desirable, and either a central refrigerating plant with pumped circulating water lines or unit-type coolers may be provided. Except where there are large employee groups, with drinking fountains closely spaced, unit coolers will generally be more economical to install.

CONTRACT PROCEDURES

Types of Estimates

Estimates of cost fall into three general classes:

1. Preliminary estimates made usually from sketch drawings and brief outline specifications to determine the approximate total cost of a project.

2. Comparative estimates made usually during the progress of design to determine the relative cost of two or more alternative arrangements of equipment, type of building, type of floor framing, and the like.

3. Detail estimates made from well-developed plans and specifications and based on a careful quantity survey of each component part of the work.

For **preliminary estimates** it is important to list all the major items, structural, mechanical, and electrical, required to complete the project since overlooking essential items that will be required later, when detailed designs are prepared, will generally affect the actual total cost to a much greater extent than inaccuracies in the amounts allowed for each of the various items included in the estimate. Fairly accurate comparative estimates can be made by preparing rough preliminary designs of two or more alternative building cross sections and then making quantity surveys for one typical bay in length, or from simple quantity surveys of alternative designs for a typical panel of floor framing.

In preliminary estimating for the cost of buildings, it is common practice to compute the **total cubic contents** of the structure and then apply some arbitrary figure based on past experience for the cost per cubic foot. The results are likely to be quite misleading, since the cost per cubic foot is affected by variations in foundation conditions, shape, story height, floor loadings, type of construction, extent of subdividing partitions, and other similar factors. The one factor of shape, all others being identical, will affect the cubic-foot cost, a long narrow building costing more than an equal area, square in plan. Considering building cost only, the most economical shape generally is that containing the greatest volume for the least surface area, namely a cube. Foundation conditions may have an important bearing on building cost; expert advice is frequently advisable. For a concrete or steel-frame multistory building, cubic-foot costs generally decrease up to about six stories, after which they increase slightly. Fireproof construction will add appreciably to the cost but is often an excellent investment. Providing earthquake resistance may add 5 percent to the building cost, and designs for high-wind conditions a like amount, but the two forces are not usually taken as acting together. The value of estimates based on cubic contents of the structure will depend upon the availability of figures for comparable structures in the same cost area.

Preliminary quantity estimates are usually more accurate where this comparison is lacking. Compute the over-all square-foot area of exterior walls, interior partitions, floors, and roof, and multiply by known cost factors for each of these. Other items, such as number of electrical outlets required and number of plumbing fixtures and sprinklers, are estimated, and their cost computed. Equipment costs can be based on preliminary quotations from manufacturers.

The following items should be considered: land cost; fees to real-estate brokers, lawyers, architects, engineers, and contractors; interest during construction; building permits; taxes including sales or use taxes in force in some states; demolition of existing structures including removal of old foundations; yard work including leveling, drainage, fencing, roads, walks, landscaping, yard lighting, and parking spaces; transportation facilities including railroad tracks, wharves, and docks; power supply; water supply; sewer and industrial-waste disposal. A contingency item of 5 to 15 percent depending on the character of the estimate and the purpose for which it is to be used should be included to provide for unforeseen conditions that may arise during the development of the project.

Working Drawings, Specifications, and Contracts

The technical staff of a given industry has special knowledge of trade practices, process requirements, operating conditions, and other fundamentals affecting successful operation in that field and is best fitted to determine the basic factors of process design and plant expansion. Unless the company is extremely large it is unlikely that they will have the specialized staff or that their own staff will have the time available to undertake the complete layout. The efficient transformation of these requirements into a completed plant extension, or new plant ready to operate, usually requires experience of a different nature. Therefore, it is generally advisable and economical to employ engineers or architects who specialize in this particular field.

Three general procedures are in common use. First, the employment on a percentage or fixed-fee basis of an engineering and construction organization skilled in the industrial field to prepare the necessary working drawings and specifications, purchase equipment and materials, and execute the work. Such an organization becomes for the duration of the project a part of the owner's organization, working under his direction and in close cooperation with his technical staff in the development of the design, purchase of equipment and materials, and their installation. This procedure permits construction work to start as soon as basic factors of arrangement and cost have been determined but in advance of the time required to complete all working drawings and specifications. Such a program will result in the earliest possible completion consistent with economical construction.

A second procedure is to employ engineers or architects of wide experience in the industrial field to prepare working drawings and specifications and then to obtain **competitive lump-sum bids** and award separate contracts for each or a combination of two or more subdivisions of the work, such as foundations, structural steel, and brickwork. This method provides direct competition restricted to units of like character and permits intelligent consideration of the bids received. Provision must be made for proper coordination of these separate contracts by experienced and skilled field supervision. This procedure requires more time than that first described since all work of a given class should be completely designed before bids for that subdivision are taken. Where construction conditions are uncertain or hazardous, the first method is likely to be more economical, or combinations of the first method for uncertain conditions and the second method for the balance may prove most advantageous.

A third procedure is to employ engineers or architects to complete all plans and specifications and then **award lump-sum contracts,** one for the entire work, or one for all building work, and one or more supplementary major contracts for equipment. This method is particularly useful where there are no serious complications or hazards affecting construction operations, but it requires considerably more time, since most of the working drawings and specifications must be complete before construction is started. It has the advantage, however, of fixing the total cost within narrow limits before the work starts, if the contracts cover the complete scope of work required and no major changes are required.

STRUCTURAL DESIGN OF BUILDINGS

BY

John A. Blume and J. P. Nicoletti

(With the assistance of Frederick Willsea)

REFERENCES: "Steel Construction," American Institute of Steel Construction. "National Design Specification for Stress-grade Lumber and Its Fastenings," National Lumber Manufacturers Assoc. "National Building Code," The National Board of Fire Underwriters. "Uniform Building Code," Pacific Coast Building Officials Conference. "Analyses of Small Reinforced Concrete Buildings for Earthquake Forces," Portland Cement Assoc. Plummer and Blume, "Reinforced Brick Masonry and Lateral Force Design," Structural Clay Products Institute. Scofield and O'Brien, "Modern Timber Engineering," Southern Pine Assoc. "Timber Design and Construction Handbook," McGraw-Hill Book Co. "Wind Forces on Structures," *Trans. ASCE*, 1961.

LOADS AND FORCES

Live loads on floors are generally regulated by the building codes in cities. For areas not regulated, the following values will serve as a guide for live loads (pounds per square foot): rooms for habitation, 40; offices, halls with fixed seats, 50; corridors, halls, and other spaces where a crowd may assemble, 100; textile mills, 50 to 100; machine shops, 50 to 200; foundries, warehouses, 200 to 300. Floor decks and beams that support only a small floor area must also be designed for any local concentrations of load that may come upon them. Girders, columns, and members that support large floor areas, except in buildings such as warehouses where the full load may extend over the whole area, may often be designed for live loads progressively reduced as the supported area becomes greater. Where live loads, such as cranes and machinery, produce **impact** or **vibration,** 25 percent or more should be added to the static loads.

Roof live loads, for snow and workmen making repairs, should be taken at not less than 30 lb per horizontal sq ft of roof for slopes up to 15 deg, and 1 lb less for each additional degree up to 45 deg. In severe climates, this load should be increased; in mild climates, it may be reduced.

Dead loads are due to the weight of the structure, partitions, and all permanent equipment not included in the live load. The weights of common building materials used in floors and roofs are given below (see also pp. 6–5 *et. seq.*).

Material	Weight, lb per sq ft	Material	Weight, lb per sq ft
Asphalt and felt, 4 ply	2	Sheathing, 1 in., wood	3
Corrugated asbestos board	5	Skylight, 3/16 to 1/4 in., glass and frame	4–5
Glass, corrugated wire	5–6	Slate, 3/16 to 1/2 in. thick	8–20
Glass, sheet, 1/8 in. thick	2	Tar and gravel, 5 ply	6
Lead, 1/8 in. thick	8	Tar and slag, 5 ply	5
Plaster ceiling (suspended)	10	Tiles, plain, 5/8 in. thick	20
Sheet metal	1–2		
Shingles, wood	2		

Earthquake effects are usually represented, for design purposes, by static lateral forces. A common rule is to provide in the building frame for resistance to horizontal forces equal to one-tenth of the dead and live load supported. Roofs and floors should be designed as horizontal beams or diaphragms, or they should be provided with horizontal bracing between points of lateral support. Concrete and masonry walls can be made to act as resisting shear elements if properly connected to roof and floor bracing systems.

WIND PRESSURE ON STRUCTURES (by William Bollay)

(See also Sec. 11)

References: Flachsbart, Die Belastung von Bauwerken durch Luftkräfte, in Kaufmann, "Angewandte Hydromechanik," Vol. 2, 1934, p. 269. Rausch, Einwirkung von Windstössen auf Hohe Bauwerke, *ZVdI*, **77,** 1933. Dryden and Hill, Wind-pressure of a Model of the Empire State Building, *NBS Jour. Research*, **10,** 1933, p. 493. Nökkentved and Irminger, Windpressure on Buildings, *Ingeniorsvidenskab. Skrifter*, A23, 1930. Göttingen Ergebnisse, Vol. 3, p. 148.

Wind pressures on walls of buildings should be assumed at 15 lb per sq ft on surfaces less than 60 ft above the ground and 20 lb per sq ft on higher surfaces. On the projected area of exposed structural-steel frames, provide for wind pressure 50 percent greater than on walls. Wind pressures normal to sloping roofs steeper than 4 in. vertical in 1 ft horizontal should be taken at 1½ lb per sq ft for each inch vertical in 1 ft horizontal, with a maximum of 20 lb per sq ft. These pressures should be increased for buildings in exposed locations and in localities where extremely high wind velocity (over 70 mph) may occur.

Natural wind is a highly turbulent flow of air over the surface of the earth. Near the ground, its velocity is reduced by friction so that at a height of 50 ft it is about 90 percent as great as at 100 ft; the distribution of velocity is represented by a formula of the type $v \approx (\text{height})^n$, where n varies with the roughness of the terrain. An average value is $n = 0.157$.

The weather-bureau records give **maximum** and **extreme wind velocities** observed in various cities. The maximum is an average velocity over 5 min, and the extreme is the average velocity over the time taken to cover a mile, *i.e.*, over ½ to 1 min depending on the speed. The critical maximum velocity as far as the strength of any structure is concerned is the maximum velocity of gusts comparable in size with the structure. In a 60 mph wind for a house about 90 ft in linear dimensions, a gust of even a second's duration would thus be giving the effective maximum wind. The only way to record such short gusts is by means of a system having very little inertia, *e.g.*, the hotwire anemometer. A British test made with such instruments on an airport tower 64 ft high showed that eddies created by neighboring trees caused a sudden increase in velocity from a mean speed of 38 mph to a peak of 85 mph and back again to the mean speed. The duration of this gust was 0.8 sec, and its linear dimension was thus about 40 ft. The ratio of the maximum velocity to the mean velocity in this case was about 2¼. When using the maximum velocities of the weather bureau, it should be kept in mind that much higher velocities will be encountered locally. On a hill, the mean velocity at the peak may be as much as 50 percent greater than in level country.

The records of the U.S. Weather Bureau (see p. 9–12) indicate maximum wind velocities of the order of 70 to 90 mph with an isolated maximum of 113 mph at North Head, Wash., and a tropical hurricane at San Juan, Puerto Rico, of 149 mph. In choosing the maximum velocity for design purposes, it is not generally economical to design such structures as telephone lines and radio masts for the very highest wind velocities that might be encountered; the latter are so rare that the increased cost of construction is greater than the cost of insurance or an occasional repair.

Flachsbart (*loc. cit.*) suggests, for ordinary purposes, a design wind of 80 (90) mph up to a height of 60 ft and 90 (100) mph for heights greater than 60 ft. The figures in parentheses refer to especially windy regions. If a structure is to be designed so strong that it will not fail under any possible winds, then, unless it is located on a mountain top, a design wind of 150 mph should be sufficiently high.

The effect of the sudden application of **gust loads** has sometimes been blamed for peculiar failures due to wind. In most cases, these failures can be explained from the pressure distributions in a steady wind. If a relatively flexible structure such as a radio tower, chimney, or skyscraper with a natural period of 1 to 5 sec is set into vibration, the stresses in the structure may be increased over those calculated from a static-load analysis. Rausch (*loc. cit.*), on the basis of a theoretical analysis, suggests that provision may be made for this effect by increasing the design wind by 5 to 25 percent, depending on the flexibility of the structure.

Even a steady wind may give rise to periodic forces which may build up into large vibrations and lead to failure of the structure when the frequency of the exciting force coincides with one of the natural frequencies of vibration of the structure (Den Hartog, "Mechanical Vibrations," 1940, p. 343). The periodic exciting force may be due to the separation of a system of **Kármán vortices** (Fig. 1) in the wake of the body. The exciting frequency n in cycles per second is related to d, the dimension of the body normal to the wind velocity V, by the equation $nd/V = C$, where $C \approx 0.207$ for circular cylinders and $C \approx 0.18$ for rectangular plates (Blenk, Fuchs, and Liebers, Measurements of Vortex Frequencies, *Luftfahrt-Forsch.*, 1935, p. 38). Dangerous vibrations related to the "flutter" of airplane wings may arise on bridges and similar flat bodies. These self-induced vibrations may be caused (1) by a negative slope of the curve of lift against angle of attack (Den Hartog, *op. cit.*, pp. 343–354) or (2) by a dynamic instability which arises when a body having two or more degrees of freedom (such as bending and torsion) moves in such a manner as to extract energy out of the air stream. The first of these vibrations will occur at one of the natural frequencies of the structure. The second type of vibration will occur at a frequency intermediate between the natural frequencies of the structure.

Fig. 1. Kármán vortices.

The wind forces and the **pressure distribution** over a structure corresponding to a design wind V can be determined by **model testing** in a wind tunnel. Extrapolation from model to full scale is based on the fact that at every other point on the body, the pressure p is proportional to the stagnation pressure q (see p. 11–79) and thus the ratio p/q = constant for a fixed point on the body, as the scale of the model or the velocity of the wind is changed. Since the principal component of the wind force is due to the pressures, the force F acting on the surface S is

$$F \approx p_{avg} \cdot S = (p/q)_{avg} \cdot qS$$

and denoting $(p/q)_{avg}$ by a normal force coefficient or **shape factor** C_N

$$F = C_N \cdot \tfrac{1}{2}\rho V^2 \cdot S = C_N \cdot qS$$

The shape factors so obtained apply to full scale for structures with sharp edges whose principal resistance is due to the pressure forces. For bodies that do not have any sharp edges perpendicular to the flow, such as spheres or streamlined bodies, the factor C_N is not constant. It depends upon the Reynolds number (see p. 3–58). For such bodies, the law for variation of the shape factor C_N must be determined experimentally before safe predictions of full-scale forces can be made from model measurements.

Experimental Results

Flat Plates in Free Air Perpendicular to the Flow. The force N normal to the plate depends upon the aspect ratio A = (length)/(width) of the plate. Writing $N = C_N \cdot qS$, the coefficient C_N varies from about 1.18 to 2 as shown in Fig. 2. About 70 percent of normal force on the plate is due to the large underpressures existing over the rear surface.

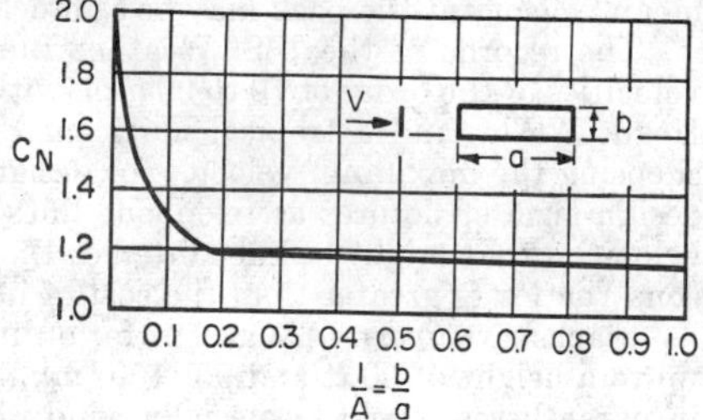

Fig. 2. Variation of "shape factor" with aspect ratio for rectangular plates perpendicular to the flow.

Flat Plates in Free Air Inclined to the Flow. The force N normal to the plate depends both upon the inclination α of the air stream with respect to the plate and upon the aspect ratio $A = a/b$, as shown in Fig. 3.

Inclined Roofs. The largest normal forces occur on the windward side; and for relatively small inclinations they are suctions. Flachsbart gives the approximate curve of Fig. 4 for the ratio of the normal force coefficient C_N of a roof inclined at an angle α to that inclined at 90 deg which was shown in Fig. 2. This curve was obtained from integrations of pressure distributions on roofs of aspect ratios 1:6. It is seen that this curve is in marked contrast with the building-code requirements which give a variation proportional to $\sin \alpha$ or $\sin^2 \alpha$.

Forces on Closed Buildings. Flachsbart (*loc. cit.*) gives measurements of pressure distributions on simplified building models as shown in Fig. 5. They show positive pressure only on the windward perpendicular faces. Suction pressures prevail over the side, top, and rear.

Figure 5(*a*) represents a building with a gabled roof at an angle of 40 deg to the horizontal. The pressure distributions are plotted for cross sections I, II, and III for

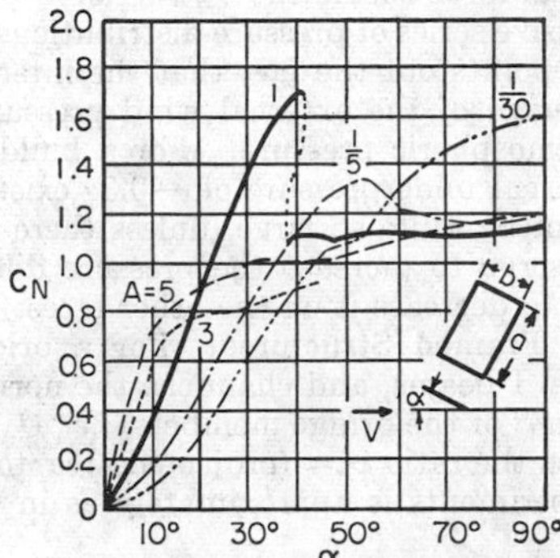

Fig. 3. Variation of "shape factor" with the inclination of the air stream for rectangular plates of various aspect ratios.

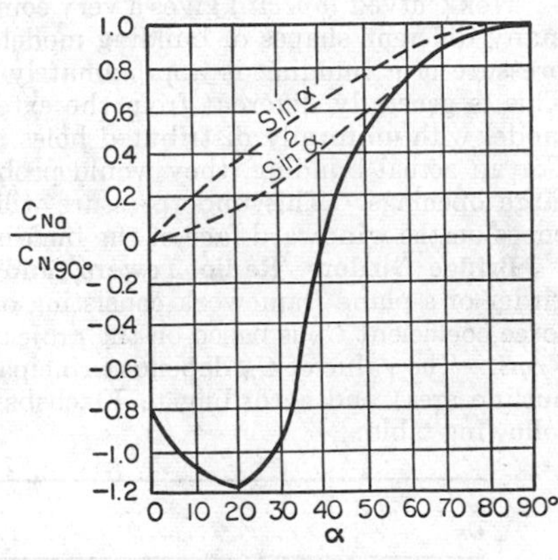

Fig. 4

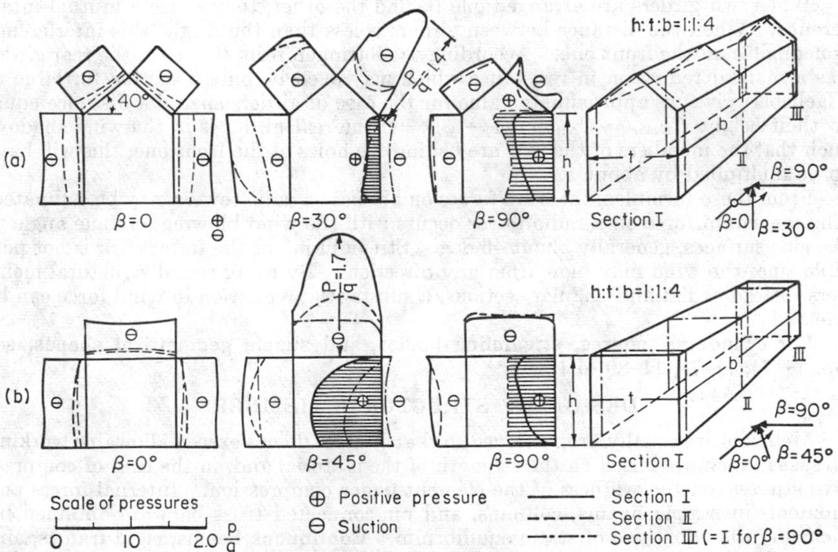

Fig. 5. Pressure distribution on two building models.

three different wind directions. When the wind blows against the end of the building ($\beta = 0$), the wind pressures are negative on the sides and on the roof, being largest at section I and decreasing toward II and III. The suction pressures at I are almost equal to the dynamic pressure q, *i.e.*, $p/q \approx -1$. Suction pressures are indicated by curves drawn outside the sections, positive pressures by curves inside. When the wind blows at an angle of 30 deg, the maximum suction of $1.4q$ is found on the roof of section I. Even when the wind blows directly against the side of the model ($\beta = 90$ deg), the pressure on the roof is partly negative on the windward side and strongly negative on the lee side. Figure 5(*b*) represents a rectangular building under similar conditions. Again the suction forces are greater than the positive pressures, reaching a maximum of $p = -1.7q$ on the roof of the building when $\beta = 45$ deg. These high suction pressures explain the lifting off of roofs and similar phenomena.

Dryden (*loc. cit.*) gives pressure distributions and force measurements on a model of the Empire State Building. He finds a normal force coefficient $C_N = 1.5$.

Nökkentved (*op. cit.*) gives a very comprehensive series of pressure distributions on many different shapes of building models. He points out the fact that the internal pressure of a building is approximately an average of the external wind pressures. This is generally different from the external atmospheric pressure. For a building model with uniformly distributed holes, an internal underpressure of $-0.3q$ existed. For an actual building, they would probably not be quite so large, unless there are large openings. This underpressure will thus serve to increase the pressure differences on the windward face of the building and to decrease it on the other faces.

Bridge Girders, Radio Towers, and Other Framed Structures. For a bridge girder or a plane framework consisting of angles, I beams, and channels, the normal force coefficient C_N is based on the projected area S of the bridge members, *i.e.*, $C_N = F/qS$. The value of C_N depends principally upon the ratio φ = (projected area/total outline area) and according to Flachsbart's experiments is approximately as in the following table:

φ	0–0.20	0.20–0.30	0.30–0.90	0.90–1.0
C_N	2.0	1.8	1.6	1.6–2.0

The last value depends upon aspect ratio as shown in Fig. 2.

When two girders are arranged one behind the other, they cause a mutual interference. When the distance between girders is less than the height this interference is negligible on the front one. According to Göttingen tests (*loc. cit.*), the rear girder has a marked reduction in resistance which may even become a suction for large φ. Flachsbart gives as approximate value for the case of girders spaced a distance equal to their height $C_{N\text{rear}} = C_{N\text{front}} \cdot (1 - \varphi)^2$. If the rear girder is in the wind shadow, such that the members of the rear are behind the holes of the front one, this will have to be multiplied by about 1.2.

From these formulas, the wind forces on bridges or radio towers may be estimated. The maximum force on a radio tower occurs with the wind blowing at some angle to the side surfaces, generally about 45 deg. Streamlining of the framework is not possible since the wind may blow from any direction. By using round structural members instead of flat and angular sections, a substantial reduction in wind force can be effected.

For **cylinders, spheres, streamline bodies,** and **simple geometrical shapes,** see pp. 11–74, 11–79, 11–89 to 11–94.

DESIGN OF STRUCTURAL MEMBERS

Members are usually proportioned so that stresses do not exceed allowable **working stresses** which are based on the strength of the material and, in the case of compressive stresses, on the stiffness of the element under compression. Internal forces and moments in **simple beams,** columns, and pin-connected truss bars are obtained by means of the equations of static equilibrium. **Continuous beams,** rigid frames, and other members characterized by practically rigid joints require for analysis additional equations derived from consideration of deflections and rotations.

Design may also be on the basis of the **ultimate strength** of members, the factor of safety being embodied in stipulated increases in the design loads. In steel-frame construction, the procedures of **plastic design** determine points where the material may be allowed to yield, forming *plastic hinges*, and the resulting redistribution of internal forces permits a more efficient use of the material.

Floors and Roofs

Flat Framing. Except in reinforced-concrete flat-slab construction, floors and roofs generally consist of flat decks supported upon beams, girders, or trusses. The decks may usually be considered a series of beamlike strips spanning between beams, and themselves designed as beams. The design of a beam consists chiefly in proportioning its cross section to resist the maximum bending and shear and providing adequate connections at its supports, without exceeding the unit stresses allowed in the materials used (see pp. 5–29 to 5–51).

Trussed Beams. Where the span of floor or roof exceeds 20 to 30 ft, **trusses** of some form may be more economical than beams of uniform section. For spans above 50 to 70 ft, trusses are usually economical. Between these limits, the line of economy is not definitely marked, but the conditions that favor the use of trusses are as follows: (1) identical trusses are repeated many times, (2) the height of the building need not be increased for the greater depth of the truss, (3) fire protection of wood or metal is not required.

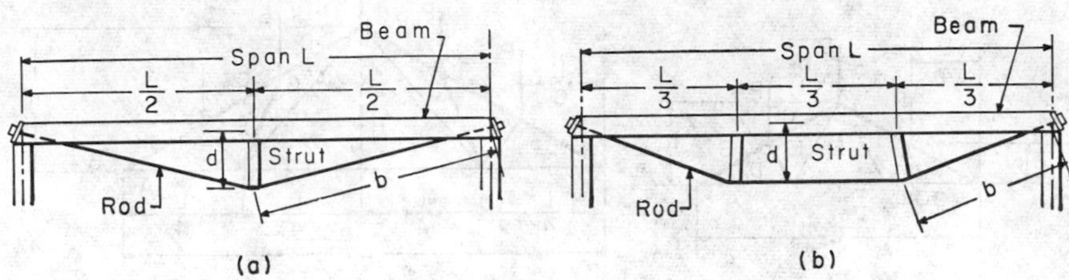

Fig. 6. Trussed beams.

A common form of small truss is shown in Fig. 6, with either one or two struts. The beams are usually of wood (rarely of steel) trussed with steel rods and wood or cast-iron struts. The rods have threaded ends, often upset, nuts, and bearing plates on the ends of the beam. Turnbuckles are sometimes used for adjusting the length of the rod. The trussed wooden beam is rarely used on spans over 40 ft. The stresses in the trussed beams shown in Fig. 6 are given in the following table, for a uniformly

	Fig. 6(*a*)	Fig. 6(*b*)
Compression in strut	$0.63W$	$0.37W$
Tension in rod	$0.31Wb/d$	$0.37Wb/d$
Compression in beam	$0.16Wl/d$	$0.12Wl/d$
Max bending in beam at strut	$WL/32$	$WL/90$

distributed load W on the whole span (or for concentrated loads at the struts each equal to the tabulated compression in the strut), assuming that the beam is a single continuous piece (or is effectively spliced) and the length of the rod is adjusted to give no deflection at the strut.

The beam should be proportioned so that $f_a/F_a + f_b/F_b$ is equal to or less than 1, where f_a is the stress due to the axial loads, f_b the stress due to bending, F_a the allowable stress for axial loads, and F_b the allowable stress due to bending.

Roof trusses usually have their top chords sloped with the roof. Common trusses for steeply pitched roofs are shown in Figs. 7 to 11, the top chord panels equal in each truss. The members shown by heavy lines are in compression under ordinary loads, those in light lines in tension. The trusses of Figs. 7 to 10 are adapted for either steel or wood. In wooden trusses, the tensile web members may be steel rods with plates, nuts, and threaded ends. The truss of Fig. 11 is usually made of steel.

The stresses in any member of these trusses under a vertical load uniformly distributed may be found by multiplying the coefficients in Tables 1 to 5 by the panel load P on the truss. For other slopes, types of trusses, or loads, see below (pp. 12–24 to 12–28). Trusses for flat roofs are commonly of one of the types shown in Figs. 12 to 18 except that the top chords conform to the slope of the roof.

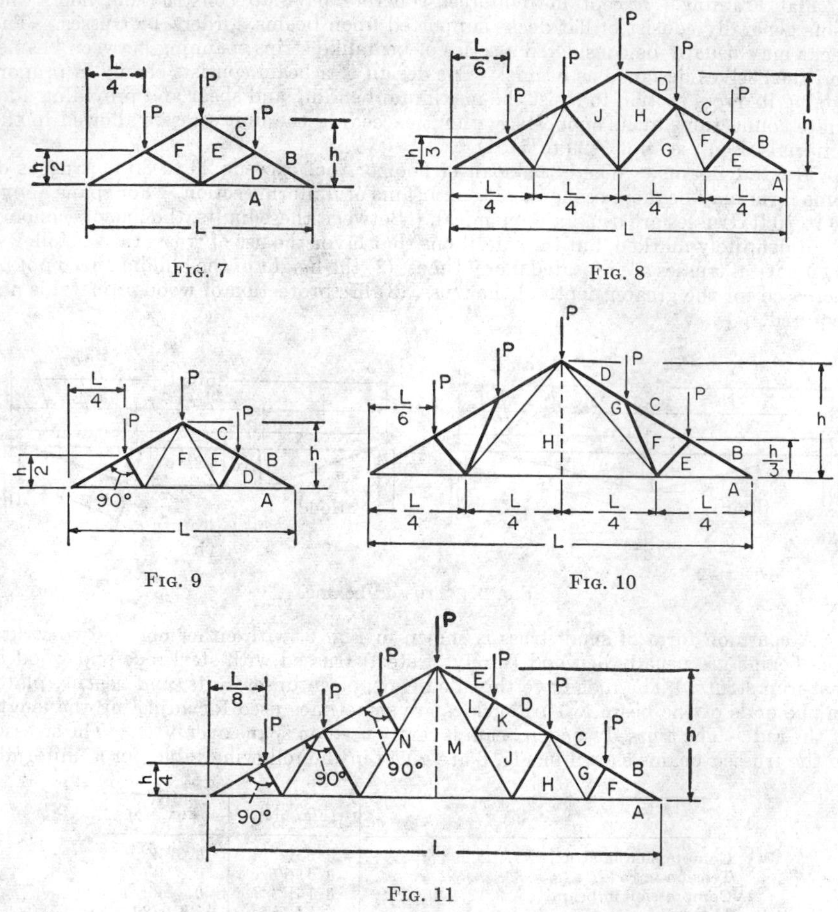

FIGS. 7 to 11. Types of steep-roof trusss.

Floor trusses normally have parallel chords. Common types are shown in Figs. 12 to 18 in which heavy lines indicate members in compression, light lines in tension, and dash lines members with only nominal stress, under equal vertical panel loads. The panel lengths l in each truss are equal. The stress in each member is written next to the member in the figure, in terms of the panel load and the lengths of members. For a truss like one of the figures turned upside down, the stresses in the chords and diagonals remain the same in magnitude but reversed in sign. Stresses in verticals must be computed (compare Figs. 12 and 13). For other loads and other types of trusses, see below, pp. 12–24 to 12–28.

Weights of Trusses. The approximate weight in pounds of a wooden truss may be taken as $W = LS(L/25 + L^2/6{,}000)$, where L is the span and S the spacing of

Table 1. Coefficients for Truss Shown in Fig. 7

Pitch h/L	Coefficients of P for stress in				
	AD	BD	CE	DE	EF
⅓	2.25	2.71	1.80	0.90	1.00
0.288*	2.60	3.00	2.00	1.00	1.00
¼	3.00	3.35	2.24	1.12	1.00
⅕	3.75	4.03	2.69	1.35	1.00

Table 2. Coefficients for Truss Shown in Fig. 8

Pitch h/L	Coefficients of P for stress in								
	AE	AG	BE	CF	DH	EF	FG	GH	HJ
⅓	3.75	3.00	4.50	3.90	3.60	0.83	0.72	1.25	2.00
0.288*	4.33	3.46	5.00	4.33	4.00	0.88	0.73	1.32	2.00
¼	5.00	4.00	5.59	4.84	4.47	0.94	0.75	1.42	2.00
⅕	6.25	5.00	6.74	5.84	5.39	1.07	0.79	1.60	2.00

Table 3. Coefficients for Truss Shown in Fig. 9

Pitch h/L	Coefficients of P for stress in					
	AD	AF	BD	CE	DE	EF
⅓	2.25	1.50	2.70	2.15	0.83	0.75
0.288*	2.60	1.73	3.00	2.50	0.87	0.87
¼	3.00	2.00	3.35	2.91	0.89	1.00
⅕	3.75	2.50	4.04	3.67	0.93	1.25

Table 4. Coefficients for Truss Shown in Fig. 10

Pitch, h/L	Coefficients of P for stress in							
	AE	AH	BE	CF	DG	EF	FG	GH
⅓	3.75	2.25	4.51	3.91	4.51	0.83	1.42	2.50
0.288*	4.33	2.60	5.00	4.33	5.00	0.88	1.45	2.65
¼	5.00	3.00	5.59	4.84	5.59	0.94	1.49	2.83
⅕	6.25	3.75	6.73	5.83	6.73	1.07	1.57	3.20

Table 5. Coefficients for Truss Shown in Fig. 11

Pitch h/L	Coefficients of P for stress in											
	AF	AH	AM	BF	CG	DK	EL	FG KL	GH JK	HJ	JM	LM
⅓	5.25	4.50	3.00	6.31	5.75	5.20	4.65	0.83	0.75	1.66	1.50	2.25
0.288*	6.06	5.20	3.46	7.00	6.50	6.00	5.50	0.87	0.87	1.73	1.73	2.60
¼	7.00	6.00	4.00	7.83	7.38	6.93	6.48	0.89	1.00	1.79	2.00	3.00
⅕	8.75	7.50	5.00	9.42	9.05	8.68	8.31	0.93	1.25	1.86	2.50	3.75

* 30 deg slope.

trusses in feet. The approximate weight of a steel roof truss may be taken as $W = \frac{1}{5}LS(\sqrt{L} + \frac{1}{8}L)$. For loads greater than 40 lb per sq ft, multiply by the load and divide by 40.

Choice of Roof Trusses. Wooden Trusses. For pitched roofs with spans up to 20 ft, the simple king-post truss, inversion of the trussed beam (Fig. 6), may be used. For spans up to 40 ft (60 ft), the trusses of Figs. 7 and 9 (Figs. 8 and 10) are good. The number of panels rarely exceeds eight or the panel length 10 ft. For flat roofs, the Howe truss (Figs. 12, 15, and 17) is built of wood with steel rods for verticals; the depth is one-eighth to one-twelfth of the span. Wooden trusses are usually spaced 10 to 15 ft. Wood is rarely used in roof trusses over 60 ft in span. Steel trusses for pitched roofs may well take the form of Figs. 8 to 11 for spans up to 100 ft. For

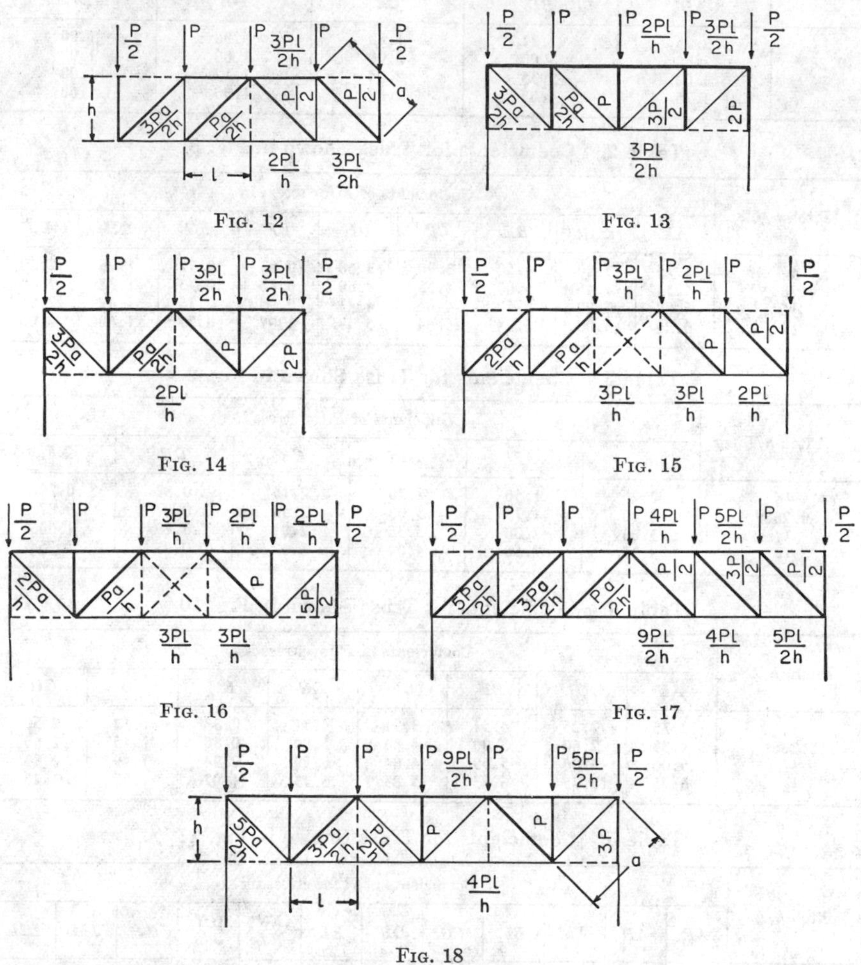

FIGS. 12 to 18. Types of floor trusses.

flat roofs, the Warren truss (Figs. 14, 16, and 18) is common in steel; the depth of the truss ranges from one-eighth to one-twelfth of the span, the spacing from 15 to 25 ft.

Stresses in Trusses

An ideal truss is a framework consisting of straight bars or members connected at their ends by frictionless ball-and-socket joints. The external forces are applied only at these ball-and-socket joints. Internal forces or stresses in such straight bars are axial, either tension or compression, without bending. Since frictionless ball-and-socket joints are impossible, and the ends of bars are often riveted or welded, the ideal truss is never realized. For purposes of analysis, the primary stresses, which are always axial, are determined on the assumption that the truss under consideration conforms to the ideal. Secondary stresses are additional stresses, generally flexural or bending, brought about by all the factors that make the actual truss different from the ideal. In the following discussion, primary stresses will be considered.

Analytical Solution of Trusses

General Procedure. After all external forces (loads and reactions) have been determined, the internal force or stress in any member is found (1) by taking a section, making an imaginary cut through the members of the truss, including the one whose stress is to be found, so as to separate the truss into two parts; (2) by isolating either of these parts; (3) by replacing each bar cut by a force, representing the stress in the bar or the force required to come to the part of the truss isolated from the other part removed; and (4) by applying the equations of statics to the part isolated.

The various ways in which sections can be taken and the equations used to determine the stresses are illustrated by a solution of the truss (Fig. 19).

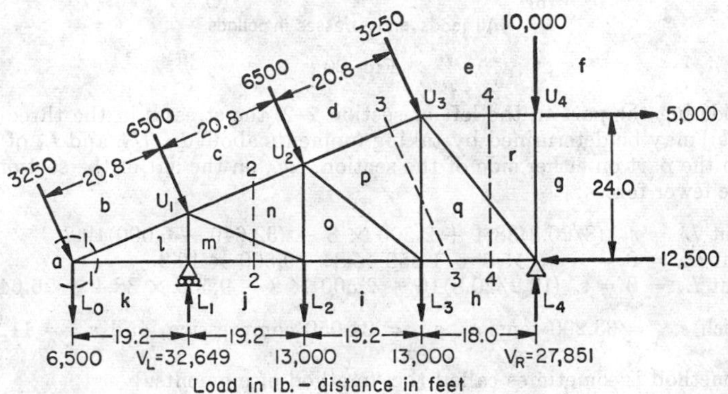

FIG. 19

A section 1–1 (Fig. 19) may be taken around a joint, L_0. Isolate the forces inside the section [Fig. 20(*a*)]. Assume the unknown stresses to be tension. Since the forces are concurrent and coplanar, two independent equations of statics will establish equilibrium. These may be either $\Sigma x = 0$ and $\Sigma y = 0$ or $\Sigma M = 0$ taken about two axes perpendicular to the plane of the forces and passing through two points selected so that neither point is the intersection of the forces, or so that the line joining the two points is not coincident with either of the unknown forces.

Using the first set of equations and taking components of all forces along horizontal and vertical axes; *e.g.*, the horizontal component of the 3,250 lb force is 1,250 and the vertical component is 3,000 lb.

$$\Sigma x = 0 = s_{lk} + s_{bl}(19.2/20.8) + 1{,}250$$
$$\Sigma y = 0 = s_{bl}(8/20.8) - 9{,}500$$

From these equations, $s_{lk} = -24{,}050$ and $s_{bl} = 24{,}700$.

The minus sign indicates that the force acts opposite to the assumed direction. If all the unknown forces are assumed to be in tension, then a plus sign in the result indicates that the stress is tension and a minus sign indicates compression.

Hence, s_{lk} is 24,050 lb compression and s_{bl} is 24,700 lb tension.

Using the $\Sigma M = 0$ twice,

$$\Sigma M \text{ about } U_1 = 0 = -s_{lk} \times 8 - 1250 \times 8 - 9{,}500 \times 19.2$$

from which $s_{lk} = 24{,}050$ lb compression.

$$\Sigma M \text{ about } L_1 = 0 = s_{bl}(8/20.8)19.2 - 9{,}500 \times 19.2$$

from which $s_{bl} = 24{,}700$ tension.

Instead of taking a section around a joint, a cut may be made vertically or inclined, cutting a number of bars such as Fig. 20(*b*) or Fig. 20(*c*). If only three members are cut, and they are neither concurrent nor parallel, the stresses can be found by taking moments of all forces on either side of the section about axes passing through the intersections of any two members.

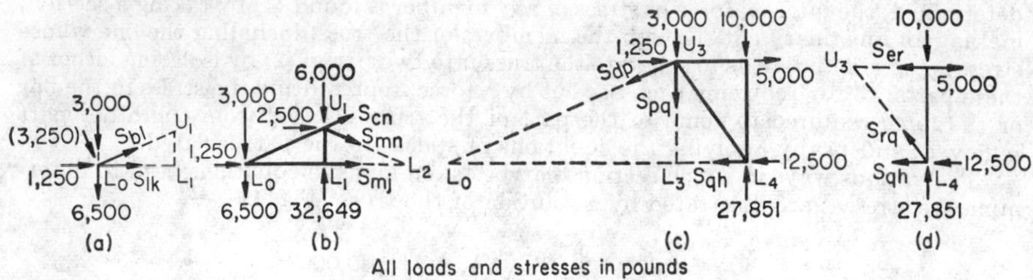

Fig. 20

Considering the part to the left of section 2–2, the stresses in the three members [Fig. 20(*b*)] may be determined by taking moments about L_0, U_1, and L_2 of all forces acting on the part on either side of the section, *e.g.*, on the left of the section because it has the fewer forces:

$$\Sigma M \text{ about } L_0 = s_{mn}(8/20.8)38.4 + 2{,}500 \times 8 - (32{,}649 - 6{,}000)19.2$$
$$\Sigma M \text{ about } U_1 = 0 = -s_{mj} \times 8 - 1{,}250 \times 8 - 9{,}500 \times 19.2$$
$$\Sigma M \text{ about } L_2 = 0 = s_{cn}(19.2/20.8)16 + 2{,}500 \times 8 - 9{,}500 \times 38.4 + 26{,}649 \times 19.2$$

from which s_{mn} = 33,290 tension, s_{mj} = 24,050 compression, and s_{cn} = 11,298 compression.

This method is sometimes called the "method of moments."

Considering the part to the right of section 3–3, the stresses in the three members [Fig. 20(*c*)] may be determined by taking moments about L_0, U_3, L_3 of all the forces acting on part or either side of the section, *e.g.*, on the right of the section because it has the fewer forces:

$$\Sigma M \text{ about } L_0 = 0 = s_{pq} \times 57.6 + 6{,}250 \times 24 + 3{,}000 \times 57.6 - (27{,}851 - 10{,}000) \times 75.6$$
$$\Sigma M \text{ about } L_3 = 0 = -s_{dp}(19.2/20.8)24 + 6{,}250 \times 24 - 17{,}851 \times 18$$
$$\Sigma M \text{ about } U_3 = 0 = s_{qh} \times 24 + 12{,}500 \times 24 - 17{,}851 \times 18$$

from which s_{pq} = 17,825 tension, s_{dp} = 7,733 compression, and s_{qh} = 888 tension.

Considering the part to the right of section 4–4, the stresses in the three members [Fig. 20(*d*)] may be found by taking moments about axes where two unknowns intersect, *e.g.*, about U_3 and L_4. Since two unknown stresses are parallel, their lines of action do not intersect. However the equation $\Sigma y = 0$; will enable one to find the stress in the member which is not parallel to the other two:

$$\Sigma M \text{ about } U_3 = 0 = s_{qh} \times 24 - (27{,}851 - 10{,}000)18 + 12{,}500 \times 24$$
$$\Sigma M \text{ about } L_4 = 0 = -s_{er} \times 24 + 5{,}000 \times 24$$
$$\Sigma y = 0 = s_{rq}(24/30) + 27{,}851 - 10{,}000$$

from which s_{qh} = 888 tension, s_{er} = 5,000 tension, and s_{rq} = 22,314 compression.

Graphical Solution of Trusses

When the external forces acting upon a truss are all in the same plane and may be assumed to act at the joints of the structure, it is often convenient to make use of graphical constructions to determine the stresses in the members. A series of stress polygons may be constructed for the forces acting at the different joints, using the methods shown on p. 3–9, but a combination diagram, using what is known as "Bow's notation," greatly simplifies the work.

The forces F_1, F_2, F_3, and F_4 (Fig. 21) are all in the same plane and form a system in equilibrium. Their lines of action all pass through the same point (o). Letters are so placed as to bring each force between two letters, these letters being usually read in a right-handed or clockwise direction around the joint. F_1, F_2, F_3, F_4 will then be designated *ab*, *bc*, *cd*, and *da*, respectively. A stress polygon (Fig. 22) is then drawn for the forces. Assume that the magnitudes, lines of action, and directions of F_1 and F_2 are known and that the lines of action only of F_3 and F_4 are known. The forces must be taken in order and the letters must be so placed that when the forces are read right-handed about the point o (Fig. 21) the sequence of the letters (in Fig. 22) will indicate the direction in which the forces act upon point o. The manner of using Bow's notation is illustrated by the following problem.

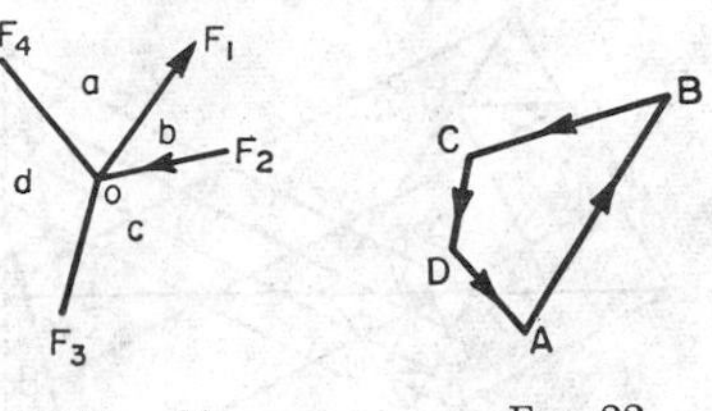

Fig. 21 Fig. 22

Bow's Notation Applied to a Truss. The truss shown in Fig. 23 is loaded with a uniformly distributed dead load which may be considered to be concentrated at the joints as shown. First plot the polygon of external forces *ABCDEFGA* (Fig. 24). As the forces act vertically, the sides of the polygon fall in the straight line *AF*. The supporting forces *GA* and *FG* are equal in this case, each being one-half the total load, so that no special construction for their determination is necessary. Start at any joint in the truss where there are not more than two unknown forces, *e.g.*, at the left end of the truss. The stress polygon for this joint is *ABHGA*. Reading the letters in a right-hand direction about the joint, the stress in the upper chord member is *BH*. This sequence of letters in the stress polygon indicates that this member acts downward and to the left on the joint and, therefore, is in compression. The stress in the lower chord member is *HG*, and this sequence of letters indicates that this member acts to the right on the joint and therefore is in tension.

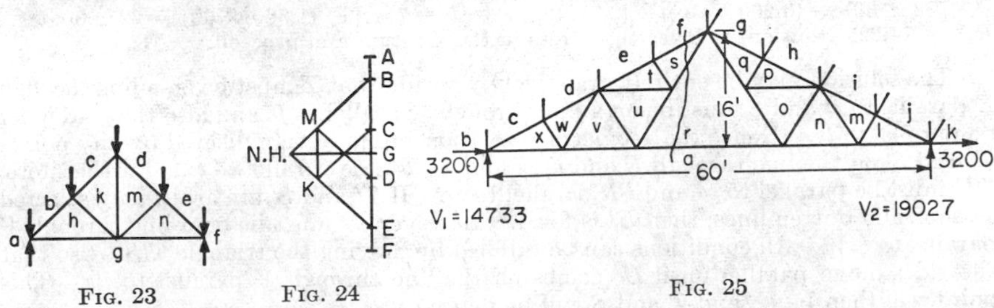

Fig. 23 Fig. 24 Fig. 25

At the joint in the middle of the upper chord there are now two unknown stresses. Draw the stress polygon *HBCKH* for the second joint. The stress *HB* is of the same magnitude as for the lower joint but acts in the opposite direction. The stress in the member *kh* is *KH* and is, therefore, compression.

Example. The truss shown in Fig. 25 is loaded with a dead load of 21,760 lb uniformly distributed over the upper chord, together with a wind load of 13,600 lb on the right side. Both ends of the truss are fixed and the horizontal components of the supporting forces are assumed to be equal. The supporting forces may be determined graphically by first assuming a roller under one end of the truss, or by the funicular polygon construction (see p. 3-8). They are often calculated and the polygon of external forces plotted from the results of the calculation. This is a desirable method, as it offers a check on this most important part of the graphical work.

The horizontal component of the wind load is $(16/34)13{,}600 = 6{,}400$ lb. The H component of each supporting force is assumed to be $6{,}400/2 = 3{,}200$ lb. The vertical component of the wind load is $(30/34)13{,}600 = 12{,}000$ lb. Taking moments about the right end of the truss, $(21{,}760 \times 30) + (13{,}600 \times 17) = 60V_1$. $\therefore V_1 = 14{,}733$; $V_2 = 21{,}760 + 12{,}000 - 14{,}733 = 19{,}027$.

The polygon of external forces can now be constructed, as in Fig. 26. The dotted part of the diagram is the combination of the dead and wind loads, assuming that they are each concentrated. The dotted line BK is the resultant of these loads. The supporting forces KA and AB are determined by plotting to scale their horizontal and vertical components as calculated. The polygon of external forces for the truss is $BCDEFGHIJKAB$, and must check with the polygon shown dotted. The forces GH, HI, IJ, and JK are the resultants of the forces acting at the joints on the right side of the truss.

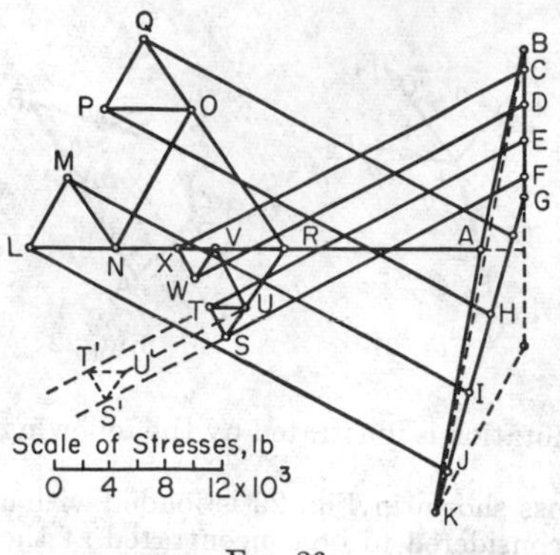

Fig. 26

When supporting forces are to be determined, the loads *may* be concentrated at the lines of action of their resultants, but when internal forces are to be determined the loads *must* be distributed at the various joints. Start with some joint of the truss where there are only two unknown forces and draw the stress diagram, Fig. 26. The magnitudes of the stresses in the different members are determined directly from the lengths of the corresponding lines and the scale used in the construction of the diagram. The nature of the stress (tension or compression) is determined by the use of Bow's notation.

A difficulty often arises that is illustrated by the truss of Fig. 25. It is impossible by the usual graphical procedure to complete the stress diagram, as it will be found that, after obtaining the stresses in the members meeting at the left end and at the next joint on both upper and lower chords, no joint with less than three unknown forces is available. To overcome this difficulty, some unknown stress may be calculated and placed on the diagram before proceeding with the graphical solution.

The stress which should be calculated in this case is that in the middle member of the lower chord. Taking moments about a point at the middle of the upper chord, $16RA = (14{,}733 \times 30) - (3{,}200 \times 16) - [2{,}720(22\frac{1}{2} + 15 + 7\frac{1}{2})] - (1{,}360 \times 30) = 227{,}600$. $\therefore$ $RA = 14{,}225$ (tension). Place this stress in the diagram and proceed.

The solution may be entirely graphical by noting that T must be on a line through E parallel to *et* and S must be on a line through f parallel to *fs* and also that TS must be parallel to *ts*. Hence the geometrical relationship may be indicated by any points T' and S' on the line through E and F as long as $T'S'$ is parallel to *ts*. Furthermore, TU must be parallel to *tu* and SR parallel to *sr*. If T' and S' are arbitrarily selected as shown in dotten lines, then U' is fixed. However, U must lie on a line through V parallel to UV. All conditions can be fulfilled by moving the triangle $T'S'U'$ so that the sides move parallel until U' comes on the line through V parallel to *uv*. This point will then be U, and T and S will be determined.

Columns and Walls

Vertical elements in building construction consist of columns, posts, or pilasters which transmit concentrated loads, walls or partitions which transmit linear loads from story to story, and rigid frames which transmit lateral as well as vertical loads.

Columns may be of timber, steel, or reinforced concrete and should be proportioned for the allowable stresses permitted for the material used and for the flexibility of the column. Care must be taken in the framing of beams and girders to avoid or to provide for the additional stresses due to connections which transfer loads to columns with large eccentricities. For instance, a beam framing to a flange of a steel column, with a seat or web connection, will produce an eccentric moment in the column equal to $Rd/2$, where R is the beam reaction and d the depth of the column section. Columns not adequately restrained against deflection of the top may be subject to considerable additional moment because of the resulting eccentricity of otherwise axial loads.

Rigid frames consist of columns and beams welded, riveted, bolted, or otherwise connected so as to produce continuity at the joints and permit the entire frame to behave as a unit. Advantages of rigid frames are the ease and simplicity of erection, increased headroom, and the resultant savings in wall heights. Rigid frames composed of rolled sections are commonly used for spans up to 100 ft in length. Built-up members have been utilized on spans to 250 ft. Welded fabrication offers particular advantages for frames utilizing variable-depth members and on parabolic-shape roofs. The distribution of moments in the statically indeterminate rigid frame is effected by the relationship of the column height to span and roof rise to column height, as well as the relative stiffness of the various members. The solution for the moments in the frame is obtained from the usual equations of statics plus one or more additional equations pertaining to the elastic deformations of the frame under load.

Walls are designed as vertical elements of unit width transmitting vertical loads from story to story. Wind, earthquake, and other lateral loads are resisted by the walls spanning as a beam vertically between floors, horizontally between columns or pilasters, or as a two-way slab spanning in each direction.

Stud walls consist of wooden studs with one or more lines of horizontal bridging. The allowable vertical load on the wall is a function of the maximum permissible load on each stud as a column and the spacing of the studs (see Table 10).

Corrugated or flat sheet steel, aluminum, or asbestos-cement sheets are commonly employed for walls of industrial or mill buildings. These sheets are usually supported on steel girts framing horizontally between columns and supported from heavier eave struts by one or more lines of vertical steel sag rods.

Reinforced-concrete or masonry walls shall be designed so that the allowable bending and/or axial stresses are not exceeded, but the minimum thicknesses of such walls should not be less than the following:

Material	Max ratio, unsupported height or length to thickness	Nominal min thickness, in.
Reinforced concrete	25	6
Plain concrete	22	7
Reinforced brick masonry	25	7
Grouted brick masonry	22	7
Plain solid masonry	20	8
Hollow-unit masonry	18	8
Stone masonry (ashlar)	14	12
Interior non-bearing concrete or masonry	48	2

Foundations

Bearing Pressure of Soils. The bearing pressure which may be allowed on soil may vary over a large range. For important structures, the nature of the underlying soil should be ascertained by borings or test pits. If the soil consists of medium or soft clay, a settlement analysis based on consolidation tests of undisturbed soil samples from the foundation strata is necessary. Structures founded upon mud, silt, peat, or artificial filling will almost certainly settle, and no foundation for a permanent structure should rest on or above such material without adequate provision for the resulting settlement. Table 6 gives a general classification of soils and the safe pressures which they may support.

These values approximate the pressures allowed by the building law in most cities. Tests, when the cost thereof is warranted by the magnitude of the project, may show higher values to be safe. The foundation for a building housing heavy vibrating machinery such as steam hammers, heavy punches, and shears should receive some allowance for possible compression and rearrangement of soil due to the vibrations transmitted through it. The foundation for a tall chimney should be designed with a comparatively low pressure upon the soil, because of the disastrous results which might occur from local settlement.

Footings. The purpose of footings is to spread the concentrated loads of building walls and columns over an area of soil so that the unit pressure will come within allowable limits. Footings are usually constructed of concrete. Brick is occasionally used but is generally more expensive than concrete. Where the depth must be kept shal-

Table 6. Safe Bearing on Soils

Nature of soil	Safe bearing capacity, tons per sq ft
Solid ledge of hard rock, such as granite, trap, etc.	25–100
Sound shale and other medium rock, requiring blasting for removal	10–15
Hardpan, cemented sand and gravel, difficult to remove by picking	8–10
Soft rock, disintegrated ledge; in natural ledge, difficult to remove by picking	5–10
Compact sand and gravel, requiring picking for removal	4–6
Hard clay, requiring picking for removal	4–5
Gravel, coarse sand, in natural thick beds	4–5
Loose, medium, and coarse sand; fine compact sand	1.5–4
Medium clay, stiff but capable of being spaded	2–4
Fine loose sand	1–2
Soft clay	1

low, or for other reasons, a grillage of steel beams may be used. Under walls, a single layer of beams may be employed; under columns, two crossed layers with the upper layer no wider than the column base. The steel is embedded in concrete for protection. Stone, where available in quantity and of the proper quality, can sometimes be used economically. Concrete is used either plain or in mass, or reinforced with steel. The offset to each side of the footing for each successive course is determined by figuring the overhanging portion as a cantilever. Plain footings of 1:2½:5 concrete or better (1,800 psi test strength) should have a thickness at least equal to the projection multiplied by $\sqrt{T}$, where T is the soil pressure, tons per sq ft. The center of pressure in the wall or column should always pass through the center of the footing. Footings in ground exposed to freezing should be carried below the possible penetration of frost.

Foundations are ordinarily placed in open excavation, with or without sheeting and bracing. When a suitable bearing soil is more than 10 or 15 ft below the surface, other methods are often desirable. Where the bearing soil is clay stiff enough to stand with undercutting, and the material immediately above it is peat or silt, the **open-caisson method** may be economical. In this method, steel cylinders 3 ft and more in diameter are sunk as excavation proceeds, the cylinders having successively smaller diameters. At the bottom of the shaft thus formed, the soil is undercut to obtain sufficient bearing area. The shaft and the enlargement at the base are then filled with concrete, the cylinders being withdrawn as the concrete is placed. The open-caisson method cannot be used where ground water flows too freely into the excavation. Where foundations under very heavy buildings must be carried to great depth to reach rock or hardpan, particularly where ground water flows freely, the **pneumatic-caisson** method is used.

Pile Foundations. Where satisfactory bearing soil is not to be had at a reasonable depth, and the open-caisson method is for any reason impracticable, piles are often used. **Wood piles** are permanent when continually submerged in water. (Marine borers may attack wood in sea water above the mud line.) A subsequent lowering of the ground-water level, however, may be disastrous, because wood will rot when damp. **Concrete piles** are less destructible, and hence are adaptable to many conditions. Wood piles are usually designed to carry 15 to 20 tons per pile. They should be straight and not less than 6 in. in diam under the bark at the tip. With a concrete pile, 25 to 60 tons or more are carried. Structural **steel** H columns with still higher capacities have been driven for piles where corrosion was not to be feared.

Methods of Driving Piles. The drop hammer and the steam hammer are usually employed in driving piles. The steam hammer, with its comparatively light blows delivered in rapid succession, is of advantage in a plastic soil, the speed with which the blows are delivered preventing the readjustment of the soil. It is also of advantage in soft soils where the driving is easy, but a light hammer may fail to drive a heavy pile satisfactorily. The water jet is sometimes used in sandy soils. Water supplied under pressure at the point of the pile through a pipe or hose run alongside it erodes the soil, allowing the pile to settle into place. To have full capacity, jetted piles should be driven after jetting stops.

Determination of Safe Loads for Piles. Piles may obtain their supporting power from friction on the sides or from bearing at the point. In the latter case, the bearing power may be limited by the strength of the pile, considered as a column, to which, however, the surrounding soil affords some lateral support. In the former case, no precise determination of the bearing power can be made. Many formulas have been developed for determining the safe bearing power in terms of the weight of the hammer, the fall, and the penetration of the pile per blow, the most generally accepted of which is that known as the *Engineering News* formula: $R = 2wh/(s + 1.0)$ for drop hammers, $R = 2wh/(s + 0.1)$ for single-acting steam hammers, $R = 2E/(s + 0.1)$ for double-acting steam hammers, where R = safe load, lb; w = weight of hammer, lb; h = fall of hammer, ft; s = penetration of last blow, in.; E = energy, ft-lb per blow transmitted to the pile. A factor of safety of 6 is assumed. This formula and similar ones are based on the determination of the energy in the falling hammer, and from this the pressure which it must exert on the top of the pile. It is a wise practice to drive test piles and determine their bearing value before proceeding with the final designs of important structures to be supported on piles. The designs then are based upon the safe bearing power so determined, and the piles are driven to the penetration which the above formula, with constants modified to fit the results of the tested piles, shows necessary to give the bearing power for which they were designed.

Concrete piles may be divided into two classes: (1) those molded in place and (2) those precast, cured, and driven. Piles of both classes, longer than 100 ft, have been driven. Piles of the first class are made by driving a mandrel into the ground and filling the hole so formed with concrete. In one well-known pile of this type (Raymond), a thin steel sheet is fitted over a tapered mandrel before driving. This shell, which is left in the ground when the mandrel is withdrawn, is filled with concrete. Another well-known pile (Simplex) of the molded-in-place type uses a hollow cylindrical mandrel which is filled with concrete after having been driven to the desired depth and raised a few feet at a time, the concrete flowing out at the bottom and filling the hole in the earth. Precast and molded-in-place piles may be reinforced with steel. Prestressing of precast concrete piles is a recent innovation giving greater assistance to handling and driving stresses. Jetting is used extensively in placing precast concrete piles, but most are driven into place. Jetting is not often practical or safe in city work because of danger to the foundations of adjoining buildings. Driving by hammer necessitates a cushioned driving head. In underpinning buildings subject to settlement, steel pipes in sections have been jacked down and filled with concrete.

Spacing of Piles. Wood piles are preferably spaced not closer than 2½ ft, and concrete piles 3 ft on centers. If driven closer than this, one pile is liable to force another up. Piles in a group must not cause excessive pressure in soil below their tips. The efficiency, or supporting value of friction piles when driven in groups, by the Converse-Labarre method, is $\dfrac{1 - d/s[(n-1)m + (m-1)n]}{90mn}$, where d = pile diameter, in. s = spacing center to center of piles, in.; m = number of rows; n = number of piles in a row.

Capping of Piles. Piles are usually capped with concrete; wood piles sometimes with timber. Timber capping to be permanent must be kept below ground-water level. Concrete is the most usual material and the most satisfactory for the reason that it gets a full bearing on all piles. The piles should be embedded 4 to 6 in. in the concrete.

Retaining Walls

A wall used to sustain the pressure of earth behind it is called a retaining wall. Retaining walls which depend for their stability upon the weight of the masonry are classed as gravity walls. Such walls built on firm soil will usually be stable when they have the following proportions: top of fill level, back vertical, base, 0.4 height; top of fill level, back battered, base, 0.5 height; top of fill steeply inclined, back vertical, base, 0.5 height; top of fill steeply inclined, back battered, base, 0.6 height. An additional factor of safety is obtained by building the face on a batter. Care should be taken in the design of a wall that the allowable soil pressure is not exceeded and that drainage is provided for the back of the wall. The foundations of retaining walls should be placed below the level of frost penetration. Retaining walls of reinforced concrete are made thin, with a broad base, and the wall either cantilevered from the base or braced with buttresses or counterforts.

It is impossible to derive formulas for the earth pressure on the back of the wall which will take account of all the actual conditions. Assuming the earth to be a loose, homogeneous, granular mass, and the coefficient of friction to be independent of the pressure, Rankine deduced the following formula for a wall with vertical back:

$$P = (\tfrac{1}{2}wh^2 + vh) \cos d(\cos d - \sqrt{\cos^2 d - \cos^2 a})/(\cos d + \sqrt{\cos^2 d - \cos^2 a})$$

the center of pressure being at a height $\tfrac{1}{3}h(wh + 3v)/(wh + 2v)$ above the base, where P = earth pressure per lin ft of the wall, lb; h = height of the wall, ft; w = weight of earth per cu ft, lb; v = weight of superposed load per sq ft of surface, lb; d = the angle with the horizontal of the earth surface behind the wall; and a = angle of repose of the earth, deg. (For values of a, see p. 10–2.) The direction of the pressure is parallel to the earth's surface. The retaining wall should have sufficient thickness at the base so that the resultant of the earth pressure P combined with the weight of the wall falls well within the base. If this resultant falls at the outside edge of the middle third, the maximum vertical pressure on the foundation (at the outer edge of the base) will be equal to $2W/T$ lb per sq ft, where W is the total vertical pressure on the base of 1 ft length of wall and T the thickness of the wall at the base, ft.

In the design of walls of buildings which must withstand earth pressure and low independent walls, where refinement is not necessary, the earth pressure is frequently assumed to be that of a fluid weighing 35 lb per cu ft.

MASONRY CONSTRUCTION

Brickwork. The strength and durability of brick masonry depend upon quality of the brick, quality of the mortar, and workmanship of laying. The strength depends also upon adequate bond and the shape of the structural unit.

Brick. Common red bricks are made of clay burned in a kiln. Quality characteristics are hardness and density. Light-colored brick are apt to be soft and porous. Brick for masonry exposed to the weather or where strength is desired should have a crushing strength of not less than 2,500 psi, and should absorb not over 20 percent of water by weight, after 5 hr immersion (see p. 6–172).

Mortar. Mortars varying over a wide range of proportions are generally classified as (1) portland-cement mortar and (2) cement-lime mortar. Average proportions are, for portland-cement mortar, 1 part cement and 4½ parts sand, by volume, to which may be added slaked-lime paste or dry hydrated lime up to one-half the volume of the cement; for cement-lime mortar, 1 part cement, 1 part lime, and 6 parts sand. Portland-cement mortar should be used for all structural brickwork (see pp. 6–221 *et seq.*).

Laying and Bonding. Brick should be laid in a full bed of mortar and shoved laterally into place to secure solid bearing and a bed of even thickness, and to fill the vertical joints. Brick should be thoroughly wet before laying, except in freezing weather. Brick laid with long dimension parallel to the face of the work are called stretchers, perpendicular to the face, headers. Bats (half-brick) should not be used except where necessary to make corners or to form patterns on the face of the wall. Walls are bonded or tied together longitudinally by overlapping stretchers in successive courses. Transverse bond is obtained by making every sixth course headers, the headers themselves overlapping in successive courses in the interior of thick walls. Variations in the arrangement of headers are often used in the face of walls for appearance. The area of cross section of full-length headers should not be less than one-twelfth the face of the wall, in bonding each pair of transverse courses of brick. Three examples of bond are shown in Fig. 27.

Arches over windows and doorways are laid in concentric rings of headers on edge, with radial joints. The radius of the arch should be 1 to 1¼ times the width of the opening.

Lateral Support. Brick walls should be supported laterally by bonding to transverse walls or buttresses, or by anchoring to floors, at intervals not exceeding 20 times the thickness. Floors and anchors must be capable of transmitting wind pressure and earthquake forces, acting outward, to transverse walls or other adequate supports, and thus to the ground. The height of piers between lateral supports should not exceed 12 times their least dimension.

Stonework. Stone masonry is divided into two general classes: rubble and ashlar (see Fig. 28). **Rubble masonry** work is built up of rough stone of irregular shape and size, coursed and uncoursed. Rubblework is used principally for retaining walls and is sometimes laid up without mortar. Mortar, when used, occupies one-fifth to one-half of the mass, the amount increasing as the stones are smaller. **Ashlar masonry** is built up of stones of rectangular shape on the exterior face of the wall and is further classified into coursed and broken ashlar, depending on whether the stones of the same course are of the same height or of different heights.

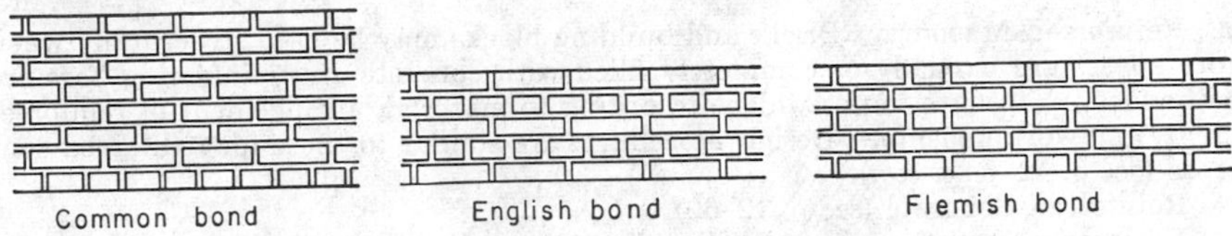

FIG. 27. Bonds used in brick laying.

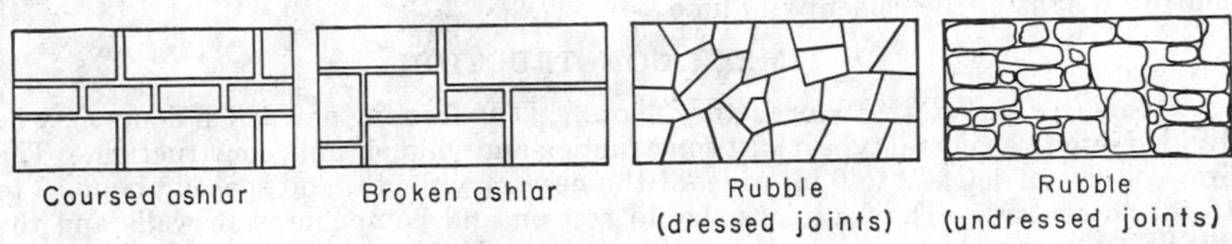

FIG. 28. Ashlar and rubble masonry.

Bond stones should extend through stone walls, in area not less than one-tenth the face of the wall. Lateral support of walls and piers should be provided, as for brickwork.

Building Blocks. Hollow blocks, either of burned clay or concrete, are used in the walls of buildings, often faced with brick or stone. Commercial sizes are designed for bonding with brick. For satisfactory quality, clay tile should have an absorption of not over 16 and concrete not over 10 percent. Clay tile tested with cells horizontal, or concrete blocks as laid, should have compressive strength not less than 700 psi gross area. Walls of hollow blocks or hollow walls of brick bonded across the air space should have lateral support at intervals not exceeding 18 times their thickness.

Faced Walls. Stone or brick facing of walls, when adequately bonded in laying to a backing of brick or hollow blocks, may be considered structurally as part of the wall, working stresses to be those allowed for the backing material.

Allowable working compressive stresses in masonry in pounds per square inch are given in the following table:

Kind of masonry	Cement mortar	Cement-lime mortar	Lime mortar
Stone ashlar	400	320	250
Rubble	300	100	80
Brickwork	175	140	75
Hollow building blocks	80	70	

The allowable stresses in brickwork may be increased 33 percent when the individual bricks have a compressive strength of 3,500 and a modulus of rupture of 600 psi.

Local pressure under concentrations of load may exceed the stresses in the table by 25 percent.

Plain Concrete (see p. 6–225). The allowable working stresses in plain concrete walls and piers are as follows:

Approx proportions	Water, gal per sack of cement	Strength, 28 days, psi	Allowable stress, psi
1-2½-5	8.00	1,500	375
1-2-4	7.50	2,000	500
1-1½-3	6.75	2,500	625
1-1-2	6.00	3,000	750

Reinforced Masonry. Bricks and building blocks may be used structurally when core spaces are partially or completely filled with concrete and reinforcing bars are embedded. Strength varies widely according to material, arrangement of reinforcement, and workmanship. Design procedures are similar to those for reinforced concrete (see p. 12–60 *et seq.*).

Reinforced Concrete (see p. 12–60).

Efflorescence on the face of brickwork can be reduced and sometimes avoided by waterproofing the mortar with an admixture of ammonium or calcium stearate, 2 percent by weight of the cement and lime.

TIMBER CONSTRUCTION

Floors (see also p. 12–10 for factory floors). The framing of wooden floors may be divided into two general types: joist construction and solid, or mill, construction. The first consists of **joists** 2 to 6 in. wide, of the necessary depth, and spaced about 12 to 16 in. on centers. The wall ends should rest on and be anchored to walls and the interior ends carried by a line of girders on columns. These joists should be securely cross-bridged not over 8 ft apart in each span to prevent twisting and to assist in distributing concentrated loads. Solid blocking should be provided at ends and at each point of support. The floor is formed of a thickness of rough boarding on which the finish flooring is laid. **Solid or mill-construction floors** are designed to do away with the small pockets which exist in joist construction and thus reduce the fire hazard. They are generally framed with beams spaced 8 to 12 ft on centers and spanning 18 to 25 ft. The wall ends of beams rest on and are anchored to the wall, and the interior ends are carried on columns and tied together to form a continuous tie across the building. Ends of timbers in masonry walls should have metal bearing plates and ½ in. space at sides and end for ventilation, to prevent rot. The ends should be beveled and the anchors placed low to avoid overturning the wall if the beams drop in a fire. In all cases, care should be taken to provide sufficient bearing at the points of support so that the allowable intensity of compression across the grain is not exceeded. In case it is desirable to omit columns, or the floor load requires a closer spacing of beams, girders are run lengthwise of the building over the columns to take the beams, the ends of which are hung in hangers or stirrup irons and tied together, over or through the girders. This is called **intermediate framing.** Steel beams are sometimes used in place of wooden beams in this type of construction, in which case a wooden strip is bolted to the top flange of the beam to take the nailing of the plank, or the plank is laid directly on top of the beam and secured by spikes driven from below and clinched over the flange. The floor is formed of 3 or 4 in. plank grooved in each edge, put together with splines and securely spiked to beams. On top of the plank is laid flooring, with a layer of sheathing paper between. In case the floor loads require an excessive thickness of plank, or in localities where heavy plank is not easily obtainable, the floor is built up of 3 × 6 in., or other sized pieces, placed on edge, and securely nailed together.

The **roofs** of buildings of joist and mill construction are framed in a manner similar to the floors of each type and should be securely anchored to the walls and columns. In case columns are not desired in the top story, steel beams or trusses of either steel or wood are used. For spans up to 35 ft, trussed beams can often be used to advantage.

For **unit stresses in timber,** see Table 4, p. 6–159. For unit stresses in wooden columns, see Table 9. Table 7 gives the properties of mill floors made of dressed plank, and of laminated floors made of planks on edge, laid close.

Timber Beams

Properties of Timber Beams. Table 8 presents those properties of wooden timbers most useful in computing their strength and deflection as beams. The "nominal size" of a timber is indicated by the breadth and depth of the section in inches. The "actual size" indicates the size of the dressed timber, according to National Lumber Manufacturers Assoc. The moment of inertia and section modulus are with the neutral axis perpendicular to the depth at the center. The **safe bending moment** in inch-pounds for a given beam is determined from the section modulus S by multiplying the tabular value by the allowable fiber stress. To select a beam to withstand safely a given bending moment, divide the bending moment in inch-pounds by the allowable fiber stress, and choose a beam whose section modulus S is equal to or larger than the quotient thus obtained. For formulas for computing bending moments, see Table 2, p. 5–31.

Table 7. Properties of Plank and Solid Laminated Floors

(b = breadth = 12 in., f = fiber stress)

Nominal thickness, or depth, in. (1)	Actual thickness d, in. (S4S) (2)	Area of section $A = bd$, sq in. (3)	Moment of inertia $I = bd^3/12$, in.^{4} (4)	Section modulus $S = bd^2/6$, cu in. (5)	Safe load, lb per sq ft on 1 ft span* f = 1,000 psi† (6)	f = 1,600 (7)	Coef of deflection, uniform load‡ E = 1,000,000 (8)	E = 1,760,000 (9)
1	25⁄32	9.38	0.478	1.218	810	1,300	47.1	26.8
1½	1 5⁄16	15.75	2.26	3.44	2,290	3,660	9.98	5.67
2	1⅝	19.50	4.29	5.28	3,520	5,630	5.25	2.98
2½	2⅛	25.5	9.59	9.03	6,020	9,630	2.35	1.336
3	2⅝	31.5	18.09	13.78	9,180	14,690	1.243	0.707
4	3⅝	43.5	47.6	26.3	17,520	28,050	0.472	0.268
5	4½	54.0	91.1	40.5	27,000	43,200	0.247	0.1404
6	5½	66.0	166.4	60.5	40,300	64,500	0.1348	0.0765
8	7½	90.0	422	112.5	75,000	120,000	0.0533	0.0303
10	9½	114.0	857	180.5	120,400	192,500	0.0263	0.0149
12	11½	138.0	1,521	264.5	176,400	282,000	0.0148	0.0084

* Divide tabular value by square of span in feet.

† For other fiber stress f, multiply tabular value by $f/1{,}000$.

‡ For deflection, in., multiply coefficient by load, lb per sq ft, and by fourth power of span in ft, and divide by 1,000,000. For other modulus of elasticity E, multiply coefficient of col. 8 by 1,000,000, and divide by E.

Maximum loads in Table 8, cols. 7 and 8, are for uniform loading. Use half the values of col. 7 for a single load concentrated at mid-span; for other loadings compute the bending moment and use the section modulus, col. 6. The values of col. 8 apply to all symmetrical loadings. For unsymmetrical loading, compute the maximum shear, which must not exceed one-half the tabular value.

The **coefficients of deflection** given are the deflections, in inches, of beams 1 ft in span, with a uniformly distributed load of 1,000,000 lb, the modulus of elasticity being taken at 1,000,000 psi. The deflection of a beam of a given span under uniformly distributed load is obtained by multiplying the coefficient of deflection of the beam by the cube of the span in feet and by the number of 1,000,000 lb units in the given load. Coefficients of deflection under concentrated loads applied at the middle of the span may be obtained by multiplying the values in the table by 1.6. The results are only approximate as the modulus of elasticity varies with the moisture content of the wood.

The deflection of beams intended to carry plastered ceilings should not exceed 1⁄360 of the span.

A convenient rule may be derived by assuming that the modulus of elasticity is 1,000 times the allowable fiber stress, which applies to all woods with sufficient accuracy for the purpose. Beams loaded uniformly to capacity in bending will then deflect

Table 8. Properties of Wooden Beams (Surfaced Size)

Nominal size, in.	Actual size $b \times d$, in., dressed (S4S) size	Area of section bd, sq in.	Weight at 40 lb per cu ft, lb per ft	Moment of inertia $I = bd^3/12$, in.^{4}	Section modulus $S = bd^2/6$, cu in.	Max safe uniform load, lb, based on: Bending on 1 ft span,* f = 1,000 psi	Max safe uniform load, lb, based on: Shear at 100† psi	Coef‡ of deflection, uniform load E = 1,000,000
(1)	(2)	(3)	(4)	(5)	(6)	(7)	(8)	(9)
2 × 4	1⅝ × 3⅝	5.89	1.64	6.45	3.56	2,370	785	3.49
3 × 4	2⅝ × 3⅝	9.52	2.64	10.4	5.75	3,830	1,269	2.16
4 × 4	3⅝ × 3⅝	13.14	3.65	14.4	7.94	5,290	1,751	1.562
2 × 6	1⅝ × 5½	8.94	2.48	22.55	8.19	5,460	1,192	0.998
3 × 6	2⅝ × 5½	14.44	4.02	36.41	13.24	8,820	1,927	0.618
4 × 6	3⅝ × 5½	19.94	5.54	50.27	18.28	12,180	2,660	0.448
6 × 6	5½ × 5½	30.3	8.40	76.3	27.7	18,490	4,040	0.295
2 × 8	1⅝ × 7½	12.19	3.39	57.1	15.3	10,200	1,621	0.394
3 × 8	2⅝ × 7½	19.69	5.47	92.3	24.6	16,400	2,620	0.244
4 × 8	3⅝ × 7½	27.2	7.55	127	34.0	22,700	3,620	0.1765
6 × 8	5½ × 7½	41.3	11.4	193	51.6	34,400	5,500	0.1162
8 × 8	7½ × 7½	56.3	15.6	264	70.3	46,900	7,500	0.0852
2 × 10	1⅝ × 9½	15.44	4.29	116	24.4	16,290	2,060	0.1931
3 × 10	2⅝ × 9½	24.9	6.93	188	39.5	26,300	3,320	0.1196
4 × 10	3⅝ × 9½	34.4	9.57	259	54.5	36,400	4,580	0.0869
6 × 10	5½ × 9½	52.3	14.5	393	82.7	55,200	6,970	0.0573
8 × 10	7½ × 9½	71.3	19.8	536	113	75,200	9,500	0.0421
10 × 10	9½ × 9½	90.3	25.0	679	143	95,300	12,030	0.0332
2 × 12	1⅝ × 11½	18.69	5.19	206	35.8	23,900	2,490	0.1092
3 × 12	2⅝ × 11½	30.2	8.39	333	57.9	38,600	4,030	0.0675
4 × 12	3⅝ × 11½	41.7	11.6	459	79.9	53,300	5,560	0.0491
6 × 12	5½ × 11½	63.3	17.5	697	121	80,800	8,430	0.0323
8 × 12	7½ × 11½	86.3	23.9	951	165	110,200	11,510	0.0237
10 × 12	9½ × 11½	109.3	30.3	1,204	209	139,600	14,570	0.01864
12 × 12	11½ × 11½	132.3	36.7	1,458	253	169,000	17,620	0.01543
4 × 14	3⅝ × 13½	48.9	13.6	743	110	73,400	6,520	0.0303
6 × 14	5½ × 13½	74.3	20.6	1,128	167	111,400	9,900	0.01987
8 × 14	7½ × 13½	101.3	28.0	1,538	228	152,000	13,500	0.01462
10 × 14	9½ × 13½	128.3	35.6	1,948	289	192,400	17,120	0.01153
12 × 14	11½ × 13½	155.3	43.1	2,360	349	233,000	20,700	0.00953
14 × 14	13½ × 13½	182.3	50.6	2,770	410	273,000	24,300	0.00812
6 × 16	5½ × 15½	85.3	23.6	1,707	220	146,800	11,380	0.01315
8 × 16	7½ × 15½	116.3	32.0	2,330	300	200,000	15,530	0.00967
10 × 16	9½ × 15½	147.3	40.9	2,950	380	254,000	19,610	0.00762
12 × 16	11½ × 15½	178.3	49.5	3,570	460	307,800	23,800	0.00630
14 × 16	13½ × 15½	209	58.1	4,190	541	360,000	27,900	0.00539
16 × 16	15½ × 15½	240	66.7	4,810	621	414,000	32,000	0.00468
8 × 18	7½ × 17½	131.3	36.4	3,350	383	255,000	17,500	0.00672
10 × 18	9½ × 17½	166.3	46.1	4,240	485	323,000	22,200	0.00531
12 × 18	11½ × 17½	201	55.9	5,140	587	391,000	26,800	0.00438
14 × 18	13½ × 17½	236	65.6	6,030	689	459,000	31,500	0.00373
16 × 18	15½ × 17½	271	75.3	6,920	791	528,000	36,200	0.00325
18 × 18	17½ × 17½	306	85.0	7,820	893	595,000	40,800	0.00288
12 × 20	11½ × 19½	224	62.3	7,110	729	485,000	29,900	0.00316
20 × 20	19½ × 19½	380	106	12,050	1,236	824,000	50,700	0.00187
24 × 24	23½ × 23½	552	153	25,400	2,160	1,440,000	73,400	0.000888
26 × 26	25½ × 25½	650	180.6	35,200	2,760	1,840,000	86,700	0.000639
28 × 28	27½ × 27½	756	210	47,700	3,470	2,320,000	100,600	0.000472
30 × 30	29½ × 29½	870	242	63,100	4,280	2,850,000	116,000	0.000356

* For total safe uniform load, pounds, on beam of span L, feet, divide tabular value by L. For fiber stress f other than 1,000 psi, multiply by f and divide by 1,000.

† For shearing stress other than 100 psi, multiply by stress and divide by 100.

‡ For deflection, inches, multiply coefficient by total load, pounds, and by cube of span, feet, and divide by 1,000,000. For other modulus of elasticity E, multiply coefficient by 1,000,000 and divide by E.

1/360 of the span when the depth in inches is 0.90 times the span in feet; and beams with central concentration, when the depth is 0.72 times the span in the same units. For such beams, the deflection in inches is, for uniform load, $0.03L^2/d$; for central concentration, $0.024L^2/d$, where L is the span, ft and d the depth, in. Variation in type of loading affects this result comparatively little.

Timber Columns

Timber columns may be either square or round and should have metal bases, usually cast iron, to cut off moisture and prevent lateral displacement. For supporting beams, they should have caps which, at roofs, may be of cast iron, or wood designed for bearing across the grain. At intermediate floors, caps should be of steel, although cast-iron caps may be used with cast-iron pintles to transmit the load from the columns above, which permit the ends of beams to extend over the shafts of the columns. In some cases hardwood bolsters may be used. Except when pintles are used or beams are of steel, columns should run down and rest directly on the cap or plate. Table 9 gives **working unit stresses for wooden columns** recommended where the building laws do not prescribe lower stresses. Use actual, not nominal, dimensions of timbers. The formula for columns on which Table 9 is based is $P/A = 0.30E/(l/d)^2$. The maximum unit stress should not exceed the allowable unit stress in compression parallel to grain c, as set forth in Table 4, p. 6–159. When computing l/d, both axes of the column should be investigated.

Table 9. Working Stresses for Timber Columns, Psi
(Compression parallel to grain)

E	*l/d*, in. per in.												
	10 or less	15	20	25	30	35	40	45	50	55*	60*	70*	80*
1,000,000	3,000	1,333	750	480	333	245	188	148	120	99	83	61	47
1,100,000	3,300	1,467	825	528	367	269	206	163	132	109	92	67	52
1,200,000	3,600	1,600	900	576	400	294	225	178	144	119	100	74	56
1,300,000	3,900	1,733	975	624	433	318	244	193	156	129	108	80	61
1,400,000	4,200	1,867	1,050	672	467	343	263	207	168	139	117	86	66
1,500,000	4,500	2,000	1,125	720	500	367	281	222	180	149	125	92	70
1,600,000	4,800	2,140	1,200	768	533	392	300	237	192	158	133	98	75
1,700,000	5,100	2,260	1,275	816	567	416	319	252	204	168	142	104	80
1,800,000	5,400	2,400	1,350	864	600	441	338	266	216	178	150	110	85
1,900,000	5,700	2,533	1,425	912	633	465	356	281	228	188	158	116	89
2,000,000	6,000	2,667	1,500	960	667	490	375	296	240	198	167	122	94

* Columns should be limited to $l/d = 50$, except for individual members in stud walls, which should be limited to $l/d = 80$.

Stud Partitions. Table 10 gives the safe load in pounds per linear foot of partition, based both on capacity of the studs as columns and bearing across the grain of the plate or sill. Stresses used are those recommended above. Note that the capacity of the studs is generally more in low partitions than the values for cross bearing unless a hardwood is used for the sill and plate. It is well, however, to provide a margin of strength in the studs to cover cutting for wires, etc.

Connections

Bolted Joints. Compression may be transmitted by merely butting the timbers, with splice pieces bolted to the sides to keep alignment and resist incidental bending and shear. The same detail (Fig. 29) serves in tension, but the entire stress must then be transmitted through the bolts and splice pieces. If of wood, these should have a thickness h equal to $\frac{1}{2}b$. In light, unimportant work, splice pieces may be spiked. Table 11 gives the allowable load in pounds for one bolt loaded at both ends (double shear) when b is at least equal to $2h$. When steel side plates are used for side members, the tabulated loads may be increased 25 percent for parallel-to-grain loading, but no increase should be made for perpendicular-to-grain loads. When a joint consists of two members (single shear), one-half the tabulated load for a

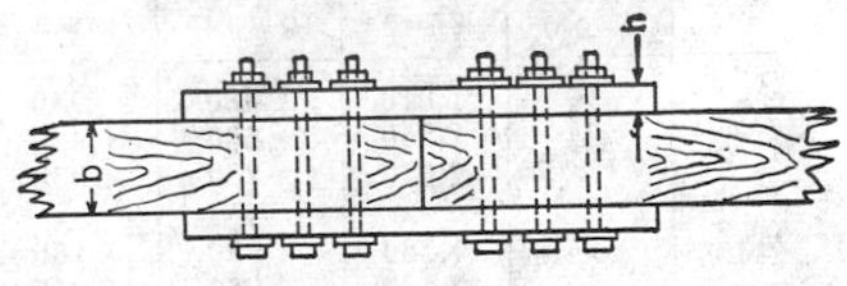

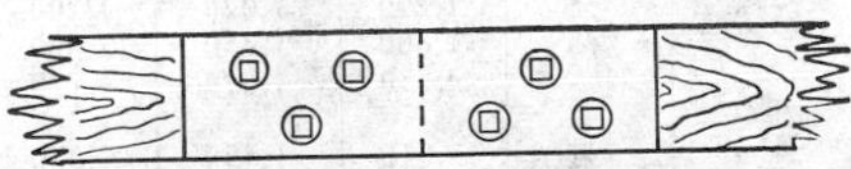

Fig. 29. Bolted splice for timber framing.

Table 10. Safe Loads on Wooden-stud Partitions

Nominal size of studs, in.	Height, ft	Safe load, lb per ft of partition; studs 12 in. on centers*							
		C = 1,000, based on compression parallel to grain c	Based on studs as columns†				Based on bearing across the grain of the plate or sill $c\perp$		
			E = 1,000,000	E = 1,320,000	E = 1,650,000	E = 1,760,000	$C\perp$ = 320	$C\perp$ = 390	$C\perp$ = 455
2 × 3	8	4,270	955	1,260	1,575	1,680	1,360	1,660	1,940
	10		615	810	1,010	1,080			
2 × 4	8	5,890	2,520	3,330	4,160	4,430	1,890	2,300	2,680
	10		1,615	2,130	2,665	2,840			
	12		1,120	1,480	1,850	1,970			
3 × 4	8	9,520	4,080	5,390	6,740	7,180	3,050	3,710	4,330
	10		2,610	3,440	4,310	4,590			
	12		1,815	2,400	3,000	3,200			
4 × 4	8	13,140	5,620	7,420	9,270	9,890	4,210	5,130	5,980
	10		3,600	4,770	5,940	6,330			
	12		2,500	3,300	4,130	4,400			
2 × 6	8	8,930	8,760	11,560	14,450	15,410	2,860	3,480	4,060
	10		5,640	7,450	9,300	9,920			
	12		3,970	5,240	6,550	6,980			
	14		2,860	3,780	4,720	5,030			
	16		2,210	2,920	3,650	3,890			
3 × 6	8	14,450	14,120	18,640	23,300	24,830	4,620	5,640	6,570
	10		9,100	12,010	15,010	16,000			
	12		6,400	8,450	10,560	11,260			
	14		4,630	6,110	7,640	8,140			
	16		3,560	4,700	5,870	6,260			
4 × 6	8	19,940	19,580	25,830	32,300	34,400	6,380	7,770	9,170
	10		12,600	16,620	20,800	22,170			
	12		8,850	11,680	14,600	15,570			
	14		6,400	8,450	10,550	11,260			
	16		4,920	6,490	8,110	8,650			

* For studs 16 in. on centers, multiply tabular value by 0.75.

† 2 × 6 studs bridged twice in height at third points; others, once at mid-height.

Table 11. Allowable Load in Pounds on One Bolt Loaded at Both Ends (Double Shear)

(For additional values and for conditions other than normal, see "National Design Specification for Stress-grade Lumber and Its Fastenings")

Length of bolt in main member, in.	Diam of bolt, in.	Douglas fir, coast and inland		Oak, red and white		Pine, southern		Redwood	
		Parallel to grain	Perpendicular to grain	Parallel to grain	Perpendicular to grain	Parallel to grain	Perpendicular to grain	Parallel to grain	Perpendicular to grain
1⅝	½	1,010	480	940	750	1,010	480	940	380
	¾	1,550	600	1,450	950	1,550	600	1,450	470
	1	2,070	730	1,930	1,140	2,070	730	1,930	570
2⅝	½	1,280	780	1,180	1,210	1,280	780	1,180	610
	¾	2,430	980	2,250	1,530	2,430	980	2,250	760
	1	3,340	1,170	3,110	1,830	3,340	1,170	3,110	920
3⅝	½	1,290	1,020	1,200	1,390	1,290	1,020	1,200	830
	¾	2,860	1,350	2,680	2,110	2,860	1,350	2,680	1,050
	1	4,430	1,620	4,120	2,530	4,430	1,620	4,120	1,270
5½	½	2,010	1,450	1,870	1,910	2,010	1,450	1,870	1,270
	¾	3,940	2,250	3,670	3,310	3,940	2,250	3,670	1,760
	1	6,440	2,680	6,000	4,190	6,440	2,680	6,000	2,090

piece twice the thickness of the thinner member shall apply. The safe load for bolts loaded at an angle θ with the grain of the wood is given by the formula $N = PQ/(P \sin^2 \theta + Q \cos^2 \theta)$, where N = allowable load per bolt in a direction at inclination θ with the direction of the grain, lb; P = allowable load per bolt in compression parallel to the grain, lb; and Q = allowable load per bolt in compression perpendicular to the grain, lb.

The size, arrangement, and **spacing of bolts** must be such that tension on the net section of the timber through the bolt holes and shear along the grain do not exceed allowable values. Bolts should be at least 7 diameters from the end of the timber for softwoods and 5 diameters for hardwoods and spaced at least 4 diameters on center parallel to the grain. Crossbolting, to prevent splitting the timber end, is sometimes desirable.

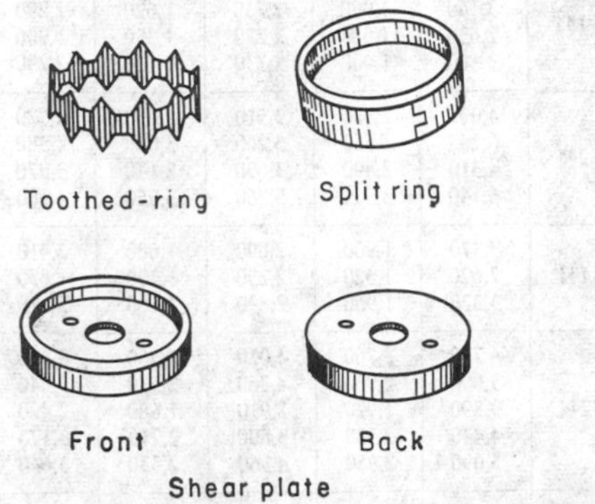

FIG. 30. Timber connectors.

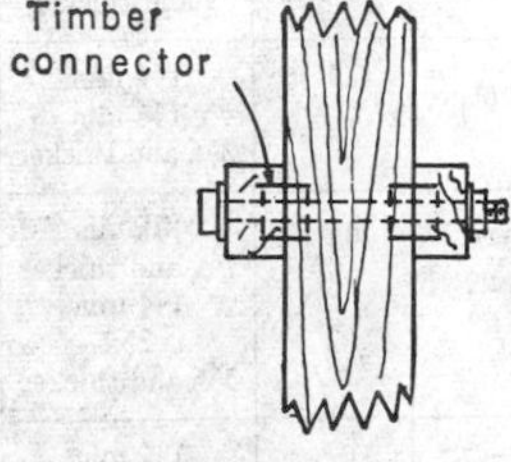

FIG. 31. Timber joint with connectors.

The efficiency of bolted timber connections may be greatly increased by the use of **ring connectors** (see Fig. 30). Split rings and shear plates are fitted into circular grooves, concentric with the bolt, in the contact surfaces, and transmit shear stresses across the joint. Grooves for split rings and shear plates are cut with a special tool, while toothed rings are usually seated by drawing together the timbers with high-strength bolts. Allowable loads for these various connectors are given in the "National Design Specification for Stress-grade Lumber and Its Fastenings," published by the National Lumber Manufacturers Assoc. Selected values are given in Table 12.

The **holding power of wire nails** is as follows ("National Design Specification for Stress-grade Lumber and Its Fastenings"): The resistance to withdrawal is proportional to the length of embedment, to the diameter of the nail (where the wood does not split), and to $G^{2.5}$, where G is the ovendry specific gravity of the wood. The safe resistance to withdrawal of common wire nails driven into the side grain of seasoned wood is given by Table 13. Nails withdrawn from green wood have generally slightly higher resistance, but nails driven into green wood may lose much of their resistance when the wood seasons. The allowable withdrawal load should be one-fourth of that given in Table 13. Cement and other coatings on nails may add materially to their resistance in softwoods. Drilling lead holes slightly smaller than the nail adds somewhat to the resistance and reduces danger of splitting. The structural design should be such that nails are not loaded in withdrawal from end grain. (See also p. 8–127.)

The safe **lateral resistance** of common wire nails driven at least half their length in the side grain of dense hardwood or two-thirds their length in softer woods is given by $P = KD^{3/2}$, where P is the lateral resistance per nail, lb; D is the diameter, in.; and K is 1,350 for cypress (southern), Douglas fir (inland region), and redwood, 1,650 for Douglas fir (coast region), and 2,040 for oak (red and white). These values are for seasoned wood and should be reduced 25 percent for woods which will remain wet or will be loaded before seasoning. For nails driven into end grain, values should be reduced one-third.

Table 12. Allowable Load in Pounds for One-connector Unit in Single Shear*
(For additional values and for conditions other than normal, see "National Design Specification for Stress-grade Lumber and Its Fastenings")

Connector unit, (diam)	Number of faces of piece with connectors on the same bolt	Net thickness of lumber, in.	Min edge distances, in.	Douglas fir, dense Douglas fir (coast region), dense Oak, red and white Pine, southern, dense		Douglas fir Douglas fir (coast region) Pine, southern		Cypress, southern and tidewater red Redwood Spruce, eastern and Sitka	
				Parallel to grain	Perpendicular to grain	Parallel to grain	Perpendicular to grain	Parallel to grain	Perpendicular to grain
2½ in. split ring, ½ in. bolt	1	1 min	1¾	2,630	1,580	2,270	1,350	1,900	1,130
		1⅝ and thicker		3,160	1,900	2,730	1,620	2,290	1,350
	2	1⅝ min		2,630	1,580	2,270	1,350	1,900	1,130
		2 and thicker		3,160	1,900	2,730	1,620	2,290	1,350
4 in. split ring, ¾ in. bolt	1	1 min	2¾	4,090	2,370	3,510	2,030	2,920	1,700
		1⅝ and thicker		6,140	3,560	5,260	3,050	4,380	2,540
	2	1⅝ min		4,310	2,490	3,690	2,140	3,070	1,780
		3 and thicker		6,140	3,560	5,260	3,050	4,380	2,540
2⅝ in. shear plate, ¾ in. bolt	1	1⅝ min	1¾	3,370	1,960	2,890	1,680	2,410	1,400
	2	1⅝ min		2,620	1,520	2,250	1,300	1,870	1,090
		2⅝ and thicker		3,370	1,960	2,890	1,680	2,410	1,400
4 in. shear plate, ¾ in. bolt	1	1⅝ min	2¾	4,750	2,760	4,070	2,360	3,390	1,970
		1¾ and thicker		5,090	2,950	4,360	2,530	3,640	2,110
	2	1¾ min		3,390	1,970	2,910	1,680	2,420	1,400
		2⅝		4,440	2,580	3,800	2,210	3,170	1,840
		3⅝ and thicker		5,090	2,950	4,360	2,530	3,640	2,110
4 in. shear plate, ⅞ in. bolt	1	1¾ min	2¾	4,750	2,760	4,070	2,360	3,390	1,970
		1¾ and thicker		5,090	2,950	4,360	2,530	3,640	2,110
	2	1¾ min		3,390	1,970	2,910	1,630	2,420	1,400
		2⅝		4,440	2,580	3,800	2,210	3,170	1,840
		3⅝ and thicker		5,090	2,950	4,360	2,530	3,640	2,110

* One connector unit consists of one split ring with its bolt in single shear or two shear plates back to back in the contact faces of a timber-to-timber joint with their bolt in single shear.

Table 13. Safe Resistance to Withdrawal of Common Wire Nails in Side Grain of Seasoned Wood

Specific gravity G	Size of nail	d	6	8	10	12	16	20	30	40	50	60
		Length, in.	2	2½	3	3¼	3½	4	4½	5	5½	6
		Diam, in.	0.113	0.131	0.148	0.148	0.162	0.192	0.207	0.225	0.244	0.263
0.39	$p = 1{,}380G^{2.5}D$ lb per in. penetration		15	17	19	19	21	25	27	30	32	34
0.42			18	21	23	23	25	30	33	35	38	41
0.45			21	25	28	28	30	36	39	42	46	49
0.48			25	29	33	33	36	42	46	50	54	58
0.51			29	34	38	38	42	49	53	58	63	68
0.54			33	39	44	44	48	57	61	67	72	78
0.57			38	44	50	50	55	65	70	76	82	89
0.60			44	50	57	57	62	74	80	87	94	101
0.63			49	57	65	65	71	84	90	98	106	115
0.66			55	64	72	72	79	94	101	110	119	128
0.69			62	71	81	81	88	105	113	123	133	143
0.72			69	79	90	90	99	117	126	137	148	160

Common wire **spikes** are larger for their lengths than nails. Their resistance to withdrawal and lateral resistance are given by the same formulas as for nails, but greater precautions need to be taken to avoid splitting. (See also p. 8–127.)

The **resistance of wood screws to withdrawal** from side grain of seasoned wood is given by the formula $P = 2{,}850G^2D$, where P = the allowable load on the screw, lb per in. penetration of the threaded portion; G = specific gravity of ovendry wood; D = diameter of screw, in. Wood screws should not be designed to be loaded in withdrawal from end grain (see also p. 8–31).

Sizes of Wood Screws

No.	6	7	8	9	10	12	14	16	18	20	24
D	0.138	0.151	0.164	0.177	0.190	0.216	0.242	0.268	0.294	0.320	0.372

Approximately two-thirds of the length of a standard screw is threaded.

The **allowable safe lateral resistance** of wood screws embedded 7 diameters in the side grain of seasoned wood is given by the formula $P = KD^2$, where P is the lateral resistance per screw, lb; D is the diameter, in.; and K is 4,000 for oak (red and white), 3,960 for Douglas fir (coast region) and southern pine, and 3,240 for cypress (southern) and Douglas fir (inland region).

The following rules should be observed: (1) the size of the lead hole in soft (hard) woods should be about 70 (90) percent of the core or root diameter of the screw; (2) lubricants such as soap may be used without great loss in holding power; (3) long, slender screws are preferable generally, but in hardwood too slender screws may reach the limit of their tensile strength; (4) in the screws themselves, holding power is favored by thin sharp threads, rough unpolished surface, full diameter under the head, and shallow slots.

The allowable **withdrawal load of lag screws** in side grain is given by the formula $p = 1{,}800D^{3/4}G^{3/2}$, where p = allowable load per inch of penetration of threaded portion of lag screw into member receiving the point, lb; D = shank diameter of lag screw, in.; G = specific gravity of ovendry wood. Use of lag screws loaded in withdrawal from end grain should be avoided. The allowable load in such case should not exceed 75 percent of that for side grain (see also p. 8–30).

The allowable **lateral resistance of lag screws** for parallel-to-grain loading with screws in side grain is given by

$P = 2{,}040D^2$ for southern cypress, and Douglas fir (inland)
$P = 2{,}280D^2$ for Douglas fir (coast) and southern pine
$P = 2{,}640D^2$ for oak, red and white

where P = allowable load per lag screw, lb; D = shank diameter of lag screw, in. The above formulas are based on wood side members having a thickness equal to 3.5 times the shank diameter and a penetration of the threaded portion into the main member of 11 shank diameters for softwoods and 7 diameters for hardwoods. Allowable lateral loads for perpendicular-to-grain loading of lag screws into side grain are obtained by multiplying the above values by a factor varying from 100 percent for 3⁄16 in. diam lag screws to 50 percent for 1 in. diam lag screws.

Lead holes for lag screws (approximately 75 percent of shank diameter) should be prebored for the threaded portion. Lead holes for the shank should be of the same diameter and length as that of the unthreaded shank. Soap or other lubricant should be used to facilitate insertion and to prevent damage to the screw. Where steel-plate side pieces are used, the allowable loads given by the formula for parallel-to-grain loading may be increased by 25 percent.

The ultimate **withdrawal load per linear inch of penetration of a round drift bolt or pin** from side grain when driven into a prebored hole having a diameter ⅛ in. less than that of the bolt diameter may be determined from the formula $p = 6{,}000G^2D$, where p = ultimate withdrawal load of penetration, lb per lin in.; G = specific gravity of ovendry wood; D = diameter of drift bolt, in. A safety factor of about 5 is suggested for general use. The allowable load in lateral resistance for a drift bolt should ordinarily be taken as less than that for a common bolt.

STEEL CONSTRUCTION

(**Note.** In the design of steel structures, 1,000 lb is frequently designated as a kilo-pound or "kip," and a stress of 1 kip per sq in. is designated as 1 ksi.)

Specifications. The following are in part condensed excerpts from the Specifications of the American Institute of Steel Construction.

Material. The ordinary structural steel of recent years, specified by ASTM A7, with yield stress of 33,000 psi is rapidly being supplanted by A36 steel with yield stress of 36,000 psi. Steels of higher strength, A440, A441, and A242, are used in special applications and for highly stressed members of conventional structures.

Ordinary unfinished machine bolts are specified by A307. The most common rivets are specified by A141. Riveting is rapidly being supplanted, both in the shop and in the field, by bolting with high-strength bolts. The most common high-strength bolts are specified by A325. High-strength rivets and extra-high-strength bolts are available for use with high-strength structural steel.

Allowable Stresses, Psi, in A36 Steel

Tension:
- On net section, except at pinholes 22,000
- On net section, at pinholes 16,000

Compression: See Table 14

Bending tension and compression on extreme fibers:
- Basic stress, reduced in certain cases 22,000
- Compact, adequately braced beams 24,000
- Rectangular bearing plates 27,000

Shear—webs of beams, gross section 14,500

Allowable stresses may be increased by one-third when produced by wind or seismic loading alone or when combined with design dead and live loads.

Allowable Stresses, Psi, in Connections

Bearing: A36 steel
- Pins in reamed, drilled, or bored holes 33,000
- Bolts and rivets 48,500
- Rollers, pounds per lin in .... 760 × diam

Shear: bearing-type connections
- A141 hot-driven rivets 15,000
- A307 bolts 10,000
- A325 bolts, when threading is excluded from shear planes 22,000

Tension:
- A325 bolts, when threading is not excluded from shear planes 15,000
- A141 hot-driven rivets 20,000
- A307 bolts 14,000
- A325 bolts 40,000

Bending in pins of A36 steel 33,000

Table 14. Allowable Stress, in Ksi, for Compression Members of A36 Steel

Main and secondary members, Kl/r not more than 120						Main members, Kl/r, 121–200				Secondary members, l/r, 121–200			
$\frac{Kl}{r}$	F_a	$\frac{Kl}{r}$	F_a	$\frac{Kl}{r}$	F_a	$\frac{Kl}{r}$	F_a	$\frac{Kl}{r}$	F_a	$\frac{l}{r}$	F_{as}	$\frac{l}{r}$	F_{as}
1	21.56	41	19.11	81	15.24	121	10.14	161	5.76	121	10.19	161	7.25
5	21.39	45	18.78	85	14.79	125	9.55	165	5.49	125	9.80	165	7.08
10	21.16	50	18.35	90	14.20	130	8.84	170	5.17	130	9.30	170	6.89
15	20.89	55	17.90	95	13.60	135	8.19	175	4.88	135	8.86	175	6.73
20	20.60	60	17.43	100	12.98	140	7.62	180	4.61	140	8.47	180	6.58
25	20.28	65	16.94	105	12.33	145	7.10	185	4.36	145	8.12	185	6.46
30	19.94	70	16.43	110	11.67	150	6.64	190	4.14	150	7.81	190	6.36
35	19.58	75	15.90	115	10.99	155	6.22	195	3.93	155	7.53	195	6.28
40	19.19	80	15.36	120	10.28	160	5.83	200	3.73	160	7.29	200	6.22

Proportion of Parts

Deflection may govern in such members as cantilevers and lightly loaded roof beams. **Buckling,** rather than strength, may govern the design of compression members. The slenderness ratio Kl/r, where Kl is the effective length of the member and r is its radius of gyration, should be limited to 200 in compression members, 240 in main tension members, and 300 in bracing and other secondary tension members. Kl should not be less than the actual unbraced length l in columns of a frame which depends on its bending stiffness for lateral stiffness. **Width-thickness ratios** are specified for projecting elements under compression. **Reversal of stress** leading to fatigue may be a controlling factor. Rules are given for **combined stresses** of tension, compression, bending, and shear.

Tension members should be proportioned for the net section, deducting for bolt or rivet holes ⅛ in. larger than the nominal diameter of the fastener.

Columns and other **compression members** subject to eccentric load or to axial load and bending are governed by special rules. A long-established rule is that $f_a/F_a + f_b/F_b$ should be equal to or less than unity, where f_a is the axial stress, f_b the bending stress, and F_a and F_b are the corresponding allowable stresses if axial or bending stress alone exist. This is still considered valid when f_b/F_a is less than 0.15. Joints shall be fully spliced, except that where reversal of stress is not expected and the joint is laterally supported, the ends of the members may be milled to plane parallel surfaces normal to the stresses and abutted with sufficient splicing to hold the connected members accurately in place. Column bases should be planed on top for the column bearing, except for rolled-steel bearing plates 4 in. or less in thickness.

Beams and girders, of rolled section or built-up, should in general be proportioned by the moment of inertia of the gross section. For A36 steel, flanges in compression should have a thickness of 1⁄16 the projecting half width, and webs should have a thickness of 1⁄320 the maximum clear distance between flanges. Web stiffeners should be provided at points of high concentrated loads; additional web stiffeners are required in plate girders. Splices in the webs of plate girders should be made by plates on both sides of the web. When two or more rolled beams or channels are used side by side to form a beam, they should be connected at separators spaced no more than 5 ft; beams deeper than 12 in. are to have at least two bolts to each separator.

The **lateral force on crane runways** due to the effect of moving crane trolleys may be assumed as 20 percent of the sum of the weights of the lifted loads and of the crane trolley (but exclusive of the other parts of the crane) applied at the top of the rail, one-half on each side of the runway, and shall be considered as acting in either direction normal to the runway rail. The **longitudinal force** may be assumed as 10 percent of the maximum wheel reactions of the crane applied at the top of the rail.

Riveted or **bolted connections** carrying calculated stress, except lacing and sag bars, should be designed to support not less than 6,000 lb. Rivets or high-strength bolts are preferred in all places, and high-strength bolting is implied in these paragraphs wherever riveting is mentioned; unfinished bolts, A307, may be used in the shop or in field connections of small unimportant structures and of secondary members, bracing, and beams.

Members in tension or compression, meeting at a joint, shall have their lines of center of gravity pass through a point, if practicable; if not, provision shall be made for the eccentricity. A group of rivets transmitting stress to a member shall have its center of gravity in the line of the stress, if practicable; if not, the group shall be designed for the resulting eccentricity. Pins and rivet groups may be so placed as to offset the effect of bending in the member due to dead load. Where stress is transmitted from one member to another by rivets through a loose filler, the filler shall be extended beyond the connected member and the extension secured by enough rivets to distribute the total stress in the member uniformly over the combined sections of the member and the filler.

The finished shank of *turned bolts* shall be long enough to provide full bearing, and washers shall be used under the nuts to grip the parts when nuts are turned tight. The holes shall be reamed, after assembly of the connected parts, to a clearance not more than 1⁄50 in. over the diameter of the bolt. (See also p. 8–32.)

The required strength of riveted connections shall be developed by the shearing and bearing values of the rivets, but rivets in shelf angles and brackets, and in connections in so far as they give stiffness to the structure, may transmit stress by tension. Rivets connecting the web to a flange subject to transverse load shall be proportioned for the resultant of the longitudinal and transverse stress. Rivets connecting any portion of a girder flange to the remainder, and thus to the web, shall be proportioned for the increment of stress in that portion, between rivets. The pitch of such rivets is determined as follows: $p = nRI/Vm$, where p is the pitch of rivets in any row, in., n is the number of rows of rivets serving the purpose in question, R is the value of one rivet, lb, whether determined by shear or bearing, V is the transverse shear in the girder, m is the product of the area of cross section of the flange portion in question, times the distance from its center of gravity to the gravity axis of the girder section, in.^{3} I is the moment of inertia of the girder section. (See also p. 8–38.)

Rivets shall be proportioned by the nominal diameter. Rivets whose grip exceeds

5 diam shall be allowed 1 percent less safe stress for each 1/16 in. excess length. The minimum distance between centers of rivet holes shall be 2⅔ diam of the rivet; but preferably not less than 3 diam.

The minimum distance from the center of any rivet hole to a sheared edge shall be 2¼ in. for 1¼ in. rivets, 2 in. for 1⅛ in. rivets, 1¾ in. for 1 in. rivets, 1½ in. for ⅞ in. rivets, 1¼ in. for ¾ in. rivets, 1⅛ in. for ⅝ in. rivets, and 1 in. for ½ in. rivets. The distance from any edge shall not exceed 12 times the thickness of the plate and shall not exceed 6 in.

Pins may be used in heavy trusses of long span where riveted field connection would become unwieldy, or for other reasons. Pinholes in rolled members should be reinforced with plates if necessary, with sufficient rivets to transmit to the member their portion of the pin pressure. Members packed on pins should be held against lateral movement.

Tie Plates. The open sides of compression members built up from plates shall be provided with lacing having tie plates at each end and at intermediate points if the lattice is interrupted. Tie plates shall be as near the ends as practicable. In main members carrying calculated stresses, the end tie plates shall have a length of not less than the distance between the lines of rivets connecting them to the flanges, and intermediate ones of not less than one-half of this distance. The thickness of tie plates shall not be less than one-fiftieth of this distance, and the rivet pitch shall not be more than 6 diam. Tie plates for tension members shall have a length not less than two-thirds that required for compression members.

Lacing bars shall be proportioned to resist a shearing stress normal to the axis of the member equal to at least two percent of the total compression stress in the member. Lacing bars shall preferably be arranged in a single system for which the ratio l/r shall not exceed 140. For double lacing this ratio shall not exceed 200. Double lacing bars shall be joined at their intersections.

The inclination of lacing bars to the axis of the members shall generally be not less than 60 deg for single lacing and 45 deg for double lacing. When the distance between the rivet lines in the flanges is more than 15 in., the lacing shall be double and riveted at the intersection if bars are used, or else shall be made of angles.

Lacing bars shall be so spaced that the ratio l/r of the flange included between their connections shall be not over three-fourths of that of the member as a whole.

Bracing provided in steel frames to resist wind and other lateral forces should preferably be of stiff members and should also serve to brace the frame during erection.

Table 15. Coefficients of Deflection for Steel Beams under Uniformly Distributed Loads

Span, ft	Fiber stress, psi		Span, ft	Fiber stress, psi		Span, ft	Fiber stress, psi		Span, ft	Fiber stress, psi	
	24,000	10,000		24,000	10,000		24,000	10,000		24,000	10,000
1	0.026	0.011	14	4.87	2.029	27	18.1	7.54	39	37.7	15.7
2	0.098	0.041	15	5.59	2.328	28	19.5	8.12	40	39.8	16.6
3	0.223	0.093	16	6.36	2.648	29	20.9	8.71	41	41.8	17.4
4	0.398	0.166	17	7.18	2.990	30	22.4	9.32	42	43.9	18.3
5	0.621	0.259	18	8.04	3.35	31	23.9	9.94	43	45.8	19.1
6	0.892	0.372	19	8.97	3.74	32	25.4	10.60	44	48.0	20.0
7	1.23	0.507	20	9.93	4.14	33	27.0	11.27	45	50.4	21.0
8	1.59	0.662	21	10.9	4.56	34	28.7	11.96	46	52.6	21.9
9	2.01	0.838	22	12.1	5.01	35	30.5	12.7	47	54.7	22.8
10	2.48	1.034	23	13.1	5.47	36	32.2	13.4	48	57.1	23.8
11	3.00	1.251	24	14.3	5.96	37	34.1	14.2	49	59.5	24.8
12	3.58	1.489	25	15.6	6.47	38	35.8	14.9	50	62.2	25.9
13	4.20	1.748	26	16.8	7.00						

For a load concentrated at mid-span, use ⅘ of the coefficient given.

Design of Members

Properties of Standard Structural Shapes. Tables 16 to 23 give the properties of American Standard channels and I beams, wide-flange beams and columns, angles, and tees. In these tables, I = moment of inertia, r = radius of gyration, S = section modulus, x = distance from gravity axis to face, V = max safe shearing strength of the web in kips, and R = max end reaction on 3½ in. seat, based on crippling of web, in kips.

A great variety of tees is produced by shearing or gas-cutting standard beams or wide-flange sections (WF) lengthwise at mid-height of the web, making two similar shapes of T section. Table 23 lists a selection of such tees.

For additional data regarding structural shapes, their strengths as beams and columns, and means of making connections, see "Steel Construction," American Institute of Steel Construction, New York.

Standard Rivet Gages. The standard gages for rivets in angles are given in Table 25, and gages for rivets in the flanges of channels and I beams in Table 26.

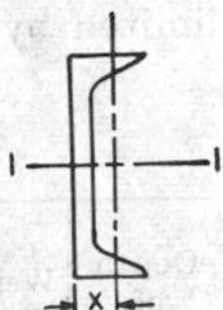

Table 16. American Standard Channels

Depth of channel, in.	Weight per ft, lb	Area of section, sq in.	Width of flange, in.	Thickness of web, in.	Axis 1–1			Axis 2–2	x, in.	V*	R*	Rows in std conn†
					I, in.⁴	r, in.	S, in.³	r, in.		1,000 lb		
15	50.0	14.64	3.716	0.716	401.4	5.24	53.6	0.87	0.80	156	93	4
	40.0	11.70	3.520	0.520	346.3	5.44	46.2	0.89	0.78	113	68	
	33.9	9.90	3.400	0.400	312.6	5.62	41.7	0.91	0.79	87	52	
12	30.0	8.79	3.170	0.510	161.2	4.28	26.9	0.77	0.68	89	63	3
	25.0	7.32	3.047	0.387	143.5	4.43	23.9	0.79	0.68	67	48	
	20.7	6.03	2.940	0.280	128.1	4.61	21.4	0.81	0.70	49	34	
10	30.0	8.80	3.033	0.673	103.0	3.42	20.6	0.67	0.65	98	81	2
	25.0	7.33	2.886	0.526	90.7	3.52	18.1	0.68	0.62	76	63	
	20.0	5.86	2.739	0.379	78.5	3.66	15.7	0.70	0.61	55	45	
	15.3	4.47	2.600	0.240	66.9	3.87	13.4	0.72	0.64	35	29	
9	20.0	5.86	2.648	0.448	60.6	3.22	13.5	0.65	0.59	58	53	2
	15.0	4.39	2.485	0.285	50.7	3.40	11.3	0.67	0.59	37	34	
	13.4	3.89	2.430	0.230	47.3	3.49	10.5	0.67	0.61	30	27	
8	18.75	5.49	2.527	0.487	43.7	2.82	10.9	0.60	0.57	56	...	2
	13.75	4.02	2.343	0.303	35.8	2.99	9.0	0.62	0.56	35	...	
	11.5	3.36	2.260	0.220	32.3	3.10	8.1	0.63	0.58	26	...	
7	14.75	4.32	2.299	0.419	27.1	2.51	7.7	0.57	0.53	43	...	1
	12.25	3.58	2.194	0.314	24.1	2.59	6.9	0.58	0.53	32	...	
	9.8	2.85	2.090	0.210	21.1	2.72	6.0	0.59	0.55	21	...	
6	13.0	3.81	2.157	0.437	17.3	2.13	5.8	0.53	0.52	38	...	1
	10.5	3.07	2.034	0.314	15.1	2.22	5.0	0.53	0.50	27.3	...	
	8.2	2.39	1.920	0.200	13.0	2.34	4.3	0.54	0.52	17.4	...	
5	9.0	2.63	1.885	0.325	8.8	1.83	3.5	0.49	0.48	23.6	...	1
	6.7	1.95	1.750	0.190	7.4	1.95	3.0	0.50	0.49	13.8	...	
4	7.25	2.12	1.720	0.320	4.5	1.47	2.3	0.46	0.46	18.6		
	5.4	1.56	1.580	0.180	3.8	1.56	1.9	0.45	0.46	10.4		
3	6.0	1.75	1.596	0.356	2.1	1.08	1.4	0.42	0.46	15.5		
	5.0	1.46	1.498	0.258	1.8	1.12	1.2	0.41	0.44	11.2		
	4.1	1.19	1.410	0.170	1.6	1.17	1.1	0.41	0.44	7.4		

* V and R values are for channels of A36 steel. † For standard connections see Table 24.

Welding (see also Sec. 13). Advantages of assembling steel frames by welding are quietness of erection compared with riveting and reduction in the amount of metal used. The saving in metal is made through (1) elimination of rivet holes which reduce the net section of tension members, (2) simplification of details, and (3) taking advantage of continuity in beams. For example of simplification, web stiffeners are made of plates with their edges welded to the web.

The AWS Building Code specifies the following working unit stresses for use in designing steel building frames, in pounds per square inch through throat of weld:

Shear, 13,600; tension, compression, and shear on section through throat of butt welds, same as corresponding allowable stress for base metal. The value of 13,600 psi for shear gives the following values per lineal inch for fillets subjected to longitudinal shear: ¼ in. fillets, 2,400 lb; ⅜ in. fillets, 3,600 lb; ½ in. fillets, 4,800 lb. Both gas and electric arc-welding processes are used.

Safe Loads for I Beams. To determine the safe load uniformly distributed, as limited by bending, for a structural steel beam on a given span, apply the formula

Table 17. American Standard I Beams

Depth of beam, in.	Weight per ft, lb	Area of section, sq in.	Width of flange, in.	Thickness of web, in.	Neutral axis perpendicular to web at center			Neutral axis coincident with center line of web			V*	R*	Rows in std conn†
					I, in.^{4}	r, in.	S, in.^{3}	I, in.^{4}	r, in.	S, in.^{3}	1,000 lb		
24	120.0	35.13	8.048	0.798	3010.8	9.26	250.9	84.9	1.56	21.1	278	117	4
	105.9	30.98	7.875	0.625	2811.5	9.53	234.3	78.9	1.60	20.0	218	92	
	100.0	29.25	7.247	0.747	2371.8	9.05	197.6	48.4	1.29	13.4	260	103	
	90.0	26.30	7.124	0.624	2230.1	9.21	185.8	45.5	1.32	12.8	217	86	
	79.9	23.33	7.000	0.500	2087.2	9.46	173.9	42.9	1.36	12.2	174	69	
20	95.0	27.74	7.200	0.800	1599.7	7.59	160.0	50.5	1.35	14.0	232	113	4
	85.0	24.80	7.053	0.653	1501.7	7.78	150.2	47.0	1.38	13.3	189	93	
	75.0	21.90	6.391	0.641	1263.5	7.60	126.3	30.1	1.17	9.4	186	88	
	65.4	19.08	6.250	0.500	1169.5	7.83	116.9	27.9	1.21	8.9	145	68	
18	70.0	20.46	6.251	0.711	917.5	6.70	101.9	24.5	1.09	7.8	186	94	4
	54.7	15.94	6.000	0.460	795.5	7.07	88.4	21.2	1.15	7.1	120	61	
15	50.0	14.59	5.640	0.550	481.1	5.74	64.2	16.0	1.05	5.7	120	71	4
	42.9	12.49	5.500	0.410	441.8	5.95	58.9	14.6	1.08	5.3	89	53	
12	50.0	14.57	5.477	0.687	301.6	4.55	50.3	16.0	1.05	5.8	120	89	3
	40.8	11.84	5.250	0.460	268.9	4.77	44.8	13.8	1.08	5.3	80	60	
	35.0	10.20	5.078	0.428	227.0	4.72	37.8	10.0	0.99	3.9	74	53	
	31.8	9.26	5.000	0.350	215.8	4.83	36.0	9.5	1.01	3.8	61	44	
10	35.0	10.22	4.944	0.594	145.8	3.78	29.2	8.5	0.91	3.4	86	72	2
	25.4	7.38	4.660	0.310	122.1	4.07	24.4	6.9	0.97	3.0	45	38	
8	23.0	6.71	4.171	0.441	64.2	3.09	16.0	4.4	0.81	2.1	51	...	2
	18.4	5.34	4.000	0.270	56.9	3.26	14.2	3.8	0.84	1.9	31	...	
7	20.0	5.83	3.860	0.450	41.9	2.68	12.0	3.1	0.74	1.6	46	...	1
	15.3	4.43	3.660	0.250	36.2	2.86	10.4	2.7	0.78	1.5	25	...	
6	17.25	5.02	3.565	0.465	26.0	2.28	8.7	2.3	0.68	1.3	40.5	...	1
	12.5	3.61	3.330	0.230	21.8	2.46	7.3	1.8	0.72	1.1	20	...	
5	14.75	4.29	3.284	0.494	15.0	1.87	6.0	1.7	0.63	1.0	35.8	...	1
	10.0	2.87	3.000	0.210	12.1	2.05	4.8	1.2	0.65	0.82	15.2		
4	9.5	2.76	2.796	0.326	6.7	1.56	3.3	0.91	0.58	0.65	18.9		
	7.7	2.21	2.660	0.190	6.0	1.64	3.0	0.77	0.59	0.58	11.0		
3	7.5	2.17	2.509	0.349	2.9	1.15	1.9	0.59	0.52	0.47	15.2		
	5.7	1.64	2.330	0.170	2.5	1.23	1.7	0.46	0.53	0.40	7.4		

Lightweight beams of each depth are usual stock sizes.
* V and R values are for beams of A36 steel.
† For standard connections see Table 24.

$W = 8fS/l$, where W is the total load, lb.; f is the fiber stress (20,000 psi or any other); S is the section modulus for the beam in question, given in Tables 16 to 23; and l is the span, in. The safe load concentrated at mid-span is one-half this amount. For other safe loads, note that fS is the safe resistance to bending in inch-pounds afforded by the beam. Compute the load, of whatever type or distribution, which will produce a maximum bending moment equal to safe moment of resistance (see pp. 5–31 to 5–34 for bending-moment formulas).

To select a beam to support a given load, compute the maximum bending moment in inch-pounds, divide by the allowable fiber stress, and refer to the table for a beam having a section modulus which is not smaller than the quotient.

Formulas for the safe loads and deflections of beams with various methods of support and of loading are given in Tables 4 and 5, pp. 5–35, 5–36.

Short beams should be investigated for crippling of the web. In the tables are given the safe end reactions for beams of A36 steel resting on a seat 3½ in. longitudinally of the beam, computed by the formula $R = 27{,}000t(a + k)$, where t = thickness of the web; a = length of the seat; and k = distance from outer face of flange to web toe of fillet; all in inches. Short beams, whose webs are stiffened against crippling, should be investigated for shear, by dividing the maximum shear, in pounds, by the area of the web, excluding the flanges.

Single angles used as beams and loaded in the plane of axis X-X or Y-Y tend to deflect laterally as well as in the plane of the loads. Unless this is prevented, as by pairing the angles back to back and securing them together, the unit fiber stress due to bending may be as much as 40 percent above that computed by dividing the bending moment by S for the axis perpendicular to the plane of the loads. The relation $f = M/S$ does not hold for single angles, and Z bars, which are unsymmetrical about both axes.

Deflection of I Beams and Other Structural Shapes. Table 15 gives **coefficients of deflection** for steel shapes under uniformly distributed loads, and is based on the formula: deflection in inches $= 30fL^2/Ed$, the table giving the values of $30fL^2/E$. (f = fiber stress, psi, L = span, ft; d = depth of section, in.; E = modulus of elasticity = 29,000,000 psi.)

To find the deflection in inches of a section symmetrical about the neutral axis, such as a beam, channel, etc., divide the coefficient in the table corresponding to given span and fiber stress by the depth of the section in inches.

To find the deflection in inches of a section which is not symmetrical about the neutral axis but which is symmetrical about an axis at right angles thereto, such as a tee or pair of angles, divide the coefficient corresponding to given span and fiber stress by twice the distance of extreme fiber from neutral axis obtained from table of elements of sections.

To find the deflection in inches of a section for any other fiber stress than those given, multiply this fiber stress by either of the coefficients in the table for the given span and divide by the fiber stress corresponding to the coefficients used.

I beams and channels loaded to a fiber stress of 20,000 psi will not deflect in excess of $\frac{1}{360}$ of the span (allowed for plastered ceilings) if the depth in inches is not less than 0.62 times the span in feet for uniform loads and 0.50 times the span for central concentration.

Beam Supports. Steel beams are supported at the ends generally (1) by means of web connections to girders and columns, (2) by resting on structural-steel seats, or (3) by resting on masonry. Limiting values of end reactions of the second type, for seats 3½ in. long, are given in Tables 16 to 18. Standard AISC web connections of the first type are called *framed beam* connections and are designated by the number of rows of rivets or bolts. These numbers are listed in Tables 16 to 18, and examples of connections are given in Fig. 32. These connections may be specified as "Standard

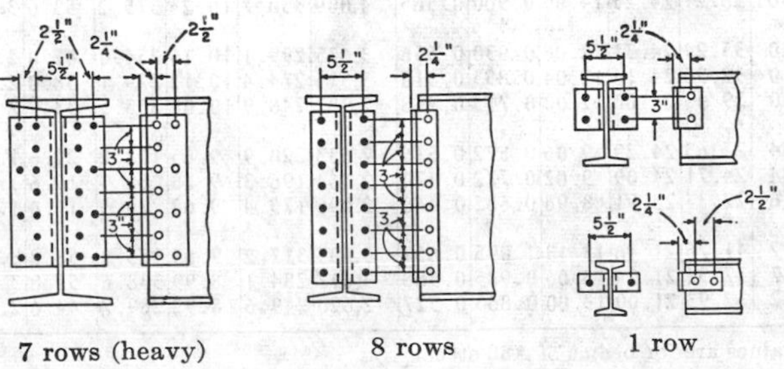

Fig. 32. Framed beam connections.

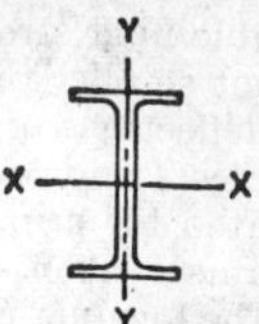

Table 18. Properties of Wide-flange Beams and Columns

Nominal size, in.	Weight per ft, lb	Area of section, sq in.	Depth of section, in.	Flange		Web thickness, in.	Neutral axis perpendicular to web at center			Neutral axis parallel to web at center			V, 1,000 lb*	R, 1,000 lb*	Rows in std conn†
				Width, in.	Thickness, in.		I, in.^{4}	S, in.^{3}	r, in.	I, in.^{4}	S, in.^{3}	r, in.			
36 × 16½	300	88.17	36.72	16.65	1.680	0.945	20,290	1,105	15.17	1,225	147.1	3.73	503	161	10
	280	82.32	36.50	16.59	1.570	0.885	18,819	1,031	15.12	1,127	135.9	3.70	468	148	
	260	76.56	36.24	16.55	1.440	0.845	17,233	951	15.00	1,020	123.3	3.65	444	138	
	245	72.03	36.06	16.51	1.350	0.802	16,092	892	14.95	944	114.4	3.62	419	129	
	230	67.73	35.88	16.47	1.260	0.765	14,988	835	14.88	870	105.7	3.59	398	121	
36 × 12	194	57.11	36.48	12.11	1.260	0.770	12,103	663	14.56	355	58.7	2.49	407	117	10
	182	53.54	36.32	12.07	1.180	0.725	11,281	621	14.52	327	54.3	2.47	382	109	
	170	49.98	36.16	12.02	1.100	0.680	10,470	579	14.47	300	50.0	2.45	357	100	
	160	47.09	36.00	12.00	1.020	0.653	9,738	541	14.38	275	45.9	2.42	341	95	
	150	44.16	35.84	11.97	0.940	0.625	9,012	502	14.29	250	41.8	2.38	325	90	
33 × 15¾	240	70.52	33.50	15.86	1.400	0.830	13,585	811	13.88	874	110.2	3.52	403	133	9
	220	64.73	33.25	15.81	1.275	0.775	12,312	740	13.79	782	99.0	3.48	374	122	
	200	58.79	33.00	15.75	1.150	0.715	11,048	669	13.71	691	87.8	3.43	342	110	
33 × 11½	152	44.71	33.50	11.56	1.055	0.635	8,147	486	13.50	256	44.3	2.39	308	92	9
	141	41.51	33.31	11.53	0.960	0.605	7,442	446	13.39	229	39.8	2.35	292	86	
	130	38.26	33.10	11.51	0.855	0.580	6,699	404	13.23	201	35.0	2.29	278	81	
30 × 15	210	61.78	30.38	15.10	1.315	0.775	9,872	649	12.64	707	93.7	3.38	341	122	8
	190	55.90	30.12	15.04	1.185	0.710	8,825	586	12.57	624	83.1	3.34	310	109	
	172	50.65	29.88	14.98	1.065	0.655	7,891	528	12.48	550	73.4	3.30	284	98	
30 × 10½	132	38.83	30.30	10.55	1.000	0.615	5,753	379	12.17	185	35.1	2.18	270	86	8
	124	36.45	30.16	10.52	0.930	0.585	5,347	354	12.11	169	32.3	2.16	256	81	
	116	34.13	30.00	10.50	0.850	0.564	4,919	327	12.00	153	29.2	2.12	245	77	
	108	31.77	29.82	10.48	0.760	0.548	4,461	299	11.85	135	25.8	2.06	237	74	
27 × 14	177	52.10	27.31	14.09	1.190	0.725	6,728	492.8	11.36	518.9	73.7	3.16	287	110	7
	160	47.04	27.08	14.02	1.075	0.658	6,018	444.5	11.31	458.0	65.3	3.12	258	99	
	145	42.68	26.88	13.96	0.975	0.600	5,414	402.9	11.26	406.9	58.3	3.09	234	88	
27 × 10	114	33.53	27.28	10.07	0.932	0.570	4,080	299.2	11.03	149.6	29.7	2.11	225	79	7
	102	30.01	27.07	10.02	0.827	0.518	3,604	266.3	10.96	129.5	25.9	2.08	203	71	
	94	27.65	26.91	9.99	0.747	0.490	3,266	242.8	10.87	115.1	23.0	2.04	191	65	
24 × 14	160	47.04	24.72	14.09	1.135	0.656	5,110	413.5	10.42	492.6	69.9	3.23	235	97	6
	145	42.62	24.49	14.04	1.020	0.608	4,561	372.5	10.34	434.3	61.8	3.19	216	88	
	130	38.21	24.25	14.00	0.900	0.565	4,009	330.7	10.24	375.2	53.6	3.13	199	80	
24 × 12	120	35.29	24.31	12.08	0.930	0.556	3,635	299.1	10.15	254.0	42.0	2.68	196	78	6
	110	32.36	24.16	12.04	0.855	0.510	3,315	274.4	10.12	229.1	38.0	2.66	179	71	
	100	29.43	24.00	12.00	0.775	0.468	2,987	248.9	10.08	203.5	33.9	2.63	163	64	
24 × 9	94	27.63	24.29	9.06	0.872	0.516	2,683	220.9	9.85	102.2	22.6	1.92	182	69	6
	84	24.71	24.09	9.02	0.772	0.470	2,364	196.3	9.78	88.3	19.6	1.89	164	62	
	76	22.37	23.91	8.98	0.682	0.440	2,096	175.4	9.68	76.5	17.0	1.85	153	56	
21 × 13	142	41.76	21.46	13.13	1.095	0.659	3,403	317.2	9.03	385.9	58.8	3.04	205	96	5
	127	37.34	21.24	13.06	0.985	0.588	3,017	284.1	8.99	338.6	51.8	3.01	181	83	
	112	32.93	21.00	13.00	0.865	0.527	2,620	249.6	8.92	289.7	44.6	2.96	160	73	

* V and R values are for beams of A36 steel.

† For standard connections see Table 24.

Table 18. Properties of Wide-flange Beams and Columns—(*Continued*)

Nominal size, in.	Weight per ft, lb	Area of section, sq in.	Depth of section, in.	Flange		Web thickness, in.	Neutral axis perpendicular to web at center			Neutral axis parallel to web at center			V, 1,000 lb*	R, 1,000 lb*	Rows in std conn†
				Width, in.	Thickness, in.		I, in.^{4}	S, in.^{3}	r, in.	I, in.^{4}	S, in.^{3}	r, in.			
21 × 9	96	28.21	21.14	9.03	0.935	0.575	2,088	197.6	8.60	109.3	24.2	1.97	176	79	5
	82	24.10	20.86	8.96	0.795	0.499	1,752	168.0	8.53	89.6	20.0	1.93	151	67	
21 × 8¼	73	21.46	21.24	8.29	0.740	0.455	1,600	150.7	8.64	66.2	16.0	1.76	140	59	5
	68	20.02	21.13	8.27	0.685	0.430	1,478	139.9	8.59	60.4	14.6	1.74	132	55	
	62	18.23	20.99	8.24	0.615	0.400	1,326	126.4	8.53	53.1	12.9	1.71	122	51	
18 × 11¾	114	33.51	18.48	11.83	0.991	0.595	2,033	220.1	7.79	255.6	43.2	2.76	159	83	4
	105	30.86	18.32	11.79	0.911	0.554	1,852	202.2	7.75	231.0	39.2	2.73	147	77	
	96	28.22	18.16	11.75	0.831	0.512	1,674	184.4	7.70	206.8	35.2	2.71	135	69	
18 × 8¾	85	24.97	18.32	8.83	0.911	0.526	1,429	156.1	7.57	99.4	22.5	2.00	140	71	4
	77	22.63	18.16	8.78	0.831	0.475	1,286	141.7	7.54	88.6	20.2	1.98	125	63	
	70	20.56	18.00	8.75	0.751	0.438	1,153	128.2	7.49	78.5	17.9	1.95	114	57	
	64	18.80	17.87	8.71	0.686	0.403	1,045	117.0	7.46	70.3	16.1	1.93	104	52	
18 × 7½	60	17.64	18.25	7.56	0.695	0.416	984	107.8	7.47	47.1	12.5	1.63	110	53	4
	55	16.19	18.12	7.53	0.630	0.390	889	98.2	7.41	42.0	11.1	1.61	102	49	
	50	14.71	18.00	7.50	0.570	0.358	800	89.0	7.38	37.2	9.9	1.59	93	44	
16 × 11½	96	28.22	16.32	11.53	0.875	0.535	1,355	166.1	6.93	207.2	35.9	2.71	127	74	4
	88	25.86	16.16	11.50	0.795	0.504	1,222	151.3	6.87	185.2	32.2	2.67	118	68	
16 × 8½	78	22.92	16.32	8.58	0.875	0.529	1,042	127.8	6.74	87.5	20.4	1.95	125	71	4
	71	20.86	16.16	8.54	0.795	0.486	936	115.9	6.70	77.9	18.2	1.93	114	64	
	64	18.80	16.00	8.50	0.715	0.443	833	104.2	6.66	68.4	16.1	1.91	103	58	
	58	17.04	15.86	8.46	0.645	0.407	746	94.1	6.62	60.5	14.3	1.88	94	52	
16 × 7	50	14.70	16.25	7.07	0.628	0.380	655	80.7	6.68	34.8	9.8	1.54	90	47	4
	45	13.24	16.12	7.03	0.563	0.346	583	72.4	6.64	30.5	8.7	1.52	81	43	
	40	11.77	16.00	7.00	0.503	0.307	515	64.4	6.62	26.5	7.6	1.50	71	37	
	36	10.59	15.85	6.99	0.428	0.299	446	56.3	6.49	22.1	6.3	1.45	69	36	
14 × 16	426	125.2	18.69	16.69	3.033	1.875	6,610	707.4	7.26	2,359	282.7	4.34	...	...	3
	398	116.9	18.31	16.59	2.843	1.770	6,013	656.9	7.17	2,169	261.6	4.31	...	...	
	370	108.8	17.94	16.47	2.658	1.655	5,454	608.1	7.08	1,986	241.1	4.27	...	...	3
	342	100.6	17.56	16.36	2.468	1.545	4,911	559.4	6.99	1,806	220.8	4.24	...	...	
	314	92.30	17.19	16.23	2.283	1.415	4,399	511.9	6.90	1,631	201.0	4.20	...	...	3
	287	84.37	16.81	16.13	2.093	1.310	3,912	465.5	6.81	1,466	181.8	4.17	...	...	
	264	77.63	16.50	16.02	1.938	1.205	3,526	427.4	6.74	1,331	166.1	4.14	...	...	3
	246	72.33	16.25	15.94	1.813	1.125	3,228	397.4	6.68	1,226	153.9	4.12	...	...	
	237	69.69	16.12	15.91	1.748	1.090	3,080	382.2	6.65	1,174	147.7	4.11	...	...	
	228	67.06	16.00	15.86	1.688	1.045	2,942	367.8	6.62	1,124	141.8	4.10	...	...	3
	219	64.36	15.87	15.82	1.623	1.005	2,798	352.6	6.59	1,073	135.6	4.08	...	...	
	211	62.07	15.75	15.80	1.563	0.980	2,671	339.2	6.56	1,028	130.2	4.07	...	...	
	202	59.39	15.63	15.75	1.503	0.930	2,538	324.9	6.54	979	124.4	4.06	...	...	
14 × 16	193	56.73	15.50	15.71	1.438	0.890	2,402	310.0	6.51	930	118.4	4.05	...	...	3
	184	54.07	15.38	15.66	1.378	0.840	2,274	295.8	6.49	882	112.7	4.04	...	...	
	176	51.73	15.25	15.64	1.313	0.820	2,149	281.9	6.45	837	107.1	4.02	...	...	
	167	49.09	15.12	15.60	1.248	0.780	2.020	267.3	6.42	790	101.3	4.01	...	...	
	158	46.47	15.00	15.55	1.188	0.730	1,900	253.4	6.40	745	95.8	4.00	...	...	3
	150	44.08	14.88	15.51	1.128	0.695	1,786	240.2	6.37	702	90.6	3.99	...	...	
	142	41.85	14.75	15.50	1.063	0.680	1,672	226.7	6.32	660	85.2	3.97	...	...	
	320‡	94.12	16.81	16.71	2.093	1.890	4,141	492.8	6.63	1,635	195.7	4.17	...	...	

* V and R values are for beams of A36 steel.
† For standard connections see Table 24.
‡ Column core section.

Table 18. Properties of Wide-flange Beams and Columns—(*Continued*)

Nominal size, in.	Weight per ft., lb	Area of section, sq in.	Depth of section, in.	Flange		Web thickness, in.	Neutral axis perpendicular to web at center			Neutral axis parallel to web at center			V, 1,000 lb*	R, 1,000 lb*	Rows in std conn†
				Width, in.	Thickness, in.		I, in.^{4}	S, in.^{3}	r, in.	I, in.^{4}	S, in.^{3}	r, in.			
14 × 14½	136	39.98	14.75	14.74	1.063	0.660	1,593	216.0	6.31	567	77.0	3.77	...	...	3
	127	37.33	14.62	14.69	0.998	0.610	1,476	202.0	6.29	527	71.8	3.76	...	...	
	119	34.99	14.50	14.65	0.938	0.570	1,373	189.4	6.26	491	67.1	3.75	120	78	
	111	32.65	14.37	14.62	0.873	0.540	1,266	176.3	6.23	454	62.2	3.73	113	73	
	103	30.26	14.25	14.57	0.813	0.495	1,165	163.6	6.21	419	57.6	3.72	102	66	
	95	27.94	14.12	14.54	0.748	0.465	1,063	150.6	6.17	383	52.8	3.71	95	61	
	87	25.56	14.00	14.50	0.688	0.420	966	138.1	6.15	349	48.2	3.70	85	55	
14 × 12	84	24.71	14.18	12.02	0.778	0.451	928	130.9	6.13	225.5	37.5	3.02	93	59	3
	78	22.94	14.06	12.00	0.718	0.428	851	121.1	6.09	206.9	34.5	3.00	87	56	
14 × 10	74	21.76	14.19	10.07	0.783	0.450	796	112.3	6.05	133.5	26.5	2.48	93	59	3
	68	20.00	14.06	10.04	0.718	0.418	724	103.0	6.02	121.2	24.1	2.46	85	54	
	61	17.94	13.91	10.00	0.643	0.378	641	92.2	5.98	107.3	21.5	2.45	76	48	
14 × 8	53	15.59	13.94	8.06	0.658	0.370	542	77.8	5.90	57.5	14.3	1.92	75	47	3
	48	14.11	13.81	8.03	0.593	0.339	484	70.2	5.86	51.3	12.8	1.91	68	43	
	43	12.65	13.68	8.00	0.528	0.308	429	62.7	5.82	45.1	11.3	1.89	61	38	
14 × 6¾	38	11.17	14.12	6.77	0.513	0.313	385	54.6	5.87	24.6	7.3	1.49	64	38	3
	34	10.00	14.00	6.75	0.453	0.287	339	48.5	5.83	21.3	6.3	1.46	58	34	
	30	8.81	13.86	6.73	0.383	0.270	289	41.8	5.73	17.5	5.2	1.41	54	32	
12 × 12	190	55.86	14.38	12.67	1.736	1.060	1,892	263.2	5.82	589.7	93.1	3.25	...	...	3
	161	47.38	13.88	12.51	1.486	0.905	1,541	222.2	5.70	486.2	77.7	3.20	...	...	
	133	39.11	13.38	12.36	1.236	0.755	1,221	182.5	5.59	389.9	63.1	3.16	...	...	
	120	35.31	13.12	12.32	1.106	0.710	1,071	163.4	5.51	345.1	56.0	3.13	...	...	3
	106	31.19	12.88	12.23	0.986	0.620	930	144.5	5.46	300.9	49.2	3.11	...	...	
	99	29.09	12.75	12.19	0.921	0.580	858	134.7	5.43	278.2	45.7	3.09	...	...	
	92	27.06	12.62	12.15	0.856	0.545	788	125.0	5.40	256.4	42.2	3.08	...	...	
	85	24.98	12.50	12.10	0.796	0.495	723	115.7	5.38	235.5	38.9	3.07	90	65	3
	79	23.22	12.38	12.08	0.736	0.470	663	107.1	5.34	216.4	35.8	3.05	84	61	
	72	21.16	12.25	12.04	0.671	0.430	597	97.5	5.31	195.3	32.4	3.04	76	55	
	65	19.11	12.12	12.00	0.606	0.390	533	88.0	5.28	174.6	29.1	3.02	69	49	
12 × 10	58	17.06	12.19	10.01	0.641	0.359	476	78.1	5.28	107.4	21.4	2.51	63	46	3
	53	15.59	12.06	10.00	0.576	0.345	426	70.7	5.23	96.1	19.2	2.48	60	44	
12 × 8	50	14.71	12.19	8.07	0.641	0.371	394	64.7	5.18	56.4	14.0	1.96	66	48	3
	45	13.24	12.06	8.04	0.576	0.336	350	58.2	5.15	50.0	12.4	1.94	59	43	
	40	11.77	11.94	8.00	0.516	0.294	310	51.9	5.13	44.1	11.0	1.94	51	37	
12 × 6½	36	10.59	12.24	6.56	0.540	0.305	280	45.9	5.15	23.7	7.2	1.50	54	37	3
	31	9.12	12.09	6.52	0.465	0.265	238	39.4	5.11	19.8	6.1	1.47	46	31	
	27	7.97	11.95	6.50	0.400	0.240	204	34.1	5.06	16.6	5.1	1.44	42	28	
10 × 10	112	32.92	11.38	10.41	1.248	0.755	718.7	126.3	4.67	235.4	45.2	2.67	...	...	2
	100	29.43	11.12	10.34	1.118	0.685	625.0	112.4	4.61	206.6	39.9	2.65	...	...	
	89	26.19	10.88	10.27	0.998	0.615	542.4	99.7	4.55	180.6	35.2	2.63	...	...	
	77	22.67	10.62	10.19	0.868	0.535	457.2	86.1	4.49	153.4	30.1	2.60	...	...	
	72	21.18	10.50	10.17	0.808	0.510	420.7	80.1	4.46	141.8	27.9	2.59	...	...	
	66	19.41	10.38	10.11	0.748	0.457	382.5	73.7	4.44	129.2	25.5	2.58	69	59	
	60	17.66	10.25	10.07	0.683	0.415	343.7	67.1	4.41	116.5	23.1	2.57	62	53	
	54	15.88	10.12	10.02	0.618	0.368	305.7	60.4	4.39	103.9	20.7	2.56	54	46	
	49	14.40	10.00	10.00	0.558	0.340	272.9	54.6	4.35	93.0	18.6	2.54	49	42	

* V and R values are for beams of A36 steel.
† For standard connections see Table 24.

Table 18. Properties of Wide-flange Beams and Columns—(*Continued*)

Nominal size, in.	Weight per ft, lb	Area of section, sq in.	Depth of section, in.	Flange		Web thickness, in.	Neutral axis perpendicular to web at center			Neutral axis parallel to web at center			V, 1,000 lb*	R, 1,000 lb*	Rows in std conn†
				Width, in.	Thickness, in.		I, in.^{4}	S, in.^{3}	r, in.	I, in.^{4}	S, in.^{3}	r, in.			
10 × 8	45	13.24	10.12	8.02	0.618	0.350	248.6	49.1	4.33	53.2	13.3	2.00	51	44	2
	39	11.48	9.94	7.99	0.528	0.318	209.7	42.2	4.27	44.9	11.2	1.98	46	39	
	33	9.71	9.75	7.96	0.433	0.292	170.9	35.0	4.20	36.5	9.2	1.94	41	35	
10 × 5¾	29	8.53	10.22	5.79	0.500	0.289	157.3	30.8	4.29	15.2	5.2	1.34	43	34	2
	25	7.35	10.08	5.76	0.430	0.252	133.2	26.4	4.26	12.7	4.4	1.31	37	29	
	21	6.19	9.90	5.75	0.340	0.240	106.3	21.5	4.14	9.7	3.4	1.25	34	27	
8 × 8	67	19.70	9.00	8.28	0.933	0.575	271.8	60.4	3.71	88.6	21.4	2.12	...	...	2
	58	17.06	8.75	8.22	0.808	0.510	227.3	52.0	3.65	74.9	18.2	2.10	...	...	
	48	14.11	8.50	8.11	0.683	0.405	183.7	43.2	3.61	60.9	15.0	2.08	...	...	
	40	11.76	8.25	8.07	0.558	0.365	146.3	35.5	3.53	49.0	12.1	2.04	...	...	
	35	10.30	8.12	8.02	0.493	0.315	126.5	31.1	3.50	42.5	10.6	2.03	37	37	
	31	9.12	8.00	8.00	0.433	0.228	109.7	27.4	3.47	37.0	9.2	2.01	33	...	
8 × 6½	28	8.23	8.06	6.54	0.463	0.285	97.8	24.3	3.45	21.6	6.6	1.62	33	33	2
	24	7.06	7.93	6.50	0.398	0.245	82.5	20.8	3.42	18.2	5.6	1.61	28	...	
8 × 5¼	20	5.88	8.14	5.27	0.378	0.248	69.2	17.0	3.43	8.5	3.2	1.20	29	27	2
	17	5.00	8.00	5.25	0.308	0.230	56.4	14.1	3.36	6.7	2.6	1.16	28	26	

Flanges of wide-flange beams and columns are not tapered, have constant thickness.

Sections without values of V and R are used chiefly for columns.

Lightweight beams for each nominal size, and beams with depth in even inches, are most usually stocked.

Designation of wide-flange beams is made by giving nominal depth and weight, thus, 8 WF 40.

* V and R values are for beams of A36 steel.

† For standard connections see Table 24.

3 row, 4 row, etc., connections." Standard AISC connections for heavier loads are called *heavy framed beam* connections. Special connections must always be designated and detailed when the end reaction exceeds the capacity of the standard connection.

The capacity of web connections is governed by the shearing of the fastener, or the bearing of the fastener on the web or on the material to which the beam is connected, or by the strength of the connecting angles. The supporting values of standard framed beam connections, using ⅞ in. fasteners in members of A36 material, are given in Table 24. For fasteners in webs thicker than 0.42 in. use the values in the column headed Double Shear; for thinner webs, bearing limits the value, and the coefficients for web bearing are to be used. For ¾ in. fasteners, multiply tabular bearing values by $6/7$ and shear values by $36/49$. Fasteners connecting the outstanding legs to the supporting metal are in double shear if two beams are framed opposite or in single shear if a beam is connected on one side only. If the supporting material of A36 steel is thinner than 0.42 in. in double-shear connections or thinner than 0.21 in. in single-shear connections, the capacity is limited by bearing. The value of any ⅞ in. fastener in bearing on A36 material is $42{,}440t$, where t is the thickness of the plate. The value of ⅞ in. A141 rivets or A325 HS bolts is 9,020 lb in single shear and 18,040 lb in double shear. The corresponding values for A307 unfinished bolts are 6,010 lb and 12,030 lb, respectively.

Steel joists consisting of lightweight rolled sections, thin for their height, or open-web trussed members fabricated by welding or otherwise, are used with economy in schools and buildings where spans are long and loads are light, and where a plaster ceiling affords sufficient fire protection. They are rarely used in industrial buildings.

Cast-iron columns were often used in the past instead of wood, to save space, in the lower stories of heavy buildings. Their use is now obsolete, but they are occa-

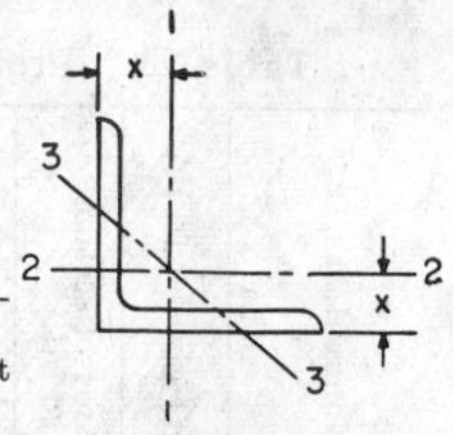

Table 19. Selected Standard Angles, Equal Legs

(One to three intermediate thicknesses in each size group are available, varying by 1/16 in.)

A single angle should never be used as a beam. Two angles, riveted at frequent intervals, may be used. See p. 12–47.

Size, in.	Weight per ft, lb	Area of section, sq in.	Axis 1-1 and axis 2-2				Axis 3-3, *r* min, in.	Net areas after deducting holes for ⅞ in. rivets	
			I, in.⁴	*r*, in.	*S*, in.³	*x*, in.		1 hole	2 holes
8 × 8 × 1⅛	56.9	16.73	98.0	2.42	17.5	2.41	1.56	15.60	14.48
1	51.0	15.00	89.0	2.44	15.8	2.37	1.56	14.00	13.00
⅞	45.0	13.23	79.6	2.45	14.0	2.32	1.57	12.36	11.48
¾	38.9	11.44	69.7	2.47	12.2	2.28	1.57	10.69	9.94
⅝	32.7	9.61	59.4	2.49	10.3	2.23	1.58	8.98	8.36
½	26.4	7.75	48.6	2.50	8.4	2.19	1.59	7.25	6.75
6 × 6 × 1	37.4	11.00	35.5	1.80	8.6	1.86	1.17	10.00	9.00
⅞	33.1	9.73	31.9	1.81	7.6	1.82	1.17	8.86	7.98
¾	28.7	8.44	28.2	1.83	6.7	1.78	1.17	7.69	6.94
⅝	24.2	7.11	24.2	1.84	5.7	1.73	1.18	6.48	5.86
½	19.6	5.75	19.9	1.86	4.6	1.68	1.18	5.25	4.75
⅜	14.9	4.36	15.4	1.88	3.5	1.64	1.19	3.98	3.61
5 × 5 × ⅞	27.2	7.98	17.8	1.49	5.2	1.57	0.97	7.10	6.23
¾	23.6	6.94	15.7	1.51	4.5	1.52	0.97	6.19	5.44
⅝	20.0	5.86	13.6	1.52	3.9	1.48	0.98	5.24	4.61
½	16.2	4.75	11.3	1.54	3.2	1.43	0.98	4.25	3.75
⅜	12.3	3.61	8.7	1.56	2.4	1.39	0.99	3.24	2.86
4 × 4 × ¾	18.5	5.44	7.7	1.19	2.8	1.27	0.78	4.69	3.94
⅝	15.7	4.61	6.7	1.20	2.4	1.23	0.78	3.98	3.36
½	12.8	3.75	5.6	1.22	2.0	1.18	0.78	3.25	2.75
⅜	9.8	2.86	4.4	1.23	1.5	1.14	0.79	2.48	2.11
¼	6.6	1.94	3.0	1.25	1.1	1.09	0.80	1.70	1.45
3½ × 3½ × ½	11.1	3.25	3.6	1.06	1.5	1.06	0.68	2.75	2.25
⅜	8.5	2.48	2.9	1.07	1.2	1.01	0.69	2.10	1.73
¼	5.8	1.69	2.0	1.09	0.79	0.97	0.69	1.44	1.19
3 × 3 × ½	9.4	2.75	2.2	0.90	1.1	0.93	0.58		
⅜	7.2	2.11	1.8	0.91	0.83	0.89	0.58		
¼	4.9	1.44	1.2	0.93	0.58	0.84	0.59		
2½ × 2½ × ½	7.7	2.25	1.2	0.74	0.72	0.81	0.49		
⅜	5.9	1.73	0.98	0.75	0.57	0.76	0.49		
¼	4.1	1.19	0.70	0.77	0.39	0.72	0.49		
2 × 2 × ⅜	4.7	1.36	0.48	0.59	0.35	0.64	0.39		
¼	3.19	0.94	0.35	0.61	0.25	0.59	0.39		
⅛	1.65	0.48	0.19	0.63	0.13	0.55	0.40		
1¾ × 1¾ × ¼	2.77	0.81	0.23	0.53	0.19	0.53	0.34		
⅛	1.44	0.42	0.13	0.55	0.10	0.48	0.35		
1½ × 1½ × ¼	2.34	0.69	0.14	0.45	0.13	0.47	0.29		
⅛	1.23	0.36	0.08	0.47	0.07	0.42	0.30		
1¼ × 1¼ × ¼	1.92	0.56	0.08	0.37	0.09	0.40	0.24		
⅛	1.01	0.30	0.04	0.38	0.05	0.36	0.25		
1 × 1 × ¼	1.49	0.44	0.04	0.29	0.06	0.34	0.20		
⅛	0.80	0.23	0.02	0.30	0.03	0.30	0.20		

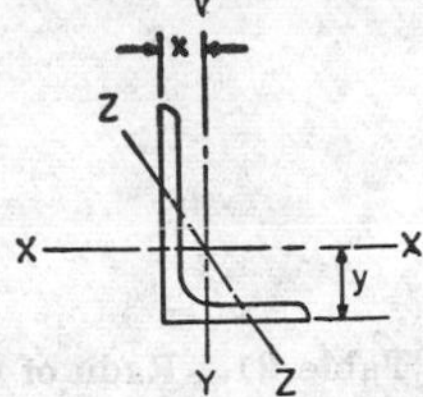

Table 20. Selected Standard Angles, Unequal Legs

(Intermediate thicknesses are available in each size group, varying by 1/16 in. among the thinner angles)

A single angle should never be used as a beam. Two angles, riveted at frequent intervals, may be used. See p. 12–47.

Size, in.	Thickness, in.	Weight per ft, lb	Area of section, sq in.	Axis X-X				Axis Y-Y				Axis Z-Z	Net areas after deducting holes for 7/8 in. rivets	
				I, in.⁴	S, in.³	r, in.	y, in.	I, in.⁴	S in.³	r, in.	x, in.	r, in.	1 hole	2 holes
8 × 6	1	44.2	13.00	80.8	15.1	2.49	2.65	38.8	8.9	1.73	1.65	1.28	12.00	11.00
	3/4	33.8	9.94	63.4	11.7	2.53	2.56	30.7	6.9	1.76	1.56	1.29	9.19	8.44
	1/2	23.0	6.75	44.3	8.0	2.56	2.47	21.7	4.8	1.79	1.47	1.30	6.25	5.75
	7/16	20.2	5.93	39.2	7.1	2.57	2.45	19.3	4.2	1.80	1.45	1.31	5.49	5.06
8 × 4	1	37.4	11.00	69.6	14.1	2.52	3.05	11.6	3.9	1.03	1.05	0.85	10.00	9.00
	3/4	28.7	8.44	54.9	10.9	2.55	2.95	9.4	3.1	1.05	0.95	0.85	7.69	6.94
	1/2	19.6	5.75	38.5	7.5	2.59	2.86	6.7	2.2	1.08	0.86	0.86	5.25	4.75
	7/16	17.2	5.06	34.1	6.6	2.60	2.83	6.0	1.9	1.09	0.83	0.87	4.62	4.18
7 × 4	7/8	30.2	8.86	42.9	9.7	2.20	2.55	10.2	3.5	1.07	1.05	0.86	7.98	7.11
	3/4	26.2	7.69	37.8	8.4	2.22	2.51	9.1	3.0	1.09	1.01	0.86	6.94	6.19
	1/2	17.9	5.25	26.7	5.8	2.25	2.42	6.5	2.1	1.11	0.92	0.87	4.75	4.25
	3/8	13.6	3.98	20.6	4.4	2.27	2.37	5.1	1.6	1.13	0.87	0.88	3.62	3.24
6 × 4	7/8	27.2	7.98	27.7	7.2	1.86	2.12	9.8	3.4	1.11	1.12	0.86	7.10	6.23
	3/4	23.6	6.94	24.5	6.3	1.88	2.08	8.7	3.0	1.12	1.08	0.86	6.19	5.44
	1/2	16.2	4.75	17.4	4.3	1.91	1.99	6.3	2.1	1.15	0.99	0.87	4.25	3.75
	3/8	12.3	3.61	13.5	3.3	1.93	1.94	4.9	1.6	1.17	0.94	0.88	3.24	2.86
	5/16	10.3	3.03	11.4	2.8	1.94	1.92	4.2	1.4	1.17	0.92	0.88	2.72	2.40
6 × 3½	1/2	15.3	4.50	16.6	4.2	1.92	2.08	4.3	1.6	0.97	0.83	0.76	4.00	3.50
	3/8	11.7	3.42	12.9	3.2	1.94	2.04	3.3	1.2	0.99	0.79	0.77	3.04	2.67
	1/4	7.9	2.31	8.9	2.2	1.96	1.99	2.3	0.85	1.01	0.74	0.78	2.06	1.81
5 × 3½	3/4	19.8	5.81	13.9	4.3	1.55	1.75	5.6	2.2	0.98	1.00	0.75	5.06	4.31
	1/2	13.6	4.00	10.0	3.0	1.58	1.66	4.1	1.6	1.01	0.91	0.75	3.50	3.00
	1/4	7.0	2.06	5.4	1.6	1.61	1.56	2.2	0.83	1.04	0.81	0.76	1.81	1.56
5 × 3	1/2	12.8	3.75	9.5	2.9	1.59	1.75	2.6	1.1	0.83	0.75	0.65	3.25	2.75
	3/8	9.8	2.86	7.4	2.2	1.61	1.70	2.0	0.89	0.84	0.70	0.65	2.48	2.11
	1/4	6.6	1.94	5.1	1.5	1.62	1.66	1.4	0.61	0.86	0.66	0.66	1.69	1.44
4 × 3½	5/8	14.7	4.30	6.4	2.4	1.22	1.29	4.5	1.8	1.03	1.04	0.72	3.68	3.05
	1/2	11.9	3.50	5.3	1.9	1.23	1.25	3.8	1.5	1.04	1.00	0.72	3.00	2.50
	3/8	9.1	2.67	4.2	1.5	1.25	1.21	3.0	1.2	1.06	0.96	0.73	2.30	1.92
	1/4	6.2	1.81	2.9	1.0	1.27	1.16	2.1	0.81	1.07	0.91	0.73	1.56	1.31
4 × 3	5/8	13.6	3.98	6.0	2.3	1.23	1.37	2.9	1.4	0.85	0.87	0.64	3.36	2.73
	1/2	11.1	3.25	5.1	1.9	1.25	1.33	2.4	1.1	0.86	0.83	0.64	2.75	2.25
	1/4	5.8	1.69	2.8	1.0	1.28	1.24	1.4	0.60	0.90	0.74	0.65	1.44	1.19
3½ × 3	1/2	10.2	3.00	3.5	1.5	1.07	1.13	2.3	1.1	0.88	0.88	0.62	2.50	
	1/4	5.4	1.56	1.9	0.78	1.11	1.04	1.3	0.59	0.91	0.79	0.63	1.31	
3½ × 2½	1/2	9.4	2.75	3.2	1.4	1.09	1.20	1.4	0.76	0.70	0.70	0.53	2.25	
	1/4	4.9	1.44	1.8	0.75	1.12	1.11	0.78	0.41	0.74	0.61	0.54	1.19	
3 × 2½	1/2	8.5	2.50	2.1	1.0	0.91	1.00	1.3	0.74	0.72	0.75	0.52		
	3/8	6.6	1.92	1.7	0.81	0.93	0.96	1.0	0.58	0.74	0.71	0.52		
	1/4	4.5	1.31	1.2	0.56	0.95	0.91	0.74	0.40	0.75	0.66	0.53		
3 × 2	1/2	7.7	2.25	1.9	1.0	0.92	1.08	0.67	0.47	0.55	0.58	0.43		
	3/16	3.07	0.90	0.84	0.41	0.97	0.97	0.31	0.20	0.58	0.47	0.44		
2½ × 2	3/8	5.3	1.55	0.91	0.55	0.77	0.83	0.51	0.36	0.58	0.58	0.42		
	3/16	2.75	0.81	0.51	0.29	0.79	0.76	0.29	0.20	0.60	0.51	0.43		
2 × 1½	1/4	2.77	0.81	0.32	0.24	0.62	0.66	0.15	0.14	0.43	0.41	0.32		
	1/8	1.44	0.42	0.17	0.13	0.64	0.62	0.09	0.08	0.45	0.37	0.33		
1¾ × 1¼	1/4	2.34	0.69	0.20	0.18	0.54	0.60	0.09	0.10	0.35	0.35	0.27		
	1/8	1.23	0.36	0.11	0.09	0.56	0.56	0.05	0.05	0.37	0.31	0.27		

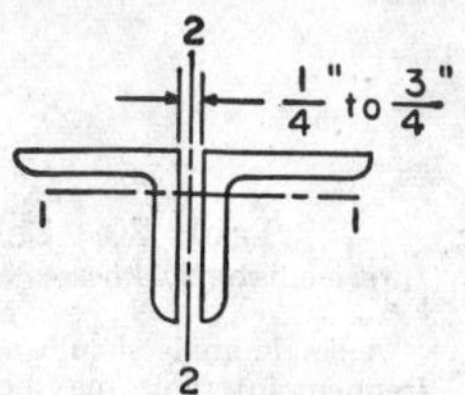

Table 21. Radii of Gyration for Two Angles, Unequal Legs

Single angle		Two angles	Radii of gyration, in.							
			Long legs vertical				Short legs vertical			
				Axis 2-2				Axis 2-2		
Size, in.	Weight per ft, lb	Area, sq in.	Axis 1-1	In contact	⅜ in. apart	¾ in. apart	Axis 1-1	In contact	⅜ in. apart	¾ in. apart
8 × 6 × 1	44.2	26.00	2.49	2.39	2.52	2.66	1.73	3.64	3.78	3.92
7/16	20.2	11.86	2.57	2.31	2.43	2.56	1.80	3.55	3.68	3.82
8 × 4 × 1	37.4	22.00	2.52	1.47	1.61	1.76	1.03	3.95	4.10	4.25
½	19.6	11.50	2.59	1.38	1.51	1.64	1.08	3.86	4.00	4.14
7 × 4 × ⅞	30.2	17.72	2.20	1.50	1.64	1.78	1.07	3.37	3.51	3.66
⅜	13.6	7.96	2.27	1.43	1.55	1.68	1.13	3.28	3.42	3.56
6 × 4 × ⅞	27.2	15.96	1.86	1.57	1.71	1.86	1.11	2.82	2.97	3.11
⅜	12.3	7.22	1.93	1.50	1.62	1.76	1.17	2.74	2.87	3.02
5 × 3½ × ¾	19.8	11.62	1.55	1.40	1.54	1.69	0.98	2.34	2.48	2.63
5/16	8.7	5.12	1.61	1.33	1.45	1.59	1.03	2.26	2.38	2.53
4 × 3½ × ⅝	14.7	8.60	1.22	1.46	1.60	1.75	1.03	1.77	1.91	2.06
5/16	7.7	4.50	1.26	1.42	1.55	1.69	1.07	1.73	1.86	2.00
4 × 3 × ⅝	13.6	7.96	1.23	1.22	1.36	1.51	0.85	1.84	1.99	2.14
¼	5.8	3.38	1.28	1.16	1.29	1.43	0.90	1.78	1.92	2.06
3½ × 3 × ½	10.2	6.00	1.07	1.25	1.38	1.53	0.88	1.56	1.70	1.85
¼	5.4	3.12	1.11	1.21	1.34	1.48	0.91	1.52	1.65	1.80
3 × 2½ × ⅜	6.6	3.84	0.93	1.02	1.16	1.31	0.74	1.34	1.48	1.63
¼	4.5	2.62	0.95	1.00	1.13	1.28	0.75	1.31	1.45	1.60
2½ × 2 × ⅜	5.3	3.10	0.77	0.82	0.96	1.11	0.58	1.13	1.27	1.43
¼	3.6	2.12	0.78	0.80	0.94	1.09	0.59	1.11	1.25	1.40

Table 22. Radii of Gyration for Two Angles, Equal Legs

Single angle		Two angles	Radii of gyration, in.			
				Axis 2-2		
Size, in.	Weight per ft, lb	Area, sq in.	Axis 1-1	In contact	⅜ in. apart	¾ in. apart
8 × 8 × 1⅛	56.9	33.46	2.42	3.42	3.55	3.69
½	26.4	15.50	2.50	3.33	3.45	3.59
6 × 6 × 1	37.4	22.00	1.80	2.59	2.72	2.87
⅜	14.9	8.72	1.88	2.49	2.62	2.76
5 × 5 × ⅞	27.2	15.96	1.49	2.17	2.31	2.45
⅜	12.3	7.22	1.56	2.09	2.22	2.35
4 × 4 × ¾	18.5	10.88	1.19	1.74	1.88	2.03
¼	6.6	3.88	1.25	1.66	1.79	1.93
3½ × 3½ × ½	11.1	6.50	1.06	1.50	1.64	1.78
¼	5.8	3.38	1.09	1.46	1.59	1.73
3 × 3 × ½	9.4	5.50	0.90	1.29	1.43	1.58
¼	4.9	2.88	0.93	1.25	1.38	1.53
2½ × 2½ × ½	7.7	4.50	0.74	1.10	1.24	1.40
¼	4.1	2.38	0.77	1.05	1.19	1.34
2 × 2 × ⅜	4.7	2.72	0.59	0.87	1.02	1.18
¼	3.19	1.88	0.61	0.85	0.99	1.14

sionally encountered in repair and alteration work to older buildings. The ratio of length to least radius of gyration l/r should not exceed 70, and the average unit stress under axial compression should not exceed $9{,}000 - 40l/r$ psi.

Steel pipe is often used for columns under light loads. Table 27 gives the safe loads on standard size pipes (ASTM A53) used as columns. For extra-strong and double extra-strong pipe used as columns, the safe loads will increase approximately in the same proportion as the weight per foot (see pp. 8–200 to 8–205).

Corrugated steel sheets used for roofs and walls are subject to stress in bending. The section modulus of corrugated sheets is approximately $3td$ in.^{3} per in. wide, where t is the thickness of the sheet and d is the over-all depth of the corrugations, in. The safe load, pounds per square foot, in bending is given by the formula $w = 25{,}000td/L^2$ where L is the span in feet. The spacing of purlins on roofs and girts on wall is usually 4 to 5 ft. Numbers 20 and 22, U.S. Standard gage, are generally used for roofing, No. 24 for siding.

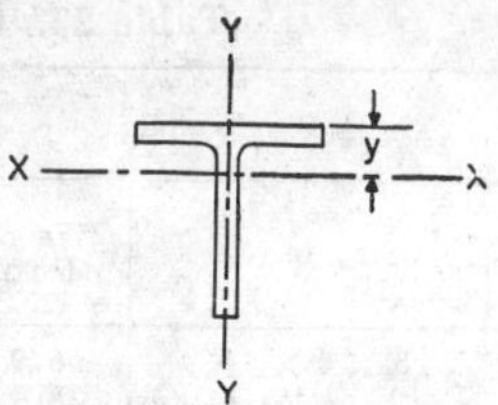

Table 23. Tees Cut from Standard Sections

Section No.	Weight per ft, lb	Area, sq in.	Depth of tee, in.	Flange		Stem thickness, in.	Axis x-x				Axis y-y		
				Width, in.	Avg thickness, in.		I, in.^{4}	S, in.^{3}	r, in.	y, in.	I, in.^{4}	S, in.^{3}	r, in.
ST 18 WF	150	44.1	18.4	16.7	1.68	0.945	1,223	85.9	5.27	4.13	613	73.6	3.73
	115	33.9	17.9	16.5	1.26	0.765	936	67.2	5.26	4.02	436	52.9	3.59
	97	28.6	18.2	12.1	1.26	0.770	904	67.3	5.63	4.81	178	29.3	2.49
	75	22.1	17.9	12.0	0.940	0.625	697	53.0	5.62	4.79	125	20.9	2.38
ST 16 WF	120	35.3	16.8	15.9	1.40	0.830	822	63.2	4.83	3.73	437	55.1	3.52
	100	29.4	16.5	15.8	1.15	0.715	684	53.3	4.82	3.67	346	43.9	3.43
	76	22.4	16.8	11.6	1.06	0.635	592	47.4	5.15	4.26	128	22.1	2.39
	65	19.1	16.6	11.5	0.855	0.580	513	42.1	5.18	4.37	101	17.5	2.29
ST 15 WF	105	30.9	15.2	15.1	1.32	0.775	578	48.7	4.33	3.31	354	46.9	3.38
	86	25.3	14.9	15.0	1.06	0.655	471	40.2	4.31	3.23	275	36.7	3.30
	66	19.4	15.2	10.6	1.00	0.615	421	37.4	4.66	3.90	92.5	17.5	2.18
	54	15.9	14.9	10.5	0.760	0.548	350	32.1	4.69	4.03	67.6	12.9	2.06
ST 13 WF	88.5	26.0	13.7	14.1	1.19	0.725	392	36.7	3.88	2.97	259	36.8	3.16
	72.5	21.3	13.4	14.0	0.975	0.600	316	29.9	3.85	2.85	204	29.1	3.09
	57	16.8	13.6	10.1	0.932	0.570	289	28.3	4.15	3.42	74.8	14.9	2.11
	47	13.8	13.4	9.99	0.747	0.490	238	23.7	4.15	3.41	57.5	11.5	2.04
ST 12 WF	80	23.5	12.4	14.1	1.14	0.656	272	27.6	3.40	2.51	246	35.0	3.23
	60	17.6	12.2	12.1	0.930	0.556	214	22.4	3.48	2.62	127	21.0	2.68
	50	14.7	12.0	12.0	0.775	0.468	177	18.7	3.46	2.54	102	17.0	2.63
	38	11.2	12.0	8.98	0.682	0.440	151	16.9	3.68	3.00	38.3	8.5	1.85
ST 10 WF	71	20.9	10.7	13.1	1.10	0.659	177	20.8	2.91	2.18	193	29.4	3.04
	48	14.1	10.6	9.04	0.935	0.575	137	17.1	3.11	2.55	54.7	12.1	1.97
	41	12.0	10.4	8.96	0.795	0.499	115	14.5	3.09	2.48	44.8	10.0	1.93
	31	9.12	10.5	8.24	0.615	0.400	93.7	11.9	3.21	2.59	26.6	6.45	1.71
ST 9 WF	57	16.8	9.24	11.8	0.991	0.595	103	13.9	2.47	1.85	128	21.6	2.76
	42.5	12.5	9.16	8.84	0.911	0.526	84.4	11.9	2.60	2.05	49.7	11.3	2.00
	32	9.40	8.94	8.72	0.686	0.403	61.8	8.82	2.56	1.93	35.2	8.07	1.93
	25	7.35	9.00	7.50	0.570	0.358	53.9	7.85	2.71	2.14	18.6	4.96	1.59
ST 8 WF	48	14.1	8.16	11.5	0.875	0.535	64.7	9.82	2.14	1.57	104	18.0	2.71
	39	11.5	8.16	8.59	0.875	0.529	60.0	9.45	2.28	1.81	43.8	10.2	1.95
	29	8.52	7.93	8.46	0.645	0.407	43.6	7.00	2.26	1.70	30.2	7.14	1.88
	18	5.30	7.93	6.99	0.428	0.299	30.7	5.10	2.41	1.90	11.1	3.17	1.45
ST 7 WF	105.5	31.0	7.88	15.8	1.56	0.980	102.2	16.2	1.81	1.57	514	65.1	4.07
	71	20.9	7.38	15.5	1.06	0.680	62.1	10.2	1.72	1.29	330	42.6	3.97
	43.5	12.8	7.00	14.5	0.688	0.420	34.9	5.88	1.65	1.08	175	24.1	3.70
	39	11.5	7.03	12.0	0.718	0.428	34.8	5.96	1.74	1.19	104	17.2	3.00
	30.5	8.97	6.96	10.0	0.643	0.378	29.2	5.13	1.80	1.25	53.6	10.7	2.45
	21.5	6.32	6.84	8.00	0.528	0.308	22.2	4.02	1.87	1.33	22.6	5.64	1.89
	15	4.41	6.93	6.73	0.383	0.270	19.0	3.55	2.08	1.59	8.77	2.61	1.41
ST 6 WF	80.5	23.7	6.94	12.5	1.49	0.905	62.6	11.5	1.63	1.47	243	38.9	3.20
	32.5	9.55	6.06	12.0	0.606	0.390	20.6	4.06	1.47	0.98	87.3	14.6	3.02
	26.5	7.80	6.03	10.0	0.576	0.345	17.7	3.54	1.51	1.02	48.0	9.60	2.48
	20	5.89	5.97	8.00	0.516	0.294	14.4	2.94	1.56	1.08	22.0	5.50	1.94
	13.5	3.98	5.98	6.50	0.400	0.240	11.4	2.39	1.69	1.21	8.3	2.55	1.44

Table 23. Tees Cut from Standard Sections—(*Continued*)

Section No.	Weight per ft, lb	Area, sq in.	Depth of tee, in.	Flange Width, in.	Flange Avg thickness, in.	Stem thickness, in.	Axis x-x I, in.^{4}	Axis x-x S, in.^{3}	Axis x-x r, in.	Axis x-x y, in.	Axis y-y I, in.^{4}	Axis y-y S, in.^{3}	Axis y-y r, in.
ST 5 WF	56	16.5	5.69	10.4	1.25	0.755	28.8	6.42	1.32	1.21	118	22.6	2.67
	24.5	7.20	5.00	10.0	0.558	0.340	10.1	2.40	1.18	0.81	46.5	9.30	2.54
	16.5	4.85	4.88	7.96	0.433	0.292	7.80	1.95	1.27	0.88	18.2	4.58	1.94
	10.5	3.10	4.95	5.75	0.340	0.240	6.31	1.62	1.43	1.06	4.87	1.69	1.25
ST 4 WF	33.5	9.85	4.50	8.29	0.933	0.575	10.9	3.07	1.05	0.94	44.3	10.7	2.12
	15.5	4.56	4.00	8.00	0.433	0.288	4.31	1.30	0.97	0.67	18.5	4.60	2.01
	12	3.53	3.97	6.50	0.398	0.245	3.53	1.08	1.00	0.70	9.10	2.80	1.61
	8.5	2.50	4.00	5.25	0.308	0.230	3.21	1.01	1.13	0.84	3.36	1.28	1.16
ST 6 I	25	7.29	6.00	5.48	0.660	0.687	25.2	6.05	1.85	1.84	7.85	2.87	1.03
	15.9	4.63	6.00	5.00	0.544	0.350	14.9	3.31	1.78	1.51	4.68	1.87	1.00
ST 5 I	12.7	3.69	5.00	4.66	0.491	0.310	7.81	2.05	1.45	1.20	3.39	1.46	0.95
ST 4 I	9.2	2.67	4.00	4.00	0.425	0.270	3.50	1.14	1.14	0.94	1.86	0.93	0.83
ST 3.5 I	7.65	2.22	3.50	3.66	0.392	0.250	2.18	0.81	0.99	0.81	1.32	0.72	0.77
ST 3 I	6.25	1.81	3.00	3.33	0.359	0.230	1.27	0.55	0.83	0.69	0.93	0.56	0.71

Table 24. Values of Standard Framed-beam Connections

(⅞ in. A141 rivets or ⅞ in. A325 HS bolts, A36 members)

AISC designation	Two angles, size	Fasteners in outstanding legs: No.	Fasteners in outstanding legs: Single* shear, 1,000 lb	Fasteners in web legs: No.	Fasteners in web legs: Double shear, 1,000 lb	Fasteners in web legs: Bearing, 1,000 lb
10 rows........	4 × 3½ × ⅜ × 2′5½″	20	180	10	180	424*t*
9 rows........	4 × 3½ × ⅜ × 2′2½″	18	164	9	164	382*t*
8 rows........	4 × 3½ × ⅜ × 1′11½″	16	144	8	144	340*t*
7 rows........	4 × 3½ × ⅜ × 1′8½″	14	126	7	126	297*t*
6 rows........	4 × 3½ × ⅜ × 1′5½″	12	108	6	108	255*t*
5 rows........	4 × 3½ × ⅜ × 1′2½″	10	90	5	90	212*t*
4 rows........	4 × 3½ × ⅜ × 0′11½″	8	72	4	72	170*t*
3 rows........	4 × 3½ × ⅜ × 0′8½″	6	54	3	54	127*t*
2 rows........	4 × 3½ × ⅜ × 0′5½″	4	56	2	36	85*t*
1 row........	6 × 4 × ⅜ × 0′3″	2	18	2	36	85*t*

* If the web of the supporting beam is thinner than 0.21 in. (0.42 in. if beams frame on both sides) bearing must also be investigated.

Table 25. Gages for Angles, Inches

Leg	8	7	6	5	4	3½	3	2½	2	1¾	1½	1⅜	1¼	1
g^1	4½	4	3½	3	2½	2	1¾	1⅜	1⅛	1	⅞	⅞	¾	⅝
g^2	3	2½	2¼	2										
g^3	3	3	2½	1¾										
Max rivet	1⅛	1	⅞	⅞	⅞	⅞	⅞	¾	⅝	½	⅜	⅜	⅜	¼

For diagonal angles, etc., gage in middle, where riveted leg equals or exceeds 3 in. for ¾ in. rivets, 3½ in. for ⅞ in. rivets. Use special gages to adapt work to multiply punch, or to secure desirable details. Rivet size may be increased in thin angles by adjusting gage lines.

Table 26. Standard Gages in Flanges of Channels and I Beams; Maximum Rivets

Section	Depth, in.	Weight per ft, lb	Gage, in.	Max rivet, in.	Depth, in.	Weight per ft, lb	Gage, in.	Max rivet, in.	Depth, in.	Weight per ft, lb	Gage, in.	Max rivet, in.	Depth, in.	Weight per ft, lb	Gage, in.	Max rivet, in.
American Standard channels	15	50	2¼	1	10	30	1¾	¾	8	18.75	1½	¾	6	13.0	1⅜	⅝
	15	40	2	1	10	20	1½	¾	8	13.75	1⅜	¾	6	10.5	1⅛	⅝
					9	20	1½	¾					5	9.0	1⅛	½
	12	30	1¾	⅞	9	15	1⅜	¾	7	14.75	1¼	⅝	4	7.25	1	½
													3	6	⅞	½
American Standard I beams	24	120	4	1	18	70	3½	⅞	10	35	2¾	¾	6	17.25	2	⅝
	20	95	4	1	15	50	3½	¾					5	14.75	1¾	½
	20	75	3½	⅞					8	23.0	2¼	¾	4	9.5	1½	½
					12	50	3	¾	7	20	2¼	⅝	3	7.5	1½	⅜
Wide-flange beams	36	. . .	5½		18	114	5½		14	. . . . .	5½		10	112	5½	
	33	. . .	5½													
	30	. . .	5½		18	60	3½		14	38	3½	1	10	29	2¾	⅞
	27	. . .	5½						12	. . . . .	5½		8	67	5½	1
	24	. . .	5½		16	96	5½	1					8	28	3½	1
	21	. . .	5½		16	50	3½	1	12	36	3½	1	8	20	2¾	⅞

Gage in channels is the distance from center of rivet holes to flat side of the channel; in I beams it is the distance between lines of rivet holes in opposite flanges.

For weights lighter than those tabulated, the gage and maximum rivet are the same as for the next heavier tabulated section.

Table 27. Safe Axial Loads for Standard Pipe Columns, Kips

(Stress according to AISC Specification for A36 material*)

(For structural-steel columns, see p. 12–48)

Nominal pipe size, in.	Outside diam, in.	Wall thickness in.	Length of column, ft										
			6	7	8	9	10	11	12	14	16	18	20
3	3.500	0.216	25.3	24.2	22.8	21.4	19.7	17.9	15.9	12.4	9.2	6.9	
3½	4.000	0.226	31.5	30.4	29.0	28.0	26.4	24.7	22.8	20.9	17.0	11.7	9.2
4	4.500	0.237	37.8	36.8	35.7	34.5	33.0	31.5	30.0	26.1	21.8	17.6	14.3
5	5.563	0.258	52.5	51.8	50.8	49.7	48.7	47.2	45.8	42.3	38.5	34.2	29.4
6	6.625	0.280	69.0	68.3	67.5	66.3	65.2	64.2	62.7	60.0	56.8	52.5	47.8
8	8.625	0.277	91.0	90.5	90.0	89.0	88.5	87.5	86.3	84.0	81.6	78.7	75.0
8	8.625	0.322	105	104	103	102	102	100	100	96.4	93.6	90.3	86.2
10	10.750	0.279	115	115	114	114	113	112	112	110	108	106	103
10	10.750	0.307	127	126	126	125	124	123	123	120	118	115	109
10	10.750	0.365	150	149	149	148	147	146	145	142	140	136	133
12	12.750	0.330	163	162	162	161	160	159	159	157	155	153	150
12	12.750	0.375	184	184	183	182	182	180	180	178	176	173	170

For dimensions of standard pipe see pp. 8–200 *et seq.* Underscored safe loads are for values of l/r more than 120 but not over 200.

* Pipe is not manufactured to A36 specification; however pipe ordered to ASTM A53, type E or S grade B, or to API standard 5L grade B will have a yield point of 35 ksi and may be designed at stresses allowed for A36 steel.

Fire Resistance. (See also p. 12–194.) The resistance to fire of building materials has been tested extensively by various agencies. Standard methods of performing these tests are established by ASTM E119. Table 28 gives the fire-resistance rating of a few of the common building materials and methods of construction as established by the National Board of Fire Underwriters from standard fire tests.

Table 28. Selected Fire-resistance Ratings

Type	Details of construction	Rating
Reinforced-concrete beams and girders	Expanded slag concrete, 1½ in. clear to reinforcement Concrete (calcareous or siliceous gravel), 1½ in. clear to reinforcement	4 hr 3 hr
Steel beams, girders, and trusses	1½ in. gypsum-perlite plaster on metal lath, ¼ in. clear of steel 1 in. gypsum-perlite plaster on metal lath Ceiling of 1 in. gypsum-perlite plaster on metal lath with 2½ in. min air space between lath and structural members	4 hr 1 hr 4 hr
Cast-iron columns, 7 in. diam and larger	2 in. concrete, cinder aggregate 1½ in. portland-cement plaster on ¾ in. rib metal lath, ½ in. max air space	2½ hr 3 hr
Reinforced-concrete columns	Concrete (limestone, calcareous gravel, traprock or slag) 1½ in. clear to reinforcement; 12 in. columns or larger Concrete (granite, sandstone, or siliceous gravel) 2½ in. clear to reinforcement; 16 in. columns or larger	4 hr 4 hr
Steel columns, 8 × 8 in. or larger	Concrete (siliceous gravel): 2½ in. clear to reinforcement 2 in. clear to reinforcement 1 in. clear to reinforcement 1½ in. gypsum-perlite plaster on metal lath spaced from flanges with ¾ in. steel furring channels 1 in. portland-cement plaster on metal lath; no fill	 4 hr 3 hr 2 hr 4 hr 1 hr
Reinforced-concrete slabs	6 in. concrete (traprock, limestone, or siliceous gravel) 1 in. clear to reinforcement 4¾ in. concrete (traprock, limestone, or siliceous gravel) ¾ in. clear to reinforcement	3 hr 2 hr
Heavy-timber floors	6 in. laminated plank floor with 1 in. finish flooring	1 hr
Wood joists	Wood floor; 1 in. tongue-and-groove subfloor and finish floor with building paper between. Ceiling of ⅝ in. Underwriters' Laboratories listed wallboard	1 hr
Brick walls	Solid walls, unplastered, with no combustible members framed in wall: 8 in. nominal 4 in. nominal	 4 hr 1 hr
Concrete masonry units	8 in. Underwriters' Laboratories listed concrete blocks, laid as specified in Underwriters' Laboratories listing 4 in. Underwriters' Laboratories listed concrete blocks; cells filled with perlite mortar and laid as specified in Underwriters' Laboratories listing	4 hr 4 hr
Steel-stud partitions	1 in. gypsum and sand plaster both sides on metal lath ⅝ in. gypsum wallboard on 3⅝ in. steel studs; attached with 2 in. cement-coated nails; joints taped and cemented	2 hr 1 hr
Wooden-stud partitions	Exterior walls; one side covered with ½ in. gypsum sheathing and wood siding; other side faced with ½ in. gypsum and sand plaster on ⅜ in. perforated gypsum lath ⅞ in. gypsum and sand plaster on metal lath each side	1 hr 1 hr
Plain or reinforced-concrete walls	Solid, unplastered (siliceous or granite aggregate): 7½ in. thick 6½ in. thick 5½ in. thick 4 in. thick	 4 hr 3 hr 2 hr 1 hr

REINFORCED CONCRETE DESIGN AND CONSTRUCTION

BY

Clyde E. Kesler

References: Ferguson, "Reinforced Concrete Fundamentals," Wiley. Dunham, "Theory and Practice of Reinforced Concrete," McGraw-Hill. Lin, "Design of Prestressed Concrete Structures," Wiley. "Building Code Requirements for Reinforced Concrete (318–63)," American Concrete Institute. Turneaure and Maurer, "Principles of Reinforced Concrete Construction," Wiley. Hool and Johnson, "Concrete Engineers' Handbook," McGraw-Hill. "Formwork for Concrete," SP-4, American Concrete Institute.

The design, theory, and notation of this chapter are in general accord with the 1963 Building Code Requirements for Reinforced Concrete of the American Concrete Institute, though many detailed provisions have been omitted.

Standard Notation

Columns

A_c = net area of concrete section of composite column = $A_g - A_s - A_r$
= area of concrete within a pipe column
A_g = over-all or gross area of column
A_r = area of steel or cast-iron core of a composite, combination, or pipe column
A_s = $p_g A_g$ = area of vertical steel
d = least lateral dimension
f_c' = compressive strength of concrete from 6 by 12 in. cylinders
f_r = allowable stress in metal core = 16,000 psi for a steel core or 10,000 psi for a cast-iron core
f_r' = allowable stress on pipe columns
f_s = nominal allowable compressive stress in vertical reinforcement for spiral columns
= 40 percent of the minimum yield strength but not to exceed 30,000 psi
f_s' = useful limit strength of spiral = 40,000 psi for intermediate-grade hot-rolled rod, 50,000 psi for hard-grade rods, and 60,000 psi for cold-drawn wire and rods, ASTM A432 grade
h = unsupported length of column
K_c = radius of gyration of concrete in pipe columns
K_s = radius of gyration of metal pipe in pipe column
P = allowable axial load on column
p_g = ratio of area of vertical reinforcement A_s to gross column area A_g
p' = ratio of volume of spiral reinforcement to volume of column core
R = ratio of gross area to core area of column

Rectangular Beams

a = area of stirrup steel within one spacing, s
A_s = area of longitudinal reinforcement
b = width of beam
d = effective depth of beam from compression face to centroid of steel
f_c = compressive unit stress in concrete
f_s = tensile unit stress in steel
jd = arm of resisting couple
kd = distance from compression face to neutral axis
M = resisting moment
n = ratio of modulus of elasticity of steel E_s to that of concrete E_c
Σo = sum of perimeters of all longitudinal bars at a section
p = steel ratio, A_s/bd
R = coefficient in formula $M = Rbd^2$
s = horizontal spacing of stirrups
u = bond stress per unit area of bar
v = shearing unit stress
V = total vertical shear
V' = vertical shear in excess of that allowed on unreinforced web
z = distance from compression face to resultant of compressive stresses

T Beams

b = width of flange
b' = width of stem
t = thickness of flange

Beams with Compression Reinforcement

C = total compressive force in concrete
C' = total compressive force in steel
d' = distance from compressive face to center of compressive steel
f_s' = compressive unit stress in steel
p' = steel ratio for compression steel
z = distance from compression face to resultant of C and C'

Two-way Slabs

C = moment coefficient from Table 6
m = ratio of short span to long span
S = length of short span
w = total uniform load per sq ft

Flat Slabs

c = diameter of circular column capital
L = span length, center to center of columns, in direction in which moments are computed
L_1 = span length, center to center of columns, perpendicular to direction in which moments are computed
t_1 = total thickness of slab at boundary of column capital
t_2 = total thickness of slab beyond boundary of drop

Footings

A = total area at top of footing or pedestal
A' = loaded area under column base
f_b = allowable working stress for concrete in column
f_c' = compressive strength of concrete in footing or pedestal

S = ratio of long side to short side

Walls

h = vertical distance between supports
t = thickness of wall

Prestressed Concrete

A_s = area of prestressed tendons
A_{sr} = area of tendon required to develop the web
A_v = area of web reinforcement placed perpendicular to the axis of the member
b = width of compression face of flexural member
b' = minimum width of web of a flanged member
d = distance from extreme compression fiber to centroid of the prestressing force
D = dead load
E = earthquake load
f_{ci}' = compressive strength of concrete at time of initial prestress
f_s' = ultimate strength of prestressing steel
f_{su} = calculated stress in prestressing steel at ultimate load
f_{sy} = nominal yield strength of prestressing steel
f_y = yield strength of shear reinforcement
L = live load including impact
M_u = ultimate resisting moment
p = A_s/bd; ratio of prestressing steel
s = longitudinal spacing of web reinforcement
t = average thickness of the compression flange of a flanged member
U = required ultimate load capacity
V_c = shear carried by concrete
V_u = shear due to specified ultimate load
W = wind load

MATERIALS

Reinforced concrete is a combination of concrete and steel acting as a unit as a result of the adhesion between the two materials. Concrete has a high compressive strength and a relatively low tensile strength. Beams of plain concrete fail by tension under very low stresses, but if reinforced by the embedment of steel in their tensile portion, they may be stressed to the compressive working limit of concrete. Reinforced concrete structures are practically monolithic, more rigid than steel and substantially fireproof. Reinforcement for concrete also prevents cracks due to changes of temperature and shrinkage in members such as walls and slabs.

Concrete. For reinforced concrete work, only first-class portland cement concrete must be used, and the aggregates must be carefully selected. The proportions are governed by the required strength, durability, economy, and the quality of the aggregates. The most common mixture for building construction contains about 5½ bags of cement per cu yd. Generally, lean mixtures must be avoided because the adhesion or bond to the steel is small, and permeability will likely be increased. Proper design of the concrete mixture and control of the proportioning, mixing, and placing of high-strength concrete, make it safe to use high design strengths. Large quantities of 5,000 to 7,000 psi strength concrete are now used. The advantages of using this mixture instead of one with leaner proportions and lower stresses are that a more workable and a more durable concrete of good density is obtained; there is an added advantage in the smaller size of the structural members. A consistency that will flow sluggishly but not be so wet as to produce a separation of the material when transported to the work must be used for all reinforced concrete work in order to embed the steel and fill the corners of the molds or forms. The use of vibration makes it desirable to use stiffer concretes than otherwise (see also pp. 6–220 *et seq.*).

Steel. Reinforcing steel may be deformed or smooth bars, welded-wire fabric, or special high-strength wire and strand for prestressed concrete. Bars with deformations on their surfaces are designed to produce mechanical bond and greater adhesion between the steel and the concrete. Plain bars are seldom used in the United States. Deformed bars are preferable for short, heavily loaded beams where large bending moments are developed in a short distance or where the construction is subjected to unusual vibration or has to resist temperature stresses. Fabric reinforcement, such as welded-wire fabric and expanded metal, is suitable in certain cases for slabs, walls, and partitions. The use of fabric in some cases results in savings in labor costs. Recently, deformed wires have been used in the manufacture of welded-wire fabric and may have some advantage with regard to the control of cracks. Deformed reinforcing bars having minimum yield points from 33,000 to 75,000 psi are now manufactured. The higher-strength steels have the advantage of allowing higher working stresses than the lower-strength grades. However, their ductility may be somewhat less, and it may not be possible to cold-bend the higher-strength bars. The ASTM specifies all the various steels used in reinforced concrete, and any steel so used should comply with these standard specifications.

Reinforcing Steel Sizes. The sizes of reinforcing bars have been standardized, and non-standard sizes are difficult to obtain. Whereas reinforcing bar sizes previously were designated by fractions of an inch, they are now referred to by numbers. Generally speaking, the number of the bar is based on the number of ⅛ in. segments included in the nominal diameter of the bar. Table 1 gives the bar sizes, nominal diameter, cross-sectional area, and perimeter.

Table 1. Dimensions of Deformed Bars

No.	Diam, in.	Area, sq in.	Perimeter, in.
2*	0.250	0.05	0.786
3	0.375	0.11	1.178
4	0.500	0.20	1.571
5	0.625	0.31	1.963
6	0.750	0.44	2.356
7	0.875	0.60	2.749
8	1.000	0.79	3.142
9	1.128	1.00	3.544
10	1.270	1.27	3.990
11	1.410	1.56	4.430
14*S*	1.693	2.25	5.32
18*S*	2.257	4.00	7.09

* No. 2 bars are obtainable in plain rounds only.

The sizes of wire used in reinforcing are given in gages. Table 2 gives various dimensions for the different gages.

Moduli of Elasticity. For concrete the modulus of elasticity E_c may be taken as $w^{1.5}33\sqrt{f_c'}$ in psi, where w is the weight of the concrete between 90 and 155 lb per cu ft. Normal weight concrete may be assumed to weigh 145 lb per cu ft. For steel the modulus of elasticity may be taken as 29,000,000 psi, except for prestressing steel for which the modulus shall be determined by tests or supplied by the manufacturer.

The **modular ratio** $n = E_s/E_c$ is of great importance in designing reinforced concrete. It may be taken as the nearest whole number but not less than six. The value of n for lightweight concrete may be taken as the same for normal weight concrete of the same strength, except in calculations for deflections.

Table 2. Dimensions of Wires

Gage	Diam, in.	Area, sq in.
0000000	0.4900	0.1886
000000	0.4615	0.1673
00000	0.4305	0.1456
0000	0.3938	0.1218
000	0.3625	0.1032
00	0.3310	0.08605
0	0.3065	0.07378
1	0.2830	0.06290
2	0.2625	0.05412
3	0.2437	0.04665
4	0.2253	0.03987
5	0.2070	0.03365
6	0.1920	0.02895
7	0.1770	0.02461
8	0.1620	0.02061
9	0.1483	0.01727
10	0.1350	0.01431

Protection of Reinforcement. Reinforcement, for both regular and prestressed concrete, must be protected by the concrete so as to prevent corrosion. The amount of cover needed for various degrees of exposure is as follows.

Member and exposure	Cover, in.
Concrete surface deposited against the ground	3
Concrete surface to come in contact with the ground after casting:	
Reinforcement larger than No. 5	2
Reinforcement smaller than No. 5	1½
Beams and girders not exposed to weather:	
Main steel	1½
Stirrups and ties	1
Joists, slabs, and walls not exposed to weather	¾
Column spirals and ties	1½

Except for joists and slabs, the cover must be at least equal to the bar diameter, and for columns the cover must be 1½ times the maximum size of the coarse aggregate.

The amount of protection recommended is a minimum, and when corrosive environments or other severe exposure occurs, the cover should be increased. The concrete in the cover should be made as impermeable as possible.

LOADS

The dead and live loads are combined in determining the cross section of members. Span lengths of continuous slabs and beams or elastic frames should be taken as the distance between centers of supports. In slabs built integrally with supports capable of full restraint, the effective span may be taken as the clear distance between supports. In case of heavy moving loads, allowance should be made for impact by increasing the live load from 25 to 100 percent.

The **live load** (pounds per square foot) to be used for design depends upon the loadings that will occur in the particular structure as well as on the requirements of the local building code. The Boston Building Code illustrates good practice and is as follows for floor loads:

Heavy manufacturing, sidewalks, heavy storage, truck garages, 250; public garages, intermediate manufacturing, and hangars, 150; stores, heavy merchandise, light storage, 125; armories, assembly halls, gymnasiums, grandstands, public portions of hotels, theaters, and public buildings, corridors and fire escapes from public assembly buildings, light merchandising stores, stairs, first and basement floors of office buildings, theater stages, 100; upper floors of public buildings, office portions of public buildings, stairs, corridors and fire escapes except from public assembly buildings, theater and assembly halls with fixed seats, light manufacturing, locker rooms, stables, 75; church auditoriums, 60; office buildings above first floor including corridors, classrooms with fixed seats, 50; residence buildings and residence portions of hotels, apartment houses, clubs, hospitals, educational and religious institutions, 40.

Live loads assumed to be affecting structural members supporting considerable tributary floor area are normally reduced owing to the fact that such areas are not all loaded at the same time. Roofs are required to support a vertical load of 30 lb per sq ft. Wind loads are taken from 10 to 30 lb per sq ft of vertical projection of the structure with the higher portions of a structure subjected to higher loads (see also p. 12–17).

Dead loads include the weight of the structural members and all fixed loads. The weights of some typical floor, wall, and ceiling constructions, exclusive of the structural concrete (Taylor, Thompson, and Smulski, *op. cit.*), are as follows.

Description	Weight, lb per sq ft
Granolithic finish per inch of thickness	12
Hardwood floors	
7/8 in. hardwood top, 13/16 in. intermediate floor, screeds, 2 in. cinder concrete fill	21
Same except 1 5/8 in. intermediate planking	23
Same except intermediate floor omitted	18
7/8 in. hardwood top, intermediate floor, 1 5/8 plank and tar base	16
3 in. wood-block floor in coal-tar pitch	10
Cinder concrete fill 2 in. thick	14
Plaster on concrete or tile (two coats)	5
Plaster on lath	10
Suspended ceiling	12

ALLOWABLE UNIT STRESSES

The following unit stresses are recommended for use in applying the design rules given here, except for prestressed concrete:

Steel reinforcement, tension:

Structural grade bars, 18,000 psi; wire fabric and bars less than 3/8 in. diam in one-way slabs of not more than 12 ft span, one-half of yield point but not to exceed 30,000 psi; deformed bars with a yield strength of 60,000 psi or more and in sizes No. 11 or less, 24,000 psi; all other reinforcement, 20,000 psi.

Steel reinforcement, compression in columns (see section on Columns).

Concrete, extreme fiber stress in compression, $0.45f_c'$.

Concrete, shearing unit stress:

Beams, no web reinforcement, $1.1\sqrt{f_c'}$ (for lightweight aggregate concrete, $0.68\sqrt{f_c'}$).

Beams with vertical or inclined web reinforcement or properly combined bent bars and vertical stirrups, $5\sqrt{f_c'}$. Reinforcement must provide for total shear.

Slabs and footings, peripheral shear, $2\sqrt{f_c'}$ (for lightweight aggregate concrete, $1.2\sqrt{f_c'}$).

Concrete, bond:

Deformed bars in tension:

(1) Top bars, horizontal bars with 12 in. of concrete cast below:

Conforming to ASTM A305, $(3.4\sqrt{f_c'})/D$, not to exceed 350 psi;

Conforming to ASTM A408, $2.1\sqrt{f_c'}$.

(2) Bars other than top bars:
Conforming to ASTM A305, $(4.8\sqrt{f_c'})/D$, not to exceed 500 psi;
Conforming to A408, $3\sqrt{f_c'}$.

Deformed bars in compression:
$6.5\sqrt{f_c'}$, not to exceed 400 psi.

Plain bars (must be hooked):
One-half of the allowable bond stresses for bars conforming to ASTM A305 but not exceeding 160 psi.

Concrete, bearing stress:

On full area, $0.25f_c'$; on partial area, $0.375f_c'$.

REINFORCED CONCRETE COLUMNS

Loads on columns include all the tributary fixed or dead loads and a proportion of the total live load depending on the likelihood of complete loading. Taylor, Thompson, and Smulski (*loc. cit.*) recommend the following for columns in buildings.

No. of floors carried by column	1	2	3	4	5	6	7	8	9 and over
Proportion of live load to be taken by columns:									
Ordinary buildings	1.00	0.85	0.80	0.75	0.70	0.65	0.60	0.55	0.50
Warehouses	1.00	0.90	0.87	0.84	0.81	0.78	0.75	0.75	0.75

Piers of short length up to four times the least diameter and loaded centrally may be built of plain concrete. Columns longer than this and also piers and columns subject to cross bending must be reinforced. An outside shell of a thickness equal to 1½ in. should be considered as fireproofing. The usual mixtures for concrete columns contain six to eight bags of cement per cu yd. For columns carrying heavy loads, the cross section may be reduced by using a high-strength mixture of concrete. As the steel is stressed only to eight or ten times the allowable stress in the concrete, the use of a large amount of steel is not economical; better economy is obtained by using rich mixtures. Reinforcement of columns usually consists of (1) longitudinal bars with ties; (2) longitudinal bars with circular spirals; (3) rigid structural shapes with longitudinal and spiral reinforcement (composite columns); (4) steel columns encased in concrete with wire mesh (combination columns). Steel pipe filled with concrete is also used for columns in concrete construction.

The following rules apply to axially loaded columns in which the unsupported length h does not exceed ten times the least lateral dimension d. For more slender columns, the allowable load given by Eqs. (**1**) and (**3**) should be multiplied by the factor $(1.3 - 0.03h/d)$.

Spirally Reinforced Columns. For columns with longitudinal reinforcement consisting of six or more bars of ⅝ in. min diam and with closely spaced spirals enclosing a circular core, the allowable axial load P is

$$P = 0.25A_g f_c' + A_s f_s \tag{1}$$

In such columns, p_g should not be less than 0.01 nor more than 0.08. The ratio p' of the volume of spiral reinforcement to the volume of column core should not be less than given by the equation

$$p' = 0.45(R - 1)\frac{f_c'}{f_s'} \tag{2}$$

The spiral wire should have a minimum diameter of ¼ in. for columns up to 18 in. in core diameter and ⅜ in. for columns of larger core diameters. The clear spacing between spiral wires should not exceed 3 in. nor be less than 1⅜ in., or 1½ times the maximum size of coarse aggregate used.

Tied Columns. For columns with longitudinal reinforcement consisting of four or more bars of ⅝ in. min diam and having separate lateral ties, the allowable axial load P shall be 85 percent of that given by Eq. (**1**). The ratio p_g for tied columns should not be less than 0.01 nor more than 0.04.

Composite Columns. For columns consisting of a structural-steel or cast-iron core thoroughly encased in concrete reinforced with both longitudinal and spiral reinforcement, the axial load P may be determined from

$$P = 0.225A_c f_c' + A_s f_s + A_r f_r \tag{3}$$

The area of metal cores should not exceed 20 percent of the gross A_g. The reinforcement limits are the same as for spirally reinforced columns. Special care must be taken in such columns with splices, connections, and provisions for transferring load to the column and to the footing.

When a larger amount of steel is used, the column may be considered as a combination column, *i.e.*, a structural steel column strengthened by the concrete. The concrete must be reinforced by welded-wire fabric having wire not smaller than 10 gage spaced vertically not more than 4 in. and horizontally not more than 8 in. Concrete must not be relied upon as a binding material, and the shapes composing the structural-steel column must be riveted together and tied by tie plates or lattice bars and in other respects designed in conformity with standard practice for structural steel. Bearing plates and brackets must be provided to take up and transfer loads.

Concrete-filled Pipe Columns. For columns made by filling steel pipe with concrete, the axial load P is

$$P = 0.25f_c'\left(1 - 0.000025\frac{h^2}{K_c^2}\right)A_c + f_r'A_r \tag{4}$$

where $f_r' = 17{,}000 - 0.485h^2/K_s^2$ when the pipe has a yield strength of at least 33,000 psi and an h/K_s ratio less than 120.

Columns Subjected to Bending. When a column is subjected to bending in addition to direct compression, the stresses due to the bending must be added to the direct compression stresses, and the resulting unit stress must not exceed the allowable unit stress for the column.

REINFORCED CONCRETE BEAMS

The live loads to be used in the design of beams carrying floor slabs may be reduced where it is not probable that the entire slab will be fully loaded at any time. The following provisions are typical:

Every plank, slab, and arch, and every floor beam carrying 100 sq ft of floor or less shall be of sufficient strength to bear safely the combined dead and live load supported by it, but the floor live loads may be reduced for other parts of the structure as follows:

In all buildings except armories, garages, gymnasiums, storage buildings, wholesale stores, and assembly halls, for all flat slabs of over 100 sq ft area reinforced in two or more directions and for all floor beams, girders, or trusses carrying over 100 ft of floor, 10 percent reduction.

For the same but carrying over 200 sq ft of floor, 15 percent reduction.

For the same but carrying over 300 sq ft of floor, 25 percent reduction.

These reductions shall not be made unless the supporting member carries more than one floor.

In public garages, for all flat slabs of over 300 sq ft area reinforced in more than one direction, and for all floor beams, girders, and trusses carrying over 300 sq ft of floor, and for all columns, walls, piers, and foundations, 25 percent reduction. These provisions do not apply to roofs.

In addition to longitudinal tension reinforcement, which is always required, compression reinforcement is sometimes provided in beams where the dimensions of the member are limited. Reinforcement against diagonal tension is provided, when required, by stirrups, bent-up bars, or both. Beam formulas are based on the following assumptions, in addition to the usual ones for homogeneous beams, (1) the concrete provides no tensile resistance in flexure, (2) the concrete is perfectly bonded to the reinforcing steel, (3) there are no initial stresses.

Rectangular Beams (Fig. 1). Beam design must provide against failure by tension, compression, diagonal tension, and bond. For tension, the resisting moment, in terms of steel stress, is

$$M_s = A_s f_s jd \tag{5}$$

For compression, the resisting moment, in terms of concrete stress is

$$M_c = f_c kjbd^2/2 \tag{6}$$

For a balanced design,

$$M_s = M_c = Rbd^2 \tag{7}$$

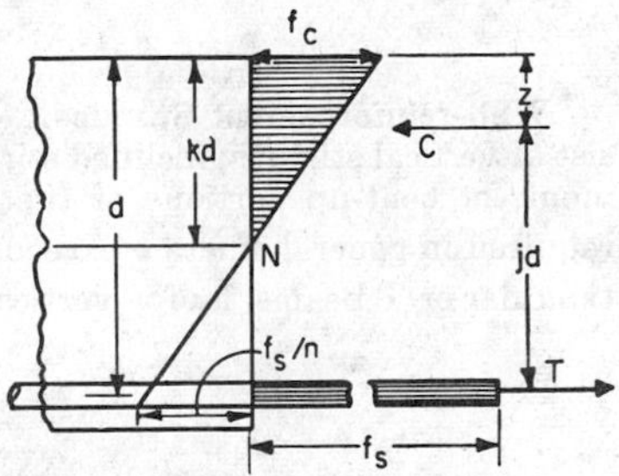

FIG. 1. Distribution of stress in a reinforced-concrete beam.

where $R = f_s pj = f_c kj/2$.

In these expressions, the neutral axis is located from the compression face by using

$$k = \sqrt{2pn + (pn)^2} - pn = \frac{1}{1 + f_s/nf_c} \tag{8}$$

the arm of the resisting couple is

$$j = 1 - \frac{k}{3} \tag{9}$$

the outermost fiber stresses are

$$f_s = \frac{M}{A_s jd} = \frac{M}{pjbd^2} \quad \text{and} \quad f_c = \frac{2M}{jkbd^2} \tag{10}$$

and the steel ratio for balanced reinforcement is

$$p = \frac{1}{(2f_s/f_c)(f_s/nf_c + 1)} \tag{11}$$

Values of these various factors for rectangular beams are given in Table 3.

The resistance to diagonal tension is governed by the allowable shearing stress. The shearing unit stress in a rectangular beam or slab may be computed as

$$v = \frac{V}{bd} \tag{12}$$

The term j is omitted on the recommendations of ACI-ASCE Committee 326. The maximum shear shall be considered as that at section a distance d from the face of the support.

Table 3. Design Factors for Rectangular Beams
(Values of p and R for balanced reinforcement)

f_s	f_c	2,500 psi concrete $n = 10$			3,000 psi concrete $n = 9$			4,000 psi concrete $n = 8$		
		k	p	R	k	p	R	k	p	R
18,000	$0.45f_c'$	0.385	0.0119	189	0.403	0.0152	237	0.445	0.0222	340
20,000	$0.45f_c'$	0.362	0.0101	178	0.378	0.0127	222	0.419	0.0189	326
24,000	$0.45f_c'$	0.320	0.0075	161	0.336	0.0095	201	0.374	0.0140	294
30,000	$0.45f_c'$	0.273	0.0051	139	0.288	0.0065	176	0.324	0.0102	273

The bond stress in either rectangular or T beams is

$$u = \frac{V}{\Sigma ojd} \tag{13}$$

Web-reinforcement Stirrups. Reinforcement against diagonal tension may consist of vertical stirrups, inclined stirrups rigidly attached to the main tension reinforcement, or bent-up portions of the main reinforcement. Such web reinforcement is required in general where v exceeds $1.1\sqrt{f_c'}$. The required stirrup spacing, for rectangular or T beams, is: for vertical stirrups,

$$s = \frac{af_sd}{V'} \tag{14}$$

and for stirrups inclined at 45 deg,

$$s = \frac{1.41af_sd}{V'} \tag{15}$$

where a is the total cross section of all legs of stirrups within each interval.

Design Procedure for Rectangular Beams. The usual procedure in designing a rectangular beam is as follows: (1) Determine the approximate ratio b/d to be used. This may be governed by architectural requirements; it frequently varies from two-thirds to one-half for small beams and may be much less for heavy girders. (2) Determine the area bd required by the allowable shearing stress v. (3) From (1) and (2), select b and d. (4) From Eq. (10), find A_s and p. If p is equal to or less than that required for balanced reinforcement [Eq. (11)], the tensile resisting moment governs, and depth d is satisfactory. If p exceeds the balanced reinforcement value, increase d or, if desired, use compression reinforcement. (5) Select bar sizes to provide A_s; see if width b will permit proper bar spacing. The bar spacing should be at least 2 diam. The clear spacing should be at least 1½ times the maximum width of aggregate particle used and never less than 1 in. (6) Check bond stresses by Eq. (**13**). (7) Design stirrups (if needed) by Eqs. (**14**) or (**15**). It is good practice to use a few stirrups even if they are not required by the shearing stress used.

For the working stresses recommended, failure of a beam is most likely to occur through tension in the bain bars or by bond and rarely through compression of the concrete.

T Beams (Fig. 2). When a floor slab and supporting beam are placed monolithically, a slab width not over one-fourth of the span length and not overhanging the beam more than eight times the slab thickness nor one-half the clear spacing between beams may be considered as a part of the beam, thus forming a T beam. If the flange is thick ($t \geq kd$), the neutral axis lies in the flange, and the beam is designed as a rectangular beam of width b, except that width b' applies in computing shearing stress. In such beams, the compression area is excessive, the steel area to be crowded into the stem is large, and the rules for bar spacing must be observed carefully. Shallow, heavily reinforced beams are not generally economical.

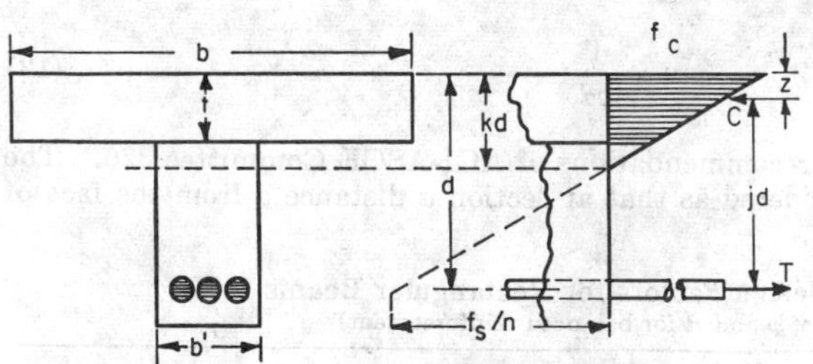

FIG. 2. Reinforced-concrete T beam.

When $t < kd$, the portion of stem between the neutral axis and the slab is commonly neglected since the error is small and on the side of safety.

The position of the neutral axis is given by

$$kd = \frac{2ndA_s + bt^2}{2nA_s + 2bt} \tag{16}$$

the position of the resultant of the compression stress is given by

$$z = \left(\frac{t}{3}\right)\frac{3kd - 2t}{2kd - t} \tag{17}$$

and the arm of the resisting couple by

$$jd = d - z \tag{18}$$

The outermost fiber stresses are

$$f_s = \frac{M}{A_s jd} \tag{19}$$

$$f_c = \frac{Mkd}{btjd(kd - \frac{1}{2}t)} \tag{20}$$

The preceding equations may be transformed to a form similar to that for rectangular beams and the beam designed as a modified rectangular beam. This is done by assuming that full allowable concrete and steel stresses will be developed using as much of the available flange width as needed. The values of k will then be those given in Table 3 for rectangular beams, and modified values of R and p (balanced reinforcement) may be found as follows, letting $t/kd = \theta$.

From Eq. (**20**)

$$M = \tfrac{1}{2}f_c kj'bd^2\theta(2 - \theta) = c_1 Rbd^2 \tag{21}$$

where $c_1 = \theta(2 - \theta)j'/j$, j' is the value of j for the T beam, and j and R are the values for rectangular beams determined from Table 2.

Solving for the steel ratio needed to balance the concrete moment,

$$f_s pj'bd^2 = c_1 Rbd^2 \qquad \text{or} \qquad p = \frac{c_1 R}{f_s j'} = c_2 R \tag{22}$$

From Eqs. (**17**) and (**18**), $j' = 1 - k\theta/3(3 - 2\theta)/(2 - \theta)$. Values of c_1 and c_2 are given in Table 4.

Table 4. Design Factors for T Beams

(Values of constant c_1 and c_2 in Eqs. (21) and (22). T beams with balanced reinforcement. f_s = 20,000 psi, $f_c = 0.45f_c'$, $k = 0.377$. Use values of R from Table 1. Compression area of stem of T beam is neglected)

$\theta = t/kd$	0.1	0.2	0.3	0.4	0.5	0.6	0.7	0.8	0.9	1.0
c_1	0.21	0.40	0.55	0.68	0.79	0.87	0.93	0.97	1.00	1.00
c_2, millionths	11	21	29	37	43	48	52	55	57	57
j'	0.982	0.964	0.947	0.931	0.916	0.903	0.893	0.885	0.879	0.877

Cases in which consideration of the compression in the stem of the T beams would result in any appreciable economy are very infrequent. In all cases, shearing stresses in T beams are computed by the equation

$$v = \frac{V}{b'd} \tag{23}$$

At the supports for continuous beams, the T flange is in tension, and all compression must be carried in the stem. An increase in resisting moment may be secured, if necessary, by increasing the beam depth by haunching, by using compression reinforcement, or by widening the beam near the supports.

Cantilever Beams. Cantilever beams must be reinforced with steel placed at the top. The maximum tensile stress in the reinforcement is at the support; therefore the bars must be extended into the support for a length sufficient to transmit the stress or to be specially anchored. Maximum stress conditions exist in the cantilever when it is fully loaded.

Beams with Compression Reinforcement (Fig. 3). Compression reinforcement is frequently used at the ends of continuous T beams or in beams where the depth is limited by special requirements. Because of these conditions, the dimensions of the beam are often prescribed in advance; further, it may be assumed that a balanced design will always be desired since, because of its cost, compression reinforcement will not be used unless actually needed.

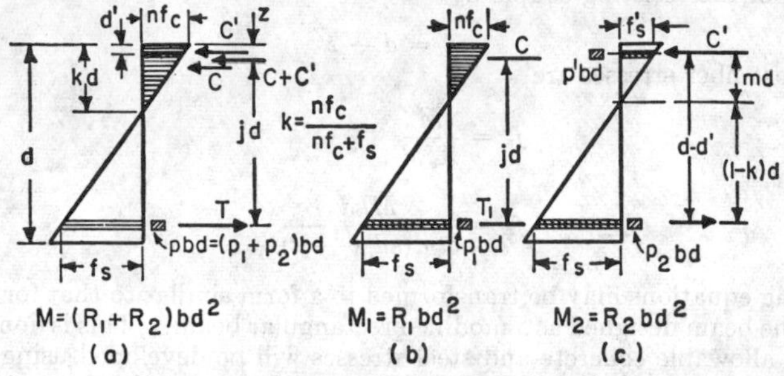

Fig. 3. Beams with compression reinforcement.

The following expressions give properties of the double-reinforced concrete beam. To find the position of the neutral axis,

$$k = \sqrt{2n\left[p + p'\frac{d'}{d}\right] + n^2(p + p')^2} - n(p + p') \tag{24}$$

the position of the resultant compression,

$$z = \frac{\frac{1}{3}k^3d + 2p'nd'[k - (d'/d)]}{k^2 + 2p'n[k - (d'/d)]} \tag{25}$$

the arm of the resisting couple,

$$jd = d - z \tag{26}$$

and the outermost fiber stresses,

$$f_c = \frac{Mk}{npjbd^2(1 - k)} \tag{27}$$

$$f_s = \frac{m}{pjbd^2} \tag{28}$$

$$f_s' = \frac{nf_c[k - (d'/d)]}{k} \tag{29}$$

The preceding general expressions contain a small error due to the failure to deduct from the concrete area the area occupied by the compression steel. The following procedure contains the same small error but leads to a simpler method of design.

Assume that the working stresses chosen will govern the position of the neutral axis and that, starting with a rectangular beam with balanced reinforcement, one may superimpose added compression and tension stresses in reinforcement which just balance one another. The stress diagram of Fig. 3(a) is thus equal to the sum of those shown in (b) and (c). If R_1 and p_1 apply to the rectangular beam of Fig. 3(b), values to be added to these quantities are found as follows. In Fig. 3(c), $p_2f_sbd = p'f_s'bd$ or $p_2/p' = f_s'/f_s = m/(1 - k)$. Hence for any compression reinforcement p' added to the beam of Fig. 3(*b*), there must be an addition to the tension reinforcement of

$$p_2 = \frac{p'm}{1 - k} \quad \textbf{(30)}$$

The total tension reinforcement is $(p_1 + p_2)bd$. Similarly, the increase in resisting moment is

$$M_2 = p_2 f_s bd(d - d') = R_2 bd^2 \quad \textbf{(31)}$$

The total moment is $M = (R_1 + R_2)bd^2$. See Table 5 for values of p_2 and R_2.

Table 5. Design Factors for Beams with Compression Reinforcement
(The following factors are to be added to the corresponding values of p and R for rectangular beams with balanced reinforcement as given in Table 3)

p'*	Additional value, p_2				Additional value, R_2			
	$d'/d =$ 0.05	0.10	0.15	0.20	$d'/d =$ 0.05	0.10	0.15	0.20
$f_s = 20{,}000$ psi $f_c' = 3{,}000$ psi $f_c = 0.45f_c'$ $k = 0.377$								
0.002	0.0012	0.0010	0.0008	0.0006	22	18	14	10
0.004	0.0023	0.0020	0.0016	0.0013	44	35	27	20
0.006	0.0035	0.0030	0.0024	0.0019	67	53	41	30
0.008	0.0047	0.0040	0.0032	0.0025	89	71	55	40
0.010	0.0059	0.0050	0.0041	0.0032	111	89	69	50
0.012	0.0070	0.0059	0.0049	0.0038	133	107	83	60
0.014	0.0082	0.0069	0.0057	0.0044	156	125	97	71
0.016	0.0094	0.0079	0.0065	0.0050	178	143	110	81
0.018	0.0105	0.0089	0.0073	0.0057	200	160	124	91
0.020	0.0117	0.0099	0.0081	0.0063	222	178	138	101
$f_s = 30{,}000$ psi $f_c' = 3{,}000$ psi $f_c = 0.45f_c'$ $k = 0.288$								
0.002	0.0007	0.0006	0.0004	0.0003	22	18	13	8
0.004	0.0015	0.0012	0.0009	0.0006	45	35	26	17
0.006	0.0022	0.0018	0.0013	0.0008	67	53	39	25
0.008	0.0030	0.0024	0.0017	0.0011	89	71	52	33
0.010	0.0037	0.0029	0.0022	0.0014	112	88	65	41
0.012	0.0045	0.0035	0.0026	0.0017	134	106	78	50
0.014	0.0052	0.0041	0.0030	0.0019	156	123	91	58
0.016	0.0060	0.0047	0.0035	0.0022	179	141	104	66
0.018	0.0067	0.0053	0.0039	0.0025	201	159	117	74
0.020	0.0075	0.0059	0.0043	0.0028	224	176	130	83

* For higher values of p', use multiplier of values given.

NOTE: Values in the table contain a slight error due to failure to deduct the area of the compression steel from the concrete area.

JOIST AND TWO-WAY SLABS

Slabs supported by steel and by concrete beams, respectively, are shown in Figs. 4 and 5. In Fig. 6, a part of the tensile portion of what would otherwise be solid slab is replaced by tiles, thus reducing the weight of the slab. Such slabs may be supported on only two sides and reinforced in one direction or supported on all four sides and reinforced in two directions. The former is commonly called a one-way slab and the latter a two-way slab. In addition to the above types of slabs, a common procedure is to use slabs reinforced in two directions but without

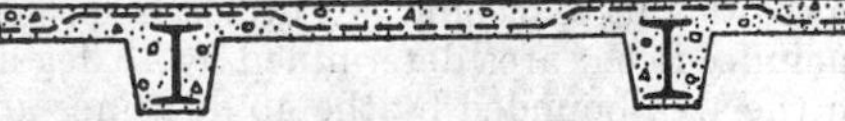

FIG. 4. Slab supported by steel beams.

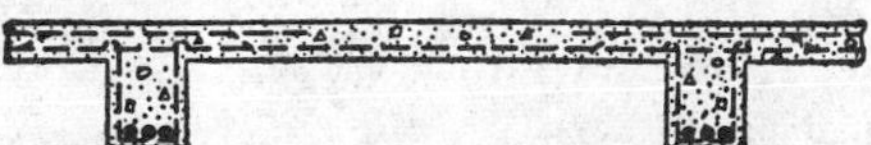

FIG. 5. Slab supported by concrete beams.

FIG. 6. Concrete floor with hollow tile.

beams or girders to transfer the loads to supporting columns. Construction of flat slabs is generally more economical than that of two-way slabs supported on beams, and such construction gives flat ceilings with consequent better distribution of light.

Joist Floor Construction. Slabs with filler units of clay or concrete tile are adapted to certain cases where long spans with flat, plastered ceilings between beams are required. The widths of the concrete beams or ribs between the lines of filler units must be determined by shear requirements but should not be less than 4 in. The depth of these ribs shall not be more than three times the width. The compression portion consists of concrete of sufficient depth above the tiles. This concrete should not be less than 2 in. nor less than one-twelfth of the clear distance between joists. The bottoms of the ribs are flush with the bottoms of the units. Care must be taken that the bond stress does not exceed the allowable working units. The beams or ribs may run in one or two directions. Their spacing is determined by the size of the units; however, the spacing is not to be greater than 30 in. face to face of the joists.

Joist floors may be constructed by using removable forms. Such slabs must be reinforced at right angles to the joists with at least the amount required for flexure.

Two-way slabs are supported by walls or beams on all sides and reinforced in two directions and may or may not be fastened securely to the supports. Such slabs may be constructed as solid, ribbed and isolated, or continuous.

If the slab is not firmly attached to the supports, special reinforcement must be provided at the exterior corners in both the bottom and top. The reinforcement in the top runs parallel and in the bottom perpendicular to the diagonal from the corner. As an alternative, the bottom reinforcement may be placed in two directions parallel to the sides of the slab. This special reinforcement shall extend in each direction from a corner a distance equal to one-fifth of the longest span, and each band shall consist of equivalent size and spacing to that required for the maximum positive moment.

For design purposes a two-way slab cast monolithically with its supports shall be considered as consisting of middle and column strips in each direction. For the usual case, a middle strip is symmetrical about the center and is one-half panel in width, and the two column strips occupy the two quarter panel areas on either side of the middle strip. When the ratio of the short to long span m is less than 0.5, the middle strip in the short direction has a width equal to the difference in span lengths and the column strips consists of the remaining area.

The critical sections for negative moments are along the faces of the supports and for the positive moment along the center lines. The moments for the middle strip can be computed from the expression

$$M = CwS^2 \tag{32}$$

where C is obtained from Table 6. For the column strips the average moments per foot of width shall be taken as two-thirds of the corresponding moments in the middle strip. The moment in a column strip may be assumed to vary from a maximum at the middle strip to a minimum at the support, and the reinforcing should be so distributed.

When continuity exists between the slab and its supports, the design of the supports takes this into account. The loads on supporting beams may be taken as the load included in the area determined by 45 deg lines from the corner for the short beams and in the area bounded by the 45 deg lines and median line for the long beams for each panel supported. The approximate bending moment for a member may be computed on an equivalent load per linear foot of beam basis as follows. For the short beam,

$$\frac{wS}{3} \tag{33}$$

and for the long beam,

$$\frac{wS}{3}\,\frac{3 - m^2}{2} \tag{34}$$

Table 6. Moment Coefficients, C
(From ACI Building Code Requirements for Reinforced Concrete, 318-63)

Moments	Short span, values of m: 1.0	0.9	0.8	0.7	0.6	0.5 and less	Long span, all values of m
Case 1, interior panels:							
Negative moment at							
Continuous edge	0.033	0.040	0.048	0.055	0.063	0.083	0.033
Discontinuous edge							
Positive moment at midspan	0.025	0.030	0.036	0.041	0.047	0.062	0.025
Case 2, one edge discontinuous:							
Negative moment at							
Continuous edge	0.041	0.048	0.055	0.062	0.069	0.085	0.041
Discontinuous edge	0.021	0.024	0.027	0.031	0.035	0.042	0.021
Positive moment at midspan	0.031	0.036	0.041	0.047	0.052	0.064	0.031
Case 3, two edges discontinuous:							
Negative moment at							
Continuous edge	0.049	0.057	0.064	0.071	0.078	0.090	0.049
Discontinuous edge	0.025	0.028	0.032	0.036	0.039	0.045	0.025
Positive moment at midspan	0.037	0.043	0.048	0.054	0.059	0.068	0.037
Case 4, three edges discontinuous:							
Negative moment at							
Continuous edge	0.058	0.066	0.074	0.082	0.090	0.098	0.058
Discontinuous edge	0.029	0.033	0.037	0.041	0.045	0.049	0.029
Positive moment at midspan	0.044	0.050	0.056	0.062	0.068	0.074	0.044
Case 5, four edges discontinuous:							
Negative moment at							
Continuous edge							
Discontinuous edge	0.033	0.038	0.043	0.047	0.053	0.055	0.033
Positive moment at midspan	0.050	0.057	0.064	0.072	0.080	0.083	0.050

The slab should be at least 3½ in. thick but not less than the perimeter of the slab divided by 180. Reinforcement spacing should be less than three times the slab thickness.

Reinforcement for all slabs must at least equal that required for shrinkage and temperature. Shrinkage and temperature reinforcement are required, as shown in Table 7, when the principal reinforcement is in one direction only.

Table 7. Shrinkage and Temperature Reinforcement

Type of reinforcement	Ratio of reinforcement area to gross concrete area
Plain bars	0.0025
Deformed bars with yield strengths less than 60,000 psi	0.0020
Deformed bars with yield strengths greater than 60,000 psi and welded wire fabric with spacing in the direction of stress not greater than 12 in.	0.0018

NOTE: Bars are not to be spaced farther than five slab thicknesses or 18 in.

FLAT SLABS

Flat-slab floors (Fig. 7) are floors without beams and girders, except as marginal beams supporting exterior walls or around stair and elevator wells. They are usually continuous over at least three spans in each direction and are supported on enlarged column heads, or **capitals.** The slab may be thickened around the capital by use of a rectangular **dropped panel,** or drop, or by continuous thickened strips forming a recessed ceiling at midpanel. The following design rules apply to rectangular panels in which the ratio of length to width does not exceed 1.33. The dropped panel is

Table 8. Moments to Be Used in Design of Interior Panels of Flat Slabs*

Design section	Flat slabs without drops		Flat slabs with drops	
	Negative	Positive	Negative	Positive
Slabs with two-way reinforcement				
Column section	$0.46M_0$	$0.22M_0$	$0.50M_0$	$0.20M_0$
Middle section	$0.16M_0$	$0.16M_0$	$0.15M_0$	$0.15M_0$

* The value of M_0 is

$$M_0 = 0.09wL_1\left(L - \frac{2}{3c}\right)^2 \tag{35}$$

NOTE: The coefficients of M_0 above may be varied not to exceed 6 percent, provided the numerical sum of positive and negative moments at the two design sections is not reduced.

It may also be noted that when c is made equal to $0.225L$, a common practice among designers, the value of M_0 becomes

$$M_0 = 0.065wL_1L^2 \tag{36}$$

generally limited in depth to not more than 1½ times the slab thickness elsewhere and in width to not less than one-third of the span.

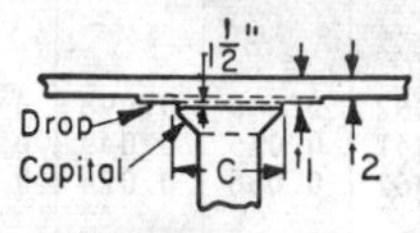

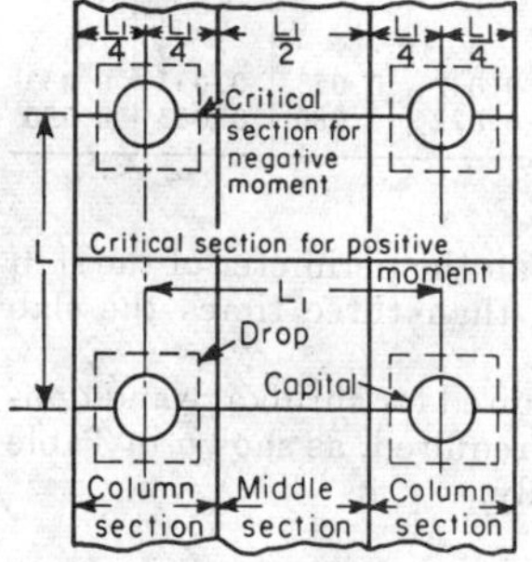

FIG. 7. Flat slab floor.

Flat-slab design is based on the requirements at four critical sections: the *column* and *middle* sections (a) for *negative* moment and (b) for *positive* moment. Reinforcement should also be at other sections as required by moments and shears. The moments given in Table 8 are less than indicated by theoretical analysis but are generally accepted as giving safe and satisfactory designs for interior panels with adjacent panels of approximately equal size.

The moments of Table 8 are used to determine the amount of reinforcement required, using Eq. (5) in the four design sections. The thickness of the slab is governed by compressive stress, shear, and rules intended to limit deflections. The negative moment in the column section governs the maximum thickness. Generally this thickness is provided by use of a drop. The total depth of drop t_1 is found as follows. Find the effective depth d required by the bending moment, the allowable compressive stress, and the assumed width of drop (use a width of $0.5L$ if no drop is used). To provide for high-stress concentrations over the sections, increase d by 20 percent and add 1½ in. for protective covering. Thus,

$$t_1 = 1.2d + 1\tfrac{1}{2}\text{ in.} \tag{37}$$

The thickness t_2 of the slab outside the drop should be at least $2t_1/3$. To avoid undue deflections, the minimum thickness t_2 should be at least as large as follows:

Slabs with drop panels one-third the span length and which extend one-fourth the slab thickness	L/40 or 4 in.
Slabs without drop panels as described above	L/36 or 5 in.

Moments in Exterior and Unusual Panels. For exterior or unusual panels of a floor or at other discontinuous edges of a slab, the bending moments for interior panels, given in Table 8, may be modified as follows, assuming that some restraint of the discontinuous edge will be produced by the marginal beam and adjoining columns:

1. *Corner or end panels on columns and beams.*
   Column section: Negative moment at first interior column and positive moment, increase 15 percent.
   Middle section: Negative moment at first interior column and positive moment, increase 30 percent.
   Both sections: Negative moment at discontinuous edge (parallel to edge), reduce 20 percent.
   Half-column section: At, and parallel to, supported edge, reduce 50 percent.
2. *Slabs supported on bearing walls or otherwise unrestrained.*
   Both sections: Positive moment, perpendicular to wall, increase 50 percent.
3. *Interior panel with beam or wall on center line of columns.*
   Middle section: Negative moment perpendicular to beam or wall, increase 30 percent.
   Column section: At, and parallel to, beam or wall, reduce 50 percent.

The thickness of exterior flat-slab panels will vary in accordance with the modifications in the bending moments just given and with the minimum thicknesses previously stated. Since the moments are relatively high in exterior panels, the required thickness of such panels is frequently greater than for interior panels. Several procedures may be followed; (1) the thickness of the whole floor may be made to conform to the maximum requirement of any panel; (2) exterior spans may be kept smaller than interior ones; and (3) compression reinforcement may be used in certain panels that govern the thickness.

Marginal and Interior Beams. Beams are generally used at edges of flat slabs. They should be designed to support direct loads plus a distributed load of one-fourth of the total of the live and dead load on the adjacent panel. Interior beams framing into columns and built monolithically with the slab should be designed as T beams to support direct loads plus one-fourth of the total of the live and dead loads on both adjacent panels, uniformly distributed.

Column Capital and Brackets. The diameter of column capital c should be at least $0.20L$, where L is the average span; the value of $c = 0.225L$ in common use generally results in a satisfactory balance between compression and diagonal tension requirements in the slab. Brackets on exterior columns may be substituted for capitals, provided the bracket is as wide as the column and the sloping face makes an angle not to exceed 45 deg with the face of the column.

Arrangement of Reinforcement. The reinforcement should be placed so as to resist not only the critical moments but also the moments at intermediate sections. At least four-tenths of all bars in each direction should be placed so as to provide reinforcement at two sections of critical negative moment and the intervening section of critical positive moment. All bars considered at a critical-moment section should extend on each side of that section to points at least one-fifteenth of the span length beyond the assumed point of inflection. Lapped splices should not exist near regions of maximum stress. At least one-third of the positive reinforcement in the column strip should extend into the drop twenty bar diameters or, if no drop exists, to a point one-eighth of the span length from the column center line.

Diagonal Tension in Flat Slabs. The maximum allowable shearing stress on a vertical section located at a distance $d/2$ outside the column capital (parallel or concentric with it) shall not exceed $2\sqrt{f_c'}$ unless shear reinforcement is provided, and then it shall not exceed $3\sqrt{f_c'}$. The nominal shear stress shall be computed as follows.

$$v = \frac{V}{b_0 d} \qquad \textbf{(38)}$$

where b_0 is taken at the distance $d/2$ indicated above.

Example of Flat-slab Design. The following design of a flat-slab floor panel with two-way reinforcement illustrates the procedure to be followed.

Assumed. Typical interior panel, 18 ft square, with drops and capital. Concrete strength, $f_c' = 3{,}000$ psi; allowable stresses $f_c = 1{,}350$ psi; $f_s = 20{,}000$ psi; $R = 222$; $n = 9$; balanced reinforcement, $p = 0.0127$; $f_sj = 17{,}480$.

Loads. Live load, 250; dead load, 90 (estimated); total, 340 lb per sq ft.

Column Capital. $c = 0.225L = 4.05$ ft; use 4 ft diam.

Dropped Panel. Min $\frac{1}{3}L = 6.0$ ft; $0.4L = 7.2$ ft; use 7 ft square.

(Use of a small width of drop requires greater drop thickness and a greater slab thickness elsewhere than required by moment or deflection considerations.) $M_0 = 0.09 \times 340 \times 18 \times 12(18 - \frac{8}{3})^2 = 1{,}554{,}000$ in.-lb. Negative moment, column section $= 0.5M_0 = 777{,}000$ in.-lb. Thickness of drop $t_1 = 1.2\sqrt{M/Rb} + 1.5 = 1.2\sqrt{777{,}000/222 \times 84} + 1.5 = 9.20$ in.

[If all panels of the floor are of approximately equal span, a constant slab thickness will generally be used. Unless exterior spans are at least 7 percent shorter than interior ones, the thickness of drop will be governed by the moment at the first row of interior columns, for which the foregoing moment must be increased 15 percent. This requires a drop thickness of $1.2(6.89) + 1.5 = 9.76$ in. Use 10.0 in. Although the thickness found for interior panels might be used throughout by adding compressive reinforcement in the drops of the first row of interior columns, it will be assumed here that it is better to use the thickness found for the exterior panel moments.]

Slab Thickness. With thickness of drop $t_1 = 10.0$ in., the slab thickness $t_2 = 2t_1/3 = 6.7$ in., say 7.0 in. This can be checked against moment requirements and against the minimum limits of $4\frac{1}{2}$ in. and $0.03L$, but none of these is greater than 7 in. For light loadings and long spans, the latter require attention. Note that a 7 in. slab gives a dead load of $7 \times 12.5 = 87.5$ lb per sq ft.

Slab Reinforcement. The reinforcement required at the various sections of the slab is as follows, considering that with $\frac{3}{4}$ in. fireproofing the protection to center of steel will be $1\frac{1}{2}$ in. at the drop and 1 in., elsewhere.

$$\text{Column section, negative moment} = 0.05M_0 = 777{,}000 \text{ in.-lb.}$$

Required $A_s = 777{,}000/(17{,}480 \times 8.5) = 5.24$ sq in. Use twenty-six No. 4 bars in the band 9 ft wide. Spacing $= 4.3$ in., $p = 5.20/(8.5 \times 84) = 0.0073$.

$$\text{Column section, positive moment} = 0.20M_0 = 311{,}000 \text{ in.-lb.}$$

Required $A_s = 311{,}000/(17{,}480 \times 6.0) = 2.97$ sq in. Use fifteen No. 4 bars in the 9 ft band. Spacing $= 7.7$ in., $p = 3.00/(6 \times 108) = 0.0046$.

$$\text{Middle section, negative or positive moment} = 0.15M_0 = 233{,}000 \text{ in.-lb.}$$

Required $A_s = 233{,}000/(17{,}480 \times 6.0) = 2.22$ sq in. Use twelve No. 4 bars in the 9 ft band. Spacing $= 9.8$ in., $p = 2.40/(6 \times 108) = 0.0036$.

It may be noted that the percentage of reinforcing is small in all cases as compared with balanced reinforcement, for which $p = 0.0127$. Hence there is no need to check compressive stresses in the concrete.

The arrangement of reinforcement may be made with reference to an assumed line of inflection, parallel to and $0.25L$ from the center line of columns. Negative reinforcement should be bent up at this point and should be carried through the region of negative moment to a point $L/15$ beyond the next line of inflection.

For the foregoing moments, all reinforcement has been held to one size of bar for convenience in ordering and handling on the job.

Of the 15 bars for positive-moment column section, one-fourth, or 4 bars, should be straight, extending in the bottom of the slab into the dropped panels at the ends a distance of 20 bar diameters. The other 11 bars may be bent up for negative moment, running past the column center line a distance $(\frac{1}{4} + \frac{1}{15})L$. Besides these 11 bars lapped in from each adjacent panel, 4 straight bars are needed to make the required 26. The straight bars have a length $(\frac{1}{2} + \frac{2}{15})L$.

In the middle section, 12 bars are required for both positive and negative moment. Of the positive-moment bars, half may be bent up and extended through the region of negative moment (6 bars from each of the two panels adjacent). The other 6 positive-moment bars should extend in the bottom of the slab to a point $L/15$ beyond the line of inflection.

Shearing Stress. Since more than half of the negative reinforcement of the column section passes through a vertical section a distance $d_1/2$ outside the capital, the allowable shearing stress on this section is $2\sqrt{f_c'} = 110$ psi, $c = 4.0$ ft, and $d_1 = 8.5$ in. $v_1 = 340(324 - 2.35^2\pi)/(4.71\pi \times 12 \times 8.5) = 69$ psi. The allowable shearing stress, a distance d_2 outside the dropped panel, is also $2\sqrt{f_c'}$. Drop width $= 7$ ft, $d_2 = 6$ in., and

$v_2 = 340(324 - 56.3)/(30 \times 12 \times 6) = 42$ psi. The shearing stress on both sections is well below the allowable value.

FOOTINGS

Footings (Fig. 8) may be classified as wall footings, isolated column footings, and combined column footings. The bending moments, shears, and bond stresses in such footings should be determined by the principles of statics on the basis of assumed or known soil-pressure distribution over the area of the footing. The bending moment on any projecting portion of a footing may be computed as the moment of the forces acting on the area to one side of a vertical plane through the critical section.

The critical section for bending in a concrete footing supporting a concrete column, pedestal, or wall should be taken at the face of the column, pedestal, or wall. For footings under metallic column bases or under masonry walls where bond with the footings is reduced to the friction value, the critical section is assumed midway between the middle and edge of the base or wall.

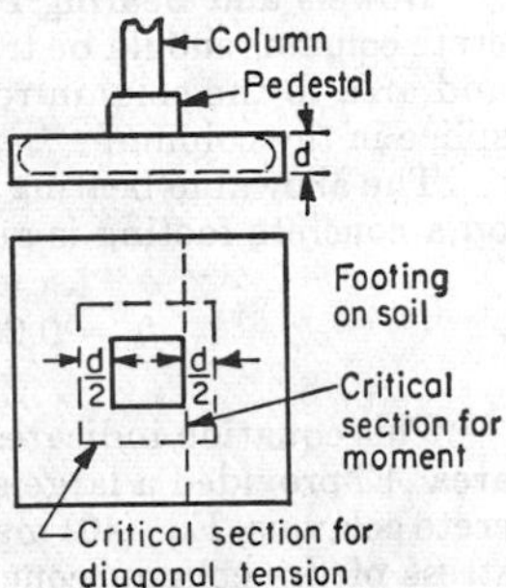

FIG. 8. Two-way reinforced-concrete footing.

The critical section for diagonal tension in footings should be taken as a vertical rectangular section lying outside the column, pedestal, or wall, a distance equal to the effective depth of the footing at the critical-moment section if the footing acts as a wide beam, *i.e.*, has one-way action, and at one-half this distance if it has two-way action. If the footing is on piles, a pile whose center is 6 in. outside the section shall be considered as producing shear and a pile 6 in. inside shall not. The shear load from intermediate piles shall be interpolated on a straight-line basis.

The critical section for bond should be taken at the same plane as for bending. Other vertical planes where abrupt changes of section occur should also be investigated for bond and shear stresses.

In sloped or stepped footings, sections other than the critical ones may require consideration. A square footing, reinforced in two directions, should have the reinforcement uniformly distributed across the entire width. Rectangular footings, reinforced in two directions, should have the reinforcement uniformly distributed across the entire width. Rectangular footings, reinforced in two directions, should have the reinforcement in the long direction uniformly distributed; in the short direction a portion, Eq. (**39**), shall be uniformly distributed across a strip equal in width to the short side and centered on the structural element supported and the remainder distributed uniformly in the outer portions. The amount included in the center strip may be computed as follows.

$$\text{Reinforcement in center strip} = \frac{2\,(\text{total reinforcement in short direction})}{S + 1} \qquad \textbf{(39)}$$

where S is the ratio of the long side to the short side.

Combined Footings. Footings supporting two or more columns may be designed with sufficient accuracy by assuming uniform soil pressure and applying the laws of statics. The footing shape must be such that the center of gravity coincides with the center of gravity of the superimposed loads; otherwise unequal settlement may occur. The longitudinal and diagonal tension reinforcement should be designed by the ordinary rules of beam design. Lateral reinforcement should be designed as for isolated footings and should preferably be concentrated in bands under and near the columns proportionate in area to the column loads. The transverse reinforcement at each column should be uniformly distributed within a width centered on the column and should not be greater than the width of the column plus twice the effective depth of the footing.

Spread or raft foundation, consisting of a slab extending over the entire area under the columns or of a slab supported by beams, may be considered as loaded by a uniform upward reaction of the ground. The principle of design is exactly the same as that applied to a floor system, except that the load acts upward instead of downward.

Concrete piles of various types are widely used for foundations as they have larger carrying capacity and greater durability under many conditions of exposure than wooden piles. Precast piles are designed as columns with allowance for driving and handling stresses. Cast-in-place piles are constructed either by driving a steel shell and filling it with concrete or by filling the hole formed by a shell as it is withdrawn. Another method forms a bulb at the bottom by means of a ram which forces the concrete into the ground. The design load or capacity of cast-in-place concrete piles is largely empirical, being based on load-test data. The concrete for precast piles is usually over 3,500 psi strength and for cast-in-place piles, over 2,500 psi strength.

Dowels and Bearing Plates. The stress in the longitudinal reinforcement of concrete columns should be transferred to the footing by means of dowels, equal in number and area to the column rods and of sufficient length to transfer the stress as in a lap splice in the column.

The allowable bearing stress f_b in the concrete at the base of a column or pedestal on a concrete footing is given by the equation

$$f_b = 0.25f_c' \sqrt[3]{A/A'} \qquad \text{or} \qquad A = \left(\frac{f_b}{0.25f_c'}\right)^3 A' \tag{40}$$

This equation indicates that a high bearing pressure f_b may be allowed on the base area A', provided a large area A exists at the top of the footing. For reinforced concrete columns, Eq. (**40**) may be applied if necessary, letting f_b be the allowable working stress of the column concrete and A' the concrete area of the column. In no case should $f_b > 0.375f_c'$.

WALLS AND PARTITIONS

Reinforced concrete is well suited to the construction of walls, especially where they have to withstand heavy pressures, such as the retaining walls of a cellar or basement, walls for coal pockets, silos, reservoirs, or grain elevators. Such walls must be designed for flexural shear and bond stresses as well as stability against overturning, sliding, and soil pressure. Drainage should be provided for by weep holes or drains. Partitions may be built of solid concrete 4 to 6 in. thick, reinforced to control temperature and shrinkage cracks. Reinforced concrete walls need to be anchored by reinforcement to adjacent structural members. All walls must be reinforced for temperature with steel placed horizontally and vertically.

The horizontal reinforcement shall not be less than 0.25 percent and the vertical reinforcement not less than 0.15 percent of the area of the reinforced section of the wall when bars are used and three-fourths of these amounts when welded fabric is used. Adequate reinforcement must be provided around all openings for windows and doors.

Retaining walls of reinforced concrete are used to resist the pressures of earth, water, and other retained materials and are usually of T or L shape. The base must be so proportioned that there is sufficient resistance to sliding and overturning and that the safe bearing strength of the soil is not exceeded. The dimensions of the concrete section and the position and amount of steel reinforcement are determined by the moments and shears at critical vertical and horizontal sections at the junction of the wall and the base. Particular attention should be given to drainage to prevent excessive water pressure behind walls retaining earth or other materials. Walls retaining water, such as tanks, should have steel tensile stresses limited to 12,000 psi unless special consideration is given to controlling cracks and should have ample reinforcement to provide for effects caused by shrinkage of the concrete and temperature change.

Bearing Walls. The allowable compressive stress for reinforced concrete bearing walls subject to concentric loads can be computed as follows.

$$f_c = 0.225f_c' \left[1 - \left(\frac{h}{40t}\right)^3\right] \tag{41}$$

For the case of concentrated loads, the effective length for computational purposes can be considered as the width of the bearing plus four times the wall thickness but not greater than the distance between loads. The wall thickness should be at least 1/25 of the unsupported height or width, whichever is smaller. For the upper 15 feet, bearing walls must be at least 6 in. thick and increase at least 1 in. in thickness for each successive 25 feet downward, except that walls of a two-story dwelling need to be only 6 in. thick over the entire height.

PRESTRESSED CONCRETE

Prestressed concrete (Fig. 9) is concrete preloaded, usually with a steel tendon, to build up initial stresses opposite those caused by the dead and live loads in service. The prestressing of the concrete is accomplished by (1) stressing the steel between anchorages before casting the concrete and then, after the concrete has hardened, transferring the load to the concrete by bond, called pretensioning; or (2) stressing the steel after casting the concrete, the steel in this case being put in place in ducts after the concrete has hardened and the stress transferred to the concrete either by bearing plates at the ends of the rods or by bond through grouting, called post-tensioning. Very high-strength steel bars or wire are used in order to keep down the space required by, and the weight of, the steel and to minimize the relative losses in steel stress due to shrinkage and creep of the concrete on relaxation of the steel. The amount of cracking can be reduced or eliminated by prestressing and thus the watertightness of structures, such as tanks and conduits, can be improved. Some loss of the prestress forces may occur from friction along curved tendons, slip at the anchorages, creep of concrete, relaxation of the steel, and elastic shortening of the concrete, and must be allowed for in the design.

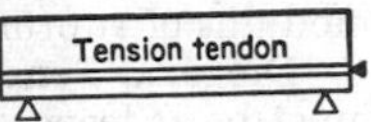

FIG. 9. Prestressed concrete beam.

Prestressed concrete members are designed by the working stress and ultimate strength design methods. The normally acceptable procedures for stress analysis of uncracked sections are usually used in the working stress design. Equations (**45**) to (**50**) may be used for the ultimate strength design.

Allowable Stresses for Working Stress Method.

Steel:	
Temporary stresses	
Maximum jacking force, not to exceed value recommended by manufacture of anchorages	$0.80f_s'$
or	
Immediately after transfer or anchoring	$0.70f_s'$
Effective prestress, the smaller of $0.60f_s'$ or $0.80f_{sy}$	
Concrete:	
Temporary stresses (immediately after transfer)	
Tension in member without auxiliary reinforcement in the tension zone	$3\sqrt{f_{ci}'}$
Compression	$0.60f_{ci}'$
Design load stresses	
Tension in the precompressed tension area	
Members not subject to freezing or corrosive atmospheres	$6\sqrt{f_c'}$
Other members	0
Compression	$0.45f_c'$

Loads for Ultimate Strength Design Method. Since design of prestressed concrete members may involve determining the ultimate strength of the members, the design load U for obtaining the ultimate strength shall be computed as follows:

No wind or earthquake load:

$$U = 1.5D + 1.8L \tag{42}$$

Wind load:

$$U = 1.25(D + L + W) \quad \text{or} \quad U = 0.9D + 1.1W \tag{43}$$

whichever is greater but not less than Eq. (**42**).

Earthquake load:

$$U = 1.25D + L + E \tag{44}$$

Flexural Strength for Ultimate Strength Method. For rectangular sections the ultimate flexural strength can be computed as

$$M_u = 0.90\left[A_sf_{su}d\left(1 - 0.59\frac{pf_{su}}{f_c'}\right)\right] \tag{45}$$

when the ratio of prestressing steel used is such that pf_{su}/f_c' is not more than 0.30. When this ratio is greater than 0.30, the ultimate moment can be computed as

$$M_u = 0.90(0.25f_c'bd^2) \tag{46}$$

For flanged sections the moment can be computed by Eq. (**45**) if the neutral axis falls within the flange. If it does not, use

$$M_u = 0.90\left[A_{sr}f_{su}d\left(1 - \frac{0.59A_{sr}f_{su}}{b'df_c'}\right) + 0.85f_c'(b - b')t(d - 0.5t)\right] \tag{47}$$

when the ratio pf_{su}/f_c' is less than 0.30. When this ratio is greater than 0.30, use

$$M_u = 0.90[0.25f_c'b'd^2 + 0.85f_c'(b - d')t(d - 0.5t)] \tag{48}$$

If the flange thickness is more than $1.4f_{su}/f_c'$, the neutral axis will usually lie in the flange; otherwise it will lie below the flange.

The total amount of prestressed and unprestressed steel must be such that the ultimate bending moment is at least 1.2 times the calculated cracking load, using a modulus of rupture of $7.5\sqrt{f_c'}$.

Diagonal Tension for the Ultimate Strength Method. The area required for shear must be at least

$$A_v = \frac{(V_u - 0.85V_c)s}{0.85df_y} \tag{49}$$

or

$$A_v = \frac{A_s}{80}\cdot\frac{f_s'}{f_y}\cdot\frac{s}{d}\sqrt{\frac{d}{b'}} \tag{50}$$

whichever is greater. For members of constant total depth, the effective depth d is that at the section of maximum moment, and the length of stirrups at the section considered must be that required at the section of maximum moment.

Bond and End Anchorage. In short beams with the steel pretensioned, high bond stresses may result near the ends and adequate transfer length must be provided. Post-tensioned beams may have end anchors, and end blocks will be required in the anchorage zone to resist the spalling and bursting stresses resulting from the concentrated loads from the prestressing steel.

Arrangement of Reinforcement. Although prestressing steel or post-tensioning ducts may be bundled together in the middle portion of the span, at each end the steel shall be spaced four times the diameter of the individual wires or three times the diameter of the strands and at least 1⅓ times the maximum size of the aggregate. Ducts may be spaced close together vertically, but horizontally must be spaced such that the concrete can be properly placed.

PRECAST CONCRETE

Precast slabs, beams, walls, and partitions as well as piles, retaining wall units, light standards, railroad crossings, and bridge slabs are being increasingly used because of the saving in time and labor cost. Such units vary in size from small slabs for use in floors of residences to large frames for industrial buildings. The small units, such as roof slabs, are cast in steel forms at central plants. Some of the larger units, such as bridge or highway slabs and wall units, are cast in wood forms at or near the place of use. A method by which wall or partition slabs are cast so that they are simply tilted into position has found wide use in housing and industrial construction. Another special adaptation is the method of casting complete floors on top of each other, then lifting into position vertically at the columns.

Particular attention must be given in the design of precast units to reduction in weight and to details to minimize the cost of erection and installation. Reduction in weight is obtained by the use of lightweight aggregates, high-strength concrete, and hollow units. Precast reinforced concrete units are seldom designed for concrete strengths of less than 3,000 psi. They are often combined with cast-in-place concrete so as to obtain the advantages of continuity. The combination of precast beams with cast-in-place slabs gives the advantage of T-beam action. Wall units are tied together by interlocking joints or by bolts. Care must be taken in shipping and handling to avoid damage to the precast units, and the design must take care of the stresses that come from such causes. All lifting devices built into the units should be designed for 100 percent impact. All units must be identified as to proper location and orientation in the structure.

Because precast units are made under conditions which allow good control of dimensions, certain restrictions can be relaxed that must be observed for cast-in-place concrete. Cover over the reinforcement for members not exposed to freezing need not be more than the nominal diameter of the steel but not less than ⅝ in. The maximum size of the coarse aggregate can be as large as one-third of the smaller dimension of the member. Precast wall panels are not limited to the minimum thickness requirements for cast-in-place walls. Precast columns may have a least dimension of 6 in. or a minimum area of 48 sq in. if this is adequate to support the loads.

To reduce the number of connections, precast units should generally be cast as large as can be properly handled. However, some joints will be needed to transfer moments, torsion, shear, and axial loads from one member to another. The integrity of the structure depends on the adequacy of the design of the various joints and connections. They may be made by use of bolts and pins or clips and keys, by welding the reinforcement or steel inserts, or by a number of other methods limited only by the ingenuity of the designer. The connections should not be the weak links in the structure. Thought as to their location will avoid many problems.

JOINTS

Contraction and expansion joints may be needed at intervals in a structure to help care for movement due to temperature changes and shrinkage. Joints at 20 to 30 ft intervals provide good crack control. A weakened plane, formed in the tension side of the member by a slot ¼ in. wide and ½ in. deep, will induce the formation of contraction cracks at selected points. Structures over 200 ft in length should have special consideration given to contraction provisions.

Construction joints are necessary in most structures because all sections cannot be cast continuously. They should be made at points of minimum shearing stress and reinforced across the joint with a steel area of not less than 0.5 percent of the area of the section cut. Provision must be made for the transfer of shear and other forces through the construction joint. Joints in columns should be made at the underside of the floor members, haunches, T beams, and column capitals.

The hardened concrete at a joint should be properly prepared for bonding with the new concrete by being cleaned, roughened, and wetted. On this surface, a coat of neat cement grout should be applied just before depositing the new concrete.

FORMS

Forms are usually built of wood or metal but in special cases may be made of plastic or fiberglass reinforced plastic. Wooden forms may be the most economical unless the construction allows for the repeated use of the same forms. Plywood and compressed wood fiber sheets, specially treated to make them waterproof, are frequently used for form faces where good surfaces are required. Forms must be designed so that they can be easily erected, removed, and reerected. The usual order of removing forms is (1) column sides, (2) joists, (3) girder and beam sides, (4) slab bottoms, and (5) girder and beam bottoms. Column forms are held together by clamps made of wood or steel, the spacing of which is smallest at the bottom and increases with the decrease in pressure. Beam forms consist of the bottom and two sides held together by clamps or cleats and supported by posts. Slab forms consist of boards or other form material supported by joists spaced 2 or 3 ft apart or other means. The joists either rest on a horizontal joist bearer fastened to the clamps of the beam or girder or are supported by stringers, or posts, or both.

Special consideration must be given to forms for prestressed concrete members. For pretensioned members the form must be constructed such that it will permit movement of the member during release of the prestressing force. For post-tensioned members, the form should provide a minimum of resistance to shortening of the member. It is also necessary to consider the deflection of the members due to the stressing force.

Design in Formwork. The formwork is an appreciable portion of the cost of most concrete structures. Any efforts, however, to reduce the cost of the forms must not go beyond the point of safe design to prevent failures which would in themselves raise the cost of construction.

All forms must conform to the dimensions and shape of the members and must be sufficiently tight to prevent leakage of the mortar. They must be properly braced and tied together to maintain their position and shape during the construction procedure.

The formwork must support all the vertical and lateral loads that may be applied until these loads can be carried by the concrete structure. Loads on the form include the weight of the forms, reinforcing steel, fresh concrete, and various construction live loads. The construction load varies with conditions but is often assumed to be 75 lb per sq ft of floor area. The formwork should also be designed to resist lateral loads produced by wind and movement of construction equipment. Most frequently the steel and concrete will not be placed in a symmetrical pattern and frequently large impact loads will occur. Because of the many varied conditions, it is frequently impossible to determine with any great precision the loads which the form must carry. The designer must therefore make safe assumptions by which the forms can be designed such that failure will not result.

Lateral pressures in forms for walls and columns are influenced by a number of factors: weight of concrete, height of placing, vibration, temperature, size and shape of form, amount and distribution of reinforcing steel, and several other variables. Formulas have been suggested for computing safe lateral pressures to be used in form design. However, because of limited test data, they are not generally accepted by all engineers.

Form Liners. Absorbent form liners are occasionally applied to the surface of forms to extract the water from the surface of the concrete, eliminate air and water voids, and produce a concrete of uniform appearance with surfaces which are superior in durability and resistance to abrasion.

The vacuum process, whereby water is absorbed from the concrete through a special form liner made of two layers of screen or wire mesh covered by a layer of cloth, has a similar effect and if properly used reduces the water content of the concrete to a depth of several inches.

Neoprene and other types of rubber have been successfully used as liners in precasting work in which a number of units are made from one form. Rubber is particularly suited for patterned work.

Plastic form liners make it easy to obtain a textured surface or a glossy smooth surface. Generally speaking, plastic liners are easily cleaned and if not too thin are suitable for a number of reuses.

Removal of Forms. The time that forms should remain in place depends on the character of the members and weather conditions. The strength of concrete must be ascertained before removing the forms. Unless special precautions are taken, concrete should not be placed below 40 F. Fresh concrete should never be subjected to temperatures below freezing. As an approximate guide for the minimum time for form removal, the following rules, which assume moist curing at not less than 70 F for the first 24 hr, may be observed.

WALLS IN MASS WORK. In summer, 1 day; in cold weather, 3 days.

THIN WALLS. In summer, 1 day; in cold weather, 5 days.

COLUMNS. In summer, 1 day; in cold weather, 4 days, provided girders are shored to prevent appreciable weight reaching the columns.

SLABS UP TO 7 FT SPAN. In summer, 4 days; in cold weather, 2 weeks.

BEAMS AND GIRDER SIDES. In summer, 1 day; in cold weather, 5 days.

BEAMS AND GIRDERS AND LONG-SPAN SLABS. In summer, 7 days; in cold weather, 2 weeks.

CONDUITS. 2 or 3 days, provided there is not a heavy fill upon them.

ARCHES. If a small size, 1 week; large arches with a heavy dead load, 3 weeks.

Forms for prestressed members may be removed when sufficient prestressing has been applied to enable them to carry their dead loads and the expected construction loads.

HEATING

BY

John O'Keefe and J. K. Whitteker

REFERENCES: *ASHRAE Guide and Data Book, Fundamentals and Equipment. ASHRAE Guide and Data Book, Applications.* "High Temperature Water for Heating and Light Process Loads," FCC Tech. Rept. No. 37 (NAS-NRC Pub. No. 753). "Underground Heat Distribution Systems," FCC Tech. Rept. No. 30R-64 (NAS-NRC Pub. No. 660). "Fan Engineering," Buffalo Forge Co. Close, "Building Insulation," American Technical Society. Handbook, National District Heating Assoc. Strock and Koral, "Handbook of Heating, Air Conditioning, and Ventilation," Industrial Press.

Notation

(These items also apply to Air Conditioning and Ventilation, pp. 12–120 *et seq.*)

ACRMA = Air-Conditioning and Refrigeration Machinery Association
AMCA = Air Moving and Conditioning Association
ARI (also ACRI) = Air-Conditioning and Refrigeration Institute
ASHRAE = American Society of Heating, Refrigerating and Air-Conditioning Engineers
ASME = American Society of Mechanical Engineers
Btuh = Btu per hour
*CBR = chemical-bacteriological-radiological
cfm = cubic feet per minute
*C_p = coefficient of performance
*DX = direct expansion
*EDR = equivalent direct radiation
F = degrees Fahrenheit
FCC = Federal Construction Council
fps = feet per second
gpm = gallons per minute
*HEPA = high efficiency particulate air
*HTHW = high temperature hot water
IBR = Institute of Boiler and Radiator Manufacturers
*L = latent
MBh = thousands of Btu's per hour
*MRT = mean radiant temperature
*MWT = mean water temperature
NBFU = National Board of Fire Underwriters
psig = pounds per square inch gage
*RSHF = room sensible heat factor
rpm = revolutions per minute
*S = sensible
SBI = Steel Boiler Institute
*SPS = standard pipe size
*TD = temperature difference
*TAC = Technical Advisory Committee on Weather Design Conditions (ASHRAE)
*THI = temperature-humidity (discomfort) index

* Except for names of organizations and items with asterisks, abbreviations are from ASAZ10.1–1941.

HEAT REQUIRED

The heating system for a building should be capable of supplying enough heat to replace structural losses and to heat outside air introduced for ventilation as well as infiltrated air. The heat generator should be capable of supplying the demand of the heat-emitting devices and other loads, of allowing for heat losses from piping and ducts, and of warming up from a cold start.

Table 1. Recommended Indoor Design Temperatures—Heating, Deg F

Residences	73–75	Operating rooms	70–95	Machine shops	60–65
Schools	68–74	Bathrooms	70–80	Foundries	50–60
Stores	65–68	Churches	68–72	Gymnasiums	55–65
Offices	70–72	Auditoriums	68–72	Steam baths	110
Hospital wards	72–74	Factories	60–65	Warm-air baths	120

Degree Days. Usually heat is not required when the mean temperature for each 24 hr period is 65 F. Each degree of declination below 65 F in mean outdoor temperature, averaged over a 24 hr period, is a degree day. A mean temperature, e.g., of 50 F is 15 degree days per day. Its main use is in estimating fuel requirements and over-all heating-system efficiency. For systems designed for stated outdoor and indoor temperatures, fuel consumption per 1,000 Btuh of heat loss is nearly proportional to the degree days.

Estimated fuel consumption per degree day for 70 F inside at 0 F outside is:

Fuel and units	Unit fuel consumption per degree day per 1,000 Btuh design heat loss		
	Utilization efficiency		
	60%	70%	80%
Gas, therms	0.00572	0.00490	0.00429
Oil, gal	0.00405	0.00347	0.00304
Coal, lb	0.0476	0.0408	0.0357

1 therm = 100,000 Btuh; 1 gal = 141,000 Btuh; 1 lb = 12,000 Btuh.

The outside design temperature recommended by the ASHRAE Technical Advisory Committee on Heating and Air Conditioning Loads is that dry-bulb temperature which will probably occur once in 13 years, and it is the temperature listed in Table 2.

Heat-loss calculations are based upon a condition of steady flow and the difference between inside and outside temperatures. The rate per hour of heat transfer through any structural element is directly proportional to its area A, the difference in temperature between the inside and outside air $t_i - t_o$, and the rate of heat flow per square foot per hour per degree temperature difference U. This latter value, called the U factor, may be applied to composite construction or to a homogeneous material. Tables of U factors covering many types of wall construction are listed in the ASHRAE Guide and Data Book and in Sec. 4. They should account for wind effect on outside surfaces. Over-all **"exposure factors"** should be avoided as they introduce substantial errors into the losses through impermeable well-insulated constructions.

Failure of the usual heat-loss formula $Q = UA(t_i - t_o)$ to account for uneven surfaces, corners, or metal members that extend from exterior to interior surfaces can result in considerable error. The error is negligible in thick, well-insulated walls, particularly those of masonry or concrete construction. Standard methods of calculation, can, however, lead to heat-loss errors of from 17 percent to more than 100 percent in curtain wall, glass wall, or complicated composite wall design. Finned through-the-wall members like beam or column flanges may increase heat losses substantially, while corner losses may exceed calculated values by as much as 17 percent. Some errors may lead to considerable overdesign in heating and air-conditioning systems (see "Heat Transfer in Large Buildings," W. Komkov, Univ. of Utah, October 1960).

Except in unusual cases, as in weave sheds, underground structures, unexposed

Table 2. Normal Degree Days and Design Outside Temperatures
(Note—all readings are at the airport except those marked † which are in the city)
(Abstracted from *ASHRAE Guide and Data Book*)

State	City	Degree days, Sept. 1–May 31	Design outside temp, deg F	State	City	Degree days, Sept. 1–May 31	Design outside temp, deg F
Alaska....	Juneau	8,088	−5	Mont.....	Helena	8,250*	−39
Ala.......	Birmingham	2,780	12	Nebr......	Omaha	6,160	−17
Ariz.......	Phoenix	1,698	36	Nev.......	Reno	6,036*	3
Ark.......	Little Rock	2,982	8	N.H.......	Concord	7,612*	−11
Calif......	San Francisco	3,421*	37	N.J.	Trenton†	5,068	2
Colo......	Denver	6,132*	−12	N.Mex....	Albuquerque	4,389	8
Conn......	Hartford	6,139	−2	N.Y.......	New York†	5,050	5
D.C.......	Washington	4,333	10	N.C.......	Raleigh	3,369	14
Fla........	Jacksonville	1,243	28	N.Dak....	Bismarck	9,033*	−31
Ga........	Atlanta	2,826	11	Ohio......	Cleveland	5,950	0
Hawaii ...	Honolulu			Okla......	Oklahoma City	3,647	−1
Idaho.....	Boise	5,890*	−10	Ore.......	Portland	4,632*	10
Ill.........	Chicago	6,310	−11	Pa........	Harrisburg	5,258	4
Ind........	Indianapolis	5,611	−8	R.I.......	Providence	6,125	1
Iowa......	Des Moines	6,446*	−13	S.C.......	Columbia	2,435	19
Kans......	Topeka	5,209	−8	S.Dak....	Rapid City	7,535*	−22
Ky........	Louisville	4,434	−2	Tenn.....	Nashville	3,513	3
La	New Orleans	1,317	26	Tex.......	Fort Worth	2,361	8
Maine....	Portland	7,681*	−9	Utah......	Salt Lake City	5,866	−1
Md........	Baltimore	4,787	8	Vt........	Burlington	7,865*	−17
Mass......	Boston	5,791	0	Va........	Richmond	3,955	11
Mich......	Detroit	6,404*	−4	Wash.....	Spokane	6,852*	−16
Minn......	Minneapolis	7,853*	−23	W.Va.....	Elkins	5,733	−4
Miss......	Vicksburg†	2,000	15	Wis.......	Milwaukee	7,206*	−15
Mo........	St. Louis	4,699	−5	Wyo......	Cheyenne	7,652*	−19

* Degree days for entire year.

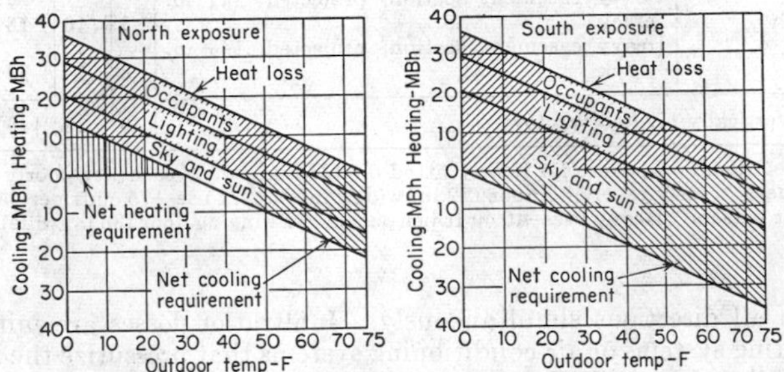

Fig. 1. Typical net heating and cooling requirements of classrooms. Basis: floor area, 1000 sq ft. Windows on one side only, 240 sq ft. Heat transmission factors: U roof, 0.15; wall, 0.25; glass, 1.13. No infiltration. Heat gains based on artificial lighting at 2.3 watts per sq ft of floor area. Occupants, 35. Solar intensity and incidence at 45 deg N. latitude, December 1. Windows shaded by venetian blinds. Since the consideration is cooling, a room temperature of 75 F, instead of 72 F, was used in the above charts. Net cooling requirement for the south exposure approaches that of the north exposure on a day when the sky has a heavy cloud cover.

areas, and heat-treating and forge shops, the liberation of **internal heat** is not deducted from the design capacity of the plant. In many installations, such as theaters, classrooms, auditoriums, and some industrial applications, it is unnecessary to supply heat during occupancy, but heat must be supplied to maintain the temperature before occupancy. Because of lights and occupants, cooling may be necessary during much of the heating season in some instances (see Fig. 1).

Infiltration losses result from leakage of outside air, mainly through cracks and openings around windows and doors, with the consequent displacement of an equal volume of room air. The volume of air that must be heated to room temperature can be estimated from Table 3 and must be accounted for in calculating the total heating load. A building in an exposed location with four exposures should be calculated for the two adjacent sides with the most infiltration. In multiroom structures, each room should be figured separately for maximum infiltration to assure correct zoning and heat-emitter capacity. However, infiltration loads properly calculated for individual rooms should not be added to yield a plant load which implies that the wind is

Table 3. Infiltration through Windows and Doors
Expressed in cubic feet per foot of crack per hour
(Adapted from the 1965 *ASHRAE Guide and Data Book*)

Type of window	Remarks	Wind velocity, mph					
		5	10	15	20	25	30
Double-hung wood-sash windows (unlocked)	Total for average window, non-weatherstripped, 1/16 in. crack and 3/64 in. clearance. Includes wood frame leakage	7	21	39	59	80	104
	Total for average window, weatherstripped	4	13	24	36	49	63
	Total for poorly fitted window, non-weatherstripped, 3/32 in. crack and 3/32 in. clearance. Includes wood frame leakage	27	69	111	154	199	249
	Total for poorly fitted window, weatherstripped	6	19	34	51	71	92
Double-hung metal windows	Non-weatherstripped, locked	20	45	70	96	125	154
	Non-weatherstripped, unlocked	20	47	74	104	137	170
	Weatherstripped, unlocked	6	19	32	46	60	76
Rolled-section steel-sash windows	Industrial pivoted, 1/16 in. crack	52	108	176	244	304	372
	Architectural projected, 1/32 in. crack	15	36	62	86	112	139
	Architectural projected, 3/64 in. crack	20	52	88	116	152	182
	Residential casement, 1/64 in. crack	6	18	33	47	60	74
	Residential casement, 1/32 in. crack	14	32	52	76	100	128
	Heavy casement section, projected, 1/64 in. crack	3	10	18	26	36	48
	Heavy casement section, projected, 1/32 in. crack	8	24	38	54	72	92
Hollow-metal, vertically pivoted window		30	88	145	186	221	242

For well-fitted doors use values for poorly fitted double-hung wood sash; for poorly fitted doors use twice these values. Freely revolving door (72 in. wide): infrequent use—75 cu ft per person. Average use—60 cu ft per person. Heavy use—40 cu ft per person. Swinging door (36 in. wide); 20 to 100 cu ft per person.

blowing from all directions simultaneously. Infiltration losses are minimized with warm-air heating systems or air-conditioning systems that pressurize the heated areas.

For **very tall multistory buildings,** the chimney effect of the inside column of warm air may result in excessive infiltration into the lower stories so that an allowance of 20 percent or more may have to be added to the calculated heat losses. It is not generally necessary to add any percentage for unusual exposures to the calculated losses of the upper floors.

Heat-conducting Areas. The areas of walls less the areas of windows and door openings are the net wall areas used in calculating heat losses for the temperature difference existing on the two sides. The building opening, not the actual glass area, is used for the area of windows and doors.

Open-roof areas are the total areas less skylights. Pitched roof losses with ceiling below are computed, except for very exact calculation, by using the ceiling area with over-all conductance coefficient U for the ceiling, air spaces, and the roof construction times the temperature difference $t_c - t_o$, where t_c is the temperature of the air at the ceiling. The practice of using the coefficient of conductance through the ceiling only and assuming that the attic space temperature is the mean of the inside and outside temperatures may result in considerable error, especially with insulated ceilings. For more exact calculations use the combined ceiling and roof coefficient $U_c = 1/R_c +$

R_r/n, where R_c and R_r are the resistances of ceiling and roof, respectively, and n is the ratio of the roof area to the ceiling area.

The suggested **indoor dry-bulb temperatures** for various occupancies are listed in Table 1. These values are at the breathing line (5 ft above the floor) or at the seating level (30 in. above the floor) for schools, offices, and similar occupancies (see Effective Temperature, p. 12–144). The ASHRAE Guide and Data Book states that for ceiling heights up to 15 ft the **increase in air temperature** per foot above the 5 ft level is 1 percent of the 5 ft level temperature.

Partitions and floors where a difference in temperature exists are included, in which case still-air coefficients are used to determine the value of U.

Basement floors of uninsulated concrete on the ground have a heat loss of approximately 0.10 Btu per sq ft per hr per deg F between basement air and ground temperature (the latter can be assumed at 50 F). Basement walls starting at ground level will have a heat loss per unit of area twice that of the floor loss. The floor loss of small buildings with concrete floors built on the ground can be computed from the exposed perimeter of the floor slab, according to Fig. 2.

Outdoor design temperature F	Heat loss per foot of exposed edge, Btu per hr	
	Recommended 2-in. edge insulation 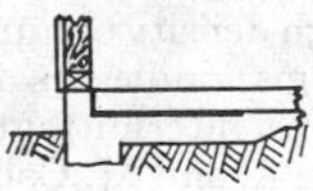	1-in. edge insulation 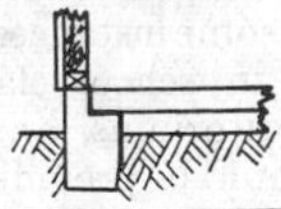
-20 to -30	50	55
-10 to -20	45	50
0 to -10	40	45
Outdoor design temperature F	1-in. edge insulation 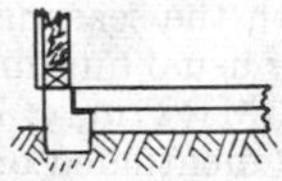	No edge insulation* 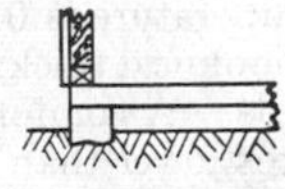
-20 to -30	60	75
-10 to -20	55	65
0 to -10	50	60

* This construction not recommended; shown for comparison only.

FIG. 2. Heat loss of concrete floors at or near grade level per foot of exposed edge. (*From 1965 ASHRAE Guide and Data Book.*)

EXAMPLE OF HEAT-LOSS CALCULATION. Assume a room in a dwelling 15 × 25 ft in plan with an 8 ft ceiling. The floor is a concrete slab on grade; the roof slope is parallel to the width of the room at 30°, creating an unfinished, unheated attic with minimum ventilating louvers; the adjacent rooms are heated. The room is exposed on the north and west and the prevailing wind direction is from the northwest at 25 mph (correction from 15 mph has been applied to glass only). Each exposed wall has two 4 × 7 ft double-hung weather-stripped windows with wood sashes.

The walls are of common brick 12 in. thick, furred and plastered on "rock lath." The ceiling is plastered on "rock lath" with 3 in. blanket rockwool insulation between joists with a 25/32 in. thick rough wood floor on top of the joists. The roof above the attic is sheathed with 25/32 in. thick wood, paper, and asphalt shingles. The floor of the room is insulated from the walls by 2 in. of foamed insulation carried 2 ft back under the floor. The room is heated to 70 F at the 5 ft level when the outside temperature is zero. Calculate the heat loss in Btuh.

Glass	112 sq ft × 1.2 Btuh/sq ft × 70 F T.D.	=	9,400 Btuh
Wall	208 sq ft × 0.21 Btuh/sq ft × 70 F T.D.	=	3,060 Btuh
Ceiling*	375 sq ft × 0.062 Btuh/sq ft × 72 F T.D.	=	1,670 Btuh
Floor (edge)	40 lin ft × 40.0 Btuh/lin ft	=	1,600 Btuh
Infiltr.	1,280 cu ft/hr × 0.018 Btuh/cu ft × 70 F	=	1,620 Btuh
	Total loss		17,350 Btuh
	Correction for attic ventilation, say 10%		167
	Adjusted total loss		17,517 Btuh

* For ceiling-roof combination, $R_c = 1/0.07 + (1/0.44)(1/1.15) = 16.3$. $U_c = 0.062$.

Intermittent Heating. Additional heat is needed to raise the temperature of air, building materials, and contents of intermittently heated buildings to the desired indoor temperature. The heat capacity of the structure and its contents, the temperature from which they must be heated, and the time allowed for heating determine the rate at which this additional heat must be supplied. A heating system designed to compensate for heat losses will usually have a 100 percent greater capacity than required for average winter weather. Since most buildings are continuously heated or have moderate "night setback" temperatures and since more time can be allowed for heat-up in extreme weather, allowance is seldom made except in boiler or furnace size. In some instances a high density of human occupancy plus the heat liberated by lighting, as in school classrooms, indicates a minimal heat-up allowance. For churches, auditoriums, and other intermittently heated large buildings, additional capacity should be provided (see A. and M. College of Texas, College Station, Texas, Engineering Experiment Station Bulletin No. 60). In extreme cases, interior heat sources produce a need for **cooling,** not heating, after occupancy. This condition may exist down to very low outdoor temperatures, as in school classrooms (see Fig. 1).

Building Insulation. Building walls and roofs may be insulated with a board form of insulation or with the blanket and loose-fill type installed between the studs and joists or in furred spaces. For localities where fuel costs are average and the minimum temperature is 0 F with the seasonal average temperature between 35 and 40 F, the economical thickness of usual building insulation is about 2 in. for roofs and 1½ in. for walls. A comfortable MRT may, however, require greater thicknesses. Temperatures lower than those mentioned or high fuel costs may also indicate the need for a greater thickness of insulation (see Secs. 4 and 6).

Vapor barriers are required whenever winter design temperatures are 20 F or lower. The development of winter air conditioning and the attempt to maintain humidities of 20 percent or more in insulated buildings have introduced the hazard of frost and ice forming in wall spaces and on roof sheathing. The interior of the walls is frequently below 32 F. Since the vapor pressure inside may be many times that of the outside, vapor flows through the building material, condensing and freezing in the wall. Air circulation in the wall is negligible so that drying out is prevented. Rot and mold may destroy the sheathing and sills of a wood structure in a few years. Difficulty in keeping paint on the walls is sometimes experienced. To prevent the passage of water vapor, vapor barriers should be applied on the **warm** side of the insulation. Building paper made up in two or more layers with asphalt between and aluminum-foil-coated paper have a high resistance to the passage of vapor.

Relative humidities that can be tolerated during cold weather are usually dictated by the state of condensation on single window glass. The elimination of all cases of single glass by the use of storm sash or Thermopane will permit a higher relative humidity.

HEAT-EMITTING UNITS

Selection of the type of heat treatment depends upon required capacity, type of heating system, application, appearance, and cost. **Heat output** of emitting units is stated in **British thermal units per hour** (Btuh), also frequently written Btu, the "h" being understood. Another method, now obsolete, stated heat output in **square feet of equivalent direct radiation** (EDR) which, originally, was a surface that emitted 240 Btuh per sq ft with a steam temperature of 215 F and room air at 70 F or 150 Btuh for 170 F average water temperature and 65 F room air. **Conversion factors** to provide adjustment for other room and heating medium temperatures are given in Table 4. Total heat output of selected emitting units must equal the calculated heat loss they are to replace. Heat should be introduced at, or directed toward, the local area of maximum heat loss, such as a cold wall or window area. Cabinet convectors, baseboard convectors, and finned tube and pipe are the most widely used types of heat-emitting units for steam and hot-water heating systems.

The term **radiator** generally means sectional cast-iron radiation. Column and large-tube radiators, no longer made, have been replaced by small-tube radiators with a spacing of 1¾ in. per section, which are made in both free-standing and wall-hung types. Because of cost, even these are being replaced by other types of heat emitters. Ratings per section are given in Table 5. Radiators are normally rated at steam temperatures of 215 F and room air of 70 F. For other heating to medium and room temperatures, the output $H_r = 240(t_s - t)^{1.3}/(215 - 70)^{1.3}$, where H_r is the Btuh per sq ft EDR for the condition of steam temperature t_s and room temperature t.

Table 4. Conversion Factors for Cast-iron Radiators and Convectors*

Temp of heating medium, deg F	Factors for direct cast-iron radiators, room temp, deg F				Factors for convectors, inlet air temp, deg F				
	50	60	70	80	50	60	65	70	80
150	1.62	1.86	2.17	2.58	1.84	2.15	2.35	2.57	3.14
160	1.44	1.62	1.86	2.17	1.59	1.84	1.98	2.15	2.57
170	1.28	1.44	1.62	1.86	1.40	1.59	1.71	1.84	2.15
180	1.15	1.28	1.44	1.62	1.24	1.40	1.49	1.59	1.84
190	1.05	1.15	1.28	1.44	1.11	1.24	1.32	1.40	1.59
200	0.96	1.05	1.15	1.28	1.00	1.11	1.17	1.24	1.40
215	0.85	0.92	1.00	1.10	0.87	0.95	1.00	1.05	1.17
230	0.76	0.81	0.88	0.96	0.76	0.83	0.87	0.91	1.00
250	0.66	0.70	0.76	0.81	0.65	0.70	0.73	0.76	0.83
270	0.58	0.62	0.66	0.70	0.56	0.60	0.63	0.65	0.70
300	0.49	0.52	0.55	0.58	0.47	0.49	0.51	0.53	0.56

* Multiply the heating capacity required by the factor opposite the heating medium and air temperatures that will actually obtain. Use the result to select a heat emitter at standard conditions: 215F heating medium and 70 F room air (radiators), 65 F entering air (convectors). For hot-water systems, many engineers use 220 F average water temperature as producing the same output as 215 F steam.

Extended surface tubing and pipe, because of its light weight, high efficiency, and quick response to load changes, has practically replaced cast iron as a heat-transfer surface. Surface extension is achieved by placing fins on the exterior of the metal tubing and pipe. The fins may be in the form of thin metal plates, square, round, or rectangular in shape, or a thin metal strip helically wound edgewise around the tube or pipe. In this way, surface extension as much as 21.5 times greater than the normal tube or pipe surface is obtained. Tube material is usually copper or aluminum, with some steel tubing used for special applications. Pipe is of steel. Solder coating of copper tubes and fins is sometimes used as a protective coating, thereby increasing the metallic bond. Finned elements, tubing, and pipe are fabricated into a variety of heat-transfer units, using the principle of convection, natural or forced (see Sec. 4), for the heating of air with hot water or electricity.

Table 5. Square-foot Rating of Direct Radiators
(Based on 240 Btu emission per hr, steam temp, 215 F, room temp, 70 F)

Sq ft rating per section small-tube cast-iron pattern radiators, spacing 1¾ in. centers				
Nominal height, in.	3 tube	4 tube	5 tube	6 tube
19	...	1.6	...	2.3
22	...	1.8	2.1	
25	1.6	2.0	2.4	3.0
32	...	...	...	3.7

The term **convector** is understood to refer to a cabinet-type unit, factory- or field-assembled, employing thermal convection for heat transfer to the room air. It has an extended surface-heating element, usually of the finned-tube type, although some cast-iron elements are used. The cabinet-type enclosure is usually of steel and surrounds the heating element tightly on four sides to prevent bypassing and to ensure air movement through the heating element from bottom to top. Openings are provided in the cabinet below and above the heating element for the entrance and egress of air (see Fig. 3).

In thermal circulation convectors, the greater the distance between the heating element and the outlet opening, the greater the heat output, within certain limits. This increase in heat output resulting from greater flue height is known as **stack effect,** where the greatest gain in output occurs between nominal heights of 20 and 32 in. Increasing stack height from 20 to 24 in. results in a 17 percent increase in heat output; to 32 in., 28 percent; and to 38 in., 34 percent. Above 38 in. the percentage gain drops off at an accelerated rate.

Linear convectors can be field-assembled to any desired length, and they are especially valuable for offsetting high heat losses along local cold areas. The heating elements may be single or multiple tube with rectangular or square fins. Single-tube units employ tube or pipe from ¾ to 2 in. in diameter. Steel tube and steel fin elements are 1¼ and 2 in. nominal tube size and are available in lengths to 14 ft in multiples of 6 in., 33 to 48 fins per ft. Copper single-tube elements are from ¾ to 1¼ in. nominal tube size and 33 to 63 fins per in. Fins on copper-tube elements may be copper or aluminum and square or rectangular. Multiple-tube convectors usually consist of two or three tubes sharing the same fin and having rectangular fins. The **maximum total length** of linear convectors that can be installed in series is limited by the carrying capacity of the tube size. In hot-water systems, this length is dependent on the permissible temperature drop and the mass flow rate of the water.

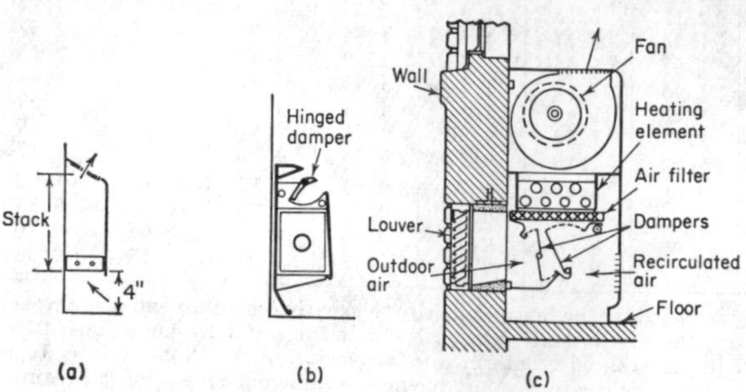

Fig. 3. Heat-emitters. (*a*) Sloping top, top outlet, wall-mounted cabinets. (*b*) Baseboard convector. (*c*) Floor-mounted unit ventilator, draw-through type.

The **heat output** of linear convectors operating with hot water is established by the Institute of Boiler and Radiator Manufacturers on a minimum velocity of 3 fps, or about 6 gpm for ¾ in., tube; 8.5 gpm for 1 in. tube; 15 gpm for 1¼ in. tube; and 32 gpm for 2 in. tube.

Enclosures for linear convectors are available in a variety of types and sizes, most of which are made in lengths up to 8 ft in increments of 6 in. In addition to enclosures resembling cabinet-type convectors, there are also expanded metal enclosures for both wall and ceiling mounting. The expanded metal enclosures have both a radiant and convection heat output and are used where cost is the paramount consideration. Sheet-metal enclosures providing a maximum of convection heating are made with either a flat or a sloping top and with top, front, or rounded outlet. Convector-element bottom should not be less than 4 in. above the floor. Enclosures are supplied in three heights to permit the stacking of as many as three single-tube elements, one above the other. This increases the heat output per foot of convector. Expansion must be given consideration and provided for in both the heating elements and the enclosures (see Sec. 5). Care must be exercised in using linear convectors in higher-temperature hot-water heating systems where temperatures exceed 250 F. At an average water temperature of 250 F, the top of the enclosure may attain a temperature of 170 F. Higher-water temperatures are considered unsafe where people may come in contact with the heat-emitting devices.

Baseboard heat emitters are convector-type units to replace conventional baseboard along the bottom of cold walls or window areas and are particularly adapted to use with forced flow hot-water heating systems but are used on steam systems and are available with electric heating elements. Heating elements for baseboard emitters are of the finned-tube type, using ½, ¾, or 1 in. nominal tube size copper tube in 3, 4, 5, 6, and 8 ft lengths. Because of the variation among manufacturers as to fin sizes and spacings, consult manufacturers' catalogues for ratings. Enclosures are formed from sheet steel with air-entrance openings in the bottom and exits in the front adjacent to the top. The over-all height varies with the manufacturer. When connected in a **series-loop** system (see Fig. 8), they replace much of the usual piping.

Baseboard units offer a minimum of interference with furniture placement. Distributing their heat output near the floor they reduce the floor-to-ceiling temperature gradient to about 2 to 4 deg. Baseboard heating-unit output is stated in Btuh per lineal foot. Testing and rating methods for baseboard-type heat emitters are established by the Institute of Boiler and Radiator Manufacturers.

Damper control of heat output from convectors is available, and while reducing heat output by convection, it has no effect on heat output by radiation. When coupled with leakage around the damper, the over-all reduction is usually less than might be expected.

Heating coils of extended surface tubing, owing to their light weight and large amount of heating surface per square foot of face area, have practically replaced other types. Normally rectangular, they are also fabricated into other shapes for special applications. Tubes are usually of copper with aluminum or copper fins. Some copper-finned units are solder-coated to provide protection and a better bond between fins and tubes.

Variations in heat transfer for a given coil size are attained by varying the **number of fins per inch** and the **number of rows** of tubes over which the air must pass. The heating medium, usually steam or hot water, flows through the interior of the tube, and the air to be treated is forced across the outside. To secure even distribution of steam, the tubes may be provided with individual orifices, distributing plates or orifices in the header, or **perforated steam-distributing pipes** extending into the individual tubes. The last arrangement attains greater uniformity in delivered air temperature, minimizes the tendency for freezing at the bottom of the coil, and is consequently used in **non-freeze** coils. Heating coils are usually given names based on their **use,** *e.g.*, a tempering, preheat, reheat, or booster coil. Heating takes place along a line of **constant dew-point temperature** (see Fig. 2, p. 4–84).

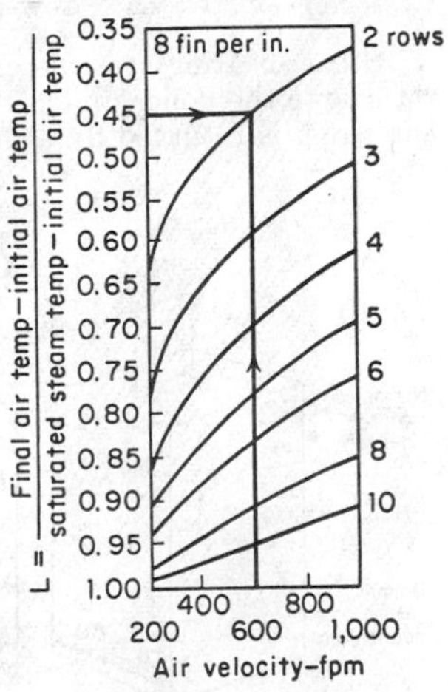

FIG. 4. Steam-heating coil capacity curves. (*From American-Standard.*)

Selection of a heating coil can only be made from a manufacturer's catalogue. When selecting a desirable face velocity (usually between 450 and 750 fpm), the coil face area is determined by total cfm/velocity = face area in square feet. The catalogue table of face area lists several choices of length and width that will provide the required area. Other tables or curves (*e.g.*, Fig. 4) permit selection of the number of rows of tubes (coil depth).

EXAMPLE. With an initial air temperature of 50 F, final air temperature 130 F, and steam temperature of 228 F, face velocity 600 fpm. (Final air temp − initial air temp)/(steam temp − initial air temp) = (130 − 50)/(228 − 50) = 0.45. Entering the curve at 0.45 and moving to the right to the intersection of the 600 fpm vertical line, both lines intersect the two-row curve.

From the principles of heat transfer it follows that an increase in the velocity of the airflow across the coil will result in a greater total transfer of heat but a lower leaving temperature.

Unit heaters are designed to supply heat by forced convection using steam, hot water, electricity, or gas or oil as the heat source. Air is forced over the heating surface by either a propeller or a centrifugal fan. **Propeller fan units** are made for either horizontal or down-blow air streams, the latter being obtainable with rotating discharges. **Centrifugal fan unit heaters** are made for horizontal, up-blast, or down-blast air streams. Fan arrangements may be either **draw-through** or **blow-through,** except that direct-fired units are always blow-through. Compared to their size, the capacity of unit heaters is large, and control of the projected air stream can be effected over considerable distance. They are used extensively in all types of commercial and industrial structures. They are available in a wide range of capacities up to 350,000 ± Btuh. Where heating requirements are large, unit heaters are usually more economical than thermal circulation types, and they permit full use of floor space. They are especially useful for spot heating, intermittent heating, and blanketing outside doors.

HEAT-DISTRIBUTION SYSTEMS

Heat is conveyed from the point of generation to heat emitters through systems of pipes or ducts, except where local direct-fired heat emitters are used (see Electric Heating and Gas Heaters, p. 12–110). Steam, hot water, and warm air are the usual media by which heat is transported from one point to another; special liquids are used to avoid freezing at low temperatures. Steam-distribution systems are classified as (1) low pressure (for systems operating at pressures below 15 psig) and (2) high pressure (operating pressures above 15 psig). A licensed engineer on all shifts is often required by law for high-pressure systems.

Low-pressure Steam-heating Systems

Steam-heating systems are classified as **gravity circulation** when the condensate returns to the boiler under its own hydraulic head or as **mechanical circulation** when the water is returned by a pump. Steam systems may be either **upfeed** (where the main is below the heat-emitting units) or **downfeed** (when the supply main is above them).

Steam systems are **one-pipe or two-pipe,** depending on whether the steam and condensate are carried in the same pipe or in separate pipes. Low-pressure systems (4 to 8 oz per sq in.) are generally called **vapor** systems. The pipe conveying steam is called the steam main, while the pipe conveying the condensate back to the boiler is the return main. The latter is called a **wet return** when it is below the water line of the boiler. A return above the water line, which may carry condensate and air, is called a **dry return.**

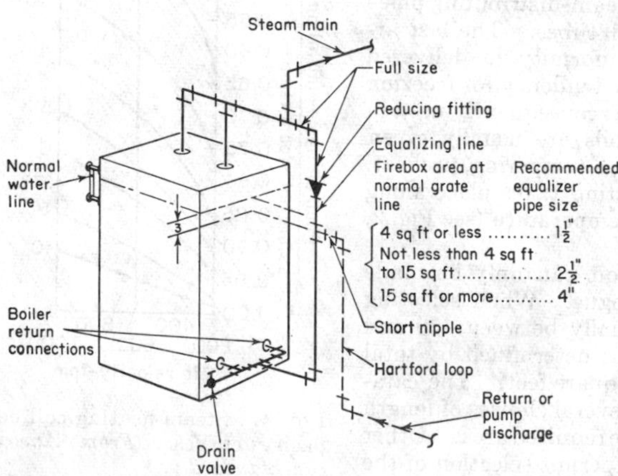

FIG. 5. Diagram of Hartford-loop return-pipe connection.

The **Hartford loop** consists of a loop or inverted trap in the condensate return formed by raising the return at the boiler to a point approximately 3 in. below the water line of the boiler and connecting at that level to the **boiler-equalizing connection,** which runs from the boiler header to the return tappings. The Hartford loop will prevent excessive loss of water from the boiler in the event of a broken return line (see Fig. 5).

One-pipe steam systems (Fig. 6) are systems in which the steam to and the condensate from the heat-emitting devices flow through the same pipe. **Heat-emitting**

devices are fitted with a bottom tapping and air-venting automatic thermostatic valves that prevent the escape of steam. **Baseboard elements** in these systems should be connected at both ends and should have a good pitch. **Valves** on one-pipe systems must be either fully opened or fully closed. No throttling or modulating position can be maintained since, if a valve is partially closed, condensate will not drain from the unit.

The **steam main** usually rises to a high point above the boiler in the same story height and then pitches downward with a slope of ½ in. per 10 ft to the end of its run, which should be not less than 18 in. above the boiler's water line. There it is dropped into a **return** near the floor and below the boiler water line, or it may be brought back to the boiler just below the steam main and above the water line, dropping at the boiler to the return connection. **Quick-vent types of air reliefs** should be used at the ends of mains.

As the main carries both steam and condensate, reductions in size are made with **eccentric** fittings to eliminate water pockets which cause water hammer. **Runouts** to radiators or risers are taken off the main at a 45 deg angle above the horizontal. As the condensate flows opposite the steam, runouts are one size (when over 8 ft long two sizes) larger than the vertical pipe and are pitched downward toward the main at ¼ in. per ft. Branch mains and risers for more than three stories are preferably connected at a 45 deg angle below the horizontal and pitch down to the far point where they drip into a return. **Piping details** are shown in Fig. 6.

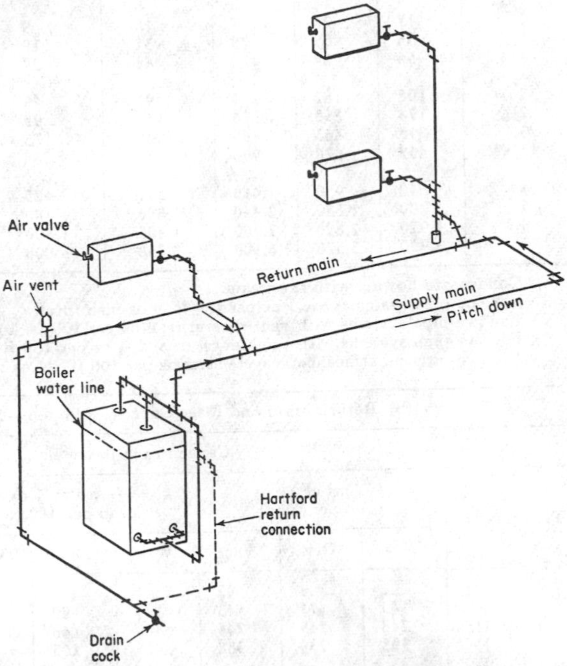

Fig. 6. Typical up-feed gravity one-pipe air-vent system. (*From 1964 ASHRAE Guide and Data Book.*)

Where condensate flows in the same pipe as the steam but opposite in direction, care must be exercised in pipe sizing to prevent **noise** and the destructive forces of **water hammer.** Steam velocities must be sufficiently low to prevent blocking the opposing flow of condensate. The sizing of **upfeed risers** is governed by this consideration. **Steam mains** should not be smaller than 2 in., and the end should not be smaller than one-half of its greatest diameter. Small systems should be sized for not greater than 2 oz drop; large systems, for 4 oz. Add to the length of the run the equivalent length of pipe represented by fittings (see Table 7). Safe capacities of pipes determined by experiment are given in Table 6. The pressure drop should not exceed one-half the initial pressure.

Vacuum-return systems are two-pipe systems in which a vacuum-heating return pump creates a partial vacuum in a receiver connected to the return line. The pump draws the air and water from the receiver and separates them, discharging the air to the atmosphere and the water to the boiler (see Fig. 7). Radiators have two tappings with a packless valve on the high supply and a thermostatic trap on the low return. **Pumps** are special forms of a water-sealed centrifugal type in which the air and water

Table 6. Steam and Return Pipe Sizing for Heating Systems

(Adapted from the 1964 *ASHRAE Guide and Data Book*)

(a) Steam-pipe Capacities for Low-pressure (3 psig) Heating Systems

Capacity in lb per hr

Nominal pipe size, in.	Pressure drop, per 100 ft in length, oz*			Two-pipe systems: Condensate flowing against steam		One-pipe systems		
	1	2	4	Vertical	Horizontal	Supply risers upfeed	Radiator valves and vertical connections	Radiator and riser runouts
¾	9	14	20	8	.....	6	...	7
1	17	26	37	14	9	11	7	7
1¼	36	53	78	31	19	20	16	16
1½	56	84	120	48	27	38	23	16
2	108	162	234	97	49	72	42	23
2½	174	258	378	159	99	116	...	42
3	318	465	660	282	175	200	...	65
3½	462	670	990	387	288	286	...	119
4	640	950	1,410	511	425	380	...	186
5	1,200	1,680	2,440	1,050	788	...	...	278
6	1,920	2,820	3,960	1,800	1,400	...	...	545
8	3,900	5,570	8,100	3,750	3,000	...	...	...

* Condensate flowing with the steam.
For one-pipe systems: use 1 oz per 100 ft, 4 oz max total.
For two-pipe systems with vented returns: 4 oz per 100 ft, 16 oz max total.
For two-pipe systems with vacuum returns: 2–4 oz per 100 ft, 32 oz max total.
For two-pipe subatmospheric systems: 2 oz per 100 ft, 24 oz max total.

(b) Return Main and Riser Capacities for Low-pressure Systems*

Capacities in lb per hr

Pipe size, in.		1/24 psi or 2/3 oz drop per 100 ft			1/16 psi or 1 oz drop per 100 ft			1/8 psi or 2 oz drop per 100 ft		
		Wet	Dry	Vac.	Wet	Dry	Vac.	Wet	Dry	Vac.
Mains	¾	.....	.....	42	.....	.....	100	.....	.....	142
	1	145	71	143	175	80	175	250	103	249
	1¼	248	149	244	300	168	300	425	217	426
	1½	393	236	388	475	265	475	675	340	674
	2	810	535	815	1,000	575	1,000	1,400	740	1,420
	2½	1,580	868	1,360	1,680	950	1,680	2,350	1,230	2,380
	3	2.130	1,560	2,180	2,680	1,750	2,680	3.750	2,250	3,800
	3½	3,300	2,200	3,250	4,000	2,500	4,000	5,500	3,230	5,680
	4	4,580	3,350	4,500	5,500	3.750	5,500	7,750	4,830	7,810
Risers	¾	.....	48	143	.....	48	175	.....	48	249
	1	.....	113	244	.....	113	300	.....	113	426
	1¼	.....	248	388	.....	248	475	.....	248	674
	1½	.....	375	815	.....	375	1,000	.....	375	1,420
	2	.....	750	1,360	.....	750	1,680	.....	750	2,380
	2½	.....	.....	2,180	.....	.....	2,680	.....	.....	3,800

* Return piping is normally sized for the same unit pressure drop as is the supply piping. Returns to a vented receiver are best sized at a lower unit pressure drop—especially if over 200 ft long.

Return runouts from thermostatic traps should be one size larger than the traps.

are separated. Another form operates on the Venturi principle, entraining the air in the water jet. Pump sets with a separate pump for air removal are available and are particularly useful in rehabilitating older systems with leaky returns (see Sec. 14 for pump details). Systems which maintain less than 5 in. Hg vacuum in the return lines are known as low vacuum systems (see Table 6 for pipe sizing).

Table 7. Equivalent Length of Pipe Due to Cast-iron Fittings

(Abstracted from NDHA Handbook, 1951, by permission)

Pipe diam, in.	Length to be added in run, ft				
	Std ell	Tee	Gate valve	Globe valve	Angle valve
2	5.17	10.3	1.21	57	28
2½	6.16	12.3	1.44	68	34
3	7.67	15.3	1.79	85	43
4	10.1	20.2	2.35	112	56
5	12.6	25.2	2.94	140	70
6	15.2	30.4	3.54	168	84

Cast-iron 45 deg ells and welding ells have approx 70 and 40 percent, respectively, of standard ells.

Condensate-pump systems are similar systems, using simple water pumps in lieu of vacuum-heating return pumps. They are used for systems serving extended surface coils and for cheaper, less extensive, distribution to direct radiation. Return piping should be generously sized and should have a good pitch. **Receivers** are vented.

Subatomospheric systems regulate steam flow into the main by a throttle valve under automatic thermostatic control and maintain a fixed vacuum differential

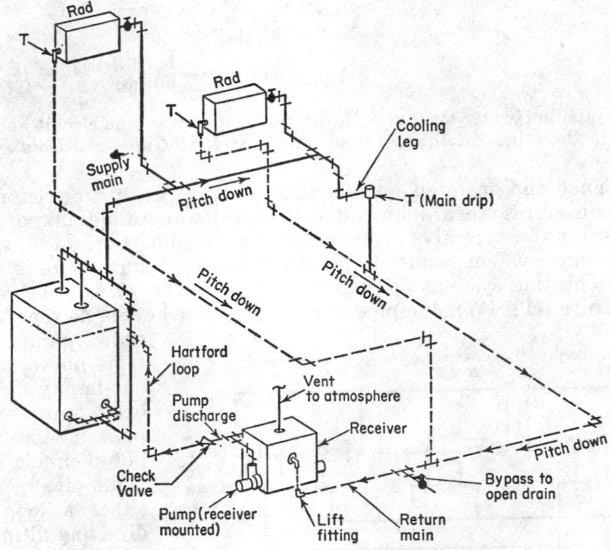

FIG. 7. Upfeed vacuum-pump system (T = thermostatic trap; C = check valve).

between supply and return by means of a **differential controller** and a vacuum pump. Operating steam pressures range from 5 psig to 23 in. Hg vacuum and return vacuum of 25 in. Hg. This results in radiator temperatures as low as 140 F in mild weather. The high vacuum requires radiator traps with vacuum-compensated thermostatic elements. Piping systems must be tight, and pipe sizes are generally the same as those for vacuum-return systems. Valves must be of the **packless type.**

Hot-water Heating Systems

Hot water has many advantages for transmission of heat from the heat generator to the heat emitters. Among them are (1) piping can run at various levels and may be offset up and down to follow building levels or terrain contours, thereby reducing the amount of excavation required as well as the number of drip points and return pump locations that would be required by a steam system; (2) warm-up heat distribution is uniform; (3) the system is adaptable to simple control from indoor and outdoor temperature and to zoning; (4) corrosion within the system is minimized by almost complete elimination of air and the absence of a need for make-up water; (5)

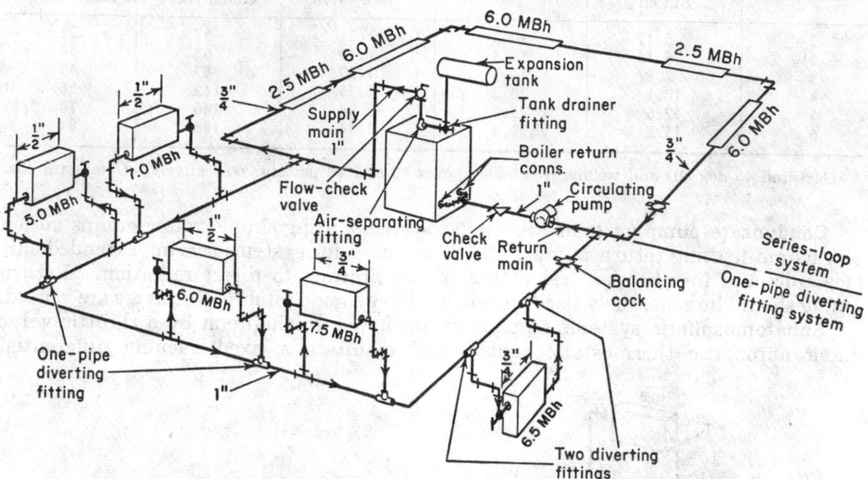

FIG. 8. One-pipe hot-water system with diverting fittings in one circuit and a series-loop arrangement in the other. (*Adapted from 1964 ASHRAE Guide and Data Book.*)

properly designed and operated systems function quietly; (6) troublesome traps and associated steam accessories are eliminated; (7) flashing losses and subsequent introduction of make-up water typical of steam systems are eliminated; and (8) savings in the cost of the piping system result if the design supply temperature is high enough.

Hot-water heating systems are categorized as gravity or forced flow, normal or high temperature (HTHW), one-pipe or two-pipe, zoned or single zone, or one-pump or two-pump. **Gravity systems,** now obsolete even for one-family dwellings, have been superseded by systems in which a centrifugal pump circulates the water. **"One-pipe"** may mean either a loop main with **diverting fittings** at branch take-offs or a loop which includes the heat emitters in a **series circuit.** **"One-pump"** and **"two-pump"** do not indicate the actual number of pumps but the number of categories (groups) of pumps. In a one-pump system the pumps in one group—there may be several in parallel—circulate water through the heat emitters as well as through the distribution system. In a two-pump system, the pumps in the central group at the heat generator circulate water through a primary loop, while pumps in the several buildings or zones circulate water through their respective secondary loops (see Figs. 8 and 9). In high-temperature systems, the same

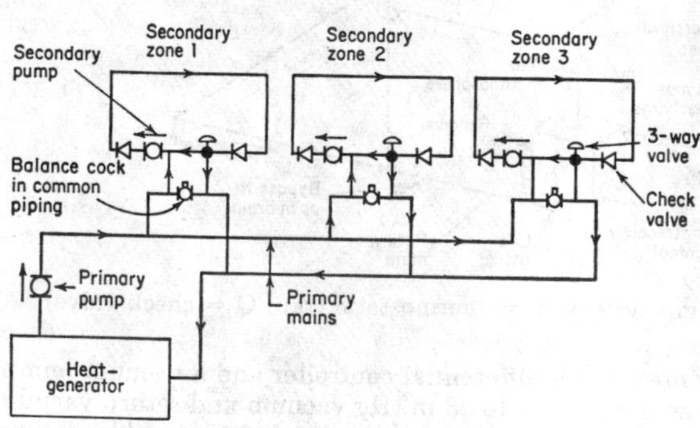

FIG. 9. Multi-zone hot-water system with primary and secondary pumping.

terms are used to differentiate between systems in which the same pumps circulate water through the heat generators and through the distribution system and those in which separate pumps are used for these two functions (see Figs. 11 and 12). Heat-emitting-device outputs may be equal to or greater than those of steam systems. Systems using supply water temperatures higher than 250 F are considered to be high-temperature systems (see p. 12–101).

Design considerations are choice of supply temperature, temperature drop, type of generator, method of pressurization, and circuiting of distribution piping. **Affecting circumstances** are type of load, heat-emitter temperature requirements, zoning requirements, steam requirements (high-temperature systems), elevation variations within the system, proportion of piping between buildings and within buildings, and the distance between heating plant and farthest heat emitter. In primary–secondary systems, two supply temperatures and two temperature drops must be selected.

Design supply temperatures of 200 to 230 F are used for residential applications; 200 to 250 F for small institutional, commercial, and industrial applications; and 250 to 450 F for larger individual and central system applications.

Economical design is achieved through the use of higher water temperatures, primary–secondary pumping, and terminal heat-emitter design for smaller flow rates. Higher supply temperatures permit greater temperature drops and smaller flow rates. This may result in reduced heat exchanger surface as long as suitable velocities are not exceeded. The pressure incurred may add to cost of exchanger. The cost of system components increases as temperature and pressure increase, such increases occurring in steps because of standardization of piping and equipment into temperature and pressure classifications. The most economical design within a pressure classification is one that takes full advantage of the maximum permissible pressure. Note that increasing temperature from 250 to 350 F results in a pressure increase of 104.8 psi but increasing temperature from 350 to 450 F requires a pressure increase of 285.37 psi.

The maximum water temperature supplied to a system is called the **design supply water** temperature. The **design average water** temperature is the design supply water temperature less one-half the **design temperature drop.** Depending upon the static head at various points in the system, design supply temperatures up to 325 F may use standard equipment designed for operating pressures of 125 psig (see p. 12–101 for equipment considerations).

Heat-emitting devices must have two connections, and they are not at a uniform temperature. The output rating of heat-emitting devices is based on the difference between mean water temperature and ambient air temperature. Temperature drops in the heat-emitting device units range from 20 to 200 F, depending on the supply water temperature and the characteristics of the device (see Table 4 for radiator conversion factors). The application of these data is approximate. Heat-transfer data are covered in Sec. 4. Most engineers consider that a design average temperature of 220 F will produce the same output as steam at 215 F. The tabular information should not be applied to extended surface coils (see p. 12–89).

Hot-water systems lend themselves to a variety of **piping and pumping arrangements.** A basic hot-water system comprises a water-heating device, which may be a direct-fired generator; a steam boiler and a heat exchanger; a means of absorbing water expansion and pressurizing the system; a closed distribution system of supply and return piping; and a circulation pump or pumps and heat-emitting devices. Systems may be divided into **zones** (see p. 12–151) to accommodate differences of exposure, population, or both. Zoning may be achieved by throttling, by varying the supply water temperature, or by starting and stopping of zone pumps, the last method being generally employed only in residential applications. Pumps in medium and large systems run continuously whenever heating is required. Piping and controls must be designed concurrently because the latter usually determines the former

In **primary–secondary systems,** a comparatively high supply temperature may be used in the primary circuit and low temperature in the secondary circuits (see Fig. 9). The water quantity circulated in the primary circuit is determined by the design water-temperature drop in this circuit. For example, a system could be designed with a primary temperature from the generator at 400 F and a return temperature of

225 F, a supply temperature in the secondary circuit of 230 F, and return temperature of 210 F. The secondary temperature drop is therefore 20 F, but the primary would be sized for a 175 F drop. The quantity circulated in the primary circuit is less than that obtained from the aggregate secondary quantity by proportioning the temperature drops by virtue of the non-simultaneity of the peaks for which the respective secondary circuits are designed.

The use of **high temperature drops** results in a more linear output control with change in flow. The primary–secondary pumping arrangement can be used to best advantage with heat emitters, such as convectors and finned radiation, which are generally unsuited for design for small flow rates.

Pipe circuits suitable for a complete system or for zone or secondary circuits on large systems are (1) series-loop with heat-emitting devices in the circuit; (2) one-pipe loop with heat-emitting devices on branch circuits; (3) two-pipe, reversed return; and two-pipe, direct return.

The **series-loop** one-pipe system (Fig. 8) is commonly used in small buildings and in subcircuits of large systems. The heat-emitting devices, which are usually baseboard or finned-tube-type units, serve as part of the piping circuit, the same water flowing successively through them. A system may consist of one or more parallel loops, the pipe in each being of a constant size. Water temperature is progressively reduced around the circuit and may require that the length of each heating element be adjusted to its actual operating temperature. When a total loop temperature drop of 20 deg is used, such compensation can usually be neglected. Series-loop systems have the advantage of low installation cost but have the disadvantage that no heating element within a circuit can be regulated on the water side without affecting all other units in the circuit. Partial control can be obtained by means of dampers in each unit (see Heat Emitters, p. 12–88).

A one-pipe **diverting-fitting system** (Fig. 8) uses a single pipe main of constant size with a special tee diverting fitting installed at connections to the heating elements. Diverting fittings create a pressure drop between the supply and return runouts, causing circulation through the heat-emitting device. A **single fitting** is usually adequate for heat-emitting devices located **above** the main since thermal head aids flow. **Two fittings** are usually required to offset the resistance of the negative thermal head when heat-emitting devices are located **below** the main. The advantage of this system over the series-loop system is that valves can be used to control output on individual heat-emitting devices. Installation cost is greater than that for the series-loop system. One-pipe diverting-fitting installations are limited to small buildings or to subcircuits of large buildings. Diverting fittings can be applied to branches from risers, providing the risers are looped. Zone-control reset of water temperature rather than modulation of circuit water flow is recommended.

Two-pipe direct- and reversed-return systems (Fig. 10) are used as mains in large installations. The total length of supply plus return piping is the same to all terminal or subcircuits in the **reversed-return system,** if the return main parallels the supply main to its end and then has an equivalent path back to the heat generator. This configuration results in a better balance of pressure drops through the piping to the subcircuits or branches. In buildings not more than four stories high, a reversed-return system is often provided for the mains only. In the two-pipe **direct-return system** the total length of supply plus return piping is unequal for the various subcircuits or branches, thus introducing radical balancing problems. The direct-return system is usually cheaper to install. In **tall buildings,** systems are divided into **vertical zones** to limit the pressure, usually to permit 125 psig construction.

Air Elimination. To reduce corrosion, piping resistance, and noise, air must be eliminated from the system. Vents may be either manual or automatic. Air is best removed from the piping immediately after the heat generator (point of maximum liberation). In low-pressure systems it is usually trapped in the expansion tank by means of a special boiler fitting with a dip tube or other air-separating device. **Closed expansion tanks** are almost universally used and are connected to the system to (1) absorb the expansion and contraction of system water with temperature variation and (2) to ensure, at all times, a controlled system pressure in the entire system above that of saturation temperature (except in steam-pressurized expansion vessels, which will be at saturation pressure). Pressurization of HTHW systems is discussed under that title.

Expansion tank size is based on the total volume of system water, the hydrostatic head at the tank, the pumping head at the tank, and the water-temperature range

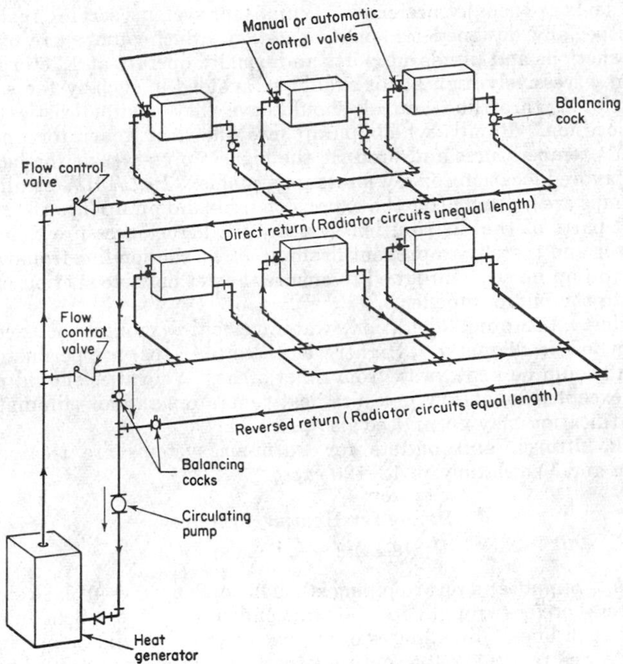

Fig. 10. Hot-water system with one circuit having a direct return and one circuit having a reversed return.

over which the system operates. For operating temperatures between 160 and 280 F, expansion tank sizes may be determined by the following ASME formula:

$$Vt = \frac{(0.00041t - 0.0466)V_s}{P_a/P_f - P_a/P_o}$$

where V_t = minimum volume of the expansion tank, gal
V_s = system volume, gal
t = maximum average operating temperature, F
P_a = pressure in expansion tank when water first enters (usually atmosphere pressure), ft of water absolute
P_f = initial fill or minimum pressure at tank, ft of water absolute
P_o = maximum operating pressure (including pumping head) at tank, ft of water absolute

P_o is determined by considerations of standard tank design and cost. The volume of water in standard pipe and tube is given in Table 3, p. 8–200. **Safety factors** of from 20 to 50 percent are used to allow for field changes and future additions to the system.

Tank Location. Tanks located near the pump suction provide higher net positive suction heads (see Sec. 14). Tanks located near the heat generator provide the maximum pressure margin above the pressure corresponding to the water temperature. In addition, this location provides for the best trapping of liberated air in the tank.

Circulating Pumps. Centrifugal pumps are used to circulate the water, pumps varying in size from the 1/12 hp. "booster" in-line type with a capacity of 5 gpm at 6 or 7 ft head to pumps handling hundreds or thousands of gallons per minute with heads limited only by the pressure characteristics of the system. Pumps with **mechanical seals** are usually preferred. Pumps for systems serving **residential areas** should be especially designed for **quiet operation.** Such pumps are often designed with larger suctions and discharge ports and usually operate at 1,750 rpm. For the latter reason, excessively high heads should be avoided in such systems. Pumps for systems employing throttling controls should have "flat" characteristics (see Sec. 14).

Pump Location. Pumps which pump into the heat generator operate at the lowest suction temperatures and produce the highest pressures at the heat generator. This is the favored location for low-pressure systems. In HTHW steam-pressurized systems, pumps are located after the expansion tank and pump into the supply line to maintain all parts of the distribution system at a higher pressure than that of the heat generator and thereby to prevent flashing. The suction line from the expansion drum to the pump must be designed to ensure the net positive suction head required at the inlet to the pump impeller.

Pipe Sizing. For quiet operation, water velocities should not exceed 4 fps in pipes 2 in. or less in diameter. Higher velocities (5 ± fps) are permissible in larger pipes, which should be kept away from quiet areas. Velocities should never be less than 2 fps (except through low-pressure heat generators and air-eliminating devices) because stratification may occur (see also p. 12–111).

Ductwork, fittings, and **outlets** for warm-air systems are treated under Air Conditioning and Ventilation, p. 12–120 *et seq.*

Piping for Heating Systems

(See also Secs. 5 and 8)

Materials. Supply and return piping is usually of Schedule-40 black steel, although some engineers prefer wrought-iron steam-condensate lines. Schedule-80 pipe is also used for such lines. Small sizes of this weight pipe should be carefully checked for capacity. See p. 12–112 for materials used in more inaccessible lines. Copper tubing is often used for hot-water systems in residences.

Expansion of Pipes. Piping must be designed to take care of its own expansion when heated. In small systems, the changes in direction of piping will usually give sufficient flexibility. Radiator and riser runouts should be made with liberal offsets. Radiator connections from risers must have sufficient pitch to assure that the expansion of the pipe will not result in a reverse pitch and form a water pocket.

Mains can be fitted with offsets, U-bends, or other forms of expansion loops. Slip joints or bellows are required where offsets are not possible but should not be installed at inaccessible locations. They are often used in series-circuit hot-water loops. **Risers** for four or more floors should be fitted with horizontal offset loops, or expansion joints can be used where the risers are exposed. The movable horizontal pipe should be supported and guided close to expansion joints to take the weight of the pipe and to assure alignment. **Steel pipe** expands approximately 0.75 in. per 100 ft per 100 F change.

Insulation of Pipes, Boilers, Furnaces, and Ducts (see also Sec. 6). Low-pressure steam and hot-water heating **pipes** are usually insulated with standard thickness glass fiber or polyurethane insulation in the lower range of temperatures and with calcium silicate and 85 percent magnesia in the higher range. **Boilers** are usually insulated with 1½ or 2 in. thickness of the same materials. **Factory-applied jackets** are favored for pipe covering, the joints being sealed with an adhesive paint followed by a flooding coat of the same paint over the entire jacket. This treatment is often left as the finished coat. **Boiler insulation** is usually finished with two coats of combination portland and asbestos cement. Some boilers are furnished by the manufacturer with insulation covered by a metal jacket. This is particularly true of scotch marine (package) boilers. **Warm-air-furnaces** are typically furnished with metal jackets with insulation applied to their inside surfaces by the manufacturer (see p. 12–114 for insulation of **aboveground** and **underground** distribution piping).

Vestibules

Adequate heating of vestibules requires judgment and experience. Essentially, the technique is to create a "bunker" of air as warm as can be tolerated when doors are closed, in order to dilute the inrush of cold air when the doors are opened. **Affecting circumstances are** (1) design outside air temperature (2) exposure and expected wind velocity, (3) pressure to be maintained in the building, (4) intensity of traffic through the vestibule, (5) presence or absence of revolving doors, (6) the distance between the two sets of doors, if only swinging doors, and (7) use of space immediately behind the vestibule, *e.g.*, personnel immobilized at desks.

Because of the large range of variations in these conditions, vestibule treatment may be anything from a single thermal convector to a patented "air curtain" replacing the vestibule altogether, as used in some department stores. Typical **active vestibules** having only **swinging doors** are usually treated with centrifugal fan unit heaters of capacity to change the entire volume of the vestibule in not more than 1 min with air delivered at 160 F.

High-temperature Hot-water Systems

The term **HTHW** is generally applied to systems with a water temperature above 250 F. The economic advantages of the system are realized more fully at higher temperatures. The design of high-temperature hot-water systems is a specialized field in which there is still controversy regarding basic elements of system design and materials to be used. The FCC Tech. Rept. No. 37 (NAS-NRC Pub. No. 753) presents a survey of practices in the United States together with a comparison of HTHW and steam systems. A survey of European practice by F. Wiese is obtainable from the International Boiler Works Co., East Stroudsburg, Pa.

Advantages. The heat conveyed per unit volume of fluid for HTHW can be as much as 25 times that for steam at the same initial temperature. Even after velocity differences and friction are accounted for, smaller pipes can be used for HTHW. The storage of heat in the total volume of water makes for reduced firing and higher operating efficiencies. The absence of pressure-reducing valves, drips, and vented receivers, and the consequently negligible losses of water and influx of air in a properly operated system tend toward lower maintenance costs. Underground piping systems can follow the contours of the terrain.

Disadvantages. Highly trained operators are needed because faulty operation of one piece of equipment can affect the entire system. The design of HTHW systems is more critical than that of steam systems because of the smaller margin for errors inherent in the medium. Utilization equipment, such as laundry machines, may not be readily available for HTHW. If power generation is involved, the use of HTHW is not indicated.

Water temperatures that would permit the use of 150 psig valves and fittings are not economical. For this reason, temperatures above 350 F should be used. Temperature drops between supply and return should be 100 F minimum and preferably between 120 and 150 F. The use of HTHW directly in heat-emitting devices for space heating is not recommended, except where such devices are located in a place remote from the occupants.

Maximum pressure drop through the HTHW generator should not exceed 10 psig. Generators should be certified by their manufacturers to be suitable for HTHW (see Sec. 9). Steam generators for process work should be built in accordance with the ASME Code for Unfired Pressure Vessels. Storage-type heat exchangers should have dry pipes, water columns, and trim similar to steam boilers. The use of higher temperature drops will be reflected by savings in piping, pumps, motors, and electrical energy consumption.

Types of Systems. Systems may be categorized as flooded or non-flooded (steam boiler), separate expansion tank or integral expansion vessel (steam boiler drum) inert gas-pressurized or steam-pressurized, or single- or double-pumped. The last distinction refers to the use of a single set of pumps for the circulation of water through the system and through the generator as opposed to separate sets of pumps for those functions (Figs. 11 and 12). **Double pumping** is usually indicated only for very large systems, systems with zones of radically differing temperature conditions, or generators with unusually high pressure drops. Some authorities are against the use of a steam boiler drum as the expansion tank and prohibit any steam space in the generator. The use of fire-tube boilers is generally not recommended.

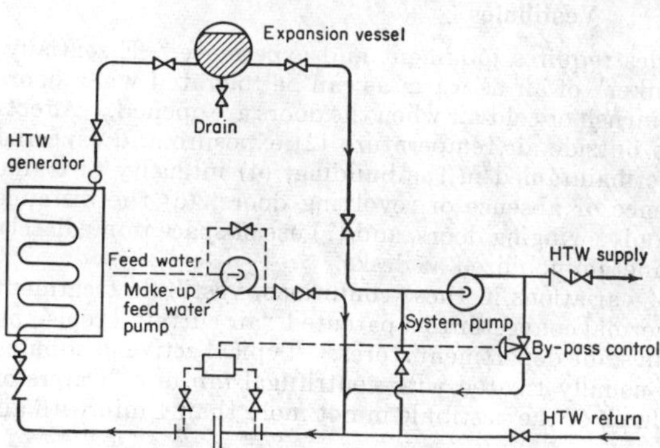

Fig. 11. High temperature water cycle—steam-pressurized, one pump. [*From Federal Construction Council Tech. Rept. No. 37 (NASNRC Publication No. 753), by permission of the Building Research Advisory Board. The complete publication can be obtained from the Printing and Publishing Office, National Academy of Sciences–National Research Council, 2101 Constitution Ave., N.W., Washington, D.C., 20418. (Price: $2).*]

Pressurization. Air should not be used to pressurize an HTHW system. Pressurizing systems should be simple because a malfunction resulting in a sudden drop may impose serious strains on the system.

Steam pressurization has the advantage of simplicity in that the relationship to the saturation temperature is automatic and the pressure in the tank is constant with constant water pressure. It has the disadvantage of a hot tank which must be on the outlet side of the generator, above the nozzle, and high enough to guarantee an adequate net positive suction head on the pump. In a **single-pumped** system, the pumping must be away from the generator (see Fig. 11).

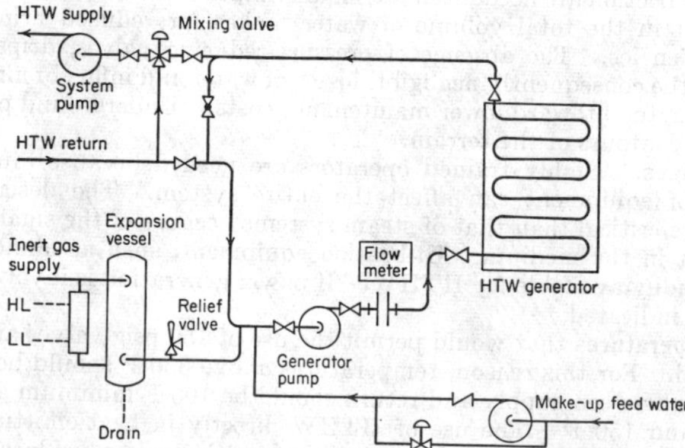

Fig. 12. High temperature water cycle—inert gas-pressurized, two pumps. [*From Federal Construction Council Tech. Rept. No. 30R (NAS-NRC Publication No. 753), by permission of the Building Research Advisory Board. The complete publication can be obtained from the Printing and Publishing Office, National Academy of Sciences–National Research Council, 2101 Constitution Ave., N.W., Washington, D.C. 20418. (Price: $2).*]

Inert-gas pressurization has the advantages of a cool tank, flexibility in locating the tank, and system pressure. It has the disadvantages of requiring more controls and a higher pressure for a given water temperature to provide a factor of safety in exceeding the saturation temperature. Two forms of gas pressurization are: (1) fixed quantity, variable pressure (smaller systems) and (2) variable gas quantity, fixed water quantity, and constant pressure (see Fig. 12). N. J. Saunders of England recommends that nitrogen-pressurized systems designed for a working pressure of 190 psig and having a maximum static head of 35 ft be operated at a maximum temperature of 360 F. For each 25 ft of additional static head (at this pressure) the maximum operating temperature should be reduced by 5 deg.

Pumps. The performance of pumps should be specified and checked under actual operating conditions. The selection of materials, bearings, method of lubrication, sealing, and cooling of seals in connection with pumps used in HTHW systems should be carefully investigated. The net positive suction head required by the pump should not exceed 80 percent of the available NPSH. Pump characteristic curves should be reasonably flat. In double-pumped systems, the generator circulating pumps should be the responsibility of the generator manufacturer (see also Sec. 14).

Controls. In addition to the usual combustion and safety controls for a high-pressure boiler, generators in HTHW systems should have separate high-temperature and high-pressure limit controllers at the outlet, automatic shutdown of firing should flow of water cease for any reason, and means of ensuring that the flow through the generators of single-pumped systems cannot fall below the design rate (see Sec. 16).

Piping. Some authorities are against the use of screwed joints, steel pipe of less than Schedule 40, copper and bronze trim, or gate valves (except as generator-isolating valves). Materials, including valve packing, should be carefully investigated (see Sec. 8). Thermal expansion should be provided by the use of expansion loops and limber in the piping configurations (see Sec. 5). Automatic-control valves should have fixed bypasses to obviate cooling down of sections of the system during periods of no demand.

Operation. Since the prime maintenance advantage of a hot-water system is inherent in a closed-circuit design, continuous blowdown should not be practiced nor should system water be flashed into steam for any purpose.

HEAT-GENERATING EQUIPMENT

(See also Sec. 9.)

The medium by which heat is conveyed from the point of generation to the point of use is usually steam, hot water, or air. Steam and hot-water boilers for low-pressure heating are built of steel or cast iron in a wide variety of types and sizes. Their construction is governed by the ASME Boiler and Pressure Vessel Code. Applicable local or state codes are usually patterned after the ASME Code.

Cast-iron boilers are generally of the sectional type and range in size from small residential units to those with gross heat outputs of 7,680 MBh.

Steel boilers may be of the **fire-tube** type, in which the gases of combustion pass through the tubes and the water circulates around them, or of the **water-tube** type, in which the gases of combustion circulate around the tubes and the water passes through them. Steel-boiler capacities range from those required for small residences up to 16,800 MBh. Fire-tube boilers in recent years have been almost exclusively of the **portable fire-box type** (furnace contained within or partially within a double construction steel box with water-cooled walls) for burning solid fuels and of the **modified scotch marine (package) type** for oil and gas firing. **Water-tube boilers** are made in a wide range of sizes, comprising low-pressure boilers in residential sizes with nonferrous tubes and steel tubes, high-pressure boilers without bottom drums with capacities from 2,300 MBh, and high-pressure boilers with two or three drums with capacities from 6,200 MBh to the sizes used in central stations. Except for the first group, these boilers are commonly known as "power" boilers and are more fully treated in Sec. 9.

Direct-fired hot-water generators resemble steam boilers operating at the same pressures, except for differences in accessories and for the fact that the generators are filled with water. Systems operating at not more than 250 F and not more than 30 psig may use **standard 30 psig hot-water heating boilers** of either **steel** (fire-tube or water-tube) or **cast iron,** if constructed in accordance with ASME Boiler and Pressure Vessel Code, Section IV, for Low Pressure Heating Boilers. Above that pressure but within the temperature limit, **steel fire-tube boilers** may be used if they are designed, tested, and stamped for a higher working pressure (160 psig max) as required by the combined static, pumping, and expansion pressures of the system. **Water-tube generators** only should be used for temperatures above 250 F or for pressures above 160 psig. The use of the usual steam drum as an expansion tank is not recommended. Water-tube generators may have thermal circulation only, forced circulation, or a combination of the two. This matter is an item of controversy within the HTHW field.

In **modified scotch marine-type generators,** thermal shock or differential tube expansion caused by radical differences in the temperature of water in contact with the tubes may be a problem in systems using relatively high temperature drops. Manufacturers have made various provisions for alleviating these conditions, including returning the water to the top of the generator and withdrawing it at the bottom.

Heating boiler **efficiencies** vary with the type of fuel used. Typical values are anthracite, hand-fired, 60 to 75 percent; bituminous coal, hand-fired, 50 to 65 percent; stoker-fired, 60 to 75 percent; and oil- or gas-fired, 70 to 80 percent. Water-tube boilers may have even higher efficiencies, depending on the sophistication of design and controls. In practice, no boiler's operating efficiency can be any better than the settings of its fuel firing system and controls will permit (see Secs. 9 and 16 for controls and measuring devices).

Method of Rating. Cast-iron heating boilers are usually rated according to the Institute of Boiler and Radiator Manufacturers and The American Gas Association codes. **Steel** heating boilers are usually rated according to the codes of the Steel Boiler Institute, the Mechanical Contractors Association of America, the American Gas Association, and the Packaged Fire-tube Branch of the American Boiler and Affiliated Industries (modified scotch marine type). There are three ways by which a boiler may be rated: (1) net load, meaning the actual connected load of heat-emitting units; (2) design load, which is the net load plus an allowance for piping loss; and (3) gross load, which is net load, plus piping tax, plus an added allowance for pick-up. The IBR's rating system indicates a ratio of net load to gross load ranging from 76 percent for small automatically fired boilers to 78 percent for the larger sizes and from 45.5 percent for small hand-fired boilers to 71 percent for the larger sizes. The SBI's rating system indicates a constant ratio of 75 percent for mechanically fired boilers. Heating boiler ratings are usually expressed in MBh, sq ft EDR_{steam}, or sq ft EDR_{water}. The use of the last term should be avoided since systems are not designed for the water temperature (180 F) that gives it validity. The term "boiler horsepower" is of little significance and misleading. It should be avoided.

Heat-transfer Rates. Cast-iron boilers have been conservatively rated at 2,400 to 3,300 Btuh per sq ft of heating surface, while steel portable fire-box boilers have been conservatively rated at 3,300 to 4,400 Btuh per sq ft. The lower end of the range should be applied to hand-fired boilers. These values should be applied to the "design load" and not to the "gross load." With the advent of "package" (modified Scotch marine) boilers, it was brought home to the industry that such values are excessively conservative when applied to carefully designed boiler–burner combinations with automatic firing of oil or gas. This type of boiler is typically rated at 6,700 Btuh per sq ft of heating surface; some manufacturers advocate as high as 11,100 Btuh per sq ft. The lower figure is presently prevalent.

Heat-release Rates. The SBI rating system for fire-box boilers indicates a heat-release rate of about 41,000 Btuh per cu ft of furnace volume at "gross load." Package boilers use considerably higher release rates. Solid-fuel burning rates are 4 to 9.5 lb per hr per sq ft of grate area when hand-fired for small boilers and 5 to 15.5 lb per hr per sq ft in the large sizes of fire-tube boilers. With mechanical firing, burning rates of 35 to 40 lb per hr per sq ft of grate area with short-term burning rates up to 55 lb per hr per sq ft are typical for the larger sizes.

A **warm-air furnace** is a self-enclosed, fuel-burning unit for heating air by transfer of heat of combustion through metal directly to the air; it is designed to discharge the heated air from its outlet directly to the space being heated or through ducts to remote spaces. Warm-air furnaces are made in a variety of types and sizes and are classified by (1) air circulation-gravity (now obsolete) or forced; (2) type of fuel burned; and (3) metal used in the heat exchanger. Furnaces are available in ratings from 15 to 8,000 MBh. Some manufacturers use stainless steel for the furnace envelope.

Circulating fans (see Sec. 14) are usually controlled from a bonnet thermostat and the burner from the room. Fan and burner delivery should be set so that the delivered air temperature is not excessively high. Bonnet thermostat differential should be set so that the delivered air temperature is not low enough to constitute a draft just before the fan stops. A satisfactory temperature is a function of the type and location of outlet.

PANEL HEATING

The term **radiant heating** is now generally confined to heating supplied by relatively small, high-temperature sources (see InfraRed Heating, p. 12–110), while **panel heating** is used for relatively large, low-temperature sources. In panel heating, the ceiling floor, walls, or combinations thereof may be used as the heat-emitting surfaces. Useful heat emission is in the form of radiation to objects and other surfaces in the space and convection to the room air (for a general treatment of radiant-heat transmission, see Sec. 4). Heat is also lost to adjacent spaces and to the outside by similar means and by conduction in the case of slabs on grade.

Wall panels are not generally favored because of their vulnerability to nails. **Floor panels** have the disadvantages of a severe limitation on surface temperature, the effect of coverings (which may be variable), and the higher mass usually involved. A floor-surface temperature higher than 85 F will probably occasion complaints of foot discomfort. Floor coils should not be run under built-in cabinet work. Narrow strips adjacent to the exposed perimeter of the room are sometimes designed for surface temperatures above 85 F. Ceiling surface temperatures should be from 100 to 120 F, the higher end of the range being used only for higher ceilings. If sufficient area is not available to offset the heat losses under the foregoing restrictions, it will be necessary to provide supplementary heat or to reduce the losses.

Heated **floor surfaces** will have the maximum convective component, with **wall surfaces** having slightly less. The convective component of heated **ceiling surfaces** is approximately 6 percent of that of floor surfaces. Ventilation and infiltration increase convection. The output of floor panels is markedly influenced by applied coverings, by edge losses, and by conductive back losses where the floor is directly on earth. The output of ceiling panels may be significantly affected by back losses to unheated attics or to the outside air, while the output of wall panels has the back loss to the outside air as a critical factor. In any case, the heat input must equal the output in all directions.

While electric heating cable, prefabricated metal panels, and warm air flowing through a pattern of flues under a floor are used to some extent, the preferred heating medium in the United States for panel heat is **water** pumped through coils of pipe or tubing which are almost always of serpentine pattern. **Ceiling coils** not embedded in a concrete slab may be in the plaster above the lath—in which case care should be exercised to ensure that they are completely enveloped by the plaster—or in the plaster below the lath (usually ⅜ in. copper tubing). Pipe is usually of SPS steel or wrought iron. Copper tubing is usually soft temper when coils are formed on the job but may be purchased in the form of **prefabricated coils** of hard temper tubing with transverse bracing of brass. The **smaller sizes** of pipe and tubing have become increasingly popular. Copper tubing is usually spaced from 4½ to 9 in. on center, while pipe is usually spaced 9 or 12 in. on center. Typical installations are shown in Fig. 13. Piping should be **tested** to not less than 150 psig for several hours before it is covered.

It is advisable to feed each coil section at its side nearest the exposure. The dimensions of coil sections (circuits) are affected by the size of pipe or tubing, the temperature drop in the water, the pumping head, and the practical size and shape, in the case of prefabricated coils. Many engineers use coils with a closer spacing of tubes in bands parallel to the exposure and a wider spacing elsewhere. **Balancing valves** and **thermometer wells,** which can be obtained in combination, should be provided for each room and in multiple for large or unusually shaped rooms. In high-grade work, balancing valves and wells are often provided for each panel circuit. A reversed-return system of mains will facilitate balancing.

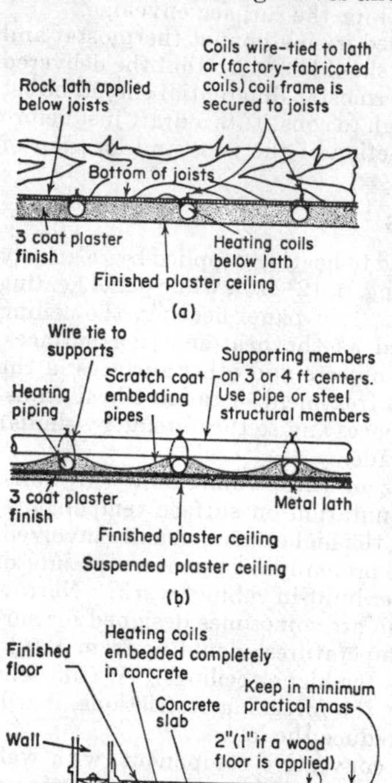

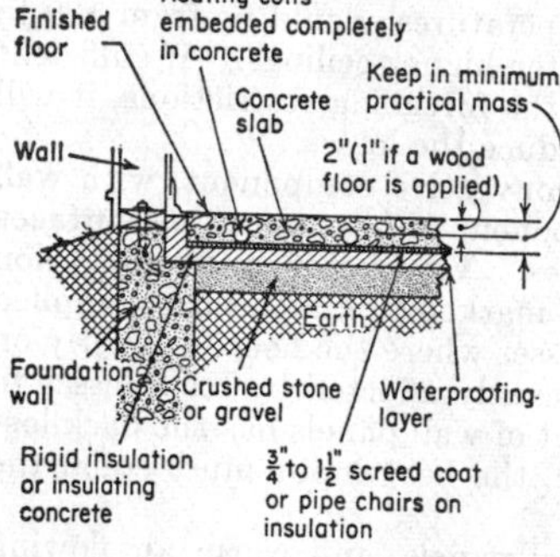

FIG. 13. Panel heat water coils. (*a*) Coils in plaster ceiling below lath. (*b*) Coils in plaster ceiling above lath. (*c*) Coils in floor slab on grade. (*Adapted from 1964 ASHRAE Guide and Data Book.*)

Specific provision for the **upward venting of air** from each panel circuit, preferably at its leaving end, is essential unless return connections proceed uniformly upward from the panel connections. Even if panel-return connections must drop, *e.g.*, to mains in a pipe trench, air-venting connections should be made **from the top** or **flush with the top** of the tube, dropping thereafter if necessary. A retarding chamber with an automatic air vent is recommended for the supply main immediately after the heat source.

Most people prefer **lower air temperatures** in rooms heated by panels. Since a feeling of warmth depends not only on dry-bulb temperature, relative humidity, and air motion but also on **mean radiant temperature,** MRT, the warmer panel surfaces and other surfaces heated by the panels produce an environment that permits lower air temperatures with equal comfort.

Design. Analytical design of panel heat involves complex procedures. The accuracy of the information regarding the space to be heated usually does not warrant a rigorous analysis. Fortunately, design methods for the usual range of conditions can be greatly simplified. For rooms with normal proportions and ceiling heights of between 7 and 12 ft, having ventilation rates of not more than two air changes per hour and maintained air temperatures of 70 F or lower, the values in Table 8 may be used with reasonable accuracy if the outside air temperature does not drop below −10 F. Insulation above ceiling coils and under floor coils radically affects the water temperature required for a given panel-unit output. Moderate insulation is assumed.

Design procedure consists of determining the **design entering water temperature** of the system by first determining the **mean water temperature,** MWT, of the **governing room** and checking it against the maximum permissible temperature (usually taken to be 140 F for coils in plaster or concrete). Water temperature drops of between 10 and 20 F are customarily used. The smaller end of this range should be used for floor coils. The entering water temperature resulting from the governing room MWT and one-half the temperature drop is then used to determine the required panel-surface areas of all other rooms. It is not necessary to use the entire surface for each panel, but non-heated portions should be kept away from exposures. If floor and ceiling panels are used, this procedure must be followed for each category.

The **governing room panel** is designed by ascertaining from Table 8 the surface temperatures required in combination with the area available. The thermal resistance to flow from the pipe coil to the room surface is then calculated, using the average of

Table 8. Panel Output and Mean Water Temperature
(Adapted from 1964 *ASHRAE Guide and Data Book*)

(a) Plaster ceiling panels—4½–9 in. spacing

Surface temperature and output per sq ft					
100 F—35 Btuh		110 F—47 Btuh		120 F—60 Btuh[b]	
rd[a]	MWT, deg F	*rd*[a]	MWT, deg F	*rd*[a]	MWT, deg F
0.3	112	0.3	125	0.3	140[c]
0.6	122	0.6	138		
1.0	136				

[a] Downward thermal resistance (deg F)(hr)(sq ft) per Btu.
[b] Use only above 9 ft 0 in.
[c] Maximum for 20 F t.d. in plaster or concrete.

(b) Concrete floor panels—9–12 in. spacing—no covering[d]

Surface temperature and output per sq ft							
85 F[e]—39 Btuh				90 F[f]—51 Btuh			
Slab thickness, in.	Pipe size, in.	*ru*[g]	MWT	Slab thickness, in.	Pipe size, in.	*ru*[g]	MWT
4	½[h] or ¾	0.60	112	4	½[h] or ¾	0.60	124
		0.50	108			0.50	118
		0.40	104			0.40	114
6	½ or ¾	0.50	108	6	½ or ¾	0.50	118
		0.45	106			0.45	116
		0.40	104			0.40	114
	1	0.60	112		1	0.60	124
		0.53	109			0.53	120
		0.45	106			0.45	116

[d] Floor coverings decrease output to fractions indicated. Increase water temperature accordingly. Check effect on adjacent rooms without floor covering.
Resilient flooring plus felt: 0.94 1 in. tile or terrzazo: 0.94
1 in. wood: 0.5 1 in. wood plus carpet and felt: 0.31
[e] Maximum for floors with foot traffic.
[f] Use only for edge strips; see[e].
[g] Upward thermal resistance (deg F)(hr)(sq ft) per Btu.
[h] Cover: 2 in., except under wood, tile, or terrazzo floors: 1 in.

the resistances along paths from the pipe to a point on the surface directly opposite it and to a point on the surface midway between pipes. It is necessary to assume a trial pipe size and spacing for this purpose. From this resistance, the **required mean water temperature** is found in Table 8.

In the case of **ceiling panels,** the loss of heat in the direction opposite the room is found by calculating the thermal resistance in that direction and applying the temperature difference between the mean water temperature and the temperature of the air to which heat is being lost. In the case of panels in the form of **concrete slabs at or near grade,** it is necessary to take account of **edge losses** as well as losses through the bottom surface. The required flow of water can be calculated from the total load on the governing panel and the selected temperature drop. Other panels are similarly calculated.

The **piping layout** is then made. Judgment should be exercised in laying out the various coil circuits to make the system as self-balancing as practicable. Velocities exceeding 4 fps should not be used in residential occupancies. The circuit of highest resistance is determined, and, from the cumulative water quantities, the pump head and gpm are established. In residential occupancies, moderate pump heads and pumps specifically designed for quiet operation should be used.

Insulation. The higher the mass of a panel, the greater will be the automatic control problem caused by "flywheel" effect (stored heat). Every effort should be made to keep the mass on the panel side of insulation to a minimum. In high-grade work, insulation is sometimes used under slabs on earth to permit the limiting of panel mass as well as to reduce back losses. The use of ceiling coils in uninsulated concrete slabs with occupied space above or the omission of insulation above the coil in other construction makes for difficult control problems in that space, particularly if it has larger glass areas facing east, south, or west. The use of a lower ceiling-surface temperature may be necessary, if the temperature of the floor above is not to exceed 85 F.

Thermostatic control from room temperature has been found to be satisfactory providing the "flywheel" effect in floor panels has been limited by adequate insulation. In high-grade work, thermostatically controlled ventilating fans have been used to offset this effect in high-mass flagged floors in enclosed terraces.

Snow Melting

Snow melting for roads, driveways, walkways, and airport surfaces is accomplished by circulating a non-freezing liquid or solution through pipes or with electric heating cables, embedded beneath the surface of the area to be protected. Limited areas can be protected by infrared radiation. Weather bureau records show that about 90 percent of all snowfall occurs at temperatures between 10 and 35 F or at an average temperature of 26 F. At 26 F the average density of snow is 6 lb per cu ft. The following information is based on this density. The assumed hourly rate of snowfall (water equivalent) for various cities is listed in Table 9. One inch of water per sq ft = 5.2 lb.

Table 9. Snowfall Data for Various Cities

(Rate in inches of water equivalent per hour per square foot)

City	Rate of snowfall	City	Rate of snowfall
Albany, N.Y.	0.16	Evansville, Ind.	0.08
Asheville, N.C.	0.08	Hartford, Conn.	0.25
Billings, Mont.	0.08	Kansas City, Mo.	0.16
Bismarck, N.Dak.	0.08	Madison, Wis.	0.08
Boise, Idaho	0.08	Minneapolis, Minn.	0.08
Boston, Mass.	0.16	Oklahoma City, Okla.	0.16
Buffalo, N.Y.	0.16	Omaha, Nebr.	0.16
Burlington, Vt.	0.08	Philadelphia, Pa.	0.16
Caribou, Maine	0.16	Pittsburgh, Pa.	0.08
Chicago, Ill.	0.08	Portland, Maine	0.16
Cincinnati, Ohio	0.08	St. Louis, Mo.	0.08
Cleveland, Ohio	0.08	Salt Lake City, Utah	0.08
Denver, Colo.	0.08	Spokane, Wash.	0.16
Detroit, Mich.	0.08	Washington, D.C.	0.16

The **heat required** per square foot of surface to melt snow at this temperature can be calculated by adding the heat required to raise the snow to 32 F (31 Btu per in. of water) to the latent heat of fusion (144 Btu per lb = 750 Btu per in. of water), yielding a total requirement of 781 Btu per in. of water. To this requirement must be added the losses to the air by convection and to the surroundings by radiation. The convective losses will be influenced by wind velocity and the ability of the water to run off the surface. Table 10 gives typical values for **total hourly heat requirements** per square foot to meet different climatic conditions and rates of snowfall.

Owing to side losses, back losses, and piping losses, an **efficiency** of 60 to 70 percent is usual, depending on the condition below and the length of supply and return piping. Where snow-melting systems occur over heated sidewalk vaults, allowance for back losses should be proportionately reduced.

Table 10. Heat Output from Slab and Fluid Temperature for Snow-melting Systems*

Rate of snowfall, in. water equiv per hr	Heat output q_o, Btu per sq ft per hr; fluid temp t_w, deg F	Air temp, deg F, (t_a) − 80 percent rel hum					
		10 F		20 F		30 F	
		Wind vel v, mph					
		5	15	5	15	5	15
0.08	q_o	127	209	102	154	75	94
	t_w	97	138	85	110	70	79
0.16	q_o	193	274	165	217	135	154
	t_w	129	170	117	142	100	109
0.25	q_o	265	364	235	287	203	221
	t_w	165	206	151	176	134	144

* Based on ¾ in. pipe on 12 in. centers with 2 in. concrete cover. Surface free from snow.

Piping Layout. Small pipes closely spaced make for the best heat distribution, but large pipes widely spaced are cheaper. A compromise is usually achieved by using ¾ or 1 in. pipe spaced on 12 to 15 in. centers or 1¼ in. pipe on 16 to 18 in. centers for parallel runs in concrete. For bituminous-paving installations, because of the lower-heat-transfer rates, ¾ or 1 in. pipe on 12 in. centers is often used.

Three types of piping circuits, known as serpentine coils, grid, and combination grid and serpentine coil, are used. A **grid** comprises a number of parallel pipe runs having their ends welded into larger pipes, usually placed at right angles to the runs so the flow will be into the supply header, then through parallel runs, and then out through the return header. Supply and return connections must be at diagonally opposite points to obtain equal flow through all runs. A **combination grid and serpentine coil** consists of three or more parallel serpentine coils connected into headers. Each flow pattern has its advantages and disadvantages. Serpentine coils are easy to form, utilize random lengths, require fewer cuts and joints, and are easily adapted to irregular areas, but they usually result in higher pumping heads and sometimes present drainage and air-binding problems. Grids have lower friction loss, can be sloped for effective drainage and venting, and require fewer balancing valves for large areas, but they do not permit the full use of random lengths. While usually the cheapest for large areas, a grid arrangement may be the most expensive for small installations.

In making the pipe installation, the paving is usually placed on a fill of crushed stone, washed gravel, or similar material. Piping should be supported so as to ensure at least 1 in. of paving on the underside of the pipe and a minimum of 2 in. of surfacing above the pipe. **Calcium chloride** and other antifreeze chemicals should not be added to concrete where the slab is to be equipped with a snow-melting system. Such chemicals in the presence of moisture promote acid conditions which are highly corrosive to all commonly used piping materials.

Freeze-up protection provided by ethylene glycol solutions or petroleum distillates have been found to be the most satisfactory. Alcohol's tendency to boil out is a health and fire hazard. A 32.5 percent ethylene glycol solution provides protection to 0 F; 38.5 percent to −10 F; 44 percent to −20 F, and 49 percent to −30 F. Excessively high concentrations of ethylene glycol should be avoided because the freezing point rises again after the eutectic has been reached. Liquid-quantity and pumping-head calculations for such solutions and fluids should be carefully checked for the effects of **specific gravity** and **specific heat.** For example, the specific gravity of a 40 percent glycol solution at 150 F is approximately 1.05 and specific heat 0.86. **Heat transfer** should also be carefully checked.

Where steam is the basic heat source, a heat exchanger is usually employed because of the danger of condensate freezing and excessive thermal stresses if steam is used directly. As in other liquid-filled heating systems, provision must be made for expansion of the liquid (see Expansion Tanks, p. 12–99).

Although fully automatic controls are available, snow-melting systems usually employ an automatic liquid temperature control and a manually operated on-off control. The system should be placed in operation well in advance of an expected snowfall. It is uneconomical to design for "catching up."

ELECTRIC HEATING

Electrical heating of space is economical in the more severe climates of the United States only in unusually well-insulated buildings, where electric rates are low or where special rates are offered for space heating. **Duct heaters** are much used, however, for reheat in air-conditioning systems as a form of zone control.

Heat emitters using electricity generally have high-temperature elements consisting of coiled Nichrome wire and may have reflectors, flues to promote convection, or fans for forced circulation of air. They are available in the form of baseboard convectors. Heaters are also made with the resistance elements embedded in glass, in which case they are designed for low operating temperatures and are used mostly for localized supplementary heat. Such heaters are usually designed with a flue for convection. The glass attains a temperature of about 340 F and, because of the surface characteristics of glass, does not burn the skin upon casual contact.

Heating cable with braid covering or jackets of Teflon and lead can be embedded in building construction for use as panel heat. It is also available in the form of mineral-insulated cable, which has a seamless copper sheath and requires special terminating fittings. The heat output per unit length of cable is controlled by the cable size used, the voltage applied, and the length of the circuit.

Air in ducts is heated electrically by means of heating elements that are built into rectangular frames or mounted on metal connection boxes. Elements are available encased in refractory material with a metal sheath. Sheaths may be obtained with fins for the advantages of cooler operation and more uniform heating of the air. Low-mass elements consist of bare Nichrome wire stretched across frames on insulators. Duct heaters are universally provided with **protective thermostats** to guard against overheating should the flow of air cease for any reason. Some engineers derate duct heaters so as to obtain a longer life.

INFRARED HEATING

Infrared heating is becoming increasingly popular for providing localized supplementary heat out-of-doors during cold weather and for snow melting. Localized heat is provided both for transient conditions, such as department store display windows, under building entrance canopies, or at outdoor teller's window of banks, and for conditions, such as loading docks and grandstands, where people are subject to low temperatures for long periods (see "The Lighting Handbook" of the Illuminating Engineering Society for additional information).

The term **"infrared"** is applied to wavelengths of radiant energy between 760 mμ and 1 mm, the beginning of the microwave band. However, because glass and the carbon dioxide in the atmosphere are increasingly opaque to wavelengths greater than 4,000 mμ, shorter wavelengths are generally used in designing sources. **Quartz** and other types of glass more transparent to infrared rays than ordinary glass are also used to improve the efficiency of sources. Any infrared source—particularly electrically heated sources—will produce a significant component of visible light, as well as the infrared radiation. This light also serves the intended function because light which strikes an object and is not transmitted by or reflected from it is converted into sensible heat. The **light contribution** of the infrared sources should be considered in designing the switching of lighting sources at the same location.

Heat-emitting Devices. Electrically heated sources are available in the form of reflector lamps and tubular quartz elements with tungsten filaments, both being gas-filled and operating at filament temperatures of about 2500 K. The **reflector lamps** are rated from 100 to 1,000 watts and have a life expectancy of about 10,000 hr or more. The **quartz lamps** are rated at 1,600 watts at 240 volts and are rated at 5,000 hr at rated voltage. Tubes are $\frac{3}{8}$ in. in diameter and 13 in. long. Commercial fixtures are generally designed for two tubes and are available for asymmetrical distribution.

Gas-heated infrared sources consist of ceramic grids which are heated by gas flames and which generally operate at a grid surface temperature of about 1650 F. They are available in ratings from 10,000 to 100,000 Btuh. The heat sources described under Electric Heating (p. 12–110) in the form of resistance elements embedded in glass also function as low-grade infrared heat sources for close applications.

The designs of infrared heat sources leave much to be desired, the output of heat in the downward direction being relatively low. The application engineering furnished by manufacturers is often vague. There is a need for accurate information relative to the components of the input energy that are emitted as **radiation in a downward direction,** radiation in other directions, and convected heat. At present, applications are usually based on the assumption that 50 percent of the input energy is directed to the surface to be heated. In the case of **reflector lamps,** 100 watt lamps spaced 10 in. on center in both directions will produce slightly over 100 watts per sq ft at a distance of 1 ft. The incident energy will vary directly as the wattage and will vary inversely as the square of the spacing and the square of the distance.

Design Criteria. The following recommendations are given in terms of **watts per square foot** incident upon the surface to be heated (1 watt equals approximately 3.4 Btuh): In an application to a grandstand in Chicago, 30 watts per sq ft has been found satisfactory. In this case, with fixtures at an average height of 24 ft above the seats, 70 to 80 ft-c of illumination were also achieved. Loading docks have been designed on a basis of 22 watts per sq ft. Consideration should be given to snow melting on the exposed portions of docks. Transient applications, such as under canopies at bank tellers' windows and under marquees at building entrances, are usually designed to snow-melting criteria.

The application of infrared heating follows the laws of radiant energy and is, therefore, analogous to the application of light sources. The guiding considerations for lighting design should be applied (see p. 12–154 *et seq.*). Sources should be kept as low as possible, although it is not desirable to locate high-temperature sources less than 9 ft above the floor. Attention should be given to the edges of the pattern of distribution, where the overlap from multiple sources is at a minimum. This is particularly essential in snow-melting applications.

CENTRAL AND DISTRICT HEATING

The distribution of steam or hot water from the plant to groups of buildings, as at universities, hospitals, large housing developments, and airports, is known as **central heating.** The use of similar distribution systems operated as commercial ventures to buildings under different ownership is known as **district heating. Steam** is usually distributed at pressures of 125 psig or more, while water is distributed as described for HTHW systems (p. 12–101). **Condensate** is usually returned to the plant in central-heating systems but often is lost to the sewer, after appropriate cooling, in district-heating systems. Laundry loads, sterilizing loads, and industrial loads, in addition to the usual domestic hot-water heating loads, are served by many such systems. The serving of laundry steam loads from HTHW systems requires extremely high temperatures for economical use of commercially available laundry equipment. Such distribution systems are run **underground, aboveground,** or as a combination of the two, the aboveground piping being kept within secondary areas.

Pipe Sizing. Pumped-water piping should be sized for an economic balance of initial cost of the piping system and the cost of pumping over the life of the system. Reasonable velocities should be maintained. Table 11 indicates suggested velocities for **hot-water distribution,** while Table 12 indicates the delivery of **steam** at various pressures through different sizes of pipe. Process piping at reduced pressures within the various buildings may also be sized from this table. A clear distinction should be made between a **condensate-pump-discharge** pipe and a **gravity-return** pipe flowing to a vented receiver. The former should be sized for the economic balance referred to, while the latter must be sized and pitched so as to produce the necessary motive power to achieve the flow rate required. Where a gravity return serves an item using high-pressure steam, it would seem reasonable to take advantage of the steam pressure to force condensate through the return system. On medium pressures, complete

Table 11. Main Velocities for Central Hot-water Distribution

Size of main, in.	2½	3	4	5	6	8	10	12
Velocity, fps	5	5½	7	8	9	10	11	12

Table 12. High and Medium Pressure Steam and Return Pipe Sizing

Pipe size, in.	Steam pipes (Schedule 40)					Return pipes (Schedule 40)		
	100 psig pressure			40 psig pressure		Capacity: lb per hr*		
	Capacity, lb per hr	Velocity, fpm	Pr. drop†	Capacity, lb per hr	Pr. drop†	Pr. drop, ½ lb per 100 ft	Pr. drop 1 lb per 100 ft	Gravity mains‡
¾						245	365	270
1	230	2,500	1.30	150	1.25	490	730	485
1¼	480	3,000	1.40	360	0.85	1,025	1,530	970
1½	750	3,500	1.50	500	0.75	1,670	2,500	1,460
2	1,450	4,000	1.40	700	0.75	3,400	5,050	2,680
2½	2,500	4,800	1.60	1,200	0.80	5,600	8,400	4,300
3	4,200	5,400	1.50	2,000	0.75	10,300	15,300	6,900
4	8,100	6,000	1.35	4,000	0.70	21,600	32,300	14,800
5	14,000	6,600	1.25	6,800	0.64	40,300	60,000	26,200
6	22,000	7,000	1.20	11,000	0.60	65,500	98,000	42,800
8	42.000	8,000	1.10	23,000	0.61			
10	75,000	9,000	1.00	42,000	0.65			

* Pressure drops based on 2 psig pressure in return for ½ lb per 100 ft drop; 1 psig pressure for 1 lb per 100 ft drop.

† lb per 100 ft.

For capacity at 125 psig, multiply by 1.20. For capacity at 150 psig, multiply by 1.40. Pressure drops vary with density for a constant velocity but not in a straight-line relationship. The difference at 150 psig pressure ranges from 38 percent (small sizes) to 50 percent (large sizes) greater pressure drop.

‡ Based on pitch of 1 in. per 60 ft and $C = 120$ in Williams and Hazen formula.

For return pipe capacities at 150 psig, multiply by 1.48. Pressures in return pipes: 5 psig for ½ lb per 100 ft drop. 10 psig for 1 lb per 100 ft drop.

dependency upon this source of motive power can produce sluggish systems. Such lines should most reasonably be designed as a compromise between a complete gravity return and a pressure return. This does not preclude the use of the inlet pressure to lift condensate initially to a well-pitched, reasonably sized return run at a high level. Returns from items having radically different inlet pressures should not be combined.

Pipe Materials. Steam piping and HTHW piping are usually of black steel with welded fittings. Condensate-return piping is variously installed as Schedule-40 black steel or Schedule-80 wrought iron or non-ferrous pipe or tubing, usually with a heavy wall thickness. The use of Schedule-80 pipe for small return lines requires careful checking of capacity. The selection of materials for condensate returns and condensate-pump discharges is discussed further below.

Underground Distribution

Underground heating distribution has been a source of endless trouble. The subject has been studied thoroughly for the Federal government by a **task group of the Building Research Advisory Board of the Federal Construction Council,** the results of their investigations and their recommendations being embodied in FCC Technical Report No. 30R (NAS-NRC Publication 660). The **task group's findings** indicate that: (1) systems are not designed with adequate attention to the **prevention of damage by water** entering supposedly adequately sealed enclosures and (2) materials are used for condensate returns and pump discharge lines which do not ensure a **life equal to that of the steam lines** enveloped with them in a common enclosure. When the condensate line fails, the entire enclosure must be disrupted to replace it, thereby interfering with the proper functioning of the steam distribution and jeopardizing its safety. The first difficulty is often aggravated by the fact that **manholes** are not rendered as resistant to the entry of water as is the pipe enclosure itself, thus permitting it to be infiltrated with water from its own manholes.

Proper design requires that a clear distinction must be made between systems that probably will be partly **submerged** for significant lengths of time, as in the case of conduits below the highest recorded water table of some duration, and conduits which will normally be completely above the water table. The assignment of a particular site situation to the second category is difficult, since the trench for the conduit may for many years represent a subsoil drainage ditch, attracting water from the adjacent more consolidated areas and submerging the conduit at least partially during heavy runoffs. The task group suggests that conduits, to be suitable for the first category, should be **pressure-tested** for complete absence of leaks through the envelope both before and after installation, that they be permanently capable of being so **tested in place,** and that they be provided with **drains** and an **air passage** around the pipe covering adequate to permit draining of the conduit and drying out of the insulation with forced hot air should water enter the conduit. The measures to be taken to render conduits in the second category reasonably safe from water damage are

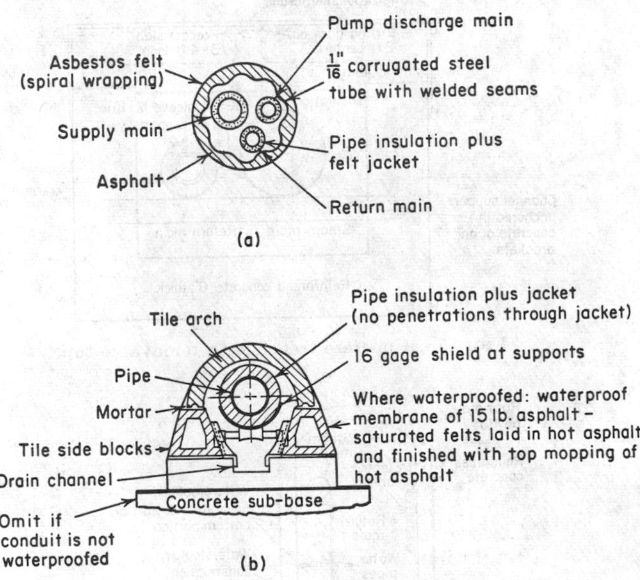

FIG. 14. Underground conduits. (*a*) Ric-Wil "presealed" shop-fabricated conduit. (*b*) Thermotile tile arch and side block-concrete base conduit.

even more open to diversity of opinion and require the judgment of persons experienced in this field and a thorough investigation of site conditions, including conditions to be expected **after the trenches for the system are completed,** which may equate with the first category.

Underground-distribution enclosures fall principally into the following types: (1) shells of metal [Fig. 14(*a*)], tile, or tile arches on concrete bases [Fig. 14(*b*)] and trenches of poured concrete or concrete block with concrete base and cover slabs (Fig. 15); (2) reinforced concrete walking tunnels (Fig. 16); (3) shells of plastic material such as polyvinyl chloride tubing over foamed plastic insulation bonded to the pipe and the jacket; (4) a thick layer of asphalt poured into an annular space between the pipe covering and a vented sheet metal jacket; (5) insulating concrete or other poured-in-place setting material (Fig. 17); and (6) granular insulating and waterproofing fill. Type 1 enclosures other than trenches are known as **"conduits."** Types 3 and 4 are also loosely referred to by the same term. They are shop-fabricated, as are the metal-shell conduit systems in Type 1. Since so-called shop-fabricated systems must be shipped in reasonable lengths, there will be field assemblies to be made. The distinction between "shop-fabricated" and "field-assembled" is that the former limits field assembly to the required joints.

Insulation and Supports (see also Secs. 6 and 8). In Type 1 enclosures, the pipe insulation should be in the form of sectional pipe covering. Loose-fill insulation should not be used. Pipe covering should be complete at every point (not interrupted for supports or protection saddles), metal bearing plates to distribute support loads being placed **outside** the waterproofing jacket. Special details must be worked out for anchors. All metal-pipe supports within such enclosures should be hot-dipped galvanized after fabrication, "fabrication" being defined to include the drilling of all holes. In the case of conduits depending upon a **plastic jacket,** the annular space between the pipe and the jacket is filled with foamed polyurethane insulation, which should be molded in place so that the insulation fills the space at uniform density and

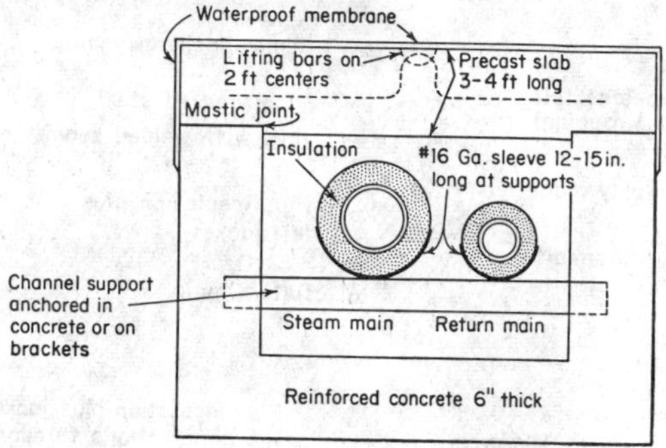

FIG. 15. Concrete trench with removable top.

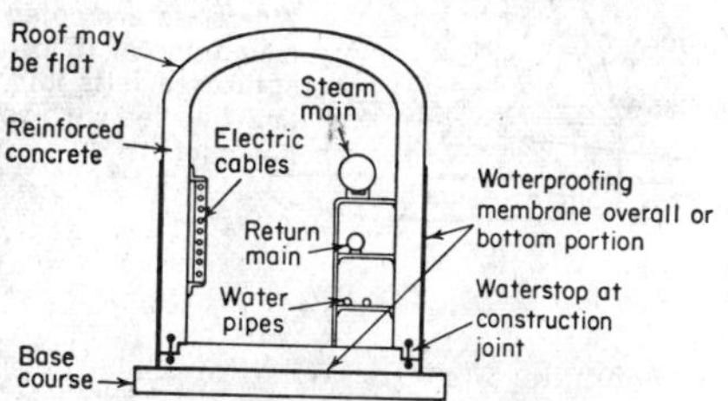

FIG. 16. Reinforced concrete tunnel.

adheres to the pipe and the jacket to form a structurally cooperative assembly. Field joints are jacketed with sleeves and stainless-steel glands resembling Dresser couplings.

In the case of conduits depending on the integrity of a **sheet-metal envelope** to exclude water, such envelopes are usually of 16 gage corrugated steel with welded seams, and they should be hot-dipped galvanized on both sides to a density of not less than 2 oz per sq ft. The envelope is then protected against corrosion, *e.g.*, by a layer of asphalt and a wrapping of asbestos felt. **Cast-iron** sectionally formed and flanged envelopes are also available at correspondingly greater cost.

Tile conduits installed on unconsolidated subsoil should have concrete bases, preferably with low-grade mesh reinforcing. The ability of split-tile systems to bridge soft spots that may form and at the same time to maintain tight joints is doubtful. Heavier tile is available for road crossings. Some engineers prefer to apply concrete with mesh over standard tile. Where trenches and tile conduit are not membrane-waterproofed, the application of glass fabric to all mortar joints with coal tar epoxy paint followed by a flooding coat of the same paint will give greater assurance against leaks. The fabric should overlap the surfaces on either side of the joint by not less than 4 in. and other sheets of fabric by not less than 2 in. Tunnels should have membrane waterproofing for at least a portion of their height.

Insulating concrete envelopes should be membrane-waterproofed and should be constructed in strict accordance with the manufacturer's instructions. Proper waterproofing requires the laying of a subbase (as indicated in Fig. 17). **Pipe supports** are of insulating concrete blocks,

Granular-fill envelopes consist of natural and synthetic insulating and waterproofing conglomerations of small granules. **Natural granular fill** is size-graded Gilsonite, a natural asphalt. Upon being heated from inside the pipe in accordance with instructions, it becomes **plastic** for a zone of thickness immediately outside the pipe, the granules **cohere** (sinter) for another zone of thickness (depending upon the amount of heat provided), and they remain **unconsolidated** for any additional thickness of fill. The sintered and unconsolidated zones both act as insulation. The plastic and sintered zones act as waterproofing, but even the unconsolidated zone is water repellent at moderate heads. **Synthetic granular fill** seeks to accomplish the same result by taking graded granules of perlite and coating them with asphaltic substances.

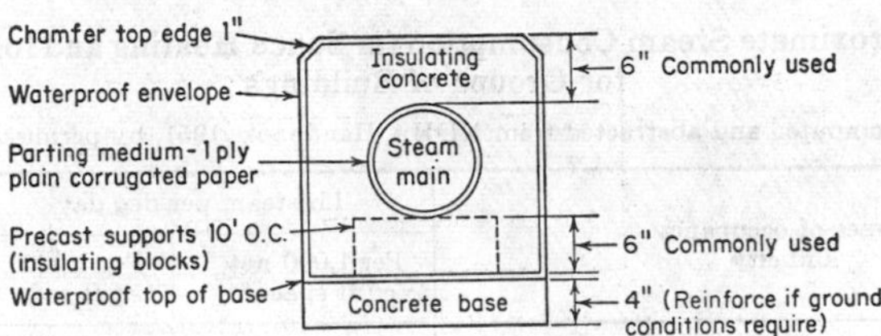

FIG. 17. Typical Z-crete underground conduit.

Manholes. Manholes should be of reinforced concrete monolithically poured, or water stops should be provided between base and monolithic walls. A **high-water signal** should be provided at such manholes to indicate failure of the drainage system, whether by malfunction of pump or clogging of gravity drain. Alarm floats should be set so as to provide ample time for action before the water level rises to the point of damage. **Gravity drains and pump discharges** should be provided with large leaf and rodent screens adequately protected by head walls and wing walls, the entire drainage system being no better than its outfalls. **Sump pumps** should be of the submersible type with any electrical items in watertight enclosures. Manholes should be ventilated by 4 in. pipes with mushroom caps in pairs, one of each pair extending to within 1 ft of the floor.

Provisions for Expansion (see also Sec. 5). Expansion joints are usually provided in tunnels, loops being preferred for the other forms of enclosures. In the case of the shop-fabricated systems, the provisions for such loops are designed into the system by the manufacturer. Expansion joints have been a source of considerable trouble. If they must be used in enclosures other than tunnels, they should be stainless-steel bellows type with pipe carefully guided on either side of the joint, in accordance with the manufacturer's instructions. The **forces on anchors** resulting from expansion joints and loops should be carefully investigated. They sometimes attain magnitudes that may be excessive for the element of the enclosure system that must act as a column to resist the force. Anchor blocks should be designed conservatively for wet-soil conditions.

Cathodic protection should be considered if the resistivity of the soil is less than 2,000 ohms per cc (see also Sec. 6).

Aboveground Systems

Pipe. Piping is often run a short distance above the ground in areas where such an arrangement will not interfere with traffic. In congested areas, *e.g.*, between industrial buildings, piping is usually run on poles, in which case the problems of expansion and pipe movement are simplified if the piping is **hung** from T members at the tops of the poles rather than placed on top of such members. Where piping is required to bridge considerable distances, *e.g.*, at double trucking lanes, **catenaries** are useful to reduce the span of the pipes. **Expansion loops** can be placed in either the horizontal or the vertical orientation. Vertical loops in steam mains require drips ahead of the loop on low piping and drips at the bottom of the loops on high piping. HTHW piping requires air vents ahead of the loops on high piping and at the far end of the high pipe on low piping. **Anchors** should be specifically designed. As with underground anchoring, the pressure on the soil should be carefully checked.

Drip assemblies for high-pressure steam mains out-of-doors in northern climates can be rendered less troublesome from the aspect of freezing up by the use of shielded-bellows thermostat traps. Drips have been successfully discharged into the condensate-pump-discharge lines by the use of long perforated tubes with a large number of small holes and closed ends. It is recommended that such tubes be either stainless steel or heavy non-ferrous pipe.

Pipe covering on aboveground piping is usually provided with a reasonably weather-

Table 13. Approximate Steam Consumption for Space Heating and for Water Heating for Groups of Buildings

(Computed and abstracted from NDHA Handbook, 1951, by permission)

Types of occupancy and city	Lb steam per deg day		Water heating, lb steam per cu ft space per year
	Per 1,000 net cu ft space*	Per 1,000 sq ft rad	
Apartments			
Dayton, Ohio	1.090*	95*	
Detroit, Mich.	1.40	86	2.83
New York, N.Y.	1.24–1.43*		
Portland, Ore.	1.05–1.24*	86–120*	
Banks			
Detroit, Mich.	0.700	26	0.77
Portland, Ore.	0.57–0.84*	42–46*	
St. Louis, Mo.	0.69	39	
Churches			
Detroit, Mich.	0.530	29	0.24
New York, N.Y.	0.370–0.640*		
St. Louis, Mo.	0.130	21	
Portland, Ore.	0.31–0.52*	30–38*	
Retail and department stores			
Baltimore, Md.	0.32–0.37	51–65	
Detroit, Mich.	0.48	28	0.95
New York, N.Y.	0.67*		
Portland, Ore.	0.18*	35*	
St. Louis, Mo.	0.26	31	
Parking garages			
Cleveland, Ohio	0.381	53	
New York, N.Y.	0.23–0.54*		
St. Louis, Mo.	0.56		
Hotels			
Baltimore, Md.	0.74–1.32	104–113	2.39
Detroit, Mich.	1.17–1.32	59–84	2.47–3.75
New York, N.Y.	0.98–2.07*		
Portland, Ore.	0.79–1.14*	78–103*	2.13–3.05
Office buildings			
Baltimore, Md.	0.35–0.88	47–92	
Detroit, Mich.	0.65–0.82	40–51	0.98
Portland, Ore.	0.51–0.94*	55–98*	
St. Louis, Mo.	0.680	28	

* Gross cubic space based on dimensions of building.

tight jacket or is installed as shop-fabricated conduit of Types 1 or 3. The modern trend is to cover such jacketing with extremely thin corrugated aluminum sheeting secured with closely spaced aluminum bands having stainless-steel catches. Fittings may be covered with heavy canvas sewn on and may be painted with asphalt-based aluminum paint, or they may be covered with manufactured sectional sheet-metal covers. Aluminum jackets of sheet-metal weight are also available for the runs of pipe at correspondingly greater expense.

Approximate Steam Consumption for Buildings and Appliances

Table 13 lists approximate **steam consumption** for **space heating** and for **water heating** for groups of buildings of various sizes heated with district steam. The steam use per cubic foot of space depends in general upon the size of the building, the larger buildings usually having lower use per cubic foot; upon the type of heating system, vacuum-return systems being generally lower; upon the type of operating control and the number of heating zones; and upon the degree of supervision and maintenance. In the Northern states, the approximate proportion of the total annual steam consumption for each month is indicated above. Tables 14 to 16 give data for various appliances and equipment.

Distribution of Heating among Different Months of the Season, Percent

Month	%	Month	%	Month	%
September	1	December	17	March	14
October	6	January	19	April	9
November	12	February	17	May	5

Table 14. Approximate Steam Consumption of Laundry Equipment, Lb per Hr*

(Abstracted in part from NDHA Handbook, 1951, by permission)

Equipment	Lb per hr
Tumbler (dryer):	
42″ × 44″	315
40″ × 94″	360
Press:	
54½″	50
Standard	105
Large shirt body	190
Ironer:	
4-roll, 110″ flatwork	335
6-roll, 110″ flatwork	415
8-roll, 120″ flatwork	480

* Pressure of 100 to 125 psig required.

Washers require hot water at the rate of 2½ gal per lb of wash. Some washers have booster steam connections for making up losses through the machine enclosure.

Table 15. Approximate Steam Consumption of Kitchen Appliances

(Steam pressure approximately 20 psig; starting-up requirements approximately double)

Appliance	Steam, lb per hr
Bain-marie, per sq ft of surface	3
Coffee urns, per gal	2.5–3
Dishwashers—per dish washed: 0.44 lb/hr wash + 0.56 lb/hr rinse =	0.10/dish
Plate warmer, per 20 cu ft	30
Soup or stock kettle, 60 gal	60
Soup or stock kettle, 40 gal	45
Steam table, per sq ft of surface	1.5
Vegetable steamer, per compartment 5 lb press	30
Silver burnisher	60

HEAT PUMPS

The term "heat pump" is usually applied to **refrigeration systems** that increase, rather than decrease, the amount of heat in a given space. Such systems are also, but erroneously, called "reverse cycle refrigeration." The process is thermally

Table 16. Approximate Steam Consumption of Hospital Equipment, Lb per Hr*

Equipment	Lb per Hr
Non-pressure instrument sterilizer (boiling), 20 min op	60
High-speed emergency instrument sterilizer, 10 min op:	
9″ × 19″	40
16″ × 24″	75
†Pressure instrument washer-sterilizer (boiling), 30 min:	
11″ diam × 11″ deep	175
Autoclave, 50 min operation:	
20″ diam × 38″	50
Laboratory type, 24″ × 24″ × 36″	95
Laboratory type, 24″ × 36″ × 48″	100
Pressure-dressing sterilizers, 50 min operation:	
24″ × 24″ × 48″	110
24″ × 36″ × 60″	170
36″ × 42″ × 84″	365
Utensil sterilizers, non-pressure (boiling), 30 min op:	
16″ × 24″ × 24″	65
20″ × 24″ × 20″	100
Water sterilizers, 2 at 15 gal, 30 min operation	190
Water still, per gal per hr capacity	12
Bedpan washer-sterilizer (nominal—momentary jet)	10

* All require 40 psig steam unless otherwise noted.
† Requires 60 psig steam.
Quantities are instantaneous rates for **pipe sizing**. Apply a factor of 0.7 for plant load before diversification.

identical whether the system is heating or cooling (see Sec. 18). A heat pump uses electrical or chemical energy to raise heat from a low temperature to a useful level of 100 F or higher. The process differs from "refrigeration" only in that the purpose is to supply rather than to extract heat, and the problem is to select a source of heat rather than a heat sink and to pump the heat up to a temperature suitable for use rather than disposal. The prime advantage is that the same equipment can be used for heating and cooling.

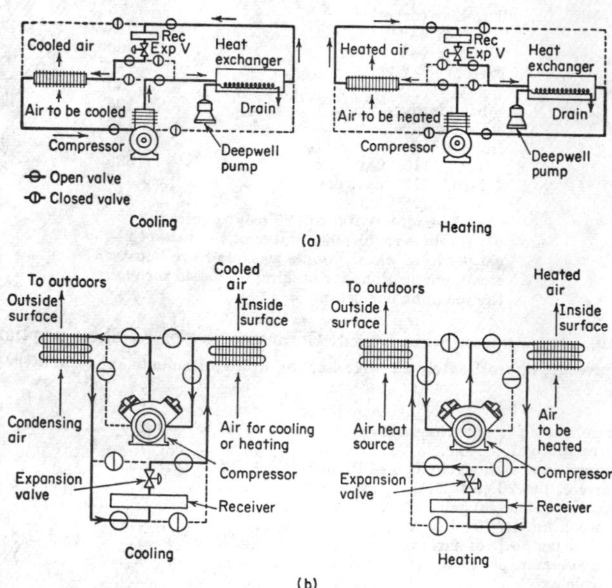

Fig. 18. Heat pump piping arrangements. (*a*) Water-to-air heat pump with water as source of heat and air as medium to transfer heat from inside surfaces. (*From Handbook of Heating and Ventilating, Strock and Koral, Industrial Press.*) (*b*) Air-to-air heat pump. (*From Modern Air-conditioning, Heating and Ventilating, Carrier, Cherne, Grant, and Roberts, Pitman.*)

Economics. The heat pump does not compare favorably with other forms of heat generation in areas with severe winters, unless unusually advantageous rates for electrical energy prevail. An example of a favorable locality is the Pacific Northwest of the United States. Because of the ratio of the **coefficients of performance** of the system in its cooling and heating functions, the selection of equipment for the latter function is often made at a level substantially less than the peak heating load. The deficiency is made up by the direct use of electrical energy or fuel as a heat source. Favorable **off-peak** electric rates should be investigated in this connection. Provision of the required heater, insulated storage, and pumping capacity will add to the initial cost, if **off-peak heating** is utilized.

The **source of heat** for the heat pump may be supplied by air, water, earth, solar energy, or waste heat. The best choice for a given area depends upon the prevailing

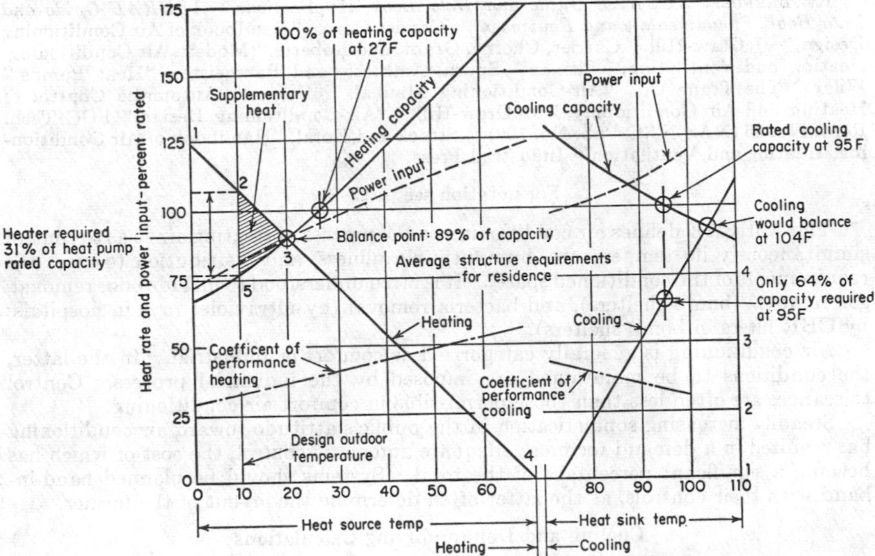

FIG. 19. Operating characteristics of single-stage unmodulated heat pump-air source, air-condensing NOTE: Power input is at capacity. (*Adapted from the 1964 ASHRAE Guide and Data Book.*)

climate, topography, and job conditions. **Air** is plentiful, easily available, and reasonably dependable as a source, but heat-pump capacity and efficiency decrease and heating requirements increase as the outdoor temperature drops. **Defrosting** of the evaporator also becomes an operating problem at evaporator temperatures below 32 F. Use of the **ground** as a heat source has been unsuccessful because the soil adjacent to the evaporator or heat-transfer arrangement soon approaches the temperature of the heat-transfer medium, thereby creating an excessively long thermal gradient to the original ground temperature. Where available, **water** is the ideal heat source.

Basic **water-to-air** and **air-to-air** heat-pump systems employing manually operated valves for change-over from summer to winter operation and vice versa are shown in Fig. 18(*a*) and (*b*). Figure 19 shows operating characteristics.

Automatic Thermostatic Control

See Air Conditioning and Ventilation, p. 12–151.

AIR CONDITIONING AND VENTILATION

BY

John O'Keefe and J. K. Whitteker

References: *ASHRAE Guide and Data Book, Applications.* *ASHRAE Guide and Data Book, Fundamentals and Equipment.* Carrier Corp., "Handbook of Air Conditioning Design," McGraw-Hill. Carrier, Cherne, Grant, and Roberts, "Modern Air Conditioning, Heating and Ventilating," Pitman. Sporn, Ambrose, and Baumeister, "Heat Pumps," Wiley. The Trane Co., "Air-Conditioning Manual." Haines, "Automatic Control of Heating and Air Conditioning," McGraw-Hill. "Air-Conditioning Design," FCC Tech. Rept. No. 35 (NAS-NRC Pub. No. 709). Strock and Koral, "Handbook of Air Conditioning, Heating and Ventilation," Industrial Press.

For notation see p. 12–83.

The ASHRAE defines air conditioning as the process of treating air so as to control simultaneously its temperature, humidity, cleanliness, and distribution to meet the requirements of the conditioned space. It is often understood to include odor removal, gas removal (bomb shelters), and bacteria removal (by ultraviolet rays in hospitals; by CBR filters in bomb shelters).

Air conditioning is generally categorized as **comfort or industrial.** In the latter, the conditions to be maintained are imposed by the industrial process. Control tolerances are often less than those permissible in comfort air conditioning.

Steadily increasing sophistication in the public's attitude toward air conditioning has resulted in a demand for more adequate **automatic control,** the cost of which has become a significant percentage of the total. Systems should be planned hand-in-hand with their controls, as the latter often determine the layout of the former.

Cooling and Dehumidifying Calculations

As a first step, **outdoor** and **indoor design conditions** consistent with the grade of the job should be established. The Technical Advisory Committee on Weather Design Conditions (**TAC**) of ASHRAE has established **outdoor conditions** that are equaled or exceeded 2½ percent, (or 5 percent) of the total hours during the four summer months. The Federal Construction Council (**FCC**) Report No. 35 makes the point that these temperatures are at airports and cover a period of 5 years. When these records are used, outdoor design **dry-bulb temperatures** are usually taken at the **5 percent level** for budget jobs and at the **2½ percent level** for first-class work. **Wet-bulb temperatures** are generally taken at the 5 percent level. Many engineers prefer to use in-town conditions that are **commonly used at the locality.** The FCC task group concurs. Table 1 gives such information for representative locations in this country.

Indoor design conditions for comfort air conditioning are usually taken at 80 F dry bulb for **transient** occupancies and for permanent occupancies in **low-budget** jobs. A temperature of 78 F dry bulb is used for **ordinary** applications, while a temperature of 75 F dry bulb or even lower is used for **first-class** work. **Indoor design relative humidities** range from less than 50 percent for **first-class** work to as high as 60 percent for **budget** jobs. However, they should fall within the **comfort zone** (Fig. 1). Most engineers no longer relate the indoor conditions to the outdoor conditions except as a cost-saving device for jobs with transient occupancies. The FCC task group concurs. For indoor conditions required by **industrial processes** see Table 2.

Table 1. Typical Outdoor Design Conditions—Summer

City	Dry bulb,* deg F	TAC dry bulb,* deg F		Wet bulb,* deg F	TAC wet bulb,† deg F	
		2½ %	5 %		2½ %	5 %
Birmingham, Ala.	95	94	93	78	78	77
Phoenix, Ariz.	108	106	104	76	76	75
Los Angeles, Cal.	92	90	87	70	70	69
Sacramento, Cal.	100	97	94	72	70	69
Denver, Colo.	93	90	89	64	64	63
Washington, D.C.	96	92	90	78	77	76
Tampa, Fla.	95	91	90	78	80	79
Atlanta, Ga.	95	92	90	76	77	76
Chicago, Ill.	96	91	88	75	76	75
Boise, Idaho	98	93	91	65	66	65
New Orleans La.	93	91	90	79	80	79
Boston, Mass.	90	88	85	75	74	73
St. Louis, Mo.	100	94	92	76	78	77
New York, N.Y.	95	90	87	75	76	75
Cincinnati, O.	96	92	90	78	77	76
Dallas, Tex.	100	99	97	78	78	78
Galveston, Tex.	95	89	88	80	81	81
Seattle, Wash.	85	79	76	65	65	64

* Commonly used.

† See text.

NOTE: The temperature-humidity index (THI), formerly called the discomfort index, with a numerical range between 70 and 80, is used in weather reporting to characterize outdoor conditions as they affect the comfort of most people. It is defined as THI = 0.4 (dry bulb, deg F + wet bulb, deg F) + 15.

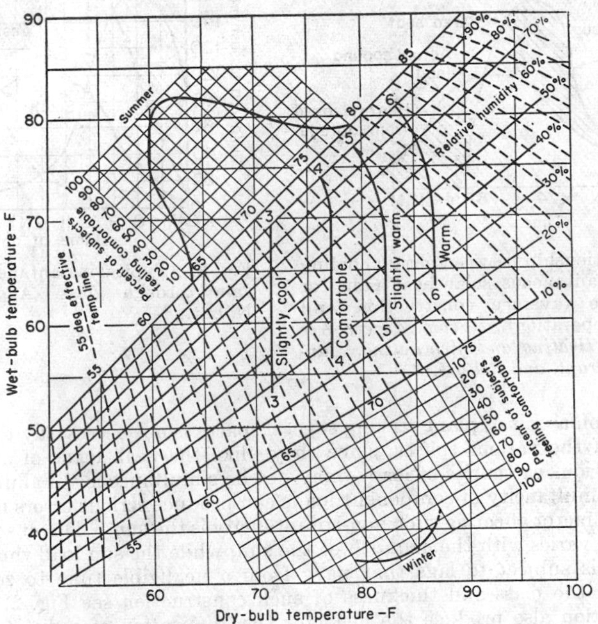

FIG. 1. Revised ASHRAE comfort chart. Air movement or turbulence 15 to 25 fpm. No panel heat or extremely low MRT in winter. NOTE: Solid lines 3-3, 4-4, 5-5 and 6-6 are for occupants acclimatized (3 hours or more) in summer. (*From ASHRAE Guide and Data Book, 1965.*)

Table 2. Typical Inside Design Conditions—Industrial

Process	Temp, deg F	Relative humidity, percent	Process	Temp, deg F	Relative humidity, percent
Dough mixing	75–80	40–50	Effervescent drugs	90	15
Bakery proof box	92–96	80–85	Photo. film drying	20–125	40–80
Drying refractories	110–150	50–90	Photo. safety film storage	60–80	45–50
Decorating ceramics	75–80	48	Thermosetting plastics	80	25–30
Chocolate dipping	60–65	50–55	Parts machining (precision)	75	45–50
Chocolate packing	65	55	Gage rooms (precision)	78	50
Chocolate storage	65–70	40–50	Printing pressroom	75	46–48
Elect. coil winding	72	15	Cotton weaving	78–80	70–85
Vacuum tube assembly	68	40	Nylon weaving	80	50–60
Glass-vinyl laminating	55	15	Rayon weaving	80	50–60
Expl. powder loading	70	40	Silk weaving	80	65–70
Drug ingredient storage	70–80	30–35	Wool weaving	80	60–70
Drug tablet coating	80	35	Cigar making	70–75	55–65

Calculations should produce several different results for use in determining the quantity of air to be introduced into a room (determined by the room load); the load to be handled by a unit serving several rooms (the aggregate load of the rooms after a diversification factor, **div. f.**, has been applied and equipment heat added); and the capacity of a refrigeration plant serving several units (the sum of the unit loads after a div. f. has been applied and piping and equipment heat gains added).

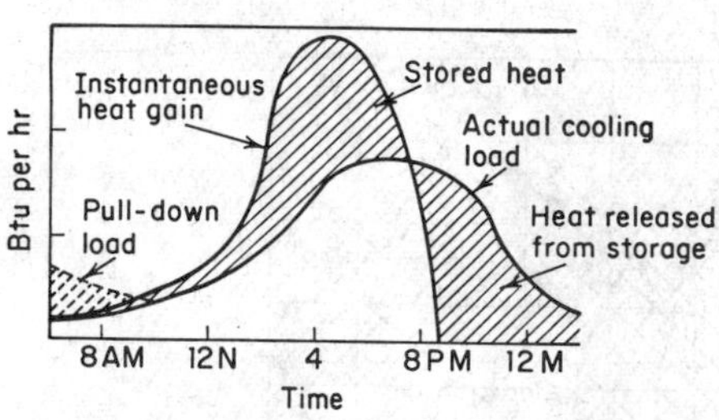

FIG. 2. Relationship between actual cooling load and instantaneous solar heat gain for west exposure (average construction and 24-hr system operation). (*From Modern Air Conditioning, Heating and Ventilating, Carrier, Cherne, Grant, and Roberts.*)

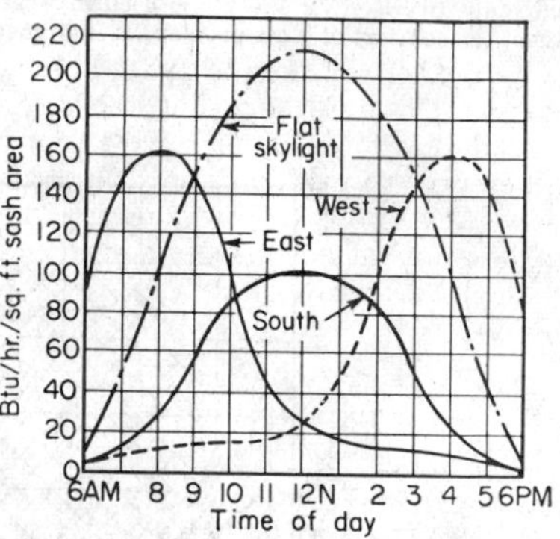

FIG. 3. Typical instantaneous solar heat gain through glass. August, 40 deg N. Lat.

The **load** on a unit or plant serving several spaces is not necessarily the sum of the peak loads of the various spaces, since they—like the peak loads of a single space under the various categories of load—may not be simultaneous. Failure to account for the non-simultaneity of component loads can produce serious errors in total loads. The principal factor affecting such non-simultaneity is the **sun.** Direct solar radiation through glass varies with the azimuth of the sun, while the sun load through opaque construction is subject to lags that vary from a negligible time to several hours, depending on the mass and thickness of such construction see Fig. 2. Shifts in a **stable population** also produce the need for the application of a **div. f.** if the total population to be served by a unit or plant can be reliably determined.

What is required is the **maximum sum of simultaneous load components** appropriate for each purpose (air quantity to room, capacity of unit, and capacity of plant). Therefore, the second step in calculating cooling loads should be to establish the **sun time** of the peak loads for each space and for each item of equipment. The peak-load time for spaces having various exposures are usually as follows: (1) **east** exposure only, no roof: **midmorning;** (2) **south** exposure only, no roof: **early afternoon;** (3) **west** exposure only and for spaces having other exposures but with **large roof areas: late afternoon.** The exact time for each exposure is affected by items such as the percent of glass area, shading of glass, and mass of walls, as affecting lag. The most expeditious procedure is usually to determine the **peak-load time** as governed by the sun and then to check it against all other possible governing factors, such as population shifts. Figure 3 shows the variation of solar radiation through glass during the day.

After the **time** of the peak load has been determined, the calculation of the space load involves the addition of the various loads that are expected to occur at that time —**not** the peak loads in each category. The categories are **transmission** (including the effect of sun on opaque construction); **radiant solar energy** through glass; **room loads** (sensible and latent); **excess fresh air load** (sensible and latent); and also **heat gains** into **ductwork** and **piping;** and heat introduced into the system by the **air-conditioning equipment** itself. In well-designed systems, **infiltration** is precluded by pressurization of the building. Figure 4 shows a typical form of **calculation sheet** which is designed to produce a room load, circulated air quantity required by the room, and a load for use as a component of a unit or plant load.

The calculation of **transmission** of heat through the building envelope is similar to the same phase of heating calculations except that (1) the outside film coefficient is based on a 7½-mph wind and (2) the effect of sun on opaque construction must be accounted for. This is done by the use of **sol-air temperatures** which are the equivalent of hypothetical outside air temperatures that would produce the same total transmission through the wall or roof as will actually be the case with the sun heating the outside surfaces of such construction. From these, **equivalent total temperature** differences can be developed for various constructions by applying the lags in heat flow from Table 3. By their use, the calculation of heat gains through sun walls and roofs is converted to a simple transmission calculation. Figure 5 shows the variation of such temperatures during the day.

Table 3. Time Lag in Periodic Heat Flow through Walls.
(Adapted from Strock and Koral, "Handbook of Air Conditioning, Heating and Ventilation," Industrial Press)

Construction	Lag, hr	Construction	Lag, hr
Walls: brick or stone		Frame: wood, plaster	
8 in.	5.5	No insulation	0.8
12 in.	8.0	Insulated	3.0
Walls: concrete or concrete block		Brick veneer, plaster	
6 in.	3.8	No insulation	3.0
8 in.	5.1	Insulated	5.5
12 in.	7.6	Roofs:†	
Glass window	0.0	Light construction	0.7–1.3
Glass block*	2.0	Medium construction	1.4–2.4
		Heavy construction	2.5–5.0

* Glass block transmits, in addition to delayed conducted load, an instantaneous sun load which for smooth-faced block is about 0.45 times that of plain window glass, and for diffusing block about 25 percent of plain glass transmission.

† Where applicable, the lags for wall materials can be used for roofs. Lags of materials added to a builtup structures are additive.

Radiant solar energy loads through glass are usually significant percentages of total loads and are subject to serious error if adequate account is not taken of all forms of **shading.** This item demands the application of mature judgment if realistic loads are to be produced. It is almost never practical to leave the windows of air-conditioned space completely unshaded. Table 4 gives **shading factors** (see Solar Heating, p. 9–212).

Skeletonized Air-conditioning Calculation Form

Conditions: Outside: ____ DB ____ WB Inside: DB ____ %RH

Time of max coincid. load: ____ (sun time) for this space ____ WB ____ DP

Time of max coincid. load: ____ (sun time) for all spaces

Any special shading of windows, skylights or glass block: ________

Solar heat: (glass & glass block) Overall coef | Btu/hr - S

East glass ____ sq ft x ____

Skylight ____ sq ft x ____

Transmission (glass & glass block) "U" TD

North ( ) ____ sq ft x ____ x ____

Transmission (walls, floors, roofs & partitions) "U" TD

North ( ) ( ) sq ft G ____ sq ft N x ____ x ____

Floor ( ) x x

Ceiling ( ) x x

Roof ( ) ( ) x x

Int. part'n ( ) x x

Other ( ) x x

Safety Factor (5%)

(% of Grand Total) TRANSMISSION TOTAL

Sun and other loads not contributing to plant load

TRANSMISSION TOTAL FOR PLANT LOAD

Internal load:					Btu/hr-S	Btu/hr-L
People:	P x		Btu/hr-S/▲	Btu/hr-L▲		
Lights:	W	x	3. 413			
Power:	HP	x	2544			
Air HP:▲	HP	x	2544			
Equipment:	x		Btu/hr-S/	Btu/hr-L		
	x		Btu/hr-S/	Btu/hr-L		
	x		Btu/hr-S/	Btu/hr-L		
Storage load▲						
Other load						

Safety factor 5%

Check Figures:
(sq ft/P)
(W/sq ft)

Internal totals

Transmission load

Tentative room totals

Room sens. ht. factor: = Tent. A. D. Pt.

Adjusted ADP ‡ Use: ADP●●

Adjust load for adjusted ADP ▲

(% of Grand Total:) Final room totals

Circulated air:●●

Room sens. ht = $\frac{}{16.2}$ = cfm @ 15° TD

USE:▲ cfm @ ° TD = cfm/sq ft

Fresh air load:●●

▲ ____ % of circ. air = ____ cfm

▲ ____ cfm/person = ____ cfm

USE: cfm x Btu/hr-S/ Btu/hr-L

(% of Grand Total:) Grand total S/L

Latent

SPACE GRAND TOTAL

Sun and other loads not contributing to Plant Load

GRAND TOTAL LOAD FOR PLANT LOAD = Tons

(Tons/sq ft)

▲ See text, tables, and figures

‡ Give consideration to part load operation in selecting apparatus dew point (generally lower 2°). Check other spaces on unit before establishing.

●● Circulated air TD, ADP, % fresh air must be same for all spaces on same unit. Check other spaces on unit before establishing.

FIG. 4. Skeletonized air-conditioning calculation form.

Room loads comprise heat from occupants, lights, appliances, equipment, and industrial processes. They require division into two categories: (1) loads that affect the occupants, (2) loads that do not affect the occupants but are imposed upon the equipment. The **sensible components** of loads in the first category are used for determining the quantity of circulated air required by the room. An example of the second category is the convected heat of recessed lighting fixtures which are used as return air inlets for the air-conditioning system. With lighting levels (and consequent heat output from the fixtures) rising steadily over the years, the careful division of room sensible heat into these two categories assumes increasing importance. Table 5 gives heat gains from **people;** Table 6 from **appliances** and **equipment.**

Room loads should be divided into **sensible** heat and **latent** heat. Sensible heat is, as its name implies, heat that can be felt and that will change the temperature of substances absorbing it. Latent heat is an expression of potential heat release and actually signifies the rate of release of water vapor

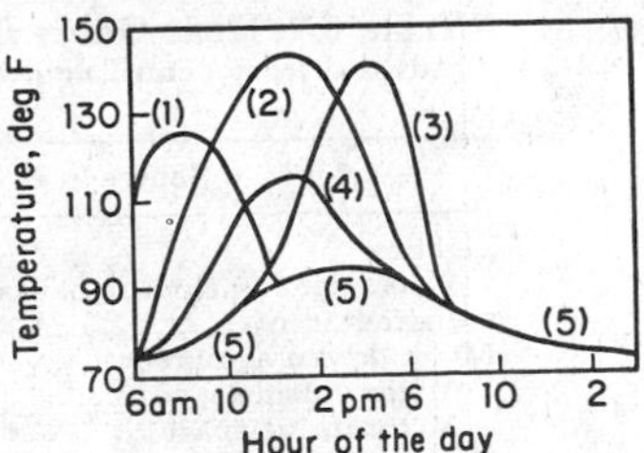

FIG. 5. Diurnal march of air and sol-air temperatures on a design day. Curves represent sol-air temperatures on (1) east wall, (2) horizontal roof, (3) west wall, (4) south wall. Curve (5) is outside air dry-bulb temperature. Sol-air temprature on a north wall (or shaded wall) is the same as air dry bulb. (*Adapted from Strock and Koral, "Handbook of Air-Conditioning, Heating and Ventilation," Industrial Press.*)

Table 4. Shading Factor for Glass Windows and Skylights
(In decimals of radiant heat transmitted without shade)
(Adapted from Strock and Koral "Handbook of Air Conditioning, Heating and Ventilation, "Industrial Press)

Total shading, regardless of source	0
Tree shade, heavy	0.20–0.25
Tree shade, light	0.50–0.60
Awning, first floor	0.25–0.30
Awning, upper floors	0.15–0.20
Inside window shade, light colored, fully drawn	0.45–0.55
Inside Venetian blind, light colored	0.45–0.55
Inside draperies, light colored	0.80–0.90

Table 5. Rates of Heat Gain from Occupants of Conditioned Spaces—Adjusted[a,b]
(Adapted from *1965 ASHRAE Guide and Data Book*)

Degree of activity	Typical application	Sensible heat, Btuh	Latent heat, Btuh
Seated at rest	Theater—matinee	180	150
	Theater—evening	195	155
Seated, very light work	Offices, hotels, apartments	195	205
Moderately active office work	Offices, hotels, apartments	200	250
Standing, light work; or walking slowly	Department store, retail store, dime store	200	250
Sedentary work	Restaurant[c]	220	330
Light bench work	Factory	220	530
Moderate dancing	Dance hall	245	605
Walking 3 mph; moderately heavy work	Factory	300	700
Heavy work; bowling[d]	Factory, bowling alley	465	985

[a] NOTE: Tabulated values are based on 80 F room dry-bulb temperature. For 78 F room dry-bulb, the total heat remains the same, but the sensible heat values should be increased by approximately 10 percent, and the latent heat values decreased accordingly.

[b] Adjusted total heat gain is based on normal percentage of men, women, and children for the application listed, with the postulate that the gain from an adult female is 85 percent of that for an adult male, and that the gain from a child is 75 percent of that for an adult male.

[c] Adjusted total heat value for sedentary work, restaurant, includes 60 Btuh for food per individual (30 Btu sensible and 30 Btu latent).

[d] For bowling figure one person per alley actually bowling, and all others as sitting (400 Btuh) or standing (550 Btuh).

Table 6. Heat Gains Due to Lighting, Equipment and Appliances
(Adapted from "Fan Engineering," Buffalo Forge Co. and *1965 ASHRAE Guide and Data Book*)

Source	Total heat gain
Lighting	
Fluorescent (including ballast).........	4.09 per watt rating
Incandescent..........................	3.41 per watt rating
Motor driven equipment	
Motor outside space....................	2544 per hp output
Motor inside space.....................	3000 per hp output
Cooking equipment, (no hood)*.........	60% of input heat†,‡ except toasters: 88%, ovens: 45%
	Latent heat: 20–35% of total, except fry kettles and food warmers: 40–60%

* For equipment effectively hooded and adequately exhausted, use 50 percent of tabular values.

† Manufactured gas: 560 Btu per cu ft; natural gas: 1130 Btu per cu ft; bottled gas: 2520 Btu per cu ft; electrical energy: 3.41 Btu per whr.

‡ Allow for on-off operation.

into the space by occupants, by cooking equipment, by gas-fired equipment vented into the space, by certain industrial processes, and by fresh air not passing through the dehumidifier. The latent heat required is the latent heat of condensation at the **temperature of the dehumidifier.** In the case of absorptive or adsorptive drying (see p. 12–134), the use of **grains of water** may be more appropriate.

The **fresh air load** to be used in the calculation of unit loads and plant loads is termed **"excess** fresh air load" because the room sensible and latent loads include the reduction of the circulated air (including its fresh air component) from the outside design conditions to the leaving dry-bulb and dew-point temperatures at the dehumidifier. It is, therefore, necessary to add only the reduction of the fresh air dry-bulb and dew-point temperatures **from the outside design conditions to the inside design conditions** (see Sec. 4). Figure 6 diagrams these relationships. Table 7 and Fig. 6 give fresh air re-

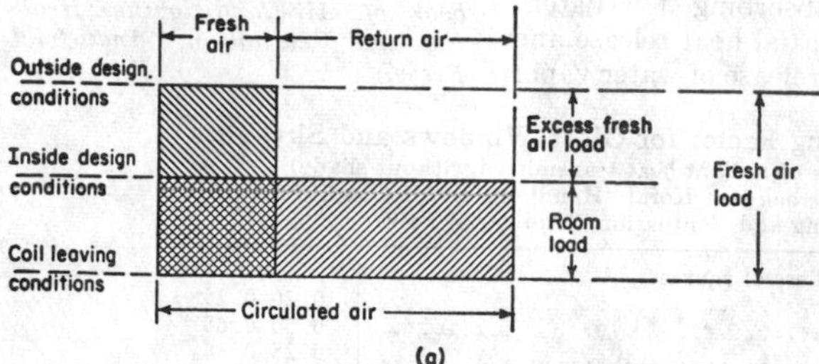

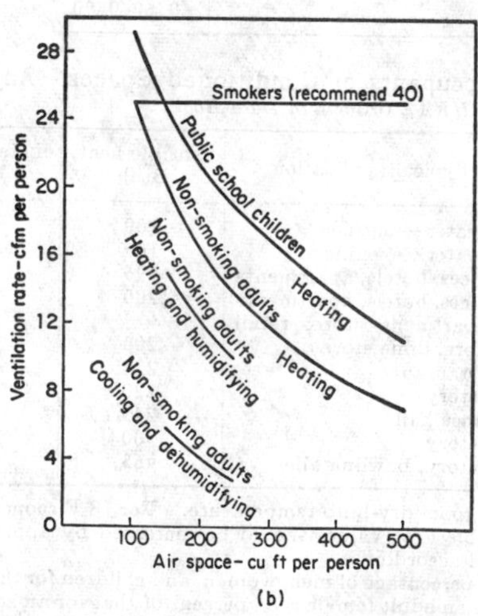

FIG. 6. Excess fresh-air load. (*a*) Relation of excess fresh-air load to other loads. (*b*) Minimum ventilation rates. NOTE: Fresh-air quantity must correspond to exhaust, see Table 7. (*From Buffalo Forge Co.*)

quirements for **ventilation** (see p. 12–143). **Pressurization** of the building requires a certain quantity of fresh air, dependent on the tightness of the construction. Well-constructed buildings usually require between 20 and 30 percent of the circulated air quantity.

Table 7. Air Quantities for Ventilation

Type of room	Cu ft per hr per occupant	Type of room	Air changes per hr
Schools*:			
Class rooms	1,500–1,800	Garages, commercial	6–10
Assembly rooms	900–1,100	Lavatories, public	10–20
Gymnasiums	1,800	Locker rooms	6–10
Hospital wards	1,800–2,400	Hospital operating rooms†	6–10
Dining room	1,200–3,000		

* Maximum. For cold weather 900 cu ft per hr per occupant is often used. Some codes permit a gradual reduction to 420 cu ft per hr per occupant in the coldest weather.

† Mechanically cooled otherwise 10–12 cu ft per hr. See NFPA Bulletin No. 56.

The loads imposed upon the air-conditioning system by its own components consist of the heat equivalent of **work** done on the circulated air by fans and on the circulated water by pumps and also of the **heat released** by motors and other air-conditioning equipment when such equipment is in air-conditioned space or the air stream of the system (see Table 6). The work done by the refrigeration machine upon the refrigerant should not be included in the calculation of the machine load, since it is included in the machine rating.

The **quantity of circulated air** required by a space is dependent on the temperature difference between the interior design dry-bulb temperature and the temperature of the conditioned air entering the space. This temperature difference in turn can be governed by the **room sensible heat factor** (RSHF), which is the ratio between the room sensible heat and the room total heat (sensible plus latent). See the discussion of the selection of cooling and dehumidifying coils for the effect of this factor on the required leaving air conditions. If the interior design conditions are to be realized but not improved (with consequent increased load on the coils and plant) the delivered air conditions so determined must not be lowered except to improve **part-load operation,** in which case the peak load must be adjusted accordingly. In many cases, engineers circulate more air than would be required by the maximum temperature difference in order to achieve a greater rate of air motion in the occupied zone. This is done by **bypassing** a portion of the circulated air around the dehumidifier.

Safety factors should be applied to calculated loads in accordance with general engineering practice. However, the factors used should be extremely moderate and care should be taken to avoid **pyramiding.** The computing of **check figures** can be highly useful for checking calculations after a backlog of such figures for various types of air-conditioning applications has been accumulated. Note the provisions for check figures in Fig. 4.

Permeability of walls to water vapor must be accounted for in industrial applications with low humidity requirements according to the formula: $w = M\,\Delta p$, where w is the vapor transmitted, grains per hr per sq ft of wall area; M is permeability of construction, perms; Δp is differential vapor pressure, in. Hg (1 psi = 2.036 in. Hg).

Cooling and Dehumidifying

Dehumidifying. Air washers are no longer being used for comfort applications, having been supplanted by **extended surface coils.** In industrial applications, washers of the glass-fiber-fill type, in which water at low pressure is distributed over such fill from above, are favored for humidification and dehumidification where close control is desired. Recirculating sprays in conjunction with such coils are also going out of use. Any system using recirculated water requires **treatment** since the water sump acts as a concentrator for solids and corrosive gases absorbed from the air.

Eliminators are required after dehumidifying coils if the face velocity exceeds about 700 fpm.

Cooling Coils. Cooling coils are categorized as **direct expansion** (DX), in which the refrigerant evaporates within the tubes, and **water** coils. Both types of coils are provided with distributing headers. Circuits leaving such headers are often orificed. **Water coils** are usually of serpentine design and are available in a single circuit or multiple circuits in parallel. Both types of coils are arranged for counterflow of cooling medium and air.

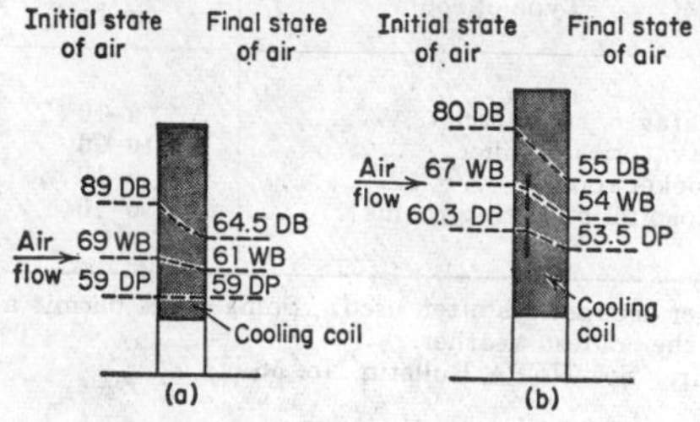

FIG. 7. Cooling coil performance. (*a*) Sensible cooling only. (*b*) Dehumidifying. (*Adapted from Trane Air-Conditioning Manual.*)

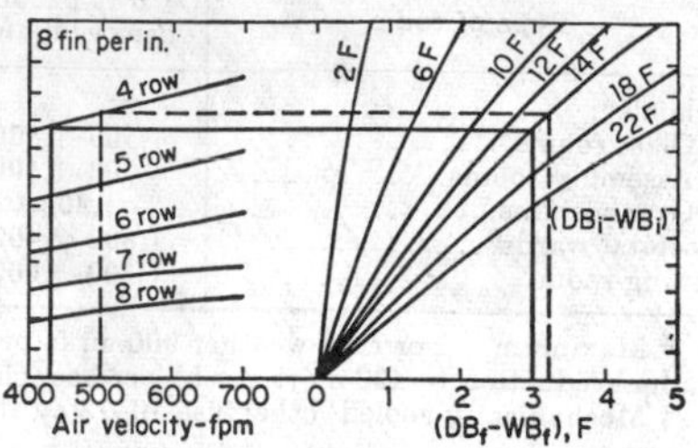

FIG. 8. Water cooling coil performance. NOTE: For an American Standard particular coil only.

The heat-transfer process through an **extended surface coil** is complicated by the fact that air passing midway between the fins and tubes is less affected than air which comes in contact with either. (See Sec. 4 for a more complete discussion of such processes.) Because of the effect produced by the evaporation of liquid on the transfer surface in a direct expansion coil, the effect of the counterflow arrangement is not as marked as in the water coil.

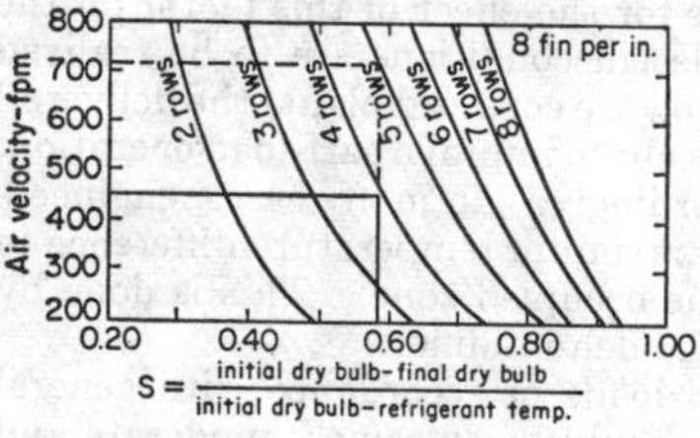

FIG. 9. Direct expansion coil performance. NOTE: For an American Standard particular coil only.

Selection. Cooling coils can be selected only from manufacturers' catalogue rating tables (see Figs. 8 and 9, which are typical curves for the selection of direct expansion and water coils, respectively). Note that manufacturers' curves or tables are for coils of particular characteristics and that no conclusion should be drawn from any curve or table relative to coils of different characteristics. Cooling coils performing **sensible** cooling only represent a simple heat-transfer process (see Sec. 4). Coils which cool and **dehumidify** operate partly **dry** (upstream section) and partly **wet** (downstream section) and the process is consequently complex. For this reason, the only practical approach to dehumidifying by the use of extended surface coils is an empirical one (see Fig. 7). Water velocities in the vicinity of 10 fps are generally used.

EXAMPLE. Cool 4,000 cfm from 83 dry bulb (DB) and 69 wet bulb (WB) to 58 dry bulb and 55 wet bulb.

For a **water** coil: entering DB − WB diff. = 83 − 69 = 14 deg; leaving DB − WB diff. = 58 − 55 = 3 deg. Referring to Fig. 8, a four-row coil at a face velocity of 430 fpm is required. Required coil face area: 4,000 cfm/430 fpm = 9.3 sq ft. Total load: 33.2 Btu per lb (69 WB) − 23.2 Btu per lb (55 WB) = 10 Btu per lb, 4,000 cfm × 60 × 10 Btu per lb/13.3 cu ft per 1 lb = 180,000 Btu per hr. NOTE: If a face velocity of 500 fpm were used, the leaving wet-bulb temperature would be 54.8 deg.

For a **DX** coil with 40 F refrigerant: entering DB − final DB = 83 − 58 = 25 deg. Entering DB − refrigerant temperature = 83 − 40 = 43 deg. Referring to Fig. 9, a four-row coil at a face velocity of 450 fpm is required. Required coil face area: 4,000 cfm/450 fpm = 8.9 sq ft. Additional information is needed to determine leaving wet-bulb temperature and load. A five-row coil with a face velocity of 710 fpm could also be used with a greater departure from saturation.

Required Leaving Condition. This condition has been known for many years as **"apparatus dew point"** and is still often referred to as such. The approach to saturation depends upon the amount of coil surface and the velocity of the air across it. The required leaving condition is determined by the room sensible heat factor (**RSHF**). Where **reheating** is used, the condition leaving the dehumidifier may be lower in dry-bulb temperature but not in dew point. (**Mixing** of air through the dehumidifier with air **bypassed** around the dehumidifier is sometimes referred to as "reheating." This is an improper use of the term.) As used here, it means the actual addition of external heat to the thermal process.

The **conditioned air** delivered to the space necessarily takes on sensible heat and water vapor in the **ratio** of their liberation from the various sources. The path of this process can be plotted from room loads on a psychrometric chart having grains per pound as the ordinate (see Fig. 10 and Sec. 4). It must, of course, be plotted in terms of heat and water vapor **per pound of dry air.** The **angle** of this path on the psychrometric chart is determined by the RSHF.

Since the path must pass through the **design room conditions,** it is common practice to plot the path backward from these conditions. Any coil leaving condition on this path will satisfy the design. The farther from the room conditions, the less air is required. If the coil leaving condition lies **above** the required path, the **room relative humidity** will be **higher** than the design value if control is from dry-bulb temperature (see **dash** line in Fig. 10). If the coil leaving condition lies **below** the required path, the **room relative humidity** will be **lower** and the coil load will be increased (see **dot-dash** line in Fig. 10).

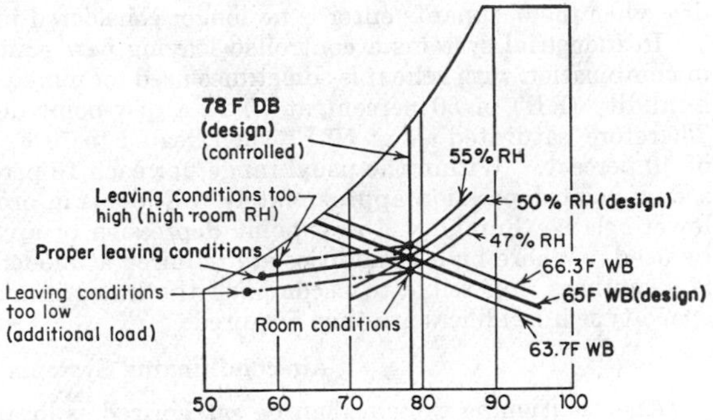

FIG. 10. Effect of improper leaving condition at dehumidifying coil.

The **entering condition** at a cooling coil and the **coil load** must account for the **fresh air** introduced for ventilation (see Fig. 6). (See Sec. 4 for a discussion of mixtures of air and water vapor.)

Evaporative Cooling

Air can be cooled by evaporating water into it, a certain **latent heat of vaporization** being given up to each pound according to the temperature of evaporation. The process takes place along a path of **constant wet-bulb temperature** and, therefore, the wet-bulb temperature is the maximum dew-point temperature that can be achieved. In practice, a saturated condition is almost never useful as a coolant in the continental United States because of the wet-bulb temperatures encountered (see Sec. 4).

The **actual wet-bulb temperature** is more significant than the **difference** between wet bulb and dew point. This fact can be demonstrated by comparing the evaporative cooling potentials at Phoenix, Ariz., with other areas (Table 1). This means of cooling is applicable to comfort air conditioning mostly in the dryer, mountainous regions of the West.

In the usual range of conditions, a cooling effect of between 1060 and 1070 Btu per lb of water evaporated will be realized. Equipment is usually considered to have a saturating efficiency of 80 percent (dry bulb lowered 80 percent of wet-bulb depression). **Larger quantities of air (100 percent fresh air)** (often up to twice as much as for typical systems cooled by refrigeration) are used.

Panel Cooling

Sensible cooling is sometimes accomplished by means of panels similar to those used in panel heating (see p. 12–105). Panels consisting of tubing attached to the upper surface of metal ceiling panels are also used. It is essential that the temperature of the panel surfaces be kept safely above the dew point of the ambient air. **Dehumidifying** is by the use of dryers in air-circulating systems (see p. 12–133).

Humidification

Humidification for **comfort** systems is effected by the admission of **water** to a system of spray nozzles, the admission of **steam** directly into the air stream or the admission of steam or electric heat to a **pan humidifier,** such functions being under the control of a **humidistat.** Humidification is going out of use for buildings where the population is reasonably constant at a level that provides ample water vapor for comfortable conditions. The fact that, in cold weather, the air may be excessively dry when the occupants enter is no longer considered justification for humidification.

In **industrial** systems a controlled leaving **dew-point** (saturated air) temperature in combination with **reheat** is sometimes used for more precise control. For a relative humidity (RH) of 50 percent at 70 F, a dew-point depression of 20 F is required. Therefore, saturated air at 50 F, when heated to 70 F, will have a relative humidity of 50 percent. Within the usual range, for each 10 percent higher relative humidity a dew-point depression approximately 5 F less is in order, while for each 10 percent lower relative humidity a dew-point depression of approximately 6 F more should be used. Where high humidities are required at moderate dry-bulb temperatures, it is sometimes impossible to accomplish the humidification in the apparatus; in-the-space-type humidifiers are then required.

Air-conditioning Systems

Air-conditioning systems can be categorized as local or distributed. **Distributed systems** may use air, chilled water, or the refrigerant as the medium. Air-distribution systems may be in the form of **high pressure** (high velocities), **low pressure** (low velocities), or a combination of the two. They may be **single-duct** or **double-duct** systems in either pressure category. **Double-duct** systems have central apparatus of the "hot deck–cold deck" type or separate apparatus for heating and cooling. **Chilled-water systems** are designed as two-pipe or, in combination with simultaneously available heating, three-pipe and four-pipe. **Three-pipe** systems have a common return from heating and cooling coils and require careful design and adjustment if the temperature of the water in the third pipe is not to exceed a tolerable range. **Four-pipe** systems have separate pairs of pipes and separate coils for cooling and heating.

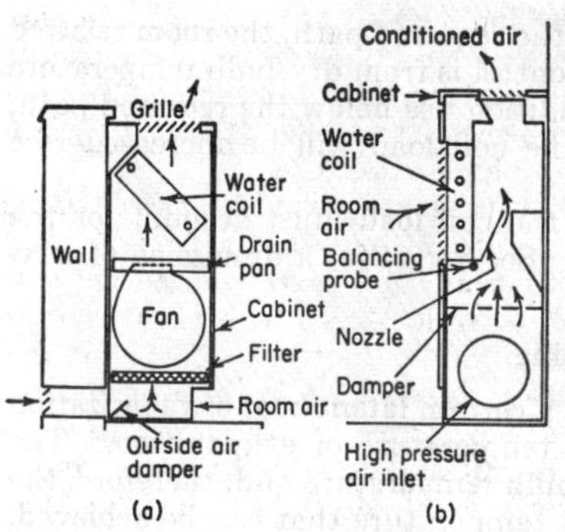

FIG. 11. Typical perimeter units. (*a*) Fan-coil unit. (*b*) Air-water induction unit. (*From Carrier Corp. Catalogue.*)

Terminal units comprise **fan-coil** units with one or two coils (see Fig. 11) and **air-water induction-type** units with sensible cooling coils in the recirculated air. The latter units induce the flow of room air into the unit by the use of high-velocity **primary air jets.** They are often connected to risers through **flexible hose.**

All **perimeter-** and **induction-**type units have the advantage of permitting extremely **local control,** thereby facilitating **zoning.** **Fan-coil units** having one coil are highly favored for moderate cost central air-conditioning systems. They are also available in horizontal models for ceiling mounting. They have the disadvantage of providing only cooling **or** heating effect, according to the medium that is being circulated at the moment. During intermediate seasons when heating may be required in the early morning and cooling after noon, their performance is less than satisfactory. **Induction units with sensible cooling coils** provide the availability of cooling and heating simultaneously (see Fig. 12), the automatic control making the choice as required. Terminal units on **all-air** systems also use high-velocity primary jets to induce a flow of room air through the unit. They require **cooled** and **heated** primary air if they are to provide the same advantage as described for air-water units.

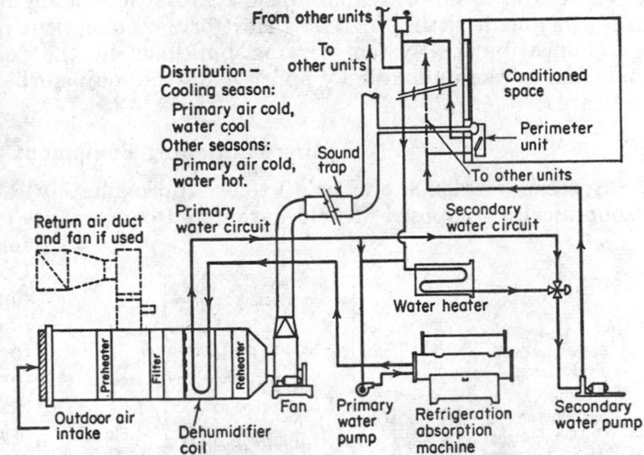

FIG. 12. Typical air-water induction unit system. NOTE: Chilled water flows in series through primary then secondary units. (*From ASHRAE Guide and Data Book, 1964.*)

Induction units are also available for use in **ceilings** over space having illumination levels of 100 ft-c or more. These units induce the flow of air from the **hung ceiling** through the unit and following ductwork by the use of primary **jets.** The automatic controls utilize the warm air thus induced to produce the required delivered air temperature. The Air Conditioning and Refrigeration Institute publishes a **Directory of Certified Room Air-Induction Units.**

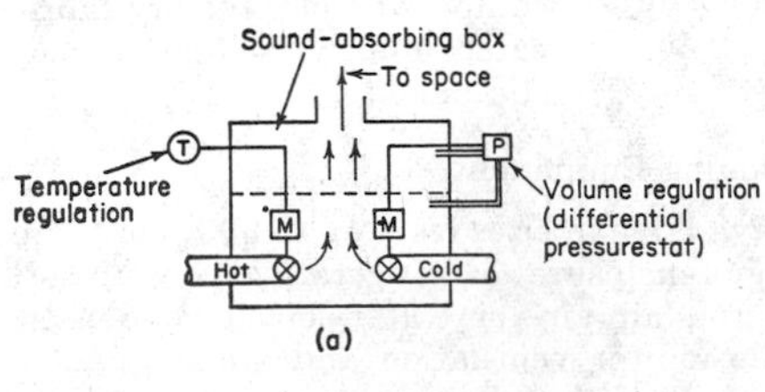

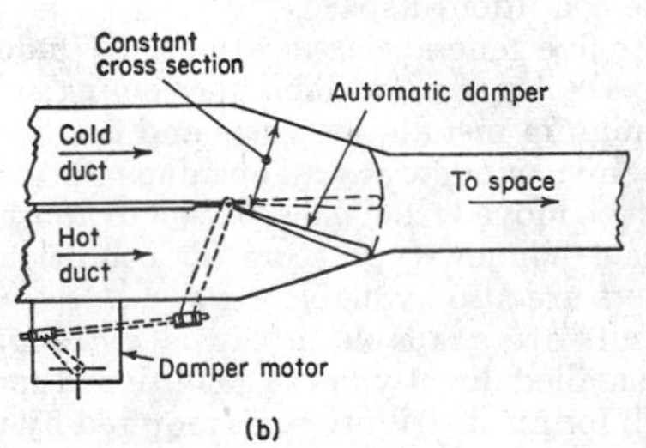

FIG. 13. Double-duct system mixing devices. (*a*) High-pressure mixing and pressure-regulating device. (*From "Fan Engineering," Buffalo Forge Co.*) (*b*) Low-pressure mixing device.

Different types of central equipment, distribution systems and terminal units may be combined as appropriate for the application. Some of these items impose limitations upon the other components of the system. For example, all types of induction terminal units require high-pressure air distribution.

High-pressure systems serving **ceiling outlets** utilize **pressure-reduction** and **sound-attenuation boxes** to permit the use of low-velocity outlets. Several outlets may be connected to one pressure-reduction box, **flexible hose** generally being used. Pressure-reduction boxes accepting hot and cold high-pressure ducts are also available. Automatic control regulates the admission of hot or cold air to produce the desired result (see Fig. 13).

High-pressure perimeter-induction systems and perimeter **fan-coil units** are often combined with **low-pressure** air systems for the interior spaces relatively unaffected by exposure.

Low-pressure double-duct systems are less used than formerly. Figure 13 shows a form of mixing damper for such systems.

Because of the high cost of refrigerants, **extended direct expansion** systems have gone out of use.

District Cooling

Despite the length of time for which district refrigeration systems circulating brine have been in use in warehouse districts, **district cooling** for air conditioning in urban areas has made little progress. Hartford, Connecticut has a large capacity chilled-water distributing system serving buildings in the central downtown area. Its installation was undoubtedly spurred by the major urban redevelopment project in that area.

Air-conditioning Equipment

Systems of 12,000 cfm or 40 tons (approximately) and larger are usually more economically composed of **field-assembled** components except when there is a need for a high degree of zoning. Components are described in detail elsewhere in this Handbook. For fans, see Sec. 14; for pumps, see Secs. 3 and 14; for piping and insulation, see Secs. 3 to 6 and 8; for refrigeration, cooling towers and evaporative condensers, see Secs. 4, 9, and 16; for automatic controls, see Sec. 16; and for noise reduction, see p. 12–177. Figure 14 shows a typical low-pressure horizontal air-handling unit and its associated devices. Smaller systems in budget jobs are generally composed of **factory-fabricated unitary** (self-contained) equipment.

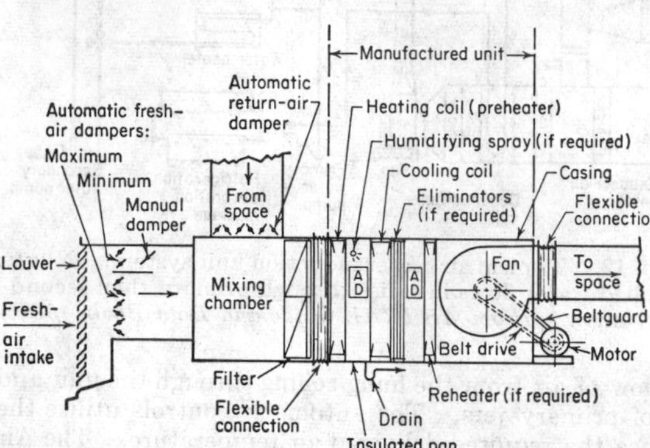

FIG. 14. Typical horizontal air-handling unit, comfort application.

Unitary Air-conditioning Equipment

Unitary or **self-contained** equipment is available in sizes from ⅓ to 30 hp or more and comprises, factory-assembled in a single enclosure, a refrigeration compressor, direct-expansion cooling coil, filters, fan, and an air- or water-cooled condenser. These units are arranged to supply outside air for ventilation and are frequently designed and styled for installation within the conditioned space.

Unitary-type equipment can be grouped into five general classifications. **Window-type** air conditioners, in capacities from ½ to 1½ hp, are available for cooling small spaces. This type of unit is designed for minimum installation costs and requires a convenient electrical outlet of proper capacity and a window or wall opening to provide air for the air condenser. Such equipment can be moved from one location to another. Figure 15 shows the general arrangement of a window-type room air conditioner. Under-window units resembling unit ventilators are also available.

Vertical self-contained air-conditioning units are available in capacities ranging from 2 to 20 hp. These units are frequently installed directly in the conditioned space and use either a discharge plenum or ductwork for air distribution, as required by the application (see Fig. 15).

In addition to the above, heavier-duty-type **remote self-contained** units are available in sizes from 2 to 30 hp or more in enclosures not styled for finished space.

"Roof-top" units (self-contained units in weatherproof housings) located directly above the conditioned space have become increasingly popular, especially for budget jobs.

Accessory equipment, such as water, steam or electric heating coils and humidifiers, is available, permitting use of all of these units for year-round air conditioning.

Manufacturers offer **residential** air conditioners which provide both summer and winter air conditioning in a single unit or in matched unit components. Research has indicated that residential air conditioning should be based on an average 24-hr heat gain rather than on an instantaneous peak, thereby reducing the required capacity by 25 to 30 percent.

The Air-Conditioning and Refrigeration Institute publishes a **Directory of Certified Unitary Air-Conditioners and Heat Pumps.**

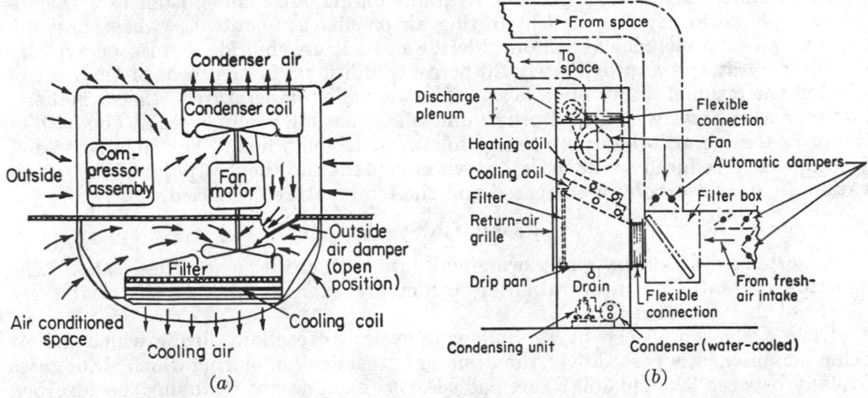

FIG. 15. Typical self-contained air-conditioning units. (*a*) Room air-conditioner; outer-wall or window type. (*b*) Vertical self-contained unit. Some units have filter at location shown for return air grille. Dot-dash lines show adaptation for use with ductwork and year round control. Discharge plenum is removed and duct connected to fan. Return air grille is blanked and filter relocated to outside the unit.

Condensing Methods

Lack of adequate water supply is becoming more and more serious in many localities. This situation has greatly accelerated acceptance of **cooling towers** or **evaporative condensers,** which reduce water consumption up to 98 percent. Some engineers select such devices for slightly higher wet-bulb temperatures than the design outside wet-bulb temperature so that they will never govern the capacity of the system. For details see Secs. 4, 9, and 16. **Air-cooled condensers** should be selected at very conservative entering air temperatures and should never be located where natural ventilation is restricted without adequate mechanical ventilation. Specific means are required to maintain adequate **head pressure** at off-peak ambient conditions. Flooding of the condenser as a control method has proved troublesome.

Dehumidification by Dryers

The function of drying equipment is to dehydrate air independently of any sensible cooling. Water vapor may be extracted by **adsorbent** or **absorbent** processes. **Adsorption** or **absorption** of vapor will take place if the saturation temperature of the vapor is greater than that corresponding to the vapor pressure of the desiccant. **Desorption** of vapor from a desiccant will take place if these conditions are reversed. The desorbed vapor will be **superheated** to the extent of the **hygroscopic depression.** The rate, in both directions, depends on the **vapor pressure difference.**

Adsorption and absorption of vapor differs from **condensation** in that (1) the vapor may be superheated by an amount not exceeding the hygroscopic depression and (2) **heat of wetting** (adsorption) or **dilution** (absorption) is **released.** Desorption of vapor differs from **evaporation** in that (1) the desorbing vapor is superheated to the extent of the hygroscopic depression, and (2) the **heat of wetting** (adsorption) or **dilution** (absorption) is **taken up** by the desiccant. The **hygroscopic depression** of a boiling solution is commonly termed the **boiling-point elevation.**

The measure of a desiccant's capacity to take on water is its **hygroscopic depression.** This is the difference between the temperature of the substance and the saturation temperature corresponding to its water-vapor pressure. It is therefore the **dew-point depression** of air **in equilibrium** with the desiccant.

Dehumidification by coils is generally more economical for comfort air conditioning. In industrial work, particularly if reheat would be needed, drying may have the advantage.

Adsorbents, such as silica gel or activated alumina, are solid substances with submicroscopic pores capable of dehydrating air on physical contact. **Absorbents** are hygroscopic solutions such as lithium chloride and calcium chloride. Adsorbers release the latent heat and approximately 20 percent additional in the form of the heat of wetting and residual reactivation heat. The wet-bulb temperature of the air is therefore increased slightly in the adsorber, unless intercooling is employed. The path of the process in an absorber more nearly follows a wet-bulb line. The effectiveness of each process is reduced as the desiccant water content and the dew point of the reactivation air (for adsorbers) is increased and the temperature decreased.

Adsorption Systems

Adsorption systems dry air by bringing it into contact with a **solid** desiccant. The moisture content (or concentration) is commonly expressed in percent of the dry weight of the adsorbent.

Drying is accomplished by the following cycle: **Adsorption,** during which the air being conditioned is passed over the desiccant; **reactivation,** during which air or gases (usually between 325 and 350 F) are passed over the desiccant removing the adsorbed water; and **purging,** during which air is passed over the desiccant to cool it and eliminate gases. The **heat** required for reactivation varies from 2100 to 2600 Btu per lb of water removed. The **reactivation air rate** is approximately 40 percent and the **purge air rate** approximately 10 percent, of the adsorption air rate. **Control** of the leaving dew point is by mixing bypassed air with dried air. The hot, dry air from an adsorber is usually **cooled** in an interchanger or by reevaporating water into it.

Desirable characteristics of an adsorbent are (1) adequate hygroscopic depression over a considerable range of water content, (2) chemical and physical stability (heat-stable at regeneration temperatures), (3) adequate mechanical strength, (4) freedom from odors, (5) reasonable bulk, (6) regeneration at reasonable temperatures, and (7) reasonable cost. Adsorbents used for air conditioning are silica gel and activated alumina. Silica gel is a hard, brittle, glass-like material manufactured from a soluble silicate and an acid. Activated alumina is 92 percent Al_2O_3 and has similar properties. The bulk density in pounds per cubic foot of activated alumina (silica gel) is 50 to 54 (30 to 45); the percentage pore volume is 33 to 52 (50 to 70); the water content when saturated, expressed as percent of the dry weight, is 20 to 25 (40 to 50); the specific heat is 0.24 (0.27).

Absorption Systems

Absorption systems condition air by bringing it into contact with a **hygroscopic solution** in a **contactor.** The air approaches a terminal dew point depressed as much as 60 F below the dry-bulb temperature. The solution may be cooled so as to reduce temperature and water vapor content of the air simultaneously; hence, the contactor may be used for any **combination** of heating, cooling, humidifying, or dehumidifying within its range. Contactors can operate **continuously,** a small percentage of the solution being diverted to the regenerator and then remixed.

The integral heat of dilution is the amount of heat evolved per pound of solute when a solution of given initial concentration is diluted with water to a stated final concentration. This heat is properly included as part of the enthalpy of the solution.

The **characteristics desired** of an absorption solution are (1) adequate hygroscopic depression over a considerable range of water content, (2) non-corrosiveness, (3) non-toxicity, (4) chemical stability (non-flammable and free from reaction with the CO_2 in the air), (5) low viscosity, (6) regeneration at reasonable temperatures, and (7) reasonable cost.

The solutions used are lithium chloride, calcium chloride, and the binary calcium chloride-calcium bromide. Of the three, **lithium chloride** is the most popular, having the greatest hygroscopic depression, lowest viscosity, and least corrosiveness. Calcium chloride is the cheapest.

AIR DISTRIBUTION

Air distribution by **mechanical** means can be categorized as residential, commercial-institutional, and industrial, the categorization referring to the type of equipment used, noise levels that can be tolerated, and velocities in ductwork. Some portions of institutional systems must comply with residential requirements. Systems can also be divided into **low pressure** (low velocity) and **high pressure** (high velocity). Table 8 lists suggested velocities for various applications. In determining the highest pressure of a system, the **class** of fan construction that will be required should be given careful consideration (see Sec. 14).

Table 8. Air Velocities for Conventional and High-velocity Systems

Duct or service	Conventional						High-velocity			
	Residences		Commercial bldgs.		Industrial bldgs.		Commercial bldgs.		Industrial bldgs.	
	Normal	Max	Normal	Max	Normal	Max	Normal	Max	Normal	Max
Main ducts.........	800	1,200	1,600	2,000	1,800	2,200	3,500	6,000	4,500	8,000
Branch ducts.......	600	1,000	1,200	1,500	1,500	1,800	2,500	4,500	3,500	6,000
Fan outlets.........	1,000	1,500	1,650	2,200	2,000	2,800	4,000	7,000	5,000	8,500
Suction connections*	700	900	900	1,200	1,000	1,400	1,700	3,300	1,800	4,500
Outside air intakes†.	500	600	500	600	500	700	500	600	500	700
Filters‡...........	250	300								
Heating coils.......	450	500	500	650	600	700	600	700	600	700
Air washers.........	500	...	500	...	500	...	500	...	500	
Dehumidifiers.......	450	500	500	650	500	650	500	650	500	650
Mod. dampers*.....	1,000	1,150	1,000	1,150	1,000	1,150	1,000	1,150	1,000	1,150

* Even in high-velocity systems, these are usually on the low-velocity side. If so, use "conventional" values. For high-pressure mixing devices see manufacturers' catalogues.

† Gross area assuming 40–50 % free area. (In high-velocity systems, these are on low-velocity side.)

‡ See Table 14.

Duct design is generally by one of four methods, (1) equal friction per foot of length, (2) arbitrarily reduced velocities, (3) static regain, and (4) self-balancing systems as used in industry for dust removal (in which dampers cannot be used). The first method does not involve designing all branches of a system for the **same** pressure drop per foot. Shorter circuits should be designed to yield approximately the same total pressure drop from the point of junction with the governing circuit, except as limited by considerations of noise production. The convenience of this method is that, when the fan resistance pressure is to be calculated, finding its friction component requires only the length of the governing circuit to yield an immediate result. The second method is actually a rule-of-thumb variant of the first. The tendency is to use a uniform reduction of velocity for the full length of the circuit, whereas the velocities should be reduced by greater increments in the smaller sizes. The third method involves the actual computation of the static regain that occurs whenever velocity is lowered, as in the first two methods. It is warranted only in special applications. The fourth method is referred to under Industrial Ventilation. Figure 16 and Table 9 give values for duct friction in **inches of water** (1 $in._w$ = 0.036 psi).

Dynamic losses in ductwork should be carefully computed. Failure to include losses in fittings less radical than elbows is a prevalent source of error. Any **turning, speeding up,** or **slowing down** of the air stream involves a dynamic loss. Table 10 gives losses in elbows while Table 11 gives losses in other fittings as well as **static regain** in diverging fittings. Table 14 gives losses through clean filters. Filter loss used in calculations should be based on allowable **"dirty"** resistance, which varies with the type of filter. Velocity head [$\text{in.}_w = (V/4005)^2$].

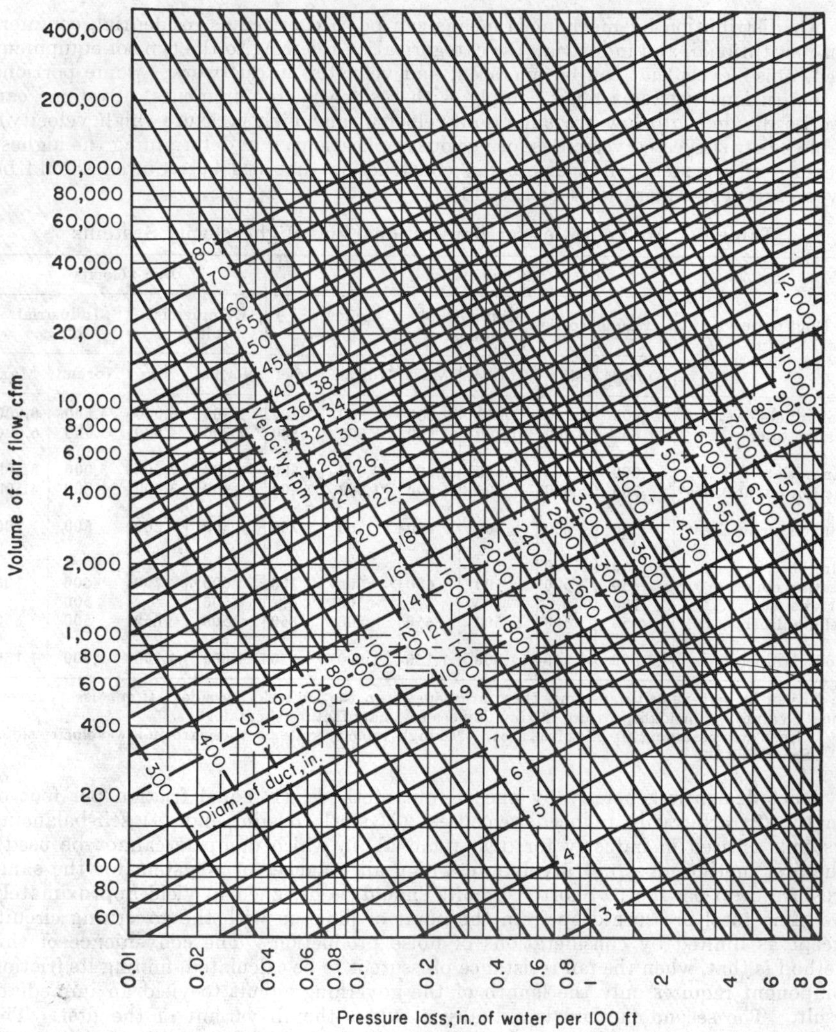

Fig. 16. Air-friction chart for round, straight galvanized duct with about 40 joints per 100 ft (based on air at 70 F and 29.92 in. barometric pressure).

Velocities in ductwork systems are often governed by acceptable **noise levels.** For **residential** areas, velocities are generally kept below 800 fpm; for **quiet commercial** areas, generally below 1,500 fpm; for **less-quiet commercial** areas generally below 1,800 fpm. These velocities apply to a **low-pressure** system with no sound attenuation from the point of application to the room. Velocities of more than 1,400 fpm over sheet metal **edges** immediately adjacent to the room, as over volume or direction

Table 9. Approximate Circular Equivalents of Rectangular Ducts for Equal Friction and Capacity

(All dimensions in inches)

Depth of duct	Breadth 4	6	8	10	12	14	16	18	20	22	24	26	28	30	32	34	36	38	40	42	44	46	48
6	5	7																					
8	6	8	9																				
10	7	8	10	11																			
12	7	9	11	12	13																		
14	8	10	12	13	14	15																	
16	8	10	12	14	15	16	18																
18	8	11	13	15	16	17	19	20															
20	8	12	14	15	17	18	20	21	22														
22	9	12	14	16	18	19	20	22	23	24													
24	9	12	15	17	18	20	21	23	24	25	26												
26	9	13	15	17	19	21	22	24	25	26	27	28											
28	10	13	16	18	20	21	23	24	26	27	28	30	31										
30	..	14	16	18	20	22	24	25	27	28	29	31	32	33									
32	..	14	17	19	21	23	24	26	28	29	30	31	33	34	35								
34	..	14	17	19	21	23	25	27	28	30	31	32	33	35	36	37							
36	..	15	17	20	22	24	26	27	29	31	32	33	35	36	37	38	39						
38	..	..	18	20	23	25	26	28	30	31	33	34	36	37	38	39	40	42					
40	..	..	18	21	23	25	27	29	31	32	34	35	36	38	39	40	41	43	44				
42	..	..	19	21	23	26	28	29	31	33	34	36	37	39	40	41	42	44	45	46			
44	..	..	19	22	24	26	28	30	32	34	35	37	38	40	41	42	43	45	46	47	48		
46	..	..	..	22	24	27	29	31	33	34	36	37	39	40	42	43	44	46	47	48	49	50	
48	..	..	..	22	25	27	29	31	33	35	37	38	40	41	43	44	45	47	48	49	50	51	53

Table 10. Losses in Elbows

(a) Loss in terms of equivalent length of straight duct (no. of diams or widths)

R/D...	Mitered		0.5†		1.0‡		1.5		2.0	
	Round	Square*	Round	Square	Round	Square	Round	Square	Round	Square
L/D...	65	75	32	50	17	11	12	4.5	10	2.4

(b) Effect of aspect ratio: fraction of $D/H = 1$ loss

R/D...........		Mitered	0.5	1.0	1.5
D/H...	2.0	0.98	1.10	1.28	1.44
	0.25	0.92	0.96	0.87	0.78

* Loss with formed vanes: 0.1 h_v; plate vanes: 0.35 h_v.
† Effect of well-placed vane: ×0.7.
‡ Vane effect: ×0.47.

regulating devices behind outlets, may produce unacceptable noise in areas of low background level. Velocities at fan outlets and in trunk ducts remote from outlets are often 10 to 12 percent higher than those listed. In ductwork on the suction side of fans, velocities are generally 10 to 20 percent lower than on the discharge side. A velocity of about 1,000 fpm is used in fresh air inlet connections and through modulating dampers. For a discussion of noise reduction, see pp. 12–177 *et seq.*

Table 11. Duct Pressure Losses and Static Regain: Entries and Transitions

Entries*

C_e = R 0.72, Sq 0.69

Round h = 90% V.P.
Square h = 106% V.P.

C_e = R 0.83, Sq 0.79

Round h = 43% V.P.
Square h = 58% V.P.

Transitions

Diverging section, static pressure regain† (in percent of velocity of approach)				Abrupt expansion, loss of total pressure (in percent of velocity pressure of approach)		
Ratio A_2/A_1	Angle θ 10	20	30	Ratio A_2/A_1	Loss in percent of velocity pressure in A_1	Static regain in A_2 in percent of velocity pressure in A_1
1.5	54	50	46	1.5	11	45
2.0	71	64	53	2.0	25	50
2.5	79	68	54	2.5	36	48
3.0	83	69	52	3.0	44	44

* Entry head losses in percent of the velocity pressure in the pipe. For entry losses in converging fittings, see Fig. 21.
† Percent of velocity pressure in $Area_1$ converted to additional static pressure in $Area_2$.

Table 12. Recommended Construction for Rectangular Low-pressure Ducts

(Adapted from *1964 ASHRAE Guide and Data Book*)

Longer side, in.	Sheet metal gage (all four sides)[a]: Steel, Gage	Aluminum alloy[b], Thickness, in.	Copper, Oz per sq ft	Transverse reinforcing, Between joints: Min reinforcing angle size and max longitudinal spacing	At joints[c], Standing S slip[d]: Min gage	Standing S slip[d]: Min angle size	Pocket lock,[e] standing seam, or standing S slip: Min. angle size
<13	26	0.020	16	None req	24	None req	
13–18	24	0.025	24	None req	24	None req	
19–30	24	0.025	24	1 × 1 × ⅛ @ 60 in.	24	None req	
31–42	22	0.032	32	1 × 1 × ⅛ @ 60 in.	22	None req	
43–48	22	0.032	32	1½ × 1½ × ⅛ @ 60 in.[f]	22	1½ × 1½ × ⅛	None req
49–54	22	0.032	32	1½ × 1½ × ⅛ @ 48 in.	22	1½ × 1½ × ⅛	None req
55–60	20	0.040	36	1½ × 1½ × ⅛ @ 48 in.	22	1½ × 1½ × ⅛	None req
61–84	20	0.040	36	1½ × 1½ × ⅛ @ 24 in.	22	1½ × 1½ × ⅛	1½ × 1½ × ⅛
85–96	18	0.050	48	1½ × 1½ × 3⁄16 @ 24 in.	22	1½ × 1½ × 3⁄16	1½ × 1½ × 3⁄16

[a] Flat areas of duct over 18 in. wide shall be stiffened by crossbreaking unless duct will have noncondutive covering or sound-absorbing lining.
[b] Suitable aluminum alloys are: Commercial Designation 3003 Temper H14 and Duct Sheet.
[c] Flat S slips and drive slips may be used at joints without angles for sizes less than 13 in. (26 gage) and from 13–18 in. (24 gage).
[d] Height: 1 in.
[e] Gage: same as standing S slips. Height: 1–42 in., length, 1½ in. for larger ducts.
[f] For aluminum or copper ducts 43–48 in. maximum dimensions, the maximum longitudinal spacing of transverse reinforcing is 48 in.

Ducts are typically constructed of galvanized steel or aluminum in accordance with Table 12. Aluminum and copper are often used for ductwork **outside** of buildings. Fittings in high-pressure ducts should be reliably airtight (see Fig. 17). High-pressure systems should have **sound traps** in fan discharge ducts. For exhaust ducts from **high humidity** areas, such as shower rooms, aluminum or copper ductwork with **seams soldered** or **welded** across the bottom and 1 in. up the sides are used to a point where an adequate amount of drier air is admixed. Such ducts should be provided with tube **drains** and a 1-in. **dam** across the bottom at their termination. Connections between ductwork of **dissimilar metals** should be provided with **non-conducting** joints.

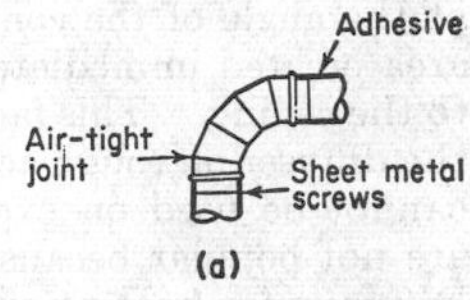

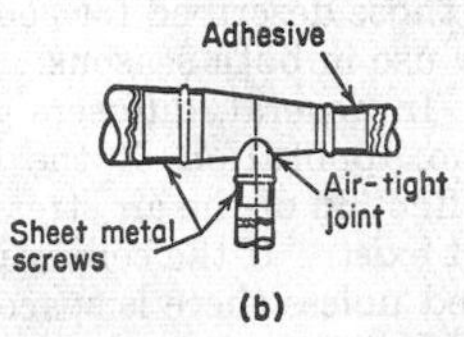

FIG. 17. High-pressure duct fittings. (*a*) 90° elbow. (*b*) Reducing tee.

Fire dampers should be provided where ducts penetrate fire walls, fire-rated partitions, or floors, except that **main exhaust** ducts and risers should **not** have fire dampers (place them at branch connections). Fire dampers should comply with the requirements of the latest edition of NBFU Pamphlet No. 90. Local ordinances often contain additional requirements. (See also p. 12–195 *et seq.*)

Warm-air heating systems for residences usually make use of asbestos cement or other non-metallic round ducts under slabs on grade and **extended plenum** arrangements where ducts are in basements or crawl spaces. The latter consist of main rectangular ducts, often unreduced in size, having moderate velocities from which round, short branches are taken off, generally with square connections. **Return branches** are often rectangular with lower velocities. "Boot" fittings are available for the connection of round ducts to narrow rectangular risers that will fit between studs and accept grilles and diffusers of typical sizes. Publications of the **National Association of Warm Air Manufacturers** give much detailed information about these systems.

Centrifugal fans are favored for most ductwork applications and are now available in **tubular** form. **Propeller** fans are appropriate where large volumes of air are to be moved against low pressures. The **noise level** created by any fan is a function of the resistance pressure, departure from the point of maximum efficiency and the characteristics of the particular fan. (See also Sec. 14.)

Air Distribution within Rooms

Criteria. Since the most serious problems arise in the introduction of air at temperatures **lower** than room temperature, the following discussion is based on this condition unless otherwise noted. Air must be introduced in the required quantity so as not to produce drafts, so as to mix with room air above the occupancy level to within 2 deg of the desired room temperature, and so as to cover the room in a reasonably uniform pattern. In general, the room should be covered by the **supply air pattern.** Returns should not be relied upon to "pull" the primary air to areas not properly covered.

A **"draft"** is a subjective thing and varies with the person, the direction of approach of air to the person, the height above the floor, the season as affecting mean radiant temperature (MRT), the air velocity, and the departure from average room temperature. For practical purposes in cooling applications, velocities higher than **35 fpm** of air more than **2 deg cooler** than average room temperature are likely to elicit complaints. The usual causes of drafts are **excessive drop** of the primary air stream (violates the second listed criterion) and **overblow** of the primary air stream with relation to a wall or another primary air stream of opposite direction, in either case causing a **cascading** of inadequately mixed air to the occupancy zone.

Outlet devices consist of grilles, registers, and diffusers. **Grilles** usually have independently movable vertical and horizontal bars, the latter for upward deflection. A **register** is a grille with a volume-regulating device attached. A **diffuser** consists of concentric elements, usually cones or pyramids arranged so as to deflect the air through a large angle and to create local high-ratio mixing. Diffusers come in round, square, rectangular, and strip shapes, and for applications on ceilings, exposed ductwork, and walls. They can be selected to produce plan patterns of one-way, two-way, three-way, four-way, or circular distribution.

The **vertical pattern** of ceiling diffusers for cooling applications is not downward at the angle of the concentric elements, as might be supposed. A negative pressure area created immediately beyond the rim of the diffuser deflects the air stream back to the ceiling. This fact may be verified by observing the ring of discoloration around the diffuser on rough acoustical tile ceilings. Diffusers designed for **ceiling application** cannot be used on exposed ductwork or under perforated ceilings. **Wall diffusers** are not popular because of the requirement for considerable wall space above them. Diffusers for **heating** only are designed to produce downward vertical patterns instead of those described for cooling outlets. **Adjustable pattern** diffusers are also available for use in both seasons.

In general, diffusers give more nearly draftless distribution than sidewall grilles. The application of the latter under low ceilings is particularly critical. **Upward deflection** of the air stream is of little benefit if space for the rise of its trajectory does not exist. If the ceiling is broken up by beam haunches, upward deflection cannot be used unless there is space under the beams.

Outlet Accessories. Grilles and diffusers are almost always equipped with accessories permitting **volume control** and, in the case of grilles, additional **directional control.** Diffusers often have **equalizing grids** at the junction of their necks with the supply duct to ensure uniform distribution of air across the diffuser.

Return and exhaust inlets usually have fixed bar or louver grilles at angles to break the line of sight into the duct. Where continuity of the surface effect is considered important, stamped lattice pattern grilles are used. **Registers** are often used where local trimming control is desired, but they should not be used for the basic balancing of high pressure-drop systems because of the likelihood of unacceptable noise levels.

Supply grilles are **selected** for throw, plan pattern of distribution, drop (as affected by velocity), and velocity (as affecting noise level). **Throw** is usually defined as the distance to a point at which the velocity is 50 fpm. For this reason, if personnel will be in fixed positions near walls, the throws should be selected 3 ft short of the actual distance. The basic formula for the throw of a grille is $T = K \times \text{cfm}/\sqrt{A}$, where T is the throw, ft; A is the daylight opening of the grille, sq in. (for 0.87 free area); and K is a constant that varies from 0.77 for straight blows to 0.55 for a spread of 42 deg each way. Supply grilles in **residential** warm-air systems are generally sized for a velocity of 300 fpm if low, and for velocities up to 600 fpm if high.

Supply diffusers are properly **selected** for noise level and ceiling height as affecting the jet velocity, patterns of distribution, and throw. Some manufacturers list throws to more than one terminal velocity. Use the remarks about the throw of sidewall grilles as a guide. **Obstructions** of limited dimensions perpendicular to the axis of the air stream will generally not cause drafts if they are more than one third of the throw from a diffuser. Where obstructions must be closer, larger, or where the throw must be shorter in one direction, sector-shaped **blanks** may be ordered to reduce the delivery of air in the direction so affected. The capacity of the diffuser should be checked against the reduced effective area.

Return and exhaust grilles and registers are **selected** on the basis of velocity. Velocities depend on location, height above the floor, and proximity to occupants. The location of large-volume inlets in corners or other restricted spaces is to be avoided, as **excessive room motion** may result. In general, inlets near the floor are sized for approximately 300 fpm, while higher inlets are sized for from 600 to 800 fpm, according to their height above the floor. **Exhaust air inlets** are in most cases located high. Return air inlets for **cooling** systems can be located high provided they do not short-circuit the primary air stream to a significant degree. Note that this is not a problem if the supply and return grilles are located several feet apart on the same wall. **Return inlets** for warm-air **heating** systems must be located **near the floor** and distributed so as to compel the general room air motion to traverse the entire room.

AIR CLEANING

(See also Sec. 7)

Air-cleaning equipment may consist of washers or scrubbers, dry or viscous filters, electrostatic precipitators, cyclones, and devices used in industrial ventilation (see description under that heading). The following pertains to air cleaning in comfort air conditioning.

Air washers, because of their bulk, their inefficiency in removing the finer particles, and their humidifying characteristics when the water is not cooled, have gone out of use for comfort applications.

Filters are universally used and are available in a wide range of designs to meet the various air-cleaning requirements. Particle size, degree of removal required, quantity and characteristics of the contaminant to be removed, condition of the air, flammability and smoke-propagating characteristics, and funds available will determine the device selected for a given application. In outside air not locally contaminated by industrial processes, **dust content** seldom exceeds 4 grains per 1,000 cu ft of air. **Particles** in atmospheric air can range in size from less than 0.01 μ (smokes) up to such things as lint, leaves and insects (see Table 13). Air cleaning may also include **odor** and **bacteria** removal, the latter a relatively recent development.

Table 13. Typical Particulate Distribution in an Industrial Atmosphere

Percent* by vol	Particle size, μ	Average, μ
28	10–30	20
52	5–10	7½
11	3–5	4
6	1–3	2
2	1–1½	¾
1	0– ½	¼

* 85 percent of viscous particles tend to be in the highest range of sizes.

Filters for dust removal are classified as viscous impingement and dry. They are also classified as unit-panel type (manually removed or cleaned in place) and automatic (moving-curtain type). **Electrostatic precipitators** are classified as low-voltage and high-voltage (industrial use). Table 14(a) shows characteristics of typical filters and precipitators.

Viscous impingement filters use viscous-coated media against which the dust particles impinge and are then held by the viscous surface. The filter may be of the **permanent-panel** type (manually cleaned), the **disposable** type which is thrown away after it has accumulated its dirt load, or the **automatic** moving-curtain type with an oil bath. They may be of the **high-velocity** type (500 = fpm face velocity), or **graduated-media** type (300 = fpm face velocity). **Throwaway** filters enjoy a popularity not warranted by long-term economic considerations. The paramountcy of initial cost is the determining factor. Permanent filters should be considered for applications to more than 5,000 cfm.

Dry-type filter media are usually fabric-like or blanket-like materials of varying thickness, and may be cellulose fibers, banded glass, wool felt, asbestos, synthetics, and similar fibers. Dry-type filters are distinguished by their **high efficiency,** small fiber size, and closeness of the fibers rather than by lack of adhesive.

Dry filters also are available in **moving-curtain** designs, both automatic and manual. Dirty medium is merely rolled up for scheduled removal. Automatic types can be **controlled** by a timer or a differential pressure switch.

Grease filters usually have a coarse metal mesh medium. They should be installed at angles well above the horizontal to prevent dripping.

HEPA filters are usually constructed of a fabric of fine fibers, such as glass or asbestos, applied to a separating medium, usually paper, in a zig-zag pattern so as to produce a deep, multilayer design. Frames are generally plywood, but fire-retarded plywood, metal and mineral board frames are available. Separators may be plastic, metal, or asbestos. **Fire ratings** should be investigated. **Efficiencies** approach 100 percent, based on 0.3-μ DOP particles. The military specification MIL-F-51068, which incorporates the test specification MIL-STD-282, is often used as the basis for purchase. HEPA filters should be preceded by **"screening"** filters to remove some of the load in the larger particle sizes.

Types of **filter tests** have proliferated. In general, American Filter Institute,

Table 14. Air-cleaning Devices

(Adapted from "Fan Engineering," Buffalo Forge Co.)
(Adapted from Mine Safety Appliance Co.)

(a) **Characteristics**

Name of device[a]		Removes[b]	Optimum		Usual face velocity,[c] fpm	Usual	
General class	Specific type		Part. size, μ	Concen-tration, grs/cu ft		Resist,[d] in. w.g.	Effi-ciency,[e] % by wt
Odor ads'rs	Shallow bed	↑	(Molecular)	<0.001	50–120	<0.3	<95−
Air washers[f]	Spray chamber	Lints,	>20	<0.005	300–500	<0.4	<25+
	wet cell	Malodors,	>5	<0.005	200–350	<0.7	>25+
Elec. precip.,[g] low volt	Two-stage, plate	gases dusts,	<1	<0.001	275–500	<0.3	<90−
	Two-stage, filter	pollens,	<1	<0.001	200–300	<0.2	>50−
Air filters, viscous	Throwaway	tobacco	>5	<0.002	300–500	<0.1	<25+
	Washable	smoke	>5	<0.002	300–500	<0.1	<25+
Air filters, dry	5–10 μ		>3	<0.001	5–25	<0.3	>50−
	2–5 μ	↓	>0.5	<0.001	5–25	<0.5	<95−
HEPA filter	Paper	Special[k]	<1	<0.001	4–6	<1	>99.95−
Indust filter	Cloth bag	↑	>0.3	>0.1	1–30	>4	>99−
	Cl. envelope		>0.3	>0.1	1–30	>4	>99−
Elec. precip.,[h] high volt	One stage, plate	Dusts,	<2	>0.1	180–600	<1	<95−
	One-stage, pipe	fumes, smokes,	<2	>0.1	180–600	<1	<99−
Dry inertial collectors	Settling ch	mists	>50	>5	300–600	<0.1	<50−
	Baffled ch		>50	>5	1,000–2,000	<0.5	<50+
	Cyclone	↓	>10	>1	2,000–4,000	<2	<80+

(b) **Filter tests**

Classes of filters	Resist, in. w.g.	Efficiency range, %					
		DOP[l] test	NBS atmos-pheric stain	AFI atmos-pheric stain	NBS artificial stain	AFI artificial weight	Bacterial tests
Viscous fiber[j]	0.08–0.12	0–2	5–12	3–10	50–60	65–75	10–60
Viscous metal	0.08–0.12	0–2	5–12	3–8	55–60	70–75	10–60
Dry, med eff	0.20–0.45	50–60	80–85	60–70	98–99+	100[i]	90–95
Dry, high eff (com)	0.35–0.55	70–85	90–95	78–88	99+	100[i]	95–99
Dry, hosp. type	0.30–0.40	95–98	99+	99+	100[i]	100[i]	99+
HEPA	0.70–1.2	99.97 min	100[i]	100[i]	100[i]	100[i]	99.99+

[a] See text.

[b] All devices bracketed do not remove all contaminants. See column headed Optimum Particle Size.

[c] Higher figures are face velocities at inlet to cell, chamber, etc. Lower figures are velocities at surface of medium.

[d] Clean resistance except for industrial filters.

[e] Signs after numerals indicate that efficiency increases with increased velocity (+) or decreased velocity (−).

[f] Water rate: 2–5 gpm per 1,000 cfm (recirculated).

[g] Power rate: 0.01–0.02 kw per 1,000 cfm.

[h] Power rate: 0.2–0.6 kw per 1,00 cfm.

[i] Test cannot detect penetration.

[j] Common furnace filter.

[k] Bacteria, radioactive or highly toxic fumes, etc.

[l] Dioctyl-phthalate smoke (0.3 μ homogeneous aerosol)

National Bureau of Standards, and Army Chemical Corps specifications are used. Table 14(*b*) shows comparative results of such tests.

Low-voltage, two-stage **electrostatic precipitators** use a potential of 12,000 volts to create the ionizing field, and 6,000 volts or more between the plates upon which the precipitation of dust occurs. The high-voltage direct current is supplied by a power pack operating from 115-volt 60-cycle single-phase service. Installation should include a **screening filter.** There is a variant of this device which uses a **charged filter** in lieu of plates. Its efficiency is radically lower.

Odor removal is sometimes incorporated into the air-cleaning arrangements to reduce the fresh air requirement. An **odor-absorber** usually consists of a bed of **activated charcoal** through which the air to be deodorized is passed. The bed is usually not more than 1 in. thick, with a face velocity of 120 fpm, providing a contact time of $\frac{1}{24}$ sec, which is sufficient for satisfactory operation. If a more shallow bed is required, the face velocity should be reduced to maintain the $\frac{1}{24}$ sec contact time. Most installations require from 5 to 50 lb of activated charcoal per 1,000 cfm. Such absorbers are not suitable for the treatment of grease-laden air.

VENTILATION

Ventilation is used to control levels of temperature, humidity, odor, and air motion for purposes of promoting human comfort or (industrial ventilation) to prevent hazard and to create ambient conditions required by certain processes. Ventilation for **comfort** may be divided into ventilation of low-occupancy spaces and ventilation of high-occupancy spaces. The former category is normally accomplished by **natural** ventilation or a minimum of the simplest kind of **mechanical** ventilation, as in residences. The latter category often requires the movement of large quantities of air through elaborate systems.

There are three prevalent **fallacies** in connection with ventilation, as follows:

1. That ventilation is required to prevent the lowering of the **oxygen** content and the rising of the **carbon dioxide** content to harmful levels and that discomfort derives from such levels. Only in almost airtight enclosures, such as bomb shelters, is this the case. **Discomfort** is caused by extremes of those conditions that are to be controlled. The "ventilation" (fresh air) component of the air circulated in air-conditioning systems is for the purpose of controlling **odor** levels. Figure 6 and Table 7 give recommended ventilation rates.

2. That if large quantities of air are introduced into a space, the space will assume the temperature of the entering air. This is true only if no heat is being absorbed or liberated within the space. The heat absorbed by (or liberated) within the space each minute must lower (raise) the temperature of the air entering the space during that minute by a finite amount according to the formula $T_2 = T_1 +$ (Btu per min/0.0178 cfm).

3. That enough mechanical ventilation can substitute for air conditioning in the hottest weather. This is not true if the same standards are applied—first, because of the fact pointed out under item 2; second, because mechanical ventilating systems of **reasonable cost** do not even produce air motion comparable to that produced by large areas of open windows. This fact can be readily demonstrated by computing the air motion through a dozen window openings measuring 3 ft by 3 ft with a 10 mph breeze blowing. Large room-type **circulating fans** will provide much more comfort from air motion.

With one important exception, the most that should be expected from mechanical ventilating systems in **extreme hot weather** is that they make conditions more tolerable than would be the case without the ventilation. The one situation in which mechanical ventilation systems contribute significantly to comfort during hot weather is where **large quantities of heat** are being liberated, as in kitchen, laundries and in industrial processes. Efficient exhausting of such heat not only promotes comfort but, if the space is air conditioned, will materially reduce the cooling load. (See also air-conditioning calculations, p. 12–120, and Air Distribution within Rooms, p. 12–139.)

Effective Temperature. The sense of **warmth** has been found by experiment to depend on the temperature, humidity, rate of motion of the air, and the mean radiant temperature (MRT). With a constant MRT, the other three parameters govern the conditions of **equal sensation of warmth** defining the "effective temperature." Figure 18 shows the combinations yielding equal effective temperatures for the conditions defined.

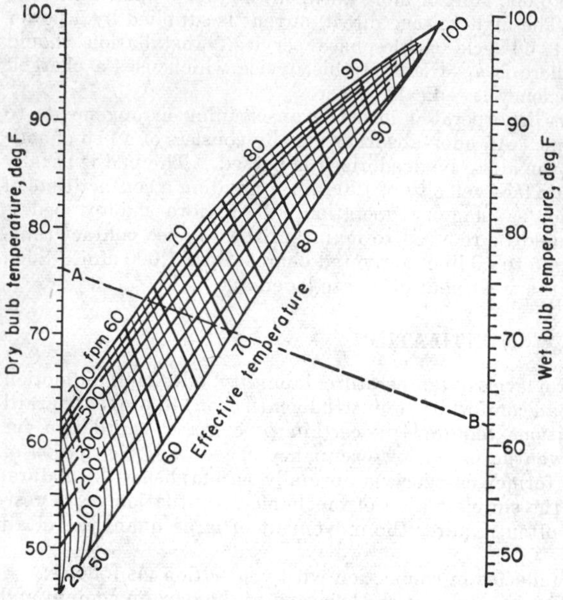

FIG. 18. Effective-temperature chart (for customary indoor clothing, light muscular work, and heating by warm air or radiators).

EXAMPLE. Dry bulb 76 F, wet bulb 62 F, air velocity 20 fpm. What is the effective temperature? *Answer:* 70.3 F. What would be the effective temperature at 100 fpm? *Answer:* 69 F.

Natural Ventilation

The movement of air through buildings without mechanical aids results from **pressure differences** created by **wind** and the **difference in temperature** between outdoors and indoors. The latter influence applies typically in cool weather, but may apply to spaces with high heat releases (kitchens, laundries, heavy industry) even in warm weather. See Table 3 under Heating (p. 12–86) for **infiltration** flow rates.

The rate of flow of air through building openings because of **stack effect** is approximately $Q = 8.4A[h(t - t_o)]^{1/2}$, where Q is in cfm; A is the net areas of inlets or outlets (which should be equal), sq ft; h is height between the inlets and outlets, ft; t and t_0 are the indoor and outdoor temperatures, deg F; and 8.4 is a coefficient including 0.58 as the effectiveness of the openings.

Mechanical Ventilation

In its simplest form, mechanical ventilation consists of propeller fans in wall or roof openings discharging to out-of-doors. In the United States, the problem is how to admit an equal quantity of air in the wintertime. Except in some locations in heavy industry, **tempering** (see p. 12–145) is required. While tempering coils are sometimes placed in **"free" intakes** (no fan), fans are normally used to permit the use of **filters** ahead of coils to prevent clogging. Such equipment combinations may be field- or factory-assembled (see p. 12–88 and Figs. 3 and 4 under Heating).

Kitchens. Except in residences, kitchens generally require an **air change** at least every 2 min. In high capacity institutional kitchens, a 1 min air change may be required. The rate may be determined by the aggregate **hood requirements.** A **common hood** is often used over ranges, ovens, steamers, and kettles in large kitchens, the portion over the ranges having **grease filters.** Because of the necessity for ready access to the grease filters, kitchen hoods are of an inefficient design (Fig. 19). For first-class results, a quantity of 100 cfm per sq ft of plan area is required at the main hood. If less than 85 cfm per sq ft is used, failure to capture heat, smoke, and steam will be significant at the ends and corners of the hood.

Dishwashers and **large coffee urns** are also hooded. Hoods should be 6 ft 6 in. above the floor. **Supply air units** usually operate as recirculating heaters until the room reaches the desired temperature, after which they operate on 100 percent fresh air.

Gravity exhausts have largely gone out of use except in heavy industry. **Mechanical exhausts** in combination with **windows** for intakes is still much used despite its draft-producing tendencies.

INDUSTRIAL VENTILATION

REFERENCES: Alden, "Design of Industrial Exhaust Systems," Industrial Press. Dalla Valle, "Exhaust Hoods," Industrial Press. Drinker and Hatch, "Industrial Dusts," McGraw-Hill. Hemeon, "Plant and Process Ventilation," Industrial Press. American Conference of Governmental Industrial Hygienists, "Industrial Ventilation," 1951. Buffalo Forge Co., "Fan Engineering."

Ventilation in industry is for the removal of dust, fumes, vapors, gases, and heat. The control of dust and vapors is achieved by eliminating the sources, preventing dispersion, and providing individual-respirator protection. Prevention of dispersion is usually accomplished by exhaust and conveying systems which maintain a flow of air into a hood, canopy, or hopper placed adjacent to, over or under the dust-producing source. The control of fumes is usually by a combination of capture and dilution.

Temperature Control

Natural Ventilation. In heavy industry, particularly in spaces with high ceilings and large volumes per occupant, **roof ventilators** are favored because of their initial and operating economies. They are available as continuous monitors, fixed round and rectangular types, and round rotating types. All are rated by their manufacturers on a basis of **temperature differential,** while some are classified as "wind driven" and are rated at a stated **wind velocity.** In connection with the latter types, it should be borne in mind that at times when air motion would be most appreciated (hot, still conditions outside), the ratings are not achieved. Natural ventilation is not as much used in light industry.

Mechanical Ventilation. In heavy industry, the economies of wall and roof fans can be realized to a greater degree (see p. 12–148). Local air **"jet"** fans are often used for **spot cooling** in areas of high heat release. Radiant **shields** are also helpful. In light industry, supplies and exhausts are more generally powered and ducted.

Table 15. Contaminant Exhaust Velocities

(From "Fan Engineering," Buffalo Forge Co. and adapted from DeBothezat Co. table, both based on the work of Allen D. Brandt.)

(a) Ranges of control (capture) velocity

Release of contaminant	Typical examples	Control velocity, fpm
With negligible velocity	Most tank operations	50–100
With low velocity	Low-pressure spraying. < 200 fpm conveyor transfer. Load–unload, mix etc.,	100–200
Actively generated	>200 fpm conveyor transfer, shakeouts, screens, etc. Melting furnaces, etc.	200–500
With high velocity	Grinding, tumbling, abrasive cleaning	500–2000

(b) Recommended minimum (conveying) velocities

Nature of contaminant	Examples	Duct velocity, fpm
Vapors, gases, smokes, fumes, and very light dusts	All vapors, gases, and smokes; zinc and aluminum oxide fumes; wood, flour and cotton lint	2,000
Medium-density dry dusts	Cotton, buffing and jute lint; wood, grain, rubber, and bakelite dust	3,000
Average industrial dust	Wool; wood, sand blast, grinding, and shoe dust; wood shavings; pulverized coal	4,000
Heavy dusts	Lead, and foundry shake-out dusts; metal turnings; jute butts	5,000
Large particles, of heavy, moist materials	Moist lead or foundry dust	5,000 and over
Sand, cement		7,000

Hoods

The **control** (capture) **velocity** of air required at the point where the contaminant will escape if not captured is dependent on the density, temperature, and kinetic energy of the contaminant. Control velocities range from less than 100 to 2,000 fpm (see Table 15). Many states and municipalities have specific requirements regarding industrial ventilation, often setting requirements for hoods (see Table 17).

Hood design should include enclosing the contaminating source as much as possible; shaping the hood to the area of contamination; having the velocity at the face of the hood as low as possible for a required velocity at the point of contamination; providing flanges or baffles to prevent air flow from ineffective areas; and directing the movement of the dust into the hood.

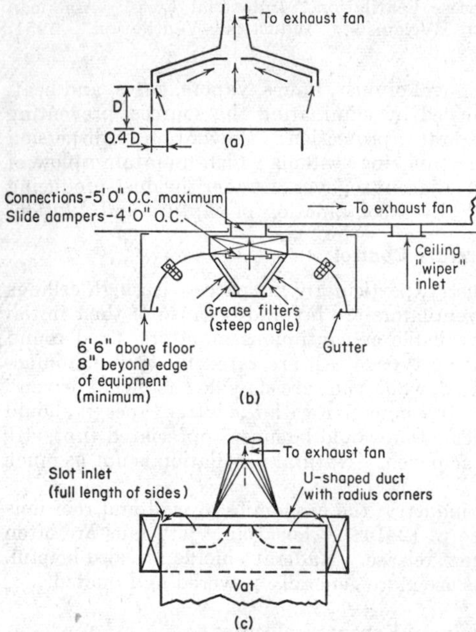

FIG. 19. Hoods for fume removal. (*a*) Efficient canopy hood. (*b*) Main kitchen hood (inefficient). NOTE: Provide CO_2 or steam smothering system. (*c*) Double-sided, slot-inlet hood for vat.

For large hoods, several pipe connections are required to produce uniform flow. Baffles and double hoods are often used (see Fig. 19).

The velocity contours of the flow of air into a pipe or hood are spheroidal (Fig. 20). Increasing the velocity of flow does not change the shape of the velocity contours; it moves them outward from the face of the hood. Properly shaping the hood will eliminate stray currents and permit a reduction in air flow without reducing the effectiveness of the hood.

To prevent the dispersion of dust at the source of generation, a capture velocity toward an exhaust hood must be sufficient to overcome the energy imparted to the dust by the machine, which may be very great for such machines as grinders. The volume of air flowing through an unobstructed circular hood for a given velocity at X is approximately $Q = V(10X^2 + A)$, where Q is in cfm; V is the center-line velocity at X ft from the face of the hood where the dust is to be captured, fpm.; A the area

Table 16. Coefficients of Entry and Entry Losses at Hoods

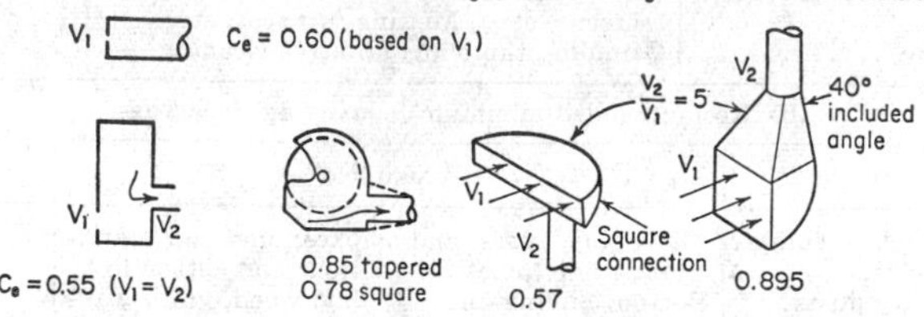

C_e	0.96	0.895	0.82	0.79	0.75	0.70	0.65	0.61	0.57
Press loss	$0.09h_v$	$0.25h_v$	$0.49h_v$	$0.60h_v$	$0.78h_v$	$1.04h_v$	$1.37h_v$	$1.69h_v$	$2.08h_v$

NOTE: Compute values for compound hoods by adding losses of slot (above), square end (Table 11), flanged end (Table 11), or converging nozzle (Fig. 21) at initial entry to similar items following, allowing for all changes in direction (use 1.15 h_v for square turns). Convert all losses to fractions of h_v in **duct** ($h_v \propto V^2$).

of the hood face, sq ft. A flanged hood or one resting on a table will permit the same velocity at X with approximately 25 percent reduction in volume.

The flow of air into a hood is $Q = 4{,}005 C_e A_t \sqrt{h_t}$, where Q is in cfm; C_e the coefficient of entry or restriction; A_t the area in sq ft of the throat, *i.e.*, the point where the pipe joins the hood; h_t the static suction in the throat, in. w.g. The coefficient of entry is determined from the relation $C_e = (h_v/h_t)^{1/2}$, in which h_v is the velocity pressure. The entrance loss into a hood is $h_e = [(1 - C_e^2)/C_e^2]h_v$ in. of water. See Table 16 and Fig. 21 for data.

Canopies, also called hoods, are suspended over vats, kettles, furnaces, etc., to remove dust, fumes, vapors. The velocity flowing through the open area under a canopy suspended over a flat surface is $V = 0.71Q/PD$, where V, is velocity, fpm; Q, the volume flowing, cfm; P, the periphery of the hood, ft; D, the distance from the bottom of hood to the surface, ft.

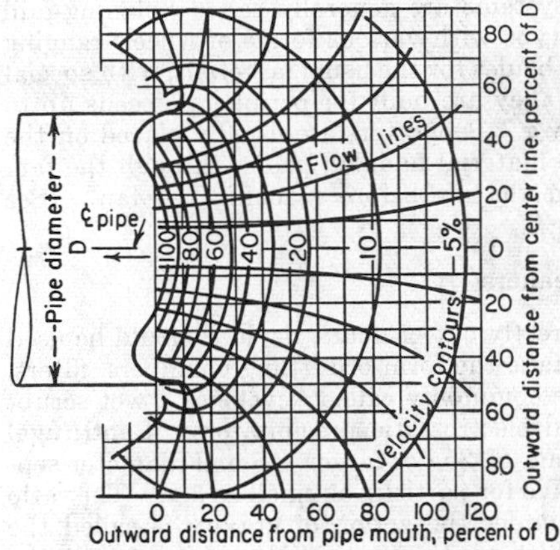

FIG. 20. Velocity contours and flow lines in radial plane into circular suction pipe. NOTE: The addition of a flange with an O.D. of twice the pipe diameter moves the contours out about 43% laterally and 17% longitudinally. These approximate the contours of a converging inlet cone of the same O.D.

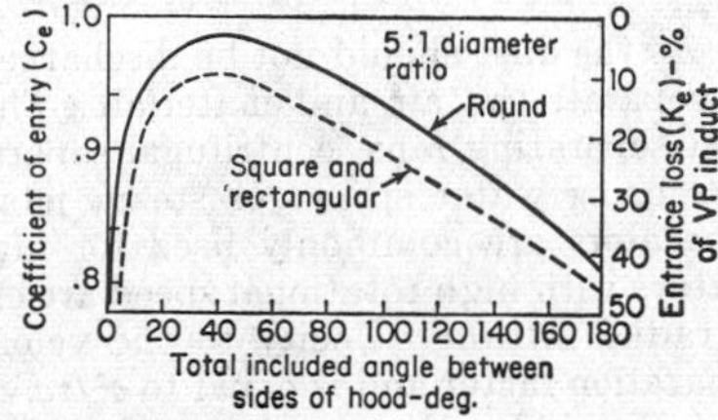

FIG. 21. Coefficients of entry and entry losses for converging inlet cones (unflanged). (*Adapted from "Fan Engineering," Buffalo Forge Co.*)

Exhaust Dust Systems

The transporting velocity for material varies with the size, specific gravity, and shape of the particles. The vertical lifting velocity must be greater than the terminal gravitational settling velocity. This has been approximately estimated as

$$V = 1{,}200(d \times s/\rho)^{1/2}$$

in which V is velocity, fpm; d, max diameter of particles, in.; s, specific gravity of material; ρ, the density of air, lb per cu ft. The horizontal transporting velocity is $V = 6{,}000 d^{0.4} s/(s + 1)$. Common practice for velocities for transporting materials is given in Table 15.

Design of the piping for exhaust systems requires consideration of the following pressure losses: hood entry loss, suction pressure in throat to maintain the flow, pressure drop due to friction in the branch and main, loss in the branch and the main at the junction, pressure drop in the separator or filter. With a velocity of 4,000 fpm ($h_v = 1$ in. w.g.) needed to convey the material and a coefficient of entry of 0.72 (equivalent to $0.93h_v$), the entry loss (h_e) is 0.93 in w.g. The static suction required in the throat is then $1 + 0.93 = 1.93$ in. w.g. The pressure drop in the pipe is usually estimated for a velocity head loss in 30 to 40 diameters. As the horizontal transporting velocity is lower than that required for the vertical lift, the main is usually made 25 percent greater in area than the areas of the branches. **Dampers** are inadvisable in solids-conveying ductwork. Elbows should have a centerline radius of 2½ × diameter.

For exhaust systems, the load of material carried in the air stream is such a small percentage of the weight of the air that only the power to move the air need be considered.

Exhaust fans used for dust-collecting systems are generally called "planing-mill exhausters." They are of the centrifugal type with various forms of wheels ranging from 6 straight blades to 18 forward curved blades for the usual materials, with special forms handling long shavings, wool, etc. They are built for peripheral speeds up to 15,000 fpm and develop as high as 16 in. w.g. Separators are usually placed on the discharge side of the fan in which case the material handled passes through the fan. Some materials are better separated from the air before reaching the fan. (See also Sec. 14).

Air Cleaners

As the dust should not be discharged directly out-of-doors, devices should be used to separate the air and material. These take the form of settling chambers, filters, dust-separating fans, centrifugal separators commonly called "cyclones," wet scrubbers using water sprays or steam jets, and electrostatic precipitators. **Centrifugal separators** are commonly used for materials of 25μ or larger. Small-diameter separators with high rotational speed are effective for particles as small as 5 μ. The ratio of radial settling velocity to the velocity under the action of gravity is called the **separation factor** and is equal to v^2/rg, in which v is the tangential velocity, fps, in the centrifugal chamber; g, the acceleration due to gravity; r, the radius of rotation, ft. The smaller the radius, the greater the separation factor; hence for large air volumes, multiple separators in parallel are indicated. The pressure drop through centrifugal separators varies with the design. For the low-pressure type, fitted with an inlet deflector, the drop is approximately 1.0 to 1.5 velocity heads. Without the inlet deflector the drop is from 2.0 to 2.5 velocity heads. This applies to velocities of 2,500 to 6,000 fpm. In very small diameter separators with high velocity and high efficiency the drop may be 3.5 to 4.0 velocity heads. Centrifugal separators are commonly used for exhaust systems handling shavings, sawdust chips, cotton, wool, buffing, and grinding materials, etc. For dust of less than 20 μ, such as in sanding operations, foundry dust, stone cutting, the efficiency of separation may be rather low.

Dust and cinder separating fans have been designed to combine the function of exhaust fan and separator into one device. For particles not too fine, they perform satisfactorily.

Cloth Filters. For the removal of fine particles, cloth is used in the form of bags, pockets, or cells. Cloth of special weave and weighing about 10 oz per sq yd is used. The air filtration rate varies from ½ to 6 fpm.

The pressure drop when clean varies from 1½ to 6 in. w.g. As the dust load on the cloth builds up, the resistance increases; shakers or rapping devices are incorporated to shake off the dust periodically. The material collected accumulates in hoppers or bins below. The filtration efficiency of a good cloth filter is about 99 per cent with usual dust in sizes as small as ½ μ. (See also Air Cleaning, p. 12–141 and Gas Cleaning, p. 7–88).

Control of Vapors, Fumes, and Gases

Vapors, mists, or fumes from degreasing, electroplating, and wire-impregnating tanks are usually removed by lateral-slot exhausts near the top of the tank. This type of exhaust is best for vapors heavier than air, but its efficiency is limited to narrow tanks. Wide tanks are usually provided with a slot extending around the whole periphery, or along the mid-section, pulling vapors from both sides over half the width of the tank.

Canopy hoods are used for the removal of gases and smokes rising from hot-water and dye vats, where the hood does not interfere with manufacturing processes. Exhaust booths are used principally in spray painting.

Table 17. Exhaust Volume, Cfm, Recommended for Various Dust-producing Machines

(Consult the state code if one exists)
(From "Industrial Ventilation," 8th ed., American Conference of Governmental Industrial Hygienists)

Machine	Volume, cfm
Double planers, 20–26 in. long, connections top and bottom, total	1,885
Table saws, 16–24 in. diameter	440
Jointers, 12–20 in. knives	550
Single-drum sanders, 400–700 sq in. areas	785
Horizontal belt sander, 9–14 in. wide connections both ends, total	1,240
Vertical disk sander, 20–30 in. diam disk, half covered, two bottom connections	700
Horizontal disk sander, 18–26 in.	550
Grinding and cutoff wheel, 19–24 in. diam 4 in. wide, good enclosure	610
Polishing and buffing wheel, 19–24 in. diam 5 in. wide, good enclosure	740

Table 18. Toxicity of Gases and Fumes, in Parts per Million Parts of Air

(Maximum allowable concentration values C_m for continuous 8 hr exposure, recommendations, American Conference of Governmental Industrial Hygienists, 1951)

Gases and vapors	C_m in ppm	Gases and vapors	C_m in ppm
Acetone	500	Gasoline	500
Ammonia	100	Hydrogen sulphide	20
Benzene (benzol)	35	Methyl chloride	100
Carbon disulphide	20	Nitrogen oxide*	25
Carbon monoxide	100	Ozone	1
Carbon tetrachloride	50	Phosgene	1
Chlorine	1	Sulphur dioxide	10
Chloroform	100	Tetrachlorethylene	100
Ethylene dichloride	75	Toluol	200
Formaldehyde	5	Turpentine	100

* Other than nitrous oxide.

Dusts and mists	Mg per cu m	Dusts and mists	Mg per cu m
Lead	0.15	Zinc oxide fumes	15
Mercury	0.10	Chromic acid mist	0.1

The ventilation requirements vary widely depending on the physical characteristics of the substance to be removed and on tank design. Suitable baffles reduce considerably the air-flow requirements. Care must be taken to keep the air flow below the critical point at which liquid particles are wiped off the surface.

Ventilation by Dilution. Many industrial operations that must be performed on open benches use solvents, which contaminate the atmosphere on evaporating. General ventilation by dilution becomes necessary. A knowledge of the maximum allowable concentration C_m, usually given in parts per million, ppm (see Table 18), permits calculation of the quantity of ventilation air required. The approximate volume of 1 lb mol of the vapor at normal atmospheric pressure and temperature is 400 cu ft. The volume of the vapor,

$$\text{Cfm} = 400 \times \text{wt of solvent per min/molecular weight of solvent}$$

The ventilation air required = $10^6 \times$ cu ft of vapor/C_m.

Some operations permit material in process, while drying, to be placed on a perforated or slatted section of the bench, through which a flow of air is maintained to an exhaust connection below, thereby trapping some of the vapor and reducing the amount of general ventilation required.

If explosive mixtures are handled, motors and switches should be explosion proof and fans should have non-ferrous wheels to avoid danger of sparks should the wheel strike the casing. In some cases **belt drives** should be wiped by grounded copper brushes. Rubber and other elastomer **hoses** may also require grounding. Humidification is advised with complete grounding of machines to prevent the building up of charges of static electricity. A relative humidity of 60 to 65 percent should be maintained; it should not be permitted to get below 55 percent without an alarm.

Fire and health hazards from flammable and toxic gases and vapors require that concentration be kept at a minimum. The approximate limits of flammability of single gases and vapors is given in Table 25, p. 7-40.

Fire hazard in exhaust systems must be considered, as many dusts form inflammable and explosive mixtures with air. Cleanouts, fire dampers, and other safety devices should be provided. The safety practices of the National Safety Council and the American Insurance Association should be complied with.

CLEAN ROOMS

The machining of small metal parts for fits having extremely close tolerances has been hampered by the presence of dirt and other airborne contaminants. The need for a high order of cleanliness at the sites of such operations has become increasingly apparent. The foreword of Federal Standard No. 209, issued by the General Services Administration, reads in part:

> Manufacturing facilities providing the environmental control necessary for this type of cleanliness are known as **clean rooms, white rooms,** and **dust controlled facilities.** Thus, a clean room may be: "A space in which **airborne contamination,** and if needed, **temperature** and **humidity** are controlled to a far higher degree than conventional air conditioned areas."

Classes. Clean rooms are categorized as Class 100, Class 10,000, or Class 100,000; the numerals represent the maximum number of particles 0.5 μ or more in diameter or length in each cubic foot of air. The latter two classes also have a requirement for particles 5.0 μ and larger, as shown in Fig. 22.

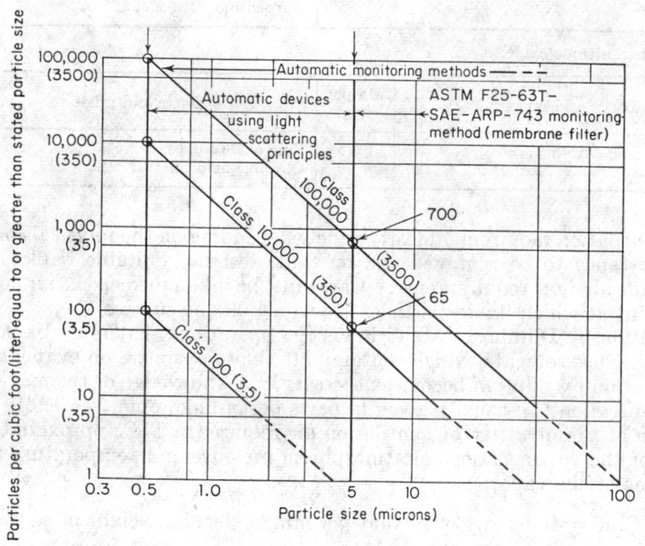

FIG. 22. Simplified control diagram for a typical central fan air-conditioning system. NOTE: Outside air (when at suitable temp.) admitted to produce predetermined mixture temperature. Return-air and exhaust-air dampers modulate in opposition to maintain constant pressure in mixing chamber.

Construction. Envelopes should be tight with non-porous, easy-to-clean surfaces having low particle-shedding properties. Floors should have a minimum practical number of joints.

Requirements. Pressure: above that of surrounding areas to ensure outward leakage. Temperature: range as required by both the product and the personnel; variations from ±0.25 F in the most critical operations to ±5 F where comfort governs. Humidity: between 30 and 45 percent with ±10 percent tolerance, except ±5 percent in humidity-sensitive areas.

Air-flow patterns are defined as either **laminar flow** or **non-laminar flow,** the former deriving from arrangements in which one whole surface of the room is the air outlet and another whole surface the air inlet. The latter is the conventional room air pattern of air conditioning and is substantially inferior for such applications. **Air motion** should be 90 fpm ± 20 fpm for laminar flow and a 3 min air change below the 12 ft level for non-laminar flow.

Filtering equipment should be HEPA filters (constituting the outlet in laminar flow rooms) preceded by screening filters (see p. 12–141). ASHRAE recommends additional filters ahead of coils, rather than screening filters so located, in order to preclude loading of the HEPA filters by dirt buildup and subsequent blowoff at the coils.

Monitoring should be by the techniques indicated in Fig. 22 and at intervals as follows: non-laminar flow, at representative locations twice each 8 hr working period; laminar flow, once a month at the first work location from the outlet and as described for non-laminar flow for downstream locations.

Work stations may be locally enclosed and treated as miniature clean rooms.

Where **radioactive particles** are liberated as a result of the use of a clean room, the **exhaust air** should be filtered as described for circulated air, and a negative pressure should be maintained in the room to ensure inward leakage. In this case, **buffer areas** with good commercial filtering of air should surround the room and entries should be air locks pressurized with air from such spaces passed through HEPA filters. Filters trapping radioactive particles are concentrators and should have shielding adequate to protect personnel. (See also Sec. 9.)

AUTOMATIC CONTROLS

(See also Sec. 16)

The form of automatic control to be used must be considered when designing the basic system since the type of control often governs layout.

Design Criteria. Since heating and air-conditioning systems are designed with capacities to produce the desired room conditions in the face of approximately **maximum** internal loads and exterior conditions approaching the **extremes,** means are required to vary their output when loads are less than maximum. In all but the simplest systems, it is impractical to perform this function manually.

An automatic control system must, if it is to produce satisfactory conditions, not only vary total heating or cooling effect but must vary such effects differently in different portions of the space as they are unequally affected by changes of load. **Zoning** is therefore required. Zones may be major portions of a building or individual rooms, according to the desired degree of sophistication and the funds available. **Corner rooms,** particularly the southeast and southwest corners, are extremely difficult to maintain at satisfactory conditions except on a room-by-room basis.

The **variable components** of load usually encountered are: (1) outside temperature and humidity, (2) sun, (3) wind, (4) occupants, (5) lights, (6) equipment producing heat and water vapor. Occupants, gas-fired equipment, and processes involving the heating of water in open containers affect the **dehumidifying** load as well as the **cooling** load.

Control Methods—Heating Systems

Control of heating systems involves **over-all** control and usually **zone** control. It may optionally involve **room-by-room** control. **Over-all** control in **steam** systems is affected by the control of the steam pressure and temperature in subatmospheric systems and by on-off control in other types. **Over-all** control in **water** systems is by varying the water temperature in accordance with the outdoor temperature (and, in good work, wind velocity), except in very small residential systems where starting and stopping of the pump is used as the only control. The **over-all** control of **indirect warm-air** systems is by throttling the flow of the heating medium through the coil or by bypassing air around the coil. **Overall** control of **direct-fired warm-air** systems is usually by stopping and starting of the firing device, the circulating fan being, in turn, started and stopped from the temperature of the air leaving the furnace. Larger systems with high outlets sometimes are controlled at the burner only, the fan running continuously. **Electric heating** systems are not usually controlled on an over-all basis.

Zone control in **steam** systems is accomplished as described for overall control except by zones. **Zone** control in **water** systems is by varying the temperature of water to the zone by mixing or by throttling the flow of water to the zone. Where throttling is used as a form of control, a high grade, externally piloted relief valve should be connected across the main so that a constant flow through the pumps and heating source may be maintained as the various zones throttle. **Zone** control of **indirect warm-air** systems is often accomplished having separate air-handling units assigned to the various zones, their coils being controlled as described for over-all control. Units with hot and cold decks and two-duct distributing systems with local mixing at the zones are presently much in favor. Where illumination levels are over 100 ft-c, induction units located in hung ceilings may be used in connection with high-pressure sytems to mix air from the hung ceiling space with primary air from the duct to the desired delivered temperature. **Zone** control of **direct-fired warm-air** units is usually by the assignment of separate units to the various zones. Deck-type units may be used as for indirect warm-air systems. **Zone** control of **electric heating** systems is usually either by local control of each heat emitter or by control of selected groups of circuits in distribution panels by means of thermostat-actuated contactors. Antifreeze protection for steam and water coils is needed.

Control Methods—Cooling and Dehumidifying

Control of cooling and dehumidifying systems involves **over-all** control only in small residential, commercial, and institutional applications where the control method is the starting and stopping of the refrigeration of package or window units. Other systems are **zoned,** the zoning in some cases being room by room. **Circulating fans** run continuously. The control of **dehumidification** in **comfort** applications is almost always by equipment selection, automatic control being of the dry-bulb temperature only. In **industrial** applications, reheat coils and dryers are often used to permit **independent control of humidity** (see Fig. 23 for a simplified control diagram).

Zone control in these systems is accomplished by varying the input to zone cooling coils, zone reheating coils, or room cooling coils. Bypasses around coils are also used. Where two-duct systems are used, air is mixed to the desired delivered temperature for each zone. Where an air-water induction-type perimeter system is used, the admission of chilled water to the sensible cooling coils in the room induction units provides room-by-room control of dry-bulb temperature. In this type of system, dehumidification is controlled by the maintenance of a fixed dew point at the primary air unit. Fan-coil type perimeter units usually have three-speed fans as the only control. Automatic modulating valves can be applied to the chilled water as well. Self-contained valve-thermostats are available for this purpose. Induction units located in hung ceilings and utilizing the heat from lighting fixtures may be used as described under control of heating. Throttling dampers are sometimes used for zone control, especially minimal room-by-room trimming. Throttling of more than one-third is not advisable without static pressure control.

During **intermediate seasons,** when the outside air is at a temperature which permits its use as a coolant, it is generally used in lieu of refrigeration. Control is accomplished by means of mixing the outside and return air by modulating dampers. Modern practice is to control the **fresh air damper** from **mixed air temperature** and the **return air damper** from **static pressure** in the mixing chamber. Since a varying input of outside air requires a varying quantity of exhaust air, the damper action just described is coordinated with an exhaust air damper so as to maintain a constant, slightly **positive pressure** in the building. Such systems require an **additional fan** on the return air system.

Thermostats should be carefully located to ensure that they measure the condition intended. **Room thermostats** should not be located so that they will be in stagnant air or in direct sunlight, or will be directly affected by the opening of exterior doors or windows, or will receive the direct heat of a fireplace or heat-producing equipment. **Outdoor thermostats** should not receive direct sunlight unless they are of types intended to take account of solar energy. **Wind-sensitive** outdoor thermostats are also available.

Automatic control systems may be electric, pneumatic, or a combination of the two. In some cases mechanical action (also called **"self-contained"**) devices are used for

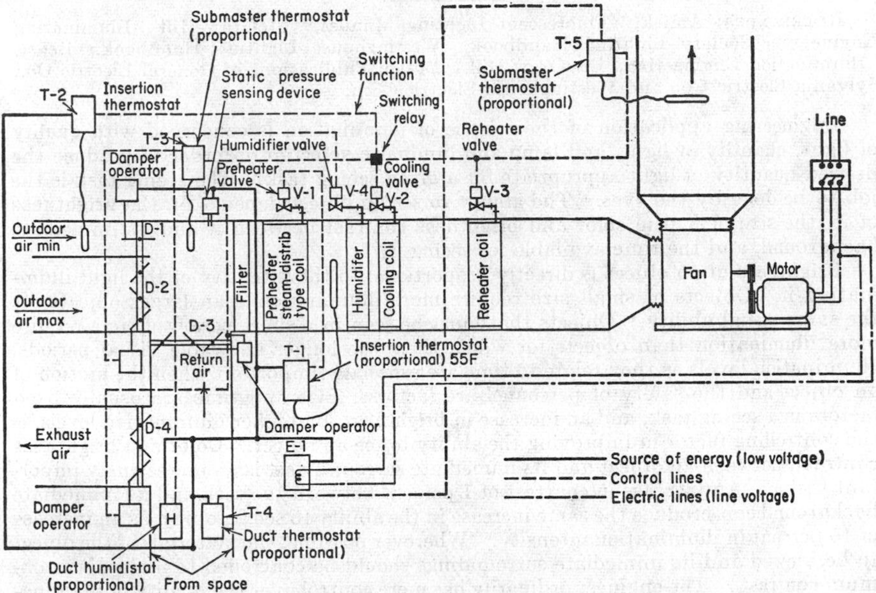

FIG. 23. Simplified control diagram.

strictly local functions, such as thermostatic water mixing valves. Electric and pneumatic control systems may have electronic components or subsystems, especially where remote reset with adjustable cut-in point and range are involved. Pneumatic systems are usually more economical for large numbers of control functions.

Nomenclature. **"Remote reset"** (also called **"submastering"**) means the resetting of a control device by another control device; e.g., the resetting of a zone water thermostat from an outside air thermostat. **"Modulation"** means a smooth varying of control effect as opposed to **"stepped"** or **"on-off"** control (also called **"two-position"** and **"positive acting"**). **"Direct acting"** means **closing** (or **increasing** control effect, such as branch-line air pressure) upon an **increase** in the value of the condition being measured. Thus a direct-acting thermostat closes its contacts, or increases the air pressure in its branch line, upon a rise in temperature. **"Tempering"** is the heating of outside air to room temperature.

Central control panels with indications of space and equipment conditions are becoming increasingly popular. It is said that, on large jobs, they pay for themselves in 3 years. Alarm annunciators are often incorporated in them.

ILLUMINATION

BY

Raymond J. Rice

REFERENCES: Amick, "Fluorescent Lighting Manual," McGraw-Hill. Illuminating Engineering Society Lighting Handbook. Westinghouse Lighting Handbook. Boast, "Illumination Engineering," McGraw-Hill. Design Publications of General Electric Co., Sylvania Electric Co., and Westinghouse Electric Corp.

Engineering application of the science of illumination is concerned with **quality** of light, **quantity** of light, and **lamp and luminaire selection** in order to produce the desired quantity of light appropriate for a given seeing task. The seeing task is the job to be done by the eyes. The ability to see an object depends on the **brightness** of it, the **size** of it, the **color and brightness contrast** between it and its immediate background, and the **time** available for seeing it.

Brightness of an object is directly proportional to the intensity of the light illuminating it. Objects of small **size** require more illumination than larger objects for the same visual ability. Objects that must be seen in a short period of time require more illumination than objects for which there are longer allowable visual periods. Illumination levels as they relate to time are especially important when the motion of an object and the safety of personnel are factors. **Size** and **time** are usually fixed factors in a seeing task, and an increase in **brightness,** by higher illumination levels, is the controlling factor in improving the ability to see an object. **Color and brightness contrast,** between an object and its immediate surroundings, is an increasingly important factor. An increase in contrast of 1 percent between the task and its immediate background can produce the same increase in the ability to see an object as an increase of 15 percent in illumination intensity. Wherever possible, the materials of the object to be viewed and its immediate surroundings should be controlled to maintain maximum contrast. The engineer ordinarily has more control over the quality of illumination so that contrasts are not veiled by glare or shadows.

Basic Units

The **candle** is the measure of intensity of a light source. The international candle is based on the light emitted by a black body heated to a specific temperature.

The **lumen** is the measure of the time rate of flow of luminous energy (light) equal to the light intercepted by a surface of one square foot, all points of which are one foot distant from a uniform point source of one candle.

The **foot-lambert,** fL, is the measure of brightness of a surface, when viewed from a particular direction, emitting, or reflecting one lumen per square foot.

Candles per sq in. is the measure of brightness of a source, when viewed from a particular direction, having an intensity of one candle per square inch of emitting surface.

The **foot-candle,** fc, is the measure of illumination at any point that is a distance of one foot from a uniform point source of one candle power. (Also equivalent to density of one lumen uniformly distributed over an area of one square foot.)

The **Angstrom unit,** A, is a measure of wavelength of radiant energy equal to 10^{-7} mm.

The **micron,** μ, is a measure of wavelength of radiant energy equal to 1×10^{-6} meters, or 1×10^4 Angstrom units.

Quality

The quality of a lighting system for a given seeing task is primarily improved by minimizing **glare.** Other considerations that determine quality are **brightness ratios, light distribution, diffusion,** and **color.**

Glare is the effect of brightness differences within a visual field sufficiently high to cause annoyance, discomfort or loss of visual perception. **Brightness** is the intensity of light emitted, transmitted, or reflected from a given surface, commonly measured in **foot-lamberts.** Brightness usually varies with direction of view and is ordinarily independent of the distance of observation. Brightness values of typical light sources are shown in Table 1.

Table 1. Approximate Brightness Values
(Westinghouse Electric Corp.)

Source	Candles per sq in.	Foot-lamberts
Inside frosted lamp, 300 watt	30	13,560
Clear lamp, 300 watt	6,000	2,712,000
White bowl lamp	15	6,780
Fluorescent lamps	2.0–7.	904–2938
Opal glass enclosing globes	1.5–5.5	678–2486
Indirect luminaire (incandescent luminous bowl)	0.5–1.0	226–452
White ceiling above direct-indirect fluorescent luminaire	0.5	226
Clear blue sky	2–3	904–1356

Direct glare results from high-brightness light sources or luminaires in the field of view that are insufficiently shielded or of too great an area. Luminaires are the principal source of direct glare; improperly shaded windows or excessively bright room surfaces are also serious contributors. Bright areas in shiny surfaces are sources of annoying **reflected glare.** Generally speaking, direct glare results from lighting sources in a zone between 45 and 90 deg from the vertical, while sources between the vertical and 45 deg from the vertical contribute to reflected glare (Fig. 1). Luminaires with lenses that polarize light (*i.e.*, a lens transmitting light waves which vibrate in one direction only) tend to reduce reflected glare in many instances. Some engineers prefer to reduce reflected glare by adjustment of the task and by optical control of the distribution pattern of the lighting fixture. Direct glare from windows is minimized by properly shielding the source of daylight with adjustable shades, blinds or louvers.

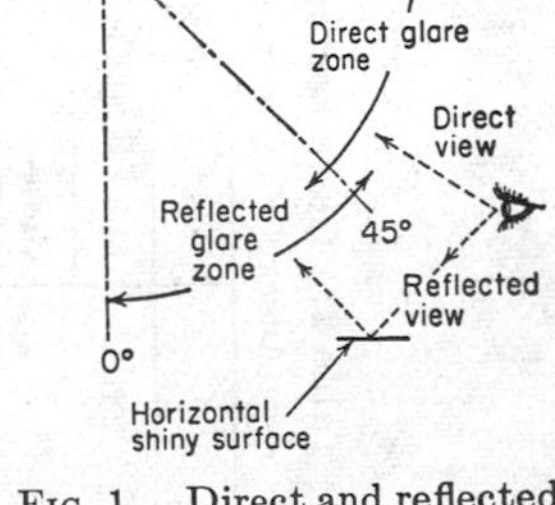

Fig. 1. Direct and reflected glare zones. It should be noted that there is no sharp line of demarcation between these zones at 45 degrees. (*IES.*)

Direct glare and reflected glare seriously reduce the ability to see an object. Direct glare causes (1) useless light to enter the eyes and (2) discomfort as the eyes attempt to screen out the direct light. Reflected glare takes the form of a bright reflection on the seeing task reducing the contrast.

Direct glare from luminaires may be minimized by controlling the light reaching the eyes from certain viewing angles. Several systems use glare factors to express the capacity of a lighting system to produce discomfort, *e.g.*, VCI (Visual Comfort Index), BCD Index (Borderline between Comfort and Discomfort), and VCF (Visual Comfort Factor). The calculation of the capacity of a lighting system to produce discomfort involves the computation of a discomfort factor for each luminaire or source of brightness within the normal field of view. The sum of these discomfort factors is the glare rating of the complete system and is used for appraisal of different lighting conditions. Table 2 gives glare factors produced with various lighting sys-

Table 2. Glare Factors for Various Lighting Systems
(Amick, "Fluorescent Lighting Manual," McGraw-Hill)

Room size	20 × 20 ft				40 × 40 ft				60 × 60 ft			
	MH* = 8½ ft		MH = 13 ft		MH = 8½ ft		MH = 13 ft		MH = 8½ ft		MH = 13 ft	
Luminaire type	Cross-wise	End-wise	Cross-wise	End-wise	Cross-wise	End-wise	Cross-wise	End-wise	Cross-wise	End-wise	Cross-wise	End-wise
Recessed commercial:												
2 ft wide troffers:												
2-lamp with clear ribbed plastic	19	34	9	22	29	43	18	33	34	46	25	39
4-lamp with clear ribbed plastic	29	50	14	33	44	63	28	48	52	66	38	57
2-lamp with low-brightness glass	18	28	12	17	25	32	17	26	28	34	21	30
4-lamp with low-brightness glass	34	55	22	35	46	64	32	53	52	67	41	60
2-lamp with dropped plastic	77	74	29	29	106	100	74	70	119	112	93	89
4-lamp with dropped plastic	133	129	55	55	180	174	127	123	210	200	159	154
2-lamp, 30° × 30° metal louvers	35	34	23	21	40	40	34	33	41	41	38	37
4-lamp, 30° × 30° metal louvers	55	52	35	32	64	61	53	50	69	66	60	57
2-lamp, 45° × 45° plastic louvers	33	34	18	18	39	41	32	33	42	44	36	38
4-lamp, 45° × 45° plastic louvers	62	69	32	39	71	80	59	66	74	84	67	77
1 ft wide troffers:												
2-lamp with clear ribbed plastic	51	67	27	44	69	76	49	65	80	76	60	71
3-lamp with clear ribbed plastic	63	87	32	57	86	98	60	84	96	100	75	92
2-lamp with low-brightness glass	35	61	26	40	43	72	33	58	50	79	38	66
3-lamp with low-brightness glass	54	86	34	52	76	101	52	83	86	109	67	94
2-lamp with dropped plastic	156	149	62	62	230	215	149	142	287	255	196	187
2-lamp, 30° × 30° metal louvers	59	56	36	33	67	64	56	53	71	68	63	60
2-lamp, 45° × 45° plastic louvers	58	58	26	26	69	69	56	56	73	73	64	64
2-lamp aluminum with louvers	5	22	5	17	6	22	5	21	6	22	6	21

* MH = luminaire mounting height.

tems in typical room environments, and Fig. 2 gives maximum acceptable glare factors for various seeing tasks.

Despite assumptions and devices designed to simplify calculation of the capacity of a lighting fixture to produce discomfort, glare calculations for specific installations are often considered cumbersome and the IES has devised a simplified method of predicting acceptability. The IES **scissors curve** method assumes a maximum room size of 100 ft square and room reflections that fall within recommended values. The scissors curve evaluation states that direct glare will not be a problem if luminaires have crosswise and endwise brightness distributions falling entirely between any straight line drawn through 250 fL at 75 deg (intersection *O* on Fig. 3) and lying between the two limiting curves *A* and *B*.

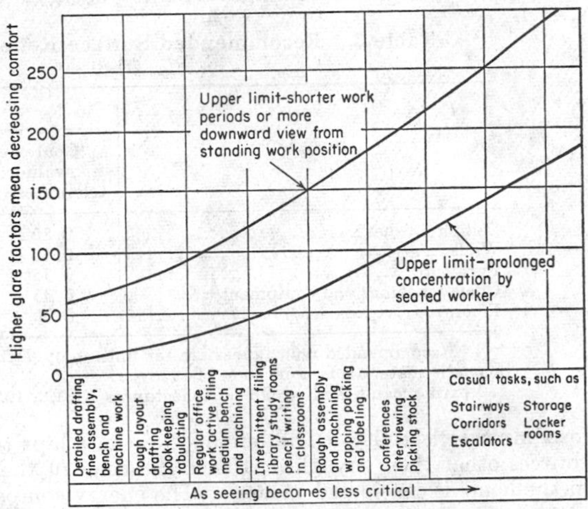

Fig. 2. Maximum acceptable glare factors for various seeing tasks. (*Amick.*)

To prevent distracting non-uniformity in brightness, the ratio of maximum to average luminaire brightnesses should preferably not exceed 3 to 1, and must not exceed 5 to 1. In no case should the maximum brightness for a given angle be more than three times the average brightness of the sloping solid line. Values required for a scissors curve evaluation are now frequently furnished by luminaire manufacturers.

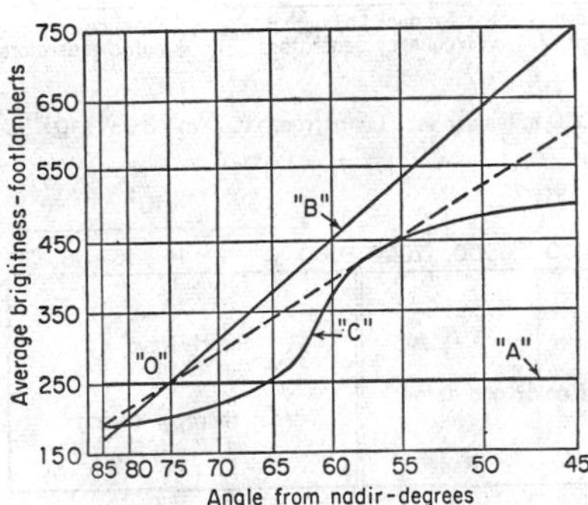

Fig. 3. Sample luminaire average brightness, scissors curve. (*IES.*)

Brightness ratios within the entire field of view involve the brightness of room and equipment surfaces as well as luminaire brightnesses. The eyes will function with minimum fatigue if the brightness contrast between the task and areas within the field of vision is a minimum. Excessive brightness ratios result in fatigue because the eye must adapt from the brightness of the task to the surroundings. An ideal, usually unattainable, is that all objects in the field of vision should have the same brightness. A ratio of the brightness of the task to that of the immediate surroundings of 3 to 1 is generally acceptable. Ratios no greater than 10 to 1 anywhere in the field of view are desirable, and 30 or 40 to 1 is the maximum permissible. These ratios can usually be achieved by having matte room surfaces with reflectances recommended in Table 3.

Distribution of illumination must be as even as possible. A quality design will have luminaires spaced so that the ratio of the intensity below the luminaire to the intensity between the luminaires is 1 to 1. Ratios of 1.5 to 1 are acceptable, and the maximum is 2 to 1. **Shadows,** on or near the task, reduce brightness. A quality installation avoids shadows with light from many sources. Proper distribution and matte room surfaces, with good reflectances, tend to eliminate shadows.

The **color** of light has no effect on visual efficiency. In certain applications color is a key variable in determining quality. Standards of color quality vary for different seeing tasks. Colors for industrial purposes can be best compared under a light source with an equal energy spectrum. Minor color differences are best distinguished when an object is viewed under a light with low energy in the spectral region of the object's maximum reflectivity. The human eye can adapt to certain colors of certain light sources other than daylight. Hence the color of the tungsten filament illumination in the home is considered natural. The energy composition of the light emitted from a tungsten filament favors the red end of the spectrum and accents flesh tints; this is considered more suitable than a light source with higher energy in the blue region of the spectrum. The effect of various color light sources on paints of different colors is often of importance. Certain colors convey a feeling of warmth, and others appear cool. The design of a lighting system must recognize psychological and traditional color factors in the achievement of quality for a particular seeing task.

Table 3. Recommended Surface Reflectances for Offices
(IES)

Surface	Reflectance	
	"Center-point" value and tolerances, percent	Equivalent range, percent
Ceiling finishes*	0.80 + 15	80–92
Walls	0.50 ± 20	40–60
Furniture	0.35 ± 25	26–44
Office machines and equipment	0.35 ± 25†	26–44
Floors	0.30 ± 30	21–39

* Recommended reflectances are for finish only. Over-all average reflectance of acoustic materials may be somewhat lower.
† American Standard Office Reflectances X2.1.3, 1954, UDC 535.312:651.2.

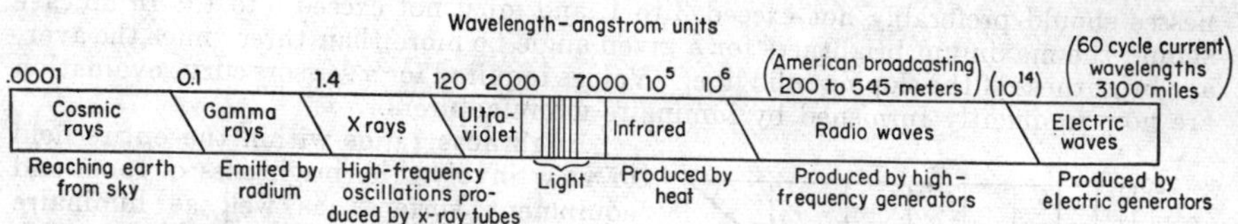

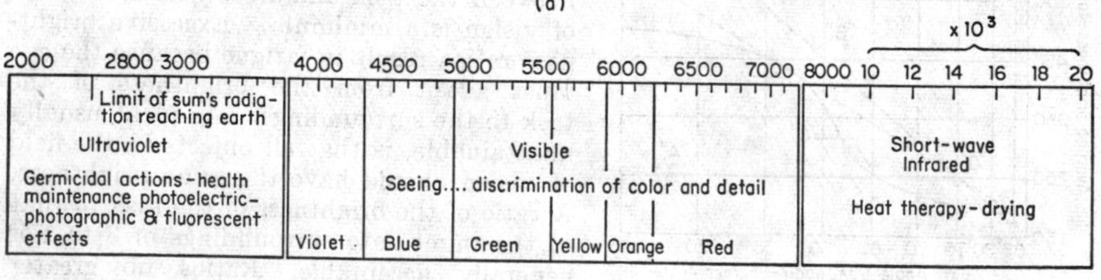

FIG. 4. (*a*) Location of light in the complete electromagnetic spectrum. (*Amick.*) (*b*) Expanded view of the electromagnetic spectrum from ultraviolet infrared regions. (*Amick.*)

Color is the sensation produced in the eye in response to light which is that portion of the electromagnetic spectrum for wavelengths of 3,800 to 7,200 Angstrom units (Fig. 4). The eye is more sensitive to energy submitted at certain wavelengths than at others. The effectiveness of energy emitted at a given wavelength, in producing a response in the eye is indicated by the relative luminosity factor, (Fig. 5).

A source of light may be emitted in (1) a narrow band of one or two frequencies, called a line spectrum, as with a mercury-vapor lamp; (2) a continuous spectrum containing varying quantities of all the frequencies in the visible spectrum, as with a tungsten lamp; or (3) an equal energy spectrum containing equal amounts of energy at each of the wavelengths in the visible spectrum.

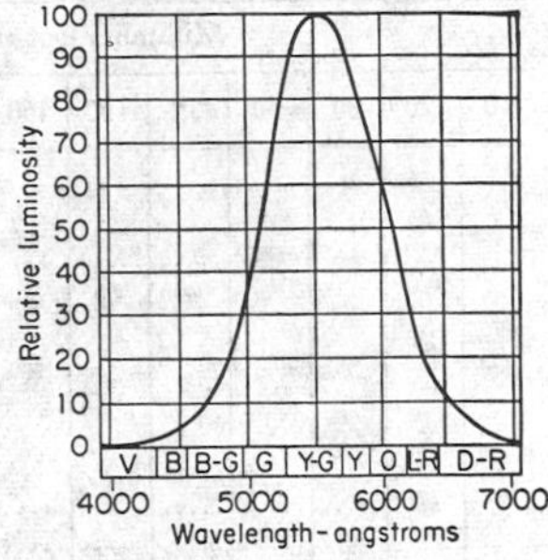

FIG. 5. Relative luminosity factors. (*Amick.*)

Color is often described by a temperature which compares the color of a light source with the color of a black body heated to varying temperatures measured in deg K (Table 4). Designation by color temperature is usually limited to colors with continuous spectrum characteristics because black bodies do not emit colors comparable to those with line-band radiation.

Objects appear to be certain colors because they have the ability to absorb light energy of particular wavelengths. The character of the reflected light determines the color of an object.

Quantity

The ability to see an object increases with the illumination level under which it is viewed. The amount of light that should be provided for a given seeing task is limited by economics and the ability to control the quality of the illumination. Ideal maximum levels are well beyond present-day standards; however, industry has accepted as **practical minimums** the new illumination levels recommended by the IES. These recommendations are the result of extensive research which analyzed the requirements of various practical tasks based on visual performance criteria.

The level of illumination is expressed in **foot-candles.** Typical required values for seeing tasks are shown in Table 5 (see also IES Lighting Handbook). Research has demonstrated increased ability to perform a given task at these recommended levels. These are maintained values at a horizontal plane 30 in. above the floor. Illumination on a vertical plane is usually one-third to one-half the level on a horizontal plane and is dependent upon a luminaire with a narrow or wide distribution pattern.

Table 4. Approximate Color Temperature
(Varying light, deg K)
(Westinghouse Electric Corp.)

Blue sky	10,000 to 30,000
Overcast sky	7000
Noon sunlight	5250
Fluorescent lamps:	
Daylight	6500
Cool white	4500
White	3500
Warm white	3000
500-watt daylight incandescent lamp	4000
Photoflood lamp	3400
General-service incandescent lamps	2500 to 3050
Candle flame	1800

Many tasks listed require a combination of general lighting plus specialized supplementary lighting. Where supplementary lighting is needed care should be taken to keep within the recommended brightness ratios. The design and installation of the combination system must provide not only a sufficient amount of light but also the proper direction of light diffusion and eye protection. As far as possible, it should eliminate direct and reflected glare as well as objectionable shadows.

Table 5. Minimum Recommended Illumination Levels for Various Tasks and Locations
(General Electric Co.)

Minimum foot-candles												
	10	20	30	50	70	100	150	200	300	500	1,000	2,000
Offices:												
Stairways, elevators, escalators, corridors		●										
Conference rooms				●								
Regular office work (reading, transcribing, active filing)						●						
Accounting, auditing, tabulating, business machine operating, etc.							●					
Cartography designing, detailed drawing								●				
Schools:												
Corridors, stairways		●										
Auditoriums (assembly only)			●									
Gymnasiums:												
General exercising			●									
Exhibition games				●								
Cafeterias				●								
Classrooms:												
Classroom work, study halls, libraries					●							
Manual arts, drafting						●						
Sewing rooms, sight-saving classes, lipreading classes, special exhibits, laboratory benches (close work), chalk boards (supplementary)							●					
Factories:												
Locker rooms, toilets, washrooms			●									
Storage (inactive)	●											
Storage (active):												
Rough bulky			●									
Medium				●								
Fine						●						
Inspection:												
Ordinary				●								
Difficult						●						
Highly difficult								●				
Very difficult										●		
Wrapping, packing, labeling				●								
Drilling, riveting					●							
Assembly:												
Medium assembly						●						
Fine assembly										●		
Extra-fine assembly, extra-fine bench and machine work, grinding fine work											●	
Woodworking:												
Sizing, planing, rough sanding, medium machine and bench work, glueing						●						
Fine sanding and finishing								●				
Printing:												
Composing room, machine composition, font assembly, sorting						●						
Proofreading, routing, finishing, proofing, tint-laying, macking							●					
Matrix making, color inspection								●				
Welding (supplementary), textile inspection (perching)												●
Shoe manufacturing (cutting, stitching, marking, etc.)									●			
Stores (clerk-service types):												
Merchandising areas						●						
Showcases and wallcases								●				
Feature displays										●		
Special appraisal areas (dark merchandise)										●		
Stores (self-service types):												
Merchandising areas								●				
Show cases and wallcases										●		
Feature displays											●	
Special appraisal areas (dark merchandise)										●		

Table 5. Minimum Recommended Illumination Levels for Various Tasks and Locations—(*Continued*)

10	20	30	50	70	100	150	200	300	500	1,000	2,000	
												Public buildings:
												Banks:
			●									Lobby (general)
				●								Writing areas in lobby
						●						Teller's stations
												Libraries:
		●										Stacks
				●								Reading, cataloging, card files, check-in, check-out
												Art galleries:
		●										General circulation areas
		●										On paintings (supplementary) minimum
					●							On statuary

(Column headings: Minimum foot-candles)

Lamps

Electric lamps are the principle source of light in common use. They convert electrical energy into light or radiant energy and are classified in two principal categories: **incandescent filament** and **gaseous discharge.**

An **incandescent-filament lamp** contains a filament which is heated by the current passing through it. The filament is enclosed in a glass bulb which has a base suitable to connect the lamp to an electrical socket. The bulb contains a specialized atmosphere which prevents oxidation of the filament at elevated temperature. The specialized atmosphere is provided by (1) evacuation of the air in the bulb or (2) replacement of the air with an inert gas. The bulb also serves to control the light from the incandescent filament, which is essentially a point source. Excessive brightness of the source is typically reduced by acid etching to frost the inside surface of the bulb. Silica coatings will also provide diffusion and can alter the color of the light emitted. Portions of the bulb's interior can be covered with reflecting material to give a predetermined direction to the emitted light. Chemical tinting of clear glass bulbs provides a variety of colors. Whenever the color that is normally produced by an incandescent filament is changed, the filtering process removes from the radiated light the energy of all wavelengths except those necessary to produce the desired color. This subtractive method of color alteration is less efficient than the generation of light of varying colors by gaseous discharge.

S F G A T PS PAR R

FIG. 6. Typical filament-lamp shapes; S-straight, F-flame, G-globe, A-general service, T-tubular, PS-pear shape, PAR-parabolic, R-reflector. (*Westinghouse.*)

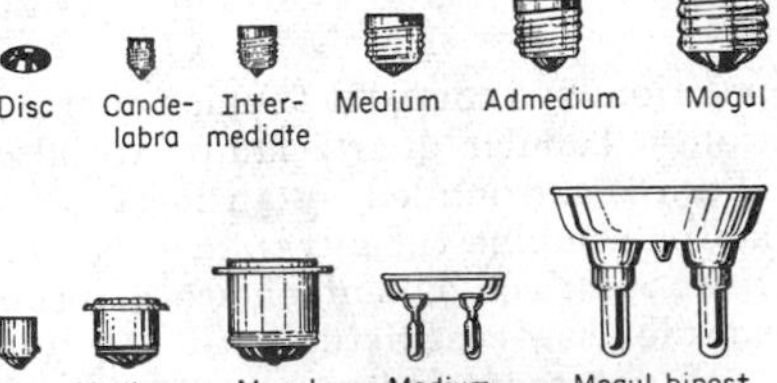

FIG. 7. Typical incandescent-lamp bases. (*Westinghouse.*)

Sizes and **shapes** of lamp bulbs are designated by a letter code followed by a numeral; the letter indicates the shape (Fig. 6), and the number indicates the diameter of the bulb in eighths of an inch. Thus a T–12 lamp has a tubular shape and is 12⁄8 or 1½ in. in diameter.

Incandescent lamps are available with several **types of bases** (Fig. 7). Most general-service lamps have medium screw bases; larger or smaller screw bases are used depending on lamp wattage. Bipost and prefocus bases accurately position the filament, as in optical projection systems. Bipost lamps also serve where ruggedness and greater heat dissipation are required.

Incandescent-lamp filaments are generally constructed of tungsten. Tungsten has a melting point slightly less than that of carbon, an early filament material, but it is superior to carbon because of its low vapor pressure, which permits higher operating temperatures without evaporation: the higher the operating temperature, the higher the efficacy (lumens per watt). Filament evaporation throughout the life of the lamp causes blackening of the bulb and thinning of the filament with consequent lower light output.

Tungsten filaments are also placed in compact quartz tubes filled with an iodine atmosphere where the tungsten iodide lighting source continuously returns evaporated tungsten particles to the filament. The inside walls do not blacken, and light output remains fairly constant throughout the life of the lamp.

Tubular quartz lamps have wide application as compact light sources for spot- and floodlighting assemblies permitting construction of smaller, less-expensive luminaires. Most tubular quartz lamps must be burned in an essentially horizontal

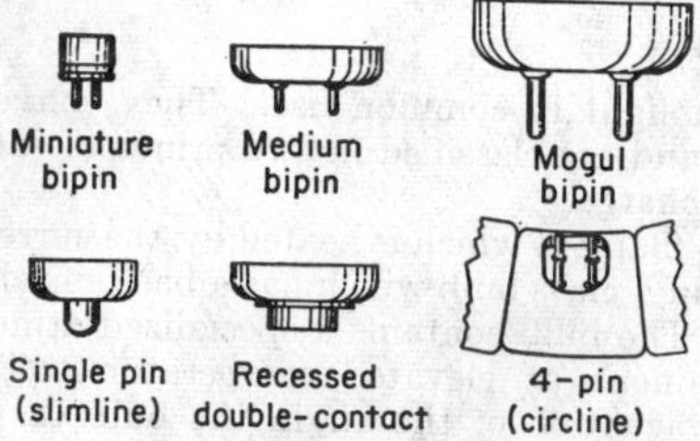

FIG. 8. Fluorescent-lamp bases. (*Amick.*)

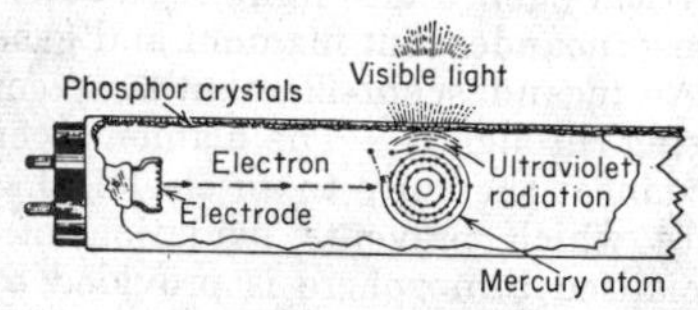

FIG. 9. Fluorescent-lamp operation. (*Westinghouse.*)

position, but compact tubular quartz lamps have been developed to burn in any position. Tubular quartz lamps are also placed inside a conventional PAR or R bulb (Fig. 6) surrounded by an inert gas which protects the filament tube leads. These lamps combine the advantages of the tubular quartz construction with the PAR and R shapes: convenient choice of beam spreads, reflectors that never get dirty, and simpler, low-cost fixtures.

Fluorescent lamps consist of a glass tube coated on the inside with fluorescent phosphor crystals; the ends of the tube are sealed with electrode-mounted bases (Fig. 8). The tube contains a highly rarefied inert gas (usually argon) and a drop of mercury (Fig. 9). When a potential is placed across the electrodes, electrons flow ionizing the gas, which quickly decreases, allowing the current to flow and the mercury to vaporize. The discharge generates ultraviolet radiation by electron collision; the radiation is absorbed by the phosphor causing it to glow and emit light.

The principal **shape** of the fluorescent lamp is the **tube,** designated by T and a numeral representing its diameter in eighths of an inch. A variation is the grooved tube in which the glass is dimpled, alternating on each side of the tube, to get higher outputs from the lamp. The groove places a higher portion of phosphor near the arc to minimize internal losses and to increase the length of the arc (1 ft on an 8 ft lamp). **Circline lamps** consist of a tube bent into a circular shape and joined in a four-pin base. **Panel lamps** are a new departure from the standard tubular shape and consist of two formed glass plates, normally 12 in. square, sealed together.

Fluorescent lamps are classified by their **starting** methods, *i.e.*, the method by which electron flow is induced. This is accomplished by a **preheat circuit,** an **instant-start circuit,** or a **rapid-start circuit.** All circuits include **ballasts** which serve as (1) autotransformers to step up supply voltage, *e.g.*, 120, 208, 240, 277 volts, to the necessary starting value, *e.g.*, 255 to 500 volts, and (2) a choke to limit the current through the lamp. Ballasts consist of a core and coil which stabilize the operation of the lamp;

a power capacitor which corrects the power factor and reduces the load on the electrical distribution system; a radio interference–suppressing capacitor which reduces feedback of radio-frequency energy to the power line; and a potting compound which fills all voids inside the ballast case, improving heat dissipation and reducing sound. Thermal protectors are sometimes included in ballasts to deenergize the ballasts upon detection of excessive temperatures that may occur toward the end of the ballast's life.

Preheat circuits contain starters (Fig. 10) which are switches, closed when power is first applied, permitting current to flow and preheat the cathode. After a predetermined period of time, the starter switch opens throwing a potential across the cathodes and striking an arc. Lamps used for preheat circuits have bi-pin bases (Fig. 8).

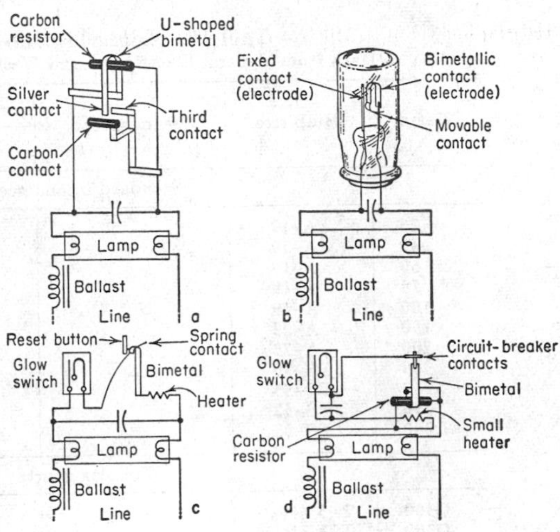

Fig. 10. Starter switches for preheat cathode circuits. (*IES.*)

Instant-start circuits have ballasts which apply sufficient voltage across the electrodes to induce current flow without preheating the cathodes. **Slimline lamps** are the principal instant-start type. They have single-pin bases because no preheating is required; are available in sizes up to 8 ft in length; and can have varying lumen outputs dependent upon the ballast current rating and wattage. Slimline lamps are available in operating amperages of 200 and 425 ma. Because of their high starting voltage, they generally employ spring-loaded push-pull lamp holders which disconnect the ballast circuit unless the lamps are properly seated in position.

Instant-start lamps are sometimes available with bi-pin bases similar to those used in preheat lamps. In these instances the lead wires from the pins are connected together inside the lamp. These lamps, marked "instant start," are not interchangeable with rapid-start equipment. Cold-cathode lamps employ the instant-start principal; have cylindrical iron cathodes; and tend to be less efficient at shorter lengths because of high wattage losses at the electrodes. They are limited to low current densities because the cathodes operate at temperatures below that necessary for satisfactory thermionic emission. Cold-cathode lamps, whose operation is not affected by dimming or flashing, have long life and are generally used for custom-built shapes and patterns that require bending.

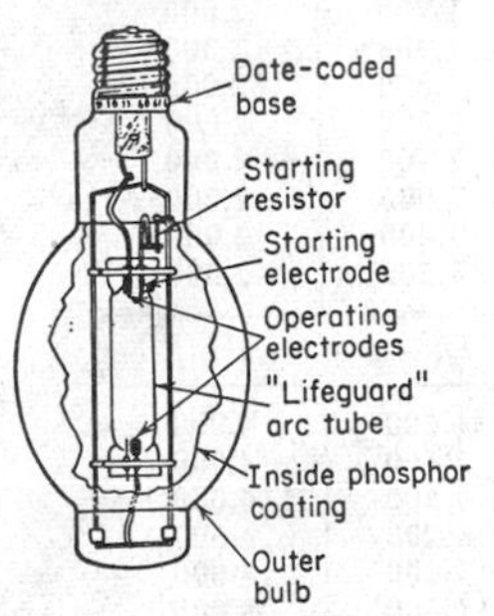

Fig. 11. Mercury-vapor lamp. (*Westinghouse.*)

Rapid-start circuits combine essential features of the preheat lamp and the rapid-start lamp. Ballasts have separate windings for the electrodes which are immediately and continuously heated when the circuit is energized. This immediate heating causes sufficient ionization in the lamp for an arc to strike from the voltage of the main ballast windings. Two-lamp rapid-start ballasts are of the series sequence type, in which the lamps start in sequence and, when fully lighted, operate in series. Rapid-start lamps are available in operating amperages from 430 to 1,500 ma.

Mercury-vapor lamps are of the gaseous-discharge type,

in which light is produced by passage of a current through high-pressure mercury vapor. A potential between two electrodes ionizes the gas permitting a current flow. The electron flow collides with the atoms of the gas temporarily altering the atomic structure. As the disturbed atoms return to their normal state, energy is given off in the form of light. The lamp consists of an inner bulb of quartz which contains the arc (Fig. 11). The starting resistor, located within the lamp, limits the starting current and creates a higher resistance path for the starting arc than for the main arc. An outer bulb shields the arc tube from changes in temperature, contains an inert gas which prevents oxidation of internal parts, provides an inner surface for coating of phosphors, and in certain instances acts as a filter to correct color. The

Table 6. Incandescent-lamp Data
(Data from General Electric Co. and Westinghouse Electric Corp.)

Watts	Bulb size	Beam spread	Lumens		Dated average life
			Initial	Beam	
Standard incandescent					
25	A–19		266		1,000
40	A–19		470		1,000
60	A–19		840		750
75	A–19		1,150		750
100	A–19		1,750		750
150	A–23		2,700		750
200	A–23		4,000		750
300	PS–30		6,000		750
500	PS–35		10,500		1,000
750	PS–52		16,500		1,000
1,000	PS–52		23,300		1,000
Tubular quartz					
Q300	T–3 4$\frac{11}{16}$″		6,000		2,000
Q300	T–3 3$\frac{1}{8}$″		5,500		2,000
Q400	T–4 3$\frac{1}{8}$″		7,400		2,000
Q500	T–3 4$\frac{11}{16}$″		10,500		2,000
Q1,000	T–6 5$\frac{5}{8}$″		21,000		2,000
Standard PAR and R					
75	R–30	50° spot	860	430	2,000
	R–30	130° flood	860	610	2,000
150	R–40	20° spot	1,950	910	2,000
	R–40	110° flood	1,950	1,530	2,000
300	R–40	35° spot	3,700	1,660	2,000
	R–40	115° flood	3,700	3,250	2,000
500	R–40	60° spot	6,500	4,240	2,000
	R–40	120° spot	6,500	5,920	2,000
150	PAR–38	30° spot	1,730	960	2,000
	PAR–38	60° flood	1,730	1,220	2,000
200	PAR–46	17° × 23° spot	2,250	1,200	2,000
		20° × 40° flood	2,250	1,300	2,000
300	PAR–56	15° × 20° spot	3,840	1,800	2,000
		20° × 35° flood	3,840	2,000	2,000
		30° × 60° flood	3,840	2,100	2,000
500	PAR–64	15° × 20° spot	6,500	3,000	2,000
		20° × 35° flood	6,500	3,400	2,000
		35° × 65° flood	6,500	3,500	2,000
Quartz PAR and R					
Q250	PAR–38	26° spot	3,200	1,600	4,000
		60° flood	3,200	2,400	4,000
Q500	PAR–56	15° × 32° spot	7,000	3,500	4,000
		20° × 42° flood	7,000	4,200	4,000
		34° × 46° flood	7,000	5,600	4,000
Q500	R–40	32° spot	17,000	11,500	3,000
Q1,000	R–40	110° flood	17,000	15,500	3,000

Table 7. Gaseous-discharge Lamp Data
(Data from General Electric Co. and Westinghouse Electric Corp.)

Watts*	Bulb size	Beam spread	Lumens†		Rated average life
			Initial	Beam	
Preheat fluorescent					
20(23)(25)	T-12 24″		1,170		7,500
25(30)	T-12 33″		1,600		7,500
30(38)(38)	T- 8 36″		2,000		7,500
90(109)(105)	T-17 60″		5,750		7,500
100(120)(115)	T-17 60″		5,200		7,500
Rapid start					
40(52)(46)	T-12 48″		3,150		12,000
30(48)(38)	T-12 36″		2,250		9,000
Instart-start					
40(60)(50)	T-12 48″		2,750		7,500
40(60)(51)	T-17 60″		2,800		7,500
Fluorescent					
25(38)(40)	T-6 42″		1,750		7,500
40(54)(52)	T-6 64″		2,660		7,500
35(54)(52)	T-8 72″		2,700		7,500
50(69)(66)	T-8 96″		3,750		7,500
Slimline					
35(56)(47)	T-12 42″		2,300		7,500
40(59)(59)	T-12 48″		2,900		9,000
50(76)(63)	T-12 60″		3,350		7.500
55(83)(69)	T-12 72″		4,250		7,500
75(102)(88)	T-12 96″		6,100		9,000
High output					
60(80)(71)	T-12 48″		3,780		9,000
85(110)(101)	T-12 72″		6,000		9,000
110(140)(121)	T-12 96″		8,900		9,000
Superhigh output					
116(138)(117)	T-12 48″		6,900		7,500
168(185)(173)	T-12 72″		10,900		7,500
218(230)(227)	T-12 96″		15,000		7,500
Power groove					
110(138)(117)	PG-17 48″		6,900		7,500
160(185)(173)	PG-17 72″		10,900		7,500
215(230)(227)	PG-17 96″		15,000		7,500
Fluorescent pane					
55(60)	FP-12 11⅝ sq.		3,040		7,500
80(100)(87)	FP-12 11⅝ sq.		4,400		7,500
Fluorescent circline					
22(25)	T- 9 8¼ O.D.		930		7,500
32(35)	T-10 12″ O.D.		1,550		7,500
40(42)	T-10 16″ O.D.		2,200		7,500

Table 7. Gaseous-discharge Lamp Data—(*Continued*)

Watts*	Bulb size	Beam spread	Lumens†		Rated average life
			Initial	Beam	
Mercury vapor					
100(120)	PAR-38	Spot	2,400		16,000
100(120)	PAR-38	Flood	2,400		16,000
100(125)	BT-25		3,350		16,000
175(210)	BT-28		7,500		16,000
250(285)(277)	BT-28		11,500		16,000
400(435)(442)	BT-37		21,000		16,000
400(435)(442)	R-60	Wide beam	18,500		16 000
400(435)(442)	R-60	Medium beam	17,500		16,000

* Numerals in parenthesis are the input wattages per *lamp* when single lamp and two-lamp 120 volt ballasts are used.

† Lumen outputs are approximate and are for cool white fluorescent lamps and standard white mercury lamps.

lower vapor pressure in fluorescent lamps results in the arc radiating most of its energy in the ultraviolet region which, in turn, produces light. With high-pressure mercury lamps, the arc of a mercury-vapor lamp produces visible light directly.

Mercury-vapor lamps are designated by ASA nomenclature; *e.g.*, in a lamp marked H33-1-GL/C: H indicates a mercury lamp; 33-1 are the ballast numbers; GL are arbitrary letters designating physical characteristics of the lamp, such as bulb size, shape, material, and finish; and C indicates the color of the light.

Mercury lamps require ballasts as do fluorescent lamps. **Reactor** ballasts may be used if the voltage is sufficiently high (*e.g.*, 480 volts). Otherwise an **autotransformer ballast** is used. Where voltages vary as much as ±13 percent, a **regulator** or **stabilizing ballast** is used to improve the lamp regulation and to lower drop-out

Table 8. Noise Ratings of Typical Indoor Ballasts
(Amick, "Fluorescent Lighting Manual," McGraw-Hill)

No. and size of lamps	Line voltage	Power factor	Certified	Rating, manufacturer		
				X	Y	Z
One 14, 15 or 20 watt switch-start	118	Low	No	A	......	A
One 20 watt trigger-start	118	Low	No	A	......	A
		High	No	B	......	B
Two 20 watt trigger-start	118	Low	No	A	......	A
		High	No	B	......	C
One 40 watt switch-start	118	Low	No	A	......	A
		High	No	A	A	A
	277	High	No	A	......	A
Two 40 watt switch-start	118	High	Yes	B	B	B
	236	High	No	B	......	B
	277	High	No	B	C	B
Two 40 watt rapid-start	118	High	Yes	B	B	B
			No	B	......	B
	277	High	Yes	B	B	B
Two 40 watt instant-start or 48 in.	118	High	Yes	D	......	D
T-12 slimline*	277	High	Yes	D	......	D
Two 96 in. T-12 slimline (series)	118	High	Yes	C	......	C
			No	C	......	C
	277	High	Yes	C	......	C
Two 96 in. T-12 slimline (lead-lag)	118	High	Yes	D	......	C
	277	High	Yes	D	......	C
Two 96 in. T-12 rapid-start	118	High	Yes	C	......	C
(800 ma)	277	High	Yes	C	......	C
Two 96 in. T-12 or T-17 (1,500 ma)	118	High	Yes	D	......	D
	277	High	Yes	D	......	D

* For lead-lag with series-type ballast, sound rating is C.

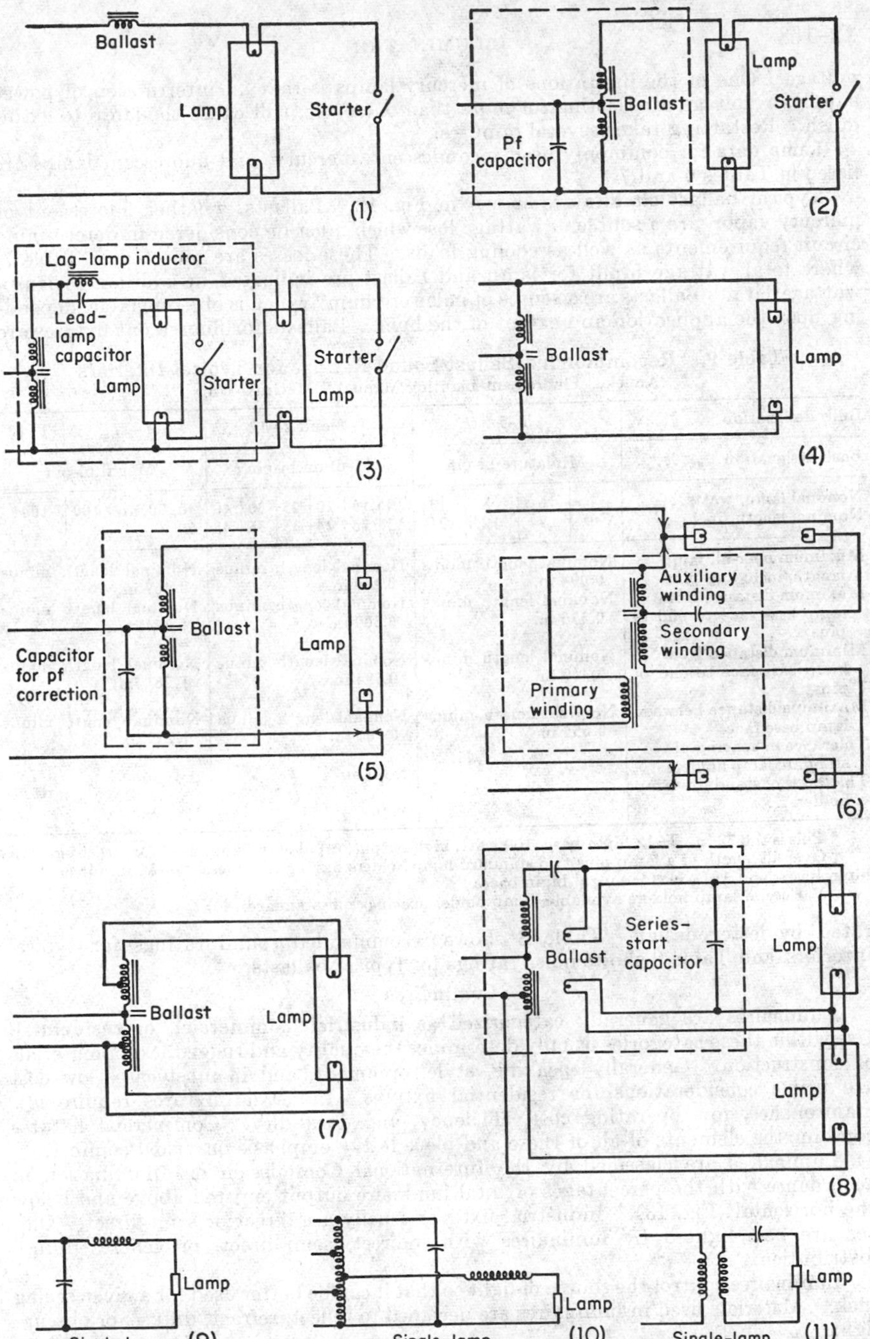

FIG. 12. Typical circuits for fluorescent and mercury ballasts. (1) Basic preheat circuit; (2) preheat circuit with autotransformer to step up voltage and capacitor to correct power factor; (3) head-lag preheat; (4) basic instant-start circuit, (5) instant-start circuit showing disconnect lampholder; (6) typical series instant-start circuit; (7) basic rapid-start circuit; (8) two-lamp series lead circuit; (9) mercury reactor ballast circuit; (10) mercury autotransformer circuit; (11) mercury stabilizing ballast circuit. (*GE*.)

voltage. One of the limitations of mercury lamps is that an interruption of power supply or voltage dip, lasting for more than one cycle, will cause the lamp to extinguish. Restarting takes several minutes.

Lamp data for commonly used incandescent, mercury, and fluorescent lamps are listed in Tables 6 and 7.

Typical **ballast circuits** are shown in Fig. 12. Ballasts, whether fluorescent or mercury vapor, are a source of wattage loss which must be considered in determining circuit requirements as well as cooling loads. These losses are reflected in Table 7, where total wattage input for lamp and ballast are indicated in addition to lamp-wattage data. Ballasts are a source of **noise** or **"hum"** which is objectionable, depending upon the application and extent of the hum. Ballasts for fluorescent fixtures are

Table 9. Recommended Ballast Sound Ratings for Typical Interiors
(Amick, "Fluorescent Lighting Manual," McGraw-Hill)

Bulb designation	T–5				T–8 and T–12						T–17	T–12
Base designation	Miniature bi-pin				Medium bi-pin						Mogul bi-pin	
Nominal lamp, watts	4	6	8	13	14	15	20	25	30	40	40, 90, and 100	100*
Nominal length, in.†	6	9	12	21	15	18	24	33	36	48	60	72
Maximum over-all lamp length, including pins	Nominal length minus 0.094 in.				Nominal length minus 0.219 in.						Nominal length minus 0.469 in.	
Maximum distance from lamp base face to end of pins	Nominal length minus 0.375 in.				Nominal length minus 0.500 in.						Nominal length minus 1.094 in.	
Minimum distance from lamp base face to end of pins	Nominal length minus 0.469 in.				Nominal length minus 0.594 in.						Nominal length minus 1.281 in.	
Maximum distance between lamp base faces	Nominal length minus 0.656 in.				Nominal length minus 0.781 in.						Nominal length minus 1.719 in.	
Tolerance in spacing of standard lamp holders	‡				± 1/32 in.						± 1/32 in.	
Thickness of standard lamp holders	‡				3/8 in.						13/16 in.	

* This is the 72 in., T–12 bipin-base, 100 watt, high-output, rapid-start lamp used for street lighting.
† Over-all length of a lamp plus two standard lamp holders having thicknesses of 3/8 in. for medium bipin bases, and 13/16 in. for mogul bipin bases.
‡ Variety of lamp holders available, lamp holder spacings not standardized.

rated by letter design. Table 8 shows recommended sound ratings for typical interiors, and Table 9 shows noise ratings for typical ballasts.

Luminaires

Luminaires are generally categorized as **industrial, commercial,** or **residential.** Use within these categories usually determines the quality and ruggedness of materials of construction. Generally speaking, style, ornament, and in most cases low cost are prime considerations for residential fixtures. Industrial fixtures require low maintenance, low operating cost, efficiency, and durability. Commercial fixtures combine the elements of all of these and place heavy emphasis on visual comfort.

Luminaires are classified by the International Commission on Illumination in accordance with the percentages of total luminaire output emitted above and below the horizontal (Fig. 13). Industrial fixtures usually are direct or semi-direct. Offices are best lighted by luminaires with indirect, semi-direct, or general diffuse distribution.

Luminaires control the source of light so that it can be better used for a given seeing task. Materials used in luminaires are designed to reflect, refract, diffuse, or obscure light.

Reflectors are commonly made of specular alzak aluminum, glass, baked-enameled coated steel, and porcelain-enameled coated steel.

Lenses with prismatic patterns refract light sources to disperse the rays or to direct them most effectively. Lenses are of glass, acrylic plastic (Plexiglas), or polystyrene. **Glass** is generally superior for incandescent fixtures because of its heat resistance. **Acrylic** lenses, in fluorescent lamps, have a light life at least twice that of **polystyrene** because of their color stability. **Translucent** glass and plastic are used in bottom lenses, louvers, and side panels to diffuse light and to obscure light sources. Baked-enamel coated-steel **louvers,** in egg-crate, concentric-ring, or cellular configurations are widely used to shield light sources from normal viewing angles.

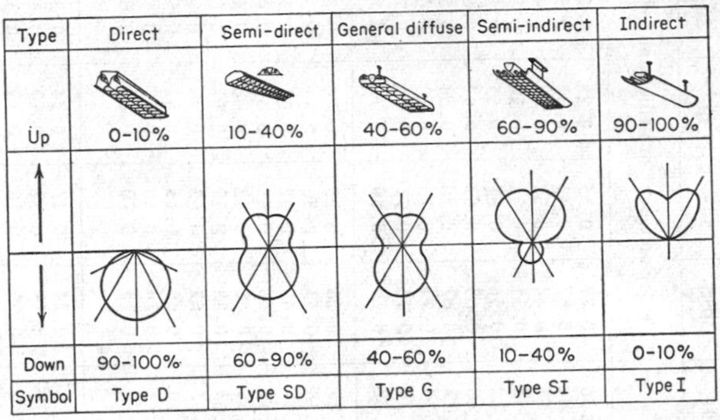

Type	Direct	Semi-direct	General diffuse	Semi-indirect	Indirect
Up	0–10%	10–40%	40–60%	60–90%	90–100%
Down	90–100%	60–90%	40–60%	10–40%	0–10%
Symbol	Type D	Type SD	Type G	Type SI	Type I

FIG. 13. Classification of general lighting units by their percentage of upward and downward light. (*Amick.*)

Fixture bodies, trims, and lens frames are commonly constructed of steel, electrogalvanized and/or treated with a rust-inhibiting coating, and painted with several coats of baked enamel. Cast aluminum is gaining favor for incandescent lighting fixtures and, with a corrosion-resistant treatment, is often used in exterior locations instead of bronze or galvanized cast iron.

Lighting Design

Illumination calculations are commonly made by the **lumen method** and the **point-by-point method.** The former utilizes the average level of illumination in foot-candles at a given working plane while the latter employs the specific foot-candle contribution at a given point. The point-by-point method is usually reserved for direct lighting sources, floodlighting, spotlighting, and streetlighting. The new IES **zonal cavity method** is a variant of the lumen method which takes into account any length of stem, a fact otherwise generally ignored. It also permits determination of the average illumination at any working plane (such as the floor); and it permits the calculation of average illumination in rooms with ceiling beams, low partitions, or obstructions; odd shaped rooms; or partially lighted rooms.

Lighting design requires determination of the room dimensions, finish, and appropriate illumination levels. With these preliminary factors determined, the type and number of fixtures can be selected.

The **lumen method** of calculation is based on the concept that the lighting level in foot-candles is equal to the number of lumens reaching a working plane divided by the area of the working plane. The number of lumens reaching the working plane equals the number of lumens emitted by a lamp or group of lamps multiplied by (1) a **maintenance factor** (*MF*) which allows for decrease in lamp lumen rating with age and by dust and dirt accumulation; and (2) the **coefficient of utilization** (*CU*) which allows for variables, such as luminaire efficiency, room proportions, and room reflectances. *CU* is the ratio of lumens received on the working plane to the lumens emitted by the lamps. Selected coefficients of utilization and maintenance factors are given in Table 10, where **"room ratio"** is defined by Eqs. (1) and (2):

For direct, semi-direct, and general diffuse luminaires

$$\text{Room ratio} = \frac{W \times L}{(\text{mounting height above working plane})(W + H)} \tag{1}$$

For semi-indirect and indirect luminaires

$$\text{Room ratio} = \frac{3\,W \times L}{2(\text{mounting height above working plane})(W + H)} \tag{2}$$

Table 10. Coefficients of Utilization for Typical Industrial and Commercial Luminaries
(General Electric Co.)

Luminaire type	Typical distribution	Floor / Ceiling / Walls / Room ratio	70% / 50%	70% / 30%	50% / 50%	50% / 30%	30% / 30%	30% / 10%
		Floor	10% reflectance					
		Ceiling	70%		50%		30%	
		Walls	50%	30%	50%	30%	30%	10%
		Room ratio	Coefficient of utilization					
1. General-service filament lamp in deep-bowl porcelain-enameled reflector with ventilated husk for good maintenance. Maintenance factors: Good—0.80 Med.—0.70 Poor—0.60 Maximum fixture spacing = mounting height × 1.1	0/100	0.6	0.36	0.29	0.35	0.28	0.28	0.24
		0.8	0.44	0.37	0.43	0.37	0.37	0.32
		1.0	0.51	0.44	0.50	0.44	0.43	0.39
		1.25	0.58	0.51	0.56	0.50	0.50	0.46
		1.5	0.62	0.56	0.61	0.55	0.55	0.51
		2.0	0.68	0.63	0.67	0.62	0.61	0.58
		2.5	0.72	0.67	0.70	0.66	0.65	0.62
		3.0	0.75	0.71	0.73	0.70	0.68	0.66
		4.0	0.79	0.76	0.77	0.74	0.73	0.71
		5.0	0.82	0.79	0.80	0.77	0.76	0.74
2. White-enameled industrial reflector for two Power Groove lamps. Shielding angle 30° cross wise. Open top improves maintenance and relieves brightness contrasts. MF's for slimline and high output units will be about 5 points higher. Maintenance factors: Good—0.70 Med.—0.65 Poor—0.60 Maximum fixture spacing = mounting height × 1.0	25/75	0.6	0.29	0.25	0.28	0.24	0.23	0.21
		0.8	0.38	0.33	0.36	0.32	0.31	0.29
		1.0	0.45	0.40	0.42	0.38	0.37	0.35
		1.25	0.51	0.45	0.48	0.43	0.41	0.40
		1.5	0.55	0.50	0.52	0.48	0.46	0.43
		2.0	0.63	0.58	0.59	0.55	0.52	0.49
		2.5	0.67	0.62	0.62	0.59	0.55	0.53
		3.0	0.70	0.66	0.65	0.62	0.58	0.56
		4.0	0.73	0.70	0.68	0.65	0.61	0.59
		5.0	0.76	0.73	0.70	0.68	0.63	0.62
3. Recessed downlight for general-service lamp. Lens and reflector provide moderately wide distribution. Maintenance factors: Good—0.75 Med.—0.65 Poor—0.55 Maximum fixture spacing = mounting height × 1.0	0/100	0.6	0.28	0.24	0.27	0.24	0.27	0.24
		0.8	0.33	0.29	0.32	0.29	0.32	0.29
		1.0	0.36	0.33	0.36	0.33	0.36	0.32
		1.25	0.40	0.37	0.40	0.36	0.39	0.36
		1.5	0.42	0.39	0.42	0.39	0.41	0.39
		2.0	0.45	0.43	0.44	0.42	0.44	0.42
		2.5	0.47	0.45	0.46	0.44	0.45	0.44
		3.0	0.48	0.46	0.48	0.46	0.47	0.45
		4.0	0.50	0.48	0.49	0.48	0.48	0.47
		5.0	0.50	0.49	0.50	0.49	0.49	0.48

Table 10. Coefficients of Utilization for Typical Industrial and Commercial Luminaries—(*Continued*)

Luminaire type	Typical distribution	Floor	10% reflectance					
		Ceiling	70%		50%		30%	
		Walls	50%	30%	50%	30%	30%	10%
		Room ratio	Coefficient of utilization					
4. General-service lamp in recessed downlight with spun aluminum reflector, fairly small bottom aperture, matte black baffle interior of housing. Maintenance factors: Good—0.80 Med.—0.70 Poor—0.65 Maximum fixture spacing = mounting height × 0.9	0 / 100	0.6	0.37	0.35	0.37	0.35	0.36	0.34
		0.8	0.41	0.39	0.41	0.39	0.41	0.39
		1.0	0.44	0.42	0.44	0.42	0.43	0.41
		1.25	0.46	0.44	0.46	0.44	0.45	0.44
		1.5	0.48	0.46	0.47	0.45	0.47	0.45
		2.0	0.49	0.48	0.49	0.47	0.48	0.47
		2.5	0.50	0.49	0.50	0.49	0.49	0.48
		3.0	0.51	0.50	0.51	0.50	0.50	0.49
		4.0	0.52	0.51	0.52	0.51	0.51	0.50
		5.0	0.53	0.52	0.52	0.51	0.51	0.51
5. Two-lamp, 12-in.-wide troffer for 40-watt or slimline lamps with clear configurated glass or plastic bottom enclosure. Maintenance factors: Good—0.75 Med.—0.70 Poor—0.60 Maximum fixture spacing = mounting height × 1.0	0 / 100	0.6	0.28	0.24	0.28	0.24	0.27	0.24
		0.8	0.35	0.31	0.35	0.31	0.34	0.31
		1.0	0.40	0.36	0.40	0.35	0.38	0.35
		1.25	0.44	0.40	0.44	0.40	0.42	0.39
		1.5	0.47	0.44	0.47	0.43	0.45	0.42
		2.0	0.51	0.47	0.50	0.47	0.49	0.46
		2.5	0.53	0.50	0.52	0.50	0.51	0.49
		3.0	0.55	0.52	0.54	0.52	0.54	0.51
		4.0	0.56	0.55	0.56	0.54	0.55	0.53
		5.0	0.58	0.58	0.57	0.56	0.56	0.55
6. Typical two-lamp, direct-indirect unit for 40-watt, slimline or high-output lamps. Metal louvers and metal or dense plastic sides provide approximately 30° × 30° shielding. Maintenance factors: Good—0.75 Med.—0.70 Poor—0.65 Maximum fixture spacing = mounting height × 1.2	45 / 55	0.6	0.24	0.18	0.23	0.18	0.21	0.17
		0.8	0.31	0.26	0.30	0.25	0.28	0.24
		1.0	0.37	0.32	0.36	0.31	0.33	0.29
		1.25	0.43	0.37	0.42	0.36	0.37	0.33
		1.5	0.48	0.42	0.45	0.40	0.41	0.36
		2.0	0.55	0.49	0.52	0.46	0.45	0.42
		2.5	0.59	0.54	0.55	0.51	0.49	0.45
		3.0	0.62	0.57	0.59	0.54	0.51	0.48
		4.0	0.66	0.63	0.62	0.59	0.53	0.51
		5.0	0.69	0.65	0.64	0.61	0.55	0.53

Table 10. Coefficients of Utilization for Typical Industrial and Commercial Luminaries—(*Continued*)

Shielding media for panels	Floor	10% reflectance*	
	Ceiling	80% reflectance	
	Walls	50%	30%
	Room ratio	Coefficient of utilization	
7. Diffusing plastic panels, usually acrylic or vinyl	0.6	0.19	0.14
	0.8	0.26	0.20
	1.0	0.32	0.25
	1.25	0.38	0.31
	1.5	0.43	0.39
	2.0	0.50	0.43
	2.5	0.55	0.49
	3.0	0.58	0.53
	4.0	0.62	0.59
	5.0	0.67	0.63
8. Clear, configurated glass or plastic brightness-controlling panels	0.6	0.22	0.17
	0.8	0.29	0.24
	1.0	0.35	0.29
	1.25	0.42	0.35
	1.5	0.46	0.40
	2.0	0.53	0.46
	2.5	0.57	0.52
	3.0	0.61	0.56
	4.0	0.65	0.61
	5.0	0.68	0.64

where H is the room height, ft, L is the room length, ft, W is the room width, ft.

Foot-candles (fc) by the lumen method formula is

$$\text{fc} = \frac{(\text{no. luminaires} \times \text{lamps per luminaire} \times \text{lumens per lamp}) \times (MF) \times (CU)}{\text{area, sq ft}}$$

After the desired foot-candle levels are determined and a luminaire type is selected, the number of luminaires is calculated. A layout is made utilizing the number of luminaires, adding or deducting those necessary to make a symmetrical and acceptable pattern. The revised quantity is then used to recalculate the foot-candle level and to determine the adequacy of the final layout. Care must be taken in a luminaire layout not to exceed the maximum fixture spacings (see Table 10 and Figs. 14 and 15).

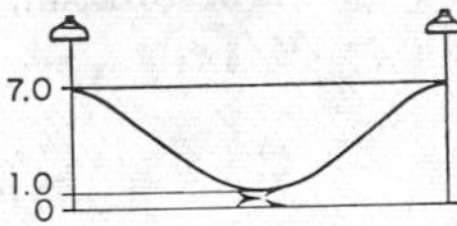

FIG. 14. Non-uniform illumination resulting from wide spacing of units.

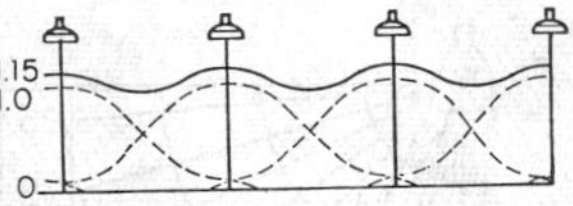

FIG. 15. Uniform illumination distribution.

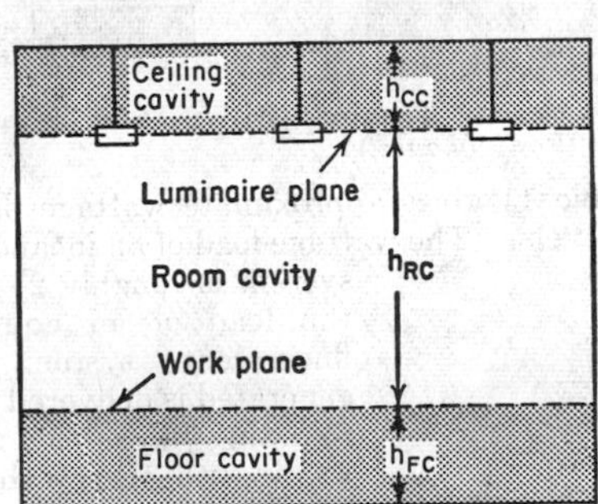

FIG. 16. Ceiling, room and floor cavity zones. (*IES.*)

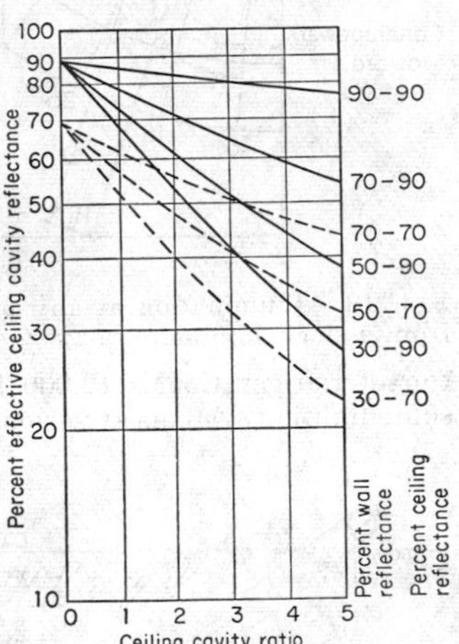

FIG. 17. Selected effective cavity reflectance curves. (*Holophane.*)

The **zonal cavity method** requires the use of data increasingly provided by equipment manufacturers. The **cavity ratio** is a prime variable defined by

$$\text{Cavity ratio} = \frac{5h(L + W)}{L \times W}$$

where h is the appropriate height of the particular cavity under consideration, *i.e.*, ceiling (h_{CC}), room (h_{RC}), or floor (h_{FC}) (Fig. 16); L is the room length, and W is the room width; all in feet. Data such as that shown in Fig. 17 enable the determination of effective cavity reflectances and coefficients of utilization. The procedure then utilizes the lumen formula as with the standard method.

The calculations of the **point-by-point method** utilize a distribution curve (Fig. 18); are based upon the inverse square law; and are valid only for the point in consideration. The illumination E, in fc, at P, and normal to SP, at distance D, ft, is $E = I/D^2$, where I is the luminous intensity or candlepower in the direction SP. The illumination on a surface is proportional to the cosine of the angle of the ray with the normal to the surface, the illumination at P, but normal to

$$OP = I \cos PSO/D^2 = I \cos^3 PSO/h^2$$

Heat from Lighting

(See also p. 12–126)

Lighting installations are a substantial source of heat; have long been a factor in the design of air-conditioning (cooling) systems; and are increasingly significant in the design of heating systems. The heating effect for 1 watt is 3.413 Btuh, and for 1 ton of refrigeration is 12,000 Btuh. Table 11 gives approximate wattage data for some lighting systems at various lighting levels. The wattage load of an incandescent system is roughly 2½ times the load of an equivalent fluorescent system. Heat generated is delivered to surrounding areas in several ways, with energy distribution for fluorescent and incandescent lamps as illustrated in Fig. 19. With the prevalent high lighting intensities of modern buildings, it is essential to control the heat generated by a lighting system. Luminaires radiate approximately 25 percent of their energy supply into the room in the form of light and invisible radiation; the remaining 75 percent is emitted by conduction or convection. Substantial portions of the energy which is not radiated into the room may be conducted away from the luminaire by an air stream or by water flowing through a coil attached to the luminaire. In the heating season, this heat energy is delivered to the perimeter of the building for effective space warming.

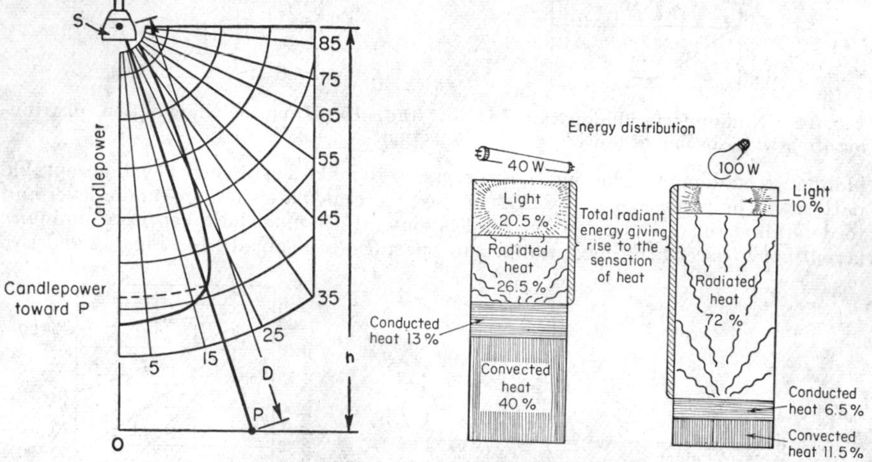

FIG. 18. Illumination at any point from a single luminaire.

FIG. 19. Energy distribution of lamps. (*Westinghouse.*)

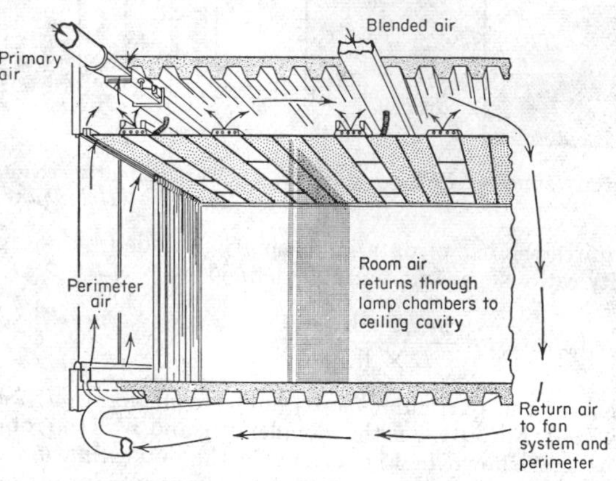

FIG. 20. Typical air-lighting system. (*Barber-Coleman.*)

In the cooling season, the heat is rejected to the exterior thus reducing the load on the cooling system. Air-handling luminaires (Fig. 20) are receiving wide acceptance.

Dimming Systems

The principal unit for dimming lighting systems is the variable-voltage autotransformer, positioned (1) manually or (2) by remotely controlled motors. The variable-voltage autotransformer has replaced the rheostat or variable resistance because of energy losses and poorer efficiency. Larger systems often use variable reactance and electronic power tubes. Filament and cold-cathode lamps lend themselves readily to dimming. Improved methods of dimming fluorescent lamps have been developed and require a dimming ballast for each lamp.

Table 11. Wattage of Lighting Systems
(AIEE)

Foot-candles	Coefficients of utilization															
	0.20	0.24	0.28	0.32	0.36	0.40	0.44	0.48	0.52	0.56	0.60	0.64	0.68	0.72	0.76	0.80
	Watts per sq. ft—50 lumens per watt, 0.70 maintenance factor															
10	1.4	1.2	1.0	0.9	0.8	0.7	0.6	0.6	0.5	0.5	0.5	0.4	0.4	0.4	0.4	0.4
20	2.9	2.4	2.0	1.8	1.6	1.4	1.3	1.2	1.1	1.0	0.9	0.9	0.8	0.8	0.7	0.7
30	4.3	3.6	3.1	2.7	2.5	2.3	2.0	1.8	1.7	1.5	1.4	1.3	1.3	1.2	1.1	1.1
50	7.2	6.0	5.1	4.5	4.0	3.6	3.2	3.0	2.8	2.6	2.4	2.2	2.1	2.0	1.9	1.8
80	11.4	9.5	8.2	7.2	6.4	5.7	5.2	4.8	4.4	4.1	3.8	3.6	3.4	3.2	3.0	2.9
100	14.3	11.9	10.2	8.9	8.0	7.2	6.5	6.0	5.3	5.1	4.8	4.5	4.2	4.0	3.8	3.6

Approximate Correction Factors for Some Typical Lamps

To find correction factor for lamps not listed here divide 50 by the lumens per watt of lamp (including ballast losses). Lamp lumen data can be found in the catalogues of lamp manufacturers.

Fluorescent lamps

Lamp type	Cool white and warm white	Deluxe cool and deluxe warm white
40 watt T-12	0.8	1.1
8′ slimline	0.8	1.1
8′ high-output	0.8	1.2
8′ 1½ amp extra-high-output	0.8	1.1

Filament lamps

100 watt	2.9
150 watt	2.8
200 watt	2.7
300, 500 watt	2.5
750, 1,000 watt	2.3

Mercury lamps	Clear	Phosphor-coated, better color	Phosphor-coated, higher efficiency	Semi-reflector better color	Semi-reflector, higher efficiency
100 watt	1.9	2.1			
250 watt	1.2	1.3			
400 watt	1.1	1.2	1.0	1.1	1.0
700 watt	1.0	1.1	0.9	1.1	
1,000 watt	1.0	1.1	0.9	1.0	

Economics

Table 12 gives a useful cost-analysis form for economic comparisons of lighting systems.

Table 12. Lighting Fixture Expense Analysis
(IES)

General information	Lighting method No. 1	Lighting method No. 2
Installation data:		
Type of installation		
No. of rows		
Luminaires per row		
Lamps per luminaire		
No. of lamps		
Watts per lamp (including accessories)		
Total watts		
Maintained foot-candles		
Calculation of complete expense		
Capital expense:		
Estimated cost of each luminaire		
Estimated cost of labor		
Estimated wiring cost per luminaire		
Cost per luminaire (luminaire plus labor plus wiring)		
Number of luminaires		
Total cost		
Assumed years life		
Total cost per year of life		
Interest on investment (per year)		
Taxes (per year)		
Insurance (per year)		
Total capital expense per year		
Energy expense:		
Total watts		
Average hours used per year		
kwh per year		
Average rate per kwh		
Total energy expense per year		
Lamp renewal expense:		
No. of lamps		
Average hours used per year		
Total lamp hours per year		
Rated lamp life in hours		
Average lamp renewals per year		
Net price each		
Replacement expense each (labor)		
Net price plus repl. expense each		
Total lamp renewal expense per year		
Cleaning expense:		
No. of washings per year		
Man-hours each (est)		
Man-hours for washing		
No. of dustings per year		
Man-hours each (est.)		
Man hours of dusting		
Total man-hours		
Expense per man-hour		
Total cleaning expense per year		
Repair expense:		
Repairs (based on experience, allocation of repair man's time, etc.)		
Est. total repair expense per year		

General information	Lighting method No. 1	Lighting method No. 2
Recapitulation:		
Total capital expense per year		
Total energy expense per year		
Total lamp renewal expense per year		
Total cleaning expense per year		
Est. total repair expense per year		
Complete lighting expense for year		
Complete lighting expense per foot-candle per year		

SOUND, NOISE, AND ULTRASONICS

BY

Benson Carlin

REFERENCES: ASA, Am. Standard Acoustic Terminology, 1951. Jour. of the Acoustical Soc. of America, 1929 et seq. Beranek, "Acoustics," McGraw-Hill. Carlin, "Ultrasonics," McGraw-Hill. Morse, "Vibration and Sound," McGraw-Hill. Harris, "Handbook of Noise Control," McGraw-Hill. Hunt, "Electroacoustics," Wiley.

Sound, Definitions. Sound is an alteration in pressure, stress, particle displacement, and particle velocity, which is propagated in an elastic material (ASA, Am. Standard Acoustic Terminology). It is longitudinal in gases but may also be transverse (shear) surface, or other types in elastic media which can support such energy. It may be reflected, diffracted, or refracted at boundaries and under suitable conditions may be changed from one form to another. In longitudinal waves, the molecules move in the direction of wave motion, in the others at right angles to it. Waves may also be plane or circular depending on the source.

The **velocity of propagation** V is a function of the elastic (Young's) modulus E and the mass density ρ of the medium. For longitudinal waves, in solids: $V = \sqrt{(E/\rho)[(1 - \mu)/(1 + \mu)(1 - 2\mu)]}$, where μ is Poisson's ratio; for shear waves, $V = \sqrt{G/\rho}$, where G is the modulus of rigidity; for surface waves, $V = 0.02\sqrt{G/\rho}$. In gases, the velocity is independent of the pressure, because the elasticity changes to compensate for the density changes; the general equation is $V = \sqrt{kp/\rho}$, where k is the ratio of specific heats and p is the pressure. The velocity in air at 68 F is 1,126 fps

Table 1. Velocity of Sound

Material	Sound velocity, fps	Density, lb per cu ft	Density × velocity, lb per sq ft per sec
Aluminum	16,740	168	2.82×10^6
Brass	11,480	530	6.08×10^6
Copper	11,670	555	6.47×10^6
Iron and soft steel	16,410	486	7.98×10^6
Lead	4,026	1125	4.54×10^6
Brick	11,980	125	1.5×10^6
Cork	1,640	15	0.025×10^6
Wood	10,000–15,000	30–50	0.3×10^6–0.75×10^6
Water	4,794	62.4	0.299×10^6
Air, dry, CO_2 free, 32 F	1,088.5	0.0808	88.0
Hydrogen	4,165	0.00560	23.3
Water vapor, 212 F	1,328	0.0372	49.4

Approximate values from Smithsonian Tables.

(33,160 cm per sec) and increases by 0.1 percent per deg F. In liquids, emprical formulas are easier to use than theoretical ones to predict actual velocities, since velocity varies in a complex way with temperature, pressure, and other factors. With sea water, a standard velocity of 5,100 fps (150,000 cm per sec) may be used. The velocity of sound in liquids and solids is usually much higher than in gases (see Table 1 and Kinsler, "Fundamentals of Acoustics," Wiley).

The **frequency** of a sound is the number of periods (cycles) occurring in unit time, customarily expressed as cycles per sec (cps); kilocycles per sec, kc = 10^3 cps; megacycles per sec, Mc = 10^6 cps. Sound frequencies are usually defined as 20 to 20,000 cps (**audible**), higher (**ultrasonic**), and lower (**infrasonic**). Frequencies as high as the thousand megacycle range (10^9 cps) are now being generated (see Table 2).

Table 2. Sound Spectrum

Frequency	Action
20–40 cps	Thunder
128 cps	Average speech (male)
250–2,750 cps	Telephone bandwidth
90–5,000 cps	Radio broadcast
15 cps–15 kc	Limits of average human hearing
10–90 kc	Ultrasonic cleaning
15–50 kc	Ultrasonic depth sounding, sonar
20 kc	Ultrasonic burglar alarm, control apparatus, door opening
30 kc	Highest frequency obtained by friction
40 kc	Highest frequency of Hartmann generator
48 kc	Bat cries
90 kc	Top limit of tuning fork
100 kc	Highest frequency of Galton whistle
500–15,000 kc	Ultrasonic pulse-echo testing
1,000 kc	Medical therapy
1,500–30,000 kc	Ultrasonic delay lines
15,000 kc	Radar trainer

The relation between frequency f and wavelength λ is $V = \lambda/f$. In air, at 1,126 cps, the wavelength is 1 ft. In nature, the waves may be simple sinusoidal, complex, or explosive (shock) depending on the source. The first is of course rare.

Attenuation of sound depends on the media of propagation and the frequency and is caused by absorption, spreading, and scattering. At audible frequencies in air attenuation is small except for the spreading of the energy over wide areas as the sound waves are propagated. By this means the intensity drops according to the inverse square law. However, in other media, the absorption, scattering, or other characteristic may be predominant.

The sound **intensity** is the average rate of sound energy transmitted through a unit area normal to the wave direction at the point considered. This is a definition of power and may be expressed in watts per sq meter. It is usual however to express power in **decibels,** db, which is a term used to give the relative magnitude of two powers by comparing the one under consideration to a standard. The sound-pressure level in decibels, db, is defined as twenty times the logarithm to the base 10 of the ratio of sound pressure to the reference sound pressure. All values are for air at 20 C and atmospheric pressure. Pressure measurements in air use a pressure reference (rms) of 0.0002 dyne per sq cm; 1 dyne per sq cm is used underwater.

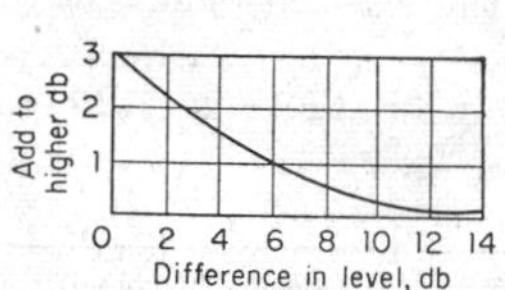

FIG. 1. Chart for the addition of decibels.

Intensity references for air are 10^{-16} watts per sq cm [equivalent to a pressure (rms) of 0.0002 dyne per sq cm, and 0.02 erg per sq cm sec, equivalent to a pressure of 1 dyne per sq cm]. Since the references are equivalent (*i.e.*, the reference pressure corresponds to the reference intensity in this particular case), numerical results are identical for plane waves using either expression $IL = 10 \log (I/I_0)$, or $PL = 20 \log (P_e/P_0)$, where IL and PL are the intensity and pressure levels, I_0 and P_0 are the reference intensity and pressure, P_e is the effective pressure, and I is the intensity in question. When making measurements with pressure or velocity microphones, it is the pressure level or velocity level which is measured and the relationship between the measurement and the intensity is unknown except in the special cases indicated.

Decibels do not add numerically as linear figures do; *i.e.*, 70 db + 70 db = 73 db since doubling power results in a 3 db increase in sound pressure. Figure 1 shows how to add decibels within 14 db of each other. If the difference is greater between two readings, ignore the weaker one.

Specific Acoustic Impedance. The relationship between the pressure and the associated particle velocity at a point in a medium is called the specific acoustic impedance; its unit is the kilogram per meter second or MKS rayl. The magnitude ρc is called the characteristic impedance of the medium, or the radiation resistance. This applies in the case of plane waves. The ρ_c of a material is one of its most useful acoustic characteristics since by means of it the amount of energy reflected at boundaries may be computed, horns may be analyzed according to the acoustic resistance at the throat, and other calculations analogous to those made in electrical design may be carried out.

The Production and Reception of Sounds

REFERENCES: Hunt, "Electroacoustics," Wiley. Mason, "Electromechanical Transducers and Wave Filters," Van Nostrand. Olsen, "Elements of Acoustical Engineering," Van Nostrand.

Transducer. A device for converting energy from one form to another, *e.g.*, from electrical to acoustic or vice versa, is called a transducer. Among these are loudspeakers, microphones, hydrophones, and piezoelectric and magnetostrictive transducers.

Loudspeakers are usually classified as direct-radiator or horn type. The direct-radiator type consists of a cone, a magnet, a voice coil moving in the magnetic field, a vibrating diaphragm coupled to the cone, and suitable supports. The attachment of a horn improves the impedance match between the speaker and the air since it is essentially an acoustic transformer. The dimensions and flare of the horn contribute to its matching ability.

One of the more common types of horn is exponential, although straight and other types are also possible. In a similar manner, mechanical transformers may be used to concentrate the energy of ultrasonic transducers. In such forms they operate to concentrate rather than to spread the energy. The operation of the speaker may be variously influenced by its enclosure, by the baffle which separates the front from the back radiation, or by its resonances.

Microphones (for gases) and **hydrophones** (for liquids) are transducers for converting mechanical to electrical energy. They may be piezoelectric, electromagnetic, magnetostrictive, or capacitive. The variation in electrical output is proportional to the effect of the acoustic field on the characteristics. Ultrasonic transducers may be any of the above types but are usually crystal (piezoelectric) or magnetostrictive. Among the common piezoelectric materials are quartz, barium titanate, lithium sulphate, A.D.P. (ammonium dihydrogen phosphate), and Rochelle salt. In sonar and high-power industrial systems, mosaics of crystals are used; in low-power, high-frequency systems, a single crystal is usual.

Whistles and **sirens** may also be used to produce intense sound fields in gases and liquids. These are devices which produce sound by passing a fluid over an obstacle, thereby creating turbulence in the fluid. When the obstacle is an edge, these are referred to as edge or E tones; when an orifice, as jet tones. Organ pipes, whistles, and nozzles for spraying are devices of this class. Frequencies up to 100,000 cps are possible, although 30,000 cps is the approximate limit at which appreciable power can be generated. Resonators may be placed in the sound field to reinforce it and to stabilize the frequency. These take the form of small pipes tuned to the approximate frequency. Common types of whistles are the Hartmann and Galton (for gases) and the jet edge (for liquids).

Sirens are devices in which a revolving disk with holes in it interrupts a jet from a nearby tube. Compressed air, steam, and water have been used. Frequencies up to 30 kc may be produced at efficiencies of 50 percent approximately; a one-horsepower motor produces between 300 and 1,000 watts (see also Jones, *Jour. Acous. Soc. Amer.*, 1946).

Transducers are generally driven by electronic generators, motor generators, or air compressors. As receivers, they activate amplifiers or indicating devices.

The Perception of Sound. The average young observer perceives sound between 20 and 20,000 cps. High-frequency response deteriorates with advancing age. The ear responds to a wide range of intensities; *e.g.*, between 500 and 5,000 cps, the ratio of tolerated intensities is about 10^{12}. The minimum intensity perceived varies with frequency. Figure 2 shows the audible frequency and intensity range for a standard listener, where the lowest curve represents the threshold of hearing and the top one the beginning of sensation in the ear. These curves show the pressure levels required for a given tone to sound as loud as the corresponding reference tone of 1,000 cps (see also Fletcher and Munson, *Jour. Acous. Soc. Amer.*, 1933).

Loudness is a subjective rather than a purely physical attribute. To provide a qualitative basis, the loudness level in **phons** is defined as the pressure level in decibels of a pure 1,000 cps tone which a typical observer judges to sound as loud as the sound in question. Observers can experimentally judge the loudness of pure or complex tones. However, this does not mean that the apparent level is proportional to its level in phons; *i.e.*, a level of 10 phons is not twice as loud as one of 5 phons. An additional expression, **sones,** defined as the loudness of a 1,000 cps tone at 40 db intensity, is necessary to compare various loudnesses. The relationship between sones and phons is shown in Fig. 3.

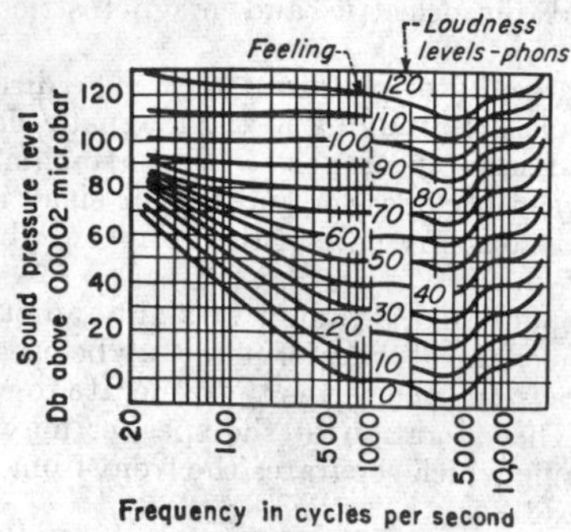

FIG. 2. Loudness contours.

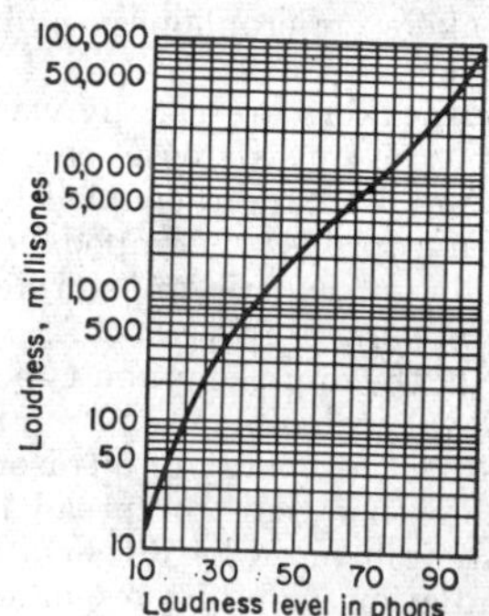

FIG. 3. Relation between loudness and loudness level.

Quality is a subjective attribute of sound in which equally loud sounds may be distinguished as to kind. Basically, differences in quality arise from differences in the distribution of energy in different parts of the frequency spectrum. In *music* this takes the form of the energy relationship of fundamental and harmonics; in *noise* it is random. These differences affect the sensation of loudness of noise and the psychological annoyance it produces. Shrill, high-pitched, and irregular sounds are usually judged less pleasant than low-pitched and regular sounds.

Among terms used to define quality are **pitch,** determined by frequency (mostly), together with intensity and wave shape (unit is the mel); **timbre,** determined by wave shape (mostly), together with intensity and frequency (see Seashore, "Psychology of Music," McGraw-Hill).

Masking describes the ability of one sound to make the ear incapable of perceiving a second one. It is measured by the shift in the threshold of audibility of the masked sound in decibels. The partial deafening of the ear by the masking effect of noise affords a direct quantitative measure of the interfering effect of the noise. If the masking is measured at several frequencies throughout the audible ranges, the overall pressure level of the sound can be computed. For any given frequency, the masking is expressed in decibels relative to the unmasked threshold for a **critical bandwidth** centered on the frequency of the masked tone. This critical bandwidth is that beyond which an increase in the pass band has little effect on the masking of a pure tone at its center frequency. Critical bandwidths vary from 40 cycles at 100 cps to 200 cycles at 6,000 cps.

Noise is an undesired sound (ASA Standard). It implies an unwanted disturbance in a useful band which interferes with the useful information. Any elastic structure may produce noise when set into vibration. Generally the motion is an unwanted concomitant of some desired function, *e.g.*, the vibration of a machine tool.

The term has a connotation of unpleasantness such as quality or loudness. Typical examples are gear noises, 60-cycle hum, motor traffic, hammer blows, pneumatic-tool operations, and hissing of gases in an orifice. Noise measurements are usually made with a **sound-level meter,** comprising a microphone, attenuator, amplifier, frequency-weighing networks, and an indicator or recorder. (Am. Std. Specifications for General-purpose Sound-level Meters, ASA Bull. SI 4–1961, and IEC Recommendations R123.) A **sound analyzer** indicates sound pressure as a function of frequency. In some cases electrical filters may be included which permit measurement in certain restricted frequency ranges. By using these instruments the components of the heterogeneous noise may be identified, and this helps to correlate it with its production. Once located, techniques for elimination follow, and the results may be used to compute masking. Individual frequencies may be identified by beating against a known source (**beat-frequency oscillator**) until a null is observed.

Contact transducers (**vibration pick-ups**) may be used to locate sources of noise, such as in partitions and machine parts. They may be piezoelectric or magnetic and may be used in place of the microphone or the sound-level meter; hydrophones may also be used.

Where the frequency distribution of the noise is significant, an analyzer may be used since the level meter tells nothing about frequency distribution. Analyzers are manufactured in various forms, *e.g.*, the octave-band analyzer, the impact-noise analyzer, and the wave analyzer, each of which uses a different method of finding out which frequency components are present.

Typical sound levels are shown in Table 3.

Table 3. Typical Sound Levels

	Decibels			Decibels	
	120	Threshold of feeling		60	Average factory
		Thunder, artillery			Noisy home
Deafening	110	Nearby riveter	Moderate	50	Average office
		Elevated train			Average conversation
	100	Boiler factory		40	Quiet radio
		Loud street noise			Quiet home or private office
Very loud	90	Noisy factory	Faint	30	Average auditorium
		Truck unmuffled			Quiet conversation
	80	Police whistle		20	Rustle of leaves
		Noisy office			Whisper
Loud	70	Average street noise	Very faint	10	Soundproof room
		Average radio			Threshold of audibility
				0	

Noise Control

REFERENCES: General Radio Co., "Handbook of Noise Measurement." Harris, "Handbook of Noise Control," McGraw-Hill. Bolt, "Handbook of Acoustic Noise Control," vol. 1, Physical Acoustics, PB 111200, Dept. of Commerce.

Noise control may be carried out at several stages (1) at the source, by design changes or by quieting procedures, (2) during transmission, by attention to the path by which it is propagated to the listener, and (3) by quieting at the listening position. It may also be controlled architecturally as by the careful placement of necessarily noisy rooms in a building.

The Source. By inspection and test procedures, a noise is tracked to its source. In some cases, design procedures which attempt to reduce the vibration or to prevent its radiation may be used. This may require the redesign of elements, such as cams, gears, housings, or provisions for cushioning. Viscous damping materials, *e.g.*, putty or tar, may be applied to the vibratory surfaces in the form of non-hardening plastic mixtures. A machine may be isolated by sections or shock mounts to prevent transmission of vibration from one section to another. Absorbing materials may be placed on walls to absorb sound after it has been radiated.

Transmission Isolation. If the vibrations of noisy machinery cannot be suppressed at the source, their transmission to the listener should be impeded. For the higher frequencies constituting noise, the most effective isolation method is the introduction of elastic discontinuities in the structure transmitting the noise (measured by the difference between density-velocity products as given in Table 1). The discontinuities may be obtained by the use of felt, cork, rubber, or springs in machinery mountings, or by the introduction of alternate lead and cork sheeting at masonry junctions. The isolation treatment should be applied as close to the source as possible in order to eliminate sound radiation from the structures transmitting the vibrations. Where this is not possible, the listening space itself may be isolated. Thus **quiet rooms,** constructed especially for noise measurements, are usually built as separate structures isolated from the main building.

Filtration. Some problems of noise transmission through air lend themselves to solution by methods of filtration. Typical examples are the transmission of sound in ventilating ducts and the noise production at engine exhaust pipes. In each of these cases, the steady flow of gas must not be impeded, but the alternating flow, representing sound transmission, must be effectively suppressed.

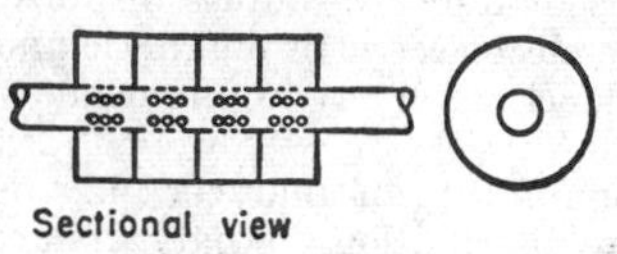

Fig. 4. Straight-through exhaust muffler.

For ventilating ducts, an acceptable degree of noise suppression may be obtained by lining the ducts (on at least two non-opposite walls) with an efficient sound absorbent for a distance of 10 to 15 ft from both the inlet and the outlet. Where the length of duct available is insufficient, or where additional noise suppression is required, baffles, covered with absorbing material, may be introduced in the duct. A plenum chamber, used to serve several ducts, should be lined with sound absorbents. If the air velocities are high, it may be necessary to introduce additional baffles at bends in the ducts to avoid noise production through turbulence.

Exhaust mufflers are usually modifications of the elementary low-pass acoustical filter, comprising a through tube to which closed cavities are coupled through small holes at intervals along the tube. Typical structures of this type (Fig. 4) produce little increase in back pressure and considerable attenuation of sound waves having frequencies above a cutoff frequency determined by the size of the holes and cavities. Porous packing, such as steel wool, in the side cavities or studied irregularity in the size and spacing of the cavities will increase the uniformity of noise suppression, whereas increasing the number of side cavities and the length of the muffler will increase the amount of suppression. Baffles in the tail pipe or irregular obstructions producing devious flow paths, *e.g.*, the stone-filled pit for stationary engine exhausts, produce muffling action at the expense of appreciable increase in exhaust back pressure.

Shielding of air-borne noise must be done by sound-opaque screens large in comparison with the wave length of the sounds whose transmission they are to impede. This is seldom possible in building interiors except by utilization of building partitions as screens. Sound is transmitted through such partitions principally by minute flexure of the wall as a whole in response to the incident sound pressure on the noisy side, with consequent reradiation on the quiet side. Reduction of sound transmission is obtained by increasing the mass per unit area of the partition, by constructing the partition of material having large viscosity for bending, such as Thermax, or by the use of double partitions, vibrationally isolated.

Sound-transmission loss is usually greater for high frequencies than for low and is measured by comparing the average sound level on each side of the partition under standardized conditions, as described in reports of the ASA Subcommittee Z-24. Average values of transmission loss, for frequencies from 125 to 4,000 cps, for typical partitions are shown in Table 4. In any specific case, a more exact measure of the effectiveness of an insulating partition can be obtained by direct comparison of the transmission-loss *vs.* frequency curve for the partition and the intensity *vs.* frequency curve for the noise. Additional data on transmission loss for a wide variety of building materials and structures are available in the NBS publications TRBM-44; BMS 17 and Supplements 1 and 2.

In general, double partitions (including floated floor constructions) provide greater transmission loss than equally heavy concrete, masonry, or brick walls but, except for special designs, less transmission loss than equally thick masonry walls. Double walls must be constructed carefully to avoid loss of vibration isolation through mechanical bridging between the opposite surfaces. Sound-absorbing fillers (e.g., mineral wool) are usually detrimental to sound insulation if in contact with both interior surfaces, and a single bridging nail may alter significantly the insulating efficiency. For maximum effectiveness, one of the wall surfaces should be hung structurally free at all four edges with the boundary cracks sealed, with felt or asphalt compounds, against sound leakage. Through piping should be made vibrationally discontinuous by introducing canvas or metallic sylphon sections, and clearance holes at the walls should be sealed. Sound leakage through small clearance cracks contributes to the low transmission loss of ordinary doors. Special self-sealing "soundproof" doors are required to maintain the effectiveness of an efficient sound-insulating partition.

Table 4. Sound-transmission Loss in Building Partitions
(Based on Sabine, "Acoustics and Architecture," McGraw-Hill)

Wall	Thickness, in.	Weight, lb per sq ft	Transmission loss, db
Wood	0.2	0.45	18.5
Plate glass	0.25	3.2	27.0
Hollow gypsum tile, unplastered	3	11.1	27.2
Brick wall, unplastered	....	22.0	33
Brick wall, plastered	6	46	43
Brick wall, plastered	10.5	93	49
Double wall; metal lath, ½ in. gypsum plaster, on staggered 2 × 4 in. wood studs	7.5	19.8	44
Double 3 in. hollow gypsum tile, unplastered, 3 in. air space	9	22.0	42.6
1 in. Thermax nailed over building paper to 3 in. Thermax laid up in mortar, ½ in. plaster on both sides	5	15	47
Double 2 in. solid-gypsum tile, unplastered, completely isolated structurally by separate foundations, 4 in. air space	8	20.4	59

Quieting. The sound level established in a room by a noise source is higher than that which the same source would produce in free space on account of successive reflections of sound at the walls. It is the function of **quieting** to avoid such enhancement of noise by providing a high degree of sound absorption at all interior reflecting surfaces exposed to the noise. Commercially available sound-absorbing materials may be cemented to flat surfaces or secured to wood or metal furring strips. They derive their absorbing property either from capillary porosity of the surface or from the dissipative vibration of surface layers. Hanging "functional absorber" units comprising vibratile matte surfaces, enclosing a volume of about 1 cu ft, can be used where surface absorbents cannot be installed conveniently. The effectiveness of sound absorbents varies with frequency, usually being greater for high and intermediate than for low frequencies. It may be measured by determining the **absorption coefficient,** defined as the fraction of sound energy diffusely incident on the material that is not reflected, or by determining the **specific acoustic impedance** of the material. The measured absorption coefficient is not a property of the material alone, but depends partly on the size and mounting of the test sample and the size and shape of the test chamber; thus comparison of the coefficients for different materials should be based only on measurements made under identical conditions. Such measurements on a wide variety of materials have been made available by the Acoustical Materials Assoc. (Chicago, Ill.), although it is to be expected that the absorption coefficients effective in various practical applications may differ somewhat from the published values.

For ordinary noise quieting, the average of absorption coefficients measured at frequencies of 250, 500, 1,000, and 2,000 cps, called the **noise-reduction coefficient,** may be used. Typical values of this coefficient for representative materials are given in Table 5. In making quantitative estimates of noise reduction, the **total sound absorption** of the room boundaries may be computed by multiplying the noise-reduction coefficient of each different material present by the total exposed area of that material and summing up the resulting products. The noise reduction is then given by

$$\text{Noise reduction in decibels} = 10 \log \frac{\text{total absorption after treatment}}{\text{total absorption before treatment}}$$

Table 5. Sound-absorption Coefficients

This tabulation is based on *Bull.* XI (1949), Acoustical Materials Assoc. All samples were cemented to plasterboard for test, except that the Sanacoustical unit is attached to wood furring with special clips, and the duct linings are laid on 24 gage sheet iron, nailed to 1 × 3 in. wood furring, 24 in. O.C.

Maker, material thickness	Absorption coef at indicated frequencies						Noise-reduction coef	Weight, lb per sq ft	Surface	AMA test No.
	128	256	512	1,024	2,048	4,096				
Armstrong Cork Co.										
Cushiontone A, ¾ in.	0.10	0.28	0.66	0.91	0.82	0.69	0.65	1.05	484 holes per sq ft, 3/16 in. diam, ⅝ in. deep. Painted by mfr	47–28
Travertone, ¾ in.	0.06	0.23	0.78	0.97	0.84	0.80	0.70	1.20	Fissured, painted	48–58
The Celotex Corp. Acousti-Celotex										
Type C-9, ¾ in.	0.11	0.23	0.80	0.93	0.58	0.50	0.65	0.96	441 holes per sq ft, 3/16 in. diam. Any paint	46–132
Type M-1, ⅝ in.	0.07	0.21	0.64	0.86	0.93	0.83	0.65	1.31	676 holes per sq ft. 5/32 in. diam. Any paint	46–12
Q-T Ductliner, . in.	0.21	0.42	0.71	0.86	0.79	0.75	0.70	1.3	Unpainted	A48–10
Johns-Manville Corp.										
Sanacoustic, KK, pad plus metal facing and pad supports 1 9/16 in.	0.25	0.58	0.96	0.97	0.85	0.72	0.85	Pad 1.28	4,608 holes per sq ft, 0.068 in. diam. Enameled metal pan backed with wool pad	46–88
Fibretone, 13/16 in.	0.14	0.37	0.69	0.80	0.76	0.73	0.65	1.17	484 holes per sq ft, 3/16 in. diam. Any paint	46–124
Airacoustic, 1 in.	0.29	0.31	0.70	0.82	0.79	0.80	0.70	1.50	Unpainted	46–71
National Gypsum Co.										
Acoustifibre, ⅝ in.	0.10	0.16	0.62	0.97	0.81	0.73	0.65	0.56	441 holes per sq ft, 3/16 in. diam, 5/16 in. deep. Painted	46–137
Owens-Corning Fiberglas Corp.										
Fiberglas Acoustical Tile, plain type, ¾ in.	0.04	0.20	0.63	0.91	0.82	0.82	0.65	0.69	Painted	A48–99
United States Gypsum Co.,										
Acoustone F, 11/16 in.	0.08	0.25	0.76	0.84	0.78	0.73	0.65	1.35	Fissured, painted	46–50
Brick wall, painted	0.012	....	0.017	....	0.023	....	0.02			
Concrete wall or floor	0.01	....	0.015	....	0.02	....	0.02			
Wood floor	0.05	....	0.03	....	0.03	....	0.03			
Cork or rubber tile on concrete	....	....	0.03–0.08	....	....	....	0.05			
Glass	0.035	....	0.027	....	0.02	....	0.02			

Table 6. Noise Reduction

(Based on ASA Tentative Standard (1940) for loudness reduction)

Factor by which total sound absorption is increased by quieting treatment	Noise reduction, db	Percentage decrease in loudness, when original loudness level is		
		60 phons	80 phons	100 phons
2	3	18	21	23
4	6	33	38	40
6	7.8	42	46	48
10	10	50	53	57
20	13	59	62	67

When the frequency spectrum of the offending noise is known, greater precision in calculation of total absorption is obtained by replacing the noise-reduction coefficient by the absorption coefficient measured at the frequency of maximum loudness level from the noise source. Subjective judgments of the loudness reduction obtained by quieting can be estimated by using the noise reduction in decibels in connection with the loudness chart of Fig. 3. Typical values of noise reduction are given in Table 6.

In general, the larger the area of absorbing material introduced and the higher its noise-reduction coefficient, the more effectively the noise is reduced. No amount of quieting treatment can reduce the level of the noise received directly from the source. If full coverage of walls and ceiling is not possible, distribution of the material in several small patches is more effective than the same total area of material concentrated in one location. Similarly, the same area of material is more effective when applied to non-opposite walls and ceiling than when concentrated on either of these areas, and more effective when located near the edges and corners of a given area than when located in the center.

Industrial Applications

(See also Sec. 5)

References: Carlin, "Ultrasonics," McGraw-Hill. Bergmann, "Ultrasonics," S. Hirzel Verlag. Goldman, "Ultrasonic Technology," Reinhold.

Acoustic waves of high powers used in industrial applications are generally called **sonic** (or **ultrasonic,** when greater than about 20,000 cps). High-intensity sonic waves, in the 10,000 cps to the megacycle range (10^6 cps), are applied to many industrial processes. The effects seem to be a function of cavitation, heating, particle acceleration, short wavelength, and other characteristics of the waves. Application categories are (1) high amplitude, and (2) low amplitude.

High-amplitude waves are used in operations such as cleaning, welding, drilling, emulsification, soldering, chemical and biological applications, medical therapy, and sonar. The energy may be continuous, pulsed, or modulated, in various ways.

Low-amplitude waves are used in operations such as material testing, burglar alarms, delay lines, or medical diagnoses. Any wave shape may be used; basically, a physical characteristic of the waves, such as velocity, is measured.

Cavitation may be defined as the formation and collapse of gas- or vapor-filled bubbles. Most significant industrial applications, *e.g.*, cleaning, take place during the vaporous phase. The amount and force of cavitation is affected by the character of the liquid and the gas in it. The bubble collapse generates powerful local forces which cause the desired action. Levels of power in the liquid of approximately 3 watts per sq cm are required for intense cavitation and are dependent upon factors such as the liquid, temperature, and external pressure; powers as low as 0.3 watts per sq cm in water will produce a threshold cavitation (see also Briggs, et al., *Jour. Acous. Soc. Amer.*, 1947).

High-amplitude Applications

(See Fig. 5)

Cleaning. An ultrasonically agitated bath will erosively clean dirt from immersed articles. A high-power generator, usually electronic, produces sonic energy which is impressed on a transducer to drive the bath. Barium titanate transducers prevail, but magnetostrictive designs may be used. 10,000 to 90,000 cps are commonly used, with the lower frequencies generally more effective. Generator tuning may be manual or by feedback from the transducer controls. Power levels of 5 ± watts per sq cm are commonly used; size (depth) of the tank may affect the output; 50 ± watts per gal is a rough empirical relationship; cavitation must exist for effective, speedy cleaning. A proper cleaning solution must be used, *i.e.*, one which supports intense cavitation and also cleans (*e.g.*, water solutions of alkalines or acids, or solvents like trichlorethylene); temperatures between 120 and 160 F prevail. Among items commonly cleaned are jewelry (lost wax castings), eyeglass frames, lenses, metal parts, and watches and clocks.

Foaming of Beverages. Air content, which determines the life of a carbonated beverage, is reduced by foaming the bottles or cans before capping. Magnetostrictive transducers at 20,000 cps and 250 watts, in contact with the containers, produce enough foam from the CO_2 to expel the air. The ultrasonic power requirement is basically small, but the losses in the coupling dictate the use of large generators. Similar techniques and apparatus may be used for the removal of gases from materials and for chemical effects such as the acceleration of iodine reactions and oxidation.

Soldering. Some materials, such as aluminum, oxidize when exposed to air so that soldering is not possible. However, an ultrasonically driven solder-bath will cause wetting of the material with solder and tinning of the surface. Magnetostrictive units are indicated because of the temperature requirements, with external heating and high tin-content solders; pots, as well as irons, may be constructed. Applications include aluminum wire, foil capacitors, and the filling of holes in castings (see also p. 13–58).

Welding. Similar equipment (between 100 and 5,000 watts output) may be used to weld thin metal or thin-to-thick sections. Such units apply the ultrasonics in a shear direction with respect to the parts to be welded. The process depends primarily on the sonic energy, the clamping force, and the amount of external heating. Either spot or lap welds are possible, but in all cases one of the sections must be thin (see also p. 13–67 and AWS Welding Handbook).

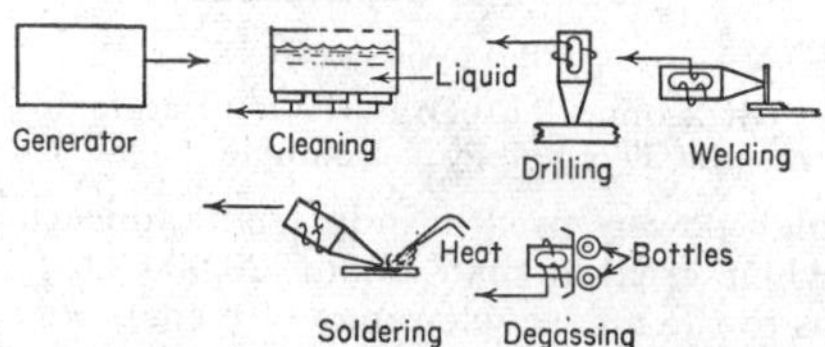

FIG. 5. High-amplitude systems.

Drilling is effected with the same sort of apparatus, but the force is longitudinal rather than shear. An abrasive is flowed over the tool head and is driven by the cavitation against the part to be drilled, causing the material to erode away. Any shape may be obtained in this manner. The head is usually mounted on a milling machine or similar apparatus. Tolerances depend principally on the physical rigidity of the system and on grit size. Applications include hard materials such as ceramics, jewels, and glasses. The same apparatus has been applied to dental drilling, but the time required and the necessity for use of a slurry has kept it from greater acceptance. However, the method is widely applied to cleaning the surface of the teeth. The technique has been applied to forming lesions in the brain and spinal column of human beings, using a focused beam of sound at $3 \pm$ Mc rather than a velocity transformer (see also p. 13–105).

A **whistle** may be operated in a gas for agglomeration or foam settling and in a liquid for emulsification. Ultrasonic fields introduce additional forces on particles suspended in a gas, causing them to come together. Materials such as smoke, dust, and fog have been experimentally treated in this way. Generally, the whistle drives a resonant cavity, generating about 150 db intensity (power output of $150 \pm$ watts) at 10 to 20 kc. Atomization of a liquid may be effected by introducing the liquid into a strong sonic field, either passing it directly over or through the whistle. The use of waves has been reported for drying solids, such as sugar, for atomically driven sound beacons under the sea, and for emulsification of liquid rubber and other materials.

Sonar. Underwater signaling and detection are among the older applications of ultrasonics and comprise the active (pulse-echo, Doppler) and passive (listening) systems. The principles of operation are similar to those of pulse-echo testing in the active case (see Albers, "Underwater Acoustics Handbook," Penn. State Univ. Press).

Among the **miscellaneous applications** of high-power ultrasonics is metal treatment, atomization of oil for burners, ultrasonic diathermy for bursitis, and ultrasonic neurosonic surgery.

Low-amplitude Applications

Testing Materials (see Sec. 5 and McMaster, "Nondestructive Testing Handbook," Ronald). The most common industrial use of low-power ultrasonic waves is for testing materials. The technique basically depends on the ability of a discontinuity in a material to reflect part of the energy hitting it. Various types of ultrasonic waves such as longitudinal, shear, or surface may be used. Transducers are usually crystal, such as barium titanate or quartz, and measure from ¼ to 1 in. diam (Fig. 6).

The basic types of ultrasonic systems are (1) pulse-echo, (2) through-transmission, and (3) resonance. The **pulse-echo system** uses a pulse ranging in length (time) from a fraction of a microsecond to several microseconds and an amplitude from 50 to 250 volts radio frequency across the transducer. The pulse travels in the material and is reflected by an interface; the time of travel is measured. The pulse-echo method has also been applied to medical mapping of the body interior and for tracing brain center-line displacement and heart valve action.

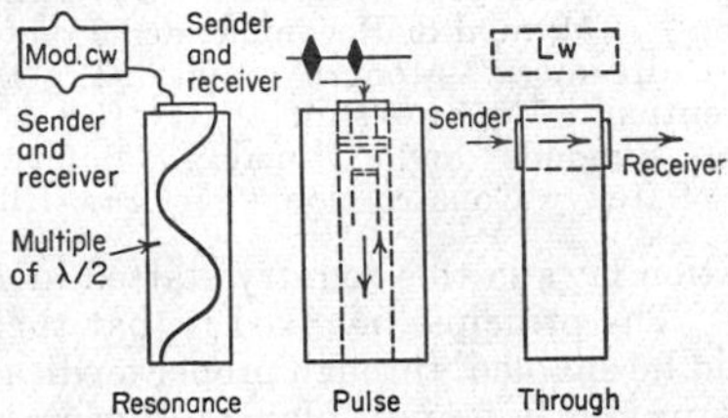

FIG. 6. Low-amplitude systems.

The **through-transmission system** places continuous pulsed or modulated waves on a transducer coupled to one side of a part with pick-up on the other side. If a flaw interrupts, the waves do not penetrate the part.

The **resonance system** uses a single transducer and varies the frequency applied to it. Within the applied frequencies is one whose wavelength is related to the thickness of the part in such a way that less power is required of the driving system. This condition is indicated, and since the wavelength within the material is known, the thickness is determined. The most common applications of the resonance system are (1) for thickness measurement when one side only is available, and (2) for finding laminations in thin sections and lack of bond (see also p. 5–110).

The **sonic burglar alarm** depends on the Doppler shift caused in a sonic field by a moving object. The unit operates at 20 kc and will find minimum objects of 0.03 sq ft in an enclosure of 100 sq ft. Magnetostrictive transducers are used coupled to diaphragms; they are not unlike radio speaker systems in appearance.

Liquid-level Sensors. Ultrasonic devices may be used to measure the level of liquid in a tank either by the pulse-echo technique or by indicating the transducer lead, *i.e.*, a transducer driven by an oscillator where the reaction of the liquid load causes a change in the driving current.

Sonic microscopes are devices in which a beam of sound illuminates a part; the shadows of the field are scanned on a cathode-ray tube (usually constructed of barium titanate) by a flying spot.

PREVENTION OF ACCIDENTS

BY

Ralph R. Meigs and Stephen F. Kimball

REFERENCES: "Accident Prevention Manual for Industrial Operations," National Safety Council. "Manual of Accident Prevention in Construction," Associated General Contractors of America, Inc. American Conference of Governmental Industrial Hygienl ists, "Industrial Ventilation—A Manual of Recommended Practice." Blake, "Industria-Safety," Prentice-Hall. DeReamer, "Modern Safety Practices," Wiley. Heinrich, "Industrial Accident Prevention," McGraw-Hill. Patty (Ed.), "Industrial Hygiene and Toxicology," Interscience. Simonds and Grimaldi, "Safety Management," Irwin. Stubbs (Ed.), "Handbook of Heavy Construction," McGraw-Hill.

Workmen's compensation laws in this country started in 1911 and have now been enacted in all the states. The principle involved is that the workingman injured or disabled in industry should be enabled, through proper medical treatment, to return to wage-earning capacity as promptly as possible and, during his period of incapacity, should receive compensation in lieu of wages, regardless of fault. The expense of medical treatment and compensation should properly be borne by industry and become a part of the cost of its products. The laws generally provide that workmen injured in industry shall be furnished the necessary medical treatment, and, in addition, compensation based on a percentage of their average weekly wages, payable periodically. Dependents of employees killed in industry are likewise compensated (see Table 1).

Table 1. Types of Occupational Accidents, Compensable Injuries
(Based on "*Accident Facts*," 1965 ed., National Safety Council, Chicago, Ill.)

Source of injury	All disabilities, %	Fatal and permanent total disabilities, %	Permanent partial disabilities, %	Temporary total disabilities, %
Handling objects, manual	22.6	13.9	9.6	28.5
Falls	20.4	17.4	18.5	21.2
Same level	10.4	4.8	9.2	11.0
Different level	10.0	12.6	9.3	10.2
Struck by falling, moving objects	13.6	9.3	19.3	11.1
Machinery	10.2	3.1	19.2	6.3
Vehicles	7.1	20.7	7.1	6.9
Motor	5.0	18.0	4.3	5.2
Other	2.1	2.7	2.8	1.7
Stepping on, striking against objects	6.9	2.3	5.6	7.6
Hand tools	6.1	1.5	8.1	5.3
Electricity, heat, explosives	2.5	7.7	2.2	2.6
Harmful substances	2.5	8.2	1.1	3.0
Elevators, hoists, conveyors	2.2	3.6	3.8	1.5
Engines, motors	0.4	0.7	0.7	0.2
Other	5.5	11.6	4.8	5.8
Total	100.0	100.0	100.0	100.0

Many states have supplemented their workmen's compensation laws by providing comparable benefits in cases of incapacity or death due to occupational disease. Some states make these provisions applicable only in case of specified occupational diseases; others make them of general application to cases of any disease directly attributable to the employment. At the present time, all states and the District of Columbia provide for compensation benefits in occupational-disease cases either by enlarging the scope of the workmen's compensation law, by separate legislative enactment, or by judicial construction.

The enactment of workmen's compensation laws has been followed in many jurisdictions by more stringent provisions relating to factory inspections for the prevention of accidents in industry and of occupational disease.

The enactment of workmen's compensation and occupational-disease laws has increased materially the cost of insurance to industry. The increased cost and the certainty with which it is applied have put a premium on accident-prevention work. This cost can be materially reduced by the installation of safety devices. Experience has shown that approximately 80 percent of all industrial accidents are preventable.

The logical time to install safety devices is when new machines are being built, while general construction work is being done, or when alterations or repairs are being made; results can be accomplished with a minimum of expense and delay at the time plans and specifications are being prepared.

Checking for Safety. In order to make sure that the question of safety will not be overlooked, it is well to have all plans, specifications, and drawings checked for safety, making special provision for this in each set of specifications and in the title plate of each drawing.

BUILDINGS

Plant Arrangement. A fundamental factor in effective accident prevention is the provision of ample ground space in the plant site to reduce crowding of buildings, congestion of plant traffic, unusual fire hazards, unsafe yard conditions, etc. One-story buildings have definite advantages in regard to fire hazards, building collapse, and natural lighting.

Where a plant is located near a main line of a railroad, consideration for safe access by employees and vehicular traffic should be given serious attention. Safe passageways from one building to another are also important. Blind corners, doorways opening onto yard railway tracks, etc., should be avoided as much as possible, and, where such conditions must necessarily exist, safety railings, gates, signs, or gongs should be installed to warn pedestrians of danger.

Because of their inherent hazards of fire and explosion, the storage, handling, and utilization of *flammable liquids* should be carefully controlled. The National Fire Codes, promulgated by the NFPA, are considered authoritative in establishing minimum safeguards necessary to control these hazards. It is necessary in any event to conform to the requirements of any applicable state and local code.

Buildings in which **dusty operations** are carried on should be so designed as to present a minimum area of projections, ledges, and resting places for dust accumulations.

Floors, Stairways, Aisles, etc. Probably the most important factor to be considered in connection with floors, stairways, etc., concerns **slipperiness.** Floors and stairs should be free from projecting nails, boltheads, etc., as noiseless as possible, wear well, and be strong enough to carry safely any static or moving load. The weight of modern industrial machinery and material handling equipment should be carefully considered in checking floor-load calculations. Floors and stairways should be kept clear of unnecessary obstructions over which workmen may trip.

Spilling of oil, water, acid, etc., should be prevented to eliminate slipping hazards. Splash guards, drip collectors, etc., can be designed in many instances to reduce slippage. Excessive spillage of dusty materials onto the floor is sometimes taken care of by installing floor gratings beneath which pits or conveyor systems are located to collect the falling material.

Ample aisle space is very important, especially in foundries where men carry ladles of molten metal and where there is considerable shop traffic involving power-driven trucks, etc. Aisles should be clearly marked off to assist in keeping them clear. One-way traffic is often advantageous.

Stairways should be provided with **handrails** on both sides, and an intermediate middle handrail should be installed on stairways over 88 in. in width. Non-slip treads on stairs are desirable. Stairways should be adequately lighted (see p. 12–11).

Exits and Fire Escapes (see Life Safety Code NFPA). As far as practicable, all doors should open outward or with the natural direction of egress; they must not block passageways from other floors or parts of the building.

For factories, not less than two means of exit should be provided on every floor, including basements, of all buildings or sections; these exits should be separated in such a manner that they are not liable to be cut off by a single local fire. The location of stairways around or adjacent to passenger elevators is undesirable unless there is separation by fire walls.

Outside fire escapes are inferior to stairways as means of egress. Where they are used, they should be located on blank walls or arranged so that persons on them will be protected from flames issuing from windows or openings underneath by use of wired glass in standard metal frames, fire doors, etc. Outside fire escapes, to provide maximum protection for persons using them during fire, should be enclosed in non-combustible towers which will protect against weather, smoke, or fire, with access through or over some intermediate balcony or structure to the building proper.

Lighting (see p. 12–154). Adequate light has a definite bearing on the prevention of accidents. Workrooms should be well lighted to reduce eye strain and the possibility of permanent eye impairment and also to remove any danger of employees falling over obstructions or being caught in machinery in darkened areas.

Ventilation (see p. 12–145). A lack of adequate ventilation in a workroom tends to bring on fatigue and reduces the alertness of workmen thus making them more susceptible to accidents. Where injurious dusts or noxious vapors are encountered, it is necessary to provide for their removal by the installation of adequate local exhaust systems (see p. 12–147 and ACGIH "Industrial Ventilation" and ASA Standard, "Fundamentals Governing the Design and Operation of Local Exhaust Systems").

Identification of Piping (see p. 8–252). It is desirable that a plan of identifying the contents of various pipelines be adopted so that in case of an emergency it will be possible to determine quickly the service of all pipelines involved.

MECHANICAL GUARDING IN MACHINE DESIGN

The most logical time at which to consider the safeguarding of a machine is during its design. In this stage, features of safe operation can be incorporated so that there will be a minimum of specific guarding required on the finished machine. The following points are fundamental considerations concerning accident prevention which should be taken into account in machine design.

Care should be taken in arranging clearances of moving parts to avoid shearing or crushing points in which hands or other parts of operator's body might be caught or injured.

Arrangements should be made so that adjustments, inspections, and hand lubrications can be done safely.

Machines should be so designed that the operator is not required to stand in an uncomfortable position, reach over moving parts, or exert himself in awkward positions.

Machines should be designed so that there will be little danger of the operator tripping over parts of the frame or striking against projecting parts during normal operation movements.

Careful attention should be given to strength of all parts whose failure might result in injury to operator.

All guards, covers, or enclosures should be designed strong enough to prevent the possibility of their giving way and permitting an accident in case the operator should fall or be thrown against them.

Point-of-operation Guarding. The point of operation on a machine is taken to be that zone where the work of the machine is actually performed and where the operator, by manipulating the material being processed, is exposed to a hazard from moving parts of the machine. Guards for point-of-operation protection are placed on the machines as additional equipment. The first requirement for a successful guard of this type is that it shall be convenient and not interfere with the operator's movement or affect the output of the machine. The following statements describe several basic principles which may be utilized in point-of-operation guarding.

Where possible, the **danger point** should be completely **covered** by a barrier or enclosure before the hazardous operation of the machine begins. This may be accomplished for example on a treadle-controlled machine by having the treadle operate the guard which when in proper location will in turn operate the machine.

Operator's hands may be kept out of dangerous positions by installing **starting devices** so located that, to operate the machines, both hands of the operator must be out of the danger zone.

Feeding devices may be used so that material to be processed is placed in a feeding mechanism at a point where there is no exposure to moving parts. Special holders or feeding tongs can also be used to place work in hazardous positions.

Electronic controls, which operate by the interruption of a light beam or other energy source to protect the danger zone, may be used to start and stop machines.

Electrical interlocks on guarding devices may be utilized in operating circuits so that unless a guard is in proper position the circuit is open and no current will flow until the machine is safely protected by the guard being brought into proper position.

Automation has minimized the hazards associated with the manual handling of stock and has eliminated the need for repetitive exposure at the point of operation, but the urgency of making repairs or adjustments introduces the need for special precautions covering maintenance work, such as locking out the power source.

ELECTRICAL EQUIPMENT

In considering electrical equipment for industrial establishments, it should be borne in mind that the **hazard** to human life **increases with** increase in **voltage,** and economy in transmission wiring and copper parts, which is achieved through the use of high-voltage motors, may be offset by increased danger of accident. For small motors, lights, and general service inside industrial plants, installations of 110 or 220 volts are recommended.

All **switches, fuse boxes, terminals, starting rheostats, motors,** etc., located within 8 ft of a floor or working platform, should be **enclosed** or guarded in such a manner as will prevent accidental contact with live parts, irrespective of voltage. **Switches** should be arranged so that they can be **locked** in the open position, to guard against a switch being thrown in accidentally while men are at work on the lines or equipment that the switch controls. **Equipment for operation at 550 volts and higher** should be isolated from other operating equipment, in separate rooms or enclosures, with provision for locking up these enclosures. **All metallic cases, frames,** and **supports** of such equipment should be permanently grounded; foundation bolts should not be depended upon for this purpose, but substantial ground conductors should be used. It is preferable to have these ground wires accessible for inspection. **All low voltage secondary circuits** of 300 volts or less (such as light, motor, and meter circuits) should be permanently grounded whenever a neutral point is available for the purpose. Secondary circuits of 250 volts or less should be permanently grounded even though a neutral point is not available. Whenever grounding has to be omitted, the frame or casing of the apparatus should be permanently grounded, and all live parts of the secondary circuit should be shielded to prevent accidental contact therewith. It is also desirable to have floors or platforms adjacent to switchboards built of non-conducting material, or suitably insulated. In the absence of such construction, rubber mats may be used.

Portable electric lamps, tools, and machines are subjected to severe operating conditions. Many electric-shock fatalities have occurred on electric portables, even with 110 volt lighting circuits. Cable used to service portable equipment should be high-grade rubber-covered cord designed for the service, not ordinary twisted lamp cord. Its mechanical attachment to both the portable and the attachment plug or source of power should be designed to prevent sharp bending or chafing that would break down the insulation. All portable lamps should have non-metallic sockets (such as rubber, composition, or porcelain). The heavier portable tools and machines cannot practically have their metallic parts insulated from contact by the operator, and protection from shock due to accidental charge thereon must be provided by means of a special grounding wire. Such protective grounding should be in the form of an additional wire in the cable that feeds the portable, one end permanently connected to the machine frame and the other connecting to ground through an additional pole in both the attachment plug and the receptacle to which the device is to be attached.

OCCUPATIONAL-DISEASE PREVENTION

In any industrial operation where a toxic material is being processed in such a manner that those persons engaged in or working near the operation are exposed to appreciable quantities of dusts, fumes, vapor, or gas, it is important that adequate control measures be adopted. The following statements cover the major considerations involved in the application of effective control to industrial occupational disease.

Contaminants. The physical and chemical characteristics of a contaminant should be known. In the case of dusts or fumes, the chemical nature, particle size, solubility, etc., should be determined. For gases or vapors, the composition, vapor pressure, flash point, etc., are important factors. In all atmospheric contamination, the quantity of material in the worker's breathing zone must be known before the degree of hazard can be evaluated. The chemical characteristics are important in the selection of materials to be used in the construction of any control equipment where corrosion, etc., might be factors.

A careful investigation should be made to determine accurately the sources from which the contaminant is being produced or from which it is being dispersed. The most common types of dust-producing operations are crushing, screening, grinding, polishing, etc. Dispersion of dust is encountered in practically all dry-handling operations of fine materials. Vapors and fumes are produced by chemical processes and reactions and are most commonly found in connection with the use of solvents.

A number of testing instruments and procedures have been developed for determining quantitatively the concentrations or amounts of various toxic material in the atmosphere of a work room (see ACGIH, "Air Sampling Instruments" and reports of U.S. Public Health Service and U.S. Bureau of Mines; see also AIHA Hygienic Guide Series and ACGIH, "Annual Threshold Limits"). In general, the seriousness of any exposure involving a health hazard is directly proportional to the dosage (concentration and length of time of the exposure). Engineering control should be directed to the reduction of these two factors.

Local Ventilation at the Source of Contaminant. Removal by means of exhaust hoods, enclosures, etc., so located as to prevent the escape into occupied areas of any appreciable amount of contaminant at its source is the most effective method of control. For details of hood design, piping, collectors, fan characteristics, and for general principles of exhaust design system, see p. 12–147 and ASA Standard, "Fundamentals Governing the Design and Operation of Local Exhaust Systems"; AFS, "Engineering Manual for Control of In-plant Environment in Foundries."

Natural ventilation has a limited application in industrial occupational-disease control. It is important with a natural-ventilation system to maintain close supervision of adjustments as required by changes in temperature, wind directions, etc. Regular tests of air content should be made to check on the degree of dilution being obtained. This method of control is not recommended for exposures where severe hazards exist owing to extreme toxicity or high concentrations.

Isolation. Under some circumstances, the isolation of a hazardous operation, physically, or in point of time, is indicated. For example, a hazardous operation may be carried on in a separated room in which all contamination can be confined or it may be carried on outside of regular working hours when no one except the persons engaged in the operation will be present. By isolating an operation, the number of persons exposed to any accompanying hazard may be reduced to a minimum.

Process Revision. The possibility of substituting a less toxic material should be borne in mind; *e.g.*, high-boiling petroleum naphtha for benzol in rubber cements, thinners, etc.; dolomite lime for quartz in foundry-parting compounds. It may be possible to reduce the concentrations of objectionable contaminants and the time of exposure by changing handling operations, by substituting mechanical feeds or conveyors for manual operations, or by installing automatic machinery or controls so as to dispense with the presence of an attendant. An automatic temperature- or pressure-control device, in connection with a chemical process, may reduce materially the time of an operator's exposure as well as prevent the production of excess or undesirable fumes or gases. An enclosed feed-conveyor system handling dry material and automatically weighing it may be utilized to eliminate a severe exposure that would result from hand shoveling, etc.

Physical Hazards. In addition to exposures to toxic gases, vapors, dusts, fumes, etc., there are several physical conditions such as abnormal pressures, temperatures, and humidities as well as radiation (including ultraviolet; infrared; X-ray; α, β, and γ rays from radioactive substances; radiation from handling radioactive isotopes), all of which may in case of excessive exposure prove detrimental to the health of exposed persons. Evaluation depends on physical methods of measurement. Protective measures include shielding from radiation (see p. 9–167) and control of time of exposure rather than ventilation as in the case of atmospheric contamination. For monitoring for radioactivity, see p. 9–181.

Personal Respiratory Protection

Where it is not practicable to control an air contamination in the breathing zone of workmen by adequate exhaust ventilation, etc., and it is necessary for men to be exposed to harmful amounts of dust, smoke, fumes, gases or to work in an atmosphere with a deficiency of oxygen, personal respiratory equipment should be provided. Such equipment is not, in general, suited for prolonged daily use because of the inherent features of discomfort and inconvenience to the wearer. For emergency or temporary situations or until effective control of contamination can be developed and applied, personal respiratory protection should be given very careful consideration where harmful exposures are encountered (see "The Respirator Manual," prepared jointly by the American Industrial Hygiene Association and the American Conference of Governmental Industrial Hygienists).

The U.S. Bureau of Mines (Schedules 19 and 21) has developed certain standards for approval of respiratory protection devices. The equipment may be either (1) **supplied-air respirators** (hose type), devices that supply clean, respirable air through a hose line extending from a source outside the contaminated zone to the wearer; (2) **supplied-oxygen respirators** (self-contained type of oxygen-breathing apparatus), devices that supply oxygen to the wearer from a source of supply that he carries as part of the respirator; or (3) **filter-type respirators** which may be either chemical-filter respirators, devices that remove the harmful constituents from air passing through them by chemical reactions, absorption, and adsorption, including ordinary gas masks and chemical respirators; or mechanical-filter respirators, devices that remove the harmful constituents from air passing through them by mechanical filtration, including dust, mist, or fume respirators.

Safety Codes and Published Material

The United States of America Standards Institute publishes a series of USA Standards. A complete list of these Standards can be secured from the Institute's headquarters at 10 E. 40th St., New York, N. Y. 10016. State and local ordinances should be complied with wherever they exist.

The National Safety Council, 425 N. Michigan Ave., Chicago, Ill. 60611 publishes a series of Industrial Data Sheets and Safe Practice Pamphlets covering the safeguarding of industrial operations. The Council also prepares literature, posters, films, and other safety educational material. The annual publication *Accident Facts* reports current trends in accident experience on an over-all basis.

Various U.S. government agencies, such as the Bureau of Mines, the Bureau of Labor Statistics, the National Bureau of Standards, and the Division of Labor Standards, publish statistical information concerning industrial-accident occurrence and accident prevention. The National Fire Protection Assoc., 60 Batterymarch St., Boston, Mass. 02110, promulgates fire codes and publishes information of all types relating to fire protection.

FIRE PROTECTION

BY

Arthur L. Brown

REFERENCES: "Fire Protection Handbook," "National Fire Codes," "Fire Inspection Manual," National Fire Protection Association. "Handbook of Industrial Loss Prevention," McGraw-Hill. "Uniform Building Code," International Conference of Building Officials.

IMPORTANCE OF FIRE PROTECTION

The continued use or availability for use of facilities is the aim of all business, whether industrial, mercantile, professional, scientific, or educational. Destruction of or damage to the facilities cripples the attainment of their purpose.

Monetary compensation for destroyed property and for resulting lost profits can be obtained by the purchase of insurance. Reputation, good will, and other intangible factors may be irreparably damaged. Loss of life is not recoverable. Loss by fire is largely an avoidable, non-productive tax resulting from carelessness, ignorance, or incompetence. The annual fire loss in the United States, as estimated and published by the National Fire Protection Assoc., has increased quite steadily, and for each of the years from 1960 to 1964 has exceeded 1.5 billion dollars. The number of losses has exceeded 2 million. Building fires have made up about 80 percent of the amount of loss but only about 40 percent of the number.

Fire-loss Prevention. Neither insurance organizations nor legally established regulatory bodies assume the responsibility of management for conserving its own resources and operating its facilities safely, although they may detect deficiencies or a lack of compliance with regulations and may serve in a consulting capacity. Fire loss prevention is an indispensable element in industry and business. It does not exist without top management direction and support.

The designation **"fire protection"** usually encompasses the entire field of **prevention of loss by fire,** including both the causes for the occurrence of fires and methods for minimizing the consequences of unprevented fires. In the consideration of fire safety it is customary to include other destructive agencies such as some types of explosion, lightning, electric current, wind, earthquake, and some features of nuclear energy and radioactive contamination. Safety to life and the prevention of personal injury cannot be ignored.

Fire protection engineering is increasingly recognized on the professional level. It involves the application of basic scientific and technical principles to the reduction of loss by fire and other commonly associated hazards. The Society of Fire Protection Engineers has established a well-defined scope for fire-protection engineering practice. Fire-protection engineering is an essential element in well-designed buildings and in safe operating practices.

Limitation of Loss. With the increasing size of individual businesses it is difficult to limit values of property subject to a single destructive occurrence to an amount that will not be catastrophic to the owner or operator or to others having a financial interest. Principles and methods for preventing large losses by fire and other perils are well known to fire-protection engineers and, to a lesser but increasing extent, to architects and industrial engineers.

Sources of Fire-protection Information. Much specific, detailed, and technical information is given in the standards, codes, and rules of the National Fire-Protection

Assoc., Factory Mutual Engineering Division, Factory Insurance Assoc., American Insurance Association, Am. Soc. for Testing and Materials, American Standards Assoc., Underwriters' Laboratories, Inc., and may also be found in the procedures of many insurance companies and inspection bureaus.

The NFPA "Handbook of Fire Protection" and the Factory Mutual "Handbook of Industrial Loss Prevention" are especially comprehensive references. The most complete and readily available source of standards is the "National Fire Codes," prepared and published by the NFPA, currently in ten volumes as follows: 1—Flammable Liquids; 2—Gases; 3—Combustible Solids, Dusts, and Explosives; 4—Building Construction and Facilities; 5—Electrical; 6—Sprinklers, Fire Pumps and Water Tanks; 7—Alarms and Special Extinguishing Systems; 8—Portable and Manual Fire-control Equipment; 9—Occupancy Standards and Process Hazards; 10—Transportation. Many of the standards have been adopted by insurance inspection and advisory groups, such as the American Insurance Association, and by Federal, state and municipal regulatory bodies and have been incorporated into building codes and other regulations.

CONSTRUCTION

Building construction and the protection of buildings and their contents against fire are frequently governed by local building codes and ordinances and by insurance standards. When new construction or changes are planned, the property owner should have the advice of a competent fire-protection engineer and should consult local authorities and his insurance carrier to avoid delay and the possibility of expensive changes later.

Some construction features which have increasing importance in fire-loss prevention are (1) the trend toward large fire areas which present high values to possible loss and make manual fire-fighting difficult; (2) blank wall, air-conditioned, and artifically lighted buildings which interfere with ready access; and (3) mechanization of materials handling, resulting in conveyor systems that interconnect areas and in larger storage areas and high-piled stock which made fires difficult to extinguish. These cause increased cost of fire protection and emphasize the need for automatic fire-control methods, sources of dependable water supplies, and special extinguishing systems. A measure that should be adopted where practical is the use of outdoor, totally enclosed process equipment, with shelters provided only for control rooms, laboratories, and some maintenance functions.

Types of Construction. **Fire resistive** refers to types that withstand considerable fire without serious damage, such as reinforced concrete or protected steel. **Noncombustible** refers to any construction that contains no elements of burnable material but which may be structurally damaged by fire, such as unprotected metal. **Combustible** means structures entirely of combustible materials or having combustible elements of such character and distribution that a fire can spread and contribute fuel so that severe damage results. Combustible types of construction are frequently subdivided into (1) "heavy timber," also called "plank on timber," "mill" or "slow burning" this has masonry walls with floors and roof of plank on heavy timbers; (2) "ordinary construction" this has masonry walls with floors and roof made of boards on joist and is sometimes called "quick burning"; (3) "wood frame" this has all of its elements of wood, except that the exterior may be surfaced with a non-combustible sheathing.

Many types of construction have composite elements that may include combustible materials. Insulation, acoustic materials, and surface treatments may aid the start and contribute to the rapid spread of fire. A roof of interlocking metal sheets, with asphalt on its upper surface as part of a vapor barrier or as an adhesive for insulation or weather surfacing, can, if initially heated by a local interior exposing fire, furnish gaseous fuel through the joints to produce a spreading damaging fire. Owing to the difficulty and cost of protection, enclosed spaces at roofs, ceilings, in walls, and below floors should be avoided. Important steel structural members and steel supports for heavy equipment that may be exposed to severe fire should have heat-insulating protection.

Fire Performance of Building Materials. A wide variation in the kind and amount of fire protection needed is governed by the fire performance of materials used in construction and by the combustibility of building contents. Completely non-combustible construction avoids the need for sprinkler protection, provided that contents are also certain to be non-combustible. Knowledge of the fire performance of materials, based upon tests made by qualified laboratories, is essential before they are adopted (see also Sec. 6). Fire performance is in two categories, fire resistance and fire hazard.

Fire resistance measures the susceptibility of materials to damage by exposure to fire and is usually measured as the time period of exposure, without significant damage, to a standard fire exposure as specified by standard fire tests, such as "ASTM E-119 Fire Tests of Building Construction and Materials," and expressed as a **Fire-resistance Classification** in hours as, ½ hr, 2 hr, 6 hr, etc.

Fire-hazard indicators are also in two generally recognized categories. In both of these the system used by the Underwriters' Laboratories is widely recognized. The **listing** of specific appliances and materials indicates that the products comply with the Laboratories' test requirements, with particular reference to fire-preventive and fire-protective capabilities when the manufacturer's instructions and limitations of use have been followed. The **Fire-hazard Classification** of materials and products is related mainly to burning characteristics. It has a numerical basis determined by (1) flame spread, (2) fuel contributed, (3) smoke developed. A Fire-hazard Classification of 0 indicates a material with a fire performance equivalent to that of asbestos-cement board. A value of 100 corresponds to the behavior of red oak lumber. Building codes and other regulations generally prescribe limiting values for Fire-hazard Classifications.

Protection against Exposure Fires. Protection of buildings or other structures against fires in nearby property must sometimes be provided. A practical barrier against a conflagration is the presence of fire-resistive buildings along the exposed side. Usually the most severe exposure is localized, and protection against it may be provided by a blank brick or concrete wall, by wired-glass metal-frame windows, or by open sprinklers alone or in combination. The relative value of various safeguards against exposure fires has been estimated to be roughly blank brick or concrete walls, 100; tin-clad shutters, 60; wired-glass windows, metal frames, glass block (4 in. minimum thickness), 40; wired-glass windows, wooden frames, 20; plain glass windows, 5; additional value of open sprinklers with any of the foregoing, except blank fire walls, 30; open windows, 0.

Horizontal Cutoffs. Provide effective fire walls between important buildings, and subdivide large building areas in order to limit the probable maximum damage from a single fire.

Vertical Cutoffs. Enclose stairs, elevator wells, vertical conveyors, chutes, and other floor openings with adequate fire-resistive walls, having fire doors or their equivalent at openings to prevent the rapid spread of fire and heat upward from floor to floor.

Isolation of Hazards. Cut off hazardous occupancies by fire-resistive partitions or fire walls or, if the degree of hazard warrants, isolate them in separate buildings. Make provision for adequate ventilation and for explosion vents where needed.

Floor Leakage. Provide drained, watertight floors over large values susceptible to water damage.

Storehouses and Vaults. Provide suitable storehouses for large quantities of combustible raw stock, tools, and patterns, and for valuable finished goods. Provide reliable vaults for the storage of business records and valuable drawings.

Safeguards during Building Construction. A building under construction is more vulnerable to fire than the same building completed and in use with normal fire protection. As construction progresses, concentrations of readily combustible materials appear at new locations from day to day. So do many potential ignition sources—temporary heaters, welders' torches, riveters' forges, roofers' tar kettles, and workers' discarded matches or cigarettes. If fire starts, wall and floor openings create draft and help flames to spread rapidly. Many serious construction fires have taken place. Most can be prevented. Guard against cutting and welding hazards by proper supervision of operations. Plan in advance for effective notification of, and coordinated fire-fighting operations with, any available public fire department.

Start installation of the fire-protective equipment—including water supplies, yard mains, and hydrants—as soon as construction of the building starts. Make layouts for sprinklers as soon as building drawings are completed, and let contracts without delay. It is sometimes possible to arrange for limited temporary protection by providing connections for hose from the piping system which furnishes water for construction uses. Have hose and nozzles available as soon as the yard piping, hydrants, and water supplies are ready. Distribute ample hand extinguishing equipment throughout the premises, including contractor's temporary buildings.

Temporary Heating. Arrange any needed heat safely. Use coke as fuel for salamanders, rather than wood trash or rubbish. Oil-fired heaters, if well-designed and properly located, are safer. Unit heaters are still better and are recommended if an adequate steam supply is available. Locate salamanders or oil heaters away from woodwork or tarpaulins. Keep the floor clean and free from combustible material. Flame-proofed, water-repellent tarpaulins are available, and their use is advised. The tarpaulin–salamander–wooden-form combination has caused many serious fires, particularly in reinforced concrete construction work during freezing weather. Scaffolding constructed of metal, or of fire-retardant treated wood, largely avoids a serious fire hazard. Locate construction sheds a safe distance from a building under erection, never inside.

Temporary Storage. Keep combustible storage out of buildings under construction, as far as possible. Under no condition erect canvas tents or wooden shelters inside. A safe location and good fire protection are important for valuable equipment or machinery, delivered before the building is ready for its installation.

AUTOMATIC SPRINKLERS

Advantages of Automatic Sprinklers. Automatic sprinklers are the most dependable and effective means of fire protection. The advantages are (1) automatic sprinklers go into operation soon after a fire starts, and before it has gained dangerous proportions; (2) the automatic sprinklers that open are over, and in the vicinity of, the fire; (3) fires at all locations, including out-of-the-way places, are controlled as effectively as fires easily seen and reached; (4) sprinklers operate where fire fighters could not enter or would be driven out by heat or smoke; (5) sprinklers are always ready; (6) only sprinklers that are needed to control a fire operate, so that water is used to better advantage than from hose streams.

Where Sprinklers Are Needed. Automatic sprinklers are needed for complete protection where there is an appreciable amount of combustible material in either building construction or in building contents, *e.g.*, (1) throughout buildings having floors or roofs of sufficient combustibility to contribute to a spreading fire, whether or not the contents are combustible; (2) in wholly non-combustible buildings where contents are combustible, including the storage or use of flammable liquids; (3) in concealed spaces, such as attics and under low roofs, if they contain any combustibles, including heat insulation and exposed electrical wiring; (4) in vacant spaces beneath a combustible first floor of a building, unless the floor is completely tight, the space sealed against entry, and no possible sources of ignition are present; (5) in dryers, large ducts, closets, and small offices, unless there is no fuel for a fire in either the construction or the contents; (6) under wide storage shelves or work tables over 4 ft in width having any combustible stock, and under canopies over platforms where combustible materials may be present.

Sprinklers over Electrical Equipment. If the construction is fire-resistive or adequately fireproofed, sprinklers can generally be omitted in electric-generator rooms and over switchboards. If voltages exceed 600, it is generally better to replace combustible roofs or ceilings with non-combustible construction or to protect all exposed woodwork with metal lath and cement plaster, rather than to install sprinklers. Metal shields or hoods may be used to protect generators, switchboards, or other important electrical equipment from possible water damage.

Automatic-sprinkler Equipment. The responsibility for the design of automatic-sprinkler systems should be given only to experienced and responsible parties. Approval of preliminary layouts and working plans are usually required by municipal or insurance inspection bureaus before installation is started. Sprinkler installation is a well-established trade by itself. Standards for the Installation of Sprinkler Systems are given in complete detail in a publication under that name by the National Fire Protection Assoc.

Dry-pipe Systems. The ordinary wet-pipe sprinkler system cannot be used where subject to temperatures below freezing. A dry-pipe system must be substituted. In the dry-pipe system the sprinkler piping contains air under pressure instead of water. When a sprinkler is opened by fire, the air pressure falls and water is admitted automatically by the operation of a dry-pipe valve.

Special Sprinkler Systems. The deluge system is a special type of sprinkler equipment frequently used in hazardous occupancies, such as airplane hangars and storage areas for flammable liquids or materials, where a flash fire could spread before the regular automatic sprinklers became operative, and where the prompt discharge of a large amount of water over a considerable area is needed. The deluge system has sprinkler heads with the fusible element removed. Water is controlled by a quick-opening valve (deluge valve) operated by heat-sensitive elements distributed over the area protected. Piping and heads are arranged as in a standard sprinkler system, with larger pipe sizes.

Preaction systems are actuated by heat-sensitive devices which trip a controlling valve and admit water to the otherwise dry sprinkler piping before the regular closed automatic-sprinkler heads operate. The system has the advantage of giving an alarm before sprinklers operate. Accidental opening of automatic sprinklers or mechanical breakage of piping does not result in the discharge of water.

Deluge and other systems actuated by heat-sensitive or other special devices introduce additional mechanical equipment and lose the simplicity of the standard automatic-sprinkler system. Some additional skilled maintenance is required. Various arrangements for mechanically supervising the condition of such equipment can be provided.

Non-freeze sprinkler systems are small and are sometimes used in relatively unimportant locations where it is impracticable to provide heat. They consist of special piping connections to wet-pipe systems, with a non-freezing solution in the exposed piping. Glycerin is acceptable for this purpose. They should be limited to systems with less than 20 heads. It is better to provide heat, to connect to existing dry-pipe systems, or to provide small dry-pipe valves. Non-freeze systems are preferable to shutting off the sprinklers and draining the piping during the winter. No portion of an automatic-sprinkler system connected to a public water supply should be filled with a non-freeze liquid without determining that the arrangement will comply with water department health regulations.

Outside sprinklers are used for protection against fire from outside sources. Windows in outside walls present the most frequent problem. Outside sprinklers may be operated either manually or automatically. The effectiveness of these systems depends on the water-supply valve opening in time. They can sometimes be adapted to automatic control by a thermostatically operated deluge valve.

Types of Automatic-sprinkler Heads. Approved automatic-sprinkler heads are well standardized as to the rate of water discharge, pattern of discharge, and temperature operating characteristics. The essential elements of an automatic sprinkler are a nozzle, a closing device that is released at a definite temperature, and a deflector that produces the desired distribution pattern. Temperature ratings appropriate for the location must be selected. The ratings for normal atmospheric temperatures, not substantially above 100 F, are 135 to 165 F. Ratings for other ceiling temperature ranges are as follows:

Max ceiling temp, deg F	Sprinkler rating, deg F
101–150	175–212
151–225	250–286
226–300	325–360

Heads of higher rating are obtainable for ambient temperatures up to 500 F. Corrosion-resistant heads, usually wax-coated, are obtainable for use in corrosive atmospheres.

Sprinkler-flow Alarms. The flow of water from a sprinkler system may be made to sound an alarm which gives warning of both a fire and accidental leakage from the system. This alarm may be either a hydraulic gong or an electric bell, or both. If the property has no constant attendance, or if added security is desired, central-station supervisory service is available in many industrial centers. This service transmits water-flow alarms to public fire departments and can perform numerous other supervisory functions.

Location and Spacing of Automatic Sprinklers. As the purpose of an automatic-sprinkler system is to protect both building and contents, the water-distribution pattern and the quantity of water applied must be held within close limits. Sprinklers customarily are installed so that the discharge from one head is allowed for each 60 to 130 sq ft of floor area. The distance between adjacent heads should not exceed 15 ft. Spacing averages 80 to 120 sq ft per head with 8 to 12 ft between heads.

Recent developments in sprinkler-system design for the more severe hazards produced by high piled combustible goods or flammable liquids are leading to standards including a **discharge density** in terms of gallons per minute per square foot of floor area. In this consideration building contents, rather than building construction, are the determining factor. Densities called for have commonly been in a range of 0.15 to 0.3 gpm per sq ft of floor area. High-piled storage of combustible materials, such as rolled paper, imposes a severe hazard which may call for a water density of 0.6 gpm per sq ft, or more.

The number of heads, to be supplied through pipes of standard sizes, with ordinary hazards and reasonably uniform water discharge, is as follows:

Size of pipe, in.	1	1¼	1½	2	2½	3	3½	4	5	6	8
Max No. of sprinklers	2	3	5	10	20	40	65	100	160	275	400

Not more than eight sprinklers should be on one branch line on either side of a cross main. For deluge systems, with which all heads are open and must be supplied simultaneously, and for especially hazardous occupancies where a large proportion of the automatic heads are expected to operate, larger pipe sizes are required as follows:

Size of pipe, in.	1	1¼	1½	2	2½	3	3½	4	5	6
Max No. of sprinklers	1	2	5	8	15	27	40	55	90	150

WATER SUPPLIES FOR FIRE PROTECTION

(See also Sec. 3 for hydraulics, Sec. 8 for piping, Sec. 9 for engines, Sec. 14 for pumps)

Insurance companies or their inspection and engineering bureaus should be consulted concerning water-supply requirements for fire service. In addition to providing water for automatic sprinklers, the supply should be adequate for hydrants and hose streams. Common water supplies are public water systems, gravity tanks or private reservoirs, and fire pumps taking suction from aboveground suction tanks, rivers, or ponds. Two or more independent supplies are usually needed for larger properties. Strong, dependable public water systems alone are adequate only for small plants, of good construction, having safe occupancies, and not dangerously exposed.

The "primary" water supply automatically maintains pressure on the property fire system at all times. The "secondary" supply supplements it as needed. The **primary supply** should not be less than 500 gpm available at a pressure that will be effective for automatic sprinklers at the highest plant elevation. A **secondary water supply** serves several purposes. The most important usually is to provide more water, frequently at higher pressure than is available from the constant primary supply. A secondary supply is also of value in maintaining protection at any time the primary supply may be interrupted due to public supply deficiencies or to the necessity of taking tanks or reservoirs out of service for repairs and maintenance.

High water demands for special hazard protection, especially where large areas must have deluge-system protection, can seldom be met by connections to public water systems. Fire pumps and suction reservoirs can give the added volume of water at desirably high pressure for the expected duration of the total demand, which is made up of the anticipated sprinkler demand and an allowance for the number of hose streams likely to be used. Large airplane hangars, large building areas containing flammable liquids, or very extensive properties that could have a general fire, approaching conflagration proportions, can have an estimated total demand of 5,000 gpm or even more.

Gravity Water Tanks. The smallest gravity tank on a tower considered advisable for fire protection is 25,000 gal, which may be suitable for the protection of small properties. Water from tanks of such limited size should be reserved for automatic sprinklers only. Tanks of 50,000 to 100,000 gal capacity may provide either the primary or secondary supplies for large properties of moderate hazard. Tanks combining fire service and domestic or industrial supplies in a single structure are allowable, provided that the amount needed for the fire supply cannot be withdrawn into the industrial-use system.

Gravity tanks should be at such elevation that the bottom of the tank will be at least 35 ft above the highest sprinkler to be supplied. The bottom of large tanks, intended to provide water for hose streams as well as sprinklers, should be at least 75 ft, and preferably 100 ft, above ground level.

Pressure Tanks. Hydropneumatic steel tanks can be used for primary water supplies for demands of short duration, such as needed to bring automatic fire pumps into full operation. Under some conditions they can be used to facilitate the automatic control of the automatic fire pumps by providing a rapid drop in the control pressure. High cost and limited capacity deter the general use of pressure tanks.

Private Fire Pumps. Well-located fire pumps with ample suction supplies and capable of maintaining high pressure over a long period provide a very satisfactory secondary supply. Centrifugal fire pumps of approved design are in common use. Practically all new installations use centrifugal pumps driven by electric motors, gasoline or diesel engines, or steam turbines. The electric-motor-driven centrifugal pump is most desirable because of simplicity of control and operation. Gasoline-engine drives are used to a limited extent where other reliable sources of power are not available, or as auxiliary units in connection with other pumps.

Adequate suction and reliable power supply are essential for fire pumps. The suction supply should be sufficient to operate the pump at rated capacity for at least 1½ hr at the smaller plants, and an inexhaustible suction supply is desirable for good protection of the largest industrial properties.

An automatically controlled, electrically driven centrifugal fire pump is sometimes used as a booster pump when the public water is of good volume but too low in pressure for direct use in sprinkler systems.

Fire pumps are used in capacities of 500, 750, 1,000 1,500, and occasionally 2,000 or 2,500 gpm. The 750 and 1,000 gpm sizes are most common.

Fire-department Connections. For properties where the public water supply is at comparatively low pressure but adequate in quantity, fire-department connections to the plant fire-service piping can serve as a valuable auxiliary for pumpers to deliver water into the fire system at high pressures. In city properties, particularly, fire-department connections are usually a part of the sprinkler system.

UNDERGROUND WATER PIPING FOR FIRE SERVICE

Complete specifications or standards covering all of the main features of underground piping for fire service are given in NFPA National Fire Codes, vol. 6, "Sprinklers, Fire Pumps, and Water Tanks," and the Factory Mutual "Handbook of Industrial Loss Prevention." The "Handbook of Cast-iron Pipe," published by the Cast-iron Pipe Research Association, contains much useful information.

Underground Mains. Buried underground piping should be so located that hydrants and control valves are at a safe distance from possible falling building walls. A complete loop system around buildings or groups of buildings, with multiple supplies preferably connected at opposite sides and with prudently located division valves, affords the best hydraulic characteristics for heavy flows and for freedom from impairments. Pipe trenches should allow careful laying and uniform support for the pipe. Foreign materials should be kept out of the pipe. Pipe should be anchored at bends, dead ends, and branch connections. The system should be hydraulically tested for 2 hr at a minimum pressure of 200 psi or at least 50 psi in excess of the maximum static pressure if it is to be more than 150 psi. Leakage at joints must be less than specified amounts. Underground piping should be thoroughly flushed before it is connected to indoor piping. Pipe should be buried well below the deepest frost penetration as shown by weather charts. In the coldest areas a cover of at least 5 ft is necessary. In the southern states 2½ ft may be adequate, except that under roadways a greater cover may be needed for protection against traffic loads. Clearance to prevent breakage by settlement is needed at foundation walls.

Soil Corrosion. Rapid external corrosion of cast-iron pipe may be expected if the mains pass under coal piles, through cinder fill, or where pickling liquors, acids, alkalies, or salts penetrate the soil. Cast-iron pipe covered with heavy coating of asphalt, or Transite pipe should be used to offset soil corrosion in such locations. Backfill should be of clean sand or gravel. (See pp. 6–124 *et seq.*)

Type of Pipe. Pipe for underground use is usually cast iron or asbestos-cement. Ordinarily the working water-pressure rating does not need to exceed 150 psi. Representative specifications for pipe suitable for fire service are: "Specifications for Cast-iron Pit-cast Pipe" (ASA. A21.2 or AWWA C102), "Specifications for Cast-iron Pipe Centrifugally Cast in Sand-lined Molds" (ASA 21.8 or AWWA C108); asbestos-cement pipe should conform to "Tentative Standard Specifications for Asbestos-cement Water Pipe" (AWWA C400) or "Commodity Federal Specification SS-P-55/A." Specific approval from insurance companies or inspection bureaus is usually required for the use of asbestos-cement pipe (see also pp. 8–194 *et seq.*).

OUTSIDE HYDRANTS AND HOSE

Location of Hydrants. Where space permits, outdoor hydrants and hose provide a supplement to automatic sprinklers and afford means for fighting fires in combustible yard storage, in railroad cars and vehicles, and small combustible unsprinkled sheds. Recommended space between hydrants varies from 150 to 300 ft, depending upon the type of buildings and the character of outdoor combustibles. Hose for outdoor use, 2½ in. in size, is made of woven cotton or modern synthetic fiber and rubber-lined.

STANDPIPES AND INSIDE HOSE

Standpipe systems furnish the best means of obtaining effective fire streams in the upper stories of buildings. They are designed for small hose streams used by the occupants and for large hose streams to be used by public or plant fire departments. Outlets may be designed to supply both. In buildings of unusual height, standpipes are sometimes supplied by a series of fire pumps and tanks at different elevations.

Small hose is of particular value in areas with hazardous occupancies, such as opener, picker, spinning, and woodworking rooms. Hose should be 1½ in. cotton, rubber-lined, or unlined linen, with ⅜ or ½ in. nozzles. Spray-type nozzles are usually best for the hazards mentioned. The water supply should preferably be taken from a connection independent of the sprinkler piping so that hose streams will be available when the sprinklers are shut off after a fire or during sprinkler repairs or changes. Small hose, for fire service only, in locations of ordinary hazards, may be connected to wet-pipe sprinkler systems, but in no case should hose connections be made to sprinkler lines smaller than 2½ in. diam. (See also p. 8–252.)

SPECIAL FORMS OF FIRE PROTECTION

Special types of protection are adapted to the control of unusual hazards, such as flammable liquids. Equipment should be secured from makers specializing in the form of protection required, but such use does not supplant general building protection by automatic sprinklers.

Water Spray. A dense strong spray of water from suitably designed nozzles is effective for controlling fires in flammable liquids of moderate hazard, for unusually flammable solid materials, and for surface fires of ordinary combustible materials. Such a system may be most appropriate for the protection of transformers and other oil-filled electric equipment and for systems handling fuel or lubricating oil under pressure. The entire zone to be protected must be within reach of the strong spray. Water pressures of 50 psi prevail with properly designed equipment. (See also p. 3–55.)

Foam. Foams for fire control provide a blanketing action to exclude air and in some cases to give useful insulating effect. Foams are commonly designated as "chemical foam" and "air foam," depending upon their service or method of production. For flammable-liquid fires, foam is available for manual or automatic application with a selection of characteristics appropriate for a wide variety of conditions. The amount of foam varies from ½ cu ft to several cubic feet per square foot of surface protected. Rate of application and means of distribution largely determine its effectiveness. A sprinkler system, designated as "Foam-water," provides an initial discharge of very fluid foam backed up by a sprinkler discharge of water. Special **alcohol-type** foam is needed for application to alcohols, alcohol-type liquids, and organic solvents, all of which seriously break down the commonly used foams. **High-expansion** foams are receiving increasing attention and use. They are easily produced in a **high-expansion foam generator** by blowing air through a screen wet with a continuous spray of water having a bubble-producing additive. The foam is very light and fluid and can be applied to fill completely and quickly a room or other enclosed area of considerable size. One gallon of foam-producing liquid can form as much as 1,000 gal of foam. Ordinary foam-producing liquids yield only about 10 gal of foam per gal of liquid.

Carbon Dioxide. For (1) flammable liquids; (2) electric equipment, such as large enclosed electric generators; and (3) hazards where a space-filling effect by an inert atmosphere is needed, or where a non-wetting extinguishing agent is desired. Carbon dioxide for fire extinguishing is available in small cylinders for manual use; or in banks of large cylinders, or in refrigerated storage tanks for piped-extinguishing systems.

Dry chemical extinguishers and extinguishing systems are mainly used for flammable liquids and electrical fires. They are effective also on surface fires in combustible fibers. Multi-purpose dry-chemical extinguishers have special ingredients which make them suitable for fires in ordinary combustibles.

PORTABLE HAND EXTINGUISHERS

Hand-operated extinguishers and small hose are effective when employees are on hand to attack fires immediately after discovery. They are frequently used to put out the final vestiges of fires brought under control by automatic sprinklers. Common types of hand extinguishers are the fire pail and water; the hand pump tank; and extinguishers called soda-acid, non-freeze, foam, carbon dioxide, dry chemical, and vaporizing liquid. Dry compounds, applied by shovel or scoop from bulk containers, are available for fires in combustible metals, such as magnesium, powdered aluminum, zirconium, sodium, and potassium.

SECTION 13

SHOP PROCESSES

BY

CARL R. LOPER, JR., Associate Professor, Minerals and Metals Engineering, University of Wisconsin.

E. V. CRANE, Consulting Engineer, Chief Engineer and Research Director (retired), E. W. Bliss Company.

EDWARD A. FENTON, Technical Director, American Welding Society.

SEROPE KALPAKJIAN, Associate Professor, Department of Mechanical and Aerospace Engineering, Illinois Institute of Technology.

JAMES A. BROADSTON, Director, Logistics, Rocketdyne, a Division of North American Aviation, Inc.

RICHARD W. PERKINS, Assistant Professor of Mechanical and Aerospace Engineering, Syracuse University.

CONTENTS

FOUNDRY PRACTICE AND EQUIPMENT

By CARL R. LOPER, Jr.

WORKING METALS AND PLASTICS

By E. V. CRANE

WELDING

By EDWARD A. FENTON

METAL-REMOVAL PROCESSES AND EQUIPMENT

By SEROPE KALPAKJIAN

SURFACE-TEXTURE DESIGNATION, PRODUCTION, AND CONTROL

By JAMES A. BROADSTON

WOODCUTTING TOOLS AND MACHINES

By RICHARD W. PERKINS

FOUNDRY PRACTICE AND EQUIPMENT

BY

Carl R. Loper, Jr.

REFERENCES: Publications of the American Foundrymen's Society: "Cast Metals Handbook," "Alloy Cast Irons Handbook," "The Cupola and Its Operation," "Copper-base Alloys Foundry Practice," "Foundry Sand Handbook," "Statistical Quality Control for Foundries," "Symposium on Principles of Gating," "Time and Motion Study for the Foundry," "Patternmaker's Manual"; Caine, "Design of Ferrous Castings." "Ferrous Foundry Process Control," SAE. "Steel Castings Handbook," Steel Founders' Society of America. "American Malleable Iron Handbook," Malleable Founders' Society. Heine and Rosenthal, "Principles of Metal Casting," McGraw-Hill. Cady, "Precision Investment Castings," Reinhold. Marek, "Fundamentals in the Production and Design of Castings," Wiley. Cook, "Engineered Castings," McGraw-Hill. "Casting Design Handbook," ASM.

BASIC STEPS IN MAKING SAND CASTINGS

The basic steps involved in making sand castings are:

1. **Patternmaking.** Patterns are required to make molds. The mold is made by packing molding sand around the pattern. The mold is usually made in two parts so that the pattern can be withdrawn, the top half being referred to as the **cope,** and the bottom half as the **drag.** When the pattern is withdrawn, the cope is replaced on the drag, the imprint of the pattern providing the cavity which ultimately is filled with metal to form the casting.

2. If the casting is to be hollow, additional patterns, referred to as **core boxes,** are needed to shape the sand forms, or **cores,** that are placed in the mold cavity to form the interior surfaces of castings. Thus the void between the mold and core eventually becomes the casting.

3. **Molding** is the operation necessary to prepare a mold for receiving the metal. It consists of ramming sand around the pattern placed in a support, or **flask,** removing the pattern, setting cores in place, cutting the **feeding system** to direct the metal if this feeding system is not a part of the pattern, removing the pattern, and closing the mold.

4. **Melting and pouring** are the processes of preparing molten metal of the proper composition and temperature and pouring this into the mold from transfer **ladles.**

5. **Cleaning** is all the operations required to remove the **gates** and **risers** that comprise the feeding system and to remove the adhering sand, scale, and other foreign material that must be removed before the casting is ready for shipment or other processing. Inspection for defects follows, and additional processing, such as heat-treatment, surface finishing, or machining may be necessary.

PATTERNS

Since patterns are the forms for the castings, the castings can be no better than the patterns from which they are made. Where close tolerances or smooth casting finishes are desired, it is particularly important that patterns be carefully designed, constructed, and finished.

Patterns serve a variety of functions, the more important being (1) to shape the mold cavity to produce castings, (2) to make corrections for the characteristics of the metal cast, (3) to provide accurate dimensions, (4) to provide a means of getting liquid metal into the mold (gating system), and (5) to provide a means to support cores.

Usual allowances built into the pattern to ensure dimensional accuracy include the following: (1) **Draft,** the taper on the vertical walls of the casting which is necessary to extract the pattern from the mold without disturbing the mold walls. (2) **Shrinkage allowance,** a correction to compensate for the solidification shrinkage of the metal and its contraction during cooling. These allowances vary with the type of metal and size of casting. Typical allowances for cast iron are 1/8 to 1/12 in. per ft; for steel, 1/8 to 1/4 in. per ft; and for aluminum, 1/16 to 5/32 in. per ft; however, a designer should consult appropriate references (AFS, "Cast Metals Handbook"; ASM, "Casting Design Handbook"; "Design of Ferrous Castings") or the foundry. These allowances also include a size tolerance for the process so that the casting is dimensionally correct. (See also Sec. 6.) (3) **Machine-finish allowance** is necessary if machining operations are to be used in order that stock is provided for machining. Tabulated data are available in the references cited for shrinkage allowances. (4) If a casting is prone to distortion, a pattern may be intentionally distorted to compensate. This is a **distortion allowance.**

Patterns vary in complexity, depending on the size and number of castings required. **Loose patterns** are single prototypes of the casting and are used only when a few castings are needed. They are usually constructed of wood, but metal, plaster, plastics, or other suitable material may be used. The gating system for feeding the the casting is cut into the sand by hand. Some loose patterns may be split into two parts to facilitate molding.

Gated patterns incorporate a gating system along with the pattern to eliminate hand cutting.

Match-plate patterns have the cope and drag portions of the pattern mounted on opposite sides of a wooden or metal plate, and are designed to speed up the molding process. Gating systems are also usually attached. These patterns are generally used with some type of molding machine and are recommended where a large number of castings are required.

For fairly large castings or where an increase in production rate is desired, the cope and drag portions of the pattern may be mounted on separate plates, referred to as **cope- and drag-pattern** plates. These may thus be used on separate molding machines by separate workers and combined on the molding floor prior to pouring.

Special Patterns and Devices. For extremely large castings, **skeleton** patterns may be employed. Large molds of a symmetrical nature may be made for forming the sand mold by **sweeps,** which provide the contour of the casting through the movement of a template around an axis.

Follow boards are used to support irregularly shaped patterns which require an irregular parting line between cope and drag. A **master pattern** is used as an original to make up a number of similar patterns that will be used directly in the foundry.

MOLDING PROCESSES AND MATERIALS

Molding Processes

Green Sand. Most castings are made in **green sand,** *i.e.*, sand bonded with clay or bentonite and properly tempered with water to give it **green strength.** Miscellaneous additions may be used for special properties. This method is adaptable to high production of small- or medium-sized castings because the mold can be poured immediately after forming, and the sand can be reused and reprocessed after the casting has solidified.

Dry-sand Molds. These molds are made with green sand but are baked prior to use. The surface is usually given a refractory wash before baking to prevent erosion and to produce a better surface finish. Somewhat the same effects are obtained if the mold is allowed to **air-dry** by leaving it open for a period of time before pouring, or if it is **skin-dried** by using a torch, infrared lamps, or heating elements directed at the mold-cavity surface.

Core molding makes use of assembled cores to construct the mold. The sand is prepared by mixing with oil or cereal, forming in core boxes, and baking. This process is used where the intricacy of the casting justifies the extra costs involved.

Carbon Dioxide Process Molds. These molds are made in a manner similar to the green-sand process but use sand bonded with sodium silicate. When the mold is finished, carbon dioxide gas is passed through the sand to produce a very hard mold with many of the advantages of dry-sand and core molds but requiring no baking.

Floor and Pit Molding. When large castings are to be produced, these may be either directly on the floor of the foundry or formed in pits in the floor which serve as the flask. **Loam molding** is a variation of floor molding in which molding material composed of 50 percent sand and 50 percent clay (approx) is troweled onto a brickwork surface and brought to dimension by use of patterns, sweeps, or templates.

Shell Molding (C Process). Sand castings having close dimensional tolerances and smooth finish can be produced by a process using a synthetic-resin binder. The sand and resin mixture is dumped onto a preheated metal pattern, which causes the resin in the mixture to set as a thin shell over the pattern. When the shell has reached the proper thickness, the excess sand is removed by rotating the pattern to dump out the sand. The remaining shell is then cured on the pattern and subsequently removed by stripping it off, using mold-release pins which have been properly spaced and that are mechanically or hydraulically made to protrude through the pattern. Mating shell halves are then bonded together with a cement or by a suitable backing, and poured.

Plaster Molds. Plaster or plaster-bonded molds are used for casting certain aluminum or copper-base alloys. Dimensional accuracy and excellent surface finish make this a useful process for making rubber-tire molds, match plates, etc.

A variation of this method of molding is the **Antioch process,** using mixtures of 50 percent silica sand, 40 percent gypsum cement, 8 percent talc, and small amounts of sodium silicate, portland cement, and magnesium oxide. These dry ingredients are mixed with water and poured over the pattern. After the mixture is poured, the mold is steam-treated in an autoclave and then allowed to set in air before drying in an oven. When the mold has cooled it is ready for pouring. Tolerances of ± 0.005 in. on small castings and ± 0.015 in. on large castings are obtained by this process.

The **lost-wax, investment, or precision-casting, process** permits the accurate casting of highly alloyed steels and of non-ferrous alloys which are impossible to forge and difficult to machine. The procedure consists of making an accurate metal die into which the wax or plastic patterns are cast. The patterns are assembled on a sprue and the assembly sprayed, brushed, or dipped in a slurry of a fine-grained, highly-refractory aggregate, and a proprietary bonding agent composed chiefly of ethyl silicate. This mixture is then allowed to set. The pattern is coated repeatedly with coarser slurries until a shell of the aggregate is produced around the pattern. The molds are allowed to stand until the aggregate has set, after which they are heated in an oven in an inverted position so that the wax will run out. After the wax is removed, the molds are baked in a preheat furnace. The molds may then be supported with loose sand and poured in any conventional manner.

All dimensions can be held to a tolerance of ± 0.005 in. with some critical dimensions held to 0.002 in. Most castings produced by this process are small.

Faithful reproduction and accurate tolerances can also be attained by the **Shaw process,** which combines the advantages of the dimensional control of precision molds with the ease of production of conventional molding. The process makes use of wood or metal patterns and a refractory mold bonded with an ethyl silicate base material. Since the mold is rubbery when stripped from the pattern, some back draft is permissible.

In the **cement-sand process** portland cement is used as the sand binder. A typical mixture has 11 percent portland cement, 89 percent silica sand, and water 4½ to 7 percent of the total sand and cement. New sand is used for facing the mold and is backed with ground-up sand which has been rebonded. Cores are made of the same material. The molds and cores must air-dry 24 to 72 hr before pouring. The process can be used for either ferrous or non-ferrous castings. This molding mixture practically eliminates the generation of gases, forms a hard surface which resists the erosive action of the metal, and produces castings with good surfaces and accurate dimensions.

Permanent-mold Casting Methods

In the **permanent-mold casting method,** fluid metal is poured by hand into metal molds and around metal cores without external pressure. The molds are held together by C clamps or by a screw or toggle.

Metals suitable for this type of casting are lead, zinc, aluminum and magnesium alloys, certain bronzes, and cast iron.

For making iron castings of this type, a number of metal-mold units are usually mounted on a turntable. The individual operations, such as coating the mold, placing the cores, closing the mold, pouring, opening the mold, and ejection of the casting, are performed as each mold passes certain stations. The molds are preheated before the first casting is poured. The process produces castings having a dense, fine-grained structure, free from shrink holes or blowholes. The tool changes are relatively low, and better surface and closer tolerances are obtained than with the sand-cast method. It does not maintain tolerances as close or sections as thin as the die-casting or the plaster-casting methods.

Yellow brasses, which are high in zinc, should not be cast by the permanent-mold process because the zinc oxide fouls the molds or dies.

The **semipermanent-mold casting method** differs from the permanent-mold casting in that sand cores are used, in some places, instead of metal cores. The same metals may be cast by this method. This process is used where cored openings are so irregular in shape, or so undercut, that metal cores would be too costly or too difficult to handle. The structure of the metal cast around the sand cores is like that of a sand casting. The advantages of permanent-mold casting in tolerances, density, appearance, etc., exist only in the section cast against the metal mold.

Graphite molds may be used as short-run permanent molds since they are easier to machine to shape and can be used for higher-melting-point alloys, *e.g.*, steel. The molds are softer, however, and more susceptible to erosive damage. Steel railroad-car wheels may be made in these molds and can be cast by filling the mold by **low-pressure casting** methods.

In the **slush casting** process, the cast metal is allowed partially to solidify next to the mold walls to produce a thin-walled hollow casting where the excess liquid metal is is poured out of the permanent mold.

In **centrifugal casting** the metal is under centrifugal force, developed by rotating the mold at high speed. This process, used in the manufacture of bronze, steel, and iron castings, has the advantage of producing sound castings with a minimum of risers. In **true centrifugal castings** the metal is poured directly into a mold which is rotated around its own axis.

In **pressure casting,** for asymmetrical castings which cannot be spun around their own axes, the mold cavities are arranged around a common sprue located on the neutral axis of the mold. The molds used in the centrifugal-casting process may be metal cores or dry sand, depending on the type of casting and the metal cast.

Most of the cast-iron pipe produced in the United States is centrifugally cast by the **de Lavaud process,** which employs water-cooled metal molds. The U.S. Army produces gun barrels at the Watertown Arsenal by the centrifugal process. Other types of castings currently being produced are gear blanks, bushings, pistons, piston rings, alloy-steel tubes, liners, valve bodies, and sheaves.

Die-casting machines consist of a basin holding molten metal, a metallic mold or die, and a metal-transferring device which automatically withdraws molten metal from the basin and forces it under pressure into the die. Two forms of die-casting machines are in general use. Lead, tin, and zinc alloys containing aluminum are handled in **piston machines.** Aluminum alloys and pure zinc, or zinc alloys free from aluminum, rapidly attack the iron in the piston and cylinder and require a different type of casting machine. The pressures in a piston machine range from a few hundred to 5,000 psi. Zinc-aluminum alloys use about 1,000 psi. (See also pp. 6–84, 6–86, 6–93, 6–98.)

The **gooseneck machine** has a cast-iron gooseneck which dips the molten metal out of the melting pot and transfers it to the die. The pressure is applied to the molten metal by compressed air after the gooseneck is brought in contact with the die. The operation pressures average 350 to 500 psi, with a maximum of about 700. This machine, developed primarily for aluminum alloys, is sometimes used for zinc-aluminum alloys, especially for large castings, but, owing to the lower pressure, the casting is likely to be less dense than when made in the piston machine. It is seldom used for magnesium alloys.

In **cold-chamber machines** the molten-metal reservoir is separated from the casting machine, and just enough metal for one casting is ladled by hand into a small chamber, from which it is forced into the die under high pressure. The pressures, ranging from a few thousand to 10,000 psi and more, are produced by a hydraulic system connected to the piston in the hot metal chamber. The alloy is kept so close to its melting temperature that it is in a slushlike condition. The process is applicable to aluminum alloys, magnesium alloys, zinc alloys, and even high-melting-point alloys like brasses and bronzes, since the pouring well, cylinder, and piston are exposed to the high temperature for only a short time. The production rates are lower than those obtained with the piston or gooseneck machines.

All metal-mold external-pressure castings have close tolerances, sharp outlines and contours, fine smooth surface, and high rate of production, with low labor cost. They have a hard skin, owing to the rapid chilling of the surface of the casting from the metal mold and a softer core.

The dies usually consist of two blocks of steel, each containing a part of the cavity, which are locked together while the casting is being made and drawn apart when it is ready for ejection. One-half of the die (next to the ejector nozzle) is stationary; the other half moves on a carriage. The dies are preheated before using and are either air- or water-cooled to maintain the desired operating temperature. Die life varies with the alloy and dimensional tolerances required. Retractable and removable metal cores are used to form internal surfaces. Inserts can be cast into the piece by placing them on locating pins in the die.

A wide range of sizes and shapes can be made by these processes, including threaded pieces and gears. Holes can be accurately located. The process is best suited to large-quantity production.

Table 1. Design and Cost Features of Basic Casting Methods
(Cook, "Engineered Castings," McGraw-Hill)

Design and cost features	Process					
	Sand casting	Shell-mold casting	Permanent-mold casting	Plaster-mold casting	Investment casting	Die casting
Choice of materials	Wide—ferrous and non-ferfous	Wide—except for low-carbon steels	Restricted—brass, bronze, aluminum, some gray iron	Narrow—brass, bronze, aluminum	Wide—includes hard-to-forge and machine materials	Narrow—zinc, aluminum, brass, magnesium
Complexity	Considerable	Moderate	Moderate	Considerable	Greatest	Considerable
Size range	Great	Limited	Moderate	Moderate	Moderate	Moderate
Minimum section, in.	3/32	1/16	0.100	0.010	0.010	0.025
Tolerances, in. per ft*	1/16–1/8	1/32–3/32	1/32–7/64	1/32–5/64	0.003–0.006	1/32–1/16
Surface smoothness, microin., rms	250–300	150–200	90–125	90–125	90–125	60–125
Design feature remaiks	Basic casting method of the industry	Considered to be a good low-cost casting method	Production economics with substantial quantities	Little finishing required	Best for parts too complicated for other casting methods	Most economical where applicable
Tool and die costs	Low	Low to moderate	Medium	Medium	Low to moderate	High
Optimum lot size	Wide—range from few pieces to huge quantities	More required than sand castings	Best when requirements are in thousands	From one to several hundred	Wide—but best for small quantities	Substantial quantities required
Direct labor costs	High	Moderate	Moderate	High	Very high	Low to medium
Finishing costs	High	Low	Low to moderate	Low	Low	Low
Scrap costs	Moderate	Low	Low	Low	Low	Low

* Closer at extra cost.

MOLDING EQUIPMENT AND MECHANIZATION

Flasks may be filled with sand by hand shoveling, gravity feed from overhead hoppers, continuous belt feeding from a bin, sand slingers, and, for large molds, by an overhead crane equipped with a grab bucket.

Hand ramming is the simplest method of compacting sand. To increase the rate, pneumatic rammers are used. The method is slow, the sand is rammed in layers, and it is difficult to gain uniform density.

More uniform results and higher production rates are obtained by **squeezing machines.** Hand-operated squeezers are limited to small molds and are becoming obsolete; **air-operated machines,** using air at 80 to 100 psi, permit an increase in the allowable size of molds as well as in the production rate. These machines are suitable for shallow molds. Squeezer molding machines produce greatest sand density at the top of the flask and softest near the parting line of the pattern.

In jolt molding machines the pattern is placed on a platen attached to the top of an air cylinder. After the table is raised, a quick-release port opens and the piston, platen, and mold drop free against the top of the cylinder or striking pads. The impact packs the sand. The densities produced by this machine are greatest next to the parting line of the pattern and softest near the top of the flask. This procedure can be used for any flask that can be rammed on a molding machine. As a separate unit, it is used primarily for medium and large work. The largest units will jolt a combined weight of sand, flask, and pattern of 100,000 lb. Where plain jolt machines are used on large work, it is usual to ram the top of the flask manually with an air hammer.

Jolt squeeze machines use both the jolt and the squeeze procedures. The platen is mounted on two air cylinders: a small sylinder to jolt and a large one to squeeze the mold. They are widely used for small and medium work, and with match-plate or gated patterns. Pattern-stripping devices can be incorporated with jolt or squeezer machines to permit mechanical removal of the pattern. Pattern removal can also be accomplished by using jolt-rockover-draw or jolt-squeeze-rollover-draw machines.

The **sand slinger** is the most widely applicable type of ramming machine. It consists of an impeller mounted on the end of a double-jointed arm which is fed with sand by belt conveyors mounted on the arm. The impeller rotating at high speed gives sufficient velocity to the sand to ram it in the mold by impact. The head may be directed to all parts of the flask manually on the larger machines and may be automatically controlled on smaller units used for the high-speed production of small molds.

Vibrators are used on all pattern-drawing machines to free the pattern from the grip of the sand before drawing. Their use reduces mold damage to a minimum when the pattern is removed, and has the additional advantage of producing castings of more uniform size than can be secured by hand-rapping the pattern. Pattern damage is also kept to a minimum. Vibrators are usually air-operated, but some electrically operated types are in use.

Flasks generally consist of two parts: the upper section, called the **cope,** and the bottom section, the **drag.** When more than two parts are used, the intermediate sections are called **cheeks.** Flasks are classified as tight, snap, and slip. **Tight flasks** are those in which the flask remains until the metal is poured. **Snap flasks** are hinged on one corner and have a locking device on the diagonally opposite corner. In use, these flasks are removed as soon as the mold is closed. **Slip flasks** are of solid construction tapered from top to bottom on all four sides so that they can be removed as soon as the mold is closed. Snap or slip flasks permit the molder to make any number of molds with one flask. Before pouring snap- or slip-flask molds, a wood or metal pouring jacket is placed around the mold and a weight set on the top to keep the cope from lifting. The cope and drag sections on all flasks are maintained in proper alignment by flask pins and guides.

Tight flasks can be made in any size and are fabricated of wood, rolled steel, cast steel, cast iron, magnesium, or aluminum. Wood, aluminum, and magnesium are used only for small- and medium-sized flasks. Snap and slip flasks are made of wood, aluminum, or magnesium, and are generally used for molds not over 20 by 20 in.

Mechanization of Sand Preparation

In addition to the various types of molding machines, the modern foundry makes use of a variety of equipment to handle the sand and castings.

Sand Preparation and Handling. Sand is prepared in **mullers,** which serve to mix the sand, bonding agent, and water. **Aerators** are used in conjunction to loosen the sand to make it more amenable to molding. **Sand cutters** that operate over a heap on the foundry floor may be used instead of mullers. Delivery of the sand to the molding floor may be by means of dump or scoop trucks or by belt conveyors. At the molding floor the molds may be placed on the floor or delivered by conveyors to a pouring station. After pouring, the castings are removed from the flasks and adhering sand at a **shakeout** station. This may be a mechanically operated jolting device that shakes the loose sand from flask and casting. The used sand, in turn, is returned to the storage bins by belt conveyor or other means. Small castings may be poured by using **stack-molding** methods. In this case, each flask has a drag cavity molded in its upper surface and a cope cavity in its lower surface. These are stacked one on the other to a suitable height and poured from a common sprue.

There is an almost infinite variety of equipment and methods available to the foundry, ranging from simple, worksaving devices to completely mechanized units, including completely automatic molding machines. Because of this wide selection available, the degree to which a foundry can be mechanized depends almost entirely on the economics of the operations, rather than the availability or lack of availability of a particular piece of equipment.

MOLDING SAND

Molding sand consists of silica grains held together by some bonding material, usually clay or bentonite.

Grain size greatly influences the surface finish of a casting. The proper grain size is determined by the size of the casting, the quality of surface required, and the surface tension of the molten metal. The grain size should be approximately uniform when maximum permeability is desired.

Naturally bonded sands are mixtures of silica and clay as taken from the pits. Modification may be necessary to produce a satisfactory mixture. This type of sand is used in gray iron, malleable iron, and non-ferrous foundries (except magnesium).

Synthetically bonded sands are produced by combining clay-free silica sand with clay or bentonite. These sands can be compounded to suit foundry requirements. They are more uniform than naturally bonded sands but require more careful mixing and control. Steel foundries, gray-iron and malleable-iron foundries, and magnesium foundries use this type of sand.

Special additives may be used in addition to the basic sand, clay, and water. These include cereals, ground pitch, sea coal, gilsonite, fuel oil, wood flour, silica flour, iron oxide, perlite, molasses, dextrin, and proprietary materials. These all serve the purpose of altering specific properties of the sand to give better results.

The properties of the sand that are of major interest to the foundryman are **permeability,** or the venting power, of the sand; **green compressive strength; green shear strength; deformation,** or the sand movement under a given load; **dry compressive strength;** and **hot strength,** *i.e.*, strength at elevated temperatures. Several auxiliary tests are often made, including moisture content, clay content, and grain-size determination.

The foundry engineer or metallurgist is usually entrusted with the control of the sand properties, and he makes the adjustments required to keep it in good condition.

Facing sands, for giving better surface to the casting, are used for gray-iron, malleable-iron, steel, and magnesium castings. The iron sands usually contain **sea coal,** a finely ground coal which keeps the sand from adhering to the casting by generating a gas film when in contact with the hot metal. Steel facings contain silica flour or other very fine highly refractory material to form a dense surface which the metal cannot readily penetrate.

Mold washes are coatings applied to the mold or core surface to improve the finish of the casting. They are applied either wet or dry. The usual practice is to brush or spray the wet mold washes and to brush or rub on the dry ones. Graphite or silica flour mixed with clay and molasses water is frequently used.

Core Sands and Core Binders

Green-sand cores are made from standard molding-sand mixtures, sometimes strengthened by adding a binder, such as dextrin, which hardens the surface. Cores of this type are very fragile and are usually made with an arbor or wires on the inside to facilitate handling. Their collapsibility is useful in preventing hot tearing of the casting.

Dry-sand cores are made from silica sand and a binder (usually oil) which hardens under the action of heat. The amount of oil used should be the minimum which will produce the necessary core strength.

Core binders are either organic, such as core oil, which are destroyed under heat, or inorganic, which are not destroyed.

Organic Binders. The main organic binder is **core oil.** Pure linseed oil is used extensively as one of the basic ingredients in blended-oil core binders. These consist primarily of linseed oil, resin, and a thinner, such as high-grade kerosene. They have good wetting properties, good workability, and better oxidation characteristics than straight linseed oil.

Corn flour produces good green strength and dry strength when used in conjunction with oil. Cores made with this binder are quick drying in the oven and burn out rapidly and completely in the mold.

Dextrin produces a hard surface and weak center because of the migration of dextrin and water to the surface. Used with oil, it produces a hard smooth surface but does not produce a green bond as good as that with corn flour.

Commercial **protein binders,** such as gelatin, casein, and glues, improve flowability of the sand, have high binding power, rapid drying, fair resistance to moisture, and low burning-out point, with only a small volume of gas evolved on burning. They are used where high collapsibility of the core is essential.

Other binders include paper-mill by-products, which absorb moisture readily, have high dry strength, low green strength, high gas ratio, and high binding power for clay materials.

Coal tar pitch and **petroleum pitch** flow with heat and freeze around the grains on cooling. These compounds have low moisture-absorption rates and are used extensively for large iron cores. They can be used effectively with impure sands.

Wood and gum rosin, plastic resins, and rosin by-products are used to produce collapsibility in cores. They must be well ground. They tend to cake in hot weather, and large amounts are required to get desired strength.

Plastics of the **urea-** and **phenol-formaldehyde** groups and **furan resins** are being used for core binders. They have the advantage of low-temperature baking, collapse readily, and produce only small amounts of gas. These can be used in **dielectric baking ovens** or in the **shell molding, hot box, or air setting** processes for making cores.

Inorganic binders include fire clay, southern bentonite, western bentonite, and iron oxide.

Cores can also be made by mixing sand with sodium silicate. When this mixture is in the core box, it is infiltrated with CO_2, which causes the core to harden. This is called the **CO_2 process.**

Coremaking Methods

Cores are made by the methods employed for sand molds. In addition, **core blowers** and **extrusion machines** are used.

Core blowers force sand into the core box by compressed air at about 100 psi. They can be used for making all types of small- and medium-sized cores. The cores produced are very uniform, and production rates up to 200 boxes per hr per machine are achieved.

Screw-feed machines are used largely for plain cylindrical cores of uniform cross section. The core sand is extruded through a die onto a core plate. The use of these machines is limited to the production of stock cores, which are cut to the desired length after baking.

Core Ovens. Core-oven walls are constructed of inner and outer layers of sheet metal separated by rock wool or Fiberglas insulation and with interlocked joints. Combustion chambers are refractory-lined, and the hot gases are circulated by fans. They are designed for operating at temperatures ranging from 300 to 650 F. Baking temperatures are approximately: urea-formaldehyde binder, 300 to 350 F; flour, starch, or dextrin, 350 to 375 F with a maximum of 410 F; pitch and resin, 350 to 400 F; dextrin, below 400 F; phenol formaldehyde, 425 to 450 F; cores bonded with oil, 400 to 450 F, but 500 F will not injure.

Core driers are light skeleton cast-iron or aluminum boxes, the internal shape of which conforms closely to the cope portion of the core. They are used to support, during baking, cores which cannot be placed on a flat plate.

CASTING ALLOYS

In general, the types of alloys that can be produced as wrought metals can also be prepared as castings. Certain alloys, however, cannot be forged or rolled and can only be produced as castings.

A very general subdivision is into **ferrous,** or iron-base alloys, and **non-ferrous** alloys. The non-ferrous group includes aluminum-base, copper-base, magnesium-base, nickel-base, and other miscellaneous alloys.

Ferrous Alloys

Steel Castings. (See also p. 6–58.) Steel castings may be classified as:

1. Low carbon ($C < 0.20$ percent). These are relatively soft and not readily heat-treatable.
2. Medium carbon ($C > 0.20$ percent < 0.50 percent). These castings are somewhat harder and amenable to strengthening by heat-treatment.
3. High carbon ($C > 0.50$ percent). These steels are used where maximum hardness and wear resistance are desired.

In addition to the classification based on carbon content, which determines the maximum hardness obtainable in steel, the castings can be also classified as **low-alloy** content ($<$ 8 percent) or **high-alloy** content ($>$ 8 percent).

The low-alloy steels behave essentially as plain-carbon steels but have a higher **hardenability,** which is a measure of ability to be hardened by heat-treatment. The high-alloy steels are designed to produce some specific property, like corrosion resistance, heat resistance, wear resistance, or some other special property.

Malleable-iron Castings. The carbon content of malleable iron ranges from about 2.00 to 2.80 percent and may reach as high as 3.30 percent if the iron is melted in a cupola. Silicon ranging from 0.90 to 1.80 percent is an additional alloying element required to aid the annealing of the iron. As cast, this iron is hard and brittle and is rendered soft and malleable by a long heat-treating or annealing cycle. This product is usually marketed to meet one of two ASTM classes, the 32510 grade and the 35018 grade. The former has minimum standards of 50,000 psi tensile strength, 32,500 psi yield strength, and 10 percent minimum elongation, while standards for the latter are 53,000 psi, 35,000 psi, and 18 percent elongation, respectively, for these properties. (See also p. 6–57.)

Malleable iron can also be heated in a number of ways to produce **pearlitic malleable** that may reach 90,000 psi in tensile strength, 70,000 psi in yield strength, and a minimum elongation in 2 in. of 2 percent.

Gray-iron Castings. Gray iron is an alloy of iron, carbon, and silicon, containing a higher percentage of these last two elements than found in malleable iron. Much of the carbon is present in the elemental form as graphite. Other elements present include managanese, phosphorus, and sulphur. Because the properties are controlled by proper proportioning of the carbon and silicon and by the cooling rate of the casting, it is usually sold on the basis of specified properties rather than composition. The carbon content will usually range between 3.00 and 4.00 percent and the silicon will be between 1.00 and 3.00 percent, the higher values of carbon being used with the lower silicon values (usually), and vice versa. As evidence of the fact that gray iron should not be considered as a material having a single set of properties, the ASTM and AFS recognize seven classes, ranging in tensile strength from 20,000 to 60,000 psi or over. The high strengths are obtained by proper adjustment of the carbon and silicon contents or by alloying. (See also pp. 6–52 *et seq.*)

An important variation of gray iron is **nodular iron,** in which the graphite appears as nodules rather than as flakes. This iron is prepared by treating the metal in the ladle with additives that usually include magnesium in alloy form. Nodular iron can exceed 100,000 psi as cast and is much more ductile than gray iron, measuring about 2 to 5 percent elongation at these higher strengths, and even higher percentages if the strength is lower. (See also p. 6–56.)

Non-ferrous Alloys

Aluminum-base Castings. Aluminum is alloyed with copper, silicon, magnesium, zinc, nickel, and other elements to produce a wide variety of casting alloys having specific characteristics of foundry properties, mechanical properties, machinability, and/or corrosion resistance. Alloys are produced for use in sand casting, permanent-mold casting, or die casting. Some alloys are heat-treatable using **solution** and **age-hardening** treatments. These alloys range in strength from about 17,000 psi to as high as 43,000 psi in some die-cast alloys. (See also p. 6–84.)

Copper-base Alloys. The alloying elements used with copper include zinc (brasses), tin (bronzes), nickel (nickel bronze), aluminum (aluminum bronze), silicon (silicon bronze), and beryllium (beryllium bronze). The brasses and tin bronzes may contain lead for machinability. Various combinations of zinc and tin, or of tin or zinc with other elements, are also available. With the exception of some of the aluminum bronzes and beryllium bronze, most of the copper-base alloys cannot be hardened by heat-treatment. Certain copper-base alloys may exceed 100,000 psi in tensile strength. (See also p. 6–78.)

Special Casting Alloys. Other metals cast in the foundry include **magnesium-base alloys** for light weight, **nickel-base alloys** for high-temperature applications, **titanium-base alloys** for strength-to-weight ratio, etc. The magnesium-base alloys require special precautions during melting and pouring to avoid burning. They can be heat-treated and may exceed 40,000 psi in tensile strength. Most magnesium alloys have excellent machinability. (See also pp. 6–81, 6–93, 6–101, 6–102, 6–106.)

MELTING FURNACES

The melting furnaces used for castings, arranged for each metal in the approximate order of their general use, are as follows:

Steel. Electric (direct-arc, acid), open-hearth (acid), open-hearth (basic), electric (direct-arc, basic), Bessemer, induction (high-frequency).

Cast Iron. Cupola, air furnace (reverberatory), electric (direct-arc).

Malleable Iron. Duplexing (cupola and air furnace or electric furnace), air furnace, cupola, rotary furnace (Brackelsberg), open-hearth (acid).

Brass and Bronze. Crucible, electric (indirect-arc), induction (low-frequency), air furnace, induction (high-frequency).

Aluminum. Crucible furnace with metal or refractory crucibles, induction (low-frequency).

Magnesium. Crucible furnace with steel crucibles, induction (high-frequency).

Annealing Furnaces. (See pp. 7–64 to 7–71.)

CLEANING AND INSPECTION

Tumbling barrels consist of a power-driven drum in which the castings are tumbled in contact with hard-iron stars or balls. Their impact removes the sand and scale.

In **air-blast cleaning units,** compressed air forces silica sand or chilled-iron shot into violent contact with the castings, which are tumbled in a barrel, rotated on a table, or passed between multiple orifices on a conveyor. Large rooms are sometimes utilized, with an operator directing the nozzle. These machines are equipped with hoppers and elevators to return the sand or shot to the magazine. Dust-collecting systems are required.

In centrifugal-blast cleaning units, a rotating impeller is used to impart the necessary velocity to the chilled-iron shot or grit abrasive. The velocities are not so high as with air, but the volume of abrasive is much greater. The construction is otherwise similar to the air-blast machine.

Water in large volume at pressures of 250 to 600 psi is used to remove sand and cores from medium and large castings. The stream is directed by an operator located outside the cleaning chamber or room.

High-pressure water and sand cleaning (**Hydroblast**) employs water at 1,200 to 1,900 psi mixed with molding sand which has been washed off the casting. A sand classifier is incorporated in the sand-reclamation system.

Pneumatic chipping hammers may be used to clean large castings where the sand is badly burned on and for deep pockets.

Removal of Gates and Risers and Finishing Castings. The following tabulation shows the most generally used methods for removing gates and risers (marked R) and for finishing (marked F).

Steel. Oxyacetylene (R), hand hammer or sledge (R), grinders (F), chipping hammer (F), and machining (F).

Cast Iron. Chipping hammer (R, F), hand hammer or sledge (R), abrasive cutoff (R), power saw (R), and grinders (F).

Malleable Iron. Hand hammer or sledge (R), grinders (F), shear (F), and machining (F).

Brass and Bronze. Chipping hammer (R, F), shear (R, F), hand hammer or sledge (R), abrasive cutoff (R), power saw (R), belt sanders (F), grinders (F), and machining (F).

Aluminum. Chipping hammer (R), shear (R), hand hammer or sledge (R), power saw (R), grinders (F), and belt sander (F).

Magnesium. Band saw (R), machining (F), and flexible-shaft machines with steel burr cutters (F).

Casting Inspection

Castings are inspected for dimensional accuracy, hardness, surface finish, physical properties, internal soundness, and cracks. For **hardness,** see p. 5–15; for **physical properties,** see p. 5–18.

Internal soundness is checked by cutting or breaking up pilot castings or by nondestructive testing using X ray, gamma ray, and fluoroscope.

Destructive testing tells only the condition of the piece tested and does not ensure that other pieces not tested will be sound. It is the most commonly used procedure at the present time.

X ray, gamma ray, and the fluoroscope have made possible the non-destructive checking of castings to determine internal soundness on all castings produced. Shrinks, cracks, tears, and gas holes can be determined and repairs made before the castings are shipped.

Magnetic-powder tests (**Magnaflux**) are used to locate structural discontinuities in iron and steel except austenitic steels, but they are not applicable to most nonferrous metals or their alloys. The method is most useful for the location of surface discontinuities, but it may indicate deep-seated defects if the magnetizing force is sufficient to produce a leakage field at the surface.

In this test a magnetic flux is induced in ferromagnetic material. Any abrupt discontinuity in its path results in a local flux-leakage field. If finely divided particles of ferromagnetic material are brought into the vicinity, they offer a low reluctance path to the leakage field and take a position that outlines approximately its effective boundaries. The casting to be inspected is magnetized and its surface dusted with the magnetic powder. A low-velocity air stream blows the excess powder off and leaves the defect outlined by the powder particles. The powder may be applied while the magnetizing current is flowing (**continuous method**) or after the current is off (**residual method**). It may be applied dry or suspended in a light petroleum distillate similar to kerosene. The dry-powder method using d-c magnetization is recommended. Expert interpretation of the tests is necessary for satisfactory results.

CASTING DESIGN

Design for the best utilization of metal in the cast form requires a knowledge of metal solidification characteristics, foundry practices, and the metallurgy of the metal being used. Metals exhibit certain peculiarities in the formation of solid metal during freezing and also undergo shrinkage in the liquid state during the freezing process and after freezing, and the casting must be designed to take these factors into consideration. Knowledge concerning the freezing process will also be of assistance in determining the fluidity of the metal, its resistance to **hot tearing,** and its tendency to evolve dissolved gases. For economy in production, casting design should take into consideration those factors in molding and coring that will lead to the simplest procedures. Elimination of expensive cores, irregular parting lines, and deep drafts in the casting can often be accomplished with a slight modification of the original design. Combination of the foregoing factors with the selection of the right metal for the job is an important facet of casting design. Consultation with the plant metallurgist or foundry engineer is recommended as a first step in the development of a well-designed casting. The references, ASM "Casting Design Handbook," and "Design of Ferrous Castings" are recommended.

WORKING METALS AND PLASTICS

BY

E. V. Crane

(See also Secs. 5 and 6)

References: Crane, "Plastic Working of Metals and Power Press Operations," Wiley. Woodworth, "Punches, Dies and Tools for Manufacturing in Presses," Henley. Jones, "Die Design and Die Making Practice," Industrial Press. Stanley, "Punches and Dies," McGraw-Hill. Woodworth, "Dies—Their Construction and Use," Henley. Dowd and Curtis, "Punches, Dies and Gages," McGraw-Hill. DeGarmo, "Materials and Processes in Manufacturing," Macmillan. "Modern Plastics Encyclopedia and Engineers Handbook," Plastics Catalogue Corp., New York. Jevons, "The Metallurgy of Deep Drawing and Pressing," Wiley. "The Tool Engineers Handbook," McGraw-Hill. Bridgman "Large Plastic Flow and Fracture," McGraw-Hill. "Cold Working of Metals," ASM. Pearson, "The Extrusion of Metals," Wiley. Shockley, "Imperfections in Nearly Perfect Crystals," Wiley.

STRUCTURE

Yieldable structural forces between the particles composing a material to be worked are the key to its behavior. Simple internal structures contain only a single element, as pure copper, silver, or iron. Relatively more difficult to work are the solid solutions in which one element tends to distribute uniformly in the structural pattern of another. Thus silver and gold form a continuous series of solid-solution alloys as their proportions vary. Next are alloys in which strongly bonded molecular groups dispersed through or along the grain boundaries of softer metals offer increasing resistance to working, as does iron carbide (Fe_3C) in solution in iron. Molecules may become complex groups of many atoms, as in the plastics. Such molecules may bond strongly together in chain relationships, as in polymers and rubbery elastomers. In other cases, mixtures may be used in which filling materials supply bulk, hardness, or other characteristics and are held together in a matrix of metallic, plastic, or ceramic bonding materials.

Bonding forces are supplied by electrical fields characteristic of individual atoms. These forces in turn are subject to modification by temperature as energy is added, increasing electron activity. The atom of each individual element includes a closely associated group of neutrons and positively charged protons at its core and a corresponding number of smaller negatively charged electrons, grouped in orbits around that core. Table 1, p. 6–4, shows the atomic number of the element, which also designates the normal number of electrons in its orbits.

The **particles** which comprise an atom are so small that most of its volume is empty space. For a similar energy state, there is some rough uniformity in the outside size of atoms. In general, therefore, the more complex elements have their larger number of particles more densely packed and so are heavier. For each element, the energy pattern of its electrical charges in motion determines the field characteristics of that atom and which of the orderly arrangements it will seek to assume with relation to others like it in the orderly crystalline form. The table (p. 6–4) lists typical crystal patterns, with an explanation at the foot of the page.

Space lattice is the term used to describe the orderly arrangement of rows and layers of atoms in the crystalline form. This orderly state is also described as balanced, unstrained, or **annealed.** The working or deforming of materials distorts the orderly arrangement, unbalancing the forces between atoms. Cubic patterns or space lattices characterize the more ductile or workable materials. Hexagonal and more complex patterns tend to be more brittle or more rigid. Flaws, irregularities, or distortions, with corresponding unbalanced strains among adjacent atoms, may occur in the pattern or along grain boundaries. **Slip-plane** movements in working to new shapes tend to slide the once orderly layers of atoms within the grain-boundary limitations of individual crystals. Such sliding movement tends to take place at 45 deg to the direction of the applied load because much higher stresses are required to pull atoms directly apart or to push them straight together.

Chemical combinations, in liquid or solid solutions, or molecular compounds depend upon relative field patterns of elements or upon actual displacement of one or more electrons from the outer orbit of a donor element to the outer orbit of a receptor element. Thus the molecules of hard iron carbide, Fe_3C, may be held in solid solution in soft pure iron (ferrite) in increasing proportions up to 0.83 percent of carbon in iron, which is described as **pearlite.** Zinc may occupy solid-solution positions in the copper space lattice up to about 45 percent, the range of the ductile red and yellow brasses. Typical of the plastics, cellulose triacetate, $C_6H_7O_2(O_2CCH_3)_3$, combines 12 carbon atoms, 16 hydrogen atoms, and 8 oxygen atoms into a complex molecule having a molecular weight nearly six times that of an iron atom. But since the mass is distributed among the 36 lighter atoms of carbon, hydrogen, and oxygen, the plastic weighs less than one-sixth of the same volume of iron.

Thermal Changes. Adding heat (energy) increases electron activity and therefore also the mobility of the atom. Probability of brittle failure at low temperatures usually becomes less as temperature increases. Transition temperatures from one state to another differ for different elements. Thermal transitions therefore become more complex as such differing elements are combined in alloys and compounds. As temperatures rise, a **stress-relieving** range is reached at which the most severely strained atoms are able to ease themselves around into less strained positions. At somewhat higher temperatures, **annealing** or **recrystallization** of worked or distorted structure takes place. Old grain boundaries disappear and small new grains begin to grow, aligning nearby atoms into their orderly lattice pattern. The more severely the material has been worked, the lower is the temperature at which recrystallization begins. Grain growth is more rapid at higher temperatures. In working materials above their recrystallization range, as in forging, the relief of interatomic strains becomes more nearly spontaneous as the temperature is increased. **Creep** takes place when materials are under some stress above the recrystallization range, and the thermal mobility permits individual atoms to ease around to relieve that stress, with an accompanying gradual change of shape. Thus a wax candle droops due to gravity on a hot day. Lead, which recrystallizes below room temperature, will creep when used for roofing or spouting. Steels in rockets and jet engines begin to creep around 1300 to 1500 F. Creep is more rapid as the temperature rises farther above the recrystallization range.

PLASTICITY

Plasticity is that property of materials which commends them to the mass-production techniques of pressure-forming desired shapes. It is understood more easily if several types of plasticity are considered.

Solvents—water, oils, acetone, and waxes—contribute to the workability of clays, paper, wood, plaster, concrete, and some of the synthetic plastics. The term **soluplastic** applies when a material can be restored to a workable state by replenishing the plasticizing solvent. Thus paper is stored in a proper humidity and wood is placed in a steam chamber to render them formable. The term **solusetting** describes forming processes in which chemical change takes place such that plasticity cannot be restored by reapplication of the solvent. Thus plaster, concrete, and baked ceramics take a chemical set. Glass fabric and epoxy set quickly to a master form.

Crystoplastic describes materials, notably metals, which can be worked in the stable crystalline state, below the recrystallization range. Metals which crystallize in the cubic patterns have a wider plastic range than those of hexagonal pattern. Alloying narrows the range and increases the resistence to working. Tensile or compressive testing of an annealed specimen can be used to show the plastic range which lies between the initial yield point and the point of ultimate tensile or compressive failure.

The **plastic range,** as of an annealed metal, is illustrated in Fig. 1. Changing values of **true stress** are determined by dividing the applied load at any instant by the cross-section area at that instant. As material is worked, a progressive increase in elastic limit and yield point registers the slip-plane movement or work hardening which has taken place and the consequent reduction in residual plasticity. This changing yield point or resistance, shown in Fig. 1, is divided roughly into three characteristic ranges. The contour of the lower range can be varied by non-uniformity of grain sizes or by small displacements resulting from prior direction of working. Random large, soft grains yield locally under slight displacement, with resulting **surface markings,** described as *orange peel, alligator skin,* or *stretcher strain markings.* These can be prevented by preparatory roller leveling, which gives protection in the case of steel for perhaps a day, or by a 3 to 5 percent temper pass of cold-rolling, which may stress relieve in perhaps three months, permitting recurrent trouble. The middle range covers most drawing and forming operations. Its upper limit is the point of normal tensile failure. The upper range requires that metal be worked primarily in compression to inhibit the start of tensile fracture. Severe extrusion, spring-temper rolling, and music-wire drawing use this range.

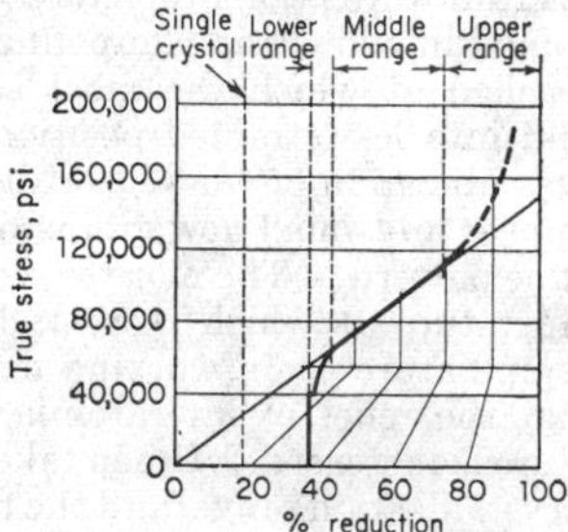

FIG. 1. Three ranges of crystoplastic work hardening of a low-carbon steel. (*ASME, 1954, W. S. Wagner, E. W. Bliss Co.*)

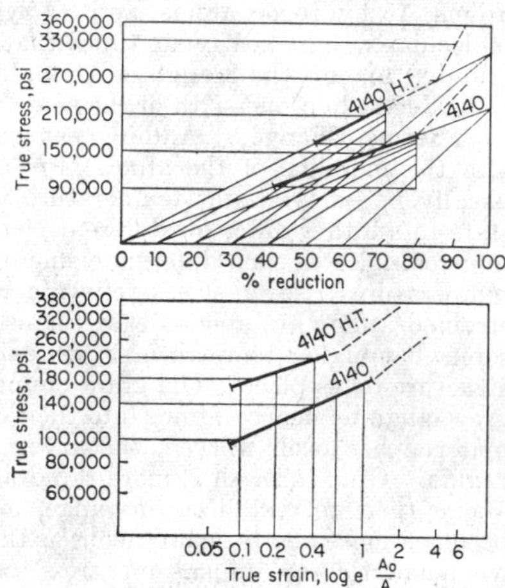

FIG. 2. High-range plasticity (dotted) of 4140 steel, showing also the effect of dispersion hardening. Two plotting methods. (*ASME, 1958, Crane and Wagner, E. W. Bliss Co.*)

Dispersion hardening of metal alloys by heat treatment (see Fig. 2) reduces the plastic range and increases the resistance to work hardening. Figure 2 also shows the common methods of plotting change of true stress against **percentage of reduction**—*e.g.*, reduction of thickness in rolling or compressive working, of area in wire drawing, ironing, or tensile testing, or of diameter in cup drawing or reducing operations—and against **true strain,** which is the $\log_e$ of change of area, for convenience in higher mathematics.

The term **thermoplastic** describes the working range of temperatures between recrystallization and fluidity. As the temperature increases, the material offers less resistance to flow and can be worked more severely; or at higher temperatures, it can be forced through more difficult passageways. The thermoplastic materials are not subject to chemical change and will resoften when reheated.

For metals, thermoplastic working is usually described as **hot forging,** except for tin and lead, which recrystallize below room temperature. Forgings may be etched to show **flow lines,** which are usually made up of old-grain boundaries. Where these show, recrystallization has not yet taken place, and some work hardening is retained to improve physical properties. Zinc and magnesium, which are typical of the hexagonal-structure metals, take only small amounts of cold working but can be drawn or otherwise worked severely at rather moderate temperatures (Zn, 200 to 400 F; Mg, 500 to 700 F). Note that, while hexagonal-pattern metals are less easily worked than cubic-pattern metals, they are for that same reason structurally more rigid for a similar relative weight. Advantageous forging temperatures change with alloy composition: copper, 1800 to 1900 F; red brass, Cu 70, Zn 30, 1600 to 1700 F; yellow brass, Cu 60, Zn 40, 1200 to 1500 F. See Section 6 for general physical properties of metals.

Thermoplastic synthetic plastics usually recrystallize a little above or below room temperature. They are usually too brittle for working purposes at lower temperatures. Plasticizing waxes may be used in a solid-solution relationship to improve flexibility in wrapping foils. Such plasticizers tend to leach out as moisture is taken up or lost on damp or dry days. Moisture sensitivity varies considerably among the plastics. Extrusion-, injection-, and compression-molding temperatures are usually in the range of 200 to 500 F, depending upon the plastic, the production rate, and the die passageways.

Physical properties of the plastics (Table 1) and of the metals (Secs. 5 and 6) are similar in principle though varying widely with materials, alloys, and their temperature or degree of work hardening. Figure 3 shows a stress-strain curve for a typical thermoplastic. Note the increasing elastic limit and decreasing plasticity at lower and lower temperatures. Note also Figure 1, p. 6–13, showing increasing elastic limit and decreasing plasticity of substantially pure iron with increasing amounts of work hardening by cold-rolling. The rate at which such work hardening takes place is greatly increased, and the remaining plasticity reduced, as alloying becomes more complex.

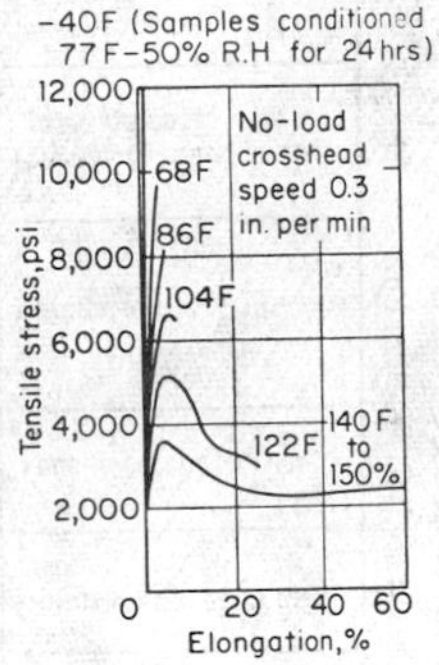

Thermosetting plastics are those in which a chemical change takes place with heat, so that the process is not reversible and reheating does not restore plasticity. Such thermosetting resins as the phenolics, ureas, melamines, and shellac are used in many or most cases with a variety of fillers for bulk, reinforcement, abrasive grinding, appearance, or resistance to heat, wear, water, or chemicals. While there is some injection molding, most working of thermosetting mixtures is in compression molding, transfer molding, and multiplaten laminating.

FIG. 3. Tensile stress-strain curves for thermoplastic lucite. (*E. I. Du Pont de Nemours & Co.*)

Elastomers, synthetic and natural rubbers, should probably be included under the thermosetting molding and forming techniques, although such work as rubber-glove production using molds dipped in solution and then heat-cured would be solusetting.

Ceramics industries, with roots farthest in the past, remain more of an art by reason of the chance variety of metallic oxides in the natural clays. In the forming stage, the process is soluplastic and control of the plasticizing water is critical. The subsequent firing is an irreversible solusetting process, and for production purposes, there are two stages where time and temperature are critical with respect to shrinkage and cracking: In the first, water which was holding clay platelettes in solution is evaporated; and in the second, water which was in chemical combination is driven off. This is prior to decorative glazing. Fillers are used with clay binders for specialized purposes, such as iron powders for electronic items.

PLASTIC-WORKING TECHNIQUES

Reference should be made to a vast file of papers on plasticity, flow research, processes, techniques, and materials and to applicable bibliographies, especially as indexed in the Engineering Societies Library, 345 E. 47 St., New York 10017. The library provides a research service by mail at a moderate fee.

In the **metalworking** operations, as distinguished from metal cutting, material is forced to move into new shapes by plastic flow. **Hot working** is carried on above the recovery temperature, and spontaneous recovery, or annealing, occurs about as fast as the properties of the material are altered by the deformation. This process is limited by the chilling of the material in the tools, scaling of the material, and the life of the

Table 1. Properties of Plastics

("Plastics and Plasticity," E. W. Bliss Co.)

	Yield point at 77 F, approx psi	Hot-shearing temp., approx deg F	Knife-edge cutting load at 77 F, lb lineal in.	Shearing strength at 77 F, psi	Compression-molding pressure, psi	Injection-molding pressure, psi	Compressive strength, psi	Tensile strength, psi	Elongation in 2 in., %	Powder-to-solid compression ratio	Modulus of elasticity, psi	Lowest recrystallization temp, approx deg F	Forming compression-molding temp, approx deg F	Injection-molding temp, approx deg F	Thermal coef of expansion, in./in. deg F	Weight, lb/cu in.
THERMOSETTING MIXTURES																
Phenol-formaldehyde (no filler)		200 250		10,000	2,000 5,000		10,000 30,000	7,000 12,000	1.1	1–2.6	700,000 1,000,000		300 340		0.000013 0.00003	0.046
Phenol-formaldehyde (wood-flour filler)		200 250			2,000 4,500	2,000 10,000	16,000 36,000	6,000 11,000	0.6	2.2–3	1,000,000 1,500,000		280 360	275 375	0.000020 0.000041	0.0481 0.055
Phenol-formaldehyde (mineral filler)		200 250			2,000 6,000	2,000 15,000	18,000 36,000	4,000 8,000	0.6	2–8	1,000,000 4,500,000		270 350	275 350	0.000014 0.00002	0.061 0.075
Phenol-formaldehyde (macerated-fabric filler)		200 250			2,000 8,000		20,000 32,000	5,500 8,000	0.7	2.5–15	700,000 1,200,000		270 350		0.00001 0.00003	0.049 0.053
Phenol-formaldehyde (sisal-felt filler)		200 250			300 3,000	10,000 20,000	10,000 35,000	7,000 12,000		2–5			275 350	275 350	0.0001 0.00003	0.025 0.050
Phenol-formaldehyde (paper laminate)	4,000 18,000	200 250		12,500	1,000 3,000		20,000 40,000	7,000 18,000	1.5	1.5–3	400,000 3,000,000		275 350		0.000009 0.000013	0.047 0.049
Phenol-formaldehyde (cotton-fabric laminate)	3,000 8,000	200 250		15,000	1,000 3,000		30,000 44,000	8,000 12,000	1–2	1.5–3	350,000 1,500,000		275 350		0.000009 0.00001	0.047 0.049
Phenol-formaldehyde (glass-fabric laminate)	4,500 28,000	200 250			1,000 3,000		42,000 47,000	14,000 20,000	2		1,000,000 2,000,000		275 350			0.050 0.057
Phenol-formaldehyde (asbestos-cloth laminate)		200 250			1,000 3,000		18,000 45,000	7,000 12,000		1.6	350,000 1,500,000		300 350		0.000009 0.000013	0.056 0.086
Birch plywood (phenolic binder)					200 2,000		5,700	13,100			1,400,000					0.0288
Urea-formaldehyde (alpha-cellulose filler)				13,000	1,500 6,000		20,000 24,000	5,500 7,000		2.5–3	1,200,000 1,500,000		290 325		0.0000138 0.000016	0.052 0.054
Urea-formaldehyde (cotton-fabric laminate)	600 2,500				1,500 6,000		7,000 8,700	5,100 6,900	8–22		560,000		290 325			0.044

Melamine-formaldehyde (alpha-cellulose filler)					1,500 6,000					2.0–2.3			280 340			0.0537
Melamine-formaldehyde (asbestos filler)					1,000 4,000		30,000	5,500 7,000	0.30–0.45	2.1–2.5	1,600,000		280 330		0.00001 0.000025	0.0612 0.087
Aniline-formaldehyde (no filler)					1,500 6,000		20,000 23,000	8,500 10,000		2.5–3	500,000 600,000		300 340		0.00002 0.00003	0.044 0.045
Casein-formaldehyde					2,000 2,500		5,300 27,000	10,000	2.5		510,000 570,000		200 225		0.00004	0.0487
Phenol-furfural (wood-floor filler)					1,000 4,000	300 10,000	28,000 36,000	6,000 11,000		2.5–3	1,000,000 2,500,000		330 400	250 375	0.00001	0.047 0.050
Phenol-furfural (mineral filler)					1,000 4,000	300 15,000	24,000 36,000	5,000 10,000		2.5–6	1,000,000 4,500,000		330 360	250 375	0.00001	0.057 0.072
Phenol-furfural (fabric filler)					1,000 8,000	300 30,000	26,000 30,000	6,500 8,000		4–15	700,000 1,200,000	2	300 360	250 375	0.000025	0.047 0.050
Phenol-lignin (laminate)					1,500 2,000		25,000 30,000	7,500 12,000		2–3	800,000 2,000,000		365		0.000011 0.000013	0.049 0.051
Columbia allyl resin 39 (paper laminate)							15,000 31,000	10,000 21,000								0.048
Columbia allyl resin 39 (fabric laminate)							29,000	1,000 7,500	4		550,000		160 240		0.000013 0.000023	0.049
Columbia allyl resin 39 (glass-cloth laminate)	12,700						52,000 60,000	30,400 39,000			1,700,000		160 240		0.00001	0.062
Columbia allyl resin 39 (sheet)								6,000			350,000	140	160 240		0.000049	0.047
Shellac					1,000 2,500	1,000 1,200	10,000 17,000	900 2,000		2–3	500,000 600,000		240	180 260		0.039 0.098
Rubber-sulphur								1,000 4,000	600		400					0.035 0.045
Ceramic "prestite" (flint feldspar, ball clay, china clay)							48,000	5,000			10,000,000	1200			0.000002 0.000006	0.088

Table 1. Properties of Plastics—(*Continued*)

	Yield point at 77 F, approx psi	Hot-shearing temp., approx deg F	Knife-edge cutting load at 77 F, lb lineal in.	Shearing strength at 77 F, psi	Compression-molding pressure, psi	Injection-molding pressure, psi	Compressive strength, psi	Tensile strength, psi	Elongation in 2 in., %	Powder-to-solid compression ratio	Modulus of elasticity, psi	Lowest recrystallization temp, approx deg F	Forming compression-molding temp, approx deg F	Injection-molding temp, approx deg F	Thermal coef of expansion, in./in. deg F	Weight, lb/cu in.
SYNTHETIC THERMOPLASTICS																
Cellulose acetate	5,000	77+	400 500	6,000 10,000	500 5,000	3,000 30,000	5,000 27,000	2,200 14,600	7.3–43	2–2.6	300,000	30–40	250 350	300 420	0.000044 0.000088	0.045 0.050
Cellulose nitrate (celluloid)		120 150	300 400		2,000 5,000		20,000 30,000	5,000 12,000	10–50		200,000 400,000		185 250		0.000066 0.000088	0.049 0.050
Cellulose acetate butyrate				6,000	500 5,000	8,000 30,000	7,500 30,400	2,500 7,500	5 90	2–2.8	200,000 350,000		260 370	340 420		
Ethyl cellulose	1,500 3,500			7,500	1,500 5,000	3,000 30,000	10,000 12,000	2,000 9,000	10–40	2.2–2.5	100,000 500,000		300 360	350 425	0.000055 0.000077	0.041
Methyl methacrylate	7,000 9,000	200		11,500	2,000 7,500	10,000 35,000	10,000 12,500	6,000 9,000	1–5	1.7–2.2	300,000 500,000	100–110	280 350	325 475	0.000036 0.000052	0.0417 0.0435
Nylon, molded								5,000 10,500	30–60				450	300 500		
Vinyl chloride								1,000 10,000			350,000 400,000				0.000038	0.0486
Vinylidene chloride	26,000			8,000 10,500	250 5,000	10,000 30,000	7,500 8,500	4,000 8,000	15–25		70,000 200,000	30–40	250 350	300 400	0.000087	0.0595 0.0633
Polystyrene (vinyl benzene)				8,000	1,000 5,000	10,000 30,000	11,500 15,000	5,000 9,000	2–5	2–2.3	170,000 470,000	−78	275 350	300 500	0.000033 0.000044	0.038 0.0385
Soluplastics: Vulcanized fiber		180	400	4,000			20,000 32,000	5,000 12,000								0.036 0.054
Aircraft spruce (douglas fir)							5,000	10,000			1,300,000					0.017

tools at the required temperatures. **Cold working** is carried on at room temperature and may be applied to most of the common metals. Since, in most cases, no recovery occurs at this temperature, the properties of the metal are altered in the direction of increasing strength and brittleness throughout the working process, and there is consequently a limit to which cold working may be carried without danger of fracture.

A convenient way of representing the action of the common metals when cold-worked consists of plotting the actual stress in the material against the percentage reduction in thickness. Within the accuracy required for shop use, the relationship is linear, as in Fig. 4. The lower limit of stress shown is the yield point at the softest temper, or anneal, commercially available, while the upper limit is the limit of tensile action, or the stress at which fracture, rather than flow, occurs. This latter value does not correspond to the commercially quoted "tensile strength" of the metal, but rather to the "true tensile strength," which is the stress that exists at the reduced section of a tensile specimen at fracture and which is higher than the nominal value in inverse proportion to the reduction of area of the material.

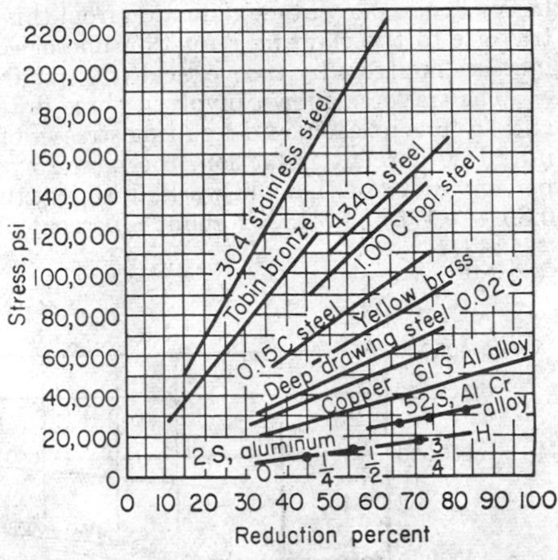

Fig. 4. Plastic range chart of commonly worked metals.

As an example of the construction and use of the cold-working plots shown in Fig. 4, the action of a very-low-carbon deep-drawing steel has been shown in Fig. 5. Starting

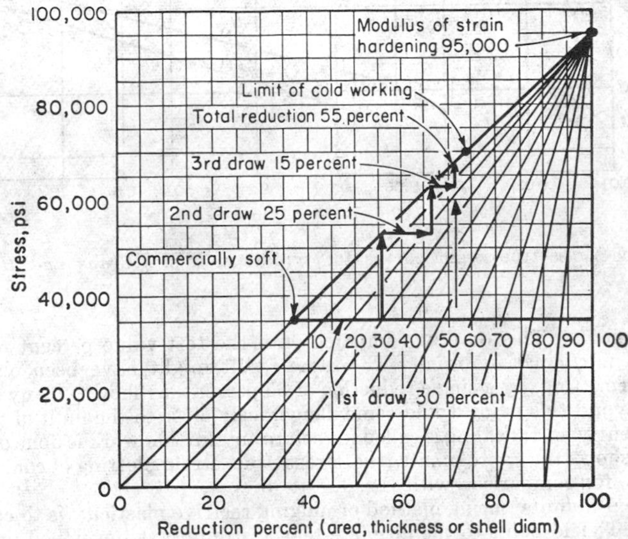

Fig. 5. Graphical solution of metalworking problem.

with the annealed material with a yield point of 35,000 psi, the steel was drawn to sucessive reductions of thickness up to about 58 percent, and the corresponding stresses plotted as the heavy straight line. The entire graph was then extrapolated to 100 percent reduction, giving the **modulus of strain hardening** as indicated, and to zero stress so that all materials might be plotted on the same graph. Lines of equal reduction are slanting lines through the point marking the modulus of strain hardening at theoretical 100 percent reduction. Starting at any initial condition of previous cold work on the heavy line, a percentage reduction from this condition will be indicated by a horizontal traverse to the slanting reduction line of corresponding magnitude and the resulting increase in stress by the vertical traverse from this point to the heavy line.

The traverse shown involved three draws from the annealed condition of 30, 25, and 15 percent each, and resulting stresses of 53,000, 63,000, and 68,000 psi. After the initial 30 percent reduction, the next 25 percent uses (1.00 − 0.30) × 0.25, or 17.5 percent more of the cold-working range; the next 15 percent reduction uses (1.00 − 0.30 − 0.175) × 0.15, or about 8 percent of the original range totaling 30 + 17.5 +

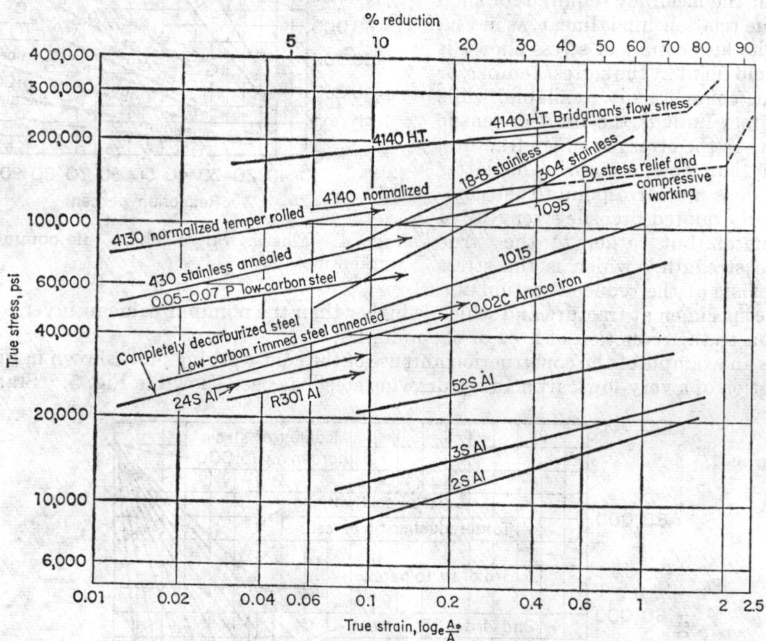

FIG. 6. True-stress–true-strain curves for typical metals. (*Crane and Hauf, E. W. Bliss Co.*)

8 = 55.5 percent. This may be compared with the test value percent reduction in area for the particular material. The same result might have been obtained, die operation permitting, by a single reduction of 55 percent, as shown. Any appreciable reduction beyond this point would come dangerously close to the limit of plastic flow, and consequently an annealing is called for before any further work is done on the piece.

Figure 6 shows the approximate **true-stress–true-strain** plotting of common plastic range values, for comparison with Fig. 4.

A practical manufacturing method of judging relative plasticity is to compute the ratio of initial yield point to the ultimate tensile strength as developed in the tensile test. Thus a General Motors research memo in 1955 listed steel with an 0.51 **yield-tensile ratio** (22,000 psi yp/43,000 psi U.T.S.) as being suitable for really severe draws of exposed parts. When the ratio reached about 0.75, the steel should be used only for flat parts or possibly those with a bend of not more than 90 deg. The higher ratios obviously represent a narrowing range of workability or residual plasticity.

Rolling Operations

Rolling of sheets, coils, bars, and shapes is a primary process using plastic ranges both above and below recrystallization to prepare metals for further working or for fabrication. Metal squeezed in the bite area of the rolls moves out lengthwise with very little spreading in width. This compressive working above the yield point of the metal may be aided in some cases by maintaining a substantial tensile strain in the direction of rolling.

A cast or forged billet or slab is usually preheated for the preliminary breakdown stage of rolling, although considerable progress is being made with pouring some metals directly into the first pair of rolls. A reversing hot mill may achieve 5,000 percent elongation of an original billet in a series of manual or automatic passes. Alternatively, the billet may pass progressively through, say, 10 hot mills in rapid succession. Such a production setup requires precise control so that each mill stand will run enough faster than the previous one to make up for the elongation of the metal that has taken place. Hot-rolled steel may be sold for many purposes with the black mill scale on it. Alternatively, it may be acid-pickled to remove the scale and treated with oil or lime for corrosion protection. To prevent scale from forming in hot-rolling, a non-oxidizing atmosphere may be maintained in the mill area, a highly special plant design.

Pack rolling of a number of sheets stacked together provides means of retaining enough heat to hot-roll thin sheets, as for high-silicon electric steels.

Cold-rolling is practical in production of thin coil stock with the more ductile metals. The number of passes or amount of reduction between anneals is determined by the rate of work hardening of the metal. Successive stands of cold-rolling help to retain heat generated in working. Tension provided by mill reels and between stands helps to increase the practical reduction per step. Bright annealing in a controlled atmosphere avoids surface pockmarks, which are difficult to get out. For high-finish stock, the rolls must be maintained with equal finish.

Protective coating is best exemplified by high-speed tinplate mills in which coil stock passes continuously through the necessary series of cleaning, plating, and heating steps. Zinc and other metals are also applied by plating but not on the same scale. **Clad** sheets (high-strength aluminum alloys with pure aluminum surface for protection against electrolytic oxidation) are produced by rolling together; *e.g.*, an alloy-aluminum billet is hot-rolled together with plates of pure aluminum above and below it through a series of reducing passes, with precautions to ensure clean adhesion.

On the other hand, prevention of adhesion, as by a separating film, is essential in the final stages of **foil rolling,** where two coils may have to be rolled together. Such foil may then be **laminated** with suitable adhesive to paper backing materials for wrapping purposes. (See also Sec. 6.)

Shape rolling of structural shapes and rails is usually a **hot** operation with roll-pass contours designed to distribute the displacement of metal in a series of steps dictated largely by experience. **Contour rolling** of relatively thin stock into tubular, channel, interlocking, or varied special cross sections is usually done cold in a series of roll stands for lengthwise bending and setting operations. There is also a wide range of simple bead-rolling, flange-rolling, and seam-rolling operations in relatively thin meterials, especially in connection with the production of barrels, drums, and other containers.

Oscillating or **segmental rolling** probably developed first in the manually fed contour rolling of agricultural implements. In some cases, the suitably contoured pair of roll inserts or roll dies oscillates before the workman, to form hot or cold metal. In other cases, the rolls rotate constantly, toward the operator. The working contour takes only a portion of the circumference, so a substantial clearance angle leaves a space between the rolls. This permits the operator to insert the blank to the tong grip between the rolls and against a fixed gage at the back. Then, as rotation continues, the roll dies grip and form the blank, moving it back to the operator. This process is sometimes automated; such units as **tube-reducing mills** oscillate an entire rolling-mill assembly and feed the work over a mandrel and into the contoured rolls, advancing it and possibly turning it between reciprocating strokes of the roll stands for cold reduction, improved concentricity, and (possibly), the tapering or forming of special sections.

Spinning operations (Fig. 7) apply a rolling-point pressure to relatively limited-lot production of cup, cone, and disk shapes, from floor lamps and TV tube housings to car wheels and large tank ends. Where substantial metal thickness is required, powerful machines and hydraulic servo controls may be used. Some of the large, heavy sections and difficult metals are spun hot.

Rolling operations are distinguished by the relatively rapid and continuous application of working pressure along a limited line of contract. In determining the working area, consider the lineal dimension (width of coil), the bite or reduction in thickness, and the roll-face deflection, which tends to increase the contact area. Approximations

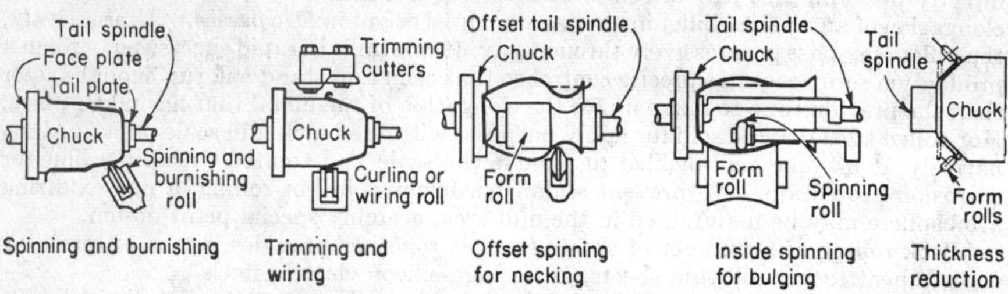

FIG. 7. Spinning operations.

of rolling-mill load and power requirements have been worked out in literature of the AISE and ASME.

Shearing

The shearing group of operations includes such **power-press operations** as blanking, piercing, perforating, shaving, broaching, trimming, slitting, and parting. Shearing operations traverse the entire plastic range of metals to the point of failure.

The maximum pressure P, in pounds, required in shearing operations is given by the equation $P = \pi Dts = Lts$, where s is the resistance of the material to shearing, psi; t is the thickness of the material, in.; L is the length of cut, in., which is the circumference of a round blank πD or the periphery of a rectangular or irregular blank. Approximate values of s are given in Table 2.

Shear (Fig. 8) is the advance of that portion of the shearing edge which first comes in contact with the material to be sheared over the last portion to establish contact, measured in the direction of motion. It should be a function of the thickness t. Shear reduces the maximum pressure because, instead of shearing the whole length of cut at once, the shearing action takes place progressively, shearing on only a portion of the length at any instant. This is illustrated in Figs. 9 and 10, which show the relationships of metal thickness, instantaneous pressure, clearance, and shear for conditions of adequate and of insufficient clearance, respectively. The maximum pressure for any case where the shear is equal to or greater than t is given by the equation $P_{max} = P_{avg} \times t/\text{shear}$, where P_{avg} is the average value of the pressure on a punch, with shear $= t$, from the time it strikes the metal to the time it leaves.

Distortion results from shearing at an angle (Fig. 8) and accordingly, in blanking, where the blank should be flat, the punch should be flat and the shear should be on the die. Conversely, in hole punching, where the scrap is punched out, the die should be flat and the shear should be on the punch. Where there are a number of punches, the effect of shear may be obtained by stepping the punches.

Crowding results during the plastic deformation period, before the fracture occurs, in any shearing operation. Accordingly, when small delicate punches are close to a large punch, they should be stepped shorter than the large punch by at least a third of the metal thickness.

Clearance between the punch and die is required for a clean cut and durability. An old rule of thumb places the clearance all around the punch at 8 to 10 percent of the metal thickness for soft metal and up to 12 percent for hard metal. Actually, hard

Table 2. Approximate Resistance to Shearing in Dies

Material	Annealed state		Hard, cold-worked	
	Resistance to shearing, psi	Penetration to fracture, percent	Resistance to shearing, psi	Penetration to fracture, percent
Lead	3,500	50	Anneals at room temperature	
Tin	5,000	40	Anneals at room temperature	
Aluminum 2S, 3S	9–11,000	60	13–16,000	30
Aluminum 52S, 61S, 62S	12–18,000	.....	24–30,000	
Aluminum 75S	22,000	.....	46,000	
Zinc	14,000	50	19,000	25
Copper	22,000	55	28,000	30
Brass	33–35,000	50–55	52,000	25–30
Bronze 90–10	......	.....	40,000	
Tobin bronze	36,000	25	42,000	
Steel 0.10C	35,000	50	43,000	38
Steel 0.20C	44,000	40	55,000	28
Steel 0.30C	52,000	33	67,000	22
Steel 0.40C	62,000	27	78,000	17
Steel 0.60C	80,000	20	102,000	9
Steel 0.80C	97,000	15	127,000	5
Steel 1.00C	115,000	10	150,000	2
Stainless steel	57,000	39		
Silicon steel	65,000	30		
Nickel	35,000	55		

Available test data do not agree closely. The above table is subject to verification with closer control of metal analysis, rolling and annealing conditions, die clearances. In dinking dies, steel-rule dies, hollow cutters, etc., cutting-edge resistance is substantially independent of thickness: cotton glove cloth (stack, 2 or 3 in. thick), 240 lb per in.; kraft paper (stack tested, 0.20 in. thick), 385 lb per in., celluloid (11/32 in. thick, warmed in water to 120 to 150 F), 300 lb per in.

metal requires less clearance for a clean fracture than soft, but it will stand more. In some cases, with delicate punches, clearance is as high as 25 percent. Where the hole diameter is important, the punch should be the desired diameter and the clearance should be added to the die diameter. Conversely, where the blank size is important, the die and blank dimensions are the same and clearance is deducted from the punch dimensions.

The **work per stroke,** as measured by the area under the pressure-distance curve (Figs. 9 or 10), is not affected by shear; thus the area under each of the curves in Fig. 9 is the same. It may be approximated as the product of the maximum pressure and the

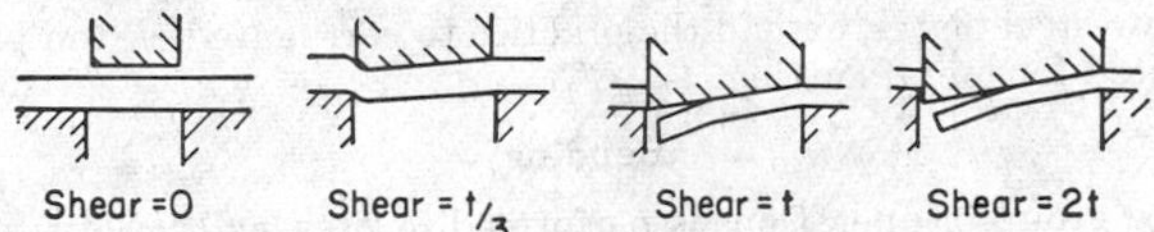

FIG. 8. Diagrams illustrating shear.

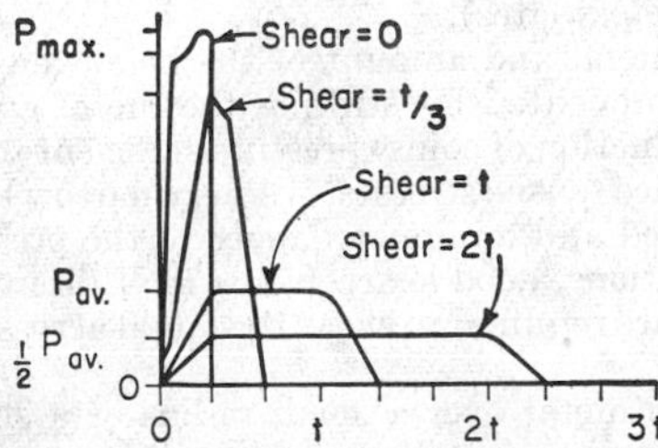

FIG. 9. Influence of shear with clearance adequate for clean fracture.

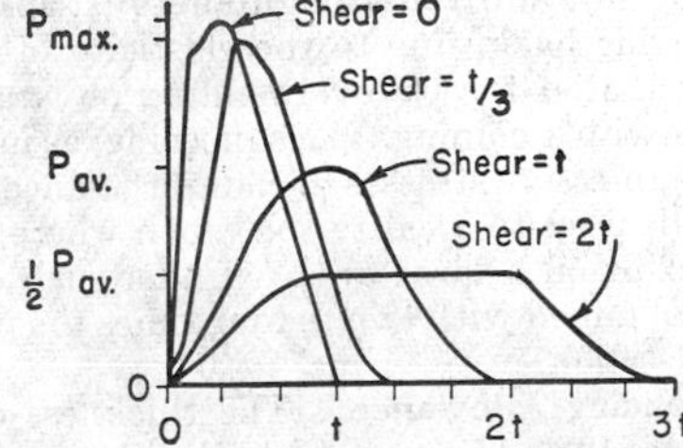

FIG. 10. Influence of shear with insufficient clearance.

metal thickness, although it is only about 20 to 80 percent of that product depending upon the clearance and the ductility of the metal. Reducing the clearance causes secondary fractures and increases the work done. With sufficient clearance for a clean fracture, the work is a little less than the product of the maximum pressure, the metal thickness, and the percentage reduction in thickness at which the fracture occurs. Approximate values for this are given in Table 2. The **power required** may be obtained from the work per stroke plus a 10 to 20 percent friction allowance.

Shaving. A sheared edge may be squared up roughly by shaving once, allowing for the shaving of mild sheet steel about 10 percent of the metal thickness. This allowance may be increased somewhat for thinner material and should be decreased for thicker and softer material. In making several cuts, the amount removed is reduced each time. For extremely fine finish a round-edged burnishing die or punch, say 0.001 or 0.0015 in. tight, may be used. Aluminum parts may be blanked (as for impact extrusion) with a fine finish by putting a 30 deg bevel, approx one-third the metal thickness on the die opening, with a near metal-to-metal fit on the punch and die, and pushing the blank through the highly polished die.

Squaring shears for sheet or plate may have their blades arranged in either of the ways shown in Fig. 11. The square-edged blades in (*a*) may be reversed to give four cutting edges before they are reground. Single-edged blades, as shown in (*b*), may have a clearance angle on the side where the blades pass, to reduce the working friction. They may also be ground at an angle or rake, on the face which comes in contact with the metal. This reduces the bending and consequent distortion at the edge. Either type of blade distorts also in the other direction owing to the angle of shear on the length of the blades (see Fig. 8). Cutting speed is 3 to 30 fpm, depending in part upon the thickness of the material.

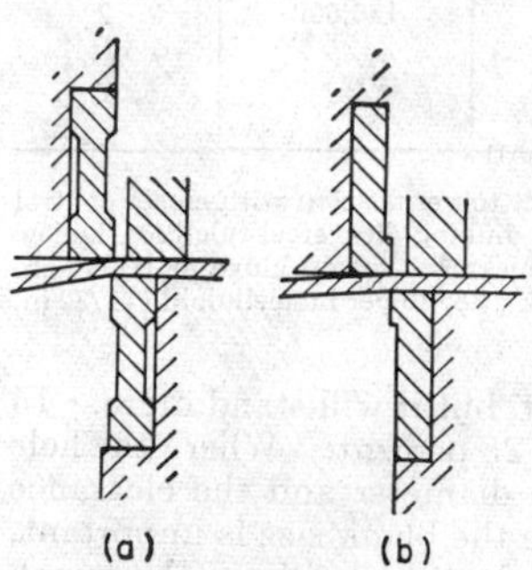

FIG. 11. Squaring shears.

Circular cutters for slitters and circle shears may also be square-edged (on most slitters) or knife-edged (on circle shears). According to one rule their diameter should be not less than 70 times the metal thickness. Cutting speeds vary from 50 to 200 fpm, depending largely upon metal thickness (inverse proportion).

Knife-edge hollow cutters working against end-grain maple blocks represent an old practice in cutting leather, rubber, and cloth in multiple thicknesses. **Steel-rule dies,** made up of knife-edge hard-steel strip economically mounted against a steel plate in a wood matrix with rubber strippers and cutting against hard saw-steel plates, extend the practice to corrugated-carton production and even some limited-lot metal cutting.

Bending

The bending group of operations is performed in **presses** (variety), **brakes** (metal furniture, cornices, roofing), **bulldozers** (heavy rolled sections), **multiple-roll forming machines** (molding, etc.), **draw benches** (door trim, molding, etc.), **forming rolls** (cylinders), and **roll straighteners** (strips, sheets, plates).

Spring back, due to the elasticity of the metal and amount of the bend, may be compensated for by overbending or largely prevented by striking the metal at the radius with a **coining** (*i.e.*, squeezing, as in production of coins) pressure sufficient to set up compressive stresses to counterbalance surface tensile stresses. A very narrow bead may be used to localize the pinch where needed and minimize danger to the press in squeezing on a large area. Under such conditions, good sharp bends in V dies have been obtained with two to four times the pressure required to shear the metal across the same section.

Bending Allowance. The thickness of the metal over a small radius or a sharp corner is 10 or 15 percent less than before bending because the metal moves more easily in tension than in compression. For the same reason the neutral axis of the metal moves in toward the center of the corner radius. Therefore, in figuring the length of blank L to be allowed for the bend up to an inside radius r of two or three times the metal thickness t, the length may be figured closely as along a neutral line at $0.4t$ out from the inside radius. Thus, with reference to Fig. 12, for any angle a in deg and other dimensions in in., $L = (r + 0.4t)2\pi a/360 = (r + 0.4t)a/57.3$.

The factor $0.4t$, which locates the neutral axis, is subject to some variation (say 0.35 to $0.45t$) according to radius, condition of metal, and angle. In figuring allowances for sharp bends, note that the metal builds up on the compression side of the corner. Therefore, in locating the neutral axis, consider an inside radius r of about $0.05t$ as a minimum.

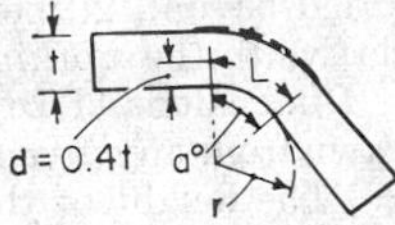

FIG. 12. Bending allowance.

Roll straighteners work on the principle of bending the metal beyond its elastic limit in one direction over rolls small enough in diameter, in proportion to the metal thickness, to give a permanent set, and then taking that bend out by repeatedly reversing it in direction and reducing it in amount. Metal is also straightened by gripping and stretching it beyond its elastic limit and also by hammering; the results of the latter operation depend entirely upon the skill of the operator.

For approximating **bending loads,** the beam formula may be used but must be very materially increased because of the short spans. Thus, for a span of about four times the depth of section, the bending load is about 50 percent more than that indicated by the beam formula. It increases from this to nearly the shearing resistance of the section where some **ironing** (*i.e.* the thinning of the metal when clearance between punch and die is less than the metal thickness) occurs. Where hit-home dies do a little coining to "set" the bend, the pressure may range from two or three times the shearing resistance, with striking beads and proper care, up to very much higher figures.

The work to roll-bend a sheet or plate t in. thick with a volume of V cu in., into curved shape of radius r in., has been given as $W = CS(t/r)V/48$ ft-lb, in which S is the tensile strength and C is an experience factor between 1.4 and 2.

Drawing

Drawing includes operations in which metal is pulled or drawn, in suitable containing tools, from flat sheets or blanks into cylindrical cups or rectangular or irregular shapes, deep or shallow. It also includes reducing operations on shells, tube, wire, etc., in which the metal being drawn is pulled through dies to reduce the diameter or size of the shape. All drawing and reducing operations, by an applied tensile stress in the material, set up circumferential compressive stresses which crowd the metal into the desired shape. The relation of the shape or diameter before drawing to the shape or diameter after drawing determines the magnitude of the stresses. Excessive draws or reductions cause thinning or tearing out near the bottom of a shell. Severe cold-drawing operations require very ductile material and, in consequence of the amount of plastic deformation, harden the metal rapidly and necessitate annealing to restore the ductility for further working.

The **pressure used in drawing** is limited to the load to shear the bottom of the shell out, except in cases where the side wall is ironed thinner, when wall friction makes somewhat higher loads possible. It is less than this limit for round shells which are shorter than the limiting height and also for rectangular shells. Drawing occurs only around the corner radii of rectangular shells, the straight sides being merely free bending.

A **holding pressure** is required in most initial drawing and some redrawing, to prevent the formation of wrinkles due to the circumferential compressive stresses. Where the blank is relatively thin compared with its diameter, the blank-holding pressure for round work is likely to vary up to about one-third of the drawing pressure. For material heavy enough to provide sufficient internal resistance to wrinkling, no pressure is required. Where a drawn shape is very shallow, the metal must be stretched beyond its elastic limit in order to hold its shape, making it necessary to use higher blankholding loads, often in excess of the drawing pressure. To grip the edges sufficiently to do this, it is often advisable to use **draw beads** on the blank-holding surfaces if sufficient pressure is available to form these beads.

Some shells, which are very thick or very shallow compared with their diameter, do not require a blank holder. Blank-holding pressure may be obtained through toggle, crank, or cam mechanisms built into the machine or by means of air cylinders, spring-pressure attachments, or rubber bumpers under the bolster plate. The length of car springs should be about 18 in. per in. of draw to give a fairly uniform drawing pressure and long life. The use of car springs has been largely superseded by hydraulic and pneumatic cushions. Rubber bumpers may be figured on a basis of about 7.5 psi of cross-sectional area per 1 percent of compression. In practice they should never be loaded beyond 20 percent compression, and as with springs, the greater the length relative to the working stroke, the more uniform is the pressure.

Dimensions of Drawn Shells. The smallest and deepest round shell that can be drawn from any given blank has a diameter d of 65 to 50 percent of the blank diameter D. The height of these shells is $h = 0.35d$ to $0.75d$, approximately. Higher shells have occasionally been drawn with ductile material and large punch and die radii. Greater thickness of material relative to the diameter also favors deeper drawing.

The area of the bottom and of the side walls added together may be considered as equal to the area of the blank for approximations. If the punch radius is appreciable, the area of a neutral surface about $0.4t$ out from the inside of the shell may be taken for approximations. Accurate blank sizes may be obtained only by trial, as the metal tends to thicken toward the top edge and to get thinner toward the bottom of the shell wall in drawing.

Approximate diameters of blanks for shells are given by the expression $\sqrt{d^2 + 4dh}$, where d is the diameter and h the height of the shell.

In **redrawing** to smaller diameters and greater depths the amount of reduction is usually decreased in each step. Thus in double-action redrawing with a blank holder, the successive reductions may be 25, 20, 16, 13, 10 percent, etc. This progression is modified by the relative thickness and ductility of the metal. Single-action redrawing without a blank holder necessitates smaller steps and depends upon the shape of the dies and punches. The steps may be 19, 15, 12, 10 percent, etc. Smaller reductions per operation seem to make possible greater total reductions between annealings.

Rectangular shells may be drawn to a depth of four to six times their corner radius. It is sometimes desirable, where the sheet is relativley thin, to use draw beads at the corners of the shell or near reverse bends in irregular shapes to hold back the metal and assist in the prevention of wrinkles.

Work in drawing is approximately the product of the length of the draw, and the maximum punch pressure, as the load rises quickly to the peak, remains fairly constant, and drops off sharply at the end of the draw unless there is stamping or wall friction. To this, add the work of blank holding which, in the case of cam and toggle pressure, is the product of the blank-holding pressure and the spring of the press at that pressure (which is small). For single-action presses with spring, rubber, or air-drawing attachments it is the product of the average blank-holding pressure and the length of draw.

Rubber-die forming, especially of the softer metals and for limited-lot production, uses one relatively hard member of metal, plaster, or plastic with a hard powder filler to control contour. The mating member may be a rubber or neoprene mattress or a hydraulically inflatable bag, confined and at 3,000 to 7,000 psi. Babbitt, oil, and water have also been used directly as the mobile member. A large hydraulic press, often with a sliding table or tables, and even static containers with adequate pumping systems are used.

Hot drawing above the recrystallization range applies single- and double-action drawing principles. For light gages of plastics, paper, and hexagonal-lattice metals such as magnesium, dies and punches may be heated by gas or electricity. For thick steel plate and heat-treatable alloys, the mass of the blank may be sufficient to hold the heat required.

Lubricants for Presswork. Many jobs may be done dry, but better results and longer life of dies are obtained by the use of a lubricant. Lard or sperm oil is used when punching iron, steel, or copper. Petroleum jelly is used for drawing aluminum. A soap solution is commonly used for drawing brass, copper, or steel. One manufacturer uses 90 percent mineral oil, 5 percent rosin, and 5 percent oleic acid for light work and an emulsion of a mineral oil, degras, and a pigment consisting of chalk, sulphur, or lithopone for heavy work. (See also Sec. 6.)

For heavy drawing operations and extrusion, steels may have a zinc phosphate coating bonded on, and a zinc or sodium stearate bonded to that, to withstand pressures over 300,000 psi. An anodized coating for aluminum may be used as a host for the lubricant. It is reported that such a chemical treatment plus a lacquer or plastic coating and plus a lubricant is effective for severe ironing operations.

The problem is to prevent local pressure welding from starting as galling or pickup, with resulting scratching, by maintaining a fluid film separation between metal surfaces. At moderate pressures, almost any viscous liquid lubricant will do the job. Rust protection and easy removal of the lubricant are often major factors in the choice.

Shock-wave forming for limited lots is developing in several ways. **Explosive forming,** especially for large-area drawn or formed shapes, usually requires one metal contour-control die immersed in fluid as in a lake. Explosives manufacturers have developed means of computing the charge and the distance that it should be suspended above the blank to be formed. The space back of the blank in the die has to be evacuated. A blank-holding ring to minimize wrinkle formation in the flange area is bolted very tightly to the die, with an O-ring seal to prevent leakage.

Electrohydraulic forming is similar to explosive forming except that the shock wave is imparted electrically from a large battery of capacitors. ASTM Papers SP-1963 184, 185, and 186, by engineers of Republic Aviation Corp., describe the electrodes, tool buildup, and impact distribution demonstrating this method at 10,000 volts and 155,000 joules capacity. **Magnetic forming** uses the same source of power but does not require a fluid medium. A flexible pancake coil under a pending Republic patent delivers the magnetic shock pulse.

Squeezing

The squeezing group of operations are those in which the metal is worked in compression. Resultant tensile strains occur, however; in cases where the metal is thin compared with its area and there is an appreciable movement of the metal, there results a pyramiding of pressure toward the center of the die which may prove serious. The metal is incompressible (beyond about 1 percent), and consequently, to reduce the thickness of any volume of metal in the center of the blank, its area must be increased which involves spreading or stretching all the metal around it. The surrounding metal acts like shrunk bands and offers a resistance increasing toward the center and often many times the mere compressive resistance of the material.

Squeezing operations and particularly the squeezing of steel are practically the severest of all press operations. They may be divided into four general classifications according to severity, although in every group there will be found examples of working to the limit of what the die steels will stand, which may be taken at about 100 tons per sq in. The severer operations, such as cold bottom extrusion and wall extrusion, are limited to the softer metals. Squeezing operations ordinarily require pressure through a very short distance, the pressure starting at the compressive yield strength of the material over the surface being squeezed and rising to a maximum at bottom stroke. This maximum is greatest when the metal is thin compared with its area or when the die is entirely closed as for coining. Care must be taken, on all squeezing operations, in the setting of presses and avoidance of double blanks or extra-heavy blanks as the presses must be stiff. In squeezing solidly across bottom center the mechanical advantage is such that a small difference in thickness or setup can make a very large difference in pressure exerted. For this reason high-speed self-contained hydraulic presses, with automatic pressure-control and size blocks, are now finding favor for some of this work.

Sizing, or the flattening or surfacing of parts of forgings or castings, is usually the least severe of the squeezing group. Tolerances are ordinarily closer than for the milling operations which are supplanted. When extremely close tolerances are required, say plus or minus one thousandth, arrange substantial size blocks to take half or two-thirds of the total load. These take up uniformly the bearing-oil films and any slight deflection of the bed and bolster and minimize the error in spring back due to variation in thickness, hardness, and area of the rough forging or casting. The usual amount left for squeezing is 1/32 to 1/16 in. Presses may be selected for this service on a basis of 60 to 80 tons per sq in., although 100 tons is more often used in the automobile trade for reserve capacities. When figuring from experimental results obtained in testing machines, the recorded loads are usually doubled in selecting a press, in order to allow for the difference among the speed of the machines, the positive action, and a safety margin.

Swaging or cold forging involves squeezing of the blank to an appreciably different shape. Success in performing such operations on steel usually depends upon squeezing a relatively small area with freedom to flow without restraint. Dies for this work must usually be substantially backed up with hardened steel plates. The edge of the blank after coining is usually ragged and must be trimmed for appearance.

Hot forging is similar in certain respects to the above but permits much greater movement of metal. Hot forging may be done in drop hammers, percussion presses, power presses, or forging machines, when dies are used; or in steam hammers, helve hammers, or hydraulic presses, on plain anvils.

The pressure exerted by hydraulic presses and steam hammers for jobbing work should be about as follows:

Ingot diam, in.	5	8	12	16	24	36	48	60	72
Press, tons	100	200	400	600	1,000	1,500	2,000	3,000	4,000
Hammer, tons	½	1	3	5	10	20	40	80	120

Drop hammers are rated according to weight of ram. For carbon steel they may be selected on a basis of 50 to 55 lb of ram weight per square inch of projected area of the forging, including as much of the flash as is squeezed. This allowance should be increased to 60 lb for 0.20 carbon steel, 70 lb for 0.30 carbon steel, and up to about 130 lb for tungsten steel (The Billings and Spencer Co., Hartford, Conn.).

In figuring the **forging pressure,** multiply the projected area of the forging, including the portion of the flash that is squeezed, by approximately one-third of the cold compressive strength of the material. Another method gives the forging pressure at three to four times the compressive strength of the material at forging temperatures times the projected area, for presses; or at ten times the compressive strength at forging temperatures times the projected area, for hammers. The pressure builds up to a rather high figure at bottom stroke owing to the cooling of the metal particularly in the flash and to the small amount of relief for excess metal which the flash allows.

For **brass press forgings** a good mixture is about Cu, 59; Zn, 39; Pb, 2 percent forged at 1300 to 1400 F. The power curve in press forging rises sharply, from the compressive strength at forging heat times the projected area of the slug to three or more times that quantity at bottom stroke. A large flash area assists in driving the metal into deep die recesses.

In **heading operations,** hot or cold, the length of wire or rod that can be gathered into a head, without side restraint, in a single operation, is limited to three times the diameter. In coining and then heading large heads, cold, wire of about 0.08 carbon must be used to avoid excessive strain-hardening.

Forging Dies. Drop-forge dies are usually of steel or steel castings. A good all-round grade of **steel** is a 0.60 percent carbon open-hearth. Dies of this steel will forge mild steel, copper, and tool steel satisfactorily if the number of forgings required is not too large. For a large number of tool-steel forgings, tool-steel dies of 0.80 to 0.90 percent carbon may be used and for extreme conditions, 3½ percent nickel steel.

Die blocks of alloy steels have special value for the production of drop forgings in large quantities. Metals Handbook, 1961, recommends the following alloy steel compositions: for hot forgings, 0.60 C, 0.25 Cr, or 0.70 C, 0.20 V; for cold forgings, 0.85 C, 0.20 V; for drop-hammer work, 0.55 C, 1.00 Cr, 0.45 Mo, or 0.50 C, 1.60 Ni, 1.00 Cr, 0.30 Mo; for forging presses, 0.55 C, 2.00 Ni, 1.00 Cr, 0.75 Mo, or 0.35 C, 5.00 Cr, 1.50 Mo. Steels recommended for hot die inserts include the above and also 0.55C, 1.00 Si, 1.25 Cr, 2.50 W, as well as tungsten steels of 9.00, 12.00, and 15.00 W.

For large massive dies or for intermittent service, chrome-nickel-molybdenum alloys are preferred. In closed die work, where the dies must dissipate considerable heat, the tungsten steels are preferred, with resulting increase in wear resistance but decrease in toughness.

For very large pieces with deep impressions, **cast-steel** dies are sometimes used. For large dies liable to spring in hardening, 0.85 **carbon steel** high in manganese is sometimes used unhardened.

Good **die-block proportions** for width and depth are as follows:

Width, in.	8	10	12	14
Depth, in.	6	7	7	7 or 8

For ordinary work, 1½ in. of metal between impression and edge of block is sufficient.

Dimensions of **dovetailed die shanks**: for hammers up to 1,200 lb, 4 in. wide and 1⅛ in. deep, with sides dovetailed at angles of 6 deg with the vertical; for hammers from 1,200 to 3,000 lb in size, 6 in. wide and 1½ in. deep, with 6 deg angles.

The **minimum draft for** the **impressions** is 7 deg, although for parts difficult to draw this may be increased up to 15 deg. It is not uncommon to have several drafts in the same impression.

Open-hearth and tool-steel **dies** are **hardened** by heating in a carbonizing box packed in charcoal and dipping face downward over a jet of brine. The jet is allowed to strike into the impression, thus freeing the face of steam and producing uniform hardness. After hardening, they are drawn in an oil bath to a temperature of 500 to 550 F.

The forging production per pair of dies is largely affected by the size and shape of the impression, the material forged, the material in the dies, the quality of heating of stock to be forged, and the care exercised in use. It may vary from a few hundred pieces to 50,000 or more. A normal **life** for a pair of dies under average conditions may be 20,000 pieces.

Coining, Stamping, and Embossing. The metal is well confined in closed dies in which it is forced to flow to fill the shape. The government gives the following pressures: silver quarter, 100 tons; nickel (0.25 Ni, 0.75 Cu), 90 tons; copper cent, 40 tons. In stamping designs, lettering, etc., in sheet metal the thickness is so little compared with the area that there is practically no relief for excess pressure. Where sharp designs are required, as in stamping panels, the dies should be arranged to strike on a narrow line (say $\frac{1}{32}$ in.) around the outline. If a sharp design is not obtained, it is often best to correct deflection in the machine by shimming or more substantial backing. Increasing the pressure only aggravates the condition and may break the press. General practice for light over-all stamping is to allow 5 to 10 tons per square inch of area that is to be stamped, except in areas where the yield point must be exceeded.

Extrusion is the severest of the squeezing processes. The metal is forced to flow rapidly through an orifice, being otherwise confined and subject largely to the laws of hydraulics, with allowances for restraint of flow and for work hardening. Power-press **impact extrusion** began with tin and lead collapsible tubes. It has been extended to the backward and forward extrusion of aluminum, brass, and copper in pressure ranges of 30 to 60 or more tons per sq in., and mild steel at pressures up to 165 tons per sq in. Hot impact extrusion of steel, as in projectile piercing, ranges from about 25 to 50 tons per sq in. **Forward extrusion** of long tubes, rods, and shapes usually performed hot in hydraulic presses has been extended from the softer metals to the extrusion of steels. Most work is done horizontally because of the lengths of the extrusions. Some vertical mechanical-press equipment is used in hot extrusion of steel tubing. **Screw extrusion** of the plastics requires closely controlled heating of the barrel around the feeding screw, which is between the feeding hopper and the contour die. Preheating for extrusion is in approximately the same range as temperatures for injection molding (Table 1).

Powder compacting apparently began with drug pills and carbon electrodes. A reasonable uniformity of particle size, fairly free of fines, is desirable for automatic feeding. The powders tend to arch and clog, particularly in narrow sections, so that vibrating devices are sometimes added. Ejectors are often timed so that they help to draw the powder into the die in which it is to be compacted. The volume of the powder fill is usually about three times the volume (depth) of the finished compact. Compacting pressures vary from as little as 1 tsi to about 20 tsi for the metals. Humidity, oxidation, and even static electricity are often problems in the storage and use of powders. Metal powders usually require careful blending with $\frac{1}{2}$ to 1 percent of metallic soap (*e.g.*, zinc stearate) to lubricate ejection from the compacting die and perhaps to provide a temporary bonding. Die or mold surfaces must be polished in the direction of ejection to a high finish to facilitate stripping. Ejecting pressures may range from 10 to 100 percent of the compacting pressure, depending on the contour. Thus a gear is much harder to strip than a rectangular contour.

Sintering of metal-powder compacts at temperatures below the melting point provides the time and electron activity needed to establish bonded strength between particles. An initial lower temperature permits volatilization of much of the lubricant. A reducing atmosphere is often needed to eliminate oxides. Both batch and conveyor-type continuous furnaces are used. For some sintered carbides, the compacting pressure and sintering action are combined in a hydraulic press using carbon dies and induction heating.

Molding under pressure of synthetic plastics or rubbers requires control of temperature, heating time, and in some cases cooling time to suit the material and volume being handled. **Compression molding** usually requires the loading of preformed compacts or blanks in heated dies. Preforms may also be preheated electronically to save press time. **Transfer molding** usually first closes the die or mold with a large hydraulic cylinder to hold the joint line tight against flash and then forces the charge into the cavity by means of a smaller cylinder. **Injection molding** makes this process automatic by adding a hopper to maintain a supply of powder, a controlled injection stroke to meter the correct amount of powder, a controlled heating zone to bring the charge up to temperature before it is injected into the mold cavities, an ejecting means, and automatic cycle timing.

Laminating of plastic bonded sheet materials uses steam or electrically heated plates or platens in hydraulic presses. Where more than one set of hot plates is used, the method of suspension opens the plate spacing for removal and reloading. Thus a dozen or more sheets of plywood can be cured at once, using sheet Tago glue interleaved between wood plies. Layers of fabric or other filler material are also cured in sheet or other forms, the curing times depending upon thermal conductivity and reaction time and temperatures required. Different materials may be bonded together, *e.g.*, plywood, metal foil, and patterned plastics for table tops.

EQUIPMENT FOR WORKING METALS AND PLASTICS

REFERENCE: *Thomas Register* (of machinery builders, etc), Thomas Publishing Co., New York 1.

The **mass-production** industries use an extremely wide variety of machines to force materials to flow plastically into desired shapes (as compared to the more gradual methods of obtaining shapes by cutting away surplus material in machine tools). The application of working pressure may use hydraulic, pneumatic, mechanical, or electrical means to apply pressing, hammering, or rolling forces. Mechanically and hydraulically actuated devices cover much the same range. In general, the mechanical equipment is faster, easier to maintain, and more efficient to operate by reason of energy-storing flywheels. The hydraulic equipment is more flexible and more easily adjusted to limited lots in pressure, positions, and strokes. Mechanical handling or feeding devices incorporated in or serving many of these more or less specialized machines further extend their productivity.

Power presses consist of a frame of substantial construction with devices for holding the dies or tools and a moving member or slide for actuating one portion of the dies. This slide usually receives its movement from a crankshaft furnished with a clutch for intermittent operation and a flywheel to supply the sudden power requirement. **Hydraulic presses** have no crankshaft, clutch, or flywheel but employ rams actuated by pumps.

The crankshaft is ordinarily the limiting factor in the pressure capacity of the machine and accordingly is often taken as the basis for tonnage ratings. There is no uniform basis for this rating, owing to variations in shaft proportions and materials and in the different relative severity of various press operations. The following valuation is tentative and is based on the shaft diameter in the main bearings. The bending strength is figured at a section through the center of the crankpin and the combined bending and torsional strength at the inside ends of the main bearings, taking the bending fulcrum at a distance out from these points equal to one-third the length of the main bearings. In the case of double-crank presses and twin-drive arrangements, the relative proportion of the torsional load must be varied to suit, but, except in the cases of long strokes, it is usually small. The working strength is based upon a stress in the extreme fibers of 28,000 psi. The limit bearing capacities are taken approximately at 5,000 psi on the crankpins and 2,500 psi average over the main bearings for ordinary steel on cast-iron press bearings with proper grooving. On the knuckle-joint-type presses with hardened tool-steel bearing surfaces and flood lubrication, the bearings will take up to about 30,000 psi. On eccentric-type shafts where the main bearings support right up to the oversize pin on each side, the limiting factor is the bearing load. The shaft is practically in shear, so that is has a considerable overload capacity (about $7d^2$ tons). In Table 3, uniform-diameter single crankshafts are those in which for manufacturing reasons the diameter is the same at the crankpin and at the main bearings. Other crankshafts have an oversize crankpin to balance the bending load at the center with the combined bending and torsional load at the side. The strength of the shaft is figured at mid-stroke, and the stroke and tonnage capacity are given in terms of the diameter d at the main bearings. Where the working load comes on only near the bottom stroke, the shaft press capacity may be figured as if the stroke were shorter in proportion.

Table 3 gives the rated capacities of a series of power presses as a function of the shaft diameter.

The speed of operation of the press depends upon the energy requirement and the crankpin velocity. The latter determines the velocity of impact on the tools. In blanking, the blow varies directly with the contact speed and the thickness and hardness of the material. On drawing operations the variation depends upon contact speed, ductility of material, lubricant, etc.

Table 3. Power-press Shaft Capacities

(E. W. Bliss Co.)

Type of press crankshaft	Max stroke, in.	Capacity, tons
Single crank, single drive, uniform diameter	d	$2.8d^2$
Single crank, single drive, oversize crankpin	d	$3.5d^2$
Single crank, single drive, oversize crankpin	$2\ d$	$2.2d^2$
Single crank, single drive, oversize crankpin	$3\ d$	$1.6d^2$
Single crank, twin drive, oversize crankpin	$2\ d$	$3.5d^2$
Single crank, twin drive, oversize crankpin	$3\ d$	$2.7d^2$
Double crank, single drive, oversize crankpin	$0.75d$	$5.5d^2$
Double crank, single drive, oversize crankpin	d	$4.4d^2$
Double crank, single drive, oversize crankpin	$2\ d$	$2.5d^2$
Double crank, single drive, oversize crankpin	$3\ d$	$1.7d^2$
Double crank, twin drive, oversize crankpin	$1.5\ d$	$5.5d^2$
Double crank, twin drive, oversize crankpin	$3\ d$	$3.2d^2$
Single eccentric, single or twin drive	$0.5\ d$	$4.3d^2$

The energy required per stroke is practically the product of the average load and the working distance, plus friction allowance, assumed at about 16 percent. On short-stroke operations, such as blanking, the working energy is supplied almost entirely by slowing down the flywheel; motor or belt pull serves merely to return the flywheel to speed during the large part of the cycle in which no work is done. In drawing operations, the working period is considerable, and in many cases the belt takes the largest part of the working load. In this case, add to the available flywheel energy, the work done by the belt. This amounts, for example, to 70 lb per in. of width of the belt, multiplied by the ratio of the belt velocity to the crankpin velocity, multiplied by the length of the working stroke on the crank circle in feet. The maximum flywheel slowdown has been assumed as up to 10 percent for continuous operation and up to 20 percent for intermittent operation. The following formula is based upon average press-flywheel proportions and a slowdown of 10 percent. The result may be doubled for 20 percent slowdown.

The flywheel capacity per stroke at 10 percent slowdown in inch-tons equals $WD^2N^2/5{,}260{,}000{,}000$, where W is the weight of the flywheel, lb, D is the diameter, in., and N is the rpm.

The difference between non-geared and geared presses is only in speed of operation and the relatively greater flywheel capacity.

Press frames are designed for stiffness and usually have a considerable excess strength. Good practice is to figure cast-iron sections on a basis of about 2,000 to 3,000 psi. **C-frame presses** are subjected to an appreciable arc spring amounting ordinarily to between 0.0005 and 0.002 in. per ton, because the center of gravity of the frame section is a considerable distance back of the working center line of the press. **Straightsided presses** eliminate that portion of the spring or deflection which is on an arc. **Built-up frame presses** are held together with steel tie rods shrunk in under an initial tension in excess of the working load so that they minimize stretch in that portion of the press.

Power presses are built in a very wide variety of styles and sizes with shafts ranging from 1 to 21 in. diam. Over a large part of this range they are built with C frames for convenience, straight-sided frames for heavier and thinner work, eccentric shafts for heavy forgings and stampings, double crankshafts for wide jobs, four-point presses for large panel work, underdrive presses in high-production plants where repairs to presses would interfere with flow of production, and knuckle-joint presses for intensely high pressures at the very bottom of the stroke. All these are classified as single-action presses and are used for most of the operations previously discussed.

Double-action presses combine the functions of blank holding with drawing. In the smaller sizes, such presses have cams mounted on the cheeks of the crankshaft to actuate the outer or blank-holding slide. In larger machines, toggle mechanisms are provided to actuate the outer slide, with the advantage that the blank-holding load is taken on the frame instead of the crankshaft. Both of these types afford a considerable power saving over single-action presses equipped with drawing attachments, because the latter must add the blank-holding pressure to the working load for the full depth of the draw.

Types of presses include **foot presses,** in which the pendulum type has the lowest mechanical advantage and the longest stroke; the **lever type,** which has higher mechanical advantage and shorter strokes; **toggle or knuckle type,** which has the highest mechanical advantage and works through the shortest stroke with considerable advantage obtainable from the use of tie rods on fine stamping or embossing work; long-stroke rack and pinion-driven presses; triple-action drawing presses; cam-actuated presses; etc.

Screw presses consist of a conventional frame and a slide which is forced down by a steep pitch screw on the upper end of which is a flywheel or weight bar. Hand-operated machines are used for die testing and for small production stamping, embossing, forming, and other work requiring more power than foot presses. Power-driven screw presses are built with a friction drive for the flywheel and automatic control to limit the stroke. Such presses are built in comparatively large sizes and used to a considerable extent for press forging. They lack the accuracy and speed of power presses built for this work but have a safety factor which power presses have not, in that their action is not positive. In this they closely resemble a drop hammer, although their motion is slower. The energy available for work in these presses is $\frac{1}{2}I_fv^2 + \frac{1}{2}I_sv^2$, in which I_f is the moment of inertia of the flywheel, I_s is the moment of inertia of the spindle, and v is the angular velocity of both.

Self-contained fast-acting **hydraulic presses** are being increasingly used. Equipped with motor-driven variable-displacement oil hydraulic pumps, the speed and pressure of the operating ram or rams are under instant and automatic control; this is particularly advantageous for deep drawing operations. The punch can be brought into initial contact with the work without shock and moved with a uniform controlled velocity through the drawing portion of the cycle. The drawing of stainless steels and alloy aluminums (in which the control of drawing speed is vital), as well as the hot drawing of magnesium, are best done on hydraulic presses. (See also Sec 14.)

The hydraulic press is used in the rubber pad, or "Guerin," process of blanking or forming metals, in which, a laminated-rubber pad replaces one half—usually the female half—of a die. In forming aluminum the practice has developed of using inexpensive dies of soft metal, vulcanized fiber, plastic, wood, or plaster; and cast dies in industries which, like the aircraft industry, require short runs on many different sizes of shapes and parts.

The older accumulator type of hydraulic press construction is still used for hot extrusion and some forging work.

Drop Hammers or Presses. Small belt-lift and board-lift drop presses are used for variety of sheet-metal operations on hardware, cutlery, silverware, etc. Large-area rope-lift drop hammers are used for stamping metal ceilings and the like, usually having a hard die and a soft babbitt or steel punch. Board-lift drop hammers with heads weighing up to 5,000 lb are widely used in the production of steel drop forgings. The energy available for work is the product of the weight of the ram and the length of fall. The following table gives the shaft diameters of trimming presses (for removing the flash) ordinarily used with drop hammers for trimming the same range of forgings.

Drop-hammer Ram Weights and Suitable Trimming-press Shaft Diameters

(E. W. Bliss Co.)

Ram weight, lb	600	800	1,000	1,200	1,500	2,000	2,500	3,000	5,000	8,000
Press shaft diam, in	3½	4	4½	5	5½	6	6½	7	8	9

Helve hammers (Bradley type) are usually belt-driven and carry the hammer face or swage on the end of a beam. The belt is provided with a tightening device, treadle-controlled, permitting the operator to regulate the number and speed of the blows. They are **used for general** and duplicate **forging,** welding, plating drawing, swaging, collaring, spindle making, etc. **Commercial sizes** are 15, 25, 40, 60, 80, 100, 200, 300, and 500 lb. The 200 lb size requires approximately 2 hp to operate.

Strap hammers carry the hammer slung from a strap, usually of leather. The control and operation are the same as for the helve type. They are **adapted for general work,** tool dressing, and the like. **Commercial sizes** are 15, 30, 50, 75, 100, 125, 150, and 200 lb.

Board Drop Hammer. Let W = work of blow, ft-lb; H = weight of hammer and die, lb; g = acceleration due to gravity (= 32.2 ft per sec per sec); h = actual hammer stroke, ft; and v = terminal velocity of hammer, fps. Then, if the hammer and die fall of their own weight, $W = (H/g)v^2/2 = Hh = 0.015\ Hv^2$ (approx). The **lifting power** $L = fF$ when the board is lifted by one roller (when both rollers are driven $L = 2fF$), where f = coefficient of friction of roll and board and F = force with which rolls are pressed together. Since $f = 0.25$ (approx), $L = 0.25F$ and $0.5F$ (approx), respectively.

Part of the lifting power must at first accelerate the motion of the hammer head. Consequently, $L = bH$, where b is a constant which is always > 1.

The motion of the hammer is accelerated with the effort $(b - 1)\ H$ until the speed v has been attained. The friction driving wheels or belt must consequently slip at first. Disregarding frictional resistances, **time** (in seconds) **required to lift hammer** $= t_1 = [0.016v/(b - 1)] + (h/v)$, and the **duration of drop** $= t_2 = 0.124\sqrt{h}$. Generally v = 2.5 to 3.5 fps; b = 1.2 to 2; h = 3 to 6 ft; and H = 100 to 3,000 lb.

Weight of hammer, lb	250	400	600	800	1,000	1,500
Approximate hp required	2	2.5	3	3.5	4	5

Steam hammers may be divided into **three classes.** In the first, the hammer is lifted by steam and drops of its own weight; in the second, steam is admitted above the piston and through its expansion increases the force of the blow; in the third, live steam is admitted above the piston throughout the stroke and the force of the blow is from combined weight of the falling hammer and the pressure of the steam.

In the **first class,** that of the single-acting steam hammer, the lifting power $L = bH$. That part of the force of the steam equal to $(b - 1)H$ is used for accelerating the lifting motion, continuing after the steam has been cut off as long as the pressure under the piston $>H$. These hammers are **used** only **for very large work.** The **weight of** the **hammer** ranges from 25 to 125 tons, and the value of b ranges from 1.5 to 1.2. The disadvantage of this type lies in the fact that the height of the clearance under the piston is directly dependent upon the thickness of the piece of work.

In the **second class,** in which steam is admitted above the piston and allowed to expand, there is an economy in steam consumption, a greater acceleration of the hammer head, and a large number of blows per unit of time. The reliability of operation is not of the best.

To overcome this defect in operation, the **third class** was developed, in which live steam is admitted above the piston. Here the **weight of** the **hammer** head varies from 1 to 25 tons. The control is such that the weight of the hammer itself is available for light blows, and for heavier blows steam is admitted above the piston.

In comparatively small hammers where the head weighs 150 to 2,000 lb, $b = 2$ to 3.5, and the diameter of the piston rod equals 0.5 to 0.65 of the diameter of the piston. The area of the upper piston face is, consquently, 1.3 to 1.7 times that of the lower face. Up to 350 **blows per min** can be obtained, depending on the length of the stroke and the tightness of the stuffing box. These hammers are provided with an automatic reversing gear. The **number and force of** the **blows** can be regulated by throttling the steam, changing the center position of the operating valve, and changing the backlash in the operating gear. The frame of these hammers is usually C-shaped.

The **anvil** in small hammers is usually a single casting. In large hammers it is usually divided into upper and lower anvil blocks. In smaller hammers the anvil is connected with the shears and upper part of the machine. In the larger hammers, however, this is not the case, as the concussions tend to injure the hammer mechanism. For good practice the **weight of** the **anvil** ($= Q$) for hammers used in forging iron is at least eight times the weight of the hammer head; for forging steel, at least twelve times.

The pressure Q_1 exerted by the anvil block on the surface which it supports is assumed to be as follows: for blooming hammers, $Q_1 = (30 \text{ to } 60)hH + Q$; for billet-forging hammers, $Q_1 = (60 \text{ to } 95)hH + Q$; for hammers for steel forging, $Q_1 = (95 \text{ to } 125)hH + Q$.

Commercial Sizes. From mechanical arrangement, steam hammers are called steam drops and single-frame and double-frame steam hammers. Sizes of steam drops range from 400 to 30,000 lb. Sizes of single- and double-frame hammers range from 250 to 4,000 lb and 1,500 to 30,000 lb, respectively. A series of small double-frame steam hammers, known as "tilting hammers," is also made. They are used chiefly by forges producing the smaller sizes of steel bars, as squares and octagons of tool steel. Uniformity in force of blow and length of stroke are the important features. Commercial sizes range from 500 to 2,500 lb.

Pneumatic Hammers. A self-contained type of pneumatic forge hammer (the Bêché) has an air-operated ram with an air-compressing cylinder integral with the frame. The ram is raised by admitting compressed air beneath the ram piston; at the same time a partial vacuum is caused above it. The ram is forced down by a reversal of this action.

This type is made in a number of different models by the Nazel Engineering and Machine Works, Philadelphia. Tests by the maker give the force of the blows for the various sizes and the capacity in maximum sizes of stock, as follows:

Size, lb	66	165	250	350	500	770
Blow, ft-lb	268	948	1,338	2,351	4,116	6,452
Max diam of stock forged, in	2	4	5	7	8	9

Energy of Hammer Blows. Where the striking velocity of a hammer ram is greater than 10 fps, the energy E of the blow (in in.-lb) may be determined from the compression of lead cylinders. From experiments made by W. T. Sears, of the Niles-Bement-Pond Co. (*Am. Mach.*, Mar. 10, 1910), using $1\frac{1}{2} \times 1\frac{1}{2}$ in. cylinders, the following results were obtained (c = compression or shortening of cylinder, in.):

c, in.	0.2	0.4	0.6	0.8	1.0	1.2	1.3
E, in.-lb	900	3,000	6,000	10,500	18,000	34,000	54,000

For any value of c, close results may be obtained from the formula $E = (10{,}800c - 870)/(1.55 - c)$. Where the speed of compression is slow, as in **presses,** it is necessary to know the speed to estimate the energy. Sears gives the following values at two rates of speed and also quotes static-pressure results obtained at Purdue University:

c (in.)	0.2	0.4	0.6	0.8	1.0	1.2	1.25
E (0.0005 fps)	600	2,100	4,000	7,000	11,000	19,200	23,500
E (0.0007 fps)	400	1,600	3,000	5,000	8,000	14,800	18,000
R (Purdue)	400	1,400	2,600	4,100	6,600	12,000	15,000

Rotary motion is used for **working sheet** metal in a variety of machines, including bending rolls (three rolls); rolling straighteners with five, seven, or more rolls; roll forming machines, in which a series of rolls in successive pairs are used to bend the strip material step by step to some desired shape; a series of two-spindle and multiple-spindle machines used for rolling beads, threads, knurls, flanges, and trimming or curling the edges of drawn shells of cylinders; seaming machines for double seaming, crimping, curling, and other operations in the production of tin cans, pieced tinware, etc.; and spinning machines for spinning, burnishing, trimming, curling, shape forming, and thickness reduction. Various production spinning operations and tool arrangements are shown in Fig. 7.

Plate-straightening Machines. The **horsepower required** for plate-straightening machines operating on steel plate is as follows:

Thickness of plate, in	0.25	0.4	0.6	0.8	1.0	1.2	1.4	1.6
Width of plate, in	48.0	52.0	60.0	72.0	88.0	102.0	120.0	140.0
Diameter of rolls, in	5.0	8.0	10.0	12.0	13.0	14.0	15.0	16.0
Horsepower (approx)	6.0	8.0	12.0	20.0	30.0	55.0	90.0	130.0

Power required for angle-iron-straightening machines: for 4 in. angles, 12 hp; for 6 in., 18 hp; for 8 in., 25 hp.

Power or hydraulic presses are used to straighten **large rolled sections.** The presses make 20 to 30 strokes per min, and the amount of flexure is regulated by inserting wedges or pieces of flat iron. The beams are supported on rolls so they can be easily handled. The **power required for presses** of this kind is as follows:

Depth of girder, in	4	6	8	10	12	16	20	24
Horsepower (approx)	3	4	7	11	13	19	23	35

Horizontal plate-bending machines consist of two stationary rolls and a third vertical adjustable upper roll which can be fitted obliquely for taper bending and is held in bearings with spherical seats. The diameter of the rolls can be determined approximately from the equation $r^2 = bt$, in which r is the radius of the roll, b the width of the plate or sheet, and t its thickness, all in inches.

The **power requirements** of horizontal plate- and sheet-bending machines are as follows:

Thickness of plate, in	0.5	0.6	0.8	1	1.2
Horsepower for plate 120 in. wide	10.0	12.0	18.0	27.0	40.0
Horsepower for plate 240 in. wide	30.0	30.0	40.0	55.0	75.0

Vertical plate-bending machines have a hydraulically operated piston which moves an upper and a lower pair of rolls between inclined surfaces of the stationary upright and the crosshead. The bending is done piece by piece against a second stationary upright. Heavy ship plates are rigidly clamped down and bent by a roll operated by two hydraulic pistons. For angular bends or for the production of warped surfaces, the pistons can be operated independently or together. In vertical machines, angles and other rolled shapes are bent between suitably shaped rolls. Pipes are filled with sand to prevent flattening when being bent. For some work, pipes are bent hot between suitable forms operated by hydraulic pressure.

The **rotary swaging machine** for tapering, closing in, and reducing tubes, rods, and hollow articles is essentially a cage carrying a number of rollers and revolving at high speed; *e.g.*, 14 rolls in a cage revolving at 600 rpm will strike 8,400 blows per min on the work.

A rapid succession of light blows is applied to a considerable variety of commercial **riveting** operations such as pneumatic riveting. Another method riveting, described as spinning, involves rotating small rollers rapidly over the top of the rivet and at the same time applying pressure. Neither of these methods involves as intense pressures as are used in riveting by direct pressure either hot or cold. Power presses and C-frame riveters, employing hydraulic pressure or air pressure of 80 to 100 psi, are figured to apply 150,000 psi of the cross section of the body of the rivet for hot working and 300,000 psi for cold working. The plates should be pressed together by a pressure of 0.3 to 0.4 that used in riveting.

WELDING

BY

Edward A. Fenton

REFERENCES: "Welding Handbook" (5 vols.), AWS. "Recommended Practices for Resistance Welding," AWS. "Resistance Welding Manual," Resistance Welder Manufacturers' Assoc. "Resistance Welding—Theory and Use," AWS. Grover, "Manual of Design for Arc Welded Steel Structures," Air Reduction Co. "Procedure Handbook of Arc Welding Design and Practice," The Lincoln Electric Co. "The Oxyacetylene Handbook," The Linde Div. Union Carbide Corp. "Brazing Manual," AWS. "Safety in Welding and Cutting," ASA. Slottman and Roper, "Oxygen Cutting," McGraw-Hill.

FUNDAMENTALS OF WELDING

A weld is defined as a localized coalescence of metal wherein coalescence is produced by heating to suitable temperatures, with or without the application of pressure, and with or without the use of filler metal. The filler metal may have a melting point approximately the same as the base metals (as in arc or gas welding), or it may have a lower melting point but above 800 F (as in brazing). This definition distinguishes welding from mechanical joining and adhesive bonding. The 800 F limit distinguishes brazing from soldering, which is excluded. The definition includes some 37 different processes falling under six general categories: arc welding, gas welding, resistance welding, brazing, solid-state welding, and "other" processes. Of these, the first four are of wide industrial significance.

Basic **types of arc and gas welds** are shown in cross section in Fig. 1, top; at bottom are views of joints commonly used in plate and sheet fabrication. Figure 2 gives typical **dimensions** for plate-edge preparation for making butt joints with six types of

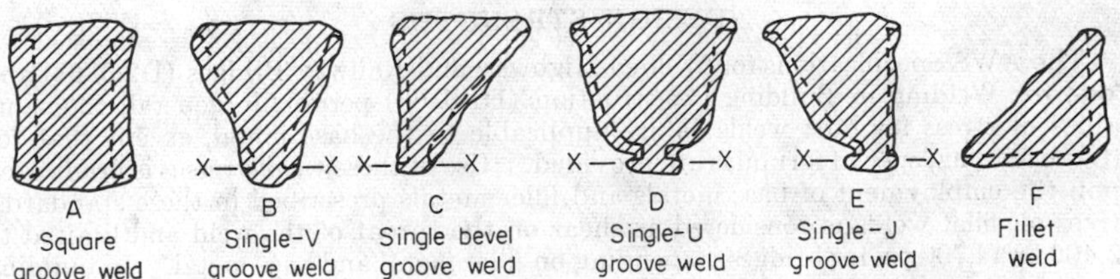

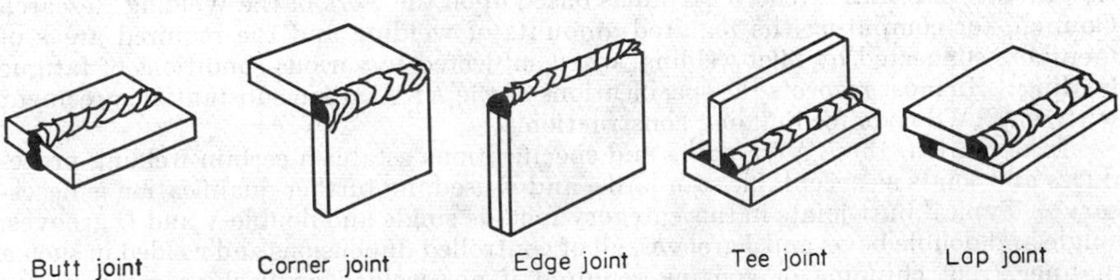

FIG. 1. Some types of welds (upper) and joints (lower).

groove welds deposited by the manual shielded-metal-arc process. The latter is still the most widely used process in the industry.

The basis for weld-groove design is to provide a shape and size of opening that will enable a sound deposition of filler metal, under given conditions, with maximum economy. For other welding processes that employ filler metals, groove dimensions may vary from those shown in Fig. 2. For instance, in submerged-arc welding, greater power input is available and deeper penetration is possible. Therefore, smaller weld grooves are required.

To establish uniform and simple drafting practice, welding symbols have been standardized by AWS and adopted by ASA. Figure 3 shows several basic symbols.

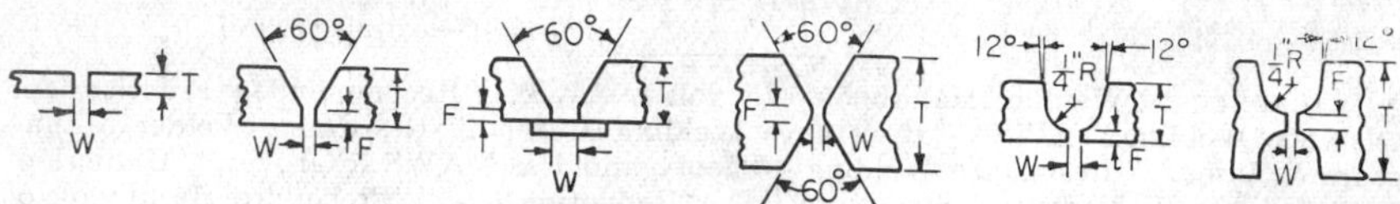

Fig. 2. Weld grooves for manual shielded-metal-arc welding. Dimensions in inches are as follows:

Groove	1	2	3	4	5	6
T	1/8–3/16	1/4 up	1/4 up	1/2 up	3/8 up	3/4 up
W	0–1/16	0–3/16	3/16–1/4	0–3/16	0–1/16	0–1/16
F	....	0–1/16	0–1/16	0–1/16	1/8 ± 1/32	1/8 ± 1/32

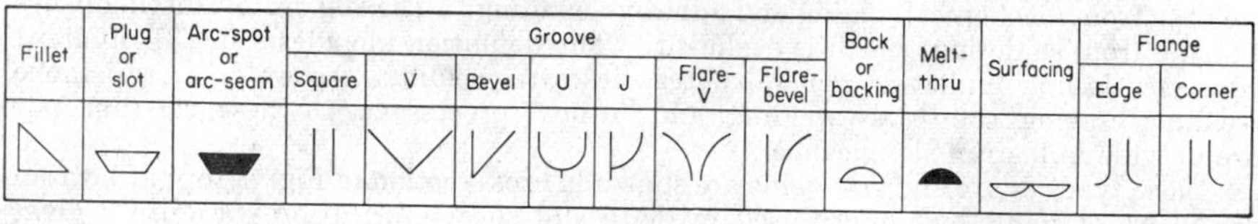

Fillet	Plug or slot	Arc-spot or arc-seam	Groove							Back or backing	Melt-thru	Surfacing	Flange	
			Square	V	Bevel	U	J	Flare-V	Flare-bevel				Edge	Corner

Fig. 3. Basic arc- and gas-weld symbols. (*AWS.*)

DESIGN STRENGTHS

The AWS Specifications for Welded Highway and Railway Bridges (D2.0–63) and Code for Welding in Building Construction (D1.0–63) permit, in general, the same values of stress for butt welds as are applicable to the base metal, except that for fatigue loading, special formulas are provided. Use of these weld stresses is predicated upon the employment of base metals and filler metals prescribed in these standards. Stress on fillet welds is considered as shear on the throat of the weld and limited to 12,400 or 14,700 psi for bridges, depending on filler metal and base metal. In building construction, such shear stresses are similarly limited to 13,600 or 15,800 psi for buildings. For both bridges and buildings, provisions are based on the use of ASTM steels A7, A36, A373, A441, and with special restrictions, A242. The bridge specification further provides extensive formulas based upon the work of the Welding Research Council, for computing the required amounts of welding and the required areas of members connected by fillet welding, when subjected to various conditions of fatigue loading. In most respects the specifications of the AISC are in substantial agreement with the AWS code for building construction.

In operation, these AWS codes and specifications establish certain welding procedures and joints as acceptable standards, and if used, no further qualification is necessary. Typical butt joints in this category include single and double V and U grooves, single and double bevel and J grooves, all of controlled dimensions and welded in such a manner (root chipping or gouging required if not welded on backing material) as to ensure fusion of the weld and base metal throughout the entire depth of the joint.

In a similar manner controlled types of fillet welds may be used without special qualification.

ARC WELDING

Arc welding is defined as a group of welding processes wherein coalescence is produced by heating with an electric arc or arcs, with or without the application of pressure and with or without the use of filler metal. The most significant processes are shielded-metal-arc welding, submerged-arc welding, gas tungsten-arc welding, gas metal-arc welding, carbon-arc welding, and arc-spot welding. Other processes exist; some have several variations. In all these cases, an arc is maintained between an electrode and the work (or between two electrodes), which form the terminals of an electric circuit. Whether direct or alternating current is employed may depend on the process, the filler metal, the type of shielding, the base metal, or other factors. Welding processes may be manual, semiautomatic (partly mechanized), or automatic (fully mechanized).

Welding Arc. More than a heat source, the arc is a complex mixture of ionized gas particles accelerated through an electric field constricted by its magnetic field, and exerting a profound effect on the transfer of filler metal. In turn, arc behavior is dependent on filler metal, base metal, type of shielding, circuit characteristics, and other factors.

In a bare-electrode d-c arc, more heat is liberated at the positive terminal (anode) than at the negative terminal (cathode); in an a-c arc, the heat is about the same at both terminals. Electrode polarity affects not only heat input but weld penetration, fluidity, and metal transfer. Through their action in the arc, shielding fluxes and gases enhance, retard, or control these effects. In d-c arc welding, the term **straight polarity** signifies that the electrode is the negative terminal; **reverse polarity,** that it is the positive terminal. The other terminal, in each case, is grounded through the work.

There is a direct relation between the length of the arc and the arc voltage—the longer the arc, the higher the voltage. The precise relationship depends on arc conditions, *i.e.*, bare-metal arcs, arcs with covered electrodes, submerged arcs, or arcs in gaseous atmospheres. Under each of these conditions there is a range of arc lengths to achieve optimum welding conditions.

Arc-welding machines may be motor-generator sets, rectifier sets, transformers, or generators driven by any of the common prime movers. Motor-generator sets consist of a d-c welding generator connected to an a-c or d-c motor. The rectifier sets employ a single- or three-phase step-down transformer, the output of which is fed through rectifiers to produce direct current. Transformer welding machines are single-phase step-down transformers which supply a-c welding power. The a-c generators usually produce power at frequencies higher than 60 cycles. Motor-generator, rectifier, and transformer units are used in shops and field locations where power lines are available. Engine-driven machines are used on field work where power is not available.

Shielding serves to exclude oxygen and nitrogen of the air from the arc and metal, thus eliminating the formation of oxides and nitrides, which decrease weld-metal ductility and, sometimes, strength. Shielding may be accomplished by (1) a flux covering applied (usually extruded) on a core wire, (2) powdered flux heaped over the weld area and the terminal end of the electrode, (3) a flow of inert or active gases, or mixtures of gases, projected around the arc and molten metal.

Shielded-metal-arc welding employs covered electrodes and can be performed with a-c or d-c power sources. The most widely used of all processes, it finds application on mild and alloy steels, stainless steels, and to a lesser extent, non-ferrous metals. The electrode is clamped in an electrode holder which has a cable leading to the power source. The work is electrically grounded. The electrode tip is touched to the work to establish the circuit and then retracted slightly, initiating the arc. In general, with mild- and low-alloy-steel electrodes, welding in the flat and horizontal positions may be performed with electrodes $5/16$ in. in diameter and smaller. In the vertical and overhead positions, electrode diameters of $3/16$ in. or less are usual. Arc voltage ranges from 20 to 40 volts approx; current from 20 to 500 amp approx, depending mainly on size of electrode.

Electrode coverings serve several purposes: (1) to facilitate the establishment and maintenance of the arc; (2) to protect the molten metal from the air; (3) to provide fluxing of the molten metals, particularly with the non-ferrous metals; (4) to provide a means of introducing alloying ingredients not contained in the core wires. A series of standard specifications covering these electrodes has been issued jointly by the ASTM and the AWS.

The Specification for Mild Steel Covered Arc-welding Electrodes (ASTM A233–64T) provides 12 classifications based on chemical requirements, mechanical properties, types of electrode covering, usability, and soundness. Usability is taken as the capability of an electrode to pass the fillet-weld test when used in the positions and with the type of current for which it is intended. Soundness is based on comparison of weld-metal radiographs with standard porosity charts. Type of covering and its condition when used are the fundamental factors determining usability and soundness. The 12 classifications are subdivided into two groups: the E60 series and the E70 series. In a classification designation such as E6010, "E" designates an electrode, the first two digits designate the minimum tensile strength in kpsi of the deposited metal in the as-welded condition, the third digit indicates the position in which the electrode is capable of making satisfactory welds, and the last digit designates the type of covering on the electrode and the type of current with which it is to be used. The main differences between the E60 and the E70 series are the mechanical properties shown in Table 1 and the absence of chemical requirements for the E60 series. In many applications, electrodes of either series may be used.

Table 1. Typical Mechanical Properties of Mild-steel Electrodes*

	E6010 E6011	E6012 E6013	E6020 E6027	E7014 E7024	E7015, E7016 E7018, E7028
Tensile strength, min psi	62,000	67,000	62,000	72,000	72,000
Yield point, min psi	50,000	55,000	50,000	60,000	60,000
Elongation in 2 in., min %	22	17	25	17	22

* All-weld-metal tension test in the as-welded condition.

E6010 and **E6011** electrodes are for all-position welding in sizes up to 3⁄16 in. and for flat and horizontal positions in larger sizes. E6010 is used with d-c, reverse polarity (dcrp); E6011 is designed for a-c but may be used with dcrp to lesser advantage. Other than this, the electrodes are used equally where the quality of the deposit is of greatest importance, particularly where radiographic requirements must be met when welding in the vertical and overhead positions. Welds are characterized by deep penetration resulting from the harsh, spray-type arc and a light, friable slag. Operating currents for these electrodes are given in Table 2. When used for welding vertically upward, currents near the lower limit are generally used. With the larger sizes of electrodes, maximum currents are somewhat limited as compared with other classifications because of spatter loss that occurs with high currents.

E6012 electrodes are designed for d-c use but are usable with a-c. In sizes up to 3⁄16 in., they are all-position electrodes; however, they are used mostly in the flat and horizontal positions. They are especially recommended for single-pass, high-speed, high-current, horizontal fillet welds. Ease of handling, good fillet-weld profile, and ability to withstand high current and to bridge gaps resulting from poor fit-up make them well suited to this type of work. Medium penetration, quiet arc, slight spatter, and dense slag are characteristics of E6012. Single-pass welds may meet radiographic standards; multipass welds do not.

E6013 electrodes, although similar to E6012, have several differences. Used with a-c or d-c, either polarity, the arc is softer, the penetration less, the slag removal easier, and the arc more easily started and maintained, especially with the smaller diameters. Originally designed for sheet-metal work with lower open-circuit voltage, the E6013 electrodes, especially in larger sizes, are used in many cases instead of the E6012. Fillet welds are flatter; radiographic quality is better.

Table 2. Typical Current Ranges in Amperes for Mild-steel Electrodes

Electrode diameter, in.	E6010 and E6011	E6012	E6013	E6020	E6027	E7014	E7015 and E7016	E7018	E7024 and E7028
1/16	....	20 to 40	20 to 40						
5/64	....	25 to 60	25 to 60						
3/32	40 to 80	35 to 85	45 to 90	....	....	80 to 125	65 to 110	70 to 100	100 to 145*
1/8	75 to 125	80 to 140	80 to 130	100 to 150	125 to 185	110 to 160	100 to 150	115 to 165	140 to 190
5/32	110 to 170	110 to 190	105 to 180	130 to 190	160 to 240	150 to 210	140 to 200	150 to 220	180 to 250
3/16	140 to 215	140 to 240	150 to 230	175 to 250	210 to 300	200 to 275	180 to 255	200 to 275	230 to 305
7/32	170 to 250	200 to 320	210 to 300	225 to 310	250 to 350	260 to 340	240 to 320	260 to 340	275 to 365
1/4	210 to 320	250 to 400	250 to 350	275 to 375	300 to 420	330 to 415	300 to 390	315 to 400	335 to 430
5/16	275 to 425	300 to 500	320 to 430	340 to 450	375 to 475	390 to 500	375 to 475	375 to 470	400 to 525*

* These values do not apply to the E7028 classification.

E6020 electrodes operate with a-c or with d-c, straight polarity (dcsp). They are designed to produce flat or slightly concave horizontal fillet welds and will produce satisfactory fillet and groove welds in the flat position. Penetration is medium when normal welding currents and techniques are used. However, this classification is considered to be the best for operating at high currents to obtain deep-penetration fillet welds. High deposition rates are obtained at the higher currents in heavy plate. The heavy, easily removed slag is honeycombed on the underside. The welds meet radiographic standards.

E6027 electrodes are the heavily, covered, **iron-powder** electrodes designed for fillet or groove welds in the flat position with a-c or d-c, either polarity. They will produce flat or slightly concave horizontal fillet welds equally with a-c or dcsp. High currents with spray-type metal transfer produce high deposition rates with medium penetration and low spatter loss. The heavy, honeycombed slag is easily removed. Weld metal varies in radiographic quality and tends to be inferior to that from E6020 electrodes.

E7014 electrodes are used with a-c or d-c, either polarity, and are designed for all-position welding in sizes up to 5⁄32 in. diam. Operating characteristics of this iron-powder electrode are a compromise between the E6013 and the E7024 types. While deposition rate falls midway between the two, penetration is the same as with E6012. This is an advantage when welding over poor fit-up. Fillet welds are flat to slightly convex, and the slag is often self-cleaning.

E7015 and **E7016** are the low-hydrogen electrodes usable in all positions in sizes up to 5⁄32 in. diam. The only difference is that the E7015 operates on dcrp while the E7016 also operates on a-c. The covering ingredients are low in hydrogen content, which enables these electrodes to avoid or reduce **underbead cracking** due to hydrogen absorption in the weld metal. To maintain this property, the electrodes must be stored in dry atmosphere or rebaked prior to use. Underbead cracking does not occur in mild steels. These electrodes were originally developed for use on high-carbon, alloy, and high-sulphur steels and have been found useful on malleable iron, spring steels, and the mild-steel side of clad plates. They are also useful in making small welds on heavy plate since they are less susceptible to cracking. For best results, the arc should be maintained as short as possible.

E7018 electrodes are low-hydrogen with high percentages of iron powder in the covering. Usable with a-c and dcrp, they are designed for the same applications as the E7015 and E7016 electrodes. They are also well suited for fillet welds in high-carbon or alloy steels. Operation is characterized by a smooth, quiet arc, very low spatter, low penetration, and high lineal speeds.

E7024 electrodes are used with a-c or d-c, either polarity, and are well suited for making fillet welds in mild steel. The iron-powder covering amounts to about 50 percent of the total weight of the electrode. The welds are slightly convex in profile, with a very smooth surface. High lineal speeds are possible, with low penetration, very low spatter, and a smooth, quiet arc.

E7028 electrodes are usable in the horizontal-fillet and flat positions. The low-hydrogen iron-powder coverings represent about 50 percent of the weight of the electrode. Deposition rate with spray-type transfer is higher than for the E7018 electrodes with the globular-type transfer. E7028 also produces more weld metal per unit weight of core wire consumed. Except for these differences, the characteristics of the E7028 electrodes are the same as for the E7018 classification.

Specifications for Low-alloy Steel Arc-welding Electrodes (ASTM A316–64T, AWS A5.5–64T) provide for six groups of classifications, at strength levels ranging from 70,000 to 120,000 psi, in increments of 10,000 psi. The system of classification follows that described for mild-steel electrodes above: the first two digits indicate the tensile strength, 70, 80, etc.; the last two digits indicate the usability and have the same significance as for the mild-steel electrodes. Electrodes may be further identified by supplementary classification to show the chemistry of the deposited metal. This is accomplished by means of a letter and digits following the normal classification. Thus E7010-A1 signifies a cellulose-type coating, usable with direct current, reverse polarity only, depositing weld metal, in all positions and of the nominal 0.50 molybdenum (carbon-molybdenum) analysis.

Specifications for Corrosion-resisting Chromium and Chromium-Nickel Steel Covered Welding Electrodes (ASTM A298–62T, AWS 5.4–62T) provide for the classification of stainless and straight chrome-steel electrodes on the basis of AISI type numbers. Usability is covered by two terminal digits, 15 and 16, which have the same significance as in the mild- and low-alloy-steel-electrode specifications for the low-hydrogen electrodes. The classification E308–15 means E, electrode; 308, the AISI type number for 19 Cr-9 Ni stainless steel; and 15 indicates the electrode usable on direct current, reverse polarity only; terminal digits 16 indicate usability on alternating or direct current, reverse polarity. The following AISI types are covered as to chemistry and mechanical properties of deposited metal: 308, 308L, 309, 309Cb, 309Mo, 310, 310Cb, 310Mo, 312, 16-8-2, 316, 316L, 317, 318, 330, 347, 349, 410, 430, 502, 505, and 7Cr.

Specifications for Copper and Copper-alloy Arc-welding Electrodes (ASTM B225–57T, AWS A5.6–57T) classifies electrodes according to principal alloying ingredients to identify the composition. Where further classification under a given alloy group is necessary, supplementary letters and numerals are employed to differentiate the several analyses. The classification ECuAl-A2 indicates E, electrode; CuAl, a copper-aluminum alloy; A2, a specific composition, *i.e.*, 9–11 percent Al, 1.5 percent Fe. The basic groups covered are copper, copper-tin (phosphor bronze), copper-nickel, copper-silicon, and copper-aluminum. The requirements cover chemical composition and mechanical properties, together with usability.

Specifications for Nickel and Nickel-base Alloy Covered Welding Electrodes (ASTM B295–54T, AWS A5.11–54T) employ chemical composition as the basis of classification. The system of classification uses a series of numbers and letters, preceded by the usual letter E to indicate electrodes. Following this letter is a number; 3 signifies that the electrode is used for welding nickel or nickel alloys to themselves; 4 indicates an electrode used for dissimilar metal combinations where the nickel-base weld metal will be diluted with steel. The next letter indicates that the metal is of the nickel-base group by means of the letter N. The digit immediately following the N denotes the welding process with which the electrode is usable, and in this case 1 indicates shielded metal arc welding. The final digit or letter identifies the composition: 0 = Monel; 1 = nickel; 2 = Inconel; 4 = "K" Monel; 9 = Inconel X; B = Hastelloy B; and C = Hastelloy C.

Specifications for Aluminum and Aluminum-alloy Arc-welding Electrodes (ASTM B184–62T, AWS A5.3–62T) provide for two classifications of covered aluminum electrodes. Classification Al–2 covers the commercially pure grade of aluminum, while Al–43 covers the 5 percent silicon-aluminum alloy.

Submerged-arc welding employs the heat of an arc between a mechanically-fed bare-metal-electrode and the work. The weld and arc are shielded by a blanket of powdered material called a "flux." The arc therefore is "submerged," *i.e.*, not visible. Welding power may be alternating or direct current, either polarity, and current densities are high. Welding currents range from 250 amp for $\frac{3}{32}$ in. wire to 2,000 amp for $\frac{3}{8}$ in. wire. As a result of these high currents, a submerged-arc weld is characterized by deep melting of the base metal and high welding speeds. Weld quality is high, readily meeting ASME Boiler Code and Piping Code requirements. Submerged-arc welding is used for welding mild and low-alloy steels, stainless steels, copper, and nickel, and alloys of these metals. The process is automatic, and either the work or the arc may be moved. Welding is performed in the flat position. A manual version retains all the essential features but provides for manually guiding the arc. Typical welding speeds and other production data are given in Table 3.

Gas tungsten-arc welding involves an arc between a single tungsten electrode and the work to be welded. A shield of monatomic inert gas, argon, helium, or mixtures of these gases is projected around the electrode. Welding may be performed with or without filler metal. When filler metal is used it is introduced separately into the arc; manually from a rod, as in gas welding; mechanically from a power-driven wire-feed reel. The inert-gas envelope permits welding such metals as aluminum, magnesium, nickel alloys, and stainless steels without flux. Welding power sources may be either alternating or direct current, either polarity. Selection of power sources depends upon metal being welded, whether manual or automatic welding, and desired results. With

Table 3. Production Data—Submerged-arc Welding

Thickness	Weld or joint type	Root opening, in.	Root face, in.	Groove angle, deg	Current, amp	Arc, volts	Speed, ipm	Electrode: Diam, in.	Electrode: Lb per ft of weld
16 gage	Square	0–1/32	....	.....	250	22	100	3/32	0.015
	groove				350	24	150	1/8	0.020
14 gage	Square	0–1/32	....	.....	325	24	100	3/32	0.020
	groove				400	26	120	1/8	0.025
12 gage	Square	0–1/32	....	.....	350	24	75	1/8	0.027
	groove				500	30	120		
10 gage	Square	0–1/16	....	.....	575	24	60	1/8	0.05
	groove				650	31	100		
3/16 in.	Square	0–1/16	....	.....	575	25	40	5/32	0.07
	groove				700	31	65		
1/4 in.	Square	0–3/32	....	.....	750	25	30	3/16	0.10
	groove				850	35	40	7/32	
5/16 in.	Square	0–3/32	....	.....	800	26	26	3/16	0.25
	groove				900	36	30	7/32	
1/4 in.	Single	0	0–1/8	50–60	625	25	28	5/32	0.10
	vee				825	32	50	3/16	0.23
3/8 in.	Single	0	0–1/8	40–60	900	28	24	1/4	0.16
	vee				1,100	36	47		0.35
1/2 in.	Single	0	3/16	60	1,075	30	19	1/4	0.38
	vee				1,175	37	23		0.45
3/4 in.	Single	0	3/16	45	1,200	32	12	1/4	0.60
	vee				1,300	39	14		0.75
1 in.	Single	0	1/8	35	1,500	35	10	5/16	0.90
	vee				1,600	41	12		1.10
1 1/4 in.	Single	0	1/8	30	1,600	37	8	5/16	1.25
	vee				1,700	41	9		1.60
1 1/2 in.	Single	0	1/8	30	1,900	38	7	3/8	1.85
	vee				2,000	43	8		2.00

a-c power sources, especially on aluminum and magnesium, it is necessary to stabilize the arc by using either a high-frequency, high-voltage pilot circuit superimposed on the welding circuit, or high open-circuit voltage.

Semiautomatic gas tungsten-arc welding involves either a fixed tungsten electrode holder with work moved under it, or else the holder is mounted on a motorized torch carriage and traverses the joint; control of arc length is manual. Automatic gas tungsten-arc welding may be employed in a similar manner, except that arc voltage, and hence arc length, is electronically controlled. Typical production data and welding conditions are provided in Table 4.

Filler metals, in the form of welding rods, for gas tungsten-arc welding are covered by a series of five AWS-ASTM specifications. The classification numbers start out with the first letter R, which indicates welding rods. The combination of numbers and letters following the R identifies the metal composition by means of chemical symbols or other standard identification, such as AISI type numbers for stainless steels. The following are the applicable specifications: Specifications for Copper and Copper-alloy Welding Rods (AWS A5.7, ASTM B259); Specifications for Corrosion-resisting Chromium and Chromium-Nickel Steel Welding Rods and Bare Electrodes (AWS A5.9, ASTM A371); Specifications for Aluminum and Aluminum-alloy Welding Rods and Bare Electrodes (AWS A5.10, ASTM B285); Specifications for Nickel and Nickel-base-alloy Bare Welding Filler Metals (AWS A5.14, ASTM B304).

Tungsten electrodes used in the gas-shielded tungsten-arc-welding process are not filler-metal electrodes since they are consumed very slowly and are not deposited in the weld. Tungsten electrodes for this process are covered by Specifications for Tungsten Arc-welding Electrodes (AWS A5.12, ASTM B297). Tungsten electrodes with small additions of thoria are also used for their improvement in arc starting and stabilization.

Gas metal-arc welding involves an arc between a continuously fed filler-metal wire and the work to be welded. A gas shield is projected around the arc and the filler wire. The gas shield may be helium or argon or mixtures of these gases; small percentages of

Table 4. Typical Production Data for Gas Tungsten-arc Welding—Flat Position

Metal	Thickness	Weld or joint design			Number of passes	Filler metal size, in.	Filler metal speed, ipm	Welding power*			Welding speed, ipm	Shielding gas		Tungsten electrode		Type§ of welding
		Type	Spacing, in.	Backing				Arc‡ volts, or length, in.	Current, amp	High frequency		Type	Flow, cfh	Type†	Size, in.	
Aluminum, type 3003	0.030 in.	Square groove	0	Yes	1	None	......	0.04	80	No	160	He	30	Th	0.040	Mech
Aluminum, type 3003	0.096 in.	Square groove	0	Yes	1	None	......	15	135	No	38	He	30	Th	3/32	Auto
Stainless steel, type 304	12 gage	Square groove	3/32	Copper	1	0.045	82	12	200	No	13	He	40	Th	3/32	Auto
Stainless steel, type 304	12–20 gage	Corner	0	Steel angle	1	None	......	12	155	No	25	He	40	Th	3/32	Auto
Stainless steel, type 321	0.029 in.	Square groove	0	Copper	1	None	......	1/32	70	Start only	72	He	20	Th	3/32	Mech
Stainless steel, type 347	0.020 in.	Square groove	0	Copper	1	None	......	1/32	55	Start only	120	He	20	Th	3/32	Mech
Stainless steel, type 410	0.010 in.	Square groove	0	Yes	1	None	......	1/32	40	Start only	130	A	12	Th	0.040	Mech
Killed steel	0.075 in.	Square groove	0	Yes	1	None	......	14	155	No	30	He	30	Th	3/32	Auto
Rimmed steel	0.062 in.	Square groove	0	Yes	1	0.045	50	14	160	No	34	He	30	Th	3/32	Auto
Monel	0.084 in.	Square groove	0.038	Copper	1	0.045	77	11	270	No	30	He	40	Th	3/32	Auto
Titanium, type AMS 4901B	0.063 in.	Square groove	0	Gas¶	1	None	......	14	115	Start only	36	He	20¶	Th	3/32	Mech

* Welding power direct current, straight polarity.
† Th = thoriated tungsten electrode.
‡ Dimensional values are arc length.
§ Mech = Mechanized welding – mechanical arc length control.
Auto = Automatic welding – automatic arc voltage control.
¶ He backing at 15 cfh; He trailing shield 25 cfh.

Table 5. Typical Production Data for Gas Metal-arc Welding—Flat Position

Metal	Thickness, in.	Weld or joint design					Number of passes	Filler metal diam, in.	Welding power			Welding speed per pass, ipm	Shielding Gas	
		Type	Bevel angle, deg	Root face, in.	Spacing, in.	Backing			Type	Arc, volts	Current, amp		Type	Flow, cfh
Aluminum	1/8	Square groove	......	......	0–1/8	....	1	3/64	d-c rp	30	110	24	A	30
Aluminum	1/4	Single vee	60	1/16	0–1/16	Grooved steel	1	1/16	d-c rp	27	200	24	A	40
Aluminum	1/2	Single vee	60	1/16	0–1/8	Grooved steel	2	3/32	d-c rp	28	320	16	A	50
Stainless steel	1/2	Double vee	90	1/8	0	....	2	1/16	d-c rp	25	300	12	A	50
Stainless steel	1/2	Single vee	70	0	1/4	Stainless steel	6	1/16	d-c rp	26	300	11	A	50
Deoxidized copper	1/4	Single vee	60	0	0	Steel	1	3/32	d-c rp	28	450	17	A	45
Cu-Al (8 Al, 2 Fe)	1/2	Single vee	60	0	0	Steel	3	1/16	d-c rp	29	300	4.1*	A	35
Cu-Si	3/8	Single vee	60	0	0	....	3	1/16	d-c rp	26	265	4.6*	A	35
Magnesium	1/4	Square butt	0	1/4	0	Grooved steel	1	1/16	d-c rp	26	195	19.2	He	60
Carbon steel	1/4	Square butt	0	1/4	1/16	Grooved copper	1	1/16	d-c rp	26	340	9.0	A + 1% O_2	40
Carbon steel	1/2	Double vee	60	1/16	1/16	....	2	1/16	d-c rp	26	340	5.0	A + 1% O_2	40
Monel	5/16	Single vee	60	3/16	0	Steel	2	1/16	d-c rp	28	325	27	A	60

* Speed of progression of total joint of number of passes indicated.

oxygen may be introduced into these inert-gas shields; carbon dioxide may also be used as the shielding gas. Welding power sources may be direct current, either polarity, or alternating current. The filler-metal wires, of small size, are fed into the arc at high speeds (175 to 225 ipm) and high current densities, usually above 50,000 amp psi. This combination of welding conditions produces high deposition rates and high welding speeds. With the smaller sizes of filler metal it is possible to weld in all positions. The use of inert-gas envelopes permits the welding of aluminum, magnesium, stainless steels, copper, nickel, and alloys without flux. The inert-gas shield protects the metal in transfer across the arc, thus providing weld metal of substantially the same composition as the filler metal. Typical production data are given in Table 5. The manually operated equipment uses wire sizes from 0.020 to 1/4 in. Automatic equipment with this process uses wire up to 1/4 in.

An important version of this process is the short-circuiting type of metal transfer which takes place when small-diameter electrode wire (1/32 to 3/64 in.) is used to form a low-current arc (50 to 225 amp). The resulting globular transfer causes a short circuit. However, by adding an inductive reactance in the power supply, a stable rate of transfer (roughly 100 times a second) can be achieved. The relatively low heat input and the strong directional transfer are desirable for welding thin sheets in any position or heavy sections in the vertical or overhead position.

Filler metals for gas metal-arc welding are supplied, level-wound on reels, spools, or coils. The standard specifications covering these filler metals are combined with other filler-metal specifications covered under welding rods or electrodes. The method of identification involves the letter E to denote an electrode wire. Following this will be either the chemical symbols of the principal elements or a type number, such as is used for stainless steels. The following specifications provide for these types of filler metals: Specifications for Copper and Copper-alloy Welding Electrodes (AWS A5.6, ASTM B225); Specifications for Corrosion-resisting Chromium and Chromium-Nickel Steel Welding Rods and Bare Electrodes (AWS A5.9, ASTM A371); Specifications for aluminum and Aluminum-alloy Welding Rods and Bare Electrodes (AWS A5.10, ASTM B285); Specifications for Nickel and Nickel-base-alloy Bare Welding Filler Metals (AWS A5.14, ASTM B304).

Arc Spot Welding. In arc spot welding, small circular welds are produced in lap joints, using a manual tool employing the gas tungsten-arc-welding process; generally no filler metal is added. In another version of arc spot welding, similar welds are produced employing the gas metal arc-welding process; in this case filler metal is added. This method may be used with either manual or automatic equipment. Equipment includes controls for regulating rate of heat input. These two methods may also be used for tack-welding members in butt, lap, tee, and corner joints.

In **carbon-arc welding,** an arc is struck between a carbon (or graphite) electrode and the parts to be welded. Straight-polarity d-c is used. The welding rod is fed into the arc and fused into the joint. For manual operation, this requires two hands, as in the case of gas welding. A fairly high rate of metal deposition is possible. In some cases, the welding rod is laid in the joint groove and the carbon arc passed slowly along the joint until the fusion is complete.

GAS WELDING

The heat for gas welding is supplied by burning a mixture of oxygen and a suitable combustible gas. The gases are mixed in a torch which gives control of the welding flame.

Acetylene is almost universally used as the combustible gas because of its high flame temperature. This temperature, estimated to be about 6000 F, is so far above the melting point of all commercial metals that it provides a means for the rapid localized melting essential in welding. The oxyacetylene flame is also used in cutting ferrous metals.

The **oxyhydrogen** flame is used in welding metals that have low melting points, such as lead, and in welding thin aluminum sheet.

With a 1:1 mixture of oxygen and acetylene the resulting flame is neutral. The neutral flame has an inside portion, consisting of a brilliant cone 1/16 to 3/4 in. long, surrounded by a faintly luminous envelope flame. When acetylene is in excess, the flame consists of three easily recognizable zones: a sharply defined inner cone, an intermediate cone of whitish color, and the bluish outer envelope. The length of the intermediate cone is a measure of the amount of excess acetylene. This flame is reducing, or carburizing.

When oxygen is in excess in the mixture, the flame resembles the neutral flame, but the inner cone is shorter, is "necked in" on the sides, is not so sharply defined, and acquires a purplish tinge. A slightly oxidizing flame may be used in braze welding and bronze surfacing, and a more strongly oxidizing flame is sometimes used in gas-welding brass, bronze, and copper.

Forehand and backhand welding are employed in oxyacetylene welding. In forehand welding the torch flame is pointed ahead in the direction of welding, and the welding rod precedes the flame. Distribution of the heat and the molten metal is obtained by imparting to the torch and rod opposite oscillating motions. In backhand welding the torch flame is pointed back in the direction of welding, and the rod is interposed between the flame and the molten pool. Distribution of the heat and molten metal is secured by a slight motion of the flame in a vertical plane in the line of the joint; the rod is rolled in the joint. Because of simplified technique, backhand welding permits the use of narrower vees (60 to 75 deg). Weld quality is generally higher with backhand welding since the molten metal has less chance to be exposed to atmosphere. Flame adjustment for backhand welding usually employs a slight excess of acetylene (carburizing) for the purpose of ensuring absence of an oxidizing condition, which is particularly harmful with welding rods containing small amounts of alloying ingredients.

It is essential that the weld should penetrate entirely through the metal. Joint designs suitable for gas welding are shown in Figs. 1 and 2. To build the weld up to the original surface, welding rods must be used to fill the V.

In **braze welding,** coalescence is produced by heating above 800 F and by using a non-ferrous filler metal having a melting point below that of the base metals. Braze welding with brass (bronze) rods is used extensively on cast iron, steel, copper, brass, etc. Since it operates at temperatures lower than base-metal melting points, it is used where control of distortion is necessary. Braze-welded joints on mild steel, made with rods of classifications RCuZn-B and RBCuZn-D, will show transverse tensile values of 60,000 to 70,000 psi. Joint designs for braze welding are similar to those used for gas and arc welding (Figs. 1 and 2).

In braze welding it is necessary to remove rust, grease, scale, etc., and to use a suitable flux to dissolve oxides and clean the metal. The parts are heated to red heat (1150 to 1350 F), and the rod is introduced into the heated zone. The brass rod melts first and "tins" the surfaces, following which additional brass is added by welding.

Welding rods for use in oxyacetylene braze welding are usually of the copper-zinc (60 Cu-40 Zn) analysis. Additions of tin, manganese, iron, nickel, and silicon are made to improve the mechanical properties and usability of the rods. These rods are covered by Specifications for Copper and Copper-alloy Welding Rods (ASTM B259–57T, AWS A5.7–57T).

Oxyacetylene welding of steel is performed without any flux. Fluxes are necessary for welding practically all other metals. The flux used depends on the metal to be welded, although fluxes for braze welding with brass rods may be used for welding brasses and copper. Fluxes are available for welding stainless steel, aluminum and its alloys, nickel and its alloys, magnesium and its alloys, and cast iron. Some non-ferrous welding fluxes (aluminum, chrominum-nickel, magnesium, etc.) contain fluorides and require adequate ventilation to remove fumes. Ventilation is also necessary in the welding or brazing of metals containing or coated with zinc, lead, or cadmium.

Welding rods for oxyacetylene welding are covered by Specifications for Iron and Steel Gas-welding Rods (AWS A5.2, ASTM A251). Six classifications, based on strength and ductility of all-weld-metal tensile-strength specimens, are provided. The significance of the classification numbers, such as GA60, is as follows: G stands for gas-welding rods; A indicates ductility (A for high values, B for lower values); 60 gives the first two digits of the stress-relieved tensile strength. Classification GA60 is commonly used for welding where high quality is required, as in pressure piping. Weld metal with this classification of rods is required to show (stress-relieved) 60,000 psi minimum tensile strength; 25 percent elongation in 2 in.

Oxyacetylene welding may be employed for the welding of practically all metals. In addition, it has the advantage of permitting welding in all positions. Welding rods are available for most commercial metals and alloys. Where rods are not available, satisfactory results may be obtained by using strips sheared from the base metal for filler metal.

Mechanized Oxyacetylene Welding. Oxyacetylene welding by machines is applied in the manufacture of steel barrels, tubing, irrigation pipes, and special forms fabricated of steel and many alloys. Multiple-flame water-cooled machine torches make welds at rates several times that possible by the most expert hand welders. Machine welding is done with and without filler metal, mostly without, on tubing and pipe, the welds being compressed in the process to make a flush or reinforced joint.

THERMAL CUTTING OF METALS

Two types of metal cutting closely allied to welding are important in the metal-fabricating industry and elsewhere: The most important is oxygen cutting; the other is arc cutting.

Oxygen cutting is based on the rapid, exothermic oxidation of iron when heated to about 1500 F in the presence of oxygen. The process is therefore usable only with the ferrous metals, especially such steel products as sheet, plate, bars, shapes, piping, tubing, forgings, and castings, and with wrought-iron products. Instead of a welding torch, a cutting torch is coupled to the gas hoses, and the oxygen-supply pressure is increased. The tip of the cutting torch contains a ring of small orifices for the preheating flame and a central orifice for the oxygen jet. When the steel is suitably heated, the oxygen is turned on, "burning" a clean, narrow cut as the torch advances. For preheating, oxygen and acetylene are commonly used; other fuel gases are hydrogen, propane, natural gas, city gas, or proprietary gases. The oxygen-cutting process finds wide application in severing, trimming, and plate-edge preparation for welding, metal removal, and gouging. Table 6 provides operating data for oxyacetylene cutting.

The **volume of oxygen** (in cubic feet per hour at 1 atm and 70 F) required to cut a heavy section ranges from 80 to 120 times the thickness, measured in inches. The supply pressure depends on the size of the cutting orifice, with higher pressures for small orifices. The volume of acetylene for preheating ranges from 10 to 15 percent of the cutting oxygen flow. In cutting heavy sections the principal object is to secure good, clean "drop" cuts; speed of cutting is secondary. For thicknesses from 12 to 48 in. the **cutting speed** varies from 6 to 2 ipm. High speeds may cause loss of cut and spoilage of metal. Production cuts have been made on steel up to 62 in. thick, using oxyacetylene cutting.

Table 6. Oxyacetylene Cutting

(Manual and machine)

Thickness, in.	¼	½	1	2	4	6	8	10
Speed, ipm, manual	16–18	12–14.5	8–12	5–7	4–5	3–4	2.5–3.5	2–3
Speed, ipm, machine	20–26	17–22	14–18	10–13	7–9	5–7	4–6	3–4
Oxygen consumption, cfh	50–90	90–125	130–200	200–300	300–400	400–500	500–650	700–1,000

Influence of Alloying Elements on Cutting. Alloying elements have two possible effects: they may increase the resistance of steel to cutting, and they may give rise to harder cut surfaces. Where an alloy steel is difficult to cut by the normal oxygen jet, an improvement is effected by tightly clamping a "waster" plate to the upper surface and cutting through both thicknesses. Another method is to weld a heavy bead on the upper surface along the proposed line of cut. Chemical-flux cutting (see p. 13–52) provides an effective means for cutting high-alloy compositions.

Steels up to 0.30 percent **carbon** can be cut without difficulty. Higher-carbon steels should be preheated to about 600 F to prevent hardening and cracking. Cast irons containing up to 4 percent carbon may be cut by special technique. Steels up to 14 percent **manganese** and 1.5 percent carbon are cut with difficulty and for best results should be preheated.

Silicon in amounts usually present has no effect. Silicon steel containing considerable amounts of carbon and manganese must be carefully preheated and postannealed for best mechanical properties.

Steels up to 5 percent **chromium** are cut without much difficulty when the surfaces are clean. If the steel is of an air-hardening type, preheat and postheat should be employed. Higher chromium and chromium-nickel steels should be cut by the chemical-flux and metal-powder methods.

Nickel up to 20 or 30 percent (if the carbon is not too high) may be cut. Up to about 7 percent nickel content, cuts are very satisfactory.

Aircraft-quality chrome-**molybdenum** steel offers no difficulties. High-molybdenum-tungsten steels, however, may be cut only by means of special techniques.

Tungsten alloys up to 12 or 14 percent may be cut very readily, but with a higher percentage of tungsten, cutting is difficult.

Vanadium in small amounts may improve cutting. The other common alloying elements have no appreciable influence.

Oxygen-cutting machines are capable of making oxygen cuts of intricate shape and of such high quality and accuracy as to require no further finishing (see Table 6). Cutting machines are frequently equipped with more than one cutting torch, centrally controlled and guided, and will oxygen-cut a number of identical shapes simultaneously, thereby effecting marked economies where a high production rate prevails. Oxygen-cutting machines may be equipped with photoelectric cells (electric eyes) for following black-and-white drawings of parts to be cut. Other machines will crawl around pipes and make one or two square or beveled cuts, as desired.

Oxygen gouging (**flame gouging**) is a form of oxygen cutting. Instead of a straight tip, a slightly curved tip is attached to the cutting torch. This enables the flame to strike the metal surface at a low angle, making shallow cuts possible. It is used for cutting weld grooves, especially to clean out the underside of root passes to make a sound back weld. It is also used for removing defective welds and surface defects.

Cutting metals under water can be accomplished with oxygen, using either a fuel gas or the electric arc to preheat the metals. Since acetylene cannot be used at pressures above 15 psig for safety reasons, its use in underwater cutting is limited to shallow depths; hydrogen is employed for greater depths. **Oxygen arc** underwater cutting is performed with a special hollow, shielded, and insulated electrode. A fully insulated electrode holder conducts current and oxygen to the electrode. Striking of the arc preheats the metal instantaneously, and the oxygen makes the cut.

The torch method consists of an oxyacetylene cutting torch surrounded by a protecting bell through which is forced compressed air. Special methods are used to permit the lighting of the torch under water.

Stainless-steel Cutting. Stainless steels (chrome-nickel and straight chrome) are virtually impossible to cut by normal oxygen-cutting procedures because chromium oxide is formed and prevents continuation of the cut. Two methods have been developed to overcome this condition. One employs a chemical flux to react with the chromium oxide. The other method uses iron powder to flux the oxide. Use of these methods permits cutting stainless steels and some non-ferrous metals with almost the same ease as oxygen cutting of mild steel. The processes have been adapted to machine gas cutting, and the results equal those with mild steel. Unstabilized varieties of stainless steel will show carbide precipitation in a zone about ⅛ to ¼ in. deep, which may be removed by grinding. Steels with alloy contents up to about 45 percent have been cut successfully. Oxygen arc cutting using a hollow electrode, similar to that employed for underwater cutting, may also be employed for manual cutting of stainless steel.

Arc-cutting processes rely on arc heat to melt a path through metal and are therefore capable of cutting non-ferrous as well as ferrous metals. As in welding, the arc is established between an electrode forming one terminal of an electric circuit and the workpiece forming the other terminal. Various means are employed to flush the molten metal from the cut. The selection of the process to be used depends on the type of cutting required.

For cutting weld grooves, for back-gouging roots of welds, or for simple removal of metal, **air carbon-arc cutting** is fast and efficient. The electrode holder is equipped to direct a jet of compressed air in line with the electrode so as to blow away the molten metal. In plate work, grooves may be cut having a width roughly equal to the size of the electrode and a depth depending on the angle of approach and speed of travel.

For piercing, severing, and other types of rough cutting, **oxygen arc cutting** may be used. Its use in underwater cutting is described above. As a result of both chemical and mechanical interactions of the flux covering, the mild-steel electrode, and the oxygen, the arc action is greatly increased. This process combines deep penetration with speed.

One of the most important cutting operations in the welding industry is the trimming and edge preparation of plates prior to forming and welding. The development of the plasma arc and its application to this type of cutting has displaced all former methods of arc cutting. **Plasma-arc cutting** employs the heavy-duty equipment needed to optimize the basic demand for a hot, thin jet capable of rapidly melting a narrow kerf in any metal and of flushing away the melt. In this process, a tungsten electrode (cathode) is centered in a tubular, water-cooled nozzle constricted at the tip to form a narrow passage about ⅛ in. or smaller in diameter. Gas is introduced into the nozzle, where it flows past the electrode, through the constricted passage, and is directed at the point to be cut in the workpiece. This point forms the anode of the circuit when a transferred arc is employed. In operation, the arc extends from the tip of the electrode, through the passage, and across the intervening distance to the workpiece. Open-circuit voltage for this arc may be 250 volts or more. However, a pilot arc drawn between the electrode and nozzle wall is needed to initiate the main arc. The heated gas quickly expands into a high-speed plasma jet with a temperature said to be in the region of 50000 F. Mixtures of argon and hydrogen or nitrogen and hydrogen are used in cutting non-ferrous metals and stainless steels. Air or oxygen is more economical for cutting carbon steels.

An alternative mode of operation makes use of the non-transferred arc. In this case, the arc is drawn between the electrode and the outer nozzle wall, the plasma jet issuing in the same manner as with the transferred arc but of shorter length.

Safety precautions are necessary to protect the user from high-voltage power, ultraviolet radiation, and fumes.

RESISTANCE WELDING

In resistance welding, coalescence is produced by the heat obtained from the resistance offered by the work to the flow of electric current in a circuit of which the work is a part, and by the application of pressure. The specific processes include **resistance spot welding, resistance seam welding, projection welding, upset welding,** and **flash welding.** Figure 4 shows diagrammatic outlines of the processes; Fig. 5 shows resistance-welding symbols.

The resistance of the welding circuit is a maximum at the interface of the parts to be joined, and the heat generated there must reach a value high enough to cause a localized fusion under pressure. There is an exception to this principle in flash butt welding, where a portion of the heat is derived from the flashing and combustion of the metal at the interface. Even in this instance a part of the heat is generated in the work. The duration of the application of the current must be short so as to limit the zone of melting; otherwise an inferior weld is produced.

Electrodes are of copper alloyed with such metals as molybdenum and tungsten, with high electrical conductivity, good thermal conductivity, and sufficient mechanical strength to withstand the high pressures to which they are subjected. The electrodes should be water-cooled. The resistance at the surfaces of contact between the work and the electrodes must be kept low. This may be accomplished by using smooth, clean work surfaces and a high electrode pressure.

In resistance spot welding (Fig. 4), the parts are lapped and held in place under pressure. The size and shape of the electrodes control the size and shape of the welds, which are usually circular.

Designing for spot welding involves six elements: tip size, edge distance, contacting overlap, spot spacing, spot-weld shear strength, and electrode clearance. For mild steel, the diameter of the tip face, in terms of sheet thickness t, may be taken as $0.1 + 2t$ for thin material, and as $\sqrt{t}$ for thicker material, dimensions in inches. Edge distance should be sufficient to provide enough metal around the weld to retain it when in

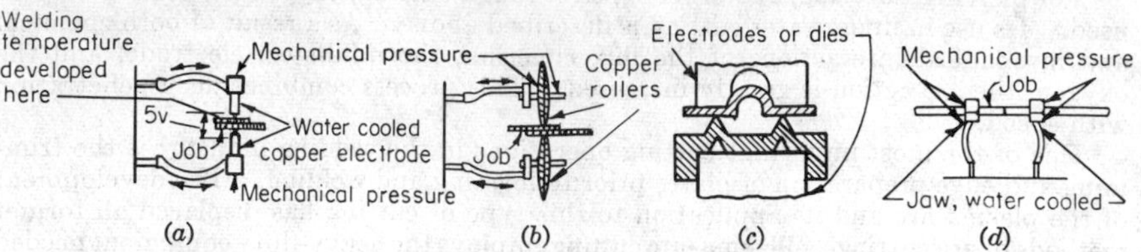

Fig. 4. (*a*) Resistance spot, (*b*) resistance seam, (*c*) projection, (*d*) flash, or upset, welding.

Type of weld			
Spot	Projection	Seam	Flash or upset

Fig. 5. Resistance-welding symbols.

molten condition. Contacting overlap is generally taken as the diameter of the weld nugget plus twice the minimum edge distance. Spot spacing must be sufficient to ensure that the welding current will not shunt through the previously made weld. Table 7 gives values of the above dimensions and also spot-weld shear-strength values based on base-metal tensile strength up to 70,000 psi.

Table 7. Spot-welding SAE 1010 Steel

(Free from scale, oxides, paint, grease, and oil)

Thickness t of thinnest outside piece, in.	Electrode diam and shape: D, in. min	Electrode diam and shape: d, in. max	Net electrode force, lb	Weld time, cycles (60 per sec)	Min shear strength, lb	Welding current (approx), amp	Diam (approx) of fused zone, in.	Min weld spacing, in.	Min contacting overlap L, in.
0.010	3/8	1/8	200	4	130	4,000	0.10	1/4	3/8
0.021	3/8	3/16	300	6	320	6,500	0.13	3/8	7/16
0.031	3/8	3/16	400	8	570	8,000	0.16	1/2	7/16
0.040	1/2	1/4	500	10	920	9,500	0.19	3/4	1/2
0.050	1/2	1/4	650	12	1,350	10,500	0.22	7/8	9/16
0.062	1/2	1/4	800	14	1,850	12,000	0.25	1	5/8
0.078	5/8	5/16	1,100	17	2,700	14,000	0.29	1 1/4	11/16
0.094	5/8	5/16	1,300	20	3,450	15,500	0.31	1 1/2	3/4
0.109	5/8	3/8	1,600	23	4,150	17,500	0.32	1 5/8	13/16
0.125	7/8	3/8	1,800	26	5,000	19,000	0.33	1 3/4	7/8

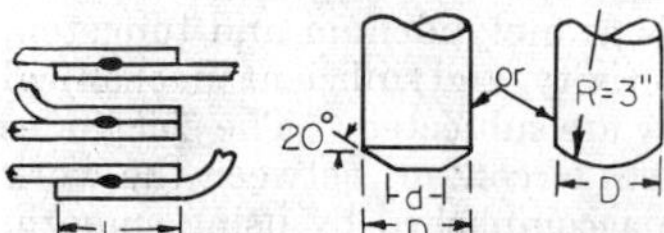

The welding conditions are governed by t of thinnest outside piece. The thickness of the assembly of sheets must not exceed $4t$; max ratio of any two thicknesses not to exceed 3:1. Electrode material conductivity min, 75 percent of copper, hardness min, 75 Rockwell B. Dimensions and contacting overlap L, as shown.

Resistance spot-welding machines vary from small, manually operated units to large, elaborately instrumented units designed to produce high-quality welds, as on aircraft parts. Portable gun-type machines are available for use where the assemblies are too large to be transported to a fixed machine. Spot welds may be made singly or in multiple, the latter being generally by special-purpose machines. Spacing of electrodes is important to avoid excessive shunting of welding current.

The **resistance seam-welding process** (Fig. 4) produces a series of spot welds made by circular or wheel-type electrodes. The weld may be a series of closely spaced individual spot welds, overlapping spot welds, or a continuous weld nugget. The weld shape for individual welds is rectangular; continuous welds are about 80 percent of the width of the roll electrode face.

Machines for seam welding may provide for the rotation of one or both rollers. Three general types are available: **longitudinal seam, circular seam,** and **universal welding machines.** Interrupters are necessary to provide control of the heat effect and allow cooling, under pressure.

Electrodes (rollers or wheels) are generally of the shape shown in Table 8. In joints with limited space, as in welding flanges to containers, one face is flat. The axes of rollers may be inclined up to 6 deg for clearance. Either roller may be driven, with the other idling, or both may be driven. Drives may be through friction rolls or knurled rollers. Wheels may range from 2 to 24 in. diam, with the average 7 to 10 in.

A **mash weld** is a seam weld in which the finished weld is only slightly thicker than the sheets, and the lap disappears. It is limited to thicknesses of about 16 gage and an overlap of 1½ times the sheet thickness. Operating the machine at reduced speed, with increased pressure and non-interrupted current, a strong quality weld may be secured that will be 10 to 25 percent greater in thickness that the sheets. The process is applicable to mild steel but has limited use on stainless steel; it cannot be used on non-ferrous metals. A modification of this technique employs a straight butt joint. This produces a slight depression at the weld, but the strength is satisfactory on some applications, *e.g.*, for the production of some electric-welded pipe and tubing.

Cleanliness of sheets is of even more importance in seam welding than in spot welding. Best results are secured with cold-rolled steel, wiped clean of oil; the next best with pickled hot-rolled steel. Grinding or polishing is sometimes satisfactory, but not sand- or shot-blasting.

Typical production data for seam welding for use with clean SAE 1010 steel are given in Table 8.

Table 8. Seam-welding SAE 1010 Steel

(Free from scale, oxides, paint, grease, and oil)

Thickness t of thinnest outside piece, in.	Electrode width and shape		Net electrode force, lb	On-time, cycles (60 per sec)	Off-time (pressure-tight), cycles	Weld speed, in. per min	Welding current (approx), amp	Welds per in.	Min contacting overlap L, in.
	W, in. min	w, in. max							
0.010	⅜	3⁄16	400	2	1	80	8,000	15	⅜
0.021	⅜	3⁄16	550	2	2	75	11,000	12	7⁄16
0.031	½	¼	700	3	2	72	13,000	10	½
0.040	½	¼	900	3	3	67	15,000	9	½
0.050	½	5⁄16	1,050	4	3	65	16,500	8	9⁄16
0.062	½	5⁄16	1,200	4	4	63	17,500	7	⅝
0.078	⅝	⅜	1,500	6	5	55	19,000	6	11⁄16
0.094	⅝	7⁄16	1,700	7	6	50	20,000	5.5	¾
0.109	¾	½	1,950	9	6	48	21,000	5	13⁄16
0.125	¾	½	2,200	11	7	45	22,000	4.5	⅞

See footnotes for Table 7.

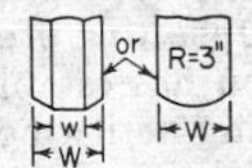

In **projection welding** (Fig. 4), the heat for welding is derived from the localization of resistance at predetermined points by means of projections, embossments, or the intersections of elements of the assembly. The projections may be made by stamping or machining. The process is essentially the same as spot welding, and the projections seem to concentrate the current and pressure. Welds may be made singly or in multiple with somewhat less difficulty than is encountered in spot welding. When made in multiple, all welds may be made simultaneously. The advantages of projection welding are (1) the heat balance for difficult assemblies is readily secured, (2) the results are generally more uniform, (3) a closer spacing of welds is possible, and (4) electrode life is increased. Sometimes it is possible to projection-weld joints that could not be welded by other means.

The design and forming of the projections are important. For sheet metal the dies must be so designed as to prevent shearing of the projection. This would weaken the weld. The weld growing from the center outward will tend to a circular shape. When projections must be formed on curved or irregular surfaces, it is preferable to elongate them to ensure that the weld initiates at a point contact. Heavy metal sections should be provided with raised V-shaped projections located so far in from the edges that the metal will not squeeze out when molten. Studs, bolts, etc., should be domed to a radius 1½ times the diameter of the stud to provide proper contact. Crossed wires may be projection-welded without any special preparation.

The **welding pressure** should be set at a value which will ensure complete flattening of the projection; too much pressure causes premature collapse of the projection. **Welding currents** will be heavy, particularly on multiple-projection assemblies; the maximum current which does not cause splashing is correct.

Projection welding may be applied to most metals except copper and red brasses. Other brasses may prove difficult to handle. Galvanized iron, terneplate, and tin plate are successfully handled. Dissimilar metals, such as steel to brass, bronze, or aluminum, may be welded with special techniques. Heavy steel sections may also be welded by projection welding.

Upset welding (Fig. 4), an early form of resistance welding, is limited to joining members of approximately equal cross section. The parts to be welded are brought together under pressure, and current is passed through the contact area. This results in creating a forge weld of symmetrical shape. Heat generated by contact resistance is a function of surface resistivity, the nature of the surfaces, the unit pressure, and other factors; the resistance is approximately inversely proportional to pressure, other factors remaining constant. Pressure and current are maintained throughout the welding cycle, although pressure is initiated at a low value (to raise the initial contact resistance) and subsequently raised to that necessary for forging. When the required upset is achieved, welding current is cut off.

In **flash welding,** the parts are brought together lightly, with current flowing, and then separated slightly; a flashing action is created at the interface. The flashing generates the greater part of the heat, the balance coming from the resistance at the joint. When the metal at the joint is molten, heavy pressure is quickly applied, and this forces out the molten metal and makes the weld in the plastic metal just in back of the molten metal. Flash welding is used more than upset welding because of greater weld strength; no need for special preparation of weld surface; lower power demand with less power consumption; faster speed and smaller upset; and less heat in the work since most heat appears at the interface. It is possible to weld dissimilar metals of widely differing melting points since flashing may be continued until both metals have reached their individual fusing temperatures.

In flashing it is necessary to move the ends together by means of the platen. The **flashing rate** must be maintained at a correct value to assure continuous flashing. If too slow, the flashing is intermittent and it is difficult to build up heat. If too fast, there is a possibility of freezing the pieces. Too short flashing time results in lowered heat and renders it impossible to secure proper upset. Too long heating time creates such a mass of plastic metal that it cannot be squeezed out properly in the upsetting cycle, resulting in improper upset.

Upsetting pressure must be applied quickly to create the weld after the flashing action has established a zone of plastic metal. The upsetting pressure provides the forging action necessary to make the weld and also to squeeze out all oxidized metal and slag. The current must be maintained during upsetting to prevent chilling. The pressure for upsetting must be sufficient to ensure complete extrusion of molten metal at the weld line beyond the original cross section. Upset pressures for welding without preheat (pressures indicated for cross section of weld area) are low-carbon steel, 10,000 psi; medium-carbon and low-alloy steels, 15,000 psi; special stainless alloys with high hot compressive strengths, 35,000 psi.

After welding, the flash and upset may be removed by chipping, grinding, machining, flame machining, die trimming, or with a high-speed sander. When the flash has been removed, the weld line should not be visible. The joint efficiency should approach 100 percent. Welds in hardenable steels may require preheating, either outside the machine or by means of the machine, to slow down the cooling rate after welding. Postheating may also be accomplished in the machine.

Multiple-impulse welding is applicable to spot-, seam-, and projection-welding processes. It consists of applying the current in a series of impulses, which may be a fraction of a cycle or a number of cycles. The welding machine must be capable of maintaining the pressure while the cyclic operations of current "on" and current "off" are in progress. The advantages of **pulsation welding** are (1) increased electrode life; (2) the welding of thicker material, frequently with the same equipment; (3) better welds in some cases; (4) reduction of "spitting" of weld metal; and (5) the successful spot welding of many thin sections stacked at greater heights. Typical production data for pulsation welding are given in Table 9.

Table 9. Pulsation-welding SAE 1010 Steel

(Free from scale, oxide, paint, grease, and oil)

Thicknesses of the two plates welded, in.	Electrode diam and shape		Net electrode force, lb	Weld time, 20 cycles on, 5 cycles off (60 cps), number of pulsations			Min shear strength, lb	Welding current (approx), amp	Diam (approx) of fused zone, in.	Min contacting overlap *L*, in.
	D, in. min	*d*, in. max		Single weld	Adjacent welds					
					1–2 in.	2–4 in.				
1/8, 1/8	1	7/16	1,800	3	5	4	5,000	18,000	3/8	7/8
1/8, 3/16	1	7/16	1,800	3	5	4	5,000	18,000	3/8	7/8
1/8, 1/4	1	7/16	1,800	3	5	4	5,000	18,000	3/8	7/8
3/16, 3/16	1 1/4	1/2	1,950	6	20	14	10,000	19,500	9/16	1 1/8
3/16, 1/4	1 1/4	1/2	1,950	6	20	14	10,000	19,500	9/16	1 1/8
3/16, 5/16	1 1/4	1/2	1,950	6	20	14	10,000	19,500	9/16	1 1/8
1/4, 1/4	1 1/4	9/16	2,150	12	24	18	15,000	21,500	3/4	1 3/8
1/4, 5/16	1 1/4	9/16	2,150	12	24	18	15,000	21,500	3/4	1 3/8
5/16, 5/16	1 1/2	5/8	2,400	15	30	23	20,000	24,000	7/8	1 1/2

Same footnote as for Table 7, except bevel angle 10 deg (instead of 20 deg) and *d* min = 1/4 in.

A continuous resistance welding process is used in the manufacture of tubular goods. The finished weld resembles a flash weld with a burr of flash ejected at the top and bottom of the weld. Steel strip is fed into the machine and is formed into a circular shape as it passes through several rolls. After the circular shape is secured, two copper rollers, one on each side of the joint, apply the welding current while side rollers apply pressure effecting the weld. Tubing has been produced by this process in low-carbon steels, low-alloy steels, and stainless steels.

In **percussion welding,** the heat for welding is secured simultaneously over the entire area of the abutting surfaces from an arc produced by a rapid discharge of stored electric energy, followed immediately by the application of pressure. The process is used only to a limited extent today.

Surfacing by Welding

Surfacing by welding is a method of applying an alloy material to a metal part so as to form a protective surface to resist abrasion, corrosion, heat, impact, or any combination of these factors. The alloy may be applied by oxyacetylene, metal arc, submerged-arc, or gas-shielded arc welding, or by the metal-spray method. New parts may be surfaced before use, or worn parts may be built up to the original size and reclaimed. The most important economy derived from surfacing results from prolonged life of parts. Surfaced parts may outwear plain or unfaced ones many times, depending on the type of hard metal used and the service to which they are subjected. To meet the various requirements of hardness, toughness, impact, abrasion-corrosion, heat resistance, and other qualities, numerous surfacing alloys are available. Practically all ferrous metals can be surfaced. Welding rods and electrodes for this work are covered by Specifications for Surfacing Welding Rods and Electrodes (ASTM A399–56T, AWS A5.13–56T). Non-ferrous alloys with low melting points cannot generally be surfaced with the alloys designed for ferrous application. However, Cu-Al covered electrodes of hard grades are available and included in the above specification. In addition, a commentary is appended to guide the user in the application and expected performance of six groups of surfacing filler metals, namely, high-speed steels, austenitic manganese steels, austenitic high-chromium iron, cobalt-base alloys, copper-base alloys, and nickel-chromium-boron alloys.

BRAZING

Brazing is another one of the general groups of welding processes, consisting of the torch, furnace, induction, dip, resistance, twin carbon arc, flow, and block-brazing processes; the first five processes are of industrial significance. Brazing may be used for joining virtually all metals and dissimilar combinations of metals, although not all combinations of dissimilar metals are satisfactory (*e.g.*, aluminum or magnesium to other metals). In brazing, coalescence is produced by heating above 800 F but below the melting point of the metals being joined. The non-ferrous filler metal used has a melting point below that of the base metal, and the filler metal is distributed in the closely fitted lap or butt joints by capillary attraction. Cleaning of the joints is essential for satisfactory brazing. The use of a flux or atmosphere to control surface cleanliness is usually necessary. Filler metal may be hand-held, and fed into the joint (face feeding), or preplaced as rings, washers, shims, slugs, etc.

Brazing with the silver-alloy types of filler metals has previously been known as **silver soldering** and **hard soldering.** Similarly, brazing with **spelter solders** has been known as **spelter brazing.** These terms are now considered obsolete, as the term "brazing" adequately covers joints made by the flow of molten filler metal by capillary attraction. "Braze welding" should not be confused with brazing. Braze welding is a method of welding employing a filler metal which melts below the melting points of the base metals jointed, but the filler metal *is not* distributed in the joint by capillary attraction. (See also pp. 6–102 and 6–106.)

Specifications for Brazing Filler Metal (ASTM B260, AWS A5.8) provide for seven basic classifications. The classification numbers use the letter B to signify brazing. Following this letter there appear the chemical symbols representing the principal alloying ingredients. The final numerals differentiate between the several analyses in a group. The BAlSi, aluminum-silicon group operates in the range of 1060 to 1150 F; the copper-phosphorus group, BCuP, operate between 1300 and 1700 F; the group carrying the symbols BAg are the widely used silver alloys which operate in a range of 1145 to 1800 F; the symbols BCu and BCuZn cover the copper and copper-zinc groups, brazing in the range of 1670 to 2100 F; a copper-gold group, BAu, operates between 1635 to 2000 F; BMg represents the magnesium group operating between 1080 to 1160 F; finally, there is the heat-resistant group, BNi, operating between 1700 and 2200 F.

Torch brazing uses acetylene, propane, or other fuel gas, burned with oxygen or air. The combination employed is governed by the brazing-temperature range of the filler metal, which is usually above the liquidus. Flux with a melting point appropriate to the brazing-temperature range and the filler metal is essential. Torch brazing may be manual or mechanized.

Furnace brazing employs the heat of a gas-fired, electrical, or other type of furnace to raise the parts to brazing temperature. Fluxes may be used, although reducing or inert atmospheres are more common since they eliminate postbraze cleaning necessary with fluxes.

Induction brazing utilizes a high-frequency current to generate the necessary heat in the part by induction. Distortion in the brazed joint can be controlled by current frequency and other factors. Fluxes or gaseous atmospheres must be used in induction brazing.

Dip brazing involves the immersion of the parts in a molten bath. The bath may be either molten brazing filler metal or molten salts, usually brazing flux. The former is limited to small parts such as electrical connections; the latter is capable of handling assemblies weighing several hundred pounds. The particular merit of dip brazing is that the joint is virtually completed all over the assembly at one time.

Resistance brazing utilizes standard resistance-welding machines to supply the heat. While theoretically any of the filler metals may be used, those of the BAg, BCuP, and BCuZn groups are most common. Either preplacement or face feeding of the filler metal may be used. Fluxes or atmospheres must be used, with flux predominating. Standard spot or projection welders may be used. Pressures are lower than those for conventional resistance welding. As currents are large, water cooling of electrodes is essential.

Step brazing is a technique that has found increasing use through the development of new brazing filler metals. This technique makes possible the brazing of several joints in succession by employing filler metals having successively lower melting points. After the first joint is brazed, any type of suitable machining or forming operation can be performed. The next joint is brazed at a lower temperature so as not to affect the first joint, etc. Another effective way of using this technique is to select a filler metal that, upon melting, combines with the base metal to form a new alloy having a melting point higher than that of the original. Precise control over filler-metal composition, brazing temperatures, and other factors is usually required.

WELDING PROCEDURES

Steel

Low-carbon Steels. (Carbon up to 0.30 by ladle analysis.) Steels in this class are readily welded by most arc and gas processes. Preheating is unnecessary unless parts are very heavy or welding is performed below 32 F. Torch-heating steel in the vicinity of welding to 70 F offsets low temperatures. Postheating is necessary only for important structures such as boilers, pressure vessels, and piping. Gas tungsten-arc welding is usable only on killed steels; rimmed steels produce porous, weak welds. Resistance welding is readily accomplished if carbon is below 0.20 percent; higher carbon requires heat-treatment to slow the cooling rate and avoid hardness. Brazing with BAg, BCu, and BCuZn filler metals is very successful.

Medium-carbon Steels. (Carbon from 0.30 to 0.45 by ladle analysis.) This class of steel may be welded by the arc, resistance, and gas processes. As the rapid cooling of the metal in the welded zone produces a harder structure, it is desirable to hold the carbon as near 0.30 percent as possible. These hard areas are proportionately more brittle and difficult to machine. The cooling rate may be diminished and hardness decreased by preheating the metal to be welded above 300 F, preferably to 500 F. The degree of preheating depends somewhat on the thickness of the section. Subsequent heating of the welded zone to 1100 or 1200 F will restore ductility and relieve strain. Brazing may also be used as noted for low-carbon steels.

High-carbon Steels. (Carbon from 0.45 to 0.80 by ladle analysis.) These steels are rarely welded except in special cases. The tendency for the metal heated above the critical range to become brittle is more pronounced than with lower- or medium-carbon steels. Thorough preheating of metal, in and near the welded zone, to a minimum of 500 F is essential. Subsequent annealing at 1350 to 1450 F is also desirable. Brazing is used with these steels, in the form of tools, and is combined with the heat-treatment cycle.

Low-alloy Steels. The weldability of low-alloy steels is dependent upon the analysis and the hardenability, those exhibiting low hardenability being welded with relative ease, while those of high hardenability requiring preheating and postheating. Sections of ¼ in. or less may be welded with mild-steel filler metal and may secure joint strengths approximating base-metal strength by virtue of alloy pickup in the weld metal, and weld reinforcement. Alloys of higher strength require filler metals of mechanical properties matching the base metal. Special alloys with creep-resistant or corrosion-resistant properties must be welded with filler metals of the same chemical analysis. Austenitic chrome-nickel shielded arc electrodes are helpful for welding hardenable alloys when preheating and postheating are not practicable. Low-hydrogen-type electrodes (either mild- or alloy-steel analyses) permit the welding of alloy steels, minimizing the occurrence of underbead cracking. No preheating is usually necessary on sections up to about ½ in.; low preheat of about 300 F is necessary for heavier sections. Brazing may also be used with these steels.

Chrome-nickel austenitic steels are excellent for welding, and under satisfactory conditions produce strong, tough, and reasonably ductile welds. Alloys containing less than 0.03 percent carbon can be welded without any subsequent heat-treatment. Alloys containing up to 0.10 percent carbon can be welded, provided the structures welded will not be used for service where high corrosion resistance is required.

Addition of titanium, columbium, or some of the other rare metals stabilizes the alloy by formation of titanium or columbium carbide in preference to chromium carbide. In general, titanium or columbium is added to the extent of about 10 times the carbon content present. Such **stabilized** steel is not entirely proof against dangerous carbide precipitation. For the welding of the stabilized analyses only stabilized filler metals should be used. In the gas tungsten-arc and gas metal-arc welding processes the stabilizer is incorporated in the filler metal. In stainless-steel covered electrodes, the columbium is frequently introduced through the coating. Since titanium cannot be successfully transferred across the metal arc with covered electrodes, columbium is the principal stabilizer employed.

Unstabilized alloys containing more than 0.07 percent carbon can generally be spot- or seam-welded without impairing their corrosion-resistant properties, provided that the welding time is made very short. The maximum safe duration of the welding time will vary inversely with the carbon content of the alloy and somewhat with the welding technique used. With alloys with 0.10 percent carbon no dangerous carbide precipitation will occur if the duration of the application of the welding current does not exceed 0.20 sec. With alloys having a carbon content of around 0.15 percent this figure should be reduced to 0.10 or 0.15 sec max. All welding will produce some carbide precipitation, and the line of demarcation between the alloys that can and cannot be welded is a compromise between the extent of the carbide precipitation and the severity of the corrosion attack to which the welded product will be subjected. No welding should be attempted without first thoroughly cleaning the surfaces to be welded. Flash welding is, in general, quite satisfactory, as most of the fused metal produced by the arc of the flash which could be expected to contain chromium oxides and nitrides is squeezed out by the upsetting operation, and the weld obtained is therefore fairly ductile. Because of the amount of heating involved, the upset welding process should be avoided. Gas tungsten-arc welding is particularly useful on stainless steels up to about $\frac{3}{16}$ in. Manual welding with this process is performed in all positions, with and without filler rods. Semiautomatic and automatic welding are performed at high speeds and yield welds of high quality. As flux is not needed, post-weld cleaning is greatly simplified. Gas metal-arc welding is especially suitable for stainless steels above $\frac{3}{16}$ in. thick. Welds of highest quality are readily produced.

Chromium Irons and Steels. Welding of the chromium irons and steels can be divided into two classes: (1) welding in which the filler metal deposited has essentially the same chemical analysis as the base metal; (2) welding in which the filler metal deposited differs in analysis and characteristics from the base metal, the filler metal commonly employed being an austenitic chromium-nickel steel of the 18 percent chromium, 8 percent nickel type, or higher-alloy analyses. An austenitic chromium-nickel filler metal is used for all welds that cannot be annealed, including field and repair welds, and a filler metal of the same analysis as the base metal for welds that can be annealed. For operation at high temperatures the expansion of the austenitic filler metal as related to the base metal must be considered. Operation at high temperature will result in warpage or high stresses and, under repeated heating and cooling, may result in failure through fatigue.

Cast Steel

In good grades of cast steel with a carbon content below 0.25 percent, welding procedures are approximately the same as for rolled steel. With a carbon content above 0.25 percent or with special alloy compositions, precautions are necessary and sometimes special procedures. Segregations of phosphorus and sulphur should be removed from areas to be welded by oxygen gouging or chipping. The problem of overcoming shrinkage in the repair of castings requires special care. Stress relieving is desirable, especially in repair work. In higher-carbon and alloy steels full annealing may be necessary.

For arc welding, a high-grade heavy-covered electrode is essential. A tough, general-purpose electrode (arc) or welding rod (gas) is used for plain-carbon castings, but filler metal of the same composition as the casting is used for alloy cast steel. Electrodes with low-hydrogen coverings are particularly useful in this work.

Multilayer welding and high currents should be employed for low-carbon castings. Low currents and small-diameter electrodes (and, in some cases, preheating and slow cooling) are necessary for high-carbon and special-alloy castings. For gas welding, only large sections are preheated, locally or generally, to a bright red.

Cast Iron

Even though cast iron has a high carbon content and is a relatively brittle and rigid material, welding can be performed successfully if proper precautions are taken. Optimum conditions for welding include the following: (1) A weld groove large enough to permit manipulation of the electrode or the welding torch and rod. The groove must be clean and free of oil, grease, and any foreign material. (2) Adequate preheat, depending on the welding process used, the type of cast iron, and the size and shape of the casting. Preheat temperature must be maintained throughout the welding operation. (3) Welding-heat input sufficient for a good weld but not enough to superheat the weld metal; *i.e.*, welding temperature should be kept as low as practicable. (4) Slow cooling after welding. Gray iron may be enclosed in asbestos, lime, or vermiculite. Other irons may require postheat treatment immediately after welding to restore mechanical properties.

Most cast-iron welding takes place in foundries, where small defects in new castings are repaired by welding. A small but growing application exists in the production of cast-iron weldments. In these cases, optimum conditions for welding usually can be realized. This is not always the case when castings that have cracked or broken in service require repair at the site. However, if optimum conditions are not realized, the over-all quality of the result will be lower. Preheating has two purposes: (1) to reduce the rate of cooling in the vicinity of the weld in order to reduce embrittlement, which reacts unfavorably to weld-shrinkage stress and to machinability; and (2) to reduce unequal expansion stresses in the relatively brittle material during heating, as well as unequal contraction stress during cooling. If the parts being welded are free of restraint, local preheat may be satisfactory. If the parts are under restraint, the effect of heating and cooling stresses may be difficult to assess. Unless a special preheat program can be devised, the best general rule is to uniformly preheat the entire casting.

Welding rods and **electrodes** for welding cast iron are described in Specifications for Welding Rods and Covered Electrodes for Welding Cast Iron (ASTM A398; AWS 5.15). In this specification, the initial letter R identifies a welding rod for gas welding and the initial letter E an electrode for arc welding. Other letters identify the composition. Thus RCI and RCuZn-A identify welding rods of gray iron and a copper-zinc alloy, respectively. ESt and ENiFe similarly identify electrodes of steel and of a nickel-iron alloy. Many different welding processes have been used to weld cast iron, the most common being manual shielded-metal-arc welding, gas welding, and braze welding.

Manual Shielded-metal-arc Welding. Of the classified electrodes, the most successful to date has been the nickel-iron electrode (ENiFe). Machinability and color match are good. Weld deposits have some ductility, which is important. Good results have been obtained in welding gray, malleable, and nodular iron. Weld grooves of about 60 deg are used, as in Fig. 2. For gray iron, the preheat is 400 to 500 F. Small-diameter electrodes (5/32 in.) are used with dcrp at about 130 amp. Beads should be kept well under 3/8 in. wide and should be staggered to avoid high temperature buildup. After welding, the casting is cooled slowly under insulation. Malleable iron may be welded in a similar manner, except that a preheat up to 300 F is used and the casting must be specially heat-treated after welding if most of the original mechanical properties are to be restored. For nodular iron using a 3/16-in. ENiFe electrode with dcrp at 185 amp, a normal bead-on-bead deposition may be used. Again, to restore some of the properties of the base metal, a special heat treatment is required. The ENiFe electrode may also be used to join various metals to cast iron. The cast-iron electrode (ECI) has a limited use, mainly because better results are obtained when gas welding with the cast-iron welding rod. The steel electrode (ESt) is no longer widely used in large repairs because of the elaborate procedure, known as **studding,** which is required. For small repairs, it yields a hard, unmachinable deposit.

Braze welding with copper-alloy or "bronze" electrodes such as ECuSn-A, ECuSn-B, and ECuAl-A2 has the advantage of being faster than with the so-called **brasses** used with gas welding. The latter process offers better heat control, however, and is generally preferred unless time is an overriding factor. In arc welding, striking the arc outside the weld groove must be avoided, as these **arc strikes** cause unmachinable hard spots.

Gas welding with the cast-iron welding rod (RCI) is a slower than arc welding but affords better heat control because of the lower temperature of the gas flame. The weld groove is chipped or ground to 75 to 90 deg to permit manipulation. Preheat is in the range of 900 to 1250 F. A neutral flame is generally employed. A little flux is spread over the starting point, and the flame is played on the groove until the walls begin to melt, starting at the root. The welding rod is dipped in flux, brought to a red heat, and then rubbed into the molten metal. The tip of the inner cone of the flame should be kept 3/16 to 7/8 in. away from the molten puddle to avoid overheating. The casting should be cooled slowly under insulation.

Braze welding with the copper-alloy gas welding rods (RBCuZn-A,-D, RCuZn-B, -C) requires that the weld groove first be cleaned of all foreign matter and of graphite by heating to red heat with an oxidizing flame or by grit blasting. Preheat is in the range of 900 to 1100 F. A neutral-to-slightly-oxidizing flame is recommended. If the temperature of the base metal is too low, the filler metal does not spread out; if too high, it collects in little balls, which are driven away by the force of the flame. To avoid overheating, the torch should be held at a smaller angle to the deposited metal than in welding. The flux should be oxidizing in order to remove graphite, and it should also remove oxide films from the base metal; otherwise the flow of the filler metal will not occur without overheating.

Wrought Iron

In metal-arc welding of wrought iron, slightly slower welding speeds should be used than for mild steel of the same thickness. In this way the metal is kept fluid longer, and gases and slag are eliminated. It may be necessary to use a slightly lower current than for the same thickness of mild steel, especially in thin sections where burning through is possible. Excessive penetration into the face of the metal should be avoided. Electrodes of classification E6010 have proved best and should be used.

Carbon-arc welding and **resistance welding** of wrought iron are the same as those of mild steel.

Nickel Alloys

Filler metals for welding nickel and nickel alloys are covered by the following specifications: Specifications for Nickel and Nickel-alloy Covered Welding Electrodes (ASTM B295, AWS A5.11); Specifications for Nickel and Nickel-alloy Bare Welding Filler Metals (ASTM B304, AWS A5.14).

Gas Welding. The oxyacetylene flame used should be very slightly reducing, with only a small feather, no longer than 1/8 in., showing beyond the tip of the luminous cone. The end of the welding rod should be kept well within the flame, so as to prevent its oxidation. Besides being reducing, the flame should be soft, rather than harsh, as is the case when too small a tip is used.

A **flux** is always used for Monel (except for gas-welding Monel with the silicon-Monel gas-welding rod for pickling service), but none should be used with pure nickel. A flux recommended by manufacturers should be used. The silicon-Monel gas-welding rod requiring no gas-welding flux was developed particularly for the welding of equipment exposed to sulphuric acid service and specifically for Monel equipment for the pickling of steel. After the flux is painted on both sides of the joint, the flame adjusted to slightly reducing conditions, and the welding begun, Monel flows freely. Nickel, which is not fluxed, flows a little sluggishly. The appearance of properly made gas welds is quite similar to that of good steel welds. For the best results on high-nickel materials there should be little puddling; the molten pool should be kept quiet, with the tip of the luminous flame just touching its surface.

Welding rods are of the same composition as the alloy being welded if uniform corrosion resistance, with lack of galvanic effects, is desired. Some leeway is possible with the deoxidizing additions. The manufacturers of nickel furnish proper welding rods where these are specified. Rods should be bright-annealed and free from oxide. Only rods tested for their weldability should be used for Monel or nickel welding.

Arc Welding. Covered electrodes are used for metal arc welding of Monel and nickel. As the presence of aluminum is desirable in or near the molten pool of Monel weld metal, a small amount of aluminum is included in the Monel-core wire. The use of a slightly alloyed Monel electrode results in developing strengths of 70,000 to 80,000 psi in single-bead and multiple-bead butt joints, metal arc-welded in flat, vertical, or overhead positions. This is the range of tensile strengths obtained in plate material. Monel and nickel electrodes carrying relatively heavy flux coatings require reverse polarity.

In the **metal arc welding** of sheets of light to medium gage between 0.037 and 0.125 in. thick, it is desirable to clamp the sheets to restrain buckling. For lighter gages, it has been found that beads made without weaving are entirely satisfactory. Electrode sizes of 3/32 (1/8) [5/32] in. with 50 to 70 (70 to 80) [80 to 140] amp are used for 12 (9) [9] gage sheets.

Gas tungsten-arc and gas metal-arc welding are successfully used on nickel and nickel alloys. No flux is necessary, and welds of high quality are consistently obtainable with both manual and automatic operation.

Nickel and high-nickel alloys may be **resistance-welded** by the spot- and flash-welding processes; seam and projection welding may also be used. Since ease of resistance welding varies as the resistivity of the material, alloys such as Inconel X may be welded more easily than pure nickel. Cleaniness is of extreme importance, and sulphur-bearing substances, such as some oils and greases, must be thoroughly removed by cleaning as they can lead to sulphur embrittlement. High unit pressures are necessary to permit adequate forging of these alloys.

Brazing with the BAg, BCu, or BNi filler metals is widely used. Because nickel and high-nickel alloys are usually employed under severe service conditions, careful attention must be given to select the proper brazing procedure and to follow procedural details. The presence, in any form, of low-melting-point elements (such as lead or sulphur) must be avoided. The same is true of oxides. Annealing or stress relieving is advisable before brazing if residual or applied stresses may be present, since the molten filler metal may cause stress cracking. The age-hardenable alloys are particularly susceptible to stress cracking and to the formation of detrimental oxides from oxygen-containing atmospheres. The most common processes are torch, furnace, induction, and resistance brazing. Generally, BAg filler metals may be used in torch brazing, while BCu and BNi filler metals are usually used in controlled-atmosphere brazing.

Aluminum and Aluminum Alloys

The **properties** that distinguish the aluminum alloys from other metals determine which welding processes can be used and which particular procedures must be followed for best results. Among the welding processes that can be used, choice is further dictated by the requirements of the end product and by economic considerations.

Physical properties of aluminum alloys that most significantly affect all welding procedures include low melting-point range (approx 900 to 1215 F), high thermal conductivity (about two to four times that of mild steel), high rate of thermal expansion (about twice that of mild steel), and high electrical conductivity (about three to five times that of mild steel). Interpreted in terms of welding, this means that, as compared with mild steel, much higher welding speeds are demanded, greater care must be exercised to avoid distortion, and for arc and resistance welding, much higher current densities are required.

It should be noted that the aluminum alloys are not quench-hardenable. However, weld cracking may result from excessive shrinkage stresses due to the high rate of thermal contraction. To offset this tendency, welding procedures, where possible, require a fast weld cycle and a narrow-weld zone, *i.e.*, a highly concentrated heat source with deep penetration, moving at a high rate of speed. Shrinkage stresses can also be reduced by using a filler metal of lower melting point than the base metal. The filler metal ER4043 is often used for this purpose.

Welding procedures also call for the removal of the thin, tough, transparent film of aluminum oxide that forms on and protects the surface of these alloys. The oxide has a melting point of about 3700 F and can therefore exist as a solid in the molten weld. Removal may be by chemical reduction or by mechanical means such as machining, filing, rubbing with steel wool, or brushing with a stainless-steel wire brush. The aluminum alloys, when molten, can dissolve relatively large amounts of hydrogen, which is given up upon cooling, causing porosity in the weld. To overcome this, all hydrogen-containing compounds, such as moisture, water vapor, oil, and grease, must be removed from the weld zone by degreasing and drying.

As classified by the Aluminum Association, the commercial wrought alloys fall into seven general types according to the principal alloying element. The **non-heat-treatable types** are the 1XXX, 3XXX, and 5XXX series—denoting, respectively, the 99 min percent pure Al, the Al-Mn series, and the Al-Mg series. Second, third, and fourth digits denote alloy modification and specific alloy. These three alloy series are supplied in the annealed form as well as in several work-hardened tempers. Since the heat of welding removes any work-hardened structure in the area near the weld, the strength of the welded joint is based on the annealed strength of the base metal, regardless of the original temper.

The **heat-treatable types** are the 2XXX, 4XXX, 6XXX, and 7XXX series—denoting, respectively, the Al-Cu, the Al-Si, the Al-Si-Mg, and the Al-Zn series. These types can achieve very high mechanical strength through solution heat treatment combined with age hardening and/or work hardening. The 6XXX series is commonly welded. While welding will remove the work hardening in the heat-affected zone, the effect on the heat-treated strength is to lower it to somewhere between the original temper and the fully annealed state. Postweld heat treatment may be effective in restoring strength, depending on the alloy and other conditions. In general, the 2XXX, 4XXX, and 7XXX series are somewhat specialized in application and weldability. Before welding any of the heat-treatable alloys, consultation with the aluminum producer is advisable.

Filler metals for welding aluminum and aluminum alloys are covered by Specifications for Aluminum and Aluminum-alloy Arc-welding Electrodes (ASTM B184, AWS A5.3-62T) and Specifications for Aluminum and Aluminum-alloy Welding Rods and Bare Electrodes (ASTM B285, AWS A5.10-61T).

Gas Tungsten-arc Welding. Most of the advances made in welding aluminum are due to this process and to the one immediately following. Welding is performed in an inert atmosphere and may be manual or mechanized. High current densities and the inherently stable tungsten arc make possible precision and high speed as well as a narrow, deeply penetrated weld zone. These are the factors that minimize distortion, reduce shrinkage stresses, and inhibit microstructural changes in the heat-treated alloys. Economically best suited for welding square-groove welds in thin gages without added filler metal, this process can also be used for welding V grooves in thicker material with cold filler metal added. Welding is effected in all positions. With a-c welding, argon is used as the shielding gas and the power supply must deliver high current with balanced wave characteristics or superimposed high-frequency current. With dcsp, helium is used as the shielding gas. Deeper penetration, a narrower weld zone, and faster speed are possible with this method. Welding with either a-c or d-c power is predicated on absolutely clean weld grooves, clean filler metal, and properly functioning equipment.

Gas metal-arc welding employs dcrp in a shielding gas that may be argon, helium, or a mixture of the two. In this process, the welding arc is formed by the filler metal, which serves as the electrode. Since the filler metal is fed from a coil as it melts in the arc, some arc instability may arise. For this reason, the process does not have the same precision as the gas tungsten-arc process for welding very thin gages. However, it is more economical for welding thicker sections due to its higher deposition rates. With a special power supply, a short-circuiting technique is possible which results in a globular transfer of weld metal with low heat input and low penetration. Thinner sections can be welded in any position. Proper functioning of equipment is mandatory, as are clean weld grooves and filler metal.

Resistance spot welding is the most widely used of the aluminum resistance-welding processes. The metal properties indicated above impose specific demands upon the three basic variables—current, force, and time—which define the operating capacity of resistance-welding equipment. Welding currents are roughly three to four times those used for equal thicknesses of mild steel, while weld times are shorter. Special power supplies and timing controls have been developed for this purpose. In addition, both the magnitude and the timing of the electrode force must be closely coordinated with the current flow. Aluminum alloys soften quickly upon heating and undergo considerable shrinkage upon solidifying. To meet these conditions, low-inertia pressure systems have been devised. They afford rapid electrode follow-up to maintain proper electrical contact during heating and proper forging force during cooling. Resistance spot welding of the aluminum alloys in the soft or annealed condition is not recommended.

The operational limits for current, force, and time will be determined somewhat by the service requirements of the end product, by the particular alloy being welded, and by the capabilities of the welding machine and its controls. Nearly all the aluminum alloys can be resistance spot-welded with excellent results. The non-heat-treatable alloys (1000, 3000, 5000 series) are the easiest to weld; most of the heat-treatable alloys (2000, 6000, 7000 series) are weldable over a narrow range of settings. Except for low-stress applications employing the 1100 or 3003 alloys, cleaning and surface preparation are highly important. Emphasis is placed on obtaining low and uniform surface-contact resistance.

Resistance seam welding makes use of electrodes in the form of wheels, which can produce a series of overlapping welds that will result in a pressure-tight seam. In other respects, this process is similar to resistance spot welding.

Flash welding finds an application in welding butt and miter joints in aluminum extrusions and butt joints in aluminum rod and bar stock as well as in dissimilar metals, such as copper to aluminum.

Aluminum brazing requires close temperature control because of the narrow range between the melting points of filler metals and base metal. A flux is required to remove the aluminum oxide film and to prevent it from reforming. After brazing, the flux must be removed completely to avoid corrosion of the aluminum. The commonly brazed alloys are 1100, 3003, 3004, 5050, the 6000 series, and the A612, C612 casting alloys. The common processes used are torch brazing, furnace brazing, and dip brazing, the latter two being preferred because closer temperature control is possible. The filler metals are Al-Si alloys and are supplied as wire, as shims, as a paste mixture of flux and alloy powder, or as brazing sheet. The latter consists of a core alloy, such as 3003 or 6951, clad on one or both sides with the filler metal. Prebraze cleaning is essential for strong joints.

Gas welding was the first process used for welding the aluminum alloys and is still used for inexpensive repairs and small jobs. A flux is required; as always, it must be removed after welding. Filler metals are covered by the welding-rod specification indicated above. Smooth, satisfactory joints can be produced in the flat position.

Out-of-position welding is very difficult. The high total heat input abets distortion, which may be overcome by suitable preheat and strategic location of weld joints.

Manual shielded-metal-arc welding using dcrp and flux-covered electrodes produces welded joints that are satisfactory in some applications. Thicknesses ranging from ⅛ to 1 in. are easily welded. Deep penetration makes possible the welding of ¼-in. square-groove welds in a single pass with a backing strip. The fluxing slag must be removed between passes and after welding. Filler-metal specifications provide two classifications having core wires equal to the ER1100 and ER4043 welding rods and bare electrodes.

Copper and Copper Alloys

In welding **commercially pure copper** it is important to select the correct type. Electrolytic, or "tough-pitch," copper contains a small percentage of copper oxide, which at welding heat leads to oxide embrittlement. For welded assemblies it is recommended that deoxidized, or oxygen-free, copper be used and that welding rods, when needed, be of the same analysis. The preferred processes for welding copper are gas tungsten-arc and gas metal-arc welding; manual shielded-metal-arc welding can also be used. It is also welded by oxyacetylene method and braze-welded; brazing with brazing filler metals conforming to BAg, BCuP, and RBCuZn-A classifications is also employed. The high heat conductivity of copper requires special consideration in welding; generally higher welding heats are necessary together with concurrent supplementary heating.

Copper alloys are extensively welded in industry. The specific procedures employed are dependent upon the analysis, and reference should be made to the AWS Welding Handbook. Filler metals for welding copper and its alloys are covered in the following specifications: Specifications for Copper and Copper-alloy Welding Electrodes (ASTM B225, AWS A5.6); Specifications for Copper and Copper-alloy Welding Rods (ASTM B259, AWS A5.7).

Other Metals

Magnesium and **magnesium alloys** can be welded in the work-hardened and heat-treated condition with joint strengths approaching that of the base metal. Gas tungsten-arc welding and gas metal-arc welding are preferred to the gas welding process. Resistance spot welding, seam welding, and flash welding are commonly performed on a number of alloys. Brazing methods are also employed on some alloys. Magnesium alloys are not generally welded to dissimilar metals or alloys.

The **reactive metals,** or so-called **exotic metals,** include titanium, zirconium, columbium (niobium), molybdenum, and tantalum. Their unusual properties make them uniquely suited to specialized applications in the aerospace and nuclear-energy fields. However, their prompt reaction to minute quantities of oxygen, nitrogen, hydrogen, and other impurities at elevated temperatures results in embrittlement. Welding operations, therefore, must be carried out under a shield of high-purity inert gases, such as argon or helium. Gas tungsten-arc welding with rigid control over cleanliness and with careful joint fixturing has been generally most successful. Electron-beam welding is unequalled but is limited by the size of the vacuum chamber. In some instances, brazing under a vacuum or in an inert atmosphere gives excellent results. Resistance spot and seam welding also have been found useful. As welding procedures have improved and welding costs reduced, many of the reactive metals have begun to find wider industrial applications.

Other Processes

A number of the welding processes of lesser industrial significance have considerable importance from a technical point of view. Most of these processes are uniquely successful in performing difficult tasks in specialized fields. Many of them promise wider use in industry, especially if present applied research-and-development programs are successful. The following are a few important examples.

Electron-beam welding makes use of a concentrated beam of electrons accelerated under a high-voltage potential and focused on a small area of the workpiece. The entire process is under high vacuum (10^{-4} mm Hg pressure) to avoid electron scattering, while providing an ideal welding environment (see also p. 13–103 *et seq.*). Energy transfer is highly efficient, resulting in narrow, deeply penetrating single-pass welds, narrow heat-affected zones, and high welding speeds. Advantages are sound welds completely free of gaseous contamination, freedom from distortion, and high joint efficiencies. Major applications are the metals and alloys which are highly reactive to gases of the atmosphere as well as to gases formed from volatilized impurities. Limitations are imposed by the size of the vacuum chamber, the difficulty in maintaining the vacuum for high production rates, and cost and maintenance of equipment. Present high-voltage equipment operating at about 150 kv and about 6 kw produces single-pass welds in most metals up to about 1½ in. thick. Present development work is aimed at higher power input, at greater thicknesses, and at the possibility of welding with the workpiece outside the vacuum chamber.

Plasma-arc welding, a more recent application of the cutting process described earlier, is a machine welding operation. The plasma arc melts completely through the joint, but by precise control of welding speed and other parameters, the molten metal reforms behind the advancing arc, resulting in a solid weld joint. The advantage is single-pass welding at high speed for limited thicknesses.

Flame spraying is a process whereby a metal or a metal compound may be sprayed on a workpiece to provide a protective coating or to build up a worn or undersized area. Metals are introduced into an oxyacetylene flame, either as a powder or as a wire that is melted in the flame, and are impelled toward the workpiece. The bond is mechanical and somewhat porous, although subsequent melting can be used to increase the density of the deposit. The workpiece is usually scored to facilitate the bond. The plasma arc is effectively used to apply the more refractory metals, carbides, and ceramics. Due to its greater heat and velocity, the bond more nearly resembles a weld.

Electroslag welding is a vertical welding process designed for welding sections of about 1 to 14 in. thick, or more, in a single pass. When welding heavy steel plates, the plates are positioned vertically about 1 in. apart. A starting plate is welded to the underside of the joint, and water-cooled copper shoes are positioned at either side to form the starting weld. Electrodes are conventionally introduced from the top or side through a wire-feeding device which curves down into the mold. Flux is introduced at the start of the weld and is fed continuously as the welding proceeds in order to maintain a molten slag blanket that covers the pool of molten weld metal. Vertical motion is accomplished by means of a relay actuated by a sensing circuit through one of the copper shoes, the essential equipment being mounted, usually, on a vertical mast. The electrically conductive slag remains molten throughout the operation, serving as the heat source and otherwise acting in the same capacity as the slag covering an open-hearth melt. The resulting weld has a dendritic structure resembling an ingot but without segregations or piping. The process is sometimes used to produce ingots of refined metal.

Solid-state welding encompasses a group of processes in which the weld is effected by bringing clean metal surfaces into intimate contact under certain specific conditions. In **friction welding,** one part is rotated at high speed with respect to the other, under pressure. The parts are heated, but not to the melting point of the metal. Rotation is stopped at the critical moment of welding. Base-metal properties across the joint show little change because the process is so rapid. **Ultrasonic welding** employs mechanical vibrations at ultrasonic frequencies plus pressure to effect the intimate contact between faying surfaces needed to produce a weld. (See also p. 12–185 *et seq.*) The welding tool is essentially a transducer that converts electrical frequencies to mechanical frequencies. By applying the tip of the tool, or anvil, to a small area in the external surface of two lapped parts, the vibrations and pressure are transmitted to the faying surfaces. Foils, thin-gage sheets, or fine wires can be spot- or seam-welded to each other or to heavier parts. In **cold welding,** the parts to be welded are permanently deformed by dies in such a way as to cause some relative displacement between the faying surfaces. Aluminum-to-copper electrical joints are a common application. **Explosive welding** is a relatively new process used to clad a metal substrate, such as steel, with a protective layer of dissimilar metal, such as aluminum. The force and speed of the explosion are directed in such a way as to cause a series of progressive shock waves that deform the faying surfaces at the moment of impact. A magnified section of the joint reveals a true weld with an interlocking wave shape and usually some alloying.

Laser-beam welding, as a process, is in the developmental stage. The coherent light beam of the laser does not affect transparent materials. A small area of intense heat can be created by focusing the beam with a condensing lens. Small parts have been spot-welded with high-energy pulses in a fraction of a second. The present goal is to obtain continuous, high-energy radiation.

METAL-REMOVAL PROCESSES AND EQUIPMENT

BY

Serope Kalpakjian

REFERENCES: Ernst and Merchant, "Chip Formation, Friction and Finish," The Cincinnati Milling Machine Co. Shaw, "Metal Cutting Principles," M.I.T. Kronenberg, "Grundzüge der Zerspanungslehre," Springer-Verlag. Black, "Theory of Metal Cutting," McGraw-Hill. ASTME, "Tool Engineers Handbook," McGraw-Hill. ASTME, "Machining with Carbides and Oxides," McGraw-Hill. Woldman and Gibbons, "Machinability and Machining of Metals," McGraw-Hill. "International Research in Production Engineering," ASME. "Machining Difficult Alloys," ASM. Machining Data, *PB* 181039, OTS, Dept. of Commerce. Machining of Superalloys and Refractory Metals, *DMIC Memo*. 134, Battelle. Roberts, Hamaker, and Johnson, "Tool Steels," ASM. "American Machinist's Handbook," McGraw-Hill. Boston, "Metal Processing," Wiley. "Manual on Cutting of Metals," ASME. DeGarmo, "Materials and Processes in Manufacturing," Macmillan. Begeman and Amstead, "Manufacturing Processes," Wiley. "Metals Handbook," ASM. Doyle, "Manufacturing Processes and Materials for Engineers," Prentice-Hall. Brierly and Siekmann, "Machining Principles and Cost Control," McGraw-Hill.

METAL-CUTTING PRINCIPLES

The proper understanding and successful solution of machining problems require a knowledge of several fields, such as mechanics, plasticity, surface phenomena, chemistry, metallurgy, and heat transfer. Investigations in machining making use of these different technical areas already have resulted in a better understanding of the problems involved and have led to improved machining conditions and equipment. The following is a brief summaiy of the present state of knowledge of the more practical aspects in this field.

Basic Mechanics of Metal Cutting

The basic mechanics of chip-type machining processes (Fig. 1) are shown, in their simplest form, in Fig. 2. A tool of a certain **rake angle** α (positive as shown) and **relief angle** moves along the surface of the workpiece at a depth of t_1. The material ahead of the tool is sheared continuously along the **shear plane,** which makes an angle of ϕ with the surface of the workpiece. This angle is called the **shear angle** and, together

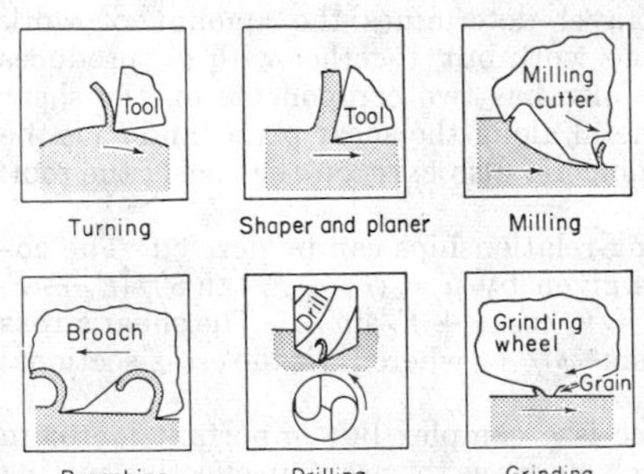

FIG. 1. Examples of chip-type machining processes.

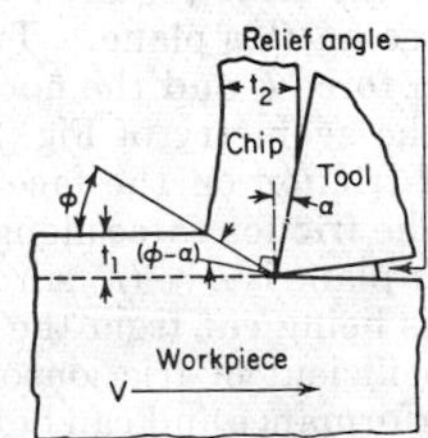

FIG. 2. Basic mechanics of the orthogonal cutting process.

with the rake angle, determines the chip thickness t_2. The ratio of t_1 to t_2 is called the **cutting ratio** r. The relationship between the shear angle, the rake angle, and the cutting ratio is given by the equation $\tan \phi = r \cos \alpha/(1 - r \sin \alpha)$. It can be readily seen that the shear angle is important in that it controls the thickness of the chip. This, in turn, has great influence on cutting performance. The **shear strain** that the material undergoes is given by the equation $\gamma = \cot \phi + \tan (\phi - \alpha)$. Shear strains in metal cutting are usually less than 5.

Investigations have shown that the shear plane may be neither a plane nor a narrow zone, as assumed in simple analysis. Various formulas have been developed which define the shear angle in terms of such factors as the rake angle and the friction angle β.

Because of the large shear strains that the chip undergoes, it becomes hard and brittle. In most cases, the chip curls away from the tool. Among possible factors contributing to chip curl is non-uniform normal stress distribution on the shear plane.

Regardless of the type of machining operation, four basic types of chips or combinations of these are found:

Continuous chips are formed by continuous deformation of the workpiece material ahead of the tool, followed by smooth flow of the chip along the tool face. These chips ordinarily are obtained in cutting ductile materials at high speeds.

Discontinuous chips consist of segments which are produced by fracture of the metal ahead of the tool. The segments may be either loosely connected to each other or unconnected. Such chips are most often found in the machining of brittle materials or in cutting ductile materials at very low speeds.

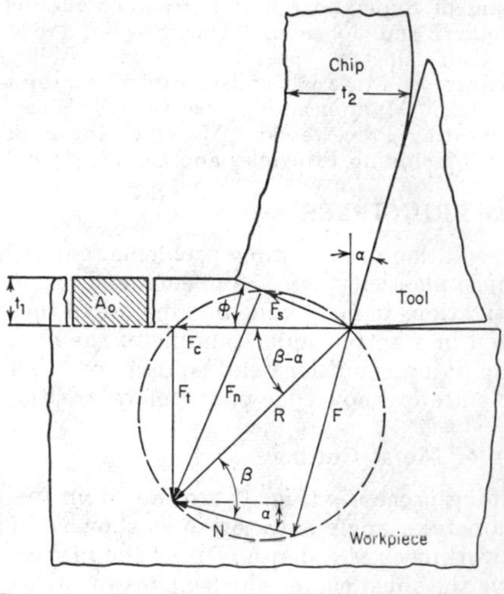

Inhomogeneous chips consist of regions of large and small strain. Such chips are characteristic of metals with low thermal conductivity or metals whose yield strength decreases sharply with temperature. Chips from titanium alloys frequently are of this type.

Built-up edge chips consist of a mass of metal which adheres to the tool face while the chip itself flows continuously along the face. This kind of chip is often encountered in machining operations and is associated with high friction between chip and tool and with poor surface finish.

FIG. 3. Force system in the orthogonal cutting process.

The **forces** acting on the cutting tool are shown in Fig. 3. The resultant force R has two components, F_c and F_t. The cutting force F_c in the direction of tool travel determines the amount of work done in cutting. The thrust force F_t does no work but, together with F_c, produces deflections of the tool. The resultant force also has two components on the shear plane: F_s is the force required to shear the metal along the shear plane, and F_n is the normal force on this plane. Two force components also exist on the face of the tool: the friction force F and the normal force N.

From the geometry of Fig. 3, the following relationships can be derived: The **coefficient of friction** on the face of the tool is given by $\mu = (F_t + F_c \tan \alpha)/(F_c - F_t \tan \alpha)$. The **friction force** along the tool is $F = F_t \cos \alpha + F_c \sin \alpha$. The **shear stress** in the shear plane is $\tau = (F_c \sin \phi \cos \phi - F_t \sin^2 \phi)/A_0$, where A_0 is the cross-sectional area that is being cut from the workpiece.

The coefficient of friction on the tool face is a complex but important factor in cutting performance and can be reduced by such means as the use of an effective cutting fluid, higher cutting speed, improved tool material and condition, or chemical additives in the workpiece material.

The net **power** consumed at the tool is calculated from the equation $P = F_cV/33{,}000$. Since F_c is a function of tool geometry, workpiece material, and process variables, it is difficult reliably to calculate its value in a particular machining operation. Charts based on experimental data are used in practice. Table 1 shows average **unit-power** requirements in hp per cu in. per min of metal removal. The power consumed is the product of unit power and rate of metal removal: P = (unit power)(vol/min).

Most of the power consumed in cutting is transformed into **heat.** Most of the heat is carried away by the chip, and the remainder is divided between the tool and the workpiece. An increase in cutting speed or feed will increase the proportion of the heat transferred to the chip. It has been observed that, in turning, the average interface **temperature** between the tool and the chip increases with cutting speed and feed, while the influence of the depth of cut on temperature has been found to be limited. Interface temperatures to the range of 1500 to 2000 F have been measured in metal cutting. The effect of a cutting fluid on temperature at speeds normally employed with carbides or oxides has been found to be negligible. However, the cutting fluid removes heat and thus avoids temperature buildup on the cutting edge.

A factor of great significance in metal cutting is **tool wear.** Many factors determine the type and rate at which wear occurs on the tool. The major critical variables that affect wear are tool temperature, hardness and type of tool material, grade and condition of workpiece, abrasiveness of the microconstituents in the workpiece material, tool geometry, feed, cutting fluid, and surface finish on the tool. The type of wear pattern that develops depends on the relative role of these variables.

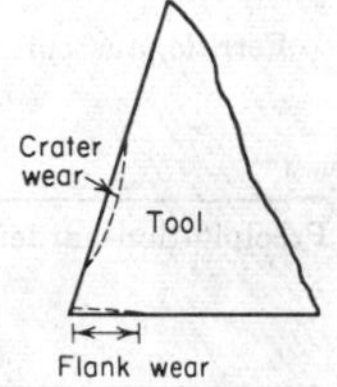

FIG. 4. Types of tool wear in cutting.

Tool wear can be classified as (1) uniform abrasive wear, such as that resulting in a straight wear land (Fig. 4); (2) crater wear on the tool face; (3) localized wear, such as the rounding of the cutting edge; (4) chipping of the cutting edge; (5) concentrated wear resulting in a deep groove at the edge of the tool.

In general, the wear on the flank or relief side of the tool is the most dependable guide for **tool life.** A wear land of 0.060 in. on high-speed steel tools or 0.030 in. for carbide tools is usually used as the end point. The cutting speed is the variable which has the greatest influence on tool life. The relationship between tool life and cutting speed is given by the well-known Taylor equation $VT^n = C$, where V is the cutting speed, fpm; T is the actual cutting time between resharpenings, min; C is a constant whose value depends on workpiece material and machine variables, numerically equal to the cutting speed that gives a tool life of 1 min; and n is the exponent whose value depends on workpiece material and other machine variables. The recommended cutting speed for a high-speed steel tool is generally the one which produces a 60-min tool life. With carbide tools, a 30-min tool life may be satisfactory.

For many years, numerous investigations have been carried out modifying this equation to obtain quantitative relationships between cutting speed, feed, depth of cut, workpiece material, tool material, etc. Some of the modified equations for turning are in the form $V_1d^xf^y = C_1$, where V_1 is the equivalent cutting speed, *i.e.*, speed at which a certain cutting time, such as 60 min, is obtained under a given set of cutting conditions between resharpenings; d is the depth of cut, in.; f is the feed per revolution, in.; x and y are exponents determined experimentally—their average value is less than 1. Two observations can be made from this equation: (1) As the feed or the depth of cut is increased, the cutting speed must be decreased in order to keep the tool life constant. (2) In doing this, the amount of metal removed for the same tool life is increased considerably. Thus, for a given tool life, a large amount of metal can be removed as a result of large depth of cut and feed with a low cutting speed. There are, however, some exceptions to this rule.

When using tool-life equations similar to the ones given above, caution should be exercised in extrapolation of the curves beyond the operating region in which they are derived. In a log-log plot, tool-life curves may be linear over a short cutting-speed range but are rarely linear over a wide range of cutting speeds. In spite of the consid-

Table 1. Average Unit-power Requirements in Machining*

Material	Hardness, BHN	Unit power† hp/cu in./min		
		Turning, HSS and carbide tools, feed—0.010 to 0.012 ipr	Drilling, HSS drills, feed—0.002 to 0.010 ipr	Milling, HSS and carbide tools, feed—0.004 to 0.008 in. per tooth
Steel	120	1.2	1.0	1.2
Free-machining plain carbon steel, plain carbon steel, free-machining alloy steel, alloy steel, cast steel, armor plate, nitriding steel, hot-work die steel, tool steel	200	1.4	1.2	1.5
	300	1.8	1.5	2.1
	400	2.0	1.8	2.4
	500	2.4	2.2	2.8
Stainless steel	140	1.6	1.2	1.6
Ferritic, austenitic, martensitic	200	1.7	1.3	1.7
	350	2.0	1.8	2.0
	440	2.3	2.1	2.3
Precipitation-hardening stainless steel	180	1.6	1.7	1.7
	400	1.8	1.9	2.1
High-temperature alloys	250	2.2	2.2	2.5
	350	2.4	2.6	2.5
Nickel alloys	180	1.6	1.2	1.7
	220	1.7	1.6	1.8
Cast iron	140	0.9	0.8	1.0
Flake-graphite cast iron, nodular or ductile cast iron, malleable cast iron	200	1.1	1.1	1.2
	280	1.9	1.6	2.0
Magnesium alloys	50‡	0.2	0.2	0.2
Aluminum alloys	100‡	0.3	0.2	0.4
Copper alloys	160	0.7	0.5	0.8
	200	1.2	1.2	1.3
Copper	150	1.2	1.1	1.2
Titanium	180	1.0	1.0	1.1
	250	1.2	1.1	1.2
	350	1.6	1.2	1.7

* "Machining Data Handbook," Ordnance Corps, 1961.

† Power requirements at spindle-drive motor, corrected for dull cutter and 80 percent spindle-drive efficiency.

‡ 500-kg load.

erable data obtained to date, no simple formulas can be given for quantitative relationships between tool life and process variables for a wide range of materials and conditions.

The major factors influencing **surface finish** (see also p. 13–106 *et seq.*) in machining are (1) the outline of the cutting tool in contact with the workpiece, (2) fragments of built-up edge left on the workpiece during cutting, and (3) vibration. Little quantitative data are available to show relationships between surface roughness and material and process variables. Improvement in surface finish may be obtained to various degrees by increasing the cutting speed and decreasing the feed and depth of cut. Changes in cutting fluid, tool geometry, and material are also important; the microstructure and chemical composition of the material have great influence on surface finish.

In cutting metal at high speeds, the chips may become very hot and cause safety hazards because of long spirals which whirl around. In such cases, **chip breakers** are introduced on the tool geometry (Fig. 5), which curl the chips and cause them to break into short sections. They can be produced by grinding on the face of the cutting tool, or they are separate pieces clamped on top of the tool.

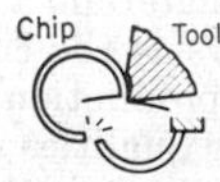

Fig. 5. Cross section of tool showing chip breaker.

A term commonly used in machining and comprising most of the items discussed above is **machinability.** This is best defined in terms of (1) tool life, (2) power requirement, and (3) surface finish. Thus, a good machinability rating would indicate a combination of long tool life, low power requirement, and good surface finish. However, it is difficult to develop quantitative relationships between these variables. Tool life is considered as the important factor and, in production, is usually expressed as the number of pieces machined between tool resharpenings. Various tables are available in literature which show the machinability rating for different materials; however, these ratings are relative. To determine the proper machining conditions for a given material, refer to the machining recommendations given later in this section. These recommendations are the result of extensive tests and data collection from industry.

Metals which machine with great difficulty at room temperature because of their high strength or high rate of strain hardening may be machined at elevated temperatures. This technique is called **hot machining** and may result in lower cutting force and longer tool life. However, since optimum conditions of machining do exist for each material, the best cutting condition with regard to temperature and cutting speed for maximum tool life must be determined experimentally. Several methods of heating the workpiece have been employed, such as a furnace for small parts, gas torch, induction coil, inert tungsten arc, and radio-frequency resistance heating. It is desirable to supply the heat just in front of the cutting tool and to machine the metal as soon as it reaches the desired temperature. Investigations have shown that, except in isolated cases where limited success was obtained, elevated-temperature machining of refractory metals and titanium alloys offers no advantages over room-temperature machining with appropriate cutting fluids.

Vibration in machine tools, a very complex behavior, is often the cause of premature tool failure or short tool life, poor surface finish, damage to the workpiece, and damage to the machine itself. Vibration may be forced or self-excited. The term **chatter** is commonly used to designate self-excited vibrations in metal-cutting machines. The excited amplitudes are usually very high and may cause damage to the machine. While there is no complete solution to all types of vibration problems, certain measures may be taken. If the vibration is being forced, it may be possible to remove or isolate the forcing element from the machine. In cases where the forcing frequency is near a natural frequency, either the forcing frequency or the natural frequency may be raised or lowered. Damping will also greatly reduce the amplitude. Self-excited vibrations are generally controlled by increasing the rigidity and damping. (See also Sec. 5.)

General experience indicates that good machining practice requires a rigid setup. The machine tool must be capable of providing the **rigidity** required for the machining conditions used. If a rigid setup is not available, the feed and/or the depth of cut must be reduced accordingly. Excessive tool overhang should be avoided, and in milling, cutters should be mounted as close to the spindle as possible. The length of end mills and drills should be kept to a minimum. Tools with large nose radius or with a long, straight cutting edge increase the possibility of chatter.

As a result of mechanical working and thermal effects, **residual stresses** exist near the surfaces of metals that have been machined or ground. These stresses may cause warping of the workpiece as well as affect the resistance to fatigue and stress corrosion. To minimize residual stresses, sharp tools, medium feeds, and medium depths of cut are recommended. In grinding, high values of the more harmful tensile stresses often result. To minimize residual stresses in grinding, the following is recommended: soft wheels dressed frequently, low wheel speeds, high work speeds, low feeds, and whenever possible, sulphurized oil. Stress relieving or shot-peening often follows grinding when the endurance limit is critical.

CUTTING-TOOL MATERIALS

As a result of research and development over many years, a wide variety of **cutting-tool materials** are now available. The selection of a proper material depends on such factors as the cutting operation involved, the machine to be used, the workpiece material, production requirements, cost, and surface finish and accuracy desired. The major qualities required in a cutting tool are (1) hot hardness, (2) impact toughness, and (3) wear resistance.

Materials for cutting tools include carbon steels, medium-alloy steels, high-speed steels, cast alloys, cemented carbides, ceramics or oxides, and diamonds. Understanding the different types of **tool steels** (see p. 6–37) requires a knowledge of the role of different alloying elements. These elements are added to (1) obtain greater hardness and wear resistance, (2) obtain greater impact toughness, (3) impart hot hardness to the steel such that its hardness is maintained at high cutting temperatures, and (4) decrease distortion and warpage during hardening.

Carbon forms a carbide with iron, making it respond to hardening and thus increasing the hardness, strength, and wear resistance. The carbon content of tool steels ranges from 0.6 to 1.4 percent. **Chromium** is added to increase wear resistance and toughness; the content ranges from 0.25 to 4.5 percent. **Cobalt** is commonly used in high-speed steels to increase hot hardness so that tools may be used at higher cutting speeds and temperatures and still maintain hardness and keen cutting edges; the content ranges from 5 to 12 percent. **Molybdenum** is a strong carbide-forming element and increases strength, wear resistance, hardness penetration, and hot hardness. It is always used in conjunction with other alloying elements, and its content ranges to 10 percent. **Tungsten** promotes hot hardness and strength; content ranges from 1.25 to 20 percent. **Vanadium** increases hot hardness and abrasion resistance; in carbon tool steels, the content is of the order of 0.20 to 0.50 percent, while in high-speed steels, it ranges from 1 to 5 percent.

Carbon tool steels (Table 2) are the oldest type of steel used for cutting metals. The steel is inexpensive, has shock resistance, can be heat-treated to obtain a wide

Table 2. Nominal Composition of Some Carbon Tool Steels

(See also p. 6–37.)

Type	Percentage			
	C	Cr	V	W
W1	0.60–1.40	....	....	....
W2	0.60–1.40	....	0.25	....
W3	0.60–1.40	....	0.50	....
W4	0.60–1.40	0.25	....	....
W5	0.60–1.40	0.50	....	....
W6	0.60–1.40	0.25	0.25	....
W7	0.60–1.40	0.50	0.20	....
F1	1.00	....	....	1.25
F2	1.25	....	....	3.50
F3	1.25	0.75	....	3.50

range of hardness, is easily formed and ground, and holds a keen cutting edge where excessive abrasion and high heat are absent. Carbon tool steels are used for drills which are to be run at relatively low speeds, taps, broaches, and reamers.

Medium-alloy tool steels have greater wear resistance than carbon steels. Alloying elements are introduced to improve hardenability with less distortion. Manganese is the chief alloying element. These steels are used widely for drills, taps and reamers but do not have sufficient hot hardness to be used in high-speed turning or milling.

Table 3. Nominal Composition of Some High-speed Steels

(See also p. 6–37.)

Type	Percentage					Application
	W	Cr	V	Mo	Co	
T1	18	4	1	....	....	General purpose
T2	18	4	2	....	....	General purpose, higher strength
T3	18	4	3	....	....	Light cuts, high speed
T4	18	4	1	....	5	Heavy cuts
T5	18	4	2	....	8	Heavy cuts, abrasion resistant
T6	20	4.5	1.5	....	12	Heavy cuts, hard material
T7	14	4	2	....	....	Planer tools
T8	14	4	2	....	5	General purpose, hard material
T15	12	4	5	....	5	Extreme abrasion resistant
M1	1.5	4	1	8	....	General purpose
M2	6	4	2	5	....	General purpose
M3	6	4	2.75	6	....	Fine-edge tools
M4	5.5	4	4	4.5	....	Abrasion resistant
M6	4	4	1.5	5	12	Heavy cuts, abrasion resistant
M7	1.75	4	2	8.75	....	Fine-edge tools, abrasion resistant
M8	5	4	1.5	5	*	General purpose, abrasion resistant
M10	....	4	2	8	....	General purpose, high strength
M15	6.5	4	5	3.5	5	Heavy cuts, abrasion resistant
M33	1.75	3.75	1	9.75	8.25	Heavy cuts, abrasion resistant

* 1.25 Cb.

Table 4. Nominal Composition of Some Cast-alloy Tool Materials

Trade name	Percentage		
	Co	Cr	W
ALX	40	33	17
Crobalt 1	48	30	14
Crobalt 2	40	33	18
Crobalt 3	40	33	20
Rexalloy	44	33	17
Stellite 98M2	38	30	18
Stellite Star J	41	32	17
Stellite No. 3	52	30	11
Stellite No. 19	53	31	10
Tantung G	47	30	15
Tantung 144	45	32	18

High-speed steels (Table 3) are the most highly alloyed group among tool steels and maintain their hardness, strength, and keen cutting edge at high operating temperatures. They are oil-hardening and are little subject to warping. With suitable procedures and equipment, they can be fully hardened with little danger of distortion or cracking.

Cast alloys (Table 4) maintain high hardness at high temperatures and have good wear resistance. Cast-alloy tools, which are cast and ground into any desired shape, are not so tough as high-speed steels and are sensitive to shock loading. These alloys are recommended for deep roughing operations at relatively high speeds and feeds. Cutting fluids are not necessary during machining and are usually used only to obtain a special surface finish.

Cemented carbides have metal carbides as key ingredients and are manufactured by powder-metallurgy techniques. They have the following properties which make them good cutting-tool materials: (1) high hardness over a wide range of temperatures; (2) high Young's modulus, two to three times that of steel; (3) no plastic flow even at very high stresses; (4) low thermal expansion; and (5) high thermal conductivity. Cemented carbides are used in the form of inserts or tips which are brazed or clamped to a steel shank. Because of the difference in coefficients of expansion, brazing should be done carefully. The mechanically fastened tool tips, called **throwaway tips,** are becoming increasingly popular. They are available in different shapes, such as square, triangular, circular, and special forms.

There are three general groups of cemented carbides in use: (1) tungsten carbide with cobalt as a binder, used in machining cast irons and non-ferrous abrasive metals; (2) tungsten carbide with cobalt as a binder, plus a solid solution of WC-TiC-TaC-NbC, for use in machining steels; and (3) titanium carbide with nickel and molybdenum as a binder, for use where cutting temperatures are high because of high cutting speeds or the strength of the workpiece material.

Rigidity is of great importance when using carbide tools. Light feeds, low speeds, and chatter are deleterious. No cutting fluid is needed, but if one is used for cooling, it should be applied in large quantities and continuously to prevent heating and quenching. To take full advantage of carbide cutting tools, rigid, higher-speed, and more powerful machine tools have been developed.

Ceramic, or **oxide,** tool tips are the newest tool materials to be used commercially. They consist primarily of fine aluminum oxide grains which have been bonded together. Minor additions of other elements help obtain optimum properties. Ceramic tools have very high abrasion resistance, are harder than cemented carbides, and have less tendency to weld to metals during cutting. However, they lack impact toughness, and premature tool failure can result by chipping or general breakage. Ceramic tools have been found to be effective for high-speed, uninterrupted cutting operations. Tool and setup geometry is important. Tool failures can be reduced by the use of rigid tool mountings and rigid machine tools. Included in oxide cutting-tool materials are also borides and cermets.

Diamonds, known as **bort,** are used where good surface finish and dimensional accuracy are desired, particularly on soft materials that are difficult to machine. The general properties of diamonds are extreme hardness, low thermal expansion, high heat conductivity, and a very low coefficient of friction. Because of brittleness, tool shape is important in the use of diamonds; special care is given to the proper mounting and crystal orientation of diamonds in order to obtain optimum use. Low values of rake angles are normally used to provide a stronger cutting edge. Diamond tools work satisfactorily at almost any speed.

Heat Treatment of Tool Steels

(See also Sec. 6)

For specific heat treatments, refer to the literature of the manufacturer of the tool steel or to the literature listed in the References.

Carbon Tool Steel. To **normalize** before hardening (after machining or forging), eliminate stresses, and obtain a uniform grain structure, heat slowly and uniformly in the furnace, at the rate of ¾ to 1 hr per in. of thickness, to 1550 to 1700 F and hold for one-half the heating time to obtain complete penetration of heat and for complete refinement of grain. Remove from the furnace and cool in air. The higher temperatures are for the higher-carbon steels.

To **anneal,** heat slowly and uniformly to 1400 to 1440 F and hold 1 to 4 hr until a complete penetration of heat is obtained. Cool slowly (not to exceed 50 F per hr) to 1000 F either in the furnace or buried in an insulating material such as lime or ashes, after which more rapid cooling may be used. The higher temperatures are for the higher-carbon range.

To **harden,** heat the steel uniformly to a temperature of 1450 to 1500 F for the lower-carbon range and 1400 to 1475 F for the higher range. Quench in water or preferably a brine solution of 10 percent by weight held at a temperature of 70 to 80 F, but remove the tool before it has cooled to 200 F. Oil may be used for quenching thin sections. The higher temperatures are for the lower-carbon range. A semimuffle or muffle furnace may be used, but lead or salt baths are often preferable. The latter requires a slightly higher temperature, owing to the more rapid transfer of heat.

To **temper,** reheat the tool, while still warm, uniformly to 300 to 550 F. Hold for 1 hr, and cool in still air.

To **forge** to shape or refine the grain structure, heat uniformly to 1800 to 2000 F. The higher temperatures are for larger sections or rapid reductions. Forge constantly but not below a temperature of 1500 F.

High-speed steel should be **annealed** after forging and machining but before it is hardened. To avoid oxidation and scaling, the tool should be packed in annealing boxes in fine sand, lime, ashes, etc. Covers should be sealed airtight with fire clay and the annealing boxes heated slowly and uniformly to a temperature of 1600 to 1650 F, allowed to soak at this temperature for 1 to 4 hr, and then permitted to cool slowly (about 50 deg per hr) to 1000 F in the furnace before being unpacked, after which cooling may be more rapid.

To **harden**, high-speed steel is **preheated** slowly and uniformly to 1450 to 1600 F. For large tools, or where distortion is to be avoided, it is often advisable to use two preheating furnaces, one held at 1100 to 1200 F and the other at 1450 to 1600 F. To **heat for quenching,** transfer the preheated tool quickly to a high-heat furnace maintained at 2300 to 2375 F (for 18–4–1 and 18–4–2 types of steel), and hold at this high heat a sufficient time for proper solution of the carbides without an excessive grain growth or damage to the surface. For small tools, 2 min is sufficient; for tools 1 in. and up, 4 to 5 min is required. The tools are quenched in oil, air, or a molten bath, the latter at approximately 1100 F. From the oil or bath quench, the tool is cooled slowly to 200 to 300 F, reheated slowly and uniformly to 1000 to 1100 F, and held for 1 to 4 hr for **tempering.**

Each type of high-speed steel must be given its own special heat treatment to secure best performance. For **forging,** the steel should be heated slowly and uniformly to 1900 to 2150 F. It is not safe to continue forging below 1700 F. Slow cooling after forging is necessary to prevent possible cracking from forging strains.

Salt Baths. With tools that cannot be ground after hardening, or where it is necessary to keep the surface in the best possible condition and preserve sharp edges, salt-bath heating will give the best results. Fresh salt has a dissolving action on the steel which disappears after the bath is used for a short time. A sludge gradually forms at the bottom of the pit and a heavy crust on the top. They must be removed periodically. From the salt bath, tools are quenched in hot water to dissolve the salts. **Lead baths** furnish temperature up to 1700 F. As the vapor from the baths is poisonous, lead furnaces should be equipped with ventilating hoods. Lead baths do not affect quenching oils used subsequently.

Cast-alloy and carbide tools require no heat treatment.

Tool Grinding

(See also p. 6–170.)

Tools should be ground to proper angles on machines by experienced operators. If a coolant of water, borax water, or emulsion is used, it should be applied in large quantities. Keen cutting edges and smooth surfaces should be formed.

Carbon-tool-steel, high-speed-steel, and cobalt-high-speed-steel tools are best rough-ground on a coarse-grain (24–36) wheel and finished on a fine-grain (60 to 100). They may be rough- and finish-machine-ground on the same wheel of aluminum oxide abrasive 24 to 36 grain L grade B vitrified bond. Resin bonded wheels are also used.

Stellite usually is ground on a soft-grade vitrified wheel of aluminum-oxide grain not coarser than 46 or finer than 60.

In grinding **sintered-carbide** tools, two types of wheels are used: (1) special silicon-carbide wheels that are hard, sharp, and bonded with an open porous structure, and (2) diamond resinoid wheels in grits from 100 to 320 grain size. For roughing, offhand or semiautomatic machine, a straight or cupped wheel in silicon-carbide abrasive 60 grain vitrified bond and soft grade is used, or a resinoid B or vitrified V wheel with 100-grain diamond may be used such as D100-P100V. For finishing, offhand or semiautomatic machine, a similar vitrified wheel of 100 grit is used, or a diamond resinoid wheel of 150 to 220 grit may be used. For offhand grinding, the wheel should be slightly crowned and the tool rocked slowly across the face of the wheel which rotates at about 4,500 fpm.

Tools finished on silicon-carbide wheels may be lapped for close-limit precision work on a Belgian iron or soft cast-iron lapping dish impregnated with No. 4 diamond powder, moistened slightly with olive oil. Grinding and lapping should be done in a direction against the cutting edge. Lapping should continue until all grinding marks are removed. It is advisable to consult the literature of the grinding-wheel manufacturers.

CUTTING FLUIDS

(See also p. 6–256)

Definition. Cutting fluids, frequently referred to as lubricants or coolants, comprise those liquids and gases which are applied to the material being cut and to the tool in order to facilitate the cutting operation.

Purpose. A cutting fluid is used (1) to keep the tool cool and prevent it from being heated to a temperature at which the hardness and resistance to abrasion are reduced; (2) to keep the work cool, thus preventing it from being machined in a warped shape to inaccurate final dimensions; (3) possibly through lubrication to reduce the power consumption, wear on the tool, and the generation of heat; (4) to provide a good finish on the work; (5) to aid in providing a satisfactory chip formation; (6) to wash away the chips (this is particularly desirable in deep-hole drilling, hacksawing, milling, and grinding); (7) to prevent corrosion of the work and machine; and (8) to lubricate moving machine parts close to the cutting tool.

Classification. Cutting fluids may be classed as follows: (1) air used as suction or blast; (2) water, either plain or containing an alkali; (3) emulsions of a soluble oil or paste; and (4) oils, such as mineral, fixed, compounded, sulphurized and, chlorinated.

Induced **air draft** is often used with internal and surface grinding and polishing operations or on grinding and boring operations on gray iron. Its main purpose is to remove the small chips or dust, although some cooling is obtained.

Aqueous solutions, containing about 1 percent by weight of an alkali, such as borax, sodium carbonate, or trisodium phosphate, have high cooling properties and have sufficient corrosion-prevention properties for some materials. They are inexpensive and are sometimes used for grinding, drilling, sawing, and light milling or turning operations.

Emulsions consist of a soluble oil or paste emulsified with water in the ratio of 1 part oil to 10 to 100 parts water, depending upon the type of product and the operation. This is a low-cost cutting fluid and is used for practically all types of cutting and grinding when machining all types of metals. The richer mixtures of oil and water, such as 1:10, are used for broaching, threading, and gear cutting, where an oil is not required to secure the desired surface finish or machine lubrication. For most operations, a solution of 1 part soluble oil to 20 parts water will be satisfactory for turret-lathe work, some screw-machine work, gear hobbing, milling, and drilling. The mix of the emulsion is often determined by the rust-prevention requirements of the metal being machined or the lubrication requirements of the machine, and not by the actual machining operation.

A variety of **oils** is used for metal cutting. They are used where lubrication rather than cooling is essential or on high-grade finishing cuts, although sometimes superior finishes are obtained with the emulsions.

Sulphurized oils are used generally as cutting fluids for rapid production involving good surface finish and close tolerances on metals difficult to machine. These sulphurized oils may be classified into four groups: (1) sulphurized mineral oils containing up to 4 percent active sulphur in straight mineral oil; (2) sulphurized mixed oils—combinations of fatty oils, such as lard, rapeseed, degras, and petroleum oils to which sulphur is added; (3) sulphurized-base oils—fatty oils containing 8 to 12 percent sulphur, which the user blends with mineral oil for individual requirements; (4) chlorinated and sulphurized, and chlorinated mineral oils.

Sulphurized oils are useful in machining low-carbon steel, hot-rolled steels, stainless steel, high-nickel alloys, and monel. They are used extensively in broaching, gear cutting, and in automatic screw-machine work involving threading and tapping.

Quantity of Cutting Fluid. Best results are obtained when any of the cutting fluids is applied to the work and tool in ample quantities, such as 3 to 5 gpm for each single-point tool. Water compounds give an increase in cutting speed of 10 to 30 percent. Emulsions are slightly less effective, the oils giving 5 to 15 percent greater speeds than dry cutting. The increase in tool life is much greater than the stated percentage of increase in cutting speed. Cutting fluids should be applied at temperatures between 70 and 85 F.

Mist cooling has been found beneficial in many cases for turning, milling, drilling, and tapping. Air is forced through a T fitting or mixing valve instead of a Venturi. With the air valve closed, conventional fluid cooling is obtained, but with both valves opened, the fluid is vaporized and the fluid-to-air ratio can be adjusted to suit the job. Favorable reports for both high-speed-steel and carbide tools have been made.

MACHINING PROCESSES AND EQUIPMENT

The general types of **machine tools** are lathes; turret lathes; screw, boring, drilling, reaming, threading, milling, and gear-cutting machines; planers and shapers; broaching, cutting-off, grinding, and polishing machines. Each of these is subdivided into many types and sizes.

"American Standards for Small Tools and Machine Tool Elements" are published by and may be obtained from the ASME. Names and addresses of machine-tool manufacturers may be obtained from various sources such as the "Mechanical Engineers' Catalog" of the ASME and the special publications of the ASTME.

General items common to all machine tools are discussed first, and individual tool types are treated later in this section.

Automation is the application of special equipment to control and perform manufacturing processes with little or no manual effort. It is applied to the manufacturing of all types of goods and processes, from the raw material to the finished product. Automation involves many items, such as handling, processing, assembly, inspecting, and packaging. Its primary objective is to lower manufacturing cost through controlled production and quality, lower labor cost, reduced damage to work by handling, higher degree of safety for personnel, and economy of floor space. Automation may be partial, such as gaging in cylindrical grinding, or it may be complete.

The conditions which play a role in decisions concerning automation are rising production costs, high percentage of rejects, lagging output, scarcity of human labor, hazardous working conditions, and work requiring repetitive operation. Factors which must be carefully studied before deciding on automation are high initial cost of equipment, maintenance problems, and type of product. (See also Sec. 16.)

Numerical control, which is a method of controlling the motions of machine components by numbers, was first applied to machine tools about a decade ago. Numerically controlled machine tools are now at work in a rapidly growing number of plants. Such machines are classified according to the type of cutting process. For instance, in drilling and boring machines, the positioning and the cutting take place sequentially, whereas in die-sinking machines, positioning and cutting take place simultaneously. The latter are often described as **continuous-path** machines, and since they require more exacting specifications, they give rise to more numerous and complex problems. Great efforts are being made to make the machines perform over a very wide range of cutting conditions without requiring adjustment, to eliminate chatter, and to improve accuracy. Information is stored on punch cards or tapes; the basic concept is that holes, representing information, are read by sensing devices which then actuate relays and other devices to control various electrical or mechanical systems. In this way, great savings can be achieved by eliminating templates; complex contours can be machined which would be almost impossible by any other method. A large variety of programming systems has been developed during the past few years.

The proper design of **machine-tool structures** requires analysis of such factors as form and materials of structures, stresses, weight, and manufacturing and performance considerations. Current thinking is that the best approach to obtain the ultimate in machine-tool accuracy is to employ both improvements in structural rigidity and compensation of deflections by use of special controls. The C-frame structure has been used extensively in the past because it provides ready accessibility to the working area of the machine. With the advent of numerical control, the box-type frame with its considerably improved static stiffness becomes practical since the need for manual access to the working area is greatly reduced. The use of a box-type structure with thin walls can provide low weight for a given stiffness. The lightweight-design principle offers high dynamic stiffness by providing a high natural frequency of the structure through combining high static stiffness with low weight rather than through the use of large mass. Manufacturing methods for structures should make the most efficient use of material. Lightweight designs can best be obtained by fabrication processes such as welding. This requires the use of steel instead of cast iron and raises the question of the lower damping capacity of steel, but the problem can be overcome by the introduction of preloaded frictional surfaces. Against the advantages of lightweight construction must be held the higher cost of labor required. New approaches to correcting lateral deviation of moving parts from their intended paths, caused by deformation under load, tolerances, wear, etc., consist of introducing additional control to sense these deviations and automatically reposition the machine elements to compensate for them.

Mass production with modern machine tools has been achieved through the development of self-contained **power-head** production units and the development of **transfer** mechanisms. Power-head units, consisting of a frame, electric driving motor, gearbox, tool spindles, etc., are available for many types of machining operations. Transfer mechanisms move the workpieces from station to station by various methods. Transfer-type machines can be arranged in several configurations, such as a straight line or a U pattern. Various types of machine tools for mass production can be built from components; this is known as the **building-block** principle. Such a system combines flexibility and adaptability with high productivity.

A new approach to optimize machining operations is **adaptive control.** While the material is being machined, the system senses operating conditions such as forces, tool-tip temperature, rate of tool wear, and surface finish and converts these data into feed and speed control that enables the machine to cut under optimum conditions for maximum productivity. Combined with numerical controls and computers, adaptive controls are expected to result in increased efficiency of metalworking operations.

Machining recommendations for turning, drilling, milling, and surface grinding of certain materials are given below. For more detailed information, the Ordnance Corps "Machining Data" is highly recommended. Sources for literature on machining can be found in such references as "Review of Metal Literature" by ASM and "U.S. Government Research and Development Reports." Specific information can also be obtained from such organizations as the Defense Metals Information Center, Battelle Memorial Institute, and Machining Data Center. Technical papers and articles on various aspects of machining appear in such periodicals as *American Machinist, Tool and Manufacturing Engineer, Microtecnic, International Journal of Machine Tool Design and Research, C.I.R.P. Annalen,* and *Journal of Engineering for Industry* (ASME); individual technical papers are also available from such societies as the ASME, ASTME, and SAE.

LATHES

Size of Lathe. It is common practice to specify the size of a lathe by giving the **swing** (diameter) and the **distance between centers** when the tailstock is flush with the end of the bed. The maximum swing over the ways is usually greater than the nominal swing. The **length of the bed** is given frequently to specify the over-all length of the bed. A lathe size is indicated thus: 14 in. (swing) by 30 in. (between centers) by 6 ft (length of bed). Lathes are made light, medium, or heavy duty. The lathes may be for heavy cuts at low speeds or for relatively light cuts at high speeds, both requiring high-power drives and rigidity.

The common **sizes of engine lathes** are as follows: 10, 12, and 13 in. × 3 to 5 ft;

14 in. × 6 ft; 16, 18, and 20 in. × 8 ft; 22 in. × 10 ft; 24, 27, 30, 36, 42, 48, 60, and 72 in. × any length of bed desired.

Lathe Centers. The tailstock center of a lathe is generally made of high-carbon steel ground to an included point angle of 60 deg. For production or high-speed work, fixed centers pointed with stellite or sintered-carbide tips are used. All centers of this type should be lubricated with a paste such as powdered lead oxide mixed with machine oil. Live centers are used generally. The point, which rotates with the work, is mounted on the shank by means of antifriction bearings.

Feed and Speed Ratios for Lathes. (See Table 5.) **Geometrical progression** is used extensively in designing machine-tool feeds and speeds. Feeds in geometrical progression are used on cylindrical grinders, boring mills, milling machines, drilling machines, etc.; but for screw-cutting lathes, the power feeds for thread cutting and turning must be in proportion to the threads per inch to be cut.

The carriage may be fed along the bed by means of a lead screw for thread cutting or through a feed rod driving through a friction clutch in the apron for general turning and facing. The lead screw is driven positively by a train of gears from the spindle. The feed rod may be driven from the spindle by a belt and change gears, pick-off change gears, or built-in easily selected quick-change gears. Most screw-cutting lathes will cut 36 differently pitched screw threads, ranging from 1½ to 80 per in. By means of gearing and a friction clutch in the apron, the feed rod (or single-splined lead screw if used for turning feeds) provides turning feeds reduced from one-half to one-tenth of these. A reduction of one-tenth the above threads gives 36 turning feeds from 15 to 800 rpm of the work per inch of tool travel, or 0.0666 to 0.00125 in. feed per revolution. The power cross feeds are often equivalent to the turning feeds.

To select the pick-off change gears for **thread cutting** if the lathe is simple-geared and the stud runs at the same speed as the spindle, choose some convenient gear for the screw and multiply its number of teeth by the number of threads per inch of the lead screw. Divide this product by the number of threads per inch to be cut. The quotient will be the number of teeth in the gear for the stud.

If the lathe is compound-geared, select at random a set of driving gears, multiply all the numbers of teeth, and multiply this product by the number of threads per inch to be cut. Then select at random all the driven gears except one. Multiply the numbers of teeth of these gears and this product by the number of threads per inch on the lead screw. Divide the first result by the second. The quotient is the number of teeth in the remaining driven gear. **Metric screw threads** may be cut on lathes having lead screws cut to a number of threads per inch by using change gears for each pitch in combination with a pair of transposing gears having 50 teeth in the driver and 127 teeth in the driven. (This is because 127 cm = 50 in.)

Multispeeds for Lathes. Step-cone pulley-driven lathes are commonly back-geared, with the gearing single, double, or triple. The single back gear adds an equal number of lower speeds, the double adds another, etc. Two-speed countershafts may be used to double the preceding spindle speeds. The diameters of the steps of mating step-cone pulleys should be such that the belt length is constant.

All geared-head lathes, which are single-pulley belt-driven or arranged for direct-motor drive through short, flat, or V belts, gears, or silent chain, increase the power of the drive and provide a means for obtaining 8, 12, 16, or 24 spindle speeds. The teeth may be of the spur, helical, or herringbone type and may be ground or lapped after hardening. Nearly all the machine tools are now being arranged for individual motor drive.

Speeds in **geometrical progression** are obtained as follows: If a is the lowest speed, b the highest, n the number of speeds, and r the ratio between each speed and the next one higher, then the various speeds are $a, ar, ar^2, ar^3, \ldots ar^{n-1}$; $r = (b/a)^{1/(n-1)}$.

In lathes of the geared-head type for toolroom work, having 12 speeds, a ratio of 1.35 is commonly used; for production work where fewer speeds are required to cover the range, 1.56 to 1.7 is used.

Variable speeds are obtained by driving with adjustable-speed d-c shunt-wound motors with stepped field-resistance control or by electronics or motor-generator system to give speed variation in infinite steps. A-c motors driving through infinitely variable speed transmissions of the mechanical or hydraulic type are also in general use.

The spindle speeds of lathes, in general, have been stepped up to from 2,000 to 2,400 rpm in many cases. They are now being constructed with rigidity and strength to take full advantage of sintered-carbide tools. The motor horsepower is greatly increased. Speed preselectors, which give speed in feet per minute as a function of work diameter, are introduced, and variable-speed drives using d-c motors with panel control are standard on many lathes. A number of manufacturers are equipping lathes with contour facing, turning, and boring attachments. They may be operated electrically, hydraulically, and pneumatically. Punched cards and tape are used for programming.

TOOL SHAPES

The standard **nomenclature** for single-point tools, such as those used on lathes, planers, and shapers, is shown in Fig. 6. Each tool consists of a shank and point. The point of a single-point tool may be formed by grinding on the end of the shank;

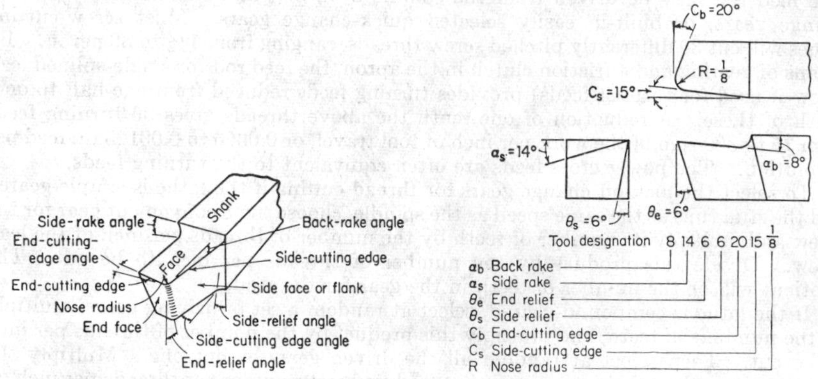

Fig. 6. Standard nomenclature for single-point cutting tools.

it may be forged on the end of the shank and subsequently ground; a tip or insert may be clamped or brazed to the end of the shank. The **best tool shape** for each material and each operation depends on many factors. For specific information and recommendations, the various sources listed in the References should be consulted.

Positive **rake angles** improve the cutting operation with regard to forces and deflection; however, a high positive rake angle may result in early failure of the cutting edge. Positive rake angles are generally used on lower-strength materials. For higher-strength materials, negative rake angles are used. **Back rake** usually controls the direction of chip flow and is of less importance than the **side rake.** The purpose of **relief angles** is to avoid interference and rubbing between the workpiece and tool flank surfaces. In general, they should be small for high-strength materials and larger for softer materials. Excessive relief angles may weaken the tool. The **side cutting-edge angle** influences the length of chip contact and the true feed. This angle is often limited by the workpiece geometry, *e.g.*, the shoulder contour. Large angles are apt to cause tool chatter. Small **end cutting-edge angles** may create excessive force normal to the workpiece, while large angles may weaken the tool point. The purpose of the **nose radius** is to give a smooth surface finish and to obtain longer tool life by increasing the strength of the cutting edge. The nose radius should be tangent to the cutting-edge angles. A large nose radius gives a stronger tool and may be used for roughing cuts; however, large radii may lead to tool chatter. A small nose radius reduces forces and is therefore preferred on thin or slender workpieces.

General recommendations for turning-tool geometries are as follows: For high-speed steel and cast-alloy tools, back rakes 0 to 20 deg, side rakes 5 to 15 deg, end relief angles 5 to 12 deg, side relief angles 5 to 12 deg, end cutting-edge angles 5 to 6 deg. For throwaway carbide tools, back rakes 0 to −5 deg, side rakes 5 to −5 deg, end and side relief angles 5 to 8 deg, end cutting-edge angle 5 deg. The softer the material, the higher the angles should be. General values for side cutting-edge angle and nose radius are 15 deg and 3/64 in., respectively.

Table 5. Turning Recommendations*

Material	Condition	Hardness, BHN	High-speed steel		Carbide	
			Speed, fpm	Feed, ipr	Speed, fpm	Feed, ipr
B-1112	Cold-drawn	135	225	0.012	700	0.015
AISI 1020	Annealed	140	160	0.010	550	0.015
AISI 4340	Annealed	200	80	0.010	400	0.015
AISI 4340	Quenched and tempered	300	50	0.008	300	0.015
AISI 4340	Quenched and tempered	400	30	0.008	225	0.012
430 stainless	Annealed	175	100	0.008	350	0.012
302 and 321 stainless	Annealed	190	70	0.008	275	0.012
410 stainless	Annealed	180	90	0.008	350	0.012
410 stainless	Quenched and tempered	300	55	0.008	225	0.012
Nickel-base high-temp alloys	Solution-treated	290	15	0.008	60	0.008
Cobalt-base high-temp alloys	Solution treated	200	20	0.008	85	0.008
Gray iron						
ASTM Class 25	Annealed	140	130	0.010	550	0.015
ASTM Class 40	Cast	200	75	0.010	350	0.015
Nodular iron						
SAE 60-40-10	Annealed	170	120	0.010	500	0.015
SAE 100-70-03	Quenched and tempered	260	55	0.010	225	0.015
Malleable iron						
Grade 32510	Malleableized	120	130	0.010	550	0.015
Grade 60003	Malleableized	220	80	0.010	350	0.015
Aluminum alloys						
Wrought alloys	Cold-drawn or solution-treated and aged	40–105†	700	0.012	Max	0.015
Magnesium alloys						
Cast alloys	Cast	35–70†	900	0.012	Max	0.012
Wrought alloys	Cold-drawn	40–80†	900	0.012	Max	0.012
Copper alloys	Wrought or cast	120–160	400	0.010	1,000	0.010
	Wrought or cast	165–180	275	0.010	750	0.010
	Wrought or cast	172–205	125	0.010	600	0.010

* Courtesy of Metcut Research Associates, Inc., Cincinnati, Ohio.
† 500-kg load for aluminum and magnesium alloys.

TURRET LATHES

Turret lathes are built in two distinct styles: the ram and the saddle types. The former is built both horizontal and vertical. Turret lathes are used for the production of parts in moderate quantities of tens, twenties, or hundreds and produce interchangeable parts at low production cost. Turret lathes may be chucking, screw machine, or universal. The universal machine may be set up to machine bar stock as a screw machine or have work held in a chuck. These machines may be semiautomatic, *i.e.*, so arranged that, after a piece is chucked and the machine started, it will complete the machining cycle automatically and come to a stop. This may be of the turret type or of the tool-slide type. They may be horizontal or vertical and single or multiple spindle.

The basic principle of the turret lathe is that, with standard tools, setups can be made quickly so that combined, multiple, and successive cuts can be made on a part. By **combined** cuts, tools on the cross slide operate simultaneously with those on the turret, *e.g.*, facing from the cross slide and boring from the turret. **Multiple** cuts permit two or more tools to operate from either or both the cross slide or turret. By **successive** cuts, one tool may follow another to rough or finish a surface; *e.g.*, a hole may be drilled, bored, and reamed at one chucking. In the tool-slide machine only roughing cuts, such as turn and face, can be made in one machine. A second machine similarly tooled must be available to make the finishing cuts.

Ram-type turret lathes have the turret mounted on a ram which slides in a separate base. This base can be clamped at any position along the bed to suit long or short work. A cross slide can be used so that combined cuts can be taken from the turret and the cross slide at the same time. Turret and cross slide can be equipped with manual or power feed. The short stroke of the turret slide limits this machine to comparatively short light work, in both the small and quantity-lot field.

Saddle-type turret lathes have the turret mounted on a saddle which slides directly on the bed. Hence, the length of stroke is limited only by the length of bed. A separate square-turret carriage with longitudinal and transverse movement can be mounted between the head and the hex-turret saddle so that combined cuts from both stations at one time are possible. The saddle type of turret lathe generally has a large hollow vertically faced turret for accurate alignment of the tools.

Turret lathes of a wide range of sizes of the ram type and, in still larger sizes, of saddle-type machines are built by a number of companies. The newer machines are made more rigid and powerful and embody more automatic features. Some have speed and feed calculators, rapid traverse on longitudinal and cross-feed, higher turning speeds, and automatic pressure lubrication.

SCREW MACHINES

When turret lathes are set up for bar stock, they are often called **screw machines.** Turret lathes that are adaptable only to bar-stock work are constructed for light work. As with turret lathes, they have spring collets for holding the bars during machining and friction fingers or rolls to feed the bar stock forward. Some bar-feeding devices are operated by hand and others semiautomatically. Some screw machines are provided with power feed, but more often both turret and cross slide are operated manually.

Automatic screw machines may be classified as single spindle or multiple spindle. Single-spindle machines rotate the bar stock from which the part is to be made. The tools are carried on a turret and on cross slides or on a circular drum and on cross slides. Multiple-spindle machines have four, five, six, or eight spindles, each carrying a bar of the material from which the piece is to be made. Capacities range from 1/8 to 6 in. diam of bar stock.

Feeds of forming tools vary with the width of the cut. The wider the forming tool and the smaller the diameter of stock, the smaller should be the feed. On multiple-spindle machines, where many tools are working simultaneously, the feeds should be such as to reduce the actual cutting time to a minimum. Often only one or two tools in a set are working up to capacity, as far as actual speed and feed are concerned.

A cutting fluid should always be used to increase tool life and to provide a better finish on the product. A rich emulsion is often satisfactory for general work, provided that it does not interfere with the lubrication of the machine. A light paraffin oil is satisfactory for brass. For aluminum, a paraffin oil plus 5 to 10 percent lard oil is very satisfactory. On most steels, a sulphurized mineral oil or a sulphurized-chlorinated oil with some fatty oil addition is best for general work.

BORING MACHINES

Boring machines are of two general types, horizontal and vertical, and are frequently referred to as horizontal boring machines and vertical boring and turning mills. A classification of boring machines comprises horizontal boring, drilling, and milling machines; vertical boring and turning mills; vertical multispindle cylinder boring mills; vertical cylinder boring mills; vertical turret boring mills (vertical turret lathes); car-wheel boring mills; diamond or precision boring machines (vertical and horizontal); and jig borers.

The **horizontal type** is made for both precision work and general manufacturing. It is particularly adapted for work not conveniently revolved, for milling, slotting, drilling, tapping, boring, and reaming long holes, and for making interchangeable parts that must be produced without jigs and fixtures. The machine is universal and has a wide range of speeds and feeds; for a face-mill operation may be followed by one with a small-diameter drill or end mill.

Vertical boring mills are adapted to a wide range of faceplate work that can be revolved. The advantage lies in the ease with which work is fastened to the horizontal table, which resembles a four-jaw independent chuck with extra radial T slots, and in the lessened effect of centrifugal forces arising from unsymmetrically balanced work. Pulleys, flywheels, gear blanks, piston heads, and electric-motor and electric-generator frames and spiders are commonly finished on these machines.

A **cylinder-boring machine** is an upright type with the spindles inclined about 15 deg to the vertical. This is a heavy-duty machine for rough- and finish-boring the cylinders of an automobile cylinder block at one setup. The cylinder block is mounted in a fixture at the lower end of the boring bars. It is fed upward hydraulically at rapid transverse against the boring tools, engaged in the boring feed, and at the end of the stroke returned to the starting point. The long boring bars, carrying inserted blades, are piloted both below and above the work.

A **jig-boring machine** has a single-spindle sliding head mounted over a table adjustable longitudinally and transversely by lead screws which roughly locate the work under the spindle. Precision setting of the table involves end-measuring rods, an inside micrometer, and an 0.0001 in. dial indicator. These machines, made in various sizes, are used for accurately finishing holes and surfaces in definite relation to one another. Measuring rods of this type are used in connection with vertical milling machines. These machines may use drills, rose or fluted reamers, or single-point boring tools. The latter are held in an adjustable **boring head** by which the tool can be moved eccentrically to change the diameter of the hole.

Precision-boring machines may have one or more spindles operating at high speeds for the purpose of boring to accurate dimensions such surfaces as wrist-pin holes in pistons and connecting-rod bushings. Diamonds or tips of sintered carbide are used as the cutters. High speeds of 600 to 1,500 fpm with shallow depths of cut of 0.005 to 0.040 in. and light feeds of 0.001 to 0.010 in. are generally used.

Tools for Boring Mills. The tools used are the same as those for lathes. In addition, many special tools are made for particular jobs, and these are frequently furnished by the machine builder.

DRILLING MACHINES

Drilling machines are intended for drilling holes, tapping, counterboring, reaming, and general boring operations. They may be **classified** into a large variety of types.

Sizes of Drilling Machines. Vertical drilling machines are usually designated by a dimension, in inches, which roughly indicates the diameter of the largest circle that can be drilled at its center under the machine. This dimensioning, however, does not hold for all makes of machines. The sizes begin with about 6 in. and continue to 50 in., the largest size commercially built. The common sizes are 20, 22, 24, 26, 28, 30, 32, 36, 42, and 50 in. Heavy-duty presses of the vertical type, with all-geared speed and feed drive, are now being constructed with a box-type column instead of the older cylindrical column. Their capacity is 20 to 30 in., and they are provided with motors from 5 to 10 hp. By shifting one lever, feeds can be increased about three times to change from drilling to reaming.

The size of a **radial drill** is designated by the length of the arm, this dimension being expressed in feet as 2, 4, 6, and 8 ft machines. This represents the radius of a piece which can be drilled in the middle.

Twist drills are the most common tools used in drilling and are made in many sizes and lengths. For years they have been grouped according to numbered sizes, 1 to 80, inclusive, corresponding approximately to Stubbs steel wire gage (Table 6); some by lettered sizes A to Z, inclusive (Table 7); some by fractional inches from 1/64 up, and the group of millimeter sizes.

Straight-shank twist drills of fractional size and long length range from 33/64 in. diam to 1 5/8 in., by 1/64 in. increments to 1 1/4 in., by 1/32 in. to 1 1/2 in., and by 1/16 in. to 2 in. **Taper-shank** drills range from 1/8 in. diam by 1/64 in. to 1 3/4 in.,

Table 6. Numbered Twist-drill Sizes

No. of drill	Diam, in.	No. of drill	Diam, in.	No. of drill	Diam. in.	No. of drill	Diam. in.	No. of drill	Diam, in.
1	0.2280	17	0.1730	33	0.1130	49	0.0730	65	0.0350
2	0.2210	18	0.1695	34	0.1110	50	0.0700	66	0.0330
3	0.2130	19	0.1660	35	0.1100	51	0.0670	67	0.0320
4	0.2090	20	0.1610	36	0.1065	52	0.0635	68	0.0310
5	0.2055	21	0.1590	37	0.1040	53	0.0595	69	0.02925
6	0.2040	22	0.1570	38	0.1015	54	0.0550	70	0.0280
7	0.2010	23	0.1540	39	0.0995	55	0.0520	71	0.0260
8	0.1990	24	0.1520	40	0.0980	56	0.0465	72	0.0250
9	0.1960	25	0.1495	41	0.0960	57	0.0430	73	0.0240
10	0.1935	26	0.1470	42	0.0935	58	0.0420	74	0.0225
11	0.1910	27	0.1440	43	0.0890	59	0.0410	75	0.0210
12	0.1890	28	0.1405	44	0.0860	60	0.0400	76	0.0200
13	0.1850	29	0.1360	45	0.0820	61	0.0390	77	0.0180
14	0.1820	30	0.1285	46	0.0810	62	0.0380	78	0.0160
15	0.1800	31	0.1200	47	0.0785	63	0.0370	79	0.0145
16	0.1770	32	0.1160	48	0.0760	64	0.0360	80	0.0135

Table 7. Lettered Twist-drill Sizes

Letter	Size	Diam, in.	Letter	Size	Diam, in.	Letter	Size	Diam, in.	Letter	Size	Diam, in.
A	15/64	0.234	H	17/64	0.266	N	......	0.302	U	......	0.368
B	......	0.238	I	......	0.272	O	5/16	0.316	V	3/8	0.377
C	......	0.242	J	......	0.277	P	21/64	0.323	W	25/64	0.386
D	......	0.246	K	9/32	0.281	Q	......	0.332	X	......	0.397
E	1/4	0.250	L	......	0.290	R	11/32	0.339	Y	13/32	0.404
F	......	0.257	M	19/64	0.295	S	......	0.348	Z	......	0.413
G	......	0.261				T	23/64	0.358			

by 1/32 in. to 2 1/4 in., by 1/16 in. to 3 1/2 in. diam. Larger drills are made by various drill manufacturers.

Tolerances have been set on the various features of all drills so that the products of different manufacturers will be interchangeable in the user's plants.

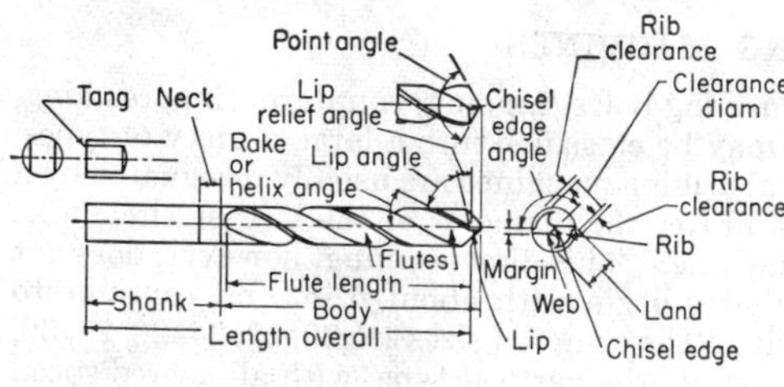

Fig. 7. Straight-shank twist drill.

Twist drills (Fig. 7) are decreased in diameter from point to shank (back taper) to prevent binding. This longitudinal clearance varies from 0.00025 to 0.0015 in. per in. of length. If the web is increased gradually in thickness from point to shank to increase the strength, it is customary to reduce the helix angle as it approaches the shank. The shape of the groove is important, that one which gives a straight cutting edge and allows a full curl to the chip being the best. The **helix angles** of the flutes vary from 0 to 45 deg. The usual **point angle** is 118 deg. Special point angles recommended for various materials are as follows:

Material	Angle	Material	Angle
Aluminum alloys	140 (45)*	Copper	100 (32)
Bakelite, hard rubber, and fiber	60–90 (32)	Slate	90 (9)
Brass and bronze	118 (0)	Steel forgings (250 Brinell +)	125–140 (32)
Soft cast iron	90 (32)	High-temperature alloys	118 (24–32)

* The values in parentheses represent the recommended helix angles in degrees.

The best all-around **relief angle** is 12 deg for hand-ground drills. They should be ground on machines to 6 deg. There are a number of **twist-drill grinders** on the market designed to give the proper point and relief angles.

Among the common **types of drills** are the combined drill and countersink or **center drill,** a short drill used to center shafts before squaring and turning; the **trepanning tool** used to cut a core from a piece of metal instead of reducing all the metal removed to chips; the **gun-barrel drill,** run at a high speed under a light feed, and used to drill small long holes; the **hog-nosed drill** used to bore out cored holes; the **oil-tube drill,** having holes or tubes in its body through which oil is forced to the cutting lips; **three- and four-fluted drills,** used to enlarge holes after a leader hole has been cored, punched, or drilled with a two-fluted drill; **twisted drills** made from flat high-speed steel or drop-forged to desired shape and then twisted. Drills are also made of solid sintered-carbide or of high-speed steel with an insert of carbide to form the chisel edge and both cutting edges. They are used primarily for drilling abrasive or very hard materials.

Speeds and feeds for drills are given in Table 8.

Table 8. Drilling Recommendations for ¼-in.-diam Drill*

Material	Condition	Hardness, BHN	High-speed steel		Cutting fluid
			Speed, fpm	Feed, ipr	
B-1112	Cold-drawn	135	200	0.007	Water-base solution
AISI 1020	Annealed	140	100	0.005	Water-base solution
AISI 4340	Annealed	200	60	0.004	Water-base solution
AISI 4340	Quenched and tempered	300	50	0.003	Active cutting oil
AISI 4340	Quenched and tempered	400	40	0.002	Active cutting oil
430 stainless	Annealed	175	50	0.003	Water-base solution
302 and 321 stainless	Annealed	190	30	0.002	Water-base solution
410 stainless	Annealed	180	50	0.003	Water-base solution
410 stainless	Quenched and tempered	300	25	0.002	Active cutting oil
Nickel-base high-temp alloys	Solution-treated	290	15	0.001	Active cutting oil
Cobalt-base high-temp alloys	Solution-treated	200	20	0.001	Active cutting oil
Gray iron					
ASTM Class 25	Annealed	140	175	0.005	Water-base solution
ASTM Class 40	Cast	200	90	0.005	Water-base solution
Nodular iron					
SAE 60-40-10	Annealed	170	150	0.005	Water-base solution
SAE 100-70-03	Quenched and tempered	260	50	0.005	Water-base solution
Malleable iron					
Grade 32510	Malleableized	120	200	0.005	Water-base solution
Grade 60003	Malleableized	220	100	0.005	Water-base solution
Aluminum alloys	Cold-drawn or solution-treated and aged	40–105†	250	0.007	Water-base solution
Magnesium alloys					
Cast alloys	Cast	35–70†	300	0.007	Mineral oil or dry
Wrought alloys	Cold-drawn	40–80†	250	0.007	Mineral oil or dry
Copper alloys	Wrought or cast	120–160	175	0.005	Water-base solution
	Wrought or cast	165–180	125	0.005	Water-base solution
	Wrought or cast	172–205	75	0.005	Water-base solution

Note: The feed should be increased with increasing drill diameter.

* Courtesy of Metcut Research Associates, Inc., Cincinnati, Ohio.

† 500-kg load for aluminum and magnesium alloys.

REAMING MACHINES

A **reamer** is a multiple-cutting-edge tool used to enlarge or finish holes, to give accurate dimensions as well as good finish. Reamers are divided into (1) rose and (2) fluted.

The **rose reamer** is a heavy-bodied tool with end cutting edges. It is used to remove considerable metal and to true up a hole preparatory to flute reaming. It is similar to the three- and four-fluted drills. Wide cylindrical lands are provided back of the flute edges.

Fluted reamers cut principally on the periphery and remove only 0.004 to 0.008 in. on the bore. Very narrow cylindrical margins are provided back of the flute edges, 0.012 to 0.015 in. wide for machine-finish reaming and 0.004 to 0.006 in. for hand reaming, to provide free cutting of the edges due to the slight body taper and also to pilot the reamer in the hole. The hole to be flute or finish reamed should be true. A rake of 5 deg is recommended for most reaming operations. A reamer may be straight or helically fluted. The latter provide much smoother cutting and give a better finish.

Expansion reamers permit a slight expansion by a wedge so that the reamer may be resharpened to its normal size or for job shop use; they provide slight variations in size. **Adjustable reamers** have means of adjusting inserted blades so that a definite size can be maintained through numerous grindings and used-up blades can be replaced with new ones. **Shell reamers** constitute the cutting portion of the tool which fits interchangeably on arbors to make many sizes available or to make replacement of worn-out shells less costly.

The **speed** of high-speed-steel reamers should be two-thirds to three-quarters and **feeds** usually are two or three times that of the corresponding drill size. Reamers float in their holding fixtures to ensure alignment, or they should be piloted in guide bushings above and below the work.

THREADING MACHINES

Threads may be formed on the inside or outside of a cylinder or cone (1) with single-point threading tools, (2) with threading chasers, (3) with taps, (4) with dies, (5) by thread milling, (6) by thread rolling, (7) by grinding. There are numerous types of taps, such as hand, machine screw, tapper, nut, pulley, boiler, mud or wash-out, staybolt, pipe, combined pipe tap and drill. Small taps usually have no radial relief. They may be made in two, three, or four flutes. Large taps may have still more flutes.

The **feed** of a tap depends upon the lead of the screw thread. The **cutting speed** depends upon numerous factors: hard tough materials, great length of hole, taper taps, and full-depth thread reduce the speed; long chamfer, fine pitches, and a good cutting fluid applied in quantity increase the speed. Taps are cut or formed by grinding. The ground-thread taps may operate at much higher speeds than the cut taps. The following speeds, in fpm, represent good practice for carbon-steel taps, with values for high-speed-steel taps in parentheses: cast brass 150 (400), rolled, drawn, and forged brass 100 (300), varieties of bronze 40 to 100 (150 to 300), cast iron and malleable iron 40 (150), low-carbon steel 30 (100), alloy and stainless steels 15 to 30 (40 to 75). For materials such as bakelite, porcelain, hard rubber, and slate, taps have been made of solid carbide.

Threading dies, used to produce external threads, may be solid, adjustable, spring adjustable, or self-opening die heads. Replacement chasers are used in die heads and may be of the fixed or self-opening type. These chasers may be of the radial type, hobbed or milled; of the tangential type; or of the circular type. Emulsions may prove satisfactory for many threading operations, such as on brass, bronze, cast iron, malleable iron, and some steels. When threading low-carbon steel, alloy steel, and Monel metal, sulphurized oils have proved satisfactory.

MILLING MACHINES

Milling machines use cutters with multiple teeth in contrast with the single-point tools of the lathe and planer. The work is generally fed past the cutter perpendicular to the cutter axis. Milling usually is face or peripheral cutting. The cutting edge has an opportunity to be cooled intermittently, as the cuts are not continuous.

Milling machines have shown marked improvement during the last few years by almost every maker. The machines are heavier, provide more power to the spindle, and give greater accuracy and convenience of operation for the effective use of carbide milling cutters at optimum cutting speeds and feeds.

Standard spindle noses and arbors for milling machines provide interchangeability of arbors and face-milling cutters, regardless of make or size of machine. The taper of the spindle end and arbor is 3½ in. per ft, to make them **self-releasing.** The retention of the shank is dependent upon a positive locking device, such as screws or draw-in bolt. When unlocked, these tapers release themselves.

Milling-machine **classification** is based on design, operation, or purpose. **Column-**

and **knee-type** milling machines have the table and saddle supported on the vertically adjustable knee gibbed to the face of the column. The table is fed longitudinally on the saddle, and the latter transversely on the knee to give three feeding motions.

Knee-type machines are made with horizontal or vertical spindles. The **horizontal** machines, plain or universal, have a swiveling table for cutting helices. The plain machines are used for jobbing or manufacturing work, the universal for toolroom work. **Vertical** milling machines with fixed or sliding heads are otherwise similar to the horizontal type. They are used for face or end mill work and are frequently provided with a rotary table for making cylindrical surfaces.

Hand millers, with feeding movements hand-controlled, are sensitive, as the cuts can be felt. They are used only on light work.

The **fixed-bed** machines have a spindle mounted in a head dovetailed to and sliding on the face of the column. The table rests directly on the bed. They are simple and rigidly built and are used primarily for high production work. These machines are usually provided with work-holding fixtures and may be constructed as plain or multiple-spindle machines, simple or duplex.

Rotary-type millers usually have a rotating table on which fixtures carrying the work are mounted. The cutter spindles are mounted over the edge of the table past which the work is fed.

Drum-type millers consist of a drum carrying the work and rotating on a horizontal axis. Both rotary and drum types are mass-production machines, there being no idle time, for the drums rotate continuously while the parts, loaded on one side of the machine, pass first the roughing and then the finishing cutters and are replaced when they return to the loading position.

In **planetary** milling machines the work is stationary on the bed or clamped to the tailstock while the cutter rotates. Plain and formed internal or external surfaces and threads are produced by inserting the cutter into the bore to be milled, feeding it to depth radially, making a sweeping cut about the bore, and withdrawing first radially and then axially.

Planer-type millers are used only on the heaviest work. They are used to machine a number of surfaces on a particular part or group of parts arranged in series in fixtures on the table.

Thread millers are used to cut threads and worms. A single formed cutter may be used or all the threads may be cut at one time by a multiple-thread cutter. In the latter case the cutter is fed into the work to the proper depth and then the work is revolved through one revolution plus 5 or 10 deg, while the cutter advances along the work the proper amount of lead.

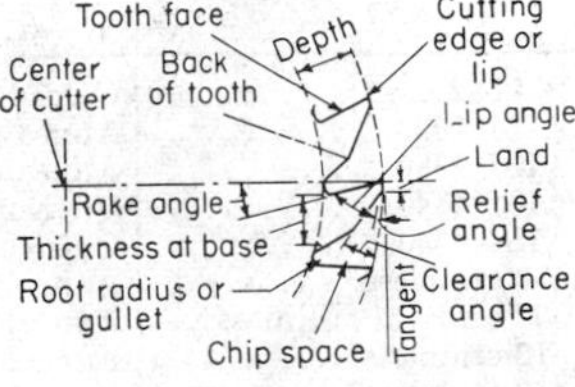

FIG. 8. Plain milling-cutter teeth.

Milling Cutters

Milling cutters are made in a wide variety of shapes and sizes. The nomenclature of tooth parts and angles is standardized as in Fig. 8. Milling cutters are generally classed as **profile cutters,** the teeth of which are sharpened on the land, and **formed cutters,** which are sharpened on the face to retain the true cross-sectional form of the cutter. They may be arbor cutters, which are mounted on an arbor and driven by a key; shank cutters, which have integral shanks to fit into the machine spindles; or face mills to be attached by keys, bolts, or screws directly to the spindle end or to a stub arbor. They also may be of the solid type or consist of bodies with inserted blades.

The tendency in **milling-cutter design** is toward moderately wide-spaced teeth. The **chip space** should be large enough to permit a reasonable number of sharpenings of the cutter and be so formed that the chips may curl without binding or heating the cutter. Less power is required when the cutting teeth are provided with a rake angle. A rake angle on high-speed-steel cutters of 12½ deg is recommended for general work. This angle is large enough to produce a distinct saving in power but is not enough to weaken the lip or cause an abnormal tendency to "hog in"; it gives a free cutting action, leaving a better finish. A 15 deg rake angle and a 5 deg relief angle are satisfactory for cutting steel; 8 deg rake and 3 to 7 deg relief for cutting cast iron; a large rake and 8 to 10 deg relief for copper, aluminum, and soft metals. Plain cutters more than ¾ in. wide are generally made with the cutting edge at a helix angle with the axis of the body up to 60 deg. With helical cutters, fewer teeth are necessary in the cutter but practically no saving in power is made. When a very deep cut is taken or a large surface is faced off, a considerable number of teeth will be in contact with the work at the same time. If the milling machine is unable to deliver enough power to the cutter to allow each tooth to take the proper thickness of chip, the thickness may be decreased, or the number of chips lessened and the thickness maintained. The latter is more efficient. Sintered-carbide cutters have a number of teeth equal to the diameter of the cutter in inches or diameter + 2.

Materials. Milling cutters are made from both carbon and high-speed steel. The latter is used more generally for production work. Cutters made from forged stock of high-speed are superior to those made from sawed-off bar stock Stellite cutters may be cast solid or with a steel core to save the metal, or stellite tool bits may be used as inserted blades in large cutters, particularly of the facing type.

The sintered carbides are used extensively as tips for blades in face milling. Rake angles of 0 to 10 deg are used on carbide teeth milling cast iron, and negative angles of 5 to 15 deg on those cutting steel. Smaller rake and larger relief angles than those used on steel or stellite cutters are used.

Speeds and Feeds of Milling Cutters. The chip per tooth should be the thickest possible consistent with the rigidity and strength of the fixture, machine, and cutter, and with the finish desired. Modern milling machines specify feeds as inches advance per minute, which equals the feed per tooth times the number of teeth in the cutter times the rpm of the cutter. (See Table 9.)

In-cut milling (climb milling) gives longer tool life and a better surface finish. The work and cutter must be supported rigidly. The longest thinnest chip is obtained

Table 9. Milling Recommendations*

Material	Condition	Hardness, BHN	High-speed steel		Carbide	
			Speed, fpm	Feed, in./tooth	Speed, fpm	Feed, in./tooth
B-1112	Cold-drawn	135	250	0.012	750	0.014
AISI 1020	Annealed	140	160	0.010	550	0.012
AISI 4340	Annealed	200	90	0.008	450	0.012
AISI 4340	Quenched and tempered	300	60	0.005	350	0.010
AISI 4340	Quenched and tempered	400	35	0.004	175	0.005
430 stainless	Annealed	175	130	0.005	380	0.008
302 and 321 stainless	Annealed	190	90	0.005	325	0.008
410 stainless	Annealed	180	120	0.005	425	0.008
410 stainless	Quenched and tempered	300	55	0.004	240	0.006
Nickel-base high-temp alloys	Solution-treated	290	20	0.003	50	0.004
Cobalt-base high-temp alloys	Solution-treated	200	25	0.003	70	0.005
Gray iron						
ASTM Class 25	Annealed	140	140	0.012	500	0.015
ASTM Class 40	Cast	200	75	0.010	350	0.012
Nodular iron						
SAE 60-40-10	Annealed	170	140	0.012	475	0.015
SAE 100-70-03	Quenched and tempered	260	50	0.008	225	0.012
Malleable iron						
Grade 32510	Malleableized	120	150	0.012	525	0.015
Grade 60003	Malleableized	220	100	0.010	325	0.012
Aluminum alloys	Cold-drawn or solution-treated and aged	40–105†	900	0.020	Max	0.020
Magnesium alloys						
Cast or wrought	Cast or cold-drawn	35–80†	1,200	0.020	Max	0.020
Copper alloys	Wrought or cast	120–160	525	0.020	1,200	0.018
	Wrought or cast	165–180	350	0.014	825	0.012
	Wrought or cast	172–205	150	0.008	550	0.010

* Courtesy of Metcut Research Associates, Inc., Cincinnati, Ohio.
† 500-kg load for aluminum and magnesium alloys.

when out-cut milling with a fine-tooth cutter at a given feed and depth of cut. The shortest thickest chip is obtained when in-cut milling with a fine-tooth cutter. With sufficient chip clearance between the teeth of the cutter, in-cut milling with fine-tooth cutters would be most efficient. To provide more chip space, coarse-tooth cutters are used. Recommended tooth shape of sintered-carbide-tipped face-milling cutters for cast iron is as follows: axial rake 0 (20); radial rake, 12 (−10); face relief, 12 (10); peripheral relief, 12 (10); face cutting-edge angle, 2 (2); peripheral cutting-edge angle, 45 (45); and a chamfer of 0.100 in. at 45 deg, or nose radius of ⅛ in. The values in parentheses are for milling steel.

GEAR-CUTTING PROCESSES

(See also Sec. 8)

Teeth in gears of the spur, helicoidal, and bevel types are formed by a milling, shaping, or hobbing process.

The four principles of action of gear-cutting machines are as follows:

1. The formed-tool principle, using a tool or cutter shaped to the tooth space.
2. The templet principle, in which the action of the cutting tool is controlled by a templet corresponding to the tooth curve.
3. The odontographic principle, in which the tool is guided by suitable mechanism, so that its path closely approximates the tooth curve.
4. The generating principle, in which a tool with a cross section differing from the desired shape of the tooth is moved in such a relation to the gear to be generated that the proper shape of tooth results.

Machines using method 1 produce spur, spiral, helical, and worm gears; 2 and 3, spur and bevel gears; and 4, spur, helical, bevel, spiral and hypoid bevel, and worm gears. In addition, methods 1 and 2 are used for such products as ratchets, sprockets, and spline shafts.

Processes for Cutting Spur Gears. Three distinct processes are used commonly for the cutting of spur gears: the **milling process,** which uses a circular form cutter corresponding to the shape of the tooth space; the **shaping process,** which is a generating process employing a tool in the form of a rack tooth or of a mating pinion; and the **hobbing process,** which also is a generating process, employing a number of straight-sided rack teeth wrapped helically around a cylindrical body.

Gears with coarse pitches are first rough cut, or stocked, which operation removes most of the metal between teeth preparatory to finishing by one of the three above-mentioned processes. This stocking is most economically done by the form-cutter or hobbing method.

Where a rack tooth is used as the generating tool, it is necessary to roll the blank and traverse the cutter after every stroke, so that the action corresponds to cutting away a small chip at every stroke, then rotate the blank through a small angle and advance the tool with the blank as if the two were meshed together. It is customary to use two tools simultaneously when this method is employed in generating straight-tooth bevel gears, the tools working on opposite sides of the same tooth.

In the shaping process a pinion-shaped cutter is used as the cutting tool. The cutter first is brought to the full depth of the space to be cut, after which the cutter and work revolve together as if they were meshed; or the work and cutter may be revolving together while the cutter is being brought to the proper depth. The motion of the cutter is reciprocating, and the relative movement of the cutter and blank constitutes the feed motion. Though the cutter itself has the form of a pinion, the generating tool used in this case is really a rack tooth which was used to generate the pinion tooth.

The **hobbing process** is very largely used where rapid production and great accuracy are required. This latter requirement could not be fulfilled by the hobbing process until means were found to grind the hobs all over and with great accuracy. As such ground hobs can be furnished now by several makers, the hobbing process is becoming more and more a favored method of producing accurate gears.

The stocking process, preparatory to finish hobbing of a gear, is often done by the hobbing process, in which case unground hobs may be used. The greater speed that may be obtained and the greater production between two successive sharpenings make the ground hob more economical than the unground hob, notwithstanding its higher price. The unground hob is useful where few gears of a kind must be cut, where the setting-up time as compared with the cutting time is relatively great, and where great accuracy is not required.

The **templet principle** is sometimes employed for very large gears, as in rolling-mill work. Such gears are not truly interchangeable with others. The machines operate on the planing or shaping principle.

For the rough cutting of large bevel gears, machines are used which employ the templet principle.

Processes for Cutting Bevel Gears. The milling method is used extensively for stocking bevel gears. Accurate straight-tooth bevel gears cannot be finished with a form cutter. The most common method of cutting bevel gears is the generating method, and the machine most commonly used for this purpose is the **bevel-gear generator** which uses a crown gear to control the motion of the straight-side basic-rack tooth used as the generating tool. Only one tool may be used, or more generally two tools are used simultaneously, working on the two sides of a tooth.

Spiral bevel gears have curved teeth which are not true spirals. A circular cutter is used, resembling a face mill. Inserted blades of a section of a straight-side rack tooth are used. In roughing, to provide rake, alternate teeth cut the opposite sides of a tooth space. After a space has been finished, the blank indexes, just as when cutting the straight-line teeth.

For finishing in production, a cutter is used which finishes only one side of the teeth. A second machine and cutter finish the other side of the teeth. Hypoid gears are machined on **hypoid generators** with the cutter placed about 2 in. below the center of the pinion. "Spiroid" gears look like hypoid gears and are for right-angle, high-ratio drives. The pinion is in the form of a conical thread with one or more threads.

Gears of this complicated shape, which cannot be ground after heat-treatment, are often lapped by running the gear and pinion together under power with an oil containing a fine abrasive poured between the meshing teeth.

Internal gears are cut by the generating principle with pinion-cutter and shaping process and with a single-point rack-tooth-cutter and generating process.

Racks are cut with the formed circular-cutter principle and the milling process and with the pinion-cutter generating process.

Helical gears are cut with the formed circular-cutter principle and the milling process, the generative principle and milling process (hobbing), and the generative principle and shaping process.

Worms are cut by the formed circular-cutter principle and milling process (thread miller); the formed-cutter principle and turning process; the pinion-cutter and generating process; and the hobbing process. Worms of large lead are finished on the sides of the teeth with a side cutting tool in a lathe or by grinding.

Worm wheels are cut by the generating principle and milling process (hobbing). Three forms of cutters are used, the straight hob, tapered hob, and fly cutter. The first requires the simplest mechanism; an ordinary miller is sufficient, but the hobs are expensive. The fly cutter is easily and accurately made but requires a complicated machine to use it. The taper hob is adapted to large work and a large number of pieces. Worms are frequently ground after hardening.

Gear Cutters. Circular formed cutters for involute tooth gears in an interchangeable standard system are made in sets of eight, to cut gears ranging from a 12-toothed pinion to a rack.

No. of cutter	1	2	3	4	5	6	7	8
No. of teeth	135–∞	55–134	35–54	27–34	21–26	17–20	14–16	12 and 13

For more accurate gears, a 15 cutter set is made by introducing a half number between each two in the foregoing list, each cutter, therefore, having a smaller range of teeth as follows:

No. of cutter	1	1½	2	2½	3	3½	4	4½
No. of teeth	135–∞	80–134	55–79	42–54	35–41	30–34	26–29	23–25

No. of cutter	5	5½	6	6½	7	7½	8
No. of teeth	21 and 22	19 and 20	17 and 18	15 and 16	14	13	12

To rough out the tooth spaces, **stocking cutters** having side rake or curved edges to break up chips are used. These leave only a small amount of metal to be removed by the regular cutter, increase the accuracy of the gears, and save wear on the finishing cutters. One stock cutter serves for all gears of the same pitch. The term stocking cutter also is applied to a concave cutter ganged beside a regular gear cutter and used to finish the periphery of a gear blank by milling ahead of the gear cutter.

Gear Finishing. The silent performance of gears has been the goal of production engineers for years. Objectionable sound waves are produced by a very slight error in tooth contour, size, spacing, or concentricity. Suitable accuracy, bearing, and surface cannot be maintained in steel gears heat-treated after machining. Gear teeth are being finished to accurate size and tooth shape with suitable bearing surface and finish after cutting by shaving and burnishing and after heat-treating by grinding and lapping. The gears are machined, sufficient metal being left on the face of the teeth to allow for distortion and for clean up after the finishing operation. **Gear-shaving** machines made with a straight-rack cutter or a circular gear cutter, run the work gear in mesh with the cutter. The cutter of accurate shape has teeth gashed or slotted at one or more points along their surface. As the work gear runs in this cutter at crossed axes of 10 to 15 deg, there is an axial sliding motion that causes minute particles of metal to be removed, thus bringing the work gear tooth to the final accuracy of the cutter within limits of 0.00025 in. "Gerac" is a process of finishing gear teeth previously roughed out. The cutter, resembling a helical gear cutter, runs in engagement with the gear at a high-degree crossed axis. The action is similar to shaving.

Burnishing of the unhardened gear is accomplished by running it under pressure with one or between three hardened burnishing gears slightly oversize.

Hardened gear teeth are finished by grinding or lapping. The **grinding** may be done with an abrasive wheel trued to the exact tooth space. Small wheels make it possible to grind gears located near a shoulder. Wheels of this type also are used for grinding hardened-steel worms up to 8 in. diam and 12 in. long. The grinding wheel may be flat on the side, tilted at an angle equal to the angle of obliquity, and generate the tooth face by a planing and rolling action.

In **lapping,** the work gear is run in mesh at crossed axes with a cast-iron lap. As they are run together, the teeth slide axially, thus abrading the whole surface of the tooth equally. An oil containing a fine abrasive is poured between the lap and gear while running. Straight-tool bevel, spiral bevel, and hypoid gears are lapped on machines which introduce a small reciprocating motion to the pinion during the lapping operation.

PLANERS AND SHAPERS

Planers are used to rough and finish large flat surfaces, although arcs and special forms can be made with proper tools and attachments. Surfaces to be finished by scraping, such as ways and long dovetails and, particularly, parts of machine tools, are, with few exceptions planed. With fixtures to arrange parts in parallel and series, quantities of small parts can be produced economically on planers. Milling planers will plane, mill, drill, and bore work at one clamping.

Planer tools are clamped to a head, comprising a clapper attached to a ram mounted in a saddle which, in turn, is mounted on the horizontal rail or attached to the face of the vertical housing. The ram is fed vertically and the whole saddle horizontally. The clapper, hinged at its upper end, permits the tool point to be swung by dragging or by positive means away from the machined surface on the non-cutting stroke; the latter is necessary for sintered-carbide tools. Large machines may have two or more tool heads on the cross rail and frequently one on each housing below the rail, known as side **heads.** The latter are used to plane down the sides of work and for undercutting.

The **size** of a planer is indicated by the width of the table, or distance between housings, the maximum height cleared under the rail (these dimensions usually being equal), and the length of the platen between pockets. In modern planers, the length of the bed is twice the length of the platen.

Cutting speeds for planers range from 20 to 200 fpm, with return speeds up to 150 or even 200 fpm on modern machines. Some planers provide cutting speeds up to 400 fpm. The tool is fed usually at the end of the non-cutting stroke. **Feeds** range from 0.005 to ⅜ in. for roughing and from ⅛ to 1½ in. for finishing. The depth of cut ranges up to 1¼ in. or even greater. **Finishing cuts** usually are very shallow with very large feeds. Finishing tools have a flat, ½ to 1½ in. wide, and the feed is such as to allow a small overlap. Finishing tools for cast iron should be of the goosenecked form with back rake but with no side rake. For steel, side rake or shear up to 60 deg is provided to prevent chatter. Carbide tools must be lifted from the work on the return stroke to avoid chipping. This is accomplished hydraulically or with electromagnets. One planer has a socket between the clapper box and rail so that a two-way tool post can be inserted. A motor on the head rotates the post to give each bit in turn proper clearance.

Shapers are used for miscellaneous planing, surfacing, notching, key seating, and production of flat surfaces on flat parts. They are essentially toolroom, repair-job, or job-shop machines. The tool is held in a holder supported on a clapper on the end of a ram which is reciprocated hydraulically or by crank and rocker arm, in a straight line. A table carrying the vise and the work feeds transversely on each return stroke.

Horizontal shapers have cutting speeds usually ranging up to 70 fpm, with return cutting speeds nearly twice that amount. Ram reciprocations vary up to 150 per min. Feeds range from 0.010 to 0.180 in. or more. In the hydraulic shaper, made in 24 and 32 in. sizes, a 10 hp motor drives an oil pump which provides uniform cutting speed and pressure throughout the stroke. Commercial sizes of shapers are 12, 14, 16, 20, 24, 28, 32, and 36 in. length of stroke. A new 48 in. all-steel shaper with a triangular ram provides speeds up to 400 fpm.

Vertical shapers or **slotters** reciprocate the ram vertically. They are made in a wide range of sizes and are used on general work for key seating, notching, facing, die making and surfacing. A rotary table with indexing attachment may be mounted on the knee which may be fed mechanically along and toward the rail. Geared slotters having 24 to 60 in. stroke require up to 20 hp motors.

Slotter tools have the cutting face on the end of the shank.

BROACHING

Broaching is a production process whereby a cutter, called a **broach,** is used to finish internal or external surfaces such as holes of circular, square, or irregular section, keyways, the teeth of internal gears, multiple spline holes, and flat surfaces. In broaching, the action of the broach itself serves as a clamping medium so that in many cases the operation may be completed in the time ordinarily taken to chuck the piece. The expense of making a broach may be large. However, the cost of maintaining its size is usually not excessive, and very little scrap work results. Broaching round holes gives greater accuracy and better finish than reaming, but, as the broach may be guided only by the work it is cutting, the hole may not be accurate with respect to previously machined surfaces. Where such accuracy is required, it is better practice to broach first and then turn other surfaces with the work mounted on a mandrel. The cutting tool or broach is usually long and is provided with many teeth so graded in size that each takes a small chip when the tool is pulled or pushed through the previously prepared leader hole or past the surface.

The main features of the broach are the pitch, the degree of taper or increase in height of each successive tooth, relief, tooth depth, and rake.

The **pitch** of the teeth, *i.e.*, the distance from one tooth to the next, depends upon tooth strength, length of cut, shape and size of chips, etc. The pitch should be as coarse as possible to provide ample chip clearance, but at least two teeth should be in contact with the work at all times. The formula $p = 0.35\sqrt{l}$ may be used, where p is pitch of the roughing teeth and l the length of hole or surface, in. An average pitch for small broaches is 1/8 to 1/4 in. and for large ones 1/2 to 1 in. Where the hole or other surface to be broached is short, the teeth are often cut on an angle or helix, so as to give more continuous cutting action by having at least two teeth cutting simultaneously.

The degree of **taper**, or increase in size per tooth, depends largely on the hardness or toughness of the material to be broached and the finish desired. The degree of taper or feed for broaching cast iron is approximately double that for steel. Usually the first few teeth coming in contact with the work are undersize but of uniform taper to take the greatest feeds per tooth, but as the finished size is approached, the teeth take smaller and smaller feeds with several teeth at the finishing end of nearly zero taper. In some cases, for soft metals and even cast iron, the large end is left plain or with rounded lands a trifle larger than the last cutting tooth so as to burnish the surface. For medium-sized broaches, the taper per tooth is 0.001 to 0.003 in. Large broaches remove 0.005 to 0.010 in. per tooth or even more. The teeth are given a **front rake** angle of 5 to 15 deg to give a curl to the chip, provide a cleaner cut surface, and reduce the power consumption. The **land** back of the cutting edge, which may be 1/64 to 1/16 in. wide, usually is provided with a land relief varying from 1 to 3 deg with a clearance of 30 to 45 deg.

The heavier the feed per tooth or the longer the surface being broached, the greater must be the **chip clearance** or space between successive teeth for the chips to accumulate. The root should be a smooth curve.

Broaches are made of carbon tool steel, finishing steel, oil-hardening steel, or high-speed steel. Broaches of complicated shape are apt to warp during the heat-treating process. For this reason, in hardening, they are often heated in a vertical cylindrical furnace and quenched by being hung in an air blast furnished from small holes along the side of pipes placed vertically about the broach. Sintered carbide is also used for the teeth of large broaches or for burnishing buttons.

Push broaches are usually shorter than pull broaches, being 6 to 14 in. long, depending on their diameter and the amount of metal to be removed. In many cases, for accuracy, four to six broaches of the push type constitute a set used in sequence to finish the surface being broached. Push broaches usually have a large cross-sectional area so as to be sufficiently rigid. With **pull broaches,** pulling tends to straighten the hole, whereas pushing permits the broaches to follow any irregularity of the leader hole. Push broaching permits the use of cheaper broaches. Pull broaches are attached to the cross head of the broaching machine by means of a key slot and key, by a threaded connection, or by a head that fits into an automatic broach puller. The threaded connection is used where the broach is not removed from the drawing head while the work is placed over the cutter, as in cutting a keyway. In enlarging holes, however, the small end of the pull broach must first be extended through the reamed, drilled, or cored hole and then fixed in the drawing head before being pulled through the work.

Broaching Machines. Push broaching is done on machines of the press type with a sort of subpress for holding the work and broach or on presses operated by power. They are usually vertical and may be driven hydraulically or by screw, rack, or crank. The pull type of broach may be either vertical or horizontal. The ram may be driven hydraulically or by screw, rack, or crank. Both are made in the duplex- and multiple-head type.

Speeds and Feeds for Broaching. Cutting speeds for broaching may range between 3 and 15 fpm for the screw- or rack-type broaching machine and between 10 and 40 fpm for the hydraulically driven broaching machines, with a non-cutting return stroke three to five times as fast. An emulsion of soluble oil is often used for broaching for general work, but some grades of steel forgings require an oil either of the compounded type or of the sulphur-base mineral or animal-oil type. In broaching cast iron where a polished or burnished finish is required, it is advisable to use a cutting compound.

CUTTING-OFF MACHINES

These machines, used for cutting off merchant bars, extruded and rolled shapes, etc., are made in six types: the lathe type using single-point cutoff tools as in screw machines, hack saws, band saws, friction-wheel saws, abrasive-wheel saws, and cold saws.

In power hack saws, the frame in which the blade is strained is reciprocated above the work which is held in a vise on the bed. The cutting feed is effected by weighting the frame, with 12 to 50 lb from small to large machines; adding weights or spring tension giving up to 180 lb; providing a positive screw feed or a friction screw feed; and by hydraulic feed mechanism giving pressures up to 300 lb between the blade and work. Speeds from 50 to 70 for hard steels, 75 to 90 for annealed steels, and 125 to 140 strokes per min for soft steels and metals are generally used. A good flow of emulsion should be used to keep the saw free from chips. The larger size machines will cut off bars up to 12 in. diam.

Hack-saw **blades** for hand frames are made 8, 10, and 12 in. long, 7/16 to 9/16 in. wide, and 0.025 in. thick. Number of teeth per inch for cutting soft steel or cast iron, 14; tool steel and angle iron, 18; brass, copper, and heavy tubing, 24; sheet metal and thin tube, 32. All sizes are made in tungsten alloy steel, all hard or flexible, but only the 10 and 12 in. are of high-speed steel.

Blades for power hack saws are made of tungsten steel, all hard, and of high-speed steel, 12, 14, 17, 18, 21, and 24 in. long, and 0.032, 0.049, and 0.065 in. thick. Each length is made in two or more widths from 5/8 to 1 in. for the 12 in. length to 1½ and 2 in. for the 24 in. length. The short lengths have 18, 14, 10, and 6 teeth per inch, and the long ones have 10, 6, and 4 teeth per inch. The coarsest teeth should be used on large work and with heavy feeds.

Band saws, vertical, horizontal, and universal, are used for cutting-off work. They are particularly useful for cutting off gates and sprues of brass, bronze, and iron castings and for cutting off high-speed and stainless steel, especially for disks of a thickness that is small as compared with the diameter. The kerf or width of cut is small with a consequently small loss in expensive material. The teeth of band saws, like those of hack saws, are set with the regular alternate type, one bent to the right and the next to the left, or with the alternate and center set, in which one tooth is bent to the right, the second to the left, and the third straight in the center. With semihigh-speed-steel saw blades, band saws should cut hard steel at 100 fpm (1 to 1½ in. per min feed); soft steel, 150 (1½ to 2); hard bronze, 250 (2); brass, 300 (2 to 3). For aluminum and brass the speeds may be much higher, even up to 1,800 fpm.

Friction sawing machines are used largely for cutting off structural shapes. Peripheral speeds of about 20,000 fpm are used. The wheels may be plain on the periphery V-notched, or with milled square notches.

Abrasive cutoff saws, which are similar to the steel friction saw, are made of thin rubber or bakelite bonded abrasive wheels. The wheels operate at speeds of 12,000 to 16,000 fpm. These wheels are excellent for cutting off tubes, shapes, and hardened high-speed steel, stellite, etc.

Cold saws are made in a wide variety of styles and sizes. Some makers list them in numbered sizes, others according to the diameter of the saw blade that the machine will carry. Cold saws of the milling-cutter type for cutoff work or deep slotting in milling machines are made from 2½ to 14 in. diam, and, for special cutoff machines, from 10 to 64 in. diam.

Cold saws may have teeth of several shapes, as radial face teeth for small fine-tooth saws less than ⅛ in. pitch; radial face teeth with a land for fine-tooth saws; alternate bevel-edged teeth on saws 10 to 36 in. diam to break up the chips, with every other tooth beveled 45 deg on each side with the next tooth plain; alternate side-beveled teeth; and the Simonds patented tooth, having one tooth beveled on the right, the next on the left, and the third beveled on both sides, each leaving slightly overlapping flats on the periphery of the teeth.

GRINDING MACHINES

Grinding machines may be classified as to purpose and type as follows: for **rough removal of stock,** the swinging-frame, portable, flexible shaft, two-wheel stand, and disk; **cutting off** or parting, the cutting-off machine; **surface finishing,** band polisher, two-wheel combination, two-wheel polishing machine, two-wheel buffing machine, and semiautomatic polishing and buffing machine; **precision grinding,** tool post, cylindrical (plain and universal), crankshaft, centerless, internal, and surface (reciprocating table with horizontal or vertical wheel spindle, and rotary table with horizontal or vertical wheel spindle); **special form** grinders, gear or worm, ball-bearing balls, cams, and threads; **tool and cutter** grinders for single-point tools, drills, and milling cutters, reamers, taps, dies, knives, etc.; **finishing and sizing,** as cylinder honing machines and lapping machines; and **pulpwood** grinders. (See also p. 13–106 *et seq.*)

All these machines, except the polishing, buffing, disk, lapping, and honing types, use **grinding wheels** made by fixing an abrasive in a binder which is usually hardened by baking. The disk type uses an abrasive disk or abrasive cloth pasted to the surface of a metal disk or a thin abrasive wheel anchored or glued to the steel wheel face. **Lapping machines** use a lapping plate charged with diamond grit or substitute or a plain soft lap formed to fit the work with an oil containing a fine abrasive (see p. 13–101); **honing machines,** such as those used to finish automotive cylinders, use several honing stones which are fixed in a body adjustable to any diameter. **Centerless grinders** are used to good advantage where large numbers of relativley small pieces must be ground and where the ground surface has no exact relation to any other surface except as a whole: the work is carried on a support between two abrasive wheels, one a normal grinding wheel, the second a rubber-bonded wheel, rotating at about one-tenth grinding speed, and is tilted 3 to 8 deg to cause the work to rotate and feed past the grinding wheel (see also p. 6–171). **Cutter grinders** are designed to grind all kinds of milling and similar toothed cutters.

Cylinder grinders are a special type for grinding the inside of cylinders of engines; one form has a planetary motion for the grinding spindle. The **cylindrical grinder** is a companion machine to the engine lathe; shafts, cylinders, rods, rolls, studs, and a wide variety of other cylindrical parts are first roughed out on the lathe, then finished accurately to size by the cylindrical grinder. The work is carried on centers, rotated slowly, and traversed past the face of a grinding wheel.

Grinding equipment of all types has been improved during the past few years so as to be more rigid, provide more power to the grinding wheel, and provide automatic cycling, loading, clamping, wheel dressing, and, in some instances, automatic feedback.

Universal grinders are cylindrical machines arranged with a swiveling table so that both straight and taper internal and external work can be ground; they are used on tool work and in refined manufacturing. **Drill grinders** are provided with rests so mounted that by a simple swinging motion, correct cutting angles are produced automatically on the lips of drills; a cupped wheel is usually employed. **Internal grinders** are used for finishing the holes in bushings, rolls, sleeves, cutters, and the like; speeds from 15,000 to 30,000 rpm are common.

Horizontal surface grinders range from small capacity, used mainly in tool making or small production work, to large sizes used for production work.

Vertical surface grinders are used for producing flat surfaces on manufacturing work. **Vertical** and **horizontal disk grinders** are used for surfacing on both cast iron and steel. Grinding machines are used for **cutting off** steel, especially tubes, structural shapes, and hard metals. A thin bakelite or rubber-bonded wheel is used, with aluminum oxide abrasive for all types of steel, aluminum, brass, bronze, nickel, Monel, and stellite; silicon carbide for cast iron, copper, carbon, glass, stone, plastics, and other non-metallic materials; and crushed diamonds for sintered carbides and quartz.

A good ground surface with **surface quality** of 50 to 200 microin. is sufficient for many purposes and is a basic requirement for further finishing operations, such as lapping, honing, and superfinishing. The size and depth of the scratches can be varied considerably by the selection of the wheel. In thread grinding, if oil is used as a coolant, it is possible to use harder and finer wheels and maintain a high productive output by running the wheel at about twice the normal speed. The fine wheel at high speed will remove stock as fast as the coarse wheel at the normal speed and will produce a much better finish.

Grinding Wheels

(See also pp. 6–170 to 6–172.)

Grinding wheels have characteristics influenced by (1) type of abrasive (aluminum oxide and silicon carbide); (2) grain size or coarseness, sometimes called the grit size; (3) grade of hardness; and (4) type of bond. (See Fig. 9.)

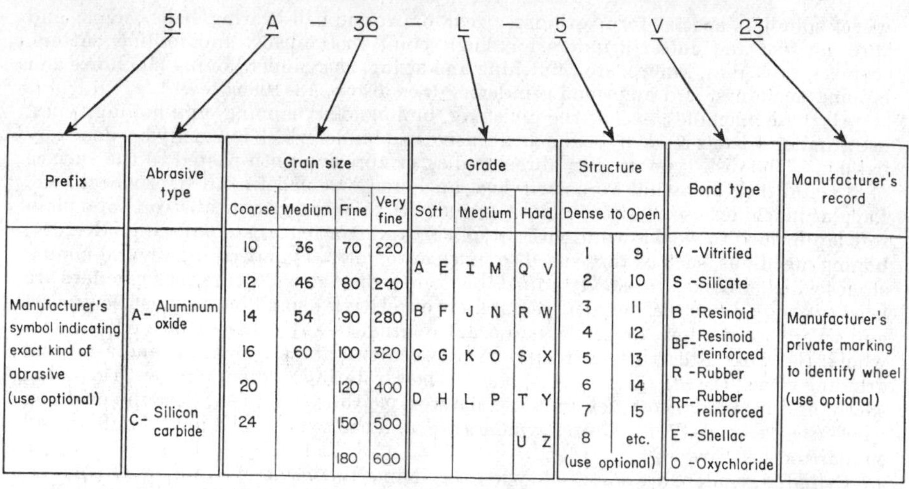

51 — A — 36 — L — 5 — V — 23
Prefix
Manufacturer's symbol indicating exact kind of abrasive (use optional)
Abrasive type
A- Aluminum oxide
C- Silicon carbide
Grain size
Coarse Medium Fine Very fine
10 36 70 220
12 46 80 240
14 54 90 280
16 60 100 320
20 120 400
24 150 500
180 600
Grade
Soft Medium Hard
A E I M Q V
B F J N R W
C G K O S X
D H L P T Y
U Z
Structure
Dense to Open
1 9
2 10
3 11
4 12
5 13
6 14
7 15
8 etc.
(use optional)
Bond type
V -Vitrified
S -Silicate
B -Resinoid
BF-Resinoid reinforced
R -Rubber
RF-Rubber reinforced
E -Shellac
O -Oxychloride
Manufacturer's record
Manufacturer's private marking to identify wheel (use optional)

FIG. 9. Grinding-wheel standard-marking-system chart.

Selection of Abrasive. **Aluminum oxide** abrasive (Alundum, Aloxite, etc.) should be used for grinding materials of high tensile strength, such as carbon steels, alloy steels, high-speed steels, annealed malleable iron, wrought iron, tough bronze, and stellite. It is widely used, is fast and free cutting, and can be used for heavy feeds on high-speed steel and alloy steels. Wheels of this abrasive hold form very well. **Silicon carbide** (Crystolon, Carborundum, etc.) should be used for grinding materials of low tensile strength, such as gray iron, chilled iron, brass and bronze, aluminum and copper, marble, granite, pearl, rubber, and leather. **Green silicon carbide** is used on sintered carbides. **Diamond grains** are used to cut very hard materials such as sintered carbide and quartz.

Selection of Grain. Use coarse grain for fast removal of stock; fine grain for fine finish. Use coarse grain for ductile materials and a finer grain for hard, dense, or brittle materials.

Factors affecting the **selection of the grade.** Use harder wheels on soft than on hard material. The shorter the arc of contact, the harder the wheel should be. The higher the work speed with relation to wheel speed, the harder the grade should be. Machines in poor condition require harder wheels than those in good condition. Skillful operators can use softer wheels than unskilled operators. Softer wheels result in more economical production. Piecework grinding usually calls for harder wheels than daywork.

Factors affecting the **selection of the process of bonding.** Wheels subjected to bending strains should be made by the shellac, resinoid, or rubber process. Extremely thin abrasive saws must be made by these processes. Use vitrified wheels for usual rapid cutting, which should be under 6,500 surface fpm; rubber or resinoid wheels at higher speeds. Use shellac or rubber wheels for highest finish where rapid production is not a factor. Use silicate wheels to replace sandstone on cutlery and other free-cutting operations.

In the grinding process, cutting is done with the highest tool pressure of all cutting methods. This advantage may be lost if too hard a wheel is used, *i.e.*, one in which the bond will not crumble under the pressure of the cut but must be forced with a pressure sufficient to displace the work. Destructive vibrations and inaccurate work are often charageable to too hard wheels.

Wheel Speeds. Surface speeds of 5,500 to 6,500 fpm are most commonly used. Vitrified and silicate wheels should not be operated faster than this, except when used on cylindrical machines, where a speed of 6,500 surface fpm may be employed. Resinoid and rubber wheels in the harder grades may be operated up to 9,000 surface fpm.

A wheel of hard bond is retentive of the grains, and in softer bonds, the grains are more easily broken up. In a wheel of proper grade for the work being done, the grains are automatically replaced when dull. If glazing occurs, the wheel is too hard and reducing the wheel speed or increasing the work speed causes it to act soft. If the wheel breaks down too rapidly, it is too soft and reversing the procedure given above will cause the wheel to act harder.

Work speeds (Table 10) depend on the size and nature of the material and on whether it is stiff enough to hold its shape. The larger the diameter, the greater the arc of contact between the wheel and work; a surface speed of work suitable for one diameter might be unsuitable for another. In roughing, for maximum production, the fastest work speed that the machine and wheel will stand should be used, as this causes each grain particle to do the maximum work. For speeds of **cylindrical work** the following values must be considered as general cases only. Steel shafts 50 to 55, hard-steel rolls 80 to 85, chilled-iron rolls 80 to 200, cast-iron auto pistons 150 to 400, auto crankshaft bearings 45 to 50, auto crankshaft pins 35 to 40 fpm. Modern surface grinders with hydraulic table reciprocation permit work speeds of 50 to 150 fpm.

Traverse feeds depend entirely on the width of the wheel. In roughing, the work should travel past the wheel ¾ to ⅞ of the width of the wheel for each revolution of the work. As the work travels past the wheel with a helical motion, the preceding rule allows a slight overlap. In finishing, a finer feed is used, generally ⅛ to ¼ of the width of the wheel for each revolution of the work.

Depth of Cut. In the roughing operation the depth of cut should be all the wheel will stand without crowding. This varies with the hardness of the material and the diameter of the work; the operator's experience is the only guide. In the finishing operation the depth of cut is always slight, 0.001 to 0.002 in. Excellent results as regards finish are obtained by letting the wheel run over the work several times without cross-feeding. This practice of letting the wheel "grind out" has been found by the majority of expert operators to give satisfactory results even with a comparatively coarse wheel. (See Table 10.)

Grinding Allowances. From 0.005 to 0.040 in. is generally removed from the diameter in rough grinding in a cylindrical machine. For finishing, 0.002 to 0.010 in. is common. Work can be finished by grinding to a tolerance of 0.0002 in. and a surface roughness of 50+ microin.

Table 10. Surface-grinding Recommendations*

Material	Condition	Hardness, BHN	Wheel speed, fpm	Table speed, fpm	Down feed, in. per pass	
					Rough	Finish
B-1112	Cold-drawn	135	6,000	60	0.001	0.0005
AISI 1020	Annealed	140	6,000	60	0.001	0.0005
AISI 4340	Annealed	200	6,000	60	0.001	0.0005
AISI 4340	Quenched and tempered	300	6,000	60	0.001	0.0005
AISI 4340	Quenched and tempered	400	6,000	60	0.001	0.0005
430 stainless	Annealed	175	6,000	60	0.001	0.0005
302 and 321 stainless	Annealed	190	5,000	50	0.001	0.0005
410 stainless	Annealed	180	5,000	50	0.001	0.0005
410 stainless	Quenched and tempered	300	5,000	50	0.001	0.0005
Nickel-base high-temp alloys	Solution-treated	290	3,000	50	0.001	0.0005
Cobalt-base high-temp alloys	Solution-treated	200	3,000	50	0.001	0.0005
Gray iron						
ASTM Class 25	Annealed	140	6,000	60	0.002	0.0005
ASTM Class 40	Cast	200	6,000	60	0.002	0.0005
Nodular iron						
SAE 60-40-10	Annealed	170	6,000	60	0.002	0.0005
SAE 100-70-03	Quenched and tempered	260	6,000	60	0.002	0.0005
Malleable iron						
Grade 32510	Malleableized	120	6,000	60	0.002	0.0005
Grade 60003	Malleableized	220	6,000	60	0.002	0.0005

* Courtesy of Metcut Research Associates, Inc., Cincinnati, Ohio.

Note: Grinding wheel: aluminum oxide, 46 grit, medium hardness, vitrified bond. Grinding fluid: water base.

Grindstones are still used for some kinds of work, particularly for the rough grinding of forgings, but the tendency is to replace them with steel wheels carrying segmental abrasive blocks. The Ohio sandstones can be safely run up to a peripheral **speed** of 2,500 to 3,000 fpm and Huron stone up to 4,000 fpm. These speeds presuppose careful setting up, large flanges, and only moderate wedging. Speeds of 600 to 800 fpm give satisfactory results in axe and offhand tool grinding. A small stream of water applied to the wheel face keeps it clean and the tool cool. The strength of grindstones is reduced by wetting, some investigations indicating by as much as 40 to 50 percent. The older form of square shaft hole is dangerous, in that it furnishes points from which fractures may easily start.

Safety. The wheel should be supported on the spindle with as close a fit as possible, a bushing being used if necessary. The flanges on the spindle of the machine should bear on the wheel at their outer edge and make contact over a thick soft paper or rubber. The inner flange should be keyed or fixed to the spindle, and the wheel should rotate true. In every case, an abrasive wheel should be well guarded so as to prevent accidents from flying particles as well as a broken wheel.

A safety code for the use, care, and protection of abrasive wheels is available from the ASA.

Truing and Dressing. The wheel face should be sharp, *i.e.*, present newly fractured crystals to the face to act as cutting tools. In **truing,** a diamond supported in the end of a soft steel rod held rigidly in the machine is passed over the face of the wheel two or three times to remove just enough material to give the wheel its true geometric shape. **Dressing** is a more severe operation of removing the dull or loaded surface of the wheel. Abrasive sticks or wheels or steel star wheels are pressed against and moved over the wheel face.

POLISHING

Polishing is an operation by which coarse scratches or tool marks or, in some instances, rough surfaces left after forging, rolling, or similar operations are removed. It is not a precision operation. Polishing wheels are built-up wheels of wood, leather, cloth, felt, etc., with the abrasive glued to the surface.

Polishing may be divided into three steps: **rough polishing, dry fining,** and **finishing** or **oiling.** The abrasive grain used for roughing usually runs from No. 20 to 80, for dry fining from No. 90 to 120, and for finishing or oiling from No. 150 to the fine flours. For the first two steps the polishing wheels are used dry. For finishing, the wheels are first worn down a little and then coated with tallow, oil, beeswax, or similar substances. This step is partly polishing and partly buffing, as additional abrasive is often added in cake form with the grease. The cutting action is freer and the life of the wheel is prolonged by making the wheel surface flexible. Buffing wheels are also used for the finishing step when tallow, etc., containing coarse or fine abrasive grains is periodically rubbed against the wheel.

To prepare a rough forging for nickel-plating may require all three steps of polishing. The first or even second polishing step may be omitted on some smooth objects or soft materials. Many steel or non-ferrous metal parts are given a high luster without being plated. When nickel-plated, the final luster or "color" is secured by a buffing operation.

Polishing wheels consisting of wooden disks faced with leather, turned to fit the form of the piece to be polished, are used for flat surfaces or on work where it is necessary to maintain square edges. A large variety of other types of wheels are now in common use. Compress wheels are used extensively and are strong, durable, and easily kept in balance. They consist of a steel center the rim of which holds a laminated surface of leather, canvas, linen, felt, rubber, etc., of various degrees of pliability. Wheels of solid leather disks of walrus hide, buffalo hide, sheepskin, or bull's neck hide, or of soft materials such as felt, canvas, and muslin, built up of disks either loose, stitched, or glued, depending on the resiliency or pliability required, are used extensively for polishing as well as buffing. Belts of cloth or leather are often charged with abrasive for polishing flat or other classes of work. Wire brushes made with coarse brass, steel, or German silver wires may be used with no abrasive for a final operation to give a satin finish to non-ferrous metals.

For ordinary operations, it is good practice to employ a **surface speed** of about 7,500 fpm. If the speed is too low, the grain is torn from the wheel too readily. Belts should have a surface speed of 2,000 to 2,500 fpm. The pins and bearings of crank and camshafts are frequently polished after they have been ground. A roughness of 20 microin. can be reduced to 2.5 to 4 microin.

Buffing is a form of finish polishing in which the surface finish is improved; very little material is removed. The powdered abrasives, usually the fine flours, are applied to the surface of the wheel by pressing a mixture of abrasive and tallow or wax against the face for a few seconds. The abrasive is replenished periodically. The wheels are made of a soft pliable material, such as soft leather, felt, linen, or muslin. Rotated at a high speed, they present a flexible face which resists pressure.

When the buffing operation is to be used as a finish polishing operation, coarse materials such as Tripoli composition, emery paste, or emery cake are used. For finish buffing gold, silver, hard rubber, etc., crocus or rouge composition (oxide of iron) may be used. For "color" buffing or bringing out a luster on solid or plated nickel, brass, copper, or even steel, a lime composition (calcium oxide), sold under various trade names, gives the best results. Other materials such as rotten stone, pumice, whiting, tin oxide, and cuttlefish bone are sometimes used for final buffing purposes.

The **sand blast** consists of particles of sand, powdered quartz, chilled-iron globules, emery, or other hard granular material blown by a jet of compressed air or of steam against a hard surface which it is desired to abrade. It is commonly used for cleaning metal castings, frosting smooth surfaces, etc. Portions of the surface which are not to be abraded can be protected by coating with a soft material such as wax, lead, or rubber. For cleaning castings, compressed air at about 90 psi is used; with a 2 hp compressor 2 sq ft of surface can be cleaned per minute, or 100 lb of small castings in a slowly rotating barrel can be cleaned in 10 to 15 min. To remove completely the hard skin of the castings takes about twice as long.

Lapping is a process of producing extremely smooth and accurate surfaces by rubbing the surface which is to be lapped against a mating form which is called a lap. The lap may either be charged with a fine abrasive and moistened with olive or lard oil or the fine abrasive may be introduced with the oil. If a part is to be lapped to a final accurate dimension, a mating form of a softer material such as soft close-grained cast iron, copper, brass, or lead is made up, which allows about 0.002 in. clearance. Aluminum oxide, silicon carbide, and diamond grits are used for lapping. "Norbide" in 320 and 600 grits also is used for rough- and finish-lapping gages of stellite, high-speed steel, chromium plate, and sintered carbide. Lapping requires considerable time. No more than 0.0002 to 0.0005 in. should be left for removal by this method. Surface plates, rings, and plugs are common forms of laps. Seating valves in a gas engine is one common illustration of lapping, the valve itself serving as the lap.

Honing is an operation similar to lapping. Instead of a metal lap charged with fine abrasive grains, a honing stone made of fine abrasives is used. Small stones of various cross-sectional shapes and 4 or 5 in. long are manufactured for honing the edges of cutting tools. Automobile cylinders are honed to secure a fine finish and accurate dimensions. This honing usually follows a light-finish reaming operation or a precision-boring operation using diamonds or carbide tools. The tool consists of several honing stones adjustable at a given radius or forced outward by springs or a wedge forced mechanically or hydraulically and is given a reciprocating (25 to 40 per min) and a rotating motion (about 300 rpm) in the cylinder which is flooded with kerosene.

Hones operate at low speeds and use universal joints to allow the tool to center itself in the work. The automatic pressure-cycle control of hone expansion, in which the pressure is reduced in steps as the final finish is reached, removes metal ten times as fast as with the spring-expanded hone. Rotational and reciprocating movements are provided to give an uneven ratio and thus prevent an abrasive grain from ever traversing its own path twice. Surface quality ranges from 0.8 to 1.8 microin., rms.

Superfinish is a honing process. Formed honing stones bear against the work previously finished to 0.0005 in. or at the most to 0.001 in. by a pressure of a few ounces which gradually increases to several pounds per square inch of stone area in proportion to the development of the increased area of contact between the work and stone. The work or tool rotates for speed and where possible is reciprocated slowly over the surface which may be finished in a matter of 20 sec to a surface quality of 1 to 3 microin. Superfinishing is applied to many types of work such as crankshaft pins and bearings, cylinder bores, pistons, valve stems, cams, and other metallic moving parts.

MACHINING OF PLASTICS

Plastics respond to metal-cutting tools similarly to the brasses. The low shear strength of these materials permits high cutting speeds and feeds but the low heat conductivity and greater resilience require increased reliefs and less rake in order to avoid undersize cutting. Hard keenly ground tools should be used. Nitrided, chromium-plated, cast non-ferrous, or even sintered-carbide tools are better, where production justifies the preparation of these tools, than the conventional high-speed-steel tools. Plastics are usually abrasive and cause the tools to wear or become dull rapidly. Dull tools generate heat and cause the tools to cut to shallow depths. The depth of cut should be small. When high production justifies the cost, diamond turning and boring tools are justified. Diamond tools maintain keen cutting edges and produce an excellent machined surface. They are particularly advantageous when a more abrasive plastic such as asbestos-filled plastic or rubber is machined.

A cutting fluid, such as a small blast of air, a stream of water, or an emulsion, improves the turning and cutting of plastics as it prevents the heating of the tool and causes the chips to remain brittle and to break rather than become sticky and gummy. A zero or slightly negative back rake and a relief angle of 8 to 12 deg should be used. Speeds of 500 to 900 fpm with light feeds and light depths of cut are desirable. When asbestos-base plastics are cut, sintered-carbide tools similar to those used on cast iron are most satisfactory. The speed may be 400 fpm with a feed of 0.010 in.

In **milling** plastics, speeds of 600 to 1,000 fpm should be used with angles similar to those on a single-point tool. From 0 to 10 deg negative rake may be used. Excellent results have been obtained by hobbing plastic gears with carbide-tipped hobs. Sintered-carbide hobs of cast-iron grade were substituted for high-speed steel to give an increase to 2,000 from 8 pieces per setting of hob, or to 2,000 from 32 per sharpening (high-speed-steel hob had four settings) and 40,000 for 20 grinds of carbide hob compared to 480 for 15 grinds of high-speed-steel hob. The gear had 8 d.p., 44 teeth, 7/8 in. face, and was made of micarta. The tooth shapes of the two cutters were alike. Air suction carried away abrasive dust.

In **drilling,** a 60 to 90 deg included-point angle is recommended with the face of the lip ground to a 0 deg rake as with brass. The relief should be 10 to 12 deg, and large polished flutes should be provided. The small-point angle is best for drilling sheets of plastic so as to prevent drill breakage at the break through and lifting of the work at that time. Usually the drill cuts under size. Drills tipped with carbide are most satisfactory and speeds of 300 to 400 fpm are generally used.

In **sawing** plastics, hollow ground saws should be used with from 4 to 8 teeth per inch, operating at speeds of 500 to 15,000 fpm. An air blast is helpful in preventing the chips from sticking to the saw. Plastics are not machined by friction sawing although razor-edge or sharp scalloped-edge blades work well on resilient materials and soft rubber, cork, etc. Abrasive saws operating at 3,500 to 6,000 fpm are used for cutting off bars and forms.

The cast phenolics are tapped and threaded with standard tools. Ground high-speed-steel **taps** with large polished flutes, with three instead of four flutes, or two instead of three flutes, are preferable. **Tapping speeds** are usually from 40 to 60 fpm; water serves as a good cutting fluid as it keeps the material brittle and prevents sticking in the flutes. As taps become worn through the abrasive action of the plastics, they will cut under size. **Thread cutting** is generally accomplished with tools similar to those used on brass.

Reaming is best accomplished in production by using tools of the expansion or adjustable type with relatively low speeds but high feeds. Less material should be removed in reaming plastics than in reaming other materials.

Polishing, buffing, and **ashing** are done on many types of plastics. Polishing is done with special compounds containing wax or a fine abrasive. Buffing wheels for plastics should have loose stitching. Ashing is done with wet pumice. Vinyl plastics can be buffed and polished with fabric wheels of standard types using light pressures.

For specific information, refer to the literature of the manufacturer or to publications such as the yearly "Modern Plastics Encyclopedia."

PRINCIPLES OF ALTERNATIVE METAL-REMOVAL PROCESSES

Electrical-discharge machining is based on the principle of erosion of metals by spark discharges. Figure 10 gives a schematic diagram of this process. The spark is a transient electric discharge through the space between two charged electrodes, which are the tool and the workpiece. The discharge occurs when the potential difference between the tool and the workpiece is large enough to cause a breakdown in the medium (which is called the **dielectric fluid** and is usually a hydrocarbon) and to procure an electrically conductive spark channel. The breakdown potential is usually established by connecting the two electrodes to the terminals of a condenser charged from a power source. The spacing between the tool and workpiece is critical; therefore, the feed is controlled by servomechanisms. The dielectric fluid has the additional functions of providing a cooling medium and carrying away particles produced by the electric discharge. The discharge can be repeated rapidly, and each time a minute amount of workpiece material is removed.

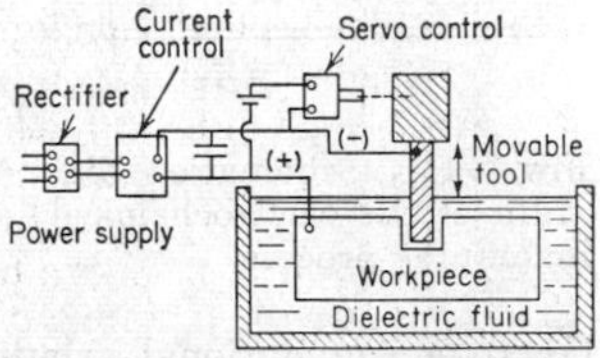

Fig. 10. Schematic diagram of the electrical-discharge machining process.

The rate of metal removal depends mostly on the average current in the discharge circuit; it is also a function of the electrode characteristics, the electrical parameters, and the nature of the dielectric fluid. In practice, this rate is normally varied by changing the number of discharges per second or the energy per discharge. Rates of metal removal may range up to 0.2 cu in. per min. However, the rates usually range down from 0.06 cu in. per min. In general, higher rates produce rougher surfaces. Surface finishes may range from 1,000 microin. in roughing cuts to less than 25 microin. in finishing cuts.

The response of materials to this process depends mostly on their thermal properties. Thermal capacity and conductivity, latent heats of melting, and vaporization are important. Hardness and strength do not necessarily have significant effect on metal-removal rates. The process is applicable to all materials which are sufficiently good conductors of electricity. The tool has great influence on permissible removal rates. It is usually made of brass, although other materials have been used successfully. Tools have been made by casting, extruding, machining, powder metallurgy, and other techniques and are made in any desired shape. Tool wear is an important consideration, and in order to control tolerances and minimize cost, the ratio of tool material removed to workpiece material removed should be low. This ratio varies with different tool and workpiece material combinations and with operating conditions. Therefore, a particular tool material may not be best for all workpieces. Tolerances as low as 0.0005 in. can be held with slow metal-removal rates.

The electrical-discharge machining process has numerous applications, such as machining cavities and dies, cutting small-diameter holes, blanking parts from sheets, cutting off rods of materials with poor machinability, and flat or form grinding. It is also applied to sharpening tools, cutters, and broaches. The process can be used to generate almost any geometry if a suitable tool can be fabricated and brought into close proximity to the workpiece.

The **electrochemical machining** process (Fig. 11) uses electrolytes which dissolve the reaction products formed on the workpiece by electrochemical action; it is similar to a reverse electroplating process. The electrolyte is pumped at high velocities through the tool. A gap of less than 0.010 in. is maintained. A d-c power supply maintains very high current densities between the tool and the workpiece. In most applications, a current density of 1,000 to 5,000 amp is required per sq in. of active cutting area. The rate of metal removal is proportional to the amount of current passing between the tool and the workpiece. Removal rates up to 1 cu in. per min can be obtained with a 10,000-amp power supply. The penetration rate is proportional to the current density for a given workpiece material.

The process leaves a burrfree surface. It is also a cold machining process and does no thermal damage to the surface of the workpiece. Tools are normally made of brass or copper, and tool wear does not exist. The amount of overcut, defined as the difference between hole diameter and tool diameter, depends upon cutting conditions. For production applications, the average overcut is around 0.015 in. The rate of penetration is between 0.100 and 0.500 in. per min. Very good surface finishes may be obtained with this process. However, sharp square corners or sharp corners and flat bottoms cannot be machined to high accuracies. The process is applied mainly to round or odd-shaped holes with straight parallel sides. It is also applied to cases where conventional methods produce burrs which are costly to remove. The process is particularly economical for materials with a hardness above 400 BHN.

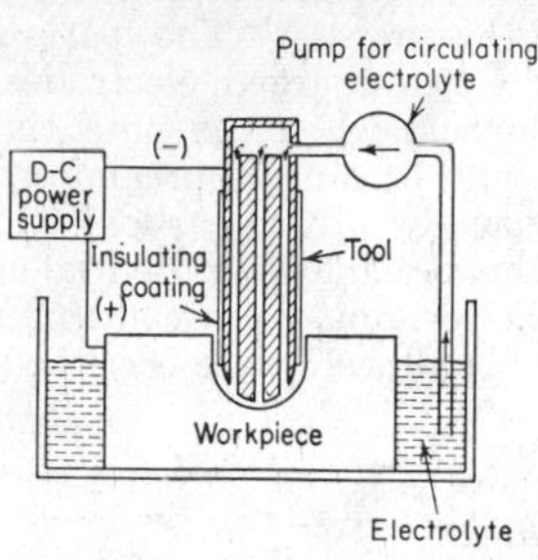

FIG. 11. Schematic diagram of the electrochemical machining process.

The **electrolytic grinding** process (Fig. 12) is a combination of electrochemical machining and abrasive grinding where most of the metal removal results from the electrolytic action. The process consists of a rotating cathode, a neutral electrolyte, and abrasive particles in contact with the workpiece. The equipment is similar to a conventional grinding machine except for the electrical accessories. The cathode usually consists of a metal-bonded diamond wheel. Graphite-filled, current-conducting abrasive wheels, made of equal parts of graphite and alumina, also have been used. An important function of the abrasive grains is to maintain a space for the electrolyte between the wheel and workpiece. The wheel runs at normal grinding speeds of 3,000 to 6,000 sfm. The abrasive particles rub against the workpiece, scrubbing off the products of the composition, thus allowing good dimensional control. In some cases, the heavy cuts are made with full electrolytic action and the final cuts are made with little electrolytic action for purposes of good surface finish and high accuracy. For best dimensional control and efficiency, the non-cutting areas of the tool should be insulated. Surface finish, precision, and metal-removal rate are influenced by the composition of the electrolyte. Aqueous solutions of sodium silicate, borax, sodium nitrate, and sodium nitrite are commonly used as electrolytes. The process is primarily used for tool and cutter sharpening and for machining of high-strength materials. It is not adapted to cavity-sinking operations. It has been successfully applied to refractory metals, high-strength steels, and nickel- and cobalt-base alloys and carbides.

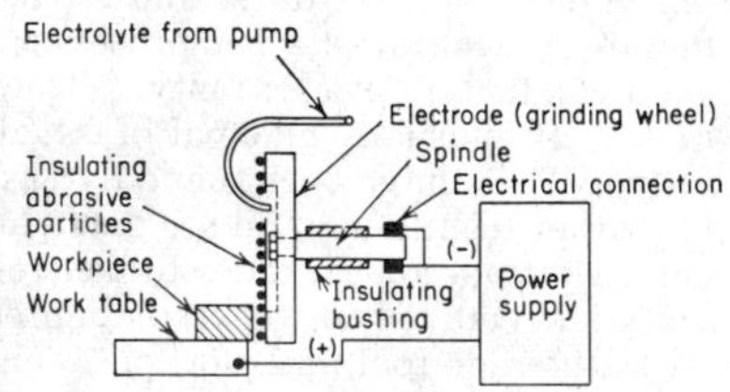

FIG. 12. Schematic diagram of the electrolytic grinding process.

Chemical milling is a process where the material is shaped by controlled chemical dissolution with chemical reagents. Selective attack on different areas of the workpiece is controlled by masking or by partial immersion. Depending on the material, the characteristics of the chemical, and the depth of cut, surface finishes can vary from 10 to 250 microin. While heavy cuts have been made successfully, lighter cuts are more characteristic of this process. Chemical milling has been applied to such materials as aluminum and magnesium alloys, steel, stainless steel, titanium, and several high-temperature alloys. Surface damage to the workpiece depends on the chemical and the workpiece material. In general, it has little or no effect on the properties of aluminum and magnesium. Less information is available on the effects on other materials.

Ultrasonic machining is a process where a tool is given a high-frequency, low-amplitude oscillation, which, in turn, transmits a high velocity to fine abrasive particles that are present between the tool and the workpiece. (See also p. 12–185 *et seq.*) Minute particles of the workpiece are chipped away on each stroke. Aluminum oxide, boron carbide, or silicone carbide grains are used in a slurry, which also carries away the debris. Grain size ranges from 200 to 1,000 (see p. 6–172 and Fig. 9). The equipment consists of an electronic oscillator, a transducer (Fig. 13), a connecting

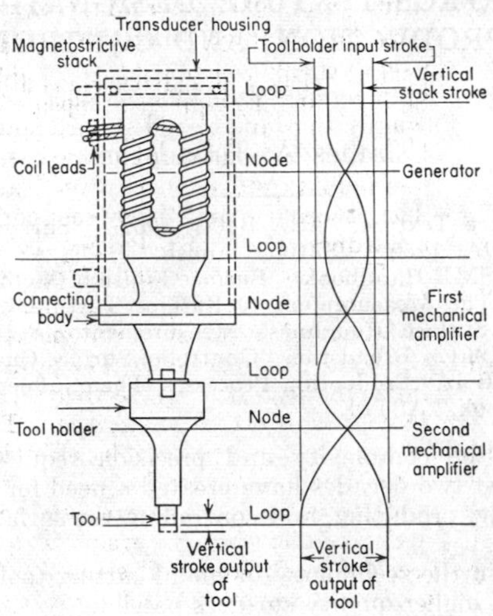

Fig. 13. Schematic diagram of a transducer used in the ultrasonic machining process. (*The Sheffield Corp.*)

cone or toolholder, and the tool. The oscillatory motion is obtained most conveniently by magnetostriction, at approximately 20,000 cps and a stroke of 0.002 to 0.005 in. The tool material is normally soft steel and is braised, soldered, or fastened mechanically to the transducer through a toolholder. The tool is ordinarily 0.003 to 0.004 in. smaller than the cavity it produces. Tolerances of 0.0005 in. or better can be obtained with fine abrasives. For best results, roughing cuts should be followed with one or more finishing operations with finer grits. The ultrasonic machining process is used in drilling holes, engraving, cavity sinking, slicing, broaching, etc. It is best suited to materials which are hard and brittle, such as ceramics, carbides, borides, ferrites, glass, precious stones, and hardened steels.

SURFACE-TEXTURE DESIGNATION, PRODUCTION, AND CONTROL

BY

James A. Broadston

REFERENCES: "Surface Texture," ASA B46.1, 1962. "Surface Roughness, Waviness and Lay," MIL-STD-10A, 1955. "Surface Finish," SAE, AS 291 C, 1962. "Metals Engineering, Design," ASME Handbook. Surface Finish of Metals, *ASM Metal Progress*, Aug., 1955. Reason, "The Measurement of Surface Texture," Cleaver-Hume. Olsen, On Standardization of Surface Roughness Measurements, *Bruel and Kjaer Technical Review*, **3**, Copenhagen, 1961. Broadston, "Control of Surface Quality," Surface Checking Gage Co., Hollywood. Bolz, "Production Processes, Their Influence on Design," Penton. "Tool Engineers Handbook," ASTM.

Rapid changes in the complexity and precision requirements of mechanical products during the past two decades have created a need for improved methods for determining, designating, producing, and controlling the surface texture of machined parts.

1. Advancements in the technology of metal-cutting tools and machinery have made the production of higher-quality surfaces possible.

2. Products are now being designed that depend upon proper quality control of critical surfaces for their successful operation as well as for long, troublefree performance in service.

3. Craftsmen who knew the function and finish requirements for all the parts they made are gradually being replaced by machine operators who are not qualified to determine the proper texture requirements for critical surfaces.

4. Remote manufacture and the necessity for controlling costs have made it preferable that finish requirements for all the critical surfaces of a part be specified on the drawing.

5. The design engineer, who best understands the over-all function of a part and all its surfaces, should be able to determine the requirement for surface-texture control where applicable and to use a satisfactory standardized method for providing this information on the drawing for use by manufacturing departments.

6. Manufacturing personnel should know what processes are able to produce surfaces within specifications and should be able to verify that the production techniques in use are under control.

7. Quality-control personnel should be able to check conformance if product quality is to be maintained and product performance and reputation ensured.

8. Test personnel should be able to operate completed products, as well as detail components, under simulated environmental conditions to determine shortcomings in design that may prevent satisfactory and troublefree performance of the product in service.

9. The design engineer should be fully cognizant of product performance and/or failure and of the reasons therefor, both in test and during customer operation, and should be able to apply such information toward the improvement of future designs.

10. Too much control may be worse than too little; hence, overuse of available techniques may hinder rather than assist, there being no payoff in producing surfaces that are more expensive than required to ensure product performance to established standards.

DESIGN CRITERIA

Surfaces produced by various processes exhibit distinct differences in texture. These differences make it possible for honed, lapped, polished, turned, milled, or ground surfaces to be easily identified. As a result of its unique character, the surface texture produced by any given process can be readily compared with other surfaces produced by the same process through the simple means of comparing the average size of its irregularities, using applicable standards and modern measurement methods. It is then possible to predict and control its performance with considerable certainty by limiting the range of the average size of its characteristic surface irregularities. Surface-texture standards make this control possible.

Variations in the texture of a critical surface of a part influence its ability to resist wear and fatigue; to assist or destroy effective lubrication; to increase or decrease its friction and/or abrasive action on other parts, and to resist corrosion, as well as affect many other properties that may be critical under certain conditions.

Clay has shown that the load-carrying capacity of nitrided shafts of varying degrees of roughness, all running at 1,500 rpm in diamond-turned lead-bronze bushings

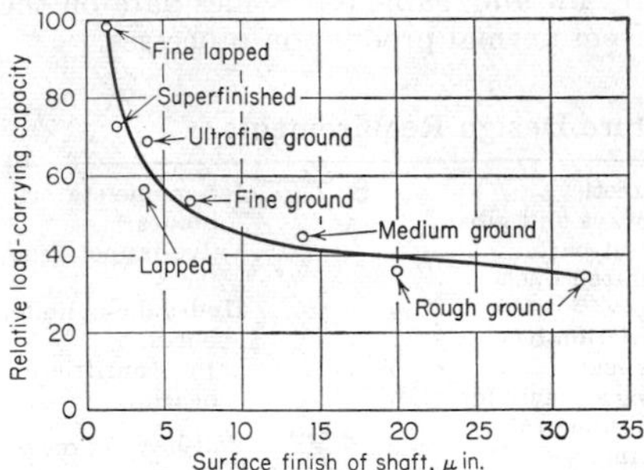

FIG. 1. Load-carrying capacity of journal bearings as related to surface roughness of shaft. (*Clay, ASM Metal Progress, Aug. 15, 1955.*)

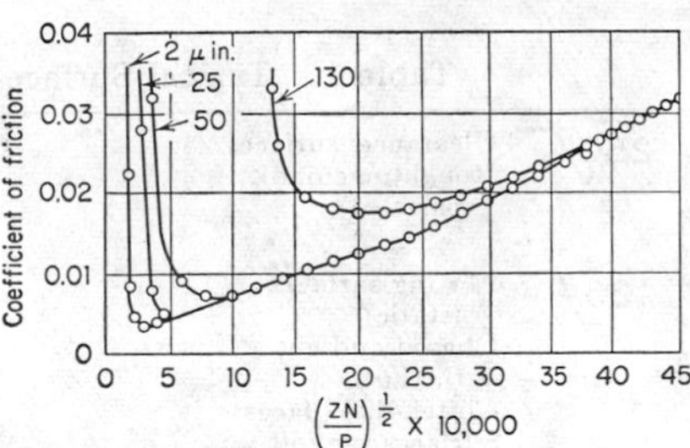

FIG. 2. Effect of surface texture on friction with hydrodynamic lubrication using a flat slider on a rotating disk. Z equals oil viscosity, centipoises; N is rubbing speed, fpm; and P is load, psi.

finished to 20 μ in., varies as shown in Fig. 1. The effects of roughness values on the friction between a flat slider on a well-lubricated rotating disk are shown in Fig. 2.

Surface-texture control should be a normal design consideration under the following conditions:

1. For those parts whose roughness must be held within closely controlled limits for optimum performance. In such cases, even the process may have to be specified. Automobile-engine cylinder walls, which should be finished to about 13 μ in. and have a circumferential (ground) or an angular (honed) lay, are an example. If too rough, excessive wear occurs; if too smooth, piston rings will not seat properly, lubrication is poor, and surfaces will seize or gall.

2. Some parts, such as antifriction bearings, cannot be made too smooth for their function. In these cases, the designer must optimize the trade-off between the added costs of production and the market value of the added performance.

3. There are some parts where surfaces must be made as smooth as possible for optimum performance, regardless of cost, such as gages, gage blocks, lenses, and carbon pressure seals.

4. In some cases, the nature of the most satisfactory finishing process may dictate the surface-texture requirements to attain production efficiency, uniformity, and control even though the individual performance of the part itself may not be dependent on the quality of the controlled surface. Hardened steel bushings, for exam-

ple, which must be ground to close tolerance for press fit into housings, could have outside diameters well beyond the roughness range specified and still perform their function satisfactorily.

5. For parts which the shop, with unjustified pride, has traditionally finished to greater perfection than is necessary, the use of proper surface-texture designations will encourage rougher surfaces on exterior and other surfaces that do not need to be finely finished.

It is the designer's responsibility to decide which surfaces of a given part are critical to its design function and which are not. This decision should be based upon a full knowledge of the part's function as well as of the performance of various surface textures that might be specified. From both a design and an economic standpoint, it may be just as unsound to specify too smooth a surface as to make it too rough—or to control it at all if not necessary. Wherever normal shop practice will produce acceptable surfaces, as in drilling, tapping, and threading, or in keyways, slots, and other purely functional surfaces, unnecessary surface-texture control will add costs which should be avoided.

Whereas each specialized field of endeavor has its own traditional criteria for determining which surface finishes are optimum for adequate performance, Table 1 provides some common examples for design review and Table 5 provides data on the surface-texture ranges that can be obtained from normal production processes.

Table 1. Typical Surface-texture Design Requirements

Symbol	Applications
250 √	Clearance surfaces; Rough machine parts
125 √	Mating surfaces (static); Chased and cut threads; Clutch-disk faces; Surfaces for soft gaskets
63 √	Piston-pin bores; Brake drums; Cylinder block, top; Gear locating faces; Gear shafts and bores; Ratchet and pawl teeth; Milled threads; Rolling surfaces; Gearbox faces; Piston crowns; Turbine-blade dovetails
32 √	Broached holes; Bronze journal bearings; Precision parts; Gear teeth; Slideways and gibs; Press-fit parts; Piston-rod bushings; Antifriction-bearing seats; Sealing surfaces for hydraulic tube fittings
16 √	Motor shafts; Gear teeth (heavy loads); Spline shafts; O-ring grooves (static); Antifriction-bearing bores and faces; Camshaft lobes; Compressor-blade airfoils
13 √	Engine cylinder bores; Piston outside diameters; Crankshaft bearings
8 √	Jet-engine stator blades; Valve-tappet cam faces; Hydraulic-cylinder bores; Lapped antifriction bearings
4 √	Ball-bearing races; Wrist pins; Hydraulic piston rods; Carbon-seal mating surfaces
2 √	Shop-gage faces; Comparator anvils
1 √	Bearing balls; Gages and mirrors; Micrometer anvils

DESIGNATION STANDARDS, SYMBOLS, AND CONVENTIONS

The precise definition and measurement of surface-texture irregularities of machined surfaces are almost impossible because the irregularities are very complex in shape and character and, being so small, do not lend themselves to direct measurement. Although both their shape and length may affect their properties, control of their average height and direction provides sufficient control of their performance. The standards do not specify the surface texture suitable for any particular application, nor the means by which it may be produced or measured. Neither are the standards concerned with other surface qualities such as appearance, luster, color, hardness, microstructure, or corrosion and wear resistance, any of which may be a governing design consideration.

The standards provide definitions of the terms used in delineating critical surface-texture qualities and a series of symbols and conventions suitable for their designation and control. The ASA B46.1, 1962, used in this section, is the standard upon which all other domestic standards, such as the MIL-STD-10A and SAE AS 291 C, as well as the British (1134, 1961) and Canadian (CSA B-95, 1962) standards are based. A declaration of accord in surface-texture standards, signed by chairmen of delegations from the three nations, provides testimony that their standards are alike in all essential aspects even though different terms are used; *i.e.*, the arithmetical average (AA) and centerline average (CLA) are identical.

The basic ASA symbol for designating surface texture is the check mark with horizontal extension shown in Fig. 3. The ISO proposes the plain symbol in Fig. 3 to indicate a requirement for a machining allowance in preference to the old ƒ symbol. The surface-texture requirement may be shown at *A*; the amount of the required

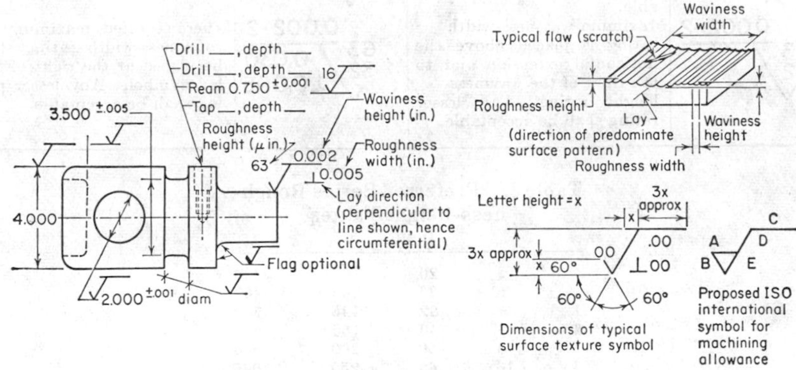

FIG. 3. Application and use of surface-texture symbols.

machining allowance may be shown at *B*, in inches; the process may be given above the line at *C*, the roughness width cutoff (sampling length) at *D*, and the lay at *E*. The ASA symbol provides spaces ror the insertion of numbers to specify a wide variety of texture characteristics, as shown in Table 2.

Control of **roughness,** the finely spaced surface-texture irregularities produced by the cutting action of tools or abrasive grains, is the most important function accomplished through the use of these standards, as roughness has a greater effect on performance than any other quality. The roughness-height index value is a number which equals the arithmetical average deviation of the minute surface irregularities from a hypothetical perfect surface, expressed in millionths of an inch (microinches, 0.000001 in.). For control purposes, roughness-height values are taken from Table 3, with those in boldface given preference.

Waviness refers to the secondary irregularities upon which roughness is superimposed, which are of significantly longer wavelength and are usually caused by machine or work deflections, chatter, heat treatment, or warping. Waviness can be measured by a dial indicator, is rated as maximum peak-to-valley distance in inches, and follows the preferred values of Table 4. For fine waviness control, techniques involving contact-area determination in percent (90, 75, 50 percent preferred) may be required. Waviness control by interferometric methods is also common, where notes, such as "Flat within XX Helium Light Bands," may be used. Dimensions may be determined from the precision length table, p. 1–75.

Lay refers to the direction of the predominant visible surface-roughness pattern. It can be controlled by use of the following approved symbols, which indicate desired

Table 2. Application of Surface-texture Ratings

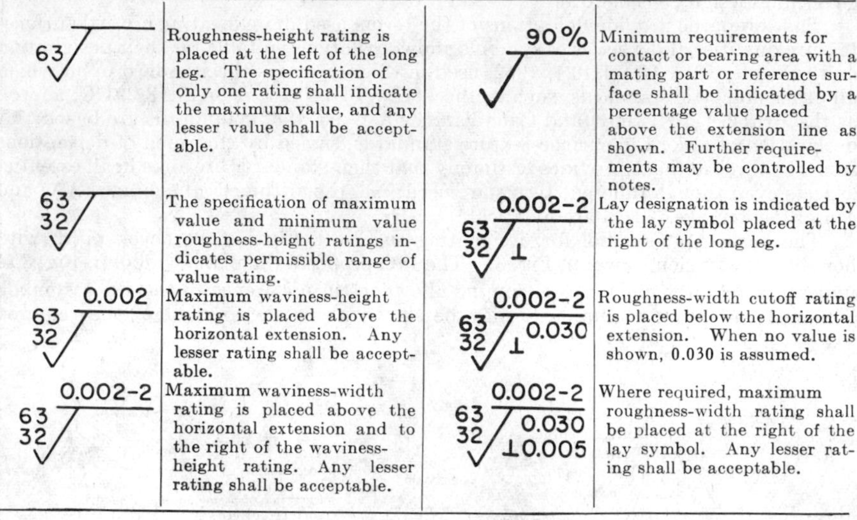

Symbol	Description	Symbol	Description
63	Roughness-height rating is placed at the left of the long leg. The specification of only one rating shall indicate the maximum value, and any lesser value shall be acceptable.	90%	Minimum requirements for contact or bearing area with a mating part or reference surface shall be indicated by a percentage value placed above the extension line as shown. Further requirements may be controlled by notes.
63 32	The specification of maximum value and minimum value roughness-height ratings indicates permissible range of value rating.	0.002–2 63 32 ⊥	Lay designation is indicated by the lay symbol placed at the right of the long leg.
0.002 63 32	Maximum waviness-height rating is placed above the horizontal extension. Any lesser rating shall be acceptable.	0.002–2 63 32 0.030 ⊥	Roughness-width cutoff rating is placed below the horizontal extension. When no value is shown, 0.030 is assumed.
0.002–2 63 32	Maximum waviness-width rating is placed above the horizontal extension and to the right of the waviness-height rating. Any lesser rating shall be acceptable.	0.002–2 63 32 0.030 ⊥0.005	Where required, maximum roughness-width rating shall be placed at the right of the lay symbol. Any lesser rating shall be acceptable.

Table 3. Preferred Series Roughness-height Values
(μ in.)

	5	20	80	320
	6	25	100	400
1	**8**	**32**	**125**	**500**
2	10	40	160	600
3	13	50	200	800
4	**16**	**63**	**250**	**1000**

Table 4. Preferred Series Waviness-height Values
(In.)

0.00002	0.00008	0.0003	0.001	0.005	0.015
0.00003	0.0001	0.0005	0.002	0.008	0.020
0.00005	0.0002	0.0008	0.003	0.010	0.030

lay direction with respect to the boundary line of the surface upon which the symbol is placed.

‖	Parallel	X	Angular	C	Circular
⊥	Perpendicular	M	Multidirectional	R	Radial

Flaws are imperfections in a surface that occur only at infrequent intervals. They are usually caused by non-uniformity of the material, or they result from damage to the surface subsequent to processing, such as scratches, dents, pits, and cracks. Flaws should not be considered in surface-texture measurements as the standards do not consider or classify them. Acceptance or rejection of parts having flaws is strictly a matter of judgment based upon whether the flaw will compromise the intended function of the part.

Surface-texture values in the standards can be called out on any drawing by a note and symbol as follows:

√ Surface texture per ASA B46.1, 1962

Table 5. Surface-roughness Ranges of Production Processes

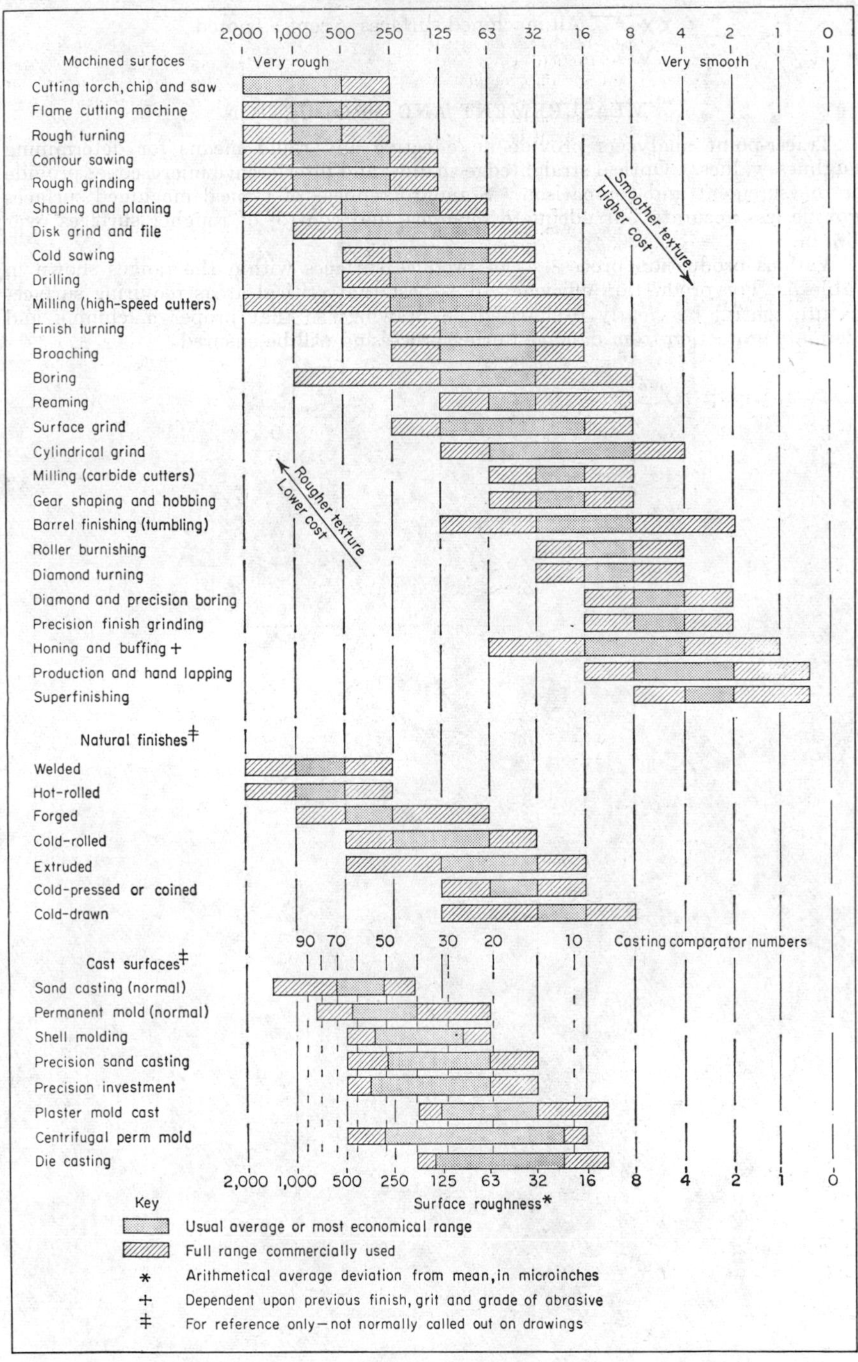

Values for non-designated surfaces can be limited by the note

XX $\surd$ All machined surfaces except as noted

MEASUREMENT AND PRODUCTION

Tracer-point analyzers provide an effective and rapid means for determining roughness values. Optical straightedge shadow and interference microscopes provide for measurement and comparison. Standard replicas of typical machined surfaces provide less accurate but adequate reference and control of rougher surfaces over 16 μ in.

Various production processes can produce surfaces within the ranges shown in Table 5. For production efficiency, it is best that critical areas requiring surface-texture control be clearly designated on drawings so that proper machining and adequate protection from damage during processing will be ensured.

WOODCUTTING TOOLS AND MACHINES

BY

Richard W. Perkins

REFERENCES: Brown and Bethel, "Lumber," Wiley. Davis, Machining and Related Characteristics of United States Hardwoods, *USDA Tech. Bull.* 1267. Harris, "A Handbook of Woodcutting," Her Majesty's Stationery Office, London, 1946. Monnett, "Knife Grinding and Woodworking Manual," Dependable Machine Co., Greensboro, N.C. Telford, Small Sawmill Operator's Handbook, *USDA Handbook* 27. Willard, "Production Woodworking Equipment," Dept. of Industrial Engineering, N.C. State College.

Sawing

Sawing machines are classified according to basic machine design, *i.e.*, band saw, gang saw, chain saw, circular saw. Saws are designated as **ripsaws** if they are designed to cut along the grain or **crosscut** saws if they are designed to cut across the grain. A **combination** saw is designed to cut reasonably well along the grain, across the grain, or along a direction at an angle to the grain (**miter**). Sawing machines are often further classified according to the specific operation for which they are used, *e.g.*, **headsaw** (the primary log-breakdown saw in a sawmill), **resaw** (saw for ripping cants into boards), **edger** (saw for edging boards in a sawmill), **variety saw** (general-purpose saw for use in furniture plants), **scroll saw** (general-purpose narrow-band saw for use in furniture plants).

The thickness of the saw blade is designated in terms of the Birmingham wire gage (BWG) (see p. 6–48). Large-diameter (40 to 60 in.) circular saw blades are tapered so that they are thicker at the center than at the rim. Typical headsaw blades range in thickness from 5 to 6 BWG for use in heavy-duty applications to 8 to 9 BWG for lighter operations. Small-diameter (6 to 30 in.) circular saws are generally flat-ground and range from 10 to 18 BWG in thickness. Band-saw and gang-saw blades are flat-ground and are generally thinner than circular saw blades designed for similar applications. For example, typical wide-band-saw blades for sawmill use range from 11 to 16 BWG in thickness. The thickness of a band-saw blade is determined by the cutting load and the diameter of the band wheel. Gang-saw blades are generally somewhat thicker than band-saw blades for similar operations. Narrow-band-saw blades for use on scroll band saws range in thickness from 20 to 25 BWG and range in width from ⅛ to about 1¾ in., depending upon the curvature of cuts to be made.

The considerable amount of heat generated at the cutting edge results in compressive stresses in the rim of the saw blade of sufficient magnitude to cause mechanical instability of the saw blades. Circular saw blades and wide-band-saw blades are commonly prestressed (or **tensioned**) to reduce the possibility of buckling. Small circular saw blades for use on power-feed ripsaws and crosscut saws are frequently provided with **expansion slots** for the same purpose.

The **shape of the cutting portion of the sawtooth** is determined by specifying the hook, face bevel, top bevel, and clearance angles. The optimum tooth shape depends primarily upon cutting direction, moisture content, and density of the work material. Sawteeth are, in general, designed in such a way that the portion of the cutting edge which is required to cut across the fiber direction is provided with the maximum effective rake angle consistent with tool strength and wear considerations. Ripsaws are designed with a hook angle between some 46 deg for inserted-tooth circular headsaws used to cut green material and 10 deg for solid-tooth saws cutting dense material at low moisture content. Ripsaws generally have zero face bevel and top bevel angle;

however, spring-set ripsaws sometimes are provided with a moderate top bevel angle (5 to 15 deg). The hook angle for crosscut saws ranges from positive 10 deg to negative 30 deg. These saws are generally designed with both top and face bevel angles of 5 to 15 deg; however, in some cases top and face bevel angles as high as 45 deg are employed. A compromise design is used for combination saws which embodies the features of both ripsaws and crosscut saws in order to provide a tool which can cut reasonably well in all directions. The clearance angle should be maintained at the smallest possible value in order to provide for maximum tooth strength. For ripsawing applications, the clearance angle should be about 12 to 15 deg. The minimum satisfactory clearance angle is determined by the nature of the work material, not from kinematical considerations of the motion of the tool through the work. In some cases of cutoff, combination, and narrow-band-saw designs where the tooth pitch is relatively small, much larger clearance angles are used in order to provide the necessary gullet volume.

A certain amount of clearance between the saw blade and the generated surface (**side clearance** or **set**) is necessary to prevent frictional heating of the saw blade. In the case of solid-tooth circular saws and band or gang saws, the side clearance is generally provided either by deflecting alternate teeth (**spring-setting**) or by spreading the cutting edge (**swage-setting**). The amount of side clearance depends upon density, moisture content, and size of the saw blade. In most cases, satisfactory results are obtained if the side clearance S is determined from the formula S (in.) = $A\frac{1}{2}[f(g-5) - f(g)]$, where g = the gage number (BWG) of the saw blade, $f(n)$ = the dimension in inches corresponding to the gage number n, and A has values from Table 1. Certain specialty circular saws such as planer, smooth-trimmer, and miter saws are hollow-ground to provide side clearance. Inserted-tooth saws, carbide-tipped saws, and chain-saw teeth are designed so that sufficient side clearance is provided for the life of the tool; consequently, the setting of such saws is unnecessary.

Table 1. Values of A for Computing Side Clearance

Saw type	Work material			
	Specific gravity less than 0.45		Specific gravity greater than 0.55	
	Air dry	Green	Air dry	Green
Circular rip and combination	0.90	1.00	0.85	0.95
Glue-joint ripsaw	0.80	....	0.60	
Circular crosscut	0.95	1.05	0.90	1.00
Wide-band saw	0.55	0.65	0.30	0.40
Narrow-band saw	0.65	....	0.55	

The **tooth speed** for sawing operations ranges from 3,000 to 17,000 fpm approx. Large tooth speeds are in general desirable in order to permit maximum work rates. The upper limit of permissible tooth speed depends in most cases on machine design considerations and not on considerations of wear or surface quality as in the case of metal cutting. Exceptionally high tooth speeds may result in charring of the work material, which is machined at slow feed rates.

In many sawing applications, **surface quality** is not of prime importance since the sawed surfaces are subsequently machined, *e.g.*, by planing, shaping, sanding; therefore, it is desirable to operate the saw at the largest feed per tooth consistent with gullet overloading. Large values of feed per tooth result in lower amounts of work required per unit volume of material cut and in lower amounts of wear per unit tool travel. Large-diameter circular saws, wide-band saws, and gang saws for ripping green material are generally designed so that the feed per tooth should be about 0.08 to 0.12 in. Small-diameter circular saws are designed so that the feed per tooth ranges from 0.03 in. for dense hardwoods to 0.05 in. for low-density softwoods. Narrow-band saws are generally operated at somewhat smaller values of feed per tooth, *e.g.*, 0.005 to 0.04 in. Smaller values of feed per tooth are necessary for applications where surface quality is of prime importance, *e.g.*, glue-joint ripsawing and variety-saw operations. The degree of gullet loading is measured by the **gullet-feed index (GFI)**, which is computed as the feed per tooth times the depth of face divided by the gullet area. The maximum GFI depends primarily upon species, moisture content, and cutting direction. It is generally conceded that the maximum GFI for ripsawing lies between 0.3 for high density, low-moisture-content material and 0.4 for low density, high-moisture-content material. For specific information, see Telford, *For. Prod. Res. Soc. Proc.*, 1949.

Saws vary considerably in design of the **gullet shape.** The primary design considerations are gullet area and tooth strength; however, special design shapes are often required for certain classes of work material, *e.g.*, for ripping frozen wood.

Materials. Saw blades and the sawteeth of solid-tooth saws are generally made of a nickel tool steel. The bits for inserted-tooth saws are usually a plain carbon tool steel; however, high-speed-steel bits or bits with a cast-alloy inlay (*e.g.*, Stellite) are sometimes used in applications where metal or gravel will not be encountered. Small-diameter circular saws of virtually all designs are made with cemented carbide tips. This design type is almost imperative in applications where highly abrasive material is cut, namely, in plywood and particle-board operations.

Sawing Power. References: Endersby, The Performance of Circular Plate Ripsaws, *For. Prod. Res. Bull.* 27, Her Majesty's Stationery Office, London, 1953. Johnston, Experimental Cut-off Saw, *For. Prod. Jour.*, June, 1962. Oehrli, Research in Cross-cutting with Power Saw Chain Teeth, *For. Prod. Jour.*, Jan., 1960. Telford, Energy Requirements for Insert-point Circular Headsaws, *Proc. For. Prod. Res. Soc.*, 1949.

An approximate relation for computing the power P, ft-lb per min required to saw is

$$P = kvb/p(A + Bt_a)$$

where k is the kerf, in.; v is the tooth speed, fpm; p is the tooth pitch, in.; A and B are constants for a given sawing operation, lb per in. and psi, respectively; and t_a is the average chip thickness, in. The average chip thickness is computed from the relation $t_a = \gamma f_t \times d/b$, where f_t is the feed per tooth; d is the depth of face; b is the length of the tool path through the workpiece, in.; and γ has the value *unity* except for saws with spring-set or offset teeth, in which case γ has the value 2. The constants A and B depend primarily upon cutting direction (ripsawing, crosscutting), moisture content below the fiber-saturation point and specific gravity of the work material, and tooth shape. The values of A and B (see Table 2) depend to some degree upon the depth of

Table 2. Constants for Sawing-power Estimation

Material			Tool		Constants	
Species	Specific gravity	Moisture content, %	Angles[e]	Sawing situation	A, lb per in.	B, psi
Beech, European[a]	0.72	12	20, 0, 12	SS, R	27.8	5,760
Birch, yellow[b]	0.55	FSP	−30, 10, 10	SS, CC	19.7	4,100
Elm, wych[a]	0.67	12	20, 0, 12	SS, R	23.2	4,840
Maple, sugar[c]	0.63	FSP	41, 0, 0	IT, R	85.6	2,995
Maple, sugar[c,f]	0.63	FSP	41, 0, 0	IT, R	48.0	4,400
Pine, northern white[c]	0.34	FSP	41, 0, 0	IT, R	27.1	1,675
Pine, northern white[c,f]	0.34	FSP	41, 0, 0	IT, R	28.2	2,085
Pine, northern white[b]	0.34	FSP	−30, 10, 10	SS, CC	0.0	3,300
Pine, ponderosa[d]	0.38–0.40	15–40	28, 25, 0	OFT, R	29.3	1,700
Pine, ponderosa[d]	0.38–0.40	15–40	28, 25, 0	OFT, CC	0.0	2,120
Poplar (*P. serotina*)[a]	0.48	12	20, 0, 12	SS, R	18.6	3,290
Redwood, California[a]	0.37	12	20, 0, 12	SS, R	15.0	2,260
Spruce, white[b]	0.32	FSP	−30, 10, 10	SS, CC	0.0	4,680

[a] Endersby.
[b] Johnston.
[c] Hoyle, unpublished report, N.Y. State College of Forestry, Syracuse, N.Y., 1958.
[d] Oehrli.
[e] The numbers represent hook angle, face bevel angle, and top bevel angle in degrees.
[f] Cutting performed on frozen material.
Note: FSP = moisture content greater than the fiber-saturation point; CC = crosscut; IT = insert-tooth; OFT = offset-tooth; R = rip; SS = spring-set.

face, saw diameter, gullet shape, gullet-feed index, saw speed, and whether the tool motion is linear or rotary; however, the effect of these variables can generally be neglected for purposes of approximation.

Planing and Molding

Machinery. Planing and molding machines employ a rotating cutterhead to generate a smooth, defectfree surface by cutting in a direction approximately along the grain. A **surfacer** (or **planer**) is designed to machine boards or panels to uniform thickness. A **facer** (or **facing planer**) is designed to generate a flat (plane) surface on the wide faces of boards. The **edge jointer** is intended to perform the same task on the edges of boards in preparation for edge-gluing into panels. A **planer-matcher** is a heavy-duty machine designed to plane rough boards to uniform width and thickness in one operation. This machine is commonly used for dressing dimension lumber and producing millwork. The **molder** is a high-production machine for use in furniture plants to generate parts of uniform cross-sectional shape.

Recommended Operating Conditions. It is of prime importance to adjust the operating conditions and knife geometry so that the machining defects are maintained at a satisfactory level. The most commonly encountered defects are torn (chipped) grain, fuzzy grain, raised and loosened grain, and chip marks. **Torn grain** is caused by the wood splitting ahead of the cutting edge and below the generated surface. It is generally associated with large cutting angle, large chip thickness, low moisture content, and low work-material density. The **fuzzy-grain** defect is characterized by small groups of wood fibers which stand up above the generated surface. This defect is caused by incomplete severing of the wood by the cutting edge and is generally associated with small cutting angles, dull knives, low-density species, high moisture content, and (often) the presence of reaction wood. The **raised-grain** defect is characterized by an uneven surface where one portion of the annual ring is raised above the remaining part. **Loosened grain** is similar to raised grain; however, loosened grain is characterized by a separation of the early wood from the late wood which is readily discernible to the naked eye. The raised- and loosened-grain defects are attributed to the crushing of springwood cells as the knife passes over the surface. (Edge-grain material may exhibit a defect similar to the raised-grain defect if machining is performed at a markedly different moisture content than that encountered at some later time.) Raised and loosened grains are associated with dull knives, excessive jointing of knives (the jointing land should not exceed $\frac{1}{32}$ in.), and high moisture content of work material. **Chip marks** are caused by chips which are forced by the knife into the generated surface as the knife enters the work material. Chip marks are associated with inadequate exhaust, low moisture content, and species (*e.g.*, birch, Douglas fir, and maple have a marked propensity toward the chip-mark defect).

Depth of cut is an important variable with respect to surface quality, particularly in the case of species which are quite prone to the torn-grain defect (*e.g.*, hard maple, Douglas fir, southern yellow pine). In most cases, the depth of cut should be less than $\frac{1}{16}$ in. The number of **marks per inch** (reciprocal of the feed per cutter) is an important variable in all cases; however, it is most important in those cases for which the torn-grain defect is highly probable. The marks per inch should be between 8 and 12 for rough planing operations and from 12 to 16 for finishing cuts. Slightly higher values may be necessary for refractory species or for situations where knots or curly grain are present. It is seldom necessary to exceed a value of 20 marks per in. The **clearance angle** should in all cases exceed a value of 10 deg. When it is desired to hone or joint the knives between sharpenings, a value of about 20 deg should be used. The optimum **cutting angle** lies between 20 and 30 deg for most planing situations; however, in the case of interlocked or wavy grain, low moisture content, or species with a marked tendency toward the torn-grain defect, it may be necessary to reduce the cutting angle to 10 or 15 deg.

Boring

Machinery. The typical general-purpose wood-boring machine has a single vertical spindle and is a hand-feed machine. Production machines are often of the vertical, multiple-spindle, adjustable-gang type or of the horizontal type with two adjustable, independently driven spindles. The former type is commonly employed in furniture plants for boring holes in the faces of parts, while the latter type is commonly used for boring dowel holes in the edges and ends of parts.

Tool Design. A wide variety of tool designs is available for specialized boring tasks; however, the most commonly used tools are the taper-head drill, the spur machine drill, and the machine bit. The **taper-head** drill is a twist drill with a point angle of 60 to 90 deg, lip clearance angle of 15 to 20 deg, chisel-edge angle of 125 to 135 deg, and helix angle of 20 to 40 deg. Taper-head drills are used for drilling screw holes and for boring dowel holes along the grain. The **spur machine** drill is equivalent to a twist drill having a point angle of 180 deg with the addition of a pyramidal point (instead of a web) and spurs at the circumference. These drills are designed with a helix angle of 20 to 40 deg and a clearance angle of 15 to 20 deg. The **machine bit** has a specially formed head which determines the configuration of the spurs. It also has a point. Machine bits are designed with a helix angle of 40 to 60 deg, cutting angle of 20 to 40 deg, and clearance angle of 15 to 20 deg. Machine bits are designed with spurs contiguous to the cutting edges (**double-spur machine bit**), with spurs removed from the vicinity of the cutting edges (**extension-lip machine bit**), and with the outlining portion of the spurs removed (**flat-cut machine bit**). The purpose of the spurs is to aid in severing wood fibers across their axes, thereby increasing hole-wall smoothness when boring across the grain. Therefore, drills or bits with spurs (double-spur machine drill and bit) are intended for boring across the grain, whereas drills or bits without spurs (taper-head drill, flat-cut machine bit) are intended for boring along the grain or at an angle to the grain.

Taper-head and spur machine drills can be sharpened until they become too short for further use; however, machine bits and other bit styles which have specially formed heads can only be sharpened a limited number of times before the spur and cutting-face configuration is significantly altered. Since most wood-boring tools are sharpened by filing the clearance face, it is important to ensure that sufficient clearance is maintained. The clearance angle should be at least 5 deg greater than the angle whose tangent (function) is the feed per revolution divided by the circumference of the drill point.

Recommended Operating Conditions. The most common defects are tearing of fibers from the end-grain portions of the hole surface and charring of hole surfaces. Rough hole surfaces are most often encountered in low-density and ring-porous species. This defect can generally be maintained at a satisfactory level by controlling the chip thickness. Charring is commonly a problem in high-density species. It can be avoided by maintaining the peripheral speed of the tool below a level which depends upon density and moisture content and by maintaining the chip thickness at a satisfactory level. Large chip thickness may result in excessive tool temperature and therefore rapid tool wear; however, large chip thickness is seldom a cause of hole charring. The following recommendations pertain to the use of spur-type drills or bits for boring material at about 6 percent moisture content across the grain. For species having a specific gravity less than 0.45, the chip thickness should be between 0.015 and 0.030 in., while the peripheral speed of the tool should not exceed 900 fpm. For material of specific gravity between 0.45 and 0.65, satisfactory results can be obtained with values of chip thickness between 0.015 and 0.045 in. and with peripheral speeds less than 700 fpm. For material of specific gravity greater than 0.65, the chip thickness should lie between 0.015 and 0.030 in., while the peripheral speed should not exceed 500 fpm. Somewhat higher values of chip thickness and peripheral speed can be employed when the moisture content of the material is higher.

Sanding

(See pp. 6–170 to 6–172.)

Machinery. Machines for production sanding of parts having flat surfaces are multiple-drum sanders, automatic-stroke sanders, and wide-belt sanders. **Multiple-drum** sanders are of the endless-bed or roll-feed type and have from two to six drums. The drum at the infeed end is fitted with a relatively coarse abrasive (40 to 100 grit), takes a relatively heavy cut (0.010 to 0.015 in.), and operates at a relatively slow surface speed (3,000 to 3,500 fpm). The drum at the outfeed end has a relatively fine

Table 3. Recommendations for Common Whitewood Sanding Operations
(Data from Graham, *Furniture Production*, July and Aug., 1961; and Martin, *Wood Working Digest*, Sept., 1961.)

		Abrasive									
		Backing		Adhesive		Mineral			Grit size		
		Material	Weight	Make coat	Size coat	1st drum	2d drum	3d drum	1st drum	2d drum	3d drum
Multiple-drum	Softwood	Paper	E	Glue	Resin	G	G	G or S	50	80	100
	Hardwood	Paper	E	Glue	Resin	A	A	A	60	100	120
	Particle board	Paper	E	Glue	Resin	G	G	G or A	40	60	80
		Fiber	0.020	Resin	Resin	S	S	S	40	60	80
	Hardboard	Paper	E	Glue	Resin	S	S	S	60	80	120
		Fiber	0.020	Resin	Resin	S	S	S	60	80	120
Wide-belt	Softwood	Paper	E	Glue	Resin	G	or	S		80–220[a]	
		Cloth	X	Resin	Resin	G	or	S		80–220[a]	
	Hardwood	Paper	E	Glue	Resin		A			80–220[a]	
		Cloth	X	Resin	Resin		A			80–220[a]	
	Burnishing	Paper	E	Glue	Glue		A			280–400	
	Particle board	Cloth	X	Resin	Resin		S			24–150[a]	
	Hardboard	Cloth	X	Resin	Resin		S			100–150	
Stroke sanding	Softwood	Paper	E	Glue	Resin		G			80;120[b]	
	Hardwood	Paper	E	Glue	Resin		A			100;150–180[b]	
		Cloth	X	Glue	Resin		A			100;150–180[b]	
	Particle board	Paper	E	Glue	Resin	A	or	S		80;120[b]	
		Cloth	X	Resin	Resin	A	or	S		80;120[b]	
	Hardboard	Paper	E	Glue	Resin	A	or	S		100;150[b]	
		Cloth	X	Resin	Resin	A	or	S		100;150[b]	
Edge sanding	Softwood	Cloth	X	Glue	Resin		G			60;100[b]	
	Hardwood	Cloth	X	Glue	Resin		A			60–150[a]	
		Cloth	X	Resin	Resin		A			60–150[a]	
Mold sanding	Softwood	Cloth	J	Glue	Glue		G			80–120[a]	
		Cloth	J	Glue	Resin		G			80–120[a]	
	Hardwood	Cloth	J	Glue	Glue	G	or	A		80–120[a]	
		Cloth	J	Glue	Resin	G	or	A		80–120[a]	

Note: G = garnet; A = aluminum oxide; S = silicon carbide.
[a] May be single- or multiple-grit operation.
[b] First number for cutting-down operations, second number for finishing operations.

abrasive paper (60 to 150 grit), takes a relatively light cut (about 0.005 in.), and operates at a somewhat higher surface speed (4,000 to 5,000 fpm). **Automatic-stroke** sanders employ a narrow abrasive belt and a reciprocating shoe which forces the abrasive belt against the work material. This machine is commonly employed in furniture plants for the final white-sanding operation prior to finish coating. The automatic-stroke sander has a relatively low rate of material removal (about one-tenth to one-third of the rate for the final drum of a multiple-drum sander) and is operated with a belt speed of 3,000 to 7,500 fpm. **Wide-belt** sanders are commonly used in board plants (plywood, particle board, hardboard). They have the advantage of higher production rates and somewhat greater accuracy than multiple-drum sanders (*e.g.*, feed rates up to 100 fpm, as opposed to about 35 fpm). Wide-belt sanders operate at surface speeds of approximately 5,000 fpm and are capable of operating at depths of cut of 0.006 to 0.020 in., depending upon work-material density.

Abrasive Tools. The abrasive tool consists of a **backing** to carry the **abrasive** and an **adhesive** coat to fix the abrasive to the backing. Backings are constructed of paper, cloth, or vulcanized fiber or consist of a cloth-paper combination. The adhesive coating (see also pp. 6–172 to 6–175) is made up of two coatings; the first coat (**make coat**) acts to join the abrasive material to the backing, while the second coat (**size coat**) acts to provide the necessary support for the abrasive particles. Coating materials are generally animal glues, urea resins, or phenolic resins. The choice of material for the make and size coats depends upon the required flexibility of the tool and the work rate required of the tool. Abrasive materials (see also pp. 6–170 to 6–172) for woodworking applications are garnet, aluminum oxide, and silicon carbide. **Garnet** is the most commonly used abrasive mineral because of its low cost and acceptable working qualities for low-work-rate situations. It is generally used for sheet goods, for sanding softwoods with all types of machines, and for sanding where the belt is loaded up (as opposed to worn out). **Aluminum oxide** abrasive is used extensively for sanding hardwoods, particle board, and hardboard. **Silicon carbide** abrasive is used for sanding and polishing between coating operations and for machine sanding of particle board and hardboard. Silicon carbide is also frequently used for the sanding of softwoods where the removal of raised fibers is a problem. The size of the abrasive particles is specified by the mesh number (the approximate number of openings per inch in the screen through which the particles will pass). (See Commercial Std CS217–59, "Grading of Abrasive Grain on Coated Abrasive Products," U.S. Government Printing Office.) Mesh numbers range from about 600 to 12. Size may also be designated by an older system of symbols which range from 10/0 (mesh No. 400) through 0 (mesh No. 80) to 4½ (mesh No. 12). Some general recommendations for common white-wood sanding operations are presented in Table 3.

SECTION 14

PUMPS AND COMPRESSORS

BY

E. F. WRIGHT, Consulting Engineer, Advance Products Division, Worthington Corporation.

IGOR J. KARASSIK, General Manager, Advance Products Division, Worthington Corporation.

WILLIAM C. KRUTZSCH, Manager-Engineering, Pump and Heat Transfer Division, Worthington Corporation.

LYMAN F. SCHEEL, Supervisor of Fluid Mechanics, The Ralph M. Parsons Company, Los Angeles and New York.

B. B. DAYTON, Chief Physicist, Consolidated Vacuum Corporation, Rochester.

J. E. McDONALD, President, Air-Boston Laboratory, Newton Lower Falls, Mass.

CONTENTS

PUMPS

BY

E. F. Wright

(For centrifugal and axial pumps, see p. 14–21.)

REFERENCES: Greene, "Pumping Machinery," Wiley. Nickel, "Direct-acting Steam Pumps," McGraw-Hill. Butler, "Modern Pumping and Hydraulic Machinery," Griffin. Kristal and Annett, "Pumps," McGraw-Hill. Standards of Hydraulic Institute.

Displacement pumps are usually divided into four general classes: (1) reciprocating power, (2) steam, (3) rotary, and (4) pistonless. A power pump is a reciprocating pump driven by power from an outside source applied to the crankshaft of the pump. A steam pump is a reciprocating pump and a steam engine built together as a unit. The power to drive the pump is furnished by the steam engine. A rotary pump is a positive-displacement pump, consisting of a fixed casing containing gears, cams, screws, vanes, plungers, or similar elements, actuated by rotation of the drive shaft. These pumps are characterized by their close running clearances and the absence of suction and discharge valves. Rotary pumps are frequently lubricated only by the fluid being pumped. Pistonless pumps utilize the direct pressure of air, gas, or steam on the fluid pumped.

RECIPROCATING POWER PUMPS

Power pumps are positive-displacement machines which, at constant speed, deliver essentially the same capacity at any pressure within the capability of the driver and the strength of the pump. The inherently high efficiency of a power pump is almost independent of pressure and capacity and is only slightly lower for a small pump than for a large pump. Thus the power pump is most useful in the field of high pressure and low capacity, where its high efficiency more than offsets the high initial cost. In some applications the constant delivery at varying pressure is a definite advantage, with the power pump acting also as a metering device. In other applications this creates a control problem to be met by varying the speed, bypassing at constant speed, or intermittently loading and unloading the pump. Many power pumps are arranged so that the size of the piston or plunger can be changed easily, thus providing a pump adaptable to a considerable range of pressure, with capacity varying inversely with pressure at constant hydraulic-power output.

High-speed Power Pumps. Modern power pumps are built with totally enclosed, self-lubricating power ends effectively protected from damage by any leakage of the fluid pumped or from dirt in the surrounding atmosphere. Piston speeds up to 300 fpm in modern short-stroke pumps with rotative speeds of 300 to 720 rpm permit direct connection to the driver or a single-reduction drive instead of the double-reduction drive usually required with older slow-speed pumps. Figure 1 shows a typical inverted vertical triplex, 3-in. stroke pump rated at 500 rpm and almost 60 hp. The suction manifold (1) communicates with three suction-valve assemblies (2) set in the individual plunger chambers in the working barrel (3). Similar discharge-valve assemblies (4) are contained partly in the discharge manifold (5) on the opposite side of the cylinder. The stuffing-box barrel (6) extends upward from the working barrel, where it is held by the stuffing-box nut (7) and studs (8). The plunger (9) and upper crosshead (10) are connected to the power-end crosshead by side rods which pass through vertical holes drilled through the cylinder forging. The power end is protected from dirt by the telescopic tubes (11) surrounding the side rods. The three-throw crankshaft is carried by a roller bearing at each end in the pump frame, and all parts are pressure-lubricated through drilled passages in the crankshaft, the connecting rods, and the crossheads. This particular pump is offered with seven different liquid ends, which can be fitted with 28 different plunger sizes to cover the range of 96 gpm displacement at 820 psi to 3.82 gpm displacement at 22,725 psi.

Conventional displacement-pump design involves intersecting bores, as in Fig. 1, where the plunger chamber enters the passage between the suction and discharge valves. This leads to stress concentration in the pulsation chamber which limits the maximum pressure, even with high-strength forgings, to about 20,000 psi. Figure 2

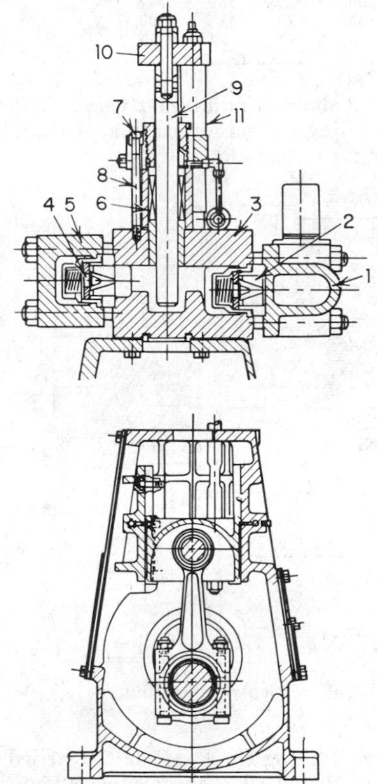

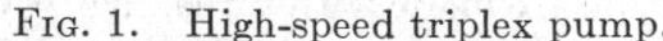

FIG. 1. High-speed triplex pump.

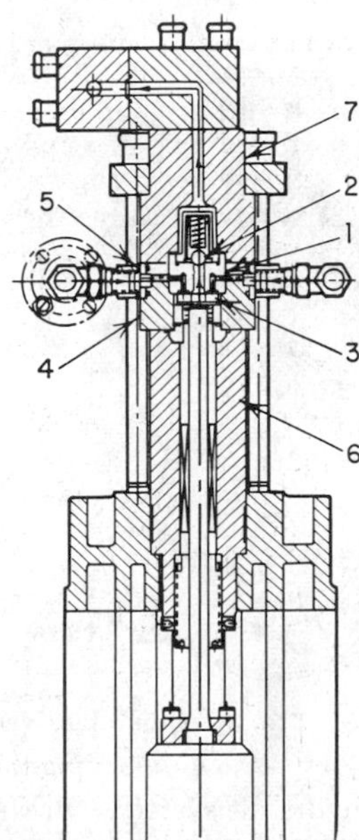

FIG. 2. "Valve-in-line" fluid end.

shows a "valve-in-line" fluid end for pressures up to 32,000 psi. Here a one-piece valve seat (1) receives both the discharge ball valve (2) and the ring-type suction valve (3). This valve seat, with its inlet passages intersecting at a right angle, is reinforced by the taper shrink fit of the valve-seat body (4). This shrink fit also seals inlet passages from discharge pressure at the top and pulsation-chamber pressure at the bottom. The suction-port ring (5) connects the suction manifolds to the valve-seat body.

The stuffing-box barrel (6), the cylinder head (7), and the lower portion of the valve-seat body are all simple cylindrical forms, well adapted to high internal pressures because of favorable stress distribution. This design also keeps the clearance volume down to a very low value, which is important at pressures where even water is appreciably compressed.

Horizontal triplex pumps are also made in a similar range of sizes for approximately the same speed with both cast and forged fluid cylinders. In the horizontal pumps, the plungers are connected directly to the power-end crossheads with the stuffing box between the cylinder and the frame, thus eliminating the upper crosshead and the side rods characteristic of the inverted vertical pump. Triplex pumps of this type are used for water flooding and salt-water disposal in the oil fields, for gathering and product pipelines, and for small hydraulic systems and hydraulic testing. (See Table 1.)

Table 1. Typical Ratings of Modern Triplex Power Pumps

Stroke, in.	2½	3	4	5	6
Rpm	690	500	420	360	300
Bhp	28	58	70	115	300
Efficiency, percent	85	86	87	88	90

Multiplex Inverted Vertical Pumps. Figure 3 shows a quintuplex vertical pump equipped with a synchronized suction-valve unloading system for use in an accumulator-type hydraulic system. Because of the heavy loading the crankshaft is carried in main bearings on either side of each crankpin with the bearing journals formed on the cheeks or webs of the crankshaft. Pumps of this type are made with three, five, seven, and nine plungers, covering a power range of 150 to 2,400 hp, operating at 225 to 360 rpm.

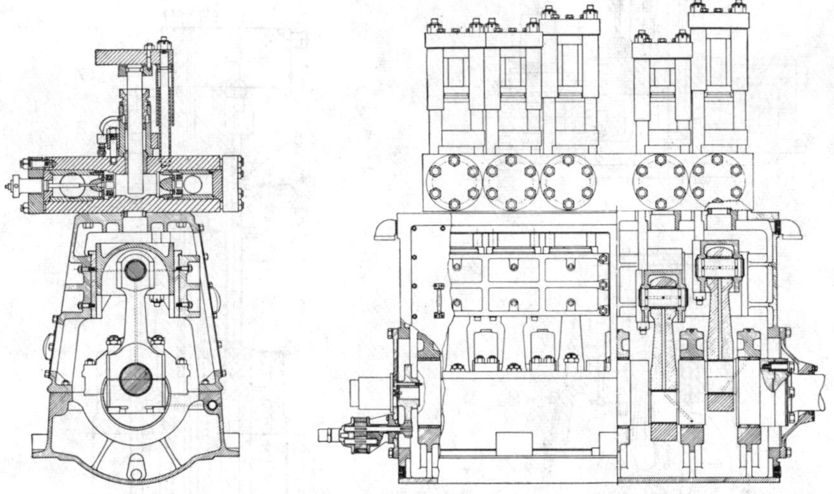

FIG. 3. Quintuplex vertical pump with suction-valve unloading.

The fluid end of this pump is arranged with the suction and discharge manifolds bored in the cylinder forging and the valve assemblies held in place with individual covers and spacers. Separate plunger barrels are used to permit the use of a range of plunger sizes for each size cylinder; for higher pressures the forged cylinders are sectionalized with two or three plunger chambers in each cylinder forging. It should be noted in the inverted construction that the only parts of the power end which are loaded in tension are the main-bearing bolts, the connecting rods, and the side rods. The plunger force presses the cylinders against the upper half of the frame, which is loaded in compression against the lower half of the frame.

The synchronized suction-valve unloading system, as shown in Fig. 4, permits this pump to operate continuously at constant speed, with the delivery starting and stopping to meet the requirements of the hydraulic system. The double-ported, or ring-type, suction valve (1) is made with several lugs extending radially inward which are engaged by the mushroom head of the valve lifter tappet (2) to hold the valve wide open when the pump is unloaded, thus permitting free flow in and out of the cylinder. This tappet is pushed to the unload position by the spring engaging the piston (3) on the valve lifter rod. When delivery is required by the system, an electrical timer energizes, in proper sequence, solenoid air valves which control the application of compressed air to the pistons on the lifting rods, thus compressing the spring and withdrawing the lifter rods to the position shown so as to permit the suction valve to open and close for normal operation. The motion of the valve lifter rod and the tappet for both loading and unloading is synchronized to take place during the early part of the suction stroke of each plunger so that the suction valve is either free to close during the latter part of the suction stroke when delivery is required, or held firmly against the stop at the start of the next discharge stroke to prevent delivery. The mushroom head of the tappet has the additional function of sealing the hole in the valve seat through which it extends when pressure is developed by the discharge stroke of the plunger.

With this system of control the rate of flow from the pump changes from zero to maximum and from maximum to zero during one-half revolution of the pump, with the rate of change following the sum of the sine-curve flow patterns of the individual plungers in operation at each instant.

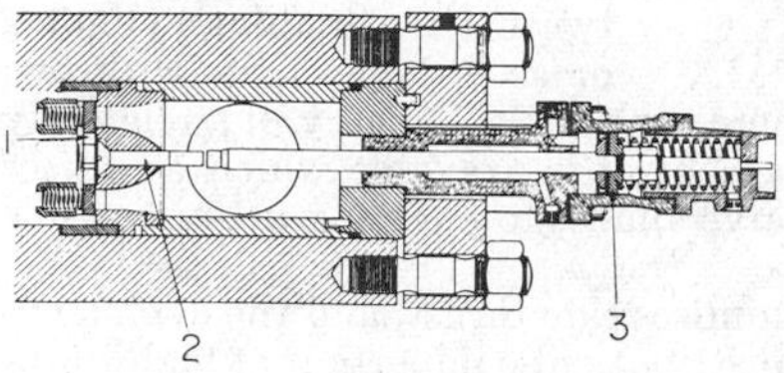

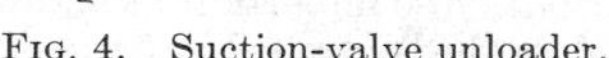

FIG. 4. Suction-valve unloader.

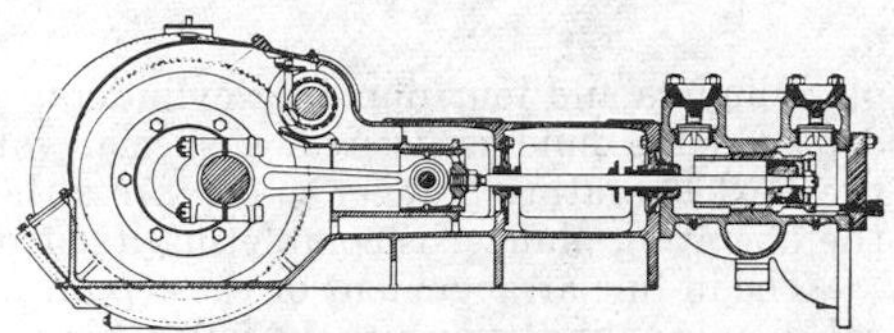

FIG. 5. Horizontal side-pot pump.

Low-speed Power Pumps. Another important type of power pump, illustrated by Fig. 5 usually operates in the speed range of 50 to 100 rpm and is built with a single reduction gear in the enclosed crankcase. Both the pinion shaft and the crankshaft are mounted in antifriction bearings, and some designs use roller bearings in both ends of the connecting rod. The horizontal duplex power end is usually self-oiling, with the gear dipping in oil and carrying it up to a distribution system from which it flows by gravity to all moving parts. The side-pot piston-pattern liquid cylinder is fitted with easily removable liners so that a range of capacity and pressure is covered by using different sizes of pistons and liners.

For general service the horizontal piston-pattern pump is used in sizes from 10 to 100 hp and pressures up to 750 psi. In oil-field use the pressure range is extended to 1,500 psi, and specially fitted slush pumps of this type for oil-well drilling are built in sizes from 100 to 750 hp.

Pumps for Very High Pressure. As pressures rise substantially above 15,000 to 20,000 psi, piston or plunger speeds must be reduced drastically to obtain acceptable packing life and to reduce the number of pressure reversals and cyclical stresses which contribute to fatigue failures. This leads to plunger sizes and loads which make crank-driven pumps impractical because of the large size, high torque, low speed, and side thrust on the crossheads. The single-acting intensifier has long been used to produce extremely high pressures for research on a laboratory scale. Based on the principle of the intensifier, the Harwood Engineering Co. has developed a line of two- and four-plunger pumps driven by double-acting oil hydraulic cylinders for pressures from 10,000 to 200,000 psi. Figure 6 shows a section through one end of a pump of this type with the compound construction used for pressures over 50,000 psi. The inner cylinder (1) is reinforced by the taper shrink fit of the outer cylinder (2). High pressure is confined to the space between the packed plunger (3) and the end closure (4), which is drilled to communicate with the external check valves. Because of the slow plunger speed of not more than 180 in. per min, the plunger chamber can be connected to the valve body with small-bore, high-pressure tubing using double-cone high-pressure fittings at each end of the tubing. The special packing (5) is located on the end of the plunger, but when it is desirable for specific applications, the packing can be in a stuffing-box surrounding the plunger.

The low-pressure or driving cylinder is a conventional double-acting hydraulic cylinder sized to develop the desired thrust with not more than 2,000-psi oil pressure. Four different sizes of oil cylinders are used to cover a range of 15 to 100 hp, and each is fitted with suitable plunger sizes and fluid cylinders to cover the desired range of pressure with corresponding capacities. Electric limit switches are used to control the hydraulic reversing valves connected to the oil cylinders. These pumps may be arranged with a single power cylinder between two pumping cylinders or as a duplex unit with two oil cylinders and four pumping cylinders. Where continuous delivery of a relatively compressible fluid is desired, a special valving control is available which advances the next operating plunger to compress the charge almost to pumping pressure while the operating plunger is completing its stroke.

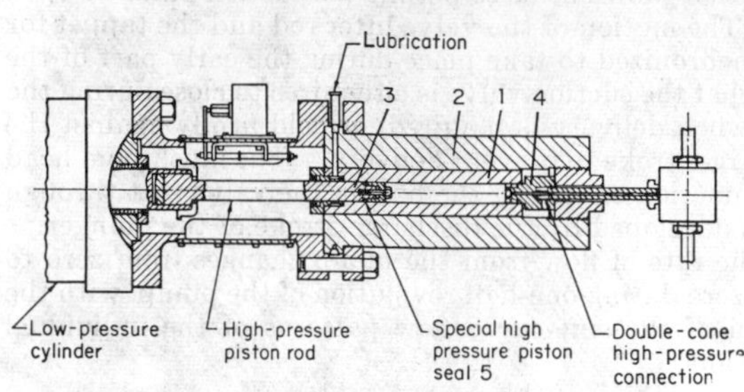

FIG. 6. Very high pressure pump.

The in-line arrangement of these pumps minimizes side thrust, and the symmetrical, simple cylinders ensure the favorable stress distribution so important at high working loads. Hydraulic shock is practically eliminated by the controlled buildup of pressure possible with the hydraulic drive, thus contributing to long life even at very high pressures. Variable-capacity primary oil pumps may be used, or oil may be bypassed to control the high-pressure pump. Pressure-control or relief valves in the oil circuits are used to limit the maximum pressure, and other safety controls are readily adaptable to the primary pump control. The almost complete lack of inertia effects in the high-pressure pump make the unit very responsive to controls and contribute to the operating safety.

Suction Lift, or Head. Liquid flows into the suction side of a pump as a result of pressure exerted on the liquid. If the liquid is exposed to the atmosphere, this pressure will be atmospheric; if the liquid is in a closed vessel (as with water above 212 F or volatile liquids such as ammonia or butane), the pressure will be the saturation pressure corresponding to the temperature of the liquid. To these pressures there will be added a positive hydrostatic head whenever the free surface of the liquid is at a higher level than that of the pump discharge valve.

The pressure exerted must at least equal the sum of the resistances to flow: (1) the vapor pressure of the liquid in the pump chamber; (2) the suction lift when the liquid level is below the pump level; (3) the pressure required to lift the suction valve and overcome the resistance of its spring; (4) the liquid friction the suction pipeline; (5) the forces required to accelerate the liquid in the suction pipeline; and (6) hydraulic losses in the pump. All these quantities are conveniently expressed in feet of the liquid.

Low-speed piston-pattern power pumps and steam pumps will usually operate satisfactorily at a considerable suction lift. Figure 7 gives the variation with temperature of permissible suction lifts for water. T, N, and M are, respectively, the theoretical suction lift, the normal suction lift, and the maximum possible under favorable conditions, all at sea level. The horizontal distance between T and M represents 8 ft head and between T and N represents 12 ft head, which are allowances to cover items (3) to (6) above. If the total of items (3) to (6) exceeds 12 ft, deduct the excess from the possible suction lift. The static suction lift is the vertical distance from the water in the suction supply to the top of the pump discharge deck. For water temperatures above 212 F, the same differential of 12 ft between T and N must be added. The broken lines show normal static suction lift at the stated altitudes.

For a liquid, such as anhydrous ammonia, whose temperature is much below room temperature, it is important to have heat insulation on the suction piping. With the ammonia at 32 F, a rise in temperature of 1 deg F would require 4.75 ft additional static head to compensate for the increased vapor pressure at the pump. Similarly, when pumping from a closed storage tank, the evaporation in the tank will lower the temperature there, thus reducing the saturation pressure and demanding an increased static head at the pump to maintain the effective pressure at the pump.

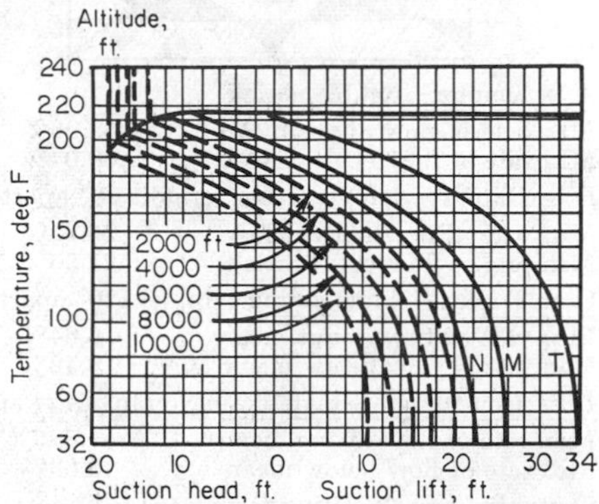

FIG. 7. Suction lifts for low-speed reciprocating pumps.

In water pumps where the water carries considerable air, there should be a large receiver in the suction line near the pump. Air should be removed from the top of the receiver by an independent vacuum pump.

The suction line should be short, with a minimum number of elbows or fittings, and any valve in it should be a gate valve. The suction pipe should slope up toward the pump with a uniform grade of at least 6 in. in 100 ft to avoid air or gas pockets. If the suction pipe is from an elevated tank, it should first drop below the pump level and then grade upward to the pump. Where pipe size is changed, eccentric reducers should be used so that the top layer of the pipe is continuous without air or gas pockets.

High-speed plunger pumps require considerably more net positive suction head than low-speed pumps and frequently will not operate with any suction lift, even on cold water. In addition, item (5), the head required to accelerate the liquid in the suction pipeline, is a much greater factor at higher rotative speeds. An empirical approximation of this quantity for crank-driven pumps is given by the equation $H = LVnC/gK$, where L is the length of the pipe, ft; n is the rpm of the pump crankshaft; H is the head of the liquid pumped to produce the required acceleration, ft; V is the mean velocity of flow in the suction line, fps; g is gravitational acceleration, ft per sec per sec; and C is a factor for the type of pump. C has the following values: simplex double-acting, 0.20; duplex double-acting, 0.115; triplex double-acting or single-acting, 0.066; sextuplex single-acting, 0.055; quintuplex single-acting, 0.040; septuplex single-acting, 0.028; nonuplex single-acting, 0.022. An increase in pump speed with an existing suction line increases H as the square of the speed because both V and n increase proportionately to the speed. The value of K varies from about 2.5 for hot oil to 1.4 for deaerated hot water. These values assume short, non-elastic suction lines.

Flow and Acceleration. Figure 8 shows the theoretical flow variation for various types of pumps as listed. Pumps with an odd number of cranks have the same flow variation for both single-acting and double-acting liquid ends. Flow curves for septuplex and nonuplex pumps are similar to the quintuplex curve, with more but smaller variations as indicated in the tabulation. The values tabulated will vary slightly with changes in crank-to-connecting-rod ratio. The curves are theoretical, being based on crosshead pin velocity for constant rotational speed, and do not represent actual flow rate. This will vary considerably from the ideal, particularly in high-speed pumps, where the valve closing and opening may lag behind the crankshaft rotation as much as 10 to 15 deg, and at high pressures, where liquid compression may cause a further lag of 5 to 10 deg, or even more if the clearance volume is relatively large.

These theoretical flow curves are frequently taken as being directly indicative of the **pressure pulsation** which can be expected in the operation of pumps of various types. However, flow curves indicate only the percentage change in flow rate at various positions of the crankshaft and in no way take into account the rate of change or departures from the ideal curve. For most operating conditions the rate of change in flow, or acceleration, is the primary factor in pressure pulsation, and the constant C in the acceleration-head formula for various types of pumps is a much better index of relative pressure pulsation at the same rotative speed. As in the acceleration-head formula, the constant C for the type of pump being considered, multiplied by the rpm, provides the best indication of probable pressure fluctuation.

A = Simplex—double acting

Max rate of flow above mean	59.96%
Min rate of flow below mean	100.0 %

B = Duplex—double acting (cranks 90° apart)

Max rate of flow above mean	26.72%
Min rate of flow below mean	21.56%

C = Triplex—single acting (cranks 120° apart)

Max rate of flow above mean	6.64%
Min rate of flow below mean	18.42%

D = Quintuplex—single acting (cranks 72° apart)

Max rate of flow above mean	1.88%
Min rate of flow below mean	5.63%

Septuplex—single acting (cranks 51 4/7° apart)

Max rate of flow above mean	1.2%
Min rate of flow below mean	2.8%

Nonuplex—single acting (cranks 40° apart)

Max rate of flow above mean	0.7%
Min rate of flow below mean	1.5%

FIG. 8. Flow-rate variation in reciprocating power pumps.

Cushion Chambers. To take up irregularities and induce a uniform flow in suction and discharge lines, cushion chambers must often be used. Their use is particularly desirable for single pumps and high-speed pumps. The volume of the cushion chamber for single pumps should be six to eight times the displacement of one plunger per stroke; for duplex and triplex pumps, three to four times. For high-speed multiplex pumps the size of chamber may be less than that indicated for a triplex pump of the same plunger size, but it is of prime importance to make the connection between the chamber and the pump as short and as large as practicable. A simple air chamber is usually satisfactory on the suction side of pumps, but at higher delivery pressures the air or gas charge is soon lost by dissolving into the fluid pumped. Here a chamber with some form of diaphragm or bladder, to hold the charge, is needed.

With deaerated water for boiler feeding, a suction chamber using steam as the cushioning medium is simple and effective. This steam cushion is maintained by jacketing the chamber with steam at a somewhat higher pressure than the maximum suction pressure. Suction cushion chambers are particularly desirable where the liquid comes to the pump under a static head, or where the suction line is relatively long.

Table 2 gives data on standard pumps of conventional design. Slower speeds are used for viscous or hot liquids and in oil-refinery service. Higher power-pump speeds

Table 2. Basic Speeds of Standard Pumps

Stroke, in.	Simplex and duplex steam		Duplex and triplex power		Stroke, in.	Simplex and duplex steam		Duplex and triplex power	
	Rpm	Fpm	Rpm	Fpm		Rpm	Fpm	Rpm	Fpm
3	74	37	105	52	10	45	75	57	95
4	71	47	90	60	12	41	81	52	104
5	64	53	80	66	15	36	90	47	117
6	60	60	74	74	18	33	99	43	129
8	51	68	64	85	24	27	108	37	148

are used where weight is a consideration, as in marine service, and also in high-pressure hydraulic-press service, where the volume of liquid pumped is comparatively small so that inertial effects are not so important.

DIRECT-ACTING STEAM PUMPS

The **direct-acting steam pump** is so named because the steam piston is connected to the pump piston by means of a rod, without crank motion or flywheel. There is no cutoff or expansion of the steam, since it is admitted at a constant rate throughout the stroke. The moving parts are cushioned and brought to rest by steam trapped in the end of the steam cylinder at the end of each stroke, with full steam pressure on the opposite side of the piston. The actual velocity of the moving piston is practically constant during 80 to 90 percent of the stroke, as contrasted to the constantly changing velocity of a power-pump piston. In single, as well as duplex, pumps there is a definite pause at the end of each stroke, which is important to the closing of the fluid-end valves. Figure 9 shows a pump-end indicator card for a direct-acting pump. Here h = total head pumped against, being the sum of h_s, the static suction lift plus suction pipe friction, and h_d, the static discharge head plus discharge pipe friction. h_i, the total head shown by an indicator card, includes internal hydraulic losses s and d on the suction and discharge strokes, respectively.

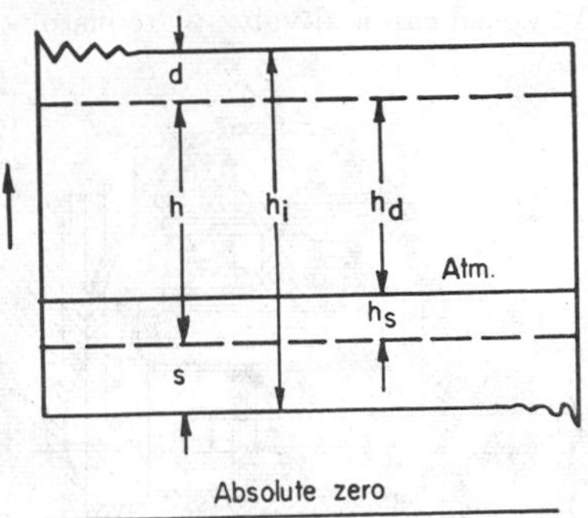

FIG. 9. Pump indicator card.

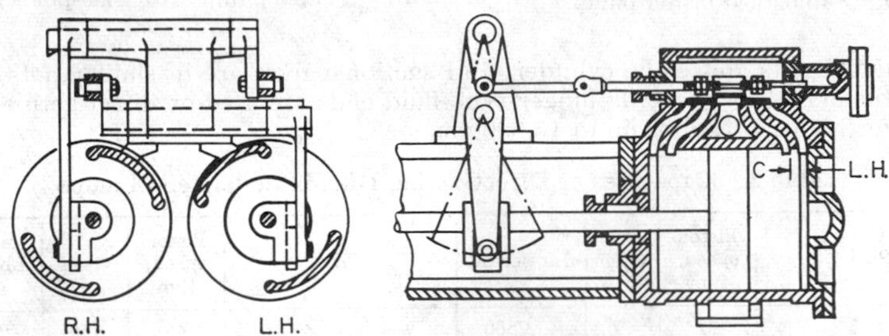

FIG. 10. Steam end of a duplex pump.

The **steam end of a duplex pump** is shown in Fig. 10. The steam piston on each side is mechanically connected to the steam valve of the opposite side. Full stroke is obtained by providing some lost motion, usually equal to one-fourth of the total stroke, between the valve rod nuts and the abutment on the steam valve. Since there is some overlapping of the strokes of the two sides a properly adjusted duplex pump will deliver a continuous flow of fluid without marked pressure fluctuation. On the other hand a duplex pump will short-stroke badly when pumping a volatile fluid if there is not sufficient suction head to prevent flashing in the fluid cylinder.

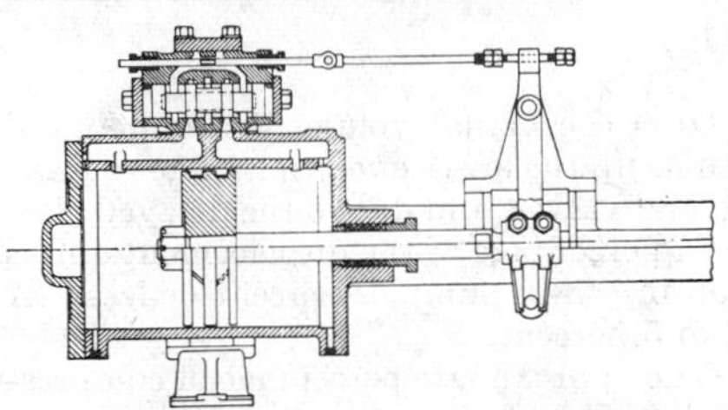

FIG. 11. Steam end of a single pump.

A typical single, or **simplex,** steam end is shown in Fig. 11. The primary elements are the main steam piston, the main piston valve, and the auxiliary slide valve. The main piston valve is steam thrown under control of the auxiliary slide valve. This additional element is necessary in a single steam end to keep it from stalling at low speed. The flow of fluid from a simplex pump is necessarily interrupted at the end of each stroke, which makes the use of cushion chambers essential if continuous delivery is required. Since a simplex pump must complete its stroke before the auxiliary valve is moved far enough to throw the main valve, it can handle volatile fluids without danger of short stroking.

Pump Ends. Double-acting fluid ends are used on all direct-acting steam pumps. A typical cap-and-valve-plate piston-pattern fluid cylinder is shown in Fig. 12. This style is used almost universally for pressures up to 250 or 350 psi, and Table 3 lists standard sizes and ratings of this type for boiler-feed service. For higher pressures side-pot fluid cylinders are usually preferred. Figure 13 shows a center-line section of a cylinder of this type fitted with a water-cooled stuffing box for temperatures up to 800 F and pressures up to 800 psi. Discharge valves are located in individual pots above the cylinder, and suction valves are in similar pots on the side of the cylinder. Forged plunger-type fluid ends are used on direct-acting steam pumps for higher pressures up to 15,000 psi.

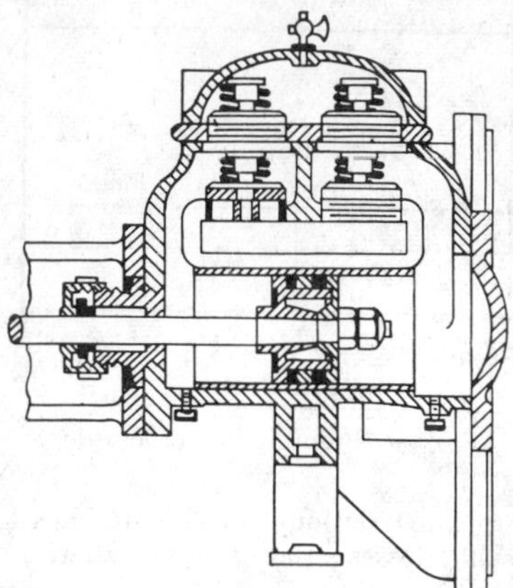

FIG. 12. Submerged piston pump.

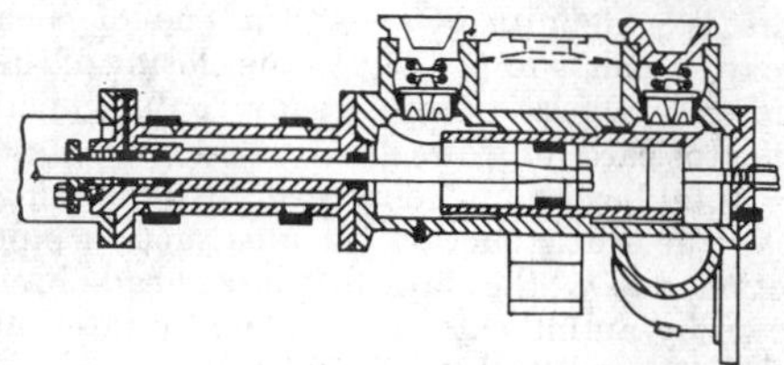

FIG. 13. Piston pump with side-pot valves.

Table 3. Capacities of Direct-acting Duplex Boiler-feed Pumps

Size	Piston speed, fpm	Gpm	Lb per hr	Size	Piston speed, fpm	Gpm	Lb per hr
3 × 2 × 3	22	7	3,500	9 × 5¼ × 10	45	100	50,000
3½ × 2¼ × 4	28	11	5,500	10 × 6 × 10	45	130	65,000
4½ × 2¾ × 4	28	17	8,500	10 × 7 × 10	45	180	90,000
5¼ × 3½ × 5	32	32	16,000	10 × 6 × 12	48	140	70,000
6 × 4 × 6	36	47	23,500	12 × 7 × 12	48	190	95,000
7½ × 5 × 6	36	73	36,500	14 × 8½ × 12	48	280	140,000
7½ × 4½ × 10	45	74	37,000				
7½ × 5 × 10	45	90	45,000				

EFFICIENCIES

Volumetric efficiency $e_v = Q_e/Q$, where Q_e = the actual volume discharged and Q = plunger displacement. This efficiency sums up the losses of capacity due to leaks past the piston packing, stuffing-box packing, and valves, and due to the delayed closing of valves. It is generally stated as a loss in percentage of the displacement and is then called **slip** = $(1 - e_v)$. The slip is small in a new pump, 2 percent or less. A normal allowance for size determination is 3 to 5 percent.

All liquids are compressible (see p. 6–9). The approximate percentage of compression for a pressure of 1,000 psi and at a temperature of 68 F for various liquids is: water, 0.29; lubricating oil, 0.44; kerosene, 0.51; gasoline, 0.70; ammonia, 0.98; *n*-butane, 1.9; isobutane, 2.4; propane, 3.9. The rate decreases with higher pressures.

For liquid hydrocarbons at high pressures, the pump must be of close-clearance design, and e_v includes loss in delivered volume due to compression of delivered liquid and loss due to liquid compressed into the clearance volume. If C = clearance volume in the plunger chamber at the inner end of the stroke divided by plunger displacement,

K = compressibility, S = slip, then $e_v = 1 - (K + CK + S)$. For $C = 0.5$, $K = 0.05$, and $S = 0.04$, then $e_v = 0.885$. For capacity measured at suction rather than discharge pressure, volumetric efficiency $e_v = 1 - s + CK/(1\text{-}K)$.

Hydraulic efficiency $e_h = h/h_i$. The hydraulic loss consists of the friction of the liquid flowing through the pump cylinder and the pressure drop through the valves. Normally this is included as a part of the mechanical efficiency. For high-speed power pumps, the valve action requires heavy springs, with resulting increase in pressure loss. Hydraulic efficiency requires careful consideration.

Mechanical efficiency $e_m = P_w/P_b$, where P_w = the water horsepower delivered by the pump, and P_b = the indicated steam horsepower of a steam pump or the horsepower input to a power pump. This efficiency gives information as to the mechanical friction in the mechanism transmitting the power to the liquid end. It can be determined only by actual experiment with different types of pumps and depends upon the size of the pump and the service. In Table 4 steam pumps are classified according to stroke and type.

Table 4. Mechanical Efficiencies of Steam-driven Pumps

(Efficiencies in percent)

Stroke, in.	Direct-acting pumps			Stroke, in.	Direct-acting pumps			Crank and fly-wheel pumps
	Piston pumps, plunger pumps	Outside center packed pumps	Pressure pumps, 1,000 lb		Piston pumps, plunger pumps	Outside center packed pumps	Pressure pumps, 1,000 lb	
3	50	47	45	12	77.5	73	69	80.0
4	55	52	50	18	82.5	78	74	85.0
5	60	57	54	24	85.0	81	77	87.5
6	65	61	58	36	87.5	83	79	90.0
10	75	71	67	48–60	90.0	85	81	92.5

The **steam consumption** of direct-acting pumps will vary from 200 lb of steam per water hp-hr for small pumps at light loads to as little as 50 lb of steam per water hp-hr for large pumps operating at 350 to 400 psi steam pressure. Where the exhaust steam can be used for feed-water heating or process work, the steam consumption is of relatively little importance since the direct-acting steam pump is not a heat engine and does not use steam expansively. Instead, it functions as a reducing valve, and the heat consumed is primarily a question of radiation loss, which can be minimized by insulation.

For pumps operating with an exhaust pressure greater than atmospheric, the steam consumption is increased in proportion to $\sqrt{p/(p - b)}$, where p = initial steam pressure at steam cylinder inlet, psig; b = exhaust pressure, psig. For superheated steam deduct 1 percent for each 10 deg F of superheat. The performance of a steam pump is often expressed as duty in foot-pounds of work done per 1,000 lb of dry steam. Duty $= 1{,}980 \times 10^6$/(steam rate, lb per water hp-hr).

PUMP VALVES

Disk Valves. For moderate pressures, disk valves on grid seats, as shown in Figs. 14 and 15, are generally used. The seats are metallic with threaded or smooth-taper fit in the valve deck. **Conical-faced wing valves** are used for high pressures as they can be ground pressure-tight more readily than flat valves. Figure 16 shows this type as applied to a forged steel cylinder with a metal-to-metal joint on the valve-hole cover. **Ball** and **Rollo valves** (Figs. 17 and 18) are used for viscous liquids.

Valves for High-speed Pumps. Figure 19 shows a **double-ported, or ring-type, valve,** as used in high-speed pumps. In closing, a single-ported valve must displace a quantity of fluid proportional to the square of the valve diameter through the outlet area, which is proportional to the first power of the diameter. In order to obtain a greater outlet area with the small lift permissible at high pump speeds and to reduce the quantity of fluid which the valve must displace in closing, the ring-type, or double-ported, valve is used, except for very small capacities. Flow from the annular seat is

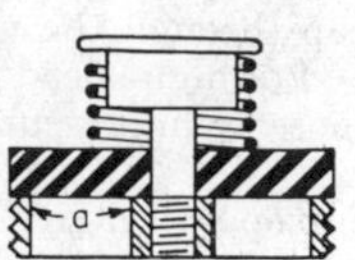

Fig. 14. Nonmetallic disk valve.

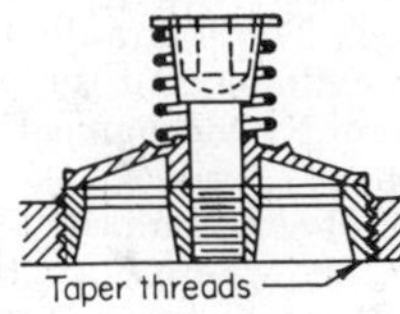

Fig. 15. Stainless-steel disk valve.

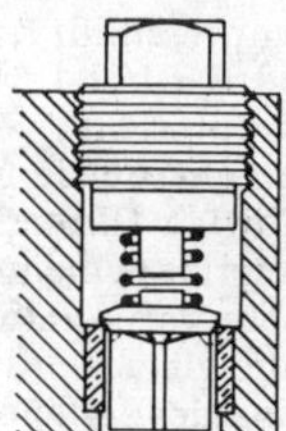

Fig. 16. Conical-faced wing valve.

Fig. 17. Ball valve.

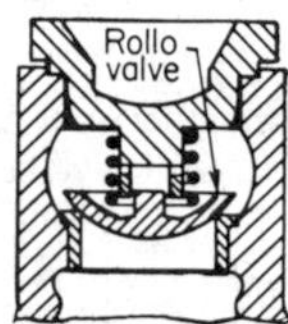

Fig. 18. Rollo valve.

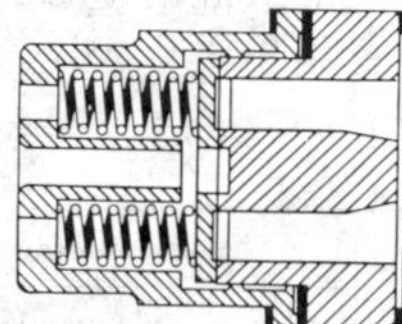

Fig. 19. Double-ported valve for high-speed pump.

both radially outward around the valve and radially inward and through the center hole in the valve.

Velocity through Valve Seats. For normal pump speeds, as in Table 2, the velocity of flow for cold water through the clear area of the valve seat is usually 200 to 250 fpm. For viscous liquids, the velocity may be 100 fpm or less; for high-pressure water pumps, 300 to 400 fpm. The velocity through the outlet port between the lifted valve and its seat is much higher and depends on the sum of the spring load and the weight of the valve; this ranges from 1 to 10 psi of valve-seat area. A load of 1 psi produces a velocity of about 600 fpm.

The area of contact of the valve seat with a plain disk valve $= pA/b$, in which $p =$ pressure on the back of the valve, psi; $A =$ area of valve on which p is acting, sq in.; and $b =$ bearing pressure of valve on seat, psi. Unit pressures are given in Table 5.

Table 5. Bearing Pressures for Valve Materials

Material	Brinell hardness	Allowable bearing pressure, psi
Bronze (regular)	60–80	3,000
Bronze (hard)	175–200	8,000
Cast iron	200	10,000
Steel (not heat-treated)	180	9,000
Steel (hardened alloy)	500–600	25,000
11–13 chrome stainless steel (hardened)	350	17,500
18–8 stainless steel	180	9,000
Monel (hardened)	260–300	13,000
Bakelite	....	2,000
Leather	....	750
Rubber (hard)	....	1,000
Rubber (soft)	....	375

For high-speed pumps, these values should be reduced to compensate for increased shock.

Valve Lift Formulas for Turbulent Flow

$B =$ diameter of seat opening, in.
$J =$ precompression load of spring with valve closed, lb

L = lift of valves at max flow, in.
p = pressure loss through valve at max flow, psi
Q = max flow rate per valve, gpm
R = spring load per in. of deflection, lb = P/f (see p. 8–101)
s = specific gravity of liquid
W = weight of valve, lb
n = number of valves per section
n_1 = number of single-acting plungers or number of working sides of double-acting piston
F = upward force on valve in deflecting flow = $Q^2s/26.9^2a$, where a is the value seat area (no ribs or wings)

$$Q = \frac{\text{total gpm} \times \pi}{nn_1} \text{ for power pumps } = \frac{\text{total gpm}}{0.75n} \text{ for simplex steam pumps}$$

$$= \frac{\text{total gpm}}{n}, \text{ for duplex steam pumps}$$

$$L = \frac{J + W - 0.3F}{R}\left(\sqrt{M\left(1 + \frac{2M}{100}\right) + 1} - 1\right) \text{ for bevel-faced wing valves}$$

$$L = \frac{J + W - 1.3F}{R}\left(\sqrt{M\left(1 + \frac{2M}{100}\right) + 1} - 1\right) \text{ for flat-faced disk valves}$$

where $M = RQ\sqrt{s}/40.5(J + W - 0.3F)^{3/2}$, for wing valves
$= RQ\sqrt{s}/58.5(J + W - 1.3F)^{3/2}$, for disk valves
$p = s[Q/72(B - L)L]^2$, for wing valves
$= s[Q/101(B - 2.4L)L]^2$, for disk valves

For the design of the valve spring, see pp. 8–101 to 8–113.

Materials for Pumps. The allowable stresses in pumps are lower than in most machinery, owing to the shocks and water hammer. The following tensile stresses, psi, may be used: cast iron, 1,500 to 1,800; high-test alloy cast iron, 2,000 to 2,500; malleable iron, 3,000; steel castings, 6,000; cast bronze, 3,000; rolled bronze, 6,000; cast Monel, 6,000; rolled Monel, 8,000; steel forgings, 6,000 to 8,000.

Table 6. Approximate Analysis of Stainless Steels

Type No.	Approximate analysis, percent						
	C*	Cr	Ni	Mo	Cu	Mn	Si
4	0.20 max	5.00	....	0.50			
5	0.15 max	13.00					
6	0.30 max	20.00	1.00				
7	0.50 max	28.00	2.00				
8	0.08 max	18.0–21.0	8.0–11.0	....	....	1.50 max	2.00 max
9	0.08 max	18.0–21.0	9.0–12.0	2.0–3.0	....	1.50 max	2.00 max
10	0.07 max	18.0–22.0	20.0–30.0	3.5 max	4.5 max	1.50 max	4.00 max

* Low-carbon alloys, only, are recommended to ensure protection from such failures as intercrystalline corrosion or intergranular attack.

The materials used for pump parts vary with the liquids handled. Corrosion-resisting steel alloys for pumps have been classified in several types in the Standards of Hydraulic Institute, as in Table 6. The Institute publishes a long list of permissible materials, from which Table 7 has been abstracted. (See also Sec. 6.)

Standard-fitted pumps have cast-iron plungers or pistons in a brass sleeve, steel rods, rubber or brass valves, brass valve seats, stems, and springs. Bronze-fitted pumps differ only in having bronze piston rods and pistons. All-iron pumps have no bronze.

Table 7. Permissible Materials for Pumps

Liquid	Materials permissible	Liquid	Materials permissible
Fatty acids	A, 8, 9, 10, 11	Glue	B, C
Fruit acids	A, 8, 9, 10, 11, 14	Glycerol (glycerin)	A, B, C
Hydrochloric acid	11, 12	Lard	B, C
Nitric acid	5, 6, 7, 8, 9, 10, 12	Limewater (milk of lime)	C
Sulphuric acid (to 65 percent)	10, 11, 12	Magnesium chloride	A, 8, 9, 10, 11, 12
Sulphuric acid (10 percent)	A, 10, 11, 12, 14	Milk	8
Tannic acid	A, 8, 9, 10, 11, 14	Molasses	A, B
Alcohol	A, B	Naphtha	B, C
Aqua ammonia	C	Fuel oil	B, C
Ammonium chloride	9, 10, 11, 12, 14	Vegetable oil	A, B, C, 8, 9, 10, 11, 14
Asphaltum	C, 5	Turpentine oil	B, C
Beer	A, 8	Potassium carbonate	C
Benzene (benzol)	B, C	Potassium chloride	A, 8, 9, 10, 11, 14
Calcium chloride brine	C	Soap liquor	C
Sodium chloride brine	A, C, 8	Soda ash (sodium carbonate)	C
Sea-water brine	A, B, C	Sugar	A, 8, 9, 10, 11, 13
Cane juice	A, B, 13	Sirup	A, 8, 9, 10, 11, 13
Creosote	B, C	Tanning liquors (veg.)	A, 8, 9, 10, 11, 12
Diphenyl	C, 3	Tar	C, 3
Ethyl acetate	C, 9, 10	Toluene (toluol)	B, C
Ethylene chloride	A, 8, 9, 10, 11, 14	Varnish	A, B, C, 8, 14
Fruit juices	A, 8, 9, 10, 11, 14	Vinegar	A, 8, 9, 10, 11, 12
Gasoline	B, C	Wood pulp	A, B, C

The letters are abbreviations of materials, as follows: A, all bronze; B, bronze fitted; C, all iron. The numbers, other than those indicating the stainless steels, represent the following materials: 1, gray iron; 2, tin bronze; 3, carbon steel; 11, a series of nickel-base alloys; 12, high-silicon cast iron; 13, austenitic cast iron; 14, Monel metal.

ROTARY PUMPS

Rotary pumps are of the positive-displacement type, usually valveless, simple, compact, light in weight, and low in first cost. They are built in capacities from a fraction of a gallon (as in domestic oil burners and refrigerators) to 5,000 gpm and above, as in marine cargo service. Though used for pressures up to 1,000 psi, their particular field is for pressures of 25 to 500 psi. Before the development of the modern centrifugal pump, large rotary pumps of lobe type were used for low-head irrigation projects in capacities as high as 35,000 gpm and showed mechanical efficiencies of 80 to 85 percent.

Rotary pumps require the maintenance of very close **clearances** between rubbing surfaces for their continued volumetric efficiency. No satisfactory method of packing the moving surfaces to compensate for wear has been developed; consequently, although some rotary pumps are used successfully for clean water, their great field of application is in pumping oils or other liquids having lubricating value and with sufficient viscosity to prevent excessive leakage. Rotary pumps are being used in the oil industry in increasing volume. They are also used for liquids of high viscosities, up to 500,000 SSU. The diameter of the discharge opening of a rotary pump designates the nominal size but does not fix the displacement.

Pigott (*Oil Gas Jour.*, May 10, 1934) **classifies rotary pumps** in the following seven groups: (1) vane type, (*a*) sliding vanes, (*b*) swinging vanes; (2) oscillating-piston or eccentric type; (3) gear type, (*a*) lobar, two and three teeth, (*b*) special-contours teeth, (*c*) spur gear, (*d*) helical and herringbone gear, (*e*) internal gear with two-teeth difference or with one-tooth difference; (4) screw type; (5) radial plunger type; (6) swashplate type; and (7) miscellaneous.

Rotary pumps up to 100 psi may be considered low pressure, from 100 to 500 psi moderate pressure, and above 500 psi high pressure; fractional to 50 gpm are small-volume pumps, 50 to 500 gal moderate-volume, and above 500 gal large-volume.

Vane Pumps. Leakage in vane-type pumps is across the tips and sides of the vanes. This leakage occurs when the vanes are under the two abutments. Since the vane tips cannot be made to fit the bore of the housing in all positions, there is line contact and low resistance to leakage. Wear may also be serious at the higher speeds unless the vanes are restrained against centrifugal force. Increasing the number of vanes materially decreases leakage.

Figure 20 is typical of the **guided-vane type.** A single rotor revolves in a case. The pumping element consists of multiple blades sliding in slots in the rotor. Impeller and case are eccentric. Centrifugal force or pressure maintains the outer end of the blades in contact with the casing bore. The blades are of hardened steel, bronze, or bakelite. This type is useful for small and moderate capacities and low pressure. Rapid wear on the points of the sliding blades and in the casing occurs where speed is high or where the liquid pumped has low lubricating value. In some constructions, the blades are made with end trunnions operating in grooves in the side plate.

Figure 21 illustrates a pump of the **swinging-vane type,** with vanes hinged or articulated. The hinge joints are subject to wear, and the comparatively small number of vanes or blades possible with this construction give a less satisfactory seal than do the multiple blades in the sliding-vane type. Swinging-vane pumps are used for moderate volume, for low pressure and vacuum, and for low speeds.

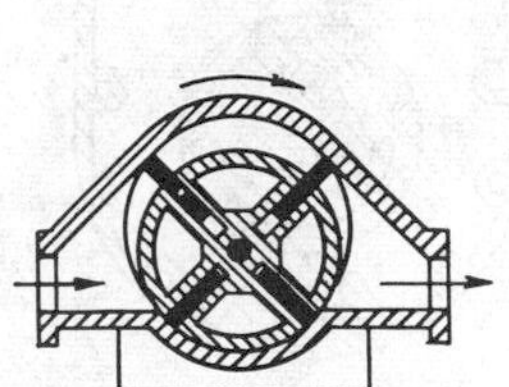

Fig. 20. Rotary pump with guided vanes.

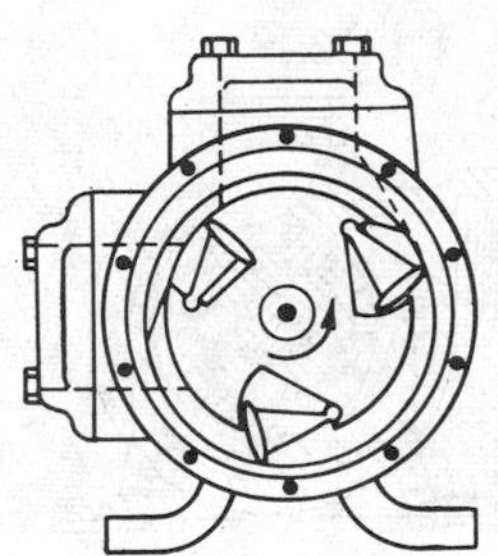

Fig. 21. Rotary pump with swinging vanes.

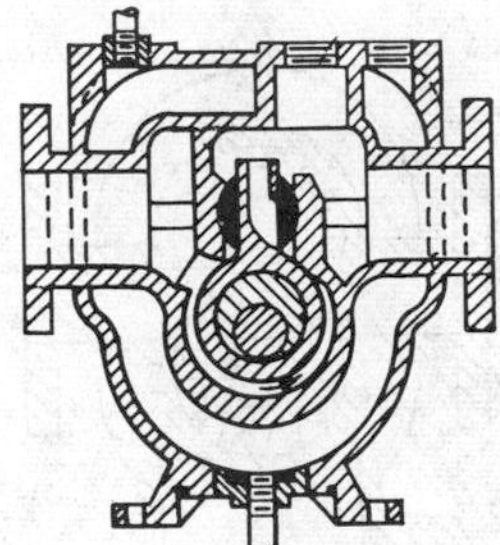

Fig. 22. Rotary pump, eccentric-piston type.

Eccentric-piston Pumps. Many pumps of this type are in service. The pump shown in Fig. 22 is of the single-shaft type with cylindrical body and with oscillating eccentric and strap. The contact between the strap and the body approximates single-line contact. Leakage, therefore, becomes excessive as wear progresses. This type is useful for small and medium capacities, low pressure, and limited speed. A jacketed construction is shown. Practically all types of rotary pumps may be jacketed for viscous materials which must be heated to be pumped or for water cooling.

Radial-plunger and Swash-plate Pumps. The rotation of the body carrying the plungers connects each plunger flow periodically to the suction port on the plunger's suction stroke and to the discharge port on its discharge stroke. These groups can be adapted for variable capacity. In Fig. 23 this is done by varying the eccentricity between the plunger-carrying body and the ring that drives the plungers; in Fig. 24 by varying the angle between the drive shaft and the plunger-carrying body. The actual machines are complicated.

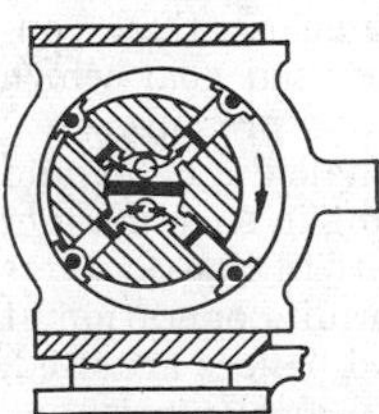

Fig. 23. Radial-plunger pump.

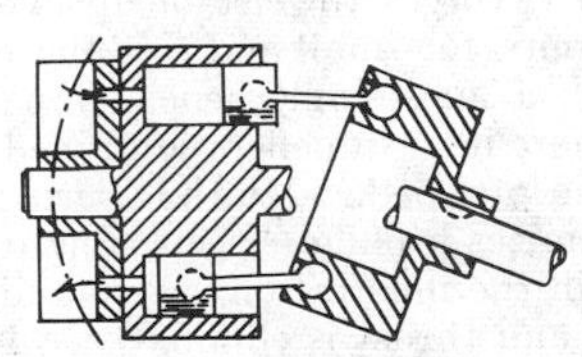

Fig. 24. Swash-plate pump.

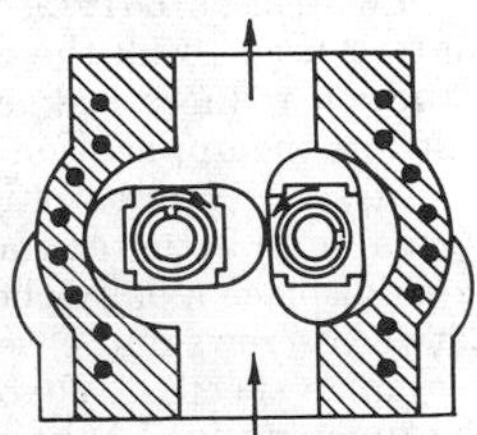

Fig. 25. Roots rotary pump, lobar type.

The **lobar type** (Fig. 25) is one of the earliest constructions used for rotary pumps and blowers. These machines are suitable for medium and large capacities and low pressures. As in the oscillating-piston type, there is line contact between the impeller and the body, and the leakage is excessive at higher pressures. The impellers are not self-actuating. Such pumps, therefore, must be built with external pilot gears capable of transmitting half the power utilized from the driving to the driven shaft.

Gear pumps (Fig. 26) are of the two-shaft type and cover a wide variety of constructions. They are used for practically all capacities and pressures. In many types, the impeller gears are self-actuating, requiring no pilot gears. The simplest form uses spur gears. The large number of teeth in contact with the casing minimizes leakages around the periphery. The utility of the straight spur-gear type is limited by trapping of liquid, which occurs on the discharge side at the point of gear intermesh, resulting in noisy operation and low mechanical efficiency, particularly at high rotative speed. Discharge pockets in the side plates may be provided to reduce the effects of trapping. Impellers in other pumps of this type are of single-helical or double-helical

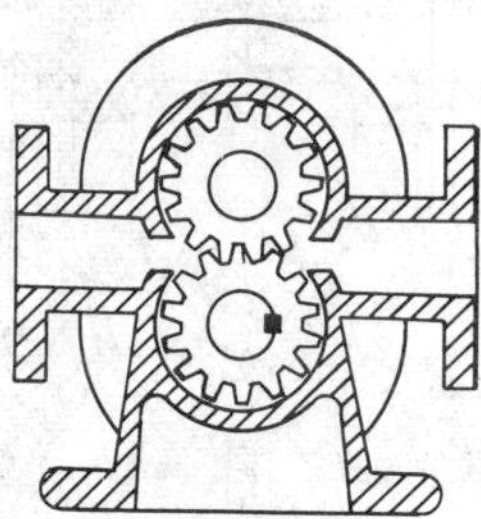

Fig. 26. Gear pump.

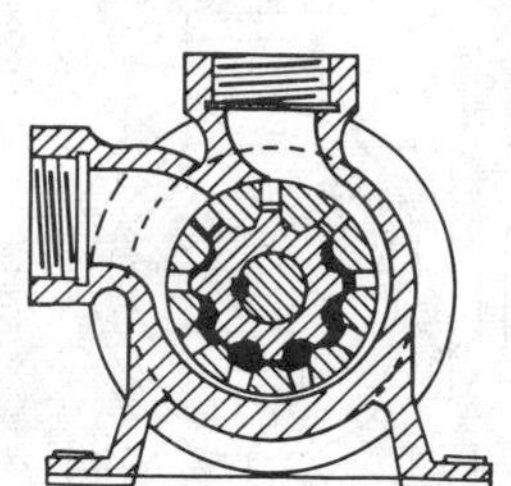

Fig. 27. Internal-gear pump, one-tooth difference.

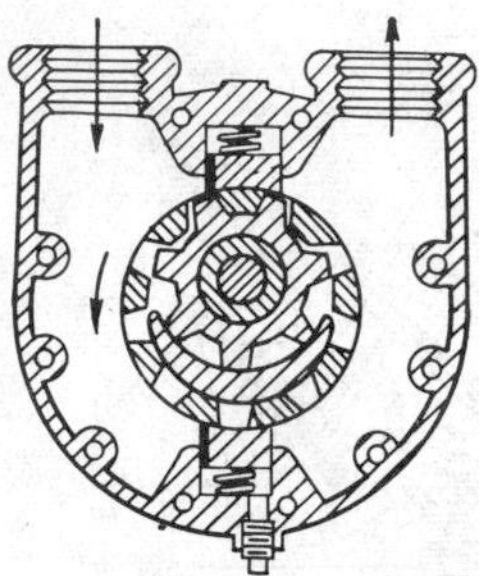

Fig. 28. Internal-gear pump, two-teeth difference.

construction with angles from 15 to 30 deg or more. With gears of single-helical type on higher pressures, considerable end thrust of the impeller gears on the pump side plates results. Either helical or herringbone gear construction largely eliminates the effects of trapping but introduces leakage losses between the teeth at the meshing point unless the teeth are cut without root clearance.

Internal-gear Pumps. One-tooth Difference (Fig. 27). In pumps of this type, an impeller mounted eccentrically with the body actuates an internal gear rotating in the body or in bearings carried in the end plates. Flow is practically continuous and without reversals. High rotative speeds may be used. In such pumps, leakage occurs around the periphery of the ring gear, over the tips of the gear teeth at open mesh, and through the contact line at full mesh. This type is particularly adaptable for high pressures and high speeds, for oils with lubricating value and considerable viscosity.

Two-teeth Difference (Fig. 28). In this construction, an abutment on one side plate is used to fill the clearance between the external and internal gear. Such construction reduces leakage but involves the use of an overhung internal gear which restricts the application to pumps for small and medium capacity and pressure.

In **screw pumps** (Fig. 29), a long single helical impeller of small diameter and special form actuates one or more idler impellers contained in a casing in such manner as to displace axially the liquid pumped. Multiple surface rather than line contacts between screws and case minimizes leakage. This construction permits operation at very high speed. Where, as in the illustration, right- and left-hand helices are used, the pumping load is balanced and thrust is eliminated. No shaft bearings or timing gears are required owing to the form of the impellers. Wear of rotating elements may be rapid with liquids of low lubricating value.

Double-screw Pumps (Fig. 30). The screw-pump construction shown incorporates right- and left-hand intermeshing helices on parallel shafts with timing gears. These pumps have been extensively used for medium and large capacities and moderate to high pressures. There is some leakage axially at the impeller contact. Impellers are carried in bearings so that wear on impellers and casing is reduced. Flow is practically continuous.

The mechanical efficiency of the better types of rotary pumps when handling oils or other liquids with lubricating value is good. Figures 31 and 32 show the characteristics of pumps of the herringbone-gear type and the internal-gear one-tooth-difference type, respectively.

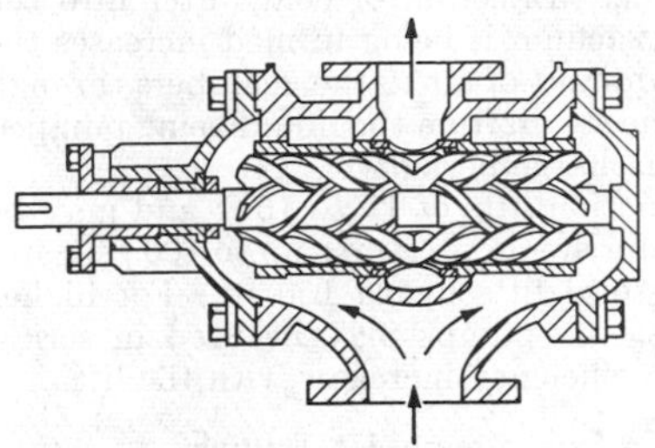

FIG. 29. Screw pump.

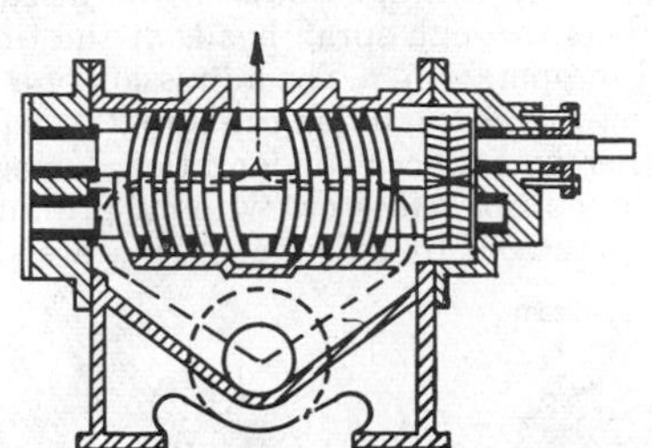

FIG. 30. Double-screw pump.

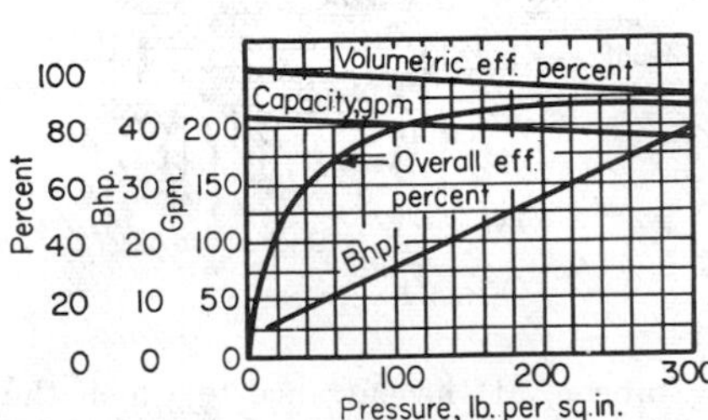

FIG. 31. Performance curves of a 600-rpm, 400-SSU, herringbone-gear pump.

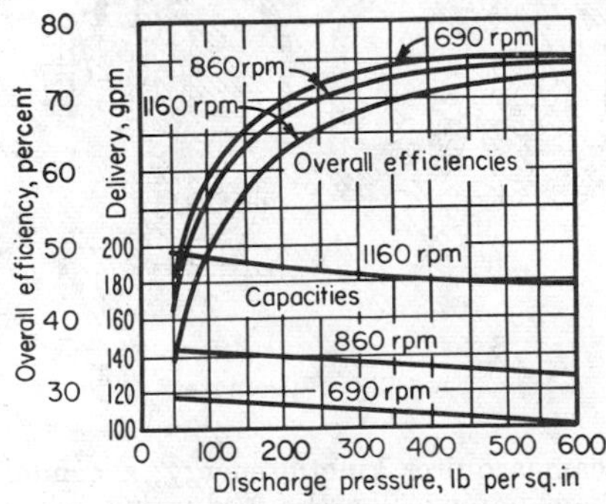

FIG. 32. Performance curves of an internal-gear, one-tooth-difference, rotary pump.

PISTONLESS PUMPS

Direct Fluid Pressure Displacement Pumps

Liquids may be pumped by the direct pressure of air, gas, or steam on the surface of the liquid. Included in such pumps are pneumatic sewage ejectors and pulsometers.

In pneumatic sewage ejectors, the liquid to be pumped enters by gravity and air is admitted to and exhausted from the pump chambers by synchronized valves operated by floats.

Pulsometers are steam-actuated expulsor pumps and are much used in draining excavations, cofferdams, quarries, mine shafts, etc. They are simple, light in weight, and rugged, have few working parts, operate without lubrication and with little attention, and need no foundation. They will satisfactorily handle water containing a considerable amount of semisolids and at temperatures up to 150 F.

The pulsometer (Fig. 33) has a central suction air chamber J, two pumping chambers AA, a discharge valve chamber, a suction valve chamber, and a foot valve in the suction line. The pumping chambers are first primed and steam is then turned on and automatically admitted to one of the two chambers depending on the position of the self-actuating ball or clapper valve C. The steam forces the contents of that chamber out through the discharge valve into the discharge line H. When the chamber is almost empty, the surface of the liquid becomes agitated, the rate of steam condensation is accelerated, the pressure drops, and the automatic steam valve C shifts and admits steam to the second chamber. The vacuum formed by further condensation in the first chamber then sucks up a new charge while the second chamber is being emptied. The cycle of operation is repeated automatically and so rapidly as to give practically continuous flow in the discharge line. Injection of cold water into the chambers through spray heads at the time the vacuum is being formed increases the speed of operation. The admission of a small amount of air to the chambers through snifting valves located in the throats separates the steam from the liquid being pumped and thereby reduces condensation during the discharge period.

The pumps will start without priming on suction lifts of 12 to 15 ft and may be used up to 20 ft by priming. They are suitable for steam pressures up to 100 psig and for total lifts up to 150 ft. For higher lifts, the pumps may be used in series. The efficiency increases with the lift.

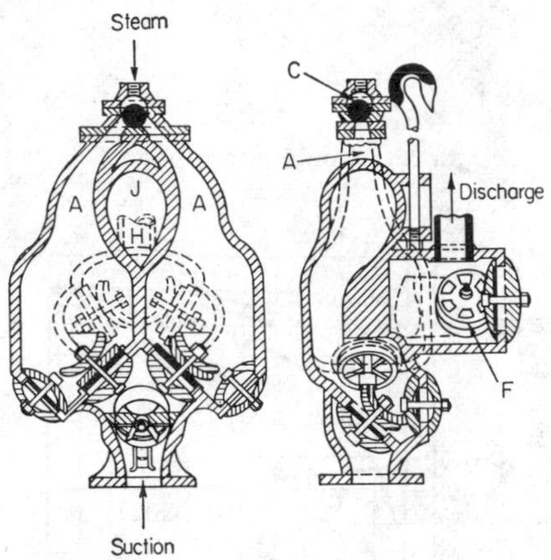

FIG. 33. Pulsometer.

Steam-jet Pumps

Injectors. An injector consists of a **steam nozzle** a (Fig. 34), in which the steam acquires kinetic energy; a **combining tube** b, at the entrance to which the steam impinges on the feed water entering at c; and a **delivery tube** d, in which the velocity head of the feed water is reduced and its static pressure increased.

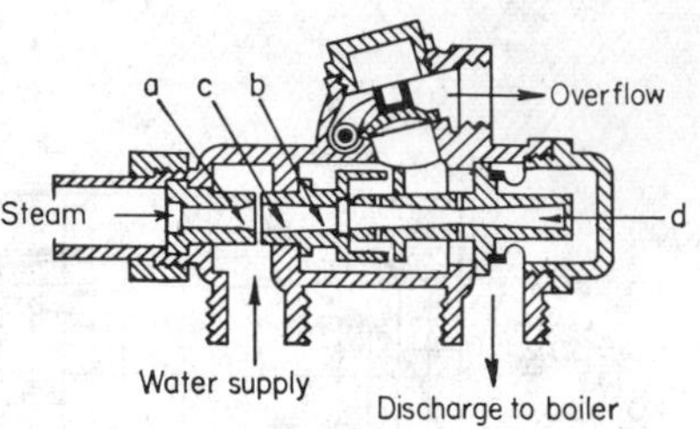

FIG. 34. Injector.

The velocity acquired by the steam in the steam nozzle can be calculated as indicated on p. 4–62. The pressure at the entrance to the combining tube is found to be 3 to 4 psia for usual feed temperatures. The quantity of feed water that can be handled is obtainable from the equation

$$(W + 1)v_m = C(v_s + Wv_w)$$

where W = weight of water discharged per lb of steam, lb; v_s = velocity of steam before impact, v_w = velocity of feed water before impact, fps; v_m = velocity of mixture after impact, fps; and C = coefficient of impact. The value of v_w is calculable when the head and lift of the feed water, the vacuum at the entrance to the combining tube, and the frictional resistances are known. Its amount is generally negligible, so that the equation becomes $(W + 1)v_m = Cv_s$. The value of C averages about 0.5.

The **actual weight of feed water handled per pound of steam** W is easily determined in an injector from a heat balance. The heat given up by the steam is equal to the heat given to the feed water plus the external work done. The external work is usually about 2 percent of the heat given up by the steam. The heat-balance equation becomes

$$0.98(H - h_2) = W(h_2 - h_1)$$

where H, h_1, and h_2 are, respectively, the enthalpies of 1 lb of steam, 1 lb of feed water, and 1 lb of the mixture.

Air-lift Pumps

The air lift consists of a drop pipe placed in a well with its lower end submerged. The depth of submergence measured from the level at which the water stands during operation to the air entrance is called the **submergence.** An air pipe delivers air at the bottom of the drop pipe and forms a mixture of air and water which is lighter than the column of solid water in the well; consequently, the mixture rises above the surrounding water. The necessary **percentage of submergence** (the percentage of the total length of pipe which is submerged in "solid" water when pumping) decreases as the lift increases. Purchas (*Proc. IMechE*, 1917) gives the following values:

Lift, ft	25	50	75	100	150	200	250	300
Submergence ÷ lift	4.0	3.0	2.33	2.0	1.7	1.38	1.22	1.0
Submergence, ft	100	150	175	200	255	275	305	300

The absolute **air pressure required,** measured in feet of water, is $B + s$, where B is the barometric pressure, ft of water, and s is the submergence, ft. The **efficiency** is about 50 percent for lifts up to 300 ft and as low as 25 percent for high lifts. The whole operating mechanism is above the ground, and the pump is able to handle dirty, gritty, or acidulous mine water, slimes from reduction plants, sewage, etc. The theoretical consumption v of free air in cubic feet per cubic foot of water pumped is given by Goodman (1899) and Purchas (*Proc. IMechE*, 1917) as follows:

$$v = l/B \ln (1 + s/B)$$

where l is the lift, ft. Multiply by from 2 to 4 for efficiency, and make the air-compressor displacement twice the quantity so found.

The air pressure required for starting is higher than that for operating and is equivalent to the height of the water level at rest above the end of the air pipe. The actual pumping level and yield of a well are seldom known in advance. After the piping is installed, the submergence is altered to suit by raising or lowering the pipe in the well. The quantity of water a well will yield depends upon its diameter. The water pipe should have a cross-sectional area (sq in.) equal to discharge in gpm ÷ 12

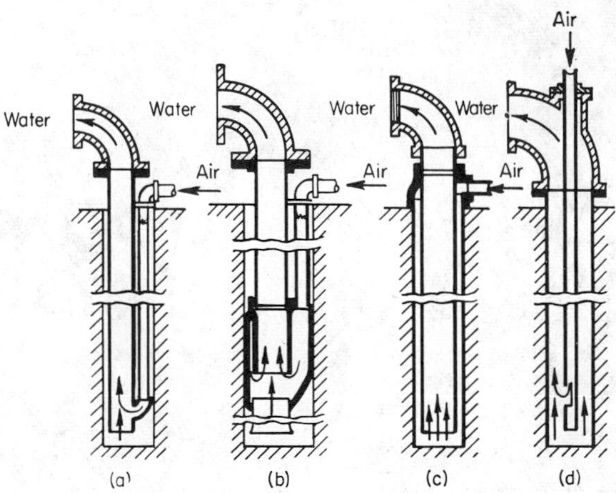

FIG. 35. Arrangements of air lifts.

to 15. Too large a pipe lets the air slip by, and too small a pipe means excessive friction and inefficient expansion of the air bubbles. The air should be injected into the water in small bubbles by the use of a foot piece provided with a large number of small holes, say about ¼ in. diam. The slip increases rapidly with increase of bubble size.

The arrangement shown at (*a*) and (*b*) (Fig. 35) is the **Pohlé, or side-inlet, method,** where the discharge and air pipes are placed side by side in the well and joined by a suitable foot piece. In (*b*), compressed air fills the annular space or ring surrounding the uptake pipe and is free to enter the rising column at all points of its periphery. The **Saunders system** is shown at (*c*). A central discharge pipe is suspended in the well, the air passing down between it and the well casing. If the well is not cased, a second pipe must be used outside of the main discharge pipe, the air, as before, filling the annular space between the two pipes. The **central air-pipe system** shown at (*d*) is used where the lift is low. The air pipe is suspended in the well without the usual discharge pipe, thereby making the well its own discharge pipe.

CENTRIFUGAL AND AXIAL PUMPS

BY

Igor J. Karassik and William C. Krutzsch

REFERENCES: (1) Theory: Stepanoff, "Centrifugal and Axial Flow Pumps," Wiley. Wislicenus, "Fluid Mechanics of Turbomachinery," McGraw-Hill. Pfleiderer, "Die Kreiselpumpen," Springer. Spannhake, "Centrifugal Pumps, Turbines and Propellers," Technology Press. (2) Practice: Karassik and Carter, "Centrifugal Pumps," F. W. Dodge. Hicks, "Pump Selection and Application," and "Pump Operation and Maintenance," McGraw-Hill. Standards of the Hydraulic Institute.

NOMENCLATURE AND MECHANICAL DESIGN

Pumps covered in this section fall into three general classes: (1) **centrifugal or radial-flow,** (2) **mixed-flow,** and (3) **axial-flow** or propeller pumps. The essential elements of a centrifugal pump are (1) the **rotating element,** consisting of the shaft and the impeller, and (2) the **stationary element,** consisting of the casing, stuffing boxes, and bearings (see Fig. 1). Other parts, such as wearing rings and shaft sleeves, are generally added to produce better-operating, more economical machines as warranted by the various services on which the pumps are to be used. Names recommended by the Hydraulic Institute for various parts are given in Table 1.

In a centrifugal pump the liquid is forced, by either atmospheric or other pressure, into a set of rotating vanes which constitute an impeller that discharges the liquid at a higher pressure and a higher velocity at its periphery. The major portion of the velocity energy is then converted into pressure energy by means of a **volute** (Fig. 1) or by a set of stationary **diffusion vanes** (Fig. 3) surrounding the impeller periphery. Pumps with volute casings are called **volute pumps;** those with diffusion vanes are called **diffuser pumps.** The latter were once commonly called turbine pumps, but this term has recently been more selectively applied to vertical deep-well centrifugal diffuser pumps, now called **vertical turbine pumps.**

Centrifugal pumps are divided into other categories, several of which relate to the impeller. First, impellers are classified according to the major direction of flow in reference to the axis of rotation. Centrifugal pumps may have (1) **radial-flow** impellers (Figs. 1, 2, and 5), (2) **axial-flow** impellers (Fig. 4), and (3) **mixed-flow** impellers, which combine radial- and axial-flow principles (Fig. 7).

Impellers are further classified according to the flow arrangement into (1) **single-suction,** with a single inlet on one side, and (2) **double-suction,** with water flowing to the impeller symmetrically from both sides. They are categorized according to their mechanical construction into (1) **closed,** with shrouds or sidewalls enclosing the waterways, (2) **open,** with no shrouds, and (3) **semiopen** or semiclosed.

If the pump is one in which the head is developed by a single impeller, it is called a **single-stage pump.** When two or more impellers operating in series are used, the unit is called a **multistage pump.** The mechanical design of the casing provides the added classification of **axially split** (Fig. 1) or **radially split** (Figs. 2 and 5), and the axis of rotation determines whether the pump is horizontal-shaft, vertical-shaft, or (occasionally) inclined-shaft. Usually these are referred to simply as **horizontal** or **vertical** units.

Horizontal centrifugal pumps are classified still further according to suction-nozzle location into (1) **end-suction,** (2) **side-suction,** (3) **bottom-suction,** and (4) **top-suction.**

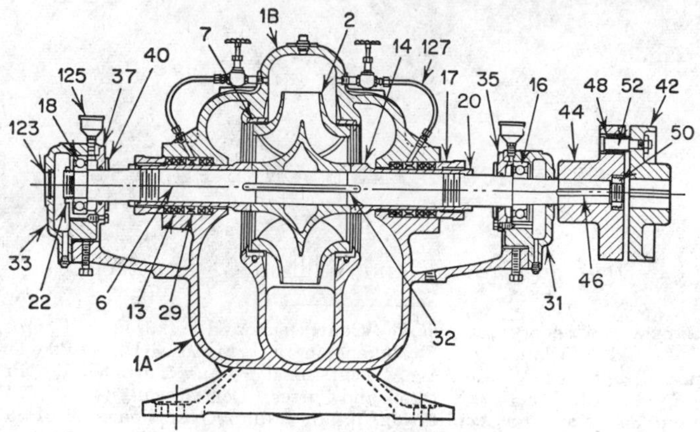

FIG. 1. Horizontal single-stage double-suction volute pump. (Numbers refer to parts listed in Table 1.)

Table 1. Recommended Names of Centrifugal-pump Parts
(These parts are called out in Figs. 1, 4, and 5.)

Item No.	Name of part	Item No.	Name of part
1	Casing	33	Bearing housing (outboard)
1A	Casing (lower half)	35	Bearing cover (inboard)
1B	Casing (upper half)	36	Propeller key
2	Impeller	37	Bearing cover (outboard)
4	Propeller	39	Bearing bushing
6	Pump shaft	40	Deflector
7	Casing ring	42	Coupling (driver half)
8	Impeller ring	44	Coupling (pump half)
9	Suction cover	46	Coupling key
11	Stuffing-box cover	48	Coupling bushing
13	Packing	50	Coupling lock nut
14	Shaft sleeve	52	Coupling pin
15	Discharge bowl	59	Handhole cover
16	Bearing (inboard)	68	Shaft collar
17	Gland	72	Thrust collar
18	Bearing (outboard)	78	Bearing spacer
19	Frame	85	Shaft-enclosing tube
20	Shaft-sleeve nut	89	Seal
22	Bearing lock nut	91	Suction bowl
24	Impeller nut	101	Column pipe
25	Suction-head ring	103	Connector bearing
27	Stuffing-box-cover ring	123	Bearing end cover
29	Seal cage	125	Grease (oil) cup
31	Bearing housing (inboard)	127	Seal piping (tubing)
32	Impeller key		

Some pumps operate with the liquid conducted to and from the unit by piping. Other pumps, usually vertical types, are submerged in their suction supply. Vertical pumps are therefore called either **dry-pit** or **wet-pit** types. If the wet-pit pumps are axial-flow, mixed-flow, or vertical-turbine types, the liquid is discharged up through the supporting drop or column pipe to a discharge point either above or below the supporting floor. These pumps are consequently designated as **above-ground discharge** or **below-ground discharge** units.

Casings

The pressure acting on the impeller in a single-volute pump-casing design is nearly uniform when the pump is operated at or near its design capacity. At other capacities, the pressures around the impeller are not uniform, causing a radial reaction (or radial thrust) which can increase substantially the pump-shaft deflection. When it becomes impractical to counteract this radial thrust through the use of a heavier shaft and heavier bearings, a **double-** or **twin-volute** design (Fig. 5) may be used.

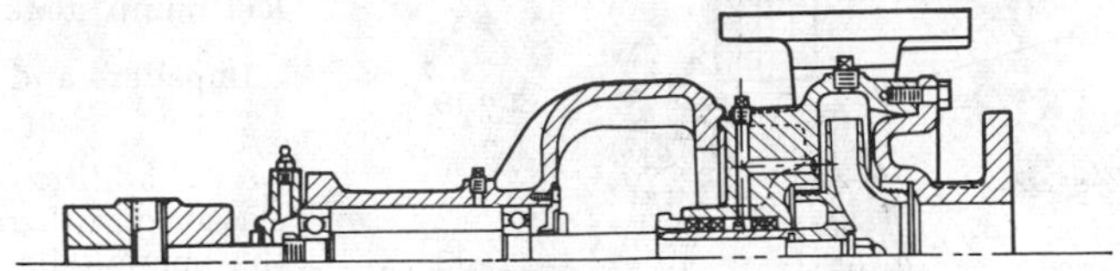

FIG. 2. Single-stage end-suction volute pump.

End-suction single-stage pumps are made of one-piece solid casings. At least one side of the casing must have an opening with a cover so that the impeller can be assembled in the pump. If the cover is on the suction side, it becomes the casing sidewall and contains the suction opening (Fig. 2). This is called the **suction cover** or **casing suction head.** Other designs are made with stuffing-box covers (Fig. 6), and still others have both casing suction covers and stuffing-box covers (Figs. 5 and 7).

In the inexpensive open-impeller pump, the impeller rotates within close clearance of the pump casing (Fig. 6). If the intended service is more severe, a side plate is mounted within the casing to provide a renewable close-clearance guide to the liquid flowing through the open impeller.

The discharge nozzle of end-suction single-stage horizontal pumps is usually in a top-vertical position (Fig. 2). However, other nozzle positions may be obtained, such as top-horizontal, bottom-horizontal, or bottom-vertical discharge.

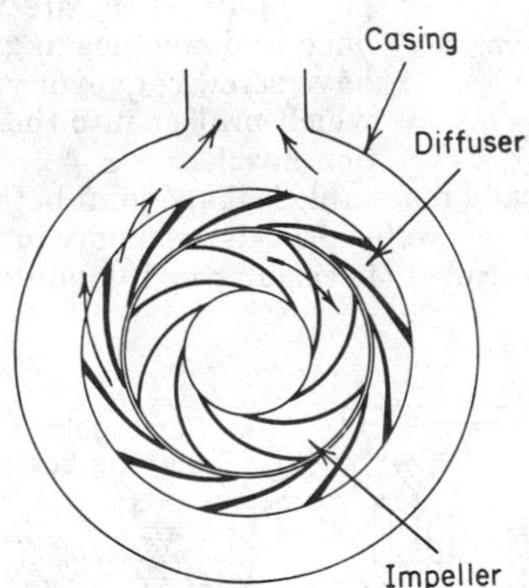

FIG. 3. Diffuser-type pump.

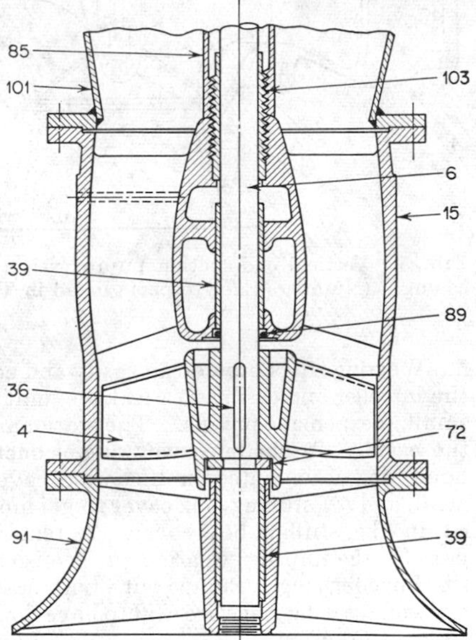

FIG. 4. Vertical wet-pit diffuser pump bowl. (Numbers refer to parts listed in Table 1.)

Practically all double-suction axially split casing pumps have a side-discharge nozzle and either a side- or a bottom-suction nozzle. Single-stage bottom-suction pumps are rarely made in sizes below 10 in. discharge-nozzle diameter.

Both axially split (Fig. 8) and radially split (Fig. 9) casings are used for multistage pumps. The choice between the two designs is dictated by the discharge pressure, with 1,300 to 2,000 psi forming the approximate limit between the two. Radially split casings are normally designed as double casings; the working parts of the pump are enclosed in an inner casing, which is then inserted into a second, or outer, casing. The space between the two casings is maintained at the discharge pressure of the last pump stage.

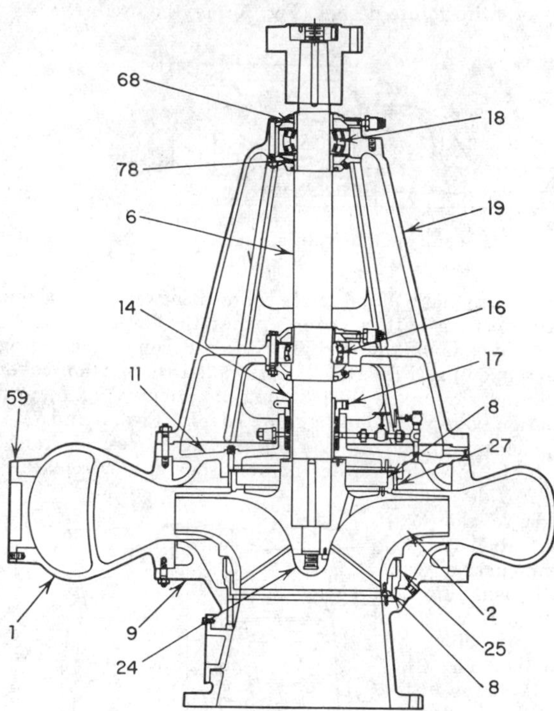

FIG. 5. Vertical end-suction pump with a double-volute casing. (Numbers refer to parts listed in Table 1.)

Impellers and Wearing Rings

In addition to being classified with reference to the suction flow into the impeller, the basic flow component, and their mechanical features, impellers are also classified with reference to their profile and to their head-capacity characteristics at a given speed. This last relationship will be described later, in the discussion of *specific speed* (p. 14–32).

Many impellers are designed for specific applications. Special non-clogging impellers with blunt edges and large waterways are used for sewage which ordinarily contains rags or stringy material. Impellers designed for handling paper-pulp stock are fully open and non-clogging and have screw conveyor vanes which project into the suction nozzle.

Wearing rings provide an easily and economically renewable leakage joint between the impeller and casing. A leakage joint without renewable parts is used only in very small, inexpensive pumps. The stationary ring is called (1) **casing ring** if mounted in the casing, (2) **suction-cover ring** or **suction-head ring** if mounted in a suction cover or head, and (3) **stuffing-box cover ring** if mounted in the stuffing-box cover. A renewable part for the impeller wearing surface is called the **impeller ring.** Pumps with both stationary and rotating rings are said to have **double-ring** construction.

There are various types of wearing-ring designs, and selection of the most desirable type depends on the liquid being handled, the pressure differential across the leakage joint, the surface speed, and the particular pump design. In general, centrifugal-pump designers use the ring construction they have found suitable for each particular pump service. The most common ring constructions are the **flat type** (Fig. 2) and the **L type** (Figs. 1 and 7).

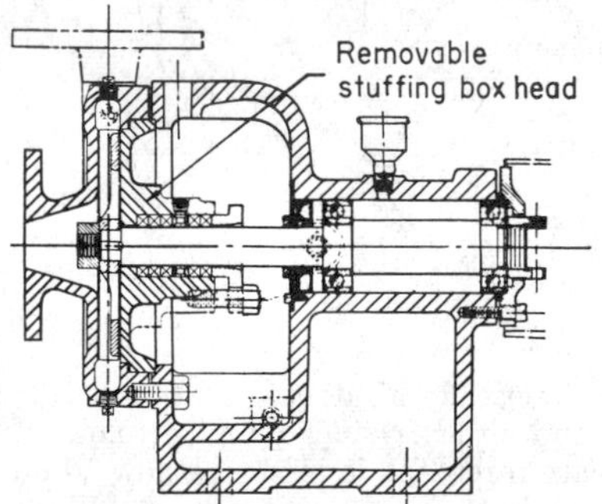

FIG. 6. End-suction pump with removable stuffing-box head.

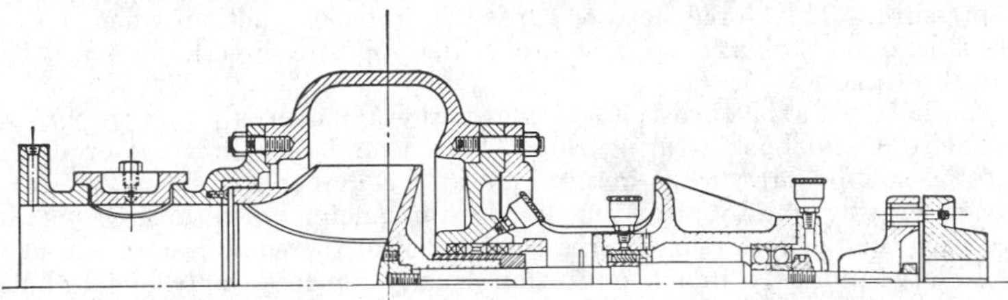

FIG. 7. End-suction pump with removable suction and stuffing-box heads.

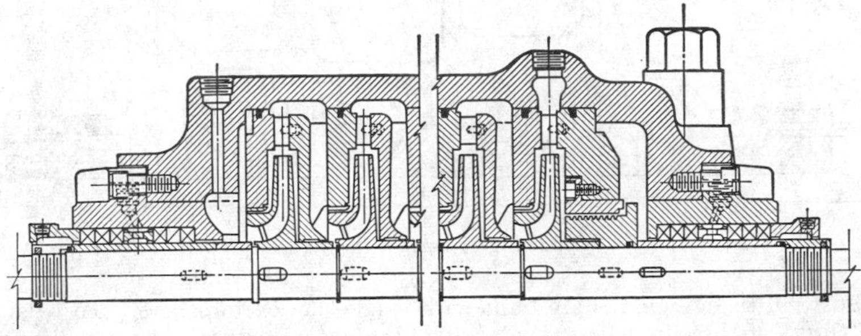

FIG. 8. Multistage pump with single-suction impellers facing in one direction and with hydraulic balancing device.

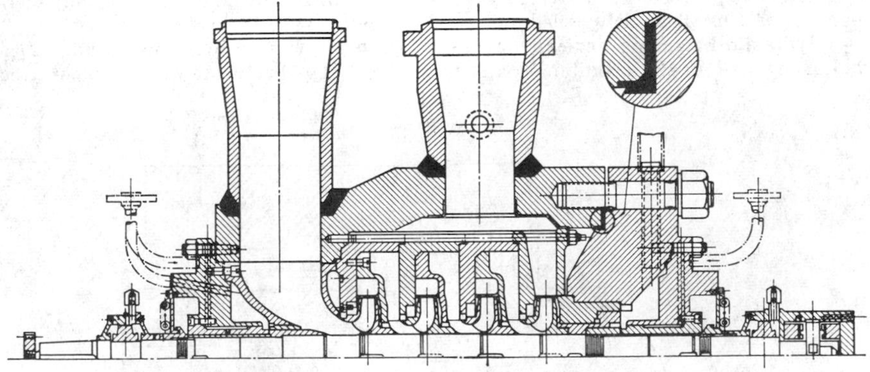

FIG. 9. Double-casing multistage pump with radially-split inner casing.

Axial Thrust in Single-stage and Multistage Pumps

Axial hydraulic thrust is the summation of unbalanced impeller forces acting in the axial direction. Theoretically, a double-suction impeller is in hydraulic balance, with the pressures on one side equal to and counterbalancing the pressures on the other. In practice, some slight unbalance may exist, and even double-suction pumps are provided with thrust bearings.

The single-suction radial-flow impeller is subject to axial thrust because a portion of the front wall is exposed to suction pressure, with a greater back-wall surface subject to discharge pressure. In addition, an overhung single-suction impeller with a single stuffing box is subject to an axial force equivalent to the product of the shaft area through the stuffing box and the difference between suction and atmospheric pressure. This force acts toward the impeller suction when the suction pressure is less than the atmospheric and in the opposite direction when it is higher than the atmospheric.

To eliminate the axial thrust of a single-suction impeller, a pump can be provided with both front and back wearing rings (Figs. 2 and 5). Pressure approximately equal to the suction pressure is maintained in a chamber located on the inner side of the back wearing ring by providing so-called **balancing holes** through the impeller. Leakage past the back wearing ring is returned into the suction area through these holes. In large pumps, a piped connection usually replaces the balancing holes.

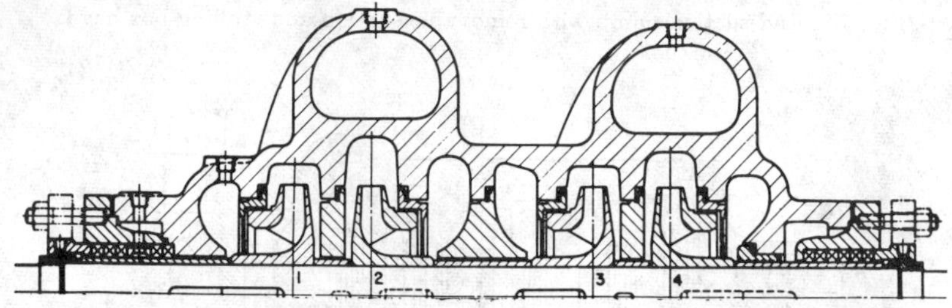

FIG. 10. Four-stage pump with opposed impellers.

Most multistage pumps are built with single-suction impellers. To balance the axial thrust of these impellers, two arrangements are used: (1) The impellers all face in the same direction and are mounted in the ascending order of the stages. The axial thrust is balanced by a hydraulic balancing device (Figs. 8 and 9). (2) An even number of single-suction impellers is used, one half of these facing in a direction opposite to the second half (Fig. 10). This mounting of single-suction impellers back to back is frequently called **opposed impellers.**

Hydraulic balancing devices may take the form of (1) a **balancing drum,** (2) a **balancing disk,** or (3) a combination of these two. The **balancing drum** is illustrated

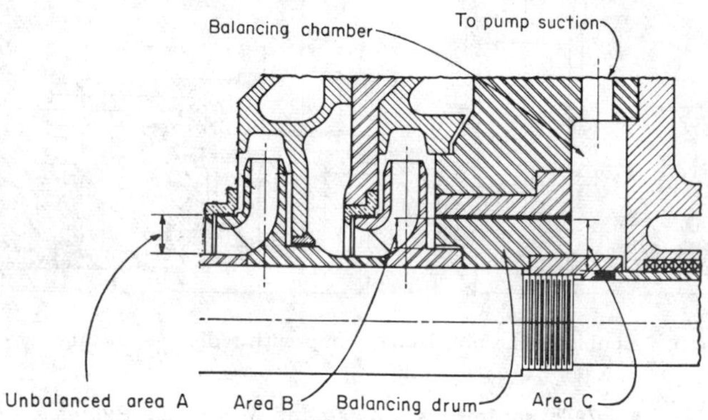

FIG. 11. Balancing drum.

in Fig. 11. The balancing chamber at the back of the last-stage impeller is separated from the pump interior by a drum mounted on the shaft. The drum is separated by a small radial clearance from the stationary portion of the balancing device, called the **balancing drum head,** which is fixed to the pump casing. The balancing chamber is connected either to the pump suction or to the vessel from which the pump takes its suction. The forces acting on the balancing drum are (1) toward the discharge end—the discharge pressure multiplied by the front balancing area (area B) of the drum;

(2) toward the suction end—the back pressure in the balancing chamber multiplied by the back balancing area (area *C*) of the drum. The first force is greater than the second, thereby counterbalancing the axial thrust exerted upon the single-suction impellers. The drum diameter can be selected to balance the axial thrust completely or to balance 90 to 95 percent of this thrust, depending on whether a slight thrust load in a specific direction on the thrust bearing is desirable.

The operation of the simple **balancing disk** is illustrated in Fig. 12. The rotating disk is separated from the balancing-disk head by a small axial clearance. The leakage through this clearance flows into the balancing chamber and from there either to the pump suction or to the suction vessel. The back of the balancing disk is subject to the balancing-chamber back pressure, whereas the disk face experiences a range of pressures. These vary from discharge pressure at its smallest diameter to back pressure at its periphery. The inner and outer disk diameters are chosen so that the difference between the total force acting on the disk face and that acting on its back will balance the impeller axial thrust. If the axial thrust of the impellers should exceed the thrust acting on the disk during operation, the latter is moved toward the disk head, reducing the axial clearance. The amount of leakage through this clearance is reduced so that the friction losses in the leakage return line are also reduced, lowering the back pressure in the balancing chamber. This automatically increases the pressure difference acting on the disk and moves it away from the disk head, increasing the clearance. Now the pressure builds up in the balancing chamber, and the disk is again moved toward the disk head until an equilibrium is reached. To ensure proper balancing-disk operation, the change in back pressure must be of an appreciable magnitude. This is accomplished by introducing a restricting orifice in the leakage return line.

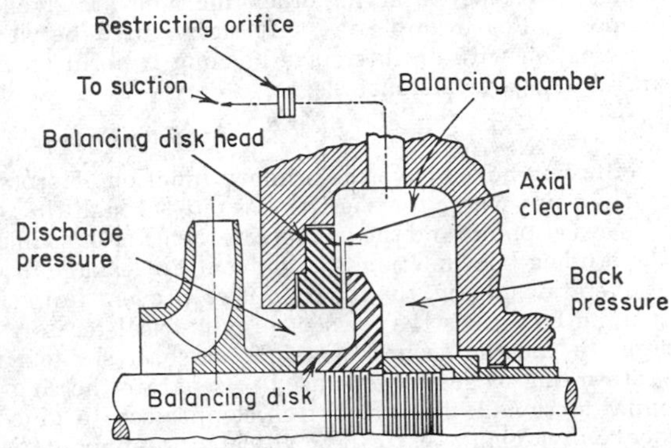

FIG. 12. Simple balancing disk.

The **combination disk and drum** (Fig. 9) is the most commonly used hydraulic balancing device. It incorporates portions rotating within radial clearances of stationary portions and a disk face rotating within an axial clearance of another portion of the stationary part. The radial clearance remains constant regardless of any axial displacement of the rotor within the casing. Such displacement, however, changes the axial clearance within the balancing device. These changes cause changes in the leakage, which in turn change the pressure drop across the radial clearances and thus increase or decrease the average value of the pressure acting on the disk face. These changes in the intermediate pressure on the disk face act to move the balancing device in whichever direction is required to restore equilibrium and axial balance.

Shafts and Shaft Sleeves

Pump-shaft diameters are usually larger than actually needed to transmit the torque because their size is dictated by the maximum permissible or desirable shaft deflection. This deflection is itself chosen to prevent possible contact at the wearing surfaces while maintaining reasonable clearances that will not affect pump efficiency too unfavorably. The first **critical speed** of a shaft is related to its deflection. It follows that a shaft design permitting a deflection of, for instance, 0.005 to 0.006 in. will have a first critical speed of 2,400 to 2,650 rpm. This is the reason for using rigid shafts (operating below their first critical speed) for pumps that operate at

1,750 rpm or lower. Multistage pumps operating at 3,600 rpm or higher use shafts of equal stiffness (for the same purpose of avoiding wearing-ring contact). However, their corresponding critical speed is about 25 to 40 percent less than their operating speed. This margin is sufficient to avoid any danger to the operation caused by critical-speed effect.

Pump shafts are usually protected from erosion, corrosion, and wear at the stuffing boxes and leakage joints and in the waterways by renewable **sleeves.** The most common shaft-sleeve function is that of protecting the shaft from wear at a stuffing box. Shaft sleeves serving other functions are given specific names to indicate their purpose. For example, a shaft sleeve used between two multistage impellers in conjunction with an interstage bushing to form an interstage leakage joint is called an **interstage** or **distance** sleeve.

Stuffing Boxes

Stuffing boxes have the primary function of protecting the pump against leakage at the point where the shaft passes out through the pump casing. If the pump handles a suction lift and the pressure at the interior stuffing-box end is below atmospheric, the stuffing-box function is to prevent air leakage into the pump. If this pressure is above atmospheric, the function is to prevent liquid leakage out of the pump. The stuffing box takes the form of a cylindrical recess that accommodates a number of rings of **packing** around the shaft or shaft sleeve. If sealing the box is desired, a **lantern ring** or **seal cage** is used to separate the rings of packing into approximately equal sections. The packing is compressed to give the desired fit on the shaft or sleeve by a gland that can be adjusted in an axial direction.

Water or some other sealing fluid can be introduced under pressure into the space provided by the seal cage, causing flow of sealing fluid in both axial directions. This is useful for pumps handling flammable or chemically active and dangerous liquids since it prevents outflow of the pumped liquid.

When a pump handles clean, cool water, stuffing-box seals are usually connected to the pump discharge or, in multistage pumps, to an intermediate stage. An **independent supply of sealing water** should be provided if any of the following conditions exist: (1) a suction lift in excess of 15 ft; (2) a discharge pressure under 10 psi; (3) hot-water handled without adequate cooling (except for boiler feed pumps, in which seal cages are not used); (4) muddy, sandy, or gritty water handled; (5) for all hot well pumps; (6) no leakage to atmosphere permitted of the liquid handled. When sealing water is taken from the pump discharge, an external connection is generally made to the seal cage through small-diameter piping (Fig. 1), or an internal-passage connection is made within the pump itself (Fig. 2).

High temperatures or pressures complicate the problem of maintaining stuffing-box packing. Pumps in these more difficult services are usually provided with jacketed, **water-cooled stuffing boxes.** If the pressure ahead of the stuffing box makes it impractical to pack the stuffing box satisfactorily, a pressure-reducing breakdown or **labyrinth** may be located ahead of the box, with the leakage past the pressure-reducing breakdown being returned to some point of lower pressure in the pumping cycle.

Basically, **stuffing-box packing** is a pressure-breakdown device that is sufficiently plastic to be adjusted for proper operation. The most common types are asbestos packing and metallic packing, the latter being composed of flexible metallic strands or foil with graphite or oil lubricant and with either an asbestos or a plastic core. Other types of packing used may be hemp, cord, braided, duck fabric, chevron, etc. Packing is supplied either in continuous coils of square cross section or in preformed, die-molded rings.

Mechanical seals are used in centrifugal pumps when it becomes impractical to use conventional packing with radial sealing surfaces. The sealing surfaces of a mechanical seal are located in a plane perpendicular to the pump shaft and consist of two highly polished surfaces running adjacently, one surface being connected to the shaft and the other to the stationary portion of the pump. These surfaces are held essentially in contact by a spring, the axial clearance between the surfaces being provided by a thin film of liquid. The flow of liquid may be only a drop every few minutes or even a haze of escaping vapor.

There are two basic seal arrangements: (1) internal assembly and (2) external assembly. Two mechanical seals may be mounted inside a stuffing box to make a **double seal assembly** (Fig. 13). Such an arrangement is used for pumps handling toxic or highly inflammable liquids. A clear, filtered, and generally inert sealing liquid is injected between two seals at a pressure slightly in excess of the pressure in the pump ahead of the seal.

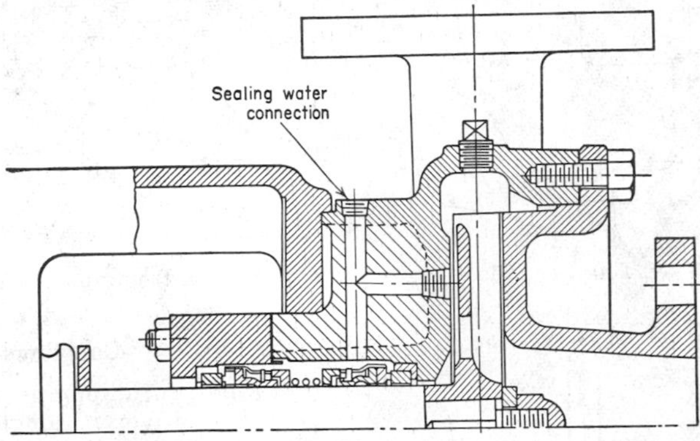

FIG. 13. Single-stage end-suction pump with double mechanical seal.

For some power-plant services, **condensate-injection sealing** is superior to either conventional packing or mechanical seals. A labyrinth breakdown bushing is substituted for the conventional packing, and the pump-shaft sleeve runs within this bushing with a small radial clearance. Cold condensate at a pressure in excess of the internal pump pressure is introduced centrally in this breakdown bushing (Fig. 9). A small portion of the injection water flows inwardly into the pump proper; the remainder flows out into a collecting chamber vented to the atmosphere and is piped back to the condenser.

Bearings

(See also Sec. 8)

All types of **bearings** are used in centrifugal pumps. Even the same basic design of pump is often made with two or more different bearings, required by varying service conditions. Two external bearings are usually used for the double-suction single-stage general-service pump, one on either side of the casing. In horizontal pumps with bearings on each end, the **inboard bearing** is the one between the casing and the coupling and the **outboard bearing** is located at the opposite end. Pumps with overhung impellers have both bearings on the same side of the casing; the bearing nearest the impeller is the inboard bearing, and the one farthest away the outboard bearing.

Ball bearings are the most common antifriction bearings used on centrifugal pumps. Roller bearings are used less often, although the spherical roller bearing is used frequently for large shaft sizes. Ball bearings used in centrifugal pumps are usually grease-lubricated, although some services use oil lubrication.

Sleeve bearings are used for large, heavy-duty pumps with shaft diameters of such proportions that the necessary antifriction bearings are not commonly available. Another application is for high-pressure multistage pumps operating at speeds of 3,600 to 9,000 rpm. Still another application is in vertical submerged pumps, such as vertical turbine pumps, in which the bearings are subject to a water contact. Most sleeve bearings are oil-lubricated.

Thrust bearings used in combination with sleeve bearings are generally Kingsbury or Kingsbury-type bearings.

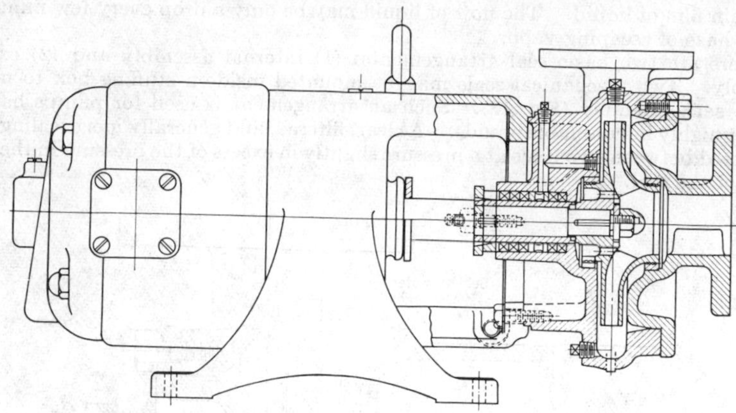

FIG. 14. Close-coupled (motor-mounted) pump.

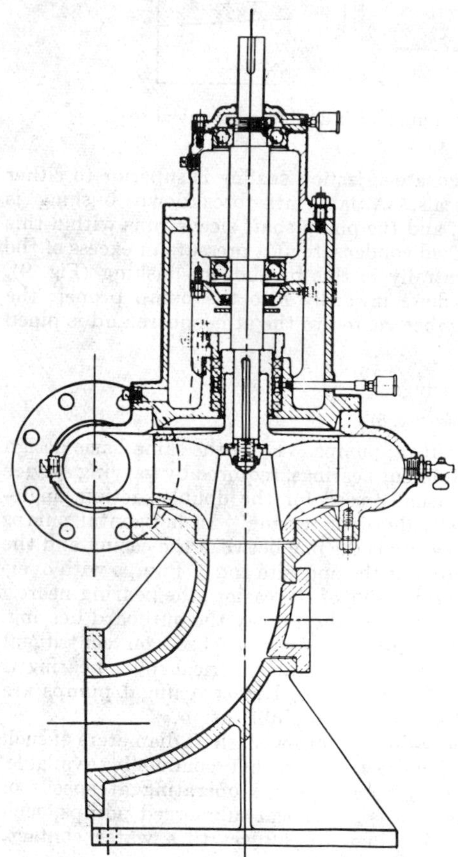

FIG. 15. Small vertical sewage pump with intermediate shafting.

Couplings

Centrifugal pumps are connected to their drivers through **couplings** of one sort or another, except for close-coupled units (Fig. 14), in which the impeller is mounted on an extension of the shaft of the driver. Couplings used with centrifugal pumps can be either **rigid** (of the clamp or compression type) or **flexible** (pin-and-buffer, gear, grid, or flexible-disk type). (See also p. 8–50.)

Pump Mounting

It is desirable that pumps and their drivers be removable from their mountings. Consequently, they are usually bolted and doweled to machined surfaces that, in turn, are firmly connected to the foundations. These machined surfaces are usually part of a common **bedplate** on which the pump and its driver have been prealigned. Bed-plates are made of either cast iron or structural steel. Cast-iron or steel **soleplates** are customarily used for vertical dry-pit pumps and also for some of the larger horizontal units.

Vertical Pumps

Dry-pit pumps with external bearings include most sewage pumps, most medium and large drainage and irrigation pumps for medium and high head, many large condenser-circulating and water-supply pumps, and many marine pumps. Some vertical dry-pit pumps are basically horizontal designs with minor modifications to adapt them for vertical-shaft drive. Other applications, such as small- and medium-sized sewage pumps, employ a purely vertical design. Most of these sewage pumps have elbow suction nozzles (Fig. 15) containing a handhole to provide easy access to the impeller. Although the driving motors are frequently mounted right on top of the pump casing, the use of vertical-shaft design permits mounting the motor at an elevation sufficiently above the pump to prevent accidental flooding. For such applications, the pump and its driver are separated by a length of shafting, which may require steady bearings between the two units.

Vertical wet-pit centrifugal pumps can be classified as (1) vertical turbine pumps, (2) propeller or modified propeller pumps, (3) sewage pumps, (4) volute pumps, and (5) sump pumps. The first of these is the most common type. **Vertical turbine pumps** (Fig. 16) are built with either closed or semiopen impellers and with either enclosed or open line shafting. The bowl assembly consists of the suction head, the impeller or impellers, the discharge bowl, the intermediate bowl or bowls, the discharge case, the various bearings, the shaft, and miscellaneous parts such as keys and impeller locking devices. The column-pipe assembly consists of the column pipe itself, the shafting above the bowl assembly, the shaft bearings, and the cover pipe or bearing retainers. The pump is suspended from the driving head, which consists of the discharge elbow, the motor or driver support, and either the stuffing box (in open shaft construction) or the assembly for providing tension on and the introduction of lubricant to the cover pipe.

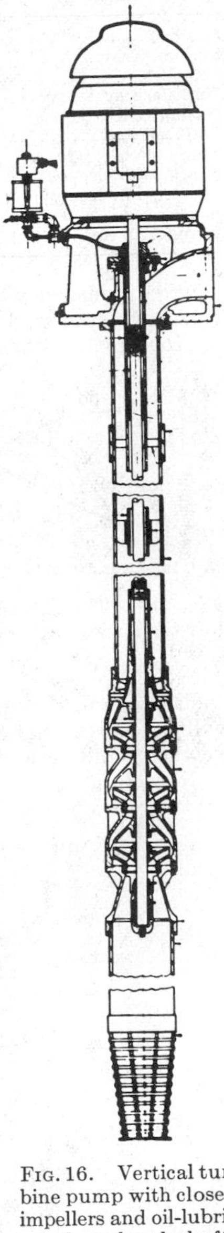

MATERIALS OF CONSTRUCTION

Centrifugal pumps can be fabricated of almost any of the known common metals or metal alloys, as well as of porcelain, glass, and even synthetics. A listing of materials commonly recommended for various liquids can be found in the Standards of the Hydraulic Institute. Table 2 indicates the materials most commonly used for various pump parts.

PUMP PERFORMANCE

The performance of a centrifugal pump is generally described in terms of the following of its **characteristics:** (1) rate of flow, or **capacity** Q, expressed in units of volume per unit of time, most frequently cfs or gpm (1 cfs = 449 gpm); (2) increase of energy content in the fluid pumped, or **head** H, expressed in units of energy per unit of mass, usually ft-lb per lb or, more simply, ft; (3) input **power** P, expressed in units of work per unit of time, bhp; (4) **efficiency** η, the ratio of useful work performed to power input, (5) **rotative speed** N, in rpm.

Since the parameters indicated are all mutually interdependent, it is customary to represent the performance of a centrifugal pump by means of **characteristic curves** similar to that shown in Fig. 17. While it is possible, within certain limits, for the pump designer to regulate the shape of these curves to suit the needs of a particular application, this is essentially a function of design capacity, head, and speed and hence for a standard production unit is determined by experiment and is not subject to modification. For any given capacity on such a characteristic curve, the relationship between performance characteristics is expressed by the equation $\eta = \gamma QH/3{,}960P$,

FIG. 16. Vertical turbine pump with closed impellers and oil-lubricated enclosed shafting.

Table 2. Materials for Various Fittings

(Materials for bearing housings, bearings, and other parts are not usually affected by the liquid handled.)

Part	Standard fitting	All-iron fitting	All-bronze fitting
Casing	Cast iron	Cast iron	Bronze
Suction head	Cast iron	Cast iron	Bronze
Impeller	Bronze	Cast iron	Bronze
Impeller ring	Bronze	Cast iron or steel	Bronze
Casing ring	Bronze	Cast iron	Bronze
Diffuser	Cast iron or bronze	Cast iron	Bronze
Stage piece	Cast iron or bronze	Cast iron	Bronze
Shaft (with sleeve)	Steel	Steel	Steel, bronze, or monel
Shaft (without sleeve)	Stainless steel or steel	Stainless steel or steel	Bronze or monel
Shaft sleeve	Bronze	Steel or stainless steel	Bronze
Gland	Bronze	Cast iron	Bronze

where η is efficiency expressed as a decimal, γ is the specific gravity of the fluid pumped, Q is in gpm, H in ft, and P in bhp.

Inasmuch as the actual performance of centrifugal pumps is determined largely by experimental means, it is highly desirable to be able to use the results of past tests as a basis for predicting the performance of future designs. To this end, an interesting and widely used characteristic number known as **specific speed,** $N_s = N\sqrt{Q}/H^{3/4}$, has been developed. In this expression, values of N, Q, and H are all for the point of best efficiency. While not dimensionless, N_s is generally expressed simply as a number since its practical application is such that units are of no consequence except for their influence on the absolute magnitude of the number itself. Specific speed is of interest to both the pump designer and the pump user essentially in two ways: (1) All geometrically similar pumps, regardless of their size, will have identical specific speeds (but all pumps of the same specific speed will not necessarily be geometrically similar). (2) Within reasonable limits, pump geometry and performance can be predicted as a function of N_s and Q. For N in rpm,

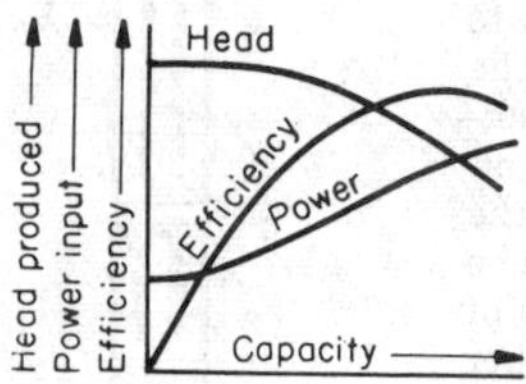

FIG. 17. Typical characteristic curves at constant speed.

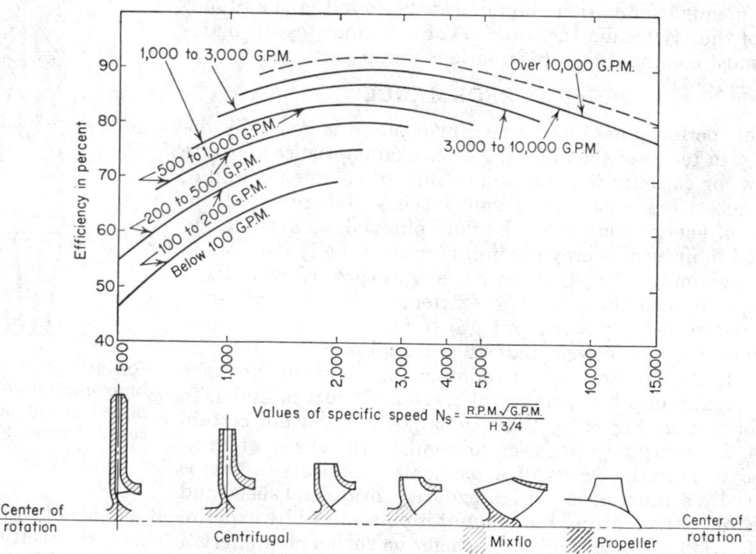

FIG. 18. Approximate relative impeller shapes and efficiency variations with specific speed.

Q in gpm, and H in ft, the practical range of N_s is approximately 500 to 15,000, and the manner in which pump efficiency and impeller design vary over this range is shown in Fig. 18. In addition, the general shape of the pump-characteristic curves will vary widely from one end of this range to the other, as illustrated by Figs. 23 and 24.

Pump Theory

The basic purpose of a centrifugal pump in any fluid-handling system is to add energy to the fluid, and since it is a dynamic machine, the pump depends entirely on changes in velocity relationships to provide the energy. While the measurable evidence of energy addition is in most cases largely in the form of static pressure, this is partially the result of velocity reductions and constraints occurring in the diffuser or casing and to this extent represents a conversion from the velocity energy produced by the impeller. Thus, any discussion of centrifugal-pump theory generally becomes a discussion of velocities occurring at various points within the pump.

The true velocity relationships existing within a pump are extremely complex and, to a substantial degree, still unknown in their ultimate detail; but for practical purposes, a one-dimensional analysis serves to illustrate the basic concepts and, indeed, has served as the basis of design for virtually all centrifugal pumps ever built.

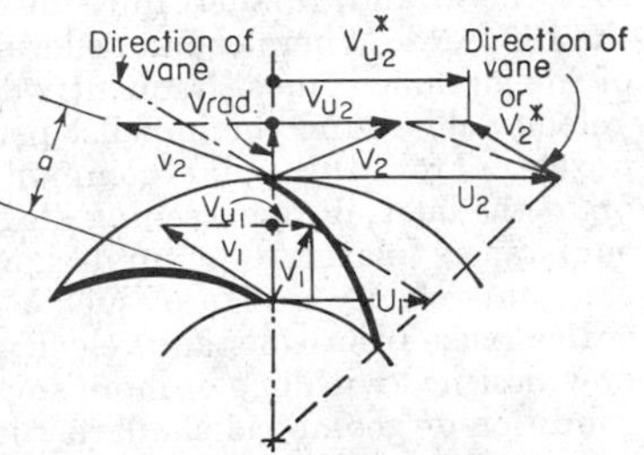

FIG. 19. Velocity diagram of a radial-flow impeller.

For radial and mixed-flow impellers ($500 \leqq N_s \leqq 7{,}500$), the velocities at the inlet and outlet of the impeller are shown by the vector diagrams in Fig. 19. The head produced by such an impeller is represented by the expression

$$H = \eta_H(U_2V_{u_2} - U_1V_{u_1})/g \tag{1}$$

where H = the head, ft; U = the circumferential velocity of the impeller at the radius being considered, fps; V_u = the average value of the circumferential component of the absolute fluid velocity, fps; and g = 32.174 ft per sec². Subscript 1 refers to the impeller inlet section, and subscript 2 to the impeller discharge section. The coefficient η_H is the hydraulic efficiency of the rotating-vane system and, for the range of specific speeds indicated above, will generally fall between 0.85 and 0.95. This hydraulic efficiency is considerably higher than pump efficiency η since it does not include mechanical losses due to bearing or packing friction, volumetric losses due to internal wearing-ring clearances, impeller-disk friction, or fluid-friction losses due to velocity conversion or boundary-layer considerations ahead of or following the impeller. For pumps in this specific-speed range, the hydraulic losses $(1 - \eta_H)$ will generally be between one-quarter and three-quarters of total pump losses $(1 - \eta)$.

For pumps arranged with an axial inlet to the impeller (such as that shown in Fig. 5), it is generally assumed that the entering flow will have no rotational component, and V_{u_1} is therefore zero. Equation (**1**) can thus be reduced to

$$H = \eta_H U_2 V_{u_2}/g \tag{2}$$

In practice, Eq. (**2**) will provide a close approximation to total head for any pump up to a specific speed of 2,000 since the term $U_1V_{u_1}$ in Eq. (**1**) is very small compared with $U_2V_{u_2}$.

It should also be noted in Fig. 19 that the relative velocity v_2 does not coincide in direction with the vane angle at the impeller discharge. The angular difference between v_2 and the direction of the vane is due to the irrotational nature of the flow between the vanes. The effect of this difference can be taken into account as the vector difference $V_{u_2}{}^* - V_{u_2} = Na/229$, where a is the shortest distance in inches taken in the radial plane between the discharge tip of any vane and the upper surface of the following vane.

The foregoing relationships provide the basis for determining impeller diameters and vane angles required to produce a given total head requirement at a specified rotative speed. It is equally necessary, of course, to provide in the design for handling a specified flow volume, and this is readily accomplished by providing the necessary cross-sectional area A between vanes to pass the required flow at velocities previously determined. A useful relationship for this purpose, in light of the units commonly employed in pump design, is $Q = AV/0.321$, where Q is in gpm, V in fps, and A in sq in.

Upon leaving the impeller, the liquid pumped enters either (1) a system of diffusing vanes surrounded by an outer casing or (2) directly into a casing designed to contain the fluid and control its velocities. Where diffusing vanes are used, they are designed on the basis of velocity relationships very similar to those employed in impeller design but with the objective being to slow the fluid down to convert velocity energy to pressure energy and, further, to reduce frictional losses in the discharge system following the diffuser. Where the impeller discharges directly into the casing, this component of the machine is most frequently designed in the form of a volute to provide constant velocity all around the impeller periphery up to the point of entry into the discharge nozzle. From this point, commonly called the **casing throat,** to the discharge flange or to the inlet of a succeeding stage, the velocity is gradually reduced. Special circumstances related to pump design or application often result in modifications to the constant-velocity design of such a casing, and variations may be found covering the entire range from constant velocity to constant area. In addition, many casings are now designed with one or more spiral vanes placed in such a way as to approximate a condition of geometric similarity in relation to the impeller, which is advantageous when a pump is operated at capacities other than those for which it is designed. A casing of this nature represents an effort by the designer to obtain an optimum balance between the desirable geometric similarity of the diffuser discharge and the manufacturing simplicity and generally high efficiency of the volute-type casing. The most common form of such a casing is the twin-volute type discussed under Nomenclature and Mechanical Design (see p. 14–22).

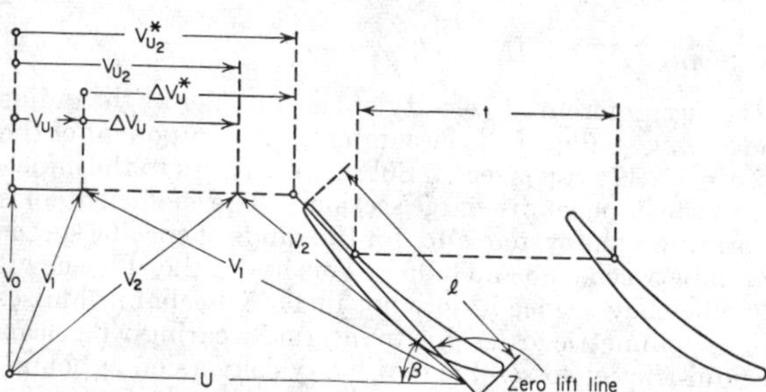

FIG. 20. Velocity diagram of an axial-flow vane system.

For axial-flow impellers ($7{,}500 \leqq N_s \leqq 15{,}000$), velocity relationships may be approximated in a manner similar to that used for lower-specific-speed pumps, but refinement of these approximations is approached in a somewhat different manner, largely because of the considerable body of knowledge available in the form of airfoil data which can be applied. Velocity diagrams for pumps of this type are shown in Fig. 20.

Considering a cylindrical stream tube intersecting the vanes of an axial-flow impeller, we can rewrite Eq. (1) in the form

$$H = \eta_H U \,\Delta V_u / g \tag{3}$$

where ΔV_u represents the increase in the tangential component of the absolute velocity as the fluid passes through the impeller. For pumps in this specific-speed range, η_H will generally fall between 0.80 and 0.90 and $(1 - \eta_H)$ will generally be between one-half and three-quarters of $(1 - \eta)$.

As in the case of radial-flow impellers, the relative velocity v_2 at the impeller exit does not coincide with the vane angle. In this case, the necessary correction can be applied by means of the expression

$$\Delta V_u = 2\Delta V_u^*/[(t/l)(2/\pi K)(1/\sin\beta) + 1] \tag{4}$$

where t is vane spacing, l is vane length, β is the discharge vane angle, and K is the coefficient determined from Fig. 21, which provides for the fact that the impeller blades are, in effect, arranged in a continuous lattice.

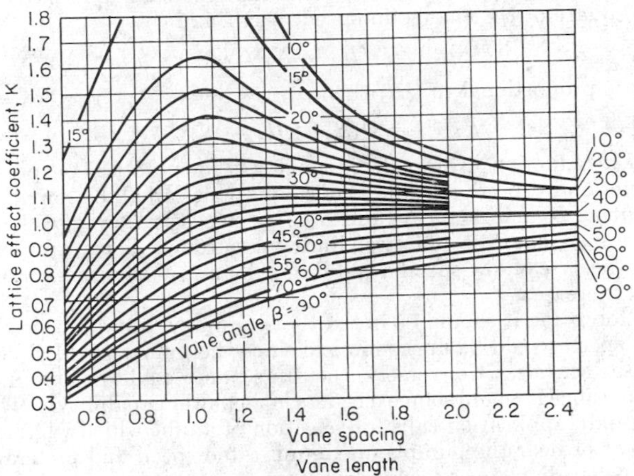

FIG. 21. Lattice-effect coefficient (Weinig).

In the design of axial-flow pumps, it is generally assumed that the head developed by the blade elements within all the cylindrical stream tubes between the impeller hub and its outer diameter will be the same. For this condition to be achieved, it will be evident from Eq. (**3**) that since U will vary directly with the radius, then ΔV_u must vary inversely with the radius. Thus vane camber (or curvature) will be greater near the hub than at the periphery. It is further generally assumed that the axial velocity is constant throughout the impeller, and to satisfy this condition, the blade angles will be greater at the hub than at the periphery, giving rise to the twist of the vane.

By designing the vane element at the hub, the periphery, and any reasonable number of radial stations between, it is possible to define the vane over its entire surface to produce the total head desired. The design capacity can be simply established from the constant axial velocity and the annular area between the hub and the periphery.

Axial-flow impellers will almost invariably discharge into a vaned diffuser designed primarily to convert into pressure the tangential component of the absolute velocity leaving the impeller, thus producing a uniform, non-rotating velocity profile at the pump discharge or at the entrance to any succeeding stage.

Pump Application

In applying any centrifugal pump to a practical fluid-handling system, the engineer generally has two variables in the pump which may be used to effect a match between it and the system, namely, speed of operation and impeller diameter. (In axial-flow pumps, impeller diameter cannot conveniently be changed, but similar results can be accomplished within a limited range by reducing vane length.) To take advantage of these variables, it is necessary to understand the similarity relationships which govern pump behavior.

The effect of change in speed can be most readily explained by referring back to Eq. (**1**). For a fixed impeller diameter, it will immediately be evident that any increase in rotative speed will result in a directly proportional increase in the peripheral velocities of the impeller at both inlet and outlet, U_1 and U_2, respectively. Furthermore, since the directions of both the relative and absolute velocities v and V, respectively, are controlled by the vane angles, it follows that both the inlet and outlet velocity diagrams remain geometrically similar; in other words, as pump speed changes, all fluid velocities change in direct proportion. Thus the effect of a speed change on pump capacity can be represented for two speeds N_1 and N_2 by the equation

$$Q_1/Q_2 = N_1/N_2$$

Referring again to Eq. (1), it will be evident that the change in head will be proportional to the square of the change in speed, resulting in

$$H_1/H_2 = N_1^2/N_2^2$$

Also, since P is proportional to QH, then

$$P_1/P_2 = Q_1H_1/Q_2H_2 = N_1^3/N_2^3$$

The effect of a reduction in impeller diameter is for practical purposes, identical to that of a reduction in speed, and the above equations can all be rewritten in the same form, substituting D_1 and D_2 for N_1 and N_2. In this case, however, there is somewhat less latitude for change, the practical limit for cutdown being approximately 25 to 30 percent in the case of low-specific-speed impellers and decreasing from this value as specific speed increases.

From the foregoing it should be noted that running a pump at speeds far below its normal rated speed would be uneconomical since the pump would obviously be overdesigned for the service. Conversely, the same pump could not be run at speeds far above its rating since it would soon exceed its horsepower capability. Thus the normal approach to pump application calls for selection of a unit which will meet the system requirements at or near the pump's maximum rated speed and preferably as close to maximum impeller diameter as possible.

A further aspect of the similarity laws, of interest primarily to pump designers, is the matter of geometrically similar pumps, or as they are commonly called, **factors of each other.** Assuming two such pumps with a size ratio f_1/f_2, then **at the same rotative speed** $H_1/H_2 = f_1^2/f_2^2$, which is the same as for a change in speed of the same ratio. In the case of capacity, however, we have, in addition to the linear increase due to velocity change, a further increase due to the change in the cross-sectional area of all fluid channels which is proportional to the square of the size factor, resulting in the relationship $Q_1/Q_2 = f_1^3/f_2^3$. The ratio of horsepower requirements becomes, therefore, $P_1/P_2 = f_1^5/f_2^5$.

Lines of geometrically similar pumps are more frequently designed, however, for constant head than for constant speed, and to have this condition apply for the size ratio indicated in the preceding paragraph, it is necessary that the speeds vary in exact inverse proportion to size ratio. Thus, **for constant head,** $N_2/N_1 = f_1/f_2$ and

$$H_1/H_2 = 1 = (f_1/f_2)^2(N_2/N_1)^2$$
$$Q_1/Q_2 = (f_1/f_2)^3(N_2/N_1) = (f_1/f_2)^2$$
$$P_1/P_2 = (H_1/H_2)(Q_1/Q_2) = (f_1/f_2)^2$$

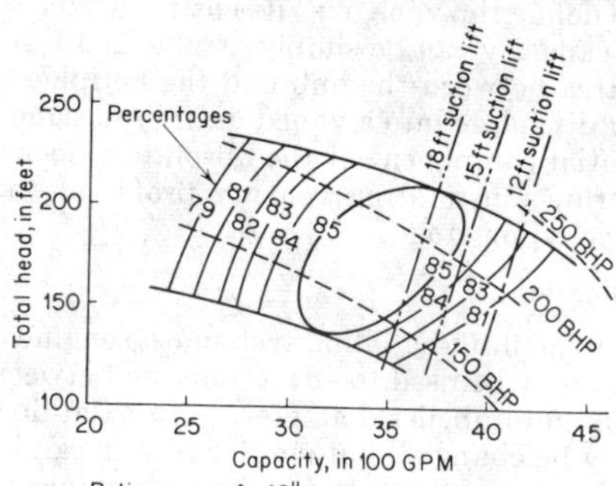

Fig. 22. Rating curve of 10-in. double-suction single-stage pump.

To simplify selection of pumps, it is customary to plot, for any given speed, performance curves to show pump characteristics over the available range of impeller diameters rather than at the single diameter which would be implicit in a curve of the type shown in Fig. 17. A typical rating curve of this nature is shown in Fig. 22. Such rating curves will vary widely in their nature with changes in N_s, and an understanding of these variations is essential to the selection of properly sized pump drivers and, in many cases, proper design of discharge piping and/or the determination of limiting ranges of pump operation. Some idea of the diversity of characteristics which is available can be obtained by a comparison between Figs. 23 and 24, both of which are plotted entirely in percentages of design values occurring at the point of best efficiency.

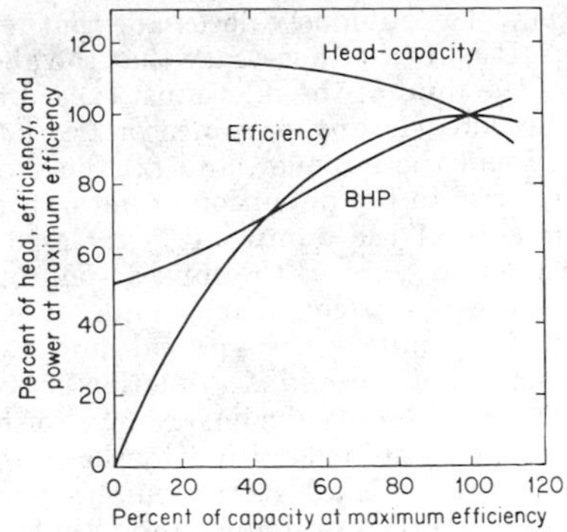

FIG. 23. Type characteristics for N_s = 1,550, single-suction impeller.

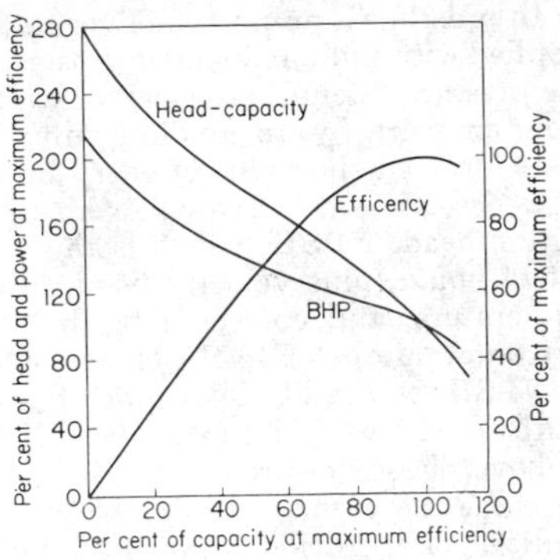

FIG. 24. Type characteristics for N_s = 10,000, single-suction impeller.

In the case of the lower-specific-speed pump shown in Fig. 23, a driving motor selected for the rated condition would be more than adequate at lower capacities, and discharge piping would be subjected to only modest overpressures. On the other hand, if the pump shown in Fig. 24 is to be operated at reduced capacities, then both motor size and discharge piping must be designed for the minimum flows to be encountered.

Selection of drivers, as well as pumps, is also influenced by **properties of the fluid** handled. Pump horsepower varies directly with the specific gravity of the liquid and is influenced in a more complex manner by viscosity. The effect of the latter is illustrated in Fig. 25. For the example shown on the chart, the pump in question is rated for 750 gpm at 100-ft head. When handling a fluid having a viscosity of 1,000 SSU, its capacity is reduced to 95 percent of that on water over its complete range of operation. Its head is reduced to 96, 94, 92, and 89 percent of its head on cold water at 60, 80, 100, and 120 percent of these reduced capacities, and its efficiency is reduced to 63.5 percent of its efficiency on water over its reduced capacity range. Thus, if the pump had a rated efficiency on cold water of 70 percent, it would now deliver 712.5 gpm at 92-ft head with an efficiency of 44.5 percent.

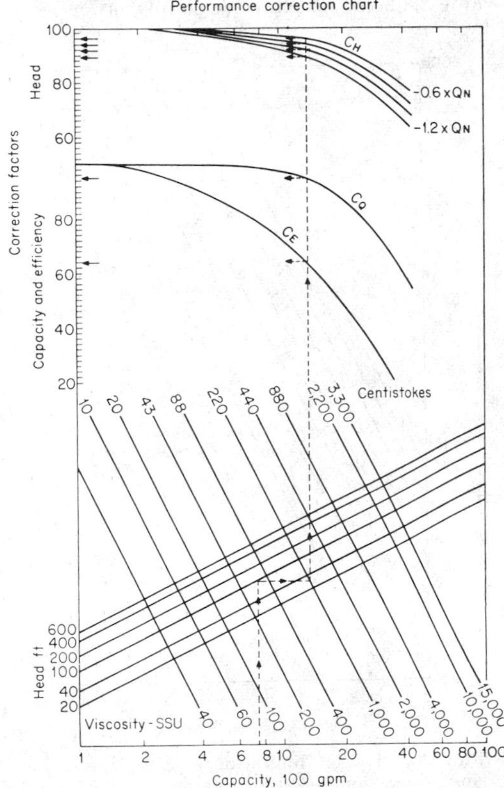

FIG. 25. Performance correction chart for effect of viscosity. (Hydraulic Institute.)

In order for a pump to deliver its rated output, it is obviously necessary that it be supplied with fluid at its inlet at the same rate. It is further necessary that the absolute pressure (including velocity head, $V^2/2g$) of the fluid at the inlet must exceed the vapor pressure by an amount sufficient to overcome (1) any entrance or frictional losses between the point of entry into the pump and the impeller, and (2) the shock losses occurring at the impeller inlet. This gives rise to the definition of **net positive suction head, NPSH,** which is the absolute pressure at the pump inlet expressed in feet of liquid, plus velocity head, minus the vapor pressure of the fluid at pumping temperature, and corrected to the elevation of the pump centerline in the case of horizontal pumps or to the entrance to the first-stage impeller for vertical pumps.

NPSH required is determined by the pump manufacturer and is a function of both pump speed and pump capacity. **NPSH available** represents the energy level of the fluid over the vapor pressure at the pump inlet and is determined entirely by the system preceding the pump. Unless NPSH available at least equals NPSH required at any condition of operation, some of the fluid will vaporize in the pump inlet and bubbles of vapor will be carried into the impeller. These bubbles will collapse violently at some point downstream of the pump inlet (usually at some point within the impeller) and produce very sharp, crackling noises, frequently accompanied by physical damage of adjacent metal surfaces. This phenomenon is known as **cavitation** and is generally highly undesirable.

A term similar to that used for pump specific speed has been developed for pump inlet characteristics and has been identified as **suction specific speed,** $S = N\sqrt{Q}/H_{sv}^{3/4}$, where H_{sv} is NPSH. For double-suction impellers, $S = N\sqrt{Q/2}/H_{sv}^{3/4}$. The value S, like N_s, is expressed simply as a number and, for general-purpose pumps, does not generally exceed 10,000, where N is in rpm, Q is in gpm; and H_{sv} is in ft.

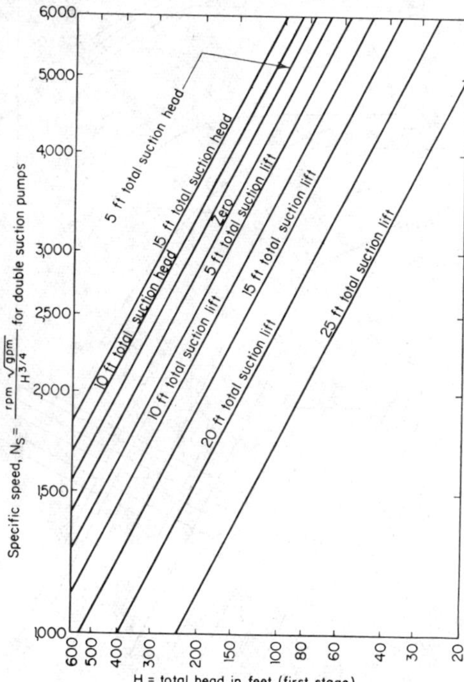

FIG. 26. Upper limits of specific speed for single-stage double-suction pumps. (Hydraulic Institute.)

Within the limits of NPSH capabilities, it is desirable to select a pump of the highest specific speed since this will produce the highest pump speed and consequently use the smallest pump. As a convenience in accomplishing this for the commonly occurring case of cold water, the Hydraulic Institute has published a series of charts defining upper limits of specific speed as a function of total head and suction lift or suction head. These charts provide conservative limits for water temperatures to 85 F. The chart for double-suction pumps is reproduced in Fig. 26.

Just as the head-capacity characteristic of a pump is represented by a curve indicating reducing head developed with increasing capacity, the head-capacity requirements of the system served by the pump can be depicted by a curve showing increased head requirements for increased flow, *i.e.*, a **system-head curve** (Fig. 27). The capacity at which a pump will operate in this system is that at which the pump head-capacity curve intersects the system-head curve.

Every system-head curve consists of (1) a total static head (which may in some cases be equal to zero) plus (2) friction losses. The total static head $H_{stat} = H_d - H_s + P_d - P_s$, where H_d and H_s are the elevations at the system's termination and origin, respectively, and P_d and P_s are the gage pressures at the same points. In the special case of a continuous fresh-water system where $P_d = P_s =$ zero (*i.e.*, atmospheric), it must be remembered that syphon recovery cannot exceed 1 atm (34 ft less vapor pressure at sea level) and that recovery will not occur if the syphon leg is broken. Thus, any system over this height will have a total static-head component at least equal to the difference between its highest elevation and H_s minus the static-head equivalent of 1 atm plus the vapor pressure, even where $H_d = H_s$.

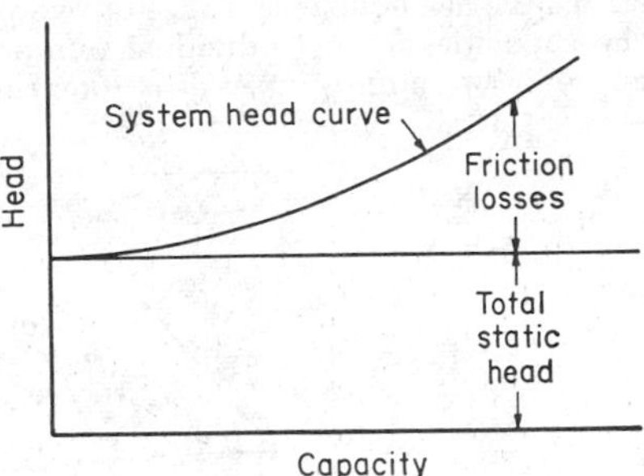

FIG. 27. System-head curve.

The **friction losses** H_{fr} are the sum of the line losses H_1, fitting losses H_f, and changes in velocity head across the system, H_v. (See Sec. 3 for calculation methods.) H_v is simply the velocity-head difference between the system's termination and origin; $H_v = V_d^2/2g - V_s^2/2g$.

In complex pumping systems, such as municipal water-supply operations, both the total static-head and the friction-loss components may be variable, *e.g.*, the former by changes in reservoir levels and the latter by the particular combination of lines being served at any given moment. This results in upper and lower limits of system-head requirements, and the intersection of these limiting curves with the pump head-capacity curve will define the capacity range over which the pump will be required to operate

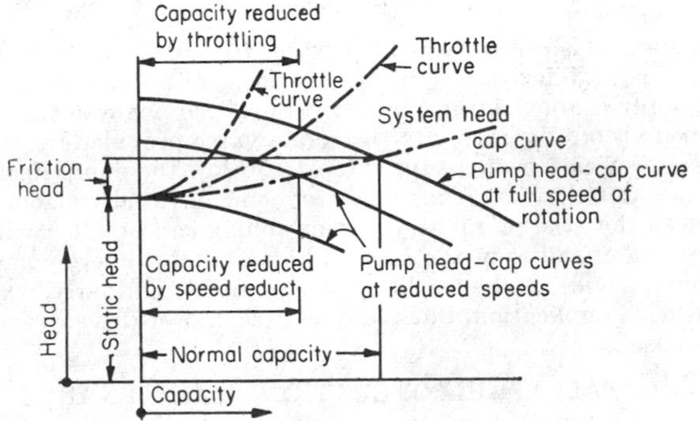

FIG. 28. Pump operation in a system.

Since the capacity at which a pump will operate corresponds to the intersection of the system-head curve with the pump head-capacity curve, any changes in pump capacity can only be obtained by varying one or the other of these two curves (Fig. 28). Thus the capacity of a centrifugal pump operating in a system can be regulated by (1) changing the pump speed or (2) throttling in the discharge piping. The former method is preferable whenever the driver permits it, because throttling always involves an appreciable waste of power.

Pump capacity should never be permitted to be reduced to zero because the fluid within the pump would have to absorb the entire power input and therefore would heat up rapidly with injurious effects on the pump. A small bypass line should be provided in the pump discharge line to permit a predetermined amount of liquid to flow through the pump if the discharge valve is closed entirely. This bypass may be operated manually or automatically.

Centrifugal pumps may sometimes be operated in **parallel** or in **series.** To construct the head-capacity curve of two pumps in parallel, it is merely necessary to add the capacities of the individual pumps for various total heads. The head-capacity curve of two pumps in series is constructed by adding the individual pump heads for

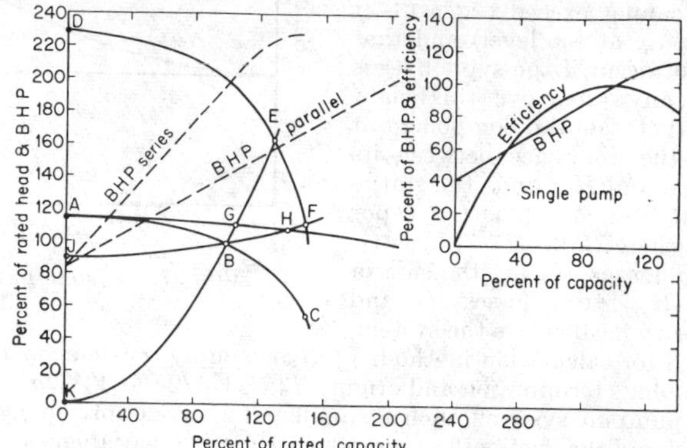

FIG. 29. Series and parallel operation of centrifugal pumps.

various capacities. Figure 29 shows series and parallel operation of two centrifugal pumps with both flat and steep system-head curves.

Priming

A centrifugal pump is primed when the waterways of the pump are filled with the liquid to be pumped. When first put into service, the waterways are filled with air. If the suction supply is above atmospheric pressure, priming is accomplished by venting the entrapped air out of the pump through a valve provided for this purpose. If the pump takes its suction from a supply located below the pump itself, the air in the pump must be evacuated by some vacuum-producing device, by placing a foot valve in the suction line so that the pump and suction piping can be filled with liquid, or by providing a priming chamber in the suction line. Almost every commercially made vacuum-producing device can be used to prime pumps. Formerly, water- and steam-jet primers had wide application, but today electric-motor-driven vacuum pumps are most frequently used.

INSTALLATION, OPERATION, MAINTENANCE

Proper installation, operation, and maintenance of centrifugal pumps will vary widely over the complete range of services to which the pumps may be applied, and satisfactory results in these areas can only be fully achieved by following the manufacturer's instructions for the size and type of unit involved. There are, however, certain general considerations which should be observed and which will seldom need to be modified under any circumstances.

In general, the location selected for installation should be as close to the source of the fluid as possible, consistent with the requirement that adequate space be made available to provide accessibility for operation, inspection, and maintenance. The pumping unit should be mounted on a foundation of sufficient size and rigidity to support the unit itself plus the weight of the fluid it will contain during operation and to maintain accurate alignment. Piping should be independently supported and anchored to avoid imposing stresses on the pump, and suction piping in particular must be designed to minimize friction losses and to present a uniform velocity profile at the pump inlet. Suction and discharge (and/or check) valves must be suitable for the pressures involved and, in the case of large units, may also require independent support. If the pump will be required to operate against a suction lift, a suitable priming system must be installed, and where it is to be provided with a head on suction, it will often be necessary to provide a venting arrangement. Care must also be exercised to ensure that all auxiliary connections for sealing, cooling, flushing, and drainage are made as required for the particular unit being installed.

Prior to initial operation of any centrifugal pump, it is necessary to make sure that the driver is connected to provide proper direction of rotation, that any shaft couplings between separate components of the entire unit are aligned within the manufacturer's stated limits, and that all bearings are provided with the proper amounts and grades of lubricants. The normal starting sequence will then be as follows: (1) open valves in all auxiliary sealing, cooling, flushing, and bypass lines; (2) open suction valve; (3) close discharge valve for low-specific-speed pumps where no check valve is installed after the pump, or open discharge valve for high-specific-speed pumps or wherever a discharge check valve has been provided; (4) prime or vent as necessary; (5) energize the driver; and (6) open discharge valve if it was previously closed in step 3.

Following start-up and until proper operation has been adequately established, it is desirable to monitor bearing temperature, stuffing-box leakage, and other outward symptoms of the unit's behavior. Securing of the pump is accomplished by a reversal of the start-up sequence, encompassing steps 6, 5, 3, and 1, in that order.

In the matter of pump maintenance, a generally accepted cardinal rule is that as long as operation continues normal, the unit should be left alone. Thus, except in special circumstances, periodic overhauls are not recommended. The amount and degree of maintenance likely to be required are influenced primarily by the nature of the service to which the pump is applied, and maintenance practices must therefore be determined largely by the user as a result of his own experience.

COMPRESSORS

BY

Lyman F. Scheel

REFERENCES: API Standards 617 and 618. Balje, ASME Paper 60-WA-231. CAGI, "Compressed Air Handbook," McGraw-Hill. Scheel, "Gas and Air Compression Machinery," McGraw-Hill. Stepanoff, "Turboblowers," Wiley. Shepherd, "Principles of Turbomachinery," Macmillan.

Notation

a = piston-rod area, sq in.
A = piston or impeller area, sq in.
acfm = actual volume, cu ft per min
ata = atmospheres of pressure absolute, 14.22 psi
atu = atmospheres of pressure gage, 14.22 psi
b = impeller-tip width, in.
c = specific heat
C = cylinder clearance, decimal fraction
c_p = specific heat at constant pressure
c_v = specific heat at constant volume
cfm = cu ft per min
cfs = cu ft per sec
d = diameter, in. or as referenced
D = diameter, ft or as referenced for specific equation
D_s = specific diameter
E_v = volumetric efficiency, decimal fraction
f = valve resistance in velocity heads
fpm = piston speed, ft per min
fps = tip speed, ft per sec
g = acceleration due to gravity, 32.2 ft per sec²
H_j = heat rejection, Btu per bhp hr
k = ratio of specific heats, c_p/c_v
K = valve-loss correction factor
L = length of piston stroke, in. or as specified for reference equation
L_{ad} = adiabatic head, ft of gas
L_w'' = head, in. of water
m = meter, metric system
$\bar{m}$ = mole weight
M* = Mach number
Mcfd = thousands of cu ft per day
MMcfd = millions of cu ft per day
MMscfd = millions of std cu ft per day
N = rpm
N_s = specific speed
P = pressure, psia
PS = European unit of power = 0.986 hp
Q = capacity or flow, as specified by equation involved
q_{ad} = pressure coefficient
R = universal gas constant, 1545.4 ft-lb per deg R per mole

R_c = ratio of compression
R_e = Reynolds number
scfm = std cu ft per min
T = absolute temperature, deg R
T = thrust, lb
U = piston speed, tip speed, or pitch-line velocity, fps
v_s = specific volume, cu ft per lb
w = weight flow, lb per sec
W = weight flow, lb per hr
X = ratio factor, as designated for specific equation
Y = pressure drop, decimal fraction
Z = compressibility factor, decimal fraction

Greek

α = ratio of piston area to minimum valve area
Δpsi = pressure loss or differential pressure
Δt = isentropic temperature rise, deg F
η = efficiency, decimal fraction
Θ = compressor-valve resistance factor (Table 1)
Λ = valve leakage factor, decimal fraction
ρ = density, lb per cu ft
σ = exponential function, $(k - 1)/k$
Σ = hp per MMcfd
τ = sonic velocity, fps
ϕ = flow coefficient

Subscripts

1 = suction conditions
2 = discharge conditions
ad = adiabatic
ag = average gas
aw = average water
b = mixture
c = compression or compressor
d = disk
dng = dry natural gas
m = mechanical
o = orifice
s = specific
v = vapor
w = water

Air Compressors

Compressed air is a form of utility energy used extensively for operations such as automatic machines, tools, material handling, and food processing. Most plant air systems are maintained at 90 to 110 psig to operate the tools and machines which require 70 to 90 psig. Instrument-control devices require 25 psig, which are usually supplied from intermediate 50-psig feeders. Other applications that require large quantities of lower-pressure air are usually installed adjacent to the operation to avoid extensive pipe systems. In addition to these permanent-utility air systems, there are innumerable portable air compressors used for construction, mining, road building, and painting. They range from 25 cfm and 2 hp to 1,200 cfm and 300 hp. Most portable compressors are now of the rotary sliding-vane (Fig. 30) and the helical-lobe (Fig. 27) types. Most permanent installations use piston compressors available as stock items in sizes ranging from 30 to 1,500 cfm, with pressures of 60, 100, and 150 psig, and to 150 hp. Engine-starting service requires 250 psig. Oil-well drilling, soot blowing, and *in situ* operations require pressures of 350 to 600 psig and considerably more power. These units are rated on the cfm piston displacement. The "free-air," or ambient, capacity is less than the piston displacement by the amount of the volumetric efficiency (see Fig. 6). The power load varies directly as the barometric pressure and inversely as the Rankine temperature. The former is depressed 0.48 psia per 1,000 ft of elevation (the average barometric pressure, in mile-high Denver, is 12.2 psia).

Gas-measurement Units

Gas, being aeriform, must be defined to have **identity.** The most widely accepted unit of measurement in the United States is the **standard cubic foot,** fixed at 60 F (519.7R) and 14.696 psia (760 mm or 29.92 in. Hg). A dry cubic foot of air at these conditions weighs 0.0763 lb and has a specific gravity of 1.000. It is common practice to accept the basic condition as 14.70 psia and 60 F. Many of the older gas-purchasing contracts are based on 14.40 psia and 60 F. The capacity of piston compressors is rated in cfm and is referred to a 14.4-psia base. This is a convenience occasioned by the canceling of 14.4 psia by 1,440 min per day [see Eq. (**10**)]. A volume at 14.4 psia base is 2 percent lighter than the same volume at 14.7 psia. Dry air has a molecular volume of 379.5 cu ft at standard conditions. The universal gas constant, **R**, is 1545.4 ft-lb per deg R per mole. When pressure is applied in units of psi, the gas contant becomes 10.73. Volume flow in the gas industry is measured in millions of std cu ft per day (MMscfd). The European standard unit of volume is the normal cu m per hr; based on 0 C and 760 mm (1.0333 kg per sq cm), it is equal to 0.625 scfm. The British use a std cu m per hr based on 60 F and 30.00 in. Hg. The European unit of absolute pressure is an "ata" and is equal to 14.22 psia. The term "atu" refers to the gage pressure in excess of ambient. The European unit of power *PS* is 0.986 hp, U.S. or British.

Types of Compressors

Compressors fall into two broad categories: displacement and rotodynamic machines. The reciprocating-piston type (Figs. 2 and 3) prevails in the former category, with capacities ranging from 30 to 9,000 cfm and suitable for pressures to 10,000 psi. The cycle is portrayed in Fig. 1, with the suction from *D* to *A*, compression from *A* to *B*, discharge from *B* to *C*, and expansion of the trapped clearance gas from *C* to *D*. Admission and delivery to the cylinder are through valves (Figs. 8 to 10), where the seating elements are motivated by the differential pressures *F*–*G* and *G*–*B*. The displacement category includes several types of rotary compressors, such as the multiple-lobe, sliding-vane, and liquid ring-seal units shown in Figs. 27 to 31. The inlet gas passes through a port, the rotor effects a cutoff, and the gas is compressed by the action of the rotor in the stator eccentric-cylinder confinement; sizes range from 40 to 20,000 cfm for low-pressure and vacuum services. The helical-lobe, axial-flow compressor can handle 800 to 13,000 cfm at 150 psi across the case, and in series they are limited to 250 psig and 450 F.

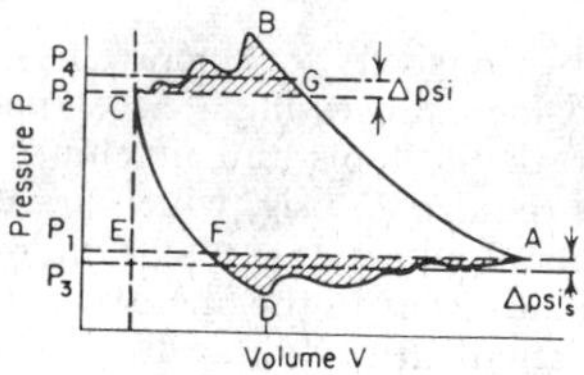

FIG. 1. Typical gas-compression-indicator diagram.

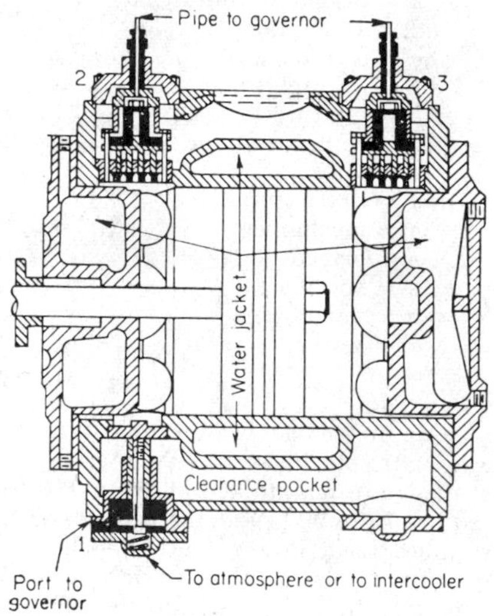

FIG. 2. Cross section of gas-compressor cylinder, showing water jackets, clearance pocket with pneumatic control, and suction-valve lift devices.

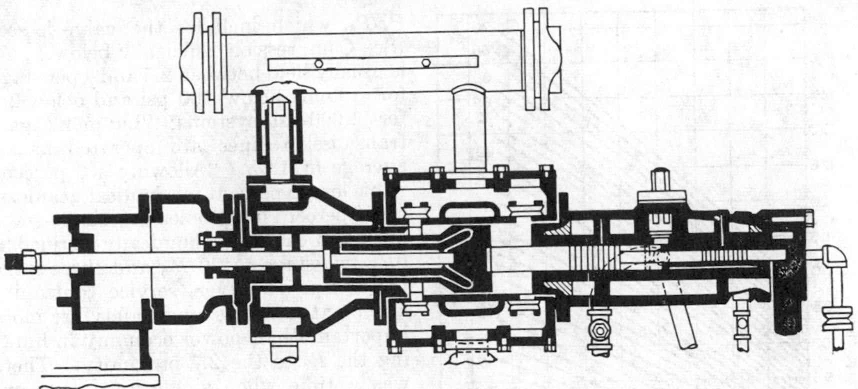

FIG. 3. Four-stage truncated tandem 4,000-psi compressor.

The rotodynamic machine depends upon its high impeller velocity (1,000 fps) to impart sufficient momentum to the gas to effect the necessary rise in pressure. The centrifugal compressor dominates this category with sizes ranging from 100-hp stock refrigeration units to 20,000-hp units for heavy chemicals and volumes up to 200,000 acfm. Figure 26 illustrates a horizontally split-case model used for pressures to 800 psi; Fig. 14 shows the vertically split-case barrel-type design for pressures to 5,000 psi. For maximum volumes, the simpler steady-flow axial compressor is used. Industrial models (Fig. 15) range from 8,000 acfm to 13 MMacfm, with ratio of compression R_c limited to 4. The aircraft jet engine uses this type of compressor for volumes of 1,700 acfm to 350 Macfm and to $R_c = 16$. (See also p. 9–150 *et seq.*) There is a mixed-flow model where the radial outflow pattern lies 45 deg with respect to the axis. There are still other designs attempting to handle smaller flow rates at higher heads and lower N_s, such as drag or regenerative compressors and partial-emission and pitot pumps (see Balje chart, Fig. 21).

Thrust Loading

The piston-rod thrust determines the load capacity of a compressor frame. The heaviest frames have a piston-rod capacity of 100,000 lb or more; the medium sizes, 14- to 18-in. stroke, have 67,000-lb capacity; 10- to 12-in. stroke, 25,000 lb; and the 5-in., balanced-opposed units, 12,000 to 18,000 lb. The specific loading on the piston rod is 10,000 psi with SAE 4140 and 7,500 psi with SAE 1050. Bearing sizes and frame structure are predicated upon this loading. (Consult manufacturer for definitive limits.) The controlling piston-rod tension load is determined from

$$\text{Tension, lb} = A(P_2 - P_1) - aP_2 \tag{1}$$

where A is the piston area and a is the rod area, both in sq in.; subscripts 1 and 2, odd and even numbers, refer to the absolute suction and discharge pressures, respectively. When compressor cylinders are unloaded by lifting the suction valve, the head end is preferably unloaded first. Working the crank end as a single-acting cylinder provides thrust reversals and permits normal lubrication to the wrist pin. When the head end works in single action, the wrist pin remains in compression for both throws, which blocks the oil flow.

Ratio of Compression

Performance is customarily evaluated on the ratio of compression $R_c = P_2/P_1$ (see Fig. 1). These pressures represent stagnation-line-connection conditions, which by strict interpretation should include the respective line-velocity head. These losses are usually negligible where line velocities are less than 50 fps and densities less than 1,000 psi. The full area of the indicator diagram is obtained by integrating

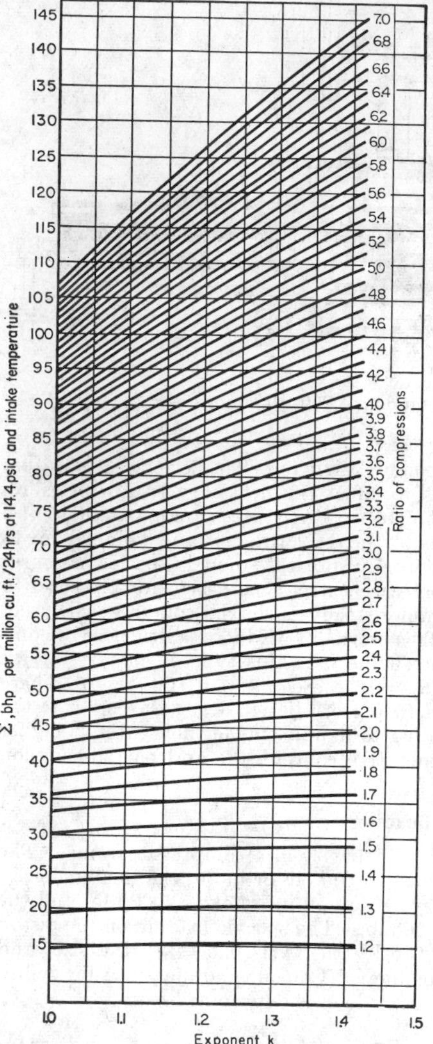

FIG. 4. Approximate horsepower to compress air or gas. If single stage, multiply cubic feet actual capacity of free gas per minute by 1,440 to obtain capacity in millions of cubic feet per 24 hours. Then capacity in 24 hours times horsepower per million as obtained from the chart will give the total horsepower. If two stage, take the square root of the total number of compressions. Read the horsepower from the chart for this ratio, multiplying the same for the two stages, to which add 3 percent for cooler loss. Note that horsepower is for 14.4 psia intake. If horsepower based on capacity at 14.7 psia, add 2 percent to horsepower.

P_4/P_3, which includes the valve losses. (See Compression Efficiency below.) R_c is usually held between 2.5 and 4 per stage for systems below 500 psi and below 2.5 for 1,000-psi systems; "big-inch" gas-transmission lines are operated at an average of $1.3R_c$. Allowing a 9 percent valve loss, 5 percent mechanical-gear loss, and 3 percent intercooler loss, single-stage operation can be economically justified to $6R_c$, two-stage to 20 R_c, and three-stage to 60 R_c. However, service continuity and plant and personnel safety are more important than power economy in limiting the R_c to the 2.7 proximity. There was a time when single-stage air compressors discharging at 100 psig and even 200 psig were commonplace and were responsible for numerous fires and explosions. Unsaturated gases from refinery processes are unstable above 220 F and form heavy gums and coke. The maintenance and service interruption resulting from such high R_c operation and subsequent temperatures are prohibitive.

Power Requirement

The power required for a given pressure rise is determined by the product of the volume and Σ, a function of R_c; *i.e.*,

$$\Sigma = [(\mathbf{K}R_c)^{\sigma} - 1]46/\sigma \qquad (2)$$

where σ is $(k - 1)/k$ and k is the ratio of specific heats. The equation includes a mechanical-gearing loss of 5 percent and is at a pressure base of 14.4 psia and 60 F. **K** is a valve-loss correction factor [see Table 2 and Eq. (**8**)]. For air, where $k = 1.40$ and $\mathbf{K} = 1.13$ for 6 percent loss in pressure through each set of valves,

$$\Sigma_{\text{air}} = 161[(1.13R_c)^{0.286} - 1] \qquad (3)$$

For dry natural gas, where $k = 1.255$ and $\bar{m} = 19$ and with the same valve loss, **K** becomes 1.08 and

$$\Sigma_{\text{dng}} = 227[(1.08R_c)^{0.203} - 1] \qquad (4)$$

Also $\Sigma_{\text{dng}} = 0.0456\bar{m}c_v\Delta t$, where c_v is the specific heat at constant volume and Δt is the isentropic temperature rise. A multiplier of 0.147 applied to the above Σ values gives the bhp per 100 cfm at 14.4 psia and 60 F. Figure 4 illustrates a popular empirical solution for Σ, wherein an arbitrary compression efficiency of 68 percent is applied at $1.5R_c$, 78 percent at $2R_c$, and 87 percent at $4R_c$. Mechanical efficiency of 95 percent is widely accepted, which includes loss allowances of 1 percent for piston-ring friction and piston-rod packing and 3 percent for gearing friction of the crosshead, slipper guides, connecting-rod pins, and crankshaft bearings. The latter losses are dissipated by convectional air circulation in frame sizes under 300 hp and into the lubricant system in larger sizes. The ring and packing losses are mostly absorbed by the jacket-water system. Where the cylinder power is less than 100 hp, these losses should be doubled.

Temperature Rise

Piston compression is essentially an adiabatic function, especially when referred to the internal cylinder conditions. The compression-temperature rise follows the equation

$$T_2 = T_1(\mathbf{K}R_c)^{\sigma/\eta} \tag{5}$$

where η represents the heat leak factor applied in a manner consistent with the thermal efficiency. These factors are less than 1.05 for normal water-jacket cylinders, 1.09 for dry-jacket cylinders, 1.11 for forced-air–cooled cylinders with fins, and 1.15 for high-velocity water-jacket cooling and the expansion cycle, curve *CFD* on Fig. 1. There was a time when water was injected into the suction of air compressors to reduce the discharge temperature; when the speed of machinery was increased and the clearance volume reduced, the practice was abandoned as hazardous. The temperature drop was substantial; η was 1.75. The scheme is still applied in chemical processes to wash out unsaturated gums and to suppress the discharge temperature of exothermic gases. The liquid is usually a light solvent of the same character as the gas and is atomized into the suction line. A short, 10-sec blast of steam every 2 or 4 hr can usually clear the gums from a cylinder.

The temperature behavior is only consistent below $4R_c$; beyond this, the cylinder cooling effect is perceptible because of the reduced mass flow at higher R_c operation. European practice of process sizing includes a **warm-up** factor, which presumes the gas is heated 20 to 40 F in passing through the hot cylinder and suction valves. Such a correction complements the volumetric efficiency by a judgment factor of 0.95 to 0.90. Thermocouple probes on the suction valve and in the flow stream show no such evidence at the ambient-temperature range. American practice has always disregarded such corrections. The warm-up factor also allows for valve and piston-ring leakage. If such leakage is perceptible, the temperature rise is usually cumulative and readily detectable by thermometry.

Compression Efficiency

Compression efficiency is an approximate method of accounting for all the power losses that occur between stagnant suction and discharge pressures. It presumes that all valve areas and gas channels offer equal resistance and that the compressor speed and character of the gas are inconsequential. The height of the crosshatched area *BCG* and *AFD* (Fig. 1) represents the Δpsi valve loss and can be evaluated from

$$\Delta\text{psi} = 1.26 \times 10^{-6}\alpha^2 f U^2 \text{ sp gr } P/Z \tag{6}$$

where f is the valve resistance in velocity heads (usually 4), α is the ratio of piston area to minimum valve area (should be about 10), U is the average piston speed (13.3 fps). Introducing these values, the equation becomes

$$\Delta\text{psi} = 0.09P \text{ sp gr}/Z = \mathbf{K}P \text{ sp gr}/Z \tag{7}$$

and

$$\mathbf{K}R_c = \left(\frac{P_2}{P_1}\right)\left(\frac{1 + \Theta \text{ sp gr}}{1 - \Theta \text{ sp gr}}\right)\left(\frac{Z_1}{Z_2}\right) \tag{8}$$

See Tables 1 and 2 for Θ and **K** correction values.

Performance Definitions

The power required and the temperature are determined by the intrinsic corrected $\mathbf{K}R_c$ value and Eqs. (**2**) and (**5**). The cylinder charge pressure and the suction-line stagnation or snubbed pressure are one and the same and are depicted as point A in Fig. 1. A horizontal projection of this point to the expansion curve CD determines the volumetric efficiency AF/AE, which is corrected for compressibility by Z_1/Z_2, and the expansion is a function of the stagnation R_c, without the **K** correction. The k value is corrected for the mean adiabatic-temperature rise in reference to the mole fraction.

Table 1. Compressor-valve Resistance Factor θ*

(Showing influence of valve area and piston-speed resistance entering and leaving the cylinder)

Piston-valve ratio, α	Piston speed, fpm and fps						
	600 10.0	700 11.7	800 13.3	900 15.0	1,000 16.7	1,100 18.3	1,200 20.0
20	0.202	0.275	0.360	0.457			
15	0.113	0.155	0.202	0.257	0.332	0.382	0.454
12	0.073	0.100	0.130	0.164	0.203	0.246	0.292
10	0.051	0.069	0.090	0.114	0.140	0.170	0.202
8	0.033	0.044	0.058	0.074	0.090	0.110	0.131
6	0.018	0.025	0.032	0.041	0.050	0.060	0.071
4	0.008	0.011	0.014	0.018	0.022	0.027	0.032

* $\theta = 1.26 \times 10^{-6}\alpha^2 fU^2$, and $\Delta\text{psi} = \theta \text{ sp gr } P/Z$.

Table 2. Valve-loss Correction Factors K*

(As applied to ratio of stagnation pressures for the intrinsic power of compression determination)

Piston-valve ratio, α	Piston speed, fpm and fps							Specific gravity
	600 10.0	700 11.7	800 13.3	900 15.0	1,000 16.7	1,100 18.3	1,200 20	
12	1.34	1.50	1.70	1.97	2.37	2.93	3.72	2.0
12	1.16	1.22	1.30	1.39	1.51	1.66	1.83	1.0
12	1.09	1.13	1.17	1.22	1.27	1.35	1.43	0.6
10	1.23	1.32	1.44	1.59	1.78	2.09	2.34	2.0
10	1.11	1.15	1.19	1.26	1.33	1.41	1.51	1.0
10	1.06	1.09	1.12	1.15	1.18	1.23	1.28	0.6
8	1.14	1.19	1.26	1.35	1.44	1.57	1.71	2.0
8	1.07	1.10	1.12	1.16	1.20	1.25	1.30	1.0
8	1.04	1.06	1.07	1.09	1.11	1.13	1.15	0.6
6	1.06	1.11	1.14	1.17	1.22	1.27	1.33	2.0
6	1.04	1.05	1.07	1.09	1.11	1.13	1.20	1.0
6	1.03	1.03	1.04	1.05	1.06	1.07	1.09	0.6

* $\mathbf{K} = (1 + \theta \text{ sp gr})/(1 - \theta \text{ sp gr})$. **K** applied to the stagnation R_c produces the intrinsic R_c experienced with the cylinder.

Cylinder Sizing

The exact displacement of a double-acting (DA) cylinder is

$$\text{cfm} = 9.1[D^2 - (d/2)^2]LN\ 10^{-4} \tag{9}$$

where D = cylinder bore, in.; d = piston-rod diameter, in.; L = stroke, in.; and N = rpm. The rod effect is negligible in cylinders larger than 10 in., and at the average piston speed of 13.3 fps, Eq. (**9**) simplifies to $4.23D^2$. Piston speed is established by effective response of the floating elements in the suction valve and the bearing design. Piston speeds of 45 fps are common for aircraft engines and experience an excellent volumetric efficiency with mechanical suction-valve gearing, as shown in Fig. 5. The capacity of a process-gas cylinder is

$$\text{MMcfd} = 10^{-4} \text{ cfm } P_1E_v/Z \tag{10}$$

EXAMPLE: Size a 50-hp air cylinder to handle 24.7 psia, 100 F to 74.0 psia, where $Z = 1.0$, $E_v = 0.70$, and $\theta = 0.09$. $R_c = 74/24.7 = 3.0$; $\mathbf{K}R_c = 3(1.09/0.91) = 3.6$; $(\mathbf{K}R_c)^{0.286} = 1.442$. From Eq. (**3**), $\Sigma = 161(1.442 - 1) = 71$ bhp/MMcfd at 60 F and 76.3 at 100 F. The air capacity is 50/76.5, or 654 Mcfd, and the cylinder displacement by Eq. (**10**) is 379 cfm, which requires a $(379/4.2)^{0.5}$, or 9.5-in. bore. A 15-in.-stroke cylinder would run; $(13.3 \times 60)/(1.25 \times 2) = 320$ rpm. The standard capacity is $654 \times (14.4/14.7) \times (520/560) = 595$ Mscfd.

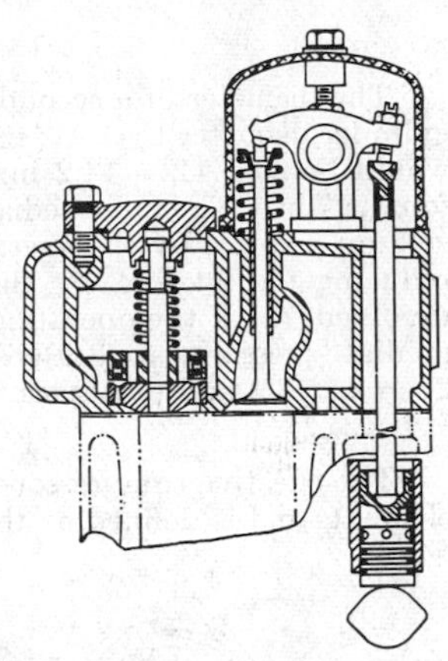

FIG. 5. Compressor cylinder head with mechanically operated suction valve and spring-loaded poppet discharge valve. (*Schramm.*)

Volumetric Efficiency

The clearance space in a cylinder is that volume (CP_2 in Fig. 1) not displaced by the piston sweep. A nominal clearance of 0.100 in. is usually allowed between the extended piston and the cylinder head. This space plus the internal access passage to the valve seat makes the total clearance 10 to 20 percent of the 10- to 20-in. piston displacement. Larger cylinders usually carry the valves in the head, and the clearance is as low as 3 percent for 42-in. bore. High-pressure cylinders smaller than 10 in. usually have a clearance less than 8 percent so as to increase the volumetric efficiency and thereby reduce the rod loading with a smaller bore. Pipeline cylinders are usually provided with 100 percent clearances because they have an optimum loading at 1.2 to 1.6R_c with a constant discharge and variable suction pressure. The volumetric efficiency is

$$E_v = 1 + C - C\Lambda R_c^{1/k} Z_1/Z_2 \qquad \textbf{(11)}$$

where C is clearance, decimal fraction, and Λ is a leakage factor, usually 1.1 (or 10 percent) at R_c below 7. (See Figs. 6 and 7.)

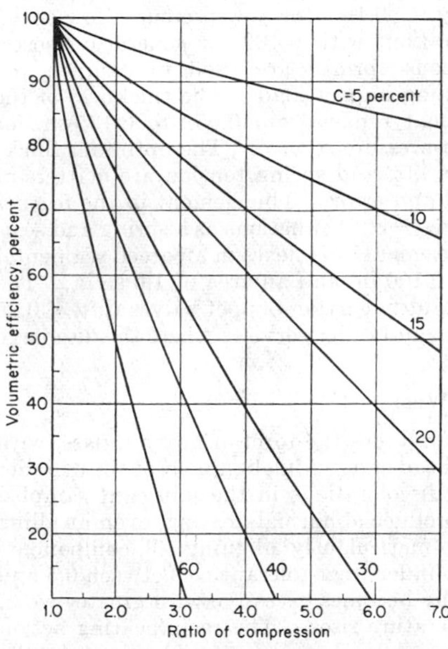

FIG. 6. Volumetric efficiency for air and diatomic gases; $k = 1.40$, $n = 1.38$, $\eta = 1.05$, $\Lambda = 1.10$ [see Eq. (**11**)].

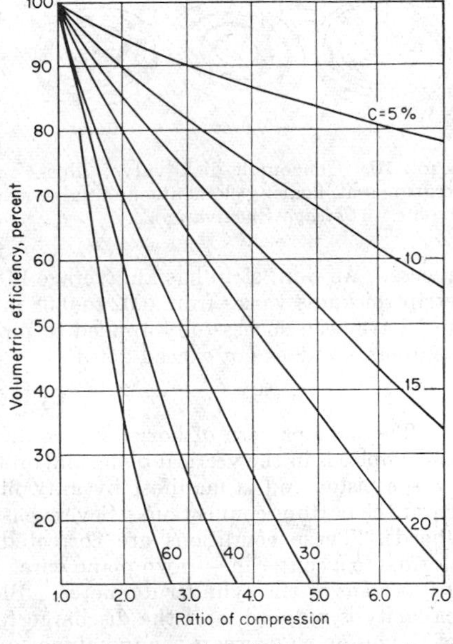

FIG. 7. Volumetric efficiency for natural gas; $\bar{m} = 17.9$, $k = 1.28$, $n = 1.22$, $\eta = 1.10$, $\Lambda = 1.10$ [see Eq. (**11**)].

Multistage Sizing

The diameter of a secondary cylinder can be estimated by dividing the preceding cylinder diameter by 1.41; *i.e.*, if the primary cylinder bore is 20 in., the second stage would be 20/1.41 = 14.2 in., the third stage would be 14.2/1.41 = 10 in., and the fourth, 7 in. The intermediate pressures are determined by multiplying the preceding suction pressure by the average ratio of compression per stage. This is obtained by reducing the total R_c by the negative exponential power of the number of stages involved; *i.e.*, if the operation is from 20 to 1,620 psia, $R_c = 81$, and $R_c^{-4} = 3$, intermediate pressures are 3(9)[27] × 1.03 (allowance for intercooler and piping losses) × 20 = 62(185) and [555] psia.

Compressor Valves

The effective compressor-valve area is fixed by the passage under the raised valve elements and is defined as the product of the element lift and the sum of the valve-

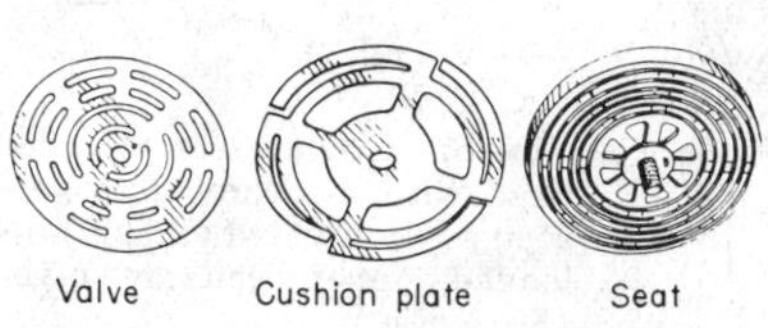

Fig. 8. Plate valve, illustrating floating element, cushion spring, and seat. (*Ingersoll-Rand.*)

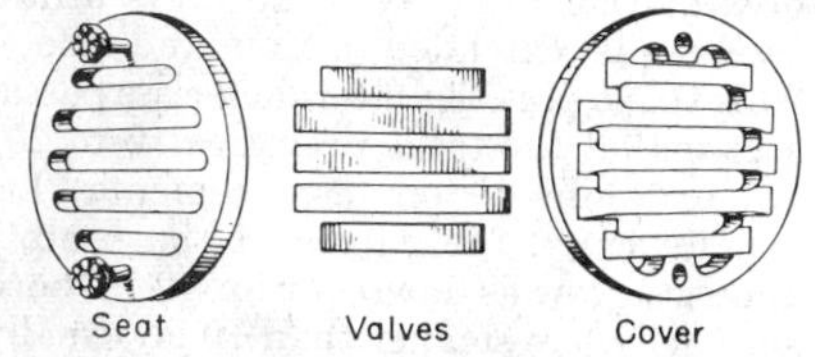

Fig. 9. Feather valve, illustrating seat, flexing elements, and valve cover. (*Worthington.*)

seat peripheries or strip edges, less the guide and end contacting surfaces. The plate- and strip-type valves (Figs. 8 and 9) are generally used in air and low-pressure service. The concentric-disk type (Fig. 10) is used in high-pressure chemical and natural-gas operations. The lift varies from 0.035 in. for high-pressure, high-speed operation to 0.180 for low-pressure, low-speed operation, with 0.100 for general purposes. Various springs are used to dampen the opening impact load. The thickness of the element ranges from 0.050 to 0.125 in. for high-pressure service. The optimum thickness, lift, and spring tension are matters of trial and error. The element in the feather valve (Fig. 9) functions as a spring and sealing element. It flexes in an arced segmental recess. An 8-in. strip has an average lift of 0.100 in. and an area of 1.6 sq in. The strip thickness varies from 0.02 to 0.08 in. Multiple nylon poppet valves (lift = 0.25 in.) have been successfully applied to pipeline and other services where the discharge temperature does not exceed 250 F.

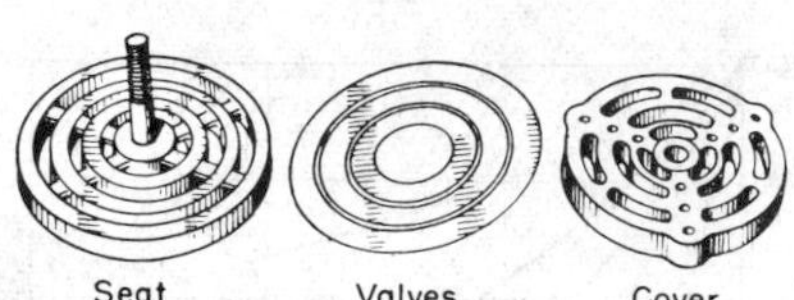

Fig. 10. Concentric-disk valve, illustrating seat, floating elements, and valve cover. (*Chicago Pneumatic.*)

Cylinder Wear

The wear pattern of horizontal compressors takes the form of an hourglass, with the emphasis in the vertical plane and on the head end. Malalignment of the cylinder or the piston rod is manifest by gray filing discolorations in the lubricant sampled from the bottom connection. Severe cases produce abnormal heating, even at idling speeds. These conditions are corrected by meticulously aligning all components normal to a centerline-drawn piano wire. Cylinder-wear tolerance is between 0.5 and 1.0 percent of the cylinder diameter. Blow-by becomes excessive with greater wear, capacity is reduced, and the discharge temperature rises. The reciprocating action of the piston rings wears the radial face of the ring lands. It is possible to square the lands by machining and fit the grooves with oversize rings or to rebuild the lands by metal spray. The latter repair can be applied to cylinder and piston surface wear, thereby maintaining the original bore. Other operators prefer to use the portable boring bar to true the cylinders to one of several regular oversized bores. When the wear exceeds 0.25 in., a liner is inserted to restore the original bore. The cylinder bore is finished within +0.003 and −0.001 in.

Piston Rings

Pistons are finished with a nominal clearance of 0.001 in. per in. of bore for sizes above 10 in. and with an 0.0015 tolerance for smaller cylinders. Piston rings in a clean, well-lubricated, cylinder may serve effectively for more than 20 years. Such wear as occurs is observed at the open end, where it continues until the section no longer sustains the pressure differential and the ring breaks into small segments. This pressure loading can be relieved by fluting the radial edge to balance the peripheral pressure. Pistons operating below 300 psi have 2 to 4 cast-iron rings; 8 to 16 rings are used for high pressures. A common one-piece snap cast piston ring has a proximate section 0.500 in. wide by 0.375 in. thick. Smaller rings are more fragile and give less service. The rings are finished to fit the cylinder and leave a 0.100-in. gap at the step-cut or diagonal opening. The inherent spring and tension of the ring effect the seal.

Segmental bronze rings are used for high pressures and where snap-ring service is inadequate. Where bronze rings are inadequate, laminated-phenolic, dense-carbon, nylon, or Teflon rings are used. These materials are reinforced with asbestos, cotton, glass, and shredded-bronze fibers and are filled with graphite and molybdenum disulphide lubricants. Phenolic materials are generally satisfactory for non-lubricated Class 1 (NL-1) service. Teflon rings reinforced with glass and bronze fibers and disulphide are rendering satisfactory NL-2 service to 400 F.

Piston-rod Packing

Piston-rod packing includes the same range of materials plus soft rubberized asbestos rings for low-pressure services. Metallic packing consists of spacer cups containing a pair of three-piece rings, alternately cut radially and tangentially. The case for pressures less than 200 psi contains three cups, and for 1,200 psi, eight cups. The pressure is presumed to be progressively reduced through each cup seal; actually the first cup facing the pressure does most of the reduction, and the subsequent rings are for reserve. The case is fed 2 to 5 drops per min of oil and is maintained under 300 F by oil circulation as needed. New packing start-up operations require maximum lubricant, and in severe instances, bright-stock oil often provides the solution. The lateral clearance of the rings in the cup must permit free-floating action for the maximum radial runout of the rod. A runout of 0.002 in. per ft of stroke is acceptable. Metallic packing can tolerate rod wear of 0.15 percent of the rod diameter, with less tolerance above 2,000 psi. The rod should be relatively hard and ground to a 10-rms finish.

Non-lubricated Cylinders

Industries such as the cryogenic and food and drug require gas compression absolutely void of contaminating lubricants. The NL-1 class does not permit any direct lubrication and tolerates the minute contamination introduced along the piston rod. This can be eliminated by an additional spacer and rod wiper, qualifying the cylinder as a class NL-2. The pistons for this service use various segmental carbon rings and riders which can be rotated externally. The life of carbon rings is reduced by low humidities. The cylinder should have a ground 10-rms finish. Custom adds 5 percent friction for such NL service, but experience indicates this is overly generous.

Lubrication

Compressor-piston lubricants serve to (1) prevent wear by providing a low-frictional supporting film between the rubbing surfaces, (2) seal close clearances, (3) protect against corrosion, and (4) transmit heat of friction and minute wear particles away from points of contact. Industrial cylinders and packers require force-feed lubricators. Viscosity is the best index of suitability: general service at pressures below 500 psi requires 400 SSU at 100 F (SAE 40), 700 SSU for 2,000 psi, and 1,000 SSU (SAE 50) for 8,000-psi operations. These oils have a viscosity in excess of 30,000 SSU at or near 40 F, which is impossible to roll for start-up. Good winterizing practice provides continuous circulation of warm jacket-water and an immersed electric heater in the oil reservoir. Crankcase oils should include a foam inhibitor, sludge dispersant, and rust inhibitor. Phosphorus extreme-pressure agents are added to high-pressure lubricants to avoid wear and scuff damage. Castor-bean and rapeseed oils are additives resistant to solvent action of condensing hydrocarbons. Phosphate esters, Cellulube, Houghto-safe, Pydraul AC, and Fluorolubes are used to resist the hazard of exothermic reaction in air compression. The crankcase lubricant consumption for 10 plants over a score of years averaged 20,000 bhp per hr per gal. Table 3 shows lubricant requirements for general process- and natural-gas operations. (See also Sec. 6.)

Table 3. Lubrication Required for Compressor Cylinders

Range of cylinder diam, in.	Film thickness, microns	Thousand hp per hr per gal	Pints per cylinder per day per 100 hp of load	Oil drops per min
24–36	0.40	13	1.5	13
15–23	0.45	19	1.0	9
10–14	0.55	24	0.8	7
7–9	0.60	32	0.6	5
4.7	1.20	24	0.8	7
3–5	1.40	27	0.7	6

Based on 12,500 drops per pt of 5,000 SSU, SAE 40 oil at 75 F with vacuum-type lubricator. Reduce drop count to one-third for pressure-type lubricator. Example: 500 bhp, 20-in. cylinder, requires 5 pt per day and feed of 45 drops per min.

Compressor Accessories

Most state laws and safe practice require a relief valve ahead of the discharge valve in every positive-displacement compressor. It is set to release at 1.25 times normal discharge or at the maximum working pressure of the cylinder, whichever is lower. The relief-valve piping system includes a manual vent valve and/or a bypass valve to the suction to facilitate start-up and shutdown operations. Quick line-sizing equations are (1) line connection, $d/1.75$; (2) bypass, $d/4.5$; (3) vent, $d/6.3$; (4) relief-valve port, $d/9$. For an 18-in.-diam cylinder, these would evaluate, respectively, to 10, 4, 3, and 2 in. diameter.

The line connection to the cylinder involves two complications: (1) to provide attenuation or adequate reservoir capacity to minimize the variation in density at the instant of charge and dispel; (2) to damper undesirable pressure waves. The former is a matter of adequate volume (six to eight single displacements) adjacent to the cylinder. A pulse bottle equal to the cylinder bore or of the next larger nominal pipe size and between 3 and 7 ft long ($\frac{1}{19}$ wavelength) is usually adequate. The wavelength is the quotient of the sonic velocity and the compressor action frequency; where τ is 1,200 fps, a DA cylinder at 360 rpm has a wavelength of 100 ft. A pulse-bottle length should avoid even quarter wavelengths to dampen the offending pressure wave. The pulse-bottle diameter may be further corrected by factor $(\tau/910)^{0.5}$. These unabated pressure waves can be destructive to piping and can make meter and control conditions difficult. Numerous baffles and chokes have been installed in the pulse bottle in an effort to diminish the pressure wave. A more logical and effective method is to install a Helmholtz resonator in the bottle outside-line connection. A simplified resonator consists of a straight tube with a bore one-third of the cylinder diameter and a length equal to the tube bore. This bore would be adequate for air at 60 F and 1 percent pressure drop. Any variation from this can be modified as indicated in Eq. (**12**) and $d_o \approx (1{,}120/\tau)$. The frequency in the tube is accelerated three to four times the source, which restricts the amplitude of the sound-pressure wave that can pass through the filter. An orifice plate can achieve the same effect with slightly more resistance. The orifice diameter is determined from

$$d_o = 0.435 d_c (\overline{m}/kTY)^{0.25} \tag{12}$$

where d_c is the cylinder bore, Y is the decimal fraction of the system pressure to be dissipated in the orifice, usually taken as 0.01, and the average piston speed U is

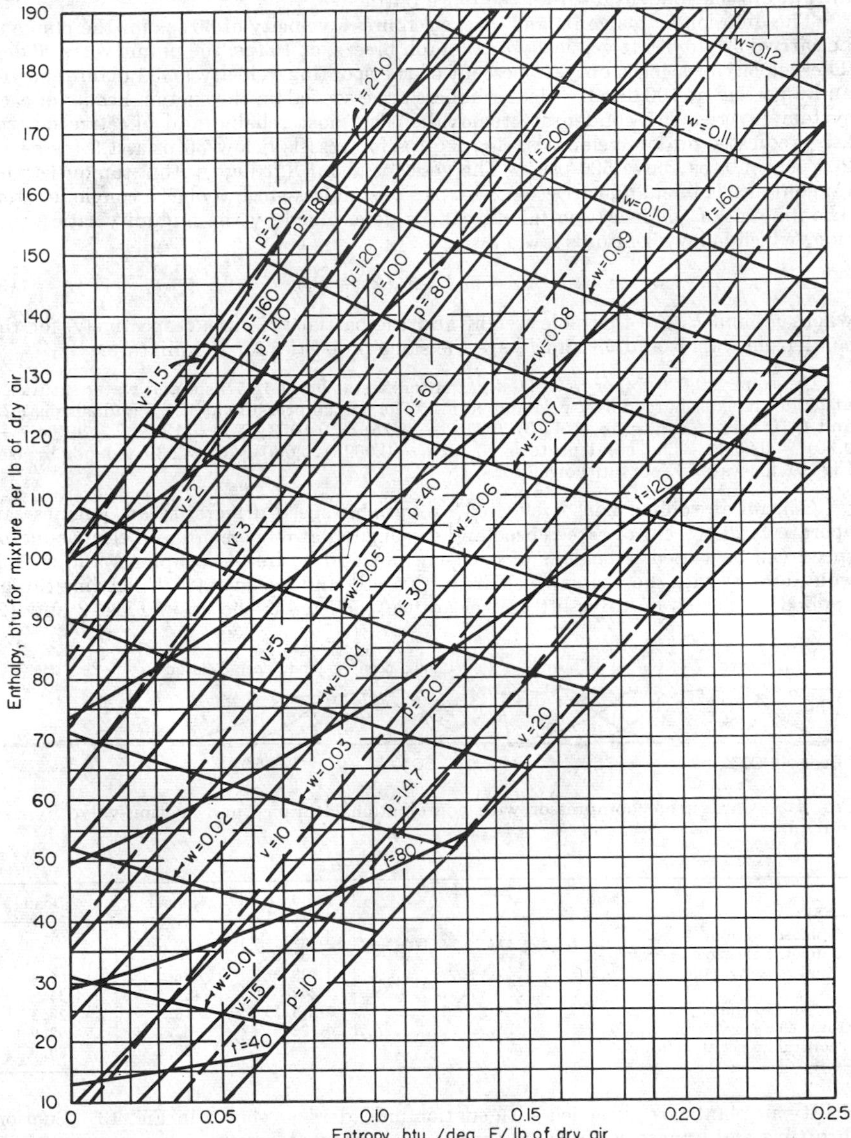

Fig. 11. Enthalpy-entropy diagram for adiabatic compression of air saturated with water vapor (neglecting all consideration of the liquid water present). w = weight of water vapor, lb per lb of dry air; v = specific volume of air-vapor mixture, cu ft per lb of dry air; p = total pressure of mixture, psia; t = temperature of mixture, deg F.

13.3 fps; d_{ox} varies directly as $(U_x/13.3)^{0.5}$. The orifice resistance can be increased on the job site until the intense vibration subsides.

These destructive pressure waves emanate from the energy released in the valve action (*BG* and *FD* in Fig. 1). It has been recently documented that these infrasonic waves tend to increase the condensation recovery beyond the expected equilibriums of Dalton's law. It is advisable to provide drain connections for the withdrawal of such condensate from the pulse bottle.

The diffusion of gas vents and stacks requires a velocity of 30 fps for the plume to be carried 300 to 500 ft vertically in a 5-mph breeze; at 15 fps, the plume veers 20 deg. The velocity of a jet is only 22 percent of the spouting velocity at 30 diam removed and 6 percent at 100 diam. Gas scrubbers are essential on the suction header of each system experiencing condensate removal. The most reliable and effective designs are predicated on low velocities, *e.g.*, 2.5 fps for vessels below 30 psia, 1.5 fps below 200 psia, 1.0 fps above 500 psia. The vessel is about 8 ft high with a top outlet and tangential side inlet and carries an 8-in. pad of stainless-steel wool as a conglomerator. The amount of condensation fallout can be determined by the humidity-ratio equation, which follows Dalton's law,

$$X_v = \bar{m}_v P_v / \bar{m}_b (P_b - P_v) \tag{13}$$

where $\bar{m}_v$ and P_v are the mole weight and the partial pressure, respectively, for the condensing vapor, and $\bar{m}_b$ and P_b are the same properties for the mixture.

Example: 20,000 lb per hr of $20\bar{m}$ gas enters a station at 16.7 psia and water saturated at 121 F; it is discharged 64.7 psia and 90 F. The partial pressure at 121 F and 90 F is 1.75 and 0.70 psia. $X_{121} = 18 \times 1.75/20(16.7 - 1.75) = 0.1053$; $X_{90} = 18 \times 0.7/20(64.7 - 0.70) = 0.0098$. The condensate is $(0.1053 - 0.0098)20{,}000/8.33 = 230$ gal per hr (see Fig. 11 for water-vapor/air corrections).

Control of volume flow is effected by variable-speed drivers; steam engines can operate at 20 percent of rated speed and gas engines at 60 percent, and electric-motor speed can be varied by means of eddy-current and hydraulic couplings and special wound rotors with rheostats, which are both costly and inefficient. Unloading can be applied by means of valve-lift and clearance pockets, as shown in Figs. 2 and 12.

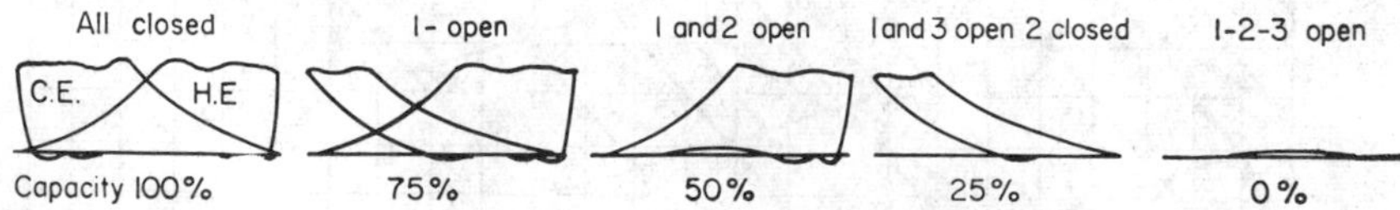

Fig. 12. Cards from compressor with combination clearance and suction-valve bypass control.

Item	Full load	¾ load	½ load
Displacement, cfm	1,546		
Volumetric efficiency, percent	86.0		
Actual capacity, cfm	1,329	996	66.4
Bhp	242	188	135
Bhp per 100 cfm	18.25	18.9	20.3
Motor efficiency, percent	92.5	92.2	90.9
Electrical hp per 100 cfm	19.73	20.5	20.9

Utility air plants are throttled with suction unloaders, as shown in Fig. 13. Suction throttling and bypass controls are used in process operations.

Cylinder Cooling

The principal purpose of a jacket-water system is to normalize cylinder-casting strains. Some cylinders have been operated **dry** for over 12 years without undue maintenance. The heat rejection to the jacket water is

$$H_j = 4(t_{ag} - t_{aw}) + 100 \qquad \text{Btu per bhp per hr} \tag{14}$$

where t_{ag} and t_{aw} represent the average gas and water temperatures, respectively; good practice would offer 155 F and 140 F, respectively, and a rejection of 160 Btu per bhp per hr. Where the temperature rise is between 2 and 5 F, the jacket-water requirement is 160 bhp/(500 × 3.2 Δt_w), or 0.1 gpm per bhp. Efforts to run cold jacket-water systems only produce liner sweating, washing of lubricant, and excessive ring wear.

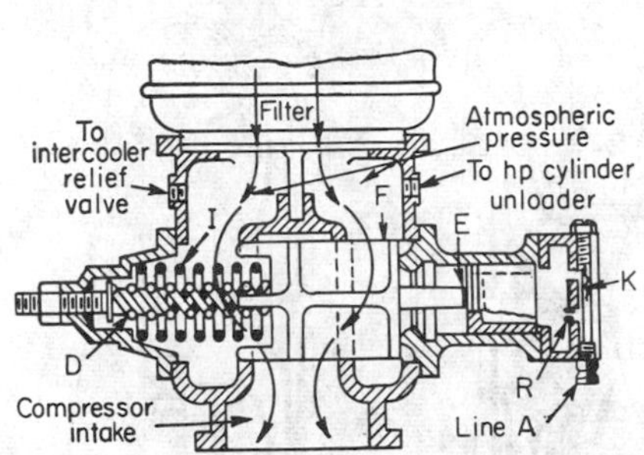

Fig. 13. Air suction unloader. Piston E moves valve to closed position as line A pressure reaches design point.

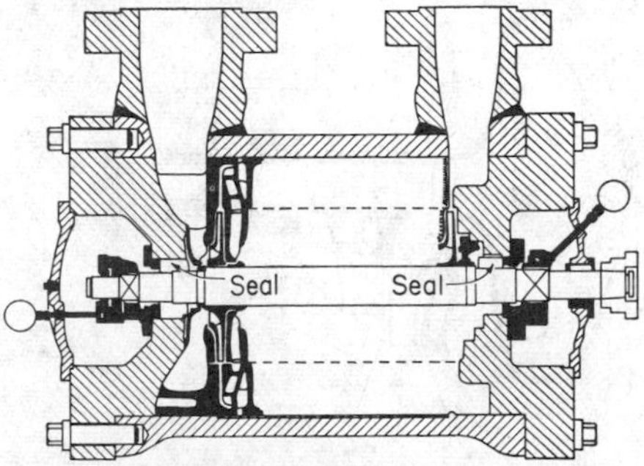

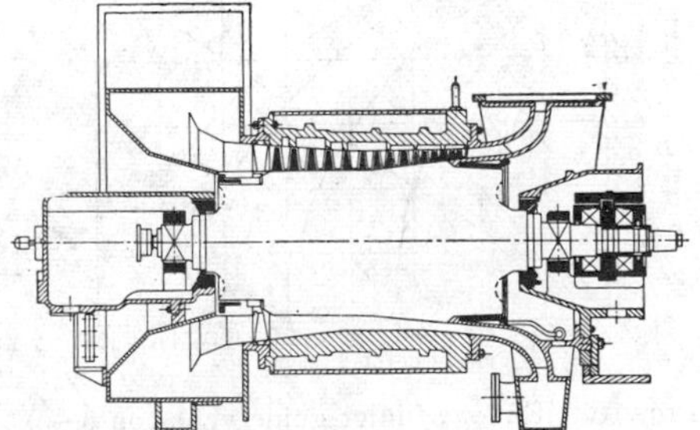

Fig. 14. Vertically split-case multistage 900- to 5,000-psi centrifugal compressor.

Turbomachines

Turbocompressor types and performances are illustrated in Figs. 14 to 20. Centrifugal and other dynamic types of compressors operate on the same analytical principles as those of centrifugal pumps and have similar components and terminology (see p. 14–21 *et seq.*). Performance is described by the capacity Q in terms of cfs (by designers) or acfm (by the trade), and the adiabatic head L_{ad}, in ft of gas compressed. Equation (**2**) can be modified to render

$$L_{ad} = \frac{1545T_1}{\bar{m}\sigma}(R_c^{\sigma} - 1) \tag{15}$$

Fig. 15. Multistage axial compressor.

Where R_c is less than 1.3, the proximate head is $144v_{sm}$ (mean specific volume) ft per psi of differential. Where the head is measured in in. of water (L_w'') for blowers, the air-fan hp is cfm × L_w''/3,500, with an average total efficiency of 55 percent. The power required to drive turbomachinery is the product of the weight flow (lb per sec) and the adiabatic head divided by 550 and the adiabatic η_{ad}, the disk and labyrinth η_d, and the mechanical η_m efficiencies. It is important that the adiabatic head and efficiency be applied in a consistent manner and not be confused by introducing polytropic or hydraulic terms. The k values should be appraised from the gas analysis for the mean adiabatic temperature. Adiabatic efficiency is the ratio of the adiabatic-head power to the dynamic power as indicated by the gas heating losses plus the labyrinth-seal and disk friction losses, usually assumed to be about 2 percent for 5,000-hp sizes. Heating-loss determination includes a detail analysis of the frictional flow at the inducer eye, the impeller, the diffuser mixing, the scroll, and the exit. The adiabatic efficiency can also be determined by the ratio of the adiabatic power to the dynamometer power less the mechanical, the disk, and the labyrinth losses. The mechanical losses are assumed to be 5 percent for units smaller than 500 hp, 2 percent for 5,000 hp, and 1 percent for units larger than 10,000 hp. An idealized performance chart for a radial and several backward-leaning vaned impellers is shown in Fig. 20. The abscissa represents the capacity in terms of the flow coefficient φ, which is the ratio of the axial inlet velocity to the impeller-tip speed U. The former is usually 0.2 M* and rarely exceeds 0.45 M* (Mach). The tip speed is usually between 900 and 1,100 fps for industrial compressors. Aeronautical and space-flight machinery operates at 1,500 to 1,800 fps, and prototypes at 2,800 fps. The optimum value of φ is 0.3, with 0.15 to 0.4 the practical range. The ordinate of Fig. 20 is the pressure coefficient q_{ad}, which is the product of the gravitational acceleration constant g (32.2) and L_{ad} divided by the square of the tip-speed fps, U^2. The negative slope lines on Fig. 21 are constant q_{ad} values and can be determined from Eq. (**16**). This and other applicable equations are

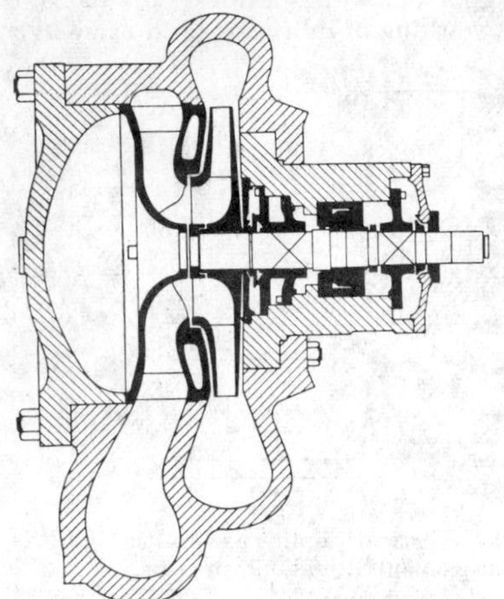

Fig. 16. Single-stage cantilever-design centrifugal compressor.

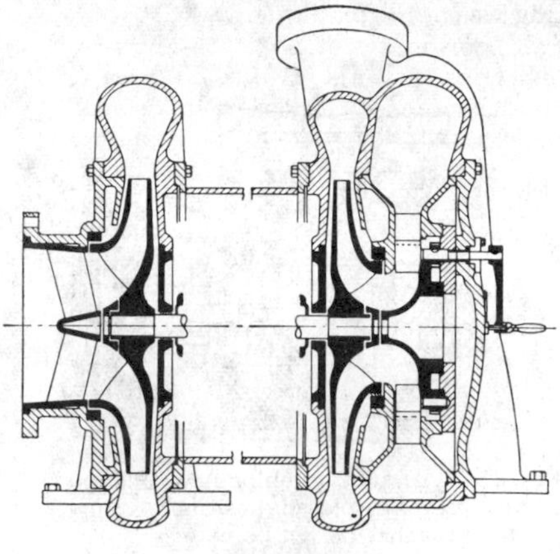

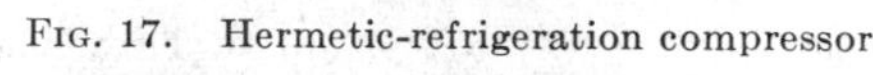

Fig. 17. Hermetic-refrigeration compressor.

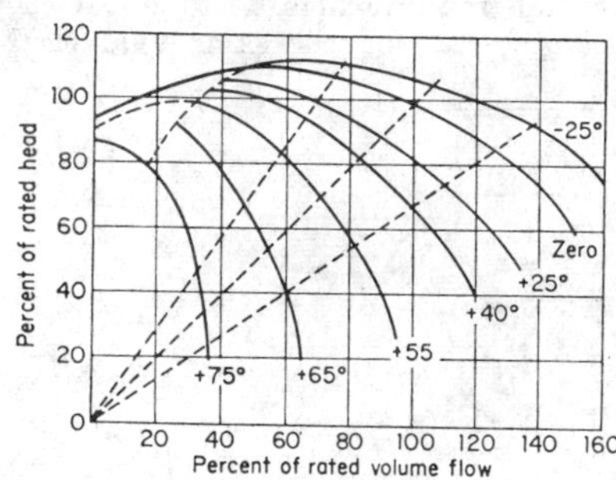

Fig. 18. Effect of inlet guide vanes on capacity and head of a centrifugal compressor. (*After Stepanoff, ASME 60-WA-130.*)

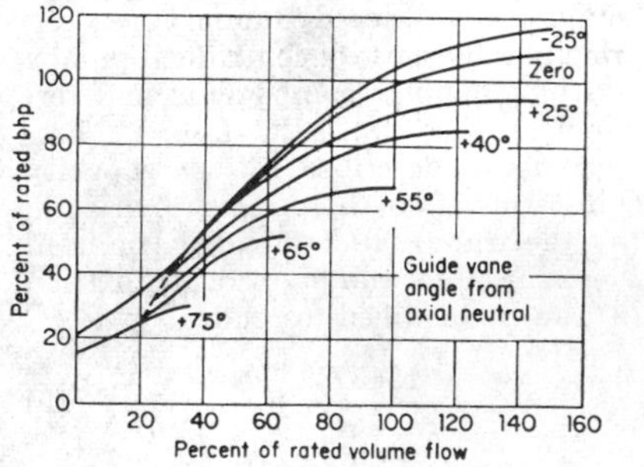

Fig. 19. Effect of inlet guide vanes on capacity and power of a centrifugal compressor. (*After Stepanoff, ASME 60-WA-130.*)

$$q_{ad} = 11{,}750/N_s{}^2D_s{}^2 \quad (16)$$

$$q_{ad} = 1.7 \times 10^{-6}L_{ad}/d^2N^2 \quad (17)$$

$$\text{MMscfd} = 32.8w/\bar{m} = 0.0091W/\bar{m} = 0.0091 \text{ moles/hr} \quad (18)$$

$$v_s = 10.73TZ/\bar{m}P = 379.5/\bar{m} \quad (19)$$

$$\text{Specific speed } N_s = NQ^{0.5}/L^{0.75} \quad (20)$$

$$\text{Specific diameter, } D_s = DL^{0.25}/Q^{0.5} \quad (21)$$

$$\text{Sonic velocity } \tau, \text{ fps} = 224(kT/m)^{0.5} \quad (22)$$

where Q is cfs; d is impeller diam in in., D in ft; w is lb per sec, and W is lb per hr.

Turbomachinery Efficiency

The optimum-performance range of the radial centrifugal compressor lies in the negative slope channel having q_{ad} values between 0.7 and 0.4 (Fig. 21). Where the volume flow exceeds this channel, an **axial** compressor is required. The axial machine is further identified as a low-head machine, having a pressure coefficient less than 0.3 and a specific speed greater than 300. The two coordinates of Fig. 21, the specific speed N_s [Eq. (**20**)] and the specific diameter D_s [Eq. (**21**)], are useful tools to determine the best efficiency that can be obtained from the optimized geometry of any turbomachine.

Where the flow rate and the head values are applied the Eqs. (**20**) and (**21**) for the coordinates of maximum efficiency for a radial compressor, $N_s = 140$ and $D_s = 1$, the optimum speed and rotor diameter are readily determined. If this speed is impractical, at half speed $N_s = 70$, $D_s = 2.0$, and η is only reduced from 85 to 82 percent; at quarter speed η is reduced to 65 percent. The efficiencies and pressure coefficients that can be realized from other forms of turbomachinery are shown with respect to their N_s and D_s orientations.

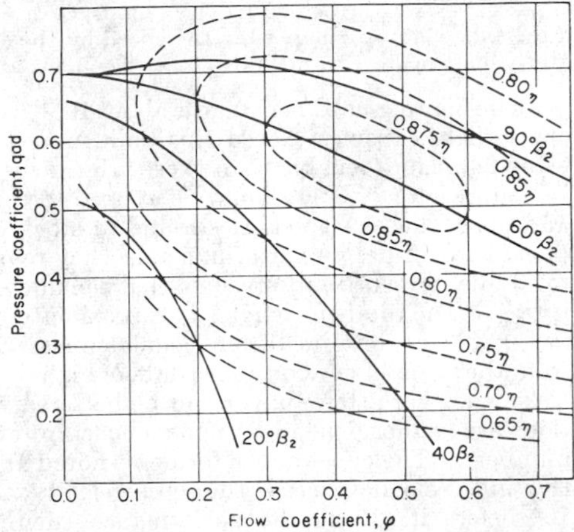

FIG. 20. Basic characteristics of centrifugal compressor, showing effects of backward-leaning impeller blades. (*After Balje, ASME 51-F-12.*)

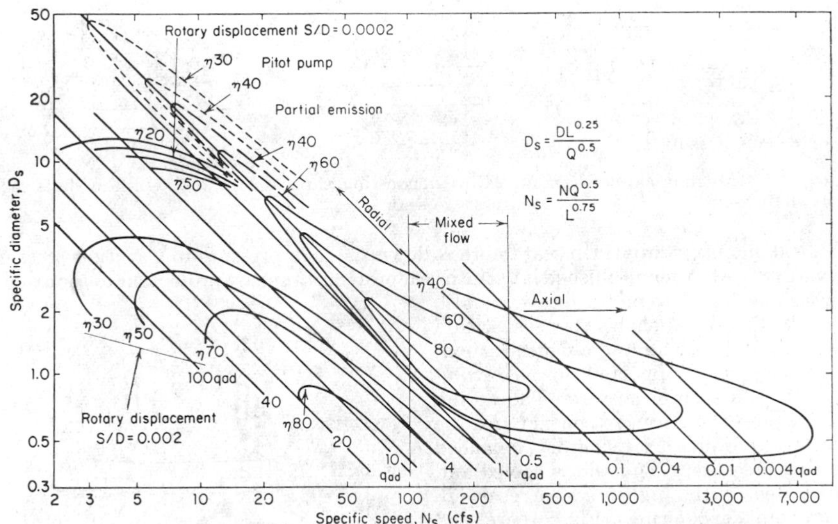

FIG. 21. Turbocompressor performance chart. (*After Balje, ASME 60-WA-231.*)

EXAMPLE: A coker-gas ($\overline{m} = 30$, $k = 1.18$) compressor is to handle 2,400 $\overline{m}$ per hr from 60 psia and 100 F to 240 psia. The flow is $2{,}400 \times 30/3{,}600 = 20$ lb per sec; $v_{s1} = 3.33$; $Q_1 = 66.6$ cfs, $Q^{0.5} = 8.15$; $R_c = 4$, $R_c^{\sigma} = 1.236$; $L_{ad} = 44{,}600$ ft. Assume six stages at

FIG. 22. Labyrinth shaft seal.

7,450 ft each; $L^{0.75} = 800$; $L^{0.25} = 9.3$. Assume $N_s = 140$ and $D_s = 1$. Then $N = 140 \times 800/8.15 = 13{,}750$ rpm, optimum efficiency is 86 percent, and the diameter is $1 \times 8.15/9.3 = 0.88$ ft. The speed can be reduced to 8,000 rpm, and $N_s = 82$, $\eta = 84$ percent, $D_s = 1.72$, and diameter = 1.50 ft. The load can be increased to $2640\bar{m}$ per hr and 54,000 ft; $Q = 73$ cfs, $Q^{0.5} = 8.65$, $L^{0.75} = 930$, and $L^{0.25} = 9.75$. By increasing the speed by the square root of the head change, $N = 8800$ rpm, $N_s = 82$, $D_s = 1.71$, and $\eta = 83$ percent.

The limiting head per stage is about 10,000 ft for industrial machines. Aircraft and space-flight capsules exceed this limit more than twofold. The efficiencies thus attained are more reliable than those arbitrarily associated with a given rotor diameter. A sizing factor of 0.90 should be applied to these efficiencies to correct for multistage and off-design characteristics found in stock designs. These efficiencies are not applicable to off-design performance. They refer to the static exhaust pressure and the total inlet pressure and presume that the inlet-line velocity V_1 equals the outlet velocity V_2. The total efficiency η is approximately equal to $\eta - 0.96(V_1/V_2)^2$. The data in Fig. 21 were obtained from calculated loss analysis using simplified assumptions and from the available performance data of high-N_s compressors and pumps. The efficiencies shown are attainable or can be bettered with precision production. These relations are further dependent upon a constant or passive M* (Mach) and R_e (Reynolds number). The effect of the former is noted at N_s values below 60 and where the relative inlet velocity exceeds the sonic velocity; the Reynolds number must be less than 10^6 before it affects the performance—neither condition is likely with industrial machinery.

Shaft Seals

The restrictive edges of the labyrinth-type shaft seal are made of a soft expendable metal, aluminum or bronze, and finished to slight-pressure interference (j5) fit. Some

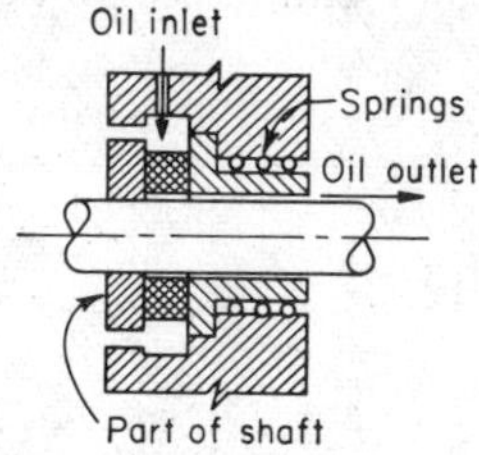

FIG. 23. Mechanical-contact shaft seal.

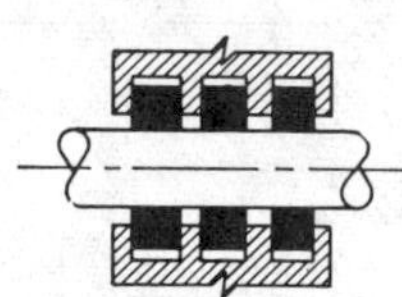

FIG. 24. Carbon-ring shaft or interstage seal.

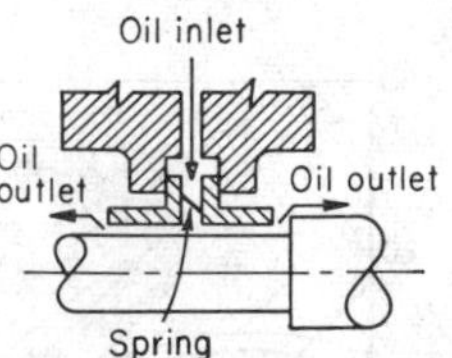

FIG. 25. Oil-film shaft seal.

applications use a labyrinth seal to break down the high pressure to a suction-pressure equalizer. Another oil-flushed labyrinth seal protects the shaft projection to the atmosphere (mechanical contact seals are also used). Figure 23 shows this seal with a rotating Stellite ring and a dense-carbon, stationary ring supported on a convolution or coil-spring carrier. The spring tension and the effective contact area are varied to produce a satisfactory, balanced sealing pressure. The seal is cooled and lubricated with high-pressure seal oil. Segmental carbon rings (Fig. 24) are used for interstage and end seals under 50 psig. The oil-film seal (Fig. 25) is applied to shafts operating at 2,500 psig. It depends upon the close clearance of the two floating bushings on the shaft and their

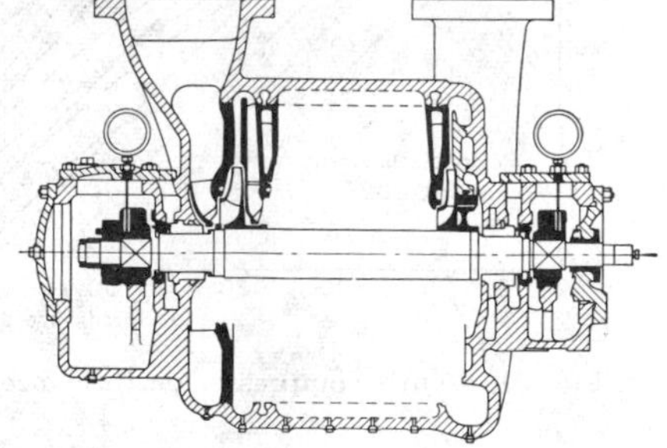

FIG. 26. Horizontally split-case multistage 800-psi centrifugal compressor.

lapped L-hub shoulder radial seals. The interior annulus is flooded with oil at 5 psi above the high-pressure gas; the interior leakage is 2 to 10 gal per day.

Thrust Pressures

A double-inlet and an open impeller have no axial thrust; a semienclosed impeller, without a frontal shroud, can impose substantial thrust, evaluated by

$$\mathbf{T}_A = Y(A_1 - A_2)\Delta\text{psi} + 0.8(A_2 - A_3)\Delta\text{psi} - P_1A_3 \tag{23}$$

where A_1 is the full impeller area, A_2 is the impeller area less the area of the inlet-eye seal, A_3 is the shaft area through the seal, all in sq in.; Δpsi is the pressure differential per stage. Y is the percentage of Δpsi acting in back of a single-stage disk: (1) without a frontal shroud and a plain back, $Y = 0.35$; (2) with 0.060-in. back ribs, $Y = 0.28$; (3) with ¼-in. equalizer holes at half radius and about 2 in. apart, $Y = 0.22$; and (4) with deep escallopes, $Y = 0.18$. For fully shrouded impellers, as used in multiple stage, $Y = 1.00$. These thrusts are balanced by opposing impeller inlet ends or, more generally, by a balancing drum wherein an equal and opposite thrust is created, equal to the product of the compressor Δpsi and the area of the drum. Stepanoff shows that radial impellers create a radial thrust, caused by the uneven volute-pressure distribution, which is

$$\mathbf{T}_R = 0.36\ \Delta\text{psi}\ db$$

where d is the impeller diameter and b is the width, including the shrouds, both in in.

Helical-screw Compressors

The helical-screw rotary compressor has a relatively high efficiency at low N_s, providing small capacities at high heads. This complements piston machinery without the problems of lubrication, maintenance, space, and vibration. It also supplements the low-N_s centrifugal compressors with more favorable efficiency. Svenska Rotor Maskiner (SRM) developed the **built-in clearance** feature for the Lysholm compressor (Fig. 27), where the compression phase of the axial sweep occupies about 300 deg of rotation. The timing between the closed discharge port and the closed suction port requires the remaining 60 deg. The gas retained in the rotor built-in clearance space is released at the point where the discharge port is closed, to the unwrapped volute space. When the operating R_c is equal to the **built-in** R_c, the pressure in the volute is balanced with the suction pressure and the compressor functions with 100 percent volumetric efficiency. If the operating R_c is greater than the built-in ratio, the capacity and the compression efficiency are reduced. If the operating R_c is less than the design R_c, the compression efficiency is reduced but the capacity is slightly improved. Figure 27 illustrates the helical form and operation sequence. The unit is sized on the diameter of the smaller male rotor, which drives the female gear via timing gears. One manufacturer drives the female element directly with the aid of a generous oil flood and seal. Industrial sizes range from 4- to 25-in. rotors, operating between 2,000 and 12,000 rpm and with capacities up to 19,000 cfm. Industrial models are limited to pitch-line velocities U of 425 fps (0.375 M*) in the small sizes and 0.32 M* in the large sizes. Good performance has been reported with tip speed of 0.6 M*. The capacity

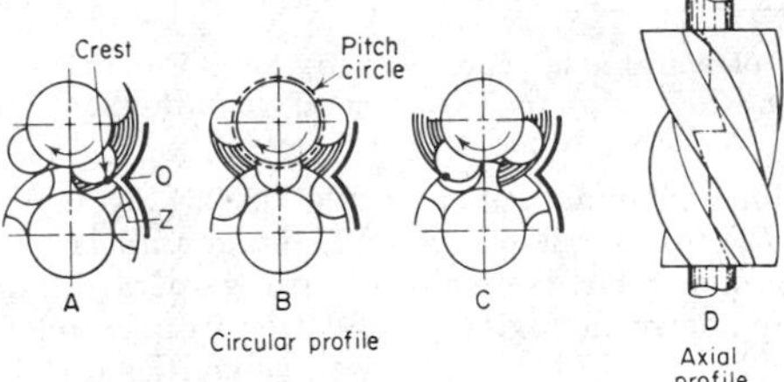

FIG. 27. Profile of SRM rotor in sequence of circular enclosure and axial sealing line.

of the helical-screw-type compressor is

$$Q_{\text{cfm}} = dLUX \tag{25}$$

The X factor is the ratio of the free cross-sectional area to the square of the rotor diameter d. The average functional X factor, including gap losses at the **built-in** R_c operation, is 0.060 for the most popular four-male-by-six-female lobe configuration. The power of compression for helical-screw-type compressors is

$$\Sigma = 50(R_c{}^{\sigma} - 1)/\sigma\eta_m \tag{26}$$

The mechanical efficiency is 98 percent for 10-in. and larger rotary machines and 91 percent for 6-in. and smaller machines. The geometric form is usually square, with $L = d$ for high-pressure models which limit the differential pressure to about 250 psi. Where $L = 1.5d$ or more, the differential pressure is usually restricted to less than 50 psi because of the limited rotor deflection within the minute case clearances. The optimum range of application for this type of compressor is shown on the left margin of Fig. 21. The lower family of curves are for rotors having a nominal clearance of $0.002d$; the upper curves have a clearance of $0.0002d$.

Other Rotary Compressors

Figure 28 illustrates an **axial-sweep** type of **screw compressor** which has an X factor of 0.165 and a commercial top speed of 140 fps in air service. The rotor sizes range from 6 to 16 in. in diameter, with capacities up to 12,500 cfm. A quick cfm-capacity check is $22dL$. The R_c is limited to 3, and the air power of compression is

$$\Sigma_{\text{air}} = 164(R_c{}^{0.375} - 1) \tag{27}$$

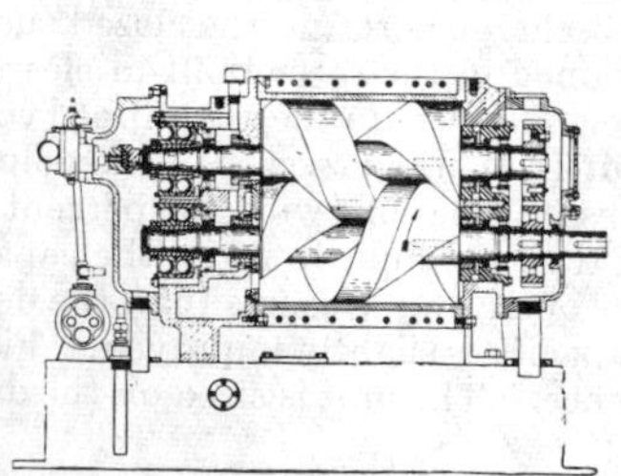

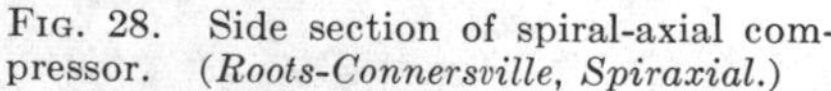

FIG. 28. Side section of spiral-axial compressor. (*Roots-Connersville, Spiraxial.*)

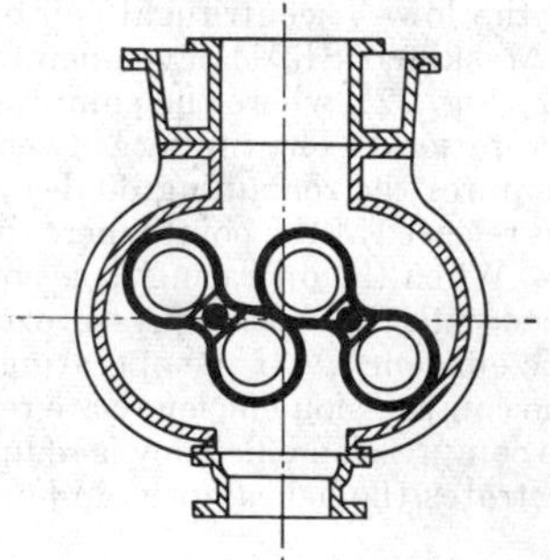

FIG. 29. End view of straight two-lobe rotary compressor. (*Roots.*)

The **straight two-lobe cycloidal rotor units** (Fig. 29) are used extensively for high vacuum and low (1.7 R_c) compression. A single-stage unit is effective from 1 mm Hg to a blank-off at 2 microns. A two-stage unit or one operating in series with the sliding-lobe vacuum pump shown in Fig. 32 is effective from 5 to 0.05 microns, or $100R_c$. The sizes range from 6 by 6 to 28 by 70 in., with capacities up to 33,000 cfm at 55-fps tip speed. The average displacement factor X is 0.30 for dry-gas and 0.26 for moisture-passage models. The static slip for this class of machinery is determined by the speed required to sustain the desired pressure at zero flow. The slippage varies directly as the square root of the change in absolute pressure and inversely as the square root of the absolute temperature and specific gravity. The speed of heavy-duty two-lobe compressors is limited to 57 fps; light models range from 25 to 35 fps.

The **sliding-vane compressor** (Fig. 30) is limited to relatively small capacities and R_c of 4.5 and has been most successful as a construction air compressor. The unit is flooded with 0.05 gal per cu ft of displacement. The oil picks up about 20 F and holds

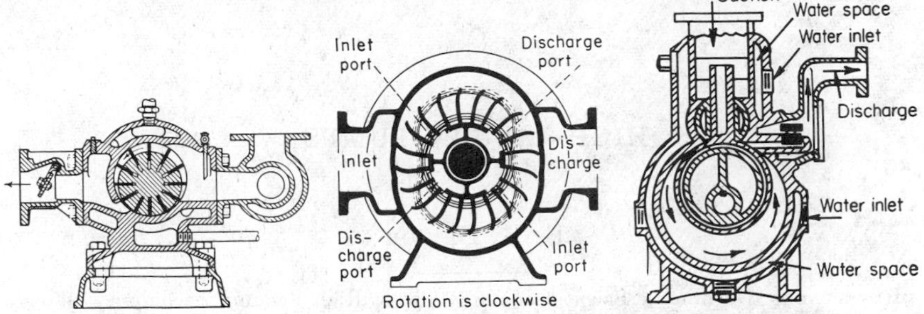

FIG. 30. Sliding-vane-type rotary compressor.

FIG. 31. Rotary compressor with liquid-ring seal. (*Nast.*®)

FIG. 32. Single-lobe-type low-micron vacuum pump. (*Kinney.*)

the discharge temperature within 100 F of ambient. The X factor is 0.060, and the limiting vane-tip speed is 60 fps. The air power required is

$$\Sigma_{\text{air}} = 164[(1.36R_c)^{0.286} - 1] \qquad \textbf{(28)}$$

The **rotary liquid-ring compressor** (Fig. 31) is used for handling highly saturated vapors, wet vacuums, and corrosive and exothermal gases. Compressor efficiency is less than 50 percent. Heat rejection from the liquid sealant is about 6,000 Btu per hp-hr of useful compression. Units are limited to capacities of 5,000 cfm; pressures of 75 psi; and vacuums to 25 in. of mercury, single-stage, and 29 in., two-stage. Figure 32 illustrates a single-lobe rotary compressor used extensively as a low-micron vacuum pump.

HIGH-VACUUM PUMPS

BY

B. B. Dayton

REFERENCES: Dushman, "Scientific Foundations of High Vacuum Technique," Wiley. Pirani and Yarwood, "Principles of Vacuum Engineering," Reinhold. Guthrie, "Vacuum Technology," Wiley. Steinherz, "Handbook of High Vacuum Engineering," Reinhold. Guthrie and Wakerling, "Vacuum Equipment and Techniques," McGraw-Hill. Reimann, "Vacuum Technique," Chapman and Hall.

The pressure of gas in a chamber at a given temperature may be reduced by allowing the gas to escape through a port into a vacuum pump, or by a pumping system comprising two or more pumps in series, which compresses the gas and discharges it into the atmosphere, or by allowing the gas (or vapor) to condense on a sufficiently cold surface or to react with a chemically active surface exposed within the chamber or within an appendage to the chamber. The movement of the gas toward the pump or trapping surface may be accelerated by heating the walls of the chamber or by ionizing the gas and applying an electric field. **Rotary mechanical pumps** and **steam ejectors** which can compress the gas from about 10^{-3} mm Hg up to atmospheric pressure are described on pp. 9–91ff, and 14–59ff; pumps and trapping techniques required to produce pressures in the "high-vacuum region" (below 10^{-3} mm Hg) are described below.

Units. The pressure unit *mm Hg* formerly used in high-vacuum technology is difficult to define precisely and has been widely replaced by the **torr** defined as (1/760) atm or exactly (1,013,250/760) dyn/cm^2 or (101,325/760) newton/m^2. The international standard mm Hg is equal to 1.000,000,14 torr. One *micron Hg* is approximately equal to one *millitorr* or 10^{-3} torr. **Pumping speed** is normally expressed in liters per second or cubic feet per minute (cfm); one liter sec^{-1} equals 2.12 cfm.

Selection of Pumps. The type of vacuum pump selected depends primarily on the lowest pressure to be attained and the possible effects of vapor contamination. The lowest pressure that the pump itself can attain without vapor traps is called the **ultimate pressure** of the pump. The *size* of the pump depends either on the time to "pump-down" from atmospheric pressure or on the pressure to be maintained in the presence of a given gas load during the process cycle and the number of pumps which can be installed in parallel. The gas load is usually expressed in terms of **throughput** defined as the product of the static pressure and the volumetric flow rate across a given section at a given temperature. Size of pump is rated in terms of volumetric pumping speed (in liter sec^{-1} or cfm) at the inlet pressure for which the speed is a maximum. As shown in Fig. 1, for rotary-piston mechanical pumps this maximum speed occurs at atmospheric pressure, but for steam ejectors and oil vapor ejectors (similar in principle and design to steam ejectors but employing water cooling on the venturi section or diffuser) the maximum speed occurs at the top of a narrow peak on the speed-pressure curve. The **diffusion pump,** Fig. 2, which employs one or more jets of vapor into which molecules from the chamber can diffuse and be carried forward into a region of higher gas pressure, has a broad plateau of maximum speed (see Fig. 1) from about 10^{-3} torr to pressures 20 times the ultimate pressure, the latter being approximately equal to the vapor pressure at room temperature of the fluid used to form the vapor jet.

The number, types, and sizes of vacuum pumps in series required to compress gas from the chamber up to atmospheric pressure usually depends on the compression ratio per pumping stage at the maximum throughput during the process cycle. For

ultrahigh vacuum systems (pressures less than 10^{-9} torr) the number of pumps or stages required to reach the lowest pressures may depend on the rate of back leakage or back diffusion through the pumps at the minimum throughput. **Compression ratio** is defined as the ratio of the outlet (exhaust or discharge) pressure to the inlet (or intake) pressure at a given throughput when pumping a gas or vapor that is not absorbed or condensed within the pump. This ratio is a variable quantity which depends in general on the ratio of the pumping speed of a given stage to the net speed of the fore-pump, or next stage of compression. However, for a given throughput there is an upper limit to the compression ratio which can be maintained across a vapor jet pumping stage at a given power input. At maximum throughput under normal operation the limiting compression ratio for single-stage ejector pumps is about 10, and for the individual stages of multistage diffusion pumps the limiting ratio is about 4. Thus, a three-stage steam ejector is required to compress air from 0.8 torr to 760 torr, a ratio of about 10^3. Oil diffusion pumps usually have from three to five stages, and a four-stage diffusion pump can compress air from 1.5×10^{-3} torr to 0.4 torr at maximum full-speed throughput, corresponding to a total compression ratio of about 4^4 or 256. The overall compression ratio can be much higher at very low throughputs, but the **forepressure** (pressure at the outlet) should not be allowed to exceed a value known as the **limiting forepressure** or **tolerable forepressure,** which is usually in the range of 0.2 to 0.6 torr for a four-stage diffusion pump.

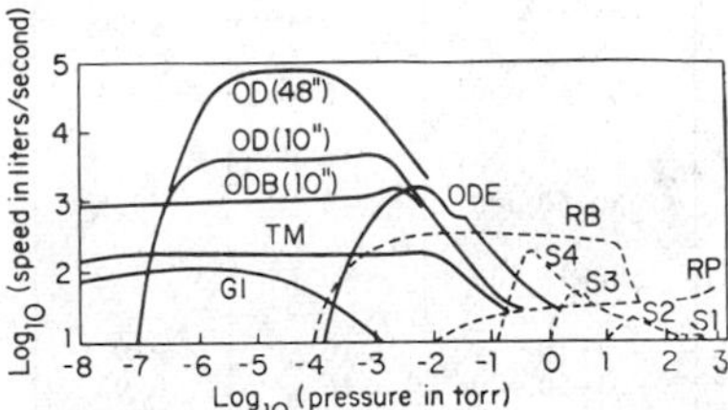

FIG. 1. Variation of pumping speed with inlet pressure for typical vacuum pumps. *OD* (48 in.) = oil diffusion pump with nominal 48 in. diam inlet flange; *OD* (10 in.) = 10 in. oil diffusion pump; *ODB* (10 in.) = 10 in. oil diffusion pump with baffle; *ODE* = oil diffusion-ejector pump; *TM* = turbomolecular pump; *GI* = getter-ion pump (sputter type); *RB* = Roots-type blower; *RP* = rotary-piston oil-sealed mechanical pump; *S*1, *S*2, *S*3, *S*4 = matching stages in series of four-stage steam ejector.

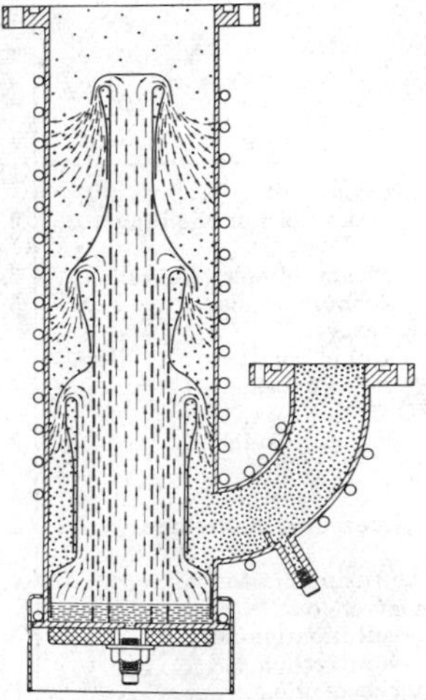

FIG. 2. Operating principle of oil diffusion pump. Arrows show vapor stream; dots represent gas molecules. Dashed lines show position of cylindrical vapor chimneys in fractionating pumps. (*Consolidated Vacuum Corporation and the Encyclopedia of Chemical Technology.*)

Oil-sealed mechanical piston pumps can be operated with high compression ratios over a pressure range from atmospheric pressure (or above) to about 10^{-3} torr. Molecular drag, centrifugal, rotary blower (*e.g.*, Roots type) pumps, and turbomolecular pumps are limited by back flow or leakage of gas from the forepressure side through the clearances between the rotor and stator, and therefore require backing pumps to reduce the forepressure from atmospheric to a sufficiently low value to permit a high vacuum to be obtained on the inlet side. Oil vapor jet pumps cannot discharge gas directly to the atmosphere because of limitations on the vapor pressure which can be generated without excessive thermal decomposition of the oil, and backing pumps must therefore be used to reduce their forepressures to values less than the vapor pressure of the oil at a safe temperature in the boiler. Some gas molecules (particularly hydrogen and helium) may succeed in diffusing back through a vapor jet from the fore vacuum to the high vacuum, and for ultrahigh vacuum systems this back diffusion must be reduced by using a sufficient number of pumping stages and vapor jets with high vapor density and velocity.

Table 1. Types and Available Sizes of High-vacuum Pumps

Type	Available sizes		Operating range		Power input, kw
	Nom. inlet diam, in.	Max. air speed, liters/sec	Ult. press, torr	Limiting forepress, torr	
Mechanical:					
rotary piston or plunger	0.5, 1.0, 1.5, 2, 3, 4, 6, 8	0.1–400	$\sim 10^{-3}$	(atm.)	0.2–30
rotary blower (Roots)	2, 4, 8, 16	40–2000	$\sim 10^{-3}$	30	0.5–20
turbomolecular	6, 10	140, 260	$<10^{-9}$	$\sim 10^{-1}$	0.4, 0.75
Ejectors:					
steam, six-stage	48	50,000	$\sim 10^{-3}$	(atm.)	
mercury vapor	1	15	$<10^{-4}$*	~ 200	7
Diffusion:					
oil, multistage	2, 3, 4, 6, 10, 12, 14, 16, 20, 24, 32, 35, 48	100–90,000	$<10^{-7}$	~ 0.5	0.3–30
mercury, multistage	2, 4, 6, 10, 24, 32, 48	50–50,000	$<10^{-10}$*	~ 0.5	0.7–20
Diffusion-ejector, oil	4, 8, 12, 24	300–16,000	$\sim 10^{-3}$	2.0	2–20
Getter-ion:					
sublimation-ion	0.3–36	$1–10^5$	$<10^{-10}$	$\sim 10^{-3}$	0.4–20
sputter-ion	0.5–36	1–50,000	$<10^{-10}$	0.02	0.1–50
Cryosorption	1, 2	1–10†	$<10^{-3}$	(atm.)	
Cryopanel	(Sized to fit inside chamber)	$10^4–10^6$†	$<10^{-10}$		

* With trap.
† N_2 speed.

Table 1 lists the types, sizes, and operating characteristics of typical commercially available pumps. The maximum (standard measured) speed (in liters per second) of oil diffusion pumps is about $18D^2$ for three-stage models and $28D^2$ for four-stage models, where D is the true inlet diameter (in inches). The larger pumps are usually water-cooled, and about 80 percent of the heat generated must be carried away by the cooling water, the remainder being lost by convection, radiation, and conduction to the surroundings. The exit temperature of the cooling water should usually not exceed 40 C, and the required rate of flow in cubic centimeters per minute of water having an inlet temperature of 20 C and an exit temperature of 30 C is about numerically equal to the power input in watts. This rule of thumb applies to either diffusion pumps or water-cooled mechanical pumps where the horsepower of the motor is converted to watts by multiplying by 746.

Diffusion Pumps. Figure 2 shows a typical diffusion pump constructed of metal. Gas molecules wandering into the top of the pump are able to penetrate the diffuse boundary of the vapor jet (downward arrows) and reach the denser forward-moving core of vapors where they are driven at an acute angle toward the pump wall and on to the next stage of pumping. The vapor condenses on the wall and drains as a liquid back to the bottom, or boiler region, where the liquid is reheated to about 200 C to create a fresh vapor supply which rises up the chimneys to feed the nozzles. The operating fluid may be mercury or a low-vapor-pressure oil. The oils are sold under various trade names and usually consist of organic or silicone compounds of molecular weight in the range from 350 to 500. **Mercury-vapor pumps** require efficient refrigerated traps to keep mercury vapor out of the chamber being evacuated. Oil diffusion pumps require some form of purging or purification of the oil during use to eliminate dissolved gases and volatile decomposition products. **Fractionating oil diffusion pumps** purify the oil by circulating it through a series of boilers, or boiler compartments, feeding vapor through separate chimneys to the various nozzles in a multistage pump. The volatile impurities are ejected with the vapor feeding the stages nearest the fore vacuum, and the purged oil of lowest vapor pressure supplies the top nozzle from which vapor molecules scattered back out of the inlet port create a partial pressure of oil vapor in the high vacuum which limits the ultimate pressure obtainable without cold traps [Hickman, *Jour. Appl. Physics* **11,** 303 (1940)].

Getter-ion or **sputter-ion pumps** (Fig. 3) employ chemically active metal layers which are continuously or intermittently deposited on the wall of the pump by either

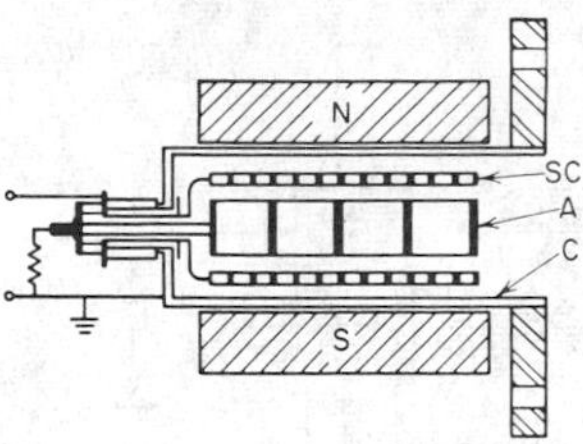

Fig. 3. Sputter-ion pump, triode type. SC = sputter cathode; A = anode; C = ion collector; N, S = magnet poles.

thermal evaporation or sputtering and which chemisorb oxygen, nitrogen, water vapor, and other active gases while the inert gases such as helium, neon and argon are "cleaned up" by ionizing them in an electric discharge and drawing the positive ions to the wall where the neutralized ions are buried by fresh deposits of metal. These pumps require a roughing pump to reduce the pressure to less than about 20 millitorr at which point the active metal (usually titanium) can be evaporated or sputtered at the required rate, but after they begin operation no backing pump is required since all of the gas is trapped at the wall. When isolated by valves from the roughing pump, the getter-ion pumps form an enclosure sealed to the vacuum system so that a power failure cannot result in leakage of atmospheric air or vapors from a forepump into the system. Sputter-ion pumps can operate continuously for more than one year at pressures below 10^{-6} torr.

Cryopumps consist of one or more exposed surfaces refrigerated to a temperature usually below 100 K, at which certain gases will be condensed and form a layer having an equilibrium vapor pressure below a specified limit. A plate cooled to 20 K, by circulating helium gas from a refrigeration unit through coils attached to the plate, will condense N_2, CO_2, CO, H_2O, O_2, A, and Xe to maintain partial pressures of these gases less than 10^{-10} torr. Hydrogen, helium, and neon are not adequately condensed at 20 K but may be "cryotrapped" in a deposit of H_2O and other gases condensing on the plate. Cryopumping is used in space simulation chambers to create the necessary low pressures and to act as a heat sink comparable to "cold black space." In this application the 20 K plates are shielded by liquid-nitrogen-cooled panels, and the whole array is shaped to cover the inside wall of the vacuum chamber (see also p. 18–28 *et seq*).

Cryosorption pumps employ a sorbent such as activated charcoal or synthetic zeolite (Molecular Sieve) cooled by liquid nitrogen or other refrigerant. They can be used to rough a system down from atmospheric pressure to a few millitorr at which getter-ion pumps may begin operation, or an additional preconditioned cryosorption pump can be valved in to reduce the pressure to 10^{-5} torr or less.

Turbomolecular pumps (U.S. Patent No. 2,918,208) employ a system of alternate high-speed rotors with inclined blades and stators with inclined slots to impel the gas molecules from the high vacuum to a forepump. They have a broad plateau of pumping speed from about 10^{-2} to 10^{-8} torr. When water and hydrogen are removed from the walls of the system by baking, these pumps can reach ultimate pressures of less than 10^{-9} torr.

Installation of Pumps. In a typical assembly of pumps for a high vacuum system (Fig. 4) the diffusion pump (A) must be located close to the chamber (B) and should always have a water-cooled or refrigerated baffle (C) over the pump inlet so that vapor scattered back from the jets (backstreaming) will be condensed and returned as liquid to the pump. The pipe or manifold, which may include a valve (D), connecting the chamber and the baffled pump should be of diameter equal to or larger than the inlet of the pump, and the length of the passage between the baffled pump and the chamber should preferably be not more than about three times the mean diameter of the passage. A space at least 6 in. high should be allowed below the diffusion pump boiler (E) for easy servicing of the heaters, draining the pump fluid, or removal of the pump from the system.

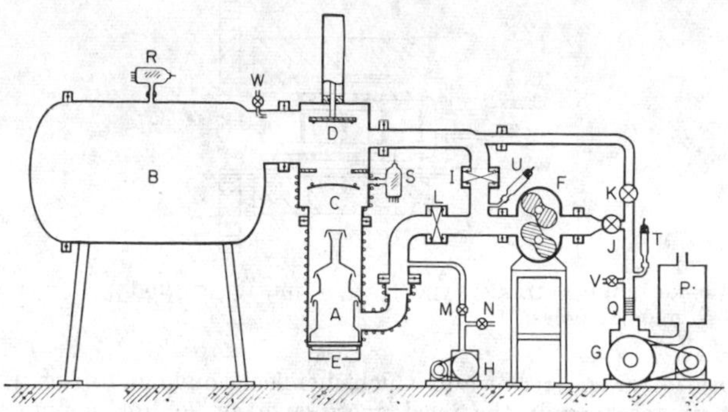

FIG. 4. Typical high-vacuum system. A = diffusion pump; B = chamber; C = baffle; D = valve; E = pump heater; F = Roots-type blower; G = roughing (mechanical) pump; H = holding (mechanical) pump; I, J, K, L, M, N = valves; P = oil reservoir and separator; Q = bellows; R, S = ion gage tubes; T, U = Pirani gage tubes; V, W = air inlet valves.

Some mechanical pumps have appreciable vibration so that they should be firmly anchored or mounted on vibration damping pads, and flexible metal bellows (Q) should be installed in the fore vacuum line. These bellows also aid in aligning the pumps during assembly. It is not necessary to have the mechanical pumps close to the chamber because the resistance to gas flow of moderate lengths of pipe having the same diameter as the inlet of these pumps is not sufficiently large to create a serious pressure drop at mean pressures above 200 millitorr. Below 200 millitorr the pressure drop along the pipe is larger, but usually the diffusion pump operation is not affected unless the limiting forepressure (about 100 to 600 millitorr) is exceeded at the pump outlet.

Vapor Contamination. The vapors evolved from vacuum systems may be condensed within mechanical pumps or the intercondensers of steam-ejector systems. If the condensed vapor is the same as the working fluid in the pump, such as water vapor condensed in "wet" vacuum pumps, no harm is done, provided that the fluid level is maintained at the optimum working value. If the condensed vapor can be separated from the working fluid by centrifuging, evaporation, filtering, or settling, suitable separating means can be installed. In certain types of rotary pumps the Gaede **gas-ballast** principle may be employed to avoid condensation by admitting air at a certain point in the compression cycle. If separation cannot be satisfactorily accomplished during operation of the pump, the vapor should be condensed in cold traps or liquid absorption columns before reaching the pump.

Baffles and **traps** are often required to prevent the backstreaming or migration of the pump operating fluid or sealing fluid into the high-vacuum chamber. Unless cooled baffles and traps or sorption traps for oil vapor are included in the connecting line, the ultimate pressure in the vacuum chamber will usually not be less than the vapor pressure of the pump fluid at ambient temperature. While a water-cooled "optically tight" baffle installed above the inlet of a diffusion pump will condense the backstreaming pump-fluid vapor and return most of the fluid to the pump, some fluid will reevaporate from such a baffle and migrate back into the vacuum chamber. To reduce the partial pressure of pump-fluid vapor below the vapor pressure at the water cooling temperature it is necessary to add a cold trap or baffle refrigerated to temperatures usually below the pour point of the fluid. These cold traps must be periodically warmed and the condensate removed to avoid inefficient cooling of the exposed surfaces during operation. The addition of an "optically tight" baffle and a cold trap over the inlet to a diffusion pump usually reduces the net pumping speed for permanent gases to less than 50 percent of the diffusion pump speed at the inlet.

Flow of Gases at Low Pressure. The pipe line between the high-vacuum pump and the vacuum chamber limits the volumetric flow so that the **net pumping speed** as measured by a vacuum gage located in the chamber is given by $S_n = S_0U/(S_0 + U)$, where S_0 is the measured speed of the pump at its inlet and U is the **conductance** of the pipe defined by $U = Q/(P_n - P_0)$ where Q is the throughput while P_n is the pressure in the chamber and P_0 is the pressure near the inlet of the pump as measured by a gage installed in a similar manner to that used to determine the pump speed S_0. When there is no loss or gain of gas within the pipe line, $Q = S_nP_n = S_0P_0 = U(P_n - P_0)$.

The conductance of a pipe depends on the geometry and the **Knudsen number,** K, (defined as the ratio of the mean free path of the gas molecules to the mean diameter of the cross section) as well as the direction and velocity of the molecules entering the pipe. For $K > 1$ the conductance for air in liters per second at 25 C of a circular pipe of length L (feet) and inside diameter D (inches) connecting a high-vacuum pump to a chamber of diameter greater than $3D$, including the "entrance correction" at the chamber, but neglecting the "exit correction" at the pump which depends on the inlet diameter and other factors, may be calculated from $U = 6.6D^3/(L + 0.11D)$. The effect of right-angle bends in the pipe for "molecular flow" ($K > 1$) and for $L > D/3$ may be approximated by adding $0.05D$ to L for each bend (where L is in feet and D in inches). A single right-angle bend in a short pipe ($L < D/3$) has practically no effect on the conductance as computed for a straight pipe of the same length along the center line [Davis, *Jour. Appl. Phys.* **5,** 358 (1954)].

When $K < 0.01$, the conductance in liters per second for air at 20 C of a long circular pipe of length L (feet) and diameter D (inches) may be calculated from $U = 0.25D^4\bar{P}/L$ where $\bar{P}$ is the mean pressure in the pipe in millitorr (microns of Hg). For $0.01 < K < 1$ the conductance for air at 20 C of a long tube can be estimated from

$$U = \frac{0.25D^4\bar{P}}{L} + \left(\frac{1 + 0.65D\bar{P}}{1 + 0.80D\bar{P}}\right)\left(\frac{6.6D^3}{L}\right)$$

The size of the primary pump, which acts as a "roughing pump" to pump the chamber down from atmospheric pressure to a pressure at which a diffusion pump or other high-vacuum pump can operate, may depend on the peak gas load during the process as well as the desired pump-down time. However, the size indicated by the peak load condition is frequently much smaller than the size required to meet the specified pump-down or roughing time. In this case, if the process cycle is much longer than the pump-down time, it is advisable to use two forepumps (primary pumps), a large one (G in Fig. 4) for roughing down and a smaller one (H in Fig. 4) for holding the vapor pumps during the roughing period and backing them during the processing period. Roots-type blowers are useful for shortening the roughing time for large chambers in the range below 20 torr and for handling unusually large bursts of gas which occur in some processes (F in Fig. 4).

An oil-sealed rotary mechanical pump is normally used as the primary pump, and the roughing time t_r (in minutes) required to evacuate a chamber of volume V (cubic feet) from atmospheric pressure to about 0.7 torr at which high-vacuum pumps begin to operate can be estimated from $t_r = 10V/C$ where C is the rated speed (cubic feet per minute) at atmospheric pressure of the rotary pump. Since the speed of the high-vacuum pumps is usually of the order of 100 times that of the forepump, the pressure should drop quickly as soon as the high-vacuum pumps "take hold," but below 10^{-4} torr the pressure may begin to decrease more slowly because of the outgassing of the materials exposed inside the vacuum system.

For most of the materials exposed in high-vacuum systems the **outgassing rate** can be assumed proportional to the exposed area, A_m, although for some very porous materials the rate is more proportional to the bulk or mass. Except for evaporation from pure liquid or solid phases, the outgassing rate normally decreases with time when the temperature is constant. For many industrial-type vacuum systems it has been found that the pressure, P, in the chamber decreases approximately according to $P = P_u + K_1 A_m / S_n t^\alpha$ where P_u is the ultimate pressure, K_1 is a constant which may be considered equal to the average outgassing rate per unit area after one hour of pumping, A_m is the exposed area, t is the total pumping time in hours, and α is an exponent which is usually nearly constant for the first few hours. For rough calculations in typical metal vacuum systems it may be assumed that $\alpha = 1$, but for systems containing large amounts of elastomers or plastics α may be closer to 0.5 [Dayton, *Trans. 6th National Vacuum Symposium*, pp. 101–119, Pergamon Press, Oxford, 1960; Kraus, *ibid*, pp. 204–5].

When the system is first evacuated after prolonged exposure to the atmosphere, most of the outgassing load for the first 10 to 100 hours is usually water vapor, and for unbaked metal systems the numerical value of K_1 is of the order of 10^{-4} when A_m is in square feet and S_n in liters per second. For systems containing large amounts of elastomers or plastics K_1 is more of the order of 10^{-3} to 10^{-2}. Systems constructed entirely of metal and glass may be heated to temperatures as high as 500 C to accelerate the outgassing, the average rate increasing by approximately a factor of 10 for each 100 C increase in temperature. In order to reach 10^{-6} torr in 10 hours in an unconditioned vacuum chamber the net pumping speed (in liters per second) should be 10 to 100 times the exposed area (in square feet).

The time t_v (in minutes) to vent a vacuum chamber of volume V (cubic feet) from pressures less than 10^{-3} torr to atmospheric pressure through a standard globe valve of nominal diameter D (inches) is given approximately by $t_v = V/100D^2$. The oil in the boiler of oil diffusion pumps should be cooled to below 100 C before opening the pump to atmospheric pressure.

CENTRIFUGAL AND AXIAL FANS

BY

J. E. McDonald

REFERENCES: Innes, "The Fan," Technical Publishing. Wislicenus, "Fluid Mechanics of Turbomachinery," McGraw-Hill. Eckert, "Axialkompressoren und Radialkompressoren," Springer. Eck, "Ventilatoren," Springer. Hagen, Parallel Operation of Fans, *Combustion*, Apr., 1936. Baumeister, "Fans" McGraw-Hill. Spannhake, "Centrifugal Pumps, Turbines, and Propellers," Technology Press. "Standard Test Code for Air Moving Devices," AMCA.

Symbols

p = total pressure, in. of water
p_s = static pressure, in. of water
p_v = velocity pressure, in. of water
V = absolute velocity, fps
v = velocity of air relative to fan wheel, fps
V_u = rotative component of velocity, fps
d = density of air, lb per cu ft
S = area, sq ft
Q = volume, cfm
T = absolute temperature, deg F
P_b = absolute or barometric pressure, in. of mercury
e = efficiency, air hp/bhp, percent
N = rpm
N_s = specific speed
D = diam of fan wheel, ft
D_s = specific diam
A = fan outlet area, sq ft

FUNDAMENTAL FORMULAS

Pressure, as usually understood, is called static pressure in fan engineering. The pressure set up by velocity impingement is called velocity pressure; the sum of the static pressure and the velocity pressure is the total pressure. Pressures, static and total, in ducts connected to fans are referred to barometric pressure as a datum.

A distinction is made in engineering practice and formally approved by the engineering societies between fans for low pressure and centrifugal compressors for high pressure. The demarcation is set at 7 percent increase in density of the air from the fan inlet to the outlet. For fan action below this density increase, the assumption of incompressibility is approved with a resulting simplification of formulas and definitions. The error due to this simplification is quantitatively insignificant.

Fan pressures are determined from readings of duct pressures. The **total pressure rise** p of a fan is the increase in total pressure through the fan as indicated by a differential reading between two impact tubes facing the air current, one in the fan inlet and one in the fan outlet.

The **static pressure** of a fan p_s is the total pressure rise p diminished by the velocity pressure in the fan outlet.

The **velocity pressure** of a fan p_v is the velocity pressure in the fan outlet.

Velocity. The velocity pressure p_v is conventionally expressed in inches of water. The relation between p_v and the velocity of a gas of density d lb per cu ft is given by

$$V = 18.3\sqrt{p_v/d}\text{ fps} = 1{,}096\sqrt{p_v/d}\text{ fpm}$$

Air horsepower, or fan power output, is the horsepower determined from the product of the volume of air Q and the pressure rise p

$$\text{Air hp} = \frac{62.3pQ}{12 \times 33{,}000} = 0.0001575pQ$$

where p is in inches of water.

In many installations, the fan velocity pressure is wasted and only the static pressure is useful. For static-pressure power p_s is substituted for p.

The **efficiency** of a fan is the ratio between the horsepower output (air horsepower) and the **horsepower input** (brake horsepower). e = air hp/bhp.

The static efficiency of a fan is the ratio between the static-pressure power and the horsepower input.

Standard air density is 0.075 lb per cu ft. This figure is the weight of 1 cu ft of air under average conditions of temperature, humidity, and barometric pressure. Manufacturers' publications of tables and curves are usually based on this standard air density.

The approximate air density is $d = 1.325P_b/T$, where P_b is the barometric pressure in in. of mercury and T is in deg F abs. For most fan testing and calculations, the density determined by this formula will introduce no appreciable error.

Fan pressures and horsepowers vary directly as the air density.

FAN CHARACTERISTICS

The performance of a fan can best be presented graphically. The accepted chart uses volumes as abscissas and pressures, horsepower inputs, and efficiencies as ordinates. The forms of the pressure and horsepower curves depend on the type of blading. They are characteristic of the particular type. Figure 1 shows a typical standard form of plotting of fan performance, with total pressure, static pressure, horsepower, and total and static efficiencies. Curves of the Fig. 1 plotting are necessarily drawn for a given size fan at a given speed.

Other plottings of more general application are also used. Fans function in close agreement with dimensional theory, and dimensionless plotting of fan curves is common practice.

A simple form of dimensionless plot is shown in Fig. 2. The abscissas are in percent

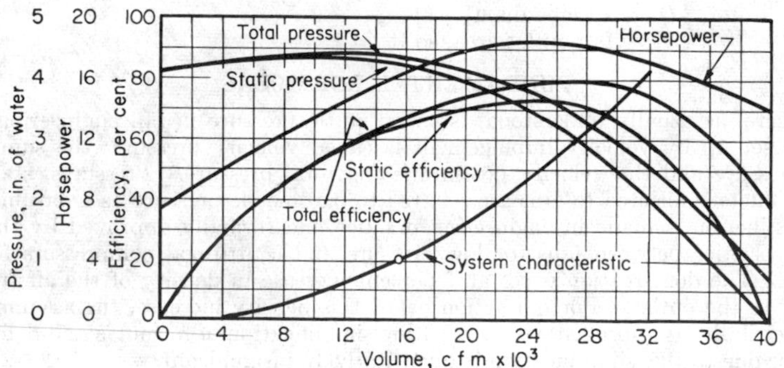

FIG. 1. Fan characteristics.

of volume at zero static pressure, the wide-open volume. The ordinates of the pressure curves are in percent of maximum pressure. Similarly horsepowers are in percent of maximum. Efficiencies are without dimension and are not changed. With the percent scales for abscissas and ordinates of a similar order of magnitude, this plotting preserves the characteristic shapes of the curves.

System Characteristics. The pressure required to deliver air through a resistance depends on the volume of flow. The relation between volume and pressure can be plotted to give a curve, the system characteristic. The system characteristic is best plotted with volumes as abscissas and pressures as ordinates. It is shown on the fan characteristic chart, Fig. 1. The crossing point of the system characteristic and the fan pressure characteristic is the point of operation.

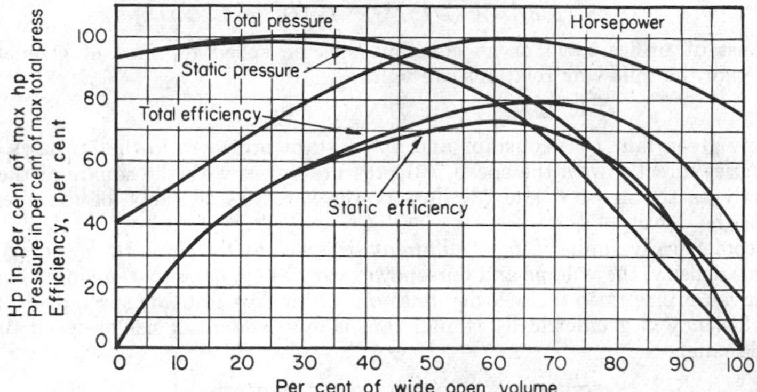

FIG. 2. Dimensionless plot of fan characteristics.

The fundamental characteristic is that of the **fixed-resistance system.** In such a system the pressure losses with ducts are considered to vary as the square of the air velocity. Deviations from the square law are negligible in normal application and may be attributed to changes in Reynolds number and Mach number. Only in rare cases of flow, at subcritical Reynolds numbers or at high Mach numbers, is it necessary to depart from the square law. In a system with fixed areas, volume is proportional to velocity, and the system characteristic may be conveniently plotted as a parabola, with pressure varying as the square of the volume. Most discussions of the relation of system and fan characteristics are limited to this parabolic form.

Compound system characteristics are frequently encountered. Further consideration may permit their analysis into a combination of fixed resistance systems. An important one is the multiple-nozzle arrangement for steam-boiler combustion. The resistance is due to the duct losses, which are substantially parabolic, to which is added the constant pressure required for nozzle combustion. The addition can be made for each nozzle giving isolated points each one of which determines its own fundamental parabolic characteristic.

Equivalent Orifice. The equivalent orifice is a useful concept. If the total pressure delivered to a system is converted to velocity, the equivalent orifice of the system is the area which, multiplied by that velocity, gives the volume flowing through the system. Physically, the equivalent orifice may be considered an ideal nozzle of 100 percent coefficient of discharge. The term is an old one in fan engineering and originally was the equivalent thin plate orifice of the same effective area as above. Allowance was made for the *vena contracta* with a coefficient of 0.625. This coefficient is subject to modification by stream forms, and the ideal nozzle concept avoids such confusion.

Orifice Ratio. O is a useful parameter that serves to relate the performance of geometrically similar fans of different sizes. In conventional notation, with p in in. of water and d in lb per cu ft,

$$O = Q/D^2\sqrt{p/d}$$

Specific Speed. N_s is a commonly used parameter which serves to relate the performance of different types of fans. It is a relative measure of the rotative speed and capacity of the various types, low values of specific speed corresponding with low rotative speeds and large wheel diameters. In the dimensionally impure form generally employed in fan application, with p in in. of water and d in lb per cu ft,

$$N_s = \frac{N\sqrt{Q}}{(p/d)^{3/4}}$$

Specific Diameter. D_s is a relative measure of wheel size required to deliver a specified volume and pressure. Customarily a plot of specific diameter against specific speed is used as a guide in fan-type selection.

$$D_s = (p/d)^{1/4} \times (D/\sqrt{Q}) \qquad [D_s' = 12 \times D_s]$$

At constant orifice ratio or at constant specific speed for fans of geometrically similar design the following relations are valid:

$$Q \propto D^3N \qquad p \propto D^2N^2d \qquad \text{hp} \propto D^5N^3d$$

For any given fan, D is constant and at constant orifice ratio the **fan laws** are (1) volume varies directly with the speed, (2) pressure varies with the square of the speed and directly as the density, and (3) horsepower varies as the cube of the speed and directly as the density.

For geometrically similar fans of different sizes but at the same tip speed πND and at the same density, the volume and horsepower vary as D^2, pressure remaining constant.

At a given orifice ratio the velocity relations of air flow to blade speed are constant, and the efficiency of geometrically similar fans is independent of size or speed throughout a wide range.

DESIGN OF CENTRIFUGAL FANS

Casing. The fan casing collects the air delivered from the impeller and directs the flow into the connected duct. It is commonly a *spiral* or *scroll.* The sides of the casing are plane and parallel. In such a space, the law of the constancy of the moment of momentum, or circulation, requires the spiral to be logarithmic.

$$\theta - \theta_0 = K \log (r/r_0)$$

Figure 3 shows a typical layout of fan spiral.

More complex forms of housing are sometimes used for various reasons, but performance at high efficiency is readily secured with the simpler logarithmic casing. The value of the constant K can be determined aerodynamically as the ratio of the tangential component to the radial component of the air velocity leaving the fan wheel. This rational procedure usually results in a casing which is much too large for commercial consideration. Experiment shows that the inner edge of the fan outlet may be located on the center line of the fan and the spiral swept from this point around to form an outlet substantially square. The outlet area should give a velocity pressure 10 percent of the static at the specified volume. K is then determined by trial and error to give the required sweep. Figure 4(a) shows a conventional spiral so determined.

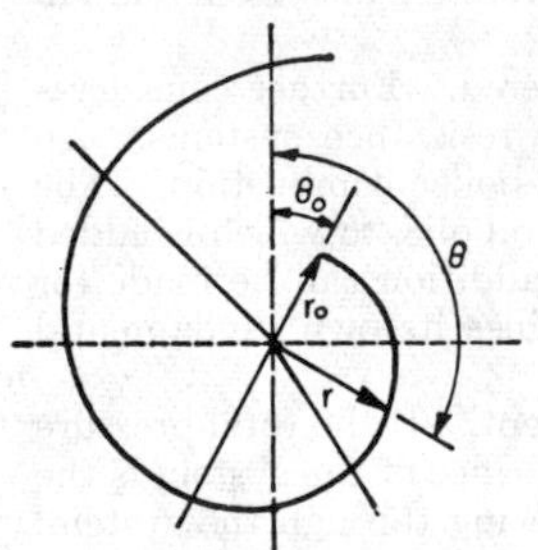

FIG. 3. Logarithmic spiral.

Modern design allows wide variation in fan outlet area for a given wheel. A good proportion, adopted as a standard by the National Assoc. of Fan Manufacturers, which conforms to the 10 percent rule above, is $A = 1.5D^2$.

Calculations for Casing of Fig. 4(a). $D = 2$ ft; $A = 6$ sq ft; $\sqrt{A} = 2.45$ ft $= r_1$; 3 in. = distance to cutoff; $r_0 = \dfrac{D}{2} + \dfrac{3}{12} = 1.25$ ft; $\theta_0 = 90$ deg; $\theta_1 = 360$ deg; $\theta_1 - \theta_0 = K \log (2.45/1.25)$ deg; $K = 922$. Equation of spiral $\theta - 90 = 922 \log (r_1/1.25)$.

Cutoff. There must be a transition from the spiral flow in the housing to the straight-line flow in the connected duct. Figure 4(b) shows the application of the principle of directing vanes to accomplish this result. Tests show that multiple vaning improves the air distribution at the fan outlet, but the performance, as determined with the test-code setup, is no better than with the arrangement of Fig. (4c), which is the most used commercial casing. The cutoff sheet extends into the outlet 10 to 40 percent, the lesser amount for the backwardly curved blade fan wheels and the greater amount for forwardly curved blades.

The cutoff sheet continues the curve of the spiral. The nearest point of the cutoff sheet to the wheel should be from 3 to 5 in. in a fan of 3 ft diam. Larger diameters

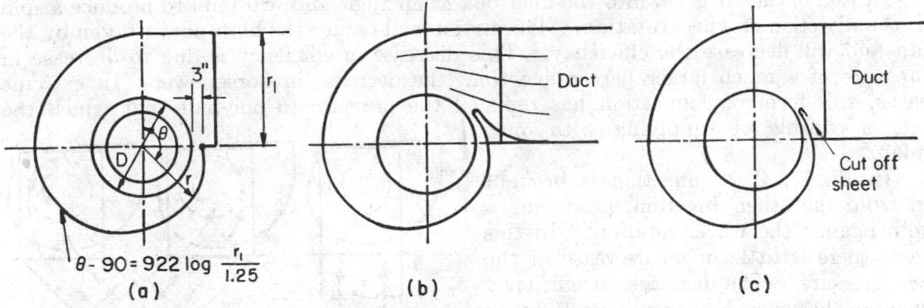

Fig. 4. Fan-casing scrolls.

require a greater distance, and smaller wheels permit less. Exact proportion is not necessary as noise rather than efficiency is the determining factor in fixing this dimension.

Width of Casing. The rule given for the size of the fan outlet, *i.e.*, a velocity pressure 10 percent of the static, and the desideratum of a substantially square outlet determine the width of the casing as well as the angle, or throw, of the spiral.

Commercial fans are probably the best guide to theoretically indeterminate dimensions. Fan housings are frequently standardized for a given wheel diameter and the same housing used for fan wheels of different types. Tests indicate consistently good performance. The discovery—a purely empirical one—that forwardly curved blade and backwardly curved blade wheels would operate successfully in the identical housing has indicated that the amount of the cross-sectional area in the housing is more important than the disposition of that area.

The flow in the casing is a complex action of a spiral flow around the fan shaft center line and a vortex around the spiral center line of the casing. This latter vortex continues spinning down the outlet duct. It can be changed, and sometimes eliminated, by changing the position of the wheel axially in the housing. Such change does not affect the true fan performance. The determination of the axial location of the wheel in the casing is a matter of structural advantage.

Fan Inlet. The fan inlet is a converging passage, preferably curved, leading from the ambient air or from an inlet duct to a smaller diameter at the entrance to the fan wheel. Some designs are improved by a small expansion of the inlet piece immediately before the wheel—the so-called Venturi passage. The upstream large end of the inlet should have an area substantially equal to the fan outlet. The smaller end at the wheel is determined by the wheel proportions and may reduce in area of passage as much as 40 percent.

The clearance between inlet and impeller is important; the clearance requirements are different with different fan types. In the backwardly curved blade fan, the inlet clearance should be small, of the order of ⅛ in. in a 3 ft diam fan. The volume recirculated through a large clearance reduces the fan output materially if clearance is as much as ½ in. With radial-blade fans, moderate clearance variations have little effect. And with the forwardly curved blade type, a large clearance not only does not harm the performance but actually is necessary for stability to minimize pulsation.

Inlet Ducts. Recent investigations have emphasized the important effect on fan performance of the actual inlet connections. The ducts leading to and from a fan are designed usually to escape beams and other limitations of space, and such duct work may seriously affect fan performance. The variation in the form of ducts is so great that no rules can be given for particular application. Figures 5 to 7 show three general forms.

In Fig. 5, the air is brought straight up to an inlet box, making a right-angle bend to get into the fan inlet. The loss in efficiency, which in this case shows itself in a drop in pressure, will amount to approximately 15 percent. This large loss is not explainable by any friction or eddy-current loss in the connection itself but is due to the poor distribution of the air flow into the wheel.

In Fig. 6, the air is led into the inlet box at an angle and will tend to produce a spin in the direction of wheel rotation. This action will reduce the horsepower taken by the fan and will decrease the efficiency. This decrease in efficiency is due to decrease in pressure of a much larger percentage than the decrease in horsepower. In extreme cases, this form of connection has reduced the pressure to one-half that which the fan is capable of supplying with open inlets.

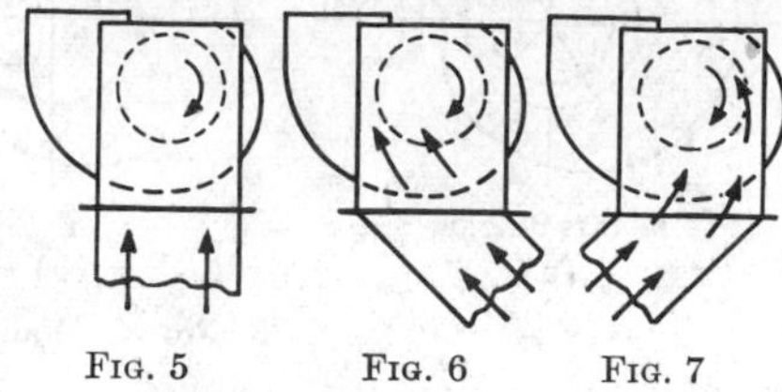

FIG. 5 FIG. 6 FIG. 7

FIGS. 5 to 7. Inlets of fan casings.

In Fig. 7, the connection is brought in from the other direction, producing a spin against the wheel rotation. In this case, there is little or no decrease in the fan pressure. The decrease in efficiency is large, however, and shows itself as an increased horsepower. An increase in horsepower of 25 percent is quite usual and may go as high as 50 percent.

Fans should be selected from tests made with the inlet connection in place. Laboratory research can determine suitable inlet ducts, called conventionally inlet boxes, of such proportions that the fan performance is affected only slightly. With such a box, even angular connections, with suitable vaning to give straight flow into the tested inlet box, will give satisfactory results.

Untested inlet connections built by the tinsmith should be avoided or proper allowance made.

Outlet Connections. The transition from the spiral flow in the housing to the flow in the duct is a turbulent change with an action similar to that of abrupt expansion. Outlet ducts continuing the fan outlet area serve to convert a portion of the high velocities into static pressure. Expanding outlet connections naturally convert a large portion of the initial velocity pressure, but, due to the varying directions of the fan outlet flow, they are not as effective as would appear. They return only 50 to 70 percent of the reduction in the velocity pressures as gain in static.

Diffuser Casing. The diffuser casing permits a circumferential discharge of air, a discharge suitable when the air is delivered into a large open space. The diffuser consists of two stationary plates continuing the sweep of the side plates of the wheel and leading the air outward to a large diameter.

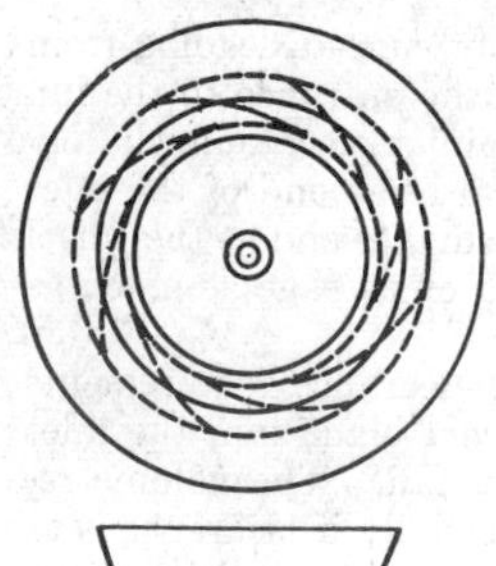

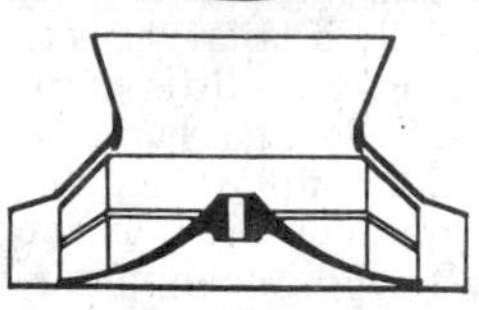

FIG. 8. Fan and diffuser casing.

The diffuser functions to convert velocity into static pressure by increasing the radius of the air spin and by increasing area. In the diffuser, no energy is imparted to the air, and constant energy requires constant circulation. Circulation is the product of tangential velocity times the circumference, and constancy of circulation requires a tangential component varying inversely with the radius.

A diffusion of the radial component of the velocity also takes place owing to an increase of area with increasing radius, but no quantitative predetermination of conversion is possible as the discharge from a fan impeller is not continuous. The discharge consists of jets from the spaces between blades, and the radial expansion of these jets does not follow any simple formula. Figure 8 shows a typical arrangement of fan and diffuser casing.

In general, diffusers and fan housings are designed empirically with some help from the theorem of constant circulation.

Fan Wheels. Fan-wheel proportions are subject to wide variation. Stresses in material or the combination of specified duty and speed are often determining factors. The significant proportions are the number of blades, the ratio of inlet diameter to wheel diameter, and the ratio of axial width to diameter. This latter ratio is important only as a maximum; reduced widths are always allowable.

The following table gives the proportions of fan wheels according to commercial practice:

Type wheel	Number of blades	Ratio of inlet diam to wheel diam	Ratio of width to diam
Forwardly curved	60	0.88	0.55
Radial tip	16–24	0.78	0.35
Backwardly curved	8–16	0.75	0.26
Paddle wheel	6–12	0.50–0.70	0.38–0.48

Fan-wheel Theory. The theory of the design of fan wheels is highly developed. The Euler equation for pressure is

$$p = (d\omega/g)(r_1 V_{u_1} - r_0 V_{u_0})$$

where r_1 and V_{u1} are the radius and rotative air velocity at exit; r_0 and V_{u0} the quantities at entrance; and ω the rotative speed of the impeller, radians per sec. The Euler equation applies to any wheel, centrifugal or propeller.

A newer analysis, applied chiefly to propeller fans, is derived from modern aeronautics and is based on the theory of circulation around an airfoil. In airfoil theory, Γ, the circulation, is

$$\Gamma = \tfrac{1}{2} C_L b v$$

where C_L is the lift coefficient, b the length of the chord, and v the effective velocity relative to the airfoil (see p. 11–72).

Applied to a fan with a number of blades Z,

$$p = d\omega Z\Gamma/2\pi g$$

This expression for p may be equated to that of the Euler equation which, for a propeller fan with r_1 equal to r_0, becomes

$$p = d\omega r(V_{u_1} - V_{u_0})/g$$

With circulation Γ per blade,

$$r(V_{u_1} - V_{u_0}) = Z\Gamma/2\pi$$

The required circulation is then

$$\Gamma = 2\pi r(V_{u_1} - V_{u_0})/Z = C_L b v/2$$

Values of C_L are available for published tests of airfoils (see p. 11–79).

Airfoil circulation is changed by the proximity of other blades, the so-called **cascade effect.** This effect varies greatly with angle and solidity of the cascade. Only when the ratio of blade spacing to blade chord is greater than 2.0 is it desirable to use uncorrected values of C_L.

For smaller values of blade spacing-to-chord ratio, corrections may be made as described under Axial Fan Design, p. 14–78, or reference may be made to cascade test data such as reported in *NACA-RM* L51G31 and *NACA-RM* L53I30b.

Propeller fans for high duties and large angles of attack have been successfully developed empirically starting with helical blades. A helix angle at the tip of 24 deg is a maximum for good efficiency.

Velocity Diagrams. The application of design formulation is best worked out with the help of diagrammatic representation of the velocity vectors. These diagrams give quantitative values for design and much information as to the fan characteristics of different types of blading.

For centrifugal fans, the Euler analysis gives satisfactory results. The Euler theory requires separate diagrams for inlet and outlet. The inlet diagrams are always the same, as they are independent of the blading.

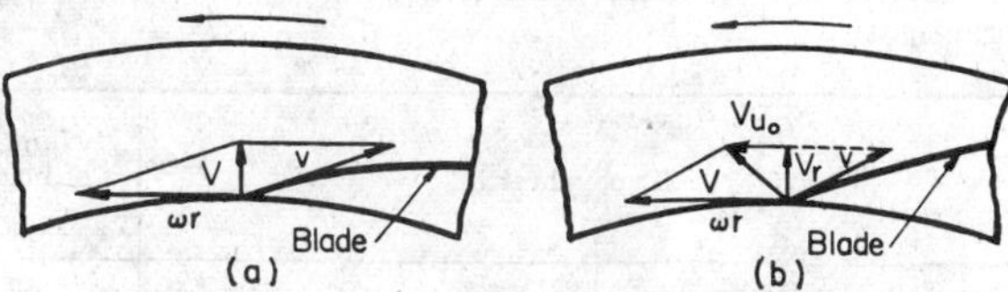

FIG. 9. Inlet-velocity diagrams.

Figure 9(*a*) shows the usual diagram for air approaching the wheel with velocity V, which combines with ωr, reversed, to give the velocity v relative to the wheel or blade. The direction of v determines the angular setting of the blade. The entrance portion of the blade may be tangent to v or inclined a few degrees from tangency dependent upon the particular blade shape contemplated.

Figure 9(*b*) shows the inlet velocity diagram for a positive value of an inlet spin V_{u0} positive in the same direction as the wheel rotation. With reverse inlet spins the action produces unsatisfactory and often unstable characteristics.

Figures 10(*a*), (*b*), and (*c*) are the outlet velocity diagrams for backwardly curved, radial, and forwardly curved blades, respectively.

The height of the diagram, indicated by the velocity vector V_r, is determined in each

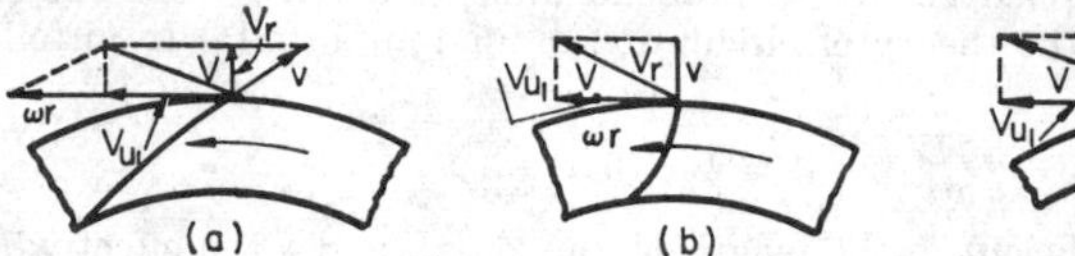

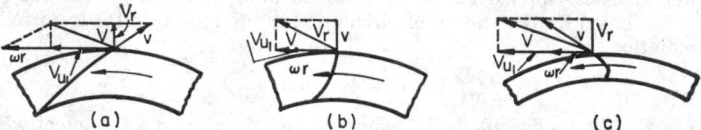

FIG. 10. Outlet-velocity diagrams.

of these cases—and also for any special inlet diagram such as Fig. 9(*b*)—from the design volume and the effective area through which that volume flows.

In Fig. 10(*b*), the relative velocity v is tangent to the blade, ωr is perpendicular to the wheel radius. The actual air velocity V is the resultant of v and ωr. V_{u1}, the rotative component of V, is projected from V to the direction of ωr.

Velocity diagrams present a rational basis for comparing the characteristics of the three types of blading. Characteristics are determined at constant speed so the ωr vector will not change. If the volume decreases, the vector V_r decreases and, as the direction of v does not change for a given blade, V_u increases with backwardly curved blades, is constant with radial blades, and decreases with forwardly curved blades.

As the pressure of the fan depends on the product of $V_u \times \omega r$, the pressure change is the same as the change in V_u, and the pressure characteristic of the backwardly curved blade fan rises with decreasing volume, is constant for the radial blade, and decreases or falls for the forwardly curved blade. Frequently, the slope of a fan characteristic is discussed in the opposite sense of increasing volumes with the designation *drooping* for the backwardly curved and *rising* for the forwardly curved blade. The decreasing volume basis is preferable as directly applicable to considerations of type desirability.

The desirable qualities of a fan are stability, successful operation in parallel, freedom from pulsation and, from the driver point of view, a non-overloading horsepower demand.

Stability. The factors of fan output are pressure and volume. Stability of operation requires that the factors change oppositely; *i.e.*, a reduction in volume should be opposed by an increase in pressure. The backwardly curved blade fan is inherently stable. The radial-blade fan is stable as to static pressure but not so where total pressure may control the action. The forwardly curved blade fan is inherently unstable.

Duct work has a characteristic also. With most ducts, the pressure decreases so much with decreased volume that even the characteristic of the forwardly curved blade fan has excess pressure requirement at reduced volume and because of duct reaction becomes stable in spite of its own unfavorable characteristic.

Parallel Operation. Two or more fans operating on a single duct system must have suitable characteristics for such operation and be properly selected as to point of operation. Parallel operation requires that the sum of the outputs of the fans equal the duct capacity and that this equality exist for only one set of conditions. In mathematical phraseology, the characteristics of the fans and duct must be satisfied and uniquely.

Figure 11 shows the graphical analysis for parallel operation of two fans. The duct characteristic is the usual parabola, and the fan characteristic is typical of the backwardly curved blade type. One fan operating on the duct will deliver the volume and pressure of their intersection *A*. If an identical fan is added to the system, the volume and pressure will be greater. The exact point of operation may be determined by constructing the "limit curve." At a series of pressures such as *P*, plot the volumes *L*

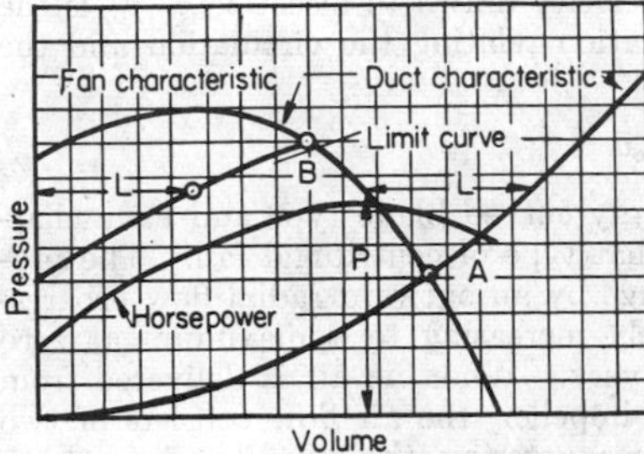

Fig. 11. Stable parallel operation of two fans.

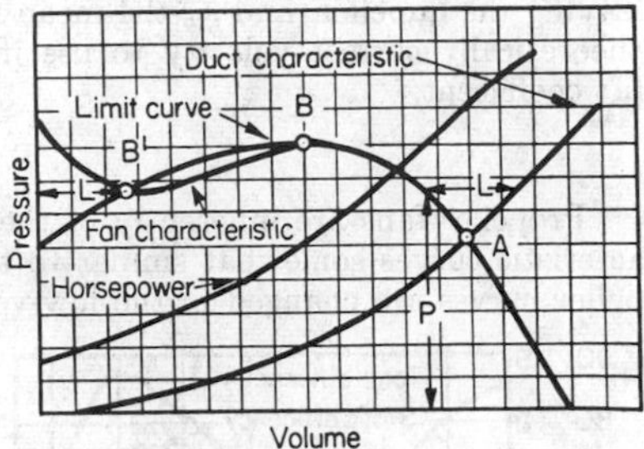

Fig. 12. Unstable parallel operation of two fans.

which when added to the volume of the fan will equal the volume of the duct characteristic. Draw the limit curve through the points. The intersection *B* of limit curve and fan characteristic gives the point of operation of each of two identical fans.

For successful operation, there should be only one such point. Further, the intersection angle should not be small or there may be hunting. The requirements are best presented by a comparison of Fig. 11, which indicates successful paralleling, with Fig. 12, which shows an incorrect combination. Figure 12 shows the analysis for forwardly curved blade fans. The limit curve is constructed in the same manner as in Fig. 11, but in Fig. 12 there are two intersections and between them a superposition of the two curves. Any attempt to parallel fans with such characteristics will be successful only by accident. The point of equal load division in both Figs. 11 and 12 was selected for efficient operation and correctly represents the comparison of the parallel operation of the two types. It is apparent that, with a different relation between duct and fan characteristics which would permit the equal division of load to occur at a larger orifice on the fan curve, successful parallel operation is possible even with the forwardly curved blade fan, but only at a sacrifice, as this region of the fan output is in the range of low efficiency.

Figures 11 and 12 show also an important advantage of the self-limiting horsepower of the backwardly curved blade fan. When two fans are installed on one duct system, the reliability of partial load operation with one fan in the event of the failure of the other unit is usually of importance. With a self-limiting-horsepower fan, there is no possibility of overloading the driving motor. With the other types of fans, the excess load with single-fan operation on a parallel system must always be considered in selecting motors.

Pulsation. Fans used for high pressures can, under some conditions, develop a severe pulsation. No exact pressure can be stated below which this action cannot occur, but it seldom happens below 15 in. of water. In most fans at one-sixth to one-third of the design volume, there is a *blowback* out of a portion of the inlet and a definite puffiness in the discharge. Fans should not be used for the higher pressures at the blowback point.

Pulsation is most severe when the fan discharges into a large duct or chamber with a volume content 5 percent or more of the volume per minute of normal fan output. A chamber of this size can be set into violent pulsation by a fan, not only at the blowback point, but also at any portion of its characteristic curve where the slope of the curve shows decreasing pressure with decreasing volume. Pulsation can also be set up by an apparently stable fan in double-inlet arrangement when there is a large difference between the flows to the two inlets.

DESIGN OF AXIAL FANS

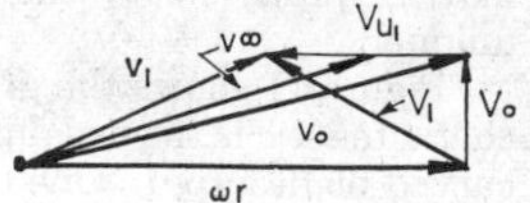

FIG. 13. Velocity diagram for propeller or axial fan.

Velocity diagrams for propeller fans are usually drawn for a uniform axial velocity. Figure 13 shows a typical propeller fan diagram where ωr is the reversed speed of the blade section under consideration, V_0, the axial velocity of the air, V_1 the air velocity leaving the impeller, and v_∞ the mean relative velocity drawn to bisect V_{u_1}. v_∞ is the theoretically correct velocity to use in the equation relating the **circulation** and the lift coefficient.

$$\Gamma = \tfrac{1}{2} C_L v_\infty b$$

Propeller fans are inherently of the backwardly curved blade type and have characteristic curves somewhat similar to those of that type of centrifugal fan. The propeller curves are changed in the low-volume range by an outward radial flow progressively increasing to a maximum at zero delivery. When no air is delivered from the impeller, the air flow consists of two eddies entering the impeller from both sides in the region near the hub and leaving near the tip. This action increases both pressure and horsepower. Figure 14 shows the **characteristic curves** of an efficient propeller fan. This fan has a small pitch angle, 15 deg at the tip. The fan performance is perfectly stable throughout the full range of the curve. This quality of stability will hold for most propeller fans up to 17 deg and with careful design, with constant circulation at the design point, even up to 20 deg. For steeper pitches, instability occurs with a break in the curve as indicated in Fig. 15.

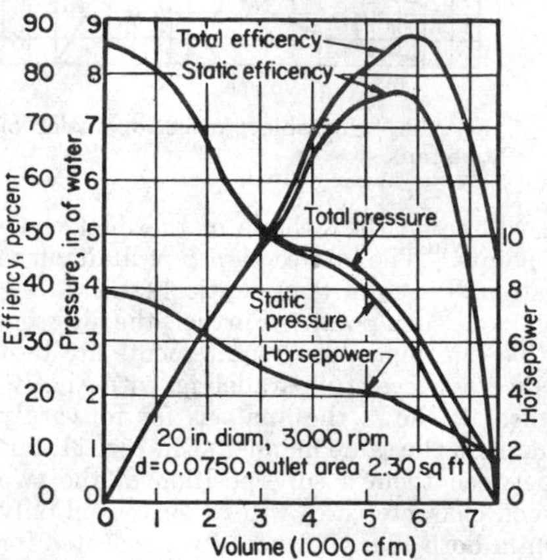

FIG. 14. Characteristic curves of stable propeller fan.

The small-pitch angle fan has the advantage of high efficiency and stable operation. Its disadvantages are low capacity and high speed. Because of this high speed, these fans are noisy for a given duty and for the higher pressures present a difficult structural design problem.

Steep-pitch fans deliver large volumes, are less noisy, and can be built for high pressures—but all at a sacrifice of stability and efficiency.

The commercially desirable propeller fan is the medium-pitch type from 17 to 20 deg. It usually has wide blades, taking up, in projected area, more than 50 percent of the circle. The cascade ratio, spacing to chord, is unity or slightly less.

Special propeller fans have been built for high efficiency and in large sizes for wind tunnels. These fans are the opposite of the commercial type. The blades are narrow compared with their radial length. The cascade ratio is 2 or more, and the lift coefficient 0.6 or less, corresponding to a low angle of attack. For a given duty, such fans may be twice the diameter of the equivalent commercial fan, but with a gain of approximately 10 percent in efficiency.

Cascade Effect. Mutual blade interference or cascade effect can be determined approximately with satisfactory results. The procedure increases the camber of the airfoil in conformity to the deviation of flow between inlet and outlet of the impeller.

In Fig. 16, v_1, v_0, v_∞, and V_{u_1} are redrawn from Fig. 13. The deviation angle is the angle between the relative velocity vectors v_1 and v_0. The dash line DE is drawn parallel to v_1 from the end of v_0. The vector v_∞ is extended, intersecting DE in B. The smooth curve AB is drawn tangent to v_0 at A and to DE at B.

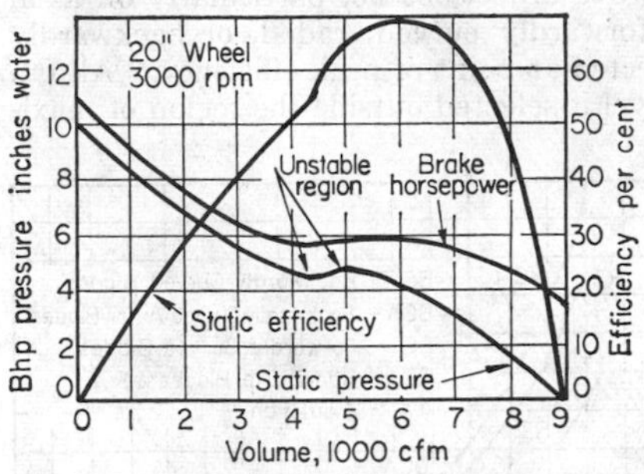

FIG. 15. Characteristic curves of a propeller fan having an unstable region.

From V_{u_1} the total circulation is calculated as

$$\Gamma = 2\pi r V_{u_1}$$

where r is the radius for which the diagram is drawn. It is usually sufficient to work out blade shapes for tip, mean, and hub radii. Γ is constant. Therefore V_{u_1} must vary inversely as the radius.

The required circulation per blade is

$$\Gamma_b = \Gamma/Z$$

where Z is the number of blades.

A suitable lift coefficient C_L may be selected from airfoil data and the curve AB rotated about A through the required angle of attack α to the position AC. AC is the corrected chord line of the airfoil. The scale is determined by the length b of the curve arc AC as calculated from Γ_b.

$$\Gamma_b = \tfrac{1}{2} C_L v_\infty b$$

Guide Vanes for Propeller Fans. The discharge from the propeller wheel necessarily has a rotation unless guide vanes are used in the inlet. The tangential component of the discharge velocity serves no useful purpose. Stationary deflecting or diffusion vanes past the wheel convert the tangential velocity into static pressure. The vanes are preferably airfoil shapes with a total circulation equal and opposite to the total circulation produced by the propeller. The number of diffusion vanes should be prime to the number of propeller blades.

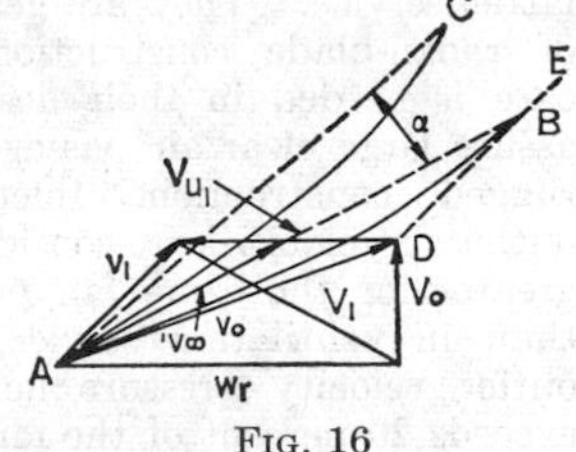

FIG. 16

The method described for the impeller blade correction may be used for the **diffusion vanes** with the absolute velocities V_d entering and V_a leaving the vanes corresponding to the relative impeller velocities V_0 and V_1 of Fig. 16. The deviation angle is the angle between the velocity vectors V_a and V_d with V_∞ as the mean.

This application of the curved stream line tends to give a factor of safety of the order of 1.05 to 1.10, with a resulting pressure slightly higher than called for by the design calculations (see *NACA-TM* 1022, 1942).

FAN APPLICATION

The choice of a fan type and size for a particular application involves (1) an aerodynamic selection influenced by volume, pressure, density, and speed requirements; and (2) a functional selection influenced by such factors as space availability, investment, operating costs, and suitability. Aerodynamic selection of type and size is a simple procedure which may be facilitated by the use of charts of various designs. One useful chart consists of a plot of specific diameter and efficiency against specific speed. In Fig. 17 are shown data for various single-inlet versions of commercially available fan types. Generally, efficiency increases and fan size decreases as specific speed increases. The fact that fan types of high specific speed are not invariably selected is governed to a large degree by functional suitability.

Guiding principles which reconcile aerodynamic and functional selection for common fan applications are:

1. Ventilation. This application may demand the production of fan pressures ranging from a fraction of an inch to 6 in. of water. Almost without exception, fans of large specific speed are economically justified (N_s = 6,000). Two governing limitations are high rotative speed, which may pose mechanical problems associated with belt drives and bearings, and noise production, which may prove objectionable, particularly on axial types. Well-designed centrifugal fans with forwardly curved, radial, or backwardly curved blading give the same noise level if selected at point of peak efficiency. All fan types, however, exhibit an increase in noise level if selected outside the region of maximum efficiency. When quiet operation is essential, sufficiently large fans should be chosen to assure operation in the region of peak efficiency. Simple dampers are usually adequate and economical for the control of air delivery with ventilation fans because the power demands are small.

2. Conveying. The transport of solid materials in high-velocity air streams is sometimes accomplished by injector action, but most frequently, the material to be conveyed passes through the fan wheel and casing. Low-specific-speed-type fans (N_s = 1,500) are used for the latter service. They are generally of radial-blade construction, and care is needed in their design to assure large clear air passages and rugged construction. Inlet and outlet air velocities are considerably greater for the same fan pressure than in ventilating service. The outlet velocity pressure normally exceeds 20 percent of the fan total pressure. Fans of this type are also broadly used in industrial systems for general exhaust or supply with pressures ranging to 15 in. of water. Output control is by simple damper, as with ventilation fans.

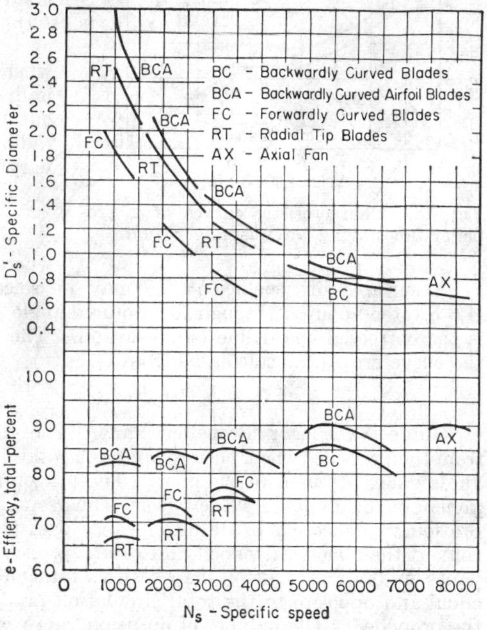

FIG. 17. Specific speed, specific diameter and efficiency for commercial single-inlet fan types.

BC—backwardly curved blades
BCA—backwardly curved airfoil blades
FC—forwardly curved blades
RT—radial-tip blades
Ax—axial fan
$D_s' = D_s \times 12$

3. Induced Draft. The exhaust, or recirculation, of the products of combustion from furnaces, kilns, boilers, sinter beds, and the like is the induced-draft application of fans. Gas temperatures from 300 to 800 F prevail. Erosive particles in varying amounts are suspended in the gas. Fans of intermediate or large specific speeds (N_s = 2,000 to 6,000) are applied, with pressures ranging from a few inches to 25 in. of water. When operating pressures are less than 10 in., and abrasive conditions are not severe, high-speed fans may be selected and evaluated on the basis of efficiency alone. At higher-pressure levels, and under severe abrasive conditions, efficiency becomes a secondary consideration, with robust fan construction of prime importance. Radial-blade unshrouded impellers with heavy, renewable liner plates are used for extreme conditions. In other cases shrouded impellers with heavy blades and liner plates are satisfactory. Fan manufacturers have developed a variety of special impellers with greatly reduced rates of erosion and of exceptional structural integrity even when severe erosion has occurred. Deep radial blades are favored since they maintain strength even when eroded to half their radial depth. The rate of erosion on backwardly inclined blades is not greater than on radial blades, but the degree of erosion which may be tolerated before rebuilding is much less because of the rapid deterioration in blade strength which occurs with reduction in effective blade thickness. Conventional backwardly inclined plate blades are consequently seldom used under severe abrasive conditions. Abrasion-resisting materials for blade liners or blade bases have not proved sufficiently effective to justify general use. Maximum wheel and casing life results from the use of (1) dust collectors ahead of the fan and/or (2) variable-speed drives with minimum fan operating speed for the specified output.

The power consumption of an induced-draft fan may be large (100 to 1,000 hp), so that control of output with sustained efficiency is desirable. When a small control range of efficient operation is required, say from 75 to 100 percent, aerodynamic controls which give an inlet spin at the fan impeller in the direction of wheel rotation are usually justifiable on the basis of the power saving. Such controls take the form of (1) multiple adjustable vanes at the fan inlet or (2) multilouvered spin-inducing dampers at the entrance to the fan inlet box. When an efficient control range of great magnitude is desired, some form of variable-speed coupling or driver is often economically justified by power saving and reduced erosion.

Gas recirculation in steam-boiler plants is a recent development using induced-draft type of equipment. Periodic operation of the gas-recirculation fan at temperatures as high as 800 F is required. The recirculation fan, unlike the usual induced-draft fan, may be subjected to abrupt gas-temperature changes of 400 to 600 F. The rapid change of wheel and shaft temperatures requires designs (1) where the wheel will not loosen on the shaft and (2) where the shaft will maintain dimensional stability. The system resistance in the gas-recirculation circuit is not fixed, and it is often necessary to produce increased pressure at reduced flow rates. The fan characteristics therefore assume major importance even at low-volume delivery. Radial-blade fans using shrouded or unshrouded wheels (N_s = 2,000) are generally preferred. Variable-speed control is not feasible because of the unusual system requirements. Control is achieved by (1) inlet spin-inducing dampers or (2) conventional dampers in the gas circuit.

4. Forced-draft fans normally handle clean air at ambient temperature. Selection is governed by mechanical reliability and efficiency. Pressure requirements vary from a few inches of water to 80 in. of water on the pressurized-type furnaces. Fans of large specific speed (N_s = 5,500) and highest attainable efficiency are justifiable economically for pressures up to 35 in. At greater pressure levels the high-specific-speed impellers, which are axially wide and radially shallow, lack the inherent structural strength required for the service and are displaced by units of lower specific speed (N_s = 3,000). The narrow, tall blades contribute to blade and shroud strength.

Backwardly inclined blading is used almost exclusively because of the premium placed on efficiency. Blades with airfoil contours and thickness ratios in the range of 15 percent have improved the structural strength and reduced aerodynamic losses so that fan efficiencies in excess of 90 percent are now attainable. Noise from air turbulence is also reduced about 5 db as a result of utilizing airfoil blades in place of formed-plate blades. System resistance characteristics in forced-draft circuits most often are not fixed, and the pressure requirement decreases much less slowly than the square of the volume flow. The nature of the fan characteristics at reduced flow rates again assumes importance, as in the case of gas-recirculation fans.

Axial fans have been applied extensively for forced draft in marine installations with pressures up to 50 in. of water. They have found limited use, however, in commercial boiler installations at pressures much above 5 in. of water because of the noise level. Efficiency equals that of the high-specific-speed, airfoil-blade, centrifugal fan, but both space requirement and investment cost are lower.

Power requirements on forced-draft fans may reach 4,000 hp on large high-pressure units, and efficiency of control at partial load is of great importance. Simple damper devices can rarely be tolerated, and variable-speed drivers are infrequently justified on economic grounds. Control is achieved, at constant speed, with spin-inducing vanes or inlet dampers in the great majority of installations.

Primary-air-supply fans draw relatively clean air at 500 to 600 F from an air heater and raise the pressure by 20 or 30 in. of water prior to passage through a coal mill ejector. Although some erosion may be anticipated when fly ash is carried from the air heater into the primary-air circuit, few special precautions are observed. The principal requirement is mechanical strength and reliability at the high peripheral wheel speeds utilized. Shrouded impellers of low specific speed ($N_s = 1{,}500$) with radial or slightly backwardly inclined blading are generally acceptable. In view of the moderate power consumption, generally less than 100 hp, simple damper devices in the inlet air duct are ample for control.

SECTION 15

ELECTRICAL AND ELECTRONICS ENGINEERING

BY

CHESTER L. DAWES, Associate Professor of Electrical Engineering Emeritus, Harvard University; Consulting Engineer.

J. HUBERT NOLAND, Professor of Electrical Engineering, University of South Carolina.

CONTENTS

ELECTRICAL ENGINEERING

BY

Chester L. Dawes

REFERENCES: Knowlton, "Standard Handbook for Electrical Engineers," McGraw-Hill. Pender and Del Mar, "Electrical Engineers' Handbook," Wiley. Dawes, "Course in Electrical Engineering," Vols. I and II, McGraw-Hill. Gray, "Principles and Practice of Electrical Engineering," McGraw-Hill. Laws, "Electrical Measurements," McGraw-Hill. Karapetoff-Dennison, "Experimental Electrical Engineering and Manual for Electrical Testing," Wiley. Langsdorf, "Principles of Direct-current Machines," McGraw-Hill. Hehre and Harness, "Electric Circuits and Machinery," Vols. I and II, Wiley. Timbie-Higbie, "Alternating Current Electricity and Its Application to Industry," Wiley. Lawrence, "Principles of Alternating-current Machinery," McGraw-Hill. Puchstein and Lloyd, "Alternating-current Machinery," Wiley. Lovell, "Generating Stations," McGraw-Hill. Underhill, "Coils and Magnet Wire" and "Magnets," McGraw-Hill. Abbott, "National Electrical Code Handbook," McGraw-Hill. Dyke, "Automobile and Gasoline Engine Encyclopedia," The Goodheart-Wilcox Co., Inc.

MAGNETIC AND ELECTRICAL UNITS

Systems of Units. There are three fundamental systems of electrical units of which two, the cgs electrostatic and the cgs electromagnetic, are based dimensionally on the centimeter, gram, and second; the third, the mks, is based on the meter, kilogram, and second. The **cgs electrostatic system** is derived from the force exerted between two unit charges of electricity concentrated at points 1 cm apart in a medium of unit capacitivity, or dielectric constant. The **cgs electromagnetic system** is derived from the force exerted between two unit magnetic poles concentrated at points 1 cm apart in a medium of unit magnetic permeability.

The **mks system,** based dimensionally on the meter, kilogram, and second, was adopted as a standard in 1935 by the International Electrotechnical Commission. There are two mks systems: the **unrationalized,** in which the mmf is equal to $4\pi NI$, where N is the number of turns and I the current in amperes; and the **rationalized** system, in which the mmf is equal to NI. In the unrationalized system the permeability of free space μ_v is equal to 10^{-7}; in the rationalized system it is equal to $4\pi\mu_v$, or $4\pi 10^{-7} = \mu_v'$. Similarly in the unrationalized system the capacitivity of free space ϵ_v is equal to 8.854×10^{-12} and in the rationalized system is equal to $4\pi\epsilon_v = \epsilon_v' = 1.113 \times 10^{-10}$. The practical electrical units such as the volt, ampere, watt, farad, henry are mks units.

When the cgs systems are used, magnetic calculations are usually made in the electromagnetic system and capacitance calculations in the electrostatic system. In Table 1 are given the relations among the units of the three systems.

Magnetic Units

(See Table 6 for relations of magnetic units)

A **unit cgs magnetic** pole is one which is concentrated at a point and which has such strength that when it is placed at a unit distance 1 cm from an exactly similar pole in a medium of unit permeability, the two poles will repel each other with a unit force (dyne). One unrationalized mks unit pole $= 10^8$ cgs unit poles; one rationalized mks unit pole $= 10^8/4\pi = 7.958 \times 10^6$ cgs unit poles. Unit mks unit poles, one meter apart in vacuum, repel or attract each other with a force of one **newton** $= 10^5$ dynes.

Magnetic potential difference $(M, \mathfrak{F})$ between two points is measured by the work involved in moving a unit magnet pole between the two points.

Magnetic field intensity (H) at a point is defined as the vector quantity which is measured by the force (mechanical) which is exerted on a unit magnetic pole placed at the point, when the point under consideration is in a vacuum.

In mediums whose permeability is unity, the cgs field intensity is given by the number of lines of force per square centimeter taken normal to their direction. The cgs unit of field intensity is the **oersted.**

Magnetic flux (Φ, ϕ) is the magnetic flow that exists in any magnetic circuit. The cgs unit is the **maxwell,** the mks unit is the **weber.** One weber $= 10^8$ maxwells.

Magnetic flux density (B) is the ratio of the flux in any cross section to the area of that cross section, the cross section being taken normal to the direction of flux. In the cgs system the unit of flux density is the **gauss** = one maxwell per sq cm; in the two mks systems the unit of flux density is the **weber per sq meter** $= 10^4$ gauss.

The force on a unit cgs magnetic pole in a field intensity of one gauss is one dyne. To produce a field intensity of one gauss requires a mmf of one gilbert per cm or 0.896 amp-turn.

Magnetomotive force ($\mathcal{F}$ and mmf) tends to produce magnetic flux and corresponds to emf in the electric circuit. The cgs unit is the **gilbert** $= 0.4\pi(ni)$, where (ni) is an ampere-turn. The unrationalized mks unit is $4\pi(ni)$, and the rationalized unit is the **ampere-turn** (ni). The respective mmfs acting on a magnetic circuit are $0.4\pi NI$, $4\pi NI$, and NI, where NI is the ampere-turns.

Relative Permeability (μ_r) is the ratio of the cgs magnetic-flux density to the magnetizing force (B/H). In the unrationalized and rationalized mks systems $\mu_r = B/\mu_v H$, and $\mu_r = B/\mu_v' H$, respectively. Actually, relative permeability is the ratio of the magnetic flux in any element of a medium to the flux that would exist if that element were replaced with air, the mmf acting on the element remaining unchanged. The term **permeability** $= \mu$ is commonly used to denote relative permeability.

Permeance ($\mathcal{P}$) of a portion of a magnetic circuit bounded by two equipotential surfaces, and by a third surface at every point of which there is a tangent having the direction of the magnetic induction, is the ratio of the flux through any cross section to the magnetic potential difference between the surfaces when taken within the portion under consideration. The equation for the permeance of the medium as defined above is $\mathcal{P} = \phi/\mathcal{F}$. Permeance is the reciprocal of reluctance.

Reluctivity (ν) of a medium is the reciprocal of its permeability. In the cgs system it is the reluctance between any two parallel faces of a one centimeter cube of the medium.

Reluctance ($\mathcal{R}$) is the reciprocal of permeance. It is the resistance to magnetic flow. In a homogeneous medium of uniform cross section, cgs reluctance is equal to the length divided by the product of the area and permeability, the length and area being expressed in centimeter units ($\mathcal{R} = L/A\mu_r$). In the mks unrationalized system the reluctance $\mathcal{R} = L/A\mu_r\mu_v$, where the length L and the area A are in meter units, μ_r is relative permeability, and μ_v is 10^{-7}. In the rationalized system, $\mathcal{R} = L/[A\mu_r(4\pi\mu_v)] = L/A\mu_r\mu_v'$, where $\mu_v' = 4\pi 10^{-7}$.

Electrical Units

(See Table 1)

Current (I, i). The practical unit of current is the ampere, which is equal to one-tenth the absolute unit of current and is the current in a conductor having a resistance of one ohm and a difference of potential of one volt between its ends. The cgs absolute unit of current is defined as follows: If one centimeter of a circuit is bent into an arc of one centimeter radius, the current is one cgs **abampere** if the magnetic field intensity at the center is one oersted, provided the remainder of the circuit produces no magnetic effect at the center of the arc. One international ampere (direct current) will deposit 0.001118 g of silver per sec from a standard silver solution. The **international ampere** equals 0.999835 absolute ampere. The absolute units, legalized by Congress, went into effect Jan. 1, 1948.

Quantity (Q). The practical unit of quantity is the **coulomb.** An **international coulomb** is the quantity of electricity which passes any section of an electric circuit in one second, when the current in the circuit is one international ampere. One **international coulomb** equals 0.999835 absolute coulomb.

Potential Difference or Electromotive Force (E, V, emf). The practical unit of electromotive force **is the volt.** The **international volt** is the voltage which will produce a current of one **international** ampere through a resistance of one international ohm. One international volt **equals** 1.000330 absolute volts. The **absolute volt** equals 10^8 cgs absolute volts. **A conductor one** centimeter long cutting flux at the rate of one maxwell per sq cm (one gauss) per sec has induced in it one cgs abvolt. A conductor one meter long cutting flux at the rate of one weber per square meter per second has induced in it one mks (practical) volt. Emf tends to cause flow of electricity.

Resistance (R, r). The practical unit of resistance is the **ohm** (Ω) and is that resistance through which the fall of potential is 1 volt when the current is 1 amp. The **international ohm** is defined as the resistance at 0 C of a column of mercury of uniform cross section, having a length of 106.300 cm and a mass of 14.521 g. One international ohm equals 1.000495 **absolute ohms.** The absolute ohm equals 10^9 cgs abohms.

Resistivity (ρ) of a material is the d-c resistance between the opposite parallel faces of a portion of the material having unit length and unit cross section. Common portions of the material are 1 cc and 1 cir-mil-foot.

Conductance (G, g). Conductance is the reciprocal of resistance and is expressed in reciprocal ohms or **mhos** (℧). "Mho" is "ohm" spelled backward.

Conductivity (γ) of a material is the d-c conductance between the opposite parallel faces of a portion of the material having unit length and unit cross section.

Capacitance (C) is that property of a system of conductors and dielectrics which permits the storage of electricity when potential difference exists between the conductors. Its value is expressed as a ratio of a quantity of electricity to a potential difference. A capacitance value is always positive.

The practical unit of capacitance is the **farad** (f) and is that capacitance the potential of which will be raised one volt by the addition of a charge of one coulomb. One **international farad** equals 0.999505 absolute farad. As the farad is too large a unit for practical purposes, the **microfarad** (μf), which is one-millionth of a farad, is generally used. For capacitors such as are used for radio purposes the **micromicrofarad** ($\mu\mu$f), or picofarad (pf) 10^{-12} farad, is a more suitable unit. The magnitude of the microfarad is 9×10^5 that of the cgs electrostatic unit (statfarad).

Relative capacitivity, or dielectric constant (ϵ_r), of a dielectric is that property which determines the electrostatic energy stored per unit volume for unit potential gradient. In the electrostatic system of units, the capacitivity of a vacuum is unity, so that the relative capacitivity of a dielectric is the ratio of capacitance with the dielectric to the capacitance with a vacuum.

In the unrationalized mks system the capacitivity ϵ_v of free space, or of a vacuum, is 1.11279×10^{-10}; in the rationalized mks system the capacitivity ϵ_v' of free space is $\epsilon_v/4\pi = 8.854 \times 10^{-12}$.

Self-inductance (L) is the property of an electric circuit which determines, for a given rate of change of current in the circuit, the emf induced in the same circuit. Thus $e_1 = -L\, di_1/dt$ where e_1 and i_1 are in the same circuit and L is the coefficient of self-inductance.

The practical unit of self-inductance is the **henry.** An electric circuit has an inductance of one henry when a rate of change of one ampere per second will induce an emf of one volt. It also follows that in such a circuit one ampere will produce 10^8 cgs linkages of magnetic lines (product of turns and flux) in the circuit, since a change of 10^8 linkages per second is required to induce one volt. One henry is equal to 10^9 cgs absolute units of self-inductance; one international henry is equal to 1.000495 absolute henrys. If the permeability is constant, $L = n\phi 10^{-8}/I$ henry, where $n\phi$ is the cgs linkages (product of turns and maxwells) and I is the amp; in both mks systems $L = n\phi/I$ henry, where $n\phi$ is the turn-weber linkages, and I is the amp.

Mutual inductance (M) is the common property of two associated electric circuits which determines for a given rate of change of current in one of the circuits, the emf induced in the other. Thus $e_1 = -M\, di_2/dt$ and $e_2 = -M\, di_1/dt$, where e_1 and i_1 are in circuit 1, e_2 and i_2 are in circuit 2, and M is the mutual inductance.

The unit of mutual inductance is the **henry.** When a change of current of 1 amp per sec in either of the two separate circuits induces an emf of 1 volt in the other circuit, their mutual inductance is 1 henry. If M is the mutual inductance of two circuits and k is the coefficient of coupling, *i.e.*, the proportion of flux produced by one circuit which links the other, then $M = k\sqrt{L_1L_2}$, where L_1 and L_2 are the respective self-inductances of the two circuits.

Energy (W) in a system is measured by the amount of work which the system is capable of doing. The **joule, or watt-second,** is the practical unit of electrical energy.

One **international joule** equals 1.000165 absolute joules. **Watt-hours** and **kilowatt-hours** are commonly used in practice. 1 joule = 10^7 ergs = 0.2389 g-cal. 1 whr = 3,600 joules = 2,655.4 ft-lb = 8,605 g-cal = 3.413 Btu = 0.001341 hp-hr.

Power (p) is the time rate of transferring or transforming energy. The practical unit of power is the **watt.** One **international watt** equals 1.000165 absolute watts. One watt is produced when one ampere flows at an emf of one volt. One watt equals 10^7 ergs per sec. One **kilowatt** equals 1,000 watts.

1 watt = 0.00134 hp = 44.25 ft-lb per min = 0.2389 g-cal per sec = 0.737 ft-lb per sec = 0.0569 Btu per min.

Active power (P) at the points of entry of a single-phase two-wire circuit or of a polyphase circuit is the time average of the values of the instantaneous power at the points of entry, the average being taken over a complete cycle of the alternating current. The value of active power is given in **watts** when the rms currents are in amperes and the rms potential differences are in volts. For sinusoidal emf and current, $P = EI \cos \theta$, where E and I are the rms values of volts and currents and θ is the phase difference of E and I.

Table 1. Electrical Units

Quantity	Symbol	Equation (mks)	Cgs unit	Mks unit	Ratio of magnitude of mks to cgs unit
Current	I, i	$I = E/R;\ I = E/Z;\ I = Q/t$	Abamp	Amp	10^{-1}
Quantity	Q, q	$Q = it;\ Q = CE$	Abcoulomb	Coulomb	10^{-1}
Electromotive force	E, e	$E = IR;\ E = W/Q$	Abvolt	Volt	10^8
Resistance	R, r	$R = E/I;\ R = \rho l/A$	Abohm	Ohm	10^9
Resistivity	ρ	$\rho = RA/l$	Abohm-cm	Ohm-cm	10^{11}
Conductance	G, g	$G = \gamma A/l$	Abmho	Mho, siemens	10^{-9}
Conductivity	γ	$\gamma = 1/\rho = l/RA$	Abmho per cm	Mho per cm	10^{-11}
Capacitance	C	$C = Q/E$	Abfarad	Farad*	10^{-9}
Relative capacitivity (dielectric constant)	ϵ_r	Numerical	....	....	1
Self-inductance	L	$L = -N\dfrac{d\phi}{di}$	Abhenry	Henry	10^9
Mutual inductance	M	$M = K\sqrt{L_1L_2}$	Abhenry	Henry	10^9
Energy	W	$W = eit$	Erg	Joule	10^7
	whr	whr = eiT	....	Watthour	36×10^9
	kwh	kwh = $eiT/1{,}000$	....	Kilowatt-hour	36×10^{12}
Apparent power	....	$P = EI$	....	Volt-amp	10^7
Active power	P, p	$P = \dfrac{dw}{dt} = ei;\ P = EI \cos \theta$	Abwatt	Watt	10^7
Reactive power	jQ	$Q = EI \sin \theta$	Abvar	Var	10^7
Power factor	p-f	$\text{p-f} = \dfrac{P}{EI} = \dfrac{P}{\sqrt{P^2 + Q^2}}$	....	....	1
Time constant	....	L/R	Sec	Sec	1
Frequency	f	$f = 1/T$	Cps	Cps	1
Period	T	$T = 1/f$	Sec	Sec	1
Angular velocity	ω	$\omega = 2\pi f$	Radians per sec	Radians per sec	1
Reactance, inductive	X_L	$X_L = 2\pi fL$	Abohm	Ohm	10^9
Reactance, capacitive	X_C	$X_C = 1/(2\pi fC)$	Abohm	Ohm	10^9
Impedance	Z	$Z = E/I = \sqrt{R^2 + (X_L - X_C)^2}$	Abohm	Ohm	10^9
Conductance	G	$G = R/Z^2$	Abmho	Mho	10^{-9}
Susceptance	B	$B = X/Z^2$	Abmho	Mho	10^{-9}
Admittance	Y	$Y = I/E = \sqrt{G^2 + B^2}$	Abmho	Mho	10^{-9}

The unit of force in the mks system is joules per meter = 10^5 dynes = 0.1019 kg and is called the *newton.*

The relations of magnetic units are given in Table 6, p. 15–20.

* 1 farad = 9×10^{11} statfarads (cgs electrostatic units).

† 1 cps = 1 hertz (Hz). This applies equally to cgs, mks, and mksa units.

Reactive power (Q) at the points of entry of a single-phase two-wire circuit, or for the special case of a sinusoidal current and sinusoidal potential difference of the same frequency, is equal to the product obtained by multiplying the rms value of the current by the rms value of the potential difference and by the sine of the angular phase difference by which the current leads or lags the potential difference. $Q = EI \sin \theta$. The unit of Q is the **var** (volt-ampere-reactive). **1 kilovar = 10^3 vars.**

Apparent power (EI) at the points of entry of a single-phase two-wire circuit is equal to the product of the rms current in one conductor multiplied by the rms potential difference between the two points of entry. Apparent power $= EI$.

Power factor (pf) is the ratio of power to apparent power. Pf $= P/EI = \cos \theta$, where θ is the phase difference between E and I, both assumed to be sinusoidal.

The **reactance** (X) of a portion of a circuit for a sinusoidal current and potential difference of the same frequency is the product of the sine of the angular phase difference between the current and potential difference times the ratio of the rms potential difference to the rms current, there being no source of power in the portion of the circuit under consideration. $X = (E/I) \sin \theta = 2\pi fL$ ohms, where f is the frequency and L the inductance in henrys; or $X = 1/2\pi fC$, where C is the capacitance in farads.

The **impedance** (Z) of a portion of an electric circuit to a completely specified periodic current and potential difference is the ratio of the rms value of the potential difference between the terminals to the rms value of the current, there being no source of power in the portion under consideration. **$Z = E/I$ ohms.**

Admittance (Y) is the reciprocal of impedance. $Y = I/E$ mhos.

The **susceptance** (B) of a portion of a circuit for a sinusoidal current and potential difference of the same frequency is the product of the sine of the angular phase difference between the current and the potential difference times the ratio of the rms current to the rms potential difference, there being no source of power in the portion of the circuit under consideration. $B = (I/E) \sin \theta$.

CONDUCTORS AND RESISTANCE

Resistivity, or **specific resistance,** is the resistance of a sample of the material having both a length and cross section of unity. The two most common resistivity samples are the centimeter cube and the circular-mil-foot. If l is the length of a conductor of uniform cross section a, then its resistance

$$R = \rho l/a \tag{1}$$

where ρ is the resistivity. With a circular-mil-foot ρ is the resistance of a circular-mil-foot and a is the cross section in circular mils. Since $v = la$ is the volume of a conductor

$$R = \rho l^2/v = \rho v/a^2 \tag{2}$$

A **circular mil** is a unit of area equal to that of a circle whose diameter is one mil (0.001 in.). It is the unit of area which is used almost entirely in this country for wires and cables. To obtain the circular mils of a solid cylindrical conductor, square its diameter expressed in mils. For example, the diameter of 000 AWG solid copper wire is 410 mils and its cross section is $(410)^2$, or 168,100, cir mils. The diameter in mils of a solid cylindrical conductor is the square root of its cross section expressed in cir mils.

A **circular-mil-foot** is a conductor having a length of one foot and a uniform cross section of one circular mil. In terms of the copper standard the resistance of a circular-mil-foot of copper at 20 C is 10.371 ohms. As a first approximation 10 ohms may frequently be used.

At 60 C a circular-mil-inch of copper has a resistance of 1.0 ohm. This is a very convenient unit of resistivity for magnet coils since the resistance is merely the length of copper in inches divided by its cross section in cir mils (see p. 15–108).

Temperature Coefficient of Resistance. The resistance of the pure metals increases with temperature. The resistance at any temperature tC is

$$R = R_0(1 + \alpha t) \tag{3}$$

where R_0 is the resistance at 0 C and α is the **temperature coefficient of resistance.** For **copper, $\alpha = 0.00427$.**

With any initial temperature t_1, the resistance at temperature t C is

$$R = R_1[1 + \alpha_1(t - t_1)] \tag{4}$$

where R_1 is the resistance at temperature t_1 C and α_1 is the temperature coefficient of resistance at temperature t_1 [see Eq. (5)].

For any initial temperature t_1 the value of α_1 is

$$\alpha_1 = 1/(234.5 + t_1) \tag{5}$$

Inferred Absolute Zero. Between 100 and 0 C the resistance of copper decreases at a rate which is practically uniform and which if continued would give a resistance of zero at −234.5 C (an easy number to remember). If the resistance at t_1 C is R_1 and the resistance at t_2 C is R_2, then

$$R_2/R_1 = (234.5 + t_2)/(234.5 + t_1) \tag{6}$$

EXAMPLE. The resistance of a copper coil at 25 C is 4.26 ohms. Determine its resistance at 45 C. Using Eq. (4) and $\alpha_1 = 1/(234.5 + 25) = 0.00385$, $R = 4.26[1 + 0.00385(45 - 25)] = 4.59$ ohms. Using Eq. (6) $R = 4.26\ (234.5 + 45)/(234.5 + 25) = 4.26 \times 1.077 = 4.59$ ohms.

The inferred absolute zero for aluminum is −228.

In Table 2 are given values of α_1 for copper and aluminum at several initial temperatures.

Table 2. Temperature Coefficients of Resistance

Initial temperature, deg C	Increase in resistance per deg C		Initial temperature, deg C	Increase in resistance per deg C	
	Copper	Aluminum		Copper	Aluminum
0	0.00427	0.00439	25	0.00385	0.00396
5	0.00418	0.00429	30	0.00378	0.00388
10	0.00409	0.00420	40	0.00364	0.00373
15	0.00401	0.00411	50	0.00352	0.00360
20	0.00393	0.00403			

The **international copper standard** of annealed copper (density, 8.99 g per cc or 0.321 lb per cu in.) at 100 percent conductivity and 20 C has a **resistivity,** for dimensions of conductors in the stated units, as follows: 0.15328 ohm (m, g); 875.20 ohms (mile, lb); 1.7241 microhms (sq cm per cm); 0.67879 microhm (sq in. per in.); 10.371 ohms (mil, ft); 0.017241 ohm (meter, sq mm).

ASTM specifications for minimum conductivities of copper wire are as follows: soft or annealed, 98.16; medium-hard-drawn, 0.460 to 0.325 in. diam, 97.66 percent; 0.324 to 0.040 in. diam, 96.60 percent; hard-drawn 0.460 to 0.325 in. diam, 97.16 percent; 0.324 to 0.040 in. diam, 96.16 percent.

The **international aluminum standard** (density, 2.70 g per cc or 0.0976 lb per cu in.) at 100 percent conductivity and 20 C has a **resistivity** for dimensions of conductors in the units stated, as follows: 0.0764 ohm (m, g); 436.0 ohms (mile, lb); 2.828 microhm (sq cm/cm); 1.113 microhm (sq in./in.); 17.01 ohms (mil, ft).

Materials. The materials generally used for the transmission and distribution of electrical energy are copper, aluminum, and sometimes iron and steel. For resistors and heaters, iron, steel, commercial alloys, and carbon are most used.

Copper is the most widely used electrical conductor. It has high conductivity, relatively low cost, good resistance to oxidation, is readily soldered, and has good mechanical characteristics such as tensile strength, toughness, and ductility. Its tensile strength together with its low linear temperature coefficient of expansion are desirable characteristics in its use for overhead transmission lines.

Aluminum is used to considerable extent for high-voltage transmission lines, because its weight is one-half that of copper for the same conductance. Moreover, the greater diameter reduces corona loss. As it has 1.4 times the linear temperature coefficient of expansion, changes in sag with temperature are greater. Because of its lower melting point, spans may fail more readily with arc-overs. In aluminum cable steel-reinforced (ACSR), the center strand is a steel cable, which gives added tensile strength. Aluminum is used occasionally for bus bars because of its large heat-dissipating surface for a given conductance. The greater cross section for a given conductance requires a greater volume of insulation for a given voltage. When the ratio of the cost of aluminum to the cost of copper becomes economically favorable, aluminum is often used for insulated wires and cables.

Steel, either **galvanized** or **copper-covered** ("copperweld"), is used for high-voltage transmission spans where tensile strength is more important than high conductance. Steel is also used for third rails.

Copper alloys and **bronzes** are of increasing importance as electrical conductors. They have lower electrical conductivity but greater tensile strength and are resistant to corrosion. **Hitenso, Calsum bronzes, Signal bronze, Phono-electric,** and **Everdur** are bronzes containing phosphorus, silicon, manganese, or zinc. Their conductivities vary from 20 to 85 percent of 100 percent conductivity copper, and they have tensile strengths up to 130,000 psi, about twice that of hard-drawn copper. Such alloys are

Table 3. Properties of Metals and Alloys

(See Table 24, p. 15–103 for properties of resistor alloys)

Metals	Resistivity, 20 C		Temperature coefficient of resistance at 20 C
	Microhms (sq cm/cm)	Ohms (mil-ft)	
Aluminum	2.828	17.01	0.00403
Antimony	42.1	251.0	0.0036
Bismuth	111.0	668.0	0.004
Brass	6.21	37.0	0.0015
Carbon: amorphous	3,800–4,100	......	(−)
Retort (graphite)	720–812*	......	(−)
Copper (drawn)	1.724	10.37	0.00393
Gold	2.44	14.7	0.0034
Iron: electrolytic	10.1	59.9	0.0064
Cast	75.2–98.8	448–588	
Wire	97.8	588	
Lead	22.0	132	0.00387
Molybdenum	5.78	34.8	
Monel metal	43.5	262	0.0019
Mercury	96.8	576	0.00089
Nickel	8.54	50.8	0.0041
Platinum	10.72	63.8	0.003
Platinum silver, 2Ag + 1Pt	24.6†	148.0	0.00031
Silver	1.628	9.8	0.0038
Steel: soft	15.9	95.8	0.0016
Glass hard	45.7	275	
Silicon (4 percent)	51.18	308	
Transformer	11.09	66.7	
Trolley wire	12.7	76.4	
Tin	11.63	70	0.0042
Tungsten	5.51	33.2	0.005
Zinc	5.97	35.58	0.0037

Max working temperature: Cu, 260 C; Ni, 600 C; Pt, 1500 C.
* Furnace electrodes, 3000 C.
† 0 C.

frequently used for trolley wires. Copper alloys having lower conductivity are usually classified as resistor materials (p. 15–102).

In Table 3 are given the electrical properties of some of the pure metals and alloys.

American Wire Gage (AWG). The AWG (formerly Brown & Sharpe gage) is based on a constant ratio between diameters of successive gage numbers. The ratio of any diameter to the next smaller is 1.123, and the corresponding ratio of cross sections is $(1.123)^2 = 1.261$, or 1¼ approximately. $(1.123)^6$ is 2.0050, so that diameters differing by 6 gage numbers have a ratio of approximately 2; cross sections differing by 3 gage

Table 4. Working Table, Standard Annealed Copper Wire, Solid

[American Wire Gage (B & S)]

Gage No.	Diam, mils	Cross section		Ohms per 1,000 ft		Ohms per mile	Weight per 1,000 ft, lb
		Cir mils	Sq in.	25 C (=77 F)	65 C (=149 F)	25 C (=77 F)	
0000	460.0	212,000	0.166	0.0500	0.0577	0.264	641.0
000	410.0	168,000	0.132	0.0630	0.0727	0.333	508.0
00	365.0	133,000	0.105	0.0795	0.0917	0.420	403.0
0	325.0	106,000	0.0829	0.100	0.116	0.528	319.0
1	289.0	83,700	0.0657	0.126	0.146	0.665	253.0
2	258.0	66,400	0.0521	0.159	0.184	0.839	201.0
3	229.0	52,600	0.0413	0.201	0.232	1.061	159.0
4	204.0	41,700	0.0328	0.253	0.292	1.335	126.0
5	182.0	33,100	0.0260	0.319	0.369	1.685	100.0
6	162.0	26,300	0.0206	0.403	0.465	2.13	79.5
7	144.0	20,800	0.0164	0.508	0.586	2.68	63.0
8	128.0	16,500	0.0130	0.641	0.739	3.38	50.0
9	114.0	13,100	0.0103	0.808	0.932	4.27	39.6
10	102.0	10,400	0.00815	1.02	1.18	5.38	31.4
11	91.0	8,230	0.00647	1.28	1.48	6.75	24.9
12	81.0	6,530	0.00513	1.62	1.87	8.55	19.8
13	72.0	5,180	0.00407	2.04	2.36	10.77	15.7
14	64.0	4,110	0.00323	2.58	2.97	13.62	12.4
15	57.0	3,260	0.00256	3.25	3.75	17.16	9.86
16	51.0	2,580	0.00203	4.09	4.73	21.6	7.82
17	45.0	2,050	0.00161	5.16	5.96	27.2	6.20
18	40.0	1,620	0.00128	6.51	7.51	34.4	4.92
19	36.0	1,290	0.00101	8.21	9.48	43.3	3.90
20	32.0	1,020	0.000802	10.4	11.9	54.9	3.09
21	28.5	810	0.000636	13.1	15.1	69.1	2.45
22	25.3	642	0.000505	16.5	19.0	87.1	1.94
23	22.6	509	0.000400	20.8	24.0	109.8	1.54
24	20.1	404	0.000317	26.2	30.2	138.3	1.22
25	17.9	320	0.000252	33.0	38.1	174.1	0.970
26	15.9	254	0.000200	41.6	48.0	220	0.769
27	14.2	202	0.000158	52.5	60.6	277	0.610
28	12.6	160	0.000126	66.2	76.4	350	0.484
29	11.3	127	0.0000995	83.4	96.3	440	0.384
30	10.0	101	0.0000789	105	121	554	0.304
31	8.9	79.7	0.0000626	133	153	702	0.241
32	8.0	63.2	0.0000496	167	193	882	0.191
33	7.1	50.1	0.0000394	211	243	1,114	0.152
34	6.3	39.8	0.0000312	266	307	1,404	0.120
35	5.6	31.5	0.0000248	335	387	1,769	0.0954
36	5.0	25.0	0.0000196	423	488	2,230	0.0757
37	4.5	19.8	0.0000156	533	616	2,810	0.0600
38	4.0	15.7	0.0000123	673	776	3,550	0.0476
39	3.5	12.5	0.0000098	848	979	4,480	0.0377
40	3.1	9.9	0.0000078	1,070	1,230	5,650	0.0200

numbers also have a ratio of approximately 2. The ratio of cross sections differing by 2 numbers is $(1.261)^2 = 1.590$, or 1.6 approximately. The ratio of cross sections differing by 10 numbers is approximately 10. The gage ordinarily extends from No. 40 to 0000 (4/0). Wires larger than 0000 must be stranded, and their cross section is given in cir mils.

The diameter of No. 10 wire is 102.0 mils. As an approximation this may be considered as being 100 mils; the cross section is 10,000 cir mils; the resistance is 1 ohm per 1,000 ft; and the weight of 1,000 ft is 31.4 (10π) lb. Also the weight of 1,000 ft of No. 2 is 200 lb. These facts give many short cuts in estimating resistances and weights of various gage numbers.

Table 5. Bare Concentric Lay Cables of Standard Annealed Copper

From *NBS Circ.* 31. See Table 20, p. 15–95 for the carrying capacity of wires.

AWG No.	Cir mils	Ohms per 1,000 ft		Weight per 1,000 ft, lb	Standard concentric stranding		
		25 C (=77 F)	65 C (=149 F)		No. of wires	Diam of wires, mils	Outside diam, mils
	2,000,000	0.00539	0.00622	6,180	127	125.5	1,631
	1,700,000	0.00634	0.00732	5,250	127	115.7	1,504
	1,500,000	0.00719	0.00830	4,630	91	128.4	1,412
	1,200,000	0.00899	0.0104	3,710	91	114.8	1,263
	1,000,000	0.0108	0.0124	3,090	61	128.0	1,152
	900,000	0.0120	0.0138	2,780	61	121.5	1,093
	850,000	0.0127	0.0146	2,620	61	118.0	1,062
	750,000	0.0144	0.0166	2,320	61	110.9	998
	650,000	0.0166	0.0192	2,010	61	103.2	929
	600,000	0.0180	0.0207	1,850	61	99.2	893
	550,000	0.0196	0.0226	1,700	61	95.0	855
	500,000	0.0216	0.0249	1,540	37	116.2	814
	450,000	0.0240	0.0277	1,390	37	110.3	772
	400,000	0.0270	0.0311	1,240	37	104.0	728
	350,000	0.0308	0.0356	1,080	37	97.3	681
	300,000	0.0360	0.0415	926	37	90.0	630
	250,000	0.0431	0.0498	772	37	82.2	575
0000	212,000	0.0509	0.0587	653	19	105.5	528
000	168,000	0.0642	0.0741	518	19	94.0	470
00	133,000	0.0811	0.0936	411	19	83.7	418
0	106,000	0.102	0.117	326	19	74.5	373
1	83,700	0.129	0.149	258	19	66.4	332
2	66,400	0.162	0.187	205	7	97.4	292
3	52,600	0.205	0.237	163	7	86.7	260
4	41,700	0.259	0.299	129	7	77.2	232

Lay Cables. In order to obtain sufficient flexibility, wires larger than 0000 are stranded, and they are designated by their circular mils. Smaller wires may be stranded also since sizes as small as No. 4 when insulated are usually too stiff for easy handling. Lay cables are made up geometrically as shown in Fig. 1. Six strands will just fit around the single central conductor; the number of strands in each succeeding layer increases by 6. The number of strands that can thus be layed up are 1, 7, 19, 37, 61, 91, 127, etc. In order to obtain sufficient flexibility with large cables, the strands themselves frequently consist of stranded cable.

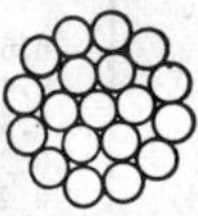

Fig. 1. Make-up of a 19-strand cable.

The **resistance of cables** is readily computed from Eq. (**1**), using the circular-mil-foot as the unit of resistivity.

Example. Determine the resistance of 3,500 ft of 800,000 cir-mil cable at 20 C. *Answer:* ρ (of a cir-mil-ft) = 10.37. $R = 10.37 \times 3{,}500/800{,}000 = 0.0454$ ohm.

ρ = 10 ohms per cir-mil-ft is often sufficiently accurate for practical purposes.

ELECTRICAL CIRCUITS

Ohm's law states that, with a steady current, the current in a circuit is *directly* proportional to the *total* emf acting in the circuit and is *inversely* proportional to the total resistance of the circuit. The law may be expressed by the following three equations:

$$I = E/R \tag{7}$$

$$E = IR \tag{8}$$

$$R = E/I \tag{9}$$

where E is the emf, volts; R the resistance, ohms; and I the current, amperes.

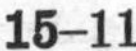

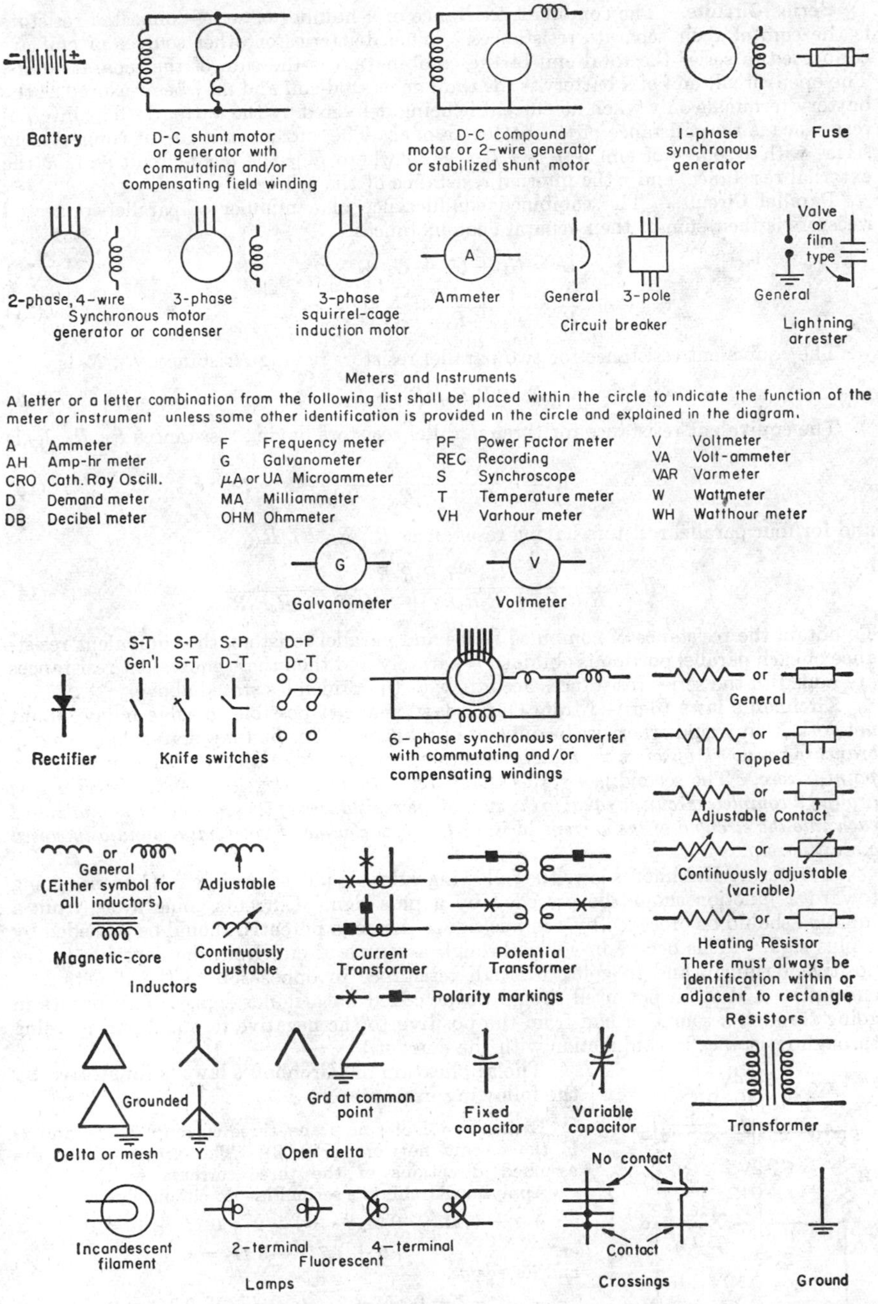

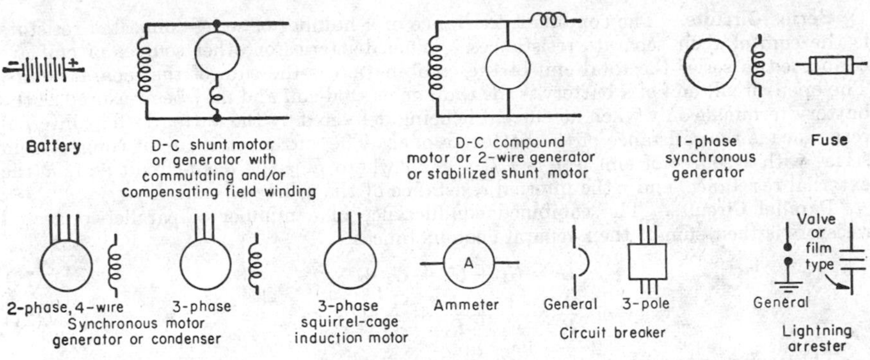

Battery
D-C shunt motor or generator with commutating and/or compensating field winding
D-C compound motor or 2-wire generator or stabilized shunt motor
1-phase synchronous generator
Fuse
2-phase, 4-wire
3-phase
Synchronous motor generator or condenser
3-phase squirrel-cage induction motor
A
Ammeter
General
3-pole
Circuit breaker
Valve or film type
General
Lightning arrester
Meters and Instruments
A letter or a letter combination from the following list shall be placed within the circle to indicate the function of the meter or instrument unless some other identification is provided in the circle and explained in the diagram.
A Ammeter
AH Amp-hr meter
CRO Cath. Ray Oscill.
D Demand meter
DB Decibel meter
F Frequency meter
G Galvanometer
μA or UA Microammeter
MA Milliammeter
OHM Ohmmeter
PF Power Factor meter
REC Recording
S Synchroscope
T Temperature meter
VH Varhour meter
V Voltmeter
VA Volt-ammeter
VAR Varmeter
W Wattmeter
WH Watthour meter
G
Galvanometer
V
Voltmeter
S-T Gen'l
S-P S-T
S-P D-T
D-P D-T
Rectifier
Knife switches
6-phase synchronous converter with commutating and/or compensating windings
or
General
or
Tapped
or
Adjustable Contact
or
Continuously adjustable (variable)
or
Heating Resistor
There must always be identification within or adjacent to rectangle
Resistors
or
General (Either symbol for all inductors)
Adjustable
Magnetic-core
Continuously adjustable
Inductors
Current Transformer
Potential Transformer
Polarity markings
Grounded
Delta or mesh
Y
Grd at common point
Open delta
Fixed capacitor
Variable capacitor
Transformer
No contact
Contact
Crossings
Ground
Incandescent filament
2-terminal
4-terminal
Fluorescent
Lamps

FIG. 2. Diagrammatic symbols for electrical machinery and apparatus. (*American Standard, "Graphical Symbols for Electrical Diagrams,"* Y 32.2, 1953).

Series Circuits. The combined resistance of a number of series-connected resistors is the sum of their separate resistances. When batteries or other sources of emf are connected in series the total emf of the combination is the sum of the separate emfs. The open-circuit emf of a battery is the total generated emf and may be measured at the battery terminals only when no current is being delivered by the battery. The internal resistance is the resistance of the battery alone. The current in a circuit connected in series with a source of emf is $I = E/(R + r)$, where E is the open-circuit emf, R the external resistance, and r the internal resistance of the source of emf.

Parallel Circuits. The combined conductance of a number of parallel-connected resistors is their sum of their separate conductances.

$$G = G_1 + G_2 + G_3 + \cdots \tag{10}$$

$$\frac{1}{R} = \frac{1}{R_1} + \frac{1}{R_2} + \frac{1}{R_3} + \cdots \tag{11}$$

The equivalent resistance for two parallel resistors having resistances R_1, R_2 is

$$R = R_1R_2/(R_1 + R_2) \tag{12}$$

The equivalent resistance for three parallel resistors having resistances R_1, R_2, R_3 is

$$R = \frac{R_1R_2R_3}{R_1R_2 + R_2R_3 + R_3R_1} \tag{13}$$

and for four parallel resistors having resistances R_1, R_2, R_3, R_4

$$R = \frac{R_1R_2R_3R_4}{R_1R_2R_3 + R_2R_3R_4 + R_3R_4R_1 + R_4R_1R_2} \tag{14}$$

To obtain the resistance of combined series and parallel resistors, the equivalent resistance of each parallel portion is obtained separately and then these equivalent resistances are added to the series resistances according to the principles stated above.

Kirchhoff's laws (derived from Ohm's law) make it possible to solve many circuit networks that would otherwise be difficult of solution. The first law states that: *In any branching network of wires the algebraic sum of the currents in all the wires that meet at a point is zero.* The second law states that: *The sum of all the electromotive forces acting around a complete circuit is equal to the sum of the resistances of its separate parts multiplied each into the strength of the current in it, or the total change of potential around any closed circuit is zero.*

In applying Kirchhoff's laws the following rules should be observed: Currents going toward a junction should be preceded by a plus sign. Currents going away from a junction should be preceded by a minus sign. A rise in potential should be preceded by a plus sign. (This occurs in going through a source of emf from the negative to the positive terminal, and in going through resistance in opposition to the direction of current.) A drop in potential should be preceded by a minus sign. (This occurs in going through a source of emf from the positive to the negative terminal and in going through resistance in conjunction with the current.)

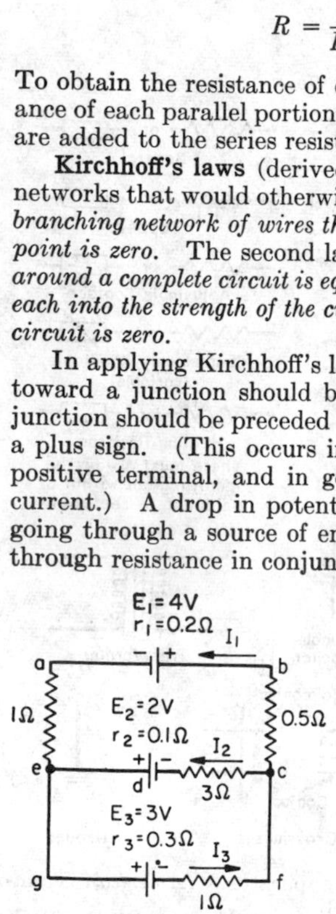

The application of Kirchhoff's laws is illustrated by the following example.

FIG. 3. Electric network and Kirchhoff's laws.

EXAMPLE. Determine the three currents I_1, I_2, and I_3 in the circuit network (Fig. 3). The arrows show the assumed directions of the three currents.

Applying Kirchhoff's second law to circuit *abcdea*,

$$+4 + 0.2I_1 + 0.5I_1 - 3I_2 + 2 - 0.1I_2 + I_1 = 0$$

or,

$$+6 + 1.7I_1 - 3.1I_2 = 0 \tag{I}$$

and for *edcfge*,

$$-2 + 0.1I_2 + 3I_2 + I_3 + 3 + 0.3I_3 = 0$$

or,

$$+1 + 3.1I_2 + 1.3I_3 = 0 \tag{II}$$

Applying Kirchhoff's first law to junction c,

$$-I_1 - I_2 + I_3 = 0 \tag{III}$$

Solving (I), (II), and (III) simultaneously gives $I_1 = -2.56$, $I_2 = +0.53$, and $I_3 = -2.03$. The minus signs before I_1 and I_3 show that the actual directions of these two currents are opposite the assumed directions.

Electrical Power. With direct currents the electrical power is given by the product of the volts and amperes. That is,

$$P = EI \quad \text{watts} \tag{15}$$

Also, by substituting for E and I Eqs. (**8**) and (**7**),

$$P = I^2R \quad \text{watts} \tag{16}$$

$$P = E^2/R \quad \text{watts} \tag{17}$$

The watt is too small a unit for many purposes. Hence, the **kilowatt** (kw) (1,000 watts) is used. 746 watts = 1 hp = 0.746 kw. 1 kw = 1.340 hp. The **kilowatt-hour (kwh)** is the common engineering unit of electrical energy.

Joule's Law. When an electric current flows through resistance, the number of heat units developed is proportional to the square of the current, directly proportional to the resistance, and directly proportional to the time that the current flows. $h = 0.2389i^2rt$, where h represents the number of gram-calories; i the current, amp; r the resistance, ohms; and t the time, sec. h (in Btu) $= 0.0009478i^2rt$.

BATTERIES

In an **electric cell,** or **battery,** chemical energy is converted into electrical energy. Strictly speaking, the word battery applies to an assembly of cells, but the word has come to mean single units or cells. A battery utilizes the potential difference which exists between different elements. When two different elements are immersed in electrolyte an emf exists tending to send current within the cell from the negative pole, which is the more highly electropositive, to the positive pole. The **poles,** or **electrodes** of a battery form the junction with the external circuit.

If the external circuit is closed, current flows from the battery at the *positive electrode,* or *cathode,* and enters the battery at the *negative electrode,* or *anode.*

In a **primary battery** the chemically reacting parts **require renewal;** in a **secondary battery,** the electrochemical processes **are reversible** to a high degree and the chemically reacting parts are restored after partial or complete discharge by reversing the direction of current through the battery.

Electromotive force of a battery is the total potential difference existing between the electrodes on open circuit. When current flows, the potential difference across the terminals drops because of the resistance drop within the cell and because of **polarization.**

Polarization. When current flows in a battery, hydrogen is deposited on the cathode. This produces two effects, both of which reduce the terminal voltage of the battery. The hydrogen in contact with the cathode constitutes a hydrogen battery which opposes the emf of the battery; the hydrogen bubbles reduce the contact area of the electrolyte with the cathode, thus increasing the battery resistance. The most satisfactory method of reducing polarization is to have present at the cathode some compound that supplies negative ions to combine with the positive hydrogen ions at the plate. In the Leclanché cell, manganese peroxide in contact with the carbon cathode serves as a depolarizer, its oxygen ion combining with the hydrogen ion to form water.

If E is the emf of the cell, E_p the emf of polarization, r the internal resistance, V the terminal voltage, when current I flows, then

$$V = (E - E_p) - Ir \tag{18}$$

Primary Batteries

The **Leclanché cell** has carbon for the positive and zinc for the negative electrode, with sal ammoniac as solution. It is used where only low values of current and intermittent service are desired. In the improved type the cathode is a porous carbon cup in which are packed lumps of manganese dioxide to serve as an insoluble oxidizing agent.

The rather high internal resistance has been reduced by using a zinc cylinder for the anode and placing it about the carbon cup and as near as possible. The emf of this cell is about 1.5 volts, but the terminal voltage drops to approximately 1 volt when in service. This type of cell now is only of importance in that it forms the basis of the dry cell.

The **copper-oxide, zinc, caustic-soda** battery is the most widely used wet primary battery at the present time as it is suited for both open- and closed-circuit work, provided the open-circuit periods are not of too long duration. The cell is made in two forms: one with multiple flat plates and the other with concentric cylindrical plates. The positive electrode is compressed cupric oxide the surface of which is reduced to metallic copper, the oxide serving as a depolarizer. The negative electrode is zinc and the electrolyte a strong caustic-soda solution (NaOH), about 1 part caustic to 4 of water. The surface is covered with mineral oil to minimize evaporation. A typical design is shown in Fig. 4. The jar is of heat-resisting glass to avoid breakage due to the heat evolved when the caustic-soda solution is mixed. The open-circuit emf is about 1 volt and the terminal voltage under load is about 0.65 volt. These batteries are extensively used in railroad service and have ratings from 250 to 1,000 amp-hr. On open-circuit work it is recommended that they be discharged for 10 min periods at least once a month.

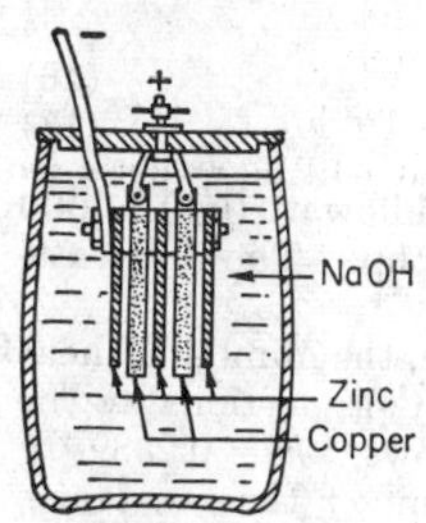

FIG. 4. Copper-oxide, zinc, caustic-soda cell.

Dry Cells. A dry cell is one in which the electrolyte exists in the form of a jelly, is absorbed in a porous medium, or is otherwise restrained from flowing from its intended position, such a cell being completely portable and the electrolyte non-spillable. There are only two forms of dry cell which are practicable, the common type developed from the Leclanché cell and the recently developed Ruben, or RM, cell. The most common type of dry cell consists of a cylindrical zinc container which serves as the negative electrode and is lined with specially prepared paper, or some similar absorbent material, to prevent the mixture of carbon and manganese dioxide, which is tamped tightly around the positive carbon electrode, from coming in contact with the zinc. The absorbent lining and the mixture are moistened with a solution of zinc chloride and sal ammoniac. In smaller cells the manganese-carbon mixture is often molded into a cylinder around the carbon electrode, the whole is then set into the zinc cup, and the space between the molded mixture and the zinc is filled with electrolyte made into a paste in such a manner that it can be solidified by either standing or heating. The top of the cell is closed with a sealing compound, and the cell is placed in a cardboard container. The emf of a dry cell when new is 1.4 to 1.6 volts.

In **block assembly** the dry cells, especially in the smaller sizes, are assembled in series and sealed in blocks of insulating compound with only two terminals and, sometimes, intermediate taps brought out. This type of battery is used for radio B and C batteries. Another construction is to build the battery up of layers in somewhat the manner of the old voltaic pile. Each cell consists of a layer of zinc, a layer of treated paper, and a flat cake of the manganese-carbon mixture. The cells are separated by layers of a special material which conducts electricity, but which is impervious to electrolyte. A sufficient number of such cells are built up to give the required voltage and the whole battery is sealed into the carton.

Dry cells and batteries fall generally into three classes: (1) the **large-size dry cells,** the No. 6, which are usually apprximately 2½ in. diam by 6 in. in height and have a capacity of about 30 amp-hr; (2) **flashlight batteries,** which are of small size, usually 1¼ in. diam by 2½ in. in height or smaller, with a capacity of about 3 amp-hr; and (3) **radio B batteries,** which consist usually of 15 or 30 cells permanently connected into a battery which is used chiefly to supply the B-battery current for radio receiving sets.

The **efficiency** of a standard-size dry battery depends on the rate at which it is discharged. Up to a certain rate the lower the discharge rate, the greater the efficiency. Above this rate the efficiency decreases (see N.B.S. *Circ.* 79, p. 39).

When used efficiently, a 6 in. dry cell will give over 30 amp-hr of service. As ordinarily used, however, the dry cell gives no more than 8 to 10 amp-hr of service and at times even less. The 1¼ by 2¼ in. flashlight battery is usually employed with a lamp taking 0.25 to 0.35 amp. Under these conditions 3 amp-hr or thereabouts may be expected if the battery is used for not more than an hour or so a day. The so-called "heavy-duty" radio battery will give about 8 to 10 amp-hr when efficiently used.

For the best results 6 in. dry cells should not be used for current drains of over 0.5 amp except for very short periods of time. Flashlight batteries should not be used for higher than the preceding current drain, and heavy-duty radio batteries will give best results if the current drain is kept below 25 milliamp.

Dry cells should be stored in a cool, dry place. Extreme heat during storage will shorten their life. The cell will not be injured by being frozen but will be as good as new after being brought back to normal temperature. In extreme cold weather dry cells may not give more than half of their normal service. At a temperature of about −30 F they freeze solid and give neither voltage nor current.

The amperage of a dry cell by definition is the current that it will give when it is short-circuited (at about 70 F) through an ammeter which with its leads has a resistance of 0.01 ohm.

The Ruben cell (Rubin, Balanced Alkaline Dry Cells, *Trans. Electrochem. Soc.*, **92,** 1947) was developed jointly by the Ruben Laboratories and P. R. Mallory & Company during World War II for the operation of radar equipment and other electronic devices which require a high ratio of ampere-hour capacity to the volume of the cell at higher current densities than were considered practicable for the Leclanché type. The anode is of amalgamated zinc, and the cathode is a mercuric oxide depolarizing material intimately mixed with graphite in order to reduce its electrical resistivity. The electrolyte is a solution of potassium hydroxide (KOH) containing potassium zincate. The cell is made in two forms. In one form the anode consists of a spirally wound corrugated strip of zinc, Fig. 5(*a*), 0.002 to 0.005 in. (0.051 to 0.13 mm) thick (1), which is amalgamated after assembly. Two strips of alkali-resistant absorbent paper (2) are interwound with the zinc foil so that the zinc protrudes at the upper side and paper at the lower side. The anode is insulated from the steel container (4) by a polystyrene sleeve (3). The cathode depolarizer is shown at (5) separated from the anode by a barrier of alkali-resistant paper (6). The cell top (7) is copper and contacts the zinc strip to form the negative terminal of the cell. The cell is sealed by an insulating grommet of neoprene (8). The cell container (4), which is inert chemically to the cell ingredients, forms the positive electrode.

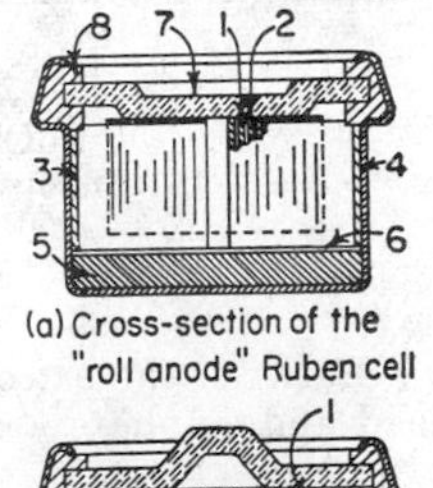

(a) Cross-section of the "roll anode" Ruben cell

(b) Cross-section of the "pressed powder anode" Ruben cell

FIG. 5. Ruben cell.

In the second or "button" type of cell, Fig. 5(*b*), the anode is a pressed powdered-zinc amalgam disk (1). The other elements of the cell are identical with those in (*a*). The button type of cell has higher volumetric efficiency than the roll type.

The no-load emf of the cell is 1.34 volts and remains essentially constant irrespective of time and temperature. Advantages of the cell are long shelf life, which enables them to be stored indefinitely; long service life, about four times that of the Leclanché dry cell of equivalent volume; small weight; a flat voltage characteristic which is advantageous for electronic uses in which the characteristics of tubes vary widely with voltage; adaptability to operating at high temperatures without deterioration; high resistance to shock.

The **Weston cell** is a primary cell used as a standard of emf. It consists of a glass H tube in the bottom of one leg of which is mercury which forms the positive or cathode; in the bottom of the other leg is cadmium amalgam forming the anode. The electrolytes consist of mercurous sulphate and cadmium sulphate. There are two forms of the Weston cell: the saturated or normal cell, and the unsaturated cell. In the normal cell the electrolyte is saturated. This is the official standard since it is more permanent than the unsaturated type and can be reproduced with far greater accuracy. When carefully made, the emfs of cells agree within a few parts in 1,000,000. There is, however, a small temperature coefficient. Although the unsaturated cell is not so reliable as the normal cell and must be standardized, it has a negligible temperature coefficient and is more convenient for general use. The manufacturers recommend that the temperature be not less than 4 C and not more than 40 C and the current should not exceed 0.0001 amp. The emf is between 1.0185 and 1.0190 volts. Since no appreciable current can be taken from the cell, a null method must be used to utilize its emf (see p. 5–42).

Storage Batteries

In a **storage battery** the electrolytic action must be **reversible** to a high degree. There are three types of storage batteries: the lead-lead-acid type, the nickel-iron-alkaline type (**Edison** battery), and the nickel-cadmium-alkali type (**Nicad**).

In the manufacture of the **lead-lead-acid cells** there are two general types of plates, or electrodes. In the **Planté type** the active material is electrically formed of pure lead by repeated reversals of the charging current. In the **Faure, or pasted plate,** type, the positive and negative plates are formed by applying a paste, largely of lead oxides (PbO_2, Pb_3O_4), to lead-antimony supporting grids. A current is passed through the plates while they are immersed in weak sulphuric acid, the positive plates being connected as anodes and the negative ones as cathodes. The paste on the positive plates is converted to lead peroxide while that on the negative plate is reduced to spongy lead.

In order to obtain high capacity per unit weight it is necessary to expose a large plate area to the action of the acid. This is done in the Planté plate by "ploughing" with sharp steel disks, and by using corrugated helical inserts as active positive material (Manchester plate). In the pasted plate a large area of the material is necessarily exposed to the action of the acid.

The chemical reactions in a lead cell may be expressed by the following equation, based on the double sulphation theory:

$$\underset{\text{positive plate}}{PbO_2} + \underset{\text{negative plate}}{Pb} + \underset{\text{sulphuric acid}}{2H_2SO_4} \underset{\text{Discharge}\;\longrightarrow}{\overset{\longleftarrow\;\text{Charge}}{=}} \underset{\text{positive and negative plates}}{2PbSO_4} + \underset{\text{water}}{2H_2O}$$

Between the extremes of complete charge and discharge, complex combinations of lead and sulphate are formed. After complete discharge a hard insoluble sulphate forms slowly on the plates, and this is reducible only by slow charging. This sulphation is objectionable and should be avoided.

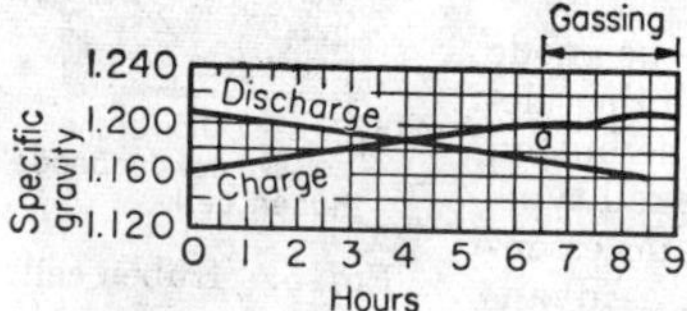

FIG. 6. Variations of specific gravity in a stationary battery.

Specific Gravity. Water is formed with discharge and sulphuric acid is formed on charge, consequently the specific gravity must decrease on discharge and increase on charge. The variation of the specific gravity for a stationary battery is shown in Fig. 6. With starting and vehicle batteries it is necessary to operate the electrolyte from between 1.280 to 1.300 when fully charged to as low as 1.100 when completely discharged. The condition of charge of a battery may be determined by its specific gravity.

Battery electrolyte may be made from concentrated sulphuric acid (oil of vitriol, sp gr 1.84) by *pouring the acid into the water* in the following proportions:

Parts Water to 1 Part Acid

Specific gravity	1.200	1.210	1.240	1.280
Volume	4.3	4.0	3.4	2.75
Weight	2.4	2.2	1.9	1.5

Freezing Temperatures of Sulphuric Acid

Specific gravity	1.180	1.200	1.240	1.280
Freezing temp, F	−6	−16	−51	−90

Voltage. The emf of a lead cell when fully charged and idle is 2.05 to 2.10 volts. Discharge lowers the voltage in proportion to the current. When charging at constant current and normal rate, the terminal voltage gradually increases from 2.14 to 2.3 volts, then increases rapidly to between 2.5 and 2.6 volts (Fig. 7). This latter interval is known as the *gassing period.* When this period is reached, the charging rate should be reduced in order to avoid waste of power and unnecessary erosion of the plates.

Practically all batteries have a **normal rating** based on the 8 hr rate of discharge. Thus a 320 amp-hr battery would have a normal rate of 40 amp. The ampere-hour capacity of batteries falls off rapidly with increase in discharge rate.

Effect of Discharge Rate on Battery Capacity

Discharge rate, hr	8	5	3	1	⅛	1/10
Percentage of rated capacity, Planté type	100	88	75	55.8	37	19.5
Percentage of rated capacity, pasted type	100	93	83	63	41	25.5

The following rule may be observed in **charging a lead battery:** The charging rate in amperes should be less than the number of ampere-hours out of the battery. For example, if 200 amp-hr are out of a battery, a charging rate of 200 amp may be used until the ampere-hours out of the battery are reduced appreciably.

There are two common methods of charging: the **constant-current method** and the **constant-potential method.**

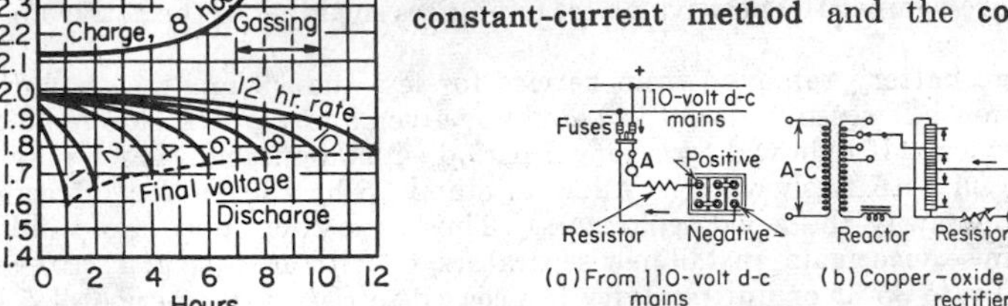

FIG. 7. Voltage curves on charge and discharge for lead cell.

FIG. 8. Connections for charging storage battery.

Figure 8(*a*) shows a common method of charging with constant current, provided a low-voltage d-c power supply is available. The resistor connected in series may be adjusted to give the required current. Several batteries may be connected in series. Figure 8(*b*) shows a more common method, using a copper-oxide or silicon rectifier, since a-c power supply is more common than d-c. The rectifier disks, mounted in a stack, are bridge-connected, the directions of rectification being indicated (see pp. 15–119 to 15–122). The polarity of the two wires may be readily determined by means of a d-c voltmeter.

The constant-potential method is to be preferred since the rate automatically tapers off as the cell approaches the charged condition. Without resistance the terminal voltage should be 2.3 volts per cell, but it is preferable to use 2.4 to 2.5 volts per cell with low resistance in series.

When a battery is being charged, its terminal voltage

$$V = E + Ir \qquad (19)$$

Compare with Eq. (**18**).

When a battery is fully charged, any rate will produce gassing, but the rate may be reduced to such a low value that gassing is practically harmless. This is called the **finishing rate.**

Portable batteries for automobile starting and lighting, airplanes, industrial trucks, electric locomotives, train lighting, and power boats employ the pasted-type plates because of their high discharge rates for a given weight and size. The separators are either of treated grooved wood; perforated hard rubber; glass-wool mats; perforated rubber, and grooved wood; ribbed microporous rubber. In low-priced short-lived batteries for automobiles, grooved wood alone is used; in the better types, the wood is reinforced with perforated hard rubber. Containers for the low-priced short-lived automobile-type starting batteries are of asphaltic compound; for other portable types they are usually of hard rubber.

The **Exide ironclad** battery is a portable type designed for propelling electric vehicles. The positive plate consists of a lead-antimony frame supporting perforated hard-rubber tubes. An irregular lead-antimony core runs down the center of each tube, and the lead peroxide paste is packed into these tubes so that shedding of active material from the positive plate cannot occur. Pasted negative plates are used. The separators are flat microporous rubber.

Stationary Batteries. The tanks of stationary batteries are made of hard rubber, a size of 25$\frac{3}{16}$ by 18$\frac{3}{16}$ and 52$\frac{1}{8}$ in. already having been attained. (Formerly glass tanks and lead-lined wooden tanks were used, but they have been superseded by hard rubber.) When the battery is used for regulating or cycling duty, the positive plates may be of the Planté type because of their long life. However, in most modern installations thick pasted plates are used. Because of the tight fit of the plate assembly within the container and the resulting pressure of the separator against the plate surfaces, shedding of active material is reduced to a minimum and long life is obtained. Pasted negative plates are used in almost all batteries.

With Planté plates, wood veneer, frequently in combination with wooden or hard-rubber dowels, is used for separation. With pasted plates, glass-wool mats are used since their pressure against the positive plates minimizes shedding of the active material, as stated above.

A lead storage battery **removed from service** for less than 9 months should be charged once a month if possible; if not, it should be given a heavy overcharge before discontinuing service. If removed for a longer period, siphon off acid (which may be used again) and fill with fresh water. Allow to stand 15 hr and siphon off water. Remove and throw away the wood separators. The battery will now stand indefinitely. To put in service again, install new separators, fill with acid (sp gr 1.210), and charge at normal rate 35 hr or until gravity has ceased to rise over a period of 5 hr. Charge at a low rate a few hours longer.

The **ampere-hour efficiency** of lead batteries is 85 to 90 percent. The **watthour efficiency** obtained from full charge to discharge at the normal rate and at rated amp-hour is 75 to 80 percent. Batteries which do regulating duty only may have a much higher watthour efficiency.

The **Edison storage cell** when fully charged has a positive plate of nickel pencils filled with a higher nickel oxide and a negative plate of flat nickel-plated-steel stampings containing metallic iron in finely divided form. The active material for the positive plate is nickel hydrate and for the negative plate, iron oxide. The electrolyte is a 21 percent solution of potassium hydrate with lithium hydroxides. The initial emf is about 1.4 volts and the average emf about 1.1 volts throughout discharge. In Fig. 9 are shown typical voltage characteristics on charge and discharge for an Edison cell. On account of the higher internal resistance of the cell the battery is not so efficient from the energy standpoint as the lead cell. The jar is welded nickel-plated steel. The battery is compact and extremely light and strong and, for these reasons, is particularly adapted for propelling electric vehicles and for boat- and train-lighting systems. The battery is rugged, and since there is no opportunity for the growth of active material on the plates or flaking of active material, the battery has long life.

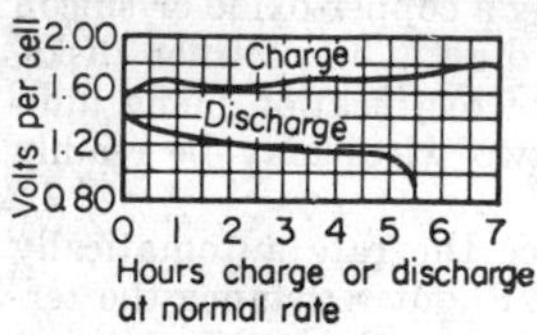

FIG. 9. Voltage during charge and discharge of Edison cell.

Nickel-Cadmium-Alkali (Nicad) Battery. Although the nickel-cadmium-alkali battery has been used in Europe for years, it has only recently been introduced into the United States. The positive active material is nickelic (black) hydroxide mixed with graphite to give it high conductivity. The negative active material is cadmium oxide. Both materials are used in powdered form and are contained within flat perforated steel pockets. These pockets are locked into steel plates, the positive and negative being alike in construction. All steel parts are nickel-plated. A complete plate group consists of a number of positive and negative plates assembled on bolts and terminal posts common to plates of the same polarity. The separators are thin strips of polystyrene, and all other battery insulation is also polystyrene. The entire plate assembly is contained within a welded-steel tank. The electrolyte is potassium hydroxide (KOH), specific gravity 1.210 at 72 F (22 C); it does not enter into any chemical reactions with the electrode materials, and its specific gravity remains constant during charge and discharge, neglecting any slight change due to the small amount of gassing. On charge, the voltage is 1.4 to 1.5 volts until near the end when it rises to 1.8 volts. On discharge, the voltage is nearly constant at 1.2 volts.

Nicad batteries are strong mechanically and are not damaged by overcharge; they hold their charge over long periods of idleness, the active material cannot flake off, the internal resistance is low, there is no corrosion, and the battery has an indefinitely long life. It is a general-purpose battery.

In the **Sonotone** nickel-cadmium battery the positive plates are nickel oxide when the battery is charged, and the negative plates are metallic cadmium. On discharge the positive plates are reduced to a state of lower oxidation, and the negative plates regain oxygen. The electrolyte is a 30 percent solution of potassium hydroxide, the specific gravity of which is 1.29 at room temperature. The case is a transparent plastic. The terminal voltage at the normal discharge rate is 1.2 volts per cell.

Rechargeable batteries, exemplified by Gould Nicad cells (Alkaline Battery Division, Gould National Batteries, Inc.), are hermetically sealed nickel-cadmium cells that contain no free alkaline electrolyte. Since there is no spillage or leakage, they can operate in any position, have long life, and require no maintenance or servicing, and their weight is small for their output. They are thus well adapted to power many types of cordless appliances such as tools, hedge shears, cameras, dictating equipment, electric razors, radios, and television sets. The electrodes consist of a plaque of microporous sintered nickel having an extremely high surface area. The electrochemical reactions differ from those of the conventional vented-type alkaline battery, a type which at the end of a charge liberates both oxygen and hydrogen gases as well as electrolytic fumes that must be vented through a valve in the top of the cell. In the sealed nickel-cadmium cell, the negative electrode (at the time that the cell is sealed) never becomes fully charged, and the evolution of hydrogen is completely suppressed. On charging, when the positive electrode has reached its full capacity, the oxygen which has evolved is channeled through the porous separator to the negative electrode and oxidizes the finely divided cadmium of the microporous plate to cadmium hydroxide, which at the same time is reduced to metallic cadmium. The cells are constructed in three different forms: the button type, the cylindrical type, and the prismatic type. Their ratings range from 20 milliamp-hr to 23 amp-hr. Their average discharge voltage is 1.22 volts, and they require 14 hr of charge at the normal rate ($\frac{1}{10}$th amp-hr rating), which for a 3.5 amp-hr cell is 0.35 amp.

Precautions in the **care of storage batteries:** An ammeter should not be connected directly across the terminals to test the condition of a cell; a battery should not be left to stand in a discharged condition; a flame should not be brought in the vicinity of a battery that is being charged; the battery should not be allowed to become heated when charging; water should never be added to the concentrated acid—always acid to the water; acid should never be equalized except when the battery is in a charged condition; a battery should never be exposed to the influence of external heat; voltmeter tests should be made when the current is flowing; batteries should always be kept clean. To replace acid lost through slopping, use a solution of 2 parts concentrated sulphuric acid in 5 parts water by weight, unless a hydrometer is at hand to enable the solution to be made up according to the specifications of the makers of the cell.

MAGNETISM

Magnetic Circuit. The magnetic circuit is analogous to the electric circuit in that the flux Φ is proportional to the magnetomotive force ($\mathfrak{F}$) and inversely proportional to the reluctance ($\mathfrak{R}$) or magnetic resistance. Thus

$$\Phi = \mathfrak{F}/\mathfrak{R} \qquad \textbf{(20)}$$

Compare with Eq. (**7**). Φ is in maxwells, where the maxwell is the cgs unit of flux, $\mathfrak{F}$ in gilberts, and B in cgs reluctance units. In the rationalized mks system, ϕ is in webers, $\mathfrak{F}$ is in ampere-turns, and $\mathfrak{R}$ is in mks reluctance units.

$$\mathfrak{R} = l/\mu_r\mu_v A \qquad \textbf{(21)}$$

where μ_r is **relative permeability** (commonly called permeability, μ), a property of the magnetic material, and μ_v is the permeability of evacuated space = unity in the cgs system; in cgs system A = square centimeter. In the rationalized mks system $\mu_v = 4\pi \times 10^{-7}$, so that

$$\mathfrak{R} = \frac{l}{\mu_r(4\pi \times 10^{-7})A} = \frac{l}{\mu_r(1.257 \times 10^{-6})A} \qquad \textbf{(22)}$$

l is in meters and A in square meters.

The unit of **flux density** in the cgs system is the *gauss*, which is equal to the number of maxwells per square centimeter taken perpendicular to their direction. One gilbert between opposite faces of a centimeter cube of a magnetic medium produces μ_r gauss. For air, $\mu_r = 1$. In the mks system the unit of flux density is *weber per square meter* = 10^4 gauss (see Table 6).

Table 6. Magnetic Units

Quantity	Symbol	Equation,* cgs	Cgs unit	Practical or rationalized mks unit	Ratio of magnitude of mks to cgs unit
Pole strength	m	$\mathbf{F} = \frac{mm'}{\mu_r l^2}$	Unit pole	$\frac{mm'}{\mu_r(4\pi)^2 10^{-7}}$	0.7958×10^7
Magnetomotive force	$\mathfrak{F}$	$\mathfrak{F} = 0.4\pi NI$	Gilbert	Amp-turn, NI	1.257
Magnetic field intensity	H	$H = \mathfrak{F}/l = \mathbf{F}/m$	Oersted	Amp-turn per m	0.01257
Magnetic flux	Φ, ϕ	$\Phi = \mathfrak{F}/\mathfrak{R}$	Maxwell	Weber	10^8
Magnetic flux density	B	$B = \Phi/A$	Gauss	Weber per sq m	10^4
Relative permeability	μ_r	$\mu_r = B/H$	Numeric	Numeric	1
Reluctivity	γ	$\gamma = H/B = 1/\mu_r$	Numeric	Numeric	1
Permeance	$\mathcal{P}$	$\mathcal{P} = \mu_r A/l$	....	....	7.96×10^7
Reluctance	$\mathfrak{R}$	$\mathfrak{R} = l/A\mu_r$	....	....	1.257×10^{-8}

* l = length; A = sectional area in sq cm; $\mathbf{F}$ = force, dynes; N = number of turns.

Magnetic-circuit calculations cannot be made with the same degree of accuracy as can electric-circuit calculations because of several factors. The cross-sectional dimensions of the magnetic circuit are large relative to its length; magnetic paths are irregular and their geometry can only be approximated as with the air gap of electric machines, which usually have slots on one or both sides of the gap.

Magnetic flux cannot be confined to definite magnetic paths, but a considerable proportion usually takes paths external to the circuit giving magnetic leakage (see Fig. 13). The relative permeability of iron varies over wide ranges with the flux density and with the previous magnetic condition (see Fig. 11). These variations of relative permeability cannot be expressed by any simple equation. Although the foregoing factors prevent the obtaining of extremely high accuracy in magnetic calculations, yet, with experience, it is possible to design magnetic circuits with a precision that is satisfactory for all practical purposes.

The **magnetomotive force** $\mathfrak{F}$ in Eq. (**20**) is expressed in **gilberts** = $0.4\pi NI$ where N is the number of turns linked with the circuit and I is the current in amp. The unit of reluctance is the reluctance of 1 cm cube of air. The total reluctance is proportional to the length and inversely proportional to the cross-sectional area of the magnetic circuit, which is analogous to electrical resistance. Hence the reluctance of any given path of uniform cross section A is $l/A\mu$, where l is the length of the path in centimeters, A its cross section in square centimeters, and μ is the permeability. Reluctances in series are added to obtain their combined reluctance. Ohm's law of the magnetic circuit becomes

$$\Phi = \frac{0.4\pi NI}{l_1/A_1\mu_1 + l_2/A_2\mu_2 + l_3/A_3\mu_3 \cdots} \text{ maxwells} \qquad \textbf{(23)}$$

where l_1, A_1, μ_1, etc., are the lengths, cross sections, and relative permeabilities of each series part of the circuit.

EXAMPLE. In Fig. 10 is shown a magnetic circuit of cast steel with a 0.4 cm air gap. The cross section of the core is 4 cm square. There are 425 turns wound on the core and the current is 10 amp. The relative permeability of the steel at the operating flux density is 1,100. Assume that the path of the flux is as shown, the average path at the corners being quarter circles. Neglect fringing at the air gap and any leakage. Determine the flux and the flux density.

Using the cgs system, the length of the magnetic path in the iron $= 12 + 8 + 8 + 5.8 + 5.8 + 4\pi = 52.2$ cm. From Eq. (**23**),

$$\Phi = \frac{0.4\pi \times 425 \times 10}{[52.2/(16 \times 1{,}100)] + (0.4/16)} = 191{,}000 \text{ maxwells}$$

$$B = \frac{191{,}000}{16} = 11{,}940 \text{ gausses}$$

Using the rationalized mks system, the length of the iron is 0.522 m, the length of the air gap is 0.004 m, and the cross section of the iron and air gap is 0.0016 sq m.

$$\Phi = \frac{425 \times 10}{\dfrac{0.522}{1{,}100 \times 4\pi \times 10^{-7} \times 0.0016} + \dfrac{0.004}{4\pi \times 10^{-7} \times 0.0016}} = 0.00191 \text{ weber}$$

Magnetization and Permeability Curves. The magnetic permeability of air is a constant and is taken as unity. The relative permeability of iron and other magnetic substances varies with the flux density. In Fig. 11 is shown a magnetization curve for cast steel in which the flux density B in gausses is plotted as a function of the field intensity, or gilberts per centimeter, H. Also the relative permeability $\mu_r = B/H$ is plotted as a function of the flux density B. Note the wide range over which the relative permeability varies. No satisfactory equation has been found to express the relation between magnetizing force and flux density and between relative permeability and flux density. If an attempt is made to solve Eq. (**23**) for flux, the factors μ_1, μ_2, etc., are unknown since they are functions of the flux density, which is being determined. The simplest method is one of trial and error, *i.e.*, a value of flux, and the corresponding permeability, is first assumed, the equation solved for the flux, and if the computed flux differs widely from the assumed flux, a second approximation is made, etc. In nearly all magnetic designs either the flux or flux density is the independent variable, and it is required to find the necessary ampere-turns

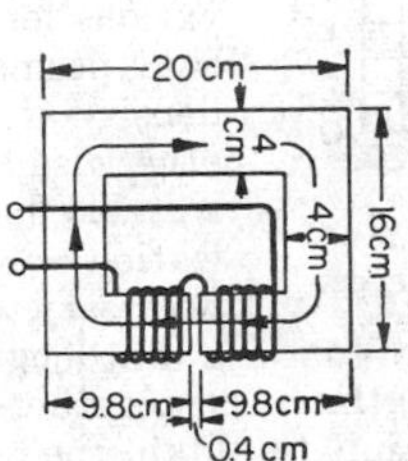

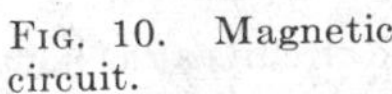

FIG. 10. Magnetic circuit.

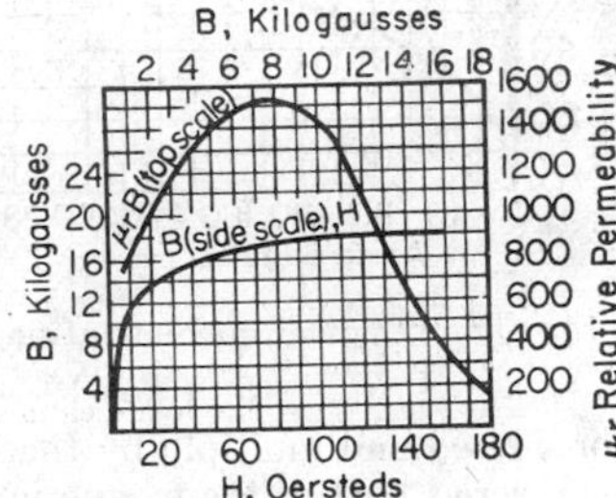

FIG. 11. Magnetization and relative-permeability curves for cast steel.

to produce them. Let the flux $\Phi = BA$ where B is the flux density in gauss. Then

$$\Phi = BA = 0.4\pi NI/(l/A\mu_r)$$

and

$$NI = Bl/0.4\pi\mu_r = 0.796Bl/\mu_r \tag{24}$$

Equation (**24**) shows that the necessary ampere-turns are proportional to the *flux density* and the length of path and are inversely proportional to the relative permeability.

With air and non-magnetic substances μ_r [Eq. (**24**)] becomes unity and

$$NI = 0.796Bl \tag{25}$$

in centimeter units. With inch units

$$NI = 0.313B'l' \tag{26}$$

where B' is the flux density, maxwells per sq in.; and l' the length of the magnetic path, in.

EXAMPLE. The average flux density in the air gap of a generator is 40,000 maxwells per sq in., and the effective length of the gap is 0.2 in. How many ampere-turns per pole are necessary for the gap?

$$NI = 0.313 \times 40{,}000 \times 0.2 = 2{,}500$$

Since the relation of μ_r to flux density B in Eq. (**24**) is not simple, the relation of ampere-turns per unit length of magnetic circuit to flux density is ordinarily shown graphically. Typical curves of this character are shown in Fig. 12, inch units being used although scales of kilogausses and gilberts per centimeter are also given. To find the kilomaxwells per square centimeter (kilogausses), divide the ordinate scale by 6.45. To determine the number of ampere-turns necessary to produce a given total flux in a magnetic circuit composed of several parts in series having various lengths, cross sections, and relative permeabilities, determine the flux density if the cross section is fixed, or otherwise choose a cross section to give a suitable flux density. From the magnetization curve obtain the ampere-turns necessary to drive this *flux density* through a unit length of the portion of the circuit considered and multiply by the length. Add together the ampere-turns required for each series part of the magnetic circuit to obtain the total ampere-turns necessary to give the assumed flux.

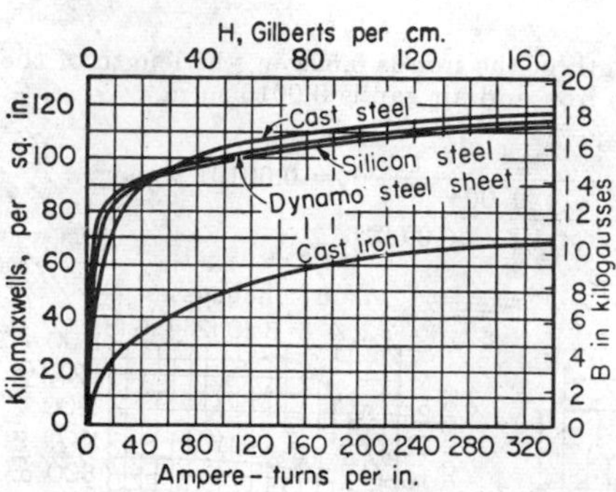

FIG. 12. Typical magnetization curves.

It is desirable to operate magnetic circuits at as high flux densities as is practicable in order to reduce the amount of iron and copper. The air gaps of dynamos are operated at average densities of 40,000 to 50,000 maxwells per sq in. Higher densities increase the exciting ampere-turns and tooth losses. At 45,000 maxwells per sq in. the flux density in the teeth may be as high as 120,000 to 130,000 maxwells per sq in. The flux densities in transformer cores are limited as a rule by the permissible losses. At 60 cycles and with silicon steel the maximum density is 60,000 to 70,000 maxwells per sq in.; at 25 cycles the density may run as high as 75,000 to 90,000 maxwells per sq in. With laminated cores, the net iron is approximately 0.9 the gross cross section.

Magnetic Leakage. It is impossible to confine all magnetic flux to any desired path since there is no known insulator of magnetic flux. Figure 13 shows the magnetic circuit of a modern four-pole dynamo. A considerable proportion of the useful magnetic flux leaks between the pole shoes and cores, rather than across the air gap. The ratio of the maximum flux, which exists in the field cores, to the useful flux, *i.e.*, the flux that crosses the air gap, is the **coefficient of leakage.** This coefficient must always be greater than unity and in carefully designed dynamos may be as low as 1.15. It is frequently as high as 1.30. Although the geometry of the leakage-flux paths is not simple, the leakage flux may be determined by approximations with a fair degree of accuracy.

Magnetic Hysteresis. The magnetization curves shown in Figs. 11 and 12 are called **normal curves.** They are taken with the magnetizing force continuously increased from zero. If at any point the magnetizing force be decreased, a greater value of flux density for any given magnetizing force will result. The effect of carrying iron through a complete cycle of magnetization, both positive and negative, is shown in Fig. 14.

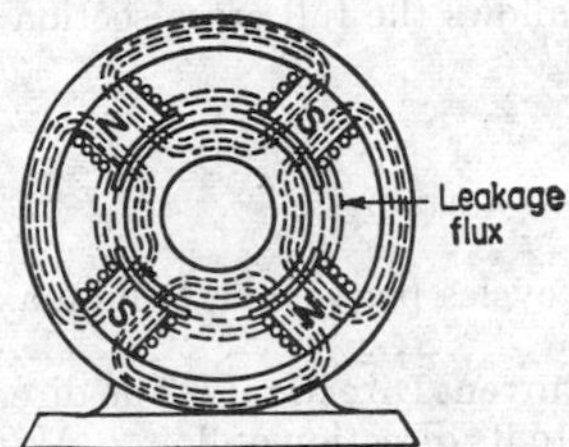

Fig. 13. Magnetic circuit of four-pole dynamo with leakage flux.

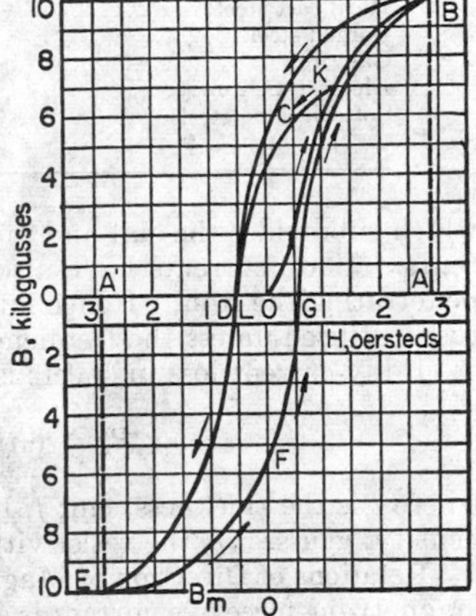

Fig. 14. Hysteresis loop for dynamo steel.

The curve OKB, taken with increasing values of magnetizing force per centimeter H is the **normal induction** curve. If, after the magnetizing force has reached the value OA, it is decreased, the magnetic flux density B will decrease in accordance with curve BCD, between A and O the values being much greater than those given by the normal curve; *i.e.*, the flux density lags the magnetizing force. At zero magnetizing force, the flux density is OC, called the **remanence.** A negative magnetizing force OD, called the **coercive force,** is required to bring the flux density to zero. If the magnetizing force is increased negatively to OA', the flux density will be given by the curve DE. If the magnetizing force is increased positively from A' to A, the flux density will be given by the curve $EFGB$, which is similar to the curve $BCDE$. OF is the negative remanence and OG again is the coercive force. The complete curve is called a **hysteresis loop.** If, when the normal curve reaches the point K, the magnetizing force is then decreased, another hysteresis loop, a portion of which is shown at KL, will be obtained. It is seen that the flux density lags the magnetizing force, throughout.

The energy dissipated per cycle is proportional to the area of the loop and is equal to $\frac{1}{4\pi}\int H\,dB$ ergs per cycle per cc. For moderately high densities the energy loss per cycle varies according to the **Steinmetz law**

$$W = \eta B_m^{1.6} \text{ ergs per cc} \tag{27}$$

where B_m is the maximum value of the flux density in gausses (Fig. 14). Table 7 gives values of the Steinmetz coefficient η, for common magnetic steels.

A permanent increase in the hysteresis constant occurs if the temperature of operation remains for some time above 80 C. This phenomenon is known as **aging** and may be much reduced by proper annealing of the iron. Silicon steels containing about 3 percent silicon have a lower hysteresis loss, somewhat larger eddy-current loss, and are practically non-aging.

Eddy-current losses, also known as Foucault-current losses, occur in iron subjected to cyclic magnetization. Eddy-current losses are reduced by laminating the iron,

Table 7. Steinmetz Coefficient

Hard tungsten steel	0.058	Annealed cast steel	0.008
Hard cast steel	0.025	Ordinary sheet iron	0.004
Forged steel	0.020	Pure iron	0.003
Cast iron	0.013	Annealed iron sheet	0.002
Electrolytic iron	0.009	Best annealed sheet	0.001
Soft machine steel	0.009	Silicon steel sheet	0.00046
		Permalloy	0.0001

which subdivides the emf and increases greatly the length of path of the parasitic currents. Eddy currents have also a screening effect, which tends to prevent the flux penetrating the iron. Hence laminating also allows the full cross section of the iron to be utilized unless the frequency is too high.

Eddy-current loss in sheets is given by

$$P_e = (\pi t f B_m)^2/6\rho 10^{16} \qquad \text{watts per cc} \tag{28}$$

where t is the thickness, cm; f, the frequency, cycles per sec; B_m, the maximum flux density, gausses; ρ, the resistivity, ohms-cm.

Relations of Direction of Magnetic Flux to Current Direction. The direction of the magnetizing force of a current is at right angles to its direction of flow. Magnetic lines about a cylindrical conductor carrying current exist in circular planes concentric with and normal to the conductor. This is illustrated in Fig. 15(a). The ⊕ sign, corresponding to the feathered end of the arrow, indicates a direction of current away from the observer; a ⊙ sign, corresponding to the tip of an arrow, indicates a direction of current toward the observer.

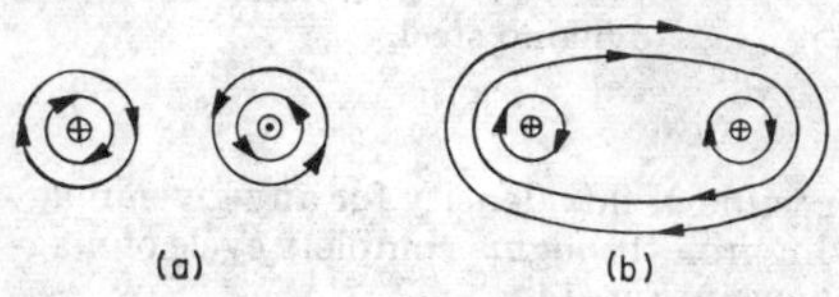

FIG. 15. (a) Currents in opposite directions. (b) Currents in the same direction.

Corkscrew Rule. The direction of the current and that of the resulting magnetic field are related to each other as the forward travel of a corkscrew and the direction in which it is rotated.

Hand Rule. Grasp the conductor in the right hand with the thumb pointing in the direction of the current. The fingers will then point in the direction of the lines of flux.

The applications of these rules are illustrated in Fig. 15. If the currents in parallel conductors are in opposite directions [Fig. 15(a)], the conductors tend to move apart; if the currents in parallel conductors are in the same direction [Fig. 15(b)], the conductors tend to come together. The magnetic lines act like stretched rubber bands and, in attempting to contract, tend to pull the two conductors together.

The relation of the direction of current in a solenoid helix to the direction of flux is shown in Fig. 16. Figure 17 shows the effect on a uniform field of placing a conductor

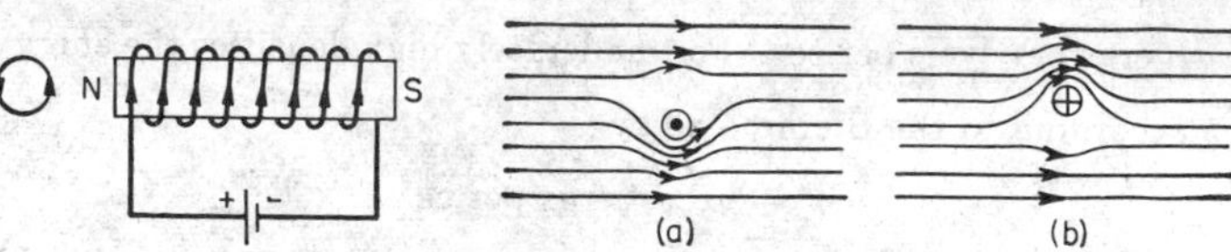

FIG. 16. Direction of current and poles in solenoid.

FIG. 17. Effect of current on uniform magnetic field.

carrying current in that field and normal to it. In (a) the direction of the current is toward the observer. By applying the corkscrew rule it is seen that the current weakens the field immediately above it and strengthens the field immediately below it. The reverse is true in (b), where the direction of the current is away from the observer.

Figure 17 is illustrative of the force developed on a conductor carrying current in a magnetic field. In (*a*) the conductor will tend to move upward owing to the stretching of the magnetic lines beneath it. Similarly, the conductor in (*b*) will tend to move downward. This principle is the basis of motor action.

For magnets and solenoids see p. 15–105.

DIELECTRIC CIRCUIT

Dynamic and Static Electricity. Electricity in motion such as an electric current is dynamic electricity; electricity at rest is static electricity. The two are identical physically. Since static electricity is frequently produced at high voltage and small quantity, the two are frequently considered as being two different types of electricity.

Capacitors

Capacitors (formerly condensers). Two conducting bodies, or electrodes, separated by a dielectric constitute a capacitor. If a positive charge is placed on one electrode of a capacitor, an equal negative charge is induced on the other. The medium between the capacitor plates is called a **dielectric.** The dielectric properties of a medium relate to its ability to conduct *dielectric lines*. This is in distinction to its **insulating** properties which relate to its property to conduct *electric current*. For example, air is an excellent insulator but ruptures dielectrically at low voltage. It is not a good dielectric so far as breakdown strength is concerned.

With capacitors

$$Q = CE \quad (29)$$

$$C = Q/E \quad (30)$$

$$E = Q/C \quad (31)$$

where Q is the quantity in coulombs, C the capacitance in farads, and E the voltage. The unit of capacitance in the practical system is the *farad*. The farad is too large a unit for practical purposes, so that either the *microfarad* (μf), 10^{-6} farad, or the *micromicrofarad* ($\mu\mu$f) = the *picofarad* (pf), 10^{-12} farad, are used. However, in voltage, current, and energy relations the capacitance must be expressed in farads.

The energy stored in a capacitor

$$W = \tfrac{1}{2}QE = \tfrac{1}{2}CE^2 = \tfrac{1}{2}Q^2/C \quad \text{joules} \quad (32)$$

FIG. 18. Parallel-electrode capacitor.

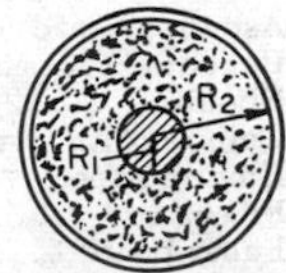

FIG. 19. Coaxial-cylinder capacitor.

Capacitance of Capacitors. The capacitance of a **parallel-electrode** capacitor (Fig. 18) is

$$C = \epsilon_r A/(4\pi d \times 9 \times 10^5) \quad \text{microfarads} \quad (33)$$

where ϵ_r is the relative capacitivity, A is the area of one electrode, sq cm; and d is the distance between electrodes, cm.

The capacitance of **coaxial cylindrical** capacitors (Fig. 19) is

$$C = 0.2171\epsilon_r l/[9 \times 10^5 \log (R_2/R_1)] \quad \text{microfarads} \quad (34)$$

where ϵ_r is the relative capacitivity and l the length, cm. Also

$$C = 0.03882\epsilon_r/\log (R_2/R_1) \quad \text{microfarads per mile} \quad (35)$$

Equation (**35**) is useful in that it is applicable to cables.

The capacitance of two **parallel cylindrical conductors** D cm between centers and having radii of r cm is

$$C = 0.01941/\log (D/r) \quad \text{microfarads per mile} \quad (36)$$

In practice, the capacitance to neutral or to an infinite conducting plane midway between the conductors and perpendicular to their plane is usually used. The capacitance to neutral

$$C = 0.03882/\log (D/r) \quad \text{microfarads per mile} \qquad \textbf{(37)}$$

Equations (**36**) and (**37**) are used for calculating the capacitance of overhead transmission lines. When computing charging current, use voltage between lines in (**36**) and to neutral in (**37**).

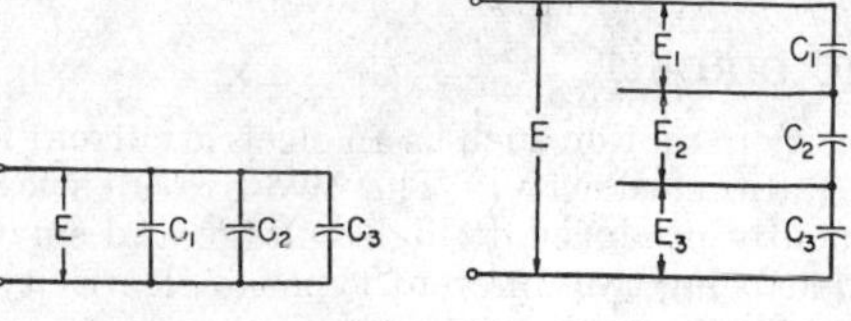

Fig. 20. Capacitances in parallel.

Fig. 21. Capacitances in series.

Capacitances in Parallel. The equivalent capacitance of capacitances in parallel (Fig. 20)

$$C = C_1 + C_2 + C_3 \qquad \textbf{(38)}$$

Capacitances in parallel are all across the same voltage. If the voltage is E, then the total quantity $Q = CE$ and $Q_1 = C_1E$, etc.

Capacitances in Series. The equivalent capacitance C of capacitances in series (Fig. 21) is found as follows:

$$1/C = 1/C_1 + 1/C_2 + 1/C_3 \qquad \textbf{(39)}$$

If the capacitances are not leaky, the charge Q is the same on each. $Q = CE$, $E_1 = Q/C_1$, $E_2 = Q/C_2$, etc.

Table 8. Insulating and Dielectric Properties of Insulating Materials

	Insulation resistance, megohms-cm	Relative capacitivity or dielectric constant	Rupturing strength	
			Volts per mil	Kilovolts per cm
Asbestos board (ebonized)	1.0×10^7	....	55	22
Bakelite	$5\text{–}30 \times 10^{11}$	4.5–5.5	450–1,400	180–550
Ebonite	$10^9\text{–}10^{12}$	1.9–3.5	1,000–2,000	390–780
Empire cloth	....	3.5–5.5	200–750	80–300
Empire paper	....	....	1,140	450
Fiber	5×10^3	2.5–5	50	20
Fuller board	11×10^9	....	120–760	47–300
Glass	17×10^9	5.4–9.9	760–3,800	300–1,500
Flint	....	6.61–9.90		
Jena-boron	....	5.5–8.1		
Gutta percha	25×10^8	2.9–4.9	200–510	80–200
Linen, varnished (see Empire cloth)				
Marble	$10^2\text{–}10^5$	8.3	50–100	20–39
Mica:				
India	10^9	7.07–7.90	4,000	1,580
Canada	$0.44\text{–}22 \times 10^6$	2.9–3.0	1,270–3,800	500–1,500
South America	39×10^6	5.9	3,800	1,500
Mica segment plate	....	....	900–1,200	350–470
Mica high-heat plate	....	....	1,000	390
Oils:				
Castor	6.6×10^4	4.7	330–480	130–190
Cottonseed	10^4	3.2	300–400	120–160
Lard	....	....	102–355	40–140
Linseed	6×10^5	3.3	300–470	120–185
Mineral	21×10^6	2.0–4.7	300–400	120–160
Paraffin	$1{,}000 \times 10^{12}$	2.41	410–550	160–215
Paper	....	1.7–2.6	110–230	43–90
Paper, treated	....	2.5–4.0	500–750	20–300
Paraffin, solid	1×10^{10}	1.9–2.5	580	230
Polyethylene	....	2.3	500–700	197–276
Polyvinyl chloride	....	6.5–12	250–450	98.5–177
Porcelain	3×10^8	5.7–6.8	240–300	95–120
Rubber (vulcanized)	$10^{14}\text{–}10^{16}$	2.0–3.5		
Rubber (compounds)	$10^{14}\text{–}10^{16}$	2.5–6	300–500	120–200
Slate	$10^2\text{–}10^4$	6–7.4	5–10	2–3.9
Transil oil	....	2.4–2.6	300	120
Petroleum jelly	....	2.16–2.2	230–330	90–130

Insulators and Dielectrics. Insulating materials are applied to electric circuits to prevent the leakage of current. Insulating materials when used with high voltage must not only have a high resistance to leakage current, but must also be able to resist dielectric puncture; *i.e.*, in addition to being a good insulator, the material must be a good dielectric. Insulation resistance is usually expressed in megohms (10^6 ohms) and the resistivity given in megohms-centimeter. The dielectric strength is usually given in terms of voltage gradient, common units being volts per mil, volts per millimeter, and kilovolts per centimeter. Insulation resistance decreases very rapidly with increase in temperature. Absorbed moisture reduces the insulation resistance, and moisture and humidity have a large effect on surface leakage. In Table 8 are given the insulating and dielectric properties of several common insulating materials (see also pp. 6–180 *et seq.*).

TRANSIENTS

Induced Emf. If a flux ϕ maxwells linking N turns of conductor changes, an emf

$$e = -N(d\phi/dt)10^{-8} \qquad \text{volts} \tag{40}$$

is induced.

Self-inductance. Let a flux ϕ link N turns. The linkages of the circuit are $N\phi$ maxwell-turns. If the permeability of the circuit is assumed constant, then the number of these linkages per ampere ($\times\ 10^{-8}$) is the **self-inductance** or **inductance** of the circuit. The unit of inductance is the **henry.** The inductance is

$$L = N\phi/(i \times 10^8) \qquad \text{henrys} \tag{41}$$

If the permeability changes with the current

$$L = N(d\phi/di)10^{-8} \qquad \text{henrys} \tag{42}$$

The energy stored in the magnetic field

$$W = \tfrac{1}{2}Li^2 \qquad \text{joules} \tag{43}$$

Emf of Self-induction. If Eq. (**41**) be written $Li = N\phi 10^{-8}$ and differentiated with respect to the time t, $L(di/dt) = N(d\phi/dt)10^{-8}$ and from Eq. (**40**)

$$e = -L(di/dt) \qquad \text{volts} \tag{44}$$

e is the emf of self-induction. If a rate of change of current of 1 amp per sec induces an emf of 1 volt, the inductance is 1 **henry** (see p. 15–4). If the flux ϕ is given in terms of the mks unit, the weber, the factor 10^{-8} should be omitted.

Current in Inductive Circuit. If a circuit containing resistance R and inductance L in series is connected across a steady voltage E, the voltage E must supply the iR drop in the circuit and at the same time overcome the emf of self-induction. That is $E = Ri + L\,di/dt$. A solution of this differential equation gives

$$i = (E/R)(1 - \epsilon^{-Rt/L}) \qquad \text{amp} \tag{45}$$

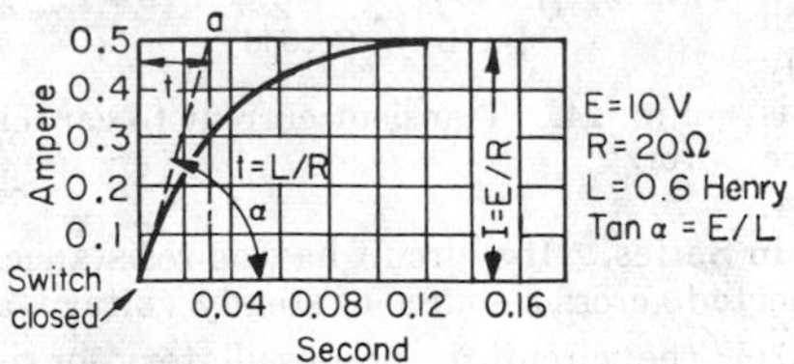

FIG. 22. Rise of current in inductive circuit.

where ϵ is the base of the natural system of logarithms.

Figure 22 shows this equation plotted when $R = 10$ volts, $R = 20\Omega$, $L = 0.6$ henry. It is to be noted that inductance causes the current to rise slowly to its Ohm's law value, $I_0 = E/R = 10/20 = 0.5$ amp. When $t = L/R$, the current has reached 63.2 percent of its Ohm's law value. L/R is the **time constant** of the circuit. In the foregoing circuit, the time constant $L/R = 0.6/20 = 0.03$ sec. The initial rate of rise of current is tan $\alpha = E/L$. If current continued at this rate, it would reach $a = E/R$ in L/R sec $[(E/L)(L/R) = E/R]$.

If a circuit containing inductance and resistance in series is short-circuited when the current is I_0, the equation of current becomes

$$i = I_0 \epsilon^{-Rt/L} \quad \text{amp} \tag{46}$$

Figure 23 shows this equation plotted when $I_0 = 0.5$ amp, $R = 20\Omega$, $L = 0.6$ henry. It is seen that inductance opposes the decay of current. Inductance always opposes change of current.

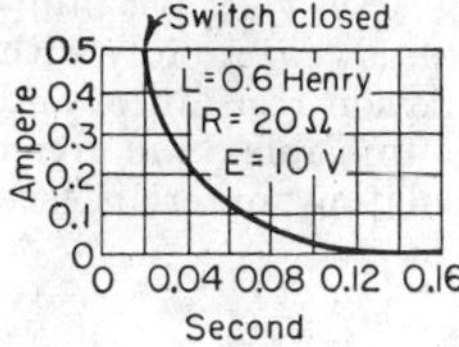

FIG. 23. Decay of current in inductive circuit.

Mutual Inductance. If two circuits having inductances L_1 and L_2 henrys are so related to each other geometrically that any portion of the flux produced by the current in one circuit links the other circuit, the two circuits possess *mutual inductance*. It follows that a change of current in one circuit causes an emf to be induced in the other. Let e_2 be induced in circuit 2 by a change di_1/dt in circuit 1. Then

$$e_2 = -M\, di_1/dt \quad \text{volts} \tag{47}$$

M is the mutual inductance of the two circuits.

$$M = k\sqrt{L_1L_2} \tag{48}$$

where k is the **coefficient of coupling** of the two circuits, or the proportion of the flux in one circuit which links the other. Also a change of current di_2/dt in circuit 2 induces an emf e_1 in circuit 1, $e_1 = -M\, di_2/dt$ (see p. 15–4).

The stored energy

$$W = \tfrac{1}{2}L_1I_1^2 + \tfrac{1}{2}L_2I_2^2 + MI_1I_2 \quad \text{joules} \tag{49}$$

where I_1 and I_2 are the currents in circuits 1 and 2.

Current in Capacitive Circuit. If capacitance C farads and resistance R ohms are connected in series across the steady voltage E, the current

$$i = (E/R)\epsilon^{-t/CR} \quad \text{amp} \tag{50}$$

If a capacitor charged to voltage E is discharged through resistance R, the current

$$i = -(E/R)\epsilon^{-t/CR} \quad \text{amp} \tag{51}$$

Except for sign, these two equations are identical and are of the same form as Eq. (**46**).

In Fig. 24 is shown the transient current to a capacitor in series with a resistor when $E = 200$ volts, $C = 4.0 \times 10^{-6}$ farad, $R = 2{,}000$ ohms. When $t = CR$, the current has reached $1/\epsilon = 0.368$ its initial value. CR is the **time constant** of the circuit. The initial rate of decrease of current is $\tan\alpha = -E/CR^2$. If the current continued at this rate it would reach zero when the time is CR sec. If, in its fully charged condition, the capacitor of Fig. 24 is discharged through the resistor R, the curve will be the negative of that shown in Fig. 24.

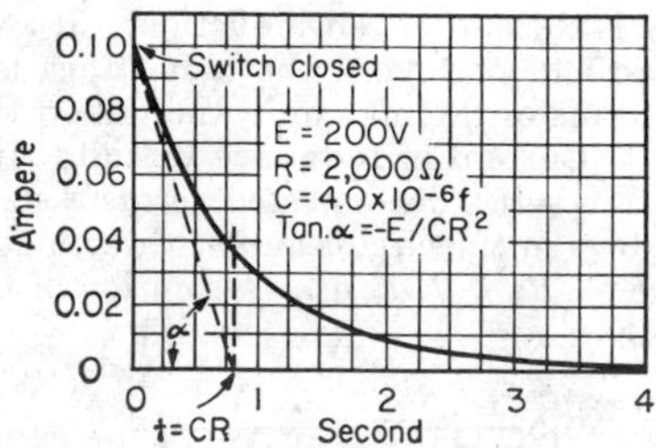

FIG. 24. Transient current to capacitor.

Resistance, Inductance, and Capacitance in Series. If a circuit having resistance, inductance, and capacitance in series is connected across a source of steady voltage, a transient condition results. If $R > \sqrt{4L/C}$, the circuit is non-oscillatory or is overdamped.

The current

$$i = \frac{EC}{\sqrt{R^2C^2 - 4LC}}\left[\epsilon^{(-\alpha+\beta)t} - \epsilon^{(-\alpha-\beta)t}\right] \quad \text{amp} \tag{52}$$

where $\alpha = R/2L$ and $\beta = (\sqrt{R^2C^2 - 4LC})/2LC$.

In Fig. 25 is shown the curve corresponding to Eq. (**52**). When $R = \sqrt{4L/C}$, the system is **critically damped** and the transient dies out rapidly without oscillation. The current

$$i = (E/L)t\epsilon^{-Rt/2L} \qquad \text{amp} \tag{53}$$

Figure 25 shows also the curve corresponding to Eq. (**53**).

If $R < \sqrt{4L/C}$, the transient is oscillatory, being a logarithmically damped sine wave. The current

$$i = \frac{2EC}{\sqrt{4LC - R^2C^2}} \epsilon^{-Rt/2L} \sin \frac{\sqrt{4LC - R^2C^2}}{2LC} t \qquad \text{amp} \tag{54}$$

The transient oscillates at a frequency very nearly equal to $1/(2\pi \sqrt{LC})$ cps. This is the **natural frequency** of the circuit.

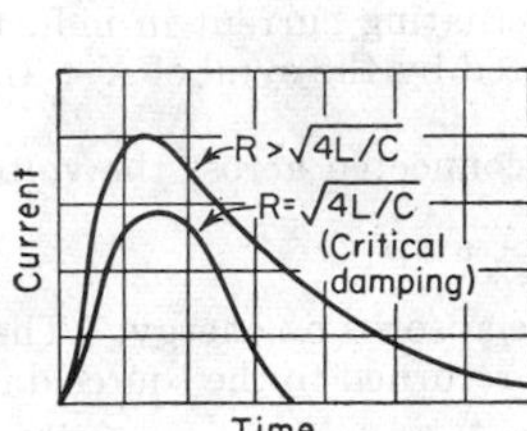

FIG. 25. Transient current in non-oscillatory circuits.

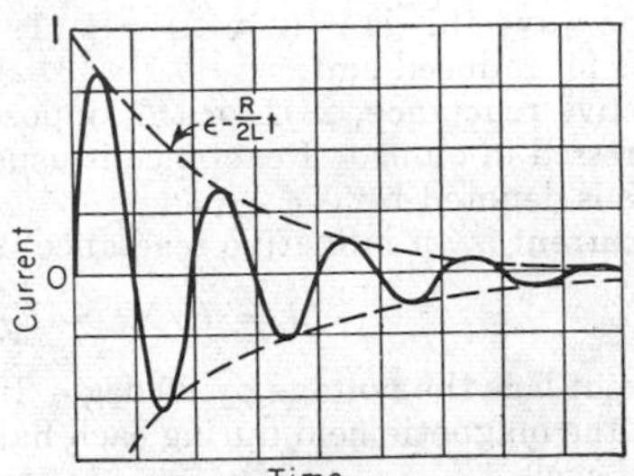

FIG. 26. Transient current in oscillatory circuit.

In Fig. 26 is shown the curve corresponding to Eq. (**54**). If the capacitor, after being charged to E volts, is discharged into the foregoing series circuits, the currents are given by Eqs. (**52**) to (**54**) multiplied by -1. Equations (**52**) to (**54**) are the same types obtained with dynamic mechanical systems with friction, mass, and elasticity.

ALTERNATING CURRENTS

Sine Waves. In the following discussion of alternating currents, sine waves of voltage and current will be assumed. That is, $e = E_m \sin \omega t$ and $i = I_m \sin (\omega t - \theta)$ where E_m and I_m are maximum values of voltage and current; ω, the angular velocity in radians per second, is equal to $2\pi f$ where f is the frequency; and θ is the angle of phase difference.

Cycle; Frequency. When any given armature coil has passed a pair of poles, the emf or current has gone through 360 electrical degrees, or 1 **cycle.** An **alternation** is one-half a cycle. The **frequency** of a synchronous machine in cycles per second is

$$f = NP/120 \qquad \text{cps} \tag{55}$$

where N is the speed in rpm and P the number of poles. In the United States and Canada the frequency of 60 cycles per second (cps) is almost universal for general lighting and power. For the a-c power supply to d-c transit systems, and for railroad electrification, a frequency of 25 cps is used in many installations. In most of Europe and Latin America the frequency of 50 cps is in general use. In order to obtain synchronous speeds up to 10,800 rpm so that direct drive can be used for planers and molders in woodworking, frequencies of from 90 to 180 cps, obtained from frequency changers, are used. In aircraft the frequency of 400 cps has become standard.

The **root-mean-square (rms), or effective, value of a current wave** produces the same heating in a given resistance as a direct current of the same ampere value. Since the heating effect of a current is proportional to i^2r, the rms value is obtained by squaring the ordinates, finding their average value, and extracting the square root, *i.e.*, the rms value

$$I = \sqrt{1/T \int_0^T i^2\, dt} \quad \text{amp}$$

where T is the time of a cycle. The rms value I of a sine wave equals $(1/\sqrt{2})I_m = 0.707I_m$.

Average Value of a Wave. The average value of a sine wave over a complete cycle is zero. For a half-cycle the average is $(2/\pi)I_m$, or 0.637 I_m, where I_m is the maximum value of the sine wave. The average value is of importance only occasionally. A d-c measuring instrument gives the average value of a pulsating wave. The average value is of use when the effects of the current are proportional to the number of coulombs, as in electrolytic work.

Form Factor. The form factor of a wave is the ratio of rms value to average value. For a sine wave this is $\pi/(2\sqrt{2}) = 1.11$. This factor is important in that it enters equations for induced emf.

Inductive reactance, $2\pi fL$ or ωL, opposes an alternating current in inductance L. It is expressed in ohms. Reactance is usually denoted by the symbol X. Inductive reactance is denoted by X_L.

The **current** is an inductive reactance X_L when connected across the voltage E is

$$I = E/X_L = E/(2\pi fL) \quad \text{amp} \tag{56}$$

This current lags the voltage by 90 deg. Inductance absorbs no energy. The energy stored in the magnetic field during each half cycle is returned to the source during the same half cycle.

Capacitive reactance is $1/(2\pi fC) = 1/\omega C$ and is denoted by X_C, where C is in *farads*. If C is given in microfarads, $X_C = 10^6/2\pi fC$. The current in a capacitive reactance X_C when connected across voltage E is

$$I = E/X_C = 2\pi fCE \quad \text{amp} \tag{57}$$

This current leads the voltage by 90 deg. Pure capacitance absorbs no energy. The energy stored in the dielectric field during each half cycle is returned to the source during the same half cycle.

Impedance opposes the flow of alternating current and is expressed in ohms. It is denoted by Z. With resistance and inductance in series

$$Z = \sqrt{R^2 + X_L^2} = \sqrt{R^2 + (2\pi fL)^2} \quad \text{ohms} \tag{58}$$

With resistance and capacitance in series

$$Z = \sqrt{R^2 + X_C^2} = \sqrt{R^2 + [1/(2\pi fC)]^2} \quad \text{ohms} \tag{59}$$

With resistance, inductance, and capacitance in series

$$Z = \sqrt{R^2 + (X_L - X_C)^2} = \sqrt{R^2 + [2\pi fL - 1/(2\pi fC)]^2} \quad \text{ohms} \tag{60}$$

The current

$$I = E/\sqrt{R^2 + [2\pi fL - 1/(2\pi fC)]^2} \quad \text{amp} \tag{61}$$

Phasor or Vector Representation. Sine waves of voltage and current can be represented by phasors, these phasors being proportional in magnitude to the waves that they represent. The angle between two phasors is also equal to the angle existing between the two waves that they represent.

Phasors may be combined as forces are combined in mechanics. Both graphical methods and the methods of complex algebra are used. Impedances and also admittances may be similarly combined, either graphically or symbolically. The usual method is to resolve series impedances into their component resistances and reactances, then combine all resistances and all reactances, from which the resultant impedance is obtained. Thus $Z_1 + Z_2 = \sqrt{(r_1 + r_2)^2 + (x_1 + x_2)^2}$, where r_1 and x_1 are the components of Z_1, etc.

Phase Difference. With resistance only in circuit the current and the voltage are in phase with each other; with inductance only in circuit the current lags the voltage by 90 deg; with capacitance only in circuit the current leads the voltage by 90 deg.

With resistance and inductance in series, the voltage leads the current by angle θ where $\tan\theta = X_L/R$. With resistance and capacitance in series, the voltage lags the current by angle θ where $\tan\theta = -X_C/R$.

With resistance, inductance, and capacitance in series, the voltage may lag, lead, or be in phase with the current.

$$\tan\theta = (X_L - X_C)/R = (2\pi fL - 1/2\pi fC)/R \qquad (62)$$

If $X_L > X_C$ the voltage leads; if $X_L < X_C$ the voltage lags; if $X_L = X_C$ the current and voltage are in phase and the circuit is in resonance.

Power Factor. In a-c circuits the power $P = I^2R$ where I is the current and R the effective resistance (see this page below). Also the power

$$P = EI\cos\theta \quad \text{watts} \qquad (63)$$

where θ is the phase angle between E and I. Cos θ is the **power factor** (pf) of the circuit. It can never exceed unity and is usually less than unity.

$$\cos\theta = P/EI \qquad (64)$$

P is often called the true power. The product EI is the **volt-amp** and is often called the apparent power.

Active or **energy** current is the projection of the total current on the voltage phasor. $I_e = I\cos\theta$. Power $= EI_e$.

Reactive, quadrature, or **wattless current** $I_q = I\sin\theta$ and is the component of the current that contributes no power but increases the I^2R losses of the system. In power systems it should ordinarily be made as low as possible or eliminated entirely.

The **vars** (volt-amp reactive) are equal to the product of the voltage and reactive current. **Vars** $= EI_q$. **Kilovars** $= EI_q/1{,}000$.

Effective Resistance. When alternating current flows in a circuit, the losses are ordinarily greater than are given by the losses in the ohmic resistance alone. For example, alternating current tends to flow near the surface of conductors (skin effect). If iron is associated with the circuit, eddy-current and hysteresis losses result. These power losses may be accounted for by increasing the ohmic resistance to a value R, where R is the *effective resistance*, $R = P/I^2$. Since the iron losses vary as $I^{1.8}$ to I^2, little error results from this assumption.

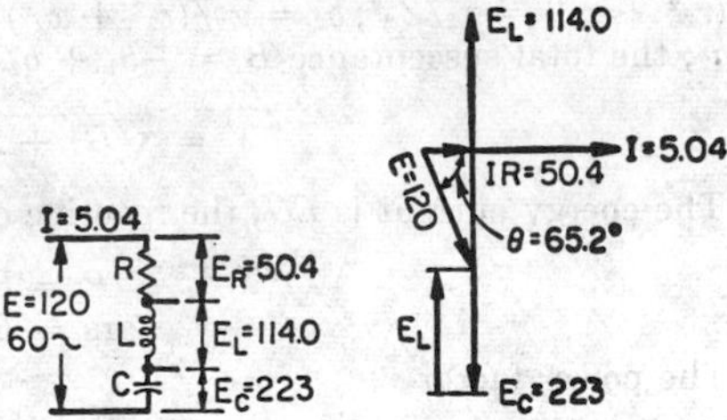

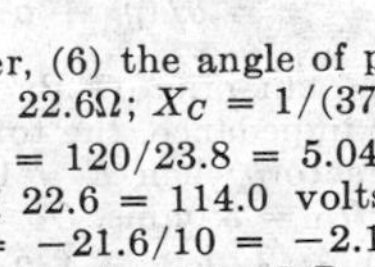

FIG. 27. Resistor, inductor, and capacitor in series.

FIG. 28. Phasor diagram for series circuit.

SOLUTION OF SERIES-CIRCUIT PROBLEM. Let a resistor R of 10 ohms, an inductor L of 0.06 henry, and a capacitor C of 60×10^{-6} farad be connected in series across 120 volt, 60-cycle mains (Fig. 27). Determine (1) the impedance, (2) the current, (3) the voltage across the resistance, the inductance, the capacitance, (4) the power factor, (5) the power, (6) the angle of phase difference.

(1) $\omega = 2\pi 60 = 377$. $X_L = 0.06 \times 377 = 22.6\Omega$; $X_C = 1/(377 \times 0.000060) = 44.2\Omega$; $Z = \sqrt{(10)^2 + (22.6 - 44.2)^2} = 23.8\Omega$; (2) $I = 120/23.8 = 5.04$ amp; (3) $E_R = IR = 5.04 \times 10 = 50.4$ volts; $E_L = IX_L = 5.04 \times 22.6 = 114.0$ volts; $E_C = IX_C = 5.04 \times 44.2 = 223$ volts; (4) $\tan\theta = (X_L - X_C)/R = -21.6/10 = -2.16$, $\theta = -65.2°$, $\cos\theta =$ pf $= 0.420$; (5) $P = 120 \times 5.04 \times 0.420 = 254$ watts; $P = I^2R = (5.04)^2 10 = 254$ watts (check); (6) From (4) $\theta = -65.2°$. Voltage lags. The phasor diagram to scale of this

circuit is shown in Fig. 28. Since the current is common for all elements of the circuit, its phasor is laid horizontally along the axis of reference.

Resonance. If the voltage E and the resistance R [Eq. (**61**)] are fixed, the maximum value of current occurs when $2\pi fL - 1/2\pi fC = 0$. The circuit so far as its terminals are concerned behaves like a non-inductive resistor. The current $I = E/R$, the power $P = EI$, and the power factor is unity.

The voltage across the inductor and the voltage across the capacitor are opposite and equal and may be many times greater than the circuit voltage. The frequency

$$f = 1/(2\pi \sqrt{LC}) \quad \text{cycles} \tag{65}$$

is the **natural frequency** of the circuit and is the frequency at which it will oscillate if the circuit is not acted upon by some external frequency (p. 15–29). This is the principle of radio sending and receiving circuits. Resonant conditions of this type should be avoided in power circuits, as the piling up of voltage may endanger apparatus and insulation.

Example. For what value of the inductance in the circuit (Fig. 27) will the circuit be in resonance, and what is the voltage across the inductor and capacitor under these conditions?

From Eq. (**65**) $L = 1(2\pi f)^2C = 0.1173$ henry. $I = E/R = 120/10 = 12$ amp. $L\omega I = I/C\omega = 0.1173 \times 377 \times 12 = 530$ volts. This voltage is over four times the line voltage.

Parallel Circuits

Parallel circuits are used for nearly all power distribution. With several series circuits in parallel it is merely necessary to find the current in each and add all the current phasors vectorially to find the total current. Parallel circuits may be solved analytically.

A series circuit has resistance r_1 and **inductive reactance** x_1. The **conductance**

$$g_1 = r_1/(r_1^2 + x_1^2) = x_1/Z_1^2 \quad \text{mhos} \tag{66}$$

the **susceptance**

$$b_1 = x_1/(r_1^2 + x_1^2) = x_1/Z_1^2 \quad \text{mhos} \tag{67}$$

Conductance is not the reciprocal of resistance unless the reactance is zero; susceptance is not the reciprocal of reactance unless the resistance is zero. With inductive reactance the susceptance is *negative;* with capacitive reactance the susceptance is *positive.*

If a second circuit has resistance r_2 and **capacitive reactance** x_2 in series, $g_2 = r_2/(r_2^2 + x_2^2) = r_2/Z_2^2$; $b_2 = x_2/(r_2^2 + x_2^2) = x_2/Z_2^2$. The total conductance $G = g_1 + g_2$; the total susceptance $B = -b_1 + b_2$. The **admittance**

$$Y = \sqrt{G^2 + B^2} = 1/Z \quad \text{mhos} \tag{68}$$

The energy current is EG; the reactive current is EB; the power

$$P = E^2G \quad \text{watts} \tag{69}$$

$$\text{vars} = E^2B \tag{70}$$

The power factor

$$pf = G/Y \tag{71}$$

Also the following relations hold:

$$r = g/(g^2 + b^2) = g/Y^2 \quad \text{ohms} \tag{72}$$

$$x = b/(g^2 + b^2) = b/Y^2 \quad \text{ohms} \tag{73}$$

Solution of a Parallel-circuit Problem. In the parallel circuit of Fig. 29 it is desired to find the joint impedance, the total current, the power in each branch, the total power, and the power factor, when $E = 100$, $f = 60$, $R_1 = 2$ ohms, $R_2 = 4$ ohms, $L_1 = 0.00795$ henry, $X_1 = 2\pi fL_1 = 3$ ohms, $C_2 = 1{,}326 \times 10^{-6}$ farad, $X_2 = 1/2\pi fC_2 = 2$ ohms, $Z_1 = \sqrt{2^2 + 3^2} = 3.6$ ohms, and $Y_1 = 1/3.6 = 0.278$ mho. *Solution:* $g_1 = R_1/(R_1^2 + X_1^2) = 2/13 = 0.154$; $b_1 = -3/13 = -0.231$; $Z_2 = \sqrt{16 + 4} = 4.47$; $Y_2 = 1/4.47 = 0.224$;

$g_2 = R_2/(R_2^2 + X_2^2) = 4/(16 + 4) = 0.2$ mho; $b_2 = 2/20 = 0.1$ mho; $G = g_1 + g_2 = 0.154 + 0.2 = 0.354$ mho; $B = b_1 + b_2 = -0.231 + 0.1 = -0.131$ mho; $Y = \sqrt{G^2 + B^2} = \sqrt{0.354^2 + (-0.131)^2} = 0.377$ mho, and joint impedance $Z = 1/0.377 = 2.65$ ohms. Phase angle $\theta = \tan^{-1} \dfrac{-0.131}{0.354} = -20.3°$. $I = EY = 100 \times 0.377 = 37.7$ amp; $P_1 = E^2g_1 = 100^2 \times 0.154 = 1{,}540$ watts; $P_2 = E^2g_2 = 100^2 \times 0.2 = 2{,}000$ watts; total power $= E^2G = 100^2 \times 0.354 = 3{,}540$ watts. Power factor $= \cos\theta = 3{,}540/(100 \times 37.7) = 93.8$ percent.

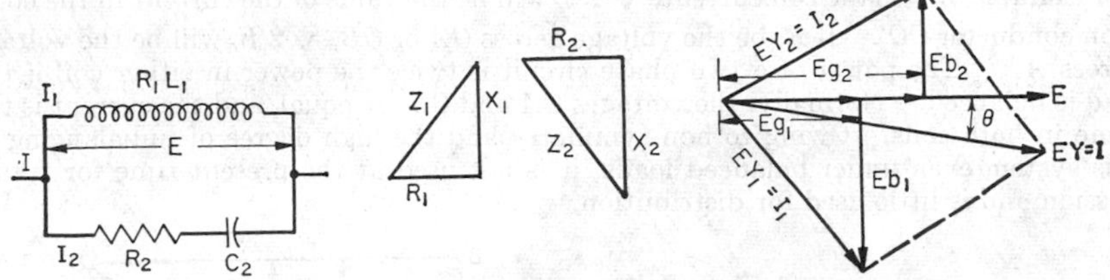

FIG. 29. Parallel circuit and phasor diagram.

With parallel circuits, unity power factor is obtained when the algebraic sum of the quadrature currents is zero. That is, $b_1 + b_2 + b_1 \cdots = 0$.

Three-phase Circuits. Alternating-current generators are usually wound with three armature circuits which are spaced 120 electrical degrees apart on the armature. Hence these coils generate emfs 120 electrical degrees apart. The coils are connected either in Y (star) or in Δ (mesh) as shown in Fig. 30. Whether Y- or Δ-connected, with a balanced load, the three coil emfs E_c and the three coil currents I_c are equal. In the Y connection the line and coil currents are equal, but the line emfs E_{AB}, E_{BC}, E_{CA} are $\sqrt{3}$ times in magnitude the coil emfs E_{OA}, E_{OB}, E_{OC}, since each is the phasor difference of two coil emfs. In the delta connection the line and coil emfs are equal, but I, the line current, is $\sqrt{3}\, I_c$, the coil current, *i.e.*, it is the phasor difference of the currents in the two coils connected to the line. The power of a coil is $E_cI_c \cos\theta$, so that the total power is $3E_cI_c \cos\theta$. If θ is the angle between *coil* current and *coil* voltage, the angle between line current and line voltage will be $(30° \pm \theta)$. In terms of line current and emf, the power is $\sqrt{3}\, EI \cos\theta$. A fourth or neutral conductor connected to O is frequently used with the Y connection. The neutral point O is frequently grounded in transmission and distribution circuits. The coil emfs are assumed to be sine waves. Under these conditions they balance, so that in the delta connection the sum of the two coil emfs at each instant is balanced by the third coil emf. Even though the third, ninth, fifteenth . . . harmonics, $3(2n + 1)f$, where $n = 0$ or an integer, exist in the coil emfs, they cannot appear between the three external line conductors of the three-phase Y-connected circuit. In the delta circuit, the same harmonics $3(2n + 1)f$ cause local currents to circulate around the mesh. This may cause a very appreciable heating. In a three-phase system the power

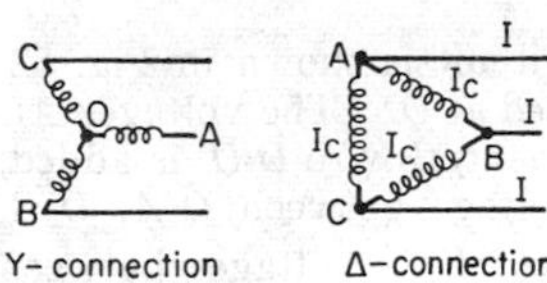

FIG. 30. Three-phase connections.

$$P = \sqrt{3}\, EI \cos\theta \quad \text{watts} \tag{74}$$

the power factor is

$$P/\sqrt{3}\, EI \tag{75}$$

and the kilovolt-amperes

$$\sqrt{3}\, EI/1{,}000 \tag{76}$$

where E and I are line voltages and currents.

Two-phase Circuits. Two-phase generators have two windings spaced 90 electrical degrees apart on the armature. These windings generate emfs differing in time phase by 90 deg. The two windings may be independent and power transmitted to the receiver though the two single-phase circuits are entirely insulated from each other. The two circuits may be combined into a two-phase three-wire circuit such as is shown in Fig. 31, where OA and OB are the generator circuits (or transformer secondaries) and $A'O'$ and $B'O'$ are the load circuits. The wire OO' is the common wire and under balanced conditions carries a current $\sqrt{2}$ times the current in wires AA' and BB'. For example, if I_c is the coil current, $\sqrt{2}\,I_c$ will be the value of the current in the common conductor OO'. If E_c be the voltage across OA or OB, $\sqrt{2}\,E_c$ will be the voltage across AB. The power of a two-phase circuit is twice the power in either coil if the load is balanced. Normally, the voltages OA and OB are equal, and the current is the same in both coils. Owing to non-symmetry and the high degree of unbalancing of this system even under balanced loads, it is not used at the present time for transmission and is little used for distribution.

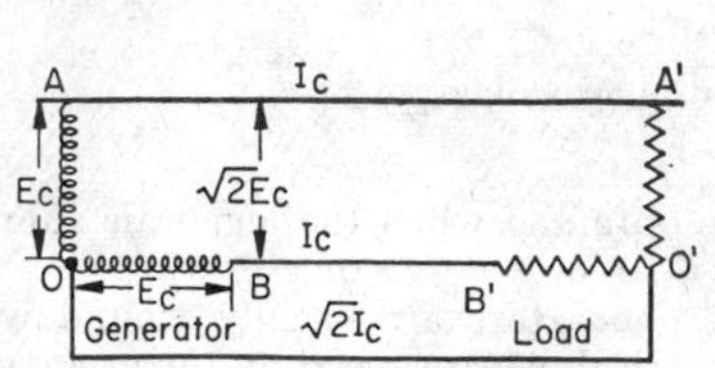

FIG. 31. Two-phase three-wire circuit.

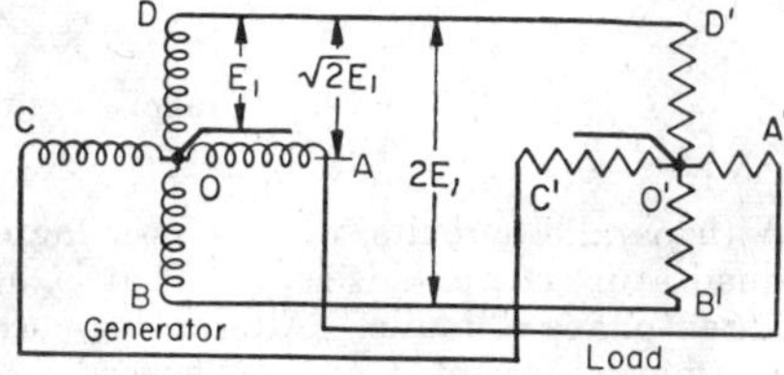

FIG. 32. Four-phase or quarter-phase circuit.

Four-phase Circuit. A four-phase or quarter-phase circuit is shown in Fig. 32. The windings AC and BD may be independent or connected at O. The voltages AC and BD are 90 deg apart as in two-phase circuits. If a neutral wire O-O' is added, three different voltages may be obtained. Let E_1 = voltage between O-A, O-B, O-C, O-D. Voltages between A-B, B-C, C-D, D-A $= \sqrt{2}\,E_1$. Voltages between A-C, B-D $= 2E_1$. Because of this multiplicity of voltages and the fact that polyphase power apparatus and lamps may be connected at the same time, this system is still used to some extent in distribution.

Advantages of Polyphase Power. The advantages of polyphase power over single-phase power are as follows: The output of synchronous generators and most other rotating machinery is from 60 to 90 percent greater when operated polyphase than when operated single phase; pulsating fluxes and corresponding iron losses which occur in many common types of machinery when operated single phase are negligible when operated polyphase; with balanced polyphase loads polyphase power is constant whereas with single phase the power fluctuates over wide limits during the cycle. Because of its minimum number of wires and the fact that it is not easily unbalanced, the three-phase system has for the most part superseded other polyphase systems. (See p. 15–61 for polyphase connections of transformers.)

ELECTRICAL INSTRUMENTS AND MEASUREMENTS

Electrical measuring devices that merely indicate, such as ammeters and voltmeters, are called **instruments**; devices that totalize with time such as watthour meters and ampere-hour meters are called **meters.** (See also Sec. 16.)

Direct-current Instruments. Direct current and voltage are both measured with an indicating instrument based on the principle of the D'Arsonval galvanometer. A coil with steel pivots and turning in jewel bearings is mounted in a magnetic field produced by permanent magnets. The motion is restrained by two small flat coiled springs which also serve to conduct the current to the coil. The deflections of the coil are read with a light aluminum pointer attached to the coil and moving over a graduated scale. The same instrument may be used for either current or voltage, but the method of connecting in circuit is different in the two cases. Usually, however, the coil of an instrument to be used as an ammeter is wound with fewer turns of coarser wire than an instrument to be used as a voltmeter and so has lower resistance. The instrument itself is frequently called a **millivoltmeter.** It cannot be used alone to measure voltage of any magnitude since its resistance is so low that it would be burned out if connected across the line. Hence a resistance r' in series with the coil is necessary as indicated in Fig. 33(*a*) in which r_c is the resistance of the coil. From 0.2 to 750 volts this resistance is usually within the instrument. For higher voltages an external resistance R called an extension coil or multiplier [Fig. 33(*b*)], is necessary. Let e be the reading of the instrument, in volts [Fig. 33(*b*)], r the internal resistance of the instrument, including r' and r_c in (*a*), R the resistance of the multiplier. Then the total voltage is

$$E = e(R + r)/r \qquad \textbf{(77)}$$

It is clear that by using suitable values of R a voltmeter may be made to have several scales.

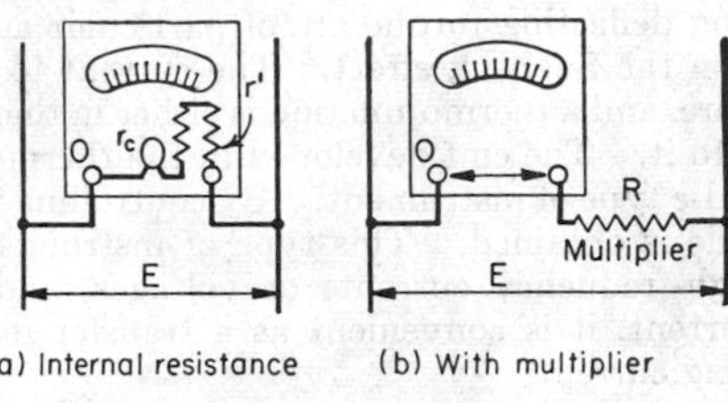

FIG. 33. Voltmeter.

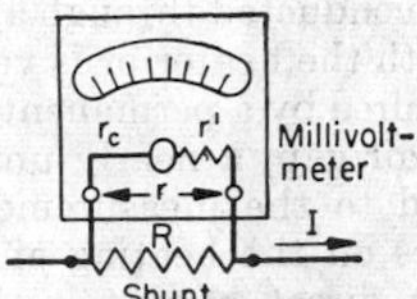

FIG. 34. Millivoltmeter with shunt.

Instruments themselves can only carry currents of the magnitudes of 0.01 to 0.06 amp. To measure larger values of current the instrument is provided with a shunt R (Fig. 34). The current divides inversely as the resistances r and R of the instrument and the shunt. A low resistance r' within the instrument is connected in series with the coil. This permits some adjustment to the deflection so that the instrument can be adapted to its shunt. Usually most of the current flows through the shunt, and the current in the instrument is negligible in comparison. Up to 50 and 75 amp the shunt may be incorporated within the instrument. For larger currents it is usually necessary to have the shunt external to the instrument and connect the instrument to the potential terminals of the shunt by means of leads. Any given instrument may have any number of ranges by providing it with a sufficient number of shunts. The range of the usual instrument of this type is approximately 50 millivolts. Although the same instrument may be used for voltmeter or ammeter, the moving coils of voltmeters are usually wound with more turns of finer wire. They take approximately 0.01 amp so that their resistance is approximately 100 ohms per volt. Instruments used as ammeters alone operate with 0.01 to 0.06 amp.

Permanent-magnet moving-coil instruments may be used to measure unidirectional pulsating currents or voltages and in such cases will indicate the average value of the periodically varying current or voltage.

Alternating-current Instruments. Instruments generally used for alternating currents may be divided into five types: **electrodynamometer, iron-vane, thermocouple, rectifier,** and **electronic.** Instruments of the **electrodynamometer** type, the most precise, operate on the principle of one coil carrying current, turning in the magnetic field produced by a second coil carrying current taken from the same circuit. If these circuits or coils are connected in series, the torque exerted on the moving system for a given relative position of the coil system is proportional to the square of the current and is not dependent on the direction of the current. Consequently, the instrument will have a compressed scale at the lower end and will usually have only the upper two-thirds of the scale range useful for accurate measurement. Instruments of this type ordinarily require 0.04 to 0.08 amp or more in the moving-coil circuit for full-scale deflection. They read the rms value of the alternating or pulsating current. The wattmeter operates on the electrodynamometer principle. The fixed coil, however, is energized by the current of the circuit, and the moving coil is connected across the potential in series with high resistance. Unless shielded magnetically the foregoing instruments will not, in general, indicate so accurately on d-c as on a-c because of the effects of external stray magnetic fields. Also reversed readings should be taken. **Iron-vane** instruments consist of a fixed coil which actuates magnetically a light movable iron vane mounted on a spindle; they are rugged, inexpensive, and may be had in ranges of 30 to 750 volts and 0.05 to 100 amp. They measure rms values and tend to have compressed scales as in the case of electrodynamometer instruments.

The compressed part of the scale may, however, be extended by changing the shape of the vanes. Such instruments operate with d-c and are accurate to within 1 percent or so. Alternating-current instruments of the **induction type** (Westinghouse Electric Corp.) must be used on a-c circuits of the frequency for which they have been designed. They are rugged and relatively inexpensive and are used principally for switchboards where a long-scale range and a strong deflecting torque are of particular advantage. **Thermocouple instruments** operate on the **Seebeck effect.** The current to be measured is conducted through a heater wire, and a thermojunction is either in thermal contact with the heater or is very close to it. The emf developed in the thermojunction is measured by a permanent-magnet d-c type of instrument. By controlling the shape of the air gap, a nearly uniform scale is obtained. This type of instrument is well adapted to the measurement of high-frequency currents or voltages, and since it operates on the heating effect of current, it is convenient as a transfer instrument between direct current and alternating current.

In the **rectifier-type instrument** the a-c voltage or current is rectified, usually by means of a small copper-oxide or a selenium-type rectifier, connected in a bridge circuit to give full-wave rectification (Fig. 35). The rectified current is measured with a d-c permanent-magnet-type instrument M. The instrument measures the **average** value of the half waves that have been rectified, and with the sine waves, the average value is 0.9 the rms value. The scale is calibrated to indicate rms values. With non-sinusoidal waves the ratio of average to rms may vary considerably from 0.9 so that the instrument may be in error up to ± 5 percent from this cause. This type of instrument is widely used in the measurement of high-frequency voltages and currents. **Electronic (vacuum-tube) voltmeters** operate on the principle of the amplification which can be obtained with a triode, or three-element vacuum tube. Since the emf to be measured is applied to the grid, the instruments take practically no current and hence are adapted to measure potential differences which would change radically were any appreciable current taken by the measuring device. This type of instrument can measure voltages from a few tenths of a volt to several hundred volts, and with a potential divider up to thousands of volts. They are also adapted to frequencies up to 100 megacycles per sec (mcps).

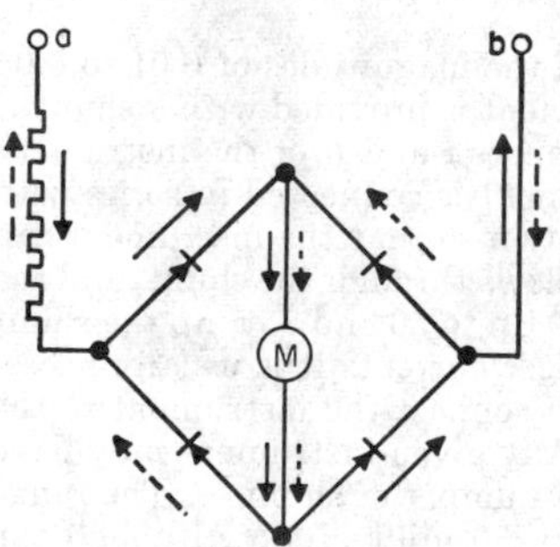

FIG. 35. Rectifier-type instrument.

Power Measurement in Single-phase Circuits. Wattmeters are not rated primarily in watts, but in amperes and volts. For example, with a low power factor the current and voltage coils may be overloaded and yet the needle be well on the scale. The current coil may be carrying several times its rated current, and yet the instrument reads zero because the potential circuit is not closed, etc. Hence it is desirable to use both an ammeter and a voltmeter in conjunction with a wattmeter when measuring power [Fig. 36(a)]. The instruments themselves consume appreciable power, and correction is often necessary unless these losses are negligible compared with the power being measured. For example, in Fig. 36(*a*), the wattmeter measures the I^2R loss in its own current coil and in the ammeter (1 to 2 watts each), as well as the loss in the voltmeter ($= E^2/R$ where R is the resistance of the voltmeter). The losses in the ammeter and voltmeter may be eliminated by short-circuiting the ammeter and disconnecting the voltmeter when reading the wattmeter. If the wattmeter is connected as shown in Fig. 36(*b*), it measures the power taken by its own potential coil (E^2/R_p) which at 110 volts is 5 to 7 watts. (R_p is the resistance of the potential circuit.) Frequently correction must be made for this power.

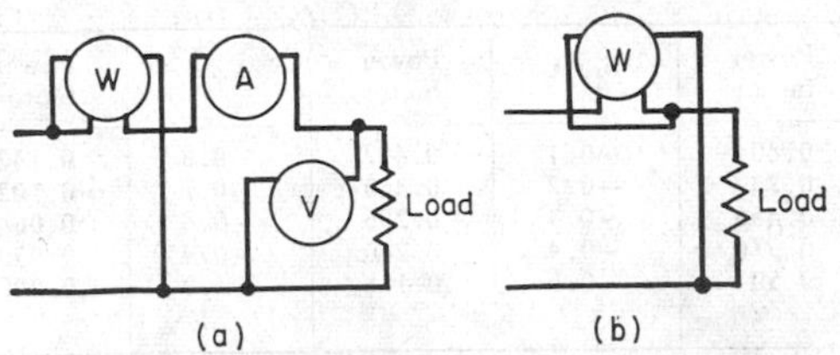

FIG. 36. Connections of instruments to single-phase load.

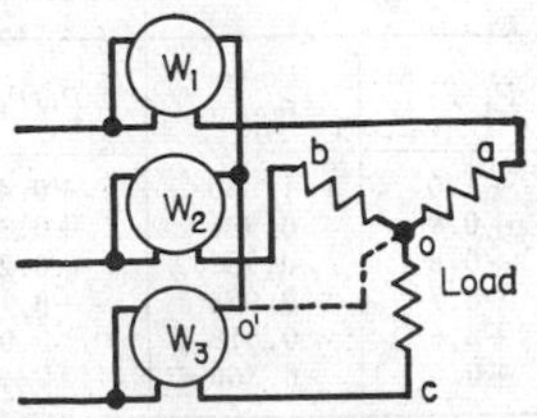

FIG. 37. Three-wattmeter method.

Power Measurement in Polyphase Circuits. Three-wattmeter Method. Let *ao*, *bo*, and *co* be any Y-connected three-phase load (Fig. 37). Three wattmeters with their current coils in each line and their potential circuits connected to neutral measure the total power, since the power in each load is measured by one of the wattmeters. The connection *oo'* may, however, be broken, and the total power is still the sum of the three readings; *i.e.*, the power $P = P_1 + P_2 + P_3$. This method is applicable to any system of n wires. The current coil of one wattmeter is connected in each of the n wires. The potential circuit of each wattmeter is connected between its own phase wire and a junction in common with all the other potential circuits. The wattmeters must be connected symmetrically, and the readings of any that read negative must be given the negative sign.

In the general case any system of n wires requires at least $n - 1$ wattmeters to measure the power correctly. The $n - 1$ wattmeters are connected in series with $n - 1$ wires. The potential circuit of each is connected between its own phase wire and the wire in which no wattmeter is connected. The application of this method to any four-wire system is shown in Fig. 38.

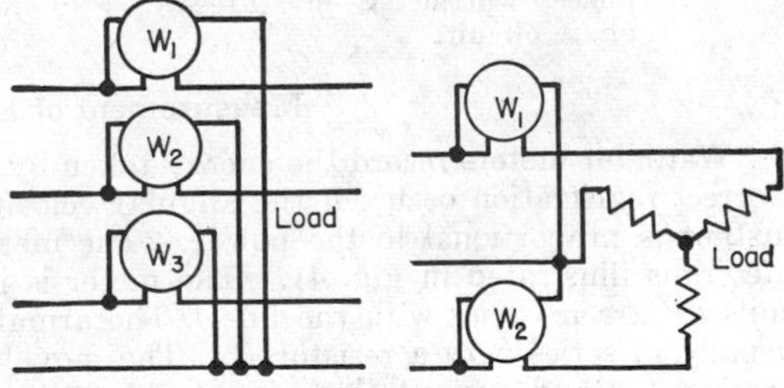

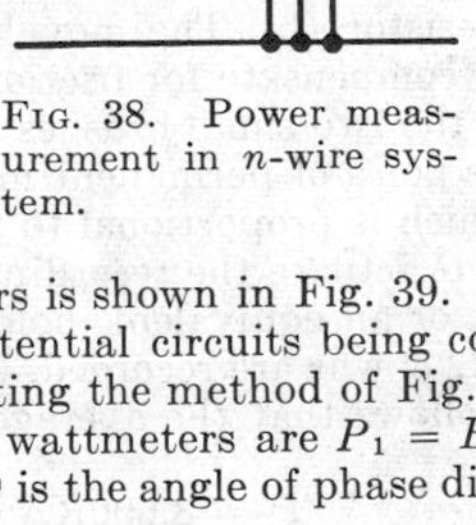

FIG. 38. Power measurement in n-wire system.

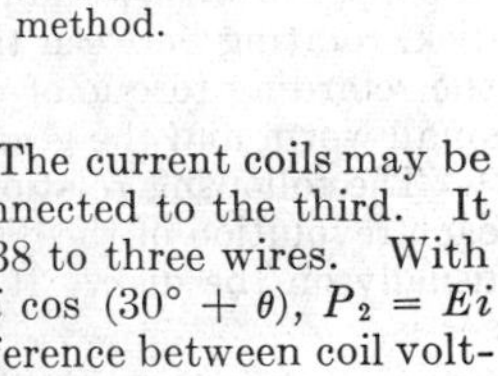

FIG. 39. Two-wattmeter method.

Three-phase Systems. The three-wattmeter method (Fig. 37) is applicable to any three-phase system. It is commonly used with the three-phase four-wire system. If the loads are balanced, $P_1 = P_2 = P_3$ and the power $P = 3P_1$.

The **two-wattmeter** method is most commonly used with three-phase three-wire systems. The method of connecting the wattmeters is shown in Fig. 39. The current coils may be connected in *any* two wires, the potential circuits being connected to the third. It will be recognized that this is adapting the method of Fig. 38 to three wires. With balanced loads the readings of the wattmeters are $P_1 = Ei \cos (30° + \theta)$, $P_2 = Ei \cos (30° - \theta)$, and $P = P_2 \pm P_1$. θ is the angle of phase difference between coil voltage and current. Since

$$P_1/P_2 = \cos (30° + \theta)/\cos (30° - \theta) \tag{78}$$

the power factor is a function of P_1/P_2. Table 9 gives values of power factor for different ratios of P_1/P_2.

$P = P_2 + P_1$ when $\theta < 60°$.

When $\theta = 60°$, pf $= \cos 60° = 0.5$, $P_1 = \cos (30° + 60°) = 0$, $P = P_2$. When $\theta > 60°$, pf < 0.5, $P = P_2 - P_1$. Also,

$$\tan \theta = \sqrt{3}\,(P_2 - P_1)/(P_2 + P_1) \tag{79}$$

Table 9. Ratio P_1/P_2 and Power Factor

P_1/P_2	Power factor	P_1/P_2	Power factor	P_1/P_2	Power factor	P_1/P_2	Power factor
+1.0	1.000	+0.4	0.804	−0.1	0.427	−0.6	0.142
+0.9	0.996	+0.3	0.732	−0.2	0.360	−0.7	0.102
+0.8	0.982	+0.2	0.656	−0.3	0.296	−0.8	0.064
+0.7	0.956	+0.1	0.576	−0.4	0.240	−0.9	0.030
+0.6	0.918	0.0	0.50	−0.5	0.188	−1.0	0.000
+0.5	0.866						

In a **polyphase wattmeter** the two single-phase wattmeter elements are combined to act on a single spindle. Hence the adding and subtracting of the individual readings are done automatically. The total power is indicated on one scale. This type of instrument is almost always used on switchboards. The connections of a portable type are shown in Fig. 40.

In the foregoing instrument connections, Y-connected loads are shown. These methods are equally applicable to delta-connected loads. The two-wattmeter method (Fig. 39) is obviously adapted to the two-phase three-wire system (Fig. 31).

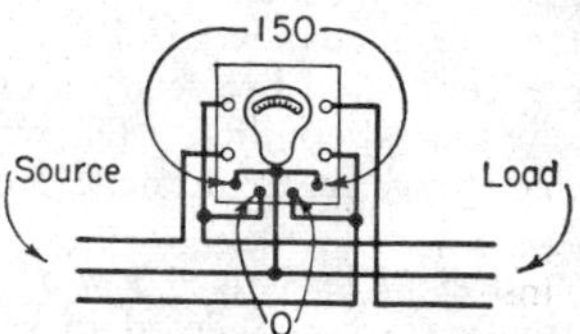

Fig. 40. Connection for polyphase wattmeter in three-phase circuit.

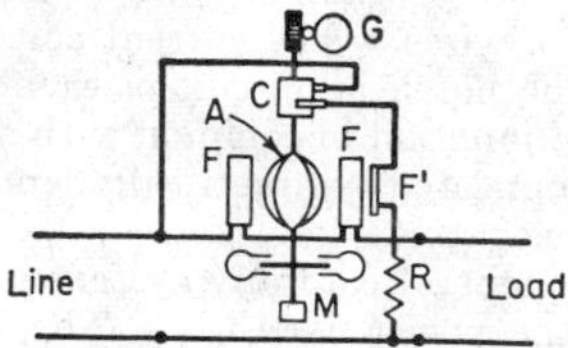

Fig. 41. Direct-current watthour meter.

Measurement of Energy

Watthour meters record the energy taken by a circuit over some interval of time. Correct registration occurs if the angular velocity of the rotating element at every instant is proportional to the power. The method of accomplishing this with d-c meters is illustrated in Fig. 41. The meter is in reality a small motor. The field coils FF are in series with the line. The armature A is connected across the line, usually in series with a resistor R. The movable field coil F' is in series with the armature A and serves to compensate for friction. C is a small commutator, either of copper or of silver, and the two small brushes are usually of silver. An aluminum disk, rotating between the poles of permanent magnets M, acts as a magnetic brake the retarding torque of which is proportional to the angular velocity of the disk. A small worm and the gears G actuate the recording dials.

The following relation, or an equivalent, holds with most types of meter. With each revolution of the disk, K whr are recorded, where K is the **meter constant** found usually on the disk. It follows that the average watts P over any period of time t sec is

$$P = 3{,}600KN/t \tag{80}$$

where N is the revolutions of the disk during that period. Hence, the meter may be calibrated by connecting standardized instruments to measure the average power taken by the load and by counting the revolutions N for t sec. Near full load, if the meter registers fast, the magnets M should be moved outward radially; if it registers slow, the magnets should be moved inwards. If the meter registers fast at light (5 to 10 percent) load, the starting coil F' should be moved further away from the armature; if it registers slow, F' should be moved nearer the armature. A meter should not register more than 1.5 percent fast or slow, and with calibrated standards it can be made to register to within 1 percent of correct.

The **induction watthour meter** is used with alternating current. Although the d-c meter registers correctly with alternating current, it is more expensive than the induction type, the commutator and brushes may cause trouble, and at low power factors compensation is necessary. In the induction watthour meter the driving torque is developed in the aluminum disk by the joint action of the alternating magnetic flux produced by the potential circuit and by the load current. The driving torque and the retarding torque are both developed in the same aluminum disk, hence no commutator and brushes are necessary. The rotating element is very light, and hence the friction torque is small. Equation (**80**) applies to this type of meter. When calibrating, the average power W for t sec is determined with a calibrated wattmeter. The friction compensation is made at light loads by changing the position of a small hollow stamping with respect to the potential lug. The meter should also be adjusted at low power factor (0.5 is customary). If the meter is slow with lagging current, resistance should be cut out of the compensating circuit; if slow with leading current, resistance should be inserted.

Power-factor Measurement. The usual method of determining power factor is by the use of voltmeter, ammeter, and wattmeter. The wattmeter gives the watts of the circuit, and the product of the voltmeter reading and the ammeter reading gives the volt-amperes. The power factor is the ratio of the two [see Eqs. (**64**) and (**75**)]. Also single-phase and three-phase power-factor indicators, which can be connected directly in circuit, are on the market.

Instrument Transformers

With voltages higher than 600 volts, and even at 600 volts, it becomes dangerous and inaccurate to connect instruments and meters directly into power lines. It is also difficult to make potential instruments for voltages in excess of 600 volts and ammeters in excess of 60-amp ratings. To insulate such instruments from high voltage and at the same time to permit the use of low-range instruments, instrument transformers are used. **Potential transformers** are identical with power transformers except that their volt-ampere rating is low, being 40 to 500 watts. Their primaries are wound for line voltage and their secondaries for 110 volts. **Current transformers** are designed to go in series with the line, and the rated secondary current is 5 amp. The secondary of a current transformer *should always be closed* when current is flowing; it should never be allowed to become open circuited under these conditions. When open circuited the voltage across the secondary becomes so high as to be dangerous and the flux becomes so large in magnitude that the transformer overheats. The secondaries of both potential and current transformers should be well grounded at one point (Figs. 42 and 43).

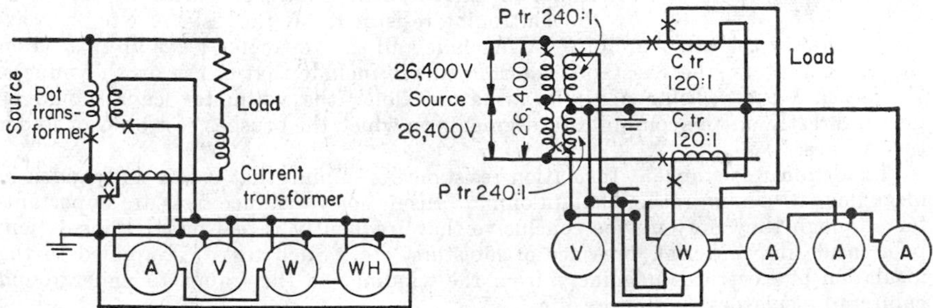

FIG. 42. Single-phase connections of instruments with transformers.

FIG. 43. Three-phase connections of instruments and instrument transformers.

Instrument transformers introduce slight errors because of small variations in their ratio with load. Also there is slight phase displacement in both current and potential transformers. The readings of the instruments must be multiplied by the instrument transformer ratios. The scales of switchboard instruments are usually calibrated to take these ratios into account.

Figure 42 shows the use of instrument transformers to measure the voltage, current, power, and kilowatt-hours of a single-phase load. Figure 43 shows the connections that would be used to measure the voltage, current, and power of a 26,400-volt, 600-amp three-phase load.

Measurement of High Voltages. Potential transformers such as those shown in Figs. 42 and 43 may be used even for very high voltages, but for voltages above 132 kv they become so large and expensive that they are used only sparingly. A convenient method used with testing transformers is the employment of a voltmeter coil, which consists of a coil of a few turns interwoven in the high-voltage winding and insulated from it. The voltage ratio is the ratio of the turns in the high-voltage winding to those in the voltmeter coil. A capacitance voltage divider consists of two or more capacitors connected in series across the high voltage to be measured. A high impedance voltmeter, such as an electronic one, is connected across the capacitor at the grounded end. The high voltage $V = V_m C_m / C$ volts, where V_m is the voltmeter reading, C the capacitance (in μf) of the entire divider, and C_m the equivalent capacitance (in μf) of the capacitor at the grounded end. A bushing potential device consists of a high-voltage-transformer bushing having a capacitance tap brought out from one of the metallic electrodes within the bushing which is near ground potential. This device is obviously a capacitance voltage divider. For testing, **sphere gaps** are used for the very high voltages. Calibration data for sphere gaps are given in the ASA standard C68.1, 1953, Measurement of Voltage in Dielectric Tests. Even when it is not being used for the measurement of voltage, it is frequently advisable to connect a sphere gap in parallel with the specimen being tested so as to prevent overvoltages. The gap is set to a slightly higher voltage than that which is desired.

Measurement of Resistance

Voltmeter-Ammeter Method. A common method of measuring resistance, known as the voltmeter-ammeter or fall-in-potential method, makes use of an ammeter and a voltmeter. In Fig. 44, the resistance to be measured is R. The current in the resistor R is I amp, which is measured by the ammeter A in series. The drop in potential across the resistor R is measured by the voltmeter V. The current shunted by the voltmeter is so small that it may generally be neglected. A correction may be applied if necessary, for the resistance of the voltmeter is generally given with the instrument. The potential difference divided by the current gives the resistance included between the voltmeter leads. As a check, determinations are generally made with several values of current, which may be varied by means of the controlling resistor r. If the resistance to be measured is that of the armature of a d-c machine and the voltmeter leads are placed on the brush holders, the resistance determined will include that of the brush contacts. To measure the resistance of the armature alone, the voltmeter leads should be placed directly on the commutator segments on which the brushes rest but not under the brushes.

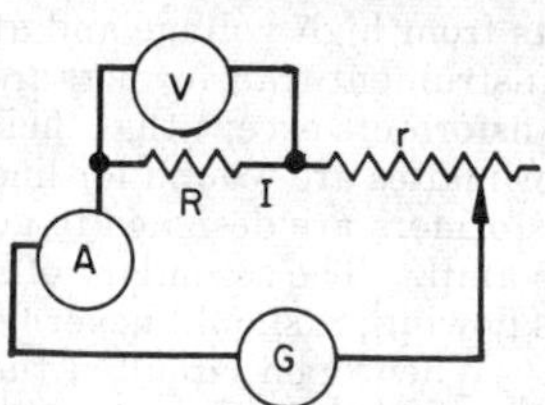

Fig. 44. Voltmeter-ammeter method for resistance measurement.

Insulation Resistance. Insulation resistance is so high that it is usually given in megohms (10^6 ohms) rather than in ohms. Insulation resistance tests are important, for although they may not be conclusive they frequently reveal flaws in insulation, poor insulating material, presence of moisture, etc. Such tests are applied to the insulation of electrical machinery from the windings to the frame, to underground cables, to insulators, capacitors, etc.

For moderately low resistances, 1 to 10 megohms, the voltmeter method given in

Fig. 45, which shows insulation measurement to the frame of the field winding of a generator, may be used. To measure the current when a voltage E is impressed across the resistor R, a high-reading voltmeter V is connected in series with R. The current under this condition with the switch connecting S and A is $E/(R + r)$, where r is the resistance of the voltmeter. A high-resistance voltmeter is necessary, since the method is in reality a comparison of the unknown insulation resistance R with the known resistance r of the voltmeter. Hence, the resistance of the voltmeter must be comparable with the unknown resistance, or the deflection of the instrument will be so small that the results will be inaccurate. To determine the impressed voltage E,

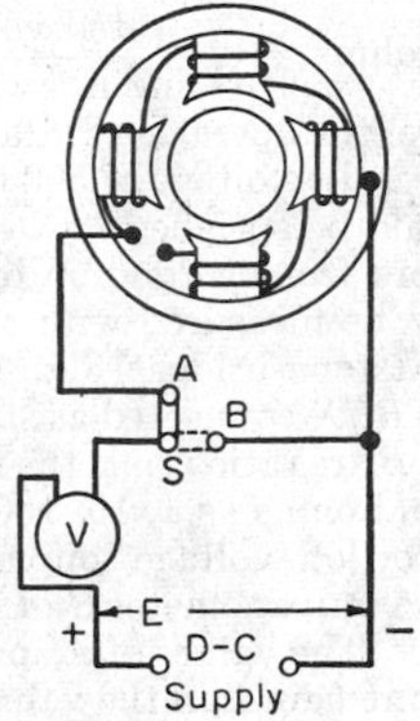

FIG. 45. Voltmeter method for insulation-resistance measurement.

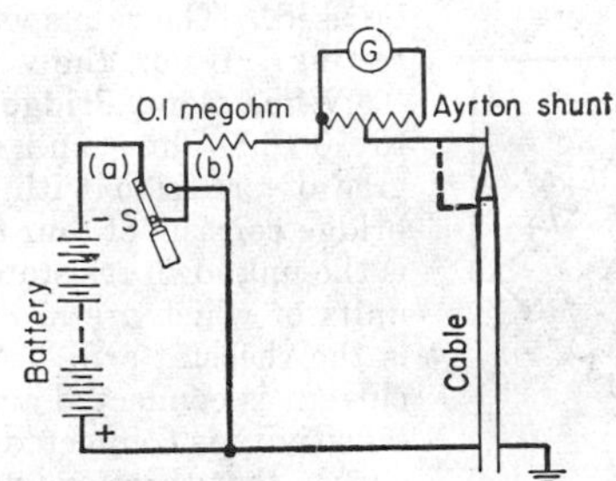

FIG. 46. Measurement of insulation resistance with galvanometer.

the same voltmeter is used. The switch S connects S and B for this purpose. With these two readings, the unknown resistance is

$$R = r(E - e)/e \tag{81}$$

where e is the deflection of the voltmeter when in series with the resistance to be measured as when S is at A. If a special voltmeter, having a resistance of 100,000 ohms per 150 volts, is available, a resistance of the order of 2 to 3 megohms may be measured very accurately.

When the insulation resistance is too high to be measured with a voltmeter, a sensitive galvanometer may be used. The connections for measuring the insulation resistance of a cable are shown in Fig. 46. The battery should have an emf of at least 100 volts. Radio B batteries are convenient for this purpose. The method involves comparing the unknown resistance with a standard 0.1 megohm. To calibrate the galvanometer the cable is short-circuited (dotted line) and the switch S is thrown to position (a). Let the galvanometer deflection be D_1 and the reading of the Ayrton shunt S_1. The short circuit is then removed. The 0.1 megohm is left in circuit since it is usually negligible in comparison with the unknown resistance X. Let the reading of the galvanometer now be D_2 and the reading of the shunt S_2. Then

$$X = 0.1\ S_2D_1/S_1D_2 \quad \text{megohms} \tag{82}$$

When the switch S is thrown to position (b), the cable is short-circuited through the 0.1 megohm and becomes discharged.

The **Megger** insulation tester is an instrument that indicates insulation resistance directly on a scale. It consists of a small hand-driven generator which generates approximately 500 volts and sometimes 1,000 volts. A clutch slips when the voltage exceeds the rated value. The current through the unknown resistance flows through a moving element consisting of two coils fastened rigidly together, but which move in different portions of the magnetic field. A pointer attached to the spindle of the moving element indicates the insulation resistance directly. These instruments have a range up to 2,000 megohms and are very convenient where portability and convenience are desirable.

The insulation resistance of electrical machinery may be of doubtful significance as far as dielectric strength is concerned. It varies widely with temperature, humidity, and cleanliness of the parts. When the insulation resistance falls below the prescribed value, it may, in most cases of good design, be brought to the required standard by cleaning and drying the machine. Hence it may be useful in determining whether or not the insulation is in proper condition for a dielectric test. The AIEE standards (5–451) specify minimum value of insulation resistance in megohms $= \dfrac{\text{rated voltage}}{\text{rating in kw} + 1{,}000}$. If the operating voltage is higher than the rated voltage, the operating voltage should be used. The rule specifies that a d-c voltage of 500 be used in testing. If not, the voltage should be specified.

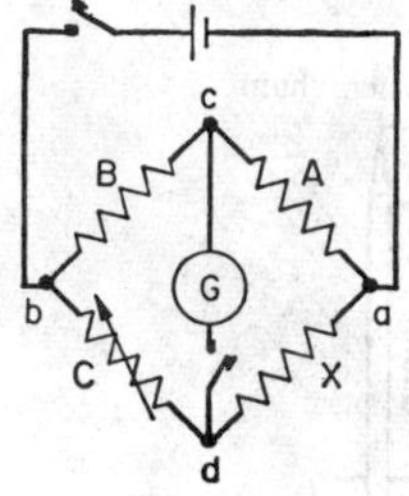

FIG. 47. Wheatstone bridge.

Wheatstone Bridge. Resistors from a fraction of an ohm to 100,000 ohms and more may be measured with a high degree of precision with the Wheatstone bridge (Fig. 47). The bridge consists of four resistors $ABCX$ connected as shown. X is the unknown resistance; A and B are ratio arms, the resistance units of which are in even decimal ohms as 1, 10, 100, etc. C is the rheostat arm. A battery or low-voltage source of direct current is connected across ab. A galvanometer G of moderate sensitivity is connected across cd. The values of A and B are so chosen that three or four significant figures in the value of C are obtained. As a first approximation it is well to make A and B equal. When the bridge is in balance,

$$X/C = A/B \tag{83}$$

The positions of the battery and galvanometer are interchangeable. There are many modifications of the bridge which adapt it to measurements of very low resistances and also to a-c measurements.

Kelvin Double Bridge. The simple Wheatstone bridge is not adapted to measuring very low resistances since the contact resistances of the test specimen become comparable with the specimen resistance. This error is avoided in the Kelvin double bridge, the diagram of which is shown in Fig. 48. The specimen X, which may be a short length of copper wire or bus bar, is connected in series with an adjustable calibrated resistor R whose resistance is comparable with that of the specimen. The arms A and B of the bridge are ratio arms usually with decimal values of 1, 10, 100 ohms. One terminal of the galvanometer is connected to X and R by means of two resistors a and b. If these resistors are set so that $a/b = A/B$, the contact resistance r between X and R is eliminated in the measurement. The contact resistances at c and d have no effect since at balance the galvanometer current is zero. The contact resistances at f and e need only be negligible compared with the resistances of arms A and B both of which are reasonably high. By means of the variable resistor Rh the value of current, as indicated by ammeter A, may be adjusted to give the necessary sensitivity. When the bridge is in balance,

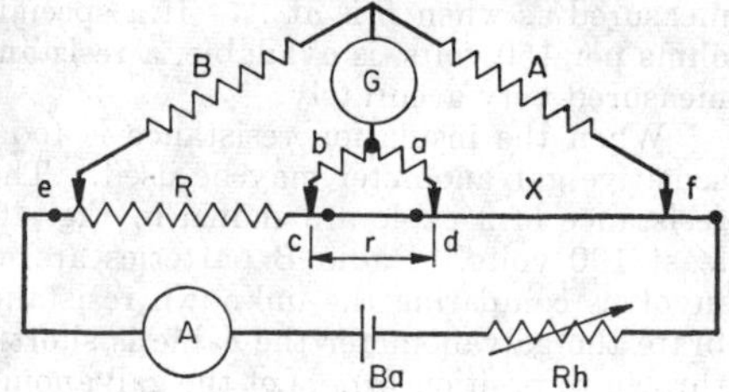

FIG. 48. Kelvin double bridge.

$$X/R = A/B \tag{84}$$

Potentiometer. The principle of the potentiometer is shown in Fig. 49. ab is a slide wire, and bc consists of a number of equal individual resistors between contacts.

A battery *Ba* the emf of which is approximately 2 volts supplies current to this wire through the adjustable rheostat *R*. A slider *m* makes contact with *ab*, and a contactor *m′* connects with the contacts in *bc*. A galvanometer *G* is in series with the wire connecting to *m*. By means of the double-throw double-pole switch *Sw*, either the standard cell or the unknown emf (*EMF*) may be connected to *mm′* through the galvanometer *G*. The potentiometer is standardized by throwing *Sw* to the standard-cell side, setting *mm′* so that their positions on *ab* and *bc* correspond to the emf of the standard cell. The rheostat *R* is then adjusted until *G* reads zero. (In commercial potentiometers a dial which may be set directly to the emf of the standard cell is usually provided.) The unknown emf is measured by throwing *Sw* to *EMF* and adjusting *m* and *m′* until *G* reads zero. The advantage of this method of measuring emf is that when the potentiometer is in balance no current is taken from either the standard cell or the source of emf. Potentiometers seldom exceed 1.6 volts in range. To measure voltage in excess of this, a *volt box* which acts as a multiplier is used. To measure current, the voltage drop across a standard resistor of suitable value is measured with the potentiometer. For example, with 50 amp a 0.01 ohm standard resistance gives a voltage drop of 0.5 volt which is well within the range of the potentiometer.

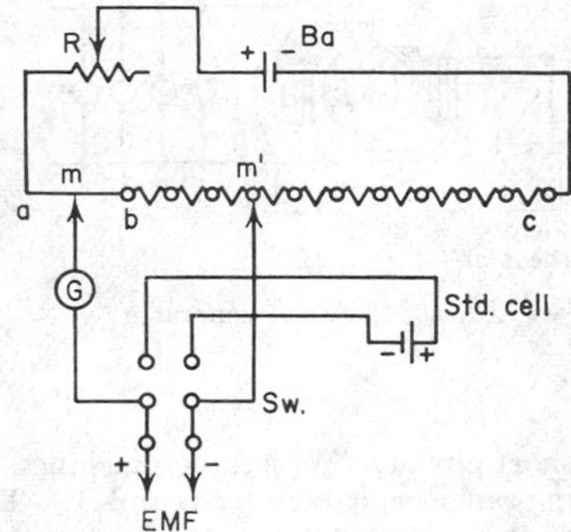

FIG. 49. Potentiometer principle.

Potentiometers of low range are used extensively with thermocouple pyrometers. Figure 49 merely illustrates the principle of the potentiometer. There are many modifications, conveniences, etc., not shown in Fig. 49.

DIRECT-CURRENT GENERATORS

All electrical machines are comprised of a magnetic circuit of iron (or steel) and an electric circuit of copper. In a generator the armature conductors are rotated so that they cut the magnetic flux coming from and entering the field poles. In the d-c generator (except the unipolar type) the emf induced in the individual conductors is alternating, but this is rectified by the commutator and brushes, so that the current to the external circuit is unidirectional.

The induced emf in a generator (or motor)

$$E = \phi ZNP/60P'10^8 \quad \text{volts} \tag{85}$$

where ϕ is the flux in maxwells entering the armature from one north pole; Z the total number of conductors on the armature; N the speed, rpm; P the number of poles; and P' the number of parallel paths through the armature.

In the mks system ϕ is in webers and 10^8 is omitted. Since with a given generator, Z, P, P' are fixed, the induced emf

$$E = K\phi N \quad \text{volts} \tag{86}$$

where K is a constant. When the armature delivers current, the terminal volts

$$V = E - I_aR_a \tag{87}$$

where I_a is the armature current and R_a the armature resistance including the brush and contact resistance, which vary somewhat.

There are three standard types of d-c generators: the **shunt generator,** the **series generator,** and the **compound generator.**

Shunt Generator. The field of the shunt generator in series with its rheostat is connected directly across the armature as shown in Fig. 50. This machine maintains approximately constant terminal voltage over its working range of load. An external characteristic of the generator is shown in Fig. 51. As load is applied the terminal voltage drops owing to the armature-resistance drop [Eq. (**87**)] and armature reaction which decreases the flux. The drop in terminal voltage reduces the field current which in turn reduces the flux, hence the induced emf, etc. At some point *B*, usually well above rated current, the foregoing reactions become cumulative and the generator commences to break down. The current reaches a maximum value and then decreases to nearly zero at short circuit. With large machines, point *B* is well above rated current, the operating range being between *O* and *A*. The voltage may be maintained constant by means of the field rheostat. Automatic regulators which operate through field resistance are frequently used to maintain constant voltage.

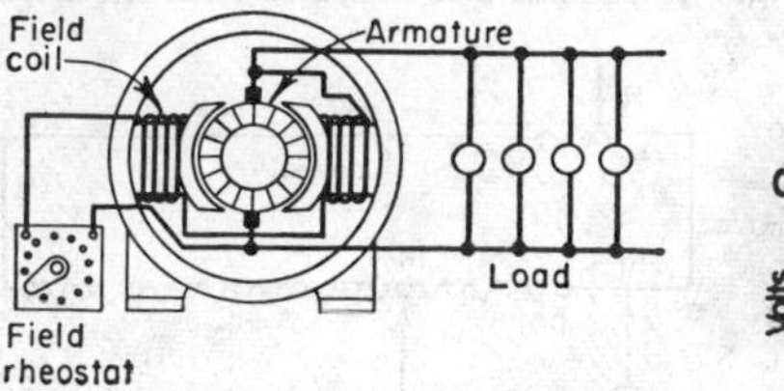

Fig. 50. Shunt generator.

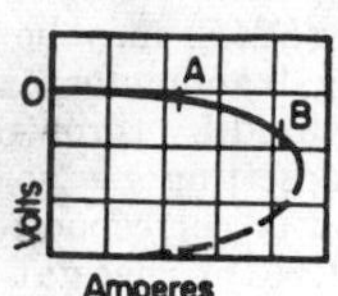

Fig. 51. Shunt-generator characteristic.

Shunt generators are commonly used in city substations which are all tied together through the network of feeders and mains. Their stability when in parallel is a distinct advantage for this service. If a generator fails to build up (1) the load may be connected; (2) the field resistance may be too high; (3) the field circuit may be open; (4) the residual magnetism may be insufficient; (5) the field connection may be reversed.

Series Generator. In the series generator (Fig. 52) the entire load current flows through the field winding, which consists of relatively few turns of wire of sufficient size to carry the entire load current without undue heating. The field excitation, and hence the terminal voltage, depends on the magnitude of the load current. The generator supplies an essentially constant current and for years was used to supply series arc lamps for street lighting requiring direct current. Except for some special applications, the series generator is now obsolete.

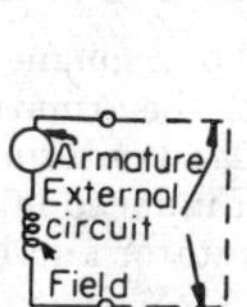

Fig. 52. Series generator.

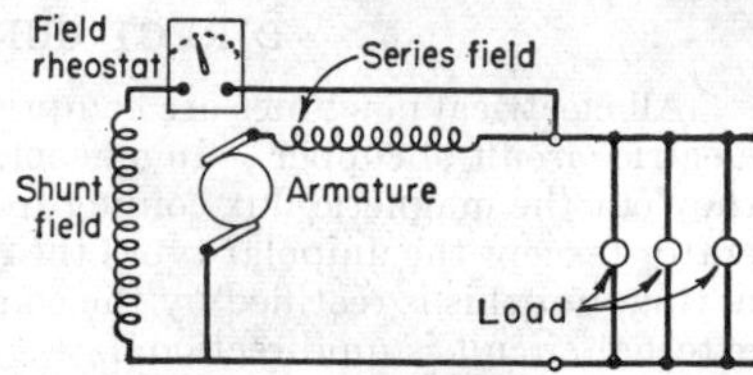

Fig. 53. Compound-wound d-c generator.

Compound-wound Generators (Fig. 53). By the addition of a series winding to a shunt generator the terminal voltage may be automatically maintained very nearly constant, or, by properly proportioning the series turns, the terminal voltage may be made to increase with load to compensate for loss of voltage in the line, so that approximately constant voltage is maintained at the load. If the shunt field is connected outside the series field (Fig. 53), the machine is **long shunt**; if the shunt field is connected inside the series field, *i.e.*, directly to the armature terminals, it is **short shunt.** So far as the operating characteristic is concerned, it makes little difference which way a machine is connected.

Compound-wound generators are chiefly used for small isolated plants and for generators supplying a purely motor load subject to rapid fluctuations such as in railway work. When first putting a compound generator in service, the shunt field must be so connected that the machine builds up. The series field is then connected so that it aids the shunt field. Figure 54 gives the characteristics of an overcompounded 200 kw 600 volt compound-wound generator.

Amplidynes. The amplidyne is a d-c generator in which a small amount of power supplied to a control field controls the generator output, the response being nearly proportional to the control field input. The amplidyne is a d-c amplifier which can supply large amounts of power. The amplifier operates on the principle of armature reaction. In Fig. 55, *NN* and *SS* are the conventional north and south poles of a d-c generator with central cavities. *BB* are the usual brushes placed at right angles to the pole axes

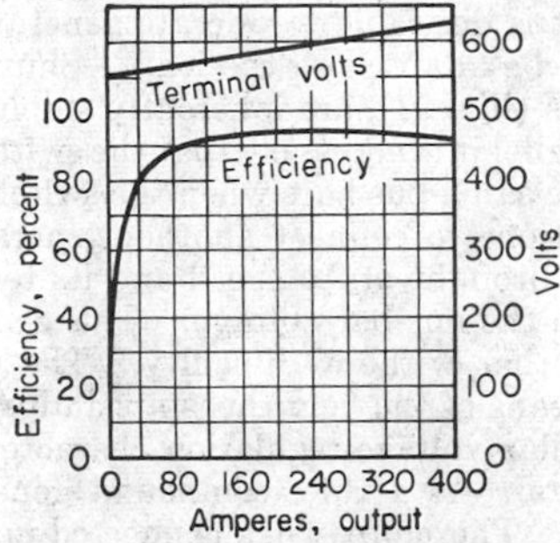

Fig. 54. Characteristics of a 200-kw compound-wound d-c generator.

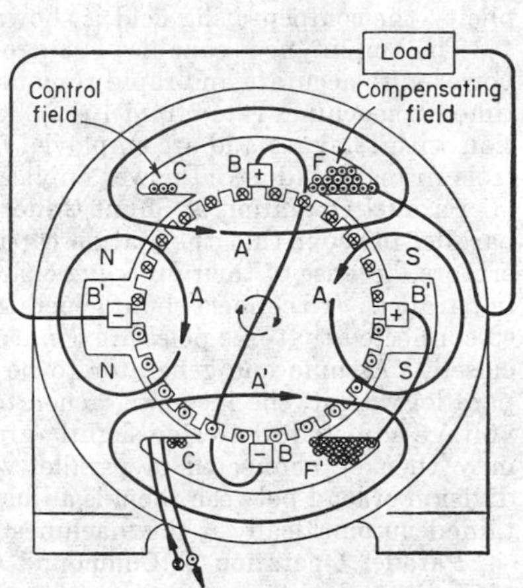

Fig. 55. Amplidyne.

of *NN* and *SS*. A control winding *CC* of small rating, as low as 100 watts, is wound on the field poles. In Fig. 55, for simplicity, the control winding is shown as being wound on one pole only. The brushes *BB* are short-circuited, so that a small excitation mmf in the control field produces a large short-circuit current along the brush axis *BB*. This large short-circuit current produces a large armature-reaction flux *AA* along brush axis *BB*. The armature rotating in this field produces a large voltage along the brush axis *B′B′*. The load or working current is taken from brushes *B′B′* as shown. In Fig. 55 the working current only is shown by the crosses and dots in the circles. The short-circuit current would be shown by crosses in the conductors to the left of brushes *BB* and by dots in the conductors to the right of brushes *BB*.

A small current in the control winding produces a high output voltage and current as a result of the large short-circuit current in brushes *BB*.

In order that the brushes *B′B′* shall not be short-circuiting conductors which are cutting the flux of poles *NN* and *SS*, cavities are cut in these poles. Also the load current from brushes *B′B′* produces an armature reaction mmf in opposition to flux *A′A′*

Table 10. Approximate Test Performance of Compound-wound D-C Generators with Commutating Poles

(Westinghouse Electric Corp.)

Kw	Rpm	Volts	Amp	Efficiencies, percent		
				¼ load	½ load	Full load
5	1,750	125	40	77.0	80.5	82.0
10	1,750	125	80	80.0	83.0	85.0
25	1,750	125	200	84.0	86.5	88.0
50	1,750	125	400	83.0	86.0	88.0
100	1,750	125	800	87.0	88.5	90.0
200	1,750	125	1,600	88.0	90.5	91.0
400	1,750	250	1,600	91.7	91.9	91.7
1,000	1,750	250	4,000	92.1	92.6	92.1

produced by the control field CC. Were this mmf not compensated, the flux $A'A'$ and the output of the machine would no longer be determined entirely by the control field. Hence there is a compensating field FF' in series with the armature, which neutralizes the armature-reaction mmf which the load current produces. For simplicity the compensating field is shown on one field pole only.

The amplidyne is capable of controlling and regulating speed, voltage, current, and power with accurate and rapid response. The amplification is from 10,000 to 250,000 times in machines rated from 1 to 50 kw. Amplidynes are frequently used in connection with **selsynes** and are employed for gun and turret control and for accurate controls in many industrial power applications.

Parallel Operation of Shunt Generators. It is desirable to operate generators in parallel in order that the station capacity may be adapted to the load. Shunt generators, because of their drooping characteristics (Fig. 51), are inherently stable when in parallel. To connect shunt generators in parallel it is necessary that the switches be so connected that like poles are connected to the same bus bars when the switches are closed. Assume one generator to be in operation; to connect another generator in parallel with it, the incoming generator is first brought up to speed and its terminal voltage adjusted to a value slightly greater than the bus-bar voltage. This generator may then be connected in parallel with the other without difficulty. The proper division of load between them is adjusted by means of the field rheostats and is maintained automatically if the machines have similar voltage-regulation characteristics.

Parallel Operation of Compound Generators. As a rule, compound generators have either flat or rising voltage characteristics. Therefore, when connected in parallel, they are inherently unstable. Stability may, however, be obtained by using an equalizer connection, Fig. 56, which connects the terminals of the generator at the junctions of the series fields. This connection is of low resistance so that any increase of current divides proportionately between the series fields of the two machines. The equalizer switch (E.S.) should be closed first and opened last, if possible. In practice, the equalizer switch is often one blade of a three-pole switch, the other two being the bus switch S, as in Fig. 56. When compound generators are used on a three-wire system, two series fields—one at each armature terminal—and two equalizers are necessary. It is possible to operate any number of compound generators in parallel provided their characteristics are not too different and the equalizer connection is used.

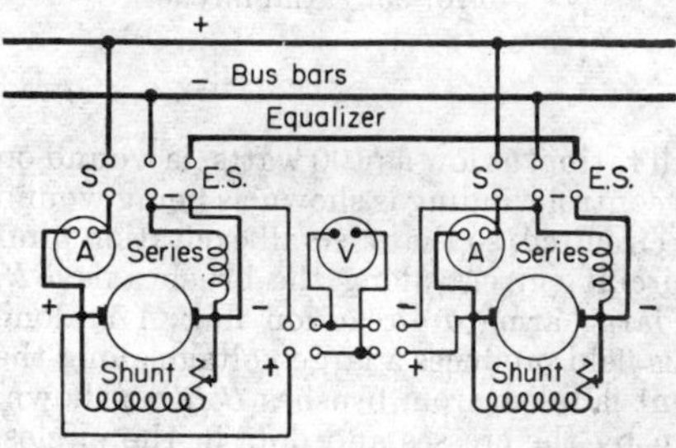

Fig. 56. Connections for compound-wound generators operating in parallel.

DIRECT-CURRENT MOTORS

Motors operate on the principle that a conductor carrying current in a magnetic field tends to move at right angles to that field (see Fig. 17). The ordinary d-c generator will operate entirely satisfactorily as a motor and will have the same rating. The conductors of the motor rotate in a magnetic field and therefore must generate an emf just as does the generator. The induced emf

$$E = K\phi N \tag{88}$$

where K is a constant ϕ the flux entering the armature from one north pole, and N the speed in rpm [see Eq. (**86**), p. 15–43]. This emf is in opposition to the terminal voltage and tends to oppose current entering the armature. Its value is

$$E = V - I_aR_a \tag{89}$$

where V is the terminal voltage, I_a the armature current, and R_a the armature resistance [compare with Eq. (**87**)]. From Eq. (**88**) it is seen that the speed

$$N = K_sE/\phi \tag{90}$$

when $K_s = 1/K$. This is the fundamental speed equation for a motor. By substituting in Eq. (**89**)

$$N = K_s(V - I_aR_a)/\phi \tag{91}$$

which is the general equation for the speed of a motor.

The internal or electromagnetic torque developed by an armature is proportional to the flux and to the armature current; *i.e.*,

$$T_t = K_t\phi I_a \tag{92}$$

when K_t is a constant. The torque at the pulley is slightly less than the internal torque by the torque necessary to overcome the rotational losses, such as friction, windage, eddy-current and hysteresis losses in the armature iron and in the pole faces.

The total mechanical power developed internally

$$P_m = EI_a \quad \text{watts} \quad = \quad EI_a/746 \quad \text{hp} \tag{93}$$

The internal torque thus becomes

$$T = EI_a 33{,}000/(2\pi \times 746N) = 7.04EI_a/N \tag{94}$$

Let VI be the motor input. The output is $VI\eta$ where η is the efficiency. The horsepower

$$P_H = VI\eta/746 \tag{95}$$

and the torque

$$T = 33{,}000P_H/2\pi N = 5{,}260P_H/N \quad \text{lb-ft} \tag{96}$$

where N is rpm.

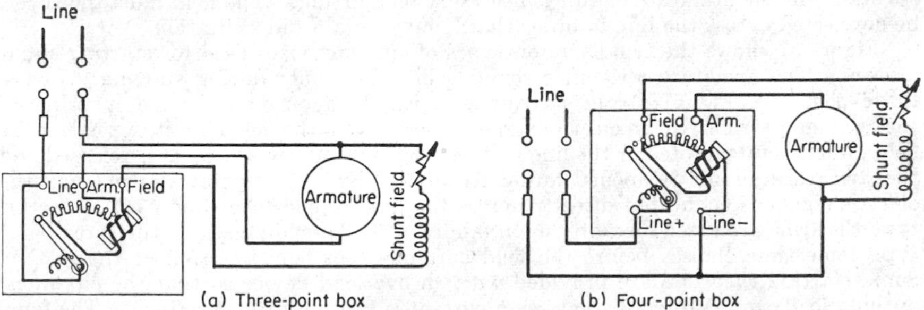

FIG. 57. Connections for shunt d-c motors and starters.

Shunt Motor. In the shunt motor (Fig. 57) the flux is substantially constant and I_aR_a is 2 to 6 percent of V. Hence from Eq. (**91**), the speed varies only slightly with load (Fig. 58), so that the motor is adapted to work requiring constant speed. The speed regulation of constant-speed motors is defined by the American Definitions of Electrical Terms C 42.10 (1957) as follows:

The speed regulation of a constant-speed direct-current motor is the change in speed when the load is reduced grad-

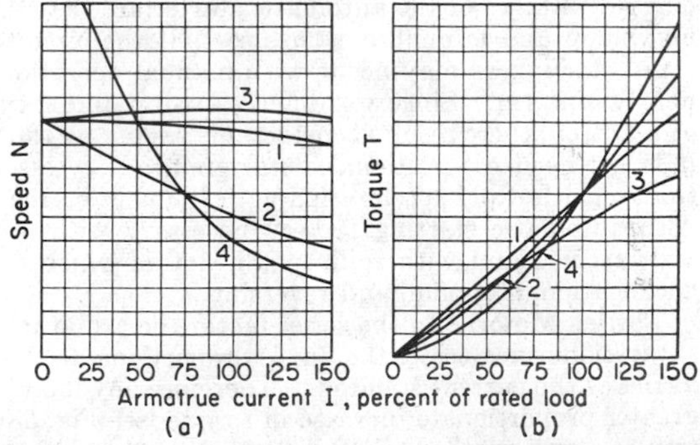

FIG. 58. Speed and torque characteristics of d-c motors. (1) Shunt motor. (2) Compound motor. (3) Differential compound motor. (4) Series motor.

ually from the rated value to zero with constant applied voltage and field rheostat setting expressed as a percent of speed at rated load.

In Fig. 61 the speed regulation under each condition is $100(ac - bc)/bc$ [see Fig. 58(a)]. Also from Eq. (**92**) it is seen that the torque is practically proportional to the armature current [see Fig. 58(b)]. The motor is able to develop full-load torque and more on starting, but the ordinary starter is not designed to carry the current necessary for starting under load. If a motor is to be started under load, the starter should be provided with resistors adapted to carry the required current without overheating. A controller is also adapted for starting duty under load.

Commutating poles have so improved commutation in d-c machines that it is possible to use a much shorter air gap than formerly. Since, with the shorter air gap, less field ampere-turns are required, the armature becomes magnetically strong with respect to the field. Hence, a sudden overload might weaken the field through armature reaction, thus causing an increase in speed; the effect may become cumulative and the motor run away. To prevent this, modern shunt motors are usually provided with a **stabilizing winding,** consisting of a few turns of the field in series with the armature and aiding the shunt field. The resulting increase of field ampere-turns with load will more than compensate for any weakening of the field through armature reaction. The series turns are so few that they have no appreciable compounding effect. The shunt motor is used to drive constant-speed line shafting, for machine tools, etc. Since its speed may be efficiently varied, it is very useful when **adjustable speeds** are necessary, such as individual drive for machine tools.

Shunt-motor Starters. At standstill the counter emf of the motor is zero and the armature resistance is very low. Hence, except in motors of very small size, series resistance in the armature circuit is necessary on starting. The field must, however, be connected across the line in order that it may obtain full excitation.

Figure 57 shows the two common types of starting boxes used for starting shunt motors. The armature resistance remains in circuit only during starting. In the **three-point box** [Fig. 57(a)] the starting lever is held, against the force of a spring, in the running position, by an electromagnet in series with the field circuit, so that, if the field circuit is interrupted or the line voltage becomes too low, the lever is released and the armature circuit is opened automatically. In the **four-point starting box** the electromagnet is connected directly across the line, as shown in Fig. 57(b). In this type the arm is released instantly upon failure of the line voltage. In the three-point type some time elapses before the field current drops enough to effect the release. Some starting rheostats are provided with an overload device so that the circuit is automatically interrupted if too large a current is taken by the armature. The four-point box is used where a wide speed range is obtained by means of the field rheostat. The electromagnet is not then affected by changes in field current.

In large motors and in many small motors, automatic starters are widely used. The advantages of the automatic starter are that the current is held between certain maximum and minimum values so that the circuit does not become opened by too rapid starting as may occur with manual operation; the acceleration is smooth and nearly uniform. Since workmen can stop and start a motor merely by the pushing of a button, there results considerable saving by the shutting down of the motor when it is not needed. Automatic starters are very essential to elevator motors in order that smooth rapid acceleration with frequent starting and stopping may be obtained. Also automatic starting is very necessary with multiple-unit operation of electric-railway cars and with rolling-mill motors which are continually subjected to rapid acceleration, stopping, and reversing.

Series Motor. In the series motor the armature and field are in series. Hence, if saturation is neglected, the flux is proportional to the current and the torque [Eq. (**92**)] varies as the current squared. Therefore any increase in current will produce a much greater proportionate increase in torque [see Fig. 58(b)]. This makes the motor particularly well adapted to traction work, cranes, hoists, elevator service, and other types of work which require large starting torques. A study of Eq. (**91**) shows that with increase in current the numerator changes only slightly, whereas the change in the denominator is nearly proportional to the change in current. Hence the speed of the series motor is practically inversely proportional to the current. With overloads the speed drops to very low values [see Fig. 58(*a*)]. With decrease in load the speed approaches infinity, theoretically. Hence the series motor should always be connected to its load by a direct drive, such as gears, so that it cannot reach unsafe speeds (see Speed Control of Motors, p. 15-50). A series-motor starting box with no-voltage release is shown in Fig. 59.

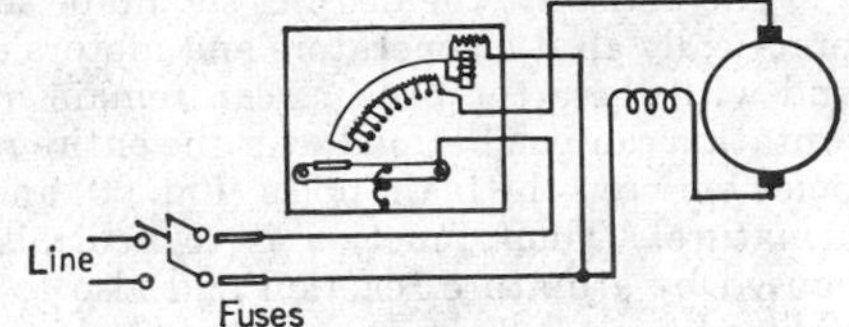

FIG. 59. Series-motor starter, no-voltage release.

Differential Compound Motors. The cumulative compound winding of a generator becomes a differential compound winding when the machine is used as a motor. Its speed may be made more nearly constant than that of a shunt motor, or, if desired, it may be adjusted to increase with increasing load.

The speed as a function of armature current is shown in Fig. 58(*a*) and the torque as a function of armature current is shown in Fig. 58(*b*).

Since the speed of the shunt motor is sufficiently constant for most purposes and the differential motor tends toward instability, particularly in starting and on overloads, the differential motor is little used.

Cumulative compound motors develop a more rapid increase in torque with load than shunt motors [Fig. 58(*b*)]; on the other hand, they have much poorer speed regulation [Fig. 58(*a*)]. Hence they are used where larger starting torque than that developed by the shunt motor is necessary, as for example with elevators. They are particularly useful where large and intermittent increases of torque occur as in drives for shears, punches, rolling mills, etc. In addition to the sudden increase in torque which the motor develops with sudden applications of load, the fact that it slows down rapidly and hence causes the rotating parts to give up some of their kinetic energy is another important advantage in that it reduces the peaks on the power plant. Performance data for compound motors are given in Tables 11 and 22.

Commutation. The brushes on the commutator of either a motor or generator should be set in such a position that the induced emf in the armature coils undergoing commutation, and hence short-circuited by the brushes, is zero. In practice, this condition can at best be only approximately realized. Frequently conditions are such that it is far from being realized. At no load, the brushes should be set in a position corresponding to the geometrical neutral of the machine, for under these conditions the induced emf in the coils short-circuited by the brushes is zero. As load is applied, two factors cause sparking under the brushes. The mmf of the armature, or **armature reaction,** distorts the flux; when the current in the coils undergoing commutation reverses, an emf of self-induction $-L\,di/dt$ tends to prolong the current flow which produces sparking. In a generator, armature reaction distorts the flux in the direction of rotation and the brushes should be advanced. In order to neutralize the emf of self-induction the brushes should be set a little ahead of the neutral plane so that the emf

Table 11. Test Performance of Compound-wound D-C Motors

(Westinghouse Electric Corp.)

Hp	Rpm	115 volts		230 volts		550 volts	
		Amp	Full-load eff, percent	Amp	Full-load eff, percent	Amp	Full-load eff, percent
1	1,750	8.4	78	4.3	79	1.86	73.0
2	1,750	16.0	80	8.0	81	3.21	82.0
5	1,750	40.0	82	20.0	83	8.40	81.0
10	1,750	75.0	85.6	37.5	85	15.4	86.5
25	1,750	182.0	87.3	91.7	87.5	38.1	88.5
50	850	.....	....	180.0	89	73.1	90.0
100	850	.....	....	350.0	90.5	149.0	91.0
200	1,750	.....	....	700.0	91	295.0	92.0

induced in the short-circuited coils by the cutting of the flux at the fringe of the next pole is opposite to this emf of self-induction. In a motor the brushes are correspondingly moved backward in the direction opposite rotation.

Theoretically, the brushes should be shifted with every change in load. However, practically all d-c generators and motors now have **commutating poles** (or **interpoles**) and with these the brushes can remain in the no-load neutral plane, and good commutation can be obtained over the entire range of load. Commutating poles are small poles between the main poles (Fig. 60) and are excited by a winding in series with the armature. Their function is to neutralize the flux distortion in the *neutral plane* caused by armature reaction and also to supply a flux that will cause an emf to be induced in the conductors undergoing commutation, opposite and equal to the emf of self-induction. Since armature reaction and the emf of self-induction are both proportional to the armature current, saturation being neglected, they are neutralized theoretically at every load. Commutating poles have made possible d-c generators and motors of very much higher voltage, greater speeds, and larger kw ratings than would otherwise be possible.

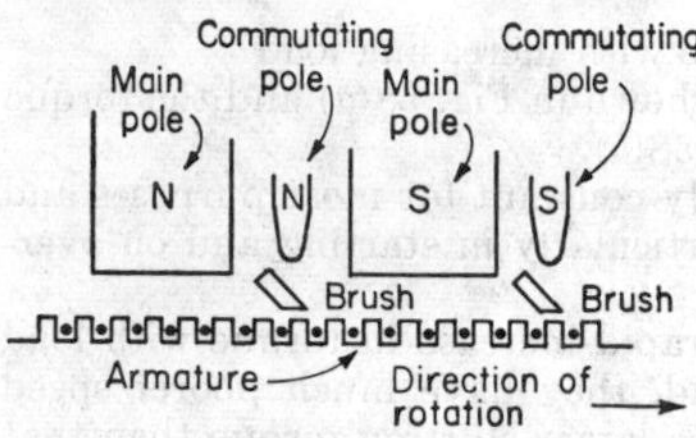

FIG. 60. Commutating poles in motor.

Occasionally, the commutating poles may be connected incorrectly. In a motor, passing from an N main pole in the direction of rotation of the armature, an N commutating pole should be encountered as shown in Fig. 60. In a generator under these conditions an S commutating pole should be encountered. The test may be easily made with a compass. If poor commutation is caused by too strong interpoles, the winding may be shunted. If the poles are too weak and the shunting cannot be reduced, they may be strengthened by inserting sheet-iron shims between the pole and the yoke thus reducing the air gap.

Although the emfs induced in the coils undergoing commutation are relatively small, the resistance of the coils themselves is low so that unless further resistance is introduced, the short-circuit currents would be large. Hence, with the exception of certain low-voltage generators, carbon brushes that have relatively large contact resistance are almost always used. Moreover, the graphite in the brushes has a lubricating action, and the usual carbon brush does not score the commutator.

Speed Control of Motors

Shunt Motors. In Eq. (**90**) the speed of a shunt motor $N = K_sE/\phi$, where K_s is a constant involving the design of the motor such as conductors on armature surface and number of poles. Obviously, in order to change the speed of a motor, without changing its construction, two factors may be varied, the counter emf E and the flux ϕ.

Armature-resistance Control. The counter emf $E = V - I_aR_a$ where V is the terminal voltage, assumed constant. R_a must be small in order that the armature heating may be maintained within permissible limits. Under these conditions the speed change with load is small. By inserting an external resistor, however, into the armature circuit the counter emf E may be made to decrease rapidly with increase in load; *i.e.*, $E = V - I_a(R_a + R)$ [see Eq. (**89**)] where R is the resistance of the external resistor. The resistor R must be inserted in the *armature* circuit only. The advantages of this method are its simplicity, the full torque of the motor is developed at any speed, and the method introduces no commutating difficulties. Its disadvantages are the very poor speed regulation with change of load (Fig. 61), the low efficiency, particularly at the lower speeds, and the fact that provision must be made to dissipate the comparatively large power losses in the series resistor. Figure 61 shows typical speed-load curves

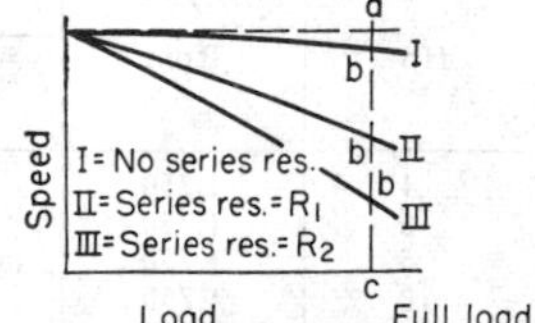

FIG. 61. Speed-load characteristics with armature-resistance control.

without and with series resistors in the armature circuit. The armature efficiency is nearly equal to the ratio of the operating speed to the no-load speed. Hence at 25 percent speed the armature efficiency is practically 25 percent. Frequently the controlling and starting resistors are one, and the device is called a **controller.** Starting rheostats themselves are not designed to carry the armature current continuously and must not be used as controllers. The armature-resistance method of speed control is frequently used to regulate the speed of ventilating fans where the power demand diminishes rapidly with decrease in speed.

Control by Changing Impressed Voltage. From Eq. (**91**) it is evident that the speed of a motor may be changed if V is changed by connecting the armature across different voltages. Speed control by this method is accomplished by having mains (usually four), which are maintained at different voltages, available at the motor.

The shunt field of the motor is generally permanently connected to one pair of mains, and the armature circuit is provided with a controller by means of which the operator can readily connect the armature to any pair of mains. Such a system gives a series of distinct and widely separated speeds and generally necessitates the use of field-resistance control, in combination, to obtain intermediate speeds. This method, known as the **multivoltage method,** has the disadvantage that the system is expensive, for it requires several generating machines, a somewhat complicated switchboard, and a number of service wires. The system is used somewhat in machine shops and is extensively used for d-c elevator starting and speed control.

In the **Ward Leonard system,** the variable voltage is obtained from a separately excited generator whose armature terminals are connected directly to the armature terminals of the working motor. The generator is driven at essentially constant speed by a d-c shunt motor if the power supply is direct current, or by an induction motor or a synchronous motor if the power supply is alternating current. The field circuit of the generator and that of the motor are connected across a constant-voltage d-c supply. The terminal voltage of the generator, and hence the voltage applied to the armature of the motor, is varied by changing the generator-field current with a field rheostat. The rheostat has a wide range of resistance so that the speed of the motor may be varied smoothly from 0 to 100 percent. Since three machines are involved the system is costly, somewhat complicated, and has low power efficiency. However, because the system is flexible and the speed may be smoothly varied over wide ranges, it is used in many applications, such as elevators, mine hoists, large printing presses, paper machines, and electric locomotives.

The **Ilgner system** is quite similar to the Ward Leonard system, except that a heavy flywheel is provided for the a-c motor–d-c generator set and the a-c motor is a wound-rotor induction motor with external variable resistance in the rotor circuit. As in the Ward Leonard system, the armature of the work motor is connected directly to the armature of the d-c generator and the field of each machine is excited from a d-c source, usually provided by a small a-c motor–d-c generator set. The system is particularly designed for sharply varying loads at widely varying speeds, such as for mine hoists and reversible rolling mills. For example, when the motor begins a hoisting operation, the field of the generator is strengthened and much of the power demanded by the motor comes from the kinetic energy stored in the flywheel, whose speed then drops only a few percent. During the descent the motor will accelerate the flywheel and frequently, through regeneration, will restore energy to it. Automatic insertion of resistance in the rotor circuit controls the rate and extent of the delivery of the kinetic energy of the flywheel.

Control by Changing Field Flux. Equation (**90**) shows that the speed of a motor is inversely proportional to the flux ϕ. The flux can be changed either by varying the shunt-field current or by varying the reluctance of the magnetic circuit. The variation of the **shunt-field current** is the simplest and most efficient of all the methods of speed control.

With the ordinary motor, speed variation of 1.5 to 1.0 is obtainable with this method. If attempt is made to obtain greater ratios, severe sparking at the brushes results, owing to the field distortion caused by the armature mmf becoming large in comparison with the weakened field of the motor. Speed ratios of 5:1 and higher are, however, obtainable with motors having commutating poles (see p. 15–48). Since the field current is a small proportion of the total current (1 to 3 percent), the rheostat losses in the field circuit are always small. This method is efficient. Also for any given speed adjustment the speed regulation is excellent, which is another advantage. Because of its simplicity, efficiency, and excellent speed regulation, the control of speed by means of the field current is by far the most common method.

Speed Control of Series Motors. The series motor is fundamentally a variable-speed motor, the speed varying widely from light load to full load and more [see Fig. 58(*a*) and p. 15–48]. From Eq. (**91**) the speed for any value of ϕ, or current, may be changed by varying the impressed voltage. Hence the speed may be controlled by inserting resistance in series with the motor. This method, which is practically the same as the armature-resistance control method for shunt motors, has the same objections of low efficiency and poor regulation with fluctuating loads. It is extensively used in controlling the speed of hoist and crane motors.

The **series-parallel** system of series-motor speed control is almost universally used in electric traction. At least two motors are necessary. The two motors are first connected in series with each other and with the starting resistor. The starting resistor is gradually cut out and, since each motor then operates at half line voltage, the speed of each is approximately half speed. Both motors take the same current, and each can develop full torque. This condition of operation is efficient since there is no external resistance in circuit. When the controller is moved to the next position, the motors are connected in parallel with each other and each in series with starting resistors. Full speed of the motors is obtained by gradually cutting out these resistors. Connecting the two motors in series on starting reduces the current to one-half the value that would be required for a given torque were both motors connected in parallel on starting. The power taken from the trolley is halved, and an intermediate running speed is efficiently obtained.

In the **multiple-unit** method of speed control which is used for electric railway trains, the starting contactors, reverser, etc., for each car are located under that car. The relays operating these control devices are actuated by energy taken from the train line consisting usually of seven wires. The train line runs the entire length of the train, the connections between the individual cars being made through the couplers. The train line is energized by the action of the motorman operating any one of the small master controllers which are located in each car. Hence corresponding relays, contactors, etc., in every car all operate simultaneously. High accelerations may be reached with this system because of the large tractive effort exerted by the wheels on every car.

SYNCHRONOUS GENERATORS

The synchronous generator is the only type of a-c generator now in general use.

Construction. In the usual synchronous generator the armature or stator, is the stationary member. This construction has many advantages. It is possible to make the slots any reasonable depth, since the tooth necks increase in cross section with increase in depth of slot; this is not true of the rotor. The large slot section which is thus obtainable gives ample space for copper and insulation. The conductors from the armature to the bus bars can be insulated throughout their entire lengths, since no rotating or sliding contacts are necessary. The insulation in a stationary member does not deteriorate as rapidly as that on a rotating member, for it is not subjected to centrifugal force or to any considerable vibration.

The **rotating member** is ordinarily the field. There are two general types of field construction: the **salient-pole type** and the **cylindrical, or non-salient-pole, type.** The salient-pole type is used almost entirely for slow and moderate-speed generators since this construction is the least expensive and permits ample space for the field ampere-turns.

It is not practicable to employ salient poles in high-speed turboalternators because of the excessive windage and the difficulty of obtaining sufficient mechanical strength. The **cylindrical type** consists of a cylindrical steel forging with radial slots in which the field copper, usually in strip form, is placed. The fields are ordinarily excited at low voltage, 125 and 250 volts, the current being conducted to the rotating member by means of slip rings and brushes. The field power is ordinarily only 1.5 percent and less of the rated power of the machine (see Table 12, p. 15–58).

Classes of Synchronous Generators. Synchronous generators may be divided into three general classes: (1) the slow-speed engine-driven type; (2) the moderate-speed water-wheel-driven type; and (3) the high-speed turbine-driven type. In (1) a hollow box frame is used as the stator support, and the field consists of a spider to which a large number of salient poles are attached, usually bolted. The speed seldom exceeds 75 to 90 rpm, although it may run as high as 150 rpm. Water-wheel generators also have salient poles which are usually dovetailed to a cylindrical spider consisting of steel plates riveted together. Their speeds range from 80 to 900 rpm and sometimes higher, although the 9,000 kva Keokuk synchronous generators rotate at only 58 rpm, operating at a very low head. The speed rating of direct-connected water-wheel generators decreases with decrease in head. It is desirable to operate synchronous generators at the highest permissible speed since the weight and costs diminish with increase in speed. Waterwheel-driven generators must be able to run at double speed, as a precaution against accident should the governor fail to shut the gate sufficiently rapidly in case of opening of the circuit breakers or should the governing mechanism become inoperative.

Turbine-driven generators operate at speeds of 720 to 3,600 rpm. Direct-connected exciters, belt-driven exciters from the generator shaft, and separately driven exciters are used. In large stations separately driven (usually motor) exciters may supply the excitation energy to excitation bus bars. Steam-driven exciters and storage batteries are frequently held in reserve. With slow-speed synchronous generators, the belt-driven exciter is frequently used because it can be driven at higher speed, thus reducing the cost.

Synchronous-generator Design. At the present time single-phase generators are seldom built. For single-phase service two phases of a standard three-phase Y-connected generator are used. A single-phase load or unbalanced three-phase load produces flux pulsations in the magnetic circuits of synchronous generators, which increase the iron losses and introduce harmonics into the emf wave. Two-phase windings consist of two similar single-phase windings displaced 90 electrical space degrees on the armature and ordinarily occupying all the slots on the armature. The most common type of winding is the three-phase lap-wound two-layer type of winding. In three-phase windings three windings are spaced 120 electrical space degrees apart, the individual phase belts being spaced 60 deg apart. Usually, all the slots on the armature are occupied. Standard voltages are 550, 1,100, 2,200, 6,600, 13,200, and 20,000 volts. It is much more difficult to insulate for 20,000 volts than it is for the lower voltages. However, if the power is to be transmitted at this voltage, its use would be justified by the saving of transformers. In machines of moderate and larger ratings it is common to generate at 6,600 and 13,200 volts if transformers must be used. The higher voltage is preferable, particularly for the higher ratings, because it reduces the cross section of the connecting leads and bus bars.

The **standard frequency** in the United States for lighting and power systems is 60 cycles per second; the few former 50 cps systems have practically all been converted to 60 cps. The frequency of 25 cps is commonly used in street-railway and subway systems to supply power to the synchronous converters and other a-c–d-c conversion apparatus; it is also commonly used in railroad electrification, particularly for single-phase series-motor locomotives (see p. 11–27). At 25 cps incandescent lamps have noticeable flicker. In European (and most other) countries 50 cps is standard. The frequency of a synchronous machine

$$f = P \times \text{rpm}/120 \qquad \text{cps (cycles per sec)} \tag{97}$$

where P is the number of poles. Synchronous generators are rated in kilovolt-amperes (kva) rather than in kilowatts, since heating, which determines the rating, is dependent only on the current, and is independent of power factor. If the kilowatt rating is specified, the power factor should also be specified.

Induced Emf. The induced emf per phase in synchronous generator

$$E = 2.22 k_b k_p \Phi f Z 10^{-8} \qquad \text{volts per phase} \tag{98}$$

k_b is the breadth factor or belt factor (usually 0.9 to 1.0) and depends on the number of slots per pole per phase, 0.958 for 3-ph, 4 slots per pole per phase; k_p is the pitch factor = 1.0 for full pitch, 0.966 for 5⁄6 pitch; Φ is the total flux in maxwells entering the armature from one north pole and is assumed to be sinusoidally distributed along the air gap; f is the frequency; and Z is the number of series conductors per phase.

Synchronous generators usually are Y-connected. The advantages are that for a given line voltage the voltage per phase is $1/\sqrt{3}$ that of the delta-connected winding; third-harmonic currents and their multiples cannot circulate in the winding as with a delta-connected winding; third-harmonic emfs and their multiples cannot exist in the line emfs; a neutral point is available for grounding.

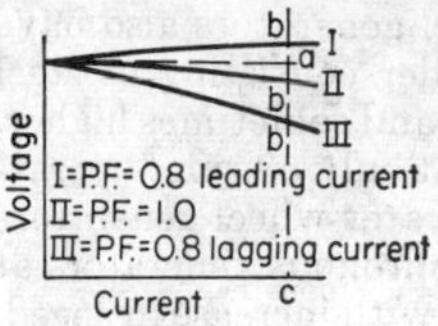

I=P.F.=0.8 leading current
II=P.F.=1.0
III=P.F.=0.8 lagging current
Voltage
Current

Fig. 62. Synchronous-generator characteristics.

Regulation. The terminal voltage of synchronous generator at constant frequency and field excitation depends not only on the current load but on the power factor as well. This is illustrated in Fig. 62 which shows the voltage-current characteristics of a synchronous generator with lagging current, leading current and in-phase current (p-f = 1.00). With leading current the voltage may actually rise with increase in load; the rate of voltage decrease with load becomes greater as the lag of the current increases. The regulation of a synchronous generator is defined by the American Definitions of Electrical Terms C42.10 (1957) as follows:

The voltage regulation of a synchronous generator is the rise in voltage with constant field current, when, with the synchronous generator operated at rated voltage and rated speed, the specified load at the specified power factor is reduced to zero, expressed as a percent of rated voltage.

For example, in Fig. 62 the regulation under each condition is

$$100(ac - bc)/bc \tag{99}$$

With leading current the regulation may be negative.

Three factors affect the regulation of synchronous generators; the **effective armature resistance,** the **armature leakage reactance,** and the **armature reaction.** With alternating current the armature loss is greater than the value obtained by multiplying the square of the armature current by the ohmic resistance. This is due to hysteresis and eddy-current losses in the iron adjacent to the conductor and to the alternating flux producing losses in the conductors themselves. Also the current is not distributed uniformly over conductors in the slot, but the current density tends to be greatest in the top of the slot. These factors all have the effect of increasing the resistance. The ratio of effective to ohmic resistance varies from 1.2 to 1.5. The **armature leakage reactance** is due to the flux produced by the armature current linking the conductors in the slots and also the end connections.

The armature mmf reacts on the field to change the value of the flux. With a single-phase generator and with an unbalanced load on a polyphase generator, the armature mmf is pulsating and causes iron losses in the field structure. With polyphase machines under a constant balanced load, the armature mmf is practically constant in magnitude and fixed in its relation to the field poles. Its direction with relation to the field-pole axis is determined by the power factor of the load.

A component of current in phase with the no-load induced emf, or the excitation emf, merely distorts the field by strengthening the trailing pole tip and weakening the leading pole tip. A component of current lagging the excitation emf by 90 deg weakens the field without distortion. A component of current leading the excitation emf by 90 deg strengthens the field without distortion. Ordinarily, both cross magnetization and one of the other components are acting simultaneously.

The foregoing effects are called **armature reaction.** Frequently the effects of armature reactance and armature reaction can be combined into a single quantity.

It is difficult to determine the regulation of synchronous generator by actual loading, even when in service, owing to the difficulty of obtaining, controlling, and absorbing the large balanced loads. Hence methods of **predetermining regulation without actually loading** the machine are used.

Synchronous-impedance Method. Both armature reactance and armature reaction have the same effect on the terminal voltage. In the synchronous-impedance method the generator is considered as having no armature reaction, but the armature reactance is increased a sufficient amount to account for the effect of armature reaction. The phasor diagram for a current I lagging the terminal voltage V by an angle θ is shown in Fig. 63. In a polyphase generator the phasor diagram is applicable to one phase, a balanced load almost always being assumed.

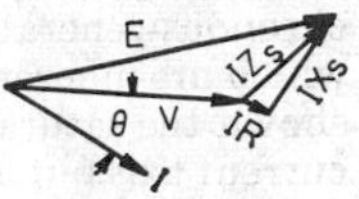

FIG. 63. Phasor diagram for synchronous-impedance method.

The power factor of the load is cos θ; IR is the effective armature-resistance drop and is parallel to I; IX_s is the synchronous-reactance drop and is at right angles to I and leading it by 90 deg. IX_s includes both the reactance drop and the drop in voltage due to armature reaction. That part of IX_s which replaces armature reaction is in reality a fictitious quantity. The synchronous-impedance drop is given by IZ_s. The no-load or open-circuit (excitation) voltage

$$E = \sqrt{(V \cos \theta + IR)^2 + (V \sin \theta \pm IX_s)^2} \qquad \text{volts} \tag{100}$$

All quantities are per phase. The negative sign is used with leading current.

$$\text{Regulation} = 100(E - V)/V \tag{101}$$

(see p. 15–54). With leading current E may be less than V and a negative regulation results.

The synchronous impedance is determined from an open-circuit and a short-circuit test, made with a weak field. The voltage E' on open circuit is divided by the current I' on short circuit for the same value of field current.

$$Z_s = E'/I' \qquad X_s = \sqrt{Z_s^2 - R^2} \qquad \text{ohms} \tag{102}$$

R is so small as compared with X_s that for all practical purposes $X_s = Z_s$. R may be determined by measuring the ohmic resistance per phase and multiplying by 1.4 to 1.5 to obtain the effective resistance. This value of R and the value of X_s obtained from Eq. (**102**) may then be substituted in Eq. (**100**) to obtain E at the specified load and power factor.

Since the synchronous reactance is determined at low saturation of the iron and used at high saturation, the method gives regulations that are too large; hence it is called the *pessimistic method*.

Mmf Method. In the mmf method the generator is considered as having no armature reactance but the armature reaction is increased by an amount sufficient to include the effect of reactance. That part of armature reaction which replaces the effect of armature reactance is in reality a fictitious quantity. To obtain the data necessary for computing the regulation, the generator is short-circuited and the field adjusted to give rated current in the armature. The corresponding value of field current I_a is read. The field is then adjusted to give voltage E' equal to rated terminal voltage + IR drop (= $V + IR$, as phasors, Fig. 64) on open circuit and the field current I' read.

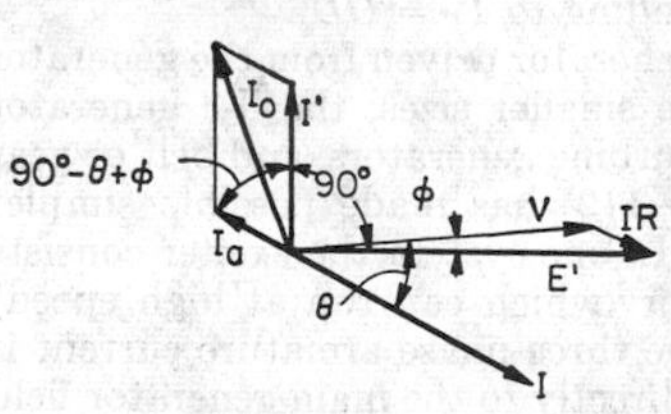

FIG. 64. Phasor diagram for mmf method.

I_a is 180 deg from the current phasor I, and I' leads E' by 90 deg (Fig. 64). The angle between I' and I_a is $90 - \theta + \phi$, but since ϕ is small, it can usually be neglected. The phasor sum of I_a and I' is I_o. The open-circuit voltage E corresponding to I_o is the no-load voltage and may be found on the saturation curve. The regulation is then found from Eq. (**101**). This method gives a value of regulation less than the actual value and hence is called the *optimistic method*. The actual regulation lies somewhere between the values obtained by the two methods but is more nearly equal to the value obtained by the mmf method.

ASA Method. The ASA method (American Standard 50, Rotating Electrical Machinery) which has become the accepted standard for the predetermination of synchronous-generator operation, eliminates in large measure the errors due to saturation which are inherent in the synchronous-impedance and mmf methods. In Fig. 65(*a*) is shown the saturation curve *OAF* of the generator. The axis *OP* is not only the field-current axis but also the axis of the current phasor *I* as well. *V* the terminal voltage is drawn θ deg from *I* or *OP*, where θ is the power-factor angle. The effective-resistance drop *IR* and the *leakage-reactance* drop *IX* are drawn parallel and perpendicular to the current phasor. E_a, the phasor sum of *V*, *IR*, and *IX*, is the internal *induced* emf. Arcs are swung with *O* as a center and *V* and E_a as radii to intercept the axis of ordi-

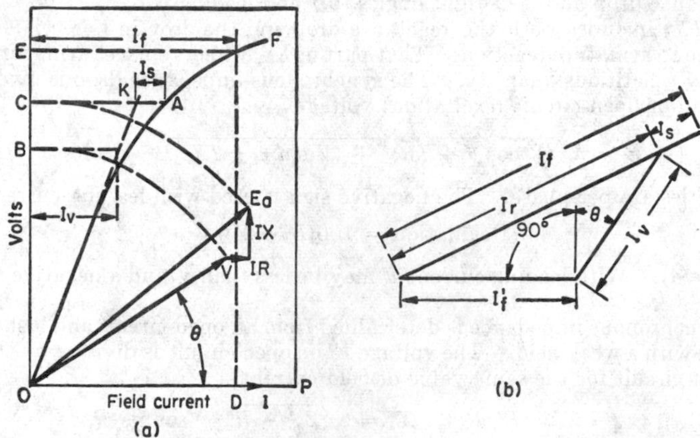

FIG. 65. ASA method of synchronous-generator regulation.

nates at *B* and *C*. *OK*, tangent to the straight portion of the saturation curve, is the *air-gap line*. If there is no saturation, I_v is the field current necessary to produce *V*, and *CK* is the field current necessary to produce E_a. The field current I_s is the increase in field current necessary to take into account the saturation corresponding to E_a.

The corresponding phasor diagram to a larger scale is shown in Fig. 65(*b*). I_f', the field current necessary to produce rated current at short circuit, corresponding to I_a (Fig. 64), is drawn horizontally. The field current I_v is drawn at an angle θ to the right of a perpendicular erected at the right-hand end of I_f'. I_r is the resultant of I_f', and I_v. I_s is added to I_r giving I_f the resultant field current. The no-load emf *E* is found on the saturation curve, Fig. 65(*a*), corresponding to $I_f = OD$.

Excitation is commonly supplied by a small d-c generator driven from the generator shaft. On account of commutation, except in the smaller sizes, the d-c generator cannot be driven at 3,600 rpm, the usual speed for turbine generators, and belt or gear drives are necessary. The silicon rectifier (p. 15–119) has made possible simpler means of excitation as well as voltage regulation. In one system the exciter consists of a small rotating-armature synchronous generator (which can run at high speed) mounted directly on the main generator shaft. The three-phase armature current is rectified by three silicon rectifiers and is conducted directly to the main generator field without any sliding contacts. The main generator field current is controlled by the current to the stationary field of the exciter generator. In another system there is no rotating exciter, the generator excitation being supplied directly from the generator terminals, the 13,800 volts, three-phase, being stepped down to 115 volts, three-phase, by small transformers and rectified by silicon rectifiers. Voltage regulation is obtained by magnetic rectifiers actuated by potential transformers connected across the generator terminals.

Most regulators such as the following operate through the field of the exciter. In the **Tirrill regulator** the field resistance of the exciter is short-circuited temporarily by contacts when the bus-bar voltage drops. Actually, the contacts are vibrating continuously, the time that they are closed depending on the value of the bus-bar voltage. The General Electric Co. manufactures a direct-acting regulator in which the regulating rheostat is part of the regulator itself. The rheostat consists of stacks of graphite plates, each plate being pivoted at the center. Tilting the plates changes the path of the current through the rheostat and thus changes the resistance. The plates are tilted by a sensitive torque armature which is actuated by variations of voltage from the normal value (for regulators employing silicon rectifiers, see p. 15–119).

Parallel Operation of Synchronous Generators. The kilowatt division of load between synchronous generators in parallel is determined entirely by the speed-load characteristics of their prime movers and not by the characteristics of the generators themselves. No appreciable adjustment of kilowatt load between synchronous generators in parallel can be made by means of their field rheostats, as with d-c generators. Consider Fig. 66, which gives the speed-load characteristics in terms of frequency, of two synchronous generators, No. 1 and No. 2, these characteristics being the speed-load characteristics of their prime movers. These speed-load characteristics are drooping, which is necessary for stable parallel operation. The total load on the two machines is $P_1 + P_2$ kw. Both machines must be operating at the same frequency f_1. Hence generator 1 must be delivering P_1 kw, and generator 2 must be delivering P_2 kw (the small generator losses being neglected). If, under the foregoing conditions, the field of either machine is strengthened, it cannot deliver a greater kilowatt load, for its prime mover can deliver more power only by dropping its speed. This is impossible, for both generators must operate always at the same frequency f_1. For any fixed total power load, the division of kilowatt load between synchronous generators can be changed only by modifying in some manner the speed-load characteristics of their prime movers, such, for example, as changing the tension in the governor spring. Synchronous generators in parallel are of themselves in stable equilibrium. If the driving torque of one machine is increased, the resulting electrical reactions between the machines cause a circulating current to flow between machines. This current puts more electrical load on the machine whose driving torque is increased and tends to produce motor action in the other machines. In an extreme case, the driving torque of one prime mover may be removed entirely, and its generator will operate as a synchronous motor, driving the prime mover mechanically.

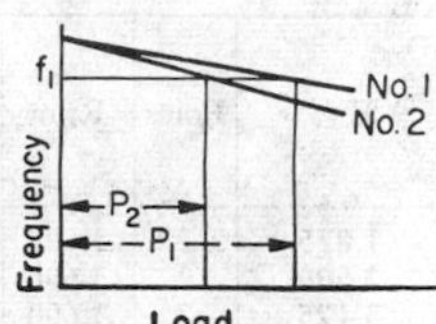

FIG. 66. Speed-load characteristics of synchronous generators in parallel.

Variations in driving torques cause currents to circulate between synchronous generators, transferring power which tends to keep the generators in synchronism. If the power transfer takes the form of recurring pulsations, it is called **hunting,** which may be reduced by building heavy copper grids called **amortisseurs, or damper windings,** into the pole faces. Turbine- and water-wheel-driven synchronous generators are much better adapted to parallel operation than are synchronous generators which are driven by reciprocating engines, because of their uniformity of torque.

Increasing the field current of synchronous generators in parallel with others causes it to deliver a greater lagging component of current. Since the character of the load determines the total current delivered by the system, the lagging components of current delivered by the other generators must decrease and may even become leading components. Likewise if the field of one generator is weakened, it delivers a greater leading component of current and the other machines deliver components of current which are more lagging. These leading and lagging currents do not affect appreciably the division of *kilowatt* load between the synchronous generators. They do, however, cause unnecessary heating in their armatures. The fields of all synchronous generators should be so adjusted that the heating due to the quadrature components of currents is a minimum. With two generators having equal armature resistances, this occurs when both deliver equal quadrature currents.

Table 12. Performance Data for Synchronous Generators

(Westinghouse Electric Corp.)

80 PERCENT PF, 3 PHASE, 60 CYCLE, 240 TO 2,400 VOLTS, HORIZONTAL-COUPLED OR BELTED-TYPE ENGINE-DRIVEN GENERATORS

Kva	Poles	Rpm	Excitation, kw	Efficiencies, percent			Approx net weight, lb
				½ load	¾ load	Full load	
25	4	1,800	0.8	81.5	85.7	87.6	900
93.8	8	900	2	87	89.5	90.9	2,700
250	12	600	5	90	91.3	92.2	6,000
500	18	400	8	91.7	92.6	93.2	10,000
1,000	24	300	14.5	92.6	93.4	93.9	16,100
3,125	48	150	40	93.4	94.2	94.6	52,000

INDUSTRIAL-SIZE TURBINE GENERATORS, DIRECT-CONNECTED TYPE, 80 PERCENT PF, 3 PHASE, 60 CYCLE, AIR-COOLED

Kva	Poles	Rpm	Excitation		Efficiency, percent			Volume of air, cfm	Voltage	Approx wt, including exciter, lb
			Kw	Volts	½ load	¾ load	Full load			
1,875	2	3,600	18	125	95.3	96.1	96.3	3,500	480–6,900	21,900
2,500	2	3,600	22	125	95.3	96.1	96.3	5,000	2,400–6,900	22,600
3,125	2	3,600	24	125	95.3	96.3	96.5	5,500	2,400–6,900	25,100
3,750	2	3,600	24	125–250	95.3	96.3	96.6	6,500	2,400–6,900	27,900
5,000	2	3,600	29	125–250	95.3	96.3	96.6	11,000	2,400–6,900	40,100
6,250	2	3,600	38	125–250	95.3	96.3	96.7	12,000	2,400–13,800	43,300
7,500	2	3,600	42	125–250	95.5	96.5	96.9	15,000	2,400–13,800	45,000
9,375	2	3,600	47	125–250	95.5	96.5	96.9	16,500	2,400–13,800	61,200

CENTRAL-STATION-SIZE TURBINE GENERATORS, DIRECT-CONNECTED TYPE, 85 PERCENT PF, 3 PHASE, 60 CYCLE, 11,500 TO 14,400 VOLTS

Kva	Poles	Rpm	Excitation		Efficiency, percent			Volume, of air, cfm	Ventilation	Approx wt, including exciter, lb
			Kw	Volts	½ load	¾ load	Full load			
13,529	2	3,600	70	250	96.3	97.1	97.3	22,000	Air-cooled	116,700
17,647	2	3,600	100	250	97.7	97.9	97.9	22,000	H_2-cooled	115,700
23,529	2	3,600	115	250	98.0	98.2	98.2	25,000	H_2-cooled	143,600
35,294	2	3,600	145	250	98.1	98.3	98.3	34,000	H_2-cooled	194,800
47,058	2	3,600	155	250	98.3	98.5	98.5	42,000	H_2-cooled	237,200
70,588	2	3,600	200	250	98.4	98.7	98.7	50,000	H_2-cooled	302,500

Armature reactance in the armature of machines in parallel is desirable. If not too great, it stabilizes their operation by producing the synchronizing action. Synchronous generators with too little reactance are sensitive, and if connected in parallel with slight phase displacement or inequality of voltage, considerable disturbance results. Armature reactance also reduces the current on short circuit, particularly during the first few cycles when the short-circuit current is a maximum. Frequently, external power-limiting reactances are connected in series to protect the generators and equipment from injury that would result from the tremendous short-circuit currents. For these reasons, poor regulation in large synchronous generators is frequently considered to be an advantage rather than a disadvantage.

Ground Resistors. Most power systems operate with a grounded neutral. When the station generators deliver current directly to the system (without intervening transformers), it is customary to ground the neutral (of the Y-connected windings) of one generator in a station; this is usually done through a grounding resistor of from 2 to 6 ohms. If the neutral of more than one generator is grounded, third-harmonic (and multiples thereof) currents can circulate between the generators. The ground resistor reduces the short-circuit currents when faults to ground occur, and hence reduces the violence of the short circuit as well as the duty of the circuit breakers. Grounding reactors are sometimes used but have limited application owing to the danger of high voltages resulting from resonant conditions.

TRANSFORMERS

Transformer Theory. The transformer is a device that transfers energy from one electric circuit to another without change of frequency and usually, but not always, with a change in voltage. The energy is transferred through the medium of a magnetic field: it is supplied to the transformer through a primary winding and is delivered by means of a secondary winding. Both windings link the same magnetic circuit. With no load on the secondary, a small current, called the exciting current, flows in the primary and produces the alternating flux. This flux links both primary and secondary windings and induces the same volts per turn in each. With a sine wave the emf

$$E = 4.44\Phi_m n f 10^{-8} \quad \text{volts} \tag{103}$$

where Φ_m is the maximum instantaneous flux in maxwells, n the turns on either winding, and f the frequency. Equation (**103**) may also be written

$$E = 4.44 B_m A n f 10^{-8} \quad \text{volts} \tag{104}$$

B_m is the maximum instantaneous flux density in the iron and A the net cross section of the iron. If B_m is in gausses, A is in sq cm; if B_m is in maxwells per sq in., A is in sq in.

In mks units, Eq. (**103**) becomes

$$E = 4.44\Phi_m n f \quad \text{volts} \tag{103a}$$

where Φ_m is in webers; Eq. (**104**) becomes

$$E = 4.44 B_m A n f \quad \text{volts} \tag{104a}$$

where B_m is in webers per sq meter and A is in sq meters.

B_m is practically fixed. In large transformers with silicon steel it varies between 60,000 and 75,000 maxwells per sq in. at 60 cycles, and between 75,000 and 90,000 maxwells per sq in. at 25 cycles. It is desirable to operate the iron at as high density as possible in order to minimize the weight of iron and copper. On the other hand, with too high densities the eddy-current and hysteresis losses become too great, and with low frequency the exciting current may become excessive. It follows from Eq. (**103**) that

$$E_1/E_2 = n_1/n_2 \tag{105}$$

where E_1 and E_2 are the primary and secondary emfs and n_1 and n_2 are the primary and secondary turns. Since the impedance drops in ordinary transformers are small, the terminal voltages of primary and secondary are also practically proportional to their number of turns. As the change in secondary terminal voltage in the ordinary constant-potential transformer over its range of operation is small (1.5 to 3 percent), the flux must remain substantially constant and the exciting current must therefore remain substantially constant. Therefore, the added ampere-turns produced by any secondary load must be balanced by opposite and equal primary ampere-turns. Since the exciting current is small compared with the load current (1.5 to 5 percent) and the two are usually out of phase, the exciting current may ordinarily be neglected. Hence,

$$n_1 I_1 = n_2 I_2 \tag{106}$$
$$I_1/I_2 = n_2/n_1 \tag{107}$$

where I_1 and I_2 are the primary and secondary currents.

When load is applied to the secondary of a transformer, the secondary ampere-turns reduce the flux slightly. This reduces the counter emf of the primary, permitting more current to enter and thus supply the increased power demanded by the secondary.

Both primary and secondary windings must necessarily have resistance. All the flux produced by the primary does not link the secondary; the counter ampere-turns of the secondary produce some flux which does not link the primary. These **leakage fluxes** produce reactance in each winding. The combined effect of the resistance and reactance produces an impedance drop in each winding when current flows. These impedance drops produce a slight drop in the secondary terminal voltage with load.

Transformer Testing. Transformer regulation and losses are so small that it is far more accurate to compute the regulation and efficiency than to determine them by actual measurement. The necessary measurements and computations are comparatively simple, and little power is involved in making the tests. In the **open-circuit** test, the power input to either winding is measured at its rated voltage. Usually it is more convenient to make this test on the low-voltage winding, particularly if it is rated at 110, 220, or 550 volts. The open-circuit power practically all goes to supply the core losses, consisting of eddy-current and hysteresis losses. Let this value of power be P_0. The eddy-current loss varies as the square of the voltage and frequency; the hysteresis loss varies as the 1.6 power of the voltage, and directly as the frequency. In the **short-circuit** test one winding is short-circuited, and the current in the other is adjusted to near its rated value. The voltage V_c, the current I_1, and the power input P_c are measured. When one winding of a transformer is short-circuited, the voltage across the other winding is 3 to 4 percent of rated value when rated current flows. Since a voltage range of from 110 to 250 volts is best adapted to measuring instruments, that winding whose rated voltage, multiplied by 0.03 or 0.04, is closest to this voltage range should be used for making the short-circuit test, the other winding being short-circuited. Practically all the power on short circuit goes to supply the copper loss of primary and secondary. If the measurements are made on the primary,

$$R_{01} = P_c/I_1^2 \tag{108}$$

$$Z_{01} = V_c/I_1 \tag{109}$$

$$X_{01} = \sqrt{Z_{01}^2 - R_{01}^2} \tag{110}$$

where R_{01}, Z_{01}, and X_{01} are the equivalent resistance, impedance, and reactance referred to the primary. Also $R_{02} = R_{01}(n_2/n_1)^2$; $Z_{02} = Z_{01}(n_2/n_1)^2$; $X_{02} = X_{01}(n_2/n_1)^2$, these quantities being the equivalent resistance, impedance, and reactance referred to the secondary. If the d-c resistances, R_1 and R_2, of the primary and secondary are measured,

$$R_{01} = R_1 + (n_1/n_2)^2R_2 \tag{111}$$

$$R_{02} = R_2 + (n_2/n_1)^2R_1 \tag{112}$$

The a-c or effective resistances, determined from Eq. (**108**), are usually 10 to 15 percent greater than these values.

Regulation. The regulation may be computed from the foregoing data as follows:

$$V_1' = \sqrt{(V_1 \cos\theta + I_1R_{01})^2 + (V_1 \sin\theta \pm I_1X_{01})^2} \tag{113}$$

$$\text{Regulation} = 100(V_1' - V_1)/V_1 \tag{114}$$

V_1 = rated primary terminal voltage; $\cos\theta$ = load power factor; I_1 = rated primary current; R_{01} = equivalent resistance referred to primary [from Eq. (**108**)]; X_{01} = equivalent reactance referred to primary. The (+) sign is used with lagging current and the (−) sign with leading current. Equations (**113**) and (**114**) are equally applicable to the secondary if the subscripts are changed.

Efficiency. The only two losses in a constant-potential transformer are the core loss in watts P_0, which is practically independent of load, and P_c the copper loss in watts, which varies as the load current squared. The efficiency for any current I_1 is

$$\eta = V_1I_1 \cos\theta/(V_1I_1 \cos\theta + P_0 + I_1^2R_{01}) \tag{115}$$

Equation (**115**) applies equally well to the secondary if the subscripts are changed. The maximum efficiency occurs when the core and copper losses are equal.

All-day Efficiency. Since transformers must usually be on the line 24 hr per day, part of which time the load may be very light, the all-day efficiency is important.

This is equal to the total energy or watthour output divided by the total energy or watthour input for the 24 hr. That is,

$$\eta = \frac{(V_1 I_1 \cos \theta_1)t_1 + \cdots}{(V_1 I_1 \cos \theta_1)t_1 + \cdots + (I_1^2 R_{01})t_1 + \cdots + 24P_0} \tag{116}$$

where t_1 is the time in hours that load $V_1 I_1 \cos \theta_1$ is being delivered, etc.

Polyphase Transformer Connections. Three-phase transformer banks may be connected Δ-Δ, Δ-Y, Y-Y, and Y-Δ. The Δ-Δ connection is very common, particularly at the lower voltages, and has the important advantage that the bank will operate V-connected if one transformer is disabled. The Δ-Y connection is advantageous for stepping up to high voltages since the secondary of the transformers need be wound only for 58 percent ($1/\sqrt{3}$) the line voltage; it is also necessary when a four-wire three-phase system is obtained from a three-wire three-phase system since "a floating neutral" on the secondary cannot occur. The Y-Y system may be used for stepping up voltage. It should not be used for obtaining a three-phase four-wire system from a three-phase three-wire system, because of the "floating neutral" on the secondary and the resulting high degree of unbalance of the secondary voltages. The Y-Δ system may be used to step down high voltages, the reverse of the Δ-Y connection. In the Δ-Y and Y-Δ systems the ratio of line voltages is obviously not that of the individual transformers. Because of different phase displacement between primaries and secondaries, a Δ-Δ bank cannot be connected in parallel (on both sides) with a Δ-Y bank, etc., even if they both have the correct voltage ratios between lines (see p. 15–33).

Three-phase transformers combine the magnetic circuits of three single-phase transformers so that they have parts in common. A material saving in cost, in weight, and in space results, the greatest saving occurring in the case and oil. The advantages of three-phase transformers are often outweighed by their lack of flexibility. The failure of a single phase shuts down the entire transformer. With three single units, one unit may be readily replaced with a single spare. The primaries of single-phase transformers may be connected in Y or Δ at will and the secondaries properly phased. The primaries, as well as the secondaries of three-phase transformers, must be phased.

For the transformation of moderate amounts of power from three-phase to three-phase, two transformers employing either the **V** or the **T connection** (Fig. 67) may be

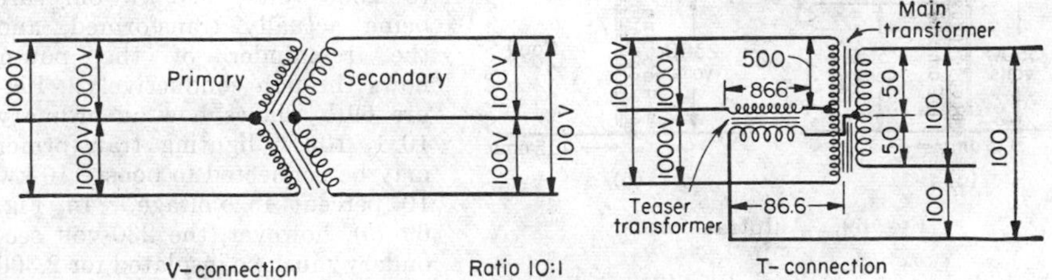

FIG. 67. Transformer connections for transforming moderate amounts of three-phase power.

used. With each connection the ratio of line voltages is the same as the transformer ratios. In the figure, ratios 10:1 are shown. In the T connection the primary and the secondary of the main transformer must be provided with a center tap to which one end of the teaser transformer is connected. The ratings of these systems are only 58 percent of the rating of the system using three similar transformers, one for each phase. Owing to dissymmetry, the terminal voltages become somewhat unbalanced even with a balanced load.

To transform from two- to three-phase or the reverse, the **T connection** of Fig. 68 is used. To make the secondary voltages symmetrical a tap (called a **Scott tap**) is brought out at 86.6 percent ($\sqrt{3}/2$) of the primary winding of the teaser transformer as shown in Fig. 68. With balanced no-load voltages the voltages become slightly unbalanced even under a symmetrical load, owing to unequal phase differences in the individual coils. The three-phase neutral O is one-third the winding of the teaser transformer from the junction. In Fig. 68(a) the transformation is from three-phase to a two-phase three-wire system. In Fig. 68(b) the transformation is from three-phase to a four-phase, five-wire system. The voltages are given on the basis of 100 volt primaries with 1:1 transformer ratios.

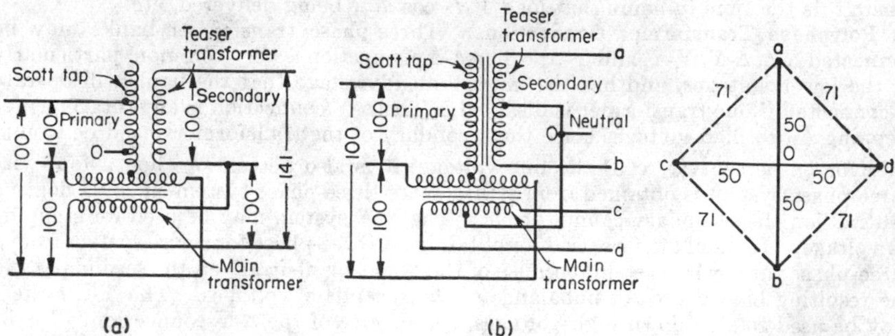

FIG. 68. Connections for transforming from three-phase to two- and four-phase power.

An **autotransformer,** also called **compensator,** consists essentially of a single winding linking a magnetic circuit. Part of the energy is transformed, and the remainder flows through conductively. Suitable taps are provided so that, if the primary voltage is applied to two of the taps, a voltage may be taken from any other two taps. The ratio of voltages is equal practically to the ratio of the turns between their taps. An autotransformer should be installed only when the ratio of transformation is not large. The ratio of power transformed to total power is $1 - n$, where n is the ratio of low-voltage to high-voltage emf. This gives the saving over the ordinary transformer and is greatest when the ratio is not far from unity. Figure 69(a) shows 100 kw being changed from 3,300 to 2,300 volts; 30.3 kw only are being actually transformed, and the remainder of the power flows through conductively. Figure 69(b) shows how an ordinary 10:1, 10-kw lighting transformer may be connected to boost 110 kw 10 percent in voltage. In Fig. 69 (b), however, the 230-volt secondary must be insulated for 2,300 volts to the core and ground. The voltage may likewise be reduced by reversing the 230-volt coil. An autotransformer should never be used when it is desired to keep dangerous primary potentials from the secondary. It is used for starting induction motors (Fig. 71) and for a number of similar purposes.

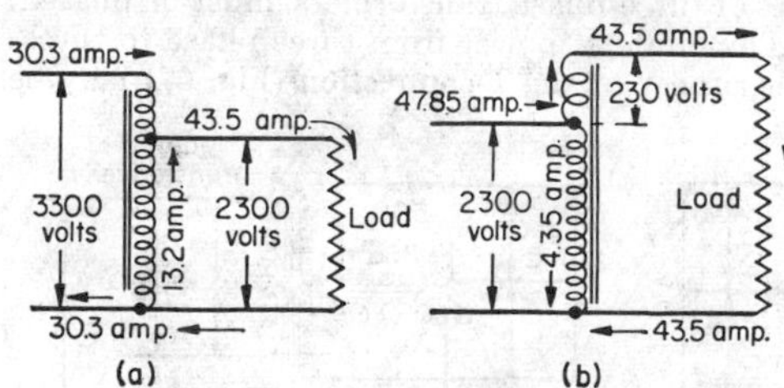

FIG. 69. Autotransformer.

Data on Transformers. Single-phase 55 deg self-cooled oil-insulated transformers for 2,300-volt primaries, 230–115 volt secondaries, and in sizes from 5 to 200 kva for 60(25) cycles have efficiencies from one-half to full load of about 98 (97 to 98.7) percent and regulation of 1.5 (1.1 to 2.1) percent with pf = 1, and 3.5 (2.7 to 4.1) percent with pf = 0.8. Power transformers with 13,200-volt primaries and 2,300-volt secondaries in sizes from 667 to 5,000 kva and for both 60 and 25 cycles have efficiencies from one-half to full load of about 99.0 percent and regulation of about 1.0 (4.2) percent with pf = 1(0.8).

ALTERNATING-CURRENT MOTORS

Polyphase Induction Motor. The polyphase induction motor is the most common type of motor used. It consists ordinarily of a stator which is wound in the same manner as the synchronous-generator stator. If two-phase current is supplied to a two-phase winding or three-phase current to a three-phase winding, a rotating magnetic field is produced in the air gap. The number of poles which this field has is the same as the number of poles that a synchronous generator employing the same stator winding would have. The speed of the rotating field, or the *synchronous speed,*

$$N = 120f/P \quad \text{rpm} \tag{117}$$

where f is the frequency and P the number of poles.

There are two general types of rotors. The **squirrel-cage type** consists of heavy copper bars short-circuited by end rings, or the bars and end rings may be an integral aluminum casting. The **wound rotor** has a polyphase winding of the same number of poles as the stator, and the terminals are brought out to slip rings so that external resistance may be introduced. The rotor conductors must be cut by the rotating field, hence the rotor cannot run at synchronous speed but must slip. The *slip,*

$$s = (N - N_2)/N \tag{118}$$

where N_2 = the rotor rpm. The rotor frequency

$$f_2 = sf \tag{119}$$

The torque is proportional to the air-gap flux and the components of rotor current in space-phase with it. The rotor currents tend to lag the emfs producing them, because of the rotor-leakage reactance. From Eq. (**119**) the rotor frequency and hence the rotor reactance ($x_2 = 2\pi f_2 L_2$) are low when the motor is running near synchronous speed, so that there is a large component of rotor current in space phase with the flux. With large values of slip the increased rotor frequency increases the rotor reactance and hence the lag of the rotor currents behind their emfs, and therefore considerable space-phase difference between these currents and the flux develops. Consequently, even with large values of current the torque may be small. The torque of the induction motor increases with slip until it reaches a maximum value called the **breakdown torque,** after which the torque decreases (see Fig. 72). The breakdown torque varies as the square of the voltage, inversely as the stator impedance and rotor reactance, and is independent of the rotor resistance.

The squirrel-cage motor develops moderate torque on starting (s = 1.0) even though the current may be three to seven times rated current. For any value of slip the torque of the induction motor varies as the square of the voltage. The torque of the squirrel-cage motor which, on starting, is only moderate is reduced in the larger motors because of the necessity for applying reduced voltage.

Polyphase squirrel-cage motors are used for constant-speed work. They are used widely on account of their rugged construction and the absence of moving electrical contacts, which makes them suitable for operation when exposed to flammable dust or gas. General-purpose squirrel-cage motors have starting torques of about 1.5 times full load torque at rated voltage. The highest torques occur at the higher rated speeds. The locked rotor currents vary between four and seven times full-load current. In the **double-squirrel-cage** type of motor there is a high-resistance winding in the top of the rotor slots and a low-resistance winding in the bottom of the slots. The low-resistance winding is made to have a high leakage reactance, either by separating the windings with a magnetic bridge, Fig. 70(*a*), or by making the slot very narrow in the area between the two windings, Fig. 70(*b*). On starting, because of the high reactance of the low-resistance winding, most of the rotor current will flow in the high-resistance winding, giving the motor a large starting torque. As the rotor approaches the low value of slip at which it normally operates, the rotor frequency and hence the rotor reactance become low and most of the rotor current

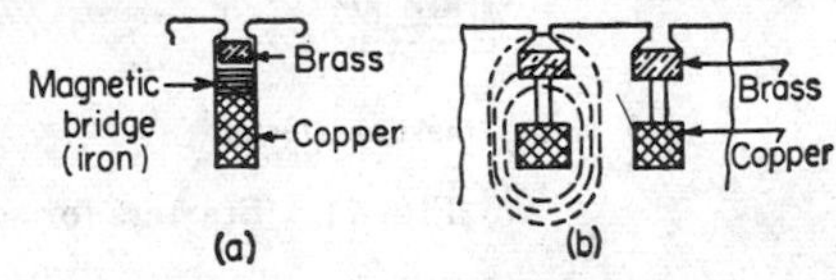

FIG. 70. Types of slot for double-squirrel-cage windings.

now flows in the low-resistance winding. The rotor operates with a low value of slip. The high starting torque of the high-resistance motor and the excellent constant-speed operating characteristics of the low-resistance squirrel-cage rotor are combined in one motor.

The National Electric Code and NEMA have **classified squirrel-cage induction motors** in accordance with the ratio of their starting to rated-load currents, and starting to rated-load torques. There are five important classes of squirrel-cage induction motors designated by design letters A, B, C, D, F, in addition to the wound-rotor motors: design A, general purpose, starting current six to seven times rated, starting torque 150 percent rated; design B, general purpose, high reactance, starting current 5½ to 6 times rated, starting torque 150 percent rated; design C, double squirrel cage, starting current 5½ to 6 times rated, starting torque (high) 225 percent rated; design D, high resistance, starting current 5½ to 6 times rated, starting torque (high) 275 percent rated. Design F is limited to motors of 30 hp and larger with 125 percent rated starting torque and starting current 3½ to 3¾ rated. Since the class D motor has a high-resistance rotor, at rated load it has high slip and is not intended for continuous duty, but rather for hoists, cranes, or punch presses, which require high starting torque, operate intermittently, and for which low efficiency near rated load is not objectionable.

Starting. It is desirable to start induction motors by direct connection across the line, since reduced voltage starters are expensive and almost always reduce the starting torque. In the larger sizes, reduced voltage may be necessary to meet starting-current restrictions, but for the most part full-voltage start predominates up to 30 hp. For larger ratings it may be necessary to employ reduced-voltage starting, but in many cases full-voltage start is employed with motors up to some few hundred horsepower by using design F motors if the required load starting torque is low.

In Fig. 71(*a*) is shown an **"across-the-line" starter** which may be operated from different push-button stations. The START push button closes the solenoid circuit

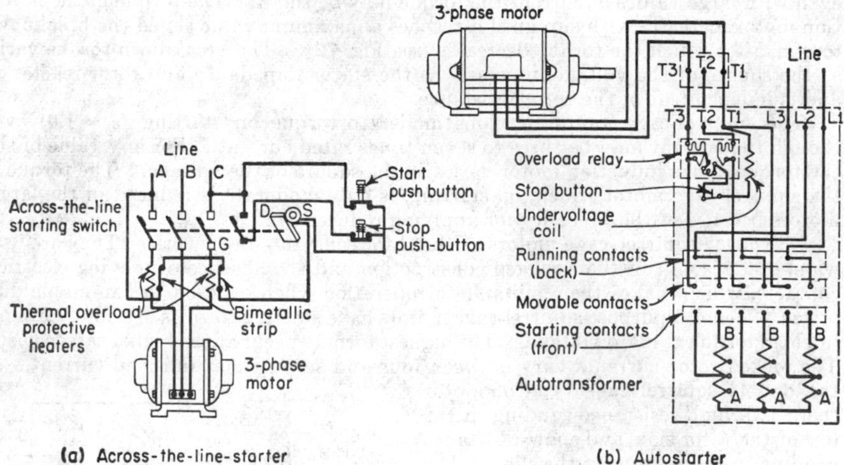

FIG. 71. Starters for squirrel-cage induction motor.

between phases *C* and *A* through two bimetallic strips in series. This energizes solenoid *S*, which attracts armature *D*, which in turn closes the starting switch and the auxiliary blade *G*. This blade keeps the solenoid circuit closed when the START push button is released. Pressing the STOP push button opens the solenoid circuit, permitting the starting switch to open. A prolonged heavy overload raises the temperature of the heaters by an amount that will cause at least one of the bimetallic strips to open the solenoid circuit, releasing the starting switch.

A common method of applying reduced-voltage start is to use a **compensator** or **autotransformer** or **autostarter** [Fig. 71(*b*)]. When the switch is in the starting position, the three windings *AB* of the three-phase autotransformer are connected in Y across the line and the motor terminals are connected to the taps which supply reduced voltage. When the switch is in the running position, the starter is entirely disconnected from the line. In modern practice, motors are protected by thermal overload relays (Fig. 71) which operate to trip the circuit breaker. Since a time element is involved in the operation of such relays, they do not respond to large starting currents, because of their short duration. To limit the current to as low a value as possible, the lowest taps that will give the motor sufficient voltage to supply the required starting torque should be used. As the torque of an induction motor varies as the square of the voltage, the compensator produces a very low starting torque.

Resistors in series with the stator may also be used to start squirrel-cage motors. They are inserted in each phase and are gradually cut out as the motor comes up to speed. The resistors are generally made of wire-type resistor units or of graphite disks enclosed within heat-resisting porcelain-lined iron tubes. The disadvantage of resistors is that if the motor is started slowly the resistor becomes very hot and may burn out. Resistor starters are less expensive than autotransformers. Their application is to motors that start with light loads at infrequent intervals.

By **introducing resistance into the rotor circuit** through slip rings, the rotor currents may be brought nearly into phase with the air-gap flux and, at the same time, any value of torque up to maximum torque obtained. As the rotor develops speed, resistance may be cut out until there is no external resistance in the rotor circuit. The speed may also be controlled by inserting resistance in the rotor circuit. However, like the armature-resistance method of speed control with shunt motors (see p. 15–50), it is inefficient and gives poor speed regulation. Figure 72 shows graphically the effect on the torque of applying reduced voltage (curves *b*, *c*) and of inserting resistance in the rotor circuit (curve *d*). As shown by curves *b* and *c*, the torque for any given slip is proportional to the square of the line voltage. The effect of introducing resistance into the rotor circuit is shown by curve *d*. The point of maximum torque is shifted toward higher values of slip. The maximum torque at starting (slip = 1.0) occurs when the rotor resistance is equal to the rotor reactance at standstill. The wound-rotor motor is used where large starting torque is necessary as in railway work, hoists, and cranes. It has better starting characteristics than the squirrel-cage motor, but, because of the necessarily higher resistance of the rotor, it has greater slip even with the rotor resistance all cut out. Obviously, the wound rotor, controller, and external resistance make it more expensive than the squirrel-cage type.

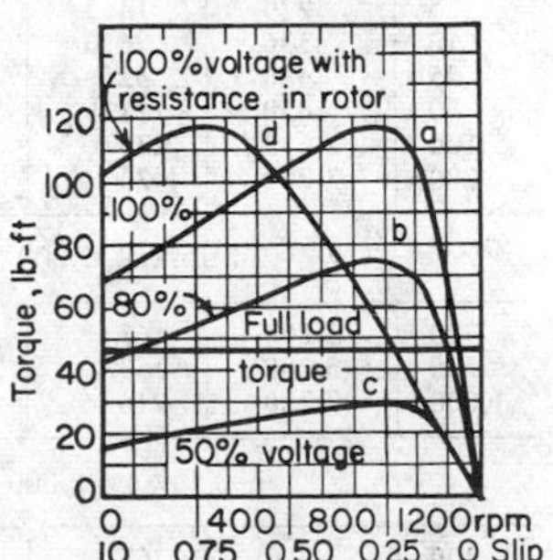

FIG. 72. Speed-torque curve of 10 hp, 60 cycle, 1,140 rpm induction motor.

One **disadvantage of induction motors** is that they take lagging current, and the power factor at half load and less is low. The speed- and torque-load characteristics of induction motors are almost identical with those of the shunt motor. The speed decreases slightly to full load, the slip being from 10 percent in small motors to 2 percent in very large motors. The torque is almost proportional to the load nearly up to the breakdown torque. The power factor is 0.8 to 0.9 at full load. The direction of rotation of any three-phase motor may be reversed by interchanging any two stator wires.

Speed Control of Induction Motors. The induction motor inherently is a constant-speed motor. From Eqs. (**117**) and (**118**) the rotor speed

$$N_2 = 120f(1 - s)/P \qquad \textbf{(120)}$$

The speed can be changed only by changing the frequency, poles, or slip. In some applications where the motors constitute the only load on the generators, as with electric propulsion of ships, their speed may be changed by changing the frequency. Even then the range is limited, for both turbines and generators must operate near their rated speeds for good efficiency. By employing two distinct windings or by reconnecting a single winding by switching it is possible to change the number of poles. Complications prevent more than two speeds being readily obtained in this manner. Elevator motors frequently have two distinct windings. Another objection to changing the number of poles is the fact that the design is a compromise, and sacrifices of desirable characteristics usually are necessary at both speeds.

Table 13. Performance Data for Induction Motors

(Westinghouse Electric Corp.)

Hp	Weight, lb	Amp	Power factor, percent			Efficiency, percent		
			½ load	¾ load	Full load	½ load	¾ load	Full load
3 Phase, 220 Volts, 60 Cycle, 1,750 Rpm, Squirrel-cage Type								
1	65	3.1	59	72.6	80.4	74.5	78.2	78.8
2	90	6.06	62.4	73.3	80.3	77.8	80.5	80.5
5	145	13.84	69.5	79.4	83.6	83	84.3	84.7
10	225	26.1	78.7	85.6	87.6	86.5	86.7	85.6
20	380	50	86.7	89	90	89	89	87.3
40	515	98	80.4	86.4	89	90.8	90.8	90.4
100	1,100	233	89.0	91	91	90	90.5	91
200	2,500	465	89.0	91	91	90	91	91.5
3 Phase, 220 Volt, 60 Cycle, 1,750 Rpm, Wound-rotor Type								
5	220	14.3	72.5	80	82.5	78	79	79.5
10	336	26.6	69	79	83	83	84.5	85
25	480	32	76.5	84.3	87.5	87	88.7	88.9
50	850	121	78.8	86.5	89.7	90.9	90.3	89.9
100	2,618	233	88	90.5	89.5	86	88	88
200	3,900	473	89	91	92	87	89	90
3 Phase, 2,300 Volt, 60 Cycle, 1,750 Rpm, Squirrel-cage Type								
300	3,200	67	84.4	88.2	90.9	90.8	92.5	92.8
700	5,200	153	85.7	89.7	91.9	91.7	93.4	93.7
1,000	7,700	216	85.9	89.9	92.1	92.1	93.8	94.1
3 Phase, 2,300 Volt, 60 Cycle, 1,750 Rpm Wound-rotor Type								
300	3,900	68	84.4	86.2	89.9	90.8	92.5	92.8
700	5,750	154	82.7	87.7	90.9	91.7	93.4	93.7
1,000	8,450	218	82.9	87.9	91.1	92.1	93.8	94.1

Note. For approximate full-load currents, see also Table 22, p. 15–100.

The change of slip by introducing resistance into the rotor circuit has been discussed under the wound-rotor motor. It is possible to introduce **counter** emfs into the rotor circuit at slip frequency, by means of special commutator machines. The power, which in resistance control is dissipated as heat, is converted into mechanical power and a portion returned to the line. This method of control is only practicable in very large units and its applications are limited. In the **concatenation method** of speed control the rotors of two wound-rotor motors are mechanically coupled together. The stator of the second motor is supplied with power from the rotor slip rings of the first motor. If both motors have the same number of poles and equal number of turns in both stator and rotor, the set will operate efficiently at a little less than half synchronous speed. The slip of the first motor is therefore slightly greater than 50 percent, and accordingly the frequency of its rotor currents is about half the line frequency. This makes the synchronous speed of the second motor about half that of the first motor. Each motor can operate at rated flux and current so that each can develop rated torque. Because of its complications this method is little used in this country.

Induction Generator. If an induction motor, while connected to a source of power, is driven above synchronous speed, it becomes an **induction,** or **asynchronous, generator** and returns electrical energy to the line without any change in connections. When driven above synchronous speed, the rotor conductors cut the rotating field in a direction opposite to that when operating as a motor, and hence the mechanical power applied to the shaft is converted into electrical power. The load increases with the negative slip; this permits induction generators to be driven by prime movers without governor control. On short-circuit, the induction generator has the desirable characteristic that after the first few cycles it does not deliver any power. It must always be used in parallel with some synchronous apparatus. Since it must take lagging current from the line for its own excitation, and in addition cannot deliver any lagging current to the system, the induction generator is little used for power supply. Induction motors are frequently used in railway work, especially in mountain systems where it is advantageous on the downgrades to permit the motors to operate as induction generators, thus acting as brakes and in addition returning energy to the line (**regenerative braking**). (See also p. 11–30.)

Single-phase Induction Motor. If one phase of a three-phase motor is opened while the motor is running, it will continue to operate, but with a rating of only about 60 percent of its three-phase rating. Likewise, if one phase of a two-phase motor is similarly opened, the motor will continue to operate at one-half its two-phase rating. In both cases the motor continues to operate single phase. It will not, however, start single phase. The single-phase motor runs in the direction in which it is started. There are several methods of starting single-phase induction motors. Short-circuited turns, or "shading coils," may be placed around the pole tips which retard the time phase of the flux in the pole tip, and thus a weak torque in the direction of rotation is produced. A high-resistance starting winding, displaced 90 electrical deg from the main winding, produces poles between the main poles and so provides a rotating field which is weak but is sufficient to start the motor. This is called the "split-phase" method. In order to minimize overheating this winding is ordinarily cut out by a centrifugal device when the armature reaches speed. In the larger motors a repulsion-motor start is used. The rotor is wound like an ordinary d-c armature with a commutator, but with short-circuited brushes pressing on it axially rather than radially. The motor starts as a repulsion motor, developing high torque. When it nears its synchronous speed, a centrifugal device pushes the brushes away from the commutator, and at the same time causes the segments to be short-circuited, thus converting the motor into a single-phase induction motor.

Capacitor Motors. Instead of splitting the phase by means of a high-resistance winding, it has become almost universal practice to connect a capacitor in series with the auxiliary winding (which is displaced 90 electrical deg from the main winding). With capacitance, it is possible to make the flux produced by the auxiliary winding lead that produced by the main field winding by 90 deg so that a true two-phase rotating field results and good starting torque develops. However, the 90 deg phase relation between the two fields is obtainable at only one value of speed (as at starting), and the phase relation changes as the motor comes up to speed. Frequently the auxiliary winding is disconnected either by a centrifugal switch or a relay as the motor approaches full speed, in which case the motor is called a "capacitor-start" motor. With proper design the auxiliary winding may be left in circuit permanently (frequently with additional capacitance introduced). This improves both the power factor and torque characteristics. Such a motor is called "permanent-split capacitor motor."

Phase Converter. If a polyphase induction motor is operating single-phase, polyphase emfs are generated in its stator by the combination of stator and rotor fluxes. Such a machine can be utilized, therefore, for converting single-phase power into polyphase power and, when so used, is called a **phase converter.** Unless corrective means are utilized, the polyphase emfs at the machine terminals are somewhat unbalanced. The power input, being single-phase and at a power factor less than unity, not only fluctuates but is negative for two periods during each cycle. The power output being polyphase is steady, or nearly so. The cyclic differences between the power output and the power input are accounted for in the kinetic energy stored in the rotating mass of the armature. The armature accelerates and decelerates, but only slightly, in accordance with the difference between output and input. The phase converter is used principally on railway locomotives, since a single trolley wire can be used to deliver single-phase power to the locomotive, and the converter can deliver three-phase power to the three-phase wound-rotor driving motors.

Alternating-current Commutator Motors. Inherently simple a-c motors are not adapted to high starting torques and variable speed. There are a large number of types of commutating motor that have been developed to meet the requirement of high starting torque and adjustable speed, particularly with single phase. These usually have been accompanied by compensating windings, centrifugal switches, etc., in order to overcome low power factors and commutation difficulties. With proper compensation, commutator motors may be designed to operate at a power factor of nearly unity or even to take leading current.

One of the simplest of the **single-phase commutator motors** is the a-c series railway motor such as is used on the New York, New Haven, and Hartford Railroad. It is based on the principle that the torque of the d-c series motor is in the same direction irrespective of the polarity of its line terminals. This type of motor must be used on low frequency, not over 25 cps, and is much heavier and more costly than an equivalent d-c motor. The torque and speed curves are almost identical with those of the d-c series motor. Unlike most a-c apparatus the power factor is highest at light load and decreases with increasing load. Such motors operate with direct current even better than with alternating current. For example, the New Haven locomotives also operate from the 600 volt d-c third-rail system (two motors in series) from some distance outside New York City into Grand Central Station. (See also p. 11–24.)

On account of difficulties inherent in a-c operation such as commutation and high reactance drops in the windings, it is economical to construct and operate such motors only in sizes adaptable to locomotives, the ratings being of the order of 300 to 400 hp. **Universal motors** are small simple series motors, usually of fractional horsepower, and will operate on either direct or alternating current, even at 60 cycles. They are used for vacuum cleaners, electric drills, and small utility purposes.

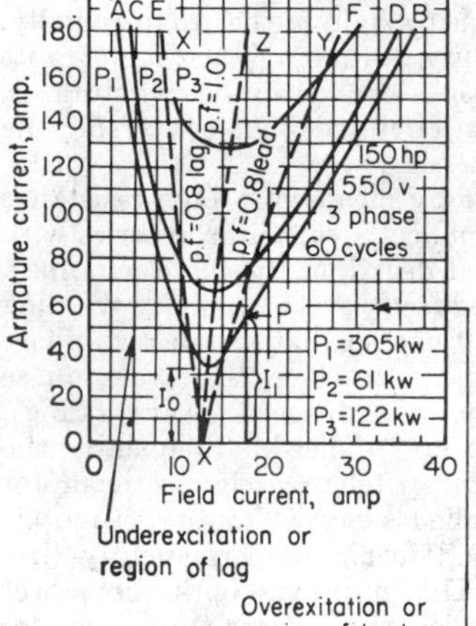

FIG. 73. V-curves of synchronous motor.

Synchronous Motor. Just as d-c shunt generators operate as motors, a synchronous generator, connected across a suitable a-c power supply, will operate as a motor and deliver mechanical power. Each conductor on the stator must be passed by a pole of alternate polarity every half cycle so that at constant frequency the rpm of the motor is constant and is equal to

$$N = 120f/P \qquad \text{rpm} \tag{121}$$

and the speed is independent of the load.

The synchronous motor has the desirable characteristic that its power factor can be varied over a wide range merely by changing the field excitation. With a weak field the motor takes a lagging current. If the load is kept constant and the excitation increased, the current decreases (Fig. 73) and the phase difference between voltage and current becomes less until the current is in phase with the voltage and the power factor is unity. The current is then at its minimum value such as I_0, and the corresponding field current is called the *normal excitation*. Further increase in field current causes the armature current to lead and the power factor to decrease. Thus *underexcitation* causes the current to *lag; overexcitation* causes the current to *lead.* The effect of varying the field current at constant values of load is shown by the V-curves (Fig. 73). Unity power factor occurs at the minimum value of armature current, corresponding to normal excitation. The power factor for any point such as P is I_0/I_1, leading current. Because of its adjustable power factor, the motor is frequently run light merely to improve power factor or to control the voltage at some part of a power system. When so used the motor is called a **synchronous condenser.** The motor may, however, deliver mechanical power and at the same time take either leading or lagging current. Its common applications are drives for motor-generator sets, ammonia compressors in refrigerating plants, rubber mills, and air compressors. The motor should not be used where fluctuations of torque are violent. As a rule, it should not be used in small sizes (under 50 hp) since it requires d-c excitation, is more difficult to start than induction motors, and falls out of step quite readily when system disturbances occur.

If situated near an inductive load the motor may be overexcited, and its leading current will neutralize entirely or in part the lagging quadrature current of the load. This reduces the I^2R loss in the transmission lines and also increases the kilowatt ratings of the system apparatus. The **synchronous condenser and motor** can also be **used to control voltage** and to stabilize power lines. If the condenser or motor is overexcited, its leading current flowing through the line reactance causes a rise in voltage at the motor; if it is underexcited, the lagging current flowing through the line reactance causes a drop in voltage at the motor. Thus within limits it becomes possible to control the voltage at the end of a transmission line by regulating the fields of synchronous condensers or motors. Long 220-kv lines and the 287-kv Hoover Dam–Los Angeles line require several thousand kva in synchronous condensers floating at their load ends merely for voltage control. If the load becomes small, the voltage would rise to very high values if the synchronous condensers were not underexcited, thus maintaining nearly constant voltage.

The synchronous motor is started as an induction motor through the action of a starting or damper winding similar to the squirrel-cage rotor winding of an induction motor. Copper or alloy bars are inserted in the faces of the salient d-c field poles, and their ends are brazed to copper segmental end-rings bolted together to form, usually, a continuous ring. The process of starting a synchronous motor is simply one of accelerating the motor to as high a speed as it will reach as an induction motor with its damper winding and then applying field excitation in order to pull the rotor into synchronism. Because of its salient poles, the synchronous motor usually pulls into synchronism without d-c field excitation.

As with the larger sizes of induction motors, synchronous motors are usually started at reduced voltage, a compensator [Fig. 71(*b*)] ordinarily being used. Sometimes the stator winding is connected in Y at starting and in Δ when running. In

Table 14. Performance Data for Coupled Synchronous Motors
(Westinghouse Electric Corp.)

Hp	Poles	Rpm	Amp	Kw-amp	Efficiencies, percent ½ load	¾ load	Full load	Weight, lb
UNITY POWER FACTOR, 3 PHASE, 60 CYCLE, 2,300 VOLTS								
50	4	1,800	10.3	0.8	86.5	89.6	91	1,200
100	8	900	20.4	1.5	88.5	91	92.1	2,400
250	12	600	50.2	2.5	90.7	92.5	93.4	4,600
500	18	400	99.3	5	92.9	93.9	94.3	7,150
1,000	24	300	197	8.4	93.7	94.6	95	15,650
4,000	48	150	781	25	94.9	95.6	95	54,000
80% POWER FACTOR, 3 PHASE, 60 CYCLE, 2,300 VOLTS								
50	4	1,800	13.2	1.1	84	87.8	88.8	2,100
100	8	900	25.8	2	87	89.5	90.6	3,000
250	12	600	63.6	2.8	89.5	91.2	92.1	6,100
500	18	400	125	7.2	92.4	93.4	93.6	9,500
1,000	24	300	248	11.6	93.3	94.2	94.4	17,500
4,000	48	150	982	40	94.6	95.3	95.5	115,000

order to minimize line disturbances, the field is ordinarily connected while reduced voltage is being applied to the stator, and the connection to the running position is made quickly so that the motor does not have opportunity to drop out of step. All starting functions may be automatically performed by the operation of relays.

It is possible to design synchronous motors for any required values of starting and pull-in torque and, by special methods, meet the low-starting inrush current limitations imposed by power companies.

For example, high-starting torque may be obtained by using high-resistance dampers, made of brass or some high-resistivity alloy. The fact that the slip may be too high for synchronizing is overcome by short-circuiting the field winding when the rotor is near synchronism. Synchronous motors may also be provided with phase-wound dampers which are connected to external resistors through slip rings. Just as with the wound-rotor induction motor, high resistance is introduced on starting, and this is cut out as the speed increases.

The **synchronous-induction motor** is fundamentally a wound-rotor slip-ring induction motor with an air gap greater than normal, and the rotor slots are larger and fewer. On starting, resistance is inserted in the rotor circuit to produce high torque, and this is cut out as the speed increases. As synchronism is approached, the rotor windings are connected to a d-c power source and the motor operates synchronously.

Timing or **clock motors** operate synchronously from a-c power systems. Figure 74(*a*) illustrates the Warren Telechron motor which operates on the hysteresis principle. The stator consists of a laminated element with an exciting coil, and each pole piece is divided, a short-circuited shading turn being placed on each of the half-poles so formed. The rotor consists of two or more hard-steel disks of the shape shown, mounted on a small shaft. The shaded poles produce a 3,600-rpm rotating magnetic field (at 60 cps), and because of hysteresis loss, the disk follows the field just as the rotor of an induction motor does. When the rotor approaches the synchronous speed of 3,600 rpm, the rotating magnetic field takes a path along the two rotor bars and locks the rotor in with it. The rotor and the necessary train of reducing gears rotate in oil sealed in a small metal can. Figure 74(*b*) shows a subsynchronous motor. Six squirrel-cage bars are inserted in six slots of a solid cylindrical iron rotor, and the spaces between the slots form six salient poles. The motor, because of the squirrel cage, starts as an induction motor, attempting to attain the speed of the rotating field, or 3,600 rpm (at 60 cps). However, when the rotor reaches 1,200 rpm, one-third synchronous speed, the salient poles of the rotor lock in with the poles of the stator and hold the rotor at 1,200 rpm.

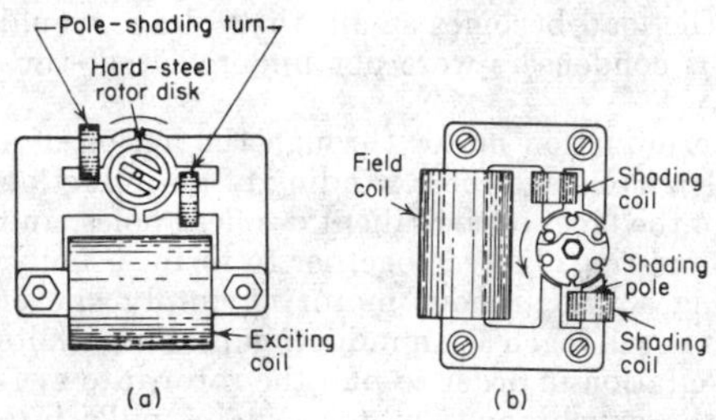

FIG. 74. Synchronous motors for timing; (*a*) Warren Telechron motor; (*b*) Holtz induction-reaction subsynchronous motor.

SYNCHRONOUS CONVERTERS

The synchronous converter is essentially a d-c generator with slip rings connected by taps to equidistant points in the armature winding. Alternating current may also be taken from and delivered to the armature. The machine may be single-phase, in which case there are two slip rings and two slip-ring taps per pair of poles; it may be three-phase, in which case there are three slip rings and three slip-ring taps per pair of poles, etc. Converters are usually used to convert alternating to direct current, in which case they are said to be operating **direct**; they may equally well convert direct to alternating current, in which case they are said to be operating **inverted.** A converter will operate satisfactorily as a d-c motor, a synchronous motor, a d-c generator, a synchronous generator, or it may deliver direct and alternating current simultaneously, when it is called a **double-current generator.**

The rating of a converter increases very rapidly with increase in the number of phases owing, in part, to better utilization of the armature copper and also because of more uniform distribution of armature heating.

Table 15. Relative Outputs of Converters

Power factor, percent	Continuous-current generator	Single-phase converter	Three-phase converter	Four-phase converter	Six-phase converter
100	100	85	132	161	194
95.5	100	78	120	145	170
90	100	74	109	128	145

Because of the materially increased rating, converters are nearly all operated six phase. The rating decreases rapidly with decrease in power factor, and hence the converter should operate near unity power factor (see Table 15). The diametrical a-c voltage is the a-c voltage between two slip-ring taps 180 electrical degrees apart. With a two-pole closed winding, *i.e.*, a winding that closes on itself when the winding is completed, the diametrical a-c voltage is the voltage between any two slip-ring taps diametrically opposite each other.

With a sine-voltage wave, the d-c voltage is the peak of the diametrical a-c voltage wave. The voltage relations for sine waves are as follows: d-c volts, 141; single phase, diametrical, 100; three phase, 87; four phase, diametrical, 100; four phase, adjacent taps, 71; six phase, diametrical, 100; six phase, adjacent taps, 50. These relations are obtained from the sides of polygons inscribed in a circle having a diameter of 100 volts, as shown in Fig. 75.

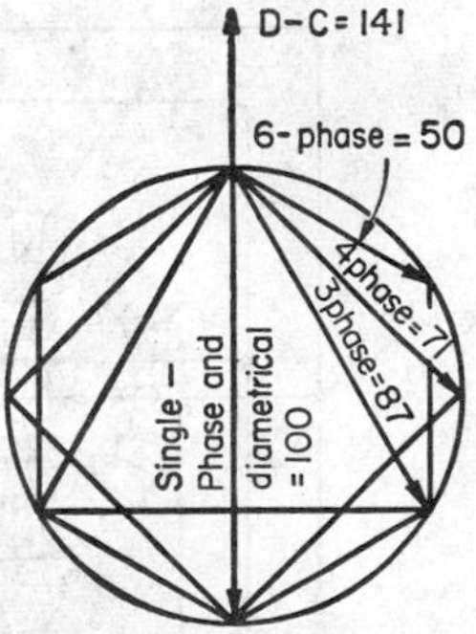

Fig. 75. Emf relations in converter.

At unity power factor and 100 percent efficiency, the ratio of alternating to direct current is as follows: two slip rings, 1.41; three slip rings, 0.94; four slip rings, 0.71; six slip rings, 0.47. At other efficiencies and power factors, divide the ratios as given by the product of the efficiency and power factor.

At unity power factor and 0.94 efficiency (a normal value) with three slip rings, the d-c and a-c currents are equal; with six slip rings the a-c current is one-half the d-c current. Twenty-five cycle converters are slightly more efficient than sixty-cycle converters.

The d-c voltage of converters may be controlled a limited amount by varying the field current. As with the synchronous motor, decreasing the field current from its normal value causes the armature current to increase and to lag (Fig. 73); increasing the field current from its normal value causes the armature current to increase and to lead. The lagging and leading currents flowing through the transformer, armature, and any other system reactance, lower and raise the voltage at the commutator. The range of d-c voltage change obtainable by this method is about 10 percent above and below normal and the power factor is changed simultaneously. The same effect may be obtained by compounding with d-c series turns.

With large units, the most satisfactory method of controlling the d-c voltage of converters is to use a synchronous generator of smaller rating and of the same number of poles mounted on the same shaft. This generator, called a **booster,** may boost or buck the converter voltage. Converters operate satisfactorily in parallel. When used to convert alternating to direct current, the machine must be in synchronism with the alternating supply. The converter may be started from the a-c end in much the same manner that synchronous motors are started. Occasionally the machine is brought to speed as a d-c motor and synchronized. When operated inverted (direct current to alternating current), some centrifugal or electrical device must be employed to prevent the converter from running away, since a highly inductive load weakens the field through armature reaction and causes the speed to increase.

Converters are cheaper, more efficient, and occupy less floor space than motor-generator sets. They are much less flexible in the matter of voltage and power-factor control. Where they cannot operate near unity power factor and where otherwise transformers are not necessary, their advantage over a motor-generator set diminishes.

Synchronous converters have efficiencies at one-half (full) load from 90 to 92.5 (92.4 to 94.3) percent, the larger sizes having the higher efficiencies. Synchronous booster efficiencies at one-half (full) load vary similarly from 91.3 to 93 (93.8 to 9.44) percent.

For the conversion of alternating to direct current at 600 volts (direct current) and higher, mercury-arc metal-tank rectifiers, particularly ignitrons, rather than motor-generator sets and synchronous converters, are in use. However, because of their small size and weight, low cost, and high efficiency, silicon rectifiers are being used almost exclusively in the newer installations (see also p. 15–117 et seq).

Selsyns. The word "selsyn" is an abbreviation of the word "self-synchronizing" and is applied to devices which are connected electrically, and in which an angular displacement of the rotating member of one device produces an equal angular displacement in the rotating member of the second device. There are several types of selsyns and they may be d-c or a-c, single-phase or polyphase. A simple and common type is shown in Fig. 76. The two stators S_1, S_2 are phase-wound stators, identical electrically with synchronous-generator or induction-motor stators. For simplicity gramme-ring windings are shown in Fig. 76. The two stators are connected three phase and

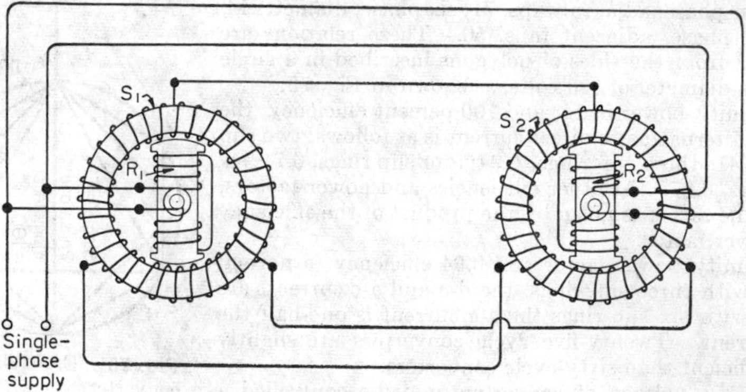

Fig. 76. Selsyn system.

are connected in parallel. There are also two bobbin-type rotors R_1, R_2, with single-phase windings, each connected to a single-phase supply such as 115 volts, 60 cycles. When R_1 and R_2 are in the same angular positions, the emfs induced in the two stators by the a-c flux of the rotors are equal and opposite, there are no interchange currents between stators, and the system is in equilibrium. However, if the angular displacement of R_1, for example, is changed, the phases of the emfs induced in the stator winding of S_1 are correspondingly changed. The emfs of the two stators then become unbalanced, currents flow from S_1 to S_2, producing torque on R_2. When R_2 attains the same angular position as R_1, the emfs in the two rotors again become equal and opposite, and the system is again in equilibrium.

If there is torque load on either rotor, a resultant current is necessary to sustain the torque, so that there must be an angular displacement between rotors. However, by the use of an auxiliary selsyn a current may be fed into the system which is proportional to the angular difference of the two rotors. This current will continue until the error is corrected. This is called *feedback*. There may be a master selsyn, controlling several secondary units.

Two similar wound-rotor induction motors with stators in parallel and rotors in parallel, with either system excited with single-phase or polyphase currents, will operate as a selsyn. Two similar wound-rotor induction motors in operation as motors will keep in exact synchronism if the stators are connected to the same supply and the rotors are connected in parallel. This system is used to maintain constant speed among different parts of a machine, which are driven by different motors.

Selsyns are used for position indicators, *e.g.*, in bridge-engine-room signal systems. They are also widely used for fire control so that from any desired position all the turrets and guns on battleships may be turned and elevated simultaneously through any desired angle with a high degree of accuracy. The selsyn itself rarely has sufficient power to perform these operations, but it actuates control through power multipliers such as amplidynes (p. 15–45).

Rating of Electrical Apparatus

The **rating** of electrical apparatus is almost always determined by the maximum temperature at which the materials in the machine, especially those employed for insulation, may be operated for long periods without deterioration. It is permissible, as far as temperature is concerned, to overload the apparatus so long as the safe temperature is not exceeded. The AIEE Standard, No. 1, Feb., 1954, classifies **insulating materials in** four general **classes**: Class O: cotton, silk, paper, and similar organic materials when neither impregnated nor immersed in a liquid dielectric. Class A: (1) cotton, silk, paper, and similar organic materials when either impregnated or immersed in a liquid dielectric; (2) molded and laminated materials with cellulose filler, phenolic resins, and other resins of similar properties; (3) films and sheets of cellulose acetate and other cellulose derivatives of similar properties; and (4) organic varnishes (enamel) as applied to conductors. Class B: mica, glass fiber, asbestos, etc., with suitable bonding substances. Other materials and combinations of materials, not necessarily inorganic, may be included in this class, if by accepted tests they can be shown to be capable of operation at Class B temperatures. Class H: materials or combinations of materials such as silicon elastomer, mica glass fiber, asbestos, etc., with suitable bonding substances such as appropriate silicone resins. Other materials or combinations of materials may be included in this class if, by experience or accepted tests, they can be shown to be capable of operation at Class H temperatures. Class C: entirely of mica, porcelain, glass, quartz and similar inorganic materials.

The values of "hottest-spot" temperatures for each class are as follows: Class O material, 90 C; Class A, 105 C; Class B, 130 C; Class H, 180 C; Class C, no limit selected.

The recommended methods of measurement are: (1) the thermometer method is preferred for uninsulated windings, exposed metal parts, gases and liquids, or surface methods generally; thermocouples are preferred for rapidly changing surface temperatures; (2) the applied-thermocouple method is suitable for making surface temperature measurements when it is desired to measure the temperature of surfaces that are accessible to thermocouples but not to liquid-in-glass thermometers; (3) the contact-thermocouple method is suitable for measuring temperatures of bare metal surfaces such as those of commutator bars and slip rings; (4) the resistance method is suitable for insulated windings, except for windings of such low resistance that measurements cannot be accurately made due to uncontrollable resistance in contacts or where it is impracticable to make connections to obtain measurements before an undesirable drop in temperature occurs; (5) the embedded-detector method is suitable for interior measurements at designated locations as specified in the standards for certain kinds of equipment, such as large rotating machines.

Efficiency of Electrical Apparatus

The losses in d-c machinery are classified as follows (American Standards for Rotating Electrical Machinery, Mar. 29, 1943): (1) shunt-field loss; (2) shunt-field-rheostat loss; (3) exciter losses; (4) friction and windage; (5) brush-friction loss; (6) ventilating loss; (7) core loss; (8) armature I^2R loss; (9) series-field loss; (10) brush contact loss; (11) stray-load losses. (1), (8), and (9) are determined by measuring the resistance of the windings and correcting to 75 C by formula $R = 309.5R_t/(234.5 + t)$, where R is resistance at 75 C and R_t is resistance at t C [see Eq. (**6**)]. (2), (3), and (6) are not chargeable to the machine but to the plant. (10) is calculated by assuming 1 volt drop for all brushes of each polarity at all loads with carbon and graphite brushes, shunts attached; 1½ volts, without shunts; ¼ volt, metal graphite brushes with shunts. (4), (5), and (7) combined ($= P_s$) may be determined by running the machine light as a motor at counter emf E and speed S corresponding to load condition. If V and I_a are the armature and terminal voltages, $P_s = VI_a - I_a^2R_a - (10)$. Also P_s may be determined by driving the machine mechanically, using a small motor, and computing its losses; (4), (5), and (7) may then be separated. (11) is taken as 1 percent of the output.

With a motor,

$$\text{Output} = \text{input} - \text{losses} = VI - [(1) + (8) + (9) + (10) + P_s + (11)] \quad \textbf{(122)}$$

With a generator,

$$\text{Input} = \text{output} + \text{losses} = VI + [(1) + (8) + (9) + (10) + P_s + (11)] \quad \textbf{(123)}$$

The motor efficiency,

$$\eta = (\text{input} - \text{losses})/\text{input} \quad \textbf{(124)}$$

The generator efficiency,

$$\eta = \text{output}/(\text{output} + \text{losses}) \quad \textbf{(125)}$$

Similar losses occur in synchronous machines.

Industrial Applications of Motors

Alternating or Direct Current. The induction motor, particularly the squirrel-cage type, is preferable to the d-c motor for constant-speed work, for the initial cost is less and the absence of a commutator reduces maintenance. Also there is less fire hazard in many industries, such as sawmills, flour mills, textile mills, and powder mills. The use of the induction motor in such places as cement mills is advantageous since with d-c motors the grit makes the maintenance of commutators difficult.

For variable-speed work like cranes, hoists, elevators, and for adjustable speeds, the d-c motor characteristics are superior to induction-motor characteristics. Even then, it may be desirable to use induction motors since their less desirable characteristics are more than balanced by their simplicity and the fact that a-c power is available, and to obtain d-c power conversion apparatus is usually necessary. Direct-current power is supplied at 115 and 230 volts, 230 volts being preferable because of the saving in copper. In certain railway shops where 550 volts is available, 550 volt motors may be used, but their use, particularly in small sizes, is undesirable because of commutator difficulties. Alternating current is almost always 60 cycles, three-phase, and 220, 440, and 550 volts are all used for smaller motors. For larger motors, 1,150, 2,300, and even 6,600 volts may be used. Where both lights and motors are to be supplied from the same a-c system, the 208–120 volt four-wire three-phase system is now in common use (see p. 15–89). This gives 208 volts three-phase for the motors, and 120 volts to neutral for the lights.

Electric Drives

Cranes and Hoists. The d-c series motor is best adapted to cranes and hoists. When the load is heavy the motor slows down automatically and develops increased torque thus reducing the peaks on the electrical system. With light loads, the speed increases rapidly, thus giving a lively crane. The series motor is also well adapted to moving the bridge itself and also the trolley along the bridge. Where alternating current only is available and it is not economical to convert it, the slip-ring type of induction motor, with external-resistance speed control, is the best type of a-c motor. Squirrel-cage motors with high resistance end rings to give high starting torque are used. (Class D motors, p. 15–73. Also see Ilgner system, p. 15–51.)

Woodworking Machinery. The log chain which hauls logs from a pond up the inclined slip to the log deck is usually driven by 25 to 75 hp wound-rotor induction motors, the rating depending on the height, the size of logs, and the speed. **Circular saws** are usually driven by a belted squirrel-cage induction motor running at 1,140 and 1,720 rpm, the speeds of the saws being much greater than those of the motors. Squirrel-cage motors operating at 3,600 rpm (synchronous speed) are designed for direct connection. The ratings for woodworking shops vary from 3 to 5 hp for cutoff, 7½ to 15 hp for rip, and about 25 hp for heavy duty. **Band saws** are the first saws to operate on the logs, the head saws having band wheels from 8 to 12 ft in diameter. Such wheels have high inertia and require motors with large starting torque to bring them up to speed rapidly. For this reason wound-rotor induction motors are frequently used. Another advantage is that their higher values of slip permit them to slow down under severe cutting conditions, thus causing the rotating system to give up some of its stored kinetic energy. Synchronous motors are now commonly used, their constant speed producing a straighter cut. Also, electrically, they improve the system power factor. However, they must be provided with damper windings designed to produce high starting torque, and at the same time provide high transient torque when severe cutting conditions are suddenly encountered. In woodworking shops where wheels from 20 to 42 in. are employed, squirrel-cage induction motors are used, the horsepowers varying from 1 to 7½ hp and the speeds from 900 to 660 rpm. **Planers** may be driven at high speed by belted squirrel-cage induction motors. In modern practice the motor is an integral part of the machine, using direct drive. Since speeds of 6,000 to 10,000 rpm are necessary and at 60 cycles the maximum speed obtainable is 3,600 rpm, the two-pole motors are supplied at higher frequencies from frequency changers. This is economical only with a number of planers. (See Sec. 13.)

Pumps. Single-acting **reciprocating pumps** should be driven with compound motors and duplex and triplex pumps with shunt motors, if direct current is used. Squirrel-cage and slip-ring motors are satisfactory with a-c supply. To reduce starting torque a by-pass in the pump is frequently opened until the motor comes up to speed. Constant head requires constant torque, and variable capacity under these conditions necessitates variable speed. For efficient operation, field control should be used with d-c motors and pole changing with induction motors. (See Sec. 14.)

Centrifugal pumps may be driven by shunt, compound, squirrel-cage, and slip-ring motors. Since such pumps require very small starting torque and operate at high speed, up to 3,600 rpm, both general-purpose squirrel-cage induction motors and synchronous motors make ideal drives. In the larger ratings the synchronous motor is favored because of its ability to improve power factor. (See Sec. 14.)

Compressors. Shunt motors ordinarily are used where d-c power is already available as in mines or with d-c electric railways. For light intermittent duty and heavy industrial medium duty and up to 30 hp, low-starting-current, normal-torque squirrel-cage induction motors (Class B, p. 15–64) with full voltage magnetic starters are used. Above 30 hp, the usual installation will be a normal-starting-current, normal-torque motor (Class A) with a reduced-voltage starter. Above 75 hp and for large heavy duty, the direct-connected synchronous motor is now almost universally used. It is not only efficient but operates to improve the system power factor. With many compressors, a large flywheel effect is desirable, to minimize the pulsations of torque which are reflected in the electric system. (See Sec. 14.)

SWITCHBOARDS

Switchboards may, in general, be divided into four classes: direct-control panel type; remote mechanical-control panel type; direct-control truck type; electrically operated. With **direct-control panel-type boards** the switches, rheostats, bus bars, meters, and other apparatus are mounted on or near the board and the switches and rheostats are operated directly, or by operating handles if they are mounted in back of the board. The voltages, for both direct current and alternating current, are usually limited to 600 volts and less but may operate up to 2,500 volts a-c if oil circuit breakers are used. Such panels are not recommended for capacities greater than 3,000 kva. **Remote mechanical-control panel-type boards** are a-c switchboards with the bus bars and connections removed from the panels and mounted separately away from the load. The oil circuit breakers are operated by levers and rods. This type of board is designed for heavier duty than the direct-control type and is used up to 25,000 kva. **Direct-control truck-type switchboards** for 15,000 volts or less consist of equipment enclosed in steel compartments completely assembled by the manufacturers. The high-voltage parts are enclosed, and the equipment is interlocked to prevent mistakes in operation. This equipment is designed for low- and medium-capacity plants and auxiliary power in large generating stations. **Electrically operated switchboards** employ solenoid or motor-operated circuit breakers, rheostats, etc., controlled by small switches mounted on the panels. This makes it possible to locate the high-voltage and other equipment independently of the location of the switchboard.

In all large stations the switching equipment and buses are always mounted entirely either in separate buildings or in outdoor enclosures. Such equipment is termed **bus structures** and is electrically operated from the main control board.

Marble has high dielectric qualities and was formerly used exclusively for the panels. It is now used occasionally where its appearance is desired for architectural

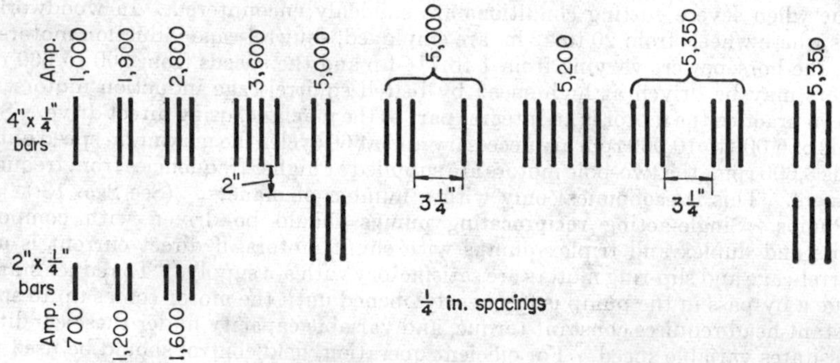

Fig. 77. Carrying capacity of bus bars.

purposes. Slate is used extensively and is finished in black enamel, marine, and natural black. Ebony asbestos is also used frequently, is lighter than marble or slate, has high dielectric strength and insulation resistivity, and can be readily cut, drilled, and machined. Steel panels, usually ⅛ in. thick, are light, economical in construction and erection, and at the present time are favored over other types.

Switchboards should be erected at least 3 or 4 ft from the wall. For panels supplying circuits of 750 volts or less the frames should be insulated from ground, and for higher voltages all frames should be grounded. For low-potential work, the conductors on the rear of the switchboard are usually made up of flat copper strip, known as **bus-bar** copper. The size required is based upon a current density of about 1,000 amp per sq in. Figure 77 gives the approximate continuous d-c carrying capacity of copper bus bars for different arrangements and spacings for 35 C temperature rise.

Switchboards must be individually adapted for each specific electrical system. Space permits the showing of the diagrams of only three boards each for a typical electrical system (Fig. 78).

Equipment of Standard Panels. Following are enumerated the various parts required in the equipment of standard panels for varying services:

Generator or Synchronous-converter Panel, Direct-current Two-wire System: 1 circuit breaker; 1 ammeter; 1 handwheel for rheostat; 1 voltmeter; 1 main switch (3-pole single throw or double throw) or 2 single-pole switches.

Generator or Synchronous-converter Panel, Direct-current Three-wire System: 2 circuit breakers; 2 ammeters; 2 handwheels for field rheostats; 2 field switches; 2 potential receptacles for use with voltmeter; 3 switches; 1 four-point starting switch.

Generator or Synchronous-motor Panel, Three-phase Three-wire System: 3 ammeters; 1 three-phase wattmeter; 1 voltmeter; 1 field ammeter; 1 double-pole field switch; 1 handwheel for field rheostats: 1 synchronizing receptacle (four-point); 1 potential receptacle (eight-point); 1 field rheostat; 1 triple-pole oil switch; 1 power-factor indicator; 1 synchronizer; 2 series transformers; 1 governor control switch.

Synchronous-converter Panel, Three-phase: 1 ammeter; 1 power-factor indicator; 1 synchronizing receptacle; 1 triple-pole oil circuit breaker; 2 current transformers; 1 potential transformer; 1 watthour meter (polyphase); 1 governor control switch.

Induction Motor Panel, Three-phase: 1 ammeter; series transformers; 1 oil switch.

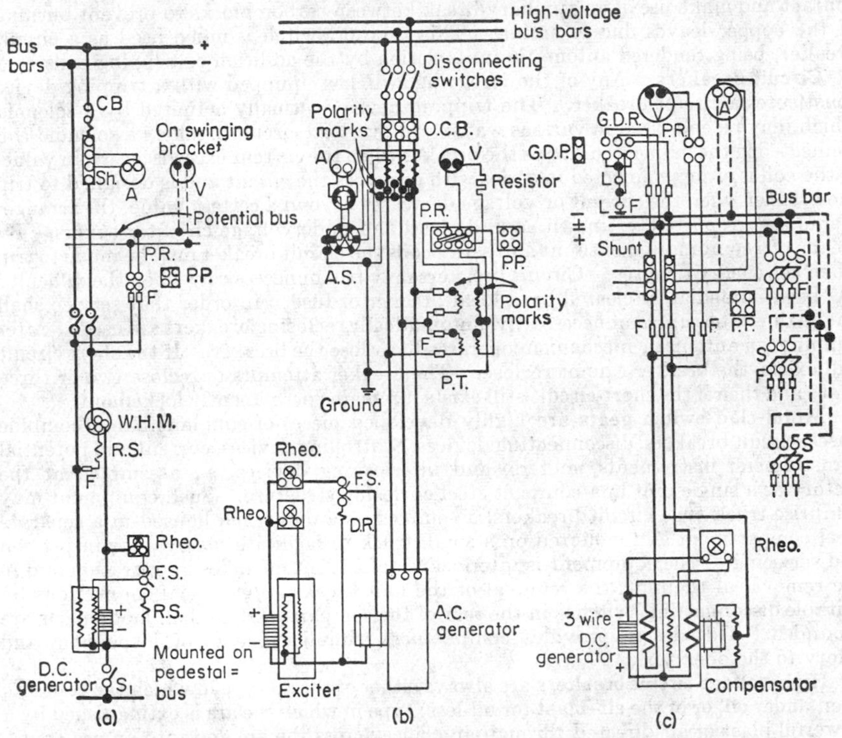

FIG. 78. Switchboard wiring diagrams for generators.

(*a*) Diagram for 125-volt or 250-volt d-c generator; (*b*) diagram for three-phase synchronous generator and exciter for small or isolated plant; (*c*) diagram for three-wire d-c generator for small or isolated plant.

SYMBOLS: *A*, ammeter; *A.S.*, three-way ammeter switch; *C.B.*, circuit breaker; *C.T.*, current transformer; *D.R.*, discharge resistor; *F.*, fuse; *F.S.*, field switch; *G.D.P.*, ground detector plug; *G.D.R.*, ground detector receptacle; *L.*, ground detector lamp; *O.C.*, overload coil; *O.C.B.*, oil circuit breaker; *P.P.*, potential ring; *P.R.*, potential receptacle; *P.T.*, potential transformer; *Rheo.*, rheostat; *R.S.*, resistor; *S*, switch; *Sh.*, shunt; *V.*, voltmeter; *W.H.M.*, watt-hour meter.

Feeder Panel, Direct-current, Two-wire and Three-wire: 1 single-pole circuit breaker; 1 ammeter; 2 single-pole main switches; potential receptacles (1 four-point for 2-wire panel; 1 four-point and 1 eight-point for 3-wire panel).

Feeder Panel, Three-wire, Three-phase and Single-phase: 3 ammeters; 1 automatic oil switch (3-pole for three-phase, 2-pole for single-phase); 2 series transformers; 1 shunt transformer; 1 wattmeter; 1 voltmeter; 1 watthour meter; 1 handwheel for control of potential regulator.

Exciter Panel (for 1 or 2 exciters): 1 ammeter (2 for 2 exciters); 1 field rheostat (2 for 2 exciters); 1 four-point receptacle (2 for 2 exciters); 1 equalizing rheostat for regulator.

Switches. The current-carrying parts of switches are usually designed for a current density of 1,000 amp per sq in. At contact surfaces, the current density should be kept down to about 50 amp per sq in. **Knife switches** are used on low-tension circuits and, in most cases, are mounted on the front of the board. They should be mounted to throw vertically, with the blade side of the switch dead or disconnected from the source of power when open, to lessen the danger of accidental contact. **Copper-brush switches** substitute a leaved copper brush with a wiping contact for the knife-blade contact and make use of an auxiliary break between carbon blocks to prevent burning of the copper leaves due to arcing. This type of switch is much used as a circuit breaker, being rendered automatic in its action by the addition of tripping coils.

Circuit Breakers. Any of the foregoing switches equipped with a tripping device constitutes a circuit breaker. The tripping device is usually actuated by a solenoid which may be energized in various ways. In overload circuit breakers a solenoid coil connected in the main circuit trips the breaker when the current exceeds a certain value. If the coil is either connected in series with or across the circuit and is designed to trip the breaker when the current or voltage decreases beyond a certain value, the arrangements are, respectively, known as underload and undervoltage circuit breakers. By means of a combination of shunt and series coils the circuit breaker may be made to trip when the energy reverses. Circuit breakers may trip unnecessarily when the difficulty has been immediately cleared by a local breaker or fuse. In order that service shall not be thus interrupted unnecessarily, **automatically reclosing breakers** are used. After tripping, an automatic mechanism operates to reclose the breaker. If the short circuit still exists, the breaker cannot reclose. The breaker attempts to reclose two or three times and then if the short-circuit still exists it remains permanently locked out.

Metal-clad switch gears are highly developed pieces of equipment that combine buses, circuit breakers, disconnecting devices, controlling devices, current and potential transformers, instruments, meters, and interlocking devices, all assembled at the factory as a single unit in a compact steel enclosing structure. Such equipment may comprise truck-type circuit breakers, assembled as a unit, each housed in a separate steel compartment and mounted on a small truck to facilitate removal for inspection and servicing. The equipment is interlocked to prevent mistakes in operation and in the removal of the unit; the removal of the unit breaks all electrical connections by suitable disconnecting switches in the rear of the compartment, and all metal parts are grounded. This design provides compactness, simplicity, ease of inspection, and safety to the operator.

High-voltage circuit breakers are always either of the oil type in which the contacts open under **oil,** or of the **air-blast** (or oil-less) type in which the arc is extinguished by a powerful blast of air directed through an orifice across the arc and into an arc chute. The tripping of high-voltage circuit breakers is initiated by an abnormal current acting through the secondary of a current transformer on an inverse-time relay in which the time of closing the relay contacts is an inverse-time function of the current; that is, the greater the current the shorter the time of closing. The breaker is tripped by a d-c tripping coil, the d-c circuit being closed by the relay contacts. Modern circuit breakers should open the circuit within six cycles from the time of the closing of the relay contacts.

Air-blast circuit breakers have received wide acceptance in all fields in recent years, both for indoor work and for outdoor applications. Indoor breakers are available up to 40 kv and interrupting capacities up to 2,500,000 kva. Outdoor breakers are available in ratings up to that of the new (1964) EHV (extra-high voltage) 500-kv 3-pole breaker made by Westinghouse, the first breaker capable of interrupting 35,000,000 kva and the first 500-kv breaker installed in the United States. Its operating rating is 3,000 amp, 500 kv, its height is 30 ft, and its weight is 40 tons. The arc-extinction medium is sulfur hexafluoride (SF_6), an inert non-toxic gas. There are two gas pressures: 45 psig for insulation and 220 psig for arc quenching.

POWER TRANSMISSION

Power for long-distance transmission is usually generated at 6,600, 13,200 and 18,000 volts and is stepped up to the transmission voltage by delta-Y-connected transformers. The transmission voltage is roughly 1,000 volts per mile. Preferred or standard transmission voltages are 22, 33, 44, 66, 110, 132, 154, 220, 287 and 330 kv. High-voltage lines across country are located on private rights of way. When they reach urban areas, the power must be carried underground to the substations which must be located near the load centers in the thickly settled districts. In many cases it is possible to go directly to underground cables since these are now practicable up to 132 kv between three-phase line conductors (76.2 kv to ground). High-voltage cables are expensive in both first cost and maintenance, and it may be more economical to step down the voltage before transmitting the power by underground cables. Within a city, alternating current may be distributed from a substation at 13,200, 6,600, or 2,300 volts, being stepped down to 550, 440, and 230 volts, three-phase for power and 230–115 volts single-phase three-wire for lights, by transformers at the consumers' premises. **Direct current** at 1,200 or 600 volts for railways, 230–115 volts for lighting and power, is supplied by motor-generator sets, synchronous converters, and rectifiers. **Constant current** for series street-lighting systems is obtained through constant-current transformers.

Transmission Systems

Power is almost always transmitted three-phase. The following fundamental relations apply to any transmission system. The weight of conductor required to transmit power by any given system with a given percentage power loss varies directly with the power, directly as the square of the distance, and inversely as the square of the voltage. The cross-sectional area of the conductors with a given percentage power loss varies directly with the power, directly with the distance, and inversely as the square of the voltage.

For two systems of the same length transmitting the same power at different voltages and with the same power loss for both systems, the cross-sectional area and weight of the conductors will vary inversely as the square of the voltages. The foregoing relations between the cross section or weight of the conductor and transmission distance and voltage hold for all systems, whether d-c, single-phase, three-phase, or four-phase. With the power, distance, and power loss fixed, all symmetrical systems having equal voltages to neutral require equal weights of conductor. Thus, the three symmetrical systems shown in Fig. 79 all deliver the same power, have the same power

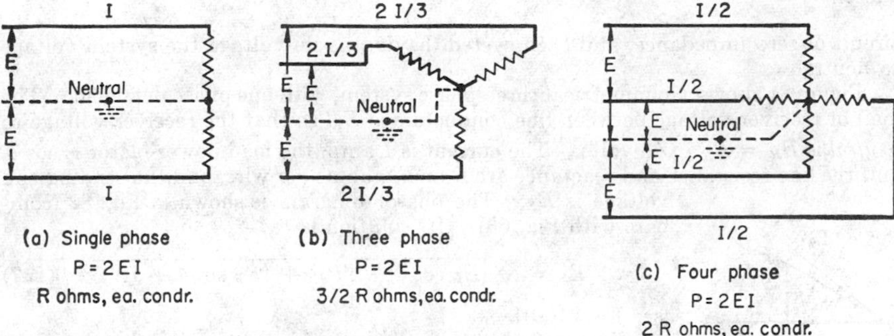

FIG. 79. Three equivalent symmetrical transmission, or distribution, systems.

loss and equal voltages to neutral, and the transmission distances are all assumed to be equal. They all require the same weight of conductor since the weights are inversely proportional to all resistances. (No actual neutral conductor is used.) The respective power losses are (1) $2I^2R$ watts; (2) $3(2I/3)^2(3R/2) = 2I^2R$ watts; (3) $4(I/2)^2(2R) = 2I^2R$ watts; which are all equal.

Size of Transmission Conductor. Kelvin's law states, "The most economical area of conductor is that for which the annual cost of energy wasted is equal to the interest on that portion of the capital outlay which can be considered proportional to the weight of copper used." In Fig. 80 are shown the annual interest cost, the annual cost of I^2R loss, and the total cost as functions of circular-mils cross section for both typical overhead conductors and three-conductor cables. Note that the total-cost curves have very flat minimums, and usually other factors such as the character of the load and the voltage regulation, are taken into consideration.

In addition to resistance, overhead power lines have inductive reactance to alternating currents. The inductive reactance

$$X = 2\pi f \left(80 + 741.1 \log \frac{D - r}{r} \right) 10^{-6} \quad \text{ohms per conductor mile} \qquad \textbf{(126)}$$

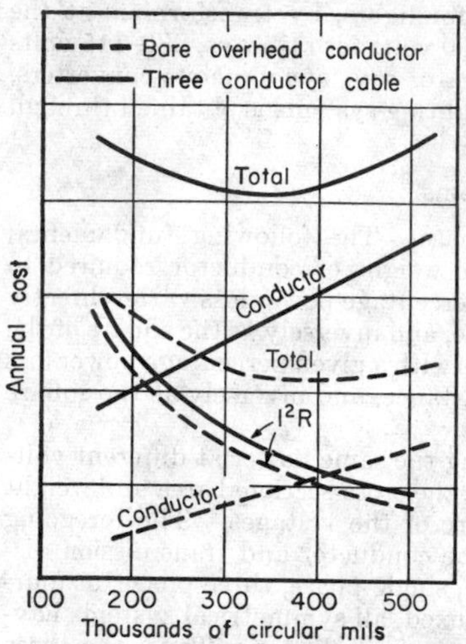

FIG. 80. Most economical sizes of overhead and underground conductors.

where f is the frequency, D the distance between the centers of conductors, and r their radius. Table 16 gives the inductive reactance per mile at 60 cycles and the resistance of stranded and solid copper conductor. (See Table 20, p. 15–95.)

Any **symmetrical system** having n conductors may be divided into n equal single-phase systems, each consisting of one wire and a return circuit of zero impedance, and each system having as its voltage the system voltage to neutral.

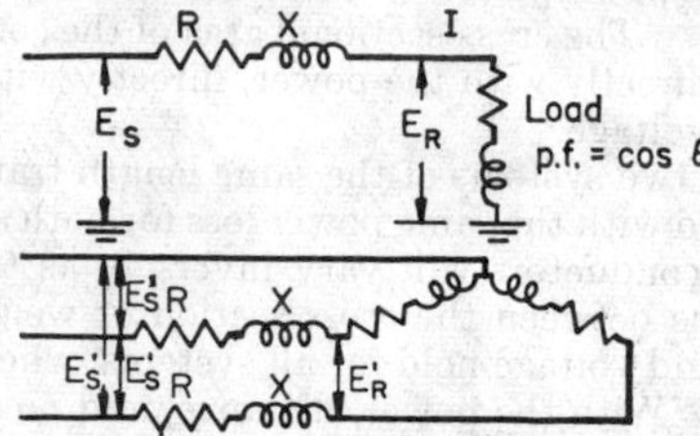

FIG. 81. Three-phase power system.

Figure 81 shows a symmetrical three-phase system, with one phase detached. The load or receiver voltage between line conductors is E_R' so that the receiver voltage to *neutral* is $E_R = E_R'/\sqrt{3}$ volts. The current is I amp, the load power factor is $\cos \theta$, and the line resistance and reactance are R and X ohms per wire, and the sending-end voltage is E_S. The phasor diagram is shown in Fig. 82 (compare with Fig. 63). Its solution is

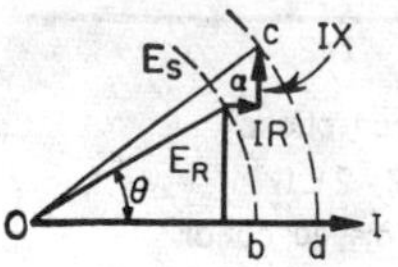

$$E_S = \sqrt{(E_R \cos \theta + IR)^2 + (E_R \sin \theta + IX)^2} \qquad \textbf{(127)}$$

[see Eq. (**100**)].

FIG. 82. Phasor diagram for power line.

Figure 83 (Mershon diagram) shows the right-hand portion of Fig. 82 plotted to large scale, the arc 00 corresponding to the arc ab (Fig. 82). The abscissa 0 (Fig. 83) corresponds to point b (Fig. 82) and is the load voltage E_R taken as 100 percent. The concentric circular arcs 0–40 are given in percentage of E_R. To find the sending-end voltage E_S for any power factor $\cos \theta$, compute first the resistance drop IR and the reactance drop IX in percentage of E_R. Then follow the ordinate corresponding to the load power factor to the inner arc 00 (a, Fig. 82). Lay off the percentage IR drop horizontally to the right, and the percentage IX drop vertically upwards. The arc at which the IX drop terminates (c, Fig. 82) when added to 100 percent gives the sending-end voltage E_S in percent of the load voltage E_R.

Table 16. Resistance and Inductive Reactance per Single Conductor

Size, cir mils or AWG	No. of strands	O.D., in.	Ohms per mile	60 cps, Spacing, ft: 1	2	3	4	5	6	7	8	10	12	15	20	30
Hard-drawn Copper, Stranded																
500,000	37	0.814	0.1130	0.443	0.527	0.576	0.611	0.638	0.660	0.679	0.695	0.722	0.745	0.772	0.807	0.856
400,000	19	0.725	0.1426	0.458	0.542	0.591	0.626	0.653	0.675	0.694	0.710	0.737	0.760	0.787	0.822	0.871
300,000	19	0.628	0.1900	0.476	0.560	0.609	0.644	0.671	0.693	0.712	0.728	0.755	0.778	0.805	0.840	0.889
250,000	19	0.574	0.2278	0.487	0.571	0.620	0.655	0.682	0.704	0.723	0.739	0.766	0.789	0.816	0.851	0.900
0000	19	0.528	0.2690	0.497	0.581	0.630	0.665	0.692	0.714	0.733	0.749	0.776	0.799	0.826	0.861	0.917
000	7	0.464	0.339	0.518	0.602	0.651	0.686	0.713	0.735	0.754	0.770	0.797	0.820	0.847	0.882	0.931
00	7	0.414	0.428	0.532	0.616	0.665	0.700	0.727	0.749	0.768	0.784	0.811	0.834	0.861	0.896	0.945
0	7	0.368	0.538	0.546	0.630	0.679	0.714	0.741	0.763	0.782	0.798	0.825	0.848	0.875	0.910	0.959
Hard-drawn Copper, Solid																
0000	..	0.4600	0.264	0.510	0.594	0.643	0.678	0.705	0.727	0.746	0.762	0.789	0.812	0.839	0.874	0.923
000	..	0.4096	0.333	0.524	0.608	0.657	0.692	0.719	0.741	0.760	0.776	0.803	0.826	0.853	0.888	0.937
00	..	0.3648	0.420	0.538	0.622	0.671	0.706	0.733	0.755	0.774	0.790	0.817	0.840	0.867	0.902	0.951
0	..	0.3249	0.528	0.552	0.636	0.685	0.720	0.747	0.769	0.788	0.804	0.831	0.854	0.881	0.916	0.965
1	..	0.2893	0.665	0.566	0.650	0.699	0.734	0.761	0.783	0.802	0.818	0.845	0.868	0.895	0.930	0.979

EXAMPLE. Let it be desired to transmit 20,000 kw, three-phase, 80 percent power factor, lagging current, a distance of 60 miles. The voltage at the receiving end is 66,000 volts, 60 cycles, and the line loss must not exceed 10 percent of the power delivered. The conductor spacing must be 7 ft (84 in.). Determine the sending-end voltage and the actual efficiency. $I = 20{,}000{,}000/(66{,}000 \times 0.80 \times \sqrt{3}) = 218.8$ amp. $3 \times 218.8^2 \times R' = 0.10 \times 20{,}000{,}000$. $R' = 13.9$ ohms $= 0.232$ ohm per mile. By referring to Table 16, 250,000 cir mils copper having a resistance of 0.2278 ohm per mile may be used. The total resistance $R = 60 \times 0.2278 = 13.67$ ohms. The reactance $X = 60 \times 0.723 = 43.38$ ohms. The volts to neutral at the load, $E_R = 66{,}000/\sqrt{3} = 38{,}100$ volts. $\cos\theta = 0.80$; $\sin\theta = 0.60$. Using Eq. (**127**), $E_S = \sqrt{[(38{,}100 \times 0.80) + (218.8 \times 13.67)]^2 + [(38{,}100 \times 0.60) + (218.8 \times 43.38)]^2} = 46{,}500$ volts to neutral or $\sqrt{3} \times 46{,}500 = 80{,}500$ between lines at the sending end. The line loss is $3(218.8)^2 \times 13.67 = 1963$ kw. The efficiency $\eta = 20{,}000/(20{,}000 + 1963) = 0.911$, or 91.1 percent. This same line is solved by means of the Mershon diagram as follows: Let $E_R = 38{,}100$ volts $= 100$ percent. $IR = 218.8 \times 13.67 = 2{,}991$ volts $= 7.85$ percent. $IX = 218.8 \times 43.38 = 9{,}490$ volts $= 24.9$ percent. Follow the 0.80 power-factor ordinate (Fig. 83) to its intersection with the arc 00; from this point go 7.85 percent horizontally to the right and then 24.9 percent vertically. (These percentages are measured on the horizontal scale.) This last distance terminates on the 22.5 percent arc. The sending-end voltage to neutral is then $1.225 \times 38{,}100 = 46{,}500$ volts, so that the sending-end voltage between line conductors is $E_S' = 46{,}500\sqrt{3} = 80{,}530$ volts.

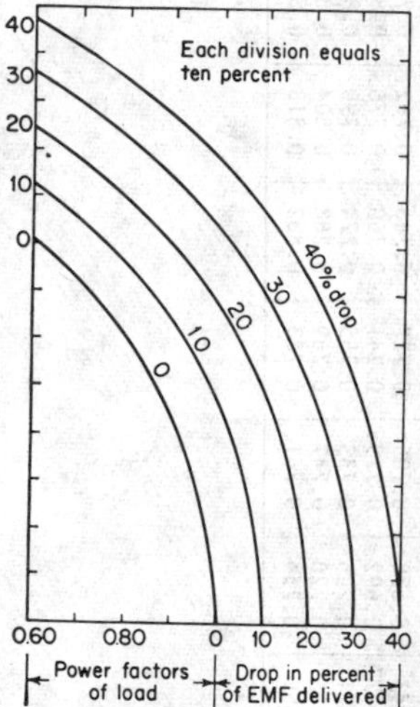

FIG. 83. Mershon diagram for determining voltage drop in a-c power lines.

In Table 16 the spacing is the distance between the centers of the two conductors of a single-phase system or the distance between the centers of each pair of conductors of a three-phase system if they are equally spaced. If they are not equally spaced, the geometric mean distance GMD is used, where $GMD = \sqrt[3]{D_1D_2D_3}$ [Fig. 84(*a*)]. With the flat horizontal spacing shown in Fig. 84(*b*), $GMD = \sqrt[3]{2D^3} = 1.26D$.

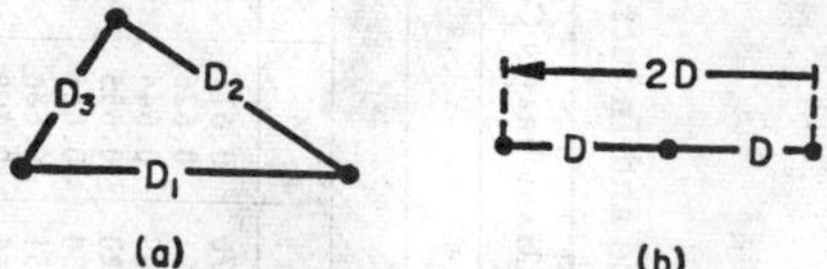

FIG. 84. Unequal spacing of three-phase conductors. (*a*) $GMD = \sqrt[3]{D_1D_2D_3}$; (*b*) flat horizontal spacing: $GMD = 1.26D$.

In addition to copper, aluminum cable steel-reinforced (ACSR), Table 17, is used for transmission conductor. For the same resistance it is lighter than copper, and with high voltages the larger diameter reduces corona loss.

Until 1966, 345 kv was the highest operating voltage in the United States. The first 500 kv system put into operation (1966) was a 350 mile transmission loop of the Virginia Electric and Power Company; the longest transmission distance was 170 miles. The towers, about 94 ft high, are of corrosion-resistant steel, and the conductors are 61-strand cables of aluminum alloy, rather than the usual aluminum cable with a steel core (ACSR). The conductor diameter is 1.65 in. with two "bundled" conductors per phase and 18 in. spacing. The standard span is 1,600 ft, the conductor spacing is flat with 30-ft spacing between phase-conductor centers, and the minimum clearance to ground is 34 to 39 ft. To maintain a minimum clearance of 11 ft to the towers and 30 ft spacing between phases, vee insulator strings, each consisting of twenty-four 10-in. disks, are used with each phase. The highest EHV system in North America is the 735 kv line of the Quebec Hydroelectric Power Commission (1966).

Table 17. Properties of Aluminum Cable Steel-reinforced (ACSR)
(Aluminum Co. of America)

Cir mils or AWG		No. of wires		O.D., in.	Cross section, sq in.		Total lb per mile	Ohms per mile of single conductor at 25 C				
									200 amp		600 amp	
Aluminum	Copper equivalent	Aluminum	Steel		Aluminum	Total		0 amp d-c	25 cycles	60 cycles	25 cycles	60 cycles
1,590,000	1,000,000	54	19	1.545	1.249	1.4071	10,777	0.0587	0.0589	0.0594	0.0592	0.0607
1,431,000	900,000	54	19	1.465	1.124	1.2664	9,699	0.0652	0.0654	0.0659	0.0657	0.0671
1,272,000	800,000	54	19	1.382	0.9990	1.1256	8,621	0.0734	0.0736	0.0742	0.0738	0.0752
1,192,500	750,000	54	19	1.338	0.9366	1.0553	8,082	0.0783	0.0785	0.0791	0.0787	0.0801
1,113,000	700,000	54	19	1.293	0.8741	0.9850	7,544	0.0839	0.0841	0.0848	0.0843	0.0857
1,033,500	650,000	54	7	1.246	0.8117	0.9170	7,019	0.0903	0.0906	0.0913	0.0908	0.0922
954,000	600,000	54	7	1.196	0.7493	0.8464	6,479	0.0979	0.0980	0.0985	0.0983	0.0997
874,500	550,000	54	7	1.146	0.6868	0.7759	5,940	0.107	0.107	0.108	0.107	0.109
795,000	500,000	26	7	1.108	0.6244	0.7261	5,770	0.117	0.117	0.117	0.117	0.117
715,500	450,000	54	7	1.036	0.5620	0.6348	4,859	0.131	0.131	0.133	0.131	0.133
636,000	400,000	54	7	0.977	0.4995	0.5642	4,319	0.147	0.147	0.149	0.147	0.149
556,500	350,000	26	7	0.927	0.4371	0.5083	4,039	0.168	0.168	0.168	0.168	0.168
477,000	300,000	26	7	0.858	0.3746	0.4357	3,462	0.196	0.196	0.196	0.196	0.196
397,500	250,000	26	7	0.783	0.3122	0.3630	2,885	0.235	0.235	0.235	0.235	0.235
336,400	0000	26	7	0.721	0.2642	0.3073	2,442	0.278	0.278	0.278	0.278	0.278
266,800	000	26	7	0.642	0.2095	0.2367	1,936	0.350	0.350	0.350	0.350	0.350
0000	00	6	1	0.563	0.1662	0.1939	1,542	0.441	0.443	0.446	0.447	0.464
000	0	6	1	0.502	0.1318	0.1537	1,223	0.556	0.557	0.561	0.562	0.579
00	1	6	1	0.447	0.1045	0.1219	970	0.702	0.703	0.707	0.706	0.718
0	2	6	1	0.398	0.0829	0.0967	769	0.885	0.885	0.889	0.887	0.893

High-voltage direct-current transmission has a greater potential for savings and at greater ability to transmit large blocks of power longer distances than has three-phase transmission. For the same crest voltage there is a saving of 50 percent in the weight of the conductor. Because of the power stability limit due to inductive and capacitive effects (inherent with a-c transmission), the ability to transmit large blocks of power long distances has not kept pace with power developments, even at the present highest a-c transmission voltage of 500 kv. With direct current there is no such power stability limit.

Where cables are necessary, as under water, the capacitive charging current may, with a-c, become so large that it absorbs a large proportion, if not all, of the cable-carrying capability. For example, at 132 kv, three-phase (76 kv to ground), with a 500 MCM cable, at 36 miles, the charging current at 60 cps is equal to the entire cable capability so that no capability remains for the load current. With direct current there is no charging current, only the negligible leakage current, and there are no a-c dielectric losses. Furthermore, the d-c voltage at which a given cable can operate is twice the a-c voltage.

The high d-c transmission voltage is obtained by converting the a-c power voltage to d-c by means of mercury-arc rectifiers; at the receiving end of the line the d-c voltage is inverted back to a power-frequency voltage by means of mercury-arc inverters.

In one system power is supplied to Gotland, an island 60 miles off the Swedish coast, at 100 kv d-c, 200 amp (20,000 kv), by a single-core submarine cable. Similarly, power is interchanged between France and Great Britain with two 31-mile single-core submarine cables across the English Channel. The voltage is 200 kv between cores, 100 kv to ground, and the maximum power is 160 megawatts. Similar d-c systems are in successful operation in the U.S.S.R. A high-voltage d-c line for transmitting large blocks of power from the Pacific Northwest to the Southwest is in the design stage.

Corona is a reddish-blue electrical discharge which occurs when the voltage-gradient in air exceeds 30 kv peak, 21.1 kv rms, at 76 cm pressure. This electrical discharge is caused by ionization of the air, and becomes more or less concentrated at irregularities on the conductor surface and on the outer strands of stranded conductors. Corona is accompanied by a hissing sound; it produces ozone and, in the presence of moisture, nitrous acid. On high-voltage lines corona produces a substantial power loss, corrosion of the conductors, and radio and television interference. The fair-weather loss increases as the square of the voltage above a critical value e_0 and is greatly increased by fog, smoke, rainstorms, sleet, and snow (see Fig. 85). To reduce corona, the diameter of high-voltage conductors is increased to values much greater than would be required for the necessary conductance cross section. This is accomplished by the use of hollow, segmented conductors and by the use of aluminum cable, steel-reinforced (ACSR), which often has inner layers of jute to increase the diameter. In extra-high-voltage lines (400 kv and greater), corona is reduced by the use of "bundled" conductors in which each phase consists of two or three conductors spaced about 16 in. from one another.

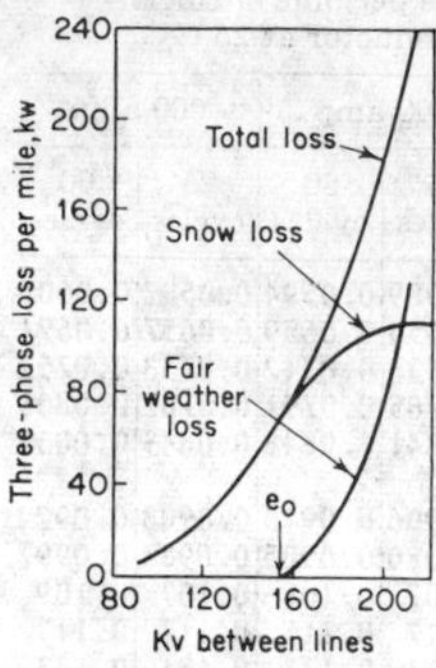

FIG. 85. Corona loss with snowstorm.

Underground Power Cables

Insulations for power cables include heat-resisting, low water-absorptive synthetic rubber compounds, varnished cloth, impregnated paper, cross-linked polyethylene thermosetting compounds, and thermoplastics such as polyvinyl chloride (PVC) and polyethylene (PE) compounds (see Sec. 6).

Properly chosen **rubber-insulated cables** may be used in wet locations with a nonmetallic jacket for protective covering instead of a metallic sheath. Commonly used jackets are flame-resisting, such as neoprene and PVC. Such cables are relatively light in weight, easy to train in ducts and manholes, and easily spliced. When distribution voltages exceed 2,000 volts phase-to-phase, an ozone-resisting type of compound is required. Such rubber insulation may be used in cables carrying up to 28,000 volts between lines in three-phase grounded systems. The insulation wall will be thicker than with varnished cloth, polyethylene, or paper.

Varnished-cloth cables are made by applying varnish-treated closely woven cloth in the form of tapes, helically, to the metallic conductor. Simultaneously a viscous compound is applied between layers which fills in any voids at laps in the taping and imparts flexibility when the cable is bent by permitting movement of one tape upon another. This type of insulation has higher dielectric loss than impregnated paper but is suitable for the transmission of power up to 28,000 volts between phases over short distances. Such insulated cables may be used in dry locations with flame-resisting fibrous braid, reinforced neoprene tape, or PVC jacket and are often further protected with an interlocked metallic tape armor; but in wet locations these cables should be protected by a continuous metallic sheath such as lead or aluminum. Since varnish-cloth-insulated cable has high ozone-resistance, heat-resistance, and impulse strength, it is well adapted for station or powerhouse wiring or for any service where the temperature is high or where there are sudden increases in voltage for short periods. Since the varnish is not affected by mineral oils, such cables make excellent leads for transformers and oil switches.

PVC is readily available in several fast, bright colors and is often chosen for color-coded multiconductor control cables. It has inherent flame and oil resistance, and as single conductor wire and cable with the proper wall thickness for a particular application, it usually does not need any outside protective covering. On account of its high dielectric constant and high power factor, its use is limited to low voltages, *i.e.*, under 1,000 volts, except for series-lighting circuits.

Polyethylene, because of its excellent electrical characteristics, first found use when it was adapted especially for high-frequency cables used in radio and radar circuits; for certain telephone, communication, and signal cables; and for submarine cables. Submarine telephone cables with built-in repeaters laid first in the Atlantic Ocean and then in the Pacific are insulated with polyethylene. Because of polyethylene's thermal characteristics, the standard maximum conductor operating temperature is

75 C. It is commonly used for power cables (including large usage for underground residential distribution), with transmissions up to 15,000 volts. Successful installations have been in service at 46 kv and some at 69 kv. The upper limit has not been reached, inasmuch as work is in progress on higher-voltage polyethylene power cables as a result of advancements in the art of compounding.

Cross-linked polyethylene is another insulation which is gaining in favor in the power field. For power cable insulations, the cross-linking process is most commonly obtained chemically. It converts polyethylene from a thermoplastic to a thermosetting material; the result is a compound with a unique combination of properties, including resistance to heat and oxidation, thus permitting an increase in maximum conductor operating temperature to 90 C. Since the service record with this compound has been good at voltages which have been gradually increased to 15 kv, it is expected that its voltage range also will be extended in the future.

Impregnated-paper insulation is used for very high-voltage cables whose range has been extended to 345 kv in recent years. To eliminate the detrimental effects of moisture and to maintain proper impregnation of the paper, such cables must have a continuous metallic sheath such as lead or aluminum or be enclosed within a steel pipe; the operation of the cable depends absolutely on the integrity of that enclosure. In three-conductor belted-type cables the individual insulated conductors are surrounded

Table 18. Carrying Capacity of Power Cables in Underground Ducts, Amp*
(5,000 volts, 75 percent load factor, 20 C ambient temp, three loaded ducts per bank)

Size, AWG or MCM	Rubber or PVC				Varnished cambric		Impregnated paper	
	60 C		75 C		85 C		85 C	
	Single conductor	Three conductors	Single conductor†	Three conductors	Single conductor†	Three conductors	Single conductor†	Three conductors
8	67	48	76	55	83	56	83	56
6	89	65	100	71	109	73	109	73
4	116	84	135	93	142	96	142	96
2	151	108	173	119	186	124	186	124
1	172	123	199	137	214	141	214	141
0	197	140	230	154	245	162	245	162
00	225	159	264	174	283	185	283	185
000	258	180	303	197	324	211	324	211
0,000	295	207	348	226	371	240	371	240
250	325	224	385	252	409	263	409	263
300	372	240	424	275	459	292	459	292
350	395	267	546	302	500	319	500	320
400	435	282	502	323	540	343	540	344
500	485	319	571	364	611	386	611	390
600	555	350	635	400	679	420	679	430
700	608	378	691	434	742	458	741	466
750	628	383	718	448	771	475	771	482
800	653	...	744	...	797	...	797	
1,000	709	425	840	...	898	...	898	
1,250	793	...	940	...	1,012	...	1,012	
1,500	865	...	1,032	...	1,110	...	1,110	
1,750	927	...	1,112	...	1,204	...	1,204	
2,000	978	...	1,187	...	1,290	...	1,300	

* Note: This is a general table. For complete and up-to-date ampacity (ampere-carrying capacity) values for various conductor temperatures and installation conditions, refer to IEEE Publication S-135, "AIEE-IPCEA Power Cable Ampacities," vols. I and II. Each volume contains 317 pages of ampacity tables and cable constants covering all conductor sizes, voltages, and operating temperatures with paper, rubber, thermoplastic, varnished-cloth, and asbestos insulations in ducts, directly buried conduits, ladders, raceways, trays, and in air.

† Sheaths assumed to be open-circuited. If sheaths are bonded together, the sheath currents will reduce the carrying capacity from 25 to 40 percent. The foregoing values are based on three loaded ducts. Values are reduced as number of loaded ducts increases.

by a belt or wall of impregnated paper over which the lead sheath is applied. When all three conductors are within one sheath, their inductive effects practically neutralize one another and eddy-current loss in the sheath is negligible. In the type-H cable, each of the individual conductors is surrounded with a perforated metallic covering, either aluminum foil backed with a paper tape or thin perforated metal tapes wound over the paper. All three conductors are then enclosed within the metal sheath. The metallic coverings being grounded electrically, each conductor acts as a single-conductor cable. This construction eliminates "tangential" stresses within the insulation and reduces pockets or voids. When paper tapes are wound on the conductor, impregnated with an oil or a petrolatum compound, and covered with a lead sheath, they are called **solid type.**

Three-conductor cables are now operating at 33,000 volts, and single-conductor cables at 66,000 volts between phases (38,000 volts to ground). In New York and Chicago, special hollow-conductor oil-filled single-conductor cables are operating successfully at 132,000 volts (76,000 volts to ground). In France, cables are operating at 345 kv between conductors.

Other methods of installing underground cables are to draw them into steel pipes, usually without the sheaths, and to fill the pipes with oil under pressure (**oilstatic**) or **nitrogen** under 200 lb pressure. The ordinary medium-high-voltage underground cables are usually drawn into duct lines. With a straight run and ample clearance the length of cable between manholes may reach 600 to 1,000 ft. Ordinarily, the distance is more nearly 400 to 500 ft. With bends of small radius the distance must be further reduced.

Cable ratings are based on the permissible operating temperatures of the insulation and environmental installation conditions.

POWER DISTRIBUTION

Distribution Systems. The choice of the system of power distribution is determined by the type of power that is available and by the nature of the load. To transmit a given power over a given distance with a given power loss (I^2R), the weight of conductor varies inversely as the square of the voltage. Incandescent lamps will not operate economically at voltages much higher than 120 volts; the most suitable voltages for d-c motors are 230 and 550 volts, although 550 volts is practically obsolete, except for railway motors; for a-c motors, standard voltages are 220, 440, and 550 volts, three-phase. When power for lighting is to be distributed in a district where the consumers are relatively far apart, alternating current is used, being distributed at high voltage (1,150, 2,300, 4,000, 6,900, and 13,800 volts) and transformed at the consumer's premises, or by transformers on poles or located in manholes or vaults under the street or sidewalks, to 230–115 volts three-wire for lighting and domestic customers, and to 230, 440, and 550 volts, three-phase, for power. In thickly settled city districts, where large cables are necessary, d-c distribution from substations is frequently used. Direct current is best suited for elevator and printing-press motors which constitute a considerable portion of the power load; alternating current produces considerable reactive voltage drop in the cables, which gives poorer voltage regulation. These d-c systems were installed early in the industry when a storage-battery reserve was considered necessary. With two or more sources of supply and with highly improved protection from short circuits by quick-acting relays, a-c systems have become highly reliable and, wherever economically feasible, are replacing d-c systems. (See Low-voltage A-C Network, p. 15–89.)

Series Circuits. Where the devices to be supplied with power are nearly of the same current rating, are located relatively far apart, and are ordinarily used simultaneously, it is often more economical to supply **power at constant current** than at constant potential. To operate at constant current, the power-consuming devices and the power source are all in series with the same current in all. In cutting any individual device out of service, an equivalent resistance must be inserted in its place to maintain the same current in the circuit, or else some means must be provided at the power source to adjust automatically the total voltage so as to maintain constant current. If, in a series circuit operating with direct current, the resistance of each of the power-consuming devices is R_d, the resistance of the line is R, the current is I, the generator voltage when all the devices are operating is E, and the number of the receiving devices is n, $E = nIR_d + IR$, where $IR = e$ is the resistance drop in the line. Now $e = \rho lI/A$, where ρ is the resistivity of the material in ohms per cir mil-foot, l the length of the conductor in feet, and A the sectional area of the conductor in cir mils. If the permissible voltage drop e has been decided upon, the proper cross section of conductor $A = \rho lI/e$. For mechanical reasons, conductors smaller than No. 6 AWG are not generally used. This method of distribution is used almost exclusively for **street-lighting systems** in which the lamps are located over considerable areas. The power is supplied by a constant-current transformer which maintains constant current irrespective of the number of lamps in the circuit. The necessarily high voltage is not objectionable, as circuits placed on poles or underground can be safely and satisfactorily operated at voltages of 1,100 to 3,000 volts per circuit. Standard currents are 4.4, 5.5, and 6.6 amp. In some systems it is more economical to supply street-lighting power from the low-voltage parallel system, time switches being used to connect and disconnect the lamps.

Parallel Circuits. **Power** is usually distributed **at constant potential,** and all the devices or receivers in the circuit are connected in parallel, giving a constant-potential system, Fig. 86(*a*). If conductors of constant cross section are used and all the loads, L_1, L_2, etc., are operating, there will be a greater voltage IR drop per unit length of wire in the portion of the circuit AB and CD than in the other portions; also the voltage will not be the same for the different lamps but will decrease along the mains with distance from the generating end.

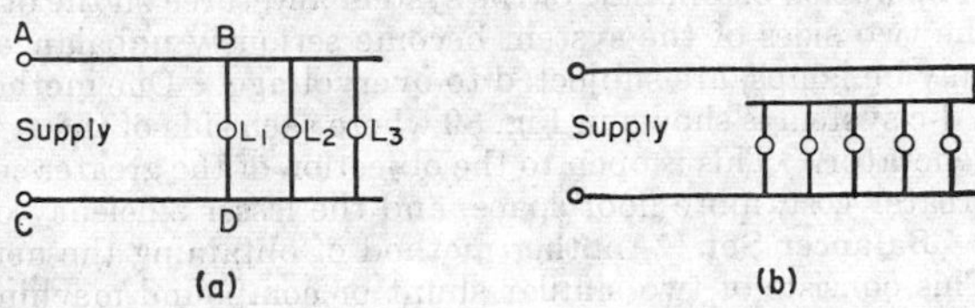

FIG. 86. (*a*) Parallel circuit. (*b*) Loop circuit.

Loop Circuits. A more nearly equal voltage for each load is obtained in the loop system, Fig. 86(*b*). The electrical distance from one generator terminal to the other through any receiver is the same as that through any other receiver, and the voltage at the receivers may be maintained more nearly equal, but at the expense of additional conductor material.

Series-parallel Circuit. For incandescent lamps the power must be at low voltage (115 volts) and the voltage variations must be small. If the transmission distance is considerable or the loads are large, a large or perhaps prohibitive investment in conductor material would be necessary. In some special cases, lamps may be operated in groups of two in series as shown in Fig. 87. The transmitting voltage is thus doubled,

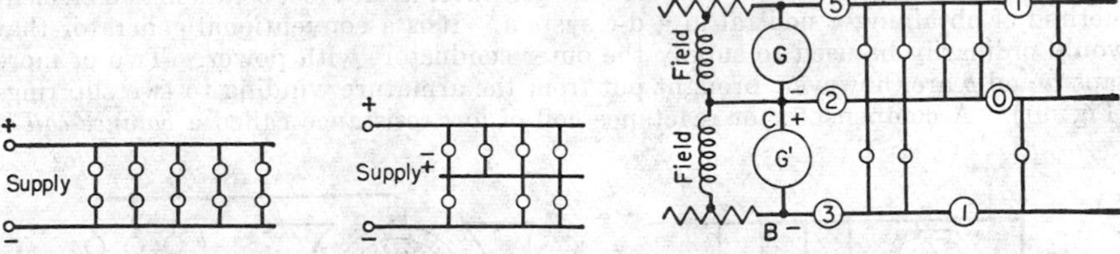

FIG. 87. Series-parallel system.

FIG. 88. Three-wire system.

FIG. 89. Three-wire system with two generators.

and, for a given number of lamps, the current is halved, the permissible voltage drop (IR) in conductors doubled, the conductor resistance quadrupled, the weight of conductor material thus being reduced to 25 percent of that necessary for simple parallel operation.

Three-wire System. In the series-parallel system the loads must be used in pairs and both units of the pair must have the same power rating. To overcome these objections and at the same time to obtain the economy in conductor material of operating at higher voltage, the three-wire system is used. It consists merely of adding a third wire or neutral to the system of Fig. 87 as shown in Fig. 88.

If the neutral wire is of the same cross section as the two outer wires, this system requires only 37.5 percent the copper required by an equivalent two-wire system. Since the neutral ordinarily carries less current than the outers, it is usually smaller and the ratio of copper to that of the two-wire system is even less than 37.5 percent (see Table 19, p. 15–93).

When the loads on each half of the system are equal, there will be no current in the middle or neutral wire, and the condition is the same as that shown in Fig. 87. When the loads on the two sides are unequal, there will be a current in the neutral wire equal to the difference of the currents in the outside wires. For example, if each of the loads in the system shown in Fig. 89 takes 1 amp, the current in each part of the system will be given by the numbers on the ammeters shown connected in the system.

The three-wire system shown in Fig. 88 is not practicable because no means are provided for holding the neutral at its correct potential. If, for example, four loads are in operation on one side of the system and three on the other, as shown, the voltages on the two sides of the system become seriously unbalanced and the three loads, which may be lamps, are subjected to overvoltage. One method of supplying the neutral in a d-c system is shown in Fig. 89 where each side of the system is supplied by a separate generator. This is open to the objection of the greater complications of two machines, greater cost, more floor space, and the lesser efficiency of two machines.

Balancer Set. Another method of obtaining the neutral is to use a balancer set. This consists of two similar shunt or compound machines coupled together with the armatures connected in series across the outer lines as shown in Fig. 90. When the loads are balanced, there is no neutral current and the two machines merely run idle as motors, being connected in series across the outer conductors. If the load on one side of the system becomes greater than that on the other side, the machine on the more heavily loaded side operates as a generator and pumps some of the neutral current to its side of the line. The remainder of the neutral current goes through the other machine supplying it with the power that enables it to operate as a motor and drive the generator. For example, in Fig. 90, the load on the positive side of the system is greater than that on the negative side. Hence, the machine G on the positive side is operating as a generator and the machine M is operating as a motor. If the machines are compounded so that when operating as a generator the winding is cumulative and hence is differential when a motor, the voltage unbalance with change in load can be made practically zero.

Since balancer sets take power continuously, they are used for the most part on large systems of high diversity where the percentage unbalance is small, so that the power rating of the set is but a small percentage of the power of the system.

Three-wire Generator. The three-wire generator is the most common and efficient method of obtaining a neutral in a d-c system. It is a conventional generator that would ordinarily be used to supply the outer conductors with power. Two or more taps a and b are, however, brought out from the armature winding to two slip rings (Fig. 91). A compensator or reactance coil of low resistance called a *balance coil* is

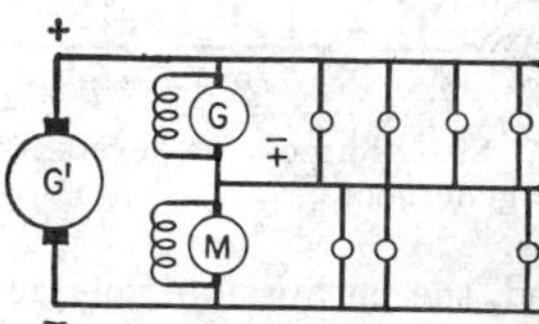

Fig. 90. Motor-generator balancer.

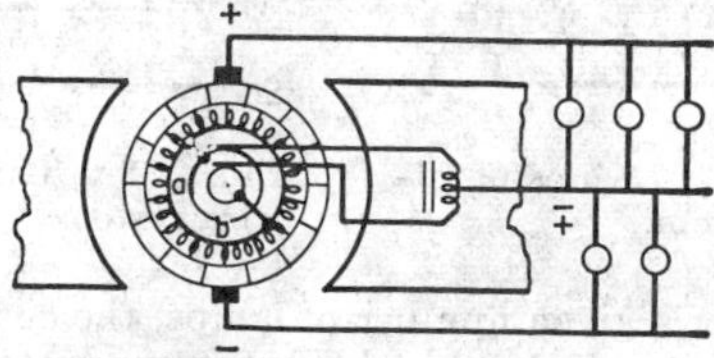

Fig. 91. Three-wire generator.

connected across the slip rings. The neutral of the three-wire system is connected to its center point. The voltage across the slip rings is alternating. Because of its choking action, but little alternating current flows in the balance coil. The unbalanced direct current in the neutral flows back through the balance coil to the armature. The inductance of the balance coil has no effect on the steady direct current, and the resistance of the balance coil is low so that there is little voltage drop due to the direct current. Two or more balance coils with their neutrals connected may be used. With two such balance coils, the second balance coil is connected to slip rings that are tapped to the armature winding at points 90 electrical degrees from the first.

Feeders and Mains. Where d-c power is supplied to a large district, improved voltage regulation is obtained by having centers of distribution. Power is supplied from the station bus bars directly to the **centers of distribution** by large cables known as **feeders.** Power is distributed from the distribution centers to the consumers through the **mains.** As there are no loads connected to the feeders between the generating station and the centers of distribution, the voltage at the latter points may be maintained constant. Pilot wires from the centers of distribution often run back to the station voltmeter, assisting the operator in maintaining the potential constant at the centers. This system provides a means of maintaining very close voltage regulation at the consumer's premises.

Alternating-current Three-wire Distribution. With the exception of the thickly settled districts of a few of the large cities, where power is still distributed as direct current, practically all energy for lighting and small motor work is transmitted at 1,150, 2,300, or 4,000 volts a-c to transformers which step down the voltage to 230 and 115 volts for three-wire domestic and lighting systems as well as 230, 440, and 550 volts, three-phase, for power. For the three-wire systems the transformers are so designed that the secondary or low-voltage winding will deliver power at 230 volts, and the middle or neutral wire is obtained by connecting to the center or mid-point of this winding (see Fig. 92).

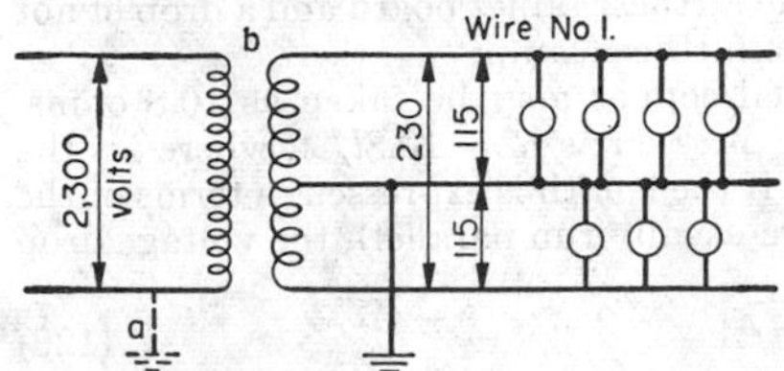

FIG. 92. Three-wire 230–115 volt a-c system.

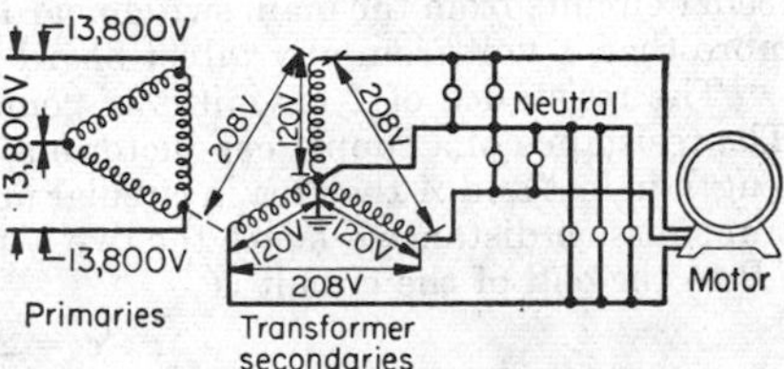

FIG. 93. 208–120 volt secondary network (single unit).

Grounding. The neutral wire of the secondary circuit of the transformer should be grounded on the pole (or in the manhole) and at the service switch in the building supplied. If, as a result of a lightning stroke or a fault in the transformer insulation, the transformer primary circuit becomes grounded at *a* (Fig. 92) and the transformer insulation between primary and secondary windings is broken down at *b* and if there were no permanent ground connection in the secondary neutral wire, the potential of wire No. 1 would be raised 2,300 volts above ground potential. This constitutes a very serious hazard to life for persons coming in contact with the 115 volt system. The National Electrical Code requires the use of a ground wire not smaller than No. 6 AWG copper; on secondary circuits, grounds should be provided at least every 500 ft. With the neutral grounded (Fig. 92), voltages to ground on the secondary system cannot exceed 115 volts.

A common and economical method of supplying business and thickly settled districts with high load densities is to employ a 208–120-volt, three-phase, four-wire **low-voltage a-c network.** The network operates with 208 volts between outer wires giving 120 volts to neutral (Fig. 93). Motors are connected across the three outer wires operating 208 volts, three-phase. Lamp loads are connected between outer wires and the grounded neutral. The network is supplied directly from 13,800 volt feeders by 13,800–208-volt three-phase transformer units, usually located in manholes, vaults, or outdoor enclosures. This system thus eliminates the necessity for transformation in the substation. A large number of such units feed the network, so that the secondaries are all in parallel. Each transformer is provided with an overload reverse-energy circuit breaker (network protector), so that a feeder and its transformer are isolated if trouble develops in either. This system is flexible since units can be easily added or removed in accordance with the rapid changes in local loads that occur particularly in downtown business districts.

Voltage Drops. In a-c distribution systems the voltage drop from transformer to consumer in lighting mains should not exceed 2 percent in first-class systems, in order that the lamps along the mains may all operate at nearly the same voltage and the annoying flicker of lamps may not occur with the switching of appliances. This may require a much larger conductor than the most economical size. In transmission lines and in feeders where there are no intermediate loads and where means of regulating the voltage are provided, the drop is not limited to the low values that are necessary with mains and the matter of economy may be given consideration.

WIRING CALCULATIONS

Wiring Calculations for Direct-current Circuits. (These same calculations can be used for a-c if the reactance can be neglected, per p. 15–31.) The determination of the proper size of conductor is influenced by a number of factors. Except for short distances, the minimum size of conductor recommended by the National Board of Fire Underwriters in Table 20, which is based on the maximum permissible current for each type of insulation, cannot be used; the size of conductor must be larger in order that the voltage drop (IR) shall not be too great. With branch circuits supplying an incandescent-lamp load, this drop should not be more than a small percentage of the voltage between wires. Good practice in interior wiring allows a drop of not more than 3 volts in feeder circuits from the main switchboard to the farthest tablet board and a drop of not more than 1 volt from any tablet board to the farthest lamp.

The resistance of 1 cir mil-ft of commercial copper may be taken as 10.8 ohms. The resistance of a copper conductor may be expressed as $R = 10.8l/A$, where l is the length in feet and A the area in circular mils. If the length is expressed in terms of the transmission distance d (since the two wires are usually run parallel), the voltage drop IR to the end of the circuit is

$$e = 21.6Id/A \tag{128}$$

and the size of conductor in circular mils necessary to give the permissible voltage drop e is

$$A = 21.6Id/e \tag{129}$$

If e is expressed as a percentage x of the voltage E between conductors, then

$$A = 2{,}160Id/xE \tag{130}$$

Example. Determine the size of conductor to supply power to a 10 hp, 220 volt d-c motor 500 ft from the switchboard with 5 volts drop. Assume a motor efficiency of 86 percent. The motor will then require a current of $(10 \times 746)/(0.86 \times 220) = 39.4$ amp. From Eq. (**129**), $A = 21.6 \times 39.4 \times 500/5 = 85{,}100$ cir mils. The next largest wire is No. 0 AWG.

The calculation of the size conductor for d-c three-wire circuits is made in practically the same manner. With a balanced circuit there is no current in the neutral wire, and the current in each outside wire will be equal to one-half the sum of the currents taken by all the receiving devices connected between neutral and outside wires plus the sum of the currents taken by the receivers connected between the outside wires. Using this total current and neglecting the neutral wire, make calculations for the size of the outside wires by means of Eq. (**129**). The neutral wire should have the same cross section as the outside wires in interior wiring.

EXAMPLE. Determine the size wire which should be used for the three-wire main of Fig. 94. Allowable drop is 3 volts and the distance to the load center 40 ft; circuit loaded with two groups of receivers each taking 60 amp connected between the neutral and the outside wires, and one group of receivers taking 20 amp connected across the outside wires. *Solution:* load = $(60 + 60)/2 + 20 = 80$ amp. Substituting in Eq. (**129**), cir mils = $21.6Id/e = 21.6 \times 80 \times 40/3 = 23{,}030$ cir mils.

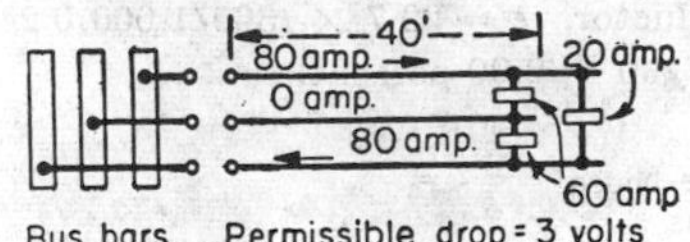

FIG. 94. Three-wire 230–115 volt main.

Referring to Tables 19 and 20, No. 6 wire, which has a cross section of 26,250 cir mils, is the next size larger. This size of wire would satisfy the voltage-drop requirements, but rubber-insulated No. 6 has a safe carrying capacity of but 55 amp. The current in the circuit is 80 amp. Therefore, rubber-insulated wire, No. 3, which has a carrying capacity of 80 amp, should be used. The neutral wire should be the same size as the outside wires.

Wiring calculations for a-c circuits are essentially the same as for d-c circuits, but other factors such as power factor, reactance, and skin effect may require consideration. Skin effect becomes pronounced only when very large conductors are used for alternating current. For interior wiring, conductors larger than 700,000 cir mils should not be used, and many prefer not to use conductors larger than 300,000 cir mils. Should the required copper cross section exceed these values, a number of conductors may be operated in parallel.

For voltages under 5,000 the effect of line capacitance may be neglected. With ordinary single-phase interior wiring, where the effect of line reactance may be neglected and where the power factor of the load (incandescent lamps) is nearly 100 percent, the calculations are made the same as for d-c circuits. Three-wire a-c circuits of ordinary length with incandescent lamp loads are also determined in the same manner. When the load is other than incandescent lamps, it is necessary to know the power factor of the load in order to make calculations. When the exact power factor cannot be accurately determined, the following approximate values may be used: incandescent lamps, 0.95 to 1.00; lamps and motors, 0.75 to 0.85; motors, 0.5 to 0.80. Equation (**131**) gives the value of current in a single-phase circuit.

$$I = \frac{P \times 1{,}000}{E \times pf} \qquad \textbf{(131)}$$

where I is the current, amp; P the kilowatts; E the load voltage; and pf the power factor of the load. The size of conductor is then determined by substituting this value of I in Eq. (**129**) or (**130**).

For three-phase three-wire a-c circuits the current per wire

$$I = 1{,}000P/\sqrt{3}\,Epf = 580P/Epf \qquad \textbf{(132)}$$

Computations are usually made of voltage drop *per wire* (see Fig. 95). Hence, if reactance can be neglected, the conductor cross section in cir mils is one-half that given by Eq. (**129**). That is,

$$A = 10.8Id/e \quad \text{cir mils} \qquad \textbf{(133)}$$

where e in Eq. (**133**) is the voltage drop per wire. The voltage drop between any two wires is $\sqrt{3}\,e$. The percent voltage drop should be in terms of the voltage to *neutral*. That is, percent drop $= [e/(E/\sqrt{3})]100 = [\sqrt{3}\,e/E]100$ (see p. 15–80, and Fig. 81).

EXAMPLE. In Fig. 95, load 10 kw; voltage of circuit 230; power factor 0.85; distance 360 ft; allowable drop per wire 4 volts. Substituting in Eq. (**132**), $I = (580 \times 10)/(230 \times$

0.85) = 29.7 amp. Substituting in Eq. (**133**), $A = 10.8 \times 29.7 \times 360/4 = 28{,}900$ cir mils.

The next larger commercially available standard-size wire (see Table 19) is 41,700 cir mils corresponding to AWG No. 4. From Table 20 this will carry 70 amp with rubber insulation, and is therefore ample in section for 29.7 amp. Three No. 4 wires would be used for this circuit.

From Table 19 the resistance of 1,000 feet of No. 4 copper wire is 0.249 ohm. Hence, the voltage drop per conductor, $e = 29.7 \times (360/1{,}000)0.249 = 2.66$ volts. Percent voltage drop $= \sqrt{3} \times 2.66/230 = 2.00$ percent.

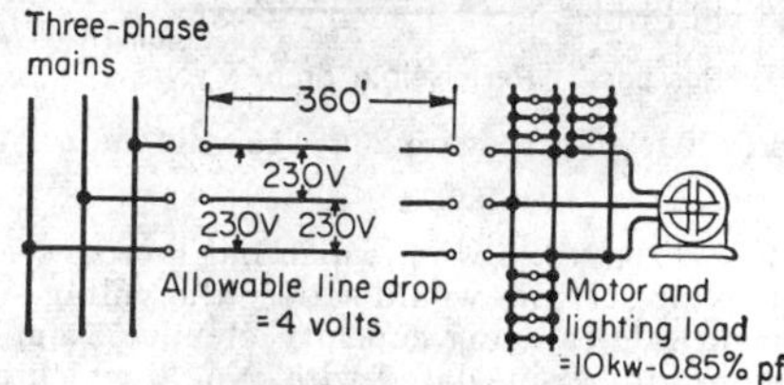

FIG. 95. Three-phase lamp and induction-motor load.

Where all the wires of a circuit, two wires for a single-phase, four wires for a four-phase (see Fig. 32, p. 15–34, and Fig. 79(*c*), p. 15–79), and three wires for a three-phase circuit, are carried in the same conduit or where the wires are separated less than 1 in. between centers, the effect of line (inductive) reactance may ordinarily be neglected. Where circuit conductors are large and widely separated from one another and the circuits are long, the inductive reactance may increase the voltage drop by a considerable amount over that due to resistance alone. Such problems are treated the same as high-voltage problems (p. 15–80). Line reactance decreases somewhat as the size of wire increases and decreases as the distance between wires decreases.

EXAMPLE. Determine the size of wire necessary for the branch to the 50 hp, 60-cycle, 250-volt, single-phase induction motor of Fig. 96. The name-plate rating of the motor

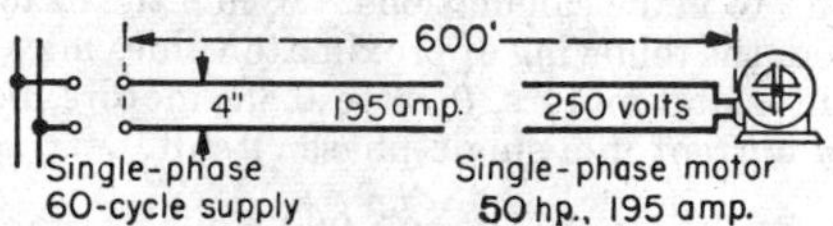

FIG. 96. Single-phase induction-motor or branch circuit.

is 195 amp, and its full-load power factor is 0.85. The wires are run open and separated 4 in.; length of circuit, 600 ft. The line drop must not exceed 7 percent, or $0.07 \times 250 = 17.5$ volts.

Solution. To ascertain approximately the size of conductor, substitute in Eq. (**129**) giving cir mils $= 21.6 \times 195 \times 600/17.5 = 144{,}400$. Referring to Table 19, the next larger size wire is No. 000 or 167,800 cir mils. This size would be ample if there were no line reactance. In order to allow for reactance drop, a larger conductor is selected and the corresponding voltage drop determined. Inasmuch as this is a motor branch, the code rules require that the carrying capacity be sufficient for a 25 percent overload. Therefore the conductor should be capable of carrying $195 \times 1.25 = 244$ amp. From Table 20, a 350,000 cir-mil conductor rubber-insulated cable would be required to carry 244 amp. Resistance drop (see Table 19), $IR = 195 \times 0.061 \times 0.6 = 7.14$ volts. $7.14/250 = 2.86$ percent. From Table 19, $X = 0.128 \times 0.6 = 0.0768$ ohm. $IX = 195 \times 0.768 = 14.98$ volts. $14.98/250 = 5.99$ percent. Using the Mershon diagram (Fig. 83), follow the ordinate corresponding to power factor, 0.85, until it intersects the smallest circle. From this point, lay off horizontally the percentage resistance drop, 2.86. From this last point, lay off vertically the percentage reactance drop 5.99. This last point lies about on the 6.0 percent circle, showing that with 195 amp the difference between the sending-end and receiving-end voltages is $0.06 \times 250 = 15.0$ volts which is within the specified limits.

Table 19. Resistance and 60-cycle Reactance for Wires with Small Spacings, Ohms

(See also Table 16, p. 15–81)

AWG and size of wire, cir mils	Resistance in 1,000 ft of line (2,000 ft of wire), copper	Reactance in 1,000 ft of line (2,000 ft of wire) at 60 cps for the distance given in inches between centers of conductors										
		½	1	2	3	4	5	6	9	12	18	24
14– 4,107	5.06	0.138	0.178	0.218	0.220	0.233	0.244	0.252	0.271	0.284	0.302	
12– 6,530	3.18	0.127	0.159	0.190	0.210	0.223	0.233	0.241	0.260	0.273	0.292	
10– 10,380	2.00	0.116	0.148	0.180	0.199	0.212	0.223	0.231	0.249	0.262	0.281	
8– 16,510	1.26	0.106	0.138	0.169	0.188	0.201	0.212	0.220	0.238	0.252	0.270	0.284
6– 26,250	0.790	0.095	0.127	0.158	0.178	0.190	0.201	0.209	0.228	0.241	0.260	0.272
4– 41,740	0.498	0.085	0.117	0.149	0.167	0.180	0.190	0.199	0.217	0.230	0.249	0.262
2– 66,370	0.312	0.074	0.106	0.138	0.156	0.169	0.180	0.188	0.206	0.220	0.238	0.252
1– 83,690	0.248	0.068	0.101	0.132	0.151	0.164	0.174	0.183	0.201	0.214	0.233	0.246
0–105,500	0.196	0.063	0.095	0.127	0.145	0.159	0.169	0.177	0.196	0.209	0.228	0.241
00–133,100	0.156	0.057	0.090	0.121	0.140	0.153	0.164	0.172	0.190	0.204	0.222	0.236
000–167,800	0.122	0.052	0.085	0.116	0.135	0.148	0.158	0.167	0.185	0.199	0.217	0.230
0000–211,600	0.098	0.046	0.079	0.111	0.130	0.143	0.153	0.161	0.180	0.193	0.212	0.225
250,000	0.085	.....	0.075	0.106	0.125	0.139	0.148	0.157	0.175	0.189	0.207	0.220
300,000	0.075	.....	0.071	0.103	0.120	0.134	0.144	0.153	0.171	0.185	0.203	0.217
350,000	0.061	.....	0.067	0.099	0.188	0.128	0.141	0.149	0.168	0.182	0.200	0.213
400,000	0.052	.....	0.064	0.096	0.114	0.127	0.138	0.146	0.165	0.178	0.197	0.209
500,000	0.042	.....	.....	0.090	0.109	0.122	0.133	0.141	0.160	0.172	0.192	0.202
600,000	0.035	.....	.....	0.087	0.106	0.118	0.128	0.137	0.155	0.169	0.187	0.200
700,000	0.030	.....	.....	0.083	0.102	0.114	0.125	0.133	0.152	0.165	0.184	0.197
800,000	0.026	.....	.....	0.080	0.099	0.112	0.122	0.130	0.148	0.162	0.181	0.194
900,000	0.024	.....	.....	0.077	0.096	0.109	0.119	0.127	0.146	0.159	0.178	0.191
1,000,000	0.022	.....	.....	0.075	0.094	0.106	0.117	0.125	0.144	0.158	0.176	0.188

For other frequencies the reactance will be in direct proportion to the frequency.

Also Eq. (**127**), p. 15–80 may be used. $\cos\theta = 0.85$; $\sin\theta = 0.527$.

$$E_s = \sqrt{[(250 \times 0.85) + 7.14]^2 + [(250 \times 0.527) + 14.98]^2} = 264.3 \text{ volts.}$$

$$264.3/250 = 105.7 \text{ percent}$$

In the calculation of three-phase three-wire circuits where line reactance must be considered, the method given on p. 15–80 may be used. The system is considered as being three single-phase systems having a ground return the resistance and inductance of which are zero, and the voltages are equal to the line voltages divided by $\sqrt{3}$. When the three conductors are spaced unequally, the value of *GMD* given on p. 15–82 and in Fig. 84 should be used in Tables 16 and 19. (When the value of resistance or reactance per 1,000 ft of *conductor* is desired, the values in Table 20 should be divided by 2.)

INTERIOR WIRING

BY

R. T. Gibbs

Interior wiring requirements are based, for the most part, on the "National Electrical Code" (N.E.C.), which has been adopted by the National Fire Protection Association and ASA. The local requirements must be complied with rather than the code since the code itself is legal only when made so by the local authorities.

Insulated Wires. The types of insulated wire in common use for low-voltage (20 to 600 volts) wiring are: rubber-covered (R) (140 F-60 C) for dry locations; thermoplastic (T) (140 F) for dry locations; heat-resistant rubber (RH) (167 F); for dry locations; moisture- and heat-resistant rubber (RHW) (167 F); moisture- and heat-resistant thermoplastic (THW) (167 F); and nylon-protected moisture- and heat-resistant thermoplastic (THWN) (167 F). With the exception of MI (mineral-insulated) and lead-covered insulations, the insulations without the type letter W cannot be used in wet locations. The thermoplastic insulations are thinner than the rubber while the nylon-protected thermoplastic insulation (THWN) has even a smaller overall cross section, which probably would result in its being able to use larger AWG sizes in rewiring existing conduits. Varnished cambric insulation (V) (185 F), asbestos and varnished cambric (AVA) (230 F), lead-covered varnished cambric (AVL) (230 F), mineral-insulated and metal-sheathed (MI) (185 F), silicone asbestos (SA) (194 F), impregnated asbestos (AI) and (AIA) (257 F) have limited use in certain sizes for special applications.

Fixture wires, as small as 18 AWG and with voltages up to 600 volts, are limited to the following types: RF-2 and FF-2 (140 F); RFH-2 and FFH-2 (167 F); TF and TFF (140 F); SF-2 and SFF-2 (392 F). Types RF-1, FF1 (140 F); RFH-1 (167 F); AF (302 F); SF-1 (392 F) and SFF-1 (302 F) are limited to fixtures on 300 volt circuits.

Table 20 gives the current-carrying capacity for not more than three insulated copper wires in a raceway or cable. The current-carrying capacity for not more than three **insulated aluminum wires** can be determined by using the multiplying factors in the table footnotes.

Methods of interior wiring are described below in the 24 approved systems.

1. Open wiring on insulators is seldom used now but is included in N.E.C. for dry places with potentials up to 600 volts. When permitted locally, the wires can be supported with two-wire porcelain cleats for voltages up to 300. For voltages from 300 to 600 and in damp locations for voltages up to 300, knobs or single-wire cleats must be used which will separate the wire 1 in. from the surface. Where wires pass through floors, timbers, or walls, or when within 2 in. of other wires or piping, porcelain tubes must be used.

2. Concealed knob-and-tube wiring is sometimes permitted in wiring wooden buildings in the process of construction. Conductors are supported on knobs between the floors and partitions, and porcelain tubes are used whenever the wires pass through timbers or other barriers.

3. Bare bars of copper or aluminum, for feeders not over 600 volts, may be used, with special permission, for large currents. They may be installed in a channel or shaft of non-combustible material in a building of fire-resistive construction, but not in damp or wet locations or where there are corrosive vapors, except in storage-battery rooms. The maximum current density for copper is limited to 1,000 amp per sq in. in unventilated enclosures and 1,200 amp per sq in. in ventilated enclosures.

Table 20. Allowable Current-carrying Capacities of Copper* Conductors, Amp

(Not more than three conductors in raceway or cable.† Based on room temperature of 86 F)

Size AWG MCM	Temp rating 60 C (140 F) Rubber type R type RW‡ Type RU type RUW (14-2) Type RH-RW§ Thermoplastic type T‡ type TW	Temp rating 75 C (167 F) Rubber type RH‡ Type RUH (14-2) Type RH-RW§ RHW THW THWN	Temp rating 85–90 C (185 F) Paper Thermoplastic asbestos type TA Silicone type SA Var-cam type V Asbestos var-cam type AVB MI cable RHH¶
	A	B	C
14	15	15	25
12	20	20	30
10	30	30	40
8	40	45	50
6	55	65	70
4	70	85	90
3	80	100	105
2	95	115	120
1	110	130	140
0	125	150	155
00	145	175	185
000	165	200	210
0000	195	230	235
250	215	255	270
300	240	285	300
350	260	310	325
400	280	335	360
500	320	380	405
600	355	420	455
700	385	460	490
750	400	475	500
800	410	490	515
900	435	520	555
1,000	455	545	585
1,250	495	590	645
1,500	520	625	700
1,750	545	650	735
2,000	560	665	775

Correction Factors for Room Temperatures over 86 F

Temp, deg F	104	113	122	131	140	158	167	176
Column A	0.82	0.71	0.58	0.41	0.00			
Column B	0.88	0.82	0.75	0.67	0.58	0.35	0.00	
Column C	0.90	0.85	0.80	0.74	0.67	0.52	0.43	0.30

* **For aluminum wire** the allowable carrying capacity of No. 12 is 15 amp (75 percent of Cu), that of No. 10 is 25 amp (83 percent of Cu). In general the allowable carrying capacity is 77 percent (rounded off to the nearest 5) from 12 to 4, 79 percent from 3 to 0000, 81 percent from 250 to 900 MCM, and 83 percent from 1,000 to 2,000 MCM.

† For four to six conductors the current is 80 percent, for seven to 24 conductors the current is 70 percent, for 25 to 42 conductors the current is 60 percent, and for 43 and above the current is 50 percent.

‡ The code rubber insulation in the above National Electric Code table includes those made from natural and synthetic rubber, neoprene, and other vulcanizable materials. Because thermoplastic insulation, as distinct from thermosetting, may stiffen at temperatures below 14 F, care should be used in its installation at such temperatures.

§ RH-RW, use Column A for wet locations and Column B for dry locations.

¶ The current-carrying capacities for Type RHH conductors for sizes 14, 12, and 10 are the same as for Type RH conductors in the table; the C column shows the capacities of the remaining RHH sizes.

4. Continuous cable supports, such as cable racks, cable troughs, or cable baskets, into which control or power cable assemblies may be laid are usually long, continuous steel or aluminum open troughs that may be installed in fire-resistive construction, but not run through a fire wall. The cable racks may support the systems of wiring listed under "Methods of interior wiring" 5 to 10, 13 to 16, and 23. No taps or splices are to be made in the troughs. The cross-sectional area of all the cable assemblies is not to exceed 40 percent of the trough area. Where cable assemblies of more than three conductors are used in ventilated racks and no horizontal spacing is maintained between the cables, the current-carrying capacity is reduced by the factors given in the footnote of Table 20. However, if spacing between cable assemblies of at least one-quarter of the cable diameters for not more than three conductor cables is maintained, the current reduction factors are higher, ranging from 0.93 for two-cable assemblies to 0.82 for six cables.

5. Mineral-insulated metal-sheathed cable, type MI, is completely non-combustible and consists of a copper tubing enclosing copper conductors insulated with compressed magnesium oxide. Special moisture-tight terminal fittings are employed, and the completed system must be tested for insulation resistance. The cable is relatively small but somewhat more expensive than other types of wiring.

6. Aluminum-sheathed, type ALS, is a factory-assembled cable in a seamless aluminum tube for both exposed and concealed work in dry or wet locations.

7. Metal-clad or armored-cable wiring, types AC and MC, in two- or three-wire assemblies, give good protection from mechanical injury and are preferable to exposed cleat or concealed knob-and-tube wiring from the viewpoint of fire safety. Armored cable can be secured in place with metal straps held by screws or nails. Types MC are power cables of No. 4 AWG or larger for copper and No. 2 or larger for aluminum.

Where armored cable enters junction or outlet boxes, the armor must be secured to the box by a connector or clamp so as to be mechanically firm and to make a good electrical connection. The armor must be at ground potential. In order to prevent the sharp edges of the armor from cutting the insulation on the wire where the cable enters a metal box, a fiber bushing with a rounded edge must be used between the conductors and armor and a connector fitting must be used at the end of the armor. One of the conductors in the cable has a white braid and must be the neutral or grounded conductor throughout the system. Metal-clad cable must have lead-covered conductors if exposed to weather or continuous moisture or when used for underground runs or embedded in masonry.

8. Non-metallic sheathed cable, types NM and NMC, is a fabricated assembly in sizes from 14 to 2 AWG and may be used in many locations in place of armored cable since added insulation is applied over the ordinary insulated conductors. A bare equipment-grounding conductor may be enclosed for grounding metal cabinets, fittings, and switch and outlet boxes. Type NM may be used in normally dry locations, while NMC may be used in damp or corrosive locations. Where NMC is embedded in plaster, it must be protected against damage from nails by a metal cover. In exposed locations, where necessary, it must be protected from mechanical injury by pipe or guard strips, and where it passes through floors it must be enclosed in a rigid conduit extending 6 in. above the floor.

9. Service-entrance cable, types ASE, SE, and USE must have a covering that, under normal conditions, will withstand exposure to atmospheric conditions and will prevent leakage that may be detrimental to adjacent objects. Type ASE has a steel tape with a saturated braid. Type USE is accepted for use underground, it is also used where the service conductors are not enclosed in conduit. Since service cable may be No. 6 and, under certain conditions, No. 8, it also may be used for interior wiring of appliances such as ranges and clothes dryers, i.e., appliances that require larger currents than the usual branch lighting circuits.

10. Underground feeder and branch-circuit cable, type UF, has an outer moisture-resistant covering. It may be buried in earth or used in wet, dry, or corrosive locations for interior wiring in other than hoistways, garages, and service-entrance cable, or in any hazardous location.

11. Non-metallic extensions are unbroken lengths of two-conductor assemblies for surface extensions from existing outlets in offices or residences on 120 volt, 15 or 20 amp branch circuits. The extensions must not extend beyond the room in which they originate or come within 2 in. of the floor.

The extensions may also be used as **aerial cables** for industrial purposes where the nature of the occupancy requires a highly flexible means of connecting equipment that cannot be supplied by one of the other general methods. The cable must be supported by a messenger wire that is a part of the cable. The messenger wire must be supported at least every 20 ft and have an 8 ft clearance over benches, 10 ft over pedestrian areaways, and 14 ft over vehicular floor areas. The messenger wire may be used as an equipment ground wire.

12. Underplaster extensions from existing outlet may be made with the suitable cable, conduit, tubing, or raceway in buildings of fire-resistive construction.

13. Rigid metal conduit is employed throughout buildings of concrete or other fireproof construction and frequently is required in other types of buildings, especially in commercial garages, theaters, motion-picture studios, hoistways, and in hazardous locations. In general ½ in. (trade-size) conduit is the smallest permitted. When conduit is bent, the radius of the bend should not effectively reduce the internal diameter of the conduit, and the radius of the inner edge of the bend should not be less than about six times the internal diameter. More than four 90 deg bends between junction boxes must be avoided. Conduit sizes as given in Table 21 apply only to complete conduit systems and do not apply to short sections of conduit used for the protection of exposed wiring from mechanical injury. The entire conduit system must be installed, and all the mechanical work on the building should be completed before the wires are drawn in. Where the conduit enters knockout holes in junction boxes or cabinets, the conduit may be clamped to the box by a threadless clamp fitting or by a bushing with rounded edges on the end of the pipe inside the cabinet and a locknut on the outside. Where conductors leave the conduit or other metal-protecting casings to open wiring or concealed knob-and-tube work, each wire must pass through a separate bushed hole in a proper terminal fitting.

14. Rigid non-metallic conduit is a new tubing (with fittings) of fiber, asbestos cement, soapstone, and rigid polyvinyl chloride. It is supplied in 10 ft lengths. When equipment grounding is required, a separate grounding conductor is necessary. The conduit can be used in concrete walls, floors, ceilings, and cinder fill, and in wet locations such as dairies, laundries, and canneries when the conduit system is made watertight. It may also be used where subject to corrosive influences if the straps, bolts, screws, and accessories are also protected against corrosion.

15. Electrical metallic tubing has a much thinner metal wall than standard conduit and is not threaded but secured in the fittings by threadless couplings and connectors. Tubing may be used in place of conduit except in certain hazardous locations and where it would be subjected to severe mechanical injury. Tubing shall not be larger than 2 in. electrical trade size.

16. Flexible metal conduit is installed where the necessary bending of rigid conduit is difficult and also in short lengths to motors where some change in position is necessary in order to tighten belts, chains, etc. It must not be used in wet or hazardous locations, hoistways, or storage-battery rooms.

17. Liquid-tight flexible metal conduit has a liquid-tight jacket with suitable terminal fittings and may be used in the wiring of machine tools or where exposed to oil or gasoline and where flexibility of connection is required.

18. Surface metal raceways (metal moldings) are installed chiefly as branch-circuit extensions to the existing wiring in completed buildings. Their use is limited to systems that do not exceed 300 volts between conductors and to conductors not larger than No. 6. Although moldings must not be concealed, metallic molding may pass through dry partitions or walls if there are no breaks inside the partition.

19. Multi-outlet assemblies, both metallic and non-metallic, may be used on surfaces in dry locations where they are not subject to severe mechanical injury or corrosive vapors and are not in hoistways or hazardous locations. The metal assembly may

Table 21. Maximum Number of Conductors in Trade Sizes of Conduit or Tubing

New Work or Rewiring—Types RF-2, RFH-2, R, RH, RW, RHH, RHW, RH-RW

New Work—FEP, FEPB, RUH, RUW, T, TF, THHN, THW, THWN, TW

(Derating factors for more than three conductors in raceways, see footnotes of Table 20)

Size AWG or MCM	Maximum number of conductors in conduit or tubing (based upon % conductor fill, Table 3, Chap. 9, N.E.C., for new work)*											
	½ in.	¾ in.	1 in.	1¼ in.	1½ in.	2 in.	2½ in.	3 in.	3½ in.	4 in.	5 in.	6 in.
18	7	12	20	35	49	80	115	176				
16	6	10	17	30	41	68	98	150				
14	4	6	10	18	25	41	58	90	121	155		
12	3	5	8	15	21	34	50	76	103	132	208	
10	1	4	7	13	17	29	41	64	86	110	173	
8	1	3	4	7	10	17	25	38	52	67	105	152
6	1	1	3	4	6	10	15	23	32	41	64	93
4	1	1	1	3†	5	8	12	18	24	31	49	72
3	...	1	1	3	4	7	10	16	21	28	44	63
2	...	1	1	3	3	6	9	14	19	24	38	55
1	...	1	1	1	3	4	7	10	14	18	29	42
0	...	...	1	1	2	4	6	9	12	16	25	37
00	...	...	1	1	1	3	5	8	11	14	22	32
000	...	...	1	1	1	3	4	7	9	12	19	27
0000	...	...	...	1	1	2	3	6	8	10	16	23
250	...	...	...	1	1	1	3	5	6	8	13	19
300	...	...	...	1	1	1	3	4	5	7	11	16
350	...	...	...	1	1	1	1	3	5	6	10	15
400	...	...	...	...	1	1	1	3	4	6	9	13
500	...	...	...	...	1	1	1	3	4	5	8	11
600	...	...	...	...	...	1	1	1	3	4	6	9
700	...	...	...	...	...	1	1	1	3	3	6	8
750	...	...	...	...	...	1	1	1	3	3	5	8
800	...	...	...	...	...	1	1	1	2	3	5	7
900	...	...	...	...	...	1	1	1	1	3	4	7

* For combinations of conductors of different sizes, see Tables 3 and 4, Chap. 9, N.E.C., 1965.

† Where an existing service run of conduit or electrical metallic tubing does not exceed 50 ft in length and does not contain more than the equivalent of two quarter bends from end to end, two No. 4 insulated and one No. 4 bare conductors may be installed in 1 in. conduit or tubing.

(For conductor types with smaller diameters over the newer insulations see Tables 1A and 1B in 1965 N.E.C., pp. 70-391, 70-392.)

be surrounded by the building finish and the non-metallic may be recessed in a baseboard.

20. Underfloor raceways are used chiefly in the floors of offices so that lighting and power wires can be brought up from the floor to desks or other office fixtures located over the raceway. They are usually installed below the surface of concrete or other flooring material. A fitting or a junction box must extend through the floor to the surface to mark the line of the duct, and care must be taken that the center of the duct follows a straight line between markers or junction boxes. Conductors of signaling and lighting systems must not be in the same raceway unless separated by a partition.

21. Cellular metal-floor raceways are hollow spaces or cells in a metal-floor structure supporting the floors which, together with suitable transverse headers or raceways with proper fittings, may be approved as enclosures for electrical conductors. Conductors shall not be installed in cellular metal-floor raceways (1) where subject to corrosive vapor; (2) in any hazardous location; (3) in commercial garages, except for supplying ceiling outlets or extensions to the area below the floor but not above; nor (4) in storage-battery rooms. No electric conductors shall be installed in any cell or header which contains a pipe for steam, water, air, gas, drainage, or other service than electrical.

22. Cellular concrete-floor raceways are precast concrete spaces or cells in a floor with continuous metal transverse header ducts which have a top surface flush with the floor finish and are grounded to the metal enclosure of the distribution center. This type of raceway is limited to about the same conditions of installation as the cellular metal-floor raceways.

23. Wireways or sheet-metal troughs which have hinged or removable covers for housing and protecting electrical wires and cables and in which the conductors are laid in place after the wireway has been installed as a complete system can be used only for exposed work. Wireways should not be used where they may be subjected to severe mechanical injury or corrosive vapors or in any hazardous location. There should not be more than 30 conductors, and the total area of all the conductors should not exceed 20 percent of the cross section of the trough. For outdoor use the wireway must be of a raintight construction.

24. Busways are bare or insulated copper or aluminum bus bars enclosed in exposed metal ducts for use in feeders, mains, or branch circuits in dry places that are not subject to severe mechanical injury or corrosive vapors and are not in hazardous locations. Branches may be made from the busways with busway, conduit, tubing, or plug-in devices. Busways are often used for power-distribution systems in industrial plants and machine shops.

In all metallic protecting systems, such as conduit, armored cable, or metal raceways, joints and splices in conductors must be made only in junction boxes or other proper fittings; therefore, these fittings can be located only in accessible places and never concealed in partitions. Splices or joints in the wire must never be in the conduit piping, raceway, or metallic tubing itself, for the splices may become a source of trouble as a result of corrosion or grounding if water should enter the conduit.

Switching Arrangements. Small quick-break switches must be set in or on a metal box or fitting and may be of the push, tumbler, or rotary type. The following types of switches are used to control lighting circuits: (1) single-pole, (2) double-pole, (3) three-point or three-way, (4) four-way, in combination with three-way switches to control lights from three or more stations, (5) electrolier.

Alternating-current Systems. All conductors of an a-c system must be placed in the same metallic casing so that their resultant magnetic field is nearly zero. If this is not done, eddy currents are set up causing heating and excessive loss. With single conductors in a casing, an excessive reactance drop may result.

Service wires are the conductors that bring the electric power into a building and should enter the building as near as possible to the service switch, so that when the switch is open all the electrical conductors and equipment inside the building will be "dead." The service wires must be rubber- or thermoplastic-covered from the point of support on the outside of the building to the service switch or cutout and must be No. 6 wire or larger except for installations consisting of two-wire branch circuits where No. 8 wire may be permitted. A minimum of 100 amp, three-wire service is recommended for all single-family residences.

Generally, when the conductors from overhead lines enter a building, the wires are encased in rigid conduit equipped with a weather cap or a service entrance cable (type ASE armored or SE type, unarmored) may be attached directly to the building wall. The inner end of the service enters a metal service cabinet in which the service fuses and switch are located. Service conductors may also terminate at an air-break or oil-immersed switch in a metal case or on a panel board which is accessible to qualified persons only.

All underground service wires must be connected to the interior wiring through a blade of the service switch or circuit breaker and be fused or automatically interrupted at the service switch. A service switch controlling a three-wire d-c or a single-phase system having a grounded neutral wire does not need to open that conductor.

The single-line diagram, Fig. 97, indicates a simplified interior arrangement of circuits and the necessary protection of the conductors and terminal load. Where a reduction is made in the wire size a protective device shall be installed to limit the conductor current to a safe value. Large motors and other terminal loads should also have over-current protection.

Table 22. Approximate Full-load Currents of Motors

Hp	Three-phase a-c motors, squirrel-cage and wound-rotor induction type, amp			Single-phase a-c motors, amp		D-c motors, amp	
	220 volts*	440 volts	550 volts	115 volts	230 volts	120 volts	240 volts
½	2	1	0.8	9.8	4.9	5.2	2.6
¾	2.8	1.4	1.1	13.8	6.9	7.4	3.7
1	3.5	1.8	1.4	16	8	9.4	4.7
1½	5	2.5	2.0	20	10	13.2	6.6
2	6.5	3.3	2.6	24	12	17	8.5
3	9	4.5	4	34	17	25	12.2
5	15	7.5	6	56	28	40	20
7½	22	11	9	80	40	58	29
10	27	14	11	100	50	76	38
15	40	20	16	.....	....	....	55
20	52	26	21	.....	....	....	72
25	64	32	26	.....	....	....	89
30	78	39	31	.....	....	....	106
40	104	52	41	.....	....	....	140
50	125	63	50	.....	....	....	173
60	150	75	60	.....	....	....	206
75	185	93	74	.....	....	....	255
100	246	123	98	.....	....	....	341
125	310	155	124	.....	....	....	425
150	360	180	144	.....	....	....	506
200	480	240	192	.....	....	....	675

These values of full-load currents are average for all speeds and frequencies of continuous-duty motors.

* For full-load currents of 208 and 200 volt motors, increase the corresponding 220 volt full-load currents by 6 and 10 percent, respectively.

The required size of wire, for the motor branch circuits, the fuse ratings and the setting of the protective devices for starting and for running protection of motors are given in Table 23. The values of full-load motor current are given in Table 22. Tables 22 and 23 are taken from the 1962 National Electrical Code.

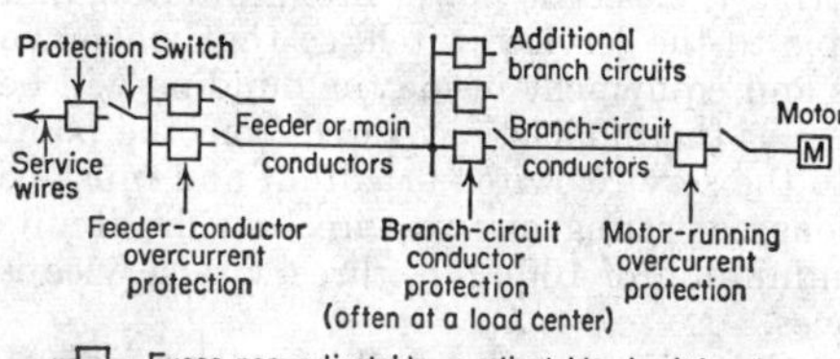

Fig. 97. Motor and wiring protection. See Table 23 for selection of conductor sizes and protective devices.

Grounding of direct- and alternating-current systems of 300 volts and less is usually required. Inside a building the **grounded conductor** (one of the two conductors in two-wire system and the **neutral conductor** in a three-wire or a four-wire system) should have a *white or natural gray covering* throughout to distinguish it from the ungrounded conductors. This identified grounded conductor must not be fused or be opened unless the other conductors are opened simultaneously. *Green wires* only shall be used for grounding electrical equipment, such as motors, as well as conduits, armor, boxes, and such metallic enclosures. Four-wire circuits have *black, white, red, and blue* conductors.

Direct-current systems need be grounded only at the generating stations because the grounded wire is electrically connected to one of the conductors in all the circuits throughout the system. In a-c systems, since one section can be insulated from the other by a transformer, each section of 300 volts or under is grounded at the individual services. The conductor grounding the a-c system should not be less than No. 8 cop-

Table 23. For Selecting Wire Sizes of Branch Circuits and Fuse Sizes and Circuit-breaker Settings for Motor Running Protection

(See Table 22 for full-load motor current and also Fig. 97)

Full-load current rating of motor, amp[a]	Min size of copper wire, AWG of cir mils in raceways (2 or 3 conductors): Types R, RW, RU, RUW (14-2) RH-RW,[d] T, TW	Types RH, RUH (14-2) RH-RW,[d] RHW, RHW, THW, THWN	For running protection of[b] motors, amp[c]: Max rating of fuses or non-adjustable devices	Max setting of adjustable protective devices	Max allowable rating of branch-circuit fuses,[c] amp: Squirrel-cage and synchronous motors, full voltage starting[e] with code letters F to V[f] and without code letters	Squirrel-cage and synchronous motors, full voltage starting[e] with code letters B to E[f] and autotransformer starting, code letters F to V. Also above motors without code letters up to 30 amp	Squirrel-cage and synchronous motors with autotransformer starting with code letters B to E. Also above motors without code letters[g] above 30 amp[g]	All motors with code letter A, slip-ring a-c and d-c motors without code letters
(1)	(2)	(3)	(4)	(5)	(6)	(7)[g]	(8)[h]	(9)[h]
4	14	14	6[i]	5[i]	15	15	15	15
6	14	14	8[i]	7.5[i]	20	15	15	15
8	14	14	10[i]	10[i]	25	25	20	15
10	14	14	15[i]	12.5[i]	30	25	20	15
12	14	14	15	15	40	30	25	20
15	12	12	20	18.75	45	40	30	25
18	10	10	25	22.5	60	45	40	30
20	10	10	25	25	60	50	40	30
24	10	10	30	30	80	60	50	40
28	8	8	35	35	90	70	60	45
32	8	8	40	40	100	80	70	50
36	6	8	45	45	110	90	80	60
40	6	6	50	50	100	100	80	60
48	4	6	60	60	150	125	100	80
56	4	4	70	70	175	150	120	90
64	3	4	80	80	200	175	150	100
72	2	3	90	90	225	200	150	110
80	1	3	100	100	250	200	175	125
96	0	1	125	120	300	250	200	150
120	000	0	150	150	400	300	250	200
140	0000	00	175	175	450	350	300	225
160	250,000	000	200	200	500	400	350	250
200	350,000	250,000	250	250	600	500	400	300

[a] For full-load motor current ratings of values between those listed here, see 1965 N.E.C. Table 430-146, pp. 70-228 to 70-231 and Table 310-12, p. 70-108.

[b] The current values shown in columns (4) and (5) for the running protection of motors must be reduced by 8 percent for all motors other than the open type marked with a 40 C rise.

[c] The motor over-current protection should be based on the motor name plate current. The current-carrying capacity of the conductors, switches, and branch-circuit over-current devices should be based on the full-load currents for the horsepower ratings of Table 22 rather than on the name plate current of the motor. Since especially low-speed or high-torque motors may require higher currents than those in Table 22, the name plate currents then should be used.

[d] For RH-RW wire use column (2) for wet or damp locations and column (3) for dry locations.

[e] Including those motors with resistor or reactance in the starting circuit as well as single-phase motors.

[f] Code letters marked on motor name plates indicate a ratio of current taken with the rotor locked to rated current. Letter A indicates 0 to 3.14; B to E, 3.15 to 4.99; F to R, 5.0 to 14.0; S to V, 16 and up.

[g] Including high-reactance squirrel-cage motors designed to limit the starting current by means of deep-slot secondaries or double-wound secondaries and generally started on full voltage.

[h] For columns (8) and (9) the fuse ratings are smaller than for columns (6) and (7), and the ratings of non-adjustable overload-trip circuit breakers to be used in place of fuses are the same as for fuses. However, since circuit breakers are available only in sizes 15, 20, 30, 40, 50, 70, 100, 125, 150, 175, 200, 225, 300, 350, 400, 500, 600, 700, and 800 amp, the next larger size circuit breaker should be selected where the fuse rating is between these sizes. For columns (6) and (7) with larger fuses than columns (8) and (9), the thermal-delay circuit breaker ratings are often less than that of the fuses. For these values see 1965 N.E.C. Table 430-146, pp. 70-228 to 70-231.

[i] For the running protection of 1 hp or less not permanently installed, the protection given in columns (6), (7), and (9) may be considered sufficient, but if the motor is permanently installed or located out of sight from the controller location or operator, the values in columns (4) or (5) should be used.

per wire and must be without a joint or a splice and run from the supply side of the service switch.

The service conduit that protects the service wires on the outside of the building must be grounded by a wire at least as large as No. 8, run directly to ground.

The entire metallic system surrounding the conductors must be at ground potential. It is only necessary to ground the metallic system, including motors and other equipment, at one point, provided that each section makes a good electrical connection with the next.

Overload Protection. A fuse or circuit breaker must be provided in all ungrounded conductors. Induction motors are usually protected by overload or thermal relays operating as automatic circuit breakers. To protect wiring properly, an automatic cutout must be installed at every point where a change is made in the size of the wire. Fuses or circuit breakers should not be placed either in a grounded line or in a ground wire. (See Fig. 97.)

Fuses, cutout bases, and **switches** are manufactured and change sizes, as follows: Edison plug (125 volts only), 0 to 30 amp; spring-clip cartridge (ferrule contact), 0 to 30, 31 to 60 amp; knife-blade cartridge type, 61 to 100, 101 to 200, 201 to 400, 401 to 600 amp; for 601 amp and larger, knife-blade cartridge type with equal-size fuses in parallel may be used except for the protection of a branch motor circuit where a circuit breaker can be installed.

Since the rating of a fuse is only about 90 percent of the current that it will carry indefinitely, and since it may also take a few minutes before the heat due to slightly excessive current would be sufficient to melt the fuse wire and hence open the circuit, insulation may be permanently damaged if the fuses are larger than the current-carrying capacities given by Tables 20 and 23.

Demand Calculations for Building Feeder Sizes. The **demand factor** or **demand** is the ratio of maximum demand to the total connected load. This depends on the type of building, whether hotel, theater, factory, etc. The demand factor for any particular class of installation decreases as the floor area increases. Values of demand factors are found in the 1965 National Electrical Code, Art. 220.

Load centers are panels or cabinets which act as distribution centers and which are supplied by feeder or main conductors, and from which the current to several branch circuits is taken. In each branch circuit there is usually a small combined switch and circuit breaker. Load centers for widely different types of circuits such as single-phase two-wire, single-phase three-wire, and three-phase are readily obtainable from several manufacturers.

RESISTOR MATERIALS

For use in rheostats, electric furnaces, ovens, heaters, and many electrical appliances, a resistor material with high melting point and high resistivity, which does not disintegrate or corrode at high temperatures, is necessary. These requirements are met by the nickel-chromium and nickel-chromium-iron alloys. For electrical instruments and measuring apparatus, the resistor material should have high resistivity, low temperature coefficient, and, for many uses, low thermoelectric power against copper. The properties of resistor materials are given in Table 24. Most of these materials are available in ribbon as well as in wire form. Cast-iron and steel wire are efficient and economical resistor materials for many uses, such as power-absorbing rheostats and motor starters and controllers. (See also Sec. 6.)

Advance has a low temperature coefficient and is useful in many types of measuring instrument and precision equipment. Because of its high thermoelectric power to copper, it is valuable for thermoelements and pyrometers. It is non-corrosive and is used to a large extent in industrial and radio rheostats. **Hytemco** is a nickel-iron alloy characterized by a high temperature coefficient and is used advantageously where self-regulation is required as in immersion heaters and heater pads. **Magno** is a manganese-nickel alloy used in the manufacture of incandescent lamps and radio tubes. **Manganin** is a copper-manganese-nickel alloy which, because of its very low temperature coefficient and its low thermal emf with respect to copper, is very valuable for high-precision electrical measuring apparatus. It is used for the resistance units in

Table 24. Properties of Metals, Alloys, and Resistor Materials

Material	Composition	Sp gr	Microhms-cm at 20 C	Ohms cir-mil-ft at 20 C	Temp coef of resistance per deg C	Temp range, deg C	Max safe working temp, deg C	Approx melting point, deg C
Advance	Cu 0.55; Ni 0.45	8.9	40	294	±0.00002	20–100	500	1210
Comet	Ni 0.30; Cr 0.05; Fe 0.65	8.15	95	570	0.00088	20–500	600	1480
Bronze, commercial	Cu; Zn	8.7	4.2	25	0.0020	0–100	....	1015
Hytemco	Ni 0.50; Fe 0.50	8.46	20	120	0.0045	20–100	600	1425
Magno	Ni 0.955; Mn 0.045	8.75	20	120	0.0036	20–100	400	1435
Manganin	Cu 0.84; Mn 0.12; Ni 0.04	8.19	48.2	290	±0.000015	15–35	100	1020
Monel metal	Ni 0.67; Cu 0.28	8.9	42.6	256	0.00198	20–100	425	1350
Nichrome	Ni 0.60; Fe 0.25; Cr 0.15	8.247	112	675	0.00017	20–100	930	1350
Nichrome V	Ni 0.80; Cr 0.20	8.412	108	650	0.00013	20–100	1100	1400
Nickel, pure	Ni 0.99	8.9	10	60	0.0050	0–100	400	1450
Platinum	Pt	21.45	10.616	63.80	0.003	......	....	1755
Silver	Ag	10.5	1.622	9.755	0.00361	......	....	960
Tungsten	W	19.3	5.523	33.22	0.00524	......	....	3370

bridges, for shunts, multipliers, and similar measuring devices. **Nichrome V** is a nickel-chromium alloy free from iron, is non-corrosive, non-magnetic, withstands high temperatures, and has high resistivity. It is recommended as material for heating elements in electric furnaces, hot-water heaters, ranges, radiant heaters, and high-grade electrical appliances. **Pure nickel** is used to satisfy the high requirements in the fabrication of radio tubes, such as the elimination of all gases and impurities in the metal parts. It has also other uses such as in incandescent lamps, for combustion boats, laboratory accessories, and resistance thermometers. (See also p. 7–94.)

Carbon withstands high temperatures and has high resistance; its temperature coefficient is negative; it will safely carry about 125 amp per sq in. Amorphous carbon has a resistivity of 3,800 to 4,100 microhms-cm, retort carbon about 720 microhms, and graphite about 812 microhms-cm. The properties of any particular kind of carbon depend on the temperature at which it was fired. Carbon for rheostats may best be used in the form of compression rheostats.

MAGNETS

A permanent magnet is one that retains a considerable amount of magnetism indefinitely. Permanent magnets are used in electrical instruments, telephone receivers, loudspeakers, magnetos, tachometers, magnetic chucks, and for many purposes where a constant magnetic field or a constant source of magnetism is desired. The magnetic material should have high retentivity, a high remanence, and a high coercive force (see Fig. 14, p. 15–23). These properties are usually found with hardened steel and its alloys.

Since permanent magnets must operate on the molecular mmf imparted to them when magnetized, they must necessarily operate on the portion *CDO* of the hysteresis loop, Fig. 14, p. 15–23. The area *CDO* is proportional to the *stored energy* within the magnet and is a criterion of its usefulness as a permanent-magnetic material. In the left half of Fig. 98, are given the *B-H* characteristics of several permanent-magnetic materials; these include 5 to 6 percent tungsten steel (curve 1); 3½ percent chrome magnet steel (curve 2); cobalt magnet steel, containing 16 to 36 percent cobalt and 5 to 9 percent chromium and in some alloys tungsten (curve 3); and the carbon-free aluminum-nickel-cobalt-steel alloys called Alnico. There are many grades of Alnico; the characteristics of three of them are shown by curves 4, 5, 6. Their composition is as follows:

Curve	Alnico No.	Composition, percent					
		Al	Ni	Co	Cu	Ti	Fe
4	5	8	14	24	3	....	51
5	6	8	14	24	3	1.25	49.75
6	12	6	18	35	..	8.0	33

All the Alnicos can be made by the sand or the precision-casting (lost-wax) process, but the most satisfactory method is by the sintering process.

If the alloys are held in a magnetic field during heat-treatment, a *magnet grain* is established and the magnetic properties in the direction of the field are greatly

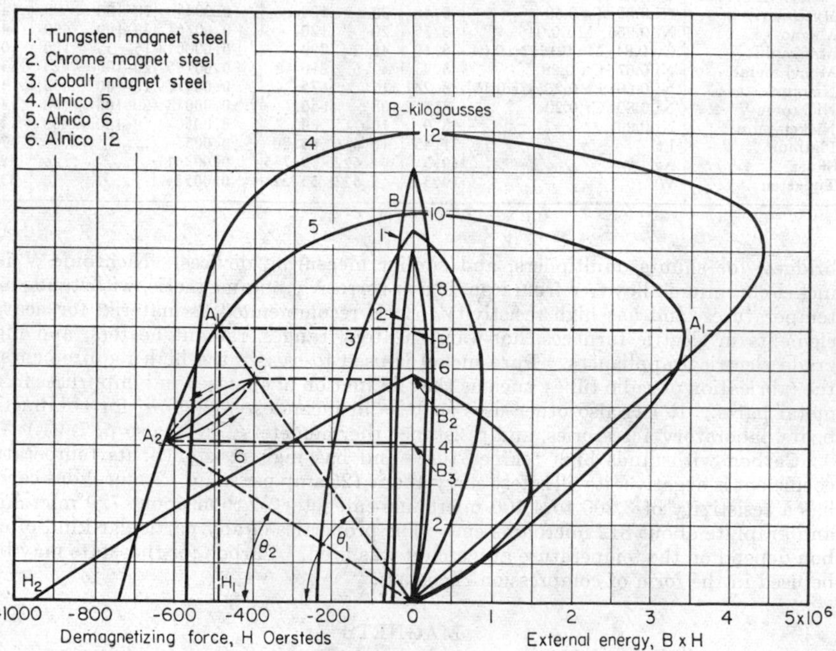

FIG. 98. Characteristics of permanent magnet materials.

increased. The alloys are hard, can be formed only by casting or sintering, and cannot be machined except by grinding.

The curves in the right half of Fig. 98 are "external energy" curves and give the product of B and H. The optimum point of operation is at the point of maximum energy as is indicated at A_1 on curve 5.

Considering curve 5, if the magnetic circuit remained closed, the magnet would operate at point B. To utilize the flux, an air gap must be introduced. The air gap acts as a demagnetizing force, $H_1(= B_1A_1)$, and the magnet operates at point A_1 on the HB curve. The line OA_1 is called the *air-gap line* and its slope is given by tan $\theta_1 = B_1/H_1$ where $H_1 = B_g l_g/l_m$ and $B_1/B_g = A_g/A_m$. B_g is the flux density in the gap in gausses; l_g the length of the gap in centimeters; l_m the length of the magnet in centimeters; A_g and A_m are the areas of the gap and magnet in square centimeters.

If the air gap is lengthened, the magnet will operate at A_2 corresponding to a lesser flux density B_3 and the new air-gap line is OA_2. If the gap is now closed to its original value, the magnet will not return to operation at point A_1 but will operate at some point C on the line OA_1. If the air gap is varied between the two foregoing values, the magnet will operate along the *minor hysteresis loop* A_2C. Return to point A_1 can be accomplished only by remagnetizing and coming back down the curve from B to A_1.

Alnico magnets corresponding to curves 4 and 5 are best adapted to operation with short air gaps, since the introduction of a long air gap will demagnetize the magnet materially. On the other hand, a magnet with a long air gap will operate most satisfactorily on curve 6 on account of the high coercive force H_2. With change in the length of the air gap, the operation will be essentially along that curve and the magnet will lose little of its original magnetization.

There are several other grades of Alnico with characteristics between curves 4, 5, and 6.

The steels for permanent magnets are cut in strips, heated to a red-hot temperature, and forged into shape, usually in a "bulldozer." If they are to be machined, they are cooled in mica dust to prevent air hardening. They are then ground, tumbled, and tempered.

Permanent magnets are magnetized either by placing them over a bus bar carrying a large direct current or by placing them across the poles of a powerful electromagnet.

Unless permanent magnets are subjected to artificial aging, they gradually weaken until after a long period they become stabilized usually at from 85 to 90 percent of their initial strength. With magnets for electrical instruments, where a constant field strength is imperative, artificial aging is accomplished by mechanical vibration or by immersion in oil at 250 F for a period of a few hours.

In an **electromagnet** the magnetic field is produced by an electric current. The core is usually made of soft iron or mild steel because, the permeability being higher, a stronger magnetic field may be obtained. Also since the retentivity is low, there is little trouble due to the sticking of armatures when the circuit is opened. Electromagnets may have the form of simple solenoids, iron-clad solenoids, plunger electromagnets, electromagnets with external armatures, and lifting magnets, which are circular in form with a flat holding surface.

A **solenoid** is a winding of insulated conductor and is wound helically; the direction of winding may be either right or left. A **portative electromagnet** is one designed only for holding material brought in contact with it. A **tractive electromagnet** is one designed to exert a force on the load through some distance and thus do work. The **range** of an electromagnet is the distance through which the plunger will perform work when the winding is energized. For long range of operation, the plunger type of tractive magnet is best suited, for the length of core is governed practically by the range of action desired, and the area of the core is determined by the pull. **Solenoid and plunger** is a solenoid provided with a movable iron rod or bar called a plunger. When the coil is energized, the iron rod becomes magnetized and the mutual action of the field in the solenoid on the poles created on the plunger causes the plunger to move within the solenoid. This force becomes zero only when the magnetic centers of the plunger and solenoid coincide. If the load is attached to the plunger, work will be done until the force to be overcome is equal to the force that the solenoid exerts on the plunger. When the iron of the plunger is not saturated, the strength of magnetic field in the solenoid and the induced poles are both proportional to the exciting current, so that the pull varies as the *current squared*. When the plunger becomes highly saturated, the pull varies almost *directly* with the current.

The **maximum uniform pull** occurs when the end of the plunger is at the center of the solenoid and is equal to

$$F = CAnI/l \quad \text{lb} \tag{134}$$

where A is the cross-sectional area of the plunger, sq in.; n the number of turns; I the current, amp; l the length of the solenoid, in.; and C the pull, psi per amp turn per in. C depends on the proportions of the coil, the degree of saturation, the length, and the physical and chemical purity of the plunger. Table 25 gives values of C for several different solenoids.

Curve 1, Fig. 99, shows the characteristic pull of an open-magnetic circuit solenoid, 12 in. long, having 10,000 amp-turns or 833 amp-turns per in.

Table 25. Maximum Pull per Sq In. of Core for Solenoids with Open Magnetic Circuit

(From data by Underhill, *Elec. World*, 45, 1906, pp. 796, 881)

Length of coil l, in.	Length of plunger, in.	Core area A, sq in.	Total ampere-turns $I \times n$	Max pull P, psi	$1{,}000 \times C$	Length of coil l, in.	Length of plunger, in.	Core area A, sq in.	Total ampere-turns $I \times n$	Max pull P, psi	$1{,}000 \times C$
6	Long	1.0	15,900	22.4	9.0	12	Long	1.0	11,200	8.75	9.4
9	Long	1.0	11,330	11.5	9.1	12	Long	1.0	20,500	16.75	9.8
9	Long	1.0	14,200	14.6	9.2	18	36	1.0	18,200	9.8	9.7
10	10	2.76	40,000	40.2	10.0	18	36	1.0	41,000	22.5	9.8
10	10	2.76	60,000	61.6	10.3	18	18	1.0	18,200	9.8	9.7
10	10	2.76	80,000	80.8	10.1	18	18	1.0	41,000	22.5	9.8

When a **strong pull** is desired at the end of the stroke, a stop may be used as shown in Fig. 100. Curve 2, Fig. 99, shows the pull obtained by adding a stop to the plunger.

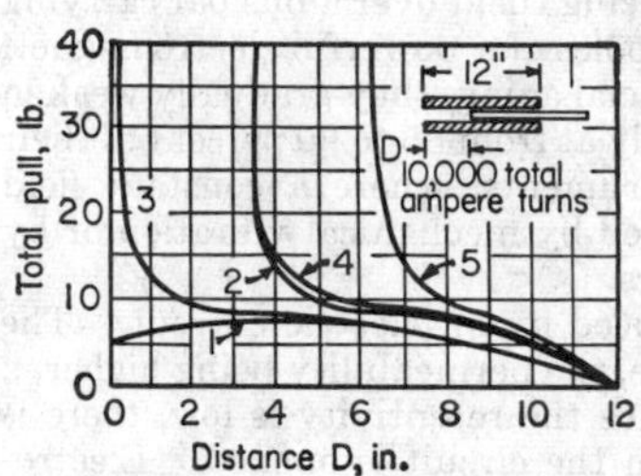

Fig. 99. Pull of solenoid on plunger. (1) Coil and plunger; (2) coil and plunger with stop; (3) iron-clad coil and plunger; (4) and (5) same as (3) with different lengths of stop.

It will be noted that, except when the end of the plunger is near the stop, the stop adds little to the solenoid pull. The pull is made up of two components: one due to the attraction between plunger and winding and the other to the attraction between plunger and stop. The equation for the pull is

$$P = AIn[(In/l_a^2C_1^2) + (C/l)] \quad \text{lb} \qquad (135)$$

where A is the area of the core, sq in.; n is the number of turns; l_a is the length of gap between core and stop; and C and C_1 are constants. At the beginning of the stroke the second member of the equation is predominant, and at the end of the stroke the first member represents practically the entire pull. Approximate values of C and C_1 are $C_1 = 2{,}660$ (for l greater than $10d$), $C = 0.0096$, where d is the diameter of the plunger, in.

The **range of uniform pull** may be extended by the use of conical ends of stop and plunger, as shown in Fig. 101. A stronger magnet mechanically may be obtained by using an iron-clad solenoid, Fig. 102, in which an iron return path is provided for the flux. Except for low flux densities and short air gaps the dimensions of the iron return path are of no practical importance, and the fact that an iron return path is used does

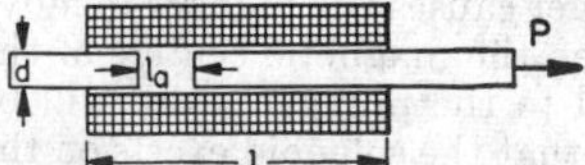

Fig. 100. Solenoid with stop.

Fig. 101. Conical plunger and stop.

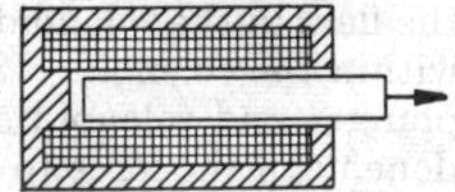

Fig. 102. Iron-clad solenoid.

not affect the pull curve except at short air gaps. This is illustrated in Fig. 99 where curves 3, 4, and 5 are typical pull curves for this same solenoid when it is made iron-clad, each curve corresponding to a different position of the stop.

Mechanical jar at the end of the stroke may be prevented by leaving the end of the solenoid open. The plunger then comes to equilibrium when its middle is at the middle of the winding, thus providing a magnetic cushion effect. Electromagnets with external armatures are best adapted for **short-range** work, and the best type is the horseshoe magnet. The pull for short-range magnets is expressed by the equation

$$F = B^2A/72{,}134{,}000 \qquad \text{lb} \qquad (136)$$

where B is the flux density in maxwells per square inch and A the area of the core in square inches. A greater holding power is obtained if the surfaces of the armature and core are not machined to an absolutely smooth contact surface. If the surface is slightly irregular, the area of contact A is reduced but the flux density B is increased approximately in proportion (if the iron is being operated below saturation), and the pull is increased since it varies as the square of the density B. Non-magnetic stops should be used if it is desired that the armature may be released readily when the current is interrupted.

Lifting magnets are of the portative type in that their function is merely to hold the load. The actual lifting is performed by the hoisting apparatus. A lifting magnet is shown in Fig. 13, p. 10–15. The magnet is almost toroidal in shape. The coil shield is of manganese steel which is very hard and thus resists wear and is practically non-magnetic. The holding power is given by Eq. (**136**), where A is the area of the holding surface in square inches. It is difficult to calculate accurately the holding force of a lifting magnet for it depends on the magnetic characteristics of the load, the area of contact, and the manner in which the load is applied.

Rapid action in a magnet may be obtained by reducing the time constant (see p. 15–27) of the winding and by subdividing the metal parts to reduce induced currents which have a demagnetizing effect when the circuit is closed. The movement of the plunger through the winding causes the winding and its bobbin to be cut by a magnetic field; if the bobbin is of metal and not slotted longitudinally, it is a short-circuited turn linked by a changing magnetic field and hence currents are induced in it. These currents oppose the flux and hence reduce the pull during the transient period. They also cause some heating. Where it is found impossible to reduce the time constant sufficiently, an electromagnet designed for a voltage much lower than normal is often used. A resistor is connected in series which is short-circuited during the stroke of the plunger. At the completion of the stroke the plunger automatically opens the short circuit, reducing the current to a value which will not overheat the magnet under continuous operation. The extremely short time of overload produces very rapid action but does not injure the winding. The solenoids on many automatic motor-starting panels are designed in this manner.

When **slow action** is desired, it can be obtained by using solid cores and yoke and by using a heavy metallic spool or bobbin for the winding. A separate winding short-circuited on itself is also used to some extent.

Sparking at switch terminals may be reduced or eliminated by neutralizing the inductance of the winding. This is accomplished by winding a separate short-circuited coil with its wires parallel to those of the active winding. (This method can be used with d-c magnets only.) This is not economical, since one-half the winding space is wasted. By connecting a capacitor across the switch terminals, the energy of the inductive discharge on opening the circuit may be absorbed. For the purpose of neutralizing the inductive discharge and causing a quick release, a small **reverse current** may be sent through the coil winding automatically on opening the circuit. Sleeves of tin, aluminum, or copper foil placed over the various layers of the winding absorb energy when the circuit is broken and reduce the energy dissipated at the switch terminals. This scheme can be used for d-c magnets only. **Sticking** of the parts of the magnetic circuit due to residual magnetism may be prevented by the use of non-magnetic stops. In the case of lifting magnets subjected to rough usage and hard blows (as in a steel works), these stops usually consist of plates of manganese steel, which are extremely hard and non-magnetic.

Alternating-current Tractive Magnets. Because of the iron losses due to eddy currents, the magnetic circuits of a-c electromagnets should be composed of laminated iron or steel. The magnetic circuit of large magnets is usually built up of thin sheets of sheet metal held together by means of suitable clamps. Small cores of circular cross section usually consist of a bundle of soft iron wires. Since the iron losses increase with the flux density, it is not advisable to operate at as high a density as with direct current. The current instead of being limited by the resistance of the winding is now determined almost entirely by the inductive reactance as the resistance is small. With the removal of the load the current rises to high values. The pull of a-c magnets is nearly constant irrespective of the length of air gap.

In a **single-phase magnet** the pull varies from zero to a maximum and back to zero twice every cycle, which may cause considerable chattering of the armature against the stop. This may be prevented by the use of a spring or, in the case of a solenoid coil, by allowing the plunger to seek its position of equilibrium in the coil. **Chattering** may also be prevented by the use of a short-circuited winding or shading coil around one tip of the pole piece or by the use of polyphase. In a **two-phase magnet** the pull is constant and equal to the maximum instantaneous pull produced by one phase so long as the voltage is a sine function. In a **three-phase magnet** under the same conditions the pull is constant and equal to 1.5 times the maximum instantaneous pull of one phase. Should the load become greater than the minimum instantaneous pull, there will be chattering as in a single-phase magnet.

Heating of Magnets. The lifting capacity of an electromagnet is limited by the permissible current-carrying capacity of the winding, which, in turn, is dependent on the amount of heat energy that the winding can dissipate per unit time without exceeding a given temperature rise. Coils wound with wire having cotton insulation will, in general, be operating at a safe temperature if the average power expended does not exceed 0.5 watt per sq in. of heat-dissipating surface.

Design of Exciting Coil. Let n be the number of turns, l the mean length of turn in inches ($l = 2\pi r$, where r is the mean radius, in.), A the cross section of wire in cir mils. The resistance of 1 cir mil-ft of copper is practically 12 ohms at 60 C, or 1 ohm per cir mil-in. Hence the resistance, $R = nl/A$ ohms; the current, $I = EA/nl$; the amp-turns, $nI = EA/l$; the power to be dissipated, $P = E^2A/nl$ watts. From the foregoing equations the cross section of wire and the number of turns may be calculated.

Space Factor of Winding. Space factor of a coil is the ratio of the space occupied by the conductor to the total volume of the coil or winding. Only in the theoretical case of uninsulated square or rectangular conductor may the space factor be 100 percent. For wire of circular section with insulation of negligible thickness, wound as shown in Fig. 103(*a*), the space factor will be 78.5 percent. When the turns of wire are "bedded," as shown in Fig. 103(*b*) (the case in most windings, particularly with smaller wires), there is a theoretical gain of about 7 percent in space factor. Experiments have shown that in most cases this gain is about neutralized in practice by the flattening out of the insulation of the wire due to the tension used in winding. When wound in a haphazard manner, the space factors of magnet wires vary according to size, substantially as follows:

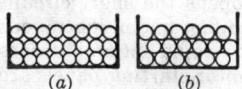

(*a*) (*b*)

FIG. 103. Winding space factor.

	Double cotton covered				Single cotton covered			
Size, AWG	0	5	10	15	20	25	30	35
Space factor, percent	60	53.8	45.5	35.1	32.2	32	25.7	16

Magnet wire is a soft insulated copper wire of high conductivity. It may be obtained in square, rectangular, and circular section, but the round or cylindrical wire is used almost entirely in the smaller sizes. Ribbons are frequently used in the larger sizes. **Cotton covering** is used on large- and medium-sized wires where the space occupied by the cotton is small relative to the conductor cross section so that the space factor remains high. Cotton is also used where the insulation is to be impregnated with, or is to absorb, a liquid insulation. **Nylon** (replacing silk), used on the smaller sizes of wire, has a higher space factor than cotton. **Paper insulation,** consisting of one or more thin strips of dense high-quality paper applied helically over bare or enamel-covered conductors, is used sometimes with transformer windings where a high space factor is important. **Enameled** wire, a film-insulated copper conductor produced with oleoresinous enamels, is used particularly with the smaller wires. It is rated by the AIEE as Class A insulation (p. 15–73). It is wound either layer upon layer or with paper between adjacent layers. **Enamel and cotton** and **enamel and nylon** are used in combination. The advantage lies in high dielectric strength, mechanical protection for the enamel, high space factor, and opportunity to impregnate if desired. Synthetic materials such as **Formvar** and **Formex** are being used as insulation. Formvar is a vinyl acetal resin varnish and is a Class A material. It has film toughness, will withstand excessive elongation, has exceptional adherence to conductors, will not become brittle after prolonged exposure to maximum operating temperatures. **Glass-fiber** insulation such as **Fiberglas** is a continuous spun-glass fiber applied to bare or film-insulated (enamel or Formvar) magnet wire. It must be compound- or varnish-treated to give it abrasion resistance. The glass itself can withstand high temperature and resists acids. **Silotex** is a wire insulated with glass-fiber yarn over the conductor and affixed to it with silicone varnish. It is designated as Class H insulation. **Asbestos-covered** magnet wire is used where the temperature is high. It combines resistance to heat and abrasion, can resist mild acids, has good dielectric strength, and is fireproof.

Table 26 gives the diameters of magnet wire with the different types of insulation. For further data on electrical insulating materials, see pp. 6–180 *et seq.*

Table 26. Diameters of Round Magnet Wire

(Anaconda Wire & Cable Co.)

Wire size	Nominal diam, bare, in.	Nominal diam over insulation, in.							
		PE	HPE	SF, NE	HF, HNE	SCC	SCE	SVC, SX	SVSF
8	0.1285	......	......	0.1306	0.1324	0.1359	0.1380	0.1345	0.1374
9	0.1144	......	......	0.1165	0.1182	0.1208	0.1229	0.1204	0.1233
10	0.1019	0.1039	0.1056	0.1039	0.1056	0.1074	0.1094	0.1069	0.1096
11	0.0907	0.0927	0.0943	0.0927	0.0943	0.0953	0.0973	0.0957	0.0984
12	0.0808	0.0827	0.0842	0.0827	0.0842	0.0854	0.0873	0.0858	0.0884
13	0.0720	0.0739	0.0753	0.0739	0.0753	0.0766	0.0785	0.0770	0.0796
14	0.0641	0.0660	0.0673	0.0660	0.0673	0.0687	0.0706	0.0691	0.0717
15	0.0571	0.0589	0.0602	0.0589	0.0602	0.0617	0.0635	0.0621	0.0646
16	0.0508	0.0525	0.0539	0.0525	0.0539	0.0554	0.0571	0.0558	0.0582
17	0.0453	0.0469	0.0483	0.0469	0.0483	0.0499	0.0515	0.0503	0.0526
18	0.0403	0.0418	0.0432	0.0418	0.0432	0.0449	0.0464	0.0453	0.0475
19	0.0359	0.0374	0.0387	0.0374	0.0387	0.0405	0.0420	0.0409	0.0431
20	0.0320	0.0334	0.0346	0.0334	0.0346	0.0366	0.0380	0.0370	0.0389
21	0.0285	0.0299	0.0310	0.0299	0.0310	0.0331	0.0345	0.0335	0.0354
22	0.0253	0.0266	0.0277	0.0266	0.0277	0.0299	0.0312	0.0303	0.0322
23	0.0226	0.0239	0.0249	0.0239	0.0249	0.0272	0.0285	0.0276	0.0294
24	0.0201	0.0213	0.0224	0.0213	0.0224	0.0247	0.0259	0.0251	0.0268
25	0.0179	0.0190	0.0201	0.0190	0.0201	0.0220	0.0231	0.0211	0.0227
26	0.0159	0.0170	0.0180	0.0170	0.0180	0.0200	0.0211	0.0191	0.0206
27	0.0142	0.0152	0.0161	0.0152	0.0161	0.0183	0.0193	0.0174	0.0189
28	0.0126	0.0136	0.0144	0.0136	0.0144	0.0167	0.0177	0.0158	0.0172
29	0.0113	0.0122	0.0130	0.0122	0.0130	0.0154	0.0163	0.0145	0.0159
30	0.0100	0.0109	0.0116	0.0109	0.0116	0.0141	0.0150	0.0132	0.0145
31	0.0089	0.0097	0.0105	0.0097	0.0105	0.0130	0.0138	0.0121	0.0133
32	0.0080	0.0088	0.0095	0.0088	0.0095	0.0121	0.0129	0.0112	0.0124
33	0.0071	0.0078	0.0085	0.0079	0.0085	0.0112	0.0119	0.0103	0.0115
34	0.0063	0.0069	0.0075	0.0070	0.0075	0.0104	0.0110	0.0095	0.0106
35	0.0056	0.0062	0.0067	0.0063	0.0067	0.0097	0.0103	0.0088	0.0099
36	0.0050	0.0055	0.0060	0.0056	0.0060	0.0087	0.0092	0.0082	0.0092
37	0.0045	0.0050	0.0055	0.0051	0.0055	0.0082	0.0087		
38	0.0040	0.0044	0.0049	0.0045	0.0049	0.0077	0.0081		
39	0.0035	0.0039	0.0043	0.0040	0.0043	0.0072	0.0076		
40	0.0031	0.0034	0.0038	0.0036	0.0038	0.0068	0.0071		

PE, plain enamel (single thickness)
HPE, heavy plain enamel (double thickness)
SF, single Formvar
NE, single nylon enamel
HF, heavy Formvar
HNE, heavy nylon enamel
SCC, single cotton covered
SCE, single cotton enamel
SVC, single Vitrotex cover
SX, single Silotex (silicone bond)
SVSF, single Vitrotex, single Formvar

AUTOMOBILE IGNITION SYSTEMS

The ignition system in an automobile produces the spark which ignites the combustible mixture in the engine cylinders. This is accomplished by a high-voltage, or high-tension, spark between metal points in a spark plug. (A spark plug is an insulated bushing screwed into the cylinder head.) Spark plugs usually have porcelain insulation, but for some special uses, such as in airplane engines, mica may be used. There are two general sources for the energy necessary for ignition; one is the electrical system of the car which is maintained by the generator and the battery (*battery ignition*), and the other is a *magneto*.

Battery ignition is most widely used since it is simple, reliable, and low in cost, and the electrical system is a part of the car equipment. The high voltage for the spark is obtained from an ignition coil which consists of a primary coil of relatively few turns and a secondary coil of a large number of turns, both coils being wound on a common magnetic core consisting of either thin strips of iron or small iron wires. In a 6-volt system the resistance of the primary coil is from 0.9 to 2 ohms and the inductance is from 5 to 10 mh. The number of secondary turns varies from 9,000 to 25,000, and the ratio of primary to secondary turns varies from 1:40 to 1:100.

The coil operates on the following principle: It stores energy in a magnetic field relatively slowly and then releases it suddenly. The power developed ($p = dw/dt$) is thus relatively large (w = stored energy). The high emf e_2 which is required for the spark is induced by the sudden change in the flux ϕ in the core of the coil when the primary current is suddenly interrupted, $e_2 = -n_2(d\phi/dt)$, where n_2 is the number of secondary turns. For satisfactory ignition, peak voltages from 10,000 to 20,000 volts are desirable. Figure 104 shows the relation between the volts required to produce a spark and pressure with compressed air.

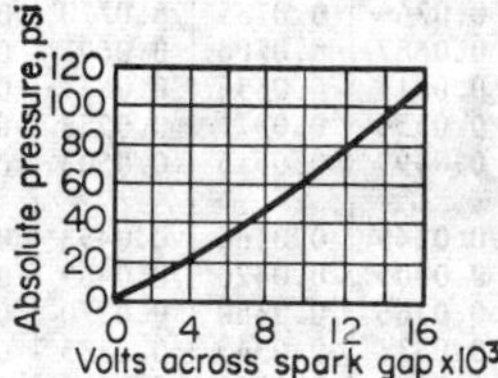

FIG. 104. Pressure-voltage curve for spark plus.

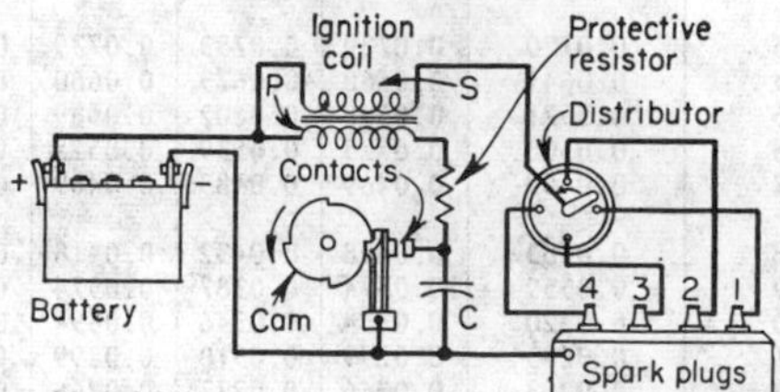

FIG. 105. Battery-ignition system.

A battery ignition system for a four-cylinder engine is shown diagrammatically in Fig. 105. The primary circuit supplied by the battery consists of the primary coil P, a protective resistor, and a set of contacts, or "points" operated by a four-lobe cam, all in series. In order to reduce arcing and burning of the contacts and to produce a sharp break in the current, a capacitor C of from 0.15 to 0.40 μf is connected across the contacts. The energy, which would otherwise appear as an arc at the contacts, is stored in the capacitor ($\frac{1}{2}ce^2$) and is dissipated when the contacts close again. The contacts, which are of pure tungsten, are operated by a four-lobe cam which is driven at one-half engine speed. A strong spring tends to keep the contacts open.

The secondary S of the ignition coil is connected between the battery positive terminal and the distributor. The lobes of the cam force the contacts together long enough to build up a magnetic field in the coil, and then through the joint action of the spring and the abrupt dropoff in the lobe of the cam, the primary current is suddenly interrupted, causing a high emf to be induced in the secondary S. The distributor arm connects the high-voltage terminal of the secondary to the spark plug of the cylinder which is firing at that instant. In a four-cylinder engine the firing order may be 1-3-4-2 or 1-2-4-3, the latter being shown in Fig. 105. The protective resistor in series with the primary of the ignition coil has a high temperature coefficient so that if the ignition switch is inadvertently left closed the resistor will heat up and limit the current. In this type of ignition system there is but a single spark for each explosion.

High-speed Distributors. It is difficult to design the type of cam shown in Fig. 105 for eight- and even six-cylinder motors so that it operates well at high speeds. After each break takes place the cam follower must ride for considerable distance upon the next lobe before the contacts are closed. At high speed this does not give time for the flux in the iron core to build up to its full value. In the Delco-Remy distributor (Fig. 106) two breaker arms are connected in parallel; one coil and one capacitor are used. One set of contacts is open when the other is just breaking but closes a few degrees after the break occurs. This closes the primary of the ignition coil immediately after the break and increases the time that the primary of the ignition coil is closed and permits the flux in the iron to reach its full value. The interrupter shown in Fig. 106 is designed for an eight-cylinder motor.

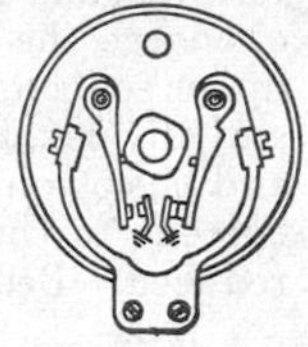

Fig. 106. Delco-Remy eight-cylinder interrupter.

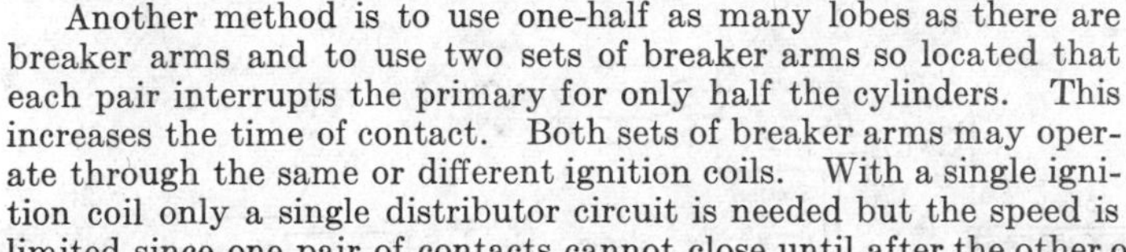

Another method is to use one-half as many lobes as there are breaker arms and to use two sets of breaker arms so located that each pair interrupts the primary for only half the cylinders. This increases the time of contact. Both sets of breaker arms may operate through the same or different ignition coils. With a single ignition coil only a single distributor circuit is needed but the speed is limited since one pair of contacts cannot close until after the other opens. With two coils there is no such limitation.

The spark should advance with increase in engine speed so as to allow for the time lag in the explosion. To take care of this **automatically** most timers are now equipped with centrifugally operated weights which advance the breaker cam with respect to the engine drive as the speed increases.

AUTOMOBILE LIGHTING AND STARTING SYSTEMS

Automobile lighting and starting systems initially operated at 6 volts, but at the present time nearly all cars, except the smaller ones, operate at **12 volts.** This is due to the fact that larger engines, particularly V-8s, are now common and require more starting power. With 12 volts, for the same power, the starting current is halved, and the effect of resistance in the leads, connections, and brushes is materially reduced. In some systems the positive side of the system is grounded, but more often the negative side is grounded.

A late development is the use in some cars of an **a-c generator,** or alternator, combined with a rectifier as the generating unit rather than the usual d-c generator. One advantage is the elimination of the commutator, made up of segments, which requires some maintenance owing to the sparking and wear of the carbon brushes. With the alternator the d-c field rotates, and brushes operating on smooth slip rings require almost no maintenance. Also, the system is greatly simplified by the fact that rectifiers are "one-way" devices, and the battery *cannot* deliver current back to the generator when its voltage drops below that of the battery. Thus, no cutout relay, such as is required with d-c generators, is necessary. This a-c development is the result of recent advances in the development of germanium and silicon semiconductor rectifiers (see p. 15–115).

Figure 107 shows a schematic diagram of the Ford system (adapted initially to trucks). The generator stator is wound three-phase Y-connected, and the field is bipolar supplied with d-c through slip rings and brushes. The rectifier diodes are connected double-way bridge circuit (see 15–119) to supply the battery through the ammeter.

Regulator. The function of the regulator is to control the generator current so that its value is adapted to the battery voltage which is related to the condition of charge of the battery (see Fig. 7). Thus, when the battery voltage drops (indicating a lowered condition of charge), the current should be increased, and, conversely, when the battery voltage increases (indicating a high condition of charge), the current should be decreased.

Neglecting for the moment the starting procedure, when the ignition switch is thrown to the normal "on" position at c, the coil actuating the field relay is connected to the battery + terminal and causes the relay contacts a to close. This energizes the regulator circuits, and, if the two upper voltage regulator contacts b are closed as shown, the rotating field of the alternator is connected directly to the battery + terminal, and the field current is then at its maximum value and produces a high generator voltage and large output current. At the same time the voltage regulator coil in series with the 0.3- and 14-ohm resistors is connected between the battery + terminal and ground. If the voltage of the battery rises owing to its higher condition of charge, the current to the voltage regulator coil increases, causing it to open the two upper contacts at b. Current from the battery now flows through the 0.3-ohm resistor and divides, some going through the 10-ohm resistor and dividing between the field and the 50-ohm resistor, and the remainder going to the voltage regulator coil. The current to the rotating field is thus reduced, causing the alternator output to be reduced. Because of the 0.3 ohm now in circuit, the current to the coil of the voltage

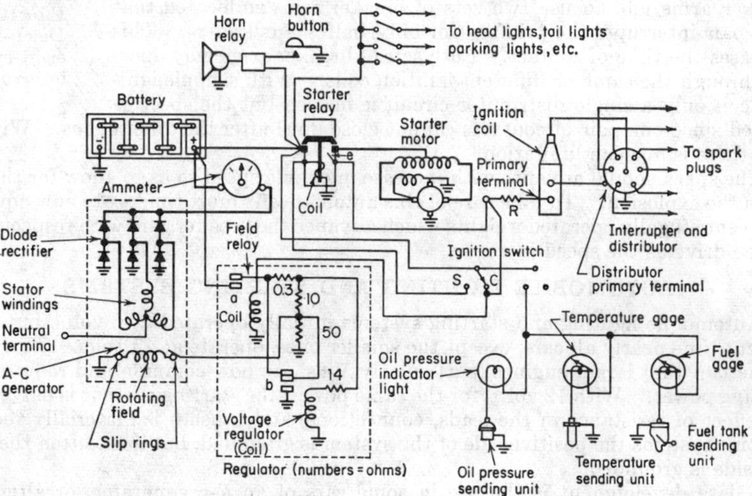

FIG. 107. Schematic diagram of Ford lighting and starting system.

regulator is reduced to such a value that it holds the center contact at b in the mid, or open, position. If the battery voltage rises to an even higher value, the regulator coil becomes strong enough to close the lower contacts at b; this short-circuits the field, reducing its current almost to zero, and thus reducing the alternator output to zero. On the other hand when the battery voltage drops, the foregoing sequence is reversed, and the contacts at b operate to increase the current to the alternator field.

As was mentioned earlier, the battery cannot supply current to the alternator because of the "one-way" characteristic of the rectifier. Thus, when the alternator voltage drops below that of the battery and even when the alternator stops running, its current automatically becomes zero. The alternator has a normal rectifier open-circuit voltage of about 14 volts and a rating of 20 amp.

Starting. In most cases, for starting, the ignition key is turned far to the right and held there until the motor starts. Then, when the key is released, the ignition switch contacts assume a normal operating position. Thus, in Fig. 107, when the ignition-switch contact is in the starting position S, the starter relay coil becomes connected by a lead to the battery + terminal and thus becomes energized, closing the relay contacts. The starter motor is then connected to the battery to crank the engine. At the time that the contact closes it makes contact with a small metal brush e which connects the battery + terminal to the primary terminal of the ignition coil through the protective resistor R. After the motor starts, the ignition switch contacts spring to the normal operating position C, and the starter relay switch opens, thereby breaking contact with the small brush e. However, when contact C is closed, the ignition coil primary terminal is now connected through leads to the battery + terminal. The interrupter, the ignition coil, and the distributor now operate in the manner described earlier (see Fig. 105); the system shown in Fig. 107, is that for a six-cylinder engine.

The connection of **accessories** to the electric system is illustrated in Fig. 107 for the horn, head and other lights, and temperature and fuel gages.

Magneto Ignition

Principle of Magneto. A magneto is an electric generator in which the magnetic flux is provided by one or more permanent magnets. It is a self-contained unit and is used advantageously for ignition where a generator and a battery are not needed to supply power to other accessories. The design of magnetos was radically changed when Alnico, with its very high retentivity (Fig. 98), became available as a permanent-magnet material. One method of utilizing Alnico magnets is to insert the bar magnets in the frame of the magneto (Fig. 108). The rotor is a soft-iron bobbin. A primary

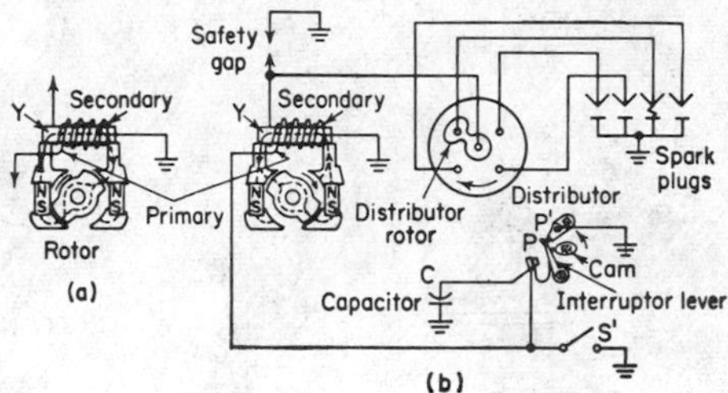

Fig. 108. Magneto-ignition system.

winding of relatively few turns and a secondary winding of a relatively large number of turns are wound over the laminated yoke Y. The position of the rotor shown in (a) provides a low reluctance path for the magnetic flux of the left-hand magnet and a high reluctance path for the magnetic flux of the right-hand magnet so that the flux goes through the yoke from left to right as shown. When the rotor turns one-eighth of a revolution, it becomes horizontal; obviously, each of the magnets acts in opposition relative to the yoke, and the flux therein becomes zero. In (b), which also shows the external electrical connections, the rotor is shown as having turned one-fourth of a revolution, or 90 deg, from its position in (a).

The rotor now provides a low-reluctance path for the right-hand magnet and a high-reluctance path for the left-hand one. Thus the magnetic flux now goes through the yoke from right to left. It follows that in each 90 deg interval the flux in the yoke undergoes a complete reversal. It will be recognized that this is an **inductor** type of a-c generator.

In the diagram in (b), one end each of the primary and of the secondary are grounded together. The other end of the primary is connected to an insulated interrupter lever having a contact point P. This makes intermittent contact with the grounded contact point P'. The contact point P is actuated by a cam which is driven by the same shaft as the magneto rotor and is in a definite relation to it. A switch S' is provided to ground and thus short-circuit the secondary when it is desired to stop the engine. A capacitor C is connected between the point P and ground to absorb the energy of the spark which occurs when the contacts open.

With the contacts closed, the primary is short-circuited, and the varying flux in the core produced by the rotation of the rotor induces an alternating current in the winding which in turn produces an alternating flux in the core. With the rotation of the rotor the current in the secondary rises cyclically to maximum values, and at these instants the cam causes the points PP' to open suddenly, interrupting the current in the primary and thus causing a sudden collapse of the flux in the core. This induces a high-impulse emf in the secondary which is transmitted to the distributor and thence to the proper spark plug as shown.

On starting, the speed of the magneto may be so low that the emf is not sufficient to produce a hot spark. This difficulty may be met by **impulse starting,** in which the rotor is driven through a spring. During cranking the rotor is restrained from turning until the engine comes to the proper firing position, at which time the rotor is suddenly released. The energy stored in the spring produces a high, instantaneous, angular velocity to the rotor, resulting in a high emf and hot spark.

Inductor-type magnetos, having a large number of rotor poles and arranged differently from those shown in Fig. 108, are used for airplane-engine ignition. In another magneto design the rotor is a solid cylindrical Alnico magnet, permanently magnetized with an N- and an S-pole diametrically opposite. The frame is laminated, and there is a yoke with primary and secondary windings. When the rotor rotates, its N- and S-poles produce an alternating flux in the yoke which induces a short-circuit current in the primary winding and the method of producing the spark is then the same as with Fig. 108(b).

ELECTRONICS

BY

J. Hubert Noland

REFERENCES: Terman, "Electronic and Radio Engineering," McGraw-Hill. Chute, "Electronics in Industry," McGraw-Hill. Cage, "Theory and Applications of Industrial Electronics," McGraw-Hill. Alley and Atwood, "Electronic Engineering," Wiley. Angelo, "Electronic Circuits," McGraw-Hill. RCA Receiving Tube Manual. RCA Transistor Manual. GE Transistor Manual.

The subject of electronics includes physical electronics as used in vacuum tubes and gas-filled tubes, solid-state physics as applied to semiconductor devices, and circuits making use of these components such as rectifiers, amplifiers, control circuits, and a wide variety of related applications.

RECTIFYING DEVICES

A **diode** is a non-linear two-terminal circuit element which has low resistance to current flow in one direction and high resistance in the other direction. An **ideal diode** would have zero resistance in the forward direction and infinite resistance in the reverse and would be a perfect rectifying device.

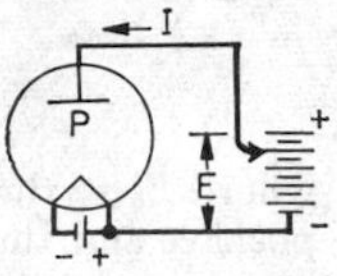

FIG. 1. Diode or two-electrode tube.

A **vacuum diode** (Fig. 1) consists of two electrodes, an anode (or plate) and a heated cathode, both enclosed in a metal or glass envelope containing a very high vacuum approximately 10^{-6} mm Hg. Emission current per unit area of the cathode is given by

$$I = AT^2\epsilon^{-e\phi/kT} \tag{1}$$

where

A = a constant depending upon cathode material (about 60 amp/cm² for most metals)
T = absolute temperature of the cathode
e = electronic charge (1.6×10^{-19} coulomb)
k = Boltzmann's constant (1.38×10^{-23} joule/°K)
ϕ = work function of the surface

Since for appreciable emission, the surface must be very hot, very few materials are suitable. Those commonly used are pure tungsten, thoriated tungsten, and nickel coated with a layer of barium or strontium oxide. The coated cathodes are much more efficient and operate at lower temperatures but deteriorate with age. From Table 1, it is seen that metals like copper would melt before they would emit appreciably.

Table 1. Comparison of Possible Cathode Materials

Material	ϕ, ev	Melting point, °K	Operating temp, °K
Copper	4.1	1,356	Unsatisfactory
Nickel	5.0	1,725	Unsatisfactory
Tungsten	4.52	3,643	2,500
Thoriated tungsten	2.6	3,643	1,900
Oxide-coated	1.0	1,725	1,100

Commonly, oxide-coated cathodes are used in receiving-type tubes, thoriated-tungsten cathodes in medium- to high-power applications, and pure tungsten for high-voltage operation where positive-ion bombardment would destroy the coating.

When the filament of the tube is used for the cathode, the alternating current used for heating causes the temperature of the filament to vary cyclically with the power frequency, and an undesirable hum is introduced. This effect may be minimized by use of an indirectly heated cathode which consists of a small cylinder of oxide-coated nickel heated by an internal insulated filament.

When an emf E is applied between the plate and the cathode so that the plate is positive, the electrons emitted by the cathode are drawn to the plate. The relation of the current to the voltage, for three different temperatures of the filament, is given in Fig. 2. At any given filament temperature T, the current increases rapidly at first with an increase in voltage and then at some point the current becomes essentially constant. This is **temperature saturation** and occurs when the voltage is sufficiently high so that it draws all the electrons emitted by the filament at the given temperature. When the temperature is increased to temperatures T_2 and T_3, more electrons are emitted, and saturation occurs at higher values of current. When the voltage is low enough so that not all electrons are drawn to the plate, a cloud of electrons surrounds the cathode and produces a **space charge.** Increasing the plate voltage draws electrons from this cloud, and plate current is given by the equation

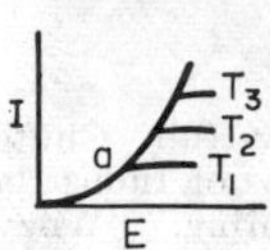

FIG. 2. Volt-ampere characteristics of vacuum diode.

$$I_b = KE_b^{3/2} \tag{2}$$

where E_b is the anode voltage with respect to the cathode. When the cathode is positive and the plate negative, the electrons are all drawn to the cathode, and there is no current. Hence this tube has unidirectional conduction and approximates the characteristics of the ideal diode.

The actual current-voltage curve (Fig. 2) does not exhibit complete saturation, but current continues to increase with voltage owing to the **Schottky effect.** This effect is produced by the potential gradient at the cathode which becomes positive when the space charge is removed and temperature saturation is reached. This potential gradient helps some electrons, which otherwise have insufficient kinetic energy, to escape from the surface of the cathode. Another anomaly occurs at zero plate voltage where slight current will still flow owing to some electrons being emitted with sufficient kinetic energy to reach the anode and give it a slight negative charge.

Gas Diodes. If the tube envelope contains a gas such as argon, neon, or mercury vapor at a pressure of the order of 10^{-3} mm Hg, the characteristics are quite different. As the plate is made positive, the electron flow begins as in a vacuum tube. When the emitted electrons have sufficient energy (10.4 electron volts for mercury vapor), they ionize the gas, and the cloud of positive ions effectively neutralizes the negative space charge in the interelectrode space. Plate current could then increase to the value limited by the emission capability of the cathode. In practical circuits, current is limited by the external circuit, and the gas tube is essentially a switch with a constant voltage drop.

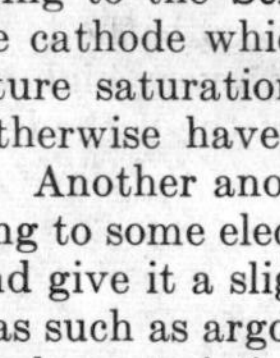

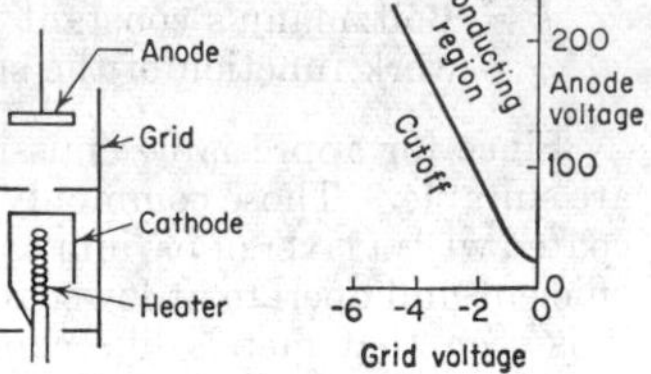

FIG. 3. Electrode structure of thyratron.

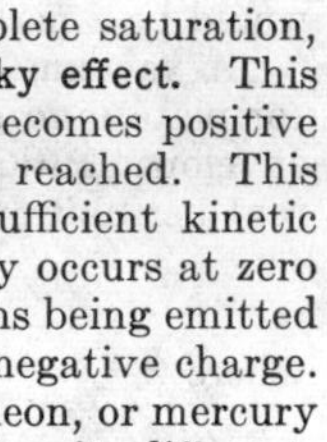

FIG. 4. Control characteristic of thyratron.

Thyratrons (Fig. 3). The addition of a grid surrounding the cathode makes it possible to prevent the firing of a gas tube by holding this grid sufficiently negative as shown in the thyratron control characteristic (Fig. 4). After conduction starts, however, the grid is surrounded by positive ions and has no control of current magnitude. Conduction may be stopped only by reducing the current to zero long enough for the tube to deionize. The actual control characteristic is influenced by the tube temperature and filament voltage so that it would, more correctly, be shown as a band rather than as a line.

A fundamental half-wave rectifier circuit using a thyratron is shown in Fig. 5. The point in the cycle at which conduction begins may be controlled by changing the magnitude of the d-c voltage in the grid circuit or by changing the phase of the a-c bias with respect to the plate supply. If the magnitude of the a-c bias is large compared to the critical grid voltage, the firing point is not greatly affected by control characteristic variations. With the phase of the a-c bias lagging the plate voltage by 90 deg, tube current may be controlled smoothly from full off to full on by adjusting the d-c voltage. This is then a d-c power amplifier with considerable power gain.

Ignitrons (Fig. 6). For large current rectifiers or for the control of large a-c loads, ignitrons are often used. The various sizes of ignitrons available can handle up to 10,000 amp on intermittent duty. The ignitron has no filament but uses a pool of liquid mercury as its cathode. If an arc can be started within the tube, large quantities of electrons are emitted from "hot spots" on the pool and are drawn to the large graphite anode whenever it is positive. These large currents produce considerable heating within the tube, and ignitrons are usually enclosed in a water-cooled jacket. To start the arc, an ignitor rod made of a pointed piece of boron carbide is mounted so that it touches the mercury surface. The ignitor forms a high-resistance contact with the mercury, and a pulse of current in the ignitor causes local heating and tiny arcs between the pool and the rod. This causes ionization, and the electron flow transfers to the more positive anode. A simple half-wave circuit using an ignitron is shown in Fig. 7. A more elaborate circuit which could vary the point of application of ignitor voltage would be able to delay firing of the tube and thus control the average output voltage.

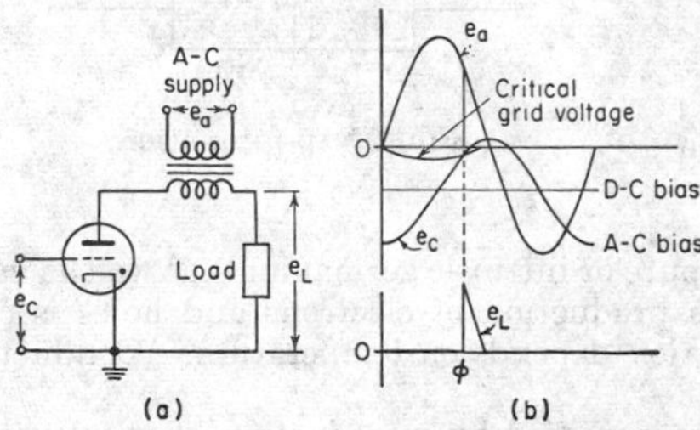

FIG. 5. Operation of thyratron as controlled rectifier.

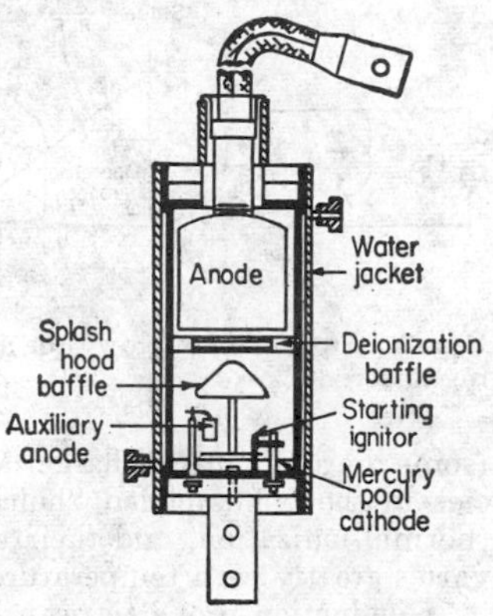

FIG. 6. Structure of ignitron. (*General Electric Company.*)

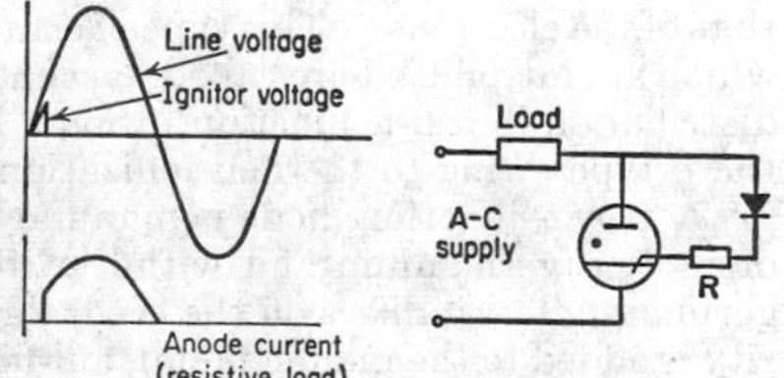

FIG. 7. Operation of ignitron as controlled rectifier.

Glow Tubes. A cold-cathode or glow tube contains an anode and an unheated cathode in a gas-filled envelope. Over its operating range, the voltage drop between the plasma and the cathode is constant at a value determined by the gas used and the material of the cathode. When the current is increased until the glow discharge completely covers the cathode, the voltage rises. Typical tubes have ratings of 75, 105, or 150 volts over a current range of 5 to 40 ma. They may be used as voltage regulators in low-power applications in a circuit of the general form of Fig. 8, with voltage across the load being held constant in spite of variations of E_s or R_L so long as the intersection of the load line occurs on the constant voltage portion of the tube characteristic.

Semiconductor Diodes. A semiconductor diode consists of two semiconducting materials with different electrical properties which are joined at a surface called the

junction, as illustrated in Fig. 9. Semiconductors are solid materials which are neither good conductors nor good insulators. Germanium is an example of a semiconductor, and silicon is also used. The atom of germanium has four electrons in its outermost shell loosely bound to the atom. In a germanium crystal, each atom shares two electrons with four neighbors, forming a diamond-crystal lattice structure. In a good insulator, these valence electrons are tightly bound, and no free electrons are available for conduction; in a conductor, there are large quantities of free electrons which provide mechanism for conduction. Between these two extremes, semiconductors have valence electrons which are loosely bound (some are available as charge carriers in pure or intrinsic germanium) as well as vacancies in the bonds called "holes." This production of electrons and holes is called thermal ionization, and their concentration depends on temperature. Conductivity varies greatly with temperature.

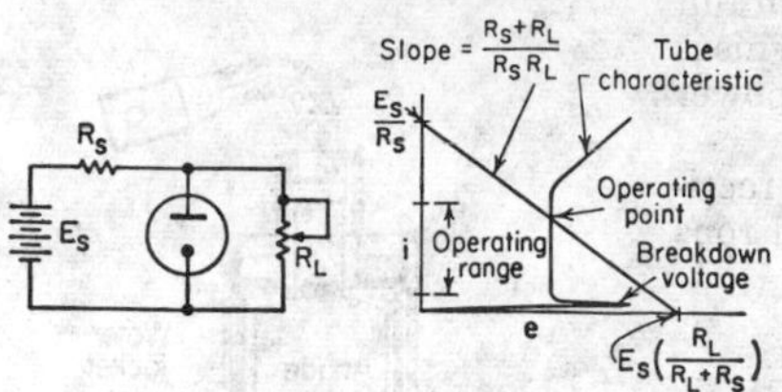

Fig. 8. Operation of glow tube as voltage regulator.

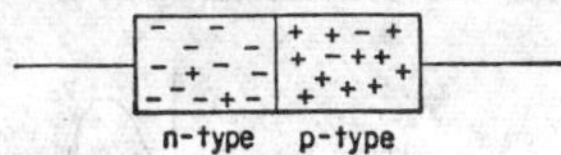

Fig. 9. p-n junction.

Conduction properties can be greatly increased by introduction of impurities (in the order of one part per million) into the crystal. When atoms with five valence electrons, such as antimony, arsenic, or phosphorus are introduced, the fifth electron is very loosely bound and is free to conduct at room temperature. Impurities of this type are called **donors,** and the crystal is called an **n-type.**

On the other hand, when atoms with three valence electrons such as those of aluminum, boron, indium are introduced, the lattice bonds are unsatisfied, and an electron from a neighboring region may jump into the incomplete bond, leaving a vacancy behind. This migration of the electrons, which may be considered as a movement of the "holes," is equivalent to a movement of positive charge in a direction opposite that of the electrons. This type of semiconductor is called a **p-type,** and the impurities which are introduced are called **"acceptors."** Figure 9 indicates the hole and electron distribution in a p-n junction. Some holes exist in the n-type and some electrons in the p-type owing to thermal ionization.

A grown-junction diode is manufactured by touching a seed crystal to the surface of molten germanium and withdrawing it at a slow and steady rate. The molten germanium crystallizes on the seed, forming a uniform crystal. If an acceptor impurity is added to the molten metal, a p-type crystal is formed. When this is of sufficient size, a donor impurity is added which outnumbers the acceptor material, and the crystal becomes n-type. This crystal can then be cut into many diodes.

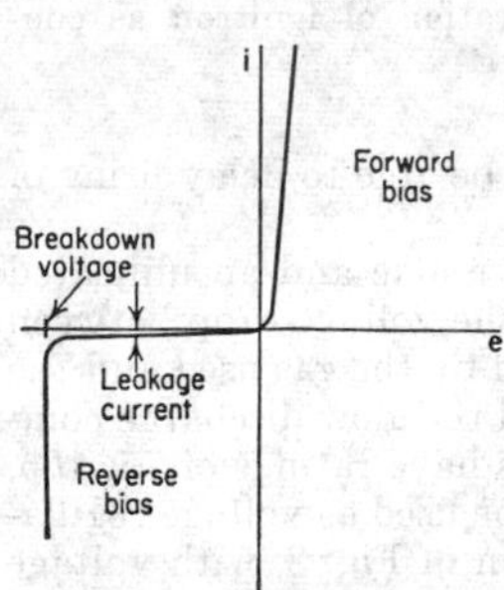

Fig. 10. Volt-ampere characteristics of junction diode.

More precise control over manufacturing tolerances can be achieved with the alloy-junction diode, which is made by placing a bit of indium on a wafer of n-type germanium. The combination is then heated above the melting point of indium, and the two metals alloy together, producing a p-type region.

The volt-ampere characteristics of a semiconductor diode are shown in Fig. 10 and its principle of operation in Fig. 11. When a forward voltage is applied, holes in the p region move toward and across the junction, and electrons in the n region move into the p region. After crossing the junction, recombination occurs, and current can flow easily with this polarity. With reverse polarity, both holes and electrons move away from the junction, and current flow is very small. When the breakdown or zener voltage is reached, however, the electric field is strong enough to break down the covalent bonds, and the current increases to a large value, limited by the external circuit. No damage is caused by this reverse current unless the power rating is exceeded. In this region, the voltage is essentially constant over a large current range, and the diode may be used as a voltage regulator. For this application, it is replacing the cold-cathode glow tube. A diode used for this purpose is usually called a **zener diode.**

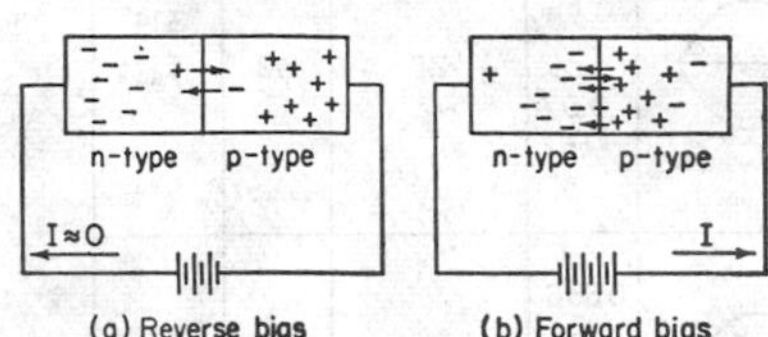

FIG. 11. Operation of junction diode.

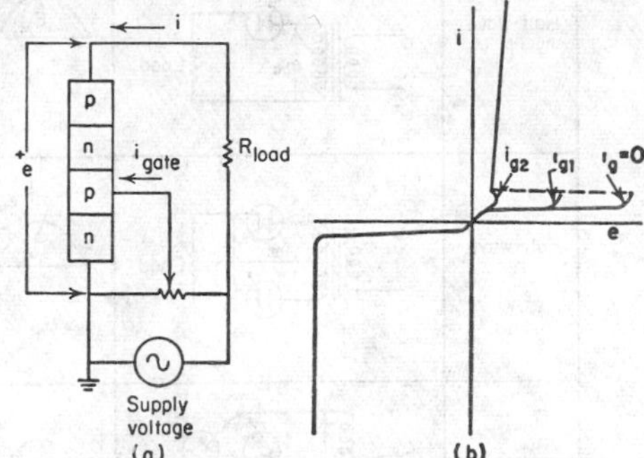

FIG. 12. Silicon controlled rectifier (SCR).

Silicon Controlled Rectifier. A semiconductor device which can be used as a controlled rectifier is a four-layer p-n-p-n device that is diagrammed in Fig. 12. Desired characteristics have been obtained more easily using silicon than germanium. With no gate current, current flow is blocked by the collector junction until a large voltage is exceeded, at which point it fires and becomes essentially a short circuit. This critical anode voltage decreases as the gate current increases until the characteristic is essentially that of a single p-n junction.

Controlled rectifiers can be turned on in less than a microsecond; control is regained by decreasing current to a value below the holding current. Performance is thus similar to a conventional thyratron, and the SCR is supplanting the thyratron for many applications.

Metallic or Disk Rectifiers. Selenium rectifiers are based on the unilateral conduction property of a thin layer of crystalline selenium when it is deposited on a backplate of either aluminum or iron. The thickness is about 0.05 mm. A low-melting alloy is sprayed on the selenium surface, forming the "counter-electrode." The forward direction of current is from backplate to counter-electrode. The cells, or units, consist of either circular or square discs with a hole in the center. These units are then stacked over a cylindrical metal stud insulated by a phenolic tube. Light springs pressing on the peripheries or edges assure good contact. The sizes of the disks range from $\frac{9}{32}$ in. diam and 1 in. square to $4\frac{3}{8}$ in. diam to 5 in. × 6 in. rectangular. The applied rms voltage per cell varies from 18 to 26 volts, giving, with single-phase full-wave center tap, a d-c voltage of 6 volts and, with a full-wave bridge circuit, a d-c voltage of 12 volts. Higher load voltages are readily obtained by adding cells to the stack. The cells operate at a current density of from 0.4 to 1.5 psia. Single-phase efficiency is from 50 to 75 percent and for three-phase, 80 to 85 percent. The d-c voltage regulation is about 15 percent. The principal application is the charging of batteries (see Chute).

RECTIFIER CIRCUITS

Rectifier Circuits—Resistive Load. Several common rectifier circuits with voltage waveforms are given in Fig. 13. It is to be noted that three phase circuits have smaller ripple of higher fundamental frequency, making filtering easier, if needed at all. Bridge circuits give lower peak inverse voltage and do not require center-tapped secondaries, but cathodes are not all at the same potential. This necessitates the use of several filament transformers in tube circuits.

Type	Circuit	Output voltage waveform	E_{dc} (avg)	Ripple fundamental frequency	% ripple	Peak inverse voltage
Half-wave 1ϕ	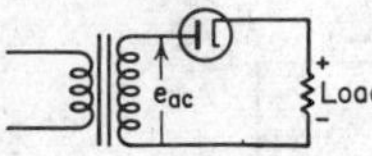 e_{ac}, Load	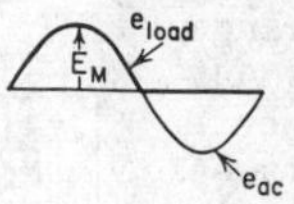 e_{load}, E_M, e_{ac}	0.318 E_M 0.45 E_{ac}	F	121	3.14 E_{dc}
Full-wave 1ϕ	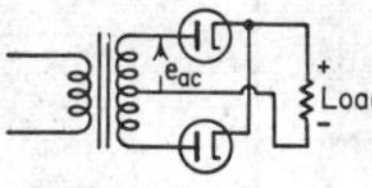 e_{ac}, Load	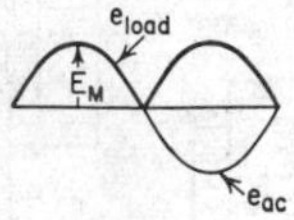 e_{load}, E_M, e_{ac}	0.636 E_M 0.9 E_{ac}	2F	48	3.14 E_{dc}
Bridge 1ϕ	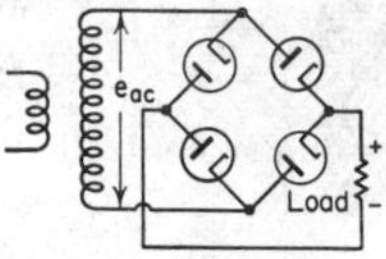 e_{ac}, Load	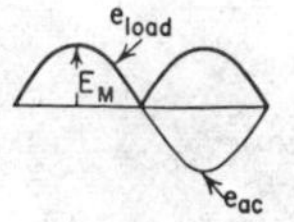 e_{load}, E_M, e_{ac}	0.636 E_M 0.9 E_{ac}	2F	48	1.57 E_{dc}
Half-wave 3ϕ	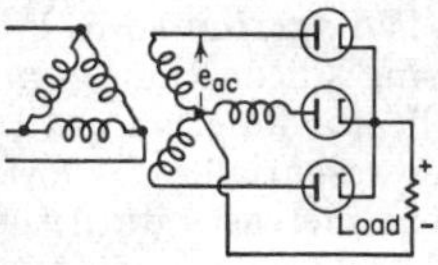 e_{ac}, Load	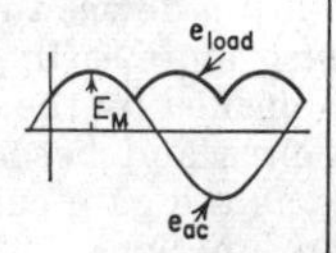 e_{load}, E_M, e_{ac}	0.827 E_M 1.17 E_{ac}	3F	18	2.09 E_{dc}

E_M = maximun value of e_{ac}
E_{ac} = effective value of e_{ac}
E_{dc} = average value of d-c load voltage
F = line frequency
% ripple = 100 x rms ripple/E_{dc}

Fig. 13. Comparison of rectifier circuits.

For an input a-c voltage of $e = E \sin \omega t$, Fourier analysis of load voltage for the half-wave rectifier gives

$$e_L = \frac{E}{\pi} + \frac{E}{2} \sin \omega t - \frac{2E}{\pi} \left(\tfrac{1}{3} \cos 2\omega t + \tfrac{1}{15} \cos 4\omega t + \tfrac{1}{35} \cos 6\omega t + \cdots \right) \tag{3}$$

For the full-wave rectifier,

$$e_L = \frac{2E}{\pi} - \frac{4E}{\pi} \left(\tfrac{1}{3} \cos 2\omega t + \tfrac{1}{15} \cos 4\omega t + \tfrac{1}{35} \cos 6\omega t + \cdots \right) \tag{4}$$

With a pure resistance load, load current is simply e_L/R.

In general, vacuum-tube rectifiers are used in low-power applications, medium-power applications make use of gas tubes, and pool-cathode mercury tubes are used for high power. Recently, semiconductor diodes have been used for all types of applications except those demanding highest voltages or currents.

Semiconductor Rectifier Circuits. While semiconductors have a simpler circuitry system because they do not require filament transformers, they are more subject to destruction by over-voltage during switching transients or by momentary overcurrents.

To provide protection from switching transients, a safety factor of 2.5 to 3 on peak inverse voltage (PIV) should be used. Furthermore, if the load cannot absorb transient energy (*i.e.*, if it is inductive or can be disconnected), a surge suppressor must be used. This consists of an R-C (resistor-capacitor) series circuit of appropriate design, which may be connected across the load terminals if a full-wave circuit is used, across primary or secondary windings, or across each diode. A non-linear resistance which breaks down and becomes conducting at voltages higher than some critical value may also be used.

Over-current protection against slight, long-sustained overloads may easily be accomplished with fuses or circuit breakers. Protection against short-circuit conditions is more difficult, since ordinary fuses or breakers generally will not operate rapidly enough. Current-limiting fuses or current-limiting impedances should be used to hold the maximum current within the half-cycle peak overload rating of the diode used.

Series operation of diodes may be used if a single diode has insufficient PIV. A voltage-balancing network, consisting of a resistor, in parallel with each diode should be used. The value of this resistance is found from the relationship

	No. diodes in series	K
$R = \dfrac{V}{KI}$	2	1.0
	3	1.2
	4	1.5
	5	1.7
	6	2.0

V = rated PIV of diode; K = a factor depending on number of diodes in series; I = maximum reverse current of diode. (Table from Semiconductor Diode Source Book, published by Westinghouse Electric Corp., Youngwood, Pa.)

Rectifier Circuits—Inductive Load. When an inductive load such as a motor field is supplied, steady-state load current can be found by dividing the series representation of the load voltage [Eq. (4)] by the load impedance; remember that X_L is different for each ripple component. Transient solution may be found by Laplace transform methods (Gibson and Tuteur, "Control System Components," McGraw-Hill).

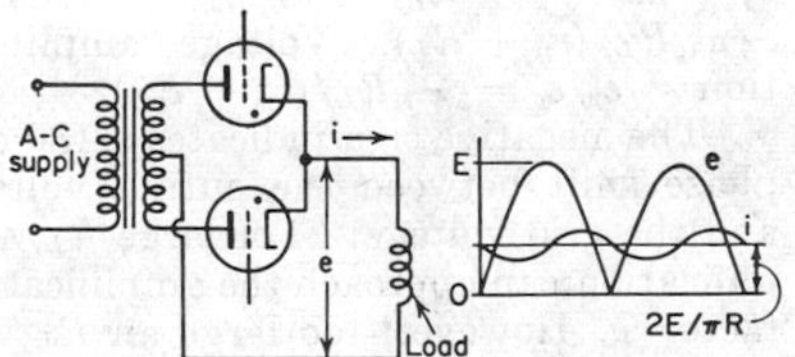

FIG. 14. Full-wave rectifier—inductive load.

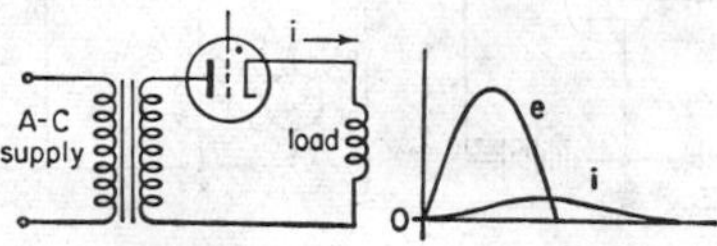

FIG. 15. Half-wave rectifier—inductive load.

With a **full-wave rectifier,** the current increases gradually after the switch is closed at a rate determined by L/R until it reaches an average value of $2E/\pi R$. Both circuit and waveform are given in Fig. 14. With a **half-wave rectifier** as shown in Fig. 15, the current increases slightly on the positive half cycle but is forced back to zero on the negative half cycle. This circuit can be made usable by connecting a **"free-wheeling" diode** across the load which conducts during the negative half cycle and provides a low resistance path for load current. The average load current is $E/\pi R$. Circuit and waveforms are given in Fig. 16.

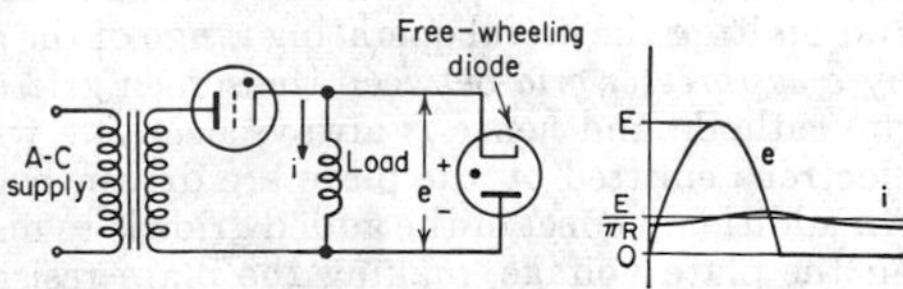

FIG. 16. Half-wave rectifier with "free-wheeling" diode.

The advantage of this circuit over the full-wave rectifier is that a center-tapped supply transformer is not required. For a controlled rectifier, only one thyratron or silicon controlled rectifier is required along with the free-wheeling diode.

AMPLIFYING DEVICES

In the **triode** (DeForest), a grid is inserted between the cathode and plate but very close to the cathode. A relatively small change of voltage applied between grid and cathode has a much greater effect on electron flow than the same voltage applied between plate and cathode. Consequently (Fig. 17), $\Delta i_b = (\partial i_b/\partial e_b)\,\Delta e_b + (\partial i_b/\partial e_c)\,\Delta e_c$ and $i_p = (1/r_p)e_p + g_m e_g$, where $\Delta i_b = i_p$ = change of plate current, $\Delta e_b = e_p$ = change of plate voltage, $\Delta e_c = e_g$ = change of grid voltage, and by definition,

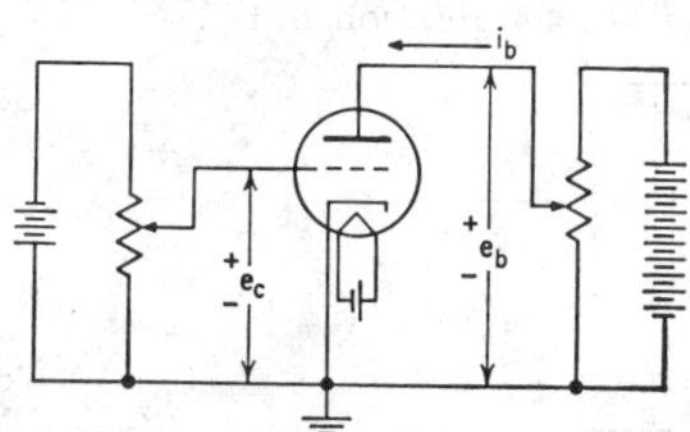

FIG. 17. Triode or three-electrode tube, Type 6J5.

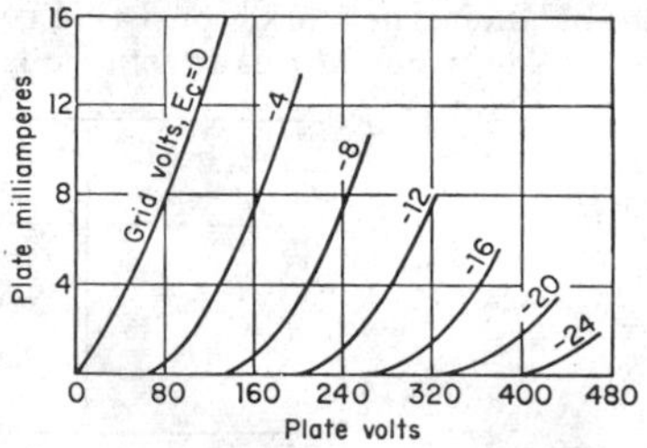

FIG. 18. Triode plate characteristics.

$\partial e_b/\partial i_b = r_p$ = plate resistance, $\partial i_b/\partial e_c = g_m$ = mutual conductance, and $\partial e_b/\partial e_c = r_p g_m = \mu$ = amplification factor.

The relationship between these two voltages and the plate current is usually given in graphical form (Fig. 18). For small signals, the values of μ, g_m, and r_p may be determined at the quiescent operating point (*i.e.*, without input signal) and considered constant over the operating range. The tube is then replaced by the equivalent plate circuit of Fig. 19(*b*). For this circuit, $i_p = \mu e_g/(r_p + R_L)$ and $e_0 = -i_p R_L = -\mu e_g R_L/(r_p + R_L)$. Voltage amplification $= e_0/e_g = -\mu R_L/(r_p + R_L)$.

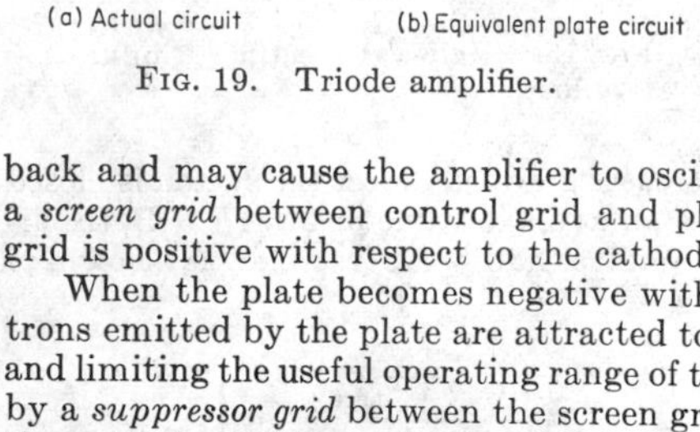

(*a*) Actual circuit (*b*) Equivalent plate circuit

FIG. 19. Triode amplifier.

The negative sign indicates a 180 deg phase shift between the output voltage and the grid voltage. For large R_L, amplification can approach the amplification factor μ. However, too large an R_L will reduce power output.

With radio-frequency amplification, the capacitance between grid and plate is objectionable in that it produces feedback and may cause the amplifier to oscillate. In the **tetrode** or four-electrode tube, a *screen grid* between control grid and plate serves as an electrostatic shield. This grid is positive with respect to the cathode but normally less positive than the plate.

When the plate becomes negative with respect to the screen, any secondary electrons emitted by the plate are attracted to the screen, thus reducing the plate current and limiting the useful operating range of the amplifier. This effect may be eliminated by a *suppressor grid* between the screen grid and the plate. This grid is connected to the cathode and hence is always negative with respect to the plate. Therefore any electrons emitted by the plate are driven back. Such a tube is a **pentode** (Fig. 20). An additional effect of the added grids is to make the plate current even less dependent on the plate voltage, making the plate resistance and the amplification factor much larger than for the triode. Calculations are performed in the same manner as those given above for the triode.

Graphical Analysis. While the equivalent plate circuit is useful for analysis of small-signal operation in the linear range, graphical analysis is particularly useful in that it shows operating principles very clearly and also shows the distortion and nonlinear effects that can be caused by large signals or poorly chosen values of supply voltages or load resistor. The volt-ampere characteristic of the load resistor (the *load line*) is drawn on the tube characteristics in such a manner that at any value of plate current the voltage drop across the tube and the voltage across the load resistor will add graphically to give the plate supply voltage. Consequently, at any grid voltage, the plate current may be found from the intersection of the load line with the line for this particular grid voltage, and values of plate current, plate voltage, and load voltage may be read directly from the curve. This method is illustrated in Fig. 20(*b*) where a pentode is used for the example.

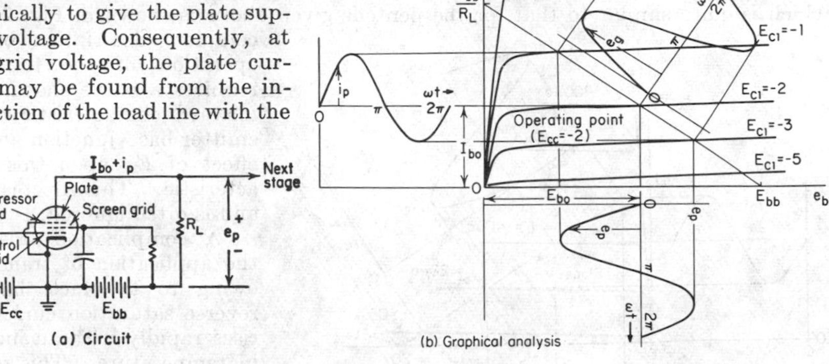

FIG. 20. Pentode amplifier.

Transistors. A transistor (Fig. 21) is a bar of semiconductor material to which impurities have been added to produce two relatively long sections of p-type material separated by a thin section of n-type. These regions are designated emitter, base, and collector. Equally useful is one in which emitter and collector are n-type, and the base is p-type. Transistors are thus described as p-n-p or n-p-n.

The transistor is a three-terminal device consisting of two p-n junctions, each having the characteristics of the junction diode similar to Fig. 10. There are three possible circuit configurations of the transistor, depending upon which element (emitter, base, or collecter) is common to both input and output. In any connection, there are four significant variables: input voltage and current and output voltage and current.

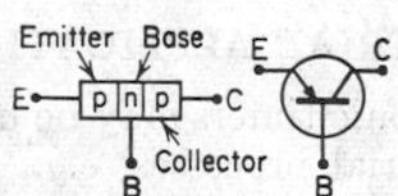

FIG. 21. Pictorial and schematic representation of p-n-p transistor.

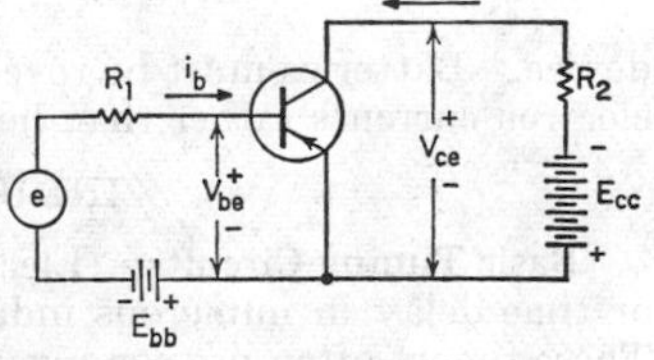

FIG. 22. p-n-p transistor amplifier circuit (common emitter).

In all three connections, the current-voltage characteristic of one junction is dependent upon the current across the other junction. The common-emitter connection (Fig. 22) is most frequently used in simple amplifiers. The voltage E_{cc} is greater in magnitude than E_{bb}, causing the collector-base junction to be reversed-biased. With $E_{bb} = 0$, a small current (reverse saturation current, Fig. 10) flows in the base-collector junction. When a small forward bias E_{bb} is applied to the emitter-base junction, a current will flow consisting of holes leaving the emitter and electrons leaving the base. The relative impurity concentration in emitter and base is such that most of this current is carried by the majority carriers in the emitter or holes in the p-n-p transistor. If the base is very thin, most of the holes which cross the emitter-base junction will be attracted to the negatively biased collector. This current in R_2 causes a voltage across this resistor. The current in the base connection consists of the relatively few electrons supplied by the base plus the holes from the emitter which are not captured by the collector. Therefore a small change in base current will produce a much larger change in collector current. For this reason, the transistor is frequently described as a current amplifier in contrast to the vacuum triode which is usually treated as a voltage amplifier. In Fig. 22 practical values of batteries and resistors would also produce voltage amplification.

Graphical Analysis. A graphical analysis of the operation of a transistor amplifier which is quite similar to that for the pentode given above is shown in Fig. 23. A complete description of the operation of the transistor requires a curve showing the forward characteristic of the emitter-base junction and the effect of E_{cc} upon this characteristic. This effect is small and is often ignored.

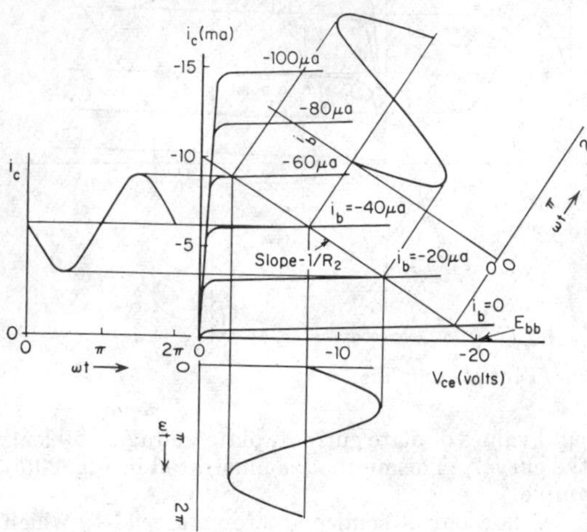

FIG. 23. Graphical analysis of transistor amplifier (common emitter).

A complication arises in the application of transistors owing to the fact that the reverse saturation current I_{c0} rises rapidly with an increase in temperature. This results in an upward shift of all the lines in Fig. 23 and corresponding changes in operating characteristics. Special circuits are often used to provide "bias stabilization" against changes in operating temperature.

The above description applies to the p-n-p transistor but is applicable to the n-p-n device. Batteries must be reversed, and emitter and collector currents are primarily electron currents rather than hole currents.

INDUSTRIAL APPLICATIONS

Basic Timing Circuits. Electronic timers may be used for controlling elapsed time or time delay in numerous industrial processes, *e.g.*, in the control of spot welders. These timers often use some variation of the circuit of Fig. 24, in which contact S is initially closed, and capacitor C is charged to the voltage E_{cc}, which holds the grid of the tube well below cutoff. When contact S is opened, the capacitor discharges through R at a rate determined by the RC time constant, and the grid voltage gradually approaches zero. At some point the tube will conduct sufficiently to energize the relay ITD.

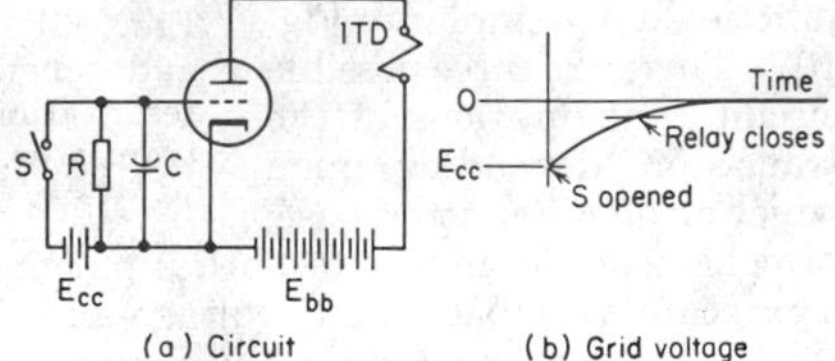

FIG. 24. Time-delay-relay circuit.

An a-c version of the time delay relay is shown in Fig. 25. With the control contacts open, the tube will conduct cathode-to-grid through $R3$ and $R2$ when terminal 1 of the a-c supply is positive. This builds up a negative charge on the grid side of capacitor C with the voltage across C determined by the setting of $R1$. When the control contacts are closed, the tube will not conduct until this capacitor has sufficiently discharged, thereby producing a delay determined by the RC time constant and the setting of $R1$. The a-c time-delay relay has two advantages: it does not require a d-c power supply, and a thyratron with its higher current capability and positive "turn-on" can be used. Several of these circuits may be used in a "weld-sequence" timer.

Ignitron Contactor. The ignitron of Fig. 6 may be used in a "back-to-back" connection to serve as the heavy-duty switch that is needed in the primary of a resistance-welding transformer (see Fig. 26). With control contacts open, no ignitor current

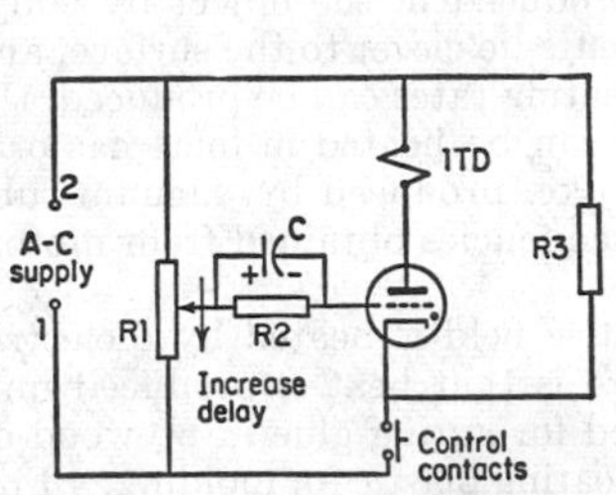

FIG. 25. A-C time-delay relay.

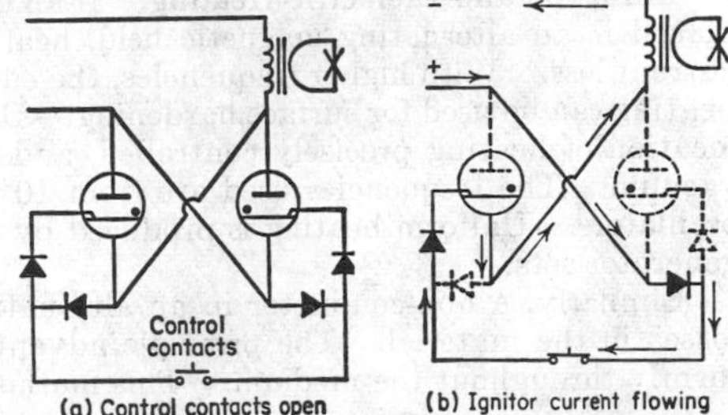

FIG. 26. Ignitron contactor.

can flow, and tubes cannot fire. Figure 26(*b*) shows a path for the ignitor current on one half-cycle with the control contacts closed. When the tube fires, the current flow transfers to the anode. The rectifiers in the ignitor circuit prevent reverse current which would damage the ignitor. Figure 27 shows oscillograms of the supply voltage, the ignitor current, and the load current as produced with the inductive load of the normal spot welder.

The control contacts of Fig. 26 may be actuated by a timer using the principles of Fig. 25, in which case welding current is permitted to flow for an adjustable number of cycles. The contacts may be a pair of back-to-back thyratrons, which can delay the firing point within the cycle and control the magnitude of the current, thereby providing "heat control." The duration of firing of the thyratrons is controlled by the timer circuit.

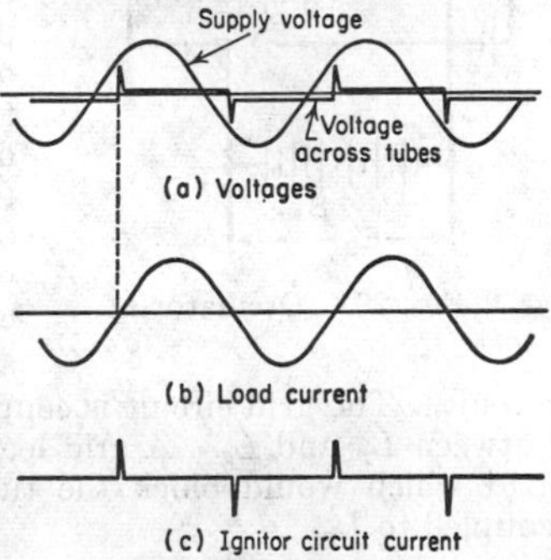

FIG. 27. Waveforms for ignitor contactor with welder load.

Electronic Motor Control. Circuits using thyratrons or silicon controlled rectifiers are often used to control the speed of a d-c motor. A simplified circuit is shown in Fig. 28(*a*), with waveforms shown in Fig. 28(*b*). The field must be supplied by a full-wave rectifier or by a circuit with a "free-wheeling" diode (see Fig. 16). Control of the thyratron is essentially the same as in Fig. 5, the principal difference being that the thyratron anode voltage must exceed the motor CEMF before it can conduct. Referring to Fig. 28(*b*), it would be possible to fire the thyratron as early as point *A*, but the control circuit delays firing until point *B*. With negligible armature inductance, conduction would cease at point *C*, but inductance delays cut off to point *D*. If the slider on the potentiometer is moved upward, the tube will be fired

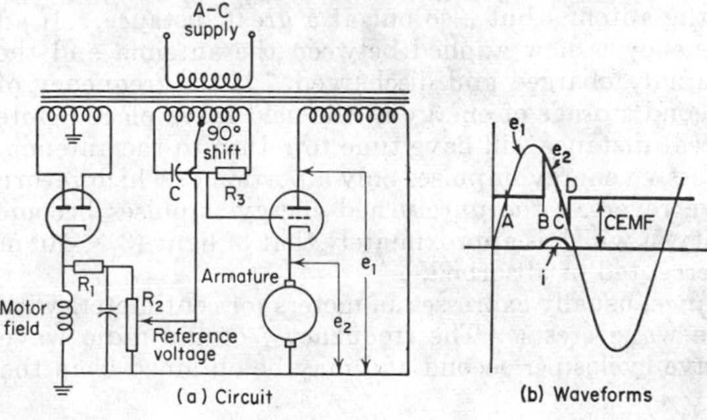

FIG. 28. Rectifier operated d-c motor.

earlier in the cycle, the armature current will increase, and the motor will speed up.

The control circuit described above attempts to hold the armature terminal voltage approximately constant; more elaborate circuits provide compensation for increased *IR* drop with increased loads, current limit protection, dynamic braking, and other safety features.

Induction and Dielectric Heating. If an object which is an electrical conductor is placed in an alternating magnetic field, heating is produced in the object by eddy-current loss. With higher frequencies, the eddy currents lie closer to the surface, and heating can be used for surface hardening. Higher heating rates can be produced, the location of heating precisely controlled, and objects can be heated in inert gas or a vacuum. The frequencies used are from 10 to 1,000 kc, produced by vacuum-tube oscillators. Uniform heating is produced by lower frequencies obtained from motor-generator sets.

Similarly, a non-conductor in an alternating electric field is heated by dielectric losses in the material. The principle advantage here is that heat is produced uniformly throughout the medium. This method is used for curing glue in plywood or furniture and for preheating plastic for molding. Frequencies used are from 1 to 50 mc obtained from vacuum-tube oscillators.

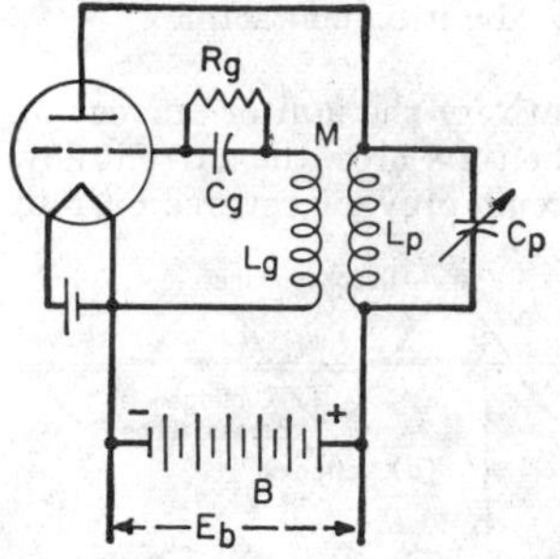

Fig. 29. Oscillator.

A vacuum tube or transistor may become a power **oscillator** or a generator of alternating current. A tube may be made to oscillate by connecting an oscillatory circuit consisting of inductance and capacitance in parallel, in the plate circuit. A portion of the energy of the plate circuit is fed back into the grid circuit, the direction of the connection being such that the emf due to the plate circuit is substantially in phase with the grid emf and so reinforces it. In Fig. 29 a simple oscillator is shown. The oscillatory circuit consisting of the inductance L_p and capacitance C_p in parallel is called the **tank circuit.** The frequency of oscillation, $f = 1/2\pi \sqrt{L_pC_p}$, is the *natural frequency* of the tank circuit. The grid circuit is coupled to the plate circuit by the mutual inductance M between L_p and L_g. A grid leak R_g prevents the accumulation of electrons on the grid which would block the tube. The load on the oscillator may be inductively coupled to L_p.

RADIO

Radiation of Electrical Energy. When a capacitor is charged, the energy represented by the charge is stored in the dielectric medium of the capacitor; it is possible to utilize part of this energy for the purpose of radio communication. If a radio aerial or antenna (which, with the earth, forms a capacitor) is electrically charged, the stored energy will exist not only near the antenna but also out at a great distance. If an alternating voltage of high frequency is now applied between the antenna and the ground, this capacitor will be rapidly charged and discharged. If the frequency of reversal is sufficiently high, a second storage of energy in the field takes place before all the first energy stored at a great distance will have time to return to the antenna. Thus the antenna sends out successive energy impulses only a portion of which return to the system on each successive reversal; the unreturned energy impulses become electromagnetic waves the velocity of which is approximately that of light (3×10^8 m per sec in space or air) until intercepted or absorbed.

The **wave length** λ is the distance, usually expressed in meters (or centimeters with microwaves), between successive wave crests. The **frequency** f of the radio wave propagation is the number of wave cycles per second and may be obtained from the equation

$$\lambda f = 3 \times 10^8 \quad \text{m per sec} \tag{5}$$

Table 2. Partial Table of Frequency Allocations
(For a complete listing of frequency allocations, see "Reference Data for Radio Engineers," published by International Telephone and Telegraph Company)

Frequency, Mc	Utilization
0.535–1.605	Commercial broadcast band
27.255	Citizens' personal radio
54–72	Television channels 2–4
76–88	Television channels 5–6
88–108	Frequency-modulation broadcasting
174–216	Television channels 7–13
460–470	Citizens' personal radio
470–890	Television channels 14–83

Table 3. Frequency Bands

Designation	Frequency	Wavelength
VLF, very low frequency	3–30 kc	100–10 kilometers
LF, low frequency	30–300 kc	10–1 kilometer
MF, medium frequency	300–3,000 kc	1,000–100 meters
HF, high frequency	3–30 mc	100–10 meters
VHF, very high frequency	30–300 mc	10–1 meter
UHF, ultra-high frequency	300–3,000 mc	100–10 cm
SHF, super-high frequency	3,000–30,000 mc	10–1 cm
EHF, extremely high frequency	30,000–300,000 mc	10–1 mm

Wavelength in meters = $300/f$ in megacycles.

For example, if the wave length is 300 m, the frequency $f = (3 \times 10^8)/(300 \times 10^3) = 1{,}000$ kilocycles (kc). (See Tables 2 and 3 for allocations.) **Continuous carrier waves** used in broadcasting are produced by tube oscillators which ordinarily have an oscillating circuit, composed of inductance and capacitance in parallel, connected in the plate circuit. The oscillator (Fig. 29) is an example of a method which can be used for producing carrier waves.

Modulation. The frequency of the carrier wave is far beyond the limits of audibility and is also far too high to operate such conversion devices as telephones or loudspeakers. In order to transmit and receive speech and music, the carrier wave must be modulated by the **audiofrequency** (a-f) waves produced by the voice and by music. There are at least three methods by which this may be accomplished: **amplitude modulation** (a-m), **frequency modulation** (f-m), and **phase modulation** (p-m).

In amplitude modulation, the amplitude of the carrier wave is varied in accordance with the amplitude of the a-f wave. The envelope of the carrier wave thus becomes the a-f wave, as shown in Fig. 30. There are several methods of modulating the carrier wave by amplitude modulation.

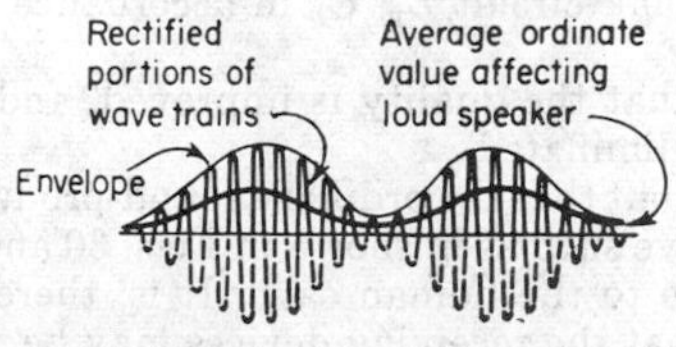

FIG. 30. Modulation wave and rectification.

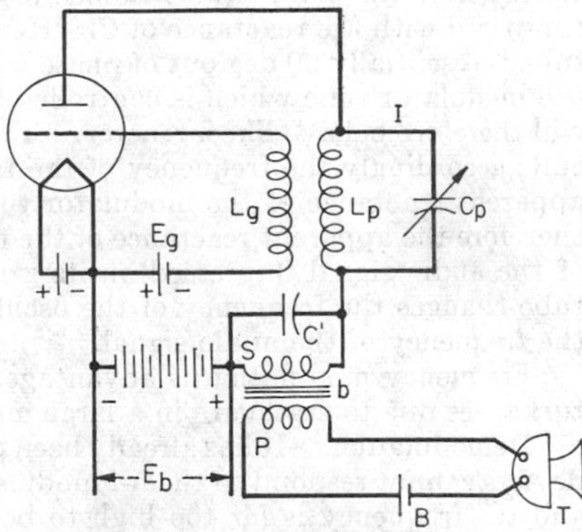

FIG. 31. Plate modulation.

A common method is to introduce into the plate circuit of a tube, oscillating at the carrier frequency, an additional emf of audio frequency, the peak value of which is somewhat less than the steady plate voltage E_b. Figure 31 shows a simple plate modulation circuit. The carrier-frequency-tuned tank circuit L_pC_p and grid circuit are similar to those in Fig. 29. The secondary S of an a-f transformer b is introduced into the plate circuit. The primary current of this transformer comes from the microphone circuit consisting of a battery B and a microphone T. The capacitor C' bypasses the carrier-frequency current around the secondary S of the a-f transformer b. Ordinarily there is not sufficient power in the microphone circuit, so that an amplifier is inserted between the microphone and the transformer b.

Frequency modulation is also being widely used. The amplitude of the carrier wave remains constant, but its frequency is varied in accordance with the frequency of the a-f, or modulating, wave.

The principle is illustrated in Fig. 32 which shows a carrier wave of constant amplitude but with an increase in frequency at the intervals *a-a*. The amount by which the frequency varies from the average, often called the **frequency deviation,** is proportional to the amplitude of the modulating frequency. For example, if the frequency of the carrier wave is 500,000 cps, it could be modulated by a 500 cycle a-f wave by having its instantaneous frequency varied between 499,990 and 500,010 cps. Thus the changes in frequency at *a, a* (Fig. 32), would occur 500 times per sec. With a

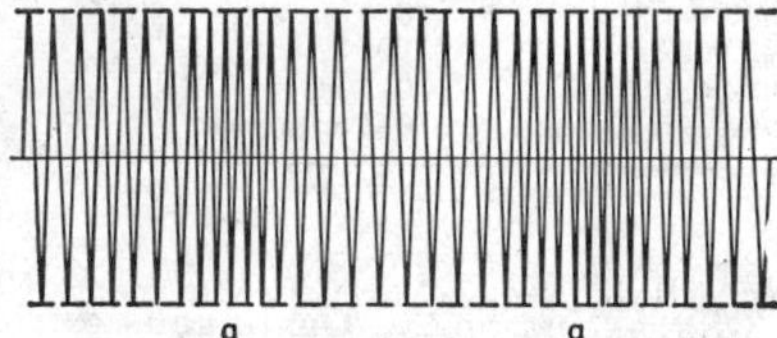

FIG. 32. Frequency-modulated wave.

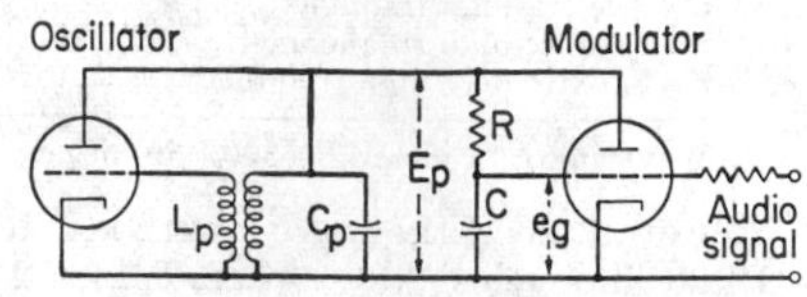

FIG. 33. Frequency modulation with reactance tube.

1,000 cycle a-f wave, the same changes in modulation such as *a, a* would occur 1,000 times per sec.

One method of frequency modulation is shown in Fig. 33. At the left-hand side is the usual oscillator similar to that shown in Fig. 29, L_p and C_p being the inductor and capacitor of the tuned tank circuit. A resistor R and a capacitor C are connected in series across the plate circuit of the modulator, the resistance of R being very high as compared with the reactance of C. Hence the emf e_g across the grid of the modulator tube is essentially 90 deg out of phase with the plate voltage E_p. Thus the current in the modulator tube which is controlled by e_g will be 90 deg out of phase with E_p and will therefore behave like a reactor. This reactor tube is in parallel with the tank circuit; accordingly the frequency of the tank circuit will be determined in part by the apparent reactance of the modulator tube. The current in the modulator tube and therefore the apparent reactance of the tube will change in accordance with the emf e_g of the audio signal impressed on its grid. The varying reactance of the modulator tube changes the frequency of the oscillatory tank circuit L_p, C_p in accordance with the frequency of the audio signal.

Frequency modulation is advantageous in that the quality is improved, and disturbances due to static are in a large measure eliminated.

Demodulation. It has already been pointed out that the ordinary sound-producing devices cannot respond to the h-f modulated wave such as in shown in Figs. 30 and 32, and the frequency is far too high to be audible to the human ear. It is, therefore, necessary to **demodulate** such waves in order that the receiving devices may be actuated by a-f currents similar to those used for modulating. This is called **detection.**

Amplitude demodulation may be accomplished with any type of rectifying tube such as the diode of Fig. 1. However, if the tube operates near the lower part of the *I-E* curve [Fig. 34(*a*) (which is analogous to Fig. 2)] the sensitivity is low. This is overcome in part by connecting a positive polarizing voltage E_p in series with the tube, as shown in Fig. 34(*b*). If an alternating emf wave e is impressed on the tube, it is not perfectly rectified but produces an a-c wave i_p. Owing to the curvature of the characteristic, the current wave i_p is dissymmetrical, the positive wave being larger than the negative wave (shown shaded). The average current is increased from I_p to I_p' and the existence of an audio emf is detected. In Fig. 34(*b*) the capacitor *C* shunts the h-f components of the rectified portions of the wave trains, Fig. 30, around the telephones

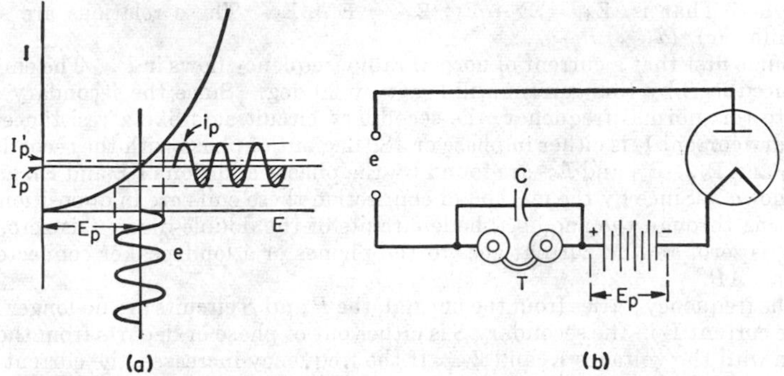

FIG. 34. Detection with diode.

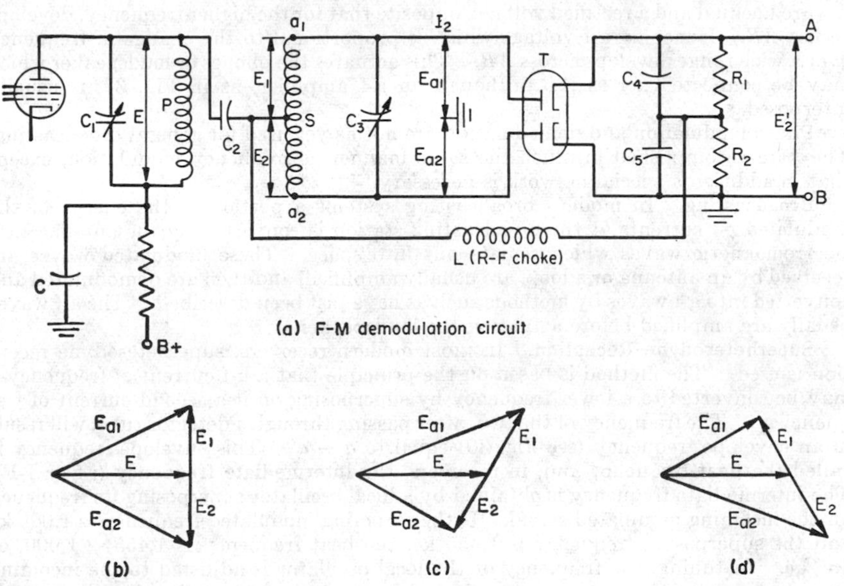

FIG. 35. Frequency demodulation.

or loudspeaker *T*. This general method of detection is used in the receiver of Fig. 36, except that a double diode is used.

The most common method of **demodulating f-m waves** is the use of a **discriminator.** The method is shown in Fig. 35. In the circuit diagram in (*a*), *P* and *S* are two coupled coils each tuned by capacitors C_1 and C_3, respectively, so as to be resonant at the normal or unmodulated intermediate frequency. C_2, a blocking capacitor which has negligible impedance at radio frequencies, is connected from the upper end of *P* to the center tap of *S*. *T* is a double-diode rectifier tube, although two single diodes can also be used, as shown at T in Fig. 37. The two capacitors C_4 and C_5 are equal and their capacitances are such that for radio frequencies the two cathodes of the diode are essentially at ground potential. Also, C_2 and C are blocking capacitors which have negligible reactance at radio frequencies. Hence, for radio frequencies the primary P and the r-f choke L are in parallel. Also the voltage of a_1 above ground $\mathbf{E}_{a1}$ is the phasor sum of $\mathbf{E}$ and $\mathbf{E}_1$ and the voltage of a_2 above ground $\mathbf{E}_{a2}$ is the phasor sum of $\mathbf{E}$ and $\mathbf{E}_2$. That is, $\mathbf{E}_{a1} = \mathbf{E} + \mathbf{E}_1$; $\mathbf{E}_{a2} = \mathbf{E} + \mathbf{E}_2$. These relations are shown in Fig. 35 (*b*), (*c*), (*d*).

Assume first that a current of normal radio frequency flows in P. The emfs $\mathbf{E}_1$ and $\mathbf{E}_2$ induced in S by this current will lag it by 90 deg. Since the secondary circuit is tuned to this normal frequency, the secondary circuit acts like a resistance and the secondary current $\mathbf{I}_2$ is either in phase or 180 deg out of phase with the secondary voltages $\mathbf{E}_1$ and $\mathbf{E}_2$. $\mathbf{E}_{a1}$ and $\mathbf{E}_{a2}$ are found by the phasor addition of $\mathbf{E}$ and $\mathbf{E}_1$, and $\mathbf{E}$ and $\mathbf{E}_2$ as shown. Since by the method of connection these emfs are in opposition, the net emf acting through the anode-cathode circuits of the double-diode T is zero, and the emf $\mathbf{E}_2'$ is zero, and no current goes to the phones or a loudspeaker connected across terminals AB.

If the frequency varies from the normal, the P and S circuits are no longer resonant and the current $\mathbf{I}_2$ in the secondary S is either out of phase or departs from the 180 deg relation with the voltages $\mathbf{E}_1$ and $\mathbf{E}_2$. If the frequency increases, the current lags and the phasor diagram will have the form shown in (*c*). $\mathbf{E}_{a1}$ and $\mathbf{E}_{a2}$ are no longer equal and a resultant rectified voltage develops across AB. Similarly, if the frequency decreases, the current leads, and the phasor diagram is shown in (*d*). Again $\mathbf{E}_{a1}$ and $\mathbf{E}_{a2}$ are unequal and a rectified voltage, opposite that for the higher frequency, develops across AB. Hence an a-f voltage which is proportional to the change of frequency over a wide range develops across AB. This actuates the phones or loudspeaker which may be connected across AB, although an a-f amplifier, as in Fig. 37, is usually interposed.

Phase modulation and demodulation are not as yet used for general broadcasting. They are accomplished in much the same manner as frequency modulation, except that in addition a special network is necessary.

Broadcasting. In modern broadcasting systems a portion of the energy of the modulated r-f currents at the broadcasting station is converted by the antenna into electromagnetic waves which radiate out into space. These modulated waves are received by an antenna or a loop, are usually amplified, and then are demodulated and converted into a-f waves by methods such as have just been described. The a-f waves usually are amplified before actuating the loudspeaker.

Superheterodyne Reception. In most modern receivers, superheterodyne reception is used. The method is based on the principle that a h-f current of frequency a may be converted to a lower frequency by superposing on it a second current of frequency a'. The frequency of the two, after passing through a detector tube, will result in an envelope frequency (see Fig. 30) equal to $a - a'$. This envelope frequency is called the **beat frequency** and, in receivers, the **intermediate frequency** (i-f or I-F). The intermediate frequency is obtained by a local oscillator superposing its frequency on the incoming modulated signal. If the incoming modulated frequency is 1,000 kc and the superposing frequency is 1,455 kc, the beat frequency is 1,455 − 1,000, or 455 kc. In tuning, the frequency of the local oscillator is adjusted to the incoming frequency so that the beat or intermediate frequency always remains the same. This simplifies the design of the amplifier and the circuits of the i-f stages since they can be adapted to fixed frequencies and thus operate under optimum conditions.

Receivers. Most receivers are designed to operate from an a-c supply of 110 to 120 volts, the usual domestic voltage. This a-c supply goes to the primary of a transformer in which one of the secondary windings steps up the voltage for the plate supply (B voltage), and low-voltage windings supply the heaters of the several tubes as well as the rectifier heaters (see Fig. 36). A full-wave rectifier and filter converts the a-c plate supply, which may be 300 volts or more, to direct current. Frequently the electromagnet of the loudspeaker is used as the choke coil of the filter. The low hum resulting from the ripples in the 60 cycle rectified wave usually is not objectionable.

The d-c plate supply or B voltage is arranged to supply all plate circuits. Screen grids are sometimes connected to a voltage divider connected across the d-c plate supply voltage. Such a divider may consist of a resistor and a capacitor in series (Figs. 36 and 37), the grid being connected to the junction of the two.

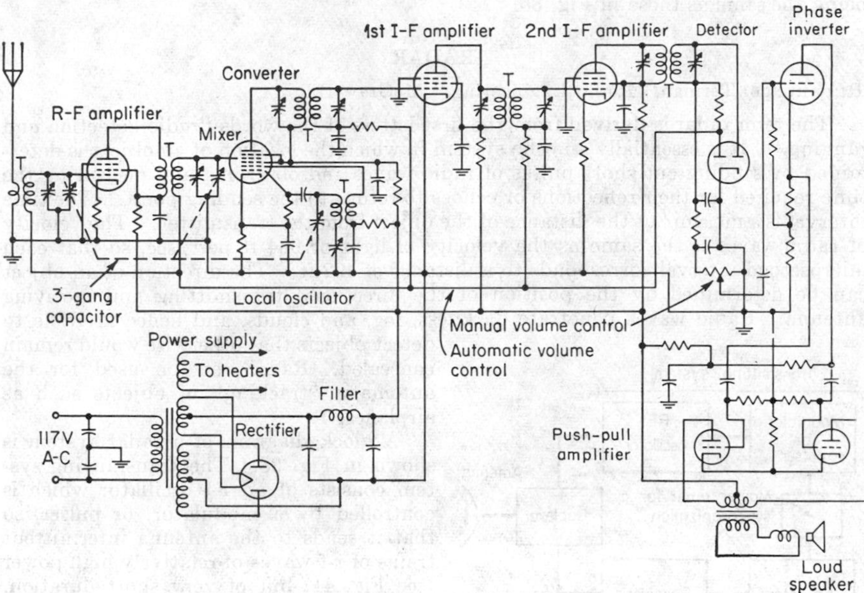

FIG. 36. Typical superheterodyne receiver with amplitude modulation.

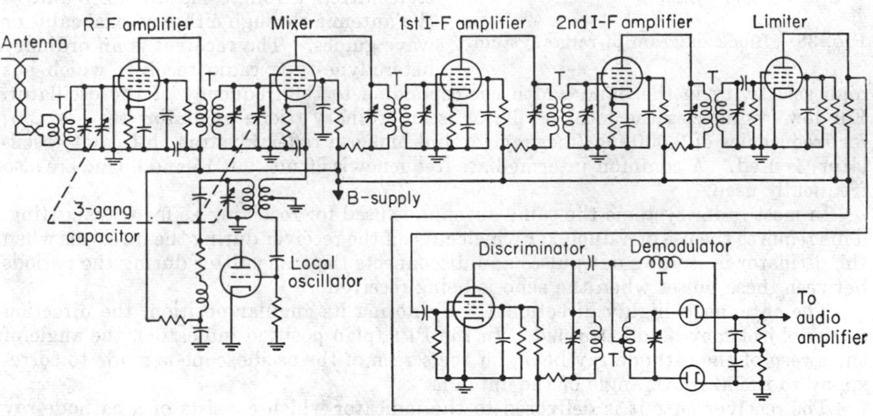

FIG. 37. Circuits for frequency-modulation superheterodyne receiver.

In the a-m system (Fig. 36), the r-f energy of the signal from the antenna is amplified by the r-f amplifier and is "mixed" with the frequency from the local oscillator to give the intermediate frequency. Two i-f amplifiers (first and second) amplify the energy of the signal, and the diode detector converts the intermediate frequency into audio frequency. This is amplified by the combination of the phase inverter and push-pull amplifier, and the audio frequency then operates the loudspeaker.

The f-m system (Fig. 37) operates in much the same manner except that demodulation is accomplished by the discriminator. The limiter reduces the amplification when the volume exceeds a predetermined value. In Fig. 37 the rectifier and filter system for the B-voltage supply and the amplification system for the loudspeaker are omitted, being the same as those in Fig. 36.

RADAR

Reference: Terman, "Radio Engineering," McGraw-Hill.

The term **radar** is **derived** from the first letters of the words "*ra*dio *d*etection *a*nd *r*anging." It is essentially an echo system in which the location of an object is determined by sending out short pulses of radio waves and observing and measuring the time required for their reflections or echoes to return to the sending point. The time interval is a measure of the distance of the object from the transmitter. The velocity of radio waves is the same as the velocity of light or 984 ft per μsec, so that each microsecond interval corresponds to a distance of 492 ft. The direction of an object can be determined by the position of the directional transmitting and receiving antenna. Radio waves penetrate darkness, fog, and clouds, and hence are able to detect objects that otherwise would remain concealed. Radar can be used for the automatic "tracking" of objects such as airplanes.

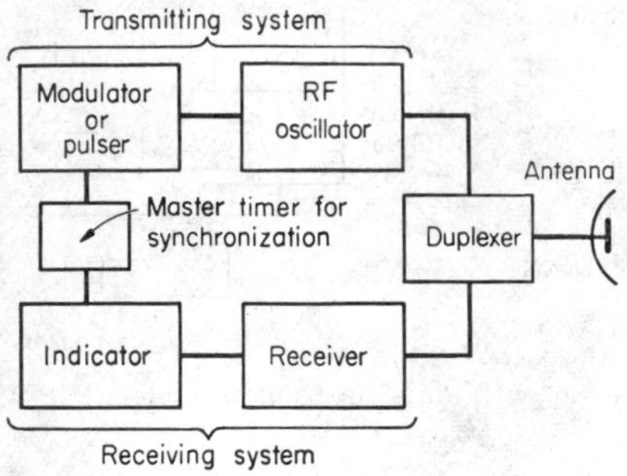

Fig. 38. Block diagram of radar system.

A block diagram of a radar system is shown in Fig. 38. The transmitting system consists of an r-f oscillator which is controlled by a modulator, or pulser, so that it sends to the antenna intermittent trains of r-f waves of relatively high power (see Fig. 41) but of very short duration, corresponding to the pulses received by the modulator. The energy of the oscillator is transmitted through the duplexer and to the antenna through either coaxial cable or wave guides. The **receiver** is an ordinary heterodyne-type radio receiver which has high sensitivity in the band width corresponding to the frequency of the oscillator. For low frequencies the local oscillator is an ordinary triode oscillator (see Fig. 29); for frequencies of 2,000 mc (megacycle) and higher a reflex **klystron** (h-f cavity oscillator) is used. A common intermediate frequency is 30 mc, but 15 and 60 mc are also frequently used.

In most radar systems the same antenna is used for receiving as for transmitting. This requires the use of a **duplexer** which cuts off the receiver during the intervals when the oscillator is sending out pulses and disconnects the transmitter during the periods between these pulses when the echo is being received.

The antenna is highly directional. By noting its angular position, the direction of the object may be determined. In the PPI (plan position indicator), the angle of the sweep of the cathode-ray beam on the screen of the oscilloscope is made to correspond to the azimuth angle of the antenna.

The receiver output is delivered to the indicator which consists of a cathode-ray tube or oscilloscope. The pulses which are received, corresponding to echoes from the target, must be synchronized with the sending pulses in order that the distance to the target may be determined. This is accomplished by synchronization of the sweep circuit of the oscilloscope with the pulses by the master timer.

Pulses. One method of pulsing is the **line pulser.** In Fig. 39(*a*) *ab-cd* is a smooth line in air. During the non-pulsing period (Fig. 41), the line capacitance is slowly charged from a high-voltage d-c source of about 10,000 volts [step-up transformer and rectifier, Fig. 39(*a*)] through a charging impedance. At the instant that the pulse is to occur, a thyratron trigger switch short-circuits the line through an impedance

Z_L equal to the surge impedance of the line. The energy stored in the line then discharges through the impedance Z_L without reflection. The voltage developed in Z_L is equal to $E/2$, where E is the voltage to which the line is charged. The trigger switch is usually a hydrogen-filled thyratron. Hydrogen is preferable to mercury vapor because of its faster action in the tube. The thyratron is triggered at definite intervals by a tube which delivers short voltage pulses (Fig. 41), the number of which varies usually from 360 to 10,000 per sec. In a line in air, the duration of the pulse is the time required for the wave of stored energy in the line to travel from one end of the line and return. Thus, a 1 μsec wave would require a line length of $984/2 =$ 492 ft. Such lines usually occupy too much space so that an artificial line of a few sections, shown in Fig. 39(*b*), is used. Such a line, due to its "lumpiness," will produce ripples in the pulse wave as shown in Fig. 41. The charging impedance (Fig. 39) is essentially infinite to the line discharge current because of the high rate of change of the latter so that practically none of the discharge current goes through it and the rectifier. When the energy of the line has been dissipated, the gas of the thyratron deionizes, the thyratron becomes an open circuit, the grid assumes control and awaits the next pulse before triggering again, after which the process is repeated. The timing of the pulses is accomplished by the master timer (Fig. 38). These pulses act through the modulator or pulser to modulate the oscillator pulses (Fig. 41).

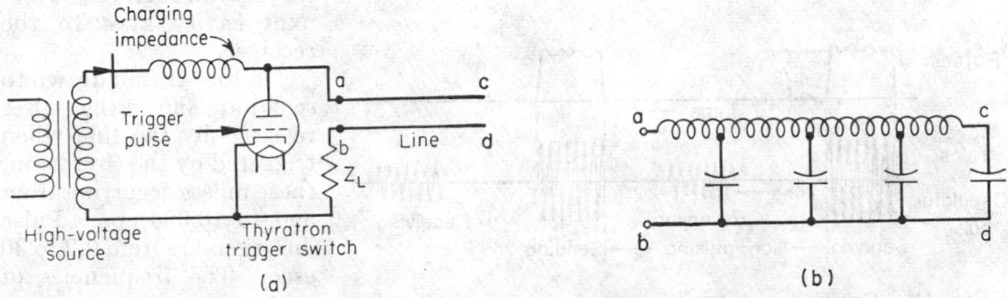

FIG. 39. Line pulser. (*a*) Smooth line; (*b*) lumpy artificial line.

Duplexer. The function of the duplexer is to cut off or isolate the receiver during the pulsing period, and to cut off the transmitter between pulses. This is accomplished by providing paths of the correct wave length so as to form loops and nodes at the right points in the wave-guide system in combination with cavity-tube combinations. Figure 40 shows the general connections. The two elements which operate to cut the transmitter and receiver on and off at the correct instants are the "TR (transmit-receive) box" and the "anti TR box." Each of these represents a short gap in special cold-cathode tubes containing gas at low pressure and associated with resonant cavities. The transmitting system shown is ordinarily a wave-guide system consisting either of coaxial cable or hollow rectangular metallic tubes. The distances *ab, ac,* and *cd* are all made odd multiples of a quarter wave length, the factor unity being used in the figure.

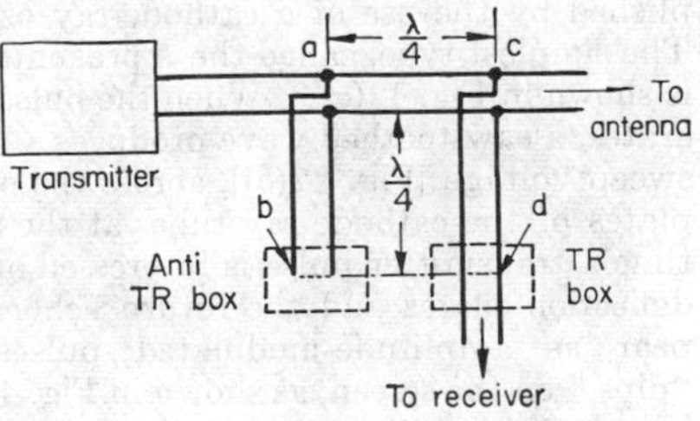

FIG. 40. Duplexer system.

Within each TR tube there is a short air gap. When the transmitter is in operation, the distances *ab* and *cd* being quarter wave lengths, loops form at *b* and *d* causing high voltage across the gaps which break them down and produce short circuits as indicated in dotted lines. This in turn forms nodes at *b* and *d* and loops at *a* and *c*, so that the branch circuits act as high impedance shunts across the line producing negligible effect on the waves traveling from the transmitter to the antenna. At the same time the receiver is short-circuited at *d*. When the oscillator pulse (Fig. 41) ceases, the discharges across the gaps cease, and the short circuits become open circuits. In the interval when the antenna receives the energy of the echo, the waves travel from the antenna to *c* and, implemented by the resonance in the cavity of the TR tube, go to *d*. The distance *cab* forms a half-wavelength line with an open end at *b*. Such a line oscillates with a standing half wave having a loop at the open end *b*, a node at *a*, and a loop at *c*. Hence, at *c*, looking toward the oscillator, the line offers a high impedance, and at *a* the node produces a short circuit in the transmitter. Hence, the wave energy travels through the resonant cavity at *d* to the receiver.

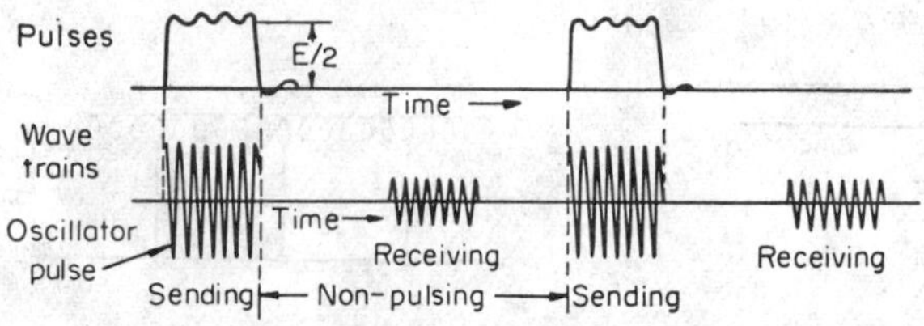

Fig. 41. Sending and receiving pulses and wave trains.

In Fig. 41 (not drawn to scale) are shown the pulses released by the line when triggered by the thyratron, these pulses occurring from 360 to 10,000 cps. Pulse durations are from 0.2 to 30 μsec. The frequencies of the corresponding wave are from 100 to 25,000 mc, the usual range being 3,000 to 10,000 mc. The higher limits give much better resolution on the radar screen or "scope." The pulses (Fig. 41) from the modulator (Fig. 38) are applied through a pulse transformer to the radar-transmitter oscillator (r-f oscillator, Fig. 38), which may consist of a triode, tetrode, magnetron, or klystron, depending on the frequency. In Fig. 41 are also shown the wave trains received from the target, returning in the intervals between the sending pulses. Actually the ratio of the amplitude of the sending to the receiving wave trains is vastly greater than that shown, although owing to differences in amplification they appear to be nearly of the same amplitude on the radar screen.

Displays. Conversion of the received radar signals to usable display is accomplished by the use of a cathode-ray oscilloscope, shown as the indicator in Fig. 38. The simplest type, called the **A presentation,** is shown in Fig. 42(*a*). When the pulser operates, a saw-toothed wave produces a linear sweep voltage [Fig. 42(*b*)], across the sweep plates of the cathode-ray tube; at the same time a transmitter pulse is impressed on the deflection plates and the return echoes appear as amplitude-modulated pulses, or "pips," on the screen, as shown in Fig. 42(*a*). The distance on the screen between the transmitter pulse and the pip caused by the echo is proportional to the distance to the target, and the screen can be calibrated in distance such as miles. [The return of the spot to its initial starting position, produced by the sweep interval *cd*, Fig. 42(*b*), is so rapid that it is not detectable by the eye.] The direction of the target may be determined by the angular position of the antenna, which can be transmitted to the operator by means of a selsyn (see p. 15–72). Different objects, such as airplanes, ships, islands, and land approaches, have characteristic pips and operators become skilled in their interpretation. A bird in flight can be recognized on the screen. Also a portion of the scale such as *ab* can be segregated and amplified for close study of the characteristics of the pips.

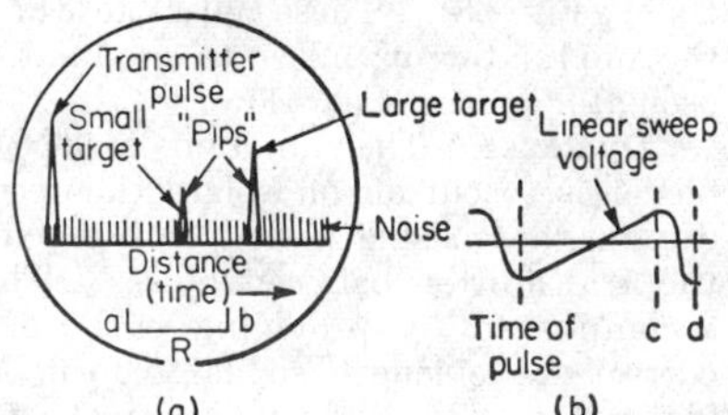

Fig. 42. Type A presentation.

Plan Position Indicator (PPI). In the PPI (Fig. 43) the direction of a radial sweep of the electron beam is synchronized with the azimuth sweep of the antenna.

The sweep of the beam is rotated continuously in synchronism with the antenna, and the received signals intensity-modulate the electron beam as it sweeps from the center of the oscilloscope screen radially outwards. In this way the direction and range position of an object can be determined from the pattern on the screen of the oscilloscope, as shown in Fig. 43.

There are two methods by which the angular direction of the cathode spot is made to correspond with the angular position of the antenna. In one method, used on board ship, two magnetic deflecting coils are rotated around the neck of the tube in synchronism with the antenna, by means of a selsyn. In the other method, used on aircraft, two fixed magnetic deflecting coils at right angles to each other and placed at the neck of the tube are supplied with current from a small two-phase synchronous generator whose rotor is driven by the antenna. Thus a rotating field, similar to that produced by the stator of an induction motor, is produced by the magnetic deflecting coils. These two rotating fields, although produced by different means, are equivalent and cause the cathode beam to sweep radially in synchronism with the antenna. Circular coordinates spaced radially corresponding to distance are obtained by impressing on the control electrode short positive pulses synchronized with the transmitted pulse but delayed by time values corresponding to the desired distances. These coordinates appear as circles on the screen (Fig. 43). Since the time of rotation of the antenna is relatively slow, it is necessary that a persistent screen be used in order that the operator may view the entire pattern. In Fig. 43 is shown a line drawing of a PPI presentation of Cape Cod, Mass., on a radar screen, taken from an airplane.

FIG. 43. Plan position indicator (PPI) of southeastern Massachusetts.

The applications of radar to war purposes are well known, such as detecting enemy ships and planes, aiming guns at them, and locating cities, rivers, mountains, and other landmarks in bombing operations. In peacetime, radar is used to navigate ships in darkness and poor visibility by locating navigational aids such as buoys and lighthouses, as well as protruding ledges, islands, and other landmarks. It can be similarly used in air navigation, as well as to operate altimeters for determining the height of the plane above ground. It is also used for aerial mapping.

There are also radio beacons, **shoran** (*shor*t-*ran*ge navigation) and **loran** (*lo*ng-*ran*ge navigation) by which ships or planes can locate their positions. In the **ground-controlled approach** (GCA) for airplanes, the ground operator picks up the plane on a PPI presentation at distances up to 30 miles, using a general surveillance radar and gives instructions to the pilot by radio as to course and procedure. As the plane approaches the landing field, it is brought into vision on the screen of a high-resolution short-range radar, and the pilot is given continual detailed instructions as to the glide path which the plane is to follow until the landing is made.

TELEVISION

References: Terman, "Radio Engineering," McGraw-Hill. Fink, "Television Engineering," McGraw-Hill. Knoll and Kazan, "Storage Tubes and Their Basic Principles," Wiley. Zworykin and Morton, "Television," Wiley.

Television is accomplished by systematically scanning a scene or the image of a scene to be reproduced, and transmitting at each instant a current or a voltage which is proportional to the light intensity of the elementary area of the scene which at the instant is being scanned. The varying voltage or current is amplified, modulated on a carrier wave, and then transmitted as a radio wave. At the receiver the radio wave enters the antenna, is amplified, and demodulated to give a voltage or a current wave similar to the original wave. This voltage or current wave is then used to control the intensity of a cathode-ray beam which is focused on a flourescent screen in a cathode-ray reproducing tube. The cathode-ray beam is caused to move over the screen in the same pattern as the scanning beam at the transmitter and in synchronism with it. Thus each small area of the receiver screen is illuminated instantaneously with light intensity corresponding to that of a similarly placed area in the original scene. This process is conducted so rapidly that, owing to persistence of vision of the eye, the reproduction of each instantaneous scene appears to be a complete picture, and the effect with successive scenes is similar to that produced by the projection of successive frames of a motion picture.

Pickup Devices. In early television experiments scanning and reproduction were conducted mechanically. The scanning device consisted of a rotating disk with a number of small holes or apertures arranged spirally toward the center. The scene to be televised was focused in these apertures and the light transmitted through them impinged on a phototube which generated a current proportional to the light intensity. At the receiver a disk similar to the scanning disk rotated in synchronism and in phase with it, and a light valve operated by the phototube current (amplified) transmitted onto a screen a light intensity proportional to the current then reproducing the picture. However, all present-day television systems operate with electronic pickup and electronic reproduction.

Image Orthicon. At the present time the image orthicon tube is used almost exclusively in the United States in broadcasting practice. It differs from the plain orthicon in that there are two electrodes, the *photocathode* and the *target*, and an electron multiplier has been added to increase the modulated current. The construction of the image orthicon is given in Fig. 44, in which, for simplicity, the horizontal deflect-

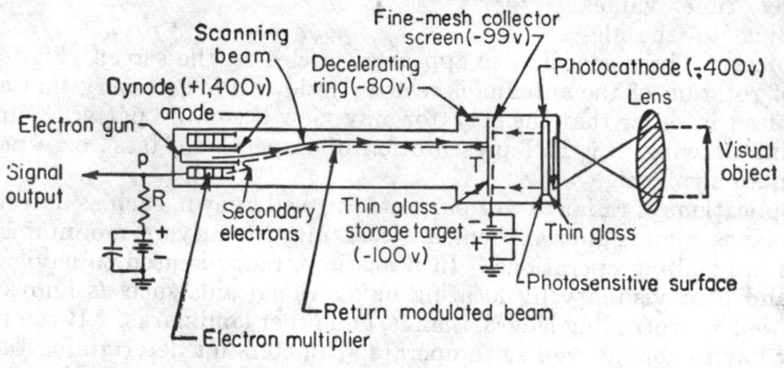

Fig. 44. Image orthicon.

ing coils, the vertical deflecting coils, and the focusing coil producing an axial magnetic field, are omitted.

The photocathode, which is located just inside the glass face of the tube, is a thin sheet of glass. The side of the glass away from the source of illumination has a continuous, electrically conducting, photosensitive surface.

The target T consists of a thin glass plate of limited conductivity which is about 0.003 mm thick and is located between the anode and photocathode, parallel to this latter and only a short distance from it. In back of the target and separated from it by about 0.05 mm (0.002 in.) is a fine-mesh collector screen which has about 1,000 meshes to the inch. In order that it may not intercept too large a proportion of the electrons coming from the photocathode, the openings constitute 75 percent of the screen area. The screen is maintained at a potential of −99 or −98 volts, or 1 or 2 volts positive with respect to the target plate.

The **process of writing** is as follows: the visual object to be televised is focused on the photosensitive surface of the photocathode by a lens, as shown in Fig. 44, and creates on it an identical electron image. Because of the fact that the target is at a potential of −100 volts and the photocathode at a potential of −400 volts, the electron image which has formed on the photocathode is drawn along the tube to the target, the target being 300 volts positive relative to the photocathode. Thus the charge image formed on the photocathode strikes the face of the target towards the source of illumination and forms a charge image on it. At the same time there occurs substantial electron multiplication due to the emission of secondary electrons. These secondary electrons, so liberated, are collected by the collector screen because of its being 1 or 2 volts positive to the target. As a result, those elements on the target included within the image pattern will become more positive because of the loss of electrons. Owing to the fact that the target is extremely thin (0.003 mm), the capacitance between the two surfaces is relatively large and the resistance is low, the target having limited conductivity. As a result, a pattern of the image more positive than the rest of the target appears on the side towards the scanning beam.

"Reading" is performed by the low-velocity electrons of the scanning beam whose velocity is reduced by the decelerating ring. When these electrons strike the target, they adhere to each point on the image pattern in proportion to the positive charge at that point. On the other hand, the electrons striking the portions of the target whose potential has not been shifted to positive in the writing process are entirely reflected. Hence, the returning beam (Fig. 44) is modulated in magnitude in accordance with the image pattern formed on the target. When the returning beam reaches the electron gun, it strikes the dynode of the first stage of an electron multiplier, as shown in Fig. 44. The secondary electrons so generated are fed into the next stage of the electron multiplier. The total of five stages produces an over-all electron multiplication of about 100. The resulting current going through the resistor R raises and lowers the potential of point p with respect to ground and thus produces the signal output, which is amplified and then transmitted.

Scanning and Blanking. In the United States the ratio of width to height of a standard television picture is 4:3, and the picture is composed of 525 lines repeated 30 times a second, this last factor being one-half 60, the prevalent electric power frequency in the United States. The scanning sequence along the individual lines is from left to right and the sequence of the lines is from top to bottom. Also, interlacing is employed, the general method of which is shown in Fig. 45. The cathode-ray spot starts at 1 in the upper left-hand corner and is swept rapidly from left to right either by a saw-tooth emf wave applied to the sweep plates or by the saw-tooth current wave applied to the sweep coils of the tube. When the spot arrives at the right-hand side of the picture, the saw-tooth wave of either emf or current in the sweep circuit acts to return the cathode-ray spot rapidly to point 3 at the left-hand side of the picture. However, during this period the cathode-ray is blanked, or entirely eliminated, by the application of a negative potential to the control grid of the tube. At the end of the

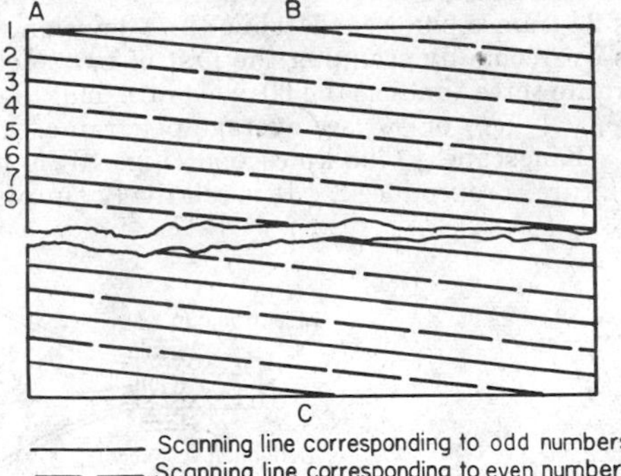

Fig. 45. Pattern of interlaced scanning.

return period, the blanking effect ceases and the spot appears at point 3 from which it again is swept across the picture and this process is repeated for 262.5 lines until the spot reaches a mid-point *C* at the bottom of the picture. It is then carried vertically and rapidly to *B*, the midpoint of the top of the picture, the beam also being blanked during this period. This process of scanning is then repeated, a second set of lines corresponding to the even numbers 2, 4, 6 being established between the lines designated by the odd numbers. These lines are shown dashed in Fig. 45. This method or pattern of scanning is called **interlacing.** The two sets of lines taken together produce a frame of 525 lines, which are repeated 30 times each second. However, owing to interlacing, the flicker frequency is 60 cps which is not noticeable, 50 cps having been determined as the threshold of flicker noticeable to the average eye. In Fig. 45, for the sake of clarity, the distances between horizontal lines are greatly exaggerated and no attempt is made to maintain proportions.

In the United States, 16 percent of the time is allocated to the horizontal retrace or blanking, corresponding to 10 μsec for each line. Similarly, 7 to 8 percent of the time is allocated for vertical blanking, corresponding to 1,250 μsec, leaving about 485 active lines.

In the television system, pulses for scanning and for blanking are superimposed on the video signal which is transmitted to the receiver and these are used to trigger the receiving sweep generators. In this manner the scanning and blanking at the receiver are kept in synchronism with those at the receiver.

Frequency Band. In order to obtain the necessary resolution of pictures, television frequencies must be high. In the United States, VHF frequencies from 54 to 88 mc (megacycles) per sec (omitting 72 to 76 mc) and 174 to 216 mc per sec are assigned for television broadcasting. A UHF band of frequencies for commercial television use is also allocated and consists of the frequencies of from 470 to 890 mc per sec (see also Tables 2 and 3).

In order to obtain the 525 lines repeated 30 times per sec, a band width of 6 mc per sec is necessary. The video, or picture, signal with the superimposed scanning and blanking pulses is amplitude-modulated, amplified, and transmitted. The carrier frequency associated with the sound transmitter is 4.5 mc per sec higher than the video carrier frequency, and is frequency-modulated with a maximum frequency deviation of 25 kc (kilocycles) per sec.

In scanning motion-picture films a complication arises because standard film rate is 24 frames per second, while the television rate is 30 frames per sec. This difficulty is overcome by scanning the first of two successive film frames twice and the second frame three times at the 60 cycle rate, making the total time for the two frames $\frac{1}{12}$ sec $(\frac{2}{60} + \frac{3}{60})$ or $\frac{1}{24}$ sec average per frame.

Kinescope. The kinescope (Fig. 46) is the terminal tube in which the televised picture is reproduced. It is relatively simple, being not unlike the cathode-ray oscilloscope tube. It has an electric gun operating at 8,000 to 20,000 volts which produces an electron beam and this is focused on a fluorescent surface within the front wall of the tube. The picture is viewed at the front wall. The horizontal and vertical deflections of the beam are normally controlled by deflection coils, as shown in Fig. 46.

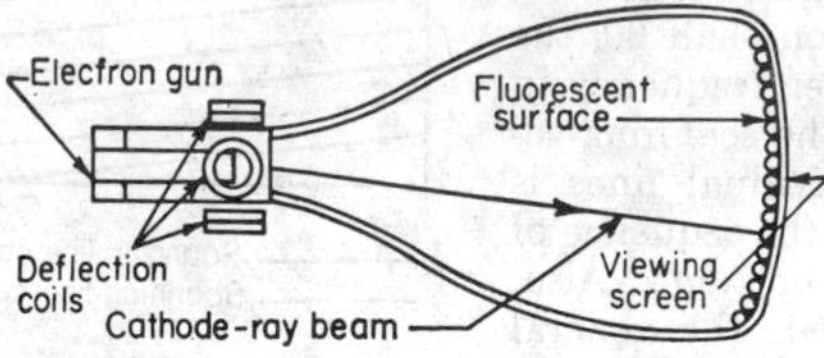

Fig. 46. Kinescope for television receiver.

Television Receivers. A block diagram for a television receiver is given in Fig 47. It is in reality a superheterodyne receiver with tuned r-f amplification, the separating of the sound and video or picture channels taking place at the intermediate frequency in the mixer. The sound channel is then conventional, a discriminator being used to demodulate the f-m wave (Fig. 35). The object of the d-c restorer is to make the picture reproduction always positive, and it consists of applying a d-c voltage at least equal in magnitude to the maximum values of the negative loops of the a-c waves. The synchronizing pulses for both the vertical and the horizontal deflections are delivered by the d-c restorer to an amplifier and the two pulses are then divided into the V and H components. The integrating and differentiating circuits are necessary to separate horizontal and vertical synchronizing signals.

As stated earlier, at any instant the magnitude of the current from the pickup tube varies in accordance with the light intensity of the part of the scene being scanned at that instant. This current is amplified and, together with the sound and synchronizing currents, is broadcast and received by the circuit shown in Fig. 47. The

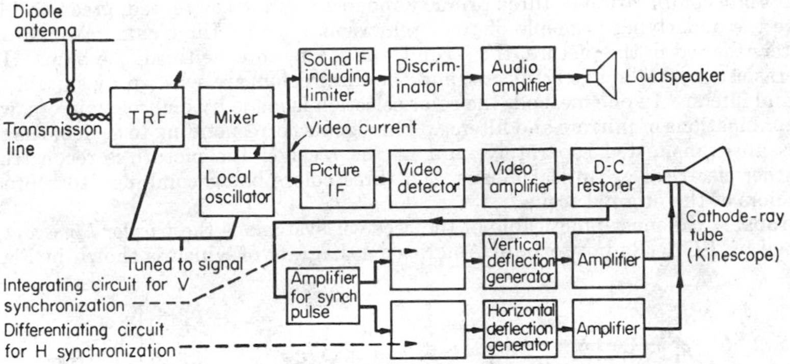

Fig. 47. Block diagram for television receiver. TRF—tuned radio frequency; IF—intermediate frequency.

video current is detected by rectification, is amplified, and is then made to control the intensity of the kinescope electron beam. Tubes produce a scanning pattern, identical with that in the pickup tube, and these tubes are triggered by the synchronizing pulses which are transmitted in the broadcast wave. Hence, the original televised scene is reproduced on the fluorescent screen of the kinescope.

Antenna. Because of the very high frequencies or very short wave lengths used in television, a half-wave doublet antenna or dipole is generally used. In its simplest form this consists of a horizontal conductor to the center of which the transmission line is connected, as shown in Fig. 47. The length of the horizontal conductor should be one-half the wave length of the received carrier signal, since the antenna is then resonant or tuned for this frequency, and the voltage and the current waves oscillate freely. However, if the antenna is resonant or tuned to the middle frequency of the television frequency band, the response is fairly uniform over the entire band, owing in part to the impedance characteristics of the transmission line and of the receiver. It is important that the impedance of the transmission line be accurately matched with that of the antenna and also with that of the receiver. Otherwise there will be reflections at the junctions, resulting in delayed spurious currents which produce a delayed image or a "ghost." The position of the antenna conductor for optimum reception is at right angles to the direction of the incoming wave. Additional elements produce a more directive and consequently a more sensitive antenna.

Since television carrier waves are short, they have quasi-optical properties and tend to travel in straight lines. Thus, mountains, buildings, and similar obstructions in the path of the rays cast shadows. Hence, it is desirable that the receiving antenna and the sending antenna be in a direct line of vision. Accordingly, for television, a special dipole type of antenna is necessary, which should be located at a high elevation, such as on a high roof. Moreover, the waves are reflected by the earth, buildings, and other objects which the waves may encounter. The reflected waves traversing a longer path will be delayed behind the direct waves, and hence cause blurring of the image. In installing an antenna it is frequently necessary to try several positions in order to avoid the effects of reflections or to use a more highly directive antenna.

Color Television. As with photography and motion pictures, it was only natural that in television the black-and-white presentation would be followed by color. There is little need to emphasize that color makes scenes appear more natural and adds beauty to them. The details are revealed more clearly to the eye, and the entertainment value of the presentation is greatly enhanced. The usual televised scenes include colors from infrared to ultraviolet, and if attempts were made to show even intermittent sections of this spectrum, a prohibitive number of information channels would be necessary. However, it has long been known that any color can be matched by the appropriate combination of three primary monochromatic colors, red, green and blue. Hence the underlying principle of color television is to use three cameras, one which registers the red in the picture, the second, the green, and the third, the blue. These cameras usually are image orthicons, and the three colors are selected by suitable mirrors and filters. In one method, the color selection is made by dichroic mirrors, which are combinations of mirrors and filters. The signals corresponding to each of the three colors are transmitted separately, and at the receiver the picture is reconstructed by either electrical or optical means, the three colors being combined to reproduce the colors of the original scene.

Probably the most practicable of the receiver systems is the *tricolor kinescope*, developed by RCA (Radio Corp. of America), a diagram of which is shown in Fig. 48.

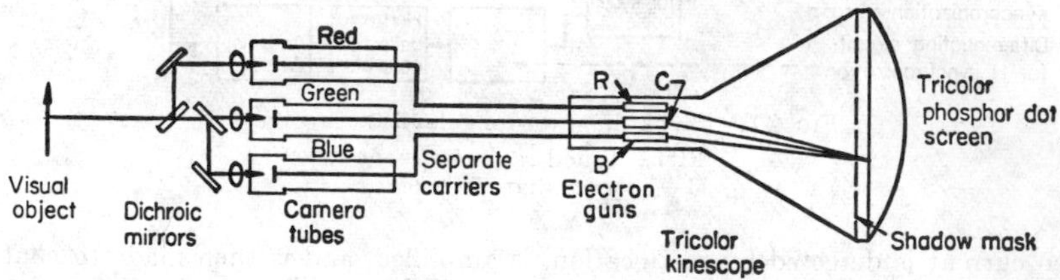

Fig. 48. Color television—simultaneous system.

The three camera tubes are conventional and each has its own carrier system. In the receiver tube there is a perforated shadow mask between the three electron guns and the screen. Each of the three electron guns responds to the signal from one of the camera tubes, and the three scanning beams, when they meet at a point on the mask, form angles of about 1 deg with one another. The perforations in the mask are arranged in a hexagonal pattern. The screen is covered with interspersed clusters, normally about 200,000, of three dots each. One dot in each cluster is a red phosphor, one a green phosphor, and the third a blue phosphor. These dots are so positioned with reference to each mask aperture that the beam from the "red" gun can strike only the red dot, that from the "green" gun can strike only the green dot, and that from the "blue" gun can strike only the blue dot. Thus, each gun operates as if it were associated with a picture tube of its own color, and three separate pictures, each in its own color, are produced on the viewing screen. But, owing to blending and superposition, a natural-color rendition of the original scene is produced. A disadvantage of this method is that about five-sixths of the beam power is dissipated in the mask so that a limit is placed on the brightness of the picture. An advantage of this system is that a black-and-white rendition of the original scene may be obtained on a black-and-white receiver with no changes whatsoever in the receiver.

Transmission. Because television waves are short and hence travel in straight lines, they do not follow the curvature of the earth, nor are they reflected by the ionosphere. Consequently, television sending antenna are located at high elevations, such as the top of the Empire State Building in New York or on top of Helderberg Mountain near Schenectady. The average radius of reception is only about 50 miles, although high-gain receiving antennas can pick up stations as far away as 150 miles. Moreover, because of the very high frequency of the television waves, programs cannot be transmitted on a nationwide hookup over the types of communication circuits that are used for voice broadcasts. There are two common methods of connecting stations for network broadcasts: coaxial cable and transmission by microwave relay stations. The coaxial cable consists of a cylindrical conductor concentric with a lead sheath and held in position by washers, spaced every foot or two along the length of the cable. In such a cable, the dielectric medium is practically air, so that the attenuation and distortion of the h-f waves used for television are minimized. Programs to many local stations are transmitted over coaxial cables.

Transmission by relay stations is accomplished by mounting amplifying stations on the top of towers which in turn are erected at the tops of high elevations such as hills or mountains. Adjacent stations are in the line of sight of each other. The received message is automatically amplified by each station and rebroadcast to the next by a directive antenna. This system is used to transmit programs over long distances.

SECTION 16

INSTRUMENTS AND CONTROLS

BY

IRVING LEFKOWITZ, Professor of Engineering, Systems Research Center, Case Institute of Technology.

GUY S. LONGOBARDO, Advisory Engineer, Advanced Systems Development Division, International Business Machines Corporation.

CONTENTS

INSTRUMENTS

BY IRVING LEFKOWITZ

AUTOMATIC CONTROLS

BY GUY S. LONGOBARDO

INSTRUMENTS

BY

Irving Lefkowitz

REFERENCES: Eckman, "Industrial Instrumentation," Wiley. Considine, "Process Instruments and Controls Handbook," McGraw-Hill. Gess and Irwin, "Flow Meter Engineering Handbook," Brown Instrument Co. ASME, "Fluid Meters, Their Theory and Application." Behar, "Handbook of Measurement and Control," Instruments Publishing Co. Harris, "Electrical Measurements," Wiley. Holzbock, "Instruments for Measurement and Control," Reinhold. American Institute of Physics, "Temperature, Its Measurement and Control in Science and Industry," Reinhold. Royds, "The Measurement and Control of Temperatures in Industry," Chemical Publishing. Sweeney, "Measurement Techniques in Mechanical Engineering," Wiley. Shoop and Tuve, "Mechanical Engineering Practice," McGraw-Hill. Cook and Rabinowicz, "Physical Measurement and Analysis," Addison-Wesley. Carroll, "Industrial Process Measuring Instruments," McGraw-Hill. Beckwith and Buck, "Mechanical Measurements," Addison-Wesley. Lion, "Instrumentation in Scientific Research," McGraw-Hill. Minnar, "ISA Transducer Compendium," Plenum Press. Considine, "Handbook of Applied Instrumentation," McGraw-Hill. Snell, "Nuclear Instruments and Their Uses," Wiley.

INTRODUCTION TO MEASUREMENT

An **instrument,** as referred to in the following sections, is a device for determining the value or magnitude of a quantity or variable. The variables of interest are those which help describe or define an object, system, or process. Thus, in a manufacturing operation, product quality is related to measurements of its various dimensions and physical properties such as hardness and surface finish. In an industrial process, measurement and control of temperature, pressure, flow rates, etc., determine quality and efficiency of production.

Measurements may be direct, such as using a micrometer to measure a dimension, or indirect, such as determining moisture in steam by measuring the temperature in a throttling calorimeter.

Because of physical limitations of the measuring device and the system under study, practical measurements always have some error. The **accuracy** of an instrument is the closeness with which its reading approaches the true value of the variable being measured. **Precision** refers to the reproducibility of the measurements; *i.e.*, with a fixed value of the variable, how much successive readings differ from one another. **Sensitivity** is the ratio of output signal or response of the instrument to a change in input or measured variable. **Resolution** relates to the smallest change in measured value to which the instrument will respond.

Error may be classified as systematic or random. Systematic errors are those due to assignable causes. These may be static or dynamic. Static errors are caused by limitations of the measuring device or the physical laws governing its behavior. A static error is introduced in a micrometer reading, for example, when excessive pressure is applied to the spindle. Dynamic errors are caused by the instrument not responding fast enough to follow the changes in measured variable; *e.g.*, a room thermometer does not show the correct temperature until several minutes after the temperature has stabilized to some steady value. Random errors are those due to causes which cannot be directly established because of random variations in the system.

Standards for measurement are established by the National Bureau of Standards. Secondary standards are prepared by very precise comparison with these primary standards and, in turn, form the basis for calibrating instruments in use. A well-known example is the Johanneson gage blocks employed in the calibration of machine tools in assembly lines.

There are three essential parts to an instrument: the **sensing element,** the **transmitting means,** and the **output or indicating element.** The sensing element responds directly to the measured quantity, producing a related motion, pressure, or electrical signal. This is transmitted by linkage, tubing, wiring, etc., to deflect a pointer or move a pen to indicate the value of the measurement on an appropriately calibrated scale or chart. The instrument may be actuated by mechanical, hydraulic, pneumatic, electrical, optical, or other energy medium. Often a combination of several energy modes is employed to obtain the accuracy, sensitivity, or form of output desired.

COUNTING OF EVENTS

Event counters are used to measure the number of items passing on a conveyor line, the number of operations of a machine, etc. Coupled with time measurements, they yield measures of average rate or frequency. They find important application, therefore, in inventory control, production analysis, and in the sequencing control of automatic machines.

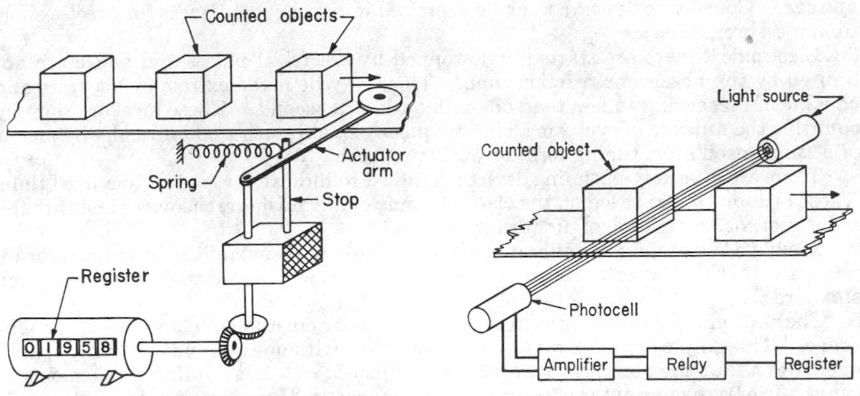

FIG. 1. Mechanical counter. FIG. 2. Photoelectric counter.

Choice of the proper counting device depends on the kind of events being counted, the necessary counting speed, and the disposition of the measurement; *i.e.*, whether it is to be indicated remotely, used to actuate a machine, etc. Errors in the total count may be introduced by events being too close together or by too much non-uniformity in the items being counted.

The **mechanical counter** is shown in Fig. 1. Motion of the event being counted deflects the arm, which through an appropriate linkage advances the count register one unit. Alternatively, motion of the actuating arm may close an electrical switch which energizes a relay coil to advance the count register one step.

Where it is desired to avoid contact with the object being counted, the **photoelectric cell** is employed (Fig. 2). A count is registered each time the light beam focused on the photocell is interrupted. This generates an electric signal which is used to actuate a relay coil (as in the above example) or an electronic counter. This system can operate at considerably higher count speeds than the mechanical or electromechanical types.

Sensing methods based on electrical capacitance and magnetic effects are extremely sensitive and fast-acting. The **magnetic pickup** responds to the motion of iron (or other magnetic material), and hence is particularly adaptable to counting machine operations.

The count is displayed by either a mechanical register as in Fig. 1, a dial-type register (as on the household watthour meter), or an electronic pulse counter with either neon-tube number indicators or digital printing output. **Electronic counters** can receive accurately at rates exceeding one million counts per second.

TIME AND FREQUENCY MEASUREMENT

Measurement of time is basic to time and motion studies, time program controls, and the measurements of velocity, frequency, and flow rate. (See also p. 1-86.)

Mechanical devices include the wide range of clocks, chronometers, and stop watches. In these, a spring tends to rotate the time indicator (clock hands) through a train of gears which is restrained by a hairspring and escapement assembly. The time measurement relates to the period of oscillation of the hairspring, which is fixed, dependent upon the dimensions and characteristics of the spring. Since the spring constant is affected somewhat by temperature, precise timepieces employ a compensating element to maintain timing accuracies over long periods. Stop watches may be obtained to read to better than 0.01 sec. The major limitation, however, is in the response time of the user.

Electric timers are simple, inexpensive, and are readily adaptable to remote-control operations. The majority of these are a-c synchronous motors geared in the proper ratio to the indicator. These depend for their accuracy on the frequency of the line voltage. Consequently, care must be exercised in using such devices for precise short time measurements.

Electronic timers are started and stopped by electrical pulses and hence are not limited by the observer's reaction time. They may be made extremely accurate and capable of measuring to less than one-millionth of a second. These measure time by counting the number of cycles in a high-frequency signal generated internally by means of a tuned oscillator, tuning fork, or quartz crystal.

There are a variety of timing devices designed to indicate or control to a fixed time. These include timers based on the charging time of a condenser, the flow of oil through a dashpot, or the release of air through a nozzle.

Timing devices may be **calibrated** by comparison with a standard instrument or by reference to the National Bureau of Standards timed radio signals and frequency standards.

The motion of fast-moving systems may be timed and studied by means of a **stroboscope.** This employs a neon tube or a rotating disk with one or more uniformly spaced apertures about the periphery such that the object is viewed at uniform increments of time. The frequency of the observed motion is measured by adjusting the stroboscopic frequency until the system appears to stand still.

Many other means exist for **measuring vibrational or rotational frequencies.** These include timing a fixed number of rotations or oscillations of the moving member. The sensing can be done by magnetic probes, phonograph-type pickups, and the like. The pulses can be counted by an electronic counter or displayed on an oscilloscope or oscillographic recorder and compared with a known frequency. Also used are reeds which vibrate when the measured oscillation excites their natural frequencies, fly-ball devices which respond directly to angular velocity, and generator-type tachometers which generate a voltage proportional to the speed.

MASS AND WEIGHT MEASUREMENT

Mass is the measure of the quantity of matter. The fundamental unit is the kilogram, which is equivalent to the mass of a cube, 10 centimeters on edge, of pure water at 4 C and standard atmospheric pressure (see Sec. 1). The standard in this country is the pound, defined by the National Bureau of Standards as 1 pound = 0.4536 kilograms.

Weight is a measure of the force of gravity acting on a mass. Since this force is in fixed proportion to the mass, the two terms are not often distinguished outside of engineering and physical calculations. Indeed, almost all practical measures of mass are based on weight.

Weighing devices fall into two major categories: balances and force-deflection systems. The device may be batch or continuous weighing, automatic or manual. Accuracies are expected to be of the order of 0.1 to better than 0.0001 percent, depending on the type and application of the scale. Calibration is normally performed by use of standard weights which have been calibrated by the National Bureau of Standards.

The **equal arm balance** compares the weight of an object with a set of standard weights. The laboratory balance shown in Fig. 3 is used for extreme precision and sensitivity. A chain poise provides fine adjustment of the final balance weight. The magnetic damper causes the balance to come to equilibrium quickly.

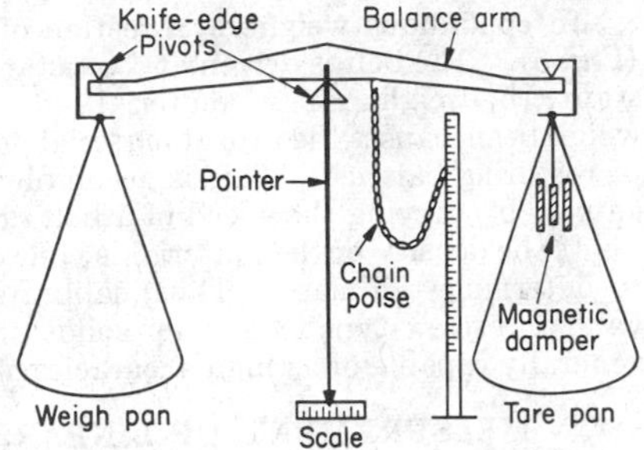

FIG. 3. Laboratory balance.

Large weighing scales operate on the same principle; however, the arms are unequal to allow multiplication between the tare and the measured weights. In this group are platform, track, hopper, and tank scales. Here balance is achieved by adjusting the position of one or more balance weights along a beam directly calibrated in weight units. In dial-indicating-type scales, balance is achieved automatically through the deflection of calibrated pendulum weights from the vertical. The deflection is greatly magnified by the pointer-actuating mechanism, providing a direct-reading weight indication on the dial.

Since the deflection of a spring (within its elastic limit) is directly proportional to the applied force, a calibrated spring serves as a simple and inexpensive weighing device. Applications include the **spring scale** and **torsion balance.** These are subject to hysteresis and temperature errors and are not used for precise work.

Other force-sensing elements are adaptable to weight measurement. Of increasing importance are strain-gage load cells because they eliminate pivot maintenance and moving parts and provide an electrical output which can be used for direct recording and control purposes. Pneumatic pressure cells are also used with similar advantages.

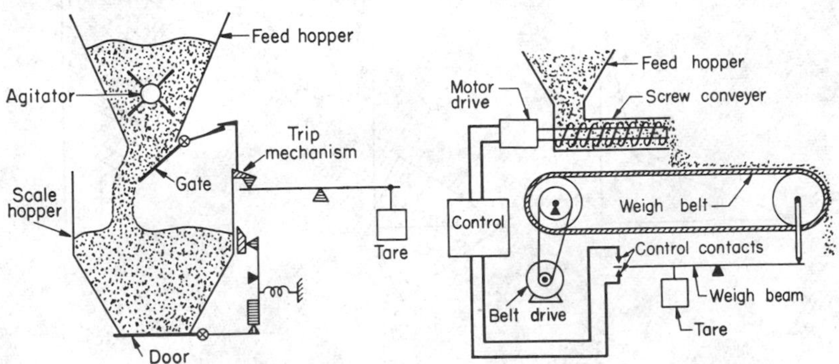

FIG. 4. Automatic batch-weighing scale. FIG. 5. Continuous-weigh scale.

In production processes, **continuous and automatic operating scales** are employed. In one type, the balancing weight is positioned by a reversible electric motor. Deflection of the beam makes an electrical contact which drives the motor in the proper direction to restore balance. The final balance position is translated by means of a potentiometer or digital encoding disk into a signal which is used for recording or control purposes.

The **batch-type scale** (Fig. 4) is adaptable to continuous flow streams of either liquids or solid particles. Material flows from the feed hopper through an adjustable gate into the scale hopper. When the weight in the scale hopper reaches that of the tare, the trip mechanism operates, closing the gate and opening the door. As soon as the scale hopper is empty, the weight of the tare forces the door closed again, resets the trip, and opens the gate to repeat the cycle. The agitator rotates while the gate is open, to prevent the solids from packing. Also, a "dribble" (partial closing of the gate just before the mechanism trips) is employed to minimize the error from the falling column of material at the instant balance is achieved. Since each dump of the scale represents a fixed weight, a counter yields the total weight of material passing through the scale.

In **continuous weighers,** a section of conveyor belt is balanced on a weigh beam (Fig. 5). The belt is driven at a constant speed; hence, if the total weight is held constant, the weight rate of material fed through the scale is fixed. Unbalance of the weigh beam causes the rate of material flow onto the belt to be changed in the direction of restoring balance. This is accomplished by a mechanical adjustment of the feed gate or by varying the speed of a belt or screw feeder drive.

If the density of the material is constant, then **volume measurements** may be used to determine the mass. Thus, calibrated tanks are frequently used for liquids and vane and screw-type feeders for solids. Though often simpler to apply, these are not generally capable of as high accuracies as are common in weighing.

MEASUREMENT OF LINEAR AND ANGULAR DISPLACEMENT

Displacement-measuring devices are employed to measure dimensions, distances between points, and some derived quantities such as velocity, area, etc. These devices fall into two major categories: those based on comparison with a known or reference length and those based on some fixed physical relationship.

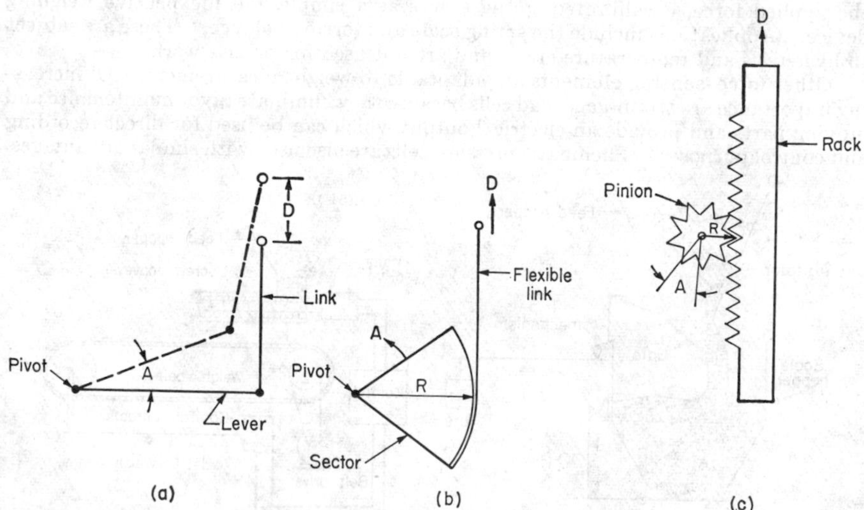

Fig. 6. Linear-rotary conversion mechanisms.

The **measurement of angles** is closely related to displacement measurements, and indeed, one is often converted into the other in the process of measurement. The common unit is the degree, which represents 1/360 of an entire rotation. The radian is used in mathematics and is related to the degree by π radians = 180 deg; 1 radian = 57.3 deg.

Figure 6 illustrates some methods of **rotary to linear conversion.** Figure 6(*a*) is a simple link and lever, Fig. 6(*b*) is a flexible link and sector, and Fig. 6(*c*) is a rack-and-pinion mechanism. These may be used to convert in either direction according to the relationship $D = RA/57.3$, where R is the mean radius of the rotating element in inches, D is the displacement in inches, and A is the degrees rotation. [This equation holds for the link and lever of Fig. 6(*a*) only if the angle change from the perpendicular is small.]

Comparative devices are generally of the manual-indicating type and include ruled or graduated devices such as the machinist's scale, folding rule, tape measure, vernier caliper (Fig. 7), micrometer (Fig. 8), etc. These vary widely in their accuracy, resolution, and measuring span, according to their intended application. Since the readings are made manually, their accuracy is very dependent on the operator's care and skill.

The **vernier** and micrometer are two methods of increasing the sensitivity and precision of reading. The vernier (Fig. 7) is an auxiliary scale which slides along the main scale. It is uniformly divided so that 10 subdivisions of the vernier correspond to exactly 9 subdivisions of the main scale. This means that each vernier subdivision is shorter than the main-scale subdivision by one-tenth the value of the main-scale subdivision. Accordingly, if the measurement (indicated by the position of the vernier index) falls between two scale subdivisions, the fraction of this interval is indicated by

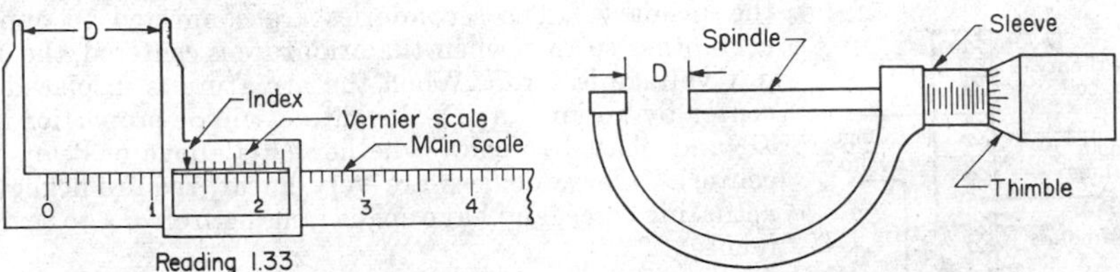

FIG. 7. Vernier caliper.

FIG. 8. Micrometer caliper.

the number of the vernier division which coincides with a main scale subdivision. Thus, in Fig. 7, the indicated reading is 1.33 in.

The **micrometer** magnifies small displacements by use of an accurately machined screw thread. In Fig. 8, one full rotation of the thimble moves the spindle 0.025 in. Since the thimble is divided into 25 divisions, each corresponds to $\frac{1}{1000}$ in. The displacement measurement is then the sum of the readings of the sleeve and thimble scales. Readings to 0.0001 in. are made by estimating the last place or by addition of a vernier to the thimble scale.

Various modifications of the above-mentioned devices are available for making special kinds of measurements; *e.g.*, **depth gages** for measuring the depth of a hole or cavity, **inside and outside calipers** (Fig. 7) for measuring the internal and external dimensions respectively of an object, **protractors** for angular measurement, etc.

For line production and inspection work, **"go-no-go" gages** provide a rapid and accurate means of dimension measurement and control. Since the measured values are fixed, the dependence on the operator's skill is considerably reduced. Such gages can be very complex in form to embrace a multidimensional object. They can also take the more general forms of the **feeler, wire, or thread-gage** sets. Of particular importance are **precision gage blocks,** which are used as standards for calibrating other measuring devices.

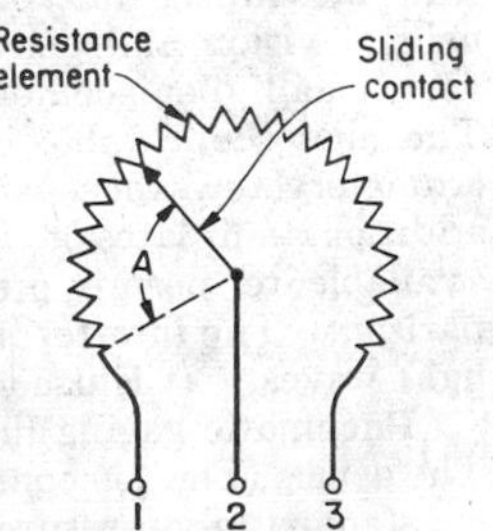

FIG. 9. Potentiometer.

The **kymograph** is a mechanically actuated displacement recorder. The motion acts through a linkage to effect a proportional deflection of the pen.

Displacement can be measured electrically through its effect on the resistance, inductance, or capacitance of an appropriate sensing element.

The **potentiometer** is comparatively inexpensive, accurate, and flexible in application. It consists of a fixed linear resistance over which slides a rotating contact keyed to the input shaft (Fig. 9). The resistance or voltage (assuming constant voltage across terminals 1 and 3) measured across terminals 1 and 2 is directly proportional to the angle A. For straight-line motion, a mechanism of the type shown in Fig. 6 converts to rotary motion (or a rectilinear-type potentiometer can be used directly). (See also p. 15–42.)

The **synchro, differential, and "E" transformers** are devices in which the input motion changes the inductive coupling between primary and secondary coils. These avoid the limitations of wear, friction, and resolution of the potentiometer; however, they require an a-c supply and usually an electronic amplifier for the output. (See also p. 15–39.)

The **synchro** is a rotating device which is used to transmit rotary motions to a remote location for indication or control action. It is particularly useful where the rotation is continuous or covers a wide range.

The **differential transformer** consists of a primary and two secondary coils wound around a common core (Fig. 10). An armature (iron) is free to move vertically along the axis of the coils. An a-c voltage is applied to the primary. A voltage is induced in each secondary coil proportional to the relative length of armature linking it with the primary. The secondaries are connected to oppose each other so that when the armature is centered, the output voltage is zero. When the armature is displaced off center by an amount D, the output will be proportional to D (and phased to show whether D is above or below the center). These devices are very linear, require negligible actuating force, and have spans ranging from 0.1 to several inches.

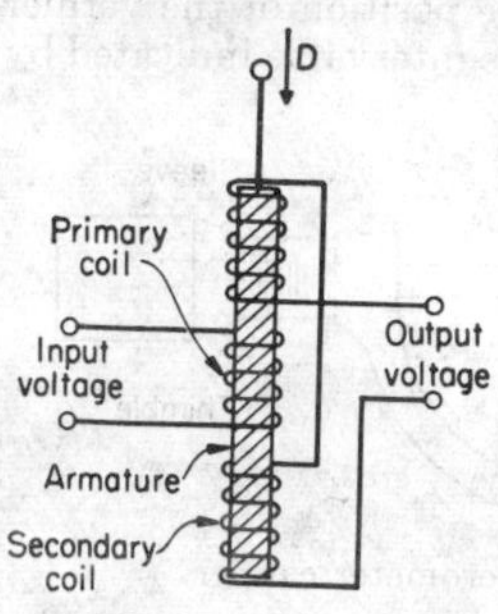

FIG. 10. Differential transformer.

The **"E" transformer** is very similar to the above except that the coils are wound around a laminated iron core in the shape of an E (with the primary and secondaries occupying the center and outside legs respectively). The magnetic path is completed through an armature whose motion, either rotary or translational, varies the induced voltage in the secondaries, as in the device of Fig. 10. This, too, is sensitive to extremely small motions.

A method that is readily applied if a strain-gage analyzer is handy is the measure of the deflection of a cantilever spring with strain gages bonded to its surface (see Strain Gages, pp. 5–77 and 16–10).

The **change of capacitance** with the displacement of the capacitor plates is extremely sensitive, but limited to very small displacements. Often, one plate is fixed within the instrument; the other is formed by the object being measured. The capacitance may be measured by means of an impedance bridge or by determining the resonant frequency of a tuned circuit.

Many optical instruments are available for obtaining precise measurements. The **transit and level** are used in surveying for measuring angles and vertical distances (see p. 18–54). A telescope with fine cross hairs permits accurate sighting. The angle scales are generally equipped with verniers. The **measuring microscope** magnifies the field of vision and permits measurement of very small displacements and dimensions. The microscope table is equipped with micrometer screws for sensitive adjustment. In addition, templates of scales, angles, etc., are available to permit measurement by comparison. The **interferometer** is based on the interference patterns of surface-reflected light waves. It is used for measurements of the order of millionths of an inch.

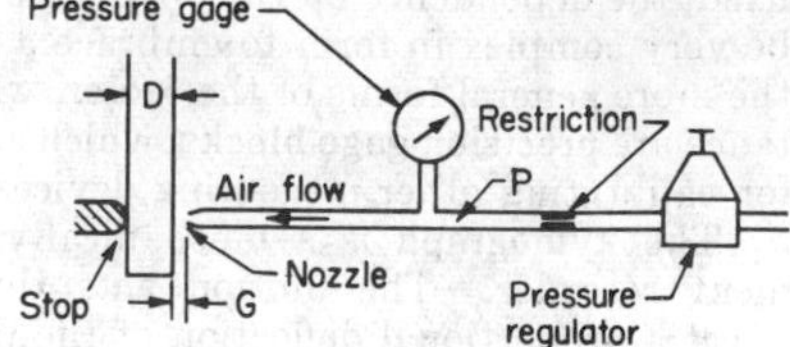

FIG. 11. Pneumatic gage.

Pneumatic gaging finds an important place in line inspection and quality control. The device (Fig. 11) consists of a nozzle fixed in position relative to a stop or jig. Air at constant supply pressure passes through a restriction and discharges through the nozzle. The nozzle back pressure P depends on the gap G between the measured surface and the nozzle opening. If the measured dimension D increases, then G decreases, restricting the discharge of air, increasing P. Conversely, when D decreases, P decreases. Thus, the pressure gage indicates deviation of the dimension from some normal value. With proper design, this pressure is directly proportional to the deviation, limited, however, to a few thousandths of an inch span. The device is extremely sensitive (better than 0.0001 in.), rugged, and, with periodic calibration against a standard, quite accurate. The gage is adaptable to automatic line operation where the pressure signal is recorded or used to actuate **"reject"** or **"accept" controls.** Further, any number of nozzles may be used in a jig to check a multiplicity of dimensions. In another form of this device, the flow of air is measured with a rotameter in place of the back pressure.

The advent of automatically controlled machine tools has brought about the need for very accurate displacement measurement over a wide range. Most commonly applied for this purpose is the calibrated **lead screw** which measures linear displacement in terms of its angular rotation. Several **digital** systems have recently been developed which extend greatly the resolution and accuracy limitations of the lead screw. In these, a uniformly spaced optical or inductive grid is displaced relative to a sensing element. The number of grid lines counted is a direct measure of the displacement.

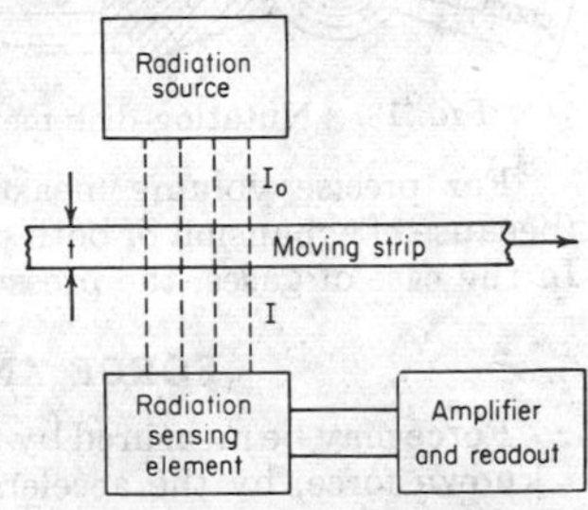

FIG. 12. Radiation-type thickness gauge.

Measurement of strip thickness or coating thickness is achieved by **X-ray** or **beta-radiation-type** gauges (Fig. 12). A constant radiation source (X-ray tube or radioisotope) provides an incident intensity I_0; the radiation intensity I after passing through the absorbing material is measured by an appropriate device (scintillation counter, Geiger-Müller tube, etc.). The thickness t is determined by the equation $I = I_0 e^{-kt}$, where k is a constant dependent on the material and the measuring device. The major advantage here is that measurements are continuous and non-destructive and require no contact. The method is extended to measure liquid level and density.

MEASUREMENT OF AREA

Area measurements are made for the purpose of determining surface area of an object or area inside a closed curve relating to some desired physical quantity. Dimensions are expressed as a length squared; *e.g.*, square inches. The areas of simple forms are readily obtained by formula. The area of a complex form may be determined by subdividing into simple forms of known area. In addition, various numerical methods are available (see **Simpson's rule,** p. 2–18) for estimating the area under irregular curves.

Area measuring devices include various **flow integrators** (used with flowmeters) and the **polar planimeter.** The latter consists of two arms pivoted to each other. A tracer at the end of one arm is guided around the boundary curve of the area, causing rotation of a recorder wheel proportional to the area enclosed.

MEASUREMENT OF FLUID VOLUME

For a liquid of known density, volume is a quick and simple means of measuring the amount (or mass) of liquid present. Conversely, measuring the weight and volume of a given quantity of material permits calculation of its density. Volume has the dimensions of length cubed; *e.g.*, cubic inches, cubic feet. The volume of simple forms may be obtained by formula.

A volumetric device is any container which has a known and fixed calibration of volume contained *vs.* the level of liquid. The device may be calibrated at only one point (**pipette, volumetric flask**) or may be graduated over its entire volume (**burette, graduated cylinder, volumetric tank**). In the case of the tank, a sight glass may be calibrated directly in liquid volume.

Volumetric measure of continuous flow streams is obtained with the **displacement meter.** This is available in various forms: the nutating disk, reciprocating piston, rotating vane, etc. The **nutating-disk meter** (Fig. 13) is relatively inexpensive and hence is widely used (water meters, etc.). Liquid entering the meter causes the disk to nutate or "roll" as the liquid makes its way around the chamber to the outlet. A pin on the disk causes a counter to rotate, thereby counting the total number of rolls of the disk. Meter accuracy is limited by leakage past the disk and friction. The **piston meter** is like a piston pump operated backwards. It is used for more precise measure (available to 0.1 percent accuracy).

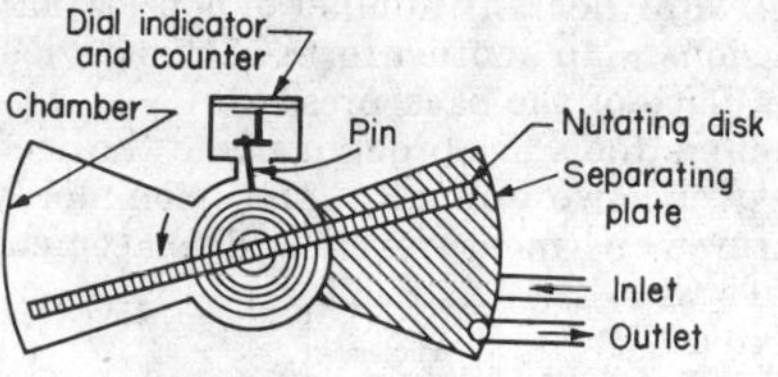

FIG. 13. Nutating-disk meter.

Volumetric gas measurement is commonly made with a **bellows meter.** Two bellows are alternately filled and exhausted with the gas. Motion of the bellows actuates a register to indicate the total flow. Various liquid-sealed displacement meters are also available for this purpose.

For precise volume measurements, corrections for temperature must be made (because of expansion of both the material being measured and the volumetric device). In the case of gases, the pressure also must be noted.

FORCE AND TORQUE MEASUREMENT

Force may be measured by the deflection of an elastic element, by balancing against a known force, by the acceleration produced in an object of known mass, or by its effects on the electrical or other properties of a stress-sensitive material. The common unit of force is the pound. **Torque** is the product of a force and the perpendicular distance to the axis of rotation. Thus, torque tends to produce rotational motion and is expressed in units of pound-feet. Torque may be measured by the angular deflection of an elastic element or, where the moment arm is known, by any of the force-measuring methods.

Since weight is the force of gravity acting on a mass, any of the weight-measuring devices already discussed can be used to measure force. Common methods employ the deflection of springs or cantilever beams.

The **strain gage** is a wire element whose resistance changes with applied stress. Measure of the resistance change can be translated into a measure of the force applied. The gage may be bonded or unbonded. In the bonded case, the gage is cemented to the surface of an elastic member and measures the strain of the member. Since the gage is very sensitive to temperature, the readings must be compensated. For this purpose, four gages are connected in a Wheatstone-bridge circuit such that the temperature effect cancels itself. A four-element unbonded gage is shown in Fig. 14. Note that as the applied force increases, the tension on two of the elements increases while that on the other two decreases. (See also Sec. 5.)

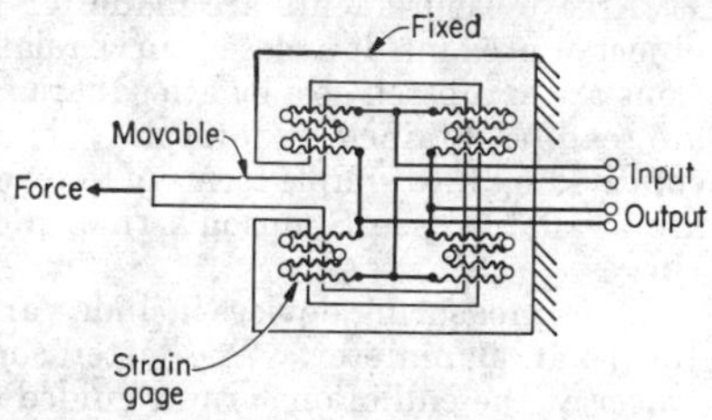

FIG. 14. Unbonded strain-gage board.

The **piezoelectric** effect is useful in measuring rapidly varying forces because of its high-frequency response and negligible displacement characteristics. Quartz, rochelle salt, and barium titanate are common piezoelectric materials. They have the property of varying an output voltage in direct relation to the mechanical stress applied. The voltage must be measured with a device having a very high input impedance. Accuracy is limited because of temperature dependence and some hysteresis effect.

Forces may also be measured with any of the pressure devices described in the next section by balancing against a fluid pressure acting on a fixed area.

PRESSURE AND VACUUM MEASUREMENT

Pressure is defined as the force per unit area exerted by a fluid. Pressure devices normally measure with respect to atmospheric pressure (mean value = 14.7 psi), $p_a = p_g + 14.7$, where p_a = total or *absolute* pressure and p_g = *gage* pressure, both psi. Conventionally, gage pressure and vacuum refer to pressures above and below atmospheric, respectively. Common units are pounds per square inch, inches of mercury, feet of water.

Pressure devices are based on (1) measure of an equivalent height of liquid column; (2) measure of the force exerted on a fixed area; (3) measure of some change in electrical or physical characteristics of the fluid.

The **manometer** measures pressure according to the relationship, $p = \rho h$, where h is the height of liquid of density ρ (assumed constant) supported by a pressure p. Thus, pressures are often expressed directly in terms of the equivalent height (head) of manometer liquid (*e.g.*, inches of water or mercury). Usual manometer fluids are water or mercury, although other fluids are available for special ranges.

The **U-tube manometer** [Fig. 15(*a*)] expresses the pressure difference $p_1 - p_2$ as the difference in levels h. If p_2 is exposed to the atmosphere, then the manometer reads the gage pressure of p_1. If the p_2 tube is evacuated and sealed ($p_2 = 0$), then the absolute value of p_1 is indicated. A common modification is the **well-type manometer** [Fig. 15(*b*)]. The scale is specially calibrated to take into account changes of level

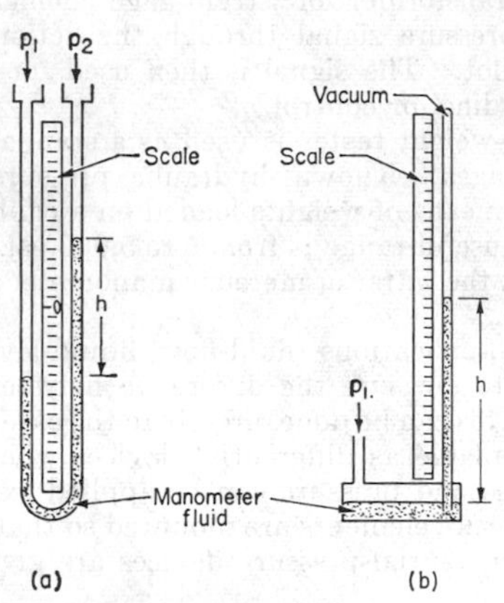

FIG. 15. Manometers: (*a*) U-tube type; (*b*) well type.

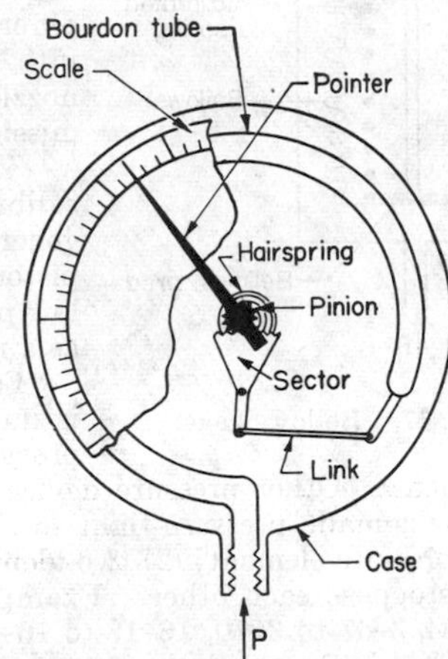

FIG. 16. Bourdon-tube gage.

inside the well so that only a single-tube reading is required. In particular, Fig. 15(*b*) illustrates the form usually applied to measurement of atmospheric pressure (**mercury barometer**).

The sensitivity of readings may be increased by inclining the manometer tubes to the vertical (**inclined manometer**), by use of low-specific-gravity manometer fluids, or by application of optical-magnification or level-sensing devices. Accuracy is influenced by surface-tension effects (reading of the meniscus) and changes in fluid density (due to temperature changes and impurities).

By definition, pressure times the area acted upon equals the force exerted. The pressure may act on a diaphragm, bellows, or other element of fixed area. The force is then measured with any force-measuring device, *e.g.*, spring deflection, strain gage, weight balance, etc. Very commonly, the unknown pressure is balanced against an air or hydraulic pressure, which in turn is measured with a gage. By use of unequal-area diaphragms, the pressure can thus be amplified or attenuated as required. Further, it permits isolating the process fluid which may be corrosive, viscous, etc.

The **Bourdon-tube gage** (Fig. 16) is the most commonly used pressure device. It consists of a flattened tube of spring bronze or steel bent into a circle. Pressure inside the tube tends to straighten it. Since one end of the tube is fixed to the pressure inlet, the other end moves proportionally to the pressure difference existing between the inside and outside of the tube. The motion rotates the pointer through a pinion-

and-sector mechanism. For amplification of the motion, the tube may be bent through several turns to form spiral or helical elements as are used in pressure recorders.

In the **diaphragm gage,** the pressure acts on a diaphragm in opposition to a spring or other elastic member. The deflection of the diaphragm is therefore proportional to the pressure. Since the force increases with the area of the diaphragm, very small pressures can be measured by the use of large diaphragms. The diaphragm may be metallic (brass, stainless steel) for strength and corrosion resistance, or non-metallic (leather, neoprene, rubber) for high sensitivity and large deflection. With a stiff diaphragm, the total motion must be very small to maintain linearity.

The **bellows gage** (Fig. 17) is somewhat similar to the diaphragm gage, with the advantage, however, of providing a much wider range of motion. The force acting on the bottom of the bellows is balanced by the deflection of the spring. This motion is transmitted to the output arm, which then actuates a pointer or recorder pen.

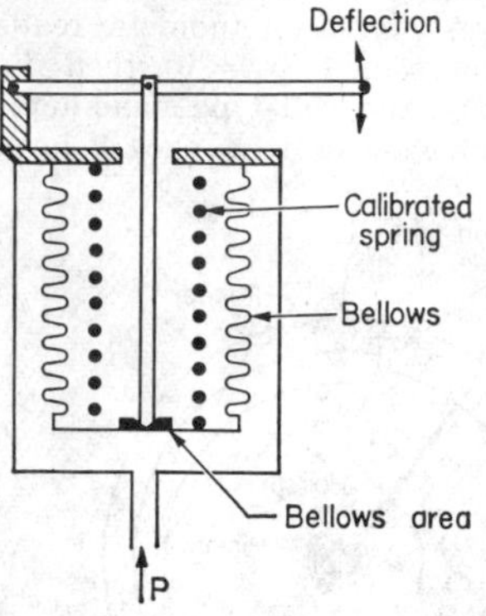

FIG. 17. Bellows gage.

The motion (or force) of the pressure element may be converted into an electrical signal by use of a differential transformer or strain-gage element, or into an air-pressure signal through the action of a nozzle and pilot. The signal is then used for transmission, recording, or control.

The **dead-weight tester** is used as a standard for calibrating gages. Known hydraulic pressures are generated by means of weights loaded on a calibrated piston. The useful range is from 5 to 5,000 psi. For low pressures, the water or mercury manometer serves as a reference.

For many applications (fluid flow, liquid level), it is important to measure the **difference between two pressures.** This can be done directly in the case of the manometer. Other pressure devices are available as differential devices where (1) the case is made pressure-tight so that the second pressure can be applied external to the pressure element; (2) two identical pressure elements are mounted so that their outputs oppose each other. Examples of differential-pressure devices are given on pp. 3–54, 3–67 to 3–70, 16–18 to 16–21.

Similar devices to those discussed are used to measure **vacuum,** the only difference being a shift in range or at most a relocation of the zeroing spring. When the vacuum is high (absolute pressure near zero) variations in atmospheric pressure become an important source of error. It is here that absolute-pressure devices are employed.

Any of the differential-pressure elements can be converted to an **absolute-pressure device** by sealing one pressure side to a perfect vacuum. A common instrument for the range 0 to 30 in. Hg employs two bellows of equal area set back to back. One bellows is completely evacuated and sealed; the other is connected to the measured pressure. The output is a bellows displacement, as in Fig. 17.

There are many instruments for high-vacuum work (0.001 to 10,000 μ range; see also p. 14–62). These are based on the characteristic properties of gases at low pressures. The **McLeod gage** amplifies the pressure to be measured by compressing the gas a known amount and then measuring its pressure with a mercury manometer. The ratio of initial to final pressure is equal to the ratio of final to initial volume (for common gases). This gage serves as a standard for low pressures. It has also been mechanized for automatic operation.

The **Pirani gage** (Fig. 18) is based on the change of heat conductivity of a gas with pressure and the change of electrical resistance of a wire with temperature. The wire is electrically heated with a constant current. Its temperature changes with pressure, producing a voltage across the bridge network. The compensating cell corrects for room-temperature changes.

The **thermocouple gage** is similar to the Pirani gage, except that a thermocouple is used to measure the temperature difference between the resistance elements in the measuring and compensating cells, respectively.

The **ionization gage** measures the ion current generated by bombardment of the molecules of the gas by the electron stream in a triode-type tube. This gage is limited to pressures below 1 μ. It is, however, extremely sensitive.

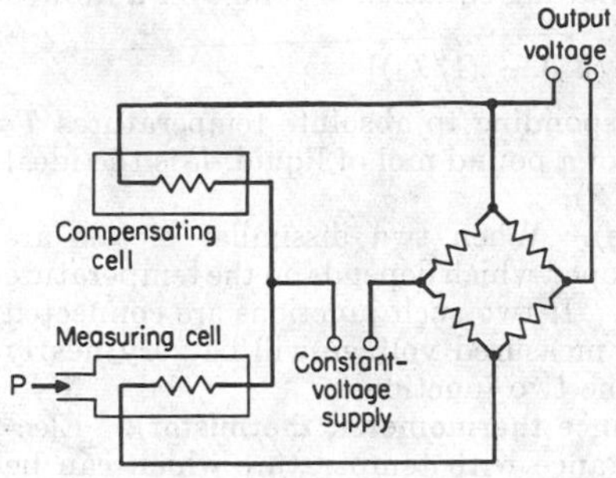

FIG. 18. Pirani gage.

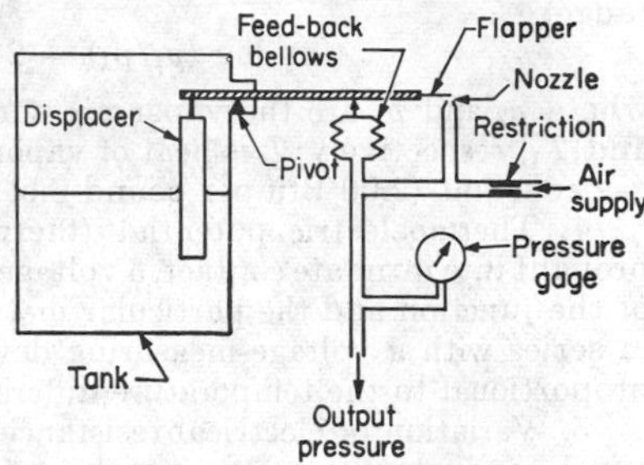

FIG. 19. Displacer-type level meter.

LIQUID-LEVEL MEASUREMENT

Level instruments are used for determining (or controlling) the height of liquid in a vessel or the location of the interface between two liquids of different specific gravity. In large storage tanks the level is indicated by a **calibrated tape or chain** which is attached to a float riding the liquid surface. For measuring small changes in level, the **fixed displacer** is common (Fig. 19). The buoyant force is proportional to the volume of displacer submerged and hence changes directly with the level. The force is balanced by the air pressure acting in the bellows, which in turn is generated by the flapper and nozzlé. A pressure gage (or recorder) indicates the level.

The level is often measured by means of a **differential-pressure meter** connected to taps in the top and bottom of the tank. As indicated in the discussion on manometers, the pressure difference is equal to the height times the density of the liquid. Where the liquid is corrosive or contains solids, then liquid seals, water purge, or air purge may be used to isolate the meter from the process.

For special applications, the dielectric, conducting, or absorption properties of the liquid can be used. Thus, in one model the liquid rises between two plates of a condenser, producing a **capacitance change** proportional to the change in level, and in another the **radiation** from a small radioactive source is measured. Since the liquid has a high absorption for the rays (compared with the vapor space), the intensity of the measured radiation decreases with the increase in level. An important advantage of this type is that it requires no external connections to the process (see p. 16–9).

TEMPERATURE MEASUREMENT

The common temperature scales (Fahrenheit and Celsius, or Centigrade) are based on the freezing and boiling points of water (see pp. 4–2 *et seq.* for discussion of temperature standards, units, and conversion equations).

Temperature is measured in a number of different ways. Some of the more useful are as follows:

1. Thermal expansion of a gas (**gas thermometer**). At constant volume, the pressure p of an (ideal) gas is directly proportional to its absolute temperature T. Thus, $p = (p_0/T_0)T$, where p_0 is the pressure at some known temperature T_0.

2. Thermal expansion of a liquid or solid (**mercury thermometer, bimetallic element**). Substances tend to expand with temperature. Thus, a change in temperature $t_2 - t_1$ causes a change in length $l_2 - l_1$ or a change in volume $V_2 - V_1$, according to the expressions

$$l_2 - l_1 = a'(t_2 - t_1) \quad \text{or} \quad V_2 - V_1 = a'''(t_2 - t_1)$$

where a' and a''' are the linear and volumetric coefficients of thermal expansion, respectively (see pp. 4–6 to 4–8). For many substances, a' and a''' are reasonably constant over a limited temperature range. For solids, $a''' = 3a'$. For mercury at room temperature, a''' is approximately 0.00018 per deg C.

3. Vapor pressure of a liquid (**vapor bulb thermometer**). The vapor pressure of all liquids increases with temperature. The following equation is valid over a limited range:

$$\log (p_2/p_1) = 2.3L/R[(1/T_2) - (1/T_1)]$$

where p_2 and p_1 are the vapor pressures corresponding to absolute temperatures T_2 and T_1, respectively; L is heat of vaporization of a pound mol of liquid, R is the ideal gas constant (2.00 Btu per pound mol per deg F).

4. Thermoelectric potential (**thermocouple**). When two dissimilar metals are brought into intimate contact, a voltage is developed which depends on the temperature of the junction and the particular metals used. If two such junctions are connected in series with a voltage-measuring device, the measured voltage will be very nearly proportional to the temperature difference of the two junctions.

5. Variation of electrical resistance (**resistance thermometer, thermistor**). Electrical conductors experience a change in resistance with temperature which can be measured with a Wheatstone-bridge circuit. The relationship for platinum is very exact and hence serves as a primary standard over a wide temperature range. The Callendar equation is used in precise work:

$$t = 100 \frac{R_t - R_0}{R_{100} - R_0} + c(t - 100)t$$

where t = measured temperature, C; R_0, R_{100}, and R_t represent the resistance of the platinum element at 0, 100, and t C, respectively; c is a constant $= 1.5 \times 10^{-4}$ per deg C (approximately).

6. Change in radiation (**radiation and optical pyrometers**). A body radiates energy proportional to the fourth power of its absolute temperature. This principle is particularly adaptable to the measurement of very high temperatures where either the total quantity of radiation or its intensity within a narrow wave-length band may be measured. In the former type (radiation pyrometer), the radiation is focused on a heat-sensitive element (*e.g.*, a thermocouple) and its rise in temperature is measured. In the latter type (optical pyrometer) the intensity of the radiation is compared optically with a heated filament of fixed intensity. Important relationships used in the design of these instruments are the Wien and Stefan-Boltzmann laws, given (in modified form):

$$\lambda_m = 5{,}220/T_2 \qquad q = 1.72 \times 10^{-9} \epsilon A (T_2^4 - T_1^4)$$

where λ_m = wave length of maximum intensity, microns; q = radiation, Btu per hr; A = radiation surface, sq ft; ϵ = mean emissivity of the surfaces; T_2, T_1 = absolute temperatures (deg Rankine) of the radiating and receiving surfaces, respectively. The emissivity depends on the material and form of the surfaces involved (see p. 4–108).

7. Change in physical or chemical state (**Seger cones, Tempilsticks**). The temperatures at which substances melt or initiate chemical reaction are often known and reproducible characteristics. Commercial products are available which cover the temperature range from about 120 to 3600 F in intervals ranging from 12 to 70 F. The temperature-sensing element may be used as a solid which softens and changes shape at the critical temperature, or it may be applied as a paint or crayon which changes color or surface appearance.

The most commonly used temperature device is the **mercury-in-glass thermometer.** As the temperature increases, the mercury in the bulb expands and rises through a fine capillary in the graduated thermometer stem. Useful range extends from −30 to 900 F. In many applications of the mercury thermometer, the stem is not exposed to the measured temperature; hence a correction is required (except where the thermometer has been calibrated for **partial immersion**). Recommended formula for the correction K to be added to the thermometer reading is $K = 0.00009D(t_1 - t_2)$, where D = the number of degrees of exposed mercury filament, deg F; t_1 = thermometer reading, deg F; t_2 = the temperature at about the middle of the exposed portion of stem, deg F.

For **industrial applications** the thermometer is encased in a metal protective well and case (Fig. 20). A threaded union fitting is provided so that the thermometer can be installed into a line or vessel under pressure. For **control** or **alarm indications** at fixed temperatures, the glass stem may be provided with electrical contacts such that when the mercury in the capillary rises to the contact point, an external relay circuit is energized.

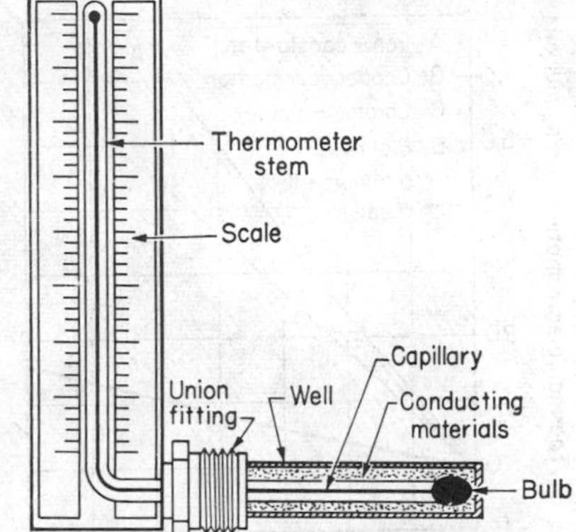

Fig. 20. Industrial thermometer.

Thermal expansion of a solid is employed in the simple **bimetal** (used in thermostats) and the bimetallic helix (Fig. 21). The bimetallic element is made by welding together two strips of metal having different coefficients of expansion. A change in temperature then causes the element to bend or twist an amount proportional to the temperature. A common bimetallic pair consists of invar (iron-nickel alloy) and brass.

A popular industrial-type instrument employs the deflection of a **pressure spring** to indicate (or record) the temperature (Fig. 22). The sensing element is a metal bulb containing some specific gas or liquid. The bulb connects with the pressure spring (in the form of a spiral or helix) through a capillary tube which is usually enclosed in a protective sheath or armor. Increasing temperature causes the fluid in the bulb to expand in volume or increase in pressure. This forces the pressure spring to unwind and move the pen or pointer an appropriate distance upscale.

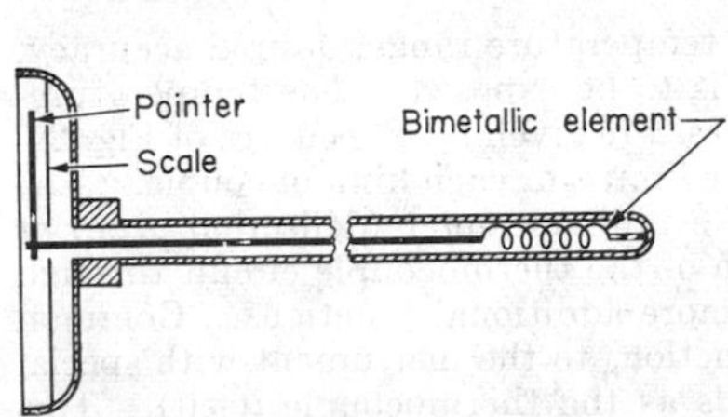

Fig. 21. Bimetallic temperature gage.

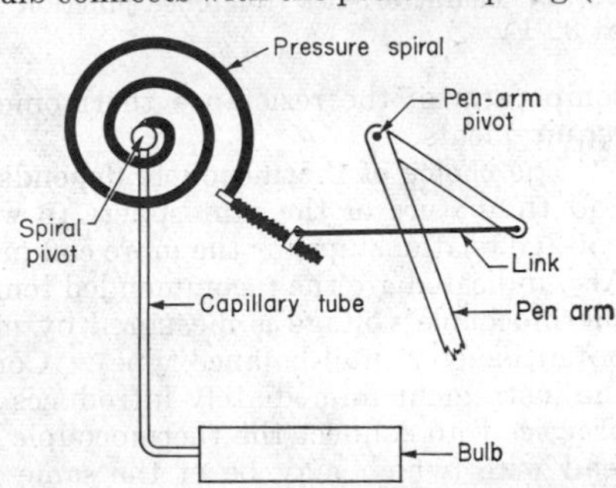

Fig. 22. Pressure-spring element.

The **bulb fluid** may be mercury (mercury system), nitrogen under pressure (gas system), or a volatile liquid (vapor-pressure system). Mercury and gas systems have linear scales; however, they must be compensated to avoid ambient temperature errors. The capillary may range up to 200 ft in length with, however, considerable reduction in speed of response.

For transmitting temperature readings over any distance (up to 1,000 ft), the **pneumatic transmitter** (Fig. 23) is better suited than the methods outlined thus far. This instrument has the additional advantages of greater compactness, higher response

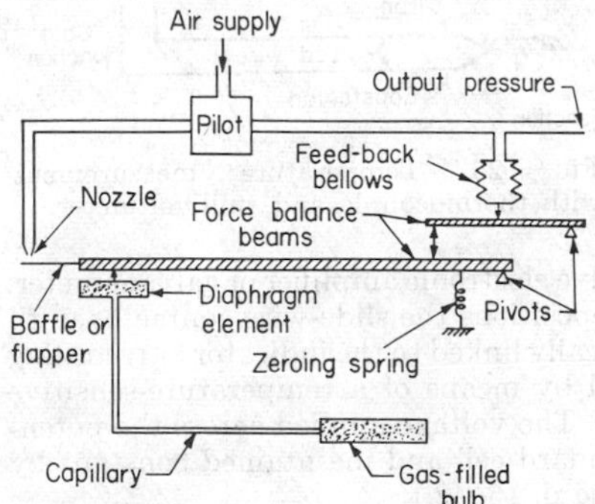

Fig. 23. Pneumatic temperature transmitter.

speeds, and generally better accuracy. The bulb is filled with gas under pressure which acts on the diaphragm. As increase in bulb temperature increases the upward force acting on the main beam, tending to rotate it clockwise. This causes the baffle or flapper to move closer to the nozzle, increasing the nozzle back pressure. This acts on the pilot, producing an increase in output pressure, which increases the force exerted by the feedback bellows. The system returns to equilibrium when the increase in bellows pressure exactly balances the effect of the increased diaphragm pressure. Since the lever ratios are fixed, this results in a direct proportionality between bulb temperature and output air pressure. For precision, compensating elements are built into the instrument to correct for the effects of changes in barometric pressure and ambient temperature.

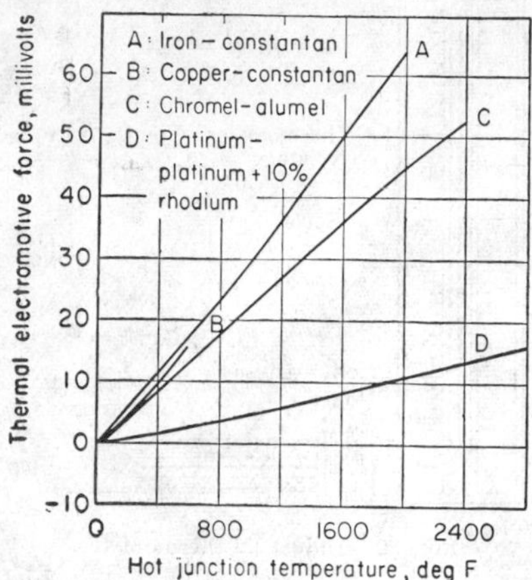

Fig. 24. Thermocouple temperature-voltage characteristics (reference junction at 32 F).

Electrical systems based on the thermocouple or resistance thermometer are particularly applicable where many different temperatures are to be measured, where transmission distances are large, or where high sensitivity and rapid response are required. The thermocouple is used with high temperatures; the resistance thermometer for low temperatures and high accuracy requirements.

The **choice of thermocouple** depends on the temperature range, desired accuracy, and the nature of the atmosphere to which it is to be exposed. The temperature-voltage relationships for the more common of these are given by the curves of Fig. 24. Also indicated are the recommended temperature limits for each kind of couple. The thermocouple voltage is measured by means of a millivoltmeter (deflection type) or potentiometer (null-balance type). Completion of the thermocouple circuit through the instrument immediately introduces one or more additional junctions. Common practice is to connect the thermocouple (hot junction) to the instrument with special lead wire (which may be of the same materials as the thermocouple itself). This assures that the **cold junction** will be inside the instrument case, where compensation can be effectively applied. A **deflection-type instrument** is shown in Fig. 25, where the millivoltmeter is similar in design to that in Fig. 39. A bimetal strip provides a zero shift of the galvanometer hairspring to compensate for changes in cold-junction temperature. Accordingly, the instrument scale is calibrated directly in thermocouple temperature. In the **potentiometer instrument,** the thermocouple voltage is compared with the voltage of a precisely calibrated potentiometer (slide-wire). Any difference between the two is detected by means of a sensitive electronic amplifier or galvanometer. The error signal drives a servomotor which repositions the slide-wire contactor until balance is achieved. The slide-wire is mechanically linked to the indicator or recording pen. Cold-junction compensation is achieved by means of a temperature-sensitive resistor placed into the potentiometer circuit. The voltage applied across the potentiometer is checked periodically against a standard cell and maintained constant by means of a self-standardizing circuit. (See also p. 15–42.)

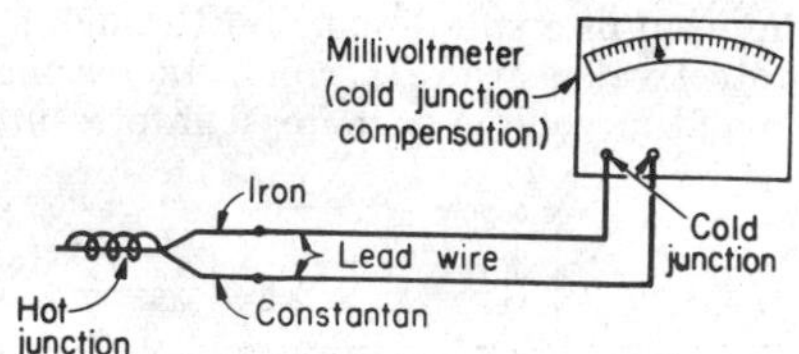

Fig. 25. Temperature measurement with thermocouple and millivoltmeter.

The **resistance thermometer** employs the same instrument described above, omitting the cold-junction compensation and the standardization circuit. The resistance bulb forms one leg of a Wheatstone bridge (Fig. 26), the slide-wire forming the opposite leg. An upset of the balance of the circuit causes a current flow through the amplifier, which actuates the motor to drive the slide-wire to a new position of balance. The relationship at balance is $R_T = (R_1/R_2)(R_s + R_3 + R_4)$, where R is the resistance of the designated arm of the bridge. (See also p. 15–42.)

The resistance bulb consists of a copper or platinum wire coil sealed in a protective metal tube. The **thermistor** has a very large temperature coefficient of resistance and may be substituted in low-accuracy, low-cost applications.

By use of a **selector switch,** any number of temperatures may be measured with the same instrument. The switch connects in order each thermocouple (or resistance bulb) to the potentiometer (or bridge circuit). When balance is achieved, the recorder prints the temperature value, then the switch advances on to the next position.

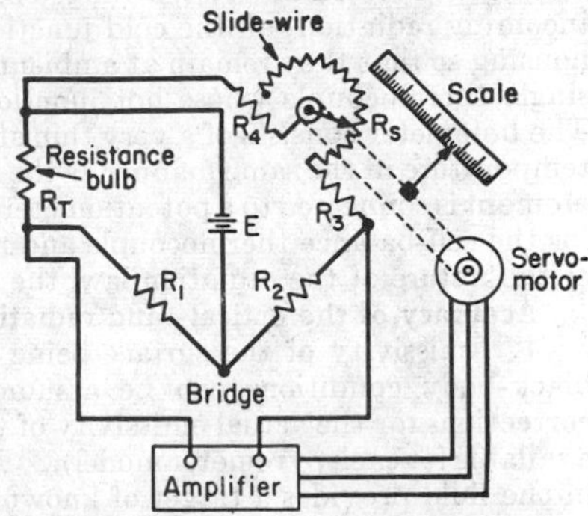

Fig. 26. Resistance thermometer with self-balance potentiometer recorder.

Optical pyrometers are applied to high-temperature measurement (in the range 1000 to 5000 F). One type is shown in Fig. 27. The surface whose temperature is to be measured (target) is focused by the lens onto the filament of a calibrated tungsten lamp. The light intensity of the filament is kept constant by maintaining a constant current flow. The intensity of the target image is adjusted by positioning the optical wedge until the image intensity appears exactly equal to that of the filament. A scale attached to the wedge is calibrated directly in temperature. The red filter is employed so that the comparison is made at a specific wave length (color) of light to make the calibration more reproducible. In another type of optical pyrometer, comparison is made by adjusting the current through the filament of the standard lamp. Here, an ammeter in series is calibrated to read temperature directly. **Automatic operation** may be had by comparing filament with image intensities with a pair of photoelectric cells

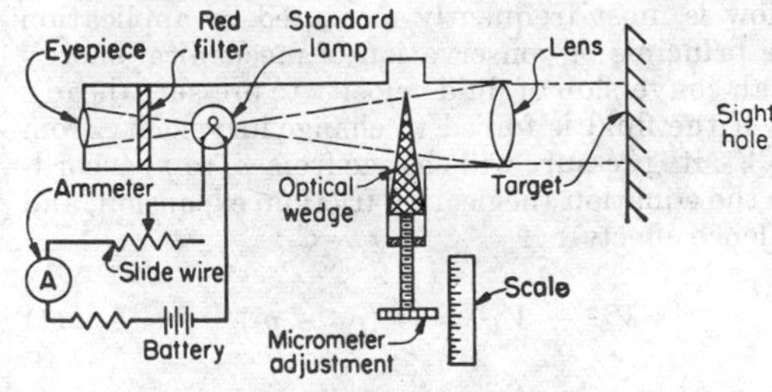

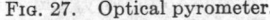

Fig. 27. Optical pyrometer.

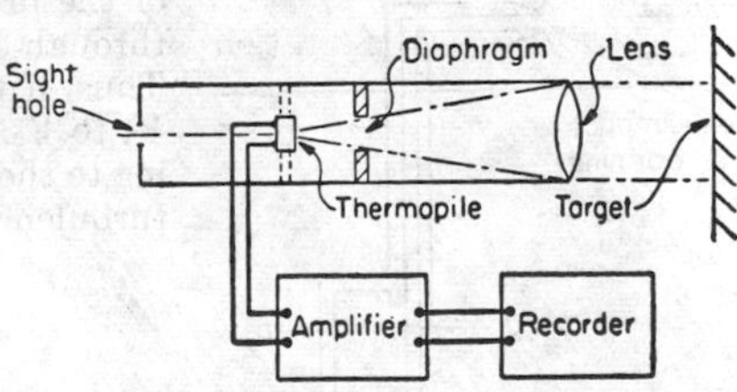

Fig. 28. Radiation pyrometer.

arranged in a bridge network. A difference in intensity produces a voltage, which is amplified to drive the slide-wire or optical wedge in the direction to restore zero difference.

The **radiation pyrometer** is normally applied to temperature measurements above 1000 F. Basically, there is no upper limit; however, the lower limit is determined by the sensitivity and cold-junction compensation of the instrument. It has been used down to almost room temperature. A common type of radiation receiver is shown in Fig. 28. A lens focuses the radiation onto a thermal sensing element. The temperature rise of this element depends on the total radiation received and the conduction of heat away from the element. The radiation relates to the temperature of the target; the conduction depends on the temperature of the pyrometer housing. In normal applications the latter factor is not very great; however, for improved accuracy a compensating coil is added to the circuit. The sensing element may be a thermopile, vacuum thermocouple, or bolometer. The **thermopile** consists of a number of thermocouples connected in series, arranged so that all the hot junctions lie in the field of the incoming radiation; all the cold junctions are in thermal contact with the pyrometer housing so that they remain at ambient temperature. The **vacuum thermocouple** is a single thermocouple whose hot junction is enclosed in an evacuated glass envelope. The **bolometer** consists of a very thin strip of nickel or platinum foil which responds to temperature in the same manner as the resistance thermometer. The **thermal sensing element** is connected to a potentiometer or bridge network of the same type as described for the self-balance thermocouple and resistance-thermometer instruments. Because of the nature of the radiation law, the scale is non-linear.

Accuracy of the optical- and radiation-type pyrometers depends on:

1. Emissivity of the surface being sighted on. For closed furnace applications, black-body conditions can be assumed (emissivity = 1). For other applications corrections for the actual emissivity of the surface must be made (correction tables are available for each pyrometer model). For measuring hot fluids, a target tube immersed in the fluid provides a target of known emissivity.
2. Radiation absorption between target and instrument. Smoke, gases, and glass lenses absorb some of the radiation and reduce the incoming signal. Use of an enclosed (or purged) target tube or direct calibration will correct this.
3. Focusing of the target on the sensing element.

MEASUREMENT OF FLUID FLOW RATE

(See also pp. 3–66 to 3–71 and pp. 4–60 to 4–68)

Flow is expressed in volumetric or weight units per unit time. Thus, gases are generally measured in cubic feet per minute (or hour), steam in pounds per hour, liquid in gallons per minute (or hour). Conversion between volumetric flow Q and weight flow W is given by the expression $W = K\rho Q$, where ρ = density of the fluid, and K is a constant dependent on the units of W, Q, and ρ. Flow rate may be measured directly by attaching a rate device to a volumetric meter of the types previously described [*e.g.*, a tachometer connected to the rotating shaft of the nutating-disk meter (Fig. 13)].

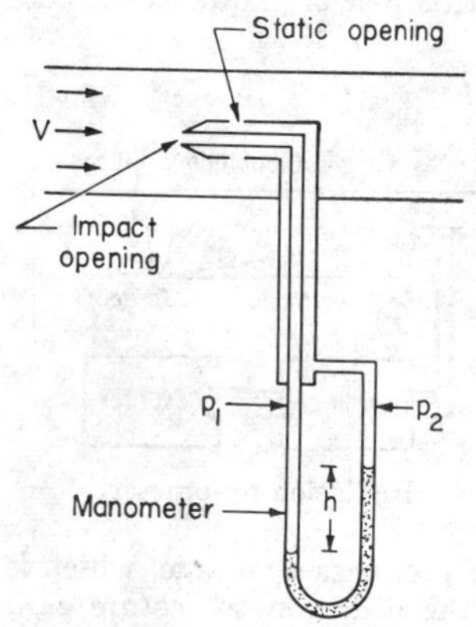

Fig. 29. Pitot tube.

Flow is most frequently measured by application of the principle of conservation of mechanical energy through conversion of fluid velocity to pressure (head). Thus, if the fluid is forced to change its velocity from V_1 to V_2, its pressure will change from p_1 to p_2 according to the equation (neglecting friction, expansion, and turbulence effects):

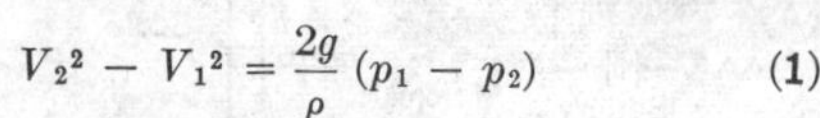

$$V_2^2 - V_1^2 = \frac{2g}{\rho}(p_1 - p_2) \tag{1}$$

where g = acceleration due to gravity, and ρ = fluid density.

Local velocity is measured with the **pitot tube** (Fig. 29), consisting of two concentric tubes connected across a differential pressure-measuring device. The tubes extend into the flow stream such that the L section is parallel to the direction of flow. The inner tube measures the impact pressure or velocity head. The outer tube has openings on the side (normal to the flow stream) so that it responds to the static pressure. Applying Eq. (**1**) and noting that, for a particle of fluid striking the impact opening, $V_1 = 0$.

$$V_2 = C_p\left[\frac{2g(p_1 - p_2)}{\rho}\right]^{1/2} = C_p\left[\frac{2g(\rho_m - \rho)h}{\rho}\right]^{1/2}$$

where h is the manometer reading, ρ_m = density of the manometer fluid, and C_p is the pitot-tube coefficient. The coefficient C_p corrects for friction and turbulence effects and is determined by calibration. For the type illustrated, the value of C_p ranges from 0.98 to 1.02. The **total volumetric flow** Q is obtained by integrating the local velocity over the entire area of the flow cross section. Thus, if V is the average velocity and A is the area, then $Q = AV$.

The **velocity distribution** depends on the flow rate and the shape of the flow channel. Hence, the average velocity is best determined by taking readings at selected points over the cross section, Table 1. When the pitot tube is preceded by a long section of straight pipe (over 50 pipe diameters) the average velocity runs normally about 0.83 of the velocity at the center of the pipe.

Table 1. Layout Measurements for Pitot-tube Traverses

Number of equal areas	Total number of readings	Distances from center of pipe to point of reading, percent of pipe diameter					
3	12	20.4	35.3	45.5			
4	16	17.7	30.5	39.4	46.6		
5	20	15.5	27.2	35.3	41.7	47.4	
6	24	14.5	25.0	32.3	38.2	43.3	47.9

Average flow rate is more directly measured by inserting a calibrated restriction in the flow line, such as the **Venturi tube** (Fig. 30). Since the volumetric flow is the same in both the pipe and the throat, the average velocity of the fluid must increase as it passes through the throat (continuity principle). Thus, $Q = A_1V_1 = A_2V_2$, where subscripts 1 and 2 refer to the pipe and throat, respectively. The volumetric flow equation in terms of the pressure drop $(p_1 - p_2)$ then becomes,

$$Q = A_1\beta^2C_DY\left[\frac{2g(p_1 - p_2)}{(1 - \beta^4)\rho}\right]^{1/2} \qquad \textbf{(2)}$$

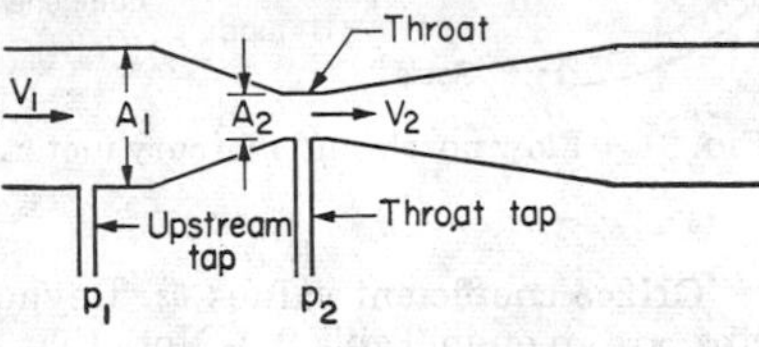

FIG. 30. Venturi tube.

where $A_1 = \pi D_1^2/4$ (pipe cross-sectional area), $\beta = d_2/d_1$ (ratio of throat to pipe diameter), C_D = discharge coefficient, Y = compressibility factor, ρ = density of the fluid. C_D depends on the nature of the flow and design of the Venturi (normal range 0.98 to 0.99). Y is unity for liquid flow and for gas or steam flow where the pressure drop is not more than 1 to 2 percent of the static pressure.

Flow nozzles (Fig. 31) are modifications of the Venturi used because of their lower cost or ease of installation. In general, the discharge coefficient approaches that of the Venturi; however, accurate values must be determined by test or obtained from the manufacturer.

The cheapest and most easily applied (hence, the most common) flow-sensing element is the **orifice** (Fig. 32). This is a thin metal plate with a sharp-edged hole accurately machined. The plate is installed between the flanges of the pipe so that (usually) the hole is concentric with the pipe. The orifice causes the flow lines to converge to much the same shape as the Venturi of Fig. 30. The flow stream continues to converge a short distance downstream from the orifice plate, then diverges back to the full pipe diameter. The point of smallest flow cross section is termed the **vena contracta;** this corresponds therefore to the point of lowest pressure.

A differential-pressure device is connected across pressure taps installed upstream and downstream from the orifice. Different **tap locations** are employed: flange taps are located 1 in. from each side of the orifice plate and are installed right in the flange; vena-contracta taps have the upstream tap 1 pipe diameter from the plate and the downstream tap at the vena contracta; pipe taps are located 2.5 and 8.0 pipe diameters upstream and downstream from the orifice, respectively.

Equation (**2**) applies to flow through orifices if β is the ratio of orifice diameter to pipe diameter and C_D is the flow coefficient of the orifice. The value of C_D depends on

β, the kind of taps used, and the Reynolds number. The Reynolds number, R, is a dimensionless number which characterizes the flow and is given by the formula (in consistent units), $R = \rho Vd/\mu$, where d = orifice diameter, V = velocity through the orifice, ρ = fluid density, and μ = absolute fluid viscosity. The **expansion factor** for orifices with flange or vena-contracta taps is $Y = 1 - (0.41 + 0.35\rho^4)(p_1 - p_2)/p_1k$, where p_1 and p_2 are upstream and downstream pressures, respectively, and k = specific heat ratio of the fluid (at 212 F and 1 atm pressure, $k_{air} = 1.40$, $k_{steam} = 1.32$).

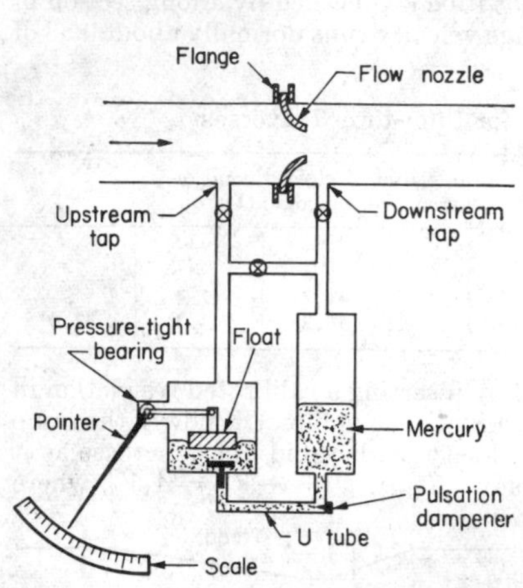

FIG. 31. Flow nozzle and mercury meter.

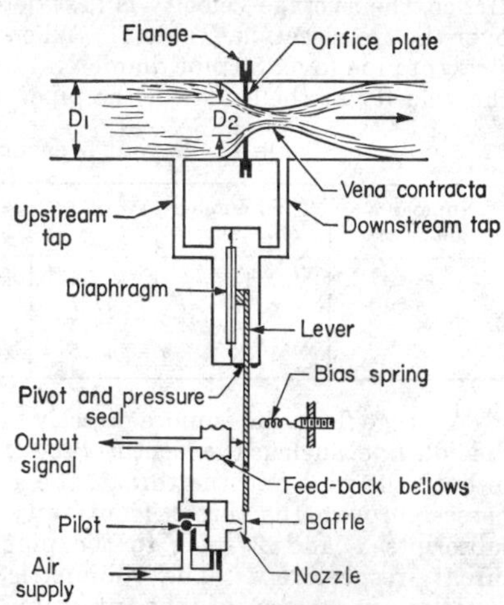

FIG. 32. Orifice plate and diaphragm-type meter.

Orifice coefficient values *vs.* Reynolds number, for an orifice with vena-contracta taps, are given in Table 2. Note that C_D ranges from 0.60 to 0.61 for most conditions. Values for flange taps are similar to those given in the table except for large orifice ratios. The values for pipe taps, however, deviate considerably (see ASME, "Fluid Meters.")

Table 2. Orifice Flow Coefficients vs. Reynolds Number for Vena-contracta Taps

Pipe size, in.	Orifice ratio, d_1/d_2	Reynolds number						
		15,000	25,000	50,000	100,000	250,000	500,000	1,000,000
2	0.1	0.615	0.611	0.606	0.603			
4	0.1	0.606	0.603	0.599	0.597			
6–10	0.1	0.602	0.600	0.596	0.594			
2	0.2	0.607	0.604	0.600	0.598			
4–10	0.2	0.603	0.600	0.598	0.596			
2–10	0.3	0.606	0.603	0.601	0.599	0.597	0.596	0.596
2–10	0.4	0.611	0.607	0.605	0.603	0.601	0.600	0.600
2–10	0.5	.....	.....	0.610	0.607	0.605	0.604	0.603
2–10	0.6	.....	...	0.614	0.611	0.609	0.608	0.607
2–10	0.7	.....	.....	.....	0.616	0.612	0.610	0.609

The tabulated orifice coefficients apply only for **straight pipe** upstream and downstream from the orifice. In most cases, satisfactory results are obtained if there are no fittings closer than 25 pipe diameters upstream and 5 diameters downstream from the orifice. The upstream limitation can be reduced a bit by employing **straightening vanes.** Reciprocating pumps in the line may introduce serious errors and require special efforts for their correction.

A wide variety of differential pressure meters is available for measuring the orifice (or other primary element) pressure drop (see pp. 16–11 and 16–19). The most frequently used types are illustrated in Figs. 31 and 32.

The **mercury meter** (Fig. 31) is basically a U-tube manometer [Fig. 15(a)] with the addition of a metal float which communicates to a pen or pointer assembly the position of the mercury level. The range of the meter is determined by the ratio of the diameters of the two manometer chambers. A needle valve in the U tube acts to dampen flow fluctuations to yield a smooth flow record.

Figure 32 shows the **diaphragm, or "dry," meter.** The orifice differential acts across a metal or rubber diaphragm, generating a force which tends to rotate the lever clockwise, moving the baffle toward the nozzle. This increases the nozzle back pressure, which acts on the pilot diaphragm to open the air supply port and increase the output pressure. This increases the force exerted by the feedback bellows, which generates a force opposing the motion of the main diaphragm. Equilibrium is reached when a change in orifice differential is exactly balanced by a proportionate change in output pressure. Often a damping device in the form of a simple oil dashpot is attached to the lever to reduce output fluctuations.

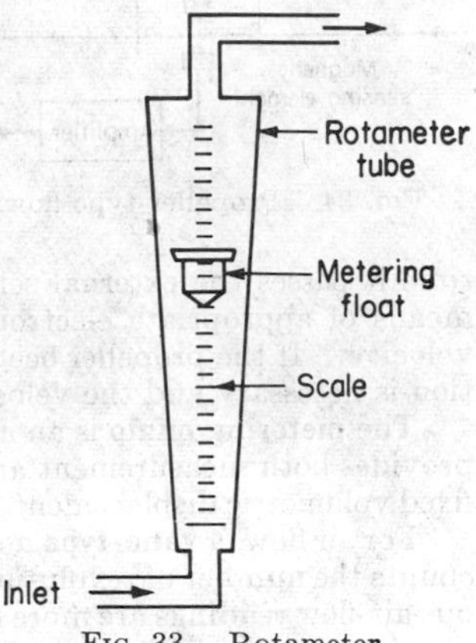

FIG. 33. Rotameter.

The flowmeter normally exhibits a square-root flow calibration [see Eq. (**2**)]. Some meters are designed to take out the square root by use of **cams, characterized floats or displacers (Ledoux bell),** or devices which describe a square-root behavior. These methods do not improve accuracy or performance but merely provide the convenience of a linear scale.

The meters described thus far are termed **"variable-head"** because the pressure drop varies with the flow, orifice ratio being fixed. In contrast, the **"variable-area"** meter maintains a constant pressure differential but varies the orifice area with flow.

The **rotameter** (Fig. 33) consists of a float positioned inside a tapered tube by action of the fluid flowing up through the tube. The flow restriction is now the annular area between the float and the tube (area increases as the float rises). The pressure differential is fixed, determined by the weight of the float and the buoyant forces. To satisfy Eq. (**2**) then, the annular area (hence the float level) must increase with flow rate. Thus the rotameter may be calibrated for direct flow reading by etching an appropriate scale on the surface of the glass tube. The calibration depends on the float dimensions, tube taper, and fluid properties. The equation for volumetric flow is

$$Q = C_R(A_T - A_F)\left[\frac{2gV_F}{\rho A_F}(\rho_F - \rho)\right]^{1/2}$$

where A_T = cross-sectional area of the tube (at the float position), A_F = effective float area, V_F = float volume, ρ_F = float density, ρ = fluid density, and C_R = rotameter coefficient (usually between 0.6 and 0.8). The coefficient varies with the fluid viscosity; however, special float designs are available which are relatively insensitive to viscosity effects. Also, fluid density compensation can be obtained.

The **rotameter reading may be transmitted** for recording and control purposes by affixing to the float a stem which connects to an armature or permanent magnet. The armature forms part of an inductance bridge whose signal is amplified electronically to drive a pen-positioning motor. For pneumatic transmission, the magnet provides magnetic coupling to a pneumatic motion transmitter external to the rotameter tube. This generates an air pressure proportional to the height of the float.

The **area meter** is similar to the rotameter in operation. Flow area is varied by motion of a piston in a straight cylinder with openings cut into the wall. The piston position is transmitted as above by an armature and inductance bridge circuit.

Primary elements for **flow in open channels** usually employ **weirs** or **open nozzles** to restrict the flow. Weir designs include the rectangular slot; the V notch; and for a linear-flow characteristic, the parabolically shaped weir (Sutro weir). The flow rate is determined from the height of the liquid surface relative to the base of the weir. This height is measured by a liquid-level device, usually float-actuated. A still well (float chamber or open standpipe) connected to the bottom of the weir or the nozzle tap is used to avoid errors in float displacement due to the motion of the flowing fluid or to the build-up of solids. (See also pp. 3–70 and 3–71.)

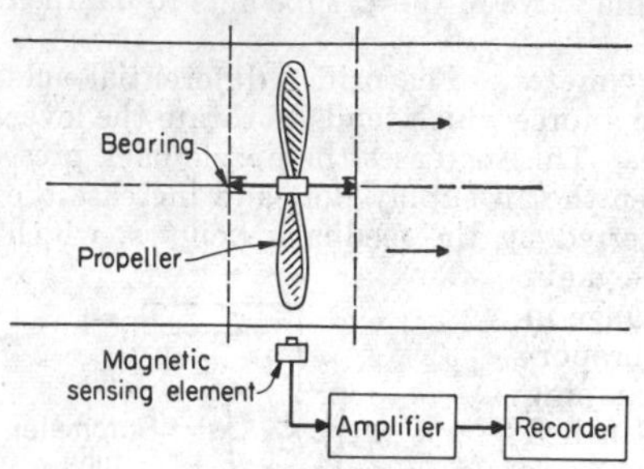

FIG. 34. Propeller-type flowmeter.

There are many other kinds of flow instruments which serve special purposes of accuracy, response, or application. The **propeller type** (Fig. 34) responds linearly to the average velocity in the path of the propeller, assuming negligible friction. The propeller may be mechanically geared to a tachometer to indicate flow rate and to a counter to show total quantity flow. The magnetic pickup (Fig. 34) minimizes friction errors. A small magnet in the tip of the propeller generates an electrical pulse every time it passes the external sensing element. The frequency of pulses (measured by means of appropriate electronic circuitry) is then proportional to the local stream velocity. If the propeller occupies only part of the flow stream, an individual calibration is necessary and the velocity distribution must remain constant.

The **metering pump** is an accurately calibrated positive displacement pump which provides both measurement and control of fluid-flow rate. The pump may be either fixed volumetric displacement–variable speed or constant speed–variable displacement.

For air flow, a **vane-type meter (anemometer)** is often used. A mechanical counter counts the number of revolutions of the vane shaft over a timed interval. Instantaneous air-flow readings are more readily obtained with the **hot-wire anemometer.** Here, a resistance wire heated by an electric current is placed in the flow stream. The temperature of the wire depends on the current and the rate at which heat is conducted away from it. This latter factor is related to the thermal properties of the air and its velocity past the wire. Air flow can be measured in terms of (1) the current through the wire to maintain a fixed temperature, (2) temperature of the wire for a fixed current, or (3) temperature rise of the air passing the wire for fixed current. The wire temperature is readily measured in terms of its resistance. The anemometer must be specially calibrated for the application.

The **electromagnetic flowmeter** is gaining importance because it has no moving parts and does not require any insertions in the flow stream. It is based on the voltage induced by the flow of charged particles of the fluid past a strong magnetic field.

Flowmeters measure rate of flow. To measure the total quantity of fluid flowing during a specified interval of time, the flow rate must be integrated over that interval. The integration may be done manually by estimating from the chart record the hourly flow averages or by measuring the area under the flow curve with a special square-root planimeter (p. 16–9). **Mechanical integrators** use a constant-speed motor to rotate a counter. A cam converts the square-root meter reading to a linear displacement such that the fraction of time that the motor is engaged to the counter is proportional to the flow rate, resulting in a counter reading proportional to the integrated flow. **Electrical integrators** are similar in principle to the watthour meter in that the speed of the integrating motor is made proportional to the magnitude of the flow signal (see p. 15–38).

POWER MEASUREMENT

Power is defined as the rate of doing work. Common units are the horsepower and the kilowatt: 1 hp = 33,000 ft-lb per min. = 0.746 kw. The power input to a rotating machine in horsepower $= 2\pi nT/33{,}000$, where n = rpm of the input shaft and T =

input torque, ft-lb. The same equation applies to the power output of an engine or motor, where n and T refer to the output shaft. Mechanical power-measuring devices (**dynamometers**) are of two types: (1) those absorbing the power and dissipating it as heat and (2) those transmitting the measured power. As indicated by the above equation, two measurements are involved: shaft speed and torque. The speed is measured directly by means of a tachometer. Torque is usually measured by balancing against weights applied to a fixed lever arm; however, other force measuring methods are also used. In the **transmission dynamometer,** the torque is measured by means of strain-gage elements bonded to the transmission shaft.

There are several kinds of **absorption dynamometers.** The **Prony brake** applies a friction load to the output shaft by means of wood blocks, flexible band, or other friction surface. The **fan brake** absorbs power by "fan" action of rotating plates on surrounding air. The **water brake** acts as an inefficient centrifugal pump to convert mechanical energy into heat. The pump casing is mounted on antifriction bearings so that the developed turning moment can be measured. In the **magnetic-drag** or **eddy-current brake,** rotation of a metal disk in a magnetic field induces eddy currents in the disk which dissipate as heat. The field assembly is mounted in bearings in order to measure the torque.

One type of **Prony brake** is illustrated in Fig. 35. The torque developed is given by $L(W - W_0)$, where L is the length of the brake arm, ft; W and W_0 are the scale loads with the brake operating and with the brake free, respectively. The brake horsepower then equals $2\pi nL(W - W_0)/33{,}000$, where n is shaft speed, rpm.

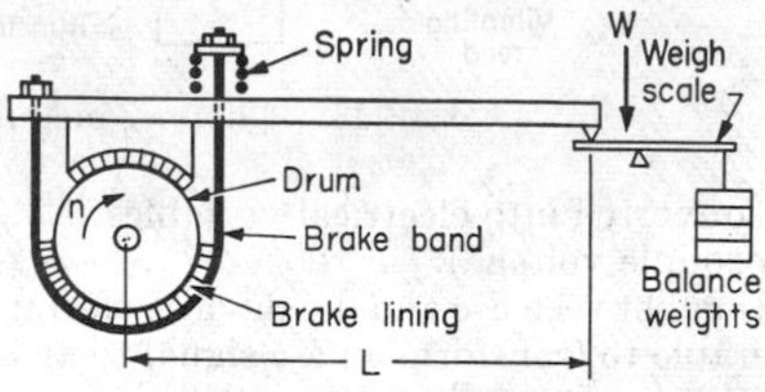

FIG. 35. Prony brake.

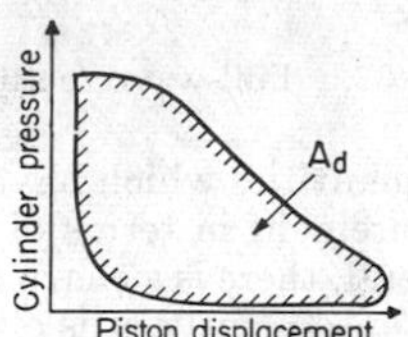

FIG. 36. Indicator diagram.

In addition to eddy-current brakes, **electric dynamometers** include calibrated generators and motors and cradle-mounted generators and motors. In calibrated machines, the efficiency is determined over a range of operating conditions and plotted. Mechanical power measurements may then be made by measuring the electrical power input (or output) to the machine. In the electric-cradle dynamometer, the motor or generator stator is mounted in trunnion bearings so that the torque may be measured by suitable scales.

The **engine indicator** is a device for plotting cylinder pressure as a function of piston (or volume) displacement. The resulting p-v diagram (Fig. 36) provides both a measure of the work done in a reciprocating engine, pump, or compressor and a means for analyzing its performance (see pp. 4–27, 4–30, 9–54, 9–104, 14–9, 14–44). If A_d is the area inside the closed curve drawn by the indicator, then the indicated horsepower for the cylinder under test $= KnA_pA_d$ where K is a proportionality factor determined by the scale factors of the indicator diagram, n = engine rpm, A_p = piston area.

The chart is mounted on a drum which rotates through an angle proportional to the piston displacement (through the agency of an appropriate **reducing motion**). A pen or stylus deflects on a line parallel to the axis of the drum and proportional to the magnitude of the cylinder pressure. The pressure measurement is commonly made by means of a lightweight, well-fitted, lubricated piston acting against a calibrated spring. The cylinder pressure acting on the underside of the indicator piston produces a compression of the spring proportional to the pressure. The resulting displacement is transmitted to the pen through a mechanical linkage. In order to avoid significant dynamic error, the natural frequency of the measuring system should be at least 10 times the rpm of the engine.

For **high-speed engines,** other techniques are required for generating the indicator diagram. **Microindicators** trace very small diagrams, which must be greatly magnified for analysis. **Optical indicators** obtain magnification by optical systems and record photographically. For example, the small motion of a pressure diaphragm may be transmitted to a mirror to deflect a beam of light proportional to the measured pressure. **Electrical indicators** employ strain gages, capacitance, or impedance elements in appropriate bridge circuits to measure the dynamic pressure signal. The diagram is usually recorded on an oscillograph properly synchronized to the engine rotation. **Very high speed indicators** utilize the piezoelectric crystal as the pressure-responsive element.

ELECTRICAL MEASUREMENTS

(See also pp. 15–34 to 15–43)

Electrical measurements serve two purposes: (1) to measure the electrical quantities themselves (*e.g.,* line voltage, power consumption, etc.) and (2) to measure other physical quantities which have been converted into electrical variables (*e.g.,* temperature measurement in terms of thermocouple voltage).

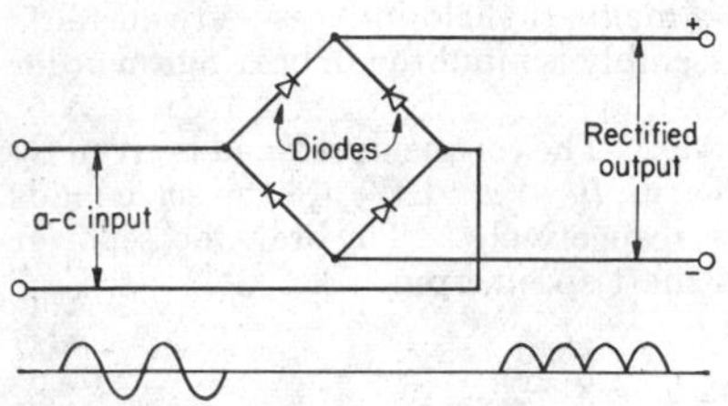

Fig. 37. Full-wave rectifier.

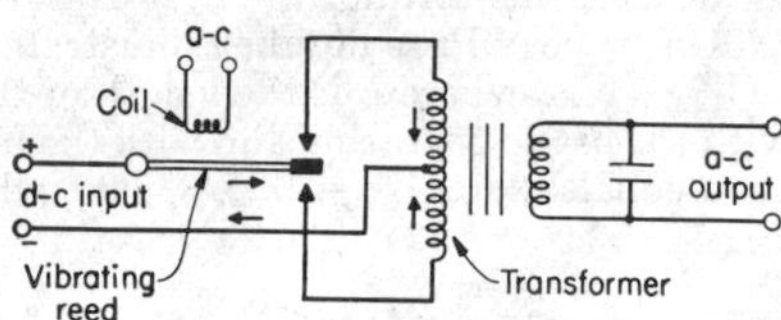

Fig. 38. Chopper modulator.

In general, there is a sharp distinction between a-c and d-c devices used in measurements. Consequently, it is often desirable to transform an a-c signal to an equivalent d-c value, and vice versa. An a-c signal is converted to d-c (rectified) by use of **selenium rectifiers, silicon or germanium diodes, or electron-tube diodes.** Full-wave rectification is accomplished by the **diode bridge,** shown in Fig. 37. The rectified signal may be passed through one or more low-pass filter stages to smooth the wave form to its average value. Similarly, there are many ways of modulating a d-c signal (converting it to alternating current). The most common method used in instrument applications is the so-called **chopper,** or **vibrator** (Fig. 38). An alternating voltage applied to the chopper coil causes the reed to vibrate at the same frequency (usually 60 or 400 cycles). The reed acts as the common terminal of a single-pole double-throw relay which alternates the direction of current flow through the primary coil of the transformer. This induces an alternating voltage (at line frequency) in the secondary coil of the transformer. The resulting output is proportional to the input signal and either in phase or 180 deg out of phase with the voltage on the chopper coil, depending on the input polarity.

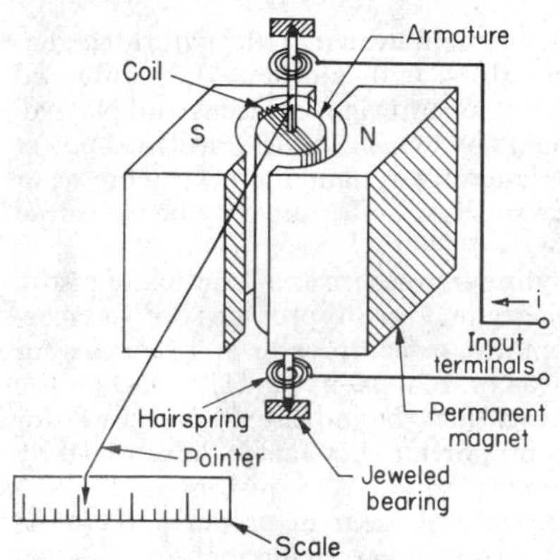

Fig. 39. D'Arsonval galvanometer.

The **galvanometer** (Fig. 39) is the most common sensing device employed in d-c measurement. The input signal is applied across a coil mounted in jeweled bearings so that it is free to rotate between the poles of a permanent magnet. Current in the coil produces a magnetic moment which tends to rotate the coil. The rotation is limited, however, by the restraining torque of the hairsprings. The resulting deflection of the coil θ is proportional to the current I:

$$\theta = \frac{NBWL}{K} I$$

where N = number of turns in the coil; W, L = coil width and length, respectively; B = magnetic field intensity; K = spring constant of the hairsprings. Galvanometer deflection is indicated by a balanced pointer attached to the coil. In very sensitive elements, the pointer is replaced by a mirror reflecting a spot of light onto a ground-glass scale; the bearings and hairspring are replaced by a torsion-wire suspension.

The galvanometer can be converted into a **d-c voltmeter, ammeter, or ohmmeter** by application of Ohm's law, $IR = E$, where I = current, amperes; E = electrical potential, volts; and R = resistance, ohms.

For a **voltmeter,** a fixed resistance R is placed in series with the galvanometer [Fig. 40(*a*)]. The current i through the galvanometer is proportional to the applied voltage E: $i = E/(r + R)$, where r = coil resistance. Different voltage ranges are obtained by changing the series resistance.

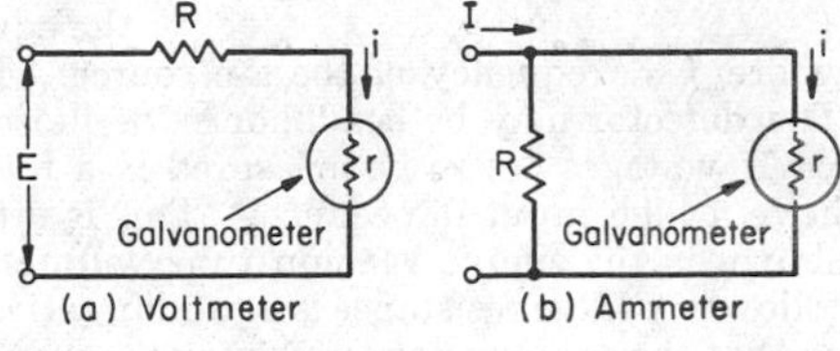

FIG. 40

An **ammeter** is produced by placing the resistance in parallel with the galvanometer [Fig. 40(*b*)]. The current then divides between the galvanometer coil and the resistor in inverse ratio to their resistance values (r and R, respectively), thus: $i = IR/(r + R)$, where i = current through the coil and I = total current to be measured. Different current ranges are obtained by using different shunt resistances.

The common **ohmmeter** consists of a battery, adjustable rheostat, and ammeter in series with the resistance to be measured. The rheostat is adjusted to give zero reading with the resistance terminals short-circuited. The specially calibrated scale then gives the correct reading of the unknown resistor.

Alternating current and voltage must be measured by special means. A d-c instrument with a rectifier input is commonly used in applications requiring high input impedance and wide frequency range. For precise measurement at power-line frequencies, the electrodynamic instrument is used. This is similar to the galvanometer except that the permanent magnet is replaced by an electromagnet. The movable coil and field coils are connected in series; hence they respond simultaneously to the same current and voltage alternations. The pointer deflection is proportional to the square of the input signal. The moving-iron-type instruments consist of a soft-iron vane or armature which moves in response to current flowing through a stationary coil. The pointer is attached to the iron to indicate the deflection on a calibrated non-linear scale. For measuring at very high frequencies, the **thermocouple voltmeter or ammeter** is used. This is based on the heating effect of the current passing through a fixed resistance R. Heat is liberated at the rate of E^2/R or I^2R watts.

Electrical power is the product of the current through the load and the voltage across the load. Thus it can be simply measured using a voltmeter and ammeter. Power is directly indicated by the wattmeter, which is similar to the electrodynamic instrument described above. Here the field coils are connected in series with the load, and the movable coil is connected across the load (to measure its voltage). The deflection of the movable coil is then proportional to the effective load power.

Precise voltage measurement (alternating or direct current) may be made by balancing the unknown voltage against a measured fraction of a known reference voltage with a **potentiometer** (Fig. 9). Balance is indicated by means of a sensitive current dectector placed in series with the unknown voltage. The potentiometer is calibrated for angular position *vs.* fractional voltage output. Accuracies to 0.05 percent are attainable, dependent on the linearity of the potentiometer and the accuracy of the reference source. The reference standard may be a Weston standard cell or a regulated voltage supply (based on diode characteristics). The balance detector may be a galvanometer or electronic amplifier.

Precise resistance measurements are made with a **Wheatstone bridge** or modification thereof (see Fig. 26). When the bridge is in balance, the resistances are in simple ratio to each other. Thus, if three of the resistances are known, a fourth can be determined. Since the bridge can be excited with alternating as well as direct current, the same principle may be employed for measuring capacitance, inductance, or a-c impedance. The **impedance bridge** is used to measure resistance, capacitance, and inductance. Various circuit elements are switched into the bridge, depending on the type and range of measurement. A circuit for capacitance measurement, for example, appears in Fig. 41. Both adjustable resistor R and inductor L are varied until the detector indicates a minimum signal. Then L and C are in series resonance and are related by the equation (assuming $R_1 = R_2$): $C = 1/(2\pi f)^2 L$, where f = frequency of the a-c source. If L is calibrated, C may be read directly. The detector may be headphones, oscilloscope, or electronic amplifier.

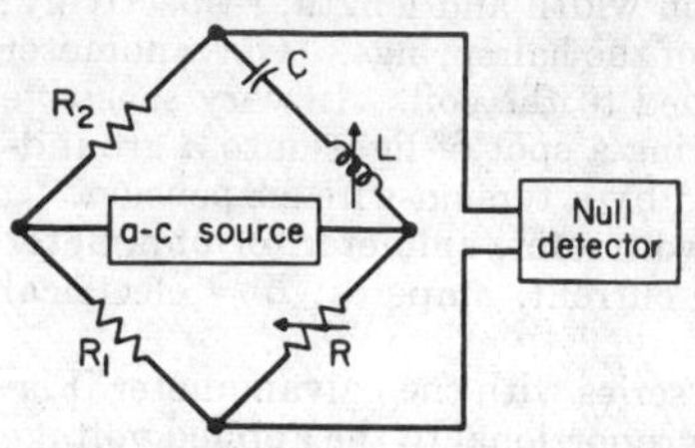

FIG. 41. Impedance bridge.

If voltages are to be measured in a high-impedance circuit, the instrument must have a high input impedance. This is often obtained by use of a **cathode follower,** shown in the simple **vacuum-tube voltmeter** application in Fig. 42. In the cathode follower, a large resistance is placed in series with the cathode, and the tube is operated so that the cathode voltage is very nearly that of the grid. The meter responds to the cathode voltage, which is essentially isolated from the input signal on the grid. Thus, the vacuum-tube voltmeter presents an impedance of many megohms to the load circuit. The rectifier and filter in the circuit are for a-c inputs.

The **cathode-ray oscilloscope** (Fig. 43) is an extremely useful and versatile device characterized by high input impedance and wide frequency range. An electron beam is focused on the phosphor-coated face of the cathode-ray tube, producing a visible spot

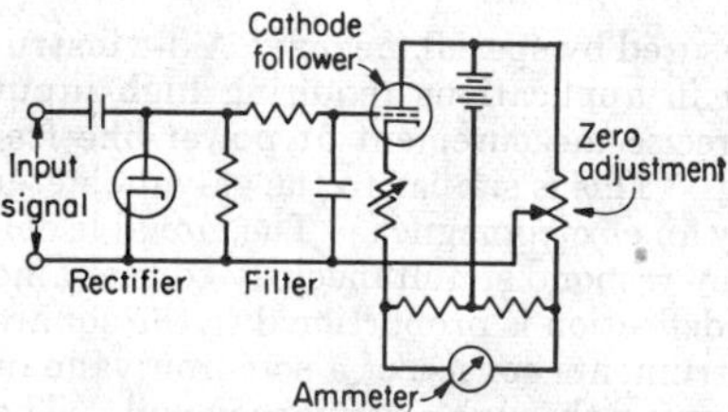

FIG. 42. Vacuum-tube voltmeter.

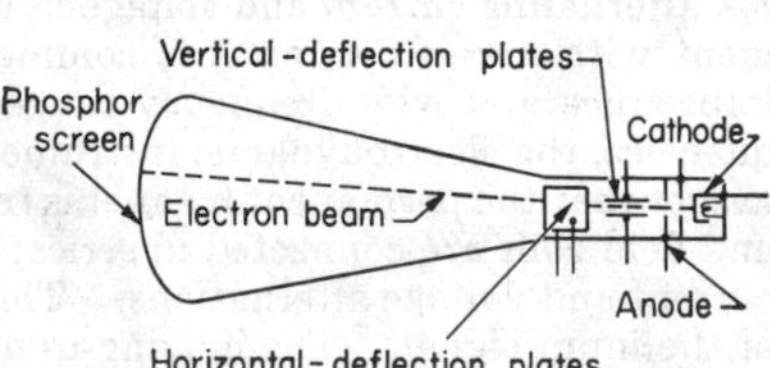

FIG. 43. Cathode-ray tube.

of light at the point of impingement. The beam is deflected by applying voltages to vertical and horizontal deflector plates. Thus, the relationship between two varying voltages can be observed by applying them to the vertical and horizontal plates, respectively. Most frequently, a saw-tooth voltage of constant period is applied to the horizontal deflection plates so that the dynamic (time-varying) characteristics of a signal may be observed. Electronic amplifiers are provided for both horizontal and vertical inputs. The instrument is used as a null indicator, to measure a-c voltage, frequency, phase relationships, and, in general, for analyzing electronic systems and for trouble shooting. Many auxiliary components, such as audio oscillators, regulated power supplies, decade resistance and capacitance standards, d-c amplifier and oscillographic recorders, find frequent application.

VELOCITY AND ACCELERATION MEASUREMENT

Velocity or speed is the time rate of change of displacement. Consequently, if the displacement measuring device provides an output signal which is a continuous (and smooth) function of time, the velocity may be measured by **differentiating** this signal either graphically or by use of a differentiating circuit. The accuracy may be very limited by noise (high-frequency fluctuations), however. More commonly, the output of an accelerometer is integrated to yield the velocity of the moving member. **Average speed** over a time interval may be determined by measuring the time required for the moving body to pass two fixed points a known distance apart. Here photoelectric or other rapid sensing devices may be used to trigger the "start" and "stop" of the timer. **Rotational speed** may be similarly measured by counting the number of rotations in a fixed time interval; a magnet attached to the rotating member is often used to provide the count signal.

The **tachometer** provides a direct measure of angular velocity. It is essentially a small permanent-magnet-type generator coupled to the rotating element; the voltage induced in the armature coil is directly proportional to the speed. The principle is also extended to rectilinear motions (restricted to small displacements) by using a straight coil moving in a fixed magnetic field.

Angular velocity may also be measured by **centrifugal force** devices (fly-ball governor). The force may be balanced against a spring with the resulting deflection calibrated in terms of the shaft speed. Alternatively, the force may be balanced against the air pressure generated by a pneumatic nozzle-baffle assembly (similar to Fig. 23).

Accelerometers measure the acceleration or time rate of change of velocity. These are commonly based on Newton's law $F = Ma$, where F is the force acting on a fixed mass M undergoing an acceleration a, all in consistent units. Either the force F may be measured directly (see p. 16–10), or the mass may be restrained by a spring and the resulting displacement measured (see pp. 16–7, 16–8).

PHYSICAL AND CHEMICAL PROPERTIES MEASUREMENT

Physical and chemical measurements are important in the control of product quality and composition. In the case of manufactured items, such properties as color, hardness, surface, roughness, etc., are of interest. Color is measured by means of a **colorimeter,** which provides comparison with color standards, or by means of a **spectrophotometer,** which analyzes the color spectrum. The **Brinell and Rockwell testers** measure surface hardness in terms of the depth of penetration of a hardened steel ball or special stylus. Testing machines with **strain-gage** elements provide measurement of the strength and elastic properties of materials. **Profilometers** are used to measure surface characteristics. In one type, the surface contour is magnified optically and the image projected onto a screen or viewer; in another, a stylus is employed to translate the surface irregularities into an electrical signal which may be recorded in the form of a highly magnified profile of the surface or presented as an averaged "roughness-factor" reading.

In the case of liquids, attributes such as density, viscosity, melting point, boiling point, transparency, etc., are important. Density measurements have already been discussed. **Viscosity** is measured with a **viscosimeter,** of which there are three main types: flow through an orifice or capillary (Saybolt), viscous drag on a cylinder rotating in the fluid (MacMichael), damping of a vibrating reed (Ultrasonic) (see pp. 3–49 to 3–52 and Fig. 38, p. 4–68). **Plasticity** and consistency are related properties which are determined with special apparatus for heating or cooling the material and observing the temperature-time curve. The **photometer, reflectometer, and turbidimeter** are devices for measuring transparency or turbidity of non-opaque liquids and solids.

A variety of properties can be measured for the purpose of determining chemical composition. **Electrical properties** include pH, conductivity, dielectric constant, oxidation potential, etc. **Physical properties** include density, refractive index, thermal conductivity, vapor pressure, melting and boiling points, etc. Of increasing industrial application are **spectroscopic measurements: infrared absorption spectra, ultraviolet and visible emission spectra, mass spectrometry** and **gas chromatography.** These are specific to particular types of compounds and molecular configurations and hence are very powerful in the analysis of complex mixtures. **X-ray diffraction** has many applications in the analysis of crystalline solids, metals, and solid solutions.

Of special importance in the realm of composition measurement is the determination of **moisture content.** A common laboratory procedure measures the loss of weight of the oven-dried sample. More rapid methods employ electrical conductance or capacitance measurements, based on the relatively high conductivity and dielectric constant values for ordinary water.

Water vapor in air (**humidity**) is measured in terms of its physical properties or effects on materials (see also Secs. 4 and 12). (1) The **psychrometer** is based on the cooling effect of water evaporating into the air stream. It consists of two thermal elements exposed to a steady air flow; one is dry, the other is kept moist. (2) The **dew-point recorder** measures the temperature at which water just starts to condense out of the air. (3) The **hygrometer** measures the change in length of such humidity-sensitive elements as hair and wood. (4) **Electric sensing elements** employ a wire-wound coil impregnated with a hygroscopic salt (one that maintains an equilibrium between its moisture content and the air humidity) such that the resistance of the coil is related to the humidity.

The **throttling calorimeter** (Fig. 44) is most commonly used for determining the moisture in steam. A sampling nozzle is located preferably in a vertical section of steampipe far removed from any fittings. Steam enters the calorimeter through a throttling orifice and into a well-insulated expansion chamber. The steam quality x (fraction dry steam) is determined from the equation $x = (h_c - h_f)/h_{fg}$, where h_c is the enthalpy of superheated steam at the temperature and pressure measured in the calorimeter, h_f and h_{fg} are, respectively, the liquid enthalpy and the heat of vaporization corresponding to line pressure. The chamber is conveniently exhausted to atmospheric pressure, then only line pressure and temperature of the throttled steam need be measured. The range of the throttling calorimeter is limited to small percentages of moisture; a **separating calorimeter** may be employed for larger moisture contents.

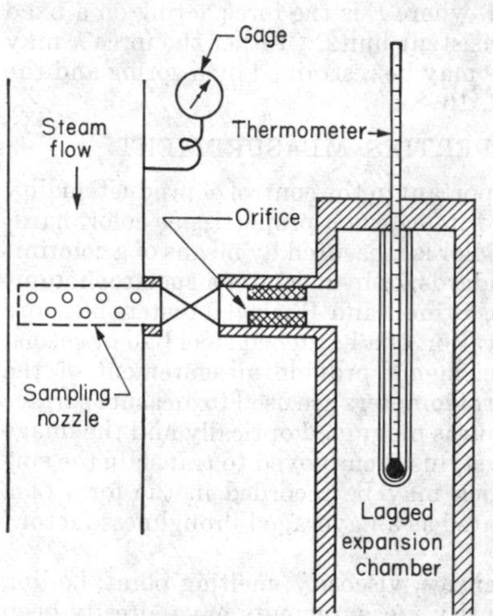

Fig. 44. Throttling calorimeter.

The **Orsat** apparatus is generally used for chemical analysis of flue gases. It consists of a graduated tube or burette designed to receive and measure volumes of gas (at constant temperature). The gas is analyzed for CO_2, O_2, CO, and N_2 by bubbling through appropriate absorbing reagents and measuring the resulting change in volume. The reagents normally employed are KOH solution for CO_2, pyrogallic acid and KOH mixture for O_2, and cuprous chloride (Cu_2Cl_2) for CO. The final remaining unabsorbed gas is assumed to be N_2. The most common errors in the Orsat analysis are due to **leakage** and poor **sampling.** The former can be checked by simple test; the latter factor can only be minimized by careful sampling procedure. Recommended procedure is the taking of several simultaneous samples from different points in the cross-sectional area of the flue-gas stream, analyzing these separately, and averaging the results.

There are many instruments for **measuring CO_2 (and other gases) automatically.** In one type, the CO_2 is absorbed in KOH, and the change in volume determined automatically. The more common type, however, is based on the difference in **thermal conductivity** of CO_2 compared to air. Two thermal conductivity cells are set into opposing arms of a Wheatstone-bridge circuit. Air is sealed into one cell (reference), and the CO_2-containing gas is passed through the other. The cell contains an electrically heated resistance element; the temperature of the element and therefore its resistance depends on the thermal conductivity of the gaseous atmosphere. As a result, the unbalance of the bridge provides a measure of the CO_2 content of the gas sample.

The same principle may be employed for analyzing other constituents of gas mixtures where there is a significant thermal-conductivity difference. A modification of this principle is also used for determining CO or other combustible gases by mixing the gas sample with air or oxygen. The combustible gas then burns on the heated wire of the test cell, producing a temperature rise which is measured as above.

Many other physical properties are employed in the determination of specific components of gaseous mixtures. An interesting example is the **oxygen analyzer,** based on the unique paramagnetic properties of oxygen.

NUCLEAR RADIATION INSTRUMENTS

(See also pp. 9–158 *et seq.*)

Nuclear radiation instrumentation is increasing in importance with two main areas of application: (1) measurement and control of radiation variables in nuclear reactor-based processes, such as nuclear power plants and (2) measurement of other physical variables based on radioactive excitation and tracer techniques. The instruments respond in general to electromagnetic radiation in the gamma and perhaps X-ray regions and to beta particles (electrons), neutrons, and alpha particles (helium nuclei).

Gas Ionization Tubes. The **ion chamber, proportional counter,** and **Geiger counter** are common instruments for radiation detection and measurement. These are different applications of the gas-ionization tube distinguished primarily by the amount of applied voltage.

A simple and very common form of the instrument consists of a gas-filled cylinder with a fine wire along the axis forming the anode and the cylinder wall itself (at ground potential) forming the cathode, as shown in Fig. 45. When a radiation particle enters the tube, its collision with gas molecules causes an ionization consisting of electrons (negatively charged) and positive ions. The electrons move very rapidly toward the positively charged wire; the heavier positive ions move relatively slowly toward the cathode. The above activity is detected by the resulting current flow in the external circuitry.

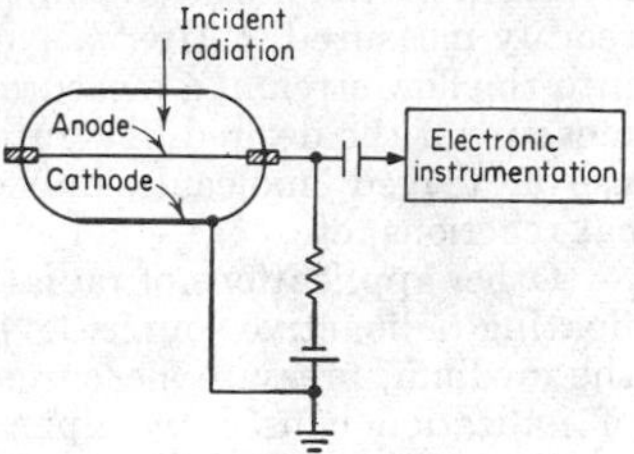

FIG. 45. Gas-ionization tube.

When the voltage applied across the tube is relatively low, the number of electrons collected at the anode is essentially equal to that produced by the incident radiation. In this voltage range, the device is called an **ion chamber.** The device may be used to count the number of radiation particles when the frequency is low; when the frequency is high, an external integrating circuit yields an output current proportional to the radiation intensity. Since the amplification factor of the ion chamber is low, high-gain electronic amplification of the current signal is necessary.

If the applied voltage is increased, a point is reached where the radiation-produced ions have enough energy to collide with other gas molecules and produce more ions which also enter into collisions so that an "avalanche" of electrons is collected at the anode. Thus, there is a very considerable amplification of the output signal. In this region, the device is called a **proportional counter** and is characterized by the voltage or current pulse being proportional to the energy content of the incident radiation signal.

With still further increase in the applied voltage, a point of saturation is reached wherein the output pulses have a constant amplitude independent of the incident radiation level. The resulting **Geiger counter** is capable of producing output pulses up to 10 volts in amplitude, thus greatly reducing the requirements on the external circuitry and instrumentation. This advantage is offset somewhat by a lower maximum counting rate and more limited ability to differentiate among the various types of radiation as compared with the proportional counter.

The **scintillation counter** is based on the excitation of a phosphor by incident radiation to produce light radiation which is in turn detected by a photomultiplier tube to yield an output voltage. The signal output is greatly amplified and nearly proportional to the energy of the initial radiation. The device may be applied to a wide range of radiations, it has a very fast response, and, by choice of phosphor material, it offers a large degree of flexibility in applications.

Applications to the Measurement of Physical Variables. The ready availability of radioactive isotopes of long half-life, such as cobalt 60, make possible a variety of industrial and laboratory measuring techniques based on radiation instruments of the type described above. Most applications are based on (1) radiation absorption, (2) tracer identification, and (3) other properties. These techniques often have the advantages of isolation of the measuring device from the system, access to a variable not observable by conventional means, or measurement without destruction or modification of the system.

In the utilization of **absorption** properties, a radioactive source is separated from the radiation-measuring device by that part of the system to be measured. The measured radiation intensity will depend on the fraction of radiation absorbed, which in turn will depend on the distance traveled through the absorbing medium and the density and nature of the material. Thus, the instrument can be adapted to measuring thickness (see Fig. 12), coating weight, density, liquid or solids level, or concentration (of certain components).

Tracer techniques are effectively used in measuring flow rates or velocities, residence time distributions, and flow patterns. In flow measurement, a sharp pulse of radioactive material may be injected into the flow stream; with two detectors placed downstream from the injection point and a known distance apart, the velocity of the pulse is readily measured. Alternatively, if a known constant flow rate of tracer is injected into the flow stream, a measure of the radiation downstream is easily converted into a measure of the desired flow rate. Other applications of tracer techniques involve the use of "tagged" molecules imbedded in the process to provide measures of wear, chemical reactions, etc.

Other applications of radiation phenomena include level measurements based on a floating radioactive source, level measurements based on the back-scattering effect of the medium, pressure measurements in the high-vacuum region based on the amount of ionization caused by alpha rays, location of interface in pipe-line transmission applications, and certain chemical analysis applications.

INDICATING, RECORDING, AND LOGGING

An important element of measurement is the display of the measured value in a form which the human operator can readily interpret. Two basic types of display are employed: analog and digital. **Analog** refers to a reading obtained from the motion of a pointer on a scale or the record of a pen moving over a chart. **Digital** refers to the reading displayed as a printed number, a series of holes on a punched card, or a sequence of pulses on magnetic tape. Further classification relates to indicating and recording functions. The **indicator** consists merely of a pointer moving over a calibrated scale. The scale may be concentric, as in the Bourdon gage (Fig. 16) or eccentric, as in the flowmeter (Fig. 31). There are also digital indicators which use neon bulbs or tubes to illuminate the specific digits corresponding to the reading. Obviously, use of the indicator is limited to cases where the variable of interest is constant during the measuring period, or at most, changes slowly.

The **recorder** is used where long-term trends or detailed variations with time are of interest, or where the response is too rapid for the human eye to follow. In the common **circular-chart recorder** (Fig. 46), the pointer is replaced by a pen which writes on a chart rotated by a constant-speed electrical or spring-wound clock. Various chart speeds are available from 1 rev per min to 1 rev every 7 days. Up to four recording pens on a single chart are available (with a print-wheel mechanism, six color-identified records may be had). The **strip-chart recorder** shown in Fig. 47 is of the type used in electronic potentiometers, where the pen is positioned by a servomotor. A constant-speed motor drives the chart vertically past the pen, which deflects horizontally. **Multipoint recording** is achieved by replacing the pen with a print-wheel assembly. A selector switch switches the input signal from one variable to another at the same time that the print wheel switches from one number (or symbol) to another. The record of each variable appears then as a sequence of dots with an identifying numeral. Up to 16 different records may be recorded on a chart (with external switching, as many as 144 records have been applied). Miniature recorders with 3- and 4-in. strip charts are gaining favor in process industries because of their compactness and readability. The pen may be pneumatically or electrically actuated. Maximum number of records per chart is two.

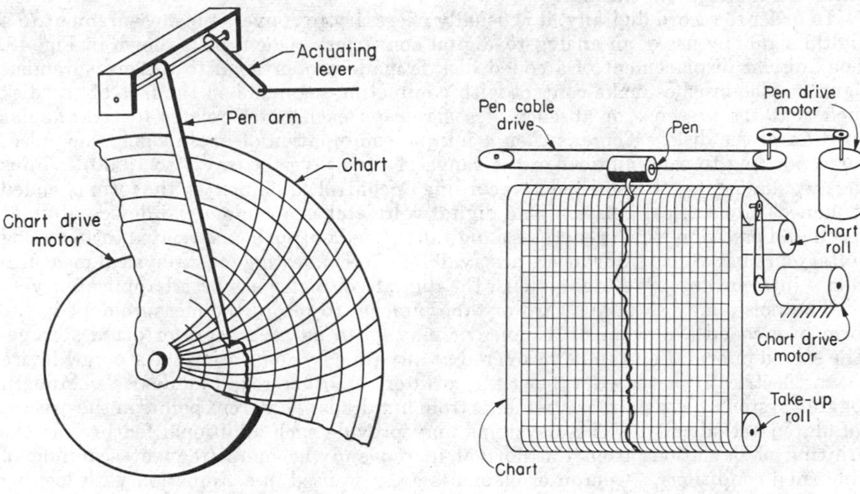

FIG. 46. Circular-chart recorder.

FIG. 47. Strip-chart recorder.

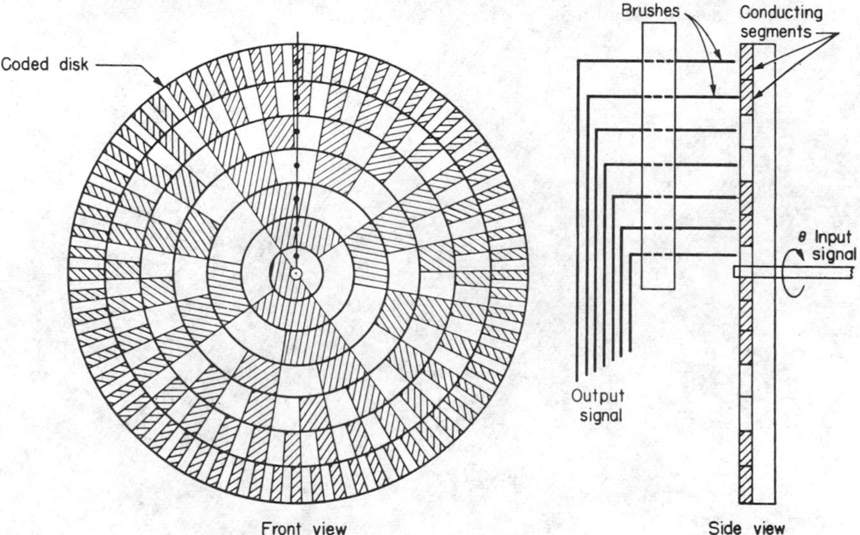

FIG. 48. Analog-to-digital converter.

For recording high-speed phenomena, the **oscillograph recorder** is used. The chart is in strip form and driven at high speed; the rate is usually adjustable. The pen (or stylus) is actuated by a galvanometer element. Recording may be with ink and standard chart paper, heated stylus and special heat-sensitive paper, or with photographic techniques using a mirror galvanometer and light-sensitive chart paper. The photoelectric oscillograph is capable of recording transient phenomena at frequencies up to several thousand cycles per second.

In quality control and time-motion studies, often a simple **on-off-type recorder** is sufficient for the purpose. Here, a pen is deflected when the machine or system is "on," not deflected whenever the system is "off." Pen actuation is usually by solenoid or other electromagnetic element.

In order to record digitally, it is usually necessary to convert the measurement to a digital signal by use of an **analog-to-digital converter.** One type is shown in Fig. 48. The angular displacement of a coded disk is made proportional to the measurement signal. The brushes make contact with conducting segments on the face of the disk such that the presence or absence of a signal on each brush relates to the angular position of the disk. There is then a unique combination of brush signals or pulses corresponding to each number in the range of the converter (say 1 to 1,000). Thus the measurement is transmitted to recording or control equipment in the form of coded sequences of electrical pulses. The **digital voltmeter** is a commercial device of great speed and precision which generates a digitally coded output signal related to an analog voltage input. Since transducers are available for converting most physical measurements into current or voltage signals, the digital voltmeter has broad applicability.

The pulses may actuate a card or tape puncher to record the measurement in the form of a coded arrangement of holes or may go to **magnetic core or drum storage.** The stored information can be recovered at any time by connecting the storage device to an electrically actuated typewriter, printer, or other read-out device. Modern **logging systems** have the measurements from hundreds of different points in the process tabulated periodically. These systems may provide such additional features as the printing of deviations from the normal in red and the more frequent scanning of abnormal conditions. Computer elements are also used in conjunction with logging systems to compute derived variables (such as operating efficiency, system losses, etc.) and to apply corrections to measured variables, *e.g.*, temperature and pressure compensation of gas-flow readings.

AUTOMATIC CONTROLS

BY

Guy S. Longobardo

References: Considine, "Process Instruments and Controls Handbook," McGraw-Hill. Thaler, "Elements of Servomechanism Theory," McGraw-Hill. Thaler and Brown, "Servomechanism Analysis," McGraw-Hill. Ahrendt, "Servomechanism Practice," McGraw-Hill. Porter, "An Introduction to Servomechanisms," Wiley. Chestnut and Mayer, "Servomechanisms and Regulating System Design," Wiley. Ahrendt and Taplin, "Automatic Feedback Control," McGraw-Hill. Brown and Campbell, "Principles of Servomechanisms," Wiley. Truxal, "Automatic Feedback Control System Synthesis," McGraw-Hill. Gardner and Barnes, "Transients in Linear Systems," Wiley. Campbell, "Process Dynamics," Wiley. Hadley and Longobardo, "Automatic Process Control," Addison-Wesley. Murphy, "Control Engineering," Van Nostrand. Savant, "Basic Feedback Control System Design," McGraw-Hill. Blackburn, Reethof, Shearer, "Fluid Power Control," Wiley. Truxal, "Control Engineers' Handbook," McGraw-Hill. Raven, "Automatic Control Engineering," McGraw-Hill. Morse, "Electrohydraulic Servomechanisms," McGraw-Hill.

INTRODUCTION

The purpose of an **automatic control** on a system is to produce a desired output when inputs to the system are changed. Inputs are in the form of commands, which the output is expected to follow, and disturbances, which the automatic control is expected to minimize. The usual form of an automatic control is a **closed-loop feedback control** which Ahrendt defines as "an operation which, in the presence of a disturbing influence, tends to reduce the difference between the actual state of a system and an arbitrarily varied desired state and which does so on the basis of this difference." The general theories and definitions of automatic control have been developed to aid the designer to meet primarily three basic specifications for the performance of the control system, namely, stability, accuracy, and speed of response.

The **nomenclature** of automatic control has been reviewed by both the ASME and the AIEE in recent years. Many terms adopted by the ASME naturally tend somewhat toward the vocabulary of the process-control engineer and in many cases are not sufficiently broad for general control application. The following terms and definitions have been selected to assist the reader and to serve as reference to a complex area of technology whose breadth crosses several professional disciplines.

Automatic regulator—an apparatus which measures the value of a quantity or condition which is subject to change with time, and operates to maintain within limits this measured value.

Controlled variable—(types) that quantity or condition of the controlled system which is directly measured or controlled.

Throttling range—that range of values through which the variable must change to cause the final control element to move from one extreme position to the other.

Set point—the value of the controlled variable that it is desired to maintain.

Deviation—the difference at any time between the controlled variable and the set point.

Corrective action—a change in the flow of the control agent initiated by the measuring means of the automatic controller.

Control agent—process energy whose flow is directly varied by the control element.

Self-regulation—that operating characteristic which inherently assists the establishment of equilibrium.

Two-position controller action—that in which the final control element is moved immediately, from one extreme to the other of its stroke, at predetermined values of the variable.

Proportional-position controller action—that in which there is continuous linear relation between the position of the final control element and the value of the controlled variable.

Floating controller action—that in which there is a predetermined relation between the values of the controlled variable and the rate of motion of a final control element.

Proportional-speed floating controller action—that in which there is a continuous linear relation between the rate of motion of the final control element and the deviation of the controlled variable.

Derivative controller action—that in which there is a predetermined relation between a derivative function of the controlled variable and the position of a final control element.

Proportional plus floating controller action (proportional + reset)—that in which proportional-position and proportional-speed floating actions are additively combined.

Proportional band—the range of scale values through which the controlled variable must pass in order that the final control element be moved through its entire range.

Floating speed—the rate of movement of a final control element corresponding to a specified deviation.

Command signal—the input which is established or varied by some means external to, and independent of, the feedback control system under consideration.

Disturbance—a signal which tends to affect the value of the controlled variable.

Response time—the time required for the controlled variable to reach a specified value after the application of a step input or disturbance.

Peak time—the time required for the controlled variable to reach its first maximum following the application of a step input.

Rise time—time required for the controlled variable to increase from one specified percentage of the final value to another, following the application of a step input.

Settling time—the time required for the absolute value of the difference between the controlled variable and its final value to become and remain less than a specified amount following the application of a step disturbance.

Compensation—a method of changing or maintaining the state of a system by employing means to offset the effects of disturbances without causal relationship between the error in the state of the system and the action of the compensating means.

These definitions have been largely abstracted from Smith, "Automatic Control Engineering"; Ahrendt, "Servomechanism Practice"; and Ahrendt and Taplin, "Automatic Feedback Control."

BASIC AUTOMATIC-CONTROL SYSTEM

The general components of a basic automatic-control system are shown in Fig. 1. Each block in the diagram represents a function which must be performed by the control. The operation may be explained as follows: (1) A command signal θ_i is applied to the input and compared with the instantaneous position of the output θ_o. (2) The result of this comparison, ϵ, representing an error, is amplified by a controller and used to position a power element. (3) The power device in turn further amplifies the error signal to supply large amounts of power to the output or load to reduce the difference between θ_i and θ_o.

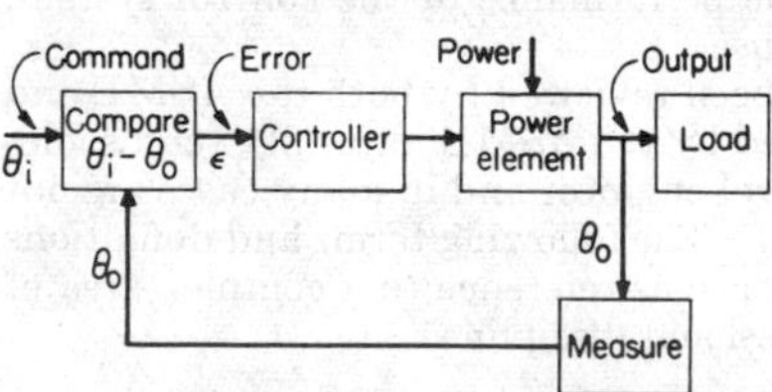

Fig. 1. Functional diagram of an automatic-control system.

TRANSIENT ANALYSIS OF A CONTROL SYSTEM

The stability, accuracy, and speed of response of a control system are determined by analyzing the *steady-state* and the *transient* performance. It is desirable to achieve the steady state in the shortest possible time, while maintaining the output within specified limits. Steady-state performance is evaluated in terms of the accuracy with which the output is controlled for a specified input. The transient performance, *i.e.*, the behavior of the output variable as the system changes from one steady-state condition to another, is evaluated in terms of such quantities as maximum overshoot, rise time, and response time (Fig. 2).

Transient-producing Disturbances. An automatic control normally has only two places where disturbances can be expected: at the input or at the load. For a purely mechanical system the input disturbance may take the form of a periodic oscillation, a displacement, a velocity, or an acceleration. Disturbances at the output are usually load changes expressed as a torque or force quantity. Non-mechanical systems have disturbances expressed in different quantities; however, they are directly analogous to the mechanical system.

The Basic Closed-loop Control. To illustrate some characteristics of a basic closed-loop control, consider a mechanical, rotational system composed of a prime mover or motor, a total system inertia J, and a viscous friction f. To control the system's output variable θ_o, a command signal θ_i must be supplied, the output variable measured and compared to the input, and the resulting signal difference used to control the flow of energy to the load. The basic control system is represented schematically in Fig. 3.

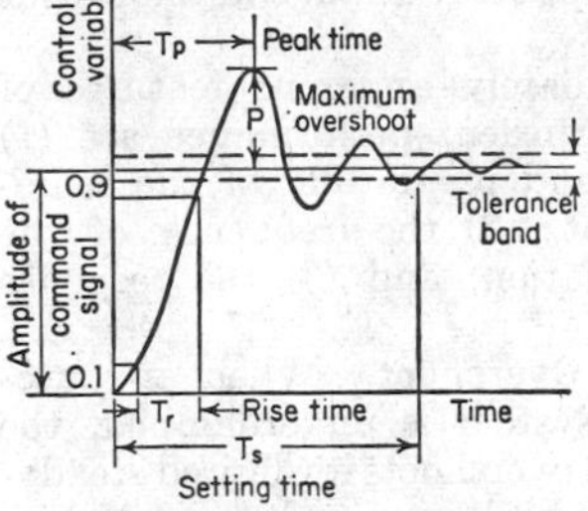

FIG. 2. System response to a unit step-function command.

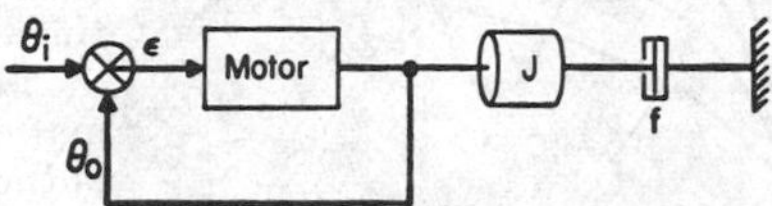

FIG. 3. A basic closed-loop control system.

The differential equation of this basic system is readily obtained from the idealized equations.

$$\text{Load torque } T_L = J\frac{d^2\theta_o}{dt^2} + f\frac{d\theta_o}{dt} \tag{1}$$

$$\text{Developed torque } T_D = K\epsilon \tag{2}$$

$$\text{Error } \epsilon = \theta_i - \theta_o \tag{3}$$

The above equations combine to yield the system differential equation:

$$J\frac{d^2\theta_o}{dt^2} + f\frac{d\theta_o}{dt} + K\theta_o = K\theta_i \tag{4}$$

Step-input Response of a Viscous-damped Control. If the control system described in Fig. 3 by Eq. (4) is subjected to a step change in the input variable θ_i, a solution $\theta_o = \theta_o(t)$ may be obtained as follows: (1) Let the ratio $\sqrt{K/J}$ be designated by the symbol ω_n and be called the **natural frequency.** (2) Let the quantity $2\sqrt{JK}$ be designated by the symbol f_c and be called the **friction coefficient** required for critical damping. (3) Let f/f_c be designated by the symbol ζ and be called the **damping ratio.** Equation (4) may then be written as

$$\frac{d^2\theta_o}{dt^2} + 2\zeta\omega_n\frac{d\theta_o}{dt} + \omega_n^2\theta_o = \omega_n^2\theta_i \tag{5}$$

For $\theta_i = 1$

$$\theta_o = 0 \ @\ t = 0$$

$$\frac{d\theta_o}{dt} = 0 \ @\ t = 0$$

The complete solution of Eq. (5) is

$$\theta_o = 1 - \frac{e^{-\zeta\omega_n t}}{\sqrt{1-\zeta^2}} \sin\left(\sqrt{1-\zeta^2}\,\omega_n t + \tan^{-1}\frac{\sqrt{1-\zeta^2}}{\zeta}\right) \tag{6}$$

Equation (6) is plotted in dimensionless form for various values of damping ratio in Fig. 4. The curves for $\zeta = 0.1$, 2, and 1 illustrate the underdamped, overdamped, and critically damped case, where any further decrease in system damping would result in overshoot. Damping is a property of the system which opposes a change in the output variable.

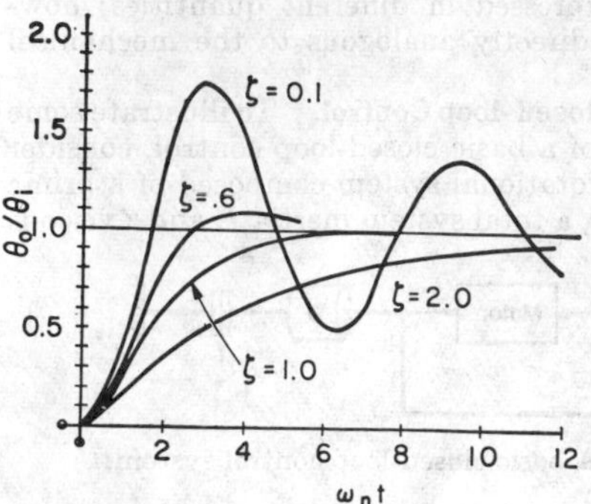

FIG. 4. Transient response of a second-order viscous-damped control to unit-step input displacement.

The immediately apparent features of an observed transient performance are (1) the existence and magnitude of the maximum overshoot, (2) the frequency of the transient oscillation, and (3) the response time.

Maximum Overshoot. When an automatic-control system is underdamped, the output variable overshoots its desired steady-state condition and a transient oscillation occurs. The first overshoot is the greatest, and it is the effect of its amplitude which must concern the control designer. The primary considerations for limiting this maximum overshoot are (1) to avoid damage to the process or machine due to excessive excursions of the controlled variable beyond that specified by the command signal, and (2) to avoid the excessive settling time associated with highly underdamped systems. Obviously, exact quantitative limits cannot generally be specified for the magnitude of this overshoot. However, experience indicates that satisfactory performance can generally be obtained if the overshoot is limited to 30 percent or less.

Transient Frequency. An undamped system oscillates about the final steady-state condition with a frequency of oscillation which should be as high as possible in order to minimize the response time. The designer must, however, avoid resonance conditions where the frequency of the transient oscillation is near the natural frequency of the system or its component parts.

Rise Time T_n, Peak Overshoot P, Peak Time T_P

These quantities are related to ζ and ω_n in Figs. 5 and 6.

Some useful formulas are listed below (Murphy).

$$\omega_n T_n \cong 1.02 + 0.48\zeta + 1.15\zeta^2 + 0.76\zeta^3 \qquad 0 \leq \zeta \leq 1$$

$$\omega_n T_s = \left.\begin{array}{ll} 17.6 - 19.2\zeta & 0.2 \leq \zeta \leq 0.75 \\ -3.8 + 9.4\zeta & 0.75 \leq \zeta \leq 1 \end{array}\right\} \text{2\% tolerance band}$$

$$P = \frac{e^{-\pi\zeta}}{\sqrt{1 - \zeta^2}}$$

$$T_P = \frac{\pi}{\omega_n \sqrt{1 - \zeta^2}}$$

Although these quantities are defined for a second-order system, they may be useful in the early design stages of higher-order systems if the response of the higher-order system is dominated by roots of the characteristic equation (p. 16-39) near the imaginary axis.

Derivative and Integral Compensation (Thaler). Four common compensation methods for improving the steady-state performance of a proportional-error control without damaging its transient response are shown in Fig. 7. They are (1) error derivative compensation, (2) input derivative compensation, (3) output derivative compensation, (4) error integral compensation.

Error Derivative Compensation. The torque equilibrium equation is

$$J\frac{d^2\theta_o}{dt^2} + f\frac{d\theta_o}{dt} = K_2\epsilon + K_1\frac{d\epsilon}{dt} \tag{7}$$

Writing Eq. (7) in terms of the input and output variables yields

$$J\frac{d^2\theta_o}{dt^2} + (f + K_1)\frac{d\theta_o}{dt} + K_2\theta_o = K_2\theta_i + K_1\frac{d\theta_i}{dt} \tag{8}$$

By adjusting K_1 and reducing f so that the quantity $(f + K_1)$ is equal to f in the uncompensated system, the system performance is affected as follows: (1) ϵ resulting from a constant-first-derivative input is reduced because of the reduction in viscous friction; (2) the transient performance of the uncompensated system is preserved unchanged.

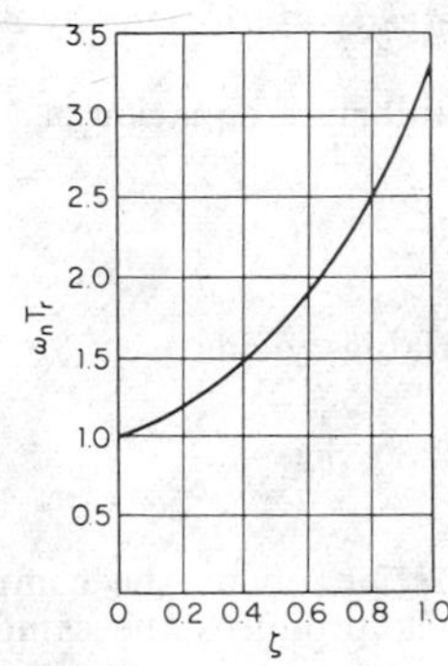

FIG. 5. Rise time T_r as a function of ζ and ω_n.

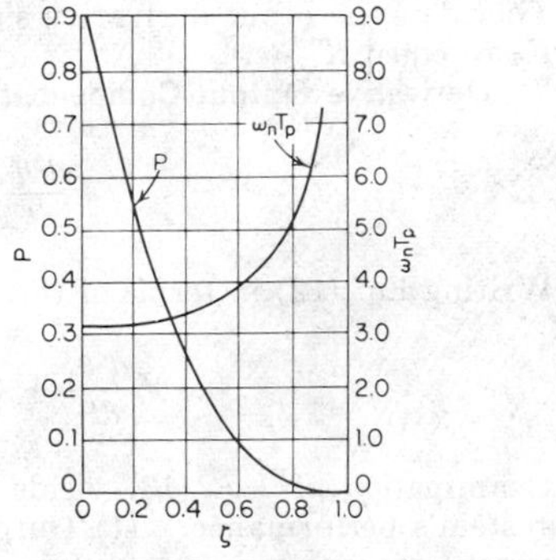

FIG. 6. Peak overshoot P and peak time T_P as functions of ζ and ω_n.

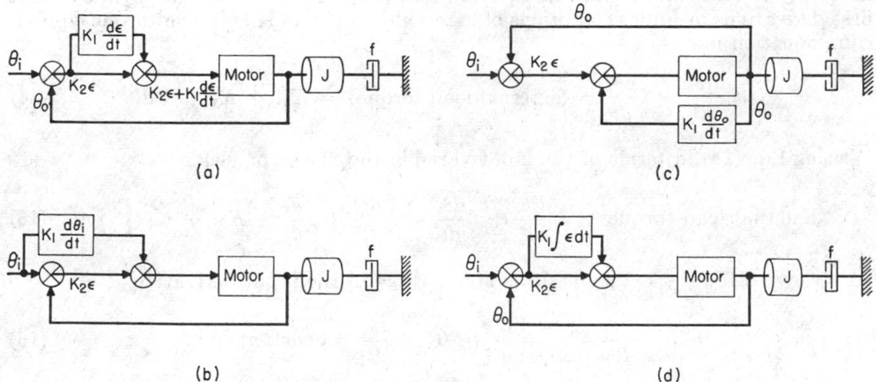

FIG. 7. Derivative and integral compensation of a basic closed-loop control system (*Thaler*): (*a*) error derivative compensation; (*b*) input derivative compensation; (*c*) output derivative compensation; (*d*) error integral compensation.

Derivative Input Compensation. The torque equilibrium equation is

$$J\frac{d^2\theta_o}{dt^2} + f\frac{d\theta_o}{dt} = K_2\epsilon + K_1\frac{d\theta_i}{dt} \tag{9}$$

Writing Eq. (**9**) in terms of the input and output variables yields

$$J\frac{d^2\theta_o}{dt^2} + f\frac{d\theta_o}{dt} + K_2\theta_o = \theta_i + K_1\frac{d\theta_i}{dt} \tag{10}$$

Examination of Eq. (**10**) yields the following information about the compensated system's performance: (1) Since the characteristic equation is unchanged from that of the uncompensated system, the transient performance is unaltered. (2) The steady-state solution to Eq. (**10**) is

$$\theta_o = \theta_i - \frac{f}{K_2}\left(1 - \frac{K_1}{K_2}\right)\frac{d\theta_i}{dt} \tag{11}$$

Therefore the input derivative signal can reduce the steady-state error by adjusting K_1 to equal K_2.

Derivative Output Compensation. The torque equilibrium equation is

$$J\frac{d^2\theta_o}{dt^2} + f\frac{d\theta_o}{dt} = K_2\epsilon \pm K_1\frac{d\theta_o}{dt} \tag{12}$$

Writing Eq. (**12**) in terms of the input and output variables yields

$$J\frac{d^2\theta_o}{dt^2} + (f \pm K_1)\frac{d\theta_o}{dt} + K_2\theta_o = K_2\theta_i \tag{13}$$

Examination of Eq. (**13**) yields the following information about the compensated system's performance. (1) Output derivative feedback produces the same system effect as does the viscous friction. This compensation, therefore, damps the transient performance. (2) Under conditions where $\theta_i = ct$, the steady-state error is increased.

Error Integral Compensation. Error integral compensation is used where it is necessary to eliminate steady-state errors resulting from input signals with constant first derivatives or under conditions of externally applied loads. The torque equilibrium equation is

$$J\frac{d^2\theta_o}{dt^2} + f\frac{d\theta_o}{dt} \pm (\text{external load torque}) = K_2\epsilon + K_1\int_0^t \epsilon\,dt \tag{14}$$

Writing Eq. (**14**) in terms of the input variable and the error yields

$$\text{External load torque} + J\frac{d^2\theta_i}{dt^2} + f\frac{d\theta_i}{dt} = J\frac{d^2\epsilon}{dt^2} + f\frac{d\epsilon}{dt} + K_2\epsilon + K_1\int_o^t \epsilon\,dt \tag{15}$$

At steady state for $t \gg 0$ and with a step change in the input derivative

$$\frac{d^2\theta_i}{dt^2} = \frac{d\epsilon}{dt} = \frac{d^2\epsilon}{dt^2} = 0 \qquad \frac{d\theta_i}{dt} = \text{constant} \tag{16}$$

Eq. (**15**) assumes the form

$$\pm\ \text{External load torque} + f\frac{d\theta_i}{dt} = K_2\epsilon + K_1\int_o^t \epsilon\,dt \tag{17}$$

Since the sum of the load torque and the term $[f(d\theta_i/dt)]$ is finite, $\epsilon = 0$, for

$$\int_0^\infty \epsilon\,dt \rightarrow \infty \tag{18}$$

If the integrating coefficient is a small number, additional torque produced by the integration action is developed very slowly, and, although the steady-state error is eventually eliminated, the transient performance is essentially unchanged. However, if K_1 is a large value, a large torque is produced in a short period of time, increasing the effective T/J ratio, and thereby decreasing the damping. The general effects of error integral compensation within its useful range are (1) steady-state error is eliminated; and (2) transient response is adversely effected, resulting in increased overshoot and the attendant increase in response time.

BLOCK-DIAGRAM REPRESENTATION

A useful representation of the mathematical relationships defining the flow of information and energy through the control system is by means of a block diagram. In the diagram the components of the control system are considered as functional blocks in series and parallel arrangements according to their position in the actual control system. Each component is represented by its **transfer function,** the ratio of the Laplace transform of the output variable to the input variable with all initial conditions taken as zero.

For example, the over-all transfer function of the control system described by Eq. (**5**) is obtained from Eq. (**5**) as

$$\frac{\theta_o(s)}{\theta_i(s)} = \frac{\omega_n{}^2}{s^2 + 2\zeta\omega_n s + \omega_n{}^2} \tag{19}$$

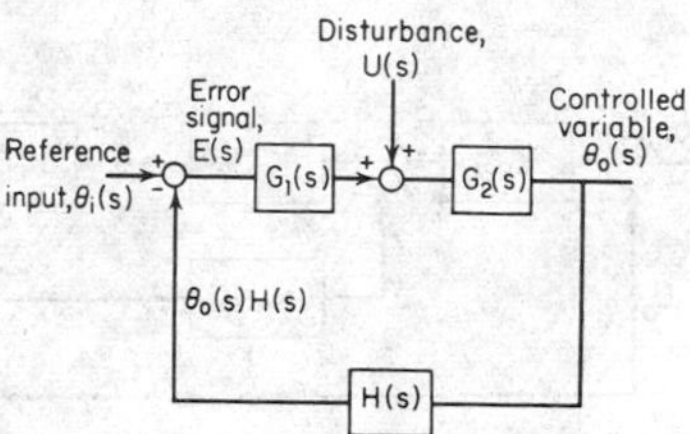

FIG. 8. Single-loop feedback control system.

Two conditions are specified: (1) the components must be described by linear differential equations (or non-linear equations linearized by suitable approximations); and (2) each block is unilateral. What occurs in one component may not affect the components preceding.

Block-diagram Algebra

The block diagram of a single-loop feedback-control system subjected to a command input $R(s)$ and a disturbance $U(s)$ is shown in Fig. 8.

When $U(s) = 0$ and the input is a reference change, the system may be reduced as follows:

$$E(s) = \theta_i(s) - \theta_o(s)H(s)$$
$$\theta_o(s) = E(s)[G_1(s)G_2(s)]$$

Therefore

$$\frac{\theta_o(s)}{\theta_i(s)} = \frac{G_1(s)G(s)}{1 + G_1(s)G_2(s)H(s)} \tag{20}$$

When $\theta_i(s) = 0$ and the input is a disturbance, the system may be reduced as follows:

$$E(s) = -\theta_o(s)H(s)$$
$$[E(s)G_1(s) + U(s)]G_2(s) = \theta_o(s)$$
$$\frac{\theta_o(s)}{U(s)} = \frac{G_2(s)}{1 + G_1(s)G_2(s)H(s)} \tag{21}$$

Equations (**20**) and (**21**) are in the form

$$\frac{\text{Response function}}{\text{Excitation function}} = \text{system function}$$

The *system function* is expressible as the ratio of two polynomials, $A(s)/B(s)$. The equation $B(s) = 0$ is the *characteristic equation.* When the excitation function is specified, inverse transformation of $\theta_o(s)$ yields $\theta_o(t)$, the transient response.

In many complex control systems, especially in the non-mechanical process-control field, auxiliary feedback paths are provided in order to adjust the system's performance. Figure 9 (a) illustrates such a condition. In analyzing such a system it is usually best to combine secondary loops into the main control loop to form an equivalent series block and transfer function. The system of Fig. 9(a) might be reduced in the following sequence.

1. Replace $K_3G_3(s)$ and $K_4H_1(s)$ with a single equivalent element

$$\frac{\theta_o}{\theta_2} = \frac{K_3G_3(s)}{1 + K_4H_1(s)K_3G_3(s)} = K_6G_6 \qquad (22)$$

The result of this first reduction is shown in Fig. 9(b).

2. Figure 9(b) can be treated in a similar fashion and a single block used to replace K_2G_2, K_6G_6, and K_5H_2

$$\frac{\theta_o}{\theta_1} = \frac{K_2G_2K_6G_6(s)}{1 + K_5H_2K_2G_2K_6G_6(s)} = K_7G_7 \qquad (23)$$

The result of this second reduction is shown in Fig. 9(c). The resulting open-loop transfer function is

$$\theta_o/\epsilon = K_1G_1K_7G_7(s) \qquad (24)$$

The closed-loop or frequency response function is

$$\frac{\theta_o}{\theta_i} = \frac{K_1G_1K_7G_7(s)}{1 + K_1G_1K_7G_7(s)} \qquad (25)$$

Equation (**25**) can, of course, be expanded to include the terms of the system's secondary loops.

(a)

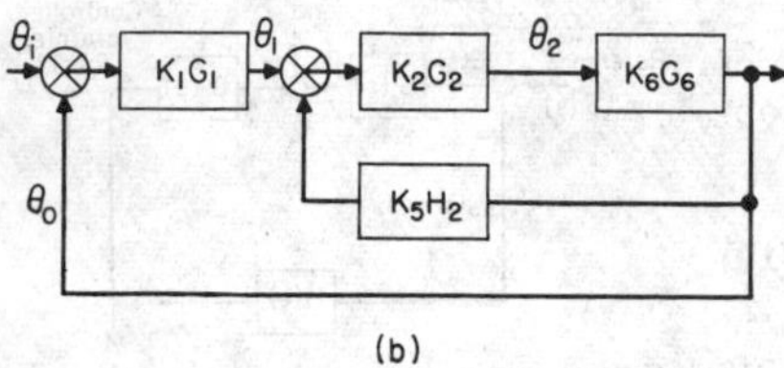

(b)

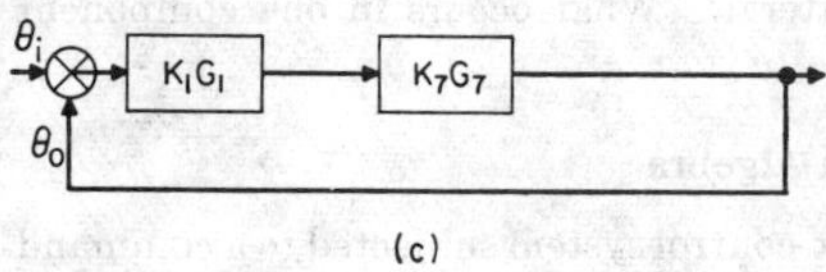

(c)

FIG. 9. Reduction of a closed-loop control system with multiple secondary loops.

STEADY-STATE PERFORMANCE

The steady-state error of a control system can be determined by using the final value theorem (see Laplace Transforms, Sec. 2) in which

$$\underset{t \to \infty}{\theta_o(t)} = \underset{s \to 0}{s\theta_o(s)} \qquad \text{[provided } \theta_o(t) \text{ is stable]}$$

The classification of control systems according to the form of the open-loop transfer function facilitates the determination of the steady-state errors when the system is subjected to various inputs.

The open-loop transfer function $\theta_o(s)/\epsilon(s) = KG(s)$ may be written

$$KG(s) = \frac{\theta_o(s)}{\epsilon(s)} = \frac{K(1 + \tau_a s)(1 + \tau_b s)(1 + \tau_c s) \cdots}{s^N(1 + \tau_1 s)(1 + \tau_2 s)(1 + \tau_3 s) \cdots} \qquad (26a)$$

The *system type* is given according to the value of N as

$$\begin{array}{ll} \text{Type 0 system} & N = 0 \\ \text{Type 1 system} & N = 1 \\ \text{Type 2 system} & N = 2 \\ \text{Type 3 system} & N = 3 \end{array} \qquad (26b)$$

Error coefficients, based on a system with unity feedback $[H(s) = 1]$, are defined as

$$\text{Positional error constant} = K_0 = \lim_{s\to 0} KG(s) \tag{27a}$$

$$\text{Velocity error constant} = K_v = \lim_{s\to 0} sKG(s) \tag{27b}$$

$$\text{Acceleration error constant} = K_a = \lim_{s\to 0} s^2KG(s) \tag{27c}$$

A summary of error coefficients for systems of different types is given in Table 1.

Table 1. Summary of Error Coefficients

N	K_0	K_v	K_a
0	Constant	0	0
1	∞	Constant	0
2	∞	∞	Constant

A summary of the errors for types 0, 1, and 2 systems, when subjected to various inputs, is given in Table 2.

Table 2. Summary of Errors

Input error	$\theta_i(t) = A$ ϵ_0/A	$\theta_i(t) = vt$ ϵ_v/v	$\theta_i(t) = at^2$ ϵ_a/a
$N = 0$	$1/1 + K_0$	∞	∞
1	0	$1/K_v$	∞
2	0	0	$1/K_a$

The higher the system type, the better is the output able to follow the higher degrees of input. Higher-type systems, however, are more difficult to stabilize, and a compromise must be made between the steady-state error and the settling time of the response. (For a detailed treatment of steady-state errors, see Savant.) Another convenient means for classifying systems is according to controller action (see Pneumatic systems).

FREQUENCY RESPONSE

Although it is the time response of the control system that is of major importance, study of the effect on transient response of changes in system parameters, either in the process or controller, is more conveniently made from a **frequency-response** analysis of the system. The **frequency response** of a system is the steady-state output of the system to input sinusoids of varying frequency. The output for a linear system can be completely described in terms of the amplitude ratio of the output sinusoid to the input sinusoid and the phase of the output sinusoid to the input sinusoid. The amplitude ratio or gain, and phase, are functions of the frequency of the input sinusoid. For purposes of system analysis the frequency response of the open-loop transfer function is more useful than that of the closed loop. Means for obtaining the closed-loop frequency response and evaluating transient performance from the open-loop frequency response are discussed below.

The frequency response can be obtained analytically from the transfer functions of the components, or system, by replacing s, the Laplace operator, with $(j\omega)$. In Table 3 are shown the frequency responses for some commonly encountered control-system elements (Considine).

The frequency response can also be obtained experimentally for systems not readily amenable to mathematical analysis by subjecting the system to input sinusoids of varying frequency.

Table 3. Frequency-response Equations for Some Common Control-system Elements
(Considine, "Process Instruments and Controls Handbook," McGraw-Hill)

Description	Transfer function $G(s)$	Frequency response $G(j\omega)$	Magnitude ratio	Phase angle
1. Dead time	$\epsilon^{-T_L s}$	$\epsilon^{-j\omega T_L}$	1	$-\omega T_L$ radians
2. First-order lag	$\frac{1}{Ts+1}$	$\frac{1}{j\omega T+1}$	$\frac{1}{\sqrt{\omega^2T^2+1}}$	$-\tan^{-1}(\omega T)$
3. Second-order lag	$\frac{1}{(Ts+1)(aTs+1)}$	$\frac{1}{-a\omega^2T^2+j(1+a)\omega T+1}$	$\frac{1}{\sqrt{(1-a\omega^2T^2)^2+(1+a)^2\omega^2T^2}}$	$-\tan^{-1}\left[\frac{(1+a)\omega T}{1-aT^2\omega^2}\right]$
4. Quadratic (underdamped)	$\frac{1}{\left(\frac{s}{\omega_n}\right)^2+\frac{2\zeta}{\omega_n}s+1}$	$\frac{1}{-\left(\frac{\omega}{\omega_n}\right)^2+j2\zeta\frac{\omega}{\omega_n}+1}$	$\frac{1}{\sqrt{\left(1-\frac{\omega^2}{\omega_n^2}\right)^2+4\zeta^2\left(\frac{\omega}{\omega_n}\right)^2}}$	$-\tan^{-1}\left[\frac{2\zeta\frac{\omega}{\omega_n}}{1-\left(\frac{\omega}{\omega_n}\right)^2}\right]$
5. Ideal proportional controller	K	K	K	0
6. Ideal proportional-plus-reset controller $T_i = \frac{1}{r}$ r = reset rate	$K\left(1+\frac{1}{T_i s}\right)$ or $K\frac{T_i s+1}{T_i s}$	$K\left(1+\frac{1}{j\omega T_i}\right)$ or $K\frac{j\omega T_i+1}{j\omega T_i}$	$K\sqrt{1+\left(\frac{1}{\omega T_i}\right)^2}$	$-\tan^{-1}\left(\frac{1}{\omega T_i}\right)$
7. Ideal proportional-plus-rate controller	$K(1+T_d s)$	$K(1+j\omega T_d)$	$K\sqrt{1+\omega^2T_d^2}$	$\tan^{-1}(\omega T_d)$
8. Ideal proportional-plus-reset-plus-rate controller	$K\left(1+T_d s+\frac{1}{T_i s}\right)$	$K\left(1+j\omega T_d+\frac{1}{j\omega T_i}\right)$ or $K\frac{j\omega T_i-\omega^2T_dT_i+1}{j\omega T_i}$	$K\sqrt{(\omega T_i)^2+(1-\omega^2T_dT_i)^2}$	$\tan^{-1}\left(\omega T_d-\frac{1}{\omega T_i}\right)$

GRAPHICAL DISPLAY OF THE FREQUENCY RESPONSE

The transient performance characteristics of the control are conveniently obtained from curves of the open-loop frequency-response function. The most common methods of graphical presentation employed are (1) the **polar** or **Nyquist plot,** where the magnitude and phase angle of the direct-transfer function $G(j\omega)H(j\omega)$ are plotted as a vector with frequency ω as a parameter and (2) the **logarithmic** or **Bode plot,** where the phase angle and log of the magnitude of $G(j\omega)H(j\omega)$ are plotted against log ω. The polar plot also enables the absolute stability of the system to be determined without the need for obtaining the roots of the characteristic equation. The logarithmic plot has the advantage of ease of plotting, especially in design, since the individual effects of cascaded elements can be gaged by superposition.

Polar plots for the frequency response of some common system components are shown in Table 4 (Considine).

For a closed system the frequency response may be derived from the polar plot of the direct-transfer function $KG(j\omega)$ (Thaler and Brown). In Fig. 10 the amplitude ratio θ_o/θ_i at any frequency ω is the ratio of the lengths of the vectors $\overline{O\beta}$ and $\overline{\alpha\beta}$. The angle formed by the vectors $\overline{\alpha\beta}$ and $\overline{O\beta}$ is the phase angle of the frequency response $\underline{/\alpha\beta O} = \underline{/\theta_o/\theta_i(j\omega)}$. The numerator of the direct-transfer function is a constant representing the gain of the control system. Changing the *gain* proportionally changes the length of each vector $\overline{O\beta}$. This technique for deriving the frequency-response function from the direct-transfer function is not applicable if the control system has a transfer function in the feedback loop.

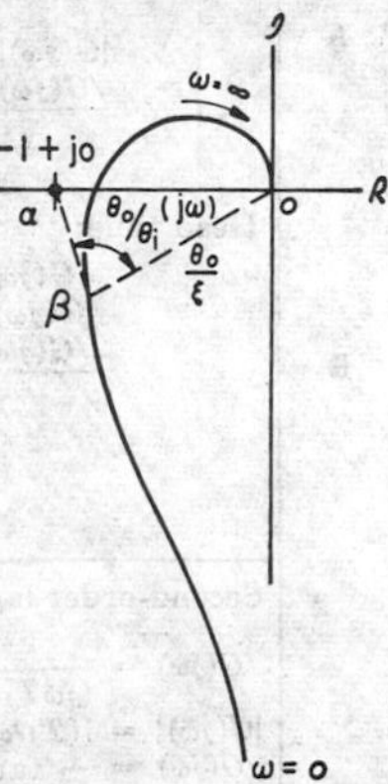

FIG. 10. Typical $\frac{\theta_o}{\epsilon}(j\omega)$ plot.

Logarithmic Plots (Bode Diagrams). The direct-transfer-function equation can be plotted on logarithmic coordinates. The first advantage of this method of data presentation is that the numerical computation of points on the curve is simplified by the fact that log magnitude *vs.* log ω may be approximated to engineering accuracy with straightline asymptotes. This may be shown as follows:

The generalized form of a direct transfer function is

$$KG(j\omega) = K\frac{(j\omega\tau_a + 1)(j\omega\tau_b + 1)\cdots}{(j\omega)^N(j\omega\tau_1 + 1)\cdots} \tag{28}$$

where there may be any number of terms in the numerator or denominator but where the denominator is of higher order. The exponent N assumes positive integral values. Since the terms of Eq. (**28**) are complex, their magnitude and phase are computed separately. Taking logs of both sides of Eq. (**28**) yields

$$\log|KG| = \log|K| + \log|j\omega\tau_a + 1| + \cdots - N\log|j\omega| - \log|j\omega\tau_1 + 1|\cdots \tag{29}$$

It is usually more convenient to express the logarithm in **decibels,** so each term of Eq. (**29**) is multiplied by 20. A decibel to amplitude-ratio conversion is given in Table 5.

$$20\log|KG| = 20\log|K| + 20\log|j\omega\tau_a + 1|\cdots \\ - 20N\log|j\omega| - 20\log(j\omega\tau_1 + 1)\cdots \tag{30}$$

The phase angle is computed as

$$\underline{/KG(j\omega)} = \underline{/K} + \tan^{-1}\omega\tau_a + \cdots - (90N)^\circ - \tan^{-1}\omega\tau_1\cdots \tag{31}$$

The computational advantage of the logarithmic form of the amplitude function is quite apparent. For such terms as $(j\omega)^N$, the decibel expression $-20N\log(j\omega)$ plots as a straight line. If $N = 1$, the slope is -6 db per octave (one octave separates any

Table 4. Polar Loci for Frequency Response of Common System Components
(Considine, "Process Instruments and Controls Handbook," McGraw-Hill)

Type	Component	Polar loci plot in $G(j\omega)$ plane
A	First-order lag: $G(j\omega) = \frac{1}{j\omega T + 1}$ $\lvert G(j\omega)\rvert = (\omega^2T^2 + 1)^{-1/2}$ $\underline{/G(j\omega)} = -\tan^{-1}(+\omega T)$	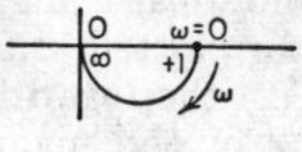 0, ∞, $\omega = 0$, +1, ω
B	Dead time: $G(j\omega) = \epsilon^{-j\omega T_L}$ $\lvert G(j\omega)\rvert = 1$ $\underline{/G(j\omega)} = -\omega T_L$ radians	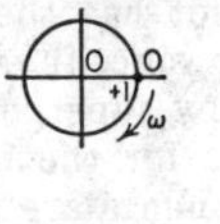 0, 0, +1, ω
C	Second-order lag: $G(j\omega) = \frac{1}{(j\omega T_1 + 1)(j\omega T_2 + 1)}$ $\lvert G(j\omega)\rvert = [(T_1{}^2\omega^2 + 1)(T_2{}^2\omega^2 + 1)]^{-1/2}$ $\underline{/G(j\omega)} = -\tan^{-1}(+\omega T_1) - \tan^{-1}(+\omega T_2)$	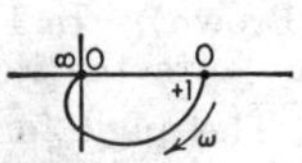 ∞, 0, 0, +1, ω
1	Proportional controller: $G(j\omega) = K$ $\lvert G(j\omega)\rvert = K$ $\underline{/G(j\omega)} = 0$	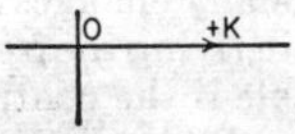 0, +K
2	Proportional-speed floating controller: $G(j\omega) = \frac{1}{j\omega T_i}$ $\lvert G(j\omega)\rvert = \frac{1}{\omega T_i}$ $\underline{/G(j\omega)} = -90°$	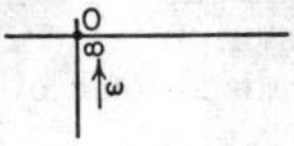 0, ∞, ω
3	Proportional-plus-rate controller: $G(j\omega) = K(1 + jT_d\omega)$ $\lvert G(j\omega)\rvert = K\sqrt{1 + \omega^2T_d{}^2}$ $\underline{/G(j\omega)} = \tan^{-1}(+\omega T_d)$	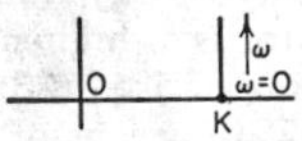 ω, 0, $\omega = 0$, K
4	Proportional-plus-reset controller: $G(j\omega) = K\left(1 + \frac{1}{j\omega T_i}\right)$ $\lvert G(j\omega)\rvert = K\sqrt{1 + \left(\frac{1}{\omega T_i}\right)^2}$ $\underline{/G(j\omega)} = -\tan^{-1}(+\omega T_i)$	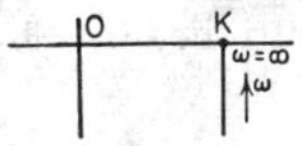 0, K, $\omega = \infty$, ω
5	Proportional-plus-reset-plus-rate controller: $G(j\omega) = K\left(1 + \frac{1}{j\omega T_i} + jT_d\omega\right)$ $\lvert G(j\omega)\rvert = K\sqrt{1 + \left(T_d\omega - \frac{1}{T_i\omega}\right)^2}$ $\underline{/G(j\omega)} = \tan^{-1}\left(T_d\omega - \frac{1}{T_i\omega}\right)$	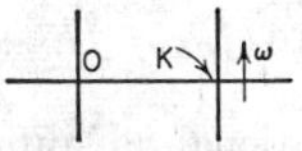 0, K, ω

two frequencies which are in a ratio of 2 or ½). If $N = 2$, the slope is -12 db per octave.

For such terms as $(j\omega\tau_a + 1)$ in the numerator of the transfer function, the decibel expression is $20 \log |j\omega\tau_a + 1|$.

For $\omega \ll 1$,
$$|j\omega\tau_a + 1| = 1 \quad \textbf{(32)}$$
$$\therefore 20 \log |j\omega\tau_a + 1| = 0 \text{ db} \quad \textbf{(33)}$$
For $\omega \gg 1$,
$$|j\omega\tau_a + 1| = j\omega\tau_a \quad \textbf{(34)}$$
$$\therefore 20 \log |j\omega\tau_a| \text{ has a slope of } +6 \text{ db per octave} \quad \textbf{(35)}$$

Table 5. Decibel to Amplitude-ratio Conversion
(Thaler)

Decibel	Amp-ratio	Decibel	Amp-ratio
60	1,000.0	0.0	1.000
50	316.2	−0.5	0.945
40	100.0	−1.0	0.894
35	56.23	−2.0	0.795
30	31.62	−3.0	0.707
25	17.78	−4.0	0.630
20	10.0	−5.0	0.562
15	5.62	−6.0	0.500
12	3.99	−8.0	0.398
9	2.82	−9.0	0.354
6	2.00	−10.0	0.316
5	1.78	−12.0	0.251
4	1.59	−15.0	0.178
3	1.41	−18.0	0.125
2	1.26	−20.0	0.100
1	1.12		
0.5	1.06		

When $\omega = 1/\tau_a$, $20 \log |j\omega\tau_a| = 0$ db. Therefore the 0 db asymptote and the +6 db per octave asymptote cross at $\omega = 1/\tau_a$. At this corner, it may be shown that the approximation yields a 3 db error. This term $(j\omega\tau_a + 1)$ is plotted in Fig. 11. For denominator terms of the form $(j\omega\tau_1 + 1)$, the asymptotes are a horizontal line at 0 db

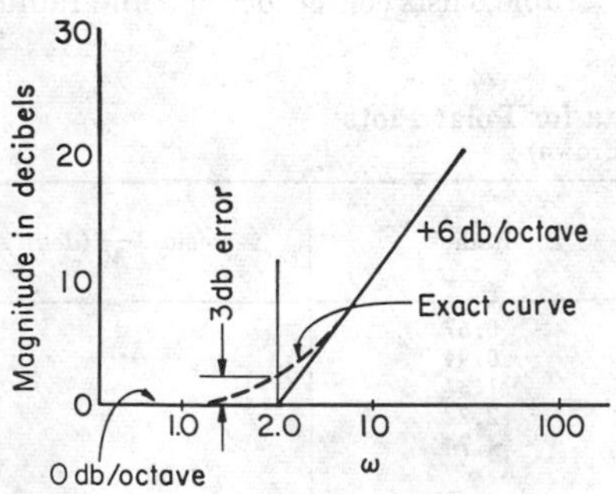

Fig. 11. Bode plot of term $(j\omega\tau_a + 1)$.

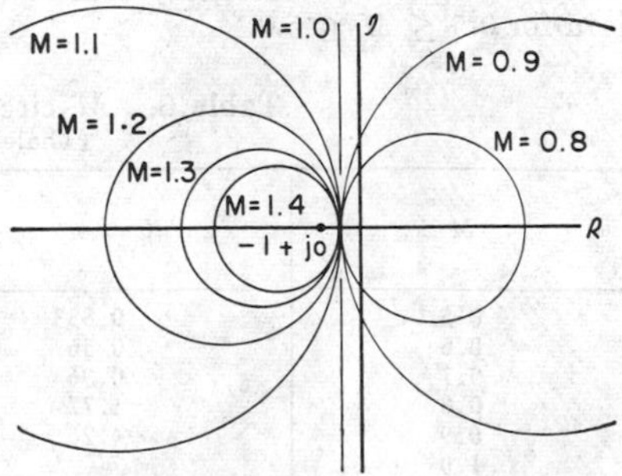

Fig. 12. M circles in the polar plane.

and a line sloping at -6 db per octave. Quadratic terms of the form $(j\omega^2)\tau_b + j\omega A + 1$ do not lend themselves quite as well to asymptotic approximation. The low-frequency asymptote has a slope of 0 db per octave and the high-frequency asymptote has a slope of ± 12 db per octave. The magnitude and phase angle values at the corner frequency $\omega = 1/\tau_b$ depend on the value of the coefficient A. The magnitude error at this frequency cannot be conveniently approximated. The phase angle is -90 deg.

To obtain a logarithmic plot of a direct transfer function, the designer must first plot the asymptotic approximations to each term of the transfer function, add the ordinate values of each term at each value of ω, and plot their sum.

Magnitude Circles. In a preceding paragraph a procedure was outlined for determining the closed-loop frequency response from the open-loop or direct transfer function by drawing a $KG(j\omega)$ vector from the origin to a point ω on the locus and computing the ratio between this vector and a vector from ω on the locus to the point $-1 + j0$. Since this technique is valid, then every point on the KG plane corresponds to some magnitude ratio and loci of constant magnitude ratio must exist. It can be shown that these loci are circles of the following dimensions and orientations:

Radius $r = M/(M^2 - 1)$ where M = closed-loop magnitude ratio θ_o/θ_i **(36)**

Center at $-M^2/(M^2 - 1)$ measured from the origin along the real axis **(37)**

A group of M circles is shown in Fig. 12.

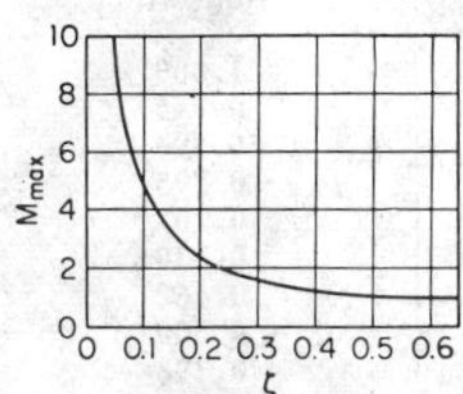

FIG. 13. M_{max} *vs.* ζ for second-order system:

$$\frac{\theta_o(s)}{\theta_i(s)} = \frac{\omega_n^2}{s^2 + 2\zeta\omega_n s + \omega_n^2}$$

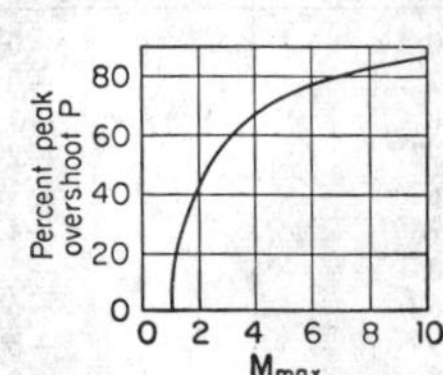

FIG. 14. P, percent peak overshoot, *vs.* M_{max} for second-order system:

$$\frac{\theta_o(s)}{\theta_i(s)} = \frac{\omega_n^2}{s^2 + 2\zeta\omega_n s + \omega_n^2}$$

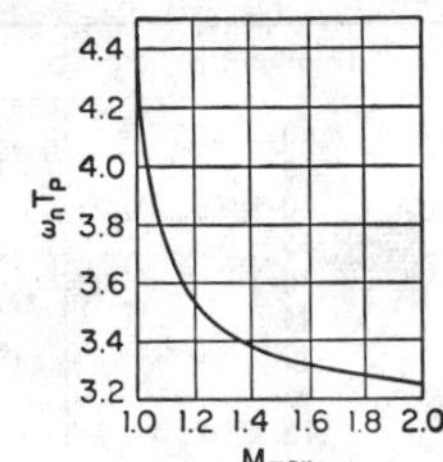

FIG. 15. Peak time T_p and natural frequency ω_n *vs.* M_{max} for second-order system:

$$\frac{\theta_o(s)}{\theta_i(s)} = \frac{\omega_n^2}{s^2 + 2\zeta\omega_n s + \omega_n^2}$$

If a direct transfer function is plotted over the M-circle curves, the frequency ω at each point of intersection of the locus with the M circles determines the closed-loop magnitude ratio at that frequency. The resonance peak occurs at a frequency ω_m which is **tangent** to the largest-value M circle. Table 6 lists center location and radius data for $0.5 \leq M \leq 5.0$.

Table 6. M-circle Data for Polar Plots
(Thaler and Brown)

M	Center	Radius	$\Psi = \sin^{-1}\frac{1}{M}$ (deg)
0.5	0.333	0.67	
0.6	0.56	0.94	
0.7	0.96	1.37	
0.8	1.77	2.22	
0.9	4.26	4.74	
1.0	∞	∞	90
1.1	−5.77	5.24	65
1.2	−3.27	2.73	56.5
1.3	−2.45	1.88	50
1.4	−2.04	1.46	46
1.5	−1.80	1.20	42
1.6	−1.64	1.03	39
1.7	−1.53	0.90	36
1.8	−1.47	0.84	34
1.9	−1.38	0.73	32
2.0	−1.33	0.67	30
2.5	−1.19	0.48	23.5
3.0	−1.12	0.38	21
3.5	−1.10	0.34	16.6
4.0	−1.07	0.266	14.5
4.5	−1.05	0.234	12.8
5.0	−1.04	0.208	11.5

For a second-order unity feedback system, with transfer function $\theta_o(s)/\theta_i(s) = \omega_n^2/(s^2 + 2\zeta\omega_n s + \omega_n^2)$,

$$M_{max} = \frac{1}{2\zeta\sqrt{1-\zeta^2}} \qquad 0 \le \zeta \le 0.707 \quad M_{max} \ge 1$$

and

$$\omega_{max} = \omega_n\sqrt{1-\zeta^2} \qquad 0 \le \zeta \le 0.707 \quad M_{max} \ge 1$$

Figures 13 to 15 graph the relationships for M_{max} *vs.* ζ, percent peak overshoot *vs.* M_{max} and peak time, and T_p and natural frequency ω_n *vs.* M_{max}. As mentioned, the transient behavior of higher-order systems dominated by zeros of the characteristic function near the imaginary axis may be approximated using these relations.

STABILITY AND PERFORMANCE OF AN AUTOMATIC CONTROL

An automatic-control system is stable if the amplitude of transient oscillations decreases with time and the system reaches a steady state. The stability of a system

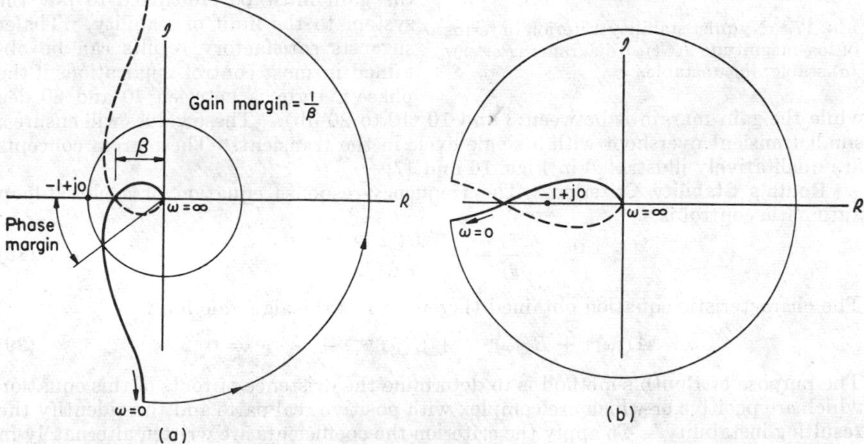

FIG. 16. Typical $KG(j\omega)$ loci illustrating application of Nyquist's stability criterion: (*a*) stable; (*b*) unstable.

may be evaluated by examining the roots of the differential equation describing the system. The presence of positive real roots or complex roots with positive real parts dictates an unstable system. Any stability test utilizing the open-loop transfer function or its plot must utilize this fact as the basis of the test.

The Nyquist Stability Criterion. The $KG(j\omega)$ locus for a typical single-loop automatic-control system plotted for all positive and negative frequencies is shown in Fig. 16. The locus for negative values of ω is the mirror image of the positive ω locus in the real axis. To complete the diagram, a semicircle (or full circle if the locus approaches $-\infty$ on the real axis) of infinite radius is assumed to connect in a positive sense, the + locus at $\omega \to 0$ with the negative locus at $\omega \to -0$. If this locus is traced in a positive sense from $\omega \to \infty$ to $\omega \to 0$, around the circle at ∞, and then along the negative-frequency locus the following may be concluded: (1) If the locus **does not** enclose the $-1 + j0$ point, the system is stable; (2) if the locus **does** enclose the $-1 + j0$ point, the system is unstable. The Nyquist criterion can also be applied to the log magnitude of $KG(j\omega)$ and phase *vs.* log ω diagrams. In this method of display, the criterion for stability reduces to the requirement that the log magnitude of $KG(j\omega)$ must cross the 0 db axis at a frequency less than the frequency at which the phase curve crosses the -180 deg line. Two stability conditions are illustrated in Fig. 17. The Nyquist criterion not only provides a simple test for the stability of an automatic-control system but also indicates the degree of stability of the system by indicating the degree to which the $KG(j\omega)$ locus avoids the $-1 + j0$ point.

The concepts of **phase margin** and **gain margin** are employed to give this quantitative indication of the degree of stability of an automatic-control system. **Phase margin** is defined as the additional negative phase shift necessary to make the phase angle of the transfer function -180 deg at the frequency where the magnitude of the $KG(j\omega)$ vector is unity. Physically, phase margin can be interpreted as the amount by which the unity KG vector has to be shifted to make a stable system unstable.

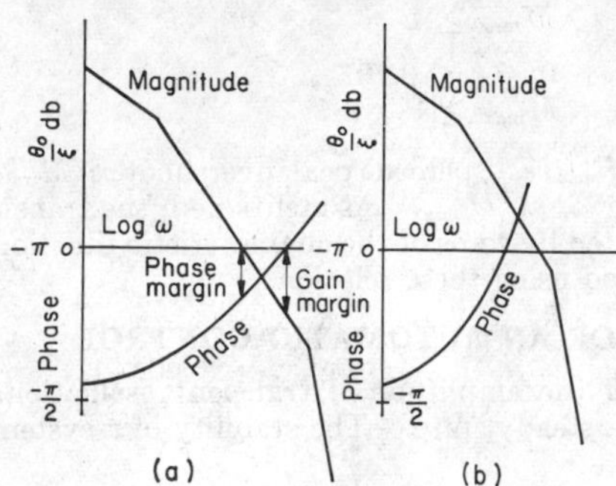

FIG. 17. Nyquist stability criterion in terms of log magnitude $KG(j\omega)$ diagrams (*Porter*): (*a*) stable; (*b*) unstable.

In a similar manner, **gain margin** is defined as the reciprocal of the magnitude of the KG vector at -180 deg. Physically, gain margin is the number by which the gain must be multiplied to put the system to the limit of stability. Thaler suggests satisfactory results can be obtained in most control applications if the phase margin is between 40 and 60 deg while the gain margin is between 3 and 10 (10 to 20 db). These values will ensure a small transient overshoot with a single cycle in the transient. The margin concepts are qualitatively illustrated in Figs. 16 and 17.

Routh's Stability Criterion. The frequency-response equation of a closed-loop automatic control is

$$\frac{\theta_o}{\theta_i} = \frac{KG(j\omega)}{1 + KG(j\omega)} \tag{38}$$

The characteristic equation obtained thereform has the algebraic form

$$A(j\omega)^n + B(j\omega)^{n-1} + C(j\omega)^{n-2} + \cdots = 0 \tag{39}$$

The purpose of Routh's method is to determine the existence of roots of this equation which are positive or which are complex with positive real parts and thus identify the resulting instability. To apply the criterion the coefficients are written alternately in two rows as

$$\begin{matrix} A & C & E & G \\ B & D & F & H \end{matrix}$$

This array is then expanded to

$$\begin{matrix} A & C & E & G \\ B & D & F & H \\ \alpha_1 & \alpha_2 & \alpha_3 & \\ \beta_1 & \beta_2 & \beta_3 & \\ \gamma_1 & \gamma_2 & & \end{matrix}$$

where α_1, α_2, α_3, β_1, β_2, β_3, γ_1 and γ_2 are computed as

$$\alpha_1 = \frac{BC - AD}{B} \qquad \beta_1 = \frac{D\alpha_1 - B\alpha_2}{\alpha_1} \qquad \gamma_1 = \frac{\beta_1\alpha_2 - \alpha_1\beta_2}{\beta_1}$$

$$\alpha_2 = \frac{BE - AF}{B} \qquad \beta_2 = \frac{F\alpha_1 - B\alpha_3}{\alpha_1} \qquad \gamma_2 = \frac{\beta_1\alpha_3 - \alpha_1\beta_3}{\beta_1}$$

$$\alpha_3 = \frac{BG - AH}{B} \qquad \beta_3 = \frac{H\alpha_1 - Bo}{\alpha_1}$$

When the array has been computed, the left-hand column (A, B, α_1, β_1, γ_1) is examined. If the signs of all the numbers in the left-hand column are the same, there are no positive real roots. If there are changes in sign, the number of positive real roots is equal to the number of changes in sign. It should be recognized that this is a test for instability; the absence of sign changes does not guarantee stability.

GENERAL DESIGN PROCEDURE

The initial performance specifications for an automatic control generally prescribe such quantities as the range of operation of the input variable and its derivatives, the maximum acceptable value of the steady-state error, and possibly other quantities, such as maximum settling time and peak overshoot. With preliminary knowledge of the nature of the input variable and the load, the designer integrates the components of the **basic** automatic-control system, develops the open-loop transfer function of this basic system, and examines its $G(s)$ locus. The system gain K is then adjusted to satisfy the steady-state error requirements and the resulting locus $KG(s)$ is again examined for stability. If instability exists at the required gain, the $KG(s)$ locus is reshaped through the use of derivative or integral compensation by means of a phase-lead or phase-lag component to display acceptable phase and gain margins. A detailed discussion of gain adjustment and phase compensation may be found in the references.

COMPONENTS

Hydraulic systems are used for rapid-response servomechanisms at high power levels. Operating system pressures are from 50 to 100 psi for slower-acting systems and up to 5,000 psi where lightweight and fast responses are required. Compared with **electrical systems** the major advantages are a rapid response in the large horsepower ranges and the capability of operating at high power-density levels since the fluid can transmit dissipated energy from the point of generation. Compared with **pneumatic systems,** hydraulic systems are faster because the fluid is essentially incompressible. Major disadvantages are vulnerability to dirt, since the components generally require close machining tolerances, and the danger of fire and explosion resulting from the flammability of the hydraulic fluids used (Blackburn).

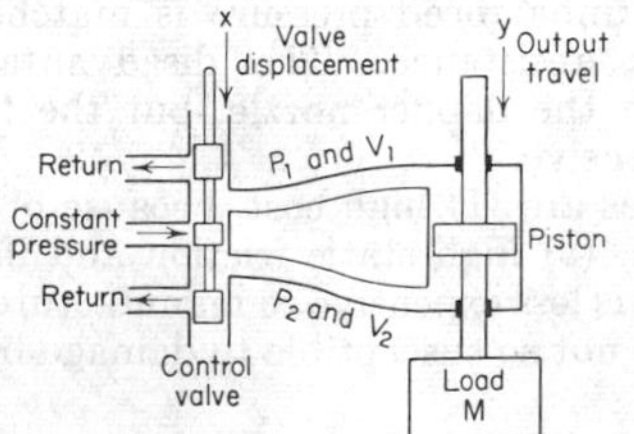

FIG. 18. Four-way valve-piston circuit (*Truxal*).

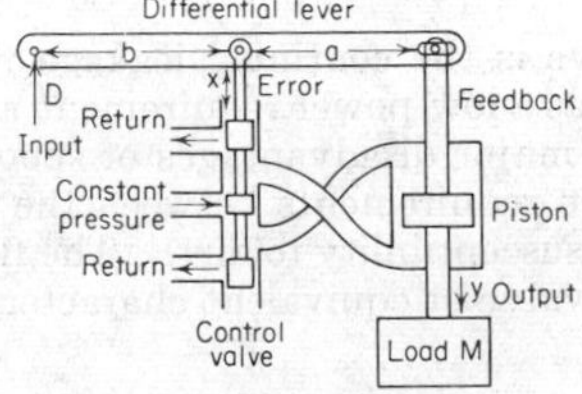

FIG. 19. Valve-piston position servo mechanical feedback (*Truxal*).

The direction and volume of flow are controlled by **servo valves** in the system. They may be single-stage or two-stage (pilot-operated) and mechanically or electrically actuated. A schematic of a spool-type four-way single-stage control piston and inertia load is shown in Fig. 18. Hydraulic fluid at constant pressure enters at the supply port. With displacement of the spool valve downward, for example, inflow to the top side of the piston moves the piston downward. Because of machining tolerances the spool dimensions are either larger (overlapped) or smaller (underlapped) than the port dimension. Underlapped valves permit leakage to the piston in the centered position; overlapped valves result in a dead zone, where motion x results in no flow until a port is opened.

The transfer function of this circuit is given as (Truxal, "Control Engineers' Handbook")

$$\frac{y}{x} = \frac{C_1 \dfrac{1}{1 + \alpha(C_1/C_2)}}{s\left[\dfrac{VM}{2BA^2}\dfrac{1}{1 + \alpha(C_1/C_2)}s^2 + \dfrac{C_1 m/C_2 + V\alpha/2BA^2}{1 + \alpha(C_1/C_2)}s + 1\right]}$$

where C_1 = servo velocity gradient, in./(sec)(in.), C_2 = servo force gradient, lb/in., α = viscous friction of load and piston, lb/(in.)(sec), B = bulk modulus of fluid, psi, M = mass of load and piston, lb/(in.)(sec^2), A = piston area, in.^{2}, and V = effective entrained fluid volume, in.^{3} (one-half of total entrained volume between valve and piston).

The velocity of the output is proportional to the input resulting in a **velocity-control** servo. To convert this system to a **position-control** servo, mechanical, hydraulic, or electrical feedback may be employed. A valve-piston position servo with **mechanical feedback** is shown in Fig. 19. Any difference between the input D and the piston position y causes a motion x, which causes the piston to move in a direction opposite to D, *i.e.*, in a direction to reduce x. The lever ratio establishes the relationship between y and D.

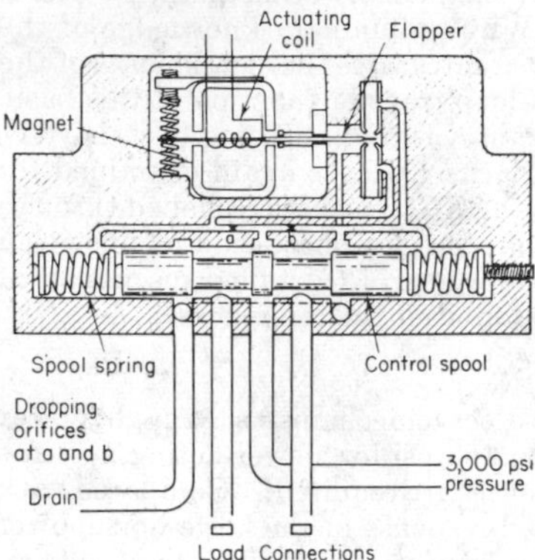

FIG. 20. Two-stage electrohydraulic servo valve. The first stage is a four-way flapper valve with a calibrated pressure output driving a second-stage spring-loaded four-way spool valve. (*Moog Servocontrols, Inc.*)

Most commercially available servo valves are two stages, permitting electrohydraulic action. The pilot stage can be operated by a low-power, short-travel electrical device, with a concomitant increase in flexibility. A typical pilot-operated servo valve is shown in Fig. 20. In this case the pilot is a double-flapper valve rather than a spool valve. (In general, small, accurate low-leakage spool valves are costly.) Upward movement of the flapper by the actuating motor results in increased pressure to the right end of the power spool. Hydraulic feedback occurs because of the increased flow across restrictor *a*. The power spool moves to the left until the unbalanced pressure is matched by the spring resistance. The disadvantage of this valve is the continual leakage flow through the flapper nozzle, but the torque motor has a low-power requirement and is inexpensive.

The major disadvantages of spool-type valves are (1) high cost, because of high-tolerance requirements between the valve lands, (2) high static friction and inertia, and (3) susceptibility to dirt. The **flapper** valve is less expensive to manufacture than a spool valve of equivalent characteristics and is not so susceptible to damage by dirt

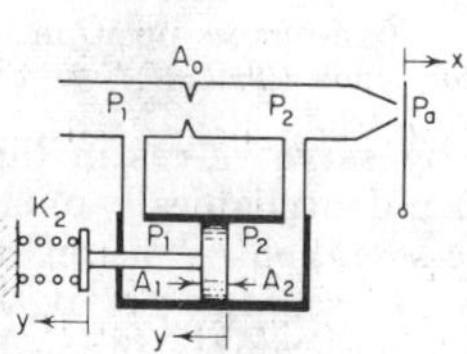

FIG. 21. Flapper valve (*Raven*).

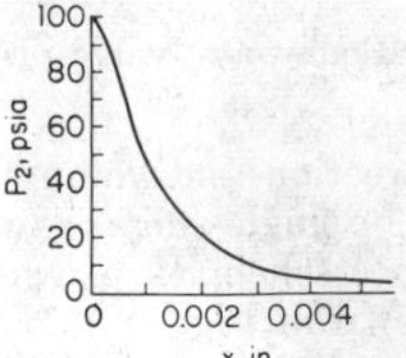

FIG. 22. Equilibrium curve of P_2 *vs.* x for a flapper valve (*Raven*).

particles. In Fig. 21, P_1, the supply pressure, is constant. Input motion of the flapper toward the nozzle increases P_2 and drives the piston toward the right. The steady-state characteristic P_2 *vs.* x is shown in Fig. 22.

PNEUMATIC SYSTEMS

Pneumatic systems are widely used in industrial control. The advantage of pneumatic over hydraulic systems is the ready availability of air and the ability to discharge it indiscriminately into the atmosphere when it is used. The most common operating pressures are of the order of 20 psig; response times are considerably slower than those of hydraulic systems.

Important components in a pneumatic control system are the valve actuator, or motor, the valve, and the controller. The most commonly used **valve actuator** is the diaphragm motor in which the output pressure from the controller is counteracted not only by the spring but also by fluid forces at the valve body. The latter may cause serious deviation from linear static static behavior with deleterious control effects. High friction at the valve stem or large unbalanced fluid forces at the valve can be overcome with valve positioners, which are essentially proportional controllers.

The **control valve** is described by its lift (L)–area (A) relationship; *e.g.*, linear valve, $L = kA$; equipercentage, $L = k \ln A/A_0$, where A_0 is area open to flow when lift is zero. This relationship is not necessarily the lift-flow characteristic of the valve when installed since the valve is but one component in a piping system in which pressure drops vary with the flow rate. The differential across the valve is usually taken as not less than one-third of the total losses of the system. Valves are generally selected according to how well they can compensate for non-linearities in the system which result in a change in the character of the control response for a given controller setting when load or set-point changes occur or when there is a variable over-all pressure drop across the system. Equipercentage valves, for example, tend to control over widely varying operating conditions, since the change in flow is always proportional to the

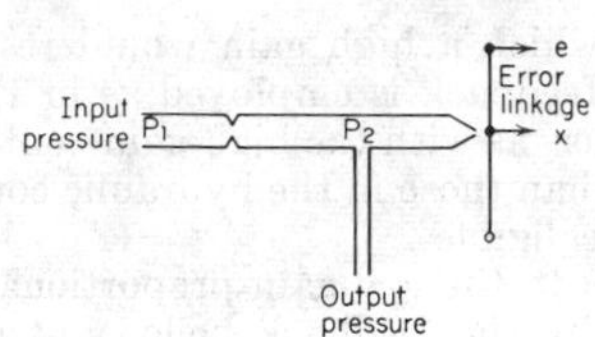

FIG. 23. Nozzle flapper amplifier.

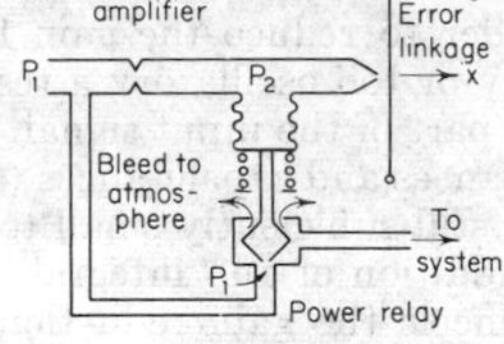

FIG. 24. Two-stage pneumatic amplifier.

flow rate. The selection of the proper valve therefore depends on study of the particular system. Regardless of the type selected, however, the size of the valve should be such that pressure drop across the valve and not that across the connecting piping controls the flow.

The **controller** modifies the error signal in a desired manner to produce an output pressure which is used to actuate the valve motor. The several controller modes used singly or in combination are (1) the proportional mode in which $P_{\text{out}}(t) = K_cE(t)$, (2) the integral mode, in which $P_{\text{out}}(t) = 1/T_1 \int E(t)\,dt$, and (3) the rate mode, in which $P_{\text{out}}(t) = T_2\, dE(t)/dt$. In these expressions $P_{\text{out}}(t)$ = controller output pressure, $E(t)$ = input error signal, K_c = proportional gain, $1/T_1$ = reset rate, and T_2 = rate time.

Since the proportional mode requires an error signal to change output pressure, set-point and load changes in a proportionally controlled system are accompanied by a steady-state error inversely proportional to the gain. For systems which, because of stability considerations, cannot tolerate high gains, the integral mode added to the proportional will eliminate the steady-state error since the output from this mode is continually varying so long as an error exists. The addition of the integral mode to a proportional controller has an adverse affect on the relative stability of the control because of the 90 deg phase lag introduced.

The **rate mode,** called "anticipatory," can take large corrective action when errors are small but have a high rate of change. The mode resists not only departures from the set point but also returns and so provides a stabilizing action. Since the rate mode cannot control to a set point, it is not used alone. When used with the proportional mode, its stabilizing influence (90 deg phase lead; see Table 3) may allow an increase in gain K_c and a consequent decrease in steady-state error.

Controller Mechanisms. A simple proportioning device is the pneumatic nozzle-flapper amplifier (Figs. 23 and 24). Since a typical nozzle area is 0.00002 in.^{2}, the controller shown is not capable of handling the large quantities of air that may be required for industrial use. For this purpose a second amplifier, or power relay (Fig. 24), is used as a second stage to the nozzle-flapper amplifier. As P_{in} (from the nozzle flapper) increases, the bellows moves the valve against the supply seat, preventing flow from the supply and allowing air from the output to bleed to the atmosphere. When P_{in} decreases, the reverse occurs.

The combination nozzle-flapper amplifier and power relay illustrated has high gain since small displacements of the flapper can result in the output traversing the full range of pressure available. Thus it can serve as an on-off controller.

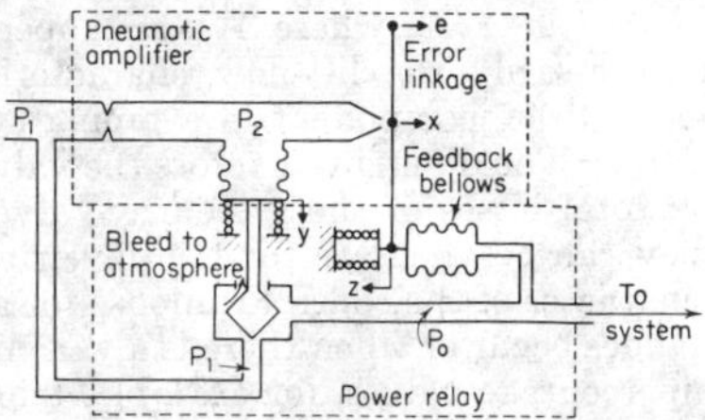

FIG. 25. Gain reduction of pneumatic amplifier by means of feedback bellows (*Raven*).

In order to reduce the gain for processes in which a high gain would result in instability or too oscillatory a response, negative feedback is employed as in Fig. 25 to cancel part of the input signal. In this controller, as with the high-gain controller, the resistances and capacitances (although higher than those in the hydraulic counterpart) are still sufficiently small to be considered negligible.

The addition of an "integral" bellows (Fig. 26) to the low-gain proportional controller cancels the gain reduction brought about by the feedback bellows at a rate determined by the restriction *a*. That is, for a step-function input, the gain and hence the output pressure increases with time, thereby fulfilling the definition of a proportional plus integral controller.

For a step input the rate mode requires an initial high gain which, as time proceeds, decays to the gain of the proportional controller. This is accomplished by delaying the feedback as in Fig. 27.

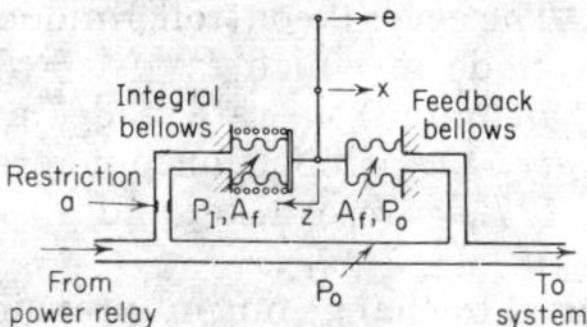

FIG. 26. Pneumatic amplifier with proportional plus integral action (*Raven*).

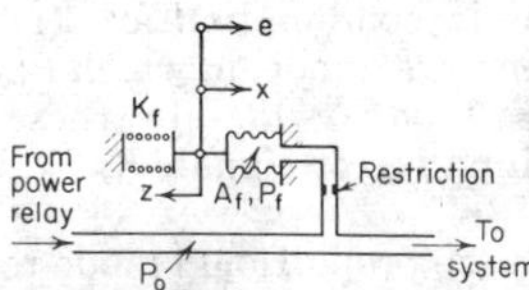

FIG. 27. Pneumatic amplifier with proportional plus rate action (*Raven*).

The selection of the proper controller can be made by methods previously outlined. Table 7 is offered as a general guide for preliminary design (Considine).

COMPUTER CONTROL

Digital computers (Sec. 2) are being used with increasing frequency in the control of diverse processes. All but a few of the digital applications are supervisory or optimizing in nature; the computer, programmed to a model of the process, accepts measured data from conventional instruments, calculates optimum control settings for conventional controllers, and corrects them automatically. The computer need not be concerned only with optimizing the variables of a process for physical stability and quality but can also be used for economic optimization.

Table 7. Process Characteristics versus Mode of Control
(Considine, "Process Instruments and Controls Handbook," McGraw-Hill)

Number of process capacities	Process reaction rate	Process time lags: Resistance capacity (R-C)	Process time lags: Dead time (transportation)	Load changes: Size	Load changes: Speed	Suitable mode of control
Single.......	Slow	Moderate to large	Small	Any	Any	Two-position. Two-position with differential gap
				Moderate	Slow	Multiposition. Proportional input
Single (self-regulating)	Fast	Small	Small	Any	Slow	Floating modes: Single speed Multispeed
					Moderate	Proportional-speed floating
Multiple.....	Slow to moderate	Moderate	Small	Small	Moderate	Proportional position
Multiple.....	Moderate	Any	Small	Small	Any	Proportional plus rate
Multiple.....	Any	Any	Small to moderate	Large	Slow to moderate	Proportional plus reset
Multiple.....	Any	Any	Small	Large	Fast	Proportional plus reset plus rate
Any.........	Faster than that of the control system	Small or nearly zero	Small to moderate	Any	Any	Wideband proportional plus fast reset

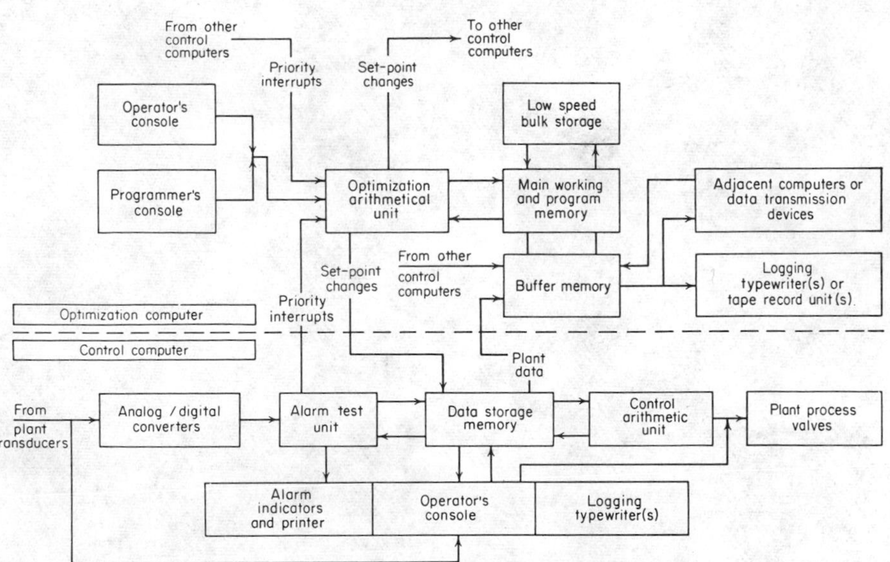

FIG. 28. Combined computer system for both direct digital and optimizing control (*Chem. Eng.*, Mar. 2, 1964).

A second use of the digital computer, still under study and not yet demonstrated conclusively as economically or technically feasible, is direct digital control (DDC) in which conventional automatic control instruments are directly displaced by a special-purpose digital computer time-shared among many control loops. The advantages of such a system are higher accuracy, more flexibility in incorporating advanced control techniques, and savings in control room costs because of compactness. Drawbacks at present are cost and reliability. A possible combined computer system for both direct digital and optimizing control is shown in Fig. 28 (*Chem. Eng.*, Mar. 2, 1964).

Applications of supervisory control computers are found in the electric utility industry, where they are applied to load-frequency control and automatic dispatch as well as closed-loop control; in the steel industry, where they are applied to rolling mills; and in the chemical industry, where they are used for closed-loop process control. At the present writing several direct digital control applications are in the planning stage.

SECTION 17

INDUSTRIAL ENGINEERING

BY

B. W. NIEBEL, Professor of Industrial Engineering, The Pennsylvania State University.
ADOLPH MATZ, Professor of Accounting, Wharton School of Finance and Commerce, University of Pennsylvania.
WESTON SMITH, Managing Director, Weston Smith Associates, New York.
E. VERNON LEWIS, Associate Professor of Mathematics, Ursinus College.
H. B. MAYNARD, President, Maynard Research Council, Pittsburgh.
WILLIAM K. HODSON, President, H. B. Maynard Company, Inc., Pittsburgh.
FRANKLIN J. LEERBURGER, Consulting Engineer, New York.

CONTENTS

INDUSTRIAL ECONOMICS AND MANAGEMENT

BY

B. W. Niebel

REFERENCES: Roscoe, "Project Economy," Irwin. Niebel, "Motion and Time Study," Irwin. Moore, "Manufacturing Management," Irwin. Folts, "Introduction to Industrial Management," McGraw-Hill. Bock and Holstein, "Production Planning and Control," Merrill. Mayer, "Production Management," McGraw-Hill.

Plant Organization

Organization generally is recognized as the foundation of management. The term, as it is used in industry and business, means the distribution of the functions of the business to the personnel logically qualified to handle them. It should be noted that the organization should be built around functions rather than individuals.

The majority of progressive concerns today are organized on a **line-and-staff** basis. The relationships usually are shown on an **organization chart,** which reveals the relationships of the major divisions and departments and the lines of direct authority from superior to subordinate. Lines of authority usually are shown as vertical lines. **Staff authority** frequently is indicated by a dotted line, which distinguishes it from direct authority. This same procedure is usually used to indicate committee relationships. Departments or activities are clearly identified within framed rectangles. The names of individuals responsible for a given department or activity often are included with their job organization titles. Although the organization chart shows the relationship of organization units, it does not clearly define the responsibilities of the individuals and the groups. Thus organization charts must be supplemented with carefully prepared job descriptions for all members of the organization. **Job descriptions** are written definitions of jobs enumerating the duties and responsibilities of each position.

A **line organization** comprises those individuals, groups, and supervising employees concerned directly with the productive operation of the business. The paths of authority are clearly defined, as each individual has but one superior from whom he obtains orders and instructions. This superior reports to but one individual, who has complete jurisdiction over his operation and supplies necessary technical information. In large and middle-sized organizations, a pure line-type enterprise cannot exist because of the complexity of our business society.

A **staff organization** involves personnel, departments, or activities that assist the line supervisor in an advisory, service, coordinating, or control capacity. It should be noted that a staff position is a full-time job and is essentially the work of a specialist. Typical staff functions are performed by the company's legal department, controller, and production control. Figure 1 illustrates a typical line-staff activity.

Committees are used in some instances. A **committee** is a group of individuals which meets to discuss problems or projects within its area of assigned responsibility in order to arrive at recommendations or decisions. A committee operates on a staff basis. Although committees are time-consuming and frequently delay action, their use combines the experience and judgment of several persons, rather than a single individual, in reaching decisions.

The control of organization is the responsibility of two groups of management: (1) **administrative management,** which has the responsibility for determining policy and co-ordinating sales, finance, production, and distribution, and (2) **production**

management, which has the responsibility for executing the policies established by administration.

In building an efficient organization, management should abide by certain principles, namely:

1. Clear separation of the various functions of the business should be established to avoid overlap or conflict in the accomplishment of tasks or in the issuance or reception of orders.
2. Each managerial position should have a definite location within the organization, with a written job specification.
3. There should be a clear distinction between line and staff operation and control.
4. A clear understanding of the authority under each position should prevail.
5. Selection of all personnel should be based on unbiased techniques.
6. A recognized line of authority should prevail from the top of the organization to the bottom, with an equally clear line of responsibility from the bottom to the top.
7. A system of communication should be well established and definitely known—it should be short, yet able to reach rapidly everyone in the organization.

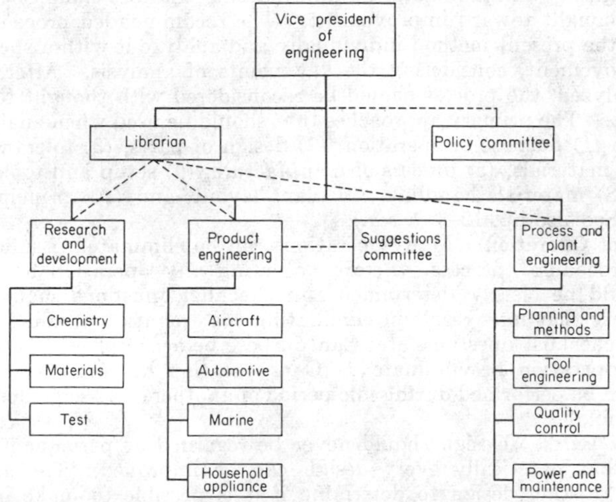

FIG. 1. Organization chart illustrating the activities reporting to the vice president of engineering.

Staff members usually have no authority over any portion of the organization that the staff unit assists. However, the department or division that is being assisted by the staff can make demands upon the staff to provide certain services. There are instances where a control type of staff may be delegated to direct the actions of certain individuals in the organization that they are servicing. When this takes place, the delegated authority may be termed **staff authority;** it is also frequently known as **functional authority** because its scope is determined by the functional speciality of the staff involved.

Good organization requires that (1) responsibilities be clearly defined; (2) responsibility be coupled with corresponding authority; (3) a change in responsibility be made only after a definite understanding exists to that effect by all persons concerned; (4) no employee be subject to definite orders from more than one source; (5) orders not be given to subordinates over the head of another executive; (6) all criticism be made in a constructive manner and be made privately; (7) promotions, wage changes, and disciplinary action always be approved by the executive immediately superior to the one directly responsible; (8) any employee whose work is subject to regular inspection or appraisal be given the facilities to maintain an independent check of the quality of his work.

Process Analysis

Process analysis is a procedure for studying all productive and non-productive operations for the purpose of optimizing cost, production output, or quality. The procedure is first to acquire all information related to the volume of the work that will be directed to the process under study, namely, the expected volume of business, the chance of repeat business, the life of the job, the chance for design changes, and the labor content of the job. This will determine the time and effort to be devoted toward improving the existing process or planning a new process.

Once an estimate is made of quantity, process life, and labor content, then all pertinent factual information should be collected on operations; facilities used for transportation and transportation distances; inspections, inspection facilities, and inspection times; storages, storage facilities, and time spent in storage; vendor operations, together with vendor prices; and all drawings and design specifications. When the information affecting cost and method is gathered, it should be presented in a form suitable for study, *e.g.*, a **flow process chart.** This chart presents graphically and chronologically all manufacturing information. Studies should be made of each event with thought toward improvement. The recommended procedure is to take each step in the present method individually and analyze it with a specific approach toward improvement, considering the key points of analysis. After each element has been analyzed, the process should be reconsidered with thought toward over-all improvement. The primary approaches that should be used when analyzing the flow chart include (1) purpose of operation, (2) design of parts, (3) tolerances and specifications, (4) materials, (5) process of manufacture, (6) setup and tools, (7) working conditions, (8) materials handling, (9) plant layout, and (10) principles of motion economy. (See also pp. 12–3 *et. seq.*)

Purpose of Operation. Many operations can be eliminated if sufficient study is given the procedural process. Before accepting any operation as necessary, its purpose should be clearly determined and **checklist questions** should be asked to stimulate ideas that may result in eliminating the operation or some component of it. Typical checklist questions are: Can purpose be accomplished better in another way? Can operation be eliminated? Can operation be combined with another? Can operation be performed during idle period of another? Is sequence of operations the best possible?

Design of Parts. Design should never be regarded as permanent. Experience has shown that practically every design can be improved. The analyst should consider the existing design to determine if it is possible to make improvements. In general, improvements can be made by (1) simplifying the design through reduction of the number of parts, (2) reducing the number of operations required to produce the design, (3) reducing the length of travel in the manufacture of the design, and (4) utilizing a better material in design.

Tolerances and Specifications. These frequently can be liberalized to decrease unit costs without detrimental effects on quality; in other instances, they should be made more rigid to facilitate manufacturing operations. Tolerances and specifications must be investigated to ensure the use of an optimum process.

Materials. Five considerations should be kept in mind relative to both the direct and the indirect material used in the process: (1) finding a less expensive material, (2) finding materials easier to process, (3) using materials more economically, (4) using salvage materials, and (5) using supplies and tools economically.

Process of Manufacture. Improvement in the process of manufacture is perhaps the salient point, and possible improvements deserving special consideration include (1) mechanizing manual operations, (2) utilizing more efficient facilities on mechanical operations, (3) operating mechanical facilities more efficiently, and (4) when changing an operation, considering the possible effects on subsequent operations. There are almost always many ways to produce a given design, and better production methods are continually being developed. By systematically questioning and investigating the manufacturing process, more effective methods will be developed.

Setup and tools have such a dominant influence on economics that consideration must include quantity to be produced, chance for repeat business, amount of labor involved, delivery requirements of the customer, and capital needed to develop the setup and provide the tools. Specifically, consideration should be given to reducing the setup time by better planning in production control, designing tooling for the full-capacity utilization of the production facility, and introducing more efficient tooling.

Good working conditions are an integral part of an optimum process as they improve the safety record, reduce absenteeism and tardiness, raise employee morale, improve public relations, and increase production. Consideration should include (1) improved lighting; (2) controlled temperature; (3) adequate ventilation; (4) sound control; (5) promotion of orderliness, cleanliness, and good housekeeping; (6) arrangement for immediate disposal of irritating and harmful dusts, fumes, gases, and fogs; (7) provision of guards at nip points and points of power transmission; (8) installation of personnel-protection equipment; (9) sponsorship and enforcement of a well-formulated first aid and safety program.

Materials Handling. The handling of materials is an essential part of each operation and frequently consumes the major share of the time. Materials handling adds nothing but cost to the product, and it should accordingly be reduced. When analyzing the flow process chart, keep in mind that the best-handled part is the least manually handled part. Whether distances of moves are large or small, points to be considered for reduction of time and energy spent in handling materials are (1) reduction of time spent in picking up material, (2) maximum use of mechanical handling equipment, (3) better use of existing handling facilities, (4) greater care in the handling of materials.

Plant Layout. Good process design requires good **plant layout.** This involves development of the workplace so that the location of the equipment introduces maximum economy during the manufacturing process. In general, plant layouts represent one or a combination of (1) product, or straight-line, layouts, and (2) process, or functional, arrangements. In the **straight-line layout,** machinery is located so the flow from one operation to the next is minimized for any product class. Thus it would not be unusual to see a surface grinder located between a milling machine and a turret lathe, with an assembly bench and plating tank in the immediate area. **Process, or functional, layout** is the grouping of similar facilities, *e.g.*, all turret lathes in one section, department, or building.

The principal advantage of **product grouping** is lower materials-handling costs since distances moved are minimized. The major disadvantages are:

1. Since a broad variety of occupations are represented in a small area, employee discontent can readily be fostered.

2. Unlike facilities grouped together result in operator training becoming more difficult since no experienced operator on a given facility may be located in the immediate area to train new employees.

3. The problem of finding competent supervisors is increased due to the variety of facilities and jobs to be supervised.

4. Greater initial investment is required because of duplicate service lines such as air, water, gas, oil, and power lines.

5. The arrangement of facilities tends to give a casual observer the thought that disorder prevails. Thus it is more difficult to promote good housekeeping.

In general, the disadvantages of product grouping are more than offset by the advantage of low handling cost if production requirements are substantial.

Process, or functional, layout gives an appearance of neatness and orderliness and, consequently, tends to promote good housekeeping; new men can be trained more readily, and it is easier to obtain experienced supervision since the requirements of supervising like facilities are not so arduous. The obvious disadvantages of process grouping are the possiblities of long moves and of backtracking on jobs that require a series of operations on diversified facilities. In planning the process, important points to be considered are: (1) For straight-line mass production, material laid aside should be in position for the next operation. (2) For diversified production, the layout should permit short moves and deliveries and the material should be convenient to the operator. (3) For multiple-machine operations, equipment should be grouped around the operator. (4) For efficient stacking, storage areas should be arranged to minimize searching and rehandling. (5) For better worker efficiency, service centers should be located close to production areas.

Principles of Motion Economy. The last of the primary approaches to process design is the analysis of the flow chart for the incorporation of basic principles of motion economy. When studying work performed at any work station, the engineer should ask: (1) Are both hands working at the same time and in opposite, symmetrical directions? (2) Is each hand going through as few motions as possible? (3) Is the workplace arranged so that long reaches are avoided? (4) Are both hands being used effectively, with neither being used as a holding device? In the event that "no" is the answer to any of these questions, then the work station should be altered to incorporate improvements related to motion economy. (See also p. 17–35 *et seq.*)

Production Control

Production control includes the scheduling of production; the dispatching of materials, tools, and supplies at the required time so that the predicted schedules can be realized; the follow-up of production orders to be sure that proposed schedules are realized; the maintenance of an adequate inventory to meet production requirements at optimum cost; and the maintenance of cost and manufacturing records to establish controls, estimating, and equipment replacement. Consideration must be given to the requirements of the customer, the available capacity, the nature of the work that precedes the production to be scheduled, and the nature of the work that succeeds the current work being scheduled.

Scheduling may be accomplished with various degrees of refinement. In low-production plants where the total number of hours required per unit of production is large, scheduling may adequately be done by departmental loading; *e.g.*, if a department has a total of 10 direct-labor employees, it has 400 available work hours per week. Every new job is scheduled by departments giving consideration to the average number of available hours within the department. A refinement of this method is to schedule groups of facilities or sections, *e.g.*, to schedule the milling machine section as a group. In high-production plants, detailed facility scheduling frequently is necessary in order to ensure optimum results from all facilities. Thus, with an 8-hr shift, each facility is recorded as having 8 available hours, and work is scheduled to each piece of equipment indicating the time that it should arrive at the work station and the time that the work should be completed.

Scheduling is frequently done on control boards utilizing commercially available devices, such as "*Productrol*," "*Sched-U-Graph*," and "*Visi-trol*." These, in effect, are mechanized versions of **Gantt charts,** where schedules are represented by paper strips cut to lengths equivalent to standard times. The strips are placed in the appropriate horizontal position adjacent to the particular order being worked; delays are conspicuously marked by red signals at the delay point. Manual posting to a ledger maintains projected schedules and cumulative loads. The digital computer is successfully used as a scheduling facility.

A recent adaptation of the Gantt chart, **PERT** (Program Evaluation and Review Techniques), is finding considerable application. This prognostic management planning and control method graphically portrays the optimum way to attain some predetermined objective, usually in terms of time. The **critical path** (CPM = Critical Path Method) consists of that sequence of events in which delay in the start or completion of any event in the sequence will cause a delay in the project completion.

In using PERT for scheduling, three time estimates are used for each activity, based upon the following questions: (1) What is the earliest time (optimistic) in which you can expect to complete this activity if everything works out ideally? (2) Under average conditions, what would be the most likely time duration for this activity? (3) What is the longest possible time (pessimistic) required to complete this activity if almost everything goes wrong? With these estimates, a probability distribution of the time required to perform the activity can be made (Fig. 2). The activity is started, and depending on how successfully events take place, the finish will occur somewhere between a and b (most likely close to m). The distribution closely approximates that of the beta distribution and is used as the typical model in PERT. The weighted linear approximation for the expected mean time, using probability theory, is given by

$$t_e = (a + 4m + b)/6$$

With the development of the project plan and the calculation of activity times (time for all jobs between successive nodes in the network, such as the time for "design of rocket ignition system"), a chain of activities through the project plan can be established which has identical early and late event times; *i.e.*, the completion time of each activity comprising this chain cannot be delayed without delaying project completion. These are the critical events. Events are represented by nodes and

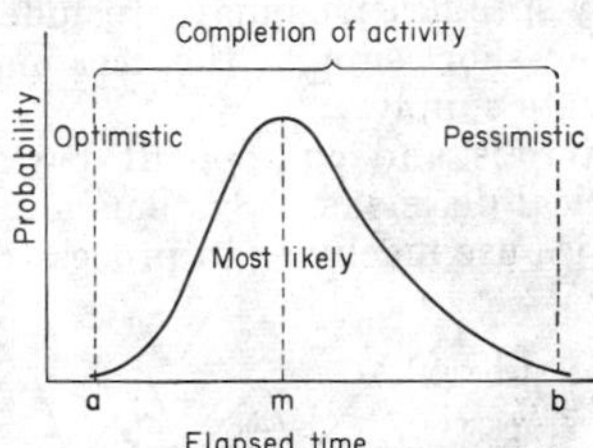

FIG. 2. Probability distribution of time required to perform an activity.

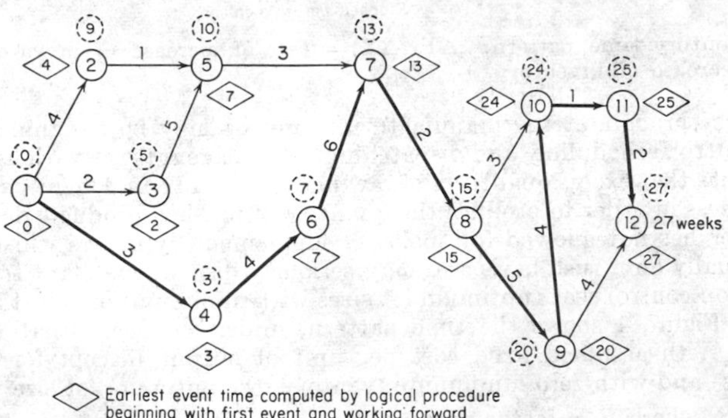

FIG. 3. Network showing critical path (heavy line). Code numbers within nodes signify events. Connecting lines with directional arrows indicate operations that are dependent on prerequisite operations. Time values shown on connecting lines represent the expected time in weeks. Diamonds associated with events show the earliest event time. Dotted circles associated with events present the latest event time.

denote instants in a logical sequence of activities at which an activity may be started or completed. This chain of critical events establishes the minimum project time. There is at least one such chain through any given project. There can, of course, be more than one chain reflecting the minimum project time. This is the concept behind the meaning of **critical path.** Figure 3 illustrates an elementary network portraying the critical path.

Control of Materials

Control of materials is critical to the smooth functioning of a plant. Raw materials and purchased parts must be on hand in the required quantities and at the time needed if production schedules are to be met. Unless management is speculating on raw materials, inventories should be at the lowest practicable level in order to minimize the capital invested and to reduce losses due to obsolescence, design changes, and deterioration. However, some minimum stock is essential if production is not to be delayed by lack of materials. The quantity for ordering replenishment stocks is determined by such factors as the lead time needed by the supplier, the reliability of the sources of supply in meeting promised delivery dates, the value of the materials, the cost of storage, and the risks of obsolescence or deterioration.

In many instances, plant management has the choice of manufacturing the components used in its product or procuring them from outside suppliers. Where a supplier specializes in certain components, he may be able to reach high-volume operations and produce more economically than can the individual users. Procurement from outside suppliers simplifies the manufacturing problem within a plant and permits management to concentrate on the phases of the process where it has critical know-how. Extreme quality specifications may preclude the use of outside suppliers. Likewise, if components are in short supply, the user may be forced to manufacture the units to ensure an adequate supply.

The control of raw materials and component parts may involve considerable clerical detail and many critical decisions. Systems and formulas will routinize this function, and larger companies use machines to process the vast amount of data.

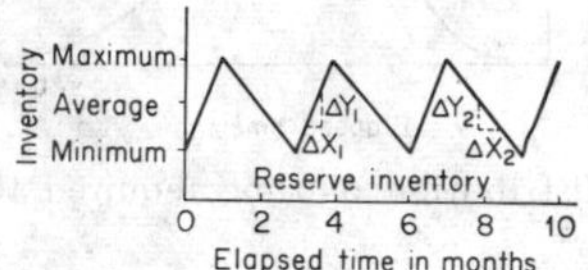

FIG. 4. Inventory time pattern. $\Delta Y_1/\Delta X_1$ = rate of increase of inventory; $\Delta Y_2/\Delta X_2$ = rate of decrease of inventory.

Shrinkage throughout the manufacturing process may be a significant factor in materials control, scheduling, and dispatching. Spoilage rates at various stages in the process require that excess quantities of raw materials and component parts be started into the process in order to produce the quantity of finished products desired. If the original order has not allowed for spoilage, supplementary orders will be necessary; these are usually on a rush basis and may seriously disrupt the plant schedule.

Production control seeks optimum lot sizes with minimum total cost and adequate inventory. Figure 4 shows the time pattern, under an ideal situation, for active inventory. With assumed fixed cost per unit of output (except for starting and storage costs) and with zero minimum inventory, the optimum lot size Q is given by $Q = \sqrt{ah/B}$, where B = factor when storage space is reserved for maximum inventory $= 0.5[1 - (\mathrm{d/r})](2s + ip)$; h = starting cost per lot (planning and setup); a = annual demand; s = annual cost of storage per unit of product; i = required yield on working capital; p = unit cost of production; d = daily demand; and r = daily rate of production during production period.

Equipment Replacement

New equipment may be acquired for a variety of reasons: (1) Existing machines may be so badly worn that they are either beyond repair or excessively costly to maintain. (2) The equipment may be incapable of holding specified quality tolerances. (3) A technical development may introduce a process producing higher-quality products. (4) Changes in the product line may require new kinds of machines. (5) An improved model which reduces operating costs may come on the market.

A decision to invest in new capital equipment involves the risk that improved models of machines may become available and render the new equipment obsolete before its mechanical life has expired. Aggressive competitors who regularly modernize their plants may force other companies to adopt a similar policy.

The **optimum time for replacement** of existing facilities is determined by an economic analysis incorporating the time value of money, the first cost of the new equipment (including unamortized portion and salvage value of old equipment), the expected life of the new equipment, the scrap value of the new equipment, and the anticipated annual return. The time value of money may be computed from $S = P(1 + i)^n$, where i = interest rate or return for a given period, n = number of interest or return periods, P = present worth of principal, and S = worth of sum n periods later.

EXAMPLE: If a new facility is anticipated to give $1,000 annual savings ($S$) over the next 5 years, company policy requires a 20 percent return (i) on capital investment, and the estimated salvage value (S') at the end of 5 years is $500, the procurement of the facility is justified if installation can be made for less than P, where

$$P = \left[\sum_{n=1}^{n=5} \frac{S}{(1 + i)^n} \right] + \frac{S'}{(1 + i)^5}$$

Wage Administration

Workers are compensated for their efforts in two principal ways: by hourly rates and by financial-type incentives. An **hourly rate** is paid to the worker for the number of hours he works and usually is not dependent upon the quantity or quality of his output. Each worker is assigned a job title depending upon his qualifications, experience, and skill. Under a structured system of wages, jobs are grouped into classifications and a similar range of rates is applied to all jobs in a classification. The bottom of the range is paid to beginners, and periodic increases to the top of the range may be automatic or may depend upon the foreman's appraisal of the individual's performance.

Job evaluation is a formal system for ranking jobs in classes. Each job is studied in relation to other jobs by analyzing such factors as responsibility, education, mental skill, manual skill, physical effort, and working conditions. A total numerical rating for job comparison is obtained by assigning points for each factor.

Merit rating is a point-scale evaluation of an individual's performance by a supervisor, considering such factors as quantity of output, quality of work, adaptability, dependability, ability to work with others, and attitude. These ratings serve as criteria for pay increases within a job classification.

The general level of hourly rates, or base rates, for a company should be determined with reference to the community level of rates. "**Going rates**" for the community are obtained from wage surveys conducted by the company, a local trade group, or a government agency. Generally a company which offers wages noticeably lower than the community rates will attract less-competent and less-permanent employees.

Under **financial-type incentives**—or **piece rates,** as they are commonly called—the worker's compensation is dependent upon his rate of output. Ordinarily, there is a minimum hourly guarantee below which pay will not decline. Penalties for substandard work may reduce the worker's pay. In some instances, a maximum for incentive earnings is established. The incentive may be calculated so that only the individual's output affects his pay, or when the individual's output cannot be measured, a group incentive may be paid, where the pay of each member of the group is determined by his base rate plus the output of the group. Group incentives tend to promote cooperation among workers. The administration of incentive plans requires careful management attention if abuses are to be avoided. Restrictions on output and deteriorated standards may lead to higher unit labor costs rather than the anticipated lower costs.

A **profit-sharing** plan is a form of group incentive whereby each participating worker receives a periodic bonus in addition to his regular pay, provided the company earns a profit. A minimum profit is usually set aside for a return on invested capital, and beyond this amount a percentage of profits goes into a pool to be shared by the employees. Many factors other than worker productivity affect profits, *e.g.*, fluctuations in sales volume, selling prices, and costs of raw materials and purchased parts. To protect the workers against adverse developments outside their control, some plans give the workers a bonus whenever the actual payroll dollars are less than the normal amount expected for a given volume of production. Bonuses may be distributed quarterly or even annually and may consequently be less encouraging than incentives paid weekly and related directly to output.

Employee Relations

Increasingly, management deals with collective bargaining units in setting conditions of work, wages, seniority, vacations, and the like. The **bargaining unit** may be affiliated with a national union or may be independent and limited to the employees of a particular plant. A union contract is usually negotiated annually, although managements have sought longer-term agreements. Some managements, by making substantial concessions, have negotiated contracts covering a 3- to 5-year period. Under these contracts, the union frequently reserves the right to reopen the wage clauses annually.

Grievance procedures facilitate the processing of minor day-to-day disputes between workers and management. Grievances most commonly occur when the worker:

1. Thinks he is unfairly treated in matters of (*a*) pay rates, (*b*) promotion, (*c*) work assignment, (*d*) distribution of overtime, (*e*) seniority, or (*f*) disciplinary action.
2. Believes he is handicapped by (*a*) lack of clear policies or working rules; (*b*) inadequate supervision; (*c*) too many bosses; (*d*) foremen who play favorites; (*e*) fellow workmen who are careless, inefficient, or uncooperative; or (*f*) lack of opportunity to show his ability.
3. Is dissatisfied with (*a*) general job conveniences (*e.g.*, washrooms), (*b*) working conditions (*e.g.*, light), (*c*) equipment and tools, (*d*) plant or office setup (*e.g.*, working space), or (*e*) protection against job hazards and accidents.

A union steward acts as the employee's representative in discussing a complaint with the foreman. If a settlement cannot be reached, the discussion may move to the general superintendent's level; the personnel manager is oftentimes involved at the various stages. Ways to reduce employee grievances are:

1. Make employee feel accepted; give him sense of "belonging."
2. Make employee feel significant; give him recognition as a person.
3. Make employee feel safe as to (*a*) job security, and (*b*) suitable working conditions.
4. Let employee experience the help of leadership.
5. Increase employee's knowledge about (*a*) the company, (*b*) its product(s), (*c*) his job, and (*d*) his next job.
6. Give employee fair and impartial treatment.
7. Give employee a chance to be heard: (*a*) Ask him for suggestions; acknowledge them; use where practicable and give credit. (*b*) Encourage him to discuss his problems and gripes; follow through if and as needed.
8. Aid the employee to make his contribution to the solution of his problem.
9. Assist employee to develop pride in his work.
10. Recognize employee's status.

An outside arbitrator may be helpful when all internal grievance procedures have been exhausted.

Selection of workers must give attention to the suitability of applicants as well as their previous training. Interviewing and tests for qualities required on the job are necessary to good placement. Induction and instruction of new men are equally important and should not be a secondary task of a busy foreman; they may be a responsibility of the personnel manager or of a subforeman. Induction includes an orientation to the total plant operations as well as to the duties of the specific job; introduction to the foreman, subforeman, and fellow workers; and an explanation of the employee's relations with the personnel department and with employee committees or groups that deal with management.

Promotions and recognition of accomplishment profoundly affect morale and require constant supervision by the personnel manager and the line managers. Training programs are used to prepare workers and apprentices for advancement; formal training programs for supervisors are used to develop the capabilities of members of management. The training sessions may be organized and conducted under the personnel manager or by outside specialists.

COST ACCOUNTING

BY

Adolph Matz

References: Dickey, "Accountants' Cost Handbook," Ronald. Matz, Curry, and Frank, "Cost Accounting," South-Western Publishing. Neuner, "Cost Accounting," Irwin. Horngren, "Cost Accounting," Prentice-Hall. Crowningsshield, "Cost Accounting," Houghton-Mifflin. Blocker and Weltmer, "Cost Accounting," McGraw-Hill. March, "Cost Accounting," McGraw-Hill.

Cost accounting, an integral part of the management process, furnishes the costs of products, operations, or functions and compares actual costs and expenses with predetermined budgets and standards. It also provides data for special cost studies involving alternative choices regarding products, operations, and functions, thus enabling management to make decisions with respect to sales policies, production methods, purchasing procedures, financial plans, and capital structure. Such information is needed to assist management in (1) setting the company's profit goal, (2) establishing departmental targets which direct activities toward the achievement of the final goal, (3) measuring and controlling progress with the aid of budgets and standards, and (4) analyzing and deciding on adjustments and improvements to keep the entire organization moving forward in balance toward established company and profit objectives.

Management and Its Functions. To be successful, management must integrate its own knowledge, skills, and practices with the know-how and experience of those who are entrusted with the task of carrying out company objectives. Management, together with its employees and workers, can achieve its objectives through performance of the three managerial functions: (1) planning and setting objectives, (2) organizing, and (3) controlling.

Planning is a basic function of the management process. Without planning there is no need to organize or control. However, planning must precede doing, and the budget is the most important planning tool of an enterprise.

Organizing is essentially the establishment of the framework within which the required activities are to be performed, together with a list of who should perform them. Creation of an organization requires the establishment of organizational or functional units generally known as departments, divisions, sections, floors, branches, etc.

Controlling is the process or procedure by which management ensures operative performance which corresponds with plans. The control process is pictured diagrammatically in Fig. 1. Recognition of accounting as an important tool in the controlling phase is evidenced by the management position of the controller, the chief accounting officer. The controller, through the issuance of performance reports, points out the areas and jobs or tasks which require corrective action. These reports should make possible "management by exception."

The effectiveness of the control of costs depends upon proper communication through control and action reports from the accountant to the various levels of operating management. An organization chart is essential to the development of a cost system and cost reports which parallel the responsibilities of individuals for implementing management plans. The coordinated development of a company's organization with the cost and budgetary system will lead to "responsibility accounting."

Annual Reports. Accounting and cost systems are in the final analysis geared to the presentation of the financial and operating results at the end of the year. (See also p. 17–21 *et seq.*) A balance sheet and income statement based on the published annual report of a company are presented below. Such statements are prepared in "conformance with generally accepted accounting principles," a phrase which is included in the certification statement thereto by the certified public accountant.

Balance Sheet (Illustrative)
Black Carbon, Inc.
December 31, 19–

Assets			
Current Assets:			
Cash		$ 5,050,000	
Accounts Receivable (net)		6,990,000	
Inventories:			
Raw Materials and Supplies	$ 1,000,000		
Work in Process	1,800,000		
Finished Goods	2,900,000	5,700,000	
Investments		1,000,000	
Deferred Charges		340,000	
Total Current Assets			$19,080,000
Property, Plant, and Equipment:			
Land		$ 4,000,000	
Buildings and Equipment	$75,500,000		
Less: Allowance for Depreciation	47,300,000	28,200,000	
Total Fixed Assets			32,200,000
Total Assets			$51,280,000
Liabilities			
Current Liabilities:			
Accounts Payable and Accruals		$ 3,580,000	
Provision for Income Taxes:			
Federal	$ 2,250,000		
State	65,000	2,315,000	
Total Current Liabilities			$ 5,895,000
Long-term Debt			5,300,000
Total Liabilities			$11,195,000
Stockholders Equity:			
Common Stock—no par value			
Authorized—2,000,000 shares			
Outstanding—1,190,000 shares		$11,900,000	
Earnings retained in the business		28,185,000	
Total Stockholders' Equity			$40,085,000
Total Liabilities and Stockholders' Equity			$51,280,000

Income Statement (Illustrative)
Black Carbon, Inc.
for the year 19—

Net Sales		$50,087,000
Cost of products:		
Material, Labor, and Overhead (excluding depreciation)	$32,150,000	
Depreciation	5,160,000	
Research and Development Costs	260,000	37,570,000
Gross Profit		$12,517,000
Less: Selling and Administrative Expenses		3,220,000
Profit from Operations		9,297,000
Other Deductions		305,000
		8,992,000
Other Income		219,000
Income before Federal and State Income Taxes		9,211,000
Less: Provision for Federal and State Income Taxes		4,055,000
Total Net Income		5,156,000
Dividends paid to shareholders		2,200,000
Income retained in the business		$ 2,956,000

Purposes of Cost Accounting. Cost accounting is charged with the task of (1) determining costs and profit for an accounting period, (2) creating inventory

values for costing and pricing purposes and, at times, controlling physical quantities, (3) aiding and participating in the creation and execution of budgets, (4) establishing costing methods and procedures that permit control and, if possible, reduction or improvement of costs, and (5) providing management with cost information in connection with problems that involve choice from among two or more alternative courses.

Classifications of Costs. The purposes of cost accouting require classifications of costs so that they are recognized (1) by the nature of the item (a natural classification), (2) in their relation to the product, (3) with respect to the accounting period to which they apply, (4) in their tendency to vary with volume or activity, (5) in their relation to departments, (6) for control and analysis, (7) for planning and decision making.

Direct material and direct labor may be listed among the items which have a **variable** nature. Factory overhead, however, must be carefully examined with regard to items of a variable and a fixed nature. It is impossible to budget and control

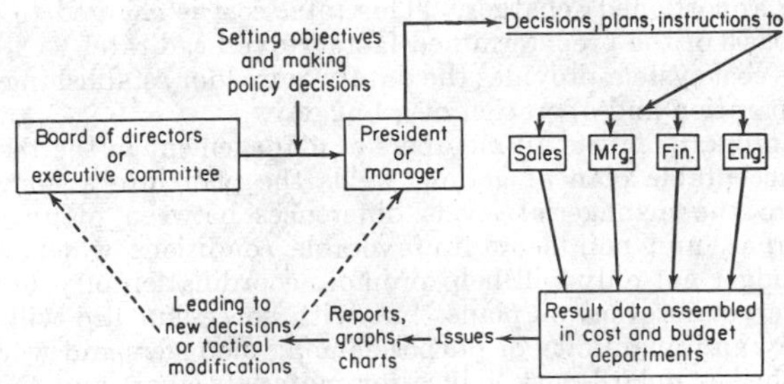

FIG. 1. Control circuit.

factory-overhead items successfully without regard to their tendency to be fixed or variable; the division is a necessary prerequisite to successful budgeting and intelligent cost planning and analysis.

In general, **variable expenses** show the following characteristics: (1) variability of total amount in direct proportion to volume, (2) comparatively constant cost per unit or product in the face of changing volume, (3) easy and reasonably accurate assignments to operating departments, and (4) incurrence controllable by the responsible department head.

The characteristics of **fixed expenses** are (1) fixed amount within a relative output range, (2) decrease of fixed cost per unit with increased output, (3) assignment to departments often made by managerial decisions or cost-allocation methods, and (4) control for incurrence resting with top management rather than departmental supervisors. Whether an expense is classified as fixed or variable may well be the result of managerial decisions.

Some **factory overhead** items are semivariable in nature; *i.e.*, they vary with production but not in direct proportion to the volume. For practical purposes, it is desirable to resolve each semivariable expense item into its variable and fixed components.

A factory is generally organized along departmental lines for production purposes. This factory departmentalization is the basis for the important classification and subsequent accumulation of costs by departments to achieve (1) cost control and (2) accurate costing. The departments of a company generally fall into two categories: (1) producing, or productive, departments, and (2) non-producing, or service, departments. A producing department is one in which manual and machine operations are performed directly upon any part of the product manufactured. A service department is one that is not directly engaged in production but renders a particular type of service for the benefit of other departments. The expense incurred in the operation

of service departments represents a part of the total factory overhead that must be absorbed in the cost of the product.

For **product costing,** the factory may be divided into departments, and departments may also be subdivided into cost centers. As a product passes through a cost center or department, it is charged with a share of the indirect expenses on the basis of a departmental factory-overhead rate. For cost-control purposes, budgets are established for departments and cost centers. Actual expenses are compared with budget allowances in order to determine the efficiency of a department and to measure the foreman's success in controlling his expenses.

Factory overhead, which is charged to a product or a job on the basis of a predetermined overhead rate, is considered indirect with regard to the product or the job to which the expense is charged. Service-department expenses are prorated to other service departments and/or to the producing departments. The prorated costs are termed **indirect departmental charges.** When all service-department expenses have been prorated to the producing departments, each producing department's total factory overhead will consist of its own direct departmental expense and the indirect (or prorated, or apportioned) charges. This total cost is charged to the product or the job on the basis of the predetermined factory-overhead rate.

A company's cost system provides the data required for establishing **standard costs** and for the preparation and operation of a **budget.**

The **budget** program enlists all members of management in the task of creating a workable and acceptable plan of action, welds the plan into a homogeneous unit, communicates to the managerial levels differences between planned activity and actual performance, and points out unfavorable conditions which need corrective action. The budget not only will help promote coordination of people, clarification of policy, and crystallization of plans, but with successful use will create greater internal harmony and unanimity of purpose among managers and workers.

The established **standard-cost** values for material, labor, and factory overhead form the foundation for the budget. Since standard costs are an invaluable aid in the process of setting prices, it is essential to set these standard costs at realistic levels. The measurement of deviations from established standards or norms is accomplished through the use of variance accounts.

Costs as a basis for planning are estimated costs which may be incurred if any one of several alternative courses of action is adopted. Different types of costs involve varying kinds of consideration in managerial planning and decision making.

Types of Cost Systems. The construction of a cost system requires a thorough understanding of (1) the organizational structure of the company, (2) the manufacturing procedure, and (3) the type of information which management requires of the cost system.

1. The organization chart gives a graphic picture of the ranking authority of superintendents, department heads, and foremen who are responsible for (*a*) providing the detailed information needed by the accounting division in order to install a successful system; (*b*) incurring expenditures in men, materials, and other cost elements, which the cost accountant must segregate and report to those in charge. The cost system with its operating accounts must correspond to organizational divisions of authority so that the individual foreman, supervisor, department head, or executive can be held "accountable" for the costs incurred in his department.

2. The manufacturing procedure and shop methods lead to a consideration of the type of pay (piece rate, incentive, day rate, etc.); the method of collecting hours worked; the control of inventories; the problem of costing tools, dies, jigs, and machinery; and many other problems connected with the factory.

3. The organizational setup on the one hand and the manufacturing procedure on the other form the background for the design of a cost system that is based on (*a*) recognition of the various cost elements, (*b*) departmentalization of factory and office, and (*c*) the chart of accounts.

Any cost system should be perfected so that it will (1) aid in the control and management of the company; (2) measure the efficiency of men, materials, and machines; (3) help in eliminating waste; (4) provide comparison within individual industries;

(5) provide a means of valuing inventories; and (6) aid in establishing selling prices. The cost system's value is greatly enhanced when it is interlocked with a **budgetary control system.** When budget figures are based upon standard costs, the greatest benefit will be derived from such a combination.

Basically, two types of cost systems exist: (1) the **actual** (or **historical**) and (2) the **standard** (or **predetermined**). The actual cost system accumulates and summarizes costs as they occur and determines a final product cost after all manufacturing operations have been completed. The job is charged with actual quantities and costs of materials used and labor expended; the overhead or burden is allocated on the basis of some predetermined overhead rate. This predetermined overhead rate shows that even the so-called actual system does not entirely live up to its name. Under a standard cost system all costs are predetermined in advance of production. Both the actual (historical) and the standard cost system may be used in connection with either (1) the job-order cost method or (2) the process cost method.

1. The Job-order Cost Method. When orders are placed in the factory for specific jobs or lots of product, which can be identified through all manufacturing processes, a job cost system is appropriate. This method has certain characteristics. A manufacturing order often corresponds to a customer's order, though sometimes a manufacturing order may be for stock. The customer's order may be obtained on the basis of a bid price computed from an estimated cost for the job. The goods in each order are kept physically separate from those of other jobs. The costs of a manufacturing order are entered on a job cost sheet which shows the total cost of the job upon completion of the order. This cost is compared with the estimated cost and with the price which the customer agreed to pay.

2. The Process Cost Method. When production proceeds in a continuous flow, when units of product are not separately identifiable, and when there are no specific jobs or lots or product, a process cost system is appropriate, for it has certain characteristics: work is ordered through the plant for a specific time period until the raw materials on hand have all been processed or until a specified quantity has been produced; goods are sold from the stock of finished goods on hand since a customer's order is not separately processed in the factory; the cost-of-production sheet is a record of the costs incurred in operating the process—or a series of processes—for a period of time. It shows the quantity produced in pounds, tons, gallons, or other units, and the cost per unit is obtained by dividing the total costs of the period by the total units produced. Performance is indicated by comparing the quantity produced and the cost per unit of the current period with similar figures of other periods or with standard cost figures.

Elements of Costs. The main items of costs are factory costs which include direct materials, direct labor and factory overhead, and selling and administrative expenses.

Materials. The cost of materials purchased is recorded from purchase invoices. When the materials are used in the factory, a decision must be made whether to charge them to operations at average prices, at costs based on the first-in, first-out method of costing, or at costs based on the last-in, first-out method of costing. Each method will lead to a slightly different cost figure. Each situation must be studied individually to determine which practice will give a maximum of accuracy in cost figures with a minimum of accounting and clerical effort. Once the choice has been made, records must be set up to charge materials to operations based on requisitions. Indirect material is necessary to the completion of the product, but its consumption with regard to the final product is either so small or so complex that it would be futile to treat it as a direct-material item.

Labor. Labor also consists of two categories: direct and indirect. Direct labor, also called **productive labor,** is expended immediately on the materials comprising the finished product. Indirect labor, in contrast to direct labor, does not affect the construction or composition of the finished product. The term includes the labor of foremen, shop clerks, general helpers, cleaners, and those employees engaged in maintenance work.

Factory Overhead. Indirect materials or factory supplies and indirect labor constitute an important segment of factory overhead. In addition, costs of fuel, power, small tools, depreciation, taxes on real estate, patent amortization, rent, inspection, supervision, social security taxes, health and accident insurance, workmen's compensation insurance, and many others fall into this large category. These expenses must be collected and allocated to jobs, processes, and departments. Many expenses are definitely applicable to a specific department and are easily assigned thereto. Other expenses relate to the entire plant and must be prorated to departments on some suitable basis. For instance, heat might be prorated to departments on the basis of cubic feet of area occupied. The expenses of the service departments are prorated to the producing departments on some basis such as service rendered in the case of a maintenance department or so much dollar payroll processed in the case of a cost department.

The charging of factory overhead to jobs or products is accomplished by means of an overhead or burden rate. This rate is essentially a ratio computed to show the relationship of the total burden of a department to some other total figure for the department. For example, the total burden cost of a department may be divided by its direct-labor cost to give a percentage-of-direct-labor rate. This percentage applied to the direct-labor cost of a job or a product gives the amount of overhead chargeable thereto. Other common types of burden rates are the labor-hour rate (departmental expenses ÷ total direct-labor hours) and the machine-hour rate (departmental expenses ÷ total machine hours available). Labor rates are most commonly used. When, however, machines perform the greater amount of the work, machine-hour rates give better results. It must be clearly understood that these rates are computed in advance of production, generally at the beginning of the year. They are used throughout the fiscal period unless seasonal fluctuations or unusual changes in expense amounts necessitate the creation of a new rate. The determination of the overhead rate is closely tied up with overhead budgets.

Departmental Classification. As mentioned above, the establishment of departmental lines is important not only for costing purposes but also for budgetary control purposes. Departmental lines are set up in order to (1) segregate basically different processes of production, (2) secure the smoothest possible flow of production, and (3) establish lines of responsibility for control over production and costs. When the costing methods are designed to fit in with the departmentalization of factory and office, costs can be accumulated within a department with production being on either the job-order or process cost method.

Budgets and Standard Costs. A budget provides management with the information necessary to attain the following major objectives of budgetary control: (1) an organized procedure for planning; (2) a means for coordinating the activities of the various divisions of a business; (3) a basis for cost control. The planning phase provides the means for formalizing and coordinating the plans of the many individuals whose decisions influence the conduct of a business. Sales, production, and expense budgets must be established. Their establishment leads necessarily to the second phase of coordination. Production must be planned in relation to expected sales, materials and labor must be acquired or hired in line with expected production requirements, facilities must be expanded only as foreseeable future needs justify, and finances must be planned in relation to volume of sales and production. The third phase of cost control is predicated on the idea that actual costs will be compared with budgeted costs, thus relating what actually happened with what should have happened. To accomplish this purpose, a good measure of what costs should be under any given set of conditions must be provided. The most important condition affecting costs is volume or rate of activity. By predetermining, through the use of the flexible budget, the expenses allowed for any given rate of activity and comparing it with the actual expense, a better measurement of the performance of an individual department is acheived and the control of costs is more readily accomplished.

In the construction of overhead budgets the volume or activity of the entire organization as well as of the individual department is of considerable importance in their relationship to existing capacity. Capacity must be looked upon as that fixed amount of plant, machinery, and personnel to which management has committed itself and with which it expects to conduct the business. Volume or activity is the variable factor in business related to capacity by the fact that volume attempts to make the best use of the existing capacity. To find a profitable solution to this relationship is one of the most difficult problems faced by business management and the cost accountant who tries to help with appropriate cost data. Volume, particularly of a department, is often expressed in terms of direct-labor hours. With different rates of capacity, a different cost per hour of labor will be computed. This relationship can be demonstrated in the following manner:

Percentage of productive capacity	60%	80%	100%
Direct-labor hours	600	800	1,000
Factory overhead			
Fixed overhead	$1,200	$1,200	$1,200
Variable overhead	600	800	1,000
Total	$1,800	$2,000	$2,200
Overhead rate per direct-labor hour	$3.00	$2.50	$2.20

The existence of fixed overhead causes a higher rate at lower capacity. It is desirable to select that overhead rate which permits a full recovery of production costs by the end of the business cycle. The above tabulation reveals another important axiom with respect to fixed and variable overhead. Fixed overhead remains constant in total but varies in respect to cost per unit or hour. Variable overhead varies in total but remains fixed in relationship to the unit or hour.

Standard Costs. The budget, as a statement of expected costs, acts as a guidepost which keeps business on a charted course. Standards, however, do not tell what the costs are expected to be but rather what they will be if certain performances are attained. In a well-managed business, costs never exceed the budget. They should constantly approach predetermined standards. The uses of standard costs are of prime importance for (1) controlling and reducing costs, (2) promoting and measuring efficiencies, (3) simplifying the costing procedures, (4) evaluating inventories, (5) calculating and setting selling prices. The success of a standard cost system depends upon the reliability and accuracy of the standards. To be effective, standards should be established for a definite period of time so that control can be exercised and variances from standards computed. Standards are set for materials, labor, and factory overhead. When actual costs differ from standard costs with respect to material and labor, two causes can generally be detected. (1) The price may be higher or lower or the rate paid a worker may be different; the difference is called a material price or a labor rate variance. (2) The quantity of the material used may be more or less than the standard quantity or the hours used by the worker may be more or less. The difference is called material-quantity variance or labor-efficiency variance, respectively. For factory overhead, the computation is somewhat more elaborate. Actual expenses are compared not only with standard expenses but also with budget figures. Various methods are in vogue, resulting in different kinds of overhead variances. Most cost accountants compute a controllable and a volume variance. The controllable variance deals chiefly with variable expenses and measures the efficiency of the foreman's ability to hold costs within the budget allowance. The volume variance portrays fixed overhead with respect to the use or non-use of existing capacity. It measures the success of management in its ability to fill capacity with sales or production volume. These two variances can be analyzed further into an expenditure and efficiency variance for the controllable variances and into an effectiveness and capacity variance for the volume variance. Such detailed analyses might bring forth additional information which would help management in making decisions. Of absolute importance for any cost system is the fact that the information must reach management promptly, with regularity, and in a report that is analytical, permitting quick comparison with targets and goals. Only in this manner can management, which includes all echelons from the foreman to the president, exercise control over costs and therewith over profits.

Cost Analysis. The analytical phase of cost accounting has become more important and influential in the last few years. Management must make many decisions, some of a short-range, others of a long-range nature. To base judgment upon good, reliable data and analyses is a major task for the controller and his staff. Cost analysis comprises such matters as analysis of distribution costs, gross-profit analysis, break-even analysis, profit-volume analysis, differential-cost analysis, direct costing, capital-expenditure analysis, return on capital employed, and price analysis. A detailed discussion of each phase mentioned lies beyond the scope of this section, but a short description is appropriate.

Distribution-cost analysis deals with allocation of selling expenses to territories, customers, channels of distribution, products, and salesmen. Once so allocated it might be possible to determine the most profitable and the least profitable commodity, product, territory, or customer. Standards have been introduced recently in these analyses. Some twenty years ago the Robinson-Patman Act, an amendment to Section 2 of the Clayton Act, gave additional impetus to the analytical phase of distribution costs.

Gross-profit analysis attempts to determine the causes for an increase or decrease in the gross profit. Any change in the gross profit is due to one or a combination of the

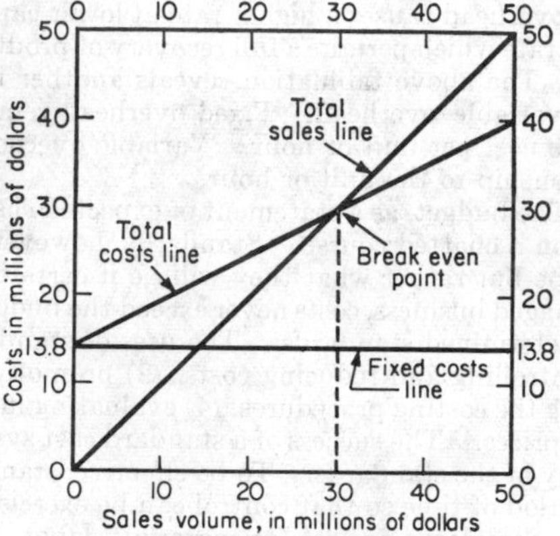

Fig. 2. Illustrative break-even chart.

following: (1) changes in the selling price of the products; (2) changes in the volume sold; (3) changes in the types of products sold, called the sales-mix; (4) changes in the cost elements. Cost elements are analyzed through budgetary control methods. Sales figures must be scrutinized to unearth the changes from the contemplated course and therewith from the final profit.

Break-even analysis, generally presented in the form of a break-even chart, constitutes one of the briefest and most easily understood devices for data presentation for policy-making decisions. The name "break-even" implies that point at which the company neither makes a profit nor suffers a loss from the operations of the business. A break-even chart can be defined as a portrayal in graphic form of the relation of production and sales to profit or, more briefly, a graphic variable income statement. The computation of the break-even point can be made by the following formula:

$$\text{Break-even sales volume} = \frac{\text{total fixed expenses}}{1 - \dfrac{\text{total variable expenses}}{\text{total sales volume}}}$$

Example. Assume fixed expenses, \$13,800,000; variable expenses, \$27,000,000; total sales volume, \$50,000,000. Computation: Break-even sales volume = \$13,800,000/[1 − (\$27,000,000/\$50,000,000)] = \$30,000,000.

Results can be obtained in chart form, Fig. 2.

Profit-volume analysis deals with the effect that a change of volume, cost, price, and product-mix will have on profits. Managements of many enterprises attempt to stimulate the public to purchase their products by conducting intensive promotion campaigns in radio, press, mail, and television. The customer, however, makes the final decision. What management wants to know is which product or model will yield the most profitable margin; which is the least profitable; what effect a reduction in sales price will have on final profit; what effect a shift in volume or product-mix will have on product costs and profits; what the new break-even point will be under such changing conditions; what the effect of expected increases in wages or other operating costs on profit will be; what the effect will be on costs, profit, and sales volume should there be an expansion of the plant. Profit-volume analysis can also be presented graphically in a so-called profit-volume-analysis graph. Using the same data as in the break-even chart, a profit-volume-analysis graph takes the form shown in Fig. 3.

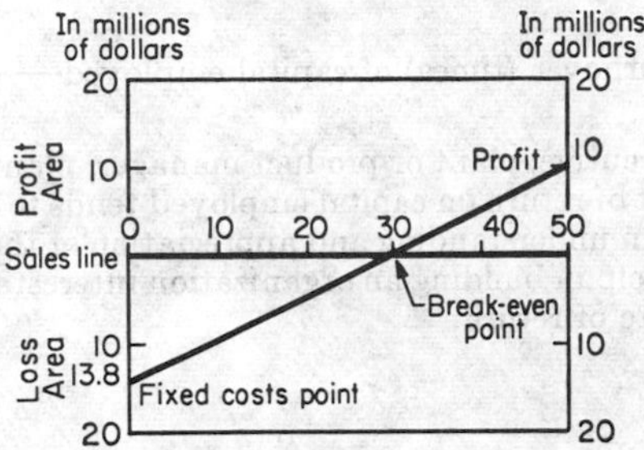

FIG. 3. Illustrative profit-volume-analysis graph.

Differential-cost analysis treats differences, as the title suggests. These differences, also called alternative courses, arise when management wants to know whether or not to take business at a special price, to risk a decline in price of total sales, to sacrifice volume for price, to shut down part of the plant, or to enlarge plant capacity. While cost accountants generally use the term **"differential,"** economists speak of **"marginal"** and engineers of **"incremental"** costs in connection with such a study. As in any of the previously discussed analyses, the classification of costs into their fixed and variable components is absolutely essential. However, while in break-even analysis the emphasis rests upon the fixed expenses, differential-cost studies stress the variable costs. The differential-cost statement presents only the differences in the following manner:

	Present business	Additional business	Total
Sales	$100,000	$10,000	$110,000
Variable costs	60,000	6,000	66,000
Marginal income	40,000	4,000	44.000
Fixed expenses	30,000	none	30,000
Profit	$ 10,000	$ 4,000	$ 14,000

This statement shows that additional business is charged with the variable expenses only because present business is absorbing all fixed expenses.

Direct costing is a costing method which charges the products with only those costs that vary directly with volume. Variable or direct costs such as direct materials, direct labor, and variable manufacturing expenses are examples of costs chargeable to the product. Costs that are a function of time rather than of production are excluded from the cost of the product. The only costs assignable to inventories are variable costs, and because they should vary in proportion to increases or decreases in production, the unit cost assigned to inventories should be uniform.

Capital-expenditure Decisions. The preparation of a capital-expenditure budget must be preceded by an analytical and decision-making process by management. This area of managerial decisions not only is important to the success of the company but also is crucial in case of errors. Financial requirements, present and anticipated costs, profits, tax considerations, and legal, personnel, and market problems must be studied and reviewed before making the final decision.

The **return-on-capital concept** aids management in making decisions with respect to proposed capital expenditures. This concept can also be used for (1) measuring operating performance, (2) profit planning and decision making, and (3) product pricing. The return on capital may be expressed as the product of two factors: the percentage of profit to sales and the rate of capital turnover. In the form of an equation, the method appears as

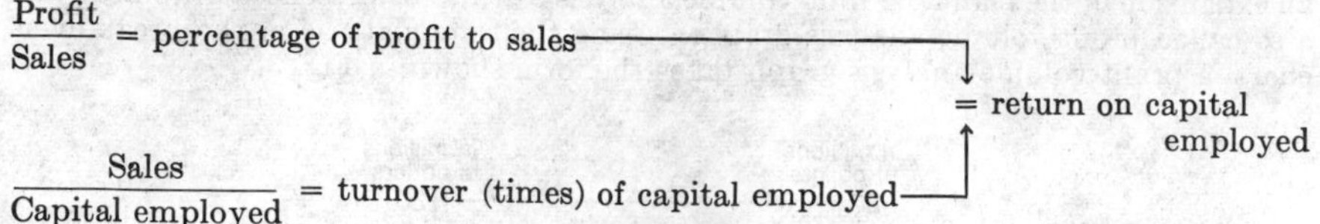

$\frac{\text{Profit}}{\text{Sales}}$ = percentage of profit to sales
= return on capital employed
$\frac{\text{Sales}}{\text{Capital employed}}$ = turnover (times) of capital employed

Whether for top executive, plant or product manager, plant engineer, salesman, or accountant, the concept of return on capital employed tends to mesh the interest of the entire organization. An understanding and appreciation of the return-on-capital concept by all employees help in building an organization interested in achieving fair profits and an adequate rate of return.

ANALYSIS OF CORPORATION ANNUAL REPORTS

BY

Weston Smith

REFERENCES: McLaren, "Annual Reports to Stockholders," Ronald. Livingston, "The American Stockholder," Lippincott. Engel, "How to Buy Stocks," Little, Brown. Bogen, "Financial Handbook" (section 5), Ronald. Greidinger, "Preparation of Financial Statements," Ronald.

The corporate annual report has become a valuable aid to engineers because it has taken on new appearance, readability, and usefulness. The reports have graduated from the elementary stage and broadened their scope. The annual report is now more than a record of stewardship by the management to the owners of the corporation. It is the most important single document which corporations produce each year. It is prepared for the shareholders, but it is distributed to the company's employees, its dealers, customers, and suppliers. In addition, it is sent to financial and editorial writers of newspapers and magazines.

Balance Sheet. (See also p. 17–12.) The comparative balance sheet provides the figures for only two days: the closing day of two fiscal years. The **Asset** side of the balance sheet lists everything owned by the company, plus those things owed to the company. The **Liability** side lists everything the company owes, plus reserves, minority interests, capital, and surplus. The assets of a solvent company are always greater than its liabilities, and the difference is called the **Net Worth.**

Current Position. Important to the average investor is the so-called **current position** or the ratio of current assets to current liabilities. Current assets include cash, government bonds, marketable securities, notes and accounts receivable, and inventories (raw materials and supplies, plus work in process or finished merchandise). Current liabilities include bank loans and commercial paper, accounts payable, debentures and other debts due within the coming year, tax accruals, and dividends declared but not paid. Deducting the current liabilities from the current assets gives the net working capital. Generally speaking the net working capital should equal total current liabilities, and if there is an excess of current assets, so much the better.

Working Capital Ratio. The working capital ratio is figured by dividing the current liabilities into the current assets, and if the ratio is better than 2 to 1, the current financial condition is satisfactory. However, a high ratio of over 6 to 1 might imply that the company has too much unemployed cash, too many unpaid bills outstanding, or an unusually large inventory of unsold merchandise.

Net Quick Asset Position. When judging the actual financial health of a corporation, it is well to check the **Net Quick Asset** position. By subtracting current liabilities from cash and equivalent and accounts receivable, the Net Quick Assets are determined. When current assets, less inventories, equal or exceed total current liabilities, a corporation is said to be in a sound financial position.

Capitalization. The average *industrial* company is in the best position when neither bonds nor preferred stock are outstanding ahead of the common stock. If there is bonded indebtedness, not more than 25 per cent of the total capitalization should be in bonds or funded debt. If both bonds and preferred stock are outstanding, the combination of funded debt and preferred stock should not exceed 50 per cent of the total capitalization.

Goodwill and Depreciation. Companies which value their goodwill, trade-marks, and patents at the nominal figure of $1, or at zero, are in a better position than those that carry this intangible asset at millions of dollars. Depreciation of plant and equipment also should be noted, especially if there is a footnote explaining the depreciation policy of the corporation.

Footnotes. It is always good policy to read all footnotes, even though they may be set in very small type, because here the independent auditors list the qualifications, exceptions, contingent liabilities, and any pending litigation. If the company has funded debt or loans outstanding which require that the management maintain a certain ratio of current assets to current liabilities or forbid any increase in dividend rate until certain requirements are met, these restrictions will be found in the footnotes.

Income Account. (See also p. 17–12.) The income account for the latest year provides a variety of information, but it is more helpful if the preceding year's income account is also available for a direct comparison. It is only within the past dozen years that the majority of publicly owned companies have been providing sales figures. Today, almost every listed corporation starts its income account with **Net Sales,** which represents actual sales after allowances, discounts, refunds, and credits for faulty or returned merchandise. A service company, such as a railroad or electric company, will start its income account with **Gross Income,** which represents payments for transportation or utility service.

Deductions from Sales. The first deduction from Net Sales is **Cost of Sales,** which includes the prices paid for raw materials, manufacturing wages, depreciation, maintenance, local taxes, fuel, and rent. Next is **Selling and Administrative Expenses,** which includes non-manufacturing payments for executive and clerical salaries, salesmen's drawing accounts and commissions, advertising, promotion and public relations, plus other general expenses. This leaves the **Net Operating Income,** to which is then added **Other Income,** and this includes interest and dividends on securities owned, income from sale of assets, and other profits not considered as operating income. The amount after adding Other Income is available for interest on bonds or other loans, and if such a deduction is made, the balance left is the **Net Income before Federal Taxes.** When the Federal taxes, or the provision for Federal taxes, is deducted the remainder is the **Net Income after Federal Taxes,** and if there are no special or non-recurring deductions, this is the amount available for dividends on the preferred stock, if any, and the common stock.

Profit Margin. The **margin of profit** is obtained by dividing the Net Sales into the Net Operating Income, sometimes called the **Net Profit from Operations.** The profit margin for one year does not mean much unless it is compared with something. If the profit margins for a series of years are available, it then can be determined whether the trend is up or down. Or a comparison can be made with the profit margins of other corporations in the same or similar industries to determine an average level for the profits on sales.

Because of the magnitude of Federal taxes, it has become popular today to determine the post-tax margin of profit, which is determined by dividing the Net Sales into the Net Income after Federal Taxes. Here again, it is necessary to have comparative post-tax profit margins for previous years or figures for competing companies in the same industry, to draw any intelligent conclusions. This is why one of the primary requisites of a modern annual report is a ten-year table of operating and financial statistics, to make quick comparisons with previous years and determine trends. But far too many corporations fail to provide any of the important ratios, such as **profit margins** (before or after taxes), **operating ratio** (percentage of all expenses to net sales or gross income), **inventory turnover, working capital ratio** (ratio of current assets to current liabilities), and so forth.

Per Share Figures. Today we are finding plenty of per share statistics in annual reports, ranging from earnings and dividends per share on the common stock, to Federal taxes and working capital per share. But very few reports provide the percentages paid out in dividends and the amount retained in the business at the end of each year. Over a period of years, the seasoned industrial company should pay out at least 50 per cent of its earnings in dividends. Growth companies often pay dividends of less than 50 per cent, because they are ploughing back a larger share of earnings to pay for expansion, new equipment, and **R & D** (Research and Development).

Annual Reports Available on Request. Today, every person who would like a copy of the annual report of a leading company can obtain one for the asking—often a postal card is all that is necessary to obtain a copy of a corporate report which is worth around a dollar a copy, and it is sent postpaid.

All engineers should read the annual report of the company for which they are working. If it is a publicly owned corporation, that is with shares in the hands of the public, there will be no difficulty in obtaining a copy. If they work for the subsidiary of a large consolidation, a copy of the annual report of the parent company should be obtained.

Copies of the annual reports of all important competitors in the same industry should be sent for to determine what their managements say about the progress of industry and how they view the future. Opinions from a dozen annual reports, representing the same industry, may cause some confusion, but it is possible to learn why some competitors are doing better, while others are having a difficult time. Such matters as overproduction, pricing, shortages, labor difficulties, litigation, and special problems will be revealed in several of the annual reports of competing companies.

The annual reports of all or most of an engineer's customer companies also may be sent for to obtain a forecast of capital expenditures for the coming year, as compared with past years. Copies of the annual reports can be obtained from your suppliers. Perhaps these annual reports will indicate future price cuts or increases. In addition, some of these annual reports may disclose new products, which are almost ready for mass distribution, as well as the improvements which have been introduced during the recent past.

Annual reports of companies making substitutes also can be obtained.

Annual report advertisements are published in the financial pages of metropolitan daily newspapers, the financial publications, and the business magazines. Each year more corporations advertise their annual reports and offer copies to the investing public. Many engineers have sent for copies of annual reports for the prime purpose of finding out if they might be good companies to work for, at a time when they are considering a change of job.

When the engineer has collected his small library of annual reports of different corporations, he should use his slide rule and pursue the elusive statistics, by computing the ratios outlined above, to determine which of the reports are as good as they look.

ENGINEERING STATISTICS AND QUALITY CONTROL

BY

E. Vernon Lewis

REFERENCES: Mood, "Introduction to the Theory of Statistics," McGraw-Hill. Burr, "Engineering Statistics and Quality Control, McGraw-Hill. Grant, "Statistical Quality Control," McGraw-Hill. Cochran and Cox, "Experimental Designs," Wiley. Ezekiel, "Methods of Correlation Analysis," Wiley. Lewis, "Statistical Analysis," Van Nostrand. Goulden, "Methods of Statistical Analysis," Wiley. Shewhart, "Economic Control of Quality of Manufactured Product," Van Nostrand. "Manual on Quality Control of Materials," ASTM.

The quantitative measurements upon which engineering depends are subject to variations from two sources: (1) differences among the true values of the measured property in "like" individuals, and (2) differences in observed values resulting from limitations of the measuring equipment. A set of observations of a designated quantity is called a **distribution.** The distribution of all conceivable measurements of a designated quantity is called a **population or universe,** while the distribution of measurements actually made is called a **sample. Descriptive statistics** provides compact methods for describing populations. **Statistical sampling** and **inference** provide methods for inferring efficiently and with known reliability the properties of populations from those of samples. **Statistical quality control** is a special group of methods particularly adapted to identifying and eliminating avoidable causes of variation in manufactured products.

DESCRIPTIVE STATISTICS

Populations may be finite or infinite. In what follows, we first consider finite populations, then indicate the modifications required for infinite ones. The list of observations in the order in which they are made is a table of **raw data.** An **array** is a rearrangement of the values in order of size. To condense the data, the total range of the data is divided into subintervals called **classes,** which may be described by (1) **class limits,** the maximum and minimum observable values to be included in the class; (2) **class boundaries,** the values midway between adjacent limits; and (3) **class marks,** the values midway between the limits or boundaries of each class. **Class intervals** are the differences between successive class marks. **Open classes** are those for which one of the limits or boundaries is undefined; they are used to cover the very extreme values in a distribution. Except for the open classes, best practice uses equal intervals for all classes. The **class frequency** is the number of observations in the class. The **class relative frequency** is the ratio of the class frequency to the total number of values. A table in which the classes and their frequencies are shown is a (frequency) **distribution table.**

A **histogram** is a graphical representation of a distribution table. It is constructed on a rectangular coordinate system with the measured values on the abscissa and the frequencies on the ordinate. Each class is represented by a bar or rectangle with its base on the horizontal axis, its sides perpendiculars at the class boundaries, and its top at the level of the class frequency. The use of equal class intervals makes both the areas and the heights of the bars proportional to the frequencies.

Study of histograms shows that distributions differ in three important characteristics: (1) the location of their central value, (2) the amount of dispersion, or scattering, of the values, and (3) the form or pattern of dispersion of values.

Measures of Central Value, or Averages

A number obtained by objective methods to locate the center of a distribution is a **measure of central value, or average.** The most useful is the **arithmetic mean,** symbolized by μ. For a population of N values of X_i, its formula in exact and abbreviated form is

$$\mu = \frac{\sum_{i=1}^{N} X_i}{N} = \Sigma X/N = (1/N)\Sigma X$$

If only a frequency table is available, the mean may be approximated by the formula

$$\mu \doteq \Sigma f_i X_i / N$$

where X_i and f_i are the mark and frequency, respectively of the ith class.

Other measures of central value are (1) the **midrange,** or value midway between the minimum and the maximum; (2) the **median,** or value such that half the values are below it; (3) the **mode,** or value which occurs most often; and (4) the **geometric mean,** or Nth root of the product of the N values, or antilog of the mean of the logs of the values. Other measures are used in highly specialized cases.

Measures of Dispersion

The most useful **measures of dispersion,** which are objectively obtained numbers indicating the scattering of the observations, are the variance and the standard deviation. The **variance,** symbolized by σ^2, is the mean of the squared deviations, or differences of the observed values from their mean. Its dimensions are thus the square of the dimensions of the measurements. This difficulty is eliminated in the **standard deviation,** symbolized by σ, which is the square root of the variance. The variance is thus

$$\sigma^2 = \frac{\sum_{i=1}^{N} (X_i - \mu)^2}{N} = \Sigma(X - \mu)^2/N$$

An algebraic identity more convenient for computation is

$$\sigma^2 = [N\Sigma X^2 - (\Sigma X)^2]/N^2$$

When $1/N$ may be exactly expressed by so few significant digits that $\mu = (1/N)\Sigma X$ may be handled without rounding on the computing equipment used, another identity is frequently more convenient:

$$\sigma^2 = (\Sigma X^2 - \mu\Sigma X)/N$$

When only a frequency table is available, the variance may be approximated by the formulas

$$\sigma^2 \doteq \Sigma f_i(X_i - \mu)^2/N = [N\Sigma f_i X_i^2 - (\Sigma f_i X_i)^2]/N^2$$
$$\doteq (\Sigma f_i X_i^2 - \mu\Sigma f_i X_i)/N$$

Form of Distribution

The histograms of distributions should be thought of as rectilinear approximations to **distribution curves,** which are smooth curves such that the area under the curves between two values of X is proportional to the frequency of observations in that interval. One distribution curve which is highly useful is the **normal, or Gaussian, distribution.** For N values with mean μ and variance σ^2, represented by a histogram with class interval c, the equation of the curve where Y is to be plotted on the frequency scale is

$$Y = \frac{Nc}{\sigma\sqrt{2\pi}} \exp\frac{-(X - \mu)^2}{2\sigma^2}$$

By **standardizing** the variable through the transformation $z = (X - \mu)/\sigma$, this becomes

$$Y = \frac{Nc}{\sigma\sqrt{2\pi}} \exp - \frac{z^2}{2}$$

while if the histogram is in relative frequencies, it becomes

$$Y' = Y/N = \frac{c}{\sigma\sqrt{2\pi}} \exp - \frac{z^2}{2}$$

and if the class interval is made equal to the standard deviation $c = \sigma$, it becomes

$$y = \frac{1}{\sqrt{2\pi}} \exp - \frac{z^2}{2}$$

which is the **standard form** of the **normal distribution.** Tables are available which show the values of y for convenient values of z. The curve can be plotted in other forms from these values through the transformations

$$Y' = (c/\sigma)y$$
$$Y = NY' = (Nc/\sigma)y$$
$$X = \mu + z\sigma$$

The curve has the following characteristics: (1) Its maximum occurs at $X = \mu$ or $z = 0$. (2) Its inflection points are at $X = \mu \pm \sigma$ or $z = \pm 1.00$. (3) It is symmetric about a vertical through its maximum. (4) It is asymptotic to the horizontal axis.

In standard form, the entire area is represented by

$$A = \int_{-\infty}^{+\infty} y\, dz$$

and the area below any stated value of z is

$$p = \int_{-\infty}^{z} y\, dz$$

The integrand is a nonintegrable form, and the lower limit produces an improper integral; but the applicable methods of calculus permit the values to be calculated. The difference between the values, say $p_2 - p_1$, associated with values z_2 and z_1 gives the area under the curve between the two z values and corresponds to the relative frequency of values in this interval. Thus frequencies determined from this distribution can be compared with those actually observed.

Many actual distributions appear not to conform to the normal distribution form. While statisticians formerly worked with many other distribution equations, current practice shows that the departures are often a consequence of one or both of the following causes:

1. The measured quantity may be non-linearly related to another quantity which is normally distributed; *e.g.*, the volumes or weights of high-grade bearing balls have a skewed distribution, but their diameters have a normal distribution.

2. The "population" considered may, in fact, be a mixture of two or more ultimate populations; *e.g.*, the diameters of rods produced on one centerless grinder may be normally distributed, but those produced by several grinders will show a more flat-topped distribution due to differences in the means and variances of the distributions from each of the grinders.

The use of the appropriate statistical and mathematical methods to identify the causes of non-normality is one of the valuable contributions of statistics to engineering.

Infinite Populations

The concept of an infinite population gives meaning to otherwise troublesome terms in engineering. Thus, the tensile strength of a specific type of material is productively considered as the mean of an unending succession of measurements of strength on an unending succession of pieces of the material. The uniformity of tensile strength is similarly considered as the variance or standard deviation of such measurements. For this purpose, the mean and variance are considered as limits

$$\mu = \lim_{N \to \infty} \Sigma X/N$$

and

$$\sigma^2 = \lim_{N \to \infty} \Sigma(X - \mu)^2/N$$

as progressively larger numbers of observations are made.

STATISTICAL INFERENCE

Although the measured values upon which engineering decisions are based are parameters of populations, limitations of time or cost, or both, require that the values be inferred from very small samples. The risk of a **misinference** (statistically called an **error**) is always present. Statistical methods permit the amount of risk to be determined and controlled but not completely eliminated. These methods fall into two different but related categories:

1. **Hypothesis Testing.** Here a value of the parameter is proposed as a hypothesis and the sample data are used to determine whether the hypothesis is valid, *e.g.*, in specifications for purchase or in development objectives.

2. **Estimation.** Here no value is hypothesized, but a usable estimate is desired, *e.g.*, in evaluating new processes and products.

Random Sampling

The terms **sample** and **population** are used to designate both the observed values and the physical entities on which they were measured. Context usually makes the particular meaning clear. All statistical methods to be discussed here assume and require that the physical sample be a **random sample,** *i.e.*, that each unit of the population have the same chance of being included in the sample. To accomplish this requires careful planning.

When the population is finite, its individuals can be identified by serial numbers and the required sample selected by the use of a table of random numbers. If a table is not available, the numbers can be placed on identical cards, disks, balls, or other objects, which can then be thoroughly mixed and from which the necessary number can be selected blindly. When the population is a mass of continuous material, it is subdivided into artificial units in such terms as location in a storage facility or time in a flowing stream. In many cases, plans for this purpose have been developed by the technical organizations involved.

When the populations are infinite, no strictly random sampling procedure is available, but every consideration should be given to ensure that the particular units used have no special characteristics known in advance. The methods of statistical quality control often help disclose departure from randomness in such cases after the data are obtained.

Estimating Statistics

From the data, **sample statistics** are computed as estimates of the population parameters. For a sample of N values of X, the **sample mean,** symbolized by $\bar{X}$, is

$$\bar{X} = \Sigma X/N = (1/N)\Sigma X$$

The **sample variance,** symbolized by s^2, is

$$\begin{aligned} s^2 &= \Sigma(X - \bar{X})^2/(N - 1) \\ &= [N\Sigma X^2 - (\Sigma X)^2]/N(N - 1) \\ &= (\Sigma X^2 - \bar{X}\Sigma X)/(N - 1) \end{aligned}$$

where the second and third forms are used under the same conditions as the similar formulas for σ^2.

Hypothesis Testing—Plan

The procedure for testing hypotheses follows the same pattern in all cases considered. To permit condensation for the specific cases, the steps will be indicated by the numbers and abbreviations whose detailed meanings are described below.

1. H_0. State the **null hypothesis,** the hypothesis specifically to be tested. Three possibilities exist: the parameter has exactly a specific value, has at least that value, or has at most that value. These are shown below in that order, but one specific hypothesis must be used in actual work.

2. **Assume.** State the assumptions made regarding conditions of sampling, prior knowledge, and proposed sample sizes.

3. **T.S.** Formulate the **test statistic,** a quantity derived from the sample statistics whose distribution is known and tabulated. These distributions are:

Name	Symbol
Standard normal	z
"Student's" t	t
Chi square over n	χ^2/n
Variance ratio	F

4. **C.R.** State the **critical region,** the range of values of the test statistic which will lead to the rejection of the null hypothesis. These values will depend upon the decision regarding the **alpha risk,** which is the risk or probability of rejecting as false an hypothesis which is true. The region is bounded by **critical values,** which will be indicated by the statistic's symbol, with a first subscript indicating the fraction of the distribution having lower values and a second subscript indicating the degrees of freedom (see below under Comments).

After this formulation, the data are obtained, the observed value of the test statistic is computed, and the decision is made. If the observed value is in the critical region, the hypothesis is rejected; otherwise, it is accepted.

Hypothesis Testing—Comments

Degrees of Freedom. The exact form of distribution of test statistics, except z, depends on the size of the sample, but in a way which is conveniently expressed in terms of the **degrees of freedom,** symbolized by n, for which detailed formulas will be given for each case.

Choice of Form of Hypothesis and Level of Alpha Risk. The cases provided herewith are condensed under the assumption that the user will secure the required protection against misinference by (1) using as the null hypothesis the form which, if it were true, would be undesirable to him, and (2) using relatively small alpha risks. The choice of alpha risk is the point at which judgment enters the process. Using the hypothesis suggested above, the smaller the alpha risk, the less will be the chance of rejecting it and so of deciding that conditions are favorable when they are not. However, for any specific sample size, there is the associated **beta risk,** which is the risk of accepting an hypothesis which is false. By appropriate choice of sample size, both risks can be controlled. This is the function of **statistical design of experiments.**

Estimation

When the use of the data involves estimation rather than testing, a value is computed from the data which is the **point estimate,** or best available estimate, of the needed parameter. A pair of values, one on either side of the point estimate, can be computed covering an interval which it can be claimed with a probability P (expressed as a percentage) of being correct will bracket the true parameter value. Such an interval and its limits are known as the $P\%$ **confidence interval** and the $P\%$ **confidence limits,** respectively.

In developing the confidence limits, the same assumptions must be made as would have been made in testing hypotheses concerning the parameter, and values of the test statistic involving a **related alpha risk,** calculated as

$$\alpha = (100 - P)/100$$

are used. Details are shown following the hypothesis-testing procedure in each applicable case.

Mean of One Population—Variance Known

1. **H**$_0$: $\mu = \mu_0$; $\mu \geq \mu_0$; $\mu \leq \mu_0$.
2. **Assume:** Random sample of N from a normal distribution, with known variance σ^2.
3. **T.S.:** $z = (\bar{X} - \mu_0)/\sigma_{\bar{x}}$, where $\sigma_{\bar{x}} = \sqrt{\sigma^2/N}$.
4. **C.R.:** $z \geq z_{1-\alpha/2}$; $z \leq z_{\alpha/2}$; $z \leq z_\alpha$; $z \geq z_{1-\alpha}$.

Confidence limits: $\mu \pm |z_{\alpha/2}|\sigma_{\bar{x}}$.

Mean of One Population—Variance Unknown

1. **H**$_0$: $\mu = \mu_0$; $\mu \geq \mu_0$; $\mu \leq \mu_0$.
2. **Assume:** Random sample of N from a normal population.
3. **T.S.:** $t = (X - \mu_0)/s_{\bar{x}}$, where $s_{\bar{x}} = \sqrt{s^2/N}$.
4. **C.R.:** $t \geq t_{1-\alpha/2,n}$; $t \leq t_{\alpha/2,n}$; $t \leq t_{\alpha,n}$; $t \geq t_{1-\alpha,n}$; where $n = N - 1$.

Confidence limits: $\mu \pm |t_{\alpha/2}|s_{\bar{x}}$.

Variance of One Population

1. **H**$_0$: $\sigma^2/\sigma_0^2 = 1$; $\sigma^2/\sigma_0^2 \geq 1$; $\sigma^2/\sigma_0^2 \leq 1$.
2. **Assume:** Random sample of N from a normal distribution.
3. **T.S.:** $\chi^2/n = s^2/\sigma_0^2$.
4. **C.R.:** $\chi^2/n \geq (\chi^2/n)_{1-\alpha/2,n}$; $\chi^2/n \leq (\chi^2/n)_{\alpha/2,n}$; $\chi^2/n \leq (\chi^2/n)_\alpha$; $\chi^2/n \geq (\chi^2/n)_{1-\alpha}$; where $n = N - 1$.

Confidence limits: upper, $s^2/(\chi^2/n)_{\alpha/2,n}$; lower, $s^2/(\chi^2/n)_{1-\alpha 2,n}$.

Difference of Two Population Means, $\Delta\mu = \mu_2 - \mu_1$—Variances Known

1. **H**$_0$: $\Delta\mu = D$; $\Delta\mu \geq D$; $\Delta\mu \leq D$.
2. **Assume:** Random samples of N_1 and N_2 from normal populations, with variances σ_1^2 and σ_2^2.
3. **T.S.:** $z = (\Delta\bar{X} - D)/\sigma_{\Delta\mu}$, where $\sigma_{\Delta\mu} = \sqrt{(\sigma_1^2/N_1) + (\sigma_2^2/N_2)}$.
4. **C.R.:** $z \geq z_{1-\alpha/2}$; $z \leq z_{\alpha/2}$; $z \leq z_\alpha$; $z \geq z_{1-\alpha}$.

Confidence limits: $\Delta\mu = \Delta\bar{X} \pm |z_{\alpha/2}|\sigma_{\Delta\mu}$.

Difference of Two Population Means, $\Delta\mu = \mu_2 - \mu_1$—Variances Unknown but Equal

1. **H**$_0$: $\Delta\mu = D$; $\Delta\mu \geq D$; $\Delta\mu \leq D$.
2. **Assume:** Random samples of N_1 and N_2 from normal populations, with σ_1^2 and σ_2^2 unknown but equal.

(Unless the equality of the variances is truly known, the H$_0$: $\sigma_1^2/\sigma_2^2 = 1$ should be tested first.)

3. **T.S.:** $t = (\Delta\bar{X} - D)/s_{\Delta\bar{x}}$, where

$$s_{\Delta\bar{x}} = \sqrt{\frac{\Sigma(X - \bar{X})_1{}^2 + \Sigma(X - \bar{X})_2{}^2}{N_1 + N_2 - 2}\,\frac{N_1 + N_2}{N_1 N_2}}$$

4. **C.R.:** $t \geq t_{1-\alpha/2,n}$; $t \leq t_{\alpha/2n}$; $t \leq t_{\alpha,n}$; $t \geq t_{1-\alpha,n}$; where $n = N_1 + N_2 - 2$.

Confidence limits: $\Delta\mu = \Delta\bar{X} \pm |t_{\alpha/2,n}|s_{\Delta\bar{x}}$.

Ratio of Two Population Variances

1. **H**$_0$: $\sigma_1^2/\sigma_2^2 = 1$; $\sigma_1^2/\sigma_2^2 \geq 1$; $\sigma_1^2/\sigma_2^2 \leq 1$.
2. **Assume:** Random samples of N_1 and N_2 from normal populations.
3. **T.S.:** $F = s_1^2/s_2^2$.
4. **C.R.:** $F \geq F_{1-\alpha/2,n_1/n_2}$; $F \leq 1/F_{\alpha/2,n_1/n_2}$; $F \geq F_{\alpha,n_1/n_2}$; $F \leq 1/F_{1-\alpha,n_1/n_2}$; where $n_1 = N_1 - 1$ and $n_2 = N_2 - 1$.

Confidence limits: Not useful.

More than Two Populations—Special Problems

The methods for examining differences among more than two population means are called **analyses of variance** and are sufficiently extensive in detail that the reader should refer to appropriate texts. The treatment of more than two variances requires the use of Bartlett's test and related methods. When two populations do not have equal variances, this fact may, itself, eliminate interest in their means. If, however, the difference of means must still be considered, approximate methods are available.

RELATIONSHIPS AMONG VARIABLES

Knowledge of the form and parameters of functions $Y = f(X_1, X_2, \ldots)$, relating independent variables Y to dependent variables X_i, is vital to engineering. When the values must be inferred from measurement subject to variation, statistical methods are available. Those needed for linear functions of one independent variable are given below. Reference is made to the more complex methods required for curvilinear and multivariate relationships.

Correlation vs. Regression

Differences in the nature of the inherent variations in the data make it necessary to distinguish two different types of problems involving linear relationships. In the **correlation** problem, the population is visualized as comprising pairs of values of X and Y, each pair measured on one individual and both measurements subject to variation. The distribution could be represented by a three-dimensional histogram with class intervals c_Y and c_X in the two variables and frequencies of values in the ith Y-class and jth X-class shown by prisms over the corresponding cell, with heights proportional to the cell frequency. Under many circumstances, these histograms are related to a smooth **distribution surface** in the same sense that two-dimensional histograms are related to distribution curves. One such surface is the **bivariate normal distribution.** In standard form, resulting from the transformations

$$y = (Y - \mu_Y)/\sigma_Y \qquad x = (X - \mu_X)/\sigma_X$$
$$c_Y = \sigma_Y \qquad c_X = \sigma_X$$

and the use of relative frequencies, it is

$$z = \frac{1}{2\pi\sqrt{1-\rho^2}} \exp\left[-\frac{1}{2\sqrt{1-\rho^2}}(x^2 - 2\rho xy + y^2)\right]$$

This surface has its maximum at $x = y = 0$. Its sections parallel to the XY-plane are circles when $\rho^2 = 0$ and ellipses of increasing eccentricity as $\rho^2 \to 1$, which degenerate to lines when $\rho^2 = 1$. The quantity ρ^2 is the **population coefficient of determination.** Its magnitude is a measure of the degree of establishment of the underlying linear relationship. Its square root ρ, with sign consistent with the slope of the major axes of the ellipses, is the **population correlation coefficient.** Data comprising a random sample from such a population are said to conform to the **linear correlation model.**

In other situations, it is possible to measure the values of X without variation and to choose the levels at will. In the population, the Y values at each level of X are visualized as being normally distributed, with mean $\mu_{Y.X}$ related to X by the regression equation

$$\mu_{Y.X} = A + BX$$

and with the same variance, $\sigma_{Y.X}^2$, at all levels of X. The quantities A and B are the **intercept** and the **regression coefficient,** respectively. The distribution surface appears as a ridge over the regression line. Data comprising a random sample of Y's at selected levels of X from such a distribution conform to a **linear regression model.**

While, in the final interpretation, the applicable model must be kept clearly in mind, many of the required statistical values may be more conveniently arrived at by using formulas strictly involved in one model as **computing devices** for the other. These uses are discussed below.

Sample Statistics

The population coefficient of determination, ρ^2, is estimated by the **sample coefficient of determination,** r^2, defined as

$$r^2 = \frac{[\Sigma(X - \bar{X})(Y - \bar{Y})]^2}{[\Sigma(X - \bar{X})^2][\Sigma(Y - \bar{Y})^2]}$$

but more readily computed from the identities

$$r^2 = \frac{[N\Sigma XY - (\Sigma X)(\Sigma Y)]^2}{[N\Sigma X^2 - (\Sigma X)^2][N\Sigma Y^2 - (\Sigma Y)^2]} = \frac{(\Sigma XY - \bar{X}\Sigma Y)^2}{(\Sigma X^2 - \bar{X}\Sigma X)(\Sigma Y^2 - \bar{Y}\Sigma Y)}$$

The last form may be used only when the means can be expressed without rounding. The sign to be affixed to the **sample correlation coefficient** r is that of the unsquared numerator of r^2.

The population regression coefficient B is estimated by the **sample regression coefficient** b, defined as

$$b = \frac{\Sigma(X - \bar{X})(Y - \bar{Y})}{\Sigma(X - \bar{X})^2}$$

but computed as

$$b = \frac{N\Sigma XY - (\Sigma X)(\Sigma Y)}{N\Sigma X^2 - (\Sigma X)^2} = \frac{\Sigma XY - \bar{X}\Sigma Y}{\Sigma X^2 - \bar{X}\Sigma X}$$

where the latter form requires unrounded values of the means. The intercept A is estimated by the **sample intercept** a, defined as

$$a = \bar{Y} - b\bar{X}$$

The **estimating equation** is thus

$$Y_c = a + bX$$

The quantity $\sigma_{Y.X}{}^2$ is estimated by the **sample variance of estimate** $s_{Y.X}{}^2$, defined as

$$s_{Y.X}{}^2 = \Sigma(Y - Y_c)^2/(N - 2)$$

but computed by the identities

$$s_{Y.X}{}^2 = (\Sigma Y^2 - a\Sigma Y - b\Sigma XY)/(N - 2) = (1 - r^2)\Sigma(Y - \bar{Y})^2/(N - 2)$$

Note the use of r^2 as a computing aid.

The procedures for testing hypotheses and estimating confidence limits are given below, following the plan used previously.

Coefficient of Determination

(Note that a simple and exact method is available only when the hypothetical value of ρ or ρ^2 is zero; for other cases and for confidence intervals, see References.)

H$_0$: $\rho^2 = 0$.
Assume: Correlation model.
T.S.: $F = r^2(N - 2)/(1 - r^2)$.
C.R.: $F \geq F_{1-\alpha,1/n}$.

Correlation Coefficient

H$_0$: $\rho = 0$; $\rho \geq 0$; $\rho \leq 0$.
Assume: Correlation model.
T.S.: $t = r\sqrt{(N - 2)/(1 - r^2)}$.
C.R.: $t \geq t_{1-\alpha/2,n}$; $t \leq t_{\alpha/2,n}$; $t \leq t_{\alpha,n}$; $t \geq t_{1-\alpha,n}$; where $n = N - 2$.

Regression Coefficient

H₀: $B = B_0$; $B \geq B_0$; $B \leq B_0$.
Assume: Regression model.
T.S.: $t = (b - B_0)/s_b$, where

$$s_b = \sqrt{s_{Y.X}^2(N-1)/s_X^2} = \sqrt{s_{Y.X}^2/\Sigma(X - \bar{X})^2}$$

C.R.: $t \geq t_{1-\alpha/2,n}$; $t \geq t_{\alpha/2,n}$; $t \leq t_{\alpha,n}$; $t \geq t_{1-\alpha,n}$; where $n = N - 2$.

Confidence limits: $B = b \pm |t_{\alpha/2,n}|s_b$. **Confidence limits for the regression line**: $\mu_{Y.X} = Y_c \pm |t_{\alpha/2,n}|\, s_{Y.X}\sqrt{(1/N) + (x_i - \bar{X})^2/\Sigma(X_i - \bar{X})^2}$. By estimating these limits at several values of X_i, plotting them, and fairing in the smooth curve, a pair of curves vertically symmetrical to the regression line, closest to it at $(\bar{X},\bar{Y})$, and progressively farther away at X_i's more remote from $\bar{X}$ is obtained.

Curvilinear and Multivariate Regression.

An extension of the ideas discussed above leads to methods for dealing with curvilinear functions of some types with one independent variable and with functions of more than one independent variable.

DATA INVOLVING COUNTS

In the foregoing methods, the data were measurements which, except for the limitations of equipment, were continuous-scale variables. In the problems now to be considered, the data comprise counts of the number of individuals in two or more categories, *e.g.*, the number of pieces accepted, reworked, or scrapped after inspection. Such counts are inherently discontinuous, and special statistical procedures are used to treat them.

Distributions

Binomial Distributions. If an infinite population involves individuals in two categories, with a fraction P in category A and a fraction $Q = 1 - P$ in category B, random samples of N individuals will have a probability (interpretable as a relative frequency) of x individuals in category A, $b(x,N)$, which is

$$b(x,N) = \binom{x}{N} P^x Q^{N-x}$$

where

$$\binom{x}{N} = N!/[x!(N-x)!]$$

is the number of combinations of N objects taking x at a time, or the binomial coefficient for N and x. The sum of these probabilities for $x = 0$ through $x = N$ is the **binomial distribution.**

The mean and variance of x are $\mu_x = PN$ and $\sigma_x^2 = PQN$, respectively.

Multinomial Distribution. If the parent population involves individuals in categories $A_1, A_2, \ldots, A_k$, with fractions $P_1, P_2, \ldots, P_k$, respectively, then the probability that a random sample of N individuals will contain $x_1, x_2, \ldots, x_k$ in the respective categories is

$$m(x_1,x_2, \ldots, x_{k-1},N) = N!\Pi P_i^{x_i}/\Pi x_i$$

where the continued product extends over the subscripts $i = 1$ through k. The sum of these probabilities over all possible samples is the **multinomial distribution.**

Poisson Distribution. If we have a small number of individuals of a specified type, whose total volume is negligible, distributed at random through an infinite space with a mean number, μ per designated unit of volume, the probability of finding x of these individuals in one of the designated units of volume is

$$p(x) = e^{-\mu}\mu^x/x!$$

and the sum of these probabilities constitutes the **Poisson distribution.** We may consider distributions over areas or lengths, instead of volumes, or we may consider events of a specified type distributed over time, *e.g.*, accidents. The values of $p(x)$ for convenient values of μ and x are available in tables.

Relations among Distributions. Although the binomial-distribution frequencies require only simple arithmetic to calculate, their computation becomes tedious. If the value of $\mu = NP$ for the binomial distribution is used for μ in the Poisson distribution, the values of $p(x)$ will be a good approximation to those of $b(x,N)$ if (1) $\mu \leq 5.0$, and (2) N is large. When these conditions are not met, the normal distribution may sometimes be used to approximate binomial frequencies by using the $\mu = NP$ and $\sigma^2 = NPQ$ from the binomial distribution as the mean and variance of the normal distribution and considering the integral values of x as class marks. This approximation is useful when (1) $P \doteq 0.5$, (2) $\mu \geq 5.0$, and (3) N is large.

Distributions from Technical Principles. In many problems, the distributions among categories will be developed from knowledge of technical principles or requirements. Similarly, observed distributions will suggest the technical principles which would induce them.

Hypothesis Testing

The procedures used below have as their test statistic χ^2, appropriate values of which are available in published tables.

Verification of Distribution

H₀: The distribution is the hypothetical distribution.

Assume: A random sample of N individuals.

T.S.: $\chi^2 = \sum_{i=1}^{k} (a_i - t_i)^2/t_i$, where k = the number of categories, a_i = the observed frequency in the ith category, and t_i = the hypothetical frequency in the ith category.

C.R.: $\chi^2 \geq (\chi^2)_{1-\alpha,n}$, where $n = k - 1$.

Comparison of Several Distributions

H₀: Several distributions are alike.

Assume: Random samples of individuals from r distributions, each involving k categories.

T.S.: $\chi^2 = \sum_{i=1}^{k} \sum_{j=1}^{r} (a_{ij} - t_{ij})^2/t_{ij}$, where a_{ij} = the observed frequency in the ith category for the jth population and t_{ij} = the corresponding hypothetical frequency. To calculate t_{ij}, let $I = \sum_{j=1}^{r} a_{ij}$ = the total frequency for all distributions in the ith category, $J = \sum_{i=1}^{k} a_{ij}$ = the number of items in the jth sample, and N = the total frequency. Then $t_{ij} = IJ/N$.

C.R.: $\chi^2 \geq (\chi^2)_{1-\alpha,n}$, where $n = (r - 1)(k - 1)$.

NOTE: The test statistic is actually an approximation, adequate for most purposes. However, when r and k are both 2, so that $n = 1$, the approximation is much improved by calculating the **T.S.** as

$$\chi^2 = \frac{(|a_{11}a_{22} - a_{12}a_{21}| - N/2)^2 N}{(a_{11} + a_{12})(a_{11} + a_{21})(a_{12} + a_{22})(a_{21} + a_{22})}$$

Other Methods

Methods are available for coping with two or more sets of categories, for testing more detailed hypotheses concerning the location of the differences among populations, and for making direct use of the properties of the parent distributions in special cases.

STATISTICAL QUALITY CONTROL

The purpose of statistical quality control is well stated in the title of the definitive American text on the subject: Shewhart, "Economic Control of Quality of Manufactured Product," Van Nostrand. Fundamentally, the distribution of values of a property of a product is visualized as resulting from a large number of causes. If these causes are constant in number, are operating individually by chance, and affect the property equally when they operate, the distribution of a measured property would be a stable normal distribution, while that of the number of defects produced would be a stable binomial distribution. If, however, some of the causes operate only intermittently (such are called **assignable causes of Type I**), the observed distribution will actually be a mixture of two or more distributions. If some causes have a much larger effect than others (such are called **assignable causes of Type II**), the distributions are characterized, in many cases, by more extreme values than would otherwise be the case.

Observed values of the property are divided into **rational subgroups**—small groups of values which may logically be believed to have originated under essentially stable conditions but which, if assignable causes of either type occur, will vary from group to group. On each group, estimates of the population parameters are made (in some cases estimates different from those discussed in the previous sections are used), and after some 20 or more groups have been obtained, these are combined into over-all estimates.

From the over-all estimates, under the assumption that no assignable causes are present, limits are computed for the individual values of the form

$$\bar{\Theta} \pm k\sigma_\theta$$

where $\bar{\Theta}$ is the mean of the group values of the estimate, σ_θ is an estimate of the standard deviation of these estimates, and k is the factor through which the economics are controlled. Under perfect control, with no assignable causes of variation, the estimates would be normally distributed and the k would have essentially the meaning of z in the normal distribution. Thus, values of $k = 3$, $k = 2.5$, and $k = 2.0$ would yield values outside limits with probabilities of approximately 0.003, 0.010, and 0.05, respectively.

If corrective action is instituted only when values fall outside limits, the number of "false alarms" will be smaller as k is increased, but the number of failures to detect changes will also be increased. The value $k = 3$ has been found useful so often that the real meaning of the k has often been overlooked. Actually, when the product is not satisfactory and the cost of corrective action is comparatively small, k's of 2 or smaller may profitably be used, while with products which are highly satisfactory or with high costs of corrective action, or both, k's above 3 are warranted. In many cases, two values of k are used—the smaller as an indication to take precautionary steps, and the larger to take full steps.

TIME AND MOTION STUDY

BY

H. B. Maynard

REFERENCES: ASME Standard Industrial Engineering Terminology. Lowry, Maynard and Stegemerten "Time and Motion Study," McGraw-Hill. Maynard and Stegemerten "Operation Analysis," McGraw-Hill. Barnes, "Motion and Time Study," Wiley. Mundel, "Motion and Time Study," Prentice-Hall. Morrow, "Time Study and Motion Economy," Ronald. Niebel, "Motion and Time Study," Irwin, Inc., Homewood, Ill. Nadler, "Motion and Time Study," McGraw-Hill. Chane, "Motion and Time Study," Harper. Maynard, Stegemerten, and Schwab, "Methods-Time Measurement," McGraw-Hill. Carroll, "How to Chart Timestudy Data," McGraw-Hill. Maynard, "Industrial Engineering Handbook," McGraw-Hill.

Scope of Time and Motion Study. Time study and motion study are two different procedures. When they are used by the industrial engineer, however, they are almost always used in conjunction with one another so that the combined name of the procedures as originally used by Frederick W. Taylor is still entirely appropriate.

According to ASME Standard Industrial Engineering Terminology, motion study is defined as

. . . . the analysis of the manual and the eye movements occurring in an operation or work cycle for the purpose of eliminating wasted movements and establishing a better sequence and coordination of movements.

In the same publication, time study is defined as

. . . the procedure by which the actual elapsed time for performing an operation or subdivisions or elements thereof is determined by the use of a suitable timing device and recorded. The procedure usually but not always includes the adjustment of the actual time as the result of performance rating to derive the time which should be required to perform the task by a workman working at a standard pace and following a standard method under standard conditions.

Attempts have been made to separate the two functions and to assign each to a specialist. Although motion study deals with method and time study deals with time, the two are nearly inseparable in practical application work. The method determines the time required, and the time determines which of two or more methods is the best. It has, therefore, been found best to have both functions handled by the same individual. Although for convenience he is usually called a "time-study man," he makes various kinds of motion or methods studies as a part of his regular work.

Aims of Time and Motion Study. The aims of time and motion study are to subject each operation of a given piece of work to close analysis, in order that every unnecessary operation may be eliminated and in order to determine the quickest and best method of performing each necessary operation; also to standardize equipment, methods, and working conditions; then and not until then to determine by scientific measurement the number of standard hours in which an average man can do the job (Lowry, Maynard, and Stegemerten, "Time and Motion Study").

The time-study man first devises the best practical method of doing a given job, a method which will result in necessary quality at the lowest cost. He then establishes by time study the time which should be taken by a normally qualified operator to perform the task. Time study is a tool of precision measurement. It determines the time taken by the worker studied to perform a given piece of work when using the method employed when the study was taken. These data cannot be used to establish accurately the time for doing the same task by a method which differs from the one being studied, any more than measuring a shaft 2 in. in diameter with micrometers will determine the diameter of another shaft of a different size.

Hence, the proper method for doing the job must be in use when the time study is made. Failure to recognize this or to act upon it is responsible for most of the inaccurate standards which are encountered.

Elements of Time and Motion Study. Figure 1 presents graphically the steps which must be taken to make a good time and motion study and shows their relation to each other and the order in which they must be performed.

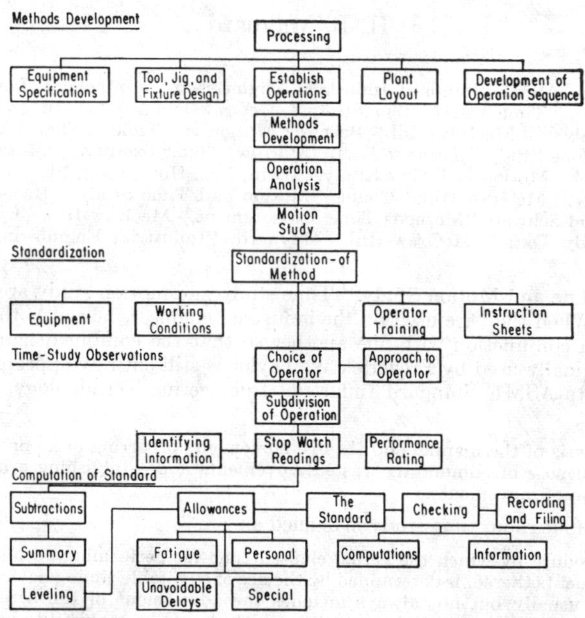

FIG. 1. Graphic analysis of the elements of time and motion study.

The first step is the development of the method. Starting with the drawing of the product, the operations which must be performed are determined and tools and equipment are specified. In large companies, this is usually done by a specialist called a process engineer. In smaller companies, processing is commonly done by the time-study man.

Next, the detailed method by which each operation should be performed is developed. The procedures used for this are known as operation analysis and motion study. They will be described in more detail presently. When the method has been developed, conditions are standardized, and the operators are trained to follow the approved method.

At this time, not before, the job is ready for time study. A suitable operator is selected, the purposes of the study are carefully explained to him, and the time-study observations are made. During the study, the time-study man rates the performance being given by the operator, either by judging the skill and effort he is exhibiting or by assessing the speed with which his motions are made as compared with what he considers to be a normal working pace. Complete identifying information which will answer any questions which may be raised in the future is also recorded either before or after the stop-watch study is made.

The final step is to compute the standard. This involves "working up the study" in the manner which will be described presently, adding allowances for fatigue and personal, unavoidable, and special delays. When all data have been checked and all related papers have been carefully identified, the standard is ready for use for control, incentive payment, or other purposes.

Operation analysis is the procedure employed to study all major factors which affect a given operation. It is used for the purpose of uncovering possibilities of improving the method. The study is made by reviewing the operation with an open mind and asking either of oneself or others questions which are likely to lead to methods-improving ideas. If this is done systematically, so that the possibility of overlooking factors which should be considered is minimized, worthwhile improvements are almost certain to result.

The 10 major factors explored during operation analysis, together with typical questions which should be asked about each factor are as follows:

1. Purpose of operation
   a. Is the result accomplished by the operation necessary?
   b. Can the purpose of the operation be accomplished better in any other way?
2. Design of product
   a. Can motions be eliminated by design changes which will not affect the functioning of the product?
   b. Is the design satisfactory for automated assembly?
3. Complete survey of all operations performed on part
   a. Can the operation being analyzed be eliminated by changing the procedure or the sequence of operations?
   b. Can it be combined with another operation?
4. Inspection requirements
   a. Are tolerance, allowance, finish, and other requirements necessary?
   b. Will changing the requirements of a previous operation make this operation easier to perform?
5. Material
   a. Is the material furnished in a suitable condition for use?
   b. Is material utilized to best advantage during processing?
6. Material handling
   a. Where should incoming and outgoing material be located with respect to the work station?
   b. Can a progressive assembly line be set up?
7. Setup and tool equipment
   a. Does the workplace layout conform to the principles of motion economy?
   b. Can the work be held in the machine by other means to better advantage?
8. Common possibilities for job improvement
   a. Can "drop delivery" be used?
   b. Can foot-operated mechanisms be used to free the hands for other work?
9. Working conditions
   a. Has safety received due consideration?
   b. Are new men properly introduced to their surroundings, and are sufficient instructions given them?
10. Method
    a. Is the repetitiveness of the job sufficient to justify more detailed motion study?
    b. Should full automation be considered?

General questions of the type given above or specific questions applying to a given department or industry may be added to the above list to provide a more complete set of questions (Maynard and Stegemerten, "Operation Analysis"). Experience has amply demonstrated that the persistent application of "the questioning attitude" will uncover numerous ideas for improving methods.

Principles of Motion Study. Operation analysis is a primary analysis which eliminates major inefficiencies. Motion study is a secondary analysis which refines the method still further. Motion study may and often does suggest further improvements in the factors considered during operation analysis, such as tools, material handling, design, and workplace layouts. In addition, it studies the human factors as well as the mechanical and sets up operations in conformance with the limitations, both physical and psychological, of those who must perform them.

The technique of motion study rests on the concept originally advanced by Frank B. and Lillian M. Gilbreth that all work is performed by using a relatively few basic operations in varying combinations and sequence. These Gilbreth Basic Elements have also been called "therbligs" and "basic divisions of accomplishment."

The basic elements together with their symbols (for definitions see ASME Industrial Engineering Terminology), grouped in accordance with their effect on accomplishment, are as follows:

Group 1 *Accomplishes*		*Group 2* *Retards accomplishment*		*Group 3* *Does not accomplish*	
Reach	R	Change direction	CD	Hold	H
Move	M	Preposition	PP	Avoidable delay	AD
Grasp	G	Search	S	Unavoidable delay	UD
Position	P	Select	SE	Rest to overcome fatigue	F
Disengage	D	Plan	PL		
Release	RL	Balancing delay	BD		
Examine	E				
Do	DO				

Group 1 is the useful group of basic elements or the ones that accomplish work. They do not necessarily accomplish it in the most effective way, however, and a study of these elements will often uncover possibilities for improvement.

Group 2 contains the basic elements that tend to retard accomplishment when present. In most cases, they do this by slowing down the group 1 basic elements. They should be eliminated wherever possible.

Group 3 is the non-accomplishment group. The greatest improvements in method usually come from the elimination of the group 3 basic elements from the cycle. This is done by rearranging the motion sequence, by providing mechanical holding fixtures, and by improving the workplace layout.

An operation may be analyzed into its basic elements either by observation or by making a frame-by-frame analysis or micromotion study of a motion picture of the operation. The time and motion study books listed in the references describe various methods of doing this (Lowry, Maynard, and Stegemerten, *op. cit.*, Morrow, "Time Study and Motion Economy," Niebel, "Motion and Time Study," Nadler, "Motion and Time Study," Chane, "Motion and Time Study"). A study of the basic elements used for performing a job will almost always result in ideas for improvement. When the time required to make each motion is known, it is even easier to develop improvements. The methods-time measurement procedure, or MTM (Maynard, Stegemerten, and Schwab, "Methods-time Measurement"), provides time standards for all types of industrially useful motions and is widely used for both methods-improvement and work-measurement purposes.

Methods improvement may be made on any operation by eliminating in so far as possible the group 2 and group 3 basic elements and by arranging the workplace so that the group 1 basic elements are performed in the shortest reasonable time. In doing this, certain laws of motion economy are followed. The following, derived from the laws originally stated by the Gilbreths, are the most important.

1. When both hands begin and complete their motions simultaneously and are not idle except during rest periods, maximum performance is approached.

2. When motions of the arms are made simultaneously in opposite directions over symmetrical paths, rhythm and automaticity develop most naturally.

3. The motion sequence which employs the fewest basic elements is the best for performing a given task.

4. When motions are confined to the lowest practical classification, maximum performance and minimum fatigue are approached. Motion classifications are: Class 1, finger motions; Class 2, finger and wrist motions; Class 3, finger, wrist, and forearm

motions; Class 4, finger, wrist, forearm, and upper-arm motions; Class 5, finger, wrist, forearm, upper-arm, and body motions.

Standardizing the Job. When an acceptable method has been devised, equipment, materials, and conditions must be standardized so that the method can always be followed. Information and records describing the standard method must be carefully made and preserved, for experience has shown that, unless this is done, minor variations creep in which may in time cause a major problem. In the case of repetitive work, a job is not standardized until each piece is delivered to the operator in the same condition, and it is possible for him to perform his work on each piece by completing a set cycle of motions, doing a definite amount of work with the same equipment under uniform working conditions.

The operator or operators must then be taught to follow the approved method. Operator training is always important if reasonable production is to be obtained, but it is an absolute necessity where methods have been devised by motion study. It is quite apparent that the operators cannot be expected to discover for themselves the method which the time-study man developed as the result of hours of concentrated study. They must, therefore, be carefully trained if they are to be expected to reach standard production. In addition, an accurate time study cannot well be made until the operator is following the approved method with reasonable proficiency.

Time-study Observations. When the method has been made as efficient as is economically justified and when standardization has been accomplished, the job is ready for time study. The time-study man can study any operator he wishes so long as that operator is using the accepted method. By applying what is known as the leveling procedure, the time-study man will arrive at the same final time standard regardless of whether he studies the fastest or the slowest worker. The time-study man's work is made somewhat easier if he studies an intelligent, cooperative operator. If only one operator is doing the job, there is, of course, no choice.

The manner in which the operator is approached at the beginning of the study is important. This is particularly true if he is not accustomed to being studied. The time-study man should be courteous and unassuming and should show a recognition of and a respect for the problems of the operator. He should be frank in his dealings with the operator and should be willing at any time to explain what he is doing and how he does it.

The first step in making time-study observations is to subdivide the operation into a number of smaller operations which will be studied and timed separately. These subdivisions are known as elements, or elemental operations. Each element is exactly described in a few well-chosen words, which are recorded on the top of the time-study form. Figure 2 shows how this is done. The beginning and ending points of these elements must be clearly recognizable so that the chances of overlapping watch readings will be minimized.

The timing is done with the aid of a stop watch or, less frequently, with a special type of "time-study machine." There are several types of stop watches as well as several methods of recording watch readings in common use. The study illustrated by Fig. 2 was made using a decimal-hour stop watch that reads directly in ten-thousandths of an hour. The readings were recorded using what is known as the continuous method of recording. In this method, the watch runs continuously from the beginning of the study to the end. Thus every moment of time is accounted for, something that may be important if the correctness of the study is ever questioned. The watch is read at the end of each elemental operation, and the reading is recorded in the "R" column under the proper element description. The elapsed time for each element is later secured by subtracting successive readings. This observation procedure gives results as accurate as any other and more accurate than some. (See also p. 16–4.)

Occasionally variations from the regular sequence of elemental operations occur. The time-study man must be prepared to handle such situations when they happen. These variations may be divided into four general classes as follows: (1) elements performed out of order, (2) elements missed by the time-study man, (3) elements omitted by the operator, (4) foreign elements.

The time study illustrated by Fig. 2 contains examples of each of these kinds of irregularity. Elements 12 and 1 on lines 12 and 13 were performed out of order. On line 3, the time-study man missed obtaining the watch readings for elements 9 and 10. On line 6, element 12 was omitted by the operator. Foreign elements A, B, C, and D

DATE 11-1-55
STUDY No. 1
SHEET No. 1
OF 1 SHEETS

ELEMENTS	Pick up part from table		Place in vise		Tighten vise		Start machine		Run table forward 4"		Engage feed		Mill slot		Stop machine		Return table 5"		Release vise		Lay aside part in totepan		Brush vise	
NUMBER	1		2		3		4		5		6		7		8		9		10		11		12	
LINE	T	R	T	R	T	R	T	R	T	R	T	R	T	R	T	R	T	R	T	R	T	R	T	R
1	06	06	06	12	23	35	03	38	08	46	02	48	72	120	16	36	13	49	12	61	09	70	11	81
2	05	86	08	94	21	215	03	18	09	27	03	30	76	306	13	19	12	31	14	45	07	52	06	58
3	07	65	07	72	21	93	02	95	10	405	03	08	70	78	12	90	—	M	—	M	—	573	08	21
4	05	26	A 07	46	14	60	03	63	08	71	03	74	73	647	13	60	16	76	12	88	08	96	08	704
5	07	11	07	18	19	37	04	41	09	50	02	52	71	823	11	34	14	48	09	57	07	64	08	72
6	07	79	08	87	17	904	03	07	10	17	02	19	72	91	11	1002	13	15	11	26	09	35	—	
7	07	42	08	50	22	72	03	75	12	87	03	90	71	1161	16	77	14	91	09	1200	06	06	07	13
8	05	18	06	24	15	39	03	42	B 10	64	02	66	76	1342	12	54	16	70	10	80	06	86	06	92
9	06	98	04	1406	12	18	02	20	13	33	03	36	74	1510	14	24	15	39	10	49	06	55	06	61
10	06	67	08	75	14	89	03	92	12	1604	04	08	71	79	12	91	16	1707	11	18	07	25	08	33
11	05	38	06	44	16	60	02	62	09	71	03	74	75	1849	13	62	12	74	09	83	08	91	07	98
12	C 05	1918	04	26	19	45	03	48	12	60	04	64	71	2035	15	50	16	66	13	79	07	86	07	99/92
13	06	92/86	07	2106/99	14	20	04	24	13	37	02	39	75	2214	14	28	15	43	11	54	08	62	09	71
14	(16)	86	07	93	13	2306	03	09	12	21	04	25	71	96	13	2409	15	24	10	34	09	43	07	50
15	06	56	08	64	17	81	03	84	13	97	03	2500	D 72	2694	16	2710	16	26	10	36	08	44	08	52
16																								
17																								
18																								
19																								
20																								

SYM.	R	T	
A	539 / 526	13	Piece in vise wrong.
B	1256 / 1244	12	Machine stopped.
C	1913 / 1898	15	Clean hands
D	2656 / 2534	122	Piece pulled out of vise
E			
F			
G			
H			
I			
J			
K			
L			
M			
N			
O			

SUMMARY

	1	2	3	4	5	6	7	8	9	10	11	12
TOTALS "T"	0083	0109	0257	0044	0160	0043	1090	0201	0203	0151	0105	0106
NO OBSERVATIONS	14	15	15	15	15	15	15	15	14	14	14	14
AVERAGE "T"	00059	00073	00171	00029	00107	00029	00727	00134	00145	00108	00075	00076
MINIMUM "T"	0005	0006	0012	0002	0008	0002	0070	0011	0012	0009	0006	0006
MAXIMUM "T"	0007	0008	0023	0004	0013	0004	0076	0016	0016	0014	0009	0011
RATING (S.E.C. ACT.)	DC100	→				→	X	→				→
LEVELING FACTOR	1.05	→				→	X	→				→
L.F. × AVE. "T"	00062	00076	00180	00030	00112	00029	00727	00141	00152	00114	00079	00079
% ALLOWANCE	15	15	15	15	15	15	10	15	15	15	15	15
TIME ALLOWED	00071	00087	00207	00035	00129	00033	00800	00162	00175	00131	00091	00091

SKILL			EFFORT		
	A1, A2	SUPER		A1, A2	EXCESSIVE
	B1, B2	EXCELLENT		B1, B2	EXCELLENT
	C1, C2	GOOD	✓ (C1)	C1, C2	GOOD
✓	D	AVERAGE		D	AVERAGE
	E1, E2	FAIR		E1, E2	FAIR
	F1, F2	POOR		F1, F2	POOR

CONDITIONS			CONSISTENCY		
	A	IDEAL		A	PERFECT
	B	EXCELLENT		B	EXCELLENT
	C	GOOD		C	GOOD
✓	D	AVERAGE		D	AVERAGE
	E	FAIR		E	FAIR
	F	POOR		F	POOR

GENERAL RATING FOR STUDY	SKILL	EFFORT	COND.	CONSY.
	0	+.05	0	—

STUDY STARTED	STUDY FINISHED	OVERALL TIME
2:54 P.M.	3:105 P.M.	.275 MIN.

FIG. 2. Face of time-study form.

occurred during regular elements 2, 5, 1, and 7, respectively. A study of these examples will show how the time-study man handles variations from the regular sequence of elements which occur during the making of a time study.

A time study to be of value for future use must tell the whole story of a job in such a way that it will be understood by anyone familiar with the time-study procedure. This will not be possible unless all identifying and other pertinent information is recorded at the time the study is made. Records should be made to show complete identification of the operator; the part or assembly; the machines, tools, and equipment used; the operation; the department in which the operation was performed; and the conditions existing at the time the study was made. Sketches are generally a desirable part of this description. Figure 3 shows the information which would be recorded on the reverse side of the time-study form illustrated by Fig. 2.

Performance Rating. The objective of a time study is to determine the time which a man giving average performance will require to do the job under average or normal conditions. It is important to understand that when the time-study man speaks of average performance, he is not referring to the mathematical average of all human beings, or even the average of all persons engaged in a given occupation. Average performance is established by definition and not statistically. It represents the time-study man's conception of the normal, steady, but unhurried performance which may reasonably be expected from anyone qualified for the work. If sufficient inducement is offered by incentives or otherwise, this performance may be considerably surpassed.

If all operators available for study worked at the average performance level, the task of establishing a standard would be easy. It would be necessary merely to average the elapsed elemental times determined from time study and add an allowance for fatigue and personal and unavoidable delays. It is seldom, however, that a performance is observed which is rated throughout as average. Therefore to establish a stand-

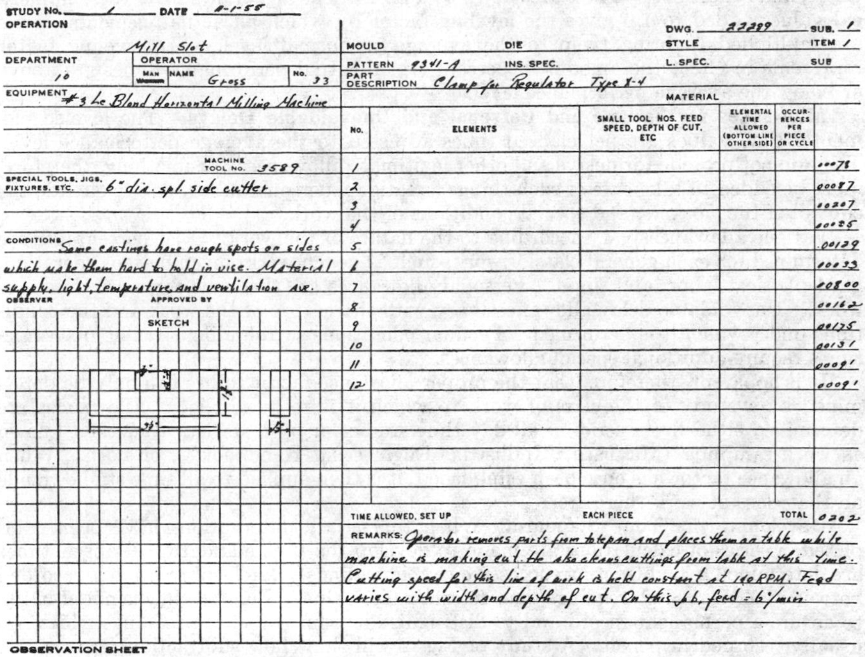

STUDY No. 1 DATE 8-1-55
OPERATION Mill Slot
DEPARTMENT 10
OPERATOR MAN NAME Gross No. 33
EQUIPMENT #3 Le Blond Horizontal Milling Machine
MACHINE TOOL No. 3589
SPECIAL TOOLS, JIGS, FIXTURES, ETC. 6" dia. spl. side cutter
CONDITIONS Some castings have rough spots on sides which make them hard to hold in vise. Material supply, light, temperature, and ventilation ave.
OBSERVER APPROVED BY
SKETCH

DWG. 22289 SUB. 1
MOULD DIE STYLE ITEM 1
PATTERN 9341-A INS. SPEC. L. SPEC. SUB
PART DESCRIPTION Clamp for Regulator Type X-4
MATERIAL

No.	ELEMENTS	SMALL TOOL NOS. FEED SPEED, DEPTH OF CUT, ETC	ELEMENTAL TIME ALLOWED (BOTTOM LINE OTHER SIDE)	OCCURRENCES PER PIECE OR CYCLE	
1					00078
2					00087
3					00207
4					00025
5					.00129
6					00033
7					00800
8					00162
9					00175
10					00131
11					00091
12					00091

TIME ALLOWED, SET UP EACH PIECE TOTAL 0202

REMARKS: Operator removes parts from totepan and places them on table while machine is making cut. He also cleans cuttings from table at this time. Cutting speed for this line of work is held constant at 140 RPM. Feed varies with width and depth of cut. On this job, feed = 6"/min

OBSERVATION SHEET

FIG. 3. Back of time-study form.

ard which represents the time which would be taken had an average performance been observed, it is necessary to use some method of adjusting the recorded elemental times when other than average performance is timed.

One of the well-known methods of doing this is the **leveling procedure.** When properly applied it gives excellent results. It must be correctly understood, of course, and the time-study man who uses it must be thoroughly trained to apply it correctly.

The procedure recognizes that when the correct method is being followed, skill, effort, and working conditions will affect the level at which the operator works. These factors are judged during the making of the time study. Skill is defined as *proficiency at following a given method.* This is not subject to variation at will by the operator but develops with practice over a period of time. Effort is defined as *the will to work.* It

Skill			*Conditions*			*Effort*		
+0.15	A1	Superskill	+0.06	A	Ideal	+0.13	A1	Excessive
+0.13	A2		+0.04	B	Excellent	+0.12	A2	
+0.11	B1	Excellent	+0.02	C	Good	+0.10	B1	Excellent
+0.08	B2		0.00	D	Average	+0.08	B2	
+0.06	C1	Good	−0.03	E	Fair	+0.05	C1	Good
+0.03	C2		−0.07	F	Poor	+0.02	C2	
0.00	D	Average				0.00	D	Average
−0.05	E1	Fair				−0.04	E1	Fair
−0.10	E2					−0.08	E2	
−0.16	F1	Poor				−0.12	F1	Poor
−0.22	F2					−0.17	F2	

FIG. 4. Leveling factors for performance rating.

is controllable by the operator within the limits imposed by skill. Conditions are those conditions which affect the operator and not those which affect the method.

Definitions have been established for different degrees of skill, effort, and conditions. Numerical factors have been established by extensive research for each degree of skill, effort, and conditions. These are shown by Fig. 4. The algebraic sum of these numerical values added to 1.0 gives the leveling factor by which all actual elemental times are multiplied to bring them to the average or normal level. The leveling factor represents in effect the amount in percent which actual performance times are above or below the average performance level.

Allowances for Fatigue and Personal and Unavoidable Delays. The leveled elemental time values are net elapsed times adjusted to the average performance level. They do not provide for delays and other legitimate allowances. Something, therefore, must be added to take care of such things as fatigue, personal needs, delays outside the control of the workers, and special conditions of the work.

Fatigue allowances vary according to the nature of the work. Flat percentages are determined for each general class of work, such as bench work, machine-tool operation, hard physical labor, and so on. Personal allowances are the same for most classes of work. Unavoidable delay allowances vary with the nature of the work and the conditions under which it is performed. Peculiar conditions surrounding specific jobs sometimes require additional special allowances.

It is apparent, therefore, that the proper allowance factor to use can only be determined by a study of the class of work to which it is to be applied. Allowances are determined either by a series of all-day time studies or by a statistical method known as work sampling (Maynard, "Industrial Engineering Handbook"), or both. When an allowance factor has once been established, it is then applied to all time studies made on that class of work thereafter.

Developing the Time Standard. When time-study observations have been completed, a series of calculations are made to develop the time standard. Elapsed times are determined by subtracting successive watch readings. Each subtraction is recorded between the two watch readings that determine its value. Elapsed time is noted in ink to ensure a permanent record and to distinguish it from the watch readings which are usually recorded in pencil. A study of Fig. 2 will show how subtractions are entered on the time-study form and later summarized.

The several elapsed times for each element are next carefully compared and examined for abnormal values. If any are found, they are circled so that they can be distinguished and excluded from the summary.

The remaining elapsed times for each element are added and are averaged by dividing by the number of elapsed time readings. The results are average elapsed times which represent the time taken by the operator during that particular study. These times must be adjusted by multiplying them by a leveling factor to bring them to the average performance level. This factor is determined by the rating of skill, effort, and conditions made during the period of observation.

Each average elapsed time is multiplied by the leveling factor, except when the element is not controlled by the operator. An element that is outside the control of the operator, such as element 7 in Fig. 2 which is a cut with power feed, should not be leveled, because it is unaffected by the ability of the operator. As long as the proper feed and speed are used, the time for performing this element will be the same whether the worker is an expert or a learner.

If workers were able to work continuously, the leveled time would be the correct value to allow for doing the operation studied, but constant application to the job is neither possible nor desirable. In the course of a day, there are certain to be occasional interruptions and delays, for which due allowance must be made in establishing the final standard. Therefore, each elemental time is increased by an allowance which covers time that will be consumed by personal and unavoidable delays, fatigue, and any special factors that may affect the job.

The numbers and descriptions of the elemental operations together with their allowed time are transcribed on the back of the time-study form as shown by Fig. 3. The number of times an elemental operation occurs on each piece or cycle of the operation is taken into account, and the total time allowed for each element is determined and recorded. The final standard for the operation is the sum of the amounts recorded in the "time allowed" column. When all computations have been checked and all supporting records have been properly identified and filed, the task of developing the time standard is complete.

Time Formulas and Standard Data. On repetitive work, time study is a satisfactory tool of work measurement. A single time study may be sufficient to establish a standard which will cover the work of one or more operators for a long period of time.

As quantities become smaller, however, the cost of establishing standards by individual time study increases until at length it becomes prohibitive. In the extreme case, where products are manufactured in quantities of one, it would require at least one time-study man for each operator if standards were established by detailed time study, and the standards would not be available until after the jobs had been completed.

In order to simplify the task of setting standards on a given class of work and in order to improve the consistency of the standards, standard data are frequently used by time-study men (Carroll, "How to Chart Timestudy Data"). A compilation of standard data in its simplest form is merely a list of all the different elements that have occurred during all the time studies made on a given class of work, with representative time values for each element. Every element that differs even slightly from any other element has its own time value.

When a job comes into the shop on which no standard has previously been established, the time-study man analyzes the job either mentally or by direct observation and determines the elements required to perform it. He then selects time values from the standard data for each element. Their sum gives the standard for the job.

This method, although a decided improvement from a time, cost, and consistency standpoint over individual time study, is capable of further refinement and improvement. On a given class of work, certain elements will be performed—for example, "pick up part"—on every piece produced, while others—such as "secure in steady rest" —will be performed only when a piece has certain characteristics. In some cases, the performance of a certain element will always require the performance of another element, *e.g.*, "start machine" will always require the subsequent performance of the element "stop machine." Then again, the time for performing certain elements—for example, "engage feed"—will be the same regardless of the characteristics of the part being worked upon, while the time for performing certain other elements—like "lay part aside"—will be affected by the size and shape of the part.

Thus it is possible to make certain combinations and groupings which will simplify the task of applying standard data. Time-study men construct various charts and tables which they still call standard data, or, in the ultimate refinement, develop time formulas (Lowry, Maynard, and Stegemerten, *op. cit.*). A time formula is a convenient arrangement of standard data which simplifies their accurate application. Much of the analysis which is necessary when applying standard data is done once and for all at the time the formula is derived. The job characteristics which make the performance of certain elements or groups of elements necessary are determined, and the formula is expressed in terms of these characteristics.

Figure 2 illustrates a detailed time study made to establish a standard on a simple milling-machine operation. The same standard can be derived much more quickly from the following time formula:

$$\text{Curve 1} + \text{Table 1} = \text{each piece time}$$

Curve 1 combines the times for the variable elements "pick up part from table," "place in vise," and "lay aside part in totepan" with the times for the constant elements "tighten vise," "start machine," "run table forward 4 in.," "engage feed," "stop machine," "release vise," and "brush vise." Table 1 combines the times for "mill slot" and "return table." The standard time for milling a slot in a brass clamp of any size is computed by determining the variable characteristics of the job from the drawing—in this case, the volume of the clamp and the perimeter of the cut—and adding together the time read from curve 1 and the time read from Table 1.

The amount of time which the use of time formulas will save the time-study man is readily apparent. It takes a certain amount of time and no little know-how to develop a time formula, but once it is available, the job of establishing accurate standards becomes a simple, fairly routine task. The time required to make and work up a time study will be from 1 to 100 or more hours, depending upon the length of the operation cycle studied. The time required to establish a standard from a time formula will, in the majority of cases, range from 1 to 15 min, depending upon the complexity of the formula and the amount of time required to determine the characteristics of the job. Where all necessary information may be obtained from the drawing of the part, the standard may generally be computed in less than 5 min.

Uses of Time Standards. Time-study data can be of value to nearly every function of a business. They are used directly by those who plan, schedule, supervise, or direct the work to which the data apply. In slightly different form, time-study data can be useful to the product- and tool-design departments, the accounting department, the sales department, the processing department, the methods department, and others. Even the president will find time standards of value as he develops policies, plans for the future of his company, and makes decisions on the day-to-day conduct of his company's business.

Some of the more common uses of time standards are in connection with

1. Wage-incentive plans
2. Plant layout
3. Plant-capacity studies
4. Production planning and control
5. Standard costs
6. Budgetary control
7. Cost-reduction activities
8. Product design
9. Tool design
10. Top-management controls
11. Equipment selection
12. Bidding for new business
13. Machine loading
14. Effective labor utilization
15. Material-handling studies

In short, wherever it is necessary to know the time required to do a given piece of work, time standards will be of value. Since it costs money to establish a time standard, any company will be well advised to endeavor to get the most for the money it spends by making full use of its time standards.

CONTROL OF MAINTENANCE COSTS

BY

William K. Hodson

References: Frank, What's Wrong with Maintenance Management Today? *Factory*, July, 1962. Maintenance Prevention, *Factory*, Jan., 1963. Cahill, Accountability—A Key to More Effective Control of Maintenance Costs, *Advanced Management*, July, 1959. Waldmann, The Development of a Maintenance Control Program, *Systems & Procedures*, Aug., 1959. Ramirez, Maintenance Cost Reporting for All Levels of Management, *NAA Bull.*, Nov., 1959. Carson and Small, Planning More Effective Maintenance, *Plant Eng.*, Aug., 1962. Lewis and Pearson, "Maintenance Management," John Rider. Morrow, Managed Maintenance, *Factory*, Jan., 1960.

Need for Controls. Industrial managers have frequently thought of maintenance and repair functions as a necessary evil. In the past, every effort was made to keep expenditures on maintenance to a minimum rather than an optimum. Since the entire cost of a maintenance activity was considered an overhead expense, there was great reluctance to add overhead on top of overhead. Consequently, in most cases, staff activities were held to a minimum. In many organizations, even clerical help was avoided to the point where foremen were largely engaged as clerks. Fortunately, the accelerated trend toward mechanization and automation has forced management to look more objectively at the role of the maintenance function. Automation has tended to reduce direct-labor costs and to increase the importance of maintenance activities. The emphasis now is toward optimizing maintenance costs rather than holding them to a minimum.

Organization. The separation of planning from performance has long been a cardinal rule of good industrial organization. Today, most production foremen are supported with strong staff organizations. These staff groups cover such activities as planning and scheduling, inventory control, quality control, methods and standards, operator training, systems and procedures, and cost controls. Because of reluctance to increase overhead, these same staff functions have been lacking in most maintenance organizations. With the growing importance of maintenance costs, in relation to total manufacturing costs, adequate staff assistance is becoming evident. Unfortunately, many old-line maintenance managers are slow to recongize this need and tend to resist changes as an encroachment on their traditional fields of responsibility. The growing importance of staff activities in maintenance functions is evident in modern organizations. These staff functions are frequently consolidated into a *Maintenance Control Section,* which assumes responsibility for all staff functions. This group provides and coordinates all staff functions and maintains records and reports, thus relieving foremen of clerical and staff activities so that they can concentrate on supervising the work force, planning the work, and coordinating efforts with other maintenance groups.

The prevalent centralized organization utilizes a number of centralized shops for such craft groups as electricians, pipe fitters, carpenters, masons, and millwrights. Strong lines of demarcation limit the work done by various crafts; *e.g.*, carpenters cannot touch electrical conduit. These restrictions on crafts are largely a carry-over from the AFL-type unions and the building trades. The trend today is to eliminate arbitrary restrictions on crafts and to observe only the restrictions inherent in the skills required to perform the work. Some organizations with simple maintenance requirements have reduced the craft groups to two—electrical and maintenance mechanics. This type of craft grouping provides maximum flexibility but sacrifices the advantages inherent in the specialization of labor. A compromise between this extreme and the extreme encountered in most building crafts provides a reasonable balance between flexibility and specialization.

Assigned maintenance groups are frequent in large organizations as they provide (1) immediate service, avoiding the geographical limitations of a centralized setup, and (2) a single production manager with all facilities to operate a complete section, or profit center, of a plant. The use of assigned maintenance forces eliminates excuses for poor performance based on inadequate maintenance support and gives the manager control of his facilities with his own maintenance force.

The productivity of assigned maintenance forces tends to be lower than that of a centralized organization. Where plant geography or profit responsibility dictate, the best compromise is a nominal-size assigned maintenance group supported by centralized crafts for the major jobs. The centralized maintenance group should also be given the responsibility for standardizing basic procedures and practices such as work orders, preventive maintenance, cost controls, and scheduling. The assigned maintenance forces will thus be forced to follow good maintenance practices and to maintain reasonable levels of productivity.

Work-order System. The basic document for any system of maintenance control is the maintenance work order. While the need for a production work order is readily accepted by most production managers, the need for a maintenance work order is frequently questioned, no doubt because of the traditional idea of keeping maintenance costs to a minimum. A system of work orders is the essential step for real control of maintenance costs.

Figure 1 illustrates a work order that has combined a number of forms and serves many uses; it includes (1) a request for work to be performed, with space for a description of the trouble; (2) space for planning the repairs and estimating the labor and materials required; (3) authorization and instruction on when the job is to be performed; (4) a parts requisition for drawing parts and posting inventory records; (5) space for posting equipment records and control reports; and (6) space for planning and scheduling. Where the volume of work orders and the complexity of the management control system justify it, a form designed for tabulating systems may be used. The work-order system should be based on the policy that no maintenance work can be performed without written authorization. For repetitive work, standing orders may be generated that are good for fixed periods of time. In emergencies, the job may be started, but the paper work must follow before any time spent can be properly charged.

Planning and Scheduling. Both short-range and long-range planning and scheduling are necessary for the effective operation of a maintenance management program.

Long-range planning and scheduling establish (1) the preventive-maintenance routines and plant overhauls, and (2) the review and analysis of historical information, with revision of the preventive routines and plant overhauls. The preventive-maintenance checklist must be subject to continuous review; a routine parts, components, and equipment replacement program must be developed and kept up to date. These functions are part of long-range planning; the maintenance jobs, by their nature, can be scheduled far in advance of actual execution, perhaps a year.

Short-range scheduling covers assignment of maintenance jobs on a day-to-day or week-to-week basis. The method of performing the job must be coordinated with the production needs to avoid conflict with the normal operation of the equipment and the work force. All repair work, except the **long-range overhaul,** falls into the short-range category.

Planning and scheduling require a control over men, equipment, and work. Plans must fully utilize the time of the maintenance man assigned. Equipment must be worked upon when free from scheduled production operations. Maintenance must be performed when both the maintenance men and the production equipment are available. The planning-and-scheduling problem is one of merging men, jobs, and equipment into a unified program. The objective of planning and scheduling is to maximize the manpower available on the most worthwhile maintenance jobs, during those periods of time that will least interfere with the normal production operation of the equipment.

The scheduling activity may be performed with tabulating equipment or computers or manually with the aid of scheduling boards. A long-range-scheduling board for preventive-maintenance activities is shown in Fig. 2, using the following letter codes: A = annually, M = monthly, and Q = quarterly. Figure 3 illustrates a section of a daily-scheduling board. The four-digit numbers, each with a letter prefix, are the work-order numbers. The prefix letter indicates the priority of the work: A = work to be completed within 48 hr, B = within a week, C = within a month. The numbers to the right of the work-order number are the estimated man-hours for the performance of the job. As the work is completed, the work order is removed and crossed out on the schedule. Uncompleted work orders are carried over to the following days; *e.g.*,

Maintenance Work Order

1 Equipment name, no. & location	Requested by 2 Initial, 3 Date	Requested Completion 4 Day, 5 time	Posted By 6	Work Order No. 7	Date Scheduled 8
9 Description of Trouble					
10 Description of Planned Work					

ESTIMATE						ACTUAL					
11 craft	12 hours	13 cost	14 material	15 quantity	16 cost	17 Employee No.	18 Hours	19 Cost	20 Material	21 Quantity	22 Cost
23 Estimated Labor			24 Estimated Material			25 Actual Labor			26 Actual Material		
27 Work estimated by			28 Work Approved by			29 Material Issued by			30 Posted to Inventory		
31 Is all material in stock?			32 If not, when can all be on hand?			33 Work Code	34 Labor Code		35 Loc. Code	36 Opr. Code	

SCHEDULED 37 start date	time	complete date	time	ACTUAL 38 start date	time	complete date	time	39 Work inspected and approved by	date

40 Where actual work varies from planned work, describe actual work performed

44 Remarks		Initial	date
	41 Posted to equipment record by		
	42 Recapped for daily report by		
	43 Recapped for monthly report by		

FIG. 1. Maintenance work order.

work order C4937, originally scheduled for Friday and not completed, was rescheduled for the following Monday—all the other jobs had a higher priority on Friday (*i.e.*, the A and B jobs were completed first).

Preventive Maintenance (PM). This is the systematic inspection, cleaning, lubricating, and servicing of equipment. The objective of PM is (1) to discover incipient malfunctions, and (2) to prevent malfunctions and breakdowns. Through regular and frequent inspection and servicing of equipment, PM reduces the number and intensity of malfunctions and breakdowns. A good maintenance program should reduce the number and intensity of breakdowns to the point where no more than 15 percent of the total maintenance effort is devoted to breakdowns or emergency work. Without the benefit of a good PM program, breakdowns and emergency work frequently account for 75 percent of the total maintenance effort.

PM is based on the scheduling of equipment inspections, cleanings, and lubrications; the written reporting of deficiencies in the equipment; the repair of these deficiencies; and the subsequent recording of the repairs into permanent equipment-history records. These records must be periodically analyzed and evaluated for causes and remedial action. PM also requires estimating, planning, scheduling, and control of maintenance repair work. An efficient PM system must have built into it controls that will indicate the need for revising the routines and procedures. All these features require an alignment of responsibilities and duties not generally found in the ordinary maintenance organization. The heart of the system centers around the effectiveness of the preventive-maintenance inspection procedures. These procedures are normally limited to (1) inspecting, (2) adjusting, (3) tightening, (4) cleaning, (5) lubricating, and (6) routine replacement of parts.

Lubricating is a part of the inspection operation only when the lubrication is a miscellaneous part of the inspection. Extensive lubrication is normally performed by

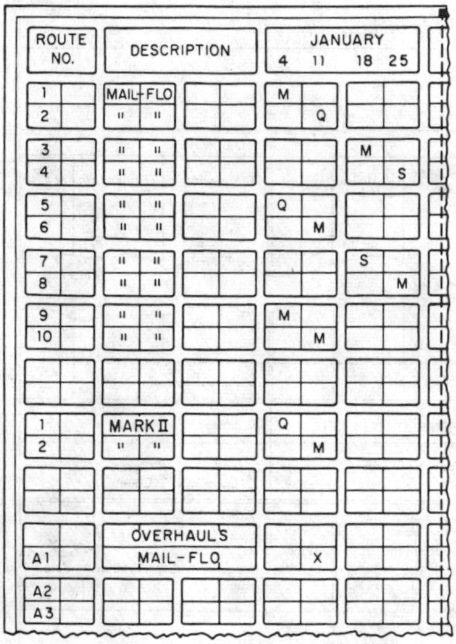

FIG. 2. Preventive-maintenance master-schedule board.

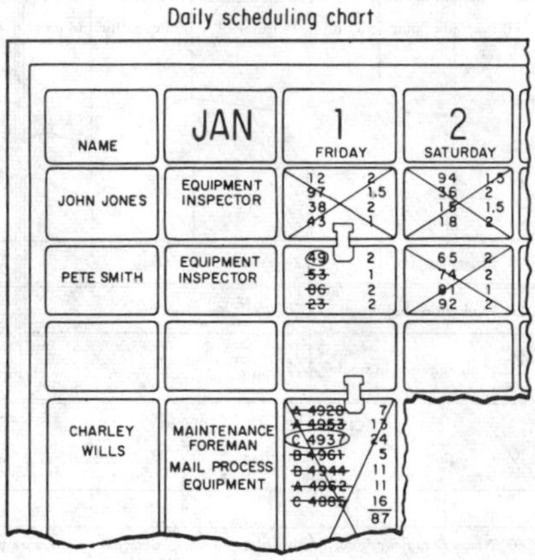

FIG. 3. Daily scheduling board.

specialists under separate schedules. PM inspection route sheets and PM cleaning and lubrication checklists provide the basic information required to perform the inspection and lubrication schedules of the PM program. The inspection checklist should designate specifically the items to be checked, *e.g.*, in Fig. 4, where the points of inspection, cleaning, adjustment, and lubrication are identified, together with the frequency of attention. If, during the course of inspection, defects are uncovered that are easily corrected (*e.g.*, belt tension), they are corrected on the spot. If the defect cannot be readily corrected, as with a pair of pliers or a screwdriver, then the defect should be noted and a work order issued upon the completion of the inspection for normal processing.

A good PM system requires maintenance of historical records on each piece of equipment. Periodic review of the records identifies points of recurrent trouble, indicating (1) faulty equipment, (2) a need to increase the PM operations, or (3) a need to increase the frequency of PM inspections, lubrications, or cleanings. A more formal **breakdown investigation report**, on major equipment, is helpful in detailing the causes of breakdown and the recommendations for improvement, which may be (1) changing the frequency of inspections, (2) modifying the equipment, (3) altering the lubrication or cleaning schedule, (4) reinstructing the equipment operator, (5) replacing the equipment.

Stores Control. A stores-control system must balance, for an optimum cost, (1) the expense caused by plant or equipment downtime against (2) the cost of procuring, storing, and issuing the spare parts. A sufficient stock of materials and parts should be on hand to minimize downtime. The varieties and quantities of parts on hand may be so extensive that it is virtually impossible to run out of any part. This will minimize downtime, but at a prohibitive price.

The major factors determining the quantity of each item to be stocked are (1) item cost, (2) usage, (3) procurement time, (4) downtime cost of the equipment involved. Items that (1) represent a high annual cost, (2) do not permit substitution in an emergency, and (3) are difficult to obtain require very close control. Conversely, items that (1) have a low annual cost, (2) will not result in equipment downtime, and (3) can be obtained quickly and easily warrant very little stores control.

PREVENTIVE MAINTENANCE INSPECTION

CHECK LIST NUMBER 1

SYSTEM Mail Flo ORIGINAL DATE OF ISSUE

EQUIPMENT Live Roller REVISION NO DATE

SUB-EQUIPMENT Feeder Lines & Side Ledge APPROVED BY

POSTAL PLANT ENGINEER

PART OR COMPONENT	NO	INSPECTION INSTRUCTIONS WEEKS	FREQUENCY 4	12	24	52
Motor & Drive Assembly		1.1 I 1 Look for obstruction of ventilation holes in motor and gear box. If obstructed in any way, remove obstruction.	X	X	X	X
		1.2 I 5 Open disconnect switch box and look for dirt & loose wiring. Blow out dirt and tighten connections. Close box.		X	X	X
		1.1 I 2 Feel motor and gear box for abnormal temperature and to detect excessive vibration when running.	X	X	X	X
		1.1 I 4 Look for damage to housing or connections.		X	X	X

FIG. 4. Inspection checklist.

Two types of records are frequently employed to limit the cost of stock-control record keeping: (1) a detailed record for items involving high unit costs and long lead times, and (2) a simplified system for low unit costs and/or short lead times. The parts are conveniently classified as A and B, and the appropriate system of controls is applied.

Inventory records may be kept on tabulating cards, by electronic computers, or by visible hand-posted systems. Figure 5 is a disbursement card showing quantities received, quantities issued, and balance on hand.

Figure 6 illustrates a **bin-card system** for controlling B parts. The card is kept at the bin, and notation is made whenever items are either placed in or withdrawn from the bin.

Some form of tool control is normally required to supervise special-purpose tools. Spring clips, mounted on a board, can be used to hold copies of tool orders or requisitions. When a special tool is issued to a worker, a tool order is filled and placed in a spring clip—there is a clip for each worker. When the tool is returned, the tool order is given to the worker as a receipt for the tool.

Work Measurement. It is difficult to control the cost of maintenance labor because of (1) the variety and number of jobs to be performed, and (2) the lack of standards with which to measure the efficiency of the work force.

The first factor, the work to be performed, can be regulated by basic policies, a PM system, and careful screening of work-order requests. Once a decision has been reached to perform a given job, however, it is difficult to measure the efficiency of the work force in carrying out the job. The control of labor performance on production work is normally accomplished by work measurement and labor standards for each

CARD NO.	NAME Filter-lubricator-regulator																		
REC'D.	DATE	WO NO.	QUANT.	BAL. O.H.	REC'D.	DATE	WO NO.	QUANT.	BAL. O.H.	REC'D.	DATE	WO NO.	QUANT.	BAL. O.H.	REC'D.	DATE	WO NO.	QUANT.	BAL. O.H.
1N5	12/14			1															

DATE	12/59	DATE	12/59
FOLLOW UP	1	MAXIMUM	7
ORDER POINT	2	ORDER QUANT.	5

P.C.D. STOCK NO.		NORMAL	OVER
	Filter-lubricator-regulator	SECTION	AISLE BIN

Fig. 5. Form used for a hand-posted record system.

operation performed. With labor standards available, it is easy to compare the standard time of the work performed with the actual time taken to do the work and arrive at a performance index. (See Fig. 8.)

Because of the irregular and non-repetitive nature of maintenance work, the application of conventional work-measurement techniques has not been too successful. Reliance must be placed upon estimates of the work. A control system, however, is

BIN CARD

Name #2863 Spacer o.q. 144

W.O. or Proc.	Date	Quant. Rec'd.	Quant. Issued
9357	1/27/60	144	
C201	3/3		10
C492	5/2		25

Fig. 6. Bin-card system.

no more effective than the accuracy of the measurements under which it is operating. Since estimates are largely a reflection of the time taken on previous jobs, they are of little value in predicting the time a job should take.

A new approach, the **Universal Maintenance Standards** (UMS), essentially combines the accuracy and consistency of engineered work standards with the ease and speed of application of estimating procedures. Work-measurement-standards data serve as the basis for the development of bench-mark jobs, with a standard time for each. The bench-mark jobs are then slotted into a series of time ranges. Four or five bench marks are developed for each time range, for each major area of each craft, in the form of a **spread sheet** (Fig. 7). Once spread sheets are available, a standards analyst can slot all work orders into one of the time ranges by comparing the work to be done with one or more of the bench-mark jobs. The figures at the top of the spread sheet show the time range for each slot in hours. The standard allowed for the job is the average of the range. For example, range F covers all jobs from 1.5 to 2.5 hr; the standard time allowed for jobs in this range is 2.0 hr. Shorter and longer jobs than those illustrated are covered by additional spread sheets.

SPREAD SHEET

CODE: 0795
CRAFT: Electrical

Task Area:	Task Area: General Installation			
	Group D (0.5) 0.7 (<0.9)	Group E (0.9) 1.2 (<1.5)	Group F (1.5) 2.0 (<2.5)	Group G (2.5) 3.0 (<3.5)
General Installation	0790-6 -- Medium size junction box, 4 tapped holes. 26 wires #12, screw clamp connection. mount and connect 0790-7 -- Medium size junction box, 4 tapped holes, 17 wires #12, screw clamp connections. mount and connect	0790-16 -- Conduit, 15' - 1 1/4" 2-30° bends, 2 condulets, 2 nipples between junction boxes, prepare conduit and install; 2 men 0790-2 -- Medium size junction box, 4 holes, 37 wires #12 crimped connections, mount and connect	0790-15 -- Conduit, 35' - 2", 2-30° bends, 2 condulets, 2 nipples between junction boxes, prepare conduit and install; 2 men 0790-17 -- Conduit, 15' - 1 1/2", 2-30° bends, 2 condulets, 2 nipples between junction boxes, prepare conduit and install; 2 men	0790-3 -- Medium size junction box, 4 holes, 85 wires #12 crimped connections, mount and connect 0790-11 -- Wires, 54-#12, measure cut, identify, install in 80', then 50' conduit 0790-19 -- Medium size junction box, splice, #12. wire, make 54

FIG. 7. Spread sheet.

MAINTENANCE PERFORMANCE REPORT

Issued by: Joe Smith

CRAFT	Actual Hours	Standard Hours	Perf. Index
Air Cond.	73.7	54.6	74.1
Lubrication	98.7	108.9	110.3
Custodians	349.0	353.0	101.1
Carpenters	267.7	232.4	86.8
Welders	264 1	220.1	83.3
Sheet Metal	225.6	173.0	76.7
Millwrights	1007.4	827.7	82.2
Plumbers	2019.3	1429.3	70.8
Electricians	1340.3	982.9	73.3
Machine Repair	1148.3	794.6	69.2
Masons	202.0	124.6	61.7
TOTAL	6996.1	5301.1	75.8

FIG. 8. Maintenance-performance report.

With this approach, one standards applicator can cover 40 maintenance craftsmen, and with standard times available, the maintenance manager is equipped with the same types of controls as the production manager.

A basic performance report is shown in Fig. 8, giving the standard hours of work produced, the time required to produce the work, and a performance index for each craft group. These standards can also be used, for instance, in planning and scheduling the work, estimating the cost of new jobs, and determining the backlog of work to be performed.

Controls and Control Reports. For an over-all evaluation of labor performance, the maintenance manager should have additional control reports. With a **time-distribution report,** the time of maintenance men can be broken down according to the type of work performed. Emergency-type jobs are generally carried out with an excess of manpower so as to bring the equipment back into operation quickly. On a planned basis, the cost of repair would be substantially less. More importantly, however, breakdowns frequently result in idle time on the part of production employees and cause loss in product or plant capacity. It is essential that emergency work be held to a minimum. A **time report** showing the percentage of emergency work to the total maintenance man-hours worked is an excellent over-all index. On certain key items of plant equipment, it may also be desirable to maintain individual equipment logs which show normal running time as well as downtime. Further, the downtime can be classified to indicate the various reasons for it. Time-distribution reports can also be used to summarize the maintenance hours spent on a particular department or piece of equipment and can consequently be used for department budgeting procedures.

Another valuable control report shows the **backlog** of maintenance work to be performed. If each work order contains either a time estimate or a standard time value, a running report of backlog can be maintained by adding the number of work-order hours received each day and subtracting the work-order hours completed. This is usually done by crafts or shops since the mix of work may be such that one craft is overloaded and another does not have sufficient work. The primary reason for this report is to guard against overloading. When backlogs become excessive, routine, planned jobs can ultimately develop into emergency jobs. On the other hand, the backlog report can also be used as a control on the work force. When backlogs become too low, there is a natural inclination to stretch out the work remaining to fit the time available. Experience will generally determine the best operating backlog range. The usual range is a minimum of several days and a maximum of one or two months. Seasonal factors, however, can strongly influence the upper limit.

Equipment-history record cards serve to accumulate the total maintenance cost for major items of equipment; they can be important in any decisions involving equipment procurement or replacement. Frequently, a low initial equipment cost will result in excessive maintenance costs.

Management has often been described as a combination of measurement and control. In the past, many maintenance activities have been operated without the benefit of either factor. They have been based largely on the philosophy of running equipment until it breaks down and then fixing it as quickly as possible. Modern maintenance-management programs, however, are based more and more on the same techniques that have proved so successful in controlling production costs—measurement plus control.

COST OF ELECTRIC POWER

BY

Franklin J. Leerburger

REFERENCES: ASME Annual Reports on Oil and Gas Power Costs. Edison Electric Institute, Annual Statistical Bulletins. *Elec. World*, Annual Steam Station Cost Surveys. FPC, "Uniform System of Accounts Prescribed for Public Utilities"; "Glossary of Important Power and Rate Terms"; Utility Cost Bulletins; "Empirical Constants for Energy Conversion"; Depreciation Practices, *Bull.* S-102; National Power Survey Repts. 1 to 21, 1963. "Handy-Whitman Index of Public Utility Construction Costs," Whitman, Requardt & Assoc. Grant, "Principles of Engineering Economy," Ronald.

This section is primarily concerned with costs of electric power from stationary plants and central stations in the United States. Caution must be exercised in comparing costs associated with generation of electricity by a large, integrated, and pooled system with those from a single generating unit or a single isolated power plant. The reliability of service, accuracy of frequency control, and adherence to a preset voltage level are generally substantially different in the case of the single plant than in that of a pooled system. In some industries (Table 1) such as the electrothermal, electrochemical, and metallurgical industries the product cost is significantly influenced by the cost of electricity. However, in most manufacturing and industrial sectors of the U.S. economy (Table 2), the price of electricity is less important than the availability of an abundant supply at accurately controlled frequency and voltage and with a high index of service reliability. (See Tables I and II, "Electric Power Distribution for Industrial Plants," 2d ed., AIEE, 1956.)

Table 1. Power Requirements for Selected Electroprocess Materials

	Approximate kwh required per lb of product
Gasoline	0.0015
Liquid sulphur	0.002
Ammonium phosphate	0.007
Sulphuric acid	0.016
Formaldehyde	0.030
Tri-sodium phosphate	0.038
Ethylene oxide	0.070
Alumina from bauxite	0.090
Nitric acid	0.180
Synthetic ethyl alcohol	0.300
Electric steel	0.330
Carbon disulphide	0.450
Benzene hexachloride	0.600
Ammonia (salt electrolysis)	0.750
Phosphoric acid (electric furnace)	1.800
Rayon	2.50
Sodium	4.50
Hydrogen peroxide	8.00
Aluminum	9.00
Magnesium	9.50
Titanium	18.20

Table 2. Power Requirements for Selected End Products

	kwh	Unit
Automobiles	1,050	Each
Wool carpets and rugs	1,480	1,000 sq yd
Cement	22	Bbl
Paper—wood pulp	384	Ton
Paper—paperboard	474	Ton
Pig iron	25	Ton
Shoes	472	1,000 pairs
Steel (not electric)	227	Ton
Sugar:		
Beet (refined-sugar base)	154	Ton
Cane (raw sugar)	220	Ton
Tobacco:		
Cigarettes	220	Million
Cigars	8,100	Million

Cost of Power Plants

An **industrial power plant** designed to meet the requirements of an isolated load involves radically different design considerations with respect to reserve capability, spinning reserve (if any), range of voltage regulation, and frequency control from those of a central station within a system of other generating stations, which in turn are pooled with adjacent systems.

A **central station** of a utility system is, in present practice, designed to meet not only the existing and prospective loads of the system in which it is to function but also the pooling and integration obligations to adjacent systems. Design will, therefore, be required to take into account factors such as scheduled maintenance, reserve capability, type of prime mover, fuel, water supplies, geographic conditions, fuel-transportation requirements, transmission limitations, labor costs, and taxes.

Whether the prime mover is a steam turbine, a hydraulic turbine, an internal-combustion engine, or a gas turbine, certain common **design considerations,** which affect cost, prevail. The nuclear steam-electric station, so far as present day practice is concerned, is a traditional steam-electric layout coupled to a steam generator of novel design. The nuclear heat-generating cycle is substituted for the traditional combustion cycle of fossil fuels. The design considerations which must be taken into account and which are common include subsurface conditions; climatic conditions which determine the type of equipment housing; quantity, quality, and temperature of water for cooling purposes; and the relative difficulty of leading water to and from the plant. Important in the case of the nuclear plant are its proximity to population centers and the sizes of the exclusion areas. In the case of fossil-burning thermal plants, the question of location near fuel source weighed against proximity to load centers will influence cost of transportation of fuel on the one hand and the transmission of electricity on the other. Internal-combustion-engine plants are sensitive to loss of capacity as elevations increase above sea level. Hydroelectric sites are frequently far removed from load centers, involving extensive transmission facilities. It is evident that most of the economic hydroelectric sites have been exploited; future developments will generally be special-purpose plants and ones installed, only as incidental to flood control, navigation, and reforestation. Pumped-storage installations are special and are really analogous to storage batteries in that they make possible the time-transfer of kilowatt hours of energy of one value to kilowatt hours of sufficiently higher value to offset the substantial losses concomitant to the transfer process. The low cost of pumped-storage installations also makes for low-cost peaking and standby capacity.

Steam-electric Plants. The economy of scale has been demonstrated in this type of facility in a most remarkable way in the past few years as manufacturers have become capable of fabricating alloy steels which permit steam-electric units to be built as big as 1 million kw, with even larger sizes projected. In a rural area, with relatively easy transportation problems, low land costs, and easy material-storage conditions, oil-fired steam-electric stations may at present cost less than $110 per kw for the first unit, with costs of additional units low enough to bring overall station costs down another $2 per kw. Under the same assumptions, units of 200,000-kw capacity might cost under $165 per kw for the first unit and perhaps $20 per kw less for the fully developed station. Coal-fired stations with additional handling facilities for fuel and ash may cost $4 to $5 per kw more than the oil-fired equivalent regardless of unit size. Extremely crowded urban conditions may add $6 to $9 per kw to the cost of an equivalent rural station. Full-outdoor and semioutdoor stations may save $5 to $10 per kw. Special cases in which natural gas is burned instead of oil or coal in outdoor and semioutdoor plants may reduce costs another $3 to $5 per kw.

The foregoing costs presume the use of modern high-pressure, high-temperature designs such as 2,400 psi and 1000 F superheat and reheat. Extremely high-pressure, supercritical stations may have special cost problems which must be considered before adoption. A report to the Joint Congressional Committee on Atomic Energy in July, 1964, introduced estimates of $97 per kw for a 1,230,000-kw supercritical plant to be completed in rural Ohio by 1967 at an anticipated heat rate of 8650 Btu per kwh. Higher-pressure and double-reheat plants cost more than conventional plants but effect reduction in heat rates. Reduction in fuel costs in specific cases must be balanced against the increased cost of the equipment. An additional plant cost of $5 per kw may be expected with pressure increase to 3,500 psi.

Hydroelectric Plants. Hydroelectric stations encounter a wider range of costs than do steam-electric stations because of widely varying costs of dams, areas flooded for pondage, intake works, discharge arrangements, heads, and rates of water flow. Costs as high as $500 per kw of capacity are not unknown, especially for small-sized units. Based on installed capacity rather than on dependable capacity, the St. Lawrence power project cost about $349 per kw, and the Niagara about $312.

Pumped-storage Hydroelectric Plants. This type of station is generally designed for emergencies and for peak-load service and is so special that costs are not comparable to high-load-factor stations. The variable factors influencing construction costs cannot be generalized, but they are substantially below the costs of high-load-factor hydroelectric plants. The projected Cornwall project of Consolidated Edison Company of New York, Inc., would consist of an outdoor-type station with reversible pump-turbine and motor-generating units. Eight units, each rated as 225,000 kw but having capability of 250,000 kw, would cost about $129,400,000 without substations and transmission facilities. This cost corresponds to $64.70 per kw of capability, or about $71.70 per kw of nameplate capacity. Off-peak pumping has been estimated at 2.6 mills per kwh of incremental cost from system thermal stations, equivalent to 3.9 mills per kwh of hydro generation.

Internal-combustion Plants. These are generally relatively small in size, and plant capacity is built up by increasing the number of engine-generator sets. The complete "package" Diesel-electric unit in standard sizes for immediate full-outdoor installation has brought station costs down to levels of about $100 per kw. Special situations, however, have developed costs that are well above this figure. The forms of internal-combustion prime movers are many and include gas engines, Diesel engines, and semi-Diesel engines, as well as kerosene and gasoline engines. For central-station service, the Diesel engine is the more widely used type of internal-combustion prime mover; this is especially true for remote-area protection and for "peak-shaving" use.

Gas-turbine Plants. Gas-turbine prime movers have gone through rapid technological improvement, to which much has been added from the turboprop machines and pure gas turbines of the airplane industry. Unit sizes are now available up to 30,000 kw, either in modular groups of prime movers driving a single generator or in complete, self-contained turbo-generator sets. There is some waste heat exhausted to the atmosphere, and this has suggested the use of specially designed waste-heat-recovery boilers in special cases. The cost of gas-turbine power plants ranges from $60 per kw to $80 per kw without waste-heat-recovery equipment.

Nuclear-power Plants. Table 3 shows costs of some existing and projected plants. The need for containment shells, shielding, instrumentation, and measures to ensure safety and the comparatively low steam pressures and temperatures (and consequent lower thermal efficiency) require larger turbines and piping than do modern fossil-fuel steam-electric stations and in the total view make for higher capital costs for nuclear-powered stations. The predicted competitive advantage of nuclear power over other forms is based on assumed unit sizes in excess of 500,000 kw. Plants actually constructed have exhibited cost overruns which should have been expected with a new technology largely adapted from the work of physicists, chemists, and mathematicians and subject to the difficulties of expanding theoretical and laboratory-prototype layouts into workable full-scale facilities. In February, 1964, the Jersey

Table 3. Nuclear-power Reactor Plants in the United States*

Date of criticality	Plant capacity, net electrical mw	Total plant cost, $ per net electrical kw	Name	Type
1959	200	183	Dresden	BW
1962	76	705	Hallam	SG
1962	255c	493	Indian Point	PW
1963	90ff	812	Fermi	FBR
1964	62	346	Path Finder	BW
1964	40	703	Peach Bottom	GC
1960	175	223	Yankee	BW
1962	71.5	366	Big Rock Point	BW
1963	50.2	410	Humboldt Bay	BW
1965	50	428	Dairyland	BW
1966	429	203	San Onofre	PW
1967	463	184	Connecticut Yankee	PW
1967	530	174	Malibu	PW
1968	500	180	Nine-mile Point	PW
1967	515/620u	132/110u	Oyster Creek	BW

* From Nucleonics, July, 1964.

Note: BW = boiling water; PW = pressurized water; SG = sodium graphite; GC = gas cooled; FBR = fast breeder reactor; *c* = includes oil-fired superheaters; *ff* = operating at reduced rating of 66 mw; *u* = initial rating guaranteed 515 mw, optimistic rating 620 mw.

Central Power and Light Company estimated that, based on a guaranteed capacity of 515,000 kw of net output, a boiling-water nuclear reactor coupled to a traditional steam-electric turbo generator would cost about $132 per kw and could be expected to safely produce 620,000 kw. At the latter output, the cost per kw would fall to about $110 per kw. At this writing, the plant has not yet been completed.

Trends of Costs. The trends of the major elements of public-utility electrical costs as experienced in the North Central region of the United States are given in Table 4.

Development of Over-all Cost of Producing Electricity

The **cost of money** needed to construct a generating station is the amount which must be paid under specific conditions to induce money to be supplied. This depends upon money-market conditions in general and upon the opinions of investors as to the soundness of the project. Thus, if a textile mill or shoe factory is considering investing in a new power plant, alternative uses for the required funds will be considered. The annual range of target returns considered as criteria by manufacturing or industrial concerns is usually between 8 and 20 percent. On the other hand, the return on investment earned by public utilities is limited by governmental agencies, usually falling between 5 and 7 percent of the difference between original cost and accrued depreciation. Plants built by government agencies are frequently financed directly from the Treasury and at government long-term borrowing rates or by revenue bonds bearing interest rates from perhaps 3½ to 5 percent.

Depreciation as an accounting concept is an annual allowance which will amortize the original cost, less net salvage realized at time of retirement, over the average

Table 4. Cost Index for North Central United States
("Handy-Whitman Index of Public Utility Construction Costs," compiled and published by Whitman, Requardt & Associates, 1304 St. Paul St., Baltimore, Md.)

January 1	Total-steam-production plant	Total-hydro-production plant
1911	100	100
1915	107	113
1920	219	221
1925	215	224
1930	219	224
1935	223	209
1940	264	247
1945	283	290
1946	290	303
1947	359	375
1948	395	415
1949	453	451
1950	450	459
1951	508	493
1952	517	513
1953	529	544
1954	562	582
1955	577	594
1956	625	638
1957	709	691
1958	745	722
1959	771	743
1960	764	763
1961	754	769
1962	735	771
1963	738	782
1964	746	799

Note: 1958 to 1964 from Bull. 79, Table 9, pp. 39 and 40.

estimated service life of the property. Numerous methods are used to compute depreciation; the so-called **straight-line** method is the most widely adopted, but a significant number of companies use some form of interest method. (See Table 5.)

Equal Annual Payments. Use may be made of interest tables which show, for any rate of interest and any number of years, the equal-annual-payment rate which will amortize an amount and also yield an annual return equal to the interest rate on the unamortized remainder.

$$\text{Equal annual payment} = \frac{i(1+i)^n}{(1+i)^n - 1}$$

where n = number of years of life and i = interest or rate of return. (See Table 6; Grant, "Principles of Engineering Economy"; and Sec. 1.)

A frequent error in estimating annual fixed charges on the basis of the first year of service life is made by using the annual rate of depreciation plus interest or return on original cost, thus failing to recognize that the interest charged in dollars in years subsequent to the first will diminish because the outstanding principal has been reduced by annual depreciation accruals.

Taxes, Insurance, and Other Fixed Charges. In the case of ownership by government or by public authority, no Federal income taxes are paid. Private business, however, has been faced with an ever-mounting tax charge on net income; the tax amounted to 12 percent in 1930, 13.75 percent in 1935, 24 percent in 1940, 40 percent in 1945, 42 percent in 1950, and 52 percent in 1952 to 1964. After 1965, the rate will drop to 48 percent, according to 1964 tax legislation. For a time, substantial taxes were levied on what were termed "excess profits." These are not presently being levied. The application of the Federal income tax depends upon a number of

Table 5. Rates for Depreciation on Depreciable Plant, Straight-line Basis
(From *FPC Bull.* S-161)

Account no.	Class of plant	Number of utilities	Depreciation rates: Full range, percent	Range of median 50%, percent	Arithmetic average, percent
	Steam production plant				
311	Structures and improvements	37	1.35– 3.33	1.70– 2.50	2.15
312	Boiler-plant equipment	37	2.22– 4.00	2.65– 3.30	2.98
313	Engines and engine-driven generators	5	2.00– 5.00	2.50– 3.33	3.16
314	Turbo-generator units	36	1.94– 4.00	2.50– 2.98	2.71
315	Accessory electric equipment	36	2.09– 4.00	2.56– 3.25	2.91
316	Miscellaneous power-plant equipment	37	2.10– 5.00	2.86– 3.50	3.23
	Hydraulic production plant				
331	Structures and improvements	24	1.23– 2.50	1.56– 1.98	1.74
332	Reservoirs, dams, and waterways	24	1.00– 3.33	1.25– 1.68	1.63
333	Water wheels, turbines, and generators	23	1.58– 3.74	2.00– 2.50	2.29
334	Accessory electric equipment	21	1.77– 3.76	2.50– 3.00	3.61
335	Miscellaneous power-plant equipment	23	2.00– 8.48	2.50– 3.80	3.42
336	Roads, railroads, and bridges	16	1.00– 3.57	1.33– 2.09	2.02
	Other production plant				
341	Structures and improvements	15	1.70– 3.33	2.00– 2.50	2.33
342	Fuel holders, producers, and accessories	14	2.00– 6.67	2.50– 4.00	3.46
343	Prime movers	12	2.05– 5.00	3.00– 4.00	3.54
344	Generators	17	2.00–10.00	3.00– 4.00	3.89
345	Accessory electric equipment	15	2.31– 4.25	3.00– 4.00	3.42
346	Miscellaneous power-plant equipment	15	2.00– 6.33	2.50– 4.25	3.73
	Transmission plant				
351	Clearing land and rights-of-way	11	1.00– 3.87	1.11– 2.22	1.71
352	Structures and improvements	41	1.33– 3.70	2.00– 2.50	2.21
353	Station equipment	44	1.47– 3.93	2.50– 3.00	2.77
354	Towers and fixtures	37	1.30– 4.00	1.83– 2.50	2.22
355	Poles and fixtures	45	2.40– 4.88	2.86– 3.45	3.24
356	Overhead conductors and devices	47	1.17– 4.00	1.74– 2.43	2.15
357	Underground conduit	18	1.20– 4.00	1.67– 2.69	2.28
358	Underground conductors and devices	18	1.50– 4.00	2.27– 3.00	2.58
359	Roads and trails	18	1.00– 5.00	2.00– 2.70	2.40
	Distribution plant				
361	Structures and improvements	43	0.59–10.00	2.00– 2.50	2.44
362	Station equipment	48	1.34– 4.38	2.72– 3.33	3.00
363	Storage-battery equipment	2	3.93– 4.55	....	4.24
364	Poles, towers, and fixtures	46	2.50– 4.75	3.29– 3.83	3.52
365	Overhead conductors and devices	45	1.50– 4.39	2.13– 3.00	2.54
366	Underground conduit	41	1.33– 4.00	1.67– 2.50	2.15
367	Underground conductors and devices	43	1.50– 4.00	2.29– 3.00	2.56
368	Line transformers	46	2.00– 5.00	2.58– 3.21	2.91
369	Services	46	2.00– 5.00	2.83– 3.81	3.20
370	Meters	46	2.30– 5.00	2.86– 3.46	3.24
371	Installations on customers' premises	30	1.08–10.00	2.88– 4.00	3.79
372	Leased property on customers' premises	14	2.22–10.00	3.10– 4.40	4.28
373	Street lighting and signal systems	44	2.00– 9.50	3.13– 4.00	3.76
	General plant				
390	Structures and improvements	42	1.33– 5.00	1.79– 2.50	2.19
391	Office furniture and equipment	42	2.37–10.00	3.80– 6.00	4.99
392	Transportation equipment	22	3.17–24.00	6.00–16.00	11.89
393	Stores equipment	40	2.00–10.00	3.80– 5.00	4.41
394	Tools; shop and garage equipment	43	1.25–12.50	3.82– 5.56	4.96
395	Laboratory equipment	40	2.22– 7.50	3.45– 5.00	4.56
396	Power-operated equipment	14	3.08–16.00	4.75– 9.00	7.09
397	Communication equipment	45	1.82–14.29	3.80– 6.67	5.98
398	Miscellaneous equipment	40	2.78– 9.80	3.80– 6.25	5.13

considerations, but primarily on the sources from which funds are raised, because interest paid on money borrowed by business owners is a deductible expense for tax purpose. A comparison of the rates of return or interest and Federal income taxes for two types of private enterprises and for governmental, municipal, and public authority is shown in Table 7.

Table 6. Equal Annual Rate Which Will Amortize Original Investment over Estimated Life and Yield Indicated Return on Difference between Original Investment and Accrued Amortization

Life, yr	Annual rate of interest or return							
	3%	4%	5%	6%	7%	8%	9%	10%
10	0.11723	0.12329	0.12950	0.13587	0.14238	0.14903	0.15582	0.16275
20	0.06722	0.07358	0.08024	0.08718	0.09439	0.10185	0.10955	0.11746
30	0.05102	0.05783	0.06505	0.07265	0.08059	0.08883	0.09734	0.10608
40	0.04326	0.05052	0.05828	0.06646	0.07501	0.08386	0.09296	0.10226
50	0.03887	0.04655	0.05478	0.06344	0.07246	0.08174	0.09123	0.10086
75	0.03367	0.04223	0.05132	0.06077	0.07044	0.08025	0.09014	0.10008
100	0.03165	0.04081	0.05038	0.06018	0.07008	0.08004	0.09002	0.10001

Table 7. Comparison of Interest or Return and Federal Income Taxes on Private and Public Projects

(F.I.T. applicable only to the first year of operations.)

	Industrial and commercial, percent	Public utility, percent	Government, municipal, or public authority, percent
Distribution of investment:			
Equity funds (stocks)	100	50	
Borrowed funds (bonds)	.....	50	100
Total	100	100	100
Rate of return or interest:			
On stocks	10*	10†	
On bonds	.....	4	4
Taxable income subject to F.I.T.:			
Average rate	10.0	7.0	4.0
Deduction for interest	.....		4.0
50% of 4%	.....	2.0	
Net taxable income	10.0	5.0	
Return on equity before 48% F.I.T.:			
10%/(100% − 48%)	19.23	.....	0
5%/(100% − 48%)	.....	9.62	0
F.I.T. as percentage of capital:			
19.23% − 10%	9.23	.....	0
9.62% − 5%	.....	4.62	0
Interest or return and F.I.T.:			
Return or interest	10.00	7.00	4.00
F.I.T	9.23	4.62	0
Total	19.23	11.62	4.00

* Many industrial organizations will not consider devoting their own funds to their own power plants unless it is justified on the basis of earning the same return as money devoted to the prime industrial objective. This may run to 20 percent.

† Many utilities do not earn this much. See public-utility earnings-price–ratio studies by leading investment houses. See also "Rate of Return Allowed in Public Utility Rate Cases," Arthur Andersen & Co.

Other taxes which are related to the cost of the plant in one way or another will vary from location to location, but generally there is no legal requirement for government, municipal, or public authorities to pay them. Insurance on the plant is a relatively small factor. Thus a reasonable allowance for local property taxes and insurance will range from 1 to 4 percent, paid by private enterprise. The rate to be paid for insurance alone on either private or public nuclear-power stations is still being developed.

The totals of the costs of money, depreciation, taxes, and insurance, when applied to the book cost of private property, usually range from 12 to 14 percent per annum.

Power plants owned by public authorities or agencies obviously enjoy lower costs of money and taxes.

Operating Expenses

In the following discussion of costs of fuel and of other operating expenses, the influence of load variations must be kept constantly in mind. The hour-by-hour loads may be considerably different from any assumed constant-load factor, especially in power plants supplying the needs of manufacturing, which may range from high-load-factor uses such as in the making of glass, paper, or aluminum to low-annual-load factor, as in food processing and canning.

Steam-electric Plants. Fossil fuels can be compared most successfully in over-all costs per million Btu; these costs will include fuel at sources, fuel-transportation costs, fuel handling and storage, and ash handling (if any). Because of the increasing interest in air pollution, the costs of minimizing this, which will vary from fuel to fuel, must be considered. In fossil-fuel plants of the Northeastern United States, public utilities have been able to buy **coal** advantageously in large quantities, and yet rail-transportation costs have about equalled mine-mouth coal costs. Total as-fired costs have ranged from 26¢ to 35¢ per million Btu. New transportation techniques advanced by the railroads include integrated trains, shuttle trains, and high-speed car unloaders. The savings in using these new methods may effect net reductions of 3¢ to 6¢ per million Btu.

New **railroad tariffs** on trainload lots are attracting increasing volume of coal shipments for utility generating stations. These rates provide for reductions of up to $1.50 per ton on trainloads of 7,000 net tons or more, originating at not more than two mines. The Pennsylvania Railroad alone reported operations in excess of 160 such unit trains per month toward the end of 1963, with unit trains moving coal at the rate of 13 million tons per year. The reduction in freight charges on coal was instrumental in discontinuing the operation of the only coal pipeline in 1963.

Residual fuel oil will have to meet this competition or lose the business, except in small plants which cannot purchase wholesale, mass-delivered coal. Residual fuel oil, which was once a large portion of the total intake of oil refineries in making gasoline, is gradually diminishing as gasoline producers develop better and better means for producing gasoline. At the beginning of the uses of crude petroleum, about one-third was turned into gasoline. With the introduction of "cracking" methods, about one-half the crude was turned into gasoline. With the commercial success of hydrogenation, more than 70 percent of crude may end in gasoline, thus substantially "drying" up the source of residuals. This economic factor must not be overlooked in planning new thermal stations. Diesel fuels (distillate) generally run about 70¢ per million Btu in the Northeastern region. Plant heat rates at high-load factors and few starts may run as low as 10300 Btu per kwh. This may also represent the heat rates for gas turbines, but at lower plant factors, heat rates for gas turbines may run as high as 15000 Btu per kwh. Natural gas boiler fuel is practical and permissible in the gas fields or near to them. As a boiler fuel in other areas, the FPC has restricted its use significantly as a matter of selective conservation, reserving natural gas to the uses of household and small commercial and industrial enterprises.

The heat rates of steam-turbo-generating stations are functions of pressure, superheat, reheat, number of stages of reheat, condenser inlet temperatures exhaust pressures at some standard vacuum, and the load or plant factor. Representative but not universally applicable heat rates, based on 2,400 psi and 1000/1000 F, seven stages of feed-water heating, and full-load exhaust temperatures at 1.5 in. Hg, are: for a nominal 1,000,000 Kw unit at 220,000-kw load, 10150 Btu per kwh; and at 912,000-Kw load, 8750 Btu per kwh. Thus, with fuel at 23¢ per million Btu, the heat alone would cost about $0.002 (2 mills) per kwh.

Operating labor for 1,000,000-kw units may range from 15¢ to 25¢ per kw per year. **Maintenance** appears to have both a "fixed" and an "incremental" element; the fixed element may approximate 6 percent of the cost of fuel, and the variable element at full load may amount to another 5 percent of the cost of fuel. Thus maintenance may, at full load, approximate 0.2 mills per kwh. At high-load factor, say 80 percent, the total operating cost might approximate 1.72 to 2.24 mills per kwh; thus:

	Cost in mills per kwh for a high-pressure conventional plant of 1,000,000-kw capacity in 1 unit (23¢ fuel)	Cost in mills per kwh for a supercritical plant of 1,230,000 kw in 2 units (17¢ fuel)
Labor	0.02 to 0.04 }	0.25
Maintenance	0.2 }	
Fuel	2.0	1.47
Total	2.22 to 2.24	1.72

Hydroelectric Plants. Operating costs are more particularly related to size and capacity and, for small plants under 100,000 kw, might be estimated at $3 per kw per year. For very large stations, the figure might approximate $2.

Nuclear Plants. The economic promise of nuclear power lies essentially in its potential for achieving fuel costs substantially lower than those of conventional thermal stations, which would make it possible to more than offset the higher capital costs. For detailed costing of fuel fabrication, net burnup, inventory charges, shipping, reprocessing irradiated material, and charges on investment in fuel, see p. 9–177 *et seq.* Totals of these component costs in terms of fuel-cycle costs on the basis of experienced load factors for plants in operation and of projected load factors for plants either under construction or being planned are as follows (in mills per kwh):

Hallam	3.3
Indian Point	5.33*
Yankee	2.8
Big Rock Point	3.75
San Onofre	1.99
Malibu	1.8
Nine-mile Point	2.17
Oyster Creek	1.73–1.65

* Includes fuel oil.

Over-all Annual Costs

In estimating fixed charges, it is necessary to decide on a method for accounting for annual depreciation. Assuming that straight-line depreciation is adopted, it then becomes necessary to estimate average service life. The whole subject is too complex to discuss in a paragraph or two, and reference to texts listed in the references should be made (see Table 5). The reciprocal of any straight-line rate is the corresponding imputed average service life of the property. Thus, for over-all, plantwide rates and assuming the following as applicable to the indicated categories, the corresponding average service lives are readily computed. (The following figures have been used for illustrative purposes.)

Type of station	Annual rate, percent	Corresponding average service life, yr
Steam-electric	3⅓	30
Hydroelectric	2	50
Diesel-electric	5	20
Nuclear	3⅓*	30

* This rate has no foundation in experience, and it it may be considerably more in the light of the prospective obsolescence associated with the rapid development of the art.

The equal annual payment will, in the selected time or service life, amortize the property and leave an annual amount available to pay interest or return, or a combination of both, as shown below:

	Average service life, yr	Private enterprise		Government, municipal, or public authority, percent
		Industrial and commercial, percent	Public utility, percent	
Steam-electric	30	10.608	7.265	5.102
Hydroelectric	50	10.086	6.344	3.887
Diesel-electric	20	11.746	8.718	6.722
Nuclear	30	10.608	7.265	5.102
Average return	...	10	6	
Interest	...	......	.....	3

The comparative fixed charges, inclusive of 4 percent for local taxes and insurance for private enterprise and ½ of 1 percent for insurance only for public ownership, are shown in Table 8.

Table 8

	Private enterprise		Government, municipal, or public authority, percent
	Industrial and commercial, percent	Public utility, percent	
Steam and nuclear:			
1. Equal annual payment	10.608	7.265	5.102
2. Less annual depreciation	3.333	3.333	
3. Line 1 − line 2	7.275	3.932	
4. Less bond interest		2.000	
5. Income after F.I.T.	7.275	1.932	
6. Income before F.I.T. of 48%	13.990	3.715	
7. F.I.T.	6.715	1.783	
8. Total line 1 + line 7	17.323	9.048	
9. Local taxes and insurance	4.000	4.000	0.500
10. Total fixed charges	21.323	13.048	5.602
Rounded to	21.3	13.0	5.6
Hydro:			
1. Equal annual payment	10.086	6.344	3.887
2. Less annual depreciation	2.000	2.000	
3. Line 1 − line 2	8.086	4.344	
4. Less bond interest		2.000	
5. Income after F.I.T.	8.086	2.344	
6. Income before F.I.T. of 48%	15.550	4.508	
7. F.I.T.	7.464	2.164	
8. Total line 1 + line 7	17.550	8.508	
9. Local taxes and insurance	4.000	4.000	0.500
10. Total fixed charges	21.550	12.508	4.387
Rounded to	21.6	12.5	4.4
Diesel:			
1. Equal annual payment	11.746	8.718	6.722
2. Less annual depreciation	5.000	5.000	
3. Line 1 − line 2	6.746	3.718	
4. Less bond interest		2.000	
5. Income after F.I.T.	6.746	1.718	
6. Income before F.I.T. of 48%	12.973	3.304	
7. F.I.T.	6.227	1.586	
8. Total line 1 + line 7	17.973	10.304	
9. Local taxes and insurance	4.000	4.000	0.500
10. Total fixed charges	21.973	14.304	7.222
Rounded to	22.0	14.3	7.2

The heavy weighting against private enterprise, compared with ownership by government, municipal, or public authority, due to cost of money alone is obvious from Table 8. Furthermore, the impact of Federal income tax accentuates this disparity.

The total cost of power may now be estimated by reference to the preceding material, assuming private ownership by public utility, related capital structure, and 80 percent load factor.

Load Factor. The load factor of a system is defined as the ratio of the energy consumed to that which might have been consumed in the same period had the peak demand represented a constant load. The load factor as applied to a particular plant is usually referred to as a **plant factor** inasmuch as the peak load to be carried by a plant within a system and the energy put-out by such a plant are within control of trained operators. When a thermal plant is new, it is usually allowed to run at a high plant factor, which is gradually diminished over service life to make way for newer and better plants, as illustrated by the following estimates:

Average age, yr	Load factor or plant factor, percent
1–5	70
6–10	65
11–15	55
16–20	40
21–25	24
26–30	16
31–35	9

The assumption that a plant will run at a high plant factor throughout its life whether it be nuclear or thermally energized is based on faulty reasoning because it assumes that the initial position in the load-duration curve will be maintained even though inevitable obsolescence brings newer and more efficient equipment into service. This decline in plant factor should be kept in mind when computing or estimating future kwh to be generated, the spread of fixed charges, and the incurring of operating expenses.

Incremental heat rate from performance data estimated for a single reheat unit rated at 1,000 mw 2,400 psi, 1000/1000 F, and, 1.5 in. Hg are:

Net load, mw		Incremental heat rate, Btu per kwh
From	To	
220	393	7880; input at 220 mw = 2233×10^6 Btu per hr
393	589	8220
589	785	8580
785	912	8710; input at 912 mw = 7980×10^6 Btu per hr

Incremental maintenance for the same 1,000-mw unit can be estimated as (1) base maintenance = 8 percent of minimum-load fuel cost; and (2) incremental maintenance = 6.4 percent of incremental fuel cost.

Lambda Dispatch. A large generating station is no longer generally designed as an isolated entity but is planned as an addition to existing systems composed of many stations and interconnected with other systems, which are themselves composed of many stations. Diversity of ownership presents some legal, but few engineering or economic, barriers to integration and pooling.

In determining the most economical use of generators to meet interconnected- and combined-system loads, the design problem resolves itself into finding the lowest over-all combined cost of production. For the moment, ignoring transmission costs, the algebraic expression for resolving the matter is

$$F_x = \text{cost of operating generating unit } x \text{ for 1 hr}$$

$$F_t = \sum_1^n F_x = \text{total cost of operating } n \text{ units in the system for 1 hr}$$

$$P_x = \text{output of unit } x \text{ during 1 hr}$$

$$P_t = \sum_1^n P_x = \text{total output of } n \text{ units equal to total load during 1 hr}$$

The search is for a value of F_t, total operating cost for given load $P_t = \sum_1^n P_x$.

Were it possible to express an operating-cost curve for each generating unit by some mathematical equation, it could be demonstrated that the minimum over-all cost would be designated as F_t = minimum when the production or output for each unit contributing to the total output satisfies the following two conditions: (1) The incremental cost at the selected level is equal for all units on the line. (2) The total output $\sum_1^n P_x$ equals the total load.

The solution of the problem by the use of the calculus is dependent on finding the incremental cost (condition 1) using a so-called **Lagrange multiplier,** symbolized λ by the originator of the method (Leon H. Kirchmayer, "Economic Operation of Power Systems," Wiley).

In the practical solution of the problem of reaching an optimum production cost for a given load, it is not possible to find λ by using mathematical production-cost curves and the methods of the calculus. It is therefore essential to resort to trial-and-error approximations of λ. This has been accomplished by assuming an incremental cost or trial value of λ and running each unit at that production level. If the total output fails to equal the load (condition 2 above), a different value of λ is tested and the operations are repeated until conditions 1 and 2 are satisfied.

Power Costs and Prices

The very large effect of costs of money and taxes, as illustrated by their impact on fixed charges, makes it essential to determine how a project is to be financed, what kind of ownership is contemplated, and what average service lives are to be expected. With respect to the effect of fixed charges on the over-all cost per kwh, it is obvious that high-load factor and pushing capability to allowable limits ("stretchout") will bring about cost reduction. High-load-factor loads have assisted the supplying electrical systems to pass on substantial cost savings; e.g.:

	Average annual price, mills per kwh	Year
ALCOA at Alcoa, Tenn.	4.69	1963
Air Reduction Carbide Plant, Ky.	3.89	1963
Diamond Alkali, Ala.	4.11	1963
Penn-Olin Chemical Co.	4.08	1963
Stauffer Chemical Co.	4.06	1963

These plants are on the TVA system, the total industrial sales of which averaged 4.29 mills per kwh in 1963. The Power Authority of the State of New York supplied ALCOA, Reynolds Metals Co., and General Motors Co. with over 3.7 billion kwh in 1963 at an average price of 4.1 mills per kwh.

Table 9 shows average experienced price trends from 1930 to 1962.

Table 9. Average Revenue per Kwh Sold, Total U.S. Electric-utility Industry
(From "Statistical Bulletin for the Year 1962," p. 65, and earlier issues, Edison Electric Institute.)

Year	Cents per kwh		
	Residential	Light and power	
		Small	Large
1962	2.41*	2.37*	0.96*
1961	2.45*	2.35*	0.97*
1960	2.47*	2.46*	0.97*
1959	2.51	2.38	0.96
1958	2.54	2.43	0.97
1957	2.56	2.44	0.94
1956	2.61	2.47	0.92
1955	2.65	2.50	0.97
1954	2.70	2.51	0.99
1953	2.74	2.51	1.00
1952	2.77	2.54	1.01
1951	2.81	2.54	1.00
1950	2.88	2.64	1.01
1945	3.41	2.79	0.93
1940	3.84	3.08	1.06
1935	5.01	3.82	1.30
1930	6.03	4.13	1.41

* Including Hawaii and Alaska.

Transmission Facilities

(See also p. 15–79 *et seq.*)

The growth of plant sizes and of unit sizes and the trend toward pooled and integrated operations of large systems, each containing arrays of plant types, have increasingly emphasized transmission facilities. Pooling and integration for purposes of

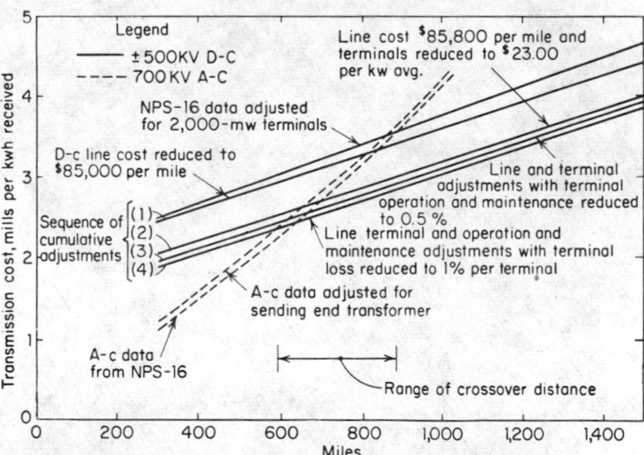

Fig. 1. A-c and d-c transmission-cost comparison; 700-kv a-c vs. ±500-kv d-c, 2000 mw delivered; 50 percent load factor. NPS-recommended annual cost ratios (NPS-O) and loss evaluation. (*National Power Survey, FPC, Rept.* 20.)

sharing regional time diversity are themselves subjects occupying the attention of the National Power Survey. There is, for example, much thought being given to the movement of perhaps 2,000 mw of power from northeastern Canada to New York State to make available electricity generated at projected low cost and high plant factor over a distance of perhaps 1,200 miles. Economic nuclear plants require that large sizes be considered—which, when juxtaposed to the site safety requirements, means large-scale transmission facilities. Foreign experience with d-c transmission holds promise of economical large-block movement over long distances. Mine-mouth generation remote from load centers, pooling and integration, nuclear developments, and economy of scale compel consideration of alternative ways of transmitting power. The traditional transmission techniques involving a-c are being reexamined as the blocks of power increase and require higher voltages to keep conductor sizes and rights-of-way within manageable limits. Long-distance a-c transmission, however, involves problems of costly compensation, switch gear, and spacing of overhead conductors. The economic interrelationships of these and many other factors are complex. Figure 1 is illustrative of the complexities for a study involving delivery of 2,000 mw at 700-kv a-c versus 500-kv d-c. (See National Power Survey, *FPC* Repts. 10, 11, 14, 16, and 20.)

Multipurpose Plants

The multipurpose power plant, in small sizes, can be used as a means of protecting an outlying area of a utility system while at the same time providing a low-first-cost plant for peaking operations. The economy of scale is sacrificed for operating expenses which would be excessive at high-load factors but which are acceptable for emergency or peak-shaving service. In other situations, both hydro and thermal plants may be used for daytime base-load operation and for providing energy at low incremental costs to pump-storage plants. In the non-utility field, the multipurpose plant frequently can be used for supplying process heat as well as electric power for industrial service. Its usefulness can also be extended to assist a local public utility on an interchange basis in hours when industrial needs are low. The allocation of costs to determine what the costs of heat and of on-peak and off-peak electricity are requires analysis beyond the scope of this book.

SECTION 18

REFRIGERATION, CRYOGENICS, OPTICS, AND MISCELLANY

BY

CARL F. KAYAN, Stevens Professor of Mechanical Engineering, Columbia University.

E. F. HAMMEL, JR., Group Leader, Cryogenics, Los Alamos Scientific Laboratory.

K. D. WILLIAMSON, JR., Cryogenics Engineer, Los Alamos Scientific Laboratory.

F. J. EDESKUTY, Associate Group Leader, Cryogenics, Los Alamos Scientific Laboratory.

F. G. BRICKWEDDE, Evan Pugh Research Professor of Physics, The Pennsylvania State University.

HEARD K. BAUMEISTER, Advisory Engineer, Systems Development Division, International Business Machines Corporation.

ALBERT HAERTLEIN, late Gordon McKay Professor of Civil Engineering, Harvard University.

FRANKLIN ROBERT JENKINS, Patent Agent, Eatonton, Ga.

EDWARD TAYLOR NEWTON, Counsellor at Law; Senior Partner, Newton, Hopkins, Jones and Ormsby, Atlanta, Ga.

CONTENTS

MECHANICAL REFRIGERATION
By CARL F. KAYAN

CRYOGENICS
By E. F. HAMMEL, Jr., K. D. WILLIAMSON, JR., F. J. EDESKUTY, and F. G. BRICKWEDDE

OPTICS
By HEARD K. BAUMEISTER

SURVEYING
By ALBERT HAERTLEIN

PATENTS FOR INVENTIONS
By FRANKLIN R. JENKINS and EDWARD T. NEWTON

MISCELLANEOUS

MECHANICAL REFRIGERATION

BY

Carl F. Kayan

REFERENCES: Publications of the ASRE and ASHRAE; "Air-conditioning Refrigerating Data Books"; *Refrigerating Engineering;* ARI Equipment Standards; ASHRAE Guide and Data Book. Merkel and Bosnjakovic, "Diagrammen und Tabellen zur Berechnung der Absorptionskältemaschinen," Springer, Berlin. Jordan and Priester, "Refrigeration and Air Conditioning," Prentice-Hall.

REFRIGERATION MACHINES AND PROCESSES

(For general theory of refrigeration, see pp. 4–59 *et seq.;* for air-conditioning uses, see pp. 12–120 *et seq.;* for cryogenics, see pp. 18–28 *et seq.*)

Refrigeration is a special aspect of heat transfer and involves the production and utilization of below-atmospheric temperatures by a number of practical processes. Substances are cooled when their heat is transferred, via a temperature drop, to solid, liquid, or gaseous media which are naturally or artificially colder, their lower temperature stemming from radiation, sensible- or latent-heat physical effects, or endothermic chemical, thermoelectric, or even magnetic effects. Effects, such as cold streams, melting ice, and sublimating solid carbon dioxide, are included.

Of particular practical use is the achievement of lowered temperature for a circulating fluid (**refrigerant**) on a continuous basis, with heat-absorption capability, by (1) expansive flow of a fluid through a pressure drop in a restriction ("expansion valve") *without* production of external work, i.e., throttling (Joule-Thomson) effect, and (2) expansive flow of a fluid (usually a gas) through a pressure drop in a machine (expander) *with* production of external work.

The integrated systems for continuous cold effect are best recognized through the similarity of format in their closed flow circuits, particularly in (1) vapor-compression and (2) gas-compression systems. Both these systems contain a high-level and a low-level heat exchanger and two pressure difference devices, a pressure generator and a pressure-reducing element, typical of energy-transport systems. In the vapor-compression system the heat exchangers are characterized by latent-heat effects; in the gas compression, by sensible-heat effects primarily. Although some cases may entail discharge of some circulant at low pressure and low temperature with subsequent fresh make-up, the closed systems are more usual. Generally, the low-level-exchanger refrigeration effect is achieved through energy input, such as work input to a compressor.

With continuous recirculation of the cycle fluid, the low-temperature heat pickup must be pumped, via energy input, to a higher level so as to discharge it to atmospheric temperature. In this sense the system acts as an **energy-transport** device or **heat pump** or, from another viewpoint, as a temperature transformer. This philosophy of energy transport may equally well be applied to more remote systems, such as thermoelectric. It is, of course, a manifestation of the principles of the Second Law, and the effectiveness of the system's operation may be evaluated numerically.

Coefficient of performance (see p. 4–60) is the ratio of useful refrigeration to the work supplied, either directly or indirectly, as energy capable of doing work. The ratio of the coefficient of performance of any actual cycle to that of the Carnot cycle operating between the same two temperature levels is called the **relative efficiency** of the cycle. Relative efficiencies must always be less than unity, but coefficients of performance can be severalfold greater than one.

Refrigeration capacity is also of interest; the capability of a system is defined in terms of an arbitrary measure of capacity, the "ton."

Units of Refrigeration. In the United States, a **standard ton of refrigeration** corresponds to a heat absorption at a rate of 288,000 Btu per day or 200 Btu per min. The heat absorption per day is approximately the heat of fusion of 1 ton of ice at 32 F. The **standard rating** of a refrigerating machine, using a condensable vapor, is the number of standard tons of refrigeration it can produce under the following conditions: (1) liquid only enters the expansion valve and vapor only enters the compressor of a compression-type unit or the absorber of an absorption system; (2) the liquid entering the expansion valve is subcooled 9 F and the vapor entering the compressor or absorber is superheated 9 F, these temperatures to be measured within 10 ft of the compressor cylinder or absorber; (3) the pressure at the compressor or absorber inlet corresponds to a saturation temperature of 5 F; and (4) the pressure at the compressor or absorber outlet corresponds to a saturation temperature of 86 F.

The **British unit of refrigeration** corresponds to a heat-absorption rate of 237.6 Btu per min with inlet and outlet pressures corresponding to saturation temperatures of 23 and 59 F, respectively. On the European continent a unit of refrigeration capacity called the **frigorie** is used. A frigorie is approximately equivalent to 50 Btu per min, or 1/4 of a standard ton of refrigeration.

PROPERTIES OF REFRIGERANTS

(For detailed properties, see Sec. 4)

Refrigerants are the transport fluids which convey the heat energy from the low-temperature level to the high-temperature level, where it can, in terms of heat transfer, give up its heat. In the broad sense, gases involved in liquefaction processes or in gas-compression cycles go through low-temperature phases and hence may be termed "refrigerants," in a way similar to the more conventional vapor-compression fluids.

According to ASA Code B79.1-1960, refrigerants are **designated by number,** to wit, "5.1.3 The identifying number of the refrigerant, or the word 'Refrigerant' or both, may be preceded by the manufacturer's trademark or trade name"; also, "5.1.4 Examples are as follows: 'Isotron' 12 or 'Isotron' Refrigerant 12; 'Genetron' 12 or 'Genetron' Refrigerant 12; 'Freon' 12 or 'Freon' Refrigerant 12 or 'Freon' 12 Refrigerant or 'F-12' Refrigerant."

One of the attributes that must be considered for vapor-compression systems is the **normal boiling point** since this is of concern in the selection of a fluid which will be above atmospheric pressure on the low side and hence free from the threat of inward air leaks. Table 1 shows some common fluids in order of ascending boiling point; included are halocarbon compounds, such as hitherto named "freons," hydrocarbons and sulphur compounds, and inorganic compounds.

The desirable thermal properties of a refrigerant are (1) convenient evaporation and condensation pressures, (2) high critical and low freezing temperatures, (3) high latent heat of evaporation and high vapor specific heat, (4) low viscosity and high film heat conductivity. Desirable practical properties include (1) low cost, (2) chemical and physical inertness under operating conditions, (3) non-corrosiveness toward ordinary construction materials, and (4) low explosive hazard both alone and mixed with air. The refrigerant should be non-poisonous and non-irritating and should not cause deterioration in the lubricant used. Leakage should be detectable by simple tests, easily performed.

The *specific volume of refrigerant* to be handled is important with reciprocating compressors, as it determines the size of the compressor; but with centrifugal compression a large volume is not objectionable and may be a positive advantage for small units. A large compression ratio is undesirable in reciprocating compressors from the standpoint of clearance losses and may make the use of compound compression necessary.

A comparison of various refrigerants based on *ideal performance* is given in Table 2. The results are for the **standard temperature range** of 5 to 86 F and also for certain other ranges. For these calculations, zero piston clearance and expansion through a throttle valve were assumed. The use of an expansion cylinder instead of a valve would have yielded work (available for supplying some of the work of compression), but this is always a negligible quantity, except when the compression pressure approaches the critical pressure, as for carbon dioxide. Theoretical *coefficients of per-*

Table 1. Selected Refrigerants and Gases in Low-temperature Applications

Refrigerant	Refrig-erant No.	Symbol	Molec-ular weight	B.P. deg F	Critical point	
					Temp, deg F	Press, psia
Helium	704	He	4.0	−452	−450	33
Hydrogen	702	H_2	2.0	−423	−400	188
Nitrogen	728	N_2	28.0	−320	−232	492
Air	729	....	29.0	−312	−220.3	547
Oxygen	732	O_2	32.0	−297	−182	730
Methane	50	CH_4	16.0	−258.9	−115.8	673
Carbon tetrafluoride	14	CF_4	88.0	−198.4	−49.9	542
Ethylene	1,150	C_2H_4	28.0	−155.0	48.8	732
Ethane	170	C_2H_6	30.0	−127.5	90.	708
Nitrous oxide	744A	N_2O	44.0	−127.0	96.5	1,050
Monochlorotrifluoromethane	13	$CClF_3$	104.5	−114.6	83.9	561
Carbon dioxide	744	CO_2	44.0	−109.3	87.8	1,071
Propane	290	C_3H_8	44.1	−44.2	202	661
Monochlorodifluoromethane	22	$CHClF_2$	86.5	−41.4	204.8	716
Ammonia	717	NH_3	17.0	−28.0	271.4	1,657
Dichlorodifluoromethane	12	CCl_2F_2	120.9	−21.6	233.6	597
Methylchloride	40	CH_3Cl	50.5	−10.8	289.4	969
Isobutane	601	C_4H_{10}	58.1	10.3	272.7	537
Sulphur dioxide	764	SO_2	64.1	14.0	314.8	1,142
Butane	600	C_4H_{10}	58.1	31.3	306	550
Dichlorotetrafluoroethane	114	$CClF_2$-$CClF_2$	170.9	38.4	294.3	474
Dichloromonofluoromethane	21	$CHCl_2F$	102.9	48.1	353.3	750
Trichloromonofluoromethane	11	CCl_3F	137.4	74.8	388.4	635
Ethyl-ether	610	$C_4H_{10}O$	74.1	94.3	522.1	381
Methylene chloride	30	CH_2Cl_2	84.9	103.6	480	670
Trichlorotrifluoroethane	113	CCl_2F-$CClF_2$	187.4	117.6	417.4	495
Water	718	H_2O	18.0	212	706.1	3,226

formance may be obtained by dividing 4.72 by the theoretical horsepower given in the table.

Ammonia is used extensively in large installations, industrial and commercial. It is toxic and because of corrosive action must be kept out of contact with copper or copper-bearing alloys. It has a high latent heat of evaporation and convenient pressure-specific volume relations. It is not miscible to any large extent with lubricating oil. **Carbon dioxide** was used for a long time as a safety refrigerant; exposure to it in a confined space is not dangerous unless concentrations are high. With cooling water at 70 F, the condensing pressure of CO_2 is high, and since its critical temperature is 87.8 F condensation will not occur at water temperatures above this. Power consumption is high on CO_2 machines. **Sulphur dioxide** has rapidly gone out of use even in the small household units where it was previously widely employed. It is extremely corrosive unless absolutely anhydrous and although not dangerous in the quantities used in a household unit (2 to 3 lb), it may be dangerous in larger installations. It is extremely irritating even in small amounts. **Methyl chloride** (CH_3Cl), an anesthetic in amounts of 5 to 10 percent by volume, has been used in air-cooled units of either moderate or small sizes. It is miscible with minerals oils; small amounts of moisture in a methyl chloride system will cause trouble by freezing in expansion valves. The series of fluoro-chloro hydrocarbons known as **Freons** or **Genetrons** are increasingly used both in small and medium-sized units. Many compounds of this type are commercially produced; those which are non-toxic, non-irritating, and non-flammable are commonly employed. They include **F-11,** trichloromonofluoromethane (CCl_3F); **F-12,** dichlorodifluoromethane (CCl_2F_2); **F-13,** monochlorotrifluoromethane ($CClF_3$); **F-21,** dichloromonofluoroethane ($CHCl_2F$); **F-22,** monochlorodifluoromethane ($CHClF_2$); **F-113,** trichlorotrifluoroethane (CCl_2FCClF_2); and **F-114,** dichlorotetrafluoroethane ($C_2Cl_2F_4$). F-12 is widely used for air conditioning and general commercial cooling. Methyl chloride, having similar physical properties, has been largely supplanted by F-12 in this field. Refrigerants containing chlorine as part of the molecule are readily detected in minute amount by passing them through a copper gauze kept hot by the essentially colorless flame of burning methyl alcohol. Even traces of

Table 2. Ideal Performance of Refrigerants for Various Temperature Ranges

Refrigerant and (number)	Operating temperature range, deg F	Suction pressure, psia	Head pressure, psia	Ratio of head to suction pressure	With dry and saturated suction vapor, per ton: Weight of vapor, lb per min	Piston displacement, cfm	Theoretical hp	Temperature at end of compression, deg F	Type of compressor
Air (729)	5–86	14.7	73.5	5.0	7.02	82.3	2.82	277.0	Recip. and exp. cyl
Water (718)	32–86	0.0885	0.6152	6.95	0.1957	647.0	0.618	332	Centrif. or ejector
	32–100	0.0885	0.9492	10.73	0.1985	656.2	0.819	420	
	40–100	0.1217	0.9492	7.80	0.1978	483.4	0.687	366	
Carbon dioxide (CO_2) (744)	5–86	332.0	1,043.0	3.14	3.61	0.960	1.827	160.3	Recip.
Ammonia (NH_3) (717)	5–86	34.27	169.2	4.94	0.421	3.44	0.99	209.8	Recip.
	20–100	48.21	211.9	4.40	0.421	2.49	0.94	212.8	
	40–100	73.32	211.9	2.89	0.427	1.70	0.65	176.0	
Freon 11 (CCl_3F) (11)	5–86	2.931	18.28	6.20	3.058	37.0	0.94	112.7	Centrif.
	20–100	4.342	23.60	5.44	3.086	26.2	0.89	122.1	
	40–100	7.032	23.60	3.36	2.945	16.08	0.63	114.2	
Freon 12 (CCl_2F_2) (12)	5–86	26.51	107.9	4.07	3.916	5.82	1.00	100.2	Recip. or centrif.
	20–100	35.75	131.6	3.68	4.054	4.54	0.97	112.5	
	40–100	51.68	131.6	2.55	3.880	3.07	0.67	108.0	
Freon 21 ($CHCl_2F$) (21)	5–86	5.243	31.23	5.96	2.364	20.87	0.94*	99.0*	Rotary
	20–100	7.699	40.04	5.20	2.404	15.61	0.94*	110.4*	
	40–100	12.32	40.04	3.25	2.315	10.19	0.68*	105.9*	
Freon 22 ($CHClF_2$) (22)	5–86	43.02	174.5	4.06	2.926	3.65	1.03	131.7	Recip.
	20–100	57.98	212.6	3.67	3.023	2.83	0.99	152.7	
	40–100	83.72	212.6	2.54	2.936	1.93	0.68	131.0	
Methylene chloride (CH_2Cl_2) (30)	5–86	1.28	10.07	8.56	1.485	74.0	0.96*	205.1*	Centrif.
	20–100	1.92	13.25	6.90	1.520	47.72	0.91*	157.1*	
	40–100	3.38	13.25	3.92	1.493	27.76	0.63*	167.7*	
Methyl chloride (CH_3Cl) (40)	5–86	21.15	94.70	4.48	1.331	5.95	0.96	178.1	Recip.
	20–100	29.16	116.7	4.00	1.363	4.51	0.90	184.4	
	40–100	43.25	116.7	2.69	1.342	3.07	0.62	157.0	
Sulphur dioxide (SO_2) (764)	5–86	11.81	66.45	5.63	1.415	9.08	0.97	191.4	Recip.
	20–100	17.18	84.52	4.92	1.453	6.52	0.92	193.4	
	40–100	27.10	84.52	3.12	1.444	4.17	0.63	162.6	
Propane (C_3H_8) (290)	5–86	42.1	155.3	3.69	1.653	4.10	1.35*	92.9*	Recip.
	20–100	55.5	187.0	3.37	1.730	3.29	1.32*	103.9*	
	40–100	78.0	187.0	2.40	1.646	2.26	0.90*	101.5*	
Ethane (C_2H_5) (170)	5–86	236.0	675.9	2.87	3.41	1.82	2.180	105	Recip.
Ethyl chloride (C_2H_5Cl) (160)	5–86	4.65	27.10	5.83	1.405	24.0	0.95*	106.3*	Rotary
	20–100	6.80	34.79	5.12	1.425	17.19	0.92*	116.1*	
	40–100	10.79	34.79	3.22	1.375	10.73	0.63*	109.9*	

* Values may be slightly in error.

such refrigerants in air give a readily detected test due to the intense green color imparted to the flame by their presence.

For industrial work, **butane** (C_4H_{10}), **propane** (C_3H_8), and, at low temperatures, **ethane** (C_2H_6) are used. **Dieline** (dichloroethylene, $C_2H_2Cl_2$) and **Carrene** (dichloromethane, CH_2Cl_2) have been used to some extent, usually in centrifugal compressors.

The pressure-temperature relations for the saturated vapors of many of the commercially important refrigerants are given in Fig. 1. If the temperature at which the refrigeration is desired and the temperature at which heat can be discarded (condenser temperature) are known, the chart is convenient for determining for any chosen refrigerant the pressures which must be maintained. For instance, if the use of methyl chloride is contemplated in an air-cooled cabinet food freezer located in a room where the air temperature may rise to 90 F, the compressor discharge must be at least 100 psia and if the cabinet cooling coil is to be held at −30 F, compressor suction will be 9 psia.

The large volumes required for F-11, dieline, and water vapor can be handled satis-

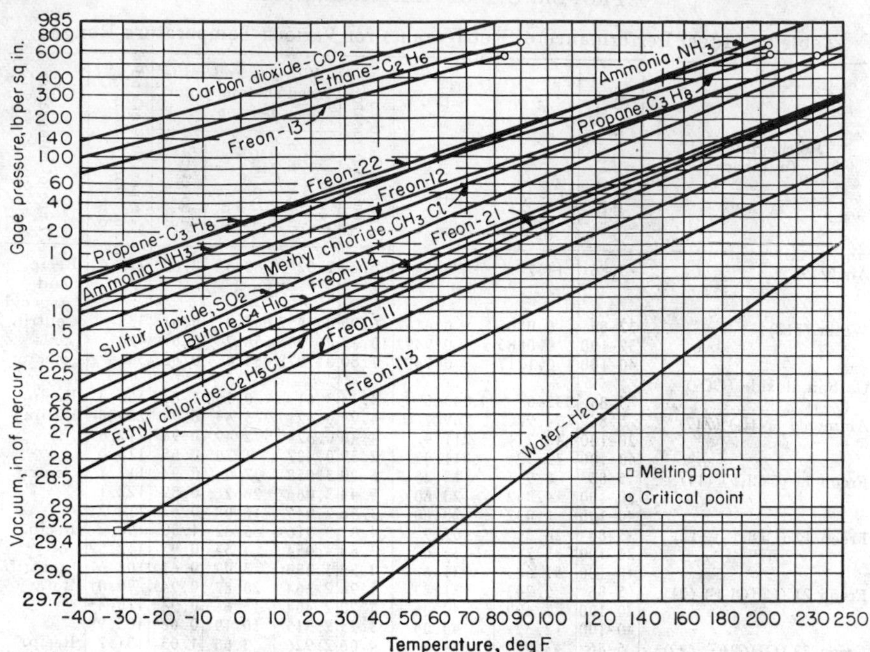

FIG. 1. Pressure-temperature relations of saturated vapors of refrigerants.

factorily by centrifugal compressors. When the evaporating pressure is below atmospheric, as in the case of dieline, ethyl chloride, sulfur dioxide, water vapor, and butane, air leaks are likely to be excessive; where the refrigerant is nearly odorless (Freon 12 and methyl chloride), leaks into the atmosphere are difficult to detect, and loss of the refrigerant may be excessive.

OVERALL CYCLES

Figure 2 represents the simple closed-circuit **vapor-compression** system. The upper heat exchanger is a vapor condenser (with some superheat), and after the throt-

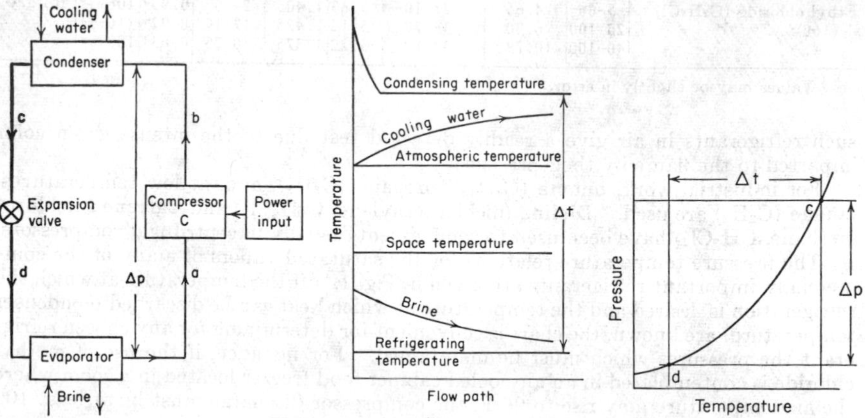

FIG. 2. Simple closed-circuit vapor-compression system.

FIG. 3. Comparative temperature relations for fluids of a simple system.

FIG. 4. Pressure-temperature curve illustrating over-all differences.

tling expansion valve, the lower one is the evaporator in which the refrigerant liquid at reduced pressure and temperature evaporates with the inward refrigeration heat flow. The refrigerant vapor is elevated by the compressor to a higher pressure and condensing temperature so that it will liquefy in its transfer of heat to the atmospheric level. Figures 3 to 5 illustrate the cycle.

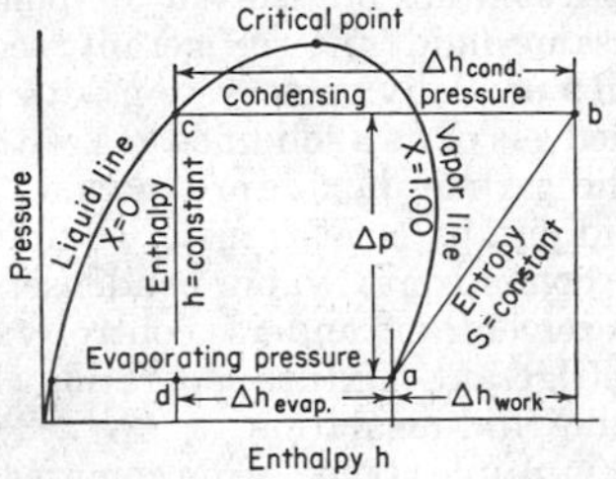

FIG. 5. Pressure-enthalpy diagram for simple ideal refrigeration cycle.

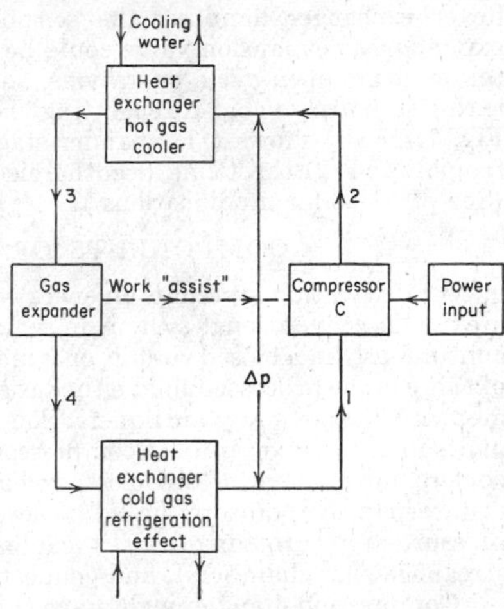

FIG. 6. Closed sensible-heat gas-compression cycle.

Figure 6 is the counterpart of Fig. 2 and represents the closed sensible-heat **gas-compression** cycle, with an expander (either displacement or turbine-type) parallel to a gas compressor which may provide a compressor-work "assist" in addition to its exhaust stream of cold gas. This is the refrigeration version of the Brayton cycle (see p. 4–28), the upper exchanger serving to cool the hot compressed gas, and the

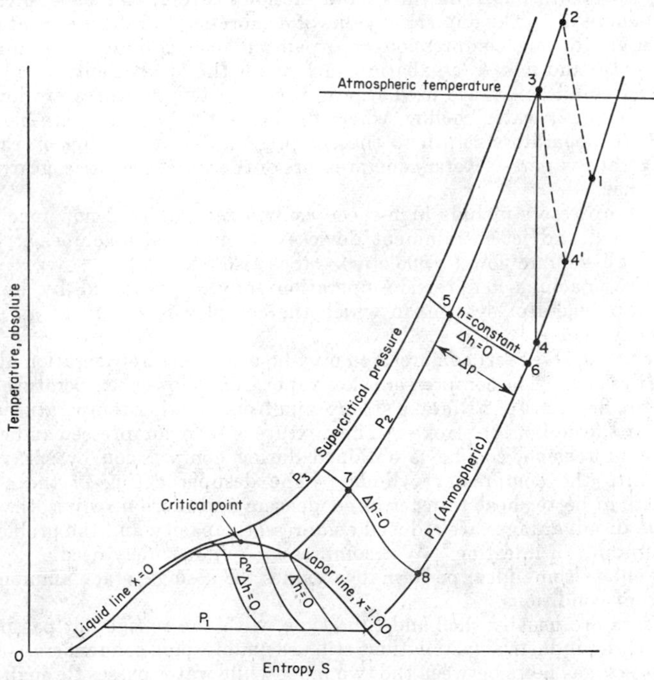

FIG. 7. Extended temperature-entropy diagram illustrating processes.

lower exchanger handling the sensible-heat refrigeration effect. In place of the expander, an expansion valve could be used; this is particularly effective on very low-temperature open-cycle operations, such as with gas liquefaction processes incorporating secondary "cold-regenerating" heat exchangers. An extended *Ts* diagram (*i.e.*, Fig. 7 for air) shows (1) expander stages 3–4 (ideal, isentropic) and 3–4′ (real, polytropic), and (2) throttling (isenthalpic process), 5–6 (high level), and 7–8 (low level). (See p. 18–26 for modifications.)

COMPONENTS OF COMPRESSION SYSTEMS

A refrigeration system is an energy-transport complex of assorted components. It may be a conventional system in which the same fluid, the refrigerant, recirculates continuously in a closed circuit, or it may entail a partially open system with discharge of some of the processed fluid either as a liquefied gas or as a solidified gas, with replacement makeup, *e.g.*, by air liquefaction and solid carbon dioxide production. Components include vapor and gas compressors; liquid pumps; heat-transfer equipment (gas coolers, intercoolers, aftercoolers, exchangers, economizers); vapor condensers and the counterpart evaporators; liquid coolers and receivers; expanders; control valves and pressure-drop throttling devices (capillaries, refrigerant-mixture separating chambers, stream-mixing chambers); and connecting piping and insulation.

Compression may be single stage (Fig. 2) or multiple stage. The **compressors** may be displacement or kinetic. The former include piston **reciprocating** machines in which the refrigerant, as vapor, is raised in pressure, usually with some simultaneous cooling. These machines may be horizontal or vertical, single acting or double acting; the vertical arrangement, with multiple cylinders in automotive arrangement and running at high rotative speeds, is common. Of utmost importance in the realized performance of a displacement compressor is the real volumetric effectiveness, or "efficiency," which measures the extent of utilization of the machine displacement volume. It is influenced by cylinder clearance volume, pressure ratio, nature of the gas, pressure drops through the valves and suction heating, and the equivalent compression exponent n. [The numerical value of n expresses the effect of heat transfer to or from the gas during compression or expansion in a cylinder. Normally it lies between $n = 1.0$ and $n = k$ (adiabatic), such as for the ideal (isentropic).]

Air-cooled compressors are used where discharge temperatures are low, such as with Refrigerant 12; **water cooling,** where discharge temperatures are high, as with ammonia. **Oil separators** return to the compressor the lubricating oil carried over by the refrigerant vapors. **Rotary compressors** of the vane, eccentric, gear, and screw types are in use.

Kinetic compressors include high-speed centrifugal and axial flow machines, usually multistaged, and jet-entrainment devices. Centrifugal machines are especially adapted to high-volume flow (>500 cfm). (See also Sec. 14.)

The entire machine-compression operation may be replaced by a secondary absorber-pump-generator system, in which the complex is known as an absorption refrigeration system.

Dual (or **multiple-effect**) **compression** may be used when refrigeration at two temperatures is desired. The compressor takes vapor from a lower temperature expansion coil during the first part of its intake stroke, and from a higher temperature expansion coil at or near the end of the stroke. The mixture is then compressed and condensed.

In **wet compression,** cooling is obtained during compression by spraying liquid refrigerant into the compressor cylinder. The desuperheating of the compressed vapors results in better heat transfer in condensers and more nearly isothermal compression; the disadvantages are reduced compressor capacity and the problem of control of the amount of injection. Wet compression is not widely used.

Table 3 shows some ideal performance values for a single-stage ammonia system under different conditions.

Condensers are usually shell-and-tube type, with the refrigerant passing outside the tubes. Older industrial installations still use **double-pipe condensers.** In double-pipe condensers, gas flows between the two pipes while water passes through the inner. The outside pipe diameter may be 2 in.; the inner, 1¼ in. In some instances, the

Table 3. Theoretical Horsepower and Theoretical Volume of Dry Ammonia Gas Pumped per Minute to Produce 1 Ton of Refrigeration

Suction pressure and temperature		Condenser pressure, psig (temperature, deg F)									
Psig	Deg F	103 (65)		127 (75)		153 (85)		182 (95)		215 (105)	
		Hp	Cfm	Hp	Cfm	Hp	Cfm	Hp	Cfm	Hp	Cfm
4	−20	1.058	5.84	1.205	5.96	1.361	6.09	1.525	6.23	1.691	6.43
6	−15	0.997	5.35	1.145	5.46	1.300	5.58	1.461	5.70	1.546	5.83
9	−10	0.903	4.66	1.045	4.76	1.193	4.86	1.347	4.97	1.435	5.08
13	−5	0.818	4.09	0.954	4.17	1.094	4.25	1.244	4.35	1.321	4.44
16	0	0.735	3.59	0.865	3.66	1.002	3.74	1.147	3.83	1.219	3.91
20	5	0.666	3.20	0.795	3.27	0.928	3.34	1.066	3.41	1.138	3.49
24	10	0.592	2.87	0.726	2.93	0.854	2.99	0.991	3.06	1.060	3.12
28	15	0.541	2.59	0.664	2.65	0.792	2.71	0.922	2.76	0.994	2.82
33	20	0.474	2.31	0.592	2.36	0.715	2.41	0.842	2.46	0.903	2.51
39	25	0.410	2.06	0.523	2.10	0.599	2.15	0.767	2.20	0.829	2.24
45	30	0.351	1.85	0.461	1.89	0.576	1.93	0.694	1.97	0.759	2.01
51	35	0.300	1.70	0.410	1.74	0.521	1.77	0.640	1.81	0.701	1.85

pipes are exposed to the atmosphere either with or without water drip. In an **evaporative condenser** the refrigerant vapor is condensed as it passes through tubes over which water is sprayed; the water is then evaporated by air flowing over the wet tubes. In this way, cooling-water requirements are reduced to from 5 to 15 percent of the water requirements of a non-evaporative condenser with no water reuse. The evaporative condenser combines in a single unit a refrigerant condenser and the atmospheric cooling tower or spray pond which is required if the cooling water is to be reused. Air-cooled finned-tube condensers with forced ventilation are widely used on small units, and shell-and-coil or double-tube water-cooled condensers on medium units.

Evaporators may have finned or plain surfaces. Defrosting may be automatic or manual. **Flooded** evaporators are operated practically full of liquid refrigerant, the level being controlled by a float valve. **Wet-expansion** evaporators are operated with a level approaching that for flooded operation; **dry-expansion** (once-through) units operate with an indefinite amount of liquid in the evaporator. Flooded or wet operation gives high heat-transfer rates, but requires larger amounts of refrigerant than dry operation. Pumped recirculation of refrigerant is used on some flooded evaporator systems to promote heat transfer, and also on shell and tube evaporators (liquid chillers), *e.g.*, in water-vapor systems. For a low-cost unit operating in limited space under conditions of motion (as on boats, trains, etc.) dry operation is preferred.

Controls are required on the liquid level of the refrigerant and on the temperature of the refrigerated space. The liquid control regulates the flow of the refrigerant into the evaporator and also serves as the pressure barrier between the high operating pressure of the condenser and the lower operating pressure of the evaporator. It may take the form of a **capillary tube** between the condenser (high side) and the evaporator (low side), in which case it is non-adjustable. Plugging due to dirt is a common difficulty. Capillary-tube liquid control is largely confined to relatively small units assembled and charged at the factory and particularly for hermetically sealed systems. The **constant-pressure expansion valve,** maintaining a constant evaporator pressure, and the **thermal expansion valve,** maintaining a constant superheat leaving the evaporator, are standard liquid controls for most commercial applications. A **low-side float** liquid control, used with a flooded evaporator operating at evaporator (low) pressure, consists of a float-operated valve to admit liquid refrigerant to the evaporator in accordance with demand so that a constant liquid level is held in it. A **high-side float** liquid control is often used with a single flooded evaporator; the float operating the valve between the evaporator and the condenser is in a float chamber containing liquid refrigerant at the condenser (high-side) pressure. As the liquid level in the float chamber falls, the valve closes, thus preventing hot gaseous refrigerant from passing from the high to the low side as is possible when using a capillary or a low-side float.

Vapor-compression Circuits

Compound Low-temperature Systems. Multistaging is advantageous as it reduces operating temperatures by intercooling and power requirements if the fluid superheats considerably on adiabatic compression, as with ammonia; with F-12 refrigerant, propane, and butane, the superheat is negligible (see Figs. 8 to 11).

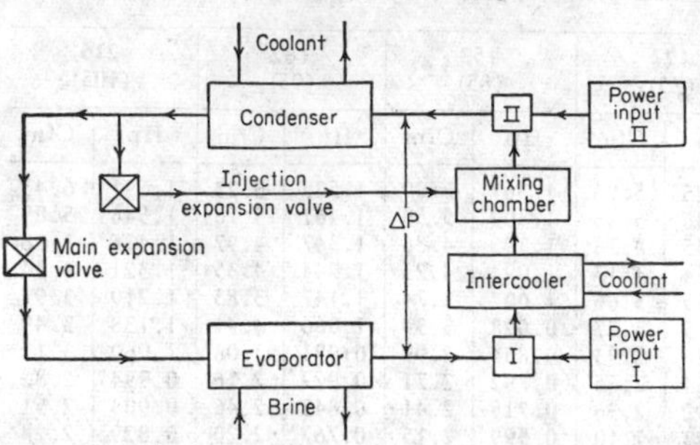

Fig. 8. Two-stage system with conventional intercooler plus refrigerant injection.

Gas Intercooler Plus Liquid Injection. Since gas temperature in the intercooler is limited by cooling water temperature, further favorable reduction of gas temperature, prior to entrance to the second stage, may be accomplished by direct injection, via an expansion valve, of refrigerant liquid (Fig. 8).

Gas Intercooler Plus Flash Intercooler. With a flash intercooler separator located midway between successive expansion valves, the gas leaving the water-cooled intercooler passes through the flash intercooler, gets cooled by direct contact with the liquid, and, augmented by the flash vapor and at reduced temperature, enters the second stage (Fig. 9).

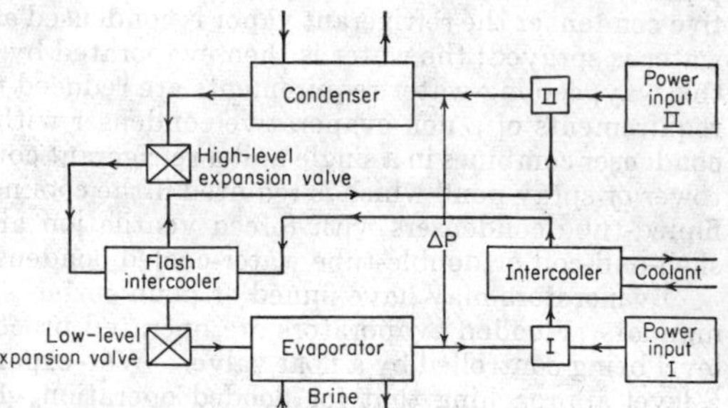

Fig. 9. Two-stage system with conventional intercooler plus flash intercooler.

Low-temperature Booster Plus Single Stage. For the addition of a second lower-temperature evaporator to an existing single-stage system, a booster for the low-temperature vapor may be employed, its output feeding into the single-stage suction. The booster is a centrifugal or rotary compressor, suitable for handling the large vapor volumes encountered at low temperatures (and pressures); the reciprocating compressor is more advantageous at high pressures (Fig. 10).

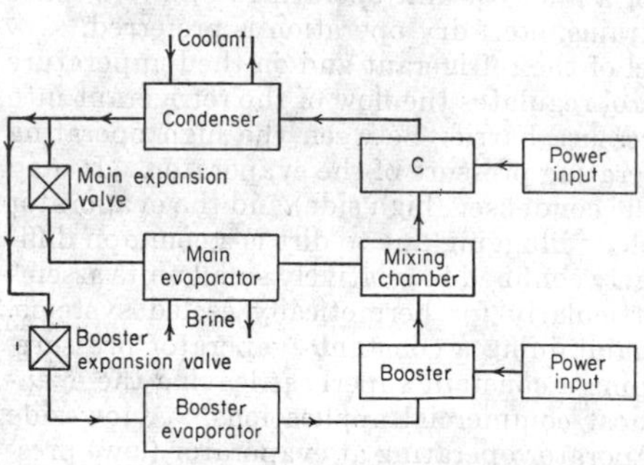

Fig. 10. Two-stage system incorporating low-temperature booster circuit.

Cascade Systems with Segregated Circuits. Here two separate circuits are employed with the low-stage vapor condensed in the second-stage evaporator. Two different refrigerants may be appropriately chosen, a lower-boiling-point refrigerant serving for the first stage. Thus, for low temperatures (< -50 F), CO_2 may be employed in the lower stage with NH_3 in the second stage condensing the CO_2. Or the same refrigerant may be used in both stages, limiting the migration of the lubricant to the low-temperature realm (Fig. 11).

Water-vapor refrigeration is necessarily limited to near-atmospheric temperature levels; it involves large suction volumes at high vacuum and utilizes a non-toxic refrigerant; this type of refrigeration was frequently used in the early days of space air-conditioning. It utilizes (1) centrifugal compressors or (2) steam-jet compressors, entraining low-density water vapor from the evaporator. The centrifugal water-vapor compressor, usually multistage, must operate at high speeds (7,000 to 10,000 rpm) with a geared electric motor or steam-turbine drive. Operation at high vacuum (Fig. 2) requires an air pump at the condenser to eliminate leakage effects.

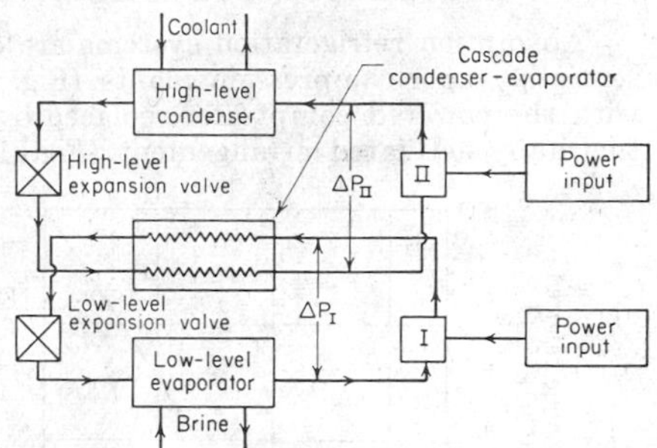

FIG. 11. Two-stage system in cascade form.

Steam-jet refrigeration systems are used where cooling to temperatures above 32 F is desired. Applications include industrial air conditioning; and cooling of city gas to condense out tar and other objectionable impurities, of gas absorbers to increase efficiency of absorption, of reaction units where heat removal and temperature control are important during chemical transformations, and of wort and mash in the brewing and other fermentation industries particularly in the summer months. Jet refrigeration has been used for cooling passenger trains and is coming into popularity for marine installations, *e.g.*, cooling of banana boats and large passenger vessels. The system is a compression-type refrigerator: it uses water as a refrigerant, a part of which is evaporated to produce cooling of the remainder; steam-jet ejectors to compress the water vapor resulting from evaporation, and a condenser, either the surface type, where refrigerant water is to be reused, or the barometric type, where refrigerant water can be discarded. The advantages of the system are: low installation cost; economical operating cost, particularly if low-cost, low-pressure steam and adequate condensing water are available; the absence of moving parts except for small liquid pumps; safety, since no noxious or toxic refrigerants are used; ability to carry considerable overload with only a small rise in refrigerating temperature level; and elimination of heat-transfer surfaces. (See Havemeyer, *Chem. Eng.*, Sept., 1948, pp. 103–106.) For considerable differences in temperatures between condensing-water temperature and refrigerating temperatures (20 F or more), cooling of the refrigerant water by evaporation in two stages operating at different pressures (and temperatures) will usually give better operating economy, but at somewhat higher installation cost.

Figure 12 shows the variation of refrigerating capacity with variation of the chilled-water temperature, capacity increasing as chilled-water temperature rises.

Household compression machines are designed for continuous automatic operation and for conservation of the charges of refrigerant and oil. These units are almost universally motor-driven air-cooled compressors, the principal exception being the Electrolux-Servel absorption unit (see p. 18-13). The compressor may be hermetically sealed, with the compressor and motor enclosed in the same casing, or may use a shaft seal, embodying some form of sylphon bellows, with an outside coil spring at the place where the crankshaft passes out of the casing. The compressor may be reciprocating, but rotary types are being increasingly used either with a floating piston ring driven by an eccentric or with sliding blades. Lubrication is by internal forced-feed circulation in most cases. The condenser may be of the radiator, coil, or plate type, cooled by natural draft, by a fan on the main motor, or by a separate motor. The refrigerant is usually Freon 12. Refrigerant feed control to the evaporator may be (1) float feed (flooded system), (2) pressure-actuated diaphragm valve, or (3) by fixed orifice. The fixed orifice may be either a plate orifice or a capillary tube. The evaporator is usually made of stainless steel. Controls are generally pressure-operated thermostatic switches. The power consumption of an average box (say 6 cu ft) is about 20 kwh per month. The heat gain of a refrigerator cabinet of the same size is about 3.3 Btu per hr per deg F.

ABSORPTION SYSTEMS

Absorption refrigeration systems are essentially vapor-compression plants (Fig. 2) with the powered compressor replaced by a thermally activated arrangement (Fig. 13) where the basic elements are absorber, pump, heat exchanger, throttle valve, and generator. Applications of this type of system are (1) ammonia-water system, for general industrial application, (2) household refrigerators (Platen, Munters, Electrolux), and (3) water and lithium bromide, for air conditioning.

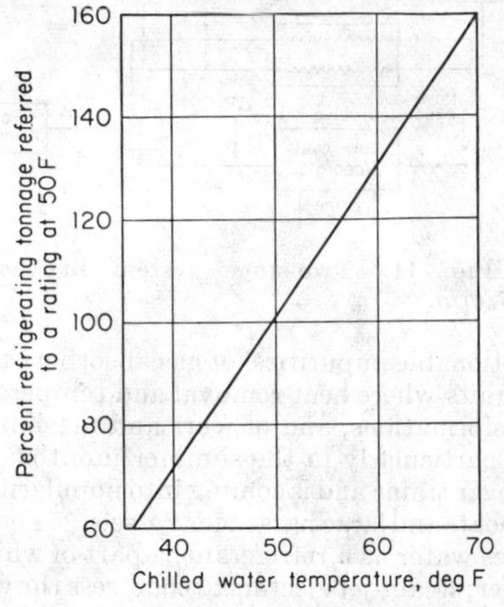

Fig. 12. Variation of refrigerating capacity with the jet chilled-water temperature in steam refrigeration.

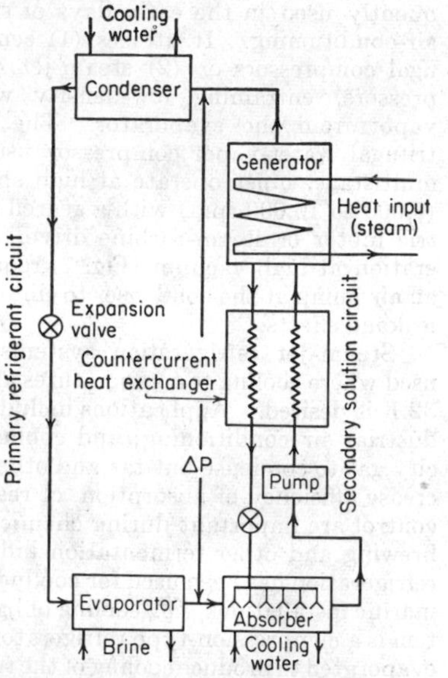

Fig. 13. Elemental absorption-system circuit.

Many combinations of soluble gas and solvent liquid have been proposed for absorption refrigeration but ammonia-water systems alone have been used industrially. Few of these are now in operation, except for the small domestic Electrolux machines (see p. 18–13), probably because they were bulky and difficult to operate efficiently.

In the absorption system, liquid ammonia vaporizes in the evaporator, producing refrigeration. The ammonia gas goes to an **absorber,** where it is absorbed by a weak solution of ammonia in water (weak liquor) at a low temperature, the heat of solution being abstracted by water (or air) and a strong liquor being formed. The strong liquor is pumped to the **generator,** where its temperature is raised by steam coils and a mixture of water vapor and ammonia vapor is evolved. This gaseous mixture passes up through the **analyzer,** where it meets the relatively cool strong liquor entering the generator and loses some of its vapor content. From the top of the analyzer ammonia and water vapor pass to the **rectifier,** often merely a cooling coil or tubular heat interchanger, where cooling water condenses more of the water vapor, the water flowing back to the analyzer and the generator and the residual ammonia gas passing to the condenser. The ammonia gas after liquefaction in the condenser goes through an expansion valve to the evaporator. Weak liquor flowing from the generator to the absorber passes through a heat exchanger, where it heats the strong liquor coming from the absorber to the generator. Efficient heat exchange is necessary in absorption units; the steam requirement may be reduced to one-third that necessary with no heat exchange. (See Stickney, *Ice and Refrig.*, May to Aug., 1936, for an analysis of the effect on the absorption cycle of the use of heat exchangers.) **Two-stage** and even

three-stage absorption systems have been proposed. Staged operation makes possible a greater temperature difference between cooling water and refrigeration temperature, but increases heat requirements almost in proportion to the number of stages. With cooling water at 80 F refrigeration may be produced at −94 F in a two-stage system; with three stages, the refrigeration may be at −200 F or even lower.

Some of the properties of ammonia-water solutions are given in Fig. 14 (from Stickney, New Tables and Chart for Ammonia Solutions, *Refrig. Eng.*, Oct., 1935). The

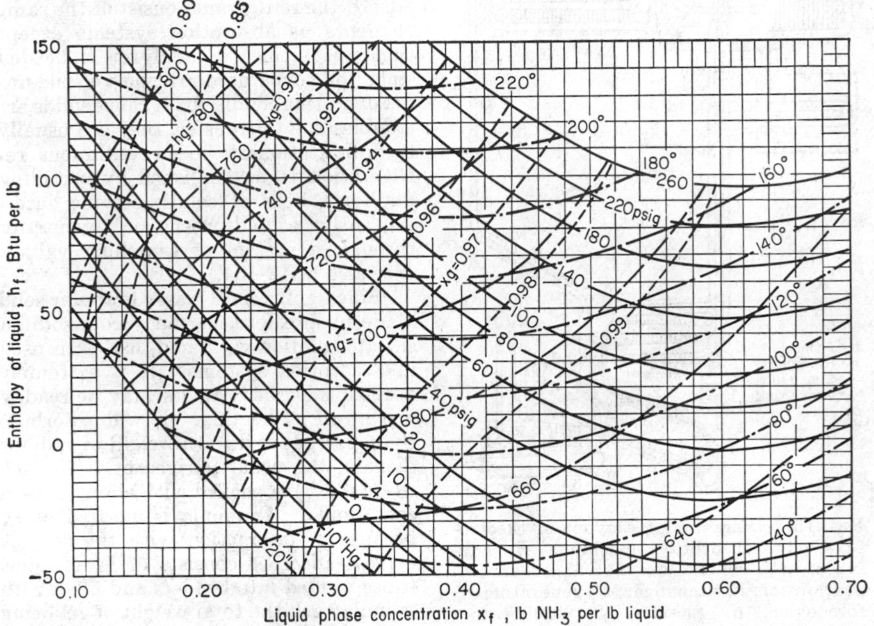

FIG. 14. Physical properties of ammonia-water solutions.

enthalpy of liquid water is assumed 0 at 32 F, the enthalpy of liquid ammonia is assumed 0 at −40 F. Six values can be read from any point, namely, gage pressure; temperature, deg F; composition (weight of ammonia per lb of mixture) and enthalpy (Btu per lb) in both the liquid and vapor phases.

EXAMPLE: A solution containing 30 percent by weight NH_3 at 120 F has a pressure of 17 psig; the enthalpy of the liquid solution is 22 and of the vapor 693 Btu per lb; the vapor in equilibrium with the solution will be 96.3 percent NH_3 by weight.

For a second-law analysis of the parts of the absorption cycle, the availability tables of Scatchard (*Refrig. Eng.*, **58**, 1947, pp. 413–419) will be found convenient.

Electrolux-Servel Absorption Process (Platen-Munters Patent). The Electrolux-Servel ammonia absorption process eliminates the use of pumps or other moving parts. The gas pressure is uniform throughout the hermetically sealed system, the difference between the vapor pressure of ammonia in the condenser and that in the evaporator being compensated by the presence of hydrogen; the sum of the partial pressures of the hydrogen and of the ammonia vapor in the evaporator is equal to the sum of the partial pressures in the condenser. The general arrangement is shown in Fig. 15.

The most prominent heat-activated absorption system for air conditioning is that involving **water and lithium bromide,** a "thermal compression" water-vapor cycle for temperatures above 32 F. This parallels the water-vapor systems (Fig. 13) in which the elevation of pressure to the condenser is accomplished either by a high volume centrifugal or by a steam-jet entrainment device. Whereas in the ammonia and water system, ammonia vapor alternately dissolves in or is disengaged from an aqueous ammonia solution, with ammonia subsequently the cycle refrigerant, here water vapor parallels the ammonia; it dissolves in (absorber) or disengages from (generator) the lithium bromide solution, and water subsequently is the cycle refrigerant.

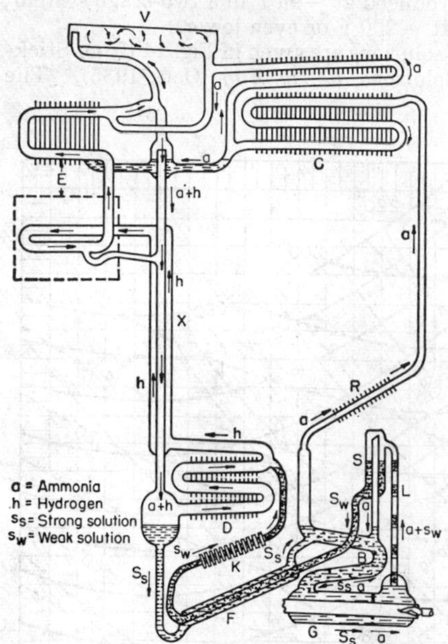

Fig. 15. Diagrammatic layout of Electrolux-Servel absorption machine. *B*, analyzer; *C*, condenser; *D*, absorber; *E*, evaporator; *F*, exchanger; *G*, generator; *K*, forecooler; *R*, rectifier; *S*, liquid-vapor separator; *V*, hydrogen reserve vessel; *X*, heat exchanger.

Adsorption systems using solids to adsorb the refrigerant consist of the same elements as absorption systems except that no rectifier or analyzer is needed since the solids used are non-volatile under operating conditions. Since solids are troublesome to transfer, they are usually held in stationary beds; continuous refrigeration is accomplished by installing duplicate beds of solids, serving intermittently as adsorber and generator through a system of switching valves. (See also p. 12–134.)

Silica gel, a hard glassy granular solid made by precipitating SiO_2 from sodium silicate solution with acid, has been used in adsorption systems. It is extremely porous; adsorbed vapors may be readily driven off by heating. It will absorb 25 to 35 percent of its own weight of sulphur dioxide, the usual refrigerant. The gel, (8–20 mesh) is packed with about 50 percent voids. Ammonia is unsatisfactory because of interaction with the gel. A typical adsorber consists of ¾ in. steel tubes welded into headers and filled with granular gel, the total weight of gel being 1,000 lb. It has an ice-melting effect of 1 to 1½ lb per 24 hr per lb of silica gel; this may be raised to 4 lb per lb by forced circulation. Fuel consumption is about 135 lb of propane per ton of refrigeration. Silica gel is used in the chemical industry as a dehydrating agent, and also in some air-conditioning and high-temperature cooling units because of its ability to absorb water. The water is eliminated and the gel restored to its original activity by raising its temperature.

AIR MACHINES

Compressed-air machines in which air is compressed, cooled, and then adiabatically expanded in an engine while doing work are obsolete for usual industrial refrigeration because of bulk and inefficiency. Their coefficient of performance is less than unity as compared with 4 or 5 for vapor machines. Operation may be closed cycle, in which the air is reused, or open cycle, in which the air is discarded after expansion. Compression ratios of about 3 seem best. In the **dense-air** closed system, the pressure at the compressor intake averages 75 and at the outlet 225 to 250 psig. The use of superatmospheric pressure throughout the cycle decreases the size, and the reuse of dried air eliminates the ice formation on engine valves which occurs with open-system operation. Air cycles are used for liquefaction of the so-called permanent gases and to an increasing extent for comfort cooling in high-speed planes where the small lightweight equipment and the safety of the cooling medium are important. High-speed (90,000 to 100,000 rpm) gas turbines are used to extract work from moderately compressed (5 to 100 psig) air.

THERMOELECTRIC COOLING

Recently thermoelectric cooling, utilizing the Peltier effect with dissimilar metallic conductors (and variously called thermoelectric refrigeration, Peltier-effect cooling, or electronic cooling), has attained practicality in units of small sizes (less than 1 ton).

The elements of a thermoelectric cooler are quite simple and are equivalent to those of a thermoelectric generator (see p. 9–204). For development of various output capacities, the number of basic elements is proportionately increased; they all act in parallel, and their outputs add together. **Semiconductor** materials, such as bismuth-telluride-selenide and bismuth-antimony-telluride alloys, are employed.

With an input to the circuit of low-voltage direct current and with heat continuously abstracted at one junction at room temperature, the other junction will become cold. Essentially each of the two junctions becomes an "activity cell," in which at the lower refrigeration temperature level, heat is converted into electrical effect, and at the higher atmospheric temperature, the electrical effect is converted into heat. This establishes the basis of "heat-pump" operation: the lower-temperature heat requirement must be supplied, essentially as in the evaporator of a vapor-compression system, by heat withdrawal via heat transfer, from all connected surroundings. The energy-transport circuit thus parallels the machine-activated circuit of Fig. 2. The amount of heat for a single-component circuit depends on the circulating electric current, on the properties and dimensions of the two conductors (P and N types), and on the resultant temperature difference between the high side room temperature and the low side input heat that is divided into two groups, useless and useful. The **useless heat** is the heat conduction between the high and low temperature through the thermoelements plus the current-generated resistance-loss heat within the elements that flows to the colder junction. The **useful heat** is the refrigeration effect in a regular evaporator. All the heat must in turn be discharged via the Peltier effect at the higher room temperature, as in the condenser of a vapor-compression system. Ultimate performance of the circuit depends on the voltage-generating nature of the two dissimilar conductors and on their electrical resistance, thermal conductivity, and physical dimensions. The different properties are mathematically combined into a **figure of merit,** Z.

METHODS OF APPLYING REFRIGERATION

In **direct expansion systems** the evaporator is placed in the space which is to be cooled; in **brine systems** a brine is cooled by contact with the evaporator surface, and the cooled brine goes to the space which is to be refrigerated. Brine systems require 40 to 60 percent more surface than do direct expansion; they have an equalizing effect due to the large heat capacity of cold brine, they are safer (particularly if the refrigerating effect must be carried considerable distance or widely distributed), and they permit closer temperature regulation than is possible with direct expansion. Brine systems are recommended for larger cold-storage plants. If two temperatures are to be held, the lower may be by direct expansion, the higher by brine cooling. Development of better controls and newer piping methods has made direct expansion more attractive than previously.

Brines used for industrial refrigeration are usually aqueous solutions of either calcium chloride or sodium chloride. Calcium chloride should not contain over 0.2 percent magnesia, calculated as magnesium chloride. The purest economically available salt should be used in making sodium chloride brines; magnesia and sulphates are especially undesirable as they cause sludge formation. Calcium chloride brines are recommended down to −45 F; sodium chloride brine should not be used below 0 F. Brines should be chemically neutral: acidic brines attack ferrous materials, alkaline brines attack zinc, ammonia in brine (resulting from leaks in the ammonia system) is especially harmful to most non-ferrous metals. Corrosion by brine is increased by the presence of oxygen, air, or carbon dioxide and by galvanic action between dissimilar metals. The contact of brine with air should be minimized. Corrosion inhibitors are widely used, a satisfactory one being about 100 lb of sodium chromate or dichromate per 1,000 cu ft of calcium chloride brine or 200 lb per 1,000 cu ft of sodium chloride brine.

Table 4. Properties of Sodium Chloride Solutions

(For variation of sp gr with temperature see Table 6)

Parts of NaCl by weight in 100 parts of the solution	Specific gravity at 60 F	Deg Baumé	Weight per gal, lb	Weight per cu ft, lb	Freezing point, deg F	Specific heat at				
						14 F	32 F	50 F	68 F	86 F
6	1.044	6.06	8.71	65.1	25.5	......	0.924	0.927	0.929	0.932
8	1.058	8.00	8.82	66.0	22.9	......	0.902	0.906	0.909	0.912
10	1.073	9.91	8.95	66.9	20.2	......	0.882	0.887	0.890	0.893
12	1.088	11.78	9.08	67.8	17.3	......	0.865	0.869	0.873	0.876
14	1.104	13.63	9.22	68.8	14.1	......	0.848	0.853	0.857	0.859
16	1.119	15.45	9.33	69.8	10.6	0.827	0.834	0.839	0.842	0.844
18	1.135	17.25	9.47	70.8	6.7	0.815	0.821	0.825	0.828	0.830
20	1.151	19.02	9.60	71.8	2.4	0.804	0.809	0.813	0.815	0.817
22	1.167	20.78	9.74	72.8	−2.5	0.794	0.798	0.801	0.803	0.804
24	1.184	22.51	9.88	73.8	+1.4	0.784	0.788	0.791	0.792	0.793

The properties of sodium and calcium chloride brines are given in Tables 4 to 7.

The density of brine is measured by a **salinometer** (or **salometer**), which is a simple hydrometer the indications on which are 4 times greater than on the corresponding Baumé scale (see p. 1–89).

It is undesirable to use a **strength of solution** of salt greater than is necessitated by its freezing temperature, as the specific heat (Tables 4 and 5) decreases as the concentration of the brine increases, and consequently the stronger the brine, the less heat a given amount of it is able to convey between certain definite temperatures and the more power is required to pump the brine. Moreover, brine which is too strong may cause clogging of pipes, etc., by depositing salt. On the other hand, if the solution is too weak it may not be able to withstand the temperature existing in the expansion coil, so that a layer of thin ice will form around the latter and interfere with the absorption of heat from the brine. The surface of the expansion coils in the brine tank should be inspected from time to time to see if any ice has formed on them. In larger plants, it is customary to use a solution with a freezing point not less than 10 deg below the lowest temperature which will be obtained in the operation of the plant. In smaller isolated

Table 5. Properties of Calcium Chloride Solutions

(For variation of sp gr with temperature see Table 6)

Parts of $CaCl_2$ by weight in 100 parts of the solution	Specific gravity at 60 F	Deg Baumé	Weight per gal, lb	Weight per cu ft, lb	Freezing point, deg F	Specific heat at					
						−4 F	14 F	32 F	50 F	68 F	86 F
6	1.050	7.0	8.76	65.52	28.0	......	......	......	......	......	......
8	1.069	9.33	8.926	66.70	24.2	......	......	0.882	0.887	0.892	0.897
10	1.087	11.57	9.076	67.83	21.4	......	......	0.853	0.858	0.863	0.868
12	1.105	13.78	9.227	68.95	18.2	......	......	0.825	0.831	0.836	0.842
14	1.124	15.96	9.377	70.08	14.4	......	......	0.799	0.805	0.811	0.817
16	1.143	18.12	9.536	71.26	9.9	......	0.768	0.775	0.781	0.787	0.792
18	1.162	20.24	9.703	72.51	4.7	......	0.745	0.752	0.759	0.764	0.769
20	1.182	22.32	9.853	73.63	−1.0	......	0.723	0.731	0.738	0.744	0.749
22	1.202	24.38	10.04	75.0	−7.3	0.695	0.704	0.711	0.718	0.724	0.729
24	1.223	26.41	10.21	76.32	−14.1	0.678	0.686	0.693	0.900	0.706	0.712
26	1.244	28.41	10.38	77.56	−22.0	0.663	0.670	0.677	0.683	0.690	0.696
28	1.265	30.39	10.56	78.94	−32.0	0.649	0.656	0.662	0.669	0.675	0.682
30	1.287	32.34	10.75	80.35	−46.0	0.638	0.643	0.648	0.655	0.661	0.668

Table 6. Specific Gravities of Brines

(To change to lb per cu ft multiply by 62.43; to change to lb per gal multiply by 8.35)

Parts by weight of salt in 100 parts of brine	Sodium chloride				Calcium chloride				Magnesium chloride			
	Temperature, deg F											
	14	32	50	68	14	32	50	68	14	32	50	68
6	......	1.046	1.044	1.041	......	1.053	1.051	1.049	......	1.053	1.051	1.049
8	......	1.061	1.059	1.056	......	1.071	1.069	1.066	......	1.070	1.069	1.067
10	......	1.077	1.074	1.071	......	1.090	1.087	1.084	......	1.089	1.087	1.084
12	......	1.093	1.090	1.086	......	1.108	1.106	1.103	1.108	1.107	1.105	1.102
14	......	1.108	1.105	1.101	......	1.127	1.124	1.121	1.127	1.126	1.123	1.121
16	1.128	1.124	1.121	1.116	1.150	1.147	1.144	1.140	1.147	1.145	1.142	1.139
18	1.144	1.140	1.136	1.132	1.170	1.167	1.163	1.159	1.166	1.164	1.161	1.158
20	1.161	1.157	1.152	1.148	1.190	1.187	1.183	1.179	1.186	1.183	1.181	1.178
22	1.178	1.173	1.169	1.164	1.211	1.208	1.203	1.199	1.206	1.203	1.201	1.197
24	1.195	1.190	1.185	1.180	1.233	1.229	1.224	1.219	1.226	1.224	1.221	1.218

Table 7. Weight of Commercial Calcium Chloride in Brine

Sp gr	1.10	1.12	1.14	1.16	1.18	1.20	1.22	1.24	1.26	1.28	1.30	1.32
Wt per gal, lb	1.41	1.70	2.00	2.30	2.59	2.90	3.20	3.50	3.83	4.13	4.46	4.78
Wt per cu ft, lb	10.55	12.72	14.96	17.20	19.37	21.69	23.94	26.18	28.62	30.89	33.36	35.75

Specific gravity is at 60 F for both brine and water. The weights are of 73 to 75 percent solid calcium chloride per gal of brine at 60 F. For flake 77 to 80 percent calcium chloride multiply the weights given by 0.94.

plants and where careful supervision is not ensured, it is customary to make the solution as strong as possible without being unstable, usually 1.240 to 1.250 sp gr.

Brine coolers may be of three types, shell-and-tube, shell-and-coil, and double pipe. The shell-and-tube type is the most widely used, the brine flowing through the tubes which are surrounded by the evaporating refrigerant. Tubes may be arranged for multipass operation. The effective heat-transfer surface varies from 8 to 15 sq ft per ton, varying with temperature and brine velocity. A submerged coil in an open brine tank is used for ice making by the can process.

Table 8. Capacity of Multipass Shell-and-tube Brine Coolers, Flooded

(Tons refrigeration)

Diameter of shell, in.	Length of shell, ft	Velocity of brine through cooler, fpm											
		75				200				400			
		Total brine, gpm	Mean temp diff, brine and ammonia, deg F			Total brine, gpm	Mean temp diff, brine and ammonia, deg F			Total brine, gpm	Mean temp diff, brine and ammonia, deg F		
			10	15	20		7½	12½	17½		5	10	15
26	6	55	5.7	8.6	11.5	140	7.74	12.9	18.1	290	7.15	14.3	21.2
26	9	55	8.5	12.8	17.2	140	11.5	19.3	26.0	290	10.7	21.4	32.0
26	12	55	11.4	17.2	22.9	140	15.5	25.8	36.2	290	14.3	28.6	42.9
34	9	90	13.6	20.5	27.4	230	18.5	30.7	43.1	440	17.1	34.1	51.1
34	12	90	18.1	27.3	36.4	230	24.6	41.0	57.4	440	22.6	45.3	68
34	18	90	27.2	41.0	54.8	230	37.0	62.0	86.2	440	34.1	68.2	101
42	12	190	33.1	50	66.5	510	45.0	74.8	105	970	41.5	83	123
42	18	190	50	75	100	510	67.4	112	157	970	62.2	124	187

The **double-pipe cooler** is usually of 2 in. inner or brine-flow pipe and 3 in. outer pipe. The commercial rating is 15 to 20 ft length of coil per ton of refrigeration.

The **shell-and-tube cooler** is used with closed heads and is erected both vertically and horizontally; brine flows through the tubes and ammonia is in the shell. It is made in sizes from 1 to 350 tons with ratings of 8 to 15 sq ft effective surface per ton, varying with the temperature and brine velocities; tubes 1 to 2½ in. arranged multipass. This type of cooler has largely displaced all other types in recent installations (Table 8).

REFRIGERANT PIPING

(See also pp. 8–194 *et seq.*)

It is important to the proper operation of a refrigeration system that the piping or mains interconnecting the compressors, condensers, evaporators, and receivers be properly sized. This piping must be considered in three categories, *viz.*, liquid lines, suction lines, and discharge lines. Essentially, pipeline sizing is governed by the permissible frictional pressure drop in each piping system. Excessive pressure drops penalize compressor efficiencies and may affect control-valve operation adversely. Liquid-line velocities for most refrigerants are in the order of 60 to 400 fpm, suction lines from 700 to 4,600 fpm, and discharge lines from 1,000 to 5,000 fpm. Pressure drops vary approximately as the square of the velocity (or tonnage) and directly as the length of the piping. For liquid lines, when evaporator is located above condenser, the following pressure drops in pounds per square inch per foot of static lift should be allowed: ammonia, 0.26; Freon 12, 0.57; Freon 22, 0.51; Freon 11, 0.64. (See also pp. 3–57 and 4–66.)

Ammonia Mains. For the average installation, Table 9 shows the maximum tons of refrigeration normally allowed for various sizes of standard pipe, based on 100 ft equivalent length of piping (measured length plus allowance for valves and fittings). The gas pressure drops per 100 ft equivalent length upon which Table 9 is based are as follows: suction lines at 5 psig = 0.25 psi, suction lines at 20 psig = 0.50 psi, suction lines at 45 psig = 1 psi, and discharge lines = 1 psi.

Standard-weight (schedule 40) steel pipe is used for ammonia mains, except for liquid lines 1½ in. and smaller where extra-strong (schedule 80) pipe is used. Joints may be either screwed, flanged, or welded, but welding is preferred.

Table 9. Maximum Tons Refrigeration for Ammonia Mains

(100 ft equivalent pipe length)

(From ASRE, Air-Conditioning Refrigerating Data Book, 1955–1956 ed., based on ARI Equipment Standards; see ASHRAE, Guide and Data Book, for more complete tables)

Pipe size, in.	Suction line			Discharge line	Liquid line	
	Suction pressure, psig				Condenser to receiver	Receiver to system
	5(−17.2 F)	20(5.5 F)	45(30 F)			
⅜	..	..	..	..	2.5	12.0
½	0.6	1.1	2.0	3.1	6.0	20.0
¾	1.2	2.2	4.1	6.0	14.0	75.0
1	2.2	4.0	7.5	11.4	24.0	137
1¼	4.4	8.0	15.0	22.4	50.0	245
1½	6.4	11.8	21.6	30.9	77.0	400
2	12.1	22.2	42.0	62.0	140	850
2½	19.1	35.5	65.0	97.5	220	1,475
3	31.5	59.0	108	160	375	2,400
3½	46.6	87.5	156	238	540	3,500
4	64.0	118	240	330	740	
5	117	208	385	560	1,320	
6	175	306	600	905	2,030	
8	362	650	1,200	1,810	4,200	
10	640	1,180	2,160	3,200		
12	940	1,850				

Freon Mains. Maximum tons refrigerant for various pressure drops per 100 ft equivalent length of Freon 12 mains are given in Table 10. For average conditions, allowable pressure drops in Freon 12 suction lines are 0.5 to 1.0 psi below 0 F evaporator temperature, 1.0 to 1.5 psi from 0 to 25 F, and 2.0 to 2.5 psi from 25 to 50 F. Discharge-line pressure drops upon which Table 10 is based are approximately 1 psi per 100 ft equivalent length. Pressure drops of 1 to 4 psi are permissible. Liquid-line pressure drops of 3 to 5 psi per 100 ft equivalent length are normal, with 10 psi usually considered maximum. To facilitate oil return in vertical suction lines with evaporator located below compressor, the velocity in the vertical section should be 1,000 fpm or more. Suction-line capacities in Table 10 may be increased 9 percent for 50 F evaporator temperature, and will decrease approximately 7 percent for each 10 F below 40 F.

Table 10. Maximum Tons Refrigeration for Freon 12 lines

(From ASRE, Air-Conditioning Refrigerating Data Book, 1955–1956 ed., based on ARI Equipment Standards; see ASHRAE, Guide and Data Book, for more complete tables)

Line sizes, in.	Suction-line (based on 105 F condensing temp) pressure drop, psi per 100 ft equivalent length at 40 F saturation						Discharge-line condensing temp		Liquid-line (based on 105 F condensing temp; 25 F evaporating temp) pressure drop, psi per 100 ft equivalent length (type L tubing)			
	½	1	2	3	4	5	115 F	90 F	3	5	10	20
⅜ O.D.	....	....	....	....	....	....	....	....	0.88	1.14	1.80	2.58
½ O.D.	0.14	0.20	0.28	0.35	0.41	0.45	....	....	2.89	3.64	5.56	8.50
⅜ IPS	0.17	0.24	0.34	0.42	0.49	0.54						
⅝ O.D.	0.25	0.35	0.51	0.62	0.73	0.81	1.43	1.15	4.86	6.81	10.2	15.8
½ IPS	0.35	0.45	0.65	0.79	0.93	1.03	1.87	1.50	4.86	6.81	10.2	15.8
⅞ O.D.	0.55	0.76	1.10	1.34	1.58	1.75	2.97	2.38	10.5	14.1	21.8	33.0
¾ IPS	0.68	0.94	1.35	1.65	1.92	2.12	3.26	2.62	9.73	12.6	18.5	27.0
1⅛ O.D.	1.26	1.80	2.57	3.17	3.76	4.15	5.05	4.05	21.4	28.2	41.3	60.8
1 IPS	1.43	2.01	2.89	3.54	4.17	4.60	5.29	4.25	21.4	28.2	41.3	60.8
1⅜ O.D.	2.21	3.12	4.45	5.50	6.38	7.05	7.72	6.19	36.9	48.1	70.5	101
1¼ IPS	2.70	3.82	5.37	6.72	7.68	8.48	9.16	7.35	36.9	48.1	70.5	101
1⅝ O.D.	3.40	4.78	6.79	8.42	9.77	10.8	10.92	8.75	62.0	80.2	114	160
1½ IPS	4.05	5.75	8.10	10.12	11.6	12.8	12.5	10.0	62.0	80.2	114	160
2⅛ O.D.	6.12	8.60	12.1	15.1	17.4	19.2	19.2	15.3				
2 IPS	7.66	10.9	15.3	19.2	22.2	24.5	20.6	16.5	124	161	231	328
2⅝ O.D.	12.0	17.1	24.0	30.1	34.6	38.2	32.2	25.9				
2½ IPS	12.0	17.1	24.0	30.1	34.6	38.2	32.2	25.9	230	297	426	607
3⅛ O.D.	19.1	27.2	38.2	47.8	55.0	60.7	51.5	39.8				
3 IPS	20.9	29.4	42.3	51.8	60.0	66.2	54.5	43.8	364	469	676	972
3⅝ O.D.	27.8	39.7	55.7	69.8	80.3	88.7	72.0	57.6				
3½ IPS	30.2	43.2	61.0	76.1	87.0	96.0	78.8	62.3	539	704	1,005	1,430
4⅛ O.D.	38.6	55.2	78.0	97.3	111	123	95.8	77.1				
4 IPS	40.7	58.6	83.0	103	118	130	101.6	81.6	753	972	1,385	1,945
5 IPS	71.3	100	141	176	203	224	171.5	137.8				
6 IPS	126	183	257	322	366	403	266	214				
8 IPS	211	297	422	523	602	664	461	370				
10 IPS	352	503	712	887	1,024	1,130	725	582				
12 IPS	550	780	1,106	1,373	1,582	1,748	1,041	836				

Freon 22 piping will, in general, be smaller for the same tonnage than Freon 12 piping. Suction lines will handle about one-third more tonnage for the same pressure drop. Liquid and discharge lines can be the same as for the equivalent tonnage of Freon 12, or slightly smaller.

Freon piping may be standard-weight steel pipe, but copper tubing is used in most cases. Medium-weight type L copper tubing is normally used for land installations, and the heavier type K copper tubing is used for marine work. Joints in the copper tubing may be flared compression fittings for tubing ¾ in. o.d. and smaller. However, hard solder (silver-base alloy melting above 1000 F) is preferred for most tubing connections. Copper tubing is almost always used for liquid lines. Steel pipe may be used for the larger suction and discharge lines but should be sandblasted on the inside and carefully cleaned before installation.

Mains for Other Refrigerants. For sizing piping for methyl chloride, sulphur dioxide, carbon dioxide, and other refrigerants, reference may be made to the latest edition of the ASRE Air-Conditioning Refrigerating Data Book—Design Volume. (For additional pipe sizing tables and charts, see Hendrickson, *Refrig. Eng.*, Oct., 1946, Determination of Refrigerant Pipe Size.)

COLD STORAGE

Insulation. For tables of conductivities, see pp. 4–95 to 4–97. Insulation used in refrigeration is often compound. The insulating value of filling material varies nearly inversely as its specific gravity. It increases to a point where the material is so loose as to permit air circulation. With most material, a specific gravity of 0.160 seems to be the limit. When any fibrous material, so far in use, is arranged so that it weighs much under this, the effect of an open air space is obtained. This does not apply to **material arranged in layers** of different densities transversely to the direction of heat flow. **Dryness of insulation** is of great importance. Insulation until the heat loss falls to 2 Btu per sq ft per deg F temp diff per 24 hr has been found to be economic in most cases in temperate climates and for plants of average efficiency.

Table 11. Cold-storage Usage and Transmission Factors

	Room volume, cu ft									
	20	50	100	500	1,000	2,000	5,000	10,000	50,000	100,000
Usage load*										
Average	4.68	2.28	1.61	1.21	1.10	0.835	0.403	0.240	0.178	0.173
Heavy	5.51	3.55	2.52	1.87	1.67	1.29	0.625	0.408	0.305	0.295
Storage temp, deg F	40 and above		25–40		15–25		0–15		−25–0	
Insulation thickness, in.	3		4		5		6		8	
Theoretical U factor†	0.086		0.066		0.055		0.046		0.035	
Practical U factor‡	0.111		0.083		0.066		0.055		0.046	
Piping U factor§	2.5		2.2		2.0		1.8		1.6	

* Btu per cu ft per 24 hr per deg F temp diff between outside and inside. Usage load includes 10 F or less of product cooling, and infiltration losses, etc., but does not include any freezing of product or fan motor loads when unit coolers are used. Values are for normal conditions and should not be used for unusual product loads.

† Theoretical U factor is based on corkboard ($k = 0.30$) with plaster on both sides, Btu per sq ft per hr per deg F temp diff.

‡ Practical U factor allows for inefficiency of joints and structural supports in insulation.

§ Piping U factor is Btu per sq ft outside pipe surface per hr per deg F temp diff between cooling medium and air (gravity circulation). Allowance has been made for frosting at the lower temperatures.

A satisfactory insulation for the **walls, ceilings, floors, partitions, etc.,** of cold-storage buildings consists of corkboard of good quality and medium density with sides and edges dipped in hot asphalt or coated with asphaltic emulsion or other cold-setting adhesive, to seal the surfaces against moisture penetration. Interior finish is usually two ⅛ in. thick coats of mastic plaster, or two ¼ in. thick coats of portland-cement plaster. In self-supporting cork partition walls, ½ in. thick portland-cement mortar is often used as a strengthening core between layers. Vapor seal should be on the warm side.

The standard thickness for temperatures down to 32 F is two layers of 2 in. corkboard; to this is added 1 in. for each 15 F below (see Table 11). **Piping, fittings, shell vessels, etc.,** should be covered with molded covering and fitting covers in which the cork as molded weighs 1.1 lb per board ft approx. This molded covering should have the inner and outer surfaces sealed with a rubberized or asphaltic mastic and made up with the joints thoroughly cemented and filled. Standard **brine pipe covering** for temperatures down to 0 F varies from 2 to 3 in. in thickness with the diameter of the pipe. "Special thick" brine covering for temperatures below 0 F is 3 to 4 in. thick. Final treatment may be plaster, canvas, paint, or sheet metal.

Either aluminum or stainless steel, about 0.022 in. thick, applied in multiple layer, with ⅝ in. air spaces between layers, is now used as insulation in low-temperature test rooms. The outer layer may be $\frac{1}{16}$ in. thick or heavier for mechanical protection.

The scope of insulation has enlarged greatly, with cellular plastics (prefoamed or foamed-in-place) such as polystyrene and polyurethane, with powders (vacuum and gas-filled cavities), and with preformed insulated panels for field assembly into complete refrigerated warehouse constructions.

Cold-storage Temperatures. A great deal of research and experience are required to obtain authoritative information on optimum temperatures and humidities for various products in cold storage. Table 12 is representative of good practice. The safe storage period depends upon the product and the storage temperature, and operational techniques vary greatly. Modern cold-storage warehouses of the larger concerns are cooled by brine which is furnished at two different temperatures only. The higher temperature for the mild-temperature warehouses is 10 to 12 F, and the low-temperature brine for the freezers is −10 to −12 F. All temperatures above that of the brine are obtained by regulating the amount of brine circulated in any particular set of coils. In the low-temperature warehouses, the piping is arranged for two classes of service: (1) **sharp freezers,** where the goods which are to be frozen are kept while their temperature is brought down quickly to the holding temperature (say in from 6 to 10 hr) after which they are stored in (2) **holding rooms** where the desired temperature is maintained.

The system of cooling which is now being installed in the highest type of warehouses consists of a coil room containing the necessary brine coils, through which the air from the different rooms is circulated by a pressure blower. The inlet and outlet of each room are so arranged that the cooled circulating air will cover the entire room in its transit; this is usually accomplished by having the cold-air inlet in the center of the room and two return outlets—one at each end of the room. The piping ratio for the coil rooms in this system, assuming a high-grade insulation with 2 to 4 Btu transmission per sq ft per 24 hr per deg temp diff, should be 1 sq ft of external pipe surface to 15 cu ft of space to be cooled (with brine at −10 to −12 F) for warehouses carrying temperatures of zero and below, and 1 sq ft of pipe surface to 24 cu ft of space to be cooled (with brine at 10 to 12 F) in warehouses carrying mild temperatures of from 30 to 40 F. Another system is used in which the blower and coils are supplemented by coils in the rooms. With this arrangement, it is possible to reduce temperatures quickly and hold them with the coils.

The average coil transmission in cold-storage rooms without forced circulation of the air is about 2 Btu per sq ft of outside metal surface per hr per deg F temp diff with horizontal piping and 2.5 Btu with vertical piping. When forced air circulation is used, the transmission rate will increase to 20 Btu or more. In **brine circulation,** the brine, at same compressor back pressure, has a higher temperature than the ammonia, and consequently 1½ times as much pipe or more is used in brine circulation as in direct expansion for a given back pressure.

Piping of Rooms. The **size of pipe** usually employed for piping rooms varies from 1 to 2 in. with either brine circulation or direct expansion.

The extra cost of liberal piping allowance will often be offset by the consequent improvement in the efficiency of operation of the compressor. An expansion valve should be provided for every 500 ft length of 1 in. pipe, every 650 ft of 1¼ in. pipe, and every 1,000 ft of 2 in. pipe when direct expansion is used.

Table 12. Product Storage Data

(Bush Manufacturing Co., West Hartford, Conn.)

Product	Quick-freeze temp, deg F	Storage temp		Humidity, % R.H.	Specific heat		Latent heat	Freezing point	Respiration, Btu per lb per day
		Long	Short		Above freezing	Below freezing			
Apples	—15	30–32	38–42	85–88	0.86	0.45	121.0	28.4	0.75
Asparagus	—30	32	40	85–90	0.95	0.44	134.0	29.8	
Bacon, fresh	....	0–5	36–40	80	0.55	0.31	30.0	25.0	
Bananas	....	56–72	56–72	85–95	0.80	0.42	108.0	28.0	4.18
Beans, green	....	32–34	40–45	85–90	0.92	0.47	128	29.7	3.3
Beans, dried	....	36–40	50–60	70	0.30	0.237	18		
Beef, fresh, fat	—15	30–32	38–42	84	0.60	0.35	79		
Beef, fresh, lean	—15	30–32	38–42	85	0.77	0.40	100		
Beets, topped	....	32–35	45–50	95–98	0.86	0.47	129	31.1	2.0
Blackberries	—15	31–32	42–45	80–85	0.89	0.46	125	28.9	
Broccoli	....	32–35	40–45	90–95	0.92	0.47	130	29.2	
Butter	+15	.....	40–45	....	0.64	0.34	15	15.0	
Cabbage	—30	32	45	90–95	0.93	0.47	130	31.2	
Carrots, topped	—30	32	40–45	95–98	0.87	0.45	120	29.6	1.73
Cauliflower	....	32	40–45	85–90	0.93	0.47	132	30.1	
Celery	—30	31–32	45–50	90–95	0.95	0.48	135	29.7	2.27
Cheese	+15	32–38	39–45	.....	0.70				
Cherries	....	31–32	40	80–85	0.87	0.45	120	26.0	6.6
Chocolate coatings	....	45–50	.....	.....	0.3				
Corn, green	....	31–32	45	85–90	0.80	0.43	108	29.0	4.1
Cranberries	....	36–40	40–45	85–90	0.90	0.46	124	27.3	
Cream	....	34	40–45	.....	0.88	0.37	84		
Cucumbers	....	45–50	45–50	80–85	0.97	0.47	137	30.5	
Dates, cured	....	28	55–60	50–60	0.83	0.44	104		
Eggs, fresh	—10	30–31	38–45	.....	0.76	0.40	98	31.0	
Eggplants	....	45–50	46–50	85–90	0.94	0.47	132	30.4	
Flowers	....	35–40		85–90					
Fish, fresh, iced	—15	25	25–30		0.82	0.41	105	30.0	
Fish, dried	....	30–40	.....	60–70	0.56	0.34	65		
Furs	....	32–34	40–42	40–60					
Furs, to shock	....	15	15						
Grapefruit	....	32	32	85–90	0.91	0.46	126	28.4	0.5
Grapes	....	30–32	35–40	80–85	0.86	0.44	116	27.0	0.5
Ham, fresh	....	28	36–40	80	0.68	0.38	87		
Honey	....	31–32	45–50	....	0.35	0.26	26		
Ice cream	—20	.....	0–10	.....	0.5–0.8	0.45	96		
Lard	....	32–34	40–45	80	0.52	0.31	90		
Lemons	....	55–58	.....	80–85	0.92	0.46	127	28.1	0.4
Lettuce	....	32	45	90–95	0.96	0.48	136	31.2	8.0
Liver, fresh	....	32–34	36–38	83	0.72	0.42	94		
Lobster, boiled	....	25	36–40	.....	0.81	0.42	105		
Maple syrup	....	31–32	45	.....	0.24	0.215	7.0		
Meat, brined	....	31–32	40–45	.....	0.75	0.36	75.0		
Melons	....	34–40	40–45	75–85	0.92	0.35	115	28.5	1.0
Milk	....	34–36	40–45	.....	0.92	0.46	124	31.0	
Mushrooms	....	32–35	55–60	80–85	0.93	0.47	130	30.2	
Mutton	....	32–34	34–42	82	0.81	0.39	96	29.0	
Nut meats	....	32–50	35–40	65–75	0.30	0.24	14	20.0	
Oleomargarine	....	34–36	.....	.....	0.65	0.34	35	15.0	
Onions	....	32	50–60	70–75	0.91	0.46	120	30.1	1.0
Oranges	....	32–34	50	85–90	0.90	0.46	124	27.9	0.7
Oysters	....	.....	32–35	.....	0.85	0.45	120.0		
Parsnips	—30	32–34	34–40	90–95	0.82	0.45	120.0	28.9	
Peaches, fresh	....	31–32	50	85–90	0.90	0.46	126	29.4	1.0
Pears, fresh	....	29–31	40	85–90	0.86	0.45	118	28.0	6.6

Table 12. Product Storage Data—(*Continued*)

Product	Quick-freeze temp, deg F	Storage temp Long	Storage temp Short	Humidity, % R.H.	Specific heat Above freezing	Specific heat Below freezing	Latent heat	Freezing point	Respiration, Btu per lb per day
Peas, green	....	32	40–45	85–90	0.80	0.42	108	30.0	
Peas, dried	....	35–40	50–60		0.28	0.22	14		
Peppers	....	32	40–45	85–90	0.94	0.47	.....	30.1	2.35
Pineapples, ripe	....	40–45	50	85–90	0.88	0.45	122	29.9	
Plums	....	31–32	40–45	80–85	0.88	0.45	123	28.0	
Pork, fresh	....	30	36–40	85	0.60	0.38	66	28.0	
Potatoes, white	−30	36–50	45–60	85–90	0.77	0.44	105	28.9	0.85
Poultry, dressed	−10	28–30	29–32	.....	0.80	0.41	99	27	
Pumpkins	....	50–55	55–60	70–75	0.92	0.47	130	30.2	
Quinces	....	31–32	40–45	80–85	0.90	....	.....	28.1	
Raspberries	....	31–32	40–45	80–85	0.89	0.46	125	30.0	3.3
Sardines, canned	....	....	35–40	.....	0.76	0.410	101		
Sausage, fresh	....	31–36	36–40	80	0.89				
Sauerkraut	....	33–36	36–38	85	0.91	0.47	128	26	
Squash	....	50–55	55–60	70–75	0.92	0.47	130	29.3	
Spinach	....	32	45–50	85	0.94	0.48	132	30.8	
Strawberries	−15	31–32	42–45	80–85	0.92	0.48	129	30.0	3.3
Tomatoes, ripe	....	40–50	55–70	85–90	0.95	0.48	135	30.4	0.5
Turnips	....	32	40–45	95–98	0.93	0.40	137	30.5	1.0
Veal	−15	28–30	36–40	.....	0.71	0.39	91	29	

Values of **over-all coefficients of heat transfer** in Btu per hour per square foot per deg F for refrigerating practice are given in Tables 11 and 13. (See pp. 4–90 *et seq.*)

Brine circulation is generally preferred to direct expansion so as to avoid danger from escaping ammonia or other refrigerant in case the pipes should leak. An advantage of the brine system is that there is always a considerable mass of refrigerated brine which can be drawn on in case the machinery should have to be stopped for any reason. In small plants, the general machinery may be stopped at night and only the brine pump be kept going to distribute the surplus refrigeration which has been accumulated in the brine during the day. Brine piping must consist of two lines, a flow and a return, usually of the same size. Brine storage is seldom used in large plants because of its bulk, its first cost, and the practical inability to store much refrigeration.

Table 13. Over-all Coefficients of Heat Transfer
(Btu per sq ft per hr per deg F)

Application	U	Application	U
Can ice-making piping		Brine coolers	
Old-style feed, non-flooded	12–15	Shell and tube	45–100
Flooded	20–40	Double pipe	150–300
High-velocity raceway trunk coils	80–110	Cooling coils	
Ammonia condensers		Boiling refrigerant to air in unit coolers	4–8
Submerged (obsolete)	30–40	Water to air in unit coolers	5–9
Atmospheric, gas entering at top	60–65	Brine to unagitated air	2.2–2.8
Atmospheric, drip or bleeder	125–200	Direct expansion to unagitated air*	1.6–2.5
Flooded	125–150	Water cooler, shell and coil	15–25
Shell and tube	150–300	Water cooler, shell and tube	50–150
Double pipe	150–250	Water cooler, shell and finned tube (Freon)	30–150
Baudelot coolers, counterflow, atmospheric type		Liquid-ammonia cooler, shell and coil accumulator	45
Milk coolers	75	Air dehydrator	
Cream coolers	60	Shell and coil (brine in coil), 1st coil	5.0
Oil coolers	10	Shell and coil (brine in coil), 2d coil	3.0
Water coolers		Double pipe	6–7
Direct expansion	60–150	Superheat remover, shell and tube	15–25
Flooded	100–200		

Forced circulation of the air increases the coefficient to 1½ to 2½ times the values for still air. One inch of frost decreases the value 25 percent.

* U factor increases to 3.3 at 15 deg temp diff with ammonia recirculation systems.

The **brine coils** in each cooled space are in parallel across the supply and return pipes. It has been common practice to allow 100 to 120 running feet of **pipe** per circuit for low temperatures, and 400 to 440 for high temperatures. The **tons refrigeration produced by brine** at various temperature differences and rates of pumping may be calculated approximately as follows: tons refrigeration = gpm × deg F range/28.

Air Conditioning of Low-temperature Storage Rooms. Bacterial growth and chemical decomposition are retarded by lowering the **temperature** of perishable goods. Too low a temperature will freeze the goods and may result in spoilage. A holding temperature above the freezing point of the article is best for storage conditions. The maintenance of a proper relative **humidity** in a storage space holding unwrapped goods is as important as the maintenance of the proper temperature. High humidity favors the growth of mold and bacteria. Low humidities rob the product of moisture resulting in losses in value through impaired appearance and lost weight. **Air motion** is of importance in maintaining uniform conditions throughout the storage space. Too high air velocities cause excessive drying, and stagnant air through high humidities will cause mold. An optimum air motion falling between stagnation on one side and excessive drying on the other must be selected.

Low-temperature conditioning for storage purposes is preferably accomplished by the use of **cold-diffuser methods.** The cold diffuser connected to or located in the storage space consists of a fan and cooling means. The cooling means may be either a brine or cold-water spray or a surface-type cooler using brine, or a volatile refrigerant such as ammonia, Freon, etc. Unitary equipment, performing the functions of the cold diffuser, is commercially available. For the requirements for various perishable products, see ASHRAE Guide and Data Books and Table 12.

Quick freezing is freezing in 2 hr or less; as employed for foods the temperatures may be as low as −20 to −50 F. The methods of freezing include direct immersion in cold brine or a brine spray with the commodity held in a metal container. Another procedure is the use of a freezing tunnel approximately 50 ft long, equipped with a stainless-steel conveyor belt. The commodities to be frozen pass through this tunnel in 15 to 30 min. The speed of the belt is variable, and the heat transfer is accomplished by high-velocity air circulation at a number of points in the tunnel, the circulation being transverse to the belt. The circulating air is cooled by brine sprays which maintain the required temperature and the high humidity necessary to prevent shrinkage. In another process, packages of the material to be quick-frozen are clamped between steel platens containing evaporating refrigerant. Successful results are obtained with temperatures as high as 0 F. Storage may be at −5 to −10 F and transportation at 10 F or lower.

Cold-storage lockers for individual family use are used in large numbers, particularly in suburban and rural areas. Lockers are rented usually on a yearly basis. A locker plant may have several hundred rental steel lockers, 72 × 20 × 30 in., 6 cu ft capacity each, placed in rooms at about 0 F; a room for cutting and wrapping the meat; and a sharp freezer room held at about −20 F. Two compressors are frequently specified or a single compressor using automatic control valves on the separate rooms. Ammonia and Freon 12, operating under direct expansion, are commonly used.

ICE MAKING

Ice refrigeration is economical for some applications. The use of natural ice is fast disappearing. Manufactured ice is made by several methods. In the can system, galvanized cans containing 300 to 400 lb of water are immersed in brine for 25 to 40 hr for freezing. Air dissolved in the water separates as bubbles causing opacity unless the water is agitated during the early stages of cooling, and any dissolved impurities come out of solution to form a central off-color core in the ice block unless the core is removed and replaced with fresh water just before freezing. The time and investment required for making ice in cans are often uneconomical. In the **Flakice** method (Crosby Field, *Trans. ASME*, May, 1951, pp. 347–357) refrigerant is sprayed against the inner wall of a flexible, slowly rotating cylinder which is partially immersed in a tank of water. As the cylinder rotates, a thin layer of ice forms on the outside and then is broken off as further rotation causes the cylinder surface to flex under the action of an internal cam.

For a patent history of small ice machines of this type, refer to Crosby Field, *Refrig. Eng.*, **58**, Dec., 1950 p. 1163. In the **Pak-Ice** process (Taylor, *Refrig. Eng.*, **22**, 1931, p. 307) liquid ammonia is evaporated in an annular space formed by two concentric cylinders, the inner being corrugated. Water sprayed on the inner corrugated surface quickly freezes in a thin layer about 0.01 inch thick and is continually removed by mechanical scrapers. In an **extrusion method** (Watt, *Trans. ASME*, 1949) a slightly tapered circular or rectangular vertical cylinder with large end up is open at the top, but closed by a ram at the bottom. This cylinder has a jacket in which refrigerant is evaporated directly against the cylinder walls. Water enters the cylinder and freezes to a tapered block at the start of the operation. As soon as this occurs, the ram lifts (about ¼ in.), shearing the ice block from the cold cylinder walls. Water admitted to this space quickly freezes, the ram again operates and the block of ice is again lifted, and shearing occurs again between the freshly formed ice and the cylinder walls, but not at the fresh ice and old ice interface. In this way, a continuous cylinder of ice is formed by the series of nested ice shells. The installation and upkeep costs are small and so is the space required per ton of ice produced; a pilot-plant 1 ton unit requires 3 sq ft of floor space.

The refrigeration tonnage required for making 1 ton of ice varies from 1.4 with 50 F inlet water temperature to about 1.7 if the water to be frozen enters as high as 80 F.

SKATING RINKS

Rinks for ice skating, hockey, or curling vary in size from about 400 sq ft area to 16,000 sq ft or more. Construction of the ice floor is important. For a low-cost, efficient unit, brine pipes are laid directly in sand, which is kept wet during freezing to increase heat transfer. As freezing progresses, a layer of ice is built up by spraying water on the surface. The expense of maintaining such a floor in a satisfactory level condition may be considerable, and corrosion of the pipes, from the outside in, in contact with the wet sand may be excessive, particularly during shutdown periods. Moreover, it is not possible to use such a floor for other purposes. When a floor for diversified activities is needed, it is usual to provide a lower layer of insulation, primarily to prevent sweating on ceilings under the floor, surmounted by a concrete slab in which the steel pipes carrying the brine are imbedded and on which the ice layer is formed. This construction protects the pipe from external corrosion, affords fast freezing, and makes possible use of the floor in a few hours for purposes where an ice surface is not desired. Floor pipes are usually 1 or 1¼ in. diam spaced 3 to 6 in. on centers; care must be exercised to ensure a uniform distribution of brine. Brine flow may be 10 gal per min per ton of refrigeration, corresponding to about 1 gal per min per 10 to 20 sq ft of piping surface. In a few installations, cold brine is sprayed directly against the under side of a steel floor on which the ice layer is frozen. Close control of ice surface temperature is necessary for good skating, usually 27 F ± 1.0. Refrigeration capacity should be from 0.4 to 0.85 ton per 100 sq ft of floor surface, although the load may be much higher for open-air rinks or other unusual conditions.

REFRIGERATION IN THE CHEMICAL INDUSTRIES

The use of refrigeration in petroleum and other industries is widespread. In petroleum processing, refrigeration is used (1) to control vapor pressure of highly volatile constituents (methane, ethane, propane, and butane), such control being necessary during distillation, during processing, and for recovery of gasoline fractions from natural gas; (2) to shift the solubility relationship so that undesired constituents such as asphalt and wax in lubricating oils may be removed by precipitation; (3) to produce selective chemical reaction such as occurs when sulphuric acid is used to remove gum-forming constituents from light fuels or when an alkylate fuel fraction is formed by combining a low molecular weight unsaturated with a similar saturated hydrocarbon. Alkylate is a valuable and important constituent of aviation fuels.

For (1), temperatures ranging from −35 F or lower to as high as 50 or 60 F are required, the refrigerant being ammonia, propane, or butane. For the higher temperatures spray-cooled water or jet refrigerating units (see p. 18–11) are sometimes satisfactory. For (2), it is possible to use propane as a combined solvent and refrigerant, evaporation of the propane causing the required cooling, temperature level (approximately −40 F) being controlled by the pressure held on the equipment. The propane vapor is recompressed, condensed, and reused as in any compression cycle. As much as ⅓ ton of refrigeration per barrel of lubricating oil dewaxed is needed. For (3), temperatures of 20 to 60 F are general, and ammonia is a satisfactory and widely used refrigerant.

The trend in the petroleum industry, as recovery of the lightest petroleum fractions is more widely practiced, and as better and more carefully prepared products are demanded, is toward more widespread use of refrigeration and toward lower temperatures. It is to be noted that, even at low temperatures, use of refrigeration is economical if efficient heat-transfer equipment is used to cool the incoming warm streams to the temperature of the leaving cold streams; in the ideal case, refrigeration is required only for the removal of heat liberated at the low temperature.

DEEP REFRIGERATION

Dry ice (solid CO_2) is useful as a refrigerating medium in special cases. The main objection to the general use of dry ice is its cost, but the ease in its handling, its low temperature (−110 F at atmospheric pressure), its non-corrosive and non-toxic properties, its high latent heat, and the absence of liquid drip make it desirable. The heat absorbed per pound of solid CO_2 during sublimation at atmospheric pressure and −110 F is 245 Btu approx. The specific heat of the gas at constant pressure is about 0.2.

Carbon dioxide is obtained commercially either by fermentation or by burning. The gas is compressed, usually in three stages, and cooled to atmospheric temperature, thereby forming a liquid at 900 to 1,100 psia; the liquid is then throttled to below 5.3 atm pressure. During throttling, part of the CO_2 solidifies and is compressed to form a dense ice. The fraction that returns to the vapor phase is recompressed.

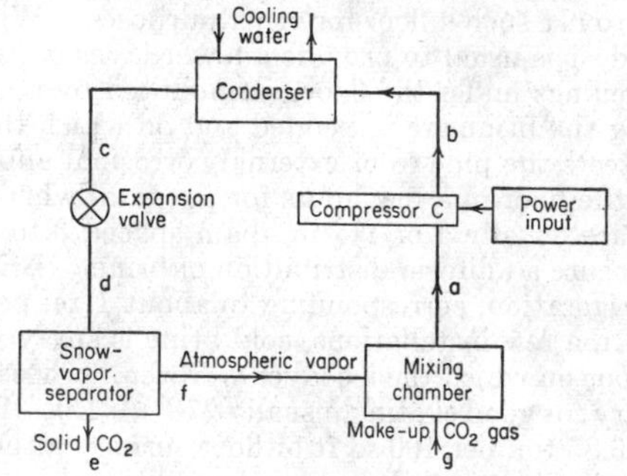

FIG. 16. Elemental dry-ice production circuit.

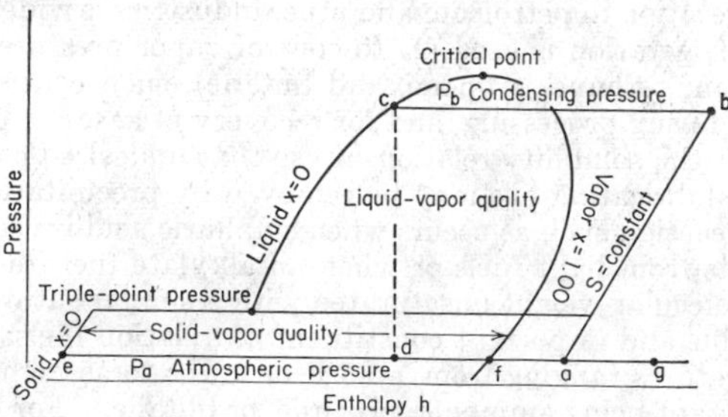

FIG. 17. Pressure-enthalpy diagram illustrating dry-ice production circuit.

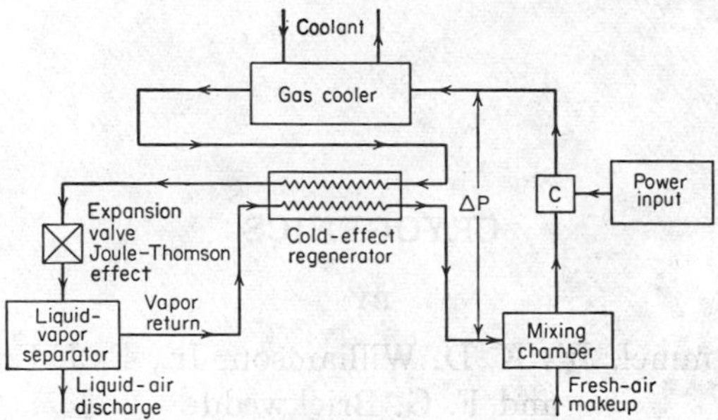

FIG. 18. Elemental Linde-system circuit.

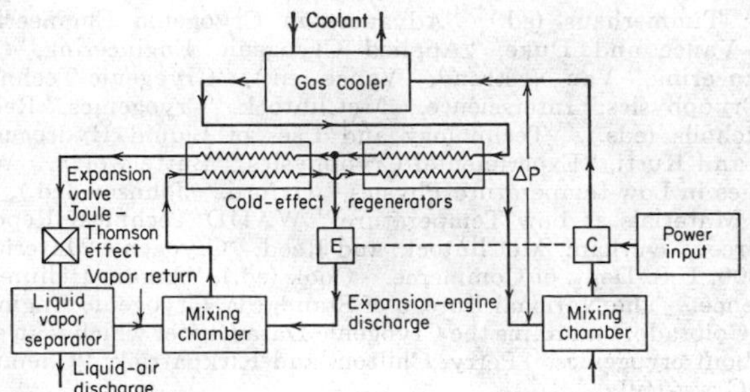

FIG. 19. Elemental Claude-system circuit.

Production of Solid Carbon Dioxide. Figure 16 shows a simple cycle and Fig. 17, the elemental Ph diagram for the production of solid carbon dioxide. From the high pressure at atmospheric temperature the liquid is throttled (isenthalpic) to atmospheric pressure, the resultant point being within the sublimation solid-vapor zone below the triple-point realm. In this resultant throttling expansion, part of the CO_2 solidifies; it is then removed in the separator from the residual vapor and is compacted to form a dense CO_2 ice. The fraction representing the vapor phase is augmented by fresh makeup gas to continue the production cycle.

Beyond the manufacture of dry ice, operations at deep refrigerations, such as air liquefaction (at −312 F approx), lead into **cryogenics** (see p. 18–28). Illustrative systems are (1) Linde (throttling) and (2) Claude (expander). In the elemental **Linde system** (Fig. 18), by virtue of the "cold-effect" regenerator, the process air is reduced in temperature by the return fraction of the air from the separator. The throttling process thus ends in the "wet zone" at atmospheric pressure with generation of low-temperature liquid air that flows from the separator. In the **Claude system** (Fig. 19), use is made of an expander (whose work output reduces the net work requirement of the compressor) and of an expansion valve with the Joule-Thomson effect.

CRYOGENICS

BY

E. F. Hammel, Jr., K. D. Williamson, Jr., F. J. Edeskuty, and F. G. Brickwedde

(Work supported by the U.S. Atomic Energy Commission.)

References: Timmerhaus (ed.), "Advances in Cryogenic Engineering" (annual), Plenum Press. Vance and Duke, "Applied Cryogenic Engineering," Wiley. Scott, "Cryogenic Engineering," Van Nostrand. Vance (ed.), "Cryogenic Technology," Wiley. Mendelssohn, "Cryophysics," Interscience. McClintock, "Cryogenics," Reinhold. Scott, Denton, and Nicholls (eds.), "Technology and Uses of Liquid Hydrogen," Pergamon. Hoare, Jackson, and Kurti, "Experimental Cryophysics," Butterworth. White, "Experimental Techniques in Low-temperature Physics," Oxford. Johnson (ed.), "Compendium of Properties of Materials at Low Temperature," WADD Technical Report 60-56, U.S. Dept. of Commerce. Durham, McClintock, and Reed, "Cryogenic Materials Data Handbook," PB 171-809, U.S. Dept. of Commerce. Cook (ed.), "Argon, Helium, and the Rare Gases," Interscience. The National Bureau of Standards, Cryogenic Engineering Laboratory at Boulder, Colorado, maintains the Cryogenic Data Center which is an excellent source of information about cryogenics. Perry, Chilton, and Kirkpatrick, "Chemical Engineers' Handbook," McGraw-Hill.

Notation

Some symbols in this section differ from the notation of engineering practice but are retained to facilitate use of the prevalent scientific sources of information.

A = area, ft^2
b.c.c. = body centered cubic lattice structure
C = specific heat, Btu per lb-deg R
C_p, C_v = specific heats at constant pressure and volume respectively, Btu per lb-deg R
f.c.c. = face centered cubic lattice structure
H = enthalpy, Btu per lb
h.c.p. = hexagonal close-packed lattice structure
κ = thermal conductivity, Btu per hr-ft-deg R
κ^* = reduced thermal conductivity
σ = electrical conductivity (reciprocal of resistivity) or pair separation for zero potential in Lennard-Jones equation
s = Boltzmann's constant
L_v = volume latent heat of vaporization
L = length, ft
LH_2 = liquid hydrogen (H_2)
LHe = liquid helium (He), He^3 = helium isotope 3
LN_2 = liquid nitrogen (N_2)
n = number of moles
NTP = normal conditions, 14.7 psia and 70 F
P = pressure, psia or torr (vacuum)
P^* = reduced pressure
R_e = electrical resistance, ohms
STP = standard conditions, 14.7 psia and 32 F
T = temperature, deg R
T^* = reduced temperature
V = volume, ft^3
α = thermal linear-expansion coefficient, R^{-1}, or accommodation coefficient
μ = micron (1 micron = 10^{-6} meters = 39.37×10^{-6} in.)
η = viscosity, lb per ft-hr
η^* = reduced viscosity
ρ = density, lb per ft^3
ρ^* = reduced density
ΔT = temp difference, deg R

Cryogenics is the study, production, and utilization of low temperatures. Cryogenic temperatures have been defined so ambiguously that "upper limits" from 220 to 400 R to the cryogenic range may be found in the literature. In this section the cryogenic range for a given property is considered to embrace the scale between absolute zero and the temperature above which the property has the expected or normal behavior. Cryogenics thus embraces the unusual and unexpected variations which appear at low temperatures and make extrapolations of properties from ambient to low temperatures unreliable.

Progressively lower temperatures become increasingly difficult to attain in practice. As the working temperature of a refrigerator is lowered, the work required to transfer a given amount of heat increases as demonstrated by the Carnot limitation, to wit, $W = Q[(T_1 - T_2)/T_2]$, where W is the work required to extract the heat Q at a low temperature T_2 and reject it at a higher temperature T_1 (see p. 4–27). The actual work is always greater than this because of inefficiencies of mechanical equipment, thermal losses associated with finite temperature differences in heat exchangers, and heat leaks from the surroundings to the cold equipment (see p. 18–2 *et seq.*).

Refrigeration Methods

(See also pp. 4–59 *et seq.*, pp. 18–2 *et seq.*)

Of the various refrigeration methods, the most commonly used to produce low temperatures are (1) the evaporation of liquid (referred to as the "cascade" method when applied in several successive stages using progressively lower-boiling liquids), (2) Joule-Thomson or isenthalpic expansion of a gas, and (3) an adiabatic expansion of a gas in a reciprocating engine or turbine or in a bomb or cylinder from which gas escapes through a throttling valve (Simon expansion). Using LHe^3, method 1 is capable of producing constant temperatures as low as 0.5 R. Numerous refrigeration cycles have been devised utilizing various combinations of these three methods. They may be used to maintain various materials or enclosures at low temperatures, or they may be utilized for gas liquefaction.

The usual method for reaching temperatures lower than 0.5 R utilizes a paramagnetic salt which is isothermally magnetized at a higher temperature followed by an adiabatic "demagnetization." Although materials can be cooled by a single adiabatic demagnetization to very low temperatures (0.003 R), this method has not as yet been successfully exploited for maintaining constant low temperatures. The continuously operating paramagnetic salt refrigerator marketed for a time has been superseded by the boiling LHe^3 refrigerator.

In the refrigerating methods referred to, refrigeration results from a four-step cycle which is approximated by: A *first stage* in which entropy is removed from the working substance at the higher temperature and heat is discharged by increasing *isothermally* some intensive variable as pressure or magnetic field intensity; a *second stage* in which the intensive variable is reduced *adiabatically* (isentropically) and the temperature falls; a *third stage* in which heat is absorbed by the working substance at the low temperature and the entropy of the working substance increases; and a *fourth stage* in which the working substance is returned to its initial state.

Gas Liquefaction

A conventional method of gas liquefaction utilizes a gas compressor, a countercurrent heat exchanger, and a throttling valve through which the gas expands isenthalpically (Joule-Thomson). (See also p. 18–26.) After expansion, the cold gas returns through the heat exchanger, in which it exchanges heat with the countercurrent compressed gas flowing to the throttling valve. It leaves the heat exchanger near the temperature of the entering compressed gas. The temperature decreases below the throttling valve until the condensing temperature is reached, and then liquefaction occurs at a rate determined by the rate of refrigeration.

The rate of liquefaction x in pounds per hour is $x = \{[H$ (expanded *gas* out) $-$ H (compressed *gas* in)$]w - q\}/[H$ (compressed *gas* in) $-$ H (*liquid* following valve)$]$, where the H's are enthalpies in Btu per pound for the final heat exchanger, w is the flow rate in the same units as x, and q is the heat leak in Btu per hour from outside into the heat exchanger. For an ideal heat exchanger the expanded gas leaves at the temperature of the entering compressed gas. In practice, there is a small difference in temperature which represents a small loss of refrigeration. For ideal gases, H is independent of P for a given T, and hence no liquefaction of an ideal gas results. The H's of air, O_2, N_2, A, CO_2, the hydrocarbons, and the normal refrigerants decrease with increasing pressure at ambient T, except at very high P's, and these gases are liquefiable by this kind of isenthalpic (Joule-Thomson) expansion (see also p. 18–26). The H's of H_2 and He at ambient T, however, increase with increasing P, even at low P's, and hence an auxiliary mechanism is required for the liquefaction of these gases. In one method, the stream of compressed gas is split in the liquefier, and a part goes to an engine in which it is cooled by an isentropic expansion with the performance of work. This part of the flow, thus cooled, is sent to a heat exchanger, where it flows counter to the other fraction of compressed gas, cooling it to a temperature below the inversion temperature (see Sec. 4). This flow of compressed gas, thus precooled, is run through another and final heat exchanger with a throttling valve at its lower end, with the result that the quantity x is liquefied.

Another method of precooling H_2 and He below their inversion temperatures makes use of a boiling liquid cryogen through which the compressed gas flows in a heat exchanger. LN_2 is used for precooling H_2, and LH_2 for He.

Uses of Liquefied Gases

Gases, such as O_2, N_2, natural gas, H_2, and He, are liquefied for transportation as liquids. Shipments have been made of LH_2 by trailer trucks in quantities of 13×10^3 gal over distances of 3,000 miles and by railway tank cars holding as much as 28×10^3 gal. LHe in 25 gal quantities is regularly shipped distances up to 2,000 miles by air, and smaller quantities have been shipped even greater distances. Liquid cryogens are used as liquid refrigerants. The aerospace, steel, and bottled-gas industries are the principal users of liquefied cryogens. Important applications as coolants can be found in vacuum technology, electronics, biology, medicine, and metal forming.

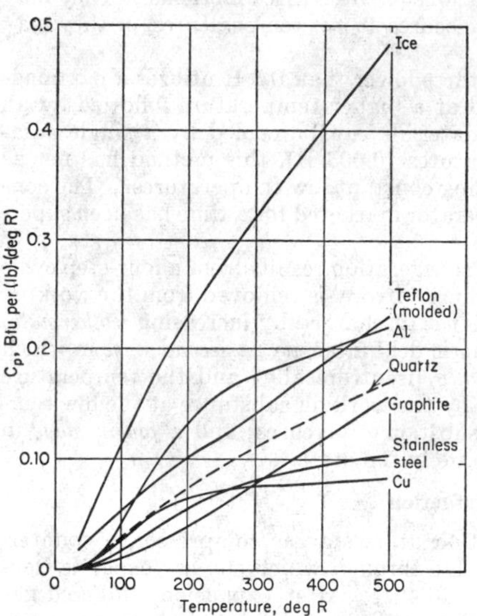

FIG. 1. Specific heats of solids at low temperatures.

Properties of Solids at Low Temperatures

(See also Sec. 4)

Specific heats of solids in general decrease with decreasing T, becoming zero at 0 deg R (Fig. 1). The downward approach to $C_p = 0$ at 0 deg R is interrupted for some substances (principally compounds) by "bumps" on the curve (excess C_p that rises to a maximum and then decreases). Paramagnetic salts undergoing transitions to either a ferromagnetic or an antiferromagnetic state are examples. This excess specific heat of a paramagnetic salt is connected with the effectiveness of the salt for reaching low temperatures by the method of adiabatic demagnetization. There are also transitions in solids from a more orderly to a less orderly arrangement of atoms and molecules in the lattice that give rise to excess C_p. The transition in solid ortho- and normal-H_2 below 20 R is an example. In Fig. 1, C_p's are plotted for various materials.

Heat is transferred in dielectrics by lattice vibrations, or waves. In good electrical conductors, heat is transferred principally by the conduction electrons, and thermal and electrical conductivities are related by the Wiedemann-Franz Law: $\kappa/\sigma T = \text{const.}$

This means that the ratio of the thermal and electrical conductivities at a given T is approximately the same for the good conductors. In the poor electrical conductors, alloys for example, both lattice waves and conduction electrons play important parts in the transfer of heat. The κ's of "pure" dielectrics and "pure" metals rise with increasing T from $\kappa = 0$ at 0 R (proportional to T for metals and to T^3 for dielectrics), reach a maximum, normally between 10 and 100 R, and then decrease to a value approximately independent of T (Fig. 3 and ice in Fig. 2). The κ's of alloys (Fig. 2)

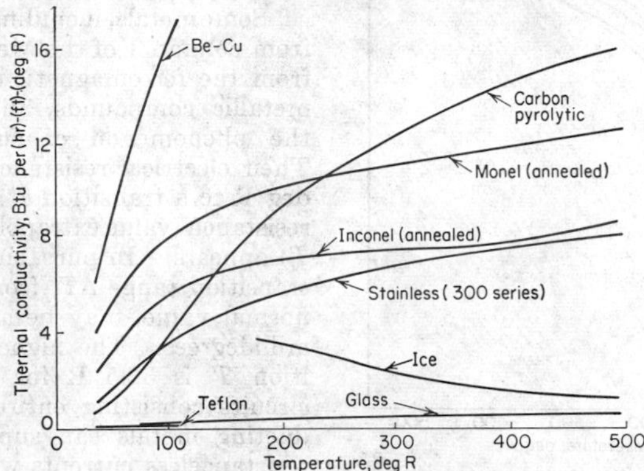

FIG. 2. Thermal conductivity of solids at low temperatures, Part 1.

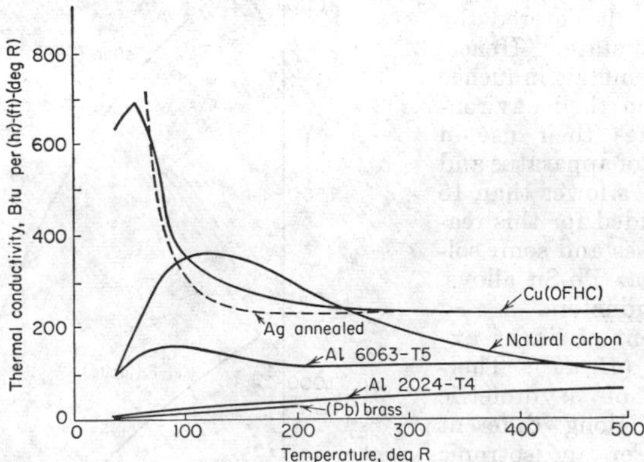

FIG. 3. Thermal conductivity of solids at low temperatures, Part 2.

are an order of magnitude smaller than for "pure" metals and *do not* exhibit the maxima characteristic of the "pure" metals at low T. Lattice disorder introduced by alloying, even in small amounts, and working a metal, even a pure metal, reduces κ. Annealing, in general, raises κ.

At 0 R, an absolutely pure and perfect single crystal of metal would have zero electrical resistance, $R_e = 0$. **Electrical resistance** arises from the scattering of the conduction electrons as they move through the lattice of metal ions under the influence of an externally applied electric field. Scattering arises for two reasons: (1) the thermal vibrations of the lattice which increase with T at a rate proportional to C of the metal, and (2) the imperfections in the regularity of the lattice as caused by impurity atoms (solid-solution alloys included), lattice vacancies, dislocations, and grain boundaries. The resistance for "pure" metals increases with T roughly proportional to

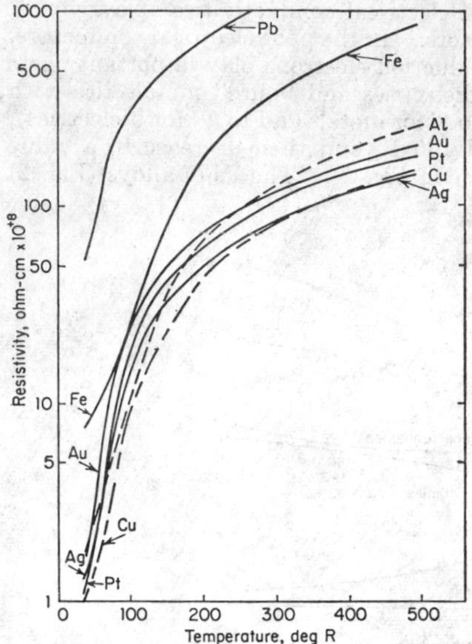

FIG. 4. Electrical resistivity of solids at low temperatures.

$C \cdot T$, except at very small T's where it is proportional to T^5 for absolutely pure crystals. The resistance due to impurities and imperfections is very roughly independent of T (Matthiessen's rule). For quite pure metals, R_e is approximately constant below 20 R. Resistivity in ohm-cm (Fig. 4) is the R_e of a cu cm.

Some metals, including elements (none from column 1 of the Mendeleeff table or from the ferromagnetic elements), intermetallic compounds, and alloys exhibit the phenomenon of **superconductivity.** Their electrical resistance is zero from 0 deg R to a transition T at which normal resistance (value extrapolated from higher T) appears. In pure, single crystals the transition range ΔT, from $R_e = 0$ to the normal value, may be as small as a few millidegrees. The highest known transition T is 32.5 R for Nb_3Sn. Closed circuits consisting entirely of superconducting metals can support persistent, resistanceless currents without an external source of voltage. A superconducting circuit maintains constant the value of the total flux enclosed by the circuit at the time it entered the superconducting state. Hence, superconducting metals influence magnetic fields in their environment. Sometimes their use in the construction of apparatus and equipment for T's lower than 15 R has been avoided for this reason. Lead brasses and some solders, in particular Pb-Sn alloys, become superconductors.

The **coefficient of linear expansion** α is $(1/L)(dL/dT)$. Thermal expansion of asymmetric crystals differs along different crystal axes. For an isotropic solid, the volume or cubical-expansion coefficient $(1/V)(dV/dT) = 3\alpha$. Expansion coefficients are in general approximately constant at ambient temperatures, but they all approach zero at 0 deg R, and the approach to zero is tangential to the T axis ($d\alpha/dT = 0$ at 0 deg R). Expansion coefficients can be negative at low temperatures, *e.g.*, stainless steel, some Invars, and fused quartz. The expansivities of some crystals are negative in some directions even though their volume coeffi-

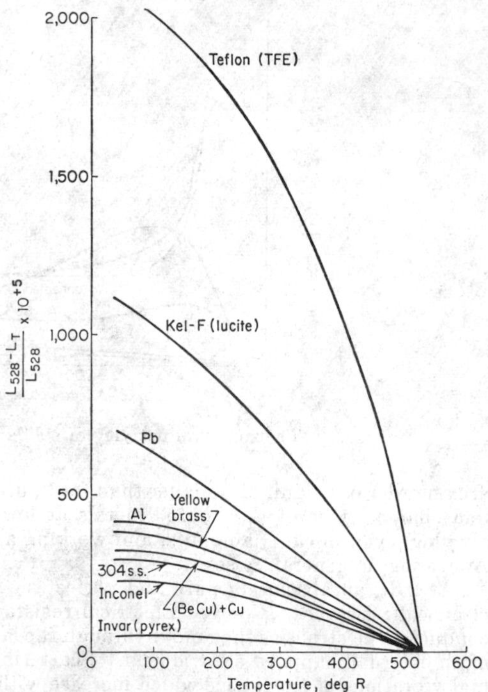

FIG. 5. Integrated expansion coefficient at low temperatures. Bracketed materials are within ~5 percent of the curve shown.

cients are positive. Cold-working may produce differences in expansivity in different directions. Annealing restores isotropy. Figure 5 shows the relative change in length, the integral of α from T to 528 R.

Because the cold interiors of cryogenic equipment must at times be warmed to ambient temperature, provisions have to be made for those changes in dimensions of the interior that result from large changes in T. Even for equipment of ordinary size, these changes can be too large for accommodation within the elastic limits of the materials of construction or of the structure. In such situations, flexibility has to be designed into the structure. Bellows and U-bends are commonly employed to obtain this flexibility in insulated transfer lines for liquid cryogens.

The **mechanical properties** important for the design and construction of cryogenic equipment are the same as for other temperatures (see also Sec. 5). Frequently, the choice of materials for the construction of cryogenic equipment will depend upon other considerations besides mechanical strength, *e.g.*, lightness (density or weight), thermal conductivity (heat transfer along structural support members), and thermal expansivity (change of dimensions when cycling between ambient and low temperatures). Frequently, mechanical properties at low temperature are significantly different from properties at ambient temperature. This makes room-temperature data unreliable for engineering use at low temperatures.

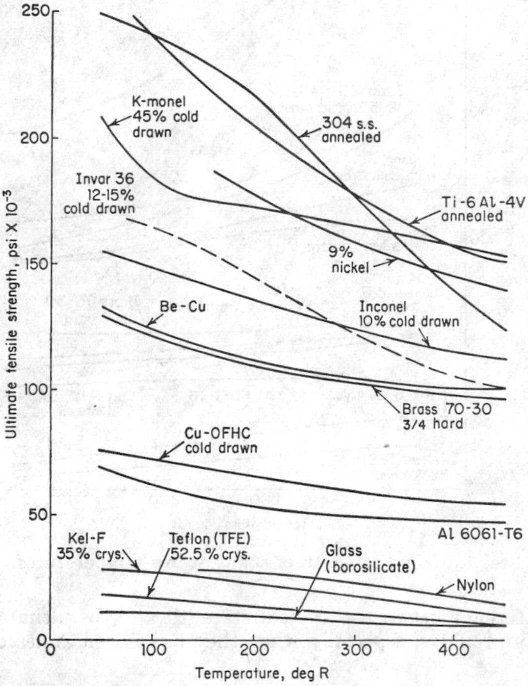

Fig. 6. Ultimate tensile strength of solids at low temperatures.

It is not possible to make generalizations that would not have numerous exceptions about the temperature variations of the mechanical properties. In this discussion, Table 1 and Figs. 6 to 8 are only illustrative guides. There is no substitute for test data on a truly representative specimen when designing for the limit of effectiveness of a cryogenic material or structure. Just as the mechanical properties at ambient temperatures are dependent upon the impurities (metallic and non-metallic), their chemical nature and concentration, the thermal history of

Table 1. Young's Modulus of Solids at Low Temperatures, psi $\times 10^{-6}$

	60 R	160 R	360 R	560 R
Al 6061-T6 longitudinal	11.3	10.95	10.45	10.0
70-30 brass	16.0	15.0	15.2	15
Be-Cu	19.5	19.0	17.5	17.5
304 SS annealed	29	29	29	28
K-Monel	30	.....	.....	26
Inconel (20% cold-drawn)	33.5	33.5	32.5	32
Teflon (TFE, 52.5% crystal)	0.62	0.50	0.27	0.05

the specimen, the amount and kind of working (microstructure and dislocations of the lattice), and the rate of loading and type of stress (uni-, bi-, and triaxial), so also are the changes, quantitative and qualitative, in the mechanical properties when changing the temperature from ambient to low temperatures.

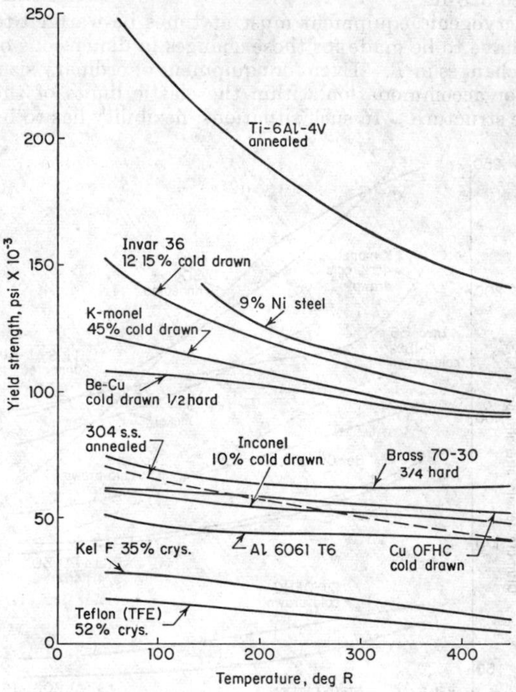

FIG. 7. Yield strength of solids at low temperatures.

Metals, non-metallic solids (glass), plastics, and elastomers are discussed in order. The metals are classed by their lattice (crystal) symmetry.

The **f.c.c. metals** and their alloys are most commonly used for the construction of cryogenic equipment. Al, Cu, Ni, their alloys, and the austenitic stainless steels of the 18-8 type (300 series) are f.c.c. They do not exhibit an impact (or a notched-tensile) ductile-to-brittle transition at low temperatures. As a general rule, which has some exceptions, the mechanical properties of these metals improve as T is reduced: (1) Young's modulus at 40 R is 5 to 20 percent larger than at 530 R, (2) the yield strength at 40 R is considerably greater than the strength at 530 R (Cu is an exception; see Fig. 7), and (3) the fatigue properties at low T are improved. There is a large difference between the yield strength and the ultimate tensile strength of these metals and alloys, especially when they have been annealed. Pb and In (f.c.c.) are used for

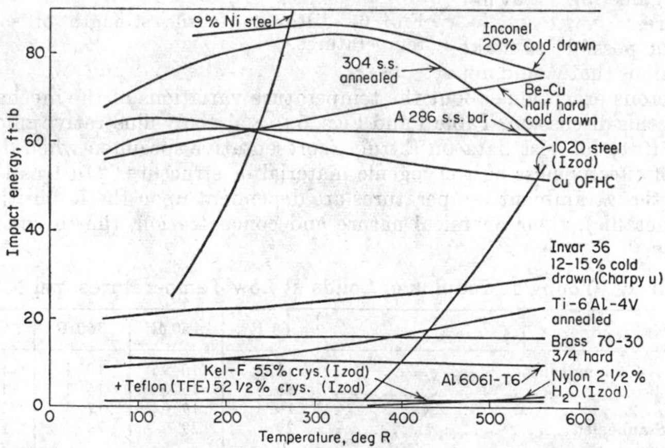

FIG. 8. Impact energy for solids at low temperatures (Charpy V unless noted). For Kel-F, nylon, and Teflon, the impact energy units are foot-pound per inch of notch width.

low-T deformable gaskets because of their creep properties. Low-T creep data are meager, but the rate of creep decreases with T.

Beta brass (f.c.c.) is ductile down to 7 R, though it is like all alloys of Cu in being less ductile than Cu itself. Thin brass is sometimes porous, and this limits its usefulness for high-vacuum enclosures at low temperatures. Free-machining brass normally contains Pb, which even in low concentrations can render the brass superconducting at LHe temperatures. In the superconducting state, it may then affect the magnetic field in its vicinity (see electrical properties, p. 18–31).

The **b.c.c. metals and alloys** are normally classed as undesirable. These include Fe, the martensitic steels (low carbon and the 400 series of stainless steels), Mo, and Nb. If not brittle at room temperature, they have a ductile-to-brittle transition at low T. Working can induce the austenite-to-martensite transition in some steels. AISI 301 austenitic stainless is an example. It remains moderately "tough" at very low T and is a valuable material for construction, but cold-drawing, in excess of 70 percent strain, induces a partial transformation of structure and reduces the elongation and notched-strength ratio to nearly zero. This same type of reduction in toughness is observed in the "heat-treatable" stainless steels. Improved tensile properties can be obtained by cold-working and by heat-treating. These alloys usually have decreased toughness at low temperatures. Alloys of V, Nb and Ta, although f.c.c., behave well as regards brittleness at low temperatures. These alloys have the advantage of being suitable for use at high T. Carbon steels, though brittle, have found special uses at low temperatures, *e.g.*, in the construction of the expansion engines of the Collins He liquefier and cryostat.

The **h.c.p. metals** exhibit properties intermediate between those of the f.c.c. and b.c.c. metals; *e.g.*, Zn undergoes a brittle-to-ductile transition, whereas Zr and pure Ti do not. Ti and some Ti alloys, having an h.c.p. structure, remain moderately ductile at low T and are excellent for many applications. They have high strength-to-weight and strength-to-thermal-conductivity ratios. The low-T properties of Ti and its alloys are extremely sensitive to even small amounts of O, N, H, and C.

Brittle materials, when in very thin sheets, can have a high degree of flexibility, and this makes them useful for some cryogenic applications. **Flexibility** cannot be used as a criterion for ductility.

There is very little information on the **strength of welds** at low temperatures. Ordinarily, normal welding practices are observed in the construction of cryogenic equipment. These practices, however, are modified in accordance with available knowledge of the performance of the metals at low T.

Non-metal materials for construction are in many cases brittle, or they are susceptible to brittle fracture. The strength of **glass,** measured at a constant rate of loading, increases on going to low T. Failure occurs at a lower stress when the glass surface contains cracks and abrasions. The strength of glass can be improved by tempering the surface, *i.e.*, by putting the surface under compression.

The **plastics** increase in strength as T is decreased, but this is accompanied by a rapid decrease in elongation in a tensile test and a decrease in impact resistance. Teflon and the glass-reinforced plastics (*e.g.*, glass-reinforced epoxy resin) retain appreciable impact resistance as T is lowered. Teflon, which is polytetrafluroethylene, can be deformed plastically at T's as low as 7 R. The amount is considerably less than at room temperature, but it is enough to make Teflon very useful for some cryogenic applications. The glass-reinforced epoxies, besides having appreciable impact resistance at low T's, also have high strength-to-weight and strength-to-thermal-conductivity ratios. Preliminary tests indicate they are vacuum-tight as well.

All the **elastomers** become brittle at low T. However, elastomers like natural rubber, nitrile rubber, Viton A, and plastics such as Mylar and nylon that become brittle at low T can be used for static seal gaskets when *highly compressed* at room temperature, prior to cooling.

Cryogenic Fluids (Cryogens)

Table 2 indicates the **temperature ranges** accessible with liquid cryogen baths. There are two inaccessible ranges: (1) between helium and hydrogen (9.36 to 24.9 R)

Table 2. Common Cryogen Properties

Cryogen	Boiling point, deg R	Triple-point		Critical temp, deg R	Critical pressure, psia	Inversion temp,* deg R	Heat of vaporization*		Liquid density,† lb/ft³	Vapor density,† lb/ft³	Gas density,‡ lb/ft³
		Temp, deg R	Pressure, psia				Btu/lb	Btu/ft³			
He^3	5.7	....	.....	6	17	72	3.6	13.4	3.72	1.50	0.0084
He^4	7.6	....	.....	9.36	33.2	92	8.8	68.6	7.80	1.04	0.0111
H_2 (equilib.)	36.5	24.9	1.02	59.4	187.7	368	192	853	4.42	0.0837	0.00561
D_2 (normal)	42.6	33.7	2.49	69.0	240	.....	131	1,343	10.25	......	0.0112
Ne	48.7	44.2	6.26	80.0	395.3	486	37.1	2,790	75.35	0.58	0.056
N_2	139.2	113.7	1.86	227.27	492.3	1,115	85.9	4,294	50.4	0.28	0.078
Air	(141.8)	....	.....	....	....	.....	88.22	4,813	54.56	0.28	0.0807
A	157.1	150.8	9.97	271.3	709.8	1,300	70.2	6,135	87.4	0.36	0.111
F_2	151	(96.4)§	.....	259.3	808	.....	74.1	6,965	94	......	0.106
O_2	162.3	97.9	0.022	278.59	736.3	1,605	91.5	6,538	71.24	......	0.089
CH_4	201.1	163.2	1.69	343.27	673	.....	219.2	5,804	26.5	0.115	0.0448

* 14.7 psia.
† At normal boiling point.
‡ At 14.7 psia and 32 F.
§ Melting point, 14.7 psia.

and (2) between neon and oxygen (80 to 97.9 R). The limiting temperatures are set by the critical and triple points. Pumping on a cryogen bath to lower the pressure results in lower temperatures ultimately reaching the triple point; except for helium, further pumping leads to solidification and poor heat-transfer characteristics. Raising the bath pressure results in higher boiling temperatures with the limit set by the critical temperature, above which a liquid phase does not exist. Cryogen baths are most frequently operated near atmospheric pressure.

The algebraic sign of the Joule-Thomson coefficient determines whether a gas cools or warms upon free expansion. Figure 9, based on the law of corresponding states,

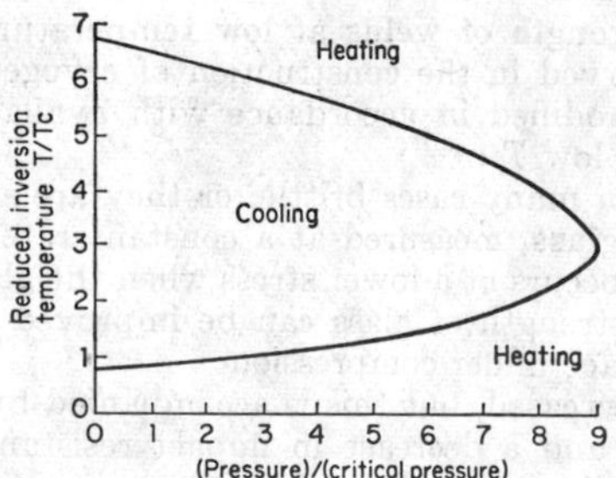

FIG. 9. Reduced inversion temperature versus reduced pressure.

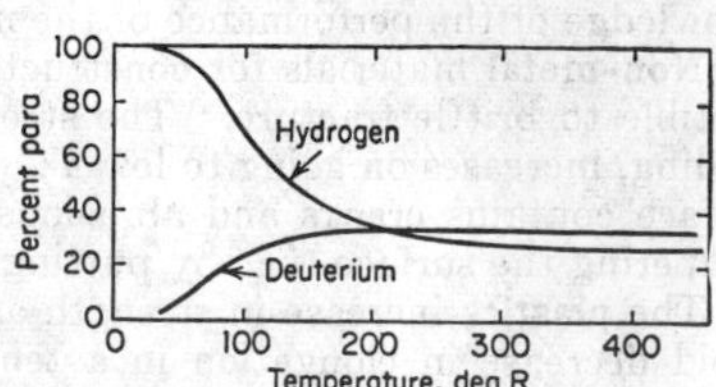

FIG. 10. Thermodynamic equilibrium composition of ortho and para varieties of H_2 and D_2: percent ortho = 100 − percent para.

allows rough calculations of inversion temperatures and pressures. Free (Joule-Thomson) expansion inside the "cooling" region results in cooling, *i.e.*, refrigeration; outside this region, heating results. Upper inversion temperatures at 14.7 psia are given in Table 2.

Volumetric latent heats (Table 3) decrease with the lower-boiling cryogens and emphasize the importance of the insulation in storing and handling LH_2 and LHe.

Two forms of **hydrogen and deuterium** exist: **ortho and para.** The ortho and para molecules differ in the relative orientation of the nuclear spins of the two atoms composing the diatomic molecule. In the ortho form of H_2 the nuclear spins of the two atoms

Table 3. Volume Latent Heats at Normal Boiling Points (B.P.) and ΔT's between Ambient and Normal Boiling-point Temperatures

Substance	$\Delta T = 540 - T_{B.P.}$, deg R	L_v, Btu/gal
Water	...	8,000
Oxygen	378	872
Nitrogen	400	574
Neon	490	371
Hydrogen	504	114
Helium 4	533	9.2

in the molecule are parallel (in the same direction), whereas in the para form the spins are antiparallel. The relative orientations for ortho and para D_2 differ from those for H_2. The thermodynamic equilibrium composition of ortho and para varieties is temperature dependent as shown in Fig. 10.

In liquid hydrogen, the uncatalyzed ortho-para reaction is second order (proportional to the square of the o-H_2 concentration) with a rate constant of 0.0114/hr. Thus, in the course of uncatalyzed liquefaction, normal LH_2 (75 percent ortho) is produced. Since the heat of conversion of o-H_2 to p-H_2 at the normal boiling point is 302 Btu/lb (greater than the heat of vaporization; see Table 2), long-term storage of normal LH_2 is impractical. Therefore, in the commercial production of LH_2 a

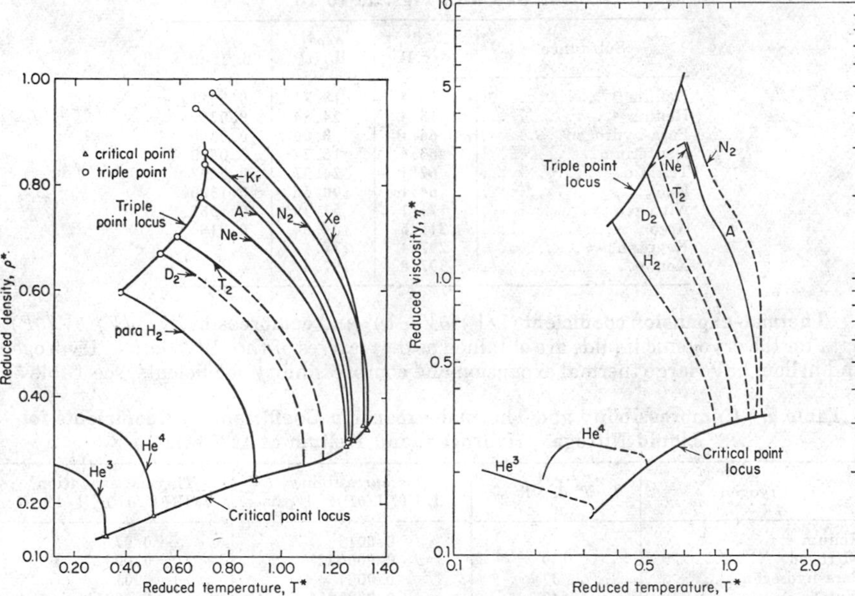

Fig. 11. Reduced density versus reduced temperature along the saturation curve for cryogenic liquids. Reduced density ρ^* must be multiplied by ρ/ρ^* given in Table 4 to obtain density in pounds per foot³. Values of T^* are obtained by dividing the desired temperature (deg R) by the value of T/T^* given in Table 4.

Fig. 12. Reduced viscosity versus reduced temperature along the saturation curve for cryogenic liquids. Reduced viscosity η^* must be multiplied by η/η^* given in Table 4 to obtain viscosity in pounds per foot-hour. Values of T^* are obtained by dividing the desired temperature (deg R) by the value of T/T^* given in Table 4.

catalyst is used to produce essentially the low-temperature equilibrium composition (greater than 95 percent para).

For pressures of no more than 150 psi and temperatures at least twice T_C, the ideal gas law ($PV = nRT$) enables one to calculate PVT data with sufficient accuracy for many engineering purposes. For cases in which the ideal gas law is not adequate or in which experimental data are not available, the procedures outlined in Sec. 4 may be used.

The theoretical prediction of PVT data for liquids is considerably more difficult than for gases. Consequently no universal equation analogous to the perfect gas law exists for extensive ranges of P and T.

A **reduced quantum mechanical correlation** of saturated liquid densities for several cryogens is shown in Fig. 11. The dashed lines for tritium (hydrogen isotope 3) and deuterium represent areas void of experimental data.

Utilization of Fig. 11 requires knowledge of the constants ϵ and σ for the Lennard-Jones function for the intermolecular potential energy $\varphi(r)$ of a pair of molecules separated by a distance r, so that $\varphi(r) = 4\epsilon[(\sigma/r)^{12} - (\sigma/r)^6]$. Here ϵ is the depth of the minimum in the potential energy of a pair of molecules, and σ is the separation of the pair at which $\varphi = 0$.

To facilitate use of Fig. 11, all required constants and conversion factors have been combined and are listed in Table 4. To obtain a density one must multiply the value of the reduced density ρ^* obtained from Fig. 11 by the appropriate factor from Table 4. T^* is obtained by dividing T by the T/T^* value from Table 4.

Table 4. Multiplication Factors for Use with Figs. 11 to 13

Substance	T/T^*, deg R	ρ/ρ^*, lb/ft^3	η/η^*, lb/ft-hr
Helium 3	18.4	18.71	0.0311
Helium 4	18.4	24.84	0.0359
Para-hydrogen	66.1	8.06	0.0360
Deuterium	63.4	16.22	0.0500
Tritium	62.1	24.37	0.0607
Neon	64.1	100.66	0.1300
Nitrogen	171.1	57.39	0.1382
Argon	215.6	104.84	0.2183
Krypton	297.4	177.1	
Xenon	397.8	197.4	

Thermal-expansion coefficient $(1/V)(\partial V/\partial T)_P$ and **compressibility** $(1/V)(\partial V/\partial P)_T$ data for the cryogenic liquids are obtained as derivatives of the PVT data. Hydrogen and helium have large thermal expansion and compressibility coefficients (see Table 5).

Table 5. Compressibility and Thermal-expansion Coefficients. Coefficients for Liquid Nitrogen, Hydrogen, and Helium at 14.7 psia

Cryogen	T, deg R	Compressibility, $1/V(\partial V/\partial P)_T$, 1/psia	Thermal expansion, $1/V(\partial V/\partial T)_P$, 1/deg R
Helium 4	6	0.0013	0.071
Nitrogen	139	0.000022	0.0032
Para-hydrogen	37	0.0001	0.01
Water	540	0.0000036	0.000115

The **viscosity** of the cryogenic liquids can be correlated by a law of corresponding states technique (see Fig. 12). Inclusion of the reduced quantum mechanical parameter in the analysis has permitted prediction of the reduced viscosities where no experimental data exist. This is shown by the dotted lines. The viscosities are obtained by multiplying the reduced viscosities η^* obtained from Fig. 12 by the appropriate factor in Table 4. For gases, kinetic theory predicts an increase of viscosity with rising temperature as shown in Fig. 13.

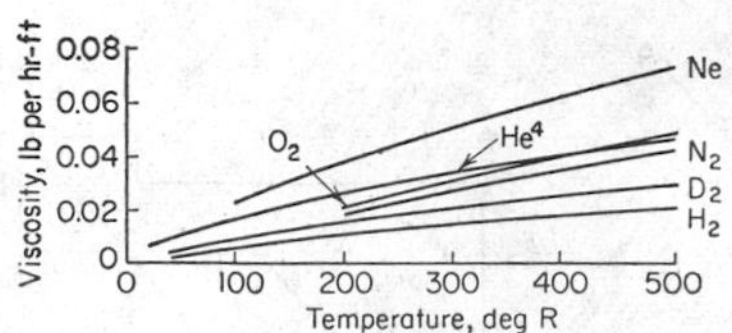

FIG. 13. Viscosity of selected gases at low temperatures and 14.7 psia.

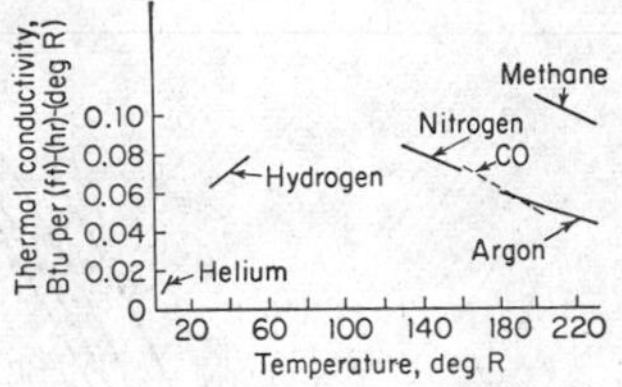

FIG. 14. Thermal conductivity of liquid cryogens at low temperatures.

Normally, the **thermal conductivities** of liquids decrease with increasing temperature, whereas the thermal conductivities of gases increase. In Fig. 14 it is seen that the liquid H_2 and He isotopes behave as gases in this respect. This is attributed to quantum mechanical effects. Figure 15 presents thermal conductivity for several gases as a function of temperature at 14.7 psia.

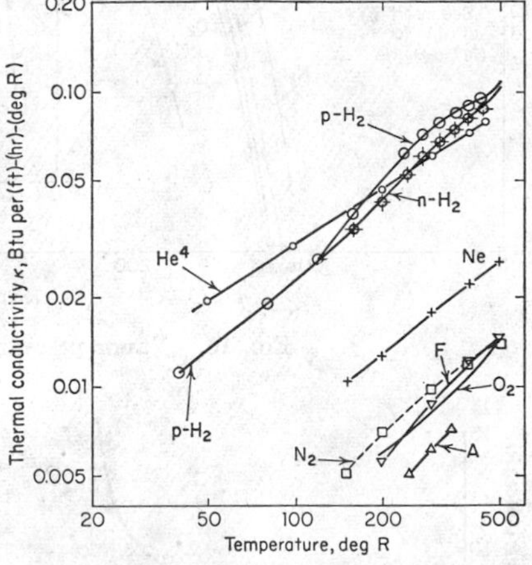

FIG. 15. Thermal conductivity of gases at low temperatures and 14.7 psia.

Figure 16 is a graph of **vapor pressures** of the common cryogens.

Figure 17 presents **specific heats** at constant pressure for several of the cryogenic liquids, while Fig. 18 presents the specific heats for liquid hydrogen and helium along the saturation curve. Specific heats of gases are given in Fig. 19.

Instrumentation

(See also Secs. 15 and 16)

The usual instrumentation problems of engineering practice are further complicated by low-temperature problems which require special calibration procedures.

Pressures are measured with normally used apparatus, *e.g.*, bourdon gages, transducers, and manometers. If the measuring device is located outside the cryogenic environment and insulated from it by a thermal barrier, no special problems are introduced. Occasionally response time requirements necessitate the placing of the transducer in the cryogen space. Then the problems of temperature compensation and calibration must be considered.

Level measurements currently utilize several methods. The differential-pressure method can in principle be used with all cryogens. With cryogens of low densities and low heats of vaporization (*e.g.*, H_2 and He) pressure oscillation occurs in the liquid leg. In the case of LH_2 these can be eliminated by the proper design of the liquid leg and the introduction of He gas which does not condense.

Direct weighing is also used to determine "levels," although difficulties are encountered owing to the large tare-to-cryogen weight ratios (as large as 20 to 1 for a full container in the case of H_2) and extraneous loadings introduced by permanently connected piping, frost, and wind. Weighing systems have nevertheless been successfully used on 50,000 gal LH_2 dewars with an accuracy in level changes of 250 gal.

With the **capacitance gage,** the sensing element consists of a concentric tube capacitor which can be calibrated to give liquid-level measurements accurate to a few tenths of a percent. An inexpensive, accurate **point-level sensor** is easily fabricated from a carbon resistor, typically 1⁄10 watt, 27 ohm. Its use depends upon the fact that its resistance is a strong function of temperature (Fig. 20). A small current (50 to 80 ma) is passed through the resistor to heat it. Since heat from the resistor is dissipated

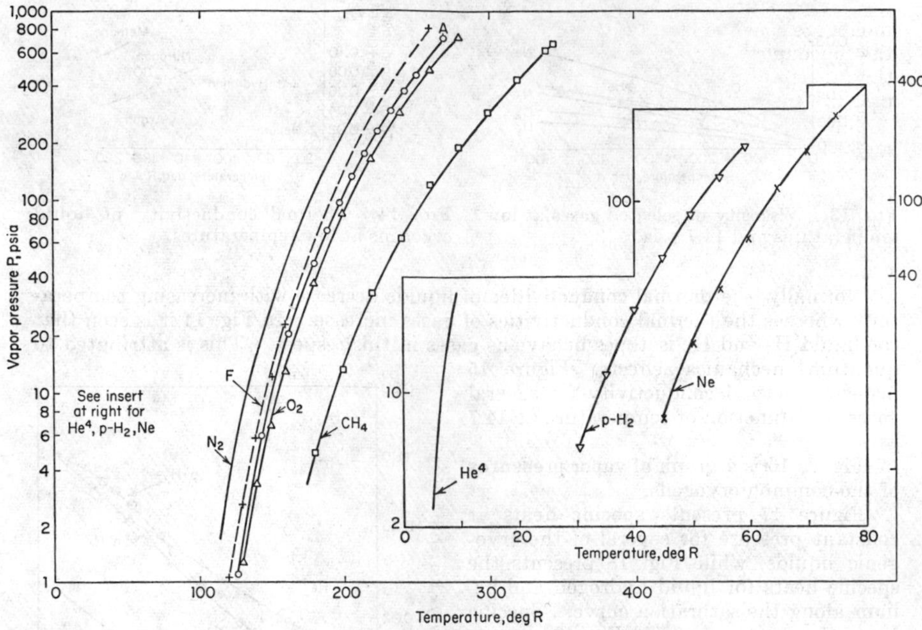

FIG. 16. Vapor pressures of the common cryogens.

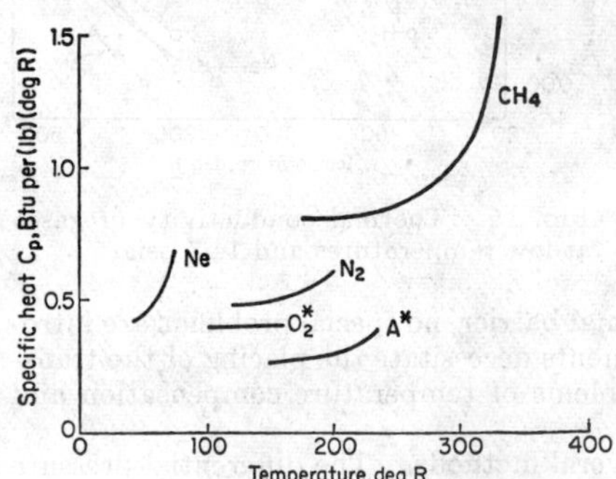

FIG. 17. Specific heat at constant pressure (C_p) for liquid cryogens at saturation pressure. Asterisk means C_p evaluated along an isobar at 14.7 psia instead of saturation pressure.

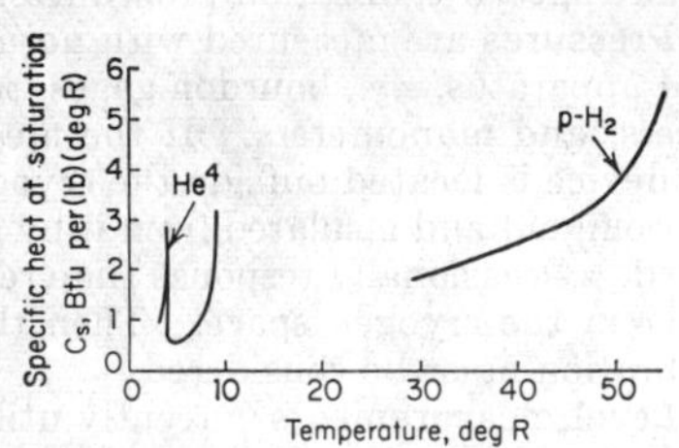

FIG. 18. Specific heats at saturation C_s along the saturation curve versus temperature for Helium 4 and para hydrogen.

more readily in the liquid than in the gas, the temperature of the resistor (and consequently the resistance) undergoes a step increase when the resistor environment changes from liquid to gas.

Flow measurements utilize orifices, venturis, and turbine-type meters. Various devices for direct mass-flow measurement exist, but none are widely used. **"Quality"** meters have been built to determine the percentage liquid in two-phase flow. The determination of quality is complicated by non-equilibrium of temperature in the gas phase.

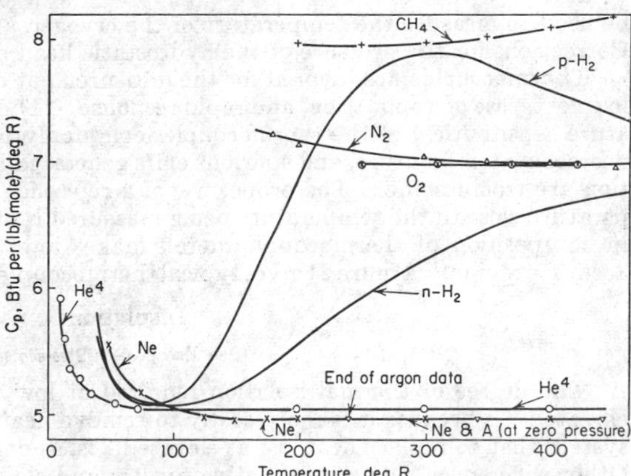

FIG. 19. Specific heat of C_p cryogen gases at 14.7 psia versus temperature.

Temperature measurements are usually made with thermocouples, resistance thermometers, and vapor-pressure thermometers.

The **vapor-pressure thermometer** depends upon a vapor-pressure–temperature relationship (see Fig. 16). In general, a small cavity is filled with a gas which has a condensation temperature in the vicinity of the temperature to be measured. If sufficient gas is present, the pressure will be that of the liquid vapor pressure at the coldest part of the measuring system. Maximum speed of response is obtained if the total quantity of gas is minimized to permit only a thin film of liquid to form. In the case of H_2, a catalyst to promote ortho-para conversion should be included in the bulb for an accurate measurement since the vapor pressure of H_2 is dependent upon its ortho-para composition (see p. 18–36).

The equilibrium vapor pressure at the surface of a liquid cryogen in a dewar may

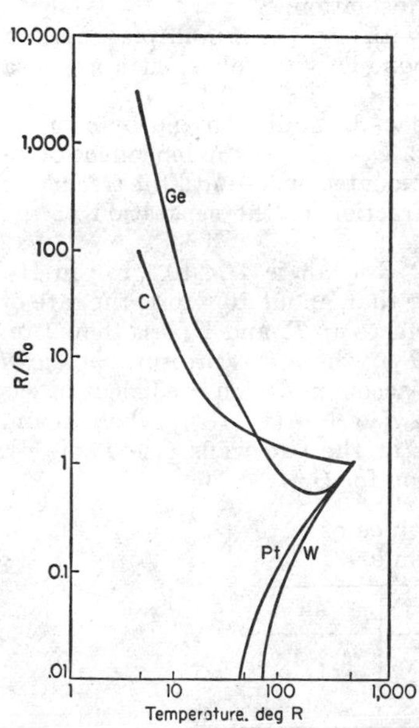

FIG. 20. Ratio of resistance R to the resistance R_0 at 492 deg R versus temperature for several resistance thermometers. (Values for germanium and carbon are representative only.)

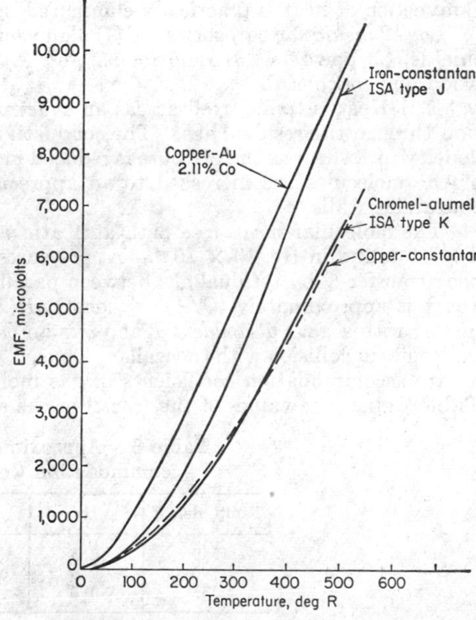

FIG. 21. EMF versus temperature for several thermocouples.

be used to measure the temperature of the cryogen and of apparatus immersed in it. Corrections for the pressure of the hydrostatic head of liquid may be required.

Thermocouples are favored for the measurement of temperatures because of their low cost, ease of application, and rapid response. The thermoelectric powers (temperature sensitivities) of the thermocouples commonly used at higher T's decrease with decreasing temperature, and spurious emfs generated in wires of non-uniform composition are troublesome. The proper use of a reference junction at a known fixed temperature close to the temperature being measured is often advantageous. Variability in composition of thermocouple metals makes individual calibrations necessary for accurate results. Figure 21 gives typical thermocouple emf-versus-temperature curves.

Insulation

(See also p. 6–203 *et seq.*)

The degree of thermal isolation required at low T's is normally greater than at elevated T's because it is more costly to remove heat leaking into a low-temperature system than to replace heat lost at elevated T's, as demonstrated by the Carnot cycle. Other differences between insulating for low and elevated temperatures are:

(1) Condensation of moisture in low-temperature insulation is possible. When this occurs, the conductance of the insulation is significantly increased. This problem is avoided by a vapor barrier on the outside of the insulation.

(2) Condensation of the atmosphere in the insulation and surface washing by the condensed liquid are possible when the insulating surfaces are below 150 R. This can result in a large added transfer of heat. It is avoided by (1) using an outer cover or surface impermeable to air, and (2) evacuating the insulating space or replacing the atmosphere in it with a non-condensable gas.

At low temperatures, as at other temperatures, the fundamental modes of heat transfer are conduction and radiation, and it is against these that insulation is used. Convection of heat is practically eliminated by the insulation.

Low-T insulation categories are (1) high vacuum, with or without multiple radiation shields, (2) powders, (3) rigid foams, and (4) low-conductivity solids, such as balsa wood and corkboard.

(1.i) **Heat is transferred across an evacuated space** by radiation and by conduction through the residual gas. The conductivity of a gas is almost independent of its density (pressure) as the pressure is reduced in an evacuated space until the free paths of the molecules are increased to an appreciable fraction of the separation of the containing walls.

The molecular *mean* free path at 1 atm and 32 F in air is 4×10^{-6} in.; in H_2, 6×10^{-6}; and in He, 10×10^{-6}. At pressures lower than about 10^{-3} torr, the rate of heat transfer Q by residual gas between parallel surfaces at T_1 and T_2 less than 1 in. apart is approximately $(Q/A) \approx$ (const) $\alpha P(T_2 - T_1)$, where P is pressure *measured* in torr with a gage *at ambient T* and α is an *over-all* accommodation coefficient of gas molecules in collision with the walls. Thus, $\alpha = \alpha_1\alpha_2/[\alpha_2 + \alpha_1(1 - \alpha_2)]$, where α_1 and α_2 are accommodation coefficients of gas molecules at the two walls (see Table 6). Table 7 gives the values of the (*const*) in the equation for Q/A.

Table 6. Approximate Values of Accommodation Coefficients, α

Temp, deg R	He	H_2	Air
540	0.3	0.3	0.8–0.9
140	0.6	0.5	1
35	0.6	1	1

The **rate of radiative heat transfer** between parallel surfaces at T_1 and $T_2 > T_1$, whose emissivities are e_1 and e_2, respectively, is $Q = e_1e_2s/[e_2 + (1 - e_2)e_1](T_2^4 - T_1^4)$, where s is the Stefan-Boltzmann constant whose value is 1.712×10^{-10} Btu/ft²-hr-deg R⁴ (see also p. 4–108 *et seq.*). Table 8 contains absorption coefficients for 550 R thermal radiation; these for most engineering purposes may be considered equivalent

Table 7. Constant in the Gas-conduction Equation

$Q/A \approx (\text{const})\ \alpha P(T_2 - T_1)$

Gas	T_2 and T_1, deg R	Const, Btu/hr-ft²-torr-deg R
N_2	<700	28
O_2	<540	26
H_2	540 and 140 or 540 and 160	93
H_2	140 and 36	70
He	Any	49

T_1—inner wall (cold).
T_2—outer wall (hot).

Table 8. Minimal Values of Absorptivity of Metal Surfaces at Various Temperatures for 540 R Thermal Radiation

Surfaces	Surface temp, deg R		
	7	140	540
Copper	0.005	0.008	0.018
Silver	0.0044	0.008	0.02
Aluminum	0.011	0.018	0.03
Chromium	......	0.08	0.08
Nickel	......	0.022	0.04
Brass	0.018	.....	0.035
Stainless steel 18-8	......	0.048	0.08
50 Pb–50 Sn solder	......	0.032	
Glass, paints, carbon	......	.....	>0.9
Nickel plate on copper	......	0.033	

to minimal values of the e's for very carefully prepared and cleaned surfaces. Organic coatings have high emissivities approaching unity (>0.9). Mechanically polished surfaces have higher e's than the minimal values. Handling a surface transfers an absorbing (high e) coating to it.

(1.ii) **Refrigerated Radiation Shield.** An LN_2 (139 R) cooled surface interposed in the insulating vacuum space of an LH_2 or an LHe container reduces the heat transferred by radiation to the LH_2 or LHe by a factor of about 250 when compared with that transferred by a surface of the same emissivity at room temperature without the interposition of the refrigerated shield. Nearly all the heat radiated by the surface at room temperature is absorbed by the LN_2, and this results in evaporation of the relatively inexpensive LN_2.

(1.iii) **A floating radiation shield** is an opaque layer (*e.g.*, a metal sheet), having surfaces of low emissivity suspended in the vacuum space with a minimum of thermal contacts with surfaces that are warmer or cooler. If the emissivity of the surfaces of the floating shield is the same as the emissivity of the vacuum-side surfaces, the floating shield decreases the *radiative* heat transfer by a factor of 2. For m floating shields arranged in series between the inner cold and outer warm surfaces, the rate of *radiative* heat transfer becomes $\dot{Q}_m$ (m floating shields) $= [1/(m+1)]\ \dot{Q}_0$ ($m = 0$).

(1.iv) **Multilayer (Super) Insulation.** The principle of multiple floating radiation shields has been extended to the use of many thin metal layers (up to 75 layers per inch) separated by thin thermal insulation. Best results have been obtained with Al foil separated by glass-fiber paper. Other materials have been used successfully, *e.g.*, nylon nets as separators and aluminized Mylar with no spacer material. The *apparent* thermal *conductivity* of glass-fiber paper, Al foil multilayer insulation is variable depending on the number of layers of foil, the thickness of the paper, and the thickness and compacting of the insulating layer. For $\Delta T = 540 - 36$ deg R, apparent mean conductivities range from 2.0 to 4.0×10^{-5} Btu/hr ft deg R. For $\Delta T = 540 - 139$

deg R, the values are about one-third larger. Using nylon nets or glass fabric or glass fibers for separating the Al-foil increases the conductance from three to seven times. The above conductivities are for the direction normal to the foil surfaces. Lateral conductivities are many thousands of times larger. An advantage of aluminized Mylar is its reduced lateral conductivity. Another advantage is its relatively low density (one-third to one-half of other multilayer insulations). If the residual gas pressure in multilayer insulation is less than 10^{-4} torr, the conductance is independent of the pressure. At 10^{-3} torr, the conductance is increased by the order of 50 percent.

(2.i) **Powder insulation** consists of finely divided materials (see Table 9). Conductances of evacuated powders may vary as much as 100 percent with variations of

Table 9. Apparent Mean Conductivity of Several Powders Determined for Insulation 1 In. Thick and a $\Delta T = 540 - 139$ deg R

Powder	Particle size	Density, lb/ft³	Gas pressure, torr	Conductivity, Btu/hr-ft-deg R
Silica aerogel	Chemically prepared 0.025 μ†	6.2	$<10^{-4}$	0.0012
		6.2	628(N_2)	0.011
		6.2	628(He)	0.036
		6.2	628(H_2)	0.046
	+10% free silicon dust, by weight	6.9	$<10^{-4}$	0.0010
Silica	Flame-prepared 0.015–0.02 μ	3.7	$<10^{-4}$	0.0012
		3.7	630(N_2)	0.011
Perlite, expanded	>540 μ	3.7	$<10^{-4}$	0.0012
	>540 μ	6.2	$<10^{-4}$	0.0010
	>540 μ	6.2	628(N_2)	0.019
	>540 μ	6.2	628(He)	0.073
	>540 μ	6.2	628(H_2)	0.084
	>177, <540 μ	8.1	$<10^{-4}$	0.0007
	>177, <540 μ	8.1	628(N_2)	0.019
	>177, <540 μ	8.1	628(He)	0.073
	>177, <540 μ	8.1	628(H_2)	0.084
	<177 μ	8.7	$<10^{-4}$	0.0006
	<177 μ	8.7	628(N_2)	0.020
	<177 μ	8.7	628(He)	0.078
	<177 μ	8.7	628(H_2)	0.084
	<540 μ	8.7	$<10^{-4}$	0.0006
Diatomaceous earth	1–100 μ	15	$<10^{-4}$	0.0009
	1–100 μ	16	$<10^{-4}$	0.0008
	1–100 μ	18	$<10^{-4}$	0.0006
Alumina, fused	>149, <290 μ	125	$<10^{-4}$	0.0010
Alumina, laminar	0.1–10 μ	4.4	$<10^{-4}$	0.0013
Mica, expanded	>540, <841 μ 30% >290, <540 μ 70%	9.4	$<10^{-4}$	0.0010
		9.4	628(N_2)	0.029
		9.4	628(He)	0.087
Lampblack		12	$<10^{-4}$	0.0007
Charcoal peach pits	>540, <841 μ	31	$<10^{-4}$	0.0010
Carbon + 7% ash*	30% <44 μ	12	$<10^{-4}$	0.0003
Talc		75	$<10^{-4}$	0.0009
Phenolic spheres	25–100 μ	12	$<10^{-3}$	0.0008
Calcium silicate (synthetic)	0.02 μ	11	$<10^{-5}$	0.0004
	0.02–0.07 μ	22	$<10^{-5}$	0.0003
	0.02–0.07 μ	22	628(N_2)	0.026
Titanium dioxide	0.11 μ	22	$<10^{-3}$	0.0009
Iron oxide (Fe_2O_3)	0.02 μ	12	10^{-3}	0.0008

* Mostly SiO_2 and Al_2O_3.
† Micron.

particle size and *apparent* density (packing) of the powder. The most commonly used powders are perlite, expanded SiO_2 (aerogel), calcium silicate, diatomaceous earth, and carbon black. The conductance of powder insulation is practically independent of gas pressure down to 10 ± torr, at which pressure it begins to decrease rapidly with decreasing pressure as the free path of the gas molecules becomes comparable with the space between powder particles. The most rapid decrease of conductance occurs between 1 and 10^{-1} torr. At 10^{-3} torr the conductance has almost reached the lower limit. Even at 10^{-2} torr the conductance is quite low. For this reason, good mechanical pumps are adequate for the evacuation of powder insulation (fine mesh filters are needed to protect the pump).

The principal function of the powder is to impede the transfer of heat by radiation. Powders are used when radiation would constitute an important heat leak. If an insulating vacuum is bounded by highly reflecting walls, such as clean Cu, Ag, or Al, and the surfaces are at 139 and 36 R, respectively, adding powder may result in an increase of heat transfer because of the paths of solid conduction through the powder.

(2.ii) **Al powder or flakes added to a powder insulation** reduces the radiative transfer through the insulation. Powdered Al is more effective than flaked Al. The conductance of highly evacuated perlite insulation ($\Delta T = 540 - 139$ deg R) may be reduced 40 percent by the addition of 25 percent of Al powder. A similar addition of Al powder to Santocel and Cab-O-Sil (diatomaceous earth) reduces the conductance by 70 percent. Metal powders are most effective with those powders that are partially transparent to infrared radiation of wavelengths longer than 3μ.

(3) **Rigid-foam Insulation.** The foams most used in cryogenic applications are the more or less closed-cell foams. Table 10 gives thermal conductivities of selected

Table 10. Apparent Mean Thermal Conductivities of Selected Foams, $\Delta T = 540 - 139$ deg R

Foam	Density, lb/ft³	Thermal conductivity,* Btu/hr-ft-deg R
Polystyrene	2.4	0.019
	2.9	0.015
Epoxy resin	5.0	0.019
Polyurethane	5.0–8.7	0.019
Rubber	5.0	0.021
Silica	10.0	0.032
Glass	8.7	0.020

* Test space pressure = 14.7 psia.

samples of insulating foams. The conductivity of a foam is dependent on the conduction through the intracellular gas, on the transfer by thermal radiation, and on solid conduction. Temperatures below the condensing T of the encased gas condense it and improve the insulation. Gases encased when polymer foams are blown gradually diffuse out of the cells and are replaced by ambient gases. The conductivities of many freon and CO_2 blown foams increase in time as much as 30 percent because of the diffusion of air into the foam. Conductivities may increase by a factor of 3 or 4 when cells are permeated with H_2 or He. Glass and silica foams appear to be the only ones having fully closed cells. The **structural rigidity** of foams may be used to eliminate the need for mechanical supports. It is possible to use rigid foams without inner liners and outer casings. Polymer foams have relatively high **thermal expansions,** even greater than the same polymer without voids. This makes cracking of the insulation a problem when it is bonded to metal. Sliding expansion joints have been used to overcome this. Mylar film bags (1 mil thick) have been used to hold cryogenic liquids inside rigid-foam insulation and plastic films outside to keep the ambient atmosphere from the insulation.

(4.) **Balsa wood and corkboard** have been used for insulating cryogens that are not very cold, *e.g.*, liquid methane (167 R) and higher-boiling cryogens. Their conductivities (Table 11) are considerably higher than for the other types of low-T insulation discussed above. Their use, therefore, is restricted to special applications, as where their ability to support internal structures mechanically is important.

Conduction of heat along structural supports passing through the insulation merits special attention for an adequate realization of the benefits of superior insulation. Ideal materials of construction would have high mechanical strength and low thermal conductivity. In Table 12, the yield strengths, in tension, of construction materials

Table 11. Thermal Conductivities of Balsa Wood and Corkboard

Material	Density, lb/ft³	Thermal conductivity, Btu/hr-ft-deg R
Balsa wood, across grain	7.3	0.027
	8.8	0.032
	20.0	0.048
Corkboard, no added binder	5.4	0.021
	7.0	0.0225
	10.6	0.025
	14.0	0.028
Corkboard with asphalt binder	14.5	0.027

Table 12. Comparison of Materials for Support Members

Material	E_y,* 1,000 psi	κ,* Btu/hr-ft-deg R	E_y/κ
Aluminum 2024	55	47	1.17
Aluminum 7075	70	50	1.4
Copper, ann.	12	274	0.044
Hastelloy† "B"	65	5.4	12
Hastelloy† "C"	48	5.9	8.1
"K" monel‡	100	9.9	10.1
Stainless steel 304, ann.	35	5.9	5.9
Stainless steel (drawn 210,000 psi)	150	5.2	29
Titanium, pure	85	21	4.0
Titanium alloy (4Al-4Mn)	145	3.5	41.4
Dacron§	20	0.088¶	227
Mylar§	10	0.088¶	113
Nylon§	20	0.18	111
Teflon§	2	0.14	14.3

* E_y is the yield stress, and κ is the average thermal conductivity between 36 and 540 R.
† Haynes Stellite Co.
‡ International Nickel Co.
§ E. I. du Pont de Nemours & Company.
¶ Room-temperature value.

are compared with their conductivities. This kind of comparison favors the nonmetallic materials in Table 12. When large quantities of cryogens are handled in the field, metals are commonly used for structural members because glass and plastics (Teflon excepted) are brittle at low T's.

Minimizing the transfer of heat through the supporting structure offers opportunities for ingenuity and inventiveness in design. The transfer is minimized by lengthening the supporting members. A stack of thin metal disks or washers, utilizing the contact resistance between adjacent disks, will increase thermal resistance without increase in length of support. A stack of 0.0008 in. stainless steel disks under a compressive stress of 1,000 psi, in vacuum, has the same thermal resistance as a solid rod 50 times the length of the stack.

Insulation Selection. Because of their smaller heats of vaporization and greater cost of production, the lowest-T cryogens (LHe and LH_2) ordinarily merit more effective insulation than the higher-boiling cryogens like LO_2 and LN_2, and these in turn are ordinarily better insulated than other cryogens boiling at still more elevated T's. The choice of insulation ordinarily involves the conditions of use of the equipment, as well as considerations of the tolerable loss of refrigeration and the cost of the insulation and its installation. If equipment is to have intermittent, rather than long, uninterrupted operating periods, the insulation heat capacity and time lag in reaching steady state are important. An insulation with large heat capacity (*e.g.*, powders) will evaporate large quantities of refrigerant and take a long time to reach steady state. Powders are compacted by mechanical shocks and vibrations. Continued mechanical loading will compact both multilayer insulation and powders. Weight and bulkiness of the insulation can be important. The heat transported by the mechanical supports and vents connecting the cold interior with the warm exterior becomes the minimum refrigeration loss, attainable only with perfect insulation of the rest of the system. A large loss of refrigeration through supports and vents ordinarily reduces the attractiveness of costly insulation having the lowest conductance.

Safety

Precautions are needed for the safe handling and storage of cryogens because (1) air can contaminate the cryogen, creating a potential explosive, either directly as when air mixes with H_2 or CH_4 or indirectly by transforming an inert cryogen like LN_2 into an oxidant (a potential hazard for combustible insulation), and (2) moisture and air can freeze on cold surfaces, clogging vents and preventing normal operation of valves.

Vent systems should be sized for sufficient exhaust velocities to prevent back-diffusion of air into the cryogen space. Storage at slightly elevated pressure is preferable to prevent in-leakage of contaminants. Condensation can also be a problem on poorly insulated lines carrying low-boiling cryogens; frost is not a hazard but the oxygen-enriched condensed air is hazardous in the presence of combustibles. The insulation of liquid vent lines is a necessary precaution. Where this is not possible, appropriately placed guttering can prevent the contact of any condensed air with combustible objects.

Any space, either containing a cryogen or being refrigerated by a cryogen, should be protected with proper **safety-relief mechanisms,** *i.e.*, relief valves or rupture disks. Such space includes less obvious ones such as the insulating vacuum space surrounding a cryogenic fluid or a section of line which can trap liquid between two valves. A heat leak to trapped liquid confined without a vent for escape of vapor may develop pressures sufficient to burst the containing vessel. Gas pressures necessary to maintain liquid density at ambient temperature are for helium, 18,000 psi; for hydrogen, 28,000 psi; and for nitrogen, 43,000 psi.

Selection of materials requires consideration of changes in physical properties with temperature. A number of otherwise suitable materials of construction become brittle at low temperature (Fig. 8). Materials must perform satisfactorily over the complete range from cryogenic to room temperature, with hydrogen-embrittlement particularly significant. While hydrogen-embrittlement is not believed to be a problem at liquid-hydrogen temperatures, it has been shown to occur at room temperature. The 300-series stainless steels and BeCu, among other alloys, do not hydrogen-embrittle.

In calculating allowable stresses, room temperature yield and tensile strengths should be used because (1) pressure testing of containers at ambient temperature is frequently necessary, and (2) in the case of large vessels, large unknown temperature gradients can exist above the liquid level both in the ullage space and in the walls of the vessel. The 300-series stainless steels are normally austenitic (f.c.c.). However, in some 300-series stainless steels austenite is partially transformed by cold-working and possibly by temperature cycling to martensite. As martensite is brittle at low T's, the ductility of these steels is reduced by this kind of treatment. For this reason, it is recommended as an added safety factor that room temperature strengths of the 300-series stainless steels be used for the design of structural members.

Careful **stress analysis** is essential and must include stresses due to (1) thermal contraction of equipment, and (2) radial, axial, and circumferential temperature gradients caused by non-uniform cooling rates. The latter are frequently encountered in the cool-down of cryogenic transfer lines (see Sec. 5).

Cryogenic equipment should be **purged** before being placed in service to remove unwanted condensables and gases forming explosive mixtures. Commonly used methods are (1) evacuating and back-filling with purge gas and (2) flowing of purge gas through the system.

The cryogen can be a direct **hazard to personnel.** Cryogen "burns" can result from direct contact with either the cryogen or uninsulated equipment containing the cryogen. The large evolution of gases associated with cryogenic spills can result in asphyxiation. Asphyxiation is a hazard in entering a warmed cryogenic vessel. Further safety details are found in the references.

OPTICS

BY

Heard K. Baumeister

REFERENCES: AIP Handbook, McGraw-Hill. Conrady, "Applied Optics and Optical Design," Dover. Jenkins and White, "Fundamentals of Optics," McGraw-Hill.

Index of Refraction. **Visible light** is a small band in the electromagnetic spectrum between 4,000 and 7,000 Å wavelengths with about 5,600 Å (green-yellow) seeming the brightest to the average person. (Å, an angstrom, $= 10^{-10}$ meters.) The **velocity** of light in a vacuum c is taken as 2.998×10^8 m/sec (9.836×10^8 fps; 186,300 mi/sec). The velocity is lower in all substances, and the ratio of the velocity of light in a vacuum c to that in a substance c' is defined as the **index of refraction,** $n = c/c'$. The index of refraction in air at standard conditions is 1.0003; it is often assumed to be unity, and the reference (air or vacuum) must be determined before using published values if the slight differences are significant in the application. Most substances, gases, liquids, and solids, have indexes between 1 and 2 (see AIP Handbook).

Dispersion. The index of refraction of substances (including optical glass) is not constant but varies with the color of the light. The dispersion v of glass is normally

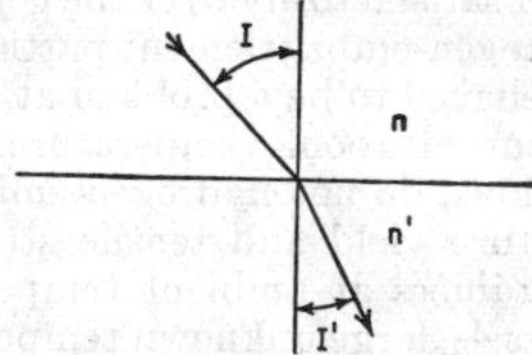

FIG. 1. Refraction at a plane surface.

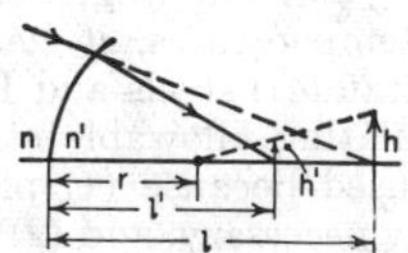

FIG. 2. Refraction at a spherical surface; all parameters shown in their positive sense.

taken as $v = (n_D - 1)/(n_F - n_C)$, where n_C, n_D, and n_F are the indexes of refraction for the three spectral lines 6,563 Å, 5,893 Å, and 4,861 Å, respectively, obtained from hydrogen (n_C and n_F) and sodium (n_D) discharge tube light sources. Most optical glasses have dispersions between 35 and 65. For special purposes, the dispersion may be determined for other colors (see AIP Handbook for further data).

Refraction. A ray of light undergoes refraction at a surface separating two regions of different indexes of refraction (see Conrady). For rays intersecting a plane surface interface, **Snell's law** holds (Fig. 1) that $n \sin I = n' \sin I'$.

For rays that are directed toward a point on the axis of a spherical interface (Fig. 2) and that are close to the axis (paraxial rays), the location of the intersection of the rays with the axis after refraction may be found from $n'/l' = (n' - n)/r + n/l$.

For two spherical surfaces close together (thin lens in air) the relationship is $1/l_2' - 1/l_1 = (n - 1)(1/r_1 - 1/r_2) = 1/f$. The **magnifications** m' for such systems are respectively $m' = h'/h = nl'/n'l$ and $m' = h'/h = l_2'/l$.

The **focal length** f of a thin lens is the distance from the image to the lens when the object is infinitely far away. The focal length for a single surface, a spherical mirror, and a thick lens is more difficult to define and interpret (see Jenkins and White), but it is analogous to that for a thin lens and is indicative of the lens power and image size.

The focal lengths of commercial lenses for use in air vary between 3 mm for microscope objectives to 100 ft for large observatory telescope objectives.

Aperture. The larger the **aperture** of an optical element, the brighter will be the image and the better the resolving power, if the rest of the system (including the eye) is capable of accommodating all the light. The aperture of telescope objectives and camera-projection lenses is usually described by the *f* **number,** *i.e.*, the ratio of the focal length to the clear diameter. Commercially available lenses usually fall between $f/1.2$ and $f/15$. The aperture of microscope objectives is usually described by the **numerical aperture** NA; that is, $n \sin U$, where n is the index of refraction of the object space and U is the half angle of the vertex of the cone of light from the object that passes through the lens. Commercially available lenses usually fall between NA/1.40 and NA/0.08.

Photometry

The **international candle** is often taken as a standard source. Other sources may be brighter because they are more intense (more candle power per unit of source area) or larger (more source area) than the standard candle. If a source emits light in all directions as intense as that emitted from the international candle in the preferred direction, it would emit 4π **lumens.** An object placed 1 ft from a 4π lumen source (or 1 ft from a standard candle in the preferred direction) would be bathed in light of **1 ft candle** intensity. This intensity at the surface is directly proportional to the intensity of the source and inversely proportional to the square of the distance between the source and surface. In this case, the surface should be normal to the direction of the light, and the size of the source should be small compared with the separation (see also pp. 12–154 *et seq.*).

Photographic film speeds are usually given as an ASA (American Standards Association) exposure index. Black-and-white films are available commercially in the ASA range from 25 to 1,000. Color films fall in the slower end of this range. A rule of thumb for exposing films on a bright, sunny day is to set the aperture of the camera at $f/16$ and the shutter speed at 1/ASA exposure index sec.

SURVEYING

BY

A. Haertlein

REFERENCES: Johnson-Smith, "Theory and Practice of Surveying," Wiley. Breed and Hosmer, "Principles and Practice of Surveying," Wiley. Tracy, "Surveying," Wiley. Raymond, "Plane Surveying," American Book. Davis and Foote, "Surveying," McGraw-Hill. Rubey, Lommel, and Todd, "Engineering Survey," Macmillan.

LINEAR MEASUREMENTS

Tapes. The linear measuring instrument most used is the **steel-ribbon tape.** For **surveying,** the **tape** is 100 or more ft long, graduated to feet, with 1 ft at the end graduated to tenths and sometimes hundredths. The **builder's tape** is graduated to feet, inches, and eights. **Linen tapes,** even when wire strands are woven in them, are useless for work of precision, but serve for laying out road and railroad earthwork and the like. They are not sufficiently precise for laying out foundations or placing machinery.

Variations in Tape Measurements Due to Temperature, Tension, and Sag. Steel tapes are usually of **standard length** at 68 F with a 10 lb pull for tapes 100 ft or less and 20 lb for tapes longer than 100 ft and in all cases supported throughout their length. They change 0.00000645 of their length per deg F change in temperature. A 100 ft tape standard at 68 F will be short 0.044 ft at 0 F and long 0.021 ft at 100 F.

A steel tape is usually standard for the pull necessary to straighten it when supported throughout its length. Additional pull stretches it at about the rate $1/28{,}000{,}000S$ of its length per pound of pull, S being its cross-sectional area in square inches. For the common **sectional area** of 0.002 sq in., a pull of 10 lb will produce an elongation of 0.02 ft in 100 ft. The sectional area of a tape may be determined by dividing the weight of the tape in pounds by its length in inches and the quotient by 0.284.

When a tape is unsupported throughout its length, the measured distance is less than that indicated by about $C_s = l(wl/P)^2/24$, in which l is the nominal length of unsupported tape; w the weight of the tape, lb per unit of length; and P the pull, lb. A 100 ft tape weighing 0.624 lb pulled with 10 lb and unsupported throughout its length would in effect be shortened by 0.016 ft. Calling the correction for temperature C_t, for pull C_p, and for **sag** C_s, the distance between two points would be given by the measured length $\pm C_t + C_p - C_s$. The **temperature correction** is **positive or negative** according as the temperature is *higher* or *lower* than standard. If a line of given length is to be measured from a given point, all the signs of the corrections are reversed (see also theory and tables for catenary curves, pp. 2–56 to 2–59).

To Measure a Horizontal Line on Sloping Ground. Most engineering linear measurements are horizontal or vertical. All land measurements mentioned in descriptions are horizontal. Vertical measurements may be made with tape or leveling instrument. When horizontal measurements are to be made on sloping ground, one of the two following methods is used: (1) The low end of the tape is raised to make the tape horizontal, the proper point on the tape or ground being transferred to the ground or tape by a plumb line held by the tapeman. When the slope is so steep that a full tape cannot be used, part of it is used—called "breaking the tape"—and it is better to pull the tape clear out, raising the several necessary sections consecutively, rather than to use one particular part of the tape several times. (2) The measurement is made along the slope, the angle of which or its rise in a tape length is determined, and the slope measurement reduced to the horizontal. In Fig. 1, the horizontal distance $B = S - R^2/2S$, approx, with an error of about 0.0013 of 1 percent for a 10 percent slope and less for flatter slopes.

To Measure or Lay Out an Angle with a Tape. In Fig. 2, from the apex of the angle A, measure equal distance d along its sides and the distance a between the ends of these measurements. Then $\sin \frac{1}{2}A = a/2d$. For small angles A (in degrees) $= 57.3\ a/d$, approx, or, if d is 100 units, A (in degrees) $= 0.573a$ (approx) $= 4a/7$ (approx). Two lines separating at the rate of n deg separate in distance at the approximate rate of $7n/4$ units per hundred.

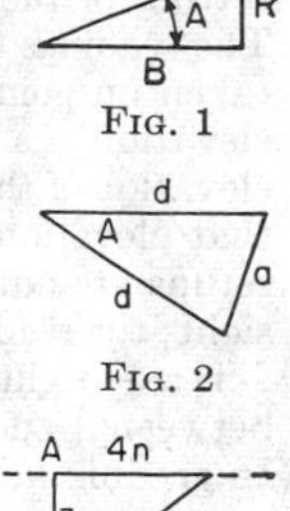

Fig. 1

Fig. 2

Fig. 3

To lay out an angle, reverse the process. From the apex, measure 100 units along one side; from the point obtained, describe an arc with a radius of $200 \sin \frac{1}{2}A$ or (approx) $7A/4$ units long; and from the apex with a radius of 100 units, describe an arc intersecting the first.

To Lay Out a Right Angle. In Fig. 3, from the point A where the angle is to be, measure along one side a distance of $4n$ units; from the point thus obtained, swing an arc with radius of $5n$ units; and from A, swing an arc with a radius of $3n$ units to intersect the first arc at B; the line joining A and B is perpendicular to the $4n$ line.

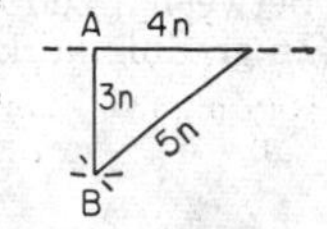

LEVELING

The **level,** shown in Fig. 4, consists of a telescope EO resting in supports YY attached to a bar B and carrying a level bubble L. The bar B is attached to a spindle D which rests in a socket carrying the ball J of a ball-and-socket joint. The bearing of the spindle carries the upper leveling plate P and the socket of the ball joint is part of the lower leveling plate P' which screws on to the tripod head T. By the leveling screws S working through plate P and resting on plate P', the upper part of the instrument may be tipped with respect to P'. In the telescope, whose objective is at O and eyepiece at E, there is a ring R carrying two fine wires at right angles. This may be adjusted so that the intersection of the wires is in the optical axis of the telescope, and one wire may be made vertical when the other will be horizontal. Figure 4 shows a **Y level,** the supports YY being in the form of Y's (wyes) in which the telescope rests and from which it may be easily removed by opening clips on the Y's. In the Y level the telescope is usually an erecting one; *i.e.,* it shows objects as they are. In another form of level, the supports are part of the telescope tube or are fastened rigidly to it and are held to the bar by screws. This is called a **dumpy level** and its (short) telescope (of large aperture) is usually inverting; *i.e.,* it shows objects upside down and right side left. When the axis of the bubble tube and the line of sight of the telescope are parallel, the line of sight will be horizontal when the bubble is brought to the center of its tube. The level is **used with** some form of **graduated rod** read by a movable target or slide and vernier or self-reading, *i.e.,* read directly by the level man.

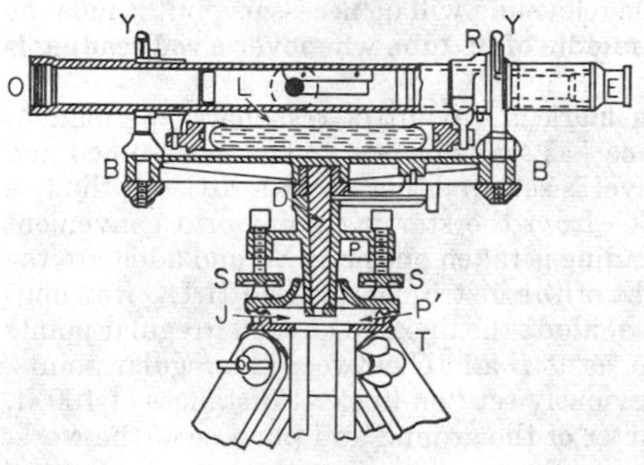

Fig. 4. Y level.

To set up the level, the legs are planted firmly, with the lower leveling plate as nearly horizontal as practicable. The telescope and frame are swung over one diagonally opposite pair of leveling screws by which the bubble is brought to the middle of the tube. The frame is then brought over the other pair of screws and leveled; back to the first pair; to the second pair, etc., until the bubble remains in the middle of its tube for any position of the telescope. The screw which clamps the spindle motion should not be used in ordinary leveling operations. The eyepiece should be focused so that the wires are sharp against a blank ground as the sky or side of a light-colored building. It will not need changing so long as the same eye uses it. If the distance varies, the objective is focused for each object looked at.

To determine the difference in level between two points, set the level nearly midway between the points, hold a rod on one, look through the level and see where the line of sight, as defined by the eye and horizontal cross wire, cuts the rod, called **rod reading.** Move the rod to the second point and read. The difference of the readings is the difference in level of the two points. If it is impossible to see both points from a single setting of the level, one or more intermediate points, called **turning points,** are used. The readings taken on points of known or assumed elevation are called **plus sights,** those taken on points whose elevations are to be determined are called **minus sights.** The elevation of a point plus the rod reading on it gives the elevation of the line of sight; the elevation of the line of sight minus the rod reading on a point of unknown elevation gives that elevation. In Fig. 5, I_1 and I_2 are intermediate points between A and B. The setups are numbered. Assuming A to be of known elevation, the reading on A is a + sight; the reading on I_1 from 1 is a − sight; the reading on I_1 from 2 is a + sight and on I_2 is a − sight. The algebraic sum of the plus and minus sights is the difference of level between A and B. Target rods may usually be read by vernier to thousandths of a foot. In grading work the nearest tenth of a foot is good; in lining shafting the finest possible

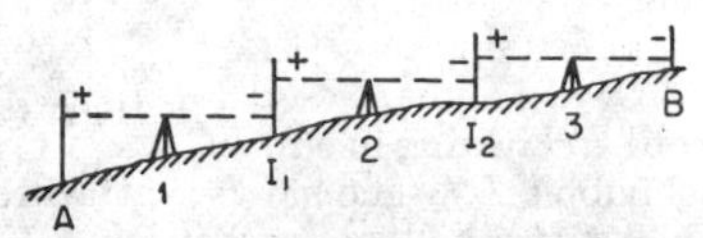

Fig. 5

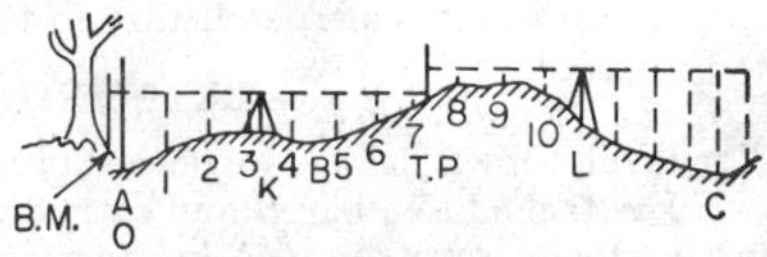

Fig. 6

reading is none too good. It is desirable that the sum of the distances to the plus sights shall approximately equal the sum of the distances to the minus sights to ensure compensation of errors of adjustment. On a side hill this may be accomplished by "zigzagging." If, when the direction of pointing is changed, the bubble leaves the middle of its tube, the instrument should be releveled with the telescope in the direction of sight. If adjustments have been properly made little releveling will be necessary, but it must be remembered that **the bubble must be in the middle of its tube whenever a rod reading is taken.**

To Make a Profile of a Line. A **bench mark** is a point of reasonably permanent character whose elevation above some surface—as sea level—is known or assumed and used as a reference point for levels. The level is set up either on or a little off the line some distance—not more than about 300 ft—from the starting point or a convenient bench mark (B.M.), as at K in Fig. 6. A reading is taken on the B.M. and added to the known or assumed elevation to get the height of the instrument, called H.I. Readings are then taken at regular intervals (or **stations**) along the line and at such irregular points as may be necessary to show change of slope, as at B and C between the regular points. The regular points are marked by stakes previously set "on line" at distances of 100 ft, 50 ft, or other distance suitable to the character of the ground and purpose of the work.

Left-hand page

This space for a heading, telling what the work is, who does it, and the date on which it is done.

Sta.	+ S	H.I.	− S	Elev.
B.M.	6.42	506.42	....	500.0
A = 0			10.4	496.0
1			8.2	98.2
2			6.1	500.3
+30			5.5	0.9
3			6.1	0.3
4			7.9	498.5
B = + 40			8.4	98.0
5			7.5	98.9
6			5.1	501.3
7			3.2	3.2
+ 10 T.P.	4.27	509.13	1.56	504.86
8			2.2	506.9

Right-hand page

This page is for remarks describing B.M.s and T.P.s or other important particulars.

When the work has proceeded as far as possible—not more than about 300 ft from the instrument for good work—a **turning point** (T.P.) is taken at a regular point or other convenient place, the instrument moved ahead and the operation continued. The first reading on the B.M. and the first reading on a T.P. after a new setup are plus sights (+ S); readings to points along the line and the first reading on a T.P. to be established are minus sights (− S).

The **notes** are taken in the following form. The elevation of a given point, both sights taken on it, and the H.I. determined from it all appear on a line with its station (Sta.) designation. In plotting the **profile,** the vertical scale is usually exaggerated from 10 to 20 times.

Adjustment of the Y level. 1. PLUMBING THE WIRE. Set up the level, and bring the vertical wire to cover a suspended plumb line or the vertical corner of a building by rotating the wire ring if necessary after loosening its screws.

2. LINE OF SIGHT. Loosen the Y clips and by means of the leveling screws and the clamp and slow motion of the spindle bring the intersection of the wires to cover a minute distant point; carefully turn the telescope upside down in the Y's keeping the eye at the glass; if the intersection remains on the point, the line of sight is in adjustment; if not, bring the intersection halfway back to the point by the screws carrying the wire ring, and repeat till the distant point is covered by the intersection of the wires in either position of the telescope.

3. THE BUBBLE TUBE. Level the bubble over two sets of screws and carefully over one set; lift the telescope from the Y's, turn it end for end and replace in the Y's; if the bubble returns to the center of the tube, its axis is parallel to the lower side of the telescope barrel and to its axis if the bearing rings are of equal diameter. For practically all work they are nearly enough so. If the bubble moves from the center of its tube, bring it halfway back by the adjusting nuts at the ends of the bubble tube, relevel, and repeat until the bubble remains in the center of its tube for both positions of the telescope.

4. THE Y'S. With the instrument leveled and more carefully over one set of screws, turn end for end on the vertical spindle and note whether the bubble remains in the middle of its tube; if not, adjust by the capstan nuts on the Y's at one end of the bar, bringing the bubble halfway back to the middle; relevel and repeat till the bubble remains in the middle through a complete revolution on the spindle. This last adjustment of the Y's is not essential to correct leveling, but is convenient in that when once set up the level requires no releveling for a change in the direction of pointing.

Adjustment of the Dumpy Level. The dumpy level is adjusted by adjusting the bubble and afterward the line of sight to it.

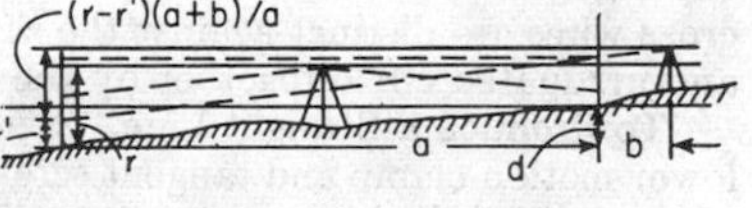

FIG. 7

1. THE BUBBLE TUBE. Set up and, having the instrument level over one set of screws, swing through 180 deg on the vertical axis; if the bubble moves from the center, bring it halfway back by the adjusting screws, relevel and repeat the test and adjustment until complete.

2. LINE OF SIGHT. Set the instrument midway between two stakes from 200 to 400 ft apart, as in Fig. 7. With the bubble in the center of the tube, read a rod on each stake. The difference in readings is the difference in level d of the two stakes. Remove the level, and set it up near one of the stakes and in line with both. If set between the two stakes and close to the near stake so that the eye end will just clear a rod held on the stake, look through the object end at the rod and with a pencil point get the reading in the middle of the small spot of light that will be seen; remove the rod to the distant stake, set a target to read the reading on the near rod + allowance for earth's curvature $\pm d$ according as the far stake is the lower or higher; turn the telescope line of sight toward the distant rod and adjust the horizontal wire till it reads on the target when the bubble is centered. Earth's curvature is approximately 0.001 ft for 200 ft distance and varies with the square of the distance. If the setup is a distance b outside the stakes which are a ft apart, read on the near stake, add earth's curvature e, and add or subtract d for the trial reading r on the distant rod; if the reading is not r but r', move the target

from r' by a distance $(r - r')\ (a \pm b)/a$, up if the result is plus, down if minus; by the wire adjusting screws bring the wire to read on the target, the bubble being kept in the middle of its tube. It is convenient to make $b = a/10$, so that $(a + b)/a = 11/10$. This is commonly called the "peg" method.

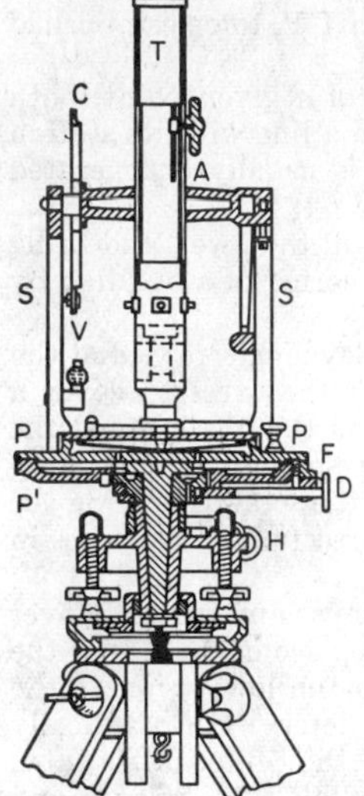

FIG. 8. Surveyor's transit.

TRANSIT WORK

Transit. The essential parts of a surveyor's transit are shown in Fig. 8. The telescope T swings on axis A in standards S resting on plate P carrying verniers seen through openings in its upper side which permit readings on a graduated circle on plate P' which may be turned on a spindle in a socket in the leveling head and clamped in position by the clamp H. The clamp D clamps the plates P and P' together, but it is still possible to move one on the other by the slow-motion or tangent screw F. A similar slow-motion screw attached to the clamp H serves to move the whole upper part of the instrument a little in a horizontal plane when the two plates are clamped together. The leveling head is like that of the level, but to the bottom of the spindle a hook is attached, from which a plumb line may be suspended for centering the transit over a point. For doing leveling and measuring vertical angles, there is a level under the telescope and a vertical circle C attached to the horizontal axis of the telescope and read by a vernier V. There is a clamp and slow-motion screw for the telescope axis of revolution. The telescope, though of shorter focal length, is like that of the level.

To set up the transit over a point, plant the legs firmly in the ground with the plumb swinging as nearly as possible over the point. At the same time, the lower plate on the leveling head should be nearly level, as judged by eye. Loosen the leveling screws of the leveling head and shift the upper part on the lower plate till the bob swings over the required point. Bring the screws again to bearing—never tight,—swing the upper part of the instrument so that the plate bubbles are, respectively, parallel to the two diagonally opposite sets of leveling screws, and by the screws bring the bubbles to the center by leveling first one and then the other in turn until both are level. Focus the eyepiece of the telescope so that the cross wires are distinct against the sky or a light ground. Set the zeros of the verniers and graduated circle together by the clamp and slow-motion screws of the plates.

To Produce a Straight Line. Set up the transit over one end of the line; with the lower motion clamp and tangent screw bring the telescopic line of sight to the other end of the line marked by a flag, a pencil, a pin, or other object; transit the telescope, *i.e.*, plunge it by revolving on its horizontal axis, and set a point (drive a stake and "center" it with a tack or otherwise) a desired distance ahead in line with the telescopic line of sight; loosen the lower motion clamp and turn the instrument in azimuth until the line of sight may be again pointed to the other end of the line; again transit and set a point beside the first point set. If the instrument is in adjustment, the two points will coincide; if not, the point marking the projection of the line lies midway between the two established points.

To Measure a Horizontal Angle. Set up the transit over the apex of the angle; with the lower motion bring the line of sight to a distant point in one side of the angle; unclamp the upper motion and bring the line of sight to a distant point in the second side of the angle, clamp and set exactly with the tangent screw; read the circle by the vernier for the angle turned.

To Measure a Vertical Angle. Set up the transit over a point marking the apex of the angle A (see Fig. 9); by the lower motion and the motion of the telescope on its horizontal axis, bring the intersection of the vertical and horizontal wires of the telescope in line with a point as much above the point defining the lower side of the angle as the telescope is above the apex; read the vertical circle; turn the telescope to a point which is the height of the instrument above the point marking the upper side of the angle and read the vertical circle. How to combine the readings to find the angle will be obvious.

To Run a Traverse. A traverse is a broken line marking the line of a road, bank of a stream, fence, ridge, or valley, or it may be the boundary of a piece of land. The bearing or azimuth and length of each portion of the line are determined, and this constitutes "running the traverse."

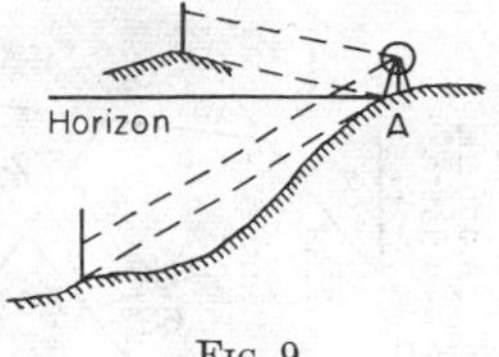

FIG. 9

The **bearing** of a line is the angle it makes east or west of a north and south line either true, magnetic, or assumed for the purpose of the survey. The bearing is read north or south so many degrees east or west, and never east or west so many degrees north or south. Thus, a line running only 1 deg north of east would have a bearing N 89° E, and one running 1 deg south of east would have a bearing S 89° E, etc.

To determine the bearing, set up over one end of the line, loosen the needle clamp, turn the telescope with its object end over the *fleur-de-lis* or north side of the compass box toward the farther end of the line, and read the needle, using the two letters between which its north end lies. It should be noticed that the compass box letters E and W are reversed to make the reading agree with the telescope pointing.

The **azimuth** of a line is the angle the line makes with a north and south line, true, magnetic, or assumed, and differs from bearing in being measured always in one direction through 360 deg, while bearing is measured in each of four directions through 90 deg. Azimuth is measured to the right or clockwise. Astronomers use the south for zero azimuth. Surveyors, with some exceptions, use the north. Lines whose bearings are N 88° E, S 38° E, S 70° W, and N 60° W have azimuths of 88 deg, 142 deg, 250 deg, and 300 deg, respectively.

To determine the azimuth of a line, set up over one end, set the horizontal circle to read the azimuth of a known line through the point of setup (as the meridian or the preceding line of a traverse), and by the lower motion turn the line of sight in the direction of the known line; loosen the upper motion and set the line of sight in the direction of the required azimuth and read the circle. Always read the same vernier and the same row of figures—those inclined to the left—since the vernier reads with these when the telescope is turned clockwise. When the preceding line of the traverse is used for orienting the transit, the "back azimuth" should be set on the circle. The **back azimuth** is the azimuth read in a direction opposite to that in which the survey proceeds, and is the forward azimuth plus 180 deg. If this gives more than 360 deg, subtract 360 deg. The distance may be measured with the tape or with the stadia, as explained on p. 18–57.

In work with the transit, bearings are not usually read by the needle except for checking. Instead, the deflection angles from one course produced to the next are measured; one course—as the initial course—is taken as a meridian, and the bearings of the other courses with respect to the assumed meridian are calculated. The true or magnetic bearing of the first course may be determined, from which the bearings of all courses will be calculated from the true or magnetic meridian. To determine the **magnetic bearing** of the first course and to establish a meridian of reference, set up the transit over the initial point, let the needle swing free; with the zeros together turn the instrument on its vertical axis by the lower motion till the needle reads north, and set a point some distance away in the line of sight. The line ranged will be the magnetic meridian. By the upper motion set the telescope in the line of the initial course; the vernier will read the angle with the meridian, from which the bearing is calculated.

In Fig. 10, the bearing of *a* is N 40° E, of *b* is N 88° 30′ E, of *c* is S 49° 20′ E = 180° − (40° + 48° 30′ + 42° 10′), of *d* is S 36° 40′ W = 86° − 49° 20′, or 40° + 48° 30′ +42° 10′ + 86° − 180°, of *e* is N 81° 20′ W = 180° − (36° 40′ + 62°). A meridian is established because the needle cannot be depended on to give exactly the same line twice. The needle pointing varies as much as 10 min or more during the day.

To Adjust a Transit. The adjustment of the transit consists in: (1) making the plate bubbles parallel to the plates, *i.e.*, perpendicular to the vertical axis; (2) making the line of sight perpendicular to the horizontal axis of revolution; (3) adjusting horizontal axis so that the line of sight may revolve in a vertical plane; (4) making the telescope bubble parallel to the line of sight; and (5) making the vernier of the vertical circle read zero when the line of sight is horizontal or determining the index error.

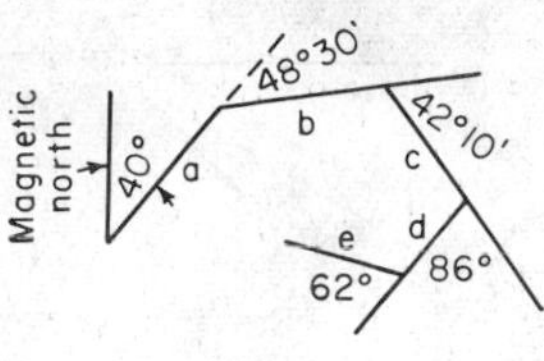

FIG. 10

1. THE PLATE BUBBLES. Set up the transit; when both plate bubbles are in the centers of their tubes turn the instrument on its vertical axis 180 deg, thus reversing the bubbles. If the bubbles remain in the centers of their tubes they are in adjustment; if not, raise or lower one end of one bubble tube with a small adjusting pin till the bubble seems to move halfway back to the center; do the same with the other tube, relevel with leveling screws, turn 180 deg to test correctness of work, and repeat till perfect.

2. LINE OF SIGHT. Set up and fix the vertical wire on a suspended plumb line or corner of a vertical building. If the wire does not coincide with the vertical line, loosen all capstan screws carrying the wire ring, rotate the ring in the barrel by the screws until the wire is vertical, and then tighten the screws. By the lower motion and the vertical swing of the telescope fix the line of sight, as defined by the vertical wire, on a distant point about on a level with the instrument or the ground under it (do not clamp the horizontal axis); transit the telescope, *i.e.*, plunge it on its horizontal axis, and, finding a minute point in the line of sight, note it carefully; turn in azimuth, *i.e.*, on the vertical axis, until the line of sight covers the first point sighted; transit and note whether line of sight covers the second point; if not, adjust the wires, moving the ring right or left as the case may be by the capstan-headed screws that carry it till the vertical wire seems to pass over ¼ the distance between the two distant points; again set on the first point, transit and note a point in line—it will be neither of the points previously noted, but if the work has been completed at the first trial, the new point will lie midway between the two previously noted points—reverse in azimuth to the first point, transit, adjust if necessary, and repeat till the adjustment is complete. Stakes centered with pins 200 or more ft either side of the transit may be used for points.

3. THE HORIZONTAL AXIS. With the transit set up near a tall building, turn the line of sight on a plumb corner near the top; plunge the telescope and note if the line of sight follows down the edge of the building; if not, raise or lower one end of the horizontal axis—one end is adjustable—until the line of sight will revolve in a vertical plane. If no vertical line is available, set the line of sight on some high point, plunge and set a point on the ground; reverse in azimuth, transit, and set again on the high point and plunge; if the line of sight cuts the point set on the ground the horizontal axis is in adjustment; if not, adjust the axis until the line of sight cuts the same point below when plunged from the high point both direct and reversed.

4. LEVEL UNDER TELESCOPE. This is adjusted by the "peg" method described for the dumpy level (see p. 18–53), except that—the plate bubbles being centered—the wires are brought to the correct target reading by tipping the telescope, and the bubble is adjusted to bring it to the center, the wires being undisturbed.

5. VERTICAL CIRCLE. If the bubble tube is parallel to the line of sight and the latter is horizontal, the bubble will be in the center of its tube and the vertical circle should read zero. If it does not, the vernier may be moved slightly after loosening the screws that hold it. If not convenient, the reading may be noted and used as an index error. If the reading indicates a small angle of elevation, all angles of elevation will be read too large; *i.e.*, the index error is to be subtracted; while depression angles will be read too small—the index error is to be added.

6. LINE OF SIGHT FOR LEVELING. For good leveling, the horizontal wire should be in the center of the telescope tube. If the eyepiece is non-adjustable, it will generally be sufficient to adjust the wire so that it appears to be in the field of view. This is not true of all instruments, and the only way to make the adjustment with certainty is to remove the telescope with its horizontal axis, place it in a pair of Y's made, for instance, by cutting notches in the ends of a wooden box of suitable size, and adjust the wires as in the Y level. (See p. 18–53.)

To Measure Distances with the Stadia. In the transit telescope are two extra horizontal wires so spaced (when fixed by the maker) that they are 1/100 of the focal length of the objective apart. When looking through the telescope at a rod held in a vertical position, 100 times the rod length S intercepted between the two extra horizontal wires plus an instrumental constant (C) is the distance (D) from the center of the instrument to the rod if the line of sight is horizontal, or $D = 100\,S + C$ (see Fig. 11). If the line of sight is inclined by a vertical angle A, as in Fig. 12, then if S is the space intercepted on the rod and C is the instrumental constant, the distance is given by the formula $D = 100\,S\cos^2 A + C\cos A$. For angles less than 5 or 6 deg, the distance is given with sufficient exactness by $D = 100\,S$. Although theory would indicate that distances may be thus determined to within 0.2 ft, yet in practice it is not well to rely on a precision greater than the nearest foot for distances of 500 ft or less.

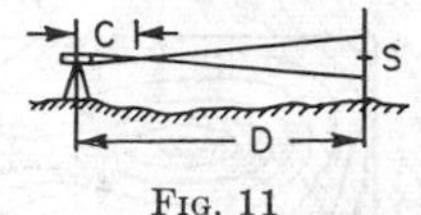

FIG. 11

The instrumental constant is usually stated on a poster in the transit box. When not so given, it may be determined by measuring several distances on level ground, reading the distances with the stadia, as $D_1 = 100\,S_1$, $D_2 = 100\,S_2$, etc., subtracting the readings from the measurements and averaging the remainders. For most transits, the so-called instrumental constant is not constant, but has an extreme variation of perhaps 0.1 ft. With different instruments its average value varies from about 0.75 to 1.25 ft. It is made up of the focal length of the objective and the distance from the objective to the horizontal axis.

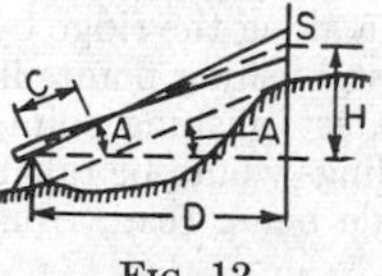

FIG. 12

For good work, the wire interval, *i.e.*, the coefficient of the rod space, should be determined daily, as it may change slightly with atmospheric changes and may not always be 100. This may be done, if C is known, by measuring $(100 + C)$ ft, $(200 + C)$ ft, etc., from the instrument, noting the rod intercepts. When C is not known, measure two distances on level ground and read the intercepts S and S_1; then, if K be the coefficient of S, C the instrumental constant, and D and D_1 the two distances, $K = (D - D_1)/(S - S_1)$, and $C = D - KS$ or $D_1 - KS_1$. Several sets of readings should be taken and average results used.

The stadia wires are sometimes adjustable as to the space between them. When so, they are not in the same plane with the line and level cross wires, and hence are not seen with the same focusing of the eyepiece. Adjustable stadia wires should be tested daily and so set that 100 shall be the coefficient of the rod intercept. This may be done by laying off $(100 + C)$ ft from the center of the instrument and adjusting the wire to cover 1 ft on a rod held at the further end of the line.

To Measure Differences of Level with Transit and Stadia. Measure the angle of elevation from the point of setup to the distant point required, according to the method already described, and read the rod intercept on a rod held *vertical* at the distant point. The rod intercept being S, its coefficient K, the instrumental constant C, angle of elevation or depression A, and difference of level H,

$$H = KS\cos A\sin A + C\sin A$$

If the rod be held normal to the line of sight,

$$H = (KS + C)\sin A$$

Tables of horizontal distances and differences of level for various vertical angles and a 100 unit rod are found in surveying textbooks.

Contour Maps. A contour map is one on which the configuration of the surface is shown by lines of equal elevation called **contour lines.** In Fig. 13, contour lines varying by 10 ft in elevation are shown. H, H are hill peaks, R, R ravines, S, S saddles or low places in the ridge $HSHSH$. The horizontal distance between adjacent contours shows the distance for a fall or rise of the contour interval—10 ft in the figure. A profile of any line as AB can be made from the contour map as shown in the lower part of the figure. Conversely, a contour map may be made from a series of profiles, properly chosen. Thus, a profile line run along the ridge $HSHSH$ and radiating profile lines from the peaks down the hills and from the saddles down the ravines would give data for projecting points of equal elevation which could be connected for contour lines. This is the best method for making contour maps of very limited areas, such as city squares or very small parks. If the ground is not too much broken, the small tract is divided into squares and levels are taken at each square corner, and between two corners on some lines if necessary to get correct profiles.

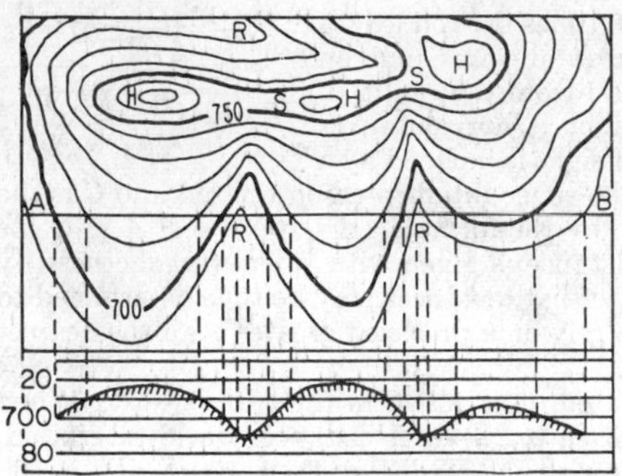

Fig. 13. Contour map.

Contours with the Transit and Stadia. When a large area of several hundred or more acres is to be contoured, or a long belt within which a railroad line is to lie, the best method is the transit and stadia method. Referring to Fig. 13, a traverse line would be run along the ridge by transit and stadia, establishing points in the saddles and on the peaks; from these, radial lines would be run, establishing points on the slopes of the hills; from each of these points a number of readings would be taken to slope-governing points, the azimuth, distance, and vertical angle being read, from which each point could be located in place and elevation.

SPECIAL PROBLEMS IN SURVEYING AND MENSURATION

Volume of Earth in Foundation and Area Grading. The volume of earth removed from a foundation pit or in grading an area may be computed in several ways, of which two follow.

1. The area (Fig. 14) is divided into squares or rectangles, levels are taken at each corner before and after grading, and the volumes are computed as a series of prisms. If A be the area (in square feet) of one of the squares or rectangles—all being equal—and h_1, h_2, h_3, h_4 be corner heights (in feet) equal to the differences of level before and after grading, the subscripts referring to the number of prisms of which h is a corner, then the volume in cubic yards is

$$Q = A(\Sigma h_1 + 2\Sigma h_2 + 3\Sigma h_3 + 4\Sigma h_4)/(4 \times 27)$$

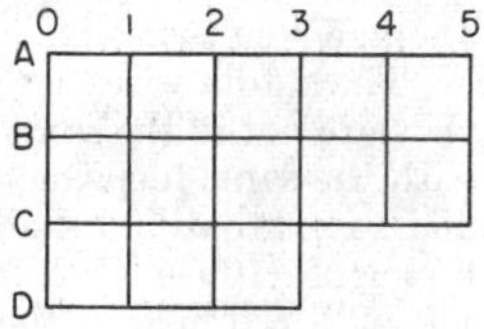

Fig. 14

In Fig. 14 the h's at A_0, D_0, D_3, C_5, and A_5 would be h_1's; those at B_0, C_0, D_1, D_2, C_4, B_5, A_4, A_3, A_2, and A_1 would be h_2's; that at C_3 an h_3; and the rest h_4's. The rectangles or squares should be of such size that their tops and bottoms are practically planes.

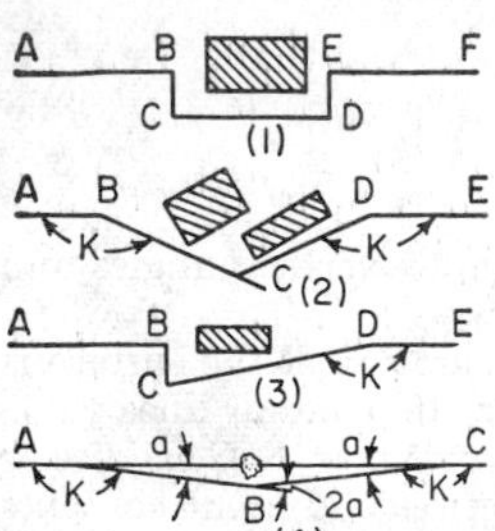

2. A large-scale profile of each line one way across the area is carefully made, as the A, B, C, and D lines of Fig. 14, the final grade line is drawn on it, and the areas in excavation and embankment are separately measured with a planimeter or by estimation from the drawing. The excavation area of profile A is averaged with that of profile B, and the result multiplied by the distance AB and divided by 27 to reduce to cubic yards. Similarly, the material between B and C is found.

Fig. 15

To Pass an Obstacle. Four cases are shown in Fig. 15. If the obstacle be large, as a building, (1) turn right angles at B, C, D, and E, making $BC = DE$ when $CD = BE$. All distances should be long enough to ensure sufficiently accurate sighting. (2) At B turn the angle K and measure BC to a convenient point. At C turn left $= 360$ deg $- 2K$; measure $CD = BC$. At D turn K for line DE. $BD = 2BC \cos (180 \text{ deg} - K)$. (3) At B lay off a right angle and measure BC. At C measure any angle to clear object and measure $CD = BC/\cos C$. At D lay off $K = 90 \text{ deg} + C$ for the line DE. $BD = BC \times \tan C$. If the obstacle is small, as a tree, (4) at A, some distance back, turn the small angle a necessary to pass the obstacle and measure AB. At B turn the angle $2a$ and measure $BC = AB$. At C turn the small angle a for the line AC, and transit, or turn the large angle $K = 180 \text{ deg} - a$. If a is but a few minutes, $AC = AB + BC$ with sufficient exactness. If only a tape is available, the right-angle method (1) above given may be used; or, an equilateral triangle ABC (Fig. 16) may be laid out, AC produced a convenient distance to F, the similar triangle DEF laid out, FE produced to H making $FH = AF$, and the similar triangle GHI then laid out for the line GH. $AH = AF$.

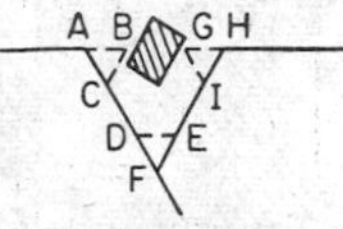

Fig. 16

To Measure the Distance across a Stream. To measure AB (Fig. 17), B being any established point, tree, stake, or building corner: (1) Set a transit over A; turn a right angle from AB and measure any distance AC; set over C and measure the angle ACB. $AB = AC \tan ACB$. (2) Set over A, turn any convenient angle BAC' and measure AC'; set over C' and measure $AC'B$. Angle $ABC' = 180 \text{ deg} - AC'B - BAC'$. $BA = AC' \times \sin AC'B/\sin ABC'$. (3) Set up on A and produce BA any measured distance to D; establish a convenient point C about opposite A and measure BAC and CAD; set over D and measure ADC; set over C, and measure DCA and ACB; solve ACD for AC, and ABC for AB. For best results the acute angles of either method should lie between 30 and 60 deg.

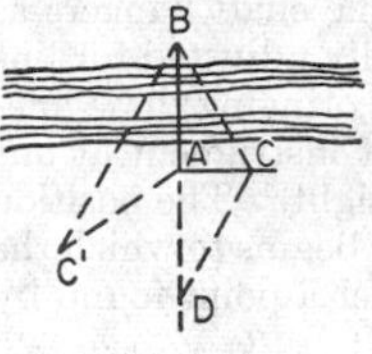

Fig. 17

To measure a visible but inaccessible distance, as AB in Fig. 18. Measure CD. Set a transit at C and measure angles ACB and BCD; set at D and measure angles CDA and ADB. $CAD = 180 \text{ deg} - (ACB + BCD + CDA)$. $AD = CD \times \sin ACD/\sin CAD$. $CBD = 180 \text{ deg} - (BCD + CDA + ADB)$. $BD = CD \times \sin BCD/\sin CBD$. In the triangle ABD, $\frac{1}{2}(B + A) = 90 \text{ deg} - \frac{1}{2}D$, where A, B and D are the angles of the triangle; $\tan \frac{1}{2}(B - A) = \cot \frac{1}{2}D(AD - BD)/(AD + BD)$; $AB = BD \sin D/\sin A = AD \sin D/\sin B$.

Setting Stakes for Trenching. A common way to give line and grade for trenching (see Fig. 19) is to set stakes K ft from the center line, driving them so that the near face is the measuring point and the top is some whole inch or tenth of a foot above the bottom grade or grade of the center or top of the pipe to be laid. The top of the pipe barrel is perhaps the better line of reference. If preferred, two stakes may be driven on opposite sides and a board nailed across, on which the center line is marked and the depth to pipe line given. When only one stake is used, a graduated pole sliding on one end of a level board at right angles is convenient for workmen and inspectors. On long grades, the grade stakes are set by "shooting in." Two grade stakes are set, one at each end of the grade, a transit is set over one, its height above grade determined, and a rod reading calculated for the distant stake such as to make the line of sight parallel to the grade line; the transit line of sight is then set at this rod reading; when the rod is taken to any intermediate stake, the height of instrument above grade less the rod reading will be the height of the top of the stake above grade. If the ground is uniform, the stakes may all be set at the same height above grade by driving them so as to give the same rod readings throughout.

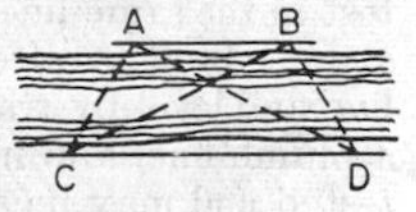

Fig. 18

To Reference a Point. The point P (Fig. 20), which must be disturbed during construction operations and will be again required as a line point in a railway, pipeline, or other survey, is referenced as follows: (1) By setting the transit over it and setting four points, A, B, and C, D on two intersecting lines. When P is again required, the transit is set over B and, with foresight on A, two temporary points close together near P but on opposite sides of the line DC are set; the transit is then set on D and, with foresight on C, a point is set in the lines DC and BA by setting it in DC under a string stretched between the two temporary points on BA. (2) Points A and E and C and F may be established instead of A, B, C, D. (3) If the ground is fairly level and is not to be much disturbed, only points A and C need be located, and these by simple tape measurement from P. They should be less than a tape length from P. When P is wanted, arcs struck from A and C with the measured distance for radii will give P at their intersection.

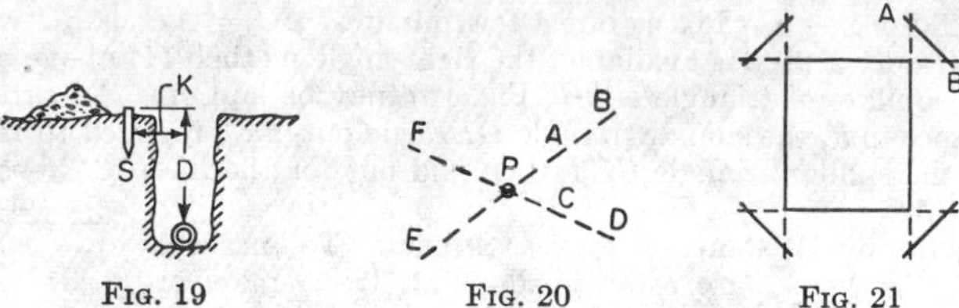

FIG. 19 FIG. 20 FIG. 21

Foundations. The corners and lines of a foundation are preserved by setting stakes outside the area to be disturbed, as in Fig. 21. Cords stretched around nails in the stakes marking the reference points will give the referenced corners at their intersections and the main lines of the building. These corners can be plumbed down to the level desired if the height of the stakes above grade is given. It is well to nail boards across the stakes at AB, putting nails in the top edge of the board to mark the points A and B, and if the ground permits, to put all the boards at the same level.

To Test the Alignment and Level of a Shaft. Having placed the shaft hangers as closely in line as possible by the use of a chalk line, the shaft is finally adjusted for line by hanging plumb lines over one side of the shaft at each hanger and bringing these lines into a line found by stretching a cord or wire or by setting a transit instrument at one end and adjusting at each hanger till its plumb line is in the line of sight. The position of the line will be known either on the floor or on the ceiling rafters or beams to which the hangers are attached. If the latter, the transit may be centered over a point found by plumbing down, and sighted to a plumb line at the farther end.

To level the shaft, an ordinary carpenter's level may be used near each hanger, or, better, a pole with an improvised sliding target may be hung over the shaft at each hanger by a hook in one end. The target is brought to the line of sight of a leveling instrument set preferably about under the middle of the shaft, by adjusting the hanger.

When the hangers are attached to inclined roof rafters, the two extreme hangers may be put in a line at right angles to the vertical planes of the rafters by the use of a square and cord. The other hangers will then be put as nearly as possible without instrumental test in the same line. The shaft being hung, the two extreme hangers, which have been attached to the rafters about midway between their limits of adjustment, are brought to line and level by trial, using a transit instrument with a well-adjusted telescope bubble, a plumb line, and inverted level rod or target pole. Each intermediate hanger is then tested and may be adjusted by trial.

To Determine the Verticality of a Stack. If the stack is not in use and its top is accessible, a board may be fitted across the top, the center of the opening found and a plumb line suspended to the bottom, where its deviation from the center will show any leaning. If the stack is in use or its top not accessible and its sides are battered, the following procedure may be followed: Referring to Fig. 22, set up a transit at any point T and measure the horizontal angles between vertical planes tangent respectively to both sides of the top and the base and also the angle a to a second point T_1. On a line through T approximately at right angles to the chimney diameter, set the transit at T_1 and perform the same operations as at T, measuring also K and the angle b. On the drawing board, lay off K to as large a scale as convenient, and from the plotted T and T_1 lay off the several angles shown in the figure. By trial, draw circumferences tangent to the two quadrilaterals formed by the intersecting tan-

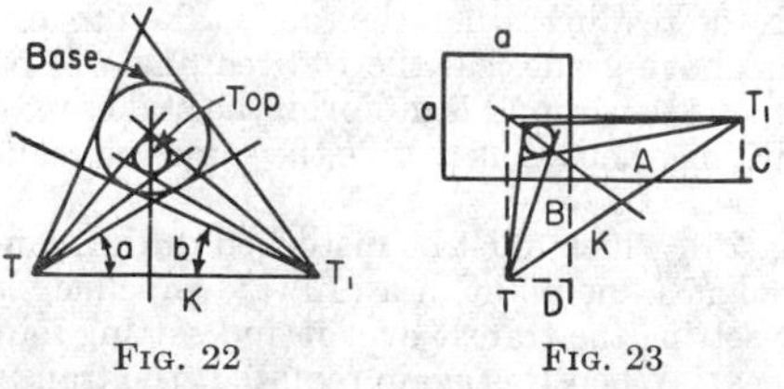

FIG. 22 FIG. 23

gents of the base and top, respectively. The line joining the centers of these circumferences will be the deviation from the vertical in direction and amount. If the base is square, T and T_1 should be established opposite the middle points of two adjacent sides, as in Fig. 23.

PATENTS FOR INVENTIONS

BY

Franklin R. Jenkins and Edward Taylor Newton

References: Deller's Edition, "Walker on Patents," Baker, Voorhis & Co., Inc. Robinson, "The Law of Patents," Little, Brown. Ellis, "Patent Assignments and Licenses," Baker, Voorhis & Co., Inc. Rules of Practice of U.S. Patent Office.

UNITED STATES OF AMERICA

[*Section references (§) refer to Patent Act of 1952, 35 U.S.C.*]

What Subject Matter Is Patentable. Any new and useful process, machine, manufacture, or composition of matter, or any new and useful improvement thereof, or any asexually reproduced distinct and new variety of plant, including cultivated sports, mutants, hybrids, and newly found seedlings, other than a tuber-propagated plant found in an uncultivated state. "Process" means art or method and includes a new use of a known process, machine, manufacture, composition of matter, or material. "Machine" includes every mechanical device, usually having relatively moving parts. "Manufacture" means articles other than machines, such as pencils and chairs for example. A "composition of matter" includes anything resulting from the chemical union or mechanical mixture of two or more substances.

Conditions for Patentability; Novelty and Loss of Right to Patent. A person shall be entitled to a patent unless (1) the invention was known or used by others in this country or patented or described in a printed publication in this or a foreign country before the invention thereof by the applicant for patent, or (2) the invention was patented or described in a printed publication in this or a foreign country or in public use or on sale in this country more than 1 year prior to the date of the application for patent in the United States, or (3) he has abandoned the invention, or (4) the invention was first patented or caused to be patented by the applicant or his legal representatives or assigns in a foreign country prior to the date of the application for patent in this country on an application filed more than 12 months before the filing of the application in the United States, or (5) the invention was described in a patent granted on an application for patent by another filed in the United States before the invention thereof by the applicant for patent, or (6) he did not himself invent the subject matter sought to be patented, or (7) before the applicant's invention thereof the invention was made in this country by another who had not abandoned, suppressed, or concealed it. In determining priority of invention there shall be considered not only the respective dates of conception and reduction to practice of the invention, but also the reasonable diligence of the one who was first to conceive and last to reduce to practice, from a time prior to conception by the other (§ 102).

Who May Apply for Patent. The original inventor or his personal representative, or inventors jointly if more than one. The existence of joint invention can be determined only by the facts of each case. The only general rule is that two or more persons are properly joined as applicants for patent if the conception grew spontaneously out of conversation between them or if in working together they both contributed to the claimed invention. The *owner* of an invention, by assignment and sale from the inventor, may not *apply* for patent, but may receive the patent as assignee.

Term of Patent. Seventeen years from the date of issue. No extensions are granted without Congressional action. The **patent grant** gives to the patentee the right to exclude others from making, using, or selling the patented subject matter during the life of the patent.

The **patent application** should be prepared by a competent solicitor. For information concerning the forms and rules, obtain from the Commissioner of Patents, Washington, D.C., a copy of the Rules of Practice of the U.S. Patent Office.

Proceedings in the U.S. Patent Office. Each application for patent found to be correct in form is examined in its turn. Rejections of claim or requirements of amendment must be answered by the applicant (or his attorney) within 6 months after the date of the official communication, or a shorter period specified by the Patent Office, or the application will be held to be abandoned.

Interferences. When an application for patent is found to interfere with, *i.e.*, to present or claim substantially the same invention as (1) another pending application, (2) a patent issued on a date less than 1 year prior to the date of the application in question, (3) a reissued patent, of which the original was granted on a date less than 1 year prior to the date of the application in question, the two interfering cases are impleaded in an action in the Patent Office called an interference, the purpose of which is to determine which of two or more rival claimants is the original and/or first inventor. The practice before the Patent Office in interference is of such a character that an interference should be conducted only by legal counsel equipped with special experience in that practice.

The first of one or more applicants to **file** applications on the same invention is prima facie the first inventor. Proving that the invention was made **before** the effective filing dates of the respective applications requires evidence generally corroborated by one or more witnesses who had **direct** knowledge of, and understood, what was being done and when, during the making of the invention. A daily **log book** for the inventor and witnesses is desirable, and any pertinence of running entries to the invention should be **clear,** as references to sketches, descriptions, etc., already in the book, and to such items as drawings, photographs, completed samples, and test reports elsewhere which should be preserved.

Cost of Obtaining a Patent. Patent Office fees and time for payment are fixed by law but attorneys' fees vary. In general, the better the protection afforded by the patent, the more it will cost.

Design Patents. The inventor of a new, original, and ornamental design for an article of manufacture may obtain a patent for such design. Design patents are granted for 3½ years, 7 years, or 14 years. Fees vary with the duration. In other respects, the requirements for design patents are substantially similar to those for mechanical patents. Design patents protect only the ornamental design of an article, *i.e.*, its shape or ornamentation, as distinguished from its mechanical construction or its functional or utilitarian attributes.

Sale or assignment of patent, to be binding, must be by an instrument in writing. To provide for constructive notice to all, an assignment must be recorded in the Patent Office within 3 months of its date.

Sales of Fractional Interests in Patents. Undivided fractions or territorial division of patent rights are advisable only in special cases, because with the best intentions the interests of joint or territorial owners are liable to interfere.

Licenses are permissions by the patentee to make, use, or sell the thing patented, and broadly speaking a license may carry any imaginable provisions the parties agree on, subject to certain restrictions upon agreements in restraint of trade, upon fixing resale prices, upon limiting the use of patented articles after their sale, upon limiting the manufacture, use, or sale of articles not covered by the patent, and other restrictions of like character, as to which a lawyer should be consulted. License contracts should be reduced to writing. License by oral arrangement, or by implication from circumstances, is as binding on the parties as if reduced to writing, the difference lying in difficulty of proof.

Relations of employer and employee, when the latter makes an invention. Unless by express contract, or by implication from circumstances, the employee agrees that his patentable inventions should be the property of the employer, the employer has no title or claim to the invention or to the patent for it. However, if the employee uses the employer's time and/or materials in making the invention, the employer has a shop right (a non-exclusive royalty-free license). The scope of such a shop right, or implied license, must be determined from the nature of the employer's business, the character of the invention involved, the circumstances that created it, and the relation, conduct, and intention of the parties. The extent of such shop right depends upon the circumstances of each case.

Many employers require or attempt to secure from their employees an express agreement that inventions shall belong to the employer, and a prospective employee should carefully read and understand any such agreement before signing.

Infringements of Patent. As the grant gives the right to prevent others from making, selling, or using, so an unlicensed manufacture, sale, or use of the thing patented is an infringement, and the maker, seller, or user may be sued in a District Court of the United States. **Suit** may be **brought** in the judicial district where the defendant resides, or where the defendant has committed acts of infringement and has a regular and established place of business. In all but very exceptional cases, the courts will not grant **preliminary injunctions** in a suit on a patent that has not previously been held valid in another contested litigation.

Marking Patented Articles. Unless the patentee has given particular notice of his patent, or general notice by marking the patented articles "Patent" followed by the number of his patent, he may not recover damages for infringement. If the patented articles themselves cannot be marked, the mark may be affixed to the packages in which they are contained. Marking requirements do not apply to process patents or to patents under which the patentee has not manufactured.

False Marking. Whoever, without the consent of the patentee, marks upon, or affixes to, or uses in advertising in connection with anything made, used, or sold by him, the name or any imitation of the name of the patentee, the patent number, or the words "patent," "patentee," or the like, with the intent of counterfeiting or imitating the mark of the patentee or of deceiving the public and inducing them to believe that the thing was made or sold by or with the consent of the patentee; or

Whoever marks upon, or affixes to, or uses in advertising in connection with any unpatented article, the word "patent" or any word or number importing that the same is patented, for the purpose of deceiving the public; or

Whoever marks upon, or affixes to, or uses in advertising in connection with any article, the words "patent applied for," "patent pending," or any word importing that an application for patent has been made, when no application for patent has been made, or if made is not pending, for the purpose of deceiving the public—

Shall be fined not more than $500 for every such offense.

Any person may sue for the penalty, in which event one-half shall go to the person suing and the other to the use of the United States (§ 292).

Damages for Infringement. § 284 provides that the successful claimant in a patent-infringement suit may be awarded "damages adequate to compensate for the infringement, but in no event less than a reasonable royalty for the use made of the invention by the infringer, together with interest and costs as fixed by the Court," and "the Court may increase the damages up to three times the amount found or assessed." § 285 provides that "the Court in exceptional cases may award reasonable attorney fees to the prevailing party." The measure of damages may be the established royalty if licenses have been granted under the patent, or it may be the profit which the claimant lost due to the infringing competition. In any event the claimant is entitled to a reasonable royalty. In the case of a design patent § 289 provides that the infringer shall also be "liable to the extent of his total profit on the infringing sales and not less than $250."

Reissues of Patent. If through inadvertence, accident, or mistake the original patent was defective, or claimed too much or too little, the error may be repaired by surrender of the patent and reissue, provided the reissue be for the same invention as was disclosed as such by the original and be applied for without unreasonable delay. No reissued patent shall be granted enlarging the scope of the claims of the original patent unless applied for within 2 years from the grant of the original patent (§ 251). The term of a reissued patent expires on the day that the original patent would have expired.

Cooperation with Attorney. The attorney who prepares a patent application should thoroughly understand both how the invention is made and how it works and try to anticipate what the inventor's competitor may wish to do; so discussion with the attorney is advisable at the outset. The action of the Patent Office will be based exclusively on the written record (Rule 2). An application contains a description and usually a drawing which essentially must enable one skilled in the art, to which the invention most closely pertains, to make and use the invention without appreciable experimentation. Neither the drawing nor the description may be substantially added to after being filed without adequate support somewhere in the application as originally filed, but the claims in a pending application may be timely amended. Each valid claim in a patent is a legal definition of what the patent owner may exclude others from making, using, or selling.

Patents as Technical Literature. The disclosures in the more recently issued patents are generally well detailed and reliable sources of information. Copies may be obtained readily at 50¢ each when identified by patent number, and they may be ordered in groups according to subclass, both according to patents already issued and according to future patents that may be issued. For details write Commissioner of Patents, Washington, D.C. 20231.

FOREIGN COUNTRIES

International Convention for the Protection of Industrial Property. The important provision of the Convention is that any person who has duly applied for a patent in one of the contracting states shall have a right of priority for 12 months in making application in the other states. Such subsequent application is unaffected by any acts accomplished in the interval, as, for example, by publication of the invention or by the working of it.

The laws and regulations in foreign countries differ so much with respect to their requirements as to novelty and patentability, the effect of a public disclosure of the invention either in the country in question or elsewhere, who may obtain a patent, the term of the patent, the cost of a patent, working of the patent, taxes, importation, compulsory licenses, revocation, and other particulars that it is not practicable to make a useful summary in the space allocated to this note. An inventor interested in foreign protection should consult a patent attorney.

MISCELLANEOUS

(Staff Contribution)

Sizes of Type

The unit of height of a line of printer's type is the "point." 1 point = 1/72 in. Six-point type is consequently 6/72 = 1/12 in. high. The sizes generally employed in books and periodicals are 6-, 7-, 8-, 9-, 10-, 11-, and 12-point. These are shown below as set in Modern No. 8A, the type face used in this book.

6-point	10-point
7-point	11-point
8-point	12-point
9-point	

This handbook is set in 8-point type (8-point Modern No. 8A) with a 1-point lead (space) between each line, with 58 text lines per page, and with a type-page width of 4½ in. One printed page of this book is equivalent to 2.76 pages of elite typewritten manuscript and 3.17 pages of pica typewritten manuscript (see Copy Preparation and Copy Fitting below).

Copy Preparation and Copy Fitting

It is recommended that manuscripts be typed on 8½- by 11-in. paper with 1½-in. margins at the top and left side, with 1-in. margins at the right and bottom, and with each page containing 26 lines, double-spaced. Some typewriters have pica type and write 10 characters per inch; others have elite type and write 12 characters per inch. One manuscript page typed as specified is equivalent to 260 words if typed in pica type and 312 words if typed in elite (assuming that each word averages six characters).

One way to find approximately how many lines of type will be equivalent to lines of manuscript copy is to type to the specifications given above at least enough lines from the particular printed article or book to fill one typewritten page. This will show the relationship between typewritten lines and lines set in type.

This is pica type
1234567890

This is elite type
123456789012

Another method is to take a number of lines from the printed article or book and type them line for line on the typewriter. This will also give the approximate number of lines of type that will be equivalent to the manuscript lines.

For a useful introduction to copy-fitting methods, including the more precise "character-count" method, see the article on copy fitting in Melcher and Larrick, "Printing and Promotion Handbook," 3d ed., McGraw-Hill.

Proofreading

When correcting proof, use ink or pencil of a different color from the marks already on the proof. Put your marks in the right or left margin, whichever is nearer to the word corrected. If there are several corrections in a single line, place them in order from left to right, separated by a slant line (*e.g.*, tr/cap/,). If the same correction is made several times in the same line with no intervening correction, make your correction once in the margin, followed by an appropriate number of slant lines. For instance, if you add an *s* to three words in a line, write in the margin s///. When you wish to insert words, put a caret at the point of insertion and write the additional words in the margin. To delete material without substituting anything, cross it out and put a delete sign in the margin. When you delete words and substitute other words, cross out the unwanted material, use a caret within the line, and write the new material in the margin; the delete sign is then unnecessary.

Occasionally you may decide that material you have deleted should be restored. Place a row of dots under the crossed-out material, cross off the delete sign in the margin, and write "stet" (let it stand).

Proofreaders' Marks

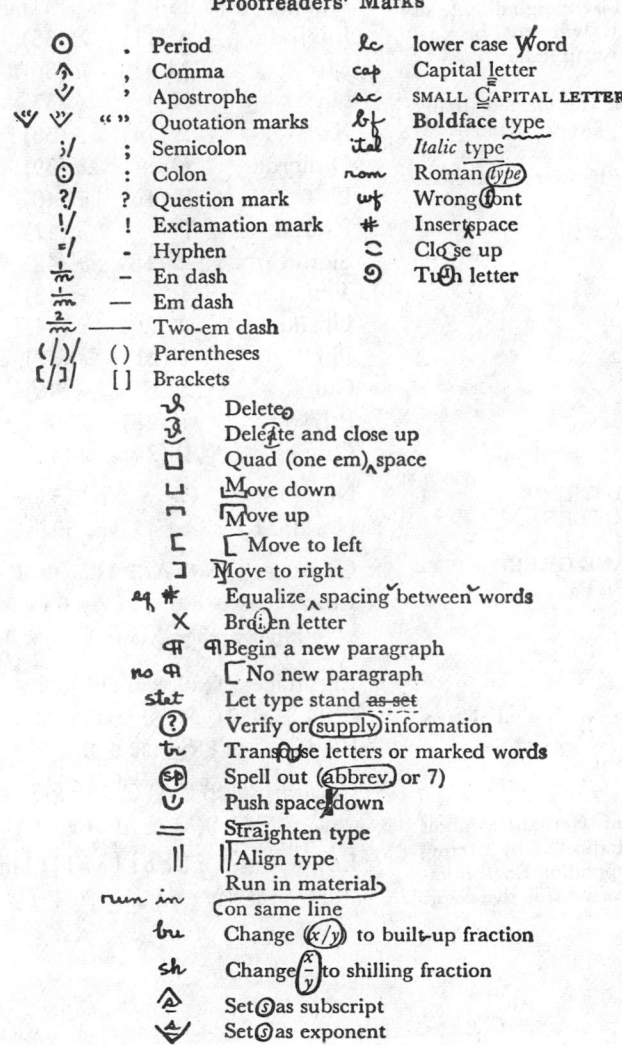

Mark			Mark	
⊙	.	Period	lc	lower case Word
^,^	,	Comma	cap	Capital letter
∨'∨	'	Apostrophe	sc	SMALL CAPITAL LETTER
∨"∨ ∨"∨	" "	Quotation marks	bf	**Boldface type**
;/	;	Semicolon	ital	*Italic* type
⊙:	:	Colon	rom	Roman (*type*)
?/	?	Question mark	wf	Wrong font
!/	!	Exclamation mark	#	Insert space
=/	-	Hyphen	⁀	Clo se up
1/en	–	En dash	⟲	Turn letter
1/em	—	Em dash		
2/em	——	Two-em dash		
(/)/	( )	Parentheses		
[/]/	[ ]	Brackets		

Mark	
ℓ	Delete
ℓ⁀	Delete and close up
□	Quad (one em) space
⊔	Move down
⊓	Move up
[	[Move to left
]	] Move to right
eq #	Equalize spacing between words
X	Broken letter
¶	¶ Begin a new paragraph
no ¶	[No new paragraph
stet	Let type stand ~~as set~~
ⓘ?	Verify or (supply) information
tr	Transpose letters or marked words
ⓢⓟ	Spell out (abbrev.) or 7)
⊥	Push space down
=	Straighten type
‖	‖ Align type
run in	Run in material on same line
bu	Change (x/y) to built-up fraction
sh	Change $\frac{x}{y}$ to shilling fraction
⋀	Set ⓢ as subscript
⋁	Set ⓢ as exponent

Special Alphabets

GREEK ALPHABET	Alpha	A	α (49), α (25)
The printer identifies Greek letters by means of the numbers in parentheses.	Beta	B	β (26), ϐ (53)
	Gamma	Γ (3)	γ (27)
	Delta	Δ (4)	δ (28), ∂ (56)
Note that the capital Greek letters A, B, E, Z, H, I, K, M, N, O, P, T, X used by the printer are like the English roman letters and may not be suitable as symbols. If used, however, they should be identified by marginal note so that they will not be improperly set in italic.	Epsilon	E	ϵ (29)
	Zeta	Z	ζ (30)
	Eta	H	η (31)
	Theta	Θ (8)	θ (32), ϑ (50)
	Iota	I	ι (33)
	Kappa	K	κ (34), $\varkappa$ (54)
	Lambda	Λ (11)	λ (35)
	Mu	M	μ (36)
Note that the form of many boldface Greek symbols is markedly different from the style of the lightface characters.	Nu	N	ν (37)
	Xi	Ξ (14)	ξ (38)
	Omicron	O	o (39)
	Pi	Π (16)	π (40)
	Rho	P	ρ (41)
	Sigma	Σ (18)	σ (42), ς (52)
	Tau	T	τ (43)
	Upsilon	Υ (20)	υ (44)
	Phi	Φ (21)	ϕ (51), φ (45)
	Chi	X	χ (46)
	Psi	Ψ (23)	ψ (47)
	Omega	Ω (24)	ω (48)

SPECIAL GREEK CHARACTERS

No. 83M 8 ϴ No. 55 ϝ
No. 83M 29 ε No. 59 ϛ

BOLDFACE GREEK ALPHABETS

Capitals: **Γ Δ Θ Λ Ξ Π Σ Φ Ψ Ω**

Lower case: **α β γ δ ε ζ η θ ι κ λ μ ν ξ ο π ϱ σ τ υ ϕ χ ψ ω α ϑ φ ς ϰ ∂**

SCRIPT

Available in capital letters only.

Lightface: $\mathcal{A} \mathcal{B} \mathcal{C} \mathcal{D} \mathcal{E} \mathcal{F} \mathcal{G} \mathcal{H} \mathcal{I} \mathcal{J} \mathcal{K} \mathcal{L} \mathcal{M} \mathcal{N} \mathcal{O} \mathcal{P} \mathcal{Q} \mathcal{R} \mathcal{S} \mathcal{T} \mathcal{U} \mathcal{V} \mathcal{W} \mathcal{X} \mathcal{Y} \mathcal{Z}$

Boldface: $\boldsymbol{\mathcal{B}} \boldsymbol{\mathcal{E}} \boldsymbol{\mathcal{C}} \boldsymbol{\mathcal{F}} \boldsymbol{\mathcal{H}} \boldsymbol{\mathcal{I}} \boldsymbol{\mathcal{M}}$

GERMAN

Script and German symbols may be indicated by circling the corresponding English letters each in a distinctive color.

Capitals: $\mathfrak{A} \mathfrak{B} \mathfrak{C} \mathfrak{D} \mathfrak{E} \mathfrak{F} \mathfrak{G} \mathfrak{H} \mathfrak{I} \mathfrak{K} \mathfrak{L} \mathfrak{M} \mathfrak{N} \mathfrak{O} \mathfrak{P} \mathfrak{Q} \mathfrak{R} \mathfrak{S} \mathfrak{T} \mathfrak{U} \mathfrak{V} \mathfrak{W} \mathfrak{X} \mathfrak{Y} \mathfrak{Z}$

Lower case: $\mathfrak{a} \mathfrak{b} \mathfrak{c} \mathfrak{d} \mathfrak{e} \mathfrak{f} \mathfrak{g} \mathfrak{h} \mathfrak{i} \mathfrak{j} \mathfrak{k} \mathfrak{l} \mathfrak{m} \mathfrak{n} \mathfrak{o} \mathfrak{p} \mathfrak{q} \mathfrak{r} \mathfrak{s} \mathfrak{t} \mathfrak{u} \mathfrak{v} \mathfrak{w} \mathfrak{x} \mathfrak{y} \mathfrak{z}$

INDEX

INDEX

IMPORTANT REFERENCE TABLES AND CHARTS